Stanley Gibbons
STAMP CATALOGUE

PART 1

British Commonwealth 2001

Including post-independence issues of Ireland

103rd edition

VOLUME 1
Great Britain and Countries A to I

Stanley Gibbons Ltd
London and Ringwood

By Appointment to Her Majesty The Queen
Stanley Gibbons Ltd, London
Philatelists

Published by **Stanley Gibbons Ltd**
Editorial, Publications Sales Offices and Distribution Centre:
5 Parkside, Christchurch Road, Ringwood,
Hants BH24 3SH.

© **Stanley Gibbons Ltd 2000**

ISBN: 0-85259-493-3

Item No. 2811 (01)

Text assembled by Black Bear Press Limited, Cambridge

Made and Printed in Great Britain by William Clowes Limited,
Beccles, Suffolk

Preface to the 2001 Edition

AMONG THE MEDALS

Stanley Gibbons Publications has always felt it important that its catalogues should be submitted to the Literature Classes of major International Philatelic Exhibitions, so that they could be impartially judged by leading collectors. The Catalogue Department contains medals awarded at various Exhibitions, stretching back to 1892. It is part of the firm's mythology that some of the earlier medals do actually contain gold!

2000 has seen two major philatelic exhibitions: "The Stamp Show 2000" in London and "WIPA 2000" in Vienna. Various catalogues were entered for each and the *Part 1 (British Commonwealth) Catalogue*, 2000 edition, sent to both. At "The Stamp Show 2000" it was awarded a Vermeil medal (83 marks) and at "WIPA 2000" a Large Vermeil (85 marks).

It was particularly encouraging to receive such an award from the very successful "home" international. Although patterns in the hobby continue to change in this country, the success of "The Stamp Show 2000" should leave everyone in no doubt that stamp collecting is very much alive.

One of the new aspects prominent at the exhibition was the use of the Internet as part of the hobby. In just a few months its impact as a source of information has been clearly demonstrated, and it has had a considerable effect on new issue listings for those countries who post even the most basic information on their websites. At least one country in the second volume of this edition has its new issues right up-to-date for the first time in many years, primarily because the dates of issue were provided on the Internet. It may take longer for e-commerce to become established in the philatelic trade, but in the years to come it is likely to alter our attitude to stamp collecting along with many other aspects of our everyday life.

Also evident at Earls Court were the growing problems surrounding new issues. Some countries continue to produce balanced programmes, in conjunction with their normal postal operations, which provide attractive stamps at a modest yearly cost. Such postal administrations recognise the educational aspect of their products and spend much time and effort on the research and production of their stamps, but unfortunately this is not always the case. Stamps for some other countries continue to appear in ever growing numbers, incorporating sheetlets and multiple miniature sheets, at an ever-escalating cost to the collector. There are also an increasing number of design and inscription errors, suggesting that very little effort is being made to achieve accuracy. Such instances are having a decidedly adverse effect on the ultimate purchaser, the collector, and there are growing signs that the amount spent on new issues is declining, with the purchaser being much more selective in this field than has been the case in the past.

PRICES

The market pattern outlined in last year's edition has remained unchanged over the past twelve months and continues to influence prices in these new volumes. Price rises, with some exceptions, have been solid rather than spectacular, but the continuing low level of inflation allows them to reflect the true scarcity of the stamps without the complications of wider economic factors.

Many stamps, quite common twenty or thirty years ago, are now becoming difficult to find as collectors compete for issues which were only

produced in limited quantities. For errors, varieties and provisional issues, such as **Batum** and **Bushire**, this leads to continuing increases year on year, but the trend is now also becoming visible for many other stamps stretching from the reign of Queen Victoria to that of King George VI. Changes in hobby trends have added emphasis to such movements. Many are neglecting "one-country" collecting, to create increased demand for such periods as King George VI or the West Indies up to 1935.

The future for stamps of the current reign is more difficult to determine. The first, recess-printed, definitive sets are probably still under-valued. Many issues from the 1960s to 1980s remain available in considerable quantities at low prices while increases for the most recent stamps are being driven largely by thematic demand. It is difficult to avoid the conclusion that a fault-line is beginning to form in the market somewhere around 1953.

This volume reflects all these trends. Many errors and varieties have increased in value, with a number of recently listed inverted watermarks priced for the first time. The West Indies revival continues, with worthwhile rises for **Antigua**, **Bahamas**, **Barbados**, **Bermuda**, **British Guiana** and **British Honduras** all extending into the King George VI period. Other activity is less predictable. From **Australia** there are many price increases for **Tasmania** (including the postal fiscals) with **Western Australia** also up, but this is balanced by the distinct lack of enthusiasm for many stamps from **Australia** itself, with some middle issues showing falls.

Stamps from the **Dominion of Canada** before 1935 show some movement, and **Newfoundland** has surged forward again.

For smaller territories there are useful increases in **Cyprus** between 1881 and 1934, and in the **Falkland Islands** prices are also up, extending from Queen Victoria to the 1968 definitive series. There has also been more interest in some of the **African colonies**, demonstrated in this volume by repricing for **Gambia** and **Gold Coast** from 1870s to the end of the reign of King George V. **Hong Kong** King Edward VII and King George V have also risen, and the strength in postal history is confirmed once again by increases for virtually all Hong Kong stamps used in **British Post Offices in China and Japan** with the exception of those from Shanghai. **Indian Convention** and **Feudatory States** show further rises.

In every instance there is a healthy balance between mint and fine used, indicating that there are now far more collectors ready to consider the latter than was the case even ten years ago. Stamps on cover continue to be popular. In this edition revised cover factors have been provided for **Bahamas** and **Japanese Occupation of Burma**.

Demand for the stamps of **Great Britain** continues unabated with price rises since the last edition for virtually all issues from the early line-engraved to the 1924 Block Cypher set. Errors and varieties have also done well, as have the key values in the Decimal Machin series from 1971 onwards. It is now recognised that a number of these are becoming increasingly difficult to find, especially those values printed in lithography. Castle high values and the Greetings stamps from booklets have now been withdrawn and further rises are to be expected here.

Guernsey and **Jersey** Second World War Occupation issues are up, and for the **Great Britain Used Abroad** enthusiast the Mail Boat section has been priced for the first time since its reintroduction some editions ago.

REVISIONS FOR THIS EDITION

The coverage of "Specimen" material has been extended by the inclusion of the much sought-after "Cancelled" in oval hand-stamps applied to various issues by Perkins Bacon in 1861. Much of the detail has been taken from *Cancelled by Perkins Bacon* by Peter Jaffé, RDP, published in 1998, and I am grateful to Mr Jaffé for giving his permission for the use of this information.

Many additional watermark varieties have been listed in this edition for the first time, including some for **Australia** postage due stamps and others on issues for **British Columbia**.

Anguilla. Following an appeal for information in *Gibbons Stamp Monthly*, it has been possible to confirm, thirty years after the stamps were issued, that some values at least of the 1969 "INDEPENDENCE" overprints were used for postal purposes. Listings are now provided for those values which have been seen commercially used from the island.

Australia. Due to its complexity the various segments of the Flora and Fauna definitives, first issued in 1996, have been relisted in their component sets.

Bermuda. Listings between 1883 and 1900 have been revised to provide a better sequence. More details of the different perforations used on the 1922–34 series are given, and there are two further plate varieties listed and illustrated on the King George VI £1.

Burma. Notes on the introduction of the 1945 Military Administration stamps have been added.

Canada—Newfoundland. The 1862–64 new colours series has been re-written to provide combined coverage of the two printings.

Cyprus. A number of Great Britain Used Abroad listings have been deleted as it has been demonstrated that the values involved were not available on the island before Great Britain stamps were withdrawn from the post offices there on 1 April 1880.

Egypt. A number of improvements have been made to the listings, including those for the British Forces, following the publication of Professor P.A.S. Smith's monumental *Egypt Stamps and Postal History*.

Fiji. A listing for the 1891–1902 ½d. perforated 10×nearly 12 has been provided.

Ghana. No. 8c, the 1d. on 4d. provisional, has been deleted following research by David Beech of the British Library. It is now generally agreed that the stamp is bogus. Two previously unrecorded 1963 stamp booklets, whose existence was confirmed by Hans-Günther Blach, have been added.

Grenadines of Grenada. Stamps from these islands are now inscribed "Carriacou & Petite Martinique".

Indian Feudatory States. John Trowbridge has provided a number of additional items for **Cochin**, including a further surcharge type for the 1909 2p. on 3p. The first issue of **Idar** has been revised following research by Peter Röver, and **Soruth** between 1864 and 1913 has been rewritten, following the publication of Ron Wood's book for the India Study Circle.

There are many other corrections and additions throughout the volume, and we are most grateful to those collectors, dealers and employees of postal administrations who have, as always, provided so much information for this edition.

David J. Aggersberg
Catalogue Editor

Stanley Gibbons Holdings Plc Addresses

STANLEY GIBBONS LIMITED, STANLEY GIBBONS AUCTIONS
399 Strand, London WC2R 0LX
Auction Room and Specialist Stamp Departments. Open Monday–Friday 9.30 a.m. to 5 p.m.
Shop. Open Monday–Friday 8.30 a.m. to 6 p.m. and Saturday 9.30 a.m. to 5.30 p.m.
Telephone 020 7836 8444, Fax 020 7836 7342, E-mail: enquiries @stanleygibbons.co.uk
and Internet: www.stanleygibbons.com for all departments

STANLEY GIBBONS PUBLICATIONS
5 Parkside, Christchurch Road, Ringwood, Hants BH24 3SH.
Telephone 01425 472363 (24 hour answer phone service), Fax 01425 470247 and E-mail info@stanleygibbons.co.uk
Publications Showroom (at above address). Open Monday–Friday 9 a.m. to 3 p.m.
Publications Mail Order. FREEPHONE 0800 611622. Monday–Friday 8.30 a.m. to 5 p.m.

FRASER'S
(a division of Stanley Gibbons Ltd)
399 Strand, London WC2R 0LX
Autographs, photographs, letters and documents.
Telephone 020 7836 8444, Fax 020 7836 7342, E-mail: info@frasersautographs.co.uk
and Internet:www.frasersautographs.com
Monday–Friday 9 a.m. to 5.30 p.m. and Saturday 10 a.m. to 4 p.m.

STANLEY GIBBONS PUBLICATIONS OVERSEAS REPRESENTATION

Stanley Gibbons Publications are represented overseas by the following sole distributors (*), distributors (**) or licensees (***).

Australia

Lighthouse Philatelic (Aust.) Pty Ltd*
PO Box 763
Strawberry Hills
New South Wales 2012
Australia

Stanley Gibbons (Australia) Pty Ltd***
Level 6, 36 Clarence Street
Sydney N.S.W. 2000
Australia

Belgium and Luxembourg**

Davo c/o Philac
Rue du Midi 48
Bruxelles 1000
Belgium

Canada*

Lighthouse Publications (Canada) Ltd
255 Duke Street
Montreal
Quebec
Canada H3C 2M2

Denmark**

Samlerforum/Davo
Ostergade 3
DK 7470 Karup
Denmark

Finland**

Davo
c/o Suomen Postimerkkeily
Ludvingkatu 5
SF-00130 Helsinki
Finland

France*

Davo France (Casteilla)
10 Rue Leon Foucault
78184 St Quentin Yvelines Cesex
France

Germany and Austria*

Leuchtturm Albenverlag Gmbh u. Co.
Am Spakenberg 45
Postfach 1340
D21495 Geesthacht
Germany

Hong Kong**

Po-on Stamp Service
GPO Box 2498
Hong Kong

Israel**

Capital Stamps
PO Box 3769
Jerusalem 91036
Israel

Italy*

Ernesto Marini Srl
Via Struppa 300
1-16165 Genova GE
Italy

Japan**

Japan Philatelic Co Ltd
PO Box 2
Suginami-Minami
Tokyo
Japan

Netherlands*

Davo Publications
PO Box 411
7400 AK Deventer
Netherlands

New Zealand***

Mowbray Collectables
PO Box 80
Wellington
New Zealand

Norway**

Davo Norge A/S
PO Box 738 Sentrum
N-01 05 Oslo
Norway

Singapore***

Stanley Gibbons (Singapore) Pte Ltd
Raffles City
PO Box 1689
Singapore 9117

South Africa**

Republic Stamp and Coin
  Accessories cc
Republic House
54A, Silwood Road
Bramley 2090
Republic of South Africa

Sweden*

Chr Winther Sorensen AB
Box 43
S-310 Knaered
Sweden

Switzerland**

Phila Service
Burgstrasse 160
CH 4125 Riehen
Switzerland

West Indies/Caribbean**

Hugh Dunphy
PO Box 413
Kingston 10
Jamaica
West Indies

Stanley Gibbons Stamp Catalogue
Complete List of Parts

1 British Commonwealth
(Annual in two volumes)

2 Austria & Hungary (5th edition, 1994)
Austria, Bosnia & Herzegovina, U.N. (Vienna), Hungary

3 Balkans (4th edition, 1998)
Albania, Bosnia & Herzegovina, Bulgaria, Croatia, Greece & Islands, Macedonia, Rumania, Slovenia, Yugoslavia

4 Benelux (4th edition, 1993)
Belgium & Colonies, Netherlands & Colonies, Luxembourg

5 Czechoslovakia & Poland (5th edition, 1994)
Czechoslovakia, Bohemia & Moravia, Slovakia, Poland

6 France (4th edition, 1993)
France, Colonies, Post Offices, Andorra, Monaco

7 Germany (5th edition, 1996)
Germany, States, Colonies, Post.Offices

8 Italy & Switzerland (5th edition, 1997)
Italy & Colonies, Fiume, San Marino, Vatican City, Trieste, Liechtenstein, Switzerland, U.N. (Geneva)

9 Portugal & Spain (4th edition, 1996)
Andorra, Portugal & Colonies, Spain & Colonies

10 Russia (5th edition, 1999)
Russia, Baltic States, Mongolia, Tuva

11 Scandinavia (4th edition, 1994)
Aland Island, Denmark, Faroe Islands, Finland, Greenland, Iceland, Norway, Sweden

12 Africa since Independence A-E (2nd edition, 1983)
Algeria, Angola, Benin, Bophuthatswana, Burundi, Cameroun, Cape Verde, Central African Republic, Chad, Comoro Islands, Congo, Djibouti, Equatorial Guinea, Ethiopia

13 Africa since Independence F-M (1st edition, 1981)
Gabon, Guinea, Guinea-Bissau, Ivory Coast, Liberia, Libya, Malagasy Republic, Mali, Mauritania, Morocco, Mozambique

14 Africa since Independence N-Z (1st edition, 1981)
Niger Republic, Rwanda, St. Thomas & Prince, Senegal, Somalia, Sudan, Togo, Transkei, Tunisia, Upper Volta, Venda, Zaire

15 Central America (2nd edition, 1984)
Costa Rica, Cuba, Dominican Republic, El Salvador, Guatemala, Haiti, Honduras, Mexico, Nicaragua, Panama

16 Central Asia (3rd edition, 1992)
Afghanistan, Iran, Turkey

17 China (6th edition, 1998)
China, Taiwan, Tibet, Foreign P.O.'s, Hong Kong, Macao

18 Japan & Korea (4th edition, 1997)
Japan, Ryukyus, Korean Empire, South Korea, North Korea

19 Middle East (5th edition, 1996)
Bahrain, Egypt, Iraq, Israel, Jordan, Kuwait, Lebanon, Oman, Qatar, Saudi Arabia, Syria, U.A.E., Yemen A.R., Yemen P.D.R.

20 South America (3rd edition, 1989)
Argentina, Bolivia, Brazil, Chile, Colombia, Ecuador, Paraguay, Peru, Surinam, Uruguay, Venezuela

21 South-East Asia (3rd edition, 1995)
Bhutan, Burma, Indonesia, Kampuchea, Laos, Nepal, Philippines, Thailand, Vietnam

22 United States (5th edition, 2000)
U.S. & Possessions, Canal Zone, Marshall Islands, Micronesia, Palau, U.N. (New York, Geneva, Vienna)

GREAT BRITAIN SPECIALISED CATALOGUES

Volume 1 Queen Victoria (11th edition, 1997)
Volume 2 King Edward VII to King George VI (11th edition, 1999)
Volume 3 Queen Elizabeth II Pre-decimal Issues (10th edition, 1998)
Volume 4 Queen Elizabeth II Decimal Definitive Issues (9th edition, 2000)
Volume 5 Queen Elizabeth II Decimal Special Issues (3rd edition, 1998, and 1998–99 Supplement (2000)

THEMATIC CATALOGUES

Collect Aircraft on Stamps (1st edition, 1994)
Collect Birds on Stamps (new edition in preparation)
Collect Chess on Stamps (2nd edition, 1999)
Collect Fish on Stamps (1st edition, 1999)
Collect Fungi on Stamps (2nd edition, 1997)
Collect Railways on Stamps (3rd edition, 1999)
Collect Shells on Stamps (1st edition, 1995)
Collect Ships on Stamps (new edition, 2000)

Stamps Added

Excluding new issues which have appeared in *Gibbons Stamp Monthly* supplements, the following are the catalogue numbers of stamps listed in this edition for the first time.

Great Britain. 40b, 611ma, 720d, 893a, 1666ma, Y1682a, 2051a, 2069a, 2081a, 2088a, 2096a, 2103a, MS2106a

Isle of Man. 775b

Anguilla. 52*a*/*g*

Australia— South Australia. 127a

Victoria. 285da

Commonwealth of Australia. 10w, 573a, MS1852c, D64aw, D64bw, D76w, D78w, D95w, O37a, O126*a*

Bahamas. 25y, 366w, 565a

Bahrain. 10w

Bangladesh. 638a, O47a/b

Barbados. 98y, 199x, D7c

Belize. 5w, 66b

Bermuda. 92a, 121a, 121da, 387bw, 782a

Botswana—Stellaland. 2c, 3b

Brunei. J4a

Burma. J31a, J57a

Canada—British Columbia and Vancouver Island. 13w, 14w, 22w, 32w

Prince Edward Island. 16c

Dominion of Canada. 895b, 988a, 1032bc/bd, 1860a, 1861a, SB218a, SB219a, SB224a, SB226a

Cayman Islands. 108i

Cyprus. 28d

Dominica. 47ay, 57x, 132c, 136a, 232b

Egypt—British Forces. ZA6

Falkland Islands Dependencies. Z132, Z134.

Fiji. 92

Ghana. 76a, SB5, SB7

Gibraltar. 76b, 573w

Grenada. 406b

Guyana. 120d., 223ca

Hong Kong. 153ab, 294b, F8w

British P.O.'s in China. Z354, Z581, Z807*b*

British P.O.'s in Japan. Z15*a*

India. 192w, 926aba, SB25, O146aw, O271a

C.E.F. C10b

Feudatory States—Cochin. 22c, 47c, O82b

Jammu and Kashmir. O7a

Kishangarh. O2a, O14*a*

Nawanagar. 15bc

Soruth. 11d, 11*e*, 18, 21, 24, 40d

Travancore. O75f

Ireland. 1057ap/apa, 1061a.

Catalogue Numbers Altered

The table below is a cross-reference of those catalogue numbers which have been altered in this edition.

Old	New
Great Britain	
1666ma	1666mb
Y1671*a*/3	Y1672/4
Y1674/96	Y1676/1701
NI78/80	NI79/82
NI81	NI84
Guernsey	
809	802
Isle of Man	
776/8	777/9
779	781
780/2	783/5
Jersey	
783/5	784/6
786/8	790/2
789/92	795/8
793/4	800/1
795/8	803/6
Antigua	
2753/77	2754/8
Australia	
47fw	47ew
1624/30	1679/85

Old	New
1631/2	1624/5
1633/7	1686/90
MS1638/90	MS1626/78
1858/61	1863/6
D64a	D64b
Bahamas	
1a	Deleted
24y	Deleted
26	27
27	26
28x	28
Belize	
66b/c	66c/d
Bermuda	
9	1a
34	28*a*
36	37
37/8	39/40
39	42
41	36
42	38

Old	New
43	41
121*a*/d	121*b*/e
Canada—Colony of Canada	
43b	Deleted
Newfoundland	
4a	Deleted
16/20	Deleted
21/4*e*	16/23
Dominion of Canada	
300a	300da
300c	300db
Cayman Islands	
872/5	884/7
Cyprus	
Z7	Deleted
Z20	Deleted
Z26	Deleted
Z39	Deleted
Dominica	
22w	22aw
2520/6	2524/30
2527/30	2520/3

Old	New
Egypt	
42c	Deleted
43c	Deleted
British Forces	
ZA6/8	ZA7/9
Falkland Islands	
245a	Deleted
Falkland Is. Dependencies	
Z131/2	Z130/1
Z134/7	Z135/8
Gambia	
2928/32	2936/40
2933/4	2928/31
2937/49	2941/53
2950/3	2932/5
2971/82	2980/91
Ghana	
8c	Deleted
SB5	SB6
SB6	SB8
Grenada	
3630/62	3631/63

Old	New
3662	3630
3672/84	3673/85
Guyana	
120d/e	120e/f
224c	224ba
224e	224da
Hong Kong	
117b	Deleted
India	
O272/3	O273/4
Feudatory States— Charkhari	
17*a*	17*b*
25a	17a
Cochin	
22c/d	22d/e
O82b	O82ba
Idar	
1/2	Rewritten
Soruth	
1/39	Rewritten

Contents

General Philatelic Information

and Guidelines to the Scope of the Part 1 (British Commonwealth) Catalogue

The notes which follow seek to reflect current practice in compiling the Part 1 (British Commonwealth) Catalogue.

It scarcely needs emphasising that the *Stanley Gibbons Stamp Catalogue* has a very long history and that the vast quantity of information it contains has been carefully built up by successive generations through the work of countless individuals. Philately itself is never static and the Catalogue has evolved and developed during this long time-span. Thus, while these notes are important for today's criteria, they may be less precise the further back in the listings one travels. They are not intended to inaugurate some unwanted series of piecemeal alterations in a widely respected work, but it does seem to us useful that Catalogue users know as exactly as possible the policies currently in operation.

PRICES

The prices quoted in this Catalogue are the estimated selling prices of Stanley Gibbons Ltd at the time of publication. They are, *unless it is specifically stated otherwise*, for examples in fine condition for the issue concerned. Superb examples are worth more; those of a lower quality considerably less.

All prices are subject to change without prior notice and Stanley Gibbons Ltd may from time to time offer stamps below catalogue price. Individual low value stamps sold at 399, Strand are liable to an additional handling charge. Purchasers of new issues are asked to note that the prices charged for them contain an element for the service rendered and so may exceed the prices shown when the stamps are subsequently catalogued. Postage and handling charges are extra.

No guarantee is given to supply all stamps priced, since it is not possible to keep every catalogued item in stock. Commemorative issues may, at times, only be available in complete sets and not as individual values.

Quotation of prices. The prices in the left-hand column are for unused stamps and those in the right-hand column are for used.

A dagger (†) denotes that the item listed does not exist in that condition and a blank, or dash, that it exists, or may exist, but no market price is known.

Prices are expressed in pounds and pence sterling. One pound comprises 100 pence (£1 = 100p).

The method of notation is as follows: pence in numerals (e.g. 10 denotes ten pence); pound and pence, up to £100, in numerals (e.g. 4·25 denotes four pounds and twenty-five pence); prices above £100 expressed in whole pounds with the "£" sign shown.

Unused stamps. Great Britain and Commonwealth: the prices for unused stamps of Queen Victoria to King George V are for lightly hinged examples. Unused prices for King Edward VIII to Queen Elizabeth II issues are for unmounted mint.

Some stamps from the King George VI period are often difficult to find in unmounted mint condition. In such instances we would expect that collectors would need to pay a high proportion of the price quoted to obtain mounted mint examples. Generally speaking lightly mounted mint stamps from this reign, issued before 1945, are in considerable demand.

Mounted mint stamps from the reign of Queen Elizabeth II are frequently available at lower prices than those quoted for the stamps unmounted.

Used stamps. The used prices are normally for stamps postally used but may be for stamps cancelled-to-order where this practice exists.

A pen-cancellation on early issues can sometimes correctly denote postal use. Instances are individually noted in the Catalogue in explanation of the used price given.

Prices quoted for bisects on cover or on large piece are for those dated during the period officially authorised.

Stamps not sold unused to the public (e.g. some official stamps) are priced used only.

The use of "unified" designs, that is stamps inscribed for both postal and fiscal purposes, results in a number of stamps of very high face value. In some instances these may not have been primarily intended for postal purposes, but if they are so inscribed we include them. We only price such items used, however, where there is evidence of normal postal usage.

Cover prices. To assist collectors, cover prices are quoted for issues up to 1945 at the beginning of each country.

The system gives a general guide in the form of a factor by which the corresponding used price of the loose stamp should be multiplied when found in fine average condition on cover.

Care is needed in applying the factors and they relate to a cover which bears a single of the denomination listed; strips and blocks would need individual valuation outside the scope. If more than one denomination is present the most highly priced attracts the multiplier and the remainder are priced at the simple figure for used singles in arriving at a total.

The cover should be of non-philatelic origin, bearing the correct postal rate for the period and distance involved and cancelled with the markings normal to the offices concerned. Purely philatelic items have a cover value only slightly greater than the catalogue value for the corresponding used stamps. This applies generally to those high-value stamps used philatelically rather than in the normal course of commerce. Low-value stamps, e.g. ¼d. and ½d., are desirable when used as a single rate on cover and merit an increase in "multiplier" value.

First-day covers in the period up to 1945 are not within the scope of the system and the multiplier should not be used. As a special category of philatelic usage, with wide variations in valuation according to scarcity, they require separate treatment.

Oversized covers, difficult to accommodate on an album page, should be reckoned as worth little more than the corresponding value of the used stamps. The condition of a cover affects its value. Except for "wreck covers", serious damage or soiling reduce the value where the postal markings and stamps are ordinary ones. Conversely, visual appeal adds to the value and this can include freshness of appearance, important addresses, old-fashioned but legible hand-writing, historic town-names, etc.

The multipliers are a base on which further value would be added to take account of the cover's postal historical importance in demonstrating such things as unusual, scarce or emergency cancels, interesting routes, significant postal markings, combination usage, the development of postal rates, and so on.

For *Great Britain*, rather than multiplication factors, the cover price is shown as a third column, following the prices for unused and used stamps. It will be extended beyond King Edward VII in subsequent editions.

Minimum price. The minimum catalogue price quoted is 10p. For individual stamps prices between 10p. and 50p. are provided as a guide for catalogue users. The lowest price *charged* for individual stamps purchased from Stanley Gibbons Ltd is 50p.

Set prices. Set prices are generally for one of each value, excluding shades and varieties, but including major colour changes. Where there are alternative shades, etc., the cheapest is usually included. The number of stamps in the set is always stated for clarity. The mint prices for sets

containing *se-tenant* pieces are based on the prices quoted for such combinations, and not on those for the individual stamps.

Varieties. Where plate or cylinder varieties are priced in a used condition the price quoted is for a fine used example with the cancellation well clear of the listed flaw.

Specimen stamps. The pricing of these items is explained under that heading.

Stamp booklets. Prices are for complete assembled booklets in fine condition with those issued before 1945 showing normal wear and tear. Incomplete booklets and those which have been "exploded" will, in general, be worth less than the figure quoted.

Repricing. Collectors will be aware that the market factors of supply and demand directly influence the prices quoted in this Catalogue. Whatever the scarcity of a particular stamp, if there is no one in the market who wishes to buy it it cannot be expected to achieve a high price. Conversely, the same item actively sought by numerous potential buyers may cause the price to rise.

All the prices in this Catalogue are examined during the preparation of each new edition by expert staff of Stanley Gibbons and repriced a necessary. They take many factors into account including supply and demand, and are in close touch with the international stamp market and the auction world.

Commonwealth cover prices and advice on postal history material originally provided by Edward B Proud.

GUARANTEE

All stamps are guaranteed genuine originals in the following terms:

If not as described, and returned by the purchaser we undertake to refund the price paid to us in the original transaction. If any stamp is certified as genuine by the Expert Committee of the Royal Philatelic Society, London, or by B.P.A. Expertising Ltd, the purchaser shall not be entitled to make any claim against us for any error, omission or mistake in such certificate.

Consumers' statutory rights are not affected by the above guarantee.

The recognised Expert Committees in this country are those of the Royal Philatelic Society, 41 Devonshire Place, London W1N 1PE, and B.P.A. Expertising Ltd, P.O. Box 137, Leatherhead, Surrey KT22 0RG. They do not undertake valuations under any circumstances and fees are payable for their services.

THE CATALOGUE IN GENERAL

Contents. The Catalogue is confined to adhesive postage stamps, including miniature sheets. For particular categories the rules are:

(*a*) Revenue (fiscal) stamps or telegraph stamps are listed only where they have been expressly authorised for postal duty.

(*b*) Stamps issued only precancelled are included, but normally issued stamps available additionally with precancel have no separate precancel listing unless the face value is changed.

(*c*) Stamps prepared for use but not issued, hitherto accorded full listing, are nowadays footnoted with a price (where possible).

(*d*) Bisects (trisects, etc.) are only listed where such usage was officially authorised.

(*e*) Stamps issued only on first day covers or in presentation packs and not available separately are not listed but may be priced in a footnote.

(*f*) New printings are only included in this Catalogue where they show a major philatelic variety, such as a change in shade, watermark or paper. Stamps which exist with or without imprint dates are listed separately; changes in imprint dates are mentioned in footnotes.

(*g*) Official and unofficial reprints are dealt with by footnote.

(*h*) Stamps from imperforate printings of modern issues which also occur perforated are covered by footnotes, but are listed where widely available for postal use.

Exclusions. The following are excluded: (*a*) non-postal revenue or fiscal stamps; (*b*) postage stamps used fiscally; (*c*) local carriage labels and private local issues; (*d*) telegraph stamps; (*e*) bogus or phantom stamps; (*f*) railway or airline letter fee stamps, bus or road transport company labels; (*g*) cut-outs; (*h*) all types of non-postal labels and souvenirs; (*i*) documentary labels for the postal service, e.g. registration, recorded delivery, air-mail etiquettes, etc.; (*j*) privately applied embellishments to official issues and privately commissioned items generally; (*k*) stamps for training postal officers.

Full listing. "Full listing" confers our recognition and implies allotting a catalogue number and (wherever possible) a price quotation.

In judging status for inclusion in the catalogue broad considerations are applied to stamps. They must be issued by a legitimate postal authority, recognised by the government concerned, and must be adhesives valid for proper postal use in the class of service for which they are inscribed. Stamps, with the exception of such categories as postage dues and officials, must be available to the general public, at face value, in reasonable quantities without any artificial restrictions being imposed on their distribution.

We record as abbreviated Appendix entries, without catalogue numbers or prices, stamps from countries which either persist in having far more issues than can be justified by postal need or have failed to maintain control over their distribution so that they have not been available to the public in reasonable quantities at face value. Miniature sheets and imperforate stamps are not mentioned in these entries.

The publishers of this catalogue have observed, with concern, the proliferation of "artificial" stamp-issuing territories. On several occasions this has resulted in separately inscribed issues for various component parts of otherwise united states or territories.

Stanley Gibbons Ltd have decided that where such circumstances occur, they will not, in the future, list these items in the SG catalogue without first satisfying themselves that the stamps represent a genuine political, historical or postal division within the country concerned. Any such issues which do not fulfil this stipulation will be recorded in the Catalogue Appendix only.

For errors and varieties the criterion is legitimate (albeit inadvertent) sale through a postal administration in the normal course of business. Details of provenance are always important; printers' waste and deliberately manufactured material are excluded.

Certificates. In assessing unlisted items due weight is given to Certificates from recognised Expert Committees and, where appropriate, we will usually ask to see them.

New issues. New issues are listed regularly in the Catalogue Supplement published in *Gibbons Stamp Monthly*, whence they are consolidated into the next available edition of the Catalogue.

Date of issue. Where local issue dates differ from dates of release by agencies, "date of issue" is the local date. Fortuitous stray usage before the officially intended date is disregarded in listing. For ease of reference, the Catalogue displays in the top corner the date of issue of the first set listed on each page.

Catalogue numbers. Stamps of each country are catalogued chronologically by date of issue. Subsidiary classes are placed at the end of the country, as separate lists, with a distinguishing letter prefix to the catalogue number, e.g. D for postage due, O for official and E for express delivery stamps.

The catalogue number appears in the extreme left column. The boldface Type numbers in the next column are merely cross-references to illus-

trations. Catalogue numbers in the *Gibbons Stamp Monthly* Supplement are provisional only and may need to be altered when the lists are consolidated. For the numbering of miniature sheets and sheetlets *see* section below.

Once published in the Catalogue, numbers are changed as little as possible; really serious renumbering is reserved for the occasions when a complete country or an entire issue is being rewritten. The edition first affected includes cross-reference tables of old and new numbers.

Our catalogue numbers are universally recognised in specifying stamps and as a hallmark of status.

Illustrations. Stamps are illustrated at three-quarters linear size. Stamps not illustrated are the same size and format as the value shown, unless otherwise indicated. Stamps issued only as miniature sheets have the stamp alone illustrated but sheet size is also quoted. Overprints, surcharges, watermarks and postmarks are normally actual size. Illustrations of varieties are often enlarged to show the detail. Stamp booklet covers are illustrated half-size, unless otherwise indicated.

Designers. Designers' names are quoted where known, though space precludes naming every individual concerned in the production of a set. In particular, photographers supplying material are usually named only where they also make an active contribution in the design stage; posed photographs of reigning monarchs are, however, an exception to this rule.

CONTACTING THE CATALOGUE EDITOR

The editor is always interested in hearing from people who have new information which will improve or correct the Catalogue. As a general rule he must see and examine the actual stamps before they can be considered for listing; photographs or photocopies are insufficient evidence.

Submissions should be made in writing to the Catalogue Editor, Stanley Gibbons Publications at the Ringwood office. The cost of return postage for items submitted is appreciated, and this should include the registration fee if required.

Where information is solicited purely for the benefit of the enquirer, the editor cannot undertake to reply if the answer is already contained in these published notes or if return postage is omitted. Written communications are greatly preferred to enquiries by telephone and the editor regrets that he or his staff cannot see personal callers without a prior appointment being made. Correspondence may be subject to delay during the production period of each new edition.

The editor welcomes close contact with study circles and is interested, too, in finding reliable local correspondents who will verify and supplement official information in countries where this is deficient.

We regret we do not give opinions as to the **genuineness of stamps, nor do we identify stamps or number them by our Catalogue.**

TECHNICAL MATTERS

The meanings of the technical terms used in the catalogue will be found in our *Philatelic Terms Illustrated* (*new edition in preparation*).

References below to "more specialised" listings are to be taken to indicate, as appropiate, the Stanley Gibbons *Great Britain Specialised Catalogue* in 5 volumes or the *Great Britain Concise Catalogue*.

1. Printing

Printing errors. Errors in printing are of major interest to the Catalogue. Authenticated items meriting consideration would include: background, centre or frame inverted or omitted; centre or subject transposed; error of colour; error

or omission of value; double prints and impressions; printed both sides; and so on. Designs *tête-bêche*, whether intentionally or by accident, are listable. *Se-tenant* arrangements of stamps are recognised in the listings or footnotes. Gutter pairs (a pair of stamps separated by blank margin) are not included in this volume. Colours only partially omitted are not listed. Stamps with embossing omitted are reserved for our more specialised listings.

Printing varieties. Listing is accorded to major changes in the printing base which lead to completely new types. In recess-printing this could be a design re-engraved; in photogravure or photolithography a screen altered in whole or in part. It can also encompass flat-bed and rotary printing if the results are readily distinguishable.

To be considered at all, varieties must be constant.

Early stamps, produced by primitive methods, were prone to numerous imperfections: the lists reflect this, recognising re-entries, retouches, broken frames, misshapen letters, and so on. Printing technology has, however, radically improved over the years, during which time photogravure and lithography have become predominant. Varieties nowadays are more in the nature of flaws and these, being too specialised for this general catalogue, are almost always outside the scope. The development of our range of specialised catalogues allows us now to list those items which have philatelic significance in their appropriate volume.

In no catalogue, however, do we list such items as: dry prints, kiss prints, doctor-blade flaws, colour shifts or registration flaws (unless they lead to the complete omission of a colour from an individual stamp), lithographic ring flaws, and so on. Neither do we recognise fortuitous happenings like paper creases or confetti flaws.

Overprints (and surcharges). Overprints of different types qualify for separate listing. These include overprints in different colours; overprints from different printing processes such as litho and typo; overprints in totally different typefaces, etc. Major errors in machine-printed overprints are important and listable. They include: overprint inverted or omitted; overprint double (treble, etc.); overprint diagonal; overprint double, one inverted; pairs with one overprint omitted, e.g. from a radical shift to an adjoining stamp; error of colour; error of type fount; letters inverted or omitted, etc. If the overprint is handstamped, few of these would qualify and a distinction is drawn. We continue, however, to list pairs of stamps where one has a handstamped overprint and the other has not.

Varieties occurring in overprints will often take the form of broken letters, slight differences in spacing, rising spaces, etc. Only the most important would be considered for footnote mention.

Sheet positions. If space permits we quote sheet positions of listed varieties and authenticated data is solicited for this purpose.

De La Rue plates. The Catalogue classifies the general plates used by De La Rue for printing British Colonial stamps as follows:

VICTORIAN KEY TYPE

Die I

1. The ball of decoration on the second point of the crown appears as a dark mass of lines.
2. Dark vertical shading separates the front hair from the bun.
3. The vertical line of colour outlining the front of the throat stops at the sixth line of shading on the neck.
4. The white space in the coil of the hair above the curl is roughly the shape of a pin's head.

Die II

1. There are very few lines of colour in the ball and it appears almost white.
2. A white vertical strand of hair appears in place of the dark shading.
3. The line stops at the eighth line of shading.
4. The white space is oblong, with a line of colour partially dividing it at the left end.

Plates numbered 1 and 2 are both Die I. Plates 3 and 4 are Die II.

GEORGIAN KEY TYPE

Die I

A. The second (thick) line below the name of the country is cut slanting, conforming roughly to the shape of the crown on each side.
B. The labels of solid colour bearing the words "POSTAGE" and "& REVENUE" are square at the inner top corners.
C. There is a projecting "bud" on the outer spiral of the ornament in each of the lower corners.

Die II

A. The second line is cut vertically on each side of the crown.
B. The labels curve inwards at the top.
C. There is no "bud" in this position.

Unless otherwise stated in the lists, all stamps with watermark Multiple Crown CA (w **8**) are Die I while those with watermark Multiple Crown Script CA (w **9**) are Die II. The Georgian Die II was introduced in April 1921 and was used for Plates 10 to 22 and 26 to 28. Plates 23 to 25 were made from Die I by mistake.

2. Paper

All stamps listed are deemed to be on "ordinary" paper of the wove type and white in colour; only departures from this are normally mentioned.

Types. Where classification so requires we distinguish such other types of paper as, for example, vertically and horizontally laid; wove and laid bâtonné; card(board); carton; cartridge; glazed; granite; native; pelure; porous; quadrillé; ribbed; rice; and silk thread.

Wove paper   Laid paper

Granite paper   Quadrillé paper

Burelé band

The various makeshifts for normal paper are listed as appropriate. The varieties of double paper and joined paper are recognised. The security device of a printed burelé band on the back of a stamp, as in early Queensland, qualifies for listing.

Descriptive terms. The fact that a paper is handmade (and thus probably of uneven thickness) is mentioned where necessary. Such descriptive terms as "hard" and "soft"; "smooth" and 'rough'; "thick", "medium" and "thin" are applied where there is philatelic merit in classifying papers. We do not, for example, even in more specialised listings, classify paper thicknesses in the Wilding and Machin definitives of Great Britain. Weight standards for the paper apply to complete reels only, so that differences on individual stamps are acceptable to the printer provided the reel conforms overall.

Coloured, very white and toned papers. A coloured paper is one that is coloured right through (front and back of the stamp). In the Catalogue the colour of the paper is given in *italics*, thus:

black/*rose* = black design on rose paper.

Papers have been made specially white in recent years by, for example, a very heavy coating of chalk. We do not classify shades of whiteness of paper as distinct varieties. There does exist, however, a type of paper from early days called toned. This is off-white, often brownish or buffish, but it cannot be assigned any definite colour. A toning effect brought on by climate, incorrect storage or gum staining is disregarded here, as this was not the state of the paper when issued.

Modern developments. Two modern developments also affect the listings: printing on self-adhesive paper and the use of metallic foils. For self-adhesive stamps *see* under "Gum", below. Care should be taken not to damage the embossing on stamps impressed on metallic foils, such as Sierra Leone 1965–67, by subjecting the album pages to undue pressure. The possibility of faked

"missing gold heads" is noted at the appropriate places in the listing of modern Great Britain.

"Ordinary" and "Chalk-surfaced" papers. The availability of many postage stamps for revenue purposes made necessary some safeguard against the illegitimate re-use of stamps with removable cancellations. This was at first secured by using fugitive inks and later by printing on chalk-surfaced paper, both of which made it difficult to remove any form of obliteration without also damaging the stamp design.

This catalogue lists these chalk-surfaced paper varieties from their introduction in 1905. Where no indication is given, the paper is "ordinary".

Our chalk-surfaced paper is specifically one which shows a black mark when touched with a silver wire. The paper used during the Second World War for high values, as in Bermuda, the Leeward Islands, etc., was thinly coated with some kind of surfacing which does not react to silver and is therefore regarded (and listed) as "ordinary". Stamps on chalk-surfaced paper can easily lose this coating through immersion in water.

Another paper introduced during the War as a substitute for chalk-surfaced is rather thick, very white and glossy and shows little or no watermark, nor does it show a black line when touched with silver. In the Bahamas high values this paper might be mistaken for the chalk-surfaced (which is thinner and poorer-looking) but for the silver test.

Some modern coated papers show little or no reaction to the silver test and, therefore, cannot be classed as chalk-surfaced.

Glazed paper. In 1969 the Crown Agents introduced a new general-purpose paper for use in conjunction with all current printing processes. It generally has a marked glossy surface but the degree varies according to the process used, being more marked in recess-printing stamps. As it does not respond to the silver test this presents a further test where previous printings were on chalky paper. A change of paper to the glazed variety merits separate listing.

Green and yellow papers. Issues of the First World War and immediate postwar period occur on green and yellow papers and these are given separate Catalogue listing. The original coloured papers (coloured throughout) gave way to surface-coloured papers, the stamps having "white backs"; other stamps show one colour on the front and a different one at the back. Because of the numerous variations a grouping of colours is adopted as follows:

YELLOW PAPERS

(1) The original *yellow* paper (throughout), usually bright in colour. The gum is often sparse, of harsh consistency and dull-looking. Used 1912–1920.

(2) The *white backs*. Used 1913–1914.

(3) A bright *lemon* paper. The colour must have a pronounced greenish tinge, different from the "yellow" in (1). As a rule, the gum on stamps using this lemon paper is plentiful, smooth and shiny, and the watermark shows distinctly. Care is needed with stamps printed in green on yellow paper (1) as it may appear that the paper is this lemon. Used 1914–1916.

(4) An experimental *orange-buff* paper. The colour must have a distinct brownish tinge. It is not to be confused with a muddy yellow (1) nor the misleading appearance (on the surface) of stamps printed in red on yellow paper where an engraved plate has been insufficiently wiped. Used 1918–1921.

(5) An experimental *buff* paper. This lacks the brownish tinge of (4) and the brightness of the yellow shades. The gum is shiny when compared with the matt type used on (4). Used 1919–1920.

(6) A *pale yellow* paper that has a creamy tone to the yellow. Used from 1920 onwards.

GREEN PAPERS

(7) The original "green" paper, varying considerably through shades of *blue-green* and *yellow-*

green, the front and back sometimes differing. Used 1912–1916.

(8) The *white backs*. Used 1913–1914.

(9) A paper blue-green on the surface with *pale olive* back. The back must be markedly paler than the front and this and the pronounced olive tinge to the back distinguish it from (7). Used 1916–1920.

(10) Paper with a vivid green surface, commonly called *emerald-green*; it has the olive back of (9). Used 1920.

(11) Paper with *emerald-green* both back and front. Used from 1920 onwards.

3. Perforation and Rouletting

Perforation gauge. The gauge of a perforation is the number of holes in a length of 2 cm. For correct classification the size of the holes (large or small) may need to be distinguished; in a few cases the actual number of holes on each edge of the stamp needs to be quoted.

Measurement. The Gibbons *Instanta* gauge is the standard for measuring perforations. The stamp is viewed against a dark background with the transparent gauge put on top of it. Though the gauge measures to decimal accuracy, perforations read from it are generally quoted in the Catalogue to the nearest half. For example:

Just over perf $12\frac{3}{4}$ to just under $13\frac{1}{4}$ = perf 13
Perf $13\frac{1}{4}$ exactly, rounded up = perf $13\frac{1}{2}$
Just over perf $13\frac{1}{4}$ to just under $13\frac{3}{4}$ = perf $13\frac{1}{2}$
Perf $13\frac{3}{4}$ exactly, rounded up = perf 14

However, where classification depends on it, actual quarter-perforations are quoted.

Notation. Where no perforation is quoted for an issue it is imperforate. Perforations are usually abbreviated (and spoken) as follows, though sometimes they may be spelled out for clarity. This notation for rectangular stamps (the majority) applies to diamond shapes if "top" is read as the edge to the top right.

P 14: perforated alike on all sides (read: "perf 14").

P 14 × 15: the first figure refers to top and bottom, the second to left and right sides (read: "perf 14 by 15"). This is a compound perforation. For an upright triangular stamp the first figure refers to the two sloping sides and second to the base. In inverted triangulars the base is first and the second figure refers to the sloping sides.

P 14–15: perforation measuring anything between 14 and 15: the holes are irregularly spaced, thus the gauge may vary along a single line or even along a single edge of the stamp (read: "perf 14 to 15").

P 14 *irregular*: perforated 14 from a worn perforator, giving badly aligned holes irregularly spaced (read: "irregular perf 14").

P comp(ound) 14 × 15: two gauges in use but not necessarily on opposite sides of the stamp. It could be one side in one gauge and three in the other; or two adjacent sides with the same gauge. (Read: "perf compound of 14 and 15".) For three gauges or more, abbreviated as "*P* 14, $14\frac{1}{2}$, 15 *or compound*" for example.

P 14, $14\frac{1}{2}$: perforated approximately $14\frac{1}{4}$ (read: "perf 14 or $14\frac{1}{2}$"). It does *not* mean two stamps, one perf 14 and the other perf $14\frac{1}{2}$. This obsolescent notation is gradually being replaced in the Catalogue.

Imperf: imperforate (not perforated).

Imperf × P 14: imperforate at top and bottom and perf 14 at sides.

Perf × imperf

P 14 × *imperf*: perf 14 at top and bottom and imperforate at sides.

Such headings as "*P* 13 × 14 (*vert*) and *P* 14 × 13 (*horiz*)" indicate which perforations apply to which stamp format—vertical or horizontal.

Some stamps are additionally perforated so that a label or tab is detachable; others have been perforated suitably for use as two halves. Listings are normally for whole stamps, unless stated otherwise.

Other terms. Perforation almost always gives circular holes; where other shapes have been used they are specified, e.g. square holes; lozenge perf. Interrupted perfs are brought about by the omission of pins at regular intervals. Perforations merely simulated by being printed as part of the design are of course ignored. With few exceptions, privately applied perforations are not listed.

In the nineteenth century perforations are often described as clean cut (clean, sharply incised holes), intermediate or rough (rough holes, imperfectly cut, often the result of blunt pins).

Perforation errors and varieties. Authenticated errors, where a stamp normally perforated is accidentally issued imperforate, are listed provided no traces of perforation (blind holes or indentations) remain. They must be provided as pairs, both stamps wholly imperforate, and are only priced in that form.

In Great Britain, numerous of these part-perforated stamps have arisen from the introduction of the Jumelle Press. This has a rotary perforator with rows of pins on one drum engaging with holes on another. Engagement is only gradual when the perforating unit is started up or stopped, giving rise to perforations "fading out", a variety mentioned above as not listed.

Stamps imperforate between stamp and sheet margin are not listed in this catalogue, but such errors on Great Britain stamps will be found in the *Great Britain Specialised Catalogue*.

Pairs described as "imperforate between" have the line of perforations between the two stamps omitted.

Imperf between (horiz pair): a horizontal pair of stamps with perfs all around the edges but none between the stamps.

Imperf between (vert pair): a vertical pair of stamps with perfs all around the edges but none between the stamps.

| imperf between (vertical pair) | Imperf horizontally (vertical pair) |

Where several of the rows have escaped perforation the resulting varieties are listable. Thus:

Imperf vert (horiz pair): a horizontal pair of stamps perforated top and bottom; all three vertical directions are imperf—the two outer edges and between the stamps.

Imperf horiz (vert pair): a vertical pair perforated at left and right edges; all three horizontal directions are imperf—the top, bottom and between the stamps.

Straight edges. Large sheets cut up before issue to post offices can cause stamps with straight edges,

i.e. imperf on one side or on two sides at right angles. They are not usually listable in this condition and are worth less than corresponding stamps properly perforated all round. This does not, however, apply to certain stamps, mainly from coils and booklets, where straight edges on various sides are the manufacturing norm affecting every stamp. The listings and notes make clear which sides are correctly imperf.

Malfunction. Varieties of double, misplaced or partial perforation caused by error or machine malfunction are not listable, neither are freaks, such as perforations placed diagonally from paper folds, nor missing holes caused by broken pins.

Centering. Well-centred stamps have designs surrounded by equal opposite margins. Where this condition affects the price the fact is stated.

Types of perforating. Where necessary for classification, perforation types are distinguished. These include:

Line perforation from one line of pins punching single rows of holes at a time.

Comb perforation from pins disposed across the sheet in comb formation, punching out holes at three sides of the stamp a row at a time.

Harrow perforation applied to a whole pane or sheet at one stroke.

Rotary perforation from toothed wheels operating across a sheet, then crosswise.

Sewing-machine perforation. The resultant condition, clean-cut or rough, is distinguished where required.

Pin-perforation is the commonly applied term for pin-roulette in which, instead of being punched out, round holes are pricked by sharp-pointed pins and no paper is removed.

Mixed perforation occurs when stamps with defective perforations are re-perforated in a different gauge.

Punctured stamps. Perforation holes can be punched into the face of the stamp. Patterns of small holes, often in the shape of initial letters, are privately applied devices against pilferage. These "perfins" are outside the scope except for Australia, Canada, Cape of Good Hope, Papua and Sudan where they were used as official stamps by the national administration. Identification devices, when officially inspired, are listed or noted; they can be shapes, or letters or words formed from holes, sometimes converting one class of stamp into another.

Rouletting. In rouletting the paper is cut, for ease of separation, but none is removed. The gauge is measured, when needed, as for perforations. Traditional French terms descriptive of the type of cut are often used and types include:

Arc roulette (percé en arc). Cuts are minute, spaced arcs, each roughly a semicircle.

Cross roulette (percé en croix). Cuts are tiny diagonal crosses.

Line roulette (percé en ligne or *en ligne droite)*. Short straight cuts parallel to the frame of the stamp. The commonest basic roulette. Where not further described, "roulette" means this type.

Rouletted in colour or *coloured roulette (percé en lignes colorées* or *en lignes de couleur)*. Cuts with coloured edges, arising from notched rule inked simultaneously with the printing plate.

Saw-tooth roulette (percé en scie). Cuts applied zigzag fashion to resemble the teeth of a saw.

Serpentine roulette (percé en serpentin). Cuts as sharply wavy lines.

Zigzag roulette (percé en zigzags). Short straight cuts at angles in alternate directions, producing sharp points on separation. U.S. usage favours "serrate(d) roulette" for this type.

Pin-roulette (originally *percé en points* and now *perforés trous d'epingle*) is commonly called pin-perforation in English.

4. Gum

All stamps listed are assumed to have gum of some kind; if they were issued without gum this is stated. Original gum (o.g.) means that which was present on the stamp as issued to the public. Deleterious climates and the presence of certain chemicals can cause gum to crack and, with early stamps, even make the paper deteriorate. Unscrupulous fakers are adept in removing it and regumming the stamp to meet the unreasoning demand often made for "full o.g." in cases where such a thing is virtually impossible.

The gum normally used on stamps has been gum arabic until the late 1960s when synthetic adhesives were introduced. Harrison and Sons Ltd for instance use *polyvinyl alcohol,* known to philatelists as PVA. This is almost invisible except for a slight yellowish tinge which was incorporated to make it possible to see that the stamps have been gummed. It has advantages in hot countries, as stamps do not curl and sheets are less likely to stick together. Gum arabic and PVA are not distinguished in the lists except that where a stamp exists with both forms this is indicated in footnotes. Our more specialised catalogues provide separate listing of gums for Great Britain.

Self-adhesive stamps are issued on backing paper, from which they are peeled before affixing to mail. Unused examples are priced as for backing paper intact, in which condition they are recommended to be kept. Used examples are best collected on cover or on piece.

5. Watermarks

Stamps are on unwatermarked paper except where the heading to the set says otherwise.

Detection. Watermarks are detected for Catalogue description by one of four methods: (1) holding stamps to the light; (2) laying stamps face down on a dark background; (3) adding a few drops of petroleum ether 40/60 to the stamp laid face down in a watermark tray; (4) by use of the Morley-Bright Detector, or other equipment, which work by revealing the thinning of the paper at the watermark (Note that petroleum ether is highly inflammable in use and can damage photogravure stamps.)

Listable types. Stamps occurring on both watermarked and unwatermarked papers are different types and both receive full listing.

Single watermarks (devices occurring once on every stamp) can be modified in size and shape as between different issues; the types are noted but not usually separately listed. Fortuitous absence of watermark from a single stamp or its gross displacement would not be listable.

To overcome registration difficulties the device may be repeated at close intervals (a *multiple watermark*), single stamps thus showing parts of several devices. Similarly, a large *sheet watermark* (or *all-over watermark*) covering numerous stamps can be used. We give informative notes and illustrations for them. The designs may be such that numbers of stamps in the sheet automatically lack watermark: this is not a listable variety. Multiple and all-over watermarks sometimes undergo modifications, but if the various types are difficult to distinguish from single stamps notes are given but not separate listings.

Papermakers' watermarks are noted where known but not listed separately, since most stamps in the sheet will lack them. Sheet watermarks which are nothing more than officially adopted papermakers' watermarks are, however, given normal listing.

Marginal watermarks, falling outside the pane of stamps, are ignored except where misplacement caused the adjoining row to be affected, in which case they are footnoted.

Watermark errors and varieties. Watermark errors are recognised as of major importance. They comprise stamps intended to be on unwatermarked paper but issued watermarked by mistake, or stamps printed on paper with the wrong watermark. Varieties showing letters omitted from the watermark are also included, but broken or deformed bits on the dandy roll are not listed unless they represent repairs.

Watermark positions. The diagram shows how watermark position is described in the Catalogue. Paper has a side intended for printing and watermarks are usually impressed so that they read normally when looked through from that printed side. However, since philatelists customarily detect watermarks by looking at the back of the stamp the watermark diagram also makes clear what is actually seen.

Illustrations in the Catalogue are of watermarks in normal positions (from the front of the stamps) and are actual size where possible.

Differences in watermark position are collectable as distinct varieties. This Catalogue now lists inverted, sideways inverted and reversed watermark varieties on Commonwealth stamps from the 1860s onwards *except* where the watermark position is completely haphazard.

Great Britain inverted and sideways inverted watermarks can be found in the *Great Britain Specialised Catalogue* and the *Great Britain Concise Catalogue*.

Where a watermark comes indiscriminately in various positions our policy is to cover this by a general note: we do not give separate listings because the watermark position in these circumstances has no particular philatelic importance. There is a general note of this sort in modern Cyprus, for example. Issues printed since 1962 by Aspioti-Elka occur with the vertical stamps having the watermark normal or inverted, while horizontal stamps are likewise found with the watermark reading upwards or downwards.

AS DESCRIBED (Read through front of stamp)		AS SEEN DURING WATERMARK DETECTION (Stamp face down and back examined)
GvR	Normal	ЯvG
ЯvG	Inverted	ӘvЯ
ЯvG	Reversed	GvR
ӘvЯ	Reversed and inverted	ЯvӘ
GvR	Sideways	ᗡᴧ⅁
GvR	Sideways inverted	ᴙᴧꓱ

Standard types of watermark. Some watermarks have been used generally for various British possessions rather than exclusively for a single colony. To avoid repetition the Catalogue classifies 17 general types, as under, with references in the headings throughout the listings being given either in words or in the form "*W* w **14**" (meaning "watermark type w **14**"). In those cases where watermark illustrations appear in the listings themselves, the respective reference reads,

for example, *W* **153**, thus indicating that the watermark will be found in the normal sequence of illustrations as (type) **153**.

The general types are as follows, with an example of each quoted.

W	Description	Example
w **1**	Large Star	St. Helena No. 1
w **2**	Small Star	Turks Is. No. 4
w **3**	Broad (pointed) Star	Grenada No. 24
w **4**	Crown (over) CC, small stamp	Antigua No. 13
w **5**	Crown (over) CC, large stamp	Antigua No. 31
w **6**	Crown (over) CA, small stamp	Antigua No. 21
w **7**	Crown CA (CA over Crown), large stamp	Sierra Leone No. 54
w **8**	Multiple Crown CA	Antigua No. 41
w **9**	Multiple Crown Script CA	Seychelles No. 158
w **9a**	do.　Error	Seychelles No. 158a
w **9b**	do.　Error	Seychelles No. 158b
w **10**	V over Crown	N.S.W. No. 327
w **11**	Crown over A	N.S.W. No. 347
w **12**	Multiple St. Edward's Crown Block CA	Antigua No. 149
w **13**	Multiple PTM	Johore No. 166
w **14**	Multiple Crown CA Diagonal	Antigua No. 426
w **15**	Multiple POST OFFICE	Kiribati No. 141
w **16**	Multiple Crown Script CA Diagonal	Ascension No. 376
w **17**	Multiple CARTOR	Brunei No. 357

CC in these watermarks is an abbreviation for "Crown Colonies" and CA for "Crown Agents". Watermarks w **1**, w **2** and w **3** are on stamps printed by Perkins, Bacon; w **4** onwards on stamps from De La Rue and other printers.

w **1**
Large Star

w **2**
Small Star

w **3**
Broad (pointed) Star

Watermark w **1**, *Large Star*, measures 15 to 16 mm across the star from point to point and about 27 mm from centre to centre vertically between stars in the sheet. It was made for long stamps like Ceylon 1857 and St. Helena 1856.

Watermark w **2**, *Small Star*, is of similar design but measures 12 to 13½ mm from point to point and 24 mm from centre to centre vertically. It was for use with ordinary-size stamps such as Grenada 1863–71.

When the Large Star watermark was used with the smaller stamps it only occasionally comes in the centre of the paper. It is frequently so misplaced as to show portions of two stars above and below and this eccentricity will very often help in determining the watermark.

Watermark w 3, *Broad* (*pointed*) *Star*, resembles w 1 but the points are broader.

w 4
Crown (over) CC

w 5
Crown (over) CC

Two *Crown* (*over*) *CC* watermarks were used: w 4 was for stamps of ordinary size and w 5 for those of larger size.

w 6
Crown (over) CA

w 7
CA over Crown

Two watermarks of *Crown CA* type were used, w 6 being for stamps of ordinary size. The other, w 7, is properly described as *CA over Crown*. It was specially made for paper on which it was intended to print long fiscal stamps: that some were used postally accounts for the appearance of w 7 in the Catalogue. The watermark occupies twice the space of the ordinary Crown CA watermark, w 6. Stamps of normal size printed on paper with w 7 watermark show it *sideways*; it takes a horizontal pair of stamps to show the entire watermark.

w 8
Multiple Crown CA

w 9
Multiple Crown
Script CA

Multiple watermarks began in 1904 with w 8, *Multiple Crown CA*, changed from 1921 to w 9, *Multiple Crown Script CA*. On stamps of ordinary size portions of two or three watermarks appear and on the large-sized stamps a greater number can be observed. The change to letters in script character with w 9 was accompanied by a Crown of distinctly different shape.

It seems likely that there were at least two dandy rolls for each Crown Agents watermark in use at any one time with a reserve roll being employed when the normal one was withdrawn for maintenance or repair.

Both the Mult Crown CA and the Mult Script CA types exist with one or other of the letters omitted from individual impressions. It is possible that most of these occur from the reserve rolls as they have only been found on certain issues. The MCA watermark experienced such problems

during the early 1920s and the Script over a longer period from the early 1940s until 1951.

During the 1920s damage must also have occurred on one of the Crowns as a substituted Crown has been found on certain issues. This is smaller than the normal and consists of an oval base joined to two upright ovals with a circle positioned between their upper ends. The upper line of the Crown's base is omitted, as are the left and right-hand circles at the top and also the cross over the centre circle.

Substituted Crown

w 9a: Error,
Crown missing

w 9b: Error,
St. Edward's Crown

The *Multiple Crown Script CA* watermark, w 9, is known with two errors recurring among the 1950–52 printings of several territories. In the first a crown has fallen away from the dandy-roll that impresses the watermark into the paper pulp. It gives w 9a, *Crown missing*, but this omission has been found in both "Crown only" (*illustrated*) and "Crown CA" rows. The resulting faulty paper was used for Seychelles, Johore and the postage due stamps of nine colonies.

When the omission was noticed a second mishap occurred, which was to insert a wrong crown in the space, giving w 9b, *St. Edward's Crown*. This produced varieties in Bahamas, St. Kitts-Nevis and Singapore and the incorrect crown likewise occurs in "Crown only" and "Crown CA" rows.

w 10
V over Crown

w 11
Crown over A

Resuming the general types, two watermarks found in issues of several Australian States are: w 10, *V over Crown*, and w 11, *Crown over A*.

w 12
Multiple St. Edward's
Crown Block CA

The *Multiple St. Edward's Crown Block CA* watermark, w 12, was introduced in 1957 and besides the change in the Crown (from that used in *Multiple Crown Script CA,* w 9) the letters reverted to block capitals. The new watermark began to appear sideways in 1966 and these stamps are generally listed as separate sets.

w 13
Multiple PTM

The watermark w 13, *Multiple PTM*, was introduced for new Malayan issues in November 1961.

w 14
Multiple Crown CA
Diagonal

By 1974 the two dandy-rolls (the "upright" and the "sideways") for w 12 were wearing out; the Crown Agents therefore discontinued using the sideways-watermark one and retained the other only as a stand-by. A new dandy-roll with the pattern of w 14, *Multiple Crown CA Diagonal*, was introduced and first saw use with some Churchill Centenary issues.

The new watermark has the design arranged in gradually spiralling rows. It is improved in design to allow smooth passage over the paper (the gaps between letters and rows had caused jolts in previous dandy-rolls) and the sharp corners and angles, where fibres used to accumulate, have been eliminated by rounding.

This watermark has no "normal" sideways position amongst the different printers using it. To avoid confusion our more specialised listings do not rely on such terms as "sideways inverted" but describe the direction in which the watermark points.

w 15
Multiple POST OFFICE

During 1981 w 15, *Multiple POST OFFICE*, was introduced for certain issues prepared by Philatelists Ltd, acting for various countries in the Indian Ocean, Pacific and West Indies.

w 16
Multiple Crown Script CA Diagonal

A new Crown Agents watermark was introduced during 1985, w 16, *Multiple Crown Script CA Diagonal*. This was very similar to the previous w 14, but showed "CA" in script rather than block letters. It was first used on the omnibus series of stamps commemorating the Life and Times of Queen Elizabeth the Queen Mother.

w 17
Multiple CARTOR

Watermark w 17, *Multiple CARTOR*, was used from 1985 for issues printed by this French firm for countries which did not normally use the Crown Agents watermark.

In recent years the use of watermarks has, to a small extent, been superseded by fluorescent security markings. These are often more visible from the reverse of the stamp (Cook Islands from 1970 onwards), but have occurred printed over the design (Hong Kong Nos. 415/30). In 1982 the Crown Agents introduced a new stock paper, without watermark, known as "C-Kurity" on which a fluorescent pattern of blue rosettes is visible on the reverse, beneath the gum. This paper was used for issues from Gambia and Norfolk Island.

6. Colours

Stamps in two or three colours have these named in order of appearance, from the centre moving outwards. Four colours or more are usually listed as multicoloured.

In compound colour names the second is the predominant one, thus:

orange-red = a red tending towards orange;
red-orange = an orange containing more red than usual.

Standard colours used. The 200 colours most used for stamp identification are given in the Stanley Gibbons Stamp Colour Key. The Catalogue has used the Stamp Colour Key as standard for describing new issues for some years. The names are also introduced as lists are rewritten, though exceptions are made for those early issues where traditional names have become universally established.

Determining colours. When comparing actual stamps with colour samples in the Stamp Colour Key, view in a good north daylight (or its best substitute: fluorescent "colour-matching" light). Sunshine is not recommended. Choose a solid portion of the stamp design; if available, marginal markings such as solid bars of colour or colour check dots are helpful. Shading lines in the design can be misleading as they appear lighter than solid colour. Postmarked portions of a stamp appear darker than normal. If more than one colour is present, mask off the extraneous ones as the eye tends to mix them.

Errors of colour. Major colour errors in stamps or overprints which qualify for listing are: wrong colours; one colour inverted in relation to the rest; albinos (colourless impressions), where these have Expert Committee certificates; colours completely omitted, but only on unused stamps (if found on used stamps the information is footnoted) and with good credentials, missing colours being frequently faked.

Colours only partially omitted are not recognised. Colour shifts, however spectacular, are not listed.

Shades. Shades in philately refer to variations in the intensity of a colour or the presence of differing amounts of other colours. They are particularly significant when they can be linked to specific printings. In general, shades need to be quite marked to fall within the scope of this Catalogue; it does not favour nowadays listing the often numerous shades of a stamp, but chooses a single applicable colour name which will indicate particular groups of outstanding shades. Furthermore, the listings refer to colours as issued: they may deteriorate into something different through the passage of time.

Modern colour printing by lithography is prone to marked differences of shade, even within a single run, and variations can occur within the same sheet. Such shades are not listed.

Aniline colours. An aniline colour meant originally one derived from coal-tar; it now refers more widely to colour of a particular brightness suffused on the surface of a stamp and showing through clearly on the back.

Colours of overprints and surcharges. All overprints and surcharges are in black unless stated otherwise in the heading or after the description of the stamp.

7. Specimen Stamps

Originally, stamps overprinted SPECIMEN were circulated to postmasters or kept in official records, but after the establishment of the Universal Postal Union supplies are sent to Berne for distribution to the postal administrations of member countries.

During the period 1884 to 1928 most of the stamps of British Crown Colonies required for this purpose were overprinted SPECIMEN in various shapes and sizes by their printers from typeset formes. Some locally produced provisionals were handstamped locally, as were sets prepared for presentation. From 1928 stamps were punched with holes forming the word SPECIMEN, each firm of printers using a different machine or machines. From 1948 the stamps supplied for U.P.U. distribution were no longer punctured.

Stamps of some other Commonwealth territories were overprinted or handstamped locally, while stamps of Great Britain and those overprinted for use in overseas postal agencies (mostly of the higher denominations) bore SPECIMEN overprints and handstamps applied by the Inland Revenue or the Post Office.

Some of the commoner types of overprints or punctures are illustrated here. Collectors are warned that dangerous forgeries of the punctured type exist.

The *Part 1* (*British Commonwealth*) *Catalogue* records those Specimen overprints or perforations intended for distribution by the U.P.U. to member countries. In addition the Specimen overprints of Australia and its dependent territories, which were sold to collectors by the Post Office, are also included.

Various Perkins Bacon issues exist obliterated with a "CANCELLED" within an oval of bars handstamp.

Perkins Bacon
"CANCELLED"
Handstamp

This was applied to six examples of those issues available in 1861 which were then given to members of Sir Rowland Hill's family. Seventy-five different stamps (including four from Chile) are recorded with this handstamp although others may possibly exist. The unauthorised gift of these "CANCELLED" stamps to the Hill family was a major factor in the loss of the Agent General for the Crown Colonies (the forerunner of the Crown Agents) contracts by Perkins Bacon in the following year. Where examples of these scarce items are known to be in private hands the catalogue provides a price.

For full details of these stamps see *CANCELLED by Perkins Bacon* by Peter Jaffé (published by Spink in 1998).

All other Specimens are outside the scope of this volume.

Specimens are not quoted in Great Britain as they are fully listed in the Stanley Gibbons *Great Britain Specialised Catalogue*.

In specifying type of specimen for individual high-value stamps, "H/S" means handstamped, "Optd" is overprinted and "Perf" is punctured. Some sets occur mixed, e.g. "Optd/Perf". If unspecified, the type is apparent from the date or it is the same as for the lower values quoted as a set.

Prices. Prices for stamps up to £1 are quoted in sets; higher values are priced singly after the colours, thus "(S. £20)". Where specimens exist in more than one type the price quoted is for the cheapest. Specimen stamps have rarely survived even as pairs; these and strips of three, four or five are worth considerably more than singles.

8. Luminescence

Machines which sort mail electronically have been introduced in recent years. In consequence some countries have issued stamps on fluorescent or phosphorescent papers, while others have marked their stamps with phosphor bands.

The various papers can only be distinguished by ultraviolet lamps emitting particular wavelengths. They are separately listed only when the stamps have some other means of distinguishing them, visible without the use of these lamps. Where this is not so, the papers are recorded in footnotes or headings.

For this Catalogue we do not consider it appropriate that collectors be compelled to have use of an ultraviolet lamp before being able to identify stamps by our listings. Some experience will also be found necessary in interpreting the results given by ultraviolet. Collectors using the lamps, nevertheless, should exercise great care in their use as exposure to their light is extremely dangerous to the eyes.

Phosphor bands are listable, since they are visible to the naked eye (by holding stamps at an angle to the light and looking along them, the bands appear dark). Stamps existing with and without phosphor bands or with differing numbers of bands are given separate listings. Varieties such as double bands, bands omitted, misplaced or printed on the back are not listed.

Detailed descriptions appear at appropriate places in the listings in explanation of luminescent papers; *see*, for example, Australia above No. 308, Canada above Nos. 472 and 611, Cook Is. above No. 249, etc.

For Great Britain, where since 1959 phosphors have played a prominent and intricate part in stamp issues, the main notes above Nos. 599, 723 and after the Decimal Machin issue (No. X841 onwards) should be studied, as well as the footnotes to individual listings where appropriate. In general the classification is as follows.

Stamps with *phosphor bands* are those where a separate cylinder applies the phosphor after the stamps are printed. Issues with "all-over" phosphor have the "band" covering the entire stamp. Parts of the stamp covered by phosphor bands, or the entire surface for "all-over" phosphor versions, appear matt. Stamps on *phosphorised paper* have the phosphor added to the paper coating before the stamps are printed. Issues on this paper have a completely shiny surface.

Further particularisation of phosphor—their methods of printing and the colours they exhibit under ultraviolet—is outside the scope. The more specialised listings should be consulted for this information.

9. Coil Stamps

Stamps issued only in coil form are given full listing. If stamps are issued in both sheets and coils the coil stamps are listed separately only where there is some feature (e.g. perforation or watermark sideways) by which singles can be distinguished. Coil strips containing different stamps *se-tenant* are also listed.

Coil join pairs are too random and too easily faked to permit of listing; similarly ignored are coil stamps which have accidentally suffered an extra row of perforations from the claw mechanism in a malfunctioning vending machine.

10. Stamp Booklets

Stamp booklets (with the exception of those from Great Britain, the Channel Islands and the Isle of Man, for which see the current editions of the *Great Britain Concise Catalogue* and *Collect Channel Islands and Isle of Man Stamps*) are now listed in this catalogue.

Single stamps from booklets are listed if they are distinguishable in some way (such as watermark or perforation) from similar sheet stamps.

Booklet panes are listed where they contain stamps of different denominations *se-tenant*, where stamp-size labels are included, or where such panes are otherwise identifiable. Booklet panes are placed in the listing under the lowest denomination present.

Particular perforations (straight edges) are covered by appropriate notes.

11. Miniature Sheets and Sheetlets

We distinguish between "miniature sheets" and "sheetlets" and this affects the catalogue numbering. An item in sheet form that is postally valid, containing a single stamp, pair, block or set of stamps, with wide, inscribed and/or decorative margins, is a *miniature sheet* if it is sold at post offices as an indivisible entity. As such the Catalogue allots a single **MS** number and describes what stamps make it up. (*See* Great Britain 1978 Historic Buildings, No. **MS**1058, as an example.) The *sheetlet* or *small sheet* differs in that the individual stamps are intended to be purchased separately for postal purposes. For sheetlets, all the component postage stamps are numbered individually and the composition explained in a footnote. (The 1978 Christmas Island Christmas sheetlet, Nos. 99/107, is an example.) Note that the definitions refer to post office sale—not how items may be subsequently offered by stamp dealers.

Production as sheetlets is a modern marketing development chosen by postal administrations to interest collectors in purchasing the item complete; if he has done so he should, as with all *se-tenant* arrangements, keep the sheetlet intact in his collection.

The Catalogue will in future no longer give full listing to designs, originally issued in normal sheets, which subsequently appear in sheetlets showing changes of colour, perforation, printing process or face value. Such stamps will be covered by footnotes.

12. Forgeries and Fakes

Forgeries. Where space permits, notes are considered if they can give a concise description that will permit unequivocal detection of a forgery. Generalised warnings, lacking detail, are not nowadays inserted, since their value to the collector is problematic.

Fakes. Unwitting fakes are numerous, particularly "new shades" which are colour changelings brought about by exposure to sunlight, soaking in water contaminated with dyes from adherent paper, contact with oil and dirt from a pocketbook, and so on. Fraudulent operators, in addition, can offer to arrange: removal of hinge marks; repairs of thins on white or coloured papers; replacement of missing margins or perforations; reperforating in true or false gauges; removal of fiscal cancellations; rejoining of severed pairs, strips and blocks; and (a major hazard) regumming. Collectors can only be urged to purchase from reputable sources and to insist upon Expert Committee certification where there is any kind of doubt.

The Catalogue can consider footnotes about fakes where these are specific enough to assist in detection.

1935 SILVER JUBILEE CROWN COLONY ISSUE

The Crown Colony Windsor Castle design by Harold Fleury is, surely, one of the most impressive produced in the 20th-century and its reproduction in the recess process by three of the leading stamp-printing firms of the era has provided a subject for philatelic research which has yet to be exhausted.

Each of the three, Bradbury, Wilkinson & Co. and Waterlow and Sons, who both produced fifteen issues, together with De La Rue & Co. who printed fourteen, used a series of vignette (centre) plates coupled with individual frame plates for each value. All were taken from dies made by Waterlow. Several worthwhile varieties exist on the frame plates, but most interest has been concentrated on the centre plates, each of which was used to print a considerable number of different stamps.

Sheets printed by Bradbury, Wilkinson were without printed plate numbers, but research has now identified eleven centre plates which were probably used in permanent pairings. A twelfth plate awaits confirmation. Stamps from some of these centre plates have revealed a number of prominent plate flaws, the most famous of which, the extra flagstaff, has been eagerly sought by collectors for many years.

Extra flagstaff
(Plate 1" R. 9/1)

Short extra flagstaff
(Plate "2" R. 2/1)

Lightning conductor
(Plate "3" R. 2/5)

Flagstaff on right-hand
turret (Plate "5" R. 7/1)

Double flagstaff (Plate
"6" R. 5/2)

De La Rue sheets were initially printed with plate numbers, but in many instances these were subsequently trimmed off. Surviving examples do, however, enable a positive identification of six centre plates, 2A, 2B, (2A), (2B), 4 and 4/ to be made. The evidence of sheet markings and plate flaws clearly demonstrates that there were two different pairs of plates numbered 2A 2B. The second pair is designated (2A) (2B) by specialist collectors to avoid further confusion. The number of major plate flaws is not so great as on the Bradbury, Wilkinson sheets, but four examples are included in the catalogue.

Diagonal line by turret
(Plate 2A R. 10/1 and 10/2)

Dot to left of chapel
(Plate 2B R. 8/3)

Dot by flagstaff (Plate 4 R. 8/4)

Dash by turret (Plate 4/ R. 3/6)

Much less is known concerning the Waterlow centre plate system as the sheets did not show plate numbers. Ten individual plates have, so far, been identified and it is believed that these were used in pairs. The two versions of the kite and log flaw from plate "2" show that this plate exists in two states.

Damaged turret
(Plate "1" R. 5/6)

Kite and vertical log
(Plate "2A" R. 10/6)

Kite and horizontal log
(Plate "2B" R. 10/6)

Bird by turret
(Plate "7" R. 1/5)

Abbreviations

Printers

A.B.N. Co	American Bank Note Co, New York.
A. & M.	Alden & Mowbray Ltd, Oxford.
Ashton-Potter	Ashton-Potter Ltd, Toronto.
Aspioti-Elka (Aspiotis)	Aspioti-Elka, Greece.
B.A.B.N.	British American Bank Note Co, Ottawa.
B.D.T.	B.D.T. International Security Printing Ltd, Dublin, Ireland.
B.W.	Bradbury Wilkinson & Co, Ltd.
Cartor	Cartor S.A., La Loupe, France.
C.B.N.	Canadian Bank Note Co, Ottawa.
Continental B.N. Co	Continental Bank Note Co.
Courvoisier	Imprimerie Courvoisier S.A., La-Chaux-de-Fonds, Switzerland.
D.L.R.	De La Rue & Co, Ltd, London, and (from 1961) Bogota, Colombia.
Edila	Editions de l'Aubetin, S.A.
Enschedé	Joh. Enschedé en Zonen, Haarlem, Netherlands.
Format	Format International Security Printers, Ltd, London.
Harrison	Harrison & Sons, Ltd, London
Heraclio Fournier	Heraclio Fournier S.A., Vitoria, Spain.
J.W.	John Waddington Security Print Ltd., Leeds
P.B.	Perkins Bacon Ltd, London.
Questa	Questa Colour Security Printers, Ltd., London
Ueberreuter	Ueberreuter (incorporating Bruder Rosenbaum), Korneuburg, Austria.
Walsall	Walsall Security Printers, Ltd.
Waterlow	Waterlow & Sons, Ltd, London.

General Abbreviations

Alph	Alphabet
Anniv	Anniversary
Comp	Compound (perforation)
Des	Designer; designed
Diag	Diagonal; diagonally
Eng	Engraver; engraved
F.C.	Fiscal Cancellation
H/S	Handstamped
Horiz	Horizontal; horizontally
Imp, Imperf	Imperforate
Inscr	Inscribed
L	Left
Litho	Lithographed
mm	Millimetres
MS	Miniature sheet
N.Y.	New York
Opt(d)	Overprint(ed)
P or P-c	Pen-cancelled
P, Pf or Perf	Perforated
Photo	Photogravure
Pl	Plate
Pr	Pair
Ptd	Printed
Ptg	Printing
R	Right
R.	Row
Recess	Recess-printed
Roto	Rotogravure
Roul	Rouletted

S	Specimen (overprint)
Surch	Surcharge(d)
T.C.	Telegraph Cancellation
T	Type
Typo	Typographed
Un	Unused
Us	Used
Vert	Vertical; vertically
W or wmk	Watermark
Wmk s	Watermark sideways

(†)=Does not exist.
(—) (or blank price column)=Exists, or may exist, but no market price is known.
/ between colours means "on" and the colour following is that of the paper on which the stamp is printed.

Colours of Stamps

Bl (blue); blk (black); brn (brown); car, carm (carmine); choc (chocolate); clar (claret); emer (emerald); grn (green); ind (indigo); mag (magenta); mar (maroon); mult (multicoloured); mve (mauve); ol (olive); orge (orange); pk (pink); pur (purple); scar (scarlet); sep (sepia); turq (turquoise); ultram (ultramarine); verm (vermilion); vio (violet); yell (yellow).

Colour of Overprints and Surcharges

(B.) = blue, (Blk.) = black, (Br.) = brown, (C.) = carmine, (G.) = green, (Mag.) = magenta, (Mve.) = mauve, (Ol.) = olive, (O.) = orange, (P.) = purple, (Pk.) = pink, (R.)=red, (Sil.) = silver, (V.) = violet, (Vm.) or (Verm.) = vermilion, (W.) = white, (Y.) = yellow.

Arabic Numerals

As in the case of European figures, the details of the Arabic numerals vary in different stamp designs, but they should be readily recognised with the aid of this illustration.

•	١	٢	٣	٤	٥	٦	٧	٨	٩
0	1	2	3	4	5	6	7	8	9

International Philatelic Glossary

English	French	German	Spanish	Italian
Agate	Agate	Achat	Agata	Agata
Air stamp	Timbre de la poste aérienne	Flugpostmarke	Sello de correo aéreo	Francobollo per posta aerea
Apple Green	Vert-pomme	Apfelgrün	Verde manzana	Verde mela
Barred	Annulé par barres	Balkenentwertung	Anulado con barras	Sbarrato
Bisected	Timbre coupé	Halbiert	Partido en dos	Frazionato
Bistre	Bistre	Bister	Bistre	Bistro
Bistre-brown	Brun-bistre	Bisterbraun	Castaño bistre	Bruno-bistro
Black	Noir	Schwarz	Negro	Nero
Blackish Brown	Brun-noir	Schwärzlichbraun	Castaño negruzco	Bruno nerastro
Blackish Green	Vert foncé	Schwärzlichgrün	Verde negruzco	Verde nerastro
Blackish Olive	Olive foncé	Schwärzlicholiv	Oliva negruzco	Oliva nerastro
Block of four	Bloc de quatre	Viererblock	Bloque de cuatro	Bloco di quattro
Blue	Bleu	Blau	Azul	Azzurro
Blue-green	Vert-bleu	Blaugrün	Verde azul	Verde azzurro
Bluish Violet	Violet bleuâtre	Bläulichviolett	Violeta azulado	Violetto azzurrastro
Booklet	Carnet	Heft	Cuadernillo	Libretto
Bright Blue	Bleu vif	Lebhaftblau	Azul vivo	Azzurro vivo
Bright Green	Vert vif	Lebhaftgrün	Verde vivo	Verde vivo
Bright Purple	Mauve vif	Lebhaftpurpur	Púrpura vivo	Porpora vivo
Bronze Green	Vert-bronze	Bronzegrün	Verde bronce	Verde bronzo
Brown	Brun	Braun	Castaño	Bruno
Brown-lake	Carmin-brun	Braunlack	Laca castaño	Lacca bruno
Brown-purple	Pourpre-brun	Braunpurpur	Púrpura castaño	Porpora bruno
Brown-red	Rouge-brun	Braunrot	Rojo castaño	Rosso bruno
Buff	Chamois	Sämisch	Anteado	Camoscio
Cancellation	Oblitération	Entwertung	Cancelación	Annullamento
Cancelled	Annulé	Gestempelt	Cancelado	Annullato
Carmine	Carmin	Karmin	Carmín	Carminio
Carmine-red	Rouge-carmin	Karminrot	Rojo carmín	Rosso carminio
Centred	Centré	Zentriert	Centrado	Centrato
Cerise	Rouge-cerise	Kirschrot	Color de ceresa	Color Ciliegia
Chalk-surfaced paper	Papier couché	Kreidepapier	Papel estucado	Carta gessata
Chalky Blue	Bleu terne	Kreideblau	Azul turbio	Azzurro smorto
Charity stamp	Timbre de bienfaisance	Wohltätigkeitsmarke	Sello de beneficenza	Francobollo di beneficenza
Chestnut	Marron	Kastanienbraun	Castaño rojo	Marrone
Chocolate	Chocolat	Schokolade	Chocolate	Cioccolato
Cinnamon	Cannelle	Zimtbraun	Canela	Cannella
Claret	Grenat	Weinrot	Rojo vinoso	Vinaccia
Cobalt	Cobalt	Kobalt	Cobalto	Cobalto
Colour	Couleur	Farbe	Color	Colore
Comb-perforation	Dentelure en peigne	Kammzähnung, Reihenzähnung	Dentado de peine	Dentellatura e pettine
Commemorative stamp	Timbre commémoratif	Gedenkmarke	Sello conmemorativo	Francobollo commemorativo
Crimson	Cramoisi	Karmesin	Carmesí	Cremisi
Deep Blue	Bleu foncé	Dunkelblau	Azul oscuro	Azzurro scuro
Deep Bluish Green	Vert-bleu foncé	Dunkelbläulichgrün	Verde azulado oscuro	Verde azzurro scuro
Design	Dessin	Markenbild	Diseño	Disegno
Die	Matrice	Urstempel, Type, Platte	Cuño	Conio, Matrice
Double	Double	Doppelt	Doble	Doppio
Drab	Olive terne	Trüboliv	Oliva turbio	Oliva smorto
Dull Green	Vert terne	Trübgrün	Verde turbio	Verde smorto
Dull Purple	Mauve terne	Trübpurpur	Púrpura turbio	Porpora smorto
Embossing	Impression en relief	Prägedruck	Impresión en relieve	Impressione a rilievo
Emerald	Vert-éméraude	Smaragdgrün	Esmeralda	Smeraldo
Engraved	Gravé	Graviert	Grabado	Inciso
Error	Erreur	Fehler, Fehldruck	Error	Errore
Essay	Essai	Probedruck	Ensayo	Saggio
Express letter stamp	Timbre pour lettres par exprès	Eilmarke	Sello de urgencia	Francobollo per espresso
Fiscal stamp	Timbre fiscal	Stempelmarke	Sello fiscal	Francobollo fiscale
Flesh	Chair	Fleischfarben	Carne	Carnicino
Forgery	Faux, Falsification	Fälschung	Falsificación	Falso, Falsificazione
Frame	Cadre	Rahmen	Marco	Cornice
Granite paper	Papier avec fragments de fils de soie	Faserpapier	Papel con filamentos	Carto con fili di seta
Green	Vert	Grün	Verde	Verde
Greenish Blue	Bleu verdâtre	Grünlichblau	Azul verdoso	Azzurro verdastro

English	French	German	Spanish	Italian
Greenish Yellow	Jaune-vert	Grünlichgelb	Amarillo verdoso	Giallo verdastro
Grey	Gris	Grau	Gris	Grigio
Grey-blue	Bleu-gris	Graublau	Azul gris	Azzurro grigio
Grey-green	Vert gris	Graugrün	Verde gris	Verde grigio
Gum	Gomme	Gummi	Goma	Gomma
Gutter	Interpanneau	Zwischensteg	Espacio blanco entre dos grupos	Ponte
Imperforate	Non-dentelé	Geschnitten	Sin dentar	Non dentellato
Indigo	Indigo	Indigo	Azul indigo	Indaco
Inscription	Inscription	Inschrift	Inscripción	Dicitura
Inverted	Renversé	Kopfstehend	Invertido	Capovolto
Issue	Émission	Ausgabe	Emisión	Emissione
Laid	Vergé	Gestreift	Listado	Vergato
Lake	Lie de vin	Lackfarbe	Laca	Lacca
Lake-brown	Brun-carmin	Lackbraun	Castaño laca	Bruno lacca
Lavender	Bleu-lavande	Lavendel	Color de alhucema	Lavanda
Lemon	Jaune-citron	Zitrongelb	Limón	Limone
Light Blue	Bleu clair	Hellblau	Azul claro	Azzurro chiaro
Lilac	Lilas	Lila	Lila	Lilla
Line perforation	Dentelure en lignes	Linienzähnung	Dentado en linea	Dentellatura lineare
Lithography	Lithographie	Steindruck	Litografía	Litografia
Local	Timbre de poste locale	Lokalpostmarke	Emisión local	Emissione locale
Lozenge roulette	Percé en losanges	Rautenförmiger Durchstich	Picadura en rombos	Perforazione a losanghe
Magenta	Magenta	Magentarot	Magenta	Magenta
Margin	Marge	Rand	Borde	Margine
Maroon	Marron pourpré	Dunkelrotpurpur	Púrpura rojo oscuro	Marrone rossastro
Mauve	Mauve	Malvenfarbe	Malva	Malva
Multicoloured	Polychrome	Mehrfarbig	Multicolores	Policromo
Myrtle Green	Vert myrte	Myrtengrün	Verde mirto	Verde mirto
New Blue	Bleu ciel vif	Neublau	Azul nuevo	Azzurro nuovo
Newspaper stamp	Timbre pour journaux	Zeitungsmarke	Sello para periódicos	Francobollo per giornali
Obliteration	Oblitération	Abstempelung	Matasello	Annullamento
Obsolete	Hors (de) cours	Ausser Kurs	Fuera de curso	Fuori corso
Ochre	Ocre	Ocker	Ocre	Ocra
Official stamp	Timbre de service	Dienstmarke	Sello de servicio	Francobollo di servizio
Olive-brown	Brun-olive	Olivbraun	Castaño oliva	Bruno oliva
Olive-green	Vert-olive	Olivgrün	Verde oliva	Verde oliva
Olive-grey	Gris-olive	Olivgrau	Gris oliva	Grigio oliva
Olive-yellow	Jaune-olive	Olivgelb	Amarillo oliva	Giallo oliva
Orange	Orange	Orange	Naranja	Arancio
Orange-brown	Brun-orange	Orangebraun	Castaño naranja	Bruno arancio
Orange-red	Rouge-orange	Orangerot	Rojo naranja	Rosso arancio
Orange-yellow	Jaune-orange	Orangegelb	Amarillo naranja	Giallo arancio
Overprint	Surcharge	Aufdruck	Sobrecarga	Soprastampa
Pair	Paire	Paar	Pareja	Coppia
Pale	Pâle	Blass	Pálido	Pallido
Pane	Panneau	Gruppe	Grupo	Gruppo
Paper	Papier	Papier	Papel	Carta
Parcel post stamp	Timbre pour colis postaux	Paketmarke	Sello para paquete postal	Francobollo per pacchi postali
Pen-cancelled	Oblitéré à plume	Federzugentwertung	Cancelado a pluma	Annullato a penna
Percé en arc	Percé en arc	Bogenförmiger Durchstich	Picadura en forma de arco	Perforazione ad arco
Percé en scie	Percé en scie	Bogenförmiger Durchstich	Picado en sierra	Foratura a sega
Perforated	Dentelé	Gezähnt	Dentado	Dentellato
Perforation	Dentelure	Zähnung	Dentar	Dentellatura
Photogravure	Photogravure, Heliogravure	Rastertiefdruck	Fotograbado	Rotocalco
Pin perforation	Percé en points	In Punkten durchstochen	Horadado con alfileres	Perforato a punti
Plate	Planche	Platte	Plancha	Lastra, Tavola
Plum	Prune	Pflaumenfarbe	Color de ciruela	Prugna
Postage Due stamp	Timbre-taxe	Portomarke	Sello de tasa	Segnatasse
Postage stamp	Timbre-poste	Briefmarke, Frei-marke, Postmarke	Sello de correos	Francobollo postale
Postal fiscal stamp	Timbre fiscal-postal	Stempelmarke als Postmarke verwendet	Sello fiscal-postal	Fiscale postale
Postmark	Oblitération postale	Poststempel	Matasello	Bollo
Printing	Impression, Tirage	Druck	Impresión	Stampa, Tiratura
Proof	Épreuve	Druckprobe	Prueba de impresión	Prova
Provisionals	Timbres provisoires	Provisorische Mark-en, Provisorien	Provisionales	Provvisori

English	French	German	Spanish	Italian
Prussian Blue	Bleu de Prusse	Preussischblau	Azul de Prusia	Azzurro di Prussia
Purple	Pourpre	Purpur	Púrpura	Porpora
Purple-brown	Brun-pourpre	Purpurbraun	Castaño púrpura	Bruno porpora
Recess-printing	Impression en taille douce	Tiefdruck	Grabado	Incisione
Red	Rouge	Rot	Rojo	Rosso
Red-brown	Brun-rouge	Rotbraun	Castaño rojizo	Bruno rosso
Reddish Lilac	Lilas rougeâtre	Rötlichlila	Lila rojizo	Lilla rossastro
Reddish Purple	Pourpre-rouge	Rötlichpurpur	Púrpura rojizo	Porpora rossastro
Reddish Violet	Violet rougeâtre	Rötlichviolett	Violeta rojizo	Violetto rossastro
Red-orange	Orange rougeâtre	Rotorange	Naranja rojizo	Arancio rosso
Registration stamp	Timbre pour lettre chargée (recommandée)	Einschreibemarke	Sello de certificado	Francobollo per lettere raccomandate
Reprint	Réimpression	Neudruck	Reimpresión	Ristampa
Reversed	Retourné	Umgekehrt	Invertido	Rovesciato
Rose	Rose	Rosa	Rosa	Rosa
Rose-red	Rouge rosé	Rosarot	Rojo rosado	Rosso rosa
Rosine	Rose vif	Lebhaftrosa	Rosa vivo	Rosa vivo
Roulette	Percage	Durchstich	Picadura	Foratura
Rouletted	Percé	Durchstochen	Picado	Forato
Royal Blue	Bleu-roi	Königblau	Azul real	Azzurro reale
Sage Green	Vert-sauge	Salbeigrün	Verde salvia	Verde salvia
Salmon	Saumon	Lachs	Salmón	Salmone
Scarlet	Écarlate	Scharlach	Escarlata	Scarlatto
Sepia	Sépia	Sepia	Sepia	Seppia
Serpentine roulette	Percé en serpentin	Schlangenliniger Durchstich	Picado a serpentina	Perforazione a serpentina
Shade	Nuance	Tönung	Tono	Gradazione de colore
Sheet	Feuille	Bogen	Hoja	Foglio
Slate	Ardoise	Schiefer	Pizarra	Ardesia
Slate-blue	Bleu-ardoise	Schieferblau	Azul pizarra	Azzurro ardesia
Slate-green	Vert-ardoise	Schiefergrün	Verde pizarra	Verde ardesia
Slate-lilac	Lilas-gris	Schieferlila	Lila pizarra	Lilla ardesia
Slate-purple	Mauve-gris	Schieferpurpur	Púrpura pizarra	Porpora ardesia
Slate-violet	Violet-gris	Schieferviolett	Violeta pizarra	Violetto ardesia
Special delivery stamp	Timbre pour exprès	Eilmarke	Sello de urgencia	Francobollo per espressi
Specimen	Spécimen	Muster	Muestra	Saggio
Steel Blue	Bleu acier	Stahlblau	Azul acero	Azzurro acciaio
Strip	Bande	Streifen	Tira	Striscia
Surcharge	Surcharge	Aufdruck	Sobrecarga	Soprastampa
Tête-bêche	Tête-bêche	Kehrdruck	Tête-bêche	Tête-bêche
Tinted paper	Papier teinté	Getöntes Papier	Papel coloreado	Carta tinta
Too-late stamp	Timbre pour lettres en retard	Verspätungsmarke	Sello para cartas retardadas	Francobollo per le lettere in ritardo
Turquoise-blue	Bleu-turquoise	Türkisblau	Azul turquesa	Azzurro turchese
Turquoise-green	Vert-turquoise	Türkisgrün	Verde turquesa	Verde turchese
Typography	Typographie	Buchdruck	Tipografia	Tipografia
Ultramarine	Outremer	Ultramarin	Ultramar	Oltremare
Unused	Neuf	Ungebraucht	Nuevo	Nuovo
Used	Oblitéré, Usé	Gebraucht	Usado	Usato
Venetian Red	Rouge-brun terne	Venezianischrot	Rojo veneciano	Rosso veneziano
Vermilion	Vermillon	Zinnober	Cinabrio	Vermiglione
Violet	Violet	Violett	Violeta	Violetto
Violet-blue	Bleu-violet	Violettblau	Azul violeta	Azzurro violetto
Watermark	Filigrane	Wasserzeichen	Filigrana	Filigrana
Watermark sideways	Filigrane couché	Wasserzeichen liegend	Filigrana acostado	Filigrana coricata
Wove paper	Papier ordinaire, Papier uni	Einfaches Papier	Papel avitelado	Carta unita
Yellow	Jaune	Gelb	Amarillo	Giallo
Yellow-brown	Brun-jaune	Gelbbraun	Castaño amarillo	Bruno giallo
Yellow-green	Vert-jaune	Gelbgrün	Verde amarillo	Verde giallo
Yellow-olive	Olive jaunâtre	Gelboliv	Oliva amarillo	Oliva giallastro
Yellow-orange	Orange jaunâtre	Gelborange	Naranja amarillo	Arancio giallastro
Zig-zag roulette	Percé en zigzag	Sägezahnartiger Durchstich	Picado en zigzag	Perforazione a zigzag

Specialist Philatelic Societies

Requests for inclusion on this page should be sent to the Catalogue Editor.

British Decimal Stamps Study Circle
Secretary—Mr. S. van Kimmenade
32 Beaufort Heights, Beaufort Road,
St. George, Bristol BS5 8JX

Great Britain Philatelic Society
Membership Secretary—Mr. A. G. Lajer
The Old Post Office, Hurst,
Berks RG10 0TR

Great Britain Decimal Stamp Book Study Circle
Membership Secretary—Mr. R. Osborne,
7 Overlord Close, Broxbourne, Herts
EN10 7TG

Great Britain Collectors' Club
Secretary/Treasurer: Ms Janet Gordon,
P.O. Box 42324, Cincinnati, Ohio
45242-0324, U.S.A.

Channel Islands Specialists Society
Membership Secretary—Mr. T. Watkins
Holmcroft, Lewes Road, Ringmer, Lewes,
East Sussex, BN8 5ES

Ascension Study Circle
Secretary—Dr. R. C. F. Baker
Greys, Tower Road, Whitstable, Kent
CT5 2ER

Australian States Study Circle
Royal Sydney Philatelic Club
Honorary Secretary—Mr. B. Palmer
G.P.O. Box 1751, Sydney, N.S.W. 1043,
Australia

British Society of Australian Philately
Secretary—Mr. A. J. Griffiths
c/o The British Philatelic Centre,
107 Charterhouse Street,
London EC1M 6PT

Society of Australasian Specialists/Oceania
Secretary—Mr. S. Leven
P.O. Box 24764, San Jose, CA 95154-4764,
U.S.A.

Bechuanalands and Botswana Society
Membership Secretary—Mr. J. Catterall
Trevessa, Upper Castle Road, St. Mawes,
Truro, Cornwall TR2 5BZ

Bermuda Collectors Society
Secretary—Mr. T. J. McMahon
P.O. Box 1949, Stuart, FL 34995, U.S.A.

British Caribbean Philatelic Study Group
Overseas Director—Mr. D. N. Druett
Pennymead Auctions, 1 Brewerton Street,
Knaresborough, North Yorkshire HG5 8AZ

British West Indies Study Circle
Membership Secretary—Mr. S. A. Sharp
34 Lovelace Drive, Pyrford, Woking, Surrey
GU22 8QY

Burma Philatelic Study Circle
Secretary—Mr. A. Meech
7208-91 Avenue, Edmonton, Alberta,
Canada T6B 0R8

Ceylon Study Circle
Secretary—Mr. R.W.P. Frost
42 Lonsdale Road, Cannington, Bridgwater,
Somerset TA5 2JS

Cyprus Study Circle
Membership Secretary— Mr. J. Wigmore,
19 Riversmeet, Appledore, Bideford,
North Devon EX39 1RE

East Africa Study Circle
Hon. Secretary—Mr. K. Hewitt
16 Ashleigh Road,
Solihull, B91 1AE

Falklands Islands Study Group
Membership Secretary—Mr. D. W. A. Jeffery
38 Bradstock Road, Stoneleigh, Epsom,
Surrey KT17 2LH

Hong Kong Study Circle
Membership Secretary—Mr. P. V. Ball
37 Hart Court, Newcastle-under-Lyme,
Staffordshire ST5 2AL

Indian Ocean Study Circle
Secretary—Mr. K. B. Fitton
50 Firlands, Weybridge, Surrey KT13 0HR

India Study Circle
Secretary—Dr. W. Fincham
10 Vallis Way, London W13 0DD

Irish Philatelic Circle
General Secretary—Mr. F. McDonald
63 Rafters Road
Drimnagh, Dublin 12, Ireland

King George V Silver Jubilee Study Circle
Secretary—Mr. N. Levinge
80 Towcester Road, Northampton
NN4 8LQ

King George VI Collectors Society
Secretary—Mr. F. R. Lockyer, OBE
98 Albany, Manor Road, Bournemouth,
Dorset BH1 3EW

Kiribati and Tuvalu Philatelic Society
Honorary Secretary—Mr. M. J. Shaw
88 Stoneleigh Avenue, Worcester Park,
Surrey KT4 8XY

Malaya Study Group
Secretary—Mr. J. Robertson
12 Lisa Court, Downsland Road,
Basingstoke, Hampshire RG21 8TU

Malta Study Circle
Hon Secretary—Mr. D. Crookes
9a Church Street
Durham DH1 3DG

New Zealand Society of Great Britain
General Secretary—Mr. K. C. Collins
13 Briton Crescent, Sanderstead,
Surrey CR2 0JN.

Orange Free State Study Circle
Secretary—Mr. J. R. Stroud
28 Oxford Street, Burnham-on-Sea,
Somerset TA8 1LQ

Pacific Islands Study Circle
Honorary Secretary—Mr. J. D. Ray
24 Woodvale Avenue, London SE25 4AE

Papuan Philatelic Society
Secretary—Mr. F. J. Prophet
5 Morcom Close, Menear Road, Boscoppa,
St. Austell, Cornwall PL25 3UF

Pitcairn Islands Study Group (U.K.)
Honorary Secretary—Mr. D. Sleep
6 Palace Gardens, 100 Court Road, Eltham,
London SE9 5NS

Rhodesian Study Circle
Secretary—Mr. R. G. Barnett
2 Cox Ley, Hatfield Heath,
Bishop's Stortford, Herts CM22 7ER

St. Helena, Ascension and Tristan da Cunha Philatelic Society
Secretary—Mr. J. Havill
205 N. Murray Blvd., #221, Colorado
Springs, CO 80916, U.S.A.

Sarawak Specialists Society (also Brunei, North Borneo and Labuan)
Secretary—Dr. J. Higgins
31 Grimston Road, South Wootton,
Kings Lynn, Norfolk PE30 3NR

South African Collectors' Society
General Secretary—Mr. R. Ross
28 Duddon Drive, Barrow-in-Furness,
Cumbria LA14 3TW

Philatelic Society of Sri Lanka
Secretary—Mr. H. Goonawardena
44A Hena Road, Mt. Lavinia 10370,
Sri Lanka.

Sudan Study Group
Secretary—Mr. N. D. Collier
34 Padleys Lane, Burton Joyce,
Nottingham NG14 5BZ

Transvaal Study Circle
Secretary—Mr. J. Woolgar
132 Dale Street, Chatham, Kent ME4 6QH

West Africa Study Circle
Secretary—Mr. J. Powell
23 Brook Street, Edlesborough, Dunstable,
Bedfordshire LU6 2JG

Select Bibliography

The literature on British Commonwealth stamps is vast, but works are often difficult to obtain once they are out of print. The selection of books below has been made on the basis of authority together with availability to the general reader, either as new or secondhand. Very specialised studies, and those covering aspects of postal history to which there are no references in the catalogue, have been excluded.

The following abbreviations are used to denote publishers:
CRL–Christie's Robson Lowe; HH–Harry Hayes; PB–Proud Bailey Co. Ltd. and Postal History Publications Co.; PC–Philip Cockrill; RPSL–Royal Philatelic Society, London; SG–Stanley Gibbons Ltd.

Where no publisher is quoted, the book is published by its author.

GENERAL. *Encyclopaedia of British Empire Postage Stamps.* Vols 1–6. Edited Robson Lowe. (CRL, 1951–1991)
Specimen Stamps of the Crown Colonies 1857–1948. Marcus Samuel. (RPSL, 1976 and 1984 Supplement)
Cancelled by Perkins Bacon. P. Jaffé. (Spink & Son Ltd, 1998)
U.P.U. Specimen Stamps. J. Bendon. (1988)
King George V Key Plates of the Imperium Postage and Revenue Design. P. Fernbank. (West Africa Study Circle, 1997)
The Commemorative Stamps of the British Commonwealth. H.D.S. Haverbeck. (Faber, 1955)
Silver Jubilee of King George V Stamps Handbook. A.J. Ainscough. (Ainweel Developments, 1985)
The Printings of King George VI Colonial Stamps. W.J.W. Potter & Lt-Col R.C.M. Shelton. (1952 and later facsimile edition)
King George VI Large Key Type Stamps of Bermuda, Leeward Islands, Nyasaland. R.W. Dickgiesser and E.P. Yendall. (Triad Publications, 1985)
Madame Joseph Forged Postmarks. D. Worboys (RPSL, 1994)
G.B. Used Abroad: Cancellations and Postal Markings. J. Parmenter. (The Postal History Society, 1993)

GREAT BRITAIN. For extensive bibliographies see *G.B. Specialised Catalogues.* Vols 1-5.
Stamps and Postal History of the Channel Islands. W. Newport. (Heineman, 1972)
ASCENSION. *Ascension. The Stamps and Postal History.* J.H. Attwood. (CRL, 1981)
AUSTRALIA. *The Postage History of New South Wales 1788–1901.* Edited J.S. White (Philatelic Assoc of New South Wales, 1988)
South Australia. The Long Stamps 1902–12. J.R.W. Purves. (Royal Philatelic Society of Victoria, 1978)
The Departmental Stamps of South Australia. A.R. Butler. (RPSL, 1978)
A Priced Listing of the Departmental Stamps of South Australia. A.D. Presgrave (2nd edition, 1999)
Stamps and Postal History of Tasmania. W.E. Tinsley. (RPSL, 1986)

The Pictorial Stamps of Tasmania 1899–1912. K.E. Lancaster. (Royal Philatelic Society of Victoria, 1986)
The Stamps of Victoria. G. Kellow. B. & K. Philatelic Publishing, 1990)
Western Australia. The Stamps and Postal History. Ed. M. Hamilton and B. Pope. (W. Australian Study Group, 1979)
Postage Stamps and Postal History of Western Australia. Vols 1–3. M. Juhl. (1981–83)
The Chapman Collection of Australian Commonwealth Stamps. R. Chapman. (Royal Philatelic Society of Victoria, 1999)
Cocos (Keeling) Islands. A Philatelic and Postal History to 1979. P. Collas & J. Hill. (B. & K. Philatelic Publishing, 1991)
Norfolk Island. A Postal and Philatelic History, 1788–1969. P. Collas & R. Breckon. (B.& K. Philatelic Publishing, 1997)
BAHAMAS. *The Postage Stamps and Postal History of the Bahamas.* H.G.D. Gisburn. (SG, 1950 and later facsimile edition)
BARBADOS. *The Stamps of Barbados.* E.A. Bayley. (1989)
Advanced Barbados Philately. H.F. Deakin. (B.W.I. Study Circle, 1997)
BATUM. *British Occupation of Batum.* P.T. Ashford. (1989)
BERMUDA. *The Postal History and Stamps of Bermuda.* M.H. Ludington (Quarterman Publications Inc., 1978)
The King George V High-value Stamps of Bermuda, 1917–1938. M. Glazer. (Calaby Publishers, 1994)
BOTSWANA. *The Postage Stamps, Postal Stationery and Postmarks of the Bechuanalands.* H.R. Holmes. (RPSL, 1971)
BRITISH OCCUPATION OF GERMAN COLONIES. *G.R.I.* R.M. Gibbs. (CRL, 1989)
BRITISH POSTAL AGENCIES IN EASTERN ARABIA. *The Postal Agencies in Eastern Arabia and the Gulf.* N. Donaldson (HH, 1975) and Supplement (Bridger & Kay Guernsey Ltd, 1994)
BRITISH WEST AFRICA. *The Postal History and Handstamps of British West Africa.* C. McCaig. (CRL, 1978)
BRUNEI. *Brunei. The Definitive Issues and Postal Cancellations to 1974.* E. Thorndike. (PC, 1983)
BURMA. *Burma Postal History.* G. Davis and D. Martin. (CRL, 1971 and 1987 Supplement).
CAMEROONS. *The Postal Arrangements of the Anglo-French Cameroons Expeditionary Force 1914–16.* R.J. Maddocks. (1996)
CANADA. *The Postage Stamps and Postal History of Newfoundland.* W.S. Boggs. (Quarterman Publications, 1975)
Stamps of British North America. F. Jarrett. (Quarterman Publications Inc, 1975)
The Postage Stamps and Postal History of Canada. W.S. Boggs. (Quarterman Publications Inc., 1974)
The First Decimal Issue of Canada 1859–68. G. Whitworth. (RPSL, 1966)
The Five Cents Beaver Stamp of Canada. G. Whitworth. (RPSL, 1985)
The Edward VII Issue of Canada. G.C. Marler. (National Postal Museum, Canada, 1975)
The Admiral Issue of Canada. G.C. Marler. (American Philatelic Society, 1982)
The Centennial Definitives of Canada. D. Gronbeck-Jones. (1972)

The Caricatures and Landscapes Definitives of Canada. D. Gronbeck-Jones (1979)
COOK ISLANDS. *The Early Cook Islands Post Office.* A.R. Burge. (Hawthorn Press, 1978)
CYPRUS. *Cyprus 1353–1986.* W. Castle. (CRL, 3rd edition, 1987)
DOMINICA. *Dominica Postal History, Stamps and Postal Stationery to 1935.* E.V. Toeg (B.W.I. Study Circle, 1994)
EGYPT. *Egypt Stamps & Postal History.* P.A.S. Smith. (James Bendon, 1999)
FALKLAND ISLANDS. *The Postage Stamps of the Falkland Islands and Dependencies.* B.S.H. Grant. (SG, 1952 and later facsimile edition)
The Falkland Islands Philatelic Digest. Nos. 1 & 2. M. Barton and R. Spafford. (HH, 1975 & 1979)
The De La Rue Definitives of the Falkland Islands 1901–29. J.P. Bunt. (1986 and 1996 Supplement)
The War Stamp Overprints of the Falkland Islands 1918–20. J.P. Bunt. (1981)
The Falkland Islands. Printings of the Pictorial Issue of 1938–49. C.E. Glass. (CRL, 1979)
The Falklands War. J.D. Davis. (1983)
FIJI. *Fiji Philatelics.* D.W.F. Alford. (Pacific Islands Study Circle, 1994)
The Postal History of Fiji 1911–1952. J.G. Rodger. (Pacific Islands Study Circle, 1991).
GAMBIA. *The Stamps and Postal History of the Gambia.* Edited J.O. Andrew. (CRL, 1985)
The Postal History of the Gambia. E.B. Proud (PB, 1994)
GHANA. *The Postal History of the Gold Coast.* E.B. Proud (PB, 1995)
The Postal Services of the Gold Coast, 1901–1957. Edited by M. Ensor. (West Africa Study Circle, 1998)
GIBRALTAR. *Posted in Gibraltar.* W. Hine-Haycock. (CRL, 1978 and 1983 Supplement)
Gibraltar. The Postal History and Postage Stamps. Vol 1 (to 1885). G. Osborn. (Gibraltar Study Circle, 1995)
GUYANA. *The Postage Stamps and Postal History of British Guiana.* W.A. Townsend and F.G. Howe. (RPSL, 1970)
HONG KONG. *The Philatelic History of Hong Kong. Vol 1.* (Hong Kong Study Circle, 1984)
Hong Kong Postage Stamps of the Queen Victoria Period. R.N. Gurevitch (1993)
Hong Kong. The 1898 10c. on 30c. Provisional Issue. A.M. Chu. (1998)
British Post Offices in the Far East. E.B. Proud. (PB, 1991)
Cancellations of the Treaty Ports of Hong Kong. H. Schoenfeld. (1988)
The Crown Colony of Wei Hai Wei. M. Goldsmith and C.W. Goodwyn. (RPSL, 1985)
INDIA. *C.E.F. The China Expeditionary Force 1900–1923.* D.S. Virk, J.C. Hume, D. Lang, G. Sattin. (Philatelic Congress of India, 1992)
India Used Abroad. V.S. Dastur. (Mysore Philatelics, 1982)
A Handbook on Gwalior Postal History and Stamps. V.K. Gupta. (1980)
The Stamps of Jammu & Kashmir. F. Staal. (The Collectors Club, 1983)
IRAQ. *The Postal History of Iraq.* P.C. Pearson and E.B. Proud. (PB, 1996)
IRELAND. *Irish Stamp Booklets 1931–1991.* C.I. Dulin (1998)

Great Britain

Great Britain Postage Stamps, GB 1
Regional Issues—
   I. Northern Ireland, GB 78
   II. Scotland, GB 78
   III. Wales, GB 79
Postage Due Stamps, GB 81
Official Stamps, GB 81
Postal Fiscal Stamps, GB 82
Channel Islands General Issue, GB 83
Guernsey, GB 83
   Alderney, GB 96
Isle of Man, GB 99
Jersey, GB 112
British Post Offices Abroad, GB 125

STAMPS ON COVER. Prices are quoted, as a third price column, for those Victorian and Edwardian issues usually found used on cover. In general these prices refer to the cheapest version of each basic stamp with other shades, plates or varieties, together with unusual frankings and postmarks, being worth more.

UNITED KINGDOM OF GREAT BRITAIN AND IRELAND

QUEEN VICTORIA
20 June 1837—22 January 1901

MULREADY ENVELOPES AND LETTER SHEETS, so called from the name of the designer, William Mulready, were issued concurrently with the first British adhesive stamps.

1d. black

Envelopes: £250 *unused*; £300 *used*.
Letter Sheets: £225 *unused*; £275 *used*.

2d. blue

Envelopes: £325 *unused*; £725 *used*.
Letter Sheets: £300 *unused*; £700 *used*.

LINE-ENGRAVED ISSUES

GENERAL NOTES

Brief notes on some aspects of the line-engraved stamps follow, but for further information and a full specialist treatment of these issues collectors are recommended to consult Volume 1 of the Stanley Gibbons *Great Britain Specialised Catalogue*.

  Alphabet I   Alphabet II

  Alphabet III   Alphabet IV

Typical Corner Letters of the four Alphabets

Alphabets. Four different styles were used for the corner letters on stamps prior to the issue with letters in all four corners, these being known to collectors as:

Alphabet I. Used for all plates made from 1840 to the end of 1851. Letters small.

Alphabet II. Plates from 1852 to mid-1855. Letters larger, heavier and broader.

Alphabet III. Plates from mid-1855 to end of period. Letters tall and more slender.

Alphabet IV. 1861. 1d. Die II, Plates 50 and 51 only. Letters were hand-engraved instead of being punched on the plate. They are therefore inconsistent in shape and size but generally larger and outstanding.

While the general descriptions and the illustrations of typical letters given above may be of some assistance, only long experience and published aids can enable every stamp to be allocated to its particular Alphabet without hesitation, as certain letters in each are similar to those in one of the others.

Blue Paper. The blueing of the paper of the earlier issues is believed to be due to the presence of prussiate of potash in the printing ink, or in the paper, which, under certain conditions, tended to colour the paper when the sheets were damped for printing. An alternative term is bleuté paper.

Corner Letters. The corner letters on the early British stamps were intended as a safeguard against forgery, each stamp in the sheet having a different combination of letters. Taking the first 1d. stamp,

printed in 20 horizontal rows of 12, as an example, the lettering is as follows:

    Row 1.   A A, A B, A C, etc. to A L.

    Row 2.   B A, B B, B C, etc. to B L.

        and so on to

    Row 20. T A, T B, T C, etc. to T L.

On the stamps with four corner letters, those in the upper corners are in the reverse positions to those in the lower corners. Thus in a sheet of 240 (12 × 20) the sequence is:

    Row 1.   A A B A C A etc. to L A
              A A A B A C   A L

    Row 2.   A B B B C B etc. to L B
              B A B B B C   B L

        and so on to

    Row 20. A T B T C T etc. to L T
              T A T B T C   T L

Placing letters in all four corners was not only an added precaution against forgery but was meant to deter unmarked parts of used stamps being pieced together and passed off as an unused whole.

Dies. The first die of the 1d. was used for making the original die of the 2d., both the No Lines and White Lines issues. In 1855 the 1d. Die I was amended by retouching the head and deepening the lines on a transferred impression of the original. This later version, known to collectors as Die II, was used for making the dies for the 1d. and 2d. with letters in all four corners and also for the 1½d.

The two dies are illustrated above No. 17 in the catalogue.

  Double letter   Guide line in corner

Guide line through value

Double Corner Letters. These are due to the workman placing his letter-punch in the wrong position at the first attempt, when lettering the plate, and then correcting the mistake; or to a slight shifting of the punch when struck. If a wrong letter was struck in the first instance, traces of a wrong letter may appear in a corner in addition to the correct one. A typical example is illustrated.

Guide Lines and Dots. When laying down the impressions of the design on the early plates, fine vertical and horizontal guide lines were marked on the plates to assist the operative. These were usually removed from the gutter margins, but could not be removed from the stamp impressions without damage to the plate, so that in such cases they appear on the printed stamps, sometimes in the corners, sometimes through "POSTAGE" or the value. Typical examples are illustrated.

Guide dots or cuts were similarly made to indicate the spacing of the guide lines. These too sometimes appear on the stamps.

Ivory Head

"Ivory Head." The so-called "ivory head" variety is one in which the Queen's Head shows white on the back of the stamp. It arises from the comparative absence of ink in the head portion of the design, with consequent absence of blueing. (*See* "Blued Paper" note above.)

Line-engraving. In this context "line-engraved" is synonymous with recess-printing, in which the engraver cuts recesses in a plate and printing (the coloured areas) is from these recesses. "Line-engraved" is the traditional philatelic description for these stamps; other equivalent terms found are "engraving in *taille-douce*" (French) or "in *intaglio*" (Italian).

Plates. Until the introduction of the stamps with letters in all four corners, the number of the plate was not indicated in the design of the stamp, but was printed on the sheet margin. By long study of identifiable blocks and the minor variations in the design, coupled with the position of the corner letters, philatelists are now able to allot many of these stamps to their respective plates. Specialist collectors often endeavour to obtain examples of a given stamp printed from its different plates and our catalogue accordingly reflects this depth of detail.

  Maltese Cross   Type of Town postmark

Type of Penny Post cancellation

Example of 1844 type postmark

Postmarks. The so-called "Maltese Cross" design was the first employed for obliterating British postage stamps and was in use from 1840 to 1844. Being hand-cut, the obliterating stamps varied greatly in detail and some distinctive types can be allotted to particular towns or offices. Local types, such as those used at Manchester, Norwich, Leeds, etc., are keenly sought. A red ink was first employed, but was superseded by black, after some earlier experiments, in February 1841. Maltese Cross obliterations in other colours are rare.

Obliterations of this type, numbered 1 to 12 in the centre, were used at the London Chief Office in 1843 and 1844.

Some straight-line cancellations were in use in 1840 at the Penny Post receiving offices, normally applied on the envelope, the adhesives then being obliterated at the Head Office. They are nevertheless known, with or without Maltese Cross, on the early postage stamps.

In 1842 some offices in S.W. England used dated postmarks in place of the Maltese Cross, usually on the back of the letter since they were not originally intended as obliterators. These town postmarks have likewise been found on adhesives.

In 1844 the Maltese Cross design was superseded by numbered obliterators of varied type, one of which is illustrated. They are naturally comparatively scarce on the first 1d. and 2d. stamps. Like the Maltese Cross they are found in various colours, some of which are rare.

Re-entry

"Union Jack" re-entry

Re-entries. Re-entries on the plate show as a doubling of part of the design of the stamp generally at top or bottom. Many re-entries are very slight while others are most marked. A typical one is illustrated.

The *Union Jack* re-entry, so called owing to the effect of the re-entry on the appearance of the corner stars (*see illustration*) occurs on stamp L K of Plate 75 of the 1d. red, Die I.

TA(TL) MA(ML)
Varieties of Large Crown Watermark

I   Two states of Large Crown Watermark   II

Watermarks. Two watermark varieties, as illustrated, consisting of crowns of entirely different shape, are found in sheets of the Large Crown paper and fall on stamps lettered M A and T A (or M L and T L when the paper is printed on the wrong side). Both varieties are found on the 1d. rose-red of 1857, while the M A (M L) variety comes also on some plates of the 1d. of 1864 (Nos. 43, 44) up to about Plate 96. On the 2d. the T A (T L) variety is known on plates 8 and 9, and the M A (M L) on later prints of plate 9. These varieties may exist inverted, or inverted reversed on stamps lettered A A and A L and H A and H L, and some are known.

In 1861 a minor alteration was made in the Large Crown watermark by the removal of the two vertical strokes, representing *fleurs-de-lis*, which projected upwards from the uppermost of the three horizontal curves at the base of the Crown. Hence two states are distinguishable, as illustrated.

CONDITION—IMPERFORATE LINE-ENGRAVED ISSUES

The prices quoted for the 1840 and 1841 imperforate Line-engraved issues are for "fine" examples. As condition is most important in assessing the value of a stamp, the following definitions will assist collectors in the evaluation of individual examples.

Four main factors are relevant when considering quality.

(a) **Impression.** This should be clean and the surface free of any rubbing or unnatural blurring which would detract from the appearance.

(b) **Margins.** This is perhaps the most difficult factor to evaluate. Stamps described as "fine", the standard adopted in this catalogue for pricing purposes, should have margins of at least approximately one half of the distance between two adjoining unsevered stamps. Stamps described as "very fine" or "superb" should have margins which are proportionally larger than those of a "fine" stamp. Examples with close margins should not, generally, be classified as "fine".

(c) **Cancellation.** On a "fine" stamp this should be reasonably clear and not noticeably smudged. A stamp described as "superb" should have a neat cancellation, preferably centrally placed or to the right.

(d) **Appearance.** Stamps, at the prices quoted, should always be without any tears, creases, bends or thins and should not be toned on either the front or back. Stamps with such defects are worth only a proportion of the catalogue price.

Good   Fine

Very Fine   Superb

The above actual size illustrations of 1840 1d. blacks show the various grades of quality. When comparing these illustrations it should be assumed that they are all from the same plate and that they are free of any hidden defects.

PRINTERS. Nos. 1/53*a* were recess-printed by Perkins, Bacon & Petch, known from 1852 as Perkins, Bacon & Co.

1   1a   2 Small Crown

(Eng Charles and Frederick Heath)

1840 (6 May).   *Letters in lower corners. Wmk Small Crown. W 2. Imperf.*

No.	Type				Un	Used	Used on cover
1	1	1d. intense black	..	..	—	£275	
2		1d. black	..	..	£3500	£190	£325
3		1d. grey-black (worn plate)	..	£3500	£275		
4	1a	2d. deep full blue	..	..	£8000	£500	
5		2d. blue	..	..	£6500	£400	£850
6		2d. pale blue	..	..	£8000	£425	

The 1d. stamp in black was printed from Plates 1 to 11. Plate 1 exists in two states (known to collectors as 1*a* and 1*b*), the latter being the result of extensive repairs.

Repairs were also made to Plates 2, 5, 6, 8, 9, 10 and 11, and certain impressions exist in two or more states.

The so-called "Royal reprint" of the 1d. black was made in 1864, from Plate 66, Die II, on paper with Large Crown watermark, inverted. A printing was also made in carmine, on paper with the same watermark, normal.

For 1d. black with "VR" in upper corners *see* No. V1 under Official Stamps.

The 2d. stamps were printed from Plates 1 and 2.

Plates of 1d. black

Plate					Un	Used
1a	..	..	..	..	£5000	£200
1b	..	..	..	..	£3500	£190
2	..	..	..	..	£3500	£190
3	..	..	..	..	£4000	£225
4	..	..	..	..	£3500	£200
5	..	..	..	..	£3500	£200
6	..	..	..	..	£3500	£200
7	..	..	..	..	£3750	£225
8	..	..	..	..	£4000	£275
9	..	..	..	..	£4500	£300
10	..	..	..	..	£5000	£400
11	..	..	..	..	£5000	£1900

Varieties of 1d. black

					Un	Used
a.	On *bleuté* paper (Plates 1 to 8)	..	from		—	£275
b.	Double letter in corner	..	from		£3750	£250
bb.	Re-entry				£3750	£250
bc.	"PB" re-entry (Plate 5, 3rd state)	..			—	£4250
cc.	Large letters in each corner (E J, I L, J C and P A) (Plate 1b)	from		£3750	£375
c.	Guide line in corner	..	..		£3750	£225
d.	,, ,, through value	..		£3750	£250
e.	Watermark inverted	..		£5000	£500
g.	Obliterated by Maltese Cross				
		In red		—	£225
		In black		—	£200
		In blue		—	£2250
		In magenta		—	£950
		In yellow		—	—
h.	Obliterated by Maltese Cross with number in centre		from		
		No. 1		—	£2900
		No. 2		—	£1900
		No. 3		—	£1900
		No. 4		—	£1900
		No. 5		—	£1900
		No. 6		—	£1900
		No. 7		—	£1900
		No. 8		—	£1900
		No. 9		—	£1900
		No. 10		—	£1900
		No. 11		—	—
		No. 12		—	£1900
i.	Obliterated "Penny Post" in black	..	from	—	£1500
j.	Obliterated by town postmark (without Maltese Cross)			
		In black	from	—	£1300
		In yellow	from	—	£7000
		In red	from	—	£1600
k.	Obliterated by 1844 type postmark in black	from	—	£550

Plates of 2d. blue

Plate				Un	Used
1	..	..	Shades from	£6500	£400
2	..	..	Shades from	£7500	£450

Varieties of 2d. blue

					Un	Used
a.	Double letter in corner	..	..		—	£500
aa.	Re-entry	..	..	..	—	£550
b.	Guide line in corner	..	..		—	£450
c.	,, ,, through value	..	..		—	£450
d.	Watermark inverted	..	..		£8000	£1000
e.	Obliterated by Maltese Cross				
		In red		—	£450
		In black		—	£400
		In blue		—	£3250
		In magenta		—	£3000

					Un	Used
f.	Obliterated by Maltese Cross with number in centre		from		
		No. 1		—	£3000
		No. 2		—	£3000
		No. 3		—	£3000
		No. 4		—	£3000
		No. 5		—	£3000
		No. 6		—	£3250
		No. 7		—	£3000
		No. 8		—	£3000
		No. 9		—	£3500
		No. 10		—	£3250
		No. 11		—	£3250
		No. 12		—	£3000
g.	Obliterated "Penny Post" in black	..	from	—	£1900
h.	Obliterated by town postmark (without Maltese Cross) in black	..	from	—	£1600
i.	Obliterated by 1844 type postmark			
		In black	from	—	£1100
		In blue	from	—	£3000

1841 (10 Feb).   *Printed from "black" plates. Wmk W 2. Paper more or less blued. Imperf.*

No.	Type			Un	Used	Used on cover
7	1	1d. red-brown (shades)	..	£600	70·00	£140
		a. "PB" re-entry (Plate 5, 3rd state)	..	..	..	—	£1300

The first printings of the 1d. in red-brown were made from Plates 1b, 2, 5 and 8 to 11 used for the 1d. black.

1d. red-brown from "black" plates

Plate					Un	Used
1b	..	..	..	..	£3500	£200
2	..	..	..	..	£2250	£150
5	..	..	..	..	£750	90·00
8	..	..	..	..	£625	70·00
9	..	..	..	..	£600	70·00
10	..	..	..	..	£625	70·00
11	..	..	..	..	£625	70·00

1841 (late Feb).   *Plate 12 onwards. Wmk W 2. Paper more or less blued. Imperf.*

					Un	Used	Used on cover
8	1	1d. red-brown	..	..	£175	10·00	15·00
8a		1d. red-brown on very blue paper	£200	10·00	
9		1d. pale red-brown (worn plates)	£275	20·00	
10		1d. deep red-brown	..	..	£200	15·00	
11		1d. lake-red	..	..	£1000	£150	
12		1d. orange-brown	..	..	£400	90·00	

Error. No letter "A" in right lower corner (Stamp B(A), Plate 77)

| 12a | 1 | 1d. red-brown | .. | .. | — | £5750 |

The error "No letter A in right corner" was due to the omission to insert this letter on stamp B A of Plate 77. The error was discovered some months after the plate was registered and was then corrected.

There are innumerable variations in the colour and shade of the 1d. "red" and those given in the above list represent colour groups each covering a wide range.

Varieties of 1d. red-brown, etc.

					Un	Used
b.	Re-entry	..	..	from	—	30·00
c.	Double letter in corner	..	from	—	20·00
d.	Double Star (Plate 75) "Union Jack" re-entry	£7500	£700	
e.	Guide line in corner	..	..		—	12·00
f.	Guide line through value	..	..		—	20·00
g.	Thick outer frame to stamp	..		—	19·00
h.	Ivory head	..	..	..	£200	15·00
i.	Watermark inverted (Plates 1b, 7, 8, 10)	..	£550	£100
j.	Left corner letter "S" inverted (Plates 78, 105, 107)	..	from	—	70·00
k.	P converted to R (Plates 30, 33, 83, 86) from	—	60·00
l.	Obliterated by Maltese Cross			
		In red		—	£1200
		In black		—	25·00
		In blue		—	£200
m.	Obliterated by Maltese Cross with number in centre			
		No. 1		—	50·00
		No. 2		—	50·00
		No. 3		—	70·00
		No. 4		—	£160
		No. 5		—	50·00
		No. 6		—	45·00
		No. 7		—	40·00
		No. 8		—	40·00
		No. 9		—	50·00
		No. 10		—	70·00
		No. 11		—	80·00
		No. 12		—	£100
n.	Obliterated "Penny Post" in black	..		—	£250
o.	Obliterated by town postmark (without Maltese Cross)			
		In black	from	—	£175
		In blue	from	—	£350
		In green	from	—	£500
		In yellow	from	—	—
		In red	from	—	£2500
p.	Obliterated by 1844 type postmark			
		In blue	from	—	60·00
		In red	from	—	£1250
		In green	from	—	£300
		In violet	from	—	£700
		In black	from	—	10·00

Stamps with thick outer frame to the design are from plates on which the frame-lines have been strengthened or recut, particularly Plates 76 and 90.

For "Union Jack" re-entry *see* General Notes to Line-engraved Issues.

In "P converted to R" the corner letter "R" is formed from the "P", the distinctive long tail having been hand-cut.

TL TL TL TL TL TL TL TL TL TL TL TL TL TL TL TL TL TL TL TL TL TL TL TL TL TL TL TL TL TL TL TL TL

TL TL TL TL TL TL TL TL TL TL TL TL TL TL TL TL TL TL TL TL TL TL TL TL TL TL TL TL TL TL TL TL TL

KEY TO LINE-ENGRAVED ISSUES

S.G. Nos.	Description	Date	Wmk	Perf	Die	Alphabet
	THE IMPERFORATE ISSUES					
1/3	1d. black	6.5.40	SC	Imp	I	I
4/6	2d. no lines	8.5.40	SC	Imp	I	I
	PAPER MORE OR LESS BLUED					
7	1d. red-brown	Feb 1841	SC	Imp	I	I
8/12	1d. red-brown	Feb 1841	SC	Imp	I	I
8/12	1d. red-brown	6.2.52	SC	Imp	I	II
13/15	2d. white lines	13.3.41	SC	Imp	I	I
	THE PERFORATED ISSUES					
	ONE PENNY VALUE					
16a	1d. red-brown	1848	SC	Roul	I	I
16b	1d. red-brown	1850	SC	16	I	I
16c	1d. red-brown	1853	SC	16	I	II
16d	1d. red-brown	1854	SC	14	I	I
17/18	1d. red-brown	Feb 1854	SC	16	I	II
22	1d. red-brown	Jan 1855	SC	14	I	II
24/5	1d. red-brown	28.2.55	SC	14	II	II
21	1d. red-brown	1.3.55	SC	16	II	II
26	1d. red-brown	15.5.55	LC	16	II	II
29/33	1d. red-brown	Aug 1855	LC	14	II	III
	NEW COLOURS ON WHITE PAPER					
37/41	1d. rose-red	Nov 1856	LC	14	II	III
36	1d. rose-red	26.12.57	LC	16	II	III
42	1d. rose-red	1861	LC	14	II	IV
	TWO PENCE VALUE					
19, 20	2d. blue	1.3.54	SC	16	I	I
23	2d. blue	22.2.55	SC	14	I	I
23a	2d. blue	5.7.55	SC	14	I	II
20a	2d. blue	18.8.55	SC	16	I	II
27	2d. blue	20.7.55	LC	16	I	II
34	2d. blue	20.7.55	LC	14	I	II
35	2d. blue	2.7.57	LC	14	I	III
36a	2d. blue	1.2.58	LC	16	I	III
	LETTERS IN ALL FOUR CORNERS					
48/9	½d. rose-red	1.10.70	W 9	14	—	
43/4	1d. rose-red	1.4.64	LC	14	II	
53a	1½d. rosy mauve	1860	LC	14	II	
51/3	1½d. rose-red	1.10.70	LC	14	II	
45	2d. blue	July 1858	LC	14	II	
46/7	2d. thinner lines	7.7.69	LC	14	II	

Watermarks: SC = Small Crown, **T 2**.
LC = Large Crown, **T 4**.
Dies: See notes above No. 17 in the catalogue.
Alphabets: See General Notes to this section.

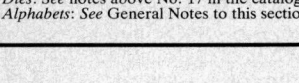

3 White lines added

1841 (13 Mar)**–51.** *White lines added. Wmk W 2. Paper more or less blued. Imperf.*

				Un	Used	Used on cover
13	3	2d. pale blue	.. ..	£1800	70·00	
14		2d. blue	.. ..	£1500	60·00	£225
15		2d. deep full blue	..	£1800	70·00	
15aa		2d. violet-blue (1851)		£7500	£600	

The 2d. stamp with white lines was printed from Plates 3 and 4. No. 15aa came from Plate 4 and the price quoted is for examples on thicker, lavender tinted paper.

Plates of 2d. blue

Plate			Un	Used
3	..	Shades from	£1500	70·00
4	..	Shades from	£1750	60·00

Varieties of 2d. blue

			Un	Used
a.	Guide line in corner			70·00
b.	„ „ through value		£1800	70·00
bb.	Double letter in corner			70·00
be.	Re-entry		£2100	80·00
c.	Ivory head		£1900	70·00
d.	Watermark inverted		£3000	£350
e.	Obliterated by Maltese Cross			
		In red	—	£6000
		In black	—	90·00
		In blue	—	£1300
f.	Obliterated by Maltese Cross with number in centre			
		No. 1	—	£240
		No. 2	—	£240
		No. 3	—	£240
		No. 4	—	£225
		No. 5	—	£325
		No. 6	—	£240
		No. 7	—	£450
		No. 8	—	£325
		No. 9	—	£450
		No. 10	—	£500
		No. 11	—	£325
		No. 12	—	£190
g.	Obliterated by town postmark (without Maltese Cross)			
		In black from	—	£550
		In blue from	—	£900

---

h.	Obliterated by 1844 type postmark			
	In black	*from*	—	60·00
	In blue	*from*	—	£400
	In red	*from*	—	£4500
	In green	*from*	—	£750

1841 (April). *Trial printing (unissued) on Dickinson silk-thread paper. No wmk. Imperf.*

16	1	1d. red-brown (Plate 11)	.. ..	£2500

Eight sheets were printed on this paper, six being gummed, two ungummed, but we have only seen examples without gum.

1848. *Wmk Small Crown, W 2. Rouletted approx 11½ by Henry Archer.*

16a	1	1d. red-brown (Plates 70, 71)	..	£4250

1850. *Wmk Small Crown, W 2. P 16 by Henry Archer.*

16b	1	1d. red-brown (Alph 1) (from Plates 90–101) ..	*from*	£700	£250

Stamp on cover, dated prior to February 1854 (*price* £375); dated during or after February 1854 (*price* £275).

1853. *Government Trial Perforations. Wmk Small Crown. W 2.*

16c		1d. red-brown (*p* 16) (Alph II) (*on cover*)	†	£5500
16d		1d. red-brown (*p* 14) (Alph I) ..		£4500

SEPARATION TRIALS. Although the various trials of machines for rouletting and perforating were unofficial, Archer had the consent of the authorities in making his experiments, and sheets so experimented upon were afterwards used by the Post Office.

As Archer ended his experiments in 1850 and plates with corner letters Alphabet II did not come into issue until 1852, perforated stamps with corner letters of Alphabet I may safely be assumed to be Archer productions, if genuine.

The Government trial perforations were done on Napier machines in 1853. As Alphabet II was by that time in use, the trials can only be distinguished from the perforated stamps listed below by being dated prior to 12 March 1854, the date when the perforated stamps were officially issued.

Die I   Die II   **4** Large Crown

Die I: The features of the portrait are lightly shaded and consequently lack emphasis.

Die II (Die I retouched): The lines of the features have been deepened and appear stronger.

The eye is deeply shaded and made more lifelike. The nostril and lips are more clearly defined, the latter appearing much thicker. A strong downward stroke of colour marks the corner of the mouth. There is a deep indentation of colour between lower lip and chin. The band running from the back of the ear to the chignon has a bolder horizontal line below it than in Die I.

The original die (Die I) was used to provide roller dies for the laying down of all the line-engraved stamps from 1840 to 1855. In that year a new master die was laid down (by means of a Die I roller die) and the impression was retouched by hand engraving by William Humphrys. This retouched die, always known to philatelists as Die II, was from that time used for preparing all new roller dies.

One Penny. The numbering of the 1d. plates recommenced at 1 on the introduction of Die II. Plates 1 to 21 were Alphabet II from which a scarce plum dies exists. Corner letters of Alphabet III appear on Plate 22 and onwards.

As an experiment, the corner letters were engraved by hand on Plates 50 and 51 in 1856, instead of being punched (Alphabet IV), but punching was again resorted to from Plate 52 onwards. Plates 50 and 51 were not put into use until 1861.

Two Pence. Unlike the 1d. the old sequence of plate numbers continued. Plates 3 and 4 of the 2d. had corner letters of Alphabet I, Plate 5 Alphabet II and Plate 6 Alphabet III. In Plate 6 the white lines are thinner than before.

1854–57. *Paper more or less blued. (a) Wmk Small Crown, W 2. P 16.*

			Un	★ Used	Used on cover
17	1	1d. red-brown (Die I) (12.3.54)	£190	15·00	30·00
18		a. Imperf three sides (horiz pair) 1d. yellow-brown (Die I)	† £275	30·00	
19	3	2d. deep blue (Plate 4) (12.3.54)	£1800	80·00	£125
		a. Imperf three sides (horiz pair)	†		
20		2d. pale blue (Plate 4)	£1900	90·00	
20a		2d. blue (Plate 5) (18.8.55)	£2250	£200	£350
21	1	1d. red-brown (Die II) (22.2.55)	£250	40·00	75·00
		a. Imperf			
		(b) Wmk Small Crown, W 2. P 14			
22	1	1d. red-brown (Die I) (1.55)	£400	50·00	90·00
23	3	2d. blue (Plate 4) (22.2.55)	£2250	£175	£275
23a		2d. blue (Plate 5) (5.7.55)	£2250	£175	£275
		b. Imperf (Plate 5)			
24	1	1d. red-brown (Die II) (27.2.55)	£350	40·00	75·00
24a		1d. deep red-brown (very blue paper) (Die II)	£400	£200	
25		1d. orange-brown (Die II)	£800	90·00	
		(c) Wmk Large Crown, W 4. P 16			
26	1	1d. red-brown (Die II) (15.5.55)	£650	55·00	£125
		a. Imperf (Plate 7)			
27	3	2d. blue (Plate 5) (20.7.55)	£2750	£200	£300
		a. Imperf		£3000	
		(d) Wmk Large Crown, W 4. P 14			
29	1	1d. red-brown (Die II) (6.55)	£175	10·00	25·00
		a. Imperf (shades) (Plates 22, 24, 25, 32, 43) ..	£1300	£1000	
30		1d. brick-red (Die II) ..	£250	35·00	

31	1	1d. plum (Die II) (2.56) ..	..	£1200	£350	
32		1d. brown-rose (Die II) ..		£250	35·00	
33		1d. orange-brown (Die II) (3.57)		£375	40·00	
34	3	2d. blue (Plate 5) (20.7.55)		£1500	50·00	£125
35		2d. blue (Plate 6) (2.7.57)		£1600	50·00	£125
		a. Imperf		—	£3500	
		b. Imperf vert (horiz pair)		†		
★17/35a		**For well-centred, lightly used**			**+125%**	

1856–58. *Wmk Large Crown, W 4. Paper no longer blued.*

				Un	Used	
		(a) P 16.				
36	1	1d. rose-red (Die II) (26.12.57)		£900	50·00	£125
36a	3	2d. blue (Plate 6) (1.2.58)		£3750	£200	£300
		(b) Die II. P 14				
37	1	1d. red-brown (11.56)		£375	£100	
38		1d. pale red (9.4.57)		75·00	15·00	
		a. Imperf		£700	£550	
39		1d. pale rose (3.57)		75·00	25·00	
40		1d. rose-red (9.57)		50·00	15·00	20·00
		a. Imperf		£700	£600	
		b. Imperf vert (horiz pair)		†		
41		1d. deep rose-red (7.57)		90·00	12·00	

1861. *Letters engraved on plate instead of punched (Alphabet IV).*

42	1	1d. rose-red (Die II) (Plates 50 and 51)		£190	30·00	50·00
		a. Imperf		—	£2100	
★36/42a		**For well-centred, lightly used**			**+125%**	

In both values, varieties may be found as described in the preceding issues—ivory heads, inverted watermarks, re-entries, and double letters in corners.

The change of perforation from 16 to 14 was decided upon late in 1854 since the closer holes of the former gauge tended to cause the sheets of stamps to break up when handled, but for a time both gauges were in concurrent use. Owing to faulty alignment of the impressions on the plates and to shrinkage of the paper when damped, badly perforated stamps are plentiful in the line-engraved issues.

5   **6**   Showing position of the plate number on the 1d. and 2d. values. (Plate 170 shown)

1858–79. *Letters in all four corners. Wmk Large Crown, W 4. Die II (1d. and 2d.). P 14.*

				Un	★ Used	Used on cover
43	5	1d. rose-red (1.4.64)		10·00	2·00	6·00
44		1d. lake-red		10·00	2·00	
		a. Imperf	*from*	£1000	£700	
★43/4a		**For well-centred, lightly used**	..		**+125%**	

Plate		Un	Used	Plate		Un	Used
71	..	25·00	3·00	133	..	80·00	9·00
72	..	30·00	4·00	134	..	10·00	2·00
73	..	25·00	3·00	135	..	90·00	26·00
74	..	20·00	2·00	136	..	90·00	20·00
76	..	35·00	2·00	137	..	20·00	2·25
77	..	£100000	£80000	138	..	18·00	2·00
78	..	90·00	2·00	139	..	30·00	16·00
79	..	30·00	2·00	140	..	18·00	2·00
80	..	22·00	2·00	141	..	£110	9·00
81	..	45·00	2·25	142	..	40·00	24·00
82	..	90·00	4·00	143	..	30·00	15·00
83	..	£110	7·00	144	..	90·00	20·00
84	..	45·00	2·25	145	..	10·00	2·25
85	..	25·00	2·25	146	..	18·00	6·00
86	..	30·00	4·00	147	..	22·00	3·00
87	..	10·00	2·00	148	..	22·00	3·00
88	..	£125	8·00	149	..	20·00	6·00
89	..	35·00	2·00	150	..	10·00	2·00
90	..	28·00	2·00	151	..	25·00	9·00
91	..	35·00	6·00	152	..	22·00	5·50
92	..	18·00	2·00	153	..	60·00	9·00
93	..	35·00	2·00	154	..	20·00	2·25
94	..	35·00	5·00	155	..	20·00	2·25
95	..	25·00	2·00	156	..	20·00	2·25
96	..	28·00	2·00	157	..	20·00	2·00
97	..	20·00	3·50	158	..	10·00	2·00
98	..	20·00	6·00	159	..	10·00	2·00
99	..	25·00	5·00	160	..	10·00	2·00
100	..	30·00	2·25	161	..	28·00	7·00
101	..	40·00	9·00	162	..	20·00	7·00
102	..	22·00	2·00	163	..	20·00	3·00
103	..	20·00	3·50	164	..	20·00	3·00
104	..	28·00	5·00	165	..	22·00	4·00
105	..	50·00	7·00	166	..	20·00	6·00
106	..	30·00	2·00	167	..	18·00	2·00
107	..	35·00	7·00	168	..	18·00	8·00
108	..	30·00	2·25	169	..	30·00	7·00
109	..	60·00	3·00	170	..	18·00	2·00
110	..	22·00	9·00	171	..	10·00	2·00
111	..	30·00	2·25	172	..	10·00	2·00
112	..	45·00	2·25	173	..	40·00	9·00
113	..	20·00	12·00	174	..	10·00	2·00
114	..	£250	12·00	175	..	30·00	3·50
115	..	90·00	2·25	176	..	25·00	2·25
116	..	75·00	9·00	177	..	18·00	2·00
117	..	20·00	2·00	178	..	20·00	3·50
118	..	25·00	2·00	179	..	20·00	2·25
119	..	18·00	2·00	180	..	20·00	5·00
120	..	10·00	2·00	181	..	20·00	2·00
121	..	32·00	9·50	182	..	75·00	9·00
122	..	10·00	2·00	183	..	25·00	3·00
123	..	18·00	2·00	184	..	10·00	2·25
124	..	18·00	2·00	185	..	20·00	3·00
125	..	18·00	2·00	186	..	30·00	2·25
127	..	30·00	2·25	187	..	18·00	2·00
129	..	18·00	8·00	188	..	22·00	10·00
130	..	22·00	2·25	189	..	30·00	7·00
131	..	60·00	16·00	190	..	20·00	6·00
132	..	90·00	22·00	191	..	10·00	2·00

Plate	Un	Used	Plate	Un	Used
192	25·00	2·00	209	20·00	9·00
193	10·00	2·00	210	22·00	12·00
194	20·00	8·00	211	38·00	20·00
195	20·00	8·00	212	20·00	11·00
196	18·00	5·00	213	20·00	11·00
197	20·00	9·00	214	25·00	18·00
198	12·00	6·00	215	25·00	18·00
199	22·00	6·00	216	25·00	18·00
200	22·00	2·00	217	22·00	7·00
201	10·00	5·00	218	18·00	8·00
202	20·00	8·00	219	45·00	70·00
203	10·00	16·00	220	10·00	7·00
204	18·00	2·25	221	30·00	16·00
205	18·00	3·00	222	40·00	40·00
206	18·00	9·00	223	45·00	60·00
207	18·00	9·00	224	50·00	50·00
208	18·00	16·00	225	£1250	£400

Error. Imperf. Issued at Cardiff (Plate 116)

			Un	Used
44*b* **5**	1d. rose-red (18.1.70)	..	£2250	£1500

The following plate numbers are also known imperf and used (No. 44a); 72, 79, 80, 81, 82, 83, 86, 87, 88, 90, 91, 92, 93, 96, 97, 98, 100, 102, 103, 104, 105, 107, 108, 109, 112, 114, 117, 120, 121, 122, 136, 137, 142, 146, 148, 158, 162, 164, 166, 171, 174, 191 and 202.

The numbering of this series of 1d. red plates follows after that of the previous 1d. stamp, last printed from Plate 68.

Plates 69, 70, 75, 126 and 128 were prepared for this issue but rejected owing to defects, and stamps from these plates do not exist, so that specimens which optimistic collectors believe to be from Plate 77) bear other plate numbers. Owing to faulty engraving or printing it is not always easy to identify the plate number. Plate 77 was also rejected but some stamps printed from it were used. One specimen is in the Tapling Collection and six or seven others are known. Plates 226 to 228 were made but not used.

Specimens from most of the plates are known with inverted watermark. The variety of watermark described in the General Notes to this section occurs on stamp M A (or M L) on plates up to about 96 (*Prices from* £110 *used*).

Re-entries in this issue are few, the best being on stamps M K and T K of Plate 71 and on S L and T L, Plate 83.

					★ Used on
			Un	Used	cover
45 **6**	2d. blue (thick lines) (7.58)	..	£225	9·00	22·00
	a. Imperf (Plate 9)	..		£3500	
	Plate				
	7	.. .. ..	£550	40·00	
	8	.. .. ..	£600	32·00	
	9	.. .. ..	£225	9·00	
	12	.. ..	£1000	£100	
46	2d. blue (thin lines) (1.7.69)	..	£250	20·00	25·00
47	2d. deep blue (thin lines)	..	£250	20·00	
	a. Imperf (Plate 13)			£2500	
	Plate				
	13	.. ..	£250	20·00	
	14	.. ..	£300	25·00	
	15	.. ..	£250	25·00	

★45/7 **For well-centred, lightly used** .. +125%

Plates 10 and 11 of the 2d. were prepared but rejected. Plates 13 to 15 were laid down from a new roller impression on which the white lines were thinner.

There are some marked re-entries and repairs, particularly on Plates 7, 8, 9 and 12.

Stamps with inverted watermark may be found and also the T A (T L) and M A (M L) watermark varieties (*see* General Notes to this section).

Though the paper is normally white, some printings showed blueing and stamps showing the "ivory head" may therefore be found.

7

Showing the plate
number (9)

9

1870 (1 Oct). *Wmk W* **9**, *extending over three stamps. P* 14.

					★ Used on
			Un	Used	cover
48 **7**	½d. rose-red	..	70·00	15·00	40·00
49	½d. rose	..	70·00	15·00	
	a. Imperf (Plates 1, 4, 5, 6, 8, 14)	*from*	£1100	£700	
	Plate				
	1	.. ..	£150	70·00	
	3	.. ..	80·00	25·00	
	4	.. ..	£110	20·00	
	5	.. ..	75·00	15·00	
	6	.. ..	70·00	15·00	
	8	.. ..	£125	70·00	
	9	.. ..	£2500	£400	
	10	.. ..	£110	15·00	
	11	.. ..	70·00	15·00	
	12	.. ..	70·00	15·00	
	13	.. ..	70·00	15·00	
	14	.. ..	70·00	15·00	
	15	.. ..	80·00	22·00	
	19	.. ..	£125	40·00	
	20	.. ..	£150	60·00	

★49/9a **For well-centred, lightly used** .. +200%

The ½d. was printed in sheets of 480 (24 × 20) so that the check letters run from A A X T to A A T X.

Plates 2, 7, 16, 17 and 18 were not completed while Plates 21 and 22, though made, were not used.

Owing to the method of perforating, the outer side of stamps in either the A or X row (ie the left or right side of the sheet) is imperf. Stamps may be found with watermark inverted or reversed, or without watermark, the latter due to misplacement of the paper when printing.

8 Position of plate Number

1870 (1 Oct). *Wmk W* **4**. *P* 14.

				★	Used on
			Un	Used	cover
51 **8**	1½d. rose-red	..	£250	40·00	£200
52	1½d. lake-red	..	£250	40·00	
	a. Imperf (Plates 1 and 3)	*from*	£2250	†	
	Plate				
	(1)	.. ..	£450	60·00	
	3	.. ..	£250	40·00	

Error of lettering. OP-PC for CP-PC (*Plate* 1)

53 **8**	1½d. rose-red	..	£5000	£750

★51/3 **For well-centred, lightly used** .. +125%

1860. *Prepared for use but not issued; blued paper. Wmk W* **4**. *P* 14.

			Un	Used
53*a* **8**	1½d. rosy mauve (Plate 1)	..	£2500	
	b. Error of lettering, OP-PC for CP-PC			

Owing to a proposed change in the postal rates, 1½d. stamps were first printed in 1860, in rosy mauve, No. 53a, but the change was not approved and the greater part of the stock was destroyed.

In 1870 a 1½d. stamp was required and was issued in rose-red.

Plate 1 did not have the plate number in the design of the stamps, but on stamps from Plate 3 the number will be found in the frame as shown above.

Plate 2 was defective and was not used.

The error of lettering OP-PC on Plate 1 was apparently not noticed by the printers, and therefore not corrected.

EMBOSSED ISSUES

Volume 1 of the Stanley Gibbons *Great Britain Specialised Catalogue* gives further detailed information on the embossed issues.

PRICES. The prices quoted are for cut-square stamps with average to fine embossing. Stamps with exceptionally clear embossing are worth more.

10　　**11**

12　　**13**

Position of die number

(Primary die engraved at the Royal Mint by William Wyon. Stamps printed at Somerset House)

1847–54. *Imperf.* (For paper and wmk see footnote.)

					Used on
			Un	Used	cover
54 **10**	1s. pale green (11.9.47)	..	£3500	£500	£600
55	1s. green	..	£3500	£550	
56	1s. deep green	..	£4000	£550	
	Die 1 (1847)	..	£3500	£500	
	Die 2 (1854)	..	£4000	£575	
57 **11**	10d. brown (6.11.48)	..	£3000	£725	£1300
	Die 1 (1848)	..	£3250	£775	
	Die 2 (1850)	..	£3000	£725	
	Die 3 (1853)	..	£3000	£725	
	Die 4 (1854)	..	£3250	£775	
	Die 5	..	£17000		
58 **12**	6d. mauve (1.3.54)	..	£3250	£575	
59	6d. dull lilac	..	£3250	£550	£650
60	6d. purple	..	£3250	£550	
61	6d. violet	..	£4500	£1100	

The 1s. and 10d. are on "Dickinson" paper with "silk" threads (actually a pale blue twisted cotton yarn). The 6d. is on paper watermarked V R in single-lined letters, W **13**, which may be found in four ways—upright, inverted, upright reversed, and inverted reversed, upright reversed being the most common.

The die numbers are indicated on the base of the bust. Only Die 1 (1 WW) of the 6d. was used for the adhesive stamps. The 10d. is from Die 1 (W.W.1 on stamps), and Dies 2 to 5 (2 W.W., 3 W.W., 4 W.W. and 5 W.W.) but the number and letters on stamps from Die 1 are seldom clear and many specimens are known without any trace of them. Because of this the stamp we previously listed as "No die number" has been deleted. That they are from Die 1 is proved by the existence of blocks showing stamps with and without the die number. The 1s. is from Dies 1 and 2 (W.W.1, W.W.2).

The normal arrangement of the "silk" threads in the paper was in

---

pairs running down each vertical row of the sheet, the space between the threads of each pair being approximately 5 mm and between pairs of threads 20 mm. Varieties due to misplacement of the paper in printing show a single thread on the first stamp from the sheet margin and two threads 20 mm apart on the other stamps of the row. Faulty manufacture is the cause of stamps with a single thread in the middle.

Through bad spacing of the impressions, which were handstruck, all values may be found with two impressions more or less overlapping. Owing to the small margin allowed for variation of spacing, specimens with good margins on all sides are not common.

Double impressions are known of all values.

Later printings of the 6d. had the gum tinted green to enable the printer to distinguish the gummed side of the paper.

SURFACE-PRINTED ISSUES

GENERAL NOTES

Volume 1 of the Stanley Gibbons *Great Britain Specialised Catalogue* gives further detailed information on the surface-printed issues.

"Abnormals". The majority of the great rarities in the surface-printed group of issues are the so-called "abnormals", whose existence is due to the practice of printing six sheets from every plate as soon as made, one of which was kept for record purposes at Somerset House, while the others were perforated and usually issued. If such plates were not used for general production or if, before they came into full use, a change of watermark or colour took place, the six sheets originally printed would differ from the main issue in plate, colour or watermark and, if issued, would be extremely rare.

The abnormal stamps of this class listed in this Catalogue and distinguished, where not priced, by an asterisk (*), are:

No.		
78	3d. Plate 3 (with white dots)	
152	4d. vermilion, Plate 16	
153	4d. sage-green, Plate 17	
109	6d. mauve, Plate 10	
124/a	6d. chestnut and 6d. pale chestnut, Plate 12	
145	6d. pale buff, Plate 13	
88	9d. Plate 3 (hair lines)	
98	9d. Plate 3 (*see* footnote to No. 98)	
113	10d. Plate 2	
91	1s. Plate 3 ("Plate 2")	
148/50	1s. green, Plate 14	
120	2s. blue, Plate 3	

Those which may have been issued, but of which no specimens are known, are 2½d. wmk Anchor, Plates 4 and 5; 3d. wmk Emblems, Plate 5; 3d. wmk Spray, Plate 21; 6d. grey, wmk Spray, Plate 18; 8d. orange, Plate 2; 1s. wmk Emblems, Plate 5. 5s. wmk Maltese Cross, Plate 4.

The 10d. Plate 1, wmk Emblems (No. 99), is sometimes reckoned among the abnormals, but was an error, due to the use of the wrong paper.

Corner Letters. With the exception of the 4d., 6d. and 1s. of 1855–57, the ½d., 1½d., 2d. and 5d. of 1880, the 1d. lilac of 1881 and the £5 (which had letters in lower corners only, and in the reverse order to the normal), all the surface-printed issues issued prior to 1887 had letters in all four corners, as in the later line-engraved stamps. The arrangement is the same, the letters running in sequence right across and down the sheets, whether these were divided into panes or not. The corner letters existing naturally depend on the number of stamps in the sheet and their arrangement.

Imprimaturs and Imperforate Stamps. The Post Office retained in their records (now in the National Postal Museum) one imperforate sheet from each plate, known as the Imprimatur (or officially approved) sheet. Some stamps have been removed from time to time for presentation purposes and have come on to the market, but these imperforates are not listed as they were not issued. Full details can be found in Volume I of the *Great Britain Specialised Catalogue*.

However, other imperforate stamps are known to have been issued and these are listed where it has been possible to prove that they do not come from the Imprimatur sheets. It is therefore advisable to purchase these only when accompanied by an Expert Committee certificate of genuineness.

Plate Numbers. All stamps from No. 75 to No. 163 bear in their designs either the plate number or, in one or two earlier instances, some other indication by which one plate can be distinguished from another. With the aid of these and of the corner letters it is thus possible to "reconstruct" a sheet of stamps from any plate of any issue or denomination.

Surface-printing. In this context the traditional designation "surface-printing" is synonymous with typo(graphy)—a philatelic term—or letterpress—the printers' term—as meaning printing from (the surface of) raised type. It is also called relief-printing, as the image is in relief (in French, *en épargne*), unwanted parts of the design having been cut away. Duplicate impressions can be electrotyped or stereotyped from an original die, the resulting *clichés* being locked together to form the printing plate.

Wing Margins. As the vertical gutters (spaces) between the panes, into which sheets of stamps of most values were divided until the introduction of the Imperial Crown watermark, were perforated through the centre with a single row of holes, instead of each vertical row of stamps on the inner side of the panes having its own line of perforation as is now usual, a proportion of the stamps in each sheet have what is called a "wing margin" about 5 mm wide on one or other side.

The stamps with "wing margins" are the watermark Emblems and Spray of Rose series (3d. 6d. 9d. 10d. 1s. and 2s.) with letters D, E, H or I in S.E. corner, and the watermark Garter series (4d. and 8d.) with letters F or G in S.E. corner. Knowledge of this lettering will enable collectors to guard against stamps with wing margin cut down and re-perforated, but note that wing margin stamps of Nos. 62 to 73 are also to be found re-perforated.

PRINTERS. The issues of Queen Victoria, Nos. 62/214, were typo by Thomas De La Rue & Co.

PERFORATIONS. All the surface-printed issues of Queen Victoria are Perf 14, with the exception of Nos. 126/9.

ALTERED CATALOGUE NUMBERS

Any Catalogue numbers altered from the last edition are shown as a list in the introductory pages.

KEY TO SURFACE-PRINTED ISSUES 1855–83

S.G. Nos.	Description	Watermark	Date of Issue
	NO CORNER LETTERS		
62	4d. carmine	Small Garter	31.7.55
63/5	4d. carmine	Medium Garter	25.2.56
66/a	4d. carmine	Large Garter	Jan 1857
69/70	6d. lilac	Emblems	21.10.56
71/3	1s. green	Emblems	1.11.56
	SMALL WHITE CORNER LETTERS		
75/7	3d. carmine	Emblems	1.5.62
78	3d. carmine (dots)	Emblems	Aug 1862
79/82	4d. red	Large Garter	15.1.62
83/5	6d. lilac	Emblems	1.12.62
86/8	9d. bistre	Emblems	15.1.62
89/91	1s. green	Emblems	1.12.62
	LARGE WHITE CORNER LETTERS		
92	3d. rose	Emblems	1.3.65
102/3	3d. rose	Spray	July 1867
93/5	4d. vermilion	Large Garter	4.7.65
96/7	6d. lilac	Emblems	7.3.65
104/7	6d. lilac	Spray	21.6.67
108/9	6d. lilac	Spray	8.3.69
122/4	6d. chestnut	Spray	12.4.72
125	6d. grey	Spray	24.4.73
98	9d. straw	Emblems	30.10.65
110/11	9d. straw	Spray	3.10.67
99	10d. brown	Emblems	11.11.67
112/14	10d. brown	Spray	1.7.67
101	1s. green	Emblems	19.1.65
115/17	1s. green	Spray	13.7.67
118/20b	2s. blue	Spray	1.7.67
121	2s. brown	Spray	27.2.80
126/7	5s. rose	Cross	1.7.67
128	10s. grey	Cross	26.9.78
129	£1 brown-lilac	Cross	26.9.78
130, 134	5s. rose	Anchor	25.11.82
131, 135	10s. grey-green	Anchor	Feb 1883
132, 136	£1 brown-lilac	Anchor	Dec 1882
133, 137	£5 orange	Anchor	21.3.82
	LARGE COLOURED CORNER LETTERS		
166	1d. Venetian red	Crown	1.1.80
138/9	2½d. rosy mauve	Anchor	1.7.75
141	2½d. rosy mauve	Orb	1.5.76
142	2½d. blue	Orb	5.2.80
157	2½d. blue	Crown	23.3.81
143/4	3d. rose	Spray	5.7.73
158	3d. rose	Crown	Jan 1881
159	3d. on 3d. lilac	Crown	1.1.83
152	4d. vermilion	Large Garter	1.3.76
153	4d. sage-green	Large Garter	12.3.77
154	4d. brown	Large Garter	15.8.80
160	4d. brown	Crown	9.12.80
145	6d. buff	Spray	15.3.73
146/7	6d. grey	Spray	20.3.74
161	6d. grey	Crown	1.1.81
162	6d. on 6d. lilac	Crown	1.1.83
156a	8d. purple-brown	Large Garter	July 1876
156	8d. orange	Large Garter	11.9.76
148/50	1s. green	Spray	1.9.73
151	1s. brown	Spray	14.10.80
163	1s. brown	Crown	24.5.81

Watermarks:		
Anchor	W **40, 47**	
Cross	W **39**	
Crown	W **49**	
Emblems	W **20**	
Large Garter	W **17**	
Medium Garter	W **16**	
Orb	W **48**	
Small Garter	W **15**	
Spray	W **33**	

14 **15** Small Garter

16 Medium Garter **17** Large Garter

1855–57. *No corner letters.*

(a) *Wmk Small Garter,* W **15.** *Highly glazed, deeply blued paper*
(31 July 1855)

			★ Used on
		Un	Used cover
62	14	4d. carmine (*shades*)	£3000 £300 £400
		a. Paper slightly blued	£3250 £300
		b. White paper	£3750 £475

(b) *Wmk Medium Garter,* W **16**

(i) *Thick, blued highly glazed paper* (25 February 1856)

63	14	4d. carmine (*shades*)	£3500 £300 £400
		a. White paper	£3250

(ii) *Ordinary thin white paper* (September 1856)

64	14	4d. pale carmine	£2500 £275 £350
		a. Stamp printed double	† —

(iii) *Ordinary white paper, specially prepared ink* (1 November 1856)

65	14	4d. rose or deep rose	£2500 £275 £375

(c) *Wmk Large Garter,* W **17.** *Ordinary white paper* (January 1857)

66	14	4d. rose-carmine	£1000 75·00 £140
		a. Rose	£900 75·00
		b. Thick glazed paper	£2250 £200
★62/6b		For well-centred, lightly used	+125%

18 **19** **20** Emblems wmk (normal)

20a Wmk error, three roses and shamrock

20b Wmk error, three roses and thistle

(d) *Wmk Emblems,* W **20**

			Un	★ Used	Used on cover
69	18	6d. deep lilac (21.10.56)	£750	£100	
70		6d. pale lilac	£675	80·00	£140
		a. Azure paper	£3500	£550	
		b. Thick paper	£1100	£250	
		c. Error. Wmk W **20a**			
71	19	1s. deep green (1.11.56)	£1750	£250	
72		1s. green	£800	£225	£275
73		1s. pale green	£800	£225	
		a. Azure paper	—	£700	
		b. Thick paper	—	£250	
		c. Imperf			
★69/73b		For well-centred, lightly used		+125%	

21 **22**

23 **24** **25** Plate 2

→ ←

A. White dots added

B. Hair lines

1862–64. *A small uncoloured letter in each corner, the 4d. wmk Large Garter,* W **17**, *the others Emblems,* W **20**.

			Un	★ Used	Used on cover
75	21	3d. deep carmine-rose (Plate 2) (1.5.62)	£1900	£225	
76		3d. bright carmine-rose	£1000	£200	£400
77		3d. pale carmine-rose	£1000	£225	
		b. Thick paper	—	£275	
78		3d. rose (with white dots, Type A, Plate 3) (8.62)	£15000	£3250	
		a. Imperf (Plate 3)	£2750		
79	22	4d. bright red (Plate 3) (15.1.62)	£1100	£100	
80		4d. pale red	£900	70·00	£150
81		4d. bright red (Hair lines, Type B, Plate 4) (16.10.63)	£1000	80·00	
82		4d. pale red (Hair lines, Type B, Plate 4)	£900	70·00	£175
		a. Imperf (Plate 4)	£2250		
83	23	6d. deep lilac (Plate 3) (1.12.62)	£1100	£100	

84	23	6d. lilac	£1000	75·00	£150
		a. Azure paper	—	£400	
		b. Thick paper	—	£125	
		c. Error. Wmk W **20b** (stamp TF)			
85		6d. lilac (Hair lines, Plate 4) (20.4.64)	£1100	£140	£240
		a. Imperf	£1750		
		b. Thick paper	£1750	£150	
		d. Error. Wmk W **20b** (stamp TF)			
86	24	9d. bistre (Plate 2) (15.1.62)	£1900	£240	£350
87		9d. straw	£1900	£225	
		a. On azure paper	—		
		b. Thick paper	£2250	£300	
		c. Error. Watermark W **20b** (stamp TF)	†	—	
88		9d. bistre (Hair lines, Plate 3) (5.62)	£7000	£2750	
89	25	1s. deep green (Plate No. 1 = Plate 2) (1.12.62)	£1300	£200	
90		1s. green (Plate No. 1 = Plate 2)	£1100	£140	£225
		a. "K" in lower left corner in white circle (stamp KD)	£4750	£625	
		aa. "K" normal (stamp KD)	—	£900	
		b. On azure paper	—		
		c. Thick paper	—	£225	
		ca. Thick paper, "K" in circle as No. 90a	—	£1300	
91		1s. deep green (Plate No. 2 = Plate 3)	£12000		
		a. Imperf	£1800		
★75/91		For well-centred, lightly used		+125%	

The 3d. as Type **21**, but with network background in the spandrels which is found overprinted SPECIMEN, was never issued.

The plates of this issue may be distinguished as follows:
3d. Plate 2. No white dots.
    Plate 3. White dots as Illustration A.
4d. Plate 3. No hair lines. Roman I next to lower corner letters.
    Plate 4. Hair lines in corners. (Illustration B). Roman II.
6d. Plate 3. No hair lines.
    Plate 4. Hair lines in corners.
9d. Plate 2. No hair lines.
    Plate 3. Hair lines in corners. Beware of faked lines.
1s. Plate 2. Numbered 1 on stamps.
    Plate 3. Numbered 2 on stamps and with hair lines.

The 9d. on azure paper (No. 87a) is very rare, only one confirmed example being known.

The variety "K" in circle, No. 90a, is believed to be due to a damaged letter having been cut out and replaced. It is probable that the punch was driven in too deeply, causing the flange to penetrate the surface, producing an indentation showing as an uncoloured circle.

The watermark variety "three roses and a shamrock" illustrated in W **20a** was evidently due to the substitution of an extra rose for the thistle in a faulty watermark bit. It is found on stamp TA of Plate 4 of the 3d., Plates 1 (No. 70c), 3, 5 and 6 of the 6d., Plate 4 of the 9d. and Plate 4 of the 1s.

A similar variety, W **20b**, but showing three roses and a thistle is found on stamp TF of the 6d. (Nos. 84/5) and 9d. (Nos. 87, 97/8).

26 **27**

28 (with hyphen) **28a** (without hyphen)

29 **30** **31**

1865–67. *Large uncoloured corner letters. Wmk Large Garter* (4d.); *others Emblems.*

			Un	★ Used	Used on cover
92	26	3d. rose (Plate 4) (1.3.65)	£600	80·00	£150
		a. Error. Wmk W **20a**	£1400	£400	
		b. Thick paper	£750	£100	
93	27	4d. dull vermilion (4.7.65)	£375	50·00	£110
94		4d. vermilion	£375	50·00	
		a. Imperf (Plates 11, 12)	£700		
95		4d. deep vermilion	£375	45·00	
		Plate			
		7 (1865)	£450	50·00	
		8 (1866)	£400	50·00	
		9 (1867)	£400	50·00	
		10 (1868)	£450	50·00	
		11 (1869)	£450	45·00	
		12 (1870)	£375	50·00	
		13 (1872)	£400	50·00	
		14 (1873)	£450	80·00	
96	28	6d. deep lilac (with hyphen) (7.3.65)	£600	90·00	
97		6d. lilac (with hyphen)	£500	70·00	£110
		a. Thick paper	£600	£100	
		b. Stamp doubly printed (Pl 6)	—	£7000	
		c. Error. Wmk W **20a** (Pl 5, 6)	—	£450	
		d. Error. Wmk W **20b** (Plate 5)			
		Plate			
		5 (1865)	£500	70·00	
		6 (1867)	£1500	£125	

Warwick & Warwick
SELLING YOUR COLLECTION?

Highest Prices

Warwick & Warwick can obtain the highest prices through our private treaty service. Whether you have a specialised collection or general surplus material, from £100 to £100,000, you can realise its true potential through Warwick & Warwick.

All Material

We have clients keen to purchase world collections, better single items, covers, proof material, quality G.B., specialised single country studies, postal history - in fact anything and everything philatelic. Whatever you have, Warwick & Warwick can sell it.

Free Valuation

Warwick & Warwick provide written valuations free of charge and without obligation. If you decline our valuation you owe us nothing except return carriage costs. You will receive the full amount tendered in the valuation with no commission or service charge deducted.

Free Visits

Warwick & Warwick will completely free of charge and without obligation arrange to visit sellers of more valuable collections anywhere in the country within 48 hours. Visits abroad can also be arranged.
Smaller collections are transported to our offices for valuation by insured security courier at no expense to the vendor.

Act Now

*Telephone us today with details of your property. Write to us or fax if you prefer. Ask for our **Service to Stamp Collectors** brochure. Alternatively visit us at Chalon House, with its large car park.*

Warwick & Warwick

Warwick & Warwick Limited, Chalon House, Scar Bank, Millers Road, Warwick, England, CV34 5DB.
Tel: 01926 499031. Fax: 01926 491906

			Un	Used	cover
98	29	9d. straw (Plate 4) (30.10.65) ..	£1000	£350	£450
		a. Thick paper	£1500	£450	
		b. Error. Wmk W **20a**	—	£550	
		c. Error. Wmk W **20b** (stamp T F)			
99	30	10d. red-brown (Pl 1) (11.11.67) ..	† £15000		
101	31	1s. green (Plate 4) (19.1.65) ..	£950	£125	£175
		a. Error. Wmk W **20a** ..	—	£500	
		b. Thick paper	£1100	£225	
		c. Imperf between (vert pair)	—	£5000	

★92/101c **For well-centred, lightly used** .. +100%

From mid-1866 to about the end of 1871 4d. stamps of this issue appeared generally with watermark inverted.

Unused examples of No. 98 from Plate 5 exist, but this was never put to press and all evidence points to such stamps originating from a portion of the Imprimatur sheet which was perforated by De La Rue in 1887 for insertion in albums to be presented to members of the Stamp Committee (*Price* £14000 *un*).

The 10d. stamps, No. 99, were printed in *error* on paper watermarked "Emblems" instead of on "Spray of Rose".

32	33 Spray of Rose	34

1867–80. *Wmk Spray of Rose, W* **33.**

			Un	★ Used	Used on cover
102	26	3d. deep rose (12.7.67) ..	£325	50·00	
103		3d. rose ..	£325	40·00	70·00
		a. Imperf (Plates 5, 6, 8) *from*	£1000		
		Plate			
		4 (1867)	£425	£100	
		5 (1868)	£325	40·00	
		6 (1870)	£350	40·00	
		7 (1871)	£425	45·00	
		8 (1872)	£375	45·00	
		9 (1872)	£375	50·00	
		10 (1873)	£425	80·00	
104	28	6d. lilac (with hyphen) (Plate 6) (21.6.67)	£725	70·00	£140
		a. Imperf			
105		6d. deep lilac (with hyphen) (Plate 6)	£725	70·00	
106		6d. purple (with hyphen) (Pl 6)	£725	90·00	
107		6d. bright violet (with hyphen) (22.7.68)	£725	75·00	
108	28a	6d. dull violet (without hyphen) (Plate 8) (8.3.69)	£475	65·00	
109		6d. mauve (without hyphen)	£400	65·00	85·00
		a. Imperf (Plate Nos. 8 and 9)	£1100	£1000	
		Plate			
		8 (1869, mauve) ..	£400	65·00	
		9 (1870, mauve) ..	£400	65·00	
		10 (1869, mauve) ..	* £15000		
110	29	9d. straw (Plate No. 4) (3.10.67)	£800	£175	£275
111		9d. pale straw (Plate No. 4) ..	£800	£190	
		a. Imperf (Plate 4) ..	£2500		
112	30	10d. red-brown (1.7.67) ..	£1500	£250	£450
113		10d. pale red-brown ..	£1500	£275	
114		10d. deep red-brown ..	£1800	£275	
		a. Imperf (Plate 1) ..	£2500		
		Plate			
		1 (1867) ..	£1500	£250	
		2 (1867) ..	£15000	£3500	
115	31	1s. deep green (13.7.67) ..	£700	28·00	
117		1s. green ..	£550	28·00	50·00
		a. Imperf between (horiz pair) (Plate 7)	£1500	£800	
		b. Imperf (Plate 4) ..	£1500	£800	
		Plate			
		4 (1867) ..	£550	32·00	
		5 (1871) ..	£600	30·00	
		6 (1871) ..	£750	28·00	
		7 (1873) ..	£750	60·00	
118	32	2s. dull blue (1.7.67) ..	£1500	£110	£450
119		2s. deep blue ..	£1500	£110	
		a. Imperf (Plate 1) ..	£3000		
120		2s. pale blue ..	£2000	£175	
		aa. Imperf (Plate 1) ..	£2750		
120a		2s. cobalt ..	£6500	£1400	
120b		2s. milky blue ..	£4250	£600	
		Plate			
		1 (1867) ..	£1500	£110	
		3 (1868) ..	*	£4000	
121		2s. brown (Plate No. 1) (27.2.80)	£8000	£1700	
		a. Imperf ..	£6000	†	
		b. No watermark ..	†	—	

★102/21 **For well-centred, lightly used** .. +75%

Examples of the 1s. from Plates 5 and 6 *without* watermark are postal forgeries used at the Stock Exchange Post Office in the early 1870's.

1872–73. *Uncoloured letters in corners. Wmk Spray, W* **33.**

			Un	★ Used	Used on cover
122	34	6d. deep chestnut (Plate 11) (12.4.72)	£575	40·00	90·00
122a		6d. chestnut (Plate 11) (22.5.72)	£500	45·00	
122b		6d. pale chestnut (Plate 11) (1872)	£475	40·00	
123		6d. pale buff (19.10.72)	£500	70·00	£190
		Plate			
		11 (1872, pale buff)	£500	70·00	
		12 (1872, pale buff)	£1100	£125	
124		6d. chestnut (Plate 12) (1872) ..	*	£1800	
124a		6d. pale chestnut (Plate 12) (1872)	*	£1800	
125		6d. grey (Plate 12) (24.4.73)	£1000	£190	£240
		a. Imperf	£2000		

★122/5 **For well-centred, lightly used** .. +50%

35	36

37

38

39 Maltese Cross	40 Large Anchor

1867–83. *Uncoloured letters in corners.*

(a) *Wmk Maltese Cross, W* **39.** *P* 15½ × 15

			Un	★ Used
126	35	5s. rose (1.7.67)	£3750	£400
127		5s. pale rose	£4000	£400
		a. Imperf (Plate 1) ..	£5500	
		Plate		
		1 (1867)	£3750	£400
		2 (1874)	£4750	£500
128	36	10s. greenish grey (Plate 1) (26.9.78)	£28000	£1300
129	37	£1 brown-lilac (Plate 1) (26.9.78)	£32000	£1900

(b) *Wmk Anchor, W* **40.** *P* 14. (i) *Blued paper*

130	35	5s. rose (25.11.82) ..	£7000	£1400
131	36	10s. grey-green (Plate 1) (2.83)	£30000	£2100
132	37	£1 brown-lilac (Plate 1) (12.82)	£38000	£3750
133	38	£5 orange (Plate 1) (21.3.82)	£24000	£5250

(ii) *White paper*

134	35	5s. rose (Plate 4) ..	£6750	£1400
135	36	10s. greenish grey (Plate 1)	£30000	£2100
136	37	£1 brown-lilac (Plate 1)	£45000	£3000
137	38	£5 orange (Plate 1) ..	£6000	£1800

★126/37 **For well-centred, lightly used** .. +75%

41	42	43

44	45	46

47 Small Anchor	48 Orb

1873–80. *Large coloured letters in the corners.*

(a) *Wmk Anchor, W* **47**

			Un	★ Used	Used on cover
138	41	2½d. rosy mauve (*blued paper*) (1.7.75)	£525	80·00	
		a. Imperf			
139		2½d. rosy mauve (*white paper*) ..	£350	65·00	£110
		Plate			
		1 (*blued paper*) (1875) ..	£525	80·00	
		1 (*white paper*) (1875) ..	£350	65·00	
		2 (*blued paper*) (1875) ..	£3750	£800	
		2 (*white paper*) (1875) ..	£350	65·00	
		3 (*white paper*) (1875) ..	£550	70·00	
		3 (*blued paper*) (1875) ..	—	£3000	

Error of Lettering L H—F L for L H—H L (Plate 2)

| 140 | 41 | 2½d. rosy mauve .. .. | £9000 | £850 | |

(b) *Wmk Orb, W* **48**

141	41	2½d. rosy mauve (1.5.76) ..	£325	35·00	70·00
		Plate			
		3 (1876)	£675	70·00	
		4 (1876)	£325	35·00	
		5 (1876)	£325	40·00	
		6 (1876)	£325	35·00	
		7 (1877)	£325	35·00	
		8 (1877)	£325	40·00	
		9 (1877)	£325	35·00	
		10 (1878)	£375	50·00	
		11 (1878)	£325	35·00	
		12 (1878)	£325	40·00	
		13 (1878)	£325	40·00	
		14 (1879)	£325	35·00	
		15 (1879)	£325	35·00	
		16 (1879)	£325	35·00	
		17 (1880)	£750	£160	
142		2½d. blue (5.2.80)	£275	30·00	40·00
		Plate			
		17 (1880)	£275	40·00	
		18 (1880)	£325	32·00	
		19 (1880)	£275	30·00	
		20 (1880)	£275	30·00	

(c) *Wmk Spray, W* **33**

143	42	3d. rose (5.7.73)	£275	30·00	50·00
144		3d. pale rose	£275	30·00	
		Plate			
		11 (1873)	£275	30·00	
		12 (1873)	£325	30·00	
		14 (1874)	£350	32·00	
		15 (1874)	£275	30·00	
		16 (1875)	£325	30·00	
		17 (1875)	£325	30·00	
		18 (1875)	£275	30·00	
		19 (1876)	£275	30·00	
		20 (1879)	£275	50·00	
145	43	6d. pale buff (Plate 13) (15.3.73)	*	£6000	
146		6d. deep grey (20.3.74) ..	£350	45·00	80·00
147		6d. grey	£325	40·00	
		Plate			
		13 (1874)	£325	40·00	
		14 (1875)	£325	40·00	
		15 (1876)	£325	40·00	
		16 (1878)	£325	40·00	
		17 (1880)	£425	65·00	
148	44	1s. deep green (1.9.73) ..	£450	65·00	
150		1s. pale green	£375	50·00	85·00
		Plate			
		8 (1873)	£450	65·00	
		9 (1874)	£450	65·00	
		10 (1874)	£425	70·00	
		11 (1875)	£425	70·00	
		12 (1875)	£375	50·00	
		13 (1876)	£375	50·00	
		14 (—)	*	£14000	
151		1s. orange-brown (Plate 13) (14.10.80)	£1750	£350	£475

(d) *Wmk Large Garter, W* **17**

152	45	4d. vermilion (1.3.76) ..	£1000	£275	£425
		Plate			
		15 (1876)	£1000	£275	
		16 (1877)	*	£14000	
153		4d. sage-green (12.3.77) ..	£550	£175	£275
		Plate			
		15 (1877)	£625	£200	
		16 (1877)	£550	£175	
		17 (1877)	*	£9000	
154		4d. grey-brown (Plate 17) (15.8.80)	£800	£300	£400
		a. Imperf	£3000		
156	46	8d. orange (Plate 1) (11.9.76) ..	£750	£225	£275

★138/56 **For well-centred, lightly used** .. +100%

1876 (July). *Prepared for use but not issued.*

| 156a | 46 | 8d. purple-brown (Plate 1) .. | £4500 | | |

49 Imperial Crown	(50)

3d.

1880–83. *Wmk Imperial Crown, W* **49.**

			Un	★ Used	Used on cover
157	41	2½d. blue (23.3.81)	£275	20·00	40·00
		Plate			
		21 (1881)	£325	28·00	
		22 (1881)	£275	28·00	
		23 (1881)	£325	28·00	
158	42	3d. rose (3.81)	£325	60·00	85·00
		Plate			
		20 (1881)	£375	80·00	
		21 (1881)	£325	60·00	

159	42	3d. on 3d. lilac (T **50**) (C.) (Plate 21) (1.1.83)			£325	£110	£325
160	45	4d. grey-brown (8.12.80)			£275	45·00	£110
		Plate					
		17 (1880)			£275	45·00	
		18 (1882)			£275	45·00	
161	43	6d. grey (1.1.81)			£250	50·00	80·00
		Plate					
		17 (1881)			£275	50·00	
		18 (1882)			£250	50·00	
162		6d. on 6d. lilac (as T **50**) (C.) (Plate 18) (1.1.83)			£275	£110	£225
		a. Slanting dots (various) *from*			£325	£110	
		b. Opt double			—	£6000	
163	44	1s. orange-brown (24.5.81)			£350	£100	£200
		Plate					
		13 (1881)			£400	£100	
		14 (1881)			£350	£100	
★157/63		**For well-centred, lightly used**				**+75%**	

The 1s. Plate 14 (line perf 14) exists in purple, but was not issued in this shade (*Price £3000 unused*). Examples were included in a few of the Souvenir Albums prepared for members of the "Stamp Committee of 1884".

52   53

54   55   56

1880–81. *Wmk Imperial Crown. W* **49.**

				★	Used on
			Un	*Used*	*cover*
164	52	½d. deep green (14.10.80)	40·00	10·00	20·00
		a. Imperf	£800		
		b. No watermark	£3500		
165		½d. pale green	40·00	15·00	
166	53	1d. Venetian red (1.1.80)	15·00	10·00	18·00
		a. Imperf	£800		
167	54	1½d. Venetian red (14.10.80)	£140	35·00	£110
168	55	2d. pale rose (8.12.80)	£175	70·00	£110
168a		2d. deep rose	£175	70·00	
169	56	5d. indigo (15.3.81)	£475	90·00	£175
		a. Imperf	£1700	£1300	
★164/9		**For well-centred, lightly used**		**+75%**	

Die I   57   Die II

1881. *Wmk Imperial Crown. W* **49.** (*a*) *14 dots in each corner, Die I* (12 July).

				★	Used on
			Un	*Used*	*cover*
170	57	1d. lilac	£110	25·00	35·00
171		1d. pale lilac	£110	25·00	

(*b*) *16 dots in each corner, Die II* (13 December)

172	57	1d. lilac	2·50	2·00	3·00
172a		1d. bluish lilac	£225	70·00	
173		1d. deep purple	2·50	2·00	
		a. Printed both sides	£450	†	
		b. Frame broken at bottom	£575	£275	
		c. Printed on gummed side	£475	†	
		d. Imperf three sides (pair)	£3000	†	
		e. Printed both sides but impression on back inverted	£500	†	
		f. No watermark	£1000	†	
		g. Blued paper	£2000		
174		1d. mauve	2·50	1·50	
		a. Imperf (pair)	£1300		
★170/4		**For well-centred, lightly used**		**+50%**	

1d. stamps with the words "PEARS SOAP" printed on the back in *orange*, *blue* or *mauve* price *from* £425, *unused*.

The variety "frame broken at bottom" (No. 173b) shows a white space just inside the bottom frame-line from between the "N" and "E" of "ONE" to below the first "N" of "PENNY", breaking the pearls and cutting into the lower part of the oval below "PEN".

MINIMUM PRICE

The minimum price quote is 10p which represents a handling charge rather than a basis for valuing common stamps. For further notes about prices see introductory pages.

KEY TO SURFACE-PRINTED ISSUES 1880–1900

S.G. Nos.	Description	Date of Issue
164/5	½d. green	14.10.80
187	½d. slate-blue	1.4.84
197/e	½d. vermilion	1.1.87
213	½d. blue-green	17.4.1900
166	1d. Venetian red	1.1.80
170/1	1d. lilac, Die I	12.7.81
172/4	1d. lilac, Die II	12.12.81
167	1½d. Venetian red	14.10.80
188	1½d. lilac	1.4.84
198	1½d. purple and green	1.1.87
168/a	2d. rose	8.12.80
189	2d. lilac	1.4.84
199/200	2d. green and red	1.1.87
190	2½d. lilac	1.4.84
201	2½d. purple on blue paper	1.1.87
191	3d. lilac	1.4.84
202/4	3d. purple on yellow paper	1.1.87
192	4d. dull green	1.4.84
205/a	4d. green and brown	1.1.87
206	4½d. green and carmine	15.9.92
169	5d. indigo	15.3.81
193	5d. dull green	1.4.84
207	5d. purple and blue, Die I	1.1.87
207a	5d. purple and blue, Die II	1888
194	6d. dull green	1.4.84
208/a	6d. purple on rose-red paper	1.1.87
195	9d. dull green	1.8.83
209	9d. purple and blue	1.1.87
210/b	10d. purple and carmine	24.2.90
196	1s. dull green	1.4.84
211	1s. green	1.1.87
214	1s. green and carmine	11.7.1900
175	2s. 6d. lilac on blued paper	2.7.83
178/9	2s. 6d. lilac	1884
176	5s. rose on blued paper	1.4.84
180/1	5s. rose	1884
177/a	10s. ultramarine on blued paper	1.4.84
182/3a	10s. ultramarine	1884
185	£1 brown-lilac, wmk Crowns	1.4.84
186	£1 brown-lilac, wmk Orbs	2.88
212	£1 green	28.1.91

Note that the £5 value used with the above series is listed as Nos. 133 and 137.

58   59

60

1883–84. *Coloured letters in the corners. Wmk Anchor, W* **40.**

(*a*) *Blued paper*

				★
			Un	*Used*
175	58	2s. 6d. lilac (2.7.83)	£3000	£800
176	59	5s. rose (1.4.84)	£4500	£1700
177	60	10s. ultramarine (1.4.84)	£16000	£4000
177a		10s. cobalt (5.84)	£18000	£6000

(*b*) *White paper*

178	58	2s. 6d. lilac	£350	£110
179		2s. 6d. deep lilac	£350	£110
		a. Error. On blued paper	£2500	£750
180	59	5s. rose	£550	£140
181		5s. crimson	£550	£140
182	60	10s. cobalt	£17000	£4250
183		10s. ultramarine	£1250	£375
183a		10s. pale ultramarine	£1250	£375
★175/83a		**For well-centred, lightly used**		**+50%**

For No. 180 perf 12 *see* second note below No. 196.

61

Broken frames, Plate 2

1884 (1 April). *Wmk Three Imperial Crowns, W* **49.**

					★
				Un	*Used*
185	61	£1 brown-lilac		£15000	£1400
		a. Frame broken		£22000	£2250

1888 (Feb). *Wmk Three Orbs. W* **48.**

186	61	£1 brown-lilac		£26000	£2250
		a. Frame broken		£34000	£3750
★185/6a		**For well-centred, lightly used**			**+50%**

The broken-frame varieties, Nos. 185a and 186a, are on Plate 2 stamps JC and TA, as illustrated. *See also* No. 212a.

62   63   64

65   66

1883 (1 Aug) (9*d.*) or **1884** (1 April) (*others*). *Wmk Imperial Crown. W* **49** (*sideways on horiz designs*).

					★	Used on
				Un	*Used*	*cover*
187	52	½d. slate-blue		17·00	7·00	12·00
		a. Imperf		£750		
188	62	1½d. lilac		85·00	35·00	£100
		a. Imperf		£750		
189	63	2d. lilac		£140	65·00	£110
		a. Imperf		£850		
190	64	2½d. lilac		70·00	12·00	24·00
		a. Imperf		£850		
191	65	3d. lilac		£175	85·00	£125
		a. Imperf		£850		
192	66	4d. dull green		£400	£175	£225
		a. Imperf		£900		
193	62	5d. dull green		£400	£175	£225
		a. Imperf		£900		
194	63	6d. dull green		£425	£200	£250
		a. Imperf		£900		
195	64	9d. dull green (1.8.83)		£750	£375	£825
		a. Imperf		£900		
196	65	1s. dull green		£550	£200	£375
		a. Imperf		£2000		
★187/96		**For well-centred, lightly used**			**+100%**	

The above prices are for stamps in the true dull green colour. Stamps which have been soaked, causing the colour to run, are virtually worthless.

Stamps of the above set and No. 180 are also found perf 12; these are official perforations, but were never issued. A second variety of the 5d. is known with a line instead of a stop under the "d" in the value; this was never issued and is therefore only known *unused* (*Price £6000*).

71   72   73

74   75   76

77   78   79

80   81   82

Die I   Die II

Die I : Square dots to right of "d".
Die II : Thin vertical lines to right of "d".

1887 (1 Jan)-**1892.** "Jubilee" issue. New types. The bicoloured stamps have the value tablets, or the frames including the value tablets, in the second colour. Wmk Imperial Crown, W **49** (Three Crowns on £1).

			Un	★ Used	Used on cover
197	71	½d. vermilion	1·50	1·00	6·00
		a. Printed on gummed side	£1000	†	
		b. Printed both sides			
		c. Doubly printed	£6000		
		d. Imperf	£1400		
197e		½d. orange-vermilion	1·50	1·00	
198	72	1½d. dull purple and pale green	15·00	7·00	22·00
		a. Purple part of design double	—	£4250	
199	73	2d. green and scarlet	£350	£200	
200		2d. grey-green and carmine	28·00	12·00	24·00
201	74	2½d. purple/blue	22·00	3·00	6·00
		a. Printed on gummed side	£2750	†	
		b. Imperf three sides	£2250		
		c. Imperf	£2500		
202	75	3d. purple/yellow	22·00	3·25	24·00
		a. Imperf	£3750		
203		3d. deep purple/yellow	22·00	3·25	
204		3d. purple/orange (1890)	£425	£175	
205	76	4d. green and purple-brown	30·00	13·00	30·00
205a		aa. Imperf			
		4d. green and deep brown	30·00	13·00	
206	77	4½d. green and carmine (15.9.92)	10·00	5·00	65·00
206a		4½d. green & deep brt carmine	£475	£350	
207	78	5d. dull purple and blue (Die I)	£475	50·00	95·00
207a		5d. dull pur & bl (Die II) (1888)	35·00	11·00	32·00
208	79	6d. purple/rose-red	30·00	10·00	28·00
208a		6d. deep purple/rose-red	30·00	11·00	
209	80	9d. dull purple and blue	60·00	40·00	75·00
210	81	10d. dull purple and carmine (shades) (24.2.90)	45·00	38·00	90·00
		aa. Imperf	£4250		
210a		10d. dull purple & dp dull carm	£400	£200	
210b		10d. dull purple and scarlet	60·00	45·00	
211	82	1s. dull green	£200	60·00	£110
212	61	£1 green (28.1.91)	£2500	£425	
		a. Frame broken	£5250	£1250	
★197/212a			Set of 14		

★197/212a For well-centred, lightly used .. +50%

The broken-frame varieties, No. 212a, are on Plate 2 stamps JC or TA, as illustrated above No. 185.
½d. stamps with "PEARS SOAP" printed on the back in *orange*, *blue* or *mauve*, price *from* £400 each.

1900. *Colours changed. Wmk Imperial Crown, W* **49.**

			Un	★ Used	Used on cover
213	71	½d. blue-green (17.4)	1·75	2·00	6·00
		a. Printed on gummed side		†	
		b. Imperf	£2000		
214	82	1s. green and carmine (11.7)	50·00	£125	£275
197/214			Set of 14	£500	£325

★213/14 For well-centred, lightly used .. +50%
The ½d., No. 213, in bright blue, is a colour changeling caused by a constituent of the ink used for some months in 1900.

KING EDWARD VII
22 January 1901–6 May 1910

PRINTINGS. Distinguishing De La Rue printings from the provisional printings of the same values made by Harrison & Sons Ltd. or at Somerset House may prove difficult in some cases. For very full guidance Volume 2 of the Stanley Gibbons *Great Britain Specialised Catalogue* should prove helpful.

Note that stamps perforated 15 × 14 must be Harrison; the 2½d., 3d. and 4d. in this perforation are useful reference material, their shades and appearance in most cases matching the Harrison perf 14 printings.

Except for the 6d. value, all stamps on chalk-surfaced paper are printed by De La Rue.

Of the stamps on ordinary paper, the De La Rue impressions are usually clearer and of a higher finish than those of the other printers. The shades are markedly different except in some printings of the 4d., 6d. and 7d. and in the 5s., 10s. and £1.

Used stamps in good, clean, unrubbed condition and with dated postmarks can form the basis of a useful reference collection, the dates often assisting in the assignment to the printers.

USED STAMPS. For well-centred, lightly used examples of King Edward VII stamps, add the following percentages to the used prices quoted below:
De La Rue printings (Nos. 215/66)—3d. values +35%, 4d. orange +100%, 6d. +75%, 7d. and 1s. +25%, all other values +50%.
Harrison printings (Nos. 267/86)—all values and perforations +75%.
Somerset House printings (Nos. 287/320)—1s. values +25%, all other values +50%.

83   84   85

86   87   88

89   90   91

92   93   94

95   96

97

(Des E. Fuchs)

1902 (1 Jan)-**10.** *Printed by De La Rue & Co. Wmk Imperial Crown (½d. to 1s.); Anchor (2s. 6d. to 10s.); Three Crowns (£1). Ordinary paper. P* 14.

			Un	Used	Used on cover
215	83	½d. dull blue-green (1.1.02)	2·00	1·50	2·50
216		½d. blue-green	2·00	1·50	
217		½d. pale yellowish grn (26.11.04)	2·00	1·50	2·50
218		½d. yellowish green	2·00	1·50	
		a. Booklet pane. Five stamps plus St. Andrew's Cross label (6.06)	£300		
		b. Doubly printed (bottom row on one pane) (Control H9)	£15000		
219		1d. scarlet (1.1.02)	2·00	1·50	2·50
220		1d. bright scarlet	2·00	1·50	
		a. Imperf (pair)	£10000		
221	84	1½d. dull purple & grn (21.3.02)	30·00	13·00	
222		1½d. slate-purple and green	32·00	12·00	22·00
223		1½d. pale dull pur & grn (chalk-surfaced paper) (8.05)	40·00	13·00	
224		1½d. slate-purple & bluish green (chalk-surfaced paper)	40·00	10·00	
225	85	2d. yellowish green & carmine-red (25.3.02)	40·00	13·00	24·00
226		2d. grey-grn & carm-red (1904)	40·00	15·00	
227		2d. pale grey-green & carm-red (chalk-surfaced paper) (4.06)	40·00	18·00	
228		2d. pale grey-grn & scar (chalk-surfaced paper) (1909)	40·00	18·00	
229		2d. dull blue-grn & carm (chalk-surfaced paper) (1907)	70·00	40·00	
230	86	2½d. ultramarine (1.1.02)	18·00	6·50	18·00
231		2½d. pale ultramarine	18·00	6·50	
232	87	3d. dull pur/orge-yell (20.3.02)	40·00	10·00	25·00
		a. Chalk-surfaced paper (3.06)	£140	50·00	
232b		3d. deep purple/orange-yellow	40·00	7·00	
232c		3d. pale reddish pur/orge-yell (chalk-surfaced paper) (3.06)	£140	40·00	
233		3d. dull reddish pur/yell (lemon back) (chalk-surfaced paper)	£140	55·00	
233b		3d. pale purple/lemon (chalk-surfaced paper)	30·00	12·00	
234		3d. pur/lemon (chalk-surfaced paper)	30·00	12·00	
235	88	4d. green & grey-brn (27.3.02)	45·00	22·00	
236		4d. green and chocolate-brown	45·00	22·00	
		a. Chalk-surfaced paper (1.06)	40·00	13·00	32·00
238		4d. dp green & choc-brn (chalk-surfaced paper) (1.06)	40·00	13·00	
239		4d. brown-orange (1.11.09)	£140	£125	
240		4d. pale orange (12.09)	20·00	13·00	32·00
241		4d. orange-red (12.09)	20·00	13·00	
242	89	5d. dull pur & ultram (14.5.02)	40·00	11·00	42·00
		a. Chalk-surfaced paper (5.06)	40·00	15·00	
244		5d. slate-pur & ultram (chalk-surfaced paper) (5.06)	40·00	15·00	

			Un	Used	Used on cover
245	83	6d. pale dull purple (1.1.02)	30·00	12·00	35·00
		a. Chalk-surfaced paper (1.06)	30·00	12·00	
246		6d. slate-purple	30·00	12·00	
248		6d. dull purple (chalk-surfaced paper) (1.06)	30·00	12·00	
249	90	7d. grey-black (4.5.10)	10·00	12·00	£150
249a		7d. deep grey-black	£100	£100	
250	91	9d. dull pur & ultram (7.4.02)	70·00	45·00	£150
		a. Chalk-surfaced paper (6.05)	70·00	50·00	
251		9d. slate-purple & ultramarine	70·00	45·00	
		a. Chalk-surfaced paper (6.05)	70·00	50·00	
254	92	10d. dull purple & carm (3.7.02)	70·00	50·00	£150
		a. No cross on crown	£250	£150	
		b. Chalk-surfaced paper (9.06)	70·00	40·00	
255		10d. slate-purple & carm (chalk-surfaced paper) (9.06)	70·00	50·00	
		a. No cross on crown	£210	£150	
256		10d. dull purple & scarlet (chalk-surfaced paper) (9.10)	60·00	60·00	
		a. No cross on crown	£200	£140	
257	93	1s. dull green & carm (24.3.02)	60·00	25·00	£100
		a. Chalk-surfaced paper (9.05)	60·00	30·00	
259		1s. dull green & scarlet (chalk-surfaced paper) (9.10)	60·00	40·00	
260	94	2s. 6d. lilac (5.4.02)	£175	75·00	£575
261		2s. 6d. pale dull purple (chalk-surfaced paper) (7.10.05)	£175	£125	
262		2s. 6d. dull pur (chalk-surfaced paper)	£175	£110	
263	95	5s. bright carmine (5.4.02)	£175	£110	£625
264		5s. deep bright carmine	£190	£110	
265	96	10s. ultramarine (5.4.02)	£500	£300	
266	97	£1 dull blue-green (16.6.02)	£1100	£450	

97a

1910 (May). *Prepared for use by De La Rue but not issued. Wmk Imperial Crown, W* **49.** *P* 14.

266a	97a	2d. Tyrian plum	£14000	

One example of this stamp is known used, but it was never issued to the public.

1911. *Printed by Harrison & Sons. Ordinary paper. Wmk Imperial Crown. (a) P* 14.

			Un	Used	Used on cover
267	83	½d. dull yellow-green (3.5.11)	2·50	1·50	4·00
268		½d. dull green	2·75	1·50	
269		½d. deep dull green	11·00	4·00	
270		½d. pale bluish green	40·00	40·00	
		a. Booklet pane. Five stamps plus St. Andrew's Cross label	£350		
		b. Wmk sideways	— £13000		
		c. Imperf (pair)	£15000		
271		½d. bright green (fine impression) (6.11)	£225	£140	
272		1d. rose-red (3.5.11)	8·00	12·00	15·00
		a. No wmk	40·00	40·00	
273		1d. deep rose-red	8·00	12·00	
274		1d. rose-carmine	55·00	30·00	
275		1d. aniline pink (5.11)	£375	£200	
275a		1d. aniline rose	£175	£140	
276	86	2½d. bright blue (10.7.11)	45·00	22·00	30·00
277	87	3d. purple/lemon (12.9.11)	60·00	£150	£450
277a		3d. grey/lemon	£2750		
278	88	4d. bright orange (12.7.11)	55·00	50·00	£150
		(b) P 15×14			
279	83	½d. dull green (30.10.11)	40·00	45·00	90·00
279a		½d. deep dull green	40·00	45·00	
280		1d. rose-red (4.10.11)	38·00	25·00	
281		1d. rose-carmine	15·00	15·00	22·00
282		1d. pale rose-carmine	22·00	12·00	
283	86	2½d. bright blue (14.10.11)	22·00	12·00	22·00
284		2½d. dull blue	22·00	12·00	
285	87	3d. purple/lemon (22.9.11)	40·00	20·00	30·00
285a		3d. grey/lemon	£2250		
286	88	4d. bright orange (11.11.11)	30·00	15·00	50·00
279/86			Set of 5	£125	80·00

1911-13. *Printed at Somerset House. Ordinary paper. Wmk as 1902-10. P* 14.

			Un	Used	Used on cover
287	84	1½d. reddish purple and bright green (13.7.11)	40·00	30·00	
288		1½d. dull purple and green	25·00	22·00	45·00
289		1½d. slate-purple & grn (9.12)	28·00	22·00	
290	85	2d. dp dull grn & red (8.8.11)	25·00	15·00	35·00
291		2d. deep dull green & carmine	25·00	15·00	
292		2d. grey-green & bright carmine (carmine shows clearly on back) (11.3.12)	25·00	20·00	
293	89	3d. dull reddish purple and bright blue (7.8.11)	30·00	15·00	60·00
294		3d. deep dull reddish purple and bright blue	28·00	15·00	
295	83	6d. royal purple (31.10.11)	45·00	70·00	
296		6d. bright magenta (chalk-surfaced paper) (31.10.11)	£2250		
297		6d. dull purple	30·00	15·00	70·00
298		6d. reddish purple (11.11)	30·00	20·00	
		a. No cross on crown (various shades)	£275		
299		6d. very dp reddish pur (11.11)	40·00	35·00	
300		6d. dark purple (3.12)	30·00	30·00	
301		6d. dull purple ("Dickinson" coated paper") (3.13)	£140	£125	
303		6d. deep plum (7.13)	28·00	60·00	
		a. No cross on crown	£300		
305	90	7d. slate-grey (1.8.12)	15·00	18·00	£100
306	91	9d. reddish purple and light blue (24.7.11)	80·00	55·00	

				Un	Used	
306a	91	9d. deep dull reddish purple & deep bright blue (9.11)		60·00	45·00	
307		9d. dull reddish purple & blue (10.11)		40·00	32·00	£120
307a		9d. deep plum and blue (7.13)		40·00	45·00	
308		9d. slate-pur & cobalt-bl (3.12)		75·00	55·00	
309	92	10d. dull purple & scar (9.10.11)		60·00	45·00	
310		10d. dull reddish pur & aniline pink		£210	£150	
311		10d. dull reddish purple & carm (5.12)		50·00	32·00	£140
		a. No cross on crown		£525		
312	93	1s. dark green & scar (13.7.11)		70·00	38·00	
313		1s. dp green & scar (9.10.11)		50·00	22·00	
314		1s. green & carmine (15.4.12)		38·00	22·00	£110
315	94	2s. 6d. dull greyish purple (15.9.11)		£350	£190	
316		2s. 6d. dull reddish purple		£140	85·00	£750
317		2s. 6d. dark purple		£140	85·00	
318	95	5s. carmine (29.2.12)		£190	85·00	6·25
319	96	10s. blue (14.1.12)		£450	£325	
320	97	£1 deep green (3.9.11)		£1000	£450	

*No. 301 was on an experimental coated paper which does not respond to the silver test.

KING GEORGE V
6 May 1910–20 January 1936

Further detailed information on the issues of King George V will be found in Volume 2 of the Stanley Gibbons *Great Britain Specialised Catalogue*.

PRINTERS. Types 98 to 102 were typographed by Harrison & Sons Ltd., with the exception of certain preliminary printings made at Somerset House and distinguishable by the controls "A.11", B.11" or "B.12" (the Harrison printings do not have a full stop after the letter). The booklet stamps, Nos. 334/7, and 344/5 were printed by Harrisons only.

WATERMARK VARIETIES. Many British stamps to 1967 exist without watermark owing to misplacement of the paper, with either inverted, reversed, or inverted and reversed watermarks. A proportion of the low-value stamps issued in booklets have the watermark inverted in the normal course of printing.

Low values with *watermark sideways* are normally from stamp rolls used in machines with sideways delivery or, from June 1940, certain booklets.

STAMPS WITHOUT WATERMARK. Stamps found without watermark, due to misplacement of the sheet in relation to the dandy roll, are not listed here, but will be found in the *Great Britain Specialised Catalogue*.

The 1½d. and 5d. 1912–22, and 2d. and 2½d., 1924–26, listed here, are from *whole* sheets completely without watermark.

98   99

For type differences with T 101/2 *see* notes below the latter.

Die A   Die B

Dies of Halfpenny

Die A. The three upper scales on the body of the right hand dolphin form a triangle; the centre jewel of the cross inside the crown is suggested by a comma.

Die B. The three upper scales are incomplete; the centre jewel is suggested by a crescent.

Die A   Die B

Dies of One Penny

Die A. The second line of shading on the ribbon to the right of the crown extends right across the wreath; the line nearest to the crown on the right hand ribbon shows as a short line at the bottom of the ribbon.

Die B. The second line of shading is broken in the middle; the first line is little more than a dot.

(Des Bertram Mackennal and G. W. Eve. Head from photograph by W. & D. Downey. Die eng J. A. C. Harrison)

1911-12. *Wmk Imperial Crown*, W **49**. *P* 15 × 14.

				Un	Used
321	98	½d. pale green (Die A) (22.6.11)		5·00	4·00
322		½d. green (Die A) (22.6.11)		5·00	4·00
		a. Error. Perf 14 (8.11)		—	£325
323		½d. bluish green (Die A)		£300	£175
324		½d. yellow-green (Die B)		8·00	1·50
325		½d. bright green (Die B)		4·50	1·50
		a. Wmk sideways		—	£2500
326		½d. bluish green (Die B)		£160	£100

				Un	Used
327	99	1d. carmine-red (Die A) (22.6.11)		4·50	2·50
		c. Wmk sideways		†	
328		1d. pale carmine (Die A) (22.6.11)		14·00	3·00
		a. No cross on crown		£325	£200
329		1d. carmine (Die B)		7·00	3·00
330		1d. pale carmine (Die B)		9·00	4·00
		a. No cross on crown		£425	£300
331		1d. rose-pink (Die B)		£100	40·00
332		1d. scarlet (Die B) (6.12)		22·00	18·00
333		1d. aniline scarlet (Die B)		£140	90·00

For note on the aniline scarlet No. 333 see below No. 343.

100 Simple Cypher

1912 (Aug). *Booklet stamps. Wmk Royal Cypher ("Simple"),* W **100**. *P* 15 × 14.

334	98	½d. pale green (Die B)		40·00	40·00
335		½d. green (Die B)		40·00	40·00
336	99	1d. scarlet (Die B)		30·00	30·00
337		1d. bright scarlet (Die B)		30·00	30·00

103 Multiple Cypher

Type differences

½d. In T **98** the ornament above "P" of "HALFPENNY" has two thin lines of colour and the beard is undefined. In T **101** the ornament has one thick line and the beard is well defined.

1d. In T **99** the body of the lion is unshaded and in T **102** it is shaded.

101   **102**

1912 (1 Jan). *Wmk Imperial Crown,* W **49**. *P* 15 × 14.

338	101	½d. deep green		15·00	8·00
339		½d. green		15·00	8·00
340		½d. yellow-green		15·00	8·00
		a. No cross on crown		70·00	30·00
341	102	1d. bright scarlet		4·00	2·00
		a. No cross on crown		60·00	30·00
		b. Printed double, one albino		£140	
342		1d. scarlet		4·00	2·00
343		1d. aniline scarlet*		£150	90·00
		a. No cross on crown		£750	

* Our prices for the aniline scarlet 1d. stamps, Nos. 333 and 343, are for specimens in which the colour is suffused on the surface of the stamp and shows through clearly on the back. Specimens without these characteristics but which show "aniline" reactions under the quartz lamp are relatively common.

1912 (Aug). *Wmk Royal Cypher ("Simple"),* W **100**. *P* 15 × 14.

344	101	½d. green		7·00	3·00
		a. No cross on crown		80·00	30·00
345	102	1d. scarlet		8·00	2·50
		a. No cross on crown		80·00	28·00

1912 (Sept–Oct). *Wmk Royal Cypher ("Multiple"),* W **103**. *P* 15 × 14.

346	101	½d. green (Oct)		12·00	8·00
		a. No cross on crown		80·00	50·00
		b. Imperf		£110	
		c. Wmk sideways		†	£1300
		d. Printed on gummed side		†	—
347		½d. yellow-green		11·00	8·00
348		½d. pale green		11·00	8·00
349	102	1d. bright scarlet		11·00	8·00
350		1d. scarlet		11·00	8·00
		a. No cross on crown		90·00	28·00
		b. Imperf		85·00	
		c. Wmk sideways		90·00	90·00
		d. Wmk sideways. No cross on crown		£600	

104   **105**   **106**

No. 357a   No. 357ab   No. 357ac

107   **108**

Die I

Die II

Dies of 2d.

Die I.— Inner frame-line at top and sides close to solid of background. *Four* complete lines of shading between top of head and oval frame-line. These four lines do *not* extend to the oval itself. White line round "TWOPENCE" thin.

Die II.— Inner frame-line farther from solid of background. *Three* lines between top of head and extending to the oval. White line round "TWOPENCE" thicker.

(Des Bertram Mackennal (heads) and G. W. Eve (frames). Coinage head (½, 1½, 2, 3 and 4d.); large medal head (1d., 2½d.); intermediate medal head (5d. to 1s.); small medal head used for fiscal stamps. Dies eng J. A. C. Harrison)

(Typo by Harrison & Sons Ltd., except the 6d. printed by the Stamping Department of the Board of Inland Revenue, Somerset House. The latter also made printings of the following which can only be distinguished by the controls: ½d. B.13; 1d. A.12; 2d. C.13; 2½d. A.12; 3d. A.12, B.13, C.13; 4d. B.13; 5d. B.13; 7d. C.13; 8d. C.13; 9d. agate B.13; 10d. C.13; 1s. C.13)

1912–24. *Wmk Royal Cypher,* W **100**. *Chalk-surfaced paper (6d.).* P 15 × 14.

351	105	½d. green (1.13)		1·00	1·00
		a. Partial double print (half of bottom row from Control G15)		£15000	
		b. Gummed both sides			
352		½d. bright green		1·00	1·00
353		½d. deep green		4·00	2·00
354		½d. yellow-green		5·00	3·00
355		½d. very yellow (Cyprus) green (1914)		£2250	
356		½d. blue-green		40·00	25·00
357	104	1d. bright scarlet (8.10.12)		1·00	1·00
		a. "Q" for "O" (R.1/4) (Control E14)		£175	£110
		ab. "Q" for "O" (R.4/11) (Control T22)		£350	£140
		ac. Reversed "Q" for "O" (R.15/9) (Control T22)		£300	£175
		ad. Inverted "Q" for "O" (R.20/3)		£375	£190
		b. Tête-bêche (pair)		£50000	†
358		1d. vermilion		5·00	2·50
359		1d. pale rose-red		15·00	2·50
360		1d. carmine-red		11·00	5·00
361		1d. scarlet-vermilion		£110	40·00
		a. Printed on back†		£225	†
362	105	1½d. red-brown (15.10.12)		4·00	1·50
		a. "PENCF" (R.1/5/12)		£180	£125
		b. Booklet pane. Four stamps plus two printed labels (2.24)		£350	
363		1½d. chocolate-brown		5·00	2·00
		a. Without wmk		£160	£110
364		1½d. chestnut		5·00	1·00
		a. "PENCF" (R.15/12)		£100	80·00
365		1½d. yellow-brown		20·00	16·00
366	106	2d. orange-yellow (Die I) (20.8.12)		7·00	3·00
367		2d. reddish orange (Die I) (11.13)		6·00	3·00
368		2d. orange (Die I)		6·00	3·00
369		2d. bright orange (Die I)		5·00	3·00
370		2d. orange (Die II) (9.21)		5·00	3·50
371	104	2½d. cobalt-blue (18.10.12)		12·00	4·00
371a		2½d. bright blue (1914)		12·00	4·00
372		2½d. blue		12·00	4·00
373		2½d. indigo-blue* (1920)		£1100	£700
373a		2½d. dull Prussian blue* (1921)		£550	£400
374	106	3d. dull reddish violet (9.10.12)		12·00	2·00
375		3d. violet		7·00	2·00
376		3d. bluish violet (11.13)		7·00	2·00
377		3d. pale violet		7·00	2·00
378		4d. deep grey-green (15.1.13)		35·00	10·00
379		4d. grey-green		12·00	2·00
380		4d. pale grey-green		22·00	5·00
381	107	5d. brown (30.6.13)		10·00	5·00
382		5d. yellow-brown		10·00	5·00
		a. Without wmk		£500	
383		5d. bistre-brown		90·00	45·00
384		6d. dull purple (1.8.13)		25·00	10·00
385		6d. reddish purple		15·00	7·00
		a. Perf 14 (10.20)		90·00	£110
386		6d. deep reddish purple		20·00	5·00
387		7d. olive (8.13)		20·00	10·00
388		7d. bronze-green (1915)		60·00	25·00
389		7d. sage-green (1917)		60·00	15·00
390		8d. black/*yellow* (1.8.13)		32·00	11·00
391		8d. black/*yellow-buff* (granite) (5.17)		40·00	15·00
392	108	9d. agate (30.6.13)		18·00	6·00
		a. Printed double, one albino			
393		9d. deep agate		25·00	10·00
393a		9d. olive-green (9.22)		£100	30·00
393b		9d. pale olive-green		£100	40·00
394		10d. turquoise-blue (1.8.13)		22·00	20·00
394a		10d. deep turquoise-blue		70·00	25·00

395	108	1s. bistre (1.8.13)	20·00	4·00
396		1s. bistre-brown	35·00	12·00
351/95		.. .. *Set of* 15	£250	£100

Imperf stamps of this issue exist but may be war-time colour trials.
† The impression of No. 361a is set sideways and is very pale.
* No. 373 comes from Control O 20 and also exists on toned paper.
No. 373a comes from Control R 21 and also exists on toned paper, but both are unlike the rare Prussian blue shade of the 1935 2½d. Jubilee issue.
See also Nos. 418/29.
For the 2d., T **106** bisected, see note under Guernsey, War Occupation Issues.

1913 (Aug). *Wmk Royal Cypher* ("*Multiple*"). W **103**. P 15×14.

397	**105**	½d. bright green		£150	£180
		a. Wmk sideways		†	£18000
398	**104**	1d. dull scarlet		£225	£225

Both these stamps were originally issued in rolls only. Subsequently sheets were found, so that horizontal pairs and blocks are known but are of considerable rarity.

109

A

110 Single Cypher

Major Re-entries on 2s. 6d.

Nos. 400a and 408a

No. 415b

(Des Bertram Mackennal. Dies eng J. A. C. Harrison. Recess)

High values, so-called "Sea Horses" design: T **109**. *Background around portrait consists of horizontal lines, Type A. Wmk Single Cypher, W* **110**. *P* 11 × 12.

1913 (30 June–Aug). *Printed by Waterlow Bros & Layton.*

399	2s. 6d. deep sepia-brown ..		£175	£110
400	2s. 6d. sepia-brown		£160	£100
	a. Re-entry (R. 2/1)		£800	£525
401	5s. rose-carmine		£300	£225
402	10s. indigo-blue (1 Aug) ..		£425	£325
403	£1 green (1 Aug)		£1300	£800
404	£1 dull blue-green (1 Aug) ..		£1300	£800
★399/404	For well-centred, lightly used ..			+35%

1915 (Oct–Dec). *Printed by De La Rue & Co.*

405	2s. 6d. deep yellow-brown (Nov) ..		£200	£110
406	2s. 6d. yellow-brown		£200	£100
407	2s. 6d. pale brown (worn plate) ..		£190	£100
408	2s. 6d. sepia (seal-brown) ..		£190	£110
	a. Re-entry (R. 2/1)		£750	£500
409	5s. bright carmine		£300	£200
410	5s. pale carmine (worn plate) ..		£375	£240
411	10s. deep blue (Dec)		£1250	£600
412	10s. blue		£1000	£550
413	10s. pale blue		£1000	£550
★405/13	For well-centred, lightly used ..			+40%

1918 (Dec)–19. *Printed by Bradbury, Wilkinson & Co, Ltd.*

413a	2s. 6d. olive-brown		90·00	50·00
414	2s. 6d. chocolate-brown		£100	50·00
415	2s. 6d. reddish brown		£110	50·00
415a	2s. 6d. pale brown		£100	45·00
	b. Major re-entry (R.1/2) ..		£525	£325
416	5s. rose-red (1.19)		£210	70·00
417	10s. dull grey-blue (1.19) ..		£1000	£550
399/417	.. .. *Set of* 4		£1700	£900
★413a/17	For well-centred, lightly used ..			+35%

DISTINGUISHING PRINTINGS. Note that the £1 value was only printed by Waterlow.
Waterlow and De La Rue stamps measure exactly 22 mm vertically. In the De La Rue printings the gum is usually patchy and yellowish, and the colour of the stamp, particularly in the 5s. tends to show through the back. The holes of the perforation are smaller than those of the other two printers, but there is a thick perforation tooth at the top of each vertical side.
In the Bradbury Wilkinson printings the height of the stamp is 22¾ or 23 mm. On most of the 22¾ mm high stamps a minute coloured guide dot appears in the margin just above the middle of the upper frame-line.
For (1934) re-engraved Waterlow printings *see* Nos. 450/2.

UNITED KINGDOM OF GREAT BRITAIN AND NORTHERN IRELAND

111   Block Cypher   **111a**

The watermark Type **111a**, as compared with Type **111**, differs as follows: Closer spacing of horizontal rows (12½ mm instead of 14½ mm). Letters shorter and rounder. Watermark thicker.

(Typo by Waterlow & Sons, Ltd (all values except 6d.) and later, 1934–35, by Harrison & Sons Ltd (all values). Until 1934 the 6d. was printed at Somerset House where a printing of the 1½d. was also made in 1926 (identifiable only by control E.26). Printings by Harrisons in 1934–35 can be identified, when in mint condition, by the fact that the gum shows a streaky appearance vertically, the Waterlow gum being uniformly applied, but Harrisons also used up the balance of the Waterlow "smooth gum" paper)

1924 (Feb)–26. *Wmk Block Cypher, W* **111**. *P* 15×14.

418	**105**	½d. green			1·00	1·00
		a. Wmk sideways (5.24)			6·00	3·25
		b. Doubly printed ..			£7500	
419	**104**	1d. scarlet			1·00	1·00
		a. Wmk sideways			15·00	15·00
		b. Experimental paper, W **111a** (10.24)			22·00	
		c. Partial double print, one inverted			£5500	
		d. Inverted "Q" for "O" (R. 20/3)			£350	
420	**105**	1½d. red-brown			1·00	1·00
		a. Tête-bêche (pair) ..			£350	£600
		b. Wmk sideways (8.24)			7·00	3·50
		c. Printed on the gummed side			£350	†
		d. Booklet pane. Four stamps plus two printed labels (3.24)			£100	
		e. Ditto. Wmk sideways			£3250	
		f. Experimental paper, W **111a** (10.24)			60·00	70·00
		g. Double impression			£8500	
421	**106**	2d. orange (Die II) (7.24)			2·50	2·50
		a. No wmk			£525	
		b. Wmk sideways (7.26)			70·00	80·00
		c. Partial double print			£13000	
422	**104**	2½d. blue (10.24)			5·00	3·00
		a. No wmk			£700	
		b. Wmk sideways			†	£3750
423	**106**	3d. violet (10.24)			10·00	2·50
424		4d. grey-green (11.24)			12·00	2·50
		a. Printed on the gummed side			£1500	†
425	**107**	5d. brown (11.24)			20·00	3·00
426		6d. reddish purple (*chalk-surfaced paper*) (9.24)			12·00	2·50
426a		6d. purple (6.26)			3·00	1·50
427	**108**	9d. olive-green (12.24)			12·00	3·50
428		10d. turquoise-blue (11.24)			35·00	40·00
429		1s. bistre-brown (10.24)			22·00	3·00
418/29		.. .. *Set of* 12			£110	60·00

There are numerous shades in this issue.
The 6d. on both chalk-surfaced and ordinary papers was printed by both Somerset House and Harrisons. The Harrisons printings have streaky gum, differ slightly in shade, and that on chalk-surfaced paper is printed in a highly fugitive ink. The prices quoted are for the commonest (Harrison) printing in each case.

112

(Des H. Nelson. Eng J. A. C. Harrison. Recess Waterlow)

1924–25. *British Empire Exhibition. W* **111**. *P* 14.

(*a*) Dated "1924" (23.4.24)

430	**112**	1d. scarlet		10·00	11·00
431		1½d. brown		15·00	15·00

(*b*) Dated "1925" (9.5.25)

432	**112**	1d. scarlet		15·00	25·00
433		1½d. brown		40·00	65·00

113   **114**   **115**

116 St. George and the Dragon

117

(Des J. Farleigh (T **113** and **115**), E. Linzell (T **114**) and H. Nelson (T **116**). Eng C. G. Lewis (T **113**), T. E. Storey (T **115**), both at the Royal Mint; J. A. C. Harrison, of Waterlow (T **114** and **116**). Typo by Waterlow from plates made at the Royal Mint, except T **116**, recess by Bradbury, Wilkinson from die and plate of their own manufacture)

1929 (10 May). *Ninth U.P.U. Congress, London.*

(*a*) W **111**. P 15×14

434	**113**	½d. green		..	..	2·25	2·25
		a. Wmk sideways		..	..	26·00	34·00
435	**114**	1d. scarlet		..	..	2·25	2·25
		a. Wmk sideways		..	..	45·00	48·00
436		1½d. purple-brown		..	..	2·25	1·75
		a. Wmk sideways		..	..	26·00	25·00
		b. Booklet pane. Four stamps plus two printed labels			..	£170	
437	**115**	2½d. blue		..	..	10·00	10·00

(*b*) W **117**. P 12

438	**116**	£1 black		..	..	£750	£550
434/7		.. .. *Set of* 4 (*to* 2½d.)				15·00	14·50

PRINTERS. All subsequent issues to 1997 were printed in photogravure by Harrison and Sons Ltd *except where otherwise stated.*

118   **119**   **120**

121   **122**

1934–36. *W* **111**. *P* 15×14.

439	**118**	½d. green (19.11.34) ..		..	30	40
		a. Wmk sideways		..	7·00	3·50
		b. Imperf three sides		..	£1250	
440	**119**	1d. scarlet (24.9.34) ..		..	30	40
		a. Imperf (pair)		..	£950	†
		b. Printed on the gummed side		..	£400	†
		c. Wmk sideways		..	11·00	4·75
		d. Double impression		..	†	£12500
		e. Imperf between (pair)		..	£1750	†
		f. Imperf three sides (pair)		..	£1250	
441	**118**	1½d. red-brown (20.8.34) ..		..	30	40
		a. Imperf (pair)		..	£325	
		b. Imperf three sides (lower stamp in vert pair) ..		..	£750	
		c. Imperf between (horiz pair)		..		
		d. Wmk sideways		..	6·00	4·00
		e. Booklet pane. Four stamps plus two printed labels (1.35) ..		..	60·00	
442	**120**	2d. orange (21.1.35) ..		..	50	75
		a. Imperf (pair)		..	£1500	
		b. Wmk sideways		..	90·00	60·00
443	**119**	2½d. ultramarine (18.3.35)		..	1·50	1·25
444	**120**	3d. violet (18.3.35)		..	1·50	1·25
445		4d. deep grey-green (2.12.35)		..	2·00	1·25
446	**121**	5d. yellow-brown (17.2.36)		..	6·00	2·75
447	**122**	9d. deep olive-green (2.12.35)		..	12·00	2·25
448		10d. turquoise-blue (24.2.36) ..		..	15·00	10·00
449		1s. bistre-brown (24.2.36) ..		..	15·00	1·25
		a. Double impression				
439/49		.. .. *Set of* 11			48·00	18·00

Owing to the need for wider space for the perforations the size of the designs of the ½d. and 2d. were once, and the 1d. and 1½d. twice reduced from that of the first printings.
There are also numerous minor variations, due to the photographic element in the process.
The ½d. imperf three sides, No. 439b, is known in a block of four, from a sheet, in which the bottom pair is imperf at top and sides.
For No. 442 bisected, see Guernsey, War Occupation Issues.

B   123

(Eng J. A. C. Harrison. Recess Waterlow)

1934 (16 Oct). *T* **109** (*re-engraved*). *Background around portrait consists of horizontal and diagonal lines.* Type B. *W* **110**. *P* 11×12.

450	109	2s. 6d. chocolate-brown	..	65·00	35·00
451		5s. bright rose-red	..	£150	80·00
452		10s. indigo	..	£325	75·00
450/2			*Set of 3*	£475	£175

There are numerous other minor differences in the design of this issue.

(Des B. Freedman)

1935 (7 May). *Silver Jubilee.* W **111**. P 15×14.

453	123	½d. green	..	75	50
454		1d. scarlet	..	1·25	1·50
455		1½d. red-brown	..	75	50
456		2½d. blue	..	4·50	5·50
456a		2½d. Prussian blue	..	£5000	£5000
453/6			*Set of 4*	6·00	7·00

The 1½d. and 2½d. values differ from T **123** in the emblem in the panel at right.

Four sheets of No. 456a, printed in the wrong shade, were issued in error by the Post Office Stores Department on 25 June 1935. It is known that three of the sheets were sold from the sub-office at 134 Fore Street, Upper Edmonton, London, between that date and 4 July.

KING EDWARD VIII
20 January–10 December 1936

Further detailed information on the stamps of King Edward VIII will be found in Volume 2 of the Stanley Gibbons *Great Britain Specialised Catalogue*.

124   125

(Des H. Brown, adapted Harrison using a photo by Hugh Cecil)

1936. W **125**. *P* 15×14.

457	124	½d. green (1.9.36)	..	30	30
		a. Double impression			
458		1d. scarlet (14.9.36)	..	60	40
459		1½d. red-brown (1.9.36)	..	30	30
		a. Booklet pane. Four stamps plus two printed labels (10.36)	..	60·00	
460		2½d. bright blue (1.9.36)	..	30	75
457/60		.. .. ..	*Set of 4*	1·25	1·60

KING GEORGE VI
11 December 1936–6 February 1952

Further detailed information on the stamps of King George VI will be found in Volume 2 of the Stanley Gibbons *Great Britain Specialised Catalogue*.

126 King George VI and Queen Elizabeth

(Des E. Dulac)

1937 (13 May). *Coronation.* W **127**. *P* 15×14.

461	126	1½d. maroon	..	50	40

127   128

129   130

King George VI and National Emblems

(Des T **128**/9, E. Dulac (head) and E. Gill (frames). T **130**, E. Dulac (whole stamp))

1937–47. W **127**. P 15×14.

462	128	½d. green (10.5.37)	..	10	25
		a. Wmk sideways (1.38)	..	50	50
		ab. Booklet pane of 4 (6.40)	..	35·00	
463		1d. scarlet (10.5.37)	..	10	25
		a. Wmk sideways (2.38)	..	16·00	9·00
		ab. Booklet pane of 4 (6.40)	..	80·00	
464		1½d. red-brown (30.7.37)	..	20	25
		a. Wmk sideways (2.38)	..	1·00	1·25
		b. Booklet pane. Four stamps plus two printed labels (8.37)	..	55·00	
		c. Imperf three sides (pair)			
465		2d. orange (31.1.38)	..	75	50
		a. Wmk sideways (2.38)	..	70·00	35·00
		b. Bisected (on cover)	..	†	28·00
466		2½d. ultramarine (10.5.37)	..	25	15
		a. Wmk sideways (6.40)	..	60·00	28·00
		b. Tête-bêche (horiz pair)			
467		3d. violet (31.1.38)	..	3·25	1·00
468	129	4d. grey-green (21.11.38)	..	60	60
		a. Imperf (pair)	..	£2000	
		b. Imperf three sides (horiz pair)	..	£2500	
469		5d. brown (21.11.38)	..	2·50	75
		a. Imperf (pair)	..	£2500	
		b. Imperf three sides (horiz pair)	..	£2000	
470		6d. purple (30.1.39)	..	1·25	60
471	130	7d. emerald-green (27.2.39)	..	3·25	60
		a. Imperf three sides (horiz pair)	..	£2000	
472		8d. bright carmine (27.2.39)	..	3·50	70
473		9d. deep olive-green (1.5.39)	..	5·50	80
474		10d. turquoise-blue (1.5.39)	..	5·00	80
		aa. Imperf (pair)	..	£3500	
474a		11d. plum (29.12.47)	..	2·00	2·00
475		1s. bistre-brown (1.5.39)	..	5·75	75
462/75			*Set of 15*	30·00	8·75

For later printings of the lower values in apparently lighter shades and different colours, see Nos. 485/90 and 503/8.

No. 465b was authorised for use in Guernsey. See notes on War Occupation Issues.

Nos. 468b and 469b are perforated at foot only and each occurs in the same sheet as Nos. 468a and 469a.

No. 471a is also perforated at foot only, but occurs on the top row of a sheet.

131 King George VI   132 King George VI

133

(Des E. Dulac (T **131**) and Hon. G. R. Bellew (T **132**). Eng J. A. C. Harrison. Recess Waterlow)

1939–48. W **133**. P 14.

476	131	2s. 6d. brown (4.9.39)	..	38·00	7·00
476a		2s. 6d. yellow-green (9.3.42)	..	7·00	1·50
477		5s. red (21.8.39)	..	14·00	2·00
478	132	10s. dark blue (30.10.39)	..	£180	21·00
478a		10s. ultramarine (30.11.42)	..	30·00	6·00
478b		£1 brown (1.10.48)	..	10·00	24·00
476/8b		.. .. ..	*Set of 6*	£250	55·00

134 Queen Victoria and King George VI.

(Des H. L. Palmer)

1940 (6 May). *Centenary of First Adhesive Postage Stamps.* W **127**. P 14½×14.

479	134	½d. green	..	30	30
480		1d. scarlet	..	1·00	50
481		1½d. red-brown	..	50	50
482		2d. orange	..	50	50
		a. Bisected (on cover)	..	†	16·00
483		2½d. ultramarine	..	2·25	1·00
484		3d. violet	..	3·00	3·25
479/84		.. .. ..	*Set of 6*	6·50	5·25

No. 482a was authorised for use in Guernsey. See notes on War Occupation Issues.

1941–42. *Head as Nos. 462/7, but lighter background.* W **127**. P 15×14.

485	128	½d. pale green (1.9.41)	..	30	30
		a. Tête-bêche (horiz pair)	..	£3000	
		b. Imperf (pair)	..	£1750	
486		1d. pale scarlet (11.8.41)	..	30	30
		a. Wmk sideways (10.42)	..	4·00	6·00
		b. Imperf (pair)	..	£2500	
		c. Imperf three sides (horiz pair)	..	£2500	

487	128	1½d. pale red-brown (28.9.42)	..	1·00	70
488		2d. pale orange (6.10.41)	..	75	75
		a. Wmk sideways (6.42)	..	28·00	19·00
		b. Tête-bêche (horiz pair)	..	£2500	
		c. Imperf (pair)	..	£2000	
		d. Imperf pane*	..	£4500	
489		2½d. light ultramarine (21.7.41)	..	30	30
		a. Wmk sideways (8.42)	..	15·00	12·00
		b. Tête-bêche (horiz pair)	..	£2500	
		c. Imperf (pair)	..	£2500	
		d. Imperf pane*	..	£2500	
		e. Imperf three sides (horiz pair)	..	£3500	
490		3d. pale violet (3.11.41)	..	2·00	1·00
485/90			*Set of 6*	4·25	3·00

The *tête-bêche* varieties are from defectively made-up stamp booklets.

Nos. 486c and 489e are perforated at foot only and occur in the same sheets as Nos. 486b and 489c.

*BOOKLET ERRORS. Those listed as "imperf panes" show one row of perforations either at the top or at the bottom of the pane of 6.

WATERMARK VARIETIES. Please note that *inverted watermarks* are outside the scope of this listing but are fully listed in the *Great Britain Specialised* and *Great Britain Concise* Catalogues. See also the notes about watermarks at the beginning of the King George V section.

135

136 Symbols of Peace and Reconstruction

(Des H. L. Palmer (T **135**) and R. Stone (T **136**))

1946 (11 June). *Victory.* W **127**. P 15×14.

491	135	2½d. ultramarine	..	30	30
492	136	3d. violet	..	30	30

137   138 King George VI and Queen Elizabeth

(Des G. Knipe and Joan Hassall from photographs by Dorothy Wilding)

1948 (26 Apr). *Royal Silver Wedding.* W **127**. P 15×14 (2½d.) or 14×15 (£1).

493	137	2½d. ultramarine	..	30	30
494	138	£1 blue	..	38·00	38·00

1948 (10 May). Stamps of 1d. and 2½d. showing seaweed-gathering were on sale at eight Head Post Offices in Great Britain, but were primarily for use in the Channel Islands and are listed there (see after Great Britain Postal Fiscals).

139 Globe and Laurel Wreath

140 "Speed"

141 Olympic Symbol

142 Winged Victory

(Des P. Metcalfe (T **139**), A. Games (T **140**), S. D. Scott (T **141**) and E. Dulac (T **142**))

1948 (29 July). *Olympic Games.* W **127**. *P* 15×14.

495	**139**	2½d. ultramarine	..	..	..	30	30
496	**140**	3d. violet				30	30
497	**141**	6d. bright purple	..	..		60	30
498	**142**	1s. brown				1·25	1·50
495/8	..	..	..	..	*Set of* 4	2·00	2·00

143 Two Hemispheres

144 U.P.U. Monument, Berne

145 Goddess Concordia, Globe and Points of Compass

146 Posthorn and Globe

(Des Mary Adshead (T **143**), P. Metcalfe (T **144**), H. Fleury (T **145**) and Hon. G. R. Bellew (T **146**))

1949 (10 Oct). *75th Anniv of Universal Postal Union.* W **127**. *P* 15×14.

499	**143**	2½d. ultramarine				30	30
500	**144**	3d. violet	..	..		30	40
501	**145**	6d. bright purple	..	..		60	75
502	**146**	1s. brown				1·25	1·50
499/502	..	..	..	..	*Set of* 4	2·00	2·75

1950–52. 4d. *as Nos.* 468 *and others as Nos.* 485/9, *but colours changed.* W **127**. *P* 15×14.

503	**128**	½d. pale orange (3.5.51)	..	30	30
		a. Imperf (pair)		£3000	
		b. *Tête-bêche* (horiz pair)	..	£3000	
		c. Imperf pane*		£4000	
504		1d. light ultramarine (3.5.51)	..	50	50
		a. Wmk sideways (5.51)	..	1·00	1·25
		b. Imperf (pair)		£2000	
		c. Imperf three sides (horiz pair)		£1600	
		d. Booklet pane. Three stamps plus three printed labels (3.52)		18·00	
		e. Ditto. Partial *tête-bêche* pane	..	£2750	
505		1½d. pale green (3.5.51)	..	50	60
		a. Wmk sideways (9.51)	..	3·00	5·00
506		2d. pale red-brown (3.5.51)	..	50	40
		a. Wmk sideways (5.51)	..	1·75	2·00
		b. *Tête-bêche* (horiz pair)	..	£3000	
		c. Imperf three sides (horiz pair)		£1500	
507		2½d. pale scarlet (3.5.51)	..	50	40
		a. Wmk sideways (5.51)	..	1·75	1·75
		b. *Tête-bêche* (horiz pair)		£2000	
508	**129**	4d. light ultramarine (2.10.50)		2·50	1·75
		a. Double impression	..	†	£5000
503/8	..	..	..	*Set of* 6	4·25	3·25

No. 504c is perforated at foot only and occurs in the same sheet as No. 504b.

No. 506c is also perforated at foot only.

*BOOKLET ERRORS. Those listed as "imperf panes" show one row of perforations either at the top or at the bottom of the pane of 6.

147 H.M.S. *Victory*

148 White Cliffs of Dover

149 St. George and the Dragon

150 Royal Coat of Arms

(Des Mary Adshead (T **147/8**), P. Metcalfe (T **149/50**). Recess Waterlow)

1951 (3 May). W **133**. *P* 11×12.

509	**147**	2s. 6d. yellow-green	..		6·00	1·00
510	**148**	5s. red	..	..	..	32·00	1·50
511	**149**	10s. ultramarine	..		21·00	8·50
512	**150**	£1 brown	..	..		32·00	20·00
509/12	..	..	..	..	*Set of* 4	80·00	25·00

151 "Commerce and Prosperity"

152 Festival Symbol

(Des E. Dulac (T **151**), A. Games (T **152**))

1951 (3 May). *Festival of Britain.* W **127**. *P* 15×14.

513	**151**	2½d. scarlet	..	..	..	30	30
514	**152**	4d. ultramarine	..	..	..	50	55

QUEEN ELIZABETH II
6 February 1952

Further detailed information on the stamps of Queen Elizabeth II will be found in volumes 3, 4 and 5 of the Stanley Gibbons *Great Britain Specialised Catalogue.*

USED PRICES. For Nos. 515 onwards the used prices quoted are for examples with circular dated postmarks.

153 Tudor Crown

154

155

156

157

158

159

160

Queen Elizabeth II and National Emblems

I   II

Types of 2½d. Type I:—In the frontal cross of the diadem, the top line is only half the width of the cross.

Type II:—The top line extends to the full width of the cross and there are signs of strengthening in other parts of the diadem.

(Des Enid Marx (T **154**), M. Farrar-Bell (T **155/6**), G. Knipe (T **157**), Mary Adshead (T **158**), E. Dulac (T **159/60**). Portrait by Dorothy Wilding)

1952–54. W **153**. *P* 15×14.

515	**154**	½d. orange-red (31.8.53)	..	10	15
516		1d. ultramarine (31.8.53)	..	20	20
		a. Booklet pane. Three stamps plus three printed labels		25·00	
517		1½d. green (5.12.52)	..	10	15
		a. Wmk sideways (15.10.54)		75	1·00
		b. Imperf pane*	..		
518		2d. red-brown (31.8.53)	..	20	15
		a. Wmk sideways (8.10.54)	..	1·50	2·25
519	**155**	2½d. carmine-red (Type I) (5.12.52)	..	10	15
		a. Wmk sideways (15.11.54)	..	12·00	12·00
		b. Type II (Booklets) (5.53)	..	1·50	1·25
520		3d. deep lilac (18.1.54)	..	1·00	90
521	**156**	4d. ultramarine (2.11.53)	..	3·00	1·40
522	**157**	5d. brown (6.7.53)	..	90	3·50
523		6d. reddish purple (18.1.54)	..	3·00	1·25
		a. Imperf three sides (pair)		£	
524		7d. bright green (18.1.54)	..	9·00	7·00
525	**158**	8d. magenta (6.7.53)	..	1·00	1·00
526		9d. bronze-green (8.2.54)	..	22·00	4·00
527		10d. Prussian blue (8.2.54)	..	18·00	4·00
528		11d. brown-purple (8.2.54)	..	30·00	20·00
529	**159**	1s. bistre-brown (6.7.53)	..	1·25	75
530	**160**	1s. 3d. green (2.11.53)	..	4·50	4·00
531	**159**	1s. 6d. grey-blue (2.11.53)	..	11·00	4·50
515/31	..	..	..	*Set of* 17	95·00	48·00

*BOOKLET ERRORS—This pane of 6 stamps is completely imperf (see No. 540a, etc.).

See also Nos. 540/56, 561/6, 570/94 and 599/618a.

For stamps as Type **157** with face values in decimal currency see Nos. 2031/3.

161

162

163

164

(Des E. Fuller (2½d.), M. Goaman (4d.), E. Dulac (1s. 3d.), M. Farrar-Bell (1s. 6d.), Portrait (except 1s. 3d.) by Dorothy Wilding)

1953 (3 June). *Coronation.* W **153**. *P* 15×14.

532	**161**	2½d. carmine-red	..	10	50
533	**162**	4d. ultramarine	..	50	2·00
534	**163**	1s. 3d. deep yellow-green	..	3·50	3·50
535	**164**	1s. 6d. deep grey-blue	..	7·00	4·50
532/5	..	..	..	*Set of* 4	10·00	9·00

165 St. Edward's Crown

166 Carrickfergus Castle

167 Caernarvon Castle

168 Edinburgh Castle

169 Windsor Castle

(Des L. Lamb. Portrait by Dorothy Wilding. Recess Waterlow (until 31.12.57) and De La Rue (subsequently))

1955–58. *W* **165.** *P* 11 × 12.

536	166	2s. 6d. black-brown (23.9.55)	..	10·00	2·50
		a. De La Rue printing (17.7.58)	..	30·00	4·00
537	167	5s. rose-carmine (23.9.55)	..	30·00	4·00
		a. De La Rue printing (30.4.58)	..	85·00	14·00
538	168	10s. ultramarine (1.9.55)	..	80·00	14·00
		a. De La Rue printing. *Dull ultramarine* (25.4.58)	..	£200	30·00
539	169	£1 black (1.9.55)	..	£130	42·00
		a. De La Rue printing (28.4.58)	..	£325	75·00
536/9		*Set of 4*		£225	55·00
536a/9a		*Set of 4*		£550	£110

See also Nos. 595/8a and 759/62.

On 1 January 1958, the contract for printing the high values, T **166** to **169** was transferred to De La Rue & Co, Ltd.

The work of the two printers is very similar, but the following notes will be helpful to those attempting to identify Waterlow and De La Rue stamps of the W **165** issue.

The De La Rue sheets are printed in pairs and have a ⊢ or ⊢-shaped guide-mark at the centre of one side-margin, opposite the middle row of perforations, indicating left- and right-hand sheets respectively.

The Waterlow sheets have a small circle (sometimes crossed) instead of a "⊢" and this is present in both side-margins opposite the 6th row of stamps, though one is sometimes trimmed off. Short dashes are also present in the perforation gutter between the marginal stamps marking the middle of the four sides and a cross is at the centre of the sheet. The four corners of the sheet have two lines forming a right-angle as trimming marks, but some are usually trimmed off. All these gutter marks and sheet-trimming marks are absent in the De La Rue printings.

De La Rue used the Waterlow die and no alterations were made to it, so that no difference exists in the design or its size, but the making of new plates at first resulted in slight but measurable variations in the width of the gutters between stamps, particularly the horizontal, as follows:

	W.	D.L.R.
Horiz gutters, mm	3.8 to 4.0	3.4 to 3.8

Later D.L.R. plates were however less distinguishable in this respect.

For a short time in 1959 the D.L.R. 2s. 6d. appeared with one dot in the bottom margin below the first stamp.

It is possible to sort singles with reasonable certainty by general characteristics. The individual lines of the D.L.R. impression are cleaner and devoid of the whiskers of colour of Waterlow's, and the whole impression lighter and softer.

Owing to the closer setting of the horizontal rows the strokes of the perforating comb are closer; this results in the topmost tooth on each side of De La Rue stamps being narrower than the corresponding teeth in Waterlow's which have two rather more than normally broad.

Shades also help. The 2s. 6d. D.L.R. is a warmer, more chocolate shade than the blackish brown of W.; the 5s. a lighter red with less carmine than W.'s; the 10s. more blue and less ultramarine; the £1 less intense black.

The paper of D.L.R. printings is uniformly white, identical with that of W. printings from February 1957 onwards, but earlier W. printings are on paper which is creamy by comparison.

In this and later issues of T **166**/9 the dates of issue given for changes of watermark or paper are those on which supplies were first sent by the Supplies Department to Postmasters.

1955–58. *W* **165.** *P* 15 × 14.

540	154	½d. orange-red (booklets 8.55, sheets 12.12.55)	..	10	15
541		a. Part perf pane* (9.9.55)	..	£1400	
541		1d. ultramarine (19.9.55)	..	30	15
		a. Booklet pane. Three stamps plus three printed labels		15·00	
		b. *Tête-bêche* (horiz pair)	..		
542		1½d. green (booklets 8.55, sheets 11.10.55)	..	30	30
		a. Wmk sideways (7.3.56)	..	50	1·00
		b. *Tête-bêche* (horiz pair)	..	£1000	
543		2d. red-brown (6.9.55)	..	40	50
		aa. Imperf between (vert pair)	..	£1750	
		a. Wmk sideways (31.7.56)	..	50	75
		ab. Imperf between (horiz pair)	..	£1750	
543*b*		2d. light red-brown (17.10.56)	..	25	30
		ba. *Tête-bêche* (horiz pair)	..	£650	
		bb. Imperf pane*			
		bc. Part perf pane*	..	£1400	
		c. Wmk sideways (5.3.57)	..	11·00	7·50
544	155	2½d. carmine-red (Type I) (28.9.55)	..	25	30
		a. Wmk sideways (Type I) (23.3.56)		2·00	2·00
		b. Type II (booklets 9.55, sheets 1957)	..	50	50
		ba. *Tête-bêche* (horiz pair)	..	£800	
		bb. Imperf pane*	..	£1000	
		bc. Part perf pane*	..		
545		3d. deep lilac (17.7.56)	..	25	30
		aa. *Tête-bêche* (horiz pair)	..	£800	
		a. Imperf three sides (pair)	..	£600	
		b. Wmk sideways (22.11.57)	..	16·00	16·00
546	156	4d. ultramarine (14.11.55)	..	30	30
547	157	5d. brown (21.9.55)	..	5·50	5·50
548		6d. reddish purple (20.12.55)	..	4·00	1·25
		aa. Imperf three sides (pair)	..	£450	
		a. Deep claret (8.5.58)	..	4·00	1·25
		ab. Imperf three sides (pair)	..	£450	
549		7d. bright green (23.4.56)	..	50·00	10·00

550	158	8d. magenta (21.12.55)	..	6·00	1·25
551		9d. bronze-green (15.12.55)	..	23·00	3·00
552		10d. Prussian blue (22.9.55)	..	19·00	3·00
553		11d. brown-purple (28.10.55)	..	50	1·75
554	159	1s. bistre-brown (3.11.55)	..	19·00	75
555	160	1s. 3d. green (27.3.56)	..	27·00	1·75
556	159	1s. 6d. grey-blue (27.3.56)	..	19·00	1·50
540/56		*Set of 18*		£150	26·00

The dates given for Nos. 540/556 are those on which they were first issued by the Supplies Dept to postmasters.

In December 1956 a completely imperforate sheet of No. 543*b* was noticed by clerks in a Kent post office, one of whom purchased it against P.O. regulations. In view of this irregularity we do not consider it properly issued.

Types of 2½d. In this issue, in 1957, Type II formerly only found in stamps from booklets, began to replace Type I on sheet stamps.

*BOOKLET ERRORS. Those listed as "imperf panes" show one row of perforations either at top or bottom of the booklet pane; those as "part perf panes" have one row of 3 stamps imperf on three sides.

170 Scout Badge and "Rolling Hitch"

171 "Scouts coming to Britain"

172 Globe within a Compass

(Des Mary Adshead (2½d.), P. Keely (4d.), W. H. Brown (1s. 3d.))

1957 (1 Aug). *World Scout Jubilee Jamboree.* W **165.** *P* 15 × 14.

557	170	2½d. carmine-red	..	15	25
558	171	4d. ultramarine	..	50	1·25
559	172	1s. 3d. green	..	5·00	4·75
557/9		*Set of 3*		5·00	5·50

173 ½d. to 1½d., 2½d., 3d. 2d.
Graphite-line arrangements
(Stamps viewed from back)

(Adapted F. Langfield)

1957 (12 Sept). *46th Inter-Parliamentary Union Conference.* W **165.** *P* 15 × 14.

560	173	4d. ultramarine	..	1·00	1·75

GRAPHITE-LINED ISSUES. These were used in connection with automatic sorting machinery, first introduced experimentally at Southampton in December 1957.

The graphite lines were printed in black on the back, beneath the gum; two lines per stamp, except for the 2d.

In November 1959 phosphor bands were introduced (see notes after No. 598).

1957 (19 Nov). *Graphite-lined issue. Two graphite lines on the back, except 2d. value, which has one line.* W **165.** *P* 15 × 14.

561	154	½d. orange-red	..	30	30
562		1d. ultramarine	..	30	50
563		1½d. green	..	30	2·00
		a. Both lines at left	..	£800	£400
564		2d. light red-brown	..	2·50	3·00
		a. Line at left	..	£500	£175
565	155	2½d. carmine-red (Type II)	..	8·00	7·50
566		3d. deep lilac	..	30	80
561/6		*Set of 6*		10·50	12·50

No. 564a results from a misplacement of the line and horizontal pairs exist showing one stamp without line. No. 563a results from a similar misplacement.

See also Nos. 587/94.

176 Welsh Dragon

177 Flag and Games Emblem

178 Welsh Dragon

(Des R. Stone (3d.), W. H. Brown (6d.), P. Keely (1s. 3d.))

1958 (18 July). *Sixth British Empire and Commonwealth Games, Cardiff.* W **165.** *P* 15 × 14.

567	176	3d. deep lilac	..	15	10
568	177	6d. reddish purple	..	25	45
569	178	1s. 3d. green	..	3·00	3·00
567/9		*Set of 3*		3·00	3·00

179 Multiple Crowns

1958–65. *W* **179.** *P* 15 × 14.

570	154	½d. orange-red (25.11.58)	..	10	10
		a. Wmk sideways (26.5.61)		30	40
		c. Part perf pane*		£1200	
		k. Chalk-surfaced paper (15.7.63)		2·75	3·00
		l. Booklet pane. No. 570a×4		3·50	
		m. Booklet pane. No. 570k×3 *se-tenant* with 574k		10·00	
		n. Booklet pane. No. 570a×2 *se-tenant* with 574l×2 (1.7.64)		2·50	
571		1d. ultramarine (booklets 11.58, sheets 24.3.59)	..	10	10
		aa. Imperf (vert pair from coil)	..		
		a. Wmk sideways (26.5.61)		1·50	1·25
		b. Part perf pane*		£1400	
		c. Imperf pane			
		l. Booklet pane. No. 571a×4		4·50	
		m. Booklet pane. No. 571a×2 *se-tenant* with 575a×2 (1d. values at left) (16.8.65)		10·00	
		ma. Ditto. 1d. values at right		11·00	
572		1½d. grn (booklets 12.58, sheets 30.8.60)	..	10	15
		a. Imperf three sides (horiz strip of 3)			
		b. Wmk sideways (26.5.61)		10·00	5·50
		l. Booklet pane. No. 572b×4		35·00	
573		2d. light red-brown (4.12.58)	..	10	10
		a. Wmk sideways (3.4.59)		85	1·50
574	155	2½d. carmine-red (Type II) (booklets 11.58, sheets 15.9.59)	..	10	10
		a. Imperf strip of 3			
		b. *Tête-bêche* (horiz pair)			
		c. Imperf pane		£1400	
		d. Wmk sideways (Type I) (10.11.60)		30	40
		da. Imperf strip of 6			
		e. Type I (wmk upright) (4.10.61)		1·00	1·00
		k. Chalk-surfaced paper (Type II) (15.7.63)		75	1·00
		l. Wmk sideways (Type II) Ord paper (1.7.64)		1·00	1·50
575		3d. deep lilac (booklets 11.58, sheets 8.12.58)	..	10	20
		a. Wmk sideways (24.10.58)		30	40
		b. Imperf pane*		£1000	
		c. Part perf pane*			
		d. Phantom "R" (Cyl 41 no dot)		£300	
		e. Phantom "R" (Cyl 37 no dot)		35·00	
		l. Booklet pane. No. 575a×4 (26.5.61)		2·75	
576	156	4d. ultramarine (29.10.58)	..	50	20
		a. Deep ultramarine†† (28.4.65)		15	50
		ab. Wmk sideways (31.5.65)		20	40
		ac. Imperf pane*		£1400	
		ad. Part perf pane*		£900	
		al. Booklet pane. No. 576ab×4 (16.8.65)		3·00	
577		4½d. chestnut (9.2.59)	..	10	30
578	157	5d. brown (10.11.58)	..	30	40
579		6d. deep claret (23.12.58)	..	30	30
		a. Imperf three sides (pair)		£500	
		b. Imperf (pair)		£600	
580		7d. bright green (26.11.58)	..	50	70
581	158	8d. magenta (24.2.60)	..	50	40
582		9d. bronze-green (24.3.59)	..	50	40
583		10d. Prussian blue (18.11.58)	..	1·00	60
584	159	1s. bistre-brown (30.10.58)	..	50	40
585	160	1s. 3d. green (17.6.59)	..	40	40
586	159	1s. 6d. grey-blue (16.12.58)	..	50	40
570/86		*Set of 17*		8·00	5·00

*BOOKLET ERRORS. See note after No. 556.

††This "shade" was brought about by making more deeply etched cylinders, resulting in apparent depth of colour in parts of the design. There is no difference in the colour of the ink.

Sideways watermark. The 2d., 2½d., 3d. and 4d. come from coils and the ½d., 1d., 1½d., 2d., 2½d., 3d. and 4d. come from booklets. In coil stamps the sideways watermark shows the top of the watermark to the left *as seen from the front of the stamp.* In the *booklet* stamps it comes equally to the left or right.

Nos. 570k and 574k only come from 2s. "Holiday Resort" Experimental undated booklets issued in 1963, in which one page contained 1 × 2½d. *se-tenant* with 3 × ½d. (See No. 570l).

No. 574l comes from coils, and the "Holiday Resort" Experimental booklets dated "1964" comprising four panes each containing two of these 2½d. stamps *se-tenant* vertically with two ½d. No. 570a (See No. 570m).

2½d. imperf No. 574a comes from a booklet with watermark upright. No. 574da is from a coil with sideways watermark.

No. 574e comes from *sheets* bearing cylinder number 42 and is also known on vertical delivery coils.

Nos. 575d and 615a occurred below the last stamp of the sheet from Cyl 41 (no dot), where an incomplete marginal rule revealed an "R". The cylinder was later twice retouched. The stamps listed show the original, unretouched "R". The rare variety, No. 575d, is best collected in a block of 4 or 6 with full margins in order to be sure that it is not No. 615a with phosphor lines removed.

No. 575e is a similar variety but from Cyl. 37 (no dot). The marginal rule is much narrower and only a very small part of the "R" is revealed. The cylinder was later retouched. The listed variety is for the original, unretouched state.

WHITER PAPER. On 18 May 1962 the Post Office announced that a whiter paper was being used for the current issue (including Nos. 595/8). This is beyond the scope of this catalogue, but the whiter papers are listed in Vol. 3 of the Stanley Gibbons *Great Britain Specialised Catalogue.*

1958 (24 Nov)–61. *Graphite-lined issue. Two graphite lines on the back, except 2d. value, which has one line.* W 179. P 15×14.

587	154	½d. orange-red (15.6.59)†	..	1·75	2·25
588		1d. ultramarine (18.12.58)	..	1·00	1·50
		a. Misplaced graphite lines (7.61)*		1·00	1·25
589		1½d. green (4.8.59)†	..	40·00	40·00
590		2d. light red-brown (24.11.58)	..	6·00	3·25
591	155	2½d. carmine-red (Type II) (9.6.59)	..	8·00	10·00
592		3d. deep lilac (24.11.58)	..	75	80
		a. Misplaced graphite lines (5.61)*		£400	£350
593	156	4d. ultramarine (29.4.59)	..	3·50	4·50
		a. Misplaced graphite lines (1961)*		£1500	
594		4½d. chestnut (3.6.59)	..	5·00	4·00
587/94			Set of 8	60·00	60·00

Nos. 587/9 were only issued in booklets or coils (587/8).

*No. 588a (in coils), and Nos. 592a and 593a (both in sheets) result from the use of a residual stock of graphite-lined stamps. As the use of graphite lines had ceased, the register of the lines in relation to the stamps was of no importance and numerous misplacements occurred—two lines close together, one line only, etc. No. 588a refers to two lines at left or at right; No. 592a refers to stamps with two lines only at left and clear of the perforations and No. 593a to stamps with two lines at left (with left line down perforations) and traces of a third line down the opposite perforations.

†The prices quoted are for stamps with the watermark inverted. (*Prices for upright watermark ½d. £7.50 un, £7.50 us; 1½d. £95 un, £70 us.*)

(Recess D.L.R. (until 31.12.62), then B.W.)

1959–68. W 179. P 11×12.

595	166	2s. 6d. black-brown (22.7.59)	..	10·00	75
		a. B.W. printing (1.7.63)	..	50	30
		k. Chalk-surfaced paper (30.5.68)	..	50	1·25
596	167	5s. scarlet-vermilion (15.6.59)	..	60·00	2·00
		a. B.W. ptg. *Red* (shades) (3.9.63)	..	1·00	60
		ab. Printed on the gummed side	..	£800	
597	168	10s. blue (21.7.59)	..	45·00	5·00
		a. B.W. ptg. *Bright ultram* (16.10.63)		3·00	3·50
598	169	£1 black (23.6.59)	..	95·00	12·00
		B.W. printing (14.11.63)	..	8·00	5·50
595/8			Set of 4	£180	17·00
595a/8a			Set of 4	11·00	9·00

The B.W. printings have a marginal Plate Number. They are generally more deeply engraved than the D.L.R., showing more of the Diadem detail and heavier lines on Her Majesty's face. The vertical perf is 11.9 to 12 as against D.L.R. 11.8.

See also Nos. 759/62.

PHOSPHOR BAND ISSUES. These are printed on the front and are wider than graphite lines. They are not easy to see but show as broad vertical bands at certain angles to the light.

Values representing the rate for printed papers (and when this was abolished in 1968 for second class mail) have one band and others two, three or four bands as stated, according to the size and format.

In the small size stamps the bands are on each side with the single band at left (*except where otherwise stated*). In the large-size commemorative stamps the single band may be at left, centre or right, varying in different designs. The bands are vertical on both horizontal and vertical designs *except where otherwise stated.*

The phosphor was originally applied typographically but later usually by photogravure and sometimes using flexography, a typographical process using rubber cylinders.

Three different types of phosphor have been used, distinguishable by the colour emitted under an ultra-violet lamp, the first being green, then blue and now violet. Different sized bands are also known. All these are fully listed in Vol. 3 of the Stanley Gibbons *Great Britain Specialised Catalogue.*

Varieties. Misplaced and missing phosphor bands are known but such varieties are beyond the scope of this Catalogue.

1959 (18 Nov). *Phosphor-Graphite issue. Two phosphor bands on front and two graphite lines on back, except 2d. value, which has one band on front and one line on back.* P 15×14. (a) W 165.

599	154	½d. orange-red	..	4·00	6·00
600		1d. ultramarine	..	9·00	7·00
601		1½d. green	..	2·00	6·00

(b) W 179

605	154	2d. light red-brown (1 band)	..	4·50	4·00
		a. Error. W 165	..	£180	£180
606	155	2½d. carmine-red (Type II)	..	20·00	13·00
607		3d. deep lilac	..	9·00	8·00
608	156	4d. ultramarine	..	12·00	25·00
609		4½d. chestnut	..	35·00	15·00
599/609			Set of 8	80·00	70·00

Examples of the 2½d., No. 606, exist showing watermark W 165 in error. It is believed that phosphor-graphite stamps of this value with this watermark were not used by the public for postal purposes.

1960 (22 June)–67. *Phosphor issue. Two phosphor bands on front, except where otherwise stated.* W 179. P 15×14.

610	154	½d. orange-red	..	10	15
		a. Wmk sideways (14.7.61)		10·00	10·00
		l. Booklet pane. No. 610a×4		40·00	
611		1d. ultramarine	..	10	10
		a. Wmk sideways (14.7.61)		35	40
		l. Booklet pane. No. 611a×4		9·00	
		m. Booklet pane. No. 611a×2 *se-tenant* with 615d×2 (1d. stamps at left) (16.8.65)		14·00	
		ma. Booklet pane. As. No. 611m, but 1d. stamps at right		14·00	
		n. Booklet pane. No. 611a×2 *se-tenant* with 615b×2†† (11.67)		8·00	
612		1½d. green	..	10	20
		a. Wmk sideways (14.7.61)		10·00	10·00
		l. Booklet pane. No. 612a×4		40·00	
613		2d. light red-brown (1 band)	..	20·00	24·00

613a	154	2d. lt red-brown (two bands) (4.10.61)		10	10
		aa. Imperf three sides***			
		ab. Wmk sideways (6.4.67)	..	25	25
614	155	2½d. carmine-red (Type II) (2 bands)*		10	50
614a		2½d. carmine-red (Type II) (1 band) (4.10.61)		50	1·00
614b		2½d. carmine-red (Type I) (1 band) (4.10.61)		42·00	35·00
615		3d. deep lilac (2 bands)	..	75	1·00
		a. Phantom "R" (Cyl 41 no dot)		35·00	
		b. Wmk sideways (14.7.61)		2·00	1·75
		l. Booklet pane. No. 615b×4		8·00	
615c		3d. deep lilac (1 side band) (29.4.65)		60	1·00
		d. Wmk sideways (16.8.65)		6·00	5·00
		e. One centre band (8.12.66)		40	50
		ea. Wmk sideways (19.6.67)		50	1·00
616	156	4d. ultramarine	..	30	30
		a. *Deep ultramarine* (28.4.65)		30	30
		aa. Part perf pane			
		ab. Wmk sideways (16.8.65)		50	50
		al. Booklet pane. No. 616ab×4		2·50	
616b		4½d. chestnut (13.9.61)		30	30
616c	157	5d. brown (9.6.67)		30	30
617		6d. deep claret (27.6.60)		50	30
617a		7d. bright green (15.2.67)		60	40
617b	158	8d. magenta (28.6.67)		60	40
617c		9d. bronze-green (29.12.66)		60	40
617d		10d. Prussian blue (30.12.66)		80	50
617e	159	1s. bistre-brown (28.6.67)		40	50
618	160	1s. 3d. green	..	2·00	2·75
618a	159	1s. 6d. grey-blue (12.12.66)		2·00	1·75
610/18a			Set of 17	8·00	7·50

The automatic facing equipment was brought into use on 6 July 1960 but the phosphor stamps may have been released a few days earlier.

The stamps with watermark sideways are from booklets except Nos. 613ab and 615ea which are from coils. No. 616ab comes from both booklets and coils.

No. 615a. See footnote after No. 586.

*No. 614 with two bands on the creamy paper was originally from cylinder 50 dot and no dot. When the change in postal rates took place in 1965 it was reissued from cylinder 57 dot and no dot on the whiter paper. Some of these latter were also released in error in districts of S.E. London in September 1964. The shade of the reissue is slightly more carmine.

***This comes from the bottom row of a sheet which is imperf at bottom and both sides.

††Booklet pane No. 611n comes from 2s. booklets of January and March 1968. The two bands on the 3d. stamp were intentional because of the technical difficulties in producing one band and two band stamps *se-tenant.*

Unlike previous one-banded phosphor stamps, No. 615c has a broad band extending over two stamps so that alternate stamps have the band at left or right (same prices either way).

180 Postboy of 1660   **181** Posthorn of 1660

(Des R. Stone (3d.), Faith Jaques (1s. 3d.))

1960 (7 July). *Tercentenary of Establishment of General Letter Office.* W 179 (*sideways on 1s. 3d.*). P 15×14 (3d.) or 14×15 (1s. 3d.).

619	180	3d. deep lilac	..	20	10
620	181	1s. 3d. green	..	4·00	4·00

182 Conference Emblem

(Des R. Stone (emblem, P. Rahikainen))

1960 (19 Sept). *First Anniv of European Postal and Telecommunications Conference. Chalk-surfaced paper.* W 179. P 15×14.

621	182	6d. bronze-green and purple	..	50	50
622		1s. 6d. brown and blue	..	7·00	5·50

183 Thrift Plant   **184** "Growth of Savings"

185 Thrift Plant

(Des P. Gauld (2½d.), M. Goaman (others))

1961 (28 Aug). *Centenary of Post Office Saving Bank. Chalk-surfaced paper.* W 179 (*sideways on 2½d.*). P 14×15 (2½d.) or 15×14 (others). A. "Timson" Machine

623A	183	2½d. black and red	..	20	20
		a. Black omitted	..	£6000	
624A	184	3d. orange-brown and violet	..	20	20
		a. Orange-brown omitted	..	£110	
625A	185	1s. 6d. red and blue	..	3·00	2·50
623A/5A			Set of 3	3·00	2·50

B. "Thrissell" Machine

623B	183	2½d. black and red	..	2·25	2·25
624B	184	3d. orange-brown and violet	..	25	25
		a. Orange-brown omitted	..	£250	

2½d. TIMSON. Cyls 1E–1F. Deeply shaded portrait (brownish black).

2½d. THRISSELL. Cyls 1D–1B or 1D (dot)–1B (dot). Lighter portrait (grey-black).

3d. TIMSON. Cyls 3D–3E. Clear, well-defined portrait with deep shadows and bright highlights.

3d. THRISSELL. Cyls 3C–3B or 3C (dot)–3B (dot). Dull portrait, lacking in contrast.

Sheet marginal examples *without* single extension perf hole on the short side of the stamps are always "Timson", as are those with large punch-hole *not* coincident with printed three-sided box guide mark.

The 3d. "Timson" perforated completely through the right-hand side margin comes from a relatively small part of the printing perforated on a sheet-fed machine.

Normally the "Timsons" were perforated in the reel, with three large punch-holes in both long margins and the perforations completely through both short margins. Only one punch-hole coincides with the guide-mark.

The "Thrissells" have one large punch-hole in one long margin, coinciding with guide-mark and one short margin imperf (except sometimes for encroachments).

186 C.E.P.T. Emblem

187 Doves and Emblem

188 Doves and Emblem

(Des M. Goaman (doves T. Kurpershoek))

1961 (18 Sept). *European Postal and Telecommunications (C.E.P.T.) Conference, Torquay. Chalk-surfaced paper.* W 179. P 15×14.

626	186	2d. orange, pink and brown	..	25	20
		a. Orange omitted	..	£10000	
627	187	4d. buff, mauve and ultramarine	..	25	20
628	188	10d. turquoise, pale green & Prussian bl		60	75
		a. Pale green omitted	..	£3750	
		b. Turquoise omitted	..	£1800	
626/8			Set of 3	1·00	1·00

189 Hammer Beam Roof, Westminster Hall   **190** Palace of Westminster

(Des Faith Jaques)

1961 (25 Sept). *Seventh Commonwealth Parliamentary Conference. Chalk-surfaced paper.* W 179 (*sideways on 1s. 3d.*). P 15×14 (6d.) or 14×15 (1s. 3d.).

629	189	6d. purple and gold	..	25	25
		a. Gold omitted	..	£475	
630	190	1s. 3d. green and blue	..	3·00	3·00
		a. Blue (Queen's head) omitted	..	£4500	

191 "Units of Productivity"

192 "National Productivity"

193 "Unified Productivity"

(Des D. Gentleman)

1962 (14 Nov). *National Productivity Year. Chalk-surfaced paper.*
W **179** (*inverted on 2½d. and 3d.*). *P* 15 × 14.

631	191	2½d. myrtle-green & carm-red (*shades*)		20	10
		p. One phosphor band	..	1·00	50
632	192	3d. light blue and violet (*shades*)		25	10
		a. Light blue (Queen's head) omitted	£725	
		p. Three phosphor bands	..	1·00	50
633	193	1s. 3d. carmine, light blue & dp green	2·25	2·25
		a. Light blue (Queen's head) omitted	£4000	
		p. Three phosphor bands	..	35·00	24·00
631/3	..	.. .. *Set of 3*	2·50	2·50
631p/3p	..	.. .. *Set of 3*	35·00	24·00

194 Campaign Emblem and Family

195 Children of Three Races

(Des M. Goaman)

1963 (21 Mar). *Freedom from Hunger. Chalk-surfaced paper. W* **179**
(*inverted*). *P* 15 × 14.

634	194	2½d. crimson and pink	..	10	10
		p. One phosphor band	..	1·00	1·25
635	195	1s. 3d. bistre-brown and yellow	..	2·50	2·50
		p. Three phosphor bands	..	35·00	24·00

196 "Paris Conference"

(Des R. Stone)

1963 (7 May). *Paris Postal Conference Centenary. Chalk-surfaced*
paper. W **179** (*inverted*). *P* 15 × 14.

636	196	6d. green and mauve	.. ..	50	50
		a. Green omitted	..	£1300	
		p. Three phosphor bands	..	7·00	7·00

197 Posy of Flowers

198 Woodland Life

(Des S. Scott (3d.), M. Goaman (4½d.))

1963 (16 May). *National Nature Week. Chalk-surfaced paper. W* **179.**
P 15 × 14.

637	197	3d. yellow, green, brown and black	..	25	20
		p. Three phosphor bands	..	50	60
638	198	4½d. black, blue, yellow, mag & brn-red	40	50
		p. Three phosphor bands	..	2·75	2·75

199 Rescue at Sea

200 19th-century Lifeboat

201 Lifeboatmen

(Des D. Gentleman)

1963 (31 May). *Ninth International Lifeboat Conference, Edinburgh.*
Chalk-surfaced paper. W **179**. *P* 15 × 14.

639	199	2½d. blue, black and red		10	10
		p. One phosphor band	..	40	50
640	200	4d. red, yellow, brown, black and blue	40	40
		p. Three phosphor bands	..	20	50
641	201	1s. 6d. sepia, yellow and grey-blue	..	3·00	3·00
		p. Three phosphor bands	..	48·00	30·00
639/41	.. .. ..	.. .. *Set of 3*	3·75	3·75
639p/41p	.. ..	.. .. *Set of 3*	48·00	30·00

202 Red Cross

203

204

(Des H. Bartram)

1963 (15 Aug). *Red Cross Centenary Congress. Chalk-surfaced paper.*
W **179**. *P* 15 × 14.

642	202	3d. red and deep lilac	..	10	10
		a. Red omitted	..	£2750	
		p. Three phosphor bands	..	60	60
		pa. Red omitted	..	£6000	
643	203	1s. 3d. red, blue and grey	..	3·25	3·00
		p. Three phosphor bands	..	40·00	38·00
644	204	1s. 6d. red, blue and bistre	..	3·00	3·00
		p. Three phosphor bands	..	35·00	30·00
642/4	.. .. ..	.. .. *Set of 3*	6·00	5·50
642p/4p	.. ..	.. .. *Set of 3*	70·00	60·00

205 Commonwealth Cable

(Des P. Gauld)

1963 (3 Dec). *Opening of COMPAC (Trans-Pacific Telephone Cable).*
Chalk-surfaced paper. W **179**. *P* 15 × 14.

645	205	1s. 6d. blue and black	.. ..	2·50	2·50
		a. Black omitted	..	£2750	
		p. Three phosphor bands	..	20·00	20·00

206 Puck and Bottom
(*A Midsummer Night's Dream*)

207 Feste (*Twelfth Night*)

208 Balcony Scene (*Romeo and Juliet*)

209 "Eve of Agincourt" (*Henry V*)

210 Hamlet contemplating Yorick's Skull
(*Hamlet*) and Queen Elizabeth II

(Des D. Gentleman. Photo Harrison & Sons (3d., 6d., 1s. 3d., 1s. 6d.).
Des C. and R. Ironside. Recess B.W. (2s. 6d.))

1964 (23 April). *Shakespeare Festival. Chalk-surfaced paper. W* **179**.
P 11 × 12 (2s. 6d.) or 15 × 14 (*others*).

646	206	3d. yell-bistre, blk & dp vio-bl (*shades*)	10	10
		p. Three phosphor bands	..	20	30
647	207	6d. yellow, orge, blk & yell-ol (*shades*)	20	30
		p. Three phosphor bands	..	60	90
648	208	1s. 3d. cerise, bl-grn, blk & sep (*shades*)	90	1·00
		p. Three phosphor bands	..	5·75	6·50
649	209	1s. 6d. violet, turq, blk & blue (*shades*)	1·25	1·00
		p. Three phosphor bands	..	11·00	6·75
650	210	2s. 6d. deep slate-purple (*shades*)	2·25	2·25
646/50	..	.. .. *Set of 5*	4·25	4·25
646p/9p	..	.. .. *Set of 4*	15·00	13·00

211 Flats near Richmond Park
("Urban Development")

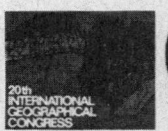
212 Shipbuilding Yards, Belfast
("Industrial Activity")

213 Beddgelert Forest Park, Snowdonia
("Forestry")

214 Nuclear Reactor, Dounreay
("Technological Development")

(Des D. Bailey)

1964 (1 July). *20th International Geographical Congress. London.*
Chalk-surfaced paper. W **179**. *P* 15 × 14.

651	211	2½d. black, olive-yell, ol-grey & turq-bl	10	10
		p. One phosphor band	..	50	40
652	212	4d. orge-brn, red-brn, rose, blk & vio	25	25
		a. Violet (face value) omitted	..	£175	
		c. Violet and red-brown (dock walls) omitted		£175	
		p. Three phosphor bands	..	75	70
653	213	8d. yellow-brown, emerald, grn & blk	60	50
		a. Green (lawn) omitted	..	£6000	
		p. Three phosphor bands	..	1·75	1·50
654	214	1s. 6d. yellow-brn, pale pk, blk & brn	3·25	3·25
		p. Three phosphor bands	..	27·00	23·00
651/4	..	.. .. *Set of 4*	4·00	4·00
651p/4p	..	.. .. *Set of 4*	27·00	23·00

A used example of the 4d. is known with the red-brown omitted.

215 Spring Gentian

216 Dog Rose

217 Honeysuckle

218 Fringed Water Lily

(Des M. and Sylvia Goaman)

1964 (5 Aug). *Tenth International Botanical Congress, Edinburgh. Chalk-surfaced paper. W* **179.** *P* 15 × 14.

655	215	3d. violet, blue and sage-green		10	10
		a. Blue omitted		£4000	
		b. Sage-green omitted		£4000	
		p. Three phosphor bands		20	30
656	216	6d. apple-green, rose, scarlet and green		20	20
		p. Three phosphor bands		2·00	1·50
657	217	9d. lemon, green, lake and rose-red		1·60	2·50
		a. Green (leaves) omitted		£4000	
		p. Three phosphor bands		4·50	3·00
658	218	1s. 3d. yellow, emerald, reddish violet and grey-green		2·50	1·90
		a. Yellow (flowers) omitted		£8000	
		p. Three phosphor bands		25·00	22·00
655/8			Set of 4	4·00	4·00
655p/8p			Set of 4	29·00	24·00

219 Forth Road Bridge

220 Forth Road and Railway Bridges

(Des A. Restall)

1964 (4 Sept). *Opening of Forth Road Bridge. Chalk-surfaced paper. W* **179.** *P* 15 × 14.

659	219	3d. black, blue and reddish violet		15	10
		p. Three phosphor bands		50	50
660	220	6d. blackish lilac, lt blue & carmine-red		45	40
		a. Light blue omitted		£1500	
		p. Three phosphor bands		4·75	4·75

221 Sir Winston Churchill

(Des D. Gentleman and Rosalind Dease, from photograph by Karsh)

1965 (8 July). *Churchill Commemoration. Chalk-surfaced paper. W* **179.** *P* 15 × 14.

I. "REMBRANDT" Machine

661	221	4d. black and olive-brown		15	10
		p. Three phosphor bands		30	30

II. "TIMSON" Machine

661a	221	4d. black and olive-brown		50	50

III. "L. & M. 4" Machine

662	–	1s. 3d. black and grey		45	40
		p. Three phosphor bands		3·75	3·75

The 1s. 3d. shows a closer view of Churchill's head.

4d. REMBRANDT. Cyls 1A–1B dot and no dot. Lack of shading detail on Churchill's portrait. Queen's portrait appears dull and coarse. This is a rotary machine which is sheet-fed.

4d. TIMSON. Cyls 5A–6B no dot. More detail on Churchill's portrait—furrow on forehead, his left eyebrow fully drawn and more shading on cheek. Queen's portrait lighter and sharper. This is a reel-fed, two-colour 12-in. wide rotary machine and the differences in impression are due to the greater pressure applied by this machine.

1s. 3d. Cyls 1A–1B no dot. The "Linotype and Machinery No. 4" machine is an ordinary sheet-fed rotary press machine. Besides being used for printing the 1s. 3d. stamps it was also employed for overprinting the phosphor bands on both values.

Two examples of the 4d. value exist with the Queen's head omitted, one due to something adhering to the cylinder and the other due to a paper fold. The stamp also exists with Churchill's head omitted, also due to a paper fold.

222 Simon de Montfort's Seal

223 Parliament Buildings (after engraving by Hollar, 1647)

(Des S. Black (6d.), R. Guyatt (2s. 6d.))

1965 (19 July). *700th Anniv of Simon de Montfort's Parliament. Chalk-surfaced paper. W* **179.** *P* 15 × 14.

663	222	6d. olive-green		10	10
		p. Three phosphor bands		1·00	1·00
664	223	2s. 6d. black, grey and pale drab		1·25	1·25

224 Bandsmen and Banner

225 Three Salvationists

(Des M. Farrar-Bell (3d.), G. Trenaman (1s. 6d.))

1965 (9 Aug). *Salvation Army Centenary. Chalk-surfaced paper. W* **179.** *P* 15 × 14.

665	224	3d. indigo, grey-blue, cerise, yell & brn		10	10
		p. One phosphor band		50	40
666	225	1s. 6d. red, blue, yellow and brown		1·00	1·00
		p. Three phosphor bands		3·00	3·25

226 Lister's Carbolic Spray

227 Lister and Chemical Symbols

(Des P. Gauld (4d.), F. Ariss (1s.))

1965 (1 Sept). *Centenary of Joseph Lister's Discovery of Antiseptic Surgery. Chalk-surfaced paper. W* **179.** *P* 15 × 14.

667	226	4d. indigo, brown-red and grey-black		10	10
		a. Brown-red (tube) omitted		£200	
		b. Indigo omitted		£2000	
		p. Three phosphor bands		15	20
		pa. Brown-red (tube) omitted		£1500	
668	227	1s. black, purple and new blue		1·00	1·50
		p. Three phosphor bands		2·75	2·75

228 Trinidad Carnival Dancers

229 Canadian Folk-dancers

(Des D. Gentleman and Rosalind Dease)

1965 (1 Sept). *Commonwealth Arts Festival. Chalk-surfaced paper. W* **179.** *P* 15 × 14.

669	228	6d. black and orange		10	10
		p. Three phosphor bands		30	30
670	229	1s. 6d. black and light reddish violet		1·25	1·50
		p. Three phosphor bands		2·50	2·50

230 Flight of Supermarine Spitfires

231 Pilot in Hawker Hurricane Mk I

232 Wing-tips of Supermarine Spitfire and Messerschmitt Bf 109

233 Supermarine Spitfires attacking Heinkel HE-111H Bomber

234 Supermarine Spitfire attacking Junkers Ju 87B "Stuka" Dive-bomber

235 Hawker Hurricanes Mk I over Wreck of Dornier Do-17Z Bomber

236 Anti-aircraft Artillery in Action

237 Air-battle over St. Paul's Cathedral

(Des D. Gentleman and Rosalind Dease (4d. ×6 and 1s. 3d.), A. Restall (9d.))

1965 (13 Sept). *25th Anniv of Battle of Britain. Chalk-surfaced paper. W* **179.** *P* 15 × 14.

671	230	4d. yellow-olive and black		30	35
		a. Block of 6. Nos. 671/6		8·00	10·00
		p. Three phosphor bands		40	50
		pa. Block of 6. Nos. 671p/6p		12·00	15·00
672	231	4d. yellow-olive, olive-grey and black		30	35
		p. Three phosphor bands		40	50
673	232	4d. red, new blue, yell-ol, ol-grey & blk		30	35
		p. Three phosphor bands		40	50
674	233	4d. olive-grey, yellow-olive and black		30	35
		p. Three phosphor bands		40	50
675	234	4d. olive-grey, yellow-olive and black		30	35
		p. Three phosphor bands		40	50
676	235	4d. olive-grey, yell-olive, new blue & blk		30	35
		a. New blue omitted		†	£3500
		p. Three phosphor bands		40	50

677	236	9d. bluish violet, orange and slate-purple	1·25	1·25
		p. Three phosphor bands	1·25	80
678	237	1s. 3d. light grey, deep grey, black, light blue and bright blue	1·25	1·25
		p. Three phosphor bands	1·25	80
671/8		Set of 8	9·50	4·25
671p/8p		Set of 8	14·00	4·25

Nos. 671/6 were issued together *se-tenant* in blocks of 6 (3×2) within the sheet.
No. 676a is only known commercially used on cover from Truro.

238 Tower and Georgian Buildings

239 Tower and "Nash" Terrace, Regent's Park

(Des C. Abbott)

1965 (8 Oct). *Opening of Post Office Tower. Chalk-surfaced paper. W **179** (sideways on 3d.). P 14 × 15 (3d.) or 15 × 14 (1s. 3d.).*

679	238	3d. olive-yell, new blue & bronze-green	10	10
		a. Olive-yellow (Tower) omitted	£750	
		p. One phosphor band	10	10
680	239	1s. 3d. bronze-green, yellow-green & bl	65	85
		p. Three phosphor bands	70	70

The one phosphor band on No. 679p was produced by printing broad phosphor bands across alternate vertical perforations. Individual stamps show the band at right or left (same prices either way).

240 U.N. Emblem

241 I.C.Y. Emblem

(Des J. Matthews)

1965 (25 Oct). *20th Anniv of U.N.O. and International Co-operation Year. Chalk-surfaced paper. W **179**. P 15 × 14.*

681	240	3d. black, yellow-orange and light blue	15	20
		p. One phosphor band	25	50
682	241	1s. 6d. black, bright purple and lt blue	1·10	1·25
		p. Three phosphor bands	3·75	3·75

242 Telecommunications Network

243 Radio Waves and Switchboard

(Des A. Restall)

1965 (15 Nov). *I.T.U. Centenary. Chalk-surfaced paper. W **179**. P 15 × 14.*

683	242	9d. red, ultram, dp slate, vio, blk & pk	25	25
		p. Three phosphor bands	60	60
684	243	1s. 6d. red, greenish bl, ind, blk & lt pk	1·60	1·75
		a. Light pink omitted	£900	
		p. Three phosphor bands	5·50	5·50

Originally scheduled for issue on 17 May 1965, supplies from the Philatelic Bureau were sent in error to reach a dealer on that date and another dealer received his supply on 27 May.

244 Robert Burns (after Skirving chalk drawing)

245 Robert Burns (after Nasmyth portrait)

(Des G. Huntly)

1966 (25 Jan). *Burns Commemoration. Chalk-surfaced paper. W **179**. P 15 × 14.*

685	244	4d. black, deep violet-blue and new blue	15	15
		p. Three phosphor bands	25	40
686	245	1s. 3d. black, slate-blue & yellow-orge	70	85
		p. Three phosphor bands	2·25	2·50

246 Westminster Abbey

247 Fan Vaulting, Henry VII Chapel

(Des Sheila Robinson. Photo Harrison (3d.). Des and eng Bradbury, Wilkinson. Recess (2s. 6d.))

1966 (28 Feb). *900th Anniv of Westminster Abbey. Chalk-surfaced paper (3d.). W **179**. P 15 × 14 (3d.) or 11 × 12 (2s. 6d.).*

687	246	3d. black, red-brown and new blue	15	20
		p. One phosphor band	30	40
688	247	2s. 6d. black	85	1·25

248 View near Hassocks, Sussex

249 Antrim, Northern Ireland

250 Harlech Castle, Wales

251 Cairngorm Mountains, Scotland

(Des L. Rosoman. Queen's portrait, adapted by D. Gentleman from coinage)

1966 (2 May). *Landscapes. Chalk-surfaced paper. W **179**. P 15 × 14.*

689	248	4d. black, yellow-green and new blue	15	15
		p. Three phosphor bands	15	15
690	249	4d. black, emerald and new blue	25	25
		p. Three phosphor bands	30	30
691	250	1s. 3d. blk, greenish yell & greenish bl	40	45
		p. Three phosphor bands	40	45
692	251	1s. 6d. black, orange and Prussian blue	60	60
		p. Three phosphor bands	60	60
689/92		Set of 4	1·25	1·25
689p/92p		Set of 4	1·25	1·25

252 Players with Ball   **253** Goalmouth Mêlée

254 Goalkeeper saving Goal

(Des D. Gentleman (4d.), W. Kempster (6d.), D. Caplan (1s. 3d.). Queen's portrait adapted by D. Gentleman from coinage)

1996 (1 June). *World Cup Football Championship. Chalk-surfaced paper. W **179** (sideways on 4d.). P 14×15 (4d.) or 15×14 (others).*

693	252	4d. red, reddish pur, brt bl, flesh & blk	15	10
		p. Two phosphor bands	15	10
694	253	6d. black, sepia, red, apple-green & blue	20	30
		a. Black omitted	85·00	
		b. Apple-green omitted	£2000	
		c. Red omitted	£2250	
		p. Three phosphor bands	20	30
		pa. Black omitted	£500	
695	254	1s. 3d. black, blue, yell, red & lt yell-ol	75	90
		a. Blue omitted	£150	
		p. Three phosphor bands	75	90
693/5		Set of 3	1·00	1·25
693p/5p		Set of 3	1·00	1·25

255 Black-headed Gull

256 Blue Tit

257 European Robin

258 Blackbird

(Des J. Norris Wood)

1966 (8 Aug). *British Birds. Chalk-surfaced paper. W **179**. P 15 × 14.*

696	255	4d. grey, black, red, emerald-green, brt blue, greenish yellow and bistre	10	15
		a. Block of 4. Nos. 696/9	1·00	2·00
		ab. Black (value), etc. omitted* (block of four)	£5000	
		ac. Black only omitted*	£4000	
		p. Three phosphor bands	10	15
		pa. Block of 4. Nos. 696/9p	1·00	2·00
697	256	4d. black, greenish yellow, grey, emerald-green, bright blue and bistre	10	15
		p. Three phosphor bands	10	15
698	257	4d. red, greenish yellow, black, grey, bistre, reddish brown & emerald-grn	10	15
		p. Three phosphor bands	10	15
699	258	4d. black, reddish brown, greenish yellow, grey and bistre**	10	15
		p. Three phosphor bands	10	15
696/9		Set of 4	1·00	50
696p/9p		Set of 4	1·00	50

Nos. 696/9 were issued together *se-tenant* in blocks of four within the sheet.
* In No. 696ab the blue, bistre and reddish brown are also omitted but in No. 696ac only the black is omitted.
** On No. 699 the black was printed over the bistre.

Other colours omitted, and the stamps affected:

d.	Greenish yellow (Nos. 696/9)		£400
pd.	Greenish yellow (Nos. 696/9)		£400
e.	Red (Nos. 696 and 698)		75·00
f.	Emerald-green (Nos. 696/8)		75·00
pf.	Emerald-green (Nos. 696/8p)		75·00
g.	Bright blue (Nos. 696/7)		£300
pg.	Bright blue (Nos. 696/7p)		£800
h.	Bistre (Nos. 696/9)		90·00
ph.	Bistre (Nos. 696/9p)		90·00
j.	Reddish brown (Nos. 698/9)		80·00
pj.	Reddish brown (Nos. 698/9p)		80·00

The prices quoted are for each stamp.

NEW INFORMATION

The editor is always interested to correspond with people who have new information that will improve or correct the Catalogue.

259 Cup Winners

1966 (18 Aug). *England's World Cup Football Victory. Chalk-surfaced paper.* W **179** (*sideways*). P 14 × 15.
700 **259** 4d. red, reddish pur, brt bl, flesh & blk   30   30
 These stamps were only put on sale at post offices in England, the Channel Islands and the Isle of Man, and at the Philatelic Bureau in London and also, on 22 August, in Edinburgh on the occasion of the opening of the Edinburgh Festival as well as at Army post offices at home and abroad.

260 Jodrell Bank Radio Telescope

261 British Motor-cars

262 "SRN 6" Hovercraft

263 Windscale Reactor

(Des D. and A. Gillespie (4d., 6d.), A. Restall (others))

1966 (19 Sept). *British Technology. Chalk-surfaced paper.* W **179**. P 15 × 14.
701 **260** 4d. black and lemon   15   15
  p. Three phosphor bands . .   15   15
702 **261** 6d. red, deep blue and orange . .   15   20
  a. Red (Mini-cars) omitted . .   £4000
  b. Deep blue (Jaguar and inscr) omitted   £2500
  p. Three phosphor bands . .   15   20
703 **262** 1s. 3d. black, orange-red, slate and light greenish blue   30   50
  p. Three phosphor bands . .   45   60
704 **263** 1s. 6d. black, yellow-green, bronze-green, lilac and deep blue   50   55
  p. Three phosphor bands . .   65   70
701/4 . .   . .   *Set of 4* 1·00   1·25
701p/4p . .   . .   . .   *Set of 4* 1·25   1·50

264

265

266

267

268

269

 All the above show battle scenes and they were issued together *se-tenant* in horizontal strips of six within the sheet.

270 Norman Ship

271 Norman Horsemen attacking Harold's Troops

(All the above are scenes from the Bayeux Tapestry)

(Des D. Gentleman. Photo, Queen's head die-stamped (6d., 1s. 3d.))

1966 (14 Oct). *900th Anniv of Battle of Hastings. Chalk-surfaced paper.* W **179** (*sideways on* 1s. 3d.). P 15 × 14.
705 **264** 4d. black, olive-green, bistre, deep blue, orange, mag, grn, blue and grey   10   15
  a. Strip of 6. Nos. 705/10 . .   2·75   6·00
  p. Three phosphor bands . .   10   25
  pa. Strip of 6. Nos. 705p/10p . .   2·75   6·00
706 **265** 4d. black, olive-green, bistre, deep blue, orange, mag, grn, blue and grey   10   15
  p. Three phosphor bands . .   10   25
707 **266** 4d. black, olive-green, bistre, deep blue, orange, mag, grn, blue and grey   10   15
  p. Three phosphor bands . .   10   25
708 **267** 4d. black, olive-green, bistre, deep blue, magenta, green, blue and grey   10   15
  p. Three phosphor bands . .   10   25
709 **268** 4d. black, olive-green, bistre, deep blue, orange, mag, grn, blue and grey   10   15
  p. Three phosphor bands . .   10   25
710 **269** 4d. black, olive-green, bistre, deep blue, orange, mag, grn, blue and grey   10   15
  p. Three phosphor bands . .   10   25
711 **270** 6d. black, olive-grn, vio, bl, grn & gold   10   10
  p. Three phosphor bands . .   10   10
712 **271** 1s. 3d. black, lilac, bronze-green, rosine, bistre-brown and gold   20   20
  a. Lilac omitted . .   £600
  p. Four phosphor bands . .   20   20
  pa. Lilac omitted   £650
705/12 . .   . .   *Set of 8* 3·00   1·50
705p/12p . .   . .   . .   *Set of 8* 3·00   1·90
 Other colours omitted on the 4d. values and the stamps affected:
  b. Olive-green (Nos. 705/10) . .   40·00
  pb. Olive-green (Nos. 705p/10p) . .   40·00
  c. Bistre (Nos. 705/10) . .   40·00
  pc. Bistre (Nos. 705p/10p) . .   45·00
  d. Deep blue (Nos. 705/10) . .   50·00
  pd. Deep blue (Nos. 705p/10p) . .   50·00
  e. Orange (Nos. 705/7 and 709/10) . .   40·00
  pe. Orange (Nos. 705p/7p and 709p/10p)   35·00
  f. Magenta (Nos. 705/10) . .   45·00
  pf. Magenta (Nos. 705p/10p) . .   45·00
  g. Green (Nos. 705/10) . .   40·00
  pg. Green (Nos. 705p/10p) . .   40·00
  h. Blue (Nos. 705/10) . .   35·00
  ph. Blue (Nos. 705p/10p) . .   50·00
  j. Grey (Nos. 705/10) . .   35·00
  pj. Grey (Nos. 705p/10p) . .   35·00
  pk. Magenta and green (Nos. 705p/10p) . .
 The prices quoted are for each stamp.
 Nos. 705 and 709, with grey and blue omitted, have been seen commercially used, posted from Middleton-in-Teesdale.
 Three examples of No. 712 in a right-hand top corner block of 10 (2 × 5) are known with the Queen's head omitted as a result of a double paper fold prior to die-stamping. The perforation is normal. Of the other seven stamps, four have the Queen's head misplaced and three are normal.

MISSING GOLD HEADS. The 6d. and 1s. 3d. were also issued with the die-stamped gold head omitted but as these can also be removed by chemical means we are not prepared to list them unless a way is found of distinguishing the genuine stamps from the fakes which will satisfy the Expert Committees.
 The same remarks apply to Nos. 713/14.

272 King of the Orient   **273** Snowman

(Des Tasveer Shemza (3d.), J. Berry (1s. 6d.) (winners of children's design competition). Photo, Queen's head die-stamped)

1966 (1 Dec). *Christmas. Chalk-surfaced paper.* W **179** (*sideways on* 3d.). P 14 × 15.
713 **272** 3d. black, blue, green, yell, red & gold   10   10
  a. Queen's head double . .   †   —
  ab. Queen's head double, one albino
  b. Green omitted . .   —   £150
  p. One phosphor band . .   10   10
714 **273** 1s. 6d. blue, red, pink, black and gold   40   70
  a. Pink (hat) omitted . .   £750
  p. Two phosphor bands . .   40   70
 See note below Nos. 679/80 which also applies to No. 713p.

274 Sea Freight

275 Air Freight

(Des C. Abbott)

1967 (20 Feb). *European Free Trade Association* (E.F.T.A.). *Chalk-surfaced paper.* W **179**. P 15 × 14.
715 **274** 9d. deep blue, red, lilac, green, brown, new blue, yellow and black . .   30   30
  a. Black (Queen's head, etc.), brown, new blue and yellow omitted . .   £650
  b. Lilac omitted . .   60·00
  c. Green omitted . .   60·00
  d. Brown (rail trucks) omitted . .   45·00
  e. New blue omitted . .   60·00
  f. Yellow omitted . .   60·00
  p. Three phosphor bands . .   30   30
  pb. Lilac omitted . .   75·00
  pc. Green omitted . .   60·00
  pd. Brown omitted . .   45·00
  pe. New blue omitted . .   60·00
  pf. Yellow omitted . .   90·00
716 **275** 1s. 6d. violet, red, deep blue, brown, green, blue-grey, new bl, yell & blk   50   50
  a. Red omitted . .   —
  b. Deep blue omitted . .   £275
  c. Brown omitted . .   45·00
  d. Blue-grey omitted . .   60·00
  e. New blue omitted . .   60·00
  f. Yellow omitted . .   60·00
  p. Three phosphor bands . .   50   50
  pa. Red omitted . .   —
  pb. Deep blue omitted . .   £275
  pc. Brown omitted . .   45·00
  pd. Blue-grey omitted . .   60·00
  pf. New blue omitted . .   60·00

276 Hawthorn and Bramble

277 Larger Bindweed and Viper's Bugloss

278 Ox-eye Daisy, Coltsfoot and Buttercup

279 Bluebell, Red Campion and Wood Anemone

The above were issued together *se-tenant* in blocks of four within the sheet.

280 Dog Violet

281 Primroses

(Des Rev. W. Keble Martin (T **276/9**), Mary Grierson (others))

1967 (24 Apr). *British Wild Flowers. Chalk-surfaced paper. W* **179.** *P* 15 × 14.

717	276	4d.	grey, lemon, myrtle-green, red, agate and slate-purple	15	10
		a.	Block of 4. Nos. 717/20	1·40	2·75
		b.	Grey double*		
		c.	Red omitted	£2250	
		f.	Slate-purple omitted		
		p.	Three phosphor bands	10	10
		pa.	Block of 4. Nos. 717p/20p	1·00	2·50
		pd.	Agate omitted	£600	
		pf.	Slate-purple omitted	£150	
718	277	4d.	grey, lemon, myrtle-green, red, agate and violet	15	10
		p.	Grey double*		
		p.	Three phosphor bands	10	10
		pd.	Agate omitted	£600	
		pe.	Violet omitted	£2000	
719	278	4d.	grey, lemon, myrtle-green, red and agate	15	10
		b.	Grey double*		
		p.	Three phosphor bands	10	10
		pd.	Agate omitted	£600	
720	279	4d.	grey, lemon, myrtle-green, reddish purple, agate and violet	15	10
		b.	Grey double*		
		c.	Reddish purple omitted	£950	
		d.	Value omitted†		
		p.	Three phosphor bands	10	10
		pd.	Agate omitted	£650	
		pe.	Violet omitted	£2000	
721	280	9d.	lavender-grey, green, reddish violet and orange-yellow	15	10
		p.	Three phosphor bands	10	10
722	281	1s. 9d.	lavender-grey, green, greenish yellow and orange	20	20
		p.	Three phosphor bands	30	20
717/22			*Set of* 6	1·50	65
717p/22p			*Set of* 6	1·25	65

*The double impression of the grey printing affects the Queen's head, value and inscription.

†No. 720d was caused by something obscuring the face value on R. 14/6 during the printing of one sheet.

PHOSPHOR BANDS. Issues from No. 723 are normally with phosphor bands only, except for the high values. However, most stamps have appeared with the phosphor bands omitted in error, but they are outside the scope of this catalogue. They are listed in Volumes 3, 4 and 5 of the Stanley Gibbons *Great Britain Specialised Catalogue* and in the *Great Britain Concise Catalogue*.

See also further notes after No. X1058.

PHOSPHORISED PAPER. Following the adoption of phosphor bands the Post Office started a series of experiments involving the addition of the phosphor to the paper coating before the stamps were printed. No. 743c was the first of these experiments to be issued for normal postal use. See also notes after No. X1058.

PVA GUM. Polyvinyl alcohol was introduced by Harrisons in place of gum Arabic in 1968. As it is almost invisible a small amount of pale yellowish colouring was introduced to make it possible to check that the stamps had been gummed. Such gum varieties are outside the scope of this catalogue, but they are listed in the *Great Britain Concise Catalogue*. See further notes *re* gum after Nos. 744 and 762.

282   **282*a***

I   II

Two types of the 2d.

I. Value spaced away from left side of stamp (cylinders 1 no dot and dot).

II. Value close to left side from new multipositive used for cylinders 5 no dot and dot onwards. The portrait appears in the centre, thus conforming to the other values.

(Des after plaster cast by Arnold Machin)

1967 (5 June)-**70**.   *Chalk-surfaced paper. Two phosphor bands except where otherwise stated. No wmk. P* 15 × 14.

723	282	½d.	orange-brown (5.2.68)	10	20
724		1d.	lt olive (*shades*) (2 bands) (5.2.68)	10	10
		a.	Imperf (coil strip)†	£1100	
		b.	Part perf pane*		
		c.	Imperf pane*	£3750	
		d.	Uncoated paper**	65·00	
		l.	Booklet pane. No. 724×2 *se-tenant* with 730×2 (6.4.68)	3·00	
		m.	Booklet pane. No. 724×4 *se-tenant* with 734×2 (6.1.69)	3·50	
		n.	Booklet pane. No. 724×6, 734×6 and 735×3 *se-tenant* (1.12.69)	8·50	
		na.	Uncoated paper**	£900	
725		1d.	yellowish olive (1 centre band) (16.9.68)	25	30
		l.	Booklet pane. No. 725×4 *se-tenant* with 732×2	4·00	
		m.	Coil strip. No. 728×2 *se-tenant* with 729, 725 and 733 (27.8.69)	1·25	
726		2d.	lake-brown (Type I) (2 bands) (5.2.68)	10	15
727		2d.	lake-brn (Type II) (2 bands) (1969)	15	15
728		2d.	lake-brown (Type II) (1 centre band) (27.8.69)	70	1·00
729		3d.	violet (*shades*) (1 centre band) (8.8.67)	10	10
		a.	Imperf (pair)	£550	
730		3d.	violet (2 bands) (6.4.68)	30	30
		a.	Uncoated paper**	£2000	
731		4d.	deep sepia (*shades*) (2 bands)	10	10
		b.	Part perf pane*	£1000	
732		4d.	dp olive-brown (*shades*) (1 centre band) (16.9.68)	10	10
		a.	Part perf pane*	£1000	
		l.	Booklet pane. Two stamps plus two printed labels	1·00	
733		4d.	brt verm (1 centre band) (6.1.69)	10	10
		a.	Tête-bêche (horiz pair)	£2500	
		b.	Uncoated paper**	6·00	
		l.	Booklet pane. Two stamps plus two printed labels (3.3.69)	1·00	
734		4d.	brt vermilion (6.1.69)	1·75	2·00
		a.	Uncoated paper**	£175	
735		5d.	royal blue (*shades*) (1.7.68)	10	10
		a.	Imperf pane*	£1200	
		b.	Part perf pane*	£800	
		c.	Imperf (pair)††	£200	
		d.	Uncoated paper**	15·00	
736		6d.	brt reddish pur (*shades*) (5.2.68)	20	20
737	282*a*	7d.	bright emerald (1.7.68)	50	30
738		8d.	bright vermilion (1.7.68)	20	30
739		8d.	light turquoise-blue (6.1.69)	75	75
740		9d.	myrtle-green (8.8.67)	60	30
741	282	10d.	drab (1.7.68)	55	50
		a.	Uncoated paper**	23·00	
742		1s.	light bluish violet (*shades*)	50	30
743		1s. 6d.	greenish blue and deep blue (*shades*) (8.8.67)	60	30
		a.	Greenish blue omitted	80·00	
		c.	Phosphorised paper. *Prussian blue and indigo* (10.12.69)	85	90
		ca.	Prussian blue omitted	£400	
744		1s. 9d.	dull orange and black (*shades*)	50	30
723/44			*Set of* 16	5·00	4·00

*BOOKLET ERRORS. See note after No. 556.

** Uncoated paper. This does not respond to the chalky test, and may be further distinguished from the normal chalk-surfaced paper by the fibres which clearly show on the surface, resulting in the printing impression being rougher, and by the screening dots which are not so evident. The 1d., 4d. and 5d. come from the £1 "Stamps for Cooks" Booklet (1970); and the 3d. and 10d. from sheets (1969). The 20p. and 50p. high values (Nos. 830/1) exist with similar errors.

† No. 724a occurs in a vertical strip of four, top stamp perforated on three sides, bottom stamp imperf three sides and the two middle stamps completely imperf.

†† No. 735c comes from the original state of cylinder 15 which is identifiable by the screening dots which extend through the gutters of the stamps and into the margins of the sheet. This must not be confused with imperforate stamps from cylinder 10, a large quantity of which was stolen from the printers early in 1970.

The 1d. with centre band (725) only came in the September 1968 booklets (PVA gum) and the coil strip (725m) (gum arabic); the 2d. with centre band (728) was only issued in the coil strip (725m); the 3d. (No. 730) appeared in booklets on 6.4.68, from coils during December 1968 and from sheets in January 1969; and the 4d. with one side band (734) only in 10s. (band at left) and £1 (band at left or right) booklets.

Gum. The 1d. (725), 3d. (729), 4d. (731 and 733), 9d., 1s., 1s. 6d. and 1s. 9d. exist with gum arabic as well as the PVA gum; the 2d. (728) and coil strip (725m) exist only with gum arabic; and the remainder exist with PVA gum only.

The 4d. (731) in shades of washed-out grey are colour changelings which we understand are caused by the concentrated solvents used in modern dry cleaning methods.

For decimal issue, see Nos. X841, etc.

---

285 "Children Coming Out of School" (L. S. Lowry)

(Des S. Rose)

1967 (10 July). *British Paintings. Chalk-surfaced paper. Two phosphor bands. No wmk. P* 14 × 15 (4d.) *or* 15 × 14 (*others*).

748	283	4d.	rose-red, lemon, brown, black, new blue and gold	10	10
		a.	Gold (value and Queen's head) omitted	£200	
		b.	New blue omitted	£2500	
749	284	9d.	Venetian red, ochre, grey-black, new blue, greenish yellow and black	20	20
		a.	Black (Queen's head and value) omitted	£400	
		b.	Greenish yellow omitted	£1300	
750	285	1s. 6d.	greenish yellow, grey, rose, new blue, grey-black and gold	60	60
		a.	Gold (Queen's head) omitted	£850	
		b.	New blue omitted	£160	
		c.	Grey (clouds and shading) omitted	95·00	
748/50			*Set of* 3	1·00	1·00

286 *Gypsy Moth IV*

(Des M. and Sylvia Goaman)

1967 (24 July). *Sir Francis Chichester's World Voyage. Chalk-surfaced paper. Three phosphor bands. No wmk. P* 15 × 14.

751	286	1s. 9d.	black, brown-red, lt emer & blue	25	25

287 Radar Screen

288 *Penicillium notatum*

289 Vickers VC-10 Jet Engines   **290** Television Equipment

(Des C. Abbott (4d., 1s.), Negus-Sharland team (others))

1967 (19 Sept). *British Discovery and Invention. Chalk-surfaced paper. Three phosphor bands* (4d.) *or two phosphor bands* (*others*). *W* **179** (*sideways on* 1s. 9d.). *P* 14 × 15 (1s. 9d.) *or* 15 × 14 (*others*).

752	287	4d.	greenish yellow, black and vermilion	10	10
753	288	1s.	blue-green, light greenish blue, slate-purple and bluish violet	15	15
754	289	1s. 6d.	black, grey, royal blue, ochre and turquoise-blue	35	35
755	290	1s. 9d.	black, grey-blue, pale olive-grey, violet and orange	50	50
		a.	Grey-blue omitted		
752/5			*Set of* 4	1·00	1·00

WATERMARK. All issues from this date are on unwatermarked paper.

283 "Master Lambton" (Sir Thomas Lawrence)   **284** "Mares and Foals in a Landscape" (George Stubbs)   **291** "The Adoration of the Shepherds" (School of Seville)   **292** "Madonna and Child" (Murillo)

293 "The Adoration of the Shepherds"
(Louis le Nain)

(Des S. Rose)

1967. *Christmas. Chalk-surfaced paper. One phosphor band (3d.) or two phosphor bands (others). P 15 × 14 (1s. 6d.) or 14 × 15 (others).*

756	291	3d. ol-yell, rose, bl, blk & gold (27.11)	10	20
		a. Gold (value and Queen's head) omitted	75·00	
		b. Printed on the gummed side	£300	
		c. Rose omitted	£500	
757	292	4d. bright purple, greenish yellow, new blue, grey-black and gold (18.10)	10	20
		a. Gold (value and Queen's head) omitted	60·00	
		b. Gold ("4D" only) omitted	£1000	
		c. Yellow (Child, robe and Madonna's face) omitted		
758	293	1s. 6d. brt purple, bistre, lemon, black, orange-red, ultram & gold (27.11)	60	60
		a. Gold (value and Queen's head) omitted	£3500	
		b. Ultramarine omitted	£350	
		c. Lemon omitted	£10000	
756/8		Set of 3	75	80

Distinct shades exist of the 3d. and 4d. values but are not listable as there are intermediate shades. For the 4d. stamps from one machine show a darker background and give the appearance of the yellow colour being omitted, but this is not so and these should not be confused with the true missing yellow No. 757c.

No. 757b comes from stamps in the first vertical row of a sheet.

(Recess Bradbury, Wilkinson)

1967–68. *No wmk. White paper. P 11 × 12.*

759	166	2s. 6d. black-brown (1.7.68)	40	50
760	167	5s. red (10.4.68)	1·00	1·00
761	168	10s. bright ultramarine (10.4.68)	5·50	8·00
762	169	£1 black (4.12.67)	4·50	6·50
759/62		Set of 4	10·00	14·00

PVA GUM. All the following issues from this date have PVA gum *except where footnotes state otherwise.*

294 Tarr Steps, Exmoor

295 Aberfeldy Bridge

296 Menai Bridge

297 M4 Viaduct

(Des A. Restall (9d.), L. Rosoman (1s. 6d.), J. Matthews (others))

1968 (29 Apr). *British Bridges. Chalk-surfaced paper. Two phosphor bands. P 15 × 14.*

763	294	4d. black, bluish violet, turq-blue & gold	10	10
		a. Printed on gummed side	25·00	
764	295	9d. red-brown, myrtle-green, ultramarine, olive-brown, black and gold	10	10
		a. Gold (Queen's head) omitted	£150	
		b. Ultramarine omitted	†	£3750
765	296	1s. 6d. olive-brown, red-orange, bright green, turquoise-green and gold	40	40
		a. Gold (Queen's head) omitted	£150	
		b. Red-orange (roof tops) omitted	£175	
766	297	1s. 9d. olive-brown, greenish yellow, dull green, deep ultramarine & gold	50	50
		a. Gold (Queen's head) omitted	£175	
763/6		Set of 4	1·00	1·00

No. 764b is only known on first day covers posted from Canterbury, Kent, or the Philatelic Bureau, Edinburgh.

298 "T U C" and Trades Unionists

299 Mrs. Emmeline Pankhurst (statue)

300 Sopwith Camel and English Electric Lightning Fighters

301 Captain Cook's *Endeavour* and Signature

(Des D. Gentleman (4d.), C. Abbott (others))

1968 (29 May). *British Anniversaries. Events described on stamps. Chalk-surfaced paper. Two phosphor bands. P 15 × 14.*

767	298	4d. emerald, olive, blue and black	10	10
768	299	9d. reddish violet, bluish grey and black	10	15
769	300	1s. olive-brown, bl, red, slate-bl & blk	40	35
770	301	1s. 9d. yellow-ochre and blackish brown	50	50
767/70		Set of 4	1·00	1·00

302 "Queen Elizabeth I"
(unknown artist)

303 "Pinkie"
(Lawrence)

304 "Ruins of St. Mary Le Port" (Piper)

305 "The Hay Wain"
(Constable)

(Des S. Rose)

1968 (12 Aug). *British Paintings. Queen's head embossed. Chalk-surfaced paper. Two phosphor bands. P 15 × 14 (1s. 9d.) or 14 × 15 (others).*

771	302	4d. blk, verm, greenish yell, grey & gold	10	10
		a. Gold (value and Queen's head) omitted	£125	
		b. Vermilion omitted*	£225	
772	303	1s. mauve, new blue, greenish yellow, black, magenta and gold	20	20
		a. Gold (value and Queen's head) omitted	£200	
773	304	1s. 6d. slate, orange, black, mauve, greenish yellow, ultramarine & gold	30	30
		a. Gold (value and Queen's head) omitted	£100	
774	305	1s. 9d. greenish yellow, black, new blue, red and gold	50	50
		a. Gold (value and Queen's head) and embossing omitted	£500	
		b. Red omitted	£10000	
771/4		Set of 4	1·00	1·00

*The effect of this is to leave the face and hands white and there is more yellow and olive in the costume.

The 4d., 1s. and 1s. 9d. are known with the embossing only omitted. No. 774a is only known with the phosphor also omitted. No. 772a exists both with or without embossing or phosphor bands.

306 Boy and Girl with Rocking Horse

307 Girl with Doll's House   **308** Boy with Train Set

(Des Rosalind Dease. Head printed in gold and then embossed)

1968 (25 Nov). *Christmas. Chalk-surfaced paper. One centre phosphor band (4d.) or two phosphor bands (others). P 15 × 14 (4d.) or 14 × 15 (others).*

775	306	4d. black, orange, vermilion, ultramarine, bistre and gold	10	10
		a. Gold omitted	£2250	
		b. Vermilion omitted*	£275	
		c. Ultramarine omitted	£175	
776	307	9d. yellow-olive, black, brown, yellow, magenta, orange, turq-green & gold	30	30
		a. Yellow omitted	65·00	
		b. Turquoise-green (dress) omitted		
777	308	1s. 6d. ultramarine, yellow-orange, brt purple, blue-green, black and gold	45	45
775/7		Set of 3	75	75

*The effect of the missing vermilion is shown on the rocking horse, saddle and faces which appear orange instead of red.

A single used example of the 4d. exists with the bistre omitted. No. 775c is only known with the phosphor also omitted. All values exist with the embossing of Queen's head omitted.

309 *Queen Elizabeth 2*

310 Elizabethan Galleon

311 East Indiaman

312 *Cutty Sark*

313 *Great Britain*

314 *Mauretania I*

(Des D. Gentleman)

1969 (15 Jan). *British Ships. Chalk-surfaced paper. Two vertical phosphor bands at right (1s.), one horizontal phosphor band (5d.) or two phosphor bands (9d.). P 15×14.*

778	309	5d. black, grey, red and turquoise	10	10
		a. Black (Queen's head, value, hull and inscr) omitted	£700	
		b. Grey (decks, etc.) omitted ..	90·00	
		c. Red (inscription) omitted ..	50·00	
779	310	9d. red, blue, ochre, brown, blk & grey	10	15
		a. Strip of 3. Nos. 779/81 ..	1·75	3·00
		ab. Red and blue omitted ..	£1500	
		ac. Blue omitted ..	£1500	
780	311	9d. ochre, brown, black and grey	10	15
781	312	9d. ochre, brown, black and grey	10	15
782	313	1s. brown, blk, grey, grn & greenish yell	40	30
		a. Pair. Nos. 782/3 ..	1·50	2·50
		ab. Greenish yellow omitted ..		
783	314	1s. red, black, brown, carmine and grey	40	30
		a. Carmine (hull overlay) omitted ..	£10000	
		b. Red (funnels) omitted ..	£10000	
		c. Carmine and red omitted ..		
778/83		*Set of 6*	2·50	1·00

The 9d. and 1s. values were arranged in horizontal strips of three and pairs respectively throughout the sheet.

No. 779ab is known only with the phosphor also omitted.

315 Concorde in Flight

316 Plan and Elevation Views

317 Concorde's Nose and Tail

(Des M. and Sylvia Goaman (4d.), D. Gentleman (9d., 1s. 6d.))

1969 (3 Mar). *First Flight of Concorde. Chalk-surfaced paper. Two phosphor bands. P 15×14.*

784	315	4d. yellow-orange, violet, greenish blue, blue-green and pale green ..	10	10
		a. Violet (value, etc.) omitted ..	£225	
		b. Yellow-orange omitted ..	£110	
785	316	9d. ultramarine, emerald, red & grey-bl	35	35
786	317	1s. 6d. deep blue, silver-grey & lt blue	50	50
		a. Silver-grey omitted ..	£275	
784/6		*Set of 3*	85	85

No. 786a affects the Queen's head which appears in the light blue colour.

318 Queen Elizabeth II. (See also Type 357)

(Des after plaster cast by Arnold Machin. Recess Bradbury, Wilkinson)

1969 (5 Mar). *P 12.*

787	318	2s. 6d. brown ..	50	30
788		5s. crimson-lake ..	2·25	60
789		10s. deep ultramarine ..	7·00	6·50
790		£1 bluish black ..	3·00	2·00
787/90		*Set of 4*	11·50	8·50

For decimal issue, see Nos. 829/31*b* and notes after No. 831*b*.

319 Page from *Daily Mail*, and Vickers FB-27 Vimy Aircraft

320 Europa and CEPT Emblems

321 ILO Emblem

322 Flags of NATO Countries

323 Vickers FB-27 Vimy Aircraft and Globe showing Flight

(Des P. Sharland (5d., 1s., 1s. 6d.), M. and Sylvia Goaman (9d., 1s. 9d.))

1969 (2 Apr). *Anniversaries. Events described on stamps. Chalk-surfaced paper. Two phosphor bands. P 15×14.*

791	319	5d. black, pale sage-green, chestnut and new blue	10	10
792	320	9d. pale turq, dp bl, lt emer-grn & blk	20	25
		a. Uncoated paper*	£1500	
793	321	1s. bright purple, deep blue and lilac	25	25
794	322	1s. 6d. red, royal blue, yellow-green, black, lemon and new blue ..	25	30
		e. Black omitted ..	60·00	
		f. Yellow-green (from flags) omitted	48·00	
		g. Lemon (from flags) omitted ..	†	—
795	323	1s. 9d. yellow-olive, greenish yellow and pale turquoise-green ..	30	35
		a. Uncoated paper* ..	£200	
791/5		*Set of 5*	1·00	1·10

*Uncoated paper. The second note after No. 744 also applies here.

No. 794g is only known used on first day cover from Liverpool.

324 Durham Cathedral

325 York Minster

326 St. Giles' Cathedral, Edinburgh

327 Canterbury Cathedral

328 St. Paul's Cathedral

329 Liverpool Metropolitan Cathedral

(Des P. Gauld)

1969 (28 May). *British Architecture. Cathedrals. Chalk-surfaced paper. Two phosphor bands. P 15×14.*

796	324	5d. grey-blk, orge, pale bluish vio & blk	10	10
		a. Block of 4. Nos. 796/9 ..	85	2·50
		ab. Block of 4. Uncoated paper**		
		b. Pale bluish violet omitted ..	£2500	
797	325	5d. grey-black, pale bluish violet, new blue and black	10	10
		b. Pale bluish violet omitted ..	£2500	
798	326	5d. grey-black, purple, green and black	10	10
		c. Green omitted ..	40·00	
799	327	5d. grey-black, green, new blue & black	10	10
800	328	9d. grey-blk, ochre, pale drab, vio & blk	15	15
		a. Black (value) omitted ..	£100	
801	329	1s. 6d. grey-black, pale turquoise, pale reddish violet, pale yellow-ol & blk	15	15
		a. Black (value) omitted ..	£1600	
		b. Black (value) double ..		
796/801		*Set of 6*	1·00	55

The 5d. values were issued together *se-tenant* in blocks of four throughout the sheet.

*The missing green on the roof top is known on R. 2/5, R. 8/5 and R. 10/5, but all from different sheets, and it only occurred in part of the printing, being "probably caused by a batter on the impression cylinder". Examples are also known with the green partly omitted.

** Uncoated paper. The second note after No. 744 also applies here.

330 The King's Gate, Caernarvon Castle

331 The Eagle Tower, Caernarvon Castle

332 Queen Eleanor's Gate, Caernarvon Castle

333 Celtic Cross, Margam Abbey

334 H.R.H. The Prince of Wales (after photo by G. Argent)

(Des D. Gentleman)

1969 (1 July). *Investiture of H.R.H. The Prince of Wales. Chalk-surfaced paper. Two phosphor bands. P 14×15.*

802	330	5d. deep olive-grey, light olive-grey, deep grey, light grey, red, pale turquoise-green, black and silver	10	10
		a. Strip of 3. Nos. 802/4 ..	70	1·50
		b. Black (value and inscr) omitted ..	£150	
		c. Red omitted* ..	£250	
		d. Deep grey omitted** ..	90·00	
		e. Pale turquoise-green omitted ..	£350	
803	331	5d. deep olive-grey, light olive-grey, deep grey, light grey, red, pale turquoise-green, black and silver ..	10	10
		b. Black (value and inscr) omitted ..	£150	
		c. Red omitted* ..	£250	
		d. Deep grey omitted** ..	90·00	
		e. Pale turquoise-green omitted ..	£325	
		f. Light grey (marks on walls, window frames, etc) omitted ..	†	£7500
804	332	5d. deep olive-grey, light olive-grey, deep grey, light grey, red, pale turquoise-green, black and silver ..	10	10
		b. Black (value and inscr) omitted ..	£150	
		c. Red omitted* ..	£250	
		d. Deep grey omitted** ..	90·00	
		e. Pale turquoise-green omitted ..	£325	
805	333	9d. deep grey, light grey, black and gold	20	10
806	334	1s. blackish yellow-olive and gold	20	10
802/6		*Set of 5*	1·00	45

The 5d. values were issued together, *se-tenant*, in strips of three throughout the sheet.

*The 5d. value is also known with the red misplaced downwards and where this occurs the red printing does not take very well on the silver background and in some cases is so faint that it could be mistaken for a missing red. However, the red can be seen under a magnifying glass and caution should therefore be exercised when purchasing copies of Nos. 802/4c.

**The deep grey affects the dark portions of the windows and doors.

No. 803f is only known commercially used on cover.

335 Mahatma Gandhi

(Des B. Mullick)

1969 (13 Aug). *Gandhi Centenary Year. Chalk-surfaced paper. Two phosphor bands. P 15 × 14.*

807	335	1s. 6d. black, green, red-orange & grey	30	30
		a. Printed on the gummed side ..	£325	

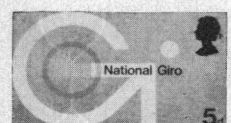

336 National Giro "G" Symbol

337 Telecommunications—International Subscriber Dialling

338 Telecommunications—Pulse Code Modulation

339 Postal Mechanisation—Automatic Sorting

(Des D. Gentleman. Litho De La Rue)

1969 (1 Oct). *Post Office Technology Commemoration. Chalk-surfaced paper. Two phosphor bands. P 13½ × 14.*

808	336	5d. new bl, greenish bl, lavender & blk	10	10
809	337	9d. emerald, violet-blue and black ..	25	25
810	338	1s. emerald, lavender and black ..	25	25
811	339	1s. 6d. brt purple, lt blue, grey-bl & blk	50	50
808/11	..	.. .. .. *Set of 4*	1·00	1·00

340 Herald Angel

341 The Three Shepherds

342 The Three Kings

(Des F. Wegner. Queen's head (and stars 4d., 5d. and scroll-work 1s. 6d.) printed in gold and then embossed)

1969 (26 Nov). *Christmas. Chalk-surfaced paper. Two phosphor bands (5d., 1s. 6d.) or one centre band (4d.). P 15 × 14.*

812	340	4d. vermilion, new blue, orange, bright purple, light green, bluish violet, blackish brown and gold ..	10	15
		a. Gold (Queen's head etc.) omitted ..	£2000	
813	341	5d. magenta, light blue, royal blue, olive-brown, green, greenish yellow, red and gold ..	25	20
		a. Light blue (sheep, etc) omitted	60·00	
		b. Red omitted*	£550	
		c. Gold (Queen's head) omitted ..	£450	
		d. Green omitted	£200	
		e. Olive-brown, red and gold omitted	£7000	

814	342	1s. 6d. greenish yell, bright purple, bluish violet, deep slate, orange, green, new blue and gold ..	50	50
		a. Gold (Queen's head etc.) omitted	90·00	
		b. Deep slate (value) omitted ..	£250	
		c. Greenish yellow omitted ..	£150	
		e. New blue omitted	60·00	
812/14		.. .. *Set of 3*	75	75

*The effect of the missing red is shown on the hat, leggings and purse which appear as dull orange.

No. 813e was caused by a paper fold and also shows the phosphor omitted.

The 5d. and 1s. 6d. values are known with the embossing omitted.

No. 813e was caused by a paper fold and also shows the phosphor omitted.

Used copies of the 5d. have been seen with the olive-brown or greenish yellow (tunic at left) omitted.

343 Fife Harling

344 Cotswold Limestone

345 Welsh Stucco

346 Ulster Thatch

(Des D. Gentleman (5d., 9d.), Sheila Robinson (1s., 1s. 6d.))

1970 (11 Feb). *British Rural Architecture. Chalk-surfaced paper. Two phosphor bands. P 15 × 14.*

815	343	5d. grey, grey-blk, blk, lemon, greenish blue, orange-brown, ultram & grn	10	15
		a. Lemon omitted	60·00	
		b. Grey (Queen's head and cottage shading) omitted	£4000	
		c. Greenish blue (door) omitted ..	†	—
816	344	9d. orange-brown, olive-yellow, bright green, black, grey-black and grey	30	25
817	345	1s. dp bl, reddish lilac, drab & new bl	30	25
		a. New blue omitted	55·00	
818	346	1s. 6d. greenish yell, blk, turq-bl & lilac	40	45
		a. Turquoise-blue omitted	£4000	
815/18		.. .. *Set of 4*	1·00	1·00

Used examples of the 5d. exist, one of which is on piece, with the greenish blue colour omitted.

347 Signing the Declaration of Arbroath

348 Florence Nightingale attending Patients

349 Signing of International Co-operative Alliance

350 Pilgrims and *Mayflower*

351 Sir William Herschel, Francis Baily, Sir John Herschel and Telescope

(Des F. Wegner (5d., 9d., and 1s. 6d.), Marjorie Saynor (1s., 1s. 9d.). Queen's head printed in gold and then embossed)

1970 (1 Apr). *Anniversaries. Events described on stamps. Chalk-surfaced paper. Two phosphor bands. P 15 × 14.*

819	347	5d. blk, yell-olive, blue, emer, greenish yellow, rose-red, gold & orange-red	10	10
		a. Gold (Queen's head) omitted ..	£400	
		b. Emerald omitted	£100	
820	348	9d. ochre, deep blue, carmine, black, blue-green, yellow-olive, gold & bl	15	15
		a. Ochre omitted	£150	
821	349	1s. green, greenish yellow, brown black, cerise, gold and light blue ..	25	35
		a. Gold (Queen's head) omitted ..	50·00	
		c. Green omitted	75·00	
		d. Brown omitted	£100	
822	350	1s. 6d. greenish yellow, carmine, deep yellow-olive, emerald, black, blue gold and sage-green ..	30	40
		a. Gold (Queen's head) omitted ..	75·00	
		b. Emerald omitted	40·00	
823	351	1s. 9d. blk, slate, lemon, gold & brt pur	30	40
		a. Lemon (trousers and document) omitted	£7500	
819/23		.. .. *Set of 5*	1·00	1·25

The 9d., 1s. and 1s. 6d. are known with the embossing omitted. No. 821c also exists with embossing omitted.

No. 823a is known mint, or used on first day cover postmarked London WC.

352 "Mr. Pickwick and Sam" (*Pickwick Papers*)

353 "Mr. and Mrs. Micawber" (*David Copperfield*)

354 "David Copperfield and Betsy Trotwood" (*David Copperfield*)

355 "Oliver asking for more" (*Oliver Twist*)

356 "Grasmere" (from engraving by J. Farrington, R.A.)

T **352/5** were issued together *se-tenant* in blocks of four throughout the sheet.

(Des Rosalind Dease. Queen's head printed in gold and then embossed)

1970 (3 June). *Literary Anniversaries. Death Centenary of Charles Dickens (novelist) (5d. ×4) and Birth Bicentenary of William Wordsworth (poet) (1s. 6d.). Chalk-surfaced paper. Two phosphor bands. P 14 × 15.*

824	352	5d. black, orange, silver, gold and mag	10	10
		a. Block of 4. Nos. 824/7 ..	1·00	2·00
		ab. Imperf (block of four)	£700	
		ac. Silver (inscr) omitted		
825	353	5d. black, magenta, silver, gold & orge	10	10
826	354	5d. black, light greenish blue, gold and yellow-bistre	10	10
		b. Yellow-bistre (value) omitted ..	£1200	
827	355	5d. black, yellow-bistre, silver, gold and light greenish blue ..	10	10
		b. Yell-bistre (background) omitted	£3000	
		c. Lt greenish blue (value) omitted*	£400	
		d. Light greenish blue and silver (inscr at foot) omitted	£6000	
828	356	1s. 6d. light yellow-olive, black, silver, gold and bright blue	20	20
		a. Gold (Queen's head) omitted ..	£250	
		b. Silver ("Grasmere") omitted ..	70·00	
		c. Bright blue (face value) omitted ..		
824/8		.. .. *Set of 5*	1·00	55

*No 827c (unlike No. 827b) comes from a sheet on which the colour was only partially omitted so that, although No. 827 was completely without the light greenish blue colour, it was still partially present on No. 826.

The 1s. 6d. is known with embossing omitted.

Essays exist of Nos. 824/7 showing the Queen's head in silver and with different inscriptions.

357 (Value redrawn)

(Des after plaster cast by Arnold Macnin. Recess B.W.)

1970 (17 June)–72. *Decimal Currency. Chalk-surfaced paper or phosphorised paper* (10p.). P 12.

829	357	10p. cerise	1·00	85
830		20p. olive-green	1·00	30
831		50p. deep ultramarine	2·00	60
831b		£1 bluish black (6.12.72)	5·00	1·00
829/31b		*Set of* 4	8·00	2·50

The 20p. and 50p. exist on thinner, uncoated paper and are listed in the *Great Britain Concise Catalogue*.

A whiter paper was introduced in 1973. The £1 appeared on 27 Sept. 1973, the 20p. on 30 Nov. 1973 and the 50p. on 20 Feb. 1974.

The 50p. was issued on 1 Feb. 1973 on phosphorised paper. This cannot be distinguished from No. 831 with the naked eye.

The £1, T **318**, was also issued, on 17 June 1970, in sheets of 100 (10 × 10) instead of panes of 40 (8 × 5) but it is not easy to distinguish from No. 790 in singles. It can be readily differentiated when in large strips or marginal pieces showing sheet markings or plate numbers.

358 Runners

359 Swimmers

360 Cyclists

(Des A. Restall. Litho D.L.R.)

1970 (15 July). *Ninth British Commonwealth Games. Chalk-surfaced paper. Two phosphor bands.* P 13½ × 14.

832	358	5d. pk, emer, greenish yell & dp yell-grn	10	10
		a. Greenish yellow omitted	£4500	
833	359	1s. 6d. light greenish blue, lilac, bistre-brown and Prussian blue	50	55
834	360	1s. 9d. yellow-orange, lilac, salmon and deep red-brown	50	55
832/4		*Set of* 3	1·00	1·10

361 1d. Black (1840)

362 1s. Green (1847)

363 4d. Carmine (1855)

(Des D. Gentleman)

1970 (18 Sept). *"Philympia 70" Stamp Exhibition. Chalk-surfaced paper. Two phosphor bands.* P 14 × 14½.

835	361	5d. grey-black, brownish bistre, black and dull purple	10	10
		a. Grey-black (Queen's head) omitted	£10000	
836	362	9d. light drab, bluish green, stone, black and dull purple	50	50
837	363	1s. 6d. carmine, lt drab, blk & dull pur	50	60
835/7		*Set of* 3	1·00	1·10

364 Shepherds and Apparition of the Angel

365 Mary, Joseph, and Christ in the Manger

366 The Wise Men bearing gifts

(Des Sally Stiff after De Lisle Psalter. Queen's head printed in gold and then embossed)

1970 (25 Nov). *Christmas. Chalk-surfaced paper. One centre phosphor band* (4d.) *or two phosphor bands* (others). P 14 × 15.

838	364	4d. brown-red, turquoise-green, pale chestnut, brn, grey-blk, gold & verm	30	30
839	365	5d. emerald, gold, blue, brown-red, ochre, grey-black and violet	30	30
		a. Gold (Queen's head) omitted	†	£2500
		b. Emerald omitted	60·00	
		c. Imperf (pair)	£250	
840	366	1s. 6d. gold, grey-black, pale turq-grn, salmon, ultram, ochre & yellow-grn	50	50
		a. Salmon omitted	80·00	
		b. Ochre omitted	50·00	
838/40		*Set of* 3	75	75

The 4d. and 5d. are known with embossing omitted, and the 1s. 6d. is known with embossing and phosphor omitted.

(New Currency. 100 new pence = £1)

"X" NUMBERS. The following definitive series has been allocated "X" prefixes to the catalogue numbers to avoid re-numbering all subsequent issues.

367

367a

NO VALUE INDICATED. Stamps as Types 367/a inscribed "2nd" or "1st" are listed as Nos. 1445/52, 1511/16, 1663a/6, 1979 and 2039/40.

ELLIPTICAL PERFORATIONS. These were introduced in 1993 and stamps showing them will be found listed as Nos. Y1667, etc.

PRINTING PROCESSES

Litho   Photo

(*Illustrations enlarged* ×6)

Litho. Clear outlines to value and frame of stamp.
Photo. Uneven lines to value and frame formed by edges of screen.

Two types of the 3p., 10p. and 26p. (Nos. X930/c, X886/b and X971/b).

I   II

I   II

Figures of face value as I (all ptgs of 3p. bright magenta except multi-value coil No. 930cl and sheets from 21.1.92 onwards, 10p. orange-brown except 1984 "Christian Heritage" £4 booklet and 26p. rosine except 1987 £1.04 "window" booklet).

Figures of face value narrower as in II (from coil No. X930cl and in sheets from 21.1.92 (3p.), 1984 "Christian Heritage" £4 booklet (10p.) or 1987 £1.04 "window" booklet (26p.)).

This catalogue includes changes of figure styles on those stamps where there is no other listable difference. Similar changes have also taken place on other values, but only in conjunction with listed colour, paper or perforation differences.

I   II

(Des from plaster cast by Arnold Machin)

1971 (15 Feb)–96. *Decimal Currency. T* **367**. *Chalk-surfaced paper.*

(a) Photo Harrison (except for some printings of Nos. X879 and X913 in sheets produced by Enschedé and issued on 12 Dec 1979 (8p.) and 19 Nov 1991 (18p.)). *With phosphor bands.* P 15 × 14.

X841	½p. turquoise-blue (2 bands)		10	10
	a. Imperf (pair)†		£900	
	l. Booklet pane. No. X841 × 2 *se-tenant* vert with X849 × 2		5·00	
	la. Ditto, *se-tenant* horiz (14.7.71)		80	
	m. Booklet pane. No. X841×5 plus label		3·50	
	n. Coil strip. No. X849, X841×2 and X844×2		35	
	o. Booklet pane. No. X841 × 3, X851 × 3 and X852 × 6 (24.5.72)		12·00	
	p. Booklet pane. No. X841 × 3, X842 and X852 × 2 (24.5.72)		75·00	
	q. Coil strip. No. X870, X849, X844 and X841 × 2 (3.12.75)		80	
	r. Booklet pane. No. X841 × 2, X844 × 3 and X852 × 6 (10.3.76)		70	
	s. Booklet pane. No. X841 × 2, X844 × 2, X873 × 2 and X881 × 4 (8½p. values at right) (26.1.77)		2·50	
	sa. Ditto. 8½p. values at left		2·50	
	t. Booklet pane. No. X841, X844, X894 × 3 and X902 (14p. value at right) (26.1.81)		2·25	
	ta. Ditto. 14p. value at left		2·25	
	u. Booklet pane. No. X841, X857 × 4 and X899 × 3 (12½p. values at left) (1.2.82)		2·50	
	ua. Ditto. 12½p. values at right		2·50	
X842	½p. turquoise-blue (1 side band) (24.5.72)		60·00	35·00
X843	½p. turquoise-bl (1 centre band) (14.12.77)		50	30
	l. Coil strip. No. X843 × 2, X875 and X845 × 2 (14.12.77)		55	
	m. Booklet pane. No. X843 × 2, X845 × 2 and X875 plus label (8.2.78)		75	
X844	1p. crimson (2 bands)		10	10
	a. Imperf (vert coil)			
	b. Pair, one imperf 3 sides (vert coil)			
	c. Imperf (pair)			
	l. Booklet pane. No. X844 × 2 *se-tenant* vert with X848 × 2		5·00	
	m. Ditto, *se-tenant* horiz (14.7.71)		80	
	n. Booklet pane. No. X844 × 2, X876 × 3 and X883 × 3 (9p. values at right) (13.6.77)		4·00	
	na. Ditto. 9p. values at left		3·00	
X845	1p. crimson (1 centre band) (14.12.77)		20	20
	l. Booklet pane. No. X879 and X845 × 2 plus label (17.10.79)		70	
	m. Coil strip. No. X879 and X845 × 2 plus 2 labels (16.1.80)		75	
	n. Booklet pane. No. X845 × 2, X860 and X898 each × 3 (5.4.83)		5·00	
	p. Booklet pane. No. X845 × 3, X863 × 2 and X900 × 3 (3.9.84)		4·00	
	q. Booklet pane. No. X845 × 2 and X896 × 4 (29.7.86)		6·00	
	s. Booklet pane. No. X845, X867 × 2 and X900 × 3 (20.10.86)		3·50	
	sa. Ditto, but with vert edges of pane imperf (29.9.87)		3·00	
X846	1p. crimson ("all-over") (10.10.79)		20	20
X847	1p. crimson (1 side band) (20.10.86)		1·25	1·60
	l. Booklet pane. X847, X901 and X912 ×2		3·00	
	m. Booklet pane. No. X847, X901×2, X912×5 and X918 with margins all round (3.3.87)		13·00	
X848	1½p. black (2 bands)		30	15
	a. Uncoated paper (1971)*		£125	
	b. Imperf (pair)			
	c. Imperf 3 sides (horiz pair)			
X849	2p. myrtle-green (face value as T **367**) (2 bands)		20	10
	a. Imperf (horiz pair)			
	l. Booklet pane. No. X849×2, X880×2 and X886×3 plus label (10p. values at right) (28.8.79)		2·50	
	la. Ditto. 10p. values at left		2·50	
	m. Booklet pane. No. X849×3, X889×2 and X895×2 plus label (12p. values at right) (4.2.80)		2·50	
	ma. Ditto. 12p. values at left		2·00	
	n. Booklet pane. No. X849, X888×3, X889 and X895×4 with margins all round (16.4.80)		3·75	
	o. Booklet pane. No. X849×6 with margins all round (16.4.80)		80	
	p. Booklet pane. No. X849, X857, X898 and X899×6 with margins all round (19.5.82)		4·50	
X850	2p. myrtle-green (face value as T **367**) ("all-over") (10.10.79)		30	15

X851	2½p. magenta (1 centre band)	25	10
	a. Imperf (pair)†	£275	
	l. Booklet pane. No. X851 × 5 plus label	2·75	
	m. Booklet pane. No. X851 × 4 plus two labels	4·00	
	n. Booklet pane. No. X851 × 3, X852 × 3 and X855 × 6 (24.5.72)	7·00	
X852	2½p. magenta (1 side band)	1·75	2·00
	l. Booklet pane. No. X852 × 2 and X855 × 4	5·00	
X853	2½p. magenta (2 bands) (21.5.75)	40	85
X854	2½p. rose-red (2 bands) (26.8.81)	75	1·00
	l. Booklet pane. No. X854 × 3, X862 × 2 and X894 × 3 (11½p. values at left)	5·00	
	la. Ditto. 11½p. values at right	6·50	
X855	3p. ultramarine (2 bands)	30	10
	a. Imperf (coil strip of 5)	£1250	
	b. Imperf (pair)†	£275	
	c. Uncoated paper (1972)*	40·00	
	l. Booklet pane. No. X855 × 5 plus label	2·00	
X856	3p. ultramarine (1 centre band) (10.9.73)	30	25
	a. Imperf (pair)†	£275	
	b. Imperf between (vert pair)†	£375	
	c. Imperf horiz (vert pair)†	£200	
X857	3p. bright magenta (Type I) (2 bands) (1.2.82)	50	50
X858	3½p. olive-grey (*shades*) (2 bands)	50	50
	a. Imperf (pair)	£375	
X859	3½p. olive-grey (1 centre band) (24.6.74)	50	15
X860	3½p. purple-brown (1 centre band) (5.4.83)	1·50	1·75
X861	4p. ochre-brown (2 bands)	30	30
	a. Imperf (pair)†	£1100	
X862	4p. greenish blue (2 bands) (26.8.81)	2·00	2·00
X863	4p. greenish blue (1 centre band) (3.9.84)	1·75	2·00
X864	4p. greenish blue (1 side band) (8.1.85)	2·25	2·50
	l. Booklet pane. No. X864×2, X901×4, X909×2 and X920 with margins all round	12·50	
X865	4½p. grey-blue (2 bands) (24.10.73)	30	25
	a. Imperf (pair)	£325	
X866	5p. pale violet (2 bands)	30	10
X867	5p. claret (1 centre band) (20.10.86)	2·25	2·25
X868	5½p. violet (2 bands) (24.10.73)	40	25
X869	5½p. violet (1 centre band) (17.3.75)	40	20
	a. Uncoated paper*	£375	
X870	6p. light emerald (2 bands)	40	15
	a. Uncoated paper*	17·00	
X871	6½p. greenish blue (2 bands) (4.9.74)	60	60
X872	6½p. greenish blue (1 centre band) (24.9.75)	50	15
	a. Imperf (vert pair)	£325	
	b. Uncoated paper*	£160	
X873	6½p. greenish blue (1 side band) (26.1.77)	80	85
X874	7p. purple-brown (2 bands) (15.1.75)	70	85
	a. Imperf (pair)	£275	
X875	7p. purple-brown (1 centre band) (13.6.77)	40	30
	a. Imperf (pair)	£140	
	l. Booklet pane. No. X875 × 10 and X883 × 10 (15.11.78)	4·50	
X876	7p. purple-brown (1 side band) (13.6.77)	80	90
X877	7½p. pale chestnut (2 bands)	40	30
X878	8p. rosine (2 bands) (24.10.73)	30	30
	a. Uncoated paper*	12·00	
X879	8p. rosine (1 centre band) (20.8.79)	30	30
	a. Uncoated paper*	£650	
	b. Imperf (pair)	£650	
	l. Booklet pane. No. X879 and X886, each × 10 (14.11.79)	5·00	
X880	8p. rosine (1 side band) (28.8.79)	1·00	1·00
X881	8½p. light yellowish green (*shades*) (2 bands) (24.9.75)	40	30
	a. Imperf (pair)	£800	
X882	9p. yellow-orange and black (2 bands)	70	40
X883	9p. deep violet (2 bands) (25.2.76)	50	30
	a. Imperf (pair)	£250	
X884	9½p. purple (2 bands) (25.2.76)	50	40
X885	10p. orge-brown & chest (2 bands) (11.8.71)	50	40
	a. Orange-brown omitted	£150	
	b. Imperf (horiz pair)	£2000	
X886	10p. orange-brn (Type I) (2 bands) (25.2.76)	50	30
	a. Imperf (pair)	£250	
	b. Type II (4.9.84)	28·00	28·00
	bl. Booklet pane. No. X886b, X901 and X909 × 7, with margins all round	29·00	
X887	10p. orange-brown (Type I) ("all-over") (3.10.79)	40	50
X888	10p. orange-brown (Type I) (1 centre band) (4.2.80)	40	30
	a. Imperf (pair)	£275	
	l. Booklet pane. No. X888×9 with margins all round (16.4.80)	2·75	
	m. Booklet pane. No. X888 and X895, each × 10 (12.11.80)	5·50	
X889	10p. orange-brown (Type I) (1 side band) (4.2.80)	1·00	1·00
X890	10½p. yellow (2 bands) (25.2.76)	60	40
X891	10½p. deep dull blue (2 bands) (26.4.78)	90	50
X892	11p. brown-red (2 bands) (25.2.76)	80	40
	a. Imperf (pair)	£2250	
X893	11½p. drab (1 centre band) (14.1.81)	60	40
	a. Imperf (pair)	£260	
	l. Booklet pane. No. X893 and X902, each × 10 (11.11.81)	7·00	
X894	11½p. drab (1 side band) (26.1.81)	80	1·00
	l. Booklet pane. No. X894 × 4 and X902 × 6 (6.5.81)	6·00	
X895	12p. yellowish green (2 bands) (4.2.80)	70	50
	l. Booklet pane. No. X895 × 9 with margins all round (16.4.80)	3·00	
X896	12p. bright emerald (1 centre band) (29.10.85)	70	50
	a. Imperf (pair)	£100	
	l. Booklet pane. No. X896 × 9 with margins all round (18.3.86)	3·00	
X897	12p. bright emerald (1 side band) (14.1.86)	1·00	1·00
	l. Booklet pane. No. X897×4 and X909×6 (12p. values at left)	5·00	
	la. Ditto. 12p. values at right	5·00	
	m. Booklet pane. No. X897×6, X909×2 and X919 with margins all round (18.3.86)	14·00	
X898	12½p. light emerald (1 centre band) (27.1.82)	50	30
	a. Imperf (pair)	£100	
	l. Booklet pane. No. X898 and X907, each × 10 (10.11.82)	7·50	

X899	12½p. light emerald (1 side band) (1.2.82)	70	70
	l. Booklet pane. No. X899 × 4 and X907 × 6 (1.2.82)	5·00	
	m. Booklet pane. No. X899 × 6 with margins all round (19.5.82)	2·50	
	n. Booklet pane. No. X899 × 4 and X908 × 6 (12½p. values at left) (5.4.83)	9·00	
	na. Ditto. 12½p. values at right	9·00	
X900	13p. pale chestnut (1 centre band) (28.8.84)	50	40
	a. Imperf (pair)	£500	
	l. Booklet pane. No. X900 × 9 with margins all round (8.1.85)	3·25	
	m. Booklet pane. No. X900 × 6 with margins all round (3.3.87)	2·50	
	n. Booklet pane. No. X900 × 4 with margins all round (4.8.87)	2·50	
	o. Booklet pane. No. X900 × 10 with margins all round (4.8.87)	5·00	
X901	13p. pale chestnut (1 side band) (3.9.84)	70	70
	l. Booklet pane. No. X901×4 and X909×6 (13p. values at left)	5·00	
	la. Ditto. 13p. values at right	5·00	
	m. Booklet pane. No. X901×6 with margins all round (4.9.84)	2·50	
	n. Booklet pane. No. X901 and X912×5 (20.10.86)	6·00	
	na. Ditto. but with vert edges of pane imperf (29.9.87)	5·00	
X902	14p. grey-blue (2 bands) (26.1.81)	1·25	75
X903	14p. deep blue (1 centre band) (23.8.88)	70	50
	a. Imperf (pair)	£275	
	l. Booklet pane. No. X903 × 4 with margins all round	4·50	
	m. Booklet pane. No. X903 × 10 with margins all round	5·00	
	n. Booklet pane. No. X903 × 4 with horiz edges of pane imperf (11.10.88)	7·00	
	p. Booklet pane. No. X903 × 10 with horiz edges of pane imperf (11.10.88)	9·00	
	q. Booklet pane. No. X903×4 with three edges of pane imperf (24.1.89)	25·00	
X904	14p. deep blue (1 side band) (5.9.88)	3·50	3·50
	l. Booklet pane. No. X904 and X914×2 plus label	4·00	
	m. Booklet pane. No. X904×2 and X914×4 with vert edges of pane imperf	6·00	
X905	15p. bright blue (1 centre band) (26.9.89)	90	60
	a. Imperf (pair)	£450	
X906	15p. bright blue (1 side band) (2.10.89)	3·00	3·00
	l. Booklet pane. No. X906×2 and X916 plus label	8·00	
	m. Booklet pane. No. X906, X916, X922, 1446, 1448, 1468, 1470 and 1472 plus label with margins all round (20.3.90)	18·00	
X907	15½p. pale violet (2 bands) (1.2.82)	75	75
	l. Booklet pane. No. X907×6 with margins all round (19.5.82)	3·00	
	m. Booklet pane. No. X907×9 with margins all round (19.5.82)	4·00	
X908	16p. olive-drab (5.4.83)	1·50	1·50
X909	17p. grey-blue (2 bands) (3.9.84)	1·00	1·00
	l. Booklet pane. No. X909×3 plus label (4.11.85)	3·00	
X910	17p. deep blue (1 centre band) (4.9.90)	1·25	1·25
	a. Imperf (pair)		
X911	17p. deep blue (1 side band) (4.9.90)	1·75	1·75
	l. Booklet pane. No. X911×3 plus label	4·50	
	m. Booklet pane. No. X911×2, X917×3 plus 3 labels with vert edges of pane imperf	4·00	
X912	18p. deep olive-grey (2 bands) (20.10.86)	1·00	1·00
X913	18p. bright green (1 centre band) (10.9.91)	75	50
	a. Imperf (pair)	£375	
X914	19p. bright orange-red (2 bands) (5.9.88)	1·75	1·75
X915	20p. dull purple (2 bands) (25.2.76)	1·50	1·00
X916	20p. brownish black (2 bands) (2.10.89)	1·75	2·00
X917	20p. bright orange-red (2 bands) (4.9.90)	1·75	1·75
X917a	25p. rose-red (2 bands) (6.2.96)	2·00	2·00
X918	26p. rosine (Type I) (2 bands) (3.3.87)	8·00	8·00
X919	31p. purple (2 bands) (18.3.86)	12·00	12·00
X920	34p. ochre-brown (2 bands) (8.1.85)	8·00	
X921	50p. ochre-brown (2 bands) (2.2.77)	2·75	90
X922	50p. ochre (2 bands) (20.3.90)	5·50	5·50

(b) Photo Harrison. On phosphorised paper. P 15×14.

X924	½p. turquoise-blue (10.12.80)	10	10
	a. Imperf (pair)	£130	
	l. Coil strip. No. X924 and X932×3 (30.12.81)	1·25	
X925	1p. crimson (12.12.79)	20	20
	a. Imperf (pair)	£750	
	l. Coil strip. No. X925 and X932×3 (14.8.84)	1·00	
	m. Booklet pane. No. X925 and X969, each × 2 (10.9.91)	2·00	
X926	2p. myrtle-green (face value as T **367**) (12.12.79)	20	20
	a. Imperf (pair)	£900	
X927	2p. deep green (face value as T **367a**) (26.7.88)	20	20
	a. Imperf (pair)	£1000	
	l. Booklet pane. No. X927×2 and X969×4 plus 2 labels with vert edges of pane imperf (10.9.91)	4·00	
X928	2p. myrtle-green (face value as T **367a**) (5.9.88)	2·50	2·50
	l. Coil strip. No. X928 and X932×3	2·75	
X929	2½p. rose-red (14.1.81)	30	30
	l. Coil strip. No. X929 and X930×3 (6.81)	1·50	
X930	3p. bright magenta (Type I) (22.10.80)	30	30
	a. Imperf (horiz pair)	£1000	
	b. Booklet pane. No. X930, X931×2 and X949×6 with margins all round (14.9.83)	4·50	
	c. Type II (10.10.89)	1·25	60
	cl. Coil strip. No. X930c and X933×3	2·75	
X931	3½p. purple-brown (30.3.83)	60	60
X932	4p. greenish blue (30.12.81)	70	70

X933	4p. new blue (26.7.88)	30	30
	a. Imperf (pair)	£1500	
	l. Coil strip. No. X933×3 and X935 (27.11.90)	1·10	
	m. Coil strip. No. X933 and X935, each ×2 (1.10.91)	90	
	n. Coil strip. No. X933 and X935×3 (31.1.95)	40	
X934	5p. pale violet (10.10.79)	40	30
X935	5p. dull red-brown (26.7.88)	30	30
	a. Imperf (pair)	£2000	
X936	6p. yellow-olive (10.9.91)	30	30
X937	7p. brownish red (29.10.85)	2·00	2·00
X938	8p. yellowish green (24.3.76)	60	60
X939	10p. orange-brown (Type I) (11.79)	50	30
X940	10p. dull orange (Type II) (4.9.90)	50	40
X941	11p. brown-red (27.8.80)	1·00	1·00
X942	11½p. ochre-brown (15.8.79)	60	50
X943	12p. yellowish green (30.1.80)	60	60
X944	13p. olive-grey (15.8.79)	70	50
X945	13½p. purple-brown (30.1.80)	70	70
X946	14p. grey-blue (14.1.81)	85	60
X947	15p. ultramarine (15.8.79)	85	85
X948	15½p. pale violet (14.1.81)	85	50
	a. Imperf (pair)	£250	
X949	16p. olive-drab (30.3.83)	70	40
	a. Imperf (pair)	£175	
	l. Booklet pane. No. X949×9 with margins all round (14.9.83)	3·75	
X950	16½p. pale chestnut (27.1.82)	1·00	1·00
X951	17p. light emerald (30.1.80)	90	60
X952	17p. grey-blue (30.3.83)	80	60
	a. Imperf (pair)	£275	
	l. Booklet pane. No. X952×6 with margins all round (4.9.84)	3·00	
	m. Booklet pane. No. X952×9 with margins all round (8.1.85)	4·50	
X953	17½p. pale chestnut (30.1.80)	1·00	1·00
X954	18p. deep violet (14.1.81)	1·00	1·00
X955	18p. deep olive-grey (28.8.84)	1·00	85
	a. Imperf (pair)	£130	
	l. Booklet pane. No. X955×9 with margins all round (3.3.87)	4·50	
	m. Booklet pane. No. X955×4 with margins all round (4.8.87)	3·00	
	n. Booklet pane. No. X955×10 with margins all round (4.8.87)	8·00	
X956	19p. bright orange-red (23.8.88)	1·00	90
	a. Imperf (pair)	£400	
	l. Booklet pane. No. X956×4 with margins all round	6·00	
	m. Booklet pane. No. X956×10 with margins all round	10·00	
	n. Booklet pane. No. X956×4 with horiz edges of pane imperf (11.10.88)	7·00	
	o. Booklet pane. No. X956×10 with horiz edges of pane imperf (11.10.88)	12·00	
	q. Booklet pane. No. X956×4 with three edges of pane imperf (24.1.89)	25·00	
X957	19½p. olive-grey (27.1.82)	1·50	1·50
X958	20p. dull purple (10.10.79)	1·00	40
X959	20p. turquoise-green (23.8.88)	1·25	85
X960	20p. brownish black (26.9.89)	1·25	75
	a. Imperf (pair)	£650	
	l. Booklet pane. No. X960×5 plus label with vert edges of pane imperf (2.10.89)	6·00	
X961	20½p. ultramarine (30.3.83)	1·60	1·40
	a. Imperf (pair)	£1100	
X962	22p. blue (22.10.80)	1·10	70
	a. Imperf (pair)	£200	
X963	22p. yellow-green (28.8.84)	1·10	80
	a. Imperf (horiz pair)	£1200	
X964	22p. bright orange-red (4.9.90)	1·00	70
X965	23p. brown-red (30.3.83)	1·25	80
	a. Imperf (horiz pair)	£900	
X966	23p. bright green (23.8.88)	1·25	70
X967	24p. violet (28.8.84)	1·60	1·25
X968	24p. Indian red (26.9.89)	2·00	1·25
	a. Imperf (horiz pair)	£2250	
X969	24p. chestnut (10.9.91)	1·00	60
	a. Imperf (pair)	£200	
X970	24p. purple (14.1.81)	1·25	1·25
X971	26p. rosine (Type I) (27.1.82)	1·25	50
	a. Imperf (pair)		
	b. Type II (4.8.87)	4·00	4·00
	bl. Booklet pane. No. X971b×4 with margins all round	18·00	
X972	26p. drab (4.9.90)	1·25	1·25
X973	27p. chestnut (23.8.88)	1·40	1·40
	l. Booklet pane. No. X973×4 with margins all round	11·00	
	m. Booklet pane. No. X973×4 with horiz edges of pane imperf (11.10.88)	25·00	
X974	27p. violet (4.9.90)	1·25	1·25
X975	28p. deep violet (30.3.83)	1·40	1·40
	a. Imperf (pair)	£1100	
X976	28p. ochre (23.8.88)	1·40	1·40
X977	28p. deep bluish grey (10.9.91)	1·25	1·25
	a. Imperf (pair)	£1500	
X978	29p. ochre-brown (27.1.82)	2·25	1·50
X979	29p. deep mauve (26.9.89)	2·25	1·50
X980	30p. deep olive-grey (26.9.89)	1·25	1·50
X981	31p. purple (30.3.83)	1·50	1·50
	a. Imperf (pair)	£1000	
X982	31p. ultramarine (4.9.90)	1·50	1·50
X983	32p. greenish blue (23.8.88)	1·75	1·75
	a. Imperf (pair)	£1000	
X984	33p. light emerald (4.9.90)	1·50	1·50
X985	34p. ochre-brown (28.8.84)	1·75	1·75
X986	34p. deep bluish grey (26.9.89)	2·00	1·75
X987	34p. deep mauve (10.9.91)	1·50	1·50
X988	35p. sepia (23.8.88)	1·75	1·50
	a. Imperf (pair)	£1000	
X989	35p. yellow (10.9.91)	1·50	1·25
X990	37p. rosine (26.9.89)	2·00	2·00
X991	39p. bright mauve (10.9.91)	1·50	1·50

(c) Photo Harrison. On ordinary paper. P 15×14

X992	50p. ochre-brown (21.5.80)	2·00	1·00
	a. Imperf (pair)	£600	
X993	75p. grey-black (face value as T **367a**) (26.7.88)	3·00	3·00

(d) Photo Harrison. On ordinary or phosphorised paper.
P 15×14

X994	50p. ochre (13.3.90)		2·00	90
	a. Imperf (pair)		£1000	

(e) Litho J.W. P 14

X996	4p. greenish blue (2 phosphor bands) (30.1.80)		30	40
X997	4p. greenish blue (phosphorised paper) (11.81)		50	30
X998	20p. dull pur (2 phosphor bands) (21.5.80)		1·50	70
X999	20p. dull pur (phosphorised paper) (11.81)		2·00	70

(f) Litho Questa. P 14 (No. X1000, X1003/4 and X1023) or 15×14 (others)

X1000	2p. emerald-green (face value as T **367**) (phosphorised paper) (21.5.80)		30	30
	a. Perf 15×14 (10.7.84)		40	30
X1001	2p. bright green & dp green (face value as T **367**a) (phosphorised paper) (23.2.88)		1·25	70
X1002	4p. greenish blue (phosphorised paper) (13.5.86)		80	80
X1003	5p. lt violet (phosphorised paper) (21.5.80)		50	30
X1004	5p. claret (phosphorised paper) (27.1.82)		60	30
	a. Perf 15×14 (21.2.84)		70	50
X1005	13p. pale chestnut (1 centre band) (9.2.88)		90	90
	l. Booklet pane. No. X1005×6 with margins all round		3·50	
X1006	13p. pale chestnut (1 side band) (9.2.88)		1·25	1·25
	l. Booklet pane. No. X1006×6, X1010, X1015 and X1021 with margins all round		22·00	
X1007	14p. deep blue (1 centre band) (11.10.88)		2·00	2·00
X1008	17p. deep blue (1 centre band) (19.3.91)		1·00	1·00
	l. Booklet pane. No. X1008×6 with margins all round		3·50	
X1009	18p. deep olive-grey (phosphorised paper) (9.2.88)		1·00	1·00
	l. Booklet pane. No. X1009×9 with margins all round		4·50	
	m. Booklet pane. No. X1009×6 with margins all round		3·00	
X1010	18p. dp ol-grey (2 phosphor bands) (9.2.88)		6·00	6·00
X1011	18p. bright green (1 centre band) (27.10.92)		1·50	1·50
	l. Booklet pane. No. X1011×6 with margins all round		7·50	
X1012	18p. bright green (1 side band) (27.10.92)		2·00	2·00
	l. Booklet pane X1012×2, X1018×2, X1022×2, 1451a, 1514a and central label with margins all round		10·00	
	m. Booklet pane. Nos. X1012, X1020, X1022 and 1451a, each × 2, and central label with margins all round (10.8.93)		11·00	
X1013	19p. brt orange-red (phosphorised paper) (11.10.88)		2·25	2·25
X1014	20p. dull pur (phosphorised paper) (13.5.86)		1·75	1·75
X1015	22p. yellow-grn (2 phosphor bands) (9.2.88)		9·00	9·00
X1016	22p. bright orange-red (phosphorised paper) (19.3.91)		1·25	1·25
	l. Booklet pane. No. X1016×9 with margins all round		5·50	
	m. Booklet pane. No. X1016×6, X1019×2 and central label with margins all round		8·00	
X1017	24p. chestnut (phosphorised paper) (27.10.92)		1·50	1·50
	l. Booklet pane. No. X1017×6 with margins all round		6·00	
X1018	24p. chestnut (2 bands) (27.10.92)		1·75	1·75
X1019	33p. lt emer (phosphorised paper) (19.3.91)		2·50	2·50
X1020	33p. lt emer (2 phosphor bands) (25.2.92)		1·50	1·50
X1021	34p. ochre-brn (2 phosphor bands) (9.2.88)		8·00	8·00
X1022	39p. bright mauve (2 bands) (27.10.92)		2·25	2·25
X1023	75p. black (face value as T **367**) (ordinary paper) (1.80)		4·00	2·50
	a. Perf 15×14 (21.2.84)		4·50	4·00
X1024	75p. brownish grey and black (face value as T **367**a) (ordinary paper) (23.2.88)		10·00	9·00

(g) Litho Walsall. P 14

X1050	2p. dp green (phosphorised paper) (9.2.93)		1·25	1·25
	l. Booklet pane. No. X1050×2 and X1053×4 plus 2 labels with vert edges of the pane imperf		4·00	
X1051	14p. deep blue (1 side band) (25.4.89)		3·50	3·50
	l. Booklet pane. No. X1051×2 and X1052×4 with vert edges of pane imperf		10·00	
X1052	19p. bright orange-red (2 phosphor bands) (25.4.89)		2·25	2·25
X1053	24p. chestnut (phosphorised paper) (9.2.93)		1·50	1·50
X1054	29p. dp mauve (2 phosphor bands) (2.10.89)		5·50	5·50
	l. Booklet pane. No. X1054×4 with three edges of pane imperf		20·00	
X1055	29p. dp mve (phosphorised paper) (17.4.90)		6·50	6·50
	l. Booklet pane. No. X1055×4 with three edges of pane imperf		24·00	
X1056	31p. ultram (phosphorised paper) (17.9.90)		2·25	2·25
	l. Booklet pane. No. X1056×4 with horiz edges of pane imperf		8·50	
X1057	33p. lt emer (phosphorised paper) (16.9.91)		1·75	1·75
	l. Booklet pane. No. X1057×4 with horiz edges of pane imperf		8·50	
X1058	39p. brt mve (phosphorised paper) (16.9.91)		2·25	2·25
	l. Booklet pane. No. X1058×4 with horiz edges of pane imperf		8·50	

*See footnote after No. 744.
†These come from sheets with gum arabic.
Nos. X842, X847, X852, X854, X857, X860, X862/4, X867, X873, X876, X880, X886b, X889, X894/5, X897, X899, X901/2, X904, X906/9, X911/12, X914, X916/20, X922, X971b, X1005/13, X1015/22 and X1050/8 come from booklets; Nos. X843 and X845 come from booklets or coils, Nos. X917a, X928 and X932 come from coils: Nos. X852, X864, X873, X876, X880, X889, X894, X897, X899, X901, X911 and X1006 were each issued with the phosphor band at the right or left from the same stamp booklet, usually in equal proportions. Nos. X847, X906 and X1012 also exist with phosphor band at the left or right, but these come from different booklets.
In addition to booklet pane No. X1012m, No. X1020 also comes from the *se-tenant* pane in the Wales £6 booklet which is listed under No. W49a in the Wales Regional Section.
Nos. X844a/b come from a strip of eight of the vertical coil. It comprises two normals, one imperforate at sides and bottom, one completely imperforate, one imperforate at top, left and bottom*

and partly perforated at right due to the bottom stamps being perforated twice. No. X844b is also known from another strip having one stamp imperforate at sides and bottom.

Nos. X848b/c come from the same sheet, the latter having perforations at the foot of the stamps only.

Multi-value coil strips Nos. X924l, X925l, X928l, X929l, X930cl and X933l/n were produced by the Post Office for a large direct mail marketing firm. Use of the first coil strip, No. X929l, is known from June 1981. From 2 September 1981 No. X929l was available from the Philatelic Bureau, Edinburgh and, subsequently, from a number of other Post Office counters.

Later coil stamps were sold at the Philatelic Bureau and Post Office philatelic counters.

PANES OF SIX FROM STITCHED BOOKLETS. Nos. X841m, X851l/m and X855l include one or two printed labels showing commercial advertisements. These were originally perforated on all four sides, but from the August 1971 editions of the 25p. and 30p. booklets and December 1971 edition of the 50p. the line of perforations between the label and the binding margin was omitted. Similar panes, with the line of perforations omitted, exist for the 3p., 3½p. and 4½p. values (Nos. X856, X858 and X865), but these are outside the scope of this listing as the labels are blank.

PART-PERFORATED SHEETS. Since the introduction of the "Jumelle" press in 1972 a number of part-perforated sheets, both definitives and commemoratives, have been discovered. It is believed that these occur when the operation of the press is interrupted. Such sheets invariably show a number of "blind" perforations, where the pins have failed to cut the paper. Our listings of imperforate errors from these sheets are for pairs showing no trace whatsoever of the perforations. Examples showing "blind" perforations are outside the scope of this catalogue.

In cases where perforation varieties affect *se-tenant* stamps fuller descriptions will be found in Vol. 4 of the *G.B. Specialised Catalogue*.

WHITE PAPER. From 1972 printings appeared on fluorescent white paper giving a stronger chalk reaction than the original ordinary cream paper.

GUM ARABIC. The following exist with gum arabic as well as PVA gum (with or without added dextrin): Nos. X841, X841n, X851, X855, X856, X861 and X870. See notes after No. 722.

DEXTRIN GUM. From 1973 printings in photogravure appeared with PVA gum to which dextrin had been added. As the resulting gum was virtually colourless bluish green colouring matter was added to distinguish it from the previous PVA gum. Questa printings in lithography from 1988 onwards used PVA gum with dextrin, but did not show the colouring agent.

"ALL-OVER" PHOSPHOR. To improve mechanised handling most commemoratives from the 1972 Royal Silver Wedding 3p. value to the 1979 Rowland Hill Death Centenary set had the phosphor applied by printing cylinder across the entire surface of the stamp, giving a matt effect. Printing of the 1, 2 and 10p. definitives, released in October 1979, also had "all-over" phosphor, but these were purely a temporary expedient pending the adoption of phosphorised paper. Nos. X883, X890 and X921 have been discovered with "all over" phosphor in addition to the normal phosphor bands. These error are outside the scope of this catalogue.

PHOSPHORISED PAPER. Following the experiments on Nos. 743c and 829 a printing of the 4½p. definitive was issued on 13 November 1974, which had, in addition to the normal phosphor bands, phosphor included in the paper coating. Because of difficulties in identifying the phosphorised paper with the naked eye this printing is not listed separately in this catalogue.

No. X938 was the first value printed on phosphorised paper without phosphor bands and was a further experiment issue to test the efficacy of this system. From 15 August 1979 phosphorised paper was accepted for use generally, the paper replacing phosphor bands on values other than those required in the second-class rate.

Stamps on phosphorised paper show a shiny surface instead of the matt areas of those printed with phosphor bands.

VARNISH COATING. Nos. X841 and X883 exist with and without a varnish coating. This cannot easily be detected without the use of an ultra-violet lamp as it merely reduces the fluorescent paper reaction.

POSTAL FORGERIES. In mid-1993 a number of postal forgeries of the 24p. chestnut were detected in the London area. These forgeries, produced by lithography, can be identified by the lack of phosphor in the paper, screening dots across the face value and by the perforations which were applied by a line machine gauging 11.

UNDERPRINTS. From 1982 various values appeared with underprints, printed on the reverse, in blue, over the gum. These were usually from special stamp booklets, sold at a discount by the Post Office, but in 1985 surplus stocks of such underprinted paper were used for other purposes.

The following Decimal Machin stamps exist with underprints:

12p. bright emerald (1 centre band)—double-lined star underprint from sheet printing (also exists without)

12½p. light emerald (1 centre band)—star with central dot underprint from booklet pane X898l

12½p. light emerald (1 centre band)—double-lined star underprint from booklet pane of 20

13p. pale chestnut (1 centre band)—double-lined star underprint from booklet pane of 10 (also exists without)

15½p. pale violet (2 bands)—star with central dot underprint from booklet pane X898l

16p. olive-drab (phosphorised paper)—double-lined D underprint from booklet pane of 10 (also exists without)

17p. grey-blue (2 bands)—double-lined star underprint from booklet pane X909l

17p. grey-blue (phosphorised paper)—double-lined D underprint from booklet pane of 10 (also exists without)

368 "A Mountain Road" (T. P. Flanagan)

369 "Deer's Meadow" (Tom Carr)

370 "Slieve na brock" (Colin Middleton)

(Layout des Stuart Rose)

1971 (16 June). *"Ulster 1971" Paintings. Chalk-surfaced paper. Two phosphor bands.* P 15 × 14.

881	368	3p.	yellow-buff, pale yellow, Venetian red, black, blue and drab	10	10
882	369	7½p.	olive-brown, brownish grey, pale olive-grey, dp bl, cobalt & grey-bl	60	60
		a.	Pale olive-grey omitted* ..	70·00	
883	370	9p.	greenish yellow, orange, grey, lavender-grey, bistre, black, pale ochre-brown, and ochre-brown ..	70	70
		a.	Orange omitted	£1500	
881/3			*Set of 3*	1·25	1·25

A used example of the 3p. has been seen with the Venetian red omitted.

371 John Keats (150th Death Anniv)

372 Thomas Gray (Death Bicentenary)

373 Sir Walter Scott (Birth Bicentenary)

(Des Rosalind Dease. Queen's head printed in gold and then embossed)

1971 (28 July). *Literary Anniversaries. Chalk-surfaced paper. Two phosphor bands.* P 15 × 14.

884	371	3p.	black, gold and greyish blue ..	10	10
		a.	Gold (Queen's head) omitted ..	95·00	
885	372	5p.	black, gold and yellow-olive ..	60	60
		a.	Gold (Queen's head) omitted ..	£175	
886	373	7½p.	black, gold and yellow-brown ..	70	70
884/6			.. .. .. *Set of 3*	1·25	1·25

The 7½p. exists with embossing omitted.

374 Servicemen and Nurse of 1921

375 Roman Centurion

376 Rugby Football, 1871

(Des F. Wegner)

1971 (25 Aug). *British Anniversaries. Events described on stamps. Chalk-surfaced paper. Two phosphor bands.* P 15 × 14.

887	374	3p.	red-orange, grey, deep blue, olive-grn, olive-brn, blk, rosine & vio-bl	10	10
		a.	Deep blue omitted*	£650	
		b.	Red-orange (nurse's cloak) omitted	£300	
		c.	Olive-brown (faces, etc.) omitted	£175	
		d.	Black omitted	£10000	
888	375	7½p.	grey, yellow-brown, vermilion, mauve, grey-black, black, silver, gold and ochre	60	60
		a.	Grey omitted	80·00	
889	376	9p.	new blue, myrtle-green, grey-blk, lemon, olive-brown, mag & yell-ol	70	70
		a.	Olive-brown omitted	£125	
		b.	New blue omitted	£2500	
		c.	Myrtle-green omitted	£2400	
887/9			*Set of 3*	1·25	1·25

*The effect of the missing deep blue is shown on the sailor's uniform, which appears as grey.

Used examples have been seen of the 3p. with grey omitted and of the 9p. with the lemon (jerseys) omitted.

377 Physical Sciences Building, University College of Wales, Aberystwyth

378 Faraday Building, Southampton University

379 Engineering Department, Leicester University

380 Hexagon Restaurant, Essex University

(Des N. Jenkins)

1971 (22 Sept). *British Architecture. Modern University Buildings. Chalk-surfaced paper. Two phosphor bands.* P 15 × 14.

890	377	3p.	olive-brn, ochre, lem, blk & yell-ol	10	10
		a.	Lemon omitted	†	£5000
		b.	Black (windows) omitted ..	£10000	
891	378	5p.	rose, black, chestnut and lilac ..	20	20
892	379	7½p.	ochre, black and purple-brown ..	65	65
893	380	9p.	pale lilac, black, sepia-brn & dp bl	1·00	1·00
		a.	Pale lilac omitted		
890/3			*Set of 4*	1·75	1·75

Mint examples of the 5p. exist with a larger "P" following the face value.

No. 890a is only known used on commercial cover from Wantage.

381 "Dream of the Wise Men"

382 "Adoration of the Magi"

383 "Ride of the Magi"

(Des Clarke-Clements-Hughes design team, from stained-glass windows, Canterbury Cathedral. Queen's head printed in gold and then embossed)

1971 (13 Oct). *Christmas. Ordinary paper. One centre phosphor band (2½p.) or two phosphor bands (others).* P 15 × 14.

894	381	2½p.	new bl, blk, lemon, emer, reddish violet, carm-red, carm-rose & gold	20	10
		a.	Imperf (pair)	£450	
895	382	3p.	black, reddish violet, lemon, new bl, carm-rose, emer, ultram & gold	20	10
		a.	Gold (Queen's head) omitted ..	£500	
		b.	Carmine-rose omitted	£1900	
		c.	Lemon (window panels) omitted	65·00	
		d.	New blue omitted	†	£7000
		e.	Reddish violet (tunics etc) omitted		
896	383	7½p.	black, lilac, lemon, emerald, new blue, rose, green and gold	1·00	1·00
		a.	Gold (Queen's head) omitted ..	90·00	
		b.	Lilac omitted	£425	
		c.	Emerald omitted	£225	
894/6			*Set of 3*	1·25	1·25

All three values are known with the embossing omitted and the 7½p. with embossing double. Used examples of the 3p. have been seen with reddish violet and embossing omitted or with lemon and carmine-rose omitted. A used example of the 7½p. exists with the lemon omitted.

WHITE CHALK-SURFACED PAPER. From No. 897 all issues, with the exception of Nos. 904/8, were printed on fluorescent white paper, giving a stronger chalk reaction than the original cream paper.

384 Sir James Clark Ross

385 Sir Martin Frobisher

386 Henry Hudson

387 Capt. Scott

(Des Marjorie Saynor. Queen's head printed in gold and then embossed)

1972 (16 Feb). *British Polar Explorers. Two phosphor bands.* P 14 × 15.

897	384	3p.	yellow-brown, indigo, slate-black, flesh, lemon, rose, brt blue & gold	10	10
		a.	Gold (Queen's head) omitted ..	£650	
		b.	Slate-black (hair, etc.) omitted ..	£2250	
		c.	Lemon omitted	£2000	
898	385	5p.	salmon, flesh, purple-brown, ochre, black and gold	20	20
		a.	Gold (Queen's head) omitted ..	£100	
899	386	7½p.	reddish violet, blue, deep slate, yellow-brown, buff, black and gold	65	65
		a.	Gold (Queen's head) omitted ..	£225	

900 387 9p. dull blue, ultramarine, black, greenish yell, pale pink, rose-red & gold 1·00 1·00
897/900 . . . . *Set of 4* 1·75 1·75
The 3p. and 5p. are known with embossing omitted and the 3p. also
exists with gold and embossing omitted. An example of the 3p. is
known used on piece with the flesh colour omitted.

388 Statuette of Tutankhamun

389 19th-century Coastguard

390 Ralph Vaughan Williams and Score

(Des Rosalind Dease (3p.), F. Wegner (7½p.), C. Abbott (9p.).
Queen's head printed in gold and then embossed (7½p., 9p.))

1972 (26 Apr). *General Anniversaries. Events described on stamps.
Two phosphor bands. P* 15 × 14.
901 388 3p. black, grey, gold, dull bistre-brown,
blackish brn, pale stone & lt brn 10 10
902 389 7½p. pale yellow, new blue, slate-blue,
violet-blue, slate and gold 60 60
903 390 9p. bistre-brown, black, sage-green, dp
slate, yellow-ochre, brown & gold 70 70
a. Gold (Queen's head) omitted . . £1300
b. Brown (facial features) omitted . . £750
c. Deep slate omitted
901/3 . . . . *Set of 3* 1·25 1·25
The 7½p. and 9p. exist with embossing omitted.

391 St. Andrew's,
Greensted-juxta-Ongar, Essex 392 All Saints, Earls Barton,
Northants

393 St. Andrew's,
Letheringsett, Norfolk 394 St. Andrew's,
Helpringham, Lincs

395 St. Mary the Virgin, Huish
Episcopi, Somerset

(Des R. Maddox. Queen's head printed in gold and then embossed)

1972 (21 June). *British Architecture. Village Churches. Ordinary
paper. Two phosphor bands. P* 14 × 15.
904 391 3p. violet-blue, black, lt yellow-olive,
emerald-green, orange-verm & gold 10 10
a. Gold (Queen's head) omitted 80·00
905 392 4p. deep yellow-olive, black, emerald,
violet-blue, orge-vermilion & gold 20 20
a. Gold (Queen's head) omitted . . £2750
b. Violet-blue omitted . . £125
906 393 5p. deep emerald, black, royal blue, lt
yellow-olive, orange-verm & gold 30 25
a. Gold (Queen's head) omitted . . £160
907 394 7½p. orange-red, black, deep yellow-ol,
royal blue, lt emerald & gold 90 90
908 395 9p. new blue, black, emerald-green, dp
yellow-olive, orange-verm & gold 1·00 1·00
904/8 . . . . *Set of 5* 2·25 2·25
The 3p., 4p., 5p. and 9p. exist with embossing omitted.
An example of the 3p. is known used on piece with the orange-
vermilion omitted.

396 Microphones, 1924–69

397 Horn Loudspeaker

398 T.V. Camera, 1972

399 Oscillator and Spark Transmitter, 1897

(Des D. Gentleman)

1972 (13 Sept). *Broadcasting Anniversaries. 75th Anniv of Marconi
and Kemp's Radio Experiments (9p.), and 50th Anniv of Daily
Broadcasting by the B.B.C. (others). Two phosphor bands. P* 15 × 14.
909 396 3p. pale brown, black, grey, greenish
yellow and brownish slate . . 10 10
a. Greenish yellow (terminals)
omitted £2000
910 397 5p. brownish slate, lake-brown,
salmon, lt brown, black & red-brn 15 20
911 398 7½p. light grey, slate, brownish slate,
magenta and black . . 85 85
a. Brownish slate (Queen's head)
omitted . . . . . . † £2000
912 399 9p. lemon, brown, brownish slate, deep
brownish slate, bluish slate & blk 85 85
a. Brownish slate (Queen's head)
omitted £1600
909/12 . . . . *Set of 4* 1·75 1·75
No. 911a is only known on first day covers posted from the
Philatelic Bureau in Edinburgh.

400 Angel holding Trumpet 401 Angel playing Lute

402 Angel playing Harp

(Des Sally Stiff. Photo and embossed)

1972 (18 Oct). *Christmas. One centre phosphor band (2½p.) or two
phosphor bands (others). P* 14 × 15.
913 400 2½p. cerise, pale reddish brown, yellow-
orange, orange-vermilion, lilac,
gold, red-brown and deep grey . . 10 15
a. Gold omitted £275
c. Deep grey omitted
914 401 3p. ultram, lavender, lt turq-blue, brt
green, gold, red-brown & bluish vio 10 15
a. Red-brown omitted . . £525
b. Bright green omitted . . 75·00
c. Bluish violet omitted . . 80·00
915 402 7½p. deep brown, pale lilac, lt cinnamon,
ochre, gold, red-brn & blackish vio 1·25 1·10
a. Ochre omitted . . . . 60·00
b. Blackish violet (shadow) omitted
913/15 . . . . *Set of 3* 1·25 1·25
All three values exist with embossing omitted.

403 Queen Elizabeth and
Duke of Edinburgh 404 "Europe"

(Des J. Matthews from photo by N. Parkinson)

1972 (20 Nov). *Royal Silver Wedding. "All-over" phosphor (3p.)
or without phosphor (20p.). P* 14 × 15.
I. "*Rembrandt*" Machine
916 403 3p. brownish black, deep blue & silver 25 25
a. Silver omitted . . £325
917 20p. brownish blk, reddish pur & silver 1·00 1·00
II. "*Jumelle*" Machine
918 403 3p. brownish black, deep blue & silver 35 35
The 3p. "JUMELLE" has a lighter shade of the brownish black
than the 3p. "Rembrandt". It also has the brown cylinders less deeply
etched, which can be distinguished in the Duke's face which is
slightly lighter, and in the Queen's hair where the highlights are
sharper.

3p. "REMBRANDT". Cyls. 3A-1B-11C no dot. Sheets of 100 (10 ×
10).
3p. "JUMELLE". Cyls. 1A-1B-3C dot and no dot. Sheets of 100
(two panes 5 × 10, separated by gutter margin).

(Des P. Murdoch)

1973 (3 Jan). *Britain's Entry into European Communities. Two
phosphor bands. P* 14 × 15.
919 404 3p. dull orange, bright rose-red, ultramarine, light lilac and black . . 10 10
920 5p. new blue, bright rose-red, ultramarine, cobalt-blue and black . . 25 50
a. Pair. Nos. 920/1 . . 1·25 1·50
921 5p. light emerald-green, bright rose-red,
ultramarine, cobalt-blue and black 25 50
919/21 . . . . *Set of 3* 1·25 1·00
Nos. 920/1 were printed horizontally *se-tenant* throughout the
sheet.

405 Oak Tree

(Des D. Gentleman)

1973 (28 Feb). *Tree Planting Year. British Trees (1st issue). Two
phosphor bands. P* 15 × 14.
922 405 9p. brownish black, apple-green, deep
olive, sepia, blackish green and
brownish grey 50 50
a. Brownish black (value and inscr)
omitted £425
b. Brownish grey (Queen's head)
omitted £275
See also No. 949.

CHALK-SURFACED PAPER. The following issues are printed on chalk-surfaced paper but where "all-over" phosphor has been applied there is no chalk reaction except in the sheet margins outside the phosphor area.

406 David Livingstone

407 H. M. Stanley

(T **406/7** were printed together, horizontally *se-tenant* within the sheet)

408 Sir Francis Drake

409 Walter Raleigh

410 Charles Sturt

(Des Marjorie Saynor. Queen's head printed in gold and then embossed)

1973 (18 Apr). *British Explorers. "All-over" phosphor.* P 14×15.

923	**406**	3p. orange-yellow, lt orge-brown, grey-black, lt turq-blue, turq-blue & gold		25	20
		a. Pair. Nos. 923/4		1·00	1·25
		b. Gold (Queen's head) omitted		45·00	
		c. Turquoise-blue (background and inscr) omitted		£375	
		d. Light orange-brown omitted		£550	
924	**407**	3p. orange-yellow, lt orge-brown, grey-black, lt turq-blue, turq-blue & gold		25	20
		b. Gold (Queen's head) omitted		45·00	
		c. Turquoise-blue (background and inscr) omitted		£375	
		d. Light orange-brown omitted		£350	
925	**408**	5p. light flesh, chrome-yellow, orange-yellow, sepia, brownish grey, grey-black, violet-blue and gold		20	30
		a. Gold (Queen's head) omitted		£100	
		b. Grey-black omitted		£525	
		c. Sepia omitted		£475	
926	**409**	7½p. light flesh, reddish brown, sepia, ultram, grey-black, brt lilac & gold		20	30
		a. Gold (Queen's head) omitted		£1750	
		b. Ultramarine (eyes) omitted		£2500	
927	**410**	9p. flesh, pale stone, grey-blue, grey-black, brown-grey, Venetian red, brown-red and gold		25	40
		a. Gold (Queen's head) omitted		£100	
		b. Brown-grey printing double .. *from*		£800	
		c. Grey-black omitted		£1100	
		d. Brown-red (rivers on map) omitted		£500	
923/7		*Set of 5*		1·50	1·25

Caution is needed when buying missing gold heads in this issue as they can be removed by using a hard eraser, etc., but this invariably affects the "all-over" phosphor. Genuine examples have the phosphor intact. Used examples off cover cannot be distinguished as much of the phosphor is lost in the course of floating.

In the 5p. value the missing grey-black affects the doublet, which appears as brownish grey, and the lace ruff, which is entirely missing. The missing sepia affects only Drake's hair, which appears much lighter.

The double printing of the brown-grey (cylinder 1F) on the 9p. is a most unusual type of error to occur in a multicoloured photogravure issue. Two sheets are known and it is believed that they stuck to the cylinder and went through a second time. This would result in the following two sheets missing the colour but at the time of going to press this error has not been reported. The second print is slightly askew and more prominent in the top half of the sheets. Examples from the upper part of the sheet showing a clear double impression of the facial features are worth a substantial premium over the price quoted.

The 3p values, the 5p. and the 9p. exist with embossing omitted.

411

412

413

(T **411/13** show sketches of W. G. Grace by Harry Furniss)

(Des E. Ripley. Queen's head printed in gold and then embossed)

1973 (16 May). *County Cricket 1873–1973. "All-over" phosphor.* P 14×15.

928	**411**	3p. black, ochre and gold		10	10
		a. Gold (Queen's head) omitted		£1800	
929	**412**	7½p. black, light sage-green and gold		80	80
930	**413**	9p. black, cobalt and gold		1·00	1·00
928/30		*Set of 3*		1·75	1·75

All three values exist with embossing omitted.

414 "Self-portrait" (Reynolds)

415 "Self-portrait" (Raeburn)

416 "Nelly O'Brien" (Reynolds)

417 "Rev. R. Walker (The Skater)" (Raeburn)

(Des S. Rose. Queen's head printed in gold and then embossed)

1973 (4 July). *British Paintings. 250th Birth Anniv of Sir Joshua Reynolds and 150th Death Anniv of Sir Henry Raeburn. "All-over" phosphor.* P 14×15.

931	**414**	3p. rose, new blue, jet-black, magenta, greenish yellow, blk, ochre & gold		10	10
		a. Gold (Queen's head) omitted		65·00	
932	**415**	5p. cinnamon, greenish yellow, new bl, lt magenta, blk, yellow-olive & gold		20	25
		a. Gold (Queen's head) omitted		80·00	
		b. Greenish yellow omitted		£375	
933	**416**	7½p. greenish yellow, new blue, light magenta, black, cinnamon and gold		55	50
		a. Gold (Queen's head) omitted		80·00	
		b. Cinnamon omitted		£4000	
934	**417**	9p. brownish rose, black, dull rose, pale yell, brownish grey, pale bl & gold		60	60
		b. Brownish rose omitted		40·00	
931/4		*Set of 4*		1·25	1·25

No. 931a is also known with the embossing also omitted or misplaced.

The 5p. and 7½p. are known with the embossing omitted.

The 9p. is known with the embossing and phosphor both omitted.

418 Court Masque Costumes

419 St. Paul's Church, Covent Garden

420 Prince's Lodging, Newmarket

421 Court Masque Stage Scene

T **418/19** and T **420/1** were printed horizontally *se-tenant* within the sheet

(Des Rosalind Dease. Litho and typo B.W.)

1973 (15 Aug). *400th Birth Anniv of Inigo Jones (architect and designer). "All-over" phosphor.* P 15×14.

935	**418**	3p. deep mauve, black and gold		10	15
		a. Pair. Nos. 935/6		35	40
936	**419**	3p. deep brown, black and gold		10	15
937	**420**	5p. blue, black and gold		50	45
		a. Pair. Nos. 937/8		1·50	1·50
938	**421**	5p. grey-olive, black and gold		50	45
935/8		*Set of 4*		1·60	1·10

422 Palace of Westminster seen from Whitehall

423 Palace of Westminster seen from Millbank

(Des R. Downer. Recess and typo B.W.)

1973 (12 Sept). *19th Commonwealth Parliamentary Conference. "All-over" phosphor.* P 15×14.

939	**422**	8p. black, brownish grey and stone		50	60
940	**423**	10p. gold and black		50	40

424 Princess Anne and Capt. Mark Phillips.

(Des C. Clements and E. Hughes from photo by Lord Litchfield)

1973 (14 Nov). *Royal Wedding. "All-over" phosphor.* P 15×14.

941	**424**	3½p. dull violet and silver		10	10
		a. Imperf (horiz pair)		£1000	
942		20p. deep brown and silver		90	90
		a. Silver omitted		£1200	

425

426

427

428

429

T 425/9 depict the carol "Good King Wenceslas" and were printed horizontally *se-tenant* within the sheet.

430 "Good King Wenceslas, the Page and Peasant"

(Des D. Gentleman)

1973 (28 Nov). *Christmas.* One centre phosphor band (3p.) or "all-over" phosphor (3½p.). P 15 × 14.

943	425	3p.	grey-black, violet-blue, slate, light brown, rose-red, rosy mauve, turquoise-grn, salmon-pink & gold	15	15
		a.	Strip of 5. Nos. 943/7	3·00	4·00
		b.	Imperf (horiz strip of 5)	£1250	
944	426	3p.	grey-black, violet-blue, slate, brown, rose-red, rosy mauve, turq-green, salmon-pink and gold	15	15
		a.	Rosy mauve omitted	£625	
945	427	3p.	grey-black, violet-blue, slate, brown, rose-red, rosy mauve, turq-green, salmon-pink and gold	15	15
		a.	Rosy mauve omitted	£625	
946	428	3p.	grey-black, violet-blue, slate, brown, rose-red, rosy mauve, turq-green, salmon-pink and gold	15	15
		a.	Rosy mauve omitted	£625	
947	429	3p.	grey-black, violet-blue, slate, brown, rose-red, rosy mauve, turq-green, salmon-pink and gold	15	15
		a.	Rosy mauve omitted	£625	
948	430	3½p.	salmon-pink, grey-black, red-brown, blue, turquoise-green, bright rose-red, rosy mauve, lavender-grey and gold	15	15
		a.	Imperf (pair)	£425	
		b.	Grey-black (value and inscr, etc) omitted	80·00	
		c.	Salmon-pink omitted	75·00	
		d.	Blue (leg, robes) omitted	£140	
		e.	Rosy mauve (robe at right) omitted	85·00	
		f.	Blue and rosy mauve omitted	£275	
		g.	Bright rose-red (King's robe) omitted	80·00	
		h.	Red-brown (logs, basket, etc) omitted		
		i.	Turquoise-green (leg, robe, etc) omitted	£2000	
		j.	Gold (background) omitted	†	£750
943/8			*Set of 6*	3·00	80

Examples of No. 948j are only known used on cover from Gloucester. The 3½p. has also been seen with the lavender-grey omitted used on piece.

The 3p. and 3½p. are normally with PVA gum with added dextrin, but the 3½p. also exists with normal PVA gum and 3p. with gum arabic.

431 Horse Chestnut

(Des. D. Gentleman)

1974 (27 Feb). *British Trees* (*2nd issue*). "All-over" phosphor. P 15 × 14.

949	431	10p.	light emerald, bright green, greenish yellow, brown-olive, black and brownish grey	50	50

432 First Motor Fire-engine, 1904

---

433 Prize-winning Fire-engine, 1863

434 First Steam Fire-engine, 1830

435 Fire-engine, 1766

(Des D. Gentleman)

1974 (24 Apr). *Bicentenary of the Fire Prevention (Metropolis) Act.* "All-over" phosphor. P 15 × 14.

950	432	3½p.	grey-black, orange-yellow, greenish yellow, dull rose, ochre and grey	10	10
		a.	Imperf (pair)	£825	
951	433	5½p.	greenish yellow, deep rosy magenta, orange-yellow, light emerald, grey-black and grey	35	35
952	434	8p.	greenish yellow, light blue-green, light greenish blue, light chestnut, grey-black and grey	45	45
953	435	10p.	grey-black, pale reddish brown, lt brown, orange-yellow and grey	50	50
950/3			*Set of 4*	1·25	1·25

The 3½p. exists with ordinary PVA gum.

436 P & O Packet, *Peninsular*, 1888

437 Farman H.F.III Biplane, 1911

438 Airmail-blue Van and Postbox, 1930

439 Imperial Airways Short S.21 Flying Boat *Maia*, 1937

(Des Rosalind Dease)

1974 (12 June). *Centenary of Universal Postal Union.* "All-over" phosphor. P 15 × 14.

954	436	3½p.	deep brownish grey, bright mauve, grey-black and gold	10	10
955	437	5½p.	pale orge, lt emer, grey-blk & gold	30	35
956	438	8p.	cobalt, brown, grey-black and gold	40	45
957	439	10p.	deep brownish grey, orange, grey-black and gold	60	50
954/7			*Set of 4*	1·25	1·25

---

440 Robert the Bruce   441 Owain Glyndŵr

442 Henry the Fifth   443 The Black Prince

(Des F. Wegner)

1974 (10 July). *Medieval Warriors.* "All-over" phosphor. P 15 × 14.

958	440	4½p.	greenish yellow, vermilion, slate-blue, red-brown, reddish brown, lilac-grey and gold	10	10
959	441	5½p.	lemon, vermilion, slate-blue red-brn, reddish brn, ol-drab & gold	20	30
960	442	8p.	deep grey, vermilion, greenish yellow, new blue, red-brown, deep cinnamon and gold	50	50
961	443	10p.	vermilion, greenish yellow, new blue, red-brown, reddish brown, light blue and gold	55	50
958/61			*Set of 4*	1·25	1·25

444 Churchill in Royal Yacht Squadron Uniform   445 Prime Minister, 1940

446 Secretary for War and Air, 1919   447 War Correspondent, South Africa, 1899

(Des C. Clements and E. Hughes)

1974 (9 Oct). *Birth Centenary of Sir Winston Churchill.* "All-over" phosphor. P 14 × 15.

962	444	4½p.	Prussian blue, pale turquoise-green and silver	15	15
963	445	5½p.	sepia, brownish grey and silver	30	25
964	446	8p.	crimson, light claret and silver	60	60
965	447	10p.	light brown, stone and silver	65	50
962/5			*Set of 4*	1·50	1·50

448 "Adoration of the Magi" (York Minster, *circa* 1355)

449 "The Nativity" (St. Helen's Church, Norwich, *circa* 1480)

450 "Virgin and Child" (Ottery St. Mary Church, *circa* 1350)

451 "Virgin and Child" (Worcester Cathedral, *circa* 1224)

(Des Peter Hatch Partnership)

1974 (27 Nov). *Christmas. Church Roof Bosses. One phosphor band (3½p.) or "all-over" phosphor (others). P 15 × 14.*

966	448	3½p. gold, light new blue, light brown, grey-black and light stone		10	10
		a. Light stone (background shading) omitted		£10000	
967	449	4½p. gold, yellow-orange, rose-red, light brown, grey-black, & lt new blue		10	10
968	450	8p. blue, gold, light brown, rose-red, dull green and grey-black		55	55
969	451	10p. gold, dull rose, grey-black, light new blue, pale cinnamon and light brown		65	65
966/9		*Set of 4*		1·25	1·25

The phosphor band on the 3½p. was first applied down the centre of the stamp but during the printing this was deliberately placed to the right between the roof boss and the value; however, intermediate positions, due to shifts, are known.

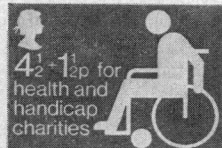

452 Invalid in Wheelchair

(Des P. Sharland)

1975 (22 Jan). *Health and Handicap Funds. "All-over" phosphor. P 15 × 14.*

970	452	4½p. + 1½p. azure and grey-blue		35	35

453 "Peace—Burial at Sea"

454 "Snowstorm—Steamer off a Harbour's Mouth"

455 "The Arsenal, Venice"

456 "St. Laurent"

(Des S. Rose)

1975 (19 Feb). *Birth Bicentenary of J. M. W. Turner (painter). "All-over" phosphor. P 15 × 14.*

971	453	4½p. grey-blk, salmon, stone, bl & grey		10	10
972	454	5½p. cobalt, greenish yellow, light yellow-brown, grey-black and rose		20	20
973	455	8p. pale yellow-orange, greenish yellow, rose, cobalt and grey-black		50	50
974	456	10p. deep blue, light yellow-ochre, light brown, deep cobalt and grey-black		60	60
971/4		*Set of 4*		1·25	1·25

457 Charlotte Square, Edinburgh

458 The Rows, Chester

T **457/8** were printed horizontally *se-tenant* within the sheet.

459 Royal Observatory, Greenwich

460 St. George's Chapel, Windsor

461 National Theatre, London

(Des P. Gauld)

1975 (23 Apr). *European Architectural Heritage Year. "All-over" phosphor. P 15 × 14.*

975	457	7p. greenish yellow, bright orange, grey-black, red-brown, new blue, lavender and gold		50	55
		a. Pair. Nos. 975/6		1·25	1·25
976	458	7p. grey-black, greenish yellow, new blue, brt orange, red-brown & gold		50	55
977	459	8p. magenta, deep slate, pale magenta, lt yellow-olive, grey-black & gold		25	25
978	460	10p. bistre-brown, greenish yellow, deep slate, emer-green, grey-blk & gold		25	25
979	461	12p. grey-blk, new bl, pale mag & gold		25	35
975/9		*Set of 5*		1·75	1·50

462 Sailing Dinghies

463 Racing Keel Yachts

464 Cruising Yachts

465 Multihulls

(Des A. Restall. Recess and photo)

1975 (11 June). *Sailing. "All-over" phosphor. P 15 × 14.*

980	462	7p. black, bluish violet, scarlet, orange-vermilion, orange and gold		20	20
981	463	8p. black, orge-verm, orange, lavender, brt mauve, brt bl, dp ultram & gold		35	35
		a. Black omitted		60·00	
982	464	10p. black, orange, bluish emerald, light olive-drab, chocolate and gold		40	40
983	465	12p. black, ultramarine, turquoise-blue, rose, grey, steel-blue and gold		45	45
980/3				1·25	1·25

On No. 981a the recess-printed black colour is completely omitted.

466 Stephenson's *Locomotion*, 1825

467 *Abbotsford*, 1876

468 *Caerphilly Castle*, 1923

469 High Speed Train, 1975

(Des B. Craker)

1975 (13 Aug). *150th Anniv of Public Railways. "All-over" phosphor. P 15 × 14.*

984	466	7p. red-brown, grey-black, greenish yellow, grey and silver		30	30
985	467	8p. brown, orange-yellow, vermilion, grey-black, grey and silver		50	50
986	468	10p. emerald-green, grey-black, yellow-orange, vermilion, grey and silver		55	55
987	469	12p. grey-black, pale lemon, vermilion, blue, grey and silver		60	60
984/7		*Set of 4*		1·75	1·75

470 Palace of Westminster

(Des R. Downer)

1975 (3 Sept). *62nd Inter-Parliamentary Union Conference. "All-over" phosphor. P 15 × 14.*

988	470	12p. light new blue, black, brownish grey and gold		50	50

471 Emma and Mr
Woodhouse (*Emma*)

472 Catherine Morland
(*Northanger Abbey*)

473 Mr. Darcy (*Pride
and Prejudice*)

474 Mary and Henry
Crawford
(*Mansfield Park*)

(Des Barbara Brown)

1975 (22 Oct). *Birth Bicentenary of Jane Austen (novelist). "All-over" phosphor. P* 14 × 15.

989	471	8½p.	blue, slate, rose-red, light yellow, dull green, grey-black and gold	20	20
990	472	10p.	slate, bright magenta, grey, light yellow, grey-black and gold	35	35
991	473	11p.	dull blue, pink, olive-sepia, slate, pale greenish yell, grey-blk & gold	40	40
992	474	13p.	bright magenta, light new blue, slate, buff, dull blue-green, grey-black and gold	45	45
989/92			*Set of* 4	1·25	1·25

475 Angels with Harp and Lute

476 Angel with Mandolin

477 Angel with Horn

478 Angel with Trumpet

(Des R. Downer)

1975 (26 Nov). *Christmas. One phosphor band* (6½p.), *phosphor-inked background* (8½p.), *"all-over" phosphor (others). P* 15 × 14.

993	475	6½p.	bluish violet, bright reddish violet, light lavender and gold	20	15
994	476	8½p.	turquoise-green, bright emerald-green, slate, lt turq-green & gold	30	30
995	477	11p.	vermilion, cerise, pink and gold	40	45
996	478	13p.	drab, brn, brt orge, buff & gold	50	50
993/6			*Set of* 4	1·25	1·25

479 Housewife

480 Policeman

481 District Nurse

482 Industrialist

(Des P. Sharland)

1976 (10 Mar). *Telephone Centenary. "All-over" phosphor. P* 15 × 14.

997	479	8½p.	greenish blue, dp rose, black & bl	20	20
		a.	Deep rose (vase and picture frame) omitted	£2000	
998	480	10p.	greenish blue, black & yellow-ol	35	35
999	481	11p.	greenish bl, dp rose, blk & brt mve	40	40
1000	482	13p.	olive-brn, dp rose, blk & orge-red	45	45
997/1000			*Set of* 4	1·25	1·25

483 Hewing Coal (Thomas Hepburn)

484 Machinery (Robert Owen)

485 Chimney Cleaning (Lord Shaftesbury)

486 Hands clutching Prison Bars (Elizabeth Fry)

(Des D. Gentleman)

1976 (28 Apr). *Social Reformers. "All-over" phosphor. P* 15 × 14.

1001	483	8½p.	lavender-grey, grey-black, black and slate-grey	20	20
1002	484	10p.	lavender-grey, grey-black, grey and slate-violet	35	35
1003	485	11p.	black, slate-grey and drab	40	40
1004	486	13p.	slate-grey, black & deep dull grn	45	45
1001/4			*Set of* 4	1·25	1·25

NEW INFORMATION

The editor is always interested to correspond with people who have new information that will improve or correct the Catalogue.

487 Benjamin Franklin (bust by Jean-Jacques Caffieri)

(Des P. Sharland)

1976 (2 June). *Bicentenary of American Revolution. "All-over" phosphor. P* 14 × 15.

1005	487	11p.	pale bistre, slate-violet, pale blue-green, black and gold	50	50

488 "Elizabeth of Glamis"

489 "Grandpa Dickson"

490 "Rosa Mundi"

491 "Sweet Briar"

(Des Kristin Rosenberg)

1976 (30 June). *Centenary of Royal National Rose Society. "All-over" phosphor. P* 14 × 15.

1006	488	8½p.	bright rose-red, greenish yellow, emerald, grey-black and gold	20	20
1007	489	10p.	greenish yellow, bright green, reddish brown, grey-black and gold	35	35
1008	490	11p.	bright magenta, greenish yellow, emerald, grey-blue, grey-black and gold	65	65
1009	491	13p.	rose-pink, lake-brown, yellow-green, pale greenish yellow, grey-black and gold	75	75
		a.	Value omitted*	£20000	
1006/9			*Set of* 4	1·75	1·75

*During repairs to the cylinder the face value on R. 1/9 was temporarily covered with copper. This covering was inadvertently left in place during printing, but the error was discovered before issue and most examples were removed from the sheets. Two mint and one used examples have so far been reported, but only one of the mint remains in private hands.

492 Archdruid

493 Morris Dancing

494 Scots Piper

495 Welsh Harpist

(Des Marjorie Saynor)

1976 (4 Aug). *British Cultural Traditions. "All-over" phosphor. P* 14 × 15.

1010	492	8½p.	yellow, sepia, bright rose, dull ultramarine, black and gold	20	20
1011	493	10p.	dull ultramarine, bright rose-red, sepia, greenish yellow, blk & gold	35	35
1012	494	11p.	bluish green, yellow-brown, yell-orge, blk, brt rose-red & gold	40	40
1013	495	13p.	dull violet-blue, yellow-orange, yell-brn, blk, bluish grn & gold	45	45
1010/13			*Set of* 4	1·25	1·25

The 8½p. and 13p. commemorate the 800th Anniv of the Royal National Eisteddfod.

496 Woodcut from
The Canterbury Tales

497 Extract from
The Tretyse of Love

498 Woodcut from
The Game and Playe of Chesse

499 Early Printing Press

(Des R. Gay. Queen's head printed in gold and then embossed)

1976 (29 Sept). *500th Anniv of British Printing.* "All-over" phosphor. P 14 × 15.

1014	496	8½p.	black, light new blue and gold ..	20	20
1015	497	10p.	black, olive-green and gold ..	35	35
1016	498	11p.	black, brownish grey and gold ..	40	40
1017	499	13p.	chocolate, pale ochre and gold ..	45	45
1014/17	..		.. .. .. *Set of* 4	1·25	1·25

500 Virgin and Child

501 Angel with Crown

502 Angel appearing to Shepherds

503 The Three Kings

(Des Enid Marx)

1976 (24 Nov). *Christmas. English Medieval Embroidery.* One phosphor band (6½p.), "all-over" phosphor (others). P 15 × 14.

1018	500	6½p.	bl, bistre-yell, brn & brt orange	15	15
		a.	Imperf (pair)	£425	
1019	501	8½p.	sage-green, yellow, brown-ochre, chestnut and olive-black	30	30
1020	502	11p.	deep magenta, brown-orange, new blue, black and cinnamon ..	45	45
		a.	Uncoated paper*	65·00	30·00
1021	503	13p.	bright purple, new blue, cinnamon, bronze-green and olive-grey	50	50
1018/21	..		.. .. .. *Set of* 4	1·25	1·25

* See footnote after No. 744.

504 Lawn Tennis

505 Table Tennis

506 Squash

507 Badminton

(Des A. Restall)

1977 (12 Jan). *Racket Sports. Phosphorised paper.* P 15 × 14.

1022	504	8½p.	emer-grn, blk, grey & bluish grn	20	20
		a.	Imperf (horiz pair) ..	£900	
1023	505	10p.	myrtle-green, black, grey-black and deep blue-green ..	35	35
1024	506	11p.	orange, pale yellow, black, slate-black and grey	40	40
1025	507	13p.	brown, grey-black, grey and bright reddish violet	45	45
1022/5	..		.. .. .. *Set of* 4	1·25	1·25

508

(Des after plaster cast by Arnold Machin)

1977 (2 Feb)–**87**. P 14 × 15.

1026	508	£1	brt yellow-green & blackish olive	3·75	40
		a.	Imperf (pair)	£650	
1026b		£1.30,	pale drab and deep greenish blue (3.8.83)	6·00	6·00
1026c		£1.33,	pale mve & grey-blk (28.8.84)	6·50	6·50
1026d		£1.41,	pale drab and deep greenish blue (17.9.85)	7·50	7·50
1026e		£1.50,	pale mauve & grey-blk (2.9.86)	6·00	6·00
1026f		£1.60,	pale drab and deep greenish blue (15.9.87)	6·50	6·50
1027		£2	light emerald and purple-brown ..	6·50	1·25
1028		£5	salmon and chalky blue	16·00	3·00
		a.	Imperf (vert pair)	£2750	
1026/8	..		.. .. .. *Set of* 8	50·00	32·00

509 Steroids—Conformational Analysis

510 Vitamin C—Synthesis

511 Starch—Chromatography

512 Salt—Crystallography

(Des J. Karo)

1977 (2 Mar). *Royal Institute of Chemistry Centenary.* "All-over" phosphor. P 15 × 14.

1029	509	8½p.	rosine, new blue, olive-yellow, brt mauve, yellow-brown, blk & gold	20	20
		a.	Imperf (horiz pair)	£900	
1030	510	10p.	bright orange, rosine, new blue, bright blue, black and gold	40	40
1031	511	11p.	rosine, greenish yellow, new blue, deep violet, black and gold	40	40
1032	512	13p.	new blue, brt green, black & gold	40	40
1029/32	..		.. .. .. *Set of* 4	1·25	1·25

513

514

515

516

T 513/16 differ in the decorations of "ER".

(Des R. Guyatt)

1977 (11 May–15 June). *Silver Jubilee.* "All-over" phosphor. P 15 × 14.

1033	513	8½p.	blackish green, black, silver, olive-grey and pale turquoise-green ..	20	20
		a.	Imperf (pair)	£700	
1034		9p.	maroon, black, silver, olive-grey and lavender (15 June)	30	30
1035	514	10p.	blackish blue, black, silver, olive-grey and ochre	30	30
		a.	Imperf (horiz pair)	£1300	
1036	515	11p.	brown-purple, black, silver, olive-grey and rose-pink	40	40
		a.	Imperf (horiz pair)	£1300	
1037	516	13p.	sepia, black, silver, olive-grey and bistre-yellow	50	50
		a.	Imperf (pair)	£1000	
1033/7	..		.. .. .. *Set of* 5	1·50	1·50

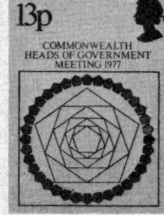

517 "Gathering of Nations"

(Des P. Murdoch. Recess and photo)

1977 (8 June). *Commonwealth Heads of Government Meeting, London.* "All-over" phosphor. P 14 × 15.

1038	517	13p.	black, blackish green, rose-car and silver	50	50

518 Hedgehog   **519** Brown Hare

520 Red Squirrel   **521** Otter

522 Badger

T **518/22** were printed horizontally *se-tenant* within the sheet.

(Des P. Oxenham)

1977 (5 Oct). *British Wildlife. "All-over" phosphor.* P 14 × 15.
1039	**518**	9p. reddish brown, grey-black, pale lemon, brt turq-bl, brt mag & gold	40	20
	a.	Horiz strip of 5. Nos. 1039/43	1·75	2·00
	b.	Imperf (vert pair)	£600	
	c.	Imperf (horiz pair, Nos. 1039/40)	£1000	
1040	**519**	9p. reddish brown, grey-black, pale lemon, brt turq-bl, brt mag & gold	40	20
1041	**520**	9p. reddish brown, grey-black, pale lemon, brt turq-bl, brt mag & gold	40	20
1042	**521**	9p. reddish brown, grey-black, pale lemon, brt turq-bl, brt mag & gold	40	20
1043	**522**	9p. grey-black, reddish brown, pale lemon, brt turq-bl, brt mag & gold	40	20
1039/43		*Set of 5*	1·75	90

523 "Three French Hens, Two Turtle Doves and a Partridge in a Pear Tree"

524 "Six Geese a-laying, Five Gold Rings, Four Colly Birds"

525 "Eight Maids a-milking, Seven Swans a-swimming"

526 "Ten Pipers piping, Nine Drummers drumming"

527 "Twelve Lords a-leaping, Eleven Ladies dancing"

T **523/7** depict the carol "The Twelve Days of Christmas" and were printed horizontally *se-tenant* within the sheet.

528 "A Partridge in a Pear Tree"

(Des D. Gentleman)

1977 (23 Nov). *Christmas. One centre phosphor band* (7p.) *or "all-over" phosphor* (9p.). P 15 × 14.
1044	**523**	7p. slate, grey, bright yellow-green, new blue, rose-red and gold	25	15
	a.	Horiz strip of 5. Nos. 1044/8	1·25	1·50
	ab.	Imperf (strip of 5, Nos. 1044/8)	£1200	
1045	**524**	7p. slate, brt yellow-grn, new bl & gold	25	15
1046	**525**	7p. slate, grey, bright yellow-green, new blue, rose-red and gold	25	15
1047	**526**	7p. slate, grey, bright yellow-green, new blue, rose-red and gold	25	15
1048	**527**	7p. slate, grey, bright yellow-green, new blue, rose-red and gold	25	15
1049	**528**	9p. pale brown, pale orange, brt emer, pale greenish yell, slate-blk & gold	25	15
	a.	Imperf (pair)	£800	
1044/9		*Set of 6*	1·25	80

529 Oil—North Sea Production Platform   **530** Coal—Modern Pithead

531 Natural Gas—Flame Rising from Sea   **532** Electricity—Nuclear Power Station and Uranium Atom

(Des P. Murdoch)

1978 (25 Jan). *Energy Resources. "All-over" phosphor.* P 14 × 15.
1050	**529**	9p. deep brown, orange-vermilion, grey-black, greenish yellow, rose-pink, new blue and silver	25	20
1051	**530**	10½p. light emerald-green, grey-black, red-brown, slate-grey, pale apple-green and silver	25	30
1052	**531**	11p. greenish blue, bright violet, violet-blue, blackish brown, grey-black and silver	30	30
1053	**532**	13p. orange-vermilion, grey-black, deep brown, greenish yellow, light brown, light blue and silver	40	40
1050/3		*Set of 4*	1·10	1·10

533 The Tower of London

534 Holyroodhouse

535 Caernarvon Castle

536 Hampton Court Palace

(Des R. Maddox (stamps), J. Matthews (miniature sheet))

1978 (1 Mar). *British Architecture. Historic Buildings. "All-over" phosphor.* P 15 × 14.
1054	**533**	9p. black, olive-brown, new blue, brt green, lt yellow-olive & rose-red	25	20
1055	**534**	10½p. black, brown-olive, orange-yell, brt grn, lt yell-olive & vio-bl	25	30
1056	**535**	11p. black, brown-olive, violet-blue, brt green, lt yellow-olive & dull bl	30	30
1057	**536**	13p. black, orange-yellow, lake-brown, bright green and light yellow-olive	40	40
1054/7		*Set of 4*	1·10	1·10
MS1058		121×89 mm. Nos. 1054/7 (*sold at* 53½p.)	1·25	1·50
	a.	Imperforate	£4250	
	b.	Lt yellow-olive (Queen's head) omitted	£3500	
	c.	Rose-red (Union Jack on 9p.) omitted	£2500	
	d.	Orange-yellow omitted	£2500	
	e.	New blue (Union Jack on 9p.) omitted	£10000	

The premium on No. MS1058 was used to support the London 1980 International Stamp Exhibition.

537 State Coach   **538** St. Edward's Crown

539 The Sovereign's Orb   **540** Imperial State Crown

(Des J. Matthews)

1978 (31 May). *25th Anniv of Coronation. "All-over" phosphor.* P 14 × 15.
1059	**537**	9p. gold and royal blue	20	20
1060	**538**	10½p. gold and brown-lake	25	30
1061	**539**	11p. gold and deep dull green	30	30
1062	**540**	13p. gold and reddish violet	45	40
1059/62		*Set of 4*	1·10	1·10

541 Shire Horse

542 Shetland Pony

543 Welsh Pony

544 Thoroughbred

(Des P. Oxenham)

1978 (5 July). *Horses. "All-over" phosphor. P* 15 × 14.

1063	541	9p. black, pale reddish brown, grey-black, greenish yellow, light blue, vermilion and gold	20	20
1064	542	10½p. pale chestnut, magenta, brownish grey, greenish yellow, greenish blue, grey-black and gold ..	35	35
1065	543	11p. reddish brown, black, light green, greenish yellow, bistre, grey-black and gold ..	40	40
1066	544	13p. reddish brown, pale reddish brown, emerald, greenish yellow, grey-black and gold ..	45	45
1063/6		*Set of* 4	1·25	1·25

545 "Penny-farthing" and 1884 Safety Bicycle

546 1920 Touring Bicycles

547 Modern Small-wheel Bicycles

548 1978 Road-racers

(Des F. Wegner)

1978 (2 Aug). *Centenaries of Cyclists Touring Club and British Cycling Federation. "All-over" phosphor. P* 15 × 14.

1067	545	9p. brown, deep dull blue, rose-pink, pale olive, grey-black and gold ..	20	20
		a. Imperf (pair)	£375	
1068	546	10½p. olive, pale yellow-orange, orange-vermilion, rose-red, light brown, grey-black and gold	25	25
1069	547	11p. orange-vermilion, greenish blue, light brown, pale greenish yellow, deep grey, grey-black and gold ..	30	30
1070	548	13p. new blue, orange-vermilion, light brn, olive-grey, grey-black & gold	45	45
		a. Imperf (pair)	£800	
1067/70 ..		.. .. *Set of* 4	1·10	1·10

549 Singing Carols round the Christmas Tree

550 The Waits

551 18th-century Carol Singers

552 "The Boar's Head Carol"

(Des Faith Jaques)

1978 (22 Nov). *Christmas. One centre phosphor band* (7p.) *or "all-over" phosphor* (others). *P* 15 × 14.

1071	549	7p. bright green, greenish yellow, magenta, new blue, black and gold	20	20
		a. Imperf (vert pair)	£350	
1072	550	9p. magenta, greenish yellow, new blue, sage-green, black and gold	25	25
		a. Imperf (pair)	£750	
1073	551	11p. magenta, new blue, greenish yellow, yellow-brown, black & gold	30	30
		a. Imperf (horiz pair)	£750	
1074	552	13p. salmon-pink, new blue, greenish yellow, magenta, black and gold	35	35
1071/4		.. .. *Set of* 4	1·10	1·10

553 Old English Sheepdog

554 Welsh Springer Spaniel

555 West Highland Terrier

556 Irish Setter

(Des P. Barrett)

1979 (7 Feb). *Dogs. "All-over" phosphor. P* 15 × 14.

1075	553	9p. grey-black, sepia, turquoise-green, pale greenish yellow, pale greenish blue and grey	20	20
1076	554	10½p. grey-black, lake-brown, apple-green, pale greenish yellow, pale greenish blue and grey ..	40	40
1077	555	11p. grey-black, claret, yellowish grn, pale greenish yell, cobalt & grey	40	40
		a. Imperf (horiz pair)	£1000	
1078	556	13p. grey-black, lake-brown, green, pale greenish yellow & dp turq-bl	40	40
1075/8 ..		.. *Set of* 4	1·25	1·25

557 Primrose   **558** Daffodil

559 Bluebell   **560** Snowdrop

(Des P. Newcombe)

1979 (21 Mar). *Spring Wild Flowers. "All-over" phosphor. P* 14 × 15.

1079	557	9p. slate-black, deep brown, pale greenish yellow, deep olive, pale new blue and silver	20	20
		a. Imperf (pair)	£400	
1080	558	10½p. greenish yellow, grey-green, steel-blue, slate-blk, new blue & silver	40	40
		a. Imperf (vert pair) ..	£1600	
1081	559	11p. slate-black, deep brown, ultra-marine, light greenish blue, pale greenish yellow and silver ..	40	40
		a. Imperf (horiz pair)	£1400	
1082	560	13p. slate-black, indigo, grey-green, sepia, ochre and silver ..	40	40
		a. Imperf (horiz pair) ..	£800	
1079/82		.. .. *Set of* 4	1·25	1·25

561

562

563

564

T **561/4** show Hands placing National Flags in Ballot Boxes.

(Des S. Cliff)

1979 (9 May). *First Direct Elections to European Assembly. Phosphorised paper. P* 15 × 14.

1083	561	9p. grey-black, vermilion, cinnamon, pale greenish yellow, pale turq-green and dull ultramarine	20	20
1084	562	10½p. grey-black, vermilion, cinnamon, pale greenish yellow, dull ultramarine, pale turq-grn & chestnut	30	30
1085	563	11p. grey-black, vermilion, cinnamon, pale greenish yellow, dull ultramarine, pale turq-grn & grey-grn	30	30
1086	564	13p. grey-black, vermilion, cinnamon, pale greenish yellow, dull ultramarine, pale turq-grn & brown	40	40
1083/6		*Set of 4*	1·10	1·10

565 "Saddling 'Mahmoud' for the Derby, 1936" (Sir Alfred Munnings)

566 "The Liverpool Great National Steeple Chase, 1839" (aquatint by F. C. Turner)

567 "The First Spring Meeting, Newmarket, 1793" (J. N. Sartorius)

568 "Racing at Dorsett Ferry, Windsor, 1684" (Francis Barlow)

(Des S. Rose)

1979 (6 June). *Horseracing Paintings. Bicentenary of the Derby (9p.). "All-over" phosphor. P* 15 × 14.

1087	565	9p. light blue, red-brown, rose-pink, pale greenish yellow, grey-black and gold	25	25
1088	566	10½p. bistre-yellow, slate-blue, salmon-pink, lt blue, grey-black and gold	30	30
1089	567	11p. rose, vermilion, pale greenish yellow, new blue, grey-black and gold	30	30
1090	568	13p. bistre-yellow, rose, turquoise, grey-black and gold	30	30
1087/90		*Set of 4*	1·10	1·10

569 *The Tale of Peter Rabbit* (Beatrix Potter) **570** *The Wind in the Willows* (Kenneth Grahame)

571 *Winnie-the-Pooh* (A. A. Milne) **572** *Alice's Adventures in Wonderland* (Lewis Carroll)

(Des E. Hughes)

1979 (11 July). *International Year of the Child. Children's Book Illustrations. "All-over" phosphor. P* 14 × 15.

1091	569	9p. deep bluish green, grey-black, bistre-brown, bright rose, greenish yellow and silver	25	20
1092	570	10½p. dull ultramarine, grey-black, ol-brown, bright rose, yellow-orge, pale greenish yellow and silver	30	35
1093	571	11p. drab, grey-black, greenish yellow, new bl, yell-orge, agate & silver	35	40
1094	572	13p. pale greenish yellow, grey-black, bright rose, deep bluish green, olive-brown, new blue and silver	65	65
1091/4		*Set of 4*	1·40	1·40

573 Sir Rowland Hill **574** Postman, *circa* 1839

575 London Postman, *circa* 1839 **576** Woman and Young Girl with Letters, 1840

(Des E. Stemp)

1979 (22 Aug–24 Oct). *Death Centenary of Sir Rowland Hill. "All-over" phosphor. P* 14 × 15.

1095	573	10p. grey-black, brown-ochre, myrtle-green, pale greenish yellow, rosine, bright blue and gold	25	25
		a. Imperf (horiz pair)	£2000	
1096	574	11½p. grey-black, brown-ochre, bright blue, rosine, bistre-brown, pale greenish yellow and gold	30	35
1097	575	13p. grey-black, brown-ochre, bright blue, rosine, bistre-brown, pale greenish yellow and gold	35	40
1098	576	15p. grey-black, brown-ochre, myrtle-green, bistre-brown, rosine, pale greenish yellow and gold	50	40
1095/8		*Set of 4*	1·25	1·25
MS1099		89×121 mm. Nos. 1095/8 (sold at 59½p.)	1·50	1·50
		(24 Oct)		
		a. Imperforate	£1200	
		b. Brown-ochre (15p. background, etc) omitted	£1000	
		c. Gold (Queen's head) omitted	£200	
		d. Brown-ochre, myrtle-green and gold omitted	£5500	
		e. Bright blue (13p. background, etc) omitted	£1200	
		f. Myrtle-green (10p. (background), 15p.) omitted	£1600	
		g. Pale greenish yellow omitted	£140	
		h. Rosine omitted	£500	
		i. Bistre-brown omitted	£800	
		j. Grey-black and pale greenish yellow omitted	£10000	

The premium on No. MS1099 was used to support the London 1980 International Stamp Exhibition.

Examples of No. MS1099 showing face values on the stamps of 9p., 10½p., 11p. and 13p., with a sheet price of 53½p., were prepared, but not issued.

577 Policeman on the Beat

578 Policeman directing Traffic

579 Mounted Policewoman

580 River Patrol Boat

(Des B. Sanders)

1979 (26 Sept). *150th Anniv of Metropolitan Police. Phosphorised paper. P* 15 × 14.

1100	577	10p. grey-black, red-brown, emerald, greenish yellow, brt blue & mag	25	25
1101	578	11½p. grey-black, bright orange, purple-brown, ultramarine, greenish yellow and deep bluish green	30	35
1102	579	13p. grey-black, red-brown, magenta, ol-grn, greenish yell & dp dull bl	35	40
1103	580	15p. grey-black, magenta, brown, slate-bl, dp brown & greenish blk	50	40
1100/3		*Set of 4*	1·25	1·25

581 The Three Kings

582 Angel appearing to the Shepherds

583 The Nativity

584 Mary and Joseph travelling to Bethlehem

585 The Annunciation

(Des F. Wegner)

1979 (21 Nov). *Christmas. One centre phosphor band (8p.) or phosphorised paper (others). P* 15 × 14.

1104	581	8p. blue, grey-black, ochre, slate-violet and gold	20	20
		a. Imperf (pair)	£500	
1105	582	10p. bright rose-red, grey-black, chestnut, chrome-yell, dp vio & gold	25	25
		a. Imperf between (vert pair)	£450	
		b. Imperf (pair)	£600	
1106	583	11½p. orange-vermilion, steel-bl, drab, grey-black, deep blue-grn & gold	30	30
1107	584	13p. bright blue, orange-vermilion, bistre, grey-black and gold	40	40
1108	585	15p. orange-vermilion, blue, bistre, grey-black, green and gold	50	45
1104/8		*Set of 5*	1·50	1·50

586 Common Kingfisher

587 Dipper

588 Moorhen

589 Yellow Wagtails

(Des M. Warren)

1980 (16 Jan). *Centenary of Wild Bird Protection Act. Phosphorised paper.* P 14 × 15.

1109	586	10p. bright blue, bright yellow-green, vermilion, pale greenish yellow, grey-black and gold	25	25
1110	587	11½p. sepia, grey-black, dull ultramarine, vermilion, grey-green, pale greenish yellow and gold	45	40
1111	588	13p. emerald-green, grey-black, bright bl, verm, pale greenish yell & gold	60	50
1112	589	15p. greenish yellow, brown, light green, slate-bl, grey-blk & gold	65	55
1109/12			Set of 4	1·75	1·75

590 *Rocket* approaching Moorish Arch, Liverpool

591 First and Second Class Carriages passing through Olive Mount cutting

592 Third Class Carriage and Sheep Truck crossing Chat Moss

593 Horsebox and Carriage Truck near Bridgewater Canal

594 Goods Truck and Mail-Coach at Manchester

T **590/4** were printed together, *se-tenant*, in horizontal strips of 5 throughout the sheet.

(Des D. Gentleman)

1980 (12 Mar). *150th Anniv of Liverpool and Manchester Railway. Phosphorised paper.* P 15 × 14.

1113	590	12p. lemon, light brown, rose-red, pale blue and grey-black	35	25
		a. Strip of 5. Nos. 1113/17	1·50	1·75
		ab. Imperf (horiz strip of 5. Nos. 1113/17)	£1200	
		ac. Lemon omitted (horiz strip of 5. Nos. 1113/17)	£7500	
1114	591	12p. rose-red, light brown, lemon, pale blue and grey-black	35	25
1115	592	12p. pale blue, rose-red, lemon, light brown and grey-black	35	25
1116	593	12p. light brown, lemon, rose-red, pale blue and grey-black	35	25
1117	594	12p. light brown, rose-red, pale blue, lemon and grey-black	35	25
1113/17			Set of 5	1·50	1·00

595 Montage of London Buildings

(Des J. Matthews. Eng G. Holt. Recess)

1980 (9 Apr–7 May). *"London 1980" International Stamp Exhibition. Phosphorised paper.* P 14½ × 14.

1118	595	50p. agate	1·50	1·50
MS1119		90 × 123 mm. No. 1118 (*sold at 75p.*) (7 May)	1·50	1·50
		a. Error. Imperf	£700	

596 Buckingham Palace

597 The Albert Memorial

598 Royal Opera House

599 Hampton Court

600 Kensington Palace

(Des Sir Hugh Casson)

1980 (7 May). *London Landmarks. Phosphorised paper.* P 14 × 15.

1120	596	10½p. grey, pale blue, rosine, pale greenish yell, yellowish green & silver	25	25
1121	597	12p. grey-black, bistre, rosine, yellowish green, pale greenish yellow and silver	30	30
		a. Imperf (vert pair)	£650	
1122	598	13½p. grey-black, pale salmon, pale olgreen, slate-blue and silver	40	40
		a. Imperf (pair)	£650	
1123	599	15p. grey-black, pale salmon, slate-blue, dull yellowish green, olive-yellow and silver	50	50
1124	600	17½p. grey, slate-blue, red-brown, sepia, yellowish green, pale greenish yellow and silver	50	50
		a. Silver (Queen's head) omitted	£175	
1120/4			Set of 5	1·75	1·75

No. 1124a shows the Queen's head in pale greenish yellow, this colour being printed beneath the silver for technical reasons.

---

601 Charlotte Brontë (*Jane Eyre*)

602 George Eliot (*The Mill on the Floss*)

603 Emily Brontë (*Wuthering Heights*)

604 Mrs. Gaskell (*North and South*)

T **601/4** show authoresses and scenes from their novels. T **601/2** also include the "Europa" C.E.P.T. emblem.

(Des Barbara Brown)

1980 (9 July). *Famous Authoresses. Phosphorised paper.* P 15 × 14.

1125	601	12p. red-brown, bright rose, bright bl, greenish yellow, grey and gold	30	30
1126	602	13½p. red-brown, dull vermilion, pale bl, pale greenish yell, grey & gold	45	45
		a. Pale blue omitted	£2500	
1127	603	15p. red-brown, vermilion, blue, lemon, grey and gold	50	55
1128	604	17½p. dull vermilion, slate-blue, ultram, pale greenish yell, grey and gold	70	70
		a. Imperf and slate-blue omitted (pair)	£800	
1125/8			Set of 4	1·75	1·75

605 Queen Elizabeth the Queen Mother

(Des J. Matthews from photograph by N. Parkinson)

1980 (4 Aug). *80th Birthday of Queen Elizabeth the Queen Mother. Phosphorised paper.* P 14 × 15.

1129	605	12p. bright rose, greenish yellow, new blue, grey and silver	1·00	1·00
		a. Imperf (horiz pair)	£1500	

606 Sir Henry Wood

607 Sir Thomas Beecham

608 Sir Malcolm Sargent

609 Sir John Barbirolli

(Des P. Gauld)

1980 (10 Sept). *British Conductors. Phosphorised paper.* P 14 × 15.

1130	**606**	12p.	slate, rose-red, greenish yellow, bistre and gold	30	30
1131	**607**	13½p.	grey-black, vermilion, greenish yellow, pale carmine-rose and gold	45	50
1132	**608**	15p.	grey-black, bright rose-red, greenish yellow, turquoise-grn & gold	55	55
1133	**609**	17½p.	black, bright rose-red, greenish yellow, dull violet-blue and gold	65	60
1130/3			*Set of 4*	1·75	1·75

610 Running

611 Rugby

612 Boxing

613 Cricket

(Des R. Goldsmith. Litho Questa)

1980 (10 Oct). *Sport Centenaries. Phosphorised paper.* P 14 × 14½.

1134	**610**	12p.	pale new blue, greenish yellow, magenta, light brown, reddish purple and gold	30	30
		a.	Gold (Queen's head) omitted	£10000	
1135	**611**	13½p.	pale new blue, olive-yellow, bright purple, orange-vermilion, blackish lilac and gold	50	50
1136	**612**	15p.	pale new blue, greenish yellow, bright purple, chalky blue & gold	50	50
		a.	Gold (Queen's head) omitted	£10000	
1137	**613**	17½p.	pale new blue, greenish yellow, magenta, dp ol, grey-brn & gold	70	70
1134/7			*Set of 4*	1·75	1·75

Centenaries:—12p. Amateur Athletics Association; 13½p. Welsh Rugby Union; 15p. Amateur Boxing Association; 17½p. First England–Australia Test Match.

Nos. 1134a and 1136a were caused by paper folds.

614 Christmas Tree

615 Candles

616 Apples and Mistletoe

617 Crown, Chains and Bell

618 Holly

(Des J. Matthews)

1980 (19 Nov). *Christmas. One centre phosphor band (10p.) or phosphorised paper (others).* P 15 × 14.

1138	**614**	10p.	black, turquoise-green, greenish yellow, vermilion and blue	25	25
		a.	Imperf (horiz pair)	£950	
1139	**615**	12p.	grey, magenta, rose-red, greenish grey and pale orange	35	35
1140	**616**	13½p.	grey-black, dull yellow-green, brown, greenish yellow and pale olive-bistre	40	40
1141	**617**	15p.	grey-black, bistre-yellow, bright orange, magenta and new blue	50	50
1142	**618**	17½p.	black, vermilion, dull yellowish green and greenish yellow	60	60
1138/42			*Set of 5*	1·90	1·90

619 St. Valentine's Day

620 Morris Dancers

621 Lammastide

622 Medieval Mummers

T **619/20** also include the "Europa" C.E.P.T. emblem.

(Des F. Wegner)

1981 (6 Feb). *Folklore, Phosphorised paper.* P 15 × 14.

1143	**619**	14p.	cerise, green, yellow-orange, salmon-pink, black and gold	35	35
1144	**620**	18p.	dull ultramarine, lemon, lake-brown, brt green, black & gold	60	60
1145	**621**	22p.	chrome-yellow, rosine, brown, new blue, black and gold	70	70
1146	**622**	25p.	brt blue, red-brown, brt rose-red, greenish yellow, black and gold	85	85
1143/6			*Set of 4*	2·25	2·25

623 Blind Man with Guide Dog

624 Hands spelling "Deaf" in Sign Language

625 Disabled Man in Wheelchair

626 Disabled Artist painting with Foot

(Des J. Gibbs)

1981 (25 Mar). *International Year of the Disabled. Phosphorised paper.* P 15 × 14.

1147	**623**	14p.	drab, greenish yellow, bright rose-red, dull purple and silver	35	35
		a.	Imperf (pair)	£600	
1148	**624**	18p.	deep blue-green, brt orange, dull vermilion, grey-black and silver	60	60
1149	**625**	22p.	brown-ochre, rosine, purple-brn, greenish blue, black and silver	70	70
1150	**626**	25p.	vermilion, lemon, pale salmon, olive-brn, new blue, blk & silver	85	85
1147/50			*Set of 4*	2·25	2·25

All known examples of No. 1147a are creased.

627 *Aglais urticae*

628 *Maculinea arion*

629 *Inachis io*

630 *Carterocephalus palaemon*

(Des G. Beningfield)

1981 (13 May). *Butterflies. Phosphorised paper.* P 14 × 15.

1151	**627**	14p.	greenish yellow, yellow-green, brt rose, brt blue, emerald & gold	35	35
		a.	Imperf (pair)	£1000	
1152	**628**	18p.	black, greenish yellow, dull yellowish green, bright mauve, bright blue, bright green and gold	80	80
1153	**629**	22p.	black, greenish yell, bronze-grn, rosine, ultramarine, lt grn & gold	90	90
1154	**630**	25p.	black, greenish yellow, bronze-green, bright rose-red, ultramarine, bright emerald and gold	1·00	1·00
1151/4			*Set of 4*	2·75	2·75

631 Glenfinnan, Scotland

632 Derwentwater, England

633 Stackpole Head, Wales

634 Giant's Causeway, Northern Ireland

635 St. Kilda, Scotland

(Des M. Fairclough)

1981 (24 June). *50th Anniv of National Trust for Scotland. British Landscapes. Phosphorised paper.* P 15 × 14.

1155	**631**	14p. lilac, dull blue, reddish brown, bistre-yellow, black and gold ..	30	30
1156	**632**	18p. bottle green, bright blue, brown, bistre-yellow, black and gold ..	40	40
1157	**633**	20p. deep turq-blue, dull blue, greenish yellow, reddish brn, black & gold	70	70
1158	**634**	22p. chrome-yellow, reddish brn, new blue, yellow-brown, black & gold	80	80
1159	**635**	25p. ultramarine, new blue, olive-green, olive-grey and gold ..	90	90
1155/9	..	.. .. .. *Set of 5*	2·75	2·75

636 Prince Charles and Lady Diana Spencer

(Des J. Matthews from photograph by Lord Snowdon)

1981 (22 July). *Royal Wedding. Phosphorised paper.* P 14 × 15.

1160	**636**	14p. grey-blk, greenish yellow, brt rose-red, ultram, pale bl, blue & silver	1·50	1·75
1161		25p. drab, greenish yellow, bright rose-red, ultramarine, grey-brown, grey-black and silver ..	2·50	2·25

637 "Expeditions"

638 "Skills"

639 "Service"

640 "Recreation"

(Des P. Sharland. Litho J.W.)

1981 (12 Aug). *25th Anniv of Duke of Edinburgh Award Scheme. Phosphorised paper.* P 14.

1162	**637**	14p. greenish yellow, magenta, pale new blue, black, emerald & silver	35	35
1163	**638**	18p. greenish yellow, magenta, pale new blue, black, cobalt and gold	60	60
1164	**639**	22p. greenish yellow, magenta, pale new blue, black, red-orge & gold	70	70
1165	**640**	25p. bright orange, mauve, pale new blue, black, flesh and bronze	80	80
1162/5	..	.. .. .. *Set of 4*	2·25	2·25

641 Cockle-dredging from *Linsey II*

642 Hauling in Trawl Net

643 Lobster Potting

644 Hoisting Seine Net

(Des B. Sanders)

1981 (23 Sept). *Fishing Industry. Phosphorised paper.* P 15 × 14.

1166	**641**	14p. slate, greenish yellow, magenta, new blue, orange-brown, olive-grey and bronze-green ..	40	40
1167	**642**	18p. slate, greenish yellow, brt crimson, ultramarine, blk & greenish slate	60	60
1168	**643**	22p. grey, greenish yellow, bright rose, dull ultram, reddish lilac & black	70	70
1169	**644**	25p. grey, greenish yellow, bright rose, cobalt and black ..	80	80
1166/9	..	.. .. .. *Set of 4*	2·25	2·25

Nos. 1166/9 were issued on the occasion of the centenary of the Royal National Mission to Deep Sea Fishermen.

645 Father Christmas

646 Jesus Christ

647 Flying Angel

648 Joseph and Mary arriving at Bethlehem

649 Three Kings approaching Bethlehem

(Des Samantha Brown (11½p.), Tracy Jenkins (14p.), Lucinda Blackmore (18p.), Stephen Moore (22p.), Sophie Sharp (25p.))

1981 (18 Nov). *Christmas. Children's Pictures. One phosphor band (11½p.) or phosphorised paper (others).* P 15 × 14.

1170	**645**	11½p. ultramarine, black, red, olive-bistre, bright green and gold	30	30
1171	**646**	14p. bistre-yellow, brt magenta, blue, greenish blue, brt grn, blk & gold	40	40
1172	**647**	18p. pale blue-green, bistre-yellow, brt magenta, ultramarine, blk & gold	60	60
1173	**648**	22p. deep turquoise-blue, lemon, magenta, black and gold	70	70
1174	**649**	25p. royal blue, lemon, bright magenta, black and gold	80	80
1170/4	..	.. .. .. *Set of 5*	2·50	2·50

650 Charles Darwin and Giant Tortoises

651 Darwin and Marine Iguanas

652 Darwin, Cactus Ground Finch and Large Ground Finch

653 Darwin and Prehistoric Skulls

(Des D. Gentleman)

1982 (10 Feb). *Death Centenary of Charles Darwin. Phosphorised paper.* P 15 × 14.

1175	**650**	15½p. dull purple, drab, bistre, black and grey-black ..	35	35
1176	**651**	19½p. violet-grey, bistre-yellow, slate-black, red-brown, grey-blk & blk	60	60
1177	**652**	26p. sage green, bistre-yellow, orange, chalky bl, grey-blk, red-brn & blk	80	80
1178	**653**	29p. grey-brown, yellow-brn, brown-ochre, black and grey-black	85	85
1175/8	..	.. .. .. *Set of 4*	2·50	2·50

654 Boys' Brigade

655 Girls' Brigade

656 Boy Scout Movement   **657** Girl Guide Movement

(Des B. Sanders)

1982 (24 Mar). *Youth Organizations. Phosphorised paper.* P 15 × 14.

1179	654	15½p.	gold, greenish yellow, pale orange, mauve, dull blue and grey-black	35	35
1180	655	19½p.	gold, greenish yellow, pale orange, bright rose, deep ultramarine, olive-bistre and grey-black	70	70
1181	656	26p.	gold, greenish yellow, olive-sepia, rosine, deep blue, deep dull green and grey-black	95	95
1182	657	29p.	gold, yellow, dull orange, cerise, dull ultram, chestnut & grey-blk	1·10	1·10
1179/82			*Set of 4*	2·75	2·75

Nos. 1179/82 were issued on the occasion of the 75th anniversary of the Boy Scout Movement; the 125th birth anniversary of Lord Baden-Powell and the centenary of the Boys' Brigade (1983).

658 Ballerina   **659** Harlequin

660 Hamlet   **661** Opera Singer

(Des A. George)

1982 (28 Apr). *Europa. British Theatre. Phosphorised paper.* P 15 × 14.

1183	658	15½p.	carm-lake, greenish bl, greenish yell, grey-blk, bottle grn & silver	35	35
1184	659	19½p.	rosine, new blue, greenish yellow, black, ultramarine and silver	60	60
1185	660	26p.	carmine-red, bright rose-red, greenish yellow, black, dull ultramarine, lake-brown and silver	90	85
1186	661	29p.	rose-red, greenish yellow, bright blue, grey-black and silver	1·25	1·25
1183/6			*Set of 4*	2·75	2·75

662 Henry VIII and *Mary Rose*

663 Admiral Blake and *Triumph*

664 Lord Nelson and H.M.S. *Victory*

665 Lord Fisher and H.M.S. *Dreadnought*

666 Viscount Cunningham and H.M.S *Warspite*

(Des Marjorie Saynor. Eng C. Slania. Recess and photo)

1982 (16 June). *Maritime Heritage. Phosphorised paper.* P 15 × 14.

1187	662	15½p.	black, lemon, bright rose, pale orange, ultramarine and grey	35	35
		a.	Imperf (pair)	£900	
1188	663	19½p.	black, greenish yellow, bright rose-red, pale orange, ultram and grey	60	60
1189	664	24p.	black, orange-yellow, bright rose-red, lake-brown, dp ultram & grey	80	80
1190	665	26p.	black, orange-yellow, bright rose, lemon, ultramarine and grey	90	90
		a.	Imperf (pair)		
1191	666	29p.	black, olive-yellow, bright rose, orange-yellow, ultram & grey	1·00	1·00
1187/91			*Set of 5*	3·25	3·25

Nos. 1187/91 were issued on the occasion of Maritime England Year, the Bicentenary of the Livery Grant by City of London to Worshipful Company of Shipwrights and the raising of *Mary Rose* from Portsmouth Harbour.

Several used examples of the 15½p. have been seen with the black recess (ship and waves) omitted.

667 "Strawberry Thief"   **668** Untitled
(William Morris)   (Steiner and Co)

669 "Cherry Orchard"   **670** "Chevron"
(Paul Nash)   (Andrew Foster)

(Des Peter Hatch Partnership)

1982 (23 July). *British Textiles. Phosphorised paper.* P 14 × 15.

1192	667	15½p.	blue, olive-yellow, rosine, deep blue-green, bistre & Prussian blue	35	35
		a.	Imperf (horiz pair)	£1000	
1193	668	19½p.	olive-grey, greenish yellow, bright magenta, dull grn, yell-brn & blk	75	75
		a.	Imperf (vert pair)	£1500	
1194	669	26p.	bright scarlet, dull mauve, dull ultramarine and bright carmine	90	90
1195	670	29p.	bronze-green, orange-yellow, turq-green, stone, chestnut & sage-grn	1·10	1·10
1192/5			*Set of 4*	2·75	2·75

Nos. 1192/5 were issued on the occasion of the 250th birth anniversary of Sir Richard Arkwright (inventor of spinning machine).

671 Development of Communications

672 Modern Technological Aids

(Des Delaney and Ireland)

1982 (8 Sept). *Information Technology. Phosphorised paper.* P 14 × 15.

1196	671	15½p.	black, greenish yellow, bright rose-red, bistre-brn, new bl & lt ochre	45	50
		a.	Imperf (pair)	£200	
1197	672	26p.	black, greenish yellow, bright rose-red, ol-bistre, new bl & lt ol-grey	80	85
		a.	Imperf (pair)	£1300	

673 Austin "Seven" and "Metro"

674 Ford "Model T" and "Escort"

675 Jaguar "SS 1" and "XJ6"

676 Rolls-Royce "Silver Ghost" and "Silver Spirit"

(Des S. Paine. Litho Questa)

1982 (13 Oct). *British Motor Cars. Phosphorised paper.* P 14½ × 14.

1198	673	15½p.	slate, orange-vermilion, bright orange, drab, yellow-green, olive-yellow, bluish grey and black	50	50
1199	674	19½p.	slate, brt orange, olive-grey, rose-red, dull vermilion, grey & black	70	70
1200	675	26p.	slate, red-brown, bright orange, turquoise-green, myrtle-green, dull blue-green, grey and olive	90	90
1201	676	29p.	slate, bright orange, carmine-red, reddish purple, grey and black	1·25	1·25
1198/201			*Set of 4*	3·00	3·00

677 "While Shepherds Watched"

678 "The Holly and the Ivy"

679 "I Saw Three Ships"

680 "We Three Kings"

681 "Good King Wenceslas"

(Des Barbara Brown)

1982 (17 Nov). *Christmas. Carols. One phosphor band (12½p.) or phosphorised paper (others). P 15 × 14.*

1202	677	12½p.	black, greenish yellow, brt scar, steel blue, red-brown & gold	30	30
1203	678	15½p.	black, bistre-yellow, brt rose-red, bright blue, bright green & gold	40	40
		a.	Imperf (pair)	£1000	
1204	679	19½p.	black, bistre-yellow, brt rose-red, dull blue, deep brown & gold	80	80
		a.	Imperf (pair)	£1300	
1205	680	26p.	black, bistre-yellow, brt magenta, brt blue, choc, gold & orange-red	90	90
1206	681	29p.	black, bistre-yellow, magenta, brt blue, chestnut, gold and brt mag	1·00	1·00
1202/6			*Set of 5*	3·00	3·00

682 Atlantic Salmon

683 Northern Pike

684 Brown Trout

685 Eurasian Perch

(Des A. Jardine)

1983 (26 Jan). *British River Fishes. Phosphorised paper. P 15 × 14.*

1207	682	15½p.	grey-black, bistre-yellow, bright purple, new blue and silver	35	35
		a.	Imperf (pair)	£1300	
1208	683	19½p.	black, bistre-yellow, olive-bistre, dp claret, silver & dp bluish green	75	75
1209	684	26p.	grey-black, bistre-yell, chrome-yellow, magenta, silver & pale bl	90	90
		a.	Imperf (pair)	£850	
1210	685	29p.	black, greenish yellow, bright carmine, new blue and silver	1·10	1·10
1207/10			*Set of 4*	2·75	2·75

All known examples of No. 1209a are creased.

686 Tropical Island   687 Desert

688 Temperate Farmland   689 Mountain Range

(Des D. Fraser)

1983 (9 Mar). *Commonwealth Day. Geographical Regions. Phosphorised paper. P 14 × 15.*

1211	686	15½p.	greenish blue, greenish yellow, bright rose, light brown, grey-black, deep claret and silver	35	35
1212	687	19½p.	brt lilac, greenish yell, mag, dull blue, grey-blk, dp dull-bl & silver	75	75
1213	688	26p.	lt blue, greenish yellow, brt mag, new blue, grey-blk, vio & silver	90	90
1214	689	29p.	dull vio-bl, reddish vio, slate-lilac, new blue, myrtle-grn, blk & silver	1·10	1·10
1211/14			*Set of 4*	2·75	2·75

690 Humber Bridge

691 Thames Flood Barrier

692 *Iolair* (oilfield emergency support vessel)

(Des. M. Taylor)

1983 (25 May). *Europa. Engineering Achievements. Phosphorised paper. P 15 × 14.*

1215	690	16p.	silver, orange-yellow, ultramarine, black and grey	45	45
1216	691	20½p.	silver, greenish yellow, bright purple, blue, grey-black and grey	1·10	1·10
1217	692	28p.	silver, lemon, brt rose-red, chestnut, dull ultramarine, blk & grey	1·25	1·25
1215/17			*Set of 3*	2·50	2·50

693 Musketeer and Pikeman, The Royal Scots (1633)   694 Fusilier and Ensign, The Royal Welch Fusiliers (mid-18th century)

695 Riflemen, 95th Rifles (The Royal Green Jackets) (1805)   696 Sergeant (khaki service uniform) and Guardsman (full dress), The Irish Guards (1900)

697 Paratroopers, The Parachute Regiment (1983)

(Des E. Stemp)

1983 (6 July). *British Army Uniforms. Phosphorised paper. P 14 × 15.*

1218	693	16p.	black, buff, deep brown, slate-black, rose-red, gold & new blue	40	40
1219	694	20½p.	black, buff, greenish yellow, slate-blk, brn-rose, gold & brt bl	70	70
1220	695	26p.	black, buff, slate-purple, green, bistre and gold	1·00	1·00
		a.	Imperf (pair)	£1300	
1221	696	28p.	black, buff, light brown, grey, dull rose, gold and new blue	1·00	1·00
1222	697	31p.	black, buff, olive-yellow, grey, deep magenta, gold and new blue	1·10	1·10
1218/22			*Set of 5*	3·75	3·75

Nos. 1218/22 were issued on the occasion of the 350th anniversary of the Royal Scots, the senior line regiment of the British Army.

698 20th-century Garden, Sissinghurst   699 19th-century Garden, Biddulph Grange

700 18th-century Garden, Blenheim   701 17th-century Garden, Pitmedden

(Des Liz Butler, Litho J.W.)

1983 (24 Aug). *British Gardens. Phosphorised paper. P 14.*

1223	698	16p.	greenish yellow, brt purple, new blue, black, bright green & silver	40	40
1224	699	20½p.	greenish yellow, brt purple, new blue, black, bright green & silver	60	60
1225	700	28p.	greenish yellow, brt purple, new blue, black, bright green & silver	1·00	1·00
1226	701	31p.	greenish yellow, brt purple, new blue, black, bright green & silver	1·10	1·10
1223/6			*Set of 4*	2·75	2·75

Nos. 1223/6 were issued on the occasion of the death bicentenary of "Capability" Brown (landscape gardener)

702 Merry-go-round

703 Big Wheel, Helter-skelter and Performing Animals

704 Side Shows

705 Early Produce Fair

(Des A. Restall)

1983 (5 Oct). *British Fairs. Phosphorised paper.* P 15 × 14.

1227	702	16p. grey-black, greenish yellow, orge-red, ochre & turquoise-blue	40	40
1228	703	20½p. grey-black, yellow-ochre, yellow-orange, brt magenta, violet & blk	75	75
1229	704	28p. grey-black, bistre-yellow, orange-red, violet and yellow-brown	95	95
1230	705	31p. grey-black, greenish yellow, red, dp turq-green, slate-violet & brn	1·00	1·00
1227/30		*Set of 4*	2·75	2·75

706 "Christmas Post" (pillar-box)

707 "The Three Kings" (chimney-pots)

708 "World at Peace" (Dove and Blackbird)

709 "Light of Christmas" (street lamp)

710 "Christmas Dove" (hedge sculpture)

(Des T. Meeuwissen)

1983 (16 Nov). *Christmas. One phosphor band (12½p.) or phosphorised paper (others).* P 15 × 14.

1231	706	12½p. black, greenish yellow, bright rose-red, bright blue, gold and grey-black	30	30
		a. Imperf (horiz pair)	£750	
1232	707	16p. black, greenish yellow, bright rose, pale new blue, gold & brown-pur	35	35
		a. Imperf (pair)	£850	
1233	708	20½p. black, greenish yellow, bright rose, new blue, gold and blue	70	70
1234	709	28p. black, lemon, bright carmine, bluish violet, gold, deep turquoise-green and purple	90	90
1235	710	31p. black, greenish yellow, brt rose, new blue, gold, green & brn-olive	1·10	1·10
1231/5		*Set of 5*	3·00	3·00

711 Arms of the College of Arms

712 Arms of King Richard III (founder)

713 Arms of the Earl Marshal of England

714 Arms of the City of London

(Des J. Matthews)

1984 (17 Jan). *500th Anniv of College of Arms. Phosphorised paper.* P 14½.

1236	711	16p. black, chrome-yellow, reddish brn, scar-verm, brt bl & grey-blk	40	40
1237	712	20½p. black, chrome-yellow, rosine, bright blue and grey-black	60	60
1238	713	28p. black, chrome-yellow, rosine, brt blue, dull green and grey-black	1·00	1·00
1239	714	31p. black, chrome-yellow, rosine, brt blue and grey-black	1·10	1·10
		a. Imperf (horiz pair)	£1800	
1236/9		*Set of 4*	2·75	2·75

715 Highland Cow

716 Chillingham Wild Bull

717 Hereford Bull

718 Welsh Black Bull

719 Irish Moiled Cow

(Des B. Driscoll)

1984 (6 Mar). *British Cattle. Phosphorised paper.* P 15 × 14.

1240	715	16p. grey-black, bistre-yellow, rosine, yellow-orge, new bl & pale drab	40	40
1241	716	20½p. grey-black, greenish yellow, magenta, bistre, dull blue-green, pale drab and light green	65	65
1242	717	26p. black, chrome-yellow, rosine, reddish brown, new blue & pale drab	85	85
1243	718	28p. black, greenish yellow, bright carmine, orange-brown, deep dull blue and pale drab	90	90
1244	719	31p. grey-black, bistre-yellow, rosine, red-brown, light blue & pale drab	1·10	1·10
1240/4		*Set of 5*	3·50	3·50

Nos. 1240/4 were issued on the occasion of the centenary of the Highland Cattle Society and the bicentenary of the Royal Highland and Agricultural Society of Scotland.

720 Liverpool Garden Festival Hall

721 Milburngate Centre, Durham

722 Bush House, Bristol

723 Commercial Street Development, Perth

(Des R. Maddox and Trickett and Webb Ltd)

1984 (10 Apr). *Urban Renewal. Phosphorised paper.* P 15 × 14.

1245	720	16p. bright emerald, greenish yellow, cerise, steel-bl, blk, silver & flesh	40	40
1246	721	20½p. bright orange, greenish yellow, deep dull blue, yellowish green, azure, black and silver	70	70
		a. Imperf (horiz pair)	£1000	
1247	722	28p. rosine, greenish yellow, Prussian blue, pale blue-green, blk & silver	1·00	1·00
1248	723	31p. blue, greenish yell, cerise, grey-blue, bright green, black & silver	1·10	1·10
		a. Imperf (pair)	£1000	
1245/8		*Set of 4*	2·75	2·75

Nos. 1245/8 were issued on the occasion of 150th anniversaries of the Royal Institute of British Architects and the Chartered Institute of Building, and to commemorate the first International Gardens Festival, Liverpool.

ROYAL MAIL POSTAGE LABELS

These imperforate labels, printed in red on phosphorised paper with grey-green background design, were issued on 1 May 1984 as an experiment by the Post Office. Special microprocessor controlled machines were installed at post offices in Cambridge, London, Shirley, (Southampton) and Windsor to provide an after-hours sales service to the public. The machines printed and dispensed the labels according to the coins inserted and the buttons operated by the customer. Values were initially available in ½p steps to 16p and in addition, the labels were sold at philatelic counters in two packs containing either 3 values (3½, 12½, 16p) or 32 values (½p to 16p).

From 28 August 1984 the machines were adjusted to provide values up to 17p. After 31 December 1984 labels including ½p values were withdrawn. The machines were withdrawn from service on 30 April 1985.

724 C.E.P.T. 25th Anniversary Logo   **725** Abduction of Europa

(Des J. Larrivière (T **724**), F. Wegner (T **725**))

1984 (15 May). *25th Anniv of C.E.P.T. ("Europa") (T **724**) and Second Elections to European Parliament (T **725**). Phosphorised paper. P 15 × 14.*

249	724	16p. greenish slate, deep blue and gold		90	90
		a. Horiz pair. Nos. 1249/50	..	1·75	1·75
		ab. Imperf (horiz pair)		£1300	
250	725	16p. greenish slate, deep blue, black and gold		90	90
251	724	20½p. Venetian red, dp magenta & gold		1·60	1·60
		a. Horiz pair. Nos. 1251/2	..	3·25	3·25
		ab. Imperf (horiz pair)			
252	725	20½p. Venetian red, deep magenta, black and gold	..	1·60	1·60
249/52		..	Set of 4	4·50	4·50

Nos. 1249/50 and 1251/2 were each printed together, *se-tenant*, in horizontal pairs throughout the sheets.

726 Lancaster House

(Des P. Hogarth)

1984 (5 June). *London Economic Summit Conference. Phosphorised paper. P 14 × 15.*

1253	726	31p. silver, bistre-yellow, brown-ochre, black, rosine, bright blue and reddish lilac	..	1·00	1·00

727 View of Earth from "Apollo 11"   **728** Navigational Chart of English Channel

729 Greenwich Observatory   **730** Sir George Airy's Transit Telescope

(Des. H. Waller. Litho Questa)

1984 (26 June). *Centenary of the Greenwich Meridian. Phosphorised paper. P 14 × 14½.*

1254	727	16p. new blue, greenish yellow, magenta, black, scar & blue-blk		40	40
1255	728	20½p. olive-sepia, light brown, pale buff, black and scarlet	..	65	65
1256	729	28p. new blue, greenish yellow, scarlet, black and bright purple		90	90
1257	730	31p. deep blue, cobalt, scarlet & black		1·10	1·10
1254/7		..	Set of 4	2·75	2·75

On Nos. 1254/7 the Meridian is represented by a scarlet line.

731 Bath Mail Coach, 1784

732 Attack on Exeter Mail, 1816

733 Norwich Mail in Thunderstorm, 1827

734 Holyhead and Liverpool Mails leaving London, 1828

735 Edinburgh Mail Snowbound, 1831

(Des K. Bassford and S. Paine. Eng C. Slania. Recess and photo)

1984 (31 July). *Bicentenary of First Mail Coach Run Bath and Bristol to London. Phosphorised paper. P 15 × 14.*

1258	731	16p. pale stone, black, grey-black and bright scarlet		70	40
		a. Horiz strip of 5 Nos. 1258/62	..	3·25	3·25
1259	732	16p. pale stone, black, grey-black and bright scarlet		70	40
1260	733	16p. pale stone, black, grey-black and bright scarlet		70	40
1261	734	16p. pale stone, black, grey-black and bright scarlet		70	40
1262	735	16p. pale stone, black, grey-black and bright scarlet		70	40
1258/62		..	Set of 5	3·25	1·75

Nos. 1258/62 were printed together, *se-tenant*, in horizontal strips of 5 throughout the sheet.

736 Nigerian Clinic

737 Violinist and Acropolis, Athens

738 Building Project, Sri Lanka

 — (in left lower area)

739 British Council Library, Middle East

(Des F. Newell and J. Sorrell)

1984 (25 Sept). *50th Anniv of the British Council. Phosphorised paper. P 15 × 14.*

1263	736	17p. grey-green, greenish yellow, bright purple, dull blue, black, pale green and yellow-green		50	50
1264	737	22p. crimson, greenish yellow, bright rose-red, dull green, black, pale drab and slate-purple		75	75
1265	738	31p. sepia, olive-bistre, red, black, pale stone and olive-brown		1·00	1·00
1266	739	34p. steel blue, yellow, rose-red, new blue, black, azure and pale blue		1·10	1·10
1263/6		..	Set of 4	3·00	3·00

740 The Holy Family

741 Arrival in Bethlehem

742 Shepherd and Lamb

743 Virgin and Child

744 Offering of Frankincense

(Des Yvonne Gilbert)

1984 (20 Nov). *Christmas. One phosphor band (13p.) or phosphorised paper (others). P 15 × 14.*

1267	740	13p. pale cream, grey-black, bistre-yellow, mag, red-brn & lake-brn		30	30
1268	741	17p. pale cream, grey-black, yellow, magenta, dull blue & dp dull bl		50	50
		a. Imperf (pair)	..		
1269	742	22p. pale cream, grey-black, olive-yellow, bright magenta, bright blue and brownish grey		70	70
1270	743	31p. pale cream, grey-black, bistre-yellow, magenta, dull bl & lt brn		1·00	1·00
1271	744	34p. pale cream, olive-grey, bistre-yellow, magenta, turquoise-green and brown-olive		1·10	1·10
1267/71		..	Set of 5	3·25	3·25

Examples of No. 1267 from the Christmas £2.30 discount stamp booklet show a blue underprint of a double-lined star printed on the reverse over the gum.

745 "Flying Scotsman"

746 "Golden Arrow"

747 "Cheltenham Flyer"

748 "Royal Scot"

749 "Cornish Riviera"

(Des T. Cuneo)

1985 (22 Jan). *Famous Trains. Phosphorised paper.* P 15 × 14.
1272 745 17p. black, lemon, magenta, dull glue,
grey-black and gold 50 50
a. Imperf (pair) .. £1800
1273 746 22p. black, greenish yellow, bright
rose, dp dull blue, grey-blk & gold 85 85
1274 747 29p. black, greenish yellow, magneta,
blue, grey-black and gold .. 1·00 1·00
1275 748 31p. black, bistre-yellow, bright magenta, new blue slate-black & gold 1·25 1·25
1276 749 34p. black, greenish yellow, bright
rose, blue, slate-black and gold .. 1·40 1·40
1272/6 .. .. *Set of 5* 4·50 4·50
Nos. 1272/6 were issued on the occasion of the 150th anniversary of
the Great Western Railway Company.

750 *Bombus terrestris*
(bee)

751 *Coccinella
septempunctata*
(ladybird)

752 *Decticus
verrucivorus*
(bush-cricket)

753 *Lucanus cervus* (stag
beetle)

754 *Anax imperator*
(dragonfly)

(Des G. Beningfield)

1985 (12 Mar). *Insects. Phosphorised paper.* P 14 × 15.
1277 750 17p. black, greenish yellow, magenta, blue,
azure, gold and slate-black .. 40 40
1278 751 22p. black, greenish yellow, bright rose-red,
dull blue-green, slate-black and gold 60 60
1279 752 29p. black, greenish yellow, bright rose,
greenish blue, grey-black, gold and
bistre-yellow.. .. .. 90 90
1280 753 31p. black, greenish yellow, rose, pale new
blue and gold .. .. .. 1·00 1·00
1281 754 34p. black, greenish yellow, magenta,
greenish blue, grey-black and gold 1·00 1·00
1277/81 .. .. *Set of 5* 3·50 3·50
Nos. 1277/81 were issued on the occasion of the centenaries of the
Royal Entomological Society of London's Royal Charter, and of the
Selborne Society.

755 "Water Music" (George
Frideric Handel)

756 "The Planets" Suite
(Gustav Holst)

757 "The First Cuckoo"
(Frederick Delius)

758 "Sea Pictures" (Edward
Elgar)

(Des W. McLean)

1985 (14 May). *Europa. European Music Year. British Composers.
Phosphorised paper.* P 14 × 14½.
1282 755 17p. black, brt yellow-grn, dp magenta,
new blue, grey-black & gold .. 65 65
a. Imperf (vert pair)
1283 756 22p. black, greenish yellow, brt mag,
new blue, grey-black and gold .. 90 90
a. Imperf (pair) .. £1300
1284 757 31p. black, greenish yellow, magenta,
greenish blue, grey-black and gold 1·40 1·40
1285 758 34p. black, olive-yellow, bistre, turq-
blue, slate and gold .. 1·50 1·50
1282/5 .. .. *Set of 4* 4·00 4·00
Nos. 1282/5 were issued on the occasion of the 300th birth
anniversary of Handel.

759 R.N.L.I. Lifeboat and Signal Flags

760 Beachy Head Lighthouse and Chart

761 "Marecs A" Communications
Satellite and Dish Aerials

762 Buoys

(Des F. Newell and J. Sorrel. Litho J.W.)

1985 (18 June). *Safety at Sea. Phosphorised paper.* P 14.
1286 759 17p. black, azure, emerald, ultramarine,
orange-yellow, vermilion, bright blue,
and chrome-yellow 50 50
1287 760 22p. black, azure, emerald, ultramarine,
orange-yellow, vermilion, bright blue
and chrome-yellow 75 75
1288 761 31p. black, azure, emerald, ultramarine,
orange-yellow, vermilion, and bright
blue .. .. 1·10 1·10
1289 762 34p. black, azure, emerald, ultramarine,
orange-yellow, vermilion, bright blue
and chrome-yellow .. .. *Set of 4* 1·25 1·25
1286/9 .. .. *Set of 4* 3·25 3·25
Nos. 1286/9 were issued on the occasion of the Bicentenary of the
unimmersible lifeboat and the 50th anniversary of radar.

763 Datapost Motorcyclist,
City of London

764 Rural Postbus

765 Parcel Delivery in
Winter

766 Town Letter Delivery

(Des P. Hogarth)

1985 (30 July). 350 *Years of Royal Mail Public Postal Service.
Phosphorised paper.* P 14 × 15.
1290 763 17p. black, greenish yellow, bright carmine, greenish blue, yellow-
brown, grey-black and silver 50 50
a. Imperf on 3 sides (vert pair) £1300
1291 764 22p. black, greenish yellow, cerise,
steel bl, lt grn, grey-blk & silver 75 75
1292 765 31p. black, greenish yellow, brt carm,
dull blue, drab, grey-blk & silver 1·10 1·10
a. Imperf (vert pair) £1300
1293 766 34p. black, greenish yellow, cerise,
ultram, lt brn, grey-blk & silver 1·25 1·25
a. Imperf between (vert pair)
1290/3 .. .. *Set of 4* 3·25 3·25
Examples of No. 1290 from the commemorative £1.53 discount
stamp booklet show a blue underprint of a double-lined D printed
on the reverse over the gum.
No. 1290a shows perforation indentations at right, but is
imperforate at top, bottom and on the left-hand side.

767 King Arthur and Merlin

768 Lady of the Lake

769 Queen Guinevere
and Sir Lancelot

770 Sir Galahad

(Des Yvonne Gilbert)

1985 (3 Sept). *Arthurian Legends. Phosphorised paper.* P 15 × 14.
1294	767	17p. grey-black, lemon, brown-lilac, ultramarine, grey-black and silver	50	50
		a. Imperf (pair)	£1800	
1295	768	22p. black, lemon, brown-lilac, pale blue, grey-black, silver & grey-blk	75	75
1296	769	31p. black, lemon, magenta, turquoise-blue, grey-black, silver & grey-blk	1·25	1·25
1297	770	34p. grey, lemon, magenta, new blue, grey-black, silver and grey-black.	1·40	1·40
1294/7		.. .. *Set of 4*	3·50	3·50

Nos. 1294/7 were issued on the occasion of the 500th anniversary of the printing of Sir Thomas Malory's *Morte d'Arthur*.

771 Peter Sellers (from photo by Bill Brandt) **772** David Niven (from photo by Cornell Lucas)

773 Charlie Chaplin (from photo by Lord Snowdon) **774** Vivien Leigh (from photo by Angus McBean)

775 Alfred Hitchcock (from photo by Howard Coster)

(Des K. Bassford)

1985 (8 Oct). *British Film Year. Phosphorised paper.* P 14½.
1298	771	17p. grey-black, ol-grey, gold & silver	55	55
1299	772	22p. black, brown, gold and silver ..	75	75
1300	773	29p. black, lavender, gold and silver ..	1·25	1·25
1301	774	31p. black, pink, gold and silver ..	1·40	1·40
1302	775	34p. black, greenish blue, gold & silver	1·60	1·60
1298/302		.. .. *Set of 5*	5·00	5·00

776 Principal Boy

777 Genie

778 Dame

779 Good Fairy

780 Pantomime Cat

(Des A. George)

1985 (19 Nov). *Christmas. Pantomime Characters. One phosphor band* (12p.) *or phosphorised paper* (others). P 15 × 14.
1303	776	12p. new blue, greenish yellow, bright rose, gold, grey-black and silver	35	30
		a. Imperf (pair)	£1300	
1304	777	17p. emerald, greenish yellow, bright rose, new blue, blk, gold & silver	45	40
		a. Imperf (pair)	£1800	
1305	778	22p. bright carmine, greenish yellow, pale new blue, grey, gold & silver	70	80
1306	779	31p. bright orange, lemon, rose, slate-purple, silver and gold	1·00	1·00
1307	780	34p. brt reddish violet, brt blue, brt rose, blk, grey-brn, gold & silver	1·10	1·10
1303/7		.. .. *Set of 5*	3·25	3·25

Examples of No. 1303 from the Christmas £2.40 stamp booklet show a blue underprint of a double-lined star printed on the reverse over the gum.

781 Light Bulb and North Sea Oil Drilling Rig (Energy)

782 Thermometer and Pharmaceutical Laboratory (Health)

783 Garden Hoe and Steelworks (Steel)

784 Loaf of Bread and Cornfield (Agriculture)

(Des K. Bassford. Litho Questa)

1986 (14 Jan). *Industry Year. Phosphorised paper.* P 14½ × 14.
1308	781	17p. gold, black, magenta, greenish yellow and new blue	45	45
1309	782	22p. gold, pale turquoise-green, black, magenta, greenish yellow and blue	70	70
1310	783	31p. gold, black, magenta, greenish yellow and new blue ..	1·10	1·10
1311	784	34p. gold, black, magenta, greenish yellow and new blue ..	1·40	1·40
1308/11		.. .. *Set of 4*	3·25	3·25

785 Dr. Edmond Halley as Comet

786 *Giotto* Spacecraft approaching Comet

787 "Twice in a Lifetime"

788 Comet orbiting Sun and Planets

(Des R. Steadman)

1986 (18 Feb). *Appearance of Halley's Comet. Phosphorised paper.* P 15 × 14.
1312	785	17p. black, bistre, rosine, blue, grey-black, gold and deep brown	45	45
1313	786	22p. orange-vermilion, greenish yellow, brt purple, new bl, blk & gold	80	80
1314	787	31p. black, greenish yellow, brt purple dp turquoise-blue, grey-blk & gold	1·10	1·10
1315	788	34p. blue, greenish yellow, magenta, deep turquoise-blue, black & gold	1·25	1·25
1312/15		.. .. *Set of 4*	3·25	3·25

789 Queen Elizabeth II in 1928, 1942 and 1952

790 Queen Elizabeth II in 1958, 1973 and 1982

(Des J. Matthews)

1986 (21 Apr). *60th Birthday of Queen Elizabeth II. Phosphorised paper.* P 15 × 14.
1316	789	17p. grey-black, turquoise-green, bright green, green and dull blue..	70	40
		a. Horiz pair. Nos. 1316/17..	1·40	1·40
1317	790	17p. grey-black, dull blue, greenish blue and indigo	70	40
1318	789	34p. grey-black, deep dull purple, yellow-orange and red ..	1·60	1·60
		a. Horiz pair. Nos. 1318/19..	3·25	3·25
1319	790	34p. grey-black, olive-brown, yellow-brown, olive-grey and red ..	1·60	1·60
1316/19		.. .. *Set of 4*	4·25	3·75

Nos. 1316/17 and 1318/19 were printed together, *se-tenant*, in horizontal pairs throughout the sheets.

NEW INFORMATION

The editor is always interested to correspond with people who have new information that will improve or correct the Catalogue.

791 Barn Owl   **792** Pine Marten

793 Wild Cat   **794** Natterjack Toad

(Des K. Lilly)

1986 (20 May). *Europa. Nature Conservation. Endangered Species. Phosphorised paper.* P 14½ × 14.

1320	791	17p. gold, greenish yellow, rose, yellow-brown, olive-grey, new blue & blk	50	50
1321	792	22p. gold, greenish yellow, reddish brn, ol-yell, turq-bl, grey-blk & blk	1·00	1·00
1322	793	31p. gold, brt yellow-green, magenta, lt brown, ultramarine, ol-brn & blk	1·50	1·50
1323	794	34p. gold, greenish yellow, bright rose-red, brt green, grey-black & black	1·75	1·75
1320/3		*Set of 4*	4·25	4·25

795 Peasants working in Fields

796 Freemen working at Town Trades

797 Knight and Retainers

798 Lord at Banquet

(Des Tayburn Design Consultancy)

1986 (17 June). *900th Anniv of Domesday Book. Phosphorised paper.* P 15 × 14.

1324	795	17p. yell-brn, verm, lemon, brt emer, orge-brn, grey & brownish grey	50	50
1325	796	22p. yellow-ochre, red, greenish blue, chestnut, grey-blk & brownish grey	75	75
1326	797	31p. yellow-brown, verm, grn, Indian red, grey-blk & brownish grey	1·25	1·25
1327	798	34p. yellow-ochre, brt scar, grey-brn, new bl, lake-brn, grey-blk & grey	1·40	1·40
1324/7		*Set of 4*	3·50	3·50

MINIMUM PRICE

The minimum price quote is 10p which represents a handling charge rather than a basis for valuing common stamps. For further notes about prices see introductory pages.

799 Athletics

800 Rowing

801 Weightlifting

802 Rifle Shooting

803 Hockey

(Des N. Cudworth)

1986 (15 July). *Thirteenth Commonwealth Games, Edinburgh and World Hockey Cup for Men, London* (34p.). *Phosphorised paper.* P 15 × 14.

1328	799	17p. black, greenish yellow, orange-vermilion, ultram, chestnut & emer	50	50
1329	800	22p. black, lemon, scarlet, new blue, royal blue, chestnut & dp ultram	70	70
1330	801	29p. grey-black, greenish yellow, scarlet, new blue, brown-ochre, brown-rose and pale chestnut	90	90
1331	802	31p. black, greenish yellow, rose, blue, dull yell-grn, chestnut & yell-grn	1·25	1·25
1332	803	34p. black, lemon, scarlet, brt blue, brt emerald, red-brown & vermilion	1·40	1·40
		a. Imperf (pair)	£1600	
1328/32		*Set of 5*	4·25	4·25

No. 1332 also commemorates the Centenary of the Hockey Association.

804   **805**
Prince Andrew and Miss Sarah Ferguson (from photo by Gene Nocon)

(Des J. Matthews)

1986 (22 July). *Royal Wedding. One phosphor band* (12p.) *or phosphorised paper* (17p.). P 14 × 15.

1333	804	12p. lake, greenish yellow, cerise, ultramarine, black and silver	60	60
1334	805	17p. steel blue, greenish yellow, cerise, ultramarine, black and gold	90	90
		a. Imperf (pair)	£850	

806 Stylised Cross on Ballot Paper

(Des J. Gibbs. Litho Questa)

1986 (19 Aug). *32nd Commonwealth Parliamentary Association Conference. Phosphorised paper.* P 14 × 14½.

1335	806	34p. pale grey-lilac, black, vermilion, yellow and ultramarine	1·25	1·25

807 Lord Dowding and Hawker Hurricane Mk I   **808** Lord Tedder and Hawker Typhoon 1B

809 Lord Trenchard and De Havilland D.H.9A   **810** Sir Arthur Harris and Avro Type 683 Lancaster

811 Lord Portal and De Havilland D.H.98 Mosquito

(Des B. Sanders)

1986 (16 Sept). *History of the Royal Air Force. Phosphorised paper.* P 14½.

1336	807	17p. pale blue, greenish yellow, bright rose, blue, black and grey-black	50	40
		a. Imperf (pair)	£950	
1337	808	22p. pale turquoise-green, greenish yell, mag, new bl, blk & grey-blk	75	85
		a. Face value omitted*	£400	
		b. Queen's head omitted*	£400	
1338	809	29p. pale drab, olive-yellow, magenta, blue, grey-black and black	1·00	1·00
1339	810	31p. pale flesh, greenish yellow, magenta, ultram, blk & grey-blk	1·25	1·25
1340	811	34p. buff, greenish yellow, magenta, blue, grey-black and black	1·50	1·50
1336/40		*Set of 5*	4·50	4·50

*Nos. 1337a/b come from three consecutive sheets on which the stamps in the first vertical row are without the face value and those in the second vertical row the Queen's head.

Nos. 1336/40 were issued to celebrate the 50th anniversary of the first R.A.F. Commands.

812 The Glastonbury Thorn

813 The Tanad Valley Plygain

814 The Hebrides Tribute

815 The Dewsbury Church Knell

816 The Hereford Boy Bishop

(Des Lynda Gray)

1986 (18 Nov–2 Dec). *Christmas. Folk Customs. One phosphor band (12p., 13p.) or phosphorised paper (others). P* 15×14.

1341	**812**	12p. gold, greenish yellow, vermilion, dp brown, emerald & dp bl (2.12)	50	50
		a. Imperf (pair)	£1000	
1342		13p. deep blue, greenish yellow, verm, deep brown, emerald and gold	30	30
1343	**813**	18p. myrtle-green, yellow, vermilion, dp blue, black, reddish brn & gold	45	45
1344	**814**	22p. vermilion, olive-bistre, dull blue, deep brown, deep green and gold	75	75
1345	**815**	31p. deep brown, yellow, vermilion, violet, dp dull green, black & gold	90	90
1346	**816**	34p. violet, lemon, vermilion, deep dull blue, reddish brown and gold	1·00	1·00
1341/6		Set of 6	3·50	3·50

No. 1341 represented a discount of 1p., available between 2 and 24 December 1986, on the current second class postage rate.

Examples of the 13p. value from special folders, containing 36 stamps and sold for £4.30, show a blue underprint of double-lined stars printed on the reverse over the gum.

817 North American Blanket Flower   **818** Globe Thistle

819 *Echeveria*   **820** Autumn Crocus

(Adapted J. Matthews)

1987 (20 Jan). *Flower Photographs by Alfred Lammer. Phosphorised paper. P* 14½×14.

1347	**817**	18p. silver, greenish yellow, rosine, deep green and black	50	50
1348	**818**	22p. silver, greenish yellow, new blue, greenish blue and black	80	80
1349	**819**	31p. silver, greenish yellow, scarlet, blue-green, deep green and black	1·25	1·25
		a. Imperf (pair)	£1700	
1350	**820**	34p. silver, greenish yellow, magenta, dull blue, deep green and black	1·40	1·40
1347/50		Set of 4	3·50	3·50

OMNIBUS ISSUES

Details, together with prices for complete sets, of the various Omnibus issues from the 1935 Silver Jubilee series to date are included in a special section following Zimbabwe at the end of Volume 2.

821 *The Principia Mathematica*   **822** *Motion of Bodies in Ellipses*

823 *Optick Treatise*   **824** *The System of the World*

(Des Sarah Godwin)

1987 (24 Mar). *300th Anniv of The Principia Mathematica by Sir Isaac Newton. Phosphorised paper. P* 14×15.

1351	**821**	18p. black, greenish yellow, cerise, blue-green, grey-black and silver	50	50
1352	**822**	22p. black, greenish yellow, brt orange, blue, brt emer, silver & bluish vio	80	80
1353	**823**	31p. black, greenish yellow, scar, new bl, bronze-grn, silver & slate-grn	1·40	1·40
1354	**824**	34p. black, greenish yellow, red, bright blue, grey-black and silver	1·50	1·50
1351/4		Set of 4	3·75	3·75

825 Willis Faber & Dumas Building, Ipswich

826 Pompidou Centre, Paris

827 Staatsgalerie, Stuttgart

828 European Investment Bank, Luxembourg

(Des Brian Tattersfield)

1987 (12 May). *Europa. British Architects in Europe. Phosphorised paper. P* 15×14.

1355	**825**	18p. black, bistre-yellow, cerise, bright blue, deep grey and grey-black	50	50
1356	**826**	22p. black, greenish yellow, carmine, bright blue, dp grey & grey-black	75	75
1357	**827**	31p. grey-black, bistre-yellow, cerise, brt blue, brt green, black & dull vio	1·25	1·25
		a. Imperf (horiz pair)	£1100	
1358	**828**	34p. black, greenish yellow, cerise, bright blue, grey-black & deep grey	1·40	1·40
1355/8		Set of 4	3·50	3·50

829 Brigade Members with Ashford Litter, 1887   **830** Bandaging Blitz Victim, 1940

831 Volunteer with fainting Girl, 1965   **832** Transport of Transplant Organ by Air Wing, 1987

(Des Debbie Cook. Litho Questa)

1987 (16 June). *Centenary of St. John Ambulance Brigade. Phosphorised paper. P* 14×14½.

1359	**829**	18p. new blue, greenish yellow, magenta, black, silver and pink	50	50
1360	**830**	22p. new blue, greenish yellow, magenta, black, silver and cobalt	75	75
1361	**831**	31p. new blue, greenish yellow, magenta, black, silver and bistre-brn	1·10	1·10
1362	**832**	34p. new blue, greenish yellow, mag. blk, silver & greenish grey	1·25	1·25
1359/62		Set of 4	3·25	3·25

833 Arms of the Lord Lyon King of Arms   **834** Scottish Heraldic Banner of Prince Charles

835 Arms of Royal Scottish Academy of Painting, Sculpture and Architecture   **836** Arms of Royal Society of Edinburgh

(Des J. Matthews)

1987 (21 July). *300th Anniv of Revival of Order of the Thistle. Phosphorised paper. P* 14½.

1363	**833**	18p. black, lemon, scarlet, blue, deep green, slate and brown	50	50
1364	**834**	22p. black, greenish yellow, carmine, new blue, dp grn, grey & lake-brn	75	75
1365	**835**	31p. black, greenish yellow, scarlet, new blue, dull grn, grey & grey-blk	1·25	1·25
1366	**836**	34p. black, greenish yellow, scarlet, dp ultram, dull grn, grey & yell-brn	1·40	1·40
1363/6		Set of 4	3·50	3·50

837 Crystal Palace, "Monarch of the Glen" (Landseer) and Grace Darling

838 *Great Eastern, Beeton's Book of Household Management* and Prince Albert

839 Albert Memorial, Ballot Box and Disraeli

840 Diamond Jubilee Emblem, Newspaper Placard for Relief of Mafeking and Morse Key

(Des M. Dempsey. Eng C. Slania. Recess and photo)

1987 (8 Sept). *150th Anniv of Queen Victoria's Accession. Phosphorised paper. P 15 × 14.*

1367	837	18p. pale stone, dp blue, lemon, rose, greenish bl, brn-ochre & grey-blk	50	50
1368	838	22p. pale stone, deep brown, lemon, rose, grey-black and brown-ochre	75	75
1369	839	31p. pale stone, dp lilac, lemon, cerise, brn-ochre, greenish bl & grey-blk	1·25	1·25
1370	840	34p. pale stone, myrtle-green, yellow-ochre, reddish brown & brn-ochre	1·40	1·40
1367/70		*Set of 4*	3·50	3·50

841 Pot by Bernard Leach

842 Pot by Elizabeth Fritsch

843 Pot by Lucie Rie

844 Pot by Hans Coper

(Des T. Evans)

1987 (13 Oct). *Studio Pottery. Phosphorised paper. P 14½ × 14.*

1371	841	18p. gold, lemon, light red-brown, chestnut, light grey and black	50	50
1372	842	26p. blue over silver, yellow-orange, bright purple, lavender, bluish violet, grey-brown and black	80	80
1373	843	31p. rose-lilac over silver, greenish yellow, cerise, new bl, grey-lilac & blk	1·25	1·25
1374	844	34p. copper, yellow-brown, reddish brown, grey-lilac and black	1·40	1·40
1371/4		*Set of 4*	3·50	3·50

845 Decorating the Christmas Tree

846 Waiting for Father Christmas

847 Sleeping Child and Father Christmas in Sleigh

848 Child reading

849 Child playing Recorder and Snowman

(Des M. Foreman)

1987 (17 Nov). *Christmas. One phosphor band (13p.) or phosphorised paper (others). P 15 × 14.*

1375	845	13p. gold, greenish yellow, rose, greenish blue and black	30	30
1376	846	18p. gold, greenish yellow, bright purple, greenish blue, brt blue & blk	50	50
1377	847	26p. gold, greenish yellow, bright purple, new blue, bright blue and black	75	75
1378	848	31p. gold, greenish yellow, scarlet, brt mag, dull rose, greenish bl & blk	1·10	1·10
1379	849	34p. gold, greenish yellow, dull rose, greenish blue, bright blue & black	1·25	1·25
1375/9		*Set of 5*	3·50	3·50

Examples of the 13p. value from special folders, containing 36 stamps and sold for £4.60, show a blue underprint of double-lined stars printed on the reverse over the gum.

850 Short-spined Seascorpion ("Bull-rout") (Jonathan Couch)

851 Yellow Waterlily (Major Joshua Swatkin)

852 Whistling ("Bewick's") Swan (Edward Lear)

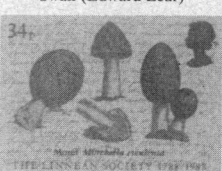

853 *Morchella esculenta* (James Sowerby)

(Des E. Hughes)

1988 (19 Jan). *Bicentenary of Linnean Society. Archive Illustrations. Phosphorised paper. P 15 × 14.*

1380	850	18p. grey-black, stone, orange-yellow, bright purple, olive-bistre & gold	60	60
1381	851	26p. black, stone, bistre-yellow, dull orange, greenish bl, gold & pale bis	95	95
1382	852	31p. black, stone, greenish yellow, rose-red, dp blue, gold & olive-bis	1·25	1·25
		a. Imperf (horiz pair)	£1300	
1383	853	34p. black, stone, yellow, pale bistre, olive-grey, gold and olive-bistre	1·40	1·40
1380/3		*Set of 4*	3·75	3·75

854 Revd William Morgan (Bible translator, 1588)   855 William Salesbury (New Testament translator, 1567)

856 Bishop Richard Davies (New Testament translator, 1567)   857 Bishop Richard Parry (editor of Revised Welsh Bible, 1620)

(Des K. Bowen)

1988 (1 Mar). *400th Anniv of Welsh Bible. Phosphorised paper. P 14½ × 14.*

1384	854	18p. grey-black, greenish yellow, cerise, blue, black and emerald	45	45
		a. Imperf (pair)	£1300	
1385	855	26p. grey-black, yellow, bright rose-red, turquoise-blue, black & orge	80	80
1386	856	31p. grey-black, chrome-yellow, carmine, new blue, grey-black and blue	1·10	1·10
1387	857	34p. grey-black, greenish yellow, cerise, turquoise-grn, blk & brt vio	1·25	1·25
1384/7		*Set of 4*	3·25	3·25

858 Gymnastics (Centenary of British Amateur Gymnastics Association)   859 Downhill Skiing (Ski Club of Great Britain)

860 Tennis (Centenary of Lawn Tennis Association)   861 Football (Centenary of Football League)

(Des J. Sutton)

1988 (22 Mar). *Sports Organizations. Phosphorised paper. P 14½.*

1388	858	18p. violet-blue, greenish yellow, rosine, brt rose, new blue & silver	45	45
1389	859	26p. violet-blue, greenish yellow, vermilion, carmine, yell-orge & silver	80	80
1390	860	31p. violet-bl, greenish yell, rose, bl, pale greenish bl, silver & brt orge	1·25	1·25
1391	861	34p. violet-blue, greenish yellow, vermilion, bl, brt emer, silver & pink	1·40	1·40
1388/91		*Set of 4*	3·50	3·50

862 *Mallard* and Mailbags on Pick-up Arms

863 Loading Transatlantic Mail on Liner *Queen Elizabeth*

864 Glasgow Tram No. 1173
and Pillar Box

865 Imperial Airways Handley
Page H.P.45 *Horatius* and
Airmail Van

(Des M. Dempsey)

1988 (10 May). *Europa. Transport and Mail Services in 1930s.*
Phosphorised paper. P 15×14.

1392	**862**	18p. brown, yellow, rose-red, dull blue, dp brown, reddish vio & blk	50	50
1393	**863**	26p. brown, yellow, orange-vermilion, dull blue, violet-bl, brt emer & blk	90	90
1394	**864**	31p. brown, yellow-orange, carmine, dull purple, vio-bl, brt grn & blk	1·10	1·10
1395	**865**	34p. brown, orange-yellow, carmine-rose, bluish vio, brt bl, sepia & blk	1·40	1·40
1392/5	..	*Set of 4*	3·50	3·50

866 Early Settler and
Sailing Clipper

867 Queen Elizabeth II with
British and Australian
Parliament Buildings

868 W. G. Grace (cricketer)
and Tennis Racquet

869 Shakespeare, John Lennon
(entertainer) and Sydney
Landmarks

(Des G. Emery. Litho Questa)

1988 (21 June). *Bicentenary of Australian Settlement. Phos-*
phorised paper. P 14½.

1396	**866**	18p. deep ultramarine, orange-yellow, scarlet, black, bluish grey & emerald	60	30
		a. Horiz pair. Nos. 1396/7 ..	1·25	1·50
1397	**867**	18p. deep ultramarine, orange-yellow, black, bluish grey and emerald ..	60	30
1398	**868**	34p. deep ultramarine, orange-yellow, scarlet, black, bluish grey & emerald	1·25	30
		a. Horiz pair. Nos. 1398/9 ..	2·50	2·50
1399	**869**	34p. deep ultramarine, orange-yellow, black, bluish grey and emerald ..	1·25	50
1396/9		*Set of 4*	3·50	1·50

Nos. 1396/7 and 1398/9 were printed together, *se-tenant*, in horizontal pairs throughout the sheets, each pair showing a background design of the Australian flag.

Stamps in similar designs were also issued by Australia.

870 Spanish Galeasse off The Lizard

871 English Fleet leaving Plymouth

872 Engagement off Isle of Wight

873 Attack of English Fire-ships, Calais

874 Armada in Storm, North Sea

(Des G. Evernden)

1988 (19 July). *400th Anniv of Spanish Armada. Phosphorised*
paper. P 15×14.

1400	**870**	18p. slate-black, yellow-orange, bright carm, brt bl, turq-bl, yell-grn & gold	85	65
		a. Horiz strip of 5. Nos. 1400/4	4·00	4·00
1401	**871**	18p. slate-black, yellow-orange, bright carm, brt bl, turq-bl, yell-grn & gold	85	65
1402	**872**	18p. slate-black, yellow-orange, bright carm, brt bl, turq-bl, yell-grn & gold	85	65
1403	**873**	18p. slate-black, yellow-orange, bright carm, brt bl, turq-bl, yell-grn & gold	85	65
1404	**874**	18p. slate-black, yellow-orange, bright carm, brt bl, turq-bl, yell-grn & gold	85	65
1400/4	..	*Set of 5*	4·00	3·00

Nos. 1400/4 were printed together, *se-tenant*, in horizontal strips of 5 throughout the sheet, forming a composite design.

875 "The Owl and the
Pussy-cat"

876 "Edward Lear as a Bird"
(self-portrait)

877 "Cat" (from alphabet
book)

878 "There was a Young Lady
whose Bonnet .." (limerick)

(Des M. Swatridge and S. Dew)

1988 (6–27 Sept). *Death Centenary of Edward Lear (artist and*
author). Phosphorised paper. P 15 × 14.

1405	**875**	19p black, pale cream and carmine	..	50	50
1406	**876**	27p black, pale cream and yellow	..	80	80

1407	**877**	32p black, pale cream and emerald	..	1·10	1·10
1408	**878**	35p black, pale cream and blue	..	1·25	1·25
1405/8	..	.. ..	*Set of 4*	3·25	3·25

MS1409 122 × 90 mm. Nos. 1405/8 (*sold at* £1.35)
(27 Sept) .. .. 8·00 8·00

The premium on No. MS1409 was used to support the "Stamp World London 90" International Stamp Exhibition.

879 Carrickfergus Castle

880 Caernarfon Castle

881 Edinburgh Castle

882 Windsor Castle

(Des from photos by Prince Andrew, Duke of York. Eng
C. Matthews. Recess Harrison)

1988 (18 Oct). *Ordinary paper.* P 15 × 14.

1410	**879**	£1 deep green	4·00	1·00
1411	**880**	£1.50, maroon	6·00	1·75
1412	**881**	£2 indigo	8·00	2·50
1413	**882**	£5 deep brown	20·00	4·50
1410/13		*Set of 4*	35·00	9·00

For similar designs, but with silhouette Queen's head see Nos. 1611/14 and 1993/6.

883 Journey to Bethlehem

884 Shepherds and Star

885 Three Wise Men

886 Nativity

887 The Annunciation

(Des L. Trickett)

1988 (15 Nov). *Christmas. Christmas Cards. One phosphor band (14p.) or phosphorised paper (others).* P 15 × 14.

1414	883	14p. gold, orange-yellow, bright mauve, bluish violet, brt blue & grey-black	45	45
		a. Error. "13p." instead of "14p."	£6000	
		b. Imperf (pair)	£750	
1415	884	19p. gold, yell-orange, brt violet, ultram, rose-red, grey-black & bright blue	50	50
		a. Imperf (pair)	£650	
1416	885	27p. gold, red, deep lavender, deep lilac, emerald, grey-black and bright blue	90	90
1417	886	32p. gold, orange-yellow, bright rose, dp mauve, violet, grey-black & brt blue	1·10	1·10
1418	887	35p. gold, green, reddish violet, bright blue, bright purple and grey-black	1·25	1·25
1414/18		Set of 5	3·75	3·75

Examples of No. 1414a were found in some 1988 Post Office Yearbooks.

888 Atlantic Puffin

889 Avocet

890 Oystercatcher

891 Northern Gannet

(Des D. Cordery)

1989 (17 Jan). *Centenary of Royal Society for the Protection of Birds. Phosphorised paper.* P 14 × 15.

1419	888	19p. grey, orange-yellow, orange-red, dull ultramarine, grey-black and silver	45	45
1420	889	27p. grey, bistre, rose, steel-blue, lavender, silver and grey-black	1·25	1·25
1421	890	32p. grey, bistre, scarlet, orange-red, lavender, silver and black	1·25	1·25
1422	891	35p. grey, lemon, rose-carmine, green, new blue, silver and black	1·50	1·50
1419/22		Set of 4	4·00	4·00

892 Rose

893 Cupid

894 Yachts

895 Fruit

896 Teddy Bear

(Des P. Sutton)

1989 (31 Jan). *Greetings Stamps. Phosphorised paper.* P 15 × 14.

1423	892	19p. black, greenish yellow, bright rose, red, new blue, light green and gold	6·25	4·50
		a. Booklet pane. Nos. 1423/7 × 2 plus 12 half stamp-size labels	55·00	
1424	893	19p. black, greenish yellow, bright rose, red, new blue, light green and gold	6·25	4·50
1425	894	19p. black, greenish yellow, bright rose, red, new blue, light green and gold	6·25	4·50
1426	895	19p. black, greenish yellow, bright rose, red, new blue, light green and gold	6·25	4·50
1427	896	19p. black, greenish yellow, bright rose, red, new blue, light green and gold	6·25	4·50
1423/7		Set of 5	28·00	20·00

Nos. 1423/7 were only issued in £1.90 booklets.

897 Fruit and Vegetables

898 Meat Products

899 Dairy Produce

900 Cereal Products

(Des Sedley Place Ltd)

1989 (7 Mar). *Food and Farming Year. Phosphorised paper.* P 14 × 14½.

1428	897	19p. brownish grey, greenish yellow, rose, new blue, black, pale grey & emerald	50	50
1429	898	27p. brownish grey, greenish yellow, bright carmine, new blue, black, pale grey and bright orange	80	80
1430	899	32p. brownish grey, greenish yellow, rose-red, new blue, black, pale grey and bistre-yellow	1·25	1·25
1431	900	35p. brownish grey, greenish yellow, bright carmine, new blue, black, pale grey and brown-red	1·40	1·40
1428/31		Set of 4	3·50	3·50

901 Mortar Board (150th Anniv of Public Education in England)

902 Cross on Ballot Paper (3rd Direct Elections to European Parliament)

903 Posthorn (26th Postal, Telegraph and Telephone International Congress, Brighton)

904 Globe (Inter-Parliamentary Union Centenary Conference, London)

(Des Lewis Moberly from firework set-pieces. Litho Questa)

1989 (11 Apr). *Anniversaries. Phosphorised paper.* P 14 × 14½.

1432	901	19p. new blue, greenish yellow, mag & blk	1·25	1·25
		a. Horiz pair. Nos. 1432/3	2·50	2·50
1433	902	19p. new blue, greenish yellow, mag & blk	1·25	1·25
1434	903	35p. new blue, greenish yellow, mag & blk	1·75	1·75
		a. Horiz pair. Nos. 1434/5	3·50	3·50
1435	904	35p. new blue, greenish yellow, mag & blk	1·75	1·75
1432/5		Set of 4	5·50	5·50

Nos. 1432/3 and 1434/5 were each printed together, *se-tenant*, in horizontal pairs throughout the sheets.

Stamps as No. 1435, but inscribed "ONE HUNDREDTH CONFERENCE" were prepared, but not issued.

905 Toy Train and Airplane

906 Building Bricks

907 Dice and Board Games

908 Toy Robot, Boat and Doll's House

(Des D. Fern)

1989 (16 May). *Europa. Games and Toys. Phosphorised paper.* P 14 × 15.

1436	905	19p. black, greenish yellow, vermilion, blue-green, blue, gold and pale ochre	50	50
1437	906	27p. black, greenish yellow, reddish orange, blue-green, blue and gold	90	90
1438	907	32p. black, greenish yellow, orange-ochre, blue-green, blue, gold and pale ochre	1·25	1·25
1439	908	35p. black, greenish yellow, reddish orange, blue-green, bl, gold & stone	1·40	1·40
1436/9		Set of 4	3·50	3·50

909 Ironbridge, Shropshire

910 Tin Mine, St. Agnes Head, Cornwall

911 Cotton Mills, New Lanark, Strathclyde

912 Pontcysyllte Aqueduct, Clwyd

(Des R. Maddox)

1989 (4–25 July). *Industrial Archaeology. Phosphorised paper.* P 14×15.

1440	909	19p. black, bistre-yellow, rose-red, apple-green, lt blue, grey-black & emerald	60	60
1441	910	27p. black, bistre-yellow, rose-red, apple-green, lt blue, grey-black & dull blue	1·00	1·00
1442	911	32p. black, yellow-orange, apple-green, yellow, dull blue, grey-black and deep reddish violet	1·10	1·10
1443	912	35p. black, yellow, bright rose, apple-green, dull blue, grey-black & verm	1·25	1·25
1440/3		Set of 4	3·50	3·50
MS1444		122×90 mm. 19p., 27p., 32p., 35p. each black, olive-yellow, bright rose-red, dull blue, apple-green, grey-black and vermilion. P 15×14 (sold at £1.40) (25 July)	6·50	6·00

The stamps in No. MS1444 are horizontal versions of Nos. 1440/3 with each design continuing onto the sheet margins.

The premium on No. MS1444 was used to support "Stamp World London 90" International Stamp Exhibition.

913

914

1989 (22 Aug)–93. *Booklet Stamps.*

(a) Photo Harrison. P 15×14

1445	913	(2nd) bright blue (1 centre band)	..	1·50	1·50
		a. Booklet pane. No. 1445×10 with horiz edges of pane imperf		8·00	
		b. Booklet pane. No. 1445×4 with three edges of pane imperf (28.11.89)		24·00	
1446		(2nd) bright blue (1 side band) (20.3.90)		2·50	2·50
1447	914	(1st) brownish black (phosphorised paper)	..	2·00	2·00
		a. Booklet pane. No. 1447×10 with horiz edges of pane imperf		10·00	
		b. Booklet pane. No. 1447×4 with three edges of pane imperf (5.12.89)		30·00	
1448		(1st) brownish black (2 bands) (20.3.90)		2·50	2·50

(b) Litho Walsall. P 14

1449	913	(2nd) bright blue (1 centre band)	..	1·00	1·00
		a. Imperf between (vert pair)			
		b. Booklet pane. No. 1449×4 with three edges of pane imperf		8·50	
		c. Booklet pane. No. 1449×4 with horiz edges of pane imperf (6.8.91)		3·00	
		d. Booklet pane. No. 1449×10 with horiz edges of pane imperf (6.8.91)		6·00	
1450	914	(1st) blackish brown (2 bands)		2·50	2·00
		a. Booklet pane. No. 1450×4 with three edges of pane imperf	..	9·00	

(c) Litho Questa. P 15×14

1451	913	(2nd) brt blue (1 centre band) (19.9.89)		1·00	1·00
1451a		(2nd) brt blue (1 side band) (25.2.92)		3·00	3·00
		al. Booklet pane. Nos. 1451a and 1514a, each × 3, with margins all round (10.8.93)		7·50	
1452	914	(1st) brownish black (phosphorised paper) (19.9.89)		2·50	2·50

Nos. 1445, 1447, 1449/51 and 1452 were initially sold at 14p. (2nd) and 19p. (1st), but these prices were later increased to reflect new postage rates.

Nos. 1446 and 1448 come from the *se-tenant* pane in the 1990 London Life £5 booklet: This pane is listed as No. X906m.

No. 1449a occurred on a miscut example of pane No. 1449d which showed an additional vertical pair beneath the last stamp in the bottom row.

No. 1451a with phosphor band at right comes from the *se-tenant* panes in the Wales and Tolkien £6 booklets. These panes are listed under Nos. 1012l and W49a (Wales Regionals). The version with band at left which appears in No. 1451al comes from the £6 Beatrix Potter booklet. No. 1446 only comes with band at right.

Nos. 1445, 1447 and 1449/50 do not exist perforated on all four sides, but come with either one or two adjacent sides imperforate.

For illustrations showing the difference between photogravure and lithography see beneath Type **367**.

For similar designs, but in changed colours, see Nos. 1511/16, for those with elliptical perforations Nos. 1663a/6 and 1979 and for self-adhesive versions Nos. 2039/40.

915 Snowflake (×10)

916 *Calliphora erythrocephala* (×5) (fly)

917 Blood Cells (×500)

918 Microchip (×600)

(Des K. Bassford. Litho Questa)

1989 (5 Sept). *150th Anniv of Royal Microscopical Society. Phosphorised paper.* P 14½×14.

1453	915	19p. gold, lemon, pale blue, grey, black and grey-black		50	50
1454	916	27p. gold, lemon, drab, black & grey-blk		1·00	1·00
1455	917	32p. gold, lemon, orange-vermilion, flesh, black and grey-black		1·25	1·25
1456	918	35p. gold, lemon, blk, brt grn & grey-blk		1·40	1·40
1453/6			*Set of 4*	3·75	3·75

919 Royal Mail Coach

920 Escort of Blues and Royals

921 Lord Mayor's Coach

922 Coach Team passing St Paul's

923 Blues and Royals Drum Horse

(Des P. Cox)

1989 (17 Oct). *Lord Mayor's Show, London. Phosphorised paper.* P 14×15.

1457	919	20p. gold, lemon, rose, orge, pale bl & blk	90	90
		a. Horiz strip of 5. Nos. 1457/61	4·00	4·00
		ab. Imperf (horiz strip of 5. Nos. 1457/61)	£5000	
		ac. Imperf (horiz strip of 4. Nos. 1457/60)	£2000	
		ad. Imperf (horiz strip of 3. Nos. 1457/9)	£950	
1458	920	20p. gold, lemon, rose, orge, pale bl & blk	90	90
1459	921	20p. gold, lemon, rose, orge, pale bl & blk	90	90
1460	922	20p. gold, lemon, rose, orge, pale bl & blk	90	90
1461	923	20p. gold, lemon, rose, orge, pale bl & blk	90	90
1457/61			*Set of 5*	4·00	4·00

This issue commemorates the 800th anniversary of the installation of the first Lord Mayor of London.

Nos. 1457/61 were printed together, *se-tenant*, in horizontal strips of 5 throughout the sheet.

Nos. 1457ab/ad come from a sheet partly imperforate at left.

924 14th-century Peasants from Stained-glass Window

925 Arches and Roundels, West Front

926 Octagon Tower

927 Arcade from West Transept

928 Triple Arch from West Front

(Des D. Gentleman)

1989 (14 Nov). *Christmas. 800th Anniversary of Ely Cathedral. One phosphor band (15p., 15p.+1p.) or phosphorised paper (others).* P 15×14.

1462	924	15p. gold, silver and blue	..	40	40
1463	925	15p. + 1p. gold, silver and blue	..	50	50
1464	926	20p. + 1p. gold, silver and rosine		60	60
		a. Imperf (pair)		£1300	
1465	927	34p. + 1p. gold, silver and emerald		1·40	1·40
1466	928	37p. + 1p. gold, silver and yellow-olive		1·40	1·40
1462/6			*Set of 5*	3·75	3·75

929 Queen Victoria and Queen Elizabeth II

(Des J. Matthews (from plaster casts by Wyon and Machin))

1990 (10 Jan–12 June). *150th Anniv of the Penny Black.*

(a) Photo Harrison. P 15×14

1467	929	15p. bright blue (1 centre band)	..	50	50
		a. Imperf (pair)		£1400	
		l. Booklet pane. No. 1467×10 with horiz edges of pane imperf (30.1.90)		7·50	
1468		15p. bright blue (1 side band) (30.1.90)		3·25	3·25
		l. Booklet pane. No. 1468×2 and 1470 plus label		5·00	
1469		20p. brownish black and cream (phosphorised paper)	..	75	75
		a. Imperf (pair)		£1000	
		l. Booklet pane. No. 1469×5 plus label with vert sides of pane imperf (30.1.90)		7·00	
		m. Booklet pane. No. 1469×10 with horiz edges of pane imperf (20.3.90)		9·00	
		n. Booklet pane. No. 1469×6 with margins all round (20.3.90)		2·50	
		r. Booklet pane. No. 1469×4 with three edges of pane imperf (17.4.90)		6·50	
1470		20p. brownish black and cream (2 bands) (30.1.90)		2·50	2·50
1471		29p. deep mauve (phosphorised paper)		1·50	1·50
1472		29p. deep mauve (2 bands) (20.3.90)		8·00	8·00
1473		34p. dp bluish grey (phosphorised paper)		1·75	1·75
1474		37p. rosine (phosphorised paper)		1·75	1·75

(b) Litho Walsall. P 14

1475	929	15p. bright blue (1 centre band) (30.1.90)		1·25	1·25
		l. Booklet pane. No. 1475×4 with three edges of pane imperf		10·00	
		m. Booklet pane. No. 1475×10 with three edges of pane imperf (12.6.90)		10·00	
1476		20p. brownish black and cream (phosphorised paper) (30.1.90)		1·50	1·50
		l. Booklet pane. No. 1476×5 plus label with vertical edges of pane imperf		7·00	
		m. Booklet pane. No. 1476×4 with three edges of pane imperf		10·00	
		n. Booklet pane. No. 1476×10 with three edges of pane imperf (12.6.90)		10·00	

(c) Litho Questa. P 15×14

1477	929	15p. bright blue (1 centre band) (17.4.90)		2·25	2·25
1478		20p. brownish black (phosphorised paper) (17.4.90)		2·25	2·25

Nos. 1475/6 do not exist perforated on all four sides, but come with either one or two adjacent sides imperforate.

Nos. 1468, 1470, 1472 and 1475/8 were only issued in stamp booklets. No. 1468 exists with the phosphor band at left or right. Nos. 1468 (band at right), 1470 and 1472 occur in the *se-tenant* pane from the 1990 London Life £5 booklet. This pane is listed as No. X906m.

For illustrations showing the difference between photogravure and lithography see beneath Type **367**.

For No. 1469 in miniature sheet see No. **MS1501**.

For Type **929** redrawn with "1st" face value see No. 2133.

930 Kitten

931 Rabbit

932 Duckling

933 Puppy

(Des T. Evans. Litho Questa)

1990 (23 Jan). *150th Anniv of Royal Society for Prevention of Cruelty to Animals. Phosphorised paper.* P 14×14½.

1479	930	20p. new blue, greenish yellow, bright magenta, black and silver	65	70
		a. Silver (Queen's head and face value) omitted	£175	
1480	931	29p. new blue, greenish yellow, bright magenta, black and silver	1·25	1·25
		a. Imperf (horiz pair)	£2500	
1481	932	34p. new blue, greenish yellow, bright magenta, black and silver	1·50	1·50
		a. Silver (Queen's head and face value) omitted	£350	
1482	933	37p. new blue, greenish yellow, bright magenta, black and silver	1·60	1·60
1479/82			Set of 4	4·50	4·50

934 Teddy Bear

935 Dennis the Menace

936 Punch

937 Cheshire Cat

938 The Man in the Moon

939 The Laughing Policeman

940 Clown

941 Mona Lisa

942 Queen of Hearts

943 Stan Laurel (comedian)

(Des Michael Peters and Partners Ltd)

1990 (6 Feb). *Greetings Stamps. "Smiles". Two phosphor bands.* P 15×14.

1483	934	20p. gold, greenish yellow, bright rose-red, new blue and grey-black	3·25	2·50
		a. Booklet pane. Nos. 1483/92 with margins all round	28·00	
1484	935	20p. gold, greenish yellow, brt rose-red, new blue, deep blue and grey-black	3·25	2·50
1485	936	20p. gold, greenish yellow, brt rose-red, new blue, deep blue and grey-black	3·25	2·50
1486	937	20p. gold, greenish yellow, brt rose-red, new blue and grey-black	3·25	2·50
1487	938	20p. gold, greenish yellow, brt rose-red, new blue and grey-black	3·25	2·50
1488	939	20p. gold, greenish yellow, brt rose-red, new blue and grey-black	3·25	2·50
1489	940	20p. gold, greenish yellow, brt rose-red, new blue and grey-black	3·25	2·50
1490	941	20p. gold, greenish yellow, bright rose-red, and grey-black	3·25	2·50
1491	942	20p. gold, greenish yellow, bright rose-red, new blue and grey-black	3·25	2·50
1492	943	20p. gold and grey-black	3·25	2·50
1483/92			Set of 10	28·00	22·00

Nos. 1483/92 were only issued in £2 booklets. The designs of Nos. 1483, 1485/7, 1489 and 1492 extend onto the pane margin.

For these designs with the face value expressed as "1st" see Nos. 1550/9.

944 Alexandra Palace ("Stamp World London 90" Exhibition)

945 Glasgow School of Art

946 British Philatelic Bureau, Edinburgh

947 Templeton Carpet Factory, Glasgow

(Des P. Hogarth)

1990 (6–20 Mar). *Europa* (Nos. 1493 *and* 1495) *and "Glasgow 1990 European City of Culture"* (Nos. 1494 *and* 1496). *Phosphorised paper.* P 14×15.

1493	944	20p. silver, lemon, flesh, grey-brown, blue, grey-black and black	50	50
		a. Booklet pane. No. 1493×4 with margins all round (20 March)	2·00	
1494	945	20p. silver, greenish yellow, dull orange, blue, grey-black and black	50	50
1495	946	29p. silver, stone, orange, olive-sepia, grey-blue, grey-black and black	1·25	1·25
1496	947	37p. silver, greenish yellow, brt emerald, salmon, olive-sepia, brt blue & black	1·40	1·40
1493/6			Set of 4	3·25	3·25

948 Export Achievement Award

949 Technological Achievement Award

(Des S. Broom. Litho Questa)

1990 (10 Apr). *25th Anniv of Queen's Awards for Export and Technology. Phosphorised paper.* P 14×14½.

1497	948	20p. new blue, greenish yellow, magenta, black and silver	75	75
		a. Horiz pair. Nos. 1497/8	1·50	1·50
1498	949	20p. new blue, greenish yellow, magenta, black and silver	75	75
1499	948	37p. new blue, greenish yellow, magenta, black and silver	1·40	1·40
		a. Horiz pair. Nos. 1499/500	2·75	2·75
1500	949	37p. new blue, greenish yellow, magenta, black and silver	1·40	1·40
1497/500			Set of 4	3·75	3·75

Nos. 1497/8 and 1499/500 were each printed together, *se-tenant*, in horizontal pairs throughout the sheets.

(Des J. Matthews and Sedley Place Design Ltd. Eng C. Matthews. Recess and photo)

1990 (3 May). *"Stamp World London 90" International Stamp Exhibition, London. Sheet,* 122×90 mm., *containing No.* 1469. *Phosphorised paper.* P 15×14.

MS1501	929	20p. brownish blk & cream (*sold at* £1)	4·50	4·50
		a. Error. Imperf	£6500	
		b. Black (recess printing) omitted	£7500	
		c. Black (recess printing) inverted	£7500	

The premium on No. MS1501 was used to support the "Stamp World London 90" International Stamp Exhibition.

On examples of No. MS1501b the 1d. black and seahorse background are omitted due to a printer's sheet becoming attached to the underside before the recess part of the design was printed. There is an albino impression visible on the reverse.

No. MS1501c shows the recess part of the design inverted in relation to the photogravure printing of Type 929.

950 Cycad and Sir Joseph Banks Building

951 Stone Pine and Princess of Wales Conservatory

952 Willow Tree and Palm House

953 Cedar Tree and Pagoda

(Des P. Leith)

1990 (5 June). *150th Anniv of Kew Gardens. Phosphorised paper.* P 14×15.

1502	950	20p. black, brt emerald, pale turquoise-green, light brown and lavender	50	50
1503	951	29p. black, brt emerald, turquoise-green, reddish orange and grey-black	80	80
1504	952	34p. Venetian red, brt green, cobalt, dull purple, turquoise-grn & yellow-green	1·25	1·25
1505	953	37p. pale violet-blue, bright emerald, red-brown, steel-blue and brown-rose	1·40	1·40
1502/5			Set of 4	3·50	3·50

954 Thomas Hardy and Clyffe Clump, Dorset

(Des J. Gibbs)

1990 (10 July). *150th Birth Anniv of Thomas Hardy (author). Phosphorised paper. P 14×15.*

| 1506 | 954 | 20p. vermilion, greenish yellow, pale lake-brown, deep brown, light red-brown and black | 1·00 | 1·00 |
| | | a. Imperf (pair) | | £1000 |

955 Queen Elizabeth the Queen Mother

956 Queen Elizabeth

957 Elizabeth, Duchess of York

958 Lady Elizabeth Bowes-Lyon

(Des J. Gorham from photographs by N. Parkinson (20p.), Dorothy Wilding (29p.), B. Park (34p.), Rita Martin (37p.))

1990 (2 Aug.). *90th Birthday of Queen Elizabeth the Queen Mother. Phosphorised paper. P 14×15.*

1507	955	20p. silver, greenish yellow, magenta, turquoise-blue and grey-black	70	70
1508	956	29p. silver, indigo and grey-blue	1·10	1·10
1509	957	34p. silver, lemon, red, new blue and grey-black	1·75	1·75
1510	958	37p. silver, sepia and stone	2·00	2·00
1507/10		*Set of 4*	5·00	5·00

1990 (7 Aug)–*92. Booklet Stamps. As T 913/14, but colours changed.*

		(a) Photo Harrison. P 15×14		
1511	913	(2nd) deep blue (1 centre band)	1·00	1·00
		a. Booklet pane. No. 1511×10 with horiz edges of pane imperf	8·50	
1512	914	(1st) brt orge-red (phosphorised paper)	1·25	1·25
		a. Booklet pane. No. 1512×10 with horiz edges of pane imperf	6·50	
		(b) Litho Questa. P 15×14		
1513	913	(2nd) deep blue (1 centre band)	2·50	2·50
1514	914	(1st) brt orge-red (phosphorised paper)	1·00	1·00
1514a		(1st) brt orange-red (2 bands) (25.2.92)	2·25	2·25
		(c) Litho Walsall. P 14		
1515	913	(2nd) deep blue (1 centre band)	1·00	1·00
		a. Booklet pane. No. 1515×4 with horiz edges of pane imperf	3·50	
		b. Booklet pane. No. 1515×10 with horiz edges of pane imperf	6·50	
1516	914	(1st) brt orge-red (phosphorised paper)	1·00	1·00
		a. Booklet pane. No. 1516×4 with horiz edges of pane imperf	3·50	
		b. Booklet pane. No. 1516×10 with horiz edges of pane imperf	6·50	
		c. Perf 13	2·75	2·75
		ca. Booklet pane. No. 1516c×4 with horiz edges of pane imperf	11·00	

Nos. 1511/14 and 1515/16 were initially sold at 15p. (2nd) and 20p. (1st), but these prices were later increased to reflect new postage rates.

Nos. 1511/12 and 1515/16 do not exist perforated on all four sides, but come with either the top or the bottom edge imperforate.

No. 1514a comes from the *se-tenant* panes in the £6 Wales, £6 Tolkien and £5.64 Beatrix Potter booklets. These panes are listed under Nos. X1012l, 1451al and W49a (Wales Regionals).

No. 1516c was caused by the use of an incorrect perforation comb.

For similar stamps with elliptical perforations see Nos. 1663a/6.

For illustrations showing the difference between photogravure and lithography see beneath Type 367.

959 Victoria Cross

960 George Cross

---

961 Distinguished Service Cross and Distinguished Service Medal

962 Military Cross and Military Medal

963 Distinguished Flying Cross and Distinguished Flying Medal

(Des J. Gibbs and J. Harwood)

1990 (11 Sept). *Gallantry Awards. Phosphorised paper. P 14×15 (vert) or 15×14 (horiz).*

1517	959	20p. grey-black, pale stone, stone, bistre-brown and bright carmine	90	90
1518	960	20p. grey-black, pale stone, flesh, grey and ultramarine	90	90
1519	961	20p. grey-black, pale stone, flesh, pale blue and ultramarine	90	90
		a. Imperf (pair)		
1520	962	20p. grey-black, pale stone, ochre, pale blue, ultramarine, scarlet and violet	90	90
1521	963	20p. grey-black, pale stone, yellow-brown, bluish grey and purple	90	90
1517/21		*Set of 5*	4·00	4·00

964 Armagh Observatory, Jodrell Bank Radio Telescope and La Palma Telescope

965 Newton's Moon and Tides Diagram with Early Telescopes

966 Greenwich Old Observatory and Early Astronomical Equipment

967 Stonehenge, Gyroscope and Navigating by Stars

(Des J. Fisher. Litho Questa)

1990 (16 Oct). *Astronomy. Phosphorised paper. P 14×14½.*

1522	964	22p. cream, grey, dull blue-grn, slate-bl, blue-grn, orange-red, gold & black	50	40
		a. Gold (Queen's head) omitted		£375
1523	965	26p. black, yellow, dull purple, pale cream, brown-rose, new blue, greenish yellow, vermilion & gold	80	90
1524	966	31p. black, cream, pale cream, yellow-orge, salmon, lemon, verm & gold	1·10	1·10
1525	967	37p. black, pale buff, olive-bistre, pale cream, pale flesh, flesh, grey, rose-red and gold	1·25	1·25
1522/5		*Set of 4*	3·25	3·25

Nos. 1522/5 commemorate the Centenary of the British Astronomical Association and the Bicentenary of the Armagh Observatory.

---

968 Building a Snowman

969 Fetching the Christmas Tree

970 Carol Singing

971 Tobogganing

972 Ice-skating

(Des J. Gorham and A. Davidson)

1990 (13 Nov). *Christmas. One phosphor band (17p) or phosphorised paper (others). P 15×14.*

1526	968	17p. gold, greenish yellow, rose, new blue and grey-black	45	35
		a. Booklet pane of 20	9·00	
1527	969	22p. gold, greenish yellow, magenta, new blue and black	55	65
		a. Imperf (horiz pair)		£450
1528	970	26p. gold, olive-yellow, pale magenta, agate, new blue, dull violet-bl & blk	80	80
1529	971	31p. gold, greenish yellow, bright rose-red, dull mauve, new blue, turquoise-blue and grey-black	1·10	1·10
1530	972	37p. gold, greenish yellow, rose, new blue and slate-green	1·25	1·25
1526/30		*Set of 5*	3·75	3·75

Booklet pane No. 1526a comes from a special £3.40 Christmas booklet and has the horizontal edges of the pane imperforate.

973 "King Charles Spaniel"

974 "A Pointer"

975 "Two Hounds in a Landscape"

976 "A Rough Dog"

977 "Fino and Tiny"

(Des Carroll, Dempsey & Thirkell Ltd)

1991 (8 Jan). *Dogs. Paintings by George Stubbs. Phosphorised paper.* P 14×14½.

1531	973	22p. gold, greenish yellow, magenta, new blue black and drab		80	80
		a. Imperf (pair)		£950	
1532	974	26p. gold, greenish yellow, magenta, new blue, black and drab		1·00	1·00
1533	975	31p. gold, greenish yellow, magenta, new blue, black and drab		1·10	1·10
		a. Imperf (pair)		£950	
1534	976	33p. gold, greenish yellow, magenta, new blue, black and drab		1·25	1·25
1535	977	37p. gold, greenish yellow, magenta, new blue, black and drab		1·40	1·40
1531/5			*Set of 5*	5·00	5·00

978 Thrush's Nest

979 Shooting Star and Rainbow

980 Magpies and Charm Bracelet

981 Black Cat

982 Common Kingfisher with Key

983 Mallard and Frog

984 Four-leaf Clover in Boot and Match Box

985 Pot of Gold at End of Rainbow

986 Heart-shaped Butterflies

987 Wishing Well and Sixpence

(Des T. Meeuwissen)

1991 (5 Feb). *Greetings Stamps. "Good Luck". Two phosphor bands.* P 15×14.

1536	978	(1st) silver, greenish yellow, magenta new blue, olive-brown and black		1·90	1·90
		a. Booklet pane. Nos. 1536/45 plus 12 half stamp-size labels with margins on 3 sides		17·00	
1537	979	(1st) silver, greenish yellow, magenta new blue, olive-brown and black		1·90	1·90
1538	980	(1st) silver, greenish yellow, magenta new blue, olive-brown and black		1·90	1·90
1539	981	(1st) silver, greenish yellow, magenta new blue, olive-brown and black		1·90	1·90
1540	982	(1st) silver, greenish yellow, magenta new blue, olive-brown and black		1·90	1·90
1541	983	(1st) silver, greenish yellow, magenta new blue, olive-brown and black		1·90	1·90
1542	984	(1st) silver, greenish yellow, magenta new blue, olive-brown and black		1·90	1·90
1543	985	(1st) silver, greenish yellow, magenta new blue, olive-brown and black		1·90	1·90
1544	986	(1st) silver, greenish yellow, magenta new blue, olive-brown and black		1·90	1·90
1545	987	(1st) silver, greenish yellow, magenta new blue, olive-brown and black		1·90	1·90
1536/45			*Set of 10*	17·00	17·00

Nos. 1536/45 were initially sold at 22p. each and were only issued in £2.20 booklets. It is intended that the price will be increased to reflect future alterations in postage rates. The backgrounds of the stamps form a composite design.

988 Michael Faraday (inventor of electric motor) (Birth Bicentenary)

989 Charles Babbage (computer science pioneer) (Birth Bicentenary)

990 Radar Sweep of East Anglia (50th anniv of operational radar network)

991 Gloster Whittle E28/39 Aircraft over East Anglia (50th anniv of first flight of Sir Frank Whittle's jet engine)

(Des P. Till (Nos. 1546/7), J. Harwood (Nos. 1548/9))

1991 (5 Mar). *Scientific Achievements. Phosphorised paper.* P 14×15.

1546	988	22p. silver, olive-brown greenish yellow, magenta, slate-blue, grey and black	65	65
		a. Imperf (pair)	£350	
1547	989	22p. silver, chrome yellow, red, grey-black, brownish grey and sepia	65	65
1548	990	31p. silver, deep turquoise-green, violet-blue, steel blue and deep dull blue	95	95
1549	991	37p. silver, olive-bistre, rose-red, turq-blue, new blue and grey-black	1·10	1·10
1546/9		*Set of 4*	3·00	3·00

992 Teddy Bear

1991 (26 Mar). *Greetings Stamps. "Smiles". As Nos. 1483/92, but inscr "1st" as in T* **992**. *Two phosphor bands.* P 15×14.

1550	992	(1st) gold, greenish yellow, bright rose-red, new blue and grey-black	1·25	1·25
		a. Booklet pane. Nos. 1550/9 plus 12 half stamp-size labels with margins on 3 sides	11·00	
1551	935	(1st) gold, greenish yellow, brt rose-red, new blue, deep blue & grey-black	1·25	1·25
1552	936	(1st) gold, greenish yellow, brt rose-red, new blue, deep blue & grey-black	1·25	1·25
1553	937	(1st) gold, greenish yellow, bright rose-red, new blue and grey-black	1·25	1·25
1554	938	(1st) gold, greenish yellow, bright rose-red, new blue and grey-black	1·25	1·25
1555	939	(1st) gold, greenish yellow, bright rose-red, new blue and grey-black	1·25	1·25
1556	940	(1st) gold, greenish yellow, bright rose-red, new blue and grey-black	1·25	1·25
1557	941	(1st) gold, greenish yellow, bright rose-red and grey-black	1·25	1·25
1558	942	(1st) gold, greenish yellow, bright rose-red, new blue and grey-black	1·25	1·25
1559	943	(1st) gold and grey-black	1·25	1·25
1550/9		*Set of 10*	11·00	11·00

Nos. 1550/9 were only issued in £2.20 booklets (sold at £2.40 from 16 September 1991 and at £2.50 from 1 November 1993). The designs of Nos. 1550, 1552/4, 1556 and 1559 extend onto the pane margin.

993 Man looking at Space **994**

995 Space looking at Man **996**

(Des J.-M. Folon)

1991 (23 Apr). *Europa. Europe in Space. Phosphorised paper.* P 14×15.

1560	993	22p. silver-mauve, greenish yellow, scar, violet-blue, brt green & blk	55	55
		a. Horiz pair. Nos. 1560/1	1·10	1·10
1561	994	22p. silver-mauve, greenish yellow, scar, violet-blue, bright blue and black	55	55
1562	995	37p. silver-mauve, bistre-yellow, dull vermilion, blue and black	1·25	1·25
		a. Horiz pair. Nos. 1562/3	2·50	2·50
1563	996	37p. silver-mauve, bistre-yellow, dull vermilion, blue and black	1·25	1·25
1560/3		*Set of 4*	3·25	3·25

Nos. 1560/1 and 1562/3 were each printed together, *se-tenant*, in horizontal pairs throughout the sheets, each pair forming a composite design.

997 Fencing **998** Hurdling

999 Diving

1000 Rugby

(Des Huntley Muir)

1991 (11 June). *World Student Games, Sheffield (Nos. 1564/6) and World Cup Rugby Championship (No. 1567). Phosphorised paper. P 14½×14.*

1564	**997**	22p. black, greenish yellow, vermilion, bright orange, ultramarine and grey	50	50
1565	**998**	26p. pale blue, greenish yellow, red, bright blue and black	80	80
1566	**999**	31p. bright blue, bistre-yellow, rose, vermilion, new blue and black	95	95
1567	**1000**	37p. yellow-orange, greenish yellow, rose, bright blue, emerald & black	1·10	1·10
1564/7		*Set of 4*	3·00	3·00

1001 "Silver Jubilee"

1002 "Mme Alfred Carrière"

1003 *Rosa moyesii*

1004 "Harvest Fayre"

1005 "Mutabilis"

(Des Yvonne Skargon. Litho Questa)

1991 (16 July). *9th World Congress of Roses, Belfast. Phosphorised paper. P 14½×14.*

1568	**1001**	22p. new blue, greenish yellow, magenta, black and silver	80	80
		a. Silver (Queen's head) omitted	£750	
1569	**1002**	26p. new blue, greenish yellow, magenta, black and silver	1·00	1·00
1570	**1003**	31p. new blue, greenish yellow, magenta, black and silver	1·10	1·10
1571	**1004**	33p. new blue, greenish yellow, magenta, black and silver	1·25	1·25
1572	**1005**	37p. new blue, greenish yellow, magenta, black and silver	1·40	1·40
1568/72		*Set of 5*	5·00	5·00

1006 Iguanodon

1007 Stegosaurus

1008 Tyrannosaurus

1009 Protoceratops

1010 Triceratops

(Des B. Kneale)

1991 (20 Aug). *150th Anniv of Dinosaurs' Identification by Owen. Phosphorised paper. P 14½×14.*

1573	**1006**	22p. grey, pale blue, magenta, bright blue, dull violet and grey-black	75	60
		a. Imperf (pair)	£1000	
1574	**1007**	26p. grey, greenish yellow, pale emerald, bright blue-green, pale bright blue, grey-black and black	90	1·10
1575	**1008**	31p. grey, light blue, magenta, brt blue, pale blue, brown and grey-black	1·10	1·10
1576	**1009**	33p. grey, dull rose, pale brt bl, brt rose-red, yellow-orge, grey-blk & blk	1·40	1·25
1577	**1010**	37p. grey, greenish yellow, turquoise-blue, dull violet, yellow-brn & blk	1·50	1·50
1573/7		*Set of 5*	5·00	5·00

1011 Map of 1816

1012 Map of 1906

1013 Map of 1959

1014 Map of 1991

(Des H. Brown. Recess and litho Harrison (24p.), Litho Harrison (28p.), Questa (33p., 39p.))

1991 (17 Sept). *Bicentenary of Ordnance Survey. Maps of Hamstreet, Kent. Phosphorised paper. P 14½×14.*

1578	**1011**	24p. black, magenta, and cream	50	50
1579	**1012**	28p. blk, brt yellow-grn, new bl, reddish orge, magenta, olive-sepia & cream	85	85
1580	**1013**	33p. dull blue-green, orange-brown, magenta, olive-grey, greenish yellow, verm, greenish grey, pale bl, bl, dull orge, apple grn & blk	1·00	1·00
1581	**1014**	39p. black, mag, greenish yell & new bl	1·25	1·25
1578/81		*Set of 4*	3·25	3·25

Mint examples of Type **1012** exist with a face value of 26p.

1015 Adoration of the Magi

1016 Mary and Baby Jesus in the Stable

1017 The Holy Family and Angel

1018 The Annunciation

1019 The Flight into Egypt

(Des D. Driver)

1991 (12 Nov). *Christmas. Illuminated Letters from "Acts of Mary and Jesus" Manuscript in Bodleian Library. Oxford. One phosphor band (18p.) or phosphorised paper (others). P 15×14.*

1582	**1015**	18p. steel-blue, greenish yellow, rose-red, orange-red, black & gold	70	40
		a. Imperf (pair)	£1750	
		b. Booklet pane of 20	8·25	
1583	**1016**	24p. bright rose-red, greenish yellow, vermilion, slate-blue, yellow-green, grey-black and gold	80	50
1584	**1017**	28p. reddish brn, bistre-yellow, orange-vermilion, orange-red, deep dull blue, grey-black and gold	85	1·00
1585	**1018**	33p. green, greenish yell, red, orange-red, blue, grey and gold	95	1·10
1586	**1019**	39p. orange-red, greenish yell, orange-vermilion, deep dull blue, olive-sepia, black and gold	1·10	1·40
1582/6		*Set of 5*	4·00	4·00

Booklet pane No. 1582b comes from special £3.60 Christmas booklet and has margins at left, top and bottom.

1020 Fallow Deer in Scottish Forest

1021 Hare on North Yorkshire Moors

1022 Fox in the Fens

1023 Redwing and Home Counties Village

1024 Welsh Mountain Sheep in Snowdonia

(Des J. Gorham and K. Bowen)

1992 (14 Jan–25 Feb). *The Four Seasons. Wintertime. One phosphor band (18p.) or phosphorised paper (others).* P 15×14.

1587	1020	18p. silver, greenish yellow, grey, dull rose, new blue and black	50	50
1588	1021	24p. silver, lemon, rose, blue & grey-blk	70	70
		a. Imperf (pair)	£325	
1589	1022	28p. silver, greenish yellow, bright rose, steel-blue and grey black	90	90
1590	1023	33p. silver, greenish yellow, brt orange, brt purple, greenish blue & grey	1·10	1·10
1591	1024	39p. silver, yellow, yellow-orange, grey, vermilion, new blue and black	1·25	1·25
		a. Booklet pane. No. 1591×4 with margins all round (25 Feb)	3·25	
1587/91		Set of 5	4·00	4·00

Booklet pane No. 1591a comes from the £6 "Cymru-Wales" booklet.

1025 Flower Spray

1026 Double Locket

1027 Key

1028 Model Car and Cigarette Cards

1029 Compass and Map

1030 Pocket Watch

1031 1854 1d. Red Stamp and Pen

1032 Pearl Necklace

1033 Marbles

1034 Bucket, Spade and Starfish

(Des Trickett and Webb Ltd)

1992 (28 Jan). *Greetings Stamps. "Memories". Two phosphor bands.* P 15×14.

1592	1025	(1st) gold, greenish yellow, magenta, ochre, light blue and grey-black	1·10	1·10
		a. Booklet pane. Nos. 1592/1601 plus 12 half stamp-size labels with margins on 3 sides	10·00	
1593	1026	(1st) gold, greenish yellow, magenta, ochre, light blue and grey-black	1·10	1·10
1594	1027	(1st) gold, greenish yellow, magenta, ochre, light blue and grey-black	1·10	1·10
1595	1028	(1st) gold, greenish yellow, magenta, ochre, light blue and grey-black	1·10	1·10
1596	1029	(1st) gold, greenish yellow, magenta, ochre, light blue and grey-black	1·10	1·10
1597	1030	(1st) gold, greenish yellow, magenta, ochre, light blue and grey-black	1·10	1·10
1598	1031	(1st) gold, greenish yellow, magenta, ochre, light blue and grey-black	1·10	1·10
1599	1032	(1st) gold, greenish yellow, magenta, ochre, light blue and grey-black	1·10	1·10
1600	1033	(1st) gold, greenish yellow, magenta, ochre, light blue and grey-black	1·10	1·10
1601	1034	(1st) gold, greenish yellow, magenta, ochre, light blue and grey-black	1·10	1·10
1592/1601		Set of 10	10·00	10·00

Nos. 1592/1601 were only issued in £2.40 booklets (sold at £2.50 from 1 November 1993 and at £2.60 from 8 July 1996). The backgrounds of the stamps form a composite design.

1035 Queen Elizabeth in Coronation Robes and Parliamentary Emblem

1036 Queen Elizabeth in Garter Robes and Archiepiscopal Arms

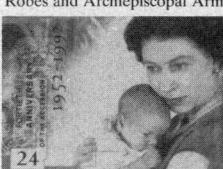

1037 Queen Elizabeth with Baby Prince Andrew and Royal Arms

1038 Queen Elizabeth at Trooping the Colour and Service Emblems

1039 Queen Elizabeth and Commonwealth Emblem

(Des Why Not Associates. Litho Questa)

1992 (6 Feb). *40th Anniv of Accession. Two phosphor bands.* P 14½×14.

1602	1035	24p. new blue, greenish yellow, magenta, black, silver and gold	1·40	1·40
		a. Horiz strip of 5. Nos. 1602/6	6·25	6·25
1603	1036	24p. new blue, greenish yellow, magenta, black, silver and gold	1·40	1·40
1604	1037	24p. new blue, greenish yellow, magenta, black and silver	1·40	1·40
1605	1038	24p. new blue, greenish yellow, magenta, black, silver and gold	1·40	1·40
1606	1039	24p. new blue, greenish yellow, magenta, black, silver and gold	1·40	1·40
1602/6		Set of 5	6·25	6·25

Nos. 1602/6 were printed together, *se-tenant*, in horizontal strips of five throughout the sheet.

1040 Tennyson in 1888 and "The Beguiling of Merlin" (Sir Edward Burne-Jones)

1041 Tennyson in 1856 and "April Love" (Arthur Hughes)

1042 Tennyson in 1864 and "I am Sick of the Shadows" (John Waterhouse)

1043 Tennyson as a Young Man and "Mariana" (Dante Gabriel Rossetti)

(Des Irene von Treskow)

1992 (10 Mar). *Death Centenary of Alfred, Lord Tennyson (poet). Phosphorised paper.* P 14½×14.

1607	1040	24p. gold, greenish yellow, magenta, new blue and black	50	50
1608	1041	28p. gold, greenish yellow, magenta, new blue and black	75	75
1609	1042	33p. gold, greenish yellow, magenta, new blue and black	1·25	1·25
1610	1043	39p. gold, greenish yellow, magenta, new blue, bistre and black	1·40	1·40
1607/10		Set of 4	3·50	3·50

1044 Carrickfergus Castle

Elliptical hole in vertical perforations

GH CASTLE

Harrison Plates (Nos. 1611/14)

GH CASTLE

Enschedé Plates (Nos. 1993/6)

(Des from photos by Prince Andrew, Duke of York. Eng C. Matthews. Recess Harrison)

1992 (24 Mar)–**95**. *Designs as Nos. 1410/13, but showing Queen's head in silhouette as T* **1044**. P 15×14 (*with one elliptical hole on each vertical side*).

1611	1044	£1 bottle green and gold†	6·00	2·00
1612	880	£1.50, maroon and gold†	4·50	3·00
1613	881	£2 indigo and gold†	6·00	4·00

1613a	1044	£3 reddish violet and gold† (22.8.95)	10·00	8·00
1614	882	£5 deep brown and gold†	15·00	7·00
		a. Gold (Queen's head) omitted		£275
1611/14		Set of 5	35·00	21·00

† The Queen's head on these stamps is printed in optically variable ink which changes colour from gold to green when viewed from different angles.

The £1·50 (5 March 1996), £2 (2 May 1996), £3 (1997) and £5 (17 September 1996) subsequently appeared on PVA (white gum) instead of the tinted PVAD previously used.

See also Nos. 1993/6.

1045 British Olympic Association Logo (Olympic Games, Barcelona)

1046 British Paralympic Association Symbol (Paralympics '92, Barcelona)

1047 *Santa Maria* (500th Anniv of Discovery of America by Columbus)

1048 *Kaisei* (Japanese cadet brigantine) (Grand Regatta Columbus, 1992)

1049 British Pavilion, "Expo '92", Seville

(Des K. Bassford (Nos. 1615/16, 1619), K. Bassford and S. Paine, Eng. C. Matthews (Nos. 1617/18). Litho Questa (Nos. 1615/16, 1619) or recess and litho Harrison (Nos. 1617/18))

1992 (7 Apr). *Europa. International Events. Phosphorised paper.* P 14×14½.

1615	1045	24p. new blue, lemon, magenta & black	1·00	1·00
		a. Horiz pair. Nos. 1615/16	2·00	2·00
1616	1046	24p. new blue, lemon, magenta & black	1·00	1·00
1617	1047	24p. black, grey, carmine, cream & gold	80	80
1618	1048	39p. black, grey, carmine, cream & gold	1·10	1·10
1619	1049	39p. new blue, lemon, magenta & black	1·10	1·10
1615/19		Set of 5	4·50	4·50

Nos. 1615/16 were printed together, *se-tenant*, throughout the sheet.

No. 1617 is known with the cream omitted used from Cornwall in September 1992.

1050 Pikeman

1051 Drummer

1052 Musketeer

1053 Standard Bearer

(Des J. Sancha)

1992 (16 June). *350th Anniv of the Civil War. Phosphorised paper.* P 14½×14.

1620	1050	24p. black, stone, bistre, scarlet, indigo, grey-green and yellow-ochre	55	55
		a. Imperf (pair)		£250
1621	1051	28p. black, yellow-ochre, ochre, rose-pink, bl, dull yell-grn & slate-lilac	70	70
1622	1052	33p. black, ochre, pale orange, lemon, reddish orange, new bl & olive-grn	1·25	1·25
1623	1053	39p. black, yellow-ochre, yell, greenish yellow, vermilion, ind & orge-brn	1·40	1·40
1620/3		Set of 4	3·50	3·50

1054 The Yeomen of the Guard

1055 The Gondoliers

1056 The Mikado

1057 The Pirates of Penzance

1058 Iolanthe

(Des Lynda Gray)

1992 (21 July). *150th Birth Anniv of Sir Arthur Sullivan (composer). Gilbert and Sullivan Operas. One phosphor band (18p.) or phosphorised paper (others).* P 14½×14.

1624	1054	18p. bluish violet, bistre-yellow, scarlet, stone, blue and grey-black	45	45
1625	1055	24p. purple-brown, lemon, scarlet, stone, blue, olive-bistre and black	70	70
		a. Imperf (pair)		£250
1626	1056	28p. rose-red, lemon, stone, new blue, bluish violet, brt emerald & black	85	85
1627	1057	33p. blue-green, orange-yellow, scarlet, olive-bistre, blue, brown-pur & blk	1·40	1·40
1628	1058	39p. deep blue, lemon, scarlet, stone, lavender, olive-bistre & lake-brown	1·50	1·50
1624/8		Set of 5	4·50	4·50

1059 "Acid Rain Kills"

1060 "Ozone Layer"

1061 "Greenhouse Effect"

1062 "Bird of Hope"

(Des Christopher Hall (24p.), Lewis Fowler (28p.), Sarah Warren (33p.), Alice Newton-Mold (39p.). Adapted Trickett and Webb Ltd)

1992 (15 Sept). *Protection of the Environment. Children's Paintings. Phosphorised paper.* P 14×14½.

1629	1059	24p. emerald, greenish yellow, pale olive-yellow, brt carmine & black	60	60
1630	1060	28p. vermilion, lemon, bright blue, new blue, brt green, ultramarine & blk	90	90
1631	1061	33p. greenish blue, greenish yellow, brt rose-red, brt green, emer, bl & blk	1·00	1·00
1632	1062	39p. emerald, greenish yellow, bright magenta, brt orange, brt blue & blk	1·10	1·10
1629/32		Set of 4	3·25	3·25

1063 European Star

(Des D. Hockney)

1992 (13 Oct). *Single European Market. Phosphorised paper.* P 15×14.

1633	1063	24p. gold, greenish yellow, bright magenta, dull ultramarine & black	1·00	1·00

1064 "Angel Gabriel", St. James's, Pangbourne

1065 "Madonna and Child", St. Mary's, Bibury

1066 "King with Gold", Our Lady and St. Peter, Leatherhead

1067 "Shepherds", All Saints, Porthcawl

1068 "Kings with Frankincense and Myrrh", Our Lady and St. Peter, Leatherhead

(Des Carroll, Dempsey and Thirkell Ltd from windows by Karl Parsons (18, 24, 33p.) and Paul Woodroffe (28, 39p.))

1992 (10 Nov). *Christmas. Stained Glass Windows. One centre band (18p.) or phosphorised paper (others).* P 15×14.

1634	1064	18p. black, greenish yellow, mauve, ultramarine, bright emerald & gold	45	45
		a. Booklet pane of 20	7·50	
1635	1065	24p. blk, greenish yell, brt pur, ultram, new blue, brt greenish yell & gold	75	75
1636	1066	28p. black, lemon, rosine, ultramarine, reddish lilac, red-orange and gold	90	90
1637	1067	33p. bright ultramarine, greenish yell, rosine, brn, yellow-orge, blk & gold	1·10	1·10
1638	1068	39p. black, lemon, rosine, bright blue, deep violet, yellow-orange and gold	1·25	1·25
1634/8		Set of 5	4·00	4·00

Booklet pane No. 1634a comes from a special £3.60 Christmas booklet and has margins at left, top and bottom.

1069 Mute Swan Cob and St. Catherine's Chapel, Abbotsbury

1070 Cygnet and Decoy

1071 Swans and Cygnet

1072 Eggs in Nest and Tithe Barn, Abbotsbury

1073 Young Swan and the Fleet

(Des D. Gentleman)

1993 (19 Jan). *600th Anniv of Abbotsbury Swannery. One phosphor band (18p) or phosphorised paper (others).* P 14×15.

1639	1069	18p. gold, greenish yellow, bistre, green, vermilion and black		1·50	1·50
1640	1070	24p. gold, cream, bright green, grey-brown, dull blue and grey-black		1·10	1·10
1641	1071	28p. gold, greenish grey, yellow-brown, myrtle-green, brown, verm & blk		1·25	1·25
1642	1072	33p. gold, ochre, apple-green, olive-brown, bright orange & grey-black		2·00	2·00
1643	1073	39p. gold, cream, bright green, cobalt, light brown and black		2·25	2·25
1639/43			Set of 5	7·00	7·00

1074 Long John Silver and Parrot (*Treasure Island*)

1075 Tweedledum and Tweedledee (*Alice Through the Looking-Glass*)

1076 William (*William* books)

1077 Mole and Toad (*The Wind in the Willows*)

1078 Teacher and Wilfrid ("The Bash Street Kids")

1079 Peter Rabbit and Mrs. Rabbit (*The Tale of Peter Rabbit*)

1080 Snowman (*The Snowman*) and Father Christmas (*Father Christmas*)

1081 The Big Friendly Giant and Sophie (*The BFG*)

1082 Bill Badger and Rupert Bear

1083 Aladdin and the Genie

(Des Newell and Sorell)

1993 (2 Feb–10 Aug). *Greetings Stamps. "Gift Giving". Two phosphor bands.* P 15×14 (*with one elliptical hole on each vertical side*).

1644	1074	(1st) gold, greenish yellow, magenta, pale brown, light blue and black		1·10	1·10
		a. Booklet pane. Nos. 1644/53		10·00	
1645	1075	(1st) gold, cream and black		1·10	1·10
1646	1076	(1st) gold, greenish yellow, magenta, cream, new blue and black		1·10	1·10
1647	1077	(1st) gold, greenish yellow, magenta, cream, new blue and black		1·10	1·10
1648	1078	(1st) gold, greenish yellow, magenta, cream, new blue and black		1·10	1·10
1649	1079	(1st) gold, greenish yellow, magenta, cream, new blue and black		1·10	1·10
		a. Booklet pane. No. 1649×4 with margins all round (10 Aug)		4·00	
1650	1080	(1st) gold, greenish yellow, magenta, cream, new blue and black		1·10	1·10
1651	1081	(1st) gold, greenish yellow, magenta, cream, new blue and black		1·10	1·10
1652	1082	(1st) gold, greenish yellow, magenta, cream, new blue and black		1·10	1·10
1653	1083	(1st) gold, greenish yellow, magenta, cream, new blue and black		1·10	1·10
1644/53			Set of 10	10·00	10·00

Nos. 1644/53 were only issued in £2.40 booklets (sold at £2.50 from 1 November 1993).

Booklet pane No. 1649a comes from the £6 (£5.64) Beatrix Potter booklet.

1084 Decorated Enamel Dial

1085 Escapement, Remontoire and Fusee

1086 Balance, Spring and Temperature Compensator

1087 Back of Movement

(Des H. Brown and D. Penny. Litho Questa)

1993 (16 Feb). *300th Birth Anniv of John Harrison (inventor of the marine chronometer). Details of "H4" Clock. Phosphorised paper.* P 14½×14.

1654	1084	24p. new blue, greenish yellow, mag, black, grey-black and pale cream		50	50
1655	1085	28p. new blue, greenish yellow, mag, black, grey-black and pale cream		85	85
1656	1086	33p. new blue, greenish yellow, mag, black, grey-black and pale cream		1·10	1·10
1657	1087	39p. new blue, greenish yellow, mag, black, grey-black and pale cream		1·25	1·25
1654/7			Set of 4	3·25	3·25

1088 Britannia

(Des B. Craddock, adapted Roundel Design Group. Litho (silver die-stamped, Braille symbol for "10" embossed) Questa)

1993 (2 Mar). *Granite paper.* P 14×14½ (*with two elliptical holes on each horizontal side*).

1658	1088	£10 greenish grey, rosine, yellow, new blue, reddish violet, vermilion, violet, bright green and silver		15·00	9·00
		a. Silver omitted		£1100	

The paper used for No. 1658 contains fluorescent coloured fibres which, together with the ink on the shield, react under U.V. light.

1089 *Dendrobium hellwigianum*

1090 *Paphiopedilum* Maudiae "Magnificum"

1091 *Cymbidium lowianum*

1092 *Vanda* Rothschildiana

1093 *Dendrobium vexillarius* var *albiviride*

(Des Pandora Sellars)

1993 (16 Mar). *14th World Orchid Conference, Glasgow. One phosphor band (18p.) or phosphorised paper (others).* P 15×14.

1659	**1089**	18p. green, greenish yellow, magenta, pale blue, apple-green and slate	40	40
		a. Imperf (pair)	£950	
1660	**1090**	24p. green, greenish yellow, bright green and grey-black	65	65
1661	**1091**	28p. green, greenish yellow, red, bright turquoise-blue and drab	90	90
1662	**1092**	33p. green, greenish yellow, pale mag, bright violet, bright green and grey	1·10	1·10
1663	**1093**	39p. green, greenish yellow, red, pale olive-yell, brt grn, vio & grey-blk	1·40	1·40
1659/63		Set of 5	4·00	4·00

FLUORESCENT PHOSPHOR BANDS. Following the introduction of new automatic sorting machinery in 1991 it was found necessary to substantially increase the signal emitted by the phosphor bands. This was achieved by adding a fluorescent element to the phosphor which appears yellow under U.V. light. This combination was first used on an experimental sheet printing of the 18p., No. X913, produced by Enschedé in 1991. All values with phosphor bands from the elliptical perforations issue, including the No Value Indicated design, originally showed this yellow fluor.

From mid-1995 printings of current sheet and booklet stamps began to appear with the colour of the fluorescent element changed to blue. As such differences in fluor colour can only be identified by use of a U.V. lamp they are outside the scope of this catalogue, but full details will be found in the *Great Britain Specialised Catalogue Volume 4*.

The first commemorative/special stamp issue to show the change to blue fluor was the Centenary of Rugby League set, Nos. 1891/5.

COMPUTER-ENGRAVED CYLINDERS. In 1991 Enschedé introduced a new method of preparing photogravure cylinders for Great Britain stamps. This new method utilised computer-engraving instead of the traditional acid-etching and produced cylinders without the minor flaws which had long been a feature of the photogravure process. Such cylinders were first used on Great Britain stamps for the printing of the 18p released on 19 November 1991 (see No. X913).

Harrison and Sons continued to use the acid-etching method until mid-1996 after which most Machin values, including N.V.I.'s, were produced from computer-engraved cylinders using a very similar process to that of Enschedé. Some values exist in versions from both cylinder production methods and can often be identified by minor differences. Such stamps are, however, outside the scope of this listing, but full details can be found in the current edition of the *Great Britain Specialised Catalogue Volume 4*.

For commemorative stamps the first Harrison issue to use computer-engraved cylinders was the Centenary of Cinema set (Nos. 1920/4).

When Walsall introduced photogravure printing in 1997 their cylinders were produced using a similar computer-engraved process.

1993 (6 Apr)–**2000**. *Booklet stamps. As T* **913/14**, *but* P 14 (*No.* 1663b) *or* 15×14 (*others*) (*both with one elliptical hole on each vertical side).*

(a) *Photo Questa* (*Nos.* 1663ab/am, 1664ab), *Harrison* (*No.* 1664), *De La Rue* (*No.* 1664al), *Walsall* (*No.* 1664am), *Harrison* (*later De La Rue*) *or Walsall* (*others*)

1663a	**913**	(2nd) brt blue (1 centre band) (7.9.93)	30	35
		ab. Perf 14 (1.12.98)	30	35
		al. Booklet pane. Nos. 1663a and 1664a×3 plus 4 labels (27.4.00)	1·50	
		am. Booklet pane. No. 1663a×2 and 1664a×6 (27.4.00)	3·00	
1663b		(2nd) brt blue (1 side band) (13.10.98)	1·00	1·00
		bl. Booklet pane. Nos. 1663b×3 and NI81b, S91a and W80a with margins all round	6·00	
1664	**914**	(1st) brt orge-red (phosphorised paper)	1·25	1·25
1664a		(1st) brt orange-red (2 phosphor bands) (4.4.95)	40	45
		ab. Perf 14 (1.12.98)	40	45
		al. Booklet pane. No. 1664a×8 with centre label and margins all round (16.2.99)	3·00	
		am. Booklet pane. No. 1664a×4 plus commemorative label at right (12.5.99)	1·60	
1664b	–	(E) dp bl (2 phosphor bands) (19.1.99)	45	50

(b) *Litho Questa* (*Nos.* 1666l, 1666m/ma, 1666n), *Walsall* (*No.* 1666la), *Enschedé* (*No.* 1666mb), *Questa or Walsall* (*others*)

1665	**913**	(2nd) bright blue (1 centre band)	1·00	1·00
1666	**914**	(1st) brt orange-red (2 phosphor bands)	80	80
		l. Booklet pane. No. 1666×4 plus commemorative label at left (27.7.94)	6·00	
		la. Ditto, but with commemorative label at right (16.5.95)	5·00	
		m. Pane. No. 1666 with margins all round (roul 8 across top corners of pane) (Boots logo on margin) (17.8.94)	1·10	
		ma. Without Boots logo above stamp (11.9.95)	1·00	
		mb. Ditto, but roul 10 across top corners of pane (20.2.97)	1·00	
		n. Booklet pane. No. 1666×9 with margins all round (16.2.99)	3·50	

Nos. 1663a/6, were issued in booklet panes showing perforations on all four edges.

No. 1663b exists with the phosphor band at the left or right from separate panes (Nos. 1663bl and 1672al) of the £6.16 Speed stamp booklet.

No. 1664b was valid for the basic European airmail rate, initially 30p.

On 6 September 1993 Nos. 1665/6 printed in lithography by Questa were made available in sheets from post offices in Birmingham, Coventry, Falkirk and Milton Keynes. These sheet stamps became available nationally on 5 October 1993. On 29 April 1997 No. 1663a printed in photogravure by Walsall became available in sheets. On the same date Nos. 1663a and 1664a were issued in coils printed by Harrison.

No. 1664am includes a commemorative label for the 50th anniversary of the Berlin Airlift or the Rugby World Cup.

No. 1666l includes a commemorative label for the 300th anniversary of the Bank of England and No. 1666la exists with labels for the birth centenary of R. J. Mitchell, 70th birthday of

Queen Elizabeth II, "Hong Kong '97" International Stamp Exhibition, Commonwealth Heads of Government Meeting, Edinburgh, or 50th birthday of Prince of Wales.

No. 1666m, printed by Questa, was provided by the Royal Mail for inclusion in single pre-packed greetings cards. The pane shows large margins at top and sides with lines of roulette gauging 8 stretching from the bottom corners to the mid point of the top edge. Examples included with greetings cards show the top two corners of the pane folded over. The scheme was originally limited to Boots and their logo appeared on the pane margin. Other card retailers subsequently participated and later supplies omitted the logo. Unfolded examples were available from the British Philatelic Bureau and from other Post Office philatelic outlets. A further printing by Enschedé in 1997 showed the roulettes gauging 10 (No. 1666mb). Blank pieces of gummed paper have been found showing the perforation and rouletting of No. 1666mb, but no printing.

In mid-1994 a number of postal forgeries of the 2nd bright blue printed in lithography were detected, after having been rejected by the sorting equipment. These show the Queen's head in bright greenish blue, have a fluorescent, rather than a phosphor, band and show matt, colourless gum on the reverse. These forgeries come from booklets of ten which also have forged covers.

For 1st in gold see No. 1979 and for self-adhesive versions in these colours see Nos. 2039/40.

1993 (27 Apr)–**2000**. *As No.* X841, *etc, but* P 14 (*No.* Y1675) *or* 15×14 (*others*) (*both with one elliptical hole on each vertical side*).

(a) *Photo*

Enschedé—20p. (Y1676), 29p., 35p. (Y1686), 36p., 38p. (Y1690), 42p. (Y1693), 43p. (Y1695)

Harrison/De La Rue—7p., 8p., 20p. (Y1678/9), 25p. (Y1680), 33p., 35p. (Y1687), 40p., 41p. (Y1694/a), 43p. (Y1696), 44p., 45p., 65p.

Walsall—10p. (Y1673a), 19p. (Y1675), 38p. (Y1691a), 43p. (Y1696a)

Enschedé or Harrison/De La Rue:—4p., 5p., 6p., 10p. (Y1673), 25p. (Y1681), 31p., 39p., 50p., £1

Enschedé, Harrison/De La Rue or Questa:—1p., 2p.

Enschedé, Harrison/De La Rue or Walsall:—30p., 37p., 63p.

Harrison/De La Rue or Questa:—19p. (Y1674), 20p. (Y1677), 26p.

De La Rue or Walsall:—38p. (Y1691), 64p.

Y1667	**367**	1p. crimson (2 bands) (8.6.93)	10	10
		l. Booklet pane. Nos. Y1667×2, Y1677 and Y1682×3 plus 2 labels (1.12.98)	5·00	
		m. Booklet pane. Nos. Y1667/8, Y1674, Y1682×3 plus 2 labels (26.4.99)	1·50	
		n. Booklet pane. Nos. Y1667×4, Y1674×3 and Y1682 with centre label and margins all round (21.9.99)	1·40	
Y1668		2p. deep green (2 bands) (11.4.95)	10	10
Y1669		4p. new blue (2 bands) (14.12.93)	10	10
Y1670		5p. dull red-brown (2 bands) (8.6.93)	10	10
Y1671		6p. yellow-olive (2 bands)	10	15
Y1672		7p. grey (2 bands) (20.4.99)	10	15
Y1672a		8p. yellow (2 bands) (25.4.00)	10	15
Y1673		10p. dull orange (2 bands) (8.6.93)	15	20
		a. Perf 14 (13.10.98)	1·25	1·25
		al. Booklet pane. Nos. Y1673a×2, 1663b and Y1696a, each × 3, with centre label and margins all round	3·00	
Y1674		19p. bistre (1 centre band) (26.10.93)	30	35
		a. Imperf (pair)	£400	
		l. Booklet pane. Nos. Y1674 and Y1682×7 (26.4.99)	3·00	
Y1675		19p. bistre (p 14) (1 side band) (15.2.00)	75	75
		l. Booklet pane. No. Y1675×4 and Y1691a×2 with margins all round	6·00	
Y1676		20p. turquoise-grn (2 bands) (14.12.93)	80	80
Y1677		20p. brt green (1 centre band) (25.6.96)	30	35
		a. Imperf (horiz pair)	£375	
		l. Booklet pane. Nos. Y1677 and Y1682×7 (1.12.98)	4·00	
Y1678		20p. bright green (1 side band) (23.9.97)	1·25	1·25
		l. Booklet pane. Nos. Y1678 and Y1682, each × 3, with margins all round	8·00	
Y1679		20p. bright green (2 bands) (20.4.99)	30	35
Y1680		25p. rose-red (phosphorised paper) (26.10.93)	1·00	1·00
		a. Imperf (pair)	£450	
		l. Booklet pane. No. Y1680×2 plus 2 labels (1.11.93)	2·00	
Y1681		25p. rose-red (2 bands) (20.12.94)	1·00	1·00
		l. Booklet pane. No. Y1681×2 plus 2 labels (6.6.95)	3·00	
Y1682		26p. red-brown (2 bands) (25.6.96)	40	45
		a. Imperf (pair)		
Y1683		29p. grey (2 bands) (26.10.93)	1·25	1·25
Y1684		30p. deep olive-grey (2 bands) (27.7.93)	45	50
Y1685		31p. deep mauve (2 bands) (25.6.96)	50	55
Y1685a		33p. grey-green (2 bands) (25.4.00)	50	55
Y1686		35p. yellow (2 bands) (17.8.93)	1·40	1·40
Y1687		35p. yell (phosphorised paper) (1.11.93)	1·40	1·40
Y1688		36p. brt ultram (2 bands) (26.10.93)	1·40	1·40
Y1689		37p. bright mauve (2 bands) (25.6.96)	55	60
Y1690		38p. rosine (2 bands) (26.10.93)	1·50	1·50
		a. Imperf (pair)	£225	
Y1691		38p. ultramarine (2 bands) (20.4.99)	55	60
		a. Perf 14 (15.2.00)	55	60
Y1692		39p. bright magenta (2 bands) (25.6.96)	60	65
Y1692a		40p. deep azure (2 bands) (25.4.00)	60	65
Y1693		41p. grey-brown (2 bands) (26.10.93)	1·60	1·60
Y1694		41p. drab (phosphorised paper) (1.11.93)	1·75	1·75
Y1694a		41p. rosine (2 bands) (25.4.00)	65	70
Y1695		43p. dp olive-brown (2 bands) (25.6.96)	1·60	1·60
Y1696		43p. sepia (2 bands) (8.7.96)	65	70
		a. Perf 14 (13.10.98)	1·50	1·50
Y1697		44p. grey-brown (2 bands) (20.4.99)	65	70
Y1697a		45p. bright mauve (2 bands) (25.4.00)	70	75
Y1698		50p. ochre (2 bands) (14.12.93)	75	80
		a. Imperf (pair)		
Y1699		63p. light emerald (2 bands) (25.6.96)	95	1·00
Y1700		64p. turquoise-green (2 bands) (20.4.99)	95	1·00
Y1700a		65p. greenish blue (2 bands) (25.4.00)	1·00	1·10
Y1701		£1 bluish violet (2 bands) (22.8.95)	1·50	1·60

(b) *Litho Walsall* (37p., 60p., 63p.), *Questa or Walsall* (25p., 35p., 41p.), *Questa* (*others*)

Y1743	**367**	1p. lake (2 bands) (8.7.96)	50	50
		l. Booklet pane. Nos. Y1743×2, Y1751 and Y1753×3 plus 2 labels	3·50	
Y1748		6p. yellow-olive (2 bands) (26.7.94)	10·00	10·00
		l. Booklet pane. Nos. Y1748, Y1750 and Y1752×4 with margins all round	14·00	
		la. 6p. value misplaced		
Y1749		10p. dull orange (2 bands) (25.4.95)	4·50	4·50
		l. Booklet pane. Nos. Y1749, Y1750 ×2, Y1752×2, Y1754/5 and Y1757 and centre label with margins all round	12·00	
Y1750		19p. bistre (1 side band) (26.7.94)	1·25	1·25
		l. Booklet pane. No. Y1750×6 with margins all round (25.4.95)	7·50	
Y1751		20p. brt yell-grn (1 centre band) (8.7.96)	1·00	1·00
		l. Booklet pane. Nos. Y1751 and Y1753×7	5·00	
Y1752		25p. red (2 bands) (1.11.93)	1·00	1·00
		l. Booklet pane. Nos. Y1752, NI72, S84 and W73, each × 2 with centre label and margins all round (14.5.96)	7·00	
Y1753		26p. chestnut (2 bands) (8.7.96)	1·00	1·00
Y1754		30p. olive-grey (2 bands) (25.4.95)	2·25	2·25
Y1755		35p. yellow (2 bands) (1.11.93)	1·50	1·50
Y1756		37p. bright mauve (2 bands) (8.7.96)	1·50	1·50
Y1757		41p. drab (shades) (1.11.93)	1·50	1·50
Y1758		60p. dull blue-grey (2 bands) (9.8.94)	2·75	2·75
Y1759		63p. light emerald (2 bands) (8.7.96)	2·75	2·75

(c) *Eng C. Slania. Recess Enschedé* (*until Mar 2000*) *or De La Rue* (*from 11 Apr 2000 onwards*)

Y1800	**367**	£1.50, red (9.3.99)	2·25	2·40
Y1801		£2 dull blue (9.3.99)	3·00	3·25
Y1802		£3 dull violet (9.3.99)	4·50	4·75
Y1803		£5 brown (9.3.99)	7·50	7·75

No. Y1701 is printed in Iriodin ink which gives a shiny effect to the solid part of the background behind the Queen's head.

Nos. Y1687 and Y1694 were only issued in coils and Nos. Y1673a, Y1675, Y1691a, Y1696a, Y1748/50, Y1752, Y1754/5 and Y1757/8 only in booklets.

No. Y1748la shows the 6p. value 22 mm to the left so that its position in the booklet pane is completely blank except for the phosphor bands. Other more minor misplacements exist.

Nos. Y1675 and Y1678 show the phosphor band at right and No. Y1750 at left or right.

The De La Rue printings of the high values, Nos. Y1800/3, cannot be identified from the original Enschedé issue as single stamps.

For 26p. in gold see No. 1978.

1094 "Family Group"
(bronze sculpture) (Henry
Moore)

1095 "Kew Gardens"
(lithograph) (Edward
Bawden)

1096 "St. Francis and the
Birds" (Stanley Spencer)

1097 "Still Life: Odyssey
I" (Ben Nicholson)

(Des A. Dastor)

1993 (11 May). *Europa. Contemporary Art. Phosphorised paper.*
P 14×14½.

1767	**1094**	24p. brownish grey, lemon, magenta, turquoise-blue, and grey-black	50	50
1768	**1095**	28p. brownish grey, buff, lt grn, yellow-brown, brt orge, new bl & grey-blk	80	80
1769	**1096**	33p. brownish grey, cream, greenish yellow, magenta, new bl & grey-blk	1·10	1·10
1770	**1097**	39p. brownish grey, cream, yell-ochre, rose-lilac, red, light blue & grey-blk	1·25	1·25
1767/70		*Set of 4*	3·25	3·25

1098 Emperor Claudius
(from gold coin)

1099 Emperor Hadrian
(bronze head)

1100 Goddess Roma
(from gemstone)

1101 Christ (Hinton St.
Mary mosaic)

(Des J. Gibbs)

1993 (15 June). *Roman Britain. Phosphorised paper with two phosphor bands.* P 14×14½.

1771	**1098**	24p. blk, pale orange, lt brown & silver	50	50
1772	**1099**	28p. black, greenish yellow, bright rose-red, silver, brt blue & grey-black	80	80
1773	**1100**	33p. black, greenish yellow, bright rose-red, silver and grey	1·10	1·10
1774	**1101**	39p. black, greenish yellow, rosine, silver, pale violet and grey	1·25	1·25
1771/4		*Set of 4*	3·25	3·25

1102 *Midland Maid* and
other Narrow Boats, Grand
Junction Canal

1103 *Yorkshire Lass* and
other Humber Keels,
Stainforth and Keadby
Canal

1104 *Valley Princess* and
other Horse-drawn Barges,
Brecknock and
Abergavenny Canal

1105 Steam Barges,
including *Pride of Scotland,*
and Fishing Boats, Crinan
Canal

(Des T. Lewery. Litho Questa)

1993 (20 July). *Inland Waterways. Two phosphor bands.*
P 14½×14.

1775	**1102**	24p. new bl, greenish yell, brt mag, blk, bl, verm, brownish grey & sage-grn	50	50
1776	**1103**	28p. new bl, greenish yell, brt mag, blk, blue, bluish grey, verm & sage-grn	80	80
1777	**1104**	33p. new bl, greenish yell, brt mag, blk, bl, verm, greenish grey & sage-grn	1·10	1·10
1778	**1105**	39p. new blue, greenish yellow, brt mag, blk, bl, verm, sage-grn & dull mve	1·25	1·25
1775/8		*Set of 4*	3·25	3·25

Nos. 1775/8 commemorate the bicentenary of the Acts of
Parliament authorising the canals depicted.

1106 Horse Chestnut

1107 Blackberry

1108 Hazel

1109 Rowan

1110 Pear

(Des Charlotte Knox)

1993 (14 Sept). *The Four Seasons. Autumn. Fruits and Leaves.
One phosphor band* (18p.) *or phosphorised paper* (*others*).
P 15×14.

1779	**1106**	18p. black, greenish yellow, cerise, bright green, gold and chestnut	40	40
1780	**1107**	24p. black, lemon, cerise, myrtle-green, gold, bright green and brown	65	65
1781	**1108**	28p. grey, lemon, emer, lake-brn & gold	1·00	1·00
1782	**1109**	33p. grey-black, greenish yellow, rosine, light green, gold and brown	1·25	1·25
1783	**1110**	39p. myrtle-green, greenish yellow, rosine, olive-sepia, gold, apple-green and deep myrtle-green	1·40	1·40
1779/83		*Set of 5*	4·25	4·25

1111 *The Reigate
Squire*

1112 *The Hound of
the Baskervilles*

1113 *The Six
Napoleons*

1114 *The Greek
Interpreter*

1115 *The Final
Problem*

(Des A. Davidson. Litho Questa)

1993 (12 Oct). *Sherlock Holmes. Centenary of the Publication of
The Final Problem. Phosphorised paper.* P 14×14½.

1784	**1111**	24p. new blue, greenish yellow, mag, black and gold	1·00	1·00
		a. Horiz strip. Nos. 1784/8	4·50	4·50
1785	**1112**	24p. new blue, greenish yellow, mag, black and gold	1·00	1·00
1786	**1113**	24p. new blue, greenish yellow, mag, black and gold	1·00	1·00
1787	**1114**	24p. new blue, greenish yellow, mag, black and gold	1·00	1·00
1788	**1115**	24p. new blue, greenish yellow, mag, black and gold	1·00	1·00
1784/8		*Set of 5*	4·50	4·50

Nos. 1785/8 were printed together, *se-tenant*, in horizontal strips
of 5 throughout the sheet.

1116

(Des J. Matthews. Litho Walsall)

1993 (19 Oct). *Self-adhesive. Two phosphor bands. Die-cut*
P 14×15 (*with one elliptical hole on each vertical side*).

1789	**1116**	(1st) orange-red	1·00	1·00
		a. Booklet pane. No. 1789×20	15·00	

No. 1789 was initially sold at 24p., which was increased to 25p.
from 1 November 1993. It was only issued in booklets containing 20
stamps, each surrounded by die-cut perforations.

For similar 2nd and 1st designs printed in photogravure by
Enschedé see Nos. 1976/7.

1117 Bob Cratchit and Tiny
Tim

1118 Mr. and Mrs. Fezziwig

1119 Scrooge

1120 The Prize Turkey

1121 Mr. Scrooge's Nephew

(Des Q. Blake)

1993 (9 Nov). *Christmas. 150th Anniv of Publication of A Christmas Carol by Charles Dickens. One phosphor band (19p.) or phosphorised paper (others). P 15×14.*

1790	1117	19p. new blue, yellow, magenta, salmon, bright emerald & grey-blk	50	50
		a. Imperf (pair)	£1500	
1791	1118	25p. yellow-orange, brn-lilac, steel-bl, lake-brown, lt grn, grey-blk & blk	80	80
1792	1119	30p. cerise, bistre-yellow, dull blue, brn-rose, pale green, grey-black & blk	1·10	1·10
1793	1120	35p. dp turquoise-green, lemon, verm, dull ultramarine, Indian red, bluish grey and black	1·25	1·25
1794	1121	41p. reddish purple, lemon, purple, light blue, salmon, bright green & black	1·40	1·40
1790/4		*Set of 5*	4·50	4·50

1122 Class 5 No. 44957 and Class B1 No. 61342 on West Highland Line

1123 Class A1 No. 60149 *Amadis* at Kings Cross

1124 Class 4 No. 43000 on Turntable at Blyth North

1125 Class 4 No. 42455 near Wigan Central

1126 Class "Castle" No. 7002 *Devizes Castle* on Bridge crossing Worcester and Birmingham Canal

(Des B. Delaney)

1994 (18 Jan). *The Age of Steam. Railway Photographs by Colin Gifford. One phosphor band (19p.) or phosphorised paper with two bands (others). P 14½.*

1795	1122	19p. dp blue-green, grey-black & black	45	45
1796	1123	25p. slate-lilac, grey-black and black	75	75
1797	1124	30p. lake-brown, grey-black and black	1·00	1·00
1798	1125	35p. deep claret, grey-black and black	1·25	1·25
1799	1126	41p. indigo, grey-black and black	1·40	1·40
1795/9		*Set of 5*	4·50	4·50

Nos. 1796/9 are on phosphorised paper and also show two phosphor bands.

MINIMUM PRICE

The minimum price quote is 10p which represents a handling charge rather than a basis for valuing common stamps. For further notes about prices see introductory pages.

1127 Dan Dare and the Mekon

1128 The Three Bears

1129 Rupert Bear

1130 Alice (*Alice in Wonderland*)

1131 Noggin and the Ice Dragon

1132 Peter Rabbit posting Letter

1133 Red Riding Hood and Wolf

1134 Orlando the Marmalade Cat

1135 Biggles

1136 Paddington Bear on Station

(Des Newell and Sorrell)

1994 (1 Feb). *Greetings Stamps. "Messages". Two phosphor bands. P 15×14 (with one elliptical hole on each vertical side).*

1800	1127	(1st) gold, greenish yellow, brt purple, bistre-yellow, new blue and black	1·00	1·00
		a. Booklet pane. Nos. 1800/9	9·00	
1801	1128	(1st) gold, greenish yellow, brt purple, bistre-yellow, new blue and black	1·00	1·00
1802	1129	(1st) gold, greenish yellow, brt purple, bistre-yellow, new blue and black	1·00	1·00
1803	1130	(1st) gold, bistre-yellow and black	1·00	1·00
1804	1131	(1st) gold, greenish yellow, brt purple, bistre-yellow, new blue and black	1·00	1·00
1805	1132	(1st) gold, greenish yellow, brt purple, bistre-yellow, new blue and black	1·00	1·00
1806	1133	(1st) gold, greenish yellow, brt purple, bistre-yellow, new blue and black	1·00	1·00
1807	1134	(1st) gold, greenish yellow, brt purple, bistre-yellow, new blue and black	1·00	1·00
1808	1135	(1st) gold, greenish yellow, brt purple, bistre-yellow, new blue and black	1·00	1·00
1809	1136	(1st) gold, greenish yellow, brt purple, bistre-yellow, new blue and black	1·00	1·00
1800/9		*Set of 10*	9·00	9·00

Nos. 1800/9 were only issued in £2.50 stamp booklets (sold at £2.60 from 8 July 1996).

1137 Castell Y Waun (Chirk Castle), Clwyd, Wales

1138 Ben Arkle, Sutherland, Scotland

1139 Mourne Mountains, County Down, Northern Ireland

1140 Dersingham, Norfolk, England

1141 Dolwyddelan, Gwynedd, Wales

1994 (1 Mar–26 July). *25th Anniv of Investiture of the Prince of Wales. Paintings by Prince Charles. One phosphor band (19p.) or phosphorised paper (others). P 15×14.*

1810	1137	19p. grey-black, greenish yellow, magenta, new blue, black and silver	50	50
1811	1138	25p. grey-black, orange-yellow, bright magenta, new blue, silver and black	90	90

1812 **1139** 30p. grey-black, greenish yellow,
    magenta, new blue, silver and black   1·00   1·00
    a. Booklet pane. No. 1812×4 with
    margins all round (26 July)   3·50
1813 **1140** 35p. greenish yellow,
    magenta, new blue, silver and black   1·25   1·25
1814 **1141** 41p. grey-black, lemon, magenta, new
    blue, silver and black   1·40   1·40
1810/14   ..   ..   *Set of 5*   4·50   4·50
  Booklet pane No. 1812a comes from the £6.04 "Northern Ireland" booklet.

1142 Bather at
Blackpool

1143 "Where's my
Little Lad?"

1144 "Wish You were
Here!"

1145 Punch and Judy
Show

1146 "The Tower
Crane" Machine

(Des M. Dempsey and B. Dare. Litho Questa)

1994 (12 Apr). *Centenary of Picture Postcards. One side band
(19p.) or two phosphor bands (others). P* 14×14½.
1815 **1142** 19p. new blue, greenish yell, mag & blk   50   50
1816 **1143** 25p. new blue, greenish yell, mag & blk   85   85
1817 **1144** 30p. new blue, greenish yell, mag & blk   1·00   1·00
1818 **1145** 35p. new blue, greenish yell, mag & blk   1·25   1·25
1819 **1146** 41p. new blue, greenish yell, mag & blk   1·40   1·40
1815/19   ..   ..   ..   *Set of 5*   4·50   4·50

1147 British Lion and French Cockerel
over Tunnel

1148 Symbolic Hands over Train

(Des G. Hardie (T **1147**), J.-P. Cousin (T **1148**))

1994 (3 May). *Opening of Channel Tunnel. Phosphorised paper.
P* 14×14½.
1820 **1147** 25p. ultram, brt orange, scar, new blue,
    emerald, turquoise-blue & silver   85   85
    a. Horiz pair. Nos. 1820/1 ..   1·75   1·75
1821 **1148** 25p. ultram, scar, new bl, emer & silver   85   85

1822 **1147** 41p. new blue, brt orge, scar, turquoise-
    blue, emerald, ultramarine & silver   1·60   1·60
    a. Horiz pair. Nos. 1822/3 ..   3·25   3·25
    ab. Imperf (horiz pair)   £700
1823 **1148** 41p. ultram, scar, new bl, emer & silver   1·60   1·60
1820/3   ..   ..   ..   *Set of 4*   4·50   4·50
  Nos. 1820/1 and 1822/3 were printed together, *se-tenant*, in horizontal pairs throughout the sheets.
  Stamps in similar designs were also issued by France.

1149 Groundcrew replacing
Smoke Canisters on
Douglas Boston of 88 Sqn

1150 H.M.S. *Warspite*
(battleship) shelling
Enemy Positions

 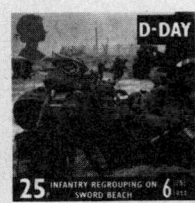

1151 Commandos landing
on Gold Beach

1152 Infantry regrouping
on Sword Beach

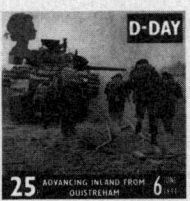

1153 Tank and Infantry
advancing, Ouistreham

(Des K. Bassford from contemporary photographs. Litho Questa)

1994 (6 June). *50th Anniv of D-Day. Two phosphor bands.
P* 14½×14.
1824 **1149** 25p. pink, greenish yell, blackish lilac,
    slate-black, brt scarlet & silver-grey   1·10   1·10
    a. Horiz strip of 5. Nos. 1824/8 ..   4·75   4·75
1825 **1150** 25p. pink, greenish yell, blackish lilac,
    slate-black, brt scarlet & silver-grey   1·10   1·10
1826 **1151** 25p. pink, greenish yell, blackish lilac,
    slate-black, brt scarlet & silver-grey   1·10   1·10
1827 **1152** 25p. pink, greenish yell, blackish lilac,
    slate-black, brt scarlet & silver-grey   1·10   1·10
1828 **1153** 25p. pink, greenish yell, blackish lilac,
    slate-black, brt scarlet & silver-grey   1·10   1·10
1824/8   ..   ..   ..   *Set of 5*   4·75   4·75
  Nos. 1824/8 were printed together, *se-tenant*, in horizontal strips of 5 throughout the sheet.

1154 The Old Course, St.
Andrews

1155 The 18th Hole,
Muirfield

1156 The 15th Hole
("Luckyslap"), Carnoustie

1157 The 8th Hole ("The
Postage Stamp"), Royal
Troon

1158 The 9th Hole,
Turnberry

(Des P. Hogarth)

1994 (5 July). *Scottish Golf Courses. One phosphor band (19p.) or
phosphorised paper (others). P* 14½×14.
1829 **1154** 19p. yellow-green, olive-grey, orange-
    verm, apple-green, blue & grey-blk   55   55
1830 **1155** 25p. yellow-green, lemon, brt orange,
    apple-green, blue, mag & grey-blk   80   80
1831 **1156** 30p. yellow-green, yellow, rosine, emer,
    blue-green, new blue & grey-black   1·00   1·00
1832 **1157** 35p. yellow-green, yellow, rosine, apple-
    green, new blue, dull bl & grey-blk   1·25   1·25
1833 **1158** 41p. yellow-grn, lemon, magenta, apple-
    green, dull blue, new bl & grey-blk   1·40   1·40
1829/33   ..   ..   ..   *Set of 5*   4·75   4·75
  Nos. 1829/33 commemorate the 250th anniversary of golf's first set of rules produced by the Honourable Company of Edinburgh Golfers.

1159 Royal Welsh Show,
Llanelwedd

1160 All England Tennis
Championships, Wimbledon

1161 Cowes Week

1162 Test Match, Lord's

1163 Braemar Gathering

(Des M. Cook)

1994 (2 Aug). *The Four Seasons. Summertime. One phosphor
band (19p.) or phosphorised paper (others). P* 15×14.
1834 **1159** 19p. black, greenish yell, brt magenta,
    brown, yellow-brown & new blue   50   50
1835 **1160** 25p. black, greenish yellow, magenta,
    reddish violet, yellow-grn, myrtle-
    green and new blue   ..   75   75
1836 **1161** 30p. black, greenish yellow, bright
    magenta, yellow-ochre, deep
    slate-blue, blue-green and blue ..   1·10   1·10

1837 **1162** 35p. black, greenish yellow, magenta,
slate-lilac, yellow-green, deep
bluish green and bright blue .. 1·25 1·25
1838 **1163** 41p. black, greenish yellow, bright
magenta, deep claret, light brown,
myrtle-green and bright blue .. 1·40 1·40
1834/8 .. .. *Set of 5* 4·50 4·50

1164 Ultrasonic Imaging

1165 Scanning Electron
Microscopy

1166 Magnetic Resonance
Imaging

1167 Computed Tomography

(Des P. Vermier and J-P. Tibbles. Photo Enschedé)
1994 (27 Sept). *Europa. Medical Discoveries. Phosphorised paper. P* 14×14½.
1839 **1164** 25p. greenish yellow, bright magenta,
new blue, black and silver .. 65 65
a. Imperf (vert pair) £1500
1840 **1165** 30p. greenish yellow, bright magenta,
new blue, black and silver .. 95 95
1841 **1166** 35p. greenish yellow, bright magenta,
new blue, black and silver .. 1·00 1·00
1842 **1167** 41p. greenish yellow, bright magenta,
new blue, black and silver .. 1·10 1·10
1839/42 .. .. *Set of 4* 3·25 3·25

1168 Mary and Joseph

1169 Three Wise Men

1170 Mary with Doll

1171 Shepherds

1172 Angels

(Des Yvonne Gilbert)
1994 (1 Nov). *Christmas. Children's Nativity Plays. One phosphor band* (19p) *or phosphorised paper* (others). *P* 15×14.
1843 **1168** 19p. turquoise-green, greenish yell, brt
magenta, new bl, dull bl & grey-blk 60 60
a. Imperf (pair) £175
1844 **1169** 25p. orange-brown, greenish yell, brt
mag, new bl, lt bl, bistre & grey-blk 90 90
1845 **1170** 30p. lt brown, greenish yellow, brt mag,
bl, turq-bl, new bl & brownish grey 1·00 1·00
1846 **1171** 35p. dp grey-brn, greenish yell, brt mag,
turq-bl, dull violet-bl, ochre & brn 1·10 1·10
1847 **1172** 41p. blue, greenish yellow, brt magenta,
turquoise-blue, light blue & dp grey 1·40 1·40
1843/7 .. .. *Set of 5* 4·50 4·50

1173 Sophie (black cat)

1174 Puskas (Siamese) and
Tigger (tabby)

1175 Chloe (ginger cat)

1176 Kikko (tortoiseshell) and
Rosie (Abyssinian)

1177 Fred (black and white cat)

(Des Elizabeth Blackadder. Litho Questa)
1995 (17 Jan). *Cats. One phosphor band* (19p.) *or two phosphor bands* (others). *P* 14½×14.
1848 **1173** 19p. new blue, greenish yellow,
magenta, black and brown-red 60 60
1849 **1174** 25p. new blue, greenish yellow, mag,
black and dull yellow-green .. 75 75

1850 **1175** 30p. new blue, greenish yellow, mag,
black and yellow-brown .. 1·00 1·00
1851 **1176** 35p. new blue, greenish yellow,
magenta, black and yellow 1·10 1·10
1852 **1177** 41p. new blue, greenish yellow, mag,
black and reddish orange 1·40 1·40
1848/52 .. .. *Set of 5* 4·50 4·50

1178 Dandelions

1179 Sweet Chestnut Leaves

1180 Garlic Leaves

1181 Hazel Leaves

1182 Spring Grass

1995 (14 Mar). *The Four Seasons. Springtime. Plant Sculptures by Andy Goldsworthy. One phosphor band* (19p.) *or two phosphor bands* (others). *P* 15×14.
1853 **1178** 19p. silver, greenish yellow, magenta,
green and grey-black .. 65 65
1854 **1179** 25p. silver, greenish yellow, magenta,
new blue, and black .. 75 75
1855 **1180** 30p. silver, greenish yellow, magenta,
new blue, and black .. 1·10 1·10
1856 **1181** 35p. silver, greenish yellow, magenta,
new blue, and black .. 1·10 1·10
1857 **1182** 41p. silver, greenish yellow, magenta,
new blue, blue-green and black 1·40 1·40
1853/7 .. .. *Set of 5* 4·50 4·50

1183 "La Danse a la
Campagne" (Renoir)

1184 "Troilus and Criseyde"
(Peter Brookes)

1185 "The Kiss" (Rodin)

1186 "Girls on the Town"
(Beryl Cook)

1187 "Jazz" (Andrew Mockett)

1188 "Girls performing a
Kathak Dance" (Aurangzeb
period)

1189 "Alice Keppel with her
Daughter" (Alice Hughes)

1190 "Children Playing" (L. S.
Lowry)

1191 "Circus Clowns" (Emily
Firmin and Justin Mitchell)

1192 Decoration from "All the
Love Poems of Shakespeare"
(Eric Gill)

(Des Newell and Sorrell. Litho Walsall)

1995 (21 Mar). *Greetings Stamps. "Greetings in Art". Two phosphor bands. P 14½×14 (with one elliptical hole on each vertical side).*

1858	1183	(1st) greenish yellow, new blue, magenta, black and silver		70	70
		a. Booklet pane. Nos. 1858/67		6·25	
		ab. Silver (Queen's head and "1ST") omitted		£6000	
1859	1184	(1st) greenish yellow, new blue, magenta, black and silver		70	70

1860	1185	(1st) greenish yellow, new blue, magenta, black and silver		70	70
1861	1186	(1st) greenish yellow, new blue, magenta, black and silver		70	70
1862	1187	(1st) greenish yellow, new blue, magenta, black and silver		70	70
1863	1188	(1st) greenish yellow, new blue, magenta, black and silver		70	70
1864	1189	(1st) purple-brown and silver		70	70
1865	1190	(1st) greenish yellow, new blue, magenta, black and silver		70	70
1866	1191	(1st) greenish yellow, new blue, magenta, black and silver		70	70
1867	1192	(1st) black, greenish yellow and silver		70	70
1858/67			*Set of 10*	6·25	6·25

Nos. 1858/67 were only available in £2.50 stamp booklets (sold at £2.60 from 8 July 1996).

No. 1858ab also shows the phosphor bands omitted.

1193 Fireplace
Decoration, Attingham
Park, Shropshire

1194 Oak Seedling

1195 Carved Table
Leg, Attingham Park

1196 St. David's Head,
Dyfed, Wales

1197 Elizabethan Window, Little
Moreton Hall, Cheshire

(Des T. Evans)

1995 (11–25 Apr). *Centenary of The National Trust. One phosphor band (19p.), two phosphor bands (25p., 35p.) or phosphorised paper (30p., 41p.). P 14×15.*

1868	1193	19p. grey-green, stone, grey-brown, grey-black and gold		55	55
1869	1194	25p. grey-green, greenish yellow, mag, new blue, gold and black		80	80
		a. Booklet pane. No. 1869×6 with margins all round (25 April)		3·50	
1870	1195	30p. grey-green, greenish yellow, mag, new blue, gold, black & slate-black		1·00	1·00
1871	1196	35p. grey-green, greenish yellow, magenta, blue, gold and black		1·25	1·25
1872	1197	41p. grey-green, greenish yell, brt green, slate-grn, gold, blackish brn & blk		1·40	1·40
1868/72			*Set of 5*	4·50	4·50

Booklet pane No. 1869a comes from the £6 "National Trust" booklet.

1198 British Troops and
French Civilians
celebrating

1199 Symbolic Hands and
Red Cross

1200 St. Paul's Cathedral
and Searchlights

1201 Symbolic Hand
releasing Peace Dove

1202 Symbolic Hands

(Des J. Gorham (Nos. 1873, 1875), J-M. Folon (others))

1995 (2 May). *Europa. Peace and Freedom. One phosphor band (Nos. 1873/4) or two phosphor bands (others). P 14½×14.*

1873	1198	19p. silver, bistre-brown and grey-black		65	65
1874	1199	19p. silver, bistre-yellow, brt rose-red, vermilion, bright blue & slate-blue		65	65
1875	1200	25p. silver, blue and grey-black		95	95
1876	1201	25p. silver, verm, brt blue & grey-black		95	95
		a. Imperf (vert pair)			
1877	1202	30p. silver, bistre-yellow, brt magenta, pale greenish blue, grey-blk & flesh		1·10	1·10
1873/7			*Set of 5*	3·75	3·75

Nos. 1873 and 1875 commemorate the 50th anniversary of the end of the Second World War, No. 1874 the 125th anniversary of the British Red Cross Society and Nos. 1876/7 the 50th anniversary of the United Nations.

Nos. 1876/7 include the "EUROPA" emblem.

1203 *The Time Machine*

1204 *The First Men in the Moon*

1205 *The War of the Worlds*

1206 *The Shape of Things to Come*

(Des Siobhan Keaney. Litho Questa)

1995 (6 June). *Science Fiction. Novels by H. G. Wells. Two phosphor bands. P 14½×14.*

1878	1203	25p. new blue, greenish yellow, magenta, black and rosine		70	70
1879	1204	30p. new blue, greenish yellow, black, rosine and violet		1·10	1·10
1880	1205	35p. rosine, greenish yellow, violet, black and bright blue-green		1·25	1·25
1881	1206	41p. new blue, greenish yellow, magenta, black and rosine		1·40	1·40
1878/81			*Set of 4*	4·00	4·00

Nos. 1878/81 commemorate the centenary of publication of Wells's *The Time Machine*.

1207 The Swan, 1595

1208 The Rose, 1592

1209 The Globe, 1599   **1210** The Hope, 1613

1211 The Globe, 1614

(Des C. Hodges. Litho Walsall)

1995 (8 Aug). *Reconstruction of Shakespeare's Globe Theatre. Two phosphor bands.* P 14½.

1882	**1207**	25p. brownish grey, black, magenta, new blue and greenish yellow	85	85
		a. Horiz strip of 5. Nos. 1882/6	3·75	3·75
1883	**1208**	25p. brownish grey, black, magenta, new blue and greenish yellow	85	85
1884	**1209**	25p. brownish grey, black, magenta, new blue and greenish yellow	85	85
1885	**1210**	25p. brownish grey, black, magenta, new blue and greenish yellow	85	85
1886	**1211**	25p. brownish grey, black, magenta, new blue and greenish yellow	85	85
1882/6		*Set of 5*	3·75	3·75

Nos. 1882/6 were printed together, *se-tenant*, in horizontal strips of 5 throughout the sheet with the backgrounds forming a composite design.

1212 Sir Rowland Hill and Uniform Penny Postage Petition   **1213** Hill and Penny Black

1214 Guglielmo Marconi and Early Wireless   **1215** Marconi and Sinking of *Titanic* (liner)

(Des The Four Hundred, Eng C. Slania. Recess and litho Harrison)

1995 (5 Sept). *Pioneers of Communications. One phosphor band (19p.) or phosphorised paper (others).* P 14½×14.

1887	**1212**	19p. silver, red and black	55	55
1888	**1213**	25p. silver, brown and black	80	80
		a. Silver (Queen's head and face value) omitted	£210	
1889	**1214**	41p. silver, grey-green and black	1·25	1·25
1890	**1215**	60p. silver, deep ultramarine and black	1·60	1·60
1887/90		*Set of 4*	3·75	3·75

Nos. 1887/8 mark the birth bicentenary of Sir Rowland Hill and Nos. 1889/90 the centenary of the first radio transmissions.

1216 Harold Wagstaff   **1217** Gus Risman

1218 Jim Sullivan   **1219** Billy Batten

1220 Brian Bevan

(Des C. Birmingham)

1995 (3 Oct). *Centenary of Rugby League. One phosphor band (19p.) or two phosphor bands (others).* P 14×14½.

1891	**1216**	19p. blue, greenish yellow, magenta, new blue, grey-black and black	60	60
1892	**1217**	25p. slate-purple, greenish yellow, mag, new blue, grey-black & black	80	80
1893	**1218**	30p. slate-green, greenish yellow, bright purple, new blue, grey-black & blk	1·00	1·00
1894	**1219**	35p. slate-black, greenish yellow, mag, new blue and black	1·10	1·10
1895	**1220**	41p. bluish grey, orange-yellow, mag, new blue, grey-black and black	1·50	1·50
1891/5		*Set of 5*	4·50	4·50

1221 European Robin in Mouth of Pillar Box

1222 European Robin on Railings and Holly

1223 European Robin on Snow-covered Milk Bottles

1224 European Robin on Road Sign

1225 European Robin on Door Knob and Christmas Wreath

(Des K. Lilly)

1995 (30 Oct). *Christmas. Christmas Robins. One phosphor band (19p.) or two phosphor bands (others).* P 15×14.

1896	**1221**	19p. silver, greenish yellow, vermilion, orange-vermilion, bistre and black	45	45
1897	**1222**	25p. silver, greenish yellow, scarlet, pale blue, ochre and black	60	60
1898	**1223**	30p. silver, greenish yellow, rose-carmine, lt green, olive-brn & grey	90	90
1899	**1224**	41p. silver, greenish yellow, rose-red, dull blue, bistre and black	1·25	1·25
1900	**1225**	60p. silver, orange-yellow, red-orange, bistre and black	1·60	1·60
1896/1900		*Set of 5*	4·50	4·50

1226 Opening Lines of "To a Mouse" and Fieldmouse   **1227** "O my Luve's like a red, red rose" and Wild Rose

1228 "Scots, wha hae wi Wallace bled" and Sir William Wallace   **1229** "Auld Lang Syne" and Highland Dancers

(Des Tayburn Design Consultancy. Litho Questa)

1996 (25 Jan). *Death Bicentenary of Robert Burns (Scottish poet). One phosphor band (19p.) or 2 phosphor bands (others).* P 14½.

1901	**1226**	19p. cream, bistre-brown and black	55	55
1902	**1227**	25p. cream, bistre-brown, black, mag, bistre-yellow and new blue	80	80
1903	**1228**	41p. cream, bistre-brown, black, mag, bistre-yellow and new blue	1·25	1·25
1904	**1229**	60p. cream, bistre-brown, black, mag, bistre-yellow and new blue	1·60	1·60
1901/4		*Set of 4*	3·75	3·75

1230 "MORE! LOVE" (Mel Calman)

1231 "Sincerely" (Charles Barsotti)

1232 "Do you have something for the HUMAN CONDITION?" (Mel Calman)

1233 "MENTAL FLOSS" (Leo Cullum)

1234 "4.55 P.M." (Charles Barsotti)

1235 "Dear lottery prize winner" (Larry)

1236 "I'm writing to you because…." (Mel Calman)

1237 "FETCH THIS, FETCH THAT" (Charles Barsotti)

1238 "My day starts before I'm ready for it" (Mel Calman)

1239 "THE CHEQUE IN THE POST" (Jack Ziegler)

(Des M. Wolff. Litho Walsall)

1996 (26 Feb–11 Nov). *Greeting Stamps. Cartoons. "All-over" phosphor.* P 14½×14 (*with one elliptical hole on each vertical side*).

1905	1230	(1st) black and bright mauve	..	70	70
		a. Booklet pane. Nos. 1905/14	..	6·25	
		p. Two phosphor bands (11 Nov)		70	70
		pa. Booklet pane. Nos. 1905p/14p		6·25	
1906	1231	(1st) black and blue-green	..	70	70
		p. Two phosphor bands (11 Nov)	..	70	70
1907	1232	(1st) black and new blue	..	70	70
		p. Two phosphor bands (11 Nov)	..	70	70
1908	1233	(1st) black and bright violet	..	70	70
		p. Two phosphor bands (11 Nov)	..	70	70
1909	1234	(1st) black and vermilion	..	70	70
		p. Two phosphor bands (11 Nov)	..	70	70
1910	1235	(1st) black and new blue	..	70	70
		p. Two phosphor bands (11 Nov)	..	70	70
1911	1236	(1st) black and vermilion	..	70	70
		p. Two phosphor bands (11 Nov)	..	70	70
1912	1237	(1st) black and bright violet	..	70	70
		p. Two phosphor bands (11 Nov)	..	70	70
1913	1238	(1st) black and blue-green	..	70	70
		p. Two phosphor bands (11 Nov)	..	70	70
1914	1239	(1st) black and bright mauve	..	70	70
		p. Two phosphor bands (11 Nov)	..	70	70
1905/14	..	..	*Set of 10*	6·25	6·25
1905p/14p		..	*Set of 10*	6·25	6·25

Nos. 1905/14 were issued in £2.50 stamp booklets (sold at £2.60 from 8 July 1996), together with a pane of twenty half stamp-sized labels. The stamps and labels were attached to the booklet cover by a common gutter margin.

1240 "Muscovy Duck"

1241 "Lapwing"

1242 "White-fronted Goose"

1243 "Bittern"

1244 "Whooper Swan"

(Des Moseley Webb)

1996 (12 Mar). *50th Anniv of the Wildfowl and Wetlands Trust. Bird paintings by C. F. Tunnicliffe. One phosphor band* (19p.) *or phosphorised paper* (others). P 14×14½.

1915	1240	19p. sepia, orange-yellow, brown, pale buff, grey and gold	50	50
1916	1241	25p. bistre-brown, greenish yell, mag, new blue, pale buff, gold & black	70	70
1917	1242	30p. bistre-brown, greenish yell, mag, new bl, pale buff, gold & grey-blk	80	80
1918	1243	35p. sepia, pale orange, lake-brn, brn-olive, pale buff, gold & grey-black	1·25	1·25
1919	1244	41p. sepia, greenish yellow, magenta, new bl, pale buff, gold & grey-blk	1·60	1·60
1915/19	..	.. .. *Set of 5*	4·25	4·25

1245 The Odeon, Harrogate

1246 Laurence Olivier and Vivien Leigh in *Lady Hamilton* (film)

1247 Old Cinema Ticket

1248 Pathé News Still

1249 Cinema Sign, The Odeon, Manchester

(Des The Chase)

1996 (16 Apr). *Centenary of Cinema. One phosphor band* (19p.) *or two phosphor bands* (others). P 14×14½.

1920	1245	19p. black, greenish yellow, silver, bright magenta and new blue	50	50
1921	1246	25p. black, greenish yellow, silver, bright magenta and new blue	70	70
1922	1247	30p. black, greenish yellow, silver, bright magenta and new blue	90	90
1923	1248	35p. black, red and silver	1·25	1·25
1924	1249	41p. black, greenish yellow, silver, bright magenta and new blue	1·60	1·60
1920/4	..	.. .. *Set of 5*	4·50	4·50

1250 Dixie Dean

1251 Bobby Moore

1252 Duncan Edwards

1253 Billy Wright

1254 Danny Blanchflower

(Des H. Brown. Litho Questa)

1996 (14 May). *European Football Championship. One phosphor band* (19p.) *or two phosphor bands* (others). P 14½×14.

1925	1250	19p. vermilion, black, pale grey and grey	40	40
		a. Booklet pane. No. 1925×4 with margins all round	1·50	
1926	1251	25p. brt emerald, blk, pale grey & grey	70	70
		a. Booklet pane. No. 1926×4 with margins all round	2·25	
1927	1252	35p. orge-yellow, blk, pale grey & grey	1·25	1·25
		a. Booklet pane. No. 1927/9, each × 2, with margins all round	6·50	
1928	1253	41p. new blue, black, pale grey and grey	1·40	1·40
1929	1254	60p. brt orange, black, pale grey & grey	1·75	1·75
1925/9	..	.. .. *Set of 5*	5·00	5·00

1255 Athlete on Starting Blocks

1256 Throwing the Javelin

1257 Basketball

1258 Swimming

1259 Athlete celebrating and
Olympic Rings

(Des N. Knight. Litho Questa)

1996 (9 July). *Olympic and Paralympic Games, Atlanta. Two phosphor bands.* P 14½×14.

1930	1255	26p. greenish grey, silver, rosine, black, magenta, bistre-yellow & new blue	1·00	1·00
		a. Horiz strip of 5. Nos. 1930/4	4·50	4·50
1931	1256	26p. greenish grey, silver, rosine, black, magenta, bistre-yellow & new blue	1·00	1·00
1932	1257	26p. greenish grey, silver, rosine, black, magenta, bistre-yellow & new blue	1·00	1·00
1933	1258	26p. greenish grey, silver, rosine, black, magenta, bistre-yellow & new blue	1·00	1·00
1934	1259	26p. greenish grey, silver, rosine, black, magenta, bistre-yellow & new blue	1·00	1·00
1930/4		Set of 5	4·50	4·50

Nos. 1930/4 were printed together, *se-tenant*, in horizontal strips of 5 throughout the sheet.

1260 Prof. Dorothy
Hodgkin (scientist)

1261 Dame Margot
Fonteyn (ballerina)

1262 Dame Elisabeth
Frink (sculptress)

1263 Dame Daphne du
Maurier (novelist)

1264 Dame Marea Hartman
(sports administrator)

(Des Stephanie Nash)

1996 (6 Aug). *Europa. Famous Women. One phosphor band (20p.) or two phosphor bands (others).* P 14½.

1935	1260	20p. dull blue-grn, brownish grey & blk	50	50
1936	1261	26p. dull mauve, brownish grey & black	70	70
		a. Imperf (horiz pair)	£300	
1937	1262	31p. bronze, brownish grey and black	90	90
1938	1263	37p. silver, brownish grey and black	1·25	1·25
1939	1264	43p. gold, brownish grey and black	1·40	1·40
1935/9		Set of 5	4·25	4·25

Nos. 1936/7 include the "EUROPA" emblem.

1265 *Muffin the Mule*

1266 *Sooty*

1267 *Stingray*

1268 *The Clangers*

1269 *Dangermouse*

(Des Tutssells. Photo Enschedé)

1996 (3 Sept)–97. *50th Anniv of Children's Television. One phosphor band (20p.) or two phosphor bands (others).* P 14½×14.

1940	1265	20p. deep claret, black, magenta, rosine and greenish yellow	55	55
		a. Perf 15×14 (23.9.97)	1·00	1·00
		ab. Booklet pane. No. 1940a×4 with margins all round	4·00	
1941	1266	26p. bright blue, black, deep grey-blue, magenta and greenish yellow	80	80
1942	1267	31p. greenish blue, black, new blue, magenta and greenish yellow	1·00	1·00
1943	1268	37p. dull violet-blue, black, new blue, magenta and greenish yellow	1·40	1·40
1944	1269	43p. bright purple, black, new blue, magenta and greenish yellow	1·60	1·60
1940/4		Set of 5	4·75	4·75

No. 1940a comes from stamp booklets and was printed by Harrison & Sons Ltd.

1270 Triumph TR3

1271 MG TD

1272 Austin-Healey 100   **1273** Jaguar XK120

1274 Morgan Plus 4

(Des S. Clay)

1996 (1 Oct). *Classic Sports Cars. One phosphor band (20p.) or two phosphor bands (others).* P 14½.

1945	1270	20p. silver, greenish yellow, bright scarlet, vermilion, new blue & blk	70	70
1946	1271	26p. silver, greenish yellow, magenta, greenish blue and black	80	80
		a. Imperf (pair)		
1947	1272	37p. silver, greenish yellow, brt mag, deep turq-blue, new blue & black	1·10	1·10
		a. Imperf (pair)		
1948	1273	43p. silver, greenish yellow, magenta, greenish blue and black	1·25	1·25
		a. Imperf (horiz pair)		
1949	1274	63p. silver, greenish yellow, magenta, greenish blue, stone and black	1·75	1·75
1945/9		Set of 5	5·00	5·00

On Nos. 1946/9 the left-hand phosphor band on each stamp is three times the width of that on the right.

1275 The Three Kings

1276 The Annunciation

1277 The Journey to Bethlehem

1278 The Nativity

1279 The Shepherds

(Des Laura Stoddart)

1996 (28 Oct). *Christmas. One phosphor band (2nd class) or two phosphor bands (others). P 15×14.*

1950	1275	(2nd)	gold, greenish yellow, magenta, blue, black and light brown	60	60
1951	1276	(1st)	gold, yellow, cerise, new blue, black and light brown	75	75
1952	1277	31p.	gold, orange-yellow, cerise, blue, black and light brown	85	85
1953	1278	43p.	gold, greenish yellow, magenta, new blue, grey-black & lt brown	1·25	1·25
1954	1279	63p.	gold, greenish yellow, magenta, new blue, black and light brown	1·60	1·60
1950/4			*Set of 5*	4·75	4·75

1280 *Gentiana acaulis* (Georg Ehret)

1281 *Magnolia grandiflora* (Ehret)

1282 *Camellia japonica* (Alfred Chandler)

1283 *Tulipa* (Ehret)

1284 *Fuchsia* "Princess of Wales" (Augusta Withers)

1285 *Tulipa gesneriana* (Ehret)

1286 *Guzmania splendens* (Charlotte Sowerby)

1287 *Iris latifolia* (Ehret)

1288 *Hippeastrum rutilum* (Pierre-Joseph Redoute)

1289 *Passiflora coerulea* (Ehret)

(Des Tutssels. Litho Walsall)

1997 (6 Jan). *Greeting Stamps. 19th-century Flower Paintings. Two phosphor bands. P 14½×14 (with one elliptical hole on each vertical side).*

1955	1280	(1st) greenish yellow, new blue, magenta, black, blue-green & gold	70	70
		a. Booklet pane. Nos. 1955/64	6·25	
		ab. Gold, blue-green and phosphor omitted		
1956	1281	(1st) greenish yellow, new blue, magenta, black, blue-green & gold	70	70
1957	1282	(1st) greenish yellow, new blue, magenta, black, blue-green & gold	70	70
1958	1283	(1st) greenish yellow, new blue, magenta, black, blue-green & gold	70	70
1959	1284	(1st) greenish yellow, new blue, magenta, black, blue-green & gold	70	70
1960	1285	(1st) greenish yellow, new blue, magenta, black, blue-green & gold	70	70
1961	1286	(1st) greenish yellow, new blue, magenta, black, blue-green & gold	70	70
1962	1287	(1st) greenish yellow, new blue, magenta, black, blue-green & gold	70	70
1963	1288	(1st) greenish yellow, new blue, magenta, black, blue-green & gold	70	70
1964	1289	(1st) greenish yellow, new blue, magenta, black, blue-green & gold	70	70
1955/64		*Set of 10*	6·25	6·25

Nos. 1955/64 were issued in £2.60 stamp booklets together with a pane of twenty half-sized labels. The stamp and labels were attached to the booklet cover by a common gutter margin.

1290 "King Henry VIII"

1291 "Catherine of Aragon"

1292 "Anne Boleyn"

1293 "Jane Seymour"

1294 "Anne of Cleves"

1295 "Catherine Howard"

1296 "Catherine Parr"

(Des Kate Stephens from contemporary paintings. Photo Harrison)

1997 (21 Jan). *450th Death Anniv of King Henry VIII. Two phosphor bands. P 15 (No. 1965) or 14×15 (others).*

1965	1290	26p.	gold, greenish yellow, bright purple, new blue and black	80	80
			a. Imperf (pair)		
1966	1291	26p.	gold, greenish yellow, bright carmine, new blue and black	85	85
			a. Horiz strip of 6. Nos. 1966/71	4·50	4·50
1967	1292	26p.	gold, greenish yellow, bright carmine, new blue and black	85	85
1968	1293	26p.	gold, greenish yellow, bright carmine, new blue and black	85	85
1969	1294	26p.	gold, greenish yellow, bright carmine, new blue and black	85	85
1970	1295	26p.	gold, greenish yellow, bright carmine, new blue and black	85	85
1971	1296	26p.	gold, greenish yellow, bright carmine, new blue and black	85	85
1965/71			*Set of 7*	4·75	4·75

Nos. 1966/71 were printed together, *se-tenant*, in horizontal strips of six throughout the sheet.

1297 St. Columba in Boat

1298 St. Columba on Iona

1299 St. Augustine with King Ethelbert

1300 St. Augustine with Model of Cathedral

(Des Claire Melinsky. Photo Enschedé)

1997 (11 Mar). *Religious Anniversaries. Two phosphor bands. P 14½.*

1972	1297	26p.	greenish yellow, magenta, new blue, grey-black and gold	70	70
			a. Imperf (pair)		
1973	1298	37p.	greenish yellow, magenta, new blue, grey-black and gold	1·00	1·00
1974	1299	43p.	greenish yellow, magenta, new blue, grey-black and gold	1·40	1·40
1975	1300	63p.	greenish yellow, magenta, new blue, grey-black and gold	1·90	1·90
1972/5			*Set of 4*	4·50	4·50

Nos. 1972/3 commemorate the 1400th death anniversary of St. Columba and Nos. 1974/5 the 1400th anniversary of the arrival of St. Augustine of Canterbury in Kent.

1301

1302

(Des J. Matthews. Photo Enschedé)

1997 (18 Mar). *Self-adhesive. One centre phosphor band (2nd) or two phosphor bands (1st). P* 14×15 *die-cut (with one elliptical hole on each vertical side).*
1976 1301 (2nd) bright blue .. .. .. 1·00 1·00
1977 1302 (1st) bright orange-red .. .. 1·00 1·00
Nos. 1976/7, which were priced at 20p. and 26p., were each sold in rolls of 100 with the stamps separate on the backing paper.

(Photo Harrison (No. 1978), Harrison (booklets) or Walsall (sheets and booklets) (No. 1979))

1997 (21 Apr–23 Sept). *Royal Golden Wedding* (1st issue). *Designs as T 367 and 914 but colours changed. Two phosphor bands. P* 15×14 *(with one elliptical hole on each vertical side).*
1978 367 26p. gold 80 80
    a. Imperf (horiz pair) £2000
    l. Booklet pane Nos. 1978/9, each
     × 4, and centre label with margins
     all round (23 Sept) .. .. 3·50
1979 914 (1st) gold 80 80
See also Nos. 2011/14.

1303 *Dracula*   1304 *Frankenstein*

1305 *Dr. Jekyll and Mr. Hyde*   1306 *The Hound of the Baskervilles*

(Des I. Pollock. Photo Walsall)

1997 (13 May). *Europa. Tales and Legends. Horror Stories. Two phosphor bands. P* 14×15.
1980 1303 26p. grey-black, black, new blue,
    magenta and greenish yellow .. 90 90
1981 1304 31p. grey-black, black, new blue,
    magenta and greenish yellow .. 1·10 1·10
1982 1305 37p. grey-black, black, new blue,
    magenta and greenish yellow .. 1·40 1·40
1983 1306 43p. grey-black, black, new blue,
    magenta and greenish yellow .. 1·60 1·60
1980/3 .. .. .. Set of 4 4·50 4·50
Nos. 1980/3 commemorate the birth bicentenary of Mary Shelley (creator of Frankenstein) with the 26p. and 31p. values incorporating the "EUROPA" emblem.
Each value has features printed in fluorescent ink which are visible under ultra-violet light.

1307 Reginald Mitchell and Supermarine Spitfire MkIIA

1308 Roy Chadwick and Avro Lancaster MkI

1309 Ronald Bishop and De Havilland Mosquito B MkXVI

1310 George Carter and Gloster Meteor T Mk 7

1311 Sir Sidney Camm and Hawker Hunter FGA Mk9

(Des Turner Duckworth. Photo Harrison)

1997 (10 June). *British Aircraft Designers. One phosphor band* (20p.) *or two phosphor bands* (others). *P* 15×14.
1984 1307 20p. silver, greenish yellow, magenta,
    new blue, black and grey .. 55 55
1985 1308 26p. silver, greenish yellow, magenta,
    new blue, black and grey .. 95 95
1986 1309 37p. silver, greenish yellow, magenta,
    new blue, black and grey .. 1·10 1·10
1987 1310 43p. silver, greenish yellow, magenta,
    new blue, black and grey .. 1·40 1·40
1988 1311 63p. silver, greenish yellow, magenta,
    new blue, black and grey .. 1·90 1·90
1984/8 .. .. .. Set of 5 5·25 5·25

1312 Carriage Horse and Coachman   1313 Lifeguards Horse and Trooper

1314 Blues and Royals Drum Horse and Drummer   1315 Duke of Edinburgh's Horse and Groom

(Des J.-L. Benard. Litho Walsall)

1997 (8 July). *"All the Queen's Horses". 50th Anniv of the British Horse Society. One phosphor band* (20p.) *or two phosphor bands* (others). *P* 14½.
1989 1312 20p. scarlet-vermilion, black, magenta,
    new blue and greenish yellow .. 70 70
1990 1313 26p. scarlet-vermilion, black, magenta,
    new blue and greenish yellow .. 1·00 1·00
1991 1314 43p. scarlet-vermilion, black, magenta,
    new blue and greenish yellow .. 1·40 1·40
1992 1315 63p. scarlet-vermilion, black, magenta,
    new blue and greenish yellow .. 1·90 1·90
1989/92 .. .. .. Set of 4 4·50 4·50

GH CASTLE

Harrison Nos. 1611/14

GH CASTLE

Enschedé Nos. 1993/6

Differences between Harrison and Enschedé:
  Harrison – "C" has top serif and tail of letter points to right. "A" has flat top. "S" has top and bottom serifs.
  Enschedé – "C" has no top serif and tail of letter points upwards. "A" has pointed top. "S" has no serifs.

(Des from photos by Prince Andrew, Duke of York. Eng Inge Madle. Recess (Queens head by silk screen process) Enschedé)

1997 (29 July). *Designs as Nos. 1612/14 with Queen's head in silhouette as T 1044, but re-engraved with differences in inscription as shown above. P* 15×14 *(with one elliptical hole on each vertical side).*
1993 880 £1.50, deep claret and gold† .. 3·50 3·00
1994 881 £2 indigo and gold† .. .. 5·00 4·00
    a. Gold (Queen's head) omitted .. £550
1995 1044 £3 violet and gold† .. .. 7·00 9·00
    a. Gold (Queen's head) omitted .. £2500
1996 882 £5 deep brown and gold† .. 13·00 8·00
    a. Gold (Queen's head) omitted .. £2500
1993/6 .. .. .. Set of 4 25·00 22·00
†The Queen's head on these stamps is printed in optically variable ink which changes colour from gold to green when viewed from different angles.
No. 1996a occurs on R. 5/8 and 6/8 from some sheets.

1316 Haroldswick, Shetland   1317 Painswick, Gloucestershire

1318 Beddgelert, Gwynedd   1319 Ballyroney, County Down

(Des T. Millington. Photo Enschedé)

1997 (12 Aug). *Sub-Post Offices. One phosphor band* (20p.) *or two phosphor bands* (others). *P* 14½.
1997 1316 20p. greenish yellow, brt magenta, new
    blue, grey-black, rosine & bl-grn 65 65
1998 1317 26p. greenish yellow, brt magenta, new
    blue, grey-black, rosine & bl-grn 80 80
1999 1318 43p. greenish yellow, brt magenta, new
    blue, grey-black, rosine & bl-grn 1·40 1·40
2000 1319 63p. greenish yellow, brt magenta, new
    blue, grey-black, rosine & bl-grn 1·90 1·90
1997/2000 .. .. Set of 4 4·25 4·25
Nos. 1997/2000 were issued on the occasion of the Centenary of the National Federation of Sub-Postmasters.

PRINTERS. Harrison and Sons Ltd became De La Rue Security Print on 8 September 1997. This was not reflected in the sheet imprints until mid-1998.

1320 *Noddy*   1321 *Famous Five*

1322 *Secret Seven*   1323 *Faraway Tree*

1324 *Malory Towers*

(Des C. Birmingham. Photo Enschedé)

1997 (9 Sept). *Birth Centenary of Enid Blyton (children's author).*
One phosphor band (20p) or two phosphor bands (others).
P 14×14½.

2001	**1320**	20p. greenish yellow, magenta, new blue, grey-black & deep grey-blue	55	55
2002	**1321**	26p. greenish yellow, magenta, new blue, grey-black & deep grey-blue	95	95
2003	**1322**	37p. greenish yellow, magenta, new blue, grey-black & deep grey-blue	1·10	1·10
2004	**1323**	43p. greenish yellow, magenta, new blue, grey-black & deep grey-blue	1·40	1·40
2005	**1324**	63p. greenish yellow, magenta, new blue, grey-black & deep grey-blue	1·90	1·90
2001/5		*Set of 5*	5·25	5·25

1325 Children and Father Christmas pulling Cracker

1326 Father Christmas with Traditional Cracker

1327 Father Christmas riding Cracker

1328 Father Christmas on Snowball

1329 Father Christmas and Chimney

(Des J. Gorham and M. Thomas (1st), J. Gorham (others). Photo Harrison)

1997 (27 Oct). *Christmas. 150th Anniv of the Christmas Cracker.*
One phosphor band (2nd) or two phosphor bands (others).
P 15×14.

2006	**1325**	(2nd) gold, greenish yellow, bright magenta, new blue & grey-black	70	70
		a. Imperf (pair)	£1100	
2007	**1326**	(1st) gold, greenish yellow, bright magenta, new blue & grey-black	80	80
2008	**1327**	31p. gold, greenish yellow, brt mag, new blue, brt blue & grey-black	90	90
		a. Imperf (pair)		
2009	**1328**	43p. gold, greenish yellow, brt mag, pale new blue & grey-black	1·40	1·40
2010	**1329**	63p. gold, greenish yellow, bright magenta, new blue & grey-black	1·75	1·75
2006/10		*Set of 5*	5·00	5·00

1330 Wedding Photograph, 1947

1331 Queen Elizabeth II and Prince Philip, 1997

(Des D. Driver (20p., 43p.), Lord Snowdon (26p., 63p.). Photo Harrison)

1997 (13 Nov). *Royal Golden Wedding (2nd issue). One phosphor band (20p.) or two phosphor bands (others).* P 15.

2011	**1330**	20p. gold, yellow-brown and grey-black	75	75
2012	**1331**	26p. gold, bistre-yellow, magenta, new blue, grey-black and greenish grey	95	95
2013	**1330**	43p. gold, bluish green and grey-black	1·60	1·60
2014	**1331**	63p. gold, bistre-yellow, magenta, new blue, grey-black & lavender-grey	2·25	2·25
2011/14		*Set of 4*	5·00	5·00

1332 Common Dormouse

1333 Lady's Slipper Orchid

1334 Song Thrush

1335 Shining Ram's-horn Snail

1336 Mole Cricket

1337 Devil's Bolete

(Des R. Maude. Litho Questa)

1998 (20 Jan). *Endangered Species. One side phosphor band (20p.) or two phosphor bands (others).* P 14×14½.

2015	**1332**	20p. black, new blue, mag, greenish yellow, dp bl & pale lavender-grey	50	50
		a. Imperf (pair)		
2016	**1333**	26p. black, new blue, mag, greenish yellow, dp blue & pale yell-olive	60	60
2017	**1334**	31p. black, new blue, mag, greenish yellow, dp blue & pale bluish grey	80	80
2018	**1335**	37p. black, new blue, mag, greenish yellow, dp bl & pale greenish grey	1·00	1·00
2019	**1336**	43p. black, new blue, mag, greenish yellow, dp blue & pale dull mauve	1·10	1·10
2020	**1337**	63p. black, new blue, mag, greenish yellow, dp blue & pale grey-brown	1·60	1·60
2015/20		*Set of 6*	5·00	5·00

1338 Diana, Princess of Wales (photo by Lord Snowdon)

1339 At British Lung Foundation Function, April 1997 (photo by John Stillwell)

1340 Wearing Tiara, 1991 (photo by Lord Snowdon)

1341 On Visit to Birmingham, October 1995 (photo by Tim Graham)

1342 In Evening Dress, 1987 (photo by Terence Donovan)

(Des B. Robinson. Photo Harrison)

1998 (3 Feb). *Diana, Princess of Wales Commemoration. Two phosphor bands.* P 14×15.

2021	**1338**	26p. purple, greenish yellow, magenta, new blue and black	90	90
		a. Horiz strip of 5. Nos. 2021/5	4·00	4·00
		ab. Imperf (horiz strip of 5. Nos. 2021/5)		
		ac. Imperf (horiz strip of 4. Nos. 2021/4)		
		ad. Imperf (horiz strip of 3. Nos. 2021/3)		
2022	**1339**	26p. purple, greenish yellow, magenta, new blue and black	90	90
2023	**1340**	26p. purple, greenish yellow, magenta, new blue and black	90	90
2024	**1341**	26p. purple, greenish yellow, magenta, new blue and black	90	90
2025	**1342**	26p. purple, greenish yellow, magenta, new blue and black	90	90
2021/5		*Set of 5*	4·00	4·00

Nos. 2021/5 were printed together, *se-tenant*, in horizontal strips of five throughout the sheet.

On No. 2021ac the right-hand stamp in the strip of 5 is perforated between the stamp and right margin only.

1343 Lion of England and Griffin of Edward III

1344 Falcon of Plantagenet and Bull of Clarence

1345 Lion of Mortimer and Yale of Beaufort

1346 Greyhound of Richmond and Dragon of Wales

1347 Unicorn of Scotland and Horse of Hanover

(Des J. Matthews. Recess and litho Harrison)

1998 (24 Feb). *650th Anniv of the Order of the Garter. The Queen's Beasts. Two phosphor bands. P* 15×14.

2026	1343	26p. silver, green, brt blue, carmine-red, verm, lemon, grey-blk & blk	90	90
		a. Horiz strip of 5. Nos. 2026/30 ..	4·00	4·00
		ab. Missing green (on Nos. 2026, 2028/9) (horiz strip of 5) ..		
2027	1344	26p. silver, green, brt blue, carm-red, verm, lemon, grey, grey-blk & blk	90	90
2028	1345	26p. silver, green, brt blue, carm-red, verm, lemon, grey, grey-blk & blk	90	90
2029	1346	26p. silver, green, brt blue, carm-red, verm, lemon, grey, grey-blk & blk	90	90
2030	1347	26p. silver, green, brt blue, vermilion, lemon, grey, grey-black & black	90	90
2026/30		*Set of* 5	4·00	4·00

Nos. 2026/30 were printed together, *se-tenant*, in horizontal strips of five throughout the sheet.

The phosphor bands on Nos. 2026/30 are only half the height of the stamps and do not cover the silver parts of the designs.

1348

(Des G. Knipe, adapted Dew Gibbons Design Group. Photo Walsall)

1998 (10 Mar). *As T* **157** (*Wilding definitive of 1952–54*) *but with face values in decimal currency as T* **1348**. *One side phosphor band* (20p.) *or two phosphor bands* (*others*). *P* 14 (*with one elliptical hole on each vertical side*).

2031	1348	20p. light green	75	75
		b. Booklet pane. No. 2031×6 with margins all round ..	4·00	
		c. Booklet pane. Nos. 2031×4 and 2032/3, each × 2 and central label with margins all round ..	6·00	
2032		26p. red-brown	75	75
		a. Booklet pane. No. 2032×9 ..	6·00	
		b. Booklet pane. Nos. 2032/3, each × 3 ..	5·50	
2033		37p. light purple	1·50	1·50
2031/3		*Set of* 3	3·25	3·25

Nos. 2031/3 were only issued in £7.49 stamp booklets. No. 2031 exists with the phosphor band at left or right

1349 St. John's Point Lighthouse, County Down

1350 Smalls Lighthouse, Pembrokeshire

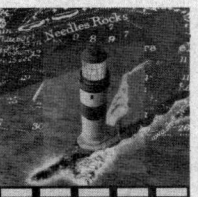

1351 Needles Rock Lighthouse, Isle of Wight, *c* 1900

1352 Bell Rock Lighthouse, Arbroath, mid-19th-century

1353 Eddystone Lighthouse, Plymouth, 1698

(Des D. Davis and J. Boon. Litho Questa)

1998 (24 Mar). *Lighthouses. One side phosphor band* (20p.) *or two phosphor bands* (*others*). *P* 14½×14.

2034	1349	20p. gold, greenish yellow, magenta, new blue and black	50	50
2035	1350	26p. gold, greenish yellow, magenta, new blue and black	70	70
2036	1351	37p. gold, greenish yellow, magenta, new blue and black	1·00	1·00
2037	1352	43p. gold, greenish yellow, magenta, new blue and black	1·40	1·40
2038	1353	63p. gold, greenish yellow, magenta, new blue and black	1·90	1·90
2034/8		*Set of* 5	5·00	5·00

Nos. 2034/8 commemorate the 300th anniversary of the first Eddystone Lighthouse and the final year of manned lighthouses.

(Photo Enschedé (coils) or Walsall (sheets))

1998 (6 Apr). *Self-adhesive Stamps. Designs as T* **913/14**. *One centre phosphor band* (2nd), *or two phosphor bands* (1st). *P* 15×14 *die-cut* (*with one elliptical hole on each vertical side*).

2039		(2nd) bright blue	30	35
2040		(1st) bright orange-red ..	40	45

Nos. 2039/40, initially sold for 20p. and 26p., were first issued in rolls of 200 with the surplus self-adhesive paper removed.

2nd and 1st self-adhesive stamps as Nos. 2039/40 were issued in sheets, printed in photogravure by Walsall Security Printers, on 15 June 1998. These are similar to the previous Enschedé coil printings, but the sheets retain the surplus self-adhesive paper around each stamp. Stamps from sheets have square perforation tips instead of the rounded versions to be found on the coils.

1354 Tommy Cooper

1355 Eric Morecambe

1356 Joyce Grenfell

1357 Les Dawson

1358 Peter Cook

(Des G. Scarfe. Litho Walsall)

1998 (23 Apr). *Comedians. One side phosphor band* (20p.) *or two phosphor bands* (*others*). *P* 14½×14.

2041	1354	20p. vermilion, black, rose-pink, new blue and greenish-yellow ..	50	50
2042	1355	26p. verm, black, rose-pink & new blue	80	80
2043	1356	37p. vermilion, black, rose-pink, new blue and greenish-yellow ..	1·10	1·10
2044	1357	43p. vermilion, black, rose-pink, new blue and pale orange ..	1·25	1·25
2045	1358	63p. vermilion, black, deep rose-pink, new blue and greenish-yellow ..	1·90	1·90
2041/5		.. .. *Set of* 5	5·00	5·00

Stamps as Type **1356** but with a face value of 30p., were prepared but not issued. Mint examples and a first day cover have been reported.

1359 Hands forming Heart

1360 Adult and Child holding Hands

1361 Hands forming Cradle

1362 Hand taking Pulse

(Des V. Frost from photos by A. Wilson. Litho Questa)

1998 (23 June). *50th Anniv of the National Health Service. One side phosphor band* (20p.) *or two phosphor bands* (*others*). *P* 14×14½.

2046	1359	20p. deep claret, black, grey-brown, pale cream and cream ..	50	50
2047	1360	26p. deep grey-green, black, grey-brown, pale cream and cream ..	70	70
2048	1361	43p. deep lilac, black, grey-brown, pale cream and cream ..	1·25	1·25
2049	1362	63p. deep dull blue, black, grey-brown, pale cream and cream ..	1·90	1·90
2046/9		.. .. *Set of* 4	3·75	3·75

1363 *The Hobbit* (J. R. R. Tolkien)

1364 *The Lion, The Witch and the Wardrobe* (C. S. Lewis)

1365 *The Phoenix and the Carpet* (E. Nesbit)

1366 *The Borrowers* (Mary Norton)

1367 *Through the Looking Glass* (Lewis Carroll)

(Des P. Malone. Photo D.L.R.)

1998 (21 July). *Famous Children's Fantasy Novels. One centre phosphor band (20p.) or two phosphor bands (others).* P 15×14.

2050	**1363**	20p. silver, greenish yellow, bright magenta, new blue, black and gold	50	50
2051	**1364**	26p. silver, greenish yellow, bright magenta, new blue, black and gold	80	80
		a. Imperf (pair) ..	£650	
2052	**1365**	37p. silver, greenish yellow, bright magenta, new blue, black and gold	1·10	1·10
2053	**1366**	43p. silver, greenish yellow, bright magenta, new blue, black and gold	1·25	1·25
2054	**1367**	63p. silver, greenish yellow, bright magenta, new blue, black and gold	1·90	1·90
2050/4		*Set of 5*	5·00	5·00

Nos. 2050/4 commemorate the birth centenary of C. S. Lewis and the death centenary of Lewis Carroll.

1368 Woman in Yellow Feathered Costume   **1369** Woman in Blue Costume and Headdress

1370 Group of Children in White and Gold Robes   **1371** Child in "Tree" Costume

(Des T. Hazael. Photo Walsall)

1998 (25 Aug). *Europa. Festivals. Notting Hill Carnival. One centre phosphor band (20p.) or two phosphor bands (others).* P 14×14½.

2055	**1368**	20p. gold, black, new blue, bright magenta and greenish yellow	50	50
2056	**1369**	26p. gold, grey-black, new blue, bright magenta and greenish yellow	70	70
2057	**1370**	43p. gold, grey-black, new blue, bright magenta and bistre-yellow	1·10	1·10
2058	**1371**	63p. gold, grey-black, new blue, bright magenta and greenish yellow	1·75	1·75
2055/8		*Set of 4*	3·50	3·50

The 20p. and 26p. incorporate the "EUROPA" emblem.

1372 Sir Malcolm Campbell's *Bluebird*, 1925

1373 Sir Henry Segrave's *Sunbeam*, 1926

1374 John G. Parry Thomas's *Babs*, 1926

1375 John R. Cobb's *Railton Mobil Special*, 1947

1376 Donald Campbell's *Bluebird CN7*, 1964

(Des Roundel Design Group. Photo De La Rue)

1998 (29 Sept–13 Oct). *British Land Speed Record Holders. One centre phosphor band (20p.) or two phosphor bands (others).* P 15×14.

2059	**1372**	20p. rosine, greenish yellow, magenta, new blue, black and silver	50	50
		a. Perf 14½×13½ (1 side phosphor band) (13 Oct) ..	1·00	1·00
		ac. Booklet pane. No. 2059a×4 with margins all round ..	3·00	
2060	**1373**	26p. rosine, greenish yellow, magenta, new blue, black and silver ..	70	70
		a. Rosine (face value) omitted ..		
2061	**1374**	30p. rosine, greenish yellow, magenta, new blue, black and silver ..	1·00	1·00
2062	**1375**	43p. rosine, greenish yellow, magenta, new blue, black and silver ..	1·10	1·10
2063	**1376**	63p. rosine, greenish yellow, magenta, new blue, black and silver ..	1·75	1·75
2059/63		*Set of 5*	4·50	4·50

Nos. 2059/63 commemorate the 50th death anniversary of Sir Malcolm Campbell.

No. 2059a, which occurs with the phosphor band at left or right, comes from stamp booklets and was printed by Walsall. There are minor differences of design between No. 2059 and No. 2059a. The latter also omits the copyright symbol and date.

No. 2060a occurs on the fourth vertical row of several sheets. Other examples exist with either the "2" or the "6" omitted.

1377 Angel with Hands raised in Blessing

1378 Angel praying

1379 Angel playing Flute

1380 Angel playing Lute

1381 Angel praying

(Des Irene von Treskow. Photo De La Rue)

1998 (2 Nov). *Christmas. Angels. One centre phosphor band (20p.) or two phosphor bands (others).* P 15×14.

2064	**1377**	20p. gold, greenish yellow, magenta, new blue and grey-black ..	50	50
		a. Imperf (pair)		
2065	**1378**	26p. gold, greenish yellow, magenta, new blue and grey-black	70	70
		a. Imperf (pair)		
2066	**1379**	30p. gold, greenish yellow, magenta, new blue and grey-black ..	1·00	1·00
2067	**1380**	43p. gold, greenish yellow, magenta, new blue and grey-black	1·10	1·10
		a. Imperf (pair)		
2068	**1381**	63p. gold, greenish yellow, magenta, new blue and grey-black	1·75	1·75
2064/8		*Set of 5*	4·50	4·50

1382 Greenwich Meridian and Clock (John Harrison's chronometer)   **1383** Industrial Worker and Blast Furnace (James Watt's discovery of steam power)

1384 Early Photos of Leaves (Henry Fox-Talbot's photographic experiments)   **1385** Computer inside Human Head (Alan Turing's work on computers)

(Des D. Gentleman (20p.), P. Howson (26p.), Z. and Barbara Baran (43p.), E. Paolozzi (63p.). Photo Enschedé (26p.) or De La Rue (others))

1999 (12 Jan–21 Sept). *Millennium Series. The Inventors' Tale. One centre phosphor band (20p.) or two phosphor bands (others).* P 14×14½.

2069	**1382**	20p. silver, deep grey, pale olive-grey, greenish grey, grey-black & brt rose-red	30	35
		a. Imperf (horiz pair)		
2070	**1383**	26p. silver, black, new blue, bright magenta and greenish yellow	40	45
2071	**1384**	43p. silver, greenish yellow, bright crimson, new blue, blk & brt mag	65	70
2072	**1385**	63p. silver, greenish blue, greenish yellow, cerise, new blue, blk & pale lemon	95	1·00
		a. Perf 13½×14 (21 Sept) ..	1·00	1·00
		ab. Booklet pane. No. 2072a×4 with margins all round ..	3·75	
2069/72		*Set of 4*	2·25	2·50

No. 2072a comes from £6.99 stamp booklets, and was printed by Questa.

1386 Airliner hugging Globe (International air travel)   **1387** Woman on Bicycle (Development of the bicycle)

1388 Victorian Railway Station (Growth of public transport)   **1389** Captain Cook and Maori (Captain James Cook's voyages)

(Des G. Hardie (20p.), Sara Fanelli (26p.), J. Lawrence (43p.), A. Klimowski (63p.). Photo Enschedé (20p., 63p.) or De La Rue (26p.). Litho Enschedé (43p.))

1999 (2 Feb). *Millennium Series. The Travellers' Tale. One centre phosphor band (20p.) or two phosphor bands (others).* P 14×14½.

2073	**1386**	20p. silver, vermilion, grey-blk, bluish violet, greenish blue & pale grey	30	35
2074	**1387**	26p. silver, greenish yellow, cerise, new blue, black and vermilion	40	45
2075	**1388**	43p. grey-black, stone and bronze	65	70
2076	**1389**	63p. silver, grey-black, new blue, brt magenta & greenish yellow ..	95	1·00
2073/6		*Set of 4*	2·25	2·50

COVER PRICES

Cover factors are quoted at the beginning of each country for most issues to 1945. An explanation of the system can be found on page x. The factors quoted do not, however, apply to philatelic covers.

1390

1999 (16 Feb). (*a*) *Embossed and litho Walsall. Self-adhesive. Die-cut perf* 14×15.
2077 1390 (1st) grey (face value) (Queen's head in
colourless relief) (phosphor back-
ground around head) .. .. 1·00 1·00
   l. Booklet pane. No. 2077×4 with
   margins all round .. .. 3·50
(*b*) *Eng. C. Slania. Recess Enschedé. P* 14×14½
2078 1390 (1st) grey-black (2 phosphor bands) .. 1·00 1·00
   l. Booklet pane. No. 2078×4 with
   margins all round .. .. 3·50
(*c*) *Typo Harrison. P* 14×15
2079 1390 (1st) black (2 phosphor bands) .. 1·00 1·00
   l. Booklet pane. No. 2079×4 with
   margins all round .. .. 3·50
Nos. 2077/9 were only issued in £7·54 stamp booklets.

1391 Vaccinating Child   **1392** Patient on Trolley
(pattern in cow markings)   (nursing care)
(Jenner's development of
smallpox vaccine)

1393 Penicillin Mould   **1394** Sculpture of Test-tube
(Fleming's discovery of   Baby (development of in
penicillin)   vitro fertilization)

(Des P. Brookes (20p.), Susan Macfarlane (26p.), M. Dempsey (43p.), A. Gormley (63p.). Photo Questa)

1999 (2 Mar–21 Sept). *Millennium Series. The Patients' Tale. One centre phosphor band* (20p.) *or two phosphor bands* (*others*). *P* 13½×14.
2080 1391 20p. greenish yellow, bright magenta,
new blue, black and silver .. 30 35
   a. Booklet pane. No. 2080×4 with
   margins all round (21 Sept) .. 1·25
2081 1392 26p. greenish yellow, bright magenta,
new blue, blk, silver & dp turq-bl 40 45
   a. Imperf (pair) .. ..
2082 1393 43p. greenish yell, brt mag, new blue,
black, dp bluish green & silver .. 65 70
2083 1394 63p. greenish yellow, bright magenta,
new blue, black, silver & blue-blk 95 1·00
2080/3 .. .. *Set of 4* 2·25 2·50

1395 Dove and Norman   **1396** Pilgrim Fathers and
Settler (medieval migration   Red Indian (17th-century
to Scotland)   migration to America)

1397 Sailing Ship and   **1398** Hummingbird and
Aspects of Settlement   Superimposed Stylised Face
(19th-century migration to   (20th-century migration to
Australia)   Great Britain)

(Des J. Byrne (20p.), W. McLean (26p.), J. Fisher (43p.), G. Powell (63p.). Litho (20p.) or photo (others) Walsall)

1999 (6 Apr–12 May). *Millennium Series. The Settlers' Tale. One centre phosphor band* (20p.) *or two phosphor bands* (*others*). *P* 14×14½.
2084 1395 20p. gold, silver, black, magenta, blue
and greenish yellow .. 30 35
2085 1396 26p. greenish yellow, magenta, new
blue, grey-black and silver .. 40 45
   a. Booklet pane. Nos. 2085 and 2089
   with margins all round (12 May) 80
2086 1397 43p. greenish yellow, magenta, new
blue, grey-black, gold & chocolate 65 70
2087 1398 63p. greenish yellow, magenta, new bl,
reddish vio, dp reddish vio & gold 95 1·00
2084/7 .. .. *Set of 4* 2·25 2·50

1399 Woven Threads   **1400** Salts Mill, Saltaire
(woollen industry)   (cotton industry)

1401 Hull on Slipway   **1402** Lloyd's Building (City
(shipbuilding)   of London Finance centre)

(Des P. Collingwood (19p.), D. Hockney (26p.), B. Sanderson (44p.), B. Neiland (64p.). Litho (19p.) or photo (others) De La Rue)

1999 (4 May). *Millennium Series. The Workers' Tale. One centre phosphor band* (19p.) *or two phosphor bands* (*others*). *P* 14×14½.
2088 1399 19p. drab, greenish yellow, cerise, new
blue, grey-black and bronze .. 30 35
   a. Bronze (Queen's head) omitted
2089 1400 26p. silver, greenish yellow, rosine,
new blue and grey-black .. 40 45
2090 1401 44p. silver, greenish yellow, orange-
red, brt blue, yell-brn & grey-blk 70 75
2091 1402 64p. silver, greenish yellow, rosine,
new blue and grey-black .. 1·00 1·10
2088/91 .. .. *Set of 4* 2·40 2·50
For No. 2089 printed by Walsall in photogravure, see booklet pane No. 2085a.

1403 Freddie Mercury (lead   **1404** Bobby Moore with
singer of Queen) ("Popular   World Cup, 1966 ("Sport")
Music")

1405 Dalek from *Dr. Who*   **1406** Charlie Chaplin (film
(science-fiction series)   star) ("Cinema")
("Television")

(Des P. Blake (19p.), M. White (26p.), Lord Snowdon (44p.), R. Steadman (63p.). Photo Enschedé)

1999 (1 June). *Millennium Series. The Entertainers' Tale. One centre phosphor band* (19p.) *or two phosphor bands* (*others*). *P* 14×14½.
2092 1403 19p. greenish yellow, bright magenta,
new blue, grey-black and gold .. 30 35
2093 1404 26p. greenish yellow, brt magenta, new
blue, grey-black, gold & stone .. 40 45
2094 1405 44p. greenish yellow, bright magenta,
new blue, grey-black and silver 70 75
2095 1406 64p. greenish yellow, bright magenta,
new blue, grey-black and silver 1·00 1·10
2092/5 .. .. *Set of 4* 2·40 2·50

1407 Prince Edward and Miss Sophie
Rhys-Jones

1408

(Adapted J. Gibbs from photos by John Swannell. Photo De La Rue)

1999 (15 June). *Royal Wedding. Two phosphor bands. P* 15×14.
2096 1407 26p. vermilion, black, grey-blk & silver 60 60
   a. Imperf (pair) .. ..
2097 1408 64p. new blue, black, grey-blk & silver 1·40 1·40

1409 Suffragette behind   **1410** Water Tap (Right to
Prison Window (Equal   Health)
Rights for Women)

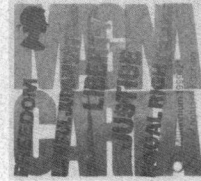

1411 Generations of School   **1412** "MAGNA CARTA"
Children (Right to Education)   (Human Rights)

(Des Natasha Kerr (19p.), M. Craig-Martin (26p.), A. Drummond (44p.), A. Kitching (64p.). Photo De La Rue)

1999 (6 July). *Millennium Series. The Citizens' Tale. One centre band* (19p.) *or two phosphor bands* (*others*). *P* 14×14½.
2098 1409 19p. silver, greenish yellow, cerise, new
blue and grey-black .. 30 35
2099 1410 26p. grey-black, new blue, brt mauve,
rosine, turquoise-grn & apple-grn 40 45
2100 1411 44p. bright blue, greenish yellow,
cerise, new blue and grey-black 70 75
2101 1412 64p. gold, greenish yellow, cerise, new
blue and grey-black .. 1·00 1·10
2098/101 .. .. *Set of 4* 2·40 2·50

1413 Molecular Structures   **1414** Galapagos Finch and
(DNA Decoding)   Fossilized Skeleton
   (Darwin's Theory of
   Evolution)

1415 Rotation of Polarised   **1416** Saturn (development of
Light by Magnetism (Faraday's   astronomical telescopes)
work on Electricity)

(Des M. Curtis (19p.), R. Harris Ching (26p.), C. Gray (44p.), from Hubble Space Telescope photograph (64p.). Photo (19p., 64p.) or litho (26p., 44p.) Questa)

1999 (3 Aug–21 Sept). *Millennium Series. The Scientists' Tale.* One centre phosphor band (19p.) or two phosphor bands (*others*). P 13½×14 (19p., 64p.) or 14×14½ (26p., 44p.).

2102	**1413**	19p. bright magenta, greenish yellow, new blue, black, black and silver	30	35
2103	**1414**	26p. greenish yellow, brt magenta, new blue, black, bronze & reddish vio	40	45
		a. Imperf (pair)		
		b. Perf 14½×14 (21 Sept) ..	40	45
		ba. Booklet pane. No. 2103a×4 with margins all round	1·60	
2104	**1415**	44p. greenish yellow, bright magenta, new blue, black and gold	70	75
		a. Perf 14½×14 (21 Sept) ..	70	75
		ab. Booklet pane. No. 2104a×4 with margins all round	2·75	
2105	**1416**	64p. bright magenta, greenish yellow, new blue, black and silver	1·00	1·10
2102/5		*Set of 4*	2·40	2·50

Nos. 2103b and 2104a only come from £6.99 stamp booklets.

(Photo De La Rue)

1999 (11 Aug). *Solar Eclipse. Sheet 89×121 mm. Two phosphor bands. P 14×14½.*

MS2106		No. 2105×4 (*sold at £2.56*)	3·75	4·00
		a. Imperf		

1417 Upland Landscape (Strip Farming) **1418** Horse-drawn Rotary Seed Drill (Mechanical Farming)

1419 Man peeling Potato (Food Imports) **1420** Aerial View of Combine Harvester (Satellite Agriculture)

(Des D. Tress (19p.), C. Wormell (26p.), Tessa Traeger (44p.), R. Cooke (64p.). Photo De La Rue)

1999 (7–21 Sept). *Millennium Series. The Farmers' Tale.* One centre phosphor band (19p.) or two phosphor bands (*others*). P 14×14½.

2107	**1417**	19p. grey-black, greenish yellow, cerise, new blue and silver ..	30	35
2108	**1418**	26p. chestnut, orange-brown, violet-bl, grey-blk, pale turq-grn & silver	40	45
		a. Booklet pane. No. 2108×2 with margins all round (21 Sept)	80	
2109	**1419**	44p. silver, yellow-brn, brn & grey-blk	70	75
2110	**1420**	64p. deep brown, greenish yellow, magenta, new blue and silver	1·00	1·10
2107/10		*Set of 4*	2·40	2·50

The 19p. includes the "EUROPA" emblem.
Booklet pane No. 2108a was printed in photogravure by Walsall.

1421 Robert the Bruce (Battle of Bannockburn, 1314) **1422** Cavalier and Horse (English Civil War)

1423 War Graves Cemetery, The Somme (World Wars) **1424** Soldiers with Boy (Peace-keeping)

(Des A. Davidson (19p.), R. Kelly (26p.), D. McCullin (44p.), C. Corr (64p.). Litho (19p.) or photo (*others*) Walsall)

1999 (5 Oct). *Millennium Series. The Soldiers' Tale.* One centre phosphor band (19p.) or two phosphor bands (*others*). P 14×14½.

2111	**1421**	19p. black, stone and silver ..	30	35
2112	**1422**	26p. lemon, black, grey, silver, black and gold	40	45
2113	**1423**	44p. grey-black, black and silver	70	75
2114	**1424**	64p. greenish yellow, red-orange, brt magenta, pale new bl, blk & brt bl	1·00	1·10
2111/14		*Set of 4*	2·40	2·50

1425 "Hark the herald angels sing" and Hymnbook (John Wesley) **1426** King James I and Bible (Authorised Version of Bible)

1427 St. Andrews Cathedral, Fife ("Pilgrimage") **1428** Nativity ("First Christmas")

(Des B. Neuenschwander (19p.), Clare Melinsky (26p.), Catherine Yass (44p.), C. Aitchison (64p.). Photo De La Rue)

1999 (2 Nov). *Millennium Series. The Christians' Tale.* One centre phosphor band (19p.) or two phosphor bands (*others*). P 14×14½.

2115	**1425**	19p. gold, stone, greenish yellow, bright crimson, deep dull blue, black and yellow-ochre	30	35
2116	**1426**	26p. gold, greenish yellow, brt scarlet, emerald, dull violet & black	40	45
2117	**1427**	44p. gold, greenish yellow, bright magenta, new blue, blk & ultram	70	75
2118	**1428**	64p. gold, bistre-yell, cerise, brt emer, bistre, slate-bl, pale new bl & blk	1·00	1·10
2115/18		*Set of 4*	2·40	2·50

1429 "World of the Stage" (Allen Jones) **1430** "World of Music" (Bridget Riley)

1431 "World of Literature" (Lisa Milroy) **1432** "New Worlds" (Sir Howard Hodgkin)

(Photo Walsall)

1999 (7 Dec). *Millennium Series. The Artists' Tale.* One centre phosphor band (19p.) or two phosphor bands (*others*). P 14×14½.

2119	**1429**	19p. greenish yellow, bright magenta, new blue, black and silver	30	35
2120	**1430**	26p. lemon, orange, pale new blue, violet-blue and black	40	45
2121	**1431**	44p. greenish yellow, bright magenta, new blue, black and gold	70	75
2122	**1432**	64p. greenish yell, yell, brt turq-grn, brt mag, new bl, blk, gold & silver	1·00	1·10
2119/22		*Set of 4*	2·40	2·50

NEW INFORMATION

The editor is always interested to correspond with people who have new information that will improve or correct the Catalogue.

1433 Clock Face and Map of North America **1434** Clock Face and Map of Asia

1435 Clock Face and Map of Middle East **1436** Clock Face and Map of Europe

(Des D. Gentleman. Photo De La Rue)

1999 (14 Dec). *Millennium Series. "Millennium Timekeeper". Sheet 120×89 mm. Each design silver, deep grey, pale olive-grey, greenish grey, grey-black and bright rose-red. Two phosphor bands. P 14×14½.*

MS2123 64p. Type **1433**; 64p. Type **1434**; 64p. Type **1435**; 64p. Type **1436** .. .. 4·00 4·25

No. MS2123 also exists overprinted "EARLS COURT, LONDON 22–28 MAY 2000 THE STAMP SHOW 2000" from Exhibition Premium Passes, costing £10, available from 1 March 2000.

1437 Queen Elizabeth II

(Des A. Machin, adapted R. Scholey. Photo De La Rue or Walsall (No. 2124), Walsall (No. 2124al, 2124bl), Questa (No. 2124b))

2000 (6 Jan–21 Mar). *New Millennium. Two phosphor bands. P 15×14 (with one elliptical hole on each vertical side).*

2124	**1437**	(1st) olive-brown ..	40	45
		al. Booklet pane. No. 2124×4 plus commemorative label at right (21 Mar)	1·60	
		b. Perf 14	40	45
		bl. Booklet pane. No. 2124b×8 with central label and margins all round (15 Feb)	3·25	

Printings by Questa on Walsall were from stamp booklets.
The label in booklet pane No. 2124al shows Postman Pat and publicizes "Stamp Show 2000".

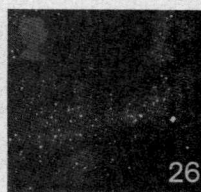

1438 Barn Owl (World Owl Trust, Muncaster) **1439** Night Sky (National Space Science Centre, Leicester)

1440 River Goyt and Textile Mills (Torrs Walkway, New Mills) **1441** Cape Gannets (Seabird Centre, North Berwick)

(Litho (44p.), photo (others) Questa)

2000 (18 Jan). *Millennium Projects (1st series). "Above and Beyond".* One centre phosphor band (19p.) or two phosphor bands (*others*). P 14×14½ (44p.) or 13½×14 (*others*).

2125	**1438**	19p. greenish yellow, magenta, pale new blue, black and silver	30	35
2126	**1439**	26p. greenish yellow, magenta, pale new blue, black and silver	40	45
2127	**1440**	44p. black, bistre-brown, buff & silver	70	75
2128	**1441**	64p. greenish yellow, magenta, blue, black, silver and orange	1·00	1·10
2125/8		*Set of 4*	2·40	2·50

1442 Millennium Beacon (Beacons across The Land) | 1443 Garratt Steam Locomotive No. 143 pulling Train in Snowdonia (Rheilffordd Eryri, Welsh Highland Railway)

1451 Reed Beds, River Braid (ECOS, Ballymena) | 1452 South American Leaf-cutter Ants ("Web of Life" Exhibition, London Zoo)

1444 Lightning (Dynamic Earth Centre, Edinburgh) | 1445 Multicoloured Lights (Lighting Croydon's Skyline)

1453 Solar Sensors (Earth Centre, Doncaster) | 1454 Hydroponic Leaves (Project SUZY, Teeside)

(Photo De La Rue)

2000 (1 Feb). *Millennium Projects (2nd series). "Fire and Light".* One centre phosphor band (19p.) or two phosphor bands (others). P 14×14½.

2129	1442	19p. silver, greenish yellow, bright magenta, new blue and black ..	30	35
2130	1443	26p. silver, greenish yellow, bright magenta, new blue and black ..	40	45
2131	1444	44p. silver, greenish yellow, bright magenta, new blue and black ..	70	75
2132	1445	64p. silver, greenish yellow, bright magenta, pale greenish blue & blk	1·00	1·10
2129/32		.. .. .. Set of 4	2·40	2·50

(Photo De La Rue)

2000 (4 Apr). *Millennium Projects (4th series). "Life and Earth".* One phosphor band (2nd) or two phosphor bands (others). P 14×14½.

2138	1451	(2nd) silver, greenish yellow, magenta, new blue, black and grey	30	35
2139	1452	(1st) silver, greenish yellow, magenta, new blue and black ..	40	45
2140	1453	44p. silver, greenish yellow, magenta, blue and black ..	70	75
2141	1454	64p. silver, greenish yellow, magenta, new blue and grey-black ..	1·00	1·10
2138/41		.. .. Set of 4	2·40	2·50

1446 Queen Victoria and Queen Elizabeth II

(Des J. Matthews. Photo Walsall)

2000 (15 Feb). *T 929 redrawn with "1st" face value as T 1446. Two phosphor bands. P 14 (with one elliptical hole on each vertical side).*

2133	1446	(1st) brownish black and cream ..	75	75
		l. Booklet pane. No. 2133×6 with margins all round ..	2·75	

No. 2133 was only issued in £7.50 stamp booklets.

1455 Pottery Glaze (Ceramica Museum, Stoke-on-Trent) | 1456 Bankside Galleries (Tate Modern, London)

1457 Cycle Lane Road Marking (Cycle Network Artworks) | 1458 People of Salford (Lowry Centre, Salford)

(Photo Enschedé)

2000 (2 May). *Millennium Projects (5th series). "Art and Craft".* One phosphor band (2nd) or two phosphor bands (others). P 14×14½.

2142	1455	(2nd) greenish yellow, magenta, new blue, black, silver & grey-brown	30	35
2143	1456	(1st) greenish yellow, magenta, new blue, black and silver ..	40	45
2144	1457	45p. greenish yellow, magenta, new blue, black and silver ..	70	75
2145	1458	65p. greenish yellow, magenta, new blue, black, dull silver and silver	1·00	1·10
2142/5		.. .. .. Set of 4	2·40	2·50

1447 Beach Pebbles (Turning the Tide, Durham Coast) | 1448 Frog's Legs and Water Lilies (National Pondlife Centre, Merseyside)

1449 Cliff Boardwalk (Parc Arfordirol, Llanelli Coast) | 1450 Reflections in Water (Portsmouth Harbour Development)

(Litho (44p.), photo (others) Walsall)

2000 (7 Mar). *Millennium Projects (3rd series). "Water and Coast".* One phosphor band (19p.) or two phosphor bands (others). P 14×14½.

2134	1447	19p. silver, black, dull silver, sage-grn, olive-grey, orge-yell & pale grey	30	35
2135	1448	26p. new blue, silver, black, greenish yellow and magenta ..	40	45
2136	1449	44p. black, grey and silver ..	70	75
2137	1450	64p. black, grey, deep bluish green, greenish blue, cobalt, grey-green and brownish grey	1·00	1·10
2134/7		.. .. Set of 4	2·40	2·50

REGIONAL ISSUES

For Regional Issues of Guernsey, Jersey and the Isle of Man, *see* after Great Britain Postal Fiscals.

Printers (£ s. d. stamps of all regions):—Photo Harrison & Sons. Portrait by Dorothy Wilding Ltd.

DATES OF ISSUE. Conflicting dates of issue have been announced for some of the regional issues, partly explained by the stamps being released on different dates by the Philatelic Bureau in Edinburgh or the Philatelic Counter in London and in the regions. We have adopted the practice of giving the earliest known dates, since once released the stamps could have been used anywhere in the U.K.

I. NORTHERN IRELAND

N 1   N 2   N 3

(Des W. Hollywood (3d., 4d., 5d.), L. Pilton (6d., 9d.), T. Collins (1s. 3d., 1s. 6d.))

1958–67. *W* **179.** *P* 15 × 14.

NI1	N 1	3d. deep lilac (18.8.58)	..	20	10
		p. One centre phosphor band (9.6.67)		20	15
NI2		4d. ultramarine (7.2.66)	..	20	15
		p. Two phosphor bands (10.67)	..	20	15
NI3	N 2	6d. deep claret (29.9.58)	..	25	25
NI4		9d. bronze-green (2 phosphor bands) (1.3.67)	..	40	80
NI5	N 3	1s. 3d. green (29.9.58)	..	40	80
NI6		1s. 6d. grey-blue (2 phosphor bands) (1.3.67)		40	80

1968–69. *No wmk. Chalk-surfaced paper. One centre phosphor band* (*Nos.* NI8/9) *or two phosphor bands* (*others*). *P* 15 × 14.

NI 7	N 1	4d. deep bright blue (27.6.68)	..	20	15
NI 8		4d. olive-sepia (4.9.68)	..	20	15
NI 9		4d. bright vermilion (26.2.69)	..	20	20
NI10		5d. royal blue (4.9.68)	..	20	20
NI11	N 3	1s. 6d. grey-blue (20.5.69)	..	2.75	4.00

No. NI7 was only issued in Northern Ireland with gum arabic. After it had been withdrawn from Northern Ireland but whilst still on sale at the philatelic counters elsewhere, about fifty sheets with PVA gum were sold over the London Philatelic counter on 23 October 1968, and some were also on sale at the British Philatelic Exhibition Post Office in October, without any prior announcement. The other values exist with PVA gum only.

N 4

(Des J. Mathews after plaster cast by Arnold Machin)

1971 (7 July)**–93.** *Decimal Currency. Chalk-surfaced paper. Type* N **4.** (a) *Photo Harrison. With phosphor bands. P* 15×14.

NI12	2½p. bright magenta (1 centre band)	..	80	30
NI13	3p. ultramarine (2 bands)	..	40	15
NI14	3p. ultramarine (1 centre band) (23.1.74)		20	15
NI15	3½p. olive-grey (2 bands) (23.1.74)	..	20	20
NI16	3½p. olive-grey (1 centre band) (6.11.74)	..	20	25
NI17	4½p. grey-blue (2 bands) (6.11.74)	..	30	30
NI18	5p. reddish violet (2 bands)	..	1.50	1.50
NI19	5½p. violet (2 bands) (23.1.74)	..	20	20
NI20	5½p. violet (1 centre band) (21.5.75)	..	20	20
NI21	6½p. greenish blue (1 centre band) (14.1.76)	..	20	20
NI22	7p. purple-brown (1 centre band) (18.1.78)	..	35	25
NI23	7½p. chestnut (2 bands)	..	2.25	2.25
NI24	8p. rosine (2 bands) (23.1.74)	..	40	40
NI25	8½p. yellow-green (2 bands) (14.1.76)	..	40	40
NI26	9p. deep violet (2 bands) (18.1.78)	..	40	40
NI27	10p. orange-brown (2 bands) (20.10.76)	..	50	50
NI28	10p. orange-brown (1 centre band) (23.7.80)	..	50	50
NI29	10½p. steel-blue (2 bands) (18.1.78)	..	50	50
NI30	11p. scarlet (2 bands) (20.10.76)	..	50	50

(b) *Photo Harrison. On phosphorised paper. P* 15 × 14.

NI31	12p. yellowish green (23.7.80)	..	50	50
NI32	13½p. purple-brown (23.7.80)	..	80	80
NI33	15p. ultramarine (23.7.80)	..	80	80

(c) *Litho Questa. P* 14 (11½p., 12½p., 14p. (*No.* NI38), 15½p., 16p., 18p. (*No.* NI45), 19½p., 20½p., 22p. (*No.* NI53), 26p. (*No.* NI60), 28p. (*No.* NI62) *or* 15×14 (*others*).

NI34	11½p. drab (1 side band) (8.4.81)	..	85	85
NI35	12p. bright emerald (1 side band) (7.1.86)	..	85	85
NI36	12½p. light emerald (1 side band) (24.2.82)	..	75	75
	a. Perf 15×14 (28.2.84)	..	4.25	4.25
NI37	13p. pale chestnut (1 side band) (23.10.84)	..	1.25	90
NI38	14p. grey-bl (phosphorised paper) (8.4.81)	..	90	75
NI39	14p. deep blue (1 centre band) (8.11.88)	..	90	75
NI40	15p. bright blue (1 centre band) (28.11.89)	..	90	75
NI41	15½p. pale violet (phosphorised paper) (24.2.82)	..	90	80
NI42	16p. drab (phosphorised paper) (27.4.83)	..	1.00	1.00
	a. Perf 15×14 (28.2.84)	..	9.50	8.00
NI43	17p. grey-blue (phosphorised paper) (23.10.84)	..	1.00	1.00
NI44	17p. deep blue (1 centre band) (4.12.90)	..	90	90
NI45	18p. dp vio (phosphorised paper) (8.4.81)	..	1.00	1.00
NI46	18p. deep olive-grey (phosphorised paper) (6.1.87)	..	90	90
NI47	18p. bright green (1 centre band) (3.12.91)	..	85	85
	a. Perf 14 (31.12.92*)	..	2.00	2.00
NI48	18p. bright green (1 side band) (10.8.93)	..	2.75	2.75
	l. Booklet pane. Nos. NI48, NI59, S61, S71, W49 and W60 with margins all round		6.00	

NI49	19p. bright orange-red (phosphorised paper) (8.11.88)		90	90
NI50	19½p. olive-grey (phosphorised paper) (24.2.82)	..	1.75	2.25
NI51	20p. brownish black (phosphorised paper) (28.11.89)		90	90
NI52	20½p. ultram (phosphorised paper) (27.4.83)		4.00	4.00
NI53	22p. blue (phosphorised paper) (8.4.81)		1.25	1.25
NI54	22p. yellow-green (phosphorised paper) (23.10.84)		1.25	1.25
NI55	22p. bright orange-red (phosphorised paper) (4.12.90)		1.25	1.00
NI56	23p. bright green (phosphorised paper) (8.11.88)		1.25	1.25
NI57	24p. Indian red (phosphorised paper) (28.11.89)		1.25	1.25
NI58	24p. chestnut (phosphorised paper) (3.12.91)		1.00	1.00
NI59	24p. chestnut (2 bands) (10.8.93)		2.25	2.25
NI60	26p. rosine (phosphorised paper) (24.2.82)		1.25	1.60
	a. Perf 15×14 (27.1.87)		3.75	3.75
NI61	26p. drab (phosphorised paper) (4.12.90)		1.25	1.25
NI62	28p. deep violet-blue (phosphorised paper) (27.4.83)		1.25	1.25
	a. Perf 15×14 (27.1.87)		1.25	1.25
NI63	28p. deep bluish grey (phosphorised paper) (3.12.91)		1.25	1.25
NI64	31p. bright purple (phosphorised paper) (23.10.84)		1.75	1.75
NI65	32p. greenish blue (phosphorised paper) (8.11.88)		1.50	1.50
NI66	34p. deep bluish grey (phosphorised paper) (28.11.89)		1.75	1.75
NI67	37p. rosine (phosphorised paper) (4.12.90)		1.75	1.75
NI68	39p. bright mauve (phosphorised paper) (3.12.91)		1.75	1.75

*Earliest known date of use.

No. NI47a was caused by the use of a reserve perforating machine for some printings in the second half of 1992.

Nos. NI48 and NI59 only come from booklets.

From 1972 printings were made on fluorescent white paper and from 1973 printings had dextrin added to the PVA gum (see notes after the 1971 Decimal Machin issue).

(Des J. Matthews after plaster cast by Arnold Machin)

1993 (7 Dec)**–2000.** *Chalk-surfaced paper.* (a) *Litho Questa. One phosphor band* (19p., 20p.) *or two phosphor bands* (*others*). *P* 15×14 (*with one elliptical hole on each vertical side*).

NI69	N 4	19p. bistre (1 centre band)	75	75
NI70		19p. bistre (1 side band) (26.7.94)	2.50	2.50
	a. Booklet pane. Nos. NI70×2, NI72×4, NI74, NI76 and centre label with margins all round	6.50	
	b. Booklet pane. Nos. NI70, NI72, NI74 and NI76 with margins all round	3.50	
	d. Booklet pane. Nos. NI70, NI72, S82, S84, W71 and W73 (25.4.95)	7.00	
	da. Part perf pane*		
NI71		20p. brt green (1 centre band) (23.7.96)	1.00	1.00
NI72		25p. red	1.00	1.00
NI73		26p. red-brown (23.7.96)	1.00	1.00
NI74		30p. deep olive-grey	1.25	1.25
NI75		37p. bright mauve (23.7.96)	1.50	1.50
NI76		41p. grey-brown	1.50	1.50
NI77		63p. light emerald (23.7.96)	2.50	2.50

(b) *Photo Walsall* (19p., 20p., 26p. (*No.* NI81b), 38p., 40p., 63p., 64p., 65p.), *Harrison or Walsall* (26p. (*No.* NI81), 37p.). *P* 14 (*No.* NI80) *or* 15×14 (*others*) (*both with one elliptical hole on each vertical side*).

NI78	N 4	19p. bistre (1 centre band) (8.6.99)	30	35
NI79		20p. bright green (1 centre band) (1.7.97)	50	50
NI80		20p. bright green (1 side band) (13.10.98)	1.50	1.50
	l. Booklet pane. Nos. NI80, S90a, W79a, and Y1696a×3 with margins all round	5.50	
NI81		26p. chestnut (2 bands) (1.7.97)	40	45
	al. Booklet pane. Nos. NI81/2, S91/2 and W80/1 with margins all round (23.9.97)	3.50	
	b. Perf 14 (13.10.98)	1.00	1.00
NI82		37p. bright mauve (2 bands) (1.7.97)	1.00	1.00
NI83		38p. ultramarine (2 bands) (8.6.99)	60	65
NI83a		40p. deep azure (2 bands) (25.4.00)	60	65
NI84		63p. light emerald (2 bands) (1.7.97)	1.50	1.50
NI85		64p. turquoise-green (2 bands) (8.6.99)	95	95
NI86		65p. greenish blue (2 bands) (25.4.00)	1.00	1.10

Nos. NI70, NI80 and NI81b only come from stamp booklets. No. NI70 exists with phosphor band at left or right.

*No, NI70da, which comes from the 1995 National Trust £6 booklet, shows the top two values in the pane of 6 (Nos. S82, S84) completely imperforate and the two Wales values below partly imperforate.

No. NI81al which was printed by Harrison, comes from the 1997 B.B.C. £6.15 booklet.

N 5

(Des J. Matthews. Photo Walsall)

2000 (15 Feb–25 Apr). *Type* N **4** *redrawn with* "1st" *face value as Type* N **5.** *Two phosphor bands. P* 14 (*with one elliptical hole on each vertical side*).

NI96	N 5	(1st) bright orange-red	40	45
		al. Booklet pane. Nos. NI96, S108 and W97, each × 3 with margins all round	3.50	
		b. Perf 15×14 (25 Apr)	40	45

No. NI96 was only issued in £7.50 stamp booklets. No. NI96b was issued in sheets.

II. SCOTLAND

S 1   S 2   S 3

(Des G. Huntly (3d., 4d., 5d.), J. Fleming (6d., 9d.), A. Imrie (1s. 3d., 1s. 6d.))

1958–67. *W* **179.** *P* 15 × 14.

S1	S 1	3d. deep lilac (18.8.58)	..	20	15
		p. Two phosphor bands (29.1.63)	15.00	2.00
		pa. One side phosphor band (30.4.65)	20	30
		pb. One centre phosphor band (9.11.67)	20	15
S2		4d. ultramarine (7.2.66)	..	20	10
		p. Two phosphor bands	20	20
S3	S 2	6d. deep claret (29.9.58)	..	20	15
		p. Two phosphor bands (29.1.63)	20	30
S4		9d. bronze-green (2 phosphor bands) (1.3.67)	50	50
S5	S 3	1s. 3d. green (29.9.58)	..	50	50
S6		1s. 6d. grey-blue (2 phosphor bands) (1.3.67)	35	30

The one phosphor band on No. S1pa was produced by printing broad phosphor bands across alternate vertical perforations. Individual stamps show the band at right or left (same prices either way).

1967–70. *No wmk. Chalk-surfaced paper. One centre phosphor band* (S7, S9/10) *or two phosphor bands* (*others*). *P* 15 × 14.

S 7	S 1	3d. deep lilac (16.5.68)	..	10	15
S 8		4d. deep bright blue (28.11.67)	..	10	15
S 9		4d. olive-sepia (4.9.68)	..	10	10
S10		4d. bright vermilion (26.2.69)	..	10	10
S11		5d. royal blue (4.9.68)	..	10	10
S12	S 2	9d. bronze-green (28.9.70)	..	5.50	7.00
S13	S 3	1s. 6d. grey-blue (12.12.68)	..	1.75	1.50

Nos. S7/8 exist with both gum arabic and PVA gum; others with PVA gum only.

S 4

(Des J. Matthews after plaster cast by Arnold Machin)

1971 (7 July)**–93.** *Decimal Currency. Chalk-surfaced paper. Type* S **4.** (a) *Photo Harrison. With phosphor bands. P* 15 × 14

S14	2½p. bright magenta (1 centre band)	..	30	15
S15	3p. ultramarine (2 bands)	..	30	15
	a. Imperf (pair)†	..	£425	
S16	3p. ultramarine (1 centre band) (23.1.74)	..	15	15
S17	3½p. olive-grey (2 bands) (23.1.74)	..	20	20
S18	3½p. olive-grey (1 centre band) (6.11.74)	..	20	20
S19	4½p. grey-blue (2 bands) (6.11.74)	..	20	20
S20	5p. reddish violet (2 bands)	..	1.00	1.00
S21	5½p. violet (2 bands) (23.1.74)	..	20	20
S22	5½p. violet (1 centre band) (21.5.75)	..	20	20
	a. Imperf (pair)		£375	
S23	6½p. greenish blue (1 centre band) (14.1.76)	..	20	20
S24	7p. purple-brown (1 centre band) (18.1.78)	..	30	30
S25	7½p. chestnut (2 bands)	..	1.25	1.25
S26	8p. rosine (2 bands) (23.1.74)	..	40	40
S27	8½p. yellow-green (2 bands) (14.1.76)	..	40	40
S28	9p. deep violet (2 bands) (18.1.78)	..	40	40
S29	10p. orange-brown (2 bands) (20.10.76)	..	50	50
S30	10p. orange-brown (1 centre band) (23.7.80)	..	50	50
S31	10½p. steel-blue (2 bands) (18.1.78)	..	50	50
S32	11p. scarlet (2 bands) (20.10.76)	..	50	50

(b) *Photo Harrison. On phosphorised paper. P* 15 × 14

S33	12p. yellowish green (23.7.80)	..	50	50
S34	13½p. purple-brown (23.7.80)	..	80	80
S35	15p. ultramarine (23.7.80)	..	80	80

(c) *Litho J.W. One side phosphor band* (11½p., 12p., 12½p., 13p.) *or phosphorised paper* (*others*). *P* 14

S36	11½p. drab (8.4.81)	..	90	70
S37	12p. bright emerald (7.1.86)	..	2.00	1.75
S38	12½p. light emerald (24.2.82)	..	80	80
S39	13p. pale chestnut (23.10.84)	..	80	80
S40	14p. grey-blue (8.4.81)	..	80	80
S41	15p. pale violet (24.2.82)	..	80	80
S42	16p. drab (27.4.83)	..	80	80
S43	17p. grey-blue (23.10.84)	..	3.75	3.00
S44	18p. deep violet (8.4.81)	..	1.00	1.00
S45	19p. olive-grey (24.2.82)	..	1.75	1.75
S46	20½p. ultramarine (27.4.83)	..	4.00	4.00
S47	22p. blue (8.4.81)	..	1.25	1.25
S48	22p. yellow-green (23.10.84)	..	2.25	2.00
S49	26p. rosine (24.2.82)	..	1.25	1.25
S50	28p. deep violet-blue (27.4.83)	..	1.25	1.25
S51	31p. bright purple (23.10.84)	..	2.00	2.00

(d) *Litho Questa. P* 15×14

S52	12p. bright emerald (1 side band) (29.4.86)	2.00	2.00
S53	13p. pale chestnut (1 side band) (4.11.86)	80	80
S54	14p. deep blue (1 side band) (21.3.89)	70	70
	l. Booklet pane. No. S54×6 with margins all round (21.3.89)	2.75	
S55	14p. deep blue (1 side band) (21.3.89)	1.00	
	l. Booklet pane. Nos. S55×5, S63×2, S68 and centre label with margins all round	16.00	
	la. Error. Booklet pane imperf		
S56	15p. bright blue (1 centre band) (28.11.89)	80	80
	a. Imperf three sides (block of 4)	£275	
S57	17p. grey-bl (phosphorised paper) (29.4.86)	4.25	3.50
S58	17p. deep blue (1 centre band) (4.12.90)	80	80
S59	18p. ol-grey (phosphorised paper) (6.1.87)	90	90

S60	18p. bright green (1 centre band) (3.12.91)	80	80
	a. Perf 14 (26.9.92*)	1·25	1·25
S61	18p. brt green (1 side band) (10.8.93)	2·50	2·50
S62	19p. bright orange-red (phosphorised paper) (8.11.88)	90	90
	l. Booklet pane. No. S62×9 with margins all round (21.3.89)	5·50	
	m. Booklet pane. No S62×6 with margins all round (21.3.89)	3·50	
S63	19p. bright orange-red (2 bands) (21.3.89)	1·75	1·75
S64	20p. brownish black (phosphorised paper) (28.11.89)	1·00	1·00
S65	22p. yell-grn (phosphorised paper) (27.1.87)	1·00	1·00
S66	22p. bright orange-red (phosphorised paper) (4.12.90)	1·25	1·00
S67	23p. brt grn (phosphorised paper) (8.11.88)	1·25	1·25
S68	23p. bright green (2 bands) (21.3.89)	12·00	12·00
S69	24p. Indian red (phosphorised paper) (28.11.89)	1·25	1·25
S70	24p. chestnut (phosphorised paper) (3.12.91)	1·00	1·00
	a. Perf 14 (10.92*)	2·50	2·50
S71	24p. chestnut (2 bands) (10.8.93)	2·25	2·25
S72	26p. rosine (phosphorised paper) (27.1.87)	2·75	2·75
S73	26p. drab (phosphorised paper) (4.12.90)	1·25	1·25
S74	28p. deep violet-blue (phosphorised paper) (27.1.87)	1·25	1·25
S75	28p. deep bluish grey (phosphorised paper) (3.12.91)	1·25	1·25
	a. Perf 14 (18.2.93*)	4·00	4·00
S76	31p. brt pur (phosphorised paper) (29.4.86)	2·00	2·00
S77	32p. greenish blue (phosphorised paper) (8.11.88)	1·50	1·50
S78	34p. deep bluish grey (phosphorised paper) (28.11.89)	1·75	1·75
S79	37p. rosine (phosphorised paper) (4.12.90)	1·75	1·75
S80	39p. brt mve (phosphorised paper) (3.12.91)	1·75	1·75
	a. Perf 14 (11.92)	2·75	2·75

*Earliest known date of use.
†Exists only with gum arabic.

Nos. S55, S61, S63, S68 and S71 only come from booklets.

No. S56a occurred in the second vertical row on two sheets. The error is best collected as a block of four to include the left-hand vertical pair imperforate on three sides.

Nos. S60a, S70a, S75a and S80a were caused by the use of a reserve perforating machine for some printings in late 1992.

From 1972 printings were on fluorescent white paper. Nos. S14/15 exist with PVA and gum arabic and the remainder with PVA only. From 1973 printings had extra dextrin added (see notes after the 1971 Decimal Machin issue).

(Des J. Matthews after plaster cast by Arnold Machin)

1993 (7 Dec)–**98.** *Chalk-surfaced paper.* (*a*) *Litho Questa. One phosphor band* (19p., 20p.) *or two phosphor bands* (*others*). *P* 15×14 (*with one elliptical hole on each vertical side*).

S81	S 4	19p. bistre (1 centre band)	75	75
S82		19p. bistre (1 side band) (25.4.95)	2·50	2·50
S83		20p. bright green (1 centre band) (23.7.96)	1·00	1·00
S84		25p. red	1·00	1·00
S85		26p. red-brown (23.7.96)	1·00	1·00
S86		30p. deep olive-grey	1·25	1·25
S87		37p. bright mauve (23.7.96)	1·50	1·50
S88		41p. grey-brown	1·50	1·50
S89		63p. light emerald (23.7.96)	2·50	2·50

(*b*) *Photo Walsall* (20p., 26p. (*No.* S91a), 63p.), *Harrison or Walsall* (26p. (*No.* S91), 37p.). *P* 14 (*No.* S90a) *or* 15×14 (*others*) (*both with one elliptical hole on each vertical side*).

S90	S 4	20p. bright green (1 centre band) (1.7.97)	50	50
S90a		20p. bright green (1 side band) (13.10.98)	1·50	1·50
S91		26p. chestnut (2 bands) (1.7.97)	75	75
		a. Perf 14 (13.10.98)	1·00	1·00
S92		37p. bright mauve (2 bands) (1.7.97)	1·00	1·00
S93		63p. light emerald (2 bands) (1.7.97)	1·50	1·50

Nos. S82, S90a and S91a only come from booklets.

The Harrison printings of the Nos. S91/2 are from booklet pane No. NI79al.

S 5 Scottish Flag   S 6 Scottish Lion   S 7 Thistle

S 8 Tartan

1999 (8 June)–**2000.** *One centre band* (2nd) *or two phosphor bands* (*others*). *P* 15×14 (*with one elliptical hole on each vertical side*).

S94	S 5	(2nd) new blue, blue and silver	30	35
S95	S 6	(1st) greenish yellow, dp rose-red, rose-red and silver	40	45
S96	S 7	(E) bright lilac, deep lilac and silver	45	50
S97	S 8	64p. greenish yellow, bright magenta, new blue, grey-black and silver	1·00	1·10
S98		65p. greenish yellow, brt magenta, new blue, grey-black & silver (25.4.00)	1·00	1·10
S94/8		Set of 5	3·00	3·50

Nos. S94, S95 and S96 were initially sold at 19p., 26p. and 30p., the latter representing the basic European airmail rate.

S 9

(Des J. Matthews. Photo Walsall)

2000 (15 Feb). *Type* S **4** *redrawn with* "1st" *face value as Type* S **9.** *Two phosphor bands. P* 14 (*with one elliptical hole on each vertical side*).

S108	S 9	(1st) bright orange-red	40	45

No. S108 was only issued in £7.50 stamp booklets.

III. WALES

From the inception of the Regional stamps, the Welsh versions were tendered to members of the public at all Post Offices within the former County of Monmouthshire but the national alternatives were available on request. By August 1961 the policy of "dual stocking" of definitive stamps was only maintained at Abergavenny, Chepstow, Newport and Pontypool. Offices with a Monmouthshire postal address but situated outside the County, namely Beachley, Brockweir, Redbrook, Sedbury, Tutshill, Welsh Newton and Woodcroft, were not supplied with the Welsh Regional stamps.

With the re-formation of Counties, Monmouthshire became known as Gwent and was also declared to be part of Wales. From 1 July 1974, therefore, except for the offices mentioned above, only Welsh Regional stamps were available at the offices under the jurisdiction of Newport, Gwent.

W 1   W 2   W 3

(Des R. Stone)

1958–67. *W* 179. *P* 15×14.

W1	W 1	3d. deep lilac (18.8.58)	20	10
		p. One centre phosphor band (16.5.67)	20	15
W2		4d. ultramarine (7.2.66)	20	15
		p. Two phosphor bands (10.67)	20	15
W3	W 2	6d. deep claret (29.9.58)	50	20
W4		9d. bronze-green (2 phosphor bands) (1.3.67)	50	50
W5	W 3	1s. 3d. green (29.9.58)	50	50
W6		1s. 6d. grey-blue (2 phosphor bands) (1.3.67)	50	50

1967–69. *No wmk. Chalk-surfaced paper. One centre phosphor band* (W7, W9/10) *or two phosphor bands* (*others*). *P* 15×14.

W 7	W 1	3d. deep lilac (6.12.67)	20	10
W 8		4d. ultramarine (21.6.68)	20	10
W 9		4d. olive-sepia (4.9.68)	20	10
W10		4d. bright vermilion (26.2.69)	20	20
W11		5d. royal blue (4.9.68)	20	10
W12	W 3	1s. 6d. grey-blue (1.8.69)	3·00	3·75

The 3d. exists with gum arabic only; the remainder with PVA gum only.

W 4 With "p"   W 5 Without "p"

(Des J. Matthews after plaster cast by Arnold Machin)

1971 (7 July)–**93.** *Decimal Currency. Chalk-surfaced paper. Type* W **4.** (*a*) *Photo Harrison. With phosphor bands. P* 15×14

W13	2½p. bright magenta (1 centre band)	20	15
	a. Imperf (pair)†	£375	
W14	3p. ultramarine (2 bands)	25	15
W15	3p. ultramarine (1 centre band) (23.1.74)	20	20
W16	3½p. olive-grey (2 bands) (23.1.74)	20	30
W17	3½p. olive-grey (1 centre band) (6.11.74)	20	30
W18	4½p. grey-blue (2 bands) (6.11.74)	30	20
W19	5p. reddish violet (2 bands)	1·00	1·00
W20	5½p. violet (2 bands) (23.1.74)	20	30
W21	5½p. violet (1 centre band) (21.5.75)	20	30
	a. Imperf (pair)	£425	
W22	6½p. greenish blue (1 centre band) (14.1.76)	20	20
W23	7p. purple-brn (1 centre band) (18.1.78)	30	30
W24	7½p. chestnut (2 bands)	1·25	1·50
W25	8p. rosine (2 bands) (23.1.74)	40	40
W26	8½p. yellow-green (2 bands) (14.1.76)	40	40
W27	9p. deep violet (2 bands) (18.1.78)	40	40
W28	10p. orange-brown (2 bands) (20.10.76)	40	40
W29	10p. orange-brn (1 centre band) (23.7.80)	40	40
W30	10½p. steel-blue (2 bands) (18.1.78)	50	50
W31	11p. scarlet (2 bands) (20.10.76)	50	50

(*b*) *Photo Harrison. On phosphorised paper. P* 15×14

W32	12p. yellow-green (23.7.80)	50	50
W33	13½p. purple-brown (23.7.80)	80	80
W34	15p. ultramarine (23.7.80)	80	80

(*c*) *Litho Questa. P* 14 (11½p., 12½p., 14p. (*No.* W39), 15½p., 16p., 18p. (*No.* W46), 19½p., 20½p., 22p. (*No.* W54), 26p. (*No.* W61), 28p. (*No.* W63)) *or* 15×14 (*others*).

W35	11½p. drab (1 side band) (8.4.81)	1·00	80
W36	12p. bright emerald (1 side band) (7.1.86)	1·50	1·25
W37	12½p. light emerald (1 side band) (24.2.82)	1·00	80
	a. Perf 15×14 (10.1.84)	6·00	6·00
W38	13p. pale chestnut (1 side band) (23.10.84)	75	75
W39	14p. grey-bl (phosphorised paper) (8.4.81)	80	80
W40	14p. deep blue (1 centre band) (8.11.88)	80	80
W41	15p. bright blue (1 centre band) (28.11.89)	80	80
W42	15½p. pale violet (phosphorised paper) (24.2.82)	1·00	80
W43	16p. grey-blue (phosphorised paper) (27.4.83)	2·00	1·50
	a. Perf 15×14 (10.1.84)	2·00	1·75
W44	17p. grey-blue (phosphorised paper) (23.10.84)	1·00	90
W45	17p. deep blue (1 centre band) (4.12.90)	1·00	90
W46	18p. deep violet (8.4.81)	1·00	90
W47	18p. deep olive-grey (phosphorised paper) (6.1.87)	1·00	90
W48	18p. bright green (1 centre band) (3.12.91)	75	75
	a. Booklet pane. No. W48×6 with margins all round (25.2.92)	2·75	
	b. Perf 14 (12.1.93*)	2·50	2·50
W49	18p. bright green (1 side band) (25.2.92)	2·50	2·50
	a. Booklet pane. No. X1020×2, 1451a, 1514a, W49×2, W60×2 and centre label with margins all round	10·00	
W50	19p. bright orange-red (phosphorised paper) (8.11.88)	1·00	80
W51	19½p. olive-grey (phosphorised paper) (24.2.82)	2·00	2·00
W52	20p. brownish black (phosphorised paper) (28.11.89)	1·00	1·00
W53	20½p. ultram (phosphorised paper) (27.4.83)	4·00	4·00
W54	22p. blue (phosphorised paper) (8.4.81)	1·25	1·25
W55	22p. yellow-green (phosphorised paper) (23.10.84)	1·25	1·25
W56	22p. bright orange-red (phosphorised paper) (4.12.90)	1·00	1·00
W57	23p. brt grn (phosphorised paper) (8.11.88)	1·25	1·25
W58	24p. Indian red (phosphorised paper) (28.11.89)	1·25	1·25
W59	24p. chestnut (phosphorised paper) (3.12.91)	1·25	1·25
	a. Booklet pane. No. W59×6 with margins all round (25.2.92)	4·75	
	b. Perf 14 (14.9.92*)	2·75	2·75
W60	24p. chestnut (2 bands) (25.2.92)	1·50	1·50
W61	26p. rosine (phosphorised paper) (24.2.82)	1·50	1·50
	a. Perf 15×14 (27.1.87)	5·00	5·00
W62	26p. drab (phosphorised paper) (4.12.90)	1·25	1·25
W63	28p. deep violet-blue (phosphorised paper) (27.4.83)	1·25	1·25
	a. Perf 15×14 (27.1.87)	1·25	1·25
W64	28p. deep bluish grey (phosphorised paper) (3.12.91)	1·25	1·25
W65	31p. bright purple (phosphorised paper) (23.10.84)	1·50	1·50
W66	32p. greenish blue (phosphorised paper) (8.11.88)	1·75	1·75
W67	34p. deep bluish grey (phosphorised paper) (28.11.89)	1·75	1·75
W68	37p. rosine (phosphorised paper) (4.12.90)	1·75	1·75
W69	39p. bright mauve (phosphorised paper) (3.12.91)	1·75	1·75

*Earliest known date of use.
†Exists with gum arabic.

Nos. W48b and W59b were caused by the use of a reserve perforating machine for some printings in late 1992.

Nos. W49 and W60 only come from booklets. No. W49 exists with phosphor band at left or right from different booklets.

From 1972 printings were on fluorescent white paper. Nos. W13/14 exist with PVA and gum arabic and the remainder with PVA only. From 1973 printings had extra dextrin added (see notes after the 1971 Decimal Machin issue).

(Des J. Matthews after plaster cast by Arnold Machin. Litho Questa)

1993 (7 Dec)–**96.** *Chalk-surfaced paper. One phosphor band* (19p., 20p.) *or two phosphor bands* (*others*). *P* 15×14 (*with one elliptical hole on each vertical side*).

W70	W 4	19p. bistre (1 centre band)	75	75
W71		19p. bistre (1 side band) (25.4.95)	2·50	2·50
W72		20p. brt green (1 centre band) (23.7.96)	1·00	1·00
W73		25p. red	1·00	1·00
W74		26p. red-brown (23.7.96)	1·00	1·00
W75		30p. deep olive-grey	1·25	1·25
W76		37p. bright mauve (23.7.96)	1·50	1·50
W77		41p. grey-brown	1·50	1·50
W78		63p. light emerald (23.7.96)	2·50	2·50

No. W71 only comes from booklets.

(Photo Walsall (20p., 26p. (*No.* W80a), 63p.), Harrison or Walsall (26p. (*No.* W80), 37p.))

1997 (1 July)–**98.** *Chalk-surfaced paper. One phosphor band* (20p.) *or two phosphor bands* (*others*). *P* 14 (*No.* W79a) *or* 15×14 (*others*) (*both with one elliptical hole on each vertical side*).

W79	W 5	20p. bright green (1 centre band)	40	40
W79a		20p. brt green (1 side band) (13.10.98)	1·50	1·50
W80		26p. chestnut	75	75
		a. Perf 14 (13.10.98)	1·00	1·00
W81		37p. bright mauve	1·00	1·00
W82		63p. light emerald	1·50	1·50

Nos. W79a and W80a were only issued in booklets.

The Harrison printings of Nos. W80/1 come from booklet pane No. NI79al.

PRICES OF SETS

Set prices are given for many issues, generally those containing three stamps or more. Definitive sets include one of each value or major colour change, but do not cover different perforations, die types or minor shades. Where a choice is possible the set prices are based on the cheapest versions of the stamps included in the listings.

W 6 Leek   W 7 Welsh Dragon   W 8 Daffodil

W 9 Prince of
Wales Feathers

(Des D. Petersen (2nd), T. & G. Petersen (1st), I. Rees (E),
R. Evans (64p, 65p.). Adapted Tutssels. Photo Walsall)

1999 (8 June)–**2000.** *One centre band* (2nd) *or two phosphor
bands* (others). P 15×14 (*with one elliptical hole on each vertical
side*).

W83	W 6	(2nd) orange-brown, yellow-orge & blk	30	35
W84	W 7	(1st) blue-grn, greenish yell, silver & blk	40	45
W85	W 8	(E) greenish blue, deep greenish blue		
		and grey-black	45	50
W86	W 9	64p. violet, gold, silver and black ..	1·00	1·10
W87		65p. violet, gold, silver & blk (25.4.00)	1·00	1·10
W83/7	..	.. .. *Set of* 5	3·00	3·50

Nos. W83, W84 and W85 were initially sold at 19p., 26p. and
30p., the latter representing the basic European airmail rate.

W 10

(Des J. Matthews. Photo Walsall)

2000 (15 Feb). *Type* W 10 *redrawn with "1af/st" face value as
Type* W 10. *Two phosphor bands. P 14* (*with one elliptical hole on
each vertical side*).

W97	W 10	(1st) bright orange-red	40	45

No. W97 was only issued in £7.50 stamp booklets.

STAMP BOOKLETS

For a full listing of Great Britain stamp booklets see the *Great Britain Concise Catalogue* published each Spring.

POSTAGE DUE STAMPS

PERFORATIONS. All postage due stamps to No. D101 are perf 14×15.

D 1   D 2

(Des G. Eve. Typo Somerset House (early trial printings of ½d., 1d., 2d., and 5d.; all printings of 1s.) or Harrison (later printings of all values except 1s.)).

1914 (20 Apr)–**22.** W 100 (*Simple Cypher*) *sideways.*

D1	D 1	½d. emerald	50	50
D2		1d. carmine	50	50
		a. *Pale carmine*	75	75
D3		1½d. chestnut (1922)	48·00	15·00
D4		2d. agate	50	70
D5		3d. violet (1918)	5·00	1·00
		a. *Bluish violet*	6·00	3·50
D6		4d. dull grey-green (12.20)	18·00	18·00
D7		5d. brownish cinnamon	6·00	4·00
D8		1s. bright blue (1915)	40·00	5·00
		a. *Deep bright blue*	40·00	5·00
D1/8		Set of 8	90·00	30·00

The 1d. is known bisected and used to make up a 1½d. rate on understamped letters from Ceylon (1921) or Tasmania (1922, Palmers Green) and the 2d. bisected and used as 1d. at Christchurch, Malvern, Streatham and West Kensington in 1921.

1924. As 1914–22, but on thick chalk-surfaced paper.

D9	D 1	1d. carmine	2·25	3·50

(Typo Waterlow and (from 1934) Harrison)

1924–31. W 111 (*Block Cypher*) *sideways.*

D10	D 1	½d. emerald (6.25)	1·25	1·00
D11		1d. carmine (4.25)	60	60
D12		1½d. chestnut (10.24)	45·00	20·00
D13		2d. agate (7.24)	1·00	50
D14		3d. dull violet (10.24)	1·50	50
		a. Printed on gummed side	75·00	†
		b. Experimental paper W 111*a*	38·00	35·00
D15		4d. dull grey-green (10.24)	15·00	3·00
D16		5d. brownish cinnamon (1.31)	32·00	24·00
D17		1s. deep blue (9.24)	10·00	1·60
D18	D 2	2s. 6d. purple/*yellow* (5.24)	45·00	
D10/18		Set of 9	£130	50·00

The 2d. is known bisected to make up the 2½d. rate at Perranwell Station, Cornwall, in 1932.

1936–37. W 125 (E 8 R) *sideways.*

D19	D 1	½d. emerald (6.37)	7·50	8·00
D20		1d. carmine (5.37)	1·50	2·00
D21		2d. agate (5.37)	7·00	11·00
D22		3d. dull violet (3.37)	1·50	2·25
D23		4d. dull grey-green (12.36)	23·00	26·00
D24		5d. brownish cinnamon (11.36)	45·00	25·00
		a. *Yellow-brown* (1937)	16·00	23·00
D25		1s. deep blue (12.36)	11·00	9·00
D26	D 2	2s. 6d. purple/*yellow* (5.37)	£250	9·00
D19/26		Set of 8 (cheapest)	£300	80·00

The 1d. is known bisected (Solihull, 3 July 1937).

1937–38. W 127 (G VI R) *sideways.*

D27	D 1	½d. emerald (5.38)	9·00	5·00
D28		1d. carmine (5.38)	3·00	75
D29		2d. agate (5.38)	2·50	75
D30		3d. violet (12.37)	12·00	1·00
D31		4d. dull grey-green (9.37)	65·00	12·00
D32		5d. yellow-brown (11.38)	14·00	2·00
D33		1s. deep blue (10.37)	60·00	2·00
D34	D 2	2s. 6d. purple/*yellow* (9.38)	60·00	2·50
D27/34		Set of 8	£200	23·00

The 2d. is known bisected in June 1951 (Boreham Wood, Harpenden and St. Albans) and on 30 October 1954 (Harpenden).

DATES OF ISSUE. The dates for Nos. D35/68 are those on which stamps were first issued by the Supplies Department to postmasters.

1951–52. *Colours changed and new value* (1½d.). W 127 (G VI R) *sideways.*

D35	D 1	½d. orange (18.9.51)	1·00	3·00
D36		1d. violet-blue (6.6.51)	1·50	1·50
D37		1½d. green (11.2.52)	1·75	9·00
D38		4d. blue (14.8.51)	30·00	12·00
D39		1s. ochre (6.12.51)	35·00	14·00
D35/9		Set of 5	60·00	30·00

The 1d. is known bisected (Dorking, 1952, and Camberley, 6 April 1954).

1954–55. W 153 (*Mult Tudor Crown and* E 2 R) *sideways.*

D40	D 1	½d. orange (8.6.55)	7·00	6·00
D41		2d. agate (28.7.55)	5·00	5·00
D42		3d. violet (4.5.55)	55·00	35·00
D43		4d. blue (14.7.55)	20·00	22·00
		a. Imperf (pair)	£250	
D44		5d. yellow-brown (19.5.55)	25·00	10·00
D45	D 2	2s. 6d. purple/*yellow* (11.54)	11·00	4·00
D40/5		Set of 6	£190	75·00

1955–57. W 165 (*Mult St. Edward's Crown and* E 2 R) *sideways.*

D46	D 1	½d. orange (16.7.56)	1·25	3·00
D47		1d. violet-blue (7.6.56)	6·00	2·00
D48		1½d. green (2.3.56)	6·00	6·00
D49		2d. agate (22.5.56)	40·00	4·00
D50		3d. violet (5.3.56)	7·00	1·75
D51		4d. blue (24.4.56)	22·00	4·50
D52		5d. brown-ochre (23.3.56)	32·00	2·50
D53		1s. ochre (22.11.55)	70·00	2·50

D54	D 2	2s. 6d. purple/*yellow* (28.6.57)	£140	10·00
D55		5s. scarlet/*yellow* (25.11.55)	80·00	28·00
D46/55		Set of 10	£350	55·00

The 1d. is known bisected in June 1957 (London S.E.D.O.), the 2d. in June 1956, the 3d. in April/May 1957 (London S.E.D.O.) and the 4d. in April 1957 (Poplar).

1959–63. W 179 (*Mult St Edward's Crown*) *sideways.*

D56	D 1	½d. orange (18.10.61)	20	1·25
D57		1d. violet-blue (9.5.60)	20	75
D58		1½d. green (5.60)	1·25	3·50
D59		2d. agate (14.9.59)	1·50	75
D60		3d. violet (24.3.59)	40	50
D61		4d. blue (17.12.59)	40	30
D62		5d. yellow-brown (6.11.61)	60	1·00
D63		6d. purple (29.3.62)	60	30
D64		1s. ochre (11.4.60)	1·40	30
D65	D 2	2s. 6d. purple/*yellow* (11.5.61)	5·00	45
D66		5s. scarlet/*yellow* (8.5.61)	9·00	1·00
D67		10s. blue/*yellow* (2.9.63)	11·00	6·00
D68		£1 black/*yellow* (2.9.63)	45·00	8·50
D56/68		Set of 13	65·00	22·00

Whiter paper. The note after No. 586 also applies to Postage Due stamps.

The 1d. is known bisected (Newbury, December 1962 and March 1963).

1968–69. *Typo. No wmk. Chalk-surfaced paper.*

D69	D 1	2d. agate (11.4.68)	25	75
D70		3d. violet (9.9.68)	30	75
D71		4d. blue (6.5.68)	40	75
D72		5d. orange-brown (3.1.69)	5·00	8·00
D73		6d. purple (9.9.68)	60	1·25
D74		1s. ochre (19.11.68)	2·00	1·75
D69/74		Set of 6	7·50	12·00

The 2d. and 4d. exist with gum arabic and PVA gum; remainder with PVA gum only.

1968–69. *Photo. No wmk. Chalk-surfaced paper. PVA gum.*

D75	D 1	4d. blue (12.6.69)	6·00	6·00
D76		8d. red (3.10.68)	1·25	1·25

Nos. D75/6 are smaller, 21½×17½ mm.

D 3   D 4

(Des J. Matthews. Photo Harrison)

1970 (17 June)–**75.** *Decimal Currency. Chalk-surfaced paper.*

D77	D 3	½p. turquoise-blue (15.2.71)	30	30
D78		1p. deep reddish purple (15.2.71)	30	30
D79		2p. myrtle-green (15.2.71)	30	30
D80		3p. ultramarine (15.2.71)	30	30
D81		4p. yellow-brown (15.2.71)	30	30
D82		5p. violet (15.2.71)	30	30
D83		7p. red-brown (21.8.74)	35	60
D84	D 4	10p. carmine	30	60
D85		11p. slate-green (18.6.75)	60	75
D86		20p. olive-brown	60	60
D87		50p. ultramarine	1·50	75
D88		£1 black	3·50	1·00
D89		£5 orange-yellow and black (2.4.73)	38·00	3·00
D77/89		Set of 13	40·00	8·00

Later printings were on fluorescent white paper, some with dextrin added to the PVA gum (see notes after X1058 of Great Britain).

 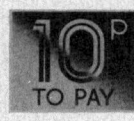

D 5   D 6

(Des Sedley Place Design Ltd. Photo Harrison)

1982 (9 June). *Chalk-surfaced paper.*

D 90	D 5	1p. lake	15	25
D 91		2p. bright blue	25	25
D 92		3p. deep mauve	15	30
D 93		4p. deep blue	25	30
D 94		5p. sepia	25	30
D 95	D 6	10p. light brown	30	40
D 96		20p. olive-green	50	40
D 97		25p. deep greenish blue	75	90
D 98		50p. grey-black	1·50	1·00
D 99		£1 red	3·00	1·00
D100		£2 turquoise-blue	6·00	75
D101		£5 dull orange	14·00	1·00
D90/101		Set of 12	24·00	6·00

D 7

(Des Sedley Place Design Ltd. Litho Questa)

1994 (15 Feb). P 15×14 (*with one elliptical hole on each vertical side*).

D102	D 7	1p. red, yellow and black	10	20
D103		2p. magenta, purple and black	10	20
D104		5p. yellow, red-brown and black	15	20
D105		10p. yellow, emerald and black	30	40
D106		20p. blue-green, violet and black	50	60
D107		25p. cerise, rosine and black	60	70
D108		£1 violet, magenta and black	2·25	2·50
D109		£1.20, greenish blue, blue-green & black	2·75	3·00
D110		£5 greenish black, green-green and black	12·00	12·00
D102/10		Set of 9	17·00	18·00

Following changes in the method of collecting money due on unpaid or underpaid mail the use of postage due stamps was restricted from April 1995 to mail addressed to business customers and to Customs V.A.T. charges levied by the Royal Mail on behalf of the Customs and Excise. The use of postage due stamps ceased completely on 28 January 2000.

OFFICIAL STAMPS

In 1840 the 1d. black (Type 1), with "V R" in the upper corners, was prepared for official use, but never issued for postal purposes. Obliterated specimens are those which were used for experimental trials of obliterating inks, or those that passed through the post by oversight.

V 1

1840. *Prepared for use but not issued; "V" "R" in upper corners. Imperf.*

			Used on
		Un	*Used* *cover*
V1	V 1	1d. black	£6000 £6500

The following Official stamps would be more correctly termed Departmental stamps as they were exclusively for the use of certain government departments. Until 1882 official mail used ordinary postage stamps purchased at post offices, the cash being refunded once a quarter. Later the government departments obtained Official stamps by requisition.

Official stamps were on sale to the public for a short time at Somerset House but they were not sold from post offices. The system of only supplying the Government departments was open to abuse so that all Official stamps were withdrawn on 13 May 1904.

OVERPRINTS, PERFORATIONS, WATERMARKS. All Official stamps were overprinted by Thomas De La Rue & Co. and are perf 14. They are on Crown watermarked paper unless otherwise stated.

INLAND REVENUE

These stamps were used by revenue officials in the provinces, mail to and from Head Office passing without a stamp. The London Office used these stamps only for foreign mail.

I.R.   **I. R.**

OFFICIAL   **OFFICIAL**

(O 1)   (O 2)

Optd with Types O 1 (½d. *to* 1s.) *or* O 2 (*others*)

1882–1901. *Stamps of Queen Victoria.* (a) *Issues of 1880–81.*

				★ *Used on*
			Un	*Used cover*
O 1		½d. deep green (1.11.82)	20·00	20·00 60·00
O 2		½d. pale green	20·00	20·00
O 3		1d. lilac (Die II) (1.10.82)	3·00	2·00 20·00
		a. Optd in blue-black	90·00	50·00
		b. "OFFICIAL" omitted	—	£2750
O 4		6d. grey (Plate 18) (3.11.82)	95·00	30·00

No. O3 with the lines of the overprint transposed is an essay.

		(b) *Issues of 1884–88*		
O 5		½d. slate-blue (8.5.85)	35·00	22·00 90·00
O 6		2½d. lilac (12.3.85)	£150	55·00 £675
O 7		1s. dull green (12.3.85)	£2750	£575
O 8		5s. rose (*blued paper*) (wmk Anchor) (12.3.85)	£3000	£550
O 9		5s. rose (wmk Anchor) (3.90)	£1600	£475
		a. Raised stop after "R"	£1800	£475
		b. Optd in blue-black	£2400	£475
O 9c		10s. cobalt (*blued paper*) (wmk Anchor) (12.3.85)	£5750	£1000
O 9d		10s. ultramarine (*blued paper*) (wmk Anchor) (12.3.85)	£5750	£1900
O10		10s. ultram (wmk Anchor) (3.90)	£3000	£650
		a. Raised stop after "R"	£3750	£675
		b. Optd in blue-black	£4000	£900
O11		£1 brown-lilac (wmk Crowns) (12.3.85)		£22000
		a. Frame broken		£27000
O12		£1 brown-lilac (wmk Orbs) (3.90)	£30000	
		a. Frame broken		£32000

		(c) *Issues of 1887–92*		
O13		½d. vermilion (15.5.88)	2·50	1·50 28·00
		a. Without "I.R."	£2250	
		b. Imperf	£1400	
		c. Opt double (imperf)	£1700	
O14		2½d. purple/*blue* (2.92)	70·00	6·00 £225
O15		1s. dull green (9.89)	£240	40·00 £1300
O16		£1 green (6.92)	£4000	£600
		a. No stop after "R"		£900
		b. Frame broken	£6250	£1100

Nos. O3, O13, O15 and O16 may be found with two varieties of overprint, namely, 1882 printings, *thin letters*, and 1894 printings, *thicker letters*.

		(d) *Issues of 1887 and 1900*		
O17		½d. blue-green (4.01)	6·00	4·50 £110
O18		6d. purple/*rose-red* (1.7.01)	£175	40·00
O19		1s. green and carmine (12.01)	£850	£250
★O1/19		For well-centred, lightly used		+35%

1902–04. *Stamps of King Edward VII. Ordinary paper.*

O20		½d. blue-green (4.2.02)	22·00	3·00 £110
O21		1d. scarlet (4.2.02)	15·00	2·00 75·00
O22		2½d. ultramarine (19.2.02)	£475	£100
O23		6d. pale dull purple (14.3.04)	£90000	£70000
O24		1s. dull green and carmine (29.4.02)	£600	£150
O25		5s. bright carmine (29.4.02)	£4750	£2000
		a. Raised stop after "R"	£5250	£2200

O26	10s. ultramarine (29.4.02)	..	£17000 £10000
	a. Raised stop after "R"	..	£20000 £13000
O27	£1 dull blue-green (29.4.02)	..	£14000 £8000

OFFICE OF WORKS

These were issued to Head and Branch (local) offices in London and to Branch (local) offices at Birmingham, Bristol, Edinburgh, Glasgow, Leeds, Liverpool, Manchester and Southampton. The overprints on stamps of value 2d. and upwards were created later in 1902, the 2d. for registration fees and the rest for overseas mail.

O.W.

OFFICIAL

(O 3)

Optd with Type O 3

1896 (24 Mar)–02. *Stamps of Queen Victoria.*

O31	½d. vermilion	..	..	£110	60·00	£275
O32	½d. blue-green (2.02)		..	£190	95·00	
O33	1d. lilac (Die II)		..	£190	60·00	£300
O34	5d. dull purple and blue (II)(29.4.02)		£900	£210	
O35	10d. dull purple and carmine (28.5.02)	£1500	£300		

1902 (11 Feb)–03. *Stamps of King Edward VII. Ordinary paper.*

O36	½d. blue-green (2.02)	..	..	£425	£110	£1000
O37	1d. scarlet	..	..	£425	£110	£225
O38	2d. yellowish green & carmine-red (29.4.02)		£750	£110	£1300
O39	2½d. ultramarine (29.4.02)		£850	£300	
O40	10d. dull purple & carmine (28.5.03)	£5500	£2000		

★O31/40 For well-centred, lightly used   +25%

ARMY

Letters to and from the War Office in London passed without postage. The overprinted stamps were distributed to District and Station Paymasters nationwide, including Cox and Co., the Army Agents, who were paymasters to the Household Division.

ARMY   **ARMY**   **ARMY**

OFFICIAL   **OFFICIAL**   **OFFICIAL**

(O 4)   (O 5)   (O 6)

1896 (1 Sept)–01. *Stamps of Queen Victoria optd with Type O 4 (½d., 1d.) or O 5 (2½d., 6d.).*

O41	½d. vermilion	..	..	2·50	1·50	28·00
	a. "OFFICIAI" (R. 13/7)		..	45·00	25·00	
	b. Lines of opt transposed		..	£1250		
O42	½d. blue-green (6.00)		..	2·50	4·50	
O43	1d. lilac (Die II)		..	2·50	1·50	45·00
	a. "OFFICIAI" (R. 13/7)		..	45·00	25·00	
O44	2½d. purple/*blue*		..	6·00	3·50	£325
O45	6d. purple/*rose-red* (20.9.01)		18·00	20·00	£525

Nos. O41a and O43a occur on sheets overprinted by Forme 1.

1902–03. *Stamps of King Edward VII optd with Type O 4 (Nos. O48/50) or Type O 6 (No. O52). Ordinary paper.*

O48	½d. blue-green (11.2.02)	..	3·00	1·50	75·00
O49	1d. scarlet (11.2.02)	..	3·00	1·50	75·00
	a. "ARMY" omitted	..	†	—	
O50	6d. pale dull purple (23.8.02)	80·00	35·00	
O52	6d. pale dull purple (12.03)	..	£1000	£350	

GOVERNMENT PARCELS

These stamps were issued to all departments, including the Head Office, for use on parcels weighing over 3 lb. Below this weight government parcels were sent by letter post to avoid the 55% of the postage paid from accruing to the railway companies, as laid down by parcel-post regulations. Most government parcels stamps suffered heavy postmarks in use.

GOVT
PARCELS

(O 7)

Optd as Type O 7

1883 (1 Aug)–86. *Stamps of Queen Victoria.*

				★
			Un	Used
O61	1½d. lilac (1.5.86)	..	£125	30·00
	a. No dot under "T"	..	£150	32·00
	b. Dot to left of "T"	..	£125	32·00
O62	6d. dull green (1.5.86)	..	£825	£300
O63	9d. dull green	..	£675	£190
O64	1s. orange-brown (wmk Crown, Pl 13)	£450	80·00
	a. No dot under "T"	..	£500	90·00
	b. Dot to left of "T"	..	£500	90·00
O64c	1s. orange-brown (Pl 14)	..	£775	£125
	ca. No dot under "T"	..	£850	£110
	cb. Dot to left of "T"			

1887–90. *Stamps of Queen Victoria.*

O65	1½d. dull purple and pale green (29.10.87)	25·00	3·00
	a. No dot under "T"	..	20·00	7·00
	b. Dot to right of "T"	..	18·00	6·00
	c. Dot to left of "T"	..	18·00	6·00
O66	6d. purple/*rose-red* (19.12.87)	60·00	12·00
	a. No dot under "T"	..	70·00	14·00
	b. Dot to right of "T"	..	70·00	14·00
	c. Dot to left of "T"	..	70·00	12·00
O67	9d. dull purple and blue (21.8.88)	70·00	16·00

O68	1s. dull green (25.3.90)	..	..	£150	80·00
	a. No dot under "T"	..	..	£175	85·00
	b. Dot to right of "T"	..	£175	85·00
	c. Dot to left of "T"	..	£200	90·00
	d. Optd in blue-black			

1891–1900. *Stamps of Queen Victoria.*

O69	1d. lilac (Die II) (18.6.97)		30·00	9·00
	a. No dot under "T"	..	32·00	21·00
	b. Dot to left of "T"	..	32·00	21·00
	c. Opt inverted	..	£1000	£850
	d. Ditto. Dot to left of "T"	£1000	£550
O70	2d. grey-green and carmine (24.10.91)	50·00	8·00
	a. No dot under "T"	..	60·00	10·00
	b. Dot to left of "T"	..	60·00	10·00
O71	4½d. green and carmine (29.9.92)	£125	80·00
	b. Dot to right of "T"			
O72	1s. green and carmine (11.00)	£175	55·00
	a. Opt inverted	..	†	£4000

★O61/72 For well-centred lightly used   +100%

The "no dot under T" variety occurred on R.12/3 and 20/2. The "dot to left of T" comes four times in the sheet on R.2/7, 6/7, 7/9 and 12/9. The best example of the "dot to right of T" is on R.20/1. All three varieties were corrected around 1897.

1902. *Stamps of King Edward VII. Ordinary paper.*

O74	1d. scarlet (30.10.02)	..	17·00	6·00
O75	2d. yellowish green & carmine-red (29.4.02)	70·00	18·00
O76	6d. pale dull purple (19.2.02)	..	£110	18·00
	a. Opt double, one albino	..	£4500	
O77	9d. dull purple and ultramarine (28.8.02)	£240	60·00
O78	1s. dull green and carmine (17.12.02)	..	£375	90·00

BOARD OF EDUCATION

BOARD
OF
EDUCATION

(O 8)

Optd with Type O 8

1902 (19 Feb). *Stamps of Queen Victoria.*

				Un	Used on Cover
					Used
O81	5d. dull purple and blue (II)	..	£600	£140	
O82	1s. green and carmine	..	£1100	£450	

1902 (19 Feb)–04. *Stamps of King Edward VII. Ordinary paper.*

O83	½d. blue-green	..	35·00	10·00	£300
O84	1d. scarlet	..	35·00	9·00	£325
O85	2½d. ultramarine	..	£600	70·00	
O86	5d. dull purple & ultram (6.2.04)	£2400	£1100	
O87	1s. dull green & carmine (23.12.02)	£40000	£30000	

ROYAL HOUSEHOLD

R.H.

OFFICIAL

(O 9)

1902. *Stamps of King Edward VII optd with Type O 9. Ordinary paper.*

O91	½d. blue-green (29.4.02)	..	£175	£110	£650
O92	1d. scarlet (19.2.02)	..	£150	£100	£500

ADMIRALTY

ADMIRALTY   **ADMIRALTY**

OFFICIAL   **OFFICIAL**

(O 10)   (O 11)
            (with different "M")

1903 (1 Apr). *Stamps of King Edward VII optd with Type O 10. Ordinary paper.*

O101	½d. blue-green	..	12·00	10·00
O102	1d. scarlet	..	7·00	4·00	£225
O103	1½d. dull purple and green	70·00	55·00
O104	2d. yellowish green & carmine-red	£140	70·00
O105	2½d. ultramarine	..	£150	55·00
O106	3d. purple/*yellow*	..	£140	55·00

1903–04. *Stamps of King Edward VII optd with Type O 11. Ordinary paper.*

O107	½d. blue-green (9.03)	..	12·00	7·00	£325
O108	1d. scarlet (12.03)	..	11·00	6·00	65·00
O109	1½d. dull purple and green (2.04)	£225	£125	
O110	2d. yellowish green and carmine-red (3.04)	£450	£225	
O111	2½d. ultramarine (3.04)	..	£575	£325	
O112	3d. dull purple/*orange-yell* (12.03)	£400	£120	

Stamps of various issues perforated with a Crown and initials ("H.M.O.W.", "O.W.", "B.T." or "S.O.") or with initials only ("H.M.S.O." or "D.S.I.R.") have also been used for official purposes, but these are outside the scope of the catalogue.

POSTAL FISCAL STAMPS

PRICES. Prices in the used column are for stamps with genuine postal cancellations dated from the time when they were authorised for use as postage stamps. Beware of stamps with fiscal cancellations removed and fraudulent postmarks applied.

VALIDITY. The 1d. Surface-printed stamps were authorised for postal use from 1 June 1881 and at the same time the 1d. postage issue, No. 166, was declared valid for fiscal purposes. The 3d. and 6d. values, together with the Embossed issues were declared valid for postal purposes by another Act effective from 1 January 1883.

SURFACE-PRINTED ISSUES

(Typo Thomas De La Rue & Co)

F 1   F 2
Rectangular Buckle

F 3   F 4
Octagonal Buckle

F 5   F 6
Double-lined Anchor   Single-lined Anchor

1853–57. P 15½ × 15. (a) Wmk F 5 (inverted) (1853–55).

				Un	Used	Used on cover
F1	F 1	1d. light blue (10.10.53)		15·00	18·00	80·00
F2	F 2	1d. ochre (10.53)	..	60·00	40·00	£175
		a. Tête-bêche (in block of four)	£8000		
F3	F 3	1d. pale turquoise-blue (12.53)	20·00	18·00	£140
F4		1d. light blue/*blue* (12.53)	40·00	25·00	£160
F5	F 4	1d. reddish lilac/*blue glazed paper* (25.3.55)	60·00	14·00	£110

Only one example is known of No. F2a outside the National Postal Museum and the Royal Collection.

(b) Wmk F 6 (1856–57)

F6	F 4	1d. reddish lilac (*shades*)	5·50	4·00	80·00
F7		1d. reddish lilac/*bluish* (*shades*) (1857)	5·50	4·00	80·00

INLAND   REVENUE

(F 7)

1860 (3 Apr). No. F7 optd with Type F 7, in red.

F8	F 4	1d. dull reddish lilac/*blue*	..	£400	£325	£550

BLUE PAPER. In the following issues we no longer distinguish between bluish and white paper. There is a range of papers from white or greyish to bluish.

F 8   F 9

F 10

1860–67. *Bluish to white paper.* P 15½ × 15. (a) Wmk F 6 (1860).

F 9	F 8	1d. reddish lilac (May)	6·00	6·00	80·00
F10	F 9	3d. reddish lilac (June)	£250	90·00	£175
F11	F 10	6d. reddish lilac (Oct)	£100	75·00	£200

(b) W 40. (*Anchor 16 mm high*) (1864)

F12	F 8	1d. pale reddish lilac (Nov)		4·75	4·75	65·00
F13	F 9	3d. pale reddish lilac	..	90·00	70·00	£160
F14	F 10	6d. pale reddish lilac	..	90·00	70·00	£160

(c) W 40. (*Anchor 18 mm high*) (1867)

F15	F 8	1d. reddish lilac	..	13·00	6·00	£130
F16	F 9	3d. reddish lilac	..	70·00	65·00	£175
F17	F 10	6d. reddish lilac	..	80·00	45·00	£170

For stamps perf 14, see Nos. F24/7.

F 11   **F 12**

Four Dies of Type F 12

Die 1. Corner ornaments small and either joined or broken; heavy shading under chin

Die 2. Ornaments small and always broken; clear line of shading under chin

Die 3. Ornaments larger and joined; line of shading under chin extended half way down neck

Die 4. Ornaments much larger; straight line of shading continued to bottom of neck

1867–81. *White to bluish paper. P* 14. (*a*) W 47 (*Small Anchor*).

F18	F 11	1d. purple (1.9.67)	..	8·00	5·00	60·00
F19	F 12	1d. purple (Die 1) (6.68)	..	1·75	1·50	40·00
F20		1d. purple (Die 2) (6.76)	..	10·00	10·00	£180
F21		1d. purple (Die 3) (3.77)	..	4·00	4·00	75·00
F22		1d. purple (Die 4) (7.78)	..	3·00	2·50	65·00

(b) W 48 (*Orb*)

F23	F 12	1d. purple (Die 4) (1.81)	..	2·00	1·50	40·00

1881. *White to bluish paper. P* 14.

(a) W 40 (*Anchor 18 mm high*) (Jan)

F24	F 9	3d. reddish lilac	..	£350	£225	£350
F25	F 10	6d. reddish lilac	..	£190	75·00	£175

(b) W 40 (*Anchor 20 mm high*) (May)

F26	F 9	3d. reddish lilac	..	£275	70·00	£175
F27	F 10	6d. reddish lilac	..	£150	90·00	£275

ISSUES EMBOSSED IN COLOUR

(Made at Somerset House)

The embossed stamps were struck from dies not appropriated to any special purpose on paper which had the words "INLAND REVENUE" previously printed, and thus became available for payment of any duties for which no special stamps had been provided.

The die letters are included in the embossed designs and holes were drilled for the insertion of plugs showing figures indicating dates of striking.

F 13   **F 14**

INLAND   INLAND

REVENUE   REVENUE

(F 15)   (F 16)

1860 (3 Apr)–**71.** *Types F* **13/14** *and similar types embossed on bluish paper. Underprint Type F* **15.** *No wmk. Imperf.*

					Un	Used
F28	2d. pink (Die A) (1.1.71)	..	..	..	£140	£140
F29	3d. pink (Die C)	..	..	..	£100	95·00
	a. Tête-bêche (vert pair)	..	..	..	£1200	
F30	3d. pink (Die D)	..	..	..	£350	
F31	6d. pink (Die T)	..	..	..	£700	
F32	6d. pink (Die U)	..	..	..	£100	90·00
	a. Tête-bêche (vert pair)	..	..	..	£1400	
F33	9d. pink (Die C) (1.1.71)	..	..	..	£250	
F34	1s. pink (Die E) (28.6.61)	..	..	..	£350	£150
F35	1s. pink (Die F) (28.6.61)	..	..	..	£125	£100
	a. Tête-bêche (vert pair)	..	..	..	£600	
F36	2s. pink (Die K) (6.8.61)	..	..	..	£275	£175
F37	2s. 6d. pink (Die N) (28.6.61)	..	..	..	£850	
F38	2s. 6d. pink (Die O) (28.6.61)	..	..	..	85·00	85·00

1861–71. *As last but perf* 12½.

F39	2d. pink (Die A) (8.71)	..	..	..	£250	£130
F40	3d. pink (Die C)	..	..	..		
F41	3d. pink (Die D)	..	..	..		
F42	9d. pink (Die C) (8.71)	..	..	..	£275	£140
F43	1s. pink (Die E) (8.71)	..	..	..	£200	£130
F44	1s. pink (Die F) (8.71)	..	..	..	£180	£100
F45	2s. 6d. pink (Die O) (8.71)	..	..	..	£120	65·00

1874 (Nov). *Types as before embossed on white paper. Underprint Type F* **16,** *in green. W* 47 (*Small Anchor*). *P* 12½.

F46	2d. pink (Die A)	..	..	..	—	£175
F47	9d. pink (Die C)	..	..	..		
F48	1s. pink (Die F)	..	..	..	£190	£100
F49	2s. 6d. pink (Die O)	..	..	..	—	£150

1875 (Nov)–**80.** *As last but colour changed and on white or bluish paper.*

F50	2d. vermilion (Die A) (1880)	..	..	..	£275	£100
F51	9d. vermilion (Die C) (1876)	..	..	..	£275	£150
F52	1s. vermilion (Die E)	..	..	..	£175	75·00
F53	1s. vermilion (Die F)	..	..	..	£175	75·00
F54	2s. 6d. vermilion (Die O) (1878)	..	..	..	£225	£100

1882 (Oct). *As last but W* 48 (*Orbs*).

F55	2d. vermilion (Die A)	..	..	..		
F56	9d. vermilion (Die C)	..	..	..		
F57	1s. vermilion (Die E)	..	..	..		
F58	2s. 6d. vermilion (Die O)	..	..	..	£500	£250

The sale of Inland Revenue stamps up to the 2s. value ceased from 30 December 1882 and stocks were called in and destroyed. The 2s. 6d. value remained on sale until 2 July 1883 when it was replaced by the 2s. 6d. "Postage & Revenue" stamp. Inland Revenue stamps still in the hands of the public continued to be accepted for revenue and postal purposes.

CONTROLS. Since the 1967 edition of the Part 1 Catalogue the priced lists of stamps with control letters have been transferred to Volumes 1 and 2 of the Stanley Gibbons *Great Britain Specialised Catalogue.*

TELEGRAPH STAMPS. A priced listing of the Post Office telegraph stamps appears in Volume 1 of the Stanley Gibbons *Great Britain Specialised Catalogue.* The last listing for the private telegraph companies in the Part 1 Catalogue was in the 1940 edition and for military telegraphs the 1941 edition.

ISLAND ISSUES

Several islands off the coast of Great Britain have issued local stamps (usually termed British Private Local Issues or Local Carriage Labels) ostensibly to cover the cost of ferrying mail to the nearest mainland post office. No official post offices operate on most of these islands. As these stamps are not recognised as valid for national or international mail they are not listed here. The following islands are known to have issued stamps from the dates shown:

Bardsey, Gwynedd (from 1979); *Bernera, Hebrides* (from 1977); *Brecqhou, Channel Is.* (1969); *Caldey, Dyfed* (from 1973); *Calf of Man, Isle of Man* (1962–73); *Calve, Hebrides* (from 1984); *Canna, Hebrides* (from 1958); *Carn Iar, Hebrides* (1961–62); *Davaar, Argyllshire* (from 1964); *Drake's Island, Devon* (1973–82); *Easdale, Argyllshire* (from 1988); *Eynhallow, Orkney* (from 1973); *Gairsay, Orkney* (from 1980); *Grunay, Shetland* (from 1981); *Gugh, Isles of Scilly* (1972–80 and from 1995); *Herm, Channel Is.* (1949–69); *Heston, Wigtownshire* (1960s); *Hilbre, Cheshire* (1960s); *Hildasay, Shetland* (from 1997); *Jethou, Channel Is.* (1960–69); *Lihou, Channel Is.* (1966–69); *Lundy, Devon* (from 1929); *Pabay, Skye* (1962–70, 1972–81 and from 1982); *St. Kilda, Hebrides* (1968–71); *St. Martin's and St. Mary's, Isles of Scilly* (from 1995); *Sanda, Argyllshire* (from 1962); *Shuna, Argyllshire* (from 1949); *Soay, Skye* (1965–67); *Staffa, Hebrides* (from 1969); *Steep Holm, Avon* (1980–87); *Stroma, Caithness* (1962–70 and from 1988) and *Summer Isles, Hebrides* (1970–88 and from 1992). Those issued for Soay have been declared bogus by a committee of the Philatelic Traders Society.

Issues of the *Commodore Shipping Co* (1950–69), the *Alderney Shipping Co* (1969–75) and the *Isle of Sark Shipping Co* (from 1969) were/are for use on parcels carried by ship between Guernsey and Alderney and Sark. They are not valid for the carriage of letters and postcards.

Issues inscribed Alderney (1975–83 and from 1990) are issued in conjunction with an internal parcel delivery service. They are not valid for use on letters or postcards.

CHANNEL ISLANDS

GENERAL ISSUE

C 1 Gathering Vraic

C 2 Islanders gathering Vraic

(Des J. R. R. Stobie (1d.) or from drawing by E. Blampied (2½d.). Photo Harrison)

1948 (10 May). *Third Anniv of Liberation. W* **127** *of Great Britain. P* 15 × 14.

C1	C 1	1d. scarlet	..	..	30	30
C2	C 2	2½d. ultramarine	..	..	30	30

Supplies of these stamps were also available from eight head post offices on the mainland of Great Britain.

GUERNSEY

WAR OCCUPATION ISSUES

Stamps issued under British authority during the German Occupation

BISECTS. On 24 December 1940 authority was given, by Post Office notice, that prepayment of penny postage could be effected by using half a British 2d. stamp, diagonally bisected. Such stamps were first used on 27 December 1940.

The 2d. stamps generally available were those of the Postal Centenary issue, 1940 (S.G. 482) and the first colour of the King George VI issue (S.G. 465). These are listed under Nos. 482a and 465b. A number of the 2d. King George V, 1912–22, and of the King George V photogravure stamp (S.G. 442) which were in the hands of philatelists, were also bisected and used.

1

1a Loops (*half actual size*)

(Des E. W. Vaudin. Typo Guernsey Press Co Ltd)

1941–44. *Rouletted.* (*a*) *White paper. No wmk.*

1	1	½d. light green (7.4.41)	..	..	3·25	2·50
		a. Emerald-green (6.41)	..	..	4·25	2·50
		b. Bluish green (11.41)	..	..	45·00	20·00
		c. Bright green (2.42)	..	..	28·00	11·00
		d. Dull green (9.42)	..	..	4·25	3·25
		e. Olive-green (2.43)	..	..	32·00	20·00
		f. Pale yellowish green (7.43 and later) (shades)	..	..	3·25	2·75
		g. Imperf (pair)	..	..	£200	
		h. Imperf between (horiz pair)	..	..	£700	
		i. Imperf between (vert pair)	..	..	£800	
2		1d. scarlet (18.2.41)	..	..	2·75	1·50
		a. Pale vermilion (7.43) (etc.)	..	..	2·75	1·50
		b. Carmine (1943)	..	..	3·00	3·00
		c. Imperf (pair)	..	..	£150	75·00
		d. Imperf between (horiz pair)	..	..	£700	
		da. Imperf vert (centre stamp of horiz strip of 3)	..	..		
		e. Imperf between (vert pair)	..	..	£800	
		f. Printed double (scarlet shade)	..	..	£100	
3		2½d. ultramarine (12.4.44)	..	..	4·50	4·50
		a. Pale ultramarine (7.44)	..	..	4·50	4·50
		b. Imperf (pair)	..	..	£500	
		c. Imperf between (horiz pair)	..	..	£1000	

(b) *Bluish French bank-note paper. W* 1a (*sideways*)

4	1	½d. bright green (11.3.42)	..	..	21·00	22·00
5		1d. scarlet (9.4.42)	..	..	12·00	24·00

The dates given for the shades of Nos. 1/3 are the months in which they were printed as indicated on the printer's imprints. Others are issue dates.

REGIONAL ISSUES

DATES OF ISSUE. Conflicting dates of issue have been announced for some of the regional issues, partly explained by the stamps being released on different dates by the Philatelic Bureau in Edinburgh or the Philatelic Counter in London and in the regions. We have adopted the practice of giving the earliest known dates, since once released the stamps could have been used anywhere in the U.K.

2   **3**

(Des E. A. Piprell. Portrait by Dorothy Wilding Ltd. Photo Harrison & Sons)

1958 (18 Aug.)–67. *W* 179 *of Great Britain. P* 15 × 14.

6	2	2½d. rose-red (8.6.64)	..	35	40
7	3	3d. deep lilac	..	35	30
		p. One centre phosphor band (24.5.67)		25	25
8		4d. ultramarine (7.2.66)	..	30	30
		p. Two phosphor bands (24.10.67)		25	25
6/8p.			*Set of 3*	70	75

1968–69. *No wmk. Chalk-surfaced paper. PVA gum*. One centre phosphor band* (Nos. 10/11) *or two phosphor bands* (others). *P* 15 × 14.

9	3	4d. pale ultramarine (16.4.68)	..	10	30
10		4d. olive-sepia (4.9.68)	..	15	20
11		4d. bright vermilion (26.2.69)	..	15	30
12		5d. royal blue (4.9.68)	..	15	30
9/12			*Set of 4*	50	1·00

No. 9 was not issued in Guernsey until 22 April.
* PVA Gum. See note after No. 722 of Great Britain.

INDEPENDENT POSTAL ADMINISTRATION

4 Castle Cornet and Edward the Confessor

5 View of Sark

Two Types of 1d. and 1s. 6d.:

I. Latitude inscr "40° 30′ N".
II. Corrected to "49° 30′ N".

(Des R. Granger Barrett. Photo Harrison (½d. to 2s. 6d.); Delrieu (others))

1969 (1 Oct.)–70. *Designs as T* **4**/**5**. *P* 14 (½d. to 2s. 6d.) *or* 12½ (others).

13		½d. deep magenta and black	..	10	10
14		1d. bright blue and black (I)	..	10	10
14b		1d. bright blue and black (II) (12.12.69)		30	30
		c. Booklet stamp with blank margins		40	40
15		1½d. yellow-brown and black	..	10	10
16		2d. gold, bright red, deep blue and black		10	10
17		3d. gold, pale greenish yellow, orge-red & blk		15	15
		a. Error. Wmk w **12**		£1200	
18		4d. multicoloured	..	25	25
		a. Booklet stamp with blank margins (12.12.69)		40	45
		ab. Yellow omitted	..	£250	
		ac. Emerald (stem) omitted	..	£110	
19		5d. gold, brt vermilion, bluish violet & black		25	15
		a. Booklet stamp with blank margins (12.12.69)		50	50
		b. Gold (inscr etc.) omitted (booklets)	..	£500	
20		6d. gold, pale greenish yellow, light bronze-green and black		30	30
21		9d. gold, bright red, crimson and black		40	30
22		1s. gold, bright vermilion, bistre and black		30	30
23		1s. 6d. turquoise-green and black (I)		30	30
23b		1s. 6d. turquoise-green and black (II) (4.2.70)		2·25	1·75
24		1s. 9d. multicoloured	..	1·25	1·50
		a. Emerald (stem) omitted ..	..	£325	
25		2s. 6d. bright reddish violet and black	..	5·00	4·25
26		5s. multicoloured	..	3·25	3·25
27		10s. multicoloured	..	26·00	22·00
		a. Perf 13½×13 (4.3.70)	..	48·00	40·00
28		£1 multicoloured	..	2·00	1·75
		a. Perf 13½×13 (4.3.70)	..	2·00	2·00
13/28			*Set of 16*	35·00	30·00

Designs: Horiz as T **4**—1d. (*both*), 1s. 6d. (*both*), Map and William I; 1½d. Martello Tower and Henry II; 2d. Arms of Sark and King John; 3d. Arms of Alderney and Edward III; 4d. Guernsey Lily and Henry V; 5d. Arms of Guernsey and Queen Victoria; 1s. 9d. Guernsey and Queen Victoria; 1s. 9d. Guernsey Lily and Elizabeth I; 2s. 6d. Martello Tower and King John. Horiz as T **5**—10s. View of Alderney; £1, View of Guernsey.

The booklet panes consist of single perforated stamps with wide margins all round intended to fit automatic machines designed for the Great Britain 2s. booklets. They are therefore found with three margins when detached from booklets or four margins when complete.

There was no postal need for the ½d. and 1½d. values as the ½d. coin had been withdrawn prior to their issue in anticipation of decimalisation. These values were only on sale at the Philatelic Bureau and the Crown Agents as well as in the U.S.A.

Nos. 14b and 23b are known only on thin paper and Nos. 13, 14, 16, 17, 20, 21, 22, 23, 24 and 25 also exist on thin paper.

19 Isaac Brock as Colonel   **23** H.M.S. *L103* (landing craft) entering St. Peter's Harbour

(Litho Format)

1969 (1 Dec.). *Birth Bicentenary of Sir Isaac Brock. T* **19** *and similar multicoloured designs. P* 13½ × 14 (2s. 6d.) *or* 14 × 13½ (others).

29	**19**	4d. Type **19**	..	20	20
30		5d. Sir Isaac Brock as Major-General	..	20	20
31		1s. 9d. Isaac Brock as Ensign	..	1·40	1·25
32		2s. 6d. Arms and flags (*horiz*)	..	1·40	1·25
29/32			*Set of 4*	2·75	2·50

(Des and photo Courvoisier)

1970 (9 May). *25th Anniv of Liberation. T* **23** *and similar designs. Granite paper. P* 11½.

33		4d. blue and pale blue	..	40	40
34		5d. brown-lake and pale grey	..	40	40
35		1s. 6d. bistre-brown and buff	..	2·50	2·50
33/5			*Set of 3*	3·00	3·00

Designs: Horiz—5d. H.M.S. *Bulldog* and H.M.S. *Beagle* (destroyers) entering St. Peter's Port. Vert—1s. 6d. Brigadier Snow reading Proclamation.

26 Guernsey "Toms"   **32** St. Peter Church, Sark

(Des and photo Courvoisier)

1970 (12 Aug.). *Agriculture and Horticulture. T* **26** *and similar horiz designs. Multicoloured. Granite paper. P* 11½.

36		4d. Type **26**	..	80	20
37		5d. Guernsey Cow	..	90	20
38		9d. Guernsey Bull	..	4·50	2·75
39		1s. 6d. Freesias	..	5·50	3·00
36/9			*Set of 4*	10·00	5·50

(Des and photo Courvoisier)

1970 (11 Nov.). *Christmas. Guernsey Churches* (1st series). *T* **32** *and similar multicoloured designs. Granite paper. P* 11½.

40		4d. St. Anne's Church, Alderney (*horiz*)	..	35	20
41		5d. St. Peter's Church (*horiz*)	..	45	25
42		9d. Type **32**	..	1·75	1·10
43		1s. 6d. St. Tugual Chapel, Herm	..	2·00	1·50
40/3			*Set of 4*	4·00	2·75

See also Nos. 63/6.

INVALIDATION. The regional issues for Guernsey were invalidated for use in Guernsey and Jersey on 1 November 1969 but remained valid for use in the rest of the United Kingdom. Nos. 13/43 (except Nos. 28/a) and Nos. D1/7 were invalidated on 14 February 1972.

34 Martello Tower and King John

(Photo Harrison (½p. to 10p.), Delrieu (others))

1971 (6 Jan.)–73. *Decimal Currency. Designs as Nos.* 13/27, *but values inscr in decimal currency as in T* **34**. *Chalk-surfaced paper. P* 14 (½ p. to 10p.) *or* 13½×13 (20p., 50p.).

44		½p. deep magenta and black (15.2.71)	..	10	15
		a. Booklet stamp with margins (*glazed, ordinary paper*)		15	20
		ab. Ditto. Chalk-surfaced paper (2.4.73)		15	20
45		1p. bright blue and black (II) (15.2.71)		10	10
46		1½p. yellow-brown and black (15.2.71)		15	15
47		2p. multicoloured (15.2.71)	..	15	15
		a. Booklet stamp with margins (*glazed, ordinary paper*)		20	20
		ab. Ditto. Chalk-surfaced paper (2.4.73)		20	20
		ac. Emerald (stem) omitted	..	£1200	
		b. Glazed, ordinary paper (15.2.71)		20	20
48		2½p. gold, brt verm, bluish vio & blk (15.2.71)		15	10
		a. Bright vermilion omitted	..	£500	
		b. Booklet stamp with margins (*glazed, ordinary paper*)		20	20
		ba. Chalk-surfaced paper (2.4.73)		20	20
49		3p. gold, pale greenish yellow, orange-red and black (15.2.71)		20	20
50		3½p. mult (*glazed, ordinary paper*) (15.2.71)	..	25	25
51		4p. multicoloured (15.2.71)	..	35	25

52		5p. turquoise-green and black (II) (15.2.71)		30	25
53		6p. gold, pale greenish yellow, light bronze-green and black (15.2.71)		30	35
54		7½p. gold, brt verm, bistre & black (15.2.71)		40	45
55		9p. gold, brt red, crimson & black (15.2.71)		50	75
56		10p. bright reddish violet and black	..	2·25	1·75
		a. Ordinary paper. *Bright reddish violet and deep black* (1.9.72)		1·75	1·75
57		20p. multicoloured (*glazed, ordinary paper*)	..	1·00	1·00
		a. *Shade** (25.1.73)	..	1·00	1·00
58		50p. multicoloured (*glazed, ordinary paper*)	..	2·00	2·00
44/58			*Set of 15*	7·00	7·00

*No. 57 has the sky in a pale turquoise-blue; on No. 57a it is pale turquoise-green.

BAILIWICK OF GUERNSEY

35 Hong Kong 2 c. of 1862

(Des and recess D.L.R.)

1971 (2 June). *Thomas De La Rue Commemoration. T* **35** *and similar horiz designs. P* 14 × 13½.

59		2p. dull purple to brown-purple*	..	50	30
60		2½p. carmine-red	..	50	30
61		4p. deep bluish green	..	2·50	2·25
62		7½p. deep blue	..	2·75	2·25
59/62			*Set of 4*	5·50	4·50

Designs: (each incorporating portraits of Queen Elizabeth II and Thomas De La Rue as in T **35**)—2½p. Great Britain 4d. of 1855–7; 4p. Italy 5 c. of 1862; 7½p. Confederate States 5 c. of 1862.

* These colours represent the extreme range of shades of this value. The majority of the printing, however, is in an intermediate shade.

36 Ebenezer Church, St. Peter Port

(Des and photo Courvoisier)

1971 (27 Oct.). *Christmas. Guernsey Churches* (2nd series). *T* **36** *and similar multicoloured designs. Granite paper. P* 11½.

63		2p. Type **36**	..	25	25
64		2½p. Church of St. Pierre du Bois	..	25	25
65		5p. St. Joseph's Church, St. Peter Port (*vert*)		2·25	1·75
66		7½d. Church of St. Philippe de Torteval (*vert*)		2·25	1·75
63/6			*Set of 4*	4·50	3·50

37 *Earl of Chesterfield* (1794)

(Des and photo Courvoisier)

1972 (10 Feb.). *Mail Packet Boats* (1st series). *T* **37** *and similar horiz designs. Multicoloured. Granite paper. P* 11½.

67		2p. Type **37**	..	15	15
68		2½p. *Dasher* (1827)	..	20	20
69		7½p. *Ibex* (1891)	..	90	1·00
70		9p. *Alberta* (1900)	..	1·50	1·40
67/70			*Set of 4*	2·50	2·50

See also Nos. 80/3.

38 Guernsey Bull

(Photo Courvoisier)

1972 (22 May). *World Conference of Guernsey Breeders, Guernsey. Granite paper. P* 11½.

71	**38**	5p. multicoloured	..	75	60

39 Bermuda Buttercup   **40** Angels adoring Christ

(Des and photo Courvoisier)

1972 (24 May). *Wild Flowers. T 39 and similar multicoloured designs. Granite paper. P 11½.*

72	2p.	Type **39**	15	20
73	2½p.	Heath Spotted Orchid (*vert*)	15	20
74	7½p.	Kaffir Fig	1·00	90
75	9p.	Scarlet Pimpernel (*vert*)	1·40	1·25
72/5		Set of 4	2·50	2·25

(Des and photo Courvoisier)

1972 (20 Nov). *Royal Silver Wedding and Christmas. T 40 and similar vert designs showing stained-glass windows from Guernsey Churches. Multicoloured. Granite paper. P 11½.*

76	2p.	Type **40**	10	10
77	2½p.	The Epiphany	15	15
78	7½p.	The Virgin Mary	60	55
79	9p.	Christ	75	60
76/9		Set of 4	1·50	1·25

See also Nos. 89/92.

(Des and photo Courvoisier)

1973 (9 Mar). *Mail Packet Boats (2nd series). Multicoloured designs as T 37. Granite paper. P 11½.*

80	2½p.	St. Julien (1925)	20	10
81	3p.	Isle of Guernsey (1930)	30	20
82	7½p.	St. Patrick (1947)	1·10	60
83	9p.	Sarnia (1961)	1·25	75
80/3		Set of 4	2·50	1·50

41 Supermarine Sea Eagle

42 "The Good Shepherd"

(Des and photo Courvoisier)

1973 (4 July). *50th Anniv of Air Service. T 41 and similar horiz designs. Multicoloured. Granite paper. P 11½.*

84	2½p.	Type **41**	10	10
85	3p.	Westland Wessex trimotor	15	15
86	5p.	De Havilland D.H.89 Dragon Rapide	30	25
87	7½p.	Douglas DC-3	90	50
88	9p.	Vickers Viscount 800 *Anne Marie*	1·00	55
84/8		Set of 5	2·25	1·40

(Des and photo Courvoisier)

1973 (24 Oct). *Christmas. T 42 and similar vert designs showing stained-glass windows from Guernsey Churches. Multicoloured. Granite paper. P 11½.*

89	2½p.	Type **42**	10	10
90	3p.	Christ at the well of Samaria	10	10
91	7½p.	St. Dominic	30	30
92	20p.	Mary and the Child Jesus	60	60
89/92		Set of 4	1·00	1·00

43 Princess Anne and Capt. Mark Phillips

(Des G. Anderson. Photo Courvoisier)

1973 (14 Nov). *Royal Wedding. Granite paper. P 11½.*

93	**43**	25p. multicoloured	1·00	75

44 John Lockett, 1875

(Des and photo Courvoisier)

1974 (15 Jan). *150th Anniv of Royal National Lifeboat Institution. T 44 and similar horiz designs. Multicoloured. Granite paper. P 11½.*

94	2½p.	Type **44**	10	10
95	3p.	Arthur Lionel, 1912	10	10
96	8p.	Euphrosyne Kendal, 1954	45	45
97	10p.	Arun, 1972	45	45
94/7		Set of 4	1·00	1·00

MINIMUM PRICE

The minimum price quote is 10p which represents a handling charge rather than a basis for valuing common stamps. For further notes about prices see introductory pages.

45 Private, East Regt, 1815

46 Driver, Field Battery, Royal Guernsey Artillery, 1848

(Photo Courvoisier (½ to 10p.) or Delrieu (others))

1974 (2 Apr)–**78**. *Designs as T 45/6. Multicoloured.*

    (a) *Vert designs as T 45. Granite paper. P 11½.*

98	½p.	Type **45**	10	10
	a.	Booklet strip of 8 (98 × 5 and 102 × 3)†	30	
	b.	Booklet pane of 16 (98 × 4, 102 × 6 and 103 × 6)†	65	
99	1p.	Officer, 2nd North Regt, 1825	10	10
	a.	Booklet strip of 8 (99 × 4, 103, 105 × 2 and 105a) (8.2.77)†	80	
	b.	Booklet strip of 4 (99, 101 × 2 and 105a) (7.2.78)†	50	
100	1½p.	Gunner, Guernsey Artillery, 1787	10	10
101	2p.	Gunner, Guernsey Artillery, 1815	10	10
102	2½p.	Corporal, Royal Guernsey Artillery, 1868	10	10
103	3p.	Field Officer, Royal Guernsey Artillery, 1895	10	10
104	3½p.	Sergeant, 3rd Regt, 1867	10	10
105	4p.	Officer, East Regt, 1822	15	15
105a	5p.	Field Officer, Royal Guernsey Artillery, 1895 (29.5.76)	15	15
106	5½p.	Colour-Sergeant of Grenadiers, East Regt, 1833	20	25
107	6p.	Officer, North Regt, 1832	20	25
107a	7p.	Officer, East Regt, 1822 (29.5.76)	25	25
108	8p.	Field Officer, Rifle Company, 1868	25	30
109	9p.	Private, 4th West Regt, 1785	30	30
110	10p.	Field Officer, 4th West Regt, 1824	30	30

    (b) *Size as T 46. P 13 × 13½ (20, 50p.) or 13½ × 13 (£1)*

111	20p.	Type **46** (1.4.75)	55	40
112	50p.	Officer, Field Battery, Royal Guernsey Artillery, 1868 (1.4.75)	1·50	1·25
113	£1	Cavalry Trooper, Light Dragoons, 1814 (*horiz*) (1.4.75)	3·25	2·50
98/113		Set of 18	7·00	6·00

The ½p. and 2¼p. with the red colour omitted are chemically produced fakes.

† Nos. 98a/b come from special booklet sheets of 88 (8 × 11), and Nos. 99a/b from separate booklet sheets of 80 (2 panes 8 × 5). These sheets were put on sale in addition to the normal sheets. The strips and panes have the left-hand selvedge stuck into booklet covers, except for No. 99b which was loose, and then folded and supplied in plastic wallets.

47 Badge of Guernsey and U.P.U. Emblem

(Photo Courvoisier)

1974 (7 June). *U.P.U. Centenary. T 47 and similar horiz designs. Multicoloured. Granite paper. P 11½.*

114	2½p.	Type **47**	10	10
115	3p.	Map of Guernsey	10	10
116	8p.	U.P.U. Building, Berne, and Guernsey flag	45	45
117	10p.	"Salle des Etats"	45	45
114/17		Set of 4	1·00	1·00

48 "Cradle Rock"

49 Guernsey Spleenwort

(Des and photo Delrieu)

1974 (21 Sept). *Renoir Paintings. T 48 and similar multicoloured designs. P 13.*

118	3p.	Type **48**	10	10
119	5½p.	"Moulin Huet Bay"	15	15
120	8p.	"Au Bord de la Mer" (*vert*)	40	40
121	10p.	Self-portrait (*vert*)	45	45
118/21		Set of 4	1·00	1·00

(Des and photo Courvoisier)

1975 (7 Jan). *Guernsey Ferns. T 49 and similar vert designs. Multicoloured. Granite paper. P 11½.*

122	3½p.	Type **49**	15	10
123	4p.	Sand Quillwort	15	10
124	8p.	Guernsey Quillwort	40	40
125	10p.	Least Adder's Tongue	60	50
122/5		Set of 4	1·25	1·00

50 Victor Hugo House

51 Globe and Seal of Bailiwick

(Des and photo Courvoisier)

1975 (6 June). *Victor Hugo's Exile in Guernsey. T 50 and similar multicoloured designs. Granite paper. P 11½.*

126	3½p.	Type **50**	10	10
127	4p.	Candie Gardens (*vert*)	20	10
128	8p.	United Europe Oak, Hauteville (*vert*)	40	40
129	10p.	Tapestry Room, Hauteville	50	50
126/9		Set of 4	1·10	1·00
MS130		114 × 143 mm. Nos. 126/9	1·10	1·00

(Des and photo Delrieu)

1975 (7 Oct). *Christmas. Multicoloured designs each showing Globe as T 51. P 13.*

131	4p.	Type **51**	10	10
132	6p.	Guernsey flag	15	15
133	10p.	Guernsey flag and Alderney shield (*horiz*)	45	35
134	12p.	Guernsey flag and Sark shield (*horiz*)	50	50
131/4		Set of 4	1·10	1·00

52 Les Hanois

(Des and photo Courvoisier)

1976 (10 Feb). *Lighthouses. T 52 and similar horiz designs. Multicoloured. Granite paper. P 11½.*

135	4p.	Type **52**	10	10
136	6p.	Les Casquets	20	25
137	11p.	Quesnard	50	45
138	13p.	Point Robert	55	60
135/8		Set of 4	1·25	1·25

53 Milk Can

(Des and photo Courvoisier)

1976 (29 May). *Europa. T 53 and similar horiz design. Granite paper. P 11½.*

139	10p.	chestnut and greenish black	40	40
140	25p.	slate and deep dull blue	85	85

Design:—25p. Christening Cup.

54 Pine Forest, Guernsey

(Des and photo Courvoisier)

1976 (3 Aug). *Bailiwick Views. T 54 and similar multicoloured designs. Granite paper. P 11½.*

141	5p.	Type **54**	15	10
142	7p.	Herm and Jethou	15	20
143	11p.	Grand Greve Bay, Sark (*vert*)	55	45
144	13p.	Trois Vaux Bay, Alderney (*vert*)	55	65
141/4		Set of 4	1·25	1·25

55 Royal Court House, Guernsey

56 Queen Elizabeth II

(Des and photo Courvoisier)

1976 (14 Oct). *Christmas. Buildings. T* **55** *and similar horiz designs. Multicoloured. Granite paper. P* 11½.
145	5p.	Type **55**	15	10
146	7p.	Elizabeth College, Guernsey	15	15
147	11p.	La Seigneurie, Sark	55	50
148	13p.	Island Hall, Alderney	55	65
145/8		*Set of* 4	1·25	1·25

(Des R. Granger Barrett. Photo Courvoisier)

1977 (8 Feb). *Silver Jubilee. T* **56** *and similar vert design. Multi-coloured. Granite paper. P* 11½.
149	7p.	Type **56**	25	25
150	35p.	Queen Elizabeth (half-length portrait)	1·00	1·00

57 Woodland, Talbot's Valley   58 Statue-menhir, Castel

(Des and photo Courvoisier)

1977 (17 May). *Europa. T* **57** *and similar horiz design. Multicoloured. Granite paper. P* 11½.
151	7p.	Type **57**	35	35
152	25p.	Pastureland, Talbot's Valley	90	90

(Des and photo Courvoisier)

1977 (2 Aug). *Prehistoric Monuments. T* **58** *and similar multicoloured designs. Granite paper. P* 11½.
153	5p.	Type **58**	10	10
154	7p.	Megalithic tomb, St. Saviour (*horiz*)	15	15
155	11p.	Cist, Tourgis (*horiz*)	55	55
156	13p.	Statue-menhir, St. Martin	60	60
153/6		*Set of* 4	1·25	1·25

59 Mobile First Aid Unit

(Des P. Slade and M. Horder. Photo Courvoisier)

1977 (25 Oct). *Christmas and St. John Ambulance Centenary. T* **59** *and similar multicoloured designs. Granite paper. P* 11½.
157	5p.	Type **59**	10	10
158	7p.	Mobile radar unit	15	15
159	11p.	Marine Ambulance *Flying Christine II* (*vert*)	55	55
160	13p.	Cliff rescue (*vert*)	60	60
157/60		*Set of* 4	1·25	1·25

60 View from Clifton, circa 1830

(Des, recess and litho D.L.R.)

1978 (7 Feb). *Old Guernsey Prints* (1st series). *T* **60** *and similar horiz designs. P* 14 × 13½.
161	5p.	black and pale apple-green	10	10
162	7p.	black and stone	15	15
163	11p.	black and light pink	55	55
164	13p.	black and light azure	60	60
161/4		*Set of* 4	1·25	1·25

Designs:—7p. Market Square, St. Peter Port, *circa* 1838; 11p. Petit-Bô Bay, *circa* 1839; 13p. The Quay, St. Peter Port, *circa* 1830.
See also Nos. 249/52.

61 *Prosperity* Memorial   62 Queen Elizabeth II

GB 86

(Des R. Granger Barrett. Litho Questa)

1978 (2 May). *Europa. T* **61** *and similar vert design. Multicoloured. P* 14½.
165	5p.	Type **61**	35	35
166	7p.	Victoria Monument	40	40

(Des R. Granger Barrett from bust by Arnold Machin. Photo Courvoisier)

1978 (2 May). *25th Anniv of Coronation. Granite paper. P* 11½.
167	**62**	20p. black, grey and bright blue	75	75

1978 (28 June). *Royal Visit. Design as No.* 167 *but inscr.* "VISIT OF H.M. THE QUEEN AND H.R.H. THE DUKE OF EDIN-BURGH JUNE 28–29, 1978 TO THE BAILIWICK OF GUERNSEY".
168	**62**	7p. black, grey and bright green	50	50

63 Northern Gannet

(Des J.W. Photo Courvoisier)

1978 (29 Aug). *Birds. T* **63** *and similar horiz designs. Multicoloured. Granite paper. P* 11½.
169	5p.	Type **63**	15	15
170	7p.	Firecrest	25	25
171	11p.	Dartford Warbler	60	45
172	13p.	Spotted Redshank	70	55
169/72		*Set of* 4	1·50	1·25

64 Solanum

(Des and photo Courvoisier)

1978 (31 Oct). *Christmas. T* **64** *and similar designs. Granite paper. P* 11½.
173	5p.	multicoloured	10	10
174	7p.	multicoloured	20	20
175	11p.	multicoloured	40	40
176	13p.	dp blue-green, grey & greenish yellow	50	50
173/6		*Set of* 4	1·10	1·10

Designs: *Horiz*—7p. Christmas Rose. *Vert*—11p. Holly; 13p. Mistletoe.

65 One Double Coin.   66 Ten Shillings William I
1830   Commemorative Coin,
                1966

66a Seal of the Bailiwick

(Des R. Reed and Courvoisier (£5). Photo Courvoisier)

1979 (13 Feb)–**83.** *Designs as T* **65/6a.** *Granite paper. P* 11½.
177	½p. multicoloured		10	10
	a. Booklet pane of 10. Nos. 177×2, 178×3, 179×2, 181, 183 and 187 (6.5.80)		1·00	
	b. Booklet pane of 10. Nos. 177×2, 178, 179×2, 183×2 and 187×3 (6.5.80)		1·50	
178	1p. multicoloured		10	10
	a. Booklet strip of 4. Nos. 178×2, 179 and 182		60	
179	2p. multicoloured		10	10
	a. Booklet strip of 5. Nos. 179, 182×2 and 184×2		1·25	

180	4p.	multicoloured	10	10
	a. Booklet pane of 10. Nos. 180 and 184, each × 5 (24.2.81)		1·75	
	b. Booklet pane of 15. Nos. 180, 184 and 190, each × 5 (24.2.81)		3·50	
	c. Booklet pane of 10. Nos. 180×2, 185×3 and 191×5 (14.3.83)		3·00	
	d. Booklet pane of 15. Nos. 180, 185 and 191, each × 5 (14.3.83)		3·75	
181	5p.	grey-black, silver and chestnut (*shades*)	15	10
	b. Booklet pane. Nos. 181×5, 184×4 and 191 (2.2.82)		2·25	
	c. Booklet pane. Nos. 181, 184 and 191, each × 5 (2.2.82)		3·75	
182	6p.	grey-black, silver and brown-red	15	15
183	7p.	grey-black, silver and brown-red	15	20
184	8p.	grey-black, silver and brown	20	20
185	9p.	multicoloured	25	20
186	10p.	multicoloured (green background)	50	50
187	10p.	mult (orange background) (5.2.80)	35	30
188	11p.	multicoloured	25	30
189	11½p.	multicoloured (5.2.80)	25	30
190	12p.	multicoloured	30	30
191	13p.	multicoloured	30	30
192	14p.	grey-black, silver and dull blue	30	30
193	15p.	grey-black, silver and bistre	35	35
194	20p.	grey-black, silver and dull brown	50	45
195	50p.	grey-black, orange-red & silver (5.2.80)	1·00	75
196	£1	grey-blk, yellowish grn & silver (5.2.80)	2·00	1·50
197	£2	grey-black, new blue and silver (5.2.80)	4·00	2·50
198	£5	multicoloured (22.5.81)	10·00	8·50
177/98		*Set of* 22	19·00	16·00

Coins: *Vert as T* **65**—1p. Two doubles, 1899; 2p. Four doubles, 1902; 4p. Eight doubles 1959; 5p. Three pence, 1956; 6p. Five new pence, 1968; 7p. Fifty new pence, 1969; 8p. Ten new pence, 1970; 9p. Half new penny, 1971; 10p. (*both*), One new penny, 1971; 11p. Two new pence, 1971; 11½p. Half penny, 1979; 12p. One penny, 1977; 13p. Two pence, 1977; 14p. Five pence, 1977; 15p. Ten pence, 1977; 20p. Twenty-five pence, 1972. *Horiz as T* **66**—£1 Silver Jubilee commemorative crown, 1977; £2 Royal Silver Wedding crown, 1972.

Nos. 177a/b, 178a, 179a, 180a/d and 181b/c come from special booklet sheets of 40 (8 × 5) (Nos. 177a and 178a); 30 (6 × 5) (Nos. 177b, 180a/b, 180d and 181 b/c), 25 (5 × 5) (No. 179a) or 20 (4 × 5) (No. 180c). These were put on sale in addition to the normal sheets, being first separated into strips, then folded and either affixed by the selvedge to booklet covers or supplied loose in plastic wallets.

67 Pillar-box and Postmark,   68 Steam Tram, 1879
1853, Mail Van
and Postmark, 1979

(Des R. Granger Barrett. Photo Courvoisier)

1979 (8 May). *Europa. Communications. T* **67** *and similar vert design. Multicoloured. Granite paper. P* 11½.
201	6p.	Type **67**	30	30
202	8p.	Telephone, 1897 and telex machine, 1979	30	30

(Photo Courvoisier)

1979 (7 Aug). *History of Public Transport. T* **68** *and similar horiz designs. Multicoloured. Granite paper. P* 11½.
203	6p.	Type **68**	15	15
204	8p.	Electric tram, 1896	20	20
205	11p.	Motor bus, 1911	55	55
206	13p.	Motor bus, 1979	60	60
203/6		*Set of* 4	1·25	1·25

69 Bureau and Postal Headquarters   70 Major-General
Le Marchant

(Des R. Granger Barrett. Photo Courvoisier)

1979 (1 Oct). *Christmas and 10th Anniv of Guernsey Postal Administration. T* **69** *and similar horiz designs. Multicoloured. Granite paper. P* 11½.
207	6p.	Type **69**	15	15
208	8p.	"Mails and telegrams"	25	15
209	13p.	"Parcels"	50	55
210	15p.	"Philately"	60	60
207/10		*Set of* 4	1·25	1·25
MS211	120 × 80 mm. Nos. 207/10		1·00	70

One copy of a pre-release sample as No. 210, but with a face value of 11p., is known. Such stamps were not sold for postal purposes.

(Des and photo Courvoisier)

1980 (6 May). *Europa. Personalities. T* **70** *and similar vert design. Multicoloured. Granite paper. P* 11½.
212	10p.	Type **70**	45	45
213	13½p.	Admiral Lord De Saumarez	55	50

71 Policewoman with Lost Child

(Litho J.W.)

1980 (6 May). *60th Anniv of Guernsey Police Force.* T **71** *and similar horiz designs. Multicoloured.* P 13½ × 14.
214	7p. Type **71**		20	20
215	15p. Police motorcyclist escorting lorry		55	55
216	17½p. Police dog-handler		65	65
214/16		*Set of 3*	1·25	1·25

72 Golden Guernsey Goat

(Des P. Lambert. Photo Delrieu)

1980 (5 Aug). *Golden Guernsey Goats.* T **72** *and similar horiz designs showing goats.* P 13.
217	7p. multicoloured		20	20
218	10p. multicoloured		30	35
219	15p. multicoloured		55	45
220	17½p. multicoloured		65	60
217/20		*Set of 4*	1·50	1·40

73 "Sark Cottage"

(Photo Courvoisier)

1980 (15 Nov). *Christmas. Peter le Lievre Paintings.* T **73** *and similar multicoloured designs. Granite paper.* P 11½.
221	7p. Type **73**		25	20
222	10p. "Moulin Huet"		35	25
223	13½p. "Boats at Sea"		40	35
224	15p. "Cow Lane" (*vert*)		50	40
225	17½p. "Peter le Lievre" (*vert*)		65	50
221/5		*Set of 5*	2·00	1·50

74 Polyommatus icarus   75 Sailors paying respect to "Le Petit Bonhomme Andriou" (rock resembling head of a man)

(Photo Harrison)

1981 (24 Feb). *Butterflies.* T **74** *and similar horiz designs. Multicoloured.* P 14.
226	8p. Type **74**		25	25
227	12p. *Vanessa atalanta*		40	40
228	22p. *Aglais urticae*		90	70
229	25p. *Lasiommata megera*		1·00	90
226/9		*Set of 4*	2·25	2·00

(Des C. Abbott. Litho Questa)

1981 (22 May). *Europa. Folklore.* T **75** *and similar vert design.* P 14½.
230	12p. gold, red-brown and cinnamon		45	45
231	18p. gold, indigo and azure		55	55
	Design:—18p. Fairies and Guernsey Lily.			

76 Prince Charles   77 Sark Launch

(Des C. Abbott. Litho Questa)

1981 (29 July). *Royal Wedding.* T **76** *and similar multicoloured designs.* P 14½.
232	8p. Type **76**		50	50
	a. Horiz strip of 3. Nos. 232/4		1·50	1·50
233	8p. Prince Charles and Lady Diana Spencer		50	50
234	8p. Lady Diana		50	50

235	12p. Type **76**		90	90
	a. Horiz strip of 3. Nos. 235/7		2·75	2·75
236	12p. As No. 233		90	90
237	12p. As No. 234		90	90
238	25p. Royal family (49 × 32 *mm*)		1·50	1·50
232/8		*Set of 7*	5·00	5·00
MS239	104 × 127 mm. Nos. 232/8. P 14		6·50	6·50

The 8 and 12p. values were each printed together, *se-tenant*, in horizontal strips of 3 throughout the sheets.

(Des and photo Courvoisier)

1981 (25 Aug). *Inter-island Transport.* T **77** *and similar horiz designs. Multicoloured. Granite paper.* P 11½.
240	8p. Type **77**		20	20
241	12p. Britten Norman "Short nose" Trislander airplane		40	40
242	18p. Hydrofoil		60	50
243	22p. Herm catamaran		75	65
244	25p. *Sea Trent* (coaster)		90	75
240/4		*Set of 5*	2·50	2·25

78 Rifle Shooting   79 Sir Edgar MacCulloch (founder-president) and Guille-Allès Library, St. Peter Port

(Des P. le Vasseur. Litho Questa)

1981 (17 Nov). *International Year for Disabled Persons.* T **78** *and similar horiz designs. Multicoloured.* P 14½.
245	8p. Type **78**		20	20
246	12p. Riding		35	35
247	22p. Swimming		65	55
248	25p. "Work"		75	60
245/8		*Set of 4*	1·75	1·50

(Des, recess and litho D.L.R.)

1982 (2 Feb). *Old Guernsey Prints* (*2nd series*). *Prints from sketches by T. Compton. Horiz designs as* T **60**. P 14 × 13½.
249	8p. black and pale blue		20	20
250	12p. black and pale turquoise-green		35	35
251	22p. black and pale yellow-brown		65	65
252	26p. black and pale rose-lilac		65	65
249/52		*Set of 4*	1·75	1·75

Designs:—8p. Jethou; 12p. Fermain Bay; 22p. The Terres; 25p. St. Peter Port.

(Des G. Drummond. Photo Courvoisier)

1982 (28 Apr). *Centenary of La Société Guernesiaise.* T **79** *and similar horiz designs. Multicoloured. Granite paper.* P 11½.
253	8p. Type **79**		20	20
254	13p. French invasion fleet crossing English Channel, 1066 ("History")		35	35
255	20p. H.M.S. *Crescent*, 1793 ("History")		45	45
256	24p. Dragonfly ("Entomology")		70	70
257	26p. Common Snipe caught for ringing ("Ornithology")		80	80
258	29p. Samian Bowl, 160–200 A.D. ("Archaeology")		85	85
253/8		*Set of 6*	3·00	3·00

The 13 and 20p. values also include the Europa C.E.P.T. emblem in the designs.

80 "Sea Scouts"   81 Midnight Mass

(Des W.L.G. Creative Services Ltd. Litho Questa)

1982 (13 July). *75th Anniv of Boy Scout Movement.* T **80** *and similar vert designs. Multicoloured.* P 14½ × 14.
259	8p. Type **80**		20	25
260	13p. "Scouts"		50	50
261	26p. "Cub Scouts"		70	70
262	29p. "Air Scouts"		85	80
259/62		*Set of 4*	2·25	2·25

(Des Lynette Hemmant. Photo Harrison)

1982 (12 Oct). *Christmas.* T **81** *and similar horiz designs. Multicoloured.* P 14½.
263	8p. Type **81**		20	20
	a. Black (Queen's head, value and inscr) omitted			
264	13p. Exchanging gifts		30	30
265	24p. Christmas meal		75	75
266	26p. Exchanging cards		75	75
267	29p. Queen's Christmas message		80	80
263/7		*Set of 5*	2·50	2·50

NEW INFORMATION

The editor is always interested to correspond with people who have new information that will improve or correct the Catalogue.

82 Flute Player and Boats   83 Building Albert Pier Extension, 1850s

(Des Sally Stiff. Photo Harrison)

1983 (18 Jan). *Centenary of Boys' Brigade.* T **82** *and similar horiz designs. Multicoloured.* P 14.
268	8p. Type **82**		25	25
269	13p. Cymbal player and tug 'o' war		40	40
270	24p. Trumpet player and bible class		85	85
271	26p. Drummer and cadets marching		90	90
272	29p. Boys' Brigade band		95	95
268/72		*Set of 5*	3·00	3·00

(Des C. Abbott. Photo Courvoisier)

1983 (14 Mar). *Europa. Development of St. Peter Port Harbour.* T **83** *and similar horiz designs. Multicoloured. Granite paper.* P 11½.
273	13p. Type **83**		35	35
	a. Horiz pair. Nos. 273/4		70	70
274	13p. St. Peter Port Harbour, 1983		35	35
275	20p. St. Peter Port, 1680		75	75
	a. Horiz pair. Nos. 275/6		1·50	1·50
276	20p. Artist's impression of future development scheme		75	75
273/6		*Set of 4*	2·00	2·00

The two designs of each value were issued together, *se-tenant*, in horizontal pairs throughout the sheets.

84 "View at Guernsey" (Renoir)

(Des and photo Courvoisier)

1983 (6 Sept). *Centenary of Renoir's Visit to Guernsey.* T **84** *and similar multicoloured designs, showing paintings. Granite paper.* P 11 × 11½ (13p.) or 11½ (others).
277	9p. Type **84**		25	25
278	13p. "Children on the Seashore" (25 × 39 *mm*)		45	45
279	26p. "Marine, Guernesey"		80	80
280	28p. "La Baie du Moulin Huet à travers les Arbres"		1·10	1·10
281	31p. "Brouillard à Guernesey"		1·25	1·25
277/81		*Set of 5*	3·50	3·50

85 Launching *Star of the West*, 1869, and Capt. J. Lenfestey

(Des R. Granger Barrett. Litho Questa)

1983 (15 Nov). *Guernsey Shipping* (*1st series*). *"Star of the West"* (*brigantine*). T **85** *and similar horiz designs. Multicoloured.* P 14.
282	9p. Type **85**		25	25
283	13p. Leaving St. Peter Port		40	40
284	26p. Off Rio Grande Bar		80	80
285	28p. Off St. Lucia		1·10	1·10
286	31p. Map of 1879–80 voyage		1·25	1·25
282/6		*Set of 5*	3·50	3·50

See also Nos. 415/19.

86 Dame of Sark as Young Woman

(Des Jennifer Toombs. Litho Questa)

1984 (7 Feb). *Birth Centenary of Sibyl Hathaway, Dame of Sark.* T **86** *and similar horiz designs. Multicoloured.* P 14½.
287	9p. Type **86**		25	25
288	13p. German occupation, 1940–45		40	45
289	26p. Royal Visit, 1957		90	90
290	28p. Chief Pleas		95	95
291	31p. The Dame of Sark rose		1·10	1·10
287/91		*Set of 5*	3·25	3·25

87 C.E.P.T. 25th Anniversary Logo

(Des J. Larrivière and C. Abbott. Litho Questa)

1984 (10 Apr). *Europa.* P 15 × 14½.
292	**87**	13p. cobalt, dull ultramarine and black	65	65
293		20½p. emerald, deep dull green and black	85	85

88 The Royal Court and St. George's Flag   **89** St. Apolline Chapel

(Des C. Abbott. Litho Questa)

1984 (10 Apr). *Links with the Commonwealth.* T **88** *and similar horiz design.* Multicoloured. P 14 × 14½.
294	9p. Type **88**		40	40
295	31p. Castle Cornet and Union flag		1·10	1·10

(Des C. Abbott. Litho Questa)

1984 (18 Sept)–**91**. *Views.* T **89** *and similar multicoloured designs.* Chalk-surfaced paper. P 14½.
296	1p. Little Chapel (23.7.85)	20	10
297	2p. Fort Grey (*horiz*) (23.7.85)	20	10
	a. Booklet pane. Nos. 297×2, 299×4, 300×2 and 305×2 (2.12.85)	2·75	
298	3p. Type **89**	20	10
	a. Booklet pane. Nos. 298, 299×2, 306×4 and 309×3 (30.3.87)	4·00	
299	4p. Petit Port (*horiz*)	20	10
	a. Booklet pane. Nos. 299×2, 304×3 and 307×5	3·50	
	b. Booklet pane. Nos. 299, 304 and 307, each × 5	4·50	
	c. Booklet pane. Nos. 299×4, 306b×3 and 309c×3 (28.3.88)	3·75	
	d. Booklet pane. Nos. 299, 301, 306b×3 and 309d×3 (28.2.89)	4·25	
300	5p. Little Russel (23.7.85)	20	10
	a. Booklet pane. Nos. 300×2, 301×2, 309×3 and 310b×3 (2.4.91)	4·00	
301	6p. The Harbour, Herm (*horiz*) (23.7.85)	20	15
	a. Booklet pane. Nos. 301×4, 308×4 and 310×2 (27.12.89)	4·25	
	b. Uncoated paper		
302	7p. Saints (*horiz*) (23.7.85)	20	20
303	8p. St. Saviour (23.7.85)	20	20
304	9p. New jetty (inscr "Cambridge Berth") (*horiz*)	20	25
	a. Booklet pane. Nos. 304×4 and 308×6 (19.3.85)	4·25	
	b. Booklet pane. Nos. 304×2 and 308×8 (19.3.85)	4·25	
305	10p. Belvoir, Herm (*horiz*)	25	25
	a. Booklet pane. Nos. 305 and 308, each × 5 (1.4.86)	4·25	
306	11p. La Seigneurie, Sark (*horiz*) (23.7.85)	25	25
	a. Booklet pane. Nos. 306 and 309, each × 5 (30.3.87)	4·25	
306b	12p. Petit Bot (28.3.88)	40	30
	ba. Booklet pane. Nos. 306b and 309c, each × 5	4·25	
	bb. Booklet pane. Nos. 306b and 309d, each × 4 (28.2.89)	4·75	
307	13p. St. Saviours reservoir (*horiz*)	30	30
308	14p. St. Peter Port	30	35
	a. Booklet pane. Nos. 308 and 310, each × 5 (27.12.89)	4·75	
	b. Uncoated paper		
309	15p. Havelet (23.7.85)	30	35
	a. Booklet pane. Nos. 309 and 310b, each × 5 (2.4.91)	5·75	
	b. Imperf at sides and foot (horiz pair)		
309c	16p. Hostel of St. John (*horiz*) (28.3.88)	30	35
309d	18p. Le Variouf (28.2.89)	35	40
310	20p. La Coupee, Sark (*horiz*)	50	45
	a. Uncoated paper		
310b	21p. King's Mills (*horiz*) (2.4.91)	50	45
310c	26p. Town Church (2.4.91)	70	55
	ca. Imperf at sides and foot (horiz pair)	£900	
311	30p. Grandes Rocques (*horiz*) (23.7.85)	60	65
312	40p. Torteval church	80	85
313	50p. Bordeaux (*horiz*)	1·00	1·10
314	£1 Albecq (*horiz*)	2·00	2·10
315	£2 L'Ancresse (*horiz*) (23.7.85)	4·25	4·25
296/315	Set of 25	12·50	12·50

Booklet panes Nos. 297a, 298a, 299a/c, 304a/b, 305a, 306a and 306ba have margins all round and were issued, folded and loose, within the booklet covers.

Booklet panes Nos. 299d, 300a, 301a, 306bb, 308a and 309a have the outer edges imperforate on three sides and were also issued loose within the booklet covers.

The uncoated errors, Nos. 301b, 308b and 310a, come from examples of booklet panes Nos. 301a and 308a.

For 11p., 12p., 15p. and 16p. stamps in a smaller size see Nos. 398/9a.

90 "A Partridge in a Pear Tree'   **91** Sir John Doyle and Coat of Arms

(Des R. Downer. Litho Questa)

1984 (20 Nov). *Christmas. "The Twelve Days of Christmas".* T **90** *and similar vert designs.* Multicoloured. P 14½.
316	5p. Type **90**	20	20
	a. Sheetlet of 12. Nos. 316/27	2·50	
317	5p. "Two turtle doves"	20	20
318	5p. "Three French hens"	20	20
319	5p. "Four colly birds"	20	20
320	5p. "Five gold rings"	20	20
321	5p. "Six geese a-laying"	20	20
322	5p. "Seven swans a-swimming"	20	20
323	5p. "Eight maids a-milking"	20	20
324	5p. "Nine drummers drumming"	20	20
325	5p. "Ten pipers piping"	20	20
326	5p. "Eleven ladies dancing"	20	20
327	5p. "Twelve lords a-leaping"	20	20
316/27	Set of 12	2·50	2·50

Nos. 316/27 were printed, *se-tenant*, in sheetlets of 12.

(Des E. Stemp. Photo Courvoisier)

1984 (20 Nov). *150th Death Anniv of Lieut-General Sir John Doyle.* T **91** *and similar multicoloured designs.* Granite paper. P 11½.
328	13p. Type **91**	40	40
329	29p. Battle of Germantown, 1777 (*horiz*)	1·00	1·00
330	31p. Reclamation of Braye du Valle, 1806 (*horiz*)	1·25	1·25
331	34p. Mail for Alderney, 1812 (*horiz*)	1·25	1·25
328/31	Set of 4	3·50	3·00

92 Cuckoo Wrasse   **93** Dove

(Des P. Barrett. Photo Courvoisier)

1985 (22 Jan). *Fishes.* T **92** *and similar horiz designs.* Multicoloured. Granite paper. P 11½.
332	9p. Type **92**	40	40
333	13p. Red Gurnard	60	60
334	29p. Red Mullet	1·50	1·10
335	31p. Mackerel	1·50	1·10
336	34p. Oceanic Sunfish	1·60	1·25
332/6	Set of 5	5·00	4·00

(Des C. Abbott. Litho Questa)

1985 (9 May). *40th Anniv of Peace in Europe.* P 14 × 14½.
337	**93**	22p. multicoloured	1·10	1·10

94 I.Y.Y. Emblem and Young People of Different Races   **95** Stave of Music enclosing Flags

(Des Suzanne Brehaut (9p.), Mary Harrison (31p.). Litho Questa)

1985 (14 May). *International Youth Year.* T **94** *and similar square design.* Multicoloured. P 14.
338	9p. Type **94**	40	40
339	31p. Girl Guides cooking over campfire	1·00	1·00

(Des Fiona Sloan (14p.), Katie Lillington (22p.). Litho Questa)

1985 (14 May). *Europa. European Music Year.* T **95** *and similar horiz design.* Multicoloured. P 14 × 14½.
340	14p. Type **95**	45	40
341	22p. Stave of music and musical instruments	95	1·00

96 Guide Leader, Girl Guide and Brownie   **97** Santa Claus

(Des Karon Mahy. Litho Questa)

1985 (14 May). *75th Anniv of Girl Guide Movement.* P 14.
342	**96**	34p. multicoloured	1·50	1·50

(Des C. Abbott. Photo Courvoisier)

1985 (19 Nov). *Christmas. Gift-bearers.* T **97** *and similar vert designs.* Multicoloured. Granite paper. P 12½.
343	5p. Type **97**	40	35
	a. Sheetlet of 12. Nos. 343/54	4·25	
344	5p. Lussibruden (Sweden)	40	35
345	5p. King Balthazar	40	35
346	5p. Saint Nicholas (Netherlands)	40	35
347	5p. La Befana (Italy)	40	35
348	5p. Julenisse (Denmark)	40	35
349	5p. Christkind (Germany)	40	35
350	5p. King Wenceslas (Czechoslovakia)	40	35
351	5p. Shepherd of Les Baux (France)	40	35
352	5p. King Caspar	40	35
353	5p. Baboushka (Russia)	40	35
354	5p. King Melchior	40	35
343/54	Set of 12	4·25	4·00

Nos. 343/54 were printed, *se-tenant*, in sheetlets of 12.

98 "Vraicing"

(Des and photo Harrison)

1985 (19 Nov). *Paintings by Paul Jacob Naftel.* T **98** *and similar horiz designs.* Multicoloured. P 15 × 14.
355	9p. Type **98**	30	30
356	14p. "Castle Cornet"	40	40
357	22p. "Rocquaine Bay"	90	90
358	31p. "Little Russel"	1·40	1·40
359	34p. "Seaweedgatherers"	1·50	1·50
355/9	Set of 5	4·00	4·00

99 Squadron off Nargue Island, 1809   **100** Profile of Queen Elizabeth II (after R. Maklouf)

(Des T. Thompson. Photo Courvoisier)

1986 (4 Feb). *150th Death Anniv of Admiral Lord De Saumarez.* T **99** *and similar horiz designs.* Multicoloured. Granite paper. P 11½.
360	9p. Type **99**	40	40
361	14p. Battle of the Nile, 1798	50	50
362	29p. Battle of St. Vincent, 1797	1·25	1·25
363	31p. H.M.S. *Crescent* off Cherbourg, 1793	1·40	1·40
364	34p. Battle of the Saints, 1782	1·40	1·40
360/4	Set of 5	4·50	4·00

(Des C. Abbott. Litho Questa)

1986 (21 Apr). *60th Birthday of Queen Elizabeth II.* P 14.
365	**100**	60p. multicoloured	2·50	2·50

101 Northern Gannet and Nylon Net ("Operation Gannet")   **102** Prince Andrew and Miss Sarah Ferguson

(Des P. Newcombe. Photo Courvoisier)

1986 (22 May). *Europa. Nature and Environmental Protection.* T **101** *and similar vert designs.* Multicoloured. Granite paper. P 11½.
366	10p. Type **101**	45	45
367	14p. Loose-flowered Orchid	75	75
368	22p. Guernsey Elm	1·00	1·00
366/8	Set of 3	2·00	2·00

(Des C. Abbott. Litho Questa)

1986 (23 July). *Royal Wedding.* T **102** *and similar multicoloured design.* P 14 (14p.) or 13½ × 14 (34p.).
369	14p. Type **102**	75	75
370	34p. Prince Andrew and Miss Sarah Ferguson (*different*) (47 × 30 mm)	1·50	1·50

103 Bowls   **104 Guernsey Museum and Art Gallery, Candie Gardens**

(Des R. Goldsmith. Litho Questa)

1986 (24 July). *Sport in Guernsey. T 103 and similar multicoloured designs. P 14½.*

371	10p.	Type **103**		30	30
372	14p.	Cricket		50	50
373	22p.	Squash		75	75
374	29p.	Hockey		1·25	1·25
375	31p.	Swimming (*horiz*)		1·40	1·40
376	34p.	Rifle-shooting (*horiz*)		1·50	1·50
371/6			*Set of 6*	5·00	5·00

(Des Sir Hugh Casson. Litho Questa)

1986 (18 Nov). *Centenary of Guernsey Museums. T 104 and similar horiz designs. Multicoloured. P 14½.*

377	14p.	Type **104**		60	60
378	29p.	Fort Grey Maritime Museum		1·10	1·10
379	31p.	Castle Cornet		1·10	1·10
380	34p.	National Trust of Guernsey Folk Museum		1·40	1·40
377/80			*Set of 4*	3·75	3·75

105 "While Shepherds Watched their Flocks by Night"

(Des Wendy Bramall. Photo Courvoisier)

1986 (18 Nov). *Christmas. Carols. T 105 and similar vert designs. Multicoloured. Granite paper. P 12½.*

381	6p.	Type **105**		40	40
	a.	Sheetlet of 12. Nos. 381/92		4·00	
382	6p.	"In The Bleak Mid-Winter"		40	40
383	6p.	"O Little Town of Bethlehem"		40	40
384	6p.	"The Holly and the Ivy"		40	40
385	6p.	"O Little Christmas Tree"		40	40
386	6p.	"Away in a Manger"		40	40
387	6p.	"Good King Wenceslas"		40	40
388	6p.	"We Three Kings of Orient Are"		40	40
389	6p.	"Hark the Herald Angels Sing"		40	40
390	6p.	"I Saw Three Ships"		40	40
391	6p.	"Little Donkey"		40	40
392	6p.	"Jingle Bells"		40	40
381/92			*Set of 12*	4·00	4·00

Nos. 381/92 were printed, *se-tenant*, in sheetlets of 12.

106 Duke of Richmond and Portion of Map

(Des J. Cooter. Litho Questa)

1987 (10 Feb). *Bicentenary of Duke of Richmond's Survey of Guernsey. Sheet 134 × 103 mm containing T 106 and similar horiz designs showing sections of map. Multicoloured. P 14½ × 14.*

MS393	14p. Type **106**; 29p. North-east; 31p. South-west; 34p. South-east		4·00	4·00

The stamps within No. MS393 show a composite design of the Duke of Richmond's map of Guernsey.

107 Post Office Headquarters   **108 Sir Edmund Andros and La Plaiderie, Guernsey**

(Des R. Reed. Litho Cartor)

1987 (5 May). *Europa. Modern Architecture. T 107 and similar vert designs. Multicoloured. P 13×13½.*

394	15p.	Type **107**		55	55
	a.	Horiz pair. Nos. 394/5		1·10	1·10
395	15p.	Architect's elevation of Post Office Headquarters		55	55
396	22p.	Guernsey Grammar School		80	80
	a.	Horiz pair. Nos. 396/7		1·75	1·75
397	22p.	Architect's elevation of Grammar School		80	80
394/7			*Set of 4*	2·50	2·50

Nos. 394/5 and 396/7 were each printed together, *se-tenant*, in horizontal pairs throughout the sheets.

(Photo Harrison)

1987 (15 May)–88. *Coil Stamps. Designs as Nos. 306, 306b, 309 and 309c, but smaller. P 14×14½ (11p., 16p.) or 14½×14 (12p., 15p.).*

398	11p.	La Seigneurie, Sark (22 × 18 mm)		30	40
398a	12p.	Petit Bot (18 × 22 mm) (28.3.88)		25	25
399	15p.	Havelet (18 × 22 mm)		45	55
399a	16p.	Hospital of St. John (22 × 18 mm) (28.3.88)		35	35
398/9a			*Set of 4*	1·40	1·25

(Des B. Sanders. Photo Courvoisier)

1987 (7 July). *350th Birth Anniv of Sir Edmund Andros (colonial administrator). T 108 and similar horiz designs, each showing portrait. Multicoloured. Granite paper. P 12.*

400	15p.	Type **108**		45	45
401	29p.	Governor's Palace, Virginia		1·00	1·00
402	31p.	Governor Andros in Boston		1·10	1·10
403	34p.	Map of New Amsterdam (New York), 1661		1·40	1·40
400/3			*Set of 4*	3·50	3·50

109 The Jester's Warning to Young William   **110 John Wesley preaching on the Quay, Alderney**

(Des P. le Vasseur. Litho Cartor)

1987 (9 Sept). *900th Death Anniv of William the Conqueror. T 109 and similar vert designs. Multicoloured. P 13½×14.*

404	11p.	Type **109**		45	35
405	15p.	Hastings battlefield		50	50
	a.	Horiz pair. Nos. 405/6		1·00	1·00
406	15p.	Norman soldier with pennant		50	50
407	22p.	William the Conqueror		80	75
	a.	Horiz pair. Nos. 407/8		1·60	1·50
408	22p.	Queen Matilda and Abbaye aux Dames, Caen		80	80
409	34p.	William's Coronation regalia and Halley's Comet		1·25	1·25
404/9			*Set of 6*	4·00	3·75

Nos. 405/6 and 407/8 were each printed together, *se-tenant*, in horizontal pairs throughout the sheets.

(Des R. Geary. Litho Questa)

1987 (17 Nov). *Bicentenary of John Wesley's Visit to Guernsey. T 110 and similar horiz designs. Multicoloured. P 14½.*

410	7p.	Type **110**		30	30
411	15p.	Wesley preaching at Mon Plaisir, St. Peter Port		45	45
412	29p.	Preaching at Assembly Rooms		1·25	1·25
413	31p.	Wesley and La Ville Baudu (early Methodist meeting place)		1·25	1·25
414	34p.	Wesley and first Methodist Chapel, St. Peter Port		1·25	1·25
410/14			*Set of 5*	4·00	4·00

111 *Golden Spur* off St. Sampson Harbour

(Des R. Granger Barrett. Litho B.D.T.)

1988 (9 Feb). *Guernsey Shipping (2nd series). "Golden Spur" (full-rigged ship). T 111 and similar horiz designs. Multicoloured. P 13½.*

415	11p.	Type **111**		35	35
416	15p.	*Golden Spur* entering Hong Kong harbour		50	50
417	29p.	Anchored off Macao		1·25	1·25
418	31p.	In China Tea Race		1·25	1·25
419	34p.	*Golden Spur* and map showing voyage of 1872–74		1·25	1·25
415/19			*Set of 5*	4·00	4·00

---

112 Rowing Boat and Bedford "Rascal" Mail Van   **113 Frederick Corbin Lukis and Lukis House, St. Peter Port**

(Des C. Abbott. Litho Questa)

1988 (10 May). *Europa. Transport and Communications. T 112 and similar horiz designs. Multicoloured. P 14½.*

420	16p.	Type **112**		60	60
	a.	Horiz pair. Nos. 420/1		1·25	1·25
421	16p.	Rowing boat and Vickers Viscount 800 mail plane		60	60
422	22p.	Postman on bicycle and horse-drawn carriages, Sark		95	95
	a.	Horiz pair. Nos. 422/3		1·90	1·90
423	22p.	Postmen on bicycles and carriage		95	95
420/3			*Set of 4*	2·75	2·75

Nos. 420/1 and 422/3 were each printed together, *se-tenant*, in horizontal pairs throughout the sheets, the two stamps of each value forming a composite design.

(Des Wendy Bramall. Photo Courvoisier)

1988 (12 July). *Birth Bicentenary of Frederick Corbin Lukis (archaeologist). T 113 and similar horiz designs. Multicoloured. Granite paper. P 12½.*

424	12p.	Type **113**		40	40
425	16p.	Natural history books and reconstructed pot		50	50
426	29p.	Lukis directing excavation of Le Creux ès Faies and prehistoric beaker		1·10	1·10
427	31p.	Lukis House Observatory and garden		1·25	1·25
428	34p.	Prehistoric artifacts		1·25	1·25
424/8			*Set of 5*	4·00	4·00

114 *Cougar, Rocky* and *Annabella* (powerboats) and Westland Wessex Rescue Helicopter off Jethou   **115 Joshua Gosselin and Herbarium**

(Des and photo Courvoisier)

1988 (6 Sept). *World Offshore Powerboat Championships. T 114 and similar multicoloured designs. Granite paper. P 12.*

429	16p.	Type **114**		60	60
430	30p.	*Paul Pilot* (powerboat) in Gouliot Passage		1·10	1·10
431	32p.	Start of race at St. Peter Port (*vert*)		1·25	1·25
432	35p.	Admiralty chart showing course (*vert*)		1·50	1·50
429/32			*Set of 4*	4·00	4·00

(Des M. Oxenham. Litho Cartor)

1988 (15 Nov). *Bicentenary of Joshua Gosselin's Flora Sarniensis. T 115 and similar vert designs. Multicoloured. P 13½×14.*

433	12p.	Type **115**		40	40
434	16p.	Hares-tail Grass		55	55
	a.	Horiz pair. Nos. 434/5		1·10	1·10
435	16p.	Dried Hares-tail Grass		55	55
436	23p.	Variegated Catchfly		80	80
	a.	Horiz pair. Nos. 436/7		1·60	1·60
437	23p.	Dried Variegated Catchfly		80	80
438	35p.	Rock Sea Lavender		1·40	1·40
433/8			*Set of 6*	4·00	4·00

Nos. 434/5 and 436/7 were each printed together, *se-tenant*, in horizontal pairs throughout the sheets.

116 Coutances Cathedral, France   **117 Lé Cat (Tip Cat)**

(Des R. Downer. Litho Questa)

1988 (15 Nov). *Christmas. Ecclesiastical Links. T 116 and similar vert designs. Multicoloured. P 14½.*

439	8p.	Type **116**		35	35
	a.	Sheetlet of 12. Nos. 439/50		3·75	
440	8p.	Interior of Notre Dame du Rosaire Church, Guernsey		35	35
441	8p.	Stained glass, St. Sampson's Church, Guernsey		35	35
442	8p.	Dol-de-Bretagne Cathedral, France		35	35
443	8p.	Bishop's throne, Town Church, Guernsey		35	35
444	8p.	Winchester Cathedral		35	35
445	8p.	St. John's Cathedral, Portsmouth		35	35
446	8p.	High altar, St. Joseph's Church, Guernsey		35	35

447	8p.	Mont Saint-Michel, France	..	35	35
448	8p.	Chancel, Vale Church, Guernsey	..	35	35
449	8p.	Lychgate, Forest Church, Guernsey	..	35	35
450	8p.	Marmoutier Abbey, France	..	35	35
439/50			Set of 12	3·75	3·75

Nos. 439/50 were printed, *se-tenant*, in sheetlets of 12.

(Des P. le Vasseur. Litho Cartor)

1989 (28 Feb). *Europa. Children's Toys and Games. T* **117** *and similar horiz designs. Multicoloured. P* 13½.

451	12p.	Type **117**	..	40	40
452	16p.	Girl with Cobo Alice doll	..	60	60
453	23p.	Lé Colimachaôn (hopscotch)	..	1·25	1·25
451/3			Set of 3	2·00	2·00

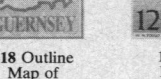

118 Outline Map of Guernsey

119 Guernsey Airways De Havilland D.H.86 Dragon Express and Mail Van

(Photo Harrison)

1989 (3 Apr–27 Dec). *Coil Stamps. No value expressed. P* 14½×14.

454	118	(–) ultramarine (27.12.89)	..	40	40
455		(–) emerald	..	60	60

No. 454 is inscribed "MINIMUM BAILIWICK POSTAGE PAID" and No. 455 "MINIMUM FIRST CLASS POSTAGE TO UK PAID". They were initially sold at 14p. and 18p., but this was changed in line with postage rate rises.

In these coils every fifth stamp is numbered on the reverse.

(Des N. Foggo. Litho B.D.T.)

1989 (5 May). *50th Anniv of Guernsey Airport (Nos. 456, 458, and 460) and 201 Squadron's Affiliation with Guernsey (Nos. 457, 459 and 461). T* **119** *and similar horiz designs. Multicoloured. P* 13½.

456	12p.	Type **119**	..	50	40
		a. Booklet pane. No. 456×6	..	2·00	
457	12p.	Supermarine Southampton II flying boat at mooring		50	40
458	18p.	B.E.A. De Havilland D.H.89 Dragon Rapide		75	75
		a. Booklet pane. No. 458×6	..	3·00	
459	18p.	Short S.25 Sunderland Mk V flying boat taking off		75	75
460	35p.	Air U.K. British Aerospace BAe 146	..	1·25	1·25
		a. Booklet pane. No. 460×6	..	6·00	
461	35p.	Avro Shackleton M.R.3	..	1·25	1·25
456/61			Set of 6	4·50	4·50

Each booklet pane has margins all round with text printed at the foot.

120 "Queen Elizabeth II" (June Mendoza)

121 *Ibex* at G.W.R. Terminal, St. Peter Port

(Des A. Theobald. Litho B.D.T.)

1989 (23 May). *Royal Visit. P* 15 × 14.

462	120	30p. multicoloured	..	1·25	1·25

(Des C. Jaques. Litho B.D.T.)

1989 (5 Sept). *Centenary of Great Western Railway Steamer Service to Channel Islands. T* **121** *and similar horiz designs. Multicoloured. P* 13½.

463	12p.	Type **121**	..	30	30
464	18p.	*Great Western* (paddle-steamer) in Little Russel		65	65
465	29p.	*St. Julien* passing Casquets Light	..	90	90
466	34p.	*Roebuck* off Portland	..	1·25	1·25
467	37p.	*Antelope* and boat train on Weymouth Quay		1·40	1·40
463/7			Set of 5	4·00	4·00
MS468		115×117 mm. Nos. 463/7	..	4·00	4·00

122 Two-toed Sloth

123 Star

(Des Anne Farncombe. Litho Cartor)

1989 (17 Nov). *10th Anniv of Guernsey Zoological Trust. Animals of the Rainforest. T* **122** *and similar vert designs. Multicoloured. P* 13½×14.

469	18p.	Type **122**	..	1·10	90
		a. Horiz strip of 5. Nos. 469/73	..	5·00	
470	29p.	Capuchin Monkey	..	1·10	90
471	32p.	White-lipped Tamarin	..	1·10	90
472	34p.	Common Squirrel-Monkey	..	1·10	90
473	37p.	Common Gibbon	..	1·10	90
469/73			Set of 5	5·00	4·00

Nos. 469/73 were printed together, *se-tenant*, in horizontal strips of five throughout the sheet.

(Des Wendy Bramall. Litho B.D.T.)

1989 (17 Nov). *Christmas. Christmas Tree Decorations. T* **123** *and similar square designs. Multicoloured. P* 13.

474	10p.	Type **123**	..	35	35
		a. Sheetlet. Nos. 474/85	..	3·75	
475	10p.	Fairy	..	35	35
476	10p.	Candles	..	35	35
477	10p.	Bird	..	35	35
478	10p.	Present	..	35	35
479	10p.	Carol-singer	..	35	35
480	10p.	Christmas cracker	..	35	35
481	10p.	Bauble	..	35	35
482	10p.	Christmas stocking	..	35	35
483	10p.	Bell	..	35	35
484	10p.	Fawn	..	35	35
485	10p.	Church	..	35	35
474/85			Set of 12	3·75	3·75

Nos. 474/85 were printed, *se-tenant*, in sheetlets of 12.

124 Sark Post Office, *c.* 1890

(Des C. Abbott. Litho Enschedé)

1990 (27 Feb). *Europa. Post Office Buildings. T* **124** *and similar horiz designs. P* 13½×14.

486	20p.	blackish brown, sepia and pale cinnamon		60	60
487	20p.	multicoloured		60	60
488	24p.	blackish brown, sepia and pale cinnamon		75	75
489	24p.	multicoloured		75	75
486/9			Set of 4	2·50	2·50

Designs:—No. 487, Sark Post Office, 1990; 488, Arcade Post Office counter, St. Peter Port, *c.* 1840; 489, Arcade Post Office counter, St. Peter Port, 1990.

125 Penny Black and Mail Steamer off St. Peter Port, 1840

(Des Jennifer Toombs. Litho Questa)

1990 (3 May). *150th Anniv of the Penny Black. T* **125** *and similar horiz designs. Multicoloured. P* 14.

490	14p.	Type **125**	..	45	45
491	20p.	Penny Red, 1841, and pillar box of 1853		60	60
492	32p.	Bisected 2d., 1940, and German Army band		1·00	90
493	34p.	Regional 3d., 1958, and Guernsey emblems		1·10	95
494	37p.	Independent postal administration 1½d., 1969, and queue outside Main Post Office		1·10	1·00
490/4			Set of 5	3·75	3·50
MS495		151×116 mm. Nos. 490/4		4·00	3·75

No. MS495 also commemorates "Stamp World London 90" International Stamp Exhibition. It was reissued on 24 August 1990 overprinted for "NEW ZEALAND 1980" and sold at this international stamp exhibition in Auckland.

126 Lt. Philip Saumarez writing Log Book

(Des R. Granger Barrett. Litho Enschedé)

1990 (26 July). *250th Anniv of Anson's Circumnavigation. T* **126** *and similar horiz designs. Multicoloured. P* 13½×14.

496	14p.	Type **126**	..	45	45
497	20p.	Anson's squadron leaving Portsmouth, 1740		60	60
498	29p.	Ships at St. Catherine's Island, Brazil		1·00	90
499	34p.	H.M.S. *Tryal* (sloop) dismasted, Cape Horn, 1741		1·10	95
500	37p.	Crew of H.M.S. *Centurion* on Juan Fernandez		1·10	1·00
496/500			Set of 5	3·75	3·50

127 Grey Seal and Pup

128 Blue Tit and Great Tit

(Des Jennifer Toombs. Litho Questa)

1990 (16 Oct). *Marine Life. T* **127** *and similar horiz designs. Multicoloured. P* 14½.

501	20p	Type **127**	..	60	60
502	26p	Bottle-nosed Dolphin	..	1·10	1·10
503	31p	Basking Shark	..	1·25	1·25
504	37p	Common Porpoise	..	1·50	1·50
501/4			Set of 4	4·00	4·00

(Des Wendy Bramall. Litho B.D.T.)

1990 (16 Oct). *Christmas. Winter Birds. T* **128** *and similar square designs. Multicoloured. P* 13.

505	10p	Type **128**	..	40	40
		a. Sheetlet of 12. Nos. 505/16	..	4·50	
506	10p	Snow Bunting	..	40	40
507	10p	Common Kestrel	..	40	40
508	10p	Common Starling	..	40	40
509	10p	Greenfinch	..	40	40
510	10p	European Robin	..	40	40
511	10p	Winter Wren	..	40	40
512	10p	Barn Owl	..	40	40
513	10p	Mistle Thrush	..	40	40
514	10p	Grey Heron	..	40	40
515	10p	Chaffinch	..	40	40
516	10p	Common Kingfisher	..	40	40
505/16			Set of 12	4·50	4·50

Nos. 505/16 were printed, *se-tenant*, in sheetlets of 12.

129 Air Raid and 1941 ½d. Stamp

(Des C. Abbott. Litho B.D.T.)

1991 (18 Feb). *50th Anniv of First Guernsey Stamps. T* **129** *and similar square designs. Multicoloured. P* 13½.

517	37p	Type **129**	..	1·25	1·25
		a. Booklet pane. Nos. 517/19	..	4·00	
518	53p	1941 1d. stamp	..	1·60	1·60
519	57p	1944 2½d. stamp	..	1·60	1·60
517/19			Set of 3	4·00	4·00

Booklet pane No. 517a exists in three versions which differ in the order of the stamps from left to right and in the information printed on the pane margins.

130 Visit of Queen Victoria to Guernsey, and Discovery of Neptune, 1846

(Des Jennifer Toombs. Litho Enschedé)

1991 (30 Apr). *Europa. Europe in Space. T* **130** *and similar horiz designs. Multicoloured. P* 13½×14.

520	21p.	Type **130**	..	65	65
521	21p.	Visit of Queen Elizabeth II and Prince Philip to Sark, and "Sputnik" (first artificial satellite), 1957		65	65
522	26p.	Maiden voyage of *Sarnia* (ferry), and "Vostok 1" (first manned space flight), 1961		90	75
523	26p.	Cancelling Guernsey stamps, and first manned landing on Moon, 1969		90	75
520/3			Set of 4	2·75	2·50

131 Children in Guernsey Sailing Trust "GP14" Dinghy

132 Pair of Oystercatchers

(Des C. Abbott. Litho B.D.T.)

1991 (2 July). *Centenary of Guernsey Yacht Club. T* **131** *and similar vert designs. Multicoloured. P* 14.

524	15p.	Type **131**	50	50
525	21p.	Guernsey Regatta	80	80
526	26p.	Lombard Channel Islands Challenge race	90	90
527	31p.	Rolex Swan Regatta	1·00	1·00
528	37p.	Old Gaffers' Association gaff-rigged yacht	1·25	1·25
524/8		*Set of* 5	4·00	4·00

MS529 163×75 mm. As Nos. 524/8, but "GUERNSEY" and face values in yellow 4·00 4·00

(Des Wendy Bramall. Litho Questa)

1991 (15 Oct). *Nature Conservation. L'Eree Shingle Bank Reserve. T* **132** *and similar horiz designs. Multicoloured. P* 14½.

530	15p.	Type **132**	60	40
	a.	Horiz strip of 5. Nos 530/4	3·00	
531	15p.	Three Turnstones	60	40
532	15p.	Dunlins and Turnstones	60	40
533	15p.	Curlew and Turnstones	60	40
534	15p.	Ringed Plover with chicks	60	40
535	21p.	Gull, Sea Campion and Sea Radish	60	50
	a.	Horiz strip of 5. Nos 535/9	3·00	
536	21p.	Yellow Horned Poppy	60	50
537	21p.	Pair of Stonechats, Hare's Foot Clover and Fennel	60	50
538	21p.	Hare's Foot Clover, Fennel and Slender Oat	60	50
539	21p.	Sea Kale on shore	60	50
530/9		*Set of* 10	5·50	4·00

Nos. 530/4 and 535/9 were each printed together, *se-tenant*, in horizontal strips of 5, throughout sheets of 20, with the backgrounds forming composite designs which continue onto the sheet margins.

133 "Rudolph the Red-nosed Reindeer" (Melanie Sharpe)

134 Queen Elizabeth II in 1952

(Litho B.D.T.)

1991 (15 Oct). *Christmas. Children's Paintings. T* **133** *and similar square designs. Multicoloured. P* 13½×13.

540	12p.	Type **133**	35	35
	a.	Sheetlet of 12. Nos. 540/51	4·00	
541	12p.	"Christmas Pudding" (James Quinn)	35	35
542	12p.	"Snowman" (Lisa Guille)	35	35
543	12p.	"Snowman in Top Hat" (Jessica Ede-Golightly)	35	35
544	12p.	"Robins and Christmas Tree" (Sharon Le Page)	35	35
545	12p.	"Shepherds and Angels" (Anna Coquelin)	35	35
546	12p.	"Nativity" (Claudine Lihou)	35	35
547	12p.	"Three Wise Men" (Jonathan Le Noury)	35	35
548	12p.	"Star of Bethlehem and Angels" (Marcia Mahy)	35	35
549	12p.	"Christmas Tree" (Laurel Garfield)	35	35
550	12p.	"Santa Claus" (Rebecca Driscoll)	35	35
551	12p.	"Snowman and Star" (Ian Lowe)	35	35
540/51		*Set of* 12	4·00	4·00

Nos. 540/51 were printed, *se-tenant*, in sheetlets of 12.

(Des C. Abbott. Litho Questa)

1992 (6 Feb). *40th Anniv of Accession. T* **134** *and similar vert designs. Multicoloured. P* 14.

552	23p.	Type **134**	70	70
553	28p.	Queen Elizabeth in 1977	75	75
554	33p.	Queen Elizabeth in 1986	85	85
555	39p.	Queen Elizabeth in 1991	1·10	1·10
552/5		*Set of* 4	3·00	3·00

135 Christopher Columbus

(Des R. Ollington. Litho Walsall)

1992 (6 Feb). *Europa. 500th Anniv of Discovery of America by Columbus. T* **135** *and similar horiz designs. Multicoloured. P* 13½×14.

556	23p.	Type **135**	60	60
557	23p.	Examples of Columbus's signature	60	60
558	28p.	Santa Maria	1·10	1·10
559	28p.	Map of first voyage	1·10	1·10
556/9		*Set of* 4	3·00	3·00

MS560 157×77 mm. Nos. 556/9 3·00 3·00

No. MS560 was reissued on 22 May 1992 overprinted for "WORLD COLUMBIAN STAMP EXPO 92" and sold at this international stamp exhibition in Chicago.

136 Guernsey Calves

137 Stock

(Des R. Goldsmith. Litho Questa)

1992 (22 May). *150th Anniv of Royal Guernsey Agricultural and Horticultural Society. Sheet, 93×71 mm, containing T* **136**. *P* 14.

MS561 **136** 75p. multicoloured 2·00 2·00

(Des R. Gorringe, Litho Walsall (Nos. 572a, 572ba, 574a, 575a, 576ba, 577a), Questa (No. 576a), Cartor (No. 582a) or B.D.T. (others))

1992 (22 May)–97. *Horticultural Exports. T* **137** *and similar multicoloured designs. P* 14 (£1, £2) *or* 13 *(others).*

562	1p.	Stephanotis floribunda (2.3.93)	10	10
563	2p.	Potted Hydrangea (2.3.93)	10	10
564	3p.	Type **137**	10	10
565	4p.	Anemones	10	10
566	5p.	Gladiolus	15	15
567	6p.	*Asparagus plumosus* and *Gypsophila paniculata* (2.3.93)	15	15
568	7p.	Guernsey Lily (2.3.93)	20	20
569	8p.	Enchantment Lily (2.3.93)	20	20
570	9p.	Clematis "Freckles" (2.3.93)	20	20
571	10p.	Alstroemeria	25	25
572	16p.	Standard Carnation (*horiz*)	35	35
	a.	Perf 14	50	50
	ac.	Booklet pane. Nos. 572a×5 and 574a×3	3·50	
	ad.	Booklet pane of 8 (2.3.93)	3·25	
572b	18p.	Standard Rose (2.1.97)	45	45
	ba.	Perf 14	45	45
	bb.	Booklet pane of 8	3·50	
573	20p.	Spray Rose	50	50
574	23p.	Mixed Freesia (*horiz*)	55	55
	a.	Perf 14	60	60
	ac.	Booklet pane of 8	4·25	
575	24p.	Standard Rose (*horiz*) (2.3.93)	60	60
	a.	Perf 14	60	60
	ab.	Booklet pane of 8	4·75	
576	25p.	Iris "Ideal" (*horiz*) (18.2.94)	60	60
	a.	Perf 14½×15	60	60
	ab.	Booklet pane of 4	2·50	
576b	26p.	Freesia "Pink Glow" (*horiz*) (2.1.97)	60	60
	ba.	Perf 14	60	60
	bb.	Booklet pane of 4	2·75	
577	28p.	Lisianthus (*horiz*) (2.3.93)	65	65
	a.	Perf 14	65	65
	ab.	Booklet pane of 4	2·75	
578	30p.	Spray Chrysanthemum (*horiz*) (2.3.93)	70	70
579	40p.	Spray Carnation	1·00	1·00
580	50p.	Single Freesia (*horiz*)	1·25	1·25
581	£1	Floral arrangement (35×26½ *mm*)	2·50	2·50
582	£2	Chelsea Flower Show exhibit (35×26½ mm) (2.3.93)	4·50	4·50
582a	£3	"Floral Fantasia" (exhibit) (35×28 *mm*) (24.1.96)	6·00	6·25
562/82a		*Set of* 24	19·50	20·00

Imprint dates: "1992", Nos. 564/6, 571/2ac, 573/4ac, 579/81; "1993", Nos. 562/3, 567/70, 572ad, 575/ab, 577/ab, 578, 582; "1994", Nos. 576/ab; "1996", No. 582a; "1997", Nos. 572b/ba, 576b/ba.

Nos. 572a, 572ba, 574a, 575a, 576a, 576ba and 577a were only issued in booklets with the upper and lower edges of the panes imperforate.

For No. 581 in miniature sheets see Nos. **MS**644 and **MS**681.

138 Building the Ship

(Des Studio Legrain. Litho Cartor)

1992 (18 Sept). *"Operation Asterix" (excavation of Roman ship). T* **138** *and similar horiz designs showing Asterix cartoon characters. Multicoloured. P* 13.

583	16p.	Type **138**	45	45
	a.	Booklet pane. Nos. 583/7 plus label with margins all round	3·50	
584	23p.	Loading the cargo	60	60
585	28p.	Ship at sea	80	80
586	33p.	Ship under attack	95	95
587	39p.	Crew swimming ashore	1·10	1·10
583/7		*Set of* 5	3·50	3·50

Booklet pane No. 583a exists with marginal inscriptions in English, French, Italian or German.

139 Tram No. 10 decorated for Battle of Flowers

140 Man in Party Hat

(Des A. Peck. Litho Enschedé)

1992 (17 Nov). *Guernsey Trams. T* **139** *and similar horiz designs. Multicoloured. P* 13½.

588	16p.	Type **139**	45	45
589	23p.	Tram No.10 passing Hougue a la Perre	60	60
590	28p.	Tram No. 1 at St. Sampsons	80	80
591	33p.	First steam tram at St. Peter Port, 1879	95	95
592	39p.	Last electric tram, 1934	1·10	1·10
588/92		*Set of* 5	3·50	3·50

(Des Wendy Bramall. Litho B.D.T.)

1992 (17 Nov). *Christmas. Seasonal Fayre. T* **140** *and similar square designs. Multicoloured. P* 13.

593	13p.	Type **140**	35	35
	a.	Sheetlet of 12. Nos. 593/604	4·00	
594	13p.	Girl and Christmas tree	35	35
595	13p.	Woman and balloons	35	35
596	13p.	Mince pies and champagne	35	35
597	13p.	Roast turkey	35	35
598	13p.	Christmas pudding	35	35
599	13p.	Christmas cake	35	35
600	13p.	Fancy cakes	35	35
601	13p.	Cheese	35	35
602	13p.	Nuts	35	35
603	13p.	Ham	35	35
604	13p.	Chocolate log	35	35
593/604		*Set of* 12	4·00	4·00

Nos. 593/604 were printed together, *se-tenant*, in sheetlets of 12 forming a composite design.

141 Rupert Bear, Bingo and Dog

142 Tapestry by Kelly Fletcher

(Des J. Harrold. Litho Walsall)

1993 (2 Feb). *Rupert Bear and Friends (cartoon characters created by Mary and Herbert Tourtel). T* **141** *and similar vert designs. Multicoloured. P* 13½×13.

605	24p.	Type **141**	1·00	1·00

MS606 116×97 mm. 16p. Airplane and castle; 16p. Professor's servant and Autumn Elf; 16p. Algy Pug; 16p. Baby Badger on sledge; 24p. Bill Badger, Willie Mouse, Reggie Rabbit and Podgy playing in snow; 24p. Type **141**; 24p. The Balloonist avoiding Gregory on toboggan; 24p. Tiger Lily and Edward Trunk 5·00 5·00

The 24p. values in No. MS606 are as Type **141**; the 16p. designs are smaller, each 25½×26 mm.

(Des B. Bell. Litho Enschedé)

1993 (7 May). *Europa. Contemporary Art. T* **142** *and similar multicoloured designs. P* 13½×14.

607	24p.	Type **142**	80	80
608	24p.	"Le Marchi a Paissaon" (etching and aquatint, Sally Reed) (48×33½ mm)	80	80
609	28p.	"Red Abstract" (painting, Molly Harris)	90	90
610	28p.	"Dress Shop, King's Road" (painting, Damon Bell) (48×33½ mm)	90	90
607/10		*Set of* 4	3·00	3·00

143 Arrest of Guernsey Parliamentarians, Fermain Bay

(Des C. Abbott. Litho Questa)

1993 (7 May). *350th Anniv of Siege of Castle Cornet. T* **143** *and similar horiz designs. Multicoloured. P* 14½×14.

611	16p.	Type **143**	40	40
612	24p.	Parliamentary ships attacking Castle Cornet	65	65
613	28p.	Parliamentary captives escaping	85	85
614	33p.	Castle cannon firing at St. Peter Port	95	95
615	39p.	Surrender of Castle Cornet, 19 December 1651	1·10	1·10
611/15		*Set of* 5	3·50	3·50

MS616 203×75 mm. Nos. 611/15 3·50 3·50

OMNIBUS ISSUES

Details, together with prices for complete sets, of the various Omnibus issues from the 1935 Silver Jubilee series to date are included in a special section following Zimbabwe at the end of Volume 2.

144 Playing Cards   **145** "The Twelve Pearls"

(Des J. Stephenson. Litho (16, 24, 28p.) or recess (33, 39p.) Enschedé)

1993 (27 July). *Birth Bicentenary of Thomas de la Rue (printer). T* **144** *and similar vert designs.* P 13½.

617	16p. multicoloured		40	40
	a. Booklet pane of 4 with margins all round	1·50		
618	24p. multicoloured		65	65
	a. Booklet pane of 4 with margins all round	2·25		
619	28p. multicoloured		80	80
	a. Booklet pane of 4 with margins all round	3·00		
620	33p. carmine-lake		95	95
	a. Booklet pane of 4 with margins all round	3·25		
621	39p. blackish green		1·10	1·10
	a. Booklet pane of 4 with margins all round	3·75		
617/21		*Set of* 5	3·50	3·50

Designs:—24p. Fountain pens; 28p. Envelope-folding machine; 33p. Great Britain 1855 4d. stamp; 39p. Thomas de la Rue and Mauritius £1 banknote.

(Des Jennifer Toombs. Litho B.D.T.)

1993 (2 Nov). *Christmas. Stained Glass Windows by Mary-Eily de Putron from the Chapel of Christ the Healer. T* **145** *and similar square designs. Multicoloured.* P 13.

622	13p. Type **145**		45	45
	a. Sheetlet. Nos. 622/33	4·00		
623	13p. "Healing rays"		45	45
624	13p. "Hand of God over the Holy City"		45	45
625	13p. "Wing and Seabirds" (facing left)		45	45
626	13p. "Christ the Healer"		45	45
627	13p. "Wing and Seabirds" (facing right)		45	45
628	13p. "The Young Jesus in the Temple"		45	45
629	13p. "The Raising of Jairus' Daughter"		45	45
630	13p. "Suffer little Children to come unto Me"		45	45
631	13p. "Pilgrim's Progress"		45	45
632	13p. "The Light of the World"		45	45
633	13p. "Raphael, the Archangel of Healing, with Tobias"		45	45
622/33		*Set of* 12	4·00	4·00

Nos. 622/33 were printed together, *se-tenant,* in sheetlets of 12.

146 Les Fouaillages (ancient burial ground)

(Des Miranda Schofield. Litho Cartor)

1994 (18 Feb). *Europa. Archaeological Discoveries. T* **146** *and similar horiz designs. Multicoloured.* P 13½.

634	24p. Type **146**		60	60
635	24p. Mounted Celtic warrior		60	60
636	30p. Jars, arrow heads and stone axe from Les Fouaillages		80	80
637	30p. Sword, spear head and torque from King's Road burial		80	80
634/7		*Set of* 4	2·50	2·50

Nos. 634/7 were each issued in small sheets of 10 (2×5) with a large inscribed margin at left. Some sheets of No. 635 were overprinted with the "Hong Kong '94" emblem on the left margin for sale at this philatelic exhibition.

147 Canadian Supermarine Spitfires Mk V over Normandy Beaches   **148** Peugeot "Type 3", 1894

(Des N. Trudgian. Litho B.D.T.)

1994 (6 June). *50th Anniv of D-Day. Sheet 93×71 mm.* P 14.
MS638 **147** £2 multicoloured   5·00   5·00

(Des R. Ollington. Litho B.D.T.)

1994 (19 July). *Centenary of First Car in Guernsey. T* **148** *and similar horiz designs. Multicoloured.* P 14½×14.

639	16p. Type **148**		45	45
	a. Booklet pane. No. 639×4 with margins all round	1·75		

640	24p. Mercedes "Simplex", 1903		70	70
	a. Booklet pane. No. 640×4 with margins all round	2·75		
641	35p. Humber tourer, 1906		1·00	1·00
	a. Booklet pane. No. 641×4 with margins all round	4·00		
642	41p. Bentley sports tourer, 1936		1·10	1·10
	a. Booklet pane. No. 642×4 with margins all round	4·25		
643	60p. MG TC Midget, 1948		1·75	1·75
	a. Booklet pane. No. 643×4 with margins all round	6·50		
639/43		*Set of* 5	4·50	4·50

(Des R. Gorringe and M. Whyte. Litho Cartor)

1994 (16 Aug). *"Philakorea '94" International Stamp Exhibition, Seoul. Sheet* 110×90 *mm containing stamp as No.* 581 *with changed imprint date.* P 13.
MS644 £1 multicoloured   2·50   2·50

149 Trident (Herm ferry)   **150** Dolls' House

(Des A. Copp. Litho Questa)

1994 (1 Oct). *25th Anniv of Guernsey Postal Administration. T* **149** *and similar horiz designs. Multicoloured.* P 14.

645	16p. Type **149**		35	35
646	24p. Handley Page HPR-7 Super Dart Herald of Channel Express		55	55
647	35p. Britten Norman Trislander G-JOEY of Aurigny Air Services		75	75
648	41p. *Bon Marin de Serk* (Sark ferry)		85	85
649	60p. Map of Bailiwick		1·40	1·40
645/9		*Set of* 5	3·75	3·75
MS650	150×100 mm. Nos. 645/9		3·75	3·75

(Des A. Peck. Litho B.D.T.)

1994 (1 Oct). *Christmas. Bygone Toys. T* **150** *and similar square designs. Multicoloured.* P 13.

651	13p. Type **150**		40	40
	a. Sheetlet. Nos. 651/6	2·00		
652	13p. Doll		40	40
653	13p. Teddy in bassinette		40	40
654	13p. Sweets in pillar box and playing cards		40	40
655	13p. Spinning top		40	40
656	13p. Building blocks		40	40
657	24p. Rocking horse		75	75
	a. Sheetlet. Nos. 657/62	3·50		
658	24p. Teddy bear		75	75
659	24p. Tricycle		75	75
660	24p. Wooden duck		75	75
661	24p. Hornby toy locomotive		75	75
662	24p. Ludo game		75	75
651/62		*Set of* 12	5·00	5·00

Nos. 651/6 and 657/62 were each printed together, *se-tenant,* in sheetlets of 6, each sheetlet forming a composite design.

151 Seafood "Face"   **152** Winston Churchill and Wireless

(Des R. Ollington. Litho Questa)

1995 (28 Feb). *Greetings Stamps. "The Welcoming Face of Guernsey". T* **151** *and similar vert designs. Multicoloured.* P 14.

663	24p. Type **151**		65	65
664	24p. Buckets and spade "face"		65	65
665	24p. Flowers "face"		65	65
666	24p. Fruit and vegetables "face"		65	65
667	24p. Sea shells and seaweed "face"		65	65
668	24p. Anchor and life belts "face"		65	65
669	24p. Glasses, cork and cutlery "face"		65	65
670	24p. Butterflies and caterpillars "face"		65	65
663/70		*Set of* 8	4·50	4·50
MS671	137×109 mm. Nos. 663/70		4·50	4·50

(Des M. Whyte. Litho Enschedé)

1995 (9 May). *50th Anniv of Liberation. T* **152** *and similar horiz designs. Multicoloured.* P 13½×14.

672	16p. Type **152**		50	50
673	24p. Union Jack and Royal Navy ships off St. Peter Port		75	75
674	35p. Royal Arms and military band		1·00	1·00
675	41p. *Vega* (Red Cross supply ship)		1·00	1·00
676	60p. Rejoicing crowd		1·75	1·75
672/6		*Set of* 5	4·50	4·50
MS677	189×75 mm. Nos. 672/6		4·50	4·50

153 Silhouette of Doves on Ground

(Des K. Bassford. Litho Walsall)

1995 (9 May). *Europa. Peace and Freedom. T* **153** *and similar horiz design. Multicoloured.* P 14.

678	25p. Type **153**		65	65
679	30p. Silhouette of doves in flight		85	85

The designs of Nos. 678/9 each provide a stereogram or hidden three-dimensional image of a single dove designed by D. Burder.

154 Prince Charles, Castle Cornet and Bailiwick Arms

(Des C. Abbott. Litho Questa)

1995 (9 May). *Royal Visit.* P 14.
680 **154** £1.50, multicoloured   4·00   4·00

(Des R. Corringe and M. Whyte. Litho Cartor)

1995 (1 Sept). *"Singapore '95" International Stamp Exhibition. Sheet* 110×90 *mm containing stamp as No.* 581 *with changed imprint date.* P 13.
MS681 £1 multicoloured   2·50   2·50

155 Part of United Nations Emblem (face value at top left)   **156** "Christmas Trees for Sale in Bern" (Cornelia Nussbrum-Weibel)

(Des K. Bassford. Litho and embossed Enschedé)

1995 (24 Oct). *50th Anniv of United Nations. T* **155** *and similar horiz designs showing different segments of the United Nations emblem. Each pale new blue and gold.* P 14×13½.

682	50p. Type **155**		1·25	1·25
	a. Block of 4. Nos. 682/5	5·00		
683	50p. Face value at top right		1·25	1·25
684	50p. Face value at bottom left		1·25	1·25
685	50p. Face value at bottom right		1·25	1·25
682/5		*Set of* 4	5·00	5·00

Nos. 682/5 were printed together, *se-tenant,* throughout the sheet with each block of 4 showing the complete emblem.

(Adapted M. Whyte from U.N.I.C.E.F. Christmas Cards. Litho B.D.T.)

1995 (16 Nov). *Christmas. 50th Anniv of U.N.I.C.E.F. T* **156** *and similar vert designs. Multicoloured.* P 13.

686	13p. Type **156** (face value at left)		40	40
	a. Horiz pair. Nos. 686/7		80	80
687	13p. "Christmas Trees for Sale in Bern" (face value at right)		40	40
688	13p. + 1p. "Evening Snowfall" (Katerina Mertikas) (face value at left)		40	40
	a. Horiz pair. Nos. 688/9		80	80
689	13p. + 1p. "Evening Snowfall) (face value at right)		40	40
690	24p. "It came upon a Midnight Clear" (Georgia Guback) (face value at left)		70	70
	a. Horiz pair. Nos. 690/1		1·40	1·40
691	24p. "It came upon a Midnight Clear" (Georgia Guback) (face value at right)		70	70
692	24p. + 2p. "Children of the World" (face value at left)		70	70
	a. Horiz pair. Nos. 692/3		1·40	1·40
693	24p. + 2p. "Children of the World" (face value at right)		70	70
686/93		*Set of* 8	4·00	4·00

Nos. 686/7, 688/9, 690/1 and 692/3 were printed together, *se-tenant,* as horizontal pairs in sheets of 12, each pair forming a composite design.

ALTERED CATALOGUE NUMBERS

Any Catalogue numbers altered from the last edition are shown as a list in the introductory pages.

157 Princess Anne (President,
Save the Children Fund) and
Children

(Des D. Miller. Litho B.D.T.)

1996 (21 Apr). *Europa. Famous Women. T* **157** *and similar horiz design. Multicoloured. P* 14.
694   25p. Type **157** 65   65
695   30p. Queen Elizabeth II and people of the
Commonwealth 85   85
The background designs of Nos. 694/5 continue on to the vertical sheet margins.

158 England v. U.S.S.R.,
1968 (value at right)

159 Maj-Gen. Brock
meeting Tecumseh
(Indian chief)

(Des M. Whyte. Litho Questa)

1996 (25 Apr). *European Football Championship. T* **158** *and similar horiz designs. Multicoloured. P* 14½×14.
696   16p. Type **158** 55   55
  a. Horiz pair. Nos. 696/7 .. .. 1·10 1·10
697   16p. England v. U.S.S.R., 1968 (value at left) 55   55
698   24p. Italy v. Belgium, 1972 (value at right) 75   75
  a. Horiz pair. Nos. 698/9 .. .. 1·50 1·50
699   24p. Italy v. Belgium, 1972 (value at left) .. 75   75
700   35p. Ireland v. Netherlands, 1988 (value at
right) 80   80
  a. Horiz pair. Nos. 700/1 .. .. 1·60 1·60
701   35p. Ireland v. Netherlands, 1988 (value at left) 80   80
702   41p. Denmark v. Germany, 1992 final (value at
right) 95   95
  a. Horiz pair. Nos. 702/3 .. .. 1·90 1·90
703   41p. Denmark v. Germany, 1992 final (value at
left) 95   95
696/703 .. .. .. *Set of 8* 5·50 5·50
Nos. 696/7, 698/9, 700/1 and 702/3 were printed together, *se-tenant*, in horizontal pairs throughout the sheets of 8 which had illustrated margins.

(Des A. Peck. Litho Enschedé)

1996 (8 June). *"CAPEX '96" International Stamp Exhibition, Toronto. Sheet* 110×90 *mm containing T* **159** *and similar horiz design. P* 13½.
MS704   24p. Type **159**; £1 Major-General Sir Isaac
Brock on horseback, 1812 .. .. 2·75 2·75

160 Ancient Greek
Runner

161 Humphrey Bogart as Philip
Marlowe

(Des K. Bassford. Litho Questa)

1996 (19 July). *Centenary of Modern Olympic Games. T* **160** *and similar designs, each black, orange-yellow and orange, showing ancient Greek athletes. P* 14.
705   16p. Type **160** 50   50
706   24p. Throwing the javelin 95   95
707   41p. Throwing the discus .. .. 1·10 1·10
708   55p. Wrestling (52×31 *mm*) .. .. 1·40 1·40
709   60p. Jumping .. .. .. 1·60 1·60
705/9 .. .. .. *Set of 5* 5·00 5·00
MS710   192×75 mm. Nos. 705/9 .. .. 5·00 5·00
No. 708 also includes the "OLYMPHILEX '96" International Stamp Exhibition, Atlanta, logo.

(Des R. Ollington. Litho Enschedé)

1996 (6 Nov). *Centenary of Cinema. Screen Detectives. T* **161** *and similar horiz designs. Multicoloured. P* 15×14.
711   16p. Type **161** 40   40
  a. Booklet pane. No. 711×3 with margins all
round .. .. .. 1·00
  b. Booklet pane. No. 711/15 with margins all
round .. .. .. 3·75
712   24p. Peter Sellers as Inspector Clouseau .. 60   60
  a. Booklet pane. No. 712×3 with margins all
round .. .. .. 1·75
713   35p. Basil Rathbone as Sherlock Holmes .. 85   85
  a. Booklet pane. No. 713×3 with margins all
round .. .. .. 2·25
714   41p. Margaret Rutherford as Miss Marple .. 90   90
  a. Booklet pane. No. 714×3 with margins all
round .. .. .. 2·50
715   60p. Warner Oland as Charlie Chan .. 1·40 1·40
  a. Booklet pane. No. 715×3 with margins all
round .. .. .. 4·00
711/15 .. .. .. *Set of 5* 3·75 3·75

162 The
Annunciation

163 Holly Blue (*Celastrina
argiolus*)

(Des P. le Vasseur. Litho B.D.T)

1996 (6 Nov). *Christmas. T* **162** *and similar multicoloured designs. P* 13.
716   13p. Type **162** 30   30
  a. Sheetlet of 12. Nos. 716/29 .. .. 3·50
717   13p. Journey to Bethlehem 30   30
718   13p. Arrival at the inn 30   30
719   13p. Angel and shepherds 30   30
720   13p. Mary, Joseph and Jesus in stable .. 30   30
721   13p. Shepherds worshipping Jesus .. 30   30
722   13p. Three Kings following star .. 30   30
723   13p. Three Kings with gifts 30   30
724   13p. The Presentation in the Temple .. 30   30
725   13p. Mary and Jesus 30   30
726   13p. Joseph warned by angel 30   30
727   13p. The Flight into Egypt 30   30
728   24p. Mary cradling Jesus (*horiz*) .. 60   60
729   25p. The Nativity (*horiz*) 60   60
716/29 .. .. .. *Set of 14* 4·25 4·25
Nos. 716/27 were printed together, *se-tenant*, in sheetlets of 12.

(Des A. Peck. Litho B.D.T.)

1997 (12 Feb). *Endangered Species. Butterflies and Moths. T* **163** *and similar horiz designs. Multicoloured. P* 14.
730   18p. Type **163** 60   60
731   25p. Hummingbird Hawk-moth (*Macro-
glossum stellatarum*) 75   75
732   26p. Emperor Moth (*Saturnia pavonia*) .. 90   90
733   37p. Brimstone (*Gonepteryx rhamni*) .. 1·10 1·10
730/3 .. .. .. *Set of 4* 3·00 3·00
MS734   92×68 mm. £1 Painted Lady (*Cynthia
cardui*). P 13½ .. .. .. 2·50 2·50
No. MS734 includes the "HONG KONG '97" International Stamp Exhibition logo on the sheet margin.

164 Gilliatt fighting Octopus

165 Shell Beach, Herm

(Des M. Wilkinson. Litho Cartor)

1997 (24 Apr). *Europa. Tales and Legends. Scenes from Les Travailleurs de la Mer by Victor Hugo. T* **164** *and similar horiz design. Multicoloured. P* 13½.
735   26p. Type **164** 65   65
736   31p. Gilliatt grieving on rock 75   75
Nos. 735/6 were each issued in small sheets of 10 (2×5) with an enlarged inscribed margin at left.

(Litho B.D.T.)

1997 (24 Apr). *Guernsey Scenes (1st series). T* **165** *and similar multicoloured designs. Self-adhesive. P* 9½ (diecut).
737   18p. Type **165** 50   50
  a. Booklet pane of 8 .. .. 3·75
738   25p. La Seigneurie, Sark (*vert*) .. 70   70
  a. Booklet pane of 8 .. .. 5·25
739   26p. Castle Cornet, Guernsey .. 70   70
  a. Booklet pane of 4 .. .. 2·75
737/9 .. .. .. *Set of 3* 1·75 1·75
Nos. 737/9 were issued in stamp booklets or as rolls of 100 (18p. and 25p.).
See also Nos. 770/3.

166 19th-century Shipyard,
St. Peter's Port

(Des C. Abbott. Litho Questa)

1997 (29 May). *"Pacific '97" World Philatelic Exhibition, San Francisco. Sheet* 110×90 *mm containing T* **166** *and similar horiz design. P* 14.
MS740   30p. brown-olive and gold; £1 multicoloured
(*Costa Rica Packet* (barque)) .. .. 3·00 3·00

NEW INFORMATION

The editor is always interested to correspond with people who have new information that will improve or correct the Catalogue.

167 Transistor Radio, Microphone
and Radio Logos

(Des Miranda Schofield. Litho Cartor)

1997 (21 Aug). *Methods of Communication. T* **167** *and similar horiz designs. Multicoloured. P* 13½×13.
741   18p. Type **167** 45   45
742   25p. Television, video camera and satellite dish 70   70
743   26p. Fax machine, telephones and mobile
phone 70   70
744   37p. Printing press, newspaper and type .. 1·00 1·00
745   43p. Stamp, coding machine and postbox .. 1·10 1·10
746   63p. C.D., computer and disk .. .. 1·60 1·60
741/6 .. .. .. *Set of 6* 5·00 5·00

168 Teddy Bear making
Cake

169 Visiting Guernsey,
1957

(Des Sally Diamond. Litho Walsall)

1997 (6 Nov). *Christmas. Teddy Bears. T* **168** *and similar vert designs. Multicoloured. P* 14½×14.
747   15p. Type **168** 45   45
748   25p. Teddy bears decorating Christmas tree .. 70   70
749   26p. Two teddy bears in armchair .. 70   70
750   37p. Teddy bear as Father Christmas .. 1·00 1·00
751   43p. Teddy bears unwrapping presents .. 1·10 1·10
752   63p. Teddy bears eating Christmas dinner .. 1·60 1·60
747/52 .. .. .. *Set of 6* 5·00 5·00
MS753   123×107 mm. Nos. 747/52 .. .. 5·00 5·00

(Des M. Whyte. Litho Questa)

1997 (20 Nov). *Golden Wedding of Queen Elizabeth and Prince Philip. T* **169** *and similar square designs. Multicoloured. P* 14½.
754   18p. Type **169** 45   45
  a. Booklet pane. Nos. 754/5, each × 3 with
margins all round .. .. 3·25
  b. Booklet pane. Nos. 754/9 with margins all
round .. .. .. 5·00
755   25p. Coronation Day, 1953 70   70
756   26p. Royal family, 1957 70   70
  a. Booklet pane. Nos. 756/7, each × 3 with
margins all round .. .. 5·00
757   37p. On royal yacht, 1972 .. .. 1·00 1·00
758   43p. Queen Elizabeth and Prince Philip at
Trooping the Colour, 1987 .. 1·10 1·10
  a. Booklet pane. Nos. 758/9, each × 3 with
margins all round .. .. 8·25
759   63p. Queen Elizabeth and Prince Philip, 1997 1·60 1·60
754/9 .. .. .. *Set of 6* 5·00 5·00
No. 755 is inscribed "1947" in error.

170 Tapestry of
11th-century
Guernsey (St.
Martin)

171 Fort Grey

(Des Sally Diamond. Litho Questa)

1998 (10 Feb). *The Millennium Tapestries Project. T* **170** *and similar vert designs each showing a different century contributed by individual parishes. Multicoloured. P* 15×14½.
760   25p. Type **170** 60   60
  a. Horiz strip of 10 or two strips of 5. Nos.
760/9 .. .. .. 5·50
  b. Booklet pane. Nos. 760/1, each × 2, and
762/3 with margins all round .. 3·50
  c. Booklet pane. Nos. 760/1, and 768/9 each
× 2 with margins all round .. 3·50
761   25p. 12th-century (St. Saviour) .. 60   60
762   25p. 13th-century (Vale) 60   60
  a. Booklet pane. Nos. 762/3, each × 2, and
764/5 with margins all round .. 3·50
763   25p. 14th-century (St. Sampson) .. 60   60
764   25p. 15th-century (Torteval) .. 60   60
  a. Booklet pane. Nos. 764/5, each × 2, and
766/7 with margins all round .. 3·50
765   25p. 16th-century (Castel) 60   60

766	25p. 17th-century (St. Andrew)		60	60
	a. Booklet pane. Nos. 766/7, each × 2, and 768/9 with margins all round		3·50	
767	25p. 18th-century (Forest)		60	60
768	25p. 19th-century (St. Pierre du Bois)		60	60
769	25p. 20th-century (St. Peter Port)		60	60
760/9		Set of 10	5·50	5·50

Nos. 760/9 were printed together, *se-tenant*, in horizontal strips of 10 throughout the sheet. These stamps were often supplied by the Guernsey Philatelic Bureau as two horizontal strips of 5.

(Des Joanna Brehaut. Litho B.D.T.)

1998 (25 Mar). *Guernsey Scenes (2nd series).* T **171** *and similar horiz designs. Multicoloured. Self-adhesive.* P 9½.

770	(20p.) Type **171**		40	45
	a. Horiz pair. Nos. 770/1		80	
	b. Booklet pane. Nos. 770/1, each × 4 with margins all round		3·25	
771	(20p.) Grand Havre		40	45
772	(25p.) Little Chapel		50	55
	a. Horiz pair. Nos. 772/3		90	
	b. Booklet pane. Nos. 772/3, each × 4 with margins all round		4·00	
773	(25p.) Guernsey Cow		50	55
770/3		Set of 4	1·75	2·00

Nos. 770/1 are inscribed "Bailiwick Minimum Postage Paid" and were initially sold at 20p. Nos. 772/3 are inscribed "UK Minimum Postage Paid" and were initially sold at 25p.

Nos. 770/3 were issued in stamp booklets or as rolls of 100, each roll containing two designs.

172 Fairey IIIC, Balloon, Sopwith Camel and Avro 504

(Des C. Abbott. Litho Cartor)

1998 (7 May). *80th Anniv of the Royal Air Force.* T **172** *and similar horiz designs. Multicoloured.* P 13½×13.

774	20p. Type **172**		50	50
775	25p. Fairey Swordfish, Tiger Moth, Supermarine Walrus and Gloster Gladiator		60	60
776	30p. Hawker Hurricane, Supermarine Spitfire, Vickers Wellington, Short Sunderland (flying boat), Westland Lysander and Bristol Blenheim		70	70
777	37p. De Havilland Mosquito, Avro Lancaster, Auster III, Gloster Meteor and Horsa glider		85	85
778	43p. Canberra, Hawker Sea Fury, Bristol Sycamore, Hawker Hunter, Handley Page Victor and BAe Lightning		95	95
779	63p. Panavia Tornado GRI, BAe Hawk, BAe Sea Harrier, Westland Lynx (helicopter) and Hawker Siddeley Nimrod		1·40	1·40
774/9		Set of 6	4·50	4·50

173 Jules Rimet (first President of F.I.F.A.)

(Des A. Peck. Litho Enschedé)

1998 (7 May). *150th Anniv of the Cambridge Rules for Football. Sheet* 110×90 *mm containing* T **173** *and similar horiz design.* P 13½×14.

MS780	30p. Type **173**; £1·75, Bobby Moore and Queen Elizabeth II, 1966		4·50	4·50

174 Girls in Traditional Costume watching Sheep Display, West Show

(Des Sally Diamond. Litho Enschedé)

1998 (11 Aug). *Europa. Festivals.* T **174** *and similar horiz designs. Multicoloured.* P 13½.

781	20p. Type **174**		50	50
782	25p. Marching band and "Battle of Flowers" exhibit, North Show		60	60
783	30p. Prince Charles, monument and tank, Liberation Day		70	70
784	37p. Goat, dahlias and show-jumping, South Show		90	90
781/4		Set of 4	2·50	2·50

The 25p. and 30p. incorporate the "EUROPA" emblem.

175 Outboard Motorboat

176 Royal Yacht *Britannia*

(Des M. Wilkinson. Litho Walsall (1p. to 75p.). Litho and embossed Walsall (£1) or Questa (£5))

1998 (11 Aug)–99. *Maritime Heritage.* T **175** *and similar multicoloured designs and* T **176**. P 14½×14 (10p., 40p., 50p., 75p.), 14×14½ (£1), 15×14½ (£5) *or* 14 (*others*).

785	1p. Type **175** (27.7.99)		10	10
786	2p. St. John Ambulance inshore rescue dinghy (27.7.99)		10	10
787	3p. Pilot boat, St. Peter Port (27.7.99)		10	10
788	4p. *Flying Christine III* (St. John Ambulance launch) (27.7.99)		10	10
789	5p. Crab fishing boat (27.7.99)		10	10
790	6p. Herm Island ferry (27.7.99)		10	10
791	7p. *Sarnia* (St. Peter Port Harbour Authority launch) (27.7.99)		15	20
792	8p. *Leopardess* (States' fisheries protection launch) (27.7.99)		15	20
793	9p. Trawler (27.7.99)		20	25
794	10p. Powerboat (30×30 *mm*) (27.7.99)		20	25
797	40p. Motor cruiser (30×30 *mm*) (27.7.99)		80	85
798	50p. Ocean-going sailing yacht (30×30 *mm*) (27.7.99)		1·00	1·10
799	75p. Motor yacht, Beaucette Marina (30×30 *mm*) (27.7.99)		1·50	1·75
800	£1 *Queen Elizabeth 2* (liner) (32×28 *mm*) (27.7.99)		2·00	2·10
802	£5 Type **176**		10·00	10·50
785/802		Set of 15	16·00	17·00

177 Modern Tree, Teletubby and Playstation

178 Elizabeth Bowes Lyon, 1907

(Des R. Ollington. Litho B.D.T)

1998 (10 Nov). *150th Anniv of the Introduction of the Christmas Tree.* T **177** *and similar horiz designs. Multicoloured.* P 13¾.

810	17p. Type **177**		40	40
811	25p. 1960s tinsel tree, toy bus and doll		60	60
812	30p. 1930s gold foil tree, panda and toy tank		70	70
813	37p. 1920s tree, model of *Bluebird* and doll		90	90
814	43p. 1900 tree, teddy bear and toy train		1·00	1·00
815	63p. 1850s tree, wooden doll and spinning top		1·50	1·50
810/15		Set of 6	4·50	4·50
MS816	160×94 mm. Nos. 810/15		4·25	4·75

(Des R. Ollington. Litho Cartor)

1999 (4 Feb). *Life and Times of Queen Elizabeth the Queen Mother.* T **178** *and similar vert designs. Multicoloured.* P 13.

817	25p. Type **178**		60	60
	a. Horiz strip of 10 or two strips of 5. Nos. 817/26		6·00	
	b. Booklet pane. Nos. 817/18, each × 2, and 819/20 with margins all round		3·50	
	c. Booklet pane. Nos. 817/18, and 825/6, each × 2, with margins all round		3·50	
818	25p. On wedding day, 1923		60	60
819	25p. Holding Princess Elizabeth, 1926		60	60
	b. Booklet pane. Nos. 819/20, each × 2, and 821/2 with margins all round		3·50	
820	25p. At Coronation, 1937		60	60
821	25p. Visiting bombed areas of London, 1940 (wearing green hat)		60	60
	b. Booklet pane. Nos. 821/2, each × 2, and 823/4 with margins all round		3·50	
822	25p. Fishing near Auckland, New Zealand, 1966		60	60
823	25p. At Guernsey function, 1963 (wearing tiara)		60	60
	b. Booklet pane. Nos. 823/4, each × 2, and 825/6 with margins all round		3·50	
824	25p. Receiving flowers on her birthday, 1992		60	60
825	25p. Presenting trophy, Sandown Park races, 1989		60	60
826	25p. Opening Royal Norfolk Regimental Museum, Norwich, 1990 (wearing blue hat)		60	60
817/26		Set of 10	5·50	5·50

Nos. 817/26 were printed together, *se-tenant*, in horizontal strips of 10 throughout the sheet.

NEW INFORMATION

The editor is always interested to correspond with people who have new information that will improve or correct the Catalogue.

179 *Spirit of Guernsey*, 1995

180 Burnet Rose and Local Carriage Label

(Des K. Wisdom. Litho Cartor)

1999 (27 Apr). *175th Anniv of Royal National Lifeboat Institution.* T **179** *and similar horiz designs. Multicoloured.* P 13½×13.

827	20p. Type **179**		50	50
828	25p. *Sir William Arnold*, 1973		60	60
829	30p. *Euphrosyne Kendal*, 1954		70	70
830	38p. *Queen Victoria*, 1929		90	90
831	44p. *Arthur Lionel*, 1912		1·10	1·10
832	64p. *Vincent Kirk Ella*, 1888		1·40	1·40
827/32		Set of 6	4·75	4·75

(Des Colleen Corlett. Litho Walsall)

1999 (27 Apr). *Europa. Parks and Gardens. Herm Island.* T **180** *and similar square designs, each showing a different local carriage label. Multicoloured.* P 13½×13.

833	20p. Type **180**		40	45
834	25p. Puffin		50	55
835	30p. Small Heath Butterfly		60	65
836	38p. Shells on Shell Beach		75	80
833/6		Set of 4	2·25	2·40

Nos. 833/6 were each issued in small sheets of 10 (2×5) with an enlarged inscribed margin at left or right.

181 Prince Edward and Miss Sophie Rhys-Jones

(Des Sally Diamond. Litho B.D.T.)

1999 (19 June). *Royal Wedding. Sheet* 93×70 *mm.* P 13½.

MS837	**181** £1 multicoloured		2·00	2·10

182 Major-General Le Marchant (founder) and Cadet at Sword Drill

183 The Nativity

(Des R. Ollington. Litho B.D.T.)

1999 (27 July). *Bicentenary of The Royal Military Academy, Sandhurst.* T **182** *and similar square designs. Multicoloured.* P 14.

838	20p. Type **182**		40	45
839	25p. The Duke of York (official sponsor) and cadet on horseback		50	55
840	30p. Field-Marshal Earl Haig and cadets on parade		60	60
841	38p. Field-Marshal Viscount Montgomery and bridging exercise		75	80
842	44p. David Niven (actor) and rifle practice		90	95
843	64p. Sir Winston Churchill and tank		1·25	1·40
838/43		Set of 6	4·25	4·75

(Des Sally Diamond. Litho Questa)

1999 (19 Oct). *Christmas. Wood Carvings by Denis Brehaut from Notre Dame Church.* T **183** *and similar vert designs. Multicoloured.* P 14×14½.

844	17p. Type **183**		35	40
845	25p. Virgin Mary and Child		50	55
846	30p. Holy Family		60	65
847	38p. Cattle around manger		75	80
848	44p. Adoration of the Shepherds		90	95
849	64p. Adoration of the Magi		1·25	1·40
844/9		Set of 6	4·25	4·75
MS850	159×86 mm. Nos. 844/9		4·25	4·75

184 "Space Bus" (Fallon
Ephgrave)

(Litho Questa)

2000 (1 Jan). *New Millennium. "Stampin' the Future" (children's
stamp design competition). T **184** and similar horiz designs.
Multicoloured. P 14×14½.*

851	20p.	Type **184**		40	45
852	25p.	"Children holding hands" (Abigail Downing)		50	55
853	30p.	"No Captivity" (Laura Martin)		60	65
854	38p.	"Post Office of the Future" (Sarah Haddow)		75	80
855	44p.	"Solar-powered car" (Sophie Medland)		90	95
856	64p.	"Woman flying" (Danielle McIver)		1·25	1·40
851/6			*Set of 6*	4·25	4·75

STAMP BOOKLETS

For a full listing of Guernsey stamp booklets see *Collect Channel Islands and Isle of Man Stamps* published each January.

POSTAGE DUE STAMPS

D 1 Castle Cornet   **D 2** St. Peter Port

(Des R. Granger Barrett. Photo Delrieu)

1969 (1 Oct). *Value in black; background colour given. No wmk.* P 12½×12.

D1	D 1	1d. plum ..	2·25	1·25
D2		2d. bright green ..	2·25	1·25
D3		3d. vermilion ..	3·75	4·00
D4		4d. ultramarine ..	5·00	5·00
D5		5d. yellow-ochre ..	5·50	5·50
D6		6d. turquoise-blue ..	6·50	6·00
D7		1s. lake-brown ..	17·00	17·00
D1/7		Set of 7	35·00	35·00

1971 (15 Feb)-**76**. *As Type* D 1 *but values in decimal currency.*

D 8	D 1	½p. plum ..	10	10
D 9		1p. bright green ..	10	10
D10		2p. vermilion ..	10	10
D11		3p. ultramarine ..	15	15
D12		4p. yellow-ochre ..	15	15
D13		5p. turquoise-blue ..	15	15
D14		6p. violet (10.2.76) ..	20	20
D15		8p. light yellow-orange (7.10.75)	30	30
D16		10p. lake-brown ..	35	35
D17		15p. grey (10.2.76) ..	60	60
D8/17		Set of 10	2·00	2·00

(Photo Delrieu)

1977 (2 Aug)-**80**. *Face value in black; background colour given.* P 13.

D18	D 2	½p. lake-brown ..	10	10
D19		1p. bright purple ..	10	10
D20		2p. bright orange ..	10	10
D21		3p. vermilion ..	10	10
D22		4p. turquoise-blue ..	15	15
D23		5p. yellow-green ..	15	15
D24		6p. turquoise-green ..	20	20
D25		8p. brown-ochre ..	25	25
D26		10p. ultramarine ..	40	40
D27		14p. green (5.2.80) ..	45	45
D28		15p. bright violet ..	45	45
D29		16p. rose-red (5.2.80) ..	55	55
D18/29		Set of 12	2·50	2·50

D 3 Milking Cow

(Litho Questa)

1982 (13 July). *Guernsey Scenes, circa 1900. Horiz designs as Type* D 3. P 14½.

D30		1p. indigo, blue-black and bright green ..	10	10
D31		2p. sepia, yellow-brown and azure	10	10
D32		3p. blackish green, black and lilac	10	10
D33		4p. bottle-green, black and dull orange	10	10
D34		5p. dp violet-blue, blue-black & turq-grn	10	10
D35		16p. deep grey-blue, deep blue and cobalt	30	35
D36		18p. steel-blue, indigo and apple-green	35	40
D37		20p. brown-olive, agate and pale blue	40	45
D38		25p. Prussian blue, blue-black and rose-pink	50	55
D39		30p. dp bluish grn, blackish ol & bistre-yell	60	65
D40		50p. olive-brown, sepia and dull violet-blue	1·00	1·10
D41		£1 light brown, brown and pale brown ..	2·00	2·10
D30/41		Set of 12	5·25	5·75

Designs:—2p. Vale Mill; 3p. Sark cottage; 4p. Quay-side, St. Peter Port; 5p. Well, Water Lane, Moulin Huet; 16p. Seaweed gathering; 18p. Upper Walk, White Rock; 20p. Cobo Bay; 25p. Saint's Bay; 30p. La Coupee, Sark; 50p. Old Harbour, St. Peter Port; £1 Greenhouses, Doyle Road, St. Peter Port.

ALDERNEY

The following issues are provided by the Guernsey Post Office for use on Alderney. They are also valid for postal purposes throughout the rest of the Bailiwick of Guernsey.

A 1 Island Map

(Des G. Drummond. Litho B.D.T. (20p. to 28p.). Photo Courvoisier (others))

1983 (14 June)-**93**. *Island Scenes. Type* A 1 *and similar horiz designs. Multicoloured. Granite paper (Nos. A1/12).* P 15×14 (20p. to 28p.) *or* 11½ (others).

A 1		1p. Type A 1 ..	10	10
A 2		4p. Hanging Rock ..	10	10
A 3		9p. States' Building, St. Anne	25	25
A 4		10p. St. Anne's Church ..	25	25
A 5		11p. Yachts in Braye Bay ..	25	25
A 6		12p. Victoria St.. St. Anne ..	30	30
A 7		13p. Map of Channel ..	30	30
A 8		14p. Fort Clonque ..	35	35
A 9		15p. Corblets Bay and Fort ..	40	40
A10		16p. Old Tower, St. Anne ..	40	40
A11		17p. Golf course and Essex Castle	45	45
A12		18p. Old Harbour ..	45	45
A12a		20p. Quesnard Lighthouse (27.12.89)	1·00	1·00
A12b		21p. Braye Harbour (2.4.91)	1·00	1·00
A12c		23p. Island Hall (6.2.92)	90	90
A12d		24p. *J. T. Daly* (steam locomotive) (2.3.93)	2·00	2·00
A12e		28p. *Louis Marchesi of Round Table* (lifeboat) (2.3.93)	2·25	2·25
A1/12e		Set of 17	9·50	9·50

Nos. A12a/e are larger, 38×27 mm.

A2 Oystercatcher

(Des and photo Harrison)

1984 (12 June). *Birds. Type* A2 *and similar horiz designs. Multicoloured.* P 14½.

A13		9p. Type A2 ..	1·50	1·50
A14		13p. Turnstone ..	1·50	2·00
A15		26p. Ringed Plover ..	5·00	4·00
A16		28p. Dunlin ..	5·00	4·00
A17		31p. Curlew ..	5·00	4·00
A13/17		Set of 5	16·00	14·00

A 3 Westland Wessex HU   **A 4** Royal
Mk 5 Helicopter of the   Engineers, 1890
Queen's Flight

(Des A. Theobald. Photo Courvoisier)

1985 (19 Mar). *50th Anniv of Alderney Airport. Type* A 3 *and similar horiz designs. Multicoloured. Granite paper.* P 11½.

A18		9p. Type A 3 ..	2·50	2·25
A19		13p. Britten Norman "long nose" Trislander	2·50	3·00
A20		29p. De Havilland D.H.114 Heron 1B	6·00	5·00
A21		31p. De Havilland D.H.89A Dragon Rapide *Sir Henry Lawrence* ..	6·50	6·00
A22		34p. Saro A.21 Windhover flying boat *City of Portsmouth* ..	7·00	6·00
A18/22		Set of 5	22·00	20·00

(Des E. Stemp. Litho Harrison)

1985 (24 Sept). *Regiments of the Alderney Garrison. Type* A 4 *and similar vert designs. Multicoloured.* P 14½.

A23		9p. Type A 4 ..	45	45
A24		14p. Duke of Albany's Own Highlanders (72nd Highland Regt), 1856	1·00	1·00
A25		29p. Royal Artillery, 1855 ..	1·50	1·50
A26		31p. South Hampshire Regiment, 1810	1·75	1·75
A27		34p. Royal Irish Regiment, 1782 ..	2·00	2·00
A23/7		Set of 5	6·00	6·00

No. A24 shows the tartan and insignia of the 78th Highland Regiment in error.

A 5 Fort Grosnez   **A 6** *Liverpool* (full-rigged
ship) 1902

(Des R. Reed. Litho Cartor)

1986 (23 Sept). *Alderney Forts. Type* A 5 *and similar vert designs. Multicoloured.* P 13×13½.

A28		10p. Type A 5 ..	1·10	1·10
A29		14p. Fort Tourgis ..	1·75	1·75
A30		31p. Fort Clonque ..	4·00	4·00
A31		34p. Fort Albert ..	4·25	4·25
A28/31		Set of 4	10·00	10·00

(Des C. Jaques. Litho Questa)

1987 (5 May). *Alderney Shipwrecks. Type* A 6 *and similar horiz designs. Multicoloured.* P 14×14½.

A32		11p. Type A 6 ..	2·00	1·75
A33		15p. *Petit Raymond* (schooner), 1906	2·25	2·00
A34		29p. *Maina* (yacht), 1910	5·50	5·25
A35		31p. *Burton* (steamer), 1911	6·00	5·75
A36		34p. *Point Law* (oil tanker), 1975	6·50	6·25
A32/6		Set of 5	20·00	19·00

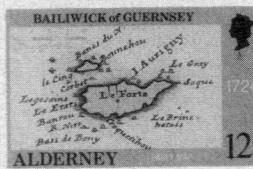

A 7 Moll's Map of 1724

(Des J. Cooter. Litho Enschedé)

1989 (7 July). *250th Anniv of Bastide's Survey of Alderney. Type* A 7 *and similar horiz designs.* P 13½×14.

A37		12p. multicoloured	45	45
A38		18p. black, greenish blue and orange-brown	60	60
A39		27p. black, greenish blue & dull yellow-green	1·25	1·25
A40		32p. black, greenish blue and bright rose-red	1·40	1·40
A41		35p. multicoloured	1·60	1·60
A37/41		Set of 5	4·75	4·75

Designs:—18p. Bastide's survey of 1739; 27p. Goodwin's map of 1831; 32p. General Staff map of 1943; 35p. Ordnance Survey map, 1988.

A 8 H.M.S. *Alderney* (bomb
ketch), 1738

(Des A. Theobald. Litho B.D.T.)

1990 (3 May). *Royal Navy Ships named after Alderney. Type* A 8 *and similar horiz designs.* P 13½.

A42		14p. black and olive-bistre ..	45	45
A43		20p. black and orange-brown ..	65	65
A44		29p. black and cinnamon ..	1·25	1·25
A45		34p. black and pale turquoise-blue ..	1·25	1·25
A46		37p. black and cobalt ..	1·40	1·40
A42/6		Set of 5	4·50	4·50

Designs:—20p. H.M.S. *Alderney* (frigate), 1742; 29p. H.M.S. *Alderney* (sloop), 1755; 34p H.M.S. *Alderney* (submarine), 1945; 37p. H.M.S. *Alderney* (patrol vessel), 1979.

A 9 Wreck of H.M.S. *Victory*,   **A 10** Two French
1744   Warships on Fire

(Des A. Theobald. Litho Cartor)

1991 (30 Apr). *Automation of The Casquets Lighthouse. Type* A 9 *and similar horiz designs. Multicoloured.* P 14×13¾.

A47		21p. Type A 9 ..	1·60	2·00
A48		26p. Lighthouse keeper's daughter rowing back to the Casquets	2·00	2·25
A49		31p. MBB-Bolkow Bo 105D helicopter leaving pad on St. Thomas Tower	2·50	2·75
A50		37p. Migrating birds over lighthouse	3·50	3·75
A51		50p. Trinity House vessel *Patricia* and arms	6·00	5·00
A47/51		Set of 5	14·00	14·00

(Des C. Abbott. Litho B.D.T.)

1992 (18 Sept). *300th Anniv of the Battle of La Hogue. Type* A 10 *and similar multicoloured designs.* P 14×15 (50p.) *or* 13½ (others).

A52		23p. Type A 10 ..	2·00	2·00
A53		28p. Crews leaving burning ships	2·75	2·75
A54		32p. French warship sinking	3·00	3·00
A55		50p. "The Battle of La Hogue" (47×32 mm)	4·50	4·50
A52/5		Set of 4	11·00	11·00

Nos. A52/4 show details of the painting on the 50p. value.

A 11 Spiny Lobster   **A 12** Blue-tailed
Damselfly, Dark Hair
Water Crowfoot and
Branched Bur-reed

(Des A. Peck. Litho Questa)

1993 (2 Nov). *Endangered Species. Marine Life.* Type A **11** *and similar horiz designs. Multicoloured.* P 14½.

A56	24p. Type A **11**	..	90	90
	a. Horiz strip of 4. Nos. A56/9	..	4·25	
A57	28p. Plumose Anemone	..	1·00	1·00
A58	33p. Starfish	..	1·25	1·25
A59	39p. Sea Urchin	..	1·60	1·60
A56/9		*Set of 4*	4·25	4·25

Nos. A56/9 were printed together, *se-tenant*, in horizontal strips of 4, throughout the sheet, the backgrounds of each strip forming a composite design.

(Des Wendy Bramall. Litho B.D.T. (No. A71a) or Questa (others))

1994 (5 May)–98. *Flora and Fauna.* Type A **12** *and similar multicoloured designs.* P 14½.

A60	1p. Type A **12**		10	10
A61	2p. White-toothed Shrew and Flax-leaved St. John's Wort		10	10
A62	3p. Fulmar and Kaffir Fig		10	10
A63	4p. Clouded Yellow (butterfly) and Red Clover		10	10
A64	5p. Bumble Bee, Prostrate Broom and Giant Broomrape		10	10
A65	6p. Dartford Warbler and Lesser Dodder ..		15	20
A66	7p. Peacock (butterfly) and Stemless Thistle		15	20
A67	8p. Mole and Bluebell		15	20
A68	9p. Great Green Grasshopper and Common Gorse ..		20	25
A69	10p. Six-spot Burnet (moth) and Viper's Bugloss		20	25
A70	16p. Common Blue (butterfly) and Pyramidal Orchid		30	35
	a. Perf 14×15		30	35
	ab. Booklet pane of 8		2·50	
A70b	18p. Small Tortoiseshell (butterfly) and Buddleia (2.1.97)		35	40
	ba. Perf 14×15		50	50
	bb. Booklet pane of 8		4·00	
A71	20p. Common Rabbit and Creeping Buttercup		40	45
	a. Perf 14×15 (25.3.98)		40	45
	ab. Booklet pane of 8		3·25	
A72	24p. Great Black-backed Gull and Sand Crocus		50	55
	a. Perf 14×15		50	55
	ab. Booklet pane of 8		3·75	
A72b	25p. Rock Pipit and Sea Stock (2.1.97)		50	55
	a. Perf 14×15		50	55
	bb. Booklet pane of 8		4·00	
A72c	26p. Sand Digger Wasp and Sea Bindweed (*horiz*) (2.1.97)		50	55
A73	30p. Atlantic Puffin and English Stonecrop		60	65
A74	40p. Emperor (moth) and Bramble		80	85
A75	50p. Pale-spined Hedgehog and Pink Oxalis		1·00	1·10
A76	£1 Common Tern and Bermuda Grass (*horiz*)		2·00	2·10
A77	£2 Northern Gannet and *Fucus vesiculosus* (seaweed) (*horiz*) (28.2.95)		4·00	4·25
A60/77		*Set of 21*	11·50	12·50

Nos. A70a, A70ba, A71a, A72a, and A72ba were only issued in booklets with the upper and lower edges imperforate.

A **13** Royal Aircraft Factory SE5A

(Des C. Abbott. Litho B.D.T.)

1995 (1 Sept). *Birth Centenary of Tommy Rose (aviator).* Type A **13** *and similar horiz designs. Multicoloured.* P 14×15.

A78	35p. Type A **13**		85	85
	a. Horiz strip of 3. Nos. A78/80		2·50	
A79	35p. Miles Master II and other Miles aircraft		85	85
A80	35p. Miles Aerovan and Miles Monitor		85	85
A81	41p. Miles Falcon Six winning King's Cup air race, 1935		1·00	1·00
	a. Horiz strip of 3. Nos. A81/3		3·00	
A82	41p. Miles Hawk Speed Six winning Manx Air Derby, 1947		1·00	1·00
A83	41p. Miles Falcon Six breaking U.K.–Cape record, 1936		1·00	1·00
A78/83		*Set of 6*	5·50	5·50

Nos. A78/80 and A81/3 were printed together, *se-tenant*, as horizontal strips of 3 in sheets of 12 (2 panes 3×2).

A **14** Returning Islanders

(Des C. Abbott. Litho B.D.T.)

1995 (16 Nov). *50th Anniv of Return of Islanders to Alderney.* Sheet 93×70 mm. P 13½.

MSA84	A **14** £1·65, multicoloured	..	4·00	4·00

A **15** Signallers training on Alderney

A **16** Cat with Butterfly

(Des A. Theobald. Litho Walsall)

1996 (24 Jan). *25th Anniv of Adoption of 30th Signal Regiment by Alderney.* Type A **15** *and similar horiz designs. Multicoloured.* P 14.

A85	24p. Type A **15**	..	65	65
	a. Horiz strip of 4. Nos. A85/8		5·00	
A86	41p. Communications station, Falkland Islands		1·10	1·10
A87	60p. Dish aerial and Land Rover, Gulf War		1·50	1·50
A88	75p. Service with United Nations		1·75	1·75
A85/8		*Set of 4*	5·00	5·00

Nos. A85/8 were printed together, *se-tenant*, in horizontal strips of 4 throughout the sheet, each strip forming a composite design.

(Des P. le Vasseur. Litho B.D.T.)

1996 (19 July). *Cats.* Type A **16** *and similar square designs. Multicoloured.* P 13½.

A89	16p. Type A **16**	..	45	45
A90	24p. Blue and White on table		65	65
A91	25p. Tabby kitten grooming Blue and White Persian kitten		65	65
A92	35p. Red Persian under table		95	95
A93	41p. White wild cat with Tortoiseshell and White in toy cart		1·10	1·10
A94	60p. Siamese playing with wool		1·75	1·75
A89/94		*Set of 6*	5·00	5·00
MSA95	144×97 mm. Nos. A89/94	..	5·00	5·00

A **17** Harold Larwood

A **18** Railway under Construction

(Des R. Ollington. Litho Walsall)

1997 (21 Aug). *150th Anniv of Cricket on Alderney.* Type A **17** *and similar vert designs. Multicoloured.* P 13½.

A 96	18p. Type A **17**	..	50	50
A 97	25p. John Arlott		65	65
A 98	37p. Pelham J. Warner		1·00	1·00
A 99	43p. W. G. Grace		1·25	1·25
A100	63p. John Wisden		1·60	1·60
A96/100		*Set of 5*	4·50	4·50
MSA101	190×75 mm. Nos. A96/100 and label		4·50	4·50

(Des R. Carter. Litho Questa)

1997 (20 Nov)–98. *Garrison Island (1st series). 150th Anniv of Harbour.* Type A **18** *and similar horiz designs. Multicoloured.* P 14½×14.

A102	18p. Type A **18**	..	45	45
	a. Horiz pair. Nos. A102/3		90	90
	b. Booklet pane. Nos. A102/5 with margins all round (10.11.98)		2·25	
	c. Booklet pane. Nos. A102/3 and A106/7 with margins all round		2·25	
A103	18p. *Ariadne* (paddle steamer) at anchor		45	45
A104	25p. Quarrying stone		65	65
	a. Horiz pair. Nos. A104/5		1·25	1·25
	b. Booklet pane. Nos. A104/5 and A108/9 with margins all round (10.11.98)		2·75	
A105	25p. Quarry railway		65	65
A106	26p. Queen Victoria and Prince Albert on Alderney		70	70
	a. Horiz pair. Nos. A106/7		1·40	1·40
	b. Booklet pane. Nos. A106/9 with margins all round (10.11.98)		3·00	
A107	26p. Royal Yacht *Victoria and Albert* and guard of honour		70	70
A108	31p. Railway workers greet Queen Victoria		80	80
	a. Horiz pair. Nos. A108/9		1·60	1·60
A109	31p. Royal party in railway wagons		80	80
A102/9		*Set of 8*	4·75	4·75

Nos. A102/3, A104/5, A106/7 and A108/9 were each printed together, *se-tenant*, as horizontal pairs throughout sheets of 10. See also Nos. A116/23 and A132/9.

MINIMUM PRICE

The minimum price quote is 10p which represents a handling charge rather than a basis for valuing common stamps. For further notes about prices see introductory pages.

A **19** Modern Superlite Helmet and Wreck of *Point Law* (oil tanker)

A **20** Stained Glass Window commemorating Mary Rogers (Chief Stewardess)

(Des Victoria Kinnersly. Litho B.D.T.)

1998 (10 Feb). *21st Anniv of Alderney Diving Club.* Type A **19** *and similar vert designs. Multicoloured.* P 13.

A110	20p. Type A **19**	..	50	50
A111	30p. Cousteau-Gagnan Demand Valve and wreck of *Stella* (steamer)		75	75
A112	37p. Heinke Closed Helmet and *Liverpool* (full-rigged ship)		90	90
A113	43p. Siebe Closed Helmet		1·00	1·00
A114	63p. Deane Open Helmet		1·50	1·50
A110/14		*Set of 5*	4·25	4·25
MSA115	190×75 mm. Nos. A110/14 and label		4·25	4·25

(Des R. Carter. Litho Questa)

1998 (10 Nov). *Garrison Island (2nd series). Horiz designs as* Type A **18**. *Multicoloured.* P 14½×14.

A116	20p. Alderney Post Office	..	50	50
	a. Horiz pair. Nos. A116/17		1·00	1·00
	b. Booklet pane. Nos. A116/19 with margins all round		2·00	
	c. Booklet pane. Nos. A116/17 and A120/1 with margins all round		2·25	
A117	20p. Traders in Victoria Street		50	50
A118	25p. Court House		60	60
	a. Horiz pair. Nos. A118/19		1·25	1·25
	b. Booklet pane. Nos. A118/19 and A122/3 with margins all round		3·00	
A119	25p. Police Station and fire engine		60	60
A120	30p. St. Anne's Church		70	70
	a. Horiz pair. Nos. A120/1		1·40	1·40
	b. Booklet pane. Nos. A120/3 with margins all round		3·00	
A121	30p. Wedding party at Albert Gate		70	70
A122	37p. *Courier* (ferry) at Braye Bay		85	85
	a. Horiz pair. Nos. A122/3		1·75	1·75
A123	37p. Fishermen at quay		85	85
A116/23		*Set of 8*	4·75	4·75

Nos. A116/17, A118/19, A120/1 and A122/3 were each printed together, *se-tenant*, as horizontal pairs throughout sheets of 10.

(Des Joanna Brehaut. Litho B.D.T.)

1999 (4 Feb). *Centenary of the Wreck of Stella (mail steamer).* Sheet 110×90 mm containing Type A **20** *and similar horiz design.* P 14.

MSA124	25p. Type A **20**; £1·75, *Stella* leaving Southampton	..	3·00	3·00

A **21** Solar Eclipse at 10.15 am

A **22** Peregine Falcon attacking Turnstone

(Des Victoria Kinnersley. Litho Enschedé)

1999 (27 Apr). *Total Eclipse of the Sun (11 August).* Type A **21** *and similar vert designs, showing stages of the eclipse. Multicoloured.* P 13½×13.

A125	20p. Type A **21**	..	50	50
A126	25p. At 10.51 am		60	60
A127	30p. At 11.14 am		70	70
A128	38p. At 11.16 am		90	90
A129	44p. At 11.17 am		1·00	1·00
A130	64p. At 11.36 am		1·50	1·50
A125/30		*Set of 6*	4·75	4·75
MSA131	191×80 mm. Nos. A125/30 and label		4·75	4·75

No. **MSA131** also includes the "PHILEX FRANCE '99", Paris, and the "iBRA '99", Nuremberg, emblems on the sheet margin.

(Des R. Carter. Litho Questa)

1999 (19 Oct). *Garrison Island (3rd series). Forts. Horiz designs as* Type A **18**. *Multicoloured.* P 14½×14.

A132	20p. Field gun and crew, Fort Grosnez, *c.* 1855		40	45
	a. Horiz pair. Nos. A132/3		80	90
	b. Booklet pane. Nos. A132/5, with margins all round		1·75	
	c. Booklet pane. Nos. A132/3 and A138/9, with margins all round		2·25	
	d. Booklet pane. Nos. A132/3 and A136/7, with margins all round		2·00	
A133	20p. Parade of 9th Bn, Royal Garrison Artillery		40	45

A134	25p. The Arsenal, Fort Albert, c. 1862	50	55
	a. Horiz pair. Nos. A134/5	1·00	1·10
	b. Booklet pane. Nos. A134/7, with margins all round	2·25	
	c. Booklet pane. Nos. A134/5 and A138/9, with margins all round	2·50	
A135	25p. Royal Engineers loading wagons	50	55
A136	30p. 2nd Bn, Royal Scots on parade	60	65
	a. Horiz pair. Nos. A136/7	1·10	1·25
	b. Booklet pane. Nos. A136/9, with margins all round	2·75	
A137	30p. Garrison at work, Fort Tourgis, c. 1865	60	65
A138	38p. Gun emplacement, Fort Houmet Herbé, c. 1870	75	80
	a. Horiz pair. Nos. A138/9	1·50	1·60
A139	38p. Royal Alderney Artillery Militia loading cannon	75	80
A132/9	Set of 8	4·50	5·00

Nos. A132/3, A134/5, A136/7 and A 138/9 were each printed together, *se-tenant*, as horizontal pairs throughout the sheet, each pair forming a composite design.

(Des R. Gorringe. Litho Questa)

2000 (4 Feb). *Endangered Species. Peregrine Falcon. Type A 22 and similar square designs. Multicoloured. P 14½×14.*

A140	21p. Type A 22	40	45
	a. Booklet pane of 10	4·00	
A141	26p. Two falcons and prey	50	55
	a. Booklet pane of 10	5·00	
A142	34p. Falcon guarding eggs	70	75
A143	38p. Falcon feeding young	75	80
A144	44p. Falcon and prey	90	95
A145	64p. Two young falcons	1·25	1·40
A140/5	Set of 6	4·50	4·75

Nos. A140/5 were each issued in sheets of 10 (2×5) with enlarged illustrated left hand margins. Nos. A142/5 include the W.W.F emblem.

Booklet panes Nos. A140a and A141a show the upper and lower edges of the panes imperforate and have margins at left and right.

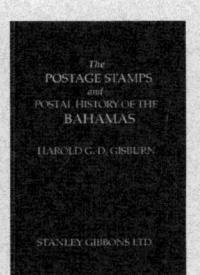

ISLE OF MAN
REGIONAL ISSUES

Although specifically issued for use in the Isle of Man, these issues were also valid for use throughout Great Britain.

DATES OF ISSUE: The note at the beginning of Guernsey also applies here.

Nos. 8/11 and current stamps of Great Britain were withdrawn from sale on the island from 5 July 1973 when the independent postal administration was established but remained valid for use there until 5 August 1973. They also remained on sale at the Philatelic Sales counters in the United Kingdom until 4 July 1974.

| 1 | 2 | 3 |

(Des J. Nicholson. Portrait by Dorothy Wilding Ltd. Photo Harrison)

1958 (18 Aug)–68. *W* 179. *P* 15 × 14.
1	1	2½d. carmine-red (8.6.64)	..	50	1·25
2	2	3d. deep lilac	..	30	20
		a. Chalk-surfaced paper (17.5.63)		12·00	10·00
		p. One centre phosphor band (27.6.68)		30	50
3		4d. ultramarine (7.2.66)	..	1·50	1·50
		p. Two phosphor bands (5.7.67)		30	30
1/3p			*Set of 3*	1·00	1·60

No. 2a was released in London sometime after 17 May 1963, this being the date of issue in Douglas.

1968–69. *No wmk. Chalk-surfaced paper. PVA gum. One centre phosphor band (Nos. 5/6) or two phosphor bands (others). P* 15 × 14.
4	2	4d. blue (24.6.68)	..	25	30
5		4d. olive-sepia (4.9.68)	..	25	40
6		4d. bright vermilion (26.2.69)	..	45	75
7		5d. royal blue (4.9.68)	..	45	75
4/7			*Set of 4*	1·25	2·00

(Des J. Matthews. Portrait after plaster cast by Arnold Machin. Photo Harrison)

1971 (7 July). *Decimal Currency. Chalk-surfaced paper. One centre phosphor band (2½p.) or two phosphor bands (others). P* 15 × 14.
8	3	2½p. bright magenta	..	20	15
9		3p. ultramarine	..	20	15
10		5p. reddish violet	..	40	50
11		7½p. chestnut	..	40	65
8/11			*Set of 4*	1·25	1·25

All values exist with PVA gum on ordinary cream paper and the 2½p. and 3p. also on fluorescent white paper.

INDEPENDENT POSTAL ADMINISTRATION

| 4 Castletown | 5 Manx Cat |

(Des J. Nicholson. Photo Courvoisier)

1973 (5 July)–75. *Horiz designs as T* 4 (½p. to 9p., 11p. and 13p.) *or vert designs as T* 5 (others). *Multicoloured. Granite paper. P* 11½.
12	½p. Type 4	..	..	10	10
13	1p. Port Erin	..	..	10	10
14	1½p. Snaefell	..	..	10	10
15	2p. Laxey	..	..	10	10
16	2½p. Tynwald Hill	..	..	10	10
17	3p. Douglas Promenade (sage-green border)		10	10
	a. Error. Olive-bistre border†		£150	£125
18	3½p. Port St. Mary (olive-brown border)	..	15	15
	a. Error. Grey-brown border†		£150	£125
19	4p. Fairy Bridge	..	..	15	15
20	4½p. As 2½p. (8.1.75)	..	..	20	20
21	5p. Peel	..	..	20	20
22	5½p. As 3p. (28.5.75)	..	..	25	25
23	6p. Cregneish	..	..	25	25
24	6p. As 2p. (28.5.75)	..	..	30	30
25	7½p. Ramsey Bay	..	..	25	25
26	8p. As 7½p. (8.1.75)	..	..	35	35
27	9p. Douglas Bay	..	..	30	35
28	10p. Type 5	..	..	40	35
29	11p. Monk's Bridge, Ballasalla (29.10.75)		30	30
30	13p. Derbyhaven (29.10.75)	..	40	40
31	20p. Manx Loaghtyn Ram	..	50	50
32	50p. Manx Shearwater	..	..	1·50	1·25
33	£1 Viking longship	..	..	3·00	2·50
12/33		*Set of 22*	8·00	7·50

†These errors occur on printings in 1974. That on the 3p. resembles the border of the ½p. and that on the 3½p. the 2p. Intermediate shades also exist, but are not covered by the listing.
Some printings from late 1973 have invisible gum.
Imprint dates: "1973", Nos. 12/19, 21, 23, 25, 27/8, 31/3; "1975", Nos. 20, 22, 24, 26, 29/30.

MINIMUM PRICE

The minimum price quote is 10p which represents a handling charge rather than a basis for valuing common stamps. For further notes about prices see introductory pages.

| 6 Viking landing on Man, A.D. 938 | 7 No. 1 *Sutherland*, 1873 |

(Des J. Nicholson. Photo Harrison)

1973 (5 July). *Inauguration of Postal Independence. P* 14.
34	6	15p. multicoloured	..	60	60

(Des J. Nicholson. Photo Harrison)

1973 (4 Aug). *Steam Railway Centenary. T* 7 *and similar horiz designs showing steam locomotives. Multicoloured. P* 15 × 14.
35	2½p. Type 7	..	..	20	20
36	3p. No. 4 *Caledonia*, 1885	..	20	20
37	7½p. No. 13 *Kissack*, 1910	..	80	90
38	9p. No. 3 *Pender*, 1873	..	1·00	90
35/8			*Set of 4*	2·00	2·00

8 Leonard Randles, First Winner, 1923

(Des J. Nicholson. Litho J.W.)

1973 (4 Sept). *Golden Jubilee of the Manx Grand Prix. T* 8 *and similar horiz design. Multicoloured. P* 14.
39	3p. Type 8	..	..	30	20
40	3½p. Alan Holmes, Double Winner, 1957	30	20

9 Princess Anne and Capt. Mark Phillips

(Des A. Larkins. Recess and litho D.L.R.)

1973 (14 Nov). *Royal Wedding. P* 13½.
41	9	25p. multicoloured	..	1·00	1·00

10 Badge, Citation and Sir William Hillary (Founder)

(Des J. Nicholson. Photo Courvoisier)

1974 (4 Mar). *150th Anniv of Royal National Lifeboat Institution. T* 10 *and similar horiz designs. Multicoloured. Granite paper. P* 11½.
42	3p. Type 10	..	..	10	10
43	3½p. Wreck of *St. George*, 1830	..	15	15
44	8p. R.N.L.B. *Manchester & Salford*, 1868–87	40	40
45	10p. R.N.L.B. *Osman Gabriel*	..	45	45
42/5		*Set of 4*	1·00	1·00

11 Stanley Woods, 1935

(Des J. Nicholson. Litho D.L.R.)

1974 (29 May). *Tourist Trophy Motor-cycle Races (1st issue). T* 11 *and similar horiz designs. Multicoloured. P* 13 × 13½.
46	3p. Type 11	..	..	10	10
47	3½p. Freddy Frith, 1937	..	10	10
48	8p. Max Deubel and Emil Horner, 1961	45	45
49	10p. Mike Hailwood, 1961	..	60	45
46/9		*Set of 4*	1·10	1·00

See also Nos. 63/6.

---

12 Rushen Abbey and Arms

(Des J. Nicholson from ideas by G. Kneale. Litho Questa (3½p., 10p.) or J.W. (others))

1974 (18 Sept). *Historical Anniversaries. T* 12 *and similar horiz designs. Multicoloured. P* 14.
50	3½p. Type 12	..	..	10	10
51	4½p. Magnus Haraldson rows King Edgar on the Dee	10	10
52	8p. King Magnus and Norse fleet	..	40	40
53	10p. Bridge at Avignon and bishop's mitre	50	50
50/3		*Set of 4*	1·00	1·00

Nos. 50 and 53 mark the 600th Death Anniv of William Russell, Bishop of Sodor and Man, and Nos. 51/2 the 1000th Anniv of the rule of King Magnus Haraldson.

13 Churchill and Bugler Dunne at Colenso, 1899

(Des G. Kneale. Photo Courvoisier)

1974 (22 Nov). *Birth Centenary of Sir Winston Churchill. T* 13 *and similar horiz designs. Multicoloured. Granite paper. P* 11½.
54	3½p. Type 13	..	..	10	10
55	4½p. Churchill and Government Buildings, Douglas	10	10
56	8p. Churchill and Manx ack-ack crew	..	25	35
57	20p. Churchill as Freeman of Douglas	75	55
54/7		*Set of 4*	1·10	1·00
MS58	121 × 91 mm. Nos. 54/7	..	1·10	1·00

No. MS58 is inscribed "30th Nov. 1974".

14 Cabin School and Names of Pioneers

(Des J. Nicholson. Photo Courvoisier)

1975 (14 Mar). *Manx Pioneers in Cleveland, Ohio. T* 14 *and similar horiz designs. Multicoloured. Granite paper. P* 11½.
59	4½p. Type 14	..	..	10	10
60	5½p. Terminal Tower Building, J. Gill and R. Carran	15	10
61	8p. Clague House Museum, and Robert and Margaret Clague	35	40
62	10p. S.S. *William T. Graves* and Thomas Quayle	50	50
59/62		*Set of 4*	1·00	1·00

15 Tom Sheard, 1923

(Des J. Nicholson. Litho J.W.)

1975 (28 May). *Tourist Trophy Motor-cycle Races (2nd issue). T* 15 *and similar horiz designs. Multicoloured. P* 13½.
63	5p. Type 15	..	..	20	15
64	7p. Walter Handley, 1925	..	30	20
65	10p. Geoff Duke, 1955	..	50	30
66	12p. Peter Williams, 1973	..	50	45
63/6		*Set of 4*	1·25	1·00

| 16 Sir George Goldie and Birthplace | 17 Title Page of Manx Bible |

(Des G. Kneale. Photo Courvoisier)

1975 (9 Sept). *50th Death Anniv of Sir George Goldie. T* 16 *and similar multicoloured designs. Granite paper. P* 11½.
67	5½p. Type 16	..	..	10	15
68	7p. Goldie and map of Africa (*vert*)	20	20
69	10p. Goldie as President of Geographical Society (*vert*)	40	30
70	12p. River scene on the Niger	..	40	45
67/70		*Set of 4*	1·00	1·00

(Des J. Nicholson. Litho Questa)

1975 (29 Oct). *Christmas and Bicentenary of Manx Bible. T 17 and similar horiz designs. Multicoloured. P 14.*

71	5½p. Type **17**		15	15
72	7p. Rev. Philip Moore and Ballaugh Old Church		20	20
73	11p. Bishop Hildesley and Bishops Court		35	35
74	13p. John Kelly saving Bible manuscript		40	40
71/4		*Set of 4*	1·00	1·00

18 William Christian listening to Patrick Henry

19 First Horse Tram, 1876

(Des and litho J.W.)

1976 (12 Mar). *Bicentenary of American Revolution. T 18 and similar vert designs. Multicoloured. P 13½.*

75	5½p. Type **18**		15	15
76	7p. Conveying the Fincastle Resolutions		20	20
77	13p. Patrick Henry and William Christian		35	35
78	20p. Christian as an Indian fighter		50	50
75/8		*Set of 4*	1·10	1·10
MS79	153 × 89 mm. Nos. 75/8. P 14		1·50	1·60

(Des J. Nicholson. Photo Courvoisier)

1976 (26 May). *Douglas Horse Trams Centenary. T 19 and similar horiz designs. Multicoloured. Granite paper. P 11½.*

80	5½p. Type **19**		10	15
81	7p. "Toast-rack" tram, 1890		15	15
82	11p. Horse-bus, 1895		45	35
83	13p. Royal tram, 1972		50	45
80/3		*Set of 4*	1·10	1·00

20 Barroose Beaker

21 Diocesan Banner

(Des J. Nicholson. Photo Courvoisier)

1976 (28 July). *Europa. Ceramic Art. T 20 and similar multicoloured designs. Granite paper. P 11½.*

84	5p. Type **20**		25	20
	a. Strip of 3. Nos. 84/6		70	60
85	5p. Souvenir teapot		25	20
86	5p. Laxey jug		25	20
87	10p. Cronk Aust food vessel (*horiz*)		40	35
	a. Strip of 3. Nos. 87/9		1·25	1·10
88	10p. Sansbury bowl (*horiz*)		40	35
89	10p. Knox urn (*horiz*)		40	35
84/9		*Set of 6*	1·75	1·50

Nos. 84/6 and 87/9 were each printed in sheets of 9 (3 × 3) the three designs being horizontally and vertically *se-tenant*.

(Des G. Kneale. Litho Questa)

1976 (14 Oct). *Christmas and Centenary of Mothers' Union. T 21 and similar vert designs. Multicoloured. P 14½.*

90	6p. Type **21**		15	15
91	7p. Onchan banner		15	15
92	11p. Castletown banner		40	35
93	13p. Ramsey banner		40	45
90/3		*Set of 4*	1·00	1·00

22 Queen Elizabeth II

(Des A. Larkins. Litho and recess D.L.R.)

1977 (1 Mar). *Silver Jubilee. T 22 and similar multicoloured designs. P 14 × 13 (7p.) or 13 × 14 (others).*

94	6p. Type **22**		20	20
95	7p. Queen Elizabeth and Prince Philip (*vert*)		20	20
96	25p. Queen Elizabeth		80	70
94/6		*Set of 3*	1·10	1·00

The 25p. is similar to T **22** but has the portrait on the right.

23 Carrick Bay from "Tom-the-Dipper"

(Des J. Nicholson. Litho Questa)

1977 (26 May). *Europa. Landscapes. T 23 and similar horiz design. Multicoloured. P 13½ × 14.*

97	6p. Type **23**		20	20
98	10p. View from Ramsey		30	30

24 F. A. Applebee, 1912

(Des J. Nicholson. Litho J.W.)

1977 (26 May). *Linked Anniversaries. T 24 and similar horiz designs. Multicoloured. P 13½.*

99	6p. Type **24**		20	15
100	7p. St. John Ambulance Brigade at Governor's Bridge, *c*. 1938		20	20
101	11p. Scouts working scoreboard		50	40
102	13p. John Williams, 1976		50	40
99/102		*Set of 4*	1·25	1·00

The events commemorated are: 70th Anniv of Manx TT; 70th Anniv of Boy Scouts; Centenary of St John Ambulance Brigade.

25 Old Summer House, Mount Morrison, Peel

(Des and photo Courvoisier)

1977 (19 Oct). *Bicentenary of the First Visit of John Wesley. T 25 and similar horiz designs. Multicoloured. Granite paper. P 11½.*

103	6p. Type **25**		15	15
104	7p. Wesley preaching in Castletown Square		20	20
105	11p. Wesley preaching outside Braddan Church		35	35
106	13p. New Methodist Church, Douglas		40	40
103/6		*Set of 4*	1·00	1·00

Nos. 104/5 are larger, 38 × 26 mm.

26 H.M.S. *Ben-My-Chree* and Short Type 184 Seaplane, 1915

(Des A. Theobald. Litho J.W.)

1978 (28 Feb). *R.A.F. Diamond Jubilee. T 26 and similar horiz designs. Multicoloured. P 13½ × 14.*

107	6p. Type **26**		20	15
108	7p. H.M.S. *Vindex* and Bristol Scout C, 1915		30	20
109	11p. Boulton Paul Defiant over Douglas Bay, 1941		45	35
110	13p. Sepecat Jaguar over Ramsey, 1977		50	40
107/10		*Set of 4*	1·25	1·00

27 Watch Tower, Langness

27a Queen Elizabeth II

(Des J. Nicholson (½p. to £1), G. Kneale (£2). Litho Questa (½p. to 16p.). Photo Courvoisier (20p. to £2))

1978 (28 Feb)–**81.** *Various multicoloured designs. (a) As T 27. P 14.*

111	½p. Type **27**		10	10
	a. Perf 14½		20	10
112	1p. Jurby Church (*horiz*)		10	10
	a. Perf 14½		20	10
113	6p. Government Buildings		30	30
114	7p. Tynwald Hill (*horiz*)		35	35
	a. Perf 14½		8·00	6·50
115	8p. Milner's Tower		25	25
	a. Perf 14½		35	35
116	9p. Laxey Wheel		35	35
	a. Perf 14½		35	35
117	10p. Castle Rushen		40	40
	a. Perf 14½		35	35
118	11p. St. Ninian's Church		40	40
	a. Perf 14½		40	40

119	12p. Tower of Refuge (*horiz*)		50	50
	a. Perf 14½		50	40
120	13p. St. German's Cathedral (*horiz*)		60	60
	a. Perf 14½		40	40
121	14p. Point of Ayre Lighthouse (*horiz*)		60	60
	a. Perf 14½		50	50
122	15p. Corrin's Tower (*horiz*)		75	75
	a. Perf 14½		40	40
123	16p. Douglas Head Lighthouse (*horiz*)		90	90
	a. Perf 14½		25·00	21·00

(b) As T 27 but size 25×31 mm. Granite paper. P 11½ (18.10.78)

124	20p. Fuchsia		40	40
125	25p. Manx cat		50	50
126	50p. Chough		1·00	1·00
127	£1 Viking warrior		2·00	2·00

(c) T 27a. P 11½ (29.9.81)

128	£2 multicoloured		4·50	4·50
111/28		*Set of 18*	11·75	11·75

Although both perforations of Nos. 111/23 were printed at the same time some did not appear in use until some time after 28 February 1978. Earliest dates for these are as follows: 1p. (112a) 8.79, 7p. (114a) 8.78, 8p. (115a) 6.80, 10p. (117a) 8.79, 12p. (119) 9.80.

28 Queen Elizabeth in Coronation Regalia

29 Wheel-headed Cross-slab

(Des G. Kneale. Litho Questa)

1978 (24 May). *25th Anniv of Coronation. P 14½ × 14.*

132	**28** 25p. multicoloured		75	75

(Des J. Nicholson. Photo Courvoisier)

1978 (24 May). *Europa. Sculpture. T 29 and similar vert designs showing Celtic and Norse Crosses. Multicoloured. Granite paper. P 11½.*

133	6p. Type **29**		20	15
	a. Strip of 3. Nos. 133/5		60	50
134	6p. Celtic wheel-cross		20	15
135	6p. Keeil Chiggyrt Stone		20	15
136	11p. Olaf Liotulfson Cross		35	30
	a. Strip of 3. Nos. 136/8		1·10	90
137	11p. Odd's and Thorleif's Crosses		35	30
138	11p. Thor Cross		35	30
133/8		*Set of 6*	1·50	1·25

Nos. 133/5 and 136/8 were each printed together, *se-tenant*, in horizontal and vertical strips of 3 throughout the sheet.

30 J. K. Ward and Ward Library, Peel

31 Hunt the Wren

(Des J.W. (7p.), G. Kneale (11p.), J. Nicholson (others). Litho J.W.)

1978 (10 June). *Anniversaries and Events. T 30 and similar horiz designs. Multicoloured. Invisible gum. P 13½.*

139	6p. Type **30**		15	15
140	7p. Swimmer, cyclist and walker (42 × 26 mm)		20	20
141	11p. American Bald Eagle, Manx arms and maple leaf (42 × 26 mm)		35	35
142	13p. Lumber camp at Three Rivers, Quebec		40	40
139/42		*Set of 4*	1·00	1·00

Commemorations:—6, 13p. James Kewley Ward (Manx pioneer in Canada); 7p. Commonwealth Games, Edmonton; 11p. 50th anniversary of North American Manx Association.

(Des J. Nicholson. Litho J.W.)

1978 (18 Oct). *Christmas. P 13.*

143	**31** 5p. multicoloured		50	50

32 P. M. C. Kermode (founder) and *Nassa kermodei*

33 Postman, 1859

(Des J. Nicholson. Litho Questa)

1979 (27 Feb). *Centenary of Natural History and Antiquarian Society. T* 32 *and similar horiz designs. Multicoloured. P* 14.

144	6p. Type **32**	15	15
145	7p. Peregrine Falcon	20	20
146	11p. Fulmar	35	35
147	13p. *Epitriptus cowini* (fly)	40	40
144/7	*Set of* 4	1·00	1·00

(Des A. Theobald. Litho Questa)

1979 (16 May). *Europa. Communications. T* 33 *and similar vert design. Multicoloured. P* 14½.

148	6p. Type **33**	25	25
149	11p. Postman, 1979	50	50

34 Viking Longship Emblem   **35** Viking Raid at Garwick

Two types of No. 150:

Type I. Wrongly inscribed "INSULAREM". "1979" imprint date.

Type II. Inscription corrected to "INSULARUM". "1980" imprint date.

(Des J. Nicholson. Litho Harrison (3, 4p.), J.W. (others))

1979 (16 May)–80. *Millenium of Tynwald. Multicoloured.*

(*a*) *Vert designs as T* **34**. *P* 14½ × 14

150	3p. Type **34** (Type I)	15	15
	a. Booklet pane. Nos. 150×4, 151×2 (4p. stamps at top)	90	
	ab. Ditto (4p. stamps in centre)	1·50	
	b. Type II (29.9.80)	10	10
	ba. Booklet pane. Nos. 150b×4, 151×2 (4p. stamps at bottom)	75	
151	4p. "Three Legs of Man" emblem	15	15

(*b*) *Horiz designs as T* **35**. *P* 13

152	6p. Type **35**	15	15
153	7p. 10th-century meeting of Tynwald	20	20
154	11p. Tynwald Hill and St. John's Church	30	30
155	13p. Procession to Tynwald Hill	45	35
150/5	*Set of* 6	1·25	1·10

See also Nos. 188/9.

The 3 and 4p. values were printed in sheets containing ten blocks of 6 and five blocks of 4 separated by blank margins. The blocks of 6 contained four 3p. values and two 4p., *se-tenant*, with the 4p. in either the top or centre rows. The blocks of 4 contain the 4p. value only.

No. 151 exists with different dates below the design.

For details of No. 150ba see after No. 189.

36 Queen and Court on Tynwald Hill

(Des G. Kneale. Litho Questa)

1979 (5 July). *Royal Visit. T* 36 *and similar horiz design. Multicoloured. P* 14½.

156	7p. Type **36**	35	35
157	13p. Queen and procession from St. John's Church to Tynwald Hill	50	50

OMNIBUS ISSUES

Details, together with prices for complete sets, of the various Omnibus issues from the 1935 Silver Jubilee series to date are included in a special section following Zimbabwe at the end of Volume 2.

37 *Odin's Raven*

(Des J. Nicholson. Litho Questa)

1979 (19 Oct). *Voyage of "Odin's Raven". P* 14 × 14½.

158	**37** 15p. multicoloured	70	70

38 John Quilliam seized by   **39** Young Girl with the Press Gang   Teddybear and Cat

(Des A. Theobald. Litho Questa)

1979 (19 Oct). *150th Death Anniv of Captain John Quilliam. T* 38 *and similar horiz designs. Multicoloured. P* 14.

159	6p. Type **38**	15	15
160	8p. Steering H.M.S. *Victory*, Battle of Trafalgar	20	20
161	13p. Capt. John Quilliam and H.M.S. *Spencer*	35	35
162	15p. Capt. John Quilliam (member of the House of Keys)	40	40
159/62	*Set of* 4	1·00	1·00

(Des Mrs E. Moore. Litho J.W.)

1979 (19 Oct). *Christmas. International Year of the Child. T* 39 *and similar vert design. Multicoloured. P* 13.

163	5p. Type **39**	25	25
164	7p. Father Christmas with young children	35	35

40 Conglomerate Arch, Langness

(Des J. Nicholson. Litho Questa)

1980 (5 Feb). *150th Anniv of Royal Geographical Society. T* 40 *and similar horiz designs. Multicoloured. P* 14½.

165	7p. Type **40**	20	20
166	8p. Braaid Circle	20	20
167	12p. Cashtal-yn-Ard	25	25
168	13p. Volcanic Rocks at Scarlett	35	35
169	15p. Sugar-loaf Rock	40	40
165/9	*Set of* 5	1·25	1·25

41 *Mona's Isle I*

(Des J. Nicholson. Photo Courvoisier)

1980 (6 May). *150th Anniv of Isle of Man Steam Packet Company. T* 41 *and similar horiz designs. Multicoloured. Granite paper. P* 11½.

170	7p. Type **41**	20	20
171	8p. *Douglas I*	20	20
172	11½p. H.M.S. *Mona's Queen II* sinking U-boat	30	30
173	12p. H.M.S. *King Orry III* at surrender of German fleet	30	30
174	13p. *Ben-My-Chree IV*	40	35
175	15p. *Lady of Mann II*	50	40
170/5	*Set of* 6	1·75	1·60
MS176	180×125 mm. Nos. 170/5	1·75	1·75

No. MS176 was issued to commemorate the "London 1980" International Stamp Exhibition.

42 Stained Glass Window, T. E. Brown Room, Manx Museum

(Des G. Kneale. Photo Courvoisier)

1980 (6 May). *Europa. Personalities. Thomas Edward Brown (poet and scholar) Commemoration. T* 42 *and similar horiz design. Multicoloured. Granite paper. P* 11½.

177	7p. Type **42**	20	20
178	13½p. Clifton College, Bristol	40	40

43 King Olav V and *Norge* (Norwegian royal yacht)

(Des J. Nicholson. Litho Questa)

1980 (13 June). *Visit of King Olav of Norway, August* 1979. *P* 14×14½.

179	**43** 12p. multicoloured	50	50
MS180	125×157 mm. Nos. 158 and 179	1·00	1·00

No. MS180 also commemorates the "NORWEX 80" Stamp Exhibition, Oslo.

44 Winter Wren and View of Calf of Man

(Des J. Nicholson. Litho J.W.)

1980 (29 Sept). *Christmas and Wildlife Conservation Year. T* 44 *and similar horiz design. Multicoloured. P* 13½ × 14.

181	6p. Type **44**	20	20
182	8p. European Robin and view of Port Erin Marine Biological Station	30	30

45 William Kermode and   **46** Peregrine Falcon Brig *Robert Quayle*, 1819

(Des A. Theobald. Litho Questa)

1980 (29 Sept). *Kermode Family in Tasmania Commemoration. T* 45 *and similar horiz designs. Multicoloured. P* 14½.

183	7p. Type **45**	20	20
184	9p. "Mona Vale", Van Diemen's Land, 1834	25	25
185	13½p. Ross Bridge, Tasmania	40	35
186	15p. "Mona Vale", Tasmania (completed 1868)	45	40
187	17½p. Robert Q. Kermode and Parliament Buildings, Tasmania	50	45
183/7	*Set of* 5	1·60	1·50

(Des J. Nicholson. Litho Harrison)

1980 (29 Sept). *Booklet stamps. Vert designs as T* 46. *Multicoloured. P* 14½ × 14.

188	1p. Type **46**	40	40
	a. Booklet pane. Nos. 151, 188 and 189 each ×2	75	
189	5p. Loaghtyn Ram	40	40

In addition to 40p. and 80p. booklets Nos. 188/9 also come from special booklet sheets of 60. These sheets contained No. 150ba and 188a, each ×5.

47 Luggers passing Red Pier, Douglas

(Des J. Nicholson. Litho Questa)

1981 (24 Feb). *Centenary of Royal National Mission to Deep Sea Fishermen. T* 47 *and similar horiz designs. Multicoloured. P* 14.

190	8p. Type **47**	25	25
191	9p. Peel Lugger *Wanderer* rescuing survivors from the *Lusitania*	30	30
192	18p. Nickeys leaving Port St. Mary Harbour	45	45
193	20p. Nobby entering Ramsey Harbour	50	50
194	22p. Nickeys *Sunbeam* and *Zebra* at Port Erin	50	50
190/4	*Set of* 5	1·75	1·75

48 "Crosh Cuirn" Superstition

(Des J. Nicholson. Litho Questa)

1981 (22 May). *Europa. Folklore. T* **48** *and similar horiz design. Multicoloured. P* 14½.
195	8p.	Type 48	..	25	25
196	18p.	"Bollan Cross" superstition	..	75	75

49 Lt. Mark Wilks (Royal Manx Fencibles) and Peel Castle

(Des A. Theobald. Litho Questa)

1981 (22 May). *150th Death Anniv of Colonel Mark Wilks. T* **49** *and similar horiz designs. Multicoloured. P* 14.
197	8p.	Type 49	..	25	25
198	20p.	Ensign Mark Wilks and Fort St. George, Madras	..	50	50
199	22p.	Governor Mark Wilks and Napoleon, St. Helena	..	70	55
200	25p.	Col. Mark Wilks (Speaker of the House of Keys) and estate, Kirby	..	80	80
197/200	..	.. .. ..	*Set of* 4	2·00	1·90

50 Miss Emmeline Goulden (Mrs. Pankhurst) and Mrs. Sophia Jane Goulden

(Des A. Theobald. Litho Questa)

1981 (22 May). *Centenary of Manx Women's Suffrage. P* 14.
201	**50**	9p. black, olive-grey and stone	..	50	50

51 Prince Charles and Lady Diana Spencer

(Des G. Kneale. Litho Harrison)

1981 (29 July). *Royal Wedding. P* 14.
202	51	9p. black, bright blue and pale blue	..	50	50
203		25p. black, bright blue and pink	..	1·50	1·50
MS204		130 × 183 mm. Nos. 202/3 × 2	..	4·50	4·50

52 Douglas War Memorial, Poppies and Commemorative Inscription

(Des A. Theobald. Photo Courvoisier)

1981 (29 Sept). *60th Anniv of The Royal British Legion. T* **52** *and similar horiz designs. Multicoloured. Granite paper. P* 11½.
205	8p.	Type 52	..	25	25
206	10p.	Major Robert Cain (war hero)	..	30	35
207	18p.	Festival of Remembrance, Royal Albert Hall	..	65	65
208	20p.	T.S.S. *Tynwald* at Dunkirk, May 1940	..	75	75
205/8	..	.. .. ..	*Set of* 4	1·75	1·75

ALTERED CATALOGUE NUMBERS

Any Catalogue numbers altered from the last edition are shown as a list in the introductory pages.

53 Nativity Scene (stained-glass window, St. George's Church)

(Des J.W. (7p.), G. Kneale (9p.). Litho J.W.)

1981 (29 Sept). *Christmas. T* **53** *and similar multicoloured design. P* 14.
209	7p.	Type 53	..	25	25
210	9p.	Children from Special School performing nativity play (48 × 30 *mm*)	..	35	35

The 7p. value also commemorates the bicentenary of St. George's Church, Douglas and the 9p. the International Year for Disabled Persons.

54 Joseph and William Cunningham (founders of Isle of Man Boy Scout Movement) and Cunningham House Headquarters

(Des G. Kneale. Litho Questa)

1982 (23 Feb). *75th Anniv of Boy Scout Movement and 125th Birth Anniv of Lord Baden-Powell. T* **54** *and similar multicoloured designs. P* 14 × 14½ (19½p.) or 13½ × 14 (others).
211	9p.	Type 54	..	30	30
212	10p.	Baden-Powell visiting Isle of Man, 1911		30	30
213	19½p.	Baden-Powell and Scout emblem (40 × 31 *mm*)	..	60	60
214	24p.	Scouts and Baden-Powell's last message		70	70
215	29p.	Scout salute, handshake, emblem and globe	..	90	90
211/15	..	.. ..	*Set of* 5	2·50	2·50

55 The Principals and Duties of Christianity (Bishop T. Wilson) (first book printed in Manx, 1707)

(Des A. Theobald. Photo Courvoisier)

1982 (1 June). *Europa. Historic Events. T* **55** *and similar horiz design. Multicoloured. Granite paper. P* 12 × 12½.
216	9p.	Type 55	..	25	25
217	19½p.	Landing at Derbyhaven (visit of Thomas, 2nd Earl of Derby, 1507)	..	50	50

56 Charlie Collier (first TT race (single cylinder) winner) and Tourist Trophy Race, 1907

(Des J. Nicholson. Litho Questa)

1982 (1 June). *75th Anniv of Tourist Trophy Motorcycle Racing. T* **56** *and similar horiz designs. Multicoloured. P* 14.
218	9p.	Type 56	..	20	20
219	10p.	Freddie Dixon (Sidecar and Junior TT winner) and Junior TT race, 1927	..	25	25
220	24p.	Jimmie Simpson (TT winner and first to lap at 60, 70 and 80 mph) and Senior TT, 1932	..	80	70
221	26p.	Mike Hailwood (winner of fourteen TT's) and Senior TT, 1961	..	85	75
222	29p.	Jock Taylor (Sidecar TT winner, 1978, 1980 and 1981) and Sidecar TT (with Benga Johansson), 1980	..	1·00	90
218/22	..	..	*Set of* 5	2·75	2·50

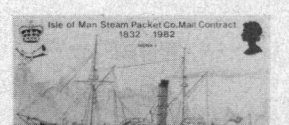

57 *Mona I*

(Des J. Nicholson. Litho Questa)

1982 (5 Oct). *150th Anniv of Isle of Man Steam Packet Company Mail Contract. T* **57** *and similar horiz design. Multicoloured. P* 13½ × 14.
223	12p.	Type 57	..	50	50
224	19½p.	*Manx Maid II*	..	75	75

58 Three Wise Men bearing Gifts **59** Princess Diana with Prince William

(Des and litho J.W.)

1982 (5 Oct). *Christmas. T* **58** *and similar multicoloured design. P* 13 × 13½ (8p.) or 13½ × 13 (11p.).
225	8p.	Type 58	..	50	50
226	11p.	Christmas snow scene (*vert*)	..	50	50

(Des G. Kneale. Litho Questa)

1982 (12 Oct). *21st Birthday of Princess of Wales and Birth of Prince William. Sheet* 100 × 83 *mm. P* 14½ × 14.
MS227	**59**	50p. multicoloured	..	3·50	3·50

60 Opening of Salvation Army Citadel, and T.H. Cannell, J.P.

(Des A. Theobald. Photo Courvoisier)

1983 (15 Feb). *Centenary of Salvation Army in Isle of Man. T* **60** *and similar horiz designs. Multicoloured. Granite paper. P* 11½.
228	10p.	Type 60	..	30	30
229	12p.	Early meeting place and Gen. William Booth	..	40	40
230	19½p.	Salvation Army band	..	60	60
231	26p.	Treating lepers and Lt.-Col. Thomas Bridson	..	90	90
228/31			*Set of* 4	2·00	2·00

61 Atlantic Puffins **61a** "Queen Elizabeth II" (Ricardo Macarron)

(Des Colleen Corlett (£5), J. Nicholson (others). Litho Questa)

1983 (15 Feb)–**85**. *Horiz designs as T* **61**, *showing sea-birds, and T* **61a**. *Multicoloured. P* 14 (20p. to £1), 14 × 13½ (£5) *or* 14½ (others).
232	1p.	Type 61	..	30	30
233	2p.	Northern Gannets	..	30	30
234	5p.	Lesser Black-backed Gulls	..	60	40
235	8p.	Common Cormorants	..	60	40
236	10p.	Kittiwakes	..	60	35
237	11p.	Shags	..	60	35
238	12p.	Grey Herons	..	70	40
239	13p.	Herring Gulls	..	70	40
240	14p.	Razorbills	..	70	40
241	15p.	Great Black-backed Gulls	..	80	50
242	16p.	Common Shelducks	..	80	50
243	18p.	Oystercatchers	..	80	60
244	20p.	Arctic Terns (14.9.83)	..	90	1·00
245	25p.	Common Guillemots (14.9.83)	..	1·00	1·00
246	50p.	Redshanks (14.9.83)	..	1·75	1·75
247	£1	Mute Swans (14.9.83)	..	3·25	3·00
248	£5	Type 61a (31.1.85)	..	12·00	12·00
232/48			*Set of* 17	24·00	21·00

Nos. 244/7 are larger, 39×26 mm.

62 Design Drawings by Robert Casement for the Great Laxey Wheel

(Des J. Nicholson. Litho Questa)

1983 (18 May). *Europa. The Great Laxey Wheel. T* **62** *and similar horiz design. P* 14.
249	10p. black, azure and buff	.. .. ..	40	35
250	20½p. multicoloured	.. .. ..	60	70

Design:—20½p. Robert Casement and the Great Laxey Wheel.

63 Nick Keig (international yachtsman) and Trimaran *Three Legs of Man III*

64 New Post Office Headquarters, Douglas

(Des J. Nicholson (10p., 31p.), Colleen Corlett (12p., 28p.). Photo Courvoisier)

1983 (18 May). *150th Anniv of King William's College. T* **63** *and similar horiz designs. Multicoloured. Granite paper. P* 11½.
251	10p. Type **63**	.. ..	20	20
252	12p. King William's College, Castletown	..	30	30
253	28p. Sir William Bragg (winner of Nobel Prize for Physics) and spectrometer	..	80	80
254	31p. General Sir George White V.C. and action at Charasiah	.. ..	1·00	1·00
251/4		*Set of 4*	2·00	2·00

(Des Colleen Corlett (10p.), J. Nicholson (15p.). Litho Questa)

1983 (5 July). *World Communications Year and 10th Anniv of Isle of Man Post Office Authority. T* **64** *and similar vert design. Multicoloured. P* 14½.
255	10p. Type **64**	.. .. ..	40	40
256	15p. As Type **6**, but inscr "POST OFFICE DECENNIUM 1983"	.. ..	60	60

65 Shepherds

(Des Colleen Corlett. Litho J.W.)

1983 (14 Sept). *Christmas. T* **65** *and similar horiz design. Multicoloured. P* 13.
257	9p. Type **65**	.. ..	50	50
258	12p. Three Kings	.. ..	50	50

66 *Manx King* (full-rigged ship)

67 C.E.P.T. 25th Anniversary Logo

(Des J. Nicholson (10p. to 31p.); Colleen Corlett, J. Nicholson and J. Smith (miniature sheet). Litho Questa)

1984 (14 Feb). *The Karran Fleet. T* **66** *and similar horiz designs. Multicoloured. P* 14.
259	10p. Type **66**	.. .. ..	40	40
260	13p. *Hope* (barque)	.. ..	55	55
261	20½p. *Rio Grande* (brig)	.. ..	85	85
262	28p. *Lady Elizabeth* (barque)	..	1·00	1·00
263	31p. *Sumatra* (barque)	.. ..	1·10	1·10
259/63		*Set of 5*	3·50	3·50

MS264 103 × 94 mm. 28p. As No. 262, 31p. *Lady Elizabeth* (as shown on Falkland Islands No. 417) (*sold at* 60p.) .. .. 3·00 3·00

No. **MS**264 was issued to commemorate links between the Isle of Man and Falkland Islands.

(Des J. Larrivière, adapted Colleen Corlett. Photo Courvoisier)

1984 (27 Apr). *Europa. Granite paper. P* 12 × 11½.
265	**67** 10p. dull orange, deep reddish brown and pale orange	..	35	35
266	20½p. light blue, deep blue and pale blue	..	70	70

68 Railway Air Services De Havilland D.H.84 Dragon Mk 2

69 Window from Glencrutchery House, Douglas

(Des A. Theobald, Litho Questa)

1984 (27 Apr). *50th Anniv of First Official Airmail to the Isle of Man and 40th Anniv of International Civil Aviation Organization. T* **68** *and similar horiz designs. Multicoloured. P* 14.
267	11p. Type **68**	.. ..	45	45
268	13p. West Coast Air Services De Havilland D.H.86A Dragon Express *Ronaldsway*	..	55	55
269	26p. B.E.A. Douglas DC-3	..	1·00	1·00
270	28p. B.E.A. Vickers Viscount 800	..	1·10	1·10
271	31p. Telair Britten Norman Islander	..	1·40	1·40
267/71	.. ..	*Set of 5*	4·00	4·00

(Des D. Swinton. Litho J.W.)

1984 (21 Sept). *Christmas. Stained-glass Windows. T* **69** *and similar vert design. Multicoloured. P* 14.
272	10p. Type **69**	.. ..	50	50
273	13p. Window from Lonan Old Church	..	50	50

70 William Cain's Birthplace, Ballasalla

(Des J. Nicholson. Litho Questa)

1984 (21 Sept). *William Cain (civic leader, Victoria) Commemoration. T* **70** *and similar horiz designs. Multicoloured. P* 14½ × 14.
274	11p. Type **70**	.. ..	35	35
275	22p. The *Anna* leaving Liverpool, 1852	..	75	75
276	28p. Early Australian railway	..	1·00	1·00
277	30p. William Cain as Mayor of Melbourne, and Town Hall	.. ..	1·10	1·10
278	33p. Royal Exhibition Building, Melbourne	..	1·25	1·25
274/8	.. ..	*Set of 5*	4·00	4·00

71 Queen Elizabeth II and Commonwealth Parliamentary Association Badge

(Des and litho J.W.)

1984 (21 Sept). *Links with the Commonwealth. 30th Commonwealth Parliamentary Association Conference. T* **71** *and similar horiz design. Multicoloured. P* 14.
279	14p. Type **71**	.. ..	50	50
280	33p. Queen Elizabeth II and Manx emblem	..	1·10	1·10

72 Cunningham House Headquarters, and Mrs. Willie Cunningham and Mrs. Joseph Cunningham (former Commissioners)

(Des Colleen Corlett. Photo Courvoisier)

1985 (31 Jan). *75th Anniv of Girl Guide Movement. T* **72** *and similar horiz designs. Multicoloured. Granite paper. P* 11½.
281	11p. Type **72**	.. ..	45	45
282	14p. Princess Margaret, Isle of Man standard and guides	.. ..	75	75
283	29p. Lady Olave Baden-Powell opening Guide Headquarters, 1955	..	1·10	1·10
284	31p. Guide uniforms from 1910 to 1985	..	1·40	1·40
285	34p. Guide handclasp, salute and early badge	..	1·60	1·60
281/5	.. ..	*Set of 5*	4·75	4·75

73 Score of Manx National Anthem

(Des D. Swinton. Photo Courvoisier)

1985 (24 Apr). *Europa. European Music Year. T* **73** *and similar horiz designs. Granite paper. P* 11½.
286	12p. black, orange-brown and chestnut		50	45
	a. Horiz pair. Nos. 286/7	..	1·00	90
287	12p. black, orange-brown and chestnut		50	45
288	22p. black, bright new blue and new blue		1·00	95
	a. Horiz pair. Nos. 288/9	..	2·10	1·90
289	22p. black, bright new blue and new blue		1·00	95
286/9	.. ..	*Set of 4*	2·75	2·50

Designs:—No. 287, William H. Gill (lyricist); 288, Score of hymn "Crofton"; 289, Dr. John Clague (composer).

Nos. 286/7 and 288/9 were printed together, *se-tenant*, in horizontal pairs throughout the sheets.

---

74 Charles Rolls in 20 h.p. Rolls-Royce (1906 Tourist Trophy Race)

(Des A. Theobald. Litho Questa)

1985 (25 May). *Century of Motoring. T* **74** *and similar horiz designs. Multicoloured. P* 14.
290	12p. Type **74**	.. ..	40	40
	a. Horiz pair. Nos. 290/1	..	85	85
291	12p. W. Bentley in 3 litre Bentley (1922 Tourist Trophy Race)	..	40	40
292	14p. F. Gerrard in E.R.A. (1950 British Empire Trophy Race)	..	55	55
	a. Horiz pair. Nos. 292/3	..	1·10	1·10
293	14p. Brian Lewis in Alfa Romeo (1934 Mannin Moar Race)	..	55	55
294	31p. Jaguar "XJ-SC" ("Roads Open" car, 1984 Motor Cycle T.T. Races)	..	1·40	1·25
	a. Horiz pair. Nos. 294/5	..	2·75	2·50
295	31p. Tony Pond and Mike Nicholson in Vauxhall "Chevette" (1981 Rothmans International Rally)		1·40	1·25
290/5	.. ..	*Set of 6*	4·25	4·00

Nos. 290/1, 292/3 and 294/5 were printed together, *se-tenant*, in horizontal pairs throughout the sheets.

75 Queen Alexandra and Victorian Sergeant with Wife

(Des Colleen Corlett. Litho Questa)

1985 (4 Sept). *Centenary of the Soldiers', Sailors' and Airmen's Families Association. T* **75** *and similar horiz designs showing Association Presidents. Multicoloured. P* 14.
296	12p. Type **75**	.. ..	40	40
297	15p. Queen Mary and Royal Air Force family	..	55	55
298	29p. Earl Mountbatten and Royal Navy family	1·10	1·10
299	34p. Prince Michael of Kent and Royal Marine with parents, 1982	..	1·25	1·25
296/9	.. ..	*Set of 4*	3·00	3·00

76 Kirk Maughold (Birthplace)

(Des A. Theobald. Litho Questa)

1985 (2 Oct). *Birth Bicentenary of Lieutenant-General Sir Mark Cubbon (Indian administrator). T* **76** *and similar multicoloured designs. P* 14.
300	12p. Type **76**	.. ..	45	45
301	22p. Lieutenant-General Sir Mark Cubbon (*vert*)	..	1·10	1·10
302	45p. Memorial Statue, Bangalore, India (*vert*)	1·90	1·90
300/2	.. ..	*Set of 3*	3·00	3·00

77 St. Peter's Church, Onchan

(Des A. Theobald. Litho J.W.)

1985 (2 Oct). *Christmas. Manx Churches. T* **77** *and similar horiz designs. Multicoloured. P* 13 × 13½.
303	11p. Type **77**	.. ..	45	45
304	14p. Royal Chapel of St. John, Tynwald	..	55	55
305	31p. Bride Parish Church	..	1·25	1·25
303/5	.. ..	*Set of 3*	2·00	2·00

78 Swimming

(Des C. Abbott. Litho Questa)

1986 (5 Feb). *Commonwealth Games, Edinburgh. T* **78** *and similar horiz designs. Multicoloured. P* 14.

306	12p.	Type **78**	40	40
307	15p.	Race walking	50	50
308	31p.	Rifle-shooting	1·50	1·50
309	34p.	Cycling	1·50	1·50
306/9		*Set of 4*	3·50	3·50

No. 309 also commemorates the 50th anniversary of Manx International Cycling Week.

79 Viking Necklace and Peel Castle   **80** Viking Longship

(Des J. Nicholson. Litho Questa)

1986 (5 Feb). *Centenary of the Manx Museum. T* **79** *and similar multicoloured designs. P* 14.

310	12p.	Type **79**	35	35
311	15p.	Meayll Circle, Rushen	45	45
312	22p.	Skeleton of Great Deer and Manx Museum (*vert*)	1·00	1·00
313	26p.	Viking longship model (*vert*)	1·25	1·25
314	29p.	Open Air Museum, Cregneash	1·40	1·40
310/14		*Set of 5*	4·00	4·00

(Des Colleen Corlett. Litho Harrison)

1986 (10 Apr). *Manx Heritage Year. Booklet stamps. T* **80** *and similar vert design. P* 14½ × 14.

315	2p.	multicoloured	25	25
		a. Booklet pane. Nos. 315 × 2 and 316 × 4	3·50	
316	10p.	black, apple green and brownish grey	75	75
		a. Booklet pane. No. 316 × 3 and 3 stamp-size labels	3·00	

Design:—10p. Celtic cross logo.
In addition to 50p. and £1·14 booklets Nos. 315/16 also come from special booklet sheets of 60 containing five each of Nos. 315a and 316a.

81 *Usnea articulata* (lichen) and *Neotinea intacta* (orchid), The Ayres   **82** Ellanbane (home of Myles Standish)

(Des J. Nicholson and Nancy Corkish. Photo Courvoisier)

1986 (10 Apr). *Europa. Protection of Nature and the Environment. T* **81** *and similar horiz designs. Multicoloured. Granite paper. P* 11½.

317	12p.	Type **81**	60	60
		a. Horiz pair. Nos. 317/18	1·25	1·25
318	12p.	Hen Harrier, Calf of Man	60	60
319	22p.	Manx Stoat, Eary Cushlin	95	95
		a. Horiz pair. Nos. 319/20	1·90	1·90
320	22p.	*Stenobothus stigmaticus* (grasshopper), St. Michael's Isle	95	95
317/20		*Set of 4*	2·75	2·75

The two designs of each value were printed together, *se-tenant*, in horizontal pairs throughout the sheets.

(Des C. Abbott. Litho Cartor)

1986 (22 May). *"Ameripex '86" International Stamp Exhibition, Chicago. Captain Myles Standish of the "Mayflower". T* **82** *and similar vert designs. Multicoloured. P* 13½.

321	12p.	Type **82**	35	35
322	15p.	*Mayflower* crossing the Atlantic, 1620	55	55
323	31p.	Pilgrim Fathers landing at Plymouth, 1620	1·40	1·40
324	34p.	Captain Myles Standish	1·60	1·60
321/4		*Set of 4*	3·50	3·50
MS325		100 × 75 mm. Nos. 323/4. P 12½	3·00	3·00

No. MS325 also commemorates the 75th anniversary of the World Manx Association.

83 Prince Andrew in Naval Uniform and Miss Sarah Ferguson   **84** Prince Philip (from photo by Karsh)

(Des Colleen Corlett. Litho B.D.T.)

1986 (23 July). *Royal Wedding. T* **83** *and similar horiz design. Multicoloured. P* 15 × 14.

326	15p.	Type **83**	75	75
327	40p.	Engagement photograph	1·75	1·50

(Des Colleen Corlett. Photo Courvoisier)

1986 (28 Aug). *Royal Birthdays. T* **84** *and similar multicoloured designs. Granite paper. P* 11½.

328	15p.	Type **84**	80	80
		a. Horiz pair. Nos. 328/9	1·60	1·60
329	15p.	Queen Elizabeth II (from photo by Karsh)	80	80
330	34p.	Queen Elizabeth and Prince Philip (from photo by Karsh) (48 × 35 *mm*)	1·75	1·75
328/30		*Set of 3*	3·00	3·00

Nos. 328/9 were printed together, *se-tenant*, in horizontal pairs throughout the sheet.
Nos. 328/30 also commemorate "Stockholmia '86" International Stamp Exhibition, Sweden and the 350th anniversary of the Swedish Post Office and are so inscribed on the margins of the sheet of twelve (Nos. 328/9) and six (No. 330).

85 European Robins on Globe and "Peace and Goodwill" in Braille   **86** North Quay

(Des Colleen Corlett. Litho Questa)

1986 (25 Sept). *Christmas. International Peace Year. T* **85** *and similar vert designs. Multicoloured. P* 14.

331	11p.	Type **85**	50	50
332	14p.	Hands releasing peace dove	55	55
333	31p.	Clasped hands and "Peace" in sign language	1·25	1·25
331/3		*Set of 3*	2·00	2·00

(Des A. Theobald. Litho Questa)

1987 (21 Jan–26 Mar). *Victorian Douglas. T* **86** *and similar horiz designs. Multicoloured. P* 14 × 14½.

334	2p.	Type **86**	10	10
		a. Booklet pane. Nos. 334 × 2, 335 × 2 and 336 × 4 (2p. stamps at top) (26.3)	4·00	
		ab. Ditto, but 2p. stamps at bottom (26.3)	4·00	
		b. Booklet pane. Nos. 334/7, each × 2 (26.3)	3·50	
335	3p.	Old Fishmarket	10	10
336	10p.	The Breakwater	35	35
337	15p.	Jubilee Clock	50	50
338	31p.	Loch Promenade	1·60	1·60
339	34p.	Beach	1·90	1·90
334/9		*Set of 6*	4·00	4·00

87 "The Old Fishmarket and Harbour, Douglas"

(Des A. Theobald. Litho Cartor)

1987 (18 Feb). *Paintings by John Miller Nicholson. T* **87** *and similar horiz designs. Multicoloured. P* 13½.

340	12p.	Type **87**	35	35
341	26p.	"Red Sails at Douglas"	90	90
342	29p.	"The Double Corner, Peel"	1·50	1·50
343	34p.	"Peel Harbour"	1·75	1·75
340/3		*Set of 4*	4·00	4·00

88 Sea Terminal, Douglas

(Des R. Maddox. Litho B.D.T.)

1987 (29 Apr). *Europa. Architecture. T* **88** *and similar horiz designs. Multicoloured. P* 13½.

344	12p.	Type **88**	60	60
		a. Horiz pair. Nos. 344/5	1·25	1·25
345	12p.	Tower of Refuge, Douglas	60	60
346	22p.	Gaiety Theatre, Douglas	1·10	1·10
		a. Horiz pair. Nos. 346/7	2·10	2·10
347	22p.	Villa Marina, Douglas	1·10	1·10
344/7		*Set of 4*	3·00	3·00

Nos. 344/5 and 346/7 were each printed, *se-tenant*, in horizontal pairs throughout the sheets.

89 Supercharged BMW 500cc Motor Cycle, 1939

(Des B. Dix. Litho Cartor)

1987 (27 May). *80th Anniv of Tourist Trophy Motor Cycle Races. T* **89** *and similar horiz designs. Multicoloured. P* 13½ × 13.

348	12p.	Type **89**	40	40
349	15p.	Manx "Kneeler" Norton 350cc, 1953	60	60
350	29p.	MV Agusta 500cc 4, 1956	1·00	1·00
351	31p.	Guzzi 500cc V8, 1957	1·10	1·10
352	34p.	Honda 250cc 6, 1967	1·40	1·40
348/52		*Set of 5*	4·00	4·00
MS353		150 × 140 mm. Nos. 348/52. P 14 × 13½	5·00	5·00

Nos. 348/53 also commemorate the Centenary of the St. John Ambulance Brigade and the miniature sheet also carries the logo of "Capex '87" International Stamp Exhibition, Toronto, on its margin.

90 Fuchsia and Wild Roses   **91** Stirring the Christmas Pudding

(Des Nancy Corkish. Litho Enschedé)

1987 (9 Sept). *Wild Flowers. T* **90** *and similar vert designs. Multicoloured. P* 14½ × 13.

354	16p.	Type **90**	60	60
355	29p.	Field Scabious and Ragwort	1·10	1·10
356	31p.	Wood Anemone and Celandine	1·25	1·25
357	34p.	Violets and Primroses	1·50	1·50
354/7		*Set of 4*	4·00	4·00

(Des Colleen Corlett. Litho Questa)

1987 (16 Oct). *Christmas. Victorian Scenes. T* **91** *and similar vert designs. Multicoloured. P* 14.

358	12p.	Type **91**	50	50
359	15p.	Bringing home the Christmas tree	75	75
360	31p.	Decorating the Christmas tree	1·25	1·25
358/60		*Set of 3*	2·25	2·25

92 Russell Brookes in Vauxhall Opel (Manx Rally winner, 1985)

(Des C. Abbott. Litho Enschedé)

1988 (10 Feb). *Motor Sport. T* **92** *and similar horiz designs. Multicoloured. P* 13½ × 14½.

361	13p.	Type **92**	75	70
362	26p.	Ari Vatanen in Ford "Escort" (Manx Rally winner, 1976)	1·25	1·10
363	31p.	Terry Smith in Repco "March 761" (Hill Climb winner, 1980)	1·40	1·25
364	34p.	Nigel Mansell in Williams/Honda (British Grand Prix winner, 1986 and 1987)	1·60	1·40
361/4		*Set of 4*	4·50	4·00

93 Horse Tram Terminus, Douglas Bay Tramway   **93a** Queen Elizabeth II taking Salute at Trooping the Colour

(Des Colleen Corlett (£2). A. Theobald (others). Litho B.D.T. (1p. to 19p., 21p., 23p.), Questa (20p. and 25p. to £2))

1988 (10 Feb)–**92**. *Manx Railways and Tramways. Horiz designs as T* **93**, *and T* **93a**. *Multicoloured. P* 13 (1p. to 19p., 21p., 23p.), 14½×15 (20p., 25p. to £1) or 14½ (£2).

365	1p.	Type **93**	10	10
366	2p.	Snaefell Mountain Railway	10	10
367	3p.	Marine Drive Tramway	10	10
		a. Booklet pane. Nos. 367 × 2, 370 and 373 × 2 (16.3.88)	4·00	
		b. Booklet pane. Nos. 367 × 2, 371 × 2 and 374 (16.10.89)	3·00	
367c	4p.	Douglas Cable Tramway (9.1.91)	10	10
		ca. Booklet pane. Nos. 367c × 3, 374 and 377a	4·00	
		cb. Booklet pane. Nos. 367c × 3, 374 × 4 and 377a	6·25	
368	5p.	Douglas Head Incline Railway	20	20
369	10p.	Douglas & Laxey Coast Electric Tramway car at Maughold Head	30	30

370	13p.	As 4p.		50	50
	a.	Booklet pane. Nos. 370×4 and 373×6 (16.3.88)		5·50	
371	14p.	Manx Northern Railway No. 4, *Caledonia*, at Gob-y-Deigan		50	50
	a.	Booklet pane. Nos. 371×4 and 374×6 (16.10.89)		5·00	
372	15p.	Laxey Mine Railway Lewin locomotive *Ant*		50	50
	a.	Booklet pane. Nos. 372 and 376×2 (14.2.90)		3·00	
	b.	Booklet pane. Nos. 372×4 and 376×6 (14.2.90)		8·00	
373	16p.	Port Erin Breakwater Tramway locomotive *Henry B. Loch*		50	50
374	17p.	Ramsey Harbour Tramway		50	50
375	18p.	Locomotive No. 7, *Tynwald*, on Foxdale line		55	55
375a	18p.	T.P.O. Special leaving Douglas, 3 July 1991 (8.1.92)		55	55
	ab.	Booklet pane. Nos. 375a×3 and 377b×2		4·00	
	ac.	Booklet pane. Nos. 375a×6 and 377b×4		8·00	
376	19p.	Baldwin Reservoir Tramway steam locomotive No. 1, *Injebreck*		60	60
377	20p.	I.M.R. No. 13, *Kissack*, near St. Johns (21.9.88)		60	60
377a	21p.	As 14p. (9.1.91)		60	60
377b	23p.	Double-deck horse tram, Douglas (8.1.92)		60	60
378	25p.	I.M.R. No. 12, *Hutchinson*, leaving Douglas (21.9.88)		70	70
379	50p.	Groudle Glen Railway locomotive *Polar Bear* (21.9.88)		1·50	1·50
380	£1	I.M.R. No. 11, *Maitland*, pulling Royal Train, 1963 (21.9.88)		3·00	3·00
380a	£2	Type 93a (14.2.90)		6·00	6·00
365/80a			Set of 21	16·00	16·00

In addition to stamp booklets Nos. 367a/b, 370a, 371a, 372a/b and 375ab/ac also come from special booklet sheets of 50 containing either ten examples of the strips of five or five examples of the strips of ten.

Nos. 367c and 377a show the Queen's head in white. The 4p. value was only issued in 50p. and £1 stamp booklets or in special booklet sheets of 50 containing five vertical strips of No. 367cb and five extra examples of both Nos. 367c and 377a.

Imprint dates: "1988", Nos. 365/7, 368/75, 376/7, 378/80; "1989", Nos. 367, 371, 374; "1990", Nos. 372, 376, 380a; "1991", Nos. 367c, 374, 377a; "1992", Nos. 375a, 377b, 379/80.

For miniature sheet containing Nos. 367c and 377a see No. MS484.

94 Laying Isle of Man—U.K. Submarine Cable

(Des C. Abbott. Litho Cartor)

1988 (14 Apr). *Europa. Transport and Communications. T **94** and similar horiz designs. Multicoloured. P 14×13½.*

381	13p.	Type **94**		60	60
	a.	Horiz pair. Nos. 381/2		1·25	1·25
382	13p.	*Flex Service 3* (cable ship)		60	60
383	22p.	Earth station, Braddan		1·00	1·00
	a.	Horiz pair. Nos. 383/4		2·00	2·00
384	22p.	"INTELSAT 5" satellite		1·00	1·00
381/4			Set of 4	3·00	3·00

Nos. 381/2 and 383/4 were each printed together, *se-tenant*, in horizontal pairs throughout the sheets. Nos. 381/2 form a composite design.

95 *Euterpe* (full-rigged ship) off Ramsey, 1863

96 "*Magellanica*"

(Des J. Nicholson. Litho Questa)

1988 (11 May). *Manx Sailing Ships. T **95** and similar horiz designs. Multicoloured. P 14.*

385	16p.	Type **95**		50	50
386	29p.	*Vixen* (topsail schooner) leaving Peel for Australia, 1853		1·10	1·10
387	31p.	*Ramsey* (full-rigged ship) off Brisbane, 1870		1·40	1·40
388	34p.	*Star of India* (formerly *Euterpe*) (barque) off San Diego, 1976		1·50	1·50
385/8			Set of 4	4·00	4·00
MS389		110 × 85 mm. Nos. 385 and 388		3·00	3·00

Nos. 386/7 also commemorate the Bicentenary of Australian Settlement.

(Des Colleen Corlett. Litho Enschedé)

1988 (21 Sept). *50th Anniv of British Fuchsia Society. T **96** and similar vert designs. Multicoloured. P 13½ × 14.*

390	13p.	Type **96**		50	50
391	16p.	"Pink Cloud"		60	60
392	22p.	"Leonora"		80	70
393	29p.	"Satellite"		1·00	1·00
394	31p.	"Preston Guild"		1·25	1·25
395	34p.	"Thalia"		1·40	1·40
390/5			Set of 6	5·00	5·00

97 Long-eared Owl

(Des Audrey North. Litho Questa)

1988 (12 Oct). *Christmas. Manx Birds. T **97** and similar horiz designs. Multicoloured. P 14.*

396	12p.	Type **97**		70	70
397	15p.	European Robin		1·00	1·00
398	31p.	Grey Partridge		1·60	1·60
396/8			Set of 3	3·00	3·00

98 Ginger Cat

99 Tudric Pewter Clock, *c.* 1903

(Des P. Layton. Litho Questa)

1989 (8 Feb). *Manx Cats. T **98** and similar horiz designs. Multicoloured. P 14.*

399	16p.	Type **98**		50	50
400	27p.	Black and white cat		1·00	1·00
401	30p.	Tortoiseshell and white cat		1·50	1·50
402	40p.	Tortoiseshell cat		1·75	1·75
399/402			Set of 4	4·25	4·25

(Des Colleen Corlett. Litho Cartor)

1989 (8 Feb). *125th Birth Anniv of Archibald Knox (artist and designer). T **99** and similar multicoloured designs. P 13.*

403	13p.	Type **99**		35	35
404	16p.	"Celtic Cross" watercolour		45	45
405	23p.	Silver cup and cover, 1902-03		75	75
406	32p.	Gold and silver brooches from Liberty's Cymric range (*horiz*)		1·40	1·40
407	35p.	Silver jewel box, 1900 (*horiz*)		1·50	1·50
403/7			Set of 5	4·00	4·00

100 William Bligh and Old Church, Onchan

(Des C. Abbott. Litho B.D.T.)

1989 (28 Apr). *Bicentenary of the Mutiny on the Bounty. T **100** and similar horiz designs. Multicoloured. P 14.*

408	13p.	Type **100**		40	40
	a.	Booklet pane. Nos. 408/10 and 412/14		4·00	
	b.	Booklet pane. Nos. 408/9 and 411/14		4·00	
409	16p.	Bligh and loyal crew cast adrift		40	40
410	23p.	Pitcairn Islands 1989 Settlement Bicentenary 90 c., No. 345		1·25	1·25
	a.	Booklet pane. Nos. 410/11, each × 3		6·00	
411	27p.	Norfolk Island 1989 Bicentenary 39 c., No. 461		1·25	1·25
412	30p.	Midshipman Peter Heywood and Tahiti		70	70
413	32p.	H.M.S. *Bounty* anchored off Pitcairn Island		75	75
414	35p.	Fletcher Christian and Pitcairn Island		80	80
408/14			Set of 7	5·00	5·00
MS415		110×85 mm. Nos. 410/11 and 414		5·00	5·00

Nos. 410/11 were only issued in £5.30 booklets and as part of No. MS415.

Booklet panes Nos. 408a/b and 410a each contain two vertical rows of three stamps, separated by a central gutter.

101 Skipping and Hopscotch

102 Atlantic Puffin

(Des Colleen Corlett. Litho Enschedé)

1989 (17 May). *Europa. Children's Games. T **101** and similar horiz designs. Multicoloured. P 13½.*

416	13p.	Type **101**		65	65
	a.	Horiz pair. Nos. 416/17		1·25	1·25
417	13p.	Wheelbarrow, leapfrog and piggyback		65	65
418	23p.	Completing model house and blowing bubbles		1·00	1·00
	a.	Horiz pair. Nos. 418/19		2·00	2·00
419	23p.	Girl with doll and doll's house		1·00	1·00
416/19			Set of 4	3·00	3·00

Nos. 416/17 and 418/19 were printed together, *se-tenant* as composite designs, in horizontal pairs throughout the sheets.

(Des W. Oliver. Litho Questa)

1989 (20 Sept). *Sea Birds. T **102** and similar vert designs. Multicoloured. P 14.*

420	13p.	Type **102**		80	80
	a.	Strip of 4. Nos. 420/3		3·00	
421	13p.	Black Guillemot		80	80
422	13p.	Common Cormorant		80	80
423	13p.	Kittiwake		80	80
420/3			Set of 4	3·00	3·00

Nos. 420/3 were printed together, *se-tenant*, in horizontal and vertical strips of 4 throughout the sheet. The sheet exists with or without perforations across the side margins.

Examples of Nos. 420/3 sold at "World Stamp Expo '89", held at Washington D.C. between 17 November and 8 December 1989, carried a commemorative inscription on the bottom sheet margin.

103 Red Cross Cadets learning Resuscitation

104 Mother with Baby, Jane Crookall Maternity Home

(Des A. Theobald. Litho Questa)

1989 (16 Oct). *125th Anniversary of International Red Cross and Centenary of Noble's Hospital, Isle of Man. T **103** and similar horiz designs. P 14.*

424	14p.	multicoloured		40	40
425	17p.	grey and orange-vermilion		65	65
426	23p.	multicoloured		90	90
427	30p.	multicoloured		1·25	1·25
428	35p.	multicoloured		1·50	1·50
424/8			Set of 5	4·25	4·25

Designs:—17p. Anniversary logo; 23p. Signing Geneva Convention, 1864; 30p. Red Cross ambulance; 35p. Henri Dunant (founder).

(Des Colleen Corlett. Litho Questa)

1989 (16 Oct). *Christmas. 50th Anniversary of Jane Crookall Maternity Home and 75th Anniversary of St. Ninian's Church, Douglas. T **104** and similar vert designs. Multicoloured. P 14½.*

429	13p.	Type **104**		55	55
430	16p.	Mother with child		70	70
431	34p.	Madonna and Child		1·25	1·25
432	37p.	Baptism, St. Ninian's Church		1·40	1·40
429/32			Set of 4	3·50	3·50

105 "The Isle of Man Express going up a Gradient"

106 Modern Postman

(Des D. Swinton. Litho B.D.T.)

1990 (14 Feb). *Isle of Man Edwardian Postcards. T **105** and similar horiz designs. Multicoloured. P 14.*

433	15p.	Type **105**		30	30
434	19p.	"A way we have in the Isle of Man"		55	55
435	32p.	"Douglas–waiting for the male boat"		1·00	1·00
436	34p.	"The last toast rack home, Douglas Parade"		1·40	1·40
437	37p.	"The last Isle of Man boat"		1·50	1·50
433/7			Set of 5	4·25	4·25

(Des A. Kellett. Litho Cartor)

1990 (18 Apr). *Europa. Post Office Buildings. T **106** and similar multicoloured designs. P 13½.*

438	15p.	Type **106**		65	65
	a.	Horiz pair. Nos. 438/9		1·25	1·25
439	15p.	Ramsey Post Office, 1990 (40×26 *mm*)		65	65
440	24p.	Postman, 1890		1·00	1·00
	a.	Horiz pair. Nos. 440/1		2·00	2·00
441	24p.	Douglas Post Office, 1890 (40×26 *mm*)		1·00	1·00
438/41			Set of 4	3·00	3·00

Nos. 438/9 and 440/1 were each printed together, *se-tenant*, in horizontal pairs throughout the sheets.

NEW INFORMATION

The editor is always interested to correspond with people who have new information that will improve or correct the Catalogue.

107 Penny Black

108 Queen Elizabeth the Queen Mother

(Des Colleen Corlett. Eng Inge Madle (No. MS447). Recess and litho (No. MS447) or litho (others) Enschedé)

1990 (3 May). *150th Anniv of the Penny Black. T **107** and similar vert designs.* P 14×13½.

442	1p. black, buff and gold		10	10
	a. Sheetlet. Horiz strip of 5. Nos. 442/6		4·50	
	b. Sheetlet. No. 442×25		3·00	
	c. Booklet pane. No. 442×8 with margins all round		1·00	
443	19p. gold, black and buff		65	65
	a. Booklet pane. Nos. 443/6×2 with margins all round		8·00	
444	32p. multicoloured		1·40	1·40
445	34p. multicoloured		1·40	1·40
446	37p. multicoloured		1·60	1·60
442/6		Set of 5	4·50	4·50
MS447	100×71 mm. £1 black, gold and buff (50×60 mm)		4·00	4·00

Designs:—19p. Wyon Medal, 1837; 32p. Wyon's stamp essay; 34p. Perkins Bacon engine-turned essay, 1839; 37p. Twopence Blue, 1840; £1 Block of four Penny Black stamps lettered IM–JN.
Sheetlet No. 442a was reissued on 24 August 1990 overprinted "From STAMP WORLD LONDON '90 to NEW ZEALAND 1990" for sale at the New Zealand exhibition.
The Penny Black stamps shown on Nos. 442b/c each have different corner letters at foot. The sheetlet of 25 was issued in conjunction with a special postal concession which allowed hand-addressed personal mail for the island to be posted for 1p. between 10 am. and 12 noon on 6 May 1990.
No. MS447 also commemorates "Stamp World London 90" International Stamp Exhibition, London.

(Des Colleen Corlett. Litho B.D.T.)

1990 (4 Aug). *90th Birthday of Queen Elizabeth the Queen Mother.* P 13×13½.

448	**108** 90p. multicoloured		4·00	4·00

No. 448 was printed in sheets of ten stamps and ten *se-tenant* inscribed labels.

109 Hawker Hurricane Mk 1, Bristol Type 142 Blenheim Mk 1 and Home Defence

(Des A. Theobald. Litho Questa)

1990 (5 Sept). *50th Anniv of Battle of Britain. T **109** and similar horiz designs. Multicoloured.* P 14.

449	15p. Type **109**		50	50
	a. Horiz pair. Nos. 449/50		1·00	1·00
450	15p. Supermarine Spitfire with Westland Lysander Mk I rescue aircraft and launch		50	50
451	24p. Rearming Hawker Hurricane Mk I fighters		1·00	1·00
	a. Horiz pair. Nos. 451/2		2·00	2·00
452	24p. Ops room and scramble		1·00	1·00
453	29p. Civil Defence personnel		1·25	1·25
	a. Horiz pair. Nos. 453/4		2·50	2·50
454	29p. Anti-aircraft battery		1·25	1·25
449/54		Set of 6	5·00	5·00

The two designs of each value were printed together, *se-tenant*, in horizontal pairs throughout the sheets of 8.

110 Churchill with Freedom of Douglas Casket

111 Boy on Toboggan and Girl posting Letter

(Des C. Abbott. Litho Cartor)

1990 (5 Sept). *25th Death Anniv of Sir Winston Churchill. T **110** and similar horiz designs. Multicoloured.* P 13½.

455	19p. Type **110**		60	60
456	32p. Churchill and London blitz		1·10	1·10
457	34p. Churchill and searchlights over Westminster		1·40	1·40
458	37p. Churchill with R.A.F. Hawker Hurricane Mk I fighters		1·40	1·40
455/8		Set of 4	4·25	4·25

(Des C. Abbott. Litho B.D.T.)

1990 (10 Oct). *Christmas. T **111** and similar vert designs. Multicoloured.* P 13×13½.

459	14p. Type **111**		40	40
460	18p. Girl on toboggan and skaters		60	60
461	34p. Boy with snowman		1·25	1·25
462	37p. Children throwing snowballs		1·40	1·40
459/62		Set of 4	3·50	3·50
MS463	123×55 mm. As Nos. 459/62, but face values in black		4·00	4·00
	a. Blue (inscriptions) omitted		£600	

112 Henry Bloom Noble and Orphans (Marshall Wane)

113 Lifeboat *Sir William Hillary*, Douglas

(Des Colleen Corlett. Litho Walsall)

1991 (9 Jan). *Manx Photography. T **112** and similar horiz designs.* P 14.

464	17p. blackish brown, pale brownish grey & blk		45	45
465	21p. deep brown and ochre		60	60
466	26p. blackish brown, stone and brownish black		90	90
467	31p. agate, pale grey-brown and black		1·25	1·25
468	40p. multicoloured		1·50	1·50
464/8		Set of 5	4·25	4·25

Designs:—21p. Douglas (Frederick Frith); 26p. Studio portrait of three children (Hilda Newby); 31p. Cashtal yn Ard (Christopher Killip); 40p. Peel Castle (Colleen Corlett).

(Des A. Peck. Litho Questa)

1991 (13 Feb). *Manx Lifeboats. T **113** and similar horiz designs. Multicoloured.* P 14.

469	17p. Type **113**		45	45
470	21p. *Osman Gabriel*, Port Erin		60	60
471	26p. *Ann and James Ritchie*, Ramsey		90	90
472	31p. *The Gough Ritchie*, Port St. Mary		1·25	1·25
473	37p. *John Batstone*, Peel		1·50	1·50
469/73		Set of 5	4·25	4·25

No. 469 is inscribed "HILARY" and No. 471 "JAMES & ANN RITCHIE", both in error.

114 "Intelsat" Communications Satellite

115 Oliver Godfrey with Indian 500cc at Start, 1911

(Des D. Miller. Litho B.D.T.)

1991 (24 Apr). *Europa. Europe in Space. T **114** and similar vert designs. Multicoloured.* P 14.

474	17p. Type **114**		80	80
	a. Vert pair. Nos. 474/5		1·60	1·60
475	17p. "Ariane" rocket launch and fishing boats in Douglas harbour		80	80
476	26p. Weather satellite and space station		1·10	1·10
	a. Vert pair. Nos. 476/7		2·25	2·25
477	26p. Ronaldsway Airport, Manx Radio transmitter and Space shuttle launch		1·10	1·10
474/7		Set of 4	3·50	3·50

Nos. 474/5 and 476/7 were each printed together, *se-tenant*, in vertical pairs throughout the sheets, each pair forming a composite design.

(Des A. Theobald. Litho Enschedé)

1991 (30 May). *80th Anniv of Tourist Trophy Mountain Course. T **115** and similar horiz designs. Multicoloured.* P 14½×13.

478	17p. Type **115**		40	40
479	21p. Freddie Dixon on Douglas "banking" sidecar, 1923		60	60
480	26p. Bill Ivy on Yamaha 125cc, 1968		85	85
481	31p. Giacomo Agostini on MV Agusta 500cc, 1972		1·25	1·25
482	37p. Joey Dunlop on RVF Honda 750cc, 1985		1·40	1·40
478/82		Set of 5	4·00	4·00
MS483	149×144 mm. Nos. 478/82		4·25	4·25

No. MS483 was reissued on 16 November 1991 overprinted for the Phila Nippon Exhibition, Japan.

(Des Colleen Corlett. Litho B.D.T.)

1991 (1 July). *9th Conference of Commonwealth Postal Administrations, Douglas. Sheet 119×77 mm containing Nos. 367c and 377a, each × 2. Multicoloured.* P 13.

MS484	Nos. 367c and 377a, each × 2		2·00	2·00

MINIMUM PRICE

The minimum price quote is 10p which represents a handling charge rather than a basis for valuing common stamps. For further notes about prices see introductory pages.

116 Laxey Hand-cart, 1920

117 Mute Swans, Douglas Harbour

(Des C. Abbott. Litho Questa)

1991 (18 Sept). *Fire Engines. T **116** and similar square designs. Multicoloured.* P 14½.

485	17p. Type **116**		40	40
486	21p. Horse-drawn steamer, Douglas, 1909		60	60
487	30p. Merryweather "Hatfield" pump, 1936		85	85
488	33p. Dennis "F8" pumping appliance, Peel, 1953		1·25	1·25
489	37p. Volvo turntable ladder, Douglas, 1989		1·40	1·40
485/9		Set of 5	4·00	4·00

(Des Colleen Corlett. Litho Cartor)

1991 (18 Sept). *Swans. T **117** and similar horiz designs. Multicoloured.* P 13.

490	17p. Type **117**		55	55
	a. Horiz pair. Nos. 490/1		1·10	1·10
491	17p. Black Swans, Curraghs Wildlife Park		55	55
492	26p. Whooper Swans, Bishop's Dub, Ballaugh		1·10	1·10
	a. Horiz pair. Nos. 492/3		2·25	2·25
493	26p. Whistling ("Bewick's") Swans, Eairy Dam, Foxdale		1·10	1·10
494	37p. Coscoroba Swans, Curraghs Wildlife Park		1·40	1·40
	a. Horiz pair. Nos. 494/5		2·75	2·75
495	37p. Whooper ("Trumpeter") Swans, Curraghs Wildlife Park		1·40	1·40
490/5		Set of 6	5·50	5·50

The two designs of each value were printed together, *se-tenant*, in horizontal pairs throughout the sheets with the backgrounds forming composite designs.

118 The Three Kings

119 North African and Italian Campaigns, 1942–43

(Des D. Swinton. Litho Walsall)

1991 (14 Oct). *Christmas. Paper Sculptures. T **118** and similar square designs. Multicoloured. (a) Sheet stamps.* P 14×14½.

496	16p. Type **118**		50	40
497	20p. Mary with manger		75	80
498	26p. Shepherds with sheep		95	95
499	37p. Choir of angels		1·25	1·25
496/9		Set of 4	3·00	3·00

(b) Booklet stamps. Self-adhesive. Stamps die-cut.

500	16p. Type **118**		1·00	1·00
	a. Booklet pane. Nos. 500×8 and 501×4		12·00	
501	20p. As No. 497		1·50	1·50

(Des A. Theobald. Litho Questa)

1992 (6 Feb). *50th Anniv of Parachute Regiment. T **119** and similar horiz designs. Multicoloured.* P 14.

502	23p. Type **119**		80	80
	a. Horiz pair. Nos. 502/3		1·60	1·60
503	23p. D-Day, 1944		80	80
504	28p. Arnhem, 1944		90	90
	a. Horiz pair. Nos. 504/5		1·75	1·75
505	28p. Rhine crossing, 1945		90	90
506	39p. Operations in Near, Middle and Far East, 1945–68		1·40	1·40
	a. Horiz pair. Nos. 506/7		2·75	2·75
507	39p. Liberation of Falkland Islands, 1982		1·40	1·40
502/7		Set of 6	5·50	5·50

The two designs of each value were printed together, *se-tenant*, in horizontal pairs throughout the sheets of 8.

120 Queen Elizabeth II at Coronation, 1953

121 Brittle-stars

(Des D. Miller. Litho B.D.T.)

1992 (6 Feb). *40th Anniv of Accession. T **120** and similar vert designs. Multicoloured.* P 14.

508	18p. Type **120**		50	50
509	23p. Queen visiting Isle of Man, 1979		70	70
510	28p. Queen in evening dress		80	80
511	33p. Queen visiting Isle of Man, 1989		1·40	1·40
512	39p. Queen arriving for film premiere, 1990		1·50	1·50
508/12		Set of 5	4·50	4·50

(Des Jennifer Toombs. Litho Questa)

1992 (16 Apr). *Centenary of Port Erin Marine Laboratory. T* **121** *and similar horiz designs. Multicoloured.* P 14×14½.

513	18p.	Type **121**	50	50
514	23p.	Phytoplankton	60	60
515	28p.	Atlantic Herring	80	80
516	33p.	Great Scallop	1·40	1·40
517	39p.	Dahlia Anemone and Delesseria	1·50	1·50
513/17		*Set of 5*	4·25	4·25

122 The Pilgrim Fathers embarking at Delfshaven

123 Central Pacific Locomotive *Jupiter*, 1869

(Des C. Abbott. Litho Enschedé)

1992 (16 Apr). *Europa. 500th Anniv of Discovery of America by Columbus. T* **122** *and similar square designs. Multicoloured.* P 14×13½.

518	18p.	Type **122**	75	75
519	18p.	*a.* Horiz pair. Nos. 518/19	1·50	1·50
519	18p.	*Speedwell* leaving Delfshaven	75	75
520	28p.	*Mayflower* setting sail for America	1·50	1·50
		a. Horiz pair. Nos. 520/1	3·00	3·00
521	28p.	*Speedwell* anchored at Dartmouth	1·50	1·50
518/21		*Set of 4*	4·00	4·00

Nos. 518/19 and 520/1 were each printed together, *se-tenant*, in separate sheets, each horizontal pair forming a composite design.
The designs of Nos. 520/1 are after the painting by L. Wilcox.

(Des A. Peck. Litho Enschedé)

1992 (22 May). *Construction of the Union Pacific Railroad, 1866–69. T* **123** *and similar horiz designs.* P 13½×14.

522	33p.	Type **123**	1·10	1·10
		a. Horiz pair. Nos. 522/3 plus label	2·25	2·25
		b. Booklet pane. Nos. 522/5×2 and MS526	11·00	
523	33p.	Union Pacific locomotive No. 119, 1869	1·10	1·10
524	39p.	Union Pacific locomotive No. 844, 1992	1·60	1·60
		a. Horiz pair. Nos. 524/5 plus label	3·25	3·25
525	39p.	Union Pacific locomotive No. 3985, 1992	1·60	1·60
522/5		*Set of 4*	5·00	5·00
MS526		105×78 mm. £1.50, Golden Spike ceremony, 10 May 1869 (60×50 *mm*)	5·50	5·50

The two designs for each value were printed in small sheets of 10 (2×5) with each horizontal pair separated by a half stamp-size label showing Union Pacific emblem or portraits of Dan and Jack Casement (railroad contractors).

Booklet pane No. 522b contains two blocks of four of Nos. 522/5 with No. MS526 between them. Miniature sheets from the booklet show a white margin and line of roulettes at left and right. In the blocks of four each horizontal pair is separated by a half stamp-size label.

124 *King Orry V* in Douglas Harbour

(Des Colleen Corlett. Litho Walsall)

1992 (18 Sept). *Manx Harbours. T* **124** *and similar horiz designs. Multicoloured.* P 14½×14.

527	18p.	Type **124**	50	50
528	23p.	Castletown	60	60
529	37p.	Port St. Mary	1·40	1·40
530	40p.	Ramsey	1·40	1·40
527/30		*Set of 4*	3·50	3·50

125 *Saint Eloi* in 1972

126 Stained Glass Window, St. German's Cathedral, Peel

(Des Colleen Corlett. Litho Walsall)

1992 (18 Sept). *"Genova '92" International Thematic Stamp Exhibition. Sheet* 111×68 *mm containing T* **125** *and similar horiz design. Multicoloured.* P 14½×14.

MS531	18p. *King Orry V* in 1992 (as in Type **124**); £1 Type **125**	4·00	4·00

(Des Colleen Corlett. Litho Questa)

1992 (13 Oct). *Christmas. Manx Churches. T* **126** *and similar vert designs. Multicoloured.* P 14½.

532	17p.	Type **126**	50	50
533	22p.	Reredos, St. Matthew the Apostle Church, Douglas	70	70

534	28p.	Stained glass window, St. George's Church, Douglas	85	85
535	37p.	Reredos, St. Mary of the Isle Catholic Church, Douglas	1·00	1·00
536	40p.	Stained glass window, Trinity Methodist Church, Douglas	1·10	1·10
532/6		*Set of 5*	3·75	3·75

127 Mansell on Lap of Honour, British Grand Prix, 1992

(Des A. Theobald. Litho Walsall)

1992 (8 Nov). *Nigel Mansell's Victory in Formula 1 World Motor Racing Championship. T* **127** *and similar horiz design. Multicoloured.* P 13½.

537	20p.	Type **127**	90	90
538	24p.	Mansell in French Grand Prix, 1992	1·10	1·10

128 H.M.S. *Amazon* (frigate)

128a Manx Red Ensign

128b Queen Elizabeth II (hologram)

(Des A. Theobald (1p. to 27p.), J. Nicholson (30p. and 40p. to £1), Colleen Corlett (£2, £5). Litho Enschedé (1p. to £1), Questa (£2) or Walsall (£5) (hologram by Applied Holographics))

1993 (4 Jan)–*97. Ships. Horiz designs as T* **128** *and* **128a/b**. *Multicoloured.* P 13½×13 (1p. *to* £1), 14½ (£2) *or* 14½×14 (£5).

539	1p.	Type **128**	10	10
540	2p.	*Fingal* (lighthouse tender)	10	10
541	4p.	*Sir Winston Churchill* (cadet schooner)	10	10
		a. Booklet pane. Nos. 541, 544 and 548, each × 2 (14.5.97)	2·50	
542	5p.	*Dar Mlodziezy* (full-rigged cadet ship)	10	10
543	20p.	*Tynwald I* (paddle-steamer), 1846	45	45
		a. Booklet pane. Nos. 543×2 and 547×3	3·00	
		b. Booklet pane. Nos. 543×4 and 547×6	5·50	
544	21p.	*Ben Veg* (freighter)	50	50
545	22p.	*Waverley* (paddle-steamer)	50	50
546	23p.	Royal Yacht *Britannia*	55	55
547	24p.	*Francis Drake* (ketch)	55	55
548	25p.	*Royal Viking Sky* (liner)	60	60
549	26p.	*Lord Nelson* (cadet barque)	65	65
550	27p.	*Europa* (liner)	65	65
551	30p.	*Snaefell V* (ferry) leaving Ardrossan (15.9.93)	75	75
552	35p.	*Seacat* (catamaran ferry) (11.1.96)	85	85
553	40p.	*Lady of Man I* (ferry) off Ramsey (15.9.93)	1·00	1·00
554	50p.	*Mona's Queen II* (paddle ferry) leaving Fleetwood (15.9.93)	1·25	1·25
555	£1	*Queen Elizabeth 2* (liner) and *Mona's Queen V* (ferry) off Liverpool (15.9.93)	2·50	2·50
556	£2	Type **128a** (12.1.94)	5·00	5·00
557	£5	Type **128b** (5.7.94)	15·00	15·00
539/57		*Set of 19*	27·00	27·00

In addition to stamp booklets Nos. 543a/b also come from a special booklet sheet of 50 (5×10) which provides either 5 examples of No. 543b or 10 of No. 543a. No. 541a comes from a special booklet sheet of 30 (5×6).

Imprint dates: "1993", Nos. 539/51, 553/5; "1994", Nos. 556/7; "1995", Nos. 543 and 547; "1996", No. 552; "1997", Nos. 541, 544, 548 and 555.

For 4p. 20p. and 24p. in similar designs, but smaller, see Nos. 687/93.

For miniature sheet containing the 23p. see No. **MS**760.

129 No. 1 Motor Car and No. 13 Trailer at Groudle Glen Hotel

(Des A. Theobald. Litho B.D.T.)

1993 (3 Feb). *Centenary of Manx Electric Railway. T* **129** *and similar horiz designs. Multicoloured.* P 14.

559	20p.	Type **129**	60	60
		a. Booklet pane. Nos. 559/62	3·50	
560	24p.	No. 9 Tunnel Car and No. 19 Trailer at Douglas Bay Hotel	90	90
561	28p.	No. 19 Motor Car and No. 59 Royal Trailer Special at Douglas Bay	1·00	1·00
562	39p.	No. 33 Motor Car, No. 45 Trailer and No. 13 Van at Derby Castle	1·40	1·40
559/62		*Set of 4*	3·50	3·50

Booklet pane. No. 559a exists in four versions, which differ in the order of the stamps within the block of four and in the information printed on the pane margins.

130 "Sir Hall Caine" (statue) (Bryan Kneale)

(Des Colleen Corlett. Litho B.D.T.)

1993 (14 Apr). *Europa. Contemporary Art. Works by Bryan Kneale. T* **130** *and similar square designs. Multicoloured.* P 14.

563	20p.	Type **130**	70	70
		a. Horiz pair. Nos. 563/4	1·40	1·40
564	20p.	"The Brass Bedstead" (painting)	70	70
565	28p.	Abstract bronze sculpture	1·00	1·00
		a. Horiz pair. Nos. 565/6	2·00	2·00
566	28p.	"Polar Bear Skeleton" (drawing)	1·00	1·00
563/6		*Set of 4*	3·00	3·00

Nos. 563/4 and 565/6 were each printed together, *se-tenant*, in horizontal pairs throughout the sheets.

131 Graham Oates and Bill Marshall (1933 International Six Day Trial) on Ariel Square Four

(Des C. Abbott. Litho Walsall)

1993 (3 June). *Manx Motor Cycling Events. T* **131** *and similar horiz designs. Multicoloured.* P 13½×14.

567	20p.	Type **131**	50	50
568	24p.	Sergeant Geoff Duke (1947 Royal Signals Display Team) on Triumph 3T Twin	70	70
569	28p.	Denis Parkinson (1953 Senior Manx Grand Prix) on Manx Norton	90	90
570	33p.	Richard Swallow (1991 Junior Classic MGP) on Aermacchi	1·25	1·25
571	39p.	Steve Colley (1992 Scottish Six Day Trial) on Beta Zero	1·40	1·40
567/71		*Set of 5*	4·25	4·25
MS572		165×120 mm. Nos. 567/71	4·50	4·50

132 *Inachis io* (Peacock)

133 Children decorating Christmas Tree

(Des Colleen Corlett. Litho Questa)

1993 (15 Sept). *Butterflies. T* **132** *and similar square designs. Multicoloured.* P 14½.

573	24p.	Type **132**	80	80
		a. Horiz strip of 5. Nos. 573/7	3·50	
574	24p.	*Argynnis aglaja* (Dark Green Fritillary)	80	80
575	24p.	*Cynthia cardui* (Painted Lady)	80	80
576	24p.	*Celastrina argiolus* (Holly Blue)	80	80
577	24p.	*Vanessa atalanta* (Red Admiral)	80	80
573/7		*Set of 5*	3·50	3·50

Nos. 573/7 were printed together, *se-tenant*, both horizontally and vertically within the sheet of 20 (5×4).
Examples of Nos. 573/7 sold at "Philakorea '94" and "Singpex '94" come with commemorative cachets on the bottom margin.

(Des Christine Haworth. Litho Questa)

1993 (12 Oct). *Christmas. T* **133** *and similar vert designs. Multicoloured.* P 14.

578	19p.	Type **133**	55	55
579	23p.	Girl with snowman	65	65
580	28p.	Boy opening presents	80	80
581	39p.	Girl with teddy bear	1·25	1·25
582	40p.	Children with toboggan	1·25	1·25
578/82		*Set of 5*	4·00	4·00

134 White-throated Robin

(Des Colleen Corlett. Litho B.D.T.)

1994 (18 Feb). *Calf of Man Bird Observatory. T* **134** *and similar multicoloured designs.* P 14.
583	20p. Type **134**	..	60	60
	a. Pair. Nos. 583/4	..	1·25	1·25
584	20p. Black-eared Wheatear	..	60	60
585	24p. Goldcrest	..	90	90
	a. Pair. Nos. 585/6	..	1·75	1·75
586	24p. Northern Oriole	..	90	90
587	30p. Common Kingfisher	..	1·10	1·10
	a. Pair. Nos. 587/8	..	2·25	2·25
588	30p. Hoopoe	..	1·10	1·10
583/8		*Set of 6*	4·75	4·75
MS589	100×71 mm. £1 Magpie (51½×61 *mm*). P 13½×13		3·25	3·25

Nos. 583/4, 585/6 and 587/8 were printed together, *se-tenant,* in horizontal and vertical pairs throughout the sheets of 10.
No. MS589 also commemorates the "Hong Kong '94" philatelic exhibition.

135 Gaiety Theatre, Douglas

(Des Colleen Corlett. Litho Cartor)

1994 (18 Feb). *Booklet Stamps. Manx Tourism Centenary. T* **135** *and similar horiz designs. Multicoloured.* P 13½.
590	24p. Type **135**	..	60	60
	a. Booklet pane. Nos. 590/9 with margins all round	..	5·50	
591	24p. Sports	..	60	60
592	24p. Artist at work and yachts racing	..	60	60
593	24p. TT Races and British Aerospace Hawk T.1's of Red Arrows display team		60	60
594	24p. Musical instruments	..	60	60
595	24p. Laxey Wheel and Manx cat	..	60	60
596	24p. Tower of Refuge, Douglas, with bucket and spade		60	60
597	24p. Cyclist	..	60	60
598	24p. Tynwald Day and classic car	..	60	60
599	24p. Santa Mince Pie train, Groudle Glen	..	60	60
590/9		*Set of 10*	5·50	5·50

Nos. 590/9 were only issued in £2.40 stamp booklets.

136 *Eubranchus tricolor* (sea slug)

(Des Jennifer Toombs. Litho Enschedé)

1994 (5 May). *Europa. Discoveries of Edward Forbes (marine biologist). T* **136** *and similar horiz designs. Multicoloured.* P 13½×14½.
600	20p. Type **136**	..	60	60
	a. Horiz strip of 3. Nos. 600/2	..	1·75	
601	20p. *Loligo forbesii* (Common Squid)	..	60	60
602	20p. Edward Forbes and signature	..	60	60
603	30p. *Solaster moretonis* (fossil starfish)	..	1·00	1·00
	a. Horiz strip of 3. Nos. 603/5	..	3·00	
604	30p. *Adamsia carciniopados* (anemone) on Hermit Crab		1·00	1·00
605	30p. *Solaster endeca* (starfish)	..	1·00	1·00
600/5		*Set of 6*	4·25	4·25

Nos. 600/2 and 603/5 were printed together, *se-tenant,* in horizontal strips of 3 throughout the sheets of 15.

137 Maj-Gen. Bedell Smith and Naval Landing Force including *Ben-My-Chree IV* (ferry)

(Des A. Theobald. Litho Questa)

1994 (6 June). *50th Anniv of D-Day. T* **137** *and similar horiz designs. Multicoloured.* P 14.
606	4p. Type **137**	..	15	15
	a. Horiz pair. Nos. 606/7	..	30	30
607	4p. Admiral Ramsay and naval ships including *Victoria* and *Lady of Man* (ferries)	..	15	15

608	20p. Gen. Montgomery and British landings	70	70
	a. Horiz pair. Nos. 608/9	1·40	1·40
609	20p. Lt-Gen. Dempsey and 2nd Army landings	70	70
610	30p. Air Chief Marshal Leigh-Mallory and U.S. paratroops and aircraft	1·00	1·00
	a. Horiz pair. Nos. 610/11	2·00	2·00
611	30p. Air Chief Marshal Tedder and British paratroops and aircraft	1·00	1·00
612	41p. Lt-Gen. Bradley and U.S. 1st Army landings	1·25	1·25
	a. Horiz pair. Nos. 612/13	2·50	2·50
613	41p. Gen. Eisenhower and American landings	1·25	1·25
606/13	*Set of 8*	5·50	5·50

The two designs for each value were printed together, *se-tenant,* in horizontal pairs throughout sheets of 8.

138 Postman Pat, Jess and Ffinlo at Sea Terminal, Douglas

139 Cycling

(Des Colleen Corlett. Litho B.D.T.)

1994 (14 Sept). *Postman Pat visits the Isle of Man. T* **138** *and similar multicoloured designs.* P 15×14.
614	1p. Type **138**	..	15	15
	a. Booklet pane. No. 614×2 with margins all round		50	
615	20p. Laxey Wheel	..	70	70
	a. Booklet pane. No. 615×2 with margins all round		1·75	
616	24p. Cregneash	..	90	90
	a. Booklet pane. No. 616×2 with margins all round		2·25	
617	30p. Manx Electric Railway trains	..	1·00	1·00
	a. Booklet pane. No. 617×2 with margins all round		2·50	
618	36p. Peel Harbour	..	1·25	1·25
	a. Booklet pane. No. 618×2 with margins all round		2·75	
619	41p. Douglas Promenade	..	1·40	1·40
	a. Booklet pane. No. 619×2 with margins all round		3·25	
614/19		*Set of 6*	4·75	4·75
MS620	110×85 mm. £1 Postman Pat (25×39 *mm*). P 13		3·00	3·00

Examples of No. MS620 from stamp booklets show a line of roulettes at left.

(Des D. Miller. Litho Walsall)

1994 (11 Oct). *Centenary of International Olympic Committee. T* **139** *and similar square designs. Multicoloured.* P 14×14½.
621	10p. Type **139**	..	30	30
622	20p. Downhill skiing	..	55	55
623	24p. Swimming	..	70	70
624	35p. Hurdling	..	95	95
625	48p. Centenary logo	..	1·40	1·40
621/5		*Set of 5*	3·50	3·50

140 Santa Train to Santon

141 Foden Steam Wagon, Highway Board Depot, Douglas

(Des Colleen Corlett. Litho Cartor)

1994 (11 Oct). *Christmas. Father Christmas in the Isle of Man. T* **140** *and similar multicoloured designs.* P 13½×14 (23p.) or 14×13½ (*others*).
626	19p. Type **140**	..	60	60
627	23p. Father Christmas and Postman Pat on mini tractor, Douglas (*vert*)		80	80
628	60p. Father Christmas and majorettes in sleigh, Port St. Mary	..	2·00	2·00
626/8		*Set of 3*	3·00	3·00

(Des A. Peck. Litho Enschedé)

1995 (8 Feb). *Steam Traction Engines. T* **141** *and similar horiz designs. Multicoloured.* P 13½×13.
629	20p. Type **141**	..	60	60
630	24p. Clayton & Shuttleworth and Fowler engines pulling dead whale	..	70	70
631	30p. Wallis and Steevens engine at Ramsey Harbour	..	85	85
632	35p. Marshall engine with threshing machine, Ballarhenny		1·10	1·10
633	41p. Marshall convertible steam roller	..	1·25	1·25
629/33		*Set of 5*	4·00	4·00

COVER PRICES

Cover factors are quoted at the beginning of each country for most issues to 1945. An explanation of the system can be found on page x. The factors quoted do not, however, apply to philatelic covers.

142 Car No. 2 and First Train, 1895

(Des A. Theobald. Litho B.D.T.)

1995 (8 Feb). *Centenary of Snaefell Mountain Railway. T* **142** *and similar horiz designs. Multicoloured.* P 14.
634	20p. Type **142**	..	70	70
	a. Booklet pane. Nos. 634/7 with margins all round		3·25	
635	24p. Car No. 4 in green livery and Car No. 3 in Laxey Valley		80	80
636	35p. Car No. 6 and Car No. 5 in 1971	..	1·10	1·10
637	42p. Goods Car No. 7 and *Caledonia* steam locomotive pulling construction train		1·25	1·25
634/7		*Set of 4*	3·50	3·50
MS638	110×87 mm. £1 Passenger car and Argus char-a-banc at Bungalow Hotel (60×37 *mm*)		3·25	3·25
	a. Booklet pane. As No. MS638 with additional margins all round showing further inscriptions at right and left		3·25	

Booklet pane No. 634a exists in three versions, which differ in the order of the stamps within the block of four.
No. MS638a from stamp booklets shows a white margin, description of the design and line of roulettes at left and an additional inscription, "1895. CENTENARY SNAEFELL MOUNTAIN RAILWAY. 1995", vertically in the margin at right.

143 Peace Doves forming Wave and Tower of Refuge, Douglas Bay

144 Spitfire, Tank and Medals

(Des Colleen Corlett and M. Magleby (20p.), Colleen Corlett (30p.). Litho Enschedé)

1995 (28 Apr). *Europa. Peace and Freedom. T* **143** *and similar vert design. Multicoloured.* P 14×13½.
639	20p. Type **143**	..	75	75
640	30p. Peace dove breaking barbed wire	..	1·00	1·00

(Des A. Theobald. Litho B.D.T.)

1995 (8 May). *50th Anniv of End of Second World War. T* **144** *and similar horiz designs. Multicoloured.* P 14.
641	10p. Type **144**	..	30	30
	a. Horiz pair. Nos. 641/2	..	60	60
642	10p. Typhoon, anti-aircraft gun and medals	..	30	30
643	20p. Lancaster, H.M.S. *Biter* (escort carrier) and medals		55	55
	a. Horiz pair. Nos. 643/4	..	1·10	1·10
644	20p. U.S. Navy aircraft, jungle patrol and medals		55	55
645	24p. Celebrations in Parliament Square	..	70	70
	a. Horiz pair. Nos. 645/6	..	1·40	1·40
646	24p. V.E. Day bonfire	..	70	70
647	40p. Street party	..	1·10	1·10
	a. Horiz pair. Nos. 647/8	..	2·25	2·25
648	40p. King George VI and Queen Elizabeth on Isle of Man in July 1945	..	1·10	1·10
641/8		*Set of 8*	4·75	4·75

The two designs for each value were printed together, *se-tenant,* in horizontal pairs throughout sheets of 8.

145 Reg Parnell in Maserati "4 CLT", 1951

(Des N. Sykes. Litho Questa)

1995 (8 May). *90th Anniv of Motor Racing on Isle of Man. T* **145** *and similar multicoloured designs.* P 14.
649	20p. Type **145**	..	60	60
650	24p. Stirling Moss in Frazer Nash, 1951	..	75	75
651	30p. Richard Seaman in Delage, 1936	..	85	85
652	36p. Prince Bira in ERA R2B "Romulus", 1937		1·00	1·00
653	41p. Kenelm Guinness in Sunbeam 1, 1914	..	1·10	1·10
654	42p. Freddie Dixon in Riley, 1934	..	1·10	1·10
649/54		*Set of 6*	4·75	4·75
MS655	103×73 mm. £1 John Napier in Arrol Johnston, 1905 (47×58 *mm*)		2·50	2·50

146 Thomas the Tank Engine
and Bertie Bus being Unloaded

147 *Amanita muscaria*

(Des O. Bell. Litho B.D.T.)

1995 (15 Aug). *50th Anniv of Thomas the Tank Engine Stories by Revd. Awdry. "Thomas the Tank Engine's Dream". T **146** and similar horiz designs. Multicoloured. P 14.*

656	20p.	Type **146**	60	60
	a. Booklet pane. Nos. 656/7 with margins all round		1·50	
	b. Booklet pane. Nos. 656 and 661 with margins all round		2·00	
657	24p.	Mail train	75	75
	a. Booklet pane. Nos. 657/8 with margins all round		1·50	
658	30p.	Bertie and engines at Ballasalla	85	85
	a. Booklet pane. Nos. 658/9 with margins all round		1·75	
659	36p.	*Viking*, the diesel engine, Port Erin	1·00	1·00
	a. Booklet pane. Nos. 659/60 with margins all round		2·00	
660	41p.	Thomas and railcar at Snaefell summit	1·10	1·10
	a. Booklet pane. Nos. 660/1 with margins all round		2·25	
661	45p.	Engines racing past Laxey Wheel	1·25	1·25
656/61		*Set of 6*	5·00	5·00

(Des Colleen Corlett. Litho Enschedé)

1995 (1 Sept). *Fungi. T **147** and similar multicoloured designs. P 13½.*

662	20p.	Type **147**	50	50
663	24p.	*Boletus edulis*	65	65
664	30p.	*Coprinus disseminatus*	85	85
665	35p.	*Pleurotus ostreatus*	95	95
666	45p.	*Geastrum triplex*	1·50	1·50
662/6		*Set of 5*	4·00	4·00
MS667	100×71 mm. £1 Shaggy Ink Cap and Bee Orchid (50×59 mm)		3·00	3·00

No. MS667 is inscribed "Singapore World Stamp Exhibition 1st–10th September 1995" on the sheet margin.

148 St. Catherine's
Church, Port Erin

149 Langness
Lighthouse

(Des Colleen Corlett. Litho B.D.T.)

1995 (10 Oct). *Christmas. T **148** and similar square designs. Multicoloured. P 14.*

668	19p.	Type **148**	50	50
669	23p.	European Robin on Holly branch	65	65
670	42p.	St. Peter's Church and wild flowers	1·25	1·25
671	50p.	Hedgehog hibernating under farm machinery	1·50	1·50
668/71		*Set of 4*	3·50	3·50

(Des D. Swinton. Litho Questa)

1996 (24 Jan). *Lighthouses. T **149** and similar multicoloured designs. P 14.*

672	20p.	Type **149**	55	55
	a. Booklet pane. No. 672×4 with margins all round		1·75	
673	24p.	Point of Ayre lighthouse (*horiz*)	65	65
	a. Booklet pane. No. 673×4 with margins all round		2·25	
674	30p.	Chicken Rock lighthouse	85	85
	a. Booklet pane. Nos. 674 and 676 each × 2 with margins all round		3·25	
675	36p.	Calf of Man lighthouse (*horiz*)	1·00	1·00
	a. Booklet pane. Nos. 675 and 677 each × 2 with margins all round		3·50	
676	41p.	Douglas Head lighthouse	1·10	1·10
677	42p.	Maughold Head lighthouse (*horiz*)	1·10	1·10
672/7		*Set of 6*	4·75	4·75

150 White Manx Cat and Celtic
Interlaced Ribbons

151 Douglas
Borough Arms

(Des Nancy Corkish. Litho B.D.T.)

1996 (14 Mar). *Manx Cats. T **150** and similar multicoloured designs. P 14.*

678	20p.	Type **150**	60	60
679	24p.	Cat and Union Jack ribbons	75	75
680	36p.	Cat on rug in German colours, mouse and Brandenburg Gate	1·00	1·00
681	42p.	Cat, U.S.A. flag and Statue of Liberty	1·25	1·25
682	48p.	Cat, map of Australia and kangaroo	1·40	1·40
678/82		*Set of 5*	4·50	4·50
MS683	100×71 mm. £1·50, Cat with kittens (51×61 mm). P 13½		4·00	4·00

For No. MS683 with "CAPEX '96" logo see No. MS712.

(Des Colleen Corlett. Litho B.D.T.)

1996 (14 Mar). *Centenary of Douglas Borough. Self-adhesive. Die-cut perf 9×10.*

684	**151**	(20p.) multicoloured	60	60

No. 684 was printed in sheets of 40, each stamp surrounded by white backing paper divided by roulettes. The actual stamps are separated from the backing paper by die-cut perforations. It was initially sold for 20p. and was only valid for postage within the Isle of Man.

(Des A. Theobald. Litho Walsall)

1996 (21 Apr). *Ships. As Nos. 541, 543 and 547, but smaller, 21×18 mm. Multicoloured. P 14.*

687	4p.	Sir Winston Churchill (cadet schooner)	15	15
	a. Booklet pane. Nos. 687, 689 and 693, each × 2		5·00	
689	20p.	*Tynwald I* (paddle-steamer), 1846	65	65
693	24p.	*Francis Drake* (ketch)	85	85
687/93		*Set of 3*	1·50	1·50

The 20p. and 24p. show the positions of the face value and Queen's head reversed.

152 Princess Anne (President,
Save the Children Fund) and
Children

(Des D. Miller. Litho B.D.T.)

1996 (21 Apr). *Europa. Famous Women. T **152** and similar horiz design. Multicoloured. P 14.*

701	24p.	Type **152**	75	75
702	30p.	Queen Elizabeth II and people of the Commonwealth	1·00	1·00

The background designs of Nos. 701/2 continue onto the vertical sheet margins.

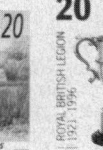

153 Alec Bennett

154 National Poppy
Appeal Trophy

(Des J. Dunne. Litho Questa)

1996 (30 May). *Tourist Trophy Motorcycle Races. Irish Winners. T **153** and similar multicoloured designs. P 14.*

703	20p.	Type **153**	65	65
704	24p.	Stanley Woods	80	80
705	45p.	Artie Bell	1·25	1·25
706	60p.	Joey and Robert Dunlop	1·75	1·75
703/6		*Set of 4*	4·00	4·00
MS707	100×70 mm. £1 R.A.F. Red Arrows display team (*vert*)		2·75	2·75

(Des C. Abbott. Litho B.D.T.)

1996 (8 June). *75th Anniv of Royal British Legion. T **154** and similar square designs. Multicoloured. P 14.*

708	20p.	Type **154**	60	60
709	24p.	Manx War Memorial, Braddan	65	65
710	42p.	Poppy appeal collection box	1·10	1·10
711	75p.	Royal British Legion badge	2·10	2·10
708/11		*Set of 4*	4·00	4·00

1996 (8 June). *"CAPEX '96" International Stamp Exhibition, Toronto. No. MS683 additionally inscribed with "CAPEX '96" exhibition logo on sheet margin.*

MS712	100×71 mm. £1·50 Cat with kittens (51×61 mm)		4·00	4·00

155 U.N.I.C.E.F. Projects in
Mexico

156 Labrador

(Des C. Abbott. Litho Enschedé)

1996 (18 Sept). *50th Anniv of U.N.I.C.E.F. T **155** and similar horiz designs. Multicoloured. P 13½×14.*

713	24p.	Type **155**	60	60
	a. Horiz pair. Nos. 713/14		1·25	1·25
714	24p.	Projects in Sri Lanka	60	60
715	30p.	Projects in Colombia	75	75
	a. Horiz pair. Nos. 715/16		1·50	1·50
716	30p.	Projects in Zambia	75	75
717	42p.	Projects in Afghanistan	1·10	1·10
	a. Horiz pair. Nos. 717/18		2·25	2·25
718	42p.	Projects in Vietnam	1·10	1·10
713/18		*Set of 6*	4·50	4·50

Nos. 713/14, 715/16 and 717/18 were each printed together, *se-tenant*, in horizontal pairs throughout the sheets.

(Des Colleen Corlett. Litho Questa)

1996 (18 Sept). *Dogs. T **156** and similar multicoloured designs. P 14½.*

719	20p.	Type **156**	55	55
	a. Booklet pane. No. 719×4 with margins all round		1·60	
720	24p.	Border Collie	65	65
	a. Booklet pane. No. 720×4 with margins all round		2·00	
721	31p.	Dalmatian	90	90
	a. Booklet pane. Nos. 721/4 with margins all round		3·50	
722	38p.	Mongrel	1·00	1·00
723	43p.	English Setter	1·25	1·25
724	63p.	Alsatian	1·75	1·75
719/24		*Set of 6*	5·50	5·50
MS725	100×71 mm. £1·20, Labrador guide dog and working Border Collie (38×50 mm). P 13½×14		3·25	3·25
	a. Booklet pane. As No. MS725, but with additional white margins all round separated by roulette		3·25	

157 "Snowman and
Pine Trees" (David
Bennett)

158 Primroses and
Cashtyl ny Ard

(Adapted Colleen Corlett. Litho Walsall)

1996 (2 Nov). *Christmas. Children's Paintings. T **157** and similar square designs. Multicoloured. P 14×14½.*

726	19p.	Type **157**	50	50
727	23p.	"Three-legged Father Christmas" (Louis White)	65	65
728	50p.	"Family around Christmas Tree" (Robyn Whelan)	1·40	1·40
729	75p.	"Father Christmas in Sleigh" (Claire Bradley)	1·90	1·90
726/9		*Set of 4*	4·00	4·00

(Des Colleen Corlett. Litho B.D.T.)

1997 (12 Feb). *Spring in Man. T **158** and similar square designs. Multicoloured. P 14.*

730	20p.	Type **158**	50	50
731	24p.	Lochtan sheep and lambs	70	70
732	43p.	Daffodils, duck and ducklings	1·10	1·10
733	63p.	Dabchick with young and frog on lily pad	1·60	1·60
730/3		*Set of 4*	3·50	3·50

159 Barn Owl

160 Moddey Dhoo, Peel Castle

(Des J. Paul. Litho B.D.T.)

1997 (12 Feb). *Owls. T **159** and similar vert designs. Multicoloured. P 14.*

734	20p.	Type **159**	60	60
	a. Booklet pane. No. 734×4 with margins all round		1·60	
735	24p.	Short-eared Owl	75	75
	a. Booklet pane. No. 735×4 with margins all round		2·00	
736	31p.	Long-eared Owl	90	90
	a. Booklet pane. Nos. 736/9 with margins all round		3·50	
737	36p.	Little Owl	1·10	1·10
738	43p.	Snowy Owl	1·25	1·25
739	56p.	Tawny Owl	1·50	1·50
734/9		*Set of 6*	5·50	5·50
MS740	100×71 mm. £1·20, Long-eared Owl (*different*) (51×60 mm). P 13		4·00	4·00
	a. Booklet pane. As No. MS740 but with additional white margins all round and with line of roulettes at left		4·00	

No. MS740 includes the "HONG KONG '97" International Stamp Exhibition Logo on the sheet margin.

(Des Colleen Corlett. Litho Enschedé)

1997 (24 Apr). *Europa. Tales and Legends.* T **160** *and similar horiz designs. Multicoloured. P* 13½×14.
741	21p.	Type **160**	..	50	50
742	25p.	Fairies in tree and cottage	..	60	60
743	31p.	Fairies at Fairy Bridge	..	80	80
744	36p.	Giant Finn Macooil and Calf of Man		1·00	1·00
745	37p.	The Buggane of St. Trinian's		1·00	1·00
746	43p.	Fynoderee and farm	..	1·25	1·25
741/6			*Set of* 6	4·50	4·50

Nos. 742/3 include the "EUROPA" emblem.

161 Sopwith Tabloid

(Des R. Carter. Litho Questa)

1997 (24 Apr). *Manx Aircraft.* T **161** *and similar horiz designs. Multicoloured. P* 14.
747	21p.	Type **161**	..	50	50
	a.	Horiz pair. Nos. 747/8	..	1·00	1·00
748	21p.	Grumman Tiger (1996 Schneider Trophy)		50	50
749	25p.	BAe ATP (15th anniv of Manx Airlines)		60	60
	a.	Horiz pair. Nos. 749/50		1·25	1·25
750	25p.	BAe 146-200 (15th anniv of Manx Airlines)		60	60
751	31p.	Boeing 757 200 (largest aircraft to land on Isle of Man)		75	75
	a.	Horiz pair. Nos. 751/2		1·50	1·50
752	31p.	Farman Biplane (1st Manx flight, 1911)		75	75
753	36p.	Spitfire	..	90	90
	a.	Horiz pair. Nos. 753/4		1·75	1·75
754	36p.	Hawker Hurricane	..	90	90
747/54			*Set of* 8	5·00	5·00

Nos. 747/8, 749/50, 751/2 and 753/4 were each printed together, *se-tenant*, in horizontal pairs, the backgrounds forming composite designs.

No. 752 is inscribed "EARMAN BIPLANE" in error.

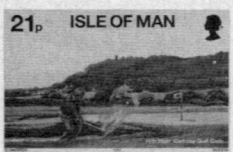

162 14th Hole, Ramsey Golf Club

(Des D. Swinton. Litho Questa)

1997 (29 May). *Golf.* T **162** *and similar multicoloured designs. P* 14.
755	21p.	Type **162**	..	50	50
	a.	Booklet pane. No. 755×3 with margins all round		1·50	
756	25p.	15th Hole, King Edward Bay Golf and Country Club		60	60
	a.	Booklet pane. No. 756×3 with margins all round		1·75	
757	43p.	17th Hole, Rowany Golf Club	..	1·10	1·10
	a.	Booklet pane. Nos. 757/8 each × 2 with margins all round		4·00	
758	50p.	8th Hole, Castletown Golf Links		1·50	1·50
755/8			*Set of* 4	3·25	3·25
MS759		100×71 mm. £1·30, Golf ball (*circular, diameter* 39 *mm*)		3·00	3·00
	a.	Booklet pane. As No. MS759, but with additional white margins all round		3·00	

No. MS759 includes the "Pacific 97" International Stamp Exhibition logo on the sheet margin.

(Litho Walsall)

1997 (1 July). *Return of Hong Kong to China. Sheet* 130×90 *mm, containing design as No.* 546 *with changed imprint date. Multicoloured.* W w **14**. *P* 13×13½.
MS760		23p. Royal Yacht *Britannia*	..	1·00	1·00

163 Steve Colley

164 Angel and Shepherd

(Des R. Organ. Litho Cartor)

1997 (17 Sept). *F.I.M. "Trial des Nations" Motorcycle Team Trials.* T **163** *and similar multicoloured design. P* 13½.
761	21p.	Type **163**	..	50	50
762	25p.	Steve Saunders (*vert*)	..	60	60
763	37p.	Sammy Miller (*vert*)	..	1·00	1·00
764	44p.	Don Smith	..	1·25	1·25
761/4			*Set of* 4	3·00	3·00

(Des Jennifer Toombs. Litho B.D.T.)

1997 (3 Nov). *Christmas.* T **164** *and similar multicoloured designs. P* 14.
765	20p.	Type **164**	..	55	55
766	24p.	Angel and King	..	70	70
767	63p.	The Nativity (54×39 *mm*)		1·50	1·50
765/7			*Set of* 3	2·50	2·50

165 Engagement of Princess Elizabeth and Lieut. Philip Mountbatten, 1947

(Des Colleen Corlett. Litho and die-stamped Questa)

1997 (3 Nov). *Golden Wedding of Queen Elizabeth and Prince Philip.* T **165** *and similar vert designs. Multicoloured* (*except No.* 768). *P* 14×14½.
768	50p.	Type **165** (sepia and gold)		1·25	1·25
	a.	Strip of 4. Nos. 768/71		4·50	
769	50p.	Wedding photograph, 1947		1·25	1·25
770	50p.	At Ascot, 1952	..	1·25	1·25
771	50p.	Golden Wedding photograph, 1997		1·25	1·25
768/71			*Set of* 4	4·50	4·50
MS772		100×72 mm. £1 Queen Elizabeth and Prince Philip at Peel, 1989 (47×58 *mm*). P 14		3·00	3·00

Nos. 768/71 were printed together, *se-tenant*, as horizontal or vertical strips of 4 throughout the sheet of 16.

166 Shamrock

167 Queen Elizabeth II and Queen Elizabeth the Queen Mother

Two Types of 4p.:
I. "WSP" imprint aligns with "N" of "MAN" (sheet stamps and 1998 booklet)
II. "WSP" ends to right of "N" of "MAN" (1999 booklet)

(Des Colleen Corlett (1p. to £1). Litho Cartor (£2·50) or Walsall (others))

1998 (12 Feb)–**99**. *Flowers. Vert designs as* T **166**, *and* T **167**. *Multicoloured. P* 13 (1, 2, 10, 20, 30p.) *or* 13×13½ (*others*).
773	1p.	Bearded Iris (2.7.98)		10	10
774	2p.	Daisy (2.7.98)		10	10
775	4p.	Type **166** (I)		10	10
	a.	Booklet pane. Nos. 775 and 778/9 each × 2		2·50	
	b.	Type II (26.4.99)		10	10
	ba.	Booklet pane. Nos. 775b×2, 780×3 and 782		2·00	
776	5p.	Silver Jubilee Rose (26.4.99)		10	15
777	10p.	Oriental Poppy (2.7.98)		20	25
778	20p.	Heath Spotted Orchid (2.7.98)		40	45
779	21p.	Cushag		40	45
780	22p.	Gorse (26.4.99)		45	50
781	25p.	Princess of Wales Rose		50	55
782	26p.	Dog Rose (26.4.99)		50	55
783	30p.	Fuchsia "Lady Thumb" (2.7.98)		60	65
784	50p.	Daffodil	..	1·00	1·10
785	£1	Spear Thistle	..	2·00	2·10
790	£2·50	Type **167** (2.7.98)		3·00	3·00
773/90			*Set of* 14	11·00	12·00

Imprint dates: "1998", Nos. 773/5, 777/9, 781, 783/5, 790; "1999", Nos. 775b/6, 780, 782.

168 Viking Figurehead

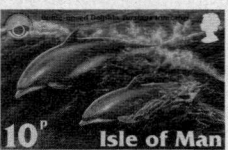

169 Bottle-nosed Dolphins

(Des A. Bell. Litho B.D.T.)

1998 (14 Feb). *Viking Longships.* T **168** *and similar vert designs. Multicoloured. P* 14.
793	21p.	Type **168**	..	50	50
794	25p.	Viking longship at sea		70	70
795	31p.	Viking longship on beach		80	80
796	75p.	Stern of ship	..	2·00	2·00
793/6			*Set of* 4	3·50	3·50
MS797		100×71 mm. £1 Viking ship at Peel Castle		2·50	2·50

(Des J. Paul. Litho Questa)

1998 (14 Mar). *U.N.E.S.C.O. International Year of the Ocean.* T **169** *and similar horiz designs. Multicoloured. P* 14.
798	10p.	Type **169**		30	30
	a.	Booklet pane. Nos. 798/9, each × 3 and 3 labels with margins all round		1·75	
	b.	Booklet pane. Nos. 798/9, 800/2 each × 2 and 1 central label with margins all round		3·50	
799	21p.	Basking Shark	..	50	50
800	25p.	Front view of Basking Shark		70	70
801	31p.	Minke Whale	..	80	80
802	63p.	Killer Whale and calf		1·60	1·60
798/802			*Set of* 5	3·50	3·50

170 Locomotive No. 12 *Hutchinson*

(Des A. Peck. Litho Questa)

1998 (2 May). *125th Anniv of Isle of Man Steam Railway.* T **170** *and similar horiz designs. Multicoloured. P* 14½×14.
803	21p.	Type **170**	..	50	50
	a.	Booklet pane. Nos. 803/6 with margins all round		2·75	
804	25p.	Locomotive No. 10 *G. H. Wood*		60	60
805	31p.	Locomotive No. 11 *Maitland*		80	80
806	63p.	Locomotive No. 4 *Loch*		1·60	1·60
803/6			*Set of* 4	3·25	3·25
MS807		119×54 mm. 25p. Pillar box and train at Douglas Station; £1 Locomotive No. 1 *Sutherland*		3·00	3·00
	a.	Booklet pane. As No. MS807 with additional margins showing diagram all round		3·50	

Booklet pane No. 803a exists in two versions, which differ in the order of the stamps within the block of four.

171 Purple Helmets Display Team

172 Princess Diana wearing Protective Clothing, Angola

(Des The Agency. Litho B.D.T.)

1998 (1 June). *Isle of Man T.T. Races and 50th Anniv of Honda* (*manufacturer*). T **171** *and similar horiz designs. Multicoloured. P* 14.
808	21p.	Type **171**	..	45	45
809	25p.	Joey Dunlop	..	55	55
810	31p.	Dave Molyneux	..	75	75
811	43p.	Naomi Taniguchi	..	1·10	1·10
812	63p.	Mike Hailwood	..	1·60	1·60
808/12			*Set of* 5	4·00	4·00

(Litho Cartor)

1998 (19 June). *Diana, Princess of Wales Commemoration.* T **172** *and similar vert designs. Multicoloured. P* 13½×13.
813	25p.	Type **172**	..	65	65
	a.	Strip of 4. Nos. 813/16		2·25	
814	25p.	Receiving award from United Cerebral Palsy Charity, New York, 1995		65	65
815	25p.	With children, South Korea, 1992		65	65
816	25p.	Wearing blue jacket, July 1993		65	65
813/16			*Set of* 4	2·25	2·25

Nos. 813/16 were printed together, *se-tenant*, both horizontally and vertically, within the sheet of 16.

173 Tynwald Day Ceremony

(Des M. Thompson. Litho Cartor)

1998 (2 July). *Europa. Festivals.* T **173** *and similar horiz design. Multicoloured. P* 13×13½.
817	25p.	Type **173**	..	65	65
818	30p.	Traditional dancers, Tynwald Fair		75	75

OMNIBUS ISSUES

Details, together with prices for complete sets, of the various Omnibus issues from the 1935 Silver Jubilee series to date are included in a special section following Zimbabwe at the end of Volume 2.

174 Father Christmas at North Pole

175 Large Oval Pillar Box, Kirk Onchan

(Des A. Bell. Litho Enschedé)

1998 (25 Sept). *Christmas. "A Very Special Delivery". T* **174** *and similar horiz designs. Multicoloured. P* 14½×14.

819	20p. Type 174	50	50
820	24p. Father Christmas checking list	60	60
821	30p. Flying over Spring Valley Sorting Office	90	90
822	43p. Passing through Baldrine village	1·10	1·10
823	63p. Father Christmas delivering presents	1·60	1·60
819/23	*Set of 5*	4·25	4·25

(Des The Agency Ltd. Litho Walsall)

1999 (4 Mar). *Local Post Boxes. T* **175** *and similar vert designs. Multicoloured. P* 14.

824	10p. Type 175	20	25
825	20p. Wall box, Ballaterson	40	45
826	21p. King Edward VII pillar box, Laxey Station	45	50
827	25p. Wall box, Spaldrick	50	55
828	44p. Small oval pillar box, Derby Road, Douglas	90	95
829	63p. Wall box, Baldrine Station	1·25	1·40
824/9	*Set of 6*	3·50	4·00

176 Cottage, Ballaglass Glen

177 *Ann and James Ritchie,* Ramsey

(Des Julia Ashby-Smyth. Litho B.D.T.)

1999 (4 Mar). *Europa. Parks and Gardens. T* **176** *and similar vert design. Multicoloured. P* 14.

830	25p. Type 176	50	55
831	30p. Glen Maye Waterfall	60	65

(Des Mainstream Media (No. MS839), R. Tomlinson (others). Litho Questa)

1999 (4 Mar). *175th Anniv of Royal National Lifeboat Institution. T* **177** *and similar multicoloured designs. P* 14.

832	21p. Type 177	45	50
	a. Booklet pane. Nos. 832/5 and 837, plus four printed labels, with margins all round	3·50	
	b. Booklet pane. Nos. 832/4, 836 and 838, plus four printed labels, with margins all round	3·50	
833	25p. *Sir William Hillary,* Douglas	50	55
834	37p. *Ruby Clery,* Peel	75	80
835	43p. *Herbert and Edith* (inshore lifeboat), Port Erin	85	90
836	43p. 1974 150th Anniv 8p. stamp	1·50	1·50
837	56p. *Gough Ritchie II,* Port St. Mary	1·10	1·25
838	56p. 1991 Manx Lifeboats 21p. stamp	1·75	1·75
832/8	*Set of 7*	6·25	6·50
MS839	100×70 mm. £1 Sir William Hillary (founder) (37×50 *mm*). P 13½×14	2·00	2·10
	a. Booklet pane. As No. MS839, but with additional margins showing lifeboats all round	2·00	

Nos. 836 and 838 were only available in £4.64 stamp booklets. No. MS839 includes the "Australia '99" World Stamp Exhibition emblem on the sheet margin.

178 Winter

179 Queen Victoria

(Des C. Alexander. Litho Walsall)

1999 (11 May). *Centenary of Yn Cheshaght Ghailckagh (Manx Gaelic Society). The Seasons. T* **178** *and similar vert designs. Multicoloured. P* 14½×14.

840	22p. Type 178	45	50
841	26p. Spring	50	55
842	50p. Summer	1·00	1·10
843	63p. Autumn	1·25	1·40
840/3	*Set of 4*	3·00	3·50

Nos. 840/3 are inscribed "Ellan Vannin", the Manx name for the Isle of Man.

(Des Colleen Corlett. Litho Walsall)

1999 (2 June). *British Monarchs of the 20th Century. Sheet* 170×75 *mm, containing T* **179** *and similar horiz designs. Multicoloured. P* 14.

MS844	26p. Type 179; 26p. King Edward VII; 26p. King George V; 26p. King Edward VIII; 26p. King George VI; 26p. Queen Elizabeth II	3·00	3·25

180 Tilling-Stevens Double Deck Bus, 1922

181 Miss Sophie Rhys-Jones

(Des P. Hearsey. Litho B.D.T.)

1999 (18 June). *Manx Buses. T* **180** *and similar horiz designs. Multicoloured. P* 14.

845	22p. Type 180	45	50
	a. Booklet pane. Nos. 845/6 and 847×2, with margins all round	2·00	
	b. Booklet pane. Nos. 845/6 and 848×2, with margins all round	2·40	
	c. Booklet pane. Nos. 845/6 and 849×2, with margins all round	2·40	
	d. Booklet pane. Nos. 845/6 and 850×2, with margins all round	2·50	
846	26p. Thornycroft BC single deck, 1928	50	55
847	28p. Cumberland ADC 416 single deck, 1927	55	60
848	37p. Straker-Squire single deck, 1914	75	80
849	38p. Thornycroft A2 single deck, 1927	75	80
850	40p. Leyland Lion LT9 single deck, 1938	80	85
845/50	*Set of 6*	3·75	4·00

(Des Catherine James. Litho B.D.T.)

1999 (19 June–1 Sept). *Royal Wedding. T* **181** *and similar multicoloured designs. P* 14.

851	22p. Type 181	45	50
852	26p. Leaving St. George's Chapel, Windsor (1 Sept)	50	55
853	39p. Prince Edward	80	85
854	44p. Miss Sophie Rhys-Jones and Prince Edward (*horiz*)	90	95
855	53p. In landau (*horiz*) (1 Sept)	1·10	1·25
851/5	*Set of 5*	3·75	4·00

1999 (2 July). *"Philexfrance 99" International Stamp Exhibition, Paris. No.* MS807 *additionally inscribed with "Philexfrance" exhibition logo on sheet margin.*

MS856	119×54 mm. 25p. Pillar box and train at Douglas Station; £1 Locomotive No. 1 *Sutherland*	2·50	2·75

182 St. Luke's Church, Baldwin

(Des N. Sayle. Litho Cartor)

1999 (22 Sept). *Christmas. Churches. T* **182** *and similar horiz designs. Multicoloured. P* 13½.

857	21p. Type 182	40	45
858	25p. St. Mark's Chapel, Malew	50	55
859	30p. St. German's Parish Church and Cathedral, Peel	60	65
860	64p. Kirk Christ Church, Rushen	1·25	1·40
857/60	*Set of 4*	2·75	3·00

183 "Massachusetts", 1967

(Des The Agency. Litho Cartor (Nos. 861/6), Walsall (MS867))

1999 (12 Oct). *Legends of Music. The Bee Gees (pop group). T* **183** *and similar horiz designs showing compact discs. Multicoloured. P* 13½.

861	22p. Type 183	45	50
862	26p. "Words", 1968	50	55
863	29p. "I've Gotta Get a Message to You", 1968	60	65
864	37p. "Ellan Vannin", 1998	75	80
865	38p. "You Win Again", 1987	75	80
866	66p. "Night Fever", 1978	1·25	1·40
861/6	*Set of 6*	4·25	4·75
MS867	Two sheets, each 119×108 mm. (a) 60p. "Immortality", 1998 (*circular, 40 mm diam*). (b) 90p. "Stayin' Alive", 1978 (*circular, 40 mm diam*). P 15	*Set of 2 sheets* 3·00	3·50

Nos. 861/6 were each printed in sheets of 9 stamps and three labels, arranged 3×4 with the labels in the third horizontal row, with enlarged illustrated right-hand margins.

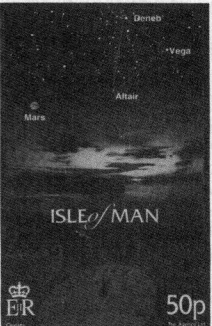

184 Sky at Sunset over Calf of Man

(Des H. Parkin and R. Berry. Litho Questa)

1999 (31 Dec). *New Millennium. Sheet,* 169×74 *mm, containing T* **184** *and similar vert designs. Multicoloured. P* 14½.

MS868	50p. Type 184; 50p. Sky at dawn over Maughold Head; £2 Constellations over Man at start of new millennium	6·00	6·25

STAMP BOOKLETS

For a full listing of Isle of Man stamp booklets see *Collect Channel Islands and Isle of Man Stamps* published each January.

POSTAGE DUE STAMPS

D 1

D 2

D 3

(Litho Questa)

1973 (5 July). P 13½×14.

D1	D 1	½p. red, black and bistre-yellow	1·75	1·50
D2		1p. red, black and cinnamon	65	65
D3		2p. red, black and light apple-green	15	20
D4		3p. red, black and grey	25	25
D5		4p. red, black and carmine-rose	35	35
D6		5p. red, black and cobalt	40	40
D7		10p. red, black and light lavender	50	50
D8		20p. red, black and pale turquoise-green	90	90
D1/8		*Set of 8*	4·50	4·25

A second printing of all values was put on sale by the Philatelic Bureau from 1 September 1973, although examples are known used from mid-August onwards. These can be distinguished by the addition of a small "A" after the date "1973" in the bottom left margin of the stamps. Spurious examples of the second printing exist with the "A" removed.

Prices quoted above are for the second printing. *Prices for set of 8 original printing £50 mint, £40 used.*

(Des and litho Questa)

1975 (8 Jan). *Arms and inscriptions in black and red; background colour given. P* 14×13½.

D 9	D 2	½p. greenish yellow	10	10
D10		1p. flesh	10	10
D11		4p. rose-lilac	10	10
D12		7p. light greenish blue	20	20
D13		9p. brownish grey	25	25
D14		10p. bright mauve	30	30
D15		50p. orange-yellow	1·25	1·25
D16		£1 turquoise-green	2·50	2·50
D9/16		*Set of 8*	4·00	4·00

(Litho B.D.T.)

1982 (5 Oct). P 15×14.

D17	D 3	1p. multicoloured	10	10
D18		2p. multicoloured	10	10
D19		5p. multicoloured	10	10
D20		10p. multicoloured	20	25
D21		20p. multicoloured	40	45
D22		50p. multicoloured	1·00	1·10
D23		£1 multicoloured	2·00	2·10
D24		£2 multicoloured	4·00	4·25
D17/24		*Set of 8*	7·75	8·25

D 4

(Des Colleen Corlett. Litho B.D.T.)

1992 (18 Sept). P 13×13½.

D25	D 4	£5 multicoloured	10·00	10·50

JERSEY

WAR OCCUPATION ISSUES

Stamps issued under British authority during the German Occupation

1

(Des Major N. V. L. Rybot. Typo *Jersey Evening Post*, St. Helier)

1941–43. *White paper (thin to thick). No wmk.* P 11.

1	1	½d. bright green (29.1.42)	.. ..	4·00	3·25
		a. Imperf between (vert pair)	..	£800	
		b. Imperf between (horiz pair)	..	£700	
		c. Imperf (pair)	..	£250	
		d. On greyish paper (1.43)	..	5·00	5·75
2		1d. scarlet (1.4.41)	..	4·25	3·25
		a. Imperf between (vert pair)	..	£800	
		b. Imperf between (horiz pair)	..	£700	
		c. Imperf (pair)	..	£275	
		d. On chalk-surfaced paper	..	40·00	38·00
		e. On greyish paper (1.43)	..	5·00	5·75

2 Old Jersey Farm

3 Portelet Bay

4 Corbière Lighthouse

5 Elizabeth Castle

6 Mont Orgueil Castle

7 Gathering Vraic (seaweed)

(Des E. Blampied. Eng H. Cortot. Typo French Govt Works, Paris)

1943–44. *No wmk.* P 13½.

3	2	½d. green (1 June)	..	8·00	7·25
		a. Rough, grey paper (6.10.43)	..	8·50	8·50
4	3	1d. scarlet (1 June)	..	2·25	1·00
		a. On newsprint (28.2.44)	..	2·50	2·00
5	4	1½d. brown (8 June)	..	4·00	4·00
6	5	2d. orange-yellow (8 June)	..	5·25	4·00
7	6	2½d. blue (29 June)	..	2·00	1·75
		a. On newsprint (25.2.44)	..	1·50	2·25
		ba. Thin paper*	..	£200	
8	7	3d. violet (29 June)	..	1·50	3·75
3/8			Set of 6	20·00	20·00

*On No. 7ba the design shows clearly through the back of the stamp.

REGIONAL ISSUES

DATES OF ISSUE. The note at the beginning of the Guernsey Regional Issues also applies here.

8

9

(Des E. Blampied (T **8**), W. Gardner (T **9**). Portrait by Dorothy Wilding Ltd. Photo Harrison & Sons)

1958 (18 Aug)–**67.** *W 179* of Great Britain. P 15 × 14.

9	8	2½d. carmine-red (8.6.64)	..	35	1·00
		a. Imperf three sides (pair)	..	£2000	
10	9	3d. deep lilac	..	35	30
		p. One centre phosphor band (9.6.67)	25	25
11		4d. ultramarine (7.2.66)	..	30	30
		p. Two phosphor bands (5.9.67)	..	25	30
9/11p	..		Set of 3	75	1·40

1968–69. *No wmk. Chalk-surfaced paper. PVA gum*. One centre phosphor band (4d. values) or two phosphor bands (5d.).* P 15 × 14.

12	9	4d. olive-sepia (4.9.68)	..	25	30
13		4d. bright vermilion (26.2.69)	..	25	40
14		5d. royal blue (4.9.68)	..	25	60
12/14	..		Set of 3	70	1·10

*PVA Gum. See note after No. 722 of Great Britain.

INDEPENDENT POSTAL ADMINISTRATION

10 Elizabeth Castle

11 Queen Elizabeth II (after Cecil Beaton)

13 Queen Elizabeth II (after Cecil Beaton)

12 Jersey Airport

(Des V. Whiteley. Photo Harrison (½d. to 1s. 9d.); Courvoisier (others))

1969 (1 Oct). *T* **10**/**13** *and similar horiz designs as T* **10** (½d. to 1s. 6d.) *or T* **12** (5s., 10s., £1). *Multicoloured. Granite paper* (2s. 6d. to £1). P 14 (½d. to 1s. 9d.) *or 12 (others).*

15		½d. Type **10**	..	10	70
16		1d. La Hougue Bie (prehistoric tomb) (shades)	15	20
		a. Booklet stamp with blank margins	75	
17		2d. Portelet Bay	..	10	15
18		3d. La Corbière Lighthouse	..	20	15
		b. Orange omitted	..	£120	
19		4d. Mont Orgueil Castle by night	..	15	10
		a. Booklet stamp with blank margins	40	
20		5d. Arms and Royal Mace	..	15	10
21		6d. Jersey Cow	..	25	30
22		9d. Chart of English Channel	..	40	75
23		1s. Mont Orgueil Castle by day	..	75	75
24		1s. 6d. As 9d.	..	1·25	1·25
25		1s. 9d. Type **11**	..	1·25	1·25
26		2s. 6d. Type **12**	..	2·00	1·75
27		5s. Legislative Chamber	..	8·00	6·00
28		10s. The Royal Court	..	24·00	16·00
		a. Error. Green border*	..	£4500	
29		£1 Type **13** (shades)	..	2·00	2·00
15/29			Set of 15	35·00	25·00

*During the final printing of the 10s. a sheet was printed in the colours of the 50p., No. 56, i.e. green border instead of slate.

The 3d. is known with the orange omitted.

There was no postal need for the ½d. value as the ½d. coin had been withdrawn prior to its issue in anticipation of decimalisation.

Nos. 16a and 19a come from 2s. booklets for the automatic machines formerly used for the Great Britain 2s. booklets (see also note after Guernsey No. 28).

Various papers were used by Harrisons. The ½d. and 1d. exist on much thicker paper from 2s. booklets and the 2d. to 1s. 9d. exist on thinner paper having white instead of creamy gum.

24 First Day Cover

25 Lord Coutanche, former Bailiff of Jersey

(Des R. Sellar. Photo Harrison)

1969 (1 Oct). *Inauguration of Post Office.* P 14.

30	24	4d. multicoloured	..	25	20
31		5d. multicoloured	..	30	30
32		1s. 6d. multicoloured	..	1·00	1·10
33		1s. 9d. multicoloured	..	1·25	1·40
30/3			Set of 4	2·50	2·75

(Des Rosalind Dease. Photo Courvoisier)

1970 (9 May). *25th Anniv of Liberation. T* **25** *and similar multicoloured designs. Granite paper* P 11½.

34	25	4d. Type **25**	..	25	25
35		5d. Sir Winston Churchill	..	25	25
36		1s. 6d. "Liberation" (Edmund Blampied) (horiz)	1·40	1·40
37		1s. 9d. S.S. *Vega* (horiz)	..	1·50	1·50
34/7			Set of 4	3·00	3·00

---

29 "A Tribute to Enid Blyton"

(Des Jennifer Toombs. Photo Courvoisier)

1970 (28 July). *"Battle of Flowers" Parade. T* **29** *and similar horiz designs. Multicoloured. Granite paper.* P 11½.

38		4d. Type **29**	..	25	25
39		5d. "Rags to Riches" (Cinderella and pumpkin)	40	40
40		1s. 6d. "Gourmet's Delight" (lobster and cornucopia)	5·50	2·50
41		1s. 9d. "We're the Greatest" (ostriches)	6·00	2·50
38/41			Set of 4	11·00	5·00

INVALIDATION. The regional issues for Jersey were invalidated for use in Jersey and Guernsey on 1 November 1969 but remained valid for use in the rest of the United Kingdom. Nos. 15/41 (except No. 29) and Nos. D1/6 were invalidated on 14 February 1972.

33 Jersey Airport

(Des V. Whiteley. Photo Harrison (½ to 9p.), Courvoisier (others))

1970 (1 Oct)–**74.** *Decimal Currency. Designs as Nos.* 15/28, *but with values inscr in decimal currency as in T* **33**, *and new horiz design as T* **10** (6p.). *Chalk-surfaced paper* (4½, 5½, 8p.), *granite paper* (10, 20, 50p.).

42		½p. Type **10** (15.2.71)	..	10	10
		a. Booklet stamp with blank margins	40	
43		1p. La Corbière Lighthouse (shades) (15.2.71)	10	10
		a. Orange omitted	..		
44		1½p. Jersey Cow (15.2.71)	..	10	10
45		2p. Mont Orgueil Castle by night (15.2.71)	10	10
		a. Booklet stamp with blank margins	1·25	
46		2½p. Arms and Royal Mace (15.2.71)	..	10	10
		a. Booklet stamp with blank margins	40	
		ab. Gold (Mace) omitted	..	£375	
		ac. Gold (Mace) printed double	£300	
47		3p. La Hougue Bie (prehistoric tomb) (15.2.71)	10	10
		a. Booklet stamp with blank margins (1.12.72)	50	
48		3½p. Portelet Bay (15.2.71)	..	15	15
		a. Booklet stamp with blank margins (1.7.74)	50	
49		4p. Chart of English Channel (15.2.71)	15	15
49a		4½p. Arms and Royal Mace (1.11.74)	..	20	20
		ab. Uncoated paper	..	£375	
50		5p. Mont Orgueil Castle by day (15.2.71)	10	15
50a		5½p. Jersey Cow (1.11.74)	..	40	25
51		6p. Martello Tower, Archirondel (15.2.71)	25	30
52		7½p. Chart of English Channel (15.2.71)	30	40
52a		8p. Mont Orgueil Castle by night (1.11.74)	25	25
53		9p. Type **11** (15.2.71)	..	50	30
54		10p. Type **33**	..	50	55
55		20p. Legislative Chamber	..	75	75
56		50p. The Royal Court	..	1·75	1·75
42/56			Set of 18	5·00	5·00

Original printings of the ½p. to 4p., 5p. and 6p. to 9p. were with PVA gum; printings from 1974 (including original printings of the 4½p. and 5½p.) have dextrin added (see notes after 1971 Great Britain Decimal Machin issue). The 10p. to 50p. have gum arabic.

The border of No. 56 has been changed from turquoise-blue to dull green.

34 White Eared-Pheasant

(Des Jennifer Toombs. Photo Courvoisier)

1971 (12 Mar). *Wildlife Preservation Trust* (1st series). *T* **34** *and similar multicoloured designs. Granite paper.* P 11½.

57		2p. Type **34**	..	50	25
58		2½p. Thick-billed Parrot (vert)	..	50	25
59		7½p. Western Black and White Colobus Monkey (vert)	6·00	3·75
60		9p. Ring-tailed Lemur	..	6·00	3·75
57/60			Set of 4	13·00	7·25

See also Nos. 73/6, 217/21, 324/9, 447/51 and 824/9.

35 Poppy Emblem and Field

36 "Tante Elizabeth" (E. Blampied)

(Des G. Drummond. Litho Questa)

1971 (15 June). *50th Anniv of Royal British Legion. T* **35** *and similar horiz designs. Multicoloured. P* 14.
61	2p.	Royal British Legion Badge	25	25
62	2½p.	Type **35**	25	25
63	7½p.	Jack Counter, V.C., and Victoria Cross	2·00	2·00
64	9p.	Crossed Tricolour and Union Jack	2·00	2·00
61/4		*Set of 4*	4·00	4·00

(Des and photo Courvoisier)

1971 (5 Oct). *Paintings. T* **36** *and similar multicoloured designs. Granite paper. P* 11½.
65	2p.	Type **36**	15	15
66	2½p.	"English Fleet in the Channel" (P. Monamy) (*horiz*)	25	20
67	7½p.	"The Boyhood of Raleigh" (Millais) (*horiz*)	2·75	2·25
68	9p.	"The Blind Beggar" (W. W. Ouless)	3·00	2·50
65/8		*Set of 4*	5·00	4·50

See also Nos. 115/18 and 213/16.

37 Jersey Fern   **38** Artillery Shako

(Des G. Drummond. Photo Courvoisier)

1972 (18 Jan). *Wild Flowers of Jersey. T* **37** *and similar vert designs. Multicoloured. Granite paper. P* 11½.
69	3p.	Type **37**	25	15
70	5p.	Jersey Thrift	60	45
71	7½p.	Jersey Orchid	2·25	2·25
72	9p.	Jersey Viper's Bugloss	2·50	2·25
69/72		*Set of 4*	5·00	4·50

(Des Jennifer Toombs. Photo Courvoisier)

1972 (17 Mar). *Wildlife Preservation Trust* (2nd series). *Multicoloured designs similar to T* **34**. *Granite paper. P* 11½.
73	2½p.	Cheetah	65	20
74	3p.	Rothschild's Mynah (*vert*)	40	35
75	7½p.	Spectacled Bear	1·40	1·50
76	9p.	Tuatara	2·00	1·75
73/6		*Set of 4*	4·00	3·25

(Des and photo Courvoisier)

1972 (27 June). *Royal Jersey Militia. T* **38** *and similar vert designs. Multicoloured. Granite paper. P* 11½.
77	2½p.	Type **38**	15	15
78	3p.	Shako (2nd North Regt)	20	20
79	7½p.	Shako (5th South-West Regt)	85	50
80	9p.	Helmet (3rd Jersey Light Infantry)	1·00	60
77/80		*Set of 4*	2·00	1·25

39 Princess Anne   **40** Armorican Bronze Coins

(Des G. Drummond from photographs by D. Groves. Photo Courvoisier)

1972 (1 Nov). *Royal Silver Wedding. T* **39** *and similar multicoloured designs. Granite paper. P* 11½.
81	2½p.	Type **39**	10	10
82	3p.	Queen Elizabeth and Prince Philip (*horiz*)	10	10
83	7½p.	Prince Charles	40	50
84	20p.	The Royal Family (*horiz*)	60	70
81/4		*Set of 4*	1·10	1·25

(Des G. Drummond. Photo Courvoisier)

1973 (23 Jan). *Centenary of La Société Jersiaise. T* **40** *and similar multicoloured designs. Granite paper. P* 11½.
85	2½p.	Silver cups	10	10
86	3p.	Gold torque (*vert*)	10	10
87	7½p.	Royal Seal of Charles II (*vert*)	40	40
88	9p.	Type **40**	50	50
85/8		*Set of 4*	1·00	1·00

41 Balloon *L'Armée de la Loire* and Letter, Paris, 1870   **42** North Western, 1870

(Des and photo Courvoisier)

1973 (16 May). *Jersey Aviation History. T* **41** *and similar horiz designs. Multicoloured. Granite paper. P* 11½.
89	3p.	Type **41**	10	10
90	5p.	Astra seaplane, 1912	15	15
91	7½p.	Supermarine Sea Eagle	60	60
92	9p.	De Havilland D.H.86 Dragon Express *Giffard Bay*	80	80
89/92		*Set of 4*	1·50	1·50

(Des G. Drummond. Photo Courvoisier)

1973 (6 Aug). *Centenary of Jersey Eastern Railway. T* **42** *and similar designs showing early locomotives. Multicoloured. Granite paper. P* 11½.
93	2½p.	Type **42**	10	10
94	3p.	*Calvados,* 1873	10	10
95	7½p.	*Carteret* at Grouville Station, 1898	60	40
96	9p.	*Caesarea,* 1873, and route map	80	50
93/6		*Set of 4*	1·50	1·00

43 Princess Anne and Capt. Mark Phillips

(Des and photo Courvoisier)

1973 (14 Nov). *Royal Wedding. Granite paper. P* 11½.
97	**43**	3p. multicoloured	10	10
98		20p. multicoloured	90	90

44 Spider Crab   **45** Freesias

(Des Jennifer Toombs. Photo Courvoisier)

1973 (15 Nov). *Marine Life. T* **44** *and similar horiz designs. Multicoloured. Granite paper. P* 11½.
99	2½p.	Type **44**	10	10
100	3p.	Conger Eel	10	10
101	7½p.	Lobster	50	50
102	20p.	Tuberculate Ormer	70	70
99/102		*Set of 4*	1·25	1·25

(Des G. Drummond. Photo Courvoisier)

1974 (13 Feb). *Spring Flowers. T* **45** *and similar vert designs. Multicoloured. Granite paper. P* 11½.
103	3p.	Type **45**	10	10
104	5½p.	Anemones	20	10
105	8p.	Carnations and Gladioli	60	40
106	10p.	Daffodils and Iris	80	50
103/6		*Set of 4*	1·50	1·00

46 First Letter-Box and Contemporary Cover   **47** John Wesley

(Des G. Drummond. Photo Courvoisier)

1974 (7 June). *U.P.U. Centenary. T* **46** *and similar horiz designs. Multicoloured. Granite paper. P* 11½.
107	2½p.	Type **46**	10	10
108	3p.	Postmen, 1862 and 1969	10	10
109	5½p.	Letter-box and letter, 1974	35	30
110	20p.	R.M.S. *Aquila* (1874) and B.A.C. One Eleven 200 (1974)	85	60
107/10		*Set of 4*	1·25	1·00

(Des, recess and litho D.L.R.)

1974 (31 July). *Anniversaries. T* **47** *and similar vert designs. P* 13 × 14.
111	3p.	agate and light cinnamon	10	10
112	3½p.	blackish violet and light azure	10	10
113	8p.	blue-black and pale rose-lilac	30	35
114	20p.	black and pale buff	70	65
	a.	Pale buff (background) omitted.		
111/14		*Set of 4*	1·00	1·00

Portraits and events:—3p. Type **47** (Bicentenary of Methodism in Jersey); 3½p. Sir William Hillary, founder (150th Anniv of R.N.L.I.); 8p. Cannon Wace, poet and historian (800th Death Anniv); 20p. Sir Winston Churchill (Birth Centenary).

48 *Catherine* and *Mary* (Royal yachts)   **49** Potato Digger

(Des and photo Courvoisier)

1974 (22 Nov). *Marine Paintings by Peter Monamy. T* **48** *and similar multicoloured designs. Granite paper. P* 11½.
115	3½p.	Type **48**	10	10
116	5½p.	French two-decker	20	15
117	8p.	Dutch vessel (*horiz*)	30	35
118	25p.	Battle of Cap La Hague, 1692 (55 × 27 mm)	80	80
115/18		*Set of 4*	1·25	1·25

(Des G. Drummond. Photo Courvoisier)

1975 (25 Feb). *19th-Century Farming. T* **49** *and similar horiz designs. Multicoloured. Granite paper. P* 11½.
119	3p.	Type **49**	10	10
120	3½p.	Cider crusher	10	15
121	8p.	Six-horse plough	35	35
122	10p.	Hay cart	55	50
119/22		*Set of 4*	1·00	1·00

50 H.M. Queen Elizabeth, the Queen Mother (photograph by Cecil Beaton)   **51** Nautilus Shell

(Des and photo Courvoisier)

1975 (30 May). *Royal Visit. Granite paper. P* 11½.
123	**50**	20p. multicoloured	1·00	1·00

(Des A. Games. Photo Courvoisier)

1975 (6 June). *Jersey Tourism. T* **51** *and similar vert designs based on holiday posters. Multicoloured. Granite paper. P* 11½.
124	5p.	Type **51**	10	10
125	8p.	Parasol	15	15
126	10p.	Deckchair	35	55
127	12p.	Sandcastle with flags of Jersey and the U.K.	60	60
124/7		*Set of 4*	1·10	1·25
MS128	146 × 68 mm. Nos. 124/7		1·00	1·10

52 Common Tern   **53** Armstrong Whitworth Siskin IIIA

(Des Jennifer Toombs. Photo Courvoisier)

1975 (28 July). *Sea Birds. T* **52** *and similar vert designs. Multicoloured. Granite paper. P* 11½.
129	4p.	Type **52**	15	15
130	5p.	British Storm Petrel	15	15
131	8p.	Brent Geese	50	40
132	25p.	Shag	85	70
129/32		*Set of 4*	1·50	1·25

(Des A. Theobald. Photo Courvoisier)

1975 (30 Oct). *50th Anniv of Royal Air Forces Association, Jersey Branch. T* **53** *and similar horiz designs. Multicoloured. Granite paper. P* 11½.
133	4p.	Type **53**	10	10
134	5p.	Supermarine Southampton I flying boat	15	15
135	10p.	Supermarine Spitfire Mk 1	50	35
136	25p.	Folland Fo.141 Gnat T.1	95	80
133/6		*Set of 4*	1·50	1·25

54 Map of Jersey Parishes

55 Parish Arms and Island Scene

(Des Courvoisier (£2). G. Drummond (others). Litho Questa (½ to 15p.). Photo Courvoisier (others))

1976–80. *Various multicoloured designs as T 54/5.*

(a) *Parish Arms and Views as T 54. P 14½.* (29 Jan)
137	½p.	Type **54**	..	10	10
138	1p.	Zoological Park	..	10	10
	a.	Booklet pane of 2 plus 2 *se-tenant* labels (5.4.76)	..	1·00	
	b.	Booklet pane of 4 (5.4.76)	..	1·00	
139	5p.	St. Mary's Church	..	15	15
	a.	Booklet pane of 4 (5.4.76)	..	50	
140	6p.	Seymour Tower	..	15	15
	a.	Booklet pane of 4 (28.2.78)	..	60	
141	7p.	La Corbière Lighthouse	..	20	20
	a.	Booklet pane of 4 (5.4.76)	..	60	
142	8p.	St. Saviour's Church	..	20	20
	a.	Booklet pane of 4 (28.2.78)	..	80	
143	9p.	Elizabeth Castle	..	25	25
	a.	Booklet pane of 4 (6.5.80)	..	1·00	
144	10p.	Gorey Harbour	..	25	25
145	11p.	Jersey Airport	..	30	25
146	12p.	Grosnez Castle	..	30	30
147	13p.	Bonne Nuit Harbour	..	35	35
148	14p.	Le Hocq Tower	..	35	40
149	15p.	Morel Farm	..	40	45

(b) *Emblems as T 55. Granite paper. P 12* (20 Aug 1976–16 Nov 1977)
150	20p.	Type **55**	..	50	50
151	30p.	Flag and map	..	75	75
152	40p.	Postal H.Q. and badge	..	1·00	1·00
153	50p.	Parliament, Royal Court and arms	..	1·25	1·00
154	£1	Lieutenant-Governor's flag and Government House	..	2·50	2·50
155	£2	Queen Elizabeth II (photograph by Alex Wilson) (*vert*) (16.11.77)	..	4·50	4·50
137/55			*Set of 19*	12·00	12·00

Nos. 156/9 are vacant.

56 Sir Walter Ralegh and Map of Virginia

(Des M. Orbell. Photo Courvoisier)

1976 (29 May). *"Links with America". T 56 and similar horiz designs. Multicoloured. Granite paper. P 11½.*
160	5p.	Type **56**	..	10	10
161	7p.	Sir George Carteret and map of New Jersey	..	15	15
162	11p.	Philippe Dauvergne and Long Island Landing	..	40	50
163	13p.	John Copley and sketch	..	45	65
160/3			*Set of 4*	1·10	1·25

57 Dr. Grandin and Map of China

58 Coronation, 1953 (photographed by Cecil Beaton)

(Des Jennifer Toombs. Photo Courvoisier)

1976 (25 Nov). *Birth Centenary of Dr. Lilian Grandin (medical missionary). T 57 and similar horiz designs. Granite paper. P 11½.*
164	5p.	multicoloured	..	10	10
165	7p.	light yellow, yellow-brown and black	..	15	15
166	11p.	multicoloured	..	50	35
167	13p.	multicoloured	..	50	50
164/7			*Set of 4*	1·10	1·00

Designs:—7p. Sampan on the Yangtze; 11p. Overland trek; 13p. Dr. Grandin at work.

(Des G. Drummond. Photo Courvoisier)

1977 (7 Feb). *Silver Jubilee. T 58 and similar vert designs. Multicoloured. Granite paper. P 11½.*
168	5p.	Type **58**	..	25	15
169	7p.	Visit to Jersey, 1957	..	30	20
170	25p.	Queen Elizabeth II (photo by Peter Grugeon)	..	90	80
168/70			*Set of 3*	1·25	1·00

59 Coins of 1871 and 1877

(Des D. Henley. Litho Questa)

1977 (25 Mar). *Centenary of Currency Reform. T 59 and similar horiz designs. Multicoloured. P 14.*
171	5p.	Type **59**	..	10	10
172	7p.	One-twelfth shilling, 1949	..	15	15
173	11p.	Silver Crown, 1966	..	40	35
174	13p.	£2 piece, 1972	..	45	50
171/4			*Set of 4*	1·00	1·00

60 Sir William Weston and *Santa Anna*, 1530

(Des A. Theobald. Litho Questa)

1977 (24 June). *St. John Ambulance Centenary. T 60 and similar horiz designs each showing a Grand Prior of the Order. Multicoloured. P 14 × 13½.*
175	5p.	Type **60**	..	10	10
176	7p.	Sir William Drogo and ambulance, 1877	..	15	15
177	11p.	Duke of Connaught and ambulance, 1917	..	40	35
178	13p.	Duke of Gloucester and stretcher-team, 1977	..	45	50
175/8			*Set of 4*	1·00	1·00

61 Arrival of Queen Victoria, 1846

(Des R. Granger Barrett. Litho Questa)

1977 (29 Sept). *125th Anniv of Victoria College. T 61 and similar multicoloured designs. P 14½.*
179	7p.	Type **61**	..	20	20
180	10½p.	Victoria College, 1852	..	25	20
181	11p.	Sir Galahad statue, 1924 (*vert*)	..	30	35
182	13p.	College Hall (*vert*)	..	35	35
179/82			*Set of 4*	1·00	1·00

62 Harry Vardon Statuette and Map of Royal Jersey Course

(Des Jennifer Toombs. Litho Questa)

1978 (28 Feb). *Centenary of Royal Jersey Golf Club. T 62 and similar horiz designs. Multicoloured. P 14.*
183	6p.	Type **62**	..	15	15
184	8p.	Harry Vardon's grip and swing	..	20	20
185	11p.	Harry Vardon's putt	..	65	50
186	13p.	Golf trophies and book by Harry Vardon	..	65	55
183/6			*Set of 4*	1·50	1·25

63 Mont Orgueil Castle

64 "Gaspé Basin" (P. J. Ouless)

(Des from paintings by Thomas Phillips. Photo Courvoisier)

1978 (1 May). *Europa. Castles. T 63 and similar horiz designs. Multicoloured. Granite paper. P 11½.*
187	6p.	Type **63**	..	20	20
188	8p.	St. Aubin's Fort	..	40	40
189	10½p.	Elizabeth Castle	..	50	50
187/9			*Set of 3*	1·00	1·00

(Des R. Granger Barrett. Litho Questa)

1978 (9 June). *Links with Canada. T 64 and similar horiz designs. Multicoloured. P 14½.*
190	6p.	Type **64**	..	15	15
191	8p.	Map of Gaspé Peninsula	..	20	20
192	10½p.	"Century" (brigantine)	..	25	30
193	11p.	Early map of Jersey	..	40	35
194	13p.	St. Aubin's Bay, town and harbour	..	45	40
190/4			*Set of 5*	1·25	1·25

65 Queen Elizabeth and Prince Philip

66 Mail Cutter, 1778–1827

(Des and photo Courvoisier)

1978 (26 June). *25th Anniv of Coronation. T 65 and similar vert design. Granite paper. P 11½.*
195	8p.	silver, black and cerise	..	30	30
196	25p.	silver, black and new blue	..	70	70

Design:—25p. Hallmarks of 1953 and 1977.

(Des Jersey P.O. Litho Harrison)

1978 (18 Oct). *Bicentenary of England-Jersey Government Mail Packet Service. T 66 and similar horiz designs. P 14½ × 14.*
197	6p.	black, yellow-brown and greenish yellow	15	15
198	8p.	black, dull yellowish grn & pale yell-grn	20	20
199	10½p.	black, ultramarine and cobalt	..	40	40
200	11p.	black, purple and pale rose-lilac	..	45	45
201	13p.	black, Venetian red and pink	..	50	50
197/201			*Set of 5*	1·50	1·50

Designs:—8p. *Flamer*, 1831–37; 10½p. *Diana*, 1877–90; 11p. *Ibex*, 1891–1925; 13p. *Caesarea*, 1960–75.

67 Jersey Calf

68 Jersey Pillar Box, *circa* 1860

(Des Jersey P.O. and Questa. Litho Questa)

1979 (1 Mar). *9th World Jersey Cattle Bureau Conference. T 67 and similar horiz design. Multicoloured. P 13½.*
202	6p.	Type **67**	..	20	20
203	25p.	"Ansom Designette" (cow presented to the Queen, 27 June 1978) (46 × 29 *mm*)	80	80

(Des Jennifer Toombs. Litho Questa)

1979 (1 Mar). *Europa. T 68 and similar vert designs. Multicoloured. P 14.*
204	8p.	Type **68**	..	25	25
	a.	Horiz pair. Nos. 204/5	..	50	50
	b.	Perf 14½	..	25	25
	ba.	Horiz pair. Nos. 204b/5b	..	50	50
205	8p.	Clearing a modern Jersey post box	..	25	25
	b.	Perf 14½	..	25	25
206	10½p.	Telephone switchboard, *circa* 1900	..	30	30
	a.	Horiz pair. Nos. 206/7	..	60	65
	b.	Perf 14½	..	30	30
	ba.	Horiz pair. Nos. 206b/7b	..	60	60
207	10½p.	Modern S.P.C. telephone system	..	30	30
	b.	Perf 14½	..	30	30
204/7			*Set of 4*	1·00	1·00

Nos. 204/5 and 206/7 were each printed together, *se-tenant*, in horizontal pairs throughout the sheets.

Although both perforations were supplied to Jersey at the same time the 8p perforated 14½ is not known used before early April.

69 Percival Mew Gull *Golden City*

70 "My First Sermon"

(Des A. Theobald. Photo Courvoisier)

1979 (24 Apr). *25th Anniv of International Air Rally. T 69 and similar horiz designs. Multicoloured. Granite paper. P 11½.*
208	6p.	Type **69**	..	15	15
209	8p.	De Havilland D.H.C.1 Chipmunk	..	20	25
210	10½p.	Druine D.31 Turbulent	..	40	25
211	11p.	De Havilland D.H.82A Tiger Moth	..	45	35
212	13p.	North American AT-6 Harvard	..	50	40
208/12			*Set of 5*	1·50	1·00

(Des Jersey P.O. and Courvoisier. Photo Courvoisier)

1979 (13 Aug). *International Year of the Child and 150th Birth Anniv of Millais. Paintings. T 70 and similar multicoloured designs. Granite paper. P 12 × 12½ (25p.) or 12 × 11½ (others).*
213	8p.	Type **70**	..	25	20
214	10½p.	"Orphans"	..	35	35
215	11p.	"The Princes in the Tower"	..	35	40
216	25p.	"Christ in the House of His Parents" (50 × 32 *mm*)	75	75
213/16			*Set of 4*	1·50	1·50

(Des Jennifer Toombs. Photo Courvoisier)

1979 (8 Nov). *Wildlife Preservation Trust (3rd series). Multicoloured designs as T 34. Granite paper.* P 11½.

217	6p.	Pink Pigeon (*vert*)		15	15
218	8p.	Orang-Utan (*vert*)		20	30
219	11½p.	Waldrapp		50	35
220	13p.	Lowland Gorilla (*vert*)		65	40
221	15p.	Rodriguez Flying Fox (*vert*)		75	50
217/21			Set of 5	2·00	1·50

71 Plan of Mont Orgueil

(Litho Enschedé)

1980 (5 Feb). *Fortresses. T 71 and similar multicoloured designs showing drawings by Thomas Phillips.* P 13 × 13½ (25p.) or 13½ × 13 (others).

222	8p.	Type **71**		30	25
223	11½p.	Plan of La Tour de St. Aubin		35	30
224	13p.	Plan of Elizabeth Castle		55	45
225	25p.	Map of Jersey showing fortresses (38 × 27 mm)		80	70
222/5			Set of 4	1·75	1·50

72 Sir Walter Raleigh

(Des Jersey Post Office and Questa. Litho Questa)

1980 (6 May). *Europa. Personalities. Links with Britain. T 72 and similar vert design. Multicoloured.* P 14.

226	9p.	Type **72**		20	20
	a.	Horiz pair. Nos. 226/7		50	50
227	9p.	Paul Ivy (engineer working on Elizabeth Castle)		20	20
228	13½p.	Sir George Carteret receiving rights to Smith's Island, Virginia, from King Charles II		45	45
	a.	Horiz pair. Nos. 228/9		90	90
229	13½p.	Lady Carteret, maid and Jean Chevalier		45	45
226/9			Set of 4	1·25	1·25

Nos. 226/7 and 228/9 were each printed together, *se-tenant*, in horizontal pairs throughout the sheets, forming composite designs.

 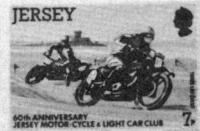

73 Planting　　**74** Three Lap Event

(Des R. Granger Barrett. Litho Questa)

1980 (6 May). *Centenary of Jersey Royal Potato. T 73 and similar vert designs. Multicoloured.* P 14.

230	7p.	Type **73**		15	15
231	15p.	Digging		35	35
232	17½p.	Weighbridge		60	60
230/2			Set of 3	1·00	1·00

(Des A. Theobald. Photo Courvoisier)

1980 (24 July). *60th Anniv of Jersey Motor-cycle and Light Car Club. T 74 and similar horiz designs. Multicoloured. Granite paper.* P 11½.

233	7p.	Type **74**		25	25
234	9p.	Jersey International Road Race		25	25
235	13½p.	Scrambling		45	45
236	15p.	Sand racing (saloon cars)		50	50
237	17½p.	National Hill Climb		55	55
233/7			Set of 5	1·75	1·75

75 *Eye of the Wind*　　**76** Detail of "The Death of Major Peirson"

(Des G. Drummond. Litho Questa)

1980 (1 Oct). *"Operation Drake" Round the World Expedition and 150th Anniv of Royal Geographical Society* (14p.). P 14.

238	7p.	Type **75**		20	20
239	9p.	Diving from inflatable dinghy		25	25
240	13½p.	Exploration of Papua New Guinea		35	35
241	14p.	Captain Scott's *Discovery*		45	35
242	15p.	Using aerial walkways, Conservation Project, Sulawesi		45	35
243	17½p.	*Eye of the Wind* and Goodyear Aerospace airship *Europa*		55	45
238/43			Set of 6	2·00	1·75

(Photo Courvoisier)

1981 (6 Jan). *Bicentenary of Battle of Jersey. Painting "The Death of Major Peirson" by J. S. Copley. T 76 and similar vert designs showing details of the work. Granite paper.* P 12½ × 12.

244	7p.	multicoloured		25	25
245	10p.	multicoloured		30	30
246	15p.	multicoloured		60	60
247	17½p.	multicoloured		80	80
244/7			Set of 4	1·75	1·75
MS248	144 × 97 mm. Nos. 244/7			2·00	2·00

Stamps from No. **MS**248 are without white margins.

77 De Bagot　　**78** Jersey Crest and Map of Channel

78a "Queen Elizabeth II"
(Norman Hepple)

(Des and photo Courvoisier (£5). Des G. Drummond. Litho Questa (others))

1981 (24 Feb)–**88**. *Arms of Jersey Families. T 77 and similar designs in black, silver and turquoise-green (½p.), black, silver and mauve (4p.), black, silver and lemon (20p.), black and dull blue (25p.), black, silver and carmine (26p.) or multicoloured (others) with T 78/a. Granite paper* (£5). P 12½×12 (£5), 15×14 (16p., 17p., 18p., 19p., 26p., 75p.) or 14 (others).

249	½p.	Type **77**		20	20
250	1p.	De Carteret		10	10
	a.	Booklet pane of 6		40	
	b.	Perf 15 × 14 (12.1.88)		25	25
251	2p.	La Cloche		10	10
	a.	Booklet pane of 6 (1.12.81)		70	
	b.	Perf 15 × 14 (15.11.84)		20	20
	ba.	Booklet pane of 6 (1.4.86)		1·00	
252	3p.	Dumaresq		20	20
	a.	Booklet pane of 6		80	
	b.	Perf 15 × 14 (27.4.84)		20	20
	ba.	Booklet pane of 6		85	
253	4p.	Payn		25	15
	a.	Perf 15 × 14 (4.3.86)		20	25
	ab.	Booklet pane of 6 (6.4.87)		90	
254	5p.	Janvrin		15	15
	a.	Perf 15 × 14 (4.3.86)		35	35
255	6p.	Poingdestre		20	20
	a.	Perf 15 × 14 (4.3.86)		50	50
256	7p.	Pipon		20	20
	a.	Booklet pane of 6		90	
257	8p.	Marett		25	25
	a.	Booklet pane of 6 (19.4.83)		1·50	
258	9p.	Le Breton		30	30
	a.	Perf 15 × 14 (27.4.84)		50	50
	ab.	Booklet pane of 6		2·75	
259	10p.	Le Maistre		30	30
	a.	Booklet pane of 6		1·50	
	b.	Perf 15 × 14 (1.4.86)		35	35
	ba.	Booklet pane of 6		1·60	
260	11p.	Bisson (28.7.81)		35	35
	a.	Booklet pane of 6 (19.4.83)		1·75	
	b.	Perf 15 × 14 (6.4.87)		40	45
	ba.	Booklet pane of 6		1·75	
261	12p.	Robin (28.7.81)		50	40
	a.	Perf 15 × 14 (27.4.84)		60	60
	ab.	Booklet pane of 6		3·00	
262	13p.	Herault (28.7.81)		40	40
	a.	Perf 15 × 14 (15.11.84)		60	60
263	14p.	Messervy (28.7.81)		45	45
	a.	Perf 15 × 14 (15.11.84)		75	75
	ab.	Booklet pane of 6 (1.4.86)		2·25	
264	15p.	Fiott (28.7.81)		45	45
	a.	Perf 15 × 14 (6.4.87)		45	45
	ab.	Booklet pane of 6		2·25	
265	16p.	Malet (25.10.85)		45	45
	a.	Booklet pane of 6 (17.5.88)		2·25	
266	17p.	Mabon (25.10.85)		50	50
266a	18p.	De St. Martin (26.4.88)		75	75
266b	19p.	Hamptonne (26.4.88)		80	80
267	20p.	Badier (28.7.81)		60	60
	a.	Perf 15 × 14 (4.3.86)		1·00	1·00
268	25p.	L'Arbalestier (23.2.82)		60	60
268a	26p.	Type **77** (26.4.88)		60	60

269	30p.	Journeaux (23.2.82)		90	90
	a.	Perf 15 × 14		1·25	1·25
270	40p.	Lempriere (23.2.82)		1·25	1·25
	a.	Perf 15×14 (6.4.87)		1·50	1·50
271	50p.	Auvergne (23.2.82)		1·50	1·50
	a.	Perf 15×14 (6.4.87)		2·00	2·00
272	75p.	Remon (23.4.87)		2·25	1·75
273	£1	Type **78** (23.2.82)		3·25	3·00
274	£5	Type **78a** (17.11.83)		15·00	12·00
249/74			Set of 29	28·00	25·00

No. 258a only occurs in the £2.16 stamp booklet issued 27 April 1984, No. 259b from the £3.12 booklet of 1 April 1986, No. 260b from the £3.60 booklet of 6 April 1987 and No. 261a from the £2.16 booklet of 27 April 1984 and the £3.84 booklet of 17 May 1988.

79 Knight of Hambye slaying Dragon

(Des Jennifer Toombs. Litho Questa)

1981 (7 Apr). *Europa. Folklore. T 79 and similar horiz designs. Multicoloured.* P 14½.

275	10p.	Type **79**		25	25
	a.	Horiz pair. Nos. 275/6		55	55
276	10p.	Servant slaying Knight of Hambye, and awaiting execution		25	25
277	18p.	St. Brelade celebrating Easter on island		50	50
	a.	Horiz pair. Nos. 277/8		1·10	1·10
278	18p.	Island revealing itself as a huge fish		50	50
275/8			Set of 4	1·50	1·40

Legends:—10p. (*both*), Slaying of the Dragon of Lawrence by the Knight of Hambye; 18p. (*both*), Voyages of St. Brelade.

Nos. 275/6 and 277/8 were each printed together, *se-tenant*, in horizontal pairs throughout the sheet.

80 The Harbour by Gaslight　　**81** Prince Charles and Lady Diana Spencer

(Des R. Granger Barrett. Photo Courvoisier)

1981 (22 May). *150th Anniv of Gas Lighting in Jersey. T 80 and similar horiz designs showing Jersey by gaslight. Multicoloured. Granite paper.* P 11½.

279	7p.	Type **80**		25	25
280	10p.	The Quay		30	30
281	18p.	Royal Square		45	45
282	22p.	Halkett Place		55	55
283	25p.	Central Market		65	65
279/83			Set of 5	2·00	2·00

(Des Jersey P.O. and Courvoisier. Photo Courvoisier)

1981 (28 July). *Royal Wedding. Granite paper.* P 11½.

284	**81**	10p.	multicoloured	75	75
285		25p.	multicoloured	1·75	1·75

82 Christmas Tree in Royal Square　　**83** Jersey, 16,000 B.C.

(Des A. Copp. Litho Questa)

1981 (29 Sept). *Christmas. T 82 and similar vert designs. Multicoloured.* P 14½.

286	7p.	Type **82**		25	25
287	10p.	East window, Parish Church, St. Helier		40	40
288	18p.	Boxing Day meet of Jersey Drag Hunt		50	50
286/8			Set of 3	1·00	1·00

(Des A. Copp. Litho Questa)

1982 (20 Apr). *Europa. Historic Events. Formation of Jersey. T 83 and similar multicoloured designs.* P 14½.

289	11p.	Type **83**		30	30
290	11p.	Jersey, 10,000 B.C. (*vert*)		30	30
291	19½p.	Jersey, 7,000 B.C. (*vert*)		70	60
292	19½p.	Jersey, 4,000 B.C.		70	60
289/92			Set of 4	1·75	1·60

84 Duke Rollo of Normandy, William the Conqueror and "Clameur de Haro" (traditional procedure for obtaining justice)

(Des R. Granger Barrett. Litho Questa)

1982 (11 June–7 Sept). *Links with France. T* **84** *and similar horiz designs. Multicoloured. P* 14.

293	8p.	Type **84**	25	25
	a.	Horiz pair. Nos. 293/4	50	50
	b.	Booklet pane. Nos. 293 and 294 each × 2 (7 Sept)	1·00	
294	8p.	John of England, Philippe Auguste of France and Siege of Rouen	25	25
295	11p.	Jean Martell (brandy merchant), early still and view of Cognac	35	35
	a.	Horiz pair. Nos. 295/6	70	70
	b.	Booklet pane. Nos. 295 and 296 each × 2 (7 Sept)	1·40	
296	11p.	Victor Hugo, "Le Rocher des Proscrits" (rock where he used to meditate) and Marine Terrace	35	35
297	19½p.	Pierre Teilhard de Chardin (philosopher) and "Maison Saint Louis" (science institute)	60	60
	a.	Horiz pair. Nos. 297/8	1·25	1·25
	b.	Booklet pane. Nos. 297 and 298 each × 2 (7 Sept)	2·50	
298	19½p.	Père Charles Rey (scientist), anemotachymeter and The Observatory, St. Louis	60	60
293/8		*Set of* 6	2·25	2·25

The two designs of each value were printed together, *se-tenant*, in horizontal pairs throughout the sheet.

Each booklet pane has margins all round and text, in English or French, printed on the binding selvedge.

85 Sir William Smith, Founder of Boys' Brigade

86 H.M.S. *Tamar* with H.M.S. *Dolphin* at Port Egmont

(Des A. Theobald. Photo Courvoisier)

1982 (18 Nov). *75th Anniv of Boy Scout Movement (Nos. 301/3) and Centenary of Boys' Brigade (Nos. 299/301). T* **85** *and similar multicoloured designs. Granite paper. P* 11½.

299	8p.	Type **85**	25	25
300	11p.	Boys' Brigade "Old Boys" band, Liberation Parade, 1945 (*vert*)	30	30
301	24p.	William Smith and Lord Baden-Powell at Royal Albert Hall, 1903	70	70
302	26p.	Lord and Lady Baden-Powell in St. Helier, 1924 (*vert*)	90	90
303	29p.	Scouts at "Westward Ho" campsite, St. Ouen's Bay	1·00	1·00
299/303		*Set of* 5	2·75	2·75

(Des R. Granger Barrett. Litho Questa)

1983 (15 Feb). *Jersey Adventurers (1st series). 250th Birth Anniv of Philippe de Carteret. T* **86** *and similar horiz designs. Multicoloured. P* 14 × 14½.

304	8p.	Type **86**	25	25
305	11p.	H.M.S. *Dolphin* and H.M.S. *Swallow* off Magellan Strait	30	30
306	19½p.	Discovering Pitcairn Island	50	50
307	24p.	Carteret taking possession of English Cove, New Ireland	70	70
308	26p.	H.M.S. *Swallow* sinking a pirate, Macassar Strait	85	75
309	29p.	H.M.S. *Endymion* leading convoy from West Indies	1·00	85
304/9		*Set of* 6	3·25	3·00

See also Nos. 417/21 and 573/8.

87 1969 5s. Legislative Chamber Definitive

(Des G. Drummond. Litho Questa)

1983 (19 Apr). *Europa. T* **87** *and similar multicoloured designs. P* 14½.

310	11p.	Type **87**	50	50
	a.	Horiz pair. Nos. 310/11	1·00	1·00
311	11p.	Royal Mace (23 × 32 *mm*)	50	50
312	19½p.	1969 10s. Royal Court definitive showing green border error	75	75
	a.	Horiz pair. Nos. 312/13	1·50	1·50
313	19½p.	Bailiff's Seal (23 × 32 *mm*)	75	75
310/13		*Set of* 4	2·25	2·25

The two designs of each value were issued together, *se-tenant*, in horizontal pairs throughout the sheets.

88 Charles Le Geyt and Battle of Minden (1759)

(Des A. Copp. Litho Questa)

1983 (21 June). *World Communications Year and 250th Birth Anniv of Charles Le Geyt (first Jersey postmaster). T* **88** *and similar horiz designs. Multicoloured. P* 14.

314	8p.	Type **88**	25	25
315	11p.	London to Weymouth mail coach	35	35
316	24p.	P.O. Mail Packet *Chesterfield* attacked by French privateer	75	75
317	26p.	Mary Godfray and the Hue Street Post Office	90	90
318	29p.	Mail steamer leaving St. Helier harbour	1·10	1·10
314/18		*Set of* 5	3·00	3·00

89 Assembly Emblem

90 "Cardinal Newman"

(Des A. Copp. Litho Questa)

1983 (21 June). *13th General Assembly of the A.I.P.L.F. (Association Internationale des Parlementaires de Langue Francaise), Jersey. P* 14½.

319	89	19½p. multicoloured	75	75

(Des and photo Courvoisier)

1983 (20 Sept). *50th Death Anniv of Walter Ouless (artist). T* **90** *and similar multicoloured designs, showing paintings. Granite paper. P* 11½.

320	8p.	Type **90**	25	25
321	11p.	"Incident in the French Revolution"	45	45
322	20½p.	"Thomas Hardy"	85	85
323	31p.	"David with the head of Goliath" (38 × 32 *mm*)	1·25	1·25
320/3		*Set of* 4	2·50	2·50

91 Golden Lion Tamarin

92 C.E.P.T. 25th Anniversary Logo

(Des W. Oliver. Litho Questa)

1984 (17 Jan). *Wildlife Preservation Trust (4th series). T* **91** *and similar vert designs. Multicoloured. P* 13½ × 14.

324	9p.	Type **91**	30	30
325	12p.	Snow Leopard	40	40
326	20½p.	Jamaican Boa	70	70
327	26p.	Round Island Gecko	1·10	1·10
328	28p.	Coscoroba Swan	1·25	1·25
329	31p.	St. Lucia Amazon	1·25	1·25
324/9		*Set of* 6	4·50	4·50

(Des J. Larriviere. Litho Questa)

1984 (12 Mar). *Europa. P* 14½ × 15.

330	**92**	9p. cobalt, dull ultramarine and black	30	30
331		12p. light green, green and black	40	40
332		20½p. rose-lilac, deep magenta and black	70	70
330/2		*Set of* 3	1·25	1·25

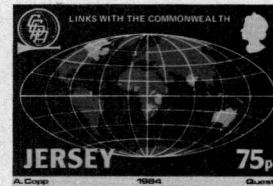

93 Map showing Commonwealth

(Des A. Copp. Litho Questa)

1984 (12 Mar). *Links with the Commonwealth. Sheet* 108 × 74 *mm. P* 15 × 14½.

MS333	**93**	75p. multicoloured	2·50	2·50

94 *Sarah Bloomshoft* at Demie de Pas Light, 1906

(Des G. Palmer. Litho Questa)

1984 (1 June). *Centenary of the Jersey R.N.L.I. Lifeboat Station T* **94** *and similar horiz designs showing famous rescues. Multicoloured. P* 14½.

334	9p.	Type **94**	40	40
335	9p.	*Hearts of Oak* and *Maurice Georges*, 1949	40	40
336	12p.	*Elizabeth Rippon* and *Hanna*, 1949	50	50
337	12p.	*Elizabeth Rippon* and *Santa Maria*, 1951	50	50
338	20½p.	*Elizabeth Rippon* and *Bacchus*, 1973	90	90
339	20½p.	*Thomas James King* and *Cythara*, 1983	90	90
334/9		*Set of* 6	3·25	3·00

95 Bristol Type 170 Freighter Mk 32

(Des G. Drummond. Litho Questa)

1984 (24 July). *40th Anniversary of International Civil Aviation Organization. T* **95** *and similar horiz designs. Multicoloured. P* 14.

340	9p.	Type **95**	30	30
341	12p.	Airspeed A.S.57 Ambassador 2	40	40
342	26p.	De Havilland D.H. 114 Heron 1B	1·10	1·10
343	31p.	De Havilland D.H.89A Dragon Rapide	1·40	1·40
340/3		*Set of* 4	3·00	3·00

96 "Robinson Crusoe leaves the Wreck"

97 "B.L.C. St Helier" Orchid

(Des R. Granger Barrett. Photo Courvoisier)

1984 (21 Sept). *Links with Australia. Paintings by John Alexander Gilfillan. T* **96** *and similar horiz designs. Multicoloured. Granite paper. P* 11½ × 12.

344	9p.	Type **96**	30	30
345	12p.	"Edinburgh Castle"	40	40
346	20½p.	"Maori Village"	75	75
347	26p.	"Australian Landscape"	95	95
348	28p.	"Waterhouse's Corner, Adelaide"	1·00	1·00
349	31p.	"Captain Cook at Botany Bay"	1·10	1·10
344/9		*Set of* 6	4·00	4·00

(Photo Courvoisier)

1984 (15 Nov). *Christmas. Jersey Orchids (1st series). T* **97** *and similar vert designs. Multicoloured. Granite paper. P* 12 × 11½.

350	9p.	Type **97**	50	45
351	12p.	"Oda Mt Bingham"	75	65

See also Nos. 433/7, 613/17 and 892/7.

98 "*Hebe* off Corbiere, 1874"

(Photo Harrison)

1985 (26 Feb). *Death Centenary of Philip John Ouless (artist). T* **98** *and similar horiz designs. Multicoloured. P* 14 × 15.

352	9p.	Type **98**	30	30
353	12p.	"*The Gaspe* engaging the *Diomede*"	40	40
354	22p.	"The Paddle-steamer *London* entering Naples, 1856"	80	80
355	31p.	"The *Rambler* entering Cape Town, 1840"	1·40	1·40
356	34p.	"St. Aubin's Bay from Mount Bingham, 1872"	1·50	1·50
352/6		*Set of* 5	4·00	4·00

99 John Ireland (composer) and Faldouet Dolmen

100 Girls' Brigade

(Des Jennifer Toombs. Litho Questa)

1985 (23 Apr). *Europa. European Music Year. T* **99** *and similar horiz designs. Multicoloured. P* 14.

357	10p.	Type **99**	40	40
358	13p.	Ivy St. Helier (actress) and His Majesty's Theatre, London	55	55
359	22p.	Claude Debussy (composer) and Elizabeth Castle	1·00	90
357/9		*Set of* 3	1·75	1·60

(Des A. Theobald. Litho Questa)

1985 (30 May). *International Youth Year. T* **100** *and similar vert designs. Multicoloured. P* 14½ × 14.

360	10p.	Type **100**	30	30
361	13p.	Girl Guides (75th anniversary) ..	50	50
362	29p.	Prince Charles and Jersey Youth Service Activities Base	1·00	1·00
363	31p.	Sea Cadet Corps ..	1·10	1·00
364	34p.	Air Training Corps ..	1·25	1·10
360/4	..	Set of 5	3·75	3·50

101 *Duke of Normandy at Cheapside*

(Des G. Palmer. Photo Courvoisier)

1985 (16 July). *The Jersey Western Railway. T* **101** *and similar horiz designs. Multicoloured. Granite paper. P* 11½.

365	10p.	Type **101** ..	55	55
366	13p.	Saddletank at First Tower ..	70	70
367	22p.	*La Moye* at Millbrook ..	1·10	1·10
368	29p.	*St. Heliers* at St. Aubin ..	1·25	1·25
369	34p.	*St. Aubyns* at Corbière ..	1·40	1·40
365/9	..	Set of 5	4·50	4·50

102 *Memorial Window to Revd. James Hemery (former Dean) and St. Helier Parish Church*

(Des R. Granger Barrett. Litho Questa)

1985 (10 Sept). *300th Anniv of Huguenot Immigration. T* **102** *and similar horiz designs. Multicoloured. P* 14.

370	10p.	Type **102** ..	30	30
	a.	Booklet pane of 4..	1·10	
371	10p.	Judge Francis Jeune, Baron St. Helier, and Houses of Parliament ..	30	30
	a.	Booklet pane of 4..	1·10	
372	13p.	Silverware by Pierre Amiraux ..	45	45
	a.	Booklet pane of 4..	1·75	
373	13p.	Francis Voisin (merchant) and Russian port..	45	45
	a.	Booklet pane of 4..	1·75	
374	22p.	Robert Brohier, Schweppes carbonation plant and bottles ..	75	75
	a.	Booklet pane of 4..	2·50	
375	22p.	George Ingouville, V.C., R.N., and attack on Viborg..	75	75
	a.	Booklet pane of 4..	2·50	
370/5	..	Set of 6	2·75	2·75

Each booklet pane has margins all round and text printed on the binding selvedge.

103 *Howard Davis Hall, Victoria College*

(Des A. Copp. Litho Cartor)

1985 (25 Oct). *Thomas Benjamin Davis (philanthropist) Commemoration. T* **103** *and similar horiz designs. Multicoloured. P* 13½.

376	10p.	Type **103** ..	40	40
377	13p.	Racing schooner *Westward* ..	60	60
378	31p.	Howard Davis Park, St. Helier ..	1·10	1·10
379	34p.	Howard Davis Experimental Farm, Trinity ..	1·25	1·25
376/9	..	Set of 4	3·00	3·00

104 *"Amaryllis belladonna"* (Pandora Sellars) **105** *King Harold, William of Normandy and Halley's Comet, 1066 (from Bayeux Tapestry)*

(Des C. Abbott. Litho Questa)

1986 (28 Jan). *Jersey Lilies. T* **104** *and similar multicoloured design. P* 15 × 14½.

380	13p.	Type **104** ..	75	75
381	34p.	"A Jersey Lily" (Lily Langtry) (Sir John Millais) (30 × 48 *mm*) ..	1·75	1·75
MS382		140 × 96 mm. Nos. 380 × 4 and 381	4·25	4·25

(Des Jennifer Toombs. Litho Cartor)

1986 (4 Mar). *Appearance of Halley's Comet. T* **105** *and similar horiz designs. Multicoloured. P* 13½ × 13.

383	10p.	Type **105** ..	40	40
384	22p.	Lady Carteret, Edmond Halley, map and Comet ..	1·00	1·00
385	31p.	Aspects of communications in 1910 and 1986 on TV screen ..	1·40	1·40
383/5	..	Set of 3	2·50	2·50

106 *Dwarf Pansy* **107** *Queen Elizabeth II (from photo by Karsh)*

(Des Pandora Sellars. Litho Questa)

1986 (21 Apr). *Europa. Environmental Conservation. T* **106** *and similar vert designs. Multicoloured. P* 14½ × 14.

386	10p.	Type **106** ..	40	40
387	14p.	Sea Stock ..	75	75
388	22p.	Sand Crocus ..	1·10	1·10
386/8	..	Set of 3	2·00	2·00

(Photo Courvoisier)

1986 (21 Apr). *60th Birthday of Queen Elizabeth II. Granite paper. P* 11½.

389	**107**	£1 multicoloured ..	3·25	3·25

No. 389 was retained in use as part of the current definitive series until replaced by No. 500.
For a £2 value in this design see No. 491*b*.

108 *Le Rât Cottage* **109** *Prince Andrew and Miss Sarah Ferguson*

(Des A. Copp. Litho Cartor)

1986 (17 June). *50th Anniv of National Trust for Jersey. T* **108** *and similar horiz designs. Multicoloured. P* 13½ × 13.

390	10p.	Type **108** ..	30	30
391	14p.	The Elms (Trust headquarters) ..	45	45
392	22p.	Morel Farm ..	80	80
393	29p.	Quétivel Mill ..	90	90
394	31p.	La Vallette ..	95	95
390/4	..	Set of 5	3·00	3·00

(Des A. Copp. Litho Cartor)

1986 (23 July). *Royal Wedding. P* 13½.

395	**109**	14p. multicoloured ..	50	50
396		40p. multicoloured ..	1·50	1·50

110 *"Gathering Vraic"* **111** *Island Map on Jersey Lily, and Dove holding Olive Branch*

(Des A. Copp. Litho Questa)

1986 (28 Aug). *Birth Centenary of Edmund Blampied (artist). T* **110** *and similar vert designs. P* 14.

397	10p.	multicoloured ..	40	40
398	14p.	black, light blue and brownish grey ..	70	70
399	29p.	multicoloured ..	1·00	1·00
400	31p.	black, pale orange and brownish grey ..	1·25	1·25
401	34p.	multicoloured ..	1·40	1·40
397/401	..	Set of 5	4·25	4·25

Designs:—14p. "Driving Home in the Rain"; 29p. "The Miller"; 31p. "The Joy Ride"; 34p. "Tante Elizabeth".

(Des G. Taylor. Litho Questa)

1986 (4 Nov). *Christmas. International Peace Year. T* **111** *and similar vert designs. Multicoloured. P* 14½.

402	10p.	Type **111** ..	40	40
403	14p.	Mistletoe wreath encircling European Robin and dove ..	60	60
404	34p.	Christmas cracker releasing dove ..	1·25	1·25
402/4	..	Set of 3	2·00	2·00

112 *Westward under Full Sail*

(Des A. Copp. Litho Cartor)

1987 (15 Jan). *Racing Schooner "Westward". T* **112** *and similar horiz designs. Multicoloured. P* 13½.

405	10p.	Type **112** ..	40	40
406	14p.	T. B. Davis at the helm ..	60	60
407	31p.	*Westward* overhauling *Britannia* ..	1·25	1·10
408	34p.	*Westward* fitting-out at St. Helier ..	1·40	1·25
405/8	..	Set of 4	3·25	3·00

113 *De Havilland D.H.86 Dragon Express Belcroute Bay*

(Des G. Palmer. Litho Questa)

1987 (3 Mar). *50th Anniv of Jersey Airport. T* **113** *and similar horiz designs. Multicoloured. P* 14.

409	10p.	Type **113** ..	30	30
410	14p.	Boeing 757 and Douglas DC-9-15 ..	50	50
411	22p.	Britten Norman "long nose" Trislander and Islander aircraft ..	70	70
412	29p.	Short 330 and Vickers Viscount 800 ..	1·10	1·10
413	31p.	B.A.C. One Eleven 500 and Handley Page H.P.R.7 Dart Herald ..	1·25	1·25
409/13	..	Set of 5	3·50	3·50

114 *St. Mary and St. Peter's Roman Catholic Church*

(Des A. Copp. Litho Questa)

1987 (23 Apr). *Europa. Modern Architecture. T* **114** *and similar horiz designs. Multicoloured. P* 15 × 14.

414	11p.	Type **114** ..	45	45
415	15p.	Villa Devereux, St. Brelade ..	65	65
416	22p.	Fort Regent Leisure Centre, St. Helier (57 × 29 *mm*) ..	90	90
414/16	..	Set of 3	1·75	1·75

115 *H.M.S. Racehorse and H.M.S. Carcass (bomb-ketches) trapped in Arctic*

(Des R. Granger Barrett. Litho Questa)

1987 (9 July). *Jersey Adventurers (2nd series). Philippe D'Auvergne. T* **115** *and similar horiz designs. Multicoloured. P* 14.

417	11p.	Type **115** ..	40	40
418	15p.	H.M.S. *Alarm* on fire, Rhode Island ..	50	50
419	29p.	H.M.S. *Arethusa* wrecked off Ushant ..	90	90
420	31p.	H.M.S. *Rattlesnake* stranded on Isle de Trinidad ..	1·00	1·00
421	34p.	Mont Orgueil Castle and fishing boats ..	1·10	1·10
417/21	..	Set of 5	3·50	3·50

See also Nos. 501/6 and 539/44.

116 *Grant of Lands to Normandy, 911 and 933*

(Des Jennifer Toombs. Litho Cartor)

1987 (9 Sept–16 Oct). *900th Death Anniv of William the Conqueror. T* **116** *and similar horiz designs. Multicoloured. P* 13½.

422	11p.	Type **116** ..	40	40
	a.	Booklet pane of 4 (16 Oct)	1·60	
423	15p.	Edward the Confessor and Duke Robert I of Normandy landing on Jersey, 1030 ..	45	45
	a.	Booklet pane of 4 (16 Oct) ..	2·00	

424	22p.	King William's coronation, 1066, and fatal fall, 1087		80	80
	a.	Booklet pane of 4 (16 Oct)		3·25	
425	29p.	Death of William Rufus, 1100, and Battle of Tinchebrai, 1106		95	95
	a.	Booklet pane of 4 (16 Oct)		4·00	
426	31p.	Civil war between Matilda and Stephen, 1135–41		1·10	1·10
	a.	Booklet pane of 4 (16 Oct)		4·50	
427	34p.	Henry inherits Normandy, 1151; John asserts ducal rights in Jersey, 1213		1·25	1·25
	a.	Booklet pane of 4 (16 Oct)		5·50	
422/7			Set of 6	4·50	4·50

Each booklet pane has margins all round and text printed on the binding selvedge.

117 "Grosnez Castle"

(Photo Courvoisier)

1987 (3 Nov). *Christmas. Paintings by John Le Capelain. T* **117** *and similar horiz designs. Multicoloured. Granite paper. P* 11½.

428	11p.	Type 117		40	40
429	15p.	"St. Aubin's Bay"		60	60
430	22p.	"Mont Orgueil Castle"		80	80
431	31p.	"Town Fort and Harbour, St. Helier"		1·10	1·10
432	34p.	"The Hermitage"		1·25	1·25
428/32			Set of 5	3·75	3·75

118 Cymbidium pontac

(Litho Questa)

1988 (12 Jan). *Jersey Orchids* (2nd series). *T* **118** *and similar multicoloured designs. P* 14.

433	11p.	Type 118		50	50
434	15p.	Odontioda Eric Young (vert)		60	60
435	29p.	Lycaste auburn "Seaford" and "Ditchling"		1·00	1·00
436	31p.	Odontoglossum St. Brelade (vert)		1·10	1·10
437	34p.	Cymbidium mavourneen "Jester"		1·25	1·25
433/7			Set of 5	4·00	4·00

119 Labrador Retriever

(Des P. Layton. Litho Questa)

1988 (2 Mar). *Centenary of Jersey Dog Club. T* **119** *and similar horiz designs. Multicoloured. P* 14.

438	11p.	Type 119		50	50
439	15p.	Wire-haired Dachshund		75	75
440	22p.	Pekingese		1·10	1·10
441	31p.	Cavalier King Charles Spaniel		1·10	1·10
442	34p.	Dalmatian		1·25	1·25
438/42			Set of 5	4·25	4·25

120 De Havilland D.H.C.7 Dash Seven Aircraft, London Landmarks and Jersey Control Tower   121 Rodriguez Fody

(Des A. Copp. Litho Cartor)

1988 (26 Apr). *Europa. Transport and Communications. T* **120** *and similar multicoloured designs. P* 14×13½ (*horiz*) *or* 13½×14 (*vert*).

443	16p.	Type 120		50	50
444	16p.	Weather radar and Jersey airport landing system (vert)		50	50
445	22p.	Hydrofoil, St. Malo and Elizabeth Castle, St. Helier		90	90
446	22p.	Port control tower and Jersey Radio maritime communication centre, La Moye (vert)		90	90
443/6			Set of 4	2·50	2·50

(Des W. Oliver. Litho Cartor)

1988 (6 July). *Wildlife Preservation Trust* (5th series). *T* **121** *and similar multicoloured designs. P* 13½×14 (*vert*) *or* 14×13½ (*horiz*).

447	12p.	Type 121		55	55
448	16p.	Volcano Rabbit (horiz)		70	70
449	29p.	White-faced Marmoset		1·10	1·10
450	31p.	Ploughshare Tortoise (horiz)		1·25	1·25
451	34p.	Mauritius Kestrel		1·40	1·40
447/51			Set of 5	4·50	4·50

122 Rain Forest Leaf Frog, Costa Rica   123 St. Clement Parish Church

(Des V. Ambrus. Photo Courvoisier)

1988 (27 Sept). *Operation Raleigh. T* **122** *and similar horiz designs. Multicoloured. Granite paper. P* 12.

452	12p.	Type 122		45	45
453	16p.	Archaeological survey, Peru		55	55
454	22p.	Climbing glacier, Chile		80	80
455	29p.	Red Cross Centre, Solomon Islands		1·00	1·00
456	31p.	Underwater exploration, Australia		1·10	1·10
457	34p.	Zebu (brigantine) returning to St. Helier		1·25	1·25
452/7			Set of 6	4·50	4·50

(Des P. Layton. Litho B.D.T.)

1988 (15 Nov). *Christmas. Jersey Parish Churches* (1st series). *T* **123** *and similar horiz designs. Multicoloured. P* 13½.

458	12p.	Type 123		35	35
459	16p.	St. Ouen		60	60
460	31p.	St. Brelade		1·00	1·00
461	34p.	St. Lawrence		1·10	1·10
458/61			Set of 4	2·75	2·75

See also Nos. 535/8 and 597/600.

124 Talbot "Type 4 CT Tourer", 1912

(Des A. Copp. Litho Questa)

1989 (31 Jan). *Vintage Cars* (1st series). *T* **124** *and similar horiz designs. Multicoloured. P* 14.

462	12p.	Type 124		40	40
463	16p.	De Dion "Bouton Type 1-D", 1920		60	60
464	23p.	Austin 7 "Chummy", 1926		75	75
465	30p.	Ford "Model T", 1926		90	90
466	32p.	Bentley 8 litre, 1930		1·10	1·10
467	35p.	Cadillac "452A -V16 Fleetwood Sports Phaeton", 1931		1·25	1·25
462/7			Set of 6	4·50	4·50

See also Nos. 591/6 and 905/10.

125 Belcroute Bay   125a Arms of King George VI

(Des G. Drummond (1p. to 75p.). Photo Courvoisier (£2), Litho Questa (£4), B.D.T. (others))

1989 (21 Mar)–**95**. *Jersey Scenes. T* **125** *and similar horiz designs, Queen's portrait as T* **107** *and T* **125a**. *Multicoloured. P* 11½×12 (£2), 15×14 (£4) *or* 13×13½ (*others*).

468	1p.	Type 125		10	10
469	2p.	High Street, St. Aubin		10	10
470	4p.	Royal Jersey Golf Course		10	10
	a.	Booklet pane of 6 with margins all round (3.5.90)		60	
471	5p.	Portelet Bay		15	15
	a.	Booklet pane of 6 with margins all round (12.2.91)		75	
472	10p.	Les Charrières D'Anneport		30	30
473	13p.	St. Helier Marina		40	40
474	14p.	Sand yacht racing, St. Ouen's Bay		40	40
	a.	Booklet pane of 6 with margins all round (3.5.90)		2·00	
	b.	Booklet pane of 8 with margins all round (22.5.92)		2·75	
475	15p.	Rozel Harbour		45	45
	a.	Booklet pane of 6 with margins all round (12.2.91)		2·00	
476	16p.	St. Aubin's Harbour		50	50
	a.	Booklet pane of 8 with margins all round (22.5.92)		3·50	
477	17p.	Jersey Airport		50	50

478	18p.	Corbière Lighthouse		55	55
	a.	Booklet pane of 6 with margins all round (3.5.90)		2·50	
479	19p.	Val de la Mare		55	55
480	20p.	Elizabeth Castle		60	60
	a.	Booklet pane of 6 with margins all round (12.2.91)		3·00	
481	21p.	Greve de Lecq (16.1.90)		50	50
482	22p.	Samarès Manor (16.1.90)		65	65
	a.	Booklet pane of 8 with margins all round (22.5.92)		4·50	
483	23p.	Bonne Nuit Harbour (16.1.90)		65	50
484	24p.	Grosnez Castle (16.1.90)		65	65
485	25p.	Augrès Manor (16.1.90)		70	70
486	26p.	Central Market (16.1.90)		75	75
487	27p.	St. Brelade's Bay (16.1.90)		80	80
488	30p.	St. Ouen's Manor (13.3.90)		85	85
489	40p.	La Hougue Bie (13.3.90)		90	90
490	50p.	Mont Orgueil Castle (13.3.90)		1·25	1·25
491	75p.	Royal Square, St Helier (13.3.90)		2·25	2·25
491b	£2	Type 107 (19.3.91)		6·00	6·00
491c	£4	Type 125a (24.1.95)		8·00	8·25
468/91c			Set of 26	25·00	25·00

126 Agile Frog   127 Toddlers' Toys

(Des W. Oliver. Litho Cartor)

1989 (25 Apr). *Endangered Jersey Fauna. T* **126** *and similar multicoloured designs. P* 13½×13 (*Nos.* 492 *and* 495), 13×13½ (*No.* 493) *or* 13½×14 (*No.* 494).

492	13p.	Type 126		1·00	1·00
493	13p.	Heteropterus morpheus (butterfly) (vert)		1·00	1·00
494	17p.	Barn Owl (vert)		1·10	1·10
495	17p.	Green Lizard		1·10	1·10
492/5			Set of 4	3·75	3·75

(Des Clare Luke. Litho Questa)

1989 (25 Apr). *Europa. Children's Toys and Games. T* **127** *and similar square designs showing clay plaques. Multicoloured. P* 14.

496	17p.	Type 127		50	50
497	17p.	Playground games		50	50
498	23p.	Party games		90	90
499	23p.	Teenage sports		90	90
496/9			Set of 4	2·50	2·50

128 Queen Elizabeth II and Royal Yacht *Britannia* in Elizabeth Harbour

(Des A. Copp. Litho Questa)

1989 (24 May). *Royal Visit. P* 14½.

500	**128**	£1 multicoloured		3·00	3·25

No. 500 was retained in use as part of the current definitive series until replaced by No. 634.

129 Philippe D'Auvergne presented to Louis XVI, 1786

(Des V. Ambrus. Litho Cartor)

1989 (7 July). *Bicentenary of the French Revolution. Philippe D'Auvergne. T* **129** *and similar horiz designs. Multicoloured. P* 13½.

501	13p.	Type 129		45	45
	a.	Booklet pane of 4		1·25	
502	17p.	Storming the Bastille, 1789		60	60
	a.	Booklet pane of 4		2·00	
503	23p.	Marie de Bouillon and revolutionaries, 1790		80	80
	a.	Booklet pane of 4		2·50	
504	30p.	Auvergne's headquarters at Mont Orgueil, 1795		1·10	1·10
	a.	Booklet pane of 4		4·25	
505	32p.	Landing arms for Chouan rebels, 1796		1·25	1·25
	a.	Booklet pane of 4		4·25	
506	35p.	The last Chouan revolt, 1799		1·40	1·40
	a.	Booklet pane of 4		4·75	
501/6			Set of 6	5·00	5·00

Each booklet pane has margins all round and text printed on the binding selvedge.

See also Nos. 539/44.

130 *St. Helier* off Elizabeth Castle

(Des G. Palmer. Litho Questa)

1989 (5 Sept). *Centenary of Great Western Railway Steamer Service to Channel Islands. T* **130** *and similar horiz designs. Multicoloured. P* 13½×14.

507	13p.	Type **130**	40	40
508	17p.	*Caesarea II* off Corbière Lighthouse	50	50
509	27p.	*Reindeer* in St. Helier harbour	1·00	1·00
510	32p.	*Ibex* racing *Frederica* off Portelet	1·25	1·25
511	35p.	*Lynx* off Noirmont	1·40	1·40
507/11		Set of 5	4·00	4·00

131 "Gorey Harbour"

132 Head Post Office, Broad Street, 1969

(Litho Enschedé)

1989 (24 Oct). *150th Birth Anniv of Sarah Louisa Kilpack (artist). T* **131** *and similar horiz designs. Multicoloured. P* 13×12½.

512	13p.	Type **131**	40	40
513	17p.	"La Corbière"	50	50
514	23p.	"Grève de Lecq"	1·00	1·00
515	32p.	"Bouley Bay"	1·25	1·25
516	35p.	"Mont Orgueil"	1·40	1·40
512/16		Set of 5	4·00	4·00

(Des P. Layton. Litho Cartor, France)

1990 (13 Mar). *Europa. Post Office Buildings. T* **132** *and similar multicoloured designs. P* 13½×14 (*vert*) or 14×13½ (*horiz*).

517	18p.	Type **132**	50	50
518	18p.	Postal Headquarters, Mont Millais, 1990	50	50
519	24p.	Hue Street Post Office, 1815 (*horiz*)	90	90
520	24p.	Head Post Office, Halkett Place, 1890 (*horiz*)	90	90
517/20		Set of 4	2·50	2·50

133 "Battle of Flowers" Parade

134 Early Printing Press and Jersey Newspaper Mastheads

(Des A. Copp. Litho Enschedé)

1990 (3 May). *Festival of Tourism. T* **133** *and similar vert designs. Multicoloured. P* 14×13½.

521	18p.	Type **133**	60	60
522	24p.	Sports	75	75
523	29p.	Mont Orgueil Castle and German Underground Hospital Museum	95	95
524	32p.	Salon Culinaire	1·00	1·00
521/4		Set of 4	3·00	3·00
MS525	151×100 mm. Nos. 521/4		3·00	3·00

(Des A. Copp. Litho Cartor)

1990 (26 June). *International Literacy Year. Jersey News Media. T* **134** *and similar horiz designs. Multicoloured. P* 13½.

526	14p.	Type **134**	55	55
527	18p.	Modern press, and offices of *Jersey Evening Post* in 1890 and 1990	60	60
528	34p.	Radio Jersey broadcaster	1·10	1·10
529	37p.	Channel Television studio cameraman	1·10	1·10
526/9		Set of 4	3·00	3·00

135 British Aerospace Hawk T.1

136 "Landsat 5" and Thematic Mapper Image over Jersey

(Des G. Palmer. Litho Questa)

1990 (4 Sept). *50th Anniv of Battle of Britain. T* **135** *and similar horiz designs. Multicoloured. P* 14.

530	14p.	Type **135**	45	45
531	18p.	Supermarine Spitfire	60	60
532	24p.	Hawker Hurricane Mk I	90	90
533	34p.	Vickers-Armstrong Wellington	1·60	1·60
534	37p.	Avro Type 683 Lancaster	1·75	1·75
530/4		Set of 5	4·75	4·75

(Des P. Layton. Litho B.D.T.)

1990 (13 Nov). *Christmas. Jersey Parish Churches (2nd series). Horiz designs as T* **123**. *Multicoloured. P* 13½.

535	14p.	St. Helier	40	40
536	18p.	Grouville	60	60
537	34p.	St. Saviour	1·25	1·25
538	37p.	St. John	1·40	1·40
535/8		Set of 4	3·25	3·25

(Des V. Ambrus. Litho Cartor)

1991 (22 Jan). *175th Death Anniv of Philippe d'Auvergne. Horiz designs as T* **129**. *Multicoloured. P* 13½.

539	15p.	Prince's Tower, La Hougue Bie	50	50
540	20p.	Auvergne's arrest in Paris	60	60
541	26p.	Auvergne plotting against Napoleon	80	80
542	31p.	Execution of George Cadoudal	1·00	1·00
543	37p.	H.M.S. *Surly* (cutter) attacking French convoy	1·25	1·25
544	44p.	Auvergne's last days in London	1·40	1·40
539/44		Set of 6	5·00	5·00

(Des A. Copp. Litho Enschedé)

1991 (19 Mar). *Europa. Europe in Space. T* **136** *and similar vert designs. Multicoloured. P* 14½×13.

545	20p.	Type **136**	55	55
546	20p.	"ERS-1" earth resources remote sensing satellite	55	55
547	26p.	"Meteosat" weather satellite	85	85
548	26p.	"Olympus" direct broadcasting satellite	85	85
545/8		Set of 4	2·50	2·50

137 1941 1d. Stamp (50th anniv of first Jersey postage stamp)

138 *Melitaea cinxia*

(Des A. Copp. Litho Cartor)

1991 (16 May). *Anniversaries. T* **137** *and similar vert designs. Multicoloured. P* 13½.

549	15p.	Type **137**	40	40
550	20p.	Steam train (centenary of Jersey Eastern Railway extension to Gorey Pier)	60	60
551	26p.	Jersey cow and Herd Book (125th anniv of Jersey Herd Book)	80	80
552	31p.	Stone-laying ceremony (from painting by P. J. Ouless) (150th anniv of Victoria Harbour)	90	90
553	53p.	Marie Bartlett and hospital (250th anniv of Marie Bartlett's hospital bequest)	1·75	1·75
549/53		Set of 5	4·00	4·00

(Des W. Oliver. Litho Enschedé)

1991 (9 July). *Butterflies and Moths. T* **138** *and similar horiz designs. Multicoloured. P* 13×12½.

554	15p.	Type **138**	40	40
555	20p.	*Euplagia quadripunctaria*	50	50
556	37p.	*Deilephila porcellus*	1·60	1·60
557	57p.	*Inachis io*	2·00	2·00
554/7		Set of 4	4·00	4·00

139 Drilling for Water, Ethiopia

140 "This is the Place for Me"

(Des A. Theobald. Litho B.D.T.)

1991 (3 Sept). *Overseas Aid. T* **139** *and similar horiz designs. Multicoloured. P* 13½×14.

558	15p.	Type **139**	50	40
559	20p.	Building construction, Rwanda	60	65
560	26p.	Village polytechnic, Kenya	80	80
561	31p.	Treating leprosy, Tanzania	1·00	1·00
562	37p.	Ploughing, Zambia	1·25	1·25
563	44p.	Immunisation clinic, Lesotho	1·40	1·40
558/63		Set of 6	5·00	5·00

(Litho Questa)

1991 (5 Nov). *Christmas. Illustrations by Edmund Blampied for J.M. Barrie's Peter Pan. T* **140** *and similar vert designs. Multicoloured. P* 14.

564	15p.	Type **140**	40	40
565	20p.	"The Island Come True"	65	65
566	37p.	"The Never Bird"	1·25	1·25
567	53p.	"The Great White Father"	1·60	1·60
564/7		Set of 4	3·50	3·50

141 Pied Wagtail

142 Shipping at Shanghai, 1860

(Des W. Oliver. Litho Cartor)

1992 (7 Jan). *Winter Birds. T* **141** *and similar vert designs. Multicoloured. P* 13½×14.

568	16p.	Type **141**	55	55
569	22p.	Firecrest	80	80
570	28p.	Common Snipe	90	90
571	39p.	Lapwing	1·40	1·40
572	57p.	Fieldfare	1·90	1·90
568/72		Set of 5	5·00	5·00

See also Nos. 635/9.

(Des V. Ambrus. Litho Cartor)

1992 (25 Feb). *Jersey Adventurers (3rd series). 150th Birth Anniv of William Mesny. T* **142** *and similar horiz designs. Multicoloured. P* 13½.

573	16p.	Type **142**	50	50
	b.	Booklet pane of 4	1·50	
574	16p.	Mesny's junk running Taiping blockade, 1862	50	50
	a.	Booklet pane of 4	1·50	
575	22p.	General Mesny outside river gate, 1874	75	75
	a.	Booklet pane of 4	2·00	
576	22p.	Mesny in Burma, 1877	75	75
	a.	Booklet pane of 4	2·00	
577	33p.	Mesny and Governor Chang, 1882	1·00	1·00
	a.	Booklet pane of 4	3·00	
578	33p.	Mesny in mandarin's sedan chair, 1886	1·00	1·00
	a.	Booklet pane of 4	3·00	
573/8		Set of 6	4·00	4·00

Each booklet pane has margins all round and text printed on the binding selvedge.

143 *Tickler* (brigantine)

(Des A. Copp. Litho Questa)

1992 (14 Apr). *Jersey Shipbuilding. T* **143** *and similar horiz designs. Multicoloured. P* 14.

579	16p.	Type **143**	50	50
580	22p.	*Hebe* (brig)	80	80
581	50p.	*Gemini* (barque)	1·60	1·60
582	57p.	*Percy Douglas* (full-rigged ship)	1·90	1·90
579/82		Set of 4	4·25	4·25
MS583	148×98 mm. Nos. 579/82		4·25	4·25

144 John Bertram (ship owner) and Columbus

145 "Snow Leopards" (Allison Griffiths)

148 Douglas DC-3 Dakota

149 "Jersey's Opera House" (Ian Rolls)

(Des N. MacKenzie. Litho Enschedé)

1993 (2 Nov). *Christmas. Stained Glass Windows by Henry Bosdet from St. Aubin on the Hill Church. T* **153** *and similar vert designs. Multicoloured. P* 14×13.

640	17p. Type **153**	45 45
641	23p. Two angels playing harps	65 65
642	39p. Two angels playing violins	1·25 1·25
643	57p. Two angels holding "Once in Royal David's City" banner	1·90 1·90
640/3	Set of 4	3·75 3·75

(Des V. Ambrus. Litho Questa)

1992 (14 Apr). *Europa. 500th Anniv of Discovery of America by Columbus. T* **144** *and similar horiz designs. P* 14×14½.

584	16p. Type **144**	70 70
585	28p. Sir George Carteret (founder of New Jersey)	85 85
586	39p. Sir Walter Ralegh (founder of Virginia)	1·25 1·25
584/6	Set of 3	2·50 2·50

(Litho Questa)

1992 (23 June). *Batik Designs. T* **145** *and similar vert designs. Multicoloured. P* 14½.

587	16p. Type **145**	50 50
588	22p. "Three Elements" (Nataly Miorin)	70 70
589	39p. "Three Men in a Tub" (Amanda Crocker)	1·25 1·25
590	57p. "Cockatoos" (Michelle Millard)	1·75 1·75
587/90	Set of 4	3·75 3·75

(Des A. Copp. Litho Enschedé)

1992 (8 Sept). *Vintage Cars (2nd series). Horiz designs as T* **124.** *Multicoloured. P* 13×12½.

591	16p. Morris Cowley "Bullnose", 1925	35 35
592	22p. Rolls Royce "20/25", 1932	50 50
593	28p. Chenard and Walcker "T5", 1924	80 80
594	33p. Packard 900 series "Light Eight", 1932	1·00 1·00
595	39p. Lanchester "21", 1927	1·25 1·25
596	50p. Buick "30 Roadster", 1913	1·75 1·75
591/6	Set of 6	5·00 5·00

(Des P. Layton. Litho B.D.T.)

1992 (3 Nov). *Christmas. Jersey Parish Churches (3rd series). Horiz designs as T* **123.** *Multicoloured. P* 13½.

597	16p. Trinity	40 35
598	22p. St. Mary	65 70
599	39p. St. Martin	1·25 1·25
600	57p. St. Peter	1·60 1·60
597/600	Set of 4	3·50 3·50

146 Farmhouse

147 *Phragmipedium Eric Young "Jersey"*

(Des A. Copp. Litho B.D.T.)

1993 (11 Jan). *Booklet Stamps. T* **146** *and similar horiz designs. Multicoloured. P* 13.

601	(–) Type **146**	50 50
	a. Booklet pane. Nos. 601/4, each × 2, with margins all round	4·50
602	(–) Trinity Church	50 50
603	(–) Daffodils and cows	50 50
604	(–) Jersey cows	50 50
605	(–) Sunbathing	60 60
	a. Booklet pane. Nos. 605/8, each × 2, with margins all round	5·00
606	(–) Windsurfing	60 60
607	(–) Crab (Queen's head at left)	60 60
608	(–) Crab (Queen's head at right)	60 60
609	(–) "Singin' in the Rain" float	75 75
	a. Booklet pane. Nos. 609/12, each × 2, with margins all round	6·50
610	(–) "Dragon Dance" float	75 75
611	(–) "Bali, Morning of the World" float	75 75
612	(–) "Zulu Fantasy" float	75 75
601/12	Set of 12	6·50 6·50

The above do not show face values, but are inscribed "BAILIWICK POSTAGE PAID" (Nos. 601/4), "U.K. MINIMUM POSTAGE PAID" (Nos. 605/8) or "EUROPE POSTAGE PAID" (Nos. 609/12). They were initially sold at 17p., 23p. or 28p. but Nos. 601/4 and 609/12 were increased to 18p. and 30p. on 10 January 1994 and Nos. 601/4 to 19p. on 4 July 1995. On 10 March 1997 Nos. 601/4 were increased to 20p., Nos. 605/8 to 24p. and Nos. 609/12 to 31p.

(Litho Enschedé)

1993 (26 Jan). *Jersey Orchids (3rd series). T* **147** *and similar vert designs. Multicoloured. P* 14×13.

613	17p. Type **147**	50 50
614	23p. *Odontoglossum Augres* "Trinity"	75 75
615	28p. *Militonia* St. Helier "Colomberie"	90 90
616	39p. *Phragmipedium pearcei*	1·50 1·50
617	57p. *Calanthe* Grouville "Grey"	2·00 2·00
613/17	Set of 5	5·00 5·00

(Des A. Theobald. Litho Questa)

1993 (1 Apr). *75th Anniv of Royal Air Force. T* **148** *and similar horiz designs. Multicoloured. P* 14.

618	17p. Type **148**	50 50
619	23p. Wight seaplane	70 70
620	28p. Avro Shackleton A.E.W.2	80 80
621	33p. Gloster Meteor Mk III and De Havilland D.H.100 Vampire FB.5	90 90
622	39p. Hawker Siddeley Harrier GR.1A	1·10 1·10
623	57p. Panavia Tornado F Mk 3	1·60 1·60
618/23	Set of 6	5·00 5·00
MS624	147×98 mm. Nos. 619 and 623	5·00 5·25

Nos. 618/24 also commemorate the 50th anniversary of the Royal Air Force Association and the 40th anniversary of the first air display on Jersey.

(Litho Cartor)

1993 (1 Apr). *Europa. Contemporary Art. T* **149** *and similar vert designs. Multicoloured. P* 13½×14.

625	23p. Type **149**	70 70
626	28p. "The Ham and Tomato Bap" (Jonathan Hubbard)	85 85
627	39p. "Vase of Flowers" (Neil MacKenzie)	1·25 1·25
625/7	Set of 3	2·50 2·50

150 1943 ½d. Occupation Stamp

151 Queen Elizabeth II (from painting by Marca McGregor)

(Des G. Drummond. Litho Cartor)

1993 (2 June). *50th Anniv of Edmund Blampied's Occupation Stamps. T* **150** *and similar horiz designs showing stamps from the 1943 issue. P* 13½.

628	17p. myrtle-green, pale green and black	40 45
629	23p. vermilion, salmon-pink and black	55 55
630	28p. chocolate, cinnamon and black	75 75
631	33p. reddish orange, salmon and black	1·00 1·00
632	39p. royal blue, cobalt and black	1·40 1·40
633	50p. bright magenta, pale mauve and black	1·50 1·50
628/33	Set of 6	5·00 5·00

Designs:—23p. 1d. value; 28p. 1½d. value; 33p. 2d. value; 39p. 2½d. value; 50p. 3d. value.

(Litho Questa)

1993 (2 June). *40th Anniv of Coronation. P* 14½.

634	**151** £1 multicoloured	3·50 3·50

No. 634 was retained in use as part of the current definitive series until replaced by No. 796.

152 Short-toed Treecreeper

153 Two Angels holding "Hark the Herald Angels Sing" Banner

(Des W. Oliver. Litho Cartor)

1993 (7 Sept). *Summer Birds. T* **152** *and similar vert designs. Multicoloured. P* 13½×14.

635	17p. Type **152**	50 50
636	23p. Dartford Warbler	75 75
637	28p. Common Wheatear	85 85
638	39p. Cirl Bunting	1·25 1·25
639	57p. Jay	1·75 1·75
635/9	Set of 5	4·50 4·50

154 *Coprinus comatus*

(Des W. Oliver. Litho Questa)

1994 (11 Jan). *Fungi. T* **154** *and similar vert designs. Multicoloured. P* 14½.

644	18p. Type **154**	45 45
645	23p. *Amanita muscaria*	70 70
646	30p. *Cantharellus cibarius*	90 90
647	41p. *Macrolepiota procera*	1·25 1·25
648	60p. *Clathrus ruber*	1·75 1·75
644/8	Set of 5	4·50 4·50

155 Pekingese

(Des P. Layton, adapted A. Copp. Litho Questa)

1994 (18 Feb). *"Hong Kong '94" International Stamp Exhibition. "Chinese Year of the Dog". Sheet* 110×75 mm. *P* 15×14½.

MS649	**155** £1 multicoloured	3·00 3·00

156 Maine Coon

157 Mammoth Hunt, La Cotte de St. Brelade

(Des P. Layton. Litho B.D.T.)

1994 (5 Apr). *21st Anniv of Jersey Cat Club. T* **156** *and similar multicoloured designs. P* 14.

650	18p. Type **156**	45 45
651	23p. British Shorthair (*horiz*)	70 70
652	35p. Persian	90 90
653	41p. Siamese (*horiz*)	1·25 1·25
654	60p. Non-pedigree	1·75 1·75
650/4	Set of 5	4·50 4·50

(Des A. Copp. Litho Enschedé)

1994 (5 Apr). *Europa. Archaeological Discoveries. T* **157** *and similar horiz designs. Multicoloured. P* 13½×14.

655	23p. Type **157**	55 55
	a. Horiz pair. Nos. 655/6	1·10 1·10
656	23p. Stone Age hunters pulling mammoth into cave	55 55
657	30p. Chambered passage, La Hougue Bie	85 85
	a. Horiz pair. Nos. 657/8	1·75 1·75
658	30p. Transporting stones	85 85
655/8	Set of 4	2·50 2·50

Nos. 655/6 and 657/8 were printed together, *se-tenant*, in horizontal pairs throughout the sheets.

158 Gliders and Towing Aircraft approaching France

(Des A. Theobald. Litho B.D.T.)

1994 (6 June). *50th Anniv of D-Day. T* **158** *and similar horiz designs. Multicoloured. P* 13½×14.

659	18p.	Type **158**	60	60
	a.	Booklet pane. Nos. 659/60, each × 3, with margins all round	2·75	
	b.	Booklet pane. Nos. 659/64, with margins all round	6·00	
660	18p.	Landing craft approaching beaches	60	60
661	23p.	Disembarking from landing craft on Gold Beach	80	80
	a.	Booklet pane. Nos. 661/2, each × 3, with margins all round	5·50	
662	23p.	British troops on Sword Beach	80	80
663	30p.	Spitfires over beaches	90	90
	a.	Booklet pane. Nos. 663/4, each × 3, with margins all round	6·00	
664	30p.	Invasion map	90	90
659/64		Set of 6	4·00	4·00

No. 659b was also available as a loose pane from the Philatelic Bureau.

159 Sailing

(Des A. Theobald. Litho Questa)

1994 (6 June). *Centenary of International Olympic Committee. T* **159** *and similar horiz designs. Multicoloured. P* 14.

665	18p.	Type **159**	45	45
666	23p.	Rifle shooting	60	60
667	30p.	Hurdling	85	85
668	41p.	Swimming	1·25	1·25
669	60p.	Hockey	1·60	1·60
665/9		Set of 5	4·25	

160 Strawberry Anemone

(Des W. Oliver. Litho Cartor)

1994 (2 Aug). *Marine Life. T* **160** *and similar horiz designs. Multicoloured. P* 13½.

670	18p.	Type **160**	50	50
671	23p.	Hermit Crab and parasitic anemone	75	75
672	41p.	Velvet Swimming Crab	1·40	1·40
673	60p.	Common Jellyfish	1·75	1·75
670/3		Set of 4	4·00	4·00

161 Condor 10 (catamaran)

(Des A. Copp. Litho Questa)

1994 (1 Oct). *25th Anniv of Jersey Postal Administration. T* **161** *and similar horiz designs. Multicoloured. P* 14.

674	18p.	Type **161**	45	45
675	23p.	Map of Jersey and pillar box	60	60
676	35p.	Vickers Type 953 Vanguard of B.E.A.	85	85
677	41p.	Shorts 360 of Aurigny Air Services	1·10	1·10
678	60p.	*Caesarea* (Sealink ferry)	1·50	1·50
674/8		Set of 5	4·00	4·00
MS679	150×100 mm. Nos. 674/8		4·50	4·50

162 "Away in a Manger"   **163** Dog and "GOOD LUCK"

(Des A. Copp. Litho Questa)

1994 (8 Nov). *Christmas. Carols. T* **162** *and similar horiz designs. Multicoloured. P* 14.

680	18p.	Type **162**	45	45
681	23p.	"Hark! the Herald Angels Sing"	60	60
682	41p.	"While Shepherds watched"	1·25	1·25
683	60p.	"We Three Kings of Orient Are"	1·60	1·60
680/3		Set of 4	3·50	3·50

(Des A. Copp. Litho B.D.T.)

1995 (24 Jan). *Greetings Stamps. T* **163** *and similar vert designs. Multicoloured. P* 13.

684	18p.	Type **163**	45	45
	a.	Horiz strip of 4. Nos. 684/7	1·75	
	b.	Booklet pane of 9. Nos. 684/92	5·50	
685	18p.	Rose and "WITH LOVE"	45	45
686	18p.	Chick and "CONGRATULATIONS"	45	45
687	18p.	Bouquet of flowers and "THANK YOU"	45	45
688	23p.	Dove with letter and "WITH LOVE"	55	55
	a.	Horiz strip of 4. Nos. 688/91	2·25	
689	23p.	Cat and "GOOD LUCK"	55	55
690	23p.	Carnations and "THANK YOU"	55	55
691	23p.	Parrot and "CONGRATULATIONS"	55	55
692	60p.	Pig and "HAPPY NEW YEAR" (25×63 mm)	1·40	1·40
684/92		Set of 9	5·00	5·00

Nos. 684/7 and 688/91 were printed together, *se-tenant*, in horizontal strips of 4 throughout sheets of 20 (4×5).

No. 692 commemorates the Chinese New Year of the Pig and was also printed in sheets of 10 (5×2).

164 Camellia "Captain Rawes"   **165** "Liberation" (sculpture, Philip Jackson)

(Des and litho Questa)

1995 (21 Mar). *Camellias. T* **164** *and similar horiz designs. Multicoloured. P* 14½.

693	18p.	Type **164**	60	60
694	23p.	"Brigadoon"	80	80
695	30p.	"Elsie Jury"	95	95
696	35p.	"Augusto L'Gouveia Pinto"	1·00	1·00
697	41p.	"Bella Romana"	1·10	1·10
693/7		Set of 5	4·00	4·00

(Des A. Theobald. Litho Cartor)

1995 (9 May). *Europa. Peace and Freedom. P* 13½.

698	**165**	23p. black and dull violet-blue	55	55
699		30p. black and rose-pink	70	75

 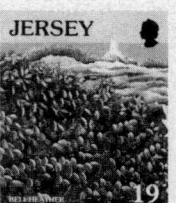

166 Bailiff and Crown Officers in Launch   **167** Bell Heather

(Des A. Theobald. Litho B.D.T.)

1995 (9 May). *50th Anniv of Liberation. T* **166** *and similar horiz designs. Multicoloured. P* 15×14.

700	18p.	Type **166**	40	40
	a.	Booklet pane. Nos. 700/1, each × 3, with margins all round	2·00	
701	18p.	*Vega* (Red Cross supply ship)	40	40
702	23p.	H.M.S. *Beagle* (destroyer)	60	60
	a.	Booklet pane. Nos. 702/3, each × 3, with margins all round	2·75	
703	23p.	British troops in Ordnance Yard, St. Helier	60	60
704	60p.	King George VI and Queen Elizabeth in Jersey	1·50	1·50
	a.	Booklet pane. Nos. 704/5, each × 3, with margins all round	7·50	
705	60p.	Unloading supplies from landing craft, St. Aubin's	1·50	1·50
700/5		Set of 6	4·50	4·50
MS706	110×75 mm. £1 Royal Family with Winston Churchill on Buckingham Palace balcony, V.E. Day (80×39 mm)		2·75	2·75
	a.	Booklet pane. As No. MS706 with additional margins all round showing arms, mace and inscriptions	2·50	

(Des N. Parlett. Litho B.D.T.)

1995 (4 July). *European Nature Conservation Year. Wild Flowers. T* **167** *and similar vert designs. Multicoloured. P* 13.

707	19p.	Type **167**	55	55
	a.	Horiz strip of 5. Nos. 707/11	2·75	
708	19p.	Sea Campion	55	55
709	19p.	Spotted Rock-rose	55	55
710	19p.	Thrift	55	55
711	19p.	Sheep's-bit Scabious	55	55
712	23p.	Field Bind-weed	65	65
	a.	Horiz strip of 5. Nos. 712/16	3·25	
713	23p.	Common Bird's-foot-trefoil	65	65
714	23p.	Sea-holly	65	65
715	23p.	Common Centaury	65	65
716	23p.	Dwarf Pansy	65	65
707/16		Set of 10	5·50	5·50

Nos. 707/11 and 712/16 were printed together, *se-tenant*, in horizontal strips of 5 throughout sheets of 20, the backgrounds forming composite designs.

168 *Precis almana*

(Des W. Oliver. Litho Questa)

1995 (1 Sept). *Butterflies. T* **168** *and similar horiz designs. Multicoloured. P* 14.

717	19p.	Type **168**	55	55
718	23p.	*Papilio palinurus*	70	70
719	30p.	*Catopsilia scylla*	90	90
720	41p.	*Papilio rumanzovia*	1·10	1·10
721	60p.	*Troides helena*	1·75	1·75
717/21		Set of 5	4·50	4·50
MS722	150×100 mm. Nos. 720/1		3·00	3·00
	a.	41p. value imperforate		

No. MS722 includes the "Singapore '95" International Stamp Exhibition logo on the sheet margin and shows the two stamp designs without frames.

169 Peace Doves and United Nations Anniversary Emblem

(Des A. Copp. Litho Enschedé)

1995 (24 Oct). *50th Anniv of United Nations. T* **169** *and similar horiz design. P* 13×14½.

723	**169**	19p. cobalt and royal blue	55	55
724	–	23p. turquoise-green and deep blue-green	65	65
725	–	41p. deep blue-green and turquoise-green	1·10	1·10
726	**169**	60p. royal blue and cobalt	1·60	1·60
723/6		Set of 4	3·50	3·50

Design:—23p., 41p. Symbolic wheat and anniversary emblem.

170 "Puss in Boots"

(Des V. Ambrus. Litho Cartor)

1995 (24 Oct). *Christmas. Pantomimes. T* **170** *and similar horiz designs. Multicoloured. P* 13½.

727	19p.	Type **170**	55	55
728	23p.	"Cinderella"	70	70
729	41p.	"Sleeping Beauty"	1·00	1·00
730	60p.	"Aladdin"	1·60	1·60
727/30		Set of 4	3·50	3·50

171 Rat with Top Hat

(Des V. Ambrus. Litho Questa)

1996 (19 Feb). *Chinese New Year ("Year of the Rat"). Sheet* 110×75 mm. *P* 13½×14.

MS731	**171**	£1 multicoloured	3·00	3·00

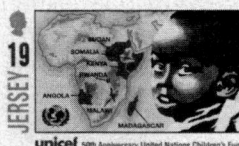

172 African Child and Map

(Des A. Copp. Litho Questa)

1996 (19 Feb). *50th Anniv of U.N.I.C.E.F. T* **172** *and similar horiz designs. Multicoloured. P* 14½.

732	19p.	Type **172**	50	50
733	23p.	Children and Globe	60	60
734	30p.	European child and map	80	80
735	35p.	South American child and map	95	95
736	41p.	Asian child and map	1·10	1·10
737	60p.	South Pacific child and map	1·60	1·60
732/7		Set of 6	5·00	5·00

173 Queen Elizabeth II (from photo by T. O'Neill)

(Litho Questa)

1996 (21 Apr). *70th Birthday of Queen Elizabeth II.* P 14×15.
738 **173** £5 multicoloured .. .. 10·00 10·50
No. 738 will be retained in use as part of the current definitive series.

174 Elizabeth Garrett (first British woman doctor)   **175** Player shooting at Goal

(Des Jennifer Toombs. Litho B.D.T.)

1996 (25 Apr). *Europa. Famous Women.* T **174** *and similar horiz design. Multicoloured.* P 13½×14.
739 23p. Type **174** 60 60
740 30p. Emmeline Pankhurst (suffragette) .. 80 80

(Des A. Theobald. Litho B.D.T.)

1996 (25 Apr). *European Football Championship, England.* T **175** *and similar horiz designs. Multicoloured.* P 13½×14.
741 19p. Type **175** 50 50
742 23p. Two players chasing ball 70 70
743 35p. Player avoiding tackle 95 95
744 41p. Two players competing for ball .. 1·10 1·10
745 60p. Players heading ball .. .. 1·75 1·75
741/5 .. .. *Set of 5* 4·50 4·50

176 Rowing

(Des A. Theobald. Litho Questa)

1996 (8 June). *Sporting Anniversaries.* T **176** *and similar horiz designs. Multicoloured.* P 14.
746 19p. Type **176** 50 50
747 23p. Judo 70 70
748 35p. Fencing 95 95
749 41p. Boxing .. .. .. 1·10 1·10
750 60p. Basketball .. .. .. 1·75 1·75
746/50 .. .. *Set of 5* 4·50 4·50
MS751 150×100 mm. £1 Olympic torch (50×37 mm). P 13½ .. .. .. 2·75 2·75
Anniversaries:—Nos. 746/8, 750/1, Centenary of Modern Olympic Games; No. 749, 50th anniv of International Amateur Boxing Association.
No. **MS**751 also includes the "CAPEX '96" International Stamp Exhibition logo.

177 Bay on North Coast

(Des A. Copp. Litho B.D.T.)

1996 (8 June). *Tourism. Beaches.* T **177** *and similar horiz designs. Multicoloured.* P 14.
752 19p. Type **177** 50 50
　a. Booklet pane. Nos. 752/3, each × 3, with
　　margins all round .. .. 2·50
　b. Booklet pane. Nos. 752/7, with margins all
　　round .. .. .. 4·25
753 23p. Portelet Bay 60 60
754 30p. Greve de Lecq Bay 80 80
　a. Booklet pane. Nos. 754/5, each × 3, with
　　margins all round .. .. 4·00
755 35p. Beauport Beach 95 95
756 41p. Plemont Bay .. .. .. 1·10 1·10
　a. Booklet pane. Nos. 756/7, each × 3, with
　　margins all round .. .. 6·00
757 60p. St. Brelade's Bay .. .. 1·60 1·60
752/7 .. .. .. *Set of 6* 5·00 5·00

178 Drag Hunt   **179** The Journey to Bethlehem

(Des P. Layton. Litho Enschedé)

1996 (13 Sept). *Horses.* T **178** *and similar horiz designs. Multicoloured.* P 13½×14.
758 19p. Type **178** 50 50
759 23p. Pony and trap 60 60
760 30p. Training racehorses on beach .. 80 80
761 35p. Show jumping 95 95
762 41p. Pony Club event .. .. 1·10 1·10
763 60p. Shire mare and foal .. .. 1·60 1·60
758/63 .. .. .. *Set of 6* 5·00 5·00

(Des V. Ambrus. Litho Cartor)

1996 (12 Nov). *Christmas.* T **179** *and similar horiz designs. Multicoloured.* P 13×13½.
764 19p. Type **179** 60 60
765 23p. The Shepherds 70 70
766 30p. The Nativity .. .. .. 1·00 1·00
767 60p. The Three Kings .. .. 1·60 1·60
764/7 .. .. .. *Set of 4* 3·50 3·50

180 Jersey Cow wearing Scarf

(Des V. Ambrus. Litho Questa)

1997 (7 Feb). *Chinese New Year ("Year of the Ox"). Sheet 110×74 mm.* P 14×13½.
MS768 **180** £1 multicoloured .. 3·00 3·00

1997 (7 Feb). *"HONG KONG '97" International Stamp Exhibition.* No. **MS**768 optd with exhibition emblem in black and "JERSEY AT HONG KONG '97" in red, both on sheet margin.
MS769 **180** £1 multicoloured .. 3·00 3·00

181 Lillie the Cow on the Beach   **182** Red-breasted Merganser

(Des A. Copp. Litho B.D.T.)

1997 (12 Feb)–99. *Tourism. "Lillie the Cow".* T **181** *and similar horiz designs. Multicoloured. Self-adhesive.* P 9½.
770 (23p.) Type **181** 70 70
　a. With copyright symbol after date
　　(2.7.99) 50 55
771 (23p.) Lillie taking photograph .. 70 70
　a. With copyright symbol after date
　　(2.7.99) 50 55
772 (23p.) Carrying bucket and spade .. 70 70
　a. With copyright symbol after date
　　(2.7.99) 50 55
773 (23p.) Eating meal at Mont Orgueil .. 70 70
　a. With copyright symbol after date
　　(2.7.99) 50 55
770/3 .. .. .. *Set of 4* 2·50 2·50
770a/3a .. .. *Set of 4* 2·00 2·10
Nos. 770/3, which are inscribed "UK MINIMUM POSTAGE PAID", come, *se-tenant*, in strips of 4 or rolls of 100 with the surplus self-adhesive paper around each stamp removed.

(Des N. Parlett. Litho Questa)

1997 (12 Feb)–99. *Seabirds and Waders.* T **182** *and similar horiz designs. Multicoloured.* P 14½.
774 1p. Type **182** 10 10
775 2p. Sanderling (28.1.98) 10 10
776 4p. Northern Gannet (11.8.98) .. 10 10
777 5p. Great Crested Grebe (28.1.98) .. 10 15
778 10p. Common Tern 20 25
779 15p. Black-headed Gull 30 35
780 20p. Dunlin 40 45
　a. With copyright symbol after date (2.4.98) 40 45
781 21p. Sandwich Tern (28.1.98) .. 40 45
782 22p. Ringed Plover (11.8.98) .. 45 50
783 23p. Bar-tailed Godwit (21.8.99) .. 45 50
784 24p. Puffin 45 50
　a. With copyright symbol after date (2.4.98) 45 50
785 25p. Brent Goose (28.1.98) .. 50 55
786 26p. Grey Plover (11.8.98) .. 50 50
787 27p. Common Scoter (21.8.99) .. 55 60
788 28p. Lesser Black-backed Gull (21.8.99) 60 65
789 29p. Little Egret (21.8.99) .. 60 65
790 30p. Fulmar (28.1.98) 60 65
791 31p. Golden Plover (11.8.98) .. 60 65
792 32p. Greenshank (11.8.98) .. 65 70
793 33p. Little Grebe (21.8.99) .. 65 70
794 34p. Common Cormorant (21.8.99) .. 70 75
795 36p. Curlew (11.8.98) 70 75
796 37p. Oystercatcher 75 80

797 40p. Turnstone (28.1.98) 80 85
798 44p. Herring Gull (11.8.98) .. 90 95
799 45p. Rock Pipit (21.8.99) .. 90 95
800 50p. Great Black-backed Gull (11.8.98) 1·00 1·10
801 60p. Avocet (28.1.98) .. .. 1·25 1·40
802 65p. Grey Heron (21.8.99) .. 1·25 1·40
803 75p. Redshank .. .. .. 1·50 1·60
804 £1 Razorbill (28.1.98) .. .. 2·00 2·10
805 £2 Shag .. .. .. 4·00 4·25
774/805 .. .. *Set of 32* 24·00 26·00
MS806 Four sheets, each 136×130 mm. (a) Nos. 774, 778/80, 784, 796, 803 and 805. (b) Nos. 775, 777, 781, 785, 790, 797, 801 and 804 (28.1.98). (c) Nos. 776, 782, 786, 791/2, 795, 798 and 800 (2.4.98). (d) Nos. 783, 787/9, 793/4, 799 and 802 (21.8.99).
.. .. *Set of 4 sheets* 24·00 26·00
Imprint dates: "1997" (without copyright symbol), Nos. 774, 778/80, 784, 796, 803, 805; "1998" (with copyright symbol), Nos. 775/7, 780a, 781/2, 784a, 785/6, 790, 792, 795, 797/8, 800/1, 804; "1999" (with copyright symbol), Nos. 783, 787/9, 793/4, 799, 802.

183 De Havilland D.H.95 Flamingo

(Des A. Theobald. Litho Enschedé)

1997 (10 Mar). *60th Anniv of Jersey Airport.* T **183** *and similar horiz designs. Multicoloured.* P 13½×14.
807 20p. Type **183** 55 55
808 24p. Handley Page H.P.R. Marathon .. 65 65
809 31p. De Havilland D.H.114 Heron .. 80 80
810 37p. Boeing 737-236 .. .. 1·00 1·00
811 43p. Britten Norman Trislander .. 1·10 1·10
812 63p. BAe 146-200 .. .. 1·75 1·75
807/12 .. .. .. *Set of 6* 5·25 5·25

184 The Bull of St. Clement   **185** Cycling

(Des Jennifer Toombs. Litho B.D.T.)

1997 (15 Apr). *Europa. Tales and Legends.* T **184** *and similar horiz designs. Multicoloured.* P 15×14.
813 20p. Type **184** 50 50
814 24p. The Black Horse of St. Ouen .. 60 60
815 31p. The Black Dog of Bouley Bay .. 70 70
816 63p. Les Fontaines des Mittes .. 1·40 1·40
813/16 .. .. .. *Set of 4* 3·00 3·00
Nos. 814/15 include the "EUROPA" emblem.

1997 (29 May). *"Pacific 97" International Stamp Exhibition, San Francisco.* No. **MS**806a optd with exhibition emblem on sheet margin.
MS817 136×130 mm. Nos. 774, 778/80, 784, 796, 803 and 805 .. .. .. 7·50 8·00

(Des A. Theobald. Litho B.D.T.)

1997 (28 June). *7th Island Games, Jersey.* T **185** *and similar horiz designs. Multicoloured.* P 13½.
818 20p. Type **185** 55 55
　a. Booklet pane. Nos. 818/19, each × 3, with
　　margins all round .. .. 2·50
　b. Booklet pane. Nos. 818/23, with margins
　　all round .. .. .. 5·25
819 24p. Archery 65 65
820 31p. Windsurfing 80 80
　a. Booklet pane. Nos. 820/1, each × 3, with
　　margins all round .. .. 4·00
821 37p. Gymnastics .. .. .. 1·00 1·00
822 43p. Volleyball .. .. .. 1·10 1·10
　a. Booklet pane. Nos. 822/3, each × 3, with
　　margins all round .. .. 6·25
823 63p. Running .. .. .. 1·75 1·75
818/23 .. .. .. *Set of 6* 5·25 5·25

186 Mallorcan Midwife Toad   **187** Ash

(Des W. Oliver. Litho Cartor)

1997 (2 Sept). *Wildlife Preservation Trust (6th series).* T **186** *and similar horiz designs. Multicoloured.* P 13.
824 20p. Type **186** 55 50
825 24p. Aye-Aye 65 65
826 31p. Echo Parakeet 80 80
827 37p. Pigmy Hog .. .. .. 1·00 1·00
828 43p. St. Lucia Whip-tail .. .. 1·10 1·10
829 63p. Madagascar Teal .. .. 1·75 1·75
824/9 .. .. .. *Set of 6* 5·25 5·25

(Des Norah Bryan. Litho Questa)

1997 (2 Sept). *Trees. T* **187** *and similar vert designs. Multicoloured. P* 14½.

830	20p.	Type **187**	55	55
831	24p.	Elder	65	65
832	31p.	Beech	80	80
833	37p.	Sweet Chestnut	1·00	1·00
834	43p.	Hawthorn	1·10	1·10
835	63p.	Common Oak	1·75	1·75
830/5		*Set of 6*	5·25	5·25

188 Father Christmas and Reindeer outside Jersey Airport

(Des Colleen Corlett. Litho B.D.T.)

1997 (11 Nov). *Christmas. T* **188** *and similar horiz designs. Multicoloured. P* 14.

836	20p.	Type **188**	55	55
837	24p.	Father Christmas with presents, St. Aubin's Harbour	65	65
838	31p.	Father Christmas in sleigh, Mont Orgueil Castle	90	90
839	63p.	Father Christmas with children, Royal Square, St. Helier	1·75	1·75
836/9		*Set of 4*	3·50	3·50

189 Wedding Photograph, 1947

(Des G. Drummond. Litho Questa)

1997 (20 Nov). *Golden Wedding of Queen Elizabeth and Prince Philip. T* **189** *and similar multicoloured designs. P* 14½.

840	50p.	Type **189**	1·50	1·50
	a.	Horiz pair. Nos. 840/1	3·00	
841	50p.	Queen Elizabeth and Prince Philip, 1997	1·50	1·50
MS842		150×100 mm. £1.50, Full-length Wedding photograph, 1947 (38×50 *mm*). P 13½	4·50	4·50

Nos. 840/1 were printed together, *se-tenant*, in horizontal pairs throughout the sheet.

190 Tiger wearing Scarf

(Des V. Ambrus. Litho Questa)

1998 (28 Jan). *Chinese New Year ("Year of the Tiger"). Sheet* 110×75 *mm. P* 14×13½.

MS843		**190** £1 multicoloured	2·50	2·50

191 J.M.T. Bristol 4 Tonner, 1923

192 Creative Arts Festival

(Des A. Copp. Litho B.D.T.)

1998 (2 Apr). *75th Anniv of Jersey Motor Transport Company. Buses. T* **191** *and similar horiz designs. Multicoloured. P* 14.

844	20p.	Type **191**	55	55
	a.	Booklet pane. Nos. 844/5, each × 3 with margins all round	2·75	
	b.	Booklet pane. Nos. 844/9 with margins all round	4·25	

845	24p.	Safety Coach Service Regent double decker, 1934	65	65
846	31p.	Slade's Dennis Lancet, *c.* 1936	75	75
	a.	Booklet pane. Nos. 846/7 each × 3 with margins all round	4·00	
847	37p.	Tantivy Leyland PLSC Lion, 1947	1·00	1·00
848	43p.	J.B.S. Morris, *c.* 1958	1·10	1·10
	a.	Booklet pane. Nos. 848/9 each × 3 with margins all round	6·25	
849	63p.	J.M.T. Titan TD4 double decker, *c.* 1961	1·50	1·50
844/9		*Set of 6*	5·00	5·00

(Des A. Copp. Litho Enschedé)

1998 (2 Apr). *Europa. National Festivals. T* **192** *and similar vert designs. Multicoloured. P* 14×13½.

850	20p.	Type **192**	60	60
851	24p.	Jazz Festival	65	65
852	31p.	Good Food Festival	85	85
853	63p.	Floral Festival	1·50	1·50
850/3		*Set of 4*	3·25	3·25

Nos. 851/2 include the "EUROPA" emblem.

193 Hobie Cat and *Duke of Normandy* (launch)

194 Bass

(Des A. Theobald. Litho Cartor)

1998 (15 May). *Opening of Elizabeth Marina, St. Helier. T* **193** *and similar vert designs. Multicoloured. P* 13.

854	20p.	Type **193**	50	50
	a.	Horiz strip of 5. Nos. 854/8	2·50	
855	20p.	Hobie Cat with white, yellow, red and green sails	50	50
856	20p.	Hobie Cats with pink, purple and orange sails	50	50
857	20p.	Bow of Hobie Cat with yellow, blue and purple sail	50	50
858	20p.	Hobie Cat heeling	50	50
859	24p.	Yacht with red, white and blue spinnaker	60	60
	a.	Horiz strip of 5. Nos. 859/63	3·00	
860	24p.	Yacht with pink spinnaker	60	60
861	24p.	Yacht with two white sails	60	60
862	24p.	Trimaran	60	60
863	24p.	Yacht with blue, white and yellow spinnaker in foreground	60	60
854/63		*Set of 10*	5·00	5·00

Nos. 854/8 and 859/63 were each printed together, *se-tenant*, in horizontal strips of five throughout the sheets and form composite designs of yacht races.

(Des W. Oliver. Litho B.D.T.)

1998 (11 Aug). *International Year of the Ocean. Fishes. T* **194** *and horiz designs. Multicoloured. P* 15×14.

864	20p.	Type **194**	50	50
865	24p.	Red Gurnard	65	65
866	31p.	Skate	80	80
867	37p.	Mackerel	1·00	1·00
868	43p.	Tope	1·10	1·10
869	63p.	Cuckoo Wrasse	1·50	1·50
864/9		*Set of 6*	5·00	5·00

195 Cider-making

196 Irises

(Des A. Copp. Litho SNP Cambec, Melbourne)

1998 (11 Aug). *Days Gone By. T* **195** *and similar horiz designs. Multicoloured. Self-adhesive. With copyright symbol after date. P* 11½ (*die-cut*).

870	(20p.)	Type **195**	40	45
871	(20p.)	Potato barrels on cart	40	45
872	(20p.)	Collecting seaweed for fertiliser	40	45
873	(20p.)	Milking Jersey cows	40	45
870/3		*Set of 4*	1·60	1·75

Imprint dates: "1998", Nos. 870/3; "1999", Nos. 870/3.

Nos. 870/3, which are inscribed "BAILIWICK MINIMUM POSTAGE PAID" and were initially sold at 20p. each, come *se-tenant* in strips of 4 or rolls of 100 with the surplus self-adhesive paper around each stamp removed.

(Des Wendy Tait. Litho Questa)

1998 (23 Oct). *Flowers. T* **196** *and similar multicoloured designs. P* 14½.

874	20p.	Type **196**	50	50
875	24p.	Carnations	65	65
876	31p.	Chrysanthemums	80	80
877	37p.	Pinks	1·00	1·00
878	43p.	Roses	1·10	1·10
879	63p.	Lilies	1·50	1·50
874/9		*Set of 6*	5·00	5·00
MS880		150×100 mm. £1.50, *Lilium* "Star Gazer" (50×37 *mm*). P 14×13½	3·50	3·50

No. MS880 includes the "ITALIA '98" stamp exhibition emblem on the margin.

197 Central Market Crib

(Des Colleen Corlett. Litho Cartor)

1998 (10 Nov). *Christmas. Cribs. T* **197** *and similar horiz designs. Multicoloured. P* 13.

881	20p.	Type **197**	45	45
882	24p.	St. Thomas's Church crib	55	55
883	31p.	Trinity Parish Church crib	65	65
884	63p.	Royal Square crib	1·40	1·40
881/4		*Set of 4*	3·00	3·00

198 Rabbit

(Des V. Ambrus. Litho Questa)

1999 (16 Feb). *Chinese New Year ("Year of the Rabbit"). Sheet* 110×75 *mm. P* 14×13½.

MS885		**198** £1 multicoloured	2·00	2·10

199 Jersey Eastern Railway Mail Train

(Des A. Theobald. Litho B.D.T.)

1999 (16 Feb). *125th Anniv of U.P.U. T* **199** *and similar horiz designs. Multicoloured. P* 14.

886	20p.	Type **199**	40	45
887	24p.	Brighton (paddle-steamer)	50	55
888	43p.	De Havilland D.H.86 Dragon Express at Jersey Airport	85	90
889	63p.	Jersey Postal Service Morris Minor van	1·25	1·40
886/9		*Set of 4*	3·00	3·25

200 *Jessie Eliza*, St. Catherine

201 *Cymbidium* Maufant "Jersey"

(Litho Questa)

1999 (16 Feb). *175th Anniv of Royal National Lifeboat Institution. T* **200** *and similar horiz design. Multicoloured. P* 14½.

890	20p.	Type **200**	1·50	1·60
	a.	Horiz pair. Nos. 890/1	3·50	
891	£1	*Alexander Coutanche*, St. Helier	2·00	2·10

Nos. 890/1 were printed together, *se-tenant*, in horizontal pairs throughout the sheet.

(Litho Enschedé)

1999 (19 Mar). *Jersey Orchids (4th series).* T **201** *and similar vert designs. Multicoloured.* P 14×13.

892	21p. Type **201**		45	50
893	25p. *Miltonia* Millbrook "Jersey"		50	55
894	31p. *Paphiopedilum* Transvaal		65	70
895	37p. *Paphiopedilum* Elizabeth Castle		75	80
896	43p. *Calanthe* Five Oaks		85	90
897	63p. *Cymbidium* Icho Tower "Trinity"		1·25	1·40
892/7		*Set of 6*	4·25	4·75
MS898	150×100 mm. £1.50, *Miltonia* Portelet.			
	P 13½		3·00	3·25

No. MS898 also includes the "Australia '99" World Stamp Exhibition, Melbourne, emblem on the margin at top left.

202 Howard Davis Park

(Des Ariel Luke. Litho Cartor)

1999 (27 Apr). *Europa. Parks and Gardens.* T **202** *and similar horiz designs. Multicoloured.* P 13×13½.

899	21p. Type **202**		45	50
900	25p. Sir Winston Churchill Memorial Park		50	55
901	31p. Coronation Park		65	70
902	63p. La Collette Gardens		1·25	1·40
899/902		*Set of 4*	2·75	3·00

Nos. 899/902 include the "EUROPA" logo at top left and all four values show the "iBRA '99" International Stamp Exhibition, Nuremberg, emblem at top right.

203 Prince Edward and Miss
Sophie Rhys-Jones

(Des A. Copp. Litho Questa)

1999 (19 June). *Royal Wedding.* P 14½.

903	**203** 35p. multicoloured (yellow background)		1·00	1·00
	a. Pair. Nos. 903/4		2·00	2·00
904	35p. multicoloured (blue background)		1·00	1·00

Nos. 903/4 were printed together, *se-tenant*, in horizontal or vertical pairs throughout the sheet.

204 Jersey-built Benz, 1899   205 West European
Hedgehog

(Des A. Copp. Litho B.D.T.)

1999 (2 July). *Vintage Cars (3rd series). Centenary of Motoring in Jersey.* T **204** *and similar horiz designs. Multicoloured.* P 14.

905	21p. Type **204**		40	45
	a. Booklet pane. Nos. 905/6, each × 3, with margins all round		2·75	
	b. Booklet pane. Nos. 905/10, with margins all round		4·25	
906	25p. Star Tourer, 1910		50	55
907	31p. Citroen "Traction Avant", 1938		60	65
	a. Booklet pane. Nos. 907/8, each × 3, with margins all round		4·00	
908	37p. Talbot BG110 Tourer, 1937		75	80
909	43p. Morris Cowley Six Special Coupé, 1934		85	90
	a. Booklet pane. Nos. 909/10, each × 3, with margins all round		6·25	
910	63p. Ford Anglia Saloon, 1946		1·25	1·40
905/10		*Set of 6*	4·25	4·75

Nos. 905a/b, 907a and 909a also include the "PhilexFrance 99" International Stamp Exhibition emblem on the margins at top right.

(Des W. Oliver. Litho Cartor)

1999 (21 Aug). *Small Mammals.* T **205** *and similar vert designs. Multicoloured.* P 13½×13.

911	21p. Type **205**		40	45
912	25p. Eurasian Red Squirrel		50	55
913	31p. Nathusius Pipistrelle		60	65
914	37p. Jersey Bank Vole		75	80
915	43p. Lesser White-toothed Shrew		85	90
916	63p. Common Mole		1·25	1·40
911/16		*Set of 6*	4·25	4·75

No. 913 is inscribed "Pipestrelle" in error.

206 Gorey Pierhead   207 Mistletoe
Light

(Des A. Copp. Litho Walsall)

1999 (5 Oct). *150th Anniv of First Lighthouse on Jersey.* T **206** *and similar vert designs. Multicoloured.* P 14.

917	21p. Type **206**		40	45
918	25p. La Corbiere		50	55
919	34p. Noirmont Point		70	75
920	38p. Demie de Pas		75	80
921	44p. Greve d'Azette		90	95
922	64p. Sorel Point		1·25	1·40
917/22		*Set of 6*	4·50	4·75

(Des Colleen Corlett. Litho B.D.T)

1999 (9 Nov). *Christmas. Festive Foliage.* T **207** *and similar vert designs. Multicoloured.* P 14.

923	21p. Type **207**		40	45
924	25p. Holly		50	55
925	34p. Ivy		70	75
926	64p. Christmas Rose		1·25	1·40
923/6		*Set of 4*	2·75	3·00

208 Jersey Crest

(Des A. Copp. Litho, die-stamped and embossed Cartor)

2000 (1 Jan). *New Millennium.* P 13½.

927	**208** £10 gold, bright red and deep carmine		20·00	21·00

The printing of No. 927 incorporates metallic die-stamping and embossing using 22 carat gold.

209 Dragon

(Des V. Ambrus. Litho Questa)

2000 (5 Feb). *Chinese New Year ("Year of the Dragon"). Sheet* 110×75 mm. P 14½×13½.

MS928	**209** £1 multicoloured		2·00	2·10

STAMP BOOKLETS

For a full listing of Jersey stamp booklets see *Collect Channel Islands and Isle of Man Stamps* published each January.

POSTAGE DUE STAMPS

D 1   D 2 Map

(Des F. Guénier. Litho Bradbury, Wilkinson)

1969 (1 Oct).   P 14×13½.

D1	D **1**	1d. bluish violet		1·50	1·50
D2		2d. sepia		2·25	2·00
D3		3d. magenta		3·00	2·75
D4	D **2**	1s. bright emerald		9·00	7·50
D5		2s. 6d. olive-grey		21·00	16·00
D6		5s. vermilion		30·00	27·00
D1/6			*Set of 6*	60·00	50·00

1971 (15 Feb)–**75.**   *As Type D **2** but values in decimal currency.*

D 7	1p. black		10	10
D 8	1p. violet-blue		10	10
D 9	2p. olive-grey		10	10
D10	3p. reddish purple		10	10
D11	4p. pale red		10	10
D12	5p. bright emerald		15	15
D13	6p. yellow-orange (12.8.74)		20	15
D14	7p. bistre-yellow (12.8.74)		20	15
D15	8p. light greenish blue (1.5.75)		30	25
D16	10p. pale olive-grey		40	35
D17	11p. ochre (1.5.75)		40	40
D18	14p. violet		45	45
D19	25p. myrtle-green (12.8.74)		90	90
D20	50p. dull purple (1.5.75)		1·50	1·50
D7/20		*Set of 14*	4·50	4·25

D **3** Arms of St. Clement and   D **4** St. Brelade
Dovecote at Samares

(Des G. Drummond. Litho Questa)

1978 (17 Jan).   *Type D **3** and similar horiz designs showing the Parish Arms given.* P 14.

D21	1p. blue-green and black		10	10
D22	2p. orange-yellow and black (St. Lawrence)		10	10
D23	3p. lake-brown and black (St. John)		10	10
D24	4p. orange-vermilion and black (St. Ouen)		10	10
D25	5p. ultramarine and black (St. Peter)		10	10
D26	10p. brown-olive and black (St. Martin)		30	30
D27	12p. greenish blue and black (St. Helier)		35	25
D28	14p. red-orange and black (St. Saviour)		35	30
D29	15p. bright magenta and black (St. Brelade)		35	30
D30	20p. yellow-green and black (Grouville)		50	40
D31	50p. deep brown and black (St. Mary)		1·10	1·10
D32	£1 chalky blue and black (Trinity)		2·25	2·25
D21/32		*Set of 12*	5·00	4·75

Parish Views shown:—2p. Handois Reservoir; 3p. Sorel Point; 4p. Pinnacle Rock; 5p. Quetivel Mill; 10p. St. Catherine's Breakwater; 12p. St. Helier Harbour; 14p. Highlands College; 15p. Beauport Bay; 20p. La Hougue Bie; 50p. Perry Farm; £1 Bouley Bay.

(Des G. Drummond. Litho Questa)

1982 (7 Sept).   *Type D **4** and similar vert designs depicting Jersey Harbours.* P 14.

D33	1p. bright turquoise-green and black		10	10
D34	2p. chrome-yellow and black		10	10
D35	3p. lake-brown and black		10	10
D36	4p. red and black		10	10
D37	5p. bright blue and black		10	10
D38	6p. yellow-olive and black		10	15
D39	7p. bright reddish mauve and black		15	20
D40	8p. bright orange-red and black		15	20
D41	9p. bright green and black		20	25
D42	10p. turquoise-blue and black		20	25
D43	20p. apple-green and black		40	45
D44	30p. bright purple and black		60	65
D45	40p. dull orange and black		80	85
D46	£1 bright reddish violet and black		2·00	2·10
D33/46		*Set of 14*	4·50	5·00

Designs:—2p. St. Aubin; 3p. Rozel; 4p. Greve de Lecq; 5p. Bouley Bay; 6p. St. Catherine; 7p. Gorey; 8p. Bonne Nuit; 9p. La Roque; 10p. St. Helier; 20p. Ronez; 30p. La Collette; 40p. Elizabeth Castle; £1 Upper Harbour Marina.

British Post Offices Abroad

The origins of the network of Post Offices, Postal Agencies and Packet Agents can be recognised from the 18th century, but the system did not become established until the expansion of trade, following the end of the Napoleonic Wars in 1815.

Many offices were provided in newly acquired dependent territories, and were then, eventually, transferred from the control of the British Post Office to the evolving local administrations.

Those in foreign countries, nearly always based on existing British Consular appointments, were mostly connected to the network of British Packet lines which had been re-established in 1814. They tended to survive until the country in which they were situated established its own efficient postal service or joined the U.P.U. The term "Post Office Agent" was employed by the British G.P.O. and "Packet Agent" by the shipping lines to describe similar functions.

Listed in this section are the Crowned-circle handstamps and G.B. stamps used in the Post Offices and Agencies situated in foreign countries. Those for the territories within the scope of this catalogue will be found under the following headings:

Prices. Catalogue prices quoted in this section, and throughout the volume, covering Crowned-circle handstamps and stamps of Great Britain used abroad are for fine used examples with the cancellation or handstamp clearly legible. Poor impressions of the cancellations and handstamps are worth much less than the prices quoted.

CROWNED-CIRCLE HANDSTAMPS

Following the introduction, in 1840, of adhesive stamps in Great Britain there was considerable pressure from a number of the dependent territories for the British Post Office to provide something similar for their use.

Such suggestions were resisted, however, because of supposed operational problems, but the decision was taken, in connection with an expansion of the Packet Service, to issue a uniform series of handstamps and date stamps to the offices abroad, both in the dependent territories and in foreign countries.

Under the regulations circulated in December 1841, letters and packets forwarded through these offices to the United Kingdom or any of its territories were to be sent unpaid, the postage being collected on delivery. Where this was not possible, for example from a British colony to a foreign country or between two foreign ports, then a *crowned-circle handstamp* was to be applied with the postage, paid in advance, noted alongside in manuscript.

Examples of these handstamps were supplied over twenty years from 1842, but many continued to fulfil other functions long after the introduction of adhesive stamps in the colony concerned.

Our listings cover the use of these handstamps for their initial purpose and the prices quoted are for examples used on cover during the pre-adhesive period.

In most instances the dates quoted are those on which the handstamp appears in the G.P.O. Record Books, but it seems to have been normal for the handstamps to be sent to the office concerned immediately following this registration.

Many of the handstamps were individually cut by hand, so that each has its own characteristics, but for the purposes of the listing they have been grouped into nine Types as shown in the adjacent column. No attempt has been made to identify them by anything but the most major differences, so that minor differences in size and in the type of the crown have been ignored.

DOUBLE CIRCLE

CC 1   CC 1a

Curved "PAID"

CC 1b   CC 1c

Curved "PAID"

CC 2

Straight "PAID"

SINGLE CIRCLE

CC 3   CC 4

Straight "PAID"

CC 5

Curved "PAID"

CC 6   CC 7

Straight "PAID"   Curved "PAID"

GREAT BRITAIN STAMPS USED ABROAD

Prices quoted are for single stamps not on cover unless otherwise stated. Stamps on cover are worth considerably more in most cases.

In many instances obliterators allocated to post offices abroad were, at a later date re-allocated to offices at home. Postmarks on issues later than those included in our lists can therefore safely be regarded as *not* having been "used abroad".

INDEX

ALTERED CATALOGUE NUMBERS

Any Catalogue numbers altered from the last edition are shown as a list in the introductory pages.

TYPES OF OBLITERATOR FOR GREAT BRITAIN STAMPS USED ABROAD

HORIZONTAL OVAL

(1)

(2)

(3)

(4)

(5)

(6)

(7)

VERTICAL OVAL

(8)

(9)

(10)

(11)

(12)

(13)

(14)

(15)

CIRCULAR DATE STAMPS

(16)

(17)

(18)

(19)

(20)

ARGENTINE REPUBLIC
BUENOS AYRES

The first regular monthly British mail packet service was introduced in 1824, replacing a private arrangement which had previously existed for some years.

Great Britain stamps were used from 1860 until the office closed at the end of June 1873. Until 1878 the British Consul continued to sell stamps which were used in combination with an Argentine value prepaying the internal rate. The British stamps on such covers were cancelled on arrival in England.

CROWNED-CIRCLE HANDSTAMPS

CC1 CC 7 BUENOS AYRES (Black or R.) (5.1.1851)
Price on cover £700

Stamps of GREAT BRITAIN cancelled "B 32" as in Types 2, 12 or 13.

1860 to 1873.
Z 1	1d. rose-red (1857)		
Z 2	1d. rose-red (1864)	From	30·00

Plate Nos. 71, 72, 73, 74, 76, 78, 79, 80, 81, 82, 85, 87, 89, 90, 91, 92, 93, 94, 95, 96, 97, 99, 101, 103, 104, 107, 108, 110, 112, 113, 114, 117, 118, 119, 120, 121, 123, 125, 127, 129, 130, 131, 135, 136, 138, 139, 140, 142, 143, 145, 147, 149, 150, 151, 155, 159, 163, 164, 166, 169, 172.

Z 3	2d. blue (1858–69)	From	25·00

Plate Nos. 8, 9, 12, 13, 14.

Z 4	3d. carmine-rose (1862)		£225
Z 5	3d. rose (1865) (Plate No. 4)		80·00
Z 6	3d. rose (1867–73)	From	40·00

Plate Nos. 4, 5, 6, 7, 8, 9, 10.

Z 7	4d. rose (1857)		55·00
Z 8	4d. red (1862) (Plate Nos. 3, 4)		60·00
Z 9	4d. vermilion (1865–73)	From	32·00

Plate Nos. 7, 8, 9, 10, 11, 12, 13.

Z10	6d. lilac (1856)		65·00
Z11	6d. lilac (1862) (Plate Nos. 3, 4)		
Z12	6d. lilac (1865–67) (Plate Nos. 5, 6)	From	48·00
Z13	6d. lilac (1867) (Plate No. 6)		80·00
Z14	6d. violet (1867–70) (Plate Nos. 6, 8, 9)	From	45·00
Z15	6d. buff (1872) (Plate No. 11)		75·00
Z16	6d. chestnut (1872) (Plate No. 11)		38·00
Z17	9d. bistre (1862)		£275
Z18	9d. straw (1862)		£225
Z19	9d. straw (1865)		£400
Z20	9d. straw (1867)		£250
Z21	10d. red-brown (1867)		£275
Z22	1s. green (1856)		£175
Z23	1s. green (1862)		£140
Z24	1s. green (1865) (Plate No. 4)		95·00
Z25	1s. green (1867–73) (Plate Nos. 4, 5, 6, 7)	From	30·00
Z26	1s. green (1873–77) (Plate No. 8)		
Z27	2s. blue (1867)		£120
Z28	5s. rose (1867) (Plate No. 1)		£350

A "B 32" obliteration was later used by Mauritius on its own stamps.

AZORES
ST. MICHAELS (SAN MIGUEL)

A British Postal Agency existed at Ponta Delgada, the chief port of the island, to operate with the services of the Royal Mail Steam Packet Company.

CROWNED-CIRCLE HANDSTAMPS

CC1 CC 1b ST. MICHAELS (27.5.1842)

BOLIVIA
COBIJA

It is believed that the British Postal Agency opened in 1862. The stamps of Great Britain were used between 1865 and 1878. They can be found used in combination with Bolivia adhesive stamps paying the local postage. The Agency closed in 1881, the town having been occupied by Chile in 1879.

CROWNED-CIRCLE HANDSTAMPS

CC1 CC 4 COBIJA (29.3.1862) .. Price on cover £4500

Stamps of GREAT BRITAIN cancelled "C 39" as Types 4, 8 or 12.

1865 to 1878.
Z 1	1d. rose-red (Plate Nos. 93, 95)		
Z 2	2d. blue (1858–69) (Plate No. 14)		
Z 3	3d. rose (1867–73) (Plate No. 6)		
Z 4	3d. rose (1873–76) (Plate Nos. 16, 19)		
Z 5	4d. sage-green (1877) (Plate No. 15)		
Z 6	6d. violet (1867–70) (Plate No. 9)		£350
Z 7	6d. buff (1872) (Plate No. 11)		
Z 8	6d. grey (1874–76) (Plate Nos. 13, (4, 15, 16)		£275
Z 9	1s. green (1867–73) (Plate Nos. 4, 5)		
Z10	1s. green (1873–77) (Plate Nos. 10, 11, 12, 13)		£275
Z11	2s. blue (1867)		£450
Z12	5s. rose (1867–74) (Plate No. 2)		

BRAZIL

The first packets ran to Brazil in 1808 when the Portuguese royal family went into exile at Rio de Janeiro. The Agencies at Bahia and Pernambuco did not open until 1851. All three agencies used the stamps of Great Britain from 1866 and these can be found used in combination with Brazil adhesive stamps paying the local postage. The agencies closed on 30 June 1874.

BAHIA
CROWNED-CIRCLE HANDSTAMPS

CC1 CC 7 BAHIA (Black, G. or R.) (6.1.1851)
Price on cover £2250

Stamps of GREAT BRITAIN cancelled "C 81" as Type 12.

1866 to 1874.
Z 1	1d. rose-red (1864–79)	From	35·00

Plate Nos. 90, 93, 96, 108, 113, 117, 135, 140, 147, 155.

Z 2	1½d. lake-red (1870–74) (Plate No. 3)		£100
Z 3	2d. blue (1858–69) (Plate Nos. 9, 12, 13, 14)		80·00
Z 4	3d. rose (1865) (Plate No. 4)		
Z 5	3d. rose (1867–73) (Plate Nos. 4, 6, 8, 9, 10)		50·00
Z 6	3d. rose (1873–79) (Plate No. 11)		

Z 7	4d. vermilion (1865–73)	From	32·00

Plate Nos. 8, 9, 10, 11, 12, 13.

Z 8	6d. lilac (1865–67) (Plate No. 5)		
Z 9	6d. lilac (1867) (Plate No. 6)		75·00
Z10	6d. violet (1867–70) (Plate Nos. 6, 8, 9)	From	50·00
Z11	6d. buff (1872–73) (Plate Nos. 11, 12)	From	90·00
Z12	6d. chestnut (1872) (Plate No. 11)		
Z13	6d. grey (1873) (Plate No. 12)		
Z14	6d. grey (1874–76) (Plate No. 13)		
Z15	9d. straw (1865)		£350
Z16	9d. straw (1867)		£200
Z17	1s. green (1865) (Plate No. 4)		90·00
Z18	1s. green (1867–73) (Plate Nos. 4, 5, 6, 7)	From	40·00
Z19	1s. green (1873–77) (Plate Nos. 8, 9)		75·00
Z20	2s. blue (1867)		£200
Z21	5s. rose (1867) (Plate No. 1)		£400

PERNAMBUCO
CROWNED-CIRCLE HANDSTAMPS

CC2 CC 7 PERNAMBUCO (Black or R.) (6.1.1851)
Price on cover £2250

Stamps of GREAT BRITAIN cancelled "C 82" as Type 12.

1866 to 1874.
Z22	1d. rose-red (1864–79)	From	35·00

Plate Nos. 85, 108, 111, 130, 131, 132, 149, 157, 159, 160, 187.

Z23	2d. blue (1858–69) (Plate Nos. 9, 12, 13, 14)	From	40·00
Z23a	3d. rose (1865) (Plate No. 4)		70·00
Z24	3d. rose (1867–73) (Plate Nos. 4, 5, 6, 7, 10)		40·00
Z25	3d. rose (1873–77) (Plate No. 11)		
Z26	4d. vermilion (1865–73)	From	30·00

Plate Nos. 9, 10, 11, 12, 13, 14.

Z27	6d. lilac (1865–67) (Plate Nos. 5, 6)		
Z28	6d. lilac (1867) (Plate No. 6)		60·00
Z29	6d. violet (1867–70) (Plate Nos. 8, 9)	From	40·00
Z30	6d. buff (1872–73) (Plate Nos. 11, 12)		50·00
Z31	6d. chestnut (1872) (Plate No. 11)		45·00
Z32	6d. grey (1873) (Plate No. 12)		
Z33	9d. straw (1865)		£350
Z34	9d. straw (1867)		£140
Z35	10d. red-brown (1867)		£200
Z36	1s. green (1865) (Plate No. 4)		80·00
Z37	1s. green (1867–73) (Plate Nos. 4, 5, 6, 7)		40·00
Z38	2s. blue (1867)		£225
Z39	5s. rose (1867–74) (Plate Nos. 1, 2)		£425

RIO DE JANEIRO
CROWNED-CIRCLE HANDSTAMPS

CC3 CC 7 RIO DE JANEIRO (Black, B., G. or R.) (6.1.1851) .. .. Price on cover £450

Stamps of GREAT BRITAIN cancelled "C 83" as Type 12.

1866 to 1874.
Z40	1d. rose-red (1857)		38·00
Z41	1d. rose-red (1864–79)	From	30·00

Plate Nos. 71, 76, 80, 82, 86, 94, 103, 113, 117, 119, 123, 130, 132, 134, 135, 146, 148, 159, 161, 166, 185, 200, 204.

Z42	2d. blue (1858–69) (Plate Nos. 9, 12, 13, 14)	From	25·00
Z43	3d. rose (1867–73) (Plate Nos. 4, 5, 6, 7, 8)	From	40·00
Z44	3d. rose (1873–77) (Plate No. 11)		
Z45	4d. vermilion (1865–73)	From	30·00

Plate Nos. 8, 9, 10, 11, 12, 13, 14.

Z46	6d. lilac (1865–67) (Plate No. 5)		
Z47	6d. lilac (1867) (Plate No. 6)		60·00
Z48	6d. violet (1867–70) (Plate Nos. 6, 8, 9)	From	30·00
Z49	6d. buff (1872) (Plate No. 11)		65·00
Z50	6d. chestnut (1872) (Plate No. 11)		35·00
Z51	6d. grey (1873) (Plate No. 12)		
Z52	9d. straw (1865)		£250
Z53	9d. straw (1867)		£120
Z54	10d. red-brown (1867)		£150
Z55	1s. green (1865) (Plate No. 4)		80·00
Z56	1s. green (1867–73) (Plate Nos. 4, 5, 6, 7)	From	25·00
Z57	1s. green (1873–77) (Plate Nos. 8, 9)		50·00
Z58	2s. blue (1867)		95·00
Z59	5s. rose (1867–74) (Plate Nos. 1, 2)	From	£300

CAPE VERDE ISLANDS

The British Packet Agency at St. Vincent opened in 1851 as part of the revised service to South America. The agency was closed by 1860.

CROWNED-CIRCLE HANDSTAMPS

CC1 CC 6 ST. VINCENT C.DE.V. (6.1.1851)
Price on cover £4250

CHILE

The British Postal Agency at Valparaiso opened on 7 May 1846, to be followed by further offices at Caldera (1858) and Coquimbo (1863). The stamps of Great Britain were introduced in 1865 and can be found used in combination with Chile adhesives paying the local postage. All three offices closed on 31 March 1881 when Chile joined the U.P.U.

CALDERA

Stamps of GREAT BRITAIN cancelled "C 37" as in Type 4.

1865 to 1881.
Z 1	1d. rose-red (1864–79)	From	40·00

Plate Nos. 71, 72, 88, 90, 95, 160, 195.

Z 2	1½d. lake-red (1870–74) (Plate No. 3)		
Z 3	2d. blue (1858–69) (Plate No. 9)		40·00
Z 4	3d. rose (1865) (Plate No. 4)		80·00
Z 5	3d. rose (1867–73) (Plate Nos. 5, 7)		
Z 6	3d. rose (1873–76)	From	35·00

Plate Nos. 11, 12, 16, 17, 18, 19.

Z 7	4d. red (1862) (Plate No. 4)		
Z 8	4d. vermilion (1865–73)	From	40·00

Plate Nos. 8, 11, 12, 13, 14.

Z 9	4d. sage-green (1877) (Plate No. 16)		
Z10	6d. lilac (1862) (Plate No. 4)		80·00
Z11	6d. lilac (1865–67) (Plate Nos. 5, 6)		
Z12	6d. violet (1867–70) (Plate Nos. 6, 8, 9)	From	45·00
Z13	6d. buff (1872) (Plate No. 11)		
Z14	6d. chestnut (1872) (Plate No. 11)		
Z15	6d. grey (1873) (Plate No. 12)		

Z16	6d. grey (1874–80)	From	40·00

Plate Nos. 13, 14, 15, 16, 17.

Z17	8d. orange (1876)		£275
Z18	9d. straw (1876)		£160
Z19	10d. red-brown (1867)		£225
Z20	1s. green (1865) (Plate No. 4)		
Z21	1s. green (1867–73) (Plate Nos. 4, 5, 6)	From	35·00
Z22	1s. green (1873–77)	From	60·00

Plate Nos. 8, 10, 11, 12, 13.

Z23	2s. blue (1867)		£200
Z23a	2s. cobalt (1867)		
Z24	2s. brown (1880)		£1600
Z25	5s. rose (1867–74) (Plate No. 2)		£425

COQUIMBO

Stamps of GREAT BRITAIN cancelled "C 40" as in Type 4.

1865 to 1881.
Z26	½d. rose-red (1870–79) (Plate No. 14)		
Z27	1d. rose-red (1857)		
Z28	1d. rose-red (1864–79) (Plate Nos. 85, 204)		
Z29	2d. blue (1858–69) (Plate Nos. 9, 14)		
Z30	3d. rose (1865)		
Z31	3d. rose (1872) (Plate No. 8)		
Z32	3d. rose (1873–76) (Plate Nos. 18, 19)	From	40·00
Z33	4d. red (1863) (Plate No. 4)		70·00
Z34	4d. vermilion (1865–73) (Plate Nos. 12, 14)		
Z35	4d. sage-green (1877) (Plate Nos. 15, 16)		£150
Z36	6d. lilac (1862) (Plate Nos. 3, 4)		65·00
Z37	6d. lilac (1865–67) (Plate No. 5)		
Z38	6d. lilac (1867) (Plate No. 6)		60·00
Z39	6d. violet (1867–70) (Plate Nos. 6, 8, 9)	From	35·00
Z40	6d. buff (1872–73) (Plate Nos. 11, 12)	From	60·00
Z41	6d. chestnut (1872) (Plate No. 11)		
Z42	6d. grey (1873) (Plate No. 12)		£120
Z43	6d. grey (1874–76) (Plate Nos. 13, 14, 15, 16)	From	35·00
Z44	8d. orange (1876)		
Z45	9d. straw (1862)		£225
Z46	9d. straw (1867)		£150
Z47	10d. red-brown (1867)		
Z48	1s. green (1865) (Plate No. 4)		80·00
Z49	1s. green (1867–73) (Plate Nos. 4, 5, 6)		35·00
Z50	1s. green (1873–77)	From	50·00

Plate Nos. 8, 10, 11, 12, 13.

Z51	2s. blue (1867)		£130
Z51a	2s. cobalt (1867)		
Z52	2s. brown (1880)		£1700
Z53	5s. rose (1867–74) (Plate Nos. 1, 2)		£375

VALPARAISO
CROWNED-CIRCLE HANDSTAMPS

CC1 CC 2 VALPARAISO (R.) (13.1.1846) Price on cover £350
CC2 CC 1 VALPARAISO. (R.) (16.7.1846) Price on cover £400

Stamps of GREAT BRITAIN cancelled "C 30", as in Types 12 and 14 or circular date stamp as Type 16.

1865 to 1881.
Z54	½d. rose-red (1870–79)	From	55·00

Plate Nos. 6, 11, 12, 13, 14.

Z55	1d. rose-red (1864–79)	From	25·00

Plate Nos. 80, 84, 85, 89, 91, 101, 106, 113, 116, 122, 123, 138, 140, 141, 146, 148, 149, 152, 157, 158, 162, 167, 175, 178, 181, 185, 186, 187, 189, 190, 195, 197, 198, 199, 200, 201, 207, 209, 210, 211, 212, 213, 214, 215, 217.

Z56	1½d. lake-red (1870–74) (Plate Nos. 1, 3)	From	55·00
Z57	2d. blue (1858–69) (Plate Nos. 9, 13, 14, 15)		35·00
Z58	2½d. rosy mauve (1875), white paper (Plate No. 2)		65·00
Z59	2½d. rosy mauve (1876) (Plate Nos. 4, 8)		50·00
Z60	3d. carmine-rose (1862)		
Z61	3d. rose (1865) (Plate No. 4)		
Z62	3d. rose (1867–73)	From	30·00

Plate Nos. 5, 6, 7, 8, 9, 10.

Z63	3d. rose (1873–76)	From	30·00

Plate Nos. 11, 12, 14, 16, 17, 18, 19.

Z63a	4d. red (1862) (Plate No. 4)		
Z63b	4d. red (1863) (Plate No. 4) (Hair lines)		
Z64	4d. vermilion (1865–73)	From	30·00

Plate Nos. 9, 10, 11, 12, 13, 14.

Z65	4d. vermilion (1876) (Plate No. 15)		£150
Z66	4d. sage-green (1877) (Plate Nos. 15, 16)		£125
Z67	4d. grey-brown (1880) wmk Large Garter (Plate No. 17)		
Z68	6d. lilac (1862) (Plate Nos. 3, 4)	From	55·00
Z69	6d. lilac (1865) (Plate Nos. 5, 6)		
Z70	6d. lilac (1867) (Plate No. 6)		
Z71	6d. violet (1867–70) (Plate Nos. 6, 8, 9)	From	35·00
Z72	6d. buff (1872–73) (Plate Nos. 11, 12)	From	45·00
Z73	6d. chestnut (1872) (Plate Nos. 11, 12)		30·00
Z74	6d. grey (1873) (Plate No. 12)		£120
Z75	6d. grey (1874–80)	From	30·00

Plate Nos. 13, 14, 15, 16, 17.

Z76	6d. grey (1881) (Plate No. 17)		
Z77	8d. orange (1876)		£180
Z78	9d. straw (1862)		
Z79	9d. straw (1865)		
Z80	9d. straw (1867)		£160
Z81	10d. red-brown (1867)		£160
Z82	1s. green (1865) (Plate No. 4)		
Z83	1s. green (1867–73) (Plate Nos. 4, 5, 6, 7)	From	25·00
Z84	1s. green (1873–77)	From	45·00

Plate Nos. 8, 9, 10, 11, 12, 13.

Z85	1s. orange-brown (1880) (Plate No. 13)		£220
Z86	2s. blue (1867)		90·00
Z86a	2s. cobalt (1867)		£1000
Z87	2s. brown (1880)		£1400
Z88	5s. rose (1867–74) (Plate Nos. 1, 2)	From	£300
Z89	10s. grey-green (1878) (wmk Cross)		£1500
Z90	£1 brown-lilac (1878) (wmk Cross)		£2500

1880.
Z91	1d. Venetian red	
Z92	1½d. Venetian red	

COLOMBIA

The system of British Postal Agencies in the area was inaugurated by the opening of the Carthagena office in 1825. In 1842 agencies at Chagres, Panama and Santa Martha were added to the system. A further office opened at Colon in 1852, this port also being known as Aspinwall. During 1872 the system was further enlarged by an office at Savanilla, although this agency was later, 1878, transferred to Barranquilla.

Stamps of Great Britain were supplied to Carthagena, Panama and Santa Martha in 1865, Colon in 1870 and Savanilla in 1872. Combination covers with Colombia stamps paying the local postage are known from Santa Martha and Savanilla as are similar covers from Panama showing Costa Rica and El Salvador stamps.

All offices, except Chagres which had ceased to operate in 1855, closed for public business on 30 June 1881. Colon and Panama continued to exist as transit offices to deal with the mail across the isthmus. Both finally closed on 31 March 1921.

CARTHAGENA
CROWNED-CIRCLE HANDSTAMPS

CC1	CC 1b	CARTHAGENA (R.) (15.1.1841)	*Price on cover*	£800
CC2	CC 1	CARTHAGENA (1.7.1846)	*Price on cover*	£700

Stamps of GREAT BRITAIN *cancelled* "C 56" *as in Type* **4**.

1865 to 1881.

Z 1	½d.	rose-red (1870–79) (Plate No. 10)		
Z 2	1d.	rose-red (1864–79)	*From*	40·00
		Plate Nos. 78, 87, 100, 111, 113, 117, 119, 125, 172, 189, 217.		
Z 3	2d.	blue (1858–69) (Plate Nos. 9, 14)	*From*	40·00
Z 4	3d.	rose (1865) (Plate No. 4)		
Z 5	3d.	rose (1865–68) (Plate Nos. 4, 5)	*From*	
Z 6	3d.	rose (1873–79) (Plate Nos. 12, 17, 18)	*From*	45·00
Z 7	4d.	vermilion (1865–73)	*From*	35·00
		Plate Nos. 7, 8, 9, 10, 11, 12, 13, 14.		
Z 8	4d.	vermilion (1876) (Plate No. 15)		£180
Z 9	4d.	sage-green (1877) (Plate Nos. 15, 16)	*From*	£160
Z10	6d.	lilac (1865–67) (Plate Nos. 5, 6)		
Z11	6d.	violet (1867–70) (Plate Nos. 6, 8)	*From*	48·00
Z12	6d.	grey (1873) (Plate No. 12)		£130
Z13	6d.	grey (1874–76) (Plate Nos. 13, 14, 15, 16)	*From*	40·00
Z14	8d.	orange (1876)		£200
Z15	9d.	straw (1865)		
Z16	1s.	green (1865)		
Z17	1s.	green (1867–73) (Plate Nos. 4, 5, 7)		40·00
Z18	1s.	green (1873–77) (Plate Nos. 8, 9, 10, 11, 12, 13)		50·00
Z19	1s.	orange-brown (1880)		
Z20	2s.	blue (1867)		£200
Z21	5s.	rose (1867) (Plate No. 1)		£400

Cancelled "C 65" (*incorrect handstamp, supplied in error*) *as T* **12**.

1866 to 1881.

Z22	½d.	rose-red (1870–79) (Plate No. 10)		
Z23	1d.	rose-red (1864–79) (Plate Nos. 100, 106, 111, 123)	*From*	50·00
Z23a	1½d.	lake-red (1870) (Plate No. 3)		
Z24	2d.	blue (1858–69) (Plate No. 9)		50·00
Z25	2d.	rose (1880)		
Z26	2½d.	blue (1880) (Plate No. 19)		
Z27	3d.	rose (1867–73) (Plate No. 9)		
Z28	3d.	rose (1873–79) (Plate Nos. 14, 17, 19, 20)		
Z29	4d.	vermilion (1865–73)	*From*	40·00
		Plate Nos. 7, 8, 9, 11, 12, 13, 14.		
Z30	4d.	vermilion (1876) (Plate No. 15)		£200
Z31	4d.	sage-green (1877) (Plate Nos. 15, 16)	*From*	£175
Z32	6d.	violet (1867–70) (Plate Nos. 6, 8)		80·00
Z33	6d.	pale buff (1872) (Plate No. 11)		
Z34	6d.	grey (1873) (Plate No. 12)		£120
Z35	6d.	grey (1874–80) (Plate Nos. 13, 15, 16, 17)		40·00
Z36	8d.	orange (1876)		£275
Z37	9d.	straw (1865)		£275
Z38	1s.	green (1865) (Plate No. 4)		85·00
Z39	1s.	green (1867) (Plate Nos. 4, 5, 6, 7)		40·00
Z40	1s.	green (1873–77) (Plate Nos. 8, 11, 12, 13)	*From*	45·00
Z41	1s.	orange-brown (1880)		
Z42	2s.	blue (1867)		£350
Z43	2s.	brown (1880)		£2000
Z44	5s.	rose (1867) (Plate Nos. 1, 2)		£425

CHAGRES
CROWNED-CIRCLE HANDSTAMPS

CC3	CC 1	CHAGRES (16.9.1846)	

COLON
CROWNED-CIRCLE HANDSTAMPS

CC4	CC 5	COLON (R.) (21.6.1854)	*Price on cover*	£3500

Stamps of GREAT BRITAIN *cancelled* "E 88" *as in Type* **12**.

1870 to 1881.

Z45	1d.	rose-red (1864–79)	*From*	35·00
		Plate Nos. 107, 121, 122, 123, 125, 127, 130, 131, 133, 136, 138, 142, 150, 151, 152, 153, 155, 156, 157, 158, 160, 169, 170, 171, 174, 176, 178, 179, 184, 187, 188, 194, 195, 201, 209, 213, 214, 217.		
Z46	1d.	Venetian red (1880)		
Z47	1½d.	lake-red (1870–74) (Plate No. 3)		90·00
Z48	2d.	blue (1858–69) (Plate Nos. 14, 15)		35·00
Z49	2d.	pale rose (1880)		
Z50	3d.	rose (1867–73) (Plate Nos. 6, 9)		
Z51	3d.	rose (1873–76)		40·00
		Plate Nos. 11, 12, 16, 18, 19, 20.		
Z52	4d.	vermilion (1865–73)	*From*	35·00
		Plate Nos. 10, 11, 12, 13, 14.		
Z53	4d.	vermilion (1876) (Plate No. 15)		
Z54	4d.	sage-green (1877) (Plate Nos. 15, 16)		£150
Z55	4d.	grey-brown (1880) *wmk* Large Garter (Plate No. 17.)		£200
Z56	4d.	grey-brown (1880) *wmk* Crown (Plate No. 17)		
Z57	6d.	violet (1867–70) (Plate Nos. 6, 8, 9)		
Z58	6d.	buff (1872) (Plate No. 11)		
Z59	6d.	chestnut (1872) (Plate No. 11)		50·00
Z60	6d.	grey (1873) (Plate No. 12)		
Z61	6d.	grey (1874–80)	*From*	35·00
		Plate Nos. 13, 14, 15, 16, 17.		
Z62	8d.	orange (1876)		
Z63	9d.	straw (1867)		£150
Z63a	10d.	red-brown (1867)		
Z64	1s.	green (1867–73) (Plate Nos. 4, 5, 6, 7)		35·00
Z65	1s.	green (1873–77)	*From*	45·00
		Plate Nos. 8, 9, 10, 11, 12, 13.		
Z66	1s.	orange-brown (1880) (Plate 13)		£250
Z67	1s.	orange-brown (1881) (Plate 13)		60·00
Z68	2s.	blue (1867)		£120

Z69	2s.	brown (1880)		£1700
Z70	5s.	rose (1867) (Plate Nos. 1, 2)		£400

PANAMA
CROWNED-CIRCLE HANDSTAMPS

CC5	CC 1	PANAMA (R.) (24.8.1846)	*Price on cover*	£1200

Stamps of GREAT BRITAIN *cancelled* "C 35" *as in Types* **4, 11** *or* **14**.

1865 to 1881.

Z 71	½d.	rose-red (1870–79)	*From*	35·00
		Plate Nos. 10, 11, 12, 13, 14, 15, 19		
Z 72	1d.	rose-red (1864–79)	*From*	25·00
		Plate Nos. 71, 72, 76, 81, 85, 87, 88, 89, 93, 95, 96, 101, 104, 114, 122, 124, 130, 138, 139, 142, 159, 168, 171, 172, 174, 177, 179, 180, 184, 185, 187, 189, 191, 192, 193, 196, 197, 200, 203, 204, 205, 207, 208, 209, 210, 211, 213, 214, 215, 218, 224		
Z 73	1½d.	lake-red (1870–74) (Plate No. 3)		50·00
Z 74	2d.	blue (1858–69)	*From*	30·00
		Plate Nos. 9, 12, 13, 14, 15.		
Z 75	2½d.	rosy mauve (1875) (Plate No. 1)		
Z 76	2½d.	rosy mauve (1876–80) (Plate Nos. 4, 12, 16)		
Z 77	2½d.	blue (1880) (Plate No. 19)		
Z 78	2½d.	blue (1880) (Plate Nos. 22, 23)		
Z 79	3d.	carmine-red (1862)		£120
Z 80	3d.	rose (1865) (Plate No. 4)		
Z 81	3d.	rose (1867–73)	*From*	30·00
		Plate Nos. 4, 5, 6, 7, 8, 9.		
Z 82	3d.	rose (1873–76)	*From*	30·00
		Plate Nos. 12, 14, 15, 16, 17, 18, 19, 20.		
Z 83	3d.	rose (1881) (Plate Nos. 20, 21)		
Z 84	4d.	red (1863) (Plate No. 4)		65·00
Z 85	4d.	vermilion (1865–73)	*From*	30·00
		Plate Nos. 7, 8, 9, 10, 11, 12, 13, 14.		
Z 86	4d.	vermilion (1876) (Plate No. 15)		£175
Z 87	4d.	sage-green (1877) (Plate Nos. 15, 16)		£130
Z 88	4d.	grey-brown (1880) *wmk* Crown	*From*	50·00
		Plate Nos. 17, 18.		
Z 89	6d.	lilac (1862) (Plate Nos. 3, 4)	*From*	60·00
Z 90	6d.	lilac (1865–67) (Plate Nos. 5, 6)	*From*	40·00
Z 91	6d.	lilac (1867) (Plate No. 6)		
Z 92	6d.	violet (1867–70) (Plate Nos. 6, 8, 9)		30·00
Z 93	6d.	buff (1872–73) (Plate Nos. 11, 12)	*From*	50·00
Z 94	6d.	chestnut (Plate No. 11)		35·00
Z 95	6d.	grey (1873) (Plate No. 12)		£120
Z 96	6d.	grey (1874–80)	*From*	35·00
		Plate Nos. 13, 14, 15, 16, 17.		
Z 97	6d.	grey (1881) (Plate No. 17)		65·00
Z 98	8d.	orange (1876)		£175
Z 99	9d.	straw (1862)		£200
Z100	9d.	straw (1865)		£225
Z101	10d.	red-brown (1867)		£190
Z102	1s.	green (1865) (Plate No. 4)		80·00
Z103	1s.	green (1867–73) (Plate Nos. 4, 5, 6, 7)	*From*	35·00
Z104	1s.	green (1873–77)	*From*	45·00
		Plate Nos. 8, 9, 10, 11, 12, 13.		
Z105	1s.	orange-brown (1880) (Plate No. 13)		£250
Z106	1s.	orange-brown (1881) (Plate No. 13)		55·00
Z107	2s.	blue (1867)		90·00
Z108	2s.	brown (1880)		£1700
Z109	5s.	rose (1867–74) (Plate Nos. 1, 2)	*From*	£350

1880.

Z110	1d.	Venetian red		30·00
Z111	2d.	rose		60·00
Z112	5d.	indigo		£110

Later stamps cancelled "C 35" are believed to originate from sailors' letters or other forms of maritime mail.

SANTA MARTHA
CROWNED-CIRCLE HANDSTAMPS

CC6	CC 1b	SANTA MARTHA (R.) (15.12.1841)	
		Price on cover £1200	

Stamps of GREAT BRITAIN *cancelled* "C 62" *as in Type* **4**.

1865 to 1881.

Z113	½d.	rose-red (1870–79) (Plate No. 6)		80·00
Z114	1d.	rose-red (1864–79) (Plate No. 106)		55·00
Z115	2d.	blue (1858–69) (Plate Nos. 9, 13)		80·00
Z116	4d.	vermilion (1865–73)	*From*	40·00
		Plate Nos. 7, 8, 9, 11, 12, 13, 14.		
Z117	4d.	sage-green (1877) (Plate No. 15)		£140
Z118	4d.	grey-brown (1880) *wmk* Large Garter		£200
		Plate No. 17.		
Z119	4d.	grey-brown (1880) *wmk* Crown (Plate No. 17)		60·00
Z120	6d.	lilac (1865–67) (Plate No. 5)		60·00
Z121	6d.	grey (1873) (Plate No. 12)		
Z122	6d.	grey (1874–76) (Plate No. 14)		
Z123	8d.	orange (1876)		£225
Z123a	9d.	bistre (1862)		
Z124	1s.	green (1865) (Plate No. 4)		90·00
Z125	1s.	green (1867–73) (Plate Nos. 5, 7)		50·00
Z126	1s.	green (1873–77) (Plate No. 8)		
Z127	2s.	blue (1867)		£275
Z128	5s.	rose (1867) (Plate No. 2)		£425

SAVANILLA (BARRANQUILLA)

Stamps of GREAT BRITAIN *cancelled* "F 69" *as in Type* **12**.

1872 to 1881.

Z129	½d.	rose-red (1870–79) (Plate No. 6)		55·00
Z130	1d.	rose-red (1864–79) (Plate Nos. 122, 171)		50·00
Z131	1½d.	lake-red (1870–74) (Plate No. 3)		90·00
Z132	3d.	rose (1867–73) (Plate No. 7)		
Z133	3d.	rose (1873–76) (Plate No. 20)		85·00
Z134	3d.	rose (1881) (Plate No. 20)		85·00
Z135	4d.	vermilion (1865–73) (Plate Nos. 12, 13, 14)		35·00
Z136	4d.	vermilion (1876) (Plate No. 15)		£175
Z137	4d.	sage-green (1877) (Plate Nos. 15, 16)		£140
Z138	4d.	grey-brown (1880) *wmk* Large Garter		£200
		Plate No. 17.		
Z139	4d.	grey-brown (1880) *wmk* Crown (Plate No. 17)		50·00
Z140	6d.	buff (1872) (Plate No. 11)		
Z141	6d.	grey (1878) (Plate Nos. 16, 17)	*From*	60·00
Z142	8d.	orange (1876)		£225
Z143	1s.	green (1867–73) (Plate Nos. 5, 7)		45·00
Z144	1s.	green (1873–77) (Plate Nos. 8, 11, 12, 13)		60·00
Z145	1s.	orange-brown (1880)		£250
Z146	2s.	blue (1867)		£170
Z147	5s.	rose (1867–74) (Plate No. 2)		£425

CUBA

The British Postal Agency at Havana opened in 1762, the island then being part of the Spanish Empire. A further office, at St. Jago de Cuba, was added in 1841.

Great Britain stamps were supplied to Havana in 1865 and to St. Jago de Cuba in 1866. They continued in use until the offices closed on 30 May 1877.

HAVANA
CROWNED-CIRCLE HANDSTAMPS

CC1	CC 1b	HAVANA (13.11.1841)	*Price on cover*	£800
CC2	CC 1c	HAVANA (1848)	*Price on cover*	£800
CC3	CC 2	HAVANA (14.7.1848)	*Price on cover*	£675

Stamps of GREAT BRITAIN *cancelled* "C 58" *as in Types* **4, 12** *or* **14**.

1865 to 1877.

Z 1	½d.	rose-red (1870) (Plate Nos. 6, 12)		50·00
Z 2	1d.	rose-red (1864–79)	*From*	40·00
		Plate Nos. 86, 90, 93, 115, 120, 123, 144, 146, 171, 174, 208.		
Z 3	2d.	blue (1858–69) (Plate Nos. 9, 14, 15)		40·00
Z 4	3d.	rose (1867–73) (Plate No. 4)		80·00
Z 5	3d.	rose (1873–76) (Plate Nos. 18, 19)		50·00
Z 6	4d.	vermilion (1865–73)	*From*	40·00
		Plate Nos. 7, 8, 10, 11, 12, 13, 14.		
Z 7	4d.	vermilion (1876) (Plate No. 15)		£250
Z 8	6d.	lilac (1865) (with hyphen) (Plate No. 5)		
Z 9	6d.	grey (1874–76) (Plate No. 15)		
Z10	8d.	orange (1876)		
Z11	9d.	straw (1867)		£200
Z12	10d.	red-brown (1867)		£250
Z13	1s.	green (1865) (Plate No. 4)		85·00
Z14	1s.	green (1867–73) (Plate Nos. 4, 5, 7)	*From*	40·00
Z15	1s.	green (1873–77) (Plate Nos. 10, 12, 13)	*From*	55·00
Z16	2s.	blue (1867)		£175
Z17	5s.	rose (1867–74) (Plate Nos. 1, 2)		£425

ST. JAGO DE CUBA
CROWNED-CIRCLE HANDSTAMPS

CC4	CC 1b	ST. JAGO-DE-CUBA (R.) (15.12.1841)	
		Price on cover £4750	

Stamps of GREAT BRITAIN *cancelled* "C 88" *as Type* **12**.

1866 to 1877.

Z18	½d.	rose-red (1870–79) (Plate Nos. 4, 6, 14)		
Z19	1d.	rose-red (1864–79)	*From*	75·00
		Plate Nos. 100, 105, 106, 109, 111, 120, 123, 138, 144, 146, 147, 148, 171, 208.		
Z20	1½d.	lake-red (1870–74) (Plate No. 3)		
Z21	2d.	blue (1858–69) (Plate Nos. 9, 12, 13, 14)		
Z22	3d.	rose (1867) (Plate No. 5)		
Z23	4d.	vermilion (1865–73)	*From*	90·00
		Plate Nos. 9, 10, 11, 12, 13, 14.		
Z24	4d.	vermilion (1876) (Plate No. 15)		£300
Z25	6d.	violet (1867–70) (Plate Nos. 6, 8, 9)	*From*	£250
Z26	6d.	buff (Plate No. 11)		
Z27	9d.	straw (1865)		
Z27a	9d.	straw (1867)		
Z28	10d.	red-brown (1867)		£350
Z29	1s.	green (1867–73) (Plate Nos. 4, 5, 6)	*From*	£250
Z30	1s.	green (1873–77) (Plate Nos. 9, 10, 12, 13)		
Z31	2s.	blue (1867)		
Z32	5s.	rose (1867) (Plate 1)		

DANISH WEST INDIES

ST. THOMAS

The British Postal Agency at St. Thomas opened in January 1809 and by 1825 was the office around which many of the packet routes were organised.

Great Britain stamps were introduced on 3 July 1865 and can be found used in combination with Danish West Indies adhesives paying the local postage.

Following a hurricane in October 1867 the main British packet office was moved to Colon in Colombia.

The British Post Office at St. Thomas closed to the public on 1 September 1877, but continued to operate as a transit office for a further two years.

CROWNED-CIRCLE HANDSTAMPS

CC1	CC 1	ST. THOMAS (R.) (20.2.49)	*Price on cover*	£450
CC2	CC 6	ST. THOMAS (R.) (1.5.1855)	*Price on cover*	£900

Stamps of GREAT BRITAIN *cancelled* "C 51" *as in Types* **4, 12** *or* **14**.

1865 to 1879.

Z 1	½d.	rose-red (1870–79)		35·00
		Plate Nos. 5, 6, 8, 10, 11, 12.		
Z 2	1d.	rose-red (1857)		
Z 3	1d.	rose-red (1864–79)	*From*	25·00
		Plate Nos. 71, 72, 79, 81, 84, 85, 86, 87, 88, 89, 90, 93, 94, 95, 96, 97, 98, 99, 100, 101, 102, 105, 106, 107, 108, 109, 110, 111, 112, 113, 114, 116, 117, 118, 119, 120, 121, 122, 123, 124, 125, 127, 129, 130, 131, 133, 134, 136, 137, 138, 139, 140, 141, 142, 144, 145, 146, 147, 148, 149, 150, 151, 152, 154, 155, 156, 157, 158, 159, 160, 161, 162, 163, 164, 165, 166, 167, 169, 170, 171, 172, 173, 174, 175, 176, 177, 178, 179, 180, 181, 182, 184, 185, 186, 187, 189, 190, 197.		
Z 4	1½d.	lake-red (1870–79) (Plate Nos. 1, 3)		60·00
Z 5	2d.	blue (1858–69)	*From*	30·00
		Plate Nos. 9, 12, 13, 14, 15.		
Z 6	3d.	rose (1865) (Plate No. 4)		65·00
Z 7	3d.	rose (1867–73)	*From*	30·00
		Plate Nos. 4, 5, 6, 7, 8, 9, 10.		
Z 8	3d.	rose (1873–76)		
		Plate Nos. 11, 12, 14, 15, 16, 17, 18, 19.		
Z 9	4d.	red (1862) (Plate Nos. 3, 4)		45·00
Z10	4d.	vermilion (1865–73)	*From*	30·00
		Plate Nos. 7, 8, 9, 10, 11, 12, 13, 14.		
Z11	4d.	vermilion (1876) (Plate No. 15)		£175
Z12	4d.	sage-green (1877) (Plate Nos. 15, 16)	*From*	£140

Z14	6d. lilac (1864) (Plate No. 4)		£100
Z15	6d. lilac (1865–67) (Plate Nos. 5, 6)	*From*	40·00
Z16	6d. lilac (1867) (Plate No. 6)		60·00
Z17	6d. violet (1867–70) (Plate Nos. 6, 8, 9)	*From*	30·00
Z18	6d. buff (1872–73) (Plate Nos. 11, 12)		65·00
Z19	6d. chestnut (1872) (Plate No. 11)		30·00
Z20	6d. grey (1873) (Plate No. 12)		£120
Z21	6d. grey (1874–76) (Plate Nos. 13, 14, 15, 16)		30·00
Z22	8d. orange (1876)		£200
Z23	9d. straw (1862)		£175
Z24	9d. bistre (1862)		£175
Z25	9d. straw (1865)		£250
Z26	9d. straw (1867)		£150
Z27	10d. red-brown (1867)		£200
Z28	1s. green (1865) (Plate No. 4)		90·00
Z29	1s. green (1867–73) (Plate Nos. 4, 5, 6, 7)	*From*	30·00
Z30	1s. green (1873–77)	*From*	55·00
	Plate Nos. 8, 9, 10, 11, 12, 13.		
Z31	2s. blue (1867)		£120
Z32	5s. rose (1867–74) (Plate Nos. 1, 2)	*From*	£350

DOMINICAN REPUBLIC

British Postal Agencies may have existed in the area before 1867, but it is only from that year that details can be found concerning offices at Porto Plata and St. Domingo. Both were closed in 1871, but re-opened in 1876.

Although postmarks were supplied in 1866 it seems likely that Great Britain stamps were not sent until the offices re-opened in 1876.

Covers exist showing Great Britain stamps used in combination with those of Dominican Republic with the latter paying the local postage. Both agencies finally closed in 1881.

PORTO PLATA

Stamps of GREAT BRITAIN *cancelled* "C 86" *or circular date stamp as in Types* **8** *or* **17**.

1876 to 1881.

Z 1	½d. rose-red (1870–79) (Plate Nos. 10, 12, 14)	*From*	60·00
Z 2	1d. rose-red (1864–79)	*From*	45·00
	Plate Nos. 123, 130, 136, 146, 151, 178, 199, 200, 205, 217.		
Z 3	1½d. lake-red (1870–74) (Plate No. 3)		£100
Z 4	2d. blue (1858–69) (Plate Nos. 14, 15)		40·00
Z 5	2½d. rosy mauve (1876–79) (Plate Nos. 13, 14)	*From*	£140
Z 6	3d. rose (1873–76) (Plate No. 18)		80·00
Z 7	3d. vermilion (1873) (Plate No. 14)		80·00
Z 8	4d. vermilion (1876) (Plate No. 15)		£200
Z 9	4d. sage-green (1877) (Plate No. 15)		£160
Z10	6d. violet (1867–70) (Plate No. 8)		
Z11	6d. grey (1874–76) (Plate No. 15)		60·00
Z12	8d. orange (1876)		£275
Z13	1s. green (1867–73) (Plate Nos. 4, 7)	*From*	45·00
Z14	1s. green (1873–77) (Plate Nos. 11, 12, 13)	*From*	45·00
Z15	2s. blue (1867)		£200
Z15a	5s. rose (1867–83) (Plate No. 2)		

ST. DOMINGO

Stamps of GREAT BRITAIN *cancelled* "C 87" *or circular date stamp as in Types* **12** *or* **16**.

1876 to 1881.

Z16	½d. rose-red (1870–79)	*From*	70·00
	Plate Nos. 5, 6, 8, 10, 11, 13.		
Z17	1d. rose-red (1864–79)	*From*	50·00
	Plate Nos. 146, 154, 171, 173, 174, 176, 178, 186, 190, 197, 220.		
Z18	1½d. lake-red (1870–74) (Plate No. 3)		£100
Z19	2d. blue (1858–69) (Plate Nos. 13, 14)		80·00
Z20	3d. rose (1873–76) (Plate No. 18)		
Z21	4d. vermilion (1865–73)	*From*	60·00
	Plate Nos. 11, 12, 14.		
Z22	4d. vermilion (1876) (Plate No. 15)		£225
Z23	4d. sage-green (1877) (Plate No. 15)		£160
Z24	6d. grey (1874–76) (Plate No. 15)		
Z25	9d. straw (1867)		
Z26	1s. green (1867) (Plate No. 4)		
Z27	1s. green (1873–77)	*From*	80·00
	Plate Nos. 10, 11, 12, 13.		
Z28	2s. blue (1867)		

ECUADOR

GUAYAQUIL

The first British Postal Agent in Guayaquil was appointed in 1848.

Great Britain stamps were supplied in 1865 and continued to be used until the agency closed on 30 June 1880. They can be found used in combination with stamps of Ecuador with the latter paying the local postage.

Stamps of GREAT BRITAIN *cancelled* "C 41" *as Type* **4**.

1865 to 1880.

Z 1	½d. rose-red (1870–79) (Plate Nos. 5, 6)		55·00
Z 2	1d. rose-red (1857)		
Z 3	1d. rose-red (1864–79)	*From*	35·00
	Plate Nos. 74, 78, 85, 92, 94, 105, 110, 115, 133, 140, 145, 166, 174, 180, 216.		
Z 4	1½d. lake-red (1870–74) (Plate No. 3)		75·00
Z 5	2d. blue (1858–69) (Plate Nos. 9, 13, 14)	*From*	35·00
Z 6	3d. carmine-rose (1862)		£175
Z 7	3d. rose (1865) (Plate No. 4)		60·00
Z 8	3d. rose (1867–73) (Plate Nos. 6, 7, 9, 10)	*From*	40·00
Z 9	3d. rose (1873–76)	*From*	40·00
	Plate Nos. 11, 12, 15, 16, 17, 18, 19, 20.		
Z10	4d. red (1862) (Plate Nos. 3, 4)		70·00
Z11	4d. vermilion (1865–73)	*From*	30·00
	Plate Nos. 7, 8, 9, 10, 11, 12, 13, 14.		
Z12	4d. vermilion (1876) (Plate No. 15)		£175
Z13	4d. sage-green (1877) (Plate Nos. 15, 16)		£150
Z14	6d. lilac (1864) (Plate No. 4)		70·00
Z15	6d. lilac (1865–67) (Plate Nos. 5, 6)		45·00
Z16	6d. lilac (1867) (Plate No. 6)		40·00
Z17	6d. violet (1867–70) (Plate Nos. 6, 8, 9)	*From*	40·00
Z18	6d. buff (1872–73) (Plate Nos. 11, 12)		75·00

Z19	6d. chestnut (1872)		
Z20	6d. grey (1873) (Plate No. 12)		
Z21	6d. grey (1874–76) (Plate Nos. 13, 14, 15, 16)	*From*	35·00
Z22	8d. orange (1876)		£200
Z23	9d. straw (1862)		£200
Z24	9d. straw (1867)		£150
Z25	10d. red-brown (1867)		£160
Z26	1s. green (1865) (Plate No. 4)		90·00
Z27	1s. green (1867–73) (Plate Nos. 4, 5, 6, 7)	*From*	30·00
Z28	1s. green (1873–77)	*From*	50·00
	Plate Nos. 8, 9, 10, 11, 12, 13.		
Z29	2s. blue (1867)		£125
Z30	2s. brown (1880)		£2000
Z31	5s. rose (1867–74) (Plate Nos. 1, 2)	*From*	£400

FERNANDO PO

The British government leased naval facilities on this Spanish island from 1827 until 1834. A British Consul was appointed in 1849 and a postal agency was opened on 1 April 1858.

The use of Great Britain stamps was authorised in 1858, but a cancellation was not supplied until 1874. The office remained open until 1877.

CROWNED-CIRCLE HANDSTAMPS

CC1 CC **4** FERNANDO-PO (R.) (19.2.1859)
Price on cover £3750

Stamps of GREAT BRITAIN *cancelled* "247" *as Type* **9**.

1874 to 1877.

Z1	4d. vermilion (1865–72) (Plate Nos. 13, 14)		
Z2	4d. vermilion (1876) (Plate No. 15)		
Z3	6d. grey (1874–76) (Plate Nos. 13, 14, 15, 16)		

GUADELOUPE

A British Packet Agency was established on Guadeloupe on 1 October 1848 and continued to function until 1874.

No. CC1 is often found used in conjunction with French Colonies (General Issues) adhesive stamps.

A similar packet agency existed on Martinique from 1 October 1848 until 1879, but no crowned-circle handstamp was issued for it.

CROWNED-CIRCLE HANDSTAMPS

CC1 CC **1** GUADALOUPE (R., B. or Black) (9.3.1849)
Price on cover £1800

HAITI

The original British Postal Agencies in Haiti date from 1830 when it is known as a Packet Agency was established at Jacmel. An office at Port-au-Prince followed in 1842, both these agencies remaining in operation until 30 June 1881.

During this period short-lived agencies also operated in the following Haitian towns: Aux Cayes (1848 to 1863), Cap Haitien (1842 to 1863), Gonaives (1849 to 1857) and St. Marc (1854 to 1861). A further agency may have operated at Le Mole around the year 1841.

Great Britain stamps were supplied to Jacmel in 1865 and to Port-au-Prince in 1869.

CAP HAITIEN

CROWNED-CIRCLE HANDSTAMPS

CC1 CC **1b** CAPE-HAITIEN (R.) (31.12.1841)
Price on cover £3000

JACMEL

CROWNED-CIRCLE HANDSTAMPS

CC2 CC **1b** JACMEL (R.) (29.6.1843) .. *Price on cover* £1000

Stamps of GREAT BRITAIN *cancelled* "C 59" *as Type* **4**.

1865 to 1881.

Z 1	½d. rose-red (1870–79)	*From*	40·00
	Plate Nos. 4, 5, 6, 10, 11, 12, 14, 15.		
Z 2	1d. rose-red (1864–79)	*From*	35·00
	Plate Nos. 74, 81, 84, 87, 95, 106, 107, 109, 122, 136, 137, 139, 148, 150, 151, 152, 156, 157, 159, 160, 162, 164, 166, 167, 170, 171, 179, 181, 183, 184, 186, 187, 189, 192, 194, 198, 200, 204, 206, 215, 219.		
Z 3	1½d. lake-red (1870–74) (Plate No. 3)		60·00
Z 4	2d. blue (1858–69) (Plate Nos. 9, 13, 14, 15)		40·00
Z 5	2½d. rosy mauve (1876) (Plate No. 4)		
Z 6	3d. rose (1867–73) (Plate Nos. 5, 6, 7, 8, 9, 10)	*From*	40·00
Z 7	3d. rose (1873–76)		40·00
	Plate Nos. 11, 12, 14, 16, 17, 18, 19.		
Z 8	4d. red (1863) (Plate No. 4) (*Hair lines*)		80·00
Z 9	4d. vermilion (1865–73)	*From*	35·00
	Plate Nos. 9, 10, 11, 12, 13, 14.		
Z10	4d. vermilion (1876) (Plate No. 15)		£200
Z11	4d. sage-green (1877) (Plate Nos. 15, 16)		£150
Z12	4d. grey-brown (1880) *wmk* Large Garter		£250
	Plate No. 17.		
Z13	4d. grey-brown (1880) *wmk* Crown (Plate No. 17)		40·00
Z14	6d. lilac (1867) (Plate Nos. 5, 6)		45·00
Z15	6d. violet (1867–70) (Plate Nos. 8, 9)		40·00
Z16	6d. buff (1872–73) (Plate Nos. 11, 12)	*From*	60·00
Z17	6d. chestnut (1872) (Plate No. 11)		
Z18	6d. grey (1873) (Plate No. 12)		
Z19	6d. grey (1874–76)	*From*	40·00
	Plate Nos. 13, 14, 15, 16, 17.		
Z20	8d. orange (1876)		£250
Z21	9d. straw (1862)		£200
Z22	9d. straw (1867)		£175
Z23	10d. red-brown (1867)		£160
Z24	1s. green (1865) (Plate No. 4)		£100
Z25	1s. green (1867–73) (Plate Nos. 4, 5, 6, 7)	*From*	30·00
Z26	1s. green (1873–77)	*From*	50·00
	Plate Nos. 8, 9, 10, 11, 12, 13.		
Z27	1s. orange-brown (1880) (Plate No. 13)		£300
Z28	2s. blue (1867)		£100
Z29	2s. brown (1880)		£2000
Z30	5s. rose (1867–74) (Plate Nos. 1, 2)	*From*	£300

1880.

Z31	½d. green (1880)		35·00
Z32	1d. Venetian red		35·00
Z33	1½d. Venetian red		50·00
Z34	2d. rose		85·00

PORT-AU-PRINCE

CROWNED-CIRCLE HANDSTAMPS

CC3 CC **1b** PORT-AU-PRINCE (R.) (29.6.1843)
Price on cover £1500

Stamps of GREAT BRITAIN *cancelled* "E 53" *as in Types* **8, 12** *or* **16**.

1869 to 1881.

Z35	½d. rose-red (1870–79)	*From*	45·00
	Plate Nos. 5, 6, 10, 11, 12, 13, 14.		
Z36	1d. rose-red (1864–79)	*From*	35·00
	Plate Nos. 87, 134, 154, 159, 167, 171, 173, 174, 177, 183, 187, 189, 193, 199, 200, 201, 202, 206, 209, 210, 218, 219.		
Z37	1½d. lake-red (1870–74) (Plate No. 3)		70·00
Z38	2d. blue (1858–69) (Plate Nos. 9, 14, 15)		40·00
Z40	2½d. rosy mauve (1876–79) (Plate Nos. 3, 9)		80·00
Z41	3d. rose (1867–73) (Plate Nos. 6, 7)		
Z42	3d. rose (1873–76) (Plate Nos. 17, 18, 20)		40·00
Z43	4d. vermilion (1865–73)	*From*	40·00
	Plate Nos. 11, 12, 13, 14.		
Z44	4d. vermilion (1876) (Plate No. 15)		£200
Z45	4d. sage-green (1877) (Plate Nos. 15, 16)	*From*	£130
Z46	4d. grey-brown (1880) *wmk* Large Garter		£250
	Plate No. 17.		
Z47	4d. grey-brown (1880) *wmk* Crown (Plate No. 17)		40·00
Z48	6d. grey (1874–76) (Plate Nos. 15, 16)		
Z49	8d. orange (1876)		£190
Z50	1s. green (1867–73) (Plate Nos. 4, 5, 6, 7)	*From*	30·00
Z51	1s. green (1873–77)	*From*	45·00
	Plate Nos. 8, 9, 10, 11, 12, 13		
Z52	1s. orange-brown (1880) (Plate No. 13)		£300
Z53	1s. orange-brown (1881) (Plate No. 13)		70·00
Z54	2s. blue (1867)		£100
Z55	2s. brown (1880)		£2000
Z56	5s. rose (1867–74) (Plate Nos. 1, 2)	*From*	£375
Z57	10s. greenish grey (1878)		£2500

1880.

Z58	½d. green		40·00
Z59	1d. Venetian red		30·00
Z60	1½d. Venetian red		40·00
Z61	2d. rose		85·00

MACAO

A British Consular Post Office opened in 1841. It had been preceded by the Macao Boat Office, possibly a private venture, which operated in the 1830s. The office closed when the consulate closed on 30 September 1845, but was back in operation by 1854.

The Agency continued to function, in conjunction with the Hong Kong Post Office, until 28 February 1884 when Portugal joined the U.P.U.

CROWNED-CIRCLE HANDSTAMPS

Z 2

CC1 – PAID AT MACAO (crowned-oval 20 mm wide) (R.) (1844) .. *Price on cover* £14000
CC2 Z **2** Crown and Macao (1881)

No. CC2 with the Crown removed was used by the Portuguese post office in Macao as a cancellation until 1890.

A locally-cut mark, as Type CC **2**, inscribed "PAGO EM MACAO" is known on covers between 1870 and 1877. It was probably used by the Portuguese postmaster to send letters via the British Post Office (*Price* £10000).

MADEIRA

The British Packet Agency on this Portuguese island was opened in 1767 and was of increased importance from 1808 following the exile of the Portuguese royal family to Brazil. The South American packets ceased to call in 1858. It appears to have closed sometime around 1860.

CROWN-CIRCLE HANDSTAMPS

CC1 CC **1b** MADEIRA (R.) (28.2.1842). . *Price on cover* £12000

MEXICO

The British Postal Agency at Vera Cruz opened in 1825, following the introduction of the Mexican Packet service. No handstamps were supplied, however, until 1842, when a similar agency at Tampico was set up.

Great Britain stamps were used at Tampico from 1867 but, apparently, were never sent to the Vera Cruz office. Combination covers exist showing the local postage paid by Mexican adhesives. The Agency at Vera Cruz closed in 1874 and that at Tampico in 1876.

TAMPICO
CROWNED-CIRCLE HANDSTAMPS
CC1 CC 1b TAMPICO (R.) (13.11.1841). . *Price on cover* £1600

No. CC1 may be found on cover, used in conjunction with Mexico adhesive stamps.

Stamps of GREAT BRITAIN cancelled "C 63" as Type 4.

1867 to 1876.

Z 1	1d. rose-red (1864–79)		*From*	80·00
	Plate Nos. 81, 89, 103, 117, 139, 147.			
Z 2	2d. blue (1858–69) (Plate Nos. 9, 14)			£100
Z 3	4d. vermilion (1865–73)		*From*	55·00
	Plate Nos. 7, 8, 10, 11, 12, 13, 14.			
Z 4	1s. green (1867–73) (Plate Nos. 4, 5, 7, 8) ..			70·00
Z 5	2s. blue (1867)			£350

VERA CRUZ
CROWNED-CIRCLE HANDSTAMPS
CC2 CC 1b VERA CRUZ (R.) (13.11.1841) *Price on cover* £1600
CC3   VERA CRUZ (Black) (*circa* 1845)
                                    Price on cover £800

No. CC3 can also be found used in conjunction with Mexico adhesive stamps.

NICARAGUA
GREYTOWN

British involvement on the Mosquito Coast of Nicaragua dates from 1655 when contacts were first made with the indigenous Misquito Indians. A formal alliance was signed in 1740 and the area was considered as a British dependency until the Spanish authorities negotiated a withdrawal in 1786.

The Misquitos remained under British protection, however, and, following the revolutionary period in the Spanish dominions, this eventually led to the appropriation, by the Misquitos with British backing, of the town of San Juan del Norte, later renamed Greytown.

The port was included in the Royal West Indian Mail Steam Packet Company's mail network from January 1842, forming part of the Jamaica District. This arrangement only lasted until September of that year, however, although packets were once again calling at Greytown by November 1844. Following the discovery of gold in California the office increased in importance, owing to the overland traffic, although the first distinctive postmark is not recorded in use until February 1856.

A subsidiary agency, without its own postmark, operated at Bluefields from 1857 to 1863.

The British Protectorate over the Misquitos ended in 1860, but the British Post Office at Greytown continued to operate, being supplied with Great Britain stamps in 1865. These are occasionally found used in combination with Nicaragua issues, which had only internal validity.

The British Post Office at Greytown closed on 1 May 1882 when the Republic of Nicaragua joined the U.P.U.

CROWNED-CIRCLE HANDSTAMPS

Z 1

CC1 Z 1 GREYTOWN (R.) (14.4.1859) .. ..

Z 2   Z 4

Z 3

Stamps of GREAT BRITAIN cancelled "C 57" as in Types Z 2 (issued 1865), Z 3 (issued 1875), or with circular postmark as Type Z 4 (issued 1864).

1865 to 1882.

Z 1	½d. rose-red (1870–79) (Plate Nos. 5, 10, 11) ..		50·00
Z 2	1d. rose-red (1864–79) (Plate Nos. 180, 197, 210) ..		45·00
Z 3	1½d. lake-red (1870) (Plate No. 3) ..		60·00
Z 4	2d. blue (1858–69) (Plate Nos. 9, 14, 15)		
Z 5	3d. rose (1873–76) (Plate Nos. 17, 18, 19, 20) ..		40·00

Z 6	3d. rose (1881) (Plate No. 20)			
Z 7	4d. vermilion (1865–73)		*From*	40·00
	Plate Nos. 8, 10, 11, 12, 13, 14.			
Z 8	4d. vermilion (1876) (Plate No. 15) ..			£200
Z 9	4d. sage-green (1877) (Plate Nos. 15, 16) ..			£140
Z10	4d. grey-brown (1880) *wmk* Large Garter ..			£250
	Plate No. 17.			
Z11	4d. grey-brown (1880) *wmk* Crown (Plate No. 17)			85·00
Z12	6d. grey (1874–76) (Plate Nos. 14, 15, 16) ..			50·00
Z13	8d. orange (1876)			
Z14	1s. green (1865) (Plate No. 4)			
Z15	1s. green (1867–73) (Plate Nos. 6, 7)			
Z16	1s. green (1873–77) (Plate Nos. 8, 10, 12, 13) ..			45·00
Z17	1s. orange-brown (1880) (Plate No. 13) ..			£250
Z18	1s. orange-brown (1881) (Plate No. 13) ..			70·00
Z19	2s. blue (1867)			£150
Z20	2s. brown (1880)			£2000
Z21	5s. rose (1867–74) (Plate Nos. 1, 2) ..			£300
Z22	5s. rose (1882) (Plate No. 4), blue *paper* ..			£1100
Z23	10s. greenish grey (1878)			£1800

1880.

Z24	1d. Venetian red		
Z25	1½d. Venetian red		45·00

PERU

British Agencies in Peru date from 1846 when offices were established at Arica and Callao. The network was later expanded to include agencies at Paita (1848), Pisco (1868) and Iquique and Islay (both 1869). This last office was transferred to Mollendo in 1877.

It is believed that a further agency existed at Pisagua, but no details exist.

Great Britain stamps were supplied from 1865 and can be found used in combination with Peru adhesives paying the local postage. The Postal Agency at Pisco closed in 1870 and the remainder in 1879, the towns of Arica, Iquique and Pisagua passing to Chile by treaty in 1883.

ARICA
CROWNED-CIRCLE HANDSTAMPS
CC1 CC 1 ARICA (Black or R.) (5.11.1850)
                             Price on cover £2750

Stamps of GREAT BRITAIN cancelled "C 36" as in Types 4 or 12.

1865 to 1879.

Z 1	½d. rose-red (1870–79)		*From*	50·00
	Plate Nos. 5, 6, 10, 11, 13.			
Z 2	1d. rose-red (1864–79)		*From*	45·00
	Plate Nos. 102, 139, 140, 163, 167.			
Z 3	1½d. lake-red (1870–74) (Plate No. 3)			
Z 4	2d. blue (1858–69) (Plate No. 14) ..			70·00
Z 5	3d. rose (1867–73) (Plate Nos. 5, 9)			
Z 6	3d. rose (1873–76)		*From*	40·00
	Plate Nos. 11, 12, 17, 18, 19.			
Z 7	4d. vermilion (1865–73)		*From*	35·00
	Plate Nos. 10, 11, 12, 13, 14.			
Z 8	4d. vermilion (1876) (Plate No. 15)			
Z 9	4d. sage-green (1877) (Plate Nos. 15, 16) ..			£140
Z10	6d. lilac (1862) (Plate Nos. 3, 4)			
Z11	6d. lilac (1865–67) (Plate No. 5)			
Z12	6d. violet (1867–70) (Plate Nos. 6, 8, 9) ..			40·00
Z13	6d. buff (1872) (Plate No. 11) ..			80·00
Z14	6d. chestnut (1872) (Plate No. 11)			
Z15	6d. grey (1873) (Plate No. 12) ..			£120
Z16	6d. grey (1874–76) (Plate Nos. 13, 14, 15, 16)		*From*	30·00
Z17	8d. orange (1876)			
Z18	9d. straw (1862)			
Z19	9d. straw (1865)			
Z20	9d. straw (1867)			£150
Z21	10d. red-brown (1867)			
Z22	1s. green (1862)			
Z23	1s. green (1865)			
Z24	1s. green (1867–73) (Plate Nos. 4, 5, 6, 7) ..		*From*	30·00
Z25	1s. green (1873–77)		*From*	50·00
	Plate Nos. 8, 9, 10, 11, 12, 13.			
Z26	2s. blue (1867)			£150
Z27	5s. rose (1867–74) (Plate Nos. 1, 2) ..			£350

CALLAO
CROWNED-CIRCLE HANDSTAMPS
CC2 CC 2 CALLAO (R.) (13.1.1846)   *Price on cover* £1000
CC3 CC 1 CALLAO (R.) (16.7.1846)   *Price on cover* £550

Nos. CC2/3 can be found used on covers from 1865 showing the local postage paid by a Peru adhesive.

Stamps of GREAT BRITAIN cancelled "C 38" as in Types 4, 12 or with circular date stamp as Type 5.

1865 to 1879.

Z28	½d. rose-red (1870–79)		*From*	35·00
	Plate Nos. 5, 6, 10, 11, 12, 13, 14.			
Z29	1d. rose-red (1864–79)		*From*	25·00
	Plate Nos. 74, 88, 89, 93, 94, 97, 108, 123,			
	127, 128, 130, 134, 137, 139, 140, 141, 143,			
	144, 145, 146, 148, 149, 156, 157, 160, 163,			
	167, 171, 172, 173, 175, 176, 180, 181, 182,			
	183, 185, 187, 190, 193, 195, 198, 199, 200,			
	201, 204, 206, 209, 210, 212, 213, 215.			
Z30	1½d. lake-red (1870–74) (Plate No. 3)			
Z31	2d. blue (1858–69)		*From*	25·00
	Plate Nos. 9, 12, 13, 14, 15.			
Z32	3d. carmine-rose (1862)			
Z33	3d. rose (1865) (Plate No. 4) ..			55·00
Z34	3d. rose (1867–73)		*From*	30·00
	Plate Nos. 5, 6, 7, 8, 9, 10.			
Z35	3d. rose (1873–76)		*From*	35·00
	Plate Nos. 11, 12, 14, 15, 16, 17, 18, 19.			
Z36	4d. red (1862) (Plate Nos. 3, 4)			
Z37	4d. vermilion (1865–73)		*From*	30·00
	Plate Nos. 8, 10, 11, 12, 13, 14.			
Z38	4d. vermilion (1876) (Plate No. 15) ..			£175
Z39	4d. sage-green (1877) (Plate Nos. 15, 16) ..			£140
Z40	6d. lilac (1862) (Plate Nos. 3, 4)			
Z40a	6d. lilac (1865) (Plate No. 5)			
Z41	6d. lilac (1867)			

Z42	6d. violet (1867–70) (Plate Nos. 6, 8, 9) ..		*From*	40·00
Z43	6d. buff (1872–73) (Plate Nos. 11, 12) ..		*From*	55·00
Z44	6d. chestnut (1872) (Plate No. 11) ..			30·00
Z45	6d. grey (1873) (Plate No. 12) ..			£120
Z46	6d. grey (1874–80) (Plate Nos. 13, 14, 15, 16)		*From*	30·00
Z47	8d. orange (1876) ..			£175
Z48	9d. straw (1862)			
Z49	9d. straw (1865) ..			£275
Z50	9d. straw (1867) ..			£160
Z51	10d. red-brown (1867) ..			£200
Z52	1s. green (1865)			
Z53	1s. green (1867–73) (Plate Nos. 4, 5, 6, 7) ..		*From*	30·00
Z54	1s. green (1873–77)		*From*	40·00
	Plate Nos. 8, 9, 10, 11, 12, 13.			
Z55	2s. blue (1867) ..			£110
Z56	5s. rose (1867–74) (Plate Nos. 1, 2) ..			£300

IQUIQUE
Stamps of GREAT BRITAIN cancelled "D 87" as Type 12.

1865 to 1879.

Z57	½d. rose-red (1870–79) (Plate Nos. 5, 6, 13, 14)			70·00
Z58	1d. rose-red (1864–79) (Plate Nos. 76, 179, 185, 205)			45·00
Z59	2d. blue (1858–69) (Plate Nos. 9, 12, 13, 14)			45·00
Z60	3d. rose (1867–73) (Plate Nos. 5, 6, 7, 8, 9)		*From*	40·00
Z61	3d. rose (1873–76) (Plate Nos. 12, 18, 19) ..			60·00
Z62	4d. vermilion (1865–73) (Plate Nos. 12, 13, 14)			45·00
Z63	4d. vermilion (1876) (Plate No. 15) ..			£200
Z64	4d. sage-green (1877) (Plate Nos. 15, 16) ..		*From*	£150
Z65	6d. mauve (1869) (Plate Nos. 8, 9)			
Z66	6d. buff (1872–73) (Plate Nos. 11, 12) ..		*From*	85·00
Z67	6d. chestnut (1872) (Plate No. 11)			
Z68	6d. grey (1873) (Plate No. 12) ..			£120
Z69	6d. grey (1874–79) (Plate Nos. 13, 14, 15, 16) ..			
Z70	8d. orange (1876) ..			£275
Z71	9d. straw (1867) ..			£175
Z72	10d. red-brown (1867)			
Z73	1s. green (1867–73) (Plate Nos. 4, 6, 7) ..		*From*	40·00
Z74	1s. green (1873–77)		*From*	50·00
	Plate Nos. 8, 9, 10, 11, 12, 13.			
Z75	2s. blue (1867)			

ISLAY (later MOLLENDO)
CROWNED-CIRCLE HANDSTAMPS
CC4 CC 1 ISLAY (Black or R.) (23.10.1850) .. ..

Stamps of GREAT BRITAIN cancelled "C 42" as Types 4 or 12.

1865 to 1879.

Z76	1d. rose-red (1864–79)		*From*	45·00
	Plate Nos. 78, 84, 87, 88, 96, 103, 125, 134.			
Z77	1½d. lake-red (1870–74) (Plate No. 3)			
Z78	2d. blue (1858–69) (Plate Nos. 9, 13, 15) ..			40·00
Z79	3d. carmine-rose (1862)			
Z80	3d. rose (1865) ..			75·00
Z81	3d. rose (1867–73) (Plate Nos. 4, 5, 6, 10) ..			40·00
Z82	4d. red (1862) (Plate Nos. 3, 4) ..			80·00
Z83	4d. vermilion (1867–73)		*From*	40·00
	Plate Nos. 9, 10, 11, 12, 13.			
Z84	4d. vermilion (1876) (Plate No. 15)			
Z85	4d. sage-green (1877) (Plate Nos. 15, 16) ..			£150
Z86	6d. lilac (1862) (Plate Nos. 3, 4) ..			80·00
Z87	6d. lilac (1865) (Plate No. 5) ..			60·00
Z88	6d. violet (1867–70) (Plate Nos. 6, 8, 9) ..		*From*	45·00
Z89	6d. buff (1873) (Plate No. 11)			
Z90	6d. grey (1873) (Plate No. 12)			
Z91	6d. grey (1874–76) (Plate Nos. 13, 14, 15, 16)		*From*	40·00
Z92	9d. straw (1865) ..			£275
Z93	9d. straw (1867) ..			£160
Z94	10d. red-brown (1867) ..			£180
Z95	1s. green (1865) (Plate No. 4)			
Z96	1s. green (1867–73) (Plate Nos. 4, 5, 6, 7) ..		*From*	40·00
Z97	1s. green (1873–77) (Plate Nos. 8, 10, 12, 13)		*From*	55·00
Z98	2s. blue (1867)			
Z99	5s. rose (1867) (Plate No. 1)			

PAITA
CROWNED-CIRCLE HANDSTAMPS
CC5 CC 1 PAITA (Black *or* R.) (5.11.1850)
                             Price on cover £3750

Stamps of GREAT BRITAIN cancelled "C 43" as Type 4.

1865 to 1879.

Z100	1d. rose-red (1864–79) (Plate Nos. 127, 147) ..			
Z101	2d. blue (1858–69) (Plate Nos. 9, 14)			
Z102	3d. rose (1867–73) (Plate Nos. 5, 6) ..			45·00
Z103	3d. rose (1876) (Plate Nos. 17, 18, 19) ..			45·00
Z104	4d. vermilion (1865–73)		*From*	45·00
	Plate Nos. 10, 11, 12, 13, 14.			
Z105	4d. sage-green (1877) (Plate No. 15)			
Z106	6d. lilac (1862) (Plate No. 3) ..			85·00
Z107	6d. lilac (1865–67) (Plate Nos. 5, 6) ..			50·00
Z108	6d. violet (1867–70) (Plate Nos. 6, 8, 9) ..			45·00
Z109	6d. buff (1872–73) (Plate Nos. 11, 12) ..		*From*	70·00
Z110	6d. chestnut (Plate No. 11) ..			42·00
Z111	6d. grey (1873)			
Z112	6d. grey (1874–76) (Plate Nos. 13, 14, 15) ..			
Z113	9d. straw (1862)			
Z114	10d. red-brown (1867) ..			£275
Z115	1s. green (1865) (Plate No. 4)			
Z116	1s. green (1867–73) (Plate No. 4) ..			45·00
Z117	1s. green (1873–77) (Plate Nos. 8, 9, 10, 13) ..			50·00
Z118	2s. blue (1867) ..			£175
Z119	5s. rose (1867) (Plate No. 1) ..			£450

PISAGUA(?)
Stamp of GREAT BRITAIN cancelled "D 65" as Type 12.

Z120	2s. blue (1867)		

PISCO AND CHINCHA ISLANDS
Stamps of GREAT BRITAIN cancelled "D 74" as Type 12.

1865 to 1870.

Z121	2d. blue (1858–69) (Plate No. 9)		
Z122	4d. vermilion (1865–73) (Plate Nos. 10, 12) ..		£300
Z123	6d. violet (1868) (Plate No. 6) ..		£1000
Z124	1s. green (1867) (Plate No. 4)		
Z125	2s. blue (1867) ..		£900

PORTO RICO

A British Postal Agency operated at San Juan from 1844. On 24 October 1872 further offices were opened at Aguadilla, Arroyo, Mayaguez and Ponce, with Naguabo added three years later.

Great Britain stamps were used during 1865–66 and from 1873 to 1877. All the British Agencies closed on 1 May 1877.

AGUADILLA

Stamps of GREAT BRITAIN cancelled "F 84" as Type **8.**

1873 *to* 1877.

Z 1	½d. rose-red (1870) (Plate No. 6)			80·00
Z 2	1d. rose-red (1864–79)			45·00
	Plate Nos. 119, 122, 139, 149, 156, 160.			
Z 3	2d. blue (1858–69) (Plate No. 14)			
Z 4	3d. rose (1867–73) (Plate Nos. 7, 8, 9)			
Z 5	3d. rose (1873–76) (Plate No. 12)			
Z 6	4d. vermilion (1865–73) (Plate Nos. 12, 13, 14)			50·00
Z 7	4d. vermilion (1876) (Plate No. 15)			£175
Z 7a	6d. pale buff (1872–73) (Plate No. 11)			
Z 8	6d. grey (1874–76) (Plate Nos. 13, 14)			
Z 9	9d. straw (1867)			£300
Z10	10d. red-brown (1867)			£200
Z11	1s. green (1867–73) (Plate Nos. 4, 5, 6, 7) .. *From*			40·00
Z12	1s. green (1873–77) .. .. .. *From*			55·00
	Plate Nos. 8, 9, 10, 11, 12.			
Z13	2s. blue (1867)			£225

ARROYO

Stamps of GREAT BRITAIN cancelled "F 83" as Type **8.**

1873 *to* 1877.

Z14	½d. rose-red (1870) (Plate No. 5)			55·00
Z15	1d. rose-red (1864–79)			50·00
	Plate Nos. 149, 150, 151, 156, 164, 174, 175.			
Z16	1½d. lake-red (1870) (Plate Nos. 1, 3)			
Z17	2d. blue (1858–69) (Plate No. 14)			
Z18	3d. rose (1867–73) (Plate Nos. 5, 7, 10)			45·00
Z19	3d. rose (1873–76) (Plate Nos. 11, 12, 14, 16, 18)			50·00
Z20	4d. vermilion (1865–73) (Plate Nos. 12, 13, 14)			40·00
Z21	4d. vermilion (1876) (Plate No. 15)			£175
Z22	6d. chestnut (1872) (Plate No. 11)			55·00
Z23	6d. pale-buff (1872) (Plate No. 11)			60·00
Z23a	6d. grey (1873) (Plate No. 12)			
Z24	6d. grey (1874–76) (Plate Nos. 13, 14, 15)			50·00
Z25	9d. straw (1867)			£225
Z26	10d. red-brown (1867)			£175
Z27	1s. green (1865) (Plate No. 4)			
Z28	1s. green (1867–73) (Plate Nos. 4, 5, 6, 7)			45·00
Z29	1s. green (1873–77)			50·00
	Plate Nos. 8, 9, 10, 11, 12, 13.			
Z30	2s. blue (1867)			£180
Z31	5s. rose (1867–74) (Plate No. 2)			

MAYAGUEZ

Stamps of GREAT BRITAIN cancelled "F 85" as Type **8.**

1873 *to* 1877.

Z32	½d. rose-red (1870) .. .. *From*			45·00
	Plate Nos. 4, 5, 6, 8, 10, 11.			
Z33	1d. rose-red (1864–79) .. .. *From*			30·00
	Plate Nos. 76, 120, 121, 122, 124, 134, 137, 140, 146, 149, 150, 151, 154, 155, 156, 157, 160, 167, 170, 171, 174, 175, 176, 178, 180, 182, 185, 186, 189.			
Z34	1½d. lake-red (1870–74) (Plate Nos. 1, 3)			40·00
Z35	2d. blue (1858–69) (Plate Nos. 13, 14, 15)			40·00
Z36	3d. rose (1867–73) (Plate Nos. 7, 8, 9, 10)			35·00
Z37	3d. rose (1873–76)			35·00
	Plate Nos. 11, 12, 14, 15, 16, 17, 18, 19.			
Z38	4d. vermilion (1865–73) (Plate Nos. 11, 12, 13, 14)			35·00
Z39	4d. vermilion (1876) (Plate No. 15)			£160
Z40	4d. sage-green (1877) (Plate No. 15)			
Z41	4d. mauve (1870) (Plate No. 9)			
Z42	6d. buff (1872) (Plate No. 11)			75·00
Z43	6d. chestnut (1872) (Plate No. 11)			65·00
Z44	6d. grey (1873) (Plate No. 12)			
Z45	6d. grey (1874–80) (Plate Nos. 13, 14, 15, 16)			40·00
Z46	8d. orange (1876)			£175
Z47	9d. straw (1867)			£140
Z48	10d. red-brown (1867)			£175
Z49	1s. green (1867–73) (Plate Nos. 4, 5, 6, 7)			30·00
Z50	1s. green (1873–77) .. .. *From*			50·00
	Plate Nos. 8, 9, 10, 11, 12.			
Z51	2s. blue (1867)			£160
Z52	5s. rose (1867–74) (Plate Nos. 1, 2)			

NAGUABO

Stamps of GREAT BRITAIN cancelled "582" as Type **9.**

1875 *to* 1877.

Z53	½d. rose-red (1870–79) (Plate Nos. 5, 12, 14)			
Z54	1d. rose-red (1864–79) (Plate Nos. 159, 165)			
Z55	3d. rose (1873–76) (Plate Nos. 17, 18)			£400
Z56	4d. vermilion (1872–73) (Plate Nos. 13, 14) .. *From*			£375
Z57	4d. vermilion (1876) (Plate No. 15)			
Z58	6d. grey (1874–76) (Plate Nos. 14, 15)			
Z59	9d. straw (1867)			
Z60	10d. red-brown (1867)			£800
Z61	1s. green (1873–77) (Plate Nos. 11, 12)			£600
Z62	2s. dull blue (1867) (Plate No. 1)			

PONCE

Stamps of GREAT BRITAIN cancelled "F 88" as Type **8.**

1873 *to* 1877.

Z63	½d. rose-red (1870) (Plate Nos. 5, 10, 12)			50·00
Z64	1d. rose-red (1864–79) .. .. *From*			35·00
	Plate Nos. 120, 121, 122, 123, 124, 146, 148, 154, 156, 157, 158, 160, 167, 171, 174, 175, 179, 186, 187.			
Z65	1½d. lake-red (1870–74) (Plate No. 3)			£100
Z66	2d. blue (1858–69) (Plate Nos. 13, 14)			40·00
Z67	3d. rose (1867–73) (Plate Nos. 7, 8, 9)			
Z68	3d. rose (1873–76) (Plate Nos. 12, 16, 17, 18, 19)			40·00
Z69	4d. vermilion (1865–73) .. .. *From*			40·00
	Plate Nos. 8, 9, 12, 13, 14.			
Z70	4d. vermilion (1876) (Plate No. 15)			£175
Z71	4d. sage-green (1877) (Plate Nos. 15, 16)			£140
Z72	6d. buff (1872–73) (Plate Nos. 11, 12)			70·00
Z73	6d. chestnut (1872) (Plate No. 11)			50·00

Z74	6d. grey (1873) (Plate No. 12)			
Z75	6d. grey (1874–76) (Plate Nos. 13, 14, 15) .. *From*			35·00
Z76	9d. straw (1867)			£200
Z77	10d. red-brown (1867)			£150
Z78	1s. green (1867–73) (Plate Nos. 4, 6, 7)			35·00
Z79	1s. green (1873–77) .. .. *From*			50·00
	Plate Nos. 8, 9, 10, 11, 12, 13.			
Z80	2s. blue (1867)			
Z81	5s. rose (1867–74) (Plate Nos. 1, 2) .. *From*			£350

SAN JUAN

CROWNED-CIRCLE HANDSTAMPS

CC1	CC **1**	SAN JUAN PORTO RICO (R. *or* Black) (25.5.1844) .. .. .. *Price on cover*		£800

No. CC1 may be found on cover, used in conjunction with Spanish colonial adhesive stamps paying the local postage.

Stamps of GREAT BRITAIN cancelled "C 61" as in Types **4, 8** *or* **14.**

1865 *to* 1866 *and* 1873 *to* 1877.

Z 82	½d. rose-red (1870) (Plate Nos. 5, 10, 15) .. *From*			30·00
Z 83	1d. rose-red (1857)			
Z 84	1d. rose-red (1864–79) .. .. *From*			30·00
	Plate Nos. 73, 74, 81, 84, 90, 94, 100, 101, 102, 107, 117, 122, 124, 125, 127, 130, 137, 138, 139, 140, 145, 146, 149, 153, 156, 159, 160, 162, 163, 169, 171, 172, 173, 174, 175, 179, 180, 182, 186.			
Z 85	1½d. lake-red (1870–74) (Plate No. 3) .. *From*			60·00
Z 86	2d. blue (1858–69) (Plate Nos. 9, 13, 14) .. *From*			30·00
Z 87	3d. rose (1865) (Plate No. 4)			60·00
Z 88	3d. rose (1867–73) .. .. *From*			30·00
	Plate Nos. 5, 6, 7, 8, 9, 10.			
Z 89	3d. rose (1873–76) .. .. *From*			30·00
	Plate Nos. 11, 12, 14, 15, 16, 17, 18.			
Z 90	4d. vermilion (1865–73) .. .. *From*			30·00
	Plate Nos. 7, 8, 9, 10, 11, 12, 13, 14.			
Z 91	4d. vermilion (1876) (Plate No. 15)			£175
Z 92	6d. lilac (1865–67) (Plate Nos. 5, 6) .. *From*			40·00
Z 93	6d. lilac (1867) (Plate No. 6)			40·00
Z 94	6d. violet (1867–70) (Plate Nos. 6, 8, 9) .. *From*			30·00
Z 95	6d. buff (1872–73) (Plate Nos. 11, 12)			60·00
Z 96	6d. chestnut (1872) (Plate No. 11)			40·00
Z 97	6d. grey (1873) (Plate No. 12)			
Z 98	6d. grey (1874–76) (Plate Nos. 13, 14, 15) .. *From*			30·00
Z 99	9d. straw (1862)			£175
Z100	9d. straw (1865)			£275
Z101	9d. straw (1867)			£150
Z102	10d. red-brown (1867)			£200
Z103	1s. green (1865) (Plate No. 4)			90·00
Z104	1s. green (1867–73) (Plate Nos. 4, 5, 6, 7) .. *From*			30·00
Z105	1s. green (1873–77) .. .. *From*			40·00
	Plate Nos. 8, 9, 10, 11, 12, 13.			
Z106	2s. blue (1867)			£110
Z107	5s. rose (1867) (Plate Nos. 1, 2) .. *From*			£300

RUSSIA

ARMY FIELD OFFICES IN THE CRIMEA

1854 *to* 1857.

	Crown between Stars			
Z 1	1d. red-brown (1841), *imperf*			£475
Z 2	1d. red-brown (1854), Die I, *wmk* Small Crown, *perf* 16			
Z 3	1d. red-brown (1855), Die II, *wmk* Small Crown, *perf* 16			£150
Z 4	1d. red-brown, Die I, *wmk* Small Crown, *perf* 14			
Z 5	1d. red-brown (1855), Die II, Small Crown, *perf* 14			
Z 6	2d. blue (1841) *imperf*			£900
Z 7	2d. blue, Small Crown (1854), *perf* 16 (Plate No. 4)			
Z 8	1s. green (1847), embossed ..			£1400
	Star between Cyphers			
Z 9	1d. red-brown (1841), *imperf*			
Z10	1d. red-brown (1854), Die I, *wmk* Small Crown, *perf* 16			70·00
Z11	1d. red-brown (1855), Die II, *wmk* Small Crown, *perf* 16			70·00
Z12	1d. red-brown (1855), Die I, *wmk* Small Crown, *perf* 14			70·00
Z13	1d. red-brown (1855), Die II, *wmk* Small Crown, *perf* 14			70·00
Z14	1d. red-brown (1855), Die II, *wmk* Large Crown, *perf* 16			90·00
Z15	1d. red-brown (1855), Die II, *wmk* Large Crown, *perf* 14			42·00
Z16	2d. blue (1841), *imperf*			£1000
Z17	2d. blue (1854) *wmk* Small Crown, *perf* 16 .. *From*			£130
	Plate Nos. 4, 5.			
Z18	2d. blue (1855) *wmk* Small Crown, *perf* 14			£175
	Plate No. 4.			
Z19	2d. blue (1855), *wmk* Large Crown, *perf* 16			£200
	Plate No. 5.			
Z20	2d. blue (1855), *wmk* Large Crown, *perf* 14			£120
	Plate No. 5.			
Z21	4d. rose (1857)			£800
Z22	6d. violet (1854), embossed			£1100
Z23	1s. green (1847), embossed			£1100

SPAIN

Little is known about the operation of British Packet Agencies in Spain, other than the dates recorded for the various postal markings in the G.P.O. Proof Books. The Agency at Corunna is said to date from the late 17th century when the Spanish packets for South America were based there. No. CC1 was probably issued in connection with the inauguration of the P & O service to Spain in 1843. The Spanish port of call was changed to Vigo in 1846 and the office at Corunna was then closed. Teneriffe became a port-of-call for the South American packets in 1817 and this arrangement continued until 1858.

CORUNNA

CROWNED-CIRCLE HANDSTAMPS

CC1	CC **1b**	CORUNNA (28.2.1842)	..

Although recorded in the G.P.O. Proof Books no example of No. CC1 on cover is known.

TENERIFFE (CANARY ISLANDS)

CROWNED-CIRCLE HANDSTAMPS

CC2	CC **7**	TENERIFFE (6.1.1851) .. *Price on cover*	£3500
CC3	CC **4**	TENERIFFE (23.10.1857) .. *Price on cover*	£3500

No. CC2/3 can be found used on covers from Spain to South America with the rate from Spain to Teneriffe paid in Spanish adhesive stamps.

UNITED STATES OF AMERICA

The network of British Packet Agencies, to operate the trans-Atlantic Packet system, was re-established in 1814 after the War of 1812.

The New York Agency opened in that year to be followed by further offices at Boston, Charleston (South Carolina), New Orleans, Savannah (Georgia) (all in 1842), Mobile (Alabama) (1848) and San Francisco (1860). Of these agencies Charleston and Savannah closed the same year (1842) as did New Orleans, although the latter was re-activated from 1848 to 1850. Mobile closed 1850, Boston in 1865, New York in 1882 and San Francisco, for which no postal markings have been recorded, in 1883.

Although recorded in the G.P.O. Proof Books no actual examples of the Crowned-circle handstamps for Charleston, Mobile, New Orleans and Savannah are known on cover.

The G.P.O. proof books record, in error, a Crowned-circle handstamp for St. Michaels, Maryland. This handstamp was intended for the agency on San Miguel in the Azores.

CHARLESTON

CROWNED-CIRCLE HANDSTAMPS

CC1	CC **1b**	CHARLESTON (15.12.1841) ..	..

MOBILE

CROWNED-CIRCLE HANDSTAMPS

CC2	CC **1b**	MOBILE (15.12.1841)	..

NEW ORLEANS

CROWNED-CIRCLE HANDSTAMPS

CC3	CC **1b**	NEW ORLEANS (15.12.1841) ..	..
CC4	CC **1**	NEW ORLEANS (27.4.1848) ..	..

NEW YORK

CROWNED-CIRCLE HANDSTAMPS

CC5	CC **1b**	NEW YORK (R.) (15.12.1841) ..	..

SAVANNAH

CROWNED-CIRCLE HANDSTAMPS

CC6	CC **1b**	SAVANNAH (15.12.1841) ..	..

URUGUAY

MONTEVIDEO

British packets commenced calling at Montevideo in 1824 on passage to and from Buenos Aires.

Great Britain stamps were in use from 1864. Combination covers exist with the local postage paid by Uruguay adhesive stamps. The agency was closed on 31 July 1873.

CROWNED-CIRCLE HANDSTAMPS

CC1	CC **5**	MONTEVIDEO (Black *or* R.) (6.1.1851)	
		Price on cover	£750

Stamps of GREAT BRITAIN cancelled "C 28" as in Types **4** *or* **12.**

1864 *to* 1873.

Z 1	1d. rose-red (1864)			50·00
	Plate Nos. 73, 92, 93, 94, 119, 148, 154, 157, 171.			
Z 2	2d. blue (1858–69) (Plate Nos. 9, 13)			45·00
Z 3	3d. rose (1865) (Plate No. 4)			
Z 4	3d. rose (1867–71) (Plate Nos. 4, 5, 7)			40·00
Z 6	4d. rose (1857)			
Z 7	4d. red (1862) (Plate No. 4)			
Z 8	4d. vermilion (1865–70) .. .. *From*			40·00
	Plate Nos. 7, 8, 9, 10, 11, 12.			
Z 9	6d. lilac (1856)			
Z10	6d. lilac (1862) (Plate No. 4)			
Z11	6d. lilac (1865–67) (Plate Nos. 5, 6)			50·00
Z12	6d. lilac (1867) (Plate No. 6)			
Z13	6d. violet (1867–70) (Plate Nos. 8, 9) .. *From*			40·00
Z14	6d. buff (1872)			
Z15	6d. chestnut (1872)			
Z16	9d. straw (1862)			
Z17	9d. straw (1865)			
Z18	9d. straw (1867)			£160
Z19	10d. red-brown (1867)			£190
Z20	1s. green (1862)			£150
Z21	1s. green (1865) (Plate No. 4)			90·00
Z22	1s. green (1867–73) (Plate Nos. 4, 5)			35·00
Z23	2s. blue (1867)			£110
Z24	5s. rose (1867) (Plate No. 1)			£350

VENEZUELA

British Postal Agencies were initially opened at La Guayra and Porto Cabello on 1 January 1842. Further offices were added at Maracaibo in 1842 and Ciudad Bolivar during January 1868. Porto Cabello closed in 1858 and Maracaibo was also short-lived. The remaining offices closed at the end of 1879 when Venezuela joined the U.P.U.

Great Britain stamps were used at La Guayra from 1865 and at Ciudad Bolivar from its establishment in 1868. They can be found used in combination with Venezuela adhesives paying the local postage.

CIUDAD BOLIVAR

Stamps of GREAT BRITAIN cancelled "D 22" as Type **12**, or circular date stamps as Types **16** or **17**.

1868 to **1879**.

Z 1	1d. rose-red (1864–79) (Plate No. 133)	..	90·00
Z 2	2d. blue (1858–69) (Plate No. 13)	..	
Z 3	3d. rose (1867–73) (Plate No. 5)	..	
Z 4	3d. rose (1873–79) (Plate No. 11)	..	£130
Z 5	4d. vermilion (1865–73) (Plate Nos. 9, 11, 12, 14)		60·00
Z 6	4d. sage-green (1877) (Plate Nos. 15, 16)	From	£140
Z 7	4d. grey-brown (1880) wmk Crown (Plate No. 17)		
Z 8	9d. straw (1867)	..	
Z 9	10d. red-brown (1867)	..	
Z10	1s. green (1867–73) (Plate Nos. 4, 5, 7)	From	£110
Z11	1s. green (1873–77) (Plate Nos. 10, 12, 13)		90·00
Z12	2s. blue (1867)	..	£300
Z13	5s. rose (1867–74) (Plate Nos. 1, 2)	..	£450

LA GUAYRA

CROWNED-CIRCLE HANDSTAMPS

CC1 CC **1b** LA GUAYRA (R.) (15.12.1841) *Price on cover* £850

Stamps of GREAT BRITAIN cancelled "C 60" as Type **4**, circular date stamp as Type **16** or with No. CC1.

1865 to **1880**.

Z14	½d. rose-red (1870) (Plate No. 6)	..	
Z15	1d. rose-red (1864–79)	From	50·00
	Plate Nos. 81, 92, 96, 98, 111, 113, 115, 131, 138, 144, 145, 154, 177, 178, 180, 196.		
Z16	1½d. lake-red (1870–74) (Plate No. 3)		
Z17	2d. blue (1858–69) (Plate Nos. 13, 14)		45·00
Z18	3d. rose (1873–76)	From	50·00
	Plate Nos. 14, 15, 17, 18, 19.		
Z19	4d. vermilion (1865–73)	From	40·00
	Plate Nos. 7, 9, 11, 12, 13, 14.		
Z20	4d. vermilion (1876) (Plate No. 15)	..	£175
Z21	4d. sage-green (1877) (Plate Nos. 15, 16)	..	£140
Z22	6d. lilac (1865) (Plate No. 5)		
Z23	6d. violet (1867–70) (Plate Nos. 6, 8)		
Z24	6d. buff (1872–73) (Plate Nos. 11, 12)	From	90·00
Z25	6d. grey (1873) (Plate No. 12)	..	£120
Z26	6d. grey (1874–76) (Plate Nos. 13, 14, 15, 16)	..	45·00
Z27	8d. orange (1876)	..	£250
Z28	9d. straw (1862)	..	
Z29	9d. straw (1867)	..	
Z30	10d. red-brown (1867)	..	
Z31	1s. green (1865) (Plate No. 4)		90·00
Z32	1s. green (1867–73) (Plate Nos. 4, 7)		
Z33	1s. green (1873–77)	From	40·00
	Plate Nos. 8, 9, 10, 11, 12, 13.		
Z34	2s. blue (1867)	..	£200
Z35	5s. rose (1867–74) (Plate Nos. 1, 2)	From	£400

MARACAIBO

CROWNED-CIRCLE HANDSTAMPS

CC2 CC **1b** MARACAIBO (31.12.1841) | .. | .. |
No examples of No. CC2 on cover have been recorded.

PORTO CABELLO

CROWNED-CIRCLE HANDSTAMPS

CC3 CC **1b** PORTO-CABELLO (R.) (15.12.1841)
Price on cover £1500

MAIL BOAT OBLITERATIONS

The following cancellations were supplied to G.P.O. sorters operating on ships holding mail contracts from the British Post Office. They were for use on mail posted on board, but most examples occur on letters from soldiers and sailors serving overseas which were forwarded to the mailboats without postmarks.

P. & O. MEDITERRANEAN AND FAR EAST MAILBOATS

The first such cancellation, "A 17" as Type **2**, was issued to the Southampton–Alexandria packet in April 1858, but no examples have been recorded.

The G.P.O. Proof Book also records "B 16", in Type **2**, as being issued for marine sorting in November 1859, but this postmark was subsequently used by the Plymouth and Bristol Sorting Carriage.

Sorting on board P. & O. packets ceased in June 1870 and many of the cancellation numbers were subsequently reallocated using Types **9**, **11** or **12**.

Stamps of GREAT BRITAIN cancelled "A 80" as Type **2**.

1859 (Mar) to **1870**.

Z1	1d. rose-red (1857), Die II, wmk Large Crown, perf 14	..	35·00
Z2	6d. lilac (1856)	..	£125

Stamps of GREAT BRITAIN cancelled "A 81" as Type **2**.

1859 (Mar) to **1870**.

Z 3	1d. rose-red (1857), Die II, wmk Large Crown, perf 14	..	35·00
Z 4	1d. rose-red (1864–79)	From	30·00
	Plate Nos. 84, 85, 86, 91, 97		
Z 5	2d. blue (1858–69) (Plate No. 9)	..	40·00
Z 6	4d. red (1862) (Plate No. 4)	..	£100

Z 7	4d. vermilion (1865–73) (Plate No. 8)	..	50·00
Z 8	6d. lilac (1856)	..	£125
Z 9	6d. lilac (1862) (Plate No. 3)	..	£100
Z10	6d. lilac (1865–67)	..	85·00
	Plate Nos. 5, 6.		
Z11	6d. lilac (1867) (Plate No. 6)	..	80·00
Z12	6d. violet (1867–70)	..	65·00
	Plate Nos. 6, 8.		
Z13	10d. red-brown (1867)	..	£400
Z14	1s. green (1856)	..	£225

Stamps of GREAT BRITAIN cancelled "A 82" as Type **2**.

1859 (Mar) to **1870**.

Z15	1d. rose-red (1857), Die II, wmk Large Crown, perf 14	..	40·00
Z16	2d. blue (1858) (Plate No. 7)	..	45·00
Z17	4d. rose (1856)	..	£180
Z18	6d. lilac (1856)	..	£160
Z19	6d. lilac (1865–67)	..	£110
	Plate Nos. 5, 6.		
Z20	6d. lilac (1867) (Plate No. 6)	..	90·00

Stamps of GREAT BRITAIN cancelled "A 83" as Type **2**.

1859 (Apr) to **1870**.

Z21	1d. rose-red (1857), Die II, wmk Large Crown, perf 14	..	35·00
Z22	1d. rose-red (1864–79)	From	30·00
	Plate Nos. 73, 74, 84, 91, 109.		
Z23	3d. carmine-rose (1862)	..	£225
Z24	4d. rose (1857)	..	£160
Z25	4d. red (1862)	..	90·00
Z26	4d. vermilion (1865–73)	..	50·00
	Plate Nos. 9, 10.		
Z27	6d. lilac (1856)	..	£125
Z28	6d. lilac (1862)	..	£100
Z29	6d. lilac (1865–67)	..	85·00
	Plate Nos. 5, 6.		
Z30	6d. violet (1867–70)	..	65·00
	Plate Nos. 6, 8.		
Z31	10d. red-brown (1867)	..	£400
Z32	1s. green (1862)	..	£225

Stamps of GREAT BRITAIN cancelled "A 84" as Type **2**.

1859 (Apr) to **1870**.

Z33	1d. rose-red (1857). Die II, wmk Large Crown, perf 14	..	90·00

Stamps of GREAT BRITAIN cancelled "A 85" as Type **2**.

1859 (Apr) to **1870**.

Z34	1d. rose-red (1857), Die II, wmk Large Crown, perf 14	..	35·00
Z35	1d. rose-red (1864–79)	From	30·00
	Plate Nos. 79, 97, 103.		
Z36	3d. carmine-rose (1862)	..	£225
Z37	4d. red (1862)	..	90·00
Z38	6d. lilac (1856)	..	£125
Z39	6d. lilac (1862)	..	£100
	Plate Nos. 3, 4.		
Z40	6d. lilac (1865–67) (Plate No. 5)	..	85·00
Z41	6d. lilac (1867) (Plate No. 6)	..	65·00
Z42	1s. green (1862)	..	£250

Stamps of GREAT BRITAIN cancelled "A 86" as Type **2**.

1859 (Apr) to **1870**.

Z43	1d. rose-red (1857), Die II, wmk Large Crown, perf 14	..	35·00
Z44	1d. rose-red (1864–79)	From	30·00
	Plate Nos. 73, 84, 94, 97, 114, 118.		
Z45	3d. rose (1865)	..	£200
Z46	3d. rose (1867–73)	..	65·00
	Plate Nos. 4, 5.		
Z47	4d. rose (1857)	..	£160
Z48	4d. red (1862) (Plate No. 4)	..	90·00
Z49	4d. vermilion (1865–73) (Plate No. 10)	..	50·00
Z50	6d. lilac (1856)	..	£125
Z51	6d. lilac (1862)	..	£100
	Plate Nos. 3, 4.		
Z52	6d. lilac (1865–67)	..	85·00
	Plate Nos. 5, 6.		
Z53	6d. lilac (1867)	..	65·00
	Plate Nos. 6, 8.		
Z54	10d. red-brown (1867)	..	£375
Z55	1s. green (1862)	..	£220

Stamps of GREAT BRITAIN cancelled "A 87" as Type **2**.

1859 (Apr) to **1870**.

Z56	1d. rose-red (1857), Die II, wmk Large Crown, perf 14	..	45·00
Z57	4d. rose (1856)	..	£200
Z58	6d. lilac (1867) (Plate No. 6)	..	£100

Stamps of GREAT BRITAIN cancelled "A 88" as Type **2**.

1859 (Apr) to **1870**.

Z59	1d. rose-red (1857), Die II, wmk Large Crown, perf 14	..	35·00
Z60	1d. rose-red (1864–79)	From	30·00
	Plate Nos. 74, 80, 85.		
Z61	4d. rose (1857)	..	£175
Z62	4d. red (1862)	..	£100
Z63	4d. vermilion (1865–73) (Plate No. 8)	..	50·00
Z64	6d. lilac (1856)	..	£125
Z65	6d. lilac (1862) (Plate No. 4)	..	£125
Z66	6d. lilac (1865–67) (Plate No. 5)	..	£100
Z67	6d. lilac (1867) (Plate No. 6)	..	85·00
Z68	6d. violet (1867–70) (Plate No. 8)	..	65·00
Z69	10d. red-brown (1867)	..	£425
Z70	1s. green (1856)	..	£250

Stamps of GREAT BRITAIN cancelled "A 89" as Type **2**.

1859 (Apr) to **1870**.

Z71	1d. rose-red (1857), Die II, wmk Large Crown, perf 14	..	90·00
Z72	6d. lilac (1856)	..	£250

Stamps of GREAT BRITAIN cancelled "A 90" as Type **2**.

1859 (June) to **1870**.

Z73	1d. rose-red (1857), Die II, wmk Large Crown, perf 14	..	55·00
Z74	4d. rose (1856)	..	
Z75	6d. lilac (1856)	..	£200
Z76	6d. lilac (1865–67)	..	£125
	Plate Nos. 5, 6.		
Z77	9d. straw (1867)	..	

Stamps of GREAT BRITAIN cancelled "A 99" as Type **2**.

1859 (June) to **1870**.

Z78	1d. rose-red (1857), Die II, wmk Large Crown, perf 14	..	35·00
Z79	1d. rose-red (1864–79)	From	30·00
	Plate Nos. 93, 97, 99, 118.		
Z80	4d. rose (1857)	..	£160
Z81	4d. red (1862)	..	90·00
Z82	4d. vermilion (1865–73) (Plate No. 11)	..	50·00
Z83	6d. lilac (1856)	..	
Z84	6d. lilac (1862)	..	£125
Z85	6d. lilac (1865–67)	..	£100
	Plate Nos. 5, 6.		
Z86	10d. red-brown (1867)	..	£400

Stamps of GREAT BRITAIN cancelled "B 03" as Type **2**.

1859 (Aug) to **1870**.

Z87	1d. rose-red (1857), Die II, wmk Large Crown, perf 14	..	45·00
Z88	1d. rose-red (1864–79)	From	35·00
	Plate Nos. 109, 116.		
Z89	3d. rose (1865) (Plate No. 4)	..	75·00
Z90	6d. lilac (1856)	..	£140
Z91	6d. lilac (1867) (Plate No. 6)	..	£110
Z92	6d. violet (1867–70)	..	80·00
	Plate Nos. 6, 8.		
Z93	10d. red-brown (1867)	..	£450

Stamps of GREAT BRITAIN cancelled "B 12" as Type **2**.

1859 (Oct) to **1870**.

Z 94	1d. rose-red (1857), Die II, wmk Large Crown, perf 14	..	45·00
Z 95	1d. rose-red (1864–79) (Plate No. 94)	..	35·00
Z 96	3d. rose (1865) (Plate No. 4)	..	75·00
Z 97	4d. red (1862)	..	£100
Z 98	4d. vermilion (1865–73) (Plate No. 8)	..	65·00
Z 99	6d. lilac (1856)	..	
Z100	6d. lilac (1862)	..	£135
Z101	6d. lilac (1865–67)	..	£110
	Plate Nos. 5, 6.		
Z102	6d. violet (1867–70) (Plate No. 8)	..	75·00

Stamps of GREAT BRITAIN cancelled "B 56" as Type **2**.

1861 (July) to **1870**.

Z103	1d. rose-red (1864–70) (Plate No. 84)	..	35·00
Z104	2d. blue (1858–69) (Plate No. 9)	..	50·00
Z105	4d. red (1862) (Plate No. 4)	..	£100
Z106	4d. vermilion (1865–73)	..	55·00
	Plate Nos. 7, 8.		
Z107	6d. lilac (1862)	..	£120
	Plate Nos. 3, 4.		
Z108	6d. lilac (1865–67)	..	£100
	Plate Nos. 5, 6.		
Z109	6d. violet (1867–70)	..	80·00
	Plate Nos. 6, 8.		

Stamps of GREAT BRITAIN cancelled "B 57" as Type **2**.

1861 (July) to **1870**.

Z110	1d. rose-red (1857). Die II, wmk Large Crown, perf 14	..	40·00
Z111	1d. rose-red (1864–79) (Plate No. 81)	..	35·00
Z112	2d. blue (1858–69) (Plate No. 9)	..	50·00
Z113	4d. red (1862)	..	£100
Z114	4d. vermilion (1865–73)	..	55·00
	Plate Nos. 7, 8.		
Z115	6d. lilac (1865–67)	..	£100
	Plate Nos. 5, 6.		

Stamps of GREAT BRITAIN cancelled "C 79" as Type **12**.

1866 (June) to **1870**.

Z116	6d. violet (1867–70)	..	75·00
	Plate Nos. 6, 8.		
Z117	10d. red-brown (1867)	..	£375

CUNARD LINE ATLANTIC MAILBOATS

These were all issued in June 1859. No examples are known used after August 1868. "B 61" is recorded as being issued in March 1862, but no examples are known. Cancellation numbers were subsequently reallocated to offices in Great Britain or, in the case of "A 91", the British Virgin Islands.

Stamps of GREAT BRITAIN cancelled "A 91" as Type **2**.

1859 (June) to **1868**.

Z130	1d. rose-red (1857), Die II, wmk Large Crown, perf 14	..	60·00
Z131	1d. rose-red (1864–79) (Plate No. 121)	..	50·00
Z132	2d. blue (1855), wmk Small Crown, perf 14	..	

Z133	2d. blue (1858–69)	.. ..	75·00
	Plate Nos. 8, 9.		
Z134	4d. rose (1857)	.. ..	£200
Z135	4d. red (1862)	.. ..	£110
Z136	6d. lilac (1856)	.. ..	£150
Z137	6d. lilac (1862)	.. ..	£125
Z138	6d. lilac (1865–67)	.. ..	£100
Z139	9d. straw (1862)	.. ..	
Z140	1s. green (1856)	.. ..	£275

Stamps of GREAT BRITAIN cancelled "A 92" as Type **2**.

1859 (June) *to* **1868**.

Z141	1d. rose-red (1857), Die II, *wmk* Large Crown, *perf* 14	.. ..	60·00
Z142	1d. rose-red (1864–79)	.. *From*	50·00
	Plate Nos. 93, 97.		
Z143	6d. lilac (1856)	.. ..	£150
Z144	6d. lilac (1862) (Plate No. 3)	.. ..	£125
Z145	6d. lilac (1865–67)	.. .. ..	£100
	Plate Nos. 5, 6.		

Stamps of GREAT BRITAIN cancelled "A 93" as Type **2**.

1859 (June) *to* **1868**.

Z146	1d. rose-red (1857), Die II, *wmk* Large Crown, *perf* 14		60·00
Z147	1d. rose-red (1864–79) (Plate No. 85)	..	50·00
Z148	6d. lilac (1856)	.. .. ..	£150
Z149	6d. lilac (1865–67) (Plate No. 6)	.. ..	£125
Z150	10d. red-brown (1867)	.. .. ..	£425

Stamps of GREAT BRITAIN cancelled "A 94" as Type **2**.

1859 (June) *to* **1868**.

Z151	1d. rose-red (1857), Die II, *wmk* Large Crown, *perf* 14	.. ..	75·00

Z152	1d. rose-red (1864–79)	.. .. ..	60·00
	Plate Nos. 74, 97.		
Z153	4d. vermilion (1865–73) (Plate No. 7)	..	85·00
Z154	6d. lilac (1856)	.. .. ..	£160
Z155	6d. lilac (1862)	.. .. ..	£135
Z156	6d. lilac (1865–67)	.. .. ..	£120
	Plate Nos. 5, 6.		

Stamps of GREAT BRITAIN cancelled "A 95" as Type **2**.

1859 (June) *to* **1868**.

Z157	1d. rose-red (1857), Die II, *wmk* Large Crown, *perf* 14	.. .. ..	55·00
Z158	1d. rose-red (1864–79)	.. *From*	45·00
	Plate Nos. 72, 89, 97.		
Z159	3d. rose (1867–73) (Plate No. 5)	..	75·00
Z160	4d. red (1862)	.. .. ..	£110
Z161	4d. vermilion (1865–73) (Plate No. 8)	..	60·00
Z162	6d. lilac (1862)	.. .. ..	£145
Z163	6d. lilac (1865–67) (Plate No. 5)	..	£125
Z164	6d. lilac (1867) (Plate No. 6)	.. ..	£110
Z165	1s. green (1856)	.. .. ..	£225

Stamps of GREAT BRITAIN cancelled "A 96" as Type **2**.

1859 (June) *to* **1868**.

Z166	1d. rose-red (1857), Die II, *wmk* Large Crown, *perf* 14	.. .. ..	60·00
Z167	4d. vermilion (1865–73) (Plate No. 7)	..	80·00
Z168	6d. lilac (1856)	.. .. ..	£150
Z169	1s. green (1856)	.. .. ..	£250

Stamps of GREAT BRITAIN cancelled "A 97" as Type **2**.

1859 (June) *to* **1868**.

Z170	1d. rose-red (1857), Die II, *wmk* Large Crown, *perf* 14	.. .. ..	60·00

Z171	1d. rose-red (1864–79) (Plate No. 71)	..	50·00
Z172	4d. red (1862) (Plate No. 3)	.. ..	£120

Stamps of GREAT BRITAIN cancelled "A 98" as Type **2**.

1859 (June) *to* **1868**.

Z173	1d. rose-red (1857), Die II, *wmk* Large Crown, *perf* 14	.. .. ..	60·00
Z174	4d. red (1862)	.. .. ..	£120
Z175	6d. lilac (1856)	.. .. ..	£160
Z176	6d. lilac (1862) (Plate No. 4)	.. ..	£135
Z177	6d. lilac (1865–67)	.. .. ..	£100
	Plate Nos. 5, 6.		

ALLAN LINE ATLANTIC MAILBOATS

British G.P.O. sorters worked on these Canadian ships between November 1859 and April 1860. Cancellations as Type 2 numbered "B 17", "B 18", "B 27", "B 28", B 29" and "B 30" were issued to them, but have not been reported used on Great Britain stamps during this period. All were subsequently reallocated to British post offices.

SPANISH WEST INDIES MAILBOATS

"D 26" was supplied for use by British mail clerks employed on ships of the Herrara Line operating between St. Thomas (Danish West Indies), Cuba, Dominican Republic and Porto Rico.

1868 *to* **1871**.

Z190	1d. rose-red (1864–79)	.. .. ..	
	Plate Nos. 98, 125.		
Z191	4d. vermilion (1865–73)	.. .. ..	£600
Z192	6d. violet (1867–70) (Plate No. 8)	.. ..	
	Plate Nos. 9, 10, 11.		
Z193	1s. green (1867) (Plate No. 4)	.. ..	

Abu Dhabi

Stamps of the BRITISH POSTAL AGENCIES IN EASTERN ARABIA were used from the oil installation on Das Island from December 1960 onwards, being postmarked at Bahrain. A British postal agency, using the same issues, postmarked "ABU DHABI" or "DAS ISLAND", operated in the shaikdom from 30 March 1963 until the introduction of Abu Dhabi issues in 1964.

An independent Arab Shaikhdom (one of the Trucial States), with a British postal administration until 31 December 1966.

(Currency. 100 naye paise = 1 rupee)

1 Shaikh Shakhbut bin Sultan

3 Ruler's Palace

(Des M. Farrar Bell. Photo Harrison (5 n.p. to 75 n.p.). Des C. T. Kavanagh (1, 2 r.), Miss P. M. Goth (5, 10 r.). Recess B.W.)

1964 (30 Mar). *T* **1, 3** *and similar designs. P* 14½ (5 to 75 n.p.) or 13 × 13½ (others).

1	**1**	5 n.p. green		1·50	2·00
2		15 n.p. red-brown		2·00	1·25
3		20 n.p. ultramarine		2·25	1·00
		a. Perf 13×13½		£225	
4		30 n.p. red-orange		3·25	1·50
5		40 n.p. reddish violet		3·25	70
6		50 n.p. bistre		3·75	2·00
7		75 n.p. black		3·75	3·25
8	**3**	1 r. emerald		4·00	1·25
9		2 r. black		7·50	3·25
10		5 r. carmine-red		16·00	9·00
11		10 r. deep ultramarine		23·00	14·00
1/11			Set of 11	60·00	35·00

Designs: As Type 1—40, 50, 75 n.p. Mountain Gazelle. As Type 3—5, 10 r. Oil rig and camels.

5   **6**   **7**
Saker Falcon

(Des V. Whiteley. Photo Harrison)

1965 (30 Mar). *Falconry. P* 14½.

12	**5**	20 n.p. light brown and grey-blue		10·00	1·75
13	**6**	40 n.p. light brown and blue		13·00	2·75
14	**7**	2 r. sepia and turquoise-green		22·00	13·00
12/14			Set of 3	40·00	16·00

(New Currency. 1,000 fils = 1 dinar)

═══

Fils فلس
(8)

1966 (1 Oct). *Nos.* 1/11 *such as T* **8** ("FILS" only on 40 f. to 70 f.) with new value expressed on remainder), by Arabian Printing and Publishing House, Bahrain. P 13 × 13½ (20 f.), others as before.

15	**1**	5 f. on 5 n.p. green		8·00	5·50
16		15 f. on 15 n.p. red-brown		8·00	5·00
17		20 f. on 20 n.p. ultramarine		9·50	7·00
		b. Perf 14½		£100	
		ba. Surch inverted		£250	£400
18		30 f. on 30 n.p. red-orange		9·00	13·00
		a. Arabic "2" for "3" in surch		£1700	
		b. Surch double, one albino		£160	
19		40 f. on 40 n.p. reddish violet		13·00	85
20		50 f. on 50 n.p. bistre		20·00	20·00
21		75 f. on 75 n.p. black		20·00	18·00
		a. Surch double, one albino		£160	
22	**3**	100 f. on 1 r. emerald		16·00	3·50
23		200 f. on 2 r. black		18·00	12·00
24		500 f. on 5 r. carmine-red		30·00	38·00
25		1 d. on 10 r. deep ultramarine		40·00	65·00
		a. Short extra bar below portrait (R. 7/3)		£300	
15/25			Set of 11	£170	£160

The Abu Dhabi Post Department took over the postal services on 1 January 1967. Later stamp issues will be found in Part 19 (*Middle East*) of this Catalogue.

Aden
see South Arabian Federation

Anguilla

Following the grant of Associated Statehood to St. Christopher, Nevis and Anguilla on 27 February 1967 the population of Anguilla agitated for independence and the St. Kitts-Nevis authorities left the island on 30 May 1967. Nos. 1/16 were issued by the Island Council and were accepted for international mail. On 7 July 1969 the Anguilla post office was officially recognised by the Government of St. Christopher, Nevis and Anguilla and normal postal communications via St. Christopher were resumed. By the Anguilla Act of 27 July 1971, Anguilla was restored to direct British control.

A degree of internal self-government with an Executive Council was introduced on 10 February 1976 and the links with St. Kitts-Nevis were officially severed on 18 December 1980.

(Currency. 100 cents = 1 Eastern Caribbean dollar)

Independent Anguilla
(1)

2 Mahogany Tree, The Quarter

1967 (4 Sept). *Nos.* 129/44 *of St. Kitts-Nevis optd as T* **1**, *by Island Press Inc, St. Thomas, U.S. Virgin Islands.*

1	½ c New lighthouse, Sombrero			28·00	20·00
2	1 c. Loading sugar cane, St. Kitts			29·00	6·50
3	2 c. Pall Mall Square, Basseterre			30·00	1·50
4	3 c. Gateway, Brimstone Hill Fort, St. Kitts			30·00	4·50
	w. Wmk inverted			—	32·00
5	4 c. Nelson's Spring, Nevis			30·00	5·50
6	5 c. Grammar School, St. Kitts			£110	18·00
7	6 c. Crater, Mt Misery, St. Kitts			55·00	9·00
8	10 c. Hibiscus			30·00	6·50
9	15 c. Sea Island cotton, Nevis			65·00	11·00
10	20 c. Boat building, Anguilla			£100	13·00
11	25 c. White-crowned Pigeon			90·00	22·00
	w. Wmk inverted			£120	38·00
12	50 c. St. George's Church Tower, Basseterre			£1800	£450
13	60 c. Alexander Hamilton			£2000	£850
14	$1 Map of St. Kitts–Nevis			£1600	£400
15	$2.50, Map of Anguilla			£1500	£300
16	$5 Arms of St. Christopher, Nevis and Anguilla			£1500	£300
1/16			Set of 16	£8000	£2250

Owing to the limited stocks available for overprinting, the sale of the above stamps was personally controlled by the Postmaster and no orders from the trade were accepted.

(Des John Lister Ltd. Litho A. & M.)

1967 (27 Nov)–**68**. *T* **2** *and similar horiz designs. P* 12½ × 13.

17	1 c. dull green, bistre-brown and pale orange		10	40
18	2 c. bluish green and black (21.3.68)		10	40
19	3 c. black and light emerald (10.2.68)		10	10
20	4 c. cobalt-blue and black (10.2.68)		10	10
21	5 c. multicoloured		10	10
22	6 c. light vermilion and black (21.3.68)		10	10
23	10 c. multicoloured		15	10
24	15 c. multicoloured (10.2.68)		60	20
25	20 c. multicoloured		80	65
26	25 c. multicoloured		60	20
27	40 c. apple green, light greenish blue and black		80	25
28	60 c. multicoloured (10.2.68)		3·00	2·75
29	$1 multicoloured (10.2.68)		1·75	3·00
30	$2.50, multicoloured (21.3.68)		2·00	3·50
31	$5 multicoloured (10.2.68)		3·00	4·25
17/31		Set of 15	11·50	14·00

Designs:—2 c. Sombrero Lighthouse; 3 c. St. Mary's Church; 4 c. Valley Police Station; 5 c. Old Plantation House, Mt Fortune; 6 c. Valley Post Office; 10 c. Methodist Church, West End; 15 c. Wall-Blake Airport; 20 c. Beech A90 King Air aircraft over Sandy Ground; 25 c. Island Harbour; 40 c. Map of Anguilla; 60 c. Hermit Crab and Starfish; $1 Hibiscus; $2.50, Local scene; $5, Spiny Lobster.

17 Yachts in Lagoon

18 Purple-throated Carib

(Des John Lister Ltd. Litho A. & M.)

1968 (11 May). *Anguillan Ships. T* **17** *and similar horiz designs. Multicoloured. P* 14.

32	10 c. Type **17**			30	10
33	15 c. Boat on beach			35	10
34	25 c. *Warspite* (schooner)			50	15
35	40 c. *Atlantic Star* (schooner)			60	20
32/5			Set of 4	1·60	40

(Des John Lister Ltd. Litho A. & M.)

1968 (8 July). *Anguillan Birds. T* **18** *and similar multicoloured designs. P* 14.

36	10 c. Type **18**			85	15
37	15 c. Bananaquit			1·10	20
38	25 c. Black-necked Stilt (*horiz*)			1·40	20
39	40 c. Royal Tern (*horiz*)			1·60	30
36/9			Set of 4	4·50	75

19 Guides' Badge and Anniversary Years

(Des John Lister Ltd. Litho A. & M.)

1968 (14 Oct). *35th Anniv of Anguillan Girl Guides. T* **19** *and similar multicoloured designs. P* 13 × 13½ (10, 25 c.) or 13½ × 13 (others).

40	10 c. Type **19**			10	10
41	15 c. Badge and silhouettes of Guides (*vert*)			15	10
42	25 c. Guides' badge and Headquarters			20	15
43	40 c. Association and Proficiency badges (*vert*)			25	15
40/3			Set of 4	65	35

20 The Three Kings

(Des John Lister Ltd. Litho A. & M.)

1968 (18 Nov). *Christmas. T* **20** *and similar designs. P* 13.

44	1 c. black and cerise			10	10
45	10 c. black and light greenish blue			10	10
46	15 c. black and chestnut			15	10
47	40 c. black and blue			15	10
48	50 c. black and dull green			20	15
44/8			Set of 5	55	30

Designs: *Vert*—10 c. The Wise Men; 15 c. Holy Family and manger. *Horiz*—40 c. The Shepherds; 50 c. Holy Family and donkey.

21 Bagging Salt

INDEPENDENCE JANUARY, 1969
(21a)

(Des John Lister Ltd. Litho A. & M.)

1969 (4 Jan). *Anguillan Salt Industry. T* **21** *and similar horiz designs. Multicoloured. P* 13.

49	10 c. Type **21**			25	10
50	15 c. Packing salt			30	10
51	40 c. Salt pond			35	10
52	50 c. Loading salt			35	10
49/52			Set of 4	1·10	30

1969 (12 Feb*). *Expiration of Interim Agreement on Status of Anguilla. Nos.* 19/22, 24 *and* 26/7 *optd with T* **21**a.

52a	3 c. black and light emerald			10	20
52b	4 c. cobalt-blue and black			10	20
52c	5 c. multicoloured			10	20
52d	6 c. light vermilion and black			10	20
52e	15 c. multicoloured			90	30
52f	25 c. multicoloured			80	30
52g	40 c. apple green, light greenish blue & blk			1·00	40
52a/g			Set of 7	2·75	1·60

*Earliest known postmark date.

The remaining values of the 1967–68 series, Nos. 17/31, also come with this overprint. The complete set exists on large first day covers postmarked 9 January 1969. The values listed above have been reported used on commercial mail from Anguilla.

---

22 "The Crucifixion"
(Studio of Massys)

(Des John Lister Ltd. Litho Format)

1969 (31 Mar). *Easter Commemoration. T* **22** *and similar vert design. P.* 13½.
53	25 c. multicoloured		25	15
54	40 c. multicoloured		35	15

Design:—40 c. "The Last Supper" (ascribed to Roberti).

23 Amaryllis

(Des John Lister Ltd. Litho Format)

1969 (10 June). *Flowers of the Caribbean. T* **23** *and similar horiz designs. Multicoloured. P* 14.
55	10 c. Type **23**		20	20
56	15 c. Bougainvillea		25	25
57	40 c. Hibiscus		50	50
58	50 c. *Cattleya* orchid		1·50	1·25
55/8		*Set of 4*	2·25	2·00

24 Superb Gaza, Channelled Turban, Chestnut Turban and Carved Star Shell

(Des John Lister Ltd. Litho A. & M.)

1969 (22 Sept). *Sea Shells. T* **24** *and similar horiz designs. Multicoloured. P* 14.
59	10 c. Type **24**		20	20
60	15 c. American Thorny Oyster		20	20
61	40 c. Scotch, Royal and Smooth Scotch Bonnets		30	30
62	50 c. Atlantic Trumpet Triton		40	30
59/62		*Set of 4*	1·00	90

(25)

(26)

(27)

(28)

(29)

1969 (Oct). *Christmas. Nos.* 17, 25/8 *optd with T* **25/29**.
63	1 c. dull green, bistre-brown & light orange		10	10
64	20 c. multicoloured		20	10
65	25 c. multicoloured		20	10
66	40 c. apple-green, light greenish blue & black		25	15
67	60 c. multicoloured		40	20
63/7		*Set of 5*	1·00	45

30 Spotted Goatfish

31 "Morning Glory"

(Des John Lister Ltd. Litho A. & M.)

1969 (1 Dec). *Fishes. T* **30** *and similar horiz designs. Multicoloured. P* 14.
68	10 c. Type **30**		30	15
69	15 c. Blue-striped Grunt		45	15
70	40 c. Nassau Grouper		55	20
71	50 c. Banded Butterflyfish		65	20
68/71		*Set of 4*	1·75	65

(Des John Lister Ltd. Litho A. & M.)

1970 (23 Feb). *Flowers. T* **31** *and similar vert designs. Multicoloured. P* 14.
72	10 c. Type **31**		30	10
73	15 c. Blue Petrea		45	10
74	40 c. Hibiscus		70	20
75	50 c. "Flame Tree"		80	25
72/5		*Set of 4*	2·00	55

32 "The Crucifixion"
(Masaccio)

33 Scout Badge and Map

(Des John Lister Ltd. Litho Format)

1970 (26 Mar). *Easter. T* **32** *and similar multicoloured designs. P* 13½.
76	10 c. "The Ascent to Calvary" (Tiepolo) (*horiz*)		15	10
77	20 c. Type **32**		20	10
78	40 c. "Deposition" (Rosso Fiorentino)		25	15
79	60 c. "The Ascent to Calvary" (Murillo) (*horiz*)		25	15
76/9		*Set of 4*	75	40

(Des John Lister Ltd. Litho A. & M.)

1970 (10 Aug). *40th Anniv of Scouting in Anguilla. T* **33** *and similar horiz designs. Multicoloured. P* 13.
80	10 c. Type **33**		15	15
81	15 c. Scout camp and cubs practising first-aid		20	20
82	40 c. Monkey Bridge		25	30
83	50 c. Scout H.Q. Building and Lord Baden-Powell		35	30
80/3		*Set of 4*	85	85

34 Boatbuilding

(Des John Lister Ltd. Litho Format)

1970 (23 Nov). *Various horiz designs as T* **34**. *Multicoloured. P* 14.
84	1 c. Type **34**		30	30
85	2 c. Road Construction		30	30
86	3 c. Quay, Blowing Point		30	20
87	4 c. Broadcaster, Radio Anguilla		30	40
88	5 c. Cottage Hospital Extension		40	40
89	6 c. Valley Secondary School		30	40
90	10 c. Hotel Extension		30	30
91	15 c. Sandy Ground		30	30
92	20 c. Supermarket and Cinema		55	30
93	25 c. Bananas and Mangoes		35	80
94	40 c. Wall Blake Airport		2·50	2·50
95	60 c. Sandy Ground Jetty		65	2·50
96	$1 Administration Buildings		1·25	1·40
97	$2.50, Livestock		1·50	3·75
98	$5 Sandy Hill Bay		2·75	3·75
84/98		*Set of 15*	11·00	16·00

35 "The Adoration of the Shepherds" (Reni)

36 "Ecce Homo"
(detail, Correggio)

(Des John Lister Ltd. Litho Questa)

1970 (11 Dec). *Christmas. T* **35** *and similar vert designs. Multicoloured. P* 13½.
99	1 c. Type **35**		10	10
100	20 c. "The Virgin and Child" (Gozzoli)		30	20
101	25 c. "Mystic Nativity" (detail, Botticelli)		30	20
102	40 c. "The Santa Margherita Madonna" (detail, Mazzola)		40	25
103	50 c. "The Adoration of the Magi" (detail, Tiepolo)		40	25
99/103		*Set of 5*	1·25	85

(Des John Lister Ltd. Litho Format)

1971 (29 Mar). *Easter. T* **36** *and similar designs. P* 13½.
104	10 c. multicoloured		15	10
105	15 c. multicoloured		25	10
106	40 c. multicoloured		30	10
107	50 c. multicoloured		30	15
104/7		*Set of 4*	90	30

Designs: *Vert*—15 c. "Christ appearing to St. Peter" (detail, Carracci). *Horiz*—40 c. "Angels weeping over the Dead Christ" (detail, Guercino); 50 c. "The Supper at Emmaus" (detail, Caravaggio).

37 Hypolimnas misippus

38 Magnanime and Aimable in Battle

(Des John Lister Ltd. Litho Questa)

1971 (21 June). *Butterflies. T* **37** *and similar horiz designs. Multicoloured. P* 14 × 14½.
108	10 c. Type **37**		1·60	70
109	15 c. *Junonia evarete*		1·60	80
110	40 c. *Agraulis vanillae*		2·00	1·25
111	50 c. *Danaus plexippus*		2·00	1·50
108/11		*Set of 4*	6·50	3·75

(Des John Lister Ltd. Litho Format)

1971 (30 Aug). *Sea-battles of the West Indies. T* **38** *and similar vert designs. Multicoloured. P* 14.
112	10 c. Type **38**		1·10	1·25
	a. Horiz strip of 5. Nos. 112/16		6·50	
113	15 c. H.M.S. *Duke, Glorieux* and H.M.S. *Agamemnon*		1·25	1·40
114	25 c. H.M.S. *Formidable* and H.M.S. *Namur* against *Ville de Paris*		1·50	1·60
115	40 c. H.M.S. *Canada*		1·60	1·75
116	50 c. H.M.S. *St. Albans* and wreck of *Hector*		1·75	1·90
112/16		*Set of 5*	6·50	7·00

Nos. 112/16 were issued in horizontal *se-tenant* strips within the sheet, to form a composite design in the order listed.

ADMINISTRATION BY BRITISH COMMISSION

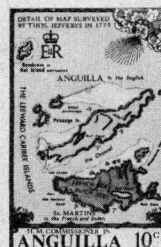

39 "The Ansidei Madonna"
(detail, Raphael)

40 Map of Anguilla and St. Martins by Thomas Jefferys (1775)

(Des John Lister Ltd. Litho Questa)

1971 (29 Nov). *Christmas. T* **39** *and similar vert designs. P* 13½.
117	20 c. multicoloured		20	25
118	25 c. multicoloured		20	25
119	40 c. multicoloured		30	35
120	50 c. multicoloured		35	40
117/20		*Set of 4*	95	1·10

Designs:—25 c. "Mystic Nativity" (detail, Botticelli); 40 c. "Adoration of the Shepherds" (detail; ascr to Murillo); 50 c. "The Madonna of the Iris" (detail; ascr to Dürer).

(Litho Format)

1972 (24 Jan). *Maps. T* **40** *and similar multicoloured designs showing maps by the cartographers given. P* 14.
121	10 c. Type **40**		25	10
122	15 c. Samuel Fahlberg (1814)		35	15
123	40 c. Thomas Jefferys (1775) (*horiz*)		50	25
124	50 c. Capt. E. Barnett (1847) (*horiz*)		60	25
121/4		*Set of 4*	1·50	65

PRICES OF SETS

Set prices are given for many issues, generally those containing three stamps or more. Definitive sets include one of each value or major colour change, but do not cover different perforations, die types or minor shades. Where a choice is possible the set prices are based on the cheapest versions of the stamps included in the listings.

41 "Jesus Buffeted"   **42** Loblolly Tree

(Des John Lister Ltd. Litho Format)

1972 (14 Mar). *Easter. Stained Glass Windows from Church of St. Michael, Bray, Berkshire. T 41 and similar vert designs. Multicoloured. P 14 × 13½.*

125	10 c. Type 41	25	25
	a. Horiz strip of 5. Nos. 125/9	1·40	
126	15 c. "The Way of Sorrows"	30	30
127	25 c. "The Crucifixion"	30	30
128	40 c. "Descent from the Cross"	35	35
129	50 c. "The Burial"	40	40
125/9	*Set of 5*	1·40	1·40

Nos. 125/9 were printed horizontally *se-tenant* within the sheet.

(Litho Questa ($10), Format (others))

1972 (30 Oct)–**75**. *T 42 and similar multicoloured designs (horiz, except 2, 4 and 6 c.). P 13½.*

130	1 c. Spear fishing	10	40
131	2 c. Type 42	10	40
132	3 c. Sandy Ground	10	40
133	4 c. Ferry at Blowing Point	90	20
134	5 c. Agriculture	15	60
135	6 c. St. Mary's Church	25	20
136	10 c. St. Gerard's Church	25	40
137	15 c. Cottage Hospital extension	25	30
138	20 c. Public library	30	35
139	25 c. Sunset at Blowing Point	40	1·50
140	40 c. Boat building	3·25	1·50
141	60 c. Hibiscus	4·00	3·50
142	$1 Magnificent Frigate Bird	8·50	7·50
143	$2.50, Frangipani	6·00	9·00
144	$5 Brown Pelican	15·00	14·00
144a	$10 Green-back turtle (20.5.75)	15·00	18·00
130/44a	*Set of 16*	48·00	50·00

43 Malcolm Miller (schooner) and Common Dolphin

(Des (from photograph by D. Groves) and photo Harrison)

1972 (20 Nov). *Royal Silver Wedding. Multicoloured; background colour given. W w 12. P 14 × 14½.*

145	43 25 c. yellow-olive (*shades*)	40	75
146	40 c. chocolate	40	75
	w. Wmk inverted	1·25	

44 Flight into Egypt   **45** "The Betrayal of Christ"

(Des John Lister Ltd. Litho Questa)

1972 (4 Dec). *Christmas. T 44 and similar vert designs. Multicoloured. P 13½.*

147	1 c. Type 44	10	10
148	20 c. Star of Bethlehem	20	20
	a. Vert strip of 4. Nos. 148/51	75	
149	25 c. Holy Family	20	20
150	40 c. Arrival of the Magi	20	25
151	50 c. Adoration of the Magi	25	20
147/51	*Set of 5*	75	85

Nos. 148/51 were printed vertically *se-tenant* within a sheet of 20 stamps.

(Des John Lister Ltd. Litho Questa)

1973 (26 Mar). *Easter. T 45 and similar vert designs. Multicoloured; bottom panel in gold and black. P 13½.*

152	1 c. Type 45	10	10
153	10 c. "The Man of Sorrows"	10	10
	a. Vert strip of 5. Nos. 153/6	55	
154	20 c. "Christ bearing the Cross"	10	15

155	25 c. "The Crucifixion"	15	15
156	40 c. "The Descent from the Cross"	15	15
157	50 c. "The Resurrection"	15	20
152/7	*Set of 6*	55	70
MS158	140 × 141 mm. Nos. 152/7. Bottom panel in gold and mauve	70	80

Nos. 153/7 were printed within one sheet, vertically *se-tenant*.

46 Santa Maria   **47** Princess Anne and Captain Mark Phillips

(Des John Lister Ltd. Litho Questa)

1973 (10 Sept). *Columbus Discovers the West Indies. T 46 and similar horiz designs. Multicoloured. P 13½.*

159	1 c. Type 46	10	10
160	20 c. Early map	1·25	1·25
	a. Horiz strip of 4. Nos. 160/3	6·00	
161	40 c. Map of voyages	1·40	1·40
162	70 c. Sighting land	1·75	1·75
163	$1.20, Landing of Columbus	2·25	2·25
159/63	*Set of 5*	6·00	6·00
MS164	193 × 93 mm. Nos. 159/63	6·00	7·00

Nos. 160/3 were printed horizontally *se-tenant* within the sheet.

(Des PAD Studio. Litho Questa)

1973 (14 Nov). *Royal Wedding. Centre multicoloured. W w 12 (sideways). P 13½.*

165	47 60 c. turquoise-green	20	15
166	$1.20, deep mauve	30	15

48 "The Adoration of the Shepherds" (Reni)   **49** "The Crucifixion" (Raphael)

(Des John Lister Ltd. Litho Questa)

1973 (2 Dec). *Christmas. T 48 and similar horiz designs. Multicoloured. P 13½.*

167	1 c. Type 48	10	10
168	10 c. "The Madonna and Child with Saints Jerome and Dominic" (Lippi)	10	10
	a. Horiz strip of 5. Nos. 168/72	75	
169	20 c. "The Nativity" (Master of Brunswick)	15	15
170	25 c. "Madonna of the Meadow" (Bellini)	15	15
171	40 c. "Virgin and Child" (Cima)	20	20
172	50 c. "Adoration of the Kings" (Geertgen)	20	20
167/72	*Set of 6*	75	75
MS173	148 × 149 mm. Nos. 167/72	80	1·60

Nos. 168/72 were printed within the sheet, horizontally *se-tenant*.

(Des John Lister Ltd. Litho Questa)

1974 (30 Mar). *Easter. T 49 and similar vert designs showing various details of Raphael's "Crucifixion". P 13½.*

174	1 c. multicoloured	10	10
175	15 c. multicoloured	10	10
	a. Vert strip of 5. Nos. 175/9	70	
176	20 c. multicoloured	15	15
177	25 c. multicoloured	15	15
178	40 c. multicoloured	15	15
179	$1 multicoloured	20	25
174/9	*Set of 6*	70	70
MS180	123 × 141 mm. Nos. 174/9	95	1·25

Nos. 175/9 were printed vertically *se-tenant* within one sheet.

50 Churchill making "Victory" Sign

(Des John Lister Ltd. Litho Questa)

1974 (24 June). *Birth Centenary of Sir Winston Churchill. T 50 and similar horiz designs. Multicoloured. P 13½.*

181	1 c. Type 50	10	10
182	20 c. Churchill with Roosevelt	20	20
	a. Horiz strip of 5. Nos. 182/6	1·50	
183	25 c. Wartime broadcast	20	20
184	40 c. Birthplace, Blenheim Palace	30	30
185	60 c. Churchill's statue	30	35
186	$1.20, Country residence, Chartwell	45	55
181/6	*Set of 6*	1·25	1·50
MS187	195 × 96 mm. Nos. 181/6	1·40	2·25

Nos. 182/6 were printed horizontally *se-tenant* within the sheet.

51 U.P.U. Emblem

(Des John Lister Ltd. Litho Questa)

1974 (27 Aug). *Centenary of Universal Postal Union. P 13½*.*

188	51 1 c. black and bright blue	10	10
189	20 c. black and pale orange	15	15
	a. Horiz strip of 5. Nos. 189/93	1·10	
190	25 c. black and light yellow	15	15
191	40 c. black and bright mauve	20	25
192	60 c. black and light emerald	30	40
193	$1.20, black and light blue	50	60
188/93	*Set of 6*	1·10	1·40
MS194	195 × 96 mm. Nos. 188/93	1·25	2·00

Nos. 189/93 were printed horizontally *se-tenant* within the sheet.
*In No. MS194 the lower row of three stamps, 40 c., 60 c. and $1.20 values, are line-perforated 15 at foot, the remaining 3 stamps being comb-perforated 13½.

52 Anguillan pointing to Star   **53** "Mary, John and Mary Magdalene" (Matthias Grünewald)

(Litho Questa)

1974 (16 Dec). *Christmas. T 52 and similar horiz designs. Multicoloured. P 14.*

195	1 c. Type 52	10	10
196	20 c. Child in Manger	10	15
	a. Horiz strip of 5. Nos. 196/200	70	
197	25 c. King's offering	10	15
198	40 c. Star over Map of Anguilla	15	15
199	60 c. Family looking at star	15	20
200	$1.20, Angels of Peace	20	30
195/200	*Set of 6*	70	95
MS201	177 × 85 mm. Nos. 195/200	1·10	1·75

Nos. 196/200 were printed horizontally *se-tenant* within the sheet.

(Litho Questa)

1975 (25 Mar). *Easter. T 53 and similar multicoloured designs showing details of the Isenheim altarpiece. P 14.*

202	1 c. Type 53	10	10
203	10 c. "The Crucifixion"	15	15
	a. Horiz strip of 5. Nos. 203/7	80	
204	15 c. "St. John the Baptist"	15	15
205	20 c. "St. Sebastian and Angels"	15	20
206	$1 "The Entombment"	20	35
207	$1.50, "St. Anthony the Hermit"	25	45
202/7	*Set of 6*	80	1·25
MS208	134 × 127 mm. Nos. 202/7. Imperf	1·00	1·75

Nos. 203/7 were printed horizontally *se-tenant* within the sheet.

54 Statue of Liberty   **55** "Madonna, Child and the Infant John the Baptist" (Raphael)

(Des John Lister Ltd. Litho Questa)

1975 (10 Nov). *Bicentenary of American Revolution. T* **54** *and similar horiz designs. Multicoloured. P* 13½*.

209	1 c. Type 54		10	10
210	10 c. The Capitol		20	10
	a. Horiz strip of 5. Nos. 210/14		1·60	
211	15 c. "Congress voting for Independence" (Pine and Savage)		30	15
212	20 c. Washington and map		30	15
213	$1 Boston Tea Party		45	40
214	$1.50, Bicentenary logo		50	60
209/14		*Set of 6*	1·25	2·50
MS215	198 × 97 mm. Nos. 209/14		1·25	2·50

Nos. 210/14 were printed horizontally *se-tenant* within the sheet.
*In No. MS215 the lower row of three stamps, 20 c., $1 and $1.50 values, are line-perforated 15 at foot, the remaining 3 stamps being comb-perforated 13½.

(Des John Lister Ltd. Litho Questa)

1975 (8 Dec). *Christmas. T* **55** *and similar vert designs showing the "Madonna and Child". Multicoloured. P* 13½.

216	1 c. Type 55		10	10
217	10 c. Cima		15	10
	a. Horiz strip of 5. Nos. 217/21		1·25	
218	15 c. Dolci		20	15
219	20 c. Dürer		20	15
220	$1 Bellini		35	35
221	$1.50, Botticelli		45	35
216/21		*Set of 6*	1·25	90
MS222	130 × 145 mm. Nos. 216/21		2·00	2·25

Nos. 217/21 were printed horizontally *se-tenant* within the sheet.

EXECUTIVE COUNCIL

(56) NEW CONSTITUTION 1976

57 Almond

TION

Italic second "O" in "CONSTITUTION". Occurs on Row 2/2 (Nos. 226, 228, 232, 235, 239), Row 3/2 (Nos. 230/1, 233/4, 236/8), Row 4/5 (Nos. 223/4, 240) or Row 5/2 (Nos. 225, 227, 229).

1976 (10 Feb–1 July). *New Constitution. Nos. 130 etc. optd with T* **56** *or surch also.*

223	1 c. Spear fishing		30	40
	a. Italic "O"		3·00	
224	2 c. on 1 c. Spear fishing		30	40
	a. Italic "O"		3·00	
225	2 c. Type 42 (1.7.76)		5·00	1·75
	a. Italic "O"		18·00	
226	3 c. on 40 c. Boat building		75	70
	a. "3 c" omitted		£300	
	b. Typo. "3 c"*		10·00	11·00
	c. Italic "O"		5·50	
227	4 c. Ferry at Blowing Point		1·00	1·00
	a. Italic "O"		6·00	
228	5 c. on 40 c. Boat building		30	50
	a. Italic "O"		3·00	
229	6 c. St. Mary's Church		30	50
	a. Italic "O"		3·00	
230	10 c. on 20 c. Public Library		30	50
	a. Italic "O"		3·00	
231	10 c. St. Gerard's Church (1.7.76)		5·00	4·00
	a. Italic "O"		18·00	
232	15 c. Cottage Hospital extension		30	90
	a. Italic "O"		3·00	
233	20 c. Public Library		30	50
	a. Italic "O"		3·00	
234	25 c. Sunset at Blowing Point		30	50
	a. Italic "O"		3·00	
235	40 c. Boat building		1·00	70
	a. Italic "O"		6·00	
236	60 c. Hibiscus		70	70
	a. Italic "O"		4·50	
237	$1 Magnificent Frigate Bird		6·00	2·25
	a. Italic "O"		20·00	
238	$2.50, Frangipani		2·25	2·25
	a. Italic "O"		8·00	
239	$5 Brown Pelican		7·50	6·50
	a. Italic "O"		24·00	
240	$10 Green-back turtle		3·00	6·00
	a. Italic "O"		17·00	
223/40		*Set of 18*	30·00	27·00

*No. 226a/b occur on R. 5/2, the "3 c" having been omitted during the normal litho surcharging.

(Des John Lister Ltd. Litho Questa)

1976 (16 Feb). *Flowering Trees. T* **57** *and similar horiz designs. Multicoloured. P* 13½.

241	1 c. Type 57		10	10
242	10 c. Autograph		20	20
	a. Horiz strip of 5. Nos. 242/6		1·25	
243	15 c. Calabash		20	20
244	20 c. Cordia		20	20
245	$1 Papaya		30	45
246	$1.50, Flamboyant		35	55
241/6		*Set of 6*	1·25	1·50
MS247	194 × 99 mm. Nos. 241/6		1·50	2·00

Nos. 242/6 were printed horizontally *se-tenant* within the sheet.

NEW INFORMATION

The editor is always interested to correspond with people who have new information that will improve or correct the Catalogue.

58 The Three Marys

59 French Ships approaching Anguilla

(Litho Questa)

1976 (5 Apr). *Easter. T* **58** *and similar multicoloured designs showing portions of the Altar Frontal Tapestry, Rheinau. P* 13½.

248	1 c. Type 58		10	10
249	10 c. The Crucifixion		10	10
	a. Horiz strip of 5. Nos. 249/53		1·75	
250	15 c. Two Soldiers		15	15
251	20 c. The Annunciation		15	15
252	$1 The complete tapestry (*horiz*)		65	65
253	$1.50, The Risen Christ		80	80
248/53		*Set of 6*	1·75	1·75
MS254	138 × 130 mm. Nos. 248/53. Imperf		1·75	2·10

Nos. 249/53 were printed horizontally *se-tenant* within the sheet.

(Des John Lister Ltd. Litho Questa)

1976 (8 Nov). *Battle for Anguilla, 1796. T* **59** *and similar horiz designs. Multicoloured. P* 13½.

255	1 c. Type 59		10	10
256	3 c. *Margaret* (sloop) leaving Anguilla		90	35
	a. Horiz strip of 5. Nos. 256/60		7·00	
257	15 c. Capture of *Le Desius*		1·25	65
258	25 c. *La Vaillante* forced aground		1·50	80
259	$1 H.M.S. *Lapwing*		2·00	1·25
260	$1.50, *Le Desius* burning		2·25	1·75
255/60		*Set of 6*	7·00	4·25
MS261	205 × 103 mm. Nos. 255/60		7·00	6·00

Nos. 256/60 were printed horizontally *se-tenant* within the sheet.

60 "Christmas Carnival" (A. Richardson)

(Litho Questa)

1976 (22 Nov). *Christmas. T* **60** *and similar horiz designs showing children's paintings. Multicoloured. P* 13½.

262	1 c. Type 60		10	10
263	3 c. "Dreams of Christmas Gifts" (J. Connor)		10	10
	a. Horiz strip of 5. Nos. 263/7		1·00	
264	15 c. "Carolling" (P. Richardson)		15	15
265	25 c. "Candle-light Procession" (A. Mussington)		20	20
266	$1 "Going to Church" (B. Franklin)		30	30
267	$1.50, "Coming Home for Christmas" (E. Gumbs)		40	40
262/7		*Set of 6*	1·00	1·10
MS268	232 × 147 mm. Nos. 262/7		1·50	1·75

Nos. 263/7 were printed horizontally *se-tenant* within the sheet.

61 Prince Charles and H.M.S. *Minerva* (frigate)

(Des John Lister Ltd. Litho Questa)

1977 (9 Feb). *Silver Jubilee. T* **61** *and similar horiz designs. Multicoloured. P* 13½.

269	25 c. Type 61		15	10
270	40 c. Prince Philip landing at Road Bay, 1964		15	10
271	$1.20, Coronation scene		20	20
272	$2.50, Coronation regalia and map of Anguilla		25	30
269/72		*Set of 4*	65	55
MS273	145 × 96 mm. Nos. 269/72		65	90

62 Yellow-crowned Night Heron

(Des John Lister Ltd. Litho Questa)

1977 (18 Apr)–78. *T* **62** *and similar horiz designs. Multicoloured. P* 13½.

274	1 c. Type 62		30	70
275	2 c. Great Barracuda		30	1·10
276	3 c. Queen or Pink Conch		1·25	1·75
277	4 c. Spanish Bayonet		40	30
278	5 c. Honeycomb Trunkfish		1·50	30
279	6 c. Cable and Wireless Building		30	30
280	10 c. American Kestrel (20.2.78)		4·00	2·00
281	15 c. Ground Orchid (20.2.78)		2·75	1·75
282	20 c. Stop-light Parrotfish (20.2.78)		2·00	75
283	22 c. Lobster fishing boat (20.2.78)		45	60
284	35 c. Boat race (20.2.78)		1·40	70
285	50 c. Sea Bean (20.2.78)		90	45
286	$1 Sandy Island (20.2.78)		60	45
287	$2.50 Manchineel (20.2.78)		1·00	1·00
288	$5 Ground Lizard (20.2.78)		2·00	1·75
289	$10 Red-billed Tropic Bird		9·00	4·25
274/89		*Set of 16*	25·00	16·00

63 "The Crucifixion" (Massys)

(Des John Lister Ltd. Litho Questa)

1977 (25 Apr). *Easter. T* **63** *and similar horiz designs showing paintings by Castagno ($1.50) or Ugolino (others), Multicoloured. P* 13½.

291	1 c. Type 63		10	10
292	3 c. "The Betrayal"		10	10
	a. Horiz strip of 5. Nos. 292/6		1·60	
293	22 c. "The Way to Calvary"		20	20
294	30 c. "The Deposition"		25	25
295	$1 "The Resurrection"		50	50
296	$1.50, "The Crucifixion"		65	65
291/6		*Set of 6*	1·60	1·60
MS297	192 × 126 mm. Nos. 291/6		1·60	1·75

Nos. 292/6 were printed horizontally *se-tenant* within the sheet.

ROYAL VISIT TO WEST INDIES

(64)

65 "Le Chapeau de Paille"

1977 (26 Oct). *Royal Visit. Nos. 269/MS273 optd with T* **64**.

298	25 c. Type 61		10	10
299	40 c. Prince Philip landing at Road Bay, 1964		10	15
300	$1.20, Coronation scene		20	25
301	$2.50, Coronation regalia and map of Anguilla		25	35
298/301		*Set of 4*	60	75
MS302	145 × 96 mm. Nos. 298/301		80	60

(Des John Lister Ltd. Litho Questa)

1977 (1 Nov). *400th Birth Anniv of Rubens. T* **65** *and similar vert designs. Multicoloured. P* 13½.

303	25 c. Type 65		15	15
304	40 c. "Helène Fourment and her Two Children"		20	25
305	$1.20, "Rubens and his Wife"		60	65
306	$2.50, "Marchesa Brigida Spinola-Doria"		75	95
303/6		*Set of 4*	1·50	1·75
MS307	93 × 145 mm. Nos. 303/6		1·75	2·10

Each value was issued in sheets of 5 stamps and 1 label.

5c

(66)

EASTER 1978

(67)

1977 (14 Nov). *Christmas. Nos. 262/8 with old date blocked out and additionally inscr "1977", some surch also as T* **66**.

308	1 c. Type 60		10	10
309	5 c. on 3 c. "Dreams of Christmas Gifts"		10	10
	a. Horiz strip of 5. Nos. 309/13		1·75	
310	12 c. on 15 c. "Carolling"		15	15
311	18 c. on 25 c. "Candle-light Procession"		20	20
312	$1 "Going to Church"		45	45
313	$2.50 on $1.50, "Coming Home for Christmas"		90	90
308/13		*Set of 6*	1·75	1·75
MS314	232 × 147 mm. Nos. 308/13		2·50	2·50

1978 (6 Mar). *Easter. Nos. 303/7 optd with T* **67**, *in gold.*

315	25 c. Type 65		15	15
316	40 c. "Helène Fourment and her Two Children"		15	20
317	$1.20, "Rubens and his Wife"		30	40
318	$2.50, "Marchesa Brigida Spinola-Doria"		40	60
315/18		*Set of 4*	90	1·25
MS319	93 × 145 mm. Nos. 315/18		1·25	1·50

68 Coronation Coach at Admiralty Arch   (69)   (70)

(Des John Lister Ltd. Litho Questa)

1978 (6 Apr). *25th Anniv of Coronation. T* **68** *and similar horiz designs. Multicoloured. P* 14.

320	22 c. Buckingham Palace	10	10
321	50 c. Type **68**	10	10
322	$1.50, Balcony scene	15	15
323	$2.50, Royal coat of arms	25	25
320/3	*Set of 4*	50	50
MS324	138 × 92 mm. Nos. 320/3	60	60

1978 (14 Aug). *Anniversaries. Nos. 283/8 optd as T* **69** *or surch as T* **70**.

325	22 c. Lobster fishing boat	20	15
	a. Opt double	£130	
	b. "C" omitted from "SECONDARY"	3·50	
326	35 c. Boat race	30	20
	a. "C" omitted from "SECONDARY"	3·75	
327	50 c. Sea Bean	30	30
	a. "I" omitted from "METHODIST"	3·75	
328	$1 Sandy Island	35	40
	a. "I" omitted from "METHODIST"	4·00	
329	$1.20 on $5 Ground Lizard	40	45
	a. "I" omitted from "METHODIST"	5·00	
330	$1.50 on $2.50, Manchineel	45	55
	a. "C" omitted from "SECONDARY"	6·00	
325/30	*Set of 6*	1·75	1·75

The 22, 35 c. and $1.50 values commemorate the 25th anniversary of Valley Secondary School; the other values commemorate the Centenary of Road Methodist Church.

Nos. 325b, 326a and 330a occur on R. 4/1 and Nos. 327a, 328a and 329a on R. 2/4.

71 Mother and Child

(Des and litho Questa)

1978 (11 Dec). *Christmas. Children's Paintings. T* **71** *and similar horiz designs. Multicoloured. P* 13½.

331	5 c. Type **71**	10	10
332	12 c. Christmas masquerade	15	10
333	18 c. Christmas dinner	15	10
334	22 c. Serenading	15	10
335	$1 Child in manger	45	20
336	$2.50, Family going to church	90	40
331/6	*Set of 6*	1·60	60
MS337	191 × 101 mm. Nos. 331/6	1·60	1·75

1979 (15 Jan). *International Year of the Child. As Nos. 331/7 but additionally inscr with emblem and "1979 INTERNATIONAL YEAR OF THE CHILD". Borders in different colours.*

338	5 c. Type **71**	10	10
339	12 c. Christmas masquerade	10	10
340	18 c. Christmas dinner	10	10
341	22 c. Serenading	10	10
342	$1 Child in manger	30	30
343	$2.50, Family going to church	50	50
338/43	*Set of 6*	90	90
MS344	205 × 112 mm. Nos. 338/43	2·25	2·50

(72)   **73** Valley Methodist Church

1979 (12 Feb). *Nos. 274/7 and 279/80 surch as T* **72**.

345	12 c. on 2 c. Great Barracuda	50	50
346	14 c. on 4 c. Spanish Bayonet	40	50
	a. Surch inverted	32·00	
347	18 c. on 3 c. Queen or Pink Conch	80	55
348	25 c. on 6 c. Cable and Wireless Building	55	50
349	38 c. on 10 c. American Kestrel	2·00	70
350	40 c. on 1 c. Type **62**	2·00	70
345/50	*Set of 6*	5·50	3·00

(Des John Lister Ltd. Litho Questa)

1979 (30 Mar). *Easter. Church Interiors. T* **73** *and similar horiz designs. Multicoloured. P* 14.

351	5 c. Type **73**	10	10
	a. Horiz strip of 6. Nos. 351/6	1·60	
352	12 c. St. Mary's Anglican Church, The Valley	10	10
353	18 c. St. Gerard's Roman Catholic Church, The Valley	15	15
354	22 c. Road Methodist Church	15	15
355	$1.50, St. Augustine's Anglican Church, East End	60	60
356	$2.50, West End Methodist Church	75	75
351/6	*Set of 6*	1·60	1·60
MS357	190 × 105 mm. Nos. 351/6	1·75	2·25

Nos. 351/6 were printed together horizontally *se-tenant*, within the sheet.

74 Cape of Good Hope 1d. "Woodblock" of 1881

(Des Stanley Gibbons Ltd. Litho Questa)

1979 (23 Apr). *Death Centenary of Sir Rowland Hill. T* **74** *and similar horiz designs showing stamps. Multicoloured. P* 14.

358	1 c. Type **74**	10	10
359	1 c. U.S.A. "inverted Jenny" of 1918	10	10
360	22 c. Penny Black ("V.R. Official")	15	15
361	35 c. Germany 2 m. *Graf Zeppelin* of 1928	20	20
362	$1.50, U.S.A. $5 Columbus of 1893	40	60
363	$2.50, Great Britain £5 orange of 1882	60	95
358/63	*Set of 6*	1·25	1·75
MS364	187 × 123 mm. Nos. 358/63	1·25	2·10

75 Wright *Flyer I* (1st powered flight, 1903)

(Des John Lister Ltd. Litho Questa)

1979 (21 May). *History of Powered Flight. T* **75** *and similar horiz designs. Multicoloured. P* 14.

365	5 c. Type **75**	15	10
366	12 c. Louis Blériot at Dover after Channel crossing, 1909	20	10
367	18 c. Vickers FB-27 Vimy (1st non-stop crossing of Atlantic, 1919)	25	15
368	22 c. Ryan NYP Special *Spirit of St. Louis* (1st solo Atlantic flight by Charles Lindbergh, 1927)	25	20
369	$1.50, Airship LZ-127 *Graf Zeppelin*, 1928	60	60
370	$2.50, Concorde, 1979	2·25	90
365/70	*Set of 6*	3·25	1·75
MS371	200×113 mm. Nos. 365/70	3·25	2·50

76 Sombrero Island

(Des John Lister Ltd. Litho Questa)

1979 (20 Aug). *Outer Islands. T* **76** *and similar horiz designs. Multicoloured. P* 14.

372	5 c. Type **76**	10	10
373	12 c. Anguillita Island	10	10
374	18 c. Sandy Island	15	15
375	25 c. Prickly Pear Cays	15	15
376	$1 Dog Island	30	40
377	$2.50, Scrub Island	60	70
372/7	*Set of 6*	1·10	1·40
MS378	180×91 mm. Nos. 372/7	2·25	2·25

77 Red Poinsettia

(Des John Lister Ltd. Litho Format)

1979 (22 Oct). *Christmas. Flowers. T* **77** *and similar diamond-shaped designs. Multicoloured. P* 14½.

379	22 c. Type **77**	15	20
380	35 c. Kalanchoe	20	30
381	$1.50, Cream Poinsettia	40	50
382	$2.50, White Poinsettia	60	70
379/82	*Set of 4*	1·25	1·50
MS383	146 × 164 mm. Nos. 379/82	1·75	2·25

COVER PRICES

Cover factors are quoted at the beginning of each country for most issues to 1945. An explanation of the system can be found on page x. The factors quoted do not, however, apply to philatelic covers.

78 Exhibition Scene

(Des R. Granger Barrett. Litho Format)

1979 (10 Dec). *"London 1980" International Stamp Exhibition (1st issue). T* **78** *and similar horiz designs. Multicoloured. P* 13.

384	35 c. Type **78**	15	20
	a. Perf 14½	15	20
385	50 c. Earls Court Exhibition Centre	15	25
	a. Perf 14½	20	25
386	$1.50, Penny Black and Two-penny Blue stamps	25	60
	a. Perf 14½	30	60
387	$2.50, Exhibition logo	45	95
	a. Perf 14½	50	95
384/7	*Set of 4*	90	1·75
MS388	150×94 mm. Nos. 384/7	1·40	2·00
	a. Perf 14½	1·40	2·00

Nos. 384a/7a come from booklets and also exist from uncut booklet sheets of 10.

See also Nos. 407/10.

79 Games Site

(Des John Lister Ltd. Litho Format)

1980 (14 Jan). *Winter Olympic Games, Lake Placid, U.S.A. T* **79** *and similar horiz designs. Multicoloured. P* 13.

389	5 c. Type **79**	10	10
390	18 c. Ice-hockey	10	10
391	35 c. Ice-skating	15	20
392	50 c. Bobsleighing	15	20
393	$1 Skiing	30	35
394	$2.50, Luge-tobogganing	40	40
389/94	*Set of 6*	80	1·50
MS395	136 × 128 mm. Nos. 389/94	1·60	2·00

Nos. 389/94 also exist perforated 14½ (*Price for set of 6* £1·10 *mint*, £1·50 *used*) from additional sheetlets of 10. Stamps perforated 13 are from normal sheets of 40.

 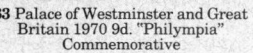

80 Salt ready for Reaping   (81)   (82)

50th Anniversary Scouting 1980   75th Anniversary Rotary 1980

(Des John Lister Ltd. Litho Questa)

1980 (14 Apr). *Salt Industry. T* **80** *and similar horiz designs. Multicoloured. P* 14.

396	5 c. Type **80**	10	10
397	12 c. Tallying salt	10	10
398	18 c. Unloading salt flats	15	15
399	22 c. Salt storage heap	15	15
400	$1 Salt for bagging and grinding	30	40
401	$2.50, Loading salt for export	50	70
396/401	*Set of 6*	1·10	1·40
MS402	180 × 92 mm. Nos. 396/401	1·10	1·75

Nos. 396/7, 398/9 and 400/1 were each printed in the same sheet, but with the values in separate panes.

1980 (16 Apr). *Anniversaries. Nos. 280, 282 and 287/8 optd with T* **81** (10 c., $2.50) *or* **82** (*others*).

403	10 c. American Kestrel	1·00	15
404	20 c. Stop-light Parrotfish	80	20
405	$2.50, Manchineel	1·75	1·25
406	$5 Ground Lizard	2·50	1·90
403/6	*Set of 4*	5·50	3·25

Commemorations:—10 c., $2.50, 50th anniversary of Anguilla Scout Movement; others, 75th anniversary of Rotary International.

83 Palace of Westminster and Great Britain 1970 9d. "Philympia" Commemorative   **84** Queen Elizabeth the Queen Mother

(Des Stamp Magazine. Litho Rosenbaum Bros, Vienna)

1980 (6 May). *"London 1980" International Stamp Exhibition (2nd issue). T* **83** *and similar horiz designs showing famous landmarks and various international stamp exhibition commemorative stamps. Multicoloured. P* 13½.

407	50 c. Type **83**		55	65
408	$1.50, City Hall, Toronto and Canada 1978			
	$1.50, "CAPEX"		85	1·00
409	$2.50, Statue of Liberty and U.S.A. 1976 13 c.			
	"Interphil"		1·10	1·40
407/9		*Set of 3*	2·25	2·75
MS410	157 × 130 mm. Nos. 407/9		2·25	2·75

(Des R. Granger Barrett from photograph by N. Parkinson. Litho Rosenbaum Bros, Vienna)

1980 (4 Aug). *80th Birthday of Queen Elizabeth the Queen Mother.* P 13½.

411	**84** 35 c. multicoloured		45	30
412	50 c. multicoloured		60	40
413	$1.50, multicoloured		1·25	1·00
414	$3 multicoloured		2·25	2·00
411/14		*Set of 4*	4·00	3·25
MS415	160 × 110 mm. Nos. 411/14		5·50	3·50

85 Brown Pelicans

SEPARATION 1980

(86)

(Des John Lister Ltd. Litho Questa)

1980 (13 Nov). *Christmas. Birds. T* **85** *and similar vert designs. Multicoloured. P* 13½.

416	5 c. Type **85**		30	10
417	22 c. Great Blue Heron		75	20
418	$1.50, Barn Swallow		1·75	60
419	$3 Ruby-throated Hummingbird		2·25	1·40
416/19		*Set of 4*	4·50	2·10
MS420	126 × 160 mm. Nos. 416/19		8·50	6·50

1980 (18 Dec). *Separation of Anguilla from St. Kitts-Nevis. Nos. 274, 277, 279/89, 341 and 418/19 optd as T* **86** *or surch also.*

421	1 c. Type **62**		10	40
422	2 c. on 4 c. Spanish Bayonet		10	40
423	5 c. on 15 c. Ground orchid		15	45
424	5 c. on $1.50, Barn Swallow		15	45
425	5 c. on $3 Ruby-throated Hummingbird		15	45
426	10 c. American Kestrel		20	60
427	12 c. on $1 Sandy Island		20	60
428	14 c. on $2.50, Manchineel		20	60
429	15 c. Ground orchid		25	60
430	18 c. on $5 Ground Lizard		25	60
431	20 c. Stop-light Parrotfish		25	60
432	22 c. Lobster fishing boat		25	60
433	25 c. on 15 c. Ground orchid		30	65
434	35 c. Boat race		30	65
435	38 c. on 22 c. Serenading		30	65
436	40 c. on 1 c. Type **62**		30	65
437	50 c. Sea Bean		35	75
438	$1 Sandy Island		50	1·00
439	$2.50, Manchineel		1·00	2·25
440	$5 Ground Lizard		2·25	3·75
441	$10 Red-billed Tropic Bird		5·00	6·00
442	$10 on 6 c. Cable and Wireless Building		5·00	6·00
421/42		*Set of 22*	16·00	26·00

87 First Petition for Separation, 1825

(Des John Lister Ltd. Litho Format)

1980 (18 Dec). *Separation of Anguilla from St. Kitts-Nevis. T* **87** *and similar horiz designs. Multicoloured. P* 14.

443	18 c. Type **87**		10	10
444	22 c. Referendum ballot paper, 1967		15	10
445	35 c. Airport blockade, 1967		15	15
446	50 c. Anguilla flag		20	20
447	$1 Separation celebrations, 1980		30	35
443/7		*Set of 5*	80	85
MS448	178 × 92 mm. Nos. 443/7		80	1·25

Nos. 443/4 and 445/6 were each printed in the same sheet with the two values in separate panes.

ALTERED CATALOGUE NUMBERS

Any Catalogue numbers altered from the last edition are shown as a list in the introductory pages.

---

88 "Nelson's Dockyard" (R. Granger Barrett)

89 Minnie Mouse being chased by Bees

(Litho Rosenbaum Bros, Vienna)

1981 (2 Mar). *175th Death Anniv of Lord Nelson. Paintings. T* **88** *and similar horiz designs. Multicoloured. P* 14.

449	22 c. Type **88**		1·25	30
450	35 c. "Ships in which Nelson served" (Nicholas Pocock)		1·50	50
451	50 c. "H.M.S. *Victory*" (Monamy Swaine)		1·75	65
452	$3 "Battle of Trafalgar" (Clarkson Stanfield)		2·25	2·25
449/52		*Set of 4*	6·00	3·25
MS453	82 × 63 mm. $5 "Horatio Nelson" (L. F. Abbott) and coat of arms		3·00	3·25

(Litho Questa)

1981 (30 Mar). *Easter. Walt Disney Cartoon Characters. T* **89** *and similar vert designs. Multicoloured. P* 13½ × 14.

454	1 c. Type **89**		10	10
455	2 c. Pluto laughing at Mickey Mouse		10	10
456	3 c. Minnie Mouse tying ribbon round Pluto's neck		10	10
457	5 c. Minnie Mouse confronted by love-struck bird who fancies her bonnet		10	10
458	7 c. Dewey and Huey admiring themselves in mirror		10	10
459	9 c. Horace Horsecollar and Clarabelle Cow out for a stroll		10	10
460	10 c. Daisy Duck with hat full of Easter eggs		10	10
461	$2 Goofy unwrapping Easter hat		1·40	1·40
462	$3 Donald Duck in his Easter finery		1·60	1·60
454/62		*Set of 9*	2·75	3·00
MS463	134 × 108 mm. $5 Chip and Dale making off with hat		3·50	3·50

90 Prince Charles, Lady Diana Spencer and St. Paul's Cathedral

Extra flagstaff at right of Windsor Castle (R. 1/5 of each pane)

(Des R. Granger Barrett. Litho Rosenbaum Bros, Vienna)

1981 (15 June). *Royal Wedding. T* **90** *and similar horiz designs showing Prince Charles, Lady Diana Spencer and buildings. Multicoloured. P* 14. (*a*) *No wmk.*

464	50 c. Type **90**		15	20
465	$2.50, Althorp		30	50
466	$3 Windsor Castle		35	60
	a. Extra flagstaff			
464/6		*Set of 3*	70	1·25
MS467	90 x 72 mm. $5 Buckingham Palace		1·25	1·50

(*b*) *Booklet stamps. W w* **15** (*sideways**)

468	50 c. Type **90**		25	45
	a. Booklet pane of 4		75	
	ab. Black printed twice		7·00	
	w. Wmk reading upwards		25	
	wa. Booklet pane of 4		75	
469	$3 As No. 466		40	85
	a. Booklet pane of 4		1·40	
	ab. Black printed twice		7·00	
	w. Wmk reading upwards		40	
	wa. Booklet pane of 4		1·40	

*On Nos. 468/9 the normal sideways watermark reads downwards.

Nos. 464/6 also exist from additional sheetlets of two stamps and one label with changed background colours (*Price for set of 3 80p mint or used*).

Nos. 468/9 come from $14 stamp booklets.

Nos. 468ab and 469ab show the black features of the portraits strengthened by a further printing applied by typography. This is particularly visible on the Prince's suit and on the couple's hair.

---

91 Children playing in Tree

(Des Susan Csomer. Litho Rosenbaum Bros, Vienna)

1981 (31 July–30 Sept). *35th Anniv of U.N.I.C.E.F. T* **91** *and similar horiz designs. Multicoloured. P* 14.

470	5 c. Type **91**		20	30
471	10 c. Children playing by pool		20	30
472	15 c. Children playing musical instruments		20	30
473	$3 Children playing with pets (30 Sept)		2·50	3·00
470/3		*Set of 4*	2·75	3·50
MS474	78 × 106 mm. $4 Children playing football (*vert*) (30 Sept)		3·50	4·50

(Litho Questa)

1981 (2 Nov). *Christmas. Horiz designs as T* **89** *showing scenes from Walt Disney's cartoon film "The Night before Christmas". P* 13½.

475	1 c. multicoloured		10	10
476	2 c. multicoloured		10	10
477	3 c. multicoloured		10	10
478	5 c. multicoloured		10	10
479	7 c. multicoloured		10	10
480	10 c. multicoloured		10	10
481	12 c. multicoloured		10	10
482	$2 multicoloured		3·25	1·25
483	$3 multicoloured		3·25	1·60
475/83		*Set of 9*	6·00	2·75
MS484	130 × 105 mm. $5 multicoloured		5·50	3·50

92 Red Grouper

(93)

(Des R. Granger Barrett. Litho Questa)

1982 (1 Jan). *Horiz designs as T* **92**. *Multicoloured. P* 13½ × 14.

485	1 c. Type **92**		15	60
486	5 c. Ferry service, Blowing Point		30	60
487	10 c. Island dinghies		20	60
488	15 c. Majorettes		20	60
489	20 c. Launching boat, Sandy Hill		40	60
490	25 c. Corals		1·25	60
491	30 c. Little Bay cliffs		30	75
492	35 c. Fountain Cave interior		1·25	80
493	40 c. Sunset over Sandy Island		30	75
494	45 c. Landing at Sombrero		50	80
495	60 c. Seine fishing		3·00	2·25
496	75 c. Boat race at sunset, Sandy Ground		80	1·75
497	$1 Bagging lobster at Island Harbour		2·25	1·75
498	$5 Brown Pelicans		14·00	10·00
499	$7.50, Hibiscus		11·00	11·00
500	$10 Queen Triggerfish		14·00	12·00
485/500		*Set of 16*	45·00	40·00

1982 (22 Mar). *No. 494 surch with T* **93**.

501	50 c. on 45 c. Landing at Sombrero		50	35

94 Anthurium and *Heliconius charithonia*

95 Lady Diana Spencer in 1961

(Des R. Granger Barrett. Litho Questa)

1982 (5 Apr). *Easter. Flowers and Butterflies. T* **94** *and similar vert designs. Multicoloured. P* 14.

502	10 c. Type **94**		45	15
503	35 c. Bird of Paradise and *Junonia evarete*		1·10	40
504	75 c. Allamanda and *Danaus plexippus*		1·50	70
505	$3 Orchid Tree and *Biblis hyperia*		2·25	2·25
502/5		*Set of 4*	4·75	3·25
MS506	65 × 79 mm. $5 Amaryllis and *Dryas julia*		2·75	3·50

(Des R. Granger Barrett. Litho Ueberreuter)

1982 (17 May–30 Aug). *21st Birthday of Princess of Wales. T* **95** *and similar vert designs. Multicoloured. P* 14.

507	10 c. Type **95**		30	20
	a. Booklet pane of 4 (30 Aug)		1·00	
508	30 c. Lady Diana Spencer in 1968		50	25
509	40 c. Lady Diana in 1970		50	30
	a. Booklet pane of 4 (30 Aug)		1·75	
510	60 c. Lady Diana in 1974		55	35
	a. Booklet pane of 4 (30 Aug)		2·00	
511	$2 Lady Diana in 1981		80	1·10
	a. Booklet pane of 4 (30 Aug)		3·00	
512	$3 Lady Diana in 1981 (*different*)		2·25	1·40
507/12		*Set of 6*	4·50	3·25
MS513	72 × 90 mm. $5 Princess of Wales		5·50	3·00
MS514	125 × 125 mm. As Nos. 507/12, but with buff borders		6·00	4·75

96 Pitching Tent

(Litho Ueberreuter)

1982 (5 July). *75th Anniv of Boy Scout Movement. T 96 and similar horiz designs. Multicoloured. P 14.*
515	10 c. Type 96			45	20
516	35 c. Scout band			85	50
517	75 c. Yachting ..			1·25	90
518	$3 On parade			3·00	2·75
515/18			*Set of 4*	5·00	4·00
MS519	90 × 72 mm. $5 Cooking			4·50	4·00

(Litho Format)

1982 (3 Aug). *World Cup Football Championship, Spain. Horiz designs as T 89 showing scenes from Walt Disney's cartoon film "Bedknobs and Broomsticks". P 11.*
520	1 c. multicoloured		..	10	10
521	3 c. multicoloured		..	10	10
522	4 c. multicoloured		..	10	10
523	5 c. multicoloured		..	10	10
524	7 c. multicoloured		..	10	10
525	9 c. multicoloured		..	10	10
526	10 c. multicoloured		..	10	10
527	$2.50 multicoloured		..	2·25	1·75
528	$3 multicoloured		..	2·25	2·00
520/8			*Set of 9*	4·50	3·75
MS529	126×101 mm. $5 mult. P 14×13½			5·50	6·00

COMMONWEALTH GAMES 1982
(97)

1982 (18 Oct). *Commonwealth Games, Brisbane. Nos. 487, 495/6 and 498 optd with T 97.*
530	10 c. Island dinghies			15	25
	a. "S" omitted from "GAMES" ..			1·75	
531	60 c. Seine fishing ..			45	60
	a. "S" omitted from "GAMES"			2·75	
532	75 c. Boat race at sunset, Sandy Ground			60	80
	a. "S" omitted from "GAMES" ..			3·25	
533	$5 Brown Pelicans			3·25	3·75
	a. "S" omitted from "GAMES"			9·00	
530/3			*Set of 4*	4·00	4·75

The "S" omitted variety occurs on R.2/2 of the right-hand pane for all values.

(Litho Questa)

1982 (29 Nov). *Birth Centenary of A. A. Milne (author). Horiz designs as T 89 showing scenes from various "Winnie the Pooh" stories. P 14 × 13½.*
534	1 c. multicoloured		..	10	10
535	2 c. multicoloured		..	15	10
536	3 c. multicoloured		..	20	10
537	5 c. multicoloured		..	25	15
538	7 c. multicoloured		..	25	20
539	10 c. multicoloured		..	25	15
540	12 c. multicoloured		..	35	20
541	20 c. multicoloured		..	55	25
542	$5 multicoloured		..	5·50	6·50
534/42			*Set of 9*	6·75	7·00
MS543	120 × 93 mm. $5 multicoloured			7·00	7·50

98 Culture

99 "I am the Lord Thy God"

(Des R. Granger Barrett. Litho Ueberreuter)

1983 (28 Feb). *Commonwealth Day. T 98 and similar horiz designs. Multicoloured. P 14.*
544	10 c. Type 98			10	15
545	35 c. Anguilla and British flags			30	30
546	75 c. Economic co-operation			60	80
547	$2.50, Salt industry (salt pond)			3·75	4·25
544/7			*Set of 4*	4·25	5·00
MS548	76 × 61 mm. $5 World map showing position of Commonwealth countries			3·00	2·50

(Litho Questa)

1983 (31 Mar). *Easter. The Ten Commandments. T 99 and similar vert designs. Multicoloured. P 14.*
549	1 c. Type 99			10	10
550	2 c. "Thou shalt not make any graven image"			10	10
551	3 c. "Thou shalt not take My Name in vain"			10	10
552	10 c. "Remember the Sabbath Day"			20	10
553	35 c. "Honour thy father and mother"			45	20
554	60 c. "Thou shalt not kill"			80	40
555	75 c. "Thou shalt not commit adultery"			90	50
556	$2 "Thou shalt not steal"			2·25	1·50
557	$2.50 "Thou shalt not bear false witness" ..			2·50	1·50
558	$5 "Thou shalt not covet"			3·75	2·75
549/58			*Set of 10*	10·00	6·50
MS559	126×102 mm. $5 "Moses receiving the Tablets" (16th-century woodcut)			2·50	3·00

100 Leatherback Turtle

101 Montgolfier Hot Air Balloon, 1783

(Des R. Granger Barrett. Litho Questa)

1983 (10 Aug). *Endangered Species. Turtles. T 100 and similar horiz designs. Multicoloured. P 13½.*
560	10 c. Type 100		..	1·75	65
	a. Perf 12			2·50	1·00
561	35 c. Hawksbill Turtle			3·00	1·25
	a. Perf 12			4·25	2·50
562	75 c. Green Turtle ..			4·25	2·50
	a. Perf 12			5·50	4·50
563	$1 Loggerhead Turtle			4·75	4·00
	a. Perf 12			6·50	5·50
560/3			*Set of 4*	12·00	7·50
MS564	93×72 mm. $5 Leatherback Turtle (*different*)			7·00	3·00

(Des R. Granger Barrett. Litho Questa)

1983 (22 Aug). *Bicentenary of Manned Flight. T 101 and similar vert designs. Multicoloured. P 13½.*
565	10 c. Type 101			30	30
566	60 c. Blanchard and Jeffries crossing English Channel by balloon, 1785			85	60
567	$1 Henri Giffard's steam-powered dirigible airship, 1852			1·25	85
568	$2.50, Otto Lilienthal and biplane glider, 1890–96			2·00	1·75
565/8			*Set of 4*	4·00	3·25
MS569	72×90 mm. $5 Wilbur Wright flying round Statue of Liberty, 1909			2·75	3·25

102 Boys' Brigade Band and Flag

(Des R. Granger Barrett. Litho Questa)

1983 (12 Sept). *Centenary of Boys' Brigade. T 102 and similar horiz design. Multicoloured. P 13½.*
570	10 c. Type 102			25	15
571	$5 Brigade members marching			3·00	2·75
MS572	96 × 115 mm. Nos. 570/1 ..			3·25	3·75

150TH ANNIVERSARY ABOLITION OF SLAVERY ACT
(103)

1983 (24 Oct). *150th Anniv of the Abolition of Slavery (1st issue). Nos. 487, 493 and 497/8 optd with T 103.*
573	10 c. Island dinghies			15	10
	a. Opt inverted ..			35·00	
574	40 c. Sunset over Sandy Island			25	25
575	$1 Bagging lobster at Island Harbour			60	50
576	$5 Brown Pelicans			5·00	2·75
573/6	..		*Set of 4*	5·50	3·25

See also Nos. 616/24.

104 Jiminy on Clock
(*Cricket on the Hearth*)

(Litho Format)

1983 (14 Nov). *Christmas. Walt Disney Cartoon Characters. T 104 and similar vert designs depicting scenes from Dickens' Christmas stories. Multicoloured. P 13½.*
577	1 c. Type 104			10	10
578	2 c. Jiminy with fiddle (*Cricket on the Hearth*)			10	10
579	3 c. Jiminy among toys (*Cricket on the Hearth*)			10	10
580	4 c. Mickey as Bob Cratchit (*A Christmas Carol*)			10	10
581	5 c. Donald Duck as Scrooge (*A Christmas Carol*)			10	10

582	6 c. Mini and Goofy in *The Chimes* ..			10	10
583	10 c. Goofy sees an imp appearing from bells (*The Chimes*)			10	10
584	$2 Donald Duck as Mr. Pickwick (*The Pickwick Papers*)			3·50	2·00
585	$3 Disney characters as Pickwickians (*The Pickwick Papers*) ..			3·50	2·25
577/85			*Set of 9*	6·75	4·25
MS586	130 × 104 mm. $5 Donald Duck as Mr. Pickwick with gifts (*The Pickwick Papers*)			6·00	8·00

105 100 Metres Race

(Litho Questa)

1984 (20 Feb–24 Apr). *Olympic Games, Los Angeles. T 105 and similar horiz designs showing Mickey Mouse in Decathlon events. Multicoloured. A. Inscr. "1984 Los Angeles". P 14 × 13½.*
587A	1 c. Type 105			10	10
588A	2 c. Long jumping			10	10
589A	3 c. Shot-putting			10	10
590A	4 c. High jumping			10	10
591A	5 c. 400 metres race			10	10
592A	6 c. Hurdling			10	10
593A	10 c. Discus-throwing			10	10
594A	$1 Pole-vaulting			3·00	1·25
595A	$4 Javelin-throwing			3·50	3·50
587A/95A			*Set of 9*	8·00	4·75
MS596A	117×93 mm. $5 1500 metres race			6·50	4·00

B. *Inscr "1984 Olympics Los Angeles" and Olympic emblem. P 14×13½ (No. MS596B) or 12 (others) (24 Apr)*
587B	1 c. Type 105			10	10
588B	2 c. Long jumping			10	10
589B	3 c. Shot-putting			10	10
590B	4 c. High jumping			10	10
591B	5 c. 400 metres race			10	10
592B	6 c. Hurdling			10	10
593B	10 c. Discus-throwing			10	10
594B	$1 Pole-vaulting			3·50	2·75
595B	$4 Javelin-throwing			7·00	7·00
587B/95B			*Set of 9*	10·00	9·00
MS596B	117×93 mm. $5 1500 metres race			6·50	4·00

Nos. 587B/95B were each printed in small sheets of 6 stamps including one *se-tenant* stamp-size label in position 2.

106 "Justice"

(107)

(Des and litho Questa)

1984 (19 Apr). *Easter. T 106 and similar vert designs showing details from "La Stanza della Segnatura" by Raphael. Multicoloured. P 13½ × 14.*
597	10 c. Type 106 ..			15	10
598	25 c. "Poetry"			20	20
599	35 c. "Philosophy"			30	30
600	40 c. "Theology"			30	30
601	$1 "Abraham and Paul"			85	95
602	$2 "Moses and Matthew"			1·60	2·00
603	$3 "John and David"			2·25	2·75
604	$4 "Peter and Adam"			2·50	3·00
597/604			*Set of 8*	7·25	8·50
MS605	83 × 110 mm. $5 "Astronomy" ..			3·50	3·00

1984 (24 Apr–17 May). *Nos. 485, 491 and 498/500 surch as T 107.*
606	25 c. on $7.50, Hibiscus (17 May)			45	35
607	35 c. on 30 c. Little Bay cliffs ..			50	40
608	60 c. on 1 c. Type 92			55	45
609	$2.50 on $5 Brown Pelicans			2·25	1·50
	a. Surch at left with decimal point*			18·00	
610	$2.50 on $10 Queen Triggerfish			1·75	1·50
	a. Surch at right without decimal point*			18·00	
606/10			*Set of 5*	5·00	3·75

*The surcharge on No. 609 shows the figures at right of the design and without a decimal point. On No. 610 they are to the left and include a decimal point. No. 609a shows, in error, the surcharge for No. 610 and No. 610a that intended for No. 609.

108 Australia 1913 1d. Kangaroo Stamp

(Des K. Cato. Litho Leigh-Mardon Ltd, Melbourne)

1984 (16 July). *"Ausipex 84" International Stamp Exhibition, Melbourne. T 108 and similar horiz designs showing Australian stamps. Multicoloured. P 13½ × 14.*

611	10 c. Type 108		40	20
612	75 c. 1914 6d. Laughing Kookaburra		1·25	85
613	$1 1932 2d. Sydney Harbour Bridge		1·75	1·25
614	$2.50, 1938 10s. King George VI		2·25	2·25
611/14		Set of 4	5·00	4·00
MS615	95 × 86 mm. $5 £1 Bass and £2 Admiral King		4·50	6·00

109 Thomas Fowell Buxton

(Des R. Granger Barrett. Litho Questa)

1984 (1 Aug). *150th Anniv of Abolition of Slavery (2nd issue). T 109 and similar horiz designs. Multicoloured. P 14.*

616	10 c. Type 109		10	10
617	25 c. Abraham Lincoln		25	25
618	35 c. Henri Christophe		35	35
619	60 c. Thomas Clarkson		50	50
620	75 c. William Wilberforce		60	60
621	$1 Olaudah Equiano		70	70
622	$2.50, General Charles Gordon		1·60	1·60
623	$5 Granville Sharp		3·00	3·00
616/23		Set of 8	6·50	6·50
MS624	150 × 121 mm. Nos. 616/23. P 12		6·50	8·00

U.P.U. CONGRESS HAMBURG 1984
(110)

PRINCE HENRY BIRTH 15.9.84
(111)

1984 (13 Aug). *Universal Postal Union Congress, Hamburg. Nos. 486/7 and 498 optd as T 110 or surch also (No. 626).*

625	5 c. Ferry services, Blowing Point		20	10
626	20 c. on 10 c. Island dinghies		30	15
627	$5 Brown Pelicans		4·50	3·50
625/7		Set of 3	4·50	3·50

1984 (31 Oct). *Birth of Prince Henry. Nos. 507/14 optd as T 111.*

628	10 c. Type 95		10	10
	a. Booklet pane of 4		90	
629	30 c. Lady Diana Spencer in 1968		20	25
630	40 c. Lady Diana in 1970		25	30
	a. Booklet pane of 4		1·25	
631	60 c. Lady Diana in 1974		40	45
	a. Booklet pane of 4		1·60	
632	$2 Lady Diana in 1981		1·00	1·25
	a. Booklet pane of 4		4·00	
633	$3 Lady Diana in 1981 (different)		1·10	1·75
628/33		Set of 6	2·75	3·75
MS634	72 × 90 mm. $5 Princess of Wales		2·00	3·00
MS635	125 × 125 mm. As Nos. 628/33, but with buff borders		2·50	4·00

On No. MS634 the lines of overprint are larger, being placed vertically each side of the portrait.

112 Christmas in Sweden

(Litho Questa)

1984 (12 Nov). *Christmas. Walt Disney Cartoon Characters. T 112 and similar horiz designs showing national scenes. Multicoloured. P 12 ($2) or 14 × 13½ (others).*

636	1 c. Type 112		10	10
637	2 c. Italy		10	10
638	3 c. Holland		10	10
639	4 c. Mexico		10	10
640	5 c. Spain		10	10
641	10 c. Disneyland, U.S.A.		10	10
642	$1 Japan		2·75	2·00
643	$2 Anguilla		3·50	4·00
644	$4 Germany		5·50	6·50
636/44		Set of 9	11·00	11·50
MS645	126 × 102 mm. $5 England		7·00	5·00

No. 643 was printed in sheetlets of 8 stamps.

STANLEY GIBBONS STAMP COLLECTING SERIES

Introductory booklets on *How to Start, How to Identify Stamps* and *Collecting by Theme*. A series of well illustrated guides at a low price. Write for details.

---

113 Icarus in Flight   114 Barn Swallow

(Des H. Herni (60 c.), S. Diouf (75 c.), adapted R. Granger Barrett. Litho Ueberreuter)

1984 (3 Dec). *40th Anniv of International Civil Aviation Organization. T 113 and similar multicoloured designs. P 14.*

646	60 c. Type 113		60	75
647	75 c. "Solar Princess" (abstract)		80	90
648	$2.50, I.C.A.O. emblem (vert)		2·25	3·00
646/8		Set of 3	3·25	4·25
MS649	65 × 49 mm. $5 Map of air routes serving Anguilla		3·00	4·25

(Litho Questa)

1985 (29 Apr). *Birth Bicentenary of John J. Audubon (ornithologist). T 114 and similar multicoloured designs. P 14.*

650	10 c. Type 114		80	65
651	60 c. American Wood Stork		1·50	1·25
652	75 c. Roseate Tern		1·50	1·25
653	$5 Osprey		4·50	5·00
650/3		Set of 4	7·50	7·25
MS654	Two sheets, each 73 × 103 mm. (a) $4 Western Tanager (horiz); (b) $4 Solitary Vireo (horiz)	Set of 2 sheets	8·00	5·00

Nos. 650/3 were each issued in sheetlets of five stamps and one stamp-size label, which appears in the centre of the bottom row.

115 The Queen Mother visiting King's College Hospital, London
116 White-tailed Tropic Bird

(Des J.W. Litho Questa)

1985 (2 July). *Life and Times of Queen Elizabeth the Queen Mother. T 115 and similar vert designs. Multicoloured. P 14.*

655	10 c. Type 115		10	10
656	$2 The Queen Mother inspecting Royal Marine Volunteer Cadets, Deal		80	1·25
657	$3 The Queen Mother outside Clarence House		1·10	1·50
655/7		Set of 3	1·75	2·50
MS658	56 × 85 mm. $5 At Ascot, 1979		1·75	2·50

Nos. 655/7 also exist perforated 12×12½ from additional sheetlets of five stamps and one label (*Price for set of 3 £1.75 mint, £2.50 used*).

(Des R. Granger Barrett. Litho Questa)

1985 (22 July)–**86.** *Birds. T 116 and similar horiz designs. Multicoloured. P 13½ × 14.*

659	5 c. Brown Pelican (11.11.85)		1·50	1·25
660	10 c. Mourning Dove (11.11.85)		1·50	1·25
661	15 c. Magnificent Frigate Bird (inscr "Man-o-War") (11.11.85)		1·50	1·25
662	20 c. Antillean Crested Hummingbird (11.11.85)		1·50	1·25
663	25 c. Type 116		1·50	1·25
664	30 c. Caribbean Elaenia (11.11.85)		1·50	1·25
665	35 c. Black-whiskered Vireo (11.11.85)		6·00	5·00
665a	35 c. Lesser Antillean Bullfinch (10.3.86)		1·50	1·25
666	40 c. Yellow-crowned Night Heron (11.11.85)		1·50	1·25
667	45 c. Pearly-eyed Thrasher (30.9.85)		1·50	1·25
668	50 c. Laughing Gull (30.9.85)		1·50	1·25
669	65 c. Brown Booby (30.9.85)		1·50	1·25
670	80 c. Grey Kingbird (30.9.85)		2·00	2·75
671	$1 Audubon's Shearwater (30.9.85)		2·00	2·75
672	$1.35, Roseate Tern		1·50	2·75
673	$2.50, Bananaquit (11.11.85)		4·50	6·00
674	$5 Belted Kingfisher		3·75	7·00
675	$10 Green Heron (30.9.85)		6·50	9·00
659/75		Set of 18	38·00	45·00

GIRL GUIDES 75TH ANNIVERSARY 1910–1985
(117)

1985 (14 Oct). *75th Anniv of Girl Guide Movement. Nos. 486, 491, 496 and 498 optd with T 117.*

676	5 c. Ferry service, Blowing Point		20	20
677	30 c. Little Bay cliffs		40	35
678	75 c. Boat race at sunset, Sandy Ground		60	85
679	$5 Brown Pelicans		6·50	6·50
	a. Opt double		85·00	
676/9		Set of 4	7·00	7·00

---

118 Goofy as Huckleberry Finn Fishing

(Des Walt Disney Productions. Litho Questa)

1985 (11 Nov). *150th Birth Anniv of Mark Twain (author). T 118 and similar horiz designs showing Walt Disney cartoon characters in scenes from "Huckleberry Finn". Multicoloured. P 12 ($1) or 14 × 13½ (others).*

680	10 c. Type 118		35	20
681	60 c. Pete as Pap surprising Huck		1·25	85
682	$1 "Multiplication tables"		1·75	1·25
683	$3 The Duke reciting Shakespeare		3·25	4·00
680/3		Set of 4	6·00	5·75
MS684	127 × 102 mm. $5 "In school but out"		6·50	6·50

No. 682 was printed in sheetlets of 8 stamps.

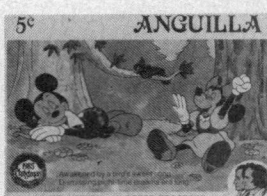

119 Hansel and Gretel (Mickey and Minnie Mouse) awakening in Forest

(Des Walt Disney Productions. Litho Questa)

1985 (11 Nov). *Birth Bicentenaries of Grimm Brothers (folklorists). T 119 and similar horiz designs showing Walt Disney cartoon characters in scenes from "Hansel and Gretel". Multicoloured. P 12 (90 c.) or 14 × 13½ (others).*

685	5 c. Type 119		20	20
686	50 c. Hansel and Gretel find the gingerbread house		75	45
687	90 c. Hansel and Gretel meeting the Witch		1·25	90
688	$4 Hansel and Gretel captured by the Witch		3·25	3·75
685/8		Set of 4	5·00	4·75
MS689	126 × 101 mm. $5 Hansel and Gretel riding on swan		6·50	7·00

No. 687 was printed in sheetlets of 8 stamps.

120 Statue of Liberty and *Danmark* (Denmark)

(Litho Format)

1985 (14 Nov). *Centenary of the Statue of Liberty (1986). T 120 and similar multicoloured designs showing the Statue of Liberty and cadet ships. P 15.*

690	10 c. Type 120		50	50
691	20 c. Eagle (U.S.A.)		70	70
692	60 c. Amerigo Vespucci (Italy)		1·00	1·50
693	75 c. Sir Winston Churchill (Great Britain)		1·00	1·75
694	$2 Nippon Maru (Japan)		1·50	2·50
695	$2.50, Gorch Fock (West Germany)		1·50	2·50
690/5		Set of 6	5·50	8·50
MS696	96 × 69 mm. $5 Statue of Liberty (vert)		7·00	4·50

80TH ANNIVERSARY ROTARY 1985
(121)

INTERNATIONAL YOUTH YEAR
(122)

1985 (18 Nov). *80th Anniv of Rotary (10, 35 c.) and International Youth Year (others). Nos. 487, 491 and 497 surch or optd as T 121 (10 c., 35 c.) or 122 (others).*

697	10 c. Island dinghies		15	15
698	35 c. on 30 c. Little Bay cliffs		40	30
699	$1 Bagging lobster at Island Harbour		90	80
700	$5 on 30 c. Little Bay cliffs		3·75	4·00
697/700		Set of 4	4·75	4·75

123 Johannes Hevelius
(astronomer) and Mayan
Temple Observatory

124 The
Crucifixion

(Des W. Hanson. Litho Questa)

1986 (17 Mar). *Appearance of Halley's Comet. T* **123** *and similar horiz designs. Multicoloured. P* 14.
701	5 c. Type **123**.			25	25
702	10 c. "Viking Lander" space vehicle on Mars, 1976			25	25
703	60 c. Comet in 1664 (from *Theatri Cosmicum*, 1668)			85	85
704	$4 Comet over Mississippi riverboat, 1835 (150th birth anniv of Mark Twain)			3·50	3·50
701/4			*Set of 4*	4·25	4·25
MS705	101×70 mm. $5 Halley's Comet over Anguilla			4·50	5·50

(Des R. Granger Barrett. Litho Questa)

1986 (27 Mar). *Easter. T* **124** *and similar designs showing stained glass windows from Chartres Cathedral. P* 14×13½.
706	10 c. multicoloured			20	20
707	25 c. multicoloured			35	35
708	45 c. multicoloured			65	65
709	$4 multicoloured			3·25	3·75
706/9			*Set of 4*	4·00	4·50
MS710	93×75 mm. $5 multicoloured (*horiz*). P 13½×14			5·50	7·00

125 Princess
Elizabeth inspecting
Guards, 1946

(126)

AMERIPEX 1986

(Litho Questa)

1986 (21 Apr). *60th Birthday of Queen Elizabeth II. T* **125** *and similar vert designs. P* 14.
711	20 c. black and yellow			20	20
712	$2 multicoloured			1·50	1·50
713	$3 multicoloured			1·75	1·75
711/13			*Set of 3*	3·00	3·00
MS714	120×85 mm. $5 black and grey-brown			2·75	3·50

Designs:—$2 Queen at Garter Ceremony; $3 At Trooping the Colour; $5 Duke and Duchess of York with baby Princess Elizabeth, 1926.

1986 (22 May). *"Ameripex" International Stamp Exhibition, Chicago. Nos. 659, 667, 671, 673 and 675 optd with T* **126**.
715	5 c. Brown Pelican			40	40
716	45 c. Pearly-eyed Thrasher			70	45
717	$1 Audubon's Shearwater			1·25	85
718	$2.50, Bananaquit			2·25	2·50
719	$10 Green Heron			6·00	7·50
715/19			*Set of 5*	9·50	10·50

127 Prince Andrew
and Miss Sarah
Ferguson

(128)

INTERNATIONAL YEAR OF PEACE

(Des and litho Questa)

1986 (23 July). *Royal Wedding. T* **127** *and similar vert designs. Multicoloured. P* 14.
720	10 c. Type **127**			20	15
	a. Perf 12			15	15
721	35 c. Prince Andrew			45	35
	a. Perf 12			35	35
722	$2 Miss Sarah Ferguson			1·50	1·50
	a. Perf 12			1·60	1·60
723	$3 Prince Andrew and Miss Sarah Ferguson (*different*)			2·00	2·00
	a. Perf 12			2·25	2·25
720/3			*Set of 4*	3·75	3·50
MS724	119×90 mm. $6 Westminster Abbey			5·50	6·50
	a. Perf 12			5·50	6·50

1986 (29 Sept). *International Peace Year. Nos. 616/24 optd with T* **128**.
725	10 c. Type **109**			25	25
726	25 c. Abraham Lincoln			45	45
727	55 c. Henri Christophe			55	55
728	60 c. Thomas Clarkson			80	80
729	75 c. William Wilberforce			90	90
730	$1 Olaudah Equiano			1·00	1·00
731	$2.50, General Gordon			2·00	2·00
732	$5 Granville Sharp			3·00	3·00
725/32			*Set of 8*	8·00	8·00
MS733	150×121 mnm. Nos. 725/32			12·00	14·00

129 Trading Sloop

130 Christopher
Columbus with
Astrolabe

(Des R. Granger Barrett. Litho Questa)

1986 (25 Nov). *Christmas. Ships. T* **129** *and similar multicoloured designs. P* 14.
734	10 c. Type **129**			90	50
735	45 c. *Lady Rodney* (cargo liner)			1·75	1·10
736	80 c. *West Derby* (19th-century sailing ship)			2·50	2·50
737	$3 *Warspite* (local sloop)			4·75	5·50
734/7			*Set of 4*	9·00	8·50
MS738	130×100 mm. $6 Boat race day (*vert*)			13·00	15·00

(Des Mary Walters. Litho Questa)

1986 (22 Dec). *500th Anniv of Discovery of America (1992) (1st issue). T* **130** *and similar multicoloured designs. P* 14.
739	5 c. Type **130**			30	30
740	10 c. Columbus on board ship			50	35
741	35 c. *Santa Maria*			1·25	90
742	80 c. King Ferdinand and Queen Isabella of Spain (*horiz*)			1·50	1·60
743	$4 Caribbean Indians smoking tobacco (*horiz*)			3·25	4·25
739/43			*Set of 5*	6·00	6·50
MS744	Two sheets, each 96×66 mm. (a) $5 Caribbean Manatee (*horiz*). (b) $5 Dragon Tree		*Set of 2 sheets*	12·00	14·00

See also Nos. 902/6.

131 *Danaus plexippus*

(Des R. Vigurs. Litho Questa)

1987 (14 Apr). *Easter. Butterflies. T* **131** *and similar horiz designs. Multicoloured. P* 14.
745	10 c. Type **131**			85	50
746	80 c. *Anartia jatrophae*			2·50	2·50
747	$1 *Heliconius charithonia*			2·75	2·50
748	$2 *Junonia evarete*			4·50	5·00
745/8			*Set of 4*	9·50	9·50
MS749	90×69 mm. $6 *Dryas julia*			11·00	13·00

132 Old Goose Iron and Modern
Electric Iron

(133)

(Des R. Vigurs. Litho Questa)

1987 (25 May). *20th Anniv of Separation from St. Kitts–Nevis. T* **132** *and similar horiz designs. Multicoloured. P* 14.
750	10 c. Type **132**			20	25
751	35 c. Old East End School and Albena Lake-Hodge Comprehensive College			25	25
752	45 c. Past and present markets			30	30
753	80 c. Previous sailing ferry and new motor ferry, Blowing Point			60	60
754	$1 Original mobile office and new telephone exchange			65	75
755	$2 Open-air meeting, Burrowes Park, and House of Assembly in session			1·25	1·50
750/5			*Set of 6*	3·00	3·75
MS756	159×127 mm. Nos. 750/5			6·00	8·00

1987 (13 June). *"Capex '87" International Stamp Exhibition, Toronto. Nos. 665a, 667, 670 and 675 optd with T* **133** *in red.*
757	35 c. Lesser Antillean Bullfinch			80	70
758	45 c. Pearly-eyed Thrasher			90	70
759	80 c. Grey Kingbird			1·50	1·25
760	$10 Green Heron			7·00	8·50
757/60			*Set of 4*	9·00	10·00

---

20 YEARS OF PROGRESS

1967 – 1987

(134)

1987 (4 Sept). *20th Anniv of Independence. Nos. 659, 661/4 and 665a/75 optd as T* **134** *in red or surch additionally in black (No. 762).*
761	5 c. Brown Pelican			1·00	1·00
762	10 c. on 15 c. Magnificent Frigate Bird			1·00	1·00
763	15 c. Magnificent Frigate Bird			1·25	1·25
764	20 c. Antillean Crested Hummingbird			1·25	1·25
765	25 c. Type **116**.			1·25	1·25
766	30 c. Caribbean Elaenia			1·25	1·25
767	35 c. Lesser Antillean Bullfinch			1·25	1·25
768	35 c. Yellow-crowned Night Heron			1·25	1·25
769	45 c. Pearly-eyed Thrasher			1·25	1·25
	a. Opt double, one albino			42·00	
770	50 c. Laughing Gull			1·25	1·25
771	65 c. Brown Booby			1·50	1·75
772	80 c. Grey Kingbird			1·50	1·75
773	$1 Audubon's Shearwater			1·50	1·75
774	$1.35, Roseate Tern			2·00	2·25
775	$2.50, Bananaquit			2·25	3·50
776	$5 Belted Kingfisher			3·50	5·00
777	$10 Green Heron			6·00	8·50
761/77			*Set of 17*	27·00	32·00

135 Wicket Keeper and Game in Progress

(Des R. Granger Barrett. Litho Questa)

1987 (5 Oct). *Cricket World Cup. T* **135** *and similar horiz designs. Multicoloured. P* 13½×14.
778	10 c. Type **135**.			75	50
779	35 c. Batsman and local Anguilla team			1·25	60
780	45 c. Batsman and game in progress			1·40	70
781	$2.50, Bowler and game in progress			3·25	4·50
778/81			*Set of 4*	6·00	5·75
MS782	100×75 mm. $6 Batsman and game in progress (*different*)			11·00	13·00

136 West Indian Top Shell

(Des R. Granger Barrett. Litho Questa)

1987 (2 Nov). *Christmas. Sea Shells and Crabs. T* **136** *and similar horiz designs. Multicoloured. P* 13½×14.
783	10 c. Type **136**.			75	40
784	35 c. Ghost Crab			1·25	60
785	50 c. Spiny Caribbean Vase			2·00	1·40
786	$2 Great Land Crab			3·25	4·75
783/6			*Set of 4*	6·50	6·50
MS787	101×75 mm. $6 Queen or Pink Conch			8·00	10·00

40TH WEDDING ANNIVERSARY

H.M. QUEEN ELIZABETH II

H.R.H. THE DUKE OF EDINBURGH

(137)

1987 (16 Dec). *Royal Ruby Wedding. Nos. 665a, 671/2 and 675 optd with T* **137** *in carmine.*
788	35 c. Lesser Antillean Bullfinch			40	30
789	$1 Audubon's Shearwater			1·00	80
790	$1.35, Roseate Tern			1·10	90
791	$10 Green Heron			5·25	6·00
788/91			*Set of 4*	7·00	7·25

138 *Crinum
erubescens*

139 Relay Racing

(Des R. Vigurs. Litho Questa)

1988 (28 Mar). *Easter. Lilies.* T **138** *and similar vert designs. Multicoloured.* P 14×13½.

792	30 c. Type **138**	40	25
793	45 c. Spider Lily	50	25
794	$1 *Crinum macowanii*	1·25	75
795	$2.50, Day Lily	1·50	2·25
792/5	Set of 4	3·25	3·25
MS796	100×75 mm. $6 Easter Lily	2·75	3·75

(Des R. Vigurs. Litho Questa)

1988 (25 July). *Olympic Games, Seoul.* T **139** *and similar vert designs. Multicoloured.* P 14×13½.

797	35 c. Type **139**	40	30
798	45 c. Windsurfing	55	45
799	50 c. Tennis	1·25	1·10
800	80 c. Basketball	2·75	2·75
797/800	Set of 4	4·50	4·25
MS801	104×78 mm. $6 Athletics	3·00	4·00

140 Common Sea Fan

(Des R. Vigurs. Litho Questa)

1988 (28 Nov). *Christmas. Marine Life.* T **140** *and similar horiz designs. Multicoloured.* P 13½ × 14.

802	35 c. Type **140**	45	30
803	80 c. Coral Crab	1·00	70
804	$1 Grooved Brain Coral	1·25	95
805	$1.60, Queen Triggerfish	1·60	2·25
802/5	Set of 4	3·75	3·75
MS806	103 x 78 mm. $6 West Indies Spiny Lobster	3·00	4·00

H.R.H. PRINCESS
ALEXANDRA'S
VISIT NOVEMBER 1988
(141)

1988 (14 Dec). *Visit of Princess Alexandra. Nos.* 665a, 670/1 *and* 673 *optd with* T **141**.

807	35 c. Lesser Antillean Bullfinch	90	60
808	80 c. Grey Kingbird	1·60	1·40
809	$1 Audubon's Shearwater	1·75	1·60
810	$2.50, Bananaquit	3·00	4·25
807/10	Set of 4	6·50	7·00

142 Wood Slave

143 "Christ Crowned with Thorns" (detail) (Bosch)

(Des R. Vigurs. Litho Questa)

1989 (20 Feb). *Lizards.* T **142** *and similar horiz designs. Multicoloured.* P 14 × 13½.

811	45 c. Type **142**	55	40
812	80 c. Slippery Back	85	75
813	$2.50, *Iguana delicatissima*	2·25	3·25
811/13	Set of 3	3·25	4·00
MS814	101 × 75 mm. $6 Tree Lizard	2·75	4·00

(Des R. Vigurs. Litho Questa)

1989 (23 Mar). *Easter. Religious Paintings.* T **143** *and similar vert designs. Multicoloured.* P 14 × 13½.

815	35 c. Type **143**	30	20
816	80 c. "Christ bearing the Cross" (detail) (Gerard David)	55	55
817	$1 "The Deposition" (detail) (Gerard David)	60	60
818	$1.60, "Pietà" (detail) (Rogier van der Weyden)	90	1·60
815/18	Set of 4	2·10	2·75
MS819	103 × 77 mm. $6 "Crucified Christ with the Virgin Mary and Saints" (detail) (Raphael)	2·75	4·00

MINIMUM PRICE

The minimum price quote is 10p which represents a handling charge rather than a basis for valuing common stamps. For further notes about prices see introductory pages.

144 University Arms

20th
ANNIVERSARY
MOON
LANDING

(145)

(Des R. Vigurs. Litho Questa)

1989 (24 Apr). *40th Anniv of University of the West Indies.* P 14 × 13½.

820	**144** $5 multicoloured	2·40	3·00

1989 (31 July). *20th Anniv of First Manned Landing on Moon. Nos.* 670/2 *and* 674 *optd with* T **145**.

821	80 c. Grey Kingbird	90	80
822	$1 Audubon's Shearwater	1·00	90
823	$1.35, Roseate Tern	1·25	1·40
824	$5 Belted Kingfisher	4·00	4·75
821/4	Set of 4	6·50	7·00

146 Lone Star House, 1930

(Des J. Vigurs. Litho Questa)

1989 (11 Dec). *Christmas. Historic Houses.* T **146** *and similar horiz designs. Multicoloured.* P 13½×14.

825	5 c. Type **146**	15	20
826	35 c. Whitehouse, 1906	45	35
827	45 c. Hodges House	55	45
828	80 c. Warden's Place	1·00	1·40
825/8	Set of 4	1·90	2·25
MS829	102×77 mm. $6 Wallblake House, 1787	3·25	4·50

147 Bigeye ("Blear Eye")

148 The Last Supper

(Des J. Vigurs. Litho Questa)

1990 (2 Apr)–92. *Fishes.* T **147** *and similar horiz designs. Multicoloured.* P 13½×14. A. *Without imprint date at foot.*

830A	5 c. Type **147**	60	75
831A	10 c. Long-spined Squirrelfish ("Redman")	60	75
832A	15 c. Stop-light Parrotfish ("Speckletail")	45	45
833A	25 c. Blue-striped Grunt	50	60
834A	30 c. Yellow Jack	50	60
835A	35 c. Red Hind	75	75
836A	40 c. Spotted Goatfish	60	60
837A	45 c. Queen Triggerfish ("Old Wife")	60	60
838A	50 c. Coney ("Butter Fish")	60	60
839A	65 c. Smooth Trunkfish ("Shell Fish")	60	60
840A	80 c. Yellow-tailed Snapper	70	70
841A	$1 Banded Butterflyfish ("Katy")	80	80
842A	$1.35, Nassau Grouper	1·25	1·25
843A	$2.50 Blue Tang ("Doctor Fish")	1·75	2·00
844A	$5 Queen Angelfish	2·75	3·50
845A	$10 Great Barracuda	4·75	6·00
830A/45A	Set of 16	16·00	18·00

B. *With imprint date* (10.6.92)

830B	5 c. Type **147**	40	50
831B	10 c. Long-spined Squirrelfish ("Redman")	40	50
835B	35 c. Red Hind	50	50
830B/5B	Set of 3	1·10	1·40

(Des M. Pollard. Litho Questa)

1990 (2 Apr). *Easter.* T **148** *and similar vert designs. Multicoloured.* P 14×13½.

846	35 c. Type **148**	65	20
847	45 c. The Trial	65	65
848	$1.35, The Crucifixion	1·75	1·90
849	$2.50, The Empty Tomb	2·25	3·50
846/9	Set of 4	4·75	5·25
MS850	114×84 mm. $6 The Resurrection	6·50	7·50

149 G.B. 1840
Penny Black

WORLD CUP FOOTBALL
CHAMPIONSHIPS 1990
(150)

(Litho Questa)

1990 (30 Apr). *"Stamp World London 90" International Stamp Exhibition.* T **149** *and similar multicoloured designs showing stamps.* P 14.

851	25 c. Type **149**	50	25
852	50 c. G.B. 1840 Twopenny Blue	85	50
853	$1.50, Cape of Good Hope 1861 1d. "woodblock" (*horiz*)	1·75	2·00
854	$2.50, G.B. 1882 £5 (*horiz*)	2·25	2·75
851/4	Set of 4	4·75	5·00
MS855	86×71 mm. $6 Penny Black and Twopence Blue (*horiz*)	6·50	7·50

1990 (24 Sept). *Anniversaries and Events. Nos.* 841A/4A *optd as* T **150**.

856	$1 Banded Butterflyfish (optd "EXPO '90")	1·25	1·00
857	$1.35, Nassau Grouper (optd "1990 INTERNATIONAL LITERACY YEAR")	1·50	1·25
858	$2.50, Blue Tang (optd with T **150**)	2·75	3·25
859	$5 Queen Angelfish (optd "90TH BIRTHDAY H.M. THE QUEEN MOTHER")	4·00	5·00
856/9	Set of 4	8·50	9·50

151 Mermaid Flag

(Des R. Vigurs. Litho Questa)

1990 (5 Nov). *Island Flags.* T **151** *and similar horiz designs. Multicoloured.* P 13½×14.

860	50 c. Type **151**	80	40
861	80 c. New Anguilla official flag	1·25	90
862	$1 Three Dolphins flag	1·40	95
863	$5 Governor's official flag	3·75	5·50
860/3	Set of 4	6·50	7·00

152 Laughing Gulls

1991
(153)

(Des R. Vigurs. Litho Questa)

1990 (26 Nov). *Christmas. Sea Birds.* T **152** *and similar horiz designs. Multicoloured.* P 13½×14.

864	10 c. Type **152**	60	40
865	35 c. Brown Booby	1·00	50
866	$1.50, Bridled Tern	2·00	2·00
867	$3.50, Brown Pelican	3·25	3·75
864/7	Set of 4	6·25	6·00
MS868	101×76 mm. $6 Little Tern	7·00	9·00

1991 (30 Apr). *Easter. Nos.* 846/50 *optd with* T **153**.

869	35 c. Type **148**	55	35
870	45 c. The Trial	65	45
871	$1.35, The Crucifixion	1·50	1·75
872	$2.50, The Empty Tomb	2·25	3·50
869/72	Set of 4	4·50	5·50
MS873	114 × 84 mm. $6 The Resurrection	6·50	7·50

On No. MS873 the "1990" inscription on the sheet margin has also been obliterated.

154 Angel

155 Angels with Palm Branches outside St. Gerard's Church

(Des Michele Lavalette. Litho Questa)

1991 (16 Dec). *Christmas. T* **154** *and similar designs.*
P 14×13½ (5 c., 35 c.) or 13½×14 (others).

874	5 c. dull violet, chestnut and black		30	30
875	35 c. multicoloured		75	55
876	80 c. multicoloured		1·60	1·60
877	$1 multicoloured		1·75	1·75
874/7		Set of 4	4·00	3·75
MS878	131×97 mm. $5 mult. P 13½×14		4·50	6·00

Designs: *Vert*—35 c. Father Christmas. *Horiz*—80 c. Church and house; $1 Palm trees at night; $5 Anguilla village.

(Des Lucia Butler. Litho Questa)

1992 (21 Apr). *Easter. T* **155** *and similar multicoloured designs. P* 13½×14 (80 c., $5) or 14×13½ (others).

879	35 c. Type **155**		45	25
880	45 c. Angels singing outside Methodist Church		55	35
881	80 c. Village (horiz)		1·10	90
882	$1 Congregation going to St. Mary's Church		1·25	1·00
883	$5 Dinghy regatta (horiz)		4·00	6·00
879/83		Set of 5	6·50	7·75

$1.60

(156)   157 Anguillan Flags

1992 (10 June). *As No. 834, but with imprint date, surch with T* **156**.

884	$1.60 on 30 c. Yellow Jack		1·40	1·40

(Litho Questa)

1992 (10 Aug). *25th Anniv of Separation from St. Kitts-Nevis. T* **157** *and similar square designs. Multicoloured. P* 14.

885	80 c. Type **157**		1·00	90
886	$1 Present official seal		1·25	1·10
887	$1.60, Anguillan flags at airport		2·25	2·25
888	$2 Royal Commissioner's official seal		2·25	2·25
885/8		Set of 4	6·00	6·00
MS889	116×117 mm. $10 "Independent Anguilla" overprinted stamps of 1967 (85×85 mm)		7·00	8·00

158 Dinghy Race

(Des Michele Lavalette. Litho Questa)

1992 (12 Oct). *Sailing Dinghy Racing. T* **158** *and similar designs. P* 13½×14 (horiz) or 14×13½ (vert).

890	20 c. multicoloured		70	55
891	35 c. multicoloured		90	60
892	45 c. multicoloured		95	60
893	80 c. multicoloured		1·75	2·25
	a. Vert pair. Nos. 893/4		3·50	4·50
894	80 c. black and pale azure		1·75	2·25
895	$1 multicoloured		1·75	2·00
890/5		Set of 6	7·00	7·50
MS896	129×30 mm. $6 multicoloured		4·25	5·00

Designs: *Vert*—35 c. Stylized poster; 80 c. (No. 893) *Blue Bird* in race; 80 c. (No. 894) Construction drawings of *Blue Bird* by Douglas Pyle; $1 Stylized poster (different). *Horiz* (as T **158**)—45 c. Dinghies on beach. (97×32 mm)—$6 Composite design as 20 and 45 c. values.

Nos. 893/4 were printed together, *se-tenant*, in vertical pairs throughout the sheet.

159 Mucka Jumbie on Stilts

(Litho Questa)

1992 (7 Dec). *Christmas. Local Traditions. T* **159** *and similar horiz dsigns. Multicoloured. P* 14.

897	20 c. Type **159**		25	20
898	70 c. Masqueraders		60	50
899	$1.05, Baking in old style oven		85	85
900	$2.40, Collecting presents from Christmas tree		1·50	2·25
897/900		Set of 4	2·75	3·50
MS901	128×101 $5 As No. 900		3·50	4·50

No. MS901 also contains labels in designs as Nos. 897/9, but without face values.

160 Columbus landing in New World

 (overlaps) 161 "Kite Flying" (Kyle Brooks)

(Des Michele Lavalette. Litho Questa)

1992 (15 Dec). *500th Anniv of Discovery of America by Columbus (2nd issue). T* **160** *and similar designs. P* 14.

902	80 c. multicoloured		1·25	1·10
903	$1 brownish black and yellow-brown		1·25	1·10
904	$2 multicoloured		2·25	2·75
905	$3 multicoloured		2·75	3·50
902/5		Set of 4	6·75	7·75
MS906	78×54 mm. $6 multicoloured		6·50	7·50

Designs: *Vert*—$1 Christopher Columbus; $6 Columbus and map of West Indies. *Horiz*—$2 Fleet of Columbus; $3 *Pinta*.

(Litho Questa)

1993 (29 Mar). *Easter. Children's Paintings. T* **161** *and similar vert designs. Multicoloured. P* 14.

907	20 c. Type **161**		65	30
908	45 c. "Clifftop Village Service" (Kara Connor)		85	45
909	80 c. "Morning Devotion on Sombrero" (Junior Carty)		1·60	1·40
910	$1.50, "Hill Top Church Service" (Leana Harris)		2·25	3·00
907/10		Set of 4	4·75	4·75
MS911	90×110 mm. $5 "Good Friday Kites" (Marvin Hazel and Kyle Brooks) (39×53 mm)		4·50	5·50

162 Salt Picking

163 Lord Great Chamberlain presenting Spurs of Chivalry to Queen

(Des Penny Slinger. Litho Questa)

1993 (23 June). *Traditional Industries. T* **162** *and similar horiz designs. Multicoloured. P* 14.

912	20 c. Type **162**		1·00	50
913	80 c. Tobacco growing		1·10	90
914	$1 Cotton picking		1·25	1·00
915	$2 Harvesting sugar cane		2·00	3·00
912/15		Set of 4	4·75	4·75
MS916	111×85 mm. $6 Fishing		7·00	9·00

(Des John Lister Ltd. Litho Questa)

1993 (16 Aug). *40th Anniv of Coronation. T* **163** *and similar vert designs. Multicoloured. P* 14.

917	80 c. Type **163**		75	50
918	$1 The Benediction		85	70
919	$2 Queen Elizabeth II in Coronation robes		1·25	1·60
920	$3 St. Edward's Crown		1·75	2·25
917/20		Set of 4	4·25	4·50
MS921	114×95 mm. $6 The Queen and Prince Philip in Coronation coach		7·00	7·50

164 Carnival Pan Player

165 Mucka Jumbies Carnival Characters

(Des Penny Slinger. Litho Questa)

1993 (23 Aug). *Anguilla Carnival. T* **164** *and similar horiz designs. Multicoloured. P* 13½×14.

922	20 c. Type **164**		30	20
923	45 c. Revellers dressed as pirates		50	30
924	80 c. Revellers dressed as stars		80	65
925	$1 Mas dancing		90	80
926	$2 Masked couple		1·75	2·50
927	$3 Revellers dressed as commandos		2·25	2·75
922/7		Set of 6	6·00	6·50
MS928	123×94 mm. $5 Revellers in fantasy costumes		6·00	7·00

(Litho Questa)

1993 (7 Dec). *Christmas. T* **165** *and similar multicoloured designs. P* 14×13½.

929	20 c. Type **165**		30	30
930	35 c. Local carol singers		50	30
931	45 c. Christmas home baking		60	35
932	$3 Decorating Christmas tree		2·40	3·50
929/32		Set of 4	3·50	4·00
MS933	123×118 mm. $4 Mucka Jumbies and carol singers (58½×47 mm). P 14		2·75	4·00

166 Travelling Branch Mail Van at Sandy Ground

167 Princess Alexandra, 1988

(Litho Questa)

1994 (11 Feb). *Delivering the Mail. T* **166** *and similar multicoloured designs. P* 14.

934	20 c. Type **166**		70	45
935	45 c. *Betsy R* (mail schooner) at The Forest (vert)		1·00	50
936	80 c. Mail van at old Post Office		1·50	1·25
937	$1 Jeep on beach, Island Harbour (vert)		1·50	1·25
938	$4 New Post Office		3·50	5·00
934/8		Set of 5	7·50	7·75

(Litho Questa)

1994 (18 Feb). *Royal Visitors. T* **167** *and similar vert designs. Multicoloured. P* 14.

939	45 c. Type **167**		55	35
940	50 c. Princess Alice, 1960		60	45
941	80 c. Prince Philip, 1993		90	75
942	$1 Prince Charles, 1973		1·10	85
943	$2 Queen Elizabeth II, 1994		1·75	2·50
939/43		Set of 5	4·50	4·50
MS944	162×90 mm. Nos. 939/43		6·00	7·00

168 "The Crucifixion"

169 Cameroun Player and Pontiac Silverdome, Detroit

(Litho Questa)

1994 (6 Apr). *Easter. Stained-glass Windows. T* **168** *and similar vert designs. Multicoloured. P* 14×15.

945	20 c. Type **168**		40	40
946	45 c. "The Empty Tomb"		55	45
947	80 c. "The Resurrection"		90	90
948	$3 "Risen Christ with Disciples"		2·75	3·75
945/8		Set of 4	4·25	5·00

(Des R. Vigurs. Litho Questa)

1994 (3 Oct). *World Cup Football Championship, U.S.A. T* **169** *and similar horiz designs. Multicoloured. P* 14.

949	20 c. Type **169**		45	30
950	70 c. Argentine player and Foxboro Stadium, Boston		85	65
951	$1.80, Italian player and RFK Memorial Stadium, Washington		1·75	2·00
952	$2.40, German player and Soldier Field, Chicago		2·00	2·75
949/52		Set of 4	4·50	5·25
MS953	112×85 mm. $6 American and Colombian players		6·00	7·00

170 "The Nativity" (Gustave Doré)

171 Pair of Zenaida Doves

(Des R. Vigurs. Litho Questa)

1994 (22 Nov). *Christmas. Religious Paintings.* T **170** *and similar vert designs. Multicoloured.* P 14.

954	20 c. Type 170		35	30
955	30 c. "The Wise Men guided by the Star" (Doré)		45	30
956	35 c. "The Annunciation" (Doré)		50	35
957	45 c. "Adoration of the Shepherds" (detail) (Poussin)		55	45
958	$2.40, "The Flight into Egypt" (Doré)		1·50	2·75
954/8		Set of 5	3·00	3·75

(Des R. Vigurs. Litho Questa)

1995 (10 Apr). *Easter. Zenaida Doves.* T **171** *and similar horiz designs. Multicoloured.* P 13½×14.

959	20 c. Type 171		50	40
960	45 c. Dove on branch		75	50
961	50 c. Guarding nest		80	55
962	$5 With chicks		5·50	6·50
959/62		Set of 4	6·75	7·25

172 Trygve Lie (first Secretary-General) and General Assembly

(Des R. Vigurs. Litho Questa)

1995 (26 June). *50th Anniv of United Nations.* T **172** *and similar multicoloured designs.* P 14×13½ (vert) or 13½×14 (others).

963	20 c. Type 172		30	30
964	80 c. Flag and building showing "50"		60	65
965	$1 Dag Hammarskjöld and U. Thant (former Secretary-Generals) and U.N. Charter		70	75
966	$5 U.N. Building (vert)		4·00	5·50
963/6		Set of 4	5·00	6·50

173 Anniversary Emblem and Map of Anguilla

(Des R. Vigurs. Litho Questa)

1995 (15 Aug). *25th Anniv of Caribbean Development Bank.* T **173** *and similar horiz design. Multicoloured.* P 13½×14.

967	45 c. Type 173		1·50	1·75
	a. Horiz pair. Nos. 967/8		4·50	5·50
968	$5 Bank building and launches		3·00	3·75

Nos. 967/8 were printed together, se-tenant, in horizontal pairs throughout sheets of 10.

174 Blue Whale

(Litho Questa)

1995 (24 Nov). *Endangered Species. Whales.* T **174** *and similar multicoloured designs.* P 14×13½ (45 c.) or 13½×14 (others).

969	20 c. Type 174		70	50
970	45 c. Right Whale (vert)		1·10	50
971	$1 Sperm Whale		1·75	1·50
972	$5 Humpback Whale		6·00	7·00
969/72		Set of 4	8·50	8·50

175 Palm Tree   176 Deep Water Gorgonia

(Litho Questa)

1995 (12 Dec). *Christmas.* T **175** *and similar square designs. Multicoloured.* P 14½.

973	10 c. Type 175		30	30
974	25 c. Balloons and fishes		50	35
975	45 c. Shells		35	35
976	$5 Fishes in shape of Christmas Tree		6·00	7·00
973/6		Set of 4	6·75	7·25

(Des Michele Lavalette. Litho Cot Printery Ltd, Barbados)

1996 (21 June). *Corals.* T **176** *and similar horiz designs. Multicoloured.* P 14×14½.

977	20 c. Type 176		65	40
978	80 c. Common Sea Fan		1·25	90
979	$5 Venus Sea Fern		4·75	6·00
977/9		Set of 3	6·00	6·50

177 Running   178 Siege of Sandy Hill Fort

(Des Iris Lewis. Litho Cot Printery Ltd, Barbados)

1996 (12 Dec). *Olympic Games, Atlanta.* T **177** *and similar vert designs. Multicoloured.* P 14.

980	20 c. Type 177		30	20
981	80 c. Javelin throwing and wheelchair basketball		80	70
982	$1 High jumping and hurdles		85	85
983	$3.50, Olympic rings and torch with Greek and American flags		2·75	3·25
980/3		Set of 4	4·25	4·50

(Des Iris Lewis. Litho Cot Printery Ltd, Barbados)

1996 (12 Dec). *Bicentenary of the Battle for Anguilla.* T **178** *and similar multicoloured designs.* P 14.

984	60 c. Type 178		75	60
985	75 c. French troops destroying church (horiz)		80	70
986	$1.50, Naval battle (horiz)		1·75	1·75
987	$4 French troops landing at Rendezvous Bay		2·75	3·75
984/7		Set of 4	5·50	6·00

179 Gooseberry

(Des Michele Lavalette. Litho Questa)

1997 (30 Apr). *Fruit.* T **179** *and similar horiz designs. Multicoloured.* P 14.

988	10 c. Type 179		10	10
989	20 c. West Indian Cherry		10	10
990	40 c. Tamarind		15	20
991	50 c. Pomme-surette		20	25
992	60 c. Sea Almond		25	30
993	75 c. Sea Grape		35	40
994	80 c. Banana		35	40
995	$1 Genip		45	50
996	$1.10, Coco Plum		50	55
997	$1.25, Pope		55	60
998	$1.50, Pawpaw		65	70
999	$2 Sugar Apple		85	90
1000	$3 Soursop		1·25	1·40
1001	$4 Pomegranate		1·75	1·90
1002	$5 Cashew		2·10	2·25
1003	$10 Mango		4·25	4·50
998/1003		Set of 16	13·50	14·50

180 West Indian Iguanas hatching

1997 (13 Oct). *Endangered Species. West Indian Iguanas.* T **180** *and similar horiz designs. Multicoloured. Litho.* P 13½×14.

1004	20 c. Type 180		60	75
	a. Strip of 4. Nos. 1004/7		3·50	
1005	50 c. On rock		80	1·00
1006	75 c. On branch		90	1·10
1007	$3 Head of West Indian Iguana		1·75	2·00
1004/7		Set of 4	3·50	4·25

Nos. 1004/7 were printed together, se-tenant, in horizontal and vertical strips of 4 throughout the sheet.

181 "Juluca, Rainbow Deity"   182 Diana, Princess of Wales

(Des Clair Twaron and N. Graulke. Litho Cot Printery Ltd, Barbados)

1997 (17 Nov). *Ancient Stone Carvings from Fountain Cavern.* T **181** *and similar horiz designs. Multicoloured.* P 14×14½.

1008	30 c. Type 181		45	35
1009	$1.25, "Lizard with front legs extended"		90	90
1010	$2.25, "Chief"		1·60	2·00
1011	$2.75, "Jocahu, the Creator"		2·00	2·25
1008/11		Set of 4	4·50	5·00

(Des R. Vigurs. Litho Questa)

1998 (14 Apr). *Diana, Princess of Wales Commemoration.* T **182** *and similar vert designs. Multicoloured.* P 14×13½.

1012	15 c. Type 182		60	75
	a. Strip of 4. Nos. 1012/15		4·50	
1013	$1 Wearing yellow blouse		1·25	1·40
1014	$1.90, Wearing tiara		1·50	1·60
1015	$2.25, Wearing blue short-sleeved Red Cross blouse		1·60	1·75
1012/15		Set of 4	4·50	5·00

Nos. 1012/15 were printed together, se-tenant, in horizontal and vertical strips of 4 throughout the sheet.

183 "Treasure Island" (Valarie Alix)

(Litho Cot Printery Ltd, Barbados)

1998 (24 Aug). *International Arts Festival.* T **183** *and similar multicoloured designs.* P 14.

1016	15 c. Type 183		25	30
1017	30 c. "Posing in the Light" (Melsadis Fleming) (vert)		35	40
1018	$1 "Pescadores de Anguilla" (Juan Garcia) (vert)		70	80
1019	$1.50, "Fresh Catch" (Verna Hart)		1·00	1·25
1020	$1.90, "The Bell Tower of St. Mary's" (Ricky Racardo Edwards) (vert)		1·25	1·50
1016/20		Set of 5	3·25	3·75

184 Roasting Corn-cobs on Fire

(Litho Cot Printery, Ltd, Barbados)

1998 (18 Nov). *Christmas. "Hidden Beauty of Anguilla".* T **184** *and similar horiz designs showing children's paintings. Multicoloured.* P 14.

1021	15 c. Type 184		20	20
1022	$1 Fresh fruit and market stallholder		60	50
1023	$1.50, Underwater scene		80	80
1024	$3 Cacti and view of sea		1·40	2·00
1021/4		Set of 4	2·75	3·25

185 University of West Indies Centre, Anguilla

(Des R. Vigurs. Litho Cartor)

1998 (31 Dec). *50th Anniv of University of West Indies.* T **185** *and similar horiz design. Multicoloured.* P 13½.

1025	$1.50, Type 185		80	80
1026	$1.90, Man with torch and University arms		1·10	1·10

Nos. 1025/6 are on fluorescent paper. A printing on ordinary paper disappeared in transit and was not issued in Anguilla.

186 Sopwith Camel and Bristol F2B
Fighters

(Des R. Vigurs. Litho Cartor)

1998 (31 Dec). *80th Anniv of Royal Air Force. T **186** and similar horiz designs. Multicoloured. P 13½.*

1027	30 c. Type **186**		30	30
1028	$1 Supermarine Spitfire Mk II and Hawker Hurricane Mk I		65	55
1029	$1.50, Avro Lancaster		90	90
1030	$1.90, Panavia Tornado F3 and Harrier GR7		1·10	1·40
1027/30		Set of 4	2·75	2·75

Nos. 1027/30 are on fluorescent paper. A printing on ordinary paper disappeared in transit and was not issued in Anguilla.

187 Saturn 5 Rocket and "Apollo 11" Command Module   188 Albena Lake Hodge

(Des R. Vigurs. Litho Cartor)

1999 (6 May). *30th Anniv of First Manned Landing on Moon. T **187** and similar horiz designs. Multicoloured. P 13½.*

1031	30 c. Type **187**		25	25
1032	$1 Astronaut Edwin Aldrin, Lunar Module *Eagle* and first footprint on Moon		55	55
1033	$1.50, Lunar Module leaving Moon's surface		75	75
1034	$1.90, Recovery of Command Module		90	1·00
1031/4		Set of 4	2·25	2·25

(Litho Cot Printery Ltd, Barbados)

1999 (5 July). *Anguillan Heroes and Heroines (1st series). T **188** and similar vert designs. Each black, light green and cream. P 14½×14.*

1035	30 c. Type **188**		25	25
1036	$1 Collins O. Hodge		55	55
1037	$1.50, Edwin Wallace Rey		75	75
1038	$1.90, Walter G. Hodge		90	1·00
1035/8		Set of 4	2·25	2·25

STAMP BOOKLETS

1977 (9 Feb). *Silver Jubilee. Multicoloured cover showing Crown and map of Anguilla. Stapled.*
SB1 $8.70, booklet containing 25 c., 40 c., $1.20 and $2.50 (Nos. 269/72), each in pair .. .. 1·75
   a. Stamps with margin at right .. .. 3·50
   No. SB1 was produced from normal sheets and can be found stapled at the left or the right. A further printing was later produced from specially prepared sheets, so that stamps from Booket No. SB1a occur with small vertical margins at the right of each pair, in addition to the binding margin at left.

1978. *25th Anniv of Coronation. Multicoloured cover, 105×38 mm, showing Royal coat-of-arms and map of Anguilla. Stapled.*
SB2 $9.44, booklet containing 22 c., 50 c., $1.50 and $2.50 (Nos. 320/3), each in pair .. .. 1·75
   a. Stamps with margin at right .. .. 2·00
   No. SB2 exists with three different scenes on the back cover. A second printing of No. SB2 exists with a sheet arrangement as described for No. SB1a.

1979. *Death Centenary of Sir Rowland Hill. Multicoloured cover, 104×39 mm, showing design from "Mulready" envelope on the front and coral beaches on the back. Stapled.*
SB3 $9.18, booklet containing 1 c. ×2, 22 c., 35 c., $1.50 and $2.50 (Nos. 358/63), each in pair .. 2·50
   No. SB3 exists with three different scenes on the back cover.

1980. *"London 1980" International Stamp Exhibition. Three multicoloured covers, each 109×39 mm, showing designs from Anguilla stamps, either No. 384, 385 or 387, on front and different views of Anguilla on back. Stapled.*
SB4 $9.70, booklet (any cover) containing 35 c., 50 c., $1.50 and $2.50 (Nos. 384a/7a), each in pair   2·50
   Set of 3 different cover designs .. .. 7·00

1981 (15 June). *Royal Wedding. Multicoloured covers, each 105×65 mm, showing Prince of Wales emblem on front and local scene on back. Stapled.*
SB5 $14 booklet containing two panes of 4 (either Nos. 468a, 469a or Nos. 468wa, 469wa) .. .. 2·00
   No. SB5 exists with three different scenes on the back cover.

1982 (30 Aug). *21st Birthday of Princess of Wales. Multicoloured cover, 105×65 mm, showing Prince of Wales emblem on front and coral beach on back. Stapled.*
SB6 $12.40, booklet containing four panes of 4 (Nos. 507a, 509a, 510a, 511a) .. .. .. 7·00

1984 (31 Oct). *Birth of Prince Henry. Booklet No. SB6 optd "PRINCE HENRY BIRTH 15.9.84" on cover.*
SB7 $12.40, booklet containing four panes of 4 (Nos. 628a, 630a, 631a, 632a) .. .. 7·50

1996 (5 June). *Black on salmon cover, 105×71 mm, showing flag and map of Anguilla. Stamps attached by selvedge.*
SB8 $5 booklet containing Nos. 894 and 959, each ×5   3·00
   It is understood that fourteen other combinations of contents with 20 c. and 80 c. face values exist.

1998 (13 Mar). *Cover as No. SB8, but surch "EC $9.00".*
SB9 $9 booklet containing Nos. 792 and 998, each ×5   5·00
   It is understood that other combinations of contents with 30 c. and $1.50 face values exist.

1998 (12 Nov). *Multicoloured cover, 105×71 mm, showing outline map of Anguilla and flag emblem. Stamps attached by selvedge.*
SB10 $6.50, booklet containing Nos. 1017/18, each ×5, plus 5 printed labels .. .. 3·50
   It is understood that other combinations of contents with 30 c. and $1 face values exist.

1999 (25 May). *Multicoloured cover, 103×72 mm, showing new General Post Office. Stamps attached by selvedge.*
SB11 $6.50, booklet containing Nos. 1027/8, each ×5, plus 5 labels from sheet gutters .. .. 2·75

Antigua

The first mention of a local postmaster for Antigua is in 1760, but the earliest straight-line mark, inscribed "ANTE/GOA", is known on a letter of 1757. Mail services before 1850 were somewhat haphazard, until St. John's was made a branch office of the British G.P.O. in 1850. A second office, at English Harbour, opened in 1857.

The stamps of Great Britain were used between May 1858 and the end of April 1860, when the island postal service became the responsibility of the local colonial authorities. In the interim period, between the take-over and the appearance of Antiguan stamps, the crowned-circle handstamps were again utilised and No. CC1 can be found used as late as 1869.

For illustrations of the handstamp and postmark types see BRITISH POST OFFICES ABROAD notes, following GREAT BRITAIN.

ST. JOHN'S

CROWNED-CIRCLE HANDSTAMPS

CC1 CC **1** ANTIGUA (St. John's) (22.3.1850) (R.)
Price on cover £550

Stamps of GREAT BRITAIN cancelled "A 02" as Type **2**.

1858 to **1860**.
Z1	1d. rose-red (1857), perf 14				£500
Z2	2d. blue (1855), perf 14 (Plate No. 6)				£900
Z3	2d. blue (1858) (Plate Nos. 7, 8, 9)				£600
Z4	4d. rose (1857)				£500
Z5	6d. lilac (1856)				£160
Z6	1s. green (1856)				£1500

ENGLISH HARBOUR

CROWNED-CIRCLE HANDSTAMPS

CC2 CC **3** ENGLISH HARBOUR (10.12.1857)
Price on cover £4250

Stamps of GREAT BRITAIN cancelled "A 18" as Type **2**.

1858 to **1860**.
Z7	2d. blue (1858) (Plate No. 7)				£5000
Z8	4d. rose (1857)				£5000
Z9	6d. lilac				£2000
Z10	1s. green (1856)				£2750

PRICES FOR STAMPS ON COVER TO 1945

No. 1	from × 8
Nos. 2/4	†
Nos. 5/10	from × 15
Nos 13/14	from × 20
No. 15	from × 50
Nos. 16/18	from × 30
Nos. 19/23	from × 12
No. 24	from × 40
Nos. 25/30	from × 10
Nos. 31/51	from × 4
Nos. 52/4	from × 10
Nos. 55/61	from × 4
Nos. 62/80	from × 3
Nos. 81/90	from × 4
Nos. 91/4	from × 5
Nos. 95/7	from × 4
Nos. 98/109	from × 3

CROWN COLONY

1

3 (Die I)

(Eng C. Jeens after drawing by Edward Corbould. Recess P.B.)

1862 (Aug). No wmk. (a) Rough perf 14 to 16.
1	**1**	6d. blue-green			£800	£500

(b) P 11 to 12½
2	**1**	6d. blue-green				£4500

(c) P 14 to 16 × 11 to 12½
3	**1**	6d. blue-green				£2750

(d) P 14 to 16 compound with 11 to 12½
4	**1**	6d. blue-green				£3000

Nos. 2/4 may be trial perforations. They are not known used.

1863 (Jan)–**67**. Wmk Small Star. W **w 2** (sideways on 6d.). Rough perf 14 to 16.
5	**1**	1d. rosy mauve			£120	45·00
6		1d. dull rose (1864)			95·00	35·00
		a. Imperf between (vert pair)			£16000	
7		1d. vermilion (1867)			£150	22·00
		a. Imperf between (horiz pair)			£16000	
		b. Wmk sideways			£190	38·00
8		6d. green (shades)			£425	22·00
		a. Wmk upright				— 75·00
9		6d. dark green			£450	22·00
10		6d. yellow-green			£2750	75·00

Caution is needed in buying No. 10 as some of the shades of No. 8 verge on yellow-green.

The 1d. rosy mauve exists showing trial perforations of 11 to 12½ and 14 to 16.

(Recess D.L.R. from P.B. plates)

1872. Wmk Crown CC. P 12½.
13	**1**	1d. lake			£110	15·00
		w. Wmk inverted			£110	
		x. Wmk reversed				
		y. Wmk inverted and reversed				
14		1d. scarlet			£150	17·00
		w. Wmk inverted			£200	75·00
		x. Wmk reversed				
15		6d. blue-green			£500	7·50
		w. Wmk inverted				
		x. Wmk reversed			£500	7·50
		y. Wmk inverted and reversed				

1876. Wmk Crown CC. P 14.
16	**1**	1d. lake			£110	9·00
		a. Bisected (½d.) (1883) (on cover)			† £3000	
		x. Wmk reversed				
17		1d. lake-rose			£110	9·00
		w. Wmk inverted			£160	60·00
		x. Wmk reversed				
		y. Wmk inverted and reversed				
18		6d. blue-green			£325	13·00
		x. Wmk reversed			£325	13·00
		y. Wmk inverted and reversed			—	50·00

(Recess (T 1); typo (T 3) De La Rue & Co)

1879. Wmk Crown CC. P 14.
19	**3**	2½d. red-brown			£600	£160
		a. Large "2" in "2½" with slanting foot			£8000	£2250
20		4d. blue			£250	14·00

Top left triangle detached
(Pl 2 R. 3/3 of right pane)

1882. Wmk Crown CA. P 14.
21	**3**	½d. dull green			2·50	10·00
		a. Top left triangle detached			£130	
22		2½d. red-brown			£140	55·00
		a. Large "2" in "2½" with slanting foot			£2500	£1100
23		4d. blue			£275	15·00
		a. Top left triangle detached			—	£400

1884. Wmk Crown CA. P 12.
24	**1**	1d. carmine-red			50·00	15·00
		w. Wmk inverted				
		y. Wmk inverted and reversed				

The 1d. scarlet is a colour changeling.

1884–86. Wmk Crown CA. P 14.
25	**1**	1d. carmine-red			1·75	2·75
		x. Wmk reversed				
		y. Wmk inverted and reversed				
26		1d. rose			55·00	12·00
27	**3**	2½d. ultramarine (1886)			6·00	11·00
		a. Large "2" in 2½ with slanting foot			£160	£250
		b. Top left triangle detached			£300	
28		4d. chestnut (1886)			1·75	2·75
		a. Top left triangle detached			£130	
29	**1**	6d. deep green			60·00	£120
30	**3**	1s. mauve (1886)			£160	£120
		a. Top left triangle detached			£800	
27/28, 30 Optd "Specimen"					Set of 3	£150

Nos. 25 and 26 postmarked "A 12" in place of "A 02" were used in St. Christopher.

2½ 2½ 2½

A   B   C

The variety "Large '2' in 2½" with slanting foot" occurs on the first stamp of the seventh row in both left (A) and right (B) panes (in which positions the "NN" of "PENNY" have three vertical strokes shortened) and on the first stamp of the third row of the right-hand pane (C). The "2" varies slightly in each position.

From 31 October 1890 until July 1903 Leeward Islands general issues were used. Subsequently both general issues and the following separate issues were in concurrent use until July 1956, when the general Leewards Island stamps were withdrawn.

PRICES OF SETS

Set prices are given for many issues, generally those containing three stamps or more. Definitive sets include one of each value or major colour change, but do not cover different perforations, die types or minor shades. Where a choice is possible the set prices are based on the cheapest versions of the stamps included in the listings.

4

5

(Typo D.L.R.)

1903 (July)–**09**. Wmk Crown CC. Ordinary paper. P 14.
31	**4**	½d. grey-black and grey-green			3·50	5·50
32		1d. grey-black and rose-red			5·50	1·00
		a. Bluish paper (1909)			95·00	95·00
33		2d. dull purple and brown			6·50	24·00
34		2½d. grey-black and blue			8·00	15·00
		a. Chalk-surfaced paper (1907)			17·00	42·00
35		3d. grey-green and orange-brown			9·50	20·00
36		6d. purple and black			28·00	48·00
		w. Wmk inverted			£100	
37		1s. blue and dull purple			40·00	48·00
		a. Chalk-surfaced paper (1907)			42·00	85·00
38		2s. grey-green and pale violet			70·00	90·00
39		2s. 6d. grey-black and purple			17·00	50·00
40	**5**	5s. grey-green and violet			70·00	95·00
		a. Chalk-surfaced paper (1907)			85·00	£110
31/40				Set of 10	£225	£350
31/40 Optd "Specimen"				Set of 10	£150	

1908–17. Wmk Mult Crown CA. Chalk-surfaced paper (2d. to 2s.). P 14.
41	**4**	½d. green			2·25	4·00
		w. Wmk inverted				
42		½d. blue-green (1917)			3·25	5·50
43		1d. red (1909)			4·75	2·00
44		1d. scarlet (5.8.15)			5·50	3·00
45		2d. dull purple and brown (1912)			4·25	26·00
46		2½d. ultramarine			9·50	15·00
		a. Blue			15·00	20·00
47		3d. grey-green and orange-brown (1912)			6·50	19·00
48		6d. purple and black (1911)			7·50	38·00
49		1s. blue and dull purple			15·00	70·00
50		2s. grey-green and violet (1912)			65·00	85·00
41/50				Set of 8	£100	£225
41, 43, 46 Optd "Specimen"				Set of 3	65·00	

1913. As T **5**, but portrait of King George V. Wmk Mult Crown CA. Chalk-surfaced paper. P 14.
51		5s. grey-green and violet (Optd S. £60)			70·00	£110

WAR STAMP
(7)   8

1916 (Sept)–**17**. No. 41 optd in London with T **7**.
52	**4**	½d. green (Bk.)			75	1·75
53		½d. green (R.) (1.10.17)			1·25	1·75

1918 (July). Optd with T **7**. Wmk Mult Crown CA. P 14.
54	**4**	1½d. orange			75	1·00
52/4 Optd "Specimen"				Set of 3	70·00	

(Typo D.L.R.)

1921–29. P 14. (a) Wmk Mult Crown CA. Chalk-surfaced paper.
55	**8**	3d. purple/pale yellow			4·00	11·00
56		4d. grey-black and red/pale yellow (1922)			1·75	5·50
57		1s. black/emerald			3·75	8·00
		y. Wmk inverted and reversed				
58		2s. purple and blue/blue			12·00	19·00
59		2s. 6d. black and red/blue			14·00	48·00
60		5s. green and red/pale yellow (1922)			8·50	45·00
61		£1 purple and black/red (1922)			£170	£275
55/61				Set of 7	£190	£375
55/61 Optd "Specimen"				Set of 7	£170	

(b) Wmk Mult Script CA. Chalk-surfaced paper (3d. to 4s.).
62	**8**	½d. dull green			1·75	30
63		1d. carmine-red			1·50	30
64		1d. bright violet (1923)			2·75	1·50
		a. Mauve			9·00	7·00
65		1d. bright scarlet (1929)			14·00	3·00
66		1½d. dull orange (1922)			2·50	7·00
67		1½d. carmine-red (1926)			3·75	1·75
68		1½d. pale red-brown (1929)			2·50	60
69		2d. grey (1922)			2·00	75
70		a. Wmk sideways				
71		2½d. bright blue (1922)			6·00	17·00
72		2½d. orange-yellow (1923)			2·00	17·00
73		2½d. ultramarine (1927)			3·75	5·50
74		3d. purple/pale yellow (1925)			4·00	8·50
75		6d. dull and bright purple (1922)			2·75	6·50
76		1s. black/emerald (1929)			6·00	8·00
77		2s. purple and blue/blue (1927)			10·00	55·00
78		2s. 6d. black and red/blue (1927)			20·00	26·00
79		3s. green and violet (1922)			25·00	80·00
80		4s. grey-black and red (1922)			40·00	65·00
62/80				Set of 16	£120	£250
62/80 Optd/Perf "Specimen"				Set of 18	£325	

9 Old Dockyard,
English Harbour

10 Government House,
St. John's

(Des Mrs. J. Goodwin (5s.), Waterlow (others). Recess Waterlow)

1932 (27 Jan). *Tercentenary. T* **9/10** *and similar designs. Wmk Mult Script CA. P* 12½.

81	9	½d. green	.. .. ..	2·00	6·00
82		1d. scarlet	.. .. ..	2·50	4·75
83		1½d. brown	.. .. ..	3·00	4·50
84	10	2d. grey	.. .. ..	3·75	15·00
85		2½d. deep blue	.. ..	3·75	8·50
86		3d. orange	.. ..	3·75	12·00
87	—	6d. violet	.. ..	14·00	12·00
88	—	1s. olive-green	.. ..	18·00	26·00
89	—	2s. 6d. claret	.. ..	38·00	48·00
90	—	5s. black and chocolate	..	75·00	£110
81/90			*Set of 10*	£140	£200
81/90 Perf "Specimen"			*Set of 10*	£200	

Designs: *Horiz*—6d., 1s., 2s. 6d. Nelson's *Victory. Vert*—5s. Sir Thomas Warner's *Concepcion.*
Examples of all values are known showing a forged St. Johns postmark dated "MY 18 1932".

13 Windsor Castle

(Des H. Fleury. Recess D.L.R.)

1935 (6 May). *Silver Jubilee. Wmk Mult Script CA. P* 13½ × 14.

91	13	1d. deep blue and carmine	..	2·00	2·50
		f. Diagonal line by turret	..	48·00	
92		1½d. ultramarine and grey	..	2·75	45
93		2½d. brown and deep blue	..	6·50	1·00
		g. Dot to left of chapel	..	£130	
94		1s. slate and purple	..	8·50	12·00
		h. Dot by flagstaff	.. ..	£160	
91/4			*Set of 4*	18·00	14·00
91/4 Perf "Specimen"			*Set of 4*	70·00	

For illustrations of plate varieties see Catalogue Introduction.

14 King George VI and
Queen Elizabeth

(Des D.L.R.. Recess B.W.)

1937 (12 May). *Coronation. Wmk Mult Script CA. P* 11×11½.

95	14	1d. carmine	.. ..	50	80
96		1½d. yellow-brown	.. ..	60	90
97		2½d. blue	.. ..	1·25	1·60
95/7			*Set of 3*	2·10	3·00
95/7 Perf "Specimen"			*Set of 3*	50·00	

15 English Harbour

16 Nelson's Dockyard

(Recess Waterlow)

1938 (15 Nov)–51. *T* **15, 16** *and similar designs. Wmk Mult Script CA. P* 12½.

98	15	½d. green	.. ..	30	1·00
99	16	1d. scarlet	.. ..	2·75	1·75
		a. Red (8.42 and 11.47)	..	3·50	2·00
100		1½d. chocolate-brown	..	5·50	60
		a. Dull reddish brown (12.43)	..	2·25	1·25
		b. Lake-brown (7.49)	..	26·00	13·00
101	15	2d. grey	.. ..	50	50
		a. Slate-grey (6.51)	..	6·00	4·50
102	16	2½d. deep ultramarine	..	70	80
103	—	3d. orange	.. ..	60	80
104	—	6d. violet	.. ..	2·00	90
105	—	1s. black and brown	..	3·00	1·10
		a. Black and red-brown (7.49)		30·00	9·50
		ab. Frame ptd double, once albino	..	£2750	
106	—	2s. 6d. brown-purple	..	42·00	8·50
		a. Maroon (8.42)	..	22·00	8·50
107	—	5s. olive-green	..	14·00	7·00
108	16	10s. magenta (1.4.48)	..	16·00	25·00
109	—	£1 slate-green (1.4.48)	..	25·00	35·00
98/109			*Set of 12*	75·00	70·00
98/109 Perf "Specimen"			*Set of 12*	£180	

Designs: *Horiz*—3d., 2s. 6d., £1 Fort James. *Vert*—6d., 1s., 5s. St. John's Harbour.

17 Houses of Parliament,
London

(Des and recess D.L.R.)

1946 (1 Nov). *Victory. Wmk Mult Script CA. P* 13½×14.

110	17	1½d. brown	..	15	10
111		3d. red-orange	..	15	30
110/111 Perf "Specimen"			*Set of 2*	50·00	

18 **19**
King George VI and Queen Elizabeth

(Des and photo Waterlow (T **18**). Design recess; name typo B.W. (T **19**))

1949 (3 Jan). *Royal Silver Wedding. Wmk Mult Script CA.*

112	18	2½d. ultramarine (p 14×15)	..	40	1·00
113	19	5s. grey-olive (p 11½×11)	..	8·50	6·00

20 Hermes, Globe and
Forms of Transport

21 Hemispheres, Jet-
powered Vickers Viking
Airliner and Steamer

22 Hermes and Globe

23 U.P.U. Monument

(Recess Waterlow (T **20, 23**). Designs recess, name typo B.W. (T **21/2**))

1949 (10 Oct). *75th Anniv of Universal Postal Union. Wmk Mult Script CA.*

114	20	2½d. ultramarine (p 13½–14)	..	40	50
115	21	3d. orange (p 11 × 11½)	..	1·50	1·75
116	22	6d. purple (p 11 × 11½)	..	45	1·25
117	23	1s. red-brown (p 13½–14)	..	45	75
114/17			*Set of 4*	2·50	3·75

(New Currency. 100 cents = 1 West Indian, later Eastern Caribbean, dollar)

24 Arms of
University

25 Princess Alice

(Recess Waterlow)

1951 (16 Feb). *Inauguration of B.W.I. University College. Wmk Mult Script CA. P* 14×14½.

118	24	3 c. black and brown	..	45	50
119	25	12 c. black and violet	..	65	80

26 Queen
Elizabeth II

27 Martello Tower

(Des and eng B.W. Recess D.L.R.)

1953 (2 June). *Coronation. Wmk Mult Script CA. P* 13½×13.

120	26	2 c. black and deep yellow-green	..	30	75

(Recess Waterlow until 1961, then D.L.R.)

1953 (2 Nov)–62. *Designs previously used for King George VI issue, but with portrait of Queen Elizabeth II as in T* **27**. *Wmk Mult Script CA. P* 13×13½ (*horiz*) *or* 13½×13 (*vert*).

120a	—	½ c. brown (3.7.56)	..	30	30
121		1 c. slate-grey	..	30	70
		a. Slate (7.11.61)	..	1·50	1·75
122		2 c. green	..	30	10
123		3 c. black and orange-yellow	..	40	20
		a. Black and yellow-orange (5.12.61)		1·75	2·25
124		4 c. scarlet	..	1·25	10
		a. Brown-red (11.12.62)	..	1·25	30
125		5 c. black and slate-lilac	..	2·50	40
126		6 c. yellow-ochre	..	2·00	10
		a. Dull yellow-ochre (5.12.61)	..	4·50	1·25
127	27	8 c. deep blue	..	2·25	10
128	—	12 c. violet	..	2·25	10
129	—	24 c. black and chocolate	..	2·50	15
130	27	48 c. purple and deep blue	..	7·00	2·75
131	—	60 c. maroon	..	7·50	80
132	—	$1.20, olive-green	..	2·25	70
		a. Yellowish olive (10.8.55)	..	2·25	70
133	—	$2.40, bright reddish purple	..	10·00	12·00
134	—	$4.80, slate-blue	..	15·00	23·00
120a/134			*Set of 15*	48·00	35·00

Designs: *Horiz*—½ c., 6 c., 60 c., $4.80, Fort James; 2 c., 3 c., 5 c., $2.40, Nelson's Dockyard. *Vert*—1 c., 4 c., English Harbour; 12 c., 24 c., $1.20, St. John's Harbour.
See also Nos. 149/58.

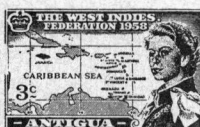

COMMEMORATION
ANTIGUA
CONSTITUTION
1960

28 Federation Map **(29)**

(Recess B.W.)

1958 (22 Apr). *Inauguration of British Caribbean Federation. W w* 12. *P* 11½ × 11.

135	28	3 c. deep green	.. ..	1·00	30
136		6 c. blue	.. ..	1·40	2·50
137		12 c. scarlet	.. ..	1·60	70
135/7			*Set of 3*	3·50	3·25

MINISTERIAL GOVERNMENT

1960 (1 Jan). *New Constitution. Nos.* 123 *and* 128 *optd with T* **29**.

138		3 c. black and orange-yellow (R.)	..	15	15
139		12 c. violet	.. ..	15	15

30 Nelson's Dockyard and
Admiral Nelson

31 Stamp of 1862 and
R.M.S.P. *Solent I* at English
Harbour

(Recess B.W.)

1961 (14 Nov). *Restoration of Nelson's Dockyard. W w* 12. *P* 11½ × 11.

140	30	20 c. purple and brown	..	90	1·00
141		30 c. green and blue	..	1·10	1·25

(Des A. W. Morley. Recess B.W.)

1962 (1 Aug). *Stamp Centenary. W w* 12. *P* 13½.

142	31	3 c. purple and deep green	..	60	10
143		10 c. blue and deep green	..	70	10
144		12 c. deep sepia and deep green	..	80	10
145		50 c. orange-brown and deep green	..	1·50	1·75
142/5			*Set of 4*	3·25	1·75

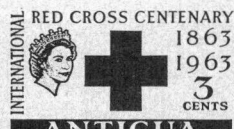

32 Protein Foods

33 Red Cross Emblem

(Des M. Goaman. Photo Harrison)

1963 (4 June). *Freedom from Hunger.* W w **12**. *P* 14×14½.
146 **32** 12 c. bluish green 15 15

(Des V. Whiteley. Litho B.W.)

1963 (2 Sept). *Red Cross Centenary.* W w **12**. *P* 13½.
147 **33** 3 c. red and black 40 50
148 12 c. red and blue .. .. 60 1·00

(Recess D.L.R.)

1963 (16 Sept)–**65**. *As 1953—61 but wmk* w **12**.
149 – ½ c. brown (13.4.65) .. .. 1·50 75
150 – 1 c. slate (13.4.65) .. .. 1·00 1·00
151 – 2 c. green 60 20
152 – 3 c. black and yellow-orange .. 45 20
153 – 4 c. brown-red 30 40
154 – 5 c. black and slate-lilac .. 20 10
    a. Black and reddish violet (15.1.65) 20 10
155 – 6 c. yellow-ochre 60 30
156 **27** 8 c. deep blue 30 20
157 – 12 c. violet 40 20
158 – 24 c. black and deep chocolate .. 4·00 70
    a. Black and chocolate-brown (28.4.65) 4·75 2·75
149/158 .. .. .. *Set of 10* 8·50 3·50

 = =

15c.
(35)

34 Shakespeare and
Memorial Theatre,
Stratford-upon-Avon

(Des R. Granger Barrett. Photo Harrison)

1964 (23 April). *400th Birth Anniv of William Shakespeare.*
W w **12**. *P* 14 × 14½.
164 **34** 12 c. orange-brown 30 10
    w. Wmk inverted .. .. 50·00

1965 (1 April). *No. 157 surch with T* **35**.
165 15 c. on 12 c. violet 10 10

36 I.T.U. Emblem

(Des M. Goaman. Litho Enschedé)

1965 (17 May). *I.T.U. Centenary.* W w **12**. *P* 11 × 11½.
166 **36** 2 c. light blue and light red .. 25 15
167 50 c. orange-yellow and ultramarine 1·25 80

37 I.C.Y. Emblem

(Des V. Whiteley. Litho Harrison)

1965 (25 Oct). *International Co-operation Year.* W w **12**. *P* 14½.
168 **37** 4 c. reddish purple and turquoise-green 20 10
169 15 c. deep bluish green and lavender .. 30 20

38 Sir Winston Churchill, and St. Paul's
Cathedral in Wartime

(Des Jennifer Toombs. Photo Harrison)

1966 (24 Jan). *Churchill Commemoration. Printed in black, cerise
and gold and with background in colours stated.* W w **12**. *P* 14.
170 **38** ½ c. new blue .. .. 10 1·75
    a. Value omitted £325
171 4 c. deep green 30 10
172 25 c. brown 85 45
173 35 c. bluish violet 95 55
170/3 .. .. .. *Set of 4* 2·00 2·50
No. 170a was caused by misplacement of the gold and also
shows "ANTIGUA" moved to the right.

39 Queen Elizabeth II and Duke of Edinburgh

(Des H. Baxter. Litho B.W.)

1966 (4 Feb). *Royal Visit.* W w **12**. *P* 11 × 12.
174 **39** 6 c. black and ultramarine .. 1·75 1·10
175 15 c. black and magenta .. 1·75 1·40

40 Footballer's Legs, Ball and Jules Rimet Cup

(Des V. Whiteley. Litho Harrison)

1966 (1 July). *World Football Cup Championships.* W w **12** (*sideways*). *P* 14.
176 **40** 6 c. violet, yellow-green, lake & yell-brn 20 50
177 35 c. chocolate, blue-grn, lake & yell-brn 60 25

41 W.H.O. Building

(Des M. Goaman. Litho Harrison)

1966 (20 Sept). *Inauguration of W.H.O. Headquarters, Geneva.*
W w **12** (*sideways*). *P* 14.
178 **41** 2 c. black, yellow-green and light blue 20 25
179 15 c. black, light purple and yellow-brown 80 25

42 Nelson's Dockyard

(Des, eng and recess B.W.)

1966 (1 Nov)–**70**. *Horiz designs as T* **42**. W w **12**. *Ordinary
paper. P* 11½×11.
180 ½ c. green and turquoise-blue .. 10 40
    a. Perf 13½ (24.6.69) .. 10 1·25
181 1 c. purple and cerise .. 10 30
    a. Perf 13½ (24.6.69) .. 10 1·25
    ab. Glazed paper (30.9.69) 60 20
182 2 c. slate-blue and yellow-orange 10 20
    a. Perf 13½ (24.6.69) .. 10 50
    ab. Glazed paper (30.9.69) 70 10
183 3 c. rose-red and black .. 10 30
    a. Perf 13½ (24.6.69) .. 15 15
184 4 c. slate-violet and brown .. 30 10
    a. Perf 13½ (24.6.69) .. 15 15
    ab. Glazed paper (6.4.70) 16·00 9·00
185 5 c. ultramarine and yellow-olive 10 10
    a. Perf 13½ (24.6.69) .. 15 10
    ab. Glazed paper (30.9.69) 40 10
186 6 c. salmon and purple .. 15 10
    a. Perf 13½ (24.6.69) .. 15 80
187 10 c. emerald and rose-red .. 15 10
    a. Perf 13½ (24.6.69) .. 15 15
    ab. Glazed paper (30.9.69) 2·75 10
188 15 c. brown and new blue .. 1·50 10
    a. Perf 13½ (*glazed paper*) (30.9.69) 55 10
189 25 c. slate-blue and sepia .. 35 20
    a. Perf 13½ (*glazed paper*) (30.9.69) 45 10
190 35 c. cerise and blackish brown .. 1·50 55
    a. Perf 13½ (*glazed paper*) (30.9.69) 60 1·00
191 50 c. dull green and black .. 1·50 2·50
    a. Perf 13½ (*glazed paper*) (30.9.69) 70 2·25
192 75 c. greenish blue and ultramarine 1·50 2·50
193 $1 cerise and yellow-olive .. 5·50 2·50
    a. Carmine and yellow-olive (14.5.68) 20·00 13·00
    b. Perf 13½ (*glazed paper*) (30.9.69) 1·25 5·00
194 $2.50, black and cerise .. 3·50 5·50
    a. Perf 13½ (*glazed paper*) (30.9.69) 1·50 8·00
195 $5 olive-green and slate-violet .. 5·50 6·50
    a. Perf 13½ (*glazed paper*) (30.9.69) 12·00 24·00
180/195 .. .. *Set of 16* 18·00 19·00
Designs:—1 c. Old Post Office, St. John's; 2 c. Health Centre;
3 c. Teachers' Training College; 4 c. Martello Tower, Barbuda; 5 c.
Ruins of Officers' Quarters, Shirley Heights; 6 c. Government
House, Barbuda; 10 c. Princess Margaret School; 15 c. Air Terminal
building; 25 c. General Post Office; 35 c. Clarence House; 50 c.
Government House, St. John's; 75 c. Administration Building; $1,
Courthouse, St. John's; $2.50, Magistrates' Court; $5, St. John's
Cathedral.

NEW INFORMATION

The editor is always interested to correspond with
people who have new information that will
improve or correct the Catalogue.

54 "Education"

55 "Science"

56 "Culture"

(Des Jennifer Toombs. Litho Harrison)

1966 (1 Dec). *20th Anniv of U.N.E.S.C.O.* W w **12** (*sideways*). *P* 14.
196 **54** 4 c. slate-violet, red, yellow and orange 15 10
197 **55** 25 c. orange-yellow, violet and deep olive 35 10
198 **56** $1 black, bright purple and orange 1·25 2·25
196/8 .. .. .. *Set of 3* 1·60 2·25

ASSOCIATED STATEHOOD

57 State Flag and Maps

(Des W. D. Cribbs. Photo Harrison)

1967 (27 Feb). *Statehood. T* **57** *and similar horiz designs.
Multicoloured.* W w **12** (*sideways**). *P* 14.
199 4 c. Type **57** 10 10
200 15 c. State Flag 10 20
    w. Wmk Crown to right of CA .. 1·75
201 25 c. Premier's Office and State Flag 10 25
202 35 c. As 15 c. 15 25
199/202 .. .. .. *Set of 4* 30 65
*The normal sideways watermark shows Crown to left of CA,
as seen from the back of the stamp.

60 Gilbert Memorial Church

(Des G. Drummond (from sketches by W. D. Cribbs). Photo
Harrison)

1967 (18 May). *Attainment of Autonomy by the Methodist
Church. T* **60** *and similar horiz designs.* W w **12**. *P* 14½ × 13½.
203 4 c. black and orange-red .. 10 10
204 25 c. black and bright green .. 15 15
205 35 c. black and bright blue .. 15 15
203/5 .. .. .. *Set of 3* 30 30
Designs:—25 c. Nathaniel Gilbert's House; 35 c. Caribbean
and Central American map.

63 Coat of Arms

64 *Susan Constant*
(settlers' ship)

(Des V. Whiteley (from sketches by W. D. Cribbs). Photo Harrison)

1967 (21 July). *300th Anniv of Treaty of Breda and Grant of New Arms.* W w **12** (sideways*). P 14½×14.
206	**63**	15 c. multicoloured		15	10
		w. Wmk Crown to right of CA		10·00	10·00
207		35 c. multicoloured		15	10

*The normal sideways watermark shows Crown to left of CA, as seen from the back of the stamp.

(Des and recess B.W.)

1967 (14 Dec). *300th Anniv of Barbuda Settlement.* T **64** and similar horiz design. W w **12**. P 11½ × 11.
208	**64**	4 c. deep ultramarine		30	10
209	–	6 c. purple		30	1·25
210	**64**	25 c. emerald		40	40
211	–	35 c. black		40	25
208/11		*Set of 4*		1·25	1·50

Design:—6, 35 c. Blaeu's map of 1665.

66 Tracking Station   **70** Limbo-dancing

(Des G. Vasarhelyi. Photo Harrison)

1968 (29 Mar). *N.A.S.A. Apollo Project. Inauguration of Dow Hill Tracking Station.* T **66** and similar vert designs in deep blue, orange-yellow and black. W w **12** (sideways). P 14½ × 14.
212	4 c. Type **66**		10	10
213	15 c. Antenna and spacecraft taking off		20	10
214	25 c. Spacecraft approaching Moon		20	10
215	50 c. Re-entry of space capsule		30	30
212/15	*Set of 4*		70	40

(Des and photo Harrison)

1968 (1 July). *Tourism.* T **70** and similar horiz designs. Multicoloured. W w **12**. P 14½ × 14.
216	½ c. Type **70**		10	20
217	15 c. Water-skiing and bathers		30	10
218	25 c. Yachts and beach		40	10
219	35 c. Underwater swimming		40	10
220	50 c. Type **70**		60	1·10
216/20	*Set of 5*		1·50	1·40

74 Old Harbour in 1768

(Des R. Granger Barrett. Recess B.W.)

1968 (31 Oct). *Opening of St. John's Deep Water Harbour.* T **74** and similar horiz designs. W w **12**. P 13.
221	2 c. light blue and carmine		10	40
222	15 c. light yellow-green and sepia		35	10
223	25 c. olive-yellow and blue		40	10
224	35 c. salmon and emerald		50	10
225	$1 black		90	2·00
221/5	*Set of 5*		2·00	2·25

Designs:—15 c. Old Harbour in 1829; 25 c. Freighter and chart of New Harbour; 35 c. New Harbour, 1968; $1, Type **74**.

78 Parliament Buildings

(Des R. Granger Barrett. Photo Harrison)

1969 (3 Feb). *Tercentenary of Parliament.* T **78** and similar square designs. Multicoloured. W w **12** (sideways). P 12½.
226	4 c. Type **78**		10	10
227	15 c. Antigua Mace and bearer		20	10
228	25 c. House of Representatives' Room		20	10
229	50 c. Coat of arms and Seal of Antigua		30	1·40
226/9	*Set of 4*		70	1·50

82 Freight Transport

(Des Jennifer Toombs. Litho D.L.R.)

1969 (14 Apr). *1st Anniv of CARIFTA (Caribbean Free Trade Area).* T **82** and similar design. W w **12** (sideways on 4 c., 15 c). P 13.
230	4 c. black and reddish purple		10	10
231	15 c. black and turquoise-blue		20	30
232	25 c. chocolate, black and yellow-ochre		25	30
233	35 c. chocolate, black and yellow-brown		25	30
230/3	*Set of 4*		65	85

Designs: *Horiz*—4, 15 c. Type **82**. *Vert*—25, 35 c. Crate of cargo.

84 Island of Redonda (Chart)

(Des R. Granger Barrett. Photo Enschedé)

1969 (1 Aug). *Centenary of Redonda Phosphate Industry.* T **84** and similar horiz design. W w **12** (sideways). P 13 × 13½.
249	15 c. Type **84**		20	10
250	25 c. Redonda from the sea		20	10
251	50 c. Type **84**		45	75
249/51	*Set of 3*		75	80

86 "The Adoration of the Magi"   (**88**)
(Marcillat)

(Des adapted by V. Whiteley. Litho Enschedé)

1969 (15 Oct). *Christmas. Stained-glass Windows.* T **86** and similar vert design. Multicoloured. W w **12** (sideways*). P 13×14.
252	6 c. Type **86**		10	10
253	10 c. "The Nativity" (unknown German artist, 15th-century)		10	10
254	35 c. Type **86**		25	10
255	50 c. As 10 c.		50	40
	w. Wmk Crown to right of CA		14·00	
252/5	*Set of 4*		80	55

*The normal sideways watermark shows Crown to left of CA, as seen from the back of the stamp.

1970 (2 Jan). *No. 189 surch with T **88**.*
256	20 c. on 25 c. slate-blue and sepia		10	10

89 Coat of Arms   **90** Sikorsky S-38 Flying Boat

(Des and photo Harrison)

1970 (30 Jan)–**73**. *Coil Stamps.* W w **12**. P 14½×14.

A. *Chalk-surfaced paper. Wmk upright* (30.1.70).
257A	**89**	5 c. blue	10	10
258A		10 c. emerald	10	15
259A		25 c. crimson	20	25
257A/9A		*Set of 3*	35	45

B. *Glazed paper. Wmk sideways* (8.3.73).
257B	**89**	5 c. blue	1·00	1·75
258B		10 c. emerald	1·10	1·75
259B		25 c. crimson	1·75	2·00
257B/9B		*Set of 3*	3·50	5·00

For these stamps with watermark W w **14**, see Nos. 541a/c.

(Des R. Granger Barrett. Litho J.W.)

1970 (16 Feb). *40th Anniv of Antigua Air Services.* T **90** and similar designs. Multicoloured. W w **12** (sideways). P 14½.
260	5 c. Type **90**		50	10
261	20 c. Dornier Do-X flying boat		1·25	10
262	35 c. Hawker Siddeley H.S. 748		1·50	10
263	50 c. Douglas C-124C Globemaster II		1·60	1·50
264	75 c. Vickers Super VC-10		1·75	2·00
260/4	*Set of 5*		6·00	3·50

91 Dickens and Scene from *Nicholas Nickleby*

(Des Jennifer Toombs. Litho Walsall)

1970 (19 May). *Death Centenary of Charles Dickens.* T **91** and similar horiz designs. W w **12** (sideways). P 14.
265	5 c. bistre, sepia and black		10	10
266	20 c. light turquoise-blue, sepia and black		20	10
267	35 c. violet-blue, sepia and black		30	10
268	$1 rosine, sepia and black		75	70
265/8	*Set of 4*		1·25	80

Designs:—20 c. Dickens and Scene from *Pickwick Papers*; 35 c. Dickens and Scene from *Oliver Twist*; $1 Dickens and Scene from *David Copperfield*.

92 Carib Indian and War Canoe   **93** "The Small Passion" (detail) (Dürer)

(Des J.W. Litho Questa)

1970 (19 Aug)–**75**. *Horiz designs as T **92**. Multicoloured. Toned paper.* W w **12** (sideways*). P 14.
269	½ c. Type **92**		10	65
270	1 c. Columbus and *Nina*		30	80
271	2 c. Sir Thomas Warner's emblem and *Concepcion*		40	1·50
	a. Whiter paper (20.10.75)		1·50	3·25
272	3 c. Viscount Hood and H.M.S. *Barfleur*		40	1·25
	w. Wmk Crown to right of CA		2·75	2·75
273	4 c. Sir George Rodney and H.M.S. *Formidable*		40	1·50
274	5 c. Nelson and H.M.S. *Boreas*		50	40
275	6 c. William IV and H.M.S. *Pegasus*		70	1·75
276	10 c. "Blackbeard" and pirate ketch		80	20
277	15 c. Captain Collingwood and H.M.S. *Pelican*		4·00	1·00
278	20 c. Nelson and H.M.S. *Victory*		1·25	40
279	25 c. *Solent I* (paddle-steamer)		1·25	40
280	35 c. George V (when Prince George) and H.M.S. *Canada* (screw corvette)		1·75	80
281	50 c. H.M.S. *Renown* (battle cruiser)		5·00	3·25
282	75 c. *Federal Maple* (freighter)		7·00	5·50
283	$1 *Sol Quest* (yacht) and class emblem		7·00	2·00
284	$2.50, H.M.S. *London* (destroyer)		7·00	7·50
285	$5 *Pathfinder* (tug)		7·00	7·50
269/85	*Set of 17*		38·00	35·00

*The normal sideways watermark shows Crown to left of CA as seen from the back of the stamp.
See also Nos. 323/34 and 426

(Des G. Drummond. Recess and litho D.L.R.)

1970 (28 Oct). *Christmas.* T **93** and similar vert design. W w **12**. P 13½ × 14.
286	**93**	3 c. black and turquoise-blue	10	10
287	–	10 c. dull purple and pink	10	10
288	**93**	35 c. black and rose-red	30	10
289	–	50 c. black and lilac	45	50
286/9		*Set of 4*	80	60

Design:—10 c., 50 c. "Adoration of the Magi" (detail) (Dürer).

94 4th King's Own Regt, 1759   **95** Market Woman casting Vote

(Des P. W. Kingsland. Litho Questa)

1970 (14 Dec). *Military Uniforms (1st series).* T **94** and similar vert designs. Multicoloured. W w **12**. P 14 × 13½.
290	½ c. Type **94**		10	10
291	10 c. 4th West India Regiment, 1804		50	10
292	20 c. 60th Regiment, The Royal American, 1809		1·00	10
293	35 c. 93rd Regiment, Sutherland Highlanders, 1826–74		1·40	15
294	75 c. 3rd West India Regiment, 1851		2·25	2·50
290/4	*Set of 5*		4·75	2·50
MS295	128 × 146 mm. Nos. 290/4		7·50	11·00

See also Nos. 303/8, 313/18, 353/8 and 380/5.

(Des Sylvia Goaman. Photo Harrison)

1971 (1 Feb). *20th Anniversary of Adult Suffrage. T* **95** *and similar vert designs. W w* **12** *(sideways). P* 14½ × 14.

296	5 c. brown	10	10
297	20 c. deep olive	10	10
298	35 c. reddish purple	10	10
299	50 c. ultramarine	15	30
296/9	*Set of* 4	30	40

People voting:—20 c. Executive; 35 c. Housewife; 50 c. Artisan.

96 "The Last Supper" **97** "Madonna and Child" (detail, Veronese)

(Des Jennifer Toombs. Litho Questa)

1971 (7 Apr). *Easter. Works by Dürer. T* **96** *and similar vert designs. W w* **12**. *P* 14 × 13½.

300	5 c. black, grey and scarlet	10	10
301	35 c. black, grey and bluish violet	10	10
302	75 c. black, grey and gold	20	30
300/2	*Set of* 3	30	35

Designs:—35 c. The Crucifixion; 75 c. The Resurrection.

(Des J. W. Litho Questa)

1971 (12 July). *Military Uniforms (2nd series). Multicoloured designs as T* **94**. *W w* **12**. *P* 13½.

303	½ c. Private, 12th Regiment, The Suffolk (1704)	10	10
	w. Wmk inverted	50·00	
304	10 c. Grenadier, 38th Regiment, South Staffs (1751)	35	15
305	20 c. Light Company, 5th Regiment, Royal Northumberland Fusiliers (1778)	65	20
306	35 c. Private, 48th Regiment, The Northamptonshire (1793)	1·10	25
307	75 c. Private, 15th Regiment, East Yorks (1805)	2·25	4·00
	w. Wmk inverted	3·25	
303/7	*Set of* 5	4·00	4·25
MS308	127×144 mm. Nos. 303/7	5·50	6·50

(Des Jennifer Toombs. Litho Questa)

1971 (4 Oct). *Christmas. T* **97** *and similar vert design. Multicoloured. W w* **12**. *P* 13½.

309	3 c. Type **97**	10	10
310	5 c. "Adoration of the Shepherds" (detail, Veronese)	10	10
311	35 c. Type **97**	25	10
312	50 c. As 5 c.	40	30
309/12	*Set of* 4	70	40

(Des J.W. Litho Questa)

1972 (1 July). *Military Uniforms (3rd series). Multicoloured designs as T* **94**. *W w* **12** *(sideways). P* 14 × 13½.

313	½ c. Battalion Company Officer, 25th Foot, 1815	10	10
314	10 c. Sergeant, 14th Foot, 1837	85	10
315	20 c. Private, 67th Foot, 1853	1·60	15
316	35 c. Officer, Royal Artillery, 1854	1·90	20
317	75 c. Private, 29th Foot, 1870	2·25	4·00
313/17	*Set of* 5	6·00	4·00
MS318	125 × 141 mm. Nos. 313/17	7·00	8·50

98 Reticulated Cowrie-Helmet

(Des J.W. Litho Questa)

1972 (1 Aug). *Shells. T* **98** *and similar horiz designs. Multicoloured. W w* **12** *(sideways). P* 14½.

319	3 c. Type **98**	50	10
320	5 c. Measled Cowrie	50	10
321	35 c. West Indian Fighting Conch	1·40	15
322	50 c. Hawk-wing Conch	1·60	3·00
319/22	*Set of* 4	3·50	3·00

1972 (2 Nov)–74. *As No.* 269 *etc., but W w* **12** *(upright) and whiter paper.*

323	½ c. Type **92**	20	40
324	1 c. Columbus and *Nina* (2.1.74)	30	90
325	3 c. Viscount Hood and H.M.S. *Barfleur* (2.1.74)	35	90
326	4 c. Sir George Rodney and H.M.S. *Formidable* (2.1.74)	50	1·75
327	5 c. Nelson and H.M.S. *Boreas* (2.1.74)	50	40
328	6 c. William IV and H.M.S. *Pegasus* (2.1.74)	50	2·50

329	10 c. "Blackbeard" and pirate ketch (2.1.74)	55	60
330	15 c. Collingwood and H.M.S. *Pelican*	75	90
	w. Wmk inverted	70·00	
331	75 c. *Federal Maple* (freighter)	7·50	3·00
332	$1 *Sol Quest* (yacht) and class emblem	3·00	1·75
333	$2.50, H.M.S. *London* (destroyer) (25.2.74)	2·75	6·50
334	$5 *Pathfinder* (tug)	4·00	10·00
323/34	*Set of* 12	25·00	26·00

See also No. 426.

99 St. John's Cathedral, Side View

(Des J.W. Litho Format)

1972 (6 Nov). *Christmas and 125th Anniversary of St. John's Cathedral. T* **99** *and similar horiz designs. Multicoloured. W w* **12**. *P* 14.

335	35 c. Type **99**	20	10
336	50 c. Cathedral interior	25	25
337	75 c. St. John's Cathedral	30	60
335/7	*Set of* 3	65	80
MS338	165 × 102 mm. Nos. 335/7. P 15	65	1·00

100 Floral Pattern

(Des (from photograph by D. Groves) and photo Harrison)

1972 (20 Nov). *Royal Silver Wedding. Multicoloured; background colour given. W w* **12**. *P* 14 × 14½.

339	**100** 20 c. bright blue	15	15
340	35 c. turquoise-blue	15	15
	w. Wmk inverted	13·00	

101 Batsman and Map

(Des G. Vasarhelyi. Litho Questa)

1972 (15 Dec). *50th Anniv of Rising Sun Cricket Club. T* **101** *and similar horiz designs. Multicoloured. W w* **12**. *P* 13½.

341	5 c. Type **101**	55	15
	w. Wmk inverted	3·75	
342	35 c. Batsman and wicket-keeper	1·25	20
343	$1 Club badge	2·25	2·75
341/3	*Set of* 3	3·50	2·75
MS344	88×130 mm. Nos. 341/3	4·50	7·50
	w. Wmk inverted	60·00	

102 Yacht and Map **103** "Episcopal Coat of Arms"

(Des M. and G. Shamir. Litho Format)

1972 (29 Dec). *Sailing Week and Inauguration of Tourist Office, New York. T* **102** *and similar square designs. Multicoloured. W w* **12**. *P* 14½.

345	35 c. Type **102**	15	10
346	50 c. Yachts	20	15
347	75 c. St. John's G.P.O.	25	25
348	$1 Statue of Liberty	25	25
345/8	*Set of* 4	75	65
MS349	100 × 94 mm. Nos. 346, 348	75	1·25

(Des PAD Studio. Litho Format)

1973 (16 Apr). *Easter. T* **103** *and similar vert designs showing stained-glass windows from St. John's Cathedral. Multicoloured. W w* **12** *(sideways*). *P* 13½.

350	5 c. Type **103**	10	10
351	35 c. "The Crucifixion"	15	10
352	75 c. "Arms of 1st Bishop of Antigua"	25	30
	w. Wmk Crown to right of CA	12·00	
350/2	*Set of* 3	40	35

*The normal sideways watermark shows Crown to left of CA on the 75 c., and to right of CA on the others, *as seen from the back of the stamp*.

(Des J.W. Litho Questa)

1973 (1 July). *Military Uniforms (4th series). Multicoloured designs as T* **94**. *W w* **12** *(sideways*). *P* 13½.

353	½ c. Private, Zacharia Tiffin's Regiment of Foot, 1701	10	10
354	10 c. Private, 63rd Regiment of Foot, 1759	40	10
355	20 c. Light Company Officer, 35th Regiment of Foot, 1828	60	15
	w. Wmk Crown to right of CA	7·50	
356	35 c. Private, 2nd West India Regiment, 1853	85	15
357	75 c. Sergeant, 49th Regiment, 1858	1·50	1·25
353/7	*Set of* 5	3·00	1·50
MS358	127×145 mm. Nos. 353/7	3·75	3·25

*The normal sideways watermark shows Crown to right of CA on the 35 and 75 c., and to left of CA on the others, *as seen from the back of the stamp*.

104 Butterfly Costumes

(Des G. Vasarhelyi. Litho Format)

1973 (30 July). *Carnival. T* **104** *and similar horiz designs. Multicoloured. P* 13½.

359	5 c. Type **104**	10	10
360	20 c. Carnival street scene	15	10
361	35 c. Carnival troupe	20	10
362	75 c. Carnival Queen	30	30
359/62	*Set of* 4	65	35
MS363	134 × 95 mm. Nos. 359/62	65	1·00

105 "Virgin of the Milk Porridge" (Gerard David) **106** Princess Anne and Captain Mark Phillips

(Des G. Vasarhelyi. Litho Format)

1973 (15 Oct). *Christmas. T* **105** *and similar vert designs. Multicoloured. P* 14½.

364	3 c. Type **105**	10	10
365	5 c. "Adoration of the Magi" (Stomer)	10	10
366	20 c. "The Granducal Madonna" (Raphael)	15	10
367	35 c. "Nativity with God the Father and Holy Ghost" (Battista)	20	10
368	$1 "Madonna and Child" (Murillo)	40	60
364/8	*Set of* 5	75	70
MS369	130× 128 mm. Nos. 364/8	1·10	1·75

(Des G. Drummond. Litho Format)

1973 (14 Nov). *Royal Wedding. T* **106** *and similar horiz design. P* 13½.

370	**106** 35 c. multicoloured	10	10
371	– $2 multicoloured	25	25
MS372	78 × 100 mm. Nos. 370/1	50	40

The $2 is as T **106** but has a different border.

Nos. 370/1 were each issued in small sheets of five stamps and one stamp-size label.

(107)

1973 (15 Dec). *Honeymoon Visit of Princess Anne and Captain Phillips. Nos.* 370/MS372 *optd with T* **107** *by lithography.*

373	**106** 35 c. multicoloured	15	10
	a. Typo opt	95	95
374	– $2 multicoloured	30	30
	a. Typo opt	2·75	2·75
MS375	78 × 100 mm. Nos. 373/4	55	55
	a. Typo opt	8·50	12·00

*The litho overprints can be distinguished from the typo by the latter being less clear, less intense, and showing through on the reverse.

108 Coats of Arms of Antigua and University

(Des PAD Studio. Litho D.L.R.)

1974 (18 Feb). *25th Anniv of University of West Indies. T* **108** *and similar horiz designs. Multicoloured. W w* **12**. *P* 13.

376	5 c. Type **108**	..	..	10	10
377	20 c. Extra-mural art	..	..	15	10
378	35 c. Antigua campus ..	..	..	20	10
379	75 c. Antigua chancellor	..	..	25	35
376/9	..	..	*Set of 4*	55	40

(Des J.W. Litho Questa)

1974 (1 May). *Military Uniforms* (5th series). *Multicoloured designs as T* **94**. *W w* **12** (*sideways**). *P* 13½.

380	½ c. Officer, 59th Foot, 1797 ..	..		10	10
381	10 c. Gunner, Royal Artillery, 1800 ..			45	10
	a. Error. Wmk T **55** of Malawi	..		60·00	
382	20 c. Private, 1st West India Regiment, 1830			70	10
383	35 c. Officer, 92nd Foot, 1843 ..	..		85	10
384	75 c. Private, 23rd Foot, 1846..	..		1·25	2·25
380/4	..	..	*Set of 5*	3·00	2·25
MS385	127 × 145 mm. Nos. 380/4 ..	..		3·00	2·50

*The normal sideways watermark shows Crown to right of CA on the 20 c., and to left of CA on the others, *as seen from the back of the stamp.*

109 English Postman, Mailcoach and Westland Dragonfly Helicopter

110 Traditional Player

(Des G. Vasarhelyi. Litho Format)

1974 (15 July). *Centenary of Universal Postal Union. T* **109** *and similar horiz designs. Multicoloured. P* 14½.

386	½ c. Type **109**	..		10	10
387	1 c. Bellman, mail steamer *Orinoco* and satellite	..		10	10
388	2 c. Train guard, post-bus and hydrofoil ..			10	10
389	5 c. Swiss messenger, Wells Fargo coach and Concorde			60	30
390	20 c. Postilion, Japanese postmen and carrier pigeon			35	10
391	35 c. Antiguan postman, Sikorsky S-88 flying boat and tracking station			45	15
392	$1 Medieval courier, American express train and Boeing 747-100 ..			1·75	2·00
386/92	..	..	*Set of 7*	3·00	2·40
MS393	141×164 mm. Nos. 386/92 plus label. P 13			3·50	2·50

On the ½ c. "English" is spelt "Enlish", and on the 2 c. "Postal" is spelt "Fostal".

(Des C. Abbott. Litho Questa)

1974 (1 Aug). *Antiguan Steel Bands. T* **110** *and similar designs. W w* **12** (*sideways on 5 c.,* 75 c. *and* MS398). *P* 13.

394	5 c. rose-red, carmine and black	..		10	10
395	20 c. brown-ochre, chestnut and black	..		10	10
396	35 c. light sage-green, blue-green and black ..			10	10
397	75 c. dull blue, dull ultramarine and black			20	65
394/7	..	..	*Set of 4*	30	75
MS398	115 × 108 mm. Nos. 394/7..	..		35	65

Designs: *Horiz*—20 c. Traditional band; 35 c. Modern band. *Vert*—75 c. Modern player.

EARTHQUAKE RELIEF
111 Footballers   **(112)**

(Des G. Vasarhelyi. Litho Format)

1974 (23 Sept). *World Cup Football Championships. T* **111** *and similar vert designs showing footballers. P* 14½.

399	**111** 5 c. multicoloured	..		10	10
400	— 35 c. multicoloured	..		15	10
401	— 75 c. multicoloured	..		30	30
402	— $1 multicoloured	..		35	40
399/402	..	..	*Set of 4*	70	70
MS403	135 × 130 mm. Nos. 399/402 plus two labels. P 13			85	90

Nos. 399/402 were each issued in small sheets of five stamps and one stamp-size label.

1974 (16 Oct). *Earthquake Relief Fund. Nos.* 400/2 *and* 397 *optd with T* **112**, *No.* 397 *surch also.*

404	35 c. multicoloured	..		20	10
405	75 c. multicoloured	..		30	25
406	$1 multicoloured	..		40	30
407	$5 on 75 c. dull blue, dull ultram & black		1·25	2·00
404/7	..	..	*Set of 4*	2·00	2·40

113 Churchill as Schoolboy and School College Building, Harrow

114 "Madonna of the Trees" (Bellini)

(Des V. Whiteley. Litho Format)

1974 (20 Oct). *Birth Centenary of Sir Winston Churchill. T* **113** *and similar horiz designs. Multicoloured. P* 14½.

408	5 c. Type **113**	..		15	10
409	35 c. Churchill and St. Paul's Cathedral	..		20	10
410	75 c. Coat of arms and catafalque	..		25	55
411	$1 Churchill, "reward" notice and South African escape route	..		40	90
408/11	..	..	*Set of 4*	90	1·50
MS412	107×82 mm. Nos. 408/11. P 13			90	1·50

(Des M. Shamir. Litho Format)

1974 (18 Nov). *Christmas. T* **114** *and similar vert designs showing "Madonna and Child" by the artists given. Multicoloured. P* 14½.

413	½ c. Type **114** ..	..		10	10
414	1 c. Raphael ..	..		10	10
415	2 c. Van der Weyden ..	..		10	10
416	3 c. Giorgione ..	..		10	10
417	5 c. Mantegna ..	..		10	10
418	20 c. Vivarini ..	..		20	10
419	35 c. Montagna ..	..		30	10
420	75 c. Lorenzo Costa ..	..		55	85
413/20	..	..	*Set of 8*	1·25	1·25
MS421	139 × 126 mm. Nos. 417/20. P 13.	..		95	1·40

$10
(115)

116 Carib War Canoe, English Harbour, 1300

1975 (14 Jan). *Nos.* 331 *and* 390/2 *surch as T* **115**.

422	50 c. on 20 c. multicoloured	..		1·25	1·75
423	$2.50, on 35 c. multicoloured	..		2·50	5·00
424	$5 on $1 multicoloured	..		5·50	7·00
425	$10 on 75 c. multicoloured	..		4·00	7·50
422/5	..	..	*Set of 4*	12·00	19·00

1975 (21 Jan). *As No.* 334, *but W w* **14** (*sideways*).

426	$5 *Pathfinder* (tug)	..	..	3·75	10·00

(Des G. Drummond. Litho Format)

1975 (17 Mar). *Nelson's Dockyard. T* **116** *and similar horiz designs. Multicoloured. P* 14½.

427	5 c. Type **116**	..		20	10
428	15 c. Ship of the line, English Harbour, 1770			80	15
429	35 c. H.M.S. *Boreas* at anchor, and Lord Nelson, 1787			1·25	15
430	50 c. Yachts during "Sailing Week", 1974			1·25	1·50
431	$1 Yacht Anchorage, Old Dockyard, 1970			1·50	2·25
427/31	..	..	*Set of 5*	4·50	3·75
MS432	130 × 134 mm. As Nos. 427/31, but in larger format, 43 × 28 mm. P 13½			3·25	2·00

117 Lady of the Valley Church

(Des R. Vigurs. Litho Format)

1975 (19 May). *Antiguan Churches. T* **117** *and similar horiz designs. Multicoloured. P* 14½.

433	5 c. Type **117**	..		10	10
434	20 c. Gilbert Memorial	..		10	10
435	35 c. Grace Hill Moravian	..		15	10
436	50 c. St. Phillips	..		20	20
437	$1 Ebenezer Methodist	..		35	50
433/7	..	..	*Set of 5*	65	75
MS438	91 × 101 mm. Nos. 435/7. P 13			65	1·25

118 Map of 1721 and Sextant of 1640

(Des PAD Studio. Litho Questa)

1975 (21 July). *Maps of Antigua. T* **118** *and similar horiz designs. Multicoloured. W w* **14** (*sideways*). *P* 14.

439	5 c. Type **118**	..		30	15
440	20 c. Map of 1775 and galleon..	..		55	15
441	35 c. Maps of 1775 and 1955	..		70	15
442	$1 1973 maps of Antigua and English Harbour	..		1·40	2·00
439/42	..	..	*Set of 4*	2·75	2·25
MS443	130 × 89 mm. Nos. 439/42 .	..		3·00	2·25

119 Scout Bugler

(Des G. Vasarhelyi. Litho Questa)

1975 (26 Aug). *World Scout Jamboree, Norway. T* **119** *and similar horiz designs. Multicoloured. P* 14.

444	15 c. Type **119**	..		25	15
445	20 c. Scouts in camp	..		30	15
446	35 c. "Lord Baden-Powell" (D. Jagger)	..		50	20
447	$2 Scout dancers from Dahomey	..		1·50	2·00
444/7	..	..	*Set of 4*	2·25	2·25
MS448	145 × 107 mm. Nos. 444/7.	..		3·25	3·50

120 *Eurema elathea*   **121** "Madonna and Child" (Correggio)

(Des. G. Vasarhelyi. Litho Questa)

1975 (30 Oct). *Butterflies. T* **120** *and similar horiz designs. Multicoloured. P* 14.

449	½ c. Type **120**	..		10	10
450	1 c. *Danaus plexippus*	..		10	10
451	2 c. *Phoebis philea*	..		10	10
452	5 c. *Hypolimnas misippus*	..		20	10
453	20 c. *Eurema proterpia*	..		75	60
454	35 c. *Battus polydamas*	..		1·40	90
455	$2 *Cynthia cardui*	..		4·00	7·50
449/55	..	..	*Set of 7*	6·00	8·50
MS456	147×94 mm. Nos 452/5..	..		6·00	9·50

No. 452 is incorrectly captioned "Marpesia petreus thetys".

(Des G. Vasarhelyi. Litho Questa)

1975 (17 Nov). *Christmas. T* **121** *and similar vert designs showing "Madonna and Child". Multicoloured. P* 14.

457	½ c. Type **121**	..		10	10
458	1 c. El Greco	..		10	10
459	2 c. Dürer	..		10	10
460	3 c. Antonello	..		10	10
461	5 c. Bellini	..		10	10
462	10 c. Dürer (*different*) ..	..		10	10
463	35 c. Bellini (*different*)..	..		40	10
464	$2 Dürer (*different*)	..		1·00	1·00
457/64	..	..	*Set of 8*	1·50	1·10
MS465	138 × 119 mm. Nos. 461/4	..		1·50	1·60

122 Vivian Richards

123 Antillean Crested Hummingbird

(Des G. Vasarhelyi. Litho Format)

1975 (15 Dec). *World Cup Cricket Winners. T* **122** *and similar multicoloured designs. P* 13½.

466	5 c. Type **122**	.. .. ..	1·25	20
467	35 c. Andy Roberts	.. .. ..	2·25	60
468	$2 West Indies team (*horiz*).	..	4·25	8·00
466/8	.. ..	*Set of* 3	7·00	8·00

(Des G. Vasarhelyi. Litho Format)

1976 (19 Jan)–78. *Various multicoloured designs as T* **123**. *P* 13½ ($2.50, $5 *and* $10) *or* 14½ (*others*). **A**. *Without imprint* (19.1.76).

469A	½ c. Type **123**	.. .. ..	20	50
470A	1 c. Imperial Amazon	.. ..	30	50
471A	2 c. Zenaida Dove	.. ..	30	50
472A	3 c. Loggerhead Kingbird	..	30	60
473A	4 c. Red-necked Pigeon	..	30	60
474A	5 c. Rufous-throated Solitaire		1·40	10
475A	6 c. Orchid Tree	.. ..	30	60
476A	10 c. Bougainvillea	.. ..	30	10
477A	15 c. Geiger Tree	.. ..	35	10
478A	20 c. Flamboyant	.. ..	35	35
479A	25 c. Hibiscus	.. ..	40	15
480A	35 c. Flame of the Wood	..	40	40
481A	50 c. Cannon at Fort James	..	55	60
482A	75 c. Premier's Office	..	60	75
483A	$1 Potworks Dam	..	75	90
484A	$2.50, Irrigation Scheme, Diamond Estate (44×28 *mm*)		1·50	4·00
485A	$5 Government House (44×28 *mm*)		3·00	6·00
486A	$10 Coolidge Airport (44×28 *mm*)		3·50	6·50
469A/86A		*Set of* 18	13·00	20·00

B. *With imprint date at foot* (1978)

469B	½ c. Type **123**	.. .. ..	50	90
470B	1 c. Imperial Amazon	.. ..	1·25	90
471B	2 c. Zenaida Dove	.. ..	1·25	90
472B	3 c. Loggerhead Kingbird	..	1·25	90
473B	4 c. Red-necked Pigeon	..	1·40	90
474B	5 c. Rufous-throated Solitaire		1·75	45
475B	6 c. Orchid Tree	.. ..	30	1·00
476B	10 c. Bougainvillea	.. ..	30	30
477B	15 c. Geiger Tree	.. ..	30	30
478B	20 c. Flamboyant	.. ..	30	75
479B	25 c. Hibiscus	.. ..	35	50
480B	35 c. Flame of the Wood	..	35	50
481B	50 c. Cannon at Fort James	..	50	70
482B	75 c. Premier's Office	..	55	80
483B	$1 Potworks Dam	..	75	90
484B	$2.50, Irrigation Scheme, Diamond Estate (44×28 *mm*)		1·75	6·00
485B	$5 Government House (44×28 *mm*)		1·50	6·50
486B	$10 Coolidge Airport (44×28 *mm*)		6·00	9·50
469B/86B		*Set of* 18	18·00	29·00

Nos. 469A, 472B, 473A, 474B, 475A/B, 476A/B, 477A, 478B, 479A/B, 480B, 481A/B, 482A/B, 483A, 484A/B, 485A/B and 486A/B exist imperforate from stock dispersed by the liquidator of Format International Security Printers Ltd.

124 Privates, Clark's Illinois Regt

125 High Jump

(Des J.W. Litho Format)

1976 (17 Mar). *Bicentenary of American Revolution. T* **124** *and similar multicoloured designs. P* 14½.

487	½ c. Type **124**	.. .. ..	10	10
488	1 c. Riflemen, Pennsylvania Militia		10	10
489	2 c. Powder horn	.. ..	10	10
	a. Imperf (*pair*)	.. ..	£160	
490	5 c. Water bottle	.. ..	10	10
491	35 c. American flags	.. ..	50	10
492	$1 *Montgomery* (American brig)		1·25	40
493	$5 *Ranger* (privateer sloop)	..	2·50	2·75
487/93		*Set of* 7	4·00	3·00
MS494	71×84 mm. $2.50 Congress flag. P 13		1·00	1·40

(Des J. W. Litho Format)

1976 (17 July). *Olympic Games, Montreal. T* **125** *and similar horiz designs. P* 14½.

495	½ c. orange-brown, bistre-yellow and black..		10	10
496	1 c. light reddish violet, bright blue & black		10	10
497	2 c. light green and black	..	10	10
498	15 c. bright blue and black	..	15	10
499	30 c. olive-brown, yellow-ochre and black		20	15
500	$1 red-orange, Venetian red and black		40	40
501	$2 rosine and black	.. ..	60	80
495/501		*Set of* 7	1·25	1·40
MS502	88×138 mm. Nos. 498/501. P 13½		1·75	2·25

Designs:—1 c. Boxing; 2 c. Pole vault; 15 c. Swimming; 30 c. Running; $1 Cycling; $2 Shot put.

126 Water Skiing

(Des J.W. Litho Questa)

1976 (26 Aug). *Water Sports. T* **126** *and similar horiz designs. Multicoloured. P* 14.

503	½ c. Type **126**	.. .. ..	10	10
504	1 c. Sailing	.. .. ..	10	10
505	2 c. Snorkeling	.. ..	10	10
506	20 c. Deep sea fishing	..	30	10
507	50 c. Scuba diving	..	50	35
508	$2 Swimming	.. ..	1·00	1·25
503/8		*Set of* 6	1·75	1·60
MS509	89 × 114 mm. Nos. 506/8 ..		1·40	1·75

127 French Angelfish **128** The Annunciation

(Des G. Drummond. Litho Questa)

1976 (4 Oct). *Fishes. T* **127** *and similar horiz designs. Multicoloured. W* w 14 (*sideways*). *P* 13½.

510	15 c. Type **127**	.. ..	50	15
511	30 c. Yellow-finned Grouper		75	30
512	50 c. Yellow-tailed Snapper		95	50
513	90 c. Shy Hamlet	..	1·25	80
510/13		*Set of* 4	3·00	1·60

(Des J.W. Litho Walsall)

1976 (15 Nov). *Christmas. T* **128** *and similar vert designs. Multicoloured. P* 13½.

514	8 c. Type **128**	.. ..	10	10
515	10 c. The Holy Family..	..	10	10
516	15 c. The Magi..	.. ..	10	10
517	50 c. The Shepherds	..	20	25
518	$1 Epiphany scene	..	30	50
514/18		*Set of* 5	60	75

129 Mercury and U.P.U. Emblem **130** Royal Family

(Des BG Studio. Litho Questa)

1976 (28 Dec). *Special Events*, 1976. *T* **129** *and similar horiz designs. Multicoloured. P* 14.

519	½ c. Type **129**	.. ..	10	10
520	1 c. Alfred Nobel	.. ..	10	10
521	10 c. Space satellite	..	30	10
522	50 c. Viv Richards and Andy Roberts..		3·50	1·75
523	$1 Bell and telephones	..	1·00	2·00
524	$2 Yacht *Freelance*	..	2·25	4·00
519/24		*Set of* 6	6·50	7·00
MS525	127 × 101 mm. Nos. 521/4		7·50	11·00

Events:—½ c. 25th Anniv of U.N. Postal Administration; 1 c. 75th Anniv of Nobel Prize; 10 c. "Viking" Space Mission; 50 c. Cricketing achievements; $1 Telephone Centenary; $2 "Operation Sail", U.S. Bicentennial.

(Des J. W. Litho Questa (Nos. 526/31); Manufactured by Walsall (Nos. 532/3))

1977 (7 Feb–26 Sept). *Silver Jubilee. T* **130** *and similar vert designs. Multicoloured.* (*a*) *Sheet stamps. P* 14 (7 Feb).

526	10 c. Type **130**..	..	10	10
527	30 c. Royal Visit, 1966	..	10	10
528	50 c. The Queen enthroned		15	15
529	90 c. The Queen after Coronation		15	25
530	$2.50, Queen and Prince Charles..		30	55
526/30		*Set of* 5	60	95
MS531	116×78 mm. $5 Queen and Prince Philip		65	85
	a. Error. Imperf	.. ..	£350	

(*b*) *Booklet stamps. Roul* 5 × *imperf* (50 *c*.) *or imperf* ($5).* *Self-adhesive* (26 Sept)

532	50 c. Design as No. 529 (24 × 42 *mm*)		35	60
	a. Booklet pane of 6..	..	1·75	
533	$5 Design as stamp from No. **MS531** (24 ×42 *mm*)		2·00	3·50
	a. Booklet pane of 1..	..	2·00	

*No. 532 was separated by various combinations of rotary knife (giving a straight edge) and roulette. No. 533 exists only with straight edges.

Stamps as Nos. 526/30 but perforated 11½ × 12, come from sheets of 5 stamps and 1 label. These were not placed on sale by the Antigua Post Office.

---

131 Making Camp **132** Carnival Costume

(Des J.W. Litho Questa)

1977 (23 May). *Caribbean Scout Jamboree, Jamaica. T* **131** *and similar horiz designs. Multicoloured. P* 14.

534	½ c. Type **131**	.. ..	10	10
535	1 c. Hiking	.. ..	10	10
536	2 c. Rock-climbing	..	10	10
537	10 c. Cutting logs	..	15	10
538	30 c. Map and sign reading		40	10
539	50 c. First aid	..	65	25
540	$2 Rafting	.. ..	1·75	2·50
534/40		*Set of* 7	2·75	2·75
MS541	127 × 114 mm. Nos. 538/40		3·75	3·75

1977. *Coil Stamps. As Nos. 257/9, but W* w 14 (*inverted on* 10 *c*.). *P* 14½×14.

541a	89	5 c. blue	.. ..	5·00	
541b		10 c. emerald	..	—	65
541c		25 c. crimson	..	9·00	

(Des C. Abbott. Litho Walsall)

1977 (18 July). *21st Anniv of Carnival. T* **132** *and similar vert designs. Multicoloured. P* 14.

542	10 c. Type **132**	.. ..	10	10
543	30 c. Carnival Queen	..	20	10
544	50 c. Butterfly costume	..	25	15
545	90 c. Queen of the band	..	35	25
546	$1 Calypso King and Queen		35	30
542/6		*Set of* 5	1·10	70
MS547	140 × 120 mm. Nos. 542/6		1·10	1·60

ROYAL VISIT
28th OCTOBER 1977
(**133**) **134** "Virgin and Child Enthroned" (Tura)

1977 (17 Oct). *Royal Visit. Nos. 526/531 optd with T* **133**. *P* 14.

548	10 c. Type **130**..	..	10	10
549	30 c. Royal Visit, 1966	..	10	10
550	50 c. The Queen enthroned		15	10
551	90 c. The Queen after Coronation		25	20
552	$2.50, Queen and Prince Charles..		45	35
548/52		*Set of* 5	80	65
MS553	116 × 78 mm. $5 Queen and Prince Philip		80	1·00
	a. Opt double	.. ..	50·00	

Nos. 548/52 also exist perf 11½×12 (*Price for set of* 5 80p *mint or used*) *from additional sheetlets of five stamps and one label.*

(Des M. Shamir. Litho Questa)

1977 (21 Nov). *Christmas. T* **134** *and similar vert designs showing* "*Virgin and Child*" *by the artists given. Multicoloured. P* 14.

554	½ c. Type **134**	.. ..	10	10
555	1 c. Crivelli	.. ..	10	10
556	2 c. Lotto	.. ..	15	10
557	8 c. Pontormo	.. ..	15	10
558	10 c. Tura (*different*)	..	30	10
559	25 c. Lotto (*different*)	..	85	60
560	$2 Crivelli (*different*)	..	80	75
554/60		*Set of* 7	1·50	75
MS561	144 × 118 mm. Nos. 557/60		1·50	2·25

135 Pineapple

(Des and litho J.W.)

1977 (29 Dec). *Tenth Anniv of Statehood. T* **135** *and similar horiz designs. Multicoloured. P* 13.

562	10 c. Type **135**	.. ..	10	10
563	15 c. State flag	.. ..	10	10
564	50 c. Police band	..	2·00	80
565	90 c. Premier V. C. Bird	..	55	80
566	$2 State Coat of Arms	..	90	1·40
562/6		*Set of* 5	3·25	2·75
MS567	126 × 99 mm. Nos. 563/6. P 14		3·25	2·75

136 Wright Glider III, 1902

(Des PAD Studio. Litho Questa)

1978 (23 Mar). *75th Anniv of Powered Flight. T **136** and similar multicoloured designs. P 14.*

568	½ c. Type 136	10	10
569	1 c. Wright Flyer I, 1903	10	10
570	2 c. Launch system and engine	10	10
571	10 c. Orville Wright (vert)	20	10
572	50 c. Wright Flyer III, 1905	50	15
573	90 c. Wilbur Wright (vert)	75	30
574	$2 Wright Type B, 1910	1·00	80
568/74	*Set of 7*	2·25	1·25
MS575	90×75 mm. $2.50, Wright Flyer I on launch system	1·25	2·50

137 Sunfish Regatta

(Des G. Drummond. Litho Format)

1978 (27 Apr). *Sailing Week. T **137** and similar horiz designs. Multicoloured. P 15.*

576	10 c. Type 137	20	10
577	50 c. Fishing and work boat race	35	20
578	90 c. Curtain Bluff race	60	35
579	$2 Power boat rally	1·10	1·25
576/9	*Set of 4*	2·00	1·75
MS580	110 × 77 mm. $2.50, Guadeloupe–Antigua race	1·50	1·75

Nos. 576/9 exist imperforate from stock dispersed by the liquidator of Format International Security Printers Ltd.

138 Queen Elizabeth and Prince Philip | **139 Glass Coach**

(Des J.W. Litho Questa (Nos. 581/6); Manufactured by Walsall (Nos. 587/9))

1978 (2 June). *25th Anniv of Coronation. Multicoloured. (a) Sheet stamps. Vert designs as T **138**. P 14.*

581	10 c. Type 138	10	10
582	30 c. Crowning	10	10
583	50 c. Coronation procession	15	10
584	90 c. Queen seated in St. Edward's Chair	20	15
585	$2.50, Queen wearing Imperial State Crown	40	40
581/5	*Set of 5*	65	65
MS586	114 × 104 mm. $5 Queen and Prince Philip	80	80

*(b) Booklet stamps. Horiz design as T **139** showing State Coaches. Imperf ($5) or roul 5 × imperf*. Self-adhesive.*

587	25 c. Type 139	15	30
	a. Booklet pane. No. 587/8 × 3	1·25	
588	50 c. Irish State Coach	25	50
589	$5 Coronation Coach	1·75	3·00
	a. Booklet pane of 1	1·75	
587/9	*Set of 3*	2·00	3·50

Nos. 581/5 also exist perf 12 (*Price for set of 5 65p mint or used*) from additional sheetlets of three stamps and one label. These stamps have changed background colours.

*Nos. 587/8 were separated by various combinations of rotary-knife (giving a straight edge) and roulette. No. 589 exists only with straight edges.

140 Player running with Ball | **141 Petrea**

(Des BG Studio. Litho Format)

1978 (17 Aug). *World Cup Football Championship, Argentina. T **140** and similar vert designs. Multicoloured. P 14½.*

590	10 c. Type 140	15	10
591	15 c. Players in front of goal	15	10
592	$3 Referee and player	2·00	1·75
590/2	*Set of 3*	2·00	1·75
MS593	126 × 88 mm. 25 c. Player crouching with ball; 30 c. Players heading ball; 50 c. Players running with ball; $2 Goalkeeper diving. (All horiz)	3·00	2·50

Nos. 590/2 were each printed in small sheets of 6 including 1 se-tenant stamp-size label.

Nos. 590/2 exist imperforate from stock dispersed by the liquidator of Format International Security Printers Ltd.

(Des G. Drummond. Litho Questa)

1978 (5 Oct). *Flowers. T **141** and similar vert designs. Multicoloured. P 14.*

594	25 c. Type 141	25	10
595	50 c. Sunflower	35	20
596	90 c. Frangipani	60	30
597	$2 Passion Flower	1·25	1·10
594/7	*Set of 4*	2·25	1·40
MS598	118 × 85 mm. $2.50, Hibiscus	1·40	1·60

142 "St Ildefonso receiving the Chasuble from the Virgin" (Rubens) | **143 1d. Stamp of 1863**

(Des BG Studio. Litho Questa)

1978 (30 Oct). *Christmas Paintings. T **142** and similar horiz designs. Multicoloured. P 14.*

599	8 c. Type 142	10	10
600	25 c. "The Flight of St. Barbara" (Rubens)	20	10
601	$2 "Madonna and Child, with St. Joseph, John the Baptist and Donor" (Sebastiano del Piombo*)	65	55
599/601	*Set of 3*	80	60
MS602	170 × 113 mm. $4 "The Annunciation" (Rubens)	1·25	1·50

*The work is incorrectly attributed to Rubens on the stamp.

(Des G. Vasarhelyi. Litho Questa)

1979 (12 Feb). *Death Centenary of Sir Rowland Hill. T **143** and similar vert designs. Multicoloured. P 14.*

603	25 c. Type 143	10	10
604	50 c. Penny Black	20	15
605	$1 Stage-coach and woman posting letter, circa 1840	30	20
606	$2 Modern mail transport	1·10	60
603/6	*Set of 4*	1·50	85
MS607	108 × 82 mm. $2.50, Sir Rowland Hill	80	90

Nos. 603/6 also exist perf 12 (*Price for set of 4 £1·50 mint or used*) from additional sheetlets of five stamps and one label.

144 "The Deposition from the Cross" (painting) | **145 Toy Yacht and Child's Hand**

(Des BG Studio. Litho Questa)

1979 (15 Mar). *Easter. Works by Dürer. T **144** and similar vert designs. P 14.*

608	10 c. multicoloured	10	10
609	50 c. multicoloured	35	20
610	$4 black, magenta and greenish yellow	1·00	90
608/10	*Set of 3*	1·25	1·00
MS611	114 × 99 mm. $2.50, multicoloured	80	80

Designs:—50 c., $2.50, "Christ on the Cross—The Passion" (wood engravings) (both different); $4 "Man of Sorrows with Hands Raised" (wood engraving).

(Des M. Rubin. Litho Questa)

1979 (9 Apr). *International Year of the Child. T **145** and similar vert designs showing toys and hands of children of different races. Multicoloured. P 14.*

612	25 c. Type 145	10	10
613	50 c. Rocket	25	15
614	90 c. Car	40	25
615	$2 Train	1·00	90
612/15	*Set of 4*	1·60	1·25
MS616	80 × 112 mm. $5 Aeroplane	1·10	1·10

146 Yellow Jack | **147 Cook's Birthplace, Marton**

(Des P. Powell. Litho Questa)

1979 (14 May). *Fishes. T **146** and similar horiz designs. Multicoloured. P 14½ × 14.*

617	30 c. Type 146	40	15
618	50 c. Blue-finned Tuna	50	25
619	90 c. Sailfish	75	40
620	$3 Wahoo	2·25	1·75
617/20	*Set of 4*	3·50	2·25
MS621	122×75 mm. $2.50, Great Barracuda	1·50	1·40

(Des J.W. Litho Questa)

1979 (2 July). *Death Bicentenary of Captain Cook. T **147** and similar vert designs. Multicoloured. P 14.*

622	25 c. Type 147	55	25
623	50 c. H.M.S. Endeavour	75	60
624	90 c. Marine chronometer	75	80
625	$3 Landing at Botany Bay	1·60	2·75
622/5	*Set of 4*	3·25	4·00
MS626	110 × 85 mm. $2.50, H.M.S. Resolution	2·25	2·00

148 The Holy Family | **149 Javelin Throwing**

(Des J.W. Litho Questa)

1979 (1 Oct). *Christmas. T **148** and similar vert designs. Multicoloured. P 14.*

627	8 c. Type 148	10	10
628	25 c. Virgin and Child on Ass	15	10
629	50 c. Shepherd and star	25	35
630	$4 Wise Men with gifts	85	2·25
627/30	*Set of 4*	1·25	1·00
MS631	113 × 94 mm. $3 Angel with trumpet. P 12	1·00	1·50

(Des Design Images Inc. Litho Questa)

1980 (18 Feb). *Olympic Games, Moscow. T **149** and similar multicoloured designs. P 14.*

632	10 c. Type 149	20	10
633	25 c. Running	20	10
634	$1 Pole vaulting	50	50
635	$2 Hurdling	70	1·50
632/5	*Set of 4*	1·40	2·00
MS636	127 × 96 mm. $3 Boxing (horiz)	80	90

150 Mickey Mouse and Aeroplane | **(151)**

(Litho Format)

1980 (24 Mar). *International Year of the Child (1979). Walt Disney Cartoon Characters. T **150** and similar multicoloured designs showing characters and transport. P 11.*

637	½ c. Type 150	10	10
638	1 c. Donald Duck driving car	10	10
639	2 c. Goofy driving taxi	10	10
640	3 c. Mickey Mouse on motorcycle with Minnie Mouse in sidecar	10	10
641	4 c. Huey, Dewey and Louie riding cycle	10	10
642	5 c. Grandma Duck, chickens and pickup truck	10	10
643	10 c. Mickey Mouse driving jeep (vert)	10	10
644	$1 Chip and Dale in sailing boat	1·75	2·00
645	$4 Donald Duck riding toy train (vert)	3·75	6·00
637/45	*Set of 9*	5·50	7·50
MS646	101 × 127 mm. $2.50, Goofy flying biplane. P 14 × 13½	4·50	3·25

See also Nos. 671/80.

1980 (6 May). *"London 1980" International Stamp Exhibition. Nos. 603/6 optd with T **151**. P 12.*

647	25 c. Type 143	20	15
648	50 c. Penny Black	30	35
649	$1 Stage-coach and woman posting letter, circa 1840	55	60
650	$2 Modern mail transport	2·75	2·75
647/50	*Set of 4*	3·50	3·50

152 "David" (statue, Donatello)

153 Rotary International 75th Anniversary Emblem and Headquarters, U.S.A.

(Des J.W. Litho Questa)

1980 (23 June). *Famous Works of Art. T* **152** *and similar multicoloured designs. P* 13½.

651	10 c. Type **152**		10	10
652	30 c. "The Birth of Venus" (painting, Sandro Botticelli) (*horiz*) ..		30	15
653	50 c. "Reclining Couple" (sarcophagus), Cerveteri (*horiz*) ..		40	40
654	90 c. "The Garden of Earthly Delights" (painting, Hieronymus Bosch) (*horiz*)		55	65
655	$1 "Portinari Altarpiece" (painting, Hugo van der Goes) (*horiz*)		65	75
656	$4 "Eleanora of Toledo and her Son Giovanni de'Medici" (painting, Agnolo Bronzino) ..		1·75	3·00
651/6		*Set of* 6	3·25	4·50
MS657	99 × 124 mm. $5 "The Holy Family" (painting, Rembrandt)		2·50	2·25

(Des G. Vasarhelyi. Litho Questa)

1980 (21 July). *75th Anniv of Rotary International. T* **153** *and similar horiz designs. Multicoloured. P* 14.

658	30 c. Type **153**		30	30
659	50 c. Rotary anniversary emblem and Antigua Rotary Club banner		40	50
660	90 c. Map of Antigua and Rotary emblem		60	70
661	$3 Paul P. Harris (founder) and Rotary emblem		2·00	3·25
658/61		*Set of* 4	3·00	4·25
MS662	102 × 78 mm. $5 Antiguan flags and Rotary emblems		1·25	2·00

154 Queen Elizabeth the Queen Mother

155 Ringed Kingfisher

(Des G. Vasarhelyi. Litho Questa)

1980 (4 Aug). *80th Birthday of Queen Elizabeth the Queen Mother. P* 14.

663	**154** 10 c. multicoloured ..		25	10
664	$2.50, multicoloured ..		1·25	1·75
MS665	68 × 90 mm. **154** $3 multicoloured. P 12		1·25	2·00

(Des Jennifer Toombs. Litho Questa)

1980 (3 Nov). *Birds. T* **155** *and similar vert designs. Multicoloured. P* 14.

666	10 c. Type **155**		70	25
667	30 c. Plain Pigeon		1·00	50
668	$1 Green-throated Carib		1·50	1·75
669	$2 Black-necked Stilt		2·00	3·50
666/9		*Set of* 4	4·75	5·50
MS670	73 × 73 mm. $2.50, Roseate Tern		6·00	4·50

(Litho Format)

1980 (23 Dec). *Christmas. Scenes from Walt Disney's Cartoon Film "Sleeping Beauty". Horiz designs as T* **150**. *P* 11.

671	½ c. multicoloured ..		10	10
672	1 c. multicoloured ..		10	10
673	2 c. multicoloured ..		10	10
674	4 c. multicoloured ..		10	10
675	8 c. multicoloured ..		10	10
676	10 c. multicoloured ..		15	10
677	25 c. multicoloured ..		20	20
678	$2 multicoloured ..		2·25	2·25
679	$2.50, multicoloured ..		2·50	2·50
671/9		*Set of* 9	4·75	4·75
MS680	126 × 101 mm. $4 multicoloured (*vert*) P 13½ × 14 ..		5·00	3·25

156 Diesel Locomotive No. 15

(Des G. Drummond. Litho Questa)

1981 (12 Jan). *Sugar Cane Railway Locomotives. T* **156** *and similar horiz designs. Multicoloured. P* 14.

681	25 c. Type **156**		15	15
682	50 c. Narrow-gauge steam locomotive		30	30
683	90 c. Diesel locomotives Nos. 1 and 10		55	60
684	$3 Steam locomotive hauling sugar cane		2·00	2·25
681/4		*Set of* 4	2·75	3·00
MS685	82 × 111 mm. $2.50, Antigua sugar factory, railway yard and sheds ..		1·75	1·75

158 "Pipes of Pan"

"INDEPENDENCE 1981"

(157)

1981 (31 Mar). *Independence. Optd with T* **157**. A. *On Nos.* 475A, 478A, 480A *and* 484A/6A.

686A	6 c. Orchid Tree	..	60	60
688A	20 c. Flamboyant	..	60	60
690A	35 c. Flame of the Wood	..	1·25	1·25
694A	$2.50, Irrigation Scheme, Diamond Estate		2·00	4·00
695A	$5 Government House	..	3·50	7·50
696A	$10 Coolidge Airport	..	6·50	11·00
686A/96A		*Set of* 6	13·00	22·00

B. *On Nos.* 475B/6B *and* 478B/86B

686B	6 c. Orchid Tree	..	10	10
687B	10 c. Bougainvillea	..	10	10
688B	20 c. Flamboyant	..	10	10
689B	25 c. Hibiscus	..	15	15
690B	35 c. Flame of the Wood	..	20	20
691B	50 c. Cannon at Fort James	..	35	35
692B	75 c. Premier's Office	..	40	40
693B	$1 Potworks Dam	..	55	55
694B	$2.50, Irrigation Scheme, Diamond Estate		1·00	1·25
695B	$5 Government House	..	1·75	2·50
696B	$10 Coolidge Airport	..	3·50	5·00
686B/96B ..		*Set of* 11	7·00	9·50

(Des J.W. Litho Questa)

1981 (5 May). *Birth Centenary of Picasso. T* **158** *and similar vert designs. Multicoloured. P* 14.

697	10 c. Type **158** ..		10	10
698	50 c. "Seated Harlequin"	..	30	30
699	90 c. "Paulo as Harlequin"	..	55	55
700	$4 "Mother and Child"	..	2·00	2·00
697/700		*Set of* 4	2·50	2·50
MS701	115 × 140 mm. $5 "Three Musicians" (detail) ..		2·00	2·75

159 Prince Charles and Lady Diana Spencer

160 Prince of Wales at Investiture, 1969

(Des J.W. Litho Questa)

1981 (23 June). *Royal Wedding (1st issue). T* **159** *and similar vert designs. Multicoloured. P* 14.

702	25 c. Type **159** ..		10	10
703	50 c. Glamis Castle	..	10	10
704	$4 Prince Charles skiing	..	80	80
702/4		*Set of* 3	80	80
MS705	96 × 82 mm. $5 Glass Coach		80	80

Nos. 702/4 also exist perforated 12 (*Price for set of 3 80p mint or used*) from additional sheetlets of five stamps and one label. These stamps have changed background colours.

(Manufactured by Walsall)

1981 (23 June). *Royal Wedding (2nd issue). T* **160** *and similar vert designs. Multicoloured ($5) or black and flesh (others). Self-adhesive. Roul* 5×*imperf*.

706	25 c. Type **160** ..		15	25
	a. Booklet pane. Nos. 706/11	..	1·50	
707	25 c. Prince Charles as baby, 1948	..	15	25
708	$1 Prince Charles at R.A.F. College, Cranwell, 1971		25	50
709	$1 Prince Charles attending Hill House School, 1956		25	50
710	$2 Prince Charles and Lady Diana Spencer		50	75
711	$2 Prince Charles at Trinity College, 1967		50	75
712	$5 Prince Charles and Lady Diana (*different*)		1·00	1·50
	a. Booklet pane of 1..			
706/12		*Set of* 7	2·50	4·00

*The 25 c. to $2 values were each separated by various combinations of rotary knife (giving a straight edge) and roulette. The $5 value exists only with straight edges. Nos. 706/12 were only issued in $11.50 stamp booklets.

161 Irene Joshua (founder)

162 Antigua and Barbuda Coat of Arms

(Des M. Diamond. Litho Questa)

1981 (28 Oct). *50th Anniv of Antigua Girl Guide Movement. T* **161** *and similar horiz designs. Multicoloured. P* 14½.

713	10 c. Type **161** ..		15	10
714	50 c. Campfire sing-song	..	45	35
715	90 c. Sailing	..	75	65
716	$2.50, Animal tending	..	1·75	2·00
713/16		*Set of* 4	2·75	2·75
MS717	110 × 85 mm. $5 Raising the flag ..		4·50	3·00

INDEPENDENT

Nos. 718/22 and 733 onwards are inscribed "ANTIGUA & BARBUDA".

(Des E. Henry. Litho Format)

1981 (1 Nov). *Independence. T* **162** *and similar multicoloured designs. P* 14½.

718	10 c. Type **162** ..		20	10
719	50 c. Pineapple, Antigua flag and map		45	20
720	90 c. Prime Minister Vere Bird		55	55
721	$2.50, St. John's Cathedral (38×25 mm)		1·50	2·75
718/21		*Set of* 4	2·40	3·25
MS722	105×79 mm. $5 Map of Antigua and Barbuda (42×42 mm) ..		3·75	2·75

163 "Holy Night" (Jacques Stella)

164 Swimming

(Des Clover Mill. Litho Format)

1981 (16 Nov). *Christmas. Paintings. T* **163** *and similar vert designs. Multicoloured. P* 14½.

723	8 c. Type **163** ..		15	10
724	30 c. "Mary with Child" (Julius Schnorr von Carolfeld)		40	15
725	$1 "Virgin and Child" (Alonso Cano)		80	90
726	$3 "Virgin and Child" (Lorenzo di Credi)		1·40	3·75
723/6		*Set of* 4	2·50	4·25
MS727	77 × 111 mm. $5 "Holy Family" (Pieter von Avon) ..		2·50	4·50

(Des M. Diamond. Litho Format)

1981 (1 Dec). *International Year for Disabled Persons. Sport for the Disabled. T* **164** *and similar horiz designs. Multicoloured. P* 15.

728	10 c. Type **164** ..		10	10
729	50 c. Discus throwing ..		20	30
730	90 c. Archery	..	40	55
731	$2 Baseball	..	1·00	1·40
728/31		*Set of* 4	1·50	2·10
MS732	108 × 84 mm. $4 Basketball		5·00	2·75

165 Scene from Football Match

166 Airbus Industrie A300

(Des Clover Mill. Litho Questa)

1982 (15 Apr). *World Cup Football Championship, Spain. T* **165** *and similar horiz designs showing scenes from different matches. P* 14.

733	10 c. multicoloured ..		30	10
734	50 c. multicoloured ..		60	35
735	90 c. multicoloured ..		1·10	70
736	$4 multicoloured ..		3·50	3·50
733/6		*Set of* 4	5·00	4·25
MS737	75 × 92 mm. $5 multicoloured		7·50	9·50

Nos. 733/6 also exist perforated 12 (*Price for set of 4, £4.50 mint or used*) from additional sheetlets of five stamps and one label. These stamps have changed inscription colours.

(Des Clover Mill. Litho Format)

1982 (17 June). *Coolidge International Airport. T **166** and similar multicoloured designs. P 14½.*

738	10 c. Type **166**	10	10
739	50 c. Hawker Siddeley H.S. 748	30	30
740	90 c. De Havilland D.H.C.6 Twin Otter	60	60
741	$2.50, Britten Norman Islander	1·75	1·75
738/41	Set of 4	2·50	2·50
MS742	99×73 mm. $5 Boeing 747-100 (*horiz*)	2·75	4·00

167 Cordia

(Des G. Drummond. Litho Questa)

1982 (28 June). *Death Centenary of Charles Darwin. Fauna and Flora. T **167** and similar multicoloured designs. P 15.*

743	10 c. Type **167**	15	10
744	50 c. Small Indian Mongoose (*horiz*)	45	40
745	90 c. Corallita	75	75
746	$3 Mexican Bulldog Bat (*horiz*)	2·00	3·25
743/6	Set of 4	3·00	4·00
MS747	107×85 mm. $5 Caribbean Monk Seal	6·50	8·00

168 Queen's House, Greenwich   **169** Princess of Wales

(Des PAD Studio. Litho Questa)

1982 (1 July). *21st Birthday of Princess of Wales. T **168/9** and similar vert design. Multicoloured. P 14½ × 14.*

748	90 c. Type **168**	45	45
749	$1 Prince and Princess of Wales	50	50
750	$4 Princess Diana (*different*)	2·00	2·00
748/50	Set of 3	2·75	2·75
MS751	102 × 75 mm. $5 Type **169**	2·75	2·50

Nos. 748/50 also exist in sheetlets of 5 stamps and 1 label.

170 Boy Scouts decorating Streets   **(171)**
for Independence Parade

(Des J.W. Litho Questa)

1982 (15 July). *75th Anniv of Boy Scout Movement. T **170** and similar horiz designs. Multicoloured. P 14.*

752	10 c. Type **170**	20	10
753	50 c. Boy Scout giving helping hand during street parade	50	40
754	90 c. Boy Scouts attending Princess Margaret at Independence Ceremony	85	75
755	$2.20, Cub Scout giving directions to tourists	1·75	2·75
752/5	Set of 4	3·00	3·50
MS756	102 × 72 mm. $5 Lord Baden-Powell	5·50	5·50

1982 (30 Aug). *Birth of Prince William of Wales. Nos. 748/51 optd with T **171**.*

757	90 c. Type **168**	45	45
758	$1 Prince and Princess of Wales	50	50
759	$4 Princess Diana (*different*)	2·00	1·50
757/9	Set of 3	2·75	2·25
MS760	102 × 75 mm. $5 Type **169**	2·40	2·50

Nos. 757/9 also exist in sheetlets of 5 stamps and 1 label.

172 Roosevelt in 1940

(Des PAD Studio. Litho Format)

1982 (20 Sept). *Birth Centenary of Franklin D. Roosevelt (Nos. 761, 763, 765/6 and MS767) and 250th Birth Anniv of George Washington (others). T **172** and similar multicoloured designs. P 15.*

761	10 c. Type **172**	20	10
762	25 c. Washington as blacksmith	45	15
763	45 c. Churchill, Roosevelt and Stalin at Yalta Conference	1·00	40
764	60 c. Washington crossing the Delaware (*vert*)	1·00	40
765	$1 "Roosevelt Special" train (*vert*)	1·25	90
766	$3 Portrait of Roosevelt (*vert*)	1·40	2·40
761/6	Set of 6	4·75	3·75
MS767	92 × 87 mm. $4 Roosevelt and Wife	2·00	1·75
MS768	92 × 87 mm. $4 Portrait of Washington (*vert*)	2·00	1·75

No. MS768 exists imperforate from stock dispersed by the liquidator of Format International Security Printers Ltd.

173 "Annunciation"

(Des Design Images. Litho Questa)

1982 (Nov). *Christmas. Religious Paintings by Raphael. T **173** and similar horiz designs. Multicoloured. P 14 × 13½.*

769	10 c. Type **173**	10	10
770	30 c. "Adoration of the Magi"	15	15
771	$1 "Presentation at the Temple"	50	50
772	$4 "Coronation of the Virgin"	2·10	2·25
769/72	Set of 4	2·50	2·75
MS773	95 × 124 mm. $5 "Marriage of the Virgin"	2·75	2·50

174 Tritons and Dolphins   **175** Pineapple Produce

(Des Design Images. Litho Format)

1983 (28 Jan). *500th Birth Anniv of Raphael. Details from "Galatea" Fresco. T **174** and similar multicoloured designs. P 14½.*

774	45 c. Type **174**	20	25
775	50 c. Sea Nymph carried off by Triton	25	30
776	60 c. Winged angel steering Dolphins (*horiz*)	30	35
777	$4 Cupids shooting arrows (*horiz*)	1·60	2·00
774/7	Set of 4	2·10	2·50
MS778	101 × 125 mm. $5 Galatea pulled along by Dolphins	2·50	2·75

(Des Artists International. Litho Questa)

1983 (14 Mar). *Commonwealth Day. T **175** and similar horiz designs. Multicoloured. P 14.*

779	25 c. Type **175**	15	15
780	45 c. Carnival	20	25
781	60 c. Tourism	30	35
782	$3 Airport	1·00	1·50
779/82	Set of 4	1·50	2·00

176 T.V. Satellite Coverage
of Royal Wedding

(Des PAD Studio. Litho Questa)

1983 (5 Apr). *World Communications Year. T **176** and similar horiz designs. Multicoloured. P 14.*

783	15 c. Type **176**	40	20
784	50 c. Police communications	2·25	1·50
785	60 c. House-to-train telephone call	2·25	1·50
786	$3 Satellite earth station with planets Jupiter and Saturn	4·75	5·00
783/6	Set of 4	8·50	7·50
MS787	100 × 90 mm. $5 "Comsat" satellite over West Indies	2·25	2·75

177 Bottle-nosed Dolphin

(Des D. Miller. Litho Format)

1983 (9 May). *Whales. T **177** and similar horiz designs. Multicoloured. P 14½.*

788	15 c. Type **177**	85	20
789	50 c. Fin Whale	1·75	1·25
790	60 c. Bowhead Whale	2·00	1·25
791	$3 Spectacled Porpoise	3·75	4·25
788/91	Set of 4	7·50	6·25
MS792	122 × 101 mm. $5 Narwhal	8·50	6·00

Nos. 788/92 exist imperforate from stock dispersed by the liquidator of Format International Security Printers Ltd.

178 Cashew Nut

(Des J.W. Litho Questa)

1983 (11 July)–**85**. *Fruits and Flowers. T **178** and similar horiz designs. Multicoloured. P 14.*

793	1 c. Type **178**	15	60
	a. Perf 12 (3.85)	20	60
794	2 c. Passion Fruit	15	60
	a. Perf 12 (3.85)	20	60
795	3 c. Mango	15	60
	a. Perf 12 (3.85)	20	60
796	5 c. Grapefruit	20	50
	a. Perf 12 (3.85)	30	50
797	10 c. Pawpaw	40	20
	a. Perf 12 (3.85)	30	20
798	15 c. Breadfruit	50	20
	a. Perf 12 (3.85)	50	20
799	20 c. Coconut	50	20
	a. Perf 12 (3.85)	60	20
800	25 c. Oleander	55	30
	a. Perf 12 (3.85)	60	20
801	30 c. Banana	60	40
	a. Perf 12 (3.85)	75	30
802	40 c. Pineapple	70	40
	a. Perf 12 (3.85)	75	30
803	45 c. Cordia	80	55
	a. Perf 12 (3.85)	85	40
804	50 c. Cassia	90	60
	a. Perf 12 (3.85)	1·25	50
805	60 c. Poui	1·50	1·00
	a. Perf 12 (3.85)	1·50	1·10
806	$1 Frangipani	2·25	1·75
	a. Perf 12 (3.85)	2·25	1·50
807	$2 Flamboyant	3·75	4·00
	a. Perf 12 (3.85)	3·75	4·00
808	$2.50, Lemon	4·50	5·50
	a. Perf 12 (12.85)	4·50	5·50
809	$5 Lignum Vitae	7·00	11·00
	a. Perf 12 (12.85)	7·00	11·00
810	$10 National flag and coat of arms	11·00	16·00
	a. Perf 12 (3.85)	11·00	16·00
793/810	Set of 18	32·00	40·00

179 Dornier Do X
Flying Boat

(Des W. Wright. Litho Format)

1983 (15 Aug). *Bicentenary of Manned Flight. T **179** and similar horiz designs. Multicoloured. P 14½.*

811	30 c. Type **179**	75	30
812	50 c. Supermarine S6B seaplane	90	60
813	60 c. Curtiss F-9C Sparrowhawk biplane and airship U.S.S. *Akron*	1·00	85
814	$4 Hot-air balloon *Pro Juventute*	3·00	5·00
811/14	Set of 4	5·00	6·00
MS815	80×105 mm. $5 Airship LZ-127 *Graf Zeppelin*	2·00	3·25

180 "Sibyls and Angels" (detail)
(Raphael)

(Des W. Wright. Litho Format)

1983 (4 Oct). *Christmas. 500th Birth Anniv of Raphael. T **180** and similar designs. P 13½.*

816	10 c. multicoloured	30	20
817	30 c. multicoloured	65	35
818	$1 multicoloured	1·50	1·25
819	$4 multicoloured	3·00	5·00
816/19	Set of 4	5·00	6·25
MS820	101 × 131 mm. $5 multicoloured	1·50	2·25

Designs: *Horiz*—10 c. to $4 Different details from "Sibyls and Angels". *Vert*—$5 "The Vision of Ezekiel".

Nos. 816/20 exist imperforate from stock dispersed by the liquidator of Format International Security Printers Ltd.

181 John Wesley (founder)

182 Discus

(Des M. Diamond. Litho Questa)

1983 (7 Nov). *Bicentenary of Methodist Church* (1984). T **181** and
similar vert designs. Multicoloured. P 14.

821	15 c. Type **181**		25	15
822	50 c. Nathaniel Gilbert (founder in Antigua)		70	50
823	60 c. St. John Methodist Church steeple		75	65
824	$3 Ebenezer Methodist Church, St. John's		2·00	4·00
821/4		*Set of 4*	3·25	4·75

183 Booker Vanguard
(freighter)

184 Chenille

(Des Artists International. Litho Format)

1984 (14 June). *Ships.* T **183** *and similar multicoloured designs.*
P 15.

830	45 c. Type **183**		1·00	55
831	50 c. Canberra (liner)		1·25	80
832	60 c. Yachts		1·50	1·00
833	$4 Fairwind (cargo liner)		3·00	7·00
830/3		*Set of 4*	6·00	8·50
MS834	107×80 mm. $5 18th-century British man-o-war (*vert*)		1·75	3·50

Nos. 830/4 exist imperforate from stock dispersed by the
liquidator of Format International Security Printers Ltd.

(Des J.W. Litho Format)

1984 (19 June). *Universal Postal Union Congress, Hamburg.*
T **184** *and similar vert designs showing flowers. Multicoloured.*
P 15.

835	15 c. Type **184**		40	15
836	50 c. Shell Flower		1·00	70
837	60 c. Anthurium		1·10	1·10
838	$3 Angels Trumpet		3·00	6·50
835/8		*Set of 4*	5·00	7·50
MS839	100 × 75 mm. $5 Crown of Thorns		1·50	3·25

Nos. 835/9 exist imperforate from stock dispersed by the
liquidator of Format International Security Printers Ltd.

(185) (186)

1984 (25 June). (a) *Nos. 702/5 surch with* T **185**

840	$2 on 25 c. Type **159**		3·00	3·00
841	$2 on 50 c. Glamis Castle		3·00	3·00
842	$2 on $4 Prince Charles skiing		3·00	3·00
840/2		*Set of 3*	8·00	8·00
MS843	96 × 82 mm. $2 on $5 Glass Coach		4·00	4·00

(b) *Nos. 748/51 surch with* T **186**

844	$2 on 90 c. Type **168** (Gold)*		2·40	2·25
845	$2 on $1 Prince and Princess of Wales (Gold)*		2·40	2·25
846	$2 on $4 Princess Diana (*different*) (Gold)*		2·40	2·25
844/6		*Set of 3*	6·50	6·00
MS847	102 × 75 mm. $2 on $5 Type **169** (Gold)		4·00	4·00

(c) *Nos. 757/60 surch with* T **186**

848	$2 on 90 c. Type **168** (Gold)*		2·40	2·25
849	$2 on $1 Prince and Princess of Wales (Gold)*		2·40	2·25
850	$2 on $4 Princess Diana (*different*) (Gold)*		2·40	2·25
848/50		*Set of 3*	6·50	6·00
MS851	102 × 75 mm. $2 on $5 Type **169** (Gold)		4·00	4·00

(d) *Nos. 779/82 surch as* T **185**

852	$2 on 25 c. Type **175**		2·25	1·25
853	$2 on 45 c. Carnival		2·25	1·25
854	$2 on 60 c. Tourism		2·25	1·25
855	$2 on $3 Airport		2·25	1·25
852/5		*Set of 4*	8·00	4·50

*Nos. 844/6 and 848/50 also exist with similar surcharges in
gold or silver on the sheetlets of five stamps and 1 label (*price for
set of 3 as Nos. 844/6, £6 mint or used*) (*price for set of 3 as Nos.
848/50, £6 mint or used*).

187 Abraham Lincoln

188 View of Moravian Mission

(Des Liane Fried. Litho Questa)

1984 (18 July). *Presidents of the United States of America.* T **187**
and similar vert designs. Multicoloured. P 14.

856	10 c. Type **187**		15	10
857	20 c. Harry Truman		20	15
858	30 c. Dwight Eisenhower		30	25
859	40 c. Ronald Reagan		50	30
860	90 c. Gettysburg Address, 1863		90	75
861	$1.10, Formation of N.A.T.O., 1949		1·25	1·25
862	$1.50, Eisenhower during Second World War		1·60	1·75
863	$2 Reagan and Caribbean Basin Initiative		1·75	2·00
856/63		*Set of 8*	6·00	6·00

(Des and litho Questa)

1984 (1 Aug). *150th Anniv of Abolition of Slavery.* T **188** *and
similar horiz designs. Multicoloured.* P 14.

864	40 c. Type **188**		80	50
865	50 c. Antigua Courthouse, 1823		90	65
866	60 c. Planting sugar-cane, Monks Hill		95	75
867	$3 Boiling house, Delaps' estate		4·00	4·75
864/7		*Set of 4*	6·00	6·00
MS868	95 × 70 mm. $5 Loading sugar, Willoughby Bay		6·50	4·75

189 Rufous-sided Towhee

190 Grass-skiing

(Des Jennifer Toombs. Litho Format)

1984 (15 Aug). *Songbirds.* T **189** *and similar vert designs. Multicoloured.* P 15.

869	40 c. Type **189**		1·25	85
870	50 c. Parula Warbler		1·40	1·10
871	60 c. House Wren		1·50	1·50
872	$2 Ruby-crowned Kinglet		2·00	3·75
873	$3 Common Flicker		2·75	5·00
869/73		*Set of 5*	8·00	11·00
MS874	76 × 76 mm. $5 Yellow-breasted Chat		2·50	6·00

(Des Bonny Redecker. Litho Questa)

1984 (21 Sept). *"Ausipex" International Stamp Exhibition,
Melbourne. Australian Sports.* T **190** *and similar vert designs.
Multicoloured.* P 14½.

875	$1 Type **190**		1·25	1·50
876	$5 Australian Football		3·75	5·50
MS877	108 × 78 mm. $5 Boomerang-throwing		3·00	4·00

191 "The Virgin and Infant with
Angels and Cherubs" (Correggio)

192 "The Blue Dancers"
(Degas)

(Litho Format)

1984 (4 Oct). *450th Death Anniv of Correggio (painter).* T **191** *and
similar vert designs. Multicoloured.* P 15.

878	25 c. Type **191**		40	20
879	60 c. "The Four Saints"		80	50
880	90 c. "St. Catherine"		1·10	90
881	$3 "The Campori Madonna"		2·25	4·25
878/81		*Set of 4*	4·00	5·25
MS882	90 × 60 mm. $5 "St. John the Baptist"		2·00	2·75

(Litho Format)

1984 (4 Oct). *150th Birth Anniv of Edgar Degas (painter).* T **192**
and similar multicoloured designs. P 15.

883	15 c. Type **192**		35	15
884	50 c. "The Pink Dancers"		80	60
885	70 c. "Two Dancers"		1·10	85
886	$4 "Dancers at the Bar"		2·50	4·75
883/6		*Set of 4*	4·25	5·75
MS887	90 × 60 mm. $5 "The Folk Dancers" (40 × 27 mm)		2·00	2·75

193 Sir Winston Churchill

194 Donald Duck fishing

(Des J. Iskowitz. Litho Format)

1984 (19 Nov). *Famous People.* T **193** *and similar multicoloured designs.* P 15.

888	60 c. Type **193**		1·10	1·50
889	60 c. Mahatma Gandhi		1·10	1·50
890	60 c. John F. Kennedy		1·10	1·50
891	60 c. Mao Tse-tung		1·10	1·50
892	$1 Churchill with General De Gaulle, Paris, 1944 (*horiz*)		1·25	1·75
893	$1 Gandhi leaving London by train, 1931 (*horiz*)		1·25	1·75
894	$1 Kennedy with Chancellor Adenauer and Mayor Brandt, Berlin, 1963 (*horiz*)		1·25	1·75
895	$1 Mao Tse-tung with Lin Piao, Peking, 1969 (*horiz*)		1·25	1·75
888/95		*Set of 8*	8·50	11·50
MS896	114 × 80 mm. $5 Flags of Great Britain, India, the United States and China		9·00	4·50

Nos. 888 and 890/5 exist imperforate from stock dispersed by
the liquidator of Format International Security Printers Ltd.

(Litho Format)

1984 (26 Nov). *Christmas. 50th Birthday of Donald Duck.*
T **194** *and similar multicoloured designs showing Walt
Disney cartoon characters.* P 11.

897	1 c. Type **194**		10	10
898	2 c. Donald Duck lying on beach		10	10
899	3 c. Donald Duck and nephews with fishing rods and fishes		10	10
900	4 c. Donald Duck and nephews in boat		10	10
901	5 c. Wearing diving masks		10	10
902	10 c. In deckchairs reading books		10	10
903	$1 With toy shark's fin		2·25	1·25
904	$2 In sailing boat		2·50	3·00
905	$5 Attempting to propel boat		5·50	6·00
897/905		*Set of 9*	9·50	9·50
MS906	Two sheets, each 125 × 100 mm. (a) $5 Nephews with crayon and paintbrushes (*horiz*). P 14 × 13½. (b) $5 Donald Duck in deckchair. P 13½ × 14	*Set of 2 sheets*	9·00	13·00

No. 904 was printed in sheetlets of 8 stamps.
Nos. 897/905 exist imperforate from stock dispersed by the
liquidator of Format International Security Printers Ltd.

195 Torch from Statue in
Madison Square Park, 1885

(Des J. Iskowitz. Litho Format)

1985 (7 Jan). *Centenary of the Statue of Liberty* (1986) (1st
issue). T **195** *and similar multicoloured designs.* P 15.

907	25 c. Type **195**		20	20
908	30 c. Statue of Liberty and scaffolding ("Restoration and Renewal") (*vert*)		20	20
909	50 c. Frederic Bartholdi (sculptor) supervising construction, 1876		30	30
910	90 c. Close-up of Statue		55	55
911	$1 Statue and cadet ship ("Operation Sail", 1976) (*vert*)		90	90
912	$3 Dedication ceremony, 1886		1·75	2·00
907/12		*Set of 6*	3·50	3·75
MS913	110×80 mm. $5 Port of New York		3·75	3·75

See also Nos. 1110/19.

196 Arawak Pot Sherd and
Indians making Clay Utensils

(Des N. Waldman. Litho Format)

1985 (21 Jan). *Native American Artefacts. T 196 and similar designs. Multicoloured. P 15.*
914	15 c. Type 196. .	15	10
915	50 c. Arawak body design and Arawak Indians tattooing	30	40
916	60 c. Head of the god "Yocahu" and Indians harvesting manioc	40	50
917	$3 Carib war club and Carib Indians going into battle	1·25	2·50
914/17	*Set of 4*	1·90	3·25
MS918	97×68 mm. $5 Taino Indians worshipping stone idol	1·50	2·50

197 Triumph 2hp "Jap", 1903

(Des BG Studio. Litho Questa)

1985 (7 Mar). *Centenary of the Motorcycle. T 197 and similar horiz designs. Multicoloured. P 14.*
919	10 c. Type 197. .	65	15
920	30 c. Indian "Arrow", 1949	1·10	40
921	60 c. BMW "R100RS", 1976	1·60	1·25
922	$4 Harley-Davidson "Model II", 1916	5·50	7·00
919/22	*Set of 4*	8·00	8·00
MS923	90×93 mm. $5 Laverda "Jota", 1975	5·50	6·50

198 Slavonian Grebe

(Litho Questa)

1985 (25 Mar). *Birth Bicentenary of John J. Audubon (ornithologist) (1st issue). T 198 and similar multicoloured designs showing original paintings. P 14.*
924	90 c. Type 198. .	1·75	1·25
925	$1 British Storm Petrel	2·00	1·25
926	$1.50, Great Blue Heron	2·50	3·25
927	$3 Double-crested Cormorant	3·75	6·00
924/7	*Set of 4*	9·00	10·50
MS928	103×72 mm. $5 White-tailed Tropic Bird (vert)	7·00	5·50

Nos. 924/7 were each issued in sheetlets of five stamps and one stamp-size label, which appears in the centre of the bottom row. See also Nos. 990/4.

199 Anaea cyanea

(Des R. Sauber. Litho Questa)

1985 (16 Apr). *Butterflies. T 199 and similar horiz designs. Multicoloured. P 14.*
929	25 c. Type 199	1·00	30
930	60 c. *Leodonta dysoni*	2·25	1·25
931	90 c. *Junea doraete*	2·75	1·50
932	$4 *Prepona pylene*	7·50	10·50
929/32	*Set of 4*	12·00	12·00
MS933	132×105 mm. $5 *Caerois gerdtrudtus*	4·50	6·00

200 Cessna 172D Skyhawk   **201** Maimonides

(Des A. DiLorenzo. Litho Questa)

1985 (30 Apr). *40th Anniv of International Civil Aviation Organization. T 200 and similar horiz designs. Multicoloured. P 14.*
934	30 c. Type 200	1·25	30
935	90 c. Fokker D.VII	2·75	1·25
936	$1.50, SPAD VII	3·75	3·25
937	$3 Boeing 747-100	5·50	7·50
934/7	*Set of 4*	12·00	11·00
MS938	97×83 mm. $5 De Havilland D.H.C.6 Twin Otter	4·50	6·00

(Des and litho Questa)

1985 (17 June). *850th Birth Anniv of Maimonides (physician, philosopher and scholar). P 14.*
939	201 $2 bright green	4·00	3·25
MS940	70×84 mm. 201 $5 reddish brown	7·00	4·50

No. 939 was printed in sheetlets of 6 stamps.

202 Young Farmers with Produce   **203** The Queen Mother attending Church

(Des Susan David. Litho Questa)

1985 (1 July). *International Youth Year. T 202 and similar horiz designs. Multicoloured. P 14.*
941	25 c. Type 202. .	20	20
942	50 c. Hotel management trainees	30	40
943	60 c. Girls with goat and boys with football ("Environment")	60	70
944	$3 Windsurfing ("Leisure")	2·00	3·25
941/4	*Set of 4*	2·75	4·00
MS945	102×72 mm. $5 Young people with Antiguan flags	2·75	3·25

(Des J.W. Litho Questa)

1985 (10 July). *Life and Times of Queen Elizabeth the Queen Mother. T 203 and similar vert designs. Multicoloured. P 14.*
946	$1 Type 203	45	60
947	$1.50, Watching children playing in London garden	60	85
948	$2.50, The Queen Mother in 1979	90	1·40
946/8	*Set of 3*	1·75	2·50
MS949	56×85 mm. $5 With Prince Edward at Royal Wedding, 1981	3·00	3·00

Stamps as Nos. 946/8, but with face values of 90 c., $1 and $3, exist from additional sheetlets of 5 plus a label issued 13 January 1986. These also have changed background colours and are perforated 12×12½ (*price for set of 3 stamps £2 mint*).

204 Magnificent Frigate Bird   **205** Girl Guides Nursing

(Des Mary Walters. Litho Questa)

1985 (1 Aug). *Marine Life. T 204 and similar vert designs. Multicoloured. P 14.*
950	15 c. Type 204	1·00	30
951	45 c. Brain Coral	2·00	95
952	60 c. Cushion Star	2·25	1·75
953	$3 Spotted Moray	7·00	9·00
950/3	*Set of 4*	11·00	11·00
MS954	110×80 mm. $5 Elkhorn Coral	8·50	7·00

(Des Y. Berry. Litho Questa)

1985 (22 Aug). *75th Anniv of Girl Guide Movement. T 205 and similar horiz designs. Multicoloured. P 14.*
955	15 c. Type 205. .	75	20
956	45 c. Open-air Girl Guide meeting	1·40	60
957	60 c. Lord and Lady Baden-Powell	1·75	90
958	$3 Girl Guides gathering flowers. .	4·25	4·50
955/8	*Set of 4*	7·50	5·75
MS959	67× 96 mm. $5 Barn Swallow (Nature study)	6·50	7·00

206 Bass Trombone   **207** Flags of Great Britain and Antigua

(Des Susan David. Litho Questa)

1985 (26 Aug). *300th Birth Anniv of Johann Sebastian Bach (composer). T 206 and similar vert designs. P 14.*
960	25 c. multicoloured	1·40	55
961	50 c. multicoloured	1·75	1·10
962	$1 multicoloured	3·25	1·75
963	$3 multicoloured	6·00	7·00
960/3	*Set of 4*	11·00	9·50
MS964	104×73 mm. $5 black and brownish grey	4·50	4·50

Designs:—50 c. English horn; $1 Violino piccolo; $3 Bass rackett; $5 Johann Sebastian Bach.

(Des Mary Walters. Litho Format)

1985 (24 Oct). *Royal Visit. T 207 and similar multicoloured designs. P 14½.*
965	60 c. Type 207. .	1·00	65
966	$1 Queen Elizabeth II (*vert*)	1·50	1·25
967	$4 Royal Yacht *Britannia*. .	3·25	6·00
965/7	*Set of 3*	5·25	7·00
MS968	110×83 mm. $5 Map of Antigua	3·00	3·25

(Des Walt Disney Productions. Litho Questa)

1985 (4 Nov). *150th Birth Anniv of Mark Twain (author). Horiz designs as T 118 of Anguilla showing Walt Disney cartoon characters in scenes from "Roughing It". Multicoloured. P 14×13½.*
969	25 c. Donald Duck and Mickey Mouse meeting Indians	60	20
970	50 c. Mickey Mouse, Donald Duck and Goofy canoeing	90	55
971	$1.10, Goofy as Pony Express rider	1·50	1·50
972	$1.50, Donald Duck and Goofy hunting buffalo	2·00	2·50
973	$2 Mickey Mouse and silver mine	2·50	3·50
969/73	*Set of 5*	6·75	7·50
MS974	127×101 mm. $5 Mickey Mouse driving stagecoach	8·00	7·50

(Des Walt Disney Productions. Litho Questa)

1985 (11 Nov). *Birth Bicentenaries of Grimm Brothers (folklorists). Horiz designs as T 119 of Anguilla showing Walt Disney cartoon characters in scenes from "Spindle, Shuttle and Needle". Multicoloured. P 14×13½.*
975	30 c. The Prince (Mickey Mouse) searches for a bride	80	40
	a. Error. Wmk w 16	95·00	
976	60 c. The Prince finds the Orphan Girl (Minnie Mouse)	1·10	80
977	70 c. The Spindle finds the Prince	1·40	90
978	$1 The Needle tidies the Girl's House	1·90	1·75
979	$3 The Prince proposes	4·00	5·50
975/9	*Set of 5*	8·50	8·50
MS980	125×101 mm. $5 The Orphan Girl and spinning wheel on Prince's horse	8·00	7·50

208 Benjamin Franklin and U.N. (New York) 1953 U.P.U. 5 c. Stamp   **209** "Madonna and Child" (De Landi)

(Litho Walsall)

1985 (18 Nov). *40th Anniv of United Nations Organization. T 208 and similar multicoloured designs showing United Nations (New York) stamps. P 13½×14.*
981	40 c. Type 208. .	1·00	70
982	$1 George Washington Carver (agricultural chemist) and 1982 Nature Conservation 28 c. stamp	2·00	2·00
983	$3 Charles Lindbergh (aviator) and 1978 I.C.A.O. 25 c. stamp	4·25	6·00
981/3	*Set of 3*	6·50	8·00
MS984	101×77 mm. $5 Marc Chagall (artist) (vert). P 14×13½.	6·00	4·75

(Des Mary Walters. Litho Format)

1985 (30 Dec). *Christmas. Religious Paintings. T 209 and similar vert designs. Multicoloured. P 15.*
985	10 c. Type 209. .	30	15
986	25 c. "Madonna and Child" (Berlinghiero)	55	25
987	60 c. "The Nativity" (Fra Angelico)	70	60
988	$4 "Presentation in the Temple" (Giovanni di Paolo) . .	1·75	4·25
985/8	*Set of 4*	3·00	3·75
MS989	113×81 mm. $5 "The Nativity" (Antoniazzo Romano)	3·00	3·75

No. MS989 exists imperforate from stock dispersed by the liquidator of Format International Security Printers Ltd.

(Litho Questa)

1986 (6 Jan). *Birth Bicentenary of John J. Audubon (ornithologist) (2nd issue). Horiz designs as T 198 showing original paintings. Multicoloured. P 12.*
990	60 c. Mallard	2·25	1·50
991	90 c. North American Black Duck	2·75	2·00
992	$1.50, Pintail	3·50	4·50
993	$3 American Wigeon	4·75	6·50
990/3	*Set of 4*	12·00	13·00
MS994	102×73 mm. $5 American Eider. P 14	7·00	5·50

Nos. 990/3 were issued in sheetlets of 5 as Nos. 924/7.

210 Football, Boots and Trophy   **211** Tug

(Des M. Donk. Litho Questa)

1986 (17 Mar). *World Cup Football Championship, Mexico.
T 210 and similar multicoloured designs. P 14.*
995	30 c. Type 210		1·25	40
996	60 c. Goalkeeper (vert)		1·75	85
997	$1 Referee blowing whistle (vert)		2·25	1·75
998	$4 Ball in net		6·00	8·50
995/8		Set of 4	10·00	10·50
MS999	87×76 mm. $5 Two players competing for ball		8·50	7·50

(Des W. Hanson. Litho Questa)

1986 (24 Mar). *Appearance of Halley's Comet (1st issue). Horiz
designs as T 123 of Anguilla. Multicoloured. P 14.*
1000	5 c. Edmond Halley and Old Greenwich Observatory		30	15
1001	10 c. Messerschmitt Me 163B Komet (fighter aircraft), 1944		30	15
1002	60 c. Montezuma (Aztec Emperor) and Comet in 1517 (from "Historias de las Indias de Neuva Espana")		1·50	70
1003	$4 Pocahontas saving Capt. John Smith and Comet in 1607		4·50	5·00
1000/3		Set of 4	6·00	5·50
MS1004	101×70 mm. $5 Halley's Comet over English Harbour, Antigua		3·50	3·75

See also Nos. 1047/51.

(Litho Questa)

1986 (21 Apr). *60th Birthday of Queen Elizabeth II. Vert
designs as T 125 of Anguilla. P 14.*
1005	60 c. black and yellow		30	35
1006	$1 multicoloured		50	55
1007	$4 multicoloured		1·40	1·90
1005/7		Set of 3	2·00	2·50
MS1008	120×85 mm. $5 black and grey-brown		2·00	3·00

Designs:—60 c. Wedding photograph, 1947; $1 Queen at
Trooping the Colour; $4 In Scotland; $5 Queen Mary and
Princess Elizabeth, 1927.

(Des A. DiLorenzo. Litho Questa)

1986 (15 May). *Local Boats. T 211 and similar vert designs.
Multicoloured. P 14.*
1009	30 c. Type 211		25	20
1010	60 c. Game fishing boat		45	35
1011	$1 Yacht		75	60
1012	$4 Lugger with auxiliary sail		2·50	3·25
1009/12		Set of 4	3·50	4·00
MS1013	108×78 mm. $5 Boats under construction		3·00	4·00

212 "Hiawatha" Express

213 Prince Andrew and Miss Sarah Ferguson

(Des W. Wright. Litho Format)

1986 (22 May). *"Ameripex '86" International Stamp Exhibition,
Chicago. Famous American Trains. T 212 and similar horiz
designs. Multicoloured. P 15.*
1014	25 c. Type 212		1·00	40
1015	50 c. "Grand Canyon" express		1·25	75
1016	$1 "Powhattan Arrow" express		1·50	1·75
1017	$3 "Empire State" express		3·00	6·00
1014/17		Set of 4	6·00	8·00
MS1018	116×87 mm. $5 Southern Pacific "Daylight" express		5·00	9·50

Nos. 1014/18 exist imperforate from stock dispersed by the
liquidator of Format International Security Printers Ltd.

(Des and litho Questa)

1986 (1 July). *Royal Wedding. T 213 and similar vert designs.
Multicoloured. P 14.*
1019	45 c. Type 213		45	35
1020	60 c. Prince Andrew		55	45
1021	$4 Prince Andrew with Prince Philip		2·25	3·50
1019/21		Set of 3	3·00	3·75
MS1022	88×88 mm. $5 Prince Andrew and Miss Sarah Ferguson (different)		4·00	4·50

214 Fly-specked Cerith

215 Nymphaea ampla (Water Lily)

(Des L. Birmingham. Litho Format)

1986 (6 Aug). *Sea Shells. T 214 and similar multicoloured
designs. P 15.*
1023	15 c. Type 214		75	50
1024	45 c. Smooth Scotch Bonnet		1·75	1·25
1025	60 c. West Indian Crown Conch		2·00	2·00
1026	$3 Ciboney Murex		6·50	10·00
1023/6		Set of 4	10·00	12·50
MS1027	109×75 mm. $5 Colourful Atlantic Moon (horiz)		7·50	8·50

(Des Mary Walters. Litho Format)

1986 (25 Aug). *Flowers. T 215 and similar horiz designs.
Multicoloured. P 15.*
1028	10 c. Type 215		20	15
1029	15 c. Queen of the Night		20	15
1030	50 c. Cup of Gold		55	55
1031	60 c. Beach Morning Glory		70	70
1032	70 c. Golden Trumpet		80	80
1033	$1 Air Plant		90	1·10
1034	$3 Purple Wreath		1·75	3·00
1035	$4 Zephyr Lily		2·00	3·75
1028/35		Set of 8	6·50	9·00
MS1036	Two sheets, each 102×72 mm. (a) $4 Dozakie. (b) $5 Four O'Clock Flower			
		Set of 2 sheets	5·00	7·50

Nos. 1028/35 exist imperforate from stock dispersed by the
liquidator of Format International Security Printers Ltd.

(216)

217 Hygrocybe occidentalis var. scarletina

1986 (15 Sept). *World Cup Football Championship Winners,
Mexico. Nos. 995/9 optd as T 216 in gold.*
1037	30 c. Type 210		65	40
1038	60 c. Goalkeeper (vert)		1·00	75
1039	$1 Referee blowing whistle (vert)		1·40	1·10
1040	$4 Ball in net		4·50	4·50
1037/40		Set of 4	6·75	6·00
MS1041	87×76 mm. $5 Two players competing for ball		4·50	4·00

The overprint on the horizontal designs is in two lines.

(Litho Format)

1986 (15 Sept). *Mushrooms. T 217 and similar vert designs.
Multicoloured. P 15.*
1042	10 c. Type 217		30	20
1043	50 c. Trogia buccinalis		70	55
1044	$1 Collybia subpruinosa		1·25	1·00
1045	$4 Leucocoprinus brebissonii		3·00	4·00
1042/5		Set of 4	4·75	5·25
MS1046	102×82 mm $5 Pyrrhoglossum pyrrhum		12·00	11·00

An unissued 3$ and examples of No. 1045 with the face value
shown as "4$" exist from stock dispersed by the liquidator of
Format International Security Printers Ltd.

(218)

219 Auburn "Speedster" (1933)

1986 (15 Oct). *Appearance of Halley's Comet (2nd issue). Nos.
1000/4 optd with T 218 (in silver on $5).*
1047	5 c. Edmond Halley and Old Greenwich Observatory		15	10
1048	10 c. Messerschmitt Me 163B Komet (fighter aircraft), 1944		20	10
1049	60 c. Montezuma (Aztec Emperor) and Comet in 1517 (from "Historias de las Indias de Neuva Espana")		1·00	65
1050	$4 Pocahontas saving Capt. John Smith and Comet in 1607		4·50	4·00
1047/50		Set of 4	5·25	4·25
MS1051	101×70 mm. $5 Halley's Comet over English Harbour, Antigua		5·50	6·50

(Des J. Martin. Litho Questa)

1986 (20 Oct). *Centenary of First Benz Motor Car. T 219 and
similar horiz designs. Multicoloured. P 14.*
1052	10 c. Type 219		15	10
1053	15 c. Mercury "Sable" (1986)		20	10
1054	50 c. Cadillac (1959)		55	30
1055	60 c. Studebaker (1950)		70	45
1056	70 c. Lagonda "V-12" (1939)		80	55
1057	$1 Adler "Standard" (1930)		1·10	75
1058	$3 DKW (1956)		2·50	2·50
1059	$4 Mercedes "500K" (1936)		3·00	3·00
1052/9		Set of 8	8·00	7·00
MS1060	Two sheets, each 99×70 mm. (a) $5 Daimler (1896). (b) $5 Mercedes "Knight" (1921)			
		Set of 2 sheets	7·00	6·50

220 Young Mickey Mouse playing Santa Claus

221 Arms of Antigua

(Des Walt Disney Co. Litho Format)

1986 (4 Nov). *Christmas. T 220 and similar horiz designs
showing Walt Disney cartoon characters as babies. Multicoloured. P 11.*
1061	25 c. Type 220		60	35
1062	30 c. Mickey and Minnie Mouse building snowman		70	40
1063	40 c. Aunt Matilda and Goofy baking		75	45
1064	60 c. Goofy and Pluto		1·00	85
1065	70 c. Pluto, Donald and Daisy Duck carol singing		1·10	1·00
1066	$1.50, Donald Duck, Mickey Mouse and Pluto stringing popcorn		1·75	2·50
1067	$3 Grandma Duck and Minnie Mouse		3·00	4·50
1068	$4 Donald Duck and Pete		3·25	4·50
		Set of 8	11·00	13·00
MS1069	Two sheets, each 127×102 mm. P 14 × 13½. (a) $5 Goofy, Donald Duck and Minnie Mouse playing reindeer. (b) $5 Mickey Mouse, Donald and Daisy Duck playing with toys.			
		Set of 2 sheets	11·00	12·00

1986 (25 Nov). *Coil stamps. T 221 and similar vert design.
Litho. P 14.*
1070	10 c. new blue		50	50
1071	25 c. orange-vermilion		75	75

Design:—25 c. Flag of Antigua.

222 Canada I (1981)

223 Bridled Burrfish

(Des J. Iskowitz. Litho Format)

1987 (5 Feb). *America's Cup Yachting Championship. T 222
and similar multicoloured designs. P 15.*
1072	30 c. Type 222		30	20
1073	60 c. Gretel II (1970)		45	50
1074	$1 Sceptre (1958)		85	1·00
1075	$3 Vigilant (1893)		2·25	3·00
1072/5		Set of 4	3·50	4·25
MS1076	113×84 mm. $5 Australia II defeating Liberty (1983) (horiz)		4·00	5·00

Nos. 1072/6 exist imperforate from stock dispersed by the
liquidator of Format International Security Printers Ltd.

(Des G. Drummond. Litho Questa)

1987 (23 Feb). *Marine Life. T 223 and similar horiz designs.
Multicoloured. P 14.*
1077	15 c. Type 223		1·75	30
1078	30 c. Common Noddy		3·00	60
1079	40 c. Nassau Grouper		2·25	70
1080	50 c. Laughing Gull		4·50	1·50
1081	60 c. French Angelfish		3·00	1·50
1082	$1 Porkfish		3·00	1·75
1083	$2 Royal Tern		6·00	5·00
1084	$3 Sooty Tern		6·00	6·00
1077/84		Set of 8	26·00	15·00
MS1085	Two sheets, each 120×94 mm. (a) $5 Banded Butterflyfish. (b) $5 Brown Booby			
		Set of 2 sheets	16·00	14·00

Nos. 1078, 1080 and 1083/5 are without the World Wildlife
Fund logo shown on Type 223.

224 Handball

225 "The Profile"

(Litho Questa)

1987 (23 Mar). *Olympic Games, Seoul (1988) (1st issue). T 224
and similar horiz designs. Multicoloured. P 14.*
1086	10 c. Type 224		40	10
1087	60 c. Fencing		65	35
1088	$1 Gymnastics		85	75
1089	$3 Football		2·25	3·50
1086/9		Set of 4	3·75	4·25
MS1090	100×72 mm. $5 Boxing gloves		3·50	4·25

See also Nos. 1222/6.

(Litho Questa)

1987 (30 Mar). *Birth Centenary of Marc Chagall (artist). T 225
and similar multicoloured designs. P 13½×14.*
1091	10 c. Type 225		20	15
1092	30 c. "Portrait of the Artist's Sister"		35	30
1093	40 c. "Bride with Fan"		40	40
1094	60 c. "David in Profile"		45	45
1095	90 c. "Fiancee with Bouquet"		60	60
1096	$1 "Self Portrait with Brushes"		65	65
1097	$3 "The Walk"		1·75	2·25
1098	$4 "Three Candles"		2·00	2·50
1091/8		Set of 8	5·75	6·50
MS1099	Two sheets, each 110×95 mm. (a) $5 "Fall of Icarus" (104×89 mm). (b) $5 "Myth of Orpheus" (104×89 mm). Imperf. Set of 2 sheets		6·50	6·00

226 *Spirit of Australia* (fastest powerboat), 1978   **227** Lee Iacocca at Unveiling of Restored Statue

(Des W. Wright. Litho Format)

1987 (9 Apr). *Milestones of Transportation.* T **226** and similar horiz designs. Multicoloured. P 15.

1100	10 c. Type **226**		40	30
1101	15 c. Werner von Siemens's electric locomotive, 1879		60	40
1102	30 c. U.S.S. *Triton* (first submerged circum-navigation), 1960		60	45
1103	50 c. Trevithick's steam carriage (first passenger-carrying vehicle), 1801		70	60
1104	60 c. U.S.S. *New Jersey* (battleship), 1942		80	70
1105	70 c. Draisine bicycle, 1818		80	80
1106	90 c. *United States* (liner) (holder of Blue Riband), 1952		1·00	1·00
1107	$1.50, Cierva C.4 (first autogyro), 1923		1·40	2·00
1108	$2 Curtiss NC-4 flying boat (first transatlantic flight), 1919		1·50	2·25
1109	$3 *Queen Elizabeth 2* (liner), 1969		2·50	3·00
1100/9		Set of 10	9·00	10·50

Nos. 1100/9 exist imperforate from stock dispersed by the liquidator of Format International Security Printers Ltd.

(Litho Questa)

1987 (23 Apr). *Centenary of Statue of Liberty* (1986) (2nd issue). T **227** and similar multicoloured designs. P 14.

1110	15 c. Type **227**		15	15
1111	30 c. Statue at sunset (side view)		20	20
1112	45 c. Aerial view of head		30	30
1113	50 c. Lee Iacocca and torch		35	35
1114	60 c. Workmen inside head of Statue (*horiz*)		35	35
1115	90 c. Restoration work (*horiz*)		50	50
1116	$1 Head of Statue		55	55
1117	$2 Statue at sunset (front view)		1·00	1·25
1118	$3 Inspecting restoration work (*horiz*)		1·25	1·75
1119	$5 Statue at night		2·00	3·00
1110/19		Set of 10	6·00	7·50

228 Grace Kelly   **229** Scouts around Camp Fire and Red Kangaroo

(Des Lynda Bruscheni. Litho Questa)

1987 (11 May). *Entertainers.* T **228** and similar vert designs. Multicoloured. P 14.

1120	15 c. Type **228**		90	40
1121	30 c. Marilyn Monroe		2·00	65
1122	45 c. Orson Welles		90	60
1123	50 c. Judy Garland		90	65
1124	60 c. John Lennon		2·75	1·10
1125	$1 Rock Hudson		1·40	1·10
1126	$2 John Wayne		2·50	2·00
1127	$3 Elvis Presley		6·50	3·50
1120/7		Set of 8	16·00	9·00

(Litho Format)

1987 (25 May). *16th World Scout Jamboree, Australia.* T **229** and similar horiz designs. Multicoloured. P 15.

1128	10 c. Type **229**		50	20
1129	60 c. Scouts canoeing and Blue-winged Kookaburra		1·00	70
1130	$1 Scouts on assault course and Ring-tailed Rock Wallaby		1·00	85
1131	$3 Field kitchen and Koala		1·50	4·00
1128/31		Set of 4	3·50	5·25
MS1132	103×78 mm. $5 Flags of Antigua, Australia and Scout Movement		2·75	3·25

Nos. 1128/32 exist imperforate from stock dispersed by the liquidator of Format International Security Printers Ltd.

230 Whistling Frog   (**231**)

(Des B. Bundock. Litho Questa)

1987 (15 June). *"Capex '87" International Stamp Exhibition, Toronto. Reptiles and Amphibians.* T **230** and similar horiz designs. Multicoloured. P 14.

1133	30 c. Type **230**		45	20
1134	60 c. Croaking Lizard		55	40
1135	$1 Antiguan Anole		80	60
1136	$3 Red-footed Tortoise		1·75	2·75
1133/6		Set of 4	3·25	3·50
MS1137	106×76 mm. $5 Ground Lizard		2·25	2·75

1987 (9 Sept). *10th Death Anniv of Elvis Presley* (entertainer). No. 1127 optd with T **231**.

1138	$3 Elvis Presley		5·50	3·75

232 House of Burgesses, Virginia ("Freedom of Speech")   **233** "Madonna and Child" (Bernardo Daddi)

(Des and litho Questa)

1987 (16 Nov). *Bicentenary of U.S. Constitution.* T **232** and similar multicoloured designs. P 14.

1139	15 c. Type **232**		10	10
1140	45 c. State Seal, Connecticut		20	25
1141	60 c. State Seal, Delaware		25	35
1142	$4 Gouverneur Morris (Pennsylvania delegate) (*vert*)		1·75	2·25
1139/42		Set of 4	2·10	2·75
MS1143	105×75 mm. $5 Roger Sherman (Connecticut delegate) (*vert*)		2·25	2·75

Nos. 1139/42 were each issued in sheetlets of five stamps and one stamp-size label, which appears in the centre of the bottom row.

(Litho Questa)

1987 (1 Dec). *Christmas. Religious Paintings.* T **233** and similar vert designs. Multicoloured. P 14.

1144	45 c. Type **233**		40	15
1145	60 c. "St. Joseph" (detail, "The Nativity" (Sano di Pietro)		55	30
1146	$1 "Virgin Mary" (detail, "The Nativity" (Sano di Pietro)		75	55
1147	$4 "Music-making Angel" (Melozzo da Forli)		2·25	3·25
1144/7		Set of 4	3·50	3·75
MS1148	99×70 mm. $5 "The Flight into Egypt" (Sano di Pietro)		2·25	2·75

234 Wedding Photograph, 1947   **235** Great Blue Heron

(Des and litho Questa)

1988 (8 Feb). *Royal Ruby Wedding.* T **234** and similar vert designs. P 14.

1149	25 c. deep brown, black and bright new blue		15	15
1150	60 c. multicoloured		30	40
1151	$2 deep brown, black and light green		90	1·10
1152	$3 multicoloured		1·40	1·60
1149/52		Set of 4	2·50	3·00
MS1153	102×77 mm. $5 multicoloured		2·25	2·75

Designs:—60 c. Queen Elizabeth II; $2 Princess Elizabeth and Prince Philip with Prince Charles at his christening, 1948; $3 Queen Elizabeth (from photo by Tim Graham), 1980; $5 Royal Family, 1952.

(Des W. Wright. Litho Questa)

1988 (1 Mar). *Birds of Antigua.* T **235** and similar multicoloured designs. P 14.

1154	10 c. Type **235**		45	40
1155	15 c. Ringed Kingfisher (*horiz*)		50	40
1156	50 c. Bananaquit (*horiz*)		90	50
1157	60 c. Purple Gallinule (*horiz*)		90	50
1158	70 c. Blue-hooded Euphonia (*horiz*)		1·00	55
1159	$1 Brown-throated Conure ("Caribbean Parakeet")		1·25	75
1160	$3 Troupial (*horiz*)		2·50	3·50
1161	$4 Purple-throated Carib (*horiz*)		2·50	3·50
1154/61		Set of 8	9·00	9·00
MS1162	Two sheets, each 115×86 mm. (a) $5 Greater Flamingo. (b) $5 Brown Pelican			
		Set of 2 sheets	4·50	5·50

NEW INFORMATION

The editor is always interested to correspond with people who have new information that will improve or correct the Catalogue.

---

236 First Aid at Daycare Centre, Antigua

(Des G. Vasarhelyi. Litho Format)

1988 (10 Mar). *Salvation Army's Community Service.* T **236** and similar horiz designs. Multicoloured. P 14×13½.

1163	25 c. Type **236**		80	65
1164	30 c. Giving penicillin injection, Indonesia		80	65
1165	40 c. Children at daycare centre, Bolivia		90	75
1166	45 c. Rehabilitation of the handicapped, India		90	75
1167	50 c. Training blind man, Kenya		1·00	1·25
1168	60 c. Weighing baby, Ghana		1·00	1·25
1169	$1 Training typist, Zambia		1·40	1·75
1170	$2 Emergency food kitchen, Sri Lanka		2·00	3·50
1163/70		Set of 8	8·00	9·50
MS1171	152×83 mm. $5 General Eva Burrows		3·75	4·50

237 Columbus' Second Fleet, 1493   **238** "Bust of Christ"

(Des I. MacLaury. Litho Questa)

1988 (16 Mar–16 May). *500th Anniv of Discovery of America by Columbus* (1992) (1st issue). T **237** and similar horiz designs. Multicoloured. P 14.

1172	10 c. Type **237**		60	40
1173	30 c. Painos Indian village and fleet (16.5)		60	45
1174	45 c. *Santa Mariagalante* (flagship) and Painos village (16.5)		70	45
1175	60 c. Painos Indians offering Columbus fruit and vegetables (16.5)		70	50
1176	90 c. Painos Indian and Columbus with Scarlet Macaw		1·25	1·00
1177	$1 Columbus landing on island		1·25	1·00
1178	$3 Spanish soldier and fleet		2·25	3·00
1179	$4 Fleet under sail (16.5)		2·50	3·00
1172/9		Set of 8	9·00	9·00
MS1180	Two sheets, each 110×80 mm. (a) $5 Queen Isabella's cross. (b) $5 Gold coin of Ferdinand and Isabella (16.5)			
		Set of 2 sheets	6·50	7·00

See also Nos. 1267/71, 1360/8, 1503/11, 1654/60 and 1670/1.

(Litho Questa)

1988 (11 Apr). *500th Birth Anniv of Titian.* T **238** and similar vert designs showing paintings. Multicoloured. P 13½×14.

1181	30 c. Type **238**		25	20
1182	40 c. "Scourging of Christ"		30	25
1183	45 c. "Madonna in Glory with Saints"		30	25
1184	50 c. "The Averoldi Polyptych" (detail)		35	35
1185	$1 "Christ Crowned with Thorns"		55	55
1186	$2 "Christ Mocked"		90	1·25
1187	$3 "Christ and Simon of Cyrene"		1·50	1·75
1188	$4 "Crucifixion with Virgin and Saints"		1·75	2·25
1181/8		Set of 8	5·50	6·25
MS1189	Two sheets, each 110×95 mm. (a) $5 "Ecce Homo" (detail). (b) $5 "Noli me Tangere" (detail)			
		Set of 2 sheets	7·00	8·50

239 Two Yachts rounding Buoy

(Des G. Drummond. Litho Format)

1988 (18 Apr). *Sailing Week.* T **239** and similar horiz designs. Multicoloured. P 15.

1190	30 c. Type **239**		20	20
1191	60 c. Three yachts		35	40
1192	$1 British yacht under way		50	55
1193	$3 Three yachts (*different*)		1·10	2·50
1190/3		Set of 4	2·00	3·25
MS1194	103×92 mm. $5 Two yachts		1·75	3·25

Nos. 1190/4 exist imperforate from stock dispersed by the liquidator of Format International Security Printers Ltd.

240 Mickey Mouse and Diver with Porpoise

(241)

(Des Walt Disney Co. Litho Questa)

1988 (3 May). *Disney EPCOT Centre, Orlando, Florida.* T **240** *and similar multicoloured designs showing cartoon characters and exhibits.* P 14×13½ (horiz) or 13½×14 (vert).

1195	1 c. Type **240**		10	10
1196	2 c. Goofy and Mickey Mouse with futuristic car (vert)		10	10
1197	3 c. Mickey Mouse and Goofy as Atlas (vert)		10	10
1198	4 c. Mickey Mouse and Edaphosaurus (prehistoric reptile)		10	10
1199	5 c. Mickey Mouse at Journey into Imagination exhibit		10	10
1200	10 c. Mickey Mouse collecting vegetables (vert)		15	10
1201	25 c. Type **240**		35	25
1202	30 c. As 2 c.		35	25
1203	40 c. As 3 c.		40	30
1204	60 c. As 4 c.		60	50
1205	70 c. As 5 c.		70	60
1206	$1.50, As 10 c.		1.50	1.75
1207	$3 Goofy and Mickey Mouse with robot (vert)		2.25	2.50
1208	$4 Mickey Mouse and Clarabelle at Horizons exhibit		2.25	2.50
1195/1208		Set of 14	8.00	8.00

MS1209 Two sheets, each 125×99 mm. (a) $5 Mickey Mouse and monorail (vert). (b) $5 Mickey Mouse flying over EPCOT Centre
Set of 2 sheets 7.00 6.50

1988 (9 May). *Stamp Exhibitions. Nos.* 1083/5 *optd as* T **241** *showing various emblems.*

1210	$2 Royal Tern (optd T **241**, Prague)	2.00	2.00
1211	$3 Sooty Tern (optd "INDEPENDENCE 40", Israel)	2.50	2.50

MS1212 Two sheets, each 120×94 mm. (a) $5 Banded Butterflyfish (optd "OLYMPHILEX '88", Seoul). (b) $5 Brown Booby (optd "FINLANDIA 88", Helsinki) Set of 2 sheets 7.00 7.00

242 Jacaranda **243** Gymnastics

(Des Mary Walters. Litho Questa)

1988 (16 May). *Flowering Trees.* T **242** *and similar vert designs. Multicoloured.* P 14.

1213	10 c. Type **242**		30	20
1214	30 c. Cordia		40	20
1215	50 c. Orchid Tree		60	40
1216	90 c. Flamboyant		70	50
1217	$1 African Tulip Tree		75	55
1218	$2 Potato Tree		1.40	1.60
1219	$3 Crepe Myrtle		1.60	2.00
1220	$4 Pitch Apple		1.75	2.75
1213/20		Set of 8	6.75	7.50

MS1221 Two sheets, each 106×76 mm. (a) $5 Cassia. (b) $5 Chinaberry Set of 2 sheets 5.00 6.00

(Des J. Martin. Litho Questa)

1988 (10 June). *Olympic Games, Seoul (2nd issue).* T **243** *and similar multicoloured designs.* P 14.

1222	40 c. Type **243**		30	25
1223	60 c. Weightlifting		40	30
1224	$1 Water polo (horiz)		60	50
1225	$3 Boxing (horiz)		1.50	2.25
1222/5		Set of 4	2.50	3.00

MS1226 114×80 mm. $5 Runner with Olympic torch 2.00 3.00

244 Danaus plexippus

(Des S. Heimann. Litho Questa)

1988 (29 Aug)–90. *Caribbean Butterflies.* T **244** *and similar horiz designs. Multicoloured.* P 14.

1227	1 c. Type **244**		30	40
1228	2 c. Greta diaphanus		40	50
1229	3 c. Calisto archebates		40	50
1230	5 c. Hamadryas feronia		50	50
1231	10 c. Mestra dorcas		60	30

1232	15 c. Hypolimnas misippus		70	30
1233	20 c. Dione juno		80	30
1234	25 c. Heliconius charithonia		80	30
1235	30 c. Eurema pyro		80	30
1236	40 c. Papilio androgeus		85	30
1237	45 c. Anteos maerula		85	30
1238	50 c. Aphrissa orbis		90	45
1239	60 c. Astraptes xagua		1.00	60
1240	$1 Heliopetes arsalte		1.50	1.00
1241	$2 Polites baracoa		2.75	3.25
1242	$2.50 Phocides pigmalion		3.25	4.00
1243	$5 Prepona amphitoe		5.00	6.00
1244	$10 Oarisma nanus		7.00	9.00
1244a	$20 Parides lycimenes (19.2.90)		14.00	16.00
1227/44a		Set of 19	38.00	38.00

245 President Kennedy and Family **246** Minnie Mouse carol singing

(Des J. Iskowitz. Litho Questa)

1988 (23 Nov). *25th Death Anniv of John F. Kennedy (American statesman).* T **245** *and similar horiz designs, each showing different inset portrait. Multicoloured.* P 14.

1245	1 c. Type **245**		10	10
1246	2 c. Kennedy commanding PT109		10	10
1247	3 c. Funeral cortege		10	10
1248	4 c. In motorcade, Mexico City		10	10
1249	30 c. As 1 c.		35	15
1250	60 c. As 4 c.		50	40
1251	$1 As 3 c.		75	75
1252	$4 As 2 c.		2.00	3.00
1245/52		Set of 8	3.25	4.00

MS1253 105 × 75 mm. $5 Kennedy taking presidential oath of office 2.50 3.25

(Des Walt Disney Co. Litho Questa)

1988 (1 Dec). *Christmas. "Mickey's Christmas Chorale".* T **246** *and similar multicoloured designs showing Walt Disney cartoon characters.* P 13½ × 14.

1254	10 c. Type **246**		30	30
1255	25 c. Pluto		45	45
1256	30 c. Mickey Mouse playing ukelele		45	45
1257	70 c. Donald Duck and nephew		80	80
1258	$1 Mordie and Ferdie carol singing		80	1.00
	a. Sheetlet. Nos. 1258/65		5.75	
1259	$1 Goofy carol singing		80	1.00
1260	$1 Chip n'Dale sliding off roof		80	1.00
1261	$1 Two of Donald Duck's nephews at window		80	1.00
1262	$1 As 10 c.		80	1.00
1263	$1 As 25 c.		80	1.00
1264	$1 As 30 c.		80	1.00
1265	$1 As 70 c.		80	1.00
1254/65		Set of 12	7.50	9.00

MS1266 Two sheets, each 127 × 102 mm. (a) $7 Donald Duck playing trumpet and Mickey and Minnie Mouse in carriage. P 13½ × 14. (b) $7 Mickey Mouse and friends singing carols on roller skates (horiz). P 14 × 13½ 8.50 8.50
Nos. 1258/65 were printed together, se-tenant as a composite design, in sheetlets of eight.

247 Arawak Warriors **248** De Havilland Comet 4 Airliner

(Des D. Miller. Litho Questa)

1989 (16 May). *500th Anniv of Discovery of America by Columbus (1992) (2nd issue). Pre-Columbian Arawak Society.* T **247** *and similar vert designs. Multicoloured.* P 14.

1267	$1.50, Type **247**		1.10	1.40
	a. Horiz strip of 4. Nos. 1267/70		4.00	
1268	$1.50, Whip dancers		1.10	1.40
1269	$1.50, Whip dancers and chief with pineapple		1.10	1.40
1270	$1.50, Family and camp fire		1.10	1.40
1267/70		Set of 4	4.00	5.00

MS1271 71 × 84 mm. $6 Arawak chief 2.50 3.00
Nos. 1267/70 were printed together, se-tenant, in horizontal strips of 4 throughout the sheet, each strip forming a composite design.

(Des W. Wright. Litho Questa)

1989 (29 May). *50th Anniv of First Jet Flight.* T **248** *and similar horiz designs. Multicoloured.* P 14.

1272	10 c. Type **248**		45	45
1273	30 c. Messerschmitt Me 262 fighter		70	45
1274	40 c. Boeing 707 airliner		75	45

1275	60 c. Canadair CL-13 Sabre ("F-86 Sabre") fighter		90	55
1276	$1 Lockheed F-104 Starfighter		1.25	90
1277	$2 Douglas DC-10 airliner		2.00	2.25
1278	$3 Boeing 747-300/400 airliner		2.50	3.00
1279	$4 McDonnell Douglas F-4 Phantom II fighter		2.50	3.00
1272/9		Set of 8	10.00	10.00

MS1280 Two sheets, each 114×83 mm. (a) $7 Grumman F-14A Tomcat fighter. (b) $7 Concorde airliner Set of 2 sheets 8.50 10.00

249 Festivale

(Des W. Wright. Litho Questa)

1989 (20 June). *Caribbean Cruise Ships.* T **249** *and similar horiz designs. Multicoloured.* P 14.

1281	25 c. Type **249**		65	40
1282	45 c. Southward		90	40
1283	50 c. Sagafjord		90	40
1284	60 c. Daphne		90	50
1285	75 c. Cunard Countess		1.00	80
1286	90 c. Song of America		1.10	1.00
1287	$3 Island Princess		2.75	3.75
1288	$4 Galileo		2.75	3.75
1281/8		Set of 8	10.00	10.00

MS1289 (a) 113 × 87 mm. $6 Norway. (b) 111 × 82 mm. $6 Oceanic Set of 2 sheets 6.50 8.00

250 "Fish swimming by Duck half-submerged in Stream"

(Litho Questa)

1989 (1 July). *Japanese Art. Paintings by Hiroshige.* T **250** *and similar horiz designs. Multicoloured.* P 14 × 13½.

1290	25 c. Type **250**		65	30
1291	45 c. "Crane and Wave"		75	40
1292	50 c. "Sparrows and Morning Glories"		80	40
1293	60 c. "Crested Blackbird and Flowering Cherry"		90	50
1294	$1 "Great Knot sitting among Water Grass"		1.25	70
1295	$2 "Goose on a Bank of Water"		2.25	2.25
1296	$3 "Black Paradise Flycatcher and Blossoms"		2.75	2.75
1297	$4 "Sleepy Owl perched on a Pine Branch"		2.75	2.75
1290/7		Set of 8	11.00	9.00

MS1298 Two sheets, each 102 × 75 mm. (a) $5 "Bullfinch flying near a Clematis Branch". (b) $5 "Titmouse on a Cherry Branch" Set of 2 sheets 8.50 7.50
Nos. 1290/7 were each printed in sheetlets of 10 containing two horizontal strips of 5 stamps separated by printed labels commemorating Emperor Hirohito.

251 Mickey and Minnie Mouse in Helicopter over River Seine

(Des Walt Disney Company. Litho Questa)

1989 (7 July). *"Philexfrance 89" International Stamp Exhibition, Paris.* T **251** *and similar multicoloured designs showing Walt Disney cartoon characters in Paris.* P 14 × 13½.

1299	1 c. Type **251**		10	10
1300	2 c. Goofy and Mickey Mouse passing Arc de Triomphe		10	10
1301	3 c. Mickey Mouse painting picture of Notre Dame		10	10
1302	4 c. Mickey and Minnie Mouse with Pluto leaving Metro station		10	10
1303	5 c. Minnie Mouse as model in fashion show		10	10
1304	10 c. Daisy Duck, Minnie Mouse and Clarabelle as Folies Bergere dancers		10	10
1305	$5 Mickey and Minnie Mouse shopping in street market		5.50	6.00
1306	$6 Mickey and Minnie Mouse, Jose Carioca and Donald Duck at pavement cafe		5.50	6.00
1299/1306		Set of 8	10.00	11.00

MS1307 Two sheets, each 127 × 101 mm. (a) $5 Mickey and Minnie Mouse in hot air balloon. P 14 × 13½. (b) $5 Mickey Mouse at Pompidou Centre cafe (vert). P 13½ × 14 Set of 2 sheets 10.00 11.00

252 Goalkeeper

253 *Mycena pura*

(Des D. Bruckner. Litho B.D.T.)

1989 (21 Aug). *World Cup Football Championship, Italy (1990). T 252 and similar multicoloured designs.* P 14.

1308	15 c. Type **252**				75	20
1309	25 c. Goalkeeper moving towards ball				85	20
1310	$1 Goalkeeper reaching for ball				1·75	1·25
1311	$4 Goalkeeper saving goal				3·25	4·75
1308/11				*Set of 4*	6·00	5·75

MS1312 Two sheets, each 75 × 105 mm. (a) $5 Three players competing for ball (*horiz*). (b) $5 Ball and players' legs (*horiz*) *Set of 2 sheets* 7·00 8·00

(Litho Questa)

1989 (12 Oct). *Fungi. T 253 and similar multicoloured designs.* P 14.

1313	10 c. Type **253**				60	40
1314	25 c. *Psathyrella tuberculata* (*vert*)				85	40
1315	50 c. *Psilocybe cubensis*				1·25	60
1316	60 c. *Leptonia caeruleocapitata* (*vert*)				1·25	70
1317	75 c. *Xeromphalina tenuipes* (*vert*)				1·50	90
1318	$1 *Chlorophyllum molybdites* (*vert*)				1·50	1·10
1319	$3 *Marasmius haematocephalus*				2·75	3·50
1320	$4 *Cantharellus cinnabarinus*				2·75	3·50
1313/20				*Set of 8*	11·00	10·00

MS1321 Two sheets, each 88×62 mm. (a) $6 *Leucopaxillus gracillimus* (*vert*). (b) $6 *Volvariella volvacea* .. .. *Set of 2 sheets* 13·00 14·00

254 Desmarest's Hutia

255 Goofy and Old Printing Press

(Des J. Barbaris. Litho B.D.T.)

1989 (19 Oct). *Local Fauna. T 254 and similar multicoloured designs.* P 14.

1322	25 c. Type **254**				70	45
1323	45 c. Caribbean Monk Seal				2·00	90
1324	60 c. Mustache Bat (*vert*) ..				1·25	90
1325	$4 American Manatee (*vert*)				6·50	6·50
1322/5				*Set of 4*	6·50	6·50

MS1326 113×87 mm. $5 West Indies Giant Rice Rat .. .. 6·50 8·00

(Des Walt Disney Co. Litho Questa)

1989 (2 Nov). *"American Philately". T 255 and similar multicoloured designs, each showing Walt Disney cartoon characters with stamps and the logo of the American Philatelic Society.* P 13¹/₂×14.

1327	1 c. Type **255**				10	10
1328	2 c. Donald Duck cancelling first day cover for Mickey Mouse				10	10
1329	3 c. Donald Duck's nephews reading recruiting poster for Pony Express riders				10	10
1330	4 c. Morty and Ferdie as early radio broadcasters				10	10
1331	5 c. Donald Duck and water buffalo watching television				10	10
1332	10 c. Donald Duck with stamp album				10	10
1333	$4 Daisy Duck with computer system				3·75	4·50
1334	$6 Donald's nephews with stereo radio, trumpet and guitar				4·75	5·50
1327/34				*Set of 8*	8·00	9·00

MS1335 Two sheets, each 127×102 mm. (a) $5 Donald's nephews donating stamps to charity. P 13¹/₂×14. (b) $5 Minnie Mouse flying mailplane upside down (*horiz*). P 14×13¹/₂ *Set of 2 sheets* 10·00 11·00

256 Mickey Mouse and Donald Duck with Camden and Amboy Locomotive *John Bull*, 1831

(Des Walt Disney Co. Litho Questa)

1989 (17 Nov). *"World Stamp Expo '89" International Stamp Exhibition, Washington (1st issue). T 256 and similar multicoloured designs showing Walt Disney cartoon characters and locomotives.* P 14×13¹/₂.

1336	25 c. Type **256**				60	50
1337	45 c. Mickey Mouse and friends with *Atlantic*, 1832				70	50
1338	50 c. Mickey Mouse and Goofy with *William Crooks*, 1861				70	50
1339	60 c. Mickey Mouse and Goofy with *Minnetonka*, 1869				80	65
1340	$1 Chip n'Dale with *Thatcher Perkins*, 1863 ..				85	75
1341	$2 Mickey and Minnie Mouse with *Pioneer*, 1848				1·75	2·25
1342	$3 Mickey Mouse and Donald Duck with cog railway locomotive *Peppersass*, 1869..				2·00	2·75
1343	$4 Mickey Mouse with Huey, Dewey and Louie aboard N.Y. World's Fair *Gimbels Flyer*, 1939 ..				2·25	2·75
1336/43				*Set of 8*	8·50	9·50

MS1344 Two sheets, each 127×101 mm. (a) $6 Mickey Mouse and locomotive *Thomas Jefferson*, 1835 (*vert*). P 13¹/₂×14. (b) $6 Mickey Mouse and friends at Central Pacific "Golden Spike" ceremony, 1869. P 14×13¹/₂ *Set of 2 sheets* 7·50 8·50

257 Smithsonian Institution, Washington

258 Launch of "Apollo 11"

(Des Design Element. Litho Questa)

1989 (17 Nov). *"World Stamp Expo '89" International Stamp Exhibition, Washington (2nd issue). Sheet 78×61 mm.* P 14.

MS1345 **257** $4 multicoloured .. .. .. 1·75 2·25

(Des J. Iskowitz. Litho B.D.T.)

1989 (24 Nov). *20th Anniv of First Manned Landing on Moon. T 258 and similar multicoloured designs.* P 14.

1346	10 c. Type **258**				40	30
1347	45 c. Aldrin on Moon				90	30
1348	$1 Module *Eagle* over Moon (*horiz*)				1·50	1·00
1349	$4 Recovery of "Apollo 11" crew after splashdown (*horiz*)				2·75	4·50
1346/9				*Set of 4*	5·00	5·50

MS1350 107×77 mm. $5 Astronaut Neil Armstrong .. .. 3·75 4·25

259 "The Small Cowper Madonna" (Raphael)

260 Star-eyed Hermit Crab

(Litho Questa)

1989 (11 Dec). *Christmas. Paintings by Raphael and Giotto. T 259 and similar vert designs. Multicoloured.* P 14.

1351	10 c. Type **259**				20	15
1352	25 c. "Madonna of the Goldfinch" (Raphael)				30	20
1353	30 c. "The Alba Madonna" (Raphael)				30	20
1354	50 c. Saint (detail, "Bologna Altarpiece") (Giotto)				50	30
1355	60 c. Angel (detail, "Bologna Altarpiece") (Giotto)				55	35
1356	70 c. Angel slaying serpent (detail, "Bologna Altarpiece") (Giotto)				65	40
1357	$4 Evangelist (detail, "Bologna Altarpiece") (Giotto)				3·00	3·75
1358	$5 "Madonna of Foligno" (detail) (Raphael)				3·00	4·00
1351/8				*Set of 8*	7·50	8·50

MS1359 Two sheets, each 71×96 mm. (a) $5 "The Marriage of the Virgin" (detail) (Raphael). (b) $5 Madonna and Child (detail, "Bologna Altarpiece") (Giotto) .. *Set of 2 sheets* 8·00 9·50

(Des Mary Walters. Litho Questa)

1990 (26 Mar). *500th Anniv of Discovery of America by Columbus (1992) (3rd issue). New World Natural History – Marine Life. T 260 and similar vert designs. Multicoloured.* P 14.

1360	10 c. Type **260**				30	20
1361	20 c. Spiny Lobster				45	25
1362	25 c. Magnificent Banded Fanworm				45	25
1363	45 c. Cannonball Jellyfish				65	40
1364	60 c. Red-spiny Sea Star				85	60
1365	$2 Peppermint Shrimp				1·75	2·25
1366	$3 Coral Crab				2·25	3·00
1367	$4 Branching Fire Coral ..				2·25	3·00
1360/7				*Set of 8*	8·00	9·00

MS1368 Two sheets, each 100×69 mm. (a) $5 Common Sea Fan. (b) $5 Portuguese Man-of-war *Set of 2 sheets* 7·00 8·00

261 *Vanilla mexicana*

262 Queen Victoria and Queen Elizabeth II

(Des Mary Walters. Litho Questa)

1990 (17 Apr). *"EXPO 90" International Garden and Greenery Exhibition, Osaka. Orchids. T 261 and similar vert designs. Multicoloured.* P 14.

1369	15 c. Type **261**				60	40
1370	45 c. *Epidendrum ibaguense*				85	40
1371	50 c. *Epidendrum secundum*				90	45
1372	60 c. *Maxillaria conferta*				1·00	50
1373	$1 *Oncidium altissimum*				1·40	85
1374	$2 *Spiranthes lanceolata*				2·00	2·25
1375	$3 *Tonopsis utricularioides*				2·25	3·00
1376	$5 *Epidendrum nocturnum*				3·25	4·25
1369/76				*Set of 8*	11·00	11·00

MS1377 Two sheets, each 102×70 mm. (a) $5 *Octomeria graminifolia*. (b) $5 *Rodriguezia lanceolata* .. .. .. *Set of 2 sheets* 6·50 8·00

(Des M. Pollard. Litho B.D.T.)

1990 (3 May). *150th Anniv of the Penny Black. T 262 and similar horiz designs.* P 14¹/₂×14.

1378	**262** 45 c. blue-green				75	40
1379	— 60 c. magenta				85	55
1380	— $5 ultramarine				3·25	5·50
1378/80				*Set of 3*	4·25	5·50

MS1381 102×80 mm. **262** $6 blackish purple 4·00 5·00 Designs:—60 c, $5 As Type **262**, but with different backgrounds.

263 *Britannia* (mail paddle-steamer), 1840

(Des M. Pollard. Litho B.D.T.)

1990 (3 May). *"Stamp World London 90" International Stamp Exhibition. T 263 and similar horiz designs.* P 13¹/₂.

1382	50 c. deep grey-green and scarlet-vermilion				75	35
1383	75 c. purple-brown and scarlet-vermilion				1·00	90
1384	$4 deep ultramarine & scarlet-vermilion				3·50	5·00
1382/4				*Set of 3*	4·75	5·50

MS1385 104×81 mm. $6 brownish black and scarlet-vermilion .. .. 3·50 5·00 Designs:—75 c. Travelling Post Office sorting van, 1892; $4 Short S.23 Empire "C" Class flying boat *Centaurus*, 1938; $6 Post Office underground railway, London, 1927.

264 Flamefish

265 "Voyager 2" passing Saturn

(Des G. Drummond. Litho Questa)

1990 (21 May). *Reef Fishes. T 264 and similar horiz designs. Multicoloured.* P 14.

1386	10 c. Type **264**				55	55
1387	15 c. Coney				70	55
1388	50 c. Long-spined Squirrelfish				1·00	60
1389	60 c. Sergeant Major				1·00	60
1390	$1 Yellow-tailed Snapper				1·25	85
1391	$2 Rock Beauty				2·00	2·50
1392	$3 Spanish Hogfish				2·50	3·25
1393	$4 Striped Parrotfish				2·50	3·25
1386/93				*Set of 8*	10·50	11·00

MS1394 Two sheets, each 99×70 mm. (a) $5 Black-barred Soldierfish. (b) $5 Four-eyed Butterflyfish .. .. .. *Set of 2 sheets* 9·00 10·00

(Des K. Gromell. Litho B.D.T.)

1990 (11 June). *Achievements in Space. T 265 and similar square designs. Multicoloured.* P 14.

1395	45 c. Type **265**				55	55
	a. Sheetlet. Nos. 1395/1414				10·00	
1396	45 c. "Pioneer 11" photographing Saturn				55	55
1397	45 c. Astronaut in transporter				55	55
1398	45 c. Space shuttle *Columbia* ..				55	55
1399	45 c. "Apollo 10" command module on parachutes				55	55
1400	45 c. "Skylab" space station				55	55
1401	45 c. Astronaut Edward White in space ..				55	55
1402	45 c. "Apollo" spacecraft on joint mission				55	55
1403	45 c. "Soyuz" spacecraft on joint mission				55	55
1404	45 c. "Mariner 1" passing Venus ..				55	55
1405	45 c. "Gemini 4" capsule				55	55
1406	45 c. "Sputnik 1"				55	55
1407	45 c. Hubble space telescope				55	55

1408	45 c. North American X-15	55	55
1409	45 c. Bell XS-1 airplane	55	55
1410	45 c. "Apollo 17" astronaut and lunar rock formation	55	55
1411	45 c. Lunar Rover	55	55
1412	45 c. "Apollo 14" lunar module	55	55
1413	45 c. Astronaut Buzz Aldrin on Moon	55	55
1414	45 c. Soviet "Lunokhod" lunar vehicle	55	55
1395/1414	*Set of 20*	10·00	10·00

Nos. 1395/1414 were printed together, *se-tenant*, in sheetlets of 20 forming a composite design.

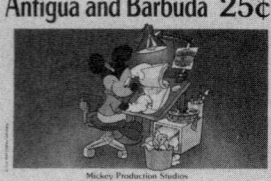

266 Queen Mother in Evening Dress **267** Mickey Mouse as Animator

(Des D. Miller. Litho Questa)

1990 (27 Aug). *90th Birthday of Queen Elizabeth the Queen Mother. T **266** and similar vert designs showing recent photographs of the Queen Mother. P 14.*

1415	15 c. multicoloured	40	15
1416	35 c. multicoloured	55	25
1417	75 c. multicoloured	85	85
1418	$3 multicoloured	2·25	3·25
1415/18	*Set of 4*	3·50	4·00
MS1419	67×98 mm. $6 multicoloured	4·00	4·50

(Des Walt Disney Co. Litho Questa)

1990 (3 Sept). *Mickey Mouse in Hollywood. T **267** and similar horiz designs showing Walt Disney cartoon characters. Multicoloured. P 14×13½.*

1420	25 c. Type **267**	45	25
1421	45 c. Minnie Mouse learning lines while being dressed	60	25
1422	50 c. Mickey Mouse with clapper board	70	30
1423	60 c. Daisy Duck making-up Mickey Mouse	75	35
1424	$1 Clarabelle Cow as Cleopatra	1·00	70
1425	$2 Mickey Mouse directing Goofy and Donald Duck	1·75	2·00
1426	$3 Mickey Mouse directing Goofy as birdman	2·25	2·75
1427	$4 Donald Duck and Mickey Mouse editing film	2·25	2·75
1420/7	*Set of 8*	8·50	8·50
MS1428	Two sheets, each 132×95 mm. (a) $5 Minnie Mouse, Daisy Duck and Clarabelle as musical stars. (b) $5 Mickey Mouse on set as director *Set of 2 sheets*	7·00	8·00

268 Men's 20 Kilometres Walk **269** Huey and Dewey asleep (*Christmas Stories*)

(Des B. Grout. Litho Questa)

1990 (1 Oct). *Olympic Games, Barcelona (1992) (1st issue). T **268** and similar vert designs. Multicoloured. P 14.*

1429	50 c. Type **268**	65	30
1430	75 c. Triple jump	85	65
1431	$1 Men's 10,000 metres	1·00	85
1432	$5 Javelin	3·25	4·75
1429/32	*Set of 4*	5·25	6·00
MS1433	100×70 mm. $6 Athlete lighting Olympic flame at Los Angeles Olympics	4·75	6·50

See also Nos. 1553/61 and 1609/17.

(Des Walt Disney Co. Litho Questa)

1990 (15 Oct). *International Literacy Year. T **269** and similar vert designs showing Walt Disney cartoon characters illustrating works by Charles Dickens. Multicoloured. P 13½×14.*

1434	15 c. Type **269**	40	25
1435	45 c. Donald Duck as Poor Jo looking at grave (*Bleak House*)	70	45
1436	50 c. Dewey as Oliver asking for more (*Oliver Twist*)	75	50
1437	60 c. Daisy Duck as The Marchioness (*Old Curiosity Shop*)	80	55
1438	$1 Little Nell giving nosegay to her grandfather (*Little Nell*)	1·10	85
1439	$2 Scrooge McDuck as Mr. Pickwick (*Pickwick Papers*)	1·75	2·00
1440	$3 Minnie Mouse as Florence and Mickey Mouse as Paul (*Dombey and Son*)	2·25	3·00
1441	$5 Minnie Mouse as Jenny Wren (*Our Mutual Friend*)	2·75	3·75
1434/41	*Set of 8*	9·50	10·00
MS1442	Two sheets, each 126×102 mm. (a) $6 Artful Dodger picking pocket (*Oliver Twist*). (b) $6 Unexpected arrivals at Mr. Peggoty's (*David Copperfield*) *Set of 2 sheets*	9·00	10·00

Winners West Germany 1 Argentina 0

(**270**) **271** Pearly-eyed Thrasher

1990 (11 Nov). *World Cup Football Championship Winners, Italy. Nos. 1308/12 optd as T **270** by Questa.*

1443	15 c. Type **252**	65	30
1444	25 c. Goalkeeper moving towards ball	65	30
1445	$1 Goalkeeper reaching for ball	1·60	1·60
1446	$4 Goalkeeper saving goal	3·50	5·00
1443/6	*Set of 4*	5·75	6·50
MS1447	Two sheets, each 75×105 mm. (a) $5 Three players competing for ball (*horiz*). (b) $5 Ball and players' legs (*horiz*) *Set of 2 sheets*	8·50	10·00

The overprint on No. **MS**1447 is larger and thicker, 31×13 mm.

(Des Jennifer Toombs. Litho B.D.T.)

1990 (19 Nov). *Birds. T **271** and similar horiz designs. Multicoloured. P 14.*

1448	10 c. Type **271**	45	30
1449	25 c. Purple-throated Carib	45	35
1450	50 c. Yellowthroat	50	40
1451	60 c. American Kestrel	1·00	70
1452	$1 Yellow-bellied Sapsucker	1·00	80
1453	$2 Purple Gallinule	2·00	2·25
1454	$3 Yellow-crowned Night Heron	2·10	2·75
1455	$4 Blue-hooded Euphonia	2·10	2·75
1448/55	*Set of 8*	8·75	9·25
MS1456	Two sheets, each 76×60 mm. (a) $6 Brown Pelican. (b) $6 Magnificent Frigate Bird *Set of 2 sheets*	13·00	15·00

272 "Madonna and Child with Saints" (detail, Sebastiano del Piombo)

(Litho Questa)

1990 (10 Dec). *Christmas. Paintings by Renaissance Masters. T **272** and similar multicoloured designs. P 14×13½ (horiz) or 13½×14 (vert).*

1457	25 c. Type **272**	40	25
1458	30 c. "Virgin and Child with Angels" (detail, Grünewald) (*vert*)	50	25
1459	40 c. "The Holy Family and a Shepherd" (detail, Titian)	60	25
1460	60 c. "Virgin and Child" (detail, Lippi) (*vert*)	75	35
1461	$1 "Jesus, St. John and Two Angels" (Rubens)	1·00	60
1462	$2 "Adoration of the Shepherds" (detail, Vincenzo Catena)	1·60	1·75
1463	$4 "Adoration of the Magi" (detail, Giorgione)	2·50	3·25
1464	$5 "Virgin and Child adored by Warrior" (detail, Vincenzo Catena)	2·75	3·25
1457/64	*Set of 8*	9·00	9·00
MS1465	Two sheets, each 71×101 mm. (a) $6 "Allegory of the Blessings of Jacob" (detail, Rubens) (*vert*). (b) $6 "Adoration of the Magi" (detail, Fra Angelico) (*vert*) *Set of 2 sheets*	3·50	4·50

273 "Rape of the Daughters of Leucippus" (detail)

(Litho Questa)

1991 (21 Jan). *350th Death Anniv of Rubens. T **273** and similar horiz designs. Multicoloured. P 14×13½.*

1466	25 c. Type **273**	55	30
1467	45 c. "Bacchanal" (detail)	75	45
1468	50 c. "Rape of the Sabine Women" (detail)	80	50
1469	60 c. "Battle of the Amazons" (detail)	90	65
1470	$1 "Rape of the Sabine Women" (different detail)	1·25	1·00
1471	$2 "Bacchanal" (different detail)	1·75	2·00
1472	$3 "Rape of the Sabine Women" (different detail)	2·25	3·00
1473	$4 "Bacchanal" (different detail)	2·25	3·00
1466/73	*Set of 8*	9·75	9·75
MS1474	Two sheets, each 101×71 mm. (a) $6 "Rape of Hippodameia" (detail). (b) $6 "Battle of the Amazons" (different detail) *Set of 2 sheets*	7·50	8·50

274 U.S. Troops cross into Germany, 1944

(Des W. Wright. Litho B.D.T.)

1991 (11 Mar). *50th Anniv of Second World War. T **274** and similar horiz designs. Multicoloured. P 14.*

1475	10 c. Type **274**	45	40
1476	15 c. Axis surrender in North Africa, 1943	50	30
1477	25 c. U.S. tanks invade Kwalajalein, 1944	60	40
1478	45 c. Roosevelt and Churchill meet at Casablanca, 1943	1·00	60
1479	50 c. Marshal Badoglio, Prime Minister of Italian anti-fascist government, 1943	80	60
1480	$1 Lord Mountbatten, Supreme Allied Commander South-east Asia, 1943	1·40	1·00
1481	$2 Greek victory at Koritza, 1940	2·00	2·25
1482	$4 Anglo-Soviet mutual assistance pact, 1941	2·50	3·00
1483	$5 Operation Torch landings, 1942	2·50	3·00
1475/83	*Set of 9*	10·50	10·50
MS1484	Two sheets, each 108×80 mm. (a) $6 Japanese attack Pearl Harbor, 1941. (b) $6 U.S.A.A.F. daylight raid on Schweinfurt, 1943 *Set of 2 sheets*	8·00	8·50

275 Locomotive *Prince Regent*, Middleton Colliery, 1812

(Des W. Hanson Studio. Litho Walsall)

1991 (18 Mar). *Cog Railways. T **275** and similar multicoloured designs. P 14.*

1485	25 c. Type **275**	75	40
1486	30 c. Snowdon Mountain Railway	75	45
1487	40 c. First railcar at Hell Gate, Manitou & Pike's Peak Railway, U.S.A.	80	55
1488	60 c. P.N.K.A. rack railway, Java	1·10	70
1489	$1 Green Mountain Railway, Maine, 1883	1·50	1·00
1490	$2 Rack locomotive *Pike's Peak*, 1891	2·25	2·50
1491	$4 Vitznau-Rigi Railway, Switzerland, and Mt Rigi hotel local post stamp	3·25	4·00
1492	$5 Leopoldina Railway, Brazil	3·25	4·00
1485/92	*Set of 8*	12·00	12·00
MS1493	Two sheets, each 100×70 mm. (a) $6 Electric towing locomotives, Panama Canal. (b) $6 Gornergracht Railway, Switzerland (*vert*) *Set of 2 sheets*	11·00	12·00

276 *Heliconius charithonia*

(Des T. Pedersen. Litho B.D.T.)

1991 (15 Apr). *Butterflies. T **276** and similar multicoloured designs. P 14.*

1494	10 c. Type **276**	55	50
1495	35 c. *Marpesia petreus*	90	50
1496	50 c. *Anartia amathea*	1·00	60
1497	75 c. *Siproeta stelenes*	1·25	85
1498	$1 *Battus polydamas*	1·50	95
1499	$2 *Historis odius*	2·25	2·50
1500	$4 *Hypolimnas misippus*	3·25	4·00
1501	$5 *Hamadryas feronia*	3·25	4·00
1494/1501	*Set of 8*	12·50	12·50
MS1502	Two sheets. (a) 73×100 mm. $6 *Vanessa cardui* caterpillar (*vert*). (b) 100×73 mm. $6 *Danaus plexippus* caterpillar (*vert*) *Set of 2 sheets*	13·00	15·00

277 Hanno the Phoenician, 450 B.C. **278** "Camille Roulin" (Van Gogh)

(Des T. Agans. Litho Questa)

1991 (22 Apr). *500th Anniv of Discovery of America by Columbus* (1992) *(4th issue). History of Exploration. T* **277** *and similar designs. P* 14.

1503	10 c. multicoloured			40	40
1504	15 c. multicoloured			55	40
1505	45 c. multicoloured			80	50
1506	60 c. multicoloured			90	60
1507	$1 multicoloured			1·25	75
1508	$2 multicoloured			2·00	2·25
1509	$4 multicoloured			2·75	3·50
1510	$5 multicoloured			2·75	3·50
1503/10			*Set of 8*	10·00	10·50

MS1511 Two sheets, each 106×76 mm. (a) $6 black and Indian red. (b) $6 black and Indian red
Set of 2 sheets 7·00 8·00

Designs: *Horiz*—15 c. Pytheas the Greek, 325 B.C.; 45 c. Erik the Red discovering Greenland, 985 A.D.; 60 c. Leif Eriksson reaching Vinland, 1000 A.D.; $1 Scylax the Greek in the Indian Ocean, 518 A.D.; $2 Marco Polo sailing to the Orient, 1259 A.D.; $4 Ship of Queen Hatshepsut of Egypt, 1493 B.C.; $5 St. Brendan's coracle, 500 A.D. *Vert*—$6 (No. **MS**1511a) Engraving of Columbus as Admiral; $6 (No. **MS**1511b) Engraving of Columbus bare-headed

(Litho Walsall)

1991 (13 May). *Death Centenary of Vincent van Gogh (artist)* (1990). *T* **278** *and similar multicoloured designs. P* 13½.

1512	5 c. Type **278**			30	30
1513	10 c. "Armand Roulin"			30	30
1514	15 c. "Young Peasant Woman with Straw Hat sitting in the Wheat"			40	30
1515	25 c. "Adeline Ravoux"			50	30
1516	30 c. "The Schoolboy"			50	40
1517	40 c. "Doctor Gachet"			60	40
1518	50 c. "Portrait of a Man"			70	40
1519	75 c. "Two Children"			90	60
1520	$2 "The Postman Joseph Roulin"			2·00	2·25
1521	$3 "The Seated Zouave"			2·50	3·00
1522	$4 "L'Arlésienne"			2·75	3·25
1523	$5 "Self-Portrait, November/December 1888"			3·00	3·50
1512/23			*Set of 12*	13·00	13·50

MS1524 Three sheets, each 102×76 mm. (a) $5 "Farmhouse in Provence" (*horiz*). (b) $5 "Flowering Garden" (*horiz*). (c) $6 "The Bridge at Trinquetaille" (*horiz*). Imperf . *Set of 3 sheets* 12·00 13·00

279 Mickey Mouse as Champion Sumo Wrestler

(Des Walt Disney Co. Litho Questa)

1991 (20 June). *"Phila Nippon '91" International Stamp Exhibition, Tokyo. T* **279** *and similar multicoloured designs showing Walt Disney cartoon characters participating in martial arts. P* 13½×14 (*vert*) or 14×13½ (*horiz*).

1525	10 c. Type **279**			40	20
1526	15 c. Goofy using the tonfa (*horiz*)			50	25
1527	45 c. Donald Duck as a Ninja (*horiz*)			80	50
1528	60 c. Mickey armed for Kung fu			1·10	65
1529	$1 Goofy with Kendo sword			1·50	1·25
1530	$2 Mickey and Donald demonstrating Aikido (*horiz*)			2·00	2·25
1531	$4 Mickey and Donald in Judo bout (*horiz*)			3·00	3·50
1532	$5 Mickey performing Yabusame (mounted archery)			3·00	3·50
1525/32			*Set of 8*	11·00	11·00

MS1533 Two sheets, each 127×102 mm. (a) $6 Mickey delivering Karate kick (*horiz*). (b) $6 Mickey demonstrating Tamashiwara
Set of 2 sheets 9·00 10·00

280 Queen Elizabeth and Prince Philip in 1976

281 Daisy Duck teeing-off

(Des D. Miller. Litho Walsall)

1991 (8 July). *65th Birthday of Queen Elizabeth II. T* **280** *and similar horiz designs. Multicoloured. P* 14.

1534	15 c. Type **280**			20	10
1535	20 c. The Queen and Prince Philip in Portugal, 1985			20	10
1536	$2 Queen Elizabeth II			1·25	1·50
1537	$4 The Queen and Prince Philip at Ascot, 1986			3·00	3·00
1534/7			*Set of 4*	3·75	4·25

MS1538 68×90 mm. $4 The Queen at National Theatre, 1986, and Prince Philip
3·00 4·00

(Des D. Miller. Litho Walsall)

1991 (8 July). *10th Wedding Anniv of Prince and Princess of Wales. Horiz designs as T* **280**. *Multicoloured. P* 14.

1539	10 c. Prince and Princess of Wales at party, 1986			30	10
1540	40 c. Separate portraits of Prince, Princess and sons			55	25
1541	$1 Prince Henry and Prince William			90	70
1542	$5 Princess Diana in Australia and Prince Charles in Hungary			3·75	4·00
1539/42			*Set of 4*	5·00	4·50

MS1543 68×90 mm. $4 Prince Charles in Hackney and Princess and sons in Majorca, 1987 4·50 5·00

(Des Walt Disney Co. Litho Questa)

1991 (7 Aug). *Golf. T* **281** *and similar multicoloured designs showing Walt Disney cartoon characters. P* 13½×14.

1544	10 c. Type **281**			55	40
1545	15 c. Goofy playing ball from under trees			65	40
1546	45 c. Mickey Mouse playing deflected shot			1·00	50
1547	60 c. Mickey hacking divot out of fairway			1·25	65
1548	$1 Donald Duck playing ball out of pond			1·50	1·10
1549	$2 Minnie Mouse hitting ball over pond			2·50	2·75
1550	$4 Donald in a bunker			3·25	3·50
1551	$5 Goofy trying snooker shot into hole			3·25	3·50
1544/51			*Set of 8*	12·50	11·50

MS1552 Two sheets, each 127×102 mm. (a) $6 Grandma Duck in senior tournament. P 13½×14. (b) $6 Mickey and Minnie Mouse on course (*horiz*). P 14×13½ . *Set of 2 sheets* 10·00 12·00

282 Moose receiving Gold Medal

283 Presidents De Gaulle and Kennedy, 1961

(Des Archie Comic Publications Inc. Litho Questa)

1991 (19 Aug). *50th Anniv of Archie Comics, and Olympic Games, Barcelona* (1992) *(2nd issue). T* **282** *and similar multicoloured designs. P* 14×13½ (*vert*) or 13½×14 (*horiz*).

1553	10 c. Type **282**			45	30
1554	25 c. Archie playing polo on a motorcycle (*horiz*)			65	30
1555	40 c. Archie and Betty at fencing class			85	45
1556	60 c. Archie joining girls' volleyball team			1·00	65
1557	$1 Archie with tennis ball in his mouth			1·25	1·00
1558	$2 Archie running marathon			2·25	2·50
1559	$4 Archie judging women's gymnastics (*horiz*)			3·75	4·00
1560	$5 Archie watching the cheer-leaders			3·75	4·00
1553/60			*Set of 8*	12·50	12·00

MS1561 Two sheets, each 128×102 mm. (a) $6 Archie heading football. (b) $6 Archie catching baseball (*horiz*) . *Set of 2 sheets* 9·50 11·00

(Des. J. Iskowitz. Litho Questa)

1991 (11 Sept). *Birth Centenary of Charles de Gaulle (French statesman). T* **283** *and similar multicoloured designs. P* 14.

1562	10 c. Type **283**			55	40
1563	15 c. General De Gaulle with Pres. Roosevelt, 1945 (*vert*)			55	40
1564	45 c. Pres. De Gaulle with Chancellor Adenauer, 1962 (*vert*)			85	40
1565	60 c. De Gaulle at Arc de Triomphe, Liberation of Paris, 1944 (*vert*)			1·00	65
1566	$1 General De Gaulle crossing the Rhine, 1945			1·25	1·00
1567	$2 General De Gaulle in Algiers, 1944			2·00	2·25
1568	$4 Presidents De Gaulle and Eisenhower, 1960			3·00	3·50
1569	$5 De Gaulle returning from Germany, 1968 (*vert*)			3·00	3·50
1562/9			*Set of 8*	11·00	11·00

MS1570 Two sheets. (a) 76×106 mm. $6 De Gaulle with crowd. (b) 106×76 mm. $6 De Gaulle and Churchill at Casablanca, 1943
Set of 2 sheets 10·00 11·00

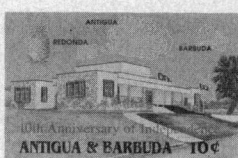

284 Parliament Building and Map

(Litho Questa)

1991 (28 Oct). *10th Anniv of Independence. T* **284** *and similar horiz design. P* 14.

1571	**284** 10 c. multicoloured			50	50

MS1572 87×97 mm. $6 Old Post Office, St. Johns, and stamps of 1862 and 1981 (50×37 mm) . . . . 5·50 7·00

285 Germans celebrating Reunification

(Des L. Fried (Nos. 1573, 1576, 1580, **MS**1583a), W. Hanson Studio (Nos. 1574, 1577, 1581, **MS**1583b), J. Iskowitz (Nos. 1575, 1582) or W. Wright (others). Litho Questa)

1991 (9 Dec). *Anniversaries and Events. T* **285** *and similar multicoloured designs. P* 14.

1573	25 c. Type **285**			30	30
1574	75 c. Cubs erecting tent			50	50
1575	$1.50, *Don Giovanni* and Mozart			2·00	1·75
1576	$2 Chariot driver and Gate at night			1·10	1·10
1577	$2 Lord Baden-Powell and members of 3rd Antigua Methodist cub pack (*vert*)			1·75	1·50
1578	$2 Lilienthal's signature and glider *Flugzeug Nr.* 5			2·25	2·25
1579	$2.50, Driver in Class P36 steam loco-motive (*vert*)			2·50	2·50
1580	$3 Statues from podium			1·75	1·75
1581	$3.50, Cubs and camp fire			1·90	1·90
1582	$4 St. Peter's Cathedral, Salzburg			3·25	3·25
1573/82			*Set of 10*	15·00	15·00

MS1583 Two sheets. (a) 100×72 mm. $4 Detail of chariot and Gate at night. (b) 89×117 mm. $5 Antiguan flag and Jamboree emblem (*vert*)
Set of 2 sheets 7·00 8·00

Anniversaries and Events:—Nos. 1573, 1576, 1580, **MS**1583a, Bicentenary of Brandenburg Gate, Germany; Nos. 1574, 1577, 1581, **MS**1583b, 17th World Scout Jamboree, Korea; Nos. 1575, 1582, Death bicentenary of Mozart; No. 1578, Centenary of Otto Lilienthal's gliding experiments; No. 1579, Centenary of Trans-Siberian Railway.

286 *Nimitz* Class Carrier and *Ticonderoga* Class Cruiser

287 "The Annunciation" (Fra Angelico)

(Des L. Birmingham. Litho Questa)

1991 (9 Dec). *50th Anniv of Japanese Attack on Pearl Harbor. T* **286** *and similar horiz designs. Multicoloured, P* 14½.

1585	$1 Type **286**			1·10	1·10
	a. Sheetlet. Nos. 1585/94			10·00	
1586	$1 Tourist launch			1·10	1·10
1587	$1 U.S.S. *Arizona* memorial			1·10	1·10
1588	$1 Wreaths on water and aircraft			1·10	1·10
1589	$1 White Tern			1·10	1·10
1590	$1 Mitsubishi A6M Zero-Sen fighters over Pearl City			1·10	1·10
1591	$1 Mitsubishi A6M Zero-Sen fighters attacking			1·10	1·10
1592	$1 Battleship Row in flames			1·10	1·10
1593	$1 U.S.S. *Nevada* (battleship) underway			1·10	1·10
1594	$1 Mitsubishi A6M Zero-Sen fighters returning to carriers			1·10	1·10
1585/94			*Set of 10*	10·00	10·00

Nos. 1585/94 were printed together, *se-tenant*, in sheetlets of 10 with the stamps arranged in two horizontal strips of 5 separated by a gutter showing the wreck of U.S.S. *Arizona*.

(Litho Walsall)

1991 (12 Dec). *Christmas. Religious Paintings by Fra Angelico. T* **287** *and similar vert designs. Multicoloured. P* 12.

1595	10 c. Type **287**			30	30
1596	30 c. "Nativity"			50	30
1597	40 c. "Adoration of the Magi"			60	30
1598	60 c. "Presentation in the Temple"			80	45
1599	$1 "Circumcision"			1·00	65
1600	$3 "Flight into Egypt"			2·50	3·00
1601	$4 "Massacre of the Innocents"			2·50	3·25
1602	$5 "Christ teaching in the Temple"			2·50	3·25
1595/1602			*Set of 8*	9·50	10·50

MS1603 Two sheets, each 102×127 mm. (a) $6 "Adoration of the Magi" (Cook Tondo). (b) $6 "Adoration of the Magi" (*different*). P 14
Set of 2 sheets 9·00 11·00

ALTERED CATALOGUE NUMBERS

Any Catalogue numbers altered from the last edition are shown as a list in the introductory pages.

288 Queen Elizabeth II and Bird Sanctuary

289 Mickey Mouse awarding Swimming Gold Medal to Mermaid

(Des D. Miller. Litho Questa)

1992 (27 Feb). *40th Anniv of Queen Elizabeth II's Accession. T 288 and similar horiz designs. Multicoloured. P 14.*

1604	10 c. Type 288		55	30
1605	30 c. Nelson's Dockyard		70	30
1606	$1 Ruins on Shirley Heights		90	70
1607	$5 Beach and palm trees		2·50	3·75
1604/7		Set of 4	4·25	4·50
MS1608	Two sheets, each 75×98 mm. (a) $6 Beach. (b) $6 Hillside foliage	Set of 2 sheets	8·00	8·50

(Des Walt Disney Co. Litho B.D.T.)

1992 (16 Mar). *Olympic Games, Barcelona (3rd issue). T 289 and similar multicoloured designs showing Walt Disney cartoon characters. P 13.*

1609	10 c. Type 289		30	30
1610	15 c. Huey, Dewey and Louie with kayak		35	30
1611	30 c. Donald Duck and Uncle Scrooge in yacht		50	35
1612	50 c. Donald and horse playing water polo		70	50
1613	$1 Big Pete weightlifting		1·00	85
1614	$2 Donald and Goofy fencing		1·60	1·60
1615	$4 Mickey and Donald playing volleyball		2·50	2·75
1616	$5 Goofy vaulting		2·50	2·75
1609/16		Set of 8	8·50	8·50
MS1617	Four sheets, each 123×98 mm. (a) $6 Mickey playing football. (b) $6 Mickey playing basketball (*horiz*). (c) $6 Minnie Mouse on uneven parallel bars (*horiz*). (d) $6 Mickey, Goofy and Donald judging gymnastics (*horiz*)	Set of 4 sheets	14·00	15·00

290 Pteranodon

291 "Supper at Emmaus" (Caravaggio)

(Des R. Frank. Litho Walsall)

1992 (6 Apr). *Prehistoric Animals. T 290 and similar multicoloured designs. P 14.*

1618	10 c. Type 290		55	30
1619	15 c. Brachiosaurus		55	30
1620	30 c. Tyrannosaurus Rex		70	35
1621	50 c. Parasaurolophus		80	50
1622	$1 Deinonychus (*horiz*)		1·25	1·00
1623	$2 Triceratops (*horiz*)		2·00	2·00
1624	$4 Protoceratops hatching (*horiz*)		2·25	2·75
1625	$5 Stegosaurus (*horiz*)		2·25	2·75
1618/25		Set of 8	9·25	9·00
MS1626	Two sheets, each 100×70 mm. (a) $6 Apatosaurus (*horiz*). (b) $6 Allosaurus (*horiz*)	Set of 2 sheets	8·50	9·50

(Litho Questa)

1992 (15 Apr). *Easter. Religious Paintings. T 291 and similar multicoloured designs. P 14×13½.*

1627	10 c. Type 291		25	25
1628	15 c. "The Vision of St. Peter" (Zurbarán)		35	25
1629	30 c. "Christ driving the Money-changers from the Temple" (Tiepolo)		55	40
1630	40 c. "Martyrdom of St. Bartholomew" (detail) (Ribera)		65	50
1631	$1 "Christ driving the Money-changers from the Temple" (detail) (Tiepolo)		1·00	1·00
1632	$2 "Crucifixion" (detail) (Altdorfer)		2·00	2·25
1633	$4 "The Deposition" (detail) (Fra Angelico)		3·00	3·25
1634	$5 "The Deposition" (different detail) (Fra Angelico)		3·00	3·25
1627/34		Set of 8	9·75	10·00
MS1635	Two sheets. (a) 102×71 mm. $6 "The Last Supper" (detail) (Masip). P 14×13½. (b) 71×102 mm. $6 "Crucifixion" (detail) (*vert*) (Altdorfer). P 13½×14	Set of 2 sheets	9·50	11·00

292 "The Miracle at the Well" (Alonso Cano)

293 Amanita caesarea

(Litho B.D.T.)

1992 (11 May). *"Granada '92" International Stamp Exhibition, Spain. Spanish Paintings. T 292 and similar multicoloured designs. P 13×13½ (vert) or 13½×13 (horiz).*

1636	10 c. Type 292		30	30
1637	15 c. "The Poet Luis de Goingora y Argote" (Velázquez)		40	30
1638	30 c. "The Painter Francisco Goya" (Vincente López Portana)		55	40
1639	40 c. "María de las Nieves Michaela Fourdinier" (Luis Paret y Alcázar)		65	50
1640	$1 "Carlos III eating before his Court" (Alcázar) (*horiz*)		1·00	1·00
1641	$2 "Rain Shower in Granada" (Antonio Munoz Degrain) (*horiz*)		2·00	2·25
1642	$4 "Sarah Bernhardt" (Santiago Rusinol i Prats)		3·00	3·25
1643	$5 "The Hermitage Garden" (Joaquim Mir Trinxet)		3·00	3·25
1636/43		Set of 8	9·75	10·00
MS1644	Two sheets, each 120×95 mm. (a) $6 "The Ascent of Monsieur Boucle's Montgolfier Balloon in the Gardens of Aranjuez" (Antonio Carnicero) (112×87 mm). (b) $6 "Olympus: Battle with the Giants" (Francisco Bayeu y Subías) (112×87 mm). Imperf	Set of 2 sheets	10·00	11·00

(Litho Walsall)

1992 (18 May). *Fungi. T 293 and similar vert designs. Multicoloured. P 14.*

1645	10 c. Type 293		60	40
1646	15 c. Collybia fusipes		75	40
1647	30 c. Boletus aereus		1·00	40
1648	40 c. Laccaria amethystina		1·00	50
1649	$1 Russula virescens		1·75	1·25
1650	$2 Tricholoma equestre ("Tricholoma auratum")		2·50	2·75
1651	$4 Calocybe gambosa		3·50	3·75
1652	$5 Lentinus tigrinus ("Panus tigrinus")		3·50	3·75
1645/52		Set of 8	13·00	12·00
MS1653	Two sheets, each 100×70 mm. (a) $6 Clavariadelphus truncatus. (b) $6 Auricularia auricula-judae	Set of 2 sheets	12·00	13·00

294 Memorial Cross and Huts, San Salvador

(Des R. Jung. Litho Questa)

1992 (25 May). *500th Anniv of Discovery of America by Columbus (5th issue). World Columbian Stamp "Expo '92", Chicago. T 294 and similar horiz designs. Multicoloured. P 14.*

1654	15 c. Type 294		30	20
1655	30 c. Martin Pinzon with telescope		45	25
1656	40 c. Christopher Columbus		55	35
1657	$1 Pinta		1·50	1·00
1658	$2 Nina		1·75	2·00
1659	$4 Santa Maria		2·75	3·50
1654/9		Set of 6	6·50	6·50
MS1660	Two sheets, each 108×76 mm. (a) $6 Ship and map of West Indies. (b) $6 Sea monster	Set of 2 sheets	8·50	10·00

295 Antillean Crested Hummingbird and Wild Plantain

296 Columbus meeting Amerindians

(Des J. Papeo. Litho Walsall)

1992 (10 Aug). *"Genova '92" International Thematic Stamp Exhibition. Hummingbirds and Plants. T 295 and similar horiz designs. Multicoloured. P 14.*

1661	10 c. Type 295		35	30
1662	25 c. Green Mango and Parrot's Plantain		50	40
1663	45 c. Purple-throated Carib and Lobster Claws		70	45
1664	60 c. Antillean Mango and Coral Plant		80	55
1665	$1 Vervain Hummingbird and Cardinal's Guard		1·10	85
1666	$2 Rufous-breasted Hermit and Heliconia		1·75	2·00
1667	$4 Blue-headed Hummingbird and Red Ginger		3·00	3·25
1668	$5 Green-throated Carib and Ornamental Banana		3·00	3·25
1661/8		Set of 8	10·00	10·00
MS1669	Two sheets, each 100×70 mm. (a) $6 Bee Hummingbird and Jungle Flame. (b) $6 Western Streamertail and Bignonia	Set of 2 sheets	10·00	11·00

(Des F. Paul ($1), J. Esquino ($2). Litho Questa)

1992 (24 Aug). *500th Anniv of Discovery of America by Columbus (6th issue). Organization of East Caribbean States. T 296 and similar vert design. Multicoloured. P 14½.*

1670	$1 Type 296		65	65
1671	$2 Ships approaching island		1·25	1·25

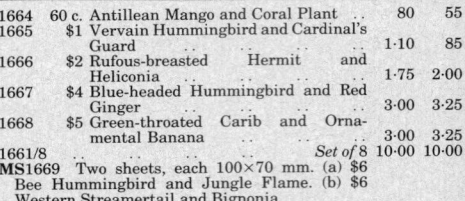

297 Ts'ai Lun and Paper

(Des L. Fried. Litho Questa)

1992 (19 Oct). *Inventors and Inventions. T 297 and similar horiz designs. Multicoloured. P 14.*

1672	10 c. Type 297		25	25
1673	25 c. Igor Sikorsky and Bolshoi Baltiskii (first four-engined airplane)		55	40
1674	30 c. Alexander Graham Bell and early telephone		55	45
1675	40 c. Johannes Gutenberg and early printing press		55	45
1676	60 c. James Watt and stationary steam engine		1·25	1·00
1677	$1 Anton van Leeuwenhoek and early microscope		1·25	1·10
1678	$4 Louis Braille and hands reading braille		3·25	3·25
1679	$5 Galileo and telescope		3·25	3·50
1672/9		Set of 8	9·75	9·50
MS1680	Two sheets, each 100×73 mm. (a) $6 Edison and Latimer's phonograph. (b) $6 Clermont (first commercial paddle-steamer)	Set of 2 sheets	9·50	11·00

298 Elvis looking Pensive

(Des J. Iskowitz. Litho Questa)

1992 (26 Oct). *15th Death Anniv of Elvis Presley. T 298 and similar vert designs. Multicoloured. P 14.*

1681	$1 Type 298		1·00	1·00
	a. Sheetlet. Nos. 1681/9		8·00	
1682	$1 Wearing black and yellow striped shirt		1·00	1·00
1683	$1 Singing into microphone		1·00	1·00
1684	$1 Wearing wide-brimmed hat		1·00	1·00
1685	$1 With microphone in right hand		1·00	1·00
1686	$1 In Army uniform		1·00	1·00
1687	$1 Wearing pink shirt		1·00	1·00
1688	$1 In yellow shirt		1·00	1·00
1689	$1 In jacket and bow tie		1·00	1·00
1681/9		Set of 9	8·00	8·00

Nos. 1681/9 were printed together, *se-tenant*, in sheetlets of 9.

299 Madison Square Gardens

(Des Kerri Schiff. Litho Questa)

1992 (28 Oct). *Postage Stamp Mega Event, New York. Sheet 100×70 mm. P 14.*

MS1690	299 $6 multicoloured	4·25	5·50

NEW INFORMATION

The editor is always interested to correspond with people who have new information that will improve or correct the Catalogue.

300 "Virgin and Child with Angels" (detail) (School of Piero della Francesca)

301 Russian Cosmonauts

(Litho Questa)

1992 (16 Nov). *Christmas. T* **300** *and similar vert designs showing details of the Holy Child from various paintings. Multicoloured. P* 13½.

1691	10 c. Type **300**		30	20
1692	25 c. "Madonna degli Alberelli" (Giovanni Bellini)		40	20
1693	30 c. "Madonna and Child with St. Anthony Abbot and St. Sigismund" (Neroccio)		50	30
1694	40 c. "Madonna and the Grand Duke" (Raphael)		60	30
1695	60 c. "The Nativity" (Georges de la Tour)		80	60
1696	$1 "Holy Family" (Jacob Jordaens)		1·10	85
1697	$4 "Madonna and Child Enthroned" (Magaritone)		3·25	3·75
1698	$5 "Madonna and Child on a Curved Throne" (Byzantine school)		3·25	3·75
1691/8		*Set of 8*	9·00	9·00

MS1699 Two sheets, each 76×102 mm. (a) $6 "Madonna and Child" (Domenco Ghirlando). (b) $6 "The Holy Family" (Pontormo) *Set of 2 sheets* 9·50 11·00

(Des W. Wright and L. Fried (Nos. 1700, 1711, **MS**1714a), W. Wright and W. Hanson (Nos. 1701, 1713, **MS**1714b), W. Wright (others). Litho Questa)

1992 (14 Dec). *Anniversaries and Events. T* **301** *and similar multicoloured designs. P* 14.

1700	10 c. Type **301**		40	40
1701	10 c. Airship LZ-127 *Graf Zeppelin,* 1929	70	55
1702	45 c. Bishop Daniel Davis		50	40
1703	75 c. Konrad Adenauer making speech	65	65
1704	$1 Bus Mosbacher and *Weatherly* (yacht)	1·00	1·00
1705	$1.50, Rain forest		1·10	1·10
1706	$2 Tiger		3·00	3·00
1707	$2 National flag, plant and emblem (*horiz*)		1·75	1·75
1708	$2 Members of Community Players company (*horiz*)		1·75	1·75
1709	$2.25, Women carrying pots		1·75	1·75
1710	$3 Lions Club emblem		2·00	2·00
1711	$4 Chinese rocket on launch tower		2·00	2·00
1712	$4 West German and N.A.T.O. flags		2·00	2·00
1713	$6 Hugo Eckener (airship pioneer)		3·00	3·00
1700/13		*Set of 14*	19·00	19·00

MS1714 Four sheets, each 100×71 mm. (a) $6 Projected European space station. (b) $6 Airship LZ-129 *Hindenburg,* 1936. (c) $6 Brandenburg Gate on German flag. (d) $6 *Danaus plexippus* (butterfly) *Set of 4 sheets* 17·00 18·00

Anniversaries and Events:—Nos. 1700, 1711, **MS**1714a, International Space Year; Nos. 1701, 1713, **MS**1714b, 75th death anniv of Count Ferdinand von Zeppelin; No. 1702, 75th anniv of Anglican Diocese of North-eastern Caribbean and Aruba; Nos. 1703, 1712, **MS**1714c, 25th death anniv of Konrad Adenauer (German statesman); No. 1704, Americas Cup Yachting Championship; Nos. 1705/6, **MS**1714d, Earth Summit '92, Rio; No. 1707, 50th anniv of Inter-American Institute for Agricultural Co-operation; No. 1708, 40th anniv of Cultural Development; No. 1709, United Nations World Health Organization Projects; No. 1710, 75th anniv of International Association of Lions Clubs.

302 Boy Hiker resting

303 Goofy playing Golf

(Litho Questa)

1993 (6 Jan). *Hummel Figurines. T* **302** *and similar vert designs. Multicoloured. P* 14.

1715	15 c. Type **302**		25	15
1716	30 c. Girl sitting on fence		40	25
1717	40 c. Boy hunter		50	35
1718	50 c. Boy with umbrella		60	45
1719	$1 Hikers at signpost		1·00	75
1720	$2 Boy hiker with pack and stick		1·75	2·00
1721	$4 Girl with young child and goat		2·75	3·00
1722	$5 Boy whistling		2·75	3·00
1715/22		*Set of 8*	9·00	9·00

MS1723 Two sheets, each 97×122 mm. (a) $1.50 ×4, As Nos. 1715/18. (b) $1.50×4, As Nos. 1719/22 *Set of 2 sheets* 13·00 14·00

(Des Euro-Disney, Paris. Litho Questa)

1993 (22 Feb). *Opening of Euro-Disney Resort, Paris. T* **303** *and similar multicoloured designs. P* 14×13½.

1724	10 c. Type **303**		40	30
1725	25 c. Chip and Dale at Davy Crockett's Campground		50	30
1726	30 c. Donald Duck at the Cheyenne Hotel	50	35
1727	40 c. Goofy at the Santa Fe Hotel	55	35
1728	$1 Mickey and Minnie Mouse at the New York Hotel		90	80
1729	$2 Mickey, Minnie and Goofy in car	1·60	1·75
1730	$4 Goofy at Pirates of the Caribbean	2·75	3·25
1731	$5 Donald at Adventureland	2·75	3·25
1724/31		*Set of 8*	9·00	9·25

MS1732 Four sheets, each 127×102 mm. (a) $6 Mickey in bellboy outfit. P 14×13½. (b) $6 Mickey on star (*vert*). P 13½×14. (c) $6 Mickey on opening poster (*vert*). P 13½×14. (d) $6 Mickey and balloons on opening poster (*vert*). P 13½×14 *Set of 4 sheets* 15·00 16·00

304 Cardinal's Guard

305 "The Destiny of Marie de' Medici" (upper detail) (Rubens)

(Des Dot Barlowe. Litho Questa)

1993 (15 Mar). *Flowers. T* **304** *and similar vert designs. Multicoloured. P* 14.

1733	15 c. Type **304**		50	30
1734	25 c. Giant Granadilla		60	30
1735	30 c. Spider Flower		60	35
1736	40 c. Gold Vine		65	35
1737	$1 Frangipani		1·00	80
1738	$2 Bougainvillea		1·60	1·75
1739	$4 Yellow Oleander		2·50	2·75
1740	$5 Spicy Jatropha		2·50	2·75
1733/40		*Set of 8*	9·50	8·50

MS1741 Two sheets, each 100×70 mm. (a) $6 Bird Lime Tree. (b) $6 Fairy Lily *Set of 2 sheets* 8·50 10·00

(Litho Walsall)

1993 (22 Mar). *Bicentenary of the Louvre, Paris. Paintings by Peter Paul Rubens. T* **305** *and similar vert designs. Multicoloured. P* 12.

1742	$1 Type **305**		65	65
	a. Sheetlet. Nos. 1742/9		4·75	
1743	$1 "The Birth of Marie de' Medici"	65	65
1744	$1 "The Education of Marie de' Medici"	65	65
1745	$1 "The Destiny of Marie de' Medici" (lower detail)		65	65
1746	$1 "Henry VI receiving the Portrait of Marie"		65	65
1747	$1 "The Meeting of the King and Marie at Lyons"		65	65
1748	$1 "The Marriage by Proxy"		65	65
1749	$1 "The Birth of Louis XIII"		65	65
1750	$1 "The Capture of Juliers"		65	65
	a. Sheetlet. Nos. 1750/7		4·75	
1751	$1 "The Exchange of the Princesses"	65	65
1752	$1 "The Regency"		65	65
1753	$1 "The Majority of Louis XIII"		65	65
1754	$1 "The Flight from Blois"		65	65
1755	$1 "The Treaty of Angouléme"		65	65
1756	$1 "The Peace of Angers"		65	65
1757	$1 "The Reconciliation of Louis and Marie de' Medici"		65	65
1742/57		*Set of 16*	9·50	9·50

MS1758 70×100 mm. $6 "Helene Fourment with a Coach" (52×85 *mm*). P 14½ 5·00 6·00

Nos. 1742/9 and 1750/7 depict details from "The Story of Marie de' Medici" and were each printed together, *se-tenant,* in sheetlets of 8 stamps and one centre label.

306 St. Lucia Amazon

(Des D. Burkhardt. Litho Questa)

1993 (5 Apr). *Endangered Species. T* **306** *and similar horiz designs. Multicoloured. P* 14.

1759	$1 Type **306**		80	80
	a. Sheetlet. Nos. 1759/70		8·50	
1760	$1 Cahow		80	80
1761	$1 Swallow-tailed Kite		80	80
1762	$1 Everglade Kite		80	80
1763	$1 Imperial Amazon		80	80
1764	$1 Humpback Whale		80	80
1765	$1 Plain Pigeon		80	80
1766	$1 St. Vincent Amazon		80	80
1767	$1 Puerto Rican Amazon		80	80
1768	$1 Leatherback Turtle		80	80

1769	$1 American Crocodile		80	80
1770	$1 Hawksbill Turtle		80	80
1759/70		*Set of 12*	8·50	8·50

MS1771 Two sheets, each 100×70 mm. (a) $6 As No. 1764. (b) $6 West Indian manatee *Set of 2 sheets* 7·00 8·00

Nos.1759/70 were printed together, *se-tenant,* in sheetlets of 12 with the background forming a composite design.

307 Queen Elizabeth II at Coronation (photograph by Cecil Beaton)

308 Princess Margaret and Antony Armstrong-Jones

(Des Kerri Schiff. Litho Questa)

1993 (2 June). *40th Anniv of Coronation (1st issue). T* **307** *and similar vert designs. P* 13½×14.

1772	30 c. multicoloured		50	50
	a. Sheetlet. Nos. 1772/5×2		8·00	
1773	40 c. multicoloured		60	60
1774	$2 indigo and black		1·50	1·75
1775	$4 multicoloured		1·90	2·00
1772/5		*Set of 4*	4·00	4·25

MS1776 70×100 mm. $6 multicoloured. P 14 4·25 4·75

Designs:—40 c. Queen Elizabeth the Queen Mother's Crown, 1937; $2 Procession of heralds; $4 Queen Elizabeth II and Prince Edward. (28½×42½ *mm*)—$6 "Queen Elizabeth II" (detail) (Dennis Fildes).

Nos. 1772/5 were printed together in sheetlets of 8, containing two *se-tenant* blocks of 4.

(Litho Questa)

1993 (2 June). *40th Anniv of Coronation (2nd issue). T* **308** *and similar multicoloured designs. P* 13½×14.

1777/1808 $1×32 either grey and black or mult 18·00 20·00

Nos. 1777/1808 were printed in four *se-tenant* sheetlets of 9 (3×3) containing eight stamps and one bottom centre label, each sheetlet showing views from a decade of the reign.

309 Edward Stanley Gibbons and Catalogue of 1865

310 Paul Gascoigne

(Des Kerri Schiff (Nos. 1809/14), D. Keren (No. **MS**1815). Litho Questa)

1993 (14 June). *Famous Professional Philatelists (1st series). T* **309** *and similar horiz designs. P* 14.

1809	$1.50, agate, black and green		1·10	1·10
1810	$1.50, multicoloured		1·10	1·10
1811	$1.50, multicoloured		1·10	1·10
1812	$1.50, multicoloured		1·10	1·10
1813	$1.50, multicoloured		1·10	1·10
1814	$1.50, multicoloured		1·10	1·10
1809/14		*Set of 6*	6·00	6·00

MS1815 98×69 mm. $3 black; $3 black 5·00 5·50

Designs:—No. 1810, Theodore Champion and France 1849 1 f. stamp; No. 1811, J. Walter Scott and U.S.A. 1918 24 c. "Inverted Jenny" error; No. 1812, Hugo Michel and Bavaria 1849 1 k. stamp; No. 1813, Alberto and Giulio Bolaffi with Sardinia 1851 5 c. stamp; No. 1814, Richard Borek and Brunswick 1865 1 gr. stamp; No. **MS**1815, Front pages of *Mekeel's Weekly Stamp News* in 1891 (misdated 1890) and 1993.

See also Nos. 1957.

(Des Rosemary DeFiglio. Litho Questa)

1993 (30 July). *World Cup Football Championship, U.S.A. (1st issue). T* **310** *and similar vert designs showing English players. Multicoloured. P* 14.

1816	$2 Type **310**		1·40	1·40
1817	$2 David Platt		1·40	1·40
1818	$2 Martin Peters		1·40	1·40
1819	$2 John Barnes		1·40	1·40
1820	$2 Gary Lineker		1·40	1·40
1821	$2 Geoff Hurst		1·40	1·40
1822	$2 Bobby Charlton		1·40	1·40
1823	$2 Bryan Robson		1·40	1·40
1824	$2 Bobby Moore		1·40	1·40
1825	$2 Nobby Stiles		1·40	1·40
1826	$2 Gordon Banks		1·40	1·40
1827	$2 Peter Shilton		1·40	1·40
1816/27		*Set of 12*	15·00	15·00

MS1828 Two sheets, each 135×109 mm. (a) $6 Bobby Moore holding World Cup. (b) $6 Gary Lineker and Bobby Robson. *Set of 2 sheets* 9·00 10·00

See also Nos. 2039/45.

311 Grand Inspector W. Heath

312 Hugo Eckener and Dr. W. Beckers with Airship LZ-127 *Graf Zeppelin* over Lake George, New York

(Des Kerri Schiff (Nos. 1830, 1837, 1840, 1844, **MS**1847b and **MS**1847e). Litho Questa)

1993 (16 Aug). *Anniversaries and Events.* T **311** *and similar designs. Deep blue-green and black (No.* **MS**1847c) *or multicoloured (others).* P 14.

1829	10 c.	Type **311**	50	30
1830	15 c.	Rodnina and Oulanov (U.S.S.R.) (pairs figure skating) (*horiz*)	30	30
1831	30 c.	Present Masonic Hall, St. John's (*horiz*)	75	50
1832	30 c.	Willy Brandt with Helmut Schmidt and George Leber (*horiz*)	30	30
1833	30 c.	"Cat and Bird" (Picasso) (*horiz*)	40	40
1834	40 c.	Previous Masonic Hall, St. John's (*horiz*)	75	50
1835	40 c.	"Fish on a Newspaper" (Picasso) (*horiz*)	40	40
1836	40 c.	Early astronomical equipment	40	40
1837	40 c.	Prince Naruhito and engagement photographs (*horiz*)	40	40
1838	60 c.	Grand Inspector J. Jeffery	1·00	60
1839	$1	"Woman Combing her Hair" (W. Slewinski) (*horiz*)	70	70
1840	$3	Masako Owada and engagement photographs (*horiz*)	1·75	1·75
1841	$3	"Artist's Wife with Cat" (Konrad Kryzanowski) (*horiz*)	1·75	1·75
1842	$4	Willy Brandt and protest march (*horiz*)	2·25	2·40
1843	$4	Galaxy	2·25	2·40
1844	$5	Alberto Tomba (Italy) (giant slalom) (*horiz*)	2·25	2·40
1845	$5	"Dying Bull" (Picasso) (*horiz*)	2·25	2·40
1846	$5	Pres. Clinton and family (*horiz*)	2·25	2·40
1829/46		*Set of 18*	19·00	18·00

MS1847 Seven sheets. (a) 106×75 mm. $5 Copernicus. (b) 106×75 mm. $6 Womens' 1500 metre speed skating medallists (*horiz*). (c) 106×75 mm. $6 Willy Brandt at Warsaw Ghetto Memorial (*horiz*). (d) 106×75 mm. $6 "Woman with a Dog" (detail) (Picasso) (*horiz*). (e) 106×75 mm. $6 Masako Owada. (f) 70×100 mm. $6 "General Confusion" (S. I. Witkiewicz). (g) 106×75 mm. $6 Pres. Clinton taking the Oath (42½×57 mm) ..... *Set of 7 sheets* 22·00 23·00

Anniversaries and Events:—Nos. 1829, 1831, 1834, 1838, 150th anniv of St. John's Masonic Lodge No. 492; Nos. 1830, 1844, **MS**1847b, Winter Olympic Games '94, Lillehammer; Nos. 1832, 1842, **MS**1847c, 80th birth anniv of Willy Brandt (German politician); Nos. 1833, 1835, 1845, **MS**1847d, 20th death anniv of Picasso (artist); Nos.1836, 1843, 450th death anniv of Copernicus (astronomer); Nos. 1837, 1840, **MS**1847e, Marriage of Crown Prince Naruhito of Japan; Nos. 1839, 1841, **MS**1847f, "Polska '93" International Stamp Exhibition, Poznań; Nos. 1846, **MS**1847g, Inauguration of U.S. President William Clinton.

(Des W. Hanson. Litho Questa)

1993 (16 Aug–11 Oct). *Aviation Anniversaries.* T **312** *and similar multicoloured designs.* P 14.

1848	30 c.	Type **312**	75	55
1849	40 c.	Chicago World's Fair from *Graf Zeppelin*	80	80
1850	40 c.	Gloster Whittle E28/39, 1941 (11 Oct)	80	80
1851	40 c.	George Washington writing balloon mail letter (*vert*) (11 Oct)	80	80
1852	$4	Pres. Wilson and Curtiss JN-4 "Jenny" (11 Oct)	3·25	3·50
1853	$5	Airship LZ-129 *Hindenburg* over Ebbets Field baseball stadium, 1937	3·25	3·50
1854	$5	Gloster Meteor in dogfight (11 Oct)	3·25	3·50
1848/54		*Set of 7*	11·50	12·00

MS1855 Three sheets. (a) 86×105 mm. $6 Hugo Eckener (*vert*). (b) 105×86 mm. $6 Consolidated PBY-5 Catalina flying boat (57×42½ mm). (c) 105×86 mm. $6 Alexander Hamilton, Washington and John Jay watching Blanchard's balloon, 1793 (*horiz*) ..... *Set of 3 sheets* 13·00 14·00

Anniversaries:—Nos. 1848/9, 1853, **MS**1855a, 125th birth anniv of Hugo Eckener (airship commander); Nos. 1850, 1854, **MS**1855b, 75th anniv of Royal Air Force; Nos. 1851/2, **MS**1855c, Bicent of First Airmail Flight.

313 Lincoln Continental

(Des W. Hanson. Litho Questa)

1993 (11 Oct). *Centenaries of Henry Ford's First Petrol Engine* (Nos. 1856, 1858, **MS**1860a) *and Karl Benz's First Four-wheeled Car (others).* T **313** *and similar horiz designs. Multicoloured.* P 14.

1856	30 c.	Type **313**	75	60
1857	40 c.	Mercedes racing car, 1914	80	65
1858	$4	Ford "GT40", 1966	3·50	3·75
1859	$5	Mercedes Benz "gull-wing" coupe, 1954	3·50	3·75
1856/9		*Set of 4*	7·75	8·00

MS1860 Two sheets. (a) 114×87 mm. $6 Ford's Mustang emblem. (b) 87×114 mm. $6 Germany 1936 12 pf. Benz and U.S.A. 1968 12 c. Ford stamps ..... *Set of 2 sheets* 9·00 10·00

314 *The Musical Farmer, 1932*

(Des Rosemary DeFiglio. Litho Questa)

1993 (25 Oct). *Mickey Mouse Film Posters.* T **314** *and similar vert designs. Multicoloured.* P 13½×14.

1861	10 c.	Type **314**	50	30
1862	15 c.	*Little Whirlwind*, 1941	55	35
1863	30 c.	*Pluto's Dream House*, 1940	70	40
1864	40 c.	*Gulliver Mickey*, 1934	70	40
1865	50 c.	*Alpine Climbers*, 1936	70	45
1866	$1	*Mr. Mouse Takes a Trip*, 1940	1·10	80
1867	$2	*The Nifty Nineties*, 1941	1·75	2·00
1868	$4	*Mickey Down Under*, 1948	2·25	3·00
1869	$5	*The Pointer*, 1939	2·25	3·00
1861/9		*Set of 9*	9·50	9·50

MS1870 Two sheets, each 125×105 mm. (a) $6 *The Simple Things*, 1953. (b) $6 *The Prince and the Pauper*, 1990 ..... *Set of 2 sheets* 9·50 10·00

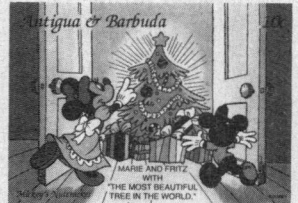

315 Marie and Fritz with Christmas Tree

(Des Alvin White Studio. Litho Questa)

1993 (8 Nov). *Christmas. Mickey's Nutcracker.* T **315** *and similar multicoloured designs showing Walt Disney cartoon characters in scenes from The Nutcracker.* P 14×13½.

1871	10 c.	Type **315**	40	30
1872	15 c.	Marie receives Nutcracker from Godfather Drosselmeir	40	30
1873	20 c.	Fritz breaks Nutcracker	45	30
1874	30 c.	Nutcracker with sword	50	30
1875	40 c.	Nutcracker and Marie in the snow	55	30
1876	50 c.	Marie and the Prince meet Sugar Plum Fairy	60	40
1877	60 c.	Marie and Prince in Crystal Hall	60	50
1878	$3	Huey, Dewey and Louie as Cossack dancers	2·25	2·50
1879	$6	Mother Ginger and her puppets	3·50	4·00
1871/9		*Set of 9*	8·25	8·00

MS1880 Two sheets, each 127×102 mm. (a) $6 Marie and Prince in sleigh. P 14×13½. (b) $6 The Prince in sword fight (*vert*). P 13½×14 ..... *Set of 2 sheets* 8·50 9·00

316 "Hannah and Samuel" (Rembrandt)

(Des Kerri Schiff. Litho Questa)

1993 (22 Nov). *Famous Paintings by Rembrandt and Matisse.* T **316** *and similar vert designs. Multicoloured.* P 13½×14.

1881	15 c.	Type **316**	30	30
1882	15 c.	"Guitarist" (Matisse)	30	30
1883	30 c.	"The Jewish Bride" (Rembrandt)	40	30
1884	40 c.	"Jacob wrestling with the Angel" (Rembrandt)	50	30
1885	60 c.	"Interior with a Goldfish Bowl" (Matisse)	70	60
1886	$1	"Mlle Yvonne Landsberg" (Matisse)	1·00	80
1887	$4	"The Toboggan" (Matisse)	2·75	3·25
1888	$5	"Moses with the Tablets of the Law" (Rembrandt)	2·75	3·25
1881/8		*Set of 8*	8·00	8·00

MS1889 Two sheets. (a) 124×99 mm. $6 "The Blinding of Samson by the Philistines" (detail) (Rembrandt). (b) 99×124 mm. $6 "The Three Sisters" (detail) (Matisse) ..... *Set of 2 sheets* 8·50 9·00

317 Hong Kong 1981 $1 Golden Threadfin Bream Stamp and Sampans, Shau Kei Wan

(Des W. Hanson. Litho Questa)

1994 (18 Feb). *"Hong Kong '94" International Stamp Exhibition (1st issue).* T **317** *and similar horiz design. Multicoloured.* P 14.

1890	40 c.	Type **317**	35	45
		a. Horiz pair. Nos. 1890/1	70	90
1891	40 c.	Antigua 1990 $2 Rock Beauty stamp and sampans, Shau Kei Wan	35	45

Nos. 1890/1 were printed together, *se-tenant*, in horizontal pairs throughout the sheet with the centre part of each pair forming a composite design.

318 Terracotta Warriors

(Des Kerri Schiff. Litho Questa)

1994 (18 Feb). *"Hong Kong '94" International Stamp Exhibition (2nd issue). Qin Dynasty Terracotta Figures.* T **318** *and similar horiz designs. Multicoloured.* P 14.

1892	40 c.	Type **318**	40	40
		a. Sheetlet. Nos. 1892/7	2·25	
1893	40 c.	Cavalryman and horse	40	40
1894	40 c.	Warriors in armour	40	40
1895	40 c.	Painted bronze chariot and team	40	40
1896	40 c.	Pekingese dog	40	40
1897	40 c.	Warriors with horses	40	40
1892/7		*Set of 6*	2·25	2·25

Nos. 1892/7 were printed together, *se-tenant*, in sheetlets of 6.

319 Mickey Mouse in Junk

320 Sumatran Rhinoceros lying down

(Litho Questa)

1994 (18 Feb). *"Hong Kong '94" International Stamp Exhibition (3rd issue).* T **319** *and similar multicoloured designs showing Walt Disney cartoon characters.* P 13½×14.

1898	10 c.	Type **319**	40	30
1899	15 c.	Minnie Mouse as mandarin	45	35
1900	30 c.	Donald and Daisy Duck on houseboat	60	45
1901	50 c.	Mickey holding bird in cage	75	60
1902	$1	Pluto and ornamental dog	1·10	90
1903	$2	Minnie and Daisy celebrating Bun Festival	1·75	2·00
1904	$4	Goofy making noodles	2·75	3·00
1905	$5	Goofy pulling Mickey in rickshaw	2·75	3·00
1898/1905		*Set of 8*	9·50	9·50

MS1906 Two sheets, each 133×109 mm. (a) $5 Mickey and Donald on harbour ferry (*horiz*). (b) $5 Mickey in traditional dragon dance (*horiz*). P 14×13½ ..... *Set of 2 sheets* 5·50 6·00

(Litho Questa)

1994 (1 Mar). *Centenary of Sierra Club (environmental protection society) (1992). Endangered Species. T* **320** *and similar multicoloured designs. P* 14.

1907	$1.50, Type **320**		1·10	1·10
	a. Sheetlet. Nos. 1907/14		7·50	
1908	$1.50, Sumatran Rhinoceros feeding		1·10	1·10
1909	$1.50, Ring-tailed Lemur on ground		1·10	1·10
1910	$1.50, Ring-tailed Lemur on branch		1·10	1·10
1911	$1.50, Red-fronted Brown Lemur on branch		1·10	1·10
1912	$1.50, Head of Red-fronted Brown Lemur		1·10	1·10
1913	$1.50, Head of Red-fronted Brown Lemur in front of trunk		1·10	1·10
1914	$1.50, Sierra Club Centennial emblem (black, buff and deep blue-green)		80	80
	a. Sheetlet. Nos. 1914/21		7·50	
1915	$1.50, Head of Bactrian Camel		1·10	1·10
1916	$1.50, Bactrian Camel		1·10	1·10
1917	$1.50, African Elephant drinking		1·10	1·10
1918	$1.50, Head of African Elephant		1·10	1·10
1919	$1.50, Leopard sitting upright		1·10	1·10
1920	$1.50, Leopard in grass (emblem at right)		1·10	1·10
1921	$1.50, Leopard in grass (emblem at left)		1·10	1·10
1907/21		*Set of 15*	15·00	15·00

MS1922 Four sheets. (a) 100×70 mm. $1.50, Sumatran Rhinoceros (*horiz*). (b) 70×100 mm. $1.50, Ring-tailed Lemur (*horiz*). (c) 70×100 mm. $1.50, Bactrian Camel (*horiz*). (d) 100×70 mm. $1.50, African Elephant (*horiz*)

Set of 4 sheets 5·00 6·00

Nos. 1907/14 and 1914/21 were printed together, *se-tenant*, in sheetlets of 8 with each sheetlet containing No. 1914 at bottom right.

321 West Highland White Terrier

322 *Spiranthes lanceolata*

(Des Jennifer Toombs. Litho Questa)

1994 (5 Apr). *Dogs of the World. Chinese New Year ("Year of the Dog"). T* **321** *and similar horiz designs. Multicoloured. P* 14×14½.

1923	50 c. Type **321**		50	50
	a. Sheetlet. Nos. 1923/34		5·50	
1924	50 c. Beagle		50	50
1925	50 c. Scottish Terrier		50	50
1926	50 c. Pekingese		50	50
1927	50 c. Dachshund		50	50
1928	50 c. Yorkshire Terrier		50	50
1929	50 c. Pomeranian		50	50
1930	50 c. Poodle		50	50
1931	50 c. Shetland Sheepdog		50	50
1932	50 c. Pug		50	50
1933	50 c. Shih Tzu		50	50
1934	50 c. Chihuahua		50	50
1935	75 c. Mastiff		50	50
	a. Sheetlet. Nos. 1935/46		5·50	
1936	75 c. Border Collie		50	50
1937	75 c. Samoyed		50	50
1938	75 c. Airedale Terrier		50	50
1939	75 c. English Setter		50	50
1940	75 c. Rough Collie		50	50
1941	75 c. Newfoundland		50	50
1942	75 c. Weimarana		50	50
1943	75 c. English Springer Spaniel		50	50
1944	75 c. Dalmatian		50	50
1945	75 c. Boxer		50	50
1946	75 c. Old English Sheepdog		50	50
1923/46		*Set of 24*	11·00	11·00

MS1947 Two sheets, each 93×58 mm. (a) $6 Welsh Corgi. (b) $6 Labrador Retriever

Set of 2 sheets 9·00 9·50

Nos. 1923/34 and 1935/46 were printed together, *se-tenant*, in sheetlets of 12.

(Litho Questa)

1994 (11 Apr). *Orchids. T* **322** *and similar vert designs. Multicoloured. P* 14.

1948	10 c. Type **322**		45	40
1949	20 c. *Ionopsis utricularioides*		60	40
1950	30 c. *Tetramicra canaliculata*		70	50
1951	50 c. *Oncidium picturatum*		80	65
1952	$1 *Epidendrum difforme*		1·25	90
1953	$2 *Epidendrum ciliare*		1·75	2·00
1954	$4 *Epidendrum ibaguense*		2·75	3·00
1955	$5 *Epidendrum nocturnum*		2·75	3·00
1948/55		*Set of 8*	10·00	9·75

MS1956 Two sheets, each 100×73 mm. (a) $6 *Rodriguezia lanceolata*. (b) $6 *Encyclia cochleata*

Set of 2 sheets 9·00 9·50

The new-issue supplement to this Catalogue appears each month in

GIBBONS STAMP MONTHLY

—from your newsagent or by postal subscription— sample copy and details on request.

---

323 Hermann E. Sieger, Germany 1931 1 m. Zeppelin Stamp and Airship LZ-127 *Graf Zeppelin*

324 *Danaus plezippus*

(Litho Questa)

1994 (6 June). *Famous Professional Philatelists (2nd series). P* 14.

1957 **323** $1.50, multicoloured · · 1·10 1·10

(Des B. Hargreaves. Litho Questa)

1994 (27 June). *Butterflies. T* **324** *and similar vert designs. Multicoloured. P* 14.

1958	10 c. Type **324**		45	40
1959	15 c. *Appias drusilla*		60	35
1960	30 c. *Eurema lisa*		70	50
1961	40 c. *Anaea troglodyta*		75	60
1962	$1 *Urbanus proteus*		1·25	90
1963	$2 *Junonia evarete*		1·90	2·00
1964	$4 *Battus polydamas*		2·75	3·00
1965	$5 *Heliconius charitonia*		2·75	3·00
1958/65		*Set of 8*	10·00	9·50

MS1966 Two sheets, each 102×72 mm. (a) $6 *Phoebis sennae*. (b) $6 *Hemiargus hanno*

Set of 2 sheets 8·00 8·50

No. 1959 is inscribed "Appisa drusilla" and No. 1965 "Heliconius charitonius", both in error.

325 Bottlenose Dolphin

326 Edwin Aldrin (astronaut)

(Des J. Genzo. Litho Questa)

1994 (21 July). *Marine Life. T* **325** *and similar multicoloured designs. P* 14.

1967	50 c. Type **325**		50	50
	a. Sheetlet. Nos. 1967/75		4·00	
1968	50 c. Killer Whale		50	50
1969	50 c. Spinner Dolphin		50	50
1970	50 c. Oceanic Sunfish		50	50
1971	50 c. Caribbean Reef Shark and Short Fin Pilot Whale		50	50
1972	50 c. Copper-banded Butterflyfish		50	50
1973	50 c. Mosaic Moray		50	50
1974	50 c. Clown Triggerfish		50	50
1975	50 c. Red Lobster		50	50
1967/75		*Set of 9*	4·00	4·00

MS1976 Two sheets, each 106×76 mm. (a) $6 Seahorse. (b) $6 Swordfish ("Blue Marlin") (*horiz*) *Set of 2 sheets* 8·00 8·50

Nos. 1967/75 were printed together, *se-tenant*, in sheetlets of 9.

(Des W. Hanson. Litho Questa)

1994 (4 Aug). *25th Anniv of First Moon Landing. T* **326** *and similar horiz designs. Multicoloured. P* 14.

1977	$1.50, Type **326**		1·25	1·25
	a. Sheetlet. Nos. 1977/82		7·00	
1978	$1.50, First lunar footprint		1·25	1·25
1979	$1.50, Neil Armstrong (astronaut)		1·25	1·25
1980	$1.50, Aldrin stepping onto Moon		1·25	1·25
1981	$1.50, Aldrin and equipment		1·25	1·25
1982	$1.50, Aldrin and U.S.A. flag		1·25	1·25
1983	$1.50, Aldrin at Tranquility Base		1·25	1·25
	a. Sheetlet. Nos. 1983/8		7·00	
1984	$1.50, Moon plaque		1·25	1·25
1985	$1.50, Eagle leaving Moon		1·25	1·25
1986	$1.50, Command module in lunar orbit		1·25	1·25
1987	$1.50, First day cover of U.S.A. 1969 10 c. First Man on Moon stamp			
1988	$1.50, Pres. Nixon and astronauts		1·25	1·25
1977/88		*Set of 12*	13·50	13·50

MS1989 72×102 mm. $6 Armstrong and Aldrin with postal official · · 3·25 4·00

Nos. 1977/82 and 1983/8 were printed together, *se-tenant*, in sheetlets of 6.

327 Edwin Moses (U.S.A.) (400 metres hurdles), 1984

(Des Kerri Schiff. Litho Questa)

1994 (4 Aug). *Centenary of International Olympic Committee. Gold Medal Winners. T* **327** *and similar horiz designs. Multicoloured. P* 14.

1990	50 c. Type **327**		30	30
1991	$1.50, Steffi Graf (Germany) (tennis), 1988		1·25	1·25

MS1992 79×110 mm. $6 Johann Olav Koss (Norway) (500, 1500 and 10,000 metre speed skating), 1994 · · 3·25 3·75

328 Antiguan Family

(Litho Questa)

1994 (4 Aug). *International Year of the Family. P* 14.

1993 **328** 90 c. multicoloured · · 40 45

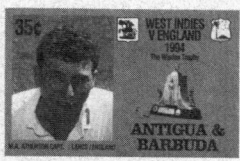

329 Mike Atherton (England) and Wisden Trophy

(Des A. Melville-Brown. Litho Questa)

1994 (4 Aug). *Centenary of First English Cricket Tour to the West Indies (1995). T* **329** *and similar multicoloured designs. P* 14.

1994	35 c. Type **329**		50	30
1995	75 c. Viv Richards (West Indies) (*vert*)		85	70
1996	$1.20, Richie Richardson (West Indies) and Wisden Trophy		1·10	1·50
1994/6		*Set of 3*	2·25	2·25

MS1997 80×100 mm. $3 English team, 1895 (black and grey-brown) · · 2·25 2·25

330 Entrance Bridge, Songgwangsa Temple

(Des Kerri Schiff. Litho Questa (Nos. 1998, 2007/9), B.D.T. (Nos. 1999/2006))

1994 (4 Aug). *"Philakorea '94" International Stamp Exhibition, Seoul. T* **330** *and similar multicoloured designs. P* 13½ (*Nos. 1999/2006*) *or* 14 (*others*).

1998	40 c. Type **330**		30	30
1999	75 c. Long-necked bottle		50	50
	a. Sheetlet. Nos. 1999/2006		3·50	
2000	75 c. Punch'ong ware jar with floral decoration		50	50
2001	75 c. Punch'ong ware jar with blue dragon pattern		50	50
2002	75 c. Ewer in shape of bamboo shoot		50	50
2003	75 c. Punch'ong ware green jar		50	50
2004	75 c. Pear-shaped bottle		50	50
2005	75 c. Porcelain jar with brown dragon pattern		50	50
2006	75 c. Porcelain jar with floral pattern		50	50
2007	90 c. Song-op Folk Village, Cheju		50	55
2008	$3 Port Sogwipo		1·75	2·00
1998/2008		*Set of 11*	6·00	6·25

MS2009 104×71 mm. $4 Ox herder playing flute (*vert*) · · 2·40 2·75

Nos. 1999/2006, each 24×47 mm, were printed together, *se-tenant*, in sheetlets of 8.

331 Short S.25 Sunderland Flying Boat

332 Travis Tritt

(Des J. Batchelor. Litho Questa)

1994 (4 Aug). *50th Anniv of D-Day. T* **331** *and similar horiz designs. Multicoloured. P* 14.

2010	40 c. Type **331**		60	30
2011	$2 Lockheed P-38 Lightning fighters attacking train		1·75	1·90
2012	$3 Martin B-26 Marauder bombers		2·25	2·50
2010/12		*Set of* 3	4·25	4·25
MS2013	108×78 mm. $6 Hawker Typhoon fighter bomber		3·50	4·00

(Des J. Iskowitz. Litho Questa)

1994 (18 Aug). *Stars of Country and Western Music. T* **332** *and similar multicoloured designs. P* 14.

2014	75 c. Type **332**		50	50
	a. Sheetlet. Nos. 2014/21		3·50	
2015	75 c. Dwight Yoakam		50	50
2016	75 c. Billy Ray Cyrus		50	50
2017	75 c. Alan Jackson		50	50
2018	75 c. Garth Brooks		50	50
2019	75 c. Vince Gill		50	50
2020	75 c. Clint Black		50	50
2021	75 c. Eddie Rabbit		50	50
2022	75 c. Patsy Cline		50	50
	a. Sheetlet. Nos. 2022/9		3·50	
2023	75 c. Tanya Tucker		50	50
2024	75 c. Dolly Parton		50	50
2025	75 c. Anne Murray		50	50
2026	75 c. Tammy Wynette		50	50
2027	75 c. Loretta Lynn		50	50
2028	75 c. Reba McEntire		50	50
2029	75 c. Skeeter Davis		50	50
2030	75 c. Hank Snow		50	50
	a. Sheetlet. Nos. 2030/7		3·50	
2031	75 c. Gene Autry		50	50
2032	75 c. Jimmie Rodgers		50	50
2033	75 c. Ernest Tubb		50	50
2034	75 c. Eddy Arnold		50	50
2035	75 c. Willie Nelson		50	50
2036	75 c. Johnny Cash		50	50
2037	75 c. George Jones		50	50
2014/37		*Set of* 24	10·50	10·50

MS2038 Three sheets. (a) 100×70 mm. $6 Hank Williams Jr. (b) 100×70 mm. $6 Hank Williams Sr. (c) 70×100 mm. $6 Kitty Wells (*horiz*)
.... *Set of* 3 *sheets* 13·00 13·00

Nos. 2014/21, 2022/9 and 2030/7 were printed together, *se-tenant*, in sheetlets of 8.

333 Hugo Sanchez (Mexico)

(Litho B.D.T.)

1994 (19 Sept). *World Cup Football Championship, U.S.A.* (*2nd issue*). *T* **333** *and similar multicoloured designs. P* 14.

2039	15 c. Type **333**		40	30
2040	35 c. Jürgen Klinsmann (Germany)		60	30
2041	65 c. Antiguan player		80	55
2042	$1.20, Cobi Jones (U.S.A.)		1·25	1·25
2043	$4 Roberto Baggio (Italy)		2·50	2·75
2044	$5 Bwalya Kalusha (Zambia)		2·50	2·75
2039/44		*Set of* 6	2·50	2·75

MS2045 Two sheets. (a) 72×105 mm. $6 Maldive Islands player (*vert*). (b) 107×78 mm. $6 World Cup trophy (*vert*) ..... *Set of* 2 *sheets* 8·00 8·50

No. 2040 is inscribed "Klinsman" in error.

334 Sir Shridath Ramphal

(Litho Questa)

1994 (26 Sept). *First Recipients of Order of the Caribbean Community. T* **334** *and similar horiz designs. Multicoloured. P* 14.

2046	65 c. Type **334**		50	40
2047	90 c. William Demas		65	60
2048	$1.20, Derek Walcott		85	1·25
2046/8		*Set of* 3	1·75	2·00

335 Pair of Magnificent Frigate Birds

336 "Virgin and Child by the Fireside" (Robert Campin)

(Des Tracy Pedersen. Litho Questa)

1994 (12 Dec). *Birds. T* **335** *and similar multicoloured designs. P* 14.

2049	10 c. Type **335**		45	45
2050	15 c. Bridled Quail Dove		50	40
2051	30 c. Magnificent Frigate Bird chick hatching		70	70
2052	40 c. Purple-throated Carib (*vert*)		70	70
2053	$1 Male Magnificent Frigate Bird in courtship display (*vert*)		1·00	1·00
2054	$1 Broad-winged Hawk (*vert*)		1·00	1·00
2055	$3 Young Magnificent Frigate Bird		2·00	2·75
2056	$4 Yellow Warbler		2·00	2·75
2049/56		*Set of* 8	7·50	8·75

MS2057 Two sheets. (a) 70×100 mm. $6 Female Magnificent Frigate Bird (*vert*). (b) 100×70 mm. $6 Black-billed Whistling Duck ducklings
.... *Set of* 2 *sheets* 7·00 7·50

Nos. 2049, 2051, 2053 and 2055 also show the W.W.F. Panda emblem.

(Litho Questa)

1994 (12 Dec). *Christmas. Religious Paintings. T* **336** *and similar vert designs. Multicoloured. P* 13½×14.

2058	15 c. Type **336**		35	30
2059	35 c. "The Reading Madonna" (Giorgione)		55	25
2060	40 c. "Madonna and Child" (Giovanni Bellini)		60	30
2061	45 c. "The Litta Madonna" (Da Vinci)		60	30
2062	65 c. "The Virgin and Child under the Apple Tree" (Lucas Cranach the Elder)		75	45
2063	75 c. "Madonna and Child" (Master of the Female Half-lengths)		85	60
2064	$1.20, "An Allegory of the Church" (Alessandro Allori)		1·25	1·25
2065	$5 "Madonna and Child wreathed with Flowers" (Jacob Jordaens)		2·75	3·75
2058/65		*Set of* 8	7·00	6·25

MS2066 Two sheets. (a) 123×88 mm. $6 "Madonna and Child with Commissioners" (detail) "Palma Vecchio". (b) 88×123 mm. $6 "The Virgin Enthroned with Child" (detail) (Bohemian master) ... *Set of* 2 *sheets* 7·50 8·00

337 Magnificent Frigate Bird

338 Head of Pachycephalosaurus

(Des W. Wright. Litho China Security Ptg Ltd, Hong Kong)

1995 (6 Feb). *Birds. T* **337** *and similar vert designs. Multicoloured. P* 15×14.

2067	15 c. Type **337**		10	10
2068	25 c. Blue-hooded Euphonia		10	10
2069	35 c. Eastern Meadowlark		15	20
2070	40 c. Red-billed Tropic Bird		15	20
2071	45 c. Greater Flamingo		20	25
2072	60 c. Yellow-faced Grassquit		25	30
2073	65 c. Yellow-billed Cuckoo		30	35
2074	70 c. Purple-throated Carib		30	35
2075	75 c. Bananaquit		35	40
2076	90 c. Painted Bunting		40	45
2077	$1.20, Red-legged Honeycreeper		50	55
2078	$2 Northern Jacana		85	90
2079	$5 Greater Antillean Bullfinch		2·10	2·25
2080	$10 Caribbean Elaenia		4·25	4·50
2081	$20 Brown Trembler		8·75	9·00
2067/81		*Set of* 15	18·00	19·00

(Des B. Regal. Litho Questa)

1995 (15 May). *Prehistoric Animals. T* **338** *and similar multicoloured designs. P* 14.

2082	15 c. Type **338**		30	30
2083	20 c. Head of Afrovenator		30	30
2084	65 c. Centrosaurus		60	60
2085	75 c. Kronosaurus (*horiz*)		60	60
	a. Sheetlet. Nos. 2085/96		6·50	
2086	75 c. Ichthyosaurus (*horiz*)		60	60
2087	75 c. Plesiosaurus (*horiz*)		60	60
2088	75 c. Archelon (*horiz*)		60	60
2089	75 c. Pair of Tyrannosaurus (*horiz*)		60	60
2090	75 c. Tyrannosaurus (*horiz*)		60	60
2091	75 c. Parasaurolophus (*horiz*)		60	60
2092	75 c. Pair of Parasaurolophus (*horiz*)		60	60
2093	75 c. Oviraptor (*horiz*)		60	60
2094	75 c. Protoceratops with eggs (*horiz*)		60	60
2095	75 c. Pteranodon and Protoceratops (*horiz*)		60	60
2096	75 c. Pair of Protoceratops (*horiz*)		60	60
2097	90 c. Pentaceratops drinking		75	75
2098	$1.20, Head of Tarbosaurus		85	85
2099	$5 Head of Styracosaurus		3·25	3·25
2082/99		*Set of* 18	11·50	12·00

MS2100 Two sheets, each 101×70 mm. (a) $6 Head of Corythosaurus (*horiz*). (b) $6 Head of Carnotaurus (*horiz*) ... *Set of* 2 *sheets* 7·50 8·00

Nos. 2085/96 were printed together, *se-tenant*, in sheetlets of 12.

339 Al Oerter (U.S.A.) (discus – 1956, 1960, 1964, 1968)

(Des R. Sauber. Litho B.D.T.)

1995 (6 June). *Olympic Games, Atlanta* (1996). *Previous Gold Medal Winners* (*1st issue*). *T* **339** *and similar multicoloured designs. P* 14.

2101	15 c. Type **339**		30	20
2102	20 c. Greg Louganis (U.S.A.) (diving – 1984, 1988)		30	20
2103	65 c. Naim Suleymanoglu (Turkey) (weightlifting – 1988)		55	40
2104	90 c. Louise Ritter (U.S.A.) (high jump – 1988)		70	70
2105	$1.20, Nadia Comaneci (Rumania) (gymnastics – 1976)		80	85
2106	$5 Olga Bondarenko (Russia) (10,000 metres – 1988)		2·50	3·00
2101/6		*Set of* 6	4·75	4·75

MS2107 Two sheets, each 106×76 mm. (a) $6 United States crew (eight-oared shell – 1964). (b) $6 Lutz Hessilch (Germany) (cycling – 1988) (*vert*) ... *Set of* 2 *sheets* 8·00 8·00

No. 2106 is inscribed "BOLDARENKO" in error. See also Nos. 2302/23.

340 Map of Berlin showing Russian Advance

341 Signatures and Earl of Halifax

(Des W. Wright. Litho Questa)

1995 (20 July). *50th Anniv of End of Second World War in Europe. T* **340** *and similar multicoloured designs. P* 14.

2108	$1.20, Type **340**		1·00	1·00
	a. Sheetlet. Nos. 2108/15		7·00	
2109	$1.20, Russian tank and infantry		1·00	1·00
2110	$1.20, Street fighting in Berlin		1·00	1·00
2111	$1.20, German tank exploding		1·00	1·00
2112	$1.20, Russian air raid		1·00	1·00
2113	$1.20, German troops surrendering		1·00	1·00
2114	$1.20, Hoisting the Soviet flag on the Reichstag		1·00	1·00
2115	$1.20, Captured German standards		1·00	1·00
2108/15		*Set of* 8	7·00	7·00

MS2116 104×74 mm. $6 Gen. Konev (*vert*) 4·00 4·50

Nos. 2108/15 were printed together, *se-tenant*, in sheetlets of 8 with the stamps arranged in two horizontal strips of 4 separated by a gutter showing a German soldier in the ruins of Berlin.

(Des L. Fried. Litho Questa)

1995 (20 July). *50th Anniv of United Nations. T* **341** *and similar vert designs. Multicoloured. P* 14.

2117	75 c. Type **341**		60	70
	a. Horiz strip of 3. Nos. 2117/19		1·60	
2118	90 c. Virginia Gildersleeve		60	70
2119	$1.20, Harold Stassen		60	70
2117/19		*Set of* 3	1·60	1·90

MS2120 100×70 mm. $6 Pres. Franklin D. Roosevelt ... 3·50 4·00

Nos. 2117/19 were printed together in sheets of 9 (3×3) containing three *se-tenant* horizontal strips, each forming a composite design.

342 Woman buying Produce from Market

343 Beach and Rotary Emblem

(Des L. Fried. Litho Questa)

1995 (20 July). *50th Anniv of Food and Agriculture Organization. T* **342** *and similar vert designs. Multicoloured. P* 14.

2121	75 c. Type **342**		60	70
	a. Horiz strip of 3. Nos. 2121/3		1·60	
2122	90 c. Women shopping		60	70
2123	$1.20, Women talking		60	70
2121/3		*Set of* 3	1·60	1·90

MS2124 100×70 mm. $6 Tractor 3·00 3·50

Nos. 2121/3 were printed together in sheets of 9 (3×3) containing three *se-tenant* horizontal strips, each forming a composite design.

(Litho Questa)

1995 (20 July). *90th Anniv of Rotary International. T **343** and similar vert design. Multicoloured. P 14.*
2125	$5 Type **343**		3·00	3·50
MS2126	74×104 mm. $6 National flag and emblem		3·50	4·00

344 Queen Elizabeth the Queen Mother

(Litho Questa)

1995 (20 July). *95th Birthday of Queen Elizabeth the Queen Mother. T **344** and similar vert designs. P 13½×14.*
2127	$1.50, orange-brown, pale brown and black		1·00	1·10
	a. Sheetlet. Nos. 2127/30×2		7·00	
2128	$1.50, multicoloured		1·00	1·10
2129	$1.50, multicoloured		1·00	1·10
2130	$1.50, multicoloured		1·00	1·10
2127/30		*Set of 4*	3·50	4·00
MS2131	102×127 mm. $6 multicoloured		3·50	4·00

Designs:—No. 2127, Queen Elizabeth the Queen Mother (pastel drawing); No. 2128, Type **344**; No. 2129, At desk (oil painting); No. 2130, Wearing green dress; No. **MS2131**, Wearing blue dress

Nos. 2128/30 were printed together in sheetlets of 8, containing two *se-tenant* horizontal strips of 4.

(Des J. Batchelor. Litho Questa)

1995 (20 July). *50th Anniv of End of Second World War in the Pacific. Horiz designs as T **340**. Multicoloured. P 14.*
2132	$1.20, Gen. Chiang Kai-shek and Chinese guerrillas		95	1·00
	a. Sheetlet. Nos. 2132/7		5·00	
2133	$1.20, Gen. Douglas MacArthur and beach landing		95	1·00
2134	$1.20, Gen. Claire Chennault and U.S. fighter aircraft		95	1·00
2135	$1.20, Brig. Orde Wingate and supply drop		95	1·00
2136	$1.20, Gen. Joseph Stilwell and U.S. supply plane		95	1·00
2137	$1.20, Field-Marshal Bill Slim and loading cow into plane		95	1·00
2132/7		*Set of 6*	5·00	5·50
MS2138	108×76 mm. $3 Admiral Nimitz and aircraft carrier		2·25	2·50

Nos. 2132/7 were printed together, *se-tenant*, in sheetlets of 6 with the stamps arranged in two horizontal strips of 3 separated by a gutter showing Japanese soldiers surrendering.

345 Family ("Caring")

346 Purple-throated Carib

1995 (31 July). *Tourism. Sheet 95×72 mm, containing T **345** and similar horiz designs. Multicoloured. Litho. P 14.*
MS2139	$2 Type **345**; $2 Market trader ("Marketing"); $2 Workers and housewife ("Working"); $2 Leisure pursuits ("Enjoying Life")		4·75	5·00

(Des Tracy Pedersen. Litho Questa)

1995 (31 Aug). *Birds. T **346** and similar vert designs. Multicoloured. P 14.*
2140	75 c. Type **346**		60	60
	a. Sheetlet. Nos. 2140/51		6·50	
2141	75 c. Antillean Crested Hummingbird		60	60
2142	75 c. Bananaquit		60	60
2143	75 c. Mangrove Cuckoo		60	60
2144	75 c. Troupial		60	60
2145	75 c. Green-throated Carib		60	60
2146	75 c. Yellow Warbler		60	60
2147	75 c. Blue-hooded Euphonia		60	60
2148	75 c. Scaly-breasted Thrasher		60	60
2149	75 c. Burrowing Owl		60	60
2150	75 c. Carib Grackle		60	60
2151	75 c. Adelaide's Warbler		60	60
2152	75 c. Ring-necked Duck		60	60
	a. Sheetlet. Nos. 2152/63		6·50	
2153	75 c. Ruddy Duck		60	60
2154	75 c. Green-winged Teal		60	60
2155	75 c. Wood Duck		60	60
2156	75 c. Hooded Merganser		60	60
2157	75 c. Lesser Scaup		60	60

2158	75 c. Black-billed Whistling Duck ("West Indian Tree Duck")		60	60
2159	75 c. Fulvous Whistling Duck		60	60
2160	75 c. Bahama Pintail		60	60
2161	75 c. Shoveler		60	60
2162	75 c. Masked Duck		60	60
2163	75 c. American Wigeon		60	60
2140/63		*Set of 24*	13·00	13·00
MS2164	Two sheets, each 104×74 mm. (a) $6 Head of Purple Gallinule. (b) $6 Heads of Blue-winged Teals	*Set of 2 sheets*	8·00	8·50

Nos. 2140/51 and 2152/63 were printed together, *se-tenant*, in sheetlets of 12 with the background forming a composite design.

347 Original Church, 1845

348 Mining Bees

(Litho Questa)

1995 (4 Sept). *150th Anniv of Greenbay Moravian Church. T **347** and similar vert designs. Multicoloured. P 14.*
2165	20 c. Type **347**		20	20
2166	60 c. Church in 1967		35	30
2167	75 c. Present church		45	40
2168	90 c. Revd. John Buckley (first minister of African descent)		55	45
2169	$1.20, Bishop John Ephraim Knight (longest-serving minister)		70	75
2170	$2 As 75 c.		1·25	1·50
2165/70		*Set of 6*	3·25	3·25
MS2171	110×81 mm. $6 Front of present church		3·50	4·00

(Des Y. Lee. Litho Questa)

1995 (7 Sept). *Bees. T **348** and similar horiz designs. Multicoloured. P 14.*
2172	90 c. Type **348**		60	60
2173	$1.20, Solitary Bee		80	80
2174	$1.65, Leaf-cutter Bee		1·10	1·10
2175	$1.75, Honey Bees		1·10	1·10
2172/5		*Set of 4*	3·25	3·25
MS2176	110×80 mm. $6 Solitary Mining Bee		3·50	3·75

349 Narcissus

350 Somali

(Des Y. Lee. Litho Questa)

1995 (7 Sept). *Flowers. T **349** and similar vert designs. Multicoloured. P 14.*
2177	75 c. Type **349**		60	60
	a. Sheetlet. Nos. 2177/88		6·50	
2178	75 c. Camellia		60	60
2179	75 c. Iris		60	60
2180	75 c. Tulip		60	60
2181	75 c. Poppy		60	60
2182	75 c. Peony		60	60
2183	75 c. Magnolia		60	60
2184	75 c. Oriental Lily		60	60
2185	75 c. Rose		60	60
2186	75 c. Pansy		60	60
2187	75 c. Hydrangea		60	60
2188	75 c. Azaleas		60	60
2177/88		*Set of 12*	6·50	6·50
MS2189	80×110 mm. $6 Calla Lily		3·50	3·75

Nos. 2177/88 were printed together, *se-tenant*, in sheetlets of 12.

No. 2186 is inscribed "Pansie" in error.

(Des Y. Lee. Litho Questa)

1995 (7 Sept). *Cats. T **350** and similar multicoloured designs. P 14.*
2190	45 c. Type **350**		40	40
	a. Sheetlet. Nos. 2190/201		4·25	
2191	45 c. Persian and butterflies		40	40
2192	45 c. Devon Rex		40	40
2193	45 c. Turkish Angora		40	40
2194	45 c. Himalayan		40	40
2195	45 c. Maine Coon		40	40
2196	45 c. Ginger non-pedigree		40	40
2197	45 c. American Wirehair		40	40
2198	45 c. British Shorthair		40	40
2199	45 c. American Curl		40	40
2200	45 c. Black non-pedigree and butterfly		40	40
2201	45 c. Birman		40	40
2190/2201		*Set of 12*	4·25	4·25
MS2202	104×74 mm. $6 Siberian kitten (*vert*)		4·00	4·25

Nos. 2190/2201 were printed together, *se-tenant*, in sheetlets of 12, with the backgrounds forming a composite design.

351 The Explorer Tent

1995 (5 Oct). *18th World Scout Jamboree, Netherlands. Tents. T **351** and similar multicoloured designs. Litho. P 14.*
2203	$1.20, Type **351**		80	80
	a. Horiz strip of 3. Nos. 2203/5		2·25	
2204	$1.20, Camper tent		80	80
2205	$1.20, Wall tent		80	80
2206	$1.20, Trail tarp		80	80
	a. Horiz strip of 3. Nos. 2206/8		2·25	
2207	$1.20, Miner's tent		80	80
2208	$1.20, Voyager tent		80	80
2203/8		*Set of 6*	4·50	4·50
MS2209	Two sheets, each 76×106 mm. (a) $6 Scout and camp fire. (b) $6 Scout with back pack (*vert*)	*Set of 2 sheets*	7·00	7·50

Nos. 2203/5 and 2206/8 were printed together, *se-tenant*, as horizontal strips of 3 in sheets of 9.

352 Trans-Gabon Diesel-electric Train

(Des B. Regal. Litho Questa)

1995 (23 Oct). *Trains of the World. T **352** and similar multicoloured designs. P 14.*
2210	35 c. Type **352**		40	40
2211	65 c. Canadian Pacific diesel-electric locomotive		60	60
2212	75 c. Santa Fe Railway diesel-electric locomotive, U.S.A.		70	70
2213	90 c. High Speed Train, Great Britain		85	85
2214	$1.20, TGV express train, France		90	90
2215	$1.20, Diesel-electric locomotive, Australia		90	90
	a. Sheetlet. Nos. 2215/23		7·00	
2216	$1.20 Pendolino "ETR 450" electric train, Italy		90	90
2217	$1.20, Diesel-electric locomotive, Thailand		90	90
2218	$1.20, Pennsylvania Railroad Type K4 steam locomotive, U.S.A.		90	90
2219	$1.20, Beyer-Garratt steam locomotive, East African Railways		90	90
2220	$1.20 Natal Govt steam locomotive		90	90
2221	$1.20, Rail gun, American Civil War		90	90
2222	$1.20, Locomotive *Lion* (red livery), Great Britain		90	90
2223	$1.20, William Hedley's *Puffing Billy* (green livery), Great Britain		90	90
2224	$6 Amtrak high speed diesel locomotive, U.S.A.		3·00	3·00
2210/24		*Set of 15*	12·00	12·00
MS2225	Two sheets, each 110×80 mm. (a) $6 Locomotive *Iron Rooster*, China (*vert*). (b) $6 "Indian-Pacific" diesel-electric locomotive, Australia (*vert*)	*Set of 2 sheets*	7·50	7·50

Nos. 2215/23 were printed together, *se-tenant*, in sheetlets of 9.

353 Dag Hammarskjöld (1961 Peace)

(Des B. Regal. Litho Walsall)

1995 (8 Nov). *Centenary of Nobel Prize Trust Fund. T **353** and similar multicoloured designs. P 14.*
2226	$1 Type **353**		75	75
	a. Sheetlet. Nos. 2226/34		6·00	
2227	$1 Georg Wittig (1979 Chemistry)		75	75
2228	$1 Wilhelm Ostwald (1909 Chemistry)		75	75
2229	$1 Robert Koch (1905 Medicine)		75	75
2230	$1 Karl Ziegler (1963 Chemistry)		75	75
2231	$1 Alexander Fleming (1945 Medicine)		75	75
2232	$1 Hermann Staudinger (1953 Chemistry)		75	75
2233	$1 Manfred Eigen (1967 Chemistry)		75	75
2234	$1 Arno Penzias (1978 Physics)		75	75
2235	$1 Shmuel Agnon (1966 Literature)		75	75
	a. Sheetlet. Nos. 2235/43		6·00	
2236	$1 Rudyard Kipling (1907 Literature)		75	75
2237	$1 Aleksandr Solzhenitsyn (1970 Literature)		75	75
2238	$1 Jack Steinberger (1988 Physics)		75	75
2239	$1 Andrei Sakharov (1975 Peace)		75	75

2240	$1 Otto Stern (1943 Physics)	75	75
2241	$1 John Steinbeck (1962 Literature) ..	75	75
2242	$1 Nadine Gordimer (1991 Literature) ..	75	75
2243	$1 William Faulkner (1949 Literature) ..	75	75
2226/43	*Set of 18*	12·00	12·00

MS2244 Two sheets, each 100×70 mm. (a) $6 Elie Wiesel (1986 Peace) (*vert*). (b) $6 The Dalai Lama (1989 Peace) (*vert*) .. *Set of 2 sheets* 7·00 7·50
Nos. 2226/34 and 2235/43 were printed together, *se-tenant*, in sheetlets of 9.

354 Elvis Presley   **355** John Lennon and Signature

1995 (8 Dec). *60th Birth Anniv of Elvis Presley. T* **354** *and similar vert designs. Multicoloured. Litho. P* 13½×14.

2245	$1 Type **354**	75	75
	a. Sheetlet. Nos. 2245/53 ..	6·00	
2246	$1 Holding microphone in right hand ..	75	75
2247	$1 In blue shirt and with neck of guitar	75	75
2248	$1 Wearing blue shirt and smiling ..	75	75
2249	$1 On wedding day	75	75
2250	$1 In army uniform	75	75
2251	$1 Wearing red shirt	75	75
2252	$1 Wearing white shirt ..	75	75
2253	$1 In white shirt with microphone ..	75	75
2245/53	*Set of 9*	6·00	6·00

MS2254 101×71 mm. $6 "Ghost" image of Elvis amongst the stars .. .. .. 3·50 3·75
Nos. 2245/54 were printed together, *se-tenant*, in sheetlets of 9.

(Litho Questa)

1995 (8 Dec). *15th Death Anniv of John Lennon (entertainer). T* **355** *and similar vert designs. Multicoloured. P* 14.

2255	45 c. Type **355**	50	40
2256	50 c. In beard and spectacles ..	50	50
2257	65 c. Wearing sunglasses ..	55	55
2258	75 c. In cap with heart badge ..	65	65
2255/8	*Set of 4*	2·00	1·90

MS2259 103×73 mm. $6 As 75 c. .. .. 5·50 6·50
Nos. 2255/8 were each issued in numbered sheets of 16 which have enlarged illustrated left-hand margins.

"Hurricane Relief"
(**356**)

357 "Rest on the Flight into Egypt" (Paolo Veronese)

1995 (14 Dec). *Hurricane Relief. Nos.* 2203/9 *optd as T* **356**.

2260	$1.20, Type 351	80	80
	a. Horiz strip of 3. Nos. 2260/2 ..	2·25	
2261	$1.20, Camper tent ..	80	80
2262	$1.20, Wall tent	80	80
2263	$1.20, Trail tarp	80	80
	a. Horiz strip of 3. Nos. 2263/5 ..	2·25	
2264	$1.20, Miner's tent	80	80
2265	$1.20, Voyager tent	80	80
2260/5	*Set of 6*	4·50	4·50

MS2266 Two sheets, each 76×106 mm. (a) $6 Scout and camp fire. (b) $6 Scout with back pack (*vert*) .. .. *Set of 2 sheets* 7·00 7·50
The overprints on No. **MS**2266 are larger, 12½×5 mm or 5×12½ mm on the vertical design.

(Litho Questa)

1995 (18 Dec). *Christmas. Religious Paintings. T* **357** *and similar vert designs. Multicoloured. P* 13½×14.

2267	15 c. Type **357**	30	30
2268	35 c. "Madonna and Child" (Van Dyck)	40	30
2269	65 c. "Sacred Conversation Piece" (Veronese)	60	50
2270	75 c. "Vision of St. Anthony" (Van Dyck)	70	55
2271	90 c. "Virgin and Child" (Van Eyck) ..	80	65
2272	$6 "The Immaculate Conception" (Giovanni Tiepolo)	3·00	3·50
2267/72	*Set of 6*	5·25	5·25

MS2273 Two sheets. (a) 101×127 mm. $5 "Christ appearing to his Mother" (detail) (Van der Weyden). (b) 127×101 mm. $6 "The Infant Jesus and the Young St. John" (Murillo) *Set of 2 sheets* 6·50 7·00

---

358 *Hygrophoropsis aurantiaca*   **359** H.M.S. *Resolution* (Cook)

(Des D. Burkhart. Litho Questa)

1996 (22 Apr). *Fungi. T* **358** *and similar vert designs. Multicoloured. P* 14.

2274	75 c. Type **358**	35	40
	a. Horiz strip of 4. Nos. 2274/7 ..	1·40	
2275	75 c. *Hygrophorus bakerensis* ..	35	40
2276	75 c. *Hygrophorus conicus* ..	35	40
2277	75 c. *Hygrophorus miniatus* (*Hygrocybe miniata*)	35	40
2278	75 c. *Suillus brevipes*	35	40
	a. Horiz strip of 4. Nos. 2278/81 ..	1·40	
2279	75 c. *Suillus luteus*	35	40
2280	75 c. *Suillus granulatus* ..	35	40
2281	75 c. *Suillus caerulescens* ..	35	40
2274/81	*Set of 8*	2·75	3·00

MS2282 Two sheets, each 105×75 mm. (a) $6 *Conocybe filaris*. (b) $6 *Hygrocybe flavescens*
Set of 2 sheets 5·00 5·25
Nos. 2274/7 and 2278/81 were each printed together in sheetlets of 12 containing three horizontal *se-tenant* strips.

(Litho B.D.T.)

1996 (25 Apr). *Sailing Ships. T* **359** *and similar horiz designs. Multicoloured. P* 14.

2283	15 c. Type **359**	10	10
2284	25 c. *Mayflower* (Pilgrim Fathers) ..	10	15
2285	45 c. *Santa Maria* (Columbus) ..	20	25
2286	75 c. *Aemilia* (Dutch galleon) ..	35	40
2287	75 c. *Sovereign of the Seas* (English galleon)	35	40
2288	90 c. H.M.S. *Victory* (Nelson) ..	40	45
2289	$1.20, As No. 2286	50	55
	a. Sheetlet. Nos. 2289/94 ..	3·00	
2290	$1.20, As No. 2287	50	55
2291	$1.20, *Royal Louis* (French galleon) ..	50	55
2292	$1.20, H.M.S. *Royal George* (ship of the line)	50	55
2293	$1.20, *Le Protecteur* (French frigate) ..	50	55
2294	$1.20, As No. 2288	50	55
2295	$1.50, As No. 2285	65	70
	a. Sheetlet. Nos. 2295/2300 ..	4·00	
2296	$1.50, *Vitoria* (Magellan) ..	65	70
2297	$1.50, *Golden Hind* (Drake) ..	65	70
2298	$1.50, As No. 2284	65	70
2299	$1.50, *Griffin* (La Salle) ..	65	70
2300	$1.50, Type **359**	65	70
2283/2300	*Set of 18*	8·50	8·75

MS2301 (a) 102×72 mm. $6 U.S.S. *Constitution* (frigate); (b) 98×67 mm. $6 *Grande Hermine* (Cartier) .. .. *Set of 2 sheets* 5·50 5·75
Nos. 2289/94 and 2295/2300 were printed together, *se-tenant*, in sheetlets of 6.

360 Florence Griffith Joyner (U.S.A.) (Gold – track, 1988)   **361** Black Skimmer

(Des R. Martin. Litho Questa)

1996 (6 May). *Olympic Games, Atlanta. Previous Medal Winners (2nd issue). T* **360** *and similar multicoloured designs. P* 14.

2302	65 c. Type **360**	30	35
2303	75 c. Olympic Stadium, Seoul (1988) (*horiz*)	35	40
2304	90 c. Allison Jolly and Lynne Jewell (U.S.A.) (Gold – yachting, 1988) (*horiz*)	40	45
2305	90 c. Wolfgang Nordwig (Germany) (Gold – pole vaulting, 1972) ..	40	45
	a. Sheetlet. Nos. 2305/13 ..	3·50	
2306	90 c. Shirley Strong (Great Britain) (Silver – 100 metres hurdles, 1984) ..	40	45
2307	90 c. Sergei Bubka (Russia) (Gold – pole vault, 1988)	40	45
2308	90 c. Filbert Bayi (Tanzania) (Silver – 3000 metres steeplechase, 1980) ..	40	45
2309	90 c. Victor Saneyev (Russia) (Gold – triple jump, 1968, 1972, 1976) ..	40	45
2310	90 c. Silke Renk (Germany) (Gold – javelin, 1992)	40	45
2311	90 c. Daley Thompson (Great Britain) (Gold – decathlon, 1980, 1984) ..	40	45
2312	90 c. Robert Richards (U.S.A.) (Gold – pole vault, 1952, 1956) ..	40	45
2313	90 c. Parry O'Brien (U.S.A.) (Gold – shot put, 1952, 1956) ..	40	45

2314	90 c. Ingrid Kramer (Germany) (Gold – Women's platform diving, 1960) ..	40	45
	a. Sheetlet. Nos. 2314/22 ..	3·50	
2315	90 c. Kelly McCormick (U.S.A.) (Silver – Women's springboard diving, 1984) ..	40	45
2316	90 c. Gary Tobian (U.S.A.) (Gold – Men's springboard diving, 1960) ..	40	45
2317	90 c. Greg Louganis (U.S.A.) (Gold – Men's diving, 1984 and 1988) ..	40	45
2318	90 c. Michelle Mitchell (U.S.A.) (Silver – Women's platform diving, 1984 and 1988) ..	40	45
2319	90 c. Zhou Jihong (China) (Gold – Women's platform diving, 1984) ..	40	45
2320	90 c. Wendy Wyland (U.S.A.) (Bronze – Women's platform diving, 1984) ..	40	45
2321	90 c. Xu Yanmei (China) (Gold – Women's platform diving, 1988) ..	40	45
2322	90 c. Fu Mingxia (China) (Gold – Women's platform diving, 1992) ..	40	45
2323	$1.20, 2000 metre tandem cycle race (*horiz*)	50	55
2302/23	*Set of 22*	8·25	9·25

MS2324 Two sheets, each 106×76 mm. (a) $5 Bill Toomey (U.S.A.) (Gold—Decathlon, 1968) (*horiz*). (b) $6 Mark Lenzi (U.S.A.) (Gold—Men's springboard diving, 1992) .. *Set of 2 sheets* 4·50 4·75
Nos. 2305/13 and 2314/22 were each printed together, *se-tenant*, in sheetlets of 9, with the backgrounds forming composite designs.

1996 (13 May). *Sea Birds. T* **361** *and similar horiz designs. Multicoloured. P* 14.

2325	75 c. Type **361**	35	40
	a. Vert strip of 4. Nos. 2325/8 ..	1·40	
2326	75 c. Black-capped Petrel ..	35	40
2327	75 c. Sooty Tern	35	40
2328	75 c. Royal Tern	35	40
2329	75 c. Pomarine Skua ("Pomarine Jaegger")	35	40
	a. Vert strip of 4. Nos. 2329/32 ..	1·40	
2330	75 c. White-tailed Tropic Bird ..	35	40
2331	75 c. Northern Gannet ..	35	40
2332	75 c. Laughing Gull	35	40
2325/32	*Set of 8*	2·75	3·25

MS2333 Two sheets, each 105×75 mm. (a) $5 Great Frigate Bird. (b) $6 Brown Pelican
Set of 2 sheets 4·50 4·75
Nos. 2325/8 and 2329/32 were each printed together, *se-tenant*, in vertical strips of 4 throughout sheets of 12.

362 Mickey and Goofy on Elephant (*Around the World in Eighty Days*)

(Litho Questa)

1996 (6 June). *Novels of Jules Verne. T* **362** *and similar horiz designs showing Walt Disney cartoon characters in scenes from the books. Multicoloured. P* 14×13½.

2334	1 c. Type **362**	10	10
2335	2 c. Mickey, Donald and Goofy entering cave (*A Journey to the Centre of the Earth*)	10	10
2336	5 c. Mickey and Minnie driving postcart (*Michel Strogoff*) ..	10	10
2337	10 c. Mickey, Donald and Goofy in space rocket (*From the Earth to the Moon*)	10	10
2338	15 c. Mickey and Goofy in balloon (*Five Weeks in a Balloon*) ..	10	10
2339	20 c. Mickey and Goofy in China (*Around the World in Eighty Days*) ..	10	10
2340	$1 Mickey, Goofy and Pluto on island (*The Mysterious Island*) ..	45	50
2341	$2 Mickey, Pluto, Goofy and Donald on Moon (*From the Earth to the Moon*)	85	90
2342	$3 Mickey being lifted by bird (*Captain Grant's Children*) ..	1·25	1·40
2343	$5 Mickey with seal and squid (*Twenty Thousand Leagues Under the Sea*)	2·10	2·25
2334/43	*Set of 10*	5·25	5·50

MS2344 Two sheets, each 124×99 mm. (a) $6 Mickey on *Nautilus* (*Twenty Thousand Leagues Under the Sea*). (b) $6 Mickey and Donald on raft (*A Journey to the Centre of the Earth*)
Set of 2 sheets 5·00 5·25

363 Bruce Lee   **364** Queen Elizabeth II

1996 (13 June). *"CHINA '96" 9th Asian International Stamp Exhibition, Peking. Bruce Lee (actor). T 363 and similar vert designs. Multicoloured. Litho P 14.*

2345	75 c. Type **363**	35	40
	a. Sheetlet. Nos. 2345/53	3·00	
2346	75 c. Bruce Lee in white shirt and red tie	35	40
2347	75 c. In plaid jacket and tie	35	40
2348	75 c. In mask and uniform	35	40
2349	75 c. Bare-chested	35	40
2350	75 c. In mandarin jacket	35	40
2351	75 c. In brown jumper	35	40
2352	75 c. In fawn shirt	35	40
2353	75 c. Shouting	35	40
2345/53	*Set of 9*	3·00	3·50
MS2354	76×106 mm. $5 Bruce Lee	2·10	2·25

Nos 2345/53 were printed together, *se-tenant*, in numbered sheetlets of 9 with enlarged illustrated left-hand margin.

(Litho Questa)

1996 (17 July). *70th Birthday of Queen Elizabeth II. T 364 and similar vert designs. Multicoloured. P 13½×14.*

2355	$2 Type **364**	85	90
	a. Strip of 3. Nos. 2355/7	2·50	
2356	$2 With bouquet	85	90
2357	$2 In garter robes	85	90
2355/7	*Set of 3*	2·50	2·75
MS2358	96×111 mm. $6 Wearing white dress	2·50	2·75

Nos. 2355/7 were printed together, *se-tenant*, in horizontal and vertical strips of 3 throughout sheets of 9.

365 Ancient Egyptian Cavalryman

366 Girl in Red Sari

1996 (24 July). *Cavalry through the Ages. T 365 and similar multicoloured designs. Litho. P 14.*

2359	60 c. Type **365**	25	30
	a. Block of 4. Nos. 2359/62	1·00	
2360	60 c. 13th-century English knight	25	30
2361	60 c. 16th-century Spanish lancer	25	30
2362	60 c. 18th-century Chinese cavalryman	25	30
2359/62	*Set of 4*	1·00	1·25
MS2363	100×70 mm. $6 19th-century French cuirassier (*vert*)	2·50	2·75

Nos. 2359/62 were printed together, *se-tenant*, in blocks of four within sheets of 16.

(Litho Questa)

1996 (30 July). *50th Anniv of U.N.I.C.E.F. T 366 and similar vert designs. Multicoloured . P 14.*

2364	75 c. Type **366**	35	40
2365	90 c. South American mother and child	40	45
2366	$1.20, Nurse with child	50	55
2364/6	*Set of 3*	1·25	1·40
MS2367	114×74 mm. $6 Chinese child	2·50	2·75

367 Tomb of Zachariah and *Verbascum sinuatum*

368 Kate Smith

(Des Jennifer Toombs. Litho Questa)

1996 (30 July). *3000th Anniv of Jerusalem. T 367 and similar vert designs. Multicoloured. P 14½.*

2368	75 c. Type **367**	35	40
2369	90 c. Pool of Siloam and *Hyacinthus orientalis*	40	45
2370	$1.20, Hurva Synagogue and *Ranunculus asiaticus*	50	55
2368/70	*Set of 3*	1·25	1·40
MS2371	66×80 mm. $6 Model of Herod's Temple and *Cercis siliquastrum*	2·75	3·00

(Des J. Iskowitz. Litho Questa)

1996 (30 July). *Centenary of Radio. Entertainers. T 368 and similar vert designs. Multicoloured. P 13½.*

2372	65 c. Type **368**	30	35
2373	75 c. Dinah Shore	35	40
2374	90 c. Rudy Vallee	40	45
2375	$1.20 Bing Crosby	50	55
2372/5	*Set of 4*	1·50	1·60
MS2376	72×104 mm. $6 Jo Stafford (28×42 mm). P 14	2·50	2·75

369 "Madonna Enthroned"

370 Robert Preston (*The Music Man*)

(Litho Questa)

1996 (25 Nov). *Christmas. Religious Paintings by Filippo Lippi. T 369 and similar vert designs. Multicoloured. P 13½×14.*

2377	60 c. Type **369**	25	30
2378	90 c. "Adoration of the Child and Saints"	40	45
2379	$1 "The Annunciation"	45	50
2380	$1.20 "Birth of the Virgin"	50	55
2381	$1.60, "Adoration of the Child"	70	75
2382	$1.75, "Madonna and Child"	70	75
2377/82	*Set of 6*	3·00	3·25
MS2383	Two sheets, each 76×106 mm. (a) $6 "Madonna and Child" (*different*). (b) $6 "The Circumcision" *Set of 2 sheets*	5·00	5·25

(Des J. Iskowitz. Litho Questa)

1997 (17 Feb). *Broadway Musical Stars. T 370 and similar vert designs. Multicoloured. P 13½×14.*

2384	$1 Type **370**	45	50
	a. Sheetlet. Nos. 2384/92	4·00	
2385	$1 Michael Crawford (*Phantom of the Opera*)	45	50
2386	$1 Zero Mostel (*Fiddler on the Roof*)	45	50
2387	$1 Patti Lupone (*Evita*)	45	50
2388	$1 Raul Julia (*Threepenny Opera*)	45	50
2389	$1 Mary Martin (*South Pacific*)	45	50
2390	$1 Carol Channing (*Hello Dolly*)	45	50
2391	$1 Yul Brynner (*The King and I*)	45	50
2392	$1 Julie Andrews (*My Fair Lady*)	45	50
2384/92	*Set of 9*	4·00	4·50
MS2393	106×76 mm. $6 Mickey Rooney (*Sugar Babies*)	2·50	2·75

Nos. 2384/92 were printed together, *se-tenant*, in sheetlets of 9 with the backgrounds forming a composite design.

ANTIGUA & BARBUDA 1c

371 Goofy and Wilbur

(Litho Questa)

1997 (17 Feb). *Walt Disney Cartoon Characters. T 371 and similar multicoloured designs. P 14×13½.*

2394	1 c. Type **371**	10	10
2395	2 c. Donald and Goofy in boxing ring	10	10
2396	5 c. Donald, Panchito and Jose Carioca	10	10
2397	10 c. Mickey and Goofy playing chess	10	10
2398	15 c. Chip and Dale with acorns	10	10
2399	20 c. Pluto and Mickey	10	15
2400	$1 Daisy and Minnie eating ice-cream	45	50
2401	$2 Daisy and Minnie at dressing table	85	90
2402	$3 Gus Goose and Donald	1·25	1·40
2394/402	*Set of 9*	3·00	3·25
MS2403	Two sheets. (a) 102×127 mm. $6 Goofy. P 14×13½. (b) 127×102 mm. $6 Donald Duck playing guitar (*vert*). P 13½×14 *Set of 2 sheets*	5·25	5·50

372 Charlie Chaplin as Young Man

373 *Charaxes porthos*

(Des J. Iskowitz. Litho Questa)

1997 (24 Feb). *20th Death Anniv of Charlie Chaplin (film star). T 372 and similar vert designs. Multicoloured. P 13½×14.*

2404	$1 Type **372**	45	50
	a. Sheetlet. Nos. 2404/12	4·25	
2405	$1 Pulling face	45	50
2406	$1 Looking over shoulder	45	50
2407	$1 In cap	45	50

2408	$1 In front of star	45	50
2409	$1 In *The Great Dictator*	45	50
2410	$1 With movie camera and megaphone	45	50
2411	$1 Standing in front of camera lens	45	50
2412	$1 Putting on make-up	45	50
2404/12	*Set of 9*	4·25	4·50
MS2413	76×106 mm. $6 Charlie Chaplin	2·50	2·75

Nos. 2404/12 were printed together, *se-tenant*, in sheetlets of 9 with the backgrounds forming a composite design.

(Des T. Wood. Litho Questa)

1997 (10 Mar). *Butterflies. T 373 and similar multicoloured designs. P 14.*

2414	90 c. Type **373**	40	45
2415	$1.10, *Charaxes protoclea protoclea*	50	55
	a. Sheetlet. Nos. 2415/23	4·50	
2416	$1.10, *Byblia ilithyia*	50	55
2417	$1.10, Black-headed Bush Shrike ("Tchagra") (bird)	50	55
2418	$1.10, *Charaxes nobilis*	50	55
2419	$1.10, *Pseudacraea boisduvali trimeni*	50	55
2420	$1.10, *Charaxes smaragdalis*	50	55
2421	$1.10, *Charaxes lasti*	50	55
2422	$1.10, *Pseudacrea poggei*	50	55
2423	$1.10, *Graphium colonna*	50	55
2424	$1.10, Carmine Bee Eater (bird)	50	55
	a. Sheetlet. Nos. 2424/32	4·50	
2425	$1.10, *Pseudacraea eurytus*	50	55
2426	$1.10, *Hypolimnas monteironis*	50	55
2427	$1.10, *Charaxes anticlea*	50	55
2428	$1.10, *Graphium leonidas*	50	55
2429	$1.10, *Graphium illyris*	50	55
2430	$1.10, *Nephronia argia*	50	55
2431	$1.10, *Graphium policenes*	50	55
2432	$1.10, *Papilio dardanus*	50	55
2433	$1.20, *Aethiopana honorius*	50	55
2434	$1.60, *Charaxes hadrianus*	70	75
2435	$1.75, *Precis westermanni*	70	75
2414/35	*Set of 22*	11·50	12·50
MS2436	Three sheets, each 106×76 mm. (a) $6 *Charaxes lactitinctus* (*horiz*). (b) $6 *Eupheadra neophron*. (c) $6 *Euxanthe tiberius* (*horiz*) *Set of 3 sheets*	7·50	7·50

Nos. 2415/23 and 2424/32 were each printed together, *se-tenant*, in sheetlets of 9 with the backgrounds forming composite designs.

No. 2430 is inscribed "Nepheronia argia" in error.

374 Convent of the Companions of Jesus, Morelia, Mexico

(Des M. Freedman and Dena Rubin. Litho Questa)

1997 (10 Apr). *50th Anniv of U.N.E.S.C.O. T 374 and similar multicoloured designs. P 14×13½ (horiz) or 13½×14 (vert).*

2437	60 c. Type **374**	25	30
2438	90 c. Fortress at San Lorenzo, Panama (*vert*)	40	45
2439	$1 Canaima National Park, Venezuela (*vert*)	45	50
2440	$1.10, Aerial view of church with tower, Guanajuato, Mexico (*vert*)	50	55
	a. Sheetlet. Nos. 2440/7 and central label	4·00	
2441	$1.10, Church facade, Guanajuato, Mexico (*vert*)	50	55
2442	$1.10, Aerial view of churches with domes, Guanajuato, Mexico (*vert*)	50	55
2443	$1.10, Jesuit Missions of the Chiquitos, Bolivia (*vert*)	50	55
2444	$1.10, Huascaran National Park, Peru (*vert*)	50	55
2445	$1.10, Jesuit Missions of La Santisima, Paraguay (*vert*)	50	55
2446	$1.10, Cartagena, Colombia (*vert*)	50	55
2447	$1.10, Fortification, Havana, Cuba (*vert*)	50	55
2448	$1.20, As No. 2444 (*vert*)	50	55
2449	$1.60, Church of San Francisco, Guatemala (*vert*)	70	75
2450	$1.65, Tikal National Park, Guatemala	70	75
	a. Sheetlet. Nos. 2450/4 and label	3·50	
2451	$1.65, Rio Platano Reserve, Honduras	70	75
2452	$1.65, Ruins of Copan, Honduras	70	75
2453	$1.65, Antigua ruins, Guatemala	70	75
2454	$1.65, Teotihuacan, Mexico	70	75
2455	$1.75, Santo Domingo, Dominican Republic (*vert*)	70	75
2437/55	*Set of 19*	9·75	10·00
MS2456	Two sheets, each 127×102 mm. (a) $6 Tikal National Park, Guatemala. (b) $6 Teotihuacan pyramid, Mexico *Set of 2 sheets*	5·00	5·25

Nos. 2440/7 and 2450/4 were each printed, *se-tenant*, in sheetlets of 8 and 5 with a label.

No. 2446 is inscribed "Columbia" in error.

OMNIBUS ISSUES

Details, together with prices for complete sets, of the various Omnibus issues from the 1935 Silver Jubilee series to date are included in a special section following Zimbabwe at the end of Volume 2.

375 Red Bishop   **376** Child's Face and U.N.E.S.C.O. Emblem

1997 (24 Apr). *Endangered Species. T* **375** *and similar vert designs. Multicoloured. Litho. P* 14.

2457	$1.20, Type **375**	50	55
	a. Sheetlet. Nos. 2457/62	3·00	
2458	$1.20, Yellow Baboon	50	55
2459	$1.20, Superb Starling	50	55
2460	$1.20, Ratel	50	55
2461	$1.20, Hunting Dog	50	55
2462	$1.20, Serval	50	55
2463	$1.65, Okapi	70	75
	a. Sheetlet. Nos. 2463/8	4·00	
2464	$1.65, Giant Forest Squirrel	70	75
2465	$1.65, Lesser Masked Weaver	70	75
2466	$1.65, Small-spotted Genet	70	75
2467	$1.65, Yellow-billed Stork	70	75
2468	$1.65, Red-headed Agama	70	75
2457/68	*Set of 12*	7·00	7·75

MS2469 Three sheets, each 106×76 mm. (a) $6 South African Crowned Crane. (b) $6 Bat-eared Fox. (c) $6 Malachite Kingfisher *Set of 3 sheets* 7·50 7·75

Nos. 2457/62 and 2463/8 were each printed together, *se-tenant*, in sheetlets of 6 with the backgrounds forming composite designs.

(Litho Questa)

1997 (12 June). *10th Anniv of Chernobyl Nuclear Disaster. T* **376** *and similar vert design. Multicoloured. P* 13½.

2470	$1.65, Type **376**	70	75
2471	$2 As Type **376**, but inscribed "CHABAD'S CHILDREN OF CHERNOBYL" at foot	85	90

377 Paul Harris and James Grant

(Des J. Iskowitz, Litho Questa)

1997 (12 June). *50th Death Anniv of Paul Harris (founder of Rotary International). T* **377** *and similar horiz design. Multicoloured. P* 14.

2472	$1.75, Type **377**	70	75

MS2473 78×107 mm. $6 Group study exchange, New Zealand .. 2·50 2·75

378 Queen Elizabeth II

(Litho Questa)

1997 (12 June). *Golden Wedding of Queen Elizabeth and Prince Philip. T* **378** *and similar horiz designs. Multicoloured. P* 14.

2474	$1 Type **378**	45	50
	a. Sheetlet. Nos. 2474/9	2·75	
2475	$1 Royal coat of arms	45	50
2476	$1 Queen Elizabeth and Prince Philip at reception	45	50
2477	$1 Queen Elizabeth and Prince Philip in landau	45	50
2478	$1 Balmoral	45	50
2479	$1 Prince Philip	45	50
2474/9	*Set of 6*	2·75	3·00

MS2480 100×71 mm. $6 Queen Elizabeth with Prince Philip in naval uniform .. 2·50 2·75

Nos. 2474/9 were printed together, *se-tenant*, in sheetlets of 6.

PRICES OF SETS

Set prices are given for many issues, generally those containing three stamps or more. Definitive sets include one of each value or major colour change, but do not cover different perforations, die types or minor shades. Where a choice is possible the set prices are based on the cheapest versions of the stamps included in the listings.

379 Kaiser Wilhelm I and Heinrich von Stephan   **380** The Ugly Sisters and their Mother

(Des J. Iskowitz. Litho Questa)

1997 (12 June). *"Pacific '97" International Stamp Exhibition, San Francisco. Death Centenary of Heinrich von Stephan (founder of the U.P.U.). T* **379** *and similar horiz designs. P* 14.

2481	$1.75, dull blue	70	75
	a. Sheetlet. Nos. 2481/3	2·10	
2482	$1.75, chestnut	70	75
2483	$1.75, deep magenta	70	75
2481/3	*Set of 3*	2·10	2·25

MS2484 82×119 mm. $6 black and violet 2·50 2·75

Designs: No. 2481, Type **379**; No. 2482, Von Stephan and Mercury; No. 2483, Carrier pigeon and loft; No. **MS**2484, Von Stephan and 15th-century Basle messenger.

Nos. 2481/3 were printed together, *se-tenant*, in sheetlets of 3 with enlarged right-hand margin.

(Des R. Sauber. Litho Questa)

1997 (12 June). *175th Anniv of Brothers Grimm's Third Collection of Fairy Tales. Cinderella. T* **380** *and similar vert designs. Multicoloured. P* 13½×14.

2485	$1.75, Type **380**	70	75
	a. Sheetlet. Nos. 2485/7	2·10	
2486	$1.75, Cinderella and her Fairy Godmother	70	75
2487	$1.75, Cinderella and the Prince	70	75
2485/7	*Set of 3*	2·10	2·25

MS2488 124×96 mm. $6 Cinderella trying on slipper .. 2·50 2·75

Nos. 2485/7 were printed together, *se-tenant*, in sheetlets of 3 with illustrated margins.

381 *Marasmius rotula*   **382** *Odontoglossum cervantesii*

(Des D. Burkhart, Litho Questa)

1997 (12 Aug). *Fungi. T* **381** *and similar horiz designs. Multicoloured. P* 14.

2489	45 c. Type **381**	20	25
2490	65 c. *Cantharellus cibarius*	30	35
2491	70 c. *Lepiota cristata*	30	35
2492	90 c. *Auricularia mesenterica*	40	45
2493	$1 *Pholiota alnicola*	45	50
2494	$1.65, *Leccinum aurantiacum*	70	75
2495	$1.75, *Entoloma serrulatum*	70	75
	a. Sheetlet. Nos. 2495/2500	4·00	
2496	$1.75, *Panaeolus sphinctrinus*	70	75
2497	$1.75, *Volvariella bombycina*	70	75
2498	$1.75, *Conocybe percincta*	70	75
2499	$1.75, *Pluteus cervinus*	70	75
2500	$1.75, *Russula foetens*	70	75
2489/2500	*Set of 12*	6·50	7·00

MS2501 Two sheets, each 106×76 mm. (a) $6 *Amanita cothurnata*. (b) $6 *Panellus serotinus* *Set of 2 sheets* 5·00 5·25

Nos. 2495/2500 were printed together, *se-tenant*, in sheetlets of 6.

(Des T. Wood. Litho Questa)

1997 (19 Aug). *Orchids of the World. T* **382** *and similar vert designs. Multicoloured. P* 14.

2502	45 c. Type **382**	20	25
2503	65 c. *Phalaenopsis* Medford Star	30	35
2504	75 c. *Vanda* Motes Resplendent	35	40
2505	90 c. *Odontonia* Debutante	40	45
2506	$1 *Iwanagaara* Apple Blossom	45	50
2507	$1.65, *Cattleya* Sophia Martin	70	75
	a. Sheetlet. Nos. 2507/14	5·50	
2508	$1.65, Dogface Butterfly	70	75
2509	$1.65, *Laeliocattleya* Mini Purple	70	75
2510	$1.65, *Cymbidium* Showgirl	70	75
2511	$1.65, *Brassolaeliocattleya* Dorothy Bertsch	70	75
2512	$1.65, *Disa blackii*	70	75
2513	$1.65, *Paphiopedilum leeanum*	70	75
2514	$1.65, *Paphiopedilum macranthum*	70	75
2515	$1.65, *Brassocattleya* Angel Lace	70	75
	a. Sheetlet. Nos. 2515/22	5·50	
2516	$1.65, *Saphrolae liocattleya* Precious Stones	70	75
2517	$1.65, Orange Theope Butterfly	70	75
2518	$1.65, *Promenaea xanthina*	70	75
2519	$1.65, *Lycasle macrobulbon*	70	75
2520	$1.65, *Amestella philippinensis*	70	75
2521	$1.65, *Masdevallia* Machu Picchu	70	75
2522	$1.65, *Phalaenopsis* Zuma Urchin	70	75
2523	$2 *Dendrobium victoria-reginae*	85	90
2502/23	*Set of 22*	13·50	14·50

MS2524 Two sheets, each 76×106 mm. (a) $6 *Miltonia* Seine. (b) $6 *Paphiopedilum gratrixanum* *Set of 2 sheets* 5·50 5·75

Nos. 2507/14 and 2515/22 were each printed together, *se-tenant*, in sheetlets of 8 with the backgrounds forming composite designs.

383 Maradona holding World Cup Trophy, 1986

(Litho Questa)

1997 (16 Oct). *World Cup Football Championship, France (1998). T* **383** *and multicoloured designs. P* 14×13½.

2525	60 c. multicoloured	25	30
2526	75 c. agate	35	40
2527	90 c. multicoloured	40	45
2528	$1 agate	45	50
	a. Sheetlet. Nos. 2528/35 and central label	3·50	
2529	$1 agate	45	50
2530	$1 agate	45	50
2531	$1 grey-black	45	50
2532	$1 agate	45	50
2533	$1 agate	45	50
2534	$1 agate	45	50
2535	$1 agate	45	50
2536	$1.20, multicoloured	50	55
2537	$1.65, multicoloured	70	75
2538	$1.75, multicoloured	70	75
2525/38	*Set of 14*	6·25	7·25

MS2539 Two sheets, each 102×127 mm. $6 multicoloured. P 13½×14. (b) $6 multicoloured. P 14×13½ *Set of 2 sheets* 5·00 5·25

Designs: *Horiz*—No. 2526, Fritzwalter, West Germany, 1954; No. 2527, Zoff, Italy, 1982; No. 2536, Moore, England, 1966; No. 2537, Alberto, Brazil, 1970; No. 2538, Matthaus, West Germany, 1990; No. **MS**2539(b), West German players celebrating, 1990. *Vert*—No. 2528, Ademir, Brazil, 1950; No. 2529, Eusebio, Portugal, 1966; No. 2530, Fontaine, France, 1958; No. 2531, Schillaci, Italy, 1990; No. 2532, Leonidas, Brazil, 1938; No. 2533, Stabile, Argentina, 1930; No. 2534, Nejedly, Czechoslovakia, 1934; No. 2535, Muller, West Germany, 1970; No. **MS**2539(a), Bebto, Brazil.

Nos. 2528/35 were printed together, *se-tenant*, in sheetlets of 8 stamps and a central label.

384 Scottish Fold Kitten

(Des R. Martin. Litho Questa)

1997 (27 Oct). *Cats and Dogs. T* **384** *and similar multicoloured designs. P* 14.

2540	$1.65, Type **384**	70	75
	a. Sheetlet. Nos. 2540/5	4·00	
2541	$1.65, Japanese Bobtail	70	75
2542	$1.65, Tabby Manx	70	75
2543	$1.65, Bicolor American Shorthair	70	75
2544	$1.65, Sorrel Abyssinian	70	75
2545	$1.65, Himalayan Blue Point	70	75
2546	$1.65, Dachshund	70	75
	a. Sheetlet. Nos. 2546/51	4·00	
2547	$1.65, Staffordshire Terrier	70	75
2548	$1.65, Shar-pei	70	75
2549	$1.65, Beagle	70	75
2550	$1.65, Norfolk Terrier	70	75
2551	$1.65, Golden Retriever	70	75
2540/51	*Set of 12*	8·00	8·50

MS2552 Two sheets, each 107×77 mm. (a) $6 Red Tabby (*vert*). (b) $6 Siberian Husky (*vert*) *Set of 2 sheets* 5·00 5·25

Nos. 2540/5 and 2546/51 were each printed together, *se-tenant*, in sheetlets of 6.

385 Original Drawing by Richard Trevithick, 1803

1997 (10 Nov). *Railway Locomotives of the World. T* **385** *and similar horiz designs. Each blackish brown. Litho. P* 14.

2553	$1.65, Type **385**		70	75
	a. Sheetlet. Nos. 2553/8		4·00	
2554	$1.65, William Hedley's *Puffing Billy*, (1813–14)		70	75
2555	$1.65, Crampton locomotive of French Nord Railway, 1858		70	75
2556	$1.65, Lawrence Machine Shop locomotive, U.S.A., 1860		70	75
2557	$1.65, Natchez and Hamburg Railway steam locomotive *Mississippi*, U.S.A., 1834		70	75
2558	$1.65, Bury "Coppernob" locomotive, Furness Railway, 1846		70	75
2559	$1.65, David Joy's *Jenny Lind*, 1847		70	75
	a. Sheetlet. Nos. 2559/64		4·00	
2560	$1.65, Schenectady Atlantic locomotive, U.S.A., 1899		70	75
2561	$1.65, Kitson Class 1800 tank locomotive, Japan, 1881		70	75
2562	$1.65, Pennsylvania Railroad express freight		70	75
2563	$1.65, Karl Golsdorf's 4 cylinder locomotive, Austria		70	75
2564	$1.65, Series "E" locomotive, Russia, 1930		70	75
2553/64		*Set of* 12	8·00	8·50

MS2565 Two sheets, each 72×100 mm. (a) $6 George Stephenson "Patentee" type locomotive, 1843. (b) $6 Brunel's trestle bridge over River Lynher, Cornwall .. *Set of* 2 *sheets* 5·00 5·25
Nos. 2553/8 and 2559/64 were each printed together, *se-tenant*, in sheetlets of 6.
No. 2554 is dated "1860" in error.

386 "The Angel leaving Tobias and his Family" (Rembrandt)   **387** Diana, Princess of Wales

(Litho B.D.T.)

1997 (2 Dec). *Christmas. Religious Paintings. T* **386** *and similar multicoloured designs. P* 14.

2566	15 c. Type **386**		10	10
2567	25 c. "The Resurrection" (Martin Knoller)		10	15
2568	60 c. "Astronomy" (Raphael)		25	30
2569	75 c. "Music-making Angel" (Melozzo da Forli)		35	40
2570	90 c. "Amor" (Parmigianino)		40	45
2571	$1.20, "Madonna and Child with Saints" (Rosso Fiorentino)		50	55
2566/71		*Set of* 6	1·60	2·10

MS2572 Two sheets, each 105×96 mm. (a) $6 "The Wedding of Tobias" (Gianantonio and Francesco Guardi) (*horiz*). (b) $6 "The Portinari Altarpiece" (Hugo van der Goes) (*horiz*)
Set of 2 *sheets* 5·00 5·25

(Litho Questa)

1998 (19 Jan). *Diana, Princess of Wales Commemoration. T* **387** *and similar vert designs. Multicoloured (except Nos. 2574, 2581/2 and* **MS**2585b*). P* 14.

2573	$1.65, Type **387**		70	75
	a. Sheetlet. Nos. 2573/8		4·00	
2574	$1.65, Wearing hoop earrings (rose-carm and black)		70	75
2575	$1.65, Carrying bouquet		70	75
2576	$1.65, Wearing floral hat		70	75
2577	$1.65, With Prince Harry		70	75
2578	$1.65, Wearing white jacket		70	75
2579	$1.65, In kitchen		70	75
	a. Sheetlet. Nos. 2579/84		4·00	
2580	$1.65, Wearing black and white dress		70	75
2581	$1.65, Wearing hat (orge-brown & black)		70	75
2582	$1.65, Wearing floral print dress (lake-brown and black)		70	75
2583	$1.65, Dancing with John Travolta		70	75
2584	$1.65, Wearing white hat and jacket		70	75
2573/84		*Set of* 12	8·00	8·50

MS2585 Two sheets, each 70×100 mm. (a) $6 Wearing red jumper. (b) $6 Wearing black dress for papal audience (lake-brown and black)
Set of 2 *sheets* 5·00 5·25
Nos. 2573/8 and 2579/84 were each printed together, *se-tenant*, in sheetlets of 6.

388 Yellow Damselfish

(Litho B.D.T.)

1998 (19 Feb). *Fishes. T* **388** *and similar horiz designs. Multicoloured. P* 14.

2586	75 c. Type **388**		35	40
2587	90 c. Barred Hamlet		40	45
2588	$1 Yellow-tailed Damselfish ("Jewelfish")		45	50
2589	$1.20, Blue-headed Wrasse		50	55
2590	$1.50, Queen Angelfish		65	70
2591	$1.65, Jackknife-fish		70	75
	a. Sheetlet. Nos. 2591/6		4·00	
2592	$1.65, Spot-finned Hogfish		70	75
2593	$1.65, Sergeant Major		70	75
2594	$1.65, Neon Goby		70	75
2595	$1.65, Jawfish		70	75
2596	$1.65, Flamefish		70	75
2597	$1.65, Rock Beauty		70	75
	a. Sheetlet. Nos. 2597/602		4·00	
2598	$1.65, Yellow-tailed Snapper		70	75
2599	$1.65, Creole Wrasse		70	75
2600	$1.65, Slender Filefish		70	75
2601	$1.65, Long-spined Squirrelfish		70	75
2602	$1.65, Royal Gramma ("Fairy Basslet")		70	75
2603	$1.75, Queen Triggerfish		75	80
2586/2603		*Set of* 18	11·50	12·00

MS2604 Two sheets, each 80×110 mm. (a) $6 Porkfish. (b) $6 Black-capped Basslet
Set of 2 *sheets* 5·25 5·50
Nos. 2591/6 and 2597/2602 were each printed together, *se-tenant*, in sheetlets of 6 with the backgrounds forming composite designs.

389 First Church and Manse, 1822–40   **390** Europa Point Lighthouse, Gibraltar

(Litho B.D.T.)

1998 (16 Mar). *175th Anniv of Cedar Hall Moravian Church. T* **389** *and similar horiz designs. Multicoloured. P* 14.

2605	20 c. Type **389**		15	20
2606	45 c. Cedar Hall School, 1840		20	25
2607	75 c. Hugh A. King, minister 1945–53		35	40
2608	90 c. Present Church building		40	45
2609	$1.20, Water tank, 1822		50	55
2610	$2 Former Manse, demolished 1978		85	90
2605/10		*Set of* 6	2·40	2·50

MS2611 100×70 mm. $6 Present church building (*different*) (50×37 *mm*) .. 2·50 2·75

(Des M. Friedman. Litho Questa)

1998 (20 Apr). *Lighthouses of the World. T* **390** *and similar multicoloured designs. P* 14.

2612	45 c. Type **390**		20	25
2613	65 c. Tierra del Fuego, Argentina (*horiz*)		30	35
2614	75 c. Point Loma, California, U.S.A. (*horiz*)		35	40
2615	90 c. Groenpoint, Cape Town, South Africa		40	45
2616	$1 Youghal, Cork, Ireland		45	50
2617	$1.20, Launceston, Tasmania, Australia		50	55
2618	$1.65, Point Abino, Ontario, Canada (*horiz*)		70	75
2619	$1.75, Great Inagua, Bahamas		75	80
2612/19		*Set of* 8	3·50	4·00

MS2620 99×70 mm. $6 Cape Hatteras, North Carolina, U.S.A. .. 2·50 2·75
No. 2613 is inscribed "Terra Del Fuego" in error.

391 Pooh and Tigger (January)   **392** Miss Nellie Robinson (founder)

(Des Walt Disney Co. Litho)

1998 (11 May). *Through the Year with Winnie the Pooh. T* **391** *and similar vert designs. Multicoloured. P* 13½×14.

2621	$1 Type **391**		45	50
	a. Sheetlet. Nos. 2621/6		2·75	
2622	$1 Pooh and Piglet indoors (February)		45	50
2623	$1 Piglet hang-gliding with scarf (March)		45	50
2624	$1 Tigger, Pooh and Piglet on pond (April)		45	50
2625	$1 Kanga and Roo with posy of flowers (May)		45	50
2626	$1 Pooh on balloon and Owl (June)		45	50
2627	$1 Pooh, Eeyore, Tigger and Piglet gazing at stars (July)		45	50
	a. Sheetlet. Nos. 2627/32		2·75	
2628	$1 Pooh and Piglet by stream (August)		45	50
2629	$1 Christopher Robin going to school (September)		45	50

2630	$1 Eeyore in fallen leaves (October)		45	50
2631	$1 Pooh and Rabbit gathering pumpkins (November)		45	50
2632	$1 Pooh and Piglet skiing (December)		45	50
2621/32		*Set of* 12	5·25	5·75

MS2633 Four sheets, each 126×101 mm. (a) $6 Pooh, Rabbit and Piglet with blanket (Spring). (b) $6 Pooh by pond (Summer). (c) $6 Pooh sweeping fallen leaves (Autumn). (d) $6 Pooh and Eeyore on ice (Winter) .. *Set of* 4 *sheets* 8·75 9·00
Nos. 2621/6 and 2627/32 were each printed together, *se-tenant*, in sheetlets of 6.

(Des M. Friedman. Litho B.D.T.)

1998 (23 July). *Centenary of Thomas Oliver Robinson Memorial School. T* **392** *and similar designs. P* 14.

2634	20 c. brown-olive and black		10	15
2635	45 c. multicoloured		20	25
2636	65 c. brown-olive and black		30	35
2637	75 c. multicoloured		35	40
2638	90 c. multicoloured		40	45
2639	$1.20, red-brown, brown-olive and black		50	55
2634/9		*Set of* 6	1·75	2·10

MS2640 106×76 mm. $6 olive-brown .. 2·50 2·75
Designs: *Horiz*—45 c. School photo, 1985: 65 c. Former school building, 1930–49: 75 c. Children with Mrs. Natalie Hurst (present headmistress): $1.20, Present school building, 1950. *Vert*—90 c. Miss Ina Loving (former teacher); $6 Miss Nellie Robinson (*different*).

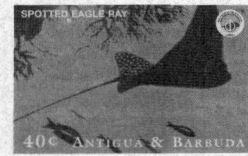

393 Spotted Eagle Ray

(Des B. Steadman (Nos. 2641/65 and **MS**2678a), R. Martin (others). Litho Questa)

1998 (17 Aug). *International Year of the Ocean. T* **393** *and similar horiz designs. Multicoloured. P* 14.
2641/65 40 c. × 25 Type **393**: Manta Ray: Hawks-bill Turtle; Jellyfish; Queen Angel-fish; Octopus; Emperor Angelfish; Regal Angelfish; Porkfish; Racoon Butterflyfish; Atlantic Barracuda; Sea Horse; Nautilus; Trumpetfish; White Tip Shark; Sunken Spanish galleon; Black Tip Shark; Long-nosed Butterflyfish; Green Moray Eel; Captain Nemo; Treasure chest; Hammerhead Shark; Divers; Lion-fish; Clown Fish
  a. Sheetlet. Nos. 2641/65 .. 3·75
2666/77 75 c. × 12 Maroon-tailed Conure; Cocoi Heron; Common Tern; Rainbow Lorikeet; Saddleback Butterflyfish; Goatfish and Cat Shark; Blue Shark and Stingray; Majestic Snapper; Nassau Grouper; Black-cap Gramma and Blue Tang; Stingrays; Stingrays and Giant Starfish
  a. Sheetlet. Nos. 2666/77 .. 4·25
2641/77 .. *Set of* 37 8·00 8·25
MS2678 Two sheets. (a) 68×98 mm. $6 Humpback Whale. (b) 98×68 mm. $6 Fiddler Ray .. *Set of* 2 *sheets* 5·00 5·25
Nos. 2641/65 and 2666/77 were each printed together, *se-tenant*, in sheetlets of 25 or 12, with the backgrounds forming composite designs.

394 *Savannah* (paddle-steamer)   **395** Flags of Antigua and CARICOM

(Des L. Schwinger. Litho Questa)

1998 (18 Aug). *Ships of the World. T* **394** *and similar multicoloured designs. P* 14½.

2679	$1.75, Type **394**		75	80
	a. Sheetlet. Nos. 2679/81		2·25	
2680	$1.75, Viking longship		75	80
2681	$1.75, Greek galley		75	80
2682	$1.75, Sailing clipper		75	80
	a. Sheetlet. Nos. 2682/4		2·25	
2683	$1.75, Dhow		75	80
2684	$1.75, Fishing catboat		75	80
2679/84		*Set of* 6	4·50	4·75

MS2685 Three sheets, each 100×70 mm. (a) $6 13th-century English warship (41×22 *mm*). (b) $6 Sailing dory (22×41 *mm*). (c) $6 Baltimore clipper (41×22 *mm*). P 14 .. *Set of* 3 *sheets* 7·50 7·75
Nos. 2679/81 and 2682/4 were printed together, *se-tenant*, in sheetlets of 3 with enlarged illustrated left-hand margins.

(Des R. Sauber. Litho Cartor)

1998 (20 Aug). *25th Anniv of Caribbean Community. P* 13½.
2686 **395** $1 multicoloured .. 45 50

396 Ford, 1896

1998 (1 Sept). *Classic Cars. T* **396** *and similar horiz designs. Multicoloured. Litho. P* 14.

2687	$1.65, Type **396**	70	75
	a. Sheetlet. Nos. 2687/92	4·00	
2688	$1.65, Ford A, 1903	70	75
2689	$1.65, Ford T, 1928	70	75
2690	$1.65, Ford T, 1922	70	75
2691	$1.65, Ford Blackhawk, 1929	70	75
2692	$1.65, Ford Sedan, 1934	70	75
2693	$1.65, Torpedo, 1911	70	75
	a. Sheetlet. Nos. 2693/8	4·00	
2694	$1.65, Mercedes 22, 1913	70	75
2695	$1.65, Rover, 1920	70	75
2696	$1.65, Mercedes-Benz, 1956	70	75
2697	$1.65, Packard V-12, 1934	70	75
2698	$1.65, Opel, 1924	70	75
2687/98	*Set of 12*	8·00	9·00

MS2699 Two sheets, each 70×100 mm. (a) $6 Ford, 1908 (60×40 mm). (b) $6 Ford, 1929 (60×40 mm). P 14×14½ *Set of 2 sheets* 5·00 5·25
Nos. 2687/92 and 2693/8 were each printed together, *se-tenant*, in sheetlets of 6.

397 Lockheed-Boeing General Dynamics Yf-22

398 Karl Benz (internal-combustion engine)

(Des E. Nisbet. Litho Questa)

1998 (22 Sept). *Modern Aircraft. T* **397** *and similar horiz designs. Multicoloured. P* 14.

2700	$1.65, Type **397**	70	75
	a. Sheetlet. Nos. 2700/5	4·00	
2701	$1.65, Dassault-Breguet Rafale BO 1	70	75
2702	$1.65, MiG 29	70	75
2703	$1.65, Dassault-Breguet Mirage 2000D	70	75
2704	$1.65, Rockwell B-1B "Lancer"	70	75
2705	$1.65, McDonnell-Douglas C-17A	70	75
2706	$1.65, Space Shuttle	70	75
	a. Sheetlet. Nos. 2706/11	4·00	
2707	$1.65, SAAB "Grippen"	70	75
2708	$1.65, Eurofighter EF-2000	70	75
2709	$1.65, Sukhoi SU 27	70	75
2710	$1.65, Northrop B-2	70	75
2711	$1.65, Lockheed F-117 "Nighthawk"	70	75
2700/11	*Set of 12*	8·00	9·00

MS2712 Two sheets, each 110×85 mm. (a) $6 F18 Hornet. (b) $6 Sukhoi SU 35 *Set of 2 sheets* 5·00 5·25
Nos. 2700/5 and 2706/11 were each printed together, *se-tenant*, in sheetlets of 6.
No. **MS**2712b is inscribed "Sukhi" in error.

1998 (10 Nov). *Millennium Series. Famous People of the Twentieth Century. Inventors. T* **398** *and similar multicoloured designs. Litho. P* 14.

2713	$1 Type **398**	45	50
	a. Sheetlet. Nos. 2713/20	3·50	
2714	$1 Early Benz car and Mercedes-Benz racing car (53×38 *mm*)	45	50
2715	$1 Atom bomb mushroom cloud (53×38 *mm*)	45	50
2716	$1 Albert Einstein (theory of relativity)	45	50
2717	$1 Leopold Godowsky Jr. and Leopold Damrosch Mannes (Kodachrome film)	45	50
2718	$1 Camera and transparencies (53×38 *mm*)	45	50
2719	$1 Heinkel He 178 (first turbo jet plane) (53×38 *mm*)	45	50
2720	$1 Dr. Hans Pabst von Ohain (jet turbine engine)	45	50
2721	$1 Rudolf Diesel (diesel engine)	45	50
	a. Sheetlet. Nos. 2721/8	3·50	
2722	$1 Early Diesel engine and forms of transport (53×38 *mm*)	45	50
2723	$1 Zeppelin airship (53×38 *mm*)	45	50
2724	$1 Count Ferdinand von Zeppelin (airship pioneer)	45	50
2725	$1 Wilhelm Conrad Rontgen (X-rays)	45	50
2726	$1 X-ray of hand (53×38 *mm*)	45	50
2727	$1 Launch of Saturn Rocket (53×38 *mm*)	45	50
2728	$1 Wernher von Braun (rocket research)	45	50
2713/28	*Set of 16*	7·00	8·00

MS2729 Two sheets, each 106×76 mm. (a) $6 Hans Geiger (Geiger counter). (b) $6 William Shockley (research into semi-conductors)
Set of 2 sheets 5·25 5·50
Nos. 2713/20 and 2721/8 were each printed together, *se-tenant*, in sheetlets of 8 with enlarged illustrated margins.
No. 2713 is inscribed "CARL BENZ" in error.

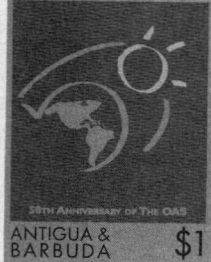

399 Stylised Americas

400 "Figures on the Seashore"

(Litho Questa)

1998 (18 Nov). *50th Anniv of Organization of American States. P* 13½×14.
2730 **399** $1 multicoloured 45 50

(Des Diana Catherines. Litho Questa)

1998 (18 Nov). *25th Death Anniv of Pablo Picasso (painter). T* **400** *and similar multicoloured designs. P* 14½.

2731	$1.20, Type **400**	50	55
2732	$1.65, "Three Figures under a Tree" (*vert*)	70	75
2733	$1.75, "Two Women running on the Beach"	75	80
2731/3	*Set of 3*	1·90	2·10

MS2734 126×102 mm. $6 "Bullfight" ... 2·50 2·75

401 Dino 246 GT-GTS

(Des F. Rivera. Litho Questa)

1998 (18 Nov). *Birth Centenary of Enzo Ferrari (car manufacturer). T* **401** *and similar horiz designs. Multicoloured. P* 14.

2735	$1.75, Type **401**	75	80
	a. Sheetlet. Nos. 2735/7	2·25	
2736	$1.75, Front view of Dino 246 GT-GTS	75	80
2737	$1.75, 365 GT4 BB	75	80
2735/7	*Set of 3*	2·25	2·40

MS2738 104×72 mm. $6 Dino 246 GT-GTS (91×34 mm). P 14×14½ 2·50 2·75
Nos. 2735/7 were printed together, *se-tenant*, in sheetlets of 3.

402 Scout Handshake

403 Mahatma Gandhi

(Des G. Bibby. Litho Questa)

1998 (18 Nov). *19th World Scout Jamboree, Chile. T* **402** *and similar horiz designs. Multicoloured. P* 14.

2739	90 c. Type **402**	40	45
2740	$1 Scouts hiking	45	50
2741	$1.20, Scout salute	50	55
2739/41	*Set of 3*	1·25	1·50

MS2742 68×98 mm. $6 Lord Baden-Powell ... 2·50 2·75

(Des M. Leboeuf. Litho Questa)

1998 (18 Nov). *50th Death Anniv of Mahatma Gandhi. T* **403** *and similar vert designs. Multicoloured. P* 14.

2743	90 c. Type **403**	40	45
2744	$1 Gandhi seated	45	50
2745	$1.20, As young man	50	55
2746	$1.65, At primary school in Rajkot, aged 7	70	75
2743/6	*Set of 4*	2·00	2·25

MS2747 100×70 mm. $6 Gandhi with staff ... 2·50 2·75

404 McDonnell Douglas Phantom F-GR1

405 Diana, Princess of Wales

(Des D. Miller. Litho Questa)

1998 (18 Nov). *80th Anniv of Royal Air Force. T* **404** *and similar horiz designs. P* 14.

2748	$1.75, Type **404**	75	80
	a. Sheetlet. Nos. 2748/51	3·00	
2749	$1.75, Two Sepecat Jaguar GR1As	75	80
2750	$1.75, Panavia Tornado F3	75	80
2751	$1.75, McDonnell Douglas Phantom F-GR2	75	80
2748/51	*Set of 4*	3·00	3·25

MS2752 Two sheets, each 90×68 mm. (a) $6 Golden Eagle (bird) and Bristol F2B Fighter. (b) $6 Hawker Hurricane and EF-2000 Eurofighter
Set of 2 sheets 5·00 5·25
Nos. 2748/51 were printed together, *se-tenant*, in sheetlets of 4 with enlarged illustrated margins.

(Litho Questa)

1998 (24 Nov). *1st Death Anniv of Diana, Princess of Wales. P* 14½×14.
2753 **405** $1.20, multicoloured ... 50 55
a. Sheetlet of 6 ... 3·00
No. 2753 was printed in sheetlets of 6 with an enlarged illustrated right margin.

406 Brown Pelican

407 Border Collie

(Litho Questa)

1998 (24 Nov). *Sea Birds of the World. T* **406** *and similar horiz designs. Multicoloured. P* 14.

2754	15 c. Type **406**	10	10
2755	25 c. Dunlin	10	15
2756	45 c. Atlantic Puffin	20	25
2757	75 c. King Eider	35	40
	a. Sheetlet. Nos. 2757/68	4·00	
2758	75 c. Inca Tern	35	40
2759	75 c. Little Auk ("Dovekie")	35	40
2760	75 c. Ross's Gull	35	40
2761	75 c. Common Noddy ("Brown Noddy")	35	40
2762	75 c. Marbled Murrelet	35	40
2763	75 c. Northern Gannet	35	40
2764	75 c. Razorbill	35	40
2765	75 c. Long-tailed Skua ("Long-tailed Jaegar")	35	40
2766	75 c. Black Guillemot	35	40
2767	75 c. Whimbrel	35	40
2768	75 c. Oystercatcher	35	40
2769	90 c. Pied Cormorant	40	45
2754/69	*Set of 16*	4·75	5·75

MS2770 Two sheets, each 100×70 mm. (a) $6 Black Skimmer. (b) $6 Wandering Albatross
Set of 2 sheets 5·00 5·25
Nos. 2757/68 were printed together, *se-tenant*, in sheetlets of 12 with the backgrounds forming a composite design.
No. 2760 is inscribed "ROSS' BULL" in error.

(Litho B.D.T.)

1998 (10 Dec). *Christmas. Dogs. T* **407** *and similar horiz designs. Multicoloured. P* 13½×14.

2771	15 c. Type **407**	10	10
2772	25 c. Dalmatian	10	15
2773	65 c. Weimaraner	30	35
2774	75 c. Scottish Terrier	35	40
2775	90 c. Long-haired Dachshund	40	45
2776	$1.20, Golden Retriever	50	55
2777	$2 Pekingese	85	90
2771/7	*Set of 7*	2·50	2·75

MS2778 Two sheets, each 75×66 mm. (a) $6 Dalmatian. (b) $6 Jack Russell Terrier
Set of 2 sheets 5·00 5·25

408 Mickey Mouse sailing

(Litho Questa)

1999 (11 Jan). *70th Birthday of Mickey Mouse. T* **408** *and similar multicoloured designs showing Walt Disney characters participating in water sports. P* 13½×14.

2779	$1 Type **408**	45	50
	a. Sheetlet. Nos. 2779/84	2·75	
2780	$1 Mickey and Goofy sailing	45	50
2781	$1 Goofy windsurfing	45	50
2782	$1 Mickey sailing and seagull	45	50
2783	$1 Goofy sailing	45	50
2784	$1 Mickey windsurfing	45	50
2785	$1 Goofy running with surfboard	45	50
	a. Sheetlet. Nos. 2785/90	2·75	
2786	$1 Mickey surfing	45	50

2787	$1 Donald Duck holding surfboard	45	50
2788	$1 Donald on surfboard (face value at right)	45	50
2789	$1 Minnie Mouse surfing in green shorts	45	50
2790	$1 Goofy surfing	45	50
2791	$1 Goofy in purple shorts waterskiing	45	50
	a. Sheetlet. Nos. 2791/6	2·75	
2792	$1 Mickey waterskiing	45	50
2793	$1 Goofy waterskiing with Mickey	45	50
2794	$1 Donald on surfboard (face value at left)	45	50
2795	$1 Goofy in yellow shorts waterskiing	45	50
2796	$1 Minnie in pink shorts surfing	45	50
2779/96	*Set of 18*	8·00	9·00

MS2797 Four sheets, each 127×102 mm. (a) $6 Goofy (*horiz*). P 14×13½. (b) $6 Donald Duck. P 13½×14. (c) $6 Minnie Mouse. P 13½×14. (d) $6 Mickey Mouse. P 13½×14 .. *Set of 4 sheets* 10·00 10·50
Nos. 2779/84, 2785/90 and 2791/6 were each printed together, *se-tenant*, in sheetlets of 6 with illustrated top margins.

409 Hell's Gate Steel Orchestra, 1996

410 Tulips

(Litho Questa)

1999 (1 Feb). *50th Anniv of Hell's Gate Steel Orchestra. T* **409** *and similar multicoloured designs.* P 14.

2798	20 c. Type 409	10	15
2799	60 c. Orchestra members, New York, 1992	25	30
2800	75 c. Orchestra members with steel drums, 1950	35	40
2801	90 c. Eustace Henry, 1964	40	45
2802	$1.20, Alston Henry playing double tenor	50	55
2798/2802	*Set of 5*	1·60	1·90

MS2803 Two sheets. (a) 100×70 mm. $4 Orchestra members, 1950 (*vert*). (b) 70×100 mm. $4 Eustace Henry, 1964 (*vert*) .. *Set of 2 sheets* 3·50 3·75

(Des S. Stines. Litho Questa)

1999 (19 Apr). *Flowers. T* **410** *and similar multicoloured designs.* P 14.

2804	60 c. Type 410	25	30
2805	75 c. Fuschia	35	40
2806	90 c. Morning Glory (*horiz*)	40	45
	a. Sheetlet. Nos. 2806/14	3·50	
2807	90 c. Geranium (*horiz*)	40	45
2808	90 c. Blue Hibiscus (*horiz*)	40	45
2809	90 c. Marigolds (*horiz*)	40	45
2810	90 c. Sunflower (*horiz*)	40	45
2811	90 c. Impatiens (*horiz*)	40	45
2812	90 c. Petunia (*horiz*)	40	45
2813	90 c. Pansy (*horiz*)	40	45
2814	90 c. Saucer Magnolia (*horiz*)	40	45
2815	$1 Primrose (*horiz*)	45	50
	a. Sheetlet. Nos. 2815/23	4·00	
2816	$1 Bleeding Heart (*horiz*)	45	50
2817	$1 Pink Dogwood (*horiz*)	45	50
2818	$1 Peony (*horiz*)	45	50
2819	$1 Rose (*horiz*)	45	50
2820	$1 Hellebores (*horiz*)	45	50
2821	$1 Lily (*horiz*)	45	50
2822	$1 Violet (*horiz*)	45	50
2823	$1 Cherry Blossom (*horiz*)	45	50
2824	$1.20, Calla Lily	50	55
2825	$1.65, Sweet Pea	70	75
2804/25	*Set of 22*	9·50	10·50

MS2826 Two sheets. (a) 76×106 mm. $6 Sangria Lily. (b) 106×76 mm. $6 Zinnias *Set of 2 sheets* 5·25 5·50
Nos. 2806/14 and 2815/23 were each printed together, *se-tenant*, in sheetlets of 9, forming composite designs

411 Elle Macpherson

412 "Luna 2" Moon Probe

1999 (26 Apr). *"Australia '99" International Stamp Exhibition, Melbourne (1st issue). Elle Macpherson (model). T* **411** *and similar vert designs. Multicoloured.* Litho. P 13½.

2827	$1.20, Type 411	50	55
	a. Sheetlet. Nos. 2827/34	4·00	
2828	$1.20, Lying on couch	50	55
2829	$1.20, In swimsuit	50	55
2830	$1.20, Looking over shoulder	50	55
2831	$1.20, Wearing cream shirt	50	55
2832	$1.20, Wearing stetson	50	55
2833	$1.20, Wearing black T-shirt	50	55
2834	$1.20, Holding tree branch	50	55
2827/34	*Set of 8*	4·00	4·50

Nos. 2827/34 were printed together, *se-tenant*, in sheetlets of 8 with enlarged illustrated margin at right.
See also Nos. 2875/93.

1999 (6 May). *Satellites and Spacecraft. T* **412** *and similar multicoloured designs.* Litho. P 14.

2835	$1.65, Type 412	70	75
	a. Sheetlet. Nos. 2835/40	4·25	
2836	$1.65, "Mariner 2" space probe	70	75
2837	$1.65, *Giotto* space probe	70	75
2838	$1.65, Rosat satellite	70	75
2839	$1.65, International Ultraviolet Explorer	70	75
2840	$1.65, *Ulysses* space probe	70	75
2841	$1.65, "Mariner 10" space probe	70	75
	a. Sheetlet. Nos. 2841/46	4·25	
2842	$1.65, "Luna 9" Moon probe	70	75
2843	$1.65, Advanced X-ray Astrophysics Facility	70	75
2844	$1.65, *Magellan* space probe	70	75
2845	$1.65, "Pioneer–Venus 2" space probe	70	75
2846	$1.65, Infra-red Astronomy Satellite	70	75
2835/46	*Set of 12*	8·50	9·00

MS2847 Two sheets, each 106×76 mm. (a) $6 "Salyut 1" space station (*horiz*). (b) $6 "MIR" space station (*horiz*) .. *Set of 2 sheets* 5·25 5·50
Nos. 2835/40 and 2841/46 were each printed together, *se-tenant*, in sheetlets of 6, with the backgrounds forming composite designs and enlarged illustrated margins at left and foot.

413 John Glenn entering "Mercury" Capsule, 1962

414 Brachiosaurus

(Des F. Rivera and Spotlight Design. Litho Questa)

1999 (6 May). *John Glenn's Return to Space. T* **413** *and similar vert designs. Multicoloured.* P 14½×14.

2848	$1.75, Type 413	80	85
	a. Sheetlet. Nos. 2848/51	3·25	
2849	$1.75, Glenn in "Mercury" mission spacesuit	80	85
2850	$1.75, Fitting helmet for "Mercury" mission	80	85
2851	$1.75, Outside pressure chamber	80	85
2848/51	*Set of 4*	3·25	3·50

Nos. 2848/51 were printed together, *se-tenant*, as a horizontal strip of 4, with the remainder of the sheetlet depicting "Mercury" and *Discovery* astronauts.

(Des Zina Saunders. Litho Questa)

1999 (25 May). *Prehistoric Animals. T* **414** *and similar multicoloured designs.* P 14.

2852	65 c. Type 414	30	35
2853	75 c. Oviraptor (*vert*)	35	40
2854	$1 Homotherium	45	50
2855	$1.10, Macrauchenia (*vert*)	50	55
2856	$1.65, Struthiomimus	75	80
	a. Sheetlet. Nos. 2856/64	6·75	
2857	$1.65, Corythosaurus	75	80
2858	$1.65, Dsungaripterus	75	80
2859	$1.65, Compsognathus	75	80
2860	$1.65, Prosaurolophus	75	80
2861	$1.65, Montanoceratops	75	80
2862	$1.65, Stegosaurus	75	80
2863	$1.65, Deinonychus	75	80
2864	$1.65, Ouranosaurus	75	80
2865	$1.65, Leptictidium	75	80
	a. Sheetlet. Nos. 2865/73	6·75	
2866	$1.65, Ictitherium	75	80
2867	$1.65, Plesictis	75	80
2868	$1.65, Hemicyon	75	80
2869	$1.65, Diacodexis	75	80
2870	$1.65, Stylinodon	75	80
2871	$1.65, Kanuites	75	80
2872	$1.65, Chriacus	75	80
2873	$1.65, Argyrolagus	75	80
2852/73	*Set of 22*	15·00	16·00

MS2874 Two sheets, each 110×85 mm. (a) $6 Eurhinodelphis. (b) $6 Pteranodon
.. *Set of 2 sheets* 5·25 5·50
Nos. 2856/64 and 2865/73 were each printed together, *se-tenant*, in sheetlets of 9, with the backgrounds forming composite designs and enlarged, inscribed margins at left.

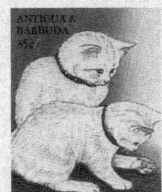

415 Two White Kittens

(Des D. Miller. Litho Questa)

1999 (25 May). *"Australia '99" International Stamp Exhibition, Melbourne (2nd issue). Cats. T* **415** *and similar vert designs. Multicoloured.* P 14½×14.

2875	35 c. Type 415	15	20
2876	45 c. Kitten with string	20	25
2877	60 c. Two kittens under blanket	25	30
2878	75 c. Two kittens in basket	35	40
2879	90 c. Kitten with ball	45	50
2880	$1 White kitten	70	75
2881	$1.65, Two kittens playing	70	75
	a. Sheetlet. Nos. 2881/6	4·25	
2882	$1.65, Black and white kitten	70	75
2883	$1.65, Black kitten and sleeping cream kitten	70	75
2884	$1.65, White kitten with green string	70	75
2885	$1.65, Two sleeping kittens	70	75
2886	$1.65, White kitten with black tip to tail	70	75
2887	$1.65, Kitten with red string	70	75
	a. Sheetlet. Nos. 2887/92	4·25	
2888	$1.65, Two long-haired kittens	70	75
2889	$1.65, Ginger kitten	70	75
2890	$1.65, Kitten playing with mouse	70	75
2891	$1.65, Kitten asleep on blue cushion	70	75
2892	$1.65, Tabby kitten	70	75
2875/92	*Set of 18*	10·00	11·00

MS2893 Two sheets, each 70×100 mm. (a) $6 Cat carrying kitten in mouth. (b) $6 Kitten in tree .. *Set of 2 sheets* 5·25 5·50
Nos. 2881/6 and 2887/92 were each printed together, *se-tenant*, in sheetlets of 6.

416 Early Leipzig–Dresden Railway Carriage and Caroline Islands 1901 Yacht Type 5 m. Stamp

(Litho Questa)

1999 (24 June). *"iBRA '99" International Stamp Exhibition, Nuremberg. T* **416** *and similar horiz designs. Multicoloured.* P 14.

2894	$1 Type 416	45	50
2895	$1.20, *Gölsdorf* steam locomotive and Caroline Islands 1901 Yacht type 1 m.	50	60
2896	$1.65, Early Leipzig–Dresden Railway carriage and Caroline Islands 1899 optd on Germany 20 pf.	70	80
2897	$1.90, *Gölsdorf* steam locomotive and Caroline Islands 1901 Yacht type 5 pf. and 20 pf.	80	85
2894/7	*Set of 4*	2·50	3·00

MS2898 165×110 mm. $6 Registration label for Ponape, Caroline Islands. P 14×14½ .. 2·50 2·75

417 "People on Balcony of Sazaido" (Hokusai)

418 Sophie Rhys-Jones

1999 (24 June). *150th Death Anniv of Katsushika Hokusai (Japanese artist). T* **417** *and similar multicoloured designs.* Litho. P 13½.

2899	$1.65, Type 417	70	75
	a. Sheetlet. Nos. 2899/904	4·25	
2900	$1.65, "Nakahara in Sagami Province"	70	75
2901	$1.65, "Defensive Positions" (two wrestlers)	70	75
2902	$1.65, "Defensive Positions" (three wrestlers)	70	75
2903	$1.65, "Mount Fuji in Clear Weather"	70	75
2904	$1.65, "Nihonbashi in Edo"	70	75
2905	$1.65, "Asakusa Honganji"	70	75
	a. Sheetlet. Nos. 2905/10	4·25	
2906	$1.65, "Dawn at Isawa in Kai Province"	70	75
2907	$1.65, "Samurai with Bow and Arrow" (with arrows on ground)	70	75
2908	$1.65, "Samurai with Bow and Arrow" (trees in background)	70	75
2909	$1.65, "Kajikazawa in Kai Province"	70	75
2910	$1.65, "A Great Wave"	70	75
2899/2910	*Set of 12*	8·50	9·00

MS2911 Two sheets, each 100×71 mm. (a) $6 "A Netsuke Workshop" (*vert*). (b) $6 "Gotenyama at Shinagawa on Tokaido Highway" (*vert*)
Set of 2 sheets 5·25 5·50
Nos. 2899/904 and 2905/10 were each printed together, *se-tenant*, in sheetlets of 6.
No. 2903 is inscribed "MOUNT FUGI" in error.

1999 (24 June). *Royal Wedding. T* **418** *and similar multicoloured designs.* Litho. P 13½.

2912	$3 Type 418	1·25	1·75
	a. Sheetlet. Nos. 2912/14	3·75	
2913	$3 Sophie and Prince Edward	1·25	1·75
2914	$3 Prince Edward	1·25	1·75
2912/14	*Set of 3*	3·75	4·00

MS2915 108×78 mm. $6 Prince Edward with Sophie Rhys-Jones and Windsor Castle (*horiz*) 2·50 2·75
Nos. 2912/14 were printed together, *se-tenant*, in sheetlets of 3 with enlarged illustrated margins.

419 Three Children

420 Crampton Type Railway Locomotive, 1855–69

1999 (24 June). *10th Anniv of United Nations Rights of the Child Convention. T* **419** *and similar vert designs. Multicoloured. Litho.* P 14.
2916	$3 Type **419**	1·25	1·75
	a. Sheetlet. Nos. 2916/18	3·75	
2917	$3 Adult hand holding child's hand	1·25	1·75
2918	$3 Dove and U.N. Headquarters	1·25	1·75
2916/18	*Set of 3*	3·75	4·00
MS2919	112×70 mm. $6 Dove	2·50	2·75

Nos. 2916/18 were printed together, *se-tenant*, in sheetlets of 3, forming a composite design.

1999 (24 June). *"PhilexFrance '99" International Stamp Exhibition, Paris. Railway Locomotives. Two sheets, each 106×81 mm, containing T* **420** *and similar design. Multicoloured. Litho.* P 14×13½.
MS2920	(a) $6 Type **420**. (b) $6 Compound type No. 232-U1 steam locomotive, 1949		
	Set of 2 sheets	5·25	5·50

421 Three Archangels from *Faust*

422 *Missa Ferdie* (fishing launch)

1999 (24 June). *250th Birth Anniv of Johann von Goethe (German writer). T* **421** *and similar designs. Litho.* P 14.
2921	$1.75, purple, bright magenta and black	80	85
	a. Sheetlet. Nos. 2921/3	2·40	
2922	$1.75, dull ultramarine, bluish violet & blk	80	85
2923	$1.75, light green and black	80	85
2921/3	*Set of 3*	2·40	2·50
MS2924	79×107 mm. $6 black & reddish brown	2·50	2·75

Designs: *Horiz*—No. 2921, Type **421**; No. 2922, Von Goethe and Von Schiller; No. 2923, Faust reclining with spirits. *Vert*—No. MS2924, Wolfgang von Goethe

Nos. 2921/3 were printed together, *se-tenant*, in sheetlets of 3 with enlarged illustrated margins.

(Litho Questa)

1999 (24 June). *Local Ships and Boats. T* **422** *and similar horiz designs. Multicoloured.* P 13×11.
2925	25 c. Type **422**	10	15
	a. Sheetlet. Nos. 2925/9	1·40	
2926	45 c. Yachts in 32nd Annual Antigua International Sailing Week	20	25
2927	60 c. *Jolly Roger* (tourist ship)	25	30
2928	90 c. *Freewinds* (cruise liner) (10th anniv of first visit)	40	45
2929	$1.20, *Monarch of the Seas* (cruise liner)	50	60
2925/9	*Set of 5*	1·40	1·50
MS2930	98×62 mm. $4 *Freewinds* (11th anniv of maiden voyage) (50×37 mm). P 14	1·75	2·10

Nos. 2925/9 were either printed together, *se-tenant*, in sheetlets of 5 or as larger sheets of one value with the stamps in rows divided by horizontal gutters carrying inscriptions.

423 Fiery Jewel (butterfly)

424 "Madonna and Child in Wreath of Flowers" (Rubens)

(Litho B.D.T.)

1999 (16 Aug). *Butterflies. T* **423** *and similar multicoloured designs.* P 14.
2931	65 c. Type **423**	30	35
2932	75 c. Hewitson's Blue Hairstreak	35	40
2933	$1 California Dog Face (*horiz*)	45	50
	a. Sheetlet. Nos. 2933/41	4·00	

2934	$1 Small Copper (*horiz*)	45	50
2935	$1 Zebra Swallowtail (*horiz*)	45	50
2936	$1 White "M" Hairstreak (*horiz*)	45	50
2937	$1 Old World Swallowtail (*horiz*)	45	50
2938	$1 Buckeye (*horiz*)	45	50
2939	$1 Apollo (*horiz*)	45	50
2940	$1 Sonoran Blue (*horiz*)	45	50
2941	$1 Purple Emperor (*horiz*)	45	50
2942	$1.20, Scarce Bamboo Page (*horiz*)	50	55
2943	$1.65, Paris Peacock (*horiz*)	75	80
2931/43	*Set of 13*	6·00	6·50
MS2944	Two sheets. (a) 85×110 mm. $6 Monarch. (b) 110×85 mm. $6 Cairns Birdwing (*horiz*)		
	Set of 2 sheets	5·25	5·50

Nos. 2933/41 were printed together, *se-tenant*, in sheetlets of 9, forming a composite design.

(Litho Questa)

1999 (23 Nov). *Christmas. Religious Paintings. T* **424** *and similar vert designs.* P 13½×14.
2945	15 c. multicoloured	10	10
2946	25 c. black, stone and yellow	10	15
2947	45 c. multicoloured	20	25
2948	60 c. multicoloured	25	30
2949	$2 multicoloured	85	90
2950	$4 black, stone and yellow	1·75	1·90
2945/50	*Set of 6*	3·25	3·50
MS2951	76×106 mm. $6 multicoloured	2·50	2·75

Designs:—25 c. "Shroud of Christ held by Two Angels" (Dürer); 45 c. "Madonna and Child enthroned between Two Saints" (Raphael); 60 c. "Holy Family with Lamb" (Raphael); $2 "The Transfiguration" (Raphael); $4 "Three Putti holding Coat of Arms" (Dürer); $6 "Coronation of St. Catharine" (Rubens)

STAMP BOOKLETS

1968 (2 Oct). *Blue cover. Stitched.*
SB1	$1.20, booklet containing 5 c., 10 c. and 15 c. (Nos. 185, 187, 188) in blocks of 4	8·50

1977 (26 Sept). *Silver Jubilee. Blue, silver and sepia cover, 165×82 mm, showing the Royal Family. Stitched.*
SB2	$8 booklet containing pane of 6 (No. 532a) and pane of 1 (No. 533a)	3·25

1978 (2 June). *25th Anniv of Coronation. Multicoloured cover, 165×92 mm, showing Coronation Coach. Stitched.*
SB3	$7.25, booklet containing pane of 6 (No. 587a) and pane of 1 (No. 589a)	2·75

1981 (23 June). *Royal Wedding. Multicoloured cover, 165×92 mm, showing Prince Charles and Lady Diana Spencer on front and Prince Charles on back. Stitched.*
SB4	$11.50, booklet containing pane of 6 (No. 706a) and pane of 1 (No. 712a)	2·50

BARBUDA
DEPENDENCY OF ANTIGUA

```
PRICES FOR STAMPS ON COVER TO 1945
        Nos. 1/11    from × 5
```

BARBUDA
(1)

1922 (13 July). *Stamps of Leeward Islands optd with T* **1**. *All Die II. Chalk-surfaced paper* (3d. to 5s.).

(a) Wmk Mult Script CA

1	**11**	½d. deep green	..	1·25	8·00
2		1d. bright scarlet	..	1·25	8·00
		x. Wmk reversed	..	£475	
3	**10**	2d. slate-grey	..	1·25	7·00
		x. Wmk reversed	..	55·00	
4	**11**	2½d. bright blue	..	1·25	7·50
		w. Wmk inverted	..	25·00	75·00
5		6d. dull and bright purple	..	1·75	16·00
6	**10**	2s. purple and blue/*blue*	..	12·00	48·00
7		3s. bright green and violet	..	30·00	75·00
8		4s. black and red (R.)	..	40·00	75·00

(b) Wmk Mult Crown CA

9	**10**	3d. purple/*pale yellow*	..	1·25	10·00
10	**12**	1s. black/*emerald* (R.)	..	1·50	8·00
11		5s. green and red/*pale yellow*	..	65·00	£130
1/11			Set of 11	£130	£325
1/11 Optd "Specimen"	..		Set of 11	£225	

Examples of all values are known showing a forged Barbuda postmark of "JU 1 23".

Stocks of the overprinted stamps were exhausted by October 1925 and issues of Antigua were then used in Barbuda until 1968.
The following issues of Barbuda were also valid for use in Antigua.

(New Currency. 100 cents = 1 Eastern Caribbean dollar)

2 Map of Barbuda   **3** Greater Amberjack

(Des R. Granger Barrett. Litho Format)

1968 (19 Nov)–**70**. *Designs as T* **2/3**. *P* 14.

12	½ c. brown, black and pink	..	20	50
13	1 c. orange, black and flesh	..	30	10
14	2 c. blackish brown, rose-red and rose		30	10
15	3 c. blackish brown, orange-yellow and lemon		30	10
16	4 c. black, bright green and apple-green		30	50
17	5 c. blue-green, black and pale blue-green		55	45
18	6 c. black, bright purple and pale lilac		40	50
19	10 c. black, ultramarine and cobalt		30	10
20	15 c. black, blue-green and turquoise-green		50	65
20a	20 c. multicoloured (22.7.70)	..	1·50	2·00
21	20 c. multicoloured (5.2.69)	..	60	25
22	35 c. multicoloured (5.2.69)	..	60	25
23	50 c. multicoloured (5.2.69)	..	60	55
24	75 c. multicoloured (5.2.69)	..	70	80
25	$1 multicoloured (6.3.69)	..	85	2·00
26	$2.50, multicoloured (6.3.69)	..	1·50	5·00
27	$5 multicoloured (6.3.69)	..	3·75	7·50
12/27		Set of 17	11·50	18·00

Designs:—½ to 15 c. Type 2. Horiz as T 3—20 c. Great Barracuda; 35 c. French Angelfish; 50 c. Porkfish; 75 c. Princess Parrotfish; $1, Long-spined Squirrelfish; $2.50, Bigeye; $5, Blue Chromis.

10 Sprinting and Aztec Sun-stone   **14** "The Ascension" (Orcagna)

(Des R. Granger Barrett. Litho Format)

1968 (20 Dec). *Olympic Games, Mexico. T* **10** *and similar horiz designs. Multicoloured. P* 14.

28	25 c. Type 10	..	45	25
29	35 c. High-jumping and Aztec statue	..	50	25
30	75 c. Dinghy-racing and Aztec lion mask	..	55	45
28/30		Set of 3	1·25	85
MS31	85×76 mm. $1 Football and engraved plate		1·75	3·25

(Des R. Granger Barret. Litho Format)

1969 (24 Mar). *Easter Commemoration. P* 14.

32	**14**	25 c. black and light blue	..	15	45
33		35 c. black and deep carmine	..	15	50
34		75 c. black and bluish lilac	..	15	55
32/4			Set of 3	40	1·40

15 Scout Enrolment Ceremony

(Des R. Granger Barrett. Litho Format)

1969 (7 Aug). *3rd Caribbean Scout Jamboree. T* **15** *and similar horiz designs. Multicoloured. P* 14.

35	25 c. Type 15	..	45	55
36	35 c. Scouts around camp fire	..	60	65
37	75 c. Sea Scouts rowing boat	..	75	85
35/7		Set of 3	1·60	1·90

(Des R. Granger Barrett. Litho Format)

1969 (20 Oct). *Christmas. P* 14.

38	**18**	½ c. multicoloured	..	10	10
39		25 c. multicoloured	..	10	15
40		35 c. multicoloured	..	10	20
41		75 c. multicoloured	..	20	35
38/41			Set of 4	30	60

19 William I (1066–87)   **(20)**

(Des R. Granger Barrett. Litho Format (Nos. 42/9) or Questa (others))

1970–71. *English Monarchs. T* **19** *and similar vert designs. Multicoloured. P* 14½ × 14.

42	35 c. Type 19 (16.2.70)	..	30	15
43	35 c. William II (2.3.70)	..	10	15
44	35 c. Henry I (16.3.70)	..	10	15
45	35 c. Stephen (1.4.70)	..	10	15
46	35 c. Henry II (15.4.70)	..	10	15
47	35 c. Richard I (1.5.70)	..	10	15
48	35 c. John (15.5.70)	..	10	15
49	35 c. Henry III (1.6.70)	..	10	15
50	35 c. Edward I (15.6.70)	..	10	15
51	35 c. Edward II (1.7.70)	..	10	15
52	35 c. Edward III (15.7.70)	..	10	15
53	35 c. Richard II (1.8.70)	..	10	15
54	35 c. Henry IV (15.8.70)	..	10	15
55	35 c. Henry V (1.9.70)	..	10	15
56	35 c. Henry VI (15.9.70)	..	10	15
57	35 c. Edward IV (1.10.70)	..	10	15
58	35 c. Edward V (15.10.70)	..	10	15
59	35 c. Richard III (2.11.70)	..	10	15
60	35 c. Henry VII (16.11.70)	..	10	15
61	35 c. Henry VIII (1.12.70)	..	10	15
62	35 c. Edward VI (15.12.70)	..	10	15
63	35 c. Lady Jane Grey (2.1.71)	..	10	15
64	35 c. Mary I (15.1.71)	..	10	15
65	35 c. Elizabeth I (1.2.71)	..	10	15
66	35 c. James I (15.2.71)	..	10	15
67	35 c. Charles I (1.3.71)	..	10	15
68	35 c. Charles II (15.3.71)	..	10	15
69	35 c. James II (1.4.71)	..	10	15
70	35 c. William III (15.4.71)	..	10	15
71	35 c. Mary II (1.5.71)	..	10	15
72	35 c. Anne (15.5.71)	..	15	15
73	35 c. George I (1.6.71)	..	15	15
74	35 c. George II (15.6.71)	..	15	15
75	35 c. George III (1.7.71)	..	15	15
76	35 c. George IV (15.7.71)	..	15	15
77	35 c. William IV (2.8.71)	..	15	60
78	35 c. Victoria (16.8.71)	..	15	60
42/78		Set of 37	3·75	6·00

See also Nos. 710/15.

1970 (26 Feb). *No. 12 surch with T* **20**.

79	**2**	20 c. on ½ c. brown, black and pink	..	10	20
		a. Surch inverted	..	50·00	
		b. Surch double	..	50·00	

21 "The Way to Calvary" (Ugolino)   **22** Oliver is introduced to Fagin (*Oliver Twist*)

(Des R. Granger Barrett. Litho Questa)

1970 (16 Mar). *Easter Paintings. T* **21** *and similar vert designs. Multicoloured P* 14.

80	25 c. Type 21	..	15	30
	a. Horiz strip of 3. Nos. 80/2		40	
81	35 c. "The Deposition from the Cross" (Ugolino)		15	30
82	75 c. Crucifix (The Master of St. Francis)		15	35
80/2		Set of 3	40	85

Nos. 80/2 were printed together, *se-tenant*, in horizontal strips of 3 throughout the sheet.

(Des R. Granger Barrett. Litho Questa)

1970 (10 July). *Death Centenary of Charles Dickens. T* **22** *and similar horiz design. Multicoloured. P* 14.

83	20 c. Type 22	..	15	20
84	75 c. Dickens and Scene from *The Old Curiosity Shop*		30	50

23 "Madonna of the Meadow" (Bellini)   **24** Nurse with Patient in Wheelchair

(Des R. Granger Barrett. Litho Questa)

1970 (15 Oct). *Christmas. T* **23** *and similar horiz designs. Multicoloured. P* 14.

85	20 c. Type 23	..	10	25
86	50 c. "Madonna, Child and Angels" (from Wilton diptych)		15	30
87	75 c. "The Nativity" (della Francesca)		15	35
85/7		Set of 3	30	80

(Des R. Granger Barrett. Litho Questa)

1970 (21 Dec). *Centenary of British Red Cross. T* **24** *and similar multicoloured designs. P* 14.

88	20 c. Type 24	..	15	30
89	35 c. Nurse giving patient magazines (*horiz*)		20	40
90	75 c. Nurse and mother weighing baby (*horiz*)		25	70
88/90		Set of 3	55	1·25

25 Angel with Vases   **26** Martello Tower

(Des R. Granger Barrett. Litho Questa)

1971 (7 Apr). *Easter. Details of the "Mond" Crucifixion by Raphael. T* **25** *and similar vert designs. Multicoloured. P* 14.

91	35 c. Type 25	..	15	75
	a. Horiz strip of 3. Nos. 91/3		40	
92	50 c. Christ crucified	..	15	85
93	75 c. Angel with vase	..	15	90
91/3		Set of 3	40	2·25

Nos. 91/3 were issued horizontally *se-tenant* within the sheet.

(Des R. Granger Barrett. Litho Questa)

1971 (10 May). *Tourism. T* **26** *and similar horiz designs. Multicoloured. P* 14.

94	20 c. Type 26	..	15	20
95	25 c. "Sailfish" dinghy	..	25	30
96	50 c. Hotel bungalows	..	25	35
97	75 c. Government House and Mystery Stone	..	25	40
94/7		Set of 4	80	1·10

27 "The Granducal Madonna" (Raphael)   **(28)**

(Des R. Granger Barrett. Litho Questa)

1971 (4 Oct). *Christmas. T* **27** *and similar vert designs. Multicoloured. P* 14.

98	½ c. Type 27	..	10	10
99	35 c. "The Ansidei Madonna" (Raphael)		10	20
100	50 c. "The Madonna and Child" (Botticelli)		15	25
101	75 c. "The Madonna of the Trees" (Bellini)		15	30
98/101		Set of 4	35	65

The contract with the agency for the distribution of Barbuda stamps was cancelled by the Antiguan Government on 15 August 1971 but the above issue was duly authorised. Four stamps (20, 35, 50 and 70 c.) were prepared to commemorate the 500th anniversary of the birth of Albrecht Dürer but their issue was not authorised.

Barbuda ceased to have separate stamps issues in 1972 but again had stamps of her own on 14 November 1973 with the following issue.

1973 (14 Nov). *Royal Wedding. Nos. 370/1 of Antigua optd with T 28.*

102	35 c. multicoloured		4·50	2·75
	a. Opt inverted		£100	
103	$2 multicoloured		1·50	1·50
	a. Opt inverted		£120	

No. MS372 of Antigua also exists with this overprint, but was not placed on sale at post offices. Examples of this sheet are known with "Specimen" overprint (*Price* £120).

(29) (30) (30a) (31)

1973 (26 Nov)–74. *T 92 etc. of Antigua optd with T 29.*

(a) On Nos. 270 etc. W w 12 (sideways)

104	1 c. Columbus and *Nina*		15	30
105	2 c. Sir Thomas Warner's emblem and *Concepcion*		25	30
106	4 c. Sir George Rodney and H.M.S. *Formidable*		30	30
107	5 c. Nelson and H.M.S. *Boreas*		40	40
108	6 c. William IV and H.M.S. *Pegasus*.		40	40
109	10 c. "Blackbeard" and pirate ketch		45	45
110	20 c. Nelson and H.M.S. *Victory*		55	60
111	25 c. *Solent I* (paddle-steamer)		55	60
112	35 c. George V (when Prince George) and H.M.S. *Canada* (screw corvette)		55	70
113	50 c. *Viscount Hood* (battle cruiser)		55	70
114	75 c. *Federal Maple* (freighter)		55	70
115	$2.50, H.M.S. *London* (destroyer) (18.2.74)		1·25	1·50

(b) On Nos. 323 etc. W w 12 (upright). White paper

116	½ c. Type 92 (11.12.73)		15	20
117	3 c. Viscount Hood and H.M.S. *Barfleur* (11.12.73)		25	25
	w. Wmk inverted		35·00	
118	15 c. Captain Collingwood and H.M.S. *Pelican* (11.12.73)		45	50
119	$1 *Sol Quest* (yacht) and class emblem (11.12.73)		55	70
120	$2.50, H.M.S. *London* (destroyer) (18.2.74)		9·00	12·00
121	$5 *Pathfinder* (tug) (26.11.73)		1·10	2·50
104/21		*Set of 18*	15·00	20·00

1973 (26 Nov). *Commemorative stamps of Antigua optd.*

(a) Nos. 353, 355 and 357/8 optd with T 30

122	½ c. Private, Zacharia Tiffin's Regt of Foot, 1701		10	10
123	20 c. Light Company Officer, 35th Regt of Foot, 1828		15	10
	aw. Wmk Crown to right of CA		7·00	
	b. Optd with T 30a		60	70
	bw. Wmk Crown to right of CA		6·00	
124	75 c. Sergeant, 49th Regt, 1858		40	15
122/4		*Set of 3*	55	25
MS125	127×145 mm. Nos. 353/7 of Antigua		2·00	3·50

(b) Nos 360/3 optd with T 31, in red

126	20 c. Carnival street scene		10	10
127	35 c. Carnival troupe		10	10
	a. Opt inverted		30·00	
128	75 c. Carnival Queen		20	25
126/8		*Set of 3*	30	40
MS129	134×95 mm. Nos. 359/62 of Antigua		1·00	2·25
	a. Albino opt			
	b. Opt double		£275	

Type 30a is a local overprint, applied by typography.

(32) (33) (34) (35)

1973 (11 Dec). *Christmas. Nos. 364/9 of Antigua optd with T 32.*

130	3 c. Type 105 (Sil.)		10	10
	a. Opt inverted		24·00	
	b. "BABRUDA" (R.4/2)		5·50	5·50
131	5 c. "Adoration of the Magi" (Stomer) (Sil.)		10	10
	a. "BABRUDA" (R.4/2)		7·00	7·00
132	20 c. "Granducal Madonna" (Raphael) (Sil.)		10	10
	a. "BABRUDA" (R.4/2)		9·00	9·00
133	35 c. "Nativity with God the Father and Holy Ghost" (Battista) (R.)		15	15
134	$1 "Madonna and Child" (Murillo) (R.)		30	30
	a. Opt inverted		45·00	
130/4		*Set of 5*	60	60
MS135	130 × 128 mm. Nos. 130/4 (Sil.)		2·75	9·00

1973 (15 Dec). *Honeymoon Visit of Princess Anne and Capt. Phillips. Nos. 373/5 of Antigua further optd with T 33.*

136	35 c. multicoloured		30	20
	a. Type 33 double, one albino		65·00	
	b. Optd on Antigua No. 373a			

137	$2 multicoloured		70	60
	a. Type 33 double, one albino		†	
	b. Optd on Antigua No. 374a		†	
MS138	78×100 mm. Nos. 136/7		5·00	7·50

1974 (18 Feb). *25th Anniv of University of West Indies. Nos. 376/9 of Antigua optd with T 34.*

139	5 c. Coat of arms		10	10
	a. Opt double, one albino		†	
140	20 c. Extra-mural art		10	10
141	35 c. Antigua campus		15	15
	a. Opt double			
142	75 c. Antigua Chancellor		15	15
139/42		*Set of 4*	30	30

No. 139a has only been seen used on first day cover. It shows the "normal" impression misplaced and very faint

1974 (1 May). *Military Uniforms. Nos. 380/4 of Antigua optd with T 35.*

143	½ c. Officer, 59th Foot, 1797		10	10
144	10 c. Gunner, Royal Artillery, 1800		10	10
	a. Horiz pair, left-hand stamp without opt		£130	
145	20 c. Private, 1st West India Regt, 1830		20	10
	a. Horiz pair, left-hand stamp without opt		£130	
146	35 c. Officer, 92nd Foot, 1843		25	10
	a. Opt inverted		50·00	
147	75 c. Private, 23rd Foot, 1846..		45	25
	a. Horiz pair, left-hand stamp without opt			
143/7		*Set of 5*	90	45

Nos. 144a, 145a and 147a come from sheets on which the overprint was so misplaced as to miss the first vertical row completely. Other stamps in these sheets show the overprint at left instead of right.

No. MS385 of Antigua also exists with this overprint, but was not placed on sale at post offices.

(36) (37 "General Postal Union") (38)

1974 (15 July). *Centenary of Universal Postal Union (1st issue). Nos. 386/92 of Antigua optd with T 36 (Nos. 148, 150, 152, 154, 156, 158 and 160) or T 37 (others), in red.*

148	½ c. English postman, mailcoach and Westland Dragonfly helicopter		10	10
149	½ c. English postman, mailcoach and Westland Dragonfly helicopter		10	10
150	1 c. Bellman, mail steamer *Orinoco* and satellite		10	10
151	1 c. Bellman, mail steamer *Orinoco* and satellite		10	10
152	2 c. Train guard, post-bus and hydrofoil		20	15
153	2 c. Train guard, post-bus and hydrofoil		20	15
154	5 c. Swiss messenger, Wells Fargo coach and Concorde		50	15
155	5 c. Swiss messenger, Wells Fargo coach and Concorde		50	15
156	20 c. Postilion, Japanese postmen and carrier pigeon		40	70
157	20 c. Postilion, Japanese postmen and carrier pigeon		40	70
158	35 c. Antiguan postman, Sikorsky S-38 flying boat and tracking station		80	1·50
159	35 c. Antiguan postman, Sikorsky S-38 flying boat and tracking station		80	1·50
160	$1 Medieval courier, American express train and Boeing 747-100		2·25	4·00
161	$1 Medieval courier, American express train and Boeing 747-100		2·25	4·00
148/61		*Set of 14*	7·50	12·00
MS162	141×164 mm. No. MS393 of Antigua overprinted with T 38, in red		3·50	6·00
	a. Albino opt			

Nos. 148/9, 150/1, 152/3, 154/5, 156/7, 158/9 and 160/1 were each printed together, *se-tenant*, in horizontal pairs throughout the sheet.

See also Nos. 177/80.

1974 (14 Aug). *Antiguan Steel Bands. Nos. 394/8 of Antigua optd with T 38.*

163	5 c. rose-red, carmine and black		10	10
164	20 c. brown-ochre, chestnut and black		10	10
165	35 c. light sage-green, blue-green and black		10	10
166	75 c. dull blue, dull ultramarine and black		20	20
163/6		*Set of 4*	35	35
MS167	115 × 108 mm. Nos. 163/6		65	80

39 Footballers (40)

(Des G. Drummond. Litho Format)

1974 (2 Sept). *World Cup Football Championships (1st issue). Various horiz designs as T 39 each showing footballers in action. P 14.*

168	39	35 c. multicoloured	10	10
169		$1.20, multicoloured	25	35
170		$2.50, multicoloured	35	50
168/70		*Set of 3*	60	75
MS171	70 × 128 mm. Nos. 168/70		85	90

Nos. 168/71 exist imperforate from stock dispersed by the liquidator of Format International Security Printers Ltd.

1974 (23 Sept). *World Cup Football Championships (2nd issue). Nos. 399/403 of Antigua optd with T 40.*

172	5 c. multicoloured		10	10
173	35 c. multicoloured		15	15
174	75 c. multicoloured		25	15
175	$1 multicoloured		25	25
172/5		*Set of 4*	60	45
MS176	135×130 mm. Nos. 172/5		75	1·50

41 Ship Letter of 1833   42 Greater Amberjack

(Des G. Drummond. Litho Format)

1974 (30 Sept). *Centenary of Universal Postal Union (2nd issue). T 41 and similar vert designs. Multicoloured. P 13½.*

177	35 c. Type 41		10	10
178	$1.20, Stamps and postmark of 1922		25	50
179	$2.50, Britten Norman Islander mailplane over map of Barbuda		35	75
177/9		*Set of 3*	60	1·25
MS180	128×97 mm. Nos. 177/9		1·00	2·00

Nos. 177/80 exist imperforate from stock dispersed by the liquidator of Format International Security Printers Ltd.

(Des G. Drummond. Litho Format)

1974 (15 Oct)–75. *Multicoloured designs as T 42. P 14×14½ (½ c. to 3 c., 25 c.), 14½×14 (4 c. to 20 c., 35 c.), 14 (50 c. to $1) or 13½ (others).*

181	½ c. Oleander, Rose Bay (6.1.75)		10	40
182	1 c. Blue Petrea (6.1.75)		15	40
183	2 c. Poinsettia (6.1.75)		15	40
184	3 c. Cassia tree (6.1.75)		15	40
185	4 c. Type 42		1·40	40
186	5 c. Holy Trinity School		15	15
187	6 c. Snorkeling		15	30
188	10 c. Pilgrim Holiness Church		15	20
189	15 c. New Cottage Hospital		15	20
190	20 c. Post Office and Treasury		15	20
191	25 c. Island jetty and boats		30	30
192	35 c. Martello Tower		30	30
193	50 c. Warden's House (6.1.75)		30	40
194	75 c. Britten Norman Islander aircraft		1·00	1·00
195	$1 Tortoise (6.1.75)		70	80
196	$2.50, Spiny lobster (6.1.75)		80	1·75
197	$5 Magnificent Frigate Bird (6.1.75)		3·50	2·50
	a. Perf 14×14½ (24.7.75)*		9·00	18·00
197b	$10 Hibiscus (19.9.75)		2·00	4·50
181/97b		*Set of 18*	10·00	13·00

*See footnote below Nos. 227/8.

The 50 c. to $1 are larger, 39 × 25 mm; the $2.50 and $5 are 45 × 29 mm; the $10 is 34 × 48 mm and the ½ c. to 3c. 25 c. and $10 are vert designs.

1974 (15 Oct). *Birth Centenary of Sir Winston Churchill (1st issue). Nos. 408/12 of Antigua optd with T 38 in red.*

198	5 c. Churchill as schoolboy, and school college building, Harrow		15	10
	a. Opt inverted		60·00	
199	35 c. Churchill and St. Paul's Cathedral		25	15
200	75 c. Coat of arms and catafalque		40	45
201	$1 Churchill, "reward" notice and South African escape route		75	70
	a. Opt inverted		60·00	
198/201		*Set of 4*	1·40	1·25
MS202	107 × 82 mm. Nos. 198/201		6·00	13·00

43 Churchill making Broadcast   (44)

(Des G. Drummond. Litho Questa)

1974 (20 Nov). *Birth Centenary of Sir Winston Churchill (2nd issue). T 43 and similar horiz designs. Multicoloured. P 13½ × 14.*

203	5 c. Type 43		10	10
204	35 c. Churchill and Chartwell		10	10
205	75 c. Churchill painting		20	20
206	$1 Churchill making "V" sign		25	30
203/6		*Set of 4*	55	60
MS207	146×95 mm. Nos. 203/6		75	2·50

1974 (25 Nov). *Christmas. Nos. 413/21 of Antigua optd with T 33.*

208	½ c. Bellini		10	10
	a. Opt inverted		45·00	
209	1 c. Raphael		10	10
210	2 c. Van der Weyden		10	10
211	3 c. Giorgione		10	10
212	20 c. Mantegna		10	10
213	20 c. Vivarini		10	10
214	35 c. Montagna		15	15
215	75 c. Lorenzo Costa		30	30
208/15		*Set of 8*	60	60
MS216	139 × 126 mm. Nos. 208/15		80	1·40

1975 (17 Mar). *Nelson's Dockyard. Nos. 427/32 of Antigua optd with T 44.*

217	5 c. Carib war canoe, English Harbour, 1300		15	15
218	15 c. Ship of the line, English Harbour, 1770		40	25
219	35 c. H.M.S. *Boreas* at anchor, and Lord Nelson, 1787		55	35
220	50 c. Yachts during "Sailing Week", 1974		60	50
221	$1 Yacht Anchorage, Old Dockyard, 1970		65	80
217/21		*Set of 5*	2·10	1·75
MS222	130 × 134 mm. As Nos. 217/21, but in larger format; 43 × 28 mm		1·75	2·75

45 Battle of the Saints, 1782

(Des G. Vasarhelyi. Litho Format)

1975 (30 May). *Sea Battles. T* **45** *and similar horiz designs showing scenes from the Battle of the Saints, 1782. Multicoloured.* P 13½.

223	35 c. Type **45**		75	65
224	50 c. H.M.S. *Ramillies*		75	75
225	75 c. *Bonhomme Richard* (American frigate) firing broadside		90	90
226	95 c. *L'Orient* (French ship of the line) burning		1·00	1·25
223/6		*Set of 4*	3·00	3·25

(46)

1975 (24 July). *"Apollo-Soyuz" Space Project. No.* 197a *optd with* T **46** *and similar ("Soyuz") opt.*

227	$5 Magnificent Frigate Bird ("Apollo")		3·25	6·00
	a. *Se-tenant* strip of 3. Nos. 227/8 and 197a		14·00	
228	$5 Magnificent Frigate Bird ("Soyuz")		3·25	6·00

Nos. 227/8 were issued together *se-tenant* in sheets of 25 (5 × 5), with the "Apollo" opts in the first and third vertical rows and the "Soyuz" opts in the second and fourth vertical rows, the fifth vertical row comprising five unoverprinted stamps (No. 197a).

47 Officer, 65th Foot, 1763   (48)

30TH ANNIVERSARY UNITED NATIONS 1945 — 1975

(Des G. Drummond. Litho Questa)

1975 (17 Sept). *Military Uniforms. T* **47** *and similar vert designs. Multicoloured.* P 13½.

229	35 c. Type **47**		75	75
230	50 c. Grenadier, 27th Foot, 1701–10		90	90
231	75 c. Officer, 21st Foot, 1793–6		1·00	1·00
232	95 c. Officer, Royal Regt of Artillery, 1800		1·25	1·25
229/32		*Set of 4*	3·50	3·50

1975 (24 Oct). *30th Anniv of United Nations. Nos.* 203/6 *optd with* T **48**.

233	5 c. Churchill making broadcast		10	10
234	35 c. Churchill and Chartwell		10	15
235	75 c. Churchill painting		15	20
236	$1 Churchill making "V" sign		20	30
233/6		*Set of 4*	40	60

BARBUDA   **BARBUDA**

(49)   (50)

1975 (17 Nov). *Christmas. Nos.* 457/65 *of Antigua optd with* T **49**.

237	½ c. Correggio		10	10
238	1 c. El Greco		10	10
239	2 c. Dürer		10	10
240	3 c. Antonello		10	10
241	5 c. Bellini		10	10
242	10 c. Dürer		10	10
243	25 c. Bellini		15	20
244	$2 Dürer		60	1·00
237/44		*Set of 8*	95	1·50
MS245	138 × 119 mm. Nos. 241/4		1·10	2·25

1975 (15 Dec). *World Cup Cricket Winners. Nos.* 466/8 *of Antigua optd with* T **50**.

246	5 c. Vivian Richards		90	1·00
247	35 c. Andy Roberts		1·75	2·00
248	$2 West Indies team		3·25	4·25
246/8		*Set of 3*	5·50	6·50

51 "Surrender of Cornwallis at Yorktown" (Trumbull)

(Des G. Vasarhelyi. Litho Format)

1976 (8 Mar). *Bicentenary of American Revolution. T* **51** *and similar horiz designs. Multicoloured.* P 13½ × 13.

249	15 c.		10	15
250	15 c. } Type **51**		10	15
251	15 c.		10	15

252	35 c.		10	15
253	35 c. } "The Battle of Princeton"		10	15
254	35 c.		10	15
255	$1		15	25
256	$1 } "Surrender of General Burgoyne at Saratoga" (W. Mercer)		15	25
257	$1		15	25
258	$2		25	40
259	$2 } "The Declaration of Independence" (Trumbull)		25	40
260	$2		25	40
249/60		*Set of 12*	1·50	2·50
MS261	140 × 70 mm. Nos. 249/54 and 255/60 (*two sheets*)		2·25	9·00

The three designs of each value were printed horizontally *se-tenant* within the sheet to form the composite designs listed. Type 51 shows the left-hand stamp of the 15 c. design.

52 Bananaquits

(Des G. Drummond. Litho Format)

1976 (30 June). *Birds. T* **52** *and similar horiz designs. Multicoloured.* P 13½.

262	35 c. Type **52**		1·00	50
263	50 c. Blue-hooded Euphonia		1·00	60
264	75 c. Royal Tern		1·25	80
265	95 c. Killdeer		1·50	85
266	$1.25, Common Cowbird		1·50	1·00
267	$2 Purple Gallinule		1·50	1·25
262/7		*Set of 6*	7·00	4·50

1976 (12 Aug). *Royal Visit to the U.S.A. As Nos.* 249/60 *but redrawn and inscr at top* "H.M. QUEEN ELIZABETH ROYAL VISIT 6TH JULY 1976 H.R.H. DUKE OF EDINBURGH".

268	15 c.		10	15
269	15 c. } As Type **51**		10	15
270	15 c.		10	15
271	35 c.		10	20
272	35 c. } As Nos. 252/4		10	20
273	35 c.		10	20
274	$1		15	50
275	$1 } As Nos. 255/7		15	50
276	$1		15	50
277	$2		25	70
278	$2 } As Nos. 258/60		25	70
279	$2		25	70
268/79		*Set of 12*	1·50	4·25
MS280	143 × 81 mm. Nos. 268/73 and 274/9 (*two sheets*)		2·50	9·00

The three designs of each value were printed horizontally *se-tenant*, imperf between.

BARBUDA   **BARBUDA**

(53)   (54)

1976 (2 Dec). *Christmas. Nos.* 514/18 *of Antigua optd with* T **53**.

281	8 c. The Annunciation		10	10
282	10 c. The Holy Family		10	10
283	15 c. The Magi		10	10
284	50 c. The Shepherds		15	15
285	$1 Epiphany scene		25	30
281/5		*Set of 5*	45	55

1976 (28 Dec). *Olympic Games, Montreal. Nos.* 495/502 *of Antigua optd with* T **54**.

286	½ c. High-jump		10	10
287	1 c. Boxing		10	10
288	2 c. Pole-vault		10	10
289	15 c. Swimming		10	10
290	30 c. Running		10	10
291	$1 Cycling		20	20
292	$2 Shot put		35	35
286/92		*Set of 7*	60	60
MS293	88 × 138 mm. Nos. 289/92		1·75	2·40

55 Post Office Tower, Telephones and Alexander Graham Bell

(Des G. Vasarhelyi. Litho Format)

1977 (31 Jan). *Telephone Centenary (1976). T* **55** *and similar horiz designs. Multicoloured.* P 13½.

294	75 c. Type **55**		15	35
295	$1.25, Dish aerial and television		20	55
296	$2 Globe and satellites		30	75
294/6		*Set of 3*	60	1·50
MS297	96 × 144 mm. Nos. 294/6. P 15		70	2·00

56 St. Margaret's Church, Westminster

1977 (7 Feb). *Silver Jubilee (1st issue). T* **56** *and similar horiz designs. Multicoloured. Litho.* P 13½ × 13.

298	75 c. Type **56**		10	15
299	75 c. Entrance, Westminster Abbey		10	15
300	75 c. Westminster Abbey		10	15
301	$1.25, Household Cavalry		15	20
302	$1.25, Coronation Coach		15	20
303	$1.25, Team of Horses		15	20
298/303		*Set of 6*	65	90
MS304	148×83 mm. As Nos. 298/303, but with silver borders. P 15		75	1·50

Nos. 298/300 and 301/3 were printed horizontally *se-tenant*, forming composite designs.

See also Nos. 323/30 and 375/8.

1977 (4 Apr). *Nos.* 469A/86A *of Antigua optd with* T **54**.

305	½ c. Antillean Crested Hummingbird		20	20
306	1 c. Imperial Amazon		30	20
307	2 c. Zenaida Dove		30	20
308	3 c. Loggerhead Kingbird		30	20
309	4 c. Red-necked Pigeon		30	20
310	5 c. Rufous-throated Solitaire		30	20
311	6 c. Orchid Tree		30	20
312	10 c. Bougainvillea		30	20
313	15 c. Geiger Tree		30	25
314	20 c. Flamboyant		30	25
315	25 c. Hibiscus		30	25
316	35 c. Flame of the Wood		35	30
317	50 c. Cannon at Fort James		40	40
318	75 c. Premier's Office		40	40
319	$1 Potworks Dam		50	60
320	$2.50, Irrigation scheme		1·00	1·60
321	$5 Government House		1·50	3·25
322	$10 Coolidge Airport		4·00	7·50
305/22		*Set of 18*	10·00	15·00

BARBUDA   **BARBUDA**   **BARBUDA**

(57)   (58)   (59)

1977 (4 Apr–20 Dec). *Silver Jubilee (2nd issue).*

(a) *Sheet stamps. Nos.* 526/31 *of Antigua optd with* T **57**.

323	10 c. Royal Family		10	15
	a. Opt double		45·00	
324	30 c. Royal Visit, 1966		10	20
325	50 c. Queen enthroned		15	30
326	90 c. Queen after Coronation		15	40
327	$2.50, Queen and Prince Charles		45	1·25
323/7		*Set of 5*	85	2·10
MS328	116×78 mm. $5 Queen Elizabeth and Prince Philip		80	1·25
	a. Error. Imperf		£600	
	b. Opt albino		25·00	
	c. Opt double			

(b) *Booklet stamps. Nos.* 532/3 *of Antigua optd with* T **58** *in silver (50 c.) or* T **59** *in gold ($5) (20 Dec)*

329	50 c. Queen after Coronation		40	70
	a. Booklet pane of 6		2·25	
330	$5 The Queen and Prince Philip		3·00	9·00
	a. Booklet pane of 1		3·00	

(60)   **61** Royal Yacht *Britannia*

BARBUDA

1977 (13 June). *Caribbean Scout Jamboree, Jamaica. Nos.* 534/41 *of Antigua optd with* T **60**.

331	½ c. Making camp		10	10
332	1 c. Hiking		10	10
333	2 c. Rock-climbing		10	10
334	10 c. Cutting logs		10	10
335	30 c. Map and sign reading		40	40
336	50 c. First aid		55	65
337	$2 Rafting		1·10	2·25
331/37		*Set of 7*	2·00	3·00
MS338	127 × 114 mm. Nos. 335/7		3·25	4·00

1977 (12 Aug). *21st Anniv of Carnival. Nos.* 542/7 *of Antigua optd with* T **60**.

339	10 c. Carnival costume		10	10
340	30 c. Carnival Queen		10	10
341	50 c. Butterfly costume		15	20
342	90 c. Queen of the band		20	30
343	$1 Calypso King and Queen		25	40
339/43		*Set of 5*	65	90
MS344	140 × 120 mm. Nos. 339/43		1·00	1·75

(Des G. Drummond. Litho Format)

1977 (27 Oct). *Royal Visit (1st issue). T* **61** *and similar horiz designs. Multicoloured.* P 14½.

345	50 c. Type **61**		10	15
346	$1.50, Jubilee emblem		25	35
347	$2.50, Union Jack and flag of Antigua		35	45
345/7		*Set of 3*	60	95
MS348	77 × 124 mm. Nos. 345/7		85	2·25

BARBUDA   BARBUDA
(62)   (63)   **64** Airship LZ-1

1977 (28 Nov–20 Dec). *Royal Visit (2nd issue). Nos. 548/53 of Antigua optd. A. With T 57. P 14 (28 Nov).*
349A	10 c. Royal Family		10	10
350A	30 c. Royal Visit, 1966		10	20
351A	50 c. Queen enthroned		15	25
352A	90 c. Queen after Coronation		15	40
353A	$2.50, Queen and Prince Charles		40	1·25
349A/53A		*Set of 5*	80	2·00
MS354A	116×78 mm. $5 Queen and Prince Philip		1·75	4·00

B. *With T 62. P 11½×12 (20 Dec)*
349B	10 c. Royal Family		10	10
	a. Blue opt		35	35
350B	30 c. Royal Visit, 1966		10	15
	a. Blue opt		90	95
351B	50 c. Queen enthroned		15	20
	a. Blue opt		2·75	1·90
352B	90 c. Queen after Coronation		20	30
	a. Blue opt		5·00	3·50
353B	$2.50, Queen and Prince Charles		45	80
	a. Blue opt		11·00	9·50
349B/53B		*Set of 5*	85	1·40

Nos. 349B/53B were each printed in small sheets of 6 including one *se-tenant* stamp-size label.

1977 (28 Nov). *Christmas. Nos. 554/61 of Antigua optd with T 63. "Virgin and Child" paintings by the artists given.*
355	½ c. Tura		10	10
356	1 c. Crivelli		10	10
357	2 c. Lotto		10	10
358	8 c. Pontormo		10	10
359	10 c. Tura		10	10
360	25 c. Lotto		15	10
361	$2 Crivelli		45	45
355/61		*Set of 7*	70	65
MS362	144 × 118 mm. Nos. 358/61		1·00	1·75

(Des I. Oliver. Litho Format)

1977 (29 Dec). *Special Events, 1977. T 64 and similar horiz designs. Multicoloured. P 14.*
363	75 c. Type **64**		30	30
	a. Nos. 363/6 in *se-tenant* block		1·10	
364	75 c. German battleship and naval airship L-31		30	30
365	75 c. Airship LZ-127 *Graf Zeppelin* in hangar		30	30
366	75 c. Gondola of military airship		30	30
367	95 c. "Sputnik 1"		35	35
	a. Nos. 367/70 in *se-tenant* block		1·25	
368	95 c. "Vostok"		35	35
369	95 c. "Voskhod"		35	35
370	95 c. Space walk		35	35
371	$1.25, Fuelling for flight		40	45
	a. Nos. 371/4 in *se-tenant* block		1·40	
372	$1.25, Leaving New York		40	45
373	$1.25, Ryan NYP Special *Spirit of St. Louis*		40	45
374	$1.25, Welcome in France		40	45
375	$2 Lion of England		50	70
	a. Nos. 375/8 in *se-tenant* block		1·75	
376	$2 Unicorn of Scotland		50	70
377	$2 Yale of Beaufort		50	70
378	$2 Falcon of Plantagenets		50	70
379	$5 ⎫		50	1·25
380	$5 ⎪ "Daniel in the Lion's Den"		50	1·25
381	$5 ⎬ (Rubens)		50	1·25
382	$5 ⎭		50	1·25
	a. Nos. 379/82 in *se-tenant* block		1·75	
363/82		*Set of 20*	6·00	11·00
MS383	132 × 156 mm. Nos. 363/82		6·00	17·00

Events:—75 c. 75th Anniv of Navigable Airships; 95 c. 20th Anniv of U.S.S.R. Space Programme; $1.25, 50th Anniv of Lindbergh's Transatlantic Flight; $2 Silver Jubilee of Queen Elizabeth II; $5 400th Birth Anniv of Rubens.

Nos. 363/66, 367/70, 371/74, 375/78 and 379/82 were printed in *se-tenant* blocks of four within the sheet.

Nos. 363/83 exist imperforate from stock dispersed by the liquidator of Format International Security Printers Ltd.

BARBUDA
(65)   **66** "Pieta" (sculpture) (detail)

1978 (15 Feb). *Tenth Anniv of Statehood. Nos. 562/7 of Antigua optd with T 65.*
384	10 c. Pineapple		10	10
385	15 c. State flag		15	10
386	50 c. Police band		1·25	40
387	90 c. Premier V. C. Bird		20	40
388	$2 State Coat of Arms		40	80
384/8		*Set of 5*	1·75	1·75
MS389	126 × 99 mm. Nos. 385/88. P 14		5·50	3·50

(Des G. Vasarhelyi. Litho Format)

1978 (23 Mar). *Easter. Works by Michelangelo. T 66 and similar horiz designs. Multicoloured. P 13½ × 14.*
390	75 c. Type **66**		15	15
391	95 c. "The Holy Family" (painting)		15	20
392	$1.25, "Libyan Sibyl" from Sistine Chapel, Rome		15	25
393	$2 "The Flood" from Sistine Chapel		20	35
390/3		*Set of 4*	60	85
MS394	117 × 85 mm. Nos. 390/3		1·60	2·00

Nos. 390/4 exist imperforate from stock dispersed by the liquidator of Format International Security Printers Ltd.

BARBUDA
(67)   **68** St. Edward's Crown

1978 (28 Mar). *75th Anniv of Powered Flight. Nos. 568/75 of Antigua optd with T 67.*
395	½ c. Wright Glider III, 1902		10	10
396	1 c. Wright Flyer I, 1903		10	10
397	2 c. Launch system and engine		10	10
398	10 c. Orville Wright		10	10
399	50 c. Wright Flyer III, 1905		25	15
400	90 c. Wilbur Wright		35	15
401	$2 Wright Type B, 1910		60	45
395/401		*Set of 7*	1·25	75
MS402	90×75 mm. $2.50, Wright Flyer I on launch system		1·50	2·25

1978 (22 May). *Sailing Week. Nos. 576/80 of Antigua optd with T 67.*
403	10 c. Sunfish regatta		20	10
404	50 c. Fishing and work boat race		40	25
405	90 c. Curtain Bluff race		55	35
406	$2 Power boat rally		85	75
403/6		*Set of 4*	1·75	1·25
MS407	110 × 77 mm. $2.50, Guadeloupe–Antigua race		1·25	1·60
	a. Albino opt		†	—

(Des J. Cooter. Litho Format)

1978 (2 June). *25th Anniv of Coronation (1st issue). T 68 and similar vert designs. Multicoloured. P 15.*
408	75 c. Type **68**		15	20
409	75 c. Imperial State Crown		15	20
410	$1.50, Queen Mary's Crown		20	30
411	$1.50, Queen Mother's Crown		20	30
412	$2.50, Queen Consort's Crown		35	50
413	$2.50, Queen Victoria's Crown		35	50
408/413		*Set of 6*	1·10	1·75
MS414	123 × 117 mm. Nos. 408/13. P 14½		1·10	1·75

The two designs for each value were issued as two *se-tenant* pairs, together with 2 labels, in small sheets of 6.

Examples of the 75 c. and $2.50 values exist in separate miniature sheets of four exist from stock dispersed by the liquidator of Format International Security Printers Ltd, as do imperforate examples of No. MS414.

1978 (2 June–12 Oct). *25th Anniv of Coronation (2nd issue).*
(a) Sheet stamps. Nos. 581/6 of Antigua optd with T 67. P 14 (2.6)
415	10 c. Queen Elizabeth and Prince Philip		10	10
416	30 c. Crowning		10	10
417	50 c. Coronation procession		10	15
418	90 c. Queen seated in St. Edward's Chair		15	20
	a. Opt triple		85·00	
419	$2.50, Queen wearing Imperial State Crown		30	60
415/19		*Set of 5*	60	1·00
MS420	114 × 103 mm. $5 Queen and Prince Philip (17.7)		1·00	1·50
	a. Albino opt		£250	

(b) Booklet stamps. Horiz designs as Nos. 587/9 of Antigua but additionally inscr "BARBUDA". Multicoloured. Roul 5 × imperf*. Self-adhesive (12.10)
421	25 c. Glass Coach		30	70
	a. Booklet pane. Nos. 421/2 × 3		1·60	
422	50 c. Irish State Coach		30	70
423	$5 Coronation Coach		1·00	2·25
	a. Booklet pane of 1		1·00	
421/3		*Set of 3*	1·75	3·25

*The 25 and 50 c. values were separated by various combinations of rotary knife (giving a straight edge) and roulette. The $5 value exists only with straight edges.

Nos. 415/19 also exist perf 12 (*Price for set of 5 55p mint or used*) from additional sheetlets of three stamps and one label, issued 12 October 1978. These stamps have different background colours from Nos. 415/19.

1978 (12 Sept). *World Cup Football Championship, Argentina. Nos. 590/3 of Antigua optd with T 67.*
424	10 c. Player running with ball		10	10
425	15 c. Players in front of goal		10	10
426	$3 Referee and player		1·00	1·25
424/6		*Set of 3*	1·00	1·25
MS427	126 × 88 mm. 25 c. Player crouching with ball; 30 c. Players heading ball; 50 c. Players running with ball; $2 Goalkeeper diving		80	90

BARBUDA
(69)   **70** Black-barred Soldierfish

1978 (20 Nov). *Flowers. Nos. 594/8 of Antigua optd with T 69.*
428	25 c. Petrea		15	20
429	50 c. Sunflower		25	40
430	90 c. Frangipani		35	45
431	$2 Passion Flower		60	90
428/31		*Set of 4*	1·25	1·75
MS432	118 × 85 mm. $2.50, Hibiscus		1·00	1·50

1978 (20 Nov). *Christmas. Paintings. Nos. 599/602 optd with T 69 in silver.*
433	8 c. "St. Ildefonso receiving the Chasuble from the Virgin"		10	10
434	25 c. "The Flight of St. Barbara"		15	15
435	$2 "Madonna and Child, with St. Joseph, John the Baptist and Donor"		60	1·25
433/5		*Set of 3*	75	1·25
MS436	170 × 113 mm. $4 "The Annunciation"		1·25	2·25

(Litho Format)

1978 (20 Nov). *Flora and Fauna. T 70 and similar horiz designs. Multicoloured. P 14½.*
437	25 c. Type **70**		1·25	1·50
438	50 c. *Cynthia cardui* (butterfly)		2·00	2·25
439	75 c. Dwarf Poinciana		1·50	2·25
440	95 c. *Heliconius charithonia* (butterfly)		2·00	2·50
441	$1.25, Bougainvillea		1·50	2·50
437/41		*Set of 5*	7·50	10·00

71 Footballers and World Cup   **72** Sir Rowland Hill

(Des J. Cooter. Litho Format)

1978 (29 Dec). *Anniversaries and Events. T 71 and similar multicoloured designs. P 14.*
442	75 c. Type **71**		30	30
443	95 c. Wright brothers and Flyer I (*horiz*)		30	40
444	$1.25, Balloon *Double Eagle II* and map of Atlantic (*horiz*)		40	45
445	$2 Prince Philip paying homage to the newly crowned Queen		40	60
442/5		*Set of 4*	1·25	1·60
MS446	122×90 mm. Nos. 442/5. Imperf		5·00	6·00

Events:—75 c. Winners of World Cup Football Championship; 95 c. 75th anniversary of powered flight; $1.25 1st Atlantic crossing by balloon; $2 25th anniversary of Coronation.

1979 (4 Apr). *Death Centenary of Sir Rowland Hill (1st issue). T 72 and similar multicoloured designs. P 14.*
447	75 c. Type **72**		25	45
448	95 c. Mail coach, 1840 (*horiz*)		25	50
449	$1.25, London's first pillar box, 1855 (*horiz*)		30	60
450	$2 Mail leaving St. Martin's Le Grand Post Office, London		45	85
447/50		*Set of 4*	1·10	2·25
MS451	129 × 104 mm. Nos. 447/50 Imperf		1·40	2·25

Nos. 447/50 were each printed in small sheets of 4 including one *se-tenant* stamp-size label.

BARBUDA
(73)   **74** Passengers alighting from Boeing 747-200

1979 (4 Apr). *Death Centenary of Sir Rowland Hill (2nd issue). Nos. 603/7 of Antigua optd with T 73 in black (No. MS456) or blue (others). P 14.*
452	25 c. Antigua 1863 1d. stamp		15	15
453	50 c. Penny Black stamp		20	20
454	$1 Stage-coach and woman posting letter, circa 1840		35	30
455	$2 Modern mail transport		80	60
452/5		*Set of 4*	1·40	1·10
MS456	108 × 82 mm. $2.50, Sir Rowland Hill		75	80

Nos. 452/5 also exist perf 12 (*Price for set of 4 £1.75 mint or used*) from additional sheetlets of four stamps and one label, issued 28 December 1979.

1979 (12 Apr). *Easter. Works by Dürer. Nos. 608/11 of Antigua optd with T 67.*
457	10 c. multicoloured		10	10
458	50 c. multicoloured		20	20
459	$4 black, magenta and greenish yellow		90	1·10
457/9		*Set of 3*	1·00	1·25
MS460	114 × 99 mm. $2.50, multicoloured		55	75

(Litho Format)

1979 (24 May). *35th Anniv of International Civil Aviation Organisation. T 74 and similar horiz designs. Multicoloured. P 13½×14.*
461	75 c. Type **74**		25	50
	a. Block of 4. Nos. 461/3 plus label		65	
462	95 c. Air traffic control		25	50
463	$1.25, Ground crew-man directing Douglas DC-8 on runway		25	50
461/3		*Set of 3*	65	1·40

Nos. 461/3 were either printed in separate sheets, or together with a stamp-size label, *se-tenant*, in blocks of 4, each block divided in the sheet by margins.

1979 (24 May). *International Year of the Child (1st issue). Nos. 612/16 of Antigua optd with T 67.*
464	25 c. Yacht		20	15
465	50 c. Rocket		30	25
466	90 c. Car		40	35
467	$2 Train		80	60
464/7		*Set of 4*	1·50	1·25
MS468	80 × 112 mm. $5 Aeroplane		1·10	1·10

BARBUDA BARBUDA
(75) (76)

1979 (1 Aug). *Fishes. Nos. 617/21 of Antigua optd with T 75.*
469	30 c. Yellow Jack	20	15
470	50 c. Blue-finned Tuna	30	20
471	90 c. Sailfish	40	30
472	$3 Wahoo	1·10	1·10
469/72	*Set of 4*	1·75	1·60
MS473	122×75 mm. $2.50, Great Barracuda (overprinted with T 73)	1·00	1·25
	a. Albino opt		

1979 (1 Aug). *Death Bicentenary of Captain Cook. Nos. 622/6 of Antigua optd with T 76.*
474	25 c. Cook's Birthplace, Marton	30	30
475	50 c. H.M.S. *Endeavour*	85	45
476	90 c. Marine chronometer	90	60
477	$3 Landing at Botany Bay	1·75	1·60
474/7	*Set of 4*	3·50	2·50
MS478	110 × 85 mm. $2.50, H.M.S. *Resolution* (overprinted with T 82)	1·25	1·50
	a. Albino opt		

77 "Virgin with the Pear" BARBUDA (78)

(Des G. Vasarhelyi. Litho Format)

1979 (24 Sept). *International Year of the Child (2nd issue). Details of Paintings by Dürer, showing the infant Jesus. T 77 and similar vert designs. Multicoloured. P 14 × 13½.*
479	25 c. Type 77	15	15
480	50 c. "Virgin with the Pink"	20	25
481	75 c. "Virgin with the Pear" (*different*)	25	30
482	$1.25, "Nativity"	25	40
479/82	*Set of 4*	75	1·00
MS483	86 × 118 mm. Nos. 479/82	1·00	1·75

1979 (21 Nov). *Christmas. Nos. 627/31 of Antigua optd with T 78.*
484	5 c. The Holy Family	10	10
485	25 c. Virgin and Child on Ass	15	10
486	50 c. Shepherd and star	25	15
487	$4 Wise Men with gifts	85	80
484/7	*Set of 4*	1·10	1·00
MS488	113 × 94 mm. $3 Angel with trumpet	80	1·10

1980 (18 Mar). *Olympic Games, Moscow. Nos. 632/6 of Antigua optd with T 67.*
489	5 c. Javelin throwing	10	10
490	25 c. Running	10	10
491	$1 Pole vaulting	30	20
492	$2 Hurdling	55	40
489/92	*Set of 4*	90	65
MS493	127 × 96 mm. $3 Boxing	70	1·10

LONDON 1980
(79)

80 "Apollo 11" Crew Badge

1980 (6 May). *"London 1980" International Stamp Exhibition. As Nos. 452/5 optd with T 79 in blue. P 12.*
494	25 c. Antigua 1863 1d. stamp	35	20
495	50 c. Penny Black stamp	45	40
496	$1 Mail coach and woman posting letter, *circa* 1840	85	65
497	$2 Modern mail transport	2·75	1·50
494/7	*Set of 4*	4·00	2·50

(Litho Format)

1980 (21 May). *10th Anniv of Moon Landing. T 80 and similar horiz designs. Multicoloured. P 13½ × 14.*
498	75 c. Type 80	25	25
499	95 c. Plaque left on Moon	25	30
500	$1.25, Rejoining mother ship	30	50
501	$2 Lunar Module	50	75
498/501	*Set of 4*	1·10	1·60
MS502	118 × 84 mm. Nos. 498/501	1·40	2·50

81 American Wigeon

(Litho Questa)

1980 (16 June). *Birds. Multicoloured designs as T 81. P 14.*
503	1 c. Type 81	70	70
504	2 c. Snowy Plover	70	70
505	4 c. Rose-breasted Grosbeak	75	70
506	6 c. Mangrove Cuckoo	75	70
507	10 c. Adelaide's Warbler	75	70
508	15 c. Scaly-breasted Thrasher	80	70
509	20 c. Yellow-crowned Night Heron	80	70
510	25 c. Bridled Quail Dove	80	70
511	35 c. Carib Grackle	85	70
512	50 c. Pintail	90	55
513	75 c. Black-whiskered Vireo	1·00	55
514	$1 Blue-winged Teal	1·25	80
515	$1.50, Green-throated Carib (*vert*)	1·50	80
516	$2 Red-necked Pigeon (*vert*)	2·25	1·25
517	$2.50, Wied's Crested Flycatcher (*vert*)	2·75	1·50
518	$5 Yellow-bellied Sapsucker (*vert*)	4·00	2·50
519	$7.50, Caribbean Elaenia (*vert*)	5·00	5·00
520	$10 Great Egret (*vert*)	5·00	5·00
503/20	*Set of 18*	27·00	22·00

1980 (29 July). *Famous Works of Art. Nos. 651/7 of Antigua optd with T 67.*
521	10 c. "David" (statue, Donatello)	10	10
522	30 c. "The Birth of Venus" (painting, Sandro Botticelli)	15	15
523	50 c. "Reclining Couple" (sarcophagus), Cerveteri	20	20
524	90 c. "The Garden of Earthly Delights" (painting, Hieronymus Bosch)	25	25
525	$1 "Portinari Altarpiece" (painting, Hugo van der Goes)	25	25
526	$4 "Eleanora of Toledo and her Son Giovanni de' Medici" (painting, Agnolo Bronzino)	80	80
521/6	*Set of 6*	1·50	1·50
MS527	99 × 124 mm. $5 "The Holy Family" (painting, Rembrandt)	1·50	1·75

1980 (8 Sept). *75th Anniv of Rotary International. Nos. 658/62 of Antigua optd with T 67.*
528	30 c. Rotary anniversary emblem and headquarters, U.S.A.	15	15
529	50 c. Rotary anniversary emblem and Antigua Rotary Club banner	20	20
530	90 c. Map of Antigua and Rotary emblem	25	25
531	$3 Paul P. Harris (founder) and Rotary emblem	65	65
528/31	*Set of 4*	1·10	1·10
MS532	102 × 77 mm. $5 Antigua flags and Rotary emblems	1·50	2·25

BARBUDA BARBUDA
(82) (83)

1980 (6 Oct). *80th Birthday of Queen Elizabeth the Queen Mother. Nos. 663/5 of Antigua optd with T 82.*
533	10 c. multicoloured	50	15
	a. Opt inverted	38·00	
	b. Opt double	30·00	
534	$2.50, multicoloured	1·25	1·50
MS535	68 × 88 mm. $3 multicoloured	1·75	1·75

1980 (8 Dec). *Birds. Nos. 666/70 of Antigua optd with T 83.*
536	10 c. Ringed Kingfisher	1·75	90
537	30 c. Plain Pigeon	2·25	1·00
538	$1 Green-throated Carib	3·25	2·50
539	$2 Black-necked Stilt	3·75	4·50
536/9	*Set of 4*	10·00	8·00
MS540	73 × 73 mm. $2.50, Roseate Tern	4·25	2·75

1981 (26 Jan). *Sugar Cane Railway Locomotives. Nos. 681/5 of Antigua optd with T 67.*
541	25 c. Diesel Locomotive No. 15	1·00	25
542	50 c. Narrow-gauge steam locomotive	1·25	35
543	90 c. Diesel locomotives Nos. 1 and 10	1·75	45
544	$3 Steam locomotive hauling sugar cane	3·25	1·40
541/4	*Set of 4*	6·50	2·25
MS545	82 × 111 mm. $2.50, Antigua sugar factory, railway yard and sheds	1·50	1·75

84 Florence Nightingale

85 Goofy in Motor-boat

(Litho Format)

1981 (9 Mar). *Famous Women. T 84 and similar vert designs. P 14 × 13½.*
546	50 c. multicoloured	15	30
547	90 c. multicoloured	40	55
548	$1 multicoloured	35	60
549	$4 black, yellow-brown and rose-lilac	50	1·75
546/9	*Set of 4*	1·25	2·75

Designs:—90 c. Marie Curie; $1 Amy Johnson; $4 Eleanor Roosevelt.
Nos. 546/9 exist imperforate from stock dispersed by the liquidator of Format International Security Printers Ltd.

(Litho Format)

1981 (15 May). *Walt Disney Cartoon Characters. T 85 and similar vert designs showing characters afloat. Multicoloured. P 13½.*
550	10 c. Type 85	55	15
551	20 c. Donald Duck reversing car into sea	65	20
552	25 c. Mickey Mouse asking tug-boat to take on more than it can handle	80	30

553	30 c. Porpoise turning the tables on Goofy	80	35
554	35 c. Goofy in sailing boat	80	35
555	40 c. Mickey Mouse and boat being lifted out of water by fish	90	40
556	75 c. Donald Duck fishing for flying-fish with butterfly net	1·00	60
557	$1 Minnie Mouse in brightly decorated sailing boat	1·10	80
558	$2 Chip and Dale on floating ship-in-bottle	1·75	1·40
550/8	*Set of 9*	7·50	4·00
MS559	127 × 101 mm. $2.50, Donald Duck	4·00	3·00

BARBUDA
(86)

1981 (9 June). *Birth Centenary of Picasso. Nos. 697/701 of Antigua optd with T 86.*
560	10 c. "Pipes of Pan"	10	10
561	50 c. "Seated Harlequin"	25	25
562	90 c. "Paulo as Harlequin"	45	45
563	$4 "Mother and Child"	1·25	1·60
560/3	*Set of 4*	1·75	2·10
MS564	115 × 140 mm. $5 "Three Musicians" (detail)	1·75	1·75

87 Buckingham Palace 88

(Des G. Drummond. Litho Format)

1981 (27 July). *Royal Wedding (1st issue). Buildings. T 87/8 and similar horiz designs. Each bicoloured*. P 11 × 11½.*
565	$1 Type 87	25	40
566	$1 Type 88	25	40
	a. Sheetlet. Nos. 565/70	2·00	
	b. Booklet pane. Nos. 565/6 × 2 in imperf between horiz pairs	2·00	
567	$1.50 } Caernarvon Castle	30	50
568	$1.50 }	30	50
	b. Booklet pane. Nos. 567/8 × 2 in imperf between horiz pairs	2·25	
569	$4 } Highgrove House	55	90
570	$4 }	55	90
	b. Booklet pane. Nos. 569/70 × 2 in imperf between horiz pairs	2·50	
565/70	*Set of 6*	2·00	3·25
MS571	75 × 90 mm. $5 black and olive-yellow (St. Paul's Cathedral—26 × 32 mm). P 11½ × 11	80	1·25

*Nos. 565/70 each exist printed in black with three different background colours, rose-pink, turquoise-green and lavender.
No. 566b was printed only in black and rose-pink. No. 568b black and turquoise-green and No. 570b black and lavender.
Nos. 565/70 were printed together, *se-tenant*, in sheetlets of 6, the two versions of each value forming a composite design.
Nos. 565/70 exist imperforate from stock dispersed by the liquidator of Format International Security Printers Ltd.

1981 (14 Aug). *Royal Wedding (2nd issue). Nos. 702/5 of Antigua optd with T 86.*
572	25 c. Prince Charles and Lady Diana Spencer	15	15
573	50 c. Glamis Castle	25	25
	a. Opt double	25·00	
574	$4 Prince Charles skiing	75	1·00
	a. Error. Optd on unissued Uganda 20s. showing Prince Charles at Balmoral	60·00	
	ab. Opt double		
572/4	*Set of 3*	1·10	1·25
MS575	95×85 mm. $5 Glass Coach	90	90

Nos. 572/4 exist perforated 12 (*Price for set of 3 £1.10 mint or used*) from additional sheetlets of five stamps and one label. These stamps have changed background colours. One sheetlet of the 25 c. is known with the overprint inverted.

89 "Integration and Travel"

(Litho Format)

1981 (14 Sept). *International Year for Disabled Persons (1st issue). T 89 and similar horiz designs. P 14.*
576	50 c. multicoloured	25	20
577	90 c. black, red-orange and blue-green	25	25
578	$1 black, light blue and bright green	30	30
579	$4 black, yellow-ochre and orange-brown	45	85
576/9	*Set of 4*	1·10	1·40

Designs:—90 c. Braille and sign language; $1 "Helping hands"; $4 "Mobility aids for disabled".
Nos. 576/9 exist imperforate from stock dispersed by the liquidator of Format International Security Printers Ltd.
See also Nos. 603/7.

BARBUDA
(90)

1981 (12 Oct). *Royal Wedding (3rd issue). Nos. 706/12 of Antigua optd with T 90 in silver.*
580	25 c. Prince of Wales at Investiture, 1969	35	55
	a. Booklet pane. Nos. 580/5	2·50	
581	25 c. Prince Charles as baby, 1948	35	55
582	$1 Prince Charles at R.A.F. College, Cranwell, 1971	40	60
583	$1 Prince Charles attending Hill House School, 1956	40	60

584	$2 Prince Charles and Lady Diana Spencer	65	80
585	$2 Prince Charles at Trinity College, 1967	65	80
586	$5 Prince Charles and Lady Diana..	2·50	3·50
	a. Booklet pane of 1..	2·50	
580/6	*Set of 7*	5·00	6·50

1981 (1 Nov). *Independence. Nos. 686B/96B of Antigua additionally optd with T 86.*

587	6 c. Orchid Tree	50	15
588	10 c. Bougainvillea	55	15
589	20 c. Flamboyant	70	20
590	25 c. Hibiscus	80	25
591	35 c. Flame of the Wood	90	30
592	50 c. Cannon at Fort James	1·10	45
593	75 c. Premier's Office	1·25	75
594	$1 Potworks Dam	1·50	80
595	$2.50, Irrigation scheme, Diamond Estate	2·50	2·75
596	$5 Government House	2·75	3·75
597	$10 Coolidge International Airport ..	4·50	6·00
587/97	*Set of 11*	15·00	14·00

BARBUDA   BARBUDA
(91)   (92)

1981 (14 Dec). *50th Anniv of Antigua Girl Guide Movement. Nos. 713/17 of Antigua optd with T 83 (No. MS602) or T 91 (others).*

598	10 c. Irene Joshua (founder)	55	10
599	50 c. Campfire sing-song	1·25	30
600	90 c. Sailing	1·75	45
601	$2.50, Animal tending	3·00	1·40
598/601	*Set of 4*	6·00	2·00
MS602	110 × 85 mm. $5 Raising the flag ..	3·50	3·50

1981 (14 Dec). *International Year for Disabled Persons (2nd issue). Nos. 728/32 of Antigua optd with T 83 (No. MS607) or T 91 (others).*

603	10 c. Swimming	20	15
604	50 c. Discus throwing ..	30	25
605	90 c. Archery	70	45
606	$2 Baseball	1·25	1·50
603/6	*Set of 4*	2·25	2·10
MS607	108 × 84 mm. $4 Basketball	2·75	2·25

1981 (22 Dec). *Christmas. Paintings. Nos. 723/7 of Antigua optd with T 92.*

608	8 c. "Holy Night" (Jacques Stella) ..	10	10
609	30 c. "Mary with Child" (Julius Schnorr von Carolfeld)	20	20
610	$1 "Virgin and Child" (Alonso Cano) (S.) ..	40	40
611	$3 "Virgin and Child" (Lorenzo di Credi) ..	1·10	1·10
608/11	*Set of 4*	1·60	1·60
MS612	77 × 111 mm. $5 "Holy Family" (Pieter von Avon)	1·75	2·25

BARBUDA $1   *S. Atlantic Fund + 50c.*
93 Princess of Wales   (94)

(Des G. Drummond. Litho Format)

1982 (21 June). *Birth of Prince William of Wales (1st issue). T 93 and similar vert portraits. W w 15. P 14.*

613	$1 multicoloured	50	50
	w. Wmk inverted	60	
614	$2.50, multicoloured	90	1·10
	a. Reddish violet (top inscr) omitted	£180	
	w. Wmk inverted ..	1·10	
615	$5 multicoloured	2·00	2·25
	w. Wmk inverted ..	2·40	
613/15	*Set of 3*	3·00	3·50
MS616	88×108 mm. $4 multicoloured. No wmk	2·00	2·10

Nos. 613/15 were issued in sheets of 10 stamps with 2 undenominated black prints, in positions 9 and 13, and 9 blank labels. These sheets exist in two different formats, with all stamps upright or with 6 stamps and one black print inverted.

1982 (28 June). *South Atlantic Fund. Nos. 580/6 such as T 94.*

617	25 c. + 50 c. Prince of Wales at Investiture, 1969	20	20
	a. Booklet pane. Nos. 617/22	2·50	
	b. Surch double	20·00	
618	25 c. +50 c. Prince Charles as baby, 1948	20	20
	b. Surch double	20·00	
619	$1 +50 c. Prince Charles at R.A.F. College, Cranwell, 1971	45	45
	b. Surch double	20·00	
620	$1 +50 c. Prince Charles attending Hill House School, 1956	45	45
	b. Surch double	20·00	
621	$2 +50 c. Prince Charles and Lady Diana Spencer	75	75
	b. Surch double	20·00	
622	$2 +50 c. Prince Charles at Trinity College, 1967	75	75
	b. Surch double	20·00	
623	$5 +50 c. Prince Charles and Lady Diana	2·00	2·00
	a. Booklet pane of 1..	2·00	
	b. Surch double	£150	
617/23	*Set of 7*	4·00	4·00

(Des G. Drummond. Litho Format)

1982 (1 July). *21st Birthday of Princess of Wales (1st issue). As Nos. 613/16 but inscribed "Twenty First Birthday Greetings to H.R.H. The Princess of Wales". W w 15. P 14.*

624	$1 multicoloured	1·00	45
	w. Wmk inverted	1·10	
625	$2.50, multicoloured	1·75	1·25
	w. Wmk inverted	1·90	
626	$5 multicoloured	2·75	2·40
	w. Wmk inverted	3·00	
624/6	*Set of 3*	5·00	3·75
MS627	88×108 mm. $4 multicoloured. No wmk	2·75	2·25

See note beneath Nos. 613/16

BARBUDA
MAIL   BARBUDA MAIL
(95)   (96)

1982 (30 Aug). *21st Birthday of Princess of Wales (2nd issue). Nos. 748/51 of Antigua optd as T 95, in silver (No. 629) or black (others).*

628	90 c. Queen's House, Greenwich	70	45
629	$1 Prince and Princess of Wales	80	50
630	$4 Princess of Wales	2·00	1·50
628/30	*Set of 3*	3·25	2·25
MS631	102 × 75 mm. $5 Princess of Wales (*different*)	1·75	2·00

The overprint on No. MS631 measures 18 × 6 mm.
Nos. 628/30 also exist from additional sheetlets of 5 stamps and 1 label overprinted with a larger overprint, 18 × 6 mm long (*price for set of 3 £3 mint or used*). On the $1 and $4 values the second line of overprint aligns to left.

1982 (12 Oct). *Birth of Prince William of Wales (2nd issue). Nos. 757/60 of Antigua further optd with T 95, in silver ($1, $4) or black (others).*

632	90 c. Queen's House, Greenwich	55	45
633	$1 Prince and Princess of Wales	60	50
634	$4 Princess of Wales	2·50	2·00
632/4	*Set of 3*	3·25	2·75
MS635	102 × 75 mm. $5 Princess of Wales (*different*)	2·75	2·50

The overprint on No. MS635 measures 18 × 6 mm.

1982 (6 Dec). *Birth Centenary of Franklin D. Roosevelt (Nos. 636, 638, 640/2) and 250th Birth Anniv of George Washington (others). Nos. 761/8 of Antigua optd as T 95 (second line ranged left on No. MS642).*

636	10 c. Roosevelt in 1940	10	10
637	30 c. Washington as blacksmith	15	15
638	45 c. Churchill, Roosevelt and Stalin at Yalta conference	35	25
639	60 c. Washington crossing the Delaware	20	25
640	$1 "Roosevelt Special" train	50	40
641	$3 Portrait of Roosevelt	60	90
636/41	*Set of 6*	1·60	1·75
MS642	92 × 87 mm. $4 Roosevelt and wife	1·00	1·75
MS643	92 × 87 mm. $4 Portrait of Washington	1·00	1·75

1982 (6 Dec). *Christmas. Religious Paintings by Raphael. Nos. 769/73 of Antigua optd with T 96.*

644	10 c. "Annunciation"	10	10
645	30 c. "Adoration of the Magi" ..	15	15
646	$1 "Presentation at the Temple"	40	40
647	$4 "Coronation of the Virgin"	1·00	1·00
644/7	*Set of 4*	1·50	1·50
MS648	95 × 124 mm. $5 "Marriage of the Virgin"	1·25	2·00

1983 (14 Mar). *500th Birth Anniv of Raphael. Details from "Galatea" Fresco. Nos. 774/8 of Antigua optd as T 95 (45, 50 c. and larger (18 × 6 mm) on MS653) or T 96 (others).*

649	45 c. Tritons and Dolphins	20	20
650	50 c. Sea Nymph carried off by Triton	20	20
651	60 c. Winged angel steering Dolphins (*horiz*)	25	25
652	$4 Cupids shooting arrows (*horiz*)	1·00	1·00
649/52	*Set of 4*	1·50	1·50
MS653	101 × 126 mm. $5 Galatea pulled along by Dolphins	1·25	2·00

1983 (14 Mar). *Commonwealth Day. Nos. 779/82 of Antigua optd as T 96.*

654	25 c. Pineapple produce	55	70
655	45 c. Carnival	80	90
656	60 c. Tourism	1·25	1·60
657	$3 Airport	2·75	4·00
654/7	*Set of 4*	4·75	6·50

1983 (12 Apr). *World Communications Year. Nos. 783/7 of Antigua optd as T 96 (Nos. 658/61) or as T 95 with second line ranged left (No. MS662).*

658	15 c. T.V. satellite coverage of Royal Wedding	75	25
659	50 c. Police communications	2·25	90
660	60 c. House-to-train telephone call	2·00	90
661	$3 Satellite earth station with planets Jupiter and Saturn	3·50	2·50
658/61	*Set of 4*	7·50	4·00
MS662	100×90 mm. $5 "Comsat" satellite over West Indies	2·25	2·50
	a. Albino opt	30·00	

97 Vincenzo Lunardi's Balloon   (98)
Flight, London, 1785

(Des G. Drummond. Litho)

1983 (13 June). *Bicentenary of Manned Flight (1st issue). T 97 and similar vert designs. Multicoloured. P 14.*

663	$1 Type 97	25	35
664	$1.50, Montgolfier brothers' balloon flight, Paris, 1783	40	55
665	$2.50, Blanchard and Jeffries' Cross-Channel balloon flight, 1785	60	90
663/5	*Set of 3*	1·10	1·60
MS666	111×111 mm. $5 Maiden flight of Airship LZ-127 *Graf Zeppelin*, 1928	2·00	2·75

See also No. 672/6.

1983 (4 July). *Whales. Nos. 788/92 of Antigua optd as T 95 (Nos. 667/70) or larger, 17 × 5½ mm (No. MS671), each with the second line ranged left.*

667	15 c. Bottle-nosed Dolphin ..	1·25	40
668	50 c. Fin Whale	4·00	1·60
669	60 c. Bowhead Whale.	4·50	1·75
670	$3 Spectacled Porpoise	5·50	4·25
667/70	*Set of 4*	14·00	7·25
MS671	122×101 mm. $5 Narwhal	3·75	4·50

1983 (12 Sept). *Bicentenary of Manned Flight (2nd issue). Nos. 811/15 of Antigua optd as T 96.*

672	30 c. Dornier Do-X flying boat	85	35
673	50 c. Supermarine S6B seaplane	1·10	60
674	60 c. Curtiss F-9C Sparrowhawk biplane and airship U.S.S. *Akron*	1·25	70
675	$4 Hot-air balloon *Pro Juventute*	4·50	4·00
672/5	*Set of 4*	7·00	5·00
MS676	80×105 mm. $5 Airship LZ-127 *Graf Zeppelin*	3·75	4·25

1983 (21 Oct). *Nos. 565/70 surch as T 98. P 11×11½.*

677	45 c. on $1 Type 87	25	45
	a. Sheetlet. Nos. 677/82	1·40	
	b. Perf 14½	1·25	2·50
	ba. Sheetlet. Nos. 677b/82b	6·50	
	bb. Error. 50 c. on $1	4·50	
	bc. Surch omitted	35·00	
678	45 c. on $1 Type 88	25	45
	b. Perf 14½	1·25	2·50
	bb. Error. 50 c. on $1	4·50	
	bc. Surch omitted	35·00	
679	50 c. on $1.50, Caernarvon Castle (left)	25	45
	b. Perf 14½	1·25	2·50
	bb. Error. 45 c. on $1.50	4·50	
	bc. Surch omitted	35·00	
680	50 c. on $1.50, Caernarvon Castle (right)	25	45
	b. Perf 14½	1·25	2·50
	bb. Error. 45 c. on $1.50	4·50	
	bc. Surch omitted	35·00	
681	60 c. on $4 Highgrove House (left)	25	45
	b. Perf 14½	1·25	2·50
	bc. Surch omitted	35·00	
682	60 c. on $4 Highgrove House (right)	25	45
	b. Perf 14½	1·25	2·50
	bc. Surch omitted	35·00	
677/82	*Set of 6*	1·40	2·50

Nos. 677bb, 678bb, 679bb and 680bb occur on the 14½ perforated sheetlets with rose-pink background.

Examples of No. 677a, and also of the errors, imperforate exist from stock dispersed by the liquidator of Format International Security Printers Ltd.

1983 (28 Oct). *Nos. 793/810 of Antigua optd with T 96.*

683	1 c. Cashew Nut	10	10
684	2 c. Passion Fruit	15	10
685	3 c. Mango	15	10
686	5 c. Grapefruit	15	10
687	10 c. Pawpaw	20	10
688	15 c. Breadfruit	40	10
689	20 c. Coconut	50	15
690	25 c. Oleander	50	15
691	30 c. Banana	55	20
692	40 c. Pineapple	65	25
693	45 c. Cordia	70	30
694	50 c. Cassia	80	30
695	60 c. Poui	80	30
696	$1 Frangipani	1·10	40
697	$2 Flamboyant	1·75	1·25
698	$2.50, Lemon	2·00	1·75
699	$5 Lignum Vitae	3·00	2·25
700	$10 National flag and coat of arms	4·50	5·50
683/700	*Set of 18*	16·00	12·00

EDWARD VII 1901 – 1910 $1

BARBUDA MAIL
(99)   100 Edward VII

1983 (28 Oct). *Christmas. 500th Birth Anniv of Raphael. Nos. 816/20 of Antigua optd with T 99 or slightly smaller (29 × 4 mm) (MS705).*

701	10 c. multicoloured	10	10
702	30 c. multicoloured	10	20
703	$1 multicoloured	30	50
704	$4 multicoloured	1·00	1·50
701/4	*Set of 4*	1·25	2·00
MS705	101 × 131 mm. $5 multicoloured..	1·40	2·50

1983 (14 Dec). *Bicentenary of Methodist Church (1984). Nos. 821/4 of Antigua optd with T 95 (in silver on 15 c. and 50 c.).*

706	15 c. John Wesley (founder)	20	15
707	50 c. Nathaniel Gilbert (founder in Antigua)	30	25
708	60 c. St. John Methodist Church steeple	30	50
709	$3 Ebenezer Methodist Church, St. John's	80	1·00
706/9	*Set of 4*	1·40	1·50

(Des G. Drummond. Litho Format)

1984 (14 Feb). *Members of British Royal Family. T **100** and similar vert portraits. Multicoloured. P 14½.*

710	$1 Type **100**	.. ..	50	1·10
711	$1 George V	.. ..	50	1·10
712	$1 George VI	.. ..	50	1·10
713	$1 Elizabeth II	.. ..	50	1·10
714	$1 Charles, Prince of Wales	..	50	1·10
715	$1 Prince William	.. ..	50	1·10
710/15		*Set of 6*	2·75	6·00

1984 (26 Apr). *Olympic Games, Los Angeles (1st issue). Nos. 825/9 of Antigua optd as T **99** (23 × 3 mm in size on Nos. 716/19).*

716	25 c. Discus	..	15	20
717	50 c. Gymnastics	..	35	40
718	90 c. Hurdling	..	50	60
719	$3 Cycling	..	1·25	1·50
716/19		*Set of 4*	2·00	2·40
MS720	82 × 67 mm. $5 Volleyball	..	2·75	3·25

1984 (12 July). *Ships. Nos. 830/4 of Antigua optd with T **95** (MS725) or T **99** (others).*

721	45 c. *Booker Vanguard* (freighter)		1·50	45
722	50 c. *Canberra* (liner)	..	1·50	50
723	60 c. Yachts	..	1·75	60
724	$4 *Fairwind* (cargo liner)	..	4·25	2·75
721/4		*Set of 4*	8·00	3·75
MS725	107×80 mm. $5 18th-century British man-o-war (*vert*)		4·50	4·25

1984 (12 July). *Universal Postal Union Congress, Hamburg. Nos. 835/9 of Antigua optd with T **95**.*

726	15 c. Chenille	..	30	15
727	50 c. Shell Flower	..	40	30
728	60 c. Anthurium	..	45	40
729	$3 Angels Trumpet	..	95	1·25
726/9		*Set of 4*	1·90	1·90
MS730	100 × 75 mm. $5 Crown of Thorns		2·00	2·50

101 Olympic Stadium, Athens, 1896   (**102**)

(Litho Format)

1984 (27 July). *Olympic Games, Los Angeles (2nd issue). T **101** and similar horiz designs. Multicoloured. P 13½.*

731	$1.50 Type **101**	..	60	90
732	$2.50, Olympic stadium, Los Angeles, 1984	80	1·50
733	$5 Athlete carrying Olympic torch	1·40	2·25
731/3		*Set of 3*	2·50	4·25
MS734	121 × 95 mm. No. 733. P 15		1·50	2·50

1984 (1 Oct). *Presidents of the United States of America. Nos. 856/63 of Antigua optd with T **95** (in silver on 10, 90 c., $1.10 and $1.50).*

735	10 c. Abraham Lincoln	..	10	10
736	20 c. Harry Truman	..	15	15
737	30 c. Dwight Eisenhower	..	20	25
738	40 c. Ronald Reagan	..	25	30
739	90 c. Gettysburg Address, 1863	50	55
740	$1.10, Formation of N.A.T.O., 1949	50	65
741	$1.50, Eisenhower during Second World War	60	70
742	$2 Reagan and Caribbean Basin Initiative	75	1·00
735/42		*Set of 8*	2·75	3·50

1984 (1 Oct). *150th Anniv of Abolition of Slavery. Nos. 864/8 of Antigua optd with T **96** (Nos. 743/6) or as T **95**, but 18 × 6½ mm (No. MS747).*

743	40 c. View of Moravian Mission	30	30
744	50 c. Antigua Courthouse, 1823	40	40
745	60 c. Planting sugar-cane, Monks Hill	45	45
746	$3 Boiling house, Delaps' Estate	1·40	1·40
743/6		*Set of 4*	2·25	2·25
MS747	95 × 70 mm. $5 Loading sugar, Willoughby Bay		2·00	2·50

1984 (21 Nov). *Songbirds. Nos. 869/74 of Antigua optd with T **95** or larger (18 × 7 mm) (No. MS753).*

748	40 c. Rufous-sided Towhee	1·50	45
749	50 c. Parula Warbler	..	1·60	50
750	60 c. House Wren	..	1·75	55
751	$2 Ruby-crowned Kinglet	3·00	1·50
752	$3 Common Flicker	..	3·25	2·25
748/52		*Set of 5*	10·00	4·75
MS753	76 × 76 mm. $5 Yellow-breasted Chat	4·00	4·50

1984 (21 Nov). *450th Death Anniv of Correggio (painter). Nos. 878/82 of Antigua optd with T **95** or larger (18 × 7 mm) No. MS758), all in silver.*

754	25 c. "The Virgin and Infant with Angels and Cherubs"		15	20
755	60 c. "The Four Saints"	..	40	45
756	90 c. "St. Catherine"	..	50	55
757	$3 "The Campori Madonna"	1·25	1·75
754/7		*Set of 4*	2·10	2·75
MS758	90 × 60 mm. $5 "St. John the Baptist"	2·25	3·25

1984 (30 Nov). *"Ausipex" International Stamp Exhibition, Melbourne. Australian Sports. Nos. 875/7 of Antigua optd with T **95** or larger (18 × 7 mm) (No. MS761).*

759	$1 Grass-skiing	..	70	75
760	$5 Australian Football	2·50	3·25
MS761	108 × 78 mm. $5 Boomerang-throwing	2·50	3·25

1984 (30 Nov). *150th Birth Anniv of Edgar Degas (painter). Nos. 883/7 of Antigua optd with T **95** (Nos. 762/5) or T **99** (No. MS766), all in silver.*

762	15 c. "The Blue Dancers"	..	10	10
763	50 c. "The Pink Dancers"	..	30	40
764	70 c. "Two Dancers"	..	45	55
765	$4 "Dancers at the Bar"	..	1·75	3·50
762/5		*Set of 4*	2·40	4·00
MS766	90 × 60 mm. $5 "The Folk Dancers" (40 × 27 mm)		2·50	2·75

1985 (18 Feb). *Famous People. Nos. 888/96 of Antigua optd with T **102** (horizontally on Nos. 771/5).*

767	60 c. Winston Churchill	..	2·00	80
768	60 c. Mahatma Gandhi	..	2·00	80
769	60 c. John F. Kennedy	..	2·00	80
770	60 c. Mao Tse-tung	..	2·00	80
771	$1 Churchill with General De Gaulle, Paris, 1944 (*horiz*)		2·25	1·00
772	$1 Gandhi leaving London by train, 1931 (*horiz*)		2·25	1·00
773	$1 Kennedy with Chancellor Adenauer and Mayor Brandt, Berlin, 1963 (*horiz*)		2·25	1·00
774	$1 Mao Tse-tung with Lin Piao, Peking, 1969 (*horiz*)		2·25	1·00
767/74		*Set of 8*	15·00	6·50
MS775	114×80 mm. $5 Flags of Great Britain, India, the United States and China		3·50	3·75

103 Lady Elizabeth Bowes-Lyon, 1907, and Camellias

104 Roseate Tern

(Des G. Drummond. Litho Format)

1985 (26 Feb). *Life and Times of Queen Elizabeth the Queen Mother (1st issue). T **103** and similar vert designs. Multicoloured. P 14×14½.*

776	15 c. Type **103**.	..	15	10
777	45 c. Duchess of York, 1926, and "Elizabeth of Glamis" roses		25	25
778	50 c. The Queen Mother after the Coronation, 1937		25	25
779	60 c. In Garter robes, 1971, and Dog Roses	25	30
780	90 c. Attending Royal Variety show, 1967, and red Hibiscus		35	45
781	$2 The Queen Mother in 1982, and blue Plumbago		65	1·10
782	$3 Receiving 82nd birthday gifts from children, and Morning Glory		90	1·60
776/82		*Set of 7*	2·50	3·50

Nos. 776/82 exist imperforate from stock dispersed by the liquidator of Format International Security Printers Ltd. See also Nos. 826/9.

(Des G. Drummond. Litho Format)

1985 (4 Apr). *Birth Bicentenary of John J. Audubon (ornithologist) (1st issue). T **104** and similar vert designs showing original paintings. Multicoloured. P 14.*

783	45 c. Type **104**.	..	25	30
784	50 c. Mangrove Cuckoo	..	25	30
785	60 c. Yellow-crowned Night Heron	30	40
786	$5 Brown Pelican	..	1·75	3·00
783/6		*Set of 4*	2·25	4·00

Nos. 783/6 exist imperforate from stock dispersed by the liquidator of Format International Security Printers Ltd. See also Nos. 794/8 and 914/17.

1985 (10 May). *Centenary of the Statue of Liberty (1986) (1st issue). Nos. 907/13 of Antigua optd horizontally with T **102**.*

787	25 c. Torch from Statue in Madison Square Park, 1885		20	20
788	30 c. Statue of Liberty and scaffolding ("Restoration and Renewal") (*vert*)		20	20
789	50 c. Frederic Bartholdi (sculptor) supervising construction, 1876		30	40
790	90 c. Close-up of Statue	..	55	55
791	$1 Statue and sailing ship ("Operation Sail", 1976) (*vert*)		60	60
792	$3 Dedication ceremony, 1886 (*vert*)	1·75	1·75
787/92		*Set of 6*	3·00	3·00
MS793	110×80 mm. $5 Port of New York	2·75	3·00

See also Nos. 987/96.

BARBUDA MAIL   BARBUDA MAIL

(**105**)   (**106**)   (**107**)

4TH AUG 1900–1985

1985 (18 July). *Birth Bicentenary of John J. Audubon (ornithologist) (2nd issue). Nos. 924/8 of Antigua optd with T **105**.*

794	90 c. Slavonian Grebe	..	4·75	3·75
795	$1 British Storm Petrel	..	5·00	4·00
796	$1.50, Great Blue Heron	..	6·00	4·75
797	$3 Double-crested Cormorant	9·00	7·00
794/7		*Set of 4*	22·00	17·00
MS798	103×72 mm. $5 White-tailed Tropic Bird (*vert*)		16·00	9·00

1985 (18 July). *Butterflies. Nos. 929/33 of Antigua optd with T **106**.*

799	25 c. *Anaea cyanea*	..	3·00	1·75
800	60 c. *Leodonta dysoni*	..	4·50	2·00
801	90 c. *Junea doraete*	..	5·50	2·50
802	$4 *Prepona pylene*	..	11·00	11·00
799/802		*Set of 4*	22·00	15·00
MS803	132×105 mm. $5 *Caerois gerdtrudtus*	15·00	8·50

1985 (2 Aug). *Centenary of the Motorcycle. Nos. 919/23 of Antigua optd with T **106**.*

804	10 c. Triumph 2hp "Jap", 1903	40	10
805	30 c. Indian "Arrow", 1949	..	70	20
806	60 c. BMW "R100RS", 1976	1·10	40
807	$4 Harley-Davidson "Model II", 1916	3·50	2·75
804/7		*Set of 4*	5·25	3·00
MS808	90×93 mm. $5 Laverda "Jota", 1975	4·00	4·00

1985 (2 Aug). *85th Birthday of Queen Elizabeth the Queen Mother. Nos. 776/82 optd with T **107**.*

809	15 c. Type **103**.	..	60	30
	a. Red (frame, flowers, etc) omitted	32·00	
810	45 c. Duchess of York, 1926, and "Elizabeth of Glamis" roses		90	50
811	50 c. The Queen Mother after the Coronation, 1937		90	50
812	60 c. In Garter robes, 1971, and Dog Roses	1·00	80
813	90 c. Attending Royal Variety show, 1967, and red Hibiscus		1·10	1·10
814	$2 The Queen Mother in 1982, and blue Plumbago		1·40	3·25
815	$3 Receiving 82nd birthday gifts from children, and Morning Glory		1·50	3·25
809/15		*Set of 7*	6·50	8·75

The 45 c. exists with the yellow omitted from stock dispersed by the liquidator of Format International Security Printers Ltd.

1985 (30 Aug). *Native American Artefacts. Nos. 914/18 of Antigua optd horizontally with T **102**.*

816	15 c. Arawak pot sherd and Indians making clay utensils		15	10
817	50 c. Arawak body design and Arawak Indians tattooing		25	25
818	60 c. Head of the god "Yocahu" and Indians harvesting manioc		35	35
819	$3 Carib war club and Carib Indians going into battle		1·25	1·50
816/19		*Set of 4*	1·75	1·90
MS820	97×68 mm. $5 Taino Indians worshipping stone idol		2·00	3·00

1985 (30 Aug). *40th Anniv of International Civil Aviation Organization. Nos. 934/8 of Antigua optd with T **106**.*

821	30 c. Cessna 172D Skyhawk	1·00	60
822	90 c. Fokker D.VII	..	1·75	1·00
823	$1.50, SPAD VII	..	2·25	3·25
824	$3 Boeing 747	..	3·75	4·50
821/4		*Set of 4*	8·00	8·50
MS825	97×83 mm. De Havilland D.H.C.6 Twin Otter		3·25	3·50

1985 (8 Nov). *Life and Times of Queen Elizabeth the Queen Mother (2nd issue). Nos. 946/9 of Antigua optd with T **95** (in silver on Nos. 826/7 and MS829).*

826	$1 The Queen Mother attending church	2·75	2·50
827	$1.50, Watching children playing in London garden		3·25	3·00
828	$2.50, The Queen Mother in 1979	4·00	3·50
826/8		*Set of 3*	9·00	8·00
MS829	56×85 mm. $5 With Prince Edward at Royal Wedding, 1981		8·50	8·50

Nos. 826/7 also exist with black and No. 828 with silver overprints (*Price for set of 3 £50 mint*).

The stamps from the sheetlets mentioned beneath Antigua No. MS949 also exist overprinted with Type **95**.

1985 (25 Nov). *850th Birth Anniv of Maimonides (physician, philosopher and scholar). Nos. 939/40 of Antigua optd with T **95**.*

830	$2 bright green	..	4·50	3·75
MS831	70×84 mm. $5 reddish brown	4·25	4·25

1985 (25 Nov). *Marine Life. Nos. 950/4 of Antigua optd with T **95** (in silver on 15 c. and $3).*

832	15 c. Magnificent Frigate Bird	3·50	75
833	45 c. Brain Coral	..	3·50	70
834	60 c. Cushion Star	..	3·50	90
835	$3 Spotted Moray	..	7·00	4·25
832/5		*Set of 4*	16·00	6·00
MS836	110×80 mm. $5 Elkhorn Coral	10·00	6·00

1986 (17 Feb). *International Youth Year. Nos. 941/5 of Antigua optd with T **95**.*

837	25 c. Young farmers with produce	15	15
838	50 c. Hotel management trainees	25	30
839	60 c. Girls with goat and boys with football ("Environment")		30	35
840	$3 Windsurfing ("Leisure")	1·50	1·60
837/40		*Set of 4*	2·00	2·10
MS841	102×72 mm. $5 Young people with Antiguan flags		2·75	3·25

1986 (17 Feb). *Royal Visit. Nos. 965/8 of Antigua optd with T **106**.*

842	60 c. Flags of Great Britain and Antigua	1·25	35
843	$1 Queen Elizabeth II (*vert*)	1·40	45
844	$4 Royal Yacht *Britannia*	4·50	2·10
842/4		*Set of 3*	6·50	2·75
MS845	110×83 mm. $5 Map of Antigua	5·00	3·50

1986 (10 Mar). *75th Anniv of Girl Guide Movement. Nos. 955/9 of Antigua optd with T 95.*
846 15 c. Girl Guides nursing .. .. 1·50 80
847 45 c. Open-air Girl Guide meeting .. 2·75 1·75
848 60 c. Lord and Lady Baden-Powell .. 2·75 2·50
849 $3 Girl Guides gathering flowers.. .. 7·50 9·50
846/9 .. .. *Set of 4* 13·00 13·00
MS850 67×96 mm. $5 Barn Swallow (Nature study) .. .. 19·00 17·00

1986 (10 Mar). *300th Birth Anniv of Johann Sebastian Bach (composer). Nos. 960/4 of Antigua optd with T 95.*
851 25 c. multicoloured .. .. .. 2·00 70
852 50 c. multicoloured .. .. .. 2·50 1·40
853 $1 multicoloured .. .. .. 3·25 2·00
854 $3 multiciloured .. .. .. 6·50 8·00
851/4 .. .. *Set of 4* 13·00 11·00
MS855 104×73 mm. $5 black and brownish grey 16·00 12·00

1986 (4 Apr). *Christmas. Religious Paintings. Nos. 985/9 of Antigua optd with T 106.*
856 10 c. "Madonna and Child" (De Landi) .. 40 20
857 25 c. "Madonna and Child" (Berlinghiero) .. 80 50
858 60 c. "The Nativity" (Fra Angelico).. .. 1·50 1·00
859 $4 "Presentation in the Temple" (Giovanni di Paolo).. .. .. 4·00 6·50
856/9 .. .. *Set of 4* 6·00 7·50
MS860 113×81 mm. $5 "The Nativity" (Antoniazzo Romano) .. .. .. 4·25 5·50

108 Queen Elizabeth II meeting Members of Legislature

(Litho Format)

1986 (21 Apr). *60th Birthday of Queen Elizabeth II (1st issue). T 108 and similar horiz designs. Multicoloured. P 15.*
861 $1 Type 108 .. .. .. 50 1·00
862 $2 Queen with Headmistress of Liberta School .. .. 60 1·10
863 $2.50, Queen greeted by Governor-General of Antigua .. .. .. 60 1·25
861/3 .. .. *Set of 3* 1·50 3·00
MS864 95×75 mm. $5 Queen Elizabeth in 1928 and 1986 (33×27 mm). P 13½×14 .. 5·00 7·00
Nos. 861/3 exist imperforate from stock dispersed by the liquidator of Format International Security Printers Ltd. See also Nos. 872/5.

109 Halley's Comet over Barbuda Beach

(Des and litho Format)

1986 (10 July). *Appearance of Halley's Comet (1st issue). T 109 and similar multicoloured designs. P 15.*
865 $1 Type 109 .. .. .. 60 1·25
866 $2.50, Early telescope and dish aerial (vert).. 1·00 2·25
867 $5 Comet and World map .. .. 1·75 3·75
865/7 .. .. *Set of 3* 3·00 6·50
Nos. 865/7 exist imperforate from stock dispersed by the liquidator of Format International Security Printers Ltd.

1986 (12 Aug). *40th Anniv of United Nations Organization. Nos. 981/4 of Antigua optd with T 96 (Nos. 868/70) or T 95 (No. MS871).*
868 40 c. Benjamin Franklin and U.N. (New York) 1953 U.P.U. 5 c. stamp .. 1·50 1·00
869 $1 George Washington Carver (agricultural chemist) and 1982 Nature Conservation 28 c. stamp .. .. 2·25 2·25
870 $3 Charles Lindbergh (aviator) and 1978 I.C.A.O. 25 c. stamp .. .. 4·00 5·00
868/70 .. .. *Set of 3* 7·00 7·50
MS871 101×77 mm. $5 Marc Chagall (artist) (vert) .. .. 11·00 12·00

1986 (12 Aug). *60th Birthday of Queen Elizabeth II (2nd issue). Nos. 1005/8 of Antigua optd with T 95 in black (No. MS875) or silver (others).*
872 60 c. black and yellow .. .. 1·75 1·25
873 $1 multicoloured .. .. .. 2·25 1·75
874 $4 multicoloured .. .. .. 3·75 4·25
872/4 .. .. *Set of 3* 7·00 6·50
MS875 120×85 mm. $5 black and grey-brown .. 7·00 8·00

1986 (28 Aug). *World Cup Football Championship, Mexico. Nos. 995/9 of Antigua optd with T 95 (30 c., $4) or T 96 (others).*
876 30 c. Football, boots and trophy .. 2·50 1·00
877 60 c. Goalkeeper (vert) .. .. 3·50 2·00
878 $1 Referee blowing whistle (vert).. 3·75 2·25
879 $4 Ball in net .. .. .. 8·00 7·00
876/9 .. .. *Set of 4* 16·00 11·00
MS880 87×76 mm. $5 Two players competing for ball. .. .. 17·00 13·00

1986 (28 Aug). *"Ameripex '86" International Stamp Exhibition, Chicago. Famous American Trains. Nos. 1014/18 of Antigua optd with T 106.*
881 25 c. "Hiawatha" express .. .. 2·00 1·50
882 50 c. "Grand Canyon" express .. 2·75 2·25
883 $1 "Powhattan Arrow" express .. 3·50 3·00
884 $3 "Empire State" express .. .. 6·00 6·50
881/4 .. .. *Set of 4* 13·00 12·00
MS885 116×87 mm $5 Southern Pacific "Daylight" express .. .. 8·50 9·00

1986 (22 Sept). *Appearance of Halley's Comet (2nd issue). Nos. 1000/4 of Antigua optd with T 96 (Nos. 886/9) or T 95 (MS890).*
886 5 c. Edmond Halley and Old Greenwich Observatory 75 55
887 10 c. Messerschmitt Me 163B Komet (fighter aircraft), 1944 .. .. 75 55
888 60 c. Montezuma (Aztec Emperor) and Comet in 1517 (from "Historias de las Indias de Neuva Espana") .. 2·50 2·00
889 $4 Pocahontas saving Capt. John Smith and Comet in 1607 .. .. 7·50 7·00
886/9 .. .. *Set of 4* 10·50 9·00
MS890 101×70 mm. $5 Halley's Comet over English Harbour, Antigua .. .. 4·75 4·75

1986 (22 Sept). *Royal Wedding. Nos. 1019/22 of Antigua optd with T 95 in silver.*
891 45 c. Prince Andrew and Miss Sarah Ferguson 75 50
892 60 c. Prince Andrew 90 65
893 $4 Prince Andrew with Prince Philip .. 3·50 4·00
891/3 .. .. *Set of 3* 4·75 4·75
MS894 88×88 mm. $5 Prince Andrew and Miss Sarah Ferguson (different) .. .. 6·00 7·00

1986 (10 Nov). *Sea Shells. Nos. 1023/7 of Antigua optd with T 106 (in silver on 15 c. to $3).*
895 15 c. Fly-specked Cerith .. .. 2·50 1·75
896 45 c. Smooth Scotch Bonnet .. 2·75 2·25
897 60 c. West Indian Crown Conch .. 3·50 2·75
898 $3 Ciboney Murex .. .. .. 8·00 9·50
895/8 .. .. *Set of 4* 15·00 14·50
MS899 109×75 mm. $5 Colourful Atlantic Moon (horiz) .. .. 20·00 18·00

1986 (10 Nov). *Flowers. Nos. 1028/36 of Antigua optd with T 106.*
900 10 c. Nymphaea ampla (water lily) .. 20 30
901 15 c. Queen of the Night 30 30
902 50 c. Cup of Gold 50 70
903 60 c. Beach Morning Glory .. 55 70
904 70 c. Golden Trumpet 70 90
905 $1 Air Plant 85 90
906 $3 Purple Wreath .. .. .. 2·25 3·00
907 $4 Zephyr Lily .. .. .. 2·75 3·50
900/7 .. .. *Set of 8* 7·50 9·25
MS908 Two sheets, each 102×72 mm. (a) $4 Dozakie. (b) $5 Four O'Clock Flower
.. .. *Set of 2 sheets* 22·00 22·00

1986 (28 Nov). *Mushrooms. Nos. 1042/6 of Antigua optd with T 106.*
909 10 c. Hygrocybe occidentalis var. scarletina . 90 50
910 50 c. Trogia buccinalis .. .. 3·25 1·75
911 $1 Collybia subpruinosa .. .. 4·75 2·75
912 $4 Leucocoprinus brebissonii .. 4·75 2·75
909/12 .. .. *Set of 4* 16·00 11·50
MS913 102×82 mm. $5 Pyrrhoglossum pyrrhum 22·00 13·00

1986 (Dec). *Birth Bicentenary of John J. Audubon (ornithologist) (3rd issue). Nos. 990/3 of Antigua optd with T 96 (in silver on 60, 90 c.).*
914 60 c. Mallard .. .. .. 3·75 1·75
915 90 c. North American Black Duck .. 4·75 2·25
916 $1.50, Pintail .. .. .. 6·00 4·75
917 $3 American Wigeon .. .. 9·50 8·50
914/17 .. .. *Set of 4* 22·00 15·00

1987 (12 Jan). *Local Boats. Nos. 1009/13 of Antigua optd with T 95.*
918 30 c. Tugboat 75 60
919 60 c. Game fishing boat .. .. 1·00 80
920 $1 Yacht .. .. 1·25
921 $4 Lugger with auxiliary sail .. 3·75 4·50
918/21 .. .. *Set of 4* 6·25 6·50
MS922 108×78 mm. $5 Boats under construction 17·00 15·00

1987 (12 Jan). *Centenary of First Benz Motor Car. Nos. 1052/60 of Antigua optd with T 95 (No. MS931) or T 96 (others).*
923 10 c. Auburn "Speedster" (1933) .. 60 30
924 15 c. Mercury "Sable" (1986) .. 75 40
925 50 c. Cadillac (1959) .. .. 1·25 60
926 60 c. Studebaker (1950) .. .. 1·25 70
927 70 c. Lagonda "V-12" (1939).. .. 1·40 1·00
928 $1 Adler "Standard" (1930) .. 1·75 1·00
929 $3 DKW (1956) .. .. .. 2·75 3·00
930 $4 Mercedes "500K" (1936) .. 2·75 3·00
923/30 .. .. *Set of 8* 11·50 9·00
MS931 Two sheets, each 99×70 mm. (a) $5 Daimler (1896). (b) $5 Mercedes "Knight" (1921)
.. .. *Set of 2 sheets* 13·00 13·00

1987 (10 Mar). *World Cup Football Championship Winners, Mexico. Nos. 1037/40 of Antigua optd with T 95 (60 c., $1) or T 96 (30 c., $4).*
932 30 c. Football, boots and trophy .. 1·25 80
933 60 c. Goalkeeper (vert) .. .. 1·75 1·00
934 $1 Referee blowing whistle (vert).. 2·25 1·75
935 $4 Ball in net .. .. .. 5·50 6·00
932/5 .. .. *Set of 4* 9·50 8·50

1987 (23 Apr). *America's Cup Yachting Championship. Nos. 1072/6 of Antigua optd horizontally as T 102.*
936 30 c. Canada I (1981). 45 40
937 60 c. Gretel II (1970) 70 50
938 $1 Sceptre (1958) .. .. .. 1·00 80
939 $3 Vigilant (1893) .. .. .. 1·75 2·75
936/9 .. .. *Set of 4* 3·50 4·50
MS940 113×84 mm. $5 Australia II defeating Liberty (1983) (horiz) .. .. 4·00 4·50

1987 (1 July). *Marine Life. Nos. 1077/85 of Antigua optd with T 95 (No. MS949) or T 96 (others).*
941 15 c. Bridled Burrfish .. .. 3·50 80
942 30 c. Common Noddy.. .. .. 4·00 85
943 40 c. Nassau Grouper .. .. 4·00 1·25
944 50 c. Laughing Gull .. .. 6·00 1·75
945 60 c. French Angelfish .. .. 6·00 1·50
946 $1 Porkfish .. .. .. 6·00 2·00
947 $2 Royal Tern .. .. .. 12·00 6·00
948 $3 Sooty Tern .. .. .. 12·00 7·00
941/8 .. .. *Set of 8* 48·00 19·00
MS949 Two sheets, each 120×94 mm. (a) $5 Banded Butterflyfish. (b) $5 Brown Booby
.. .. *Set of 2 sheets* 20·00 15·00

1987 (28 July). *Milestones of Transportation. Nos. 1100/9 of Antigua optd with T 106.*
950 10 c. Spirit of Australia (fastest powerboat), 1978 .. .. 1·25 75
951 15 c. Werner von Siemens's electric locomotive, 1879 .. .. 1·75 90
952 30 c. U.S.S. Triton (first submerged circumnavigation), 1960 .. .. 2·00 90
953 50 c. Trevithick's steam carriage (first passenger-carrying vehicle), 1801 .. 2·25 1·50
954 60 c. U.S.S. New Jersey (battleship), 1942 2·50 1·25
955 70 c. Draisine bicycle, 1818 .. 2·50 1·75
956 90 c. United States (liner) (holder of Blue Riband), 1952 .. .. 2·75 1·75
957 $1.50, Cierva C. 4 (first autogyro), 1923 3·00 3·00
958 $2 Curtiss NC-4 (first translantic flight), 1919 .. .. 4·00 4·00
959 $3 Queen Elizabeth 2 (liner), 1969 .. 4·75 4·75
950/9 .. .. *Set of 10* 23·00 18·00

![110 Shore Crab]
110 Shore Crab

(Litho Format)

1987 (15 Sept). *Marine Life. T 110 and similar multicoloured designs. P 15.*
960 5 c. Type 110 .. .. .. 10 20
961 10 c. Sea Cucumber 15 20
962 15 c. Stop-light Parrotfish 15 20
963 25 c. Banded Coral Shrimp .. 15 20
964 50 c. Spotted Drum 15 20
965 60 c. Thorny Starfish 25 40
966 75 c. Atlantic Trumpet Triton .. 35 60
967 90 c. Feather Star and Yellow Beaker Sponge 40 65
968 $1 Blue Gorgonian (vert) .. 40 65
969 $1.25, Slender Filefish (vert) .. 45 85
970 $5 Barred Hamlet (vert) .. 90 4·00
971 $7.50 Royal Gramma ("Fairy Basslet") (vert) .. .. 1·25 5·50
972 $10 Fire Coral and Banded Butterflyfish (vert) .. .. 1·50 6·50
960/72 .. .. *Set of 13* 5·50 18·00
Nos. 960/72 exist imperforate from stock dispersed by the liquidator of Format International Security Printers Ltd.

1987 (12 Oct). *Olympic Games, Seoul (1988). Nos. 1086/90 of Antigua optd with T 95 (No. MS977) or T 96 in silver (others).*
973 10 c. Handball 75 55
974 60 c. Fencing .. .. .. 1·25 70
975 $1 Gymnastics .. .. .. 1·50 1·25
976 $3 Football .. .. .. 4·00 4·00
973/6 .. .. *Set of 4* 6·00 6·00
MS977 100×72 mm. $5 Boxing gloves .. 4·25 4·25

1987 (12 Oct). *Birth Centenary of Marc Chagall (artist). Nos. 1091/9 of Antigua optd as T 95 (in silver on Nos. 983, MS986b).*
978 10 c. "The Profile" 10 10
979 30 c. "Portrait of the Artist's Sister" .. 15 15
980 40 c. "Bride with Fan" 20 30
981 60 c. "David in Profile" 25 30
982 90 c. "Fiancee with Bouquet" .. 40 50
983 $1 "Self Portrait with Brushes" .. 45 55
984 $3 "The Walk" .. .. .. 1·40 2·00
985 $4 "Three Candles" .. .. 1·75 2·25
978/85 .. .. *Set of 8* 4·25 5·50
MS986 Two sheets, each 110×95 mm. (a) $5 "Fall of Icarus" (104×89 mm). (b) $5 "Myth of Orpheus" (104×89 mm) .. .. *Set of 2 sheets* 4·50 5·50

1987 (5 Nov). *Centenary of Statue of Liberty (1986) (2nd issue). Nos 1110/19 of Antigua optd with T 95 (15, 30, 45, 50 c., $1, $2, $5) or T 96 (60, 90 c., $3), in black (50 c., $3) or silver (others).*
987 15 c. Lee Iacocca at unveiling of restored Statue 10 10
988 30 c. Statue at sunset (side view) .. 15 15
989 45 c. Aerial view of head 20 25
990 50 c. Lee Iacocca and torch .. 25 30
991 60 c. Workmen inside head of Statue (horiz) 25 30
992 90 c. Restoration work (horiz) .. 40 50
993 $1 Head of Statue 45 55
994 $2 Statue at Sunset (front view) .. 90 1·40
995 $3 Inspecting restoration work (horiz) 1·40 2·00
996 $5 Statue at night .. .. .. 2·25 1·40
987/96 .. .. *Set of 10* 5·75 7·75

1987 (5 Nov). *Entertainers. Nos. 1120/7 of Antigua optd with T 95 (in silver on $3).*
997	15 c. Grace Kelly		90	50
998	25 c. Marilyn Monroe		2·25	1·00
999	45 c. Orson Welles		1·00	75
1000	50 c. Judy Garland		1·00	85
1001	60 c. John Lennon		3·75	1·75
1002	$1 Rock Hudson		2·00	1·50
1003	$2 John Wayne		3·25	2·75
1004	$3 Elvis Presley		7·00	5·00
997/1004		*Set of 8*	19·00	13·00

1987 (5 Nov). *"Capex '87" International Stamp Exhibition, Toronto. Reptiles and Amphibians. Nos. 1133/7 of Antigua optd with T 95 (No. MS1009) or T 96 (others).*
1005	30 c. Whistling Frog		2·25	85
1006	60 c. Croaking Lizard		2·75	1·25
1007	$1 Antiguan Anole		3·00	1·40
1008	$3 Red-footed Tortoise		7·00	8·00
1005/8		*Set of 4*	13·50	10·50
MS1009	106×76 mm. $5 Ground Lizard		13·50	8·00

1988 (12 Jan). *Christmas. Religious Paintings. Nos. 1144/8 of Antigua optd with T 95.*
1010	45 c. "Madonna and Child" (Bernardo Daddi)		70	30
1011	60 c. "St. Joseph" (detail, "The Nativity" (Sano di Pietro))		85	55
1012	$1 "Virgin Mary" (detail, "The Nativity" (Sano di Pietro))		1·25	1·00
1013	$4 "Music-making Angel" (Melozzo da Forli)		3·25	4·50
1010/13		*Set of 4*	5·50	5·75
MS1014	99×70 mm. $5 "The Flight into Egypt" (Sano di Pietro)		6·00	6·00

1988 (25 Mar). *Salvation Army's Community Service. Nos. 1163/71 of Antigua optd with T 106.*
1015	25 c. First aid at daycare centre, Antigua		80	80
1016	30 c. Giving penicillin injection, Indonesia		80	80
1017	40 c. Children at daycare centre, Bolivia		85	85
1018	45 c. Rehabilitation of the handicapped, India		85	85
1019	50 c. Training blind man, Kenya		1·25	1·25
1020	60 c. Weighing baby, Ghana		1·25	1·25
1021	$1 Training typist, Zambia		1·75	1·75
1022	$2 Emergency food kitchen, Sri Lanka		2·25	2·75
1015/22		*Set of 8*	8·75	9·25
MS1023	152×83 mm. $5 General Eva Burrows		13·00	15·00

1988 (6 May). *Bicentenary of U.S. Constitution. Nos. 1139/43 of Antigua optd with T 95 ($4, $5) or T 96 (others), all in silver.*
1024	15 c. House of Burgesses, Virginia ("Freedom of Speech")		10	10
1025	45 c. State Seal, Connecticut		20	25
1026	60 c. State Seal, Delaware		25	35
1027	$4 Gouverneur Morris (Pennsylvania delegate) (vert)		1·75	3·00
1024/7		*Set of 4*	2·10	3·25
MS1028	105×75 mm. $5 Roger Sherman (Connecticut delegate) (vert)		2·75	3·25

1988 (4 July). *Royal Ruby Wedding. Nos. 1149/53 of Antigua optd with T 95.*
1029	25 c. deep brown, black and bright new blue		75	30
1030	60 c. multicoloured		1·25	65
1031	$2 deep brown, black and light green		2·50	2·25
1032	$3 multicoloured		2·75	2·75
	a. Opt triple			†
1029/32		*Set of 4*	6·50	5·50
MS1033	102×77 mm. $5 multicoloured		6·50	5·50

The only known example of No. 1032a is used, uncancelled, on cover from the Philatelic Bureau.

1988 (4 July). *Birds of Antigua. Nos. 1154/62 of Antigua optd with T 95 (10 c., $1) or T 96 (others).*
1034	10 c. Great Blue Heron		1·75	1·00
1035	15 c. Ringed Kingfisher (horiz)		2·00	1·00
1036	50 c. Bananaquit (horiz)		2·75	1·50
1037	60 c. Purple Gallinule (horiz)		2·75	1·50
1038	70 c. Blue-hooded Euphonia (horiz)		3·00	2·25
1039	$1 Brown-throated Conure ("Caribbean Parakeet")		3·25	2·25
1040	$3 Troupial (horiz)		5·00	6·00
1041	$4 Purple-throated Carib (horiz)		5·00	6·00
1034/41		*Set of 8*	23·00	19·00
MS1042	Two sheets, each 115×86 mm. (a) $5 Greater Flamingo. (b) $5 Brown Pelican	*Set of 2 sheets*	15·00	11·00

1988 (25 July–8 Dec). *500th Anniv of Discovery of America by Columbus (1992) (1st issue). Nos. 1172/80 of Antigua optd with T 96 (Nos. 1043/50) or T 95 (No. MS1051).*
1043	10 c. Columbus' second fleet, 1493		1·00	1·00
1044	30 c. Painos Indian village and fleet		1·25	80
1045	45 c. Santa Mariagalante (flagship) and Painos village		1·75	80
1046	60 c. Painos Indians offering Columbus fruit and vegetables		1·25	85
1047	90 c. Painos Indian and Columbus with Scarlet Macaw		2·50	1·50
1048	$1 Columbus landing on island		2·50	1·50
1049	$3 Spanish soldier and fleet		3·25	3·50
1050	$4 Fleet under sail		3·25	3·50
1043/50		*Set of 8*	15·00	12·00
MS1051	Two sheets, each 110×80 nn. (a) $5 Queen Isabella's cross. (b) $5 Gold coin of Ferdinand and Isabella (8 Dec) *Set of 2 sheets*		8·00	10·00

See also Nos. 1112/16, 1177/85, 1285/93, 1374/80 and 1381/2.

1988 (25 July). *500th Birth Anniv of Titian. Nos. 1181/9 of Antigua optd with T 96 (Nos. 1052/9) or T 95 (No. MS1060), all in silver.*
1052	30 c. "Bust of Christ"		15	15
1053	40 c. "Scourging of Christ"		20	25
1054	45 c. "Madonna in Glory with Saints"		20	25
1055	50 c. "The Averoldi Polyptych" (detail)		25	30
1056	$1 "Christ Crowned with Thorns"		45	50
1057	$2 "Christ Mocked"		90	1·10
1058	$3 "Christ and Simon of Cyrene"		1·40	1·75
1059	$4 "Crucifixion with Virgin and Saints"		1·75	2·25
1052/9		*Set of 8*	4·75	6·00
MS1060	Two sheets, each 110×95 mm. (a) $5 "Ecce Homo" (detail). (b) $5 "Noli me Tangere" (detail) *Set of 2 sheets*		4·50	5·50

1988 (25 Aug). *16th World Scout Jamboree, Australia. Nos. 1128/32 of Antigua optd with T 95 (No. MS1064) or T 96 (others).*
1061	10 c. Scouts around camp fire and Red Kangaroo		85	75
1062	60 c. Scouts canoeing and Blue-winged Kookaburra		2·50	95
1063	$1 Scouts on assault course and Ring-tailed Rock Wallaby		2·00	1·25
1064	$3 Field kitchen and Koala		4·00	5·00
1061/4		*Set of 4*	8·50	7·25
MS1065	103 × 78 mm. $5 Flags of Antigua, Australia and Scout Movement		2·50	3·25

1988 (25 Aug–8 Dec). *Sailing Week. Nos. 1190/4 of Antigua optd with T 95 (No. MS1070) or T 96 (others).*
1066	30 c. Two yachts rounding buoy		60	35
1067	60 c. Three yachts		1·00	70
1068	$1 British yacht under way		1·25	1·00
1069	$3 Three yachts (different)		2·25	2·75
1066/9		*Set of 4*	4·50	4·50
MS1070	103 × 92 mm. $5 Two yachts (8 Dec)		3·50	3·25

1988 (16 Sept). *Flowering Trees. Nos. 1213/21 of Antigua optd with T 95.*
1071	10 c. Jacaranda		10	10
1072	30 c. Cordia		15	15
1073	50 c. Orchid Tree		20	25
1074	90 c. Flamboyant		40	45
1075	$1 African Tulip Tree		45	50
1076	$2 Potato Tree		80	1·25
1077	$3 Crepe Myrtle		1·25	1·75
1078	$4 Pitch Apple		1·60	2·25
1071/8		*Set of 8*	4·50	6·00
MS1079	Two sheets, each 106 × 76 mm. (a) $5 Cassia. (b) $5 Chinaberry *Set of 2 sheets*		4·25	5·00

1988 (16 Sept). *Olympic Games, Seoul. Nos. 1222/6 of Antigua optd with T 95 (Nos. 1080/1, MS1084) or T 96 (Nos. 1082/3).*
1080	40 c. Gymnastics		60	40
1081	60 c. Weightlifting		80	55
1082	$1 Water polo (horiz)		1·00	90
1083	$3 Boxing (horiz)		2·25	2·50
1080/3		*Set of 4*	4·25	4·00
MS1084	114 × 80 mm. $5 Runner with Olympic torch		2·10	2·40

BARBUDA MAIL

(111)

1988 (8 Dec)–90. *Caribbean Butterflies. Nos. 1227/44a of Antigua optd with T 96 (Nos. 1085/1102) or T 111 (No. 1102a).*
1085	1 c. Danaus plexippus		30	60
1086	2 c. Greta diaphanus		30	60
1087	3 c. Calisto archebates		40	60
1088	5 c. Hamadryas feronia		40	60
1089	10 c. Mestra dorcas		50	60
1090	15 c. Hypolimnas misippus		60	40
1091	20 c. Dione juno		70	50
1092	25 c. Heliconius charithonia		75	50
1093	30 c. Eurema pyro		80	50
1094	40 c. Papilio androgeus		90	50
1095	45 c. Anteos maerula		90	50
1096	50 c. Aphrissa orbis		1·10	75
1097	60 c. Astraptes xagua		1·10	60
1098	$1 Heliopetes arsalte		1·40	1·00
1099	$2 Polites baracoa		3·00	3·50
1100	$2.50 Phocides pigmalion		3·25	4·00
1101	$5 Prepona amphitoe		4·50	5·50
1102	$10 Oarisma nanus		7·50	8·50
1102a	$20 Parides lycimenes (4.5.90)		12·00	13·00
1085/102a		*Set of 19*	35·00	38·00

BARBUDA MAIL

(112)

BARBUDA MAIL

(113)

1989 (28 Apr). *25th Death Anniv of John F. Kennedy (American statesman). Nos. 1245/53 of Antigua optd with T 96 (Nos. 1103/10) or T 112 (No. MS1111).*
1103	1 c. President Kennedy and family		10	20
1104	2 c. Kennedy commanding PT109		10	20
1105	3 c. Funeral cortege		10	20
1106	4 c. In motorcade, Mexico City		10	20
1107	30 c. As 1 c.		75	40
1108	60 c. As 4 c.		1·00	55
1109	$1 As 3 c.		1·25	95
1110	$4 As 2 c.		3·75	5·00
1103/10		*Set of 8*	6·00	7·00
MS1111	105 × 75 mm. $5 Kennedy taking presidential oath of office		3·75	5·00

1989 (24 May). *500th Anniv of Discovery of America by Columbus (1992) (2nd issue). Pre-Columbian Arawak Society. Nos. 1267/71 of Antigua optd with T 113.*
1112	$1.50, Arawak warriors		1·75	2·25
	a. Horiz strip of 4. Nos. 1112/15		6·00	
1113	$1.50, Whip dancers		1·75	2·25
1114	$1.50, Whip dancers and chief with pineapple		1·75	2·25
1115	$1.50, Family and camp fire		1·75	2·25
1112/15		*Set of 4*	6·00	8·00
MS1116	71 × 84 mm. $6 Arawak chief		3·50	4·50

1989 (29 June). *50th Anniv of First Jet Flight. Nos. 1272/80 of Antigua optd with T 111.*
1117	10 c. Hawker Siddeley Comet 4 airliner		1·25	1·00
1118	30 c. Messerschmitt Me 262 fighter		1·75	90
1119	40 c. Boeing 707 airliner		2·00	1·00
1120	60 c. Canadair CL-13 airliner ("F-86 Sabre") fighter		2·25	1·00
1121	$1 Lockheed F-104 Starfighter		2·50	1·25
1122	$3 Douglas DC-10 airliner		3·75	4·00
1123	$3 Boeing 747-300/400 airliner		4·25	4·50
1124	$4 McDonnell Douglas F-4 Phantom II fighter		4·25	4·50
1117/24		*Set of 8*	20·00	16·00
MS1125	Two sheets, each 114×83 mm. (a) $7 Grumman F-14 Tomcat fighter. (b) $7 Concorde airliner *Set of 2 sheets*		22·00	18·00

BARBUDA MAIL

(114)

BARBUDA MAIL

(115)

1989 (18 Sept). *Caribbean Cruise Ships. Nos. 1281/9 of Antigua optd as T 114, but with lines spaced (No. MS1134b), or with T 111 (others).*
1126	25 c. Festivale		90	70
1127	45 c. Southward		1·25	70
1128	50 c. Sagafjord		1·40	80
1129	60 c. Daphne		1·50	80
1130	75 c. Cunard Countess		1·60	1·60
1131	90 c. Song of America		1·75	1·75
1132	$3 Island Princess		4·00	4·75
1133	$4 Galileo		4·00	4·75
1126/33		*Set of 8*	15·00	14·00
MS1134	(a) 113×87 mm. $6 Norway. (b) 111×82 mm. $6 Oceanic *Set of 2 sheets*		24·00	24·00

1989 (14 Dec). *Japanese Art. Paintings by Hiroshige. Nos. 1290/8 of Antigua optd with T 114.*
1135	25 c. "Fish swimming by Duck half-submerged in Stream"		1·25	70
1136	45 c. "Crane and Wave"		1·75	70
1137	50 c. "Sparrows and Morning Glories"		2·00	1·00
1138	60 c. "Crested Blackbird and Flowering Cherry"		2·00	1·00
1139	$1 "Great Knot sitting among Water Grass"		2·25	1·25
1140	$2 "Goose on a Bank of Water"		3·50	3·25
1141	$3 "Black Paradise Flycatcher and Blossoms"		3·75	3·75
1142	$4 "Sleepy Owl perched on a Pine Branch"		4·00	4·00
1135/42		*Set of 8*	18·00	14·00
MS1143	Two sheets, each 102×75 mm. (a) $5 "Bullfinch flying near a Clematis Branch". (b) $5 "Titmouse on a Cherry Branch" *Set of 2 sheets*		22·00	17·00

1989 (20 Dec). *World Cup Football Championship, Italy (1990). Nos. 1308/12 of Antigua optd with T 115.*
1144	15 c. Goalkeeper		75	50
1145	25 c. Goalkeeper moving towards ball		85	50
1146	$1 Goalkeeper reaching for ball		1·50	1·25
1147	$4 Goalkeeper saving goal		3·50	4·50
1144/7		*Set of 4*	6·00	6·00
MS1148	Two sheets, each 75×105 mm. (a) $5 Three players competing for ball (horiz). (b) $5 Ball and players' legs (horiz) *Set of 2 sheets*		16·00	17·00

1989 (20 Dec). *Christmas. Paintings by Raphael and Giotto. Nos. 1351/9 of Antigua optd with T 114.*
1149	10 c. "The Small Cowper Madonna" (Raphael)		10	10
1150	25 c. "Madonna of the Goldfinch" (Raphael)		10	15
1151	30 c. "The Alba Madonna" (Raphael)		15	20
1152	50 c. Saint (detail, "Bologna Altarpiece") (Giotto)		25	30
1153	60 c. Angel (detail, "Bologna Altarpiece") (Giotto)		30	45
1154	70 c. Angel slaying serpent (detail, "Bologna Altarpiece") (Giotto)		35	50
1155	$4 Evangelist (detail, "Bologna Altarpiece") (Giotto)		1·90	2·50
1156	$5 "Madonna of Foligno" (Raphael)		2·40	3·00
1149/56		*Set of 8*	5·00	6·50
MS1157	Two sheets, each 71×96 mm. (a) $5 "The Marriage of the Virgin" (detail) (Raphael). (b) $5 Madonna and Child (detail, "Bologna Altarpiece") (Giotto) *Set of 2 sheets*		10·00	12·00

1990 (21 Feb). *Fungi. Nos. 1313/21 of Antigua optd with T 111.*
1158	15 c. Mycena pura		1·25	75
1159	25 c. Psathyrella tuberculata (vert)		1·50	65
1160	50 c. Psilocybe cubensis		2·00	1·00
1161	60 c. Leptonia caeruleocapitata (vert)		2·25	1·00
1162	75 c. Xeromphalina tenuipes (vert)		2·25	1·40
1163	$1 Chlorophyllum molybdites (vert)		2·25	1·40
1164	$3 Marasmius haematocephalus		4·50	4·75
1165	$4 Cantharellus cinnabarinus		4·50	4·75
1158/65		*Set of 8*	18·00	14·00
MS1166	Two sheets, each 88×62 mm. (a) $6 Leucopaxillus gracilimus (vert). (b) $6 Volvariella volvacea *Set of 2 sheets*		28·00	21·00

BARBUDA MAIL
(116)

1990 (30 Mar). *Local Fauna. Nos. 1322/6 of Antigua optd with T* **116** (*vertically on 60 c.*, $4).
1167	25 c.	Desmarest's Hutia		50	45
1168	45 c.	Caribbean Monk Seal		1·25	80
1169	60 c.	Mustache Bat (*vert*)		1·00	80
1170	$4	American Manatee (*vert*)		3·00	4·50
1167/70			Set of 4	5·25	6·00
MS1171	113×87 mm. $5 West Indies Giant Rice Rat			9·00	11·00

1990 (30 Mar). *20th Anniv of First Manned Landing on Moon. Nos. 1346/50 of Antigua optd with T* **116** (*vertically on* 10, 45 c. *and* $5).
1172	10 c.	Launch of "Apollo 11"		85	65
1173	45 c.	Aldrin on Moon		1·75	70
1174	$1	Module *Eagle* over Moon (*horiz*)		2·50	1·75
1175	$4	Recovery of "Apollo 11" crew after splashdown (*horiz*)		5·00	7·00
1172/5			Set of 4	9·00	9·00
MS1176	107×77 mm. $5 Astronaut Neil Armstrong			9·50	11·00

1990 (6 June). *500th Anniv of Discovery of America by Columbus* (1992) (*3rd issue*). *New World Natural History – Marine Life. Nos. 1360/8 of Antigua optd as T* **114**, *but with lines spaced.*
1177	10 c.	Star-eyed Hermit Crab		65	60
1178	20 c.	Spiny Lobster		85	60
1179	25 c.	Magnificent Banded Fanworm		85	60
1180	45 c.	Cannonball Jellyfish		1·25	60
1181	60 c.	Red-spiny Sea Star		1·50	75
1182	$2	Peppermint Shrimp		2·50	3·00
1183	$3	Coral Crab		2·75	3·50
1184	$4	Branching Fire Coral		2·75	3·50
1177/84			Set of 8	11·50	11·50
MS1185	Two sheets, each 101×69 mm. (a) $5 Common Sea Fan. (b) $5 Portuguese Man-of-war				
			Set of 2 sheets	14·00	14·00

1990 (12 July). *"EXPO 90" International Garden and Greenery Exhibition, Osaka. Orchids. Nos. 1369/77 of Antigua optd as T* **114**, *but with lines spaced.*
1186	15 c.	Vanilla mexicana		1·50	80
1187	45 c.	Epidendrum ibaguense		2·00	80
1188	50 c.	Epidendrum secundum		2·00	90
1189	60 c.	Maxillaria conferta		2·25	1·10
1190	$1	Onicidium altissimum		2·50	1·75
1191	$2	Spiranthes lanceolata		4·50	4·50
1192	$3	Tonopsis utricularioides		5·00	5·50
1193	$5	Epidendrum nocturnum		6·50	7·50
1186/93			Set of 8	24·00	21·00
MS1194	Two sheets, each 101×69 mm. (a) $6 Octomeria graminifolia. (b) $6 Rodriguezia lanceolata				
			Set of 2 sheets	14·00	14·00

1990 (14 Aug). *Reef Fishes. Nos. 1386/94 of Antigua optd with T* **111**.
1195	10 c.	Flamefish		75	75
1196	15 c.	Coney		1·00	75
1197	50 c.	Long-spined Squirrelfish		1·50	1·00
1198	60 c.	Sergeant Major		1·75	1·00
1199	$1	Yellow-tailed Snapper		2·25	1·75
1200	$2	Rock Beauty		3·50	3·75
1201	$3	Spanish Hogfish		4·00	4·25
1202	$4	Striped Parrotfish		4·00	4·25
1195/1202			Set of 8	17·00	16·00
MS1203	Two sheets, each 99×70 mm. (a) $5 Black-barred Soldierfish. (b) $5 Four-eyed Butterflyfish				
			Set of 2 sheets	23·00	22·00

$5.00

**1st Anniversary
Hurricane Hugo
16th September, 1989-1990**

━━━

(117)

1990 (17 Sept). *First Anniv of Hurricane Hugo. Nos. 971/2 surch as T* **117**.
1204	$5 on $7.50 Fairy Basslet (*vert*)			5·00	5·50
1205	$7.50 on $10 Fire Coral and Butterfly Fish (*vert*)			6·00	6·50

1990 (12 Oct). *90th Birthday of Queen Elizabeth the Queen Mother. Nos. 1415/19 of Antigua optd as T* **114**, *but with lines spaced.*
1206	15 c.	multicoloured		1·40	70
1207	35 c.	multicoloured		2·00	75
1208	75 c.	multicoloured		3·00	1·75
1209	$3	multicoloured		7·00	5·50
1206/9			Set of 4	12·00	8·00
MS1210	67×98 mm $6 multicoloured			16·00	13·00

NEW INFORMATION

The editor is always interested to correspond with people who have new information that will improve or correct the Catalogue.

BARBUDA MAIL
(118)

119 Troupial

1990 (14 Dec). *Achievements in Space. Nos. 1395/1414 of Antigua optd with T* **118** *in silver.*
1211	45 c.	"Voyager 2" passing Saturn		1·25	1·25
		a. Sheetlet. Nos. 1211/30		22·00	
1212	45 c.	"Pioneer 11" photographing Saturn		1·25	1·25
1213	45 c.	Astronaut in transporter		1·25	1·25
1214	45 c.	Space shuttle *Columbia*		1·25	1·25
1215	45 c.	"Apollo 10" command module on parachutes		1·25	1·25
1216	45 c.	"Skylab" space station		1·25	1·25
1217	45 c.	Astronaut Edward White in space		1·25	1·25
1218	45 c.	"Apollo" spacecraft on joint mission		1·25	1·25
1219	45 c.	"Soyuz" spacecraft on joint mission		1·25	1·25
1220	45 c.	"Mariner 1" passing Venus		1·25	1·25
1221	45 c.	"Gemini 4" capsule		1·25	1·25
1222	45 c.	"Sputnik 1"		1·25	1·25
1223	45 c.	Hubble space telescope		1·25	1·25
1224	45 c.	North American X-15		1·25	1·25
1225	45 c.	Bell XS-1 airplane		1·25	1·25
1226	45 c.	"Apollo 17" astronaut and lunar rock formation		1·25	1·25
1227	45 c.	Lunar Rover		1·25	1·25
1228	45 c.	"Apollo 14" lunar module		1·25	1·25
1229	45 c.	Astronaut Buzz Aldrin on Moon		1·25	1·25
1230	45 c.	Soviet "Lunokhod" lunar vehicle		1·25	1·25
1211/30			Set of 20	22·00	22·00

1990 (14 Dec). *Christmas. Paintings by Renaissance Masters. Nos. 1457/65 of Antigua optd with T* **111**.
1231	25 c.	"Madonna and Child with Saints" (detail, Sebastiano del Piombo)		75	45
1232	30 c.	"Virgin and Child with Angels" (detail, Grünewald) (*vert*)		80	45
1233	40 c.	"The Holy Family and a Shepherd" (detail, Titian)		90	45
1234	60 c.	"Virgin and Child" (detail, Lippi) (*vert*)		1·25	50
1235	$1	"Jesus, St. John and Two Angels" (Rubens)		1·60	1·10
1236	$2	"Adoration of the Shepherds" (detail, Vincenzo Catena)		2·50	3·00
1237	$4	"Adoration of the Magi" (detail, Giorgione)		3·25	4·25
1238	$5	"Virgin and Child adored by Warrior" (detail, Vincenzo Catena)		3·25	4·25
1231/8			Set of 8	13·00	13·00
MS1239	Two sheets, each 71×101 mm. (a) $6 "Allegory of the Blessings of Jacob" (detail, Rubens) (*vert*). (b) $6 "Adoration of the Magi" (detail, Fra Angelico) (*vert*)				
			Set of 2 sheets	13·00	14·00

1991 (4 Feb). *150th Anniv of the Penny Black. Nos. 1378/81 of Antigua optd with T* **116**.
1240	45 c.	blue-green		1·60	60
1241	60 c.	magenta		1·75	75
1242	$5	ultramarine		6·50	8·00
1240/2			Set of 3	8·75	8·50
MS1243	102×80 mm. $6 blackish purple			9·00	9·50

1991 (4 Feb). *"Stamp World London 90" International Stamp Exhibition. Nos. 1382/5 of Antigua optd with T* **116**.
1244	50 c.	deep grey-green and scarlet-vermilion		1·50	75
1245	75 c.	purple-brown and scarlet-vermilion		1·75	1·10
1246	$4	deep ultramarine & scarlet-vermilion		6·50	7·50
1244/6			Set of 3	8·75	8·50
MS1247	104×81 mm. $6 brownish black and scarlet-vermilion			9·00	9·50

(Des G. Drummond. Litho Questa)

1991 (25 Mar). *Wild Birds. T* **119** *and similar vert designs. Multicoloured. P* 14.
1248	60 c.	Type **119**		90	55
1249	$2	Adelaide's Warbler ("Christmas Bird")		1·75	2·00
1250	$4	Rose-breasted Grosbeak		3·50	3·75
1251	$7	Wied's Crested Flycatcher		5·00	7·00
1248/51			Set of 4	10·00	12·00

1991 (23 Apr). *Olympic Games, Barcelona* (1992). *Nos. 1429/33 of Antigua optd as T* **114**, *but with lines spaced.*
1252	50 c.	Men's 20 kilometres walk		85	70
1253	75 c.	Triple jump		1·10	85
1254	$1	Men's 10,000 metres		1·40	1·25
1255	$5	Javelin		4·50	6·00
1252/5			Set of 4	7·00	8·00
MS1256	100 × 70 mm. $6 Athlete lighting Olympic flame at Los Angeles Olympics			8·00	9·00

1991 (23 Apr). *Birds. Nos. 1448/56 of Antigua optd with T* **116** *diagonally.*
1257	10 c.	Pearly-eyed Thrasher		1·00	90
1258	25 c.	Purple-throated Carib		1·60	80
1259	50 c.	Yellowthroat		2·00	1·00
1260	60 c.	American Kestrel		2·00	1·10
1261	$1	Yellow-bellied Sapsucker		2·50	1·50
1262	$2	Purple Gallinule		3·75	4·00
1263	$3	Yellow-crowned Night Heron		4·00	5·00
1264	$4	Blue-hooded Euphonia		4·00	5·00
1257/64			Set of 8	19·00	17·00
MS1265	Two sheets, each 76×60 mm. (a) $6 Brown Pelican. (b) $6 Magnificent Frigate Bird				
			Set of 2 sheets	17·00	16·00

1991 (21 June). *350th Death Anniv of Rubens. Nos. 1466/74 of Antigua optd with T* **111**.
1266	25 c.	"Rape of the Daughters of Leucippus" (detail)		70	60
1267	45 c.	"Bacchanal" (detail)		90	60
1268	50 c.	"Rape of the Sabine Women" (detail)		1·00	75
1269	60 c.	"Battle of the Amazons" (detail)		1·10	85
1270	$1	"Rape of the Sabine Women" (different detail)		1·75	1·50
1271	$2	"Bacchanal" (different detail)		2·75	3·00
1272	$3	"Rape of the Sabine Women" (different detail)		3·00	3·50
1273	$4	"Bacchanal" (different detail)		3·00	3·50
1266/73			Set of 8	13·00	13·00
MS1274	Two sheets, each 101 × 71 mm. (a) $6 "Rape of Hippodameia" (detail). (b) $6 "Battle of the Amazons" (different detail)		Set of 2 sheets	13·00	14·00

1991 (25 July). *50th Anniv of Second World War. Nos. 1475/84 of Antigua optd diagonally with T* **116**.
1275	10 c.	U.S. troops cross into Germany, 1944		1·00	1·00
1276	15 c.	Axis surrender in North Africa, 1943		1·40	1·10
1277	25 c.	U.S. tanks invade Kwalajalein, 1944		1·75	1·10
1278	45 c.	Roosevelt and Churchill meet at Casablanca, 1943		2·75	1·50
1279	50 c.	Marshall Badoglio, Prime Minister of Italian anti-fascist government, 1943		1·90	1·50
1280	$1	Lord Mountbatten, Supreme Allied Commander South-east Asia, 1943		3·50	2·50
1281	$2	Greek victory at Koritza, 1940		4·50	4·50
1282	$4	Anglo-Soviet mutual assistance pact, 1941		5·50	6·00
1283	$5	Operation Torch landings, 1942		5·50	6·00
1275/83			Set of 9	25·00	23·00
MS1284	Two sheets, each 108×80 mm. (a) $6 Japanese attack on Pearl Harbor, 1941. (b) $6 U.S.A.A.F. daylight raid on Schweinfurt, 1943				
			Set of 2 sheets	24·00	22·00

1991 (26 Aug). *500th Anniv of Discovery of America by Columbus* (1992) (*4th issue*). *History of Exploration. Nos. 1503/11 of Antigua optd with T* **111**.
1285	10 c.	multicoloured		75	75
1286	15 c.	multicoloured		90	75
1287	45 c.	multicoloured		1·25	80
1288	60 c.	multicoloured		1·50	1·00
1289	$1	multicoloured		2·00	1·50
1290	$2	multicoloured		3·00	3·25
1291	$4	multicoloured		4·50	4·50
1292	$5	multicoloured		4·50	5·00
1285/92			Set of 8	17·00	16·00
MS1293	Two sheets, each 106×76 mm. (a) $6 black and Indian red. (b) $6 black and Indian red				
			Set of 2 sheets	17·00	17·00

1991 (18 Oct). *Butterflies. Nos. 1494/502 of Antigua optd with T* **116** *diagonally.*
1294	10 c.	Heliconius charithonia		1·00	1·00
1295	35 c.	Marpesia petreus		1·60	1·10
1296	50 c.	Anartia amathea		2·00	1·40
1297	75 c.	Siproeta stelenes		2·25	1·60
1298	$1	Battus polydamas		2·50	1·75
1299	$2	Historis odius		3·50	3·75
1300	$4	Hypolimnas misippus		4·75	6·00
1301	$5	Hamadryas feronia		4·75	6·00
1294/1301			Set of 8	20·00	20·00
MS1302	Two sheets. (a) 73×100 mm. $6 Vanessa cardui caterpillar (*vert*). (b) 100×73 mm. $6 Danaus plexippus caterpillar (*vert*)				
			Set of 2 sheets	20·00	20·00

BARBUDA MAIL
(120)

1991 (18 Nov). *65th Birthday of Queen Elizabeth II. Nos. 1534/8 of Antigua optd with T* **120**.
1303	15 c.	Queen Elizabeth and Prince Philip in 1976		1·00	1·00
1304	20 c.	The Queen and Prince Philip in Portugal, 1985		1·00	60
1305	$2	Queen Elizabeth II		2·50	2·50
1306	$4	The Queen and Prince Philip at Ascot, 1986		4·25	4·50
1303/6			Set of 4	8·00	7·50
MS1307	68×90 mm. $4 The Queen at National Theatre, 1986, and Prince Philip			8·50	8·50

1991 (18 Nov). *10th Wedding Anniv of Prince and Princess of Wales. Nos. 1539/43 of Antigua optd with T* **120**.
1308	10 c.	Prince and Princess of Wales at party, 1986		80	65
1309	40 c.	Separate portraits of Prince, Princess and sons		1·25	65
1310	$1	Prince Henry and Prince William		1·60	1·25
1311	$5	Princess Diana in Australia and Prince Charles in Hungary		5·50	6·00
1308/11			Set of 4	8·25	7·75
MS1312	68×90 mm. $4 Prince Charles in Hackney and Princess and sons in Majorca, 1987			8·50	8·50

1991 (24 Dec). *Christmas. Religious Paintings by Fra Angelico. Nos. 1595/602 of Antigua optd with T* **120**.
1313	10 c.	"The Annunciation"		60	45
1314	30 c.	"Nativity"		80	45
1315	40 c.	"Adoration of the Magi"		80	45
1316	60 c.	"Presentation in the Temple"		1·00	50
1317	$1	"Circumcision"		1·40	80
1318	$3	"Flight into Egypt"		3·25	4·00
1319	$4	"Massacre of the Innocents"		3·50	4·25
1320	$5	"Christ teaching in the Temple"		3·75	4·50
1313/20			Set of 8	13·50	14·00

1992 (20 Feb). *Death Centenary of Vincent van Gogh (artist)* (1990). *Nos. 1512/24 of Antigua optd with T* **120**.
1321	5 c.	"Camille Roulin"	40	40
1322	10 c.	"Armand Roulin"	50	50
1323	15 c.	"Young Peasant Woman with Straw Hat sitting in the Wheat"	60	60
1324	25 c.	"Adeline Ravoux"	70	70
1325	30 c.	"The Schoolboy"	70	70
1326	40 c.	"Doctor Gachet"	75	75
1327	50 c.	"Portrait of a Man"	75	75
1328	75 c.	"Two Children"	1·10	1·10
1329	$2	"The Postman Joseph Roulin"	2·50	2·75
1330	$3	"The Seated Zouave"	2·75	3·00
1331	$4	"L'Arlésienne"	3·00	3·25
1332	$5	"Self-Portrait, November/December 1888"	3·25	3·50
1321/32		*Set of 12*	15·00	16·00

MS1333 Three sheets, each 102×76 mm. (a) $5 "Farmhouse in Provence" (*horiz*). (b) $5 "Flowering Garden" (*horiz*). (c) $6 "The Bridge at Trinquetaille" (*horiz*). Imperf .. *Set of 3 sheets* 16·00 17·00

1992 (7 Apr). *Birth Centenary of Charles de Gaulle (French statesman). Nos. 1562/70 of Antigua optd with T* **111** (10 c., $1, $2, $4, $6) *or T* **114** (*others*).
1334	10 c.	Presidents De Gaulle and Kennedy, 1961	85	70
1335	15 c.	General De Gaulle with Pres. Roosevelt, 1945 (*vert*)	1·00	75
1336	45 c.	Pres. De Gaulle with Chancellor Adenauer, 1962 (*vert*)	1·40	75
1337	60 c.	De Gaulle at Arc de Triomphe, Liberation of Paris, 1944 (*vert*)	1·60	1·00
1338	$1	General De Gaulle crossing the Rhine, 1945	2·00	1·50
1339	$2	General De Gaulle in Algiers, 1944	3·25	3·50
1340	$4	Presidents De Gaulle and Eisenhower, 1960	4·50	5·00
1341	$5	De Gaulle returning from Germany, 1968 (*vert*)	4·50	5·00
1334/41		*Set of 8*	17·00	16·00

MS1342 Two sheets, (a) 76×106 mm. $6 De Gaulle with crowd. (b) 106×76 mm. $6 De Gaulle and Churchill at Casablanca, 1943
.. *Set of 2 sheets* 20·00 18·00

1992 (16 Apr). *Easter. Religious Paintings. Nos. 1627/35 of Antigua optd with T* **111**.
1343	10 c.	"Supper at Emmaus" (Caravaggio)	60	45
1344	15 c.	"The Vision of St. Peter" (Zurbarán)	70	50
1345	30 c.	"Christ driving the Money-changers from the Temple" (Tiepolo)	85	55
1346	40 c.	"Martyrdom of St. Bartholomew" (detail) (Ribera)	90	60
1347	$1	"Christ driving the Money-changers from the Temple" (detail) (Tiepolo)	1·75	1·25
1348	$2	"Crucifixion" (detail) (Altdorfer)	3·00	3·50
1349	$4	"The Deposition" (detail) (Fra Angelico)	4·50	5·00
1350	$5	"The Deposition" (different detail) (Fra Angelico)	4·50	5·00
1343/50		*Set of 8*	15·00	15·00

MS1351 Two sheets. (a) 102×71 mm. $6 "The Last Supper" (detail) (Masip). (b) 71×102 mm. $6 "Crucifixion" (detail) (Altdorfer)
.. *Set of 2 sheets* 14·00 15·00

1992 (19 June). *Anniversaries and Events. Nos. 1573/83 of Antigua optd as T* **114**, *but with lines spaced (Nos. 1358 and* MS1362b) *or with T* **111** (*others*).
1352	25 c.	Germans celebrating Reunification	60	60
1353	75 c.	Cubs erecting tent	1·25	1·25
1354	$1.50	Don Giovanni and Mozart	3·00	2·25
1355	$2	Chariot driver and Gate at night	2·25	2·25
1356	$2	Lord Baden-Powell and members of the 3rd Antigua Methodist cub pack (*vert*)	2·25	2·25
1357	$2	Lilienthal's signature and glider *Flugzeug Nr.* 5	2·25	2·25
1358	$2.50	Driver in Class P36 steam locomotive (*vert*)	3·00	2·50
1359	$3	Statues from podium	2·50	2·50
1360	$3.50	Cubs and camp fire	3·00	3·00
1361	$4	St. Peter's Cathedral, Salzburg	3·00	3·00
1352/61		*Set of 10*	21·00	20·00

MS1362 Two sheets. (a) 100×72 mm. $4 Detail of chariot and helmet. (b) 89×117 mm. $5 Antiguan flag and Jamboree emblem (*vert*)
.. *Set of 2 sheets* 12·00 13·00

1992 (12 Aug). *50th Anniv of Japanese Attack on Pearl Harbor. Nos. 1585/94 of Antigua optd as T* **114**, *but with lines spaced.*
1364	$1	*Nimitz* class carrier and *Ticonderoga* class cruiser	2·00	2·00
	a.	Sheetlet. Nos. 1364/73	18·00	
1365	$1	Tourist launch	2·00	2·00
1366	$1	U.S.S. *Arizona* memorial	2·00	2·00
1367	$1	Wreaths on water and aircraft	2·00	2·00
1368	$1	White Tern	2·00	2·00
1369	$1	Mitsubishi A6M Zero-Sen fighters over Pearl City	2·00	2·00
1370	$1	Mitsubishi A6M Zero-Sen fighters attacking	2·00	2·00
1371	$1	Battleship Row in flames	2·00	2·00
1372	$1	U.S.S. *Nevada* (battleship) underway	2·00	2·00
1373	$1	Mitsubishi A6M Zero-Sen fighters returning to carriers	2·00	2·00
1364/73		*Set of 10*	18·00	18·00

1992 (12 Oct). *500th Anniv of Discovery of America by Columbus (5th issue). World Columbian Stamp "Expo '92", Chicago. Nos. 1654/60 of Antigua optd with T* **111**.
1374	15 c.	Memorial cross and huts, San Salvador	50	50
1375	30 c.	Martin Pinzon with telescope	60	60
1376	40 c.	Christopher Columbus	70	70
1377	$1	*Pinta*	2·25	2·00
1378	$2	*Nina*	3·00	3·00
1379	$4	*Santa Maria*	4·00	4·25
1374/9		*Set of 6*	10·00	10·00

MS1380 Two sheets, each 108×76 mm. (a) $6 Ship and map of West Indies. (b) $6 Sea monster
.. *Set of 2 sheets* 14·00 15·00

1992 (12 Oct). *500th Anniv of Discovery of America by Columbus (6th issue). Organization of East Caribbean States. Nos. 1670/1 of Antigua optd with T* **111**.
1381	$1	Columbus meeting Amerindians	1·50	1·50
1382	$2	Ships approaching island	3·00	3·00

1992 (29 Oct). *Postage Stamp Mega Event, New York. No. MS1690 of Antigua optd with T* **111**.
MS1383 $6 multicoloured .. .. 6·50 7·00

1992 (3 Nov). *40th Anniv of Queen Elizabeth II's Accession. Nos. 1604/8 of Antigua optd with T* **111**.
1384	10 c.	Queen Elizabeth II and bird sanctuary	1·25	80
1385	30 c.	Nelson's Dockyard	1·75	85
1386	$1	Ruins on Shirley Heights	2·50	2·00
1387	$5	Beach and palm trees	5·50	6·50
1384/7		*Set of 4*	10·00	9·00

MS1388 Two sheets, each 75×98 mm. (a) $6 Beach. (b) $6 Hillside foliage .. *Set of 2 sheets* 18·00 17·00

1992 (8 Dec). *Prehistoric Animals. Nos. 1618/26 of Antigua optd with T* **120** (*sideways on Nos. 1391/2 and* MS1397).
1389	10 c.	Pteranodon	1·25	1·25
1390	15 c.	Brachiosaurus	1·50	1·25
1391	30 c.	Tyrannosaurus Rex	1·75	1·25
1392	50 c.	Parasaurolophus	2·00	1·50
1393	$1	Deinonychus (*horiz*)	2·50	2·00
1394	$2	Triceratops (*horiz*)	4·00	4·00
1395	$4	Protoceratops hatching (*horiz*)	5·00	5·50
1396	$5	Stegosaurus (*horiz*)	5·00	5·50
1389/96		*Set of 8*	21·00	20·00

MS1397 Two sheets, each 100×70 mm. (a) $6 Apatosaurus (*horiz*). (b) $6 Allosaurus (*horiz*)
Set of 2 sheets 22·00 20·00

1992 (8 Dec). *Christmas. Nos. 1691/9 of Antigua optd with T* **111**.
1398	10 c.	"Virgin and Child with Angels" (School of Piero della Francesca)	75	65
1399	25 c.	"Madonna Degli Alberelli" (Giovanni Bellini)	1·10	65
1400	30 c.	"Madonna and Child with St. Anthony Abbot and St. Sigismund" (Neroccio)	1·10	65
1401	40 c.	"Madonna and the Grand Duke" (Raphael)	1·25	65
1402	60 c.	"The Nativity" (George de la Tour)	1·75	70
1403	$1	"Holy Family" (Jacob Jordaens)	2·25	1·40
1404	$4	"Madonna and Child Enthroned" (Magaritone)	6·00	6·50
1405	$5	"Madonna and Child on a Curved Throne" (Byzantine school)	6·00	6·50
1398/405		*Set of 8*	18·00	16·00

MS1406 Two sheets, each 76×102 mm. (a) $6 "Madonna and Child" (Domenco Ghirlando). (b) $6 "The Holy Family" (Pontormo)
Set of 2 sheets 18·00 17·00

1993 (25 Jan). *Fungi. Nos. 1645/53 of Antigua optd with T* **120**.
1407	10 c.	Amanita caesarea	1·50	1·25
1408	15 c.	Collybia fusipes	1·75	1·25
1409	30 c.	Boletus aereus	2·00	1·50
1410	40 c.	Laccaria amethystina	2·00	1·50
1411	$1	Russula virescens	3·00	2·00
1412	$2	Tricholoma equestre ("Tricholoma auratum")	4·50	4·00
1413	$4	Calocybe gambosa	5·50	6·00
1414	$5	Lentinus tigrinus ("Panus tigrinus")	5·50	6·00
1407/14		*Set of 8*	23·00	21·00

MS1415 Two sheets, each 100×70 mm. (a) $6 Clavariadelphus truncatus. (b) $6 Auricularia auricula-judae .. *Set of 2 sheets* 23·00 21·00

1993 (22 Mar). *"Granada '92" International Stamp Exhibition, Spain. Spanish Paintings. Nos. 1636/44 of Antigua optd diagonally with T* **116**.
1416	10 c.	"The Miracle at the Well" (Alonzo Cano)	75	75
1417	15 c.	"The Poet Luis de Goingora y Argote" (Velázquez)	1·00	75
1418	30 c.	"The Painter Francisco Goya" (Vincente López Portana)	1·25	1·00
1419	40 c.	"Maria de las Nieves Michaela Fourdinier" (Luis Paret y Alcázar)	1·25	1·00
1420	$1	"Carlos III eating before his Court" (Alcázar) (*horiz*)	2·50	2·00
1421	$2	"Rain Shower in Granada" (Antonio Munoz Degrain) (*horiz*)	4·00	4·00
1422	$4	"Sarah Bernhardt" (Santiago Ruisnol i Prats)	5·50	6·00
1423	$5	"The Hermitage Garden" (Joaquim Mir Trinxet)	5·50	6·00
1416/23		*Set of 8*	19·00	19·00

MS1424 Two sheets, each 120×95 mm. (a) $6 "The Ascent of Monsieur Boucle's Montgolfier Balloon in the Gardens of Aranjuez" (Antonio Carnicero) (112×87 *mm*). (b) $6 "Olympus: Battle with the Giants" (Francisco Bayeu y Subias) (112×87 *mm*). Imperf .. *Set of 2 sheets* 14·00 15·00

1993 (10 May). *"Genova '92" International Thematic Stamp Exhibition. Hummingbirds and Plants. Nos. 1661/9 of Antigua optd with T* **120**.
1425	10 c.	Antillean Crested Hummingbird and Wild Plantain	1·00	1·00
1426	25 c.	Green Mango and Parrot's Plantain	1·25	1·00
1427	45 c.	Purple-throated Carib and Lobster Claws	1·50	1·25
1428	60 c.	Antillean Mango and Coral Plant	2·00	1·50
1429	$1	Vervain Hummingbird and Cardinal's Guard	2·25	1·75
1430	$2	Rufous-breasted Hermit and Heliconia	3·50	3·50
1431	$4	Blue-headed Hummingbird and Red Ginger	4·50	5·00
1432	$5	Green-throated Carib and Ornamental Banana	4·50	5·00
1425/32		*Set of 8*	18·00	18·00

MS1433 Two sheets, each 100×70 mm. (a) $6 Bee Hummingbird and Jungle Flame. (b) $6 Western Streamertail and Bignonia
Set of 2 sheets 14·00 15·00

1993 (29 June). *Inventors and Inventions. Nos. 1672/80 of Antigua optd with T* **111**.
1434	10 c.	Ts'ai Lun and paper	30	40
1435	25 c.	Igor Sikorsky and *Bolshoi Baltiskii* (first four-engined airplane)	90	60
1436	30 c.	Alexander Graham Bell and early telephone	80	60
1437	40 c.	Johannes Gutenberg and early printing press	80	60
1438	60 c.	James Watt and stationary steam engine	2·00	1·25
1439	$1	Anton van Leeuwenhoek and early microscope	2·00	1·50
1440	$4	Louis Braille and hands reading braille	4·00	4·50
1441	$5	Galileo and telescope	4·00	4·50
1434/41		*Set of 8*	13·50	12·50

MS1442 Two sheets, each 100×71 mm. (a) $6 Edison and Latimer's phonograph. (b) $6 *Clermont* (first commercial paddle-steamer)
Set of 2 sheets 13·00 14·00

1993 (16 Aug). *Anniversaries and Events. Nos. 1700/14 of Antigua optd with T* **111** (*Nos. 1450/1*) *or as T* **114**, *but with lines spaced (others).*
1443	10 c.	Russian cosmonauts	80	80
1444	40 c.	Airship LZ-127 *Graf Zeppelin*, 1929	1·50	1·00
1445	45 c.	Bishop Daniel Davis	50	50
1446	75 c.	Konrad Adenauer making speech	70	70
1447	$1	Bus Mosbacher and *Weatherly* (yacht)	1·50	1·25
1448	$1.50	Rain Forest	1·50	1·50
1449	$2	Tiger	4·50	3·75
1450	$2	National flag, plant and emblem (*horiz*)	2·00	2·00
1451	$2	Members of Community Players company (*horiz*)	1·75	2·00
1452	$2.25	Women carrying pots	1·75	2·00
1453	$3	Lions Club emblem	2·75	2·75
1454	$4	Chinese rocket on launch tower	3·00	3·00
1455	$4	West German and N.A.T.O. flags	3·00	3·00
1456	$6	Hugo Eckener (airship pioneer)	4·50	4·50
1443/56		*Set of 14*	27·00	26·00

MS1457 Four sheets, each 100×71 mm. (a) $6 Projected European space station. (b) $6 Airship LZ-129 *Hindenburg*, 1936. (c) $6 Brandenburg Gate on German flag. (d) $6 *Danaus plexippus* (butterfly) .. .. *Set of 4 sheets* 26·00 25·00

1993 (21 Sept). *Flowers. Nos. 1733/41 of Antigua optd with T* **114**, *but with lines spaced (Nos. 1458/65) or T* **111** (*No.* MS1466).
1458	15 c.	Cardinal's Guard	85	85
1459	25 c.	Giant Granadilla	1·10	1·10
1460	30 c.	Spider Flower	1·25	1·25
1461	40 c.	Gold Vine	1·40	1·40
1462	$1	Frangipani	2·00	2·00
1463	$2	Bougainvillea	2·75	2·75
1464	$4	Yellow Oleander	3·75	3·75
1465	$5	Spicy Jatropha	3·75	3·75
1458/65		*Set of 8*	15·00	15·00

MS1466 Two sheets, each 100×70 mm. (a) $6 Bird Lime Tree. (b) $6 Fairy Lily *Set of 2 sheets* 16·00 16·00

WORLD BIRDWATCH
9-10 OCTOBER 1993

(121)

1993 (9 Oct). *World Bird Watch. Nos. 1248/51 optd as T* **121** (*horiz opt on* $2, $4).
1467	60 c.	Type **119**	2·50	1·75
1468	$2	Adelaide's Warbler	4·50	4·00
1469	$4	Rose-breasted Grosbeak	6·00	6·50
1470	$7	Wied's Crested Flycatcher	8·00	9·50
1467/70		*Set of 4*	19·00	20·00

1993 (11 Nov). *Endangered Species. Nos. 1759/71 of Antigua optd with T* **111**.
1471	$1	St. Lucia Amazon	2·25	2·25
	a.	Sheetlet. Nos. 1471/82	24·00	
1472	$1	Cahow	2·25	2·25
1473	$1	Swallow-tailed Kite	2·25	2·25
1474	$1	Everglade Kite	2·25	2·25
1475	$1	Imperial Amazon	2·25	2·25
1476	$1	Humpback Whale	2·25	2·25
1477	$1	Plain Pigeon	2·25	2·25
1478	$1	St. Vincent Amazon	2·25	2·25
1479	$1	Puerto Rican Amazon	2·25	2·25
1480	$1	Leatherback Turtle	2·25	2·25
1481	$1	American Crocodile	2·25	2·25
1482	$1	Hawksbill Turtle	2·25	2·25
1471/82		*Set of 12*	24·00	24·00

MS1483 Two sheets, each 100×70 mm. (a) $6 As No. 1476. (b) $6 West Indian Manatee
Set of 2 sheets 22·00 19·00

1994 (6 Jan). *Bicentenary of the Louvre, Paris. Paintings by Peter Paul Rubens. Nos. 1742/9 and* MS1758 *of Antigua optd with T* **120**.
1484	$1	"The Destiny of Marie de Medici" (upper detail)	2·25	2·25
	a.	Sheetlet. Nos. 1484/91	16·00	
1485	$1	"The Birth of Marie de Medici"	2·25	2·25
1486	$1	"The Education of Marie de Medici"	2·25	2·25
1487	$1	"The Destiny of Marie de Medici" (lower detail)	2·25	2·25
1488	$1	"Henry VI receiving the Portrait of Marie"	2·25	2·25
1489	$1	"The Meeting of the King and Marie de Medici"	2·25	2·25
1490	$1	"The Marriage by Proxy"	2·25	2·25
1491	$1	"The Birth of Louis XIII"	2·25	2·25
1484/91		*Set of 8*	16·00	16·00

MS1492 70×100 mm. $6 "Helene Fourment with a Coach" (52×85 *mm*) .. .. 11·00 12·00

ANTIGUA/*Barbuda* — 1994

1994 (3 Mar). *World Cup Football Championship 1994, U.S.A.* (1st issue). Nos. 1816/28 of Antigua optd with T 114, *but with lines spaced* (Nos. 1493/1504) *or* T 111 (No. MS1505).

1493	$2 Paul Gascoigne	2.50	2.25
1494	$2 David Platt	2.50	2.25
1495	$2 Martin Peters	2.50	2.25
1496	$2 John Barnes	2.50	2.25
1497	$2 Gary Lineker	2.50	2.25
1498	$2 Geoff Hurst	2.50	2.25
1499	$2 Bobby Charlton	2.50	2.25
1500	$2 Bryan Robson	2.50	2.25
1501	$2 Bobby Moore	2.50	2.25
1502	$2 Nobby Stiles	2.50	2.25
1503	$2 Gordon Banks	2.50	2.25
1504	$2 Peter Shilton	2.50	2.25
1493/1504		Set of 12 27.00	24.00

MS1505 Two sheets, each 135×109 mm. (a) $6 Bobby Moore holding World Cup. (b) $6 Gary Lineker and Bobby Robson ... Set of 2 sheets 16.00 14.00
See also Nos. 1573/9.

1994 (21 Apr). *Anniversaries and Events.* Nos. 1829/38, 1840 *and* 1842/7 of Antigua optd with T 111.

1506	10 c. Grand Inspector W. Heath	80	60
1507	15 c. Rodnina and Oulanov (U.S.S.R.) (pairs figure skating) (*horiz*)	65	60
1508	30 c. Present Masonic Hall, St. John's (*horiz*)	1.25	80
1509	30 c. Willy Brandt with Helmut Schmidt and George Leber (*horiz*)	80	80
1510	30 c. "Cat and Bird" (Picasso) (*horiz*)	80	80
1511	40 c. Previous Masonic Hall, St. John's (*horiz*)	1.25	80
1512	40 c. "Fish on a Newspaper" (Picasso) (*horiz*)	80	80
1513	40 c. Early astronomical equipment	80	80
1514	40 c. Prince Naruhito and engagement photographs (*horiz*)	80	80
1515	60 c. Grand Inspector J. Jeffery	1.50	90
1516	$3 Masako Owada and engagement photographs (*horiz*)	2.00	2.50
1517	$4 Willy Brandt and protest march (*horiz*)	2.75	3.00
1518	$4 Galaxy	2.75	3.00
1519	$5 Alberto Tomba (Italy) (giant slalom)	2.75	3.00
1520	$5 "Dying Bull" (Picasso) (*horiz*)	2.75	3.00
1521	$5 Pres. Clinton and family (*horiz*)	2.75	3.00
1506/21		Set of 16 23.00	23.00

MS1522 Six sheets. (a) 106×75 mm. $5 Copernicus. (b) 106×75 mm. $6 Womens' 1500 metre speed skating medallists (*horiz*). (c) 106×75 mm. $6 Willy Brandt at Warsaw Ghetto Memorial (*horiz*). (d) 106×75 mm. $6 "Woman with a Dog" (detail) (Picasso) (*horiz*). (e) 106×75 mm. $6 Masako Owada. (f) 106×75 mm. $6 Pres. Clinton taking the Oath (42½×57 mm) ... Set of 6 sheets 28.00 28.00

1994 (15 June). *Aviation Anniversaries.* Nos. 1848/55 of Antigua optd with T 111 (*vertically reading down on No. 1526*).

1523	30 c. Hugo Eckener and Dr. W. Beckers with Airship LZ-127 Graf Zeppelin over Lake George, New York	1.25	90
1524	40 c. Chicago World's Fair from Graf Zeppelin	1.25	90
1525	40 c. Gloster Whittle E28/39, 1941	1.25	90
1526	40 c. George Washington writing balloon mail letter (*vert*)	1.25	90
1527	$4 Pres. Wilson and Curtiss JN-4 "Jenny"	4.50	4.50
1528	$5 Airship LZ-129 Hindenburg over Ebbets Field baseball stadium, 1937	4.50	4.50
1529	$5 Gloster Meteor in dogfight	4.50	4.50
1523/9		Set of 7 17.00	15.00

MS1530 Three sheets. (a) 86×105 mm. $6 Hugo Eckener (*vert*). (b) 105×86 mm. $6 Consolidated Catalina PBY-5 flying boat (57×42½ mm). (c) 105×86 mm. $6 Alexander Hamilton, Washington and John Jay watching Blanchard's balloon, 1793 (*horiz*) ... Set of 3 sheets 22.00 20.00

1994 (15 June). *Centenaries of Henry Ford's First Petrol Engine* (Nos. 1531, 1533, **MS**1535a) *and Karl Benz's First Four-wheeled Car* (*others*). Nos. 1856/60 of Antigua optd with T 111.

1531	30 c. Lincoln Continental	1.25	85
1532	40 c. Mercedes racing car, 1914	1.25	90
1533	$4 Ford "GT40", 1966	4.50	4.50
1534	$5 Mercedes Benz "gull-wing" coupe, 1954	4.50	4.50
1531/4		Set of 4 10.50	9.50

MS1535 Two sheets. (a) 114×87 mm. $6 Ford's Mustang emblem. (b) 87×114 mm. $6 Germany 1936 12pf. Benz and U.S.A. 1968 12 c. Ford stamps ... Set of 2 sheets 13.00 14.00

1994 (18 Aug). *Famous Paintings by Rembrandt and Matisse.* Nos. 1881/9 of Antigua optd with T 111.

1536	15 c. "Hannah and Samuel" (Rembrandt)	75	75
1537	15 c. "Guitarist" (Matisse)	75	75
1538	30 c. "The Jewish Bride" (Rembrandt)	1.10	90
1539	40 c. "Jacob wrestling with the Angel" (Rembrandt)	1.10	90
1540	60 c. "Interior with a Goldfish Bowl" (Matisse)	1.40	1.10
1541	$1 "Mlle. Yvonne Landsberg" (Matisse)	1.75	1.40
1542	$4 "The Toboggan" (Matisse)	4.50	5.00
1543	$5 "Moses with the Tablets of the Law" (Rembrandt)	4.50	5.00
1536/43		Set of 8 14.00	14.00

MS1544 Two sheets. (a) 124×99 mm. $6 "The Blinding of Samson by the Philistines" (detail) (Rembrandt). (b) 99×124 mm. $6 "The Three Sisters" (detail) (Matisse) ... Set of 2 sheets 13.00 14.00

1994 (21 Sept). *"Polska '93" International Stamp Exhibition, Poznań.* Nos. 1839, 1841 *and* 1847f of Antigua optd with T 114, *but with lines spaced* (*sideways on* $1, $3).

1545	$1 "Woman Combing her Hair" (W. Slewinski) (*horiz*)	2.00	2.00
1546	$3 "Artist's Wife with Cat" (Konrad Kryzanowski) (*horiz*)	4.00	4.00

MS1547 70×100 mm. $6 "General Confusion" (S. I. Witkiewicz) ... 8.00 9.00

1994 (21 Sept). *Orchids.* Nos. 1948/56 of Antigua optd with T 114, *but with lines spaced* (Nos. 1548/55) *or* T 111 (No. MS1556).

1548	10 c. Spiranthes lanceolata	1.00	1.00
1549	20 c. Ionopsis utricularioides	1.50	1.25
1550	30 c. Tetramicra canaliculata	1.75	1.25
1551	50 c. Oncidium picturatum	2.00	1.50
1552	$1 Epidendrum difforme	2.75	2.25
1553	$2 Epidendrum ciliare	4.50	4.00
1554	$4 Epidendrum ibaguense	6.00	6.50
1555	$5 Epidendrum nocturnum	6.00	6.50
1548/55		Set of 8 23.00	22.00

MS1556 Two sheets, each 100×73 mm. (a) $6 Rodriguezia lanceolata. (b) $6 Encyclia cochleata ... Set of 2 sheets 23.00 22.00

1994 (3 Nov). *Centenary of Sierra Club* (*environmental protection society*) (1992). *Endangered Species.* Nos. 1907/22 of Antigua optd with T 114, *but lines spaced* (Nos. 1557/71) *or* T 111 (No. MS1572).

1557	$1.50, Sumatran Rhinoceros lying down	2.00	2.00
	a. Sheetlet. Nos. 1557/64	13.50	
1558	$1.50, Sumatran Rhinoceros feeding	2.00	2.00
1559	$1.50, Ring-tailed Lemur on ground	2.00	2.00
1560	$1.50, Ring-tailed Lemur on branch	2.00	2.00
1561	$1.50, Red-fronted Brown Lemur on branch	2.00	2.00
1562	$1.50, Head of Red-fronted Brown Lemur	2.00	2.00
1563	$1.50, Head of Red-fronted Brown Lemur in front of trunk	2.00	2.00
1564	$1.50, Sierra Club Centennial emblem	1.25	1.25
	a. Sheetlet. Nos. 1564/71	13.50	
1565	$1.50, Head of Bactrian Camel	2.00	2.00
1566	$1.50, Bactrian Camel	2.00	2.00
1567	$1.50, African Elephant drinking	2.00	2.00
1568	$1.50, Head of African Elephant	2.00	2.00
1569	$1.50, Leopard sitting upright	2.00	2.00
1570	$1.50, Leopard in grass (emblem at right)	2.00	2.00
1571	$1.50, Leopard in grass (emblem at left)	2.00	2.00
1557/71		Set of 15 27.00	27.00

MS1572 Four sheets. (a) 100×70 mm. $1.50, Sumatran Rhinoceros (*horiz*). (b) 70×100 mm. $1.50, Ring-tailed Lemur (*horiz*). (c) 70×100 mm. $1.50, Bactrian Camel (*horiz*). (d) 100×70 mm. $1.50, African Elephant (*horiz*) ... Set of 4 sheets 5.00 6.00

1995 (12 Jan). *World Cup Football Championship, U.S.A.* (2nd issue). Nos. 2039/45 of Antigua optd with T 116 *diagonally in silver.*

1573	15 c. Hugo Sanchez (Mexico)	75	60
1574	35 c. Jürgen Klinsmann (Germany)	1.10	90
1575	65 c. Antiguan player	1.50	1.25
1576	$1.20, Cobi Jones (U.S.A.)	2.00	1.75
1577	$4 Roberto Baggio (Italy)	4.00	4.50
1578	$5 Bwalya Kalusha (Zambia)	4.00	4.50
1573/8		Set of 6 12.00	12.00

MS1579 Two sheets. (a) 72×105 mm. $6 Maldive Islands player (*vert*). (b) 107×78 mm. $6 World Cup trophy (*vert*) ... Set of 2 sheets 12.00 12.00

1995 (12 Jan). *Christmas. Religious Paintings.* Nos. 2058/66 of Antigua optd with T 111.

1580	15 c. "Virgin and Child by the Fireside" (Robert Campin)	65	45
1581	35 c. "The Reading Madonna" (Giorgione)	85	45
1582	40 c. "Madonna and Child" (Giovanni Bellini)	85	45
1583	45 c. "The Litta Madonna" (Da Vinci)	85	45
1584	65 c. "The Virgin and Child under the Apple Tree" (Lucas Cranach the Elder)	1.25	90
1585	75 c. "Madonna and Child" (Master of the Female Half-lengths)	1.25	1.25
1586	$1.20, "An Allegory of the Church" (Alessandro Allori)	2.00	2.25
1587	$5 "Madonna and Child wreathed with Flowers" (Jacob Jordaens)	5.00	6.00
1580/7		Set of 8 11.50	11.00

MS1588 Two sheets. (a) 123×88 mm. $6 "Madonna and Child with Commissioners" (detail) (Palma Vecchio). (b) 88×123 mm. $6 "The Virgin Enthroned with Child" (detail) (Bohemian master) ... Set of 2 sheets 11.50 12.00

1995 (24 Feb). *"Hong Kong '94" International Stamp Exhibition* (1st issue). Nos. 1890/1 of Antigua optd with T 111.

1589	40 c. Hong Kong 1981 $1 Golden Threadfin Bream stamp and sampans, Shau Kei Wan	80	80
	a. Horiz pair. Nos. 1589/90	1.60	1.60
1590	40 c. Antigua 1990 $2 Rock Beauty stamp and sampans, Shau Kei Wan	80	80

1995 (24 Feb). *"Hong Kong '94" International Stamp Exhibition* (2nd issue). Nos. 1892/7 of Antigua optd with T 111.

1591	40 c. Terracotta warriors	30	30
	a. Sheetlet. Nos. 1591/6	1.60	
1592	40 c. Cavalryman and horse	30	30
1593	40 c. Warriors in armour	30	30
1594	40 c. Painted bronze chariot and team	30	30
1595	40 c. Pekingese dog	30	30
1596	40 c. Warriors with horses	30	30
1591/6		Set of 6 1.60	1.60

1995 (24 Feb). *Centenary of International Olympic Committee.* Nos. 1990/2 of Antigua optd with T 111, *but with lines spaced.*

1597	80 c. Edwin Moses (U.S.A.) (400 metres hurdles), 1984	75	75
1598	$1.50, Steffi Graf (Germany) (tennis), 1988	3.00	3.00

MS1599 79×110 mm. $6 Johann Olav Koss (Norway) (500, 1500 and 10,000 metre speed skating), 1994 ... 5.00 6.00

1995 (4 Apr). *Dogs of the World. Chinese New Year* ("Year of the Dog"). Nos. 1923/47 of Antigua optd with T 111.

1600	50 c. West Highland White Terrier	70	70
	a. Sheetlet. Nos. 1600/11	7.50	
1601	50 c. Beagle	70	70
1602	50 c. Scottish Terrier	70	70
1603	50 c. Pekingese	70	70
1604	50 c. Dachshund	70	70
1605	50 c. Yorkshire Terrier	70	70
1606	50 c. Pomeranian	70	70
1607	50 c. Poodle	70	70
1608	50 c. Shetland Sheepdog	70	70
1609	50 c. Pug	70	70
1610	50 c. Shih Tzu	70	70
1611	50 c. Chihuahua	70	70
1612	50 c. Mastiff	70	70
	a. Sheetlet. Nos. 1612/23	7.50	
1613	50 c. Border Collie	70	70
1614	50 c. Samoyed	70	70
1615	50 c. Airedale Terrier	70	70
1616	50 c. English Setter	70	70
1617	50 c. Rough Collie	70	70
1618	50 c. Newfoundland	70	70
1619	50 c. Weimarana	70	70
1620	50 c. English Springer Spaniel	70	70
1621	50 c. Dalmatian	70	70
1622	50 c. Boxer	70	70
1623	50 c. Old English Sheepdog	70	70
1600/23		Set of 24 15.00	15.00

MS1624 Two sheets, each 93×58 mm. (a) $6 Welsh Corgi. (b) $6 Labrador Retriever ... Set of 2 sheets 13.00 13.00

1995 (18 May). *Centenary of First English Cricket Tour to the West Indies* (1995). Nos. 1994/7 of Antigua optd with T 114, *but with lines spaced.*

1625	35 c. Mike Atherton (England) and Wisden Trophy	1.00	65
1626	75 c. Viv Richards (West Indies) (*vert*)	1.75	1.75
1627	$1.20, Richie Richardson (West Indies) and Wisden Trophy	2.25	2.50
1625/7		Set of 3 4.50	4.50

MS1628 80×100 mm. $3 English team, 1895 (black and grey-brown) ... 4.75 5.00

1995 (18 May–12 July). *"Philakorea '94" International Stamp Exhibition* (1st issue). Nos. 1998/2009 of Antigua optd with T 114, *but with lines spaced* (Nos. 1629 and 1638/40) *or* T 111 (*others*).

1629	40 c. Entrance bridge, Songgwangsa Temple (12 July)	60	60
1630	75 c. Long-necked Bottle	90	90
	a. Sheetlet. Nos. 1630/7	6.50	
1631	75 c. Punch'ong ware jar with floral decoration	90	90
1632	75 c. Punch'ong ware jar with blue dragon pattern	90	90
1633	75 c. Ewer in shape of bamboo shoot	90	90
1634	75 c. Punch'ong ware green jar	90	90
1635	75 c. Pear-shaped bottle	90	90
1636	75 c. Porcelain jar with brown dragon pattern	90	90
1637	75 c. Porcelain jar with floral pattern	90	90
1638	90 c. Song-op Folk Village, Cheju (12 July)	90	90
1639	$3 Port Sogwipo (12 July)	2.50	2.50
1629/39		Set of 11 9.00	9.00

MS1640 104×71 mm. $4 Ox herder playing flute (*vert*) ... 2.75 3.50

1995 (18 May). *First Recipients of Order of the Caribbean Community.* Nos. 2046/8 of Antigua optd with T 111.

1641	65 c. Sir Shridath Ramphal	45	50
1642	90 c. William Demas	55	60
1643	$1.20, Derek Walcott	75	85
1641/3		Set of 3 1.60	1.75

1995 (12 July–29 Sept). *25th Anniv of First Moon Landing.* Nos. 1977/89 of Antigua optd with T 114, *but with lines spaced* (*vertically reading upward on Nos. 1644/55*).

1644	$1.50, Edwin Aldrin (astronaut)	1.50	1.50
	a. Sheetlet. Nos. 1644/49	8.00	
1645	$1.50, First lunar footprint	1.50	1.50
1646	$1.50, Neil Armstrong (astronaut)	1.50	1.50
1647	$1.50, Aldrin stepping onto Moon	1.50	1.50
1648	$1.50, Aldrin and equipment	1.50	1.50
1649	$1.50, Aldrin and U.S.A. flag	1.50	1.50
1650	$1.50, Aldrin at Tranquility Base	1.50	1.50
	a. Sheetlet. Nos. 1650/55	8.00	
1651	$1.50, Moon plaque	1.50	1.50
1652	$1.50, Eagle leaving Moon	1.50	1.50
1653	$1.50, Command module in lunar orbit	1.50	1.50
1654	$1.50, First day cover of U.S.A. 1969 10 c. First Man on Moon stamp	1.50	1.50
1655	$1.50, Pres. Nixon and astronauts	1.50	1.50
1644/55		Set of 12 16.00	16.00

MS1656 72×102 mm. $6 Armstrong and Aldrin with postal official (29 Sept) ... 7.00 8.00

1995 (12 July). *International Year of the Family.* No. 1993 of Antigua optd with T 114, *but with lines spaced.*

1657	90 c. Antiguan family	80	80

1995 (29 Sept). *50th Anniv of D-Day. Nos. 2010/13 of Antigua optd as T 113, but with lines spaced.*
1658	40 c. Short S.25 Sunderland flying boat		1·00	75
1659	$2 Lockheed P-38 Lightning fighters attacking train		3·00	3·00
1660	$3 Martin B-26 Marauder bombers		3·25	3·50
1658/60		*Set of 3*	6·50	6·50
MS1661	108×78 mm. $6 Hawker Typhoon fighter bomber		7·00	8·00

122 Queen Elizabeth the Queen Mother (90th birthday)

(Des G. Vasarhelyi. Litho B.D.T.)

1995 (13–27 Nov). *Anniversaries. T 122 and similar multi-coloured designs. P 13.*
1662	$7.50, Type 122 (20 Nov)		7·00	7·00
1663	$8 German bombers over St. Paul's Cathedral, London (*horiz*) (50th anniv of end of Second World War)		8·00	8·00
1664	$8 New York skyline with U.N. and national flags (*horiz*) (50th anniv of United Nations) (27 Nov)		6·50	7·50
1662/4		*Set of 3*	19·00	20·00

HURRICANE RELIEF
+ $1
(123)

BARBUDA
MAIL
(124)

1995 (13–27 Nov). *Hurricane Relief. Nos. 1662/4 surch with T 123 in silver.*
1665	$7.50 + $1 Type **122** (90th birthday) (20 Nov)		5·00	6·00
1666	$8 + $1 German bombers over St. Paul's Cathedral, London (*horiz*) (50th anniv of end of Second World War)		5·00	6·00
1667	$8 + $1 New York skyline with U.N. and national flags (*horiz*) (50th anniv of United Nations) (27 Nov)		5·00	6·00
1665/7		*Set of 3*	13·50	17·00

1996 (22 Jan). *Marine Life. Nos. 1967/76 of Antigua optd as T 114, but with lines spaced.*
1668	50 c. Bottlenose Dolphin		60	60
	a. Sheetlet. Nos. 1668/76		4·75	
1669	50 c. Killer Whale		60	60
1670	50 c. Spinner Dolphin		60	60
1671	50 c. Oceanic Sunfish		60	60
1672	50 c. Caribbean Reef Shark and Short Fin Pilot Whale		60	60
1673	50 c. Copper-banded Butterflyfish		60	60
1674	50 c. Mosaic Moray		60	60
1675	50 c. Clown Triggerfish		60	60
1676	50 c. Red Lobster		60	60
1668/76		*Set of 9*	4·75	4·75
MS1677	Two sheets, each 106×76 mm. (a) $6 Seahorse. (b) $6 Swordfish ("Blue Marlin") (*horiz*)			
		Set of 2 sheets	11·00	12·00

1996 (22 Jan). *Christmas. Religious Paintings. Nos. 2267/73 of Antigua optd with T 111.*
1678	15 c. "Rest on the Flight into Egypt" (Paolo Veronese)		50	40
1679	35 c. "Madonna and Child" (Van Dyck)		65	40
1680	65 c. "Sacred Conversation Piece" (Veronese)		80	55
1681	75 c. "Vision of St. Anthony" (Van Dyck)		90	60
1682	90 c. "Virgin and Child" (Van Eyck)		1·10	75
1683	$6 "The Immaculate Conception" (Giovanni Tiepolo)		4·25	5·50
1678/83		*Set of 5*	7·50	7·50
MS1684	Two sheets. (a) 101×127 mm. $5 "Christ appearing to his Mother" (detail) (Van der Weyden). (b) 127×101 mm. $6 "The Infant Jesus and the Young St. John" (Murillo) *Set of 2 sheets*		9·00	11·00

1996 (14 Feb). *Stars of Country and Western Music. Nos. 2014/38 of Antigua optd with T 114, but with lines spaced.*
1685	75 c. Travis Tritt		70	70
	a. Sheetlet. Nos. 1685/92		5·00	
1686	75 c. Dwight Yoakam		70	70
1687	75 c. Billy Ray Cyrus		70	70
1688	75 c. Alan Jackson		70	70
1689	75 c. Garth Brooks		70	70
1690	75 c. Vince Gill		70	70
1691	75 c. Clint Black		70	70
1692	75 c. Eddie Rabbit		70	70
1693	75 c. Patsy Cline		70	70
	a. Sheetlet. Nos. 1693/1700		5·00	
1694	75 c. Tanya Tucker		70	70
1695	75 c. Dolly Parton		70	70
1696	75 c. Anne Murray		70	70
1697	75 c. Tammy Wynette		70	70
1698	75 c. Loretta Lynn		70	70

1699	75 c. Reba McEntire		70	70
1700	75 c. Skeeter Davis		70	70
1701	75 c. Hank Snow		70	70
	a. Sheetlet. Nos. 1701/8		5·00	
1702	75 c. Gene Autry		70	70
1703	75 c. Jimmie Rodgers		70	70
1704	75 c. Ernest Tubb		70	70
1705	75 c. Eddy Arnold		70	70
1706	75 c. Willie Nelson		70	70
1707	75 c. Johnny Cash		70	70
1708	75 c. George Jones		70	70
1685/1708		*Set of 24*	15·00	15·00
MS1709	Three sheets. (a) 100×70 mm. $6 Hank Williams Jr. (b) 100×70 mm. $6 Hank Williams Sr. (c) 70×100 mm. $6 Kitty Wells (*horiz*)			
		Set of 3 sheets	15·00	15·00

1996 (14 Feb). *Birds. Nos. 2067/81 of Antigua optd with T 124.*
1710	15 c. Magnificent Frigate Bird		10	10
1711	25 c. Blue-hooded Euphonia		10	10
1712	35 c. Eastern Meadowlark		15	20
1713	40 c. Red-billed Tropic Bird		15	20
1714	45 c. Greater Flamingo		20	25
1715	60 c. Yellow-faced Grassquit		25	30
1716	65 c. Yellow-billed Cuckoo		30	35
1717	70 c. Purple-throated Carib		30	35
1718	75 c. Bananaquit		35	40
1719	90 c. Painted Bunting		40	45
1720	$1.20, Red-legged Honeycreeper		50	55
1721	$2 Northern Jacana		80	90
1722	$5 Greater Antillean Bullfinch		2·10	2·25
1723	$10 Caribbean Elaenia		4·25	4·50
1724	$20 Brown Trembler		8·75	9·00
1710/24		*Set of 15*	18·00	19·00

1996 (2 Apr). *Birds. Nos. 2050, 2052, 2054 and 2056/7 of Antigua optd with T 111.*
1725	15 c. Bridled Quail Dove		55	40
1726	40 c. Purple-throated Carib (*vert*)		75	40
1727	$1 Broad-winged Hawk (*vert*)		1·50	1·10
1728	$4 Yellow Warbler		2·75	4·00
1725/8		*Set of 4*	5·00	5·50
MS1729	Two sheets. (a) 70×100 mm. $6 Female Magnificent Frigate Bird (*vert*). (b) 100×70 mm. $6 Black-billed Whistling Duck ducklings			
		Set of 2 sheets	10·50	10·50

1996 (13 June). *Prehistoric Animals. Nos. 2082/100 of Antigua optd with T 114, but with lines spaced (Nos. 1730/2 and 1745/7) or T 111 (others).*
1730	15 c. Head of Pachycephalosaurus		60	60
1731	20 c. Head of Afrovenator		60	60
1732	65 c. Centrosaurus		70	70
1733	75 c. Kronosaurus (*horiz*)		70	70
	a. Sheetlet. Nos. 1733/44		7·50	
1734	75 c. Ichthyosaurus (*horiz*)		70	70
1735	75 c. Plesiosaurus (*horiz*)		70	70
1736	75 c. Archelon (*horiz*)		70	70
1737	75 c. Pair of Tyrannosaurus (*horiz*)		70	70
1738	75 c. Tyrannosaurus (*horiz*)		70	70
1739	75 c. Parasaurolophus (*horiz*)		70	70
1740	75 c. Pair of Parasaurolophus (*horiz*)		70	70
1741	75 c. Oviraptor (*horiz*)		70	70
1742	75 c. Protoceratops with eggs (*horiz*)		70	70
1743	75 c. Pteranodon and Protoceratops (*horiz*)		70	70
1744	75 c. Pair of Protoceratops (*horiz*)		70	70
1745	90 c. Pentaceratops drinking		90	90
1746	$1.20, Head of Tarbosaurus		1·25	1·25
1747	$5 Head of Styracosaurus		3·50	3·50
1730/47		*Set of 18*	14·00	14·00
MS1748	Two sheets, each 101×70 mm. (a) $6 Head of Corythosaurus (*horiz*) (b) $6 Head of Carnotaurus (*horiz*) *Set of 2 sheets*		11·00	11·00

1996 (16 July). *Olympic Games, Atlanta. Previous Gold Medal Winners. Nos. 2101/7 of Antigua optd diagonally with T 116.*
1749	15 c. Al Oerter (U.S.A.) (discus – 1956, 1960, 1964, 1968)		45	35
1750	20 c. Greg Louganis (U.S.A.) (diving – 1984, 1988)		45	35
1751	65 c. Naim Suleymanoglu (Turkey) (weightlifting – 1988)		75	60
1752	90 c. Louise Ritter (U.S.A.) (high jump – 1988)		1·10	85
1753	$1.20, Nadia Comaneci (Rumania) (gymnastics – 1976)		1·40	1·40
1754	$5 Olga Boldarenko (Russia) (10,000 metres – 1988)		3·50	4·00
1749/54		*Set of 6*	7·00	6·75
MS1755	Two sheets, 106×76 mm. (a) $6 United States crew (eight-oared shell – 1964) (b) $6 Lutz Hessilch (Germany) (cycling – 1988) (*vert*).			
		Set of 2 sheets	8·50	9·00

1996 (10 Sept). *18th World Scout Jamboree, Netherlands. Tents. Nos. 2203/9 of Antigua optd with T 116 diagonally.*
1756	$1.20, The Explorer Tent		1·00	1·00
	a. Horiz strip of 3. Nos. 1756/8		2·75	
1757	$1.20, Camper tent		1·00	1·00
1758	$1.20, Wall tent		1·00	1·00
1759	$1.20, Trail tent		1·00	1·00
	a. Horiz strip of 3. Nos. 1759/61		2·75	
1760	$1.20, Miner's tent		1·00	1·00
1761	$1.20, Voyager tent		1·00	1·00
1756/61		*Set of 6*	5·50	5·50
MS1762	Two sheets, each 76×106 mm. (a) $6 Scout and camp fire. (b) $6 Scout with back pack (*vert*) *Set of 2 sheets*		7·50	8·00

1996 (25 Oct). *Centenary of Nobel Prize Trust Fund. Nos. 2226/44 of Antigua optd with T 120.*
1763	$1 Dag Hammarskjold (1961 Peace)		60	60
	a. Sheetlet. Nos. 1763/71		4·75	
1764	$1 Georg Wittig (1979 Chemistry)		60	60
1765	$1 Wilhelm Ostwold (1909 Chemistry)		60	60

1766	$1 Robert Koch (1905 Medicine)		60	60
1767	$1 Karl Ziegler (1963 Chemistry)		60	60
1768	$1 Alexander Fleming (1945 Medicine)		60	60
1769	$1 Hermann Staudinger (1953 Chemistry)		60	60
1770	$1 Manfred Eigen (1967 Chemistry)		60	60
1771	$1 Arno Penzias (1978 Physics)		60	60
1772	$1 Shumal Agnon (1966 Literature)		60	60
	a. Sheetlet. Nos. 1772/80		4·75	
1773	$1 Rudyard Kipling (1907 Literature)		60	60
1774	$1 Aleksandr Solzhenitsyn (1970 Literature)		60	60
1775	$1 Jack Steinburger (1988 Physics)		60	60
1776	$1 Andrei Sakharov (1975 Peace)		60	60
1777	$1 Otto Stern (1943 Physics)		60	60
1778	$1 John Steinbeck (1962 Literature)		60	60
1779	$1 Nadine Gordimer (1991 Literature)		60	60
1780	$1 William Faulkner (1949 Literature)		60	60
1763/80		*Set of 18*	9·50	9·50
MS1781	Two sheets, each 100×70 mm. (a) $6 Elie Wiesel (1986 Peace) (*vert*). (b) $6 Dalai Lama (1989 Peace) (*vert*) *Set of 2 sheets*		8·50	9·00

1996 (14 Nov). *70th Birthday of Queen Elizabeth II. Nos. 2355/8 of Antigua optd with T 111.*
1782	$2 Queen Elizabeth II in blue dress		1·10	1·10
	a. Strip of 3. Nos. 1782/4		3·00	
1783	$2 With bouquet		1·10	1·10
1784	$2 In Garter robes		1·10	1·10
1782/4		*Set of 3*	3·00	3·00
MS1785	96×111 mm. $6 Wearing white dress		4·50	4·75

1997 (28 Jan). *Christmas. Religious Paintings by Filippo Lippi. Nos. 2377/83 of Antigua optd with T 111.*
1786	60 c. "Madonna Enthroned"		35	35
1787	90 c. "Adoration of the Child and Saints"		55	55
1788	$1 "The Annunciation"		60	60
1789	$1.20, "Birth of the Virgin"		75	75
1790	$1.60, "Adoration of the Child"		90	90
1791	$1.75, "Madonna and Child"		1·00	1·00
1786/91		*Set of 6*	3·75	3·75
MS1792	Two sheets, each 76×106 mm. (a) $6 "Madonna and Child" (*different*). (b) $6 "The Circumcision" *Set of 2 sheets*		8·00	8·50

1997 (24 Feb). *50th Anniv of Food and Agriculture Organization. Nos. 2121/4 of Antigua optd with T 114, but with lines spaced.*
1793	75 c. Woman buying produce from market		80	80
	a. Horiz strip of 3. Nos. 1793/5		2·50	
1794	90 c. Women shopping		90	90
1795	$1.20, Women talking		1·10	1·10
1793/5		*Set of 3*	2·50	2·50
MS1796	100×70 mm. $6 Tractor		5·00	6·00

1997 (24 Feb). *90th Anniv of Rotary International (1995). Nos. 2125/6 of Antigua optd with T 114, but with lines spaced.*
1797	$5 Beach and rotary emblem		4·25	4·50
MS1798	74×104 mm. $6 National flag and emblem		3·25	3·75

1997 (4 Apr). *50th Anniv of End of Second World War in Europe and the Pacific. Nos. 2108/16 and 2132/8 of Antigua optd with T 114 but with lines spaced (No. MS1813b) or with T 111 (others).*
1799	$1.20, Map of Berlin showing Russian advance		55	60
	a. Sheetlet. Nos. 1799/1806		4·25	
1800	$1.20, Russian tank and infantry		55	60
1801	$1.20, Street fighting in Berlin		55	60
1802	$1.20, German tank exploding		55	60
1803	$1.20, Russian air raid		55	60
1804	$1.20, German troops surrendering		55	60
1805	$1.20, Hoisting the Soviet flag on the Reichstag		55	60
1806	$1.20, Captured German standards		55	60
1807	$1.20, Gen. Chiang Kai-shek and Chinese guerrillas		55	60
	a. Sheetlet. Nos. 1807/12		4·25	
1808	$1.20, Gen. Douglas MacArthur and beach landing		55	60
1809	$1.20, Gen. Claire Chennault and U.S. fighter aircraft		55	60
1810	$1.20, Brig. Orde Wingate and supply drop		55	60
1811	$1.20, Gen. Joseph Stilwell and U.S. supply plane		55	60
1812	$1.20, Field-Marshal Bill Slim and loading cow onto plane		55	60
1799/1812		*Set of 14*	8·50	8·75
MS1813	Two sheets, each 100×70 mm. (a) $3 Admiral Nimitz and aircraft carrier. (b) $6 Gen. Konev (*vert*) *Set of 2 sheets*		5·75	6·25

1997 (25 Apr). *95th Birthday of Queen Elizabeth the Queen Mother. Nos. 2127/31 of Antigua optd with T 111.*
1814	$1.50, orange-brown, pale brown and black		85	90
	a. Sheetlet. Nos. 1814/17×2		6·00	
1815	$1.50, multicoloured		85	90
1816	$1.50, multicoloured		85	90
1817	$1.50, multicoloured		85	90
1814/17		*Set of 4*	3·00	3·25
MS1818	102×27 mm. $6 multicoloured		4·25	4·25

1997 (25 Apr). *50th Anniv of United Nations. Nos. 2117/20 optd with T 114 but with lines spaced.*
1819	75 c. Signatures and Earl of Halifax		35	40
	a. Horiz strip of 3. Nos. 1819/21		1·25	
1820	90 c. Virginia Gildersleeve		40	45
1821	$1.20, Harold Stassen		55	60
1819/21		*Set of 3*	1·25	1·40
MS1822	100×70 mm. $6 Pres. Franklin D. Roosevelt		3·50	4·00

1997 (30 May). *Trains of the World.* Nos. 2210/25 of *Antigua optd with T* **114**, *but with lines spaced* (No. **MS**1838) *or with T* **111** (*others*).

1823	35 c. Trans-Gabon diesel-electric train	15	20
1824	65 c. Canadian Pacific diesel-electric train	30	35
1825	75 c. Santa Fe Railway diesel-electric locomotive, U.S.A.	35	40
1826	90 c. High Speed Train, Great Britain	40	45
1827	$1.20, TGV express train, France	55	60
1828	$1.20, Diesel-electric locomotive, Australia	55	60
	a. Sheetlet. Nos. 1828/36	5·00	
1829	$1.20 Pendolino "ETR 450" electric train, Italy	55	60
1830	$1.20, Diesel-electric locomotive, Thailand	55	60
1831	$1.20, Pennslyvania Railroad steam locomotive, U.S.A.	55	60
1832	$1.20, Beyer-Garratt steam locomotive, East African Railways	55	60
1833	$1.20, Natal Govt steam locomotive	55	60
1834	$1.20, Rail gun, American Civil War	55	60
1835	$1.20, Locomotive *Lion* (red livery), Great Britain	55	60
1836	$1.20, William Hedley's *Puffing Billy* (green livery), Great Britain	55	60
1837	$6 Amtrak high-speed diesel locomotive, U.S.A.	2·75	3·00
1823/37	*Set of 15*	9·50	10·50

MS1838 Two sheets, each 110×80 mm. (a) $6 Locomotive *Iron Rooster*, China (*vert*). (b) $6 "Indian-Pacific" diesel-electric locomotive, Australia (*vert*) ... *Set of 2 sheets* 8·00 8·50

Golden Wedding of H.M. Queen Elizabeth II and H.R.H. Prince Phillip 1947 - 1997

(125)

1997 (25 July). *Golden Wedding of Queen Elizabeth II and Prince Philip* (1st issue). Nos. 1662/3 optd with *T* **125** *in gold.*

1839	$7.50, Type **122**	3·50	3·75
1840	$8 German bombers over St. Paul's Cathedral, London (*horiz*)	3·75	4·00

1997 (16 Sept). *Fungi.* Nos. 2274/82 of *Antigua optd with T* **114**, *but with lines spaced.*

1841	75 c. *Hygrophoropsis aurantiaca*	50	50
	a. Horiz strip of 4. Nos. 1841/4	1·75	
1842	75 c. *Hygrophorus bakerensis*	50	50
1843	75 c. *Hygrophorus conicus*	50	50
1844	75 c. *Hygrophorus miniatus* (*Hygrocybe miniata*)	50	50
1845	75 c. *Suillus brevipes*	50	50
	a. Horiz strip of 4. Nos. 1845/8	1·75	
1846	75 c. *Suillus luteus*	50	50
1847	75 c. *Suillus granulatus*	50	50
1848	75 c. *Suillus caerulescens*	50	50
1841/8	*Set of 8*	3·50	3·50

MS1849 Two sheets, each 106×76 mm. (a) $6 *Conocybe filaris.* (b) $6 *Hygrocybe flavescens* ... *Set of 2 sheets* 11·00 11·00

1997 (16 Sept). *Birds.* Nos. 2140/64 of *Antigua optd with T* **114** *with lines spaced* (Nos. 1850/73) *or T* **111** (No. **MS**1874).

1850	75 c. Purple-throated Carib	35	40
	a. Sheetlet. Nos. 1850/61	4·25	
1851	75 c. Antillean Crested Hummingbird	35	40
1852	75 c. Bananaquit	35	40
1853	75 c. Mangrove Cuckoo	35	40
1854	75 c. Troupial	35	40
1855	75 c. Green-throated Carib	35	40
1856	75 c. Yellow Warbler	35	40
1857	75 c. Blue-hooded Euphonia	35	40
1858	75 c. Scaly-breasted Thrasher	35	40
1859	75 c. Burrowing Owl	35	40
1860	75 c. Carib Grackle	35	40
1861	75 c. Adelaide's Warbler	35	40
1862	75 c. Ring-necked Duck	35	40
	a. Sheetlet. Nos. 1862/73	4·25	
1863	75 c. Ruddy Duck	35	40
1864	75 c. Green-winged Teal	35	40
1865	75 c. Wood Duck	35	40
1866	75 c. Hooded Merganser	35	40
1867	75 c. Lesser Scaup	35	40
1868	75 c. Black-billed Whistling Duck	35	40
1869	75 c. Fulvous Whistling Duck	35	40
1870	75 c. Bahama Pintail	35	40
1871	75 c. Shoveler	35	40
1872	75 c. Masked Duck	35	40
1873	75 c. American Wigeon	35	40
1850/73	*Set of 24*	8·50	9·50

MS1874 Two sheets, each 104×74 mm. (a) $6 Head of Purple Gallinule. (b) $6 Heads of Blue-winged Teals ... *Set of 2 sheets* 6·00 7·00

1997 (3 Nov). *Sailing Ships.* Nos. 2283/301 of *Antigua optd with T* **116** *diagonally.*

1875	15 c. H.M.S. *Resolution* (Cook)	10	10
1876	25 c. *Mayflower* (Pilgrim Fathers)	10	15
1877	45 c. *Santa Maria* (Columbus)	20	25
1878	75 c. *Aemilia* (Dutch galleon)	35	40
1879	75 c. *Sovereign of the Seas* (English galleon)	35	40
1880	90 c. H.M.S. *Victory* (Nelson)	40	45
1881	$1.20, As No. 1878	55	60
	a. Sheetlet. Nos. 1881/6	3·25	
1882	$1.20, As No. 1879	55	60
1883	$1.20, *Royal Louis* (French galleon)	55	60
1884	$1.20, H.M.S. *Royal George* (ship of the line)	55	60
1885	$1.20, *Le Protecteur* (French frigate)	55	60
1886	$1.20, As No. 1880	55	60
1887	$1.50, As No. 1877	70	75
	a. Sheetlet. Nos. 1887/92	4·25	
1888	$1.50, *Vitoria* (Magellan)	70	75
1889	$1.50, *Golden Hind* (Drake)	70	75
1890	$1.50, As No. 1876	70	75
1891	$1.50, *Griffin* (La Salle)	70	75
1892	$1.50, As No. 1875	70	75
1875/92	*Set of 18*	9·00	9·25

MS1893 (a) 102×72 mm. $6 U.S.S. *Constitution* (frigate). (b) 98×67 mm. $6 *Grande Hermine* (Cartier) ... *Set of 2 sheets* 5·50 5·75

1997 (3 Nov). *Golden Wedding of Queen Elizabeth and Prince Philip* (2nd issue). Nos. 2474/80 of *Antigua optd with T* **111**.

1894	$1 Queen Elizabeth II	70	70
	a. Sheetlet. Nos. 1894/9	3·75	
1895	$1 Royal coat of arms	70	70
1896	$1 Queen Elizabeth and Prince Philip at reception	70	70
1897	$1 Queen Elizabeth and Prince Philip in landau	70	70
1898	$1 Balmoral	70	70
1899	$1 Prince Philip	70	70
1894/9	*Set of 6*	3·75	3·75

MS1900 100×71 mm. $6 Queen Elizabeth with Prince Philip in naval uniform ... 3·75 4·00

1997 (24 Dec). *Christmas. Religious Paintings.* Nos. 2566/72 of *Antigua optd with T* **116** *diagonally.*

1901	15 c. "The Angel leaving Tobias and his Family" (Rembrandt)	20	20
1902	25 c. "The Resurrection" (Martin Knoller)	25	20
1903	60 c. "Astronomy" (Raphael)	40	40
1904	75 c. "Music-making Angel" (Melozzo da Forli)	45	45
1905	90 c. "Amor" (Parmigianino)	60	60
1906	$1.20, "Madonna and Child with Saints" (Rosso Fiorentino)	80	85
1901/6	*Set of 6*	2·40	2·40

MS1907 Two sheets, each 105×96 mm. (a) $6 "The Wedding of Tobias" (Gianantonio and Francesco Guardi) (*horiz*). (b) $6 "The Portinari Altarpiece" (Hugo van der Goes) (*horiz*) ... *Set of 2 sheets* 7·00 7·50

1998 (16 Feb). *Sea Birds.* Nos. 2325/33 of *Antigua optd with T* **111**.

1908	75 c. Black Skimmer	50	50
	a. Vert strip of 4. Nos. 1908/11	1·75	
1909	75 c. Black-capped Petrel	50	50
1910	75 c. Sooty Tern	50	50
1911	75 c. Royal Tern	50	50
1912	75 c. Pomarine Skua ("Pomarine Jaegger")	50	50
	a. Vert strip of 4. Nos. 1912/15	1·75	
1913	75 c. White-tailed Tropic Bird	50	50
1914	75 c. Northern Gannet	50	50
1915	75 c. Laughing Gull	50	50
1908/15	*Set of 8*	3·50	3·50

MS1916 Two sheets, each 105×75 mm. (a) $5 Great Frigate Bird. (b) $6 Brown Pelican ... *Set of 2 sheets* 7·00 7·50

1998 (25 Mar). *Centenary of Radio. Entertainers.* Nos. 2372/6 of *Antigua optd with T* **111**.

1917	65 c. Kate Smith	45	45
1918	75 c. Dinah Shore	50	50
1919	90 c. Rudy Vallee	60	60
1920	$1.20, Bing Crosby	75	75
1917/20	*Set of 4*	2·10	2·10

MS1921 72×104 mm. $6 Jo Stafford (28×42 mm) ... 3·50 4·00

1998 (25 Mar). *Olympic Games, Atlanta* (2nd issue). *Previous Medal Winners.* Nos. 2302/24 of *Antigua optd with T* **111** (Nos. 1923/4, 1943 *and* **MS**1944a) *or with T* **114**, *but with lines spaced* (*others*).

1922	65 c. Florence Griffith Joyner (U.S.A.) (Gold – track, 1988)	50	50
1923	75 c. Olympic Stadium, Seoul (1988) (*horiz*)	50	50
1924	90 c. Allison Jolly and Lynne Jewell (U.S.A.) (Gold – yachting, 1988) (*horiz*)	50	50
1925	90 c. Wolfgang Nordwig (Germany) (Gold – pole vaulting, 1972)	50	50
	a. Sheetlet. Nos. 1925/33	4·00	
1926	90 c. Shirley Strong (Great Britain) (Silver – 100 metres hurdles, 1984)	50	50
1927	90 c. Sergei Bubka (Russia) (Gold – pole vault, 1988)	50	50
1928	90 c. Filbert Bayi (Tanzania) (Silver – 3000 metres steeplechase, 1980)	50	50
1929	90 c. Victor Saneyev (Russia) (Gold – triple jump, 1968, 1972, 1976)	50	50
1930	90 c. Silke Renk (Germany) (Gold – javelin, 1992)	50	50
1931	90 c. Daley Thompson (Great Britain) (Gold – decathlon, 1980, 1984)	50	50
1932	90 c. Robert Richards (U.S.A.) (Gold – pole vault, 1952, 1956)	50	50
1933	90 c. Parry O'Brien (U.S.A) (Gold – shot put, 1952, 1956)	50	50
1934	90 c. Ingrid Kramer (Germany) (Gold – Women's platform diving, 1960)	50	50
	a. Sheetlet. Nos. 1934/42	4·00	
1935	90 c. Kelly McCormick (U.S.A.) (Silver – Women's springboard diving, 1984)	50	50
1936	90 c. Gary Tobian (U.S.A.) (Gold – Men's springboard diving, 1960)	50	50
1937	90 c. Greg Louganis (U.S.A.) (Gold – Men's diving, 1984 and 1988)	50	50
1938	90 c. Michelle Mitchell (U.S.A.) (Silver – Women's platform diving, 1984 and 1988)	50	50
1939	90 c. Zhou Jihong (China) (Gold – Women's platform diving, 1984)	50	50
1940	90 c. Wendy Wyland (U.S.A.) (Bronze – Women's platform diving, 1984)	50	50
1941	90 c. Xu Yanmei (China) (Gold – Women's platform diving, 1988)	50	50
1942	90 c. Fu Mingxia (China) (Gold – Women's platform diving, 1992)	50	50
1943	$1.20, 2000 metre tandem cycle race (*horiz*)	75	75
1922/43	*Set of 21*	9·50	9·50

MS1944 Two sheets, each 106×76 mm. (a) $5 Bill Toomey (U.S.A.) (Gold – decathlon, 1968) (*horiz*). (b) $6 Mark Lenzi (U.S.A.) (Gold – Men's springboard diving, 1992) ... *Set of 2 sheets* 7·00 7·50

1998 (12 May). *World Cup Football Championship, France.* Nos. 2525/39 of *Antigua optd with T* **114**.

1945	60 c. multicoloured	40	40
1946	75 c. agate	45	45
1947	90 c. multicoloured	50	50
1948	$1 agate	55	55
	a. Sheetlet. Nos. 1948/55 and central label	4·00	
1949	$1 agate	55	55
1950	$1 agate	55	55
1951	$1 grey-black	55	55
1952	$1 agate	55	55
1953	$1 agate	55	55
1954	$1 agate	55	55
1955	$1 agate	55	55
1956	$1.20, multicoloured	65	65
1957	$1.65, multicoloured	85	85
1958	$1.75, multicoloured	95	95
1945/58	*Set of 14*	7·00	7·00

MS1959 Two sheets, each 102×127 mm. (a) $6 multicoloured. (b) $6 multicoloured ... *Set of 2 sheets* 7·00 7·50

1998 (4 June). *Cavalry through the Ages.* Nos. 2359/63 of *Antigua optd with T* **111** (Nos. 1960/3) *or T* **114** (No. **MS**1964).

1960	60 c. Ancient Egyptian cavalryman	40	40
	a. Block of 4. Nos. 1960/3	1·40	
1961	60 c. 13th-century English knight	40	40
1962	60 c. 16th-century Spanish lancer	40	40
1963	60 c. 18th-century Chinese cavalryman	40	40
1960/3	*Set of 4*	1·40	1·40

MS1964 100×70 mm. $6 19th-century French cuirassier (*vert*) ... 3·75 4·00

1998 (20 July). *50th Anniv of U.N.I.C.E.F.* Nos. 2364/7 of *Antigua optd with T* **114**.

1965	75 c. Girl in red sari	50	50
1966	90 c. South American mother and child	60	60
1967	$1.20, Nurse with child	70	70
1965/7	*Set of 3*	1·60	1·60

MS1968 114×74 mm. $6 Chinese child ... 3·50 4·00

1998 (20 July). *3000th Anniv of Jerusalem.* Nos. 2368/71 of *Antigua optd with T* **111**.

1969	75 c. Tomb of Zachariah and *Verbascum sinuatum*	50	50
1970	90 c. Pool of Siloam and *Hyacinthus orientalis*	60	60
1971	$1.20, Hurva Synagogue and *Ranunculus asiaticus*	70	70
1969/71	*Set of 3*	1·60	1·60

MS1972 66×80 mm. $6 Model of Herod's Temple and *Cercis siliquastrum* ... 3·75 4·00

1998 (31 Aug). *Diana, Princess of Wales Commemoration.* Nos. 2573/85 of *Antigua optd with T* **114**, *but with lines spaced.*

1973	$1.65, Diana, Princess of Wales	1·00	1·00
	a. Sheetlet. Nos. 1973/8	5·50	
1974	$1.65, Wearing hoop earrings (rose-carmine and black)	1·00	1·00
1975	$1.65, Carrying bouquet	1·00	1·00
1976	$1.65, Wearing floral hat	1·00	1·00
1977	$1.65, With Prince Harry	1·00	1·00
1978	$1.65, Wearing white jacket	1·00	1·00
1979	$1.65, In kitchen	1·00	1·00
	a. Sheetlet. Nos. 1979/84	5·50	
1980	$1.65, Wearing black and white dress	1·00	1·00
1981	$1.65, Wearing hat (orge-brown & black)	1·00	1·00
1982	$1.65, Wearing floral print dress (lake-brown and black)	1·00	1·00
1983	$1.65, Dancing with John Travolta	1·00	1·00
1984	$1.65, Wearing white hat and jacket	1·00	1·00
1973/84	*Set of 12*	11·00	11·00

MS1985 Two sheets, each 70×100 mm. (a) $6 Wearing red jumper. (b) $6 Wearing black dress for Papal audience (lake-brown and black) ... *Set of 2 sheets* 7·00 7·50

1998 (12 Oct). *Broadway Musical Stars.* Nos. 2384/93 of *Antigua optd with T* **111**.

1986	$1 Robert Preston (*The Music Man*)	65	65
	a. Sheetlet. Nos. 1986/94	5·00	
1987	$1 Michael Crawford (*Phantom of the Opera*)	65	65
1988	$1 Zero Mostel (*Fiddler on the Roof*)	65	65
1989	$1 Patti Lupone (*Evita*)	65	65
1990	$1 Raul Julia (*Threepenny Opera*)	65	65
1991	$1 Mary Martin (*South Pacific*)	65	65
1992	$1 Carol Channing (*Hello Dolly*)	65	65
1993	$1 Yul Brynner (*The King and I*)	65	65
1994	$1 Julie Andrews (*My Fair Lady*)	65	65
1986/94	*Set of 9*	5·00	5·00

MS1995 106×76 mm. $6 Mickey Rooney (*Sugar Babies*) ... 3·50 4·00

1998 (12 Oct). *20th Death Anniv of Charlie Chaplin* (film star). Nos. 2404/13 of *Antigua optd with T* **111**.

1996	$1 Charlie Chaplin as young man	65	65
	a. Sheetlet. Nos. 1996/2004	5·00	
1997	$1 Pulling face	65	65
1998	$1 Looking over shoulder	65	65
1999	$1 In cap	65	65
2000	$1 In front of star	65	65
2001	$1 In *The Great Dictator*	65	65
2002	$1 With movie camera and megaphone	65	65

2003	$1 Standing in front of camera lens ..	65	65
2004	$1 Putting on make-up	65	65
1996/2004	*Set of 9*	5·00	5·00
MS2005	76×106 mm. $6 Charlie Chaplin ..	3·75	4·00

1998 (23 Nov). *Butterflies. Nos. 2414/36 of Antigua optd with T 114, but with lines spaced.*

2006	90 c. *Charaxes porthos* ..	60	60
2007	$1.10, *Charaxes protoclea protoclea* ..	70	70
	a. Sheetlet. Nos. 2007/15 ..	5·50	
2008	$1.10, *Byblia ilithyia*	70	70
2009	$1.10, Black-headed Bush Shrike ("Tchagra") (bird)	70	70
2010	$1.10, *Charaxes nobilis*	70	70
2011	$1.10, *Pseudacraea boisduvali trimeni*	70	70
2012	$1.10, *Charaxes smaragdalis* ..	70	70
2013	$1.10, *Charaxes lasti*	70	70
2014	$1.10, *Pseudacraea poggei* ..	70	70
2015	$1.10, *Graphium colonna* ..	70	70
2016	$1.10, Carmine Bee Eater (bird) ..	70	70
	a. Sheetlet. Nos. 2016/24 ..	5·50	
2017	$1.10, *Pseudacraea eurytus* ..	70	70
2018	$1.10, *Hypolimnas monteironis* ..	70	70
2019	$1.10, *Charaxes anticlea* ..	70	70
2020	$1.10, *Graphium leonidas* ..	70	70
2021	$1.10, *Graphium illyris* ..	70	70
2022	$1.10, *Nephronia argia* ..	70	70
2023	$1.10, *Graphium policenes* ..	70	70
2024	$1.10, *Papilio dardanus* ..	70	70
2025	$1.20, *Aethiopana honorius* ..	70	70
2026	$1.60, *Charaxes hadrianus* ..	1·00	1·00
2027	$1.75, *Precis westermanni* ..	1·10	1·10
2006/27	*Set of 21*	12·50	12·50

MS2028 Three sheets, each 106×76 mm. (a) $6 *Charaxes lactitinctus* (*horiz*). (b) $6 *Eupheadra neophron.* (c) $6 *Euxanthe tiberius* (*horiz*)

Set of 3 sheets	10·00	11·00

BARBUDA MAIL

(126)

1998 (23 Dec). *Christmas. Dogs. Nos. 2771/8 of Antigua optd with T 126 diagonally.*

2029	15 c. Border Collie	20	20
2030	25 c. Dalmatian	25	25
2031	65 c. Weimaraner	50	50
2032	75 c. Scottish Terrier	55	55
2033	90 c. Long-haired Dachshund ..	60	60
2034	$1.20, Golden Retriever	70	70
2035	$2 Pekingese	1·25	1·25
2029/35	*Set of 7*	3·50	3·50

MS2036 Two sheets, each 75×66 mm. (a) $6 Dalmatian. (b) $6 Jack Russell Terrier

Set of 2 sheets	7·00	7·50

1999 (25 Jan). *Lighthouses of the World. Nos. 2612/20 of Antigua optd with T 111.*

2037	45 c. Europa Point Lighthouse, Gibraltar	40	40
2038	65 c. Tierra del Fuego, Argentina (*horiz*)	50	50
2039	75 c. Point Loma, California, U.S.A. (*horiz*)	60	60
2040	90 c. Greenpoint, Cape Town, South Africa	70	70
2041	$1 Youghal, Cork, Ireland ..	75	75
2042	$1.20, Launceston, Tasmania, Australia	80	80
2043	$1.65, Point Abino, Ontario, Canada (*horiz*)	1·00	1·00
2044	$1.75, Great Inagua, Bahamas (*horiz*)	1·10	1·10
2037/44	*Set of 8*	5·25	5·25

MS2045 99×70 mm. $6 Cape Hatteras, North Carolina, U.S.A.

	3·50	3·75

STAMP BOOKLETS

1977 (20 Dec). *Silver Jubilee. No. SB2 of Antigua with cover optd "BARBUDA".*

SB1	$8 booklet containing pane of 6 (No. 329a) and pane of 1 (No. 330a)	5·00

1978 (12 Oct). *25th Anniv of Coronation. No. SB3 of Antigua with cover optd "BARBUDA".*

SB2	$7.25, booklet containing pane of 6 (No. 421a) and pane of 1 (No. 423a)	2·50

1981 (27 July). *Royal Wedding (1st issue). Cover printed in grey, 98×63 mm, showing crown, bells and inscription. Stitched.*

SB3	$26 booklet containing panes of four (Nos. 566b, 568b, 570b)	6·00

The panes in this booklet each consist of two imperforate-between horizontal pairs.

1981 (12 Oct). *Royal Wedding (3rd issue). No. SB4 of Antigua with cover optd "BARBUDA" in silver.*

SB4	$11.50, booklet containing pane of 6 (No. 580a) and pane of 1 (No. 586a)	5·00

1982 (28 June). *South Atlantic Fund. No. SB4 with contents surcharged.*

SB5	$15 booklet containing pane of 6 (No. 617a) and pane of 1 (No. 623a)	4·75

REDONDA
DEPENDENCY OF ANTIGUA

Appendix

The following stamps were issued in anticipation of commercial and tourist development, philatelic mail being handled by a bureau in Antigua. Since at the present time the island is uninhabited, we do not list or stock these items. It is understood that the stamps are valid for the prepayment of postage in Antigua. Miniature sheets, imperforate stamps etc., are excluded from this section.

1979

Antigua 1976 *definitive issue optd* "REDONDA". 3, 5, 10, 25, 35, 50, 75 c., $1, $2.50, $5, $10.
Antigua *Coronation Anniversary issue optd* "REDONDA". 10, 30, 50, 90 c., $2.50.
Antigua *World Cup Football Championship issue optd* "REDONDA". 10, 15 c., $3.
Death Centenary of Sir Rowland Hill. 50, 90 c., $2.50, $3.
International Year of the Child. 25, 50 c., $1, $2.
Christmas. Paintings. 8, 50, 90 c., $3.

1980

Marine Life. 8, 25, 50 c., $4.
75th Anniv of Rotary International. 25, 50 c., $1, $2.
Birds of Redonda. 8, 10, 15, 25, 30, 50 c., $1, $2, $5.
Olympic Medal Winners, Lake Placid and Moscow. 8, 25, 50 c., $3.
80th Birthday of Queen Elizabeth the Queen Mother. 10 c., $2.50.
Christmas. Paintings. 8, 25, 50 c., $4.

1981

Royal Wedding. 25, 55 c., $4.
Christmas. Walt Disney Cartoon Characters. ½, 1, 2, 3, 4, 5, 10 c., $2.50, $3.
World Cup Football Championship, Spain (1982). 30 c. × 2, 50 c. × 2, $1 × 2, $2 × 2.

1982

Boy Scout Anniversaries. 8, 25, 50 c., $3, $5.
Butterflies. 8, 30, 50 c., $2.
21st Birthday of Princess of Wales. $2, $4.
Birth of Prince William of Wales. Optd on 21st Birthday of Princess of Wales issue. $2, $4.
Christmas. Walt Disney's "One Hundred and One Dalmatians". ½, 1, 2, 3, 4, 5, 10 c., $2.50, $3.

1983

Easter. 500th Birth Anniv of Raphael. 10, 50, 90 c., $4.
Bicentenary of Manned Flight. 10, 50, 90 c., $2.50.
Christmas. Walt Disney Cartoon Characters. "Deck the Halls". ½, 1, 2, 3, 4, 5, 10 c., $2.50, $3.

1984

Easter. Walt Disney Cartoon Characters. ½, 1, 2, 3, 4, 5, 10 c., $2, $4.
Olympic Games, Los Angeles. 10, 50, 90 c., $2.50.
Christmas. 50th Birthday of Donald Duck. 45, 60, 90 c., $2, $4.

1985

Birth Bicentenary of John J. Audubon (ornithologist) (1st issue). 60, 90 c., $1, $3.
Life and Times of Queen Elizabeth the Queen Mother. $1, $1.50, $2.50.
Royal Visit. 45 c., $1, $4.
150th Birth Anniv of Mark Twain (author). 25, 50 c., $1.50, $3.
Birth Bicentenary of Grimm Brothers (folklorists). Walt Disney Cartoon Characters. 30, 60, 70 c., $4.

1986

Birth Bicentenary of John J. Audubon (ornithologist) (2nd issue). 90 c., $1, $1.50, $3.
Appearance of Halley's Comet. 5, 15, 55 c., $4.
Centenary of Statue of Liberty (1st issue). 20, 25, 30 c., $4.
60th Birthday of Queen Elizabeth II. 50, 60 c., $4.
Royal Wedding. 60 c., $1, $4.
Christmas (1st issue). Disney characters in Hans Andersen Stories. 30, 60, 70 c., $4.
Christmas (2nd issue). "Wind in the Willows" (Kenneth Grahame). 25, 50 c., $1.50, $3.

1987

"Capex '87" International Stamp Exhibition, Toronto. Disney characters illustrating Art of Animation. 25, 30, 50, 60, 70 c., $1.50, $3, $4.
Birth Centenary of Marc Chagall (artist). 10, 30, 40, 60, 90 c., $1, $3, $4.
Centenary of Statue of Liberty (2nd issue). 10, 15, 25, 30, 40, 60, 70, 90 c., $1, $2, $3, $4.
250th Death Anniv of Sir Isaac Newton (scientist). 20 c., $2.50.
750th Anniv of Berlin. $1, $4.
Bicentenary of U.S. Constitution. 30 c., $3.
16th World Scout Jamboree, Australia. 10 c., $4.

1988

500th Anniv of Discovery of America by Columbus (1992) (1st issue). 15, 30, 45, 60, 90 c., $1, $2, $3.
"Finlandia '88" International Stamp Exhibition, Helsinki. Disney characters in Finnish scenes. 1, 2, 3, 4, 5, 6 c., $5, $6.
Olympic Games, Seoul. 25, 60 c., $1.25, $3.
500th Birth Anniv of Titian. 10, 25, 40, 70, 90 c., $2, $3, $4.

1989

20th Anniv of First Manned Landing on Moon. Disney characters on Moon. ½, 1, 2, 3, 4, 5 c., $5, $6.
500th Anniv of Discovery of America by Columbus (1992) (2nd issue). Pre-Columbian Societies. 15, 45, 45, 50 c., $2, $2, $3, $3.
Christmas. Disney characters and Cars of 1950's. 25, 35, 45, 60 c., $1, $2, $3, $4.

1990

Christmas. Disney characters and Hollywood Cars. 25, 35, 40, 60 c., $1, $2, $4, $5.

1991

Nobel Prize Winners. 5, 15, 25, 40, 50 c., $1, $2, $4.

Ascension

DEPENDENCY OF ST. HELENA

Ascension, first occupied in 1815, was retained as a Royal Navy establishment from 1816 until 20 October 1922 when it became a dependency of St. Helena by Letters Patent.

Under Post Office regulations of 1850 (ratings) and 1854 (officers) mail from men of the Royal Navy serving abroad had the postage prepaid in Great Britain stamps, supplies of which were issued to each ship. Great Britain stamps used on Ascension before 1860 may have been provided by the naval officer in charge of the postal service.

The British G.P.O. assumed responsibility for such matters in 1860, but failed to send any stamps to the island until January 1867.

Until about 1880 naval mail, which made up most early correspondence, did not have the stamps cancelled until arrival in England. The prices quoted for Nos. Z1/3 and Z6 are for examples on cover showing the Great Britain stamps cancelled on arrival and an Ascension postmark struck elsewhere on the front of the envelope.

The use of British stamps ceased in December 1922.

The following postmarks were used on Great Britain stamps from Ascension:

Z 1   Z 2

Z 3   Z 4

Z 5

Postmark Type	Approx Period of Use	Diameter	Index Letter
Z 1	1862	20 mm	A
Z 2	1864–1872	20 mm	A
	1872–1878	21½ mm	A
	1879–1889	19½ mm	A
	1891–1894	21½ mm	C
	1894–1902	22 mm	A
	1903–1907	20½ mm	A
	1908–1920	21 mm	A or none
	1909–1920	23 mm	C sideways (1909), none (1910–11), B (1911–20)
Z 3	1920–1922	24 mm	none
Z 4	1897–1903 Registered	23 mm	none
Z 5	1900–1902 Registered	28 mm	C
	1903–1904 Registered	29 mm	A

Postmark Type Z 1 appears in the G.P.O. proof book for 1858, but the first recorded use is 3 November 1862.

Forged postmarks exist. Those found most frequently are genuine postmarks of the post-1922 period with earlier date slugs fraudulently inserted, namely a 20 mm postmark as Type Z 2 (because of the shape of the "O" in "ASCENSION" this is often known as the Square O postmark) and a 24 mm postmark as Type Z 3 but with the index letter A.

Stamps of GREAT BRITAIN cancelled with Types Z 2/5. Prices quoted for Nos. Z 1/6 are for complete covers.

Line-engraved issues.

Z 1	1d. red-brown (1855)	.. .. ..	£3250
Z 2	1d. rose-red (1864–79)	.. ..	*From* £1500
	Plate Nos. 71, 74, 76, 78, 83, 85, 96, 100, 102, 103, 104, 122, 134, 168, 154, 155, 157, 160, 168, 178		

Surface-printed issues (1856–1883).

Z 2a	6d. lilac (1856)	.. ..	
Z 3	6d. lilac (1865) (Plate No. 5)	..	£3250
Z 4	1s. green (1865) (Plate No. 4)	..	
Z 5	1s. green (1867) (Plate No. 7)	..	
Z 6	6d. grey (1874) (Plate Nos. 15, 16)		£2500
Z 6a	6d. on 6d. lilac (1883)	..	
Z 7	1d. lilac (1881) (16 dots)	..	32·00

1887–92.

Z 8	½d. vermilion	.. ..	48·00
Z 9	1½d. purple and green	.. ..	£200
Z10	2d. green and carmine	.. ..	£100
Z11	2½d. purple/*blue*	.. ..	45·00
Z12	3d. purple/*yellow*	.. ..	£180
Z13	4d. green and brown	.. ..	£150
Z14	4½d. green and carmine	.. ..	£400
Z15	5d. dull purple and blue	.. ..	£150
Z16	6d. purple/*rose-red*	.. ..	£130
Z17	9d. purple and blue	.. ..	£350
Z17a	10d. dull purple and carmine	..	£425
Z18	1s. green	.. .. ..	£350

1900.

Z19	½d. blue-green	.. .. ..	48·00
Z20	1s. green and carmine	.. ..	£400

King Edward VII issues (1902–1911).

Z21	½d. green	.. .. ..	32·00
Z22	1d. red	.. .. ..	18·00
Z23	1½d. purple and green	.. ..	£100
Z24	2d. green and carmine	..	75·00
Z25	2½d. blue	.. .. ..	70·00
Z26	3d. purple/*yellow*	.. ..	£100
Z27	4d. green and brown	.. ..	£325
Z28	4d. orange (1909)	.. ..	£120
Z29	5d. purple and ultramarine	..	£120
Z30	6d. purple	.. .. ..	£110
Z31	7d. grey-black (1910)	.. ..	£225
Z32	9d. purple and ultramarine (1910)	..	£200
Z32a	10d. dull purple and scarlet	..	£250
Z33	1s. green and carmine	.. ..	75·00
Z33a	2s. 6d. dull reddish purple (1911)	..	£550
Z34	5s. carmine	.. .. ..	£800
Z35	10s. ultramarine	.. ..	£1200
Z35a	£1 green	.. .. ..	£2500

1911–12.   *T 98/9 of Great Britain.*

Z36	½d. green (Die A)	.. ..	65·00
Z37	½d. yellow-green (Die B)	.. ..	32·00
Z38	1d. scarlet (Die B) ..		45·00

1912.   *T 101/2 of Great Britain.*

Z38a	½d. green	.. .. ..	45·00
Z38b	1d. scarlet	.. .. ..	45·00

1912–22.

Z39	½d. green (1913)	.. ..	29·00
Z40	1d. scarlet	.. .. ..	18·00
Z41	1½d. red-brown	.. ..	40·00
Z42	2d. orange (Die I)	.. ..	35·00
Z42a	2d. orange (Die II) (1921)	..	£275
Z43	2½d. blue	.. .. ..	45·00
Z44	3d. violet	.. .. ..	60·00
Z45	4d. grey-green (1913)	.. ..	80·00
Z46	5d. brown (1913)	.. ..	80·00
Z47	6d. purple (1913)	.. ..	70·00
Z47a	7d. green (1913)	.. ..	£250
Z47b	8d. black/*yellow* (1913)	.. ..	£275
Z48	9d. agate (1913)	.. ..	£225
Z49	9d. olive-green (1922)	.. ..	£550
Z50	10d. turquoise-blue (1913)	..	£225
Z51	1s. bistre (1913)	.. ..	£110
Z52	2s. 6d. brown (1918)	.. ..	£750
Z53	5s. rose-red (1919)	.. ..	£1000

Supplies of some values do not appear to have been sent to the island and known examples originate from maritime or, in the case of high values, philatelic mail.

PRICES FOR STAMPS ON COVER TO 1945		
Nos. 1/34	*from* × 5	
Nos. 35/7	*from* × 10	
Nos. 38/47	*from* × 6	

ASCENSION

(1)

1922 (2 Nov). *Stamps of St. Helena, showing Government House or the Wharf, optd with T 1 by D.L.R.*

Line through "P" of "POSTAGE" (R. 3/6)

(a) Wmk Mult Script CA

1	½d. black and green	.. ..	4·00	12·00
	w. Wmk reversed	.. ..	£350	
2	1d. green	.. ..	4·00	12·00
3	1½d. rose-scarlet	.. ..	14·00	48·00
4	2d. black and grey	.. ..	14·00	12·00
	a. Line through "P" of "POSTAGE"		£180	£180
5	3d. bright blue	.. ..	12·00	16·00
6	8d. black and dull purple	..	25·00	48·00
7	2s. black and blue/*blue*	..	80·00	£120
8	3s. black and violet	..	£120	£160

(b) Wmk Mult Crown CA

9	1s. black/*green* (R.)	..	27·00	48·00
1/9		*Set of 9*	£250	£400
1/9 Optd "Specimen"		*Set of 9*	£600	

Nos. 1, 4 and 6/8 are on special printings which were not issued without overprint.

Examples of all values are known showing a forged Ascension postmark dated "MY 24 23".

PLATE FLAWS ON THE 1924–33 ISSUE. Many constant plate varieties exist on both the vignette and duty plates of this issue.

The three major varieties are illustrated and listed below with prices for mint examples. Fine used stamps showing these flaws are worth a considerable premium over the mint prices quoted.

This issue utilised the same vignette plate as the St. Helena 1922–36 set so that these flaws occur there also.

2 Badge of St. Helena

Broken mainmast. Occurs on R.2/1 of all values.

Torn flag. Occurs on R.4/6 of all values except the 5d. Retouched on sheets of ½d. and 1d. printed after 1927.

Cleft rock. Occurs on R.5/1 of all values.

Broken scroll. Occurs on R. 1/4 of 1½d. only

(Typo D.L.R.)

1924 (20 Aug)–**33.** *Wmk Mult Script CA. Chalk-surfaced paper. P* 14.

10	2	½d. grey-black and black	3·25	12·00
		a. Broken mainmast ..	55·00	
		b. Torn flag	80·00	
		c. Cleft rock	48·00	
11		1d. grey-black and deep blue-green	5·50	6·50
		a. Broken mainmast ..	65·00	
		b. Torn flag	80·00	
		c. Cleft rock	55·00	
11d		1d. grey-black & brt blue-green (1933)	80·00	£350
		da. Broken mainmast ..	£325	
		dc. Cleft rock	£300	
12		1½d. rose-red	7·00	26·00
		a. Broken mainmast ..	75·00	
		b. Torn flag	75·00	
		c. Cleft rock	60·00	
		d. Broken scroll ..	80·00	
13		2d. grey-black and grey	11·00	6·00
		a. Broken mainmast ..	85·00	
		b. Torn flag	95·00	
		c. Cleft rock	75·00	
14		3d. blue	7·50	12·00
		a. Broken mainmast ..	75·00	
		b. Torn flag	75·00	
		c. Cleft rock	65·00	
15		4d. grey-black and black/*yellow*	45·00	80·00
		a. Broken mainmast ..	£190	
		b. Torn flag	£190	
		c. Cleft rock	£160	
15d		5d. purple and olive-green (8.27)	10·00	20·00
		da. Broken mainmast ..	£120	
		dc. Cleft rock	£100	
16		6d. grey-black and bright purple	48·00	85·00
		a. Broken mainmast ..	£250	
		b. Torn flag	£250	
		c. Cleft rock	£200	

17	2	8d. grey-black and bright violet		14·00	40·00
		a. Broken mainmast		£120	
		b. Torn flag		£120	
		c. Cleft rock		95·00	
18		1s. grey-black and brown		19·00	48·00
		a. Broken mainmast		£140	
		b. Torn flag		£140	
		c. Cleft rock		£120	
19		2s. grey-black and blue/*blue*		55·00	85·00
		a. Broken mainmast		£275	
		b. Torn flag		£275	
		c. Cleft rock		£225	
20		3s. grey-black and black/*blue*		80·00	85·00
		a. Broken mainmast		£375	
		b. Torn flag		£375	
		c. Cleft rock		£325	
10/20			Set of 12	£250	£425
10/20	Optd "Specimen"		Set of 12	£500	

3 Georgetown

4 Ascension Island

(Des and recess D.L.R.)

1934 (2 July). *T* **3/4** *and similar designs. Wmk Mult Script CA. P* 14.

21	3	½d. black and violet		90	80
22	4	1d. black and emerald		1·75	1·25
23	—	1½d. black and scarlet		1·75	2·25
24	4	2d. black and orange		1·75	2·50
25	—	3d. black and ultramarine		1·75	1·50
26	—	5d. black and blue		2·25	3·25
27	4	8d. black and sepia		4·25	4·75
28	—	1s. black and carmine		18·00	6·50
29	4	2s. 6d. black and bright purple		38·00	32·00
30	—	5s. black and brown		45·00	55·00
21/30			Set of 10	95·00	£100
21/30	Perf "Specimen"		Set of 10	£250	

Designs: *Horiz*—1½d. The Pier; 3d. Long Beach; 5d. Three Sisters; 1s. Sooty Tern and Wideawake Fair; 5s. Green Mountain.

1935 (6 May). *Silver Jubilee. As Nos.* 91/4 *of Antigua, but ptd by Waterlow. P* 11 × 12.

31		1½d. deep blue and scarlet		3·50	6·50
		l. Kite and horizontal log		£100	
32		2d. ultramarine and grey		11·00	22·00
		l. Kite and horizontal log		£190	
33		5d. green and indigo		17·00	24·00
		k. Kite and vertical log		£200	
		l. Kite and horizontal log		£275	
34		1s. slate and purple		23·00	27·00
		l. Kite and horizontal log		£325	
31/4			Set of 4	45·00	70·00
31/4	Perf "Specimen"		Set of 4	£160	

For illustrations of plate varieties see Catalogue Introduction.

1937 (19 May). *Coronation. As Nos.* 95/7 *of Antigua, but printed by D.L.R. P* 14.

35		1d. green		50	70
36		2d. orange		1·00	40
37		3d. bright blue		1·00	50
35/7			Set of 3	2·25	1·40
35/7	Perf "Specimen"		Set of 3	£130	

10 The Pier

Long centre bar to "E" in
"GEORGETOWN" (R. 2/3)

"Davit" flaw (R. 5/1) (all
ptgs of 1½d. and 2s. 6d.)

(Recess D.L.R.)

1938 (12 May)–**53**. *Horiz designs as King George V issue, but modified and with portrait of King George VI as in T* **10**. *Wmk Mult Script CA. P* 13½.

38	3	½d. black and violet		3·50	1·25
		a. Long centre bar to E		£110	
		b. Perf 13. *Black and bluish violet* (17.5.44)		70	1·75
		ba. Long centre bar to E		50·00	
39	—	1d. black and green		40·00	7·50
39a		1d. black and yellow-orange (8.7.40)		14·00	9·00
		b. Perf 13 (5.42)		45	60
		c. Perf 14 (17.2.49)		70	16·00
39d	—	1d. black and green, *p* 13 (1.6.49)		60	50
40	10	1½d. black and vermilion		4·00	1·40
		a. Davit flaw		£170	
		b. Perf 13 (17.5.44)		85	80
		ba. Davit flaw		85·00	
		c. Perf 14 (17.2.49)		2·25	13·00
		ca. Davit flaw		£120	
40d		1½d. black and rose-carmine, *p* 14 (1.6.49)		55	80
		da. Davit flaw		80·00	
		db. *Black and carmine*		7·00	5·00
		dba. Davit flaw		£200	
		e. Perf 13 (25.2.53)		45	6·50
		ea. Davit flaw		75·00	
41	—	2d. black and red-orange		3·75	1·00
		a. Perf 13 (17.5.44)		80	40
		b. Perf 14 (17.2.49)		2·25	35·00
41c		2d. black and scarlet, *p* 14 (1.6.49)		1·00	85
42	—	3d. black and ultramarine		£100	26·00
42a		3d. black and grey (8.7.40)		17·00	90
		b. Perf 13 (17.5.44)		70	80
42c		4d. black and ultramarine (8.7.40)		15·00	3·25
		d. Perf 13 (17.5.44)		4·50	3·00
43	—	6d. black and blue		9·00	1·50
		a. Perf 13 (17.5.44)		9·00	5·00
44	3	1s. black and sepia		16·00	1·50
		a. Perf 13 (17.5.44)		4·75	2·00
45	10	2s. 6d. black and deep carmine		42·00	9·50
		a. Frame printed double, once albino	£2750		
		b. Davit flaw		£600	£250
		c. Perf 13 (17.5.44)		35·00	32·00
		ca. Davit flaw		£500	
46	—	5s. black and yellow-brown		£110	8·50
		a. Perf 13 (17.5.44)		48·00	27·00
47	—	10s. black and bright purple		£110	42·00
		a. Perf 13 (17.5.44)		55·00	55·00
38/47a			Set of 16	£275	90·00
38/47	Perf "Specimen"		Set of 13	£475	

Designs: *Horiz*—1d. (Nos. 39/c), 2d., 4d. Green Mountain; 1d. (No. 39d), 6d., 10s. Three Sisters; 3d., 5s. Long Beach.

1946 (21 Oct). *Victory. As Nos.* 110/11 *of Antigua.*

48		2d. red-orange		40	50
49		4d. blue		40	30
48/9	Perf "Specimen"		Set of 2	£140	

1948 (20 Oct). *Royal Silver Wedding. As Nos.* 112/13 *of Antigua.*

50		3d. black		50	30
51		10s. bright purple		45·00	40·00

1949 (10 Oct). *75th Anniv of Universal Postal Union. As Nos.* 114/17 *of Antigua.*

52		3d. carmine		1·40	1·25
53		4d. deep blue		3·50	1·25
54		6d. olive		3·75	2·75
55		1s. blue-black		3·75	1·50
52/5			Set of 4	11·00	6·00

1953 (2 June). *Coronation. As No.* 120 *of Antigua.*

56		3d. black and grey-black		1·00	1·50

15 Water Catchment

(Recess B.W.)

1956 (19 Nov). *T* **15** *and similar horiz designs. Wmk Mult Script CA. P* 13.

57		½d. black and brown		10	30
58		1d. black and magenta		2·00	60
59		1½d. black and orange		30	60
60		2d. black and carmine-red		1·75	50
61		2½d. black and orange-brown		85	80
62		3d. black and blue		3·00	1·00
63		4d. black and deep turquoise-green		1·25	1·40
64		6d. black and indigo		1·25	90
65		7d. black and deep olive		1·00	1·00
66		1s. black and vermilion		1·00	90
67		2s. 6d. black and deep dull purple		27·00	6·50
68		5s. black and blue-green		35·00	17·00
69		10s. black and purple		48·00	35·00
57/69			Set of 13	£110	60·00

Designs:—1d. Map of Ascension; 1½d. View of Georgetown; 2d. Map showing cable network; 2½d. Mountain road; 3d. White-tailed Tropic Bird; 4d. Yellow-finned Tuna; 6d. Rollers on the seashore; 7d. Young turtles; 1s. Land Crab; 2s. 6d. Sooty Tern; 5s. Perfect Crater; 10s. View of Ascension from North-west.

STANLEY GIBBONS
STAMP COLLECTING SERIES

Introductory booklets on *How to Start, How to Identify Stamps* and *Collecting by Theme.* A series of well illustrated guides at a low price.
Write for details.

---

28 Brown Booby **42** Satellite Station

(Des after photos by N. P. Ashmole. Photo Harrison)

1963 (23 May). *T* **28** *and similar horiz designs. W w* **12**. *P* 14×14½.

70		1d. black, lemon and new blue		90	30
71		1½d. black, cobalt and ochre		1·25	60
		a. Cobalt omitted		75·00	
72		2d. black, grey and bright blue		1·25	30
73		3d. black, magenta and turquoise-blue		1·25	30
74		4½d. black, bistre-brown and new blue		1·25	30
		w. Wmk inverted		£190	
75		5d. bistre, black and yellow-green		1·25	30
76		7d. black, brown and reddish violet		1·25	30
77		10d. black, greenish yellow and blue-green		1·25	30
78		1s. multicoloured		1·25	30
79		1s. 6d. multicoloured		4·50	1·75
80		2s. 6d. multicoloured		6·50	8·00
81		5s. multicoloured		7·00	7·00
82		10s. multicoloured		13·00	8·00
83		£1 multicoloured		20·00	10·00
70/83			Set of 14	55·00	32·00

Designs:—1½d. White-capped Noddy; 2d. White Tern; 3d. Red-billed Tropic Bird; 4½d. Common Noddy; 6d. Sooty Tern; 7d. Ascension Frigate Bird; 10d. Blue-faced Booby; 1s. White-tailed Tropic Bird; 1s. 6d. Red-billed Tropic Bird; 2s. 6d. Madeiran Storm Petrel; 5s. Red-footed Booby (brown phase); 10s. Ascension Frigate Birds; £1 Red-footed Booby (white phase).

1963 (4 June). *Freedom from Hunger. As No.* 146 *of Antigua.*

84		1s. 6d. carmine		1·40	40

1963 (2 Sept). *Red Cross Centenary. As Nos.* 147/8 *of Antigua.*

85		3d. red and black		3·50	1·25
86		1s. 6d. red and blue		7·50	2·25

1965 (17 May). *I.T.U. Centenary. As Nos.* 166/7 *of Antigua.*

87		3d. magenta and bluish violet		1·00	65
88		6d. turquoise-blue and light chestnut		1·25	65

1965 (25 Oct). *International Co-operation Year. As Nos.* 168/9 *of Antigua.*

89		1d. reddish purple and turquoise-green		50	60
90		6d. deep bluish green and lavender		1·00	90

1966 (24 Jan). *Churchill Commemoration. As Nos.* 170/3 *of Antigua.*

91		1d. new blue		50	75
92		3d. deep green		2·75	1·25
93		6d. brown		3·50	1·50
94		1s. 6d. bluish violet		4·50	2·00
91/4				10·00	5·00

1966 (1 July). *World Cup Football Championships. As Nos.* 176/7 *of Antigua.*

95		3d. violet, yellow-green, lake and yell-brn		1·25	60
96		6d. chocolate, blue-green, lake & yellow-brn		1·50	80

1966 (20 Sept). *Inauguration of W.H.O. Headquarters, Geneva. As Nos.* 178/9 *of Antigua.*

97		3d. black, yellow-green and light blue		1·75	75
98		1s. 6d. black, light purple and yellow-brown		4·25	1·75

(Des V. Whiteley. Photo Harrison)

1966 (7 Nov). *Opening of Apollo Communications Satellite Earth Station. W w* **12**. (*sideways*). *P* 14 × 14½.

99	**42**	4d. black and reddish violet		15	15
100		8d. black and deep bluish green		15	20
101		1s. 3d. black and olive-brown		20	25
102		2s. 6d. black and turquoise-blue		25	35
99/102			Set of 4	65	85

43 B.B.C. Emblem **44** Human Rights Emblem and Chain Links

(Des B.B.C. staff. Photo, Queen's head and emblem die-stamped, Harrison)

1966 (1 Dec). *Opening of B.B.C. Relay Station. W w* **12**. *P* 14½.

103	**43**	1d. gold and ultramarine		10	20
104		3d. gold and myrtle-green		15	25
		w. Wmk inverted		75	1·25
105		6d. gold and reddish violet		15	25
106		1s. 6d. gold and red		15	25
103/6			Set of 4	50	80

1967 (1 Jan). *20th Anniv of U.N.E.S.C.O. As Nos. 196/8 of Antigua.*

107	3d. slate-violet, red, yellow and orange		2.50	1.25
108	6d. orange-yellow, violet and deep olive		3.75	1.75
109	1s. 6d. black, bright purple and orange		6.00	2.25
107/9	..	Set of 3	11.00	4.75

(Des and litho Harrison)

1968 (8 July). *Human Rights Year.* W w **12** (*sideways**). P 14½×14.

110	44 6d. light orange, red and black		25	25
111	1s. 6d. light grey-blue, red and black		35	35
112	2s. 6d. light green, red and black		40	40
	w. Wmk Crown to right of CA		£200	
110/12	..	Set of 3	90	90

*The normal sideways watermark shows Crown to left of CA, *as seen from the back of the stamp.*

45 Black Durgon ("Ascension Black-Fish")

46 H.M.S. *Rattlesnake*

(Des M. Farrar Bell. Litho D.L.R.)

1968 (23 Oct). *Fishes (1st series). T 45 and similar horiz designs.* W w **12** (*sideways**). P 13.

113	4d. black, slate and turquoise-blue		40	40
114	8d. multicoloured		50	70
	w. Wmk Crown to right of CA		£180	
115	1s. 9d. multicoloured		60	80
116	2s. 3d. multicoloured		70	85
113/16		Set of 4	2.00	2.50

Designs:—8d. Scribbled Filefish ("Leather-jacket"); 1s. 9d. Yellow-finned Tuna; 2s. 3d. Short-finned Mako.

*The normal sideways watermark shows Crown to left of CA, *as seen from the back of the stamp.*

See also Nos. 117/20 and 126/9.

(Des M. Farrar Bell. Litho D.L.R.)

1969 (3 Mar). *Fishes (2nd series). Horiz designs as T 45.* Multicoloured. W w **12** (*sideways*). P 13.

117	4d. Sailfish		1.00	90
118	6d. White Seabream ("Old Wife")		1.25	1.25
119	1s. 6d. Yellowtail		2.00	2.50
120	2s. 11d. Rock Hind ("Jack")		3.00	3.00
117/20		Set of 4	6.50	7.00

(Des L. Curtis. Photo Harrison)

1969 (1 Oct). *Royal Naval Crests (1st series). T 46 and similar vert designs.* P 14×14½.

121	4d. multicoloured		70	30
122	9d. multicoloured		90	35
123	1s. 9d. deep blue, pale blue and gold		1.40	45
124	2s. 3d. multicoloured		1.60	50
121/4		Set of 4	4.25	1.50
MS125	165×105 mm. Nos. 121/4. P 14½		7.50	12.00
	w. Wmk Crown to right of CA		£450	

Designs:—9d. H.M.S. *Weston*; 1s. 9d. H.M.S. *Undaunted*; 2s. 3d. H.M.S. *Eagle*.

*The normal sideways watermark shows Crown to left of CA, *as seen from the back of the stamp.*

See also Nos. 130/4, 149/53, 154/8 and 166/70.

(Des M. Farrar Bell. Litho D.L.R.)

1970 (6 Apr). *Fishes (3rd series). Horiz designs as T 45.* Multicoloured. W w **12** (*sideways**). P 14.

126	4d. Wahoo		4.50	2.75
127	9d. Ascension Jack ("Coalfish")		5.00	2.75
	w. Wmk Crown to right of CA		5.00	1.75
128	1s. 9d. Pompano Dolphin		5.50	3.50
129	2s. 3d. Squirrelfish ("Soldier")		5.50	3.50
	w. Wmk Crown to right of CA		70	85
126/9		Set of 4	18.00	11.50

*The normal sideways watermark shows Crown to left of CA, *as seen from the back of the stamp.*

(Des L. Curtis. Photo D.L.R.)

1970 (7 Sept). *Royal Naval Crests (2nd series). Designs as T 46.* Multicoloured. W w **12**. P 12½.

130	4d. H.M.S. *Penelope*		1.75	1.00
131	9d. H.M.S. *Carlisle*		2.25	1.50
132	1s. 6d. H.M.S. *Amphion*		2.75	2.00
133	2s. 6d. H.M.S. *Magpie*		3.25	2.00
130/3	..	Set of 4	9.00	6.00
MS134	153 × 96 mm. Nos. 130/3		14.00	13.00

50 Early Chinese Rocket

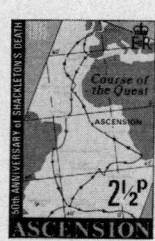

51 Course of the *Quest*

(Des V. Whiteley. Litho Format)

1971 (15 Feb). *Decimal Currency. The Evolution of Space Travel. T 50 and similar multicoloured designs.* W w **12** (*sideways on horiz designs*). P 14.

135	½p. Type 50		15	20
136	1p. Medieval Arab astronomers		20	20
137	1½p. Tycho Brahe's Observatory, quadrant and Supernova		30	30
138	2p. Galileo, Moon and telescope		40	30
139	2½p. Isaac Newton, instruments and apple		1.00	70
140	3½p. Harrison's Chronometer and H.M.S. *Deptford* (frigate), 1735		2.00	70
141	4½p. Space Rocket taking-off		1.25	70
142	5p. World's largest telescope, Palomar		1.00	70
143	7½p. World's largest radio telescope, Jodrell Bank		4.00	1.60
144	10p. "Mariner 7" and Mars		3.50	1.75
145	12½p. "Sputnik 2" and Space dog, Laika		6.00	2.00
146	25p. Walking in Space		7.00	2.25
147	50p "Apollo 11" crew on Moon		6.00	2.50
148	£1 Future Space Research Station		6.00	2.50
135/48		Set of 14	35.00	16.00

The ½p., 1p., 4½p. and 25p. are vertical, and the remainder are horizontal.

(Des L. Curtis. Photo D.L.R.)

1971 (15 Nov). *Royal Naval Crests (3rd series). Designs as T 46.* Multicoloured. W w **12**. P 13.

149	2p. H.M.S. *Phoenix*		1.50	30
150	4p. H.M.S. *Milford*		1.75	55
151	9p. H.M.S. *Pelican*		2.25	80
152	15p. H.M.S. *Oberon*		2.50	1.00
149/52		Set of 4	7.00	2.40
MS153	151×104 mm. Nos. 149/52		7.00	15.00

(Des L. Curtis. Litho Questa)

1972 (29 May). *Royal Naval Crests (4th series). Multicoloured designs as T 46.* W w **12** (*sideways**). P 14.

154	1½p. H.M.S. *Lowestoft*		60	50
155	3p. H.M.S. *Auckland*		65	75
156	6p. H.M.S. *Nigeria*		70	1.25
157	17½p. H.M.S. *Bermuda*		1.50	2.50
154/7		Set of 4	3.00	4.50
MS158	157×93 mm. Nos. 154/7		3.00	7.50
	w. Wmk Crown to right of CA		£200	

*The normal sideways watermark shows Crown to left of CA, *as seen from the back of the stamp.*

(Des J. Cooter. Litho Questa)

1972 (2 Aug). *50th Anniv of Shackleton's Death. T 51 and similar multicoloured designs.* W w **12** (*sideways on 4 and 7½p.*). P 14.

159	2½p. Type 51		55	60
160	4p. Shackleton and *Quest* (*horiz*)		60	70
161	7½p. Shackleton's cabin and *Quest* (*horiz*)		65	75
162	11p. Shackleton's statue and memorial		75	1.00
159/62		Set of 4	2.25	2.75
MS163	139 × 114 mm. Nos. 159/62 (wmk sideways)	2.25	6.00

52 Land Crab and Short-finned Mako

(Des from photograph by D. Groves) and photo Harrison)

1972 (20 Nov). *Royal Silver Wedding. Multicoloured; background colour given.* W w **12**. P 14 × 14½.

164	52 2p. bright bluish violet		15	10
165	16p. rose-carmine		35	30

(Des L. Curtis. Litho J.W.)

1973 (28 May). *Royal Naval Crests (5th series). Multicoloured designs as T 46.* W w **12** (*sideways**). P 14.

166	2p. H.M.S. *Birmingham*		2.50	1.25
167	4p. H.M.S. *Cardiff*		3.00	1.25
168	9p. H.M.S. *Penzance*		4.00	1.50
169	13p. H.M.S. *Rochester*		4.50	1.50
	w. Wmk Crown to right of CA		8.00	
166/9		Set of 4	12.50	5.50
MS170	109×152 mm. Nos. 166/9		28.00	10.00

*The normal sideways watermark shows Crown to left of CA on 2, 4, 13p. and MS170, or Crown to right of CA on 9p., *as seen from the back of the stamp.*

53 Green Turtle

(Des V. Whiteley Studio. Litho Enschedé)

1973 (28 Aug). *Turtles. T 53 and similar triangular designs.* Multicoloured. W w **12**. P 13½.

171	4p. Type 53		3.75	1.25
172	9p. Loggerhead turtle		4.00	1.50
173	12p. Hawksbill turtle		4.25	1.75
171/3		Set of 3	11.00	4.00

54 Sergeant, R.M. Light Infantry, 1900

55 Letter and H.Q., Berne

(Des G. Drummond from paintings by C. Stadden. Litho Walsall)

1973 (31 Oct). *50th Anniv of Departure of Royal Marines from Ascension. T 54 and similar vert designs.* Multicoloured. W w **12** (*sideways**). P 14.

174	2p. Type 54		2.00	1.25
175	6p. R.M. Private, 1816		3.00	1.75
176	12p. R.M. Light Infantry Officer, 1880		3.50	2.25
	w. Wmk Crown to right of CA		25.00	
177	20p. R.M. Artillery Colour Sergeant, 1910		4.00	2.50
174/7		Set of 4	11.00	7.00

*The normal sideways watermark shows Crown to left of CA, *as seen from the back of the stamp.*

1973 (14 Nov). *Royal Wedding. As Nos. 165/6 of Anguilla. Centre multicoloured.* W w **12** (*sideways*). P 13½.

178	2p. ochre		15	10
179	18p. dull blue-green		25	15

(Des PAD Studio. Litho Questa)

1974 (27 Mar). *Centenary of U.P.U. T 55 and similar horiz design.* Multicoloured. W w **12**. P 14½ × 14.

180	2p. Type 55		25	30
181	9p. Hermes and U.P.U. monument		40	45

56 Churchill as a Boy, and Birthplace, Blenheim Palace

(Des J.W. Litho Questa)

1974 (30 Nov). *Birth Centenary of Sir Winston Churchill. T 56 and similar horiz design.* Multicoloured. No wmk. P 14.

182	5p. Type 56		25	35
183	25p. Churchill as statesman, and U.N. Building		40	75
MS184	93 × 87 mm. Nos. 182/3		1.25	2.50

57 "Skylab 3" and Photograph of Ascension

(Des PAD Studio. Litho Questa)

1975 (20 Mar). *Space Satellites. T 57 and similar horiz design.* Multicoloured. W w **12** (*sideways*). P 14.

185	2p. Type 57		30	30
186	18p. "Skylab 4" command module and photograph		35	40

The date "11.1.73" given on the 2p. is incorrect, "Skylab 3" was launched in July 1973 and returned to Earth in September 1973.

The date on the 18p. is also incorrect. The photograph was taken on 6 January 1974, three days later than the date given in the caption.

58 U.S.A.F. Lockheed C-141A Starlifter

APOLLO-SOYUZ LINK 1975 (59)

(Des R. Granger Barrett. Litho Questa)

1975 (19 June). *Wideawake Airfield. T 58 and similar horiz designs.* Multicoloured. W w **12** (*sideways**). P 13½.

187	2p. Type 58		1.75	65
188	5p. R.A.F. Lockheed C-130 Hercules		2.00	85
189	9p. Vickers Super VC-10		2.25	1.40
190	24p. U.S.A.F. Lockheed C-5A Galaxy		4.00	3.00
	w. Wmk Crown to right of CA			
187/90		Set of 4	9.00	5.50
MS191	144×99 mm. Nos 187/90		17.00	22.00

*The normal sideways watermark shows Crown to left of CA, *as seen from the back of the stamp.*

1975 (18 Aug). *"Apollo–Soyuz" Space Link. Nos. 141 and 145/6 optd with T 59.*
192	4½p. Space rocket taking-off		15	20
193	12½p. Sputnik II and Space Dog, Laika		20	25
194	25p. Walking in Space		30	40
192/4		*Set of 3*	60	75

60 Arrival of Royal Navy, 1815

(Des J.W. from paintings by Isobel McManus. Litho Walsall)

1975 (22 Oct). *160th Anniv of Occupation. T 60 and similar horiz designs. Multicoloured. W w 14 (sideways*). P 14.*
195	2p. Type 60		30	25
	w. Wmk Crown to right of CA		£110	
196	5p. Water Supply, Dampiers Drip		40	40
197	9p. First landing, 1815		45	60
198	15p. The garden on Green Mountain		60	85
195/8		*Set of 4*	1·60	1·90

*The normal sideways watermark shows Crown to left of CA, as seen from the back of the stamp.

61 Yellow Canary

62 Boatswain Bird Island Sanctuary

(Des J.W. Litho Questa)

1976 (26 Apr). *Birds. Multicoloured designs as T 61 and T 62. W w 14 (sideways on horiz designs*). P 13½ (£2) or 14 (others).*
199	1p. Type 61		40	1·50
200	2p. White Tern (*vert*)		45	1·50
	w. Wmk inverted		£190	
201	3p. Common Waxbill		45	1·50
202	4p. White-capped Noddy (*vert*)		50	1·50
203	5p. Common Noddy		70	1·50
204	6p. Common Mynah		70	1·50
205	7p. Madeiran Storm Petrel (*vert*)		70	1·50
206	8p. Sooty Tern		70	1·50
	w. Wmk Crown to right of CA		£150	
207	9p. Blue-faced Booby (*vert*)		70	1·50
208	10p. Red-footed Booby		70	1·50
209	15p. Bare-throated Francolin (*vert*)		1·25	1·75
210	18p. Brown Booby (*vert*)		1·25	1·75
211	25p. Red-billed Tropic Bird		1·40	1·75
212	50p. White-tailed Tropic Bird		2·25	2·75
213	£1 Ascension Frigate Bird (*vert*)		2·75	3·25
214	£2 Type 62		5·50	7·50
199/214		*Set of 16*	18·00	30·00

*The normal sideways watermark shows Crown to left of CA, as seen from the back of the stamp.

63 G.B. Penny Red with Ascension Postmark

(Des C. Abbott. Litho J.W.)

1976 (4 May). *Festival of Stamps, London. T 63 and similar designs. W w 14 (sideways on 5 and 25p). P 13½.*
215	5p. rose-red, black and cinnamon		20	15
216	9p. green, black and greenish stone		30	20
217	25p. multicoloured		50	45
215/17		*Set of 3*	90	70
MS218	133×121 mm. No. 217 with St. Helena 318 and Tristan da Cunha 206 (wmk sideways*). P 13		1·50	2·00
	w. Wmk Crown to left of CA		£325	

Designs:—*Vert*—9p. ½d. stamp of 1922. *Horiz*—25p. Southampton Castle (liner).

*The normal sideways watermark shows Crown to right of CA, as seen from the back of the stamp.

No. MS218 was postally valid on each island to the value of 25p.

64 U.S. Base, Ascension

65 Visit of Prince Philip, 1957

(Des V. Whiteley Studio. Litho J.W.)

1976 (4 July). *Bicentenary of American Revolution. T 64 and similar horiz designs. Multicoloured. W w 14 (sideways). P 13.*
219	8p. Type 64		55	40
220	9p. NASA Station at Devils Ashpit		55	45
221	25p. "Viking" landing on Mars		85	80
219/21		*Set of 3*	1·75	1·50

(Des J. Cooter. Litho Walsall)

1977 (7 Feb). *Silver Jubilee. T 65 and similar horiz designs. Multicoloured. W w 14 (sideways on 12 and 25p). P 13½.*
222	8p. Type 65		15	15
	w. Wmk inverted		£120	
223	12p. Coronation Coach leaving Buckingham Palace		20	20
224	25p. Coronation Coach		35	40
222/4		*Set of 3*	60	65

66 Tunnel carrying Water Pipe

67 Mars Bay Location, 1877

(Des G. Drummond. Litho Harrison)

1977 (27 June). *Water Supplies. T 66 and similar multicoloured designs. W w 14 (sideways on 12 and 25p). P 14.*
225	3p. Type 66		15	15
226	5p. Breakneck Valley wells		20	20
227	12p. Break tank (*horiz*)		35	35
228	25p. Water catchment (*horiz*)		55	65
225/8		*Set of 4*	1·10	1·25

(Des J.W. Litho Questa)

1977 (3 Oct). *Centenary of Visit of Professor Gill (astronomer). T 67 and similar horiz designs. Multicoloured. W w 14 (sideways). P 13½.*
229	3p. Type 67		15	20
230	8p. Instrument sites, Mars Bay		20	25
231	12p. Sir David and Lady Gill		30	40
232	25p. Maps of Ascension		60	70
229/32		*Set of 4*	1·10	1·40

68 Lion of England

69 Queen Elizabeth II

(Des C. Abbott. Litho Questa)

1978 (2 June). *25th Anniv of Coronation. T 68/9 and similar vert design. P 15.*
233	68	25p. yellow, sepia and silver		35	50
		a. Sheetlet. Nos. 233/5 × 2		1·75	
234	69	25p. multicoloured		35	50
235	—	25p. yellow, sepia and silver		35	50
233/5			*Set of 3*	95	1·40

Design:—No. 235, Green Turtle.

Nos. 233/5 were printed together in small sheets of 6, containing two *se-tenant* strips of 3 with horizontal gutter margin between.

PRICES OF SETS

Set prices are given for many issues, generally those containing three stamps or more. Definitive sets include one of each value or major colour change, but do not cover different perforations, die types or minor shades. Where a choice is possible the set prices are based on the cheapest versions of the stamps included in the listings.

70 Flank of Sisters, Sisters' Red Hill and East Crater

71 "The Resolution" (H. Roberts)

(Des J.W. Litho Questa)

1978 (4 Sept). *Volcanic Rock Formations of Ascension. T 70 and similar horiz designs. Multicoloured. W w 14. P 14½.*
236	3p. Type 70		15	20
	a. Horiz strip of 5. Nos. 236/40		1·10	
237	5p. Holland's Crater (Hollow Tooth)		20	30
238	12p. Street Crater, Lower Valley Crater and Bear's Back		25	40
239	15p. Butt Crater, Weather Post and Green Mountain		30	45
240	25p. Flank of Sisters, Thistle Hill and Two Boats Village		35	50
236/40		*Set of 5*	1·10	1·60
MS241	185 × 100 mm. Nos. 236/40, each × 2		2·00	5·00
	a. Blue ("Ascension Island") omitted		£4000	

Nos. 236/40 were printed together, *se-tenant*, in horizontal strips of 5 throughout the sheet forming a composite design.

(Des and litho (25p. also embossed) Walsall)

1979 (19 Feb*). *Bicentenary of Captain Cook's Voyages, 1768–79. T 71 and similar vert designs. Multicoloured. P 11.*
242	3p. Type 71		40	25
243	8p. Chronometer		40	40
244	12p. Green Turtle		45	50
245	25p. Flaxman/Wedgwood medallion of Captain Cook		55	70
242/5		*Set of 4*	1·60	1·75

*This is the local date of issue; the stamps were released in London on 8 January.

72 St. Mary's Church, Georgetown

73 Landing Cable, Comfortless Cove

(Des Walsall. Litho Format)

1979 (24 May). *Ascension Day. T 72 and similar vert designs. Multicoloured. W w 14. P 14.*
246	8p. Type 72		15	20
247	12p. Map of Ascension		20	30
248	50p. "The Ascension" (painting by Rembrandt)		55	90
246/8		*Set of 3*	80	1·25

(Des G. Vasarhelyi. Litho Walsall)

1979 (15 Sept). *80th Anniv of Eastern Telegraph Company's Arrival on Ascension. T 73 and similar designs. W w 14 (inverted on 12p. or sideways on others*). P 14.*
249	3p. black and carmine		15	10
250	8p. black and yellowish green		20	20
251	12p. black and yellow		25	25
252	15p. black and bright violet		25	35
	w. Wmk Crown to right of CA		40·00	
253	25p. black and orange-brown		35	50
249/53		*Set of 5*	1·10	1·25

Designs: *Horiz*—8p. C.S. *Anglia*; 15p. C.S. *Seine*; 25p Cable and Wireless earth station. *Vert*—12p. Map of Atlantic cable network.

*The normal sideways watermark shows Crown to left of CA, as seen from the back of the stamp.

74 1938 6d. Stamp

(Des BG Studio. Litho Questa)

1979 (12 Dec). *Death Centenary of Sir Rowland Hill. T 74 and similar designs. W w 14 (sideways on 3 and 8p). P 14.*
254	3p. black, new blue & deep turquoise-blue		15	10
255	8p. black, blue-green and light green		15	20
256	12p. black, bright blue and turquoise-blue		20	25
	w. Wmk inverted		85·00	
257	50p. black, brownish grey and red		60	90
254/7		*Set of 4*	1·00	1·25

Designs: *Horiz*—8p. 1956 5s. definitive stamp. *Vert*—12p. 1924 3s. stamp; 50p. Sir Rowland Hill.

75 *Anogramma ascensionis* **76** 17th-century Bottle Post

(Des J. Cooter. Litho Format)

1980 (18 Feb). *Ferns and Grasses. T* **75** *and similar multicoloured designs.* W w **14** (*sideways on* 12 *to* 24*p.*). P 14½ × 14 (3 *to* 8*p.*) *or* 14 × 14½ (12 *to* 24*p.*).

258	3p. Type **75**	..	10	10
259	6p. *Xiphopteris ascensionense*	..	15	15
260	8p. *Sporobolus caespitosus* ..	..	15	15
261	12p. *Sporobolus durus* (*vert*)	..	15	25
262	18p. *Dryopteris ascensionis* (*vert*)	..	20	35
	a. Brown (thorns) omitted..	..	£130	
263	24p. *Marattia purpurascens* (*vert*)	..	30	50
258/63		*Set of* 6	90	1·25

(Des L. Curtis. Litho Format)

1980 (1 May). *"London 1980" International Stamp Exhibition. T* **76** *and similar horiz designs. Multicoloured.* W w **14** (*sideways*). P 13½.

264	8p. Type **76**	..	15	20
265	12p. 19th-century chance calling ship	..	20	25
266	15p. *Garth Castle* (regular mail service from 1863)	..	20	30
267	50p. *St. Helena* (mail services, 1980)	..	60	90
264/7		*Set of* 4	1·00	1·50
MS268	102×154 mm. Nos. 264/7		1·00	2·40

77 Queen Elizabeth the **78** Lubbock's Yellowtail
Queen Mother

(Des Harrison. Litho Questa)

1980 (11 Aug)*. *80th Birthday of Queen Elizabeth the Queen Mother.* W w **14** (*sideways*). P 14.

269	15p. multicoloured	..	40	40

*This was the local release date. The Crown Agents placed stocks on sale in London on 4 August.

(Des G. Drummond. Litho Enschedé)

1980 (15 Sept). *Fishes. T* **78** *and similar horiz designs. Multicoloured.* W w **14** (*sideways**). P 13×13½.

270	3p. Type **78**	..	30	15
271	10p. Resplendent Angelfish	..	45	25
272	25p. Bicoloured Butterflyfish	..	75	50
	w. Wmk Crown to right of CA	..	1·00	
273	40p. Marmalade Razorfish	..	1·00	65
	w. Wmk Crown to right of CA	..	1·50	
270/3		*Set of* 4	2·25	1·40

*The normal sideways watermark shows Crown to left of CA, as seen from the back of the stamp.

79 H.M.S. *Tortoise*

(Des D. Bowen. Litho Rosenbaum Bros, Vienna)

1980 (17 Nov). *150th Anniv of Royal Geographical Society. T* **79** *and similar multicoloured designs.* W w **14** (*sideways**). P 14 (60*p.*) *or* 13½ (*others*).

274	10p. Type **79**	..	35	40
	w. Wmk Crown to left of CA	..	85	
275	15p. "Wideawake Fair"	..	45	45
	w. Wmk Crown to left of CA	..	1·25	
276	60p. Mid-Atlantic Ridge (38×48 *mm*)	..	80	1·25
	w. Wmk Crown to left of CA	..	2·75	
274/6		*Set of* 3	1·40	2·00

*The normal sideways watermark shows Crown to right of CA, as seen from the back of the stamp.

80 Green Mountain Farm, 1881

(Des C. Abbott. Litho Format)

1981 (15 Feb). *Green Mountain Farm. T* **80** *and similar horiz designs. Multicoloured.* W w **14** (*sideways*). P 13½ × 14.

277	12p. Type **80**	..	15	35
278	15p. Two Boats, 1881 ..	..	20	40
279	20p. Green Mountain and Two Boats, 1981	..	25	50
280	30p. Green Mountain Farm, 1981	..	35	70
277/80		*Set of* 4	85	1·75

81 Cable and Wireless Earth Station

(Des G. Vasarhelyi and Walsall. Litho Walsall)

1981 (27 Apr). *"Space Shuttle" Mission and Opening of 2nd Earth Station.* W w **14** (*sideways*). P 14.

281	**81**	15p. black, bright blue and pale blue	..	30	35

82 Poinsettia

83 Solanum

(Des J. Cooter. Litho J.W.)

1981 (11 May)–**82**. *Flowers. Designs as T* **82** (1 *to* 40*p.*) *or vert as T* **83** (50*p. to* £2). *Multicoloured.* W w **14** (*sideways** *on* 1, 2, 4, 5, 8, 15, 20, 40, 50*p.*, £1 *and* £2). P 13½. A. *Without imprint date.*

282A	1p. Type **82**	..	70	70
283A	2p. Clustered Wax Flower	..	80	75
284A	3p. Kolanchoe (*vert*)	..	80	75
285A	4p. Yellow Pops	..	80	75
286A	5p. Camels Foot Creeper	..	80	75
287A	8p. White Oleander	..	80	80
288A	10p. Ascension Lily (*vert*)	..	1·40	1·25
289A	12p. Coral Plant (*vert*)	..	1·50	85
290A	15p. Yellow Allamanda	..	1·25	85
291A	20p. Ascension Euphorbia	..	1·25	1·00
	w. Wmk Crown to left of CA	..	2·00	
292A	30p. Flame of the Forest (*vert*)	..	1·25	1·25
293A	40p. Bougainvillea "King Leopold"	..	1·25	2·00
294A	50p. Type **83**	..	1·25	2·50
295A	£1 Ladies Petticoat	..	2·00	4·00
296A	£2 Red Hibiscus	..	3·75	5·50
282A/96A		*Set of* 15	17·00	21·00

B. *With imprint date* ("1982") (27.8.82)

283B	2p. Clustered Wax Flower	..	50	75
284B	3p. Kolanchoe	..	50	75
288B	10p. Ascension Lily	..	45	75
290B	15p. Yellow Allamanda	..	50	75
291B	20p. Ascension Euphorbia	..	1·00	75
295B	£1 Ladies Petticoat	..	2·00	2·75
	w. Wmk Crown to left of CA	..	9·00	
283B/95B		*Set of* 6	4·50	6·00

*The normal sideways watermark shows Crown to right of CA, *as seen from the back of the stamp.*
Nos. 283B/95B had the imprint dates printed on the stamps by typography.

84 Map by Maxwell, 1793

(Des L. Curtis. Litho Walsall)

1981 (22 May). *Early Maps of Ascension. T* **84** *and similar horiz designs.* W w **14** (*sideways*). P 14 × 14½.

297	10p. black, gold and pale blue	..	25	35
298	12p. black, gold and apple-green	..	25	35
299	15p. black, gold and stone	..	25	35
300	40p. black, gold and pale greenish yellow	..	55	70
297/300		*Set of* 4	1·10	1·60
MS301	79 × 64 mm. 5p. × 4, multicoloured		60	75

Designs:—12p. Maxwell, 1793 (*different*); 15p. Ekeberg and Chapman, 1811; 40p. Campbell, 1819; miniature sheet, Linschoten, 1599.
Stamps from No. MS301 form a composite design.

85 Wedding Bouquet **86** Prince Charles and
from Ascension Lady Diana Spencer

(Des J.W. Litho Questa)

1981 (22 July). *Royal Wedding. T* **85**/**6** *and similar vert design. Multicoloured.* W w **14.** P 14.

302	10p. Type **85**	..	15	15
303	15p. Prince Charles in Fleet Air Arm flying kit	..	25	25
304	50p. Type **86**	..	65	75
302/4 ..		*Set of* 3	95	1·00

87 "Interest" **88** Scout crossing Rope Bridge

(Des BG Studio. Litho Questa)

1981 (14 Sept). *25th Anniv of Duke of Edinburgh Award Scheme. T* **87** *and similar vert designs. Multicoloured.* W w **14.** P 14.

305	5p. Type **87**	..	15	15
306	10p. "Physical activities" ..	..	15	15
307	15p. "Service"	..	20	20
308	40p. Duke of Edinburgh	..	45	45
	w. Wmk inverted	..	24·00	
305/8		*Set of* 4	85	85

(Des A. Theobald. Litho Format)

1982 (22 Feb). *75th Anniv of Boy Scout Movement. T* **88** *and similar designs.* W w **14** (*sideways*). P 14.

309	10p. black, bright blue and azure	..	15	35
310	15p. black, orange-brown and greenish yellow	..	20	50
311	25p. black, bright mauve and pale mauve	..	30	60
312	40p. black, rosine and pale orange	..	45	70
309/12		*Set of* 4	1·00	2·10
MS313	121 × 121 mm. 10p., 15p., 25p., 40p. As Nos. 309/12 (*each diamond,* 40 × 40 *mm*). P 14½		1·00	2·50

Designs:—15p. 1st Ascension Scout Group flag; 25p. Scouts learning to use radio; 40p. Lord Baden-Powell.
Stamps from No. MS313 have an overall design showing a flag printed on the reverse beneath the gum.

89 Charles Darwin

(Des L. Curtis. Litho Questa)

1982 (19 Apr). *150th Anniv of Charles Darwin's Voyage. T* **89** *and similar horiz designs. Multicoloured.* W w **14** (*sideways*). P 14.

314	10p. Type **89**	..	25	40
315	12p. Darwin's pistols	..	30	50
316	15p. Rock Crab	..	35	55
317	40p. H.M.S. *Beagle*	..	75	95
314/17		*Set of* 4	1·50	2·25

90 Fairey Swordfish Torpedo Bomber

(Des A. Theobald. Litho Walsall)

1982 (15 June). *40th Anniv of Wideawake Airfield. T* **90** *and similar horiz designs. Multicoloured.* W w **14** (*sideways*). P 14.

318	5p. Type **90**	..	1·00	35
319	10p. North American B-25C Mitchell	..	1·25	40
320	15p. Boeing EC-135N Aria	..	1·50	55
321	50p. Lockheed C-130 Hercules	..	2·25	1·10
318/21		*Set of* 4	5·50	2·25

91 Ascension Coat of Arms   **92** Formal Portrait

(Des Jennifer Toombs. Litho Questa)

1982 (1 July).   *21st Birthday of Princess of Wales. T* **91/2** *and similar vert designs. Multicoloured. W w* **14**. *P* 14 × 14½.

322	12p. Type **91**	25	25
323	15p. Lady Diana Spencer in Music Room, Buckingham Palace	25	25
324	25p. Bride and Earl Spencer leaving Clarence House	40	40
325	50p. Type **92**	75	75
322/5	Set of 4	1·50	1·50

 (positioned as 93)

1st PARTICIPATION
COMMONWEALTH GAMES 1982
(93)   **94** Bush House, London

1982 (29 Oct).   *Commonwealth Games, Brisbane. Nos.* 290B/1B *optd with T* **93**.

326	15p. Yellow Allamanda	30	40
327	20p. Ascension Euphorbia	40	45

(Des A. Theobald. Litho Questa)

1982 (1 Dec).   *Christmas. 50th Anniv of B.B.C. External Broadcasting. T* **94** *and similar horiz designs. Multicoloured. W w* **14** *(sideways*). P.* 14.

328	5p. Type **94**	15	20
329	10p. Atlantic relay station	15	30
330	25p. Lord Reith, first director-general	30	60
	w. Wmk Crown to right of CA	3·75	
331	40p. King George V making his first Christmas broadcast, 1932	45	75
328/31	Set of 4	95	1·60

*The normal sideways watermark shows Crown to left of CA, as seen from the back of the stamp.

95 *Marasmius thwaitesii* ("*Marasmius echinosphaerus*")   **96** Aerial View of Georgetown

(Des Harrison. Litho Questa)

1983 (1 Mar).   *Fungi. T* **95** *and similar vert designs. Multicoloured. W w* **14**. *P* 14.

332	7p. Type **95**	55	30
333	12p. *Chlorophyllum molybdites*	75	45
334	15p. *Leucocoprinus cepaestripes*	90	50
335	20p. *Lycoperdon marginatum*	1·10	65
336	50p. *Marasmiellus distantifolius*	1·75	1·25
332/6	Set of 5	4·50	2·75

(Des Jennifer Toombs. Litho Format)

1983 (12 May).   *Island Views (1st series). T* **96** *and similar horiz designs. Multicoloured. W w* **14** *(sideways*). P* 14×13½.

337	12p. Type **96**	20	25
338	15p. Green Mountain farm	20	25
	w. Wmk Crown to right of CA		
339	20p. Boatswain Bird Island	35	40
340	60p. Telemetry Hill by night	70	80
337/40	Set of 4	1·25	1·50

*The normal sideways watermark shows Crown to left of CA, as seen from the back of the stamp.
See also Nos. 367/70.

97 Westland Wessex 5 Helicopter of No. 845 Naval Air Squadron

---

(Des D. Hartley-Marjoram. Litho Questa)

1983 (1 Aug).   *Bicentenary of Manned Flight. British Military Aircraft. T* **97** *and similar horiz designs. Multicoloured. W w* **14** *(sideways). P* 13½.

341	12p. Type **97**	85	65
342	15p. Avro Vulcan B.2 of No. 44 Squadron	95	75
343	20p. Hawker Siddeley H.S.801 Nimrod M.R. 2P of No. 120 Squadron	1·10	85
344	60p. Handley Page H.P.80 Victor K2 of No. 55 Squadron	2·00	2·00
341/4	Set of 4	4·50	3·75

98 Iguanid

(Des D. Nockles. Litho Questa)

1983 (20 Sept).   *Introduced Species. T* **98** *and similar horiz designs. Multicoloured. W w* **14** *(sideways). P* 14.

345	12p. Type **98**	30	30
346	15p. Rabbit	35	35
347	20p. Cat	45	45
348	60p. Donkey	1·40	1·40
345/8	Set of 4	2·25	2·25

99 Speckled Tellin (*Tellina listeri*)   **100** 1922 1½d. Stamp

(Des G. Wilby. Litho Format)

1983 (28 Nov).   *Sea Shells. T* **99** *and similar horiz designs. Multicoloured. W w* **14** *(sideways). P* 14½ × 14.

349	7p. Type **99**	20	20
350	12p. Lion's Paw Scallop (*Lyropecten nodosa*)	30	30
351	15p. Lurid Cowrie (*Cypraea lurida oceanica*)	30	35
352	20p. Ascension Nerite (*Nerita ascensionis*)	40	45
353	50p. Miniature Melo (*Micromelo undatus*)	75	1·10
349/53	Set of 5	1·75	2·25

(Des C. Abbott. Litho Questa)

1984 (3 Jan).   *150th Anniv of St. Helena as a British Colony. T* **100** *and similar vert designs showing stamps of the 1922 issue overprinted on St. Helena. Multicoloured. W w* **14**. *P* 14.

354	12p. Type **100**	30	45
355	15p. 1922 2d. stamp	35	50
356	20p. 1922 8d. stamp	35	55
357	60p. 1922 1s. stamp	70	1·40
354/7	Set of 4	1·50	2·50

101 Prince Andrew   **102** Naval Semaphore

(Des L. Curtis. Litho Questa)

1984 (10 Apr).   *Visit of Prince Andrew. Sheet, 124 × 90 mm, containing vert designs as T* **101**. *W w* **14**. *P* 14½ × 14.
MS358 12p. Type **101**; 70p. Prince Andrew in naval uniform   1·40 1·60

(Des D. Hartley-Marjoram. Litho Questa)

1984 (28 May).   *250th Anniv of "Lloyd's List" (newspaper). T* **102** *and similar vert designs. Multicoloured. W w* **14**. *P* 14½ × 14.

359	12p. Type **102**	40	30
360	15p. *Southampton Castle* (liner)	45	35
361	20p. Pier Head	55	45
362	70p. *Dane* (screw steamer)	1·60	1·50
359/62	Set of 4	2·75	2·40

NEW INFORMATION

The editor is always interested to correspond with people who have new information that will improve or correct the Catalogue.

---

103 Penny Coin and Yellow-finned Tuna   **104** Bermuda Cypress

(Des G. Drummond. Litho Questa)

1984 (26 July).   *New Coinage. T* **103** *and similar horiz designs. Multicoloured. W w* **14** *(sideways). P* 14.

363	12p. Type **103**	65	35
364	15p. Twopenny coin and donkey	75	40
365	20p. Fifty pence coin and Green Turtle	90	50
366	70p. Pound coin and Sooty Tern	2·25	1·75
363/6	Set of 4	4·00	2·75

(Des Jennifer Toombs. Litho B.D.T.)

1984 (26 Oct).   *Island Views (2nd series). Horiz designs as T* **96**. *Multicoloured. W w* **14** *(sideways). P* 13½.

367	12p. The Devil's Riding-school	30	30
368	15p. St. Mary's Church	35	35
369	20p. Two Boats Village	35	45
370	70p. Ascension from the sea	80	1·50
367/70	Set of 4	1·60	2·40

(Des N. Shewring. Litho Questa)

1985 (8 Mar).   *Trees. T* **104** *and similar vert designs. Multicoloured. W w* **14**. *P* 14½.

371	7p. Type **104**	55	20
372	12p. Norfolk Island Pine	65	30
373	15p. Screwpine	75	35
374	20p. Eucalyptus	90	45
375	65p. Spore Tree	2·25	1·40
371/5	Set of 5	4·50	2·40

105 The Queen Mother with Prince Andrew at Silver Jubilee Service   **106** 32 Pdr. Smooth Bore Muzzle-loader, c 1820, and Royal Marine Artillery Hat Plate, c 1816

(Des A. Theobald (75p.), C. Abbott (others). Litho Questa)

1985 (7 June).   *Life and Times of Queen Elizabeth the Queen Mother. T* **105** *and similar vert designs. Multicoloured. W w* **16**. *P* 14½ × 14.

376	12p. With the Duke of York at Balmoral, 1924	25	35
	w. Wmk inverted	12·00	
377	15p. Type **105**	25	40
	w. Wmk inverted	1·00	
378	20p. The Queen Mother at Ascot	30	55
	w. Wmk inverted	26·00	
379	70p. With Prince Henry at his christening (from photo by Lord Snowdon)	80	1·75
376/9	Set of 4	1·40	2·75

MS380 91×73 mm. 75p. Visiting the *Queen Elizabeth 2* at Southampton, 1968. Wmk sideways   1·10 1·60

(Des W. Fenton. Litho Walsall)

1985 (19 July).   *Guns on Ascension Island. T* **106** *and similar horiz designs. Multicoloured. W w* **14** *(sideways). P* 14 × 14½.

381	12p. Type **106**	70	90
382	15p. 7 inch rifled muzzle-loader, c 1866, and Royal Cypher on barrel	80	1·00
383	20p. 7 pdr. rifled muzzle-loader, c 1877, and Royal Artillery badge	90	1·25
384	70p. 5·5 inch gun, 1941, and crest from H.M.S. *Hood*	2·50	3·50
381/4	Set of 4	4·50	6·00

107 Guide Flag   **108** *Clerodendrum fragrans*

(Des N. Shewring. Litho Questa)

1985 (4 Oct).   *75th Anniv of Girl Guide Movement and International Youth Year. T* **107** *and similar vert designs. Multicoloured. W w* **14**. *P* 14½ × 14.

385	12p. Type **107**	75	70
	w. Wmk inverted	4·00	
386	15p. Practising first aid	85	80
	w. Wmk inverted	4·00	
387	20p. Camping	95	90
388	70p. Lady Baden-Powell	2·75	2·50
385/8	Set of 4	4·75	4·50

(Des Josephine Martin. Litho Questa)

1985 (6 Dec). *Wild Flowers. T* **108** *and similar vert designs. Multicoloured. W w* **16**. *P* 14.

389	12p. Type **108**	..	45	75
390	15p. Shell Ginger	..	55	90
391	20p. Cape Daisy	..	65	90
392	70p. Ginger Lily	..	2·00	2·50
389/92		*Set of* 4	3·25	4·50

109 Newton's Reflector Telescope   **110** Princess Elizabeth in 1926

(Des D. Hartley. Litho B.D.T.)

1986 (7 Mar). *Appearance of Halley's Comet. T* **109** *and similar vert designs. Multicoloured. W w* **16**. *P* 14.

393	12p. Type **109**	..	75	1·10
394	15p. Edmond Halley and Old Greenwich Observatory		85	1·25
395	20p. Short's Gregorian telescope and comet, 1759		95	1·25
396	70p. Ascension satellite tracking station and ICE spacecraft	..	2·75	3·50
393/6	..	*Set of* 4	4·50	6·00

(Des A. Theobald. Litho Format)

1986 (21 Apr). *60th Birthday of Queen Elizabeth II. T* **110** *and similar vert designs. Multicoloured. W w* **16**. *P* 14 × 14½.

397	7p. Type **110**	..	15	25
398	15p. Queen making Christmas broadcast, 1952		20	40
399	20p. At Garter ceremony, Windsor Castle, 1983		25	50
400	35p. In Auckland, New Zealand, 1981	..	35	80
401	£1 At Crown Agents' Head Office, London, 1983		1·00	2·25
397/401		*Set of* 5	1·75	3·75

111 1975 Space Satellites 2p. Stamp   **112** Prince Andrew and Miss Sarah Ferguson

(Des L. Curtis. Litho Walsall)

1986 (22 May). *"Ameripex '86" International Stamp Exhibition, Chicago. T* **111** *and similar horiz designs showing previous Ascension stamps. Multicoloured. W w* **16** (*sideways**). *P* 14 × 14½.

402	12p. Type **111**	..	40	60
403	15p. 1980 "London 1980" International Stamp Exhibition 50p.		45	70
404	20p. 1976 Bicentenary of American Revolution 8p.	..	55	90
	w. Wmk Crown to right of CA	..	50·00	
405	70p. 1982 40th Anniv of Wideawake Airfield 10p.	..	1·25	2·00
402/5		*Set of* 4	2·40	3·75
MS406	60×75 mm. 75p. Statue of Liberty		2·00	2·75

The normal sideways watermark shows Crown to left of CA, as seen from the back of the stamp.

(Des D. Miller. Litho Questa)

1986 (23 July). *Royal Wedding. T* **112** *and similar square design. Multicoloured. W w* **16**. *P* 14.

407	15p. Type **112**	..	25	35
408	35p. Prince Andrew aboard H.M.S. *Brazen*	..	50	75

113 H.M.S. *Ganymede* (c 1811)

(Des E. Nisbet. Litho Questa)

1986 (14 Oct). *Ships of the Royal Navy. T* **113** *and similar horiz designs. Multicoloured. W w* **16** (*sideways**) *P* 14½.

409	1p. Type **113**	..	55	1·50
410	2p. H.M.S. *Kangaroo* (c 1811)	..	60	1·50
	w. Wmk Crown to right of CA			
411	4p. H.M.S. *Trinculo* (c 1811)	..	60	1·50
412	5p. H.M.S. *Daring* (c 1811)	..	60	1·50
413	9p. H.M.S. *Thais* (c 1811)	..	70	1·50
414	10p. H.M.S. *Pheasant* (1819)	..	70	1·50
415	15p. H.M.S. *Myrmidon* (1819)	..	80	1·75

416	18p. H.M.S. *Atholl* (1825)	..	90	1·75
417	20p. H.M.S. *Medina* (1830)	..	90	1·75
418	25p. H.M.S. *Saracen* (1840)	..	1·00	2·00
419	30p. H.M.S. *Hydra* (c 1845)	..	1·00	2·00
420	50p. H.M.S. *Sealark* (1849)	..	1·25	2·50
421	70p. H.M.S. *Rattlesnake* (1868)	..	1·75	3·00
422	£1 H.M.S. *Penelope* (1889)	..	2·40	3·75
423	£2 H.M.S. *Monarch* (1897)	..	5·00	6·50
409/23		*Set of* 15	17·00	30·00

The normal sideways watermark shows Crown to left of CA, as seen from the back of the stamp.

114 Cape Gooseberry   **115** Ignition of Rocket Motors

(Des R. Gorringe. Litho Walsall)

1987 (29 Jan). *Edible Bush Fruits. T* **114** *and similar horiz designs. Multicoloured. W w* **16** (*sideways*). *P* 14.

424	12p. Type **114**	..	65	90
425	15p. Prickly Pear	..	75	1·00
426	20p. Guava	..	85	1·10
427	70p. Loquat	..	2·00	2·75
424/7		*Set of* 4	3·75	5·25

(Des D. Hartley. Litho Questa)

1987 (30 Mar). *25th Anniv of First American Manned Earth Orbit. T* **115** *and similar vert designs. Multicoloured. W w* **16**. *P* 14.

428	15p. Type **115**	..	55	75
429	18p. Lift-off	..	60	80
430	25p. Re-entry	..	75	95
431	£1 Splashdown	..	2·50	3·25
428/31		*Set of* 4	4·00	5·25
MS432	92×78 mm. 70p. "Friendship 7" capsule		1·75	2·00

116 Captains in Full Dress raising Red Ensign   **117** *Cynthia cardui*

(Des C. Collins. Litho Format)

1987 (29 June). *19th-century Uniforms (1st series). Royal Navy, 1815–20. T* **116** *and similar vert designs. Multicoloured. W w* **16**. *P* 14.

433	25p. Type **116**	..	50	60
	a. Horiz strip of 5. Nos. 433/7		2·25	
434	25p. Surgeon and seamen	..	50	60
435	25p. Seaman with water-carrying donkey	..	50	60
436	25p. Midshipman and gun	..	50	60
437	25p. Commander in undress uniform surveying		50	60
433/7		*Set of* 5	2·25	2·75

Nos. 433/7 were printed together, *se-tenant*, in horizontal strips of five throughout the sheet.
See also Nos. 478/82.

(Des I. Loe. Litho Questa)

1987 (10 Aug). *Insects (1st series). Butterflies. T* **117** *and similar horiz designs. Multicoloured. W w* **16** (*sideways*). *P* 14 × 14½.

438	15p. Type **117**	..	65	65
439	18p. *Danaus chrysippus*	..	70	75
440	25p. *Hypolimnas misippus*	..	85	85
441	£1 *Lampides boeticus*	..	2·25	2·50
438/41		*Set of* 4	4·00	4·25

See also Nos. 452/5 and 483/6.

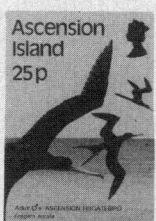

118 Male Ascension Frigate Birds   **(119)** 40TH WEDDING ANNIVERSARY

(Des N. Arlott. Litho B.D.T.)

1987 (8 Oct). *Sea Birds (1st series). T* **118** *and similar vert designs. Multicoloured. W w* **16**. *P* 14.

442	25p. Type **118**	..	1·60	1·90
	a. Horiz strip of 5. Nos. 442/6		7·00	
443	25p. Juvenile Ascension Frigate Bird, Brown Booby and Blue-faced Boobies		1·60	1·90
444	25p. Male Ascension Frigate Bird and Blue-faced Boobies		1·60	1·90

445	25p. Female Ascension Frigate Bird	..	1·60	1·90
446	25p. Adult male feeding juvenile Ascension Frigate Bird		1·60	1·90
442/6		*Set of* 5	7·00	8·50

Nos. 442/6 were printed together, *se-tenant*, in horizontal strips of five throughout the sheet, forming a composite design. See also Nos. 469/73.

1987 (9 Dec). *Royal Ruby Wedding. Nos.* 397/401 *optd with T* **119** *in silver.*

447	7p. Type **110**	..	15	15
448	15p. Queen making Christmas broadcast, 1952		25	30
449	20p. At Garter ceremony, Windsor Castle, 1983		30	40
	a. Opt double	..	60·00	
450	35p. In Auckland, New Zealand, 1981	..	50	60
451	£1 At Crown Agents' Head Office, London, 1983		1·25	1·40
447/51		*Set of* 5	2·25	2·50

(Des I. Loe. Litho Questa)

1988 (18 Jan). *Insects (2nd series). Horiz designs as T* **117**. *Multicoloured. W w* **16** (*sideways*). *P* 14 × 14½.

452	15p. *Gryllus bimaculatus* (field cricket)	..	50	50
453	18p. *Ruspolia differeus* (bush cricket)	..	55	55
454	25p. *Chilomenus lunata* (ladybird)	..	70	70
455	£1 *Diachrysia orichalcea* (moth)	..	2·25	2·25
452/5		*Set of* 4	3·50	3·50

120 Bate's Memorial, St. Mary's Church

(Des S. Noon. Litho Questa)

1988 (14 Apr). *150th Death Anniv of Captain William Bate (garrison commander, 1828–38). T* **120** *and similar horiz designs. Multicoloured. W w* **16** (*sideways*). *P* 14.

456	9p. Type **120**	..	35	35
457	15p. Commodore's Cottage	..	45	45
458	18p. North East Cottage	..	50	50
459	25p. Map of Ascension	..	70	70
460	70p. Captain Bate and marines	..	1·75	1·75
456/60		*Set of* 5	3·25	3·25

121 H.M.S. *Resolution* (ship of the line), 1667

(Des E. Nisbet. Litho Questa)

1988 (23 June). *Bicentenary of Australian Settlement. Ships of the Royal Navy. T* **121** *and similar diamond-shaped designs. Multicoloured. W w* **16** (*sideways**). *P* 14.

461	9p. Type **121**	..	80	45
	w. Wmk Crown to left of CA	..	60·00	
462	18p. H.M.S. *Resolution* (Captain Cook), 1772		1·25	70
	w. Wmk Crown to left of CA		60·00	
463	25p. H.M.S. *Resolution* (battleship), 1892		1·40	85
464	65p. H.M.S. *Resolution* (battleship), 1916	..	2·50	1·50
461/4		*Set of* 4	5·50	3·25

The normal sideways watermark shows Crown to right of CA, as seen from the back of the stamp positioned with the Royal cypher in the top left corner.

(122) SYDPEX '88 30.7.88 – 7.8.88   **123** Lloyd's Coffee House, London, 1688

1988 (30 July). *"Sydpex '88" National Stamp Exhibition, Sydney. Nos.* 461/4 *optd with T* **122**.

465	9p. Type **121**	..	50	40
466	18p. H.M.S. *Resolution* (Captain Cook), 1772		75	60
467	25p. H.M.S. *Resolution* (battleship), 1892	..	85	70
468	65p. H.M.S. *Resolution* (battleship), 1916	..	1·60	1·40
465/8		*Set of* 4	3·25	2·75

(Des N. Arlott. Litho Questa)

1988 (15 Aug). *Sea Birds (2nd series). Sooty Tern. Vert designs as T 118. Multicoloured.* W w **16**. P 14.
469	25p.	Pair displaying	1·40	1·10
	a.	Horiz strip of 5. Nos. 469/73	6·00	
470	25p.	Turning egg	1·40	1·10
471	25p.	Incubating egg	1·40	1·10
472	25p.	Feeding chick	1·40	1·10
473	25p.	Immature Sooty Tern	1·40	1·10
469/73		*Set of 5*	6·00	5·00

Nos. 469/73 were printed together, *se-tenant*, in horizontal strips of five throughout the sheet, forming a composite design of a nesting colony.

(Des E. Nisbet and D. Miller (8p., 25p.), D. Miller (others). Litho Questa)

1988 (17 Oct). *300th Anniv of Lloyd's of London. T 123 and similar multicoloured designs.* W w **14** (sideways on 18, 25p.). P 14.
474	8p.	Type **123**	25	35
475	18p.	*Alert IV* (cable ship) (*horiz*)	65	70
476	25p.	Satellite recovery in space (*horiz*)	80	90
477	65p.	*Good Hope Castle* (cargo liner) on fire off Ascension, 1973	1·75	2·00
474/7		*Set of 4*	3·00	3·50

(Des C. Collins. Litho B.D.T.)

1988 (21 Nov). *19th-century Uniforms (2nd series). Royal Marines, 1821–34. Vert designs as T 116. Multicoloured.* W w **14**. P 14.
478	25p.	Marines landing on Ascension, 1821	1·10	1·60
	a.	Horiz strip of 5. Nos. 478/82	5·00	
479	25p.	Officer and Marine at semaphore station, 1829	1·10	1·60
480	25p.	Sergeant and Marine at Octagonal Tank, 1831	1·10	1·60
481	25p.	Officers at water pipe tunnel, 1833	1·10	1·60
482	25p.	Officer supervising construction of barracks, 1834	1·10	1·60
478/82		*Set of 5*	5·00	7·00

Nos. 478/82 were printed together, *se-tenant*, in horizontal strips of five throughout the sheet.

(Des I. Loe. Litho Questa)

1989 (16 Jan). *Insects (3rd series). Horiz designs as T 117. Multicoloured.* W w **16** (sideways). P 14×14½.
483	15p.	*Trichoptilus wahlbergi* (moth)	75	50
484	18p.	*Lucilia sericata* (fly)	80	55
485	25p.	*Alceis ornatus* (weevil)	1·10	70
486	£1	*Polistes fuscatus* (wasp)	3·00	2·40
483/6		*Set of 4*	5·00	3·75

124 Two Land Crabs

125 1949 75th Anniversary of U. P. U. 1s. Stamp

(Des Doreen McGuiness. Litho Questa)

1989 (17 Apr). *Ascension Land Crabs (Gecarcinus lagostoma). T 124 and similar vert designs. Multicoloured.* W w **16**. P 14.
487	15p.	Type **124**	40	45
488	18p.	Crab with claws raised	45	50
489	25p.	Crab on rock	60	70
490	£1	Crab in surf	2·25	2·50
487/90		*Set of 4*	3·25	3·75
MS491		98 × 101 mm. Nos. 487/90	3·50	3·75

(Des D. Miller. Litho Walsall)

1989 (7 July). *"Philexfrance '89" International Stamp Exhibition, Paris, and "World Stamp Expo '89", Washington (1st issue). Sheet 104×86 mm.* W w **16**. P 14×13½.
MS492	**125**	75p. multicoloured	1·50	1·75

See also Nos. 498/503.

126 "Apollo 7" Tracking Station, Ascension

127 *Queen Elizabeth 2* (liner) and U.S.S. *John F. Kennedy* (aircraft carrier) in New York Harbour

---

(Des A. Theobald (£1), D. Miller (others). Litho Questa)

1989 (20 July). *20th Anniv of First Manned Landing on Moon. T 126 and similar multicoloured designs.* W w **16** (sideways on 18, 25p.). P 14 × 13½ (15, 70p.) or 14 (others).
493	15p.	Type **126**	65	45
494	18p.	Launch of "Apollo 7" (30 × 30 mm)	70	50
495	25p.	"Apollo 7" emblem (30 × 30 mm)	90	70
496	70p.	"Apollo 7" jettisoning expended Saturn rocket	1·75	1·75
493/6		*Set of 4*	3·50	3·00
MS497		101 × 83 mm. £1 Diagram of "Apollo 11" mission. P 14 × 13½.	2·00	2·10

(Des D. Miller. Litho Walsall)

1989 (21 Aug). *"Philexfrance 89" International Stamp Exhibition, Paris, and "World Stamp Expo '89", Washington (2nd issue). T 127 and similar vert designs showing Statue of Liberty and Centenary celebrations. Multicoloured.* W w **14**. P 14×13½.
498	15p.	Type **127**	35	35
	a.	Sheetlet. Nos. 498/503	1·90	
499	15p.	Cleaning Statue	35	35
500	15p.	Statue of Liberty	35	35
501	15p.	Crown of Statue	35	35
502	15p.	Warships and New York skyline	35	35
503	15p.	*Jean de Vienne* (French destroyer) and skyscrapers	35	35
498/503		*Set of 6*	1·90	1·90

Nos. 498/503 were printed, *se-tenant*, in sheetlets of 6.

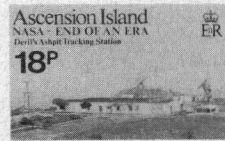

128 Devil's Ashpit Tracking Station

(Des D. Miller. Litho Questa)

1989 (30 Sept). *Closure of Devil's Ashpit Tracking Station, Ascension. T 128 and similar horiz design. Multicoloured.* W w **16** (sideways). P 14.
504	18p.	Type **128**	80	50
	a.	Sheetlet. Nos. 504/5, each × 5	7·00	
505	25p.	Launch of shuttle *Atlantis*	80	55

Nos. 504/5 were issued in sheetlets of ten containing vertical strips of five of each design, separated by a central inscribed gutter.

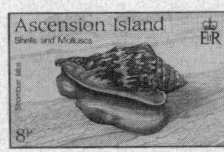

129 Bubonian Conch (*Strombus latus*)

130 Donkeys

(Des I. Loe. Litho Questa)

1989 (2 Nov). *Sea Shells. T 129 and similar horiz designs. Multicoloured.* W w **16** (sideways). P 14.
506	8p.	Type **129**	40	30
507	18p.	Giant Tun (*Tonna galea*)	70	50
508	25p.	Doris Harp (*Harpa doris*)	90	65
509	£1	Atlantic Trumpet Triton (*Charonia variegata*)	2·75	2·50
506/9		*Set of 4*	4·25	3·50

(Des G. Drummond, adapted N. Harvey. Litho Walsall)

1989 (17 Nov). *Ascension Wildlife. T 130 and similar vert design. Multicoloured.* W w **16** (sideways). P 14.
510	18p.	Type **130**	35	40
	a.	Booklet pane. No. 510×6	2·10	
511	25p.	Green Turtle	50	55
	a.	Booklet pane. No. 511×4	2·00	

Nos. 510/11 were only issued in £1 stamp booklets and come with either the left or right-hand side imperforate.

131 Seaman's Pistol, Hat and Cutlass

132 Pair of Ascension Frigate Birds with Young

(Des C. Collins. Litho Questa)

1990 (12 Feb). *Royal Navy Equipment, 1815-20. T 131 and similar vert designs. Multicoloured.* W w **16**. P 14.
512	25p.	Type **131**	65	65
	a.	Horiz strip of 5. Nos. 512/16	3·00	
513	25p.	Midshipman's belt plate, button, sword and hat	65	65
514	25p.	Surgeon's hat, sword and instrument chest	65	65

515	25p.	Captain's hat, telescope and sword	65	65
516	25p.	Admiral's epaulette, megaphone, hat and pocket	65	65
512/16		*Set of 5*	3·00	3·00

Nos. 512/16 were printed together, *se-tenant*, in horizontal strips of 5 throughout the sheet.
See also Nos. 541/5.

(Des W. Oliver. Litho Questa)

1990 (5 Mar). *Ascension Frigate Bird. T 132 and similar vert designs. Multicoloured.* W w **14**. P 14½×14.
517	9p.	Type **132**	1·50	1·00
518	10p.	Fledgeling	1·50	1·00
519	11p.	Adult male in flight	1·50	1·00
520	15p.	Female and immature birds in flight	1·75	1·25
517/20		*Set of 4*	5·50	3·75

133 Penny Black and Twopence Blue

(Des D. Miller. Litho Walsall)

1990 (3 May). *"Stamp World London 90" International Stamp Exhibition, London. T 133 and similar horiz designs. Multicoloured.* W w **14** (sideways). P 14.
521	9p.	Type **133**	50	40
522	18p.	Ascension postmarks used on G.B. stamps	70	60
523	25p.	Unloading mail at Wideawake Airfield	95	85
524	£1	Mail van and Main Post Office	2·25	2·75
521/4		*Set of 4*	4·00	4·25

134 "Queen Elizabeth, 1940" (Sir Gerald Kelly)

135 King George VI and Queen Elizabeth with Bren-gun Carrier

(Des D. Miller. Litho Questa)

1990 (4 Aug). *90th Birthday of Queen Elizabeth the Queen Mother.* W w **16**. P 14×15 (25p.) or 14½ (£1).
525	**134**	25p. multicoloured	75	75
526	**135**	£1 black and deep lilac	2·25	2·25

136 "Madonna and Child" (sculpture, Dino Felici)

137 *Garth Castle* (mail steamer), 1910

(Des D. Miller. Litho B.D.T.)

1990 (24 Oct). *Christmas. Works of Art. T 136 and similar vert designs. Multicoloured.* W w **14**. P 13½.
527	8p.	Type **136**	70	70
528	18p.	"Madonna and Child" (anon)	1·25	1·25
529	25p.	"Madonna and Child with St. John" (Johann Gebhard)	1·75	1·75
530	65p.	"Madonna and Child" (Giacomo Gritti)	3·00	4·00
527/30		*Set of 4*	6·00	7·00

(Des L. Curtis. Litho Walsall)

1990 (27 Nov). *Maiden Voyage of St. Helena II. T 137 and similar horiz designs. Multicoloured.* W w **14** (sideways). P 14×14½.
531	9p.	Type **137**	90	75
532	18p.	*St. Helena I* during Falkland Islands campaign, 1982	1·25	1·25
533	25p.	Launch of *St. Helena II*	1·75	1·75
534	70p.	Duke of York launching *St. Helena II*	3·00	4·00
531/4		*Set of 4*	6·25	7·00
MS535		100×100 mm. £1 *St. Helena II* and outline map of Ascension	3·50	5·00

No. MS535 also contains two imperforate designs of similar stamps from St. Helena and Tristan da Cunha without face values.

BRITISH FOR 175 YEARS

(138)

139 Queen Elizabeth II at Trooping the Colour

1991 (5 Feb). *175th Anniv of Occupation. Nos. 418, 420 and 422 optd with T 138 in silver by Cartor.*

536	25p. H.M.S. *Saracen* (1840)	.. ..	1·50	1·75
537	50p. H.M.S. *Sealark* (1849)	.. ..	2·00	2·50
538	£1 H.M.S. *Penelope* (1889)	.. ..	3·00	4·00
536/8		*Set of 3*	6·00	7·50

(Des D. Miller. Litho Questa)

1991 (18 June). *65th Birthday of Queen Elizabeth II and 70th Birthday of Prince Philip. T 139 and similar vert design. Multicoloured. W w 16 (sideways). P 14½ × 14.*

539	25p. Type 139		1·00	1·40
	a. Horiz pair. Nos. 539/40 separated by label		2·00	2·75
540	25p. Prince Philip in naval uniform		1·00	1·40

Nos. 539/40 were printed together, *se-tenant*, in sheetlets of 10 (2 × 5) with designs alternating and the vertical rows separated by inscribed labels.

(Des C. Collins. Litho Questa)

1991 (1 Aug). *Royal Marines Equipment, 1821–44. Vert designs as T 131. Multicoloured. W w 14. P 14.*

541	25p. Officer's shako, epaulettes, belt plate and button		1·10	1·50
	a. Horiz strip of 5. Nos. 541/5		5·00	
542	25p. Officer's cap, sword, epaulettes and belt plate		1·10	1·50
543	25p. Drum major's shako and staff		1·10	1·50
544	25p. Sergeant's shako, chevrons, belt plate and canteen		1·10	1·50
545	25p. Drummer's shako and side-drum		1·10	1·50
541/5		*Set of 5*	5·00	6·50

Nos. 541/5 were printed together, *se-tenant*, in horizontal strips of 5 throughout the sheet.

140 B.B.C. World Service Relay Station

(Des D. Miller. Litho Questa)

1991 (17 Sept). *25th Anniv of B.B.C. Atlantic Relay Station. T 140 and similar multicoloured designs. W w 16 (sideways on 15, 18p.). P 14½.*

546	15p. Type 140		90	1·10
547	18p. Transmitters at English Bay		1·00	1·25
548	25p. Satellite receiving station (*vert*)		1·25	1·40
549	70p. Antenna support tower (*vert*)		2·50	3·50
546/9		*Set of 4*	5·00	6·50

141 St. Mary's Church

(Des D. Miller. Litho Questa)

1991 (1 Oct). *Christmas. Ascension Churches. T 141 and similar horiz designs. Multicoloured. W w 16 (sideways). P 14.*

550	8p. Type 141		55	55
551	18p. Interior of St. Mary's Church		1·00	1·00
552	25p. Our Lady of Ascension Grotto		1·25	1·25
553	65p. Interior of Our Lady of Ascension Grotto		2·75	4·50
550/3		*Set of 4*	5·00	6·50

142 Black Durgon ("Blackfish")

(Des G. Drummond. Litho Walsall)

1991 (10 Dec). *Fishes. T 142 and similar horiz designs. Multicoloured. W w 14 (sideways). P 14.*

554	1p. Type 142		40	60
555	2p. Sergeant Major ("Five Finger")		50	60
556	4p. Resplendent Angelfish		60	70
557	5p. Derbio ("Silver Fish")		60	70

558	9p. Spotted Scorpionfish ("Gurnard")		70	80
559	10p. St Helena Parrotfish ("Blue Dad")		70	80
560	15p. St. Helena Butterflyfish ("Cunning Fish")		90	1·00
561	18p. Rock Hind ("Grouper")		1·00	1·00
562	20p. Spotted Moray		1·00	1·25
563	25p. Squirrelfish ("Hardback Soldierfish")		1·00	1·25
564	30p. Blue Marlin		1·25	1·40
565	50p. Wahoo		1·75	2·00
566	70p. Yellow-finned Tuna		2·25	2·75
567	£1 Blue Shark		2·75	3·50
568	£2.50, Bottlenose Dolphin		6·00	7·00
554/68		*Set of 15*	19·00	23·00

143 Holland's Crater

(Des D. Miller. Litho Questa (70p.), Walsall (others))

1992 (6 Feb). *40th Anniv of Queen Elizabeth II's Accession. T 143 and similar horiz designs. W w 14 (sideways). P 14.*

569	9p. Type 143		30	30
570	15p. Green Mountain		50	50
571	18p. Boatswain Bird Island		60	60
572	25p. Three portraits of Queen Elizabeth		80	80
573	70p. Queen Elizabeth II		2·00	2·00
569/73		*Set of 5*	3·75	3·75

The portraits shown on the 25p. are repeated from the three lower values of the set.

144 Compass Rose and *Eye of the Wind* (cadet brig)

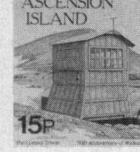

145 Control Tower, Wideawake Airfield

(Des R. Watton. Litho Walsall)

1992 (18 Feb). *500th Anniv of Discovery of America by Columbus and Re-enactment Voyages. T 144 and similar horiz designs. Multicoloured. W w 14 (sideways). P 13½×14.*

574	9p. Type 144		85	70
575	18p. Map of re-enactment voyages and *Soren Larsen* (cadet brigantine)		1·40	1·00
576	25p. *Santa Maria*, *Pinta* and *Nina*		1·75	1·25
577	70p. Columbus and *Santa Maria*		3·25	2·75
574/7		*Set of 4*	6·50	5·25

(Des N. Shewring. Litho Questa)

1992 (5 May). *50th Anniv of Wideawake Airfield. T 145 and similar square designs. Multicoloured. W w 14 (sideways). P 14.*

578	15p. Type 145		65	65
579	18p. Nose hangar		70	70
580	25p. Site preparation by U.S. Army engineers		90	90
581	70p. Laying fuel pipeline		2·25	2·25
578/81		*Set of 4*	4·00	4·00

146 Hawker Siddeley H.S.801 Nimrod

147 "Christmas in Great Britain and Ascension"

(Des N. Shewring. Litho Questa)

1992 (12 June). *10th Anniv of Liberation of Falkland Islands. Aircraft. T 146 and similar square designs. Multicoloured. W w 14 (sideways). P 14.*

582	15p. Type 146		1·25	1·25
583	18p. Vickers VC-10 landing at Ascension		1·25	1·25
584	25p. Westland Wessex HU Mk 5 helicopter lifting supplies		1·75	1·50
585	65p. Avro Vulcan B.2 over Ascension		3·00	3·75
582/5		*Set of 4*	6·50	7·00
MS586	116×116 mm. 15p. + 3p. Type 146; 18p. + 4p. As No. 583; 25p. + 5p. As No. 584; 65p. + 13p. As No. 585		4·75	6·00

The premiums on No. MS586 were for the S.S.A.F.A.

(Adapted G. Vasarhelyi. Litho Walsall)

1992 (13 Oct). *Christmas. Children's Paintings. T 147 and similar horiz designs. Multicoloured. W w 16 (sideways). P 14.*

587	8p. Type 147		60	60
588	18p. "Santa Claus riding turtle"		1·00	90
589	25p. "Nativity"		1·25	1·10
590	65p. "Nativity with rabbit"		2·75	3·50
587/90		*Set of 4*	5·00	5·50

148 Male Canary singing

149 Sopwith Snipe

(Des N. Arlott. Litho Questa)

1993 (12 Jan). *Yellow Canary. T 148 and similar vert designs. Multicoloured. W w 14. P 14½×14.*

591	15p. Type 148		75	70
592	18p. Adult male and female		85	80
593	25p. Young birds calling for food		95	95
594	70p. Adults and young birds on the wing		2·50	3·50
591/4		*Set of 4*	4·50	5·50

(Des A. Theobald. Litho Questa)

1993 (1 Apr). *75th Anniv of Royal Air Force. T 149 and similar horiz designs. Multicoloured. W w 14 (sideways). P 14.*

595	20p. Type 149		1·25	85
596	25p. Supermarine Southampton		1·25	95
597	30p. Avro Type 652 Anson		1·40	1·10
598	70p. Vickers-Armstrong Wellington		2·50	3·00
595/8		*Set of 4*	5·75	5·50
MS599	110×77 mm. 25p. Westland Lysander; 25p. Armstrong-Whitworth Meteor ("Gloster Meteor"); 25p. De Havilland D.H.106 Comet; 25p. Hawker Siddeley H.S.801 Nimrod		2·75	3·75

150 Map of South Atlantic Cable

151 Lanatana Camara

(Des D. Miller. Litho Questa)

1993 (8 June). *25th Anniv of South Atlantic Cable Company. T 150 and similar horiz designs. Multicoloured. W w 16 (sideways). P 14½.*

600	20p. Type 150		80	80
601	25p. *Sir Eric Sharpe* laying cable		90	90
602	30p. Map of Ascension		1·00	1·00
603	70p. *Sir Eric Sharpe* (cable ship) off Ascension		2·25	2·50
600/3		*Set of 4*	4·50	4·75

(Des N. Shewring. Litho Questa)

1993 (3 Aug). *Local Flowers. T 151 and similar horiz designs. Multicoloured. W w 16 (sideways). P 14×14½.*

604	20p. Type 151		80	70
605	25p. Moonflower		90	75
606	30p. Hibiscus		1·00	85
607	70p. Frangipani		2·25	2·25
604/7		*Set of 4*	4·50	4·00

152 Posting Christmas Card to Ascension

153 Ichthyosaurus

(Des N. Shewring. Litho Walsall)

1993 (19 Oct). *Christmas. T 152 and similar vert designs. Multicoloured. W w 14. P 14½×14.*

608	12p. Type 152		45	45
609	20p. Loading mail onto R.A.F. Lockheed L-1011 TriStar at Brize Norton		75	55
610	25p. Tristar over South Atlantic		85	65
611	30p. Unloading mail at Wideawake Airfield		1·10	75
612	65p. Receiving card and Georgetown Post Office		1·60	2·00
608/12		*Set of 5*	4·25	4·00
MS613	161×76 mm. Nos. 608/12		5·50	5·50

(Des N. Shewring. Litho B.D.T.)

1994 (25 Jan). *Prehistoric Aquatic Reptiles. T 153 and similar vert designs. Multicoloured. W w 14. P 14.*

614	12p. Type 153		70	70
615	20p. Metriorhynchus		85	85
616	25p. Mosasaurus		90	90
617	30p. Elasmosaurus		90	1·00
618	65p. Plesiosaurus		1·75	2·25
614/18		*Set of 5*	4·50	5·00

NEW INFORMATION

The editor is always interested to correspond with people who have new information that will improve or correct the Catalogue.

(154)

155 Young Green Turtles
heading towards Sea

1994 (18 Feb). *"Hong Kong '94" International Stamp
Exhibition. Nos. 614/18 optd with T 154.*

619	12p. Type 153		65	80
620	20p. Metriorhynchus		85	1·00
621	25p. Mosasaurus		90	1·10
622	30p. Elasmosaurus		1·00	1·25
623	65p. Plesiosaurus		1·90	2·50
619/23		Set of 5	4·75	6·00

(Des A. Robinson. Litho Questa)

1994 (22 Mar). *Green Turtles. T 155 and similar horiz designs.
Multicoloured. W w 14 (sideways). P 14.*

624	20p. Type 155		1·25	1·00
625	25p. Turtle digging nest		1·40	1·10
626	30p. Turtle leaving sea		1·50	1·25
627	65p. Turtle swimming		2·50	3·00
624/7		Set of 4	6·00	5·50

MS628 116×90 mm. 30p. Turtle leaving sea
(*different*); 30p. Turtle digging nest (*different*);
30p. Young turtles heading towards sea
(*different*); 30p. Young turtle leaving nest ... 6·50 7·50

156 *Yorkshireman* (tug)

(Des R. Watton. Litho Walsall)

1994 (14 June). *Civilian Ships used in Liberation of Falkland
Islands, 1982. T 156 and similar horiz designs. Multicoloured.
W w 16 (sideways). P 14.*

629	20p. Type 156		1·25	1·00
630	25p. St. Helena I (minesweeper support ship)		1·40	1·10
631	30p. British Esk (tanker)		1·50	1·25
632	65p. Uganda (hospital ship)		2·50	3·00
629/32		Set of 4	6·00	5·50

157 Sooty Tern Chick

(Des N. Arlott. Litho Walsall)

1994 (16 Aug). *Sooty Tern. T 157 and similar horiz designs.
Multicoloured. W w 14 (sideways). P 14½.*

633	20p. Type 157		90	1·00
634	25p. Juvenile bird		95	1·10
635	30p. Brooding adult		1·10	1·25
636	65p. Adult male performing courting display		1·75	2·50
633/6		Set of 4	4·25	5·25

MS637 77×58 mm. £1 Flock of Sooty Terns ... 3·50 4·00

158 Donkey Mare with Foal

159 *Leonurus japonicus*

(Des Josephine Martin. Litho Questa)

1994 (11 Oct). *Christmas. Donkeys. T 158 and similar horiz
designs. Multicoloured. W w 16 (sideways). P 14½.*

638	12p. Type 158		55	55
639	20p. Juvenile		75	75
640	25p. Foal		80	80
641	30p. Adult and Cattle Egrets		95	95
642	65p. Adult		1·90	3·00
638/42		Set of 5	4·50	5·50

(Des Jennifer Toombs. Litho Walsall)

1995 (10 Jan). *Flowers. T 159 and similar multicoloured
designs. W w 16 (sideways on horiz designs). P 14.*

643	20p. Type 159		1·25	1·00
644	25p. Catharanthus roseus (horiz)		1·25	1·10
645	30p. Mirabilis jalapa		1·40	1·10
646	65p. Asclepias curassavica (horiz)		2·50	3·00
643/6		Set of 4	5·75	5·75

160 Two Boats and Green
Mountain

(Des S. Noon. Litho Questa)

1995 (7 Mar). *Late 19th-century Scenes. T 160 and similar
horiz designs, each in cinnamon and reddish brown. W w 16
(sideways). P 14×14½.*

647	12p. Type 160		50	60
648	20p. Island Stewards' Store		70	70
649	25p. Navy headquarters and barracks		80	80
650	30p. Police office		1·50	1·50
651	65p. Pierhead		1·75	2·50
647/51		Set of 5	4·75	5·50

161 5.5-inch Coastal Battery

162 Male and Female
Lampides boeticus

(Des R. Watton. Litho Questa)

1995 (8 May). *50th Anniv of End of Second World War. T 161
and similar multicoloured designs. W w 16 (sideways). P 14.*

652	20p. Type 161		1·00	80
653	25p. Fairey Swordfish aircraft		1·25	1·00
654	30p. H.M.S. Dorsetshire (cruiser)		1·50	1·25
655	65p. H.M.S. Devonshire (cruiser)		2·50	3·00
652/5		Set of 4	5·50	5·50

MS656 75×85 mm. £1 Reverse of 1939–45 War
Medal (*vert*). W w 14 ... 2·50 3·25

(Des K. McGee. Litho B.D.T.)

1995 (1 Sept). *Butterflies. T 162 and similar vert designs.
Multicoloured. W w 16. P 14.*

657	20p. Type 162		1·00	75
658	25p. Vanessa cardui		1·10	80
659	30p. Male Hypolimnas misippus		1·25	85
660	65p. Danaus chrysippus		2·25	2·00
657/60		Set of 4	5·00	4·00

MS661 114×85 mm. £1 Vanessa atalanta ... 3·50 3·25
No. MS661 includes the "Singapore '95" International Stamp
Exhibition logo on the sheet margin.

163 "Santa Claus on Boat"
(Phillip Stephens)

(Des B. Dare. Litho Walsall)

1995 (10 Oct). *Christmas. Children's Drawings. T 163 and
similar horiz designs. Multicoloured. W w 14 (sideways). P 14.*

662	12p. Type 163		60	60
663	20p. "Santa sitting on Wall" (Kelly Lemon)		85	85
664	25p. "Santa in Chimney" (Mario Anthony)		90	90
665	30p. "Santa riding Dolphin" (Verena Benjamin)		1·00	1·10
666	65p. "Santa in Sleigh over Ascension" (Tom Butler)		2·00	2·50
662/6		Set of 5	4·75	5·50

164 *Cypraea lurida oceanica*

165 Queen Elizabeth
II and St. Mary's
Church

(Des I. Loe. Litho B.D.T.)

1996 (10 Jan). *Molluscs. T 164 and similar horiz designs.
Multicoloured. W w 16 (sideways). P 14.*

667	12p. Type 164		80	80
	a. Horiz strip of 4. Nos. 667/70		4·50	
668	25p. Cypraea spurca sanctaehelenae		1·25	1·25
669	30p. Harpa doris		1·25	1·25
670	65p. Umbraculum umbraculum		1·75	1·75
667/70		Set of 4	4·50	4·50

Nos. 667/70 were printed together, *se-tenant*, in horizontal
strips of 4 throughout the sheet with the backgrounds forming a
composite design.

(Des D. Miller. Litho B.D.T.)

1996 (22 Apr). *70th Birthday of Queen Elizabeth II. T 165 and
similar vert designs. W w 16. P 13½.*

671	20p. Type 165		55	55
672	25p. The Residency		60	60
673	30p. The Roman Catholic Grotto		70	70
674	65p. The Exiles' Club		1·75	1·75
671/4		Set of 4	3·25	3·25

166 American Army Jeep

167 Madeiran
Storm Petrel

(Des B. Dare. Litho Walsall)

1996 (8 June). *"CAPEX '96" International Stamp Exhibition,
Toronto. Island Transport. T 166 and similar horiz designs.
Multicoloured. W w 16 (sideways). P 14.*

675	20p. Type 166		75	75
676	25p. Citroen 7.5hp two-seater car, 1924		80	80
677	30p. Austin ten tourer car, 1930		90	90
678	65p. Series 1 Land Rover		1·75	1·75
675/8		Set of 4	3·75	3·75

(Des N. Arlott. Litho Walsall)

1996 (12 Aug). *Birds and their Young. T 167 and similar vert
designs. Multicoloured. W w 14. P 13½×13.*

679	1p. Type 167		10	10
680	2p. Red-billed Tropic Bird		10	10
681	4p. Common Mynah		10	10
682	5p. House Sparrow		10	15
683	7p. Common Waxbill		15	20
684	10p. White Tern		20	25
685	12p. Bare-throated Francolin		25	30
686	15p. Common Noddy		30	35
687	20p. Yellow Canary		40	45
688	25p. Lesser Noddy		50	55
689	30p. Red-footed Booby		60	65
690	40p. White-tailed Tropic Bird		80	85
691	50p. Brown Booby		1·25	1·40
692	£1 Blue-faced Booby		2·00	2·10
693	£2 Sooty Tern		4·00	4·25
694	£3 Ascension Frigate Bird		6·00	6·25
679/94		Set of 16	16·00	17·00

For 65p. and £1 (with "1997" imprint date) used in miniature
sheets see Nos. MS708 and MS718.
For 15p. and 35p. in designs of 7p and 20p, but 20×24 mm
from booklets see Nos. 726/7.

168 Pylons

169 Santa Claus on Dish
Aerial

(Des D. Miller. Litho Walsall)

1996 (9 Sept). *30th Anniv of B.B.C. Atlantic Relay Station.
T 168 and similar horiz designs. Multicoloured. W w 16
(sideways). P 14×14½.*

695	20p. Type 168		65	65
696	25p. Pylons (different)		70	70
697	30p. Pylons and station buildings		80	80
698	65p. Dish aerial, pylon and beach		1·75	1·75
695/8		Set of 4	3·50	3·50

(Des B. Dare. Litho Questa)

1996 (23 Sept). *Christmas. T 169 and similar horiz designs
showing Santa Claus. Multicoloured. W w 14 (sideways).
P 14×14½.*

699	12p. Type 169		35	35
700	20p. Playing golf		65	65
701	25p. In deck chair		65	65
702	30p. On top of aircraft		75	75
703	65p. On funnel of St. Helena II (mail ship)		1·75	2·00
699/703		Set of 5	3·75	4·00

170 Date Palm
171 Red Ensign and *Maersk Ascension* (tanker)

(Des R. Watton. Litho Walsall)

1997 (7 Jan). *"HONG KONG '97" International Stamp Exhibition. Trees. T* **170** *and similar vert designs. Multicoloured. W w* 14. *P* 14½×14.

704	20p. Type **170**	..	..	55	55
705	25p. Mauritius Hemp	..	..	65	65
706	30p. Norfolk Island Pine	..	..	75	75
707	65p. Dwarf Palm	..	..	1·50	1·60
704/7			*Set of 4*	3·00	3·25

(Des D. Miller. Litho Questa)

1997 (3 Feb). *"HONG KONG '97" International Stamp Exhibition. Sheet* 130×90 *mm containing design as No.* 691. *Multicoloured. W w* 14. *P* 14.

MS708	65p. Brown Booby	..	..	1·50	1·50

(Des A. Theobald. Litho Walsall)

1997 (1 Apr). *Flags. T* **171** *and similar vert designs. Multicoloured. W w* 14. *P* 14½.

709	12p. Type **171**	..	..	45	45
710	25p. R.A.F. flag and Tristar airliner		..	75	75
711	30p. N.A.S.A. emblem amd Space Shuttle *Atlantis* landing			85	85
712	65p. White Ensign and H.M.S. *Northumberland* (frigate)			1·60	1·60
709/12			*Set of 4*	3·25	3·25

172 *Solanum sodomaeum*
173 Queen Elizabeth II

(Des I. Loe. Litho Questa)

1997 (2 June). *Wild Herbs. T* **172** *and similar horiz designs. Multicoloured. W w* 14 (*sideways*). *P* 14½.

713	30p. Type **172**	..	..	90	1·00
	a. Horiz strip of 5. Nos. 713/17	..		4·00	
714	30p. *Ageratum conyzoides*	..		90	1·00
715	30p. *Leonurus sibiricus*	..		90	1·00
716	30p. *Cerastium vulgatum*	..		90	1·00
717	30p. *Commelina diffusa*	..		90	1·00
713/17			*Set of 5*	4·00	4·50

Nos. 713/17 were printed together, *se-tenant*, in horizontal strips of 5 with the backgrounds forming a composite design.

(Des D. Miller. Litho Questa)

1997 (20 June). *Return of Hong Kong to China. Sheet* 130×90 *mm containing design as No.* 692, *but with* "1997" *imprint date. W w* 14 (*inverted*). *P* 13½×13.

MS718	£1 Blue-faced Booby	..	..	2·00	2·10

(Des N. Shewring (No. **MS**725), D. Miller (others). Litho Questa (No. **MS**725), B.D.T. (others))

1997 (10 July). *Golden Wedding of Queen Elizabeth and Prince Philip. T* **173** *and similar vert designs. Multicoloured. W w* 16. *P* 13½.

719	20p. Type **173**	..	..	70	80
	a. Horiz pair. Nos. 719/20		..	1·40	1·60
720	20p. Prince Philip on horseback	..		70	80
721	25p. Queen Elizabeth with polo pony	..		80	90
	a. Horiz pair. Nos. 721/2		..	1·60	1·75
722	25p. Prince Philip in Montserrat	..		80	90
723	30p. Queen Elizabeth and Prince Philip	..		90	1·00
	a. Horiz pair. Nos. 723/4		..	1·75	2·00
724	30p. Prince William and Prince Harry on horseback			90	1·00
719/24			*Set of 6*	4·25	4·75
MS725	110×70 mm. $1·50, Queen Elizabeth and Prince Philip in landau (*horiz*). W w 14 (*sideways*). P 14×14½			3·50	3·50

Nos. 719/20, 721/2 and 723/4 were each printed together, *se-tenant*, in horizontal pairs throughout the sheets with the backgrounds forming composite designs.

(Des N. Arlott. Litho Walsall)

1997 (1 Sept). *Birds and their Young. Designs as Nos.* 683 *and* 687, *but smaller, size* 20×24 *mm. W w* 14 (*sideways*). *P* 14.

726	15p. Common Waxbill	..	..	30	35
	a. Booklet pane. Nos. 726/7, each ×2			2·00	
727	35p. Yellow Canary	..	..	70	75

Nos. 726/7 were only issued in £1 stamp booklets with the vertical edges of the booklet pane imperforate so that they exist imperforate at left or right.

174 Black Marlin
175 Interior of St. Mary's Church

(Des R. Watton. Litho Walsall)

1997 (3 Sept). *Gamefish. T* **174** *and similar horiz designs. Multicoloured. W w* 16 (*sideways*). *P* 14×14½.

728	12p. Type **174**	..	..	40	40
729	20p. Atlantic Sailfish	..	..	65	65
730	25p. Swordfish	..	..	75	75
731	30p. Wahoo	..	..	85	85
732	£1 Yellowfin Tuna	..	..	2·25	2·25
728/32			*Set of 5*	4·50	4·50

(Des G. Vasarhelyi. Litho Walsall)

1997 (1 Oct). *Christmas. T* **175** *and similar vert designs. W w* 16. *P* 14.

733	15p. Type **175**	..	..	45	45
734	35p. Falklands memorial window showing Virgin and Child			85	85
735	40p. Falklands memorial window showing Archangel			95	1·10
736	50p. Pair of stained glass windows	..		1·25	1·40
733/6			*Set of 4*	3·25	3·50

176 *Cactoblastis cactorum* (caterpillar and moth)
177 Diana, Princess of Wales, 1985

(Des I. Loe. Litho B.D.T.)

1998 (10 Feb). *Biological Control using Insects. T* **176** *and similar vert designs. W w* 14. *P* 14.

737	15p. Type **176**	..	..	50	50
738	25p. *Teleonemia scrupulosa* (lace-bug)			90	90
739	40p. *Neltumius arizonensis* (beetle)	..		1·00	1·00
740	50p. *Algarobius prosopis* (beetle)	..		1·25	1·25
737/40			*Set of 4*	3·25	3·25

(Des D. Miller. Litho Questa)

1998 (31 Mar). *Diana, Princess of Wales Commemoration. Sheet,* 145×70 *mm, containing T* **177** *and similar vert designs. Multicoloured. W w* 14 (*sideways*). *P* 14½×14.

MS741	35p. Type **177**; 35p. Wearing yellow blouse, 1992; 35p. Wearing grey jacket, 1984; 35p. Carrying bouquets (*sold at* £1·40 + 20p. *charity premium*)			3·75	3·75

178 Fairey Fawn
179 Barn Swallow

(Des A. Theobald. Litho Questa)

1998 (1 Apr). *80th Anniv of Royal Air Force. T* **178** *and similar horiz designs. Multicoloured. W w* 16 (*sideways*). *P* 14.

742	15p. Type **178**	..	..	65	65
743	35p. Vickers Vernon	..	..	1·25	1·25
744	40p. Supermarine Spitfire F.22	..		1·40	1·40
745	50p. Bristol Britannia C.2	..		1·60	1·60
742/5			*Set of 4*	4·50	4·50
MS746	110×77 mm. 50p. Blackburn Kangaroo; 50p. S.E.5a; 50p. Curtiss Kittyhawk III; 50p. Boeing Fortress II			4·75	4·75

(Des N. Arlott. Litho Walsall)

1998 (15 June). *Migratory Birds. T* **179** *and similar vert designs. Multicoloured. W w* 14. *P* 14.

747	15p. Type **179**	..	..	60	60
748	25p. House Martin	..	..	80	85
749	35p. Cattle Egret	..	..	1·00	1·10

750	40p. Common Swift	..	..	1·00	1·25
751	50p. Allen's Gallinule	..	..	1·10	1·40
747/51			*Set of 4*	4·00	4·75

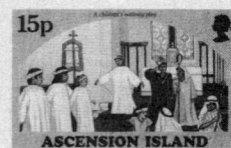

180 Cricket
181 Children in Nativity Play

(Des S. Noon. Litho Walsall)

1998 (17 Aug). *Sporting Activities. T* **180** *and similar vert designs. Multicoloured. W w* 14. *P* 14.

752	15p. Type **180**	..	..	75	75
753	35p. Golf	..	..	1·25	1·25
754	40p. Football	..	..	1·25	1·25
755	50p. Shooting	..	..	1·25	1·25
752/5			*Set of 4*	4·00	4·00

(Des N. Shewring. Litho Questa)

1998 (1 Oct). *Christmas. T* **181** *and similar horiz designs. Multicoloured. W w* 14 (*sideways*). *P* 14.

756	15p. Type **181**	..	..	45	40
757	35p. Santa Claus arriving on Ascension	..	1·00	1·00
758	40p. Santa Claus on carnival float	..	1·10	1·10
759	50p. Carol singers	..	..	1·10	1·25
756/9			*Set of 4*	3·25	3·25

182 Curtiss C-46 Commando

(Des A. Theobald. Litho Questa)

1999 (20 Jan). *Aircraft. T* **182** *and similar horiz designs. Multicoloured. W w* 14 (*sideways*). *P* 14.

760	15p. Type **182**	..	..	50	50
761	35p. Douglas C-47 Dakota	..		85	85
762	40p. Douglas C-54 Skymaster	..		95	95
763	50p. Consolidated Liberator Mk. V		1·25	1·25
760/3			*Set of 4*	3·25	3·25
MS764	120×85 mm. £1·50, Consolidated Liberator LB-30			3·75	4·00

No. **MS**764 also commemorates the 125th birth anniversary of Sir Winston Churchill.

183 *Glengorm Castle* (mail ship), 1929
184 Pair of White Terns ("Fairy Terns")

(Des J. Batchelor. Litho Questa)

1999 (5 Mar). *"Australia '99" World Stamp Exhibition, Melbourne. Ships. T* **183** *and similar horiz designs. Multicoloured. W w* 14 (*sideways*). *P* 15×14.

765	15p. Type **183**	..	..	50	50
766	35p. *Gloucester Castle* (mail ship), 1930	..	90	90
767	40p. *Durham Castle* (mail ship), 1930	..	95	95
768	50p. *Garth Castle* (mail ship), 1930	..	1·25	1·25
765/8			*Set of 4*	3·25	3·25
MS769	121×82 mm. £1 H.M.S. *Endeavour* (Cook)			2·50	2·75

(Des Doreen McGuiness. Litho Questa)

1999 (27 Apr). *Endangered Species. White Tern* ("*Fairy Tern*"). *T* **184** *and similar vert designs. Multicoloured. W w* 16. *P* 14½.

770	10p. Type **184**	..	..	30	30
	a. Strip of 4. Nos. 770/3	..		1·10	
771	10p. On branch	..	..	30	30
772	10p. Adult and fledgling	..	..	30	30
773	10p. In flight	..	..	30	30
770/3			*Set of 4*	1·10	1·10

Nos. 770/3 were printed in sheets of individual designs, or in sheets of 16 containing the four designs *se-tenant*, both horizontally and vertically.

185 Prince Edward and Miss Sophie Rhys-Jones

186 Command and Service Modules

(Des D. Miller. Litho Walsall)

1999 (19 June). *Royal Wedding.* T **185** *and similar vert design. Multicoloured.* W w **16**. *P* 14.
774	50p. Type **185**	..	1·25	1·25
775	£1 Engagement photograph	..	2·25	2·25

(Des N. Shewring. Litho Walsall)

1999 (20 July). *30th Anniv of First Manned Landing on Moon.* T **186** *and similar multicoloured designs.* W w **16**. *P* 14×13½.
776	15p. Type **186**	50	50
777	35p. Moon from "Apollo 11"	90	90
778	40p. Devil's Ashpit Tracking Station and command module	95	95
779	50p. Lunar module leaving Moon ..	1·25	1·25
776/9	*Set of* 4	3·25	3·25
MS780	90×80 mm. £1.50, Earth as seen from Moon (*circular, 40 mm diam*). *Wmk sideways.* P 14 ..	3·50	3·75

187 King George VI, Queen Elizabeth and Prime Minister Winston Churchill, 1940

188 Babies with Toys

(Des D. Miller. Litho Cartor)

1999 (20 Aug). *"Queen Elizabeth the Queen Mother's Century".* T **187** *and similar horiz designs. Multicoloured (except* £1.50) W w **16** (*sideways*). *P* 13½.
781	15p. Type **187**	50	50
782	35p. With Prince Charles at Coronation, 1953	90	90
783	40p. On her 88th Birthday, 1988 ..	95	95
784	50p. With Guards' drummers, 1988	1·25	1·25
781/4	*Set of* 4	3·25	3·25
MS785	145×70 mm. £1.50, Lady Elizabeth Bowes-Lyon, and *Titanic* (liner) (*black*)	3·50	3·75

(Des A. Robinson. Litho Questa)

1999 (6 Oct). *Christmas.* T **188** *and similar square designs. Multicoloured.* W w **16**. *P* 14.
786	15p. Type **188**	50	50
787	35p. Children dressed as clowns ..	90	90
788	40p. Getting ready for bed	95	95
789	50p. Children dressed as pirates ..	1·25	1·25
786/9	*Set of* 4	3·25	3·25

189 *Anglia* (cable ship), 1900

(Litho Cartor)

1999 (13 Dec). *Centenary of Cable & Wireless Communications plc on Ascension.* T **189** *and similar horiz designs.* W w **14** (*sideways*). *P* 13½.
790	15p. black, reddish brown and bistre-brown	30	30
791	35p. black, reddish brown and bistre-brown	70	75
792	40p. multicoloured	80	85
793	50p. black, reddish brown and bistre-brown	1·00	1·10
790/3	*Set of* 4	2·75	3·00
MS794	105×90 mm. £1.50, multicoloured	3·00	3·25

Designs:—35p. *Cambria* (cable ship), 1910; 40p. Cable network map; 50p. *Colonia* (cable ship), 1910; £1.50, *Seine* (cable ship), 1899.

STAMP BOOKLETS

1963 (23 May). *Buff cover. Stitched.*
SB1	10s.6d. booklet containing 1d., 1½d., 2d., 3d., 6d. and 1s. 6d. (Nos. 70/3, 75, 79), each in block of 4	70·00	

1971 (15 Feb). *White cover. Stitched.*
SB2	44p. booklet containing ½p., 1p., 1½p., 2p., 2½p. and 3½p. (Nos 135/40), each in block of 4	17·00
	a. "5/71" imprint on back cover ..	30·00

1981 (9 Nov)–**84**. *Printed cover, 104×58 mm, showing Ascension landscape.*
SB3	£1.20, booklet containing 2p., 3p., 10p. and 15p. (Nos. 283A/4A, 288A, 290A), each in block of 4 (black and pink cover stapled at left)	12·00
	a. Black and lemon cover stapled at right (4.84)	12·00

1982 (15 June). *Blue, red and brown cover, 101×60 mm, showing World War II aircraft. A. Cover stapled at left and inscriptions printed in brown. B. Cover stapled at right and inscriptions printed in blue.*
SB4	60p. booklet containing 5p. and 10p. (Nos. 318/19), each in block of 4 (inscr in brown. Stapled at left)..	6·00
	a. Inscr in blue. Stapled at right ..	6·00

1989 (17 Nov). *Blackish olive and deep brown cover, 54×41 mm, showing turtle and outline map of Ascension. Panes attached by selvedge.*
SB5	£1 booklet containing pane of 6 (No. 510a) ..	2·75
SB6	£1 booklet containing pane of 4 (No. 511a) ..	2·75

1989 (17 Nov). *As Nos. SB5/6, but with "Expo 89" logo printed on cover in black.*
SB7	£1 booklet containing pane of 6 (No. 510a) ..	5·50
SB8	£1 booklet containing pane of 4 (No. 511a) ..	5·50

1997 (1 Sept). *Cover as Nos. SB5/6. Pane attached by selvedge.*
SB9	£1 booklet containing pane of 4 (No. 726a) ..	2·00

POSTAGE DUE STAMPS

D 1 Outline Map of Ascension

(Des L. Curtis. Litho Questa)

1986 (9 June). W w **16**. *P* 14½×14.
D1	D 1	1p. deep brown and cinnamon ..	..	15	20
D2		2p. deep brown and bright orange	..	15	20
D3		5p. deep brown and orange-vermilion ..		15	20
D4		7p. black and bright reddish violet	..	20	30
D5		10p. black and violet-blue	..	25	35
D6		25p. black and pale emerald	..	65	75
D1/6	.. ..	*Set of* 6		1·40	1·75

Australia

The Australian colonies of New South Wales, Queensland, South Australia, Tasmania, Victoria and Western Australia produced their own issues before federation in 1901. Stamps inscribed for the individual states continued in use after federation until the end of December 1912.

NEW SOUTH WALES

PRICES FOR STAMPS ON COVER

Nos. 1/83	*from* ×2
Nos. 84/110	*from* ×3
No. 110b	*from* ×10
Nos. 111/13	*from* × 2
No. 114	—
Nos. 115/24	*from* × 2
Nos. 125/6	—
Nos. 127/53	*from* × 2
Nos. 154/70	*from* × 3
Nos. 171/2	—
No. 173	*from* × 2
Nos. 174/81	—
Nos. 186/202	*from* × 2
Nos. 203/6	*from* × 10
Nos. 207/21	*from* × 5
Nos. 222/39	*from* × 6
Nos. 240/1	*from* × 2
Nos. 241a/3	*from* × 10
Nos. 244/52	—
Nos. 253/73	*from* × 10
Nos. 274/80	—
Nos. 281/4	*from* × 15
Nos. 285/7	*from* × 2
Nos. 287c/d	*from* × 2
Nos. 288/97	*from* × 10
Nos. 298/312	*from* × 12
Nos. 313/28	*from* × 10
No. 329	—
Nos. 330/45	*from* × 12
No. 346	—
Nos. 347/60	*from* × 12
No. O1	—
Nos. O2/12	*from* × 4
Nos. O13/18	—
Nos. O19/34	*from* × 20
Nos. O35/8	—
Nos. O39/47	*from* × 40
Nos. O48/53	—
Nos. O54/8	*from* × 20
No. O59	—
Nos. D1/7	*from* × 50
Nos. D8/10	—
Nos. D11/15	*from* × 50

EMBOSSED LETTER SHEETS AND ENVELOPES. From 1 November 1838 the Sydney G.P.O. supplied envelopes and letter sheets pre-stamped with an albino embossing, as illustrated, at 1½d. each or 1s. 3d. per dozen. From January 1841 the price was reduced to 1s. per dozen. The public were also able to present their own stationery for embossing. The circular design measures approximately 29 mm in diameter and examples are known on laid or wove paper of varying colours. Embossing continued until 1 May 1852 after which the Post Office refused to carry mail which was not franked with postage stamps. The die was used for reprints in 1870 and 1898 before it was destroyed later the same year.

PRINTERS. The early issues of New South Wales were printed on a press supervised by the Inspector of Stamps. On 1 January 1857 this responsibility passed to the Government printer who produced all subsequent issues, *unless otherwise stated.*

SPECIMEN OVERPRINTS. Those listed are from U.P.U. distributions between 1892 and 1903. Further "Specimen" overprints exist, but these were used for other purposes. From 1891 examples of some of these Specimens, together with cancelled stamps, were sold to collectors by the N.S.W. Post Office.

NEW SOUTH WALES USED IN NEW CALEDONIA. From October 1859 mail for Europe from New Caledonia was routed via Sydney and franked with New South Wales stamps in combination with local issues. Such N.S.W. stamps were cancelled on arrival in Sydney.

1   2

(Eng Robert Clayton, Sydney)

1850 (1 Jan). *T* **1.** *Plate I. No clouds.* (a) *Soft yellowish paper.*

1	1d. crimson-lake	..	£4250	£450
2	1d. carmine	..	£4000	£400
3	1d. reddish rose	..	£3750	£375
4	1d. brownish red	..	£4000	£400

(b) *Hard bluish paper*

5	1d. pale red	..	£3750	£375
6	1d. dull lake	..	£4000	£400

1850 (Aug). *T* **2.** *Plate I, re-engraved by H. C. Jervis, commonly termed Plate II. With clouds.* (a) *Hard toned white to yellowish paper.*

7	1d. vermilion	..	£2500	£300
8	1d. dull carmine	..	£2500	£300
	a. No trees on hill (R.2/2)	..	£4500	£475
	b. Hill unshaded (R.2/3)	..	£4500	£475
	c. Without clouds (R.3/5)	..	£4500	£475

(b) *Hard greyish or bluish paper*

9	1d. crimson-lake	..	£2500	£300
10	1d. gooseberry-red	..	£3000	£450
11	1d. dull carmine	..	£2250	£275
12	1d. brownish red	..	£2250	£275
	a. No trees on hill (R.2/2)	..	£4500	£475
	b. Hill unshaded (R.2/3)	..	£4500	£475
	c. Without clouds (R.3/5)	..	£4500	£475

(c) *Laid paper*

13	1d. carmine	..	£4000	£475
14	1d. vermilion	..	£4500	£450
	a. No trees on hill (R.2/2)	..	—	£800
	b. Hill unshaded (R.2/3)	..	—	£800
	c. Without clouds (R.3/5)	..	—	£800

The varieties quoted with the letters "a", "b", "c" of course exist in each shade; the prices quoted are for the commonest shade, and the same applies to the following portions of this list.
Nos. 1/14 were printed in sheets of 25 (5×5).

LAID PAPER. Nos. 13/14, 34/5, 38 and 43d/e can be found showing parts of the papermaker's watermark (T. H. SAUNDERS 1847 in double-lined capitals and the figure of Britannia seated in an oval beneath a crown).

3   4   A (Pl I)

Illustrations A, B, C, and D are sketches of the lower part of the inner circular frame, showing the characteristic variations of each plate.

(Eng John Carmichael)

1850 (1 Jan). *Plate I. Vertical-lined background. T* **3.**

(a) *Early impressions, full details of clouds, etc.*

15	2d. greyish blue	..	£4500	£400
16	2d. deep blue	..	—	£450
	a. Double lines on bale (R.2/7)	..	—	£650

(b) *Intermediate impressions*

16b	2d. greyish blue	..	£3000	£275
16c	2d. deep blue	..	£3250	£325

(c) *Later impressions, clouds, etc., mostly gone, T* **4**

17	2d. blue	..	£2250	£150
18	2d. dull blue	..	£1800	£140

(d) *Stamps in the lower row partially retouched* (end Jan)

19	2d. blue	..	£3000	£275
20	2d. greyish blue	..	£2750	£225

5   B (Pl II)   C (Pl III)

(Plate entirely re-engraved by H. C. Jervis)

1850 (Apr). *T* **5.** *Plate II. Horizontal-lined background. Bale on left side supporting the seated figure, dated. Dot in centre of the star in each corner.* (a) *Early impressions.*

21	2d. indigo	..	£3500	£275
22	2d. lilac-blue	..	—	£1000
23	2d. grey-blue	..	£3500	£225
24	2d. bright blue	..	£3500	£225
	a. Fan as in Pl III, but with shading outside (R.1/1)	..	—	£375
	b. Fan as in Pl III, but without shading, and inner circle intersects the fan (R.1/2)		—	£375
	c. Pick and shovel omitted (R.1/10)		—	£375
	d. "CREVIT" omitted (R.2/1)		—	£600
	e. No whip (R.1/4, 1/8, 2/8)		—	£300

(b) *Worn impressions*

25	2d. dull blue	..	£1800	£130

26	2d. Prussian blue	..	£1900	£170
	a. Fan as in Pl III, but with shading outside (R.1/1)		—	£300
	b. Fan as in Pl III, but without shading, and inner circle intersects the fan (R.1/2)		—	£300
	c. Pick and shovel omitted (R.1/10)		—	£300
	d. "CREVIT" omitted (R.2/1)		—	£400
	e. No whip (R.1/4, 1/8, 2/8)		£2500	£225

(c) *Bottom row retouched with dots and dashes in lower spandrels* (Aug)

27	2d. Prussian blue	..	£2750	£225
28	2d. dull blue	..	£2500	£150
	a. No whip (R.2/8)		—	£250
	b. "CREVIT" omitted (R.2/1)		—	£375

(Plate re-engraved a second time by H. C. Jervis)

1850 (Sept). *Plate III. Bale not dated and single-lined, except on No. 30c which is doubled-lined. No dots in stars.*

29	2d. ultramarine	..	£2250	£170
30	2d. deep blue	..	£2250	£170
	a. No whip (R.2/3, 2/7)		—	£250
	b. Fan with 6 segments (R. 2/8)		—	£375
	c. Double lines on bale (R. 1/7, 1/10, 1/12)		—	£225

(Plate re-engraved a third time by H. C. Jervis)

1851 (Jan). *Plate IV. Double-lined bale, and circle in centre of each star.* (a) *Hard bluish grey wove paper.*

31	2d. ultramarine	..	£2750	£160
32	2d. Prussian blue	..	£2250	£130
33	2d. bright blue	..	£2500	£150
	a. Hill not shaded (R.1/12)		—	£225
	b. Fan with 6 segments (R.2/8)		—	£225
	c. No clouds (R.2/10)		—	£225
	d. Retouch (R.2/1)		—	£300
	e. No waves (R.1/9, 2/5)		—	£190

(b) *Stout yellowish vertically laid paper*

34	2d. ultramarine	..	£2750	£170
35	2d. Prussian blue	..	£3000	£180
	a. Hill not shaded (R.1/12)		—	£250
	b. Fan with 6 segments (R.2/8)		—	£250
	c. No clouds (R.2/10)		—	£250
	d. Retouch (R.2/1)		—	£325
	e. No waves (R.1/9, 2/5)		—	£200
	f. "PENOE" (R.1/10, 2/12)		—	£250

The retouch, Nos. 33d and 35d., occurs outside the left margin line on R.2/1.

6   D (Pl V)   7

(Plate re-engraved a fourth time by H. C. Jervis)

1851 (Apr). *T* **6.** *Plate V. Pearl in fan.* (a) *Hard greyish wove paper.*

36	2d. ultramarine	..	£2500	£140
37	2d. dull blue	..	£2500	£140
	a. Pick and shovel omitted (R.2/5)		—	£250
	b. Fan with 6 segments (R.2/8)		—	£250

(b) *Stout yellowish vertically laid paper*

38	2d. dull ultramarine	..	£3750	£300
	a. Pick and shovel omitted (R.2/5)		—	£425
	b. Fan with 6 segments (R.2/8)		—	£425

Nos. 15/38 were printed in sheets of 24 (12×2), although the existence of an inter-panneau *tête-bêche* pair from Plate II indicates that the printer applied two impressions of the plate to each sheet of paper. The two panes were normally separated before issue. The original plate I was re-cut four times to form Plates II to V. An interesting variety occurs on R.1/9-11 and 2/7 in all five plates. It consists of ten loops of the engine-turning on each side of the design instead of the normal nine loops.

(Eng H. C. Jervis)

1850. *T* **7.** (a) *Soft yellowish wove paper.*

39	3d. yellow-green	..	£3000	£250
40	3d. myrtle-green	..	£10000	£1000
41	3d. emerald-green	..	£3500	£275
	a. No whip (R.4/3–4)		—	£375
	b. "SIGIIIUM" for "SIGILLUM" (R.5/3)		—	£450

(b) *Bluish to grey wove paper*

42	3d. yellow-green	..	£2500	£225
43	3d. emerald-green	..	£3000	£225
	b. No whip (R.4/3–4)		—	£300
	c. "SIGIIIUM" for "SIGILLUM" (R.5/3)		—	£375

(c) *Yellowish to bluish laid paper*

43d	3d. bright green	..	£5500	£500
43e	3d. yellowish green	..	£5000	£450
	f. No whip (R.4/3–4)		—	£650
	g. "SIGIIIUM" for "SIGILLUM" (R.5/3)		—	£750

Nos. 39/43e were printed in sheets of 25 (5×5).
A used example of No. 42 is known printed double, one albino.

8   9

(Des A. W. Manning from sketch by W. T. Levine; eng on steel by John Carmichael, Sydney)

1851 (18 Dec)–**52.** *Imperf.* (a) *Thick yellowish paper*

44	**8** 1d. carmine	..	£1800	£190
	a. No leaves right of "SOUTH" (R.1/7, 3/1)		—	£375
	b. Two leaves right of "SOUTH" (R.2/5)		—	£475
	c. "WALE" (R.1/9)		—	£475

(b) *Bluish medium wove paper* (1852)
45	8	1d. carmine	£1000	£120
46		1d. scarlet..	£1000	£120
47		1d. vermilion	£900	£100
48		1d. brick-red	£900	£100
		a. No leaves right of "SOUTH" (R.1/7, 3/1)	—	£225
		b. Two leaves right of "SOUTH" (R.2/5)	—	£300
		c. "WALE" (R.1/9)	—	£300

(c) *Thick vertically laid bluish paper* (1852?)
49	8	1d. orange-brown	£3000	£350
50		1d. claret	£3000	£375
		a. No leaves right of "SOUTH" (R.1/7, 3/1)	—	£550
		b. Two leaves right of "SOUTH" ((R.2/5)	—	£650
		c. "WALE" (R.1/9)	—	£650

Nos. 44/50 were printed in sheets of 50 (10×5).

(Eng on steel by John Carmichael)
1851 (24 July). *Plate I. Imperf.* (a) *Thick yellowish wove paper*
51	8	2d. ultramarine	£800	80·00

(b) *Fine impressions, blue to greyish medium paper*
52	8	2d. ultramarine	£750	30·00
53		2d. chalky blue	£650	30·00
54		2d. dark blue	£650	30·00
55		2d. greyish blue	£650	30·00

(c) *Worn plate, blue to greyish medium paper*
56	8	2d. ultramarine	£450	30·00
57		2d. Prussian blue	£450	30·00

(d) *Worn plate, blue wove medium paper*
58	8	2d. ultramarine	£350	30·00
59		2d. Prussian blue	£325	30·00

Nos. 51/9 were printed in sheets of 50 (10×5).

(Plate II eng H. C. Jervis)
1853 (Oct). *Plate II. Stars in corners. Imperf.*
(a) *Bluish medium to thick wove paper*
60	9	2d. deep ultramarine	£1000	£110
61		2d. indigo	£1100	80·00
		a. "WAEES" (R.3/3)	—	£375

(b) *Worn plate, hard blue wove paper*
62	9	2d. deep Prussian blue	£1000	£100
		a. "WAEES" (R.3/3)	—	£375

Nos. 60/2 were printed in sheets of 50 (10×5).

1855 (Sept). *Plate III, being Plate I (T 8) re-engraved by H. C. Jervis. Background of crossed lines. Imperf.*
(a) *Medium bluish wove paper*
63		2d. Prussian blue	£475	55·00
		a. "WALES" partly covered with wavy lines (R.1/3)	—	£190

(b) *Stout white wove paper*
64		2d. Prussian blue	£475	55·00
		a. "WALES" partly covered with wavy lines (R.1/3)	—	£190

Nos. 63/4 were printed in sheets of 50 (10×5).

(Eng John Carmichael)
1852 (3 Dec). *Imperf.* (a) *Medium greyish blue wove paper*
65	8	3d. deep green	£1600	£200
66		3d. green	£1300	£140
67		3d. dull yellow-green	£1200	£100
		a. "WAEES" with centre bar of first "E" missing (R.4/7)	—	£350

(b) *Thick blue wove paper*
69	8	3d. emerald-green	£1600	£200
71		3d. blue-green	£1600	£200
		a. "WAEES" with centre bar of first "E" missing (R.4/7)	—	£550

Nos. 65/71 were printed in sheets of 50 (10×5).

1852 (Apr). *Fine background. Imperf.*
(a) *Medium white wove paper*
72	8	6d. vandyke-brown	—	£900
		a. "WALLS"	—	£1600

(b) *Medium bluish grey wove paper*
73	8	6d. vandyke-brown	£1700	£250
74		6d. yellow-brown	£1800	£275
75		6d. chocolate-brown	£1700	£250
76		6d. grey-brown	£1600	£250
		a. "WALLS" (R.2/3)	—	£550

Examples of the 6d. in vandyke-brown on thick yellowish paper are proofs.

1853 (June). *Plate I re-engraved by H. C. Jervis. Coarse background. Imperf.*
77		6d. brown	£1800	£300
78		6d. grey-brown	£1700	£300

Nos. 72/6 and 77/8 were printed in sheets of 25 (5×5).

(Eng H. C. Jervis)
1853 (May). *Medium bluish paper. Imperf.*
79	8	8d. dull yellow	£3500	£600
80		8d. orange-yellow	£3500	£600
81		8d. orange	£3750	£650
		a. No bow at back of head (R.1/9)	—	£1300
		b. No leaves right of "SOUTH" (R.3/1)	—	£1300
		c. No lines in spandrel (R.2/2, 3/2, 4/2)	—	£800

Nos. 79/81 were issued in sheets of 50 (10×5).

NOTE. All watermarked stamps from No. 82 to No. 172 have double-lined figures, as T 10.

1854 (Feb). *Wmk "1", T 10. Yellowish wove paper. Imperf.*
82	8	1d. red-orange	£170	17·00
83		1d. orange-vermilion	£170	17·00
		a. No leaves right of "SOUTH" (R.1/7, 3/1)	£350	85·00
		b. Two leaves right of "SOUTH" (R.2/5)	£475	£120
		c. "WALE" (R.1/9)	£475	£120

Nos. 82/3 were printed in sheets of 50 (10×5).

1854 (Jan). *Plate III. Wmk "2". Imperf.*
84		2d. ultramarine	£110	10·00
85		2d. Prussian blue	£110	10·00
86		2d. chalky blue	£110	8·00
		a. "WALES" partly covered by wavy lines (R.1/3)	£425	50·00

Nos. 84/6 were printed in sheets of 50 (10×5).

1854 (Mar). *Wmk "3". Imperf.*
87	8	3d. yellow-green	£200	27·00
		a. "WAEES" with centre bar of first "E" missing (R. 4/7)	—	£120
		b. Error. Wmk "2"	£3000	£1500

No. 87 was printed in sheets of 50 (10×5).

(Eng John Carmichael)
1856 (1 Jan). *For Registered Letters. T 13. No wmk. Imperf. Soft medium yellowish paper.*
88		(6d.) vermilion and Prussian blue	£700	£150
		a. Frame printed on back..	£2500	£2000
89		(6d.) salmon and indigo	£700	£170
90		(6d.) orange and Prussian blue	£700	£200
91		(6d.) orange and indigo	£700	£180

1859 (Apr)—**60.** *Hard medium bluish wove paper, with manufacturer's wmk in sans-serif, double-lined capitals across sheet and only showing portions of letters on a few stamps in a sheet.*
(a) *Imperf.*
92		(6d.) orange and Prussian blue	£800	£150

(b) *P 12* (2.60)
93		(6d.) orange and Prussian blue	£350	45·00
94		(6d.) orange and indigo	£325	50·00

1860 (Feb)—**62.** *Coarse yellowish wove paper having the manufacturer's wmk in Roman capitals.* (a) *P 12.*
95		(6d.) rose-red and Prussian blue	£250	35·00
96		(6d.) rose-red and indigo	£325	80·00
97		(6d.) salmon and indigo		

(b) *P 13* (1862)
98		(6d.) rose-red and Prussian blue	£250	50·00

1863 (May). *Yellowish wove paper. Wmk "6". P 13.*
99		(6d.) rose-red and Prussian blue	95·00	16·00
100		(6d.) rose-red and indigo	£150	20·00
101		(6d.) rose-red and pale blue	75·00	15·00
		a. Double impression of frame	—	£500

(T 14/21 and 24 printed by the New South Wales Govt Ptg Dept from plates engraved by Perkins, Bacon & Co)

Two plates of the 2d. and 6d. were used. On Plate II of the 2d. the stamps are wider apart and more regularly spaced than on Plate I.

1856 (6 Apr). *Wmk "1". Imperf.*
102	14	1d. orange-vermilion	£150	22·00
		a. Error. Wmk "2"		
103		1d. carmine-vermilion	£150	22·00
104		1d. orange-red	£150	22·00
		a. Printed on both sides	£1400	£1400

1856 (7 Jan)—**58.** *Plate I. Wmk "2". Imperf.*
105	14	2d. deep turquoise-blue	£140	8·00
106		2d. ultramarine	£130	8·00
107		2d. blue	£130	8·00
		a. Major retouch (1858)	£1800	£450
		b. Error. Wmk "1"	—	£4000
		c. Wmk "5" (3.57)	£450	60·00
		d. Error. Wmk "8"		
108		2d. pale blue	£130	8·00

The 2d. Plate I was retouched, on a total of ten positions, several times.
No. 107c comes from a printing made when supplies of the "2" paper were unavailable.

1859 (3 Aug). *Lithographic transfer of Plate I.*
110	14	2d. pale blue	—	£750
		a. Retouched	—	£2500

1860 (Jan). *Plate II. Recess. Stamps printed wider apart and with a white patch between the "A" of "WALES" and the back of the Queen's head.*
110b	14	2d. blue	£500	50·00

No. 110b was principally issued to post offices in Queensland.

1856 (10 Oct). *Wmk "3". Imperf.*
111	14	3d. yellow-green	£800	80·00
112		3d. bluish green	£850	80·00
113		3d. dull green	£850	80·00
		a. Error, Wmk "2"	—	£3000

In the 3d. the value is in block letters on a white ground.

PRICES OF SETS

Set prices are given for many issues, generally those containing three stamps or more. Definitive sets include one of each value or major colour change, but do not cover different perforations, die types or minor shades. Where a choice is possible the set prices are based on the cheapest versions of the stamps included in the listings.

(6d. and 1s. des E. H. Corbould after sketches by T. W. Levinge)
1855 (1 Dec). *Wmk "5". Imperf.*
114	15	5d. dull green	£1000	£550

1854 (1 Feb)—**59.** *Wmk "6". Imperf.*
115	17	6d. deep slate	£500	35·00
		a. Wmk sideways	†	£750
116		6d. greenish grey	£400	35·00
117		6d. slate-green	£400	35·00
		a. Printed both sides		
118		6d. bluish grey	£450	55·00
119		6d. fawn	£500	95·00
		a. Wmk "8" (15.8.59)	£1600	£110
120		6d. grey	£450	55·00
121		6d. olive-grey	£450	35·00
122		6d. greyish brown	£450	35·00
		a. Wmk "8" (15.8.59)	£1600	£110
		ab. Wmk sideways	—	£350

Nos. 119a and 122a come from a printing made when supplies of the "6" paper were unavailable.
Plate proofs of the 6d. in red-brown on unwatermarked paper exist handstamped "CANCELLED" in oval of bars (see note on Perkins Bacon "CANCELLED" in Catalogue Introduction) (Price £4000).

1855 (1 Dec). *Wmk "8". Imperf.*
125	19	8d. golden yellow	£4000	£850
126		8d. dull yellow-orange	£3500	£800

1854 (Feb)—**57.** *Wmk "12". Imperf.*
127	21	1s. rosy vermilion	£750	65·00
		a. Wmk "8" (20.6.57)	£2000	£180
128		1s. pale red	£750	65·00
129		1s. brownish red	£800	75·00

No. 127a comes from a printing made when supplies of the "12" paper were unavailable.
Plate proofs of the 1s. in deep blue on unwatermarked paper exist handstamped "CANCELLED" in oval of bars (Price £4000).

1860 (14 Feb)—**63.** *Wmk double-lined figure of value. P 12.*
131	14	1d. orange-red	£170	16·00
		ab Imperf between (pair)		
		b. Double impression		
132		1d. scarlet	£100	16·00
133		2d. pale blue (Pl I)	£500	£140
		a. Retouched	—	£1300
134		2d. greenish blue (Pl II)	90·00	10·00
136		2d. Prussian blue (Pl II)	90·00	10·00
		a. Error. Wmk "1"	—	£2750
		b. Retouched (shades)	—	£400
137		2d. Prussian blue (Pl I) (3.61)	£110	11·00
138		2d. dull blue (Pl I)	£100	10·00
139		3d. yellow-green (1860)	£1000	55·00
140		3d. blue-green	£550	42·00
141	15	5d. dull green (1863)	£100	35·00
142		5d. yellowish green (1863)	£100	35·00
143	17	6d. grey-brown	£275	45·00
144		6d. olive-brown	£275	55·00
145		6d. greenish grey	£350	45·00
146		6d. fawn	£325	65·00
147		6d. mauve	£300	35·00
148		6d. violet	£275	16·00
		a. Imperf between (pair)		
149	19	8d. lemon-yellow	—	£1400
150		8d. orange	£2250	£650
151		8d. red-orange	£2250	£650
152	21	1s. brownish red	£450	48·00
153		1s. rose-carmine	£450	48·00
		a. Imperf between (pair)		

No. 133 was made by perforating a small remaining stock of No. 108. Nos. 137/8 were printed from the original plate after its return from London, where it had been repaired.

1862–72. *Wmk double-lined figure of value.* (a) *P 13.*
154	14	1d. scarlet (1862)	60·00	8·00
155		1d. dull red	60·00	8·00
156		3d. blue-green (12.62)	48·00	11·00
157		3d. yellow-green	55·00	8·50
		a. Wmk "6" (7.72)	£100	12·00
158		3d. dull green	55·00	8·00
		a. Wmk "6" (7.72)	£100	15·00
160	15	5d. bluish green (12.63)	42·00	15·00
161		5d. bright yellow-green (8.65)	75·00	30·00
162		5d. sea-green (1866)	45·00	17·00
162a		5d. dark bluish green (11.70)	32·00	17·00
163	17	6d. reddish purple (Pl I) (7.62)	85·00	5·50
164		6d. mauve	85·00	5·50
165		6d. purple (Pl II) (1864)	60·00	4·50
		a. Wmk "5" (7.66)	£350	25·00
		b. Wmk "12" (12.66 and 1868)	£275	20·00
166		6d. violet	60·00	6·00
167		6d. aniline mauve	£900	£120
167a	19	8d. red-orange	£150	55·00
167b		8d. yellow-orange	£150	40·00
167c		8d. bright yellow	£150	40·00
168	21	1s. rose-carmine	75·00	7·50
169		1s. carmine	75·00	8·00
170		1s. crimson-lake	75·00	8·00

(b) Perf compound 12×13

171	14	1d. scarlet	..	—	£1700
172		2d. dull blue (1.62)	..	£2000	£180

Nos. 157a, 158a and 165a/b come from printings made when supplies of paper with the correct face value were unavailable.

23

1864 (June). *W* 23. *P* 13.

173	14	1d. pale red	..	40·00	14·00

24   **25**

(Des E. H. Corbould, R.I.)

1861–88. *W* 25. *Various perfs.*

174	24	5s. dull violet, p. 12 (1861)	..	£1000	£325
		a. Perf 13 (1861)		£160	28·00
175		5s. royal purple, p 13 (1872)	..	£275	45·00
176		5s. deep rose-lilac, p 13 (1875)		95·00	28·00
177		5s. deep purple, p 13 (1880)	..	£150	40·00
		a. Perf 10 (1882)		£150	40·00
178		5s. rose-lilac, p 10 (1883)	..	£110	40·00
179		5s. purple, p 12 (1885) ..		—	45·00
		a. Perf 10 × 12 (1885)		—	£120
180		5s. reddish purple, p 10 (1886)..		£110	40·00
		a. Perf 12 × 10 (1887)	..	£225	45·00
181		5s. rose-lilac, p 11 (1888)	..	—	£120

This value was replaced by Nos. 261, etc. in 1888 but reissued in 1897, *see* Nos. 297c/e.

26   **28**   **29**

(Printed by De La Rue & Co, Ltd, London and perf at Somerset House, London)

1862–65. *Surfaced paper. P* 14. (i) *W* 23.

186	26	1d. dull red (Pl I) (4.64)	..	85·00	32·00

(ii) *No wmk*

187	26	1d. dull red (Pl II) (1.65)	..	65·00	30·00
188	28	2d. pale blue (3.62)	..	70·00	30·00

(Printed from the De La Rue plates in the Colony)

1862 (12 Apr). *Wmk double-lined* "2". *P* 13.

189	28	2d. blue	..	50·00	7·00
		a. Perf 12	..	£130	30·00
		b. Perf 12 × 13	..	£400	

1864–65. *W* 23. *P* 13.

190	26	1d. dark red-brown (Pl I)	..	80·00	16·00
191		1d. brownish red (Pl II) ..		20·00	1·50
		a. Imperf between (horiz pair)	..	†	£500
192		1d. brick-red (Pl II)	..	20·00	1·50
		b. Highly surfaced paper (1865)		£200	
194	28	2d. pale blue	..	£120	3·50

Plates I and II were made from the same die; they can only be distinguished by the colour or by the marginal inscription.

1865–66. *Thin wove paper. No wmk. P* 13.

195	26	1d. brick-red	..	95·00	16·00
196		1d. brownish red	..	95·00	16·00
197	28	2d. pale blue	..	45·00	3·00

1863–69. *W* 29. *P* 13.

198	26	1d. pale red (3.69)	..	80·00	12·00
199	28	2d. pale blue	..	11·00	50
		a. Perf 12			
200		2d. cobalt-blue	..	11·00	50
201		2d. Prussian blue	..	22·00	3·50

1862 (Sept). *Wmk double-lined* "5". *P* 13.

202	28	2d. dull blue	..	60·00	8·50

32   **34**

33   **35**

1867 (Sept)–**93.** *W* 33 *and* 35.

203	32	4d. red-brown, p 13	..	42·00	3·00
204		4d. pale red-brown, p 13		42·00	3·00
205	34	10d. lilac, p 13 (Optd S. £25)	..	12·00	3·00
		a. Imperf between (pair)	..	£450	
206		10d. lilac, p 11 (1893) ..		13·00	3·00
		a. Perf 10		15·00	4·50
		b. Perf 10 and 11, compound ..		20·00	7·50
		c. Perf 12 × 11	..	£110	15·00

36   **37**   **38**

NINEPENCE

(39)

From 1871 to 1903 the 9d. is formed from the 10d. by a *black* surch. (T **39**), 15 mm long on Nos. 219 to 220h, and 13½ mm long on subsequent issues.

1871–1902. *W* 36.

207	26	1d. dull red, p 13 (8.71)	..	5·50	30
		a. Imperf vert (horiz pair)			
208		1d. salmon, p 13 (1878)	..	5·50	30
		a. Perf 10 (6.80)		£250	30·00
		b. Perf 10×13 (6.80)	..	50·00	5·00
		ba. Perf 13×10		16·00	30
		c. Scarlet. Perf 10 (6.80)		—	£180
209	28	2d. Prussian-blue, p 13 (11.71)		7·50	30
		a. Perf 11×12, comb (11.84)		£250	40·00
		b. Imperf vert (horiz pair)		—	£500
210		2d. pale blue, p 13 (1876)	..	7·50	30
		aa. "TWO PENCE" double impression at right		—	30·00
		a. Perf 10 (6.80)		£250	22·00
		b. Perf 10×13 (6.80)		£100	15·00
		ba. Perf 13×10		7·50	30
		c. Surfaced paper. Perf 13			
211	14	3d. yellow-green, p 13 (3.74)	..	18·00	2·40
		a. Perf 10 (6.80)		65·00	5·50
		b. Perf 11 (1902)		£150	£150
		c. Perf 12 (5.85)	..	—	£150
		d. Perf 10×12 (5.85)		£150	32·00
		e. Perf 11×12 (1902)		£120	32·00
212		3d bright green, p 10 (6.80)		£120	11·00
		a. Perf 13×10 (6.80)	..	£110	15·00
		b. Perf 13			
213	32	4d. pale red-brown, p 13 (8.77)		55·00	8·00
214		4d. red-brown, p 13	..	55·00	6·00
		a. Perf 10 (6.80)		£180	50·00
		b. Perf 10×13 (6.80)		£100	20·00
		c. Perf 13×10		75·00	3·50
215	15	5d. bluish green, p 10 (8.84)	..	15·00	8·00
		a. Perf 12 (5.85)		£250	£100
		b. Perf 10×13			
		c. Perf 10×12 (5.85)		£120	40·00
216	37	6d. bright mauve, p 13 (1.72)	..	42·00	1·00
		a. Imperf between (horiz pair)		—	£500
217		6d. pale lilac, p 13 (1878)	..	45·00	1·00
		a. Perf 10 (6.80)		£180	12·00
		b. Perf 10×13 (6.80)		80·00	15·00
		ba. Perf 13×10		55·00	1·00
		c. Imperf between (horiz pair). Perf 13×10		—	£500
218	19	8d. yellow, p 13 (3.77)	..	£100	17·00
		a. Perf 10 (6.80)		£250	24·00
		b. Perf 13×10 (6.80)		£170	22·00
219	34	9d. on 10d. pale red-brown, p 13 (8.71)		20·00	4·50
220		9d. on 10d. red-brown, p 13 (1878)		20·00	6·00
		a. Perf 10 (6.80)		12·00	4·50
		b. Perf 12 (5.85)		12·00	4·50
		c. Perf 11 (12.85)	..	27·00	7·00
		d. Perf 12×10 (5.85)		£250	£160
		e. Perf 10×11 or 11×10 (12.85)		42·00	9·00
		f. Perf 12×11 (12.85)		14·00	5·00
		g. Perf 12×11, comb (1.84) (Optd S. £25)		14·00	5·50
		h. In black and blue. Perf 11 (12.85)		£110	
221	38	1s. black, p 13 (4.76)	..	80·00	2·75
		a. Perf 10 (6.80)		£200	12·00
		b. Perf 10×13 (6.80)		£240	15·00
		ba. Perf 13×10		£170	4·75
		c. Perf 11			
		d. Imperf between (horiz pair)		—	£750

Collectors should note that the classification of perforations is that adopted by the Royal Philatelic Society, London. "Perf 12" denotes the perforation formerly called "11½, 12" and "perf 13" that formerly called "12½, 13".

1882 (Apr)–**97.** *W* 40.

222	26	1d. salmon, p 10	..	12·00	20
		a. Perf 13			
		b. Perf 13×10	..	30·00	1·50
223		1d. orange *to* scarlet, p 13	..	£800	£400
		a. Perf 10		8·00	20
		ab. Imperf between (horiz pair)			
		b. Perf 10×13		£120	6·00
		c. Perf 10×12 or 12×10 (4.85)		£250	65·00
		d. Perf 10×11 (12.85)		£450	£120
		e. Perf 12×11 (12.85)		—	£120
		f. Perf 11×12, comb (1.84)		5·50	30
		h. Perf 11 (12.85)		—	£130
224	28	2d. pale blue, p 13	..	£450	90·00
		a. Perf 10		14·00	30
		b. Perf 10×13 or 13×10		65·00	2·00
225		2d. Prussian blue, p 10		23·00	30
		a. Perf 10×13		£100	30·00
		b. Perf 12 (4.85)		—	£225
		c. Perf 11 (12.85)		—	£100
		d. Perf 12×11 (12.85)		£400	£100
		e. Perf 12×10 (4.85)		£225	65·00
		ea. Perf 12×10		£400	£100
		f. Perf 10×11 or 11×10 (12.85)		£450	£150
		g. Perf 11×12, comb (1.84)		12·00	20
226	14	3d. yellow-green, p 10 (1886)		6·00	80
		a. Wmk sideways (Optd S. £25)		—	£225
		b. Perf 10×12		£160	30·00
		ba. Perf 12×10		£120	15·00
		c. Perf 11		5·00	80
		ca. Imperf between (horiz pair)		£160	
		d. Perf 11×12 or 12×11		5·00	80
		e. Perf 12		9·00	1·00
		g. Imperf (pair)		£130	
227		3d. bluish green, p 10		5·00	80
		a. Wmk sideways		50·00	10·00
		b. Perf 11		5·00	80
		c. Perf 10×11		15·00	1·50
		ca. Perf 11×10 (12.85)		£100	30·00
		d. Perf 12×11		5·00	1·00
		e. Perf 10×12 or 12×10		30·00	3·00
228		3d. emerald-green, p 10 (1893)		55·00	7·50
		a. Wmk sideways		—	15·00
		b. Perf 10×11		£120	35·00
		c. Perf 10×12		50·00	3·00
		ca. Perf 12×10		75·00	5·00
		d. Perf 12×11		—	10·00
229	32	4d. red-brown, p 10		42·00	3·00
		a. Perf 10×12 (4.85)		—	£130
		b. Perf 11×12, comb (1.84)		50·00	1·25
230		4d. dark brown, p 10		42·00	3·00
		a. Perf 12 (4.85)		£250	£100
		b. Perf 10×12 (4.85)		£200	60·00
		ba. Perf 12×10		£300	£150
		c. Perf 11×12, comb (1.84)		28·00	1·00
231	15	5d. dull grn, p 10 (1890) (Optd S. £25)		13·00	90
		b. Perf 12×10 (4.85)		80·00	3·50
232		5d. bright green, p 10		35·00	4·50
		b. Perf 10×13 (12.85)		42·00	4·50
		ba. Perf 11×10		48·00	6·00
		c. Perf 12×10 (4.85)		£150	30·00
		ca. Perf 12×10		£100	70·00
233		5d. blue-green, p 10		9·00	90
		a. Perf 12 (4.85)		12·00	90
		ab. Wmk sideways		50·00	
		b. Perf 11 (12.85)		9·00	55
		c. Perf 10×11 (12.85)		27·00	1·60
		d. Perf 11×12 or 12×11 (12.85)		7·00	55
		da. Wmk sideways (p 11×12)		—	20·00
		e. Imperf (pair)		£200	
234	37	6d. pale lilac, p 10		42·00	1·00
		a. Perf 10×13 or 13×10		—	£300
		b. Perf 10×12 or 12×10 (4.85)		45·00	1·50
235		6d. mauve, p 10		42·00	1·00
		a. Perf 12 (4.85)		80·00	10·00
		b. Perf 11 (12.85)		80·00	8·00
		c. Perf 12×10 (4.85)		50·00	4·50
		ca. Perf 12×10		42·00	2·00
		cb. Imperf between (horiz pair)		—	£650
		d. Perf 11×12 (12.85)		80·00	12·00
		da. Perf 12×11		42·00	1·40
		e. Perf 11×10 (12.85)		55·00	4·00
236	19	8d. yellow, p 10 (1883)		£100	15·00
		a. Perf 12 (4.85)		£170	27·00
		b. Perf 11 (12.85)		£100	17·00
		c. Perf 10×12 (4.85)		£130	30·00
		ca. Perf 12×10		£100	25·00
236d	34	9d. on 10d. red-brown, p 11×12 (1897) (Optd S. £25)		8·00	4·50
		da. Perf 12		11·00	6·50
		db. Perf 11		11·00	7·00
		dc. Surch double, p 11		£140	£120
236e		10d. violet, p 11×12 (1897) (Optd S. £25)		12·00	3·50
		ea. Perf 12×11½		12·00	3·50
		eb. Perf 12		15·00	4·25
		ec. Perf 11		20·00	5·50
237	38	1s. black, p 10		65·00	2·00
		a. Perf 11 (12.85)		£200	9·00
		b. Perf 10×12		—	£250
		c. Perf 10×13			
		ca. Perf 13×10		£200	20·00
		d. Perf 11×12, comb (1.84)		65·00	2·00

1886–87. *W* 41.

238	26	1d. scarlet, p 10 ..	..	11·00	3·75
		a. Perf 11 × 12, comb ..		3·75	90
239	28	2d. deep blue, p 10	..	35·00	5·00
		a. Perf 11 × 12, comb ..		12·00	95
		b. Imperf			

1891 (July). *Wmk* "10" *as W* 35. *P* 10.

240	14	3d. green	..	12·00	80·00
241		3d. dark green	..	5·00	17·00

40   **41**

NEW INFORMATION

The editor is always interested to correspond with people who have new information that will improve or correct the Catalogue.

42   43

NOTE. The spacing between the Crown and "NSW" is 1 mm in T **42**, as against 2 mm in T **40**.

1903–8. W **42**.

241a	14	3d. yellow-green, p 11		7·00	90
		b. Perf 12		6·00	90
		ba. Imperf between (horiz pair)			
		c. Perf 11×12 or 12×11		6·00	90
242		3d. dull green, p 12		21·00	1·75
		a. Perf 11×12 or 12×11		8·00	1·00
		b. Perf 11			
243	15	5d. dark blue-green, p 11×12 or 12×11	6·00	90
		b. Wmk sideways		17·00	5·00
		b. Perf 11		14·00	90
		ba. Wmk sideways			
		c. Perf 12		21·00	3·50
		ca. Wmk sideways		32·00	10·00
		d. Imperf (pair)		£130	

1885–86. W **41** (*sideways*). (i). Optd "POSTAGE", *in black*.

244	43	5s. green and lilac, p 13			
		a. Perf 10			
		b. Perf 12 × 10		£325	80·00
245		10s. claret and lilac, p 13		£475	£150
		a. Perf 12			
246		£1 claret and lilac, p 13 (1886)	—	£2250
		a. Perf 12		£2250	

(ii) Overprinted in blue

247	43	10s. claret and mauve, p 10 (Optd S. £60)	£600	£170
		a. Perf 12		£170	55·00
		b. Perf 12 × 11			
248		£1 claret and rose-lilac, p 12 × 10	£2500	£1100

44

1894. Optd "POSTAGE" *in blue.* W **44** (*sideways*).

249	43	10s. claret and mauve, p 10	£275	£110
249a		10s. claret and violet, p 12	£160	42·00
		b. Perf 11		£250	80·00
		c. Perf 12 × 11		£180	50·00
250		10s. aniline crimson & violet, p 12 × 11	£160	48·00
		a. Perf 12		£250	80·00
250b		£1 claret and violet, p 12 × 11		

1903–04. Optd "POSTAGE" *in blue. Chalk-surfaced paper.* W **44** (*sideways*).

250c	43	10s. aniline crimson & violet, p 12 × 11	£160	75·00
251		10s. rosine and violet, p 12 (1904)	£160	75·00
		a. Perf 11		£200	85·00
		b. Perf 12 × 11		£160	45·00
252		10s. claret and violet, p 12 × 11 (1904)	£225	85·00

45 View of Sydney   46 Emu   47 Captain Cook

48 Queen Victoria and Arms of Colony   49 Superb Lyrebird   50 Eastern Grey Kangaroo

51 Map of Australia   52 Capt. Arthur Phillip, first Governor and Lord Carrington, Governor in 1888

(Des M. Tannenberg (1d., 6d.), Miss Devine (2d., 8d.), H. Barraclough (4d.), Govt Ptg Office (1s.), C. Turner (5s.), Mrs. F. Stoddard (20s.). Eng W. Bell.)

1888 (1 May)–**89.** *Centenary of New South Wales.* (a) W **40**. P 11×12.

253	45	1d. lilac (9.7.88)		3·75	10
		a. Perf 12 ×11½		17·00	90
		b. Perf 12		5·00	10
		c. Imperf (pair)			
		d. Mauve		3·75	10
		da. Imperf between (pair)			
		db. Perf 12×11½		6·00	25
		dc. Perf 12		5·50	25
254	46	2d. Prussian blue (1.9.88)	4·75	10
		a. Imperf (pair)		£100	
		b. Imperf between (pair)		£375	
		c. Perf 12 × 11½		9·00	10
		d. Perf 12		7·00	10
		e. Chalky blue		4·75	10
		ea. Perf 12 × 11½			
		eb. Perf 12		6·50	25
255	47	4d. purple-brown (8.10.88)	11·00	3·00
		a. Perf 12×11½		30·00	7·50
		b. Perf 12		26·00	3·25
		c. Perf 11		£300	90·00
		d. Red-brown		10·00	3·00
		da. Perf 12×11½		13·00	2·75
		db. Perf 12		13·00	2·75
		e. Orange-brown, p 12×11½	14·00	2·75
		f. Yellow-brown, p 12×11½	13·00	3·00
256	48	6d. carmine (26.11.88)	20·00	3·50
		a. Perf 12×11½		25·00	4·00
		b. Perf 12		21·00	8·50
257	49	8d. lilac-rose (17.1.89)	15·00	2·00
		a. Perf 12×11½		38·00	10·00
		b. Perf 12		15·00	2·25
		c. Magenta		75·00	9·00
		ca. Perf 12×11½		15·00	2·25
		cc. Perf 12		15·00	2·75
258	50	1s. maroon (21.2.89)	17·00	90
		a. Perf 12×11½		19·00	90
		b. Perf 12		23·00	90
		c. Violet-brown		17·00	90
		ca. Imperf (pair)		£550	
		cb. Perf 12×11½		38·00	1·25
		cc. Perf 12		38·00	90

(b) W **41**. P 11×12

259	45	1d. lilac (1888)		14·00	
		a. Mauve		12·00	85
260	46	2d. Prussian blue (1888)	48·00	3·00

(c) W **25**. P 10

261	51	5s. deep purple (13.3.89)	£180	45·00
		a. Deep violet		£180	45·00
262	52	20s. cobalt-blue		£225	£110
253/8		Optd "Specimen"	Set of 6	£150

Nos. 255c and 261/2 are line perforated, the remainder are comb.

A postal forgery exists of the 2d. on unwatermarked paper and perforated 11.

53   54

1890. W **53** (5s.) *or* **54** (20s.). P 10.

263	51	5s. lilac		£120	27·00
		a. Perf 11		£160	38·00
		ab. Imperf between (horiz pair)		
		b. Perf 12		£225	42·00
		c. Perf 10 × 11 or 11 × 10	£160	27·00
		d. Mauve		£160	27·00
		da. Perf 11		£160	38·00
264	52	20s. cobalt-blue		£300	£130
		a. Perf 11		£225	75·00
		b. Perf 11 × 10			
		c. Ultramarine, p 11	£180	75·00
		ca. Perf 12		£225	£130
		cb. Perf 11 × 12 or 12 × 11	£160	75·00
263/4		Optd "Specimen"	Set of 2	£180

55 Allegorical figure of Australia

Halfpenny (56)   **HALFPENNY** (57)

SEVEN-PENCE

1890 (22 Dec). W **40**.

281	55	2½d. ultramarine, p 11 × 12 comb (Optd S. £25)	2·50	40
		a. Perf 12 × 11½, comb		45·00	
		b. Perf 12, comb		7·00	40

1891 (5 Jan). *Surch as* T **56** *and* **57**. W **40**.

282	26	½d. on 1d. grey, p 11×12 comb	3·00	3·25
		a. Surch omitted			
		b. Surch double		£200	
283	37	7½d. on 6d. brown, p 10		5·50	2·75
		a. Perf 11		5·00	2·75
		b. Perf 12		6·00	3·25
		c. Perf 11×12 or 12×11	5·50	3·25
		d. Perf 10×12		6·00	3·25
284	38	12½d. on 1s. red, p 10		12·00	8·00
		a. "HALFPENCE" omitted			
		b. Perf 11		13·00	8·00
		c. Perf 11×12, comb	12·00	7·50
		d. Perf 12×11½, comb	11·00	7·50
		e. Perf 12, comb		15·00	7·50
282/4		Optd "Specimen"	Set of 3	70·00

58   Type I. Narrow "H" in "HALF"

1892 (21 Mar)–**99.** *Type I.* W **40**.

285	58	½d. grey, p 10		18·00	45
		a. Perf 11		60·00	5·00
		b. Perf 10×12		55·00	7·50
		c. Perf 11×12 (Optd S. £20)	2·25	10
		d. Perf 12		2·50	10
286		½d. slate, p 11×12 (1897)	2·25	10
		a. Perf 12×11½		2·25	10
		b. Perf 12		2·25	10
		c. Imperf between (horiz pair). Perf 11×12	£400	
287		½d. bluish green, p 11×12 (1899)	2·75	10
		a. Perf 12×11½		1·75	10
		b. Perf 12		1·75	10

The perforations 11×12, 12×11½, 12, are from comb machines.

The die for Type **58** was constructed from an electro taken from the die of the De La Rue 1d., Type **26**, with "ONE" replaced by "HALF" and two "½" plugs added to the bottom corners. These alterations proved to be less hard-wearing than the remainder of the die and defects were visible by the 1905 plate of No. 330. It seems likely that repairs were undertaken before printing from the next plate in late 1907 which produced stamps as Type II.

58a

58b

(Des C. Turner. Litho Govt Printing Office, Sydney)

1897. *Diamond Jubilee and Hospital Charity.* T **58**a *and* **58**b. W **40**. P 12×11 (1d.) *or* 11 (2½d.).

287c	58a	1d. (1s.) green and brown (22.6)	40·00	40·00
287d	58b	2½d. (2s. 6d.), gold, carmine & bl (28.6)	£150	£150
287c/d		Optd "Specimen"	Set of 2	£200

These stamps, sold at 1s. and 2s. 6d respectively, paid postage of 1d. and 2½d. only, the difference being given to a Consumptives' Home.

59   60   61

Dies of the 1d.

Die I   Die II

1d. Die I. The first pearl on the crown on the left side is merged into the arch, the shading under the fleur-de-lis is indistinct, the "S" of "WALES" is open.
Die II. The first pearl is circular, the vertical shading under the fleur-de-lis clear, the "S" of "WALES" not so open.

Dies of the 2½d.

Die I   Die II

2½d. Die I. There are 12 radiating lines in the star on the Queen's breast.
Die II. There are 16 radiating lines in the star and the eye is nearly full of colour.

Des D. Souter (2d., 2½d.). Eng W. Amor)

1897 (22 June)–*99*. W 40 *(sideways on 2½d.)*. P 12×11 *(2½d.)* or 11×12 *(others)*.

288	59	1d. carmine (Die I)	..	1·75	10
289		1d. scarlet (Die I)	..	1·75	10
		a. Perf 12×11½	..	4·50	40
		b. Perf 12	..	4·50	50
		ba. Imperf horiz (vert pair)		£225	
290		1d. rose-carmine (Die II) (11.97)	..	1·75	10
		a. Perf 12×11½	..	1·50	10
		b. Perf 12	..	1·50	10
		c. Imperf between (pair)		£400	
291		1d. salmon-red (Die II) (p 12×11½)	..	1·75	10
		a. Perf 12	..	3·25	30
292	60	2d. deep dull blue	..	2·50	10
		a. Perf 12×11½	..	2·50	10
		b. Perf 12	..	5·00	10
293		2d. cobalt-blue	..	3·50	10
		a. Perf 12×11½	..	3·00	10
		b. Perf 12	..	3·50	10
294		2d. ultramarine (1.12.97)	..	3·00	10
		a. Perf 12×11½	..	2·50	10
		b. Perf 12	..	2·50	10
		c. Imperf between (pair)	..	2·50	
295	61	2½d. purple (Die I)	..	6·50	1·25
		a. Perf 11½×12	..	7·50	80
		b. Perf 11	..	7·50	1·75
296		2½d. deep violet (Die II) (11.97)	..	4·50	80
		a. Perf 11½×12	..	7·50	1·25
		b. Perf 11	..	4·25	1·25
297		2½d. Prussian blue (17.1.99)	..	6·00	1·25
		a. Perf 11½×12	..	4·25	1·00
		b. Perf 12	..	3·50	1·00
288, 292, 294/5 Optd "Specimen"			Set of 4	60·00	

The perforations 11 × 12, 12 × 11½ and comb 11 are from comb machines, the perforation 11 is from a single-line machine.

1897. *Reissue of T 24.* W 25. P 11.

297c	5s. reddish purple (*shades*)	..	32·00	12·00
	ca. Imperf between (horiz pair)	..	£2750	
	d. Perf 12	..	42·00	20·00
	e. Perf 11×12 or 12×11	..	35·00	19·00

1898–99. W 40. P 11 × 12.

297f	48	6d. emerald-green (Optd S. £20)	..	30·00	9·00
		fa. Perf 12×11½	..	22·00	8·00
		fb. Perf 12	..	22·00	8·00
297g		6d. orange-yellow (1899)	..	14·00	3·25
		ga. Perf 12×11½	..	13·00	2·75
		gb. Perf 12	..	23·00	4·50
		gc. Yellow, p 12×11½	..	14·00	1·50

1899(Oct). *Chalk-surfaced paper.* W 40 *(sideways on 2½d.)*. P 12×11½ or 11½×12 *(2½d.)*, comb.

298	58	½d. blue-green (Type I)	..	1·00	10
		a. Imperf (pair)	..	65·00	75·00
299	59	1d. carmine (Die II)	..	1·75	10
		a. Imperf horiz (vert pair)	..	£200	
300		1d. scarlet (Die II)	..	1·00	10
301		1d. salmon-red (Die II)	..	1·75	10
		a. Imperf (pair)	..	65·00	75·00
302	60	2d. cobalt-blue	..	1·75	10
		a. Imperf (pair)	..	65·00	
303	61	2½d. Prussian blue (Die II)	..	2·75	70
		a. Imperf (pair)	..	80·00	
303b	47	4d. red-brown	..	9·50	3·50
		c. Imperf (pair)	..	£225	
304		4d. orange-brown	..	9·50	3·50
305	48	6d. deep orange	..	11·00	90
		a. Imperf (pair)	..	£150	
306		6d. orange-yellow	..	11·00	90
307		6d. emerald-green	..	75·00	22·00
		a. Imperf (pair)	..	£190	
308	49	8d. magenta	..	20·00	3·25
309	34	9d. on 10d. dull brown	..	8·00	4·25
		a. Surcharge double	..	90·00	£110
		b. Without surcharge	..	80·00	
310		10d. violet	..	12·00	3·75
311	50	1s. maroon	..	20·00	1·00
312		1s. purple-brown	..	20·00	1·50
		a. Imperf (pair)	..	£180	

---

62 Superb Lyrebird   63

1902–03. *Chalk-surfaced paper.* W 42 *(sideways on 2½d.)*. P 12×11½ or 11½×12 *(2½d.)*, comb.

313	58	½d. blue-green (Type I)	..	3·75	10
		a. Perf 12×11	..	3·75	
314	59	1d. carmine (Die II)	..	2·00	10
315	60	2d. cobalt-blue	..	2·50	10
316	61	2½d. dark blue (Die II)	..	5·50	10
317	47	4d. orange-brown	..	24·00	4·50
318	48	6d. yellow-orange	..	18·00	1·25
319		6d. orange	..	17·00	1·25
320		6d. orange-buff	..	22·00	1·25
321	49	8d. magenta	..	18·00	2·75
322	34	9d. on 10d. brownish orange	..	9·00	3·50
323		10d. violet	..	18·00	3·50
324	50	1s. maroon	..	21·00	80
325		1s. purple-brown	..	23·00	80
326	62	2s. 6d. green (1903) (Optd S. £35)	..	42·00	18·00

(Typo Victoria Govt Printer, Melbourne)

1903 (18 July). *Wmk double-lined V over Crown.* W w 10.

327	63	9d. brown & ultram, p 12¼ × 12½, comb (Optd S. £27)	..	10·00	1·75
328		9d. brown & dp blue, p 12¼ × 12½, comb	..	10·00	1·75
329		9d. brown and blue, p 11	..	£450	£275

Type II. Broad   66
"H" in "HALF"

1905 (Oct)–*10*. *Chalk-surfaced paper.* W 66 *(sideways on 2½d.)*. P 12×11½ or 11½×12 *(2½d.)* comb, unless otherwise stated.

330	58	½d. blue-green (Type I)	..	2·00	10
		a. Perf 11½×11	..		
		b. Type II (1908)	..	1·50	10
		ba. Perf 11½×11	..	2·00	
332	59	1d. rose-carmine (Die II)	..	1·50	10
		a. Double impression	..	£225	
		b. Perf 11½×11	..	1·75	
333	60	2d. deep ultramarine	..	1·75	10
		b. Perf 11½×11	..	2·00	
333d		2d. milky blue (1910)	..	1·75	10
		da. Perf 11	..	45·00	
		db. Perf 11½×11	..		
334	61	2½d. Prussian blue (Die II)	..	3·25	90
335	47	4d. orange-brown	..	9·50	3·50
336		4d. red-brown	..	11·00	3·50
337	48	6d. dull yellow	..	13·00	1·25
		a. Perf 11½×11	..	21·00	
338		6d. orange-yellow	..	13·00	1·25
		a. Perf 11×11½	..	27·00	
339		6d. deep orange	..	11·00	1·25
		a. Perf 11	..	£160	
339b		6d. orange-buff	..	11·00	1·25
		c. Perf 11½×11	..	17·00	2·75
340	49	8d. magenta	..	18·00	3·75
341		8d. lilac-rose	..	18·00	4·00
342	34	10d. violet	..	14·00	3·75
		a. Perf 11½×11	..	13·00	3·50
		b. Perf 11	..	13·00	3·50
343	50	1s. maroon	..	16·00	1·50
344		1s. purple-brown (1908)	..	20·00	1·50
345	62	2s. 6d. blue-green	..	42·00	20·00
		a. Perf 11½×11	..	27·00	18·00
		b. Perf 11	..	30·00	22·00

67

1905 (Dec). *Chalk-surfaced paper.* W 67. P 11.

346	52	20s. cobalt-blue	..	£150	65·00
		a. Perf 12	..	£170	75·00
		b. Perf 11 × 12 or 12 × 11	..	£140	60·00

(Typo Victoria Govt Printer, Melbourne)

1906 (Sept). *Wmk double-lined "A" and Crown,* W w 11. P 12×12½, comb.

347	63	9d. brown and ultramarine	..	7·00	1·10
		a. Perf 11	..	50·00	42·00
348		9d. yellow-brown and ultramarine	..	7·00	90

1907 (July). W w 11 *(sideways on 2½d.)*. P 12×11½ or 11½×12 *(2½d.)*, comb, unless otherwise stated.

349	58	½d. blue-green (Type I)	..	3·50	10
351	59	1d. dull rose (Die II)	..	3·50	10
352	60	2d. cobalt-blue	..	3·50	10
353	61	2½d. Prussian blue (Die II)	..	42·00	
354	47	4d. orange-brown	..	10·00	4·50
355	48	6d. orange-buff	..	27·00	6·00
356		6d. dull yellow	..	25·00	6·00
357	49	8d. magenta	..	18·00	5·00
358	34	10d. violet, p 11	..	20·00	15·00
359	50	1s. purple-brown	..	24·00	4·00
		a. Perf 11	..		
360	62	2s. 6d. blue-green	..	45·00	26·00

STAMP BOOKLETS

There are very few surviving examples of Nos. SB1/4. Listings are provided for those believed to have been issued with prices quoted for those known to still exist.

1904 (May)–*09*. *Black on red cover with map of Australia on front and picture of one of six different State G.P.O's on back. Stapled.*

SB1 £1 booklet containing two hundred and forty 1d. in four blocks of 30 and two blocks of 60
a. Red on pink cover (1909)
b. Blue on pink cover

1904 (May). *Black on grey cover as No.* SB1. *Stapled.*
SB2 £1 booklet containing one hundred and twenty 2d. in four blocks of 30

1910 (May). *Black on cream cover inscribed "COMMON-WEALTH OF AUSTRALIA/POSTMASTER-GENERAL'S DEPARTMENT". Stapled.*
SB3 2s. booklet containing eleven ½d. (No. 331), either in block of 6 plus block of 5 or block of 11, and eighteen 1d. (No. 332), either in three blocks of 6 or block of 6 plus 1 block of 12 .. .. ..£2000
Unsold stock of No. SB3 was uprated with one additional ½d. in May 1911.

1911 (Aug). *Red on pink cover as No.* SB3. *Stapled.*
SB4 2s. booklet containing twelve ½d. (No. 331), either in two blocks of 6 or block of 12, and eighteen 1d. (No. 332) either in three blocks of 6 or 1 block of 6 plus block of 12 .. .. .. £1500

OFFICIAL STAMPS

O S   O S   O S

(O 1)   (O 2)   (O 3)

The space between the letters is normally 7 mm as illustrated, except on the 5d. and 8d. (11–11½ mm), 5s. (12 mm) and 20s. (14 mm). Later printings of the 3d., W 40, are 5½ mm, and these are listed. Varieties in the settings are known on the 1d. (8 and 8½ mm), 2d. (8½ mm) and 3d. (9 mm).
Varieties of Type O 1 exist with "O" sideways.

Nos. O1/35 overprinted with Type O 1

1879. *Wmk double-lined "6".* P 13.

O1	14	3d. dull green	..	—	£400

1879 (Oct)–*85*. W 36. P 13.

O 2	26	1d. salmon	..	11·00	2·25
		a. Perf 10 (5.81)	..	£180	30·00
		b. Perf 13×10 (1881)	..	22·00	3·75
O 3	28	2d. blue	..	15·00	1·50
		a. Perf 10 (7.81)	..	£225	32·00
		b. Perf 10×13 (1881)	..	40·00	20·00
		ba. Perf 13×10	..	23·00	2·75
		d. Perf 11×12 (11.84?)	..	—	£225
O 4	14	3d. dull green (R.) (12.79)	..	£400	£250
O 5		3d. dull green (3.80)	..	£250	48·00
		a. Perf 10 (1881)	..	£140	42·00
		b. Yellow-green. Perf 10 (10.81)	..	£140	27·00
		ba. Perf 13×10 (1881)	..	£140	27·00
		bb. Perf 12 (4.85)	..	£200	50·00
		bc. Perf 10×12 or 12×10 (4.85)	..	£200	50·00
O 6	32	4d. red-brown	..	£160	8·00
		a. Perf 10 (1881)	..	—	£190
		b. Perf 10×13 (1881)	..	£200	90·00
		c. Perf 13×10	..	£150	12·00
O 7	15	5d. green, p 10 (8.84)	..	18·00	13·00
O 8	37	6d. pale lilac	..	£225	6·50
		a. Perf 10 (1881)	..	£350	42·00
		b. Perf 13×10 (1881)	..	£160	42·00
O 9	19	8d. yellow (R.) (12.79)	..	—	£160
O10		8d. yellow (1880)	..	—	16·00
		a. Perf 10 (1881)	..	£275	75·00
O11	34	9d. on 10d. brown, p 10 (30.5.80) (Optd S £60)	..	£350	
O12	38	1s. black (R.)	..	£225	7·50
		a. Perf 10 (1881)	..	—	16·00
		b. Perf 10×13 (1881)	..	—	25·00
		ba. Perf 13×10	..	—	10·00

Other stamps are known with red overprint but their status is in doubt.

1880–88. *Wmk "5/-",* W 25. (a) P 13.

O13	24	5s. deep purple (15.2.80)	..	£425	90·00
		a. Royal purple	..	—	£300
		b. Deep rose-lilac	..	£425	90·00
				(b) P 10	
O14	24	5s. deep purple (9.82)	..	£425	£160
		a. Opt double	..	† £1500	
		b. Rose-lilac (1883)	..	£300	£100
				(c) P 10 × 12	
O15	24	5s. purple (10.86)	..		
				(d) P 12 × 10	
O16	24	5s. reddish purple (1886)	..	£425	£100

                                    (e) P 12
O17 24 5s. purple .. .. † £500
                                    (f) P 11
O18 24 5s. rose-lilac (1888) .. .. £170 80·00

1880 (31 May). *Wmk "10". W 35. P 13.*
O18a 34 10d. lilac (Optd S. £60) .. .. £130 80·00
        ab. Perf 10 and 11, compound .. £200 £180
        ac. Perf 10 .. .. £200
        ad. Opt double, one albino (*p* 10)

1882–85. *W 40. P 10.*
O19 26 1d. salmon .. .. 11·00 2·25
        a. Perf 13×10 .. .. .. £130
O20   1d. orange *to* scarlet .. .. 8·50 1·75
        a. Perf 10×13 .. .. .. £130
        b. Perf 11×12, comb (1.84) .. 6·50 1·40
        c. Perf 10×12 or 12×10 (4.85) .. — £110
        d. Perf 12×11 (12.85) .. .. ..
O21 28 2d. blue .. .. 8·00 1·00
        a. Perf 10×13 or 13×10 .. £190 75·00
        c. Perf 11×12, comb (1.84) .. 7·00 1·00
        d. Ditto. Opt double .. .. — £150
        e. Perf 12×11 (12.85) .. ..
O22 14 3d. yellow-green (7 *mm*) .. 7·00 3·50
        a. Perf 12 (4.85) .. .. £120 80·00
        b. Perf 12×10 (4.85) .. ..
        c. Perf 12×11 .. .. ..
O23   3d. bluish green (7 *mm*) .. 7·00 3·50
        a. Perf 12 (4.85) .. .. £120 80·00
        b. Perf 12×10 (4.85) .. ..
        c. Perf 12×11 (12.85) .. ..
O24   3d. yellow-green (5½ *mm*) .. 7·50 3·50
        a. Wmk sideways (Optd S. £35) .. 35·00 20·00
        b. Perf 10×12 or 12×10 (4.85) .. 7·00 3·50
        c. Perf 10×11 or 11×10 (12.85) ..
O25   3d. bluish green (5½ *mm*) .. 7·00 3·50
        a. Perf 10×12 or 12×10 (4.85) .. 6·00 3·50
        c. Perf 10×11 or 11×10 (12.85) .. 5·00 3·50
O26 32 4d. red-brown .. .. .. 30·00 4·00
        a. Perf 11×12, comb (1.84) .. 12·00 3·00
        b. Perf 10×12 (4.85) .. .. — 70·00
O27   4d. dark brown .. .. .. 15·00 3·00
        a. Perf 11×12, comb (1.84) .. 12·00 3·00
        b. Perf 12 (4.85) £200 £150
        c. Perf 12×10 (4.85) .. .. £200 90·00
O28 15 5d. dull green (Optd S. £35) .. 12·00 11·00
        a. Perf 12×10 (4.85) .. ..
O29   5d. blue-green .. .. .. 13·00 12·00
        a. Perf 12 (4.85) £100
        b. Perf 10×11 .. .. .. 13·00 12·00
O30 37 6d. pale lilac .. .. .. 18·00 5·50
        a. Perf 11 (12.85) .. .. 19·00
O31   6d. mauve .. .. 18·00 5·50
        a. Perf 12 (4.85) .. .. — 45·00
        b. Perf 10×12 or 12×10 (4.85) .. 20·00 5·00
        d. Perf 11×10 (12.85) .. .. 18·00 5·50
        e. Perf 12×11 (12.85) .. .. 55·00 15·00
O32 19 8d. yellow .. .. 22·00 11·00
        a. Perf 12 (4.85) .. .. £130 38·00
        b. Perf 10×12 or 12×10 (4.85) .. 22·00 10·00
        d. Perf 11 (12.85) .. .. 22·00 11·00
        da. Opt double .. .. .. † —
        db. Opt treble .. .. .. † —
O33 38 1s. black (R.) .. .. .. 25·00 6·50
        a. Perf 10×13 .. .. .. — 55·00
        b. Perf 11×12, comb (1.84) .. 25·00 6·50
        c. Ditto. Opt double .. .. — £200

1886–87. *W 41. P 10.*
O34 26 1d. scarlet .. .. 27·00 3·50
O35 28 2d. deep blue .. .. ..
        a. Perf 11 × 12 .. .. ..

1887–89. *Nos. 247/8 overprinted in black.* (a) *With Type O 1.*
O36 43 10s. claret and mauve, *p* 12 .. — £800
                        (b) With Type O 2 (April 1889)
O37 43 10s. claret & mauve, *p* 12 (Optd S. £80) £1200 £600
        a. Perf 10 .. .. .. £2250 £1300
                        (c) With Type O 3 (Jan 1887)
O38 43 £1 claret and rose-lilac, *p* 12×10 .. £5500 £3500
Only nine examples of No. O38 are recorded, three of which are mint. One of the used stamps, in the Royal Collection, shows overprint Type O 3 double.

1888 (17 July)–90. *Optd as Type O 1.* (a) *W 40. P 11×12.*
O39 45 1d. lilac .. .. 2·00 15
        a. Perf 12 .. .. 2·00 15
        b. *Mauve* .. .. 2·00 15
        ba. Perf 12 .. .. 2·00 15
O40 46 2d. Prussian blue (15.10.88) .. 4·25 15
        a. Perf 12 .. .. 4·25 15
O41 47 4d. purple-brown (10.10.89) .. 10·00 3·00
        a. Perf 12 .. .. 13·00 3·25
        b. Perf 11 .. ..
        c. *Red-brown* .. .. .. 10·00 3·00
        ca. Opt double .. .. .. † —
        cb. Perf 12 .. .. 13·00 3·25
O42 48 6d. carmine (16.1.89) .. 8·50 4·00
        a. Perf 12 .. .. 12·00 4·00
O43 49 8d. lilac-rose (1890) .. 18·00 9·00
        a. Perf 12 .. .. 22·00 12·00
O44 50 1s. maroon (9.1.90) .. 17·00 3·00
        a. Perf 12 .. .. 17·00 3·00
        b. *Purple-brown* .. .. .. 17·00 3·00
        ba. Opt double .. .. ..
        .. 17·00 3·00
O39/44 Optd "Specimen" .. *Set of 6* £200
                        (b) W 41. P 11×12 (1889)
O45 45 1d. mauve .. ..
O46 46 2d. blue .. ..
                        (c) W 25. P 10
O47 51 5s. deep purple (R.) (9.1.90) .. £600 £500
O48 52 20s. cobalt-blue (10.3.90) .. £1600 £800

1890 (Feb)–91. *Optd as Type O 1. W 53 (5s.) or 54 (20s.) P 10.*
O49 51 5s. lilac £300 £120
        a. *Mauve* .. .. £160 50·00
        b. *Dull lilac, p* 12 .. .. £450 £130
O50 52 20s. cobalt-blue (3.91) .. £1600 £600
O49/50 Optd "Specimen" .. .. *Set of 2* £200

1891 (Jan). *Optd as Type O 1. W 40.*
                        (a) *On No. 281. P 11×12*
O54 55 2½d. ultramarine .. .. 7·00 3·00
                        (b) *On Nos. 282/4*
O55 26 ½d. on 1d. grey, *p* 11×12 .. 50·00 45·00
O56 37 7½d. on 6d. brown, *p* 10 .. 35·00 30·00
O57 38 12½d. on 1s. red, *p* 11×12 .. 60·00 55·00

1892 (May). *No. 285 optd as Type O 1. P 10.*
O58 58 ½d. grey .. .. 8·50 12·00
        a. Perf 11×12 .. .. .. 6·00 8·00
        b. Perf 12 .. .. 7·50 8·00
        c. Perf 12×11½ .. .. .. 11·00
O54/8 Optd "Specimen" .. .. *Set of 5* £160

Official stamps were withdrawn from the government departments on 31 December 1894.

POSTAGE DUE STAMPS

D 1

(Dies eng by A. Collingridge. Typo Govt Printing Office, Sydney)

1891 (1 Jan)–92. *W 40. P 10.*
D 1 D 1 ½d. green (21.1.92) .. .. 3·00 2·25
D 2   1d. green .. .. 5·00 90
        a. Perf 11 .. .. 5·00 90
        b. Perf 12 .. .. 14·00 2·50
        c. Perf 12 × 10 .. .. .. 17·00 1·75
        d. Perf 10 × 11 .. .. .. 8·00 1·25
        e. Perf 11 × 12 or 12 × 11 .. 5·50 90
D 3   2d. green .. .. 7·00 1·00
        a. Perf 11 .. .. 7·00 1·00
        b. Perf 12 .. .. — 8·00
        c. Perf 12×10 .. .. .. 16·00 3·00
        d. Perf 10×11 .. .. .. 8·50 1·50
        e. Perf 11×12 or 12×11 .. 7·50 1·00
        f. Wmk sideways .. .. 14·00 5·00
D 4   3d. green .. .. 12·00 2·75
        a. Perf 10 × 11 .. .. .. 12·00 2·75
D 5   4d. green .. .. 9·00 80
        a. Perf 11 .. .. 10·00 80
        b. Perf 10 × 11 .. .. .. 9·00 80
D 6   6d. green .. .. 18·00 2·00
D 7   8d. green .. .. 60·00 9·00
D 8   5s. green .. .. £120 35·00
        a. Perf 11 .. .. £200 75·00
        b. Perf 11 × 12 .. .. .. — £250
D 9   10s. green (early 1891) .. £225 50·00
        a. Perf 12 × 10 .. .. .. £180 85·00
D10   20s. green (early 1891) .. £300 85·00
        a. Perf 12 .. .. £300
        b. Perf 12 × 10 .. .. .. £225 £110
D1/10 Optd "Specimen" .. .. *Set of 10* £180

1900. *Chalk-surfaced paper. W 40. P 11.*
D11 D 1 ½d. emerald-green .. ..
D12   1d. emerald-green .. .. 4·50 2·00
        a. Perf 12 .. .. 12·00 3·50
        b. Perf 11 × 12 or 12 × 11 .. 4·50 1·00
D13   2d. emerald-green .. .. 8·50 2·75
        a. Perf 12 .. ..
        b. Perf 11 × 12 or 12 × 11 .. 7·50 2·50
D14   3d. emerald-green, *p* 11 × 12 or 12 × 11 17·00 5·00
D15   4d. emerald-green .. .. 9·50 3·50

New South Wales became part of the Commonwealth of Australia on 1 January 1901.

QUEENSLAND

The area which later became Queensland was previously part of New South Wales known as the Moreton Bay District. The first post office, at Brisbane, was opened in 1834 and the use of New South Wales stamps from the District became compulsory from 1 May 1854.
Queensland was proclaimed a separate colony on 10 December 1859, but continued to use New South Wales issues until 1 November 1860.
Post Offices opened in the Moreton Bay District before 10 December 1859, and using New South Wales stamps, were

Office	Opened	Numeral Cancellation
Brisbane	1834	95
Burnett's Inn (*became* Goodes Inn)	1850	108
Callandoon	1850	74
Condamine	1856	151
Dalby	1854	133
Drayton	1846	85
Gayndah	1850	86
Gladstone	1854	131
Goode's Inn	1858	108
Ipswich	1846	87
Maryborough	1849	96
Rockhampton	1858	201
Surat	1852	110
Taroom	1856	152
Toowoomba	1858	214
Warwick	1848	81

ALTERED CATALOGUE NUMBERS

Any Catalogue numbers altered from the last edition are shown as a list in the introductory pages.

PERKINS BACON "CANCELLED". For notes on these handstamps, showing "CANCELLED" between horizontal bars forming an oval, see Catalogue Introduction.

1 **2** Large Star **3** Small Star

(Dies eng W. Humphrys. Recess P.B.)

1860 (1 Nov–15 Nov). *W 2.* (a) *Imperf.*
1 1 1d. carmine-rose £2750 £800
2   2d. blue £5500 £1500
3   6d. green £4000 £800
                        (b) *Clean-cut perf* 14–15½
4 1 1d. carmine-rose £1200 £250
5   2d. blue £500 £100
        a. Imperf between (pair) ..
6   6d. green (15 Nov) .. .. £550 60·00

1860–61. *W 3.* (a) *Clean-cut perf* 14–15½
7 1 2d. blue £500 £100
        a. Imperf between (horiz pair) .. — £1000
8   3d. brown (15.4.61) .. .. £275 60·00
        a. Re-entry £200
        b. Retouch (R. 2/8) £200
9   6d. green .. .. £550 65·00
10   1s. violet (15.11.60) (H/S "CANCELLED" in oval £3500) .. £500 80·00
11   "REGISTERED" (6d.) olive-yellow (1.61) (H/S "CANCELLED" in oval £3500) £350 75·00
        a. Imperf between (pair) .. £2750
                        (b) *Clean-cut perf* 14 *at Somerset House* (7.61)
12 1 1d. carmine-rose (H/S "CANCELLED" in oval £2750) .. £110 40·00
13   2d. blue (H/S "CANCELLED" in oval £2750) .. £275 50·00
                        (c) *Rough perf* 14–15½ (9.61)
14 1 1d. carmine-rose .. .. 75·00 28·00
15   2d. blue .. .. 95·00 28·00
        a. Imperf between (horiz pair) .. £1800
16   3d. brown .. .. 50·00 30·00
        a. Imperf vert (horiz pair) .. £1800
        b. Re-entry £200 £110
        c. Retouch (R. 2/8) £110
17   6d. deep green (H/S "CANCELLED" in oval £3500) .. £110 27·00
18   6d. yellow-green .. .. £200 27·00
19   1s. violet .. .. £350 80·00
20   "REGISTERED" (6d.) orange-yellow .. 90·00 35·00
The perforation of No. 8 is that known as "intermediate between clean-cut and rough".
The 3d. re-entry which occurs on one stamp in the second row, shows doubling of the left-hand arabesque and the retouch has redrawn spandrel dots under "EN" of "PENCE", a single dot in the centre of the circle under "E" and the bottom outer frame liner closer to the spandrel's frame line.

(Printed and perforated by Thomas Ham, Brisbane)

1862–67. *Thick toned paper. No wmk.* (a) *P* 13 (1862–63).
21 1 1d. Indian red (16.12.62) .. £250 60·00
22   1d. orange-vermilion (2.63) .. 60·00 12·00
        a. Imperf (pair) .. .. — £550
        b. Imperf between (pair) ..
23   2d. pale blue (16.12.62) .. 80·00 27·00
24   2d. blue .. .. 40·00 9·00
        a. Imperf (pair) .. .. — £550
        b. Imperf between (horiz pair) .. — £900
        c. Imperf between (vert pair) .. £1200
25   3d. brown .. .. 55·00 30·00
        a. Re-entry £110
        b. Retouch (R. 2/8) £110
26   6d. apple-green (17.4.63) .. 90·00 15·00
27   6d. yellow-green .. .. 80·00 12·00
        a. Imperf between (horiz pair) .. — £1000
28   6d. pale bluish green .. £130 27·00
        a. Imperf (pair) .. .. — £550
29   1s. grey (14.7.63) (H/S S. £40) .. £130 22·00
        a. Imperf between (horiz pair) .. £1000
        b. Imperf between (vert pair) .. — £1100
The top or bottom row of perforation was sometimes omitted from the sheet, resulting in stamps perforated on three sides only.

(b) P 12½×13 (1863–67)

30	1	1d. orange-vermilion	..	60·00	27·00
31		2d. blue	..	50·00	20·00
32		3d. brown	..	65·00	25·00
		a. Re-entry	..	—	95·00
		b. Retouch (R. 2/8)	..	—	95·00
33		6d. apple-green	..	85·00	27·00
34		6d. yellow-green	..	85·00	27·00
34a		6d. pale bluish green	..		
35		1s. grey	..	£170	32·00
		a. Imperf between (horiz pair)			

The previously listed stamps perforated 13 round holes come from the same perforating machine as Nos. 21/9 after the pins had been replaced. The holes vary from rough to clean-cut.

1864–65. W 3. (a) P 13.

44	1	1d. orange-vermilion (1.65)	..	65·00	20·00
		a. Imperf between (horiz pair)	..	£450	
45		2d. pale blue (1.65)	..	55·00	16·00
46		2d. deep blue	..	55·00	16·00
		a. Imperf between (vert pair)	..	£900	
		b. Bisected (1d.) (on cover)	..		†£1900
47		6d. yellow-green (1.65)	..	£120	22·00
48		6d. deep green	..	£140	22·00
49		"REGISTERED" (6d.) orge-yell (21.6.64)		75·00	32·00
		a. Double printed	..	£750	
		b. Imperf	..		

(b) P 12½ × 13

50	1	1d. orange-vermilion	..	95·00	40·00
50a		2d. deep blue	..	£120	40·00

1866 (24 Jan). Wmk "QUEENSLAND/POSTAGE—POSTAGE/STAMPS—STAMPS" *in three lines in script capitals with double wavy lines above and below the wmk and single wavy lines with projecting sprays between each line of words. There are ornaments ("fleurons") between "POSTAGE" "POSTAGE" and between "STAMPS" "STAMPS". Single stamps only show a portion of one or two letters of this wmk. (a) P 13.*

51	1	1d. orange-vermilion	..	£130	27·00
52		2d. blue	..	50·00	17·00

(b) P 12½ × 13

52a	1	1d. orange-vermilion	..	£160	40·00
52b		2d. blue	..	£160	40·00

1866 (24 Sept). Lithographed on thick paper. No wmk. P 13.

53	1	4d. slate (H/S S. £40)	..	£150	20·00
		a. Re-entry	..	—	85·00
		b. Retouch (R. 2/8)	..	—	85·00
55		4d. lilac	..	£110	16·00
		a. Re-entry	..	—	75·00
		b. Retouch (R. 2/8)	..	—	75·00
56		4d. reddish lilac	..	£110	16·00
		a. Re-entry	..	—	75·00
		b. Retouch (R. 2/8)	..	—	75·00
57		5s. bright rose (H/S S. £50)	..	£300	85·00
58		5s. pale rose	..	£225	60·00
		a. Imperf between (vert pair)	..	£900	

The 4d. is from a transfer taken from the 3d. plate and the 5s. was taken from the 1s. plate, the final "s" being added. The alteration in the values was made by hand on the stone, and there are many varieties, such as tall and short letters in "FOUR PENCE", some of the letters of "FOUR" smudged out, and differences in the position of the two words.

4

1868–74. Wmk small truncated Star, W 4 on each stamp, and the word "QUEENSLAND" in single-lined Roman capitals four times in each sheet. (a) P 13.

59	1	1d. orange-vermilion (18.1.71)	..	45·00	4·50
60		2d. pale blue	..	45·00	4·50
61		2d. blue (3.4.68)	..	40·00	2·75
62		2d. bright blue	..	50·00	2·75
63		2d. greenish blue	..	85·00	2·50
64		2d. dark blue	..	45·00	2·50
		a. Imperf			
65		3d. olive-green (27.2.71)	..	80·00	6·00
		a. Re-entry	..	—	35·00
		b. Retouch (R. 2/8)	..	—	35·00
66		3d. greenish grey	..	95·00	5·50
		a. Re-entry	..	—	32·00
		b. Retouch (R. 2/8)	..	—	32·00
67		3d. brown	..	80·00	5·50
		a. Re-entry	..	—	32·00
		b. Retouch (R. 2/8)	..	—	32·00
68		6d. yellow-green (10.11.71)	..	£140	7·00
69		6d. green	..	£130	10·00
70		6d. deep green	..	£170	17·00
71		1s. greenish grey (13.11.72)	..	£350	38·00
72		1s. brownish grey	..	£350	38·00
73		1s. mauve (19.2.74)	..	£225	22·00
59, 61, 65, 69, 73, H/S "Specimen"			Set of 5	£180	

(b) P 12 (about Feb 1874)

74	1	1d. orange-vermilion	..	£275	24·00
75		2d. blue	..	£600	35·00
76		3d. greenish grey	..	—	£150
		a. Re-entry	..		
		b. Retouch (R. 2.8)	..		
77		3d. brown	..	£325	£150
		a. Re-entry	..		
		b. Retouch (R. 2/8)	..		
78		6d. green	..	£850	40·00
79		1s. mauve	..	£375	40·00

(c) P 13 × 12

80	1	1d. orange-vermilion	..	—	£170
81		2d. blue	..	£850	40·00
82		3d. greenish grey	..	—	£275

Reprints were made in 1895 of all five values on the paper of the regular issue, and perforated 13; the colours are:—1d. orange and orange-brown, 2d. dull blue and bright blue, 3d. deep brown, 6d. yellow-green, 1s. red-violet and dull violet. The "Registered" was also reprinted on the same paper, but perforated 12. One sheet of the 2d. reprint is known to have had the perforations missing between the fourth and fifth vertical rows.

5   6

(4d., litho. Other values recess)

1868–78. Wmk Crown and Q, W 5. (a) P 13 (1868–75).

83	1	1d. orange-vermilion (10.11.68)	..	50·00	4·50
		a. Imperf (pair)	..	£180	
84		1d. pale rose-red (4.11.74)	..	48·00	8·50
85		1d. deep rose-red	..	95·00	9·00
86		2d. pale blue (4.11.74)	..	48·00	1·75
87		2d. deep blue (20.11.68)	..	38·00	4·50
		a. Imperf (pair)	..	£300	
		b. Imperf between (vert pair)	..		
88		3d. brown (11.6.75)	..	70·00	12·00
		a. Re-entry	..	—	55·00
		b. Retouch (R. 2/8)	..	—	55·00
89		4d. yellow (1.1.75) (H/S S. £65)	..	£750	45·00
90		6d. deep green (9.4.69)	..	£120	9·00
91		6d. yellow-green	..	£100	6·50
92		6d. pale apple-green (1.1.75)	..	£130	9·00
		a. Imperf (pair)	..	£300	
93		1s. mauve	..	£150	29·00

(b) P 12 (1876–78)

94	1	1d. deep orange-vermilion	..	38·00	5·00
95		1d. pale orange-vermilion	..	40·00	5·00
		a. Imperf between (vert pair)	..		
96		1d. rose-red	..	45·00	10·00
97		1d. flesh	..	60·00	10·00
98		2d. pale blue	..	80·00	15·00
99		2d. bright blue	..	25·00	1·00
100		2d. deep blue	..	28·00	1·50
101		3d. brown	..	60·00	9·00
		a. Re-entry	..	—	45·00
		b. Retouch (R. 2/8)	..	—	45·00
102		4d. yellow	..	£600	25·00
103		4d. buff	..	£600	20·00
104		6d. deep green	..	£140	7·00
105		6d. green	..	£130	4·25
106		6d. yellow-green	..	£140	4·50
107		6d. apple-green	..	£140	7·00
108		1s. mauve	..	45·00	9·00
109		1s. purple	..	£140	5·00
		a. Imperf between (pair)	..		

(c) P 13 × 12 or 12 × 13

110	1	1d. orange-vermilion	..	—	£150
110a		1d. rose-red	..		
111		2d. deep blue	..	£1100	£250
112		4d. yellow	..	—	£300
113		6d. deep green	..	—	£300

(d) P 12½ × 13

114	1	1d. orange-vermilion	..	—	£350
115		2d. deep blue	..	—	£350
115a		6d. yellow-green	..		

(e) P 12½

115b	1	2d. deep blue	..		

Reprints exist from 1895 of the 1d., 2d., 3d., 6d. and 1s. on thicker paper, Wmk W 6, and in different shades from the originals.

1879. No wmk. P 12.

116	1	6d. pale emerald-green	..	£170	26·00
		a. Imperf between (horiz pair)	..	—	£600
117		1s. mauve (fiscal-cancel £5)	..	£100	48·00

No. 117 has a very indistinct lilac *burelé* band at back.
Nos. 116/17 can be found showing portions of a papermaker's watermark, either T. H. Saunders & Co or A. Pirie & Sons.

1881. Lithographed from transfers from the 1s. die. Wmk Crown and Q, W 6. P 12.

118	1	2s. pale blue (6 Apr)	..	70·00	22·00
119		2s. blue (fiscal-cancel £3)	..	70·00	22·00
		a. Imperf vert (horiz pair)	..		
120		2s. deep blue (fiscal-cancel £3)	..	80·00	22·00
121		2s. 6d. dull scarlet (28 Aug)	..	£120	45·00
122		2s. 6d. bright scarlet (fiscal-cancel £3)	..	£140	45·00
123		5s. pale yellow-ochre (28 Aug)	..	£160	65·00
124		5s. yellow-ochre (fiscal-cancel £4)	..	£160	65·00
125		10s. reddish brown (Mar)	..	£350	£110
		a. Imperf	..	£375	
126		10s. bistre-brown	..	£350	£110
127		20s. rose (fiscal-cancel £6)	..	£350	£110

Of the 2s. and 20s. stamps there are five types of each, and of the other values ten types of each.

Beware of fiscally used copies that have been cleaned and provided with forged postmarks.

7

Die I   Die II

Dies I and II often occur in the same sheet.

Die I. The white horizontal inner line of the triangle in the upper right-hand corner merges into the outer white line of the oval above the "L".

Die II. The same line is short and does not touch the inner oval.

1879–80. Typo. P 12. (a) Wmk Crown and Q, W 5.

128	7	1d. reddish brown (Die I) (15.5.79)	..	65·00	15·00
		a. Die II		£100	15·00
		ab. "QUEENSLAND"	..	£850	£150
129		1d. orange-brown (Die I)	..	£100	15·00
130		2d. blue (Die I) (10.4.79)	..	55·00	10·00
		a. "PENGE" (R. 12/6)	..	£650	£110
		b. "QUEENSbAND" (R. 5/6)	..	—	£110
		c. "QU" joined	..	—	£110
131		4d. orange-yellow (6.6.79)	..	£325	35·00

(b) No wmk, with lilac burelé band on back

132	7	1d. reddish brown (Die I) (21.10.79)	..	£275	35·00
		a. "QUEENSLAND"	..	£300	65·00
		ab. "QUEENSLAND"	..	—	£1400
133		2d. blue (Die I) (21.10.79)	..	£350	17·00
		a. "PENGE" (R. 12/6)	..	£3250	£600
		b. "QUEENSbAND" (R. 5/6)	..		

(c) Wmk Crown and Q, W 6

134	7	1d. reddish brown (Die I) (31.10.79)	..	35·00	5·00
		a. Imperf between (pair)	..	—	£300
		b. Die II	..	45·00	5·00
		ba. "QUEENSLAND"	..	£200	40·00
		bb. Imperf between (pair)	..	—	£300
135		1d. dull orange (Die I)	..	17·00	3·00
		a. Die II	..	20·00	3·00
		ab. "QUEENSLAND"	..	55·00	20·00
136		1d. scarlet (Die I) (7.3.81)	..	14·00	1·75
		a. Die II	..	16·00	2·25
		ab. "QUEENSLAND"	..	80·00	24·00
137		2d. blue (Die I) (10.4.79)	..	27·00	1·00
		a. "PENGE"	..	£120	40·00
		b. "QUEENSbAND"	..	£120	40·00
		c. Die II	..	29·00	3·00
138		2d. grey-blue (Die I)	..	27·00	1·00
		a. "PENGE"	..	£120	40·00
		b. "QUEENSbAND"	..	£120	40·00
		c. Die II	..	29·00	3·00
139		2d. bright blue (Die I)	..	30·00	1·00
		a. "PENGE"	..	£130	40·00
		b. "QUEENSbAND"	..	£130	40·00
		c. Imperf between (pair)	..	£450	
		d. Die II	..	32·00	3·00
140		2d. deep blue (Die I)	..	32·00	1·00
		a. "PENGE"	..	£140	40·00
		b. "QUEENSbAND"	..	£140	40·00
		c. Die II	..	26·00	4·50
141		4d. orange-yellow	..	£110	10·00
		a. Imperf between (pair)	..		
142		6d. deep green	..	65·00	4·50
		a. Imperf between (pair)	..		
143		6d. yellow-green	..	70·00	4·50
144		1s. deep violet (3.80)	..	60·00	4·50
145		1s. pale lilac	..	50·00	5·50

The variety "QO" is No. 48 in the first arrangement, and No. 44 in a later arrangement on the sheets.

All these values have been seen imperf and unused, but we have no evidence that any of them were used in this condition.

The above were printed in sheets of 120, from plates made up of 30 groups of four electrotypes. There are four different types in each group, and two such groups of four are known of the 1d. and 2d., thus giving eight varieties of these two values. There was some resetting of the first plate of the 1d., and there are several plates of the 2d.; the value in the first plate of the latter value is in thinner letters, and in the last plate three types in each group of four have the "TW" of "TWO" joined, the letters of "PENCE" are larger and therefore much closer together, and in one type the "O" of "TWO" is oval, that letter being circular in the other types.

(8)   9   10

Half-penny

1880 (21 Feb). Surch with T 8.

151	7	½d. on 1d. (No. 134) (Die I)	..	£160	90·00
		a. Die II	..	£425	£350
		ab. "QUEENSLAND"	..	£850	£700

Examples with "Half-penny" reading downwards are forged surcharges.

(Eng H. Bourne. Recess Govt Printing Office, Brisbane from plates made by B.W.)

1882 (13 Apr)–95. P 12. (a) W 5 (twice sideways). Thin paper

152	9	2s. bright blue (14.4.82)	..	65·00	18·00
153		2s. 6d. vermilion (12.7.82)	..	55·00	20·00
154		5s. rose	..	50·00	22·00
155		10s. brown (12.7.82)	..	£110	40·00
156		£1 deep green (30.5.83)	..	£250	£120
		a. Re-entry (R.1/2)	..	—	£180
		b. Retouch (R.6/4)	..	—	£180
152, 154/6 H/S "Specimen"			Set of 4	£150	

(b) W 10. Thick paper (10.11.86)

157	9	2s. bright blue	..	65·00	30·00
158		2s. 6d. vermilion	..	38·00	22·00
159		5s. rose	..	35·00	30·00

160	**9**	10s. brown	.. .. ..	95·00	45·00
161		£1 deep green	.. .. ..	£170	60·00
		a. Re-entry (R.1/2)	.. ..	—	£100
		b. Retouch (R.6/4)	.. ..	—	£100

(c) W 6 (twice sideways). Thin paper (1895)

162	**9**	2s. 6d. vermilion	.. ..	40·00	30·00
163		5s. rose	.. .. ..	45·00	20·00
164		10s. brown	.. .. ..	£180	50·00
165		£1 deep green	.. .. ..	£180	70·00
		a. Re-entry (R.1/2)	..	—	£110
		b. Retouch (R.6/4)	..	—	£110

The re-entry on the £1 shows as a double bottom frame line and the retouch occurs alongside the bottom right numeral.
See also Nos. 270/1, 272/4 and 309/12.

11	12

In T **12** the shading lines do not extend entirely across, as in T **11**, thus leaving a white line down the front of the throat and point of the bust.

1882 (1 Aug)–**91. W 6.** *(a) P* 12.

166	**11**	1d. pale vermilion-red (23.11.82)	..	3·75	30
		a. Double impression	..		
167		1d. deep vermilion-red	..	3·75	30
168		2d. blue	.. ..	5·50	30
		a. Imperf between (horiz pair)	..		
169		4d. pale yellow (18.4.83)	..	13·00	2·00
		a. "PENGE" for "PENCE" (R. 8/1)		£130	45·00
		b. "EN" joined in "PENCE" (R. 4/6)		90·00	30·00
		c. Imperf (11.91)	..		
170		6d. green (6.11.82)	..	9·50	1·00
171		1s. violet (6.2.83)	..	20·00	2·25
172		1s. lilac	.. ..	11·00	2·00
173		1s. deep mauve	..	11·00	1·75
174		1s. pale mauve	..	12·00	1·75
		a. Imperf	.. ..	†	—

(b) P 9½ × 12 (1884)

176	**11**	1d. pale red	.. ..	70·00	24·00
177		2d. blue	.. ..	£225	40·00
178		1s. mauve	.. ..	£120	30·00

The above were printed from plates made up of groups of four electrotypes as previously. In the 1d. the words of value are followed by a full stop. There are four types of the 4d., 6d., and 1s., eight types of the 1d., and twelve types of the 2d.

No. 169c is from a sheet used at Roma post office and comes cancelled with the "46" numeral postmark.

1887 (5 May)–**89. W 6.** *(a) P* 12.

179	**12**	1d. vermilion-red	..	3·25	30
180		2d. blue	.. ..	6·00	30
		a. Oval white flaw on Queen's head behind diadem (R. 12/5)	..	25·00	7·50
181		2s. deep brown (12.3.89)	..	60·00	28·00
182		2s. pale brown	..	55·00	26·00

(b) P 9½ × 12

183	**12**	2d. blue	.. ..	£180	38·00

These are from new plates; four types of each value grouped as before. The 1d. is without stop. In all values No. 2 in each group of four has the "L" and "A" of "QUEENSLAND" joined at the foot, and No. 3 of the 2d. has "P" of word "PENCE" with a long downstroke.
The 2d. is known bisected and used as a 1d. value.

13	14

1890–94. W 6 *(sideways on* ½d.*). P* 12½, 13 *(comb machine).*

184	**13**	½d. pale green	..	3·25	65
185		½d. deep green	..	3·25	65
186		½d. deep blue-green	..	3·50	65
187	**12**	1d. vermilion-red	..	2·75	15
		a. Imperf	..	30·00	30·00
		b. Oval broken by tip of bust (R.10/3)		20·00	5·00
		c. Double impression	..	†	£190
188		2d. blue (old plate)	..	4·50	15
189		2d. pale blue (old plate)	..	4·25	15
190		2d. pale blue (retouched plate)	..	4·00	30
		a. "FWO" for "TWO" (R.8/7)		—	20·00
191	**14**	2½d. carmine	.. ..	10·00	80
192	**12**	3d. brown	.. ..	8·50	1·90
193	**11**	4d. yellow	.. ..	13·00	1·75
		a. "PENGE" for "PENCE" (R.8/1)		60·00	22·00
		b. "EN" joined in "PENCE" (R.4/6)		45·00	16·00
194		4d. orange	.. ..	17·00	1·75
		a. "PENGE" for "PENCE" (R.8/1)		70·00	22·00
		b. "EN" joined in "PENCE" (R.4/6)		50·00	16·00
195		4d. lemon	.. ..	20·00	2·00
		a. "PENGE" for "PENCE" (R.8/1)		80·00	28·00
		b. "EN" joined in "PENCE" (R.4/6)		60·00	20·00
196		6d. green	.. ..	10·00	1·50
197	**12**	2s. red-brown	..	40·00	11·00
198		2s. pale brown	..	45·00	13·00

This issue is perforated by a new vertical comb machine, gauging about 12¾ × 12¾. The 3d. is from a plate similar to those of the last issue, No. 2 in each group of four types having "L" and "A" joined at the foot. The ½d. and 2½d. are likewise in groups of four types, but the differences are very minute. In the retouched plate of the 2d. the letters "L" and "A" no longer touch in No. 2 of each group and the "P" in No. 3 is normal.

1895. A. *Thick paper.* **W 10.** *(a) P* 12½, 13.

202	**12**	1d. vermilion-red (16.1.95)	..	3·00	15
		a. Oval broken by tip of bust (R. 10/3)		25·00	5·00
203		1d. red-orange	..	3·00	15
		a. Oval broken by tip of bust (R. 10/3)		25·00	5·00
204		2d. blue (retouched plate) (16.1.95)	..	3·50	20
		a. "FWO" for "TWO" (R. 8/7)	..	—	20·00

(b) P 12

205	**11**	1s. mauve (8.95)	..	12·00	3·50

B. *Unwmkd paper; with blue burelé band at back. P* 12½, 13

206	**12**	1d. vermilion-red (19.2.95)	..	2·25	15
		a. Oval broken by tip of bust (R. 10/3)		20·00	5·00
		b. "PE" of "PENNY" omitted (R. 1/2)		£110	75·00
206c		1d. red-orange	.. ..	2·25	15

C. *Thin paper. Crown and Q faintly impressed. P* 12½, 13

207	**12**	2d. blue (retouched plate) (6.95)	..	10·00	
		a. "FWO" for "TWO" (R. 8/7)	..	80·00	

15	16

17	18

1895–96. A. W 6 *(sideways on* ½d.*). (a) P* 12½, 13.

208	**15**	½d. green (11.5.95)	..	1·40	75
		a. Double impression	..		
209		½d. deep green	..	1·40	75
		a. Printed both sides	..	75·00	
210	**16**	1d. orange-red (28.2.95)	..	3·00	20
211		1d. pale red	..	2·75	20
212		2d. blue (19.6.95)	..	5·00	35
213	**17**	2½d. carmine (8.95)	..	11·00	3·50
214		2½d. rose	..	12·00	3·50
215	**18**	5d. purple-brown (10.95)	..	15·00	3·50

(b) P 12

217	**16**	1d. red (8.95)	..	32·00	11·00
218		2d. blue (8.95)	..	32·00	15·00

B. *Thick paper.* **W 10** *(sideways) (part only on each stamp).*

(a) P 12½, 13

219	**15**	½d. green (8.95)	..	2·00	75
220		½d. deep green	..	2·00	75

(b) P 12

221	**15**	½d. green	..	12·00	
222		½d. deep green	..	12·00	

C. *No wmk; with blue burelé band at back. (a) P* 12½, 13

223	**15**	½d. green (1.8.95)	..	2·00	85
		a. Without burelé band	..	40·00	
224		½d. deep green	..	2·00	

(b) P 12

225	**15**	½d. green	..	15·00	
		a. Without burelé band	..	50·00	

Nos. 223a and 225a are from the margins of the sheet.

D. *Thin paper, with Crown and Q faintly impressed. P* 12½, 13

227	**15**	½d. green	..	1·75	85
228	**16**	1d. orange-red	..	3·25	50

19

1896. W 6. *P* 12½, 13.

229	**19**	1d. vermilion	..	10·00	50

Used examples of a 6d. green as Type **19** (figures in lower corners only) are known, mostly with readable 1902 postmark dates. It is believed that this 6d. was prepared, but not officially issued (*Price* £1700 *used*).

20	21	22
23	24	25

Die I	Die II

Two Dies of 4d.:

Die I. Serif of horizontal bar on lower right 4d. is clear of vertical frame line.

Die II. Serif joins vertical frame line.

1897–1908. *Figures in all corners.* **W 6** *(sideways on* ½d.*). P* 12½, 13.

231	**20**	½d. deep green	..	3·75	3·25
		a. Perf 12	..	—	90·00
232	**21**	1d. orange-vermilion	..	2·00	15
233		1d. vermilion	..	2·00	15
		a. Perf 12 (1903)	..	3·00	70
234		2d. blue (1902)	..	2·00	15
		a. Cracked plate	..	55·00	20·00
		b. Perf 12 (1903)	..	—	5·00
235		2d. deep blue	..	2·00	15
		a. Cracked plate	..	55·00	20·00
236	**22**	2½d. rose (10.98)	..	17·00	11·00
237		2½d. purple/blue (20.1.99)	..	9·50	1·00
238		2½d. brown-purple/blue	..	9·50	1·00
239		2½d. slate/blue (5.08)	..	12·00	2·75
240	**21**	3d. brown (10.98)	..	10·00	1·25
241		3d. deep brown	..	8·00	1·25
242		3d. reddish brown (1906)	..	8·00	1·25
243		3d. grey-brown (1907)	..	10·00	1·25
244		4d. yellow (Die I) (10.98)	..	8·00	1·50
		a. Die II	..	18·00	2·25
245		4d. yellow-buff (Die I)	..	8·00	1·50
		a. Die II	..	18·00	2·25
246	**23**	5d. purple-brown	..	8·00	1·25
247		5d. dull brown (1906)	..	9·00	2·00
248		5d. black-brown (1907)	..	10·00	2·25
249	**21**	6d. green (1.4.98)	..	7·00	1·75
250		6d. yellow-green	..	6·00	1·75
251	**24**	1s. pale mauve (1.7.99)	..	13·00	1·75
252		1s. dull mauve	..	13·00	1·75
253		1s. bright mauve	..	15·00	2·50
254	**25**	1s. turquoise-green	..	30·00	13·00

The 1d. perf 12×9½ was not an authorised issue.

The cracked plate variety on the 2d. developed during 1901 and shows as a white break on the Queen's head and neck. The electro was later replaced.

1897–8. W 6 *(a) Zigzag roulette in black. (b) The same but plain. (c) Roulette (a) and also (b). (d) Roulette (b) and perf* 12½, 13. *(e) Roulette (a) and perf* 12½, 13. *(f) Compound of (a), (b), and perf* 12½, 13.

256	**21**	1d. vermilion (a)	..	8·50	7·00
257		1d. vermilion (b)	..	3·75	3·25
258		1d. vermilion (c)	..	8·50	11·00
259		1d. vermilion (d)	..	5·50	4·50
260		1d. vermilion (e)	..	65·00	80·00
261		1d. vermilion (f)	..	80·00	80·00

26	27

(Des M. Kellar)

1899–1906. W 6. *P* 12½, 13.

262	**26**	½d. deep green	..	1·75	60
		a. Grey-green	..	1·75	60
		b. Green (p 12) (1903)	..	2·25	70
		c. Pale green (1906)	..	1·75	60

Stamps of T **26** without wmk, are proofs.

(Des F. Elliott)

1900 (19 June). *Charity. T* **27** *and horiz design showing Queen Victoria in medallion inscr* "PATRIOTIC FUND 1900". **W 6.** *P* 12.

264a		1d. (6d.) claret	..	£110	£100
264b		2d. (1s.) violet	..	£275	£250

These stamps, sold at 6d. and 1s. respectively, paid postage of 1d. and 2d. only, the difference being contributed to a Patriotic Fund.

28	A	B

TWO TYPES OF "QUEENSLAND". Three different duty plates, each 120 (12×10), were produced for Type **28**. The first contained country inscriptions as Type A and was only used for No. 265. The second duty plate used for Nos. 265/6 and 282/5 contained 117 examples as Type A and 3 as Type B occurring on R. 1/6, R. 2/6 and R. 3/6. The third plate, used for Nos. 266 and 282/5, had all inscriptions as Type B.

(Typo Victoria Govt Printer, Melbourne)

1903 (4 July)–**05.** W w **10.** P 12½.
265	28	9d. brown and ultramarine (A)	..	12·00	2·25
266		9d. brown and ultramarine (B) (1905)	..	12·00	2·25

1903 (Oct). As Nos. 162 and 165. W **6** (twice sideways). P 12½, 13 (irregular line).
270	9	2s. 6d. vermilion	..	60·00	32·00
271		£1 deep green	..	£900	£500
	a.	Re-entry (R.1/2)		—	£750
	b.	Retouch (R.6/4)		—	£750

(Litho Govt Ptg Office, Brisbane, from transfers of the recess plates)

1905 (Nov)–**06.** W **6** (twice sideways).

(a) P 12½, 13 (irregular line)
272	9	£1 deep green	..	£350	£100
	a.	Re-entry (R.1/2)		—	£160
	b.	Retouch (R.6/4)		—	£160

(b) P 12
273	9	5s. rose (7.06)	..	70·00	65·00
274		£1 deep green (7.06)	..	£250	90·00
	a.	Re-entry (R.1/2)		£375	£150
	b.	Retouch (R.6/4)		£375	£150

30	**32**

Redrawn types of T 21

T **30.** The head is redrawn, the top of the crown is higher and touches the frame, as do also the back of the chignon and the point of the bust. The forehead is filled in with lines of shading, and the figures in the corners appear to have been redrawn also.

T **32.** The forehead is plain (white instead of shaded), and though the top of the crown is made higher, it does not touch the frame; but the point of the bust and the chignon still touch The figure in the right lower corner does not touch the line below, and has not the battered appearance of that in the first redrawn type. The stamps are very clearly printed, the lines of shading being distinct.

1906 (Sept). W **6.** P 12½, 13 (comb).
281	**30**	2d. dull blue (shades)	..	7·00	2·50

(Typo Victoria Govt Printer, Melbourne)

1906 (Sept)–**10.** Wmk Crown and double-lined A, W w **11.**

(a) P 12 × 12½.
282	28	9d. brown and ultramarine (A)	..	26·00	3·50
283		9d. brown and ultramarine (B)	..	13·00	3·25
283a		9d. pale brown and blue (A)	..	26·00	4·00
284		9d. pale brown and blue (B)	..	13·00	3·50

(b) P 11 (1910)
285	28	9d. brown and blue (B)	..	—	£200

33

1907–11. W **33.** (a) P 12½, 13 (comb).
286	26	½d. deep green	..	1·75	55
287		½d. deep blue-green	..	1·75	55
288	21	1d. vermilion	..	2·25	15
	a.	Imperf (pair)	..	£170	
289	30	2d. dull blue	..	2·75	15
289a		2d. bright blue (3.08)	..	11·00	2·75
290	32	2d. bright blue (4.08)	..	2·75	15
291	21	3d. pale brown (8.08)	..	12·00	1·25
292		3d. bistre-brown	..	11·00	1·40
293		4d. yellow (Die I)	..	11·00	2·00
	a.	Die II	..	24·00	3·25
294		4d. grey-black (Die I) (4.09)	..	14·00	1·90
	a.	Die II	..	29·00	3·75
295	23	5d. dull brown	..	8·00	2·50
295a		5d. sepia (12.09)	..	13·00	3·00
296	21	6d. yellow-green	..	9·00	1·75
297		6d. bright green	..	11·00	2·00
298	24	1s. violet (1908)	..	12·00	1·75
299		1s. bright mauve	..	13·00	1·75
300	25	2s. turquoise-green (8.08)	..	30·00	11·00

Stamps of this issue also exist with the irregular line perforation 12½, 13. This was used when the comb perforation was under repair.

(b) P 13×11 to 12½ (May 1911)
301	26	½d. deep green	..	5·00	2·00
302	21	1d. vermilion	..	6·00	1·00
303	32	2d. blue	..	7·50	3·00
304	21	3d. bistre-brown	..	13·00	5·00
305		4d. grey-black	..	30·00	14·00
306	23	5d. dull brown	..	20·00	14·00
307	21	6d. yellow-green	..	20·00	14·00
308	21	1s. violet	..	35·00	15·00

The perforation (b) is from a machine introduced to help cope with the demands caused by the introduction of penny postage. The three rows at top (or bottom) of the sheet show varieties gauging 13 × 11½, 13 × 11, and 13 × 12 respectively, these are obtainable in strips of three showing the three variations.

(Litho Govt Ptg Office, Brisbane)

1907 (Oct)–**12.** W **33** (twice sideways). P 12½, 13 (irregular line).
309	9	2s. 6d. vermilion	..	40·00	28·00
	a.	Dull orange (1910)	..	55·00	48·00
	b.	Reddish orange (1912)	..	£150	£180
310		5s. rose (12.07)	..	48·00	30·00
	a.	Deep rose (1910)	..	60·00	45·00
	b.	Carmine-red (1912)	..	£150	£225
311		10s. blackish brown	..	£100	45·00
	a.	Sepia (1912)	..	£300	
312		£1 bluish green	..	£170	80·00
	a.	Re-entry (R. 1/2)		—	£130
	b.	Retouch (R. 6/4)		—	£130
	c.	Deep bluish green (1910)		£375	£250
	ca.	Re-entry (R. 1/2)		—	£350
	cb.	Retouch (R. 6/4)		—	£350
	d.	Yellow-green (1912)		£750	
	da.	Re-entry (R. 1/2)			
	db.	Retouch (R. 6/4)			

The 1912 printings are on thinner, whiter paper.
The lithographic stone used for Nos. 272/4 and 309/12 took the full sheet of 30 so the varieties on the £1 recess-printed version also appear on the stamps printed by lithography.

1911. W **33.** Perf irregular compound, 10½ to 12½.
313	21	1d. vermilion	..	£350	£190

This was from another converted machine, formerly used for perforating Railway stamps. The perforation was very unsatisfactory and only one or two sheets were sold.

STAMP BOOKLETS

There are very few surviving examples of Nos. SB1/4. Listings are provided for those believed to have been issued with prices quoted for those known to still exist.

1904 (1 Jan)–**09.** Black on red cover as No. SB1 of New South Wales. Stapled.
SB1	£1 booklet containing two hundred and forty 1d. in four blocks of 30 and two blocks of 60	..	
	a. Red on pink cover (1909)	..	
	b. Blue on pink cover	..	£6000

1904 (1 Jan). Black on grey cover as No. SB1. Stapled.
SB2	£1 booklet containing one hundred and twenty 2d. in four blocks of 30	..

1910 (May). Black on cream cover as No. SB3 of New South Wales. Stapled.
SB3	2s. booklet containing eleven ½d. (No. 301), either in block of 6 plus block of 5 or block of 11, and eighteen 1d. (No. 302), either in three blocks of 6 or block of 6 plus block of 12

Unsold stock of No. SB3 was uprated with one additional ½d. in May 1911.

1911 (Aug). Red on pink cover as No. SB3. Stapled.
SB4	2s. booklet containing twelve ½d. (No. 301), either in two blocks of 6 or block of 12, and eighteen 1d. (No. 302), either in three blocks of 6 or block of 6 plus block of 12	..	£1500
	a. Red on white	..	£1500

POSTAL FISCALS

Authorised for use from 1 January 1880 until 1 July 1892

CANCELLATIONS. Beware of stamps which have had pen-cancellations cleaned off and then had faked postmarks applied. Used prices quoted are for postally used examples between the above dates.

F 1	**F 2**

1866–68. A. No wmk. P 13.
F 1	F 1	1d. blue	..	30·00	7·00
F 2		6d. deep violet	..	30·00	40·00
F 3		1s. blue-green	..	35·00	9·00
F 4		2s. brown	..	90·00	42·00
F 5		2s. 6d. dull red	..	90·00	30·00
F 6		5s. yellow	..	£200	60·00
F 6a		6s. light brown	..	£550	
F 7		10s. green	..	£350	£100
F 8		20s. rose	..	£425	£150

B. Wmk F **2.** P 13.
F 9	F 1	1d. blue	..	18·00	20·00
F10		6d. deep violet	..	30·00	30·00
F11		6d. blue	..	30·00	14·00
F12		1s. blue-green	..	35·00	14·00
F13		2s. brown	..	90·00	30·00
F13a		5s. yellow	..	£200	65·00
F14		10s. green	..	£350	£100
F15		20s. rose	..	£425	£150

COVER PRICES

Cover factors are quoted at the beginning of each country for most issues to 1945. An explanation of the system can be found on page x. The factors quoted do not, however, apply to philatelic covers.

F 3	**F 3a**

1871–2. P 12 or 13. A. Wmk Large Crown and Q, Wmk F **3a.**
F16	F **3**	1d. mauve	..	12·00	5·00
F17		6d. red-brown	..	22·00	10·00
F18		1s. green	..	35·00	10·00
F19		2s. blue	..	45·00	10·00
F20		2s. 6d. brick-red	..	65·00	25·00
F21		5s. orange-brown	..	£100	25·00
F22		10s. brown	..	£200	75·00
F23		20s. rose	..	£350	£120

B. No wmk. Blue burelé band at back.
F24	F **3**	1d. mauve	..	16·00	6·50
F25		6d. red-brown	..	22·00	10·00
F26		6d. mauve	..	65·00	30·00
F27		1s. green	..	35·00	12·00
F28		2s. blue	..	50·00	50·00
F29		2s. 6d. vermilion	..	90·00	35·00
F30		5s. yellow-brown	..	£120	40·00
F31		10s. brown	..	£225	90·00
F32		20s. rose	..	£350	£110

F 4	**F 5**

1878–9. A. No wmk. Lilac burelé band at back. P 12.
F33	F **4**	1d. violet	..	42·00	12·00

B. Wmk Crown and Q, W **5.** P 12
F34	F **4**	1d. violet	..	16·00	8·00

Stamps as Type F **5** were not issued until 1 July 1892. The existence of postal cancellations on such issues was unauthorised.

Queensland became part of the Commonwealth of Australia on 1 January 1901.

SOUTH AUSTRALIA

PRICES FOR STAMPS ON COVER
Nos. 1/3	from × 3
No. 4	†
Nos. 5/12	from × 2
Nos. 13/18	from × 3
Nos. 19/43	from × 4
Nos. 44/9b	—
Nos. 50/110	from × 3
No. 111	—
Nos. 112/34	from × 6
Nos. 135/45	from × 3
Nos. 146/66	from × 5
Nos. 167/70a	from × 10
Nos. 171/2a	—
Nos. 173/94a	from × 12
Nos. 195/208	—
Nos. 229/31	from × 12
No. 232	—
Nos. 233/42	from × 12
Nos. 268/75	from × 30
Nos. 276/9	—
Nos. 280/8	from × 30
Nos. 289/92	—
Nos. 293/304	from × 15
No. 305	—
Nos. O1/13	—
Nos. O14/36	from × 20
Nos. O37/42	from × 5
Nos. O43/4	from × 50
Nos. O45/7	—
Nos. O48/52	from × 30
No. O53	—
Nos. O54/85	from × 50
Nos. O86/7	—

SPECIMEN OVERPRINTS. Those listed are from U.P.U. distributions between 1889 and 1895. Further "Specimen" overprints exist, but these were used for other purposes.

PERKINS BACON "CANCELLED". For notes on these handstamps, showing "CANCELLED" between horizontal bars forming an oval, see Catalogue Introduction.

1

2 Large Star

(Eng Wm Humphrys. Recess P.B.)

1855 (26 Oct–1 Nov). *Printed in London. W* **2**. *Imperf.*

1	1	1d. dark green (H/S "CANCELLED" in oval £4000)		£2500	£375
2		2d. rose-carmine (*shades*) (1 Nov) (H/S "CANCELLED" in oval £3000)		£550	80·00
3		6d. deep blue (H/S "CANCELLED" in oval £3000)		£2000	£150

Prepared and sent to the Colony, but not issued

4	1	1s. vio (H/S "CANCELLED" in oval £5500)	£4750	

A printing of 500,000 of these 1s. stamps was made and delivered, but, as the colour was liable to be confused with that of the 6d. stamp, the majority of the stock was destroyed on 5 June 1857.

NOTE. Proofs of the 1d. and 6d. without wmk exist, and these are found with forged star watermarks added, and are sometimes offered as originals.

For reprints of the above and later issues, see note after No. 194.

1856–58. *Printed by Govt Ptr, Adelaide, from Perkins, Bacon plates. W* **2**. *Imperf.*

5	1	1d. deep yellow-green (15.6.58)		£5000	£400
6		1d. yellow-green (11.10.58)		—	£475
7		2d. orange-red (23.4.56)		—	75·00
8		2d. blood-red (14.11.56)		£1200	60·00
		a. Printed on both sides		—	£800
9		2d. red (*shades*) (29.10.57)		£650	40·00
		a. Printed on both sides		—	£600
10		6d. slate-blue (7.57)		£2000	£150
11		1s. red-orange (8.7.57)		—	£400
12		1s. orange (11.6.58)		£3750	£325

1858–59. W **2**. *Rouletted. (This first rouletted issue has the same colours as the local imperf issue).*

13	1	1d. yellow-green (8.1.59)		£475	45·00
14		1d. light yellow-green (18.3.59)		£475	50·00
		a. Imperf between (pair)		—	
15		2d. red (17.2.59)		£110	18·00
		a. Printed on both sides		—	£600
17		6d. slate-blue (12.12.58)		£375	25·00
18		1s. orange (18.3.59)		£800	35·00
		a. Printed on both sides		—	£1000

3

4

(5)

1860–69. *Second rouletted issue, printed (with the exception of No. 24) in colours only found rouletted or perforated. Surch with T* **5** (*Nos.* 35/7). W **2**.

19	1	1d. bright yellow-green (22.4.61)		45·00	26·00
20		1d. dull blue-green (17.12.63)		42·00	24·00
21		1d. sage-green		55·00	28·00
22		1d. pale sage-green (27.5.65)		45·00	
23		1d. deep green (1864)		£225	65·00
24		1d. deep yellow-green (1869)		90·00	
24a		2d. pale red		65·00	4·00
		b. Printed on both sides		—	£375
25		2d. pale vermilion (3.2.63)		50·00	4·00
26		2d. bright vermilion (19.8.64)		42·00	2·75
		a. Imperf between (horiz pair)		£700	£300
27	3	4d. dull violet (24.1.67)		60·00	17·00
28	1	6d. violet-blue (19.3.60)		£140	6·00
29		6d. greenish blue (11.2.63)		70·00	4·00
30		6d. dull ultramarine (25.4.64)		65·00	4·00
		a. Imperf between (horiz pair)		—	£300
31		6d. violet-ultramarine (11.4.68)		£150	6·00
32		6d. dull blue (26.8.65)		£100	6·50
		a. Imperf between (pair)		—	£600
33		6d. Prussian blue (7.9.69)		£550	50·00
33a		6d. indigo		—	55·00
34	4	9d. grey-lilac (24.12.60)		55·00	9·00
		a. Imperf between (horiz pair)		—	£1000
35		10d. on 9d. orange-red (B.) (20.7.66)		£140	15·00
36		10d. on 9d. yellow (29.7.67)		£170	22·00
37		10d. on 9d. yellow (Blk.) (14.8.69)		£1200	32·00
		a. Surch inverted at the top		—	£2500
		b. Printed on both sides		—	£800
		c. Roul × perf 10		†	—
38	1	1s. yellow (25.10.61)		£450	26·00
		a. Imperf between (vert pair)		—	£1200
39		1s. grey-brown (10.4.63)		£150	17·00
40		1s. dark grey-brown (26.5.63)		£130	17·00
41		1s. chestnut (25.8.63)		£150	11·00
42		1s. lake-brown (27.3.65)		£110	12·00
		a. Imperf between (horiz pair)		—	£400
43	4	2s. rose-carmine (24.1.67)		£160	26·00
		a. Imperf between (vert pair)		—	£750

1868–71. *Remainders of old stock subsequently perforated by the 11½–12½ machine.*

(a) Imperf stamps. P 11½–12½

44	1	1d. pale vermilion (Feb 1868)		—	£900
45		2d. vermilion (18.3.68)		—	£1000

(b) Rouletted stamps. P 11½–12½

46	1	1d. bright green (9.11.69)		—	£450
47		2d. pale vermilion (15.8.68)		£1500	£400
48		6d. Prussian blue (8.11.69)		—	£200
		aa. Horiz pair perf all round, roul between			
48a		6d. indigo		—	£300
49	4	9d. grey-lilac (29.3.71)		£1500	£160
		a. Perf × roulette		—	£180
49b	1	1s. lake-brown (23.5.70)		—	

1867–70. W **2**. P 11½–12½ × *roulette.*

50	1	1d. pale bright green (2.11.67)		£150	20·00
51		1d. bright green (1868)		£130	20·00
52		1d. grey-green (26.1.70)		£150	22·00
		a. Imperf between (horiz pair)			
53		1d. blue-green (29.11.67)		£190	32·00
54	3	4d. dull violet (July 1868)		£1400	£130
55		4d. dull purple (1869)		—	90·00
56	1	6d. bright pale blue (29.5.67)		£450	19·00
57		6d. Prussian blue (30.7.67)		£400	19·00
		a. Printed on both sides			
58		6d. indigo (1.8.69)		£500	25·00
59	4	10d. on 9d. yellow (B.) (2.2.69)		£600	30·00
		a. Printed on both sides		—	£550
60	1	1s. chestnut (April 1868)		£250	16·00
61		1s. lake-brown (3.3.69)		£250	16·00

NOTE. The stamps perf 11½, 12½, or compound of the two, are here combined in one list, as both perforations are on the one machine, and all the varieties *may* be found in each sheet of stamps. This method of classifying the perforations by the machines is by far the most simple and convenient.

3-PENCE

(6)

7 (= Victoria W **19**)

1868–79. *Surch with T* **6** (*Nos.* 66/8). W **2**. P 11½–12½.

62	1	1d. pale bright green (8.2.68)		£150	20·00
63		1d. grey-green (18.2.68)		£120	42·00
64		1d. dark green (20.3.68)		60·00	19·00
		a. Printed on both sides			
65		1d. deep yellow-green (28.6.72)		55·00	19·00
		a. Imperf between (horiz pair)		†	£500
66	3	3d. on 4d. Prussian blue (Blk.) (7.2.71)		—	£700
67		3d. on 4d. sky-blue (Blk.) (12.8.70)		£275	10·00
		a. Imperf			
		b. Rouletted		—	£500
68		3d. on 4d. deep ultramarine (Blk.) (9.72)		70·00	8·50
		a. Surch double (10.9.74)		—	£3250
		b. Additional surch on back		—	£2500
		c. Surch omitted (26.4.74)		£14000	£8000
70		4d. dull purple (1.2.68)		60·00	15·00
		a. Imperf between (horiz pair)			
71		4d. dull violet (1868)		55·00	8·00
72	1	6d. bright pale blue (23.2.68)		£300	11·00
73		6d. Prussian blue (29.9.69)		90·00	6·50
		a. Perf 11½×imperf (horiz pair)		†	£500
74		6d. indigo (1869)		£120	17·00
75	4	9d. claret (7.72)		£100	8·00
76		9d. bright mauve (1.11.72)		£100	8·00
		a. Printed on both sides		—	£300
77		9d. red-purple (15.1.74)		65·00	8·00
78		10d. on 9d. yellow (B.) (15.8.68)		£1000	26·00
		a. Wmk Crown and S A (W **10**) (1868)		—	£750
79		10d. on 9d. yellow (Blk.) (13.9.69)		£200	29·00
80	1	1s. lake-brown (9.68)		£150	11·00
81		1s. chestnut (8.10.72)		£110	16·00
82		1s. dark red-brown		90·00	11·00
83		1s. red-brown (6.1.69)		£100	11·00
84	3	2s. pale rose-pink (10.10.69)		£950	£150
85		2s. deep rose-pink (8.69)		—	£100
86		2s. crimson-carmine (16.10.69)		80·00	18·00
87		2s. carmine (1869)		70·00	11·00
		a. Printed on both sides		—	£300

No. 78a was a trial printing made to test the perforating machine on the new D.L.R. paper.

1870–71. W **2**. P 10.

88	1	1d. grey-green (6.70)		£120	15·00
89		1d. pale bright green (9.8.70)		£120	15·00
90		1d. bright green (1871)		£100	15·00
91	3	3d. on 4d. dull ultramarine (R.) (6.8.70)		£325	60·00
92		3d. on 4d. pale ultram (Blk.) (14.2.71)		£250	14·00
93		3d. on 4d. ultramarine (Blk.) (14.8.71)		£100	17·00
93a		3d. on 4d. Prussian blue (Blk.) (16.12.71)		£110	10·00
94		4d. dull lilac (1870)		£100	10·00
95		4d. dull purple (1871)		£100	10·00
96	1	6d. bright blue (19.6.70)		£180	17·00
97		6d. indigo (11.10.71)		£225	16·00
98		1s. chestnut (4.1.71)		£150	20·00

1870–73. W **2**. P 10 × 11½–12½, 11½–12½ × 10, *or compound.*

99	1	1d. pale bright green (11.10.70)		£140	14·00
		a. Printed on both sides			
100		1d. grey-green		£130	15·00
101		1d. deep green (19.6.71)		75·00	10·00
102	3	3d. on 4d. pale ultram (Blk.) (9.11.70)		£180	38·00
103		4d. dull lilac (11.5.72)		—	20·00
104		4d. slate-lilac (5.3.73)		£120	18·00
105	1	6d. Prussian blue (2.3.70)		£140	8·00
106		6d. bright Prussian blue (26.10.70)		£150	10·00
107	4	10d. on 9d. yellow (Blk.) (1.70)		£110	17·00
108	1	1s. chestnut (17.6.71)		£200	35·00
109	3	2s. rose-pink (24.4.71)		—	£170
110		2s. carmine (2.3.72)		£130	26·00

1871 (17 July). W **7**. P 10.

111	3	4d. dull lilac		£1500	£200
		a. Printed on both sides			

8 Broad Star

8 PENCE

(9)

1876–1900. W **8**. *Surch with T* **9** (*Nos.* 118/21). (*a) P* 11½–12½.

112	3	3d. on 4d. ultramarine (1.6.79)		60·00	15·00
		a. Surch double		—	£1000
113		4d. violet-slate (15.3.79)		£100	12·00
114		4d. plum (16.4.80)		50·00	6·50
115		4d. deep mauve (8.6.82)		50·00	5·50
116	1	6d. indigo (2.12.76)		£100	4·50
		a. Imperf between (horiz pair)			
117		6d. Prussian blue (7.78)		65·00	4·00
118	4	8d. on 9d. brown-orange (7.76)		60·00	5·50
119		8d. on 9d. burnt umber (1880)		65·00	5·50
120		8d. on 9d. brown (9.3.80)		65·00	5·50
		a. Imperf between (vert pair)		—	£425
121		8d. on 9d. grey-brown (10.5.81)		60·00	7·00
		a. Surch double		—	£350
122		9d. purple (9.3.80)		48·00	7·00
		a. Printed on both sides		—	£200
123		9d. rose-lilac (21.8.80)		16·00	3·25
124		9d. rose-lilac (*large holes*) (26.5.00)		10·00	3·50
125	1	1s. red-brown (3.11.77)		50·00	2·75
		a. Imperf between (horiz pair)		—	£275
126		1s. reddish lake-brown (1880)		48·00	3·00
127		1s. lake-brown (9.1.83)		55·00	2·75
		a. Printed double			
128		1s. Vandyke brown (1891)		65·00	8·00
129		1s. dull brown (1891)		42·00	2·75
130		1s. chocolate (*large holes*) (6.5.97)		24·00	3·00
		a. Imperf vert (horiz pair)		£200	
131		1s. sepia (*large holes*) (22.5.00)		24·00	3·00
		a. Imperf between (vert pair)		£150	
132	3	2s. carmine (15.2.77)		38·00	5·00
		a. Imperf between (horiz pair)		—	£450
		b. Imperf (pair)			
133		2s. rose-carmine (1885)		42·00	6·50
134		2s. rose-carmine (*large holes*) (6.12.98)		30·00	6·50

The perforation with larger, clean-cut holes resulted from the fitting of new pins to the machine.

(b) P 10

135	1	6d. Prussian blue (11.11.79)		90·00	13·00
136		6d. bright blue (1879)		£110	12·00
136a		1s. reddish lake-brown		£225	

(c) P 10 × 11½–12½, 11½–12½ × 10, *or compound*

137	3	4d. violet-slate (21.5.79)		£100	11·00
138		4d. dull purple (4.10.79)		40·00	2·25
139	1	6d. Prussian blue (29.12.77)		55·00	2·50
140		6d. bright blue		75·00	5·50
141		6d. bright ultramarine		42·00	1·75
142		1s. reddish lake-brown (9.2.85)		80·00	9·00
143		1s. dull brown (29.6.86)		£100	10·00
144	3	2s. carmine (27.12.77)		55·00	5·50
145		2s. rose-carmine (1887)		50·00	5·00
		a. Imperf between (horiz pair)		—	£425

10

11

12

1901–2. *Wmk Crown SA (wide), W* **10**. P 11½–12½ (*large holes*).

146	4	9d. claret (1.2.02)		15·00	15·00
147	1	1s. dark brown (12.6.01)		22·00	11·00
148		1s. dark reddish brown (1902)		24·00	12·00
		a. Imperf between (vert pair)			
149		1s. red-brown (aniline) (18.7.02)		22·00	13·00
150	3	2s. crimson (29.8.01)		28·00	14·00
151		2s. carmine		22·00	10·00

(Plates and electrotypes by D.L.R. Printed in Adelaide)

1868–76. W **10**. (*a) Rouletted.*

152	12	2d. deep brick-red (8.68)		55·00	3·25
153		2d. pale orange-red (5.10.68)		50·00	2·75
		a. Printed on both sides		—	£225
		b. Imperf between (horiz pair)		—	£275

(b) P 11½–12½

154	11	1d. blue-green (10.1.75)		70·00	11·00
155	12	2d. pale orange-red (5.5.69)		£850	£190

(c) P 11½–12½ × *roulette*

156	12	2d. pale orange-red (20.8.69)		—	£120

(d) P 10 × *roulette*

157	12	2d. pale orange-red (7.5.70)		£200	24·00

(e) P 10

158	11	1d. blue-green (4.75)		27·00	4·50
159	12	2d. brick-red (4.70)		13·00	45
160		2d. orange-red (1.7.70)		10·00	40
		a. Printed on both sides		—	£170

(f) P 10 × 11½–12½, 11½–12½ × 10, *or compound*

161	11	1d. blue-green (27.8.75)		50·00	15·00
162	12	2d. brick-red (19.1.71)		£400	6·00
163		2d. orange-red (3.2.71)		£100	8·50
		a. Imperf (8.76)		—	£750

1869. *Wmk Large Star, W 2. (a) Rouletted.*
164 12 2d. orange-red (13.3.69) .. 55·00 12·00
 (b) P 11½–12½ × *roulette*
165 12 2d. orange-red (1.8.69) .. — 90·00
 (c) P 11½–12½
165a 12 2d. orange-red (7.69) .. £800

1871 (15 July). *Wmk V and Crown, W 7. P 10.*
166 12 2d. brick-red .. .. 50·00 15·00

HALF-

PENNY

13 (14)

1876–1904. *Wmk Crown SA (close), W 13. (a)* P 10 (1876–85)
167 11 1d. blue-green (9.2.76) .. 7·00 20
 a. Yellowish green (11.78) .. 9·00 20
 b. Deep green (11.79) .. 9·00 20
 ba. Imperf between (horiz pair)
 bb. Printed double † —
168 12 2d. orange-red (8.76) .. 8·00 10
 a. Dull brick-red (21.5.77) .. 8·00 10
 b. Blood-red (31.10.79) .. £200 3·00
 c. Pale red (4.85) .. 8·00 10
 (b) P 10×11½–12½, 11½–12½×10 *or compound* (1877–80)
169 11 1d. deep green (11.2.80) .. 22·00 2·25
 a. Blue-green (2.3.80) .. 11·00 1·90
170 12 2d. orange-red (4.9.77) .. £120 3·00
 a. Dull brick-red (6.80) .. £120 3·00
 (c) P 11½–12½ (1877–84)
171 11 1d. blue-green (2.84) .. — £110
172 12 2d. orange-red (14.9.77) .. — £110
 a. Blood-red (1.4.80) .. — £110
 (d) P 15 (1893)
173 11 1d. green (8.5.93) .. 5·00 30
174 12 2d. pale orange (9.2.93) .. 9·50 10
 a. Orange-red .. 9·00 10
 b. Imperf between (vert pair) .. £180
 (e) P 13 (1895–1903)
175 11 1d. pale green (11.1.95) .. 5·00 20
 a. Green .. 5·00 20
 b. Imperf between (vert pair)
176 1d. rosine (8.8.99) .. 3·00 10
 a. Scarlet (23.12.03) .. 3·50 10
 b. Deep red .. 3·25 10
177 12 2d. pale orange (19.1.95) .. 4·25 10
 a. Orange-red (9.5.95) .. 5·00 10
178 2d. bright violet (10.10.99) .. 2·50 10
 (f) P 12×11½ (comb) (1904)
179 11 1d. rosine (2.2.04) .. 6·50 10
 a. Scarlet (25.7.04) .. 5·00 10
180 12 2d. bright violet (11.10.04) .. 3·75 10
Examples of the 1d. pale green with thicker lettering come from a worn plate.

1882 (1 Jan). *No. 167 surch with T 14.*
181 11 ½d. on 1d. blue-green .. 11·00 3·50

15

16

17

18

1883–99. *W 13 (sideways on ½d.). (a)* P 10 (1883–95)
182 15 ½d. chocolate (1.3.83) .. 3·00 50
 a. Imperf between (horiz pair)
 b. Red-brown (4.4.89) .. 2·75 45
 c. Brown (1895) .. 2·75 45
183 16 3d. sage-green (12.86) (Optd S. £25) 10·00 1·10
 a. Olive-green (6.6.90) .. 8·50 1·50
 b. Deep green (12.4.93) .. 6·50 90
184 17 4d. pale violet (3.90) (Optd S. £30) 8·50 1·25
 a. Aniline violet (3.1.93) .. 10·00 1·50
185 18 6d. pale blue (4.87) (Optd S. £25) 8·50 1·40
 a. Blue (5.5.87) .. 10·00 70
 (b) P 10×11½–12½, 11½–12½×10 *or compound* (1891)
186 15 ½d. red-brown (25.9.91) .. 4·50 1·75
 a. Imperf between (horiz pair) .. 85·00
 (c) P 11½–12½ (1890)
187 15 ½d. red-brown (1.90) .. 7·00 1·50
 (d) P 15 (1893–94)
188 15 ½d. pale brown (1.93) .. 3·00 60
 a. Deep brown .. 3·00 60
 b. Imperf between (horiz pair) .. 85·00
 c. Perf 12½ between (pair) .. £120 28·00
189 17 4d. purple (1.1.94) .. 10·00 2·00
 a. Slate-violet .. 15·00 1·75

190 18 6d. blue (20.11.93) .. 24·00 3·50
 (e) P 13 (1895–99)
191 15 ½d. pale brown (9.95) .. 2·75 30
 a. Deep brown (19.3.97) .. 2·75 30
192 16 3d. pale olive-green (26.7.97) .. 7·00 90
 a. Deep olive-green (27.11.99) .. 5·00 90
193 17 4d. violet (21.5.96) .. 6·00 40
194 18 6d. pale blue (3.96) .. 7·00 75
 a. Blue .. 7·00 75

REPRINTS. In 1884, and in later years, reprints on paper wmkd Crown SA, W 10, were made of Nos. 1, 2, 3, 4, 12, 13, 14, 15, 19, 24, 27, 28, 32, 33, 34, 35, 36, 37, 38, 40, 43, 44, 49a, 53, 65, 67, 67 with surcharge in red, 70, 71, 72, 73, 78, 79, 81, 83, 86, 90, 118, 119, 120, 121, 122, 155, 158, 159, 164, 181, 182. They are overprinted "REPRINT".
 In 1889 examples of the reprints for Nos. 1/3, 12, 15, 19, 27, 32/8, 44, 67, 67 surcharged in red, 70/1, 73, 83, 86, 118, 121/2, 158/9, 164 and 181/2, together with No. 141 overprinted "Specimen", were supplied to the U.P.U. for distribution.

19 (20) (21)

(Plates and electrotypes by D.L.R. Printed in Adelaide)

1886 (20 Dec)–96. *T 19* (*inscr* "POSTAGE & REVENUE"). *W 13. Parts of two or more wmks, on each stamp, sometimes sideways.* P 10.
195 2s. 6d. mauve .. .. 32·00 8·00
 a. Perf 11½–12½. Dull violet .. 28·00 6·00
 bb. Bright aniline violet .. 30·00 7·00
196 5s. rose-pink .. .. 48·00 12·00
 a. Perf 11½–12½ .. 38·00 12·00
 ab. Rose-carmine .. 38·00 14·00
197 10s. green .. .. £110 35·00
 a. Perf 11½–12½ .. 80·00 35·00
198 15s. brownish yellow .. £275
 a. Perf 11½–12½ .. £300 £120
199 £1 blue .. .. £200 90·00
 a. Perf 11½–12½ .. £150 80·00
200 £2 Venetian red £550 £200
 a. Perf 11½–12½ .. £550 £200
201 50s. dull pink £800 £250
 a. Perf 11½–12½ .. £800
202 £3 sage green £850 £250
 a. Perf 11½–12½ .. £850 £250
203 £4 lemon £1100
 a. Perf 11½–12½ .. £950
204 £5 grey £1600
 a. Perf 11½–12½ .. £1700
205 £5 brown (p 11½–12½) (1896) .. £1700 £600
206 £10 bronze £2500 £700
 a. Perf 11½–12½ .. £1800 £700
207 £15 silver £4500
 a. Perf 11½–12½ .. £4500
208 £20 claret £5000
 a. Perf 11½–12½ .. £5000
195/208 Optd "Specimen" .. Set of 14 £450
 Variations exist in the length of the words and shape of the letters of the value inscription.
 The 2s. 6d. dull violet, 5s. rose-pink, 10s., £1 and £5 brown exist perf 11½–12½ with either large or small holes; the 2s. 6d. aniline, 5s. rose-carmine, 15s., £2 and 50s. with large holes only and the remainder only with small holes.
 Stamps perforated 11½–12½ small holes, are, generally speaking, rather rarer than those with the 1895 (large holes) gauge.
 Stamps perf 10 were issued on 20 Dec 1886. Stamps perf 11½–12½ (small holes) are known with earliest dates covering the period from June 1890 to Feb 1896. Earliest dates of stamps with large holes range from July 1896 to May 1902.

1891 (1 Jan)–93. *T 17/18 surch with T 20/1. W 13. (a)* P 10
229 17 2½d. on 4d. pale grn (Br.) (Optd S. £25) 7·50 2·50
 a. Fraction bar omitted .. 90·00 75·00
 b. Deep green .. 8·00 1·75
 ba. Fraction bar omitted .. 90·00 75·00
 bb. "2" and "½" closer together .. 20·00 18·00
 bc. Imperf between (horiz pair)
 bd. Imperf between (vert pair) .. — £425
230 18 5d. on 6d. pale brn (C.) (Optd S. £25) 16·00 4·00
 a. Deep brown .. 16·00 3·75
 b. No stop after "5D" .. £150
 (b) P 10×11½–12½ or 11½–12½×10
231 17 2½d. on 4d. pale green (Br.) .. 16·00 3·00
 a. Deep green .. 16·00 3·00
 (c) P 11½–12½
232 17 2½d. on 4d. deep green .. 28·00 45·00
 (d) P 15
233 17 2½d. on 4d. green (14.10.93) .. 13·00 2·00
 a. Fraction bar omitted
 b. "2" and "½d." closer together .. 42·00 22·00

22 Red
Kangaroo

23

24 G.P.O.,
Adelaide

(Des M. Tannenberg, plates by D.L.R.)
1894 (1 Mar)–1906. *W 13. (a)* P 15
234 22 2½d. violet-blue .. 16·00 2·00
235 23 5d. brown-purple .. 16·00 2·25
234/5 Optd "Specimen" Set of 2 50·00
 (b) P 13
236 22 2½d. violet-blue (11.2.95) .. 13·00 70
237 2½d. indigo (25.3.98) .. 4·50 40
238 23 5d. brown-purple (1.96) .. 6·50 50
 a. Purple .. 6·50 45
 (c) P 12×11½ (comb)
239 22 2½d. indigo (4.7.06) .. 7·50 40
240 23 5d. dull purple (1.05) .. 8·50 85

(Typo D.L.R.)
1899 (27 Dec)–1905. *W 13. (a)* P 13
241 24 ½d. yellow-green .. 1·50
 (b) P 12×11½ (comb)
242 24 ½d. yellow-green (7.05) .. 1·50 40

25

The measurements given indicate the length of the value inscription in the bottom label. The dates are those of the earliest known postmarks.

1902–04. *As T 19, but top tablet as T 25 (thin "POSTAGE"). W 13. (a)* P 11½–12½.
268 3d. olive-green (18½ mm) (1.8.02) .. 4·00 1·25
269 4d. red-orange (17 mm) (29.11.02) .. 5·00 1·75
270 6d. blue-green (16–16½ mm) (29.11.02) .. 6·00 1·75
271 8d. ultramarine (19 mm) (25.4.02) .. 7·50 4·00
272 8d. ultramarine (16½ mm) (22.3.04) .. 7·50 4·00
 a. "EIGNT" (R. 2/9) .. £800 £1100
273 9d. rosy lake (19.9.02) .. 8·00 2·50
 a. Imperf between (vert pair) .. £300
 b. Imperf between (horiz pair)
274 10d. dull yellow (29.11.02) .. 11·00 5·00
275 1s. brown (18.8.02) .. 11·00 2·50
 a. Imperf between (horiz pair)
 b. Imperf between (vert pair) .. £450
 c. "POSTAGE" and value in red-brown 45·00 20·00
276 2s. 6d. pale violet (19.9.02) .. 28·00 12·00
 a. Bright violet (2.2.03) .. 22·00 7·00
277 5s. rose (17.10.02) .. 55·00 40·00
278 10s. green (1.11.02) .. £100 60·00
279 £1 blue (1.11.02) .. £225 £120
 (b) P 12
280 3d. olive-green (20 mm) (15.4.04) .. 7·00 1·75
 a. "POSTAGE" omitted; value below "AUSTRALIA" .. £375
281 4d. orange-red (17½–18 mm) (18.2.03) .. 6·50 1·75
282 6d. blue-green (15 mm) (14.11.03) .. 16·00 3·50
283 9d. rosy lake (2.12.03) .. 32·00 5·00

PRINTER. Stamp printing in Adelaide ceased in 1909 when the printer, J. B. Cooke, was appointed head of the Commonwealth Stamp Printing Branch in Melbourne. From 9 March 1909 further printings of current South Australia stamps were made in Melbourne.

26

TWO SHILLINGS
AND SIX PENCE
V

TWO SHILLINGS
AND SIX PENCE
X

In Type X the letters in the bottom line are slightly larger than in Type V, especially the "A", "S" and "P".

FIVE
SHILLINGS
Y

FIVE
SHILLINGS
Z

In Type Z the letters "S" and "G" are more open than in Type Y. Nos. 196/a and 277 are similar to Type Y with all letters thick and regular and the last "S" has the top curve rounded instead of being slightly flattened.

1904–11. *As T 19, but top tablet as T 26 (thick "POSTAGE"). W 13. P 12.*
284 6d. blue-green (27.4.04) .. 8·00 2·00
 a. Imperf between (vert pair)
285 8d. bright ultramarine (4.7.05) .. 7·00 3·50
 a. Value closer (15¼ mm) .. 18·00
 b. Dull ultramarine (2.4.08) .. 10·00 2·75
286 9d. rosy lake (17–17¼ mm) (18.7.04) .. 8·00 2·50
 a. Value 16½–16¾ mm (2.06) .. 18·00 4·50
 b. Brown-lake. Perf 12½ small holes (6.6.11) 13·00
287 10d. dull yellow (8.07) .. 14·00 7·00
 a. Imperf between (horiz pair) .. £350 £275
 b. Imperf between (vert pair) .. £325
288 1s. brown (12.4.04) .. 12·00 1·75
 a. Imperf between (vert pair) .. £225
 b. Imperf between (horiz pair) .. £300
289 2s. 6d. bright violet (V.) (14.7.05) .. 42·00 9·00
 a. Dull violet (X) (8.06) .. 42·00 9·00
290 5s. rose-scarlet (Y) (8.04) .. 42·00 27·00
 a. Scarlet (Z) (8.06) .. 42·00 27·00
 b. Pale rose. Perf 12½ (small holes) (Z) (7.10) 55·00 32·00
291 10s. green (26.8.08) .. £100 £130
292 £1 blue (29.12.04) .. £160 £100
 a. Perf 12½ (small holes) (7.10) £140 85·00
The "value closer" variety on the 8d. occurs six times in the sheet of 60. The value normally measures 16½ mm but in the variety it is 15¼ mm.
 The 9d., 5s. and £1, perf 12½ (small holes), are late printings made in 1910–11 to use up the Crown SA paper.
 No. 286b has the value as Type C of the 9d. on Crown over A paper.

27

1905–11. W **27**. *P* 12 × 11½ (*new comb machine*).
293 24 ½d. pale green (4.07) .. .. .. 3·00 65
    a. Yellow-green .. .. .. 3·00 65
294 11 1d. rosine (2.12.05) .. .. .. 3·25 10
    a. Scarlet (4.11) .. .. .. 3·00 20
295 12 2d. bright violet (2.2.06) .. .. 5·00 10
    aa. Imperf three sides (horiz pair) ..
    a. Mauve (4.08) .. .. 3·50 10
296 22 2½d. indigo-blue (14.9.10) .. .. 9·00 2·50
297 23 5d. brown-purple (11.3.08) .. .. 9·00 2·50
    No. 295aa is perforated at foot.

Three types of the 9d., perf 12½, distinguishable by the distance between "NINE" and "PENCE".
A. Distance 1¾ mm. B. Distance 2¼ mm. C. Distance 2½ mm.

1906–12. *T* **19** ("POSTAGE" thick as *T* **26**). W **27**. *P* 12 or 12½ (*small holes*).
298 3d. sage-green (19 mm) (26.6.06) .. 6·00 1·75
    a. Imperf between (horiz pair) .. † £600
    b. Perf 12½. *Sage-green* (17 mm) (9.12.09) 4·75 1·75
    c. Perf 12½. *Deep olive* (20 mm) (7.10) .. 26·00 6·00
    d. Perf 12½. *Yellow-olive* (14 mm) (16.12.11) 10·00 5·50
    da. Perf 12½. *Bright olive-green* (19–19¾ mm) (5.12) .. .. 9·50 6·50
    e. Perf 11 (17 mm) (10.7.11) .. £200 £180
299 4d. orange-red (10.9.06) .. .. 8·50 1·25
    a. Orange .. .. .. 8·50 1·10
    b. Perf 12½. *Orange* (27.10.09) .. 7·00 2·25
300 6d. blue-green (1.9.06) .. .. 8·00 1·75
    a. Perf 12½ (21.4.10) .. .. 6·50 2·25
    ab. Perf 12½. Imperf between (vert pair) £350 £325
301 8d. bright ultramarine (*p* 12½) (8.09) 10·00 6·00
    a. Value closer (8.09) .. .. 38·00 24·00
302 9d. brown-lake (3.2.06) .. .. 10·00 1·75
    a. Imperf between (vert pair) .. £300
    aa. Imperf between (horiz pair) .. £300
    b. Deep lake (9.5.08) .. .. 30·00 3·75
    c. Perf 12½. *Lake* (A) (5.9.09) .. 11·00 3·00
    d. Perf 12½. *Lake* (B) (7.09) .. 15·00 3·00
    e. Perf 12½. *Brown-lake* (C) .. 17·00 5·50
    ea. Perf 12½. *Deep lake*. Thin paper (C) 16·00 3·50
    f. Perf 11 (1909) .. .. — £250
303 1s. brown (30.5.06) .. .. .. 12·00 3·00
    a. Imperf between (horiz pair) .. £300
    b. Perf 12½ (10.3.10) .. .. 10·00 3·00
304 2s. 6d. bright violet (X) (10.6.09) .. 35·00 6·00
    a. Perf 12½. *Pale violet* (X) (6.10) .. 35·00 9·00
    ab. Perf 12½. *Deep purple* (X) (5.11.12) 38·00 18·00
305 5s. bright brown (*p* 12½) (Z) (24.4.11). .. 60·00
The "value closer" variety of the 8d. occurred 11 times in the sheet of 60 in the later printing only. On No. 301 the value measures 16½ mm while on No. 301a it is 15¼ mm.

The 1s. brown, perf compound of 11½ and 12½, formerly listed is now omitted, as it must have been perforated by the 12 machine, which in places varied from 11½ to 13. The 4d. has also been reported with a similar perforation.

STAMP BOOKLETS

There are very few surviving examples of Nos. SB1/4. Listings are provided for those believed to have been issued with prices quoted for those known to still exist.

1904 (1 Jan)–**09.** *Black on red cover as No. SB1 of New South Wales. Stapled.*
SB1 £1 booklet containing two hundred and forty 1d. in four blocks of 30 and two blocks of 60 ..
    a. Red on pink cover (1909) .. ..
    b. Blue on pink cover £6000

1904 (1 Jan). *Black on grey cover as No. SB1. Stapled.*
SB2 £1 booklet containing one hundred and twenty 2d. in four blocks of 30 .. ..

1910 (May). *Black on cream cover as No. SB3 of New South Wales. Stapled.*
SB3 2s. booklet containing eleven ½d. (No. 262A), either in block of 6 plus block of 5 or block of 11, and eighteen 1d. (No. 264A), either in three blocks of 6 or block of 6 plus block of 12 ..
Unsold stock of No. SB3 was uprated with one additional ½d. in May 1911.

1911 (Aug). *Red on pink cover as No. SB3. Stapled.*
SB4 2s. booklet containing twelve ½d. (No. 262A), either in two blocks of 6 or block of 12, and eighteen 1d. (No. 264A), either in three blocks of 6 or block of 6 plus block of 12 .. .. £1500

OFFICIAL STAMPS

A. Departmentals

Following suspected abuses involving stamps supplied for official use it was decided by the South Australian authorities that such supplies were to be overprinted with a letter, or letters, indicating the department of the administration to which the stamps had been invoiced.

The system was introduced on 1 April 1868 using overprints struck in red. Later in the same year the colour of the overprints was amended to blue, and, during the latter months of 1869, to black.

In 1874 the Postmaster-General recommended that this somewhat cumbersome system be replaced by a general series of "O.S." overprints with the result that the separate accounting for the Departmentals ceased on 30 June of that year. Existing stocks continued to be used, however, and it is believed that much of the

residue was passed to the Government Printer to pay postage on copies of the *Government Gazette*.

We are now able to provide a check list of these most interesting issues based on the definitive work, *The Departmental Stamps of South Australia* by A. R. Butler, FRPSL, RDP, published by the Royal Philatelic Society, London in 1978.

No attempt has been made to assign the various overprints to the catalogue numbers of the basic stamps, but each is clearly identified by both watermark and perforation. The colours are similar to those of the contemporary postage stamps, but there can be shade variations. Errors of overprint are recorded in footnotes, but not errors occurring on the basic stamps used.

Most departmental overprints are considered to be scarce to rare in used condition, with unused examples, used multiples and covers being regarded as considerable rarities.

Forgeries of a few items do exist, but most can be readily identified by comparison with genuine examples. A number of forged overprints on stamps not used for the genuine issues also occur.

A. (Architect)

Optd in red with stop. W **2**. 2d. (*roul*), 4d. (*p* 11½–12½), 6d. (*roul*), 1s. (*roul*)
Optd in red without stop. W **2**. *Roul.* 1d., 6d., 1s.
Optd in black. (*a*) W **2**. 4d. (*p* 11½–12½), 4d. (*p* 10), 4d. (*p* 10 × 11½–12½), 6d. (*p* 11½–12½), 2s. (*roul*)
  (*b*) W **10**. 2d. D.L.R. (*roul*), 2d. D.L.R. (*p* 10)

A.G. (Attorney–General)

Optd in red. W **2**. *Roul.* 1d., 2d., 6d., 1s.
Optd in blue. (*a*) W **2**. *Roul.* 6d.
  (*b*) W **10**. *Roul.* 2d. D.L.R.
Optd in black. (*a*) W **2**. 1d. (*p* 11½–12½ × roul), 4d. (*p* 11½–12½), 4d. (*p* 10), 6d. (*p* 11½–12½ × roul), 6d. (*p* 11½–12½), 1s. (*p* 11½–12½ × roul), 1s. (*p* 10)
  (*b*) W **10**. 2d. D.L.R. (*roul*), 2d. D.L.R. (*p* 10)

A.O. (Audit Office)

Optd in red. W **2**. 2d. (*roul*), 4d. (*p* 11½–12½), 6d. (*roul*)
Optd in blue. (*a*) W **2**. *P* 11½–12½. 1d., 6d.
  (*b*) W **10**. *Roul.* 2d. D.L.R.
Optd in black. (*a*) W **2**. 1d. (*p* 11½–12½), 1d. (*p* 10), 1d. (*p* 10 × 11½–12), 2d. D.L.R. (*roul*), 4d. (*p* 11½–12½), 4d. (*p* 10), 4d. (*p* 10 × 11½–12½), 6d. (*roul*), 6d. (*p* 11½–12½), 1s. (*p* 10), 1s. (*p* 11½–12½ × roul)
  (*b*) W **7**. *P* 10. 4d.
  (*c*) W **10**. 2d. D.L.R. (*roul*), 2d. D.L.R. (*p* 10)

B.D. (Barracks Department)

Optd in red. W **2**. *Roul.* 2d., 6d., 1s.

B.G. (Botanic Garden)

Optd in black. (*a*) W **2**. 1d. (*p* 11½–12½ × roul), 1d. (*p* 11½–12½), 1d. (*p* 10), 1d. (*p* 10 × 11½–12½), 2d. D.L.R. (*roul*), 6d. (*roul*), 6d. (*p* 11½–12½ × roul), 6d. (*p* 11½–12½), 6d. (*p* 10), 1s. (*p* 11½–12½ × roul), 1s. (*p* 10 × 11½–12½)
  (*b*) W **7**. *P* 10. 2d. D.L.R.
  (*c*) W **10**. 2d. D.L.R. (*roul*), 2d. D.L.R. (*p* 10)

B.M. (Bench of Magistrates)

Optd in red. W **2**. *Roul.* 2d.
Optd in black. W **10**. *Roul.* 2d. D.L.R.

C. (Customs)

Optd in red. W **2**. 1d. (*roul*), 2d. (*roul*), 4d. (*p* 11½–12½), 6d. (*roul*), 1s. (*roul*)
Optd in blue. (*a*) W **2**. *Roul.* 1d., 4d., 6d., 1s., 2s.
  (*b*) W **10**. *Roul.* 2d. D.L.R.
Optd in black. (*a*) W **2**. 1d. (*roul*), 1d. (*p* 10), 1d. (*p* 10 × 11½–12½), 2d. D.L.R. (*p* 10 × 11½–12½), 4d. (*p* 11½–12½), 4d. (*p* 10), 4d. (*p* 10 × 11½–12½), 6d. (*roul*), 6d. (*p* 11½–12½), 6d. (*p* 10), 1s. (*p* 11½–12½ × roul), 1s. (*p* 11½–12½), 2s. (*roul*)
  (*b*) W **7**. *P* 10. 2d. D.L.R.
  (*c*) W **10**. 2d. D.L.R. (*roul*), 2d. D.L.R. (*p* 10 × roul), 2d. D.L.R. (*p* 10), 2d. D.L.R. (*p* 10 × 11½–12½)
The 1d. (*W* **10**. *Roul*) with black overprint is known showing the error "G" for "C".

C.D. (Convict Department)

Optd in red. W **2**. 2d. (*roul*), 4d. (*p* 11½–12½), 6d. (*roul*), 1s. (*roul*)
Optd in black. (*a*) W **2**. 1d. (*p* 11½–12½ × roul), 2d. D.L.R. (*roul*), 2d. D.L.R. (*p* 11½–12½), 2d. D.L.R. (*p* 11½–12½ × roul), 4d. (*p* 11½–12½), 6d. (*p* 11½–12½ × roul), 1s. (*p* 11½–12½ × roul)
  (*b*) W **10**. *Roul.* 2d. D.L.R.

C.L. (Crown Lands)

Optd in red. W **2**. 2d. (*roul*), 4d. (*p* 11½–12½), 6d. (*roul*), 1s. (*roul*)
Optd in blue. (*a*) W **2**. *Roul.* 4d., 6d.
  (*b*) W **10**. *Roul.* 2d. D.L.R.
Optd in black. (*a*) W **2**. 2d. D.L.R. (*roul*), 4d. (*p* 11½–12½), 4d. (*p* 10), 4d. (*p* 10 × 11½–12½), 6d. (*roul*), 6d. (*p* 11½–12½), 1s. (*p* 11½–12½ × roul), 1s. (*p* 11½–12½), 2s. (*roul*), 2s. (*p* 11½–12½)
  (*b*) W **7**. *P* 10. 2d. D.L.R., 4d.
  (*c*) W **10**. 2d. D.L.R. (*roul*), 2d. D.L.R. (*p* 10), 2d. D.L.R. (*p* 10 × 11½–12½)
The 2s. (*W* **2**. *P* 11½–12½) with black overprint is known showing the stop omitted after "L".

C.O. (Commissariat Office)

Optd in red. W **2**. 2d. (*roul*), 4d. (*p* 11½–12½), 6d. (*roul*), 1s. (*roul*)
Optd in black. (*a*) W **2**. 4d. (*p* 11½–12½), 4d. (*p* 10), 4d. (*p* 10 × 11½–12½), 6d. (*p* 11½–12½), 1s. (*p* 11½–12½), 2s. (*p* 11½–12½)
  (*b*) W **10**. 2d. D.L.R. (*roul*), 2d. D.L.R. (*p* 10)
The 2s. (*W* **2**. *P* 11½–12½) with black overprint is known showing the stop omitted after "O".

C.P. (Commissioner of Police)

Optd in red. W **2**. 2d. (*roul*), 4d. (*p* 11½–12½), 6d. (*roul*)

C.S. (Chief Secretary)

Optd in red. W **2**. 2d. (*roul*), 4d. (*p* 11½–12½), 6d. (*roul*), 1s. (*roul*)
Optd in blue. (*a*) W **2**. *Roul.* 4d., 6d.
  (*b*) W **10**. *Roul.* 2d. D.L.R.
Optd in black. (*a*) W **2**. 2d. D.L.R. (*roul*), 4d. (*roul*), 4d. (*p* 11½–12½ × roul), 4d. (*p* 11½–12½), 4d. (*p* 10), 4d. (*p* 10 × 11½–12½), 6d. (*p* 11½–12½ × roul), 6d. (*p* 11½–12½), 6d. (*p* 10), 6d. (*p* 10 × 11½–12½), 1s. (*p* 11½–12½), 1s. (*p* 10), 1s. (*p* 10 × 11½–12½), 2s. (*p* 10 × 11½–12½)
  (*b*) W **7**. *P* 10. 4d.
  (*c*) W **10**. 2d. D.L.R. (*roul*), 2d. D.L.R. (*p* 10)

C.Sgn. (Colonial Surgeon)

Optd in red. W **2**. 2d. (*roul*), 4d. (*p* 11½–12½), 6d. (*roul*)
Optd in black. (*a*) W **2**. 2d. D.L.R. (*roul*), 4d. (*p* 11½–12½), 4d. (*p* 10), 4d. (*p* 10 × 11½–12½), 6d. (*roul*), 6d. (*p* 11½–12½), 1s. (*p* 11½–12½ × roul)
  (*b*) W **10**. 2d. D.L.R. (*roul*), 2d. D.L.R. (*p* 11½–12½ × roul), 2d. D.L.R. (*p* 10)
Two types of overprint exist on the 2d. D.L.R. (*W* **10**. *Roul*), the second type having block capitals instead of the serifed type used for the other values.

D.B. (Destitute Board)

Optd in red. W **2**. 1d. (*roul*), 2d. (*roul*), 4d. (*p* 11½–12½), 6d. (*roul*), 1s. (*roul*)
Optd in blue. (*a*) W **2**. *Roul.* 2d. D.L.R., 6d.
  (*b*) W **10**. *Roul.* 2d. D.L.R.
Optd in black. (*a*) W **2**. 1d. (*p* 11½–12½), 4d. (*p* 11½–12½), 4d. (*p* 10), 6d. (*p* 10 × 11½–12½), 1s. (*p* 10)
  (*b*) W **10**. 2d. D.L.R. (*roul*), 2d. D.L.R. (*p* 10 × 11½–12½)
The 2d. D.L.R. (*W* **10**. *P* 10) with black overprint is known showing the stop omitted after "D".

D.R. (Deeds Registration)

Optd in red. W **2**. *Roul.* 2d., 6d.

E. (Engineer)

Optd in red. W **2**. 2d. (*roul*), 4d. (*p* 11½–12½), 6d. (*roul*), 1s. (*roul*)
Optd in blue. (*a*) W **2**. *Roul.* 1s.
  (*b*) W **10**. *Roul.* 2d. D.L.R.
Optd in black. (*a*) W **2**. 4d. (*p* 11½–12½ × roul), 4d. (*p* 11½–12½), 4d. (*p* 10), 4d. (*p* 10 × 11½–12½), 6d. (*p* 11½–12½), 6d. (*p* 10 × 11½–12½), 1s. (*p* 11½–12½ × roul), 1s. (*p* 10 × 11½–12½), 2s. (*p* 10 × 11½–12½)
  (*b*) W **7**. *P* 10. 4d.
  (*c*) W **10**. 2d. D.L.R. (*roul*), 2d. D.L.R. (*p* 10)

E.B. (Education Board)

Optd in red. W **2**. 2d. (*roul*), 4d. (*p* 11½–12½), 6d. (*roul*), 1s. (*roul*)
Optd in blue. (*a*) W **2**. *Roul.* 4d., 6d.
  (*b*) W **10**. *Roul.* 2d. D.L.R.
Optd in black. (*a*) W **2**. 2d. D.L.R. (*roul*), 4d. (*roul*), 4d. (*p* 11½–12½), 4d. (*p* 10), 4d. (*p* 10 × 11½–12½), 6d. (*p* 11½–12½ × roul), 6d. (*p* 11½–12½)
  (*b*) W **7**. *P* 10. 2d. D.L.R.
  (*c*) W **10**. 2d. D.L.R. (*roul*), 2d. D.L.R. (*p* 10), 2d. D.L.R. (*p* 10 × 11½–12½)

G.F. (Gold Fields)

Optd in black. (*a*) W **2**. *Roul.* 6d.
  (*b*) W **10**. 2d. D.L.R. (*p* 10 × roul), 2d. D.L.R. (*p* 10)

G.P. (Government Printer)

Optd in red. W **2**. *Roul.* 1d., 2d., 6d., 1s.
Optd in blue. (*a*) W **2**. *Roul.* 1d., 6d., 1s., 2s.
  (*b*) W **10**. *Roul.* 2d. D.L.R.
Optd in black. (*a*) W **2**. 1d. (*roul*), 1d. (*p* 11½–12½ × roul), 1d. (*p* 11½–12½), 1d. (*p* 10), 1d. (*p* 10 × 11½–12½), 6d. (*p* 11½–12½ × roul), 6d. (*p* 10), 1s. (*p* 10), 1s. (*p* 10 × 11½–12½), 2s. (*roul*), 2s. (*p* 11½–12½), 2s. (*p* 10 × 11½–12½)
  (*b*) W **10**. 2d. D.L.R. (*roul*), 2d. D.L.R. (*p* 10)
The 1d. (*W* **2**. *Roul*) with red overprint is known showing "C.P." instead of "G.P.".

G.S. (Government Storekeeper)

Optd in red. W **2**. *Roul.* 2d., 6d., 1s.

G.T. (Goolwa Tramway)

Optd in red. W **2**. 1d. (*roul*), 2d. (*roul*), 4d. (*p* 11½–12½), 6d. (*roul*), 1s. (*roul*)
Optd in black. (*a*) W **2**. 2d. D.L.R. (*roul*), 4d. (*p* 11½–12½)
  (*b*) W **10**. 2d. D.L.R. (*roul*), 2d. D.L.R. (*p* 10)
The 2d. and 6d. (both *W* **2**. *Roul*) with red overprint are known showing the stop omitted after "T". The 1s. (*W* **2**. *Roul*) with red overprint is known showing "C.T." instead of "G.T.".

H. (Hospitals)

Optd in black. (*a*) W **7**. *P* 10. 2d. D.L.R.
  (*b*) W **10**. 2d. D.L.R. (*p* 10), 2d. D.L.R. (*p* 10 × 11½–12½)

H.A. (House of Assembly)

Optd in red. W **2**. 1d. (*roul*), 2d. (*roul*), 4d. (*p* 11½–12½), 6d. (*roul*), 1s. (*roul*)
Optd in black. (*a*) W **2**. 1d. (*p* 11½–12½), 1d. (*p* 10), 1d. (*p* 10 × 11½–12½), 2d. D.L.R. (*roul*), 4d. (*p* 10), 6d. (*roul*), 6d. (*p* 11½–12½), 1s. (*p* 11½–12½ × roul), 1s. (*p* 11½–12½)
  (*b*) W **10**. 2d. D.L.R. (*roul*), 2d. D.L.R. (*p* 10)

I.A. (Immigration Agent)

Optd in red. W **2**. 1d. (*roul*), 2d. (*roul*), 4d. (*p* 11½–12½), 6d. (*roul*)

I.E. (Intestate Estates)

Optd in black. W **10**. *P* 10. 2d. D.L.R.

I.S. (Inspector of Sheep)

Optd in red. W **2**. *Roul.* 2d., 6d.
Optd in blue. W **2**. *P* 11½–12½. 6d.
Optd in black. (*a*) W **2**. 2d. D.L.R. (*roul*), 6d. (*p* 11½–12½ × roul)
  (*b*) W **10**. 2d. D.L.R. (*roul*), 2d. D.L.R. (*p* 10)

L.A. (Lunatic Asylum)

Optd in red. W 2. 1d. (*roul*), 2d. (*roul*), 4d. (*p* 11½–12½), 6d. (*roul*), 1s. (*roul*)
Optd in black. (*a*) W 2. 4d. (*p* 11½–12½), 4d. (*p* 10), 4d. (*p* 10 × 11½–12½), 6d. (*p* 11½–12½ × *roul*), 6d. (*p* 11½–12½), 1s. (*p* 11½–12½), 2s. (*roul*)
(*b*) W 10. 2d. D.L.R. (*roul*), 2d. D.L.R. (*p* 10)

L.C. (Legislative Council)

Optd in red. W 2. Roul. 2d., 6d.
Optd in black. (*a*) W 2. Roul. 6d.
(*b*) W 10. 2d. D.L.R. (*roul*), 2d. D.L.R. (*p* 10 × *roul*)
The 2d. and 6d. (both W 2. *Roul*) with red overprint are known showing the stop omitted after "C".

L.L. (Legislative Librarian)

Optd in red. W 2. 2d. (*roul*), 4d. (*p* 11½–12½), 6d. (*roul*)
Optd in black. (*a*) W 2. P 11½–12½. 6d.
(*b*) W 10. P 10. 2d. D.L.R.
The 2d. and 6d. (both W 2. *Roul*) with red overprint are known showing the stop omitted from between the two letters.

L.T. (Land Titles)

Optd in red. W 2. 2d. (*roul*), 4d. (*p* 11½–12½), 6d. (*roul*), 1s. (*roul*)
Optd in blue. W 10. Roul. 2d. D.L.R.
Optd in black. (*a*) W 2. 4d. (*p* 11½–12½), 4d. (*p* 10), 4d. (*p* 10 × 11½–12½), 6d. (*p* 11½–12½ × *roul*), 6d. (*p* 11½–12½), 6d. (*p* 10), 6d. (*p* 10 × 11½–12½)
(*b*) W 7. P 10. 2d. D.L.R.
(*c*) W 10. 2d. D.L.R. (*roul*), 2d. D.L.R. (*p* 10)
The 2d. and 6d. (both W 2. *Roul*) with red overprint are known showing the stop omitted after "T".

M. (Military)

Optd in red. W 2. Roul. 2d., 6d., 1s.
Optd in black. W 2. 6d. (*p* 11½–12½ × *roul*), 1s. (*p* 11½–12½ × *roul*), 2s. (*roul*)

M.B. (Marine Board)

Optd in red. W 2. 1d. (*roul*), 2d. (*roul*), 4d. (*roul*), 4d. (*p* 11½–12½), 6d. (*roul*), 1s. (*roul*)
Optd in black. (*a*) W 2. 1d. (*roul*), 1d. (*p* 11½–12½), 2d. D.L.R. (*roul*), 4d. (*p* 11½–12½ × *roul*), 4d. (*p* 11½–12½), 4d. (*p* 10), 4d. (*p* 10 × 11½–12½), 6d. (*roul*), 6d. (*p* 11½–12½), 6d. (*p* 10 × 11½–12½), 1s. (*p* 11½–12½ × *roul*), 1s. (*p* 10), 1s. (*p* 10 × 11½–12½)
(*b*) W 7. P 10. 2d. D.L.R., 4d.
(*c*) W 10. 2d. D.L.R. (*roul*), 2d. D.L.R. (*p* 10)

M.R. (Manager of Railways)

Optd in red. W 2. Roul. 2d., 6d.
Optd in black. (*a*) W 2. 1d. (*p* 11½–12½), 1d. (*p* 11½–12½), 2d. D.L.R. (*roul*), 4d. (*p* 11½–12½), 6d. (*p* 11½–12½ × *roul*), 6d. (*p* 11½–12½), 10d. on 9d. (*roul*), 1s. (*roul*), 1s. (*p* 11½–12½ × *roul*), 2s. (*p* 11½–12½), 2s. (*p* 10 × 11½–12½)
(*b*) W 10. 2d. D.L.R. (*roul*), 2d. D.L.R. (*p* 10 × 11½–12½)

M.R.G. (Main Roads Gambierton)

Optd in red without stops. W 2. Roul. 2d., 6d.
Optd in blue without stops. W 10. Roul. 2d. D.L.R.
Optd in black without stops. W 10. 2d. D.L.R. (*roul*), 2d. D.L.R. (*p* 10)
Optd in black with stops. W 10. 2d. D.L.R. (*roul*), 2d. D.L.R. (*p* 10)
The 2d. D.L.R. (W 10. P 10) with black overprint is known showing the stops omitted after "M" and "R".

N.T. (Northern Territory)

Optd in black. W 2. P 11½–12½. 1d., 3d. on 4d., 4d., 6d., 1s.
(*b*) W 10. 2d. D.L.R. (*roul*), 2d. D.L.R. (*p* 10)

O.A. (Official Assignee)

Optd in red. W 2. 2d. (*roul*), 4d. (*p* 11½–12½)
Optd in blue. W 10. Roul. 2d. D.L.R.
Optd in black. (*a*) W 2. 4d. (*p* 11½–12½), 4d. (*p* 10)
(*b*) W 7. P 10. 2d. D.L.R.
(*c*) W 10. 2d. D.L.R. (*roul*), 2d. D.L.R. (*p* 10 × *roul*), 2d. D.L.R. (*p* 10)

P. (Police)

Optd in blue. (*a*) W 2. Roul. 6d.
(*b*) W 10. Roul. 2d. D.L.R.
Optd in black. (*a*) W 2. 6d. (*p* 11½–12½), 6d. (*p* 10)
(*b*) W 7. P 10. 2d. D.L.R.
(*c*) W 10. 2d. D.L.R. (*roul*), 2d. D.L.R. (*p* 11½–12½ × *roul*), 2d. D.L.R. (*p* 10), 2d. D.L.R. (*p* 10 × 11½–12½)

P.A. (Protector of Aborigines)

Optd in red. W 2. Roul. 2d., 6d.
Optd in black. (*a*) W 2. Roul. 2d. D.L.R., 6d.
(*b*) W 10. 2d. D.L.R. (*roul*), 2d. D.L.R. (*p* 10)

P.O. (Post Office)

Optd in red. W 2. Roul. 1d., 2d., 6d., 1s.
Optd in blue. W 2. Roul. 2d., 2d. D.L.R.
Optd in black. (*a*) W 2. 1d. (*p* 11½–12½), 2d. D.L.R. (*roul*), 4d. (*p* 11½–12½), 6d. (*roul*), 6d. (*p* 11½–12½), 1s. (*p* 11½–12½ × *roul*), 1s. (*p* 11½–12½), 1s. (*p* 10 × 11½–12½)
(*b*) W 10. 2d. D.L.R. (*roul*), 2d. D.L.R. (*p* 10 × *roul*), 2d. D.L.R. (*p* 10)
The 6d. (W 2. *Roul*) with red overprint is known showing the stop omitted after "O", but with two stops after "P".

P.S. (Private Secretary)

Optd in red. W 2. 1d. (*roul*), 2d. (*roul*), 4d. (*p* 11½–12½), 6d. (*roul*)
Optd in black. (*a*) W 2. 1d. (*p* 11½–12½ × *roul*), 1d. (*p* 11½–12½), 1d. (*p* 10), 3d. (*in black*) on 4d. (*p* 10), 3d. (*in red*) on 4d. (*p* 10), 3d. (*in black*) on 4d. (*p* 10), 4d. (*p* 11½–12½), 4d. (*p* 10), 4d. (*p* 10 × 11½–12½), 4d. (*p* 11½–12½ × *roul*), 6d. (*p* 11½–12½), 6d. (*p* 10), 9d. (*roul*), 9d. (*p* 11½–12½), 10d. on 9d. (*p* 10 × 11½–12½), 1s. (*p* 11½–12½ × *roul*), 2s. (*p* 11½–12½)
(*b*) W 7. P 10. 2d. D.L.R.
(*c*) W 10. 2d. D.L.R. (*roul*), 2d. D.L.R. (*p* 10)

P.W. (Public Works)

Optd in red without stop after "W". W 2. Roul. 2d., 6d., 1s.
Optd in black. (*a*) W 2. 2d. D.L.R. (*roul*), 4d. (*p* 10), 6d. (*roul*), 6d. (*p* 11½–12½), 1s. (*p* 11½–12½ × *roul*)
(*b*) W 10. 2d. D.L.R. (*roul*), 2d. D.L.R. (*p* 10)

R.B. (Road Board)

Optd in red. W 2. Roul. 2d., 6d. (*p* 11½–12½), 1s. (*roul*)
Optd in blue without stops. W 10. Roul. 2d. D.L.R.
Optd in black. (*a*) W 2. 1d. (*p* 11½–12½ × *roul*), 1d. (*p* 10), 4d. (*p* 10), 2s. (*roul*)
(*b*) W 7. P 10. 2d. D.L.R.
(*c*) W 10. 2d. D.L.R. (*roul*), 2d. D.L.R. (*p* 10)
The 6d. (W 2. *Roul*) with red overprint is known showing the stop omitted after "B".

R.G. (Registrar-General)

Optd in red. W 2. Roul. 2d., 6d., 1s.
Optd in blue. W 2. P 11½–12½ × *roul*. 6d.
Optd in black. (*a*) W 2. Roul. 2d. D.L.R., 6d. (*p* 10), 6d. (*p* 10 × 11½–12½), 1s. (*p* 11½–12½ × *roul*), 1s. (*p* 10)
(*b*) W 7. P 10. 2d. D.L.R.
(*c*) W 10. 2d. D.L.R. (*roul*), 2d. D.L.R. (*p* 10 × *roul*), 2d. D.L.R. (*p* 10 × 11½–12½)

S. (Sheriff)

Optd in red. W 2. Roul. 2d., 6d.
Optd in blue. (*a*) W 2. P 11½–12½ × *roul*. 6d.
(*b*) W 10. Roul. 2d. D.L.R.
Optd in black. (*a*) W 2. 4d. (*p* 11½–12½), 4d. (*p* 10), 6d. (*roul*), 6d. (*p* 11½–12½), 6d. (*p* 10)
(*b*) W 10. 2d. D.L.R. (*roul*), 2d. D.L.R. (*p* 10 × *roul*), 2d. D.L.R. (*p* 10 × 11½–12½)

S.C. (Supreme Court)

Optd in red. W 2. Roul. 2d., 6d.
Optd in black. W 10. P 10. 2d. D.L.R.

S.G. (Surveyor-General)

Optd in red. W 2. 2d. (*roul*), 4d. (*p* 11½–12½), 6d. (*roul*)
Optd in blue. (*a*) W 2. Roul. 4d.
(*b*) W 10. Roul. 2d. D.L.R.
Optd in black. (*a*) W 2. 2d. D.L.R. (*roul*), 4d. (*p* 11½–12½), 4d. (*p* 10), 4d. (*p* 10 × 11½–12½), 6d. (*p* 11½–12½ × *roul*), 6d. (*p* 10), 6d. (*p* 10 × 11½–12½)
(*b*) W 7. P 10. 2d. D.L.R.
(*c*) W 10. 2d. D.L.R. (*roul*), 2d. D.L.R. (*p* 10 × *roul*), 2d. D.L.R. (*p* 10)

S.M. (Stipendiary Magistrate)

Optd in red. W 2. 1d. (*roul*), 2d. (*roul*), 4d. (*roul*), 4d. (*p* 11½–12½), 6d. (*roul*), 1s. (*roul*)
Optd in blue. (*a*) W 2. Roul. 2d., 4d., 6d.
(*b*) W 10. Roul. 2d. D.L.R.
Optd in black. (*a*) W 2. 1d. (*p* 11½–12½), 1d. (*p* 10), 2d. D.L.R. (*roul*), 4d. (*roul*), 4d. (*p* 11½–12½), 4d. (*p* 10), 4d. (*p* 10 × 11½–12½), 6d. (*p* 11½–12½ × *roul*), 6d. (*p* 11½–12½), 6d. (*p* 10), 6d. (*p* 10 × 11½–12½), 1s. (*p* 11½–12½ × *roul*)
(*b*) W 7. P 10. 2d. D.L.R.
(*c*) W 10. 2d. D.L.R. (*roul*), 2d. D.L.R. (*p* 10 × *roul*), 2d. D.L.R. (*p* 10 × 11½–12½)
The 2d. and 4d. (both W 2. *Roul*) with red overprint are known showing the stop omitted after "M".

S.T. (Superintendent of Telegraphs)

Optd in red. W 2. Roul. 2d., 6d.
Optd in blue. W 10. 2d. D.L.R. (*roul*), 2d. D.L.R. (*p* 11½–12½)
Optd in black. (*a*) W 2. Roul. 2d. D.L.R., 6d.
(*b*) W 7. P 10. 2d. D.L.R.
(*c*) W 10. 2d. D.L.R. (*roul*), 2d. D.L.R. (*p* 10 × *roul*), 2d. D.L.R. (*p* 10)
The 2d. and 6d. (both W 2. *Roul*) with red overprint (2d., 6d.) or black overprint (6d.) are known showing the stop omitted after "T".

T. (Treasury)

Optd in red. W 2. 1d. (*roul*), 2d. (*roul*), 4d. (*p* 11½–12½ × *roul*), 6d. (*roul*), 1s. (*roul*)
Optd in blue. (*a*) W 2. Roul. 1d., 4d., 6d., 2s.
(*b*) W 10. Roul. 2d. D.L.R.
Optd in black. (*a*) W 2. 1d. (*p* 11½–12½), 2d. D.L.R. (*roul*), 4d. (*roul*), 4d. (*p* 11½–12½), 6d. (*roul*), 6d. (*p* 11½–12½), 1s. (*p* 11½–12½ × *roul*), 1s. (*p* 10 × 11½–12½), 2s. (*roul*), 2s. (*p* 11½–12½), 2s. (*p* 10 × 11½–12½)
(*b*) W 7. P 10. 2d. D.L.R.
(*c*) W 10. 2d. D.L.R. (*roul*), 2d. D.L.R. (*p* 10)

T.R. (Titles Registration)

Optd in black. (*a*) W 2. 4d. (*p* 11½–12½), 4d. (*p* 10 × 11½–12½), 6d. (*p* 11½–12½), 6d. (*p* 10 × 11½–12½), 1s. (*p* 11½–12½)
(*b*) W 10. P 10. 2d. D.L.R.

V. (Volunteers)

Optd in red. W 2. Roul. 2d., 6d., 1s.
Optd in black. (*a*) W 2. Roul. 6d.
(*b*) W 7. P 10. 2d. D.L.R.
(*c*) W 10. 2d. D.L.R. (*roul*), 2d. D.L.R. (*p* 10 × *roul*), 2d. D.L.R. (*p* 10)
The 2d. (W 10. P 10 × *roul*) overprinted in black is only known showing the stop omitted after "V".

VA. (Valuator of Runs)

Optd in black without stop after "V". (*a*) W 2. P 10. 4d.
(*b*) W 10. P 10. 2d. D.L.R.

VN. (Vaccination)

Optd in black without stop after "V". W 2. P 10. 4d.

W. (Waterworks)

Optd in red. W 2. Roul. 2d.
Optd in black. (*a*) W 2. P 11½–12½. 6d., 2s.
(*b*) W 10. 2d. D.L.R. (*roul*), 2d. D.L.R. (*p* 10)
The 2d. (W 2. *Roul*) with red overprint is known showing the stop omitted after "W".

B. General

O.S. (O 1) **O.S.** (O 2)

No.	Type	Description		
1874–77.		*Optd with Type* O 1. W 2. (*a*) P 10.		
O 1	3	4d. dull purple (18.2.74)	£1000	£275
		(*b*) P 11½–12½ × 10.		
O 2	1	1d. green (2.1.74)	—	£150
O 3	3	4d. dull violet (12.2.75)	60·00	5·00
O 4	1	6d. Prussian blue (20.10.75)	70·00	8·50
O 4a	3	2s. rose-pink		
O 5		2s. carmine (3.12.76)	—	90·00
		(*c*) P 11½–12½		
O 6	1	1d. deep yellow-green (30.1.74)	£1000	17·00
		a. Printed on both sides	—	£400
O 7	3	3d. on 4d. ultramarine (26.6.77)	£1400	£600
		a. No stop after "S"	—	£1000
O 8	1	4d. dull violet (13.7.74)	48·00	6·50
		a. No stop after "S"	—	30·00
O 9	1	6d. bright blue (31.8.75)	75·00	12·00
		a. "O.S." double	—	65·00
O10		6d. Prussian blue (27.3.74)	65·00	6·50
		a. No stop after "S"	—	35·00
O11	4	9d. red-purple (22.3.76)	£750	£325
		a. No stop after "S"	£1200	£550
O12	1	1s. red-brown (5.8.74)	65·00	6·00
		a. "O.S." double	—	70·00
		b. No stop after "S"	£130	35·00
O13	3	2s. crimson-carmine (13.7.75)	£100	14·00
		a. No stop after "S"	—	60·00
		b. No stops	—	75·00
		c. Stops at top of letters		
1876–85.		*Optd with Type* O 1. W 8. (*a*) P 10.		
O14	1	6d. bright blue (1879)	70·00	10·00
		(*b*) P 10 × 11½–12½, 11½–12½ × 10, *or compound*		
O15	3	4d. violet-slate (24.1.78)	65·00	6·50
O16		4d. plum (29.11.81)	38·00	2·75
O17		4d. deep mauve	26·00	2·50
		a. No stop after "S"	£100	24·00
		b. No stop after "O"		
		c. "O.S." double		
		d. "O.S." inverted	—	£100
O18	1	6d. bright blue (1877)	50·00	4·25
		a. "O.S." inverted		
		b. No stop after "O"		
O19		6d. bright ultramarine (27.3.85)	45·00	4·00
		a. "O.S." inverted		
		b. "O.S." double		
		c. "O.S." double, one inverted	—	£225
		d. No stop after "S"	—	35·00
		e. No stops after "O" & "S"		
O20		1s. red-brown (27.3.83)	40·00	6·50
		a. "O.S." inverted		
		b. No stop after "O"		
		c. No stop after "S"	—	35·00
O21	3	2s. carmine (16.3.81)	85·00	7·50
		a. "O.S." inverted	—	£130
		b. No stop after "S"	—	50·00
		(*c*) P 11½–12½		
O22	3	3d. on 4d. ultramarine	£1400	
O23		4d. violet-slate (14.3.76)	£120	6·50
O24		4d. deep mauve (19.8.79)	45·00	4·00
		a. "O.S." inverted		
		b. "O.S." double, one inverted		
		c. No stop after "S"	—	25·00
O25	1	6d. Prussian blue (6.77)	50·00	5·50
		a. "O.S." double	—	55·00
		b. "O.S." inverted		
O26	4	8d. on 9d. brown (9.11.76)	£1000	£450
		a. "O.S." double	£1600	
		b. "O" only	—	£700
O26c		9d. purple	£2250	
O27	1	1s. red-brown (12.2.78)	35·00	8·50
		a. "O.S." inverted	£190	90·00
		b. No stop after "S"	£160	38·00
O28		1s. lake-brown (8.11.83)	32·00	3·50
O29	3	2s. rose-carmine (12.8.85)	85·00	8·00
		a. "O.S." double	—	80·00
		b. "O.S." inverted	—	85·00
		c. No stop after "S"	—	35·00
1891–1903.		*Optd with Type* O 2. (*a*) W 8. P 11½–12½.		
O30	1	1s. lake-brown (18.4.91)	35·00	10·00
O31		1s. Vandyke brown	42·00	7·00
O32		1s. dull brown (2.7.96)	32·00	5·00
		a. No stop after "S"	—	50·00
O33	3	1s. sepia (*large holes*) (4.1.02)	27·00	5·00
		a. "O.S." double		
		b. No stop after "S"	—	50·00
O34	3	2s. carmine (26.6.00)	75·00	11·00
		a. No stop after "S"		
		(*b*) W 8. P 10 × 11½–12½		
O35	3	2s. rose-carmine (9.11.95)	60·00	9·00
		a. No stop after "S"	£110	
		b. "O.S." double		
		(*c*) W 10. P 11½–12½		
O36	1	1s. dull brown (1902)	38·00	6·50

1874–76. *Optd with Type O 1. W 10. (a) P 10.*
O37 11 1d. blue-green (30.9.75) .. .. 70·00 15·00
 a. "O.S." inverted
 b. No stop after "S"
O38 12 2d. orange-red (18.2.74) .. .. 14·00 85
 a. No stop after "S" .. — 20·00
 b. "O.S." double

(b) P 10 × 11½–12½, 11½–12½ × 10, or compound
O39 11 1d. blue-green (16.9.75)
 a. No stop after "S"
O40 12 2d. orange-red (27.9.76) .. .. — 4·75

(c) P 11½–12½
O41 11 1d. blue-green (13.8.75) .. .. — 14·00
 a. "O.S." inverted
 b. No stop after "S"
O42 12 2d. orange-red (20.5.74) .. .. — 80·00

1876–80. *Optd with Type O 1. W 13. (a) P 10*
O43 11 1d. blue-green (2.10.76) .. .. 11·00 40
 a. "O.S." inverted .. — 35·00
 b. "O.S." double .. 45·00 30·00
 c. "O.S." double, one inverted
 d. No stops .. — 20·00
 e. No stop after "O"
 f. No stop after "S" .. — 10·00
 g. Deep green .. 12·00 40
 ga. "O.S." double .. — 32·00
O44 12 2d. orange-red (21.9.77) .. 7·50 50
 a. "O.S." inverted .. — 18·00
 b. "O.S." double .. 55·00 27·00
 c. "O.S." double, one inverted
 d. "O.S." double, both inverted .. — 85·00
 e. No stops .. — 40·00
 f. No stop after "S" .. — 14·00
 g. No stop after "S"
 h. Dull brick-red .. 26·00 65

(b) P 10×11½–12½, 11½–12½×10 or compound
O45 11 1d. deep green (14.8.80) .. — 18·00
 a. "O.S." double
O46 12 2d. orange-red (6.4.78) .. 48·00 6·00
 a. "O.S." inverted .. — 85·00
 b. No stop after "S" .. — 40·00

(c) P 11½–12½
O47 12 2d. orange-red (15.7.80) .. — 60·00

1882 (20 Feb). *No. 181 optd with Type O 1.*
O48 11 ½d. on 1d. blue-green .. 55·00 14·00
 a. "O.S." inverted ..

1888 (15 Nov)–91. *Nos. 184 and 185a optd with Type O 1. P 10.*
O49 17 4d. pale violet (24.1.91) .. 50·00 4·00
O50 18 6d. blue .. .. 16·00 1·25
 a. "O.S." double
 b. No stop after "S"

1891. *Nos. 229b and 231a/2 optd with Type O 1. (a) P 10*
O51 17 2½d. on 4d. deep green (Br.) (1 Aug) 45·00 6·50
 a. "2" and "½" closer together .. — 42·00
 b. "O.S." inverted
 c. "O.S." double
 d. "O.S." omitted (in vert pair with
  normal) ..
 e. No stop after "S"

(b) P 10×11½–12½ or 11½–12½×10
O52 17 2½d. on 4d. deep green (Br.) (1 Oct) 50·00 9·50

(c) P 11½–12½
O53 17 2½d. on 4d. deep green (1 June) £100 50·00

1891–96. *Optd with Type O 2. W 13. (a) P 10*
O54 11 1d. deep green (22.4.91) .. 11·00 1·40
 a. "O.S." double .. 45·00 27·00
 b. "O.S." double, one inverted
 c. No stop after "S" .. 32·00 8·00
 d. Blackish blue opt .. £200 4·00
O55 12 2d. orange-red (22.4.91) .. 11·00 30
 a. "O.S." double
 b. "O.S." double, both inverted
 c. No stop after "S" .. — 9·00

(b) P 15
O56 11 1d. green (8.9.94) .. 9·00 40
 a. "O.S." double
 b. No stop after "S"
O57 12 2d. orange-red (16.6.94) .. 9·00 30
 a. "O.S." double .. — 21·00
 b. "O.S." inverted .. — 15·00

(c) P 13
O58 11 1d. green (20.5.95) .. 14·00 40
 a. No stop after "S" .. 48·00 8·00
O59 12 2d. orange-red (11.2.96) .. 12·00 30
 a. "O.S." double .. 75·00
 b. No stop after "S" .. 45·00 8·00

1891–99. *Optd with Type O 2. W 13 (sideways on ½d.). (a) P 10*
O60 15 ½d. brown (2.5.94) .. 9·50 3·75
 a. No stop after "S" .. 32·00 20·00
O61 17 4d. pale violet (13.2.91) .. 50·00 2·75
 a. "O.S." double
 b. "S." omitted .. — 48·00
 c. No stop after "S"
 d. Aniline violet (31.8.93) .. 50·00 2·50
 da. "O.S." double
 dc. No stop after "S"
O62 18 6d. blue (4.4.93) .. 17·00 1·75
 a. No stop after "S"
 b. Blackish blue opt

(b) P 10×11½–12½
O63 15 ½d. brown (26.3.95) .. 10·00 4·00

(c) P 11½–12½
O64 15 ½d. red-brown (13.6.91) .. 24·00 5·50

(d) P 15
O65 15 ½d. pale brown (8.6.95) .. 14·00 4·50
O66 17 4d. slate-violet (4.4.95) .. 50·00 2·75
 a. "O.S." double .. £150 27·00
O67 18 6d. blue (20.9.93) .. 16·00 1·25

(e) P 13
O68 15 ½d. deep brown (17.5.98) .. 9·00 4·50
 a. Opt triple, twice sideways .. £150
O69 17 4d. violet (12.96) .. 50·00 2·25
 a. "O.S." double .. £120 28·00
 b. No stop after "S" .. £120 20·00
O70 18 6d. blue (13.9.99) .. 22·00 1·50
 a. No stop after "S" .. 70·00 50·00

1891–95. *Nos. 229b, 230a and 231a optd with Type O 2. (a) P 10*
O71 17 2½d. on 4d. deep green (Br.) (18.8.94) 32·00 4·50
 a. Fraction bar omitted
 b. "2" and "½" closer together .. 75·00 20·00
 c. "O.S." inverted .. £130
 d. No stop after "S" .. — 30·00
O72 18 5d. on 6d. deep brown (C.) (2.12.91) 38·00 12·00
 a. "O.S." inverted .. £170
 b. No stop after "S" .. 95·00 32·00

(b) P 10×11½–12½
O73 17 2½d. on 4d. deep green (Br.) (17.9.95) — 38·00
 a. "O.S." double

1897–1901. *Nos. 235/6 and 238a optd with Type O 2. (a) P 15*
O74 23 5d. brown-purple (29.3.01) .. 55·00 7·00

(b) P 13
O75 22 2½d. violet-blue (5.7.97) .. 42·00 4·00
 a. No stop after "S" .. — 25·00
O76 23 5d. purple (29.9.01) .. 55·00 8·50
 a. No stop after "S"

O. S.
(O 3)

1899–1901. *Optd with Type O 3. W 13. P 13.*
O80 24 ½d. yellow-green (12.2.00) .. 9·00 4·75
 a. "O.S." inverted .. 48·00
 b. No stop after "S" .. 32·00
O81 11 1d. rosine (22.9.99) .. 10·00 95
 a. "O.S." inverted .. 42·00 30·00
 b. "O.S." double
 c. No stop after "S" .. 38·00 14·00
O82 12 2d. bright violet (1.6.00) .. 10·00 60
 a. "O.S." inverted .. 38·00 20·00
 b. "O.S." double
 c. No stop after "S" .. 27·00
O83 22 2½d. indigo (2.10.01) .. 55·00 15·00
 a. "O.S." inverted .. — 55·00
 b. No stop after "S" .. £140
O84 17 4d. violet (18.11.00) .. 48·00 2·50
 a. "O.S." inverted .. £160
 b. No stop after "S" .. £120
O85 18 6d. blue (8.10.00) .. 16·00 2·00
 a. No stop after "S" .. 50·00

1891 (May). *Optd as Type O 3 but wider. W 13. P 10.*
O86 19 2s. 6d. pale violet £2250 £1700
O87 5s. pale rose £2250 £1700
 Only one sheet (60) of each of these stamps was printed.

The use of stamps overprinted "O S" was made invalid by the Posts and Telegraph Act of 1 November 1902.

South Australia became part of the Commonwealth of Australia on 1 January 1901.

TASMANIA

PRICES FOR STAMPS ON COVER	
Nos. 1/4	*from* × 6
Nos. 5/12	*from* × 5
Nos. 14/24	*from* × 3
Nos. 25/56	*from* × 5
Nos. 57/77	*from* × 6
Nos. 78/9	
Nos. 80/90	*from* × 3
No. 91	
Nos. 92/109	*from* × 3
No. 110	
Nos. 111/23	*from* × 3
Nos. 124/6	
Nos. 127/34	*from* × 5
Nos. 135/55	*from* × 4
Nos. 156/8	*from* × 20
Nos. 159/66	*from* × 10
Nos. 167/9	*from* × 15
Nos. 170/4	*from* × 6
Nos. 216/22	*from* × 15
Nos. 223/5	
Nos. 226/7	*from* × 15
Nos. 229/36	*from* × 20
Nos. 237/57	*from* × 10
No. 258	
Nos. 259/62	*from* × 10
Nos. F1/25	—
Nos. F26/9	*from* × 15
Nos. F30/9	—

SPECIMEN OVERPRINTS. Those listed are from U.P.U. distributions between 1892 and 1904. Further "Specimen" overprints exist, but these were used for other purposes.

  1   2   3

(Eng C. W. Coard. Recess H. and C. Best at the *Courier* newspaper, Hobart)

1853 (1 Nov). *No wmk. Imperf. Twenty-four varieties in four rows of six each.*

(a) Medium soft yellowish paper with all lines clear and distinct
1 1 1d. pale blue £3250 £850
2 1d. blue £3250 £850

(b) Thin hard white paper with lines of the engraving blurred and worn
3 1 1d. pale blue £3000 £750
4 1d. blue £3000 £750

1853–55. *No wmk. Imperf. In each plate there are twenty-four varieties in four rows of six each.*

(a) Plate I. Finely engraved. All lines in network and background thin, clear, and well defined. (1853)

(i) First state of the plate, brilliant colours
5 2 4d. bright red-orange £2500 £650
 a. Double impression
6 4d. bright brownish orange .. — £800

(ii) Second state of plate, with blurred lines and worn condition of the central background
7 2 4d. red-orange £2250 £400
8 4d. orange £2000 £375
9 4d. pale orange .. .. — £375

(b) Plate II. Coarse engraving, lines in network and background thicker and blurred (1855)
10 2 4d. orange £2000 £375
 a. Double print, one albino
11 4d. dull orange £2000 £325
12 4d. yellowish orange £2000 £325

In the 4d. Plate I, the outer frame-line is thin all round. In Plate II it is, by comparison with other parts, thicker in the lower left angle.

The 4d. is known on vertically laid paper from proof sheets. Examples from Plate I have the lines close together and those from Plate II wide apart (*Price* £5000 *unused*).

In 1879 reprints were made of the 1d. in blue and the 4d., Plate I, in brownish yellow, on thin, tough, white wove paper, and perforated 11½. In 1887, a reprint from the other plate of the 4d. was made in reddish brown and in black, and in 1889 of the 1d. in blue and in black, and of the 4d. (both plates) in yellow and in black on white card, imperforate. As these three plates were defaced after the stamps had been superseded, all these reprints show two, or three thick strokes across the Queen's head.

All three plates were destroyed in July 1950.

PERKINS BACON "CANCELLED". For notes on these handstamps, showing "CANCELLED" between horizontal bars forming an oval, see Catalogue Introduction.

(Eng W. Humphrys, after water-colour sketch by E. Corbould. Recess P.B.)

1855 (17 Aug–16 Sept). *Wmk Large Star, W w 1. Imperf.*
14 3 1d. carmine (16.9) (H/S "CANCELLED" in
  oval £4500) £4000 £700
15 2d. deep green (16.9) £1800 £500
16 2d. green (16.9) (H/S "CANCELLED" in
  oval £4500) £1800 £450
17 4d. deep blue .. .. £1200 85·00
18 4d. bl (H/S "CANCELLED" in oval £3250) £1200 95·00
 Proofs of the 1d. and 4d. on thick paper, *without watermark*, are sometimes offered as the issued stamps.
 The 6d. dull lilac on this watermark was prepared, but not issued. Examples exist from a creased proof sheet (*Price* £650 *unused*).

(Recess H. and C. Best, Hobart, from P.B. plates)

1856 (Apr)–57. *No wmk. Imperf. (a) Thin white paper.*
19 3 1d. pale brick-red (4.56) £4000 £550
20 2d. dull emerald-green (1.57) .. £5000 £750
21 4d. deep blue (5.57) .. .. £600 90·00
22 4d. blue (5.57) .. .. £500 90·00
23 4d. pale blue (5.57) .. .. — £120

(b) Pelure paper
24 3 1d. deep red-brown (11.56) £3000 £600

  4   7   8

(Recess H. Best (August 1857–May 1859), J. Davies (August 1859–March 1862), J. Birchall (March 1863), M. Hood (October 1863–April 1864), Govt Printer (from July 1864), all from P.B. plates)

1857 (Aug)–69. *Wmk double-lined numerals "1", "2" or "4" as W 4 on appropriate value. Imperf.*
25 3 1d. deep red-brown .. .. £400 22·00
26 1d. red-brown .. .. £275 17·00
27 1d. brick-red (1863) .. .. £140 16·00
28 1d. dull vermilion (1865).. .. 80·00 16·00
29 1d. carmine (1867) .. .. 80·00 16·00
 a. Double print .. — £120
 b. Error. Wmkd "2" (1869)
30 2d. dull emerald-green .. — 65·00
31 2d. green .. .. — 29·00
 a. Double print .. .. — £150

32 3 2d. yellow-green .. .. £200 60·00
33 2d. deep green (1858) .. .. .. £170 32·00
34 2d. slate-green (1860) .. .. £120 48·00
35 4d. deep blue .. .. — 70·00
   a. Double print .. .. — £150
36 4d. pale blue .. .. £100 12·00
37 4d. pale blue .. .. £100 16·00
   a. Double print .. .. — £150
38 4d. bright blue .. .. £100 16·00
   a. Printed on both sides.. .. †
   b. Double print .. — £120
39 4d. cobalt-blue .. .. — 60·00

Printings before July 1864 were all carried out at the *Courier* printing works which changed hands several times during this period.

CANCELLATIONS. Beware of early Tasmanian stamps with pen-cancellations cleaned off and faked postmarks applied.

(Recess P.B.)

1858 (Jan). *Wmk double-lined numerals "6" or "12" as W 4. Imperf.*
40 7 6d. dull lilac (H/S "CANCELLED" in oval £4500) .. .. £600 70·00
41 8 1s. verm (shades) (H/S "CANCELLED" in oval £3500) .. .. £500 65·00

(Recess J. Davies (March 1860), J. Birchall (April 1863), Govt Printer (from February 1865), all from P.B. plates)

1860 (Mar)–67. *Wmk double-lined "6" as W 4. Imperf.*
44 7 6d. dull slate-grey .. .. .. £225 55·00
45 6d. grey .. .. — 60·00
46 6d. grey-violet (4.63) .. .. £140 55·00
   a. Double print .. .. — £200
47 6d. dull cobalt (2.65) .. .. £350 80·00
48 6d. slate-violet (2.65) .. .. £250 48·00
49 6d. reddish mauve (4.67).. .. £550 £150

In 1871 reprints were made of the 6d. (in mauve) and the 1s. on white wove paper, and perforated 11½. They are found with or without "REPRINT". In 1889 they were again reprinted on white card, imperforate. These later impressions are also found overprinted "REPRINT" and perforated 11½.

PERFORATED ISSUES. From 1 October 1857 the Tasmania Post Office only supplied purchasers requiring five or more complete sheets of stamps. The public obtained their requirements, at face value, from licensed stamp vendors, who obtained their stocks at a discount from the Post Office.
From 1863 onwards a number of the stamp vendors applied their own roulettes or perforations. The Hobart firm of J. Walch & Sons achieved this so successfully that they were given an official contract in July 1869 to perforate sheets for the Post Office. The Government did not obtain a perforating machine until late in 1871.

1863–71. *Double-lined numeral watermarks. Various unofficial roulettes and perforations.*
(a) By J. Walch & Sons, Hobart
(i) Roulette about 8, often imperf × roul (1863–68)
50 3 1d. brick-red .. .. — £150
51 1d. carmine £300 £100
52 2d. yellow-green .. .. — £400
53 2d. slate-green .. ..
54 4d. pale blue .. .. — £140
55 7 6d. dull lilac .. .. — £170
56 8 1s. vermilion .. .. — £500

(ii) P 10 (1864–69)
57 3 1d. brick-red .. .. 48·00 20·00
58 1d. dull vermilion .. .. 48·00 20·00
   a. Double print .. .. †
59 1d. carmine .. .. 45·00 20·00
60 2d. yellow-green .. .. £250 75·00
61 2d. slate-green £300 £130
62 4d. pale blue .. .. 95·00 10·00
63 4d. blue .. .. 95·00 10·00
   a. Double print .. .. — £110
64 7 6d. grey-violet .. .. £160 14·00
65 6d. dull cobalt .. .. £225 55·00
66 6d. slate-violet .. .. — 19·00
67 6d. reddish mauve .. .. £325 65·00
68 8 1s. vermilion .. .. £100 20·00
   a. Imperf vert (horiz pair) .. —

(iii) P 12 (1865–71—from July 1869 under contract to the Post Office)
69 3 1d. dull vermilion .. .. 48·00
   a. Double print .. .. †
70 1d. carmine .. .. 38·00 14·00
   a. Error. Wmkd "2" (pen cancel £75) .. — £1000
71 2d. yellow-green .. .. £120 40·00
72 4d. deep blue .. .. 75·00 12·00
73 4d. blue .. .. 75·00 14·00
74 4d. cobalt-blue .. .. — 30·00
75 7 6d. slate-violet .. .. £130 20·00
   a. Imperf between (vert pair) .. —
76 6d. reddish mauve .. .. 80·00 35·00
   a. Imperf between (vert or horiz pair) .. —
77 8 1s. vermilion .. .. £110 30·00
   a. Double print .. .. —
   b. Imperf between (horiz pair) .. — £150

(iv) Perf compound 10 × 12 (1865–69)
78 3 1d. carmine £1300
79 4d. blue .. .. — £900

(b) P 12½ by R. Harris, Launceston (1864–68)
80 3 1d. brick-red .. .. 55·00 24·00
81 1d. dull vermilion .. .. 50·00 18·00
82 1d. carmine .. .. 29·00 7·50
83 2d. yellow-green .. .. £250 85·00
84 2d. slate-green £225 £110
85 4d. blue .. .. £140 38·00
86 4d. bright blue .. .. £140 38·00
87 7 6d. dull cobalt .. .. £275 75·00
88 6d. slate-violet .. .. £180 42·00
89 6d. reddish mauve .. .. £375 95·00
90 8 1s. vermilion .. .. £225 80·00

(c) Imperf × oblique roulette 11½ at Oatlands (1866)
91 3 4d. blue .. .. — £375

(d) Oblique roulette 10–10½, possibly at Deloraine (1867)
92 3 1d. brick-red .. .. — £325
93 1d. carmine £900 £275
94 2d. yellow-green .. .. — £425
95 4d. bright blue .. .. — £375
96 7 6d. grey-violet .. .. — £600

(e) Oblique roulette 14–15, probably at Cleveland (1867–69)
97 3 1d. brick-red .. .. — £375
98 1d. dull vermilion .. .. — £375
99 1d. carmine .. .. — £375
100 2d. yellow-green .. .. — £425
101 4d. pale blue .. .. — £325
102 7 6d. grey-violet .. .. — £600
103 8 1s. vermilion .. .. — £750

(f) Pin-perf 5½ to 9½ at Longford (1867)
104 3 1d. carmine .. .. £300 75·00
105 2d. yellow-green .. ..
106 4d. bright blue .. .. — £160
107 7 6d. grey-violet .. .. — £150
108 6d. reddish mauve .. .. — £425
109 8 1s. vermilion .. ..

(g) Pin-perf 12 at Oatlands (1867)
110 3 4d. blue .. ..

(h) Pin-perf 13½ to 14½ (1867)
111 3 1d. brick-red .. .. — £190
112 1d. dull vermilion .. .. — £190
113 1d. carmine .. .. — £275
114 2d. yellow-green .. .. — £275
115 4d. pale blue .. .. — £160
116 7 6d. grey-violet .. .. — £375
117 8 1s. vermilion .. ..

(j) Serrated perf 19 at Hobart (1868–69)
118 3 1d. carmine (pen-cancel £9) .. £225 £100
119 2d. yellow-green .. .. — £200
120 4d. deep blue .. .. £550 95·00
121 4d. cobalt-blue .. .. — 95·00
122 7 6d. slate-violet .. .. — £375
123 8 1s. vermilion .. ..

(k) Roul 4½, possibly at Macquarie River (1868)
124 3 4d. blue .. ..
125 7 6d. reddish mauve .. ..
126 8 1s. vermilion .. ..

An example of the 1d. carmine is known perforated 10 on three sides and serrated 19 on the fourth.
For stamps perforated 11½ or 12 by the Post Office see Nos. 134a/43.

(Typo Govt Printer, Hobart, from plates made by D.L.R.)

1870 (1 Nov)–71. *Wmk single-lined numerals W 12 (2d.), 13 (1d., 4d.) or 14 (1d., 10d.). (a) P 12 by J. Walch & Sons.*
127 11 1d. rose-red (wmk "10") .. .. 30·00 8·50
   a. Imperf (pair) £300 £300
   b. Deep rose-red .. .. 50·00 6·50
128 1d. rose-red (wmk "4") (3.71) .. 48·00 8·50
   a. Imperf (pair) .. .. — £250
129 2d. yellow-green .. .. 50·00 4·50
   a. Imperf (pair) .. ..
   b. Blue-green .. .. 55·00 4·50
130 4d. blue £700 £400
131 10d. black .. .. 23·00 18·00
   a. Imperf (pair) .. .. — £170
(b) P 11½ by the Post Office (1871)
132 11 1d. rose-red (wmk "10") £900
133 2d. yellow-green .. .. 90·00 6·50
   a. Blue-green .. .. 45·00 3·25
   a. Double print
134 10d. black .. .. 26·00 18·00
The above were printed on paper obtained from New South Wales.
See also Nos. 144/55, 156/8, 159/66, 170/4, 226/7, 242 and 255/6.

(Recess P.B.)

1871. *Wmk double-lined numeral "6". P 11½ by the Post Office.*
134a 7 1s. vermilion .. ..

(Recess Govt Printer, Hobart)

1871–91. *Double-lined numeral watermarks as W 4. Perforated by the Post Office. (a) P 11½.*
135 7 6d. dull lilac .. .. 75·00 19·00
136 6d. lilac .. .. 70·00 19·00
   a. Imperf between (pair) .. — £475
137 6d. deep slate-lilac (3.75) .. 70·00 19·00
   a. Imperf (pair) .. .. — £450
138 6d. bright violet (5.78) .. .. 70·00 28·00
   a. Double print .. .. — £110
   b. Imperf between (horiz pair) .. £750
139 6d. dull reddish lilac (10.79) .. 70·00 38·00

140 8 1s. brown-red (1.73) .. .. 90·00 38·00
   a. Imperf between (horiz pair) .. —
141 1s. orange-red (3.75) .. .. 80·00 38·00
141a 1s. orange (5.78) .. ..
(b) P 12
142 7 6d. reddish purple (1884) .. .. 80·00 18·00
   a. Imperf between (horiz pair) .. £425
143 6d. dull claret (7.91) .. .. 24·00 12·00
The perforation machine used on Nos. 142/3 was previously owned by J. Walch and Sons and passed to the ownership of the Government in 1884. It may have been used to perforate left-over sheets of previous printings.

15   16
(Typo Govt Printer, Hobart, from plates made by D.L.R.)

1871 (25 Mar)–78. W 15. (a) P 11½.
144 11 1d. rose (5.71) .. .. 4·50 50
   a. Imperf (pair) (pen cancel £30) .. —
   b. Bright rose .. .. 4·50 50
   c. Carmine .. .. 6·00 50
   d. Pink .. .. 6·00 1·50
   e. Vermilion (4.75) .. .. £200 65·00
145 2d. deep green (11.72) .. .. 18·00 50
   a. Blue-green .. .. 26·00 50
   b. Yellow-green (12.75) .. .. £110 1·50
146 3d. pale red-brown .. .. 42·00 3·25
   a. Imperf (pair) £170
   b. Deep red-brown .. .. 42·00 3·75
   ba. Imperf between (pair) .. —
   c. Purple-brown (1.78) .. .. 42·00 3·25
   ca. Imperf (pair).. .. — £400
   d. Brownish purple .. .. 42·00 3·25
147 4d. pale yellow (8.8.76) .. .. 42·00 12·00
   a. Ochre (7.78) .. .. 50·00 9·00
   b. Buff .. .. 45·00 9·50
148 9d. blue (2.10.71) .. .. 16·00 5·00
   a. Imperf (pair) £160
   b. Double print
149 5s. purple (pen cancel £3.75) .. £140 42·00
   a. Imperf (pair) .. .. —
   b. Mauve .. .. £120 42·00
(b) P 12
150 11 1d. rose .. .. 60·00 5·50
   a. Carmine .. .. 65·00 7·00
151 2d. green.. .. £400 95·00
   a. Imperf (pair).. .. — £300
152 3d. red-brown .. .. 60·00 15·00
   a. Deep red-brown .. .. 60·00 15·00
153 4d. buff .. .. £225 16·00
154 9d. pale blue .. .. 28·00
155 5s. purple £250
   a. Mauve £160

(Typo D.L.R.)

1878 (28 Oct). W 16. P 14.
156 11 1d. carmine .. .. 2·75 50
   a. Rose-carmine .. .. 2·75 50
   b. Scarlet .. .. 2·75 50
157 2d. pale green .. .. 3·25 50
   a. Green.. .. 3·25 50
158 8d. dull purple-brown .. .. 14·00 4·25

(Typo Govt Printer, Hobart (some printings of 1d. in 1891 by *Mercury Press*) from plates made by Victoria Govt Printer Melbourne (½d.) or D.L.R. (others))

1880 (Apr)–91. W 16 (sideways on 1d.). (a) P 11½.
159 11 ½d. orange (8.3.89) .. .. 2·50 2·25
   a. Deep orange .. .. 2·50 2·25
160 1d. dull red (14.2.89) .. .. 4·00 1·10
   a. Vermilion-red .. .. 4·00 1·10
161 3d. red-brown .. .. 13·00 2·75
   a. Imperf (pair) £130
162 4d. deep yellow (1.83) .. .. 29·00 12·00
   a. Chrome-yellow .. .. 29·00 13·00
   b. Olive-yellow .. .. £100 22·00
   c. Buff .. .. 28·00 9·50
(b) P 12
163 11 ½d. orange .. .. 2·00 2·75
   a. Deep orange .. .. 1·90 2·75
   ab. Wmk sideways
164 1d. pink (1891) .. .. 18·00 2·75
   a. Imperf (pair) £130 £15
   b. Rosine .. .. 8·00 1·5
   c. Dull rosine .. .. 10·00 3·0
   ca. Imperf (pair) £110
165 3d. red-brown .. .. 8·00 3·2
   a. Imperf between (horiz pair) .. £550
166 4d. deep blue .. .. 50·00 13·00
   a. Chrome-yellow .. .. 70·00 13·00
   ab. Printed both sides £300

SPECIMEN AND PRESENTATION REPRINTS OF TYPE 11. In 1871 the 1d., 2d., 3d., 4d. blue, 9d., 10d. and 5s. were reprinted on soft white wove paper to be followed, in 1879, by the 4d. yellow and 8d. on rough white wove. Both these reprintings were perforated 11½. In 1886 it was decided to overprint remaining stocks with the word "REPRINT".
In 1889 Tasmania commenced sending sample stamps to the U.P.U. in Berne and a further printing of the 4d. blue was made imperforate, on white card. This, together with the 5s. in mauve on white card, both perforated 11½ and overprinted "RE-PRINT", were included in presentation sets supplied to members of the states' legislatures in 1901.

Halfpenny

(17)

d.	**d.**	
2½	**2½**	
(18) (2¼ mm between "d", and "2")	(19) (3½ mm between "d" and "2")	

1889 (1 Jan). *No. 156b surch locally with T* **17**.
167 **11** ½d. on 1d. scarlet .. .. .. 8·50 10·00
   a. "al" in "Half" printed sideways
   (R. 1/2) £700 £475
No. 167a occurred in a second printing and was later corrected.
A reprint on white card, perforated 11½ or imperforate,
overprinted "REPRINT" was produced in 1901.

1891 (1 Jan–June). *Surch locally.* W **16**. (*a*) With *T* **18**. P 11½.
168 **11** 2½d. on 9d. pale blue .. .. 7·50 3·50
   a. Surch double, one inverted .. £250 £275
   b. Deep blue (May) .. .. 8·00 4·00
     (*b*) With *T* **19**. P 12
169 **11** 2½d. on 9d. pale blue (June) .. 5·00 3·25
   a. Blue surch. .. .. .. 5·00 3·25
A reprint, using a third setting, perforated 11½ and overprinted "REPRINT" was produced in 1901.

(Typo Govt Printer, Hobart)
1891 (Apr–Aug). W **15**. (*a*) P 11½.
170 **11** ½d. orange .. .. .. 24·00 8·50
   a. Brown-orange .. .. 18·00 4·00
171 1d. rosine .. .. .. 15·00 5·00
     (*b*) P 12
172 **11** ½d. orange .. .. .. 17·00 12·00
   a. Imperf (pair) .. .. 85·00
173 1d. dull rosine .. .. 20·00 9·00
   a. Rosine .. .. 32·00 13·00
174 4d. bistre (Aug).. .. .. 16·00 8·00

20   21   21a

(Typo D.L.R.)
1892 (12 Feb)–99. W **16**. P 14.
216 **20** ½d. orange and mauve (11.92) .. 1·25 50
217 **21** 2½d. purple .. .. 2·50 1·00
218 **20** 5d. pale blue and brown .. 4·50 1·75
219 6d. violet and black (11.92) .. 5·50 2·00
220 **21a** 10d. purple-lake & deep green (30.1.99) 9·00 7·50
221 **20** 1s. rose and green (11.92) .. 6·00 1·75
222 2s. 6d. brown and blue (11.92) .. 22·00 9·00
223 5s. lilac and blue (3.2.97) .. 40·00 18·00
224 10s. mauve and brown (11.92) .. 75·00 55·00
225 £1 green and yellow (2.97) .. £225 £160
216/25 .. .. *Set of* 10 £350 £225
216/25 Optd "Specimen" .. *Set of* 10 £250
See also Nos. 243 and 257/8.

(Typo Govt Printer, Hobart)
1896. W **16**. P 12.
226 **11** 4d. pale bistre .. .. 12·00 6·00
227 9d. pale blue .. .. 8·00 2·50
   a. Blue.. .. .. 8·50 3·25

22 Lake Marion   23 Mount Wellington

24 Hobart   25 Tasman's Arch

26 Spring River, Port Davey   27 Russell Falls

28 Mount Gould, Lake St. Clair   29 Dilston Falls

30

(Eng. L. Phillips. Recess D.L.R.)
1899 (Dec)–1900. W **30**. P 14.
229 **22** ½d. deep green (31.3.00) .. 7·00 4·00
230 **23** 1d. bright lake (13.12.99)* .. 5·00 90
231 **24** 2d. deep violet (15.12.99)* .. 10·00 90
232 **25** 2½d. indigo (1900) .. .. 10·00 3·75
233 **26** 3d. sepia (1900) .. .. 8·50 3·00
234 **27** 4d. deep orange-buff (1900) .. 14·00 3·00
235 **28** 5d. bright blue (31.3.00) .. 14·00 7·50
236 **29** 6d. lake (31.3.00) .. .. 18·00 11·00
229/36 .. .. *Set of* 8 75·00 30·00
229/36 Optd "Specimen" .. *Set of* 8 £225
*Earliest known postmark dates.
See also Nos. 237/9, 240/1, 245/8, 249/54, 259 and 261/2.

DIFFERENCES BETWEEN LITHOGRAPHED AND TYPOGRAPHED PRINTINGS OF TYPES 22/9

Lithographed	Typographed
General appearance fine.	*Comparatively crude and coarse appearance.*
½d. All "V over Crown" wmk.	All "Crown over A" wmk.
1d. The shading on the path on the right bank of the river consists of very fine dots. In printings from worn stones the dots hardly show.	The shading on the path is coarser, consisting of large dots and small patches of colour.
The shading on the white mountain is fine (or almost absent in many stamps).	The shading on the mountain is coarse, and clearly defined.
2d. Three rows of windows in large building on shore, at extreme left, against inner frame.	Two rows of windows.
3d. Clouds very white.	Clouds dark.
Stars in corner ornaments have long points.	Stars have short points.
Shading of corner ornaments is defined by a coloured outer line.	Shading of ornaments terminates against white background.
4d. Lithographed only.	—
6d. No coloured dots at base of waterfall.	Coloured dots at base of waterfall.
Outer frame of value tablets is formed by outer line of design.	Thick line of colour between value tablets and outer line. Small break in inner frame below second "A" of "TASMANIA".

(Litho, using transfers from D.L.R. plates, Victoria Government Printing Office, Melbourne)
1902 (Jan)–04. *Wmk V over Crown,* W w **10** (*sideways on* ½d., 2d.). P 12½.
237 **22** ½d. green (2.03) .. .. 1·25 1·00
   a. Wmk upright
   b. Perf 11 .. .. 3·25 2·75
   c. Perf comp of 12½ and 11 .. 50·00 35·00
   d. Perf comp of 12½ and 12 ..
238 **23** 1d. carmine-red .. .. 6·00 1·00
239 **24** 2d. deep reddish violet .. 4·50 30
   a. Perf 11 .. .. 4·50 2·25
   b. Perf comp of 12½ and 11 .. 55·00 35·00
   c. Wmk upright (2.04) ..
   d. Deep rose-lilac (4.05) .. 7·50 10
   da. Perf 11 .. .. 6·50 85
   db. Perf comp of 12½ and 11 ..
237 and 239 Optd "Specimen" .. *Set of* 2 85·00
As the V and Crown paper was originally prepared for stamps of smaller size, portions of two or more watermarks appear on each stamp.
We only list the main groups of shades in this and the following issues. There are variations of shade in all values, particularly in the 2d. where there is a wide range, also in the 1d. in some issues.

(Typo, using electrotyped plates, Victoria Govt Ptg Office, Melbourne)
1902 (Oct)–04. *Wmk V over Crown,* W w **10**. P 12½.
240 **23** 1d. pale red (*wmk sideways*) .. 8·50 1·00
   a. Perf 11 .. .. 22·00 1·25
   b. Perf comp of 12½ and 11 .. £150 35·00
   c. Wmk upright (1.03) .. 22·00 5·00
   ca. Perf 11 .. .. 27·00 6·00
   d. Rose-red (*wmk upright*) (4.03) (Optd S. £40) .. 4·50 90
   da. Perf 11 .. .. 15·00 90
   db. Perf comp of 12½ and 11 .. £150 35·00

241 **23** 1d. scarlet (*wmk upright*) (9.03) .. 3·25 30
   a. Perf 11 .. .. 4·50 50
   b. Perf comp of 12½ and 11 ..
   c. Rose-scarlet (1904) .. 2·75 40
   ca. Perf 11 .. .. 3·25 50
   cb. Perf comp of 12½ and 11 .. 50·00 15·00
The 1d. scarlet of September 1903 was from new electrotyped plates which show less intense shading.

(Typo Victoria Govt Ptg Office, Melbourne)
1903–05. *Wmk V over Crown,* W w **10**. P 12½.
242 **11** 9d. blue (1905) .. .. 8·00 3·25
   a. Perf 11 .. .. 8·00 4·75
   b. Perf comp of 12½ and 11 .. — £375
   c. Wmk sideways .. 55·00 20·00
   d. Pale blue .. .. 10·00 4·50
   e. Bright blue .. .. 10·00 5·00
   f. Ultramarine £350
   g. Indigo £130
243 **20** 1s. rose and green .. 12·00 3·00
   a. Perf 11 .. .. 30·00
242/3 Optd "Specimen" .. *Set of* 2 £100

1½d.	**ONE PENNY**	
(31)	(32)	

1904 (29 Dec). *No. 218 surch with T* **31**.
244 **20** 1½d. on 5d. pale blue & brn (Optd S. £28) 1·25 60
Stamps with inverted surcharge or without surcharge *se-tenant* with stamps with normal surcharge were obtained irregularly and were not issued for postal use.

PRINTER. The Victoria Govt Ptg Office became the Commonwealth Stamp Printing Branch in March 1909.

(Litho, using transfers from D.L.R. plates, Victoria Govt Ptg Office, Melbourne)
1905 (Sept)–12. *Wmk Crown over A,* W w **11** (*sideways on horiz stamps*). P 12½.
245 **24** 2d. deep purple .. .. 4·00 15
   a. Perf 11 .. .. 12·00 20
   b. Perf comp of 12½ and 11 .. 17·00 3·00
   c. Perf comp of 12½ and 12 .. — 45·00
   d. Perf comp of 11 and 12 .. 90·00
   e. Slate-lilac (1906) .. 4·50
   ea. Perf 11 .. .. 17·00 25
   eb. Perf comp of 12½ and 11 ..
   ed. Perf comp of 11 and 12 ..
   f. Reddish lilac (1907) .. 11·00 75
   fa. Perf 11 ..
   fb. Perf comp of 12½ and 11 ..
246 **26** 3d. brown (5.06) .. .. 8·50 2·25
   a. Perf 11 .. .. 13·00 4·75
   b. Perf comp of 12½ and 11 .. 60·00
247 **27** 4d. pale yellow-brown (3.07) .. 12·00 3·25
   a. Perf 11 .. .. 17·00 3·75
   b. Orange-buff (5.09) .. 13·00 3·25
   ba. Perf 11 .. .. 16·00 3·25
   bb. Perf comp of 12½ and 11 .. £160
   c. Brown-ochre (*wmk sideways*). Perf 11 (6.11) .. 24·00 27·00
   d. Orange-yellow (3.12) .. 15·00 13·00
   da. Perf 11 .. .. 25·00 20·00
   db. Perf comp of 12½ and 11 ..
248 **29** 6d. lake (7.08) .. .. 38·00 4·25
   a. Perf 11 .. .. 45·00 4·50
   b. Perf comp of 12½ and 11 .. £140
Stamps with perf compound of 12½ and 12 or 11 and 12 are found on sheets which were sent from Melbourne incompletely perforated along the outside edge of the pane or sheet. The missing perforations were applied in Hobart using a line machine measuring 12 (11.8 is the exact gauge). This perforation can only occur on one side of a stamp.

(Typo, using electrotyped plates, Victoria Govt Ptg Office, Melbourne)
1905 (Aug)–11. *Wmk Crown over A,* W w **11** (*sideways on horiz designs*). P 12½.
249 **22** ½d. yellow-green (10.12.08) .. 1·25 20
   a. Perf 11 .. .. 1·25 20
   b. Perf comp of 12½ and 11 .. 25·00 5·00
   c. Perf comp of 11 and 12 .. 65·00
   d. Wmk upright (1909) .. 5·50 1·75
   da. Perf 11 ..
250 **23** 1d. rose-red .. .. 1·50 10
   a. Perf 11 .. .. 3·00 10
   b. Perf comp of 12½ and 11 .. 4·00 1·75
   c. Perf comp of 12½ and 12 .. 40·00 5·50
   d. Perf comp of 11 and 12 .. 45·00 20·00
   e. Wmk sideways (1908) .. 5·50 75
   ea. Perf 11 ..
   f. Imperf (pair) £150
250g 1d. carmine-red (3.10) .. 3·25 55
   ga. Perf 11 .. .. 5·50 60
   gb. Perf comp of 12½ and 11 .. 8·00 4·00
   gc. Perf comp of 12½ and 12 .. 40·00
   gd. Perf comp of 11 and 12 .. 45·00
   ge. Imperf (pair) £150
   h. Carmine-vermilion (1911) .. 8·50 2·75
   ha. Perf 11 .. .. 9·50 2·75
   hb. Perf comp of 12½ and 11 ..
   hc. Perf comp of 12½ and 12 ..
   hd. Perf comp of 11 and 12 ..
251 **24** 2d. plum (8.07) .. .. 4·75 10
   a. Wmk upright .. 9·00 1·00
   b. Perf 11 .. .. 2·50 10
   ba. Wmk upright (12.07) .. 9·00 1·00
   c. Perf comp of 12½ and 11 .. 20·00 6·00
   d. Perf comp of 12½ and 12 .. £110 45·00
   e. Perf comp of 11 and 12 .. 70·00 38·00
   f. Bright reddish violet (1910) .. 3·25 90
   fa. Perf 11 .. .. 3·25 50
   fb. Perf comp of 12½ and 11 ..

253	26	3d. brown (3.09)			6·50	2·75
		a. Wmk upright				
		b. Perf 11			13·00	3·50
		c. Perf comp of 12½ and 11			£130	
254	29	6d. carmine-lake (12.10)			16·00	18·00
		a. Perf 11			20·00	22·00
		b. Perf comp of 12½ and 11			£180	
		c. *Dull carmine-red* (3.11)			22·00	22·00
		ca. Wmk upright			27·00	
		cb. Perf 11			23·00	22·00
		cc. Perf comp of 12½ and 11			£150	

The note after No. 248 *re* perfs compound with perf 12 also applies here.

Nos. 250/f were printed from the same plates as Nos. 241/cb. Nos. 250g/hd are from a further pair of new plates and the images are sharper.

(Typo Victoria Govt Printing Office, Melbourne)

1906–13. *Wmk Crown over A, W w 11. P 12½.*

255	11	8d. purple-brown (1907)			17·00	5·00
		a. Perf 11			15·00	3·75
256		9d. blue (1907)			7·00	3·00
		a. Perf 11			7·00	3·00
		b. Perf comp of 12½ and 11 (1909)			55·00	
		c. Perf comp of 12½ and 12 (1909)			£120	
		d. Perf comp of 11 and 12			£200	
257	20	1s. rose and green (1907)			13·00	3·00
		a. Perf 11 (1907)			17·00	8·50
		b. Perf comp of 12½ and 11			22·00	
		c. Perf comp of 12½ and 12			70·00	
258		10s. mauve and brown (1906)			£110	£100
		a. Perf 11			£180	
		b. Perf comp of 12½ and 12			£200	

The note after No. 248 *re* perfs compound with perf 12, also applies here.

(Typo, using stereotyped plates, Commonwealth Stamp Ptg Branch, Melbourne)

1911 (Jan). *Wmk Crown over A, W w 11 (sideways). P 12½.*

259	24	2d. bright violet			4·75	1·75
		a. Wmk upright			16·00	2·75
		b. Perf 11			5·00	1·75
		c. Perf comp of 12½ and 11			50·00	15·00
		d. Perf comp of 12½ and 12			£150	

Stamps from this stereotyped plate differ from No. 251 in the width of the design (33 to 33¾ mm, against just over 32 mm), in the taller, bolder letters of "TASMANIA", in the slope of the mountain in the left background, which is clearly outlined in white, and in the outer vertical frame-line at left, which appears "wavy". Compare Nos. 260, etc, which are always from this plate.

1912 (Oct). *No. 259 surch with T 32. P 12½.*

260	24	1d. on 2d. bright violet (R.)			90	40
		a. Perf 11			1·50	40
		b. Perf comp of 12½ and 11			85·00	85·00

(Typo, using electrotyped plates, Commonwealth Stamp Ptg Branch, Melbourne)

1912 (Dec). *Thin paper, white gum (as Victoria, 1912). W w 11 (sideways on 3d.). P 12½.*

261	23	1d. carmine-vermilion			16·00	6·00
		a. Perf 11			16·00	6·00
		b. Perf comp of 12½ and 11				
262	26	3d. brown			42·00	48·00

STAMP BOOKLETS

There are very few surviving examples of Nos. SB1/4. Listings are provided for those believed to have been issued with prices quoted for those known to still exist.

1904 (1 Jan)–**09.** *Black on red cover as No. SB1 of New South Wales. Stapled.*
SB1 £1 booklet containing two hundred and forty 1d. in twelve blocks of 20 (5×4) ..
   a. Red on pink cover (1909)
   b. Blue on pink cover ..

1904 (1 Jan). *Black on grey cover as No. SB1. Stapled.*
SB2 £1 booklet containing one hundred and twenty 2d. in four blocks of 30 ..

1910 (May). *Black on white cover as No. SB3 of New South Wales. Stapled.*
SB3 2s. booklet containing eleven ½d. (No. 249), either in block of 6 plus block of 5 or block of 11, and eighteen 1d. (No. 250), either in three blocks of 6 or block of 6 plus block of 12 .. £2000
Unsold stock No. SB3 was uprated with one additional ½d. in May 1911.

1911 (Aug). *Red on pink cover as No. SB3. Stapled.*
SB4 2s. booklet containing twelve ½d. (No. 249), either in two blocks of 6 or block of 12, and eighteen 1d. (No. 250), either in three blocks of 6 or block of 6 plus block of 12 .. .. .. £1500

POSTAL FISCAL STAMPS

VALIDITY. Nos. F1/29 were authorised for postal purposes on 1 November 1882.

CLEANED STAMPS. Beware of postal fiscal stamps with pen-cancellations removed.

F 1

F 2

F 3

F 4

(Recess Alfred Bock, Hobart)

1863–80. *Wmk double-lined "1", W 4. (a) Imperf.*

F 1	F 1	3d. green (1.65)			70·00	45·00
F 2	F 2	2s. 6d. carmine (11.63)			75·00	45·00
F 3		2s. 6d. lake (5.80)				
F 4	F 3	5s. brown (1.64)			£180	£150
F 5		5s. sage-green (1880)			75·00	55·00
F 6	F 4	10s. orange (1.64)			£275	£150
F 7		10s. salmon (5.80)			£180	£150

(b) P 10

F 8	F 1	3d. green ..			42·00 24·00
F 9	F 2	2s. 6d. carmine			45·00
F10	F 3	5s. brown..			70·00
F11	F 4	10s. orange			45·00

(c) P 12

F12	F 1	3d. green ..			45·00 27·00
F13	F 2	2s. 6d. carmine			45·00 38·00
F14	F 3	5s. brown..			80·00
F15		5s. sage-green			35·00 27·00
F16	F 4	10s. orange			45·00 38·00
F17		10s. salmon			35·00 27·00

(d) P 12½

F18	F 1	3d. green ..			80·00
F19	F 2	2s. 6d. carmine			80·00
F20	F 3	5s. brown..			£100
F21	F 4	10s. orange-brown			70·00

(e) P 11½

F22	F 1	3d. green ..			
F23	F 2	2s. 6d. lake			42·00 35·00
F24	F 3	5s. sage-green			35·00 24·00
F25	F 4	10s. salmon			60·00 42·00

See also No. F30.

In 1879, the 3d., 2s. 6d., 5s. (brown), and 10s. (orange) were reprinted on thin, tough, white paper, and are found with or without "REPRINT". In 1889 another reprint was made on white card, imperforate and perforated 12. These are also found with or without "REPRINT".

REVENUE

F 5 Duck-billed Platypus   (F 6)

(Typo D.L.R.)

1880 (19 Apr). *W 16 (sideways). P 14.*

F26	F 5	1d. slate			11·00 3·75
F27		3d. chestnut			11·00 3·00
F28		6d. mauve			60·00 2·00
F29		1s. rose-pink			70·00 5·00
		a. Perf comp of 14 and 11			

All values are known imperf, but not used.

Reprints are known of the 1d. in *deep blue* and the 6d. in lilac. The former is on yellowish white, the latter on white card. Both values also exist on wove paper, perf 12, with the word "REPRINT".

1888 (Aug). *W 16. P 12.*

F30	F 2	2s. 6d. lake			15·00 11·00
		a. Imperf between (horiz pair)			£450

1900 (15 Nov). *Optd with Type F 6. (a) On Types F 2 and F 4.*

F31	F 2	2s. 6d. carmine (No. F13)			
		a. "REVFNUE"			
F32		2s. 6d. lake (No. F30)			£160
		a. "REVFNUE"			£250
		b. Opt inverted			£350
		c. Imperf			£170
F33	F 4	10s. salmon (No. F17) ..			
		a. "REVFNUE"			

(b) On Nos. F27 and F29

F34	F 5	3d. chestnut			15·00 15·00
		a. Double opt, one vertical			75·00 £100
F35		1s. rose-pink			

(c) On stamps as Nos. F26/9, but typo locally. W 16. P 12

F36	F 5	1d. blue			18·00
		a. Imperf between (horiz pair)			£300
		b. "REVENUE" inverted			£100
		c. "REVENUE" double			£160
		d. Pale blue			18·00
F37		6d. mauve			50·00
		a. Double print			£200
F38		1s. pink			75·00

(d) On No. 225

F39	20	£1 green and yellow ..			£150 £130
		a. Opt double, one vertical			£275 £275

It was not intended that stamps overprinted with Type F 6 should be used for postal purposes, but an ambiguity in

regulations permitted such usage until all postal fiscal stamps were invalidated on 30 November 1900.

Printings of some of the above with different watermarks, together with a 2d. as Nos. F36/8, did not appear until after the stamps had become invalid for postal purposes.

Tasmania became part of the Commonwealth of Australia on 1 January 1901.

VICTORIA

SPECIMEN OVERPRINTS. Those listed are from U.P.U. distributions in 1892 and 1897. Further "Specimen" overprints exist, but these were used for other purposes.

During the expansion of the Australian settlements in the fourth decade of the nineteenth century the growing population of the Port Phillip District in the south of New South Wales led to a movement for its creation as a separate colony. This aspiration received the approval of the British Government in 1849, but the colony of Victoria, as it was to be called, was not to be created until 1 July 1851.

In the meantime the New South Wales Legislative Council voted for the introduction of postal reforms, including the issue of postage stamps, from 1 January 1850, and this act was also to apply to the Port Phillip District where stamps inscribed "VICTORIA" would predate the creation of that colony by eighteen months.

Until the end of 1859 the stamps of Victoria, with the exception of Nos. 40 and 73, were produced by local contractors working under the supervision of the colonial administration.

HAM PRINTINGS. The first contractor was Thomas Ham of Melbourne. He was responsible for the initial printings of the "Half-Length" 1d., 2d. and 3d., together with the replacement "Queen on Throne" 2d. The first printings were produced from small sheets of 30 (5×6) laid down directly from the engraved die which showed a single example of each value. Subsequent printings, of which No. 4a was the first, were in sheets of 120 (two panes of 60) laid down using intermediate stones of various sizes. Impressions from the first printings were fine and clear, but the quality deteriorated when intermediate stones were used.

1 Queen Victoria ("Half Length")

(Lithographed by Thomas Ham, Melbourne)

1850 (3 Jan)–53. *Imperf.*

1d. Thin line at top

2d. Fine border and background

3d. White area to left of orb

(a) Original state of dies: 1d. *(tops of letters of "VICTORIA" reach to top of stamp);* 2d. *(fine border and background);* 3d. *(thicker white outline around left of orb, central band of orb does not protrude at left). No frame-lines on dies.*

1	1	1d. orange-vermilion	..	£7500	£1500
		a. Orange-brown	..	†	£750
		b. Dull chocolate-brown *(shades)*	..	£3500	£850
2		2d. lilac-mauve *(shades)* (Stone A)	..	£2250	£400
3		2d. brown-lilac *(shades)* (Stone B)	..	£2250	£250
		a. Grey-lilac	..	—	£250
4		3d. bright blue *(shades)*	..	£1800	£300
		b. Blue *(shades)*	..	£1800	£170
		ab. Retouched (between Queen's head and right border) (No. 11 in transfer-group) (8 varieties)	..	—	£275
		ac. Retouched (under "V") (No. 10 in transfer group)	..	—	£275

With the exception of No. 4a the above were printed from small stones of 30 (5×6) laid down directly from the engraved die which showed a single example of each value. There were two states of the 2d. and one for each of the other values. No. 4a is the second printing of the 3d. for which the sheet size was increased to 120, the printing stone being constructed from an intermediate stone of 15 (5×3).

1d. Thick line at top

2d. Coarse background

3d. White area small and band protruding to left of orb

(b) Second state of dies: 1d. *(more colour over top of letters of "VICTORIA");* 2d. *(fine border as (a) but with coarse background);* 3d. *(thinner white outline around left of orb, central band of orb protrudes at left).*

5	1	1d. red-brown *(shades)* (2.50)	..	£2750	£300
		a. Pale dull red-brown	..	£2000	£300
6		2d. grey-lilac *(shades)* (1.50)	..	£1100	£100
		a. Dull grey	..	£1100	£110
7		3d. blue *(shades)*	..	£1000	£110
		a. Retouched (22 varieties)	..	from £1600	£225

Printed in sheets of 120 (10×12) with the printing stones constructed from intermediate stones of 30 (5×6) for the 1d. and 2d. or 10 (5×2) for the 3d. It is believed that the use of the smaller intermediate stone for the latter resulted in the many retouches.

Frame-lines added

(c) Third state of dies: As in (b) but with frame-lines added, very close up, on all four sides.

8	1	1d. dull orange-vermilion (11.50)	..	£1300	£400
		a. Dull red *(shades)*	..	£1000	£120
9		1d. deep red-brown (5.51)	..	—	£450
		a. Brownish red *(shades)*	..	£650	£110
		b. Dull rose *(shades)*	..	£650	£110
10		2d. grey *(shades)* (8.50)	..	£850	£130
		a. Olive-grey *(shades)*	..	£1000	£130
11		3d. blue *(shades)* (12.52)	..	£400	50·00
		a. Deep blue *(shades)*	..	£500	50·00
		b. Pale greenish blue *(shades)*	..	£650	£100

Printed in sheets of 120 (12×10) produced from intermediate stones of 30 (6×5) for No. 8 and 12 (6×2) for the others.

White veil

(d) As (c) but altered to give, for the 1d. and 3d., the so-called "white veils", and for the 2d., the effect of vertical drapes to the veil.

12	1	1d. reddish brown (6.51)	..	£700	£100
		a. Bright pinky red *(shades)*	..	£450	£100
13		2d. drab (1.51)	..	£1000	£110
		a. Grey-drab	..	£1000	£110
		b. Lilac-drab	..	—	£110
		c. Red-lilac	..	—	£500
		d. Void lower left corner	..	—	£1800
14		3d. blue *(shades)* (1.53)	..	£400	45·00
		a. Deep blue *(shades)*	..	£400	45·00
		b. Greenish blue *(shades)*	..	£500	50·00
		c. Retouched (9 varieties)	..	£750	£120

Printed in sheets of 120 (12×10) produced from intermediate stones of 12 (6×2) on which the details of the veil were amended as described above.

The "void corner" error occurred on the printing stone. It is believed that only four examples still exist.

2d. Coarse border and background

(e) Fourth state of 2d. die only: Coarse border and background. Veil details as in original die.

15	1	2d. red-lilac *(shades)* (5.50)	..	£600	£180
		a. Lilac	..	£600	£180
		b. Grey	..	—	£275
		c. Dull brownish lilac	..	£400	£100
		d. Retouched lower label—value omitted	from	—	£1800
		e. Other retouches (17 varieties)	from	£1000	£225

Printed in sheets of 120 (12×10) produced from an intermediate stone of 30 (6×5).

(f) 2d. as (e), but with veils altered to give effect of vertical drapes.

16	1	2d. lilac-grey (1.51)	..	£750	£110
		a. Deep grey	..	£850	£110
		b. Brown-lilac *(shades)*	..	£600	60·00
17		2d. cinnamon *(shades)* (2.51)	..	£500	95·00
		a. Drab *(shades)*	..	£550	60·00
		b. Pale dull brown *(shades)*	..	£650	70·00
		c. Greenish grey	..	£500	60·00
		d. Olive-drab *(shades)*	..	£600	£120
		e. Buff	..	†	£130

Printed in sheets of 120 (12×10) produced from two successive intermediate stones of 30 (6×5) on which the details of the veils were amended as described above.

This was the final printing of the 2d. "Half Length" as the die for this value had been damaged. A replacement 2d. design was ordered from Thomas Ham.

For the later printings of the 1d. and 3d. in this design see Nos. 23/4, 26/31, 48/9 and 78/9.

2 Queen on Throne 3

(Recess-printed by Thomas Ham)

1852 (27 Dec). *Imperf.*

18	2	2d. reddish brown	..	£160	22·00
		a. Chestnut	..	—	£110
		b. Purple-brown	..	£225	22·00

Printed in sheets of 50 (10×5) from a hand-engraved plate of the same size. Each stamp in the sheet had individual corner letters made-up of various combinations, none of which contained the letter "J".

Reprints were made in 1891 using the original plate, on paper wmk V over Crown, both imperf and perf 12½.

For later printings of this design see Nos. 19/22 and 36/9.

CAMPBELL & CO PRINTINGS. In May 1853 the Victoria postal authorities placed an order for the 1d. and 6d. stamps in the "Queen on Throne" design with Perkins, Bacon in London. These would not arrive for some time, however, and supplies of Ham's printings were rapidly becoming exhausted. Local tenders were, therefore, solicited for further supplies of the 1d. and 3d. "Half Lengths" and the 2d. "Queen on Throne". That received from J. S. Campbell & Co was accepted. The stamps were produced by lithography, using transfers from either the "Half Length" engraved die or the 2d. "Queen on Throne" engraved plate of 50. Stamps from the Campbell & Co printings can be distinguished from later printings in lithography by the good quality paper used.

(Lithographed by J. S. Campbell & Co, Melbourne, using transfers taken from Ham's engraved plate)

1854 (Jan–July). *Good quality white or toned paper. Imperf.*

(a) Clear impressions with details around back of throne generally complete

19	2	2d. brownish purple	..	£170	22·00
		a. Grey-brown	..	£250	22·00
		b. Purple-black	..	—	22·00
		c. Dull lilac-brown *(toned paper only)*	..	£300	40·00

(b) Poor impressions with details around back of throne not fully defined

20	2	2d. violet-black (2.54)	..	£250	22·00
		a. Grey-black	..	£350	24·00
		b. Grey-lilac	..	£250	24·00
		c. Dull brown *(on toned)*	..	£250	24·00
		ca. Substituted transfer (in pair)	..	—	£2000

(c) Weak impressions with background generally white without details. Toned paper only

21	2	2d. grey-purple (7.54)	..	£130	20·00
		a. Purple-black	..	£130	20·00

(d) Printings using an intermediate stone. Impression flat and blurred. Background details usually complete. Toned paper only

22	2	2d. grey-drab *(shades)* (5.54)	..	£225	19·00
		a. Black	..	—	£100

Nos. 19/21 were produced using transfers taken directly from the original Ham engraved plate. It is believed that the different strengths of the impressions were caused by the amount of pressure exerted when the transfers were taken. The stamps were printed in sheets of 100 (2 panes 10×5). On one stone a block of four at bottom left, lettered "FL GM" over "QV RW", was damaged and the stone was repaired by using a block of four substituted transfers. These were lettered "VZ WA" over "FL GM". No. 20ca covers any one of these substituted transfers in pair with normal. As horizontal pairs these are lettered "WA HN" or "GM SX" and as vertical "VZ" over "VZ" or "WA" over "WA".

For No. 22 an intermediate stone was used to produce a printing stone of 300 (6 panes 10×5). The insertion of a further stage into the process caused the blurred appearance of stamps from this printing. No. 22a is believed to come from proof sheets issued to post offices for normal use. Examples are usually cancelled with Barred Oval 108 and Barred Numerals 1 and 2.

(Lithographed by J. S. Campbell & Co, Melbourne)

1854 (Feb–June). *Good quality wove paper. Imperf.*

23	1	1d. orange-red *(shades)*	..	£450	£110
		a. Rose	..	£2000	£275
24		3d. blue *(shades)* (6.54)	..	£475	32·00
		a. Retouch under "C" of "VICTORIA"	..	—	£120

The 1d. was produced in sheets of 192 (two panes of 96 (12×8)) and the 3d. in sheets of 320 (two panes of 160 (18×9)). Both printing stones were constructed from transfers taken from intermediate stones of 24 (6×4). The spacing between stamps is far wider than on the Ham printings. The 3d. panes of 160 were constructed using six complete transfers of 24 and three of 6 with the final impression in the bottom two rows removed.

The 1d. Campbell printings have the frame lines almost completely absent due to lack of pressure when taking transfers.

The 3d. retouch, No. 24a, occurs on R.3/5 of the intermediate stone.

CAMPBELL AND FERGUSSON PRINTINGS. Increased postal rates in early 1854 led to a requirement for a 1s. value and in April a contract for this stamp was awarded to Campbell and Fergusson (the new corporate style of J. S. Campbell & Co). Further contracts to print the 1d. and 3d. "Half Lengths" and the 2d. "Queen on Throne" followed. All were produced by lithography with the two "Half Lengths" using transfers from the original engraved die and the 2d. "Queen on Throne" transfers from Ham's original engraved plate.

All Campbell and Fergusson printings were on paper of a poorer quality than that used for the earlier contract.

(Lithographed by Campbell & Fergusson)

1854 (6 July). *Poorer quality paper. Imperf.*

25	3	1s. blue *(shades)*	..	£650	22·00
		a. Greenish blue *(shades)*	..	£750	22·00
		b. Indigo-blue	..	—	£110

No. 25 was produced in sheets of 100 (8×12) with an additional stamp appearing at the end of Rows 6 to 9. The printing stones used each contained four such sheets. They were constructed from an intermediate stone of 40 (8×5) taken from a single engraved die. Each pane of 100 showed two complete transfers of 40, one of 20 and one of a vertical strip of 4.

For this stamp rouletted or perforated see Nos. 54 and 81.

(Lithographed by Campbell & Fergusson)

1854 (July)–57. *Poorer quality paper. Imperf.*

26	1	1d. brown *(shades)*	..	£450	95·00
		a. Brick-red *(shades)*	..	£600	75·00
		b. Dull red *(shades)*	..	£650	75·00
27		1d. orange-brown *(shades)* (8.55)	..	£400	£100
		a. Dull rose-red *(shades)*	..	£400	60·00
		b. Bright rose-pink	..	£500	£100
		c. Retouched (6 varieties)	..	£1400	£400

28	1	1d. pink (*shades*) (2.55)	..	£375	32·00
		a. *Rose* (*shades*)	..	£375	32·00
		b. *Lilac-rose* (*shades*)	..	£400	32·00
		c. *Dull brown-red* (*shades*)	..	—	£110
		d. *Retouched* (8 *varieties*)	..	£750	£325
29		3d. bright blue (*shades*) (7.57)	..	£425	50·00
		a. *Greenish blue* (*shades*)	..	£375	40·00
		b. *Retouch under "C" of "VICTORIA"*	..	—	95·00
30		3d. Prussian blue (*shades*) (11.56)	..	£500	70·00
		a. *Milky blue*	..	—	—
		b. *Retouch under "C" of "VICTORIA"*	..	£750	£110
			..	—	£225
31		3d. steel-blue (*shades*) (*heavier impression*) (5.55)	..	—	42·00
		a. *Greenish blue* (*shades*)	..	£350	30·00
		b. *Blue* (*shades*)	..	£350	30·00
		c. *Deep blue* (*shades*)	..	£350	30·00
		d. *Indigo* (*shades*)	..	—	38·00

The 1d. was produced in sheets of 400 (2 panes 20×10) constructed from transfers originating from the J. S. Campbell & Co intermediate stone. Each pane contained six complete tranfers of 24, three of 12, two of 8 and one of 4.

The 3d. was produced in sheets of 320 (2 panes of 160) (No. 29), 200 (No. 30) or 400 (2 panes of 200) (No. 31.) The stone for No. 29 was constructed from transfers taken from the J. S. Campbell intermediate stone with the retouch on R.3/5 still present. The panes of 160 contained six transfers of 24 and three of 6 with the last impression in both rows 8 and 9 removed. Quality of impression is generally poor. The stone for No. 30, once again taken from the Campbell intermediate stone, was laid down in the same combination of transfers as the 1d. value. Impressions from it were, however, so poor that transfers from a new intermediate stone were used for No. 31. Impressions from this stone, on which the panes of 200 were in a similar layout to the 1d., were much further apart than those on the stones used to produce Nos. 29/30.

The Campbell and Fergusson printings of the "Half Lengths" are listed in the order in which they were printed.

CALVERT PRINTINGS. Contracts for the provision of other values required by the postal rate changes in 1853 were placed with Samuel Calvert of Melbourne who used typography as the printing process. Calvert continued to print, and later roulette, stamps for the Victoria Post Office until March 1858 when it was discovered that he had placed some of the stock in pawn.

4   5   6

(Typographed from woodblocks by Samuel Calvert)

1854 (1 Sept)—55. *Imperf.*

32	4	6d. reddish brown (13.9.54)	..	£225	27·00
		a. *Dull orange*	..	£180	18·00
		b. *Orange-yellow*	..	£180	19·00
33	5	6d. ("TOO LATE") lilac and green (1.1.55)	..	£700	£140
34	6	1s. ("REGISTERED") rose-pink and blue (1.12.54)	..	£850	£110
35	4	2s. dull bluish green/*pale yellow*	..	£1100	£140

No. 33 was provided to pay the additional fee on letters posted after the normal closure of the mails. This service was only available in the larger towns; examples are usually postmarked Castlemaine, Geelong or Melbourne. The service was withdrawn on 30 June 1857 and remaining stocks of the "TOO LATE" stamps were used for normal postal purposes.

No. 34 was issued to pay the registration fee and was so used until 5 January 1858 after which remaining stocks were used for normal purposes.

These four values were produced from individually-engraved boxwood woodblocks. The 6d. was in sheets of 100 printed by two impressions from two blocks of 25. The 2s. was in sheets of 50 from a single plate of 25. The bicoloured "TOO LATE" and "REGISTERED" stamps are unusual in that Calvert used a common woodblock "key" plate of 25 for both values combined with "duty" plates made up from metal stereos. Both values were originally in sheets of 50, but the "REGISTERED" later appeared in sheets of 100 for which a second "key" plate of 25 was utilised.

For these stamps rouletted or perforated see Nos. 53, 55/8, 60/1 and 82.

(Lithographed by Campbell & Fergusson)

1855 (Mar)—56. *Poorer quality paper. Imperf.*

(a) *Printings from stones which were not over-used; background around top of throne generally full and detail good*

36	2	2d. lilac (*shades*) (7.55)	..	£140	19·00
		a. *Purple* (*shades*)	..	£140	19·00
		b. "TVO" for "TWO"	..	£2500	£600

(b) *Early printings from stones which were over-used. Similar characteristics to those above, though detail is not quite so full. Distinctive shades.*

37	2	2d. brown	..	—	70·00
		a. *Brown-purple*	..	£170	22·00
		b. *Warm purple*	..	—	22·00
		c. *Rose-lilac*	..	—	22·00
		d. *Substituted transfer* (*pair*)	..	—	£600

(c) *Later printings from the same stones used for No. 37 when in a worn condition. Impressions heavy, coarse and overcoloured; details blurred; generally white background around top of throne.*

38	2	2d. dull lilac-mauve (1856)	..	£170	22·00
		a. *Dull mauve*	..	£170	22·00
		b. *Grey-violet*	..	—	22·00
		c. *Red-lilac*	..	—	24·00
		d. *Substituted transfer* (*pair*)	..	—	£600

(d) *Printings from a stone giving blotchy and unpleasing results, with poor definition. Mainly shows in extra colour patches found on most stamps.*

39	2	2d. dull purple (7.55)	..	—	40·00
		a. *Dull grey-lilac*	..	£180	40·00
		b. *On thick card paper*	..	—	£500

The Campbell and Fergusson 2d. "Queen on Throne" printings were in sheets of 200 (4 panes 10 × 5) constructed from transfers taken from the original Ham engraved plate.

Four separate stones were used. On Stone A a creased transfer running through R.4/8, 4/9 and 5/8 caused the "TVO" variety on the stamp from the bottom row of one pane. On Stone C the impression in the first vertical row of one pane were found to be so faulty that they were replaced by substituted transfers taken from elsewhere on the sheet causing abnormal horizontal pairs lettered "UY BF", "TX MQ", "DI WA", "SW GM" and "CH RW". The vertical pairs from the substituted transfers are lettered "UY" over "TX" and "DI" over "SW".

PERKINS BACON "CANCELLED". For notes on these handstamps, showing "CANCELLED" between horizontal bars forming an oval, see Catalogue Introduction.

7 Queen on   8 "Emblems"
   Throne

(Recess Perkins, Bacon & Co, London)

1856 (23 Oct). *Wmk Large Star*, W w 1. *Imperf.*

| 40 | 7 | 1d. yellow-green (H/S "CANCELLED" in oval £3500) | .. | £120 | 19·00 |

Supplies of this stamp, and the accompanying 6d. which was only issued rouletted (see No. 73), arrived in the colony at the end of 1854, but the 1d. was not placed on sale until almost two years later.

No. 40 was reprinted from the original plate in 1891. Examples, in either dull yellow-green or bright blue-green, are imperforate and on V over Crown watermarked paper.

(Typographed from electrotypes by Calvert)

1857 (26 Jan–6 Sept). *Imperf.* (a) *Wmk Large Star*, W w 1

41	8	1d. yellow-green (18 Feb)	..	95·00	13·00
		a. *Deep green*	..	£110	26·00
		b. *Printed on both sides*	..	†	£700
42		4d. vermilion	..	£250	10·00
		a. *Brown-vermilion*	..	£225	9·00
		b. *Printed on both sides*	..	†	£700
43		4d. dull red (20 July)	..	£160	7·50
44		4d. dull rose (6 Sept)	..	£225	7·50

(b) *No wmk. Good quality medium wove paper*

| 45 | 8 | 2d. pale lilac (25 May) | .. | £170 | 10·00 |
| | | a. *Grey-lilac* | .. | £170 | 10·00 |

Nos. 41/5 were produced in sheets of 120, arranged as four panes of 30 (6×5) (1d. and 4d.) or twelve panes of 10 (2×5) (2d.), using electrotypes taken from a single engraved die of each value. The setting of the 4d. was re-arranged before the printing of Nos. 43/4.

Only two examples of No. 41b and No. 42b have been recorded.

For this printing rouletted or perforated see Nos. 46/7, 50/2, 59, 74 and 77.

ROULETTES AND PERFORATIONS. In August 1857 a rouletting machine was provided at the G.P.O., Melbourne, to enable the counter clerks to separate stamp stocks before sale to the public. This machine produced roulettes of 7½–9 in one direction across six rows at a time. There was also a single wheel device which gauged 7–7½. Both were in use between the earliest known date of 12 August and the end of 1857.

Calvert was granted a separate contract in October 1857 to roulette the stamps he printed, but only Nos. 57/61 had been produced when it was found, in April 1858, that he had pawned a quantity of the sheets. His contracts were terminated and his successor, F. W. Robinson, used a roulette machine of a different gauge before switching to a gauge 12 perforating machine in January 1859.

1857 (12 Aug–Sept). *Rouletted 7–9 by counter clerks at G.P.O., Melbourne.*

46	8	1d. yellow-green (No. 41)	..	£300	65·00
47		2d. pale lilac (No. 45)	..	—	£225
		a. *Grey-lilac*	..	—	£225
48	1	3d. blue (*shades*) (No. 24)	..	—	£180
		a. *Retouch under "C" of "VICTORIA"*			
49		3d. bright blue (*shades*) (No. 29)	..	—	£190
		a. *Greenish blue* (*shades*)	..	£1000	£170
		b. *Retouch under "C" of "VICTORIA"*			
50	8	4d. vermilion (No. 42)	..	—	£100
51		4d. dull red (No. 43)	..	—	38·00
52		4d. dull rose (No. 44) (Sept)	..	—	26·00
53	4	6d. reddish brown (No. 32)	..	—	45·00
		a. *Dull orange*	..	—	35·00
		b. *Orange-yellow*	..	—	42·00
54	3	1s. blue (*shades*) (No. 25)	..	—	80·00
		a. *Greenish blue*	..	—	80·00
55	6	1s. ("REGISTERED") rose-pink and blue (No. 34)	..	£3500	£180
56	4	2s. dull bluish green/*pale yellow* (No. 35)	..	£3500	£350

With the exception of the 1s., Nos. 54/a these stamps are normally found rouletted on one or two sides only.

1857 (Oct). *Rouletted by Calvert.* (a) *Rouletted 7–9 on all four sides and with finer points than No. 53b*

| 57 | 4 | 6d. orange-yellow (No. 32b) | .. | — | 55·00 |

(b) *Serpentine roulette 10–10½*

| 58 | 4 | 6d. orange-yellow (No. 32b) | .. | — | 60·00 |

(c) *Serrated 18–19*

| 59 | 8 | 2d. grey-lilac (No. 45a) | .. | £500 | £350 |
| 60 | 4 | 6d. orange-yellow (No. 32b) | .. | — | 65·00 |

(d) *Compound of serrated 18–19 and serpentine roulette 10–10½*

| 61 | 4 | 6d. orange-yellow (No. 32b) | .. | — | 65·00 |

No. 59 was not covered by the contract given to Calvert, but it is believed to be a test run for the rouletting machine. No. 61 always shows serrated 18–19 on three sides and the serpentine roulette at the top or bottom of the stamp.

(Typo from electrotypes by Calvert)

1858 (14 Jan–Apr). *No wmk. Good quality white wove paper.*

(a) *Rouletted 7–9 on all four sides*

62	8	1d. pale emerald	..	£300	16·00
		a. *Emerald-green*	..	£300	16·00
63		4d. rose-pink (18 Jan)	..	£200	6·00
		a. *Bright rose*	..	£200	6·00
		b. *Reddish pink*	..	—	11·00
		c. *Imperf horiz* (*vert pair*)	..	†	£400

(b) *Imperf* (Apr)

64	8	1d. pale emerald	..	£190	11·00
		a. *Emerald-green*	..	—	14·00
65		4d. rose-pink	..	£250	23·00
		a. *Bright rose*	..	—	23·00
		b. *Reddish pink*	..	—	30·00

Nos. 62/5 were produced in sheets of 120, arranged as four panes of 30 (6×5).

The Royal Collection contains a used horizontal pair of the 4d. showing the vertical rows imperforate.

The majority of Nos. 64/5 were issued in April after Calvert's contracts had been terminated, although there is some evidence that imperforate sheets of the 4d., at least, were issued earlier. For the 1d. of this issue perforated see No. 75.

ROBINSON PRINTINGS. Calvert's contracts were cancelled in April 1858 and the work was then placed with F. W. Robinson, who had unsuccessfully tendered in 1856. The same electrotypes were used, but a perforating machine was introduced from January 1859. Robinson continued to print and perforate stamps under contract until the end of 1859 when the Victoria Post Office purchased his equipment to set up a Stamp Printing Branch and appointed him Printer of Postage Stamps.

(Typo from electrotypes by Robinson)

1858 (May–Dec). (a) *Imperf.* (i) *Coarse quality wove paper.*

| 66 | 8 | 4d. dull rose (*oily ink*) | .. | — | 60·00 |

(ii) *Smooth vertically-laid paper*

67	8	4d. dull rose (*oily ink*)	..	—	26·00
		a. *Dull rose-red*	..	—	26·00
68		4d. dull rose-red (*normal ink*) (20 May)	..	£400	15·00

(b) *Rouletted 5½–6½.* (i) *Smooth laid paper*

69	8	2d. brown-lilac (*shades*) (*horiz laid*) (June)	..	£120	5·50
		a. *Vert laid paper* (21 Sept)	..	£200	9·50
70		2d. violet (*horiz laid*) (27 Nov)	..	£150	5·50
		a. *Dull violet*	..	£180	18·00
71		4d. pale dull rose (*vert laid*) (1 June)	..	£150	3·75
		a. *Horiz laid paper*	..	†	£800
		b. *Dull rose-red*	..	£120	3·75
		c. *Rose-red*	..	£120	3·50
		ca. *Serrated 19*	..	†	£350

(ii) *Good quality wove paper*

| 72 | 8 | 1d. yellow-green (24 Dec) | .. | £275 | 23·00 |

Nos. 66/72 were produced in sheets of 120, arranged as four panes of 30 (6 × 5).

For stamps of this issue perforated see Nos. 76 and 80.

(Recess Perkins, Bacon & Co, London)

1858 (1 Nov). *Wmk Large Star*, W w 1. *Rouletted 5½–6½.*

| 73 | 7 | 6d. bright blue | .. | £130 | 13·00 |
| | | a. *Light blue* | .. | £170 | 25·00 |

No. 73 was received from London at the same time as the 1d., No. 40, but was kept in store until November 1858 when the stock was rouletted by Robinson. When issued the gum was in a poor state.

Imperforate examples exist from Perkins, Bacon remainders. Examples are known handstamped "CANCELLED" in oval of bars. *Price* £3500.

Imperforate reprints, in shades of indigo, were made from the original plate in 1891 on V over Crown watermarked paper.

1859 (Jan–May). *P 12 by Robinson.*

74	8	1d. yellow-green (No. 41)	..	—	£275
75		1d. emerald-green (No. 64a)	..	—	£275
		a. *Imperf between* (*horiz pair*)			
76		1d. yellow-green (as No. 62) (11 Jan)	..	£160	13·00
		a. *Imperf horiz* (*vert pair*)	..	—	£300
		b. *Thin, glazed* ("Bordeaux") *paper*	..	†	£150
77		2d. pale lilac (No. 45)	..	—	£225
		a. *Grey-lilac*	..	—	£225
78	1	3d. blue (*shades*) (No. 24) (2 Feb)	..	£750	£110
		a. *Retouch under "C" of "VICTORIA"*	..	—	£250
79		3d. greenish blue (*shades*) (No. 29a)	..	†	£350
		a. *Retouch under "C" of "VICTORIA"*	..	†	£1000
80	8	4d. dull rose-red (No. 68)	..	—	£300
81	3	1s. blue (*shades*) (No. 25) (4 Feb)	..	£130	15·00
		a. *Greenish blue*	..	£150	12·00
		b. *Indigo-blue*	..	—	30·00
82	4	2s. dull bluish green/*pale yellow* (No. 35) (May)	..	£250	32·00

The 1s. was reprinted in 1891 using transfers taken from the original die. These reprints were on V over Crown watermarked paper and perforated 12½/2.

For perforated 6d. black and 2s. blue both as Type 4 see Nos. 102 and 129/30.

(Typo from electrotypes by Robinson)

1859 (17 Feb–23 Dec). *P 12.* (a) *Good quality wove paper*

| 83 | 8 | 4d. dull rose | .. | £150 | 3·00 |
| | | a. *Roul 5½–6½* | .. | † | £800 |

(b) *Poorer quality wove paper*

84	8	1d. dull green (July)	..	£120	7·50
		a. *Green* (11 Nov)	..	£120	7·50
85		4d. rose-carmine (16 July)	..	£150	5·00
		a. *Rose-pink* (*thick paper*) (30 Nov)	..	—	9·00

(c) *Horizontally laid paper with the lines wide apart*

86	8	1d. dull green (18 July)	..	—	—
		a. *Laid lines close together*	..	—	16·00
		b. *Green* (*shades*) (Oct)	..	£130	9·50
87		4d. rose-pink (*shades*) (23 Dec)	..	£120	7·50
		a. *Laid lines close together*	..	—	10·00

STAMP PRINTING BRANCH. On 1 January 1860 F. W. Robinson was appointed Printer of Postage Stamps and his equipment purchased by the Post Office to establish the Stamp Printing Branch. All later Victoria issues were printed by the Branch which became part of the Victoria Government Printing Office in December 1885. In 1909 the Commonwealth Stamp Printing Office under J. B. Cooke was established in Melbourne and produced stamps for both the states and Commonwealth until 1918.

9

| 10 | 11 |

(Des and eng F. Grosse. Typo from electrotypes)

1860 (31 Jan)–**66.** *P* 12. (*a*) *No wmk*
88	9	3d. deep blue (*horiz laid paper*)		£300	26·00
		a. Light blue			
89		4d. rose-pink (*thin glazed Bordeaux paper*) (21.4.60)		—	8·50
		a. Rose		£275	13·00
		ab. Thick coarse paper (7.60)		£275	8·50

(*b*) *On paper made by T. H. Saunders of London wmkd with the appropriate value in words as W* **10**
90	9	3d. pale blue (1.61)		£120	7·00
		a. Bright blue (10.61)		£120	8·00
		b. Blue (4.63)		£130	6·00
		c. Deep blue (4.64)		£130	6·00
		d. "TREE" *for* "THREE" *in wmk*			
91		3d. maroon (13.2.66)		£100	25·00
		a. Perf 13		£120	28·00
92		4d. rose-pink (1.8.60)		—	6·00
		a. Rose-red		80·00	3·25
		b. Rose-carmine		—	8·50
		c. Dull rose		80·00	3·25
		d. Printed on "FIVE SHILLINGS" *diagonal wmk paper* (11.9.62)		£1500	20·00
93		6d. orange (25.10.60)		£3000	£200
94		6d. black (20.8.61)		£110	5·50
		a. Grey-black		£110	5·50

(*c*) *On paper made by De La Rue wmkd with the appropriate value as a single-lined numeral as W* **11**
95	9	4d. dull rose-pink (9.10.62)		90·00	5·00
		a. Dull rose		95·00	5·50
		b. Rose-red		—	5·00
		c. Roul 8 (28.7.63)		—	£250
		d. Imperf (31.7.63)		—	65·00
		e. Perf 13×12			

All three values were produced in sheets of 120, initially as four panes of 30 (6×5). Printings of the 3d. from 1864 were in a changed format of six panes of 20 (4×5).

The "TREE" watermark error comes from early printings of No. 90 on R. 10/7.

Two examples of the 4d. on Saunders paper are known bisected in 1863, but such use was unauthorised.

Nos. 95c/e were issued during July and August 1863 when the normal perforating machine had broken down.

Reprints, from new plates, were made of the 3d. and 4d. in 1891 on "V over Crown" paper and perforated 12½.

1860 (Apr)–**63.** *P* 12. (*a*) *No wmk*
| 96 | 8 | 1d. bright green (*horiz laid paper*) | | | |
| 97 | | 1d. bright green (*thin, glazed Bordeaux paper*) (25.5.60) | | — | 25·00 |

(*b*) *On paper made by T. H. Saunders of London wmkd with the appropriate value in words as W* **10**
98	8	1d. pale yellowish green (8.7.60)		65·00	4·50
		a. Yellow-green		75·00	4·75
		b. Error. Wmkd "FOUR PENCE"		†	
99		2d. brown-lilac (7.7.61)		—	19·00
100		2d. bluish slate (8.61)		£100	4·75
		a. Greyish lilac (9.61)		£110	4·75
		b. Slate-grey (1.62)		—	4·75
		c. Printed on "THREE PENCE" *wmkd paper. Pale slate* (27.12.62)		£110	10·00
		d. Bluish grey (2.63)		£120	12·00

(*c*) *On paper made by De La Rue wmkd single-lined* "2", *W* **11**
101	8	2d. dull reddish lilac (24.4.63)		£160	6·00
		a. Grey-lilac (10.63)		£150	12·00
		ab. Error. Wmkd "6"		† £4000	
		b. Grey-violet (11.63)		£100	9·00
		c. Slate (12.63)		£150	18·00

The only confirmed example of No. 98b is in the Royal Collection. There have been unconfirmed reports of the existence of another.

1861 (22 June). *On paper made by T. H. Saunders of London wmkd* "SIX PENCE" *as W* **10.** *P* 12.
| 102 | 4 | 6d. black | | £160 | 38·00 |

No. 102 was produced as an emergency measure after the decision had been taken to change the colour of the current 6d. from orange (No. 93) to black (No. 94). During the changeover the old Calvert "woodblock" plates were pressed into service to provide two month's supply.

MINIMUM PRICE

The minimum price quote is 10p which represents a handling charge rather than a basis for valuing common stamps. For further notes about prices see introductory pages.

| 12 | 13 |

(Des, eng and electrotyped De Gruchy & Leigh, Melbourne. Typo)

1861 (1 Oct)–**64.** *P* 12. (*a*) *On paper made by T. H. Saunders of London wmkd* "ONE PENNY" *as W* **10**
| 103 | 12 | 1d. pale green | | 80·00 | 6·50 |
| | | *a. Olive-green* | | — | 7·00 |

(*b*) *On paper made by De La Rue wmkd single-lined* "1" *as W* **11**
104	12	1d. olive-green (1.2.63)		60·00	7·00
		a. Pale green (9.63)		60·00	5·00
		b. Apple-green (4.64)		60·00	5·00

(*c*) *On paper supplied to Tasmania by Perkins, Bacon and wmkd double-lined* "1", *W* **4** *of Tasmania*
105	12	1d. yellow-green (10.12.63)		£110	7·50
		a. Dull green		—	7·50
		b. Imperf between (pair)		†	

All printings were in sheets of 120 containing four panes of 30 (6×5).

Reprints from new plates were made in 1891 on paper watermarked "V over Crown" and perforated 12½.

(Frame die eng F. Grosse. Typo from electrotypes)

1862 (26 Apr)–**64.** *Centre vignette cut from T* **9** *with a new frame as T* **13**.

(*a*) *On paper made by T. H. Saunders of London wmkd* "SIX PENCE" *as W* **10.** *P* 12
106	13	6d. grey		80·00	5·00
		a. Grey-black		80·00	6·50
		b. Jet-black		85·00	7·50

(*b*) *On paper made by De La Rue wmkd with single-lined* "6" *as W* **11**
107	13	6d. grey (*p* 12) (18.6.63)		70·00	4·50
		a. Jet-black		—	5·50
		b. Grey-black		70·00	4·75
		c. Perf 13. Jet-black		80·00	5·00
		ca. Grey-black		80·00	5·50

Printings before August 1863 were in sheets of 120 containing four panes of 30 (6×5). For subsequent printings of No. 107 the format was changed to six panes of 20 (4×5).

Reprints from new plates were made in 1891 on paper watermarked "V over Crown" and perforated 12½.

SINGLE-LINED NUMERAL WATERMARK PAPERS.

The first consignment of this paper, showing watermarks as W **11**, arrived in Victoria during October 1862. Five further consignments followed, all but the last supplied by De La Rue.

The complexity of the scheme for different watermarks for each value, together with the time required to obtain further supplies from Great Britain, resulted in the emergency use of paper obtained from Tasmania and of the wrong numeral watermark on certain printings.

The final order for this paper was placed, in error with the firm of T. H. Saunders of London. Although the actual watermarks are the same (the dandy rolls were the property of the Victoria Government and supplied to each firm in turn) there are considerable differences between the two types of paper. That manufactured by Saunders is of a more even quality and is smoother, thicker, less brittle and less white than the De La Rue type.

De La Rue supplied white paper watermarked "1", "2", "4", "6" and "8", blue paper watermarked "2" and green paper watermarked "2".

The Saunders consignment of October 1865 contained white paper watermarked "1", "4" and "6", blue paper watermarked "1", green paper watermarked "2" and pink paper watermarked "10".

It is helpful for comparison purposes to note that all white paper watermarked "2" or "8" can only be De La Rue and all pink paper watermarked "10" can only be Saunders.

| 14 | 15 | 16 |

| 17 | 18 |

(Des and eng F. Grosse. Typo from electrotypes)

1863–74. "Laureated" series.

(*a*) *On paper made by De La Rue wmkd with the appropriate value in single-lined numerals as W* **11**
108	14	1d. pale green (*p* 12) (9.9.64)		75·00	7·00
		a. Perf 12½×12 (9.64)			
		b. Perf 13 (10.10.64)		70·00	3·50
		c. Bluish green (p 13) (12.64)		65·00	2·75
		ca. Printed double		†	£550
		d. Green (p 12) (7.65)		70·00	3·00
		da. Perf 13		65·00	3·50
		e. Deep green (p 12) (12.65)		85·00	3·00
		ea. Perf 13		—	3·00
		eb. Perf 12×13		—	6·00
		f. Bright yellow-green (p 13) (1.67)		—	15·00

109	14	2d. violet (*p* 12) (1.4.64)		65·00	5·50
		a. Dull violet (p 12) (10.64)		70·00	5·50
		ab. Perf 12½×12			
		ac. Perf 12½			
		ad. Perf 13		70·00	4·25
		b. Dull lilac (p 13) (4.65)		55·00	4·00
		ba. Perf 12 (7.66)		—	7·00
		bb. Perf 12×13 (7.66)		—	8·50
		c. Reddish mauve (p 13) (11.65)		60·00	4·50
		d. Rose-lilac (p 13) (1.66)		55·00	5·50
		da. Perf 12×13 or 13×12 (2.66)		55·00	5·50
		e. Grey (p 12) (7.66)		85·00	7·00
		ea. Perf 13		55·00	3·00
110		4d. deep rose (*p* 12) (11.9.63)		£110	3·50
		a. Printed double		†	£500
		b. Rose-pink (p 12) (9.63)		85·00	2·50
		c. Pink (p 12) (7.5.64)		85·00	2·50
		ca. Error. Wmkd single-lined "8"		† £2000	
		cb. Perf 12½×12 (9.64)			
		d. Dull rose (p 13) (10.64)		75·00	2·50
		e. Dull rose-red (p 13) (2.65)		75·00	2·50
		ea. Perf 13 (8.65)		£120	75·00
111	16	6d. blue (*p* 13) (13.2.66)		38·00	4·50
		a. Perf 13		38·00	2·75
		b. Perf 12×13		35·00	2·25
112	14	8d. orange (*p* 13) (22.2.65)		£300	55·00
113	17	1s. blue/*blue* (*p* 13) (10.4.65)		£100	3·50
		a. Perf 13 (4.66)		£100	3·50
		ab. Imperf between (vert pair)		† £1200	
		b. Bright blue/blue (p 13) (1.66)		85·00	3·00
		c. Indigo-blue/blue (p 13) (3.68)		—	2·75
		d. Dull blue/blue (p 12) (6.74)		—	3·50

(*b*) *Emergency printings on Perkins, Bacon paper borrowed from Tasmania wmkd double-lined* "4" *as W* **4** *of Tasmania*
114	14	4d. deep rose (*p* 12) (7.1.64)		£110	3·75
		a. Pale rose (p 12)		—	3·25
		b. Dull reddish rose (p 13) (11.8.65)		£110	3·50
		ba. Perf 12		—	3·75
		bb. Perf 12×13		—	11·00
		c. Red (p 13) (4.12.65)		—	3·50

(*c*) *Emergency printings on De La Rue paper as W* **11**, *but showing incorrect single-lined numeral. P* 13
115	14	1d. brt yellow-grn (*wmkd* "8") (27.12.66)		£120	12·00
116		1d. yellow-green (*wmkd* "6") (6.67)		—	18·00
117		2d. grey (*wmkd* "8") (18.1.67)		£110	5·00
118	15	3d. lilac (*wmkd* "8") (29.9.66)		£110	22·00
119	16	10d. grey (*wmkd* "8") (21.10.65)		£450	£100
		a. Grey-black		£450	£100

(*d*) *On paper made by T. H. Saunders wmkd with the appropriate value in single-lined numerals as W* **11**
120	14	1d. deep yellow-green (*p* 12×13) (1.66)		£120	7·00
		a. Perf 13 (3.66)		65·00	3·00
		b. Perf 12 (7.66)		—	8·00
121		4d. rose-red (*p* 12) (12.12.65)		75·00	3·00
		a. Perf 12×13 or 13×12 (2.66)		£110	5·50
		b. Perf 12 (4.66)		—	4·75
122	16	6d. blue (*p* 13) (28.5.66)		32·00	1·50
		a. Perf 12		38·00	3·50
		b. Perf 12×13		32·00	1·75
		ba. Imperf between (horiz pair)		† £600	
123		10d. dull purple/*pink* (*p* 13) (22.3.66)		85·00	5·00
		a. Perf 12×13		£120	6·00
		b. Blackish brown/pink (p 13) (12.69)		90·00	5·50
		c. Purple-brown/pink (p 13) (11.70)			
124	17	1s. blue/*blue* (*p* 13) (5.12.70)		55·00	2·50
		a. Pale dull blue/blue (p 12) (1.73)		£120	3·25
		ab. Perf 13		—	7·50
		b. Indigo-blue/blue (p 12) (9.73)		—	5·00
		c. Perf 13		55·00	3·25

(*e*) *Emergency printings on Saunders paper as W* **11**, *but showing incorrect single-lined numeral. P* 13
125	14	1d. brt yellow-green (*wmkd* "4") (6.3.67)		85·00	9·00
126		1d. brt yellow-green (*wmkd* "6") (6.67)		£120	16·00
127		2d. grey (*wmkd* "4") (21.2.67)		85·00	5·00
128		2d. grey (*wmkd* "4") (13.5.67)		£140	6·00

The 1d., 2d., 4d. and 8d. were originally produced in sheets of 120 containing eight panes of 15 (3×5). The 3d. and 6d. were in sheets of 120 (12×10) and the 1d. (from February 1866), 2d. (from July 1866) and 4d. (from April 1866) subsequently changed to this format. The 10d. was in sheets of 120 containing twenty panes of 6 (2×3). The 1s. was originally in sheets of 60 containing three panes of 20 (4×5), but this changed to 120 (12×10) in April 1866.

Only single examples are thought to exist of Nos. 110a, 110ca, 113ab, and 122ba and two of No. 108ca.

For later emergency printings on these papers see Nos.153/66.

(Typo from composite woodblock and electrotype plate)

1864 (22 Nov)–**80.** (*a*) *On De La Rue paper wmkd single-lined* "2" *as W* **11**
129	4	2s. light blue/*green* (*p* 13) (22.11.64)		£150	5·50
		a. Dark blue/green (p 12) (9.65)		£170	9·50
		ab. Perf 13 (6.66)		£150	6·00
		b. Blue/green (p 13) (6.68)		£140	4·75
		c. Greenish blue/green (p 13) (7.73)		£140	5·50
		ca. Perf 12		£160	6·50
		d. Deep greenish blue/green (p 12½)		£140	5·50

(*b*) *On Saunders paper wmkd single-lined* "2" *as W* **11**
130	4	2s. dark blue/*green* (*p* 13) (23.11.67)		£160	6·50
		a. Blue/green (p 13) (10.71)		£160	5·50
		ab. Perf 12 (8.74)		£180	6·50
		c. Deep greenish blue/green (p 12½) (7.80)		£140	5·50

Nos. 129/30 were produced in sheets of 30 containing two panes of 15 (3×5). The plate contained eighteen of the original woodblock impressions and twelve electrotypes taken from them.

| 19 | 20 |

V OVER CROWN WATERMARKS. The changeover from the numeral watermarks to a general type to be used for all values was first suggested at the end of 1865, but the first supplies did not reach Melbourne until April 1867. Five different versions were used before the V over Crown watermark was superseded by the Commonwealth type in 1905. The five versions are listed as follows:

Type 19   De La Rue paper supplied 1867 to 1882. Shows four points at the top of the crown with the left and right ornaments diamond-shaped

Type 33   De La Rue paper supplied 1882 to 1895. No points at the top of the crown with the left and right ornaments oval-shaped

Type 82   Waterlow paper supplied 1896 to 1899. Wide base to crown

Type 85   Waterlow paper used for postal issues 1899 to 1905. Wide top to crown

Type 104   James Spicer and Sons paper used for postal issues August and September 1912. Narrow crown

(Typo from electrotypes)

1867–81. *Wmk V over Crown, W* **19.** (*a*) *P* 13
131	14	1d. bright yellow-green (10.8.67)		65·00	2·50
		a. Bright olive-green (1.69)		95·00	15·00
		b. Yellow-green (4.69)		65·00	2·10
		c. Dull green (3.70)		65·00	2·10
		d. Pale green (10.70)		60·00	2·10
		e. Grass-green (1871)		60·00	2·40
		f. Bluish green (shades) (7.72)		60·00	2·40
		g. Green (shades) (9.72)		60·00	2·25
132		2d. slate-grey (shades) (26.8.67)		70·00	3·50
		a. Grey-lilac (29.1.68)		70·00	4·75
		b. Lilac (26.8.68)		50·00	3·25
		c. Dull mauve (shades) (10.68)		50·00	3·25
		d. Lilac-grey (1.69)			3·50
		e. Lilac-rose (2.69)		55·00	3·00
		f. Mauve (4.69)		70·00	3·25
		g. Red-lilac (5.69)		55·00	3·00
		h. Dull lilac (6.69)		55·00	2·50
		i. Silver-grey (9.69)		£110	7·00
133	15	3d. lilac (28.8.67)		£200	27·00
		a. Grey-lilac (6.68)		£225	29·00
134		3d. yellow-orange (12.6.69)		23·00	3·00
		a. Dull orange (6.70)		21·00	1·90
		b. Orange (3.73)			2·25
		c. Bright orange (3.73)		26·00	2·50
		d. Orange-brown (glazed paper) (10.78)		26·00	5·50
135	14	4d. dull rose (28.11.67)		75·00	5·00
		Wmk sideways		†	60·00
		a. Aniline red (shades) (21.4.69)			6·50
		c. Rose-pink (11.69)			5·00
		d. Rose (shades) (8.71)		70·00	3·00
		e. Dull rose (glazed paper) (5.3.79)		70·00	3·00
		f. Dull rose-red (glazed paper) (11.79)		—	3·00
		g. Bright lilac-rose (aniline) (glazed paper) (2.80)		80·00	3·75
		h. Rosine (aniline) (glazed paper) (9.80)		£200	5·00
136	16	6d. deep blue (15.1.68)			3·00
		a. Blue (21.12.68)		22·00	1·25
		b. Indigo-blue (10.69)		22·00	1·25
		c. Prussian blue (9.72)		20·00	1·25
		d. Indigo (4.73)		22·00	1·40
		e. Dull blue (worn plate) (3.74)			1·25
		f. Dull ultramarine (2.12.75)		28·00	1·25
		g. Light Prussian blue (12.75)		42·00	1·25
		h. Dull violet-blue (7.77)			6·50
		i. Blue (glazed paper) (6.78)		32·00	1·25
		j. Dull milky-blue (glazed paper) (9.79)		28·00	1·25
		k. Prussian blue (glazed paper) (4.80)			1·25
		l. Light blue (glazed paper) (4.81)		32·00	1·25
		m. Deep blue (glazed paper) (10.81)		28·00	1·25
137	14	8d. lilac-brown/pink (24.1.77)		80·00	5·50
		a. Purple-brown/pink (2.78)		80·00	5·50
		b. Chocolate/pink (8.78)		85·00	5·00
		ba. Compound perf 13×12		†	£325
		c. Red-brown/pink (12.78)		80·00	5·00
138	17	1s. light blue/blue (11.5.75)		£100	7·00
139	18	5s. blue/yellow (26.12.67)		£1600	£300
		a. Wmk reversed			£500
140		5s. indigo-blue and carmine (I) (8.10.68)		£200	18·00
		a. Blue and carmine (4.69)		£180	13·00
		b. Pale bright blue and carmine (glazed paper) (24.7.77)			17·00
		c. Grey-blue and carmine (glazed paper) (4.78)		£170	15·00
		d. Wmk sideways. Deep lavender-blue and carmine (glazed paper) (4.6.80)		£170	15·00
141		5s. bright blue and red (II) (glazed paper) (12.5.81)		£150	13·00
		a. Indigo-blue and red (glazed paper)			17·00

(*b*) *P* 12
142	14	1d. pale green (10.71)		70·00	2·40
		a. Grass-green (1871)		60·00	2·40
		b. Bluish green (shades) (7.72)			2·40
		c. Green (shades) (9.72)		60·00	2·25
143	15	3d. dull orange (5.72)		21·00	2·10
		a. Orange (3.73)		—	2·10
		b. Bright orange (3.73)			2·50
		c. Dull orange-yellow (glazed paper) (12.80)			
144	14	4d. rose (shades) (8.71)		70·00	3·00
		a. Compound perf 12×13		—	£325
		b. Dull rose (glazed paper) (3.79)		—	3·00
		c. Dull rose-red (glazed paper) (11.79)		—	3·00
		d. Bright lilac-rose (aniline) (glazed paper) (2.80)			6·50
		e. Rosine (aniline) (glazed paper) (9.80)		80·00	4·75
145	16	6d. deep blue (2.2.72)			
		a. Prussian blue (9.72)		22·00	1·25
		b. Indigo (4.73)		28·00	1·75
		c. Dull blue (worn plate) (3.74)			
		d. Blue (glazed paper) (6.78)			1·25
		e. Dull milky-blue (glazed paper) (9.79)			1·25
		f. Light blue (glazed paper) (4.81)			2·40
146	14	8d. red-brn/pink (glazed paper) (11.80)		75·00	5·50
147	17	1s. light blue/blue (5.75)			6·50
148	18	5s. bright blue and red (II) (glazed paper) (5.81)		£140	13·00
		a. Indigo-blue and red		£225	17·00

(*c*) *P* 12½
149	15	3d. dull orange-yellow (glazed paper) (12.80)		28·00	3·25
150	14	4d. rosine (aniline) (glazed paper) (9.80)			

151	16	6d. Prussian blue (glazed paper) (4.80)			
		a. Light blue (glazed paper) (4.81)			
		b. Deep blue (glazed paper) (10.81)		28·00	1·75
152	14	8d. lilac-brown/pink (8.77)		75·00	5·50
		a. Red-brown/pink (glazed paper) (11.80)			†

The same electrotypes as the previous issues were used for this series with the exception of the 5s. which was a new value. The 1d., 2d., 3d., 4d., 6d. and 1s. plates were arranged to print sheets of 120 (12×10) and the 8d. conformed to this when reintroduced in 1877. New plates for the 1d. (1868), 2d.(1869) and 6d. (1875) were constructed by Robinson's successor, J. P. Atkinson, using the improved facilities then available.

Atkinson was also responsible for the printing of the 5s. value. The original printings in blue on yellow paper were produced in sheets of 25, or possibly 50, using a vertical strip of five electrotypes. Due to its size the 5s. did not exactly fit the watermarked paper and, to avoid a preprinted sheet number, a proportion of the printing was made on the back of the paper creating the reversed watermark variety, No. 139a. These varieties occur in the first printing only as Atkinson created a plate of 25 for the second printing in March 1868. Printings of the 5s. bicoloured to April 1880 were made from electrotypes taken from the monocoloured plate. These showed a blue line beneath the crown (Type I). In early 1881 this plate was found to be too worn for further use and a new die was made from which a plate of 100 was constructed. Stamps from this plate are without the blue line beneath the crown (Type II).

PERFORATIONS. Various perforating machines were in use during this period. The use of line machines gauging 12 ceased around 1883. Of the line machines gauging 13 two were converted to comb types in 1873 and were eventually replaced by the 12½ gauge line and comb machines first used in 1876.

(Typo from electrotypes)

1867–70. *Emergency printings on various papers due to shortages of V over Crown paper.* P 13

(*a*) *Perkins, Bacon paper borrowed from Tasmania. Wmkd double-lined numerals as W* 4 *of Tasmania*
153	14	1d. pale yellowish green (wmkd "1") (24.9.67)		65·00	3·50
		a. Deep yellow-green (10.67)		65·00	3·50
154		1d. pale yellow-green (wmkd "4") (27.5.68)		£1300	85·00
155		2d. grey-lilac (wmkd "4") (3.2.68)		£110	4·25
		a. Slate (4.68)		£110	3·50
		b. Mauve (7.68)			4·50
156		2d. mauve (wmkd "1") (30.6.68)		£110	5·50
157	15	3d. grey-lilac (wmkd "1") (8.68)		£150	38·00
158	14	4d. dull rose-red (wmkd "4") (5.68)		£110	5·00
159	16	6d. blue (wmkd "4") (20.6.68)		£150	13·00
		a. Indigo-blue		—	15·00
160		6d. blue (wmkd "1") (28.7.68)		55·00	4·25
161		6d. dull blue (wmkd "2") (1870)		†	£2250

(*b*) *Saunders paper. Wmkd in words as W* 10
162	14	1d. pale yellow-green (wmkd "SIX PENCE") (23.3.68)		£375	18·00
163		2d. slate-grey (wmkd "SIX PENCE") (6.68)		†	£2500
164	16	6d. blue (wmkd "SIX PENCE") (20.5.68)		£250	14·00
		a. Indigo-blue		—	18·00
165		6d. dull blue (wmkd "THREE PENCE") (6.12.69)		£130	6·00
		a. Deep blue		—	7·00
166		6d. dull blue (wmkd "FOUR PENCE") (21.5.70)		£250	23·00
		a. Deep blue		—	24·00

(*c*) *V over Crown, W* 19, *coloured paper*
167	14	2d. mauve/lilac (7.68)		65·00	6·50
		a. Lilac/lilac		65·00	6·00

(*d*) *Saunders single-lined numeral* "4" *as W* 11
168	16	6d. dull blue (21.5.70)		†	£1600

The supply of paper was so short during 1868 that many odds and ends were utilised. Nos. 161 (five known), 163 (one known) and 168 (ten known) are the rarest of these emergency printings.

(Printed in Melbourne from a double electrotyped plate of 240 supplied by D.L.R.)

1870 (28 Jan)**–73.** *Wmk V over Crown, W* **19.**
169	20	2d. brown-lilac (p 13)		60·00	1·50
		a. Dull lilac-mauve (9.70)		50·00	1·50
		b. Mauve (worn plate) (3.73)		50·00	1·25
170		2d. dull lilac-mauve (p 12) (28.7.71)		55·00	1·50
		a. Mauve (worn plate) (3.73)		55·00	1·00

9 9

NINEPENCE

(21)

1871 (22 Apr). *No.* 123c *surch with T* 21 *in blue.*
171	16	9d. on 10d. purple-brown/pink		£300	10·00
		a. Blackish brown/pink		£400	12·00
		b. Surch double		†	£800

(image: stamps numbered 22, 23, 24, 25, 26, 27)

(Des and eng W. Bell. Typo from electrotyped plates)

1873 (25 Mar)**–74.** *Saunders paper wmkd single-lined* "10" *as* W 11.
172	25	9d. pale brown/pink (p 13)		65·00	8·50
		a. Red-brown/pink (7.74)		60·00	9·00
173		9d. pale brown/pink (p 12)		70·00	12·00

½   ½

HALF

(28)

1873 (25 June). *No.* 131g *surch with T* 28 *in red.*
174	14	½d. on 1d. green (p 13)		48·00	12·00
		a. Grass-green		50·00	12·00
		b. Short "1" at right (R. 1/3)		—	70·00
175		½d. on 1d. green (p 12)		65·00	14·00
		a. Grass-green		65·00	14·00
		b. Short "1" at right (R. 1/3)		—	75·00

Die I   Die II

Two Dies of 2d.:
Die I. Single-lined outer oval
Die II. Double-lined outer oval

(Des and eng W. Bell. Typo from electrotyped plates)

1873–87. *Wmk V over Crown, W* **19,** (*sideways on* ½d.).
(*a*) *P* 13
176	22	½d. rose-red (10.2.74)		7·50	70
		a. Lilac-rose (1874)		8·00	90
		b. Rosine (shades) (glazed paper) (12.80)		6·50	70
		c. Pale red (glazed paper) (1882)		7·50	60
		d. Mixed perf 13 and 12		†	£250
177	23	1d. dull bluish green (14.12.75)		17·00	85
		a. Green (shades) (1877)		17·00	80
		b. Yellow-green (glazed paper) (1878)		17·00	65
178	24	2d. deep lilac-mauve (I) (1.10.73)		24·00	65
		b. Dull violet-mauve		24·00	65
		b. Dull mauve		24·00	65
		c. Pale mauve (worn plate) (glazed paper) (1.79)		25·00	80
		d. Mixed perf 13 and 12		£130	£100
179		2d. lilac-mauve (II) (glazed paper) (17.12.78)		22·00	65
		a. Grey-mauve (1.80)			65
		b. Pale mauve (6.80)		30·00	70
		c. Vert pair, lower stamp imperf horiz		†	£1200
180	26	1s. indigo-blue (16.8.76)		55·00	3·00
		a. Deep blue/blue (7.77)		60·00	3·00
		b. Pale blue/blue (8.80)		65·00	3·00
		c. Bright blue/blue (9.80)		70·00	7·50
		d. Bright blue/blue (glazed paper) (21.11.83)		70·00	5·00
		e. Pale blue/blue (glazed paper) (7.84)			
		f. Mixed perf 13 and 12		†	—

(*b*) *P* 12
181	22	½d. rose-red (1874)		8·00	1·25
		a. Lilac-rose (1874)		7·50	1·25
		b. Rosine (shades) (glazed paper) (12.80)		7·50	1·00
		c. Pale red (glazed paper) (1882)		7·50	1·10
182	23	1d. dull bluish green (1875)		19·00	1·50
		a. Green (shades) (1877)		18·00	5·00
		b. Yellow-green (glazed paper) (1878)		—	2·75
183	24	2d. deep lilac-mauve (I) (1873)		—	2·50
		a. Dull violet-mauve		—	2·25
		b. Dull mauve		27·00	1·00
		c. Pale mauve (worn plate) (glazed paper) (1879)		—	1·25
184		2d. lilac-mauve (II) (glazed paper) (1878)		28·00	80
		a. Grey-mauve (glazed paper) (1880)		—	85
		b. Pale mauve (glazed paper) (1880)		—	2·00
185	25	9d. lilac-brown/pink (1.12.75)		£100	12·00
186	26	1s. deep blue/blue (1880)		—	7·50
		a. Bright blue/blue (1880)		—	7·50

(*c*) *P* 12½
187	22	½d. rosine (shades) (glazed paper) (1880)			
		a. Pale red (glazed paper) (1882)			
188	23	1d. yellow-green (glazed paper) (1880)			
189	24	2d. grey-mauve (II) (glazed paper) (1880)			
		a. Pale mauve (1880)			
190	27	2s. deep blue/green (glazed paper) (8.7.81)		£120	18·00
		a. Light blue/green (glazed paper) (4.83)			
		ab. Wmk sideways		£130	22·00
		b. Ultramarine/green (glazed paper) (6.84)		—	28·00
		ba. Wmk sideways		—	48·00

8ᵈ   8ᵈ

EIGHTPENCE

(29)

1876 (1 July). *No.* 185 *surch with T* 29.
191	25	8d. on 9d. lilac-brown/pink		£180	15·00
		a. "F.IGHTPENCE"		—	£180

No. 191a was caused by a broken "E" and it occurred once in each sheet of 120.

1877 (24 Jan). *Saunders paper wmkd "10" as W* **11**.
192	**14**	8d. lilac-brown/*pink* (p 13)	..	—	£500
		a. *Purple-brown/pink* (2.78)	..	£100	8·00
		b. *Chocolate/pink* (8.78)	..	†	£600
		c. *Red-brown/pink* (8.79)	..	85·00	5·00
193		8d. red-brown/*pink* (p 12) (8.79)	..	—	10·00
194		8d. red-brown/*pink* (p 12½) (8.79)	..	—	50·00

Nos. 192/4 occur amongst the V over Crown printings, the two types of pink paper having become mixed.

1878. *Emergency printings on coloured papers wmkd V over Crown, W* **19**, *(sideways on ½d.). P* 13.
195	**22**	½d. rose-red/*pink* (1.3.78)	..	24·00	13·00
196	**23**	1d. yellow-green/*yellow* (5.3.78)	..	75·00	12·00
197		1d. yellow-green/*drab* (5.4.78)	..	£100	42·00
198	**24**	2d. dull violet-mauve/*lilac* (21.2.78)	..	—	£400
199		2d. dull violet-mauve/*green* (23.2.78)	..	£130	13·00
200		2d. dull violet-mauve/*brown* (21.3.78)	..	£120	13·00

There was a shortage of white V over Crown, W **19**, watermarked paper in the early months of 1878 and various coloured papers were used for printings of the ½d., 1d. and 2d. values until fresh stocks of white paper were received.

30	31	32

(Des and eng C. Naish. Typo from electrotyped plates)

1880 (3 Nov)–**84.** *Wmk V over Crown, W* **19**.
201	**30**	1d. green (p 12½) (2.84)	..	90·00	8·50
202	**31**	2d. sepia (p 12½)	..	21·00	55
		a. *Sepia-brown* (2.81)	..	19·00	55
		b. *Brown (aniline)* (5.81)	..	22·00	55
		c. *Dull black-brown* (10.81)	..	—	55
		d. *Dull grey-brown* (3.82)	..	18·00	55
203		2d. sepia (p 13)	..		
		a. Mixed perf 13 and 12	..	†	£250
204		2d. sepia (p 12)	..	—	40·00
		a. *Sepia-brown* (2.81)	..	—	40·00
		b. *Brown (aniline)* (5.81)	..	—	40·00
205		2d. mauve (*worn plate*) (p 12½) (2.84)	..	—	6·50
206	**32**	4d. rose-carmine (p 12½) (10.81)	..	50·00	5·00
		a. *Rosine* (7.82)	..	50·00	4·50

Nos. 201 and 205 are subsequent printings of stamps first produced on watermark W **33**.

33

1882–84. *Wmk V over Crown, W* **33**, *(sideways on ½d.). P* 12½.
207	**22**	½d. rosine (3.83)	..	10·00	2·00
		a. Perf 12	..	—	16·00
208	**23**	1d. yellow-green (9.82)	..	17·00	1·50
		a. Perf 12	..		
209	**30**	1d. yellow-green (29.10.83)	..	17·00	1·25
		a. *Green* (1.84)	..	15·00	1·25
		b. *Pale green* (5.84)	..	15·00	1·25
210	**31**	2d. dull grey-brown (15.8.82)	..	20·00	75
		a. *Chocolate* (3.83)	..	20·00	75
		ab. Perf 12	..	—	19·00
211		2d. mauve (20.12.83)	..	11·00	50
		a. *Worn plate* (2.84)	..	12·00	50
		b. Perf 12	..	†	£250
		c. Mixed perf 12 and 12½	..	†	£250
212	**15**	3d. yellow-orange (13.4.83)	..	30·00	6·50
		a. *Dull brownish orange*	..	35·00	8·00
213	**32**	4d. rose-red (3.83)	..	45·00	6·00
214	**16**	6d. dull violet-blue (10.11.82)	..	22·00	1·25
		a. *Indigo-blue* (11.83)	..	22·00	1·25
		b. *Light ultramarine* (8.84)	..	22·00	1·40

Reprints were made in 1891 of the "Laureated" 1d., 2d., 3d. (in yellow), 4d., 6d., 8d. (in orange-yellow), 10d. (in greenish slate) and 5s. (in blue and red), of the Bell ½d., 1d., 2d. (Die II), 9d. and 1s. and of the Naish 2d. (in brown), 4d. (in pale red) and 2s. With the exception of the Bell 9d., which was watermarked W **19**, all were watermarked W **33** and perforated 12½. Some were from new plates.

THE POST OFFICE ACT OF 1883. Following official concern as to the number of different series of adhesive stamps, both fiscal and postal, used in Victoria it was decided that the system should be unified to the extent that the postage stamps, Stamp Statute fiscals and Stamp Duty fiscals should be replaced by a single series valid for all three purposes. As the Stamp Duty series contained the largest number of values it was adopted as the basis of the new range.

The regulations for the changeover were detailed in the Post Office Act of 1883 which came into force on 1 January 1884. From that date all existing Stamp Statute (first produced in 1871) and Stamp Duty (first produced in 1879) issues became valid for postal purposes, and the previous postage stamps could be used for fiscal fees.

Until matters could be organised printings of some of the existing postage values continued and these will be found included in the listings above.

Printing of the Stamp Statute series was discontinued in early 1884.

The existing Stamp Duty range was initially supplemented by postage stamps overprinted "STAMP DUTY" for those values where the available fiscal design was considered to be too large

---

to be easily used on mail. These overprints were replaced by smaller designs inscribed "STAMP DUTY".

Stamp Statute and Stamp Duty values which became valid for postal purposes on 1 January 1884 have previously been listed in this catalogue as Postal Fiscals. Under the circumstances this distinction appears somewhat arbitary and all such stamps are now shown in the main listing. Used prices quoted are for examples with postal cancellations. In some instances prices are also provided for fiscally used and these are marked "F.C.".

34	35	36

37

(Des and dies eng J. Turner (3d., 2s. 6d.), W. Bell (others). Typo from electrotypes)

1884 (1 Jan)*. *Stamp Statute series. Vert designs as T* **34/6**, *and others showing Queen Victoria, and T* **37**. *P* 13.

(a) Wmk single-lined numerals according to face value, as W **11**, *(sideways). Paper manufactured by T. H. Saunders unless otherwise stated*
215		1s. blue/*blue*	..	45·00	17·00
		a. Perf 12	..	60·00	23·00
216		2s. blue/*green* (D.L.R. paper)	..	65·00	45·00
		a. Perf 12	..	65·00	45·00
217		2s. deep blue/*green*	..	65·00	
		a. Perf 12	..	—	45·00
		b. Wmk upright	..		
218		10s. brown-olive/*pink*	..		
219		10s. red-brown/*pink*	..	£500	£100
		a. Wmk upright. Perf 12	..		

(b) Wmk V over Crown, W **19**, *(sideways). P* 13
220		1d. pale green	..	17·00	17·00
		a. *Green (wmk upright)* (p 12½)	..	42·00	35·00
221		3d. mauve	..	£120	80·00
222		4d. rose	..	£110	60·00
223		6d. blue	..	48·00	17·00
		a. *Ultramarine*	..	42·00	12·00
		ab. Perf 12	..	48·00	15·00
224		1s. blue/*blue*	..	45·00	17·00
		a. Perf 12	..	50·00	20·00
		b. *Ultramarine/blue* (p 12½)	..	—	29·00
		ba. Perf 12	..	—	24·00
		c. *Deep blue/blue* (p 12½)	..	45·00	17·00
		ca. Perf 12	..	—	17·00
225		2s. blue/*green*	..	60·00	40·00
		a. Perf 12	..	60·00	
		b. *Deep blue/blue-green (glazed paper)*	..	60·00	45·00
		ba. Perf 12	..	60·00	50·00
226		2s. 6d. orange	..	—	55·00
		a. Perf 12	..		
		b. *Yellow (glazed paper)*	..	£120	
		ba. Perf 12	..	£120	60·00
		c. *Orange-yellow (glazed paper)* (p 12½)	..	—	65·00
		ca. Perf 12	..		
227		5s. blue/*yellow*	..	£140	45·00
		a. Perf 12	..	£150	
		b. Wmk upright	..		
		ba. Perf 12	..		
		c. *Ultram/lemon (glazed paper)* (p 12½)	..	£140	45·00
228		10s. brown/*pink*	..	£500	£100
		a. *Purple-brown/pink*	..	£500	£100
		ab. Perf 12	..		
229		£1 slate-violet/*yellow*	..	£300	85·00
		a. Wmk upright	..		
		b. *Mauve/yellow*	..		
		ba. Perf 12	..	£300	85·00
		bb. Perf 12½	..	£300	85·00
230		£5 black and yellow-green	..	£2000	£450
		a. Perf 12	..		
		b. Wmk upright. Perf 12½	..	£2000	£450

(c) Wmk V over Crown, W **33**, *(sideways)*
231		1d. yellowish green (p 12½)	..	30·00	30·00
232		2s. 6d. pale orange-yellow (p 12)	..	£120	55·00
233		£5 black & yellow-grn (*wmk upright*) (p 12)	..	—	£450

½d

HALF

(38)

1884 (1 Jan)*. *No.* 220 *surch with T* **38** *in red.*
234		½d. on 1d. pale green	..	35·00	32·00

* The dates quoted are those on which the stamps became valid for postal purposes. The ½d., 1d., 4d., 6d., 1s., 5s. and £1 were issued for fiscal purposes on 26 April 1871. The 10s. was added to the series in June 1871, the £5 in September 1871, the 2s. 6d. in July 1876 and the 3d. in October 1879.

All values of the Stamp Statue series were reprinted in 1891 on paper watermarked W **19** (5s., 10s., £1) or W **33** (others). The £5 was pulled from the original plate, but the others were produced from new electrotypes taken from the original dies.

39	40	41

42	43	44

45	46	47

48	49	50

51	52	53

54	55

56   57

58   59

60

61

(Des H. Samson and F. Oxenbould (T **39**), C. Jackson and L. Lang (all others except T **40**). Dies eng C. Jackson, J. Turner, J. Whipple, A. Williams and other employees of Sands & MacDougall. T **40** die eng C. Naish.

1884 (1 Jan*)**–96**. *Existing Stamp Duty series.*

  (a) Litho. Wmk V over Crown, W **19**, *(sideways). P* 13
235	**39**	1d. blue-green		45·00	9·00
		a. Perf 12		45·00	9·00
		b. Perf 12½			
236	**43**	1s. 6d. rosine		£130	17·00
		a. Perf 12			— 24·00
		b. Perf 12½			
237	**45**	3s. purple/*blue*		£300	26·00
		a. Perf 12			— 35·00
		b. Perf 12½			
238	**46**	4s. orange-red		75·00	16·00
		a. Perf 12		75·00	16·00
		b. Perf 12½			
239	**48**	6s. apple-green		£200	25·00
		a. Perf 12½			
240	**49**	10s. brown/*rose* (*glazed paper*)	£300	55·00
		a. Perf 12			
		b. Perf 12½			
		c. Wmk upright			
		cb. Perf 12½			
241	**50**	15s. mauve		£800	£120
242	**51**	£1 red-orange		£350	60·00
		a. Perf 12½		£350	60·00
243	**52**	£1 5s. dull rose (*wmk upright*)	£750	£140
244	**53**	£1 10s. deep grey-olive	£800	95·00
		a. Wmk upright		— £130
245	—	35s. grey-violet (*wmk upright*) (F.C. £150)	£3000	
246	**54**	£2 blue		— 85·00
247	**55**	45s. dull brown-lilac		£1400	£110
248	**56**	£5 rose-red (*wmk upright*) (F.C. £50)	£1200	£250
249	**57**	£6 blue/*pink* (*wmk upright*) (*glazed paper*) (F.C. £100)	— £475
250	**58**	£7 violet/*blue* (*wmk upright*) (F.C. £100)	— £475
251	**59**	£8 brownish red/*yellow* (*wmk upright*) (*glazed paper*) (F.C. £100)	— £600
252	**60**	£9 yellow-green/*green* (*wmk upright*) (*glazed paper*) (F.C. £100)	— £600

  (b) Typo from electrotypes
   (i) *Wmk V over Crown, W* **19**, *(sideways). P* 13
253	**39**	1d. yellowish green		32·00	8·50
		a. Perf 12		32·00	8·50
		b. Perf 12½			

254	**40**	1d. pale bistre		9·00	1·50
		a. Perf 12		9·00	2·50
		b. Perf 12½			
255	**41**	6d. dull blue		38·00	6·00
		a. Perf 12		42·00	13·00
		b. Perf 12½			
256	**42**	1s. deep blue/*blue*		55·00	4·50
		a. Perf 12		55·00	5·50
		b. Perf 12½			
		c. *Brt blue/blue* (*glazed paper*) (p 12½)	55·00	5·00
		ca. Perf 12			— 5·50
		d. *Ultramarine/blue* (*glazed paper*) (p 12½) (11.84)	90·00	5·50
257		1s. chalky *blue/lemon* (*glazed paper*) (3.3.85)	75·00	22·00
258	**44**	2s. deep blue/*green* (*glazed paper*)	£100	14·00
		a. Perf 12			— 16·00
		b. Perf 12½			— 18·00
		c. *Indigo/green*		80·00	18·00
		ca. Perf 12		£120	19·00
		cb. Perf 12½			
259	**45**	3s. *mar/bl* (*glazed paper*) (p 12½) (8.8.84)	£170	25·00
260	**47**	5s. claret/*yellow* (*glazed paper*)	50·00	4·75
		a. Perf 12		60·00	10·00
		b. Perf 12½			
		c. *Pale claret/yellow* (p 12½)	50·00	10·00
		ca. Perf 12		70·00	10·00
		d. *Reddish purple/lemon* (p 12½) (6.87)	45·00	11·00
		e. *Brown-red/yellow* (p 12½) (5.93)	75·00	22·00
261	**49**	10s. chocolate/*rose* (*glazed paper*)	— 55·00
		a. Perf 12			
		b. Perf 12½			
		c. Wmk upright			
262	**51**	£1 yellow-orange/*yellow* (p 12)	£550	75·00
		a. *Orange/yellow* (p 12½)	£500	55·00
		b. *Reddish orange/yellow* (p 12½) (9.88)	£325	55·00
263	**54**	£2 deep blue (p 12)		— 85·00
264	**61**	£10 dull mauve (p 12)			
		a. *Deep red-lilac* (p 12)	£1500	£100

  (ii) *Wmk V over Crown, W* **33**, *(sideways). P* 12½
265	**40**	1d. ochre		17·00	2·75
		a. Perf 12		17·00	2·75
266	**41**	6d. ultramarine		50·00	5·00
		a. Perf 12		50·00	5·00
267	**43**	1s. 6d. pink (1.85)		£130	25·00
		a. *Bright rose-carmine* (4.86)	£150	23·00
268	**45**	3s. drab (20.10.85)		75·00	16·00
		a. *Olive-drab* (1.93)		70·00	16·00
269	**46**	4s. red-orange (5.86)		80·00	13·00
		a. *Yellow-orange* (12.94)			
		ab. Wmk upright		£100	10·00
270	**47**	5s. rosine (8.5.96)		75·00	19·00
271	**48**	6s. pea-green (12.11.91)	£110	35·00
		a. *Apple-green* (*wmk upright*) (3.96)	£180	35·00
272	**49**	10s. dull bluish green (10.85)	£150	30·00
		a. *Grey-green* (5.86)		£110	27·00
273	**50**	15s. purple-brown (12.85)	£550	75·00
		a. *Brown* (*wmk upright*) (5.95)	£550	80·00
274	**52**	£1 5s. pink (*wmk upright*) (6.8.90)	£850	80·00
275	**53**	£1 10s. pale olive (6.88)	£600	70·00
276	**54**	£2 bright blue		— 75·00
		a. *Blue* (7.88)		£750	75·00
277	**55**	45s. lilac (15.8.90)		£2000	90·00
278	**56**	£5 rose-pink (p 12)		— £225
		a. *Pink* (p 12½)		— £325
279	**61**	£10 mauve (3.84)		£1700	90·00
		a. *Lilac* (6.85)		— £100

*This is the date on which the stamps became valid for postal use. The 1d., 1s., 1s.6d., 2s., 3s., 4s., 5s., 10s., 15s., £1, £1 10s., £2, £5 and £10 were issued for fiscal purposes on 18 December 1879 with the £1 5s., 35s., 45s., £6 and £9 added to the range later the same month and the 6s., £7 and £8 in January 1880.

Used prices for the £1 5s., £1 10s., £2 (No. 276a), 45s. and £10 watermarked W **33** are for examples from the cancelled-to-order sets sold to collectors by the Victoria postal authorities between September 1900 and 30 June 1902.

Similar Stamp Duty designs were prepared for 7s., 8s., 9s., 11s., 12s., 13s., 14s., 16s., 17s., 18s. and 19s., but were never issued.

The two different 1d. designs were reprinted in 1891 on W **33** paper.

For these designs with later watermarks see Nos. 345/50 and 369/71.

62

(Des C. Jackson and L. Lang. Dies eng C. Jackson)

1884 (1 Jan*)**–1900**. *High value Stamp Duty series.*

  (a) Recess-printed direct from the die
   (i) *Wmk V over Crown, W* **19**, *(sideways). P* 12½
280	**62**	£25 yellow-green (F.C. £55)		
		a. Wmk upright			
		b. Perf 13			
		c. *Deep green* (F.C. £55)		
		ca. Wmk upright			
281		£50 bright mauve (F.C. £85)		
		a. Wmk upright			
		b. Perf 13			
282		£100 crimson-lake (F.C. £110)		
		a. Wmk upright			
		b. Perf 13			

  (ii) *Wmk V over Crown, W* **33**, *(sideways). P* 12½
283	**62**	£25 yellow-green		
		b. *Deep green* (1.85) (F.C. £55)	— £400
		c. *Bright blue-green* (10.90) (F.C. £55)	
		a. Wmk upright			
284		£50 dull lilac-mauve (*wmk upright*) (F.C.£85)		
		a. *Black-violet* (10.90) (F.C. £65)	— £400
		ab. Wmk upright			

285	**62**	£100 crimson (F.C. £120)		
		a. Wmk upright			
		b. Perf 12 (F.C. £120)		
		c. *Aniline crimson* (*wmk upright*) (2.85) (F.C. £120)	— £475
		d. *Scarlet-red* (5.95)		— £475
		da. Wmk upright		— £375

  (b) Litho. Wmk V over Crown, W **33**, *(sideways). P* 12½
286	**62**	£25 dull yellowish green (1.86) (F.C. £45)	
		a. Wmk upright (11.87)		
		b. *Dull blue-green* (9.88) (F.C. £45)	
		ba. Wmk upright			
287		£50 dull purple (1.86) (F.C. £60)	
		a. Wmk upright			
		b. *Bright violet* (11.89) (F.C. £60)	
		ba. Wmk upright			
288		£100 rosine (1.86) (F.C. £95)	
		a. Wmk upright			

  (c) Typo from electrotyped plates. Wmk V over Crown, W **33**. *P* 12½
289	**62**	£25 dull blue-green (12.97)	— 90·00
290		£50 bright mauve (10.97)	— £150
291		£100 pink-red (10.1900)	— £200

*This is the date on which the stamps became valid for postal use. All three values were issued for fiscal purposes on 18 December 1879.

Used prices for Nos. 283b, 284a, 285c/d and 289/91 are for examples from the cancelled-to-order sets described beneath No. 279a. "F.C." indicates that the price quoted is for a stamp with a fiscal cancellation.

For the £25 and £50 with watermark W **82** see Nos. 351/2.

63

(Des and die eng C. Naish. Typo from electrotyped plates)

1884 (23 Apr)**–92**. *New design inscr "STAMP DUTY". Wmk V over Crown, W* **33** *(sideways). P* 12½.
292	**63**	2s. 6d. brown-orange		85·00	12·00
		a. *Yellow* (8.85)		80·00	11·00
		b. *Lemon-yellow* (2.92)		80·00	11·00

For this design on later watermarks see Nos. 344 and 368.

64   65   66

67   68

(Des and dies eng C. Naish. Typo from electrotyped plates)

1885 (1 Jan)**–95**. *New designs inscr "STAMP DUTY". P* 12½.

  (a) W **19**
293	**68**	8d. rose/*pink*		20·00	5·50
		a. *Rose-red/pink* (2.88)		22·00	5·50
294	**66**	1s. deep dull blue/*lemon* (11.85)	55·00	7·50
		a. *Dull blue/yellow* (6.86)		55·00	8·00
295	**68**	2s. olive/*bluish green* (12.85)	40·00	3·00

  (b) W **33**
296	**64**	½d. pale rosine		6·50	65
		a. *Deep rosine* (7.85)		7·50	1·00
		b. *Salmon* (9.85)		8·00	1·25
297	**65**	1d. yellowish green (1.85)		8·00	50
		a. *Dull pea-green* (2.85)		13·00	1·75
298	**66**	2d. lilac		6·50	30
		a. *Mauve* (1886)		6·50	30
		b. *Rosy-mauve* (1886)		8·00	50
299	**65**	3d. yellowish brown		10·00	1·00
		a. *Pale ochre* (9.86)		9·50	1·00
		b. *Bistre-yellow* (9.92)		10·00	1·00
300	**67**	4d. magenta		38·00	3·00
		a. *Bright mauve-rose* (12.86)	40·00	3·50
		b. *Error. Lilac* (12.86)		£2250	£400
301	**65**	6d. chalky blue (1.85)		50·00	2·50
		a. *Bright blue* (3.85)		32·00	2·10
		b. *Cobalt* (7.85)		32·00	2·10
302	**68**	8d. bright scarlet/*pink* (3.95)	30·00	8·00
303		2s. olive-green/*pale green* (1.90)	26·00	4·00
304		2s. apple-green (12.8.95)		25·00	35·00
		a. *Blue-green* (29.10.95)		18·00	6·50

The plates for the 1d., 6d., 1s. and 2s. were derived from the dies of the 2d. (1s.), 3d. (1d. and 6d.) and 8d. (2s.). In each instance lead moulds of six impressions were taken from the original die and the face values altered by hand creating six slightly different versions.

Two states of the 2d. die exist with the second showing a break in the top frame line near the righthand corner. This damaged die was used for seven impressions on Plate 1 and all 120 on Plate 2.

No. 300b occured during the December 1886 printing of the 4d. when about fifty sheets were printed in the colour of the 2d.

by mistake. The sheets were issued to Melbourne post offices and used examples are known postmarked between 21 December 1886 and 4 March 1887. Nine unused are also believed to exist.

Reprints of the ½d., 1d., 2d., 4d., 6d. and 1s. values were made in 1891 from the existing plates. The 1s. was watermarked W 19 and the remainder W 33.

For some of these values used with later watermarks see Nos. 336, 343, 360, 368 and X362.

(69)

1885 (Feb–Nov).   *Optd with T* **69**. *P* 12½. (*a*) W 19
305	15	3d. dull orge-yell (*glazed paper*) (B.) (Nov)		—	£130
306	26	1s. pale blue/*blue* (*glazed paper*) (*p* 13)		95·00	20·00
		a. Deep blue/blue		—	22·00
		b. Blue opt (F.C. £14)		£1200	£600
307	27	2s. ultramarine/*grn* (*glazed paper*) (Mar)		90·00	18·00
		a. Wmk sideways		£100	20·00

(*b*) W 33
308	15	3d. yellow-orange (B.) (Nov)		60·00	22·00
		a. Dull brownish orange (B.)		65·00	24·00
309	32	4d. rose-red (B.) (Nov)		55·00	24·00

Unauthorised reprints of the 4d. and 1s., both with blue overprints and watermarked W 33, were made during 1895–96. The 4d. reprint, which is in pale red, also exists without the overprint.

70   71   72

73   74   75

76   77   78

79   80

(Des S. Reading (1d. (No. 313), M. Tannenberg (2½d., 5d.), C. Naish (1s. 6d.), P. Astley (others). Dies eng C. Naish (2d., 4d. (both existing dies with lines added behind Queen's head) and 1s. 6d.), S. Reading (originally as an employee of Fergusson & Mitchell) (others). Typo from electrotyped plates)

1886 (26 July)–**96**. W 33 (*sideways on* ½d., 1s., £5, £7 *to* £9). *P* 12½.
310	70	½d. lilac-grey (28.8.86)		20·00	3·50
		a. Grey-black		—	35·00
311		½d. pink (15.2.87)		7·00	30
		a. Rosine (*aniline*) (1889)		4·75	30
		b. Rose-red (1891)		4·50	30
		c. Vermilion (1896)		5·00	35
312	71	1d. green		5·75	50
		a. Yellow-green (1887)		5·75	50
313	72	1d. dull chestnut (1.1.90)		5·00	30
		a. Deep red-brown (1890)		5·00	40
		b. Orange-brown (1890)		5·00	30
		c. Brown-red (1890)		5·00	30
		d. Yellow-brown (1891)		5·00	30
		e. Bright yellow-orange (1893)		50·00	12·00
		f. Brownish orange (1894)		4·00	30
314	73	2d. pale lilac (17.12.86)		5·50	20
		a. Pale mauve (1887)		6·50	20
		b. Deep lilac (1888, 1892)		5·00	20
		c. Purple (1894)		3·25	25
		d. Violet (1895)		3·25	20
		e. Imperf		—	£700
315	74	2½d. red-brown/*lemon* (1.1.91)		13·00	2·00
		a. Brown-red/yellow (1892)		9·00	80
		b. Red/yellow (1893)		7·00	70
316	75	4d. rose-red (1.4.87)		12·00	1·00
		a. Red (1893)		6·50	90

317	76	5d. purple-brown (1.1.91)		8·50	85
		a. Pale reddish brown (1893)		6·50	80
318	77	6d. bright ultramarine (27.8.86)		12·00	80
		a. Pale ultramarine (1887)		11·00	50
		b. Dull blue (1891)		9·50	50
319	25	9d. apple-green (18.10.92)		20·00	9·00
320		9d. carmine-rose (15.10.95)		22·00	5·50
		a. Rosine (*aniline*) (1896)		26·00	6·00
321	78	1s. dull purple-brown (14.3.87)		38·00	2·00
		a. Lake (1890)		28·00	1·75
		b. Carmine-lake (1892)		16·00	1·00
		c. Brownish red (1896)		17·00	1·60
322	79	1s. 6d. pale blue (9.88)		£130	65·00
323		1s. 6d. orange (19.9.89)		15·00	4·50
		a. Red-orange (1893)		15·00	5·00
324	80	£5 pale blue and maroon (7.2.88)†		£1000	80·00
325		£6 yellow and pale blue (1.10.87)†		£1200	£100
326		£7 rosine and black (17.10.89)†		£1400	£120
327		£8 mauve & brown-orange (2.8.90)†		£1500	£150
328		£9 apple-green and rosine (21.8.88)†		£1800	£160

†The used prices provided for these stamps are for cancelled-to-order examples.

Unauthorised reprints of the ½d. lilac-grey and 1s. 6d. pale blue were made in 1894–95 on W 33 paper and perforated 12½. These differ in shade from the originals and have rougher perforations. It should be noted that the original printing of No. 322 does not occur with inverted watermark, but the reprint does.

A single example of No. 314e is known postmarked "737" (Foster). A second, postmarked "249" (Mortlake), was reported in 1892. It is known that an imperforate sheet was sold at Mortlake P.O. in 1890. Other examples are believed to be clandestine.

A £10 value as Type **80** was prepared, but not issued.

1891 (17 June).   W 19. *P* 12½.
329	72	1d. orange-brown/*pink*		4·50	1·75

No. 329 was an emergency printing during a shortage of white W 33 paper.

81   82

(Die eng A. Williams (1½d.). Typo from electrotyped plates)

1896 (11 June)–**99**. W 82 (*sideways on* ½d., 1½d., 1s., 2s. 6d. *to* 15s.). *P* 12½.
330	70	½d. light scarlet (1.7.96)		3·00	20
		a. Carmine-rose (1897)		3·25	20
		b. Dp carmine-red (*coarse impression*) (1899)		—	1·25
		c. Wmk upright			—
331		½d. emerald (1.8.99)		8·50	1·50
332	72	1d. brown-red (13.6.96)		4·25	10
		a. Brownish orange (1897)		4·25	10
333	81	1½d. apple-green (7.10.97)		4·00	1·75
334	73	2d. violet		5·00	10
		a. Wmk sideways			†
335	74	2½d. blue (1.8.99)		7·50	4·00
336	65	3d. ochre (11.96)		7·00	55
		a. Buff (1898)		6·50	50
337	75	4d. red (6.97)		9·00	1·00
338	76	5d. red-brown (7.97)		14·00	95
339	77	6d. dull blue (9.96)		11·00	65
340	25	9d. rosine (8.96)		25·00	3·25
		a. Rose-carmine (1898)		—	3·25
		b. Dull rose (1898)		22·00	3·25
341	78	1s. brownish red (3.97)		11·00	2·00
342	79	1s. 6d. brown-orange (8.98)		28·00	10·00
343	68	2s. blue-green (4.97)		25·00	6·00
344	63	2s. 6d. yellow (9.96)		90·00	12·00
		a. Wmk upright (1898)		£100	12·00
345	45	3s. olive-drab (12.96)		55·00	17·00
		a. Wmk upright (1898)		55·00	16·00
346	46	4s. orange (9.97)		80·00	7·50
347	47	5s. rosine (2.97)		80·00	8·50
		a. Rose-carmine (1897)		80·00	8·50
		b. Wmk upright. Rosine (1899)		80·00	9·00
348	45	5s. pale yellow-green (4.99)†		80·00	23·00
349	49	10s. grey-green (4.97)		£100	16·00
		a. Blue-green (1898)		£100	16·00
350	50	15s. brown (4.97)†		£375	42·00
351	62	£25 dull bluish green (1897)†		—	£100
352		£50 dull purple (1897)†		—	£130

†The used prices provided for these stamps are for cancelled-to-order examples.

83   84

(Des M. Tannenberg. Dies eng A. Mitchelhill. Typo from electrotyped plates)

1897 (22 Oct).   *Hospital Charity Fund*. W 82 (*sideways*). *P* 12½.
353	83	1d. (1s.) blue		18·00	18·00
354	84	2½d. (2s. 6d) red-brown		85·00	70·00
353/4		Optd "Specimen"		*Set of 2*	£140

These stamps were sold at 1s. and 2s. 6d., but only had postal validity for 1d. and 2½d. with the difference going to the Fund.

1899 (1 Aug).   W 33 (*sideways*). *P* 12½.
355	81	1½d. brown-red/*yellow*		3·00	1·75

85

1899 (1 Aug)–**1901**. W 85 (*sideways on* ½d., 1s. *and* 2s. 6d. *to* 10s.). *P* 12½.
356	70	½d. emerald (12.99)		4·75	40
		a. Deep blue-green		5·00	40
		b. Wmk upright			
357	72	1d. rose-red		5·00	15
		a. Rosine (1900)		4·25	10
358		1d. olive (6.6.01)		5·00	4·00
359	73	2d. violet		6·50	10
		a. Wmk sideways			†
360	74	2½d. blue (10.99)		8·00	1·50
361	65	3d. bistre-yellow (9.99)		7·00	1·00
362		3d. slate-green (20.6.01)		21·00	7·50
363	75	4d. rose-red (12.99)		5·00	1·10
364	76	5d. red-brown (10.99)		10·00	1·10
365	77	6d. dull ultramarine (1.00)		7·50	75
366	25	9d. rose-red (9.99)		11·00	1·75
367	78	1s. brown-red (5.00)		12·00	1·75
368	79	1s. 6d. orange (2.00)		14·00	6·00
369	68	2s. blue-green (6.00)		17·00	5·50
370	63	2s. 6d. yellow (1.00)		£300	14·00
371	45	3s. pale olive (4.00)†		£130	19·00
372	47	5s. rose-red (4.00)		£100	19·00
373	49	10s. green (3.00)†		£130	20·00

†The used prices provided for these stamps are for cancelled-to-order examples.

From 1 July 1901 stamps inscribed "STAMP DUTY" could only be used for fiscal purposes.

86 Victoria Cross   87 Australian Troops in South Africa

(Des Sands and MacDougall (1d.), J. Sutherland (2d.). Dies eng S. Reading. Typo from electrotyped plates)

1900 (22 May).   *Empire Patriotic Fund*. W 85 (*sideways*). *P* 12½.
374	86	1d. (1s.) olive-brown		60·00	38·00
375	87	2d. (2s.) emerald-green		£120	£120

These stamps were sold at 1s. and 2s., but only had postal validity for 1d. and 2d. with the difference going to the Fund.

FEDERATION. The six Australian colonies were federated as the Commonwealth of Australia on 1 January 1901. Under the terms of the Post and Telegraph Act their postal services were amalgamated on 1 March 1901, but other clauses to safeguard the financial position of the individual States provided them with a large degree of independence until 13 October 1910 when issues of each state could be used throughout Australia. Postage stamps for the Commonwealth of Australia did not appear until January 1913.

It was agreed in 1901 that stamp printing should be centralised at Melbourne under J. B. Cooke of South Australia who was appointed Commonwealth Stamp Printer. By 1909 the Commonwealth Stamp Printing Branch in Melbourne was producing stamps for Papua, South Australia, Tasmania and Western Australia in addition to those of Victoria.

On federation it was decided to separate postal and fiscal stamp issues so Victoria needed urgent replacements for the current Stamp Duty series which reverted to fiscal use only on 30 June 1901.

1901 (29 Jan).   *Re-use of previous designs without* "POSTAGE" *inscr*. W 82 (2s.) *or* W 85 (*others*) (*sideways on* ½d.). *P* 12×12½.
376	22	½d. bluish green		2·00	85
		a. "VICTCRIA" (R. 7/19)		35·00	25·00
377	31	2d. reddish violet		5·50	75
378	15	3d. dull orange		15·00	1·25
379	32	4d. bistre-yellow		25·00	12·00
380	16	6d. emerald		9·00	5·50
381	26	1s. yellow		38·00	30·00
382	27	2s. blue/*pink*		42·00	15·00
383	18	5s. pale red and deep blue		45·00	35·00

88   89   90

91	92	93
94	95	96
97	98	99
100	101	102

I II III

Three die states of ½d.:
I. Outer vertical line of colour to left of "V" continuous except for a break opposite the top of "V". Triangles either end of "VICTORIA" are more or less solid colour.
II. Die re-engraved. Three breaks in outer line of colour left of "V". White lines added to left triangle.
III. Die re-engraved. As II, but equivalent triangle at right also contains white lines.

I

II

III

I and II   III

Three die states of 1d.:
I. Thick lines fill top of oval above Queen's head.
II. Die re-engraved. Lines thinner, showing white space between.
III. Die re-engraved. As II, but with bottom left value table recut to show full point separated from both "1" and the circular frame.

Two die states of 2d.:
I. Frame line complete at top right corner. Bottom right corner comes to a point.
II. Break in right frame line just below the top corner. Bottom right corner is blunted.

Two types of 1s.:
A. "POSTAGE" 6 mm long (produced by a hand punch applied twice to each impression on the previous 1s. electrotyped plate. Slight variations in position occur).
B. "POSTAGE" 7 mm long (produced from new electrotyped plates incorporating the "POSTAGE" inscriptions).

(Eng S. Reading after photo by W. Stuart (£1, £2))

1901 (29 Jan)–**10.** *Previous issues with "POSTAGE" added and new designs (£1, £2). W 85 (sideways on ½d., 1½d., £1, £2).*

(a) P 12×12½

384	88	½d. blue-green (I) (26.6.01)	1·90	30
		a. Wmk upright (1903)	2·25	30
		b. Die state II (6.04)	3·50	30
		ba. Wmk upright	3·50	5·50
385	89	1d. rose (I)	3·50	15
		a. Dull red (12.02)	3·00	15
		ab. Wmk sideways	†	—
		b. Die state II (4.01)	1·50	15
		ba. Dull red (12.02)	1·25	15
		c. Die state II. Pale rose-red (4.05)	3·00	70
		ca. Wmk sideways	50·00	50·00
386	90	1½d. maroon/yellow (9.7.01)	6·50	3·25
		a. Wmk upright. Brn-red/yell (9.01)	2·10	55
		b. Dull red-brown/yellow (1906)	2·10	55
		ba. On yellow-buff back (1908)	2·75	1·00
387	91	2d. lilac (I) (26.6.01)	7·00	30
		a. Die state II	20·00	1·50
		b. Reddish violet (1902)	7·00	30
		ba. Die state II	20·00	1·50
		c. Bright purple (II) (1905)	7·00	30
		d. Rosy mauve (II) (1905)		
388	92	2½d. dull blue	7·00	35
		a. Deep blue (1902)	7·00	35
389	93	3d. dull orange-brown (5.7.01)	7·50	1·00
		a. Chestnut (1901)	7·00	55
		b. Yellowish brown (1905)	7·00	55
		ba. Wmk sideways	11·00	15·00
390	94	4d. bistre-yellow (26.6.01)	5·50	55
		a. Brownish bistre (1905)	8·50	70
391	95	5d. reddish brown	7·50	40
		a. Purple-brown (1903)	7·00	40
392	96	6d. emerald (5.7.01)	12·00	80
		a. Dull green (1904)	14·00	85
393	97	9d. dull rose-red (5.7.01)	12·00	1·75
		a. Wmk sideways (1901)	18·00	3·75
		b. Pale red (1901)	12·00	1·25
		c. Dull brownish red (1905)	15·00	2·00
394	98	1s. yellow-orange (A) (5.7.01)	14·00	1·75
		a. Yellow (1902)	16·00	1·75
		b. Type B (4.03)	17·00	3·00
		ba. Orange (1904)	15·00	2·50
		bb. Wmk sideways (1905)	25·00	6·50
395	99	2s. blue/rose (5.7.01)	22·00	2·00

(b) P 12½

396	88	½d. blue-green (III) (6.05)	8·00	50
397	92	2½d. dull blue (1901)	£250	£250
398	100	5s. rose-red and pale blue (5.7.01)	65·00	12·00
		a. Scarlet and deep blue (12.01)	70·00	10·00
		b. Rosine and blue (12.04)	70·00	10·00
399	101	£1 carmine-rose (18.11.01)	£225	£100
400	102	£2 deep blue (2.6.02)	£500	£250

(c) P 11

401	88	½d. blue-green (I) (9.02)	5·00	2·00
		a. Wmk upright (1903)	3·25	60
		b. Die state II (6.04)	4·50	60
		c. Die state III (6.05)	5·50	85
402	89	1d. dull red (I) (12.02)	55·00	40·00
		a. Die state II	45·00	18·00
		ab. Pale red (aniline) (3.03)	6·00	1·75
		ac. Pale rose (aniline) (1904)	25·00	3·50
		b. Die state III. Pale rose-red (7.05)	45·00	25·00
403	90	1½d. dull red-brown/yellow (1910)	42·00	42·00
404	91	2d. bright purple (II) (1905)	£500	£180
		a. Rosy mauve (II) (1905)	†	—
405	93	3d. yellowish brown (1903)	5·50	4·25
		a. Wmk sideways	15·00	20·00
406	96	6d. emerald (2.03)	12·00	15·00
		a. Dull green (1905)	£325	£160
407	101	£1 rose (5.05)	£275	£130
408	102	£2 deep blue (1905)	£850	£750

(d) Compound or mixed perf 12½ and 11

409	88	½d. blue-green (I) (1901)	23·00	7·50
		a. Wmk upright (1903)	—	7·50
		b. Die state (1904)	22·00	17·00
		ba. Wmk upright	35·00	
410	89	1d. dull red (I) (1902)	—	£180
		a. Die state II	£350	£140
411	90	1½d. maroon/yellow (1903)	£500	£200
412	91	2d. reddish violet (I) (1903)	†	£300
413	93	3d. dull orange-brown (1902)	—	£450
414	96	6d. emerald (1903)	†	£400
415	100	5s. rosine and blue (12.04)	£800	

Examples of the 1d. Die state II perforated 12½ exist with two black lines printed across the face of the stamp. These were prepared in connection with stamp-vending machine trials.

1905–13. *Wmk Crown over A, W w 11 (sideways on ½d., £1, £2).*

(a) P 12×12½

416	88	½d. blue-green (shades) (III) (21.10.05)	1·60	15
		a. Wmk. upright. Thin, ready gummed paper (6.12)	3·75	4·00
417	89	1d. rose-red (III) (16.7.05)	1·25	10
		a. Pale rose (1907)	1·25	10
		b. Rose-carmine (1911)	3·50	85
		ba. Wmk sideways	11·00	4·50
		c. Thin, ready gummed paper (10.12)	4·50	1·25
418	91	2d. dull mauve (II) (13.9.05)	6·00	30
		a. Lilac (1906)	6·00	25
		b. Reddish violet (1907)	6·00	25
		c. Bright mauve (1910)	4·75	55
		ca. Thin, ready gummed paper (8.12)	26·00	5·00
419	92	2½d. blue (10.08)	3·00	40
		a. Indigo (1909)	5·00	70
420	93	3d. orange-brown (11.11.05)	7·50	95
		a. Yellow-orange (1908)	8·00	90
		b. Dull orange-buff (1909)	8·00	90
		c. Ochre (1912)	8·00	3·50
421	94	4d. yellow-bistre (15.1.06)	7·00	65
		a. Olive-bistre (1908)	7·00	65
		b. Yellow-olive (1912)	7·00	3·25
422	95	5d. chocolate (14.8.06)	7·00	1·25
		a. Dull reddish brown (1908)	7·00	1·25
		ab. Thin, ready gummed paper (19.10.12)	13·00	8·00
423	96	6d. dull green (25.10.05)	12·00	80
		a. Dull yellow-green (1907)	12·00	80
		b. Emerald (1909)	12·00	1·10
		c. Yellowish green (1911)	12·00	1·60
		d. Emerald. Thin, ready gummed paper (11.12)	18·00	12·00
424	97	9d. brown-red (11.12.05)	13·00	1·75
		a. Orange-brown (1906)	13·00	1·50
		b. Red-brown (1908)	14·00	1·50
		c. Pale dull rose (1909)	14·00	2·75
		d. Rose-carmine (1910)	9·50	1·25
425	98	1s. orange (B) (13.2.06)	8·00	2·00
		a. Yellow-orange (1906)	11·00	2·00
		b. Yellow (1908)	13·00	2·00
		ba. Thin, ready gummed paper (11.12)	28·00	18·00
		c. Pale orange. Thin, ready gummed paper (1913)	28·00	18·00

(b) P 12½

426	88	½d. blue-green (shades) (III) (1905)	2·25	50
		a. Wmk upright (1909)	13·00	2·50
		b. Thin, ready gummed paper (1912)	5·00	
		ba. Wmk upright	3·50	4·00
427	89	1d. rose-red (III) (1905)	2·50	30
		a. Rose-carmine (1911)	5·50	1·75
428	92	2½d. indigo (1909)	10·00	1·75
429	96	6d. yellowish green (1911)	17·00	6·50
430	100	5s. rose-red and ultramarine (12.07)	70·00	13·00
		a. Rose-red and blue (1911)	80·00	13·00
		ab. Wmk sideways	85·00	16·00
431	101	£1 salmon (12.2.07)	£225	£100
		a. Dull rose (1910)	£225	£100
		ab. Wmk upright (1911)	£275	£120
432	102	£2 dull blue (18.7.06)	£500	£300

(c) P 11

433	88	½d. blue-green (shades) (III) (1905)	1·60	30
		a. Wmk upright. Thin, ready gummed paper (1912)	15·00	16·00
434	89	1d. rose-red (III) (1905)	3·50	1·00
		a. Pale rose (1907)	3·50	1·00
		b. Rose-carmine (1911)	7·00	3·25
		ba. Wmk sideways	10·00	4·50
		c. Thin, ready gummed paper (10.12)	7·50	4·50
435	91	2d. lilac (II) (1906)	†	£150
		a. Reddish violet (1907)	65·00	15·00
		b. Bright mauve (1910)	25·00	8·50
436	92	2½d. blue (1908)	60·00	8·50
		a. Indigo (1909)	11·00	5·50
437	93	3d. orange-brown (1905)	10·00	7·50
		a. Yellow-orange (1908)	†	£130
		b. Dull orange-buff (1909)	15·00	16·00
		c. Ochre (1912)	8·00	4·75
438	94	4d. yellow-bistre (1906)	9·00	15·00
		a. Olive-bistre (1909)		
		b. Yellow-olive (1912)	8·50	12·00
439	95	5d. chocolate (1906)	†	£475
		a. Dull reddish brown (1908)	†	£475
440	96	6d. emerald (1909)	10·00	14·00
		a. Yellowish green (1911)	15·00	19·00
441	97	9d. rose-carmine (1910)	†	£375
442	98	1s. yellow-orange (B) (1906)	†	£180
		a. Orange (1910)	£375	
443	100	5s. rose-red and ultramarine (12.07)	70·00	9·50
444	101	£1 salmon (12.2.07)	£275	£100
445	102	£2 dull blue (1.07)	£700	£325

(d) Compound or mixed perfs 12½ and 11

446	88	½d. blue-green (shades) (III) (1905)	17·00	16·00
		a. Wmk upright. Thin, ready gummed paper (1912)	£110	80·00
447	89	1d. rose-red (III) (1905)	35·00	35·00
		a. Pale rose (1907)	—	40·00
		b. Rose-carmine (1911)	—	40·00
448	91	2d. reddish violet (II) (1907)	£350	£200
449	93	3d. orange-brown (1905)	†	£275
		a. Ochre (1912)	£250	
450	94	4d. bistre (1908)	†	£275
451	96	6d. emerald (1909)	—	£375
		a. Yellowish green (1911)	†	£250
452	97	9d. orange-brown (1906)	†	£450
		a. Red-brown (1908)	†	£450
453	98	1s. yellow-orange (1906)	£600	

(e) Rotary comb perf 11½×12¼

454	89	1d. pale rose (III) (2.10)	6·50	1·75
		a. Rose-carmine (1911)		
		ab. Thin, ready gummed paper (7.12)	3·25	3·25
		b. Rose-red. Thin, ready gummed paper (10.12)	3·25	3·25
455	91	2d. lilac (II) (1910)	9·00	1·50

The original Crown over A watermark paper used by Victoria was of medium thickness and had toned gum applied after printing. Stocks of this paper lasted until 1912 when further supplies were ordered from a new papermakers, Cowan and Sons. This paper was much thinner and was supplied with white gum already applied. The first delivery arrived in June 1912 and a second in September of the same year.

The rotary comb perforating gauging 11½×12¼ was transferred from South Australia in 1909 when J. B. Cooke moved to Melbourne.

Examples of the 1d. perforated 12½ or 11 exist with two black lines across the face of the stamp. These were prepared in connection with stamp-vending machine trials.

ONE PENNY

(103)   104

1912 (29 June). *No. 455 surch with T 103 in red.*
456	91	1d. on 2d. lilac (II)	70	45

1912 (Aug–Sept). *W 104. (a) P 12×12½*
457	89	1d. rose-carmine (III)	2·75	2·50
		a. Wmk sideways	50·00	
458	91	2d. reddish violet (II) (Sept)	3·00	3·00
		a. Lilac	5·50	4·50
459	97	9d. rose-carmine	15·00	12·00

(b) P 12½
460	88	½d. bluish green (III)	3·00	3·50

(c) P 11
461	88	½d. bluish green (III)	20·00	20·00
462	89	1d. rose-carmine (III)	28·00	13·00
463	97	9d. rose-carmine	20·00	18·00

(d) Compound or mixed perfs 12½ and 11
464	97	9d. rose-carmine	†	£425

Nos. 457/64 were emergency printings caused by the non-arrival of stocks of the Cowan thin, ready gummed Crown over A watermarked paper. Paper watermarked W 104 had been introduced in 1911 and was normally used for Victoria fiscal stamps. This watermark can be easily distinguished from the previous W 85 by its narrow crown.

STAMP BOOKLETS

There are very few surviving examples of Nos. SB1/4. Listings are provided for those believed to have been issued with prices quoted for those known to still exist.

1904 (Mar)–**09**. *Black on red cover as No. SB1 of New South Wales. Stapled.*
SB1   £1 booklet containing two hundred and forty 1d. in four blocks of 30 and two blocks of 60
    a. Red on pink cover (1909)   £6000
    b. Blue on pink cover   £5000

1904 (Mar). *Black on grey cover as No. SB1. Stapled.*
SB2   £1 booklet containing one hundred and twenty 2d. in four blocks of 30

1910 (May). *Black on white cover as No. SB3 of New South Wales. Stapled.*
SB3   2s. booklet containing eleven ½d. (No. 426, either in block of 6 plus block of 5 or block of 11, and eighteen 1d. (No. 427), either in three blocks of 6 or block of 6 plus block of 12   £2000
    a. Black on pale green cover   £2000
Unsold stock of No. SB3 was uprated with one additional ½d. in May 1911.

1911 (Aug). *Red on pink cover as No. SB3. Stapled.*
SB4   2s. booklet containing twelve ½d. (No. 426), either in two blocks of 6 or block of 12, and eighteen 1d. (No. 427), either in three blocks of 6 or block of 6 plus block of 12   £1500

POSTAGE DUE STAMPS

D 1

(Dies eng A. Williams (values) and J. McWilliams (frame). Typo)
1890 (12 Oct)–**94**. *Wmk V over Crown, W 33. P 12×12½.*
D 1	D 1	½d. dull blue and brown-lake (24.12.90)	3·25	2·25
		a. Dull blue and deep claret	2·75	3·50
D 2		1d. dull blue and brown-lake	4·75	1·40
		a. Dull blue and brownish red (1.93)	6·50	1·10
D 3		2d. dull blue and brown-lake	8·00	1·25
		a. Dull blue and brownish red (3.93)	8·50	90
D 4		4d. dull blue and brown-lake	10·00	2·00
		a. Dull blue and pale claret (5.94)	12·00	6·00
D 5		5d. dull blue and brown-lake	9·00	2·00
D 6		6d. dull blue and brown-lake	11·00	2·00
D 7		10d. dull blue and brown-lake	70·00	38·00
D 8		1s. dull blue and brown-lake	48·00	6·50
D 9		2s. dull blue and brown-lake	£110	48·00
D10		5s. dull blue and brown-lake	£160	90·00
D1/10			Set of 10	£375	£160
D1a/10		Optd "Specimen"	Set of 10	£300	

A used example of the 6d. showing compound perforation of 12×12½ and 11 exists in the Royal Collection.

1895 (17 Jan)–**96**. *Colours changed. Wmk V over Crown, W 33. P 12×12½.*
D11	D 1	½d. rosine and bluish green	3·50	1·60
		a. Pale scarlet and yellow-green (3.96)	3·50	1·50
D12		1d. rosine and bluish green	3·00	60
		a. Pale scarlet and yellow-green (3.96)	3·25	70

D13	D 1	2d. rosine and bluish green	4·50	70
		a. Pale scarlet and yellow-green (3.96)	5·00	80
D14		4d. rosine and bluish green	8·50	1·50
		a. Pale scarlet and yellow-green (3.96)	9·50	1·00
D15		5d. rosine and bluish green	8·00	7·00
		a. Pale scarlet and yellow-green (3.96)	8·50	4·75
D16		6d. rosine and bluish green	8·00	3·25
D17		10d. rosine and bluish green	15·00	10·00
D18		1s. rosine and bluish green	11·00	3·25
D19		2s. pale red & yellowish green (28.3.95)	60·00	20·00
D20		5s. pale red & yellowish green (28.3.95)	£100	40·00
D11/20			Set of 10	£180	75·00

1897 (July)–**99**. *Wmk V over Crown. W 82. P 12×12½.*
D21	D 1	1d. pale scarlet and yellow-green	4·50	80
		a. Dull red and bluish green (8.99)	6·50	75
D22		2d. pale scarlet and yellow-green	6·50	90
		a. Dull red and bluish green (6.99)	7·50	75
D23		4d. pale scarlet and yellow-green	10·00	2·25
		a. Dull red and bluish green (8.99)	14·00	1·25
D24		5d. pale scarlet and yellow-green	10·00	2·75
D25		6d. pale scarlet and yellow-green	7·50	3·00
D21/5			Set of 5	35·00	7·50

1900 (June)–**04**. *Wmk V over Crown. W 85. P 12×12½.*
D26	D 1	1d. rose-red and pale green	5·00	4·00
		a. Pale red and deep green (8.01)	3·75	3·50
		b. Scarlet and deep green (1.03)	—	22·00
		c. Aniline rosine and green (6.04)	5·50	6·50
D27		1d. rose-red and pale green	5·50	75
		a. Pale red and deep green (9.01)	5·00	35
		b. Scarlet and deep green (2.02)	6·00	50
		c. Aniline rosine and green (9.03)	5·50	85
D28		2d. rose-red and pale green (7.00)	7·00	75
		a. Pale red and deep green (9.01)	7·50	70
		b. Scarlet and deep green (2.02)	7·00	50
		c. Aniline rosine and green (9.03)	7·00	85
D29		4d. rose-red and pale green (5.01)	15·00	4·00
		a. Pale red and deep green (9.01)	14·00	1·75
		b. Scarlet and deep green (6.03)	14·00	2·50
		c. Aniline rosine and green (6.04)	15·00	3·00
D30		5d. scarlet and deep green (1.03)	11·00	5·00
D31		1s. scarlet and deep green (3.02)	16·00	5·00
D32		2s. scarlet and deep green (1.03)	£110	65·00
D33		5s. scarlet and deep green (1.03)	£130	65·00
D26/33			Set of 8	£250	£130

1905 (Dec)–**09**. *Wmk Crown over A, W w 11. P 12×12½.*
D34	D 1	½d. aniline rosine and pale green (1.06)	8·00	8·00
		a. Scarlet & pale yellow-green (7.07)	3·75	4·00
		b. Dull scarlet and pea-green (3.09)	5·50	4·50
		ba. Compound perf 12×12½ and 11	42·00	95·00
D35		1d. aniline rosine and pale green	35·00	4·75
		a. Scarlet & pale yellow-green (5.06)	5·50	1·50
		b. Dull scarlet and pea-green (1.07)	8·50	1·50
D36		2d. aniline scarlet & dp yell-grn (5.06)	7·50	1·75
		a. Dull scarlet and pea-green (11.07)	8·50	1·50
D37		4d. dull scarlet and pea-green (1908)	18·00	7·50
D34/7			Set of 4	32·00	13·00

A printing of the 5d. in dull scarlet and pea-green on this paper was prepared in 1907–08, but not put into use. A few examples have survived, either mint or cancelled-to-order from presentation sets (*Price £1000 mint, £750 cancelled-to-order*).

WESTERN AUSTRALIA

PRICES FOR STAMPS ON COVER	
Nos. 1/6	from × 6
Nos. 15/32	from × 4
Nos. 33/46	from × 5
Nos. 49/51	from × 6
Nos. 52/62	from × 10
Nos. 63/a	from × 8
No. 67	from × 6
Nos. 68/92a	from × 10
Nos. 94/102	from × 40
Nos. 103/5	from × 8
Nos. 107/10a	from × 12
Nos. 111a/b	—
Nos. 112/16	from × 25
Nos. 117/25	from × 10
Nos. 126/8	—
Nos. 129/34	from × 8
Nos. 135/6	—
Nos. 138/48	from × 12
Nos. 151/63	from × 5
Nos. 168/9	from × 20
Nos. 170/1	from × 4
Nos. 172/3	from × 40
Nos. F11/22	from × 10
Nos. T1/2	

SPECIMEN OVERPRINTS. Those listed are from U.P.U. distributions between 1889 and 1892. Further "Specimen" overprints exist, but those were used for other purposes.

1   2

---

3   4

GUM. The 1854 issues are hardly ever seen with gum and so the unused prices quoted are for examples without gum.

(Eng W. Humphrys. Recess P.B.)
1854 (1 Aug). *W 4 (sideways). (a) Imperf.*
1	1	1d. black	£800	£180

(b) Rouletted 7½ to 14 and compound
2	1	1d. black	£1300	£375

In addition to the supplies received from London a further printing, using the original plate and watermarked paper from Perkins, Bacon, was made in the colony before the date of issue. The 1d. is also known pin-perforated.

(Litho H. Samson (later A. Hillman), Government Lithographer)
1854 (1 Aug)–**55**. *W 4 (sideways). (a) Imperf.*
3	2	4d. pale blue	£225	£150
		a. Blue	£225	£150
		b. Deep dull blue	£1200	£600
		c. Slate-blue (1855)	£1300	£700
4	3	1s. salmon	—	£1600
		a. Deep red-brown	£900	£425
		b. Grey-brown (1.55)	£450	£325
		c. Pale brown (1.55)	£325	£275

(b) Rouletted 7½ to 14 and compound
5	2	4d. pale blue	£1200	£425
		a. Blue	—	£425
		b. Slate-blue (1855)	—	£1100
6	3	1s. grey-brown (1.55)	£1500	£700
		a. Pale brown (10.55)	£1500	£700

The 1s. is also known pin-perforated.
The 4d. value was prepared from the Perkins, Bacon 1d. plate. A block of 60 (5 × 12) was taken as a transfer from this plate, the frames painted out and then individually replaced by transfers taken from a single impression master plate of the frame. Four transfers were then taken from this completed intermediate stone to construct the printing stone of 240 impressions. This first printing stone was used by H. Samson to print the initial supplies in July 1854.

The intermediate stone had carried several transfer errors, the most prominent of which was the "T" of "POSTAGE" sliced at foot, which appeared on four positions of the printing stone.

3d. "T" of "POSTAGE" shaved off to a point at foot (R.7/5, 7/10, 7/15, 7/20)	£750	£550

The original printing stone also contained three scarce creased transfers, whose exact positions in the sheet have yet to be established. These were corrected during the first printing.
3e. Top of letters of "AUSTRALIA" cut off so that they are barely 1 mm high	—	£6000
f. "PEICE" instead of "PENCE"	—	£6000
g. "CE" of "Pence" close together	—	£8000

Further supplies were required in January 1855 and A. Hillman, Samson's successor, found, after printing three further sheets from the first printing stone, that two of the impressions on the intermediate stone were defective giving one inverted and one tilted frame. A second printing stone was then prepared on which the four positions of the inverted frame were individually corrected.

3h. Frame inverted (R.8/1, 8/6, 8/11, 8/16)	†	£60000
i. Tilted border (R.7/4, 7/9, 7/14, 7/19)	£850	£600

None of the creased transfers from the first printing stone appear on the second, which exhibits its own range of similar varieties.

3j. "WEST" in squeezed-down letters and "F" of "FOUR" with pointed foot (R.2/17)	£900	£650
k. "ESTERN" in squeezed-down letters and "U" of "FOUR" squeezed-up (R.3/17)	£1500	£1100
l. Small "S" in "POSTAGE" (R.4/17)	£900	£650
m. "EN" of "PENCE" shorter (R.6/4)	£800	£600
n. "N" of "PENCE" tilted to right with thin first downstroke (R.6/16)	£800	£600
o. Swan and water above "ENCE" damaged (R.6/20)	£800	£600
p. "F" of "FOUR" slanting to left (R.7/17)	£800	£600
q. "WESTERN" in squeezed-down letters only 1½ mm high (R.8/17)	£950	£700
r. "P" of "PENCE" with small head (R.9/15)	£800	£600
s. "RALIA" in squeezed-down letters only 1½ mm high (R.9/16)	£900	£650
t. "PE" of "PENCE" close together (R.10/15)	£800	£600
u. "N" of "PENCE" narrow (R.10/16)	£800	£600
v. Part of right cross-stroke and down-stroke of "T" of "POSTAGE" cut off (R.11/15)	£800	£600
w. "A" in "POSTAGE" with thin right limb (R.11/16)	£800	£600

For the third printing in October 1855 the impressions showing the inverted frame were replaced on the printing stone with fresh individual transfers of the frame. On two of the positions traces of the original frame transfer remained visible.

3x. Coloured line above "AGE" of "POSTAGE" (R.8/6)	£800	£600
y. No outer line above "GE" of "POSTAGE" and coloured line under "FOU" of "FOUR" (R.8/11)	£850	£650

The same stone was used for a further printing in December 1855 and it is believed that the slate-blue shade occurred from one of the 1855 printings.

The above varieties, with the exception of Nos. 3e/g, also occur on the rouletted stamps.

The 1s. value was produced in much the same way, based on a transfer from the Perkins, Bacon 1d. plate.

5

(Litho A. Hillman, Government Lithographer)

1857 (7 Aug)–**59.** W **4** (*sideways*). (*a*) *Imperf.*

15	**5**	2d. brown-black/*red* (26.2.58)	..	£1700	£500
		a. Printed both sides ..	..	£1900	£800
16		2d. brown-black/*Indian red* (26.2.58)		—	£800
		a. Printed both sides ..	..	£1700	£850
17		6d. golden bronze	..	£4500	£1400
18		6d. black-bronze	..	£2500	£600
19		6d. grey-black (1859) ..	..	£2500	£500

(*b*) *Rouletted* 7½ *to* 14 *and compound*

20	**5**	2d. brown-black/*red*	..	£3250	£1200
		a. Printed both sides ..	..	—	£1400
21		2d. brown-black/*Indian red*	..		£1300
22		6d. black-bronze	..	£3250	£800
23		6d. grey-black	..		£850

The 2d. and 6d. are known pin-perforated.
Prices quoted for Nos. 15/23 are for "cut-square" examples.
Collectors are warned against "cut-round" copies with corners added.

(Recess in the colony from P.B. plates)

1860 (11 Aug)–**64.** W **4** (*sideways*). (*a*) *Imperf.*

24	**1**	2d. pale orange	..	70·00	55·00
25		2d. orange-vermilion	..	70·00	55·00
25b		2d. deep vermilion	..	£250	£300
26		4d. blue (21.6.64)	..	£200	£1400
		a. Wmk upright	..	£225	
27		4d. deep blue	..	£200	£1500
28		6d. sage-green (27.7.61)	..	£1100	£400
28a		6d. deep sage-green	..	—	£500

(*b*) *Rouletted* 7½ *to* 14

29	**1**	2d. pale orange	..	£350	£150
30		2d. orange-vermilion	..	£425	£160
31		4d. deep blue	..	£1900	
32		6d. sage-green	..	£1600	£425

PERKINS BACON "CANCELLED". For notes on these handstamps, showing "CANCELLED" between horizontal bars forming an oval, see Catalogue Introduction.

(Recess P.B.)

1861. W **4** (*sideways*). (*a*) *Intermediate perf* 14–16.

33	**1**	1d. rose	..	£300	90·00
34		2d. blue	..	£130	38·00
35		4d. vermilion	..	£500	£1300
36		6d. purple-brown	..	£325	60·00
37		1s. yellow-green	..	£425	£110

(*b*) P 14 *at Somerset House*

38	**1**	1d. rose	..	£160	45·00
39		2d. blue	..	70·00	28·00
40		4d. vermilion	..	£150	£120

(*c*) *Perf clean-cut* 14–16

41	**1**	2d. blue	..	60·00	24·00
		a. Imperf between (pair)	..		
42		6d. purple-brown	..	£180	38·00
43		1s. yellow-green	..	£300	50·00

(*d*) P 14–16 *very rough* (July)

44	**1**	1d. rose-carmine (H/S "CANCELLED" in oval £5000)	..	£180	32·00
45		6d. purple/*blued* (H/S "CANCELLED" in oval £4000)	..	£750	£150
46		1s. deep green (H/S "CANCELLED" in oval £4000)	..	£950	£200

Perkins, Bacon experienced considerable problems with their perforating machine during the production of these stamps.

The initial printing showed intermediate perforation 14–16. Further supplies were then sent, in late December 1860, to Somerset House to be perforated on their comb 14 machine. The Inland Revenue Board were only able to process the three lower values, although the 6d. purple-brown and 1s. yellow-green are known from this perforation overprinted "SPECIMEN".

The Perkins, Bacon machine was repaired the following month and the 6d., 1s. and a further supply of the 2d. were perforated on it to give a clean-cut 14–16 gauge.

A final printing was produced in July 1861, but by this time the machine had deteriorated so that it produced a very rough 14–16.

(Recess D.L.R. from P.B. plates)

1863 (16 Dec)–**64.** *No wmk.* P 13.

49	**1**	1d. carmine-rose	..	48·00	3·50
50		1d. lake	..	48·00	3·50
51		6d. deep lilac (15.4.64)	..	95·00	38·00
51a		6d. dull violet (15.4.64)	..	£140	42·00

Both values exist on thin and on thick papers, the former being the scarcer.

Both grades of paper show a marginal sheet watermark, "T H SAUNDERS 1860" in double-lined large and small capitals, but parts of this watermark rarely occur on the stamps.

(Recess D.L.R. from P.B. plates)

1864 (27 Dec)–**79.** *Wmk Crown CC* (*sideways on* 1d.). P 12½.

52	**1**	1d. bistre	..	50·00	3·00
53		1d. yellow-ochre (16.10.74)	..	65·00	6·50
54		2d. chrome-yellow (18.1.65)	..	50·00	1·25
55		2d. yellow	..	50·00	1·25
		a. Wmk sideways (5.79)	..	—	15·00
		b. Error. Mauve (1879)	..	£5500	£4000
56		4d. carmine (18.1.65)	..	60·00	4·00
		a. Doubly printed	..	£5000	
57		6d. violet (18.1.65)	..	70·00	6·00
		a. Doubly printed	..	† £7000	
		b. Wmk sideways	..		£150
58		6d. indigo-violet	..	£275	28·00
59		6d. lilac (1872) ..	..	£130	6·00
60		6d. mauve (12.5.75)	..	£120	6·00
61		1s. bright green (18.1.65) (H/S S. £85)	..	95·00	12·00
62		1s. sage-green (10.68)	..	£225	23·00

Beware of fakes of No. 55b made by altering the value tablet of No. 60.

7

ONE PENNY

(**8**)

(Typo D.L.R.)

1871 (29 Oct)–**73.** *Wmk Crown CC* (*sideways*). P 14.

63	**7**	3d. pale brown (H/S S. £75)	..	32·00	4·00
		a. Cinnamon (1873)	..	32·00	3·50

1874 (10 Dec). *No. 55 surch with* T **8** *by Govt Printer.*

67	**1**	1d. on 2d. yellow (G.)	..	£170	45·00
		a. Pair, one without surch	..		
		b. Surch triple	..	† £2000	
		c. "O" of "ONE" omitted	..		

Forged surcharges of T **8** are known on stamps wmk Crown CC perf 14, and on Crown CA, perf 12 and 14.

(Recess D.L.R. from P.B. plates)

1876–81. *Wmk Crown CC* (*sideways*). P 14.

68	**1**	1d. ochre	..	48·00	1·75
69		1d. bistre (1878)	..	70·00	2·75
70		1d. yellow-ochre (1879)	..	50·00	90
71		2d. chrome-yellow	..	48·00	50
		a. Wmk upright (1877)	..	70·00	1·25
74		4d. carmine (1881)	..	£325	75·00
75		6d. lilac (1877)	..	90·00	3·25
		a. Wmk upright (1879)	..	£450	15·00
75b		6d. reddish lilac (1879)	..	90·00	5·50

(Recess D.L.R. from P.B. plates)

1882 (Mar)–**85.** *Wmk Crown CA* (*sideways*). (*a*) P 14.

76	**1**	1d. yellow-ochre	..	17·00	50
77		2d. chrome-yellow	..	22·00	50
		a. Wmk upright	..	†	—
78		4d. carmine (8.82)	..	85·00	6·50
		a. Wmk upright (1885)	..	—	25·00
79		6d. reddish lilac (1882)	..	70·00	3·00
80		6d. lilac (1884) (H/S S. £75)	..	70·00	4·00

(*b*) P 12 × 14

81	**1**	1d. yellow-ochre (2.83)	..	£1200	£150

(*c*) P 12

82	**1**	1d. yellow-ochre (2.83)	..	60·00	2·25
83		2d. chrome-yellow (6.83)	..	75·00	2·25
		a. Imperf between (pair)	..		
84		4d. carmine (5.83)	..	£130	26·00
85		6d. lilac (6.83)	..	£225	26·00

(Typo D.L.R.)

1882 (July)–**95.** *Wmk Crown CA* (*sideways*). P 14.

86	**7**	3d. pale brown	..	14·00	1·50
87		3d. red-brown (12.95)	..	8·50	1·00

The 3d. stamps in other colours, watermark Crown CA and perforated 12, are colour trials dating from 1883.

½
(**9**)

1d.
(**10**)

1d.
(**11**)

1884 (19 Feb). *Surch with* T **9**, *in red, by Govt Printer.*

89	**1**	½ on 1d. yellow-ochre (No. 76)	..	14·00	18·00
		a. Thin bar	..	70·00	85·00
90		½ on 1d. yellow-ochre (No. 82)	..	9·00	14·00

Inverted or double surcharges are forgeries made in London about 1886.

The "Thin bar" varieties occur on R12/3, R12/8, R12/13 and R12/18, and show the bar only 0.2 mm thick.

1885 (May). *Nos.* 63/a *surch, in green, by Govt Printer.*

(*a*) *Thick* "1" *with slanting top,* T **10** (*Horizontal Rows* 1/5)

91		1d. on 3d. pale brown	..	48·00	10·00
		a. Cinnamon	..	40·00	8·00
		b. Vert pair. Nos. 91/2 ..	..	£160	

(*b*) *Thin* "1" *with straight top,* T **11** (*Horizontal Row* 6)

92		1d. on 3d. pale brown	..	£120	22·00
		a. Cinnamon	..	90·00	23·00

12   **13**

14   **15**

(Typo D.L.R.)

1885 (May)–**93.** *Wmk Crown CA* (*sideways*). P 14.

94	**12**	½d. yellow-green	..	3·25	40
94a		½d. green	..	3·25	40
95	**13**	1d. carmine (2.90)	..	14·00	10
96		2d. bluish grey (6.90)	..	20·00	40
96a		2d. grey	..	19·00	40

97	**15**	2½d. deep blue (1.5.92)	..	8·50	35
97a		2½d. blue	..	8·00	35
98		4d. chestnut (7.90)	..	8·00	40
99		5d. bistre (1.5.92)	..	8·00	2·75
100		6d. bright violet (1.93)	..	15·00	1·00
101		1s. pale olive-green (4.90)	..	22·00	3·00
102		1s. olive-green	..	17·00	3·00
94, 96a, 97a/99, 101 Optd/H/S "Specimen"			*Set of* 6	£225	

(Recess D.L.R. from P.B. plates)

1888 (Mar–Apr). *Wmk Crown CA* (*sideways*). P 14.

103	**1**	1d. carmine-pink	..	14·00	2·00
104		2d. grey	..	38·00	1·00
105		4d. red-brown (April)	..	70·00	18·00
103/5 H/S "Specimen"			*Set of* 3	£150	

ONE PENNY   **Half-penny**

(**16**)   (**17**)

1893 (Feb). *Surch with* T **16**, *in green, by Govt Printer.*

107	**7**	1d. on 3d. pale brown (No. 63)	..	11·00	2·75
108		1d. on 3d. cinnamon (No. 63a)	..	11·00	3·00
		a. Double surcharge	..	£600	
109		1d. on 3d. pale brown (No. 86)	..	32·00	4·25

1895 (21 Nov). *Surch with* T **17** *by Govt Printer.* (*a*) *In green.*

110	**7**	½d. on 3d. pale brown (No. 63)	..	7·50	19·00
110a		½d. on 3d. cinnamon (No. 63a)	..	5·50	18·00
		b. Surcharge double	..	£400	

(*b*) *In red and in green*

111a	**7**	½d. on 3d. cinnamon (No. 63a)	..	70·00	£150
111b		½d. on 3d. red-brown (No. 87)	..	50·00	90·00

Green was the adopted surcharge colour but a trial had earlier been made in red on stamps watermarked Crown CC. As they proved unsatisfactory they were given another surcharge in green. The trial stamps were inadvertently issued and, to prevent speculation, a further printing of the duplicated surcharge was made, but on both papers, Crown CC (No. 111a) and Crown CA (No. 111b).

18   **19**

20   **21**

(Typo D.L.R.)

1898 (Dec)–**1907.** *Wmk W Crown A, W* **18**. P 14.

112	**13**	1d. carmine	..	4·50	10
113	**14**	2d. bright yellow (1.99)	..	11·00	1·40
114	**19**	2½d. blue (1.01)	..	8·00	30
115	**20**	6d. bright violet (10.06)	..	19·00	50
116	**21**	1s. olive-green (4.07)	..	22·00	3·50

22   **23**   **24**

25   **26**   **27**

28   **29**   **30**

31   **32**   **33**

(Typo Victoria Govt Printer, Melbourne, Commonwealth Stamp Ptg Branch from March, 1909)

1902 (Oct)–**12.** *Wmk V and Crown, W 33 (sideways on horiz designs).*

(a) P 12½ or 12½ × 12 (horiz), 12 × 12½ (vert)

117	22	1d. carmine-rose (1.03)		9·50	10
118	23	a. Wmk upright (10.02)		13·00	30
		2d. yellow (4.1.03)		9·50	1·40
		a. Wmk upright (12.7.04)		—	1·75
119	24	4d. chestnut (4.03)		9·50	90
		a. Wmk upright		£160	
120	15	5d. bistre (4.9.05)		70·00	42·00
121	25	8d. apple-green (3.03)		18·00	2·50
122	26	9d. yellow-orange (5.03)		27·00	5·00
		a. Wmk upright (11.03)		38·00	14·00
123	27	10d. red (3.03)		30·00	4·50
124	28	2s. bright red/*yellow*		75·00	16·00
		a. Wmk sideways		£150	16·00
		b. *Orange/yellow* (7.06)		40·00	8·50
		c. *Brown-red/yellow* (5.11)		40·00	8·50
125	29	2s. 6d. deep blue/*rose*		40·00	8·00
126	30	5s. emerald-green		60·00	19·00
127	31	10s. deep mauve		£140	60·00
		a. *Bright purple* (1910)		£160	85·00
128	32	£1 orange-brown (1.11.02)		£275	£150
		a. *Orange* (10.7.09)		£550	£250

(b) P 11

129	22	1d. carmine-rose		85·00	11·00
		a. Wmk upright			
130	23	2d. yellow		£110	13·00
		a. Wmk upright			
131	24	4d. chestnut		£450	£130
132	15	5d. bistre		45·00	28·00
133	26	9d. yellow-orange		65·00	50·00
134	28	2s. bright red/*yellow*		£120	75·00
		a. *Orange/yellow*		£225	£110

(c) Perf compound of 12½ or 12 and 11

135	22	1d. carmine-rose		£375	£180
136	23	2d. yellow		£450	£225
137	24	4d. chestnut			

Type **22** is similar to Type **13** but larger.

34	35

1905–12. *Wmk Crown and A, W 34 (sideways).*

(a) P 12½ or 12½ × 12 (horiz), 12 × 12½ (vert)

138	12	½d. green (6.10)		4·00	3·00
139	22	1d. rose-pink (10.05)		7·00	20
		a. Wmk upright (1.06)		6·50	20
		b. *Carmine* (1909)		8·50	30
		c. *Carmine-red* (1912)		9·50	4·50
140	23	2d. yellow (15.11.05)		6·00	1·50
		a. Wmk upright (4.10)			
141	7	3d. brown (2.06)		12·00	50
142	24	4d. bistre-brown (12.06)		12·00	3·25
		a. *Pale chestnut* (1908)		12·00	2·75
		b. *Bright brown-red* (14.10.10)		9·50	90
143	15	5d. pale olive-bistre (8.05)		13·00	3·00
		a. *Olive-green* (1.09)		13·00	3·00
		b. *Pale greenish yellow* (5.12)		55·00	55·00
144	25	8d. apple-green (22.4.12)		18·00	30·00
145	26	9d. orange (11.5.06)		23·00	3·50
		a. *Red-orange* (6.10)		32·00	3·50
		b. Wmk upright (7.12)		38·00	24·00
146	27	10d. rose (26.2.10)		22·00	13·00
148	30	5s. emerald-grn (*wmk upright*) (9.07)		75·00	55·00

(b) P 11

150	12	½d. green			
151	22	1d. rose-pink		22·00	5·50
		a. *Carmine-red*		22·00	4·50
		b. Wmk upright		22·00	9·50
152	23	2d. yellow		20·00	8·50
153	7	3d. brown		14·00	2·00
154	24	4d. yellow-brown		£475	£130
		a. *Pale chestnut*			
155	15	5d. pale olive-bistre		28·00	10·00
		a. *Olive-green*		16·00	10·00
157	26	9d. orange		75·00	80·00
		a. *Red-orange*		—	65·00
		b. Wmk upright (1912)		†	£325

(c) Perf compound of 12½ or 12 and 11

161	22	1d. rose-pink (*wmk upright*)		£225	£110
162	23	2d. yellow		£180	95·00
163	7	3d. brown		£275	£160
164	26	9d. red-orange			

1912 (Mar). *Wmk Crown and A (sideways). W 35. P 11½ × 12.*

168	20	6d. bright violet		11·00	3·75
169	21	1s. sage-green		26·00	5·50
		a. Perf 12½ (single line)		—	£250

1912 (7 Aug). *W 34 (sideways). Thin paper and white gum (as Victoria).*

170	7	3d. brown (p 12½)		45·00	45·00
		a. Wmk upright			
171		3d. brown (p 11)			
		a. Wmk upright			

ONE PENNY
(36)

1912 (6 Nov). *Nos. 140 and 162 surch with T 36 in Melbourne.*

(a) P 12½ or 12 × 12½

172	23	1d. on 2d. yellow		80	30
		a. Wmk upright		2·25	2·25

(b) Perf compound of 12½ and 11

173	23	1d. on 2d. yellow		£300	

STAMP BOOKLETS

There are very few surviving examples of Nos. SB1/4. Listings are provided for those believed to have been issued with prices quoted for those known to still exist.

1904 (1 Jan)–**09.** *Black on red cover as No. SB1 of New South Wales. Stapled.*
SB1 £1 booklet containing two hundred and forty 1d. in four blocks of 30 and two blocks of 60
   a. Red on pink cover (1909) .. £6000
   b. Blue on pink cover

1904 (1 Jan). *Black on grey cover as No. SB1. Stapled.*
SB2 £1 booklet containing one hundred and twenty 2d. in four blocks of 30

1910 (May). *Black on white cover as No. SB3 of New South Wales. Stapled.*
SB3 2s. booklet containing eleven ½d. (No. 138), either in block of 6 plus block of 5 or block of 11, and eighteen 1d. (No. 139) either in three blocks of 6 or block of 6 plus block of 12 .. £2000
Unsold stock of No. SB3 was uprated with one additional ½d. in May 1911.

1911 (Aug). *Red on pink cover as No. SB3. Stapled.*
SB4 2s. booklet containing twelve ½d. (No. 138), either in two blocks of 6 or block of 12, and eighteen 1d. (No. 139), either in three blocks of 6 or block of 6 plus block of 12 .. £1500

POSTAL FISCAL STAMPS

By the Post and Telegraph Act of 5 September 1893 the current issue of fiscal stamps up to and including the 1s. value, Nos. F11/15, was authorised for postal use.

These stamps had been initially supplied, for fiscal purposes, in February 1882 and had been preceded by a series of "I R" surcharges and overprints on postage stamps which were in use for a period of about six months. Examples of these 1881–82 provisionals can be found postally used under the terms of the 1893 Act but, as they had not been current for fiscal purposes for over eleven years, we no longer list them.

WESTERN AUSTRALIA INTERNAL REVENUE ONE PENNY

F 3

(Typo D.L.R.)

1893 (5 Sept). *Definitive fiscal stamps of Feb 1882. Wmk CA over Crown. P 14.*

F11	F 3	1d. dull purple		9·00	1·25
F12		2d. dull purple		90·00	35·00
F13		3d. dull purple		35·00	2·00
F14		6d. dull purple		38·00	3·50
F15		1s. dull purple		70·00	5·50

The 1s. value is as Type F 3 but with rectangular outer frame and circular frame surrounding swan.

Higher values in this series were not validated by the Act for postal use.

Two varieties of watermark exist on these stamps. Initial supplies showed an indistinct watermark with the base of the "A" 4 mm wide. From 1896 the paper used showed a clearer watermark on which the base of the "A" was 5 mm wide.

1897. *Wmk W Crown A, W 18. P 14.*

F19	F 3	1d. dull purple		5·50	1·25
F20		3d. dull purple		26·00	2·00
F21		6d. dull purple		26·00	2·00
F22	—	1s. dull purple		65·00	8·50

TELEGRAPH STAMPS USED FOR POSTAGE

The 1d. Telegraph stamps were authorised for postal purposes from 25 October 1886.

WESTERN AUSTRALIA TELEGRAPH ONE PENNY

T 1

1886 (25 Oct). *Wmk Crown CC.*

T1	T 1	1d. bistre (p 12½)		23·00	3·00
T2		1d. bistre (p 14)		25·00	4·00

Copies of a similar 6d. value are known postally used, but such use was unauthorised.

OFFICIAL STAMPS

Stamps of the various issues from 1854–85 are found with a circular hole punched out, the earlier size being about 3 mm. in diameter and the later 4 mm. These were used on official correspondence by the Commissariat and Convict Department, branches of the Imperial administration separate from the colonial government. This system of punching ceased by 1886. Subsequently many stamps between Nos. 94 and 148 may be found punctured, "PWD", "WA" or "OS".

Western Australia became part of the Commonwealth of Australia on 1 January 1901.

COMMONWEALTH OF AUSTRALIA

On 1 March 1901 control of the postal service passed to the federal administration although it was not until 13 October 1910 that the issues of the various states became valid for use throughout Australia. Postal rates were standardised on 1 May 1911.

The first national postage due stamps appeared in July 1902, but it was not until January 1913 that postage stamps inscribed "AUSTRALIA" were issued.

PRICES FOR STAMPS ON COVER TO 1945	
Nos. 1/19	*from* × 4
Nos. 20/3	*from* × 2
Nos. 24/30	*from* × 4
Nos. 35/47f	*from* × 3
Nos. 51/5a	*from* × 4
Nos. 55b/75	*from* × 3
Nos. 76/84	*from* × 4
Nos. 85/104	*from* × 3
Nos. 105/6	*from* × 4
Nos. 107/15	*from* × 3
No. 116	*from* × 5
Nos. 117/20	*from* × 4
Nos. 121/39a	*from* × 2
Nos. 140/a	*from* × 5
Nos. 141/4	*from* × 3
No. 146	*from* × 6
Nos. 147/53	*from* × 3
Nos. 153a/b	*from* × 2
Nos. 154/63	*from* × 3
Nos. 164/211	*from* × 2
Nos. D1/118	*from* × 8
Nos. O123/36	*from* × 5

PRINTERS. Except where otherwise stated, all Commonwealth stamps to No. 581 were printed under Government authority at Melbourne. Until 1918 there were two establishments (both of the Treasury Dept)—the Note Printing Branch and the Stamp Printing Branch. The former printed T 3 and 4.

In 1918 the Stamp Printing Branch was closed and all stamps were printed by the Note Printing Branch. In 1926 control was transferred from the Treasury to the Commonwealth Bank of Australia, and on 14 January 1960 the branch was attached to the newly established Reserve Bank of Australia.

Until 1942 stamps bore in the sheet margin the initials or names of successive managers and from 1942 to March 1952 the imprint "Printed by the Authority of the Government of the Commonwealth of Australia". After November 1952 (or Nos. D129/31 for Postage Dues) imprints were discontinued.

SPECIMEN OVERPRINTS. These come from Specimen sets, first made available to the public on 15 December 1913. In these sets the lower values were cancelled-to-order, but stamps with a face value of 7s. 6d. or 75 c. were overprinted "Specimen" in different types. These overprints are listed as they could be purchased from the Australian Post Office.

It is, however, believed that examples of No. 112 overprinted "Specimen" were distributed by the U.P.U. in 1929. Supplies of the 1902 and 1902–04 postage due stamps overprinted "Specimen" were supplied to the U.P.U. by some of the states.

The sale of the cancelled-to-order sets ceased after 1966, but high value "Specimen" overprints were retained until the end of 1994 to support philatelic funds.

1	2

Die I	Die II

Dies of Type 1 (mono-coloured values only):—

Die I.   Break in inner frame line at lower left level with top of words of value.

Die II.   Die repaired showing no break.

Die I was only used for the ½d., 1d., 2d. and 3d. Several plates were produced for each except the 3d. When the second plate of the 3d. was being prepared the damage became aggravated after making 105 out of the 120 units when the die was returned for repair. This gave rise to the *se-tenant* pairs showing the two states of the die.

Die II was used until 1945 and deteriorated progressively with damage to the frame lines and rounding of the corners.

Specialists recognise seven states of this die, but we only list the two most major of the later versions.

Die IIA. This state is as Die II, but, in addition, shows a break in the inner left-hand frame line, 9 mm from the top of the design (occurs on 1d., 2d. and 6d.).

Die IIB. As Die IIA, but now also showing break in outer frame line above "ST", and (not illustrated) an incomplete corner to the inner frame line at top right (occurs on 3d., 6d., 9d., 1s. and £1 (No. 75)).

(Des B. Young. Eng S. Reading. Typo J. B. Cooke)

1913 (2 Jan)–**14.** W 2. P 12.
1	1	½d. green (Die I) (16.1.13)		6·00	3·00
		a. Printed on the gummed side		£1000	
		bw. Wmk inverted		25·00	9·00
		c. Wmk sideways		† £3500	
2		1d. red (Die I)		8·50	1·00
		a. Wmk sideways		£600	£110
		b. *Carmine*		8·50	1·00
		cw. Wmk inverted		22·00	2·75
		d. Die II. *Red* (16.1.13)		9·00	1·00
		da. Wmk sideways		£650	£120
		db. *Carmine*		8·50	1·00
		dw. Wmk inverted		22·00	2·75
		e. Die IIA. *Red* (4.14)		15·00	1·25
		eb. *Carmine*		15·00	1·25
		ew. Wmk inverted		30·00	3·50
3		2d. grey (Die I) (15.1.13)		28·00	4·50
		w. Wmk inverted		50·00	10·00
4		2½d. indigo (Die II) (27.1.13)		29·00	13·00
5		3d. olive (Die I) (1.2.13)		48·00	8·00
		a. Imperf three sides (horiz pair)		£12000	
		b. In pair with Die II		£450	£170
		c. *Yellow-olive*		48·00	9·50
		ca. In pair with Die II		£450	£170
		dw. Wmk inverted		65·00	18·00
		e. Die II. *Olive*		£160	50·00
		ea. *Yellow-olive*		£160	50·00
		ew. Wmk inverted		£200	75·00
6		4d. orange (Die II) (15.2.13)		50·00	22·00
		a. *Orange-yellow*		£170	48·00
8		5d. chestnut (Die II) (18.1.13)		40·00	32·00
9		6d. ultramarine (Die II) (18.1.13)		48·00	20·00
		a. Retouched "E"		£1500	£500
		b. Die IIA (substituted cliché) (11.13)		£1100	£375
		w. Wmk inverted		£120	55·00
10		9d. violet (Die II) (1.2.13)		45·00	22·00
		w. Wmk inverted			
11		1s. emerald (Die II) (25.1.13)		45·00	16·00
		a. *Blue-green*		50·00	16·00
		w. Wmk inverted		£150	48·00
12		2s. brown (Die II) (30.1.13)		£160	65·00
13		5s. grey and yellow (Die II) (20.3.13)		£250	£140
14		10s. grey and pink (Die II) (20.3.13)		£600	£450
15		£1 brown & ultram (Die II) (20.3.13)		£1000	£1000
16		£2 black and rose (Die II) (8.4.13)		£2250	£1600
1/16			*Set of 15*	£3000	£3000
14/16		Optd "Specimen"	*Set of 3*	£600	

Three examples, all used, are known of No. 1c.

The 3d. was printed from two plates, one of which contained 105 stamps as Die I and 15 as Die II. The other plate contained Die I stamps only.

No. 5a. shows the stamp perforated at foot only. Examples are known from the top or bottom rows of different sheets.

No. 9a shows a badly distorted second "E" in "PENCE", which is unmistakable. It occurs on the Upper plate right pane R. 10/6 and was replaced by a substitute cliché in the November 1913 printing.

See also Nos. 24/30 (W 5), 35/45b (W 6), 73/5 (W 6, new colours), 107/14 (W 7), 132/8 (W 15), 212 (2s. re-engraved).

3

4 Laughing Kookaburra

(Des R. A. Harrison. Eng and recess T. S. Harrison)

1913 (8 Dec)–**14.** *No wmk.* P 11.
17	3	1d. red		2·50	4·50
		a. Imperf between (horiz pair)		£1700	
		b. Imperf horiz (vert pair)		£1300	
		c. *Pale rose-red*		7·00	10·00
		ca. Imperf between (vert pair)		£1500	
		cb. Imperf between (horiz pair)		£1900	
19	4	6d. claret (26.8.14)		70·00	38·00

All printings from Plate 1 of the 1d. were in the shade of No. 17c. This plate shows many retouches.

5   5a

1d. Die II

1d. Die II. The flaw distinguishing the so-called Die II, a white upward spur to the right of the base of the "1" in the left value tablet, is now known to be due to a defective roller-die. It occurred on all stamps in the second and third vertical rows of upper left plate right pane. Each of the twenty defective impressions differs slightly; a typical example is illustrated above.

(Dies eng P.B. Typo J. B. Cooke until May 1918, then T. S. Harrison)

1914 (17 July)–**20.** W 5. P 14¼×14 (*comb*).
20	5a	½d. bright green (22.2.15)		3·75	80
		a. Perf 14¼ (line) (12.15)		£2500	£250
		b. *Green* (1916)		3·75	80
		c. *Yellow-green* (1916)		22·00	10·00
		d. Thin "1" in fraction at right (Pl 5 rt pane R. 8/1)		£3000	£1100
		w. Wmk inverted		10·00	4·00
21		1d. carmine-red (*shades*) (Die I) (p 14¼ (line))		25·00	4·00
		a. Die II		£3250	£350
		bw. Wmk inverted		†	—
		c. Perf 14¼×14 (comb) (7.8.14)		7·00	50
		ca. Rusted cliché (Pl 2 rt pane R. 6/4 and 5) (9.16)		£5000	£300
		cb. Substituted cliché (Pl 2 rt pane R. 6/5) (2.18)		£800	50·00
		cc. *Pale carmine* (*shades*) (1917)		10·00	50
		cd. *Rose-red* (1917)		11·00	2·50
		ce. *Carmine-pink* (1918)		80·00	7·00
		cf. *Carmine* (*aniline*) (1920)		16·00	3·25
		cw. Wmk inverted		12·00	2·00
		d. Die II. *Carmine-red* (*shades*)		£300	6·00
		db. Substituted cliché (Pl 2 right pane R. 6/4) (2.18)		£800	50·00
		dc. *Pale carmine* (*shades*)		£300	7·00
		dw. Wmk inverted		£425	14·00
22		4d. orange (6.1.15)		27·00	2·50
		a. *Yellow-orange* (1915)		27·00	3·25
		b. *Pale orange-yellow* (1916)		60·00	11·00
		c. *Lemon-yellow* (1916)		90·00	14·00
		d. *Dull orange* (1920)		42·00	3·25
		e. Line through "FOUR PENCE" (Pl 2 right pane R. 2/6) (*all shades*) From		£300	90·00
		w. Wmk inverted		45·00	12·00
23		5d. brown (p 14¼×14 line) (22.2.15)		25·00	4·00
		aw. Wmk inverted			
		b. Perf 14¼×14 (comb) (15.8.17)		18·00	1·60
		ba. *Yellow-brown* (1920)		25·00	2·25
		bw. Wmk inverted		55·00	18·00

The variety No. 20d was caused by the engraving of a new fraction in a defective electro in 1918.

No. 21ca was caused by rusting on two positions of the steel plate 2 and shows as white patches on the back of the King's neck and on, and besides, the top of the right frame (right pane R. 6/4) and on the left frame, wattles, head and ears of kangaroo (right pane R. 6/5). These were noticed in December 1916 when the damaged impressions were removed and replaced by a pair of copper electros (Die II for R. 6/4 and Die I for R. 6/5), showing rounded corners and some frame damage, the former also showing a white spot under tail of emu. In time the tops of the crown quickly wore away.

Most of Nos. 20/3 were perforated 14 by a comb machine (exact gauge 14.25×14), but printings of the ½d. in December 1915, of the 1d. in July and August 1914 and of the 5d. until June 1917 were perforated by a line machine measuring 14.2.

See also Nos. 47/fa (W 5, rough paper), 51/5a (W 6a), 55/ba (1d. Die III), 56/66b and 76/81 (W 5, new colours), 82 (W 6a), 83/4 (no wmk), 85/104 (W 7), 124/31 (W 15).

(Typo J. B. Cooke)

1915 (15 Jan–Aug). W 5. P 12.
24	1	2d. grey (Die I)		50·00	11·00
		w. Wmk inverted		†	£550
25		2½d. indigo (Die II) (July)		50·00	27·00
26		6d. ultramarine (Die II) (April)		£130	22·00
		a. *Bright blue*		£170	48·00
		b. Die IIA. *Ultramarine* (substituted cliché) (Upper plate rt pane R. 10/6)		£1100	£325
		ba. *Bright blue*		£1400	£400
		w. Wmk inverted		†	£1100

27	1	9d. violet (Die II) (9 July)		£130	32·00
		w. Wmk inverted		£650	£225
28		1s. blue-green (Die II) (Aug)		£140	23·00
29		2s. brown (Die II) (March)		£425	90·00
30		5s. grey and yellow (Die II) (12 Feb)		£500	£250
		a. Yellow portion doubly printed		£5500	£1500
		w. Wmk inverted		£600	£300
24/30			*Set of 7*	£1300	£400

The watermark in this issue is often misplaced as the paper was made for the portrait stamps.

6   6a

Nos. 38ca and 73a
(Upper plate lt pane

(Typo J. B. Cooke (to May 1918), T. S. Harrison to February 1926), A. J. Mullett (to June 1927) and thereafter J. Ash)

1915 (12 Oct)–**28.** W 6 (*narrow Crown*). P 12.
35	1	2d. grey (Die I) (11.15)		25·00	6·00
		a. In pair with Die IIA (1917)*		£900	£400
		bw. Wmk inverted		35·00	8·50
		c. *Silver-grey* (shiny paper) (3.18)		26·00	7·00
		d. Die II. *Silver-grey* (shiny paper) (3.18)		35·00	10·00
		da. *Grey* (1920)		38·00	10·00
36		2½d. deep blue (Die II) (9.17)		23·00	9·50
		aw. Wmk inverted		50·00	20·00
		b. *Deep indigo* (1920)		27·00	8·00
		ba. "1" of fraction omitted (Lower plate left pane R. 6/3)		£9500	£3500
37		3d. yellow-olive (Die I)		27·00	3·75
		a. In pair with Die II		£200	85·00
		b. *Olive-green* (1917)		30·00	3·75
		ba. In pair with Die II		£200	85·00
		cw. Wmk inverted		38·00	7·50
		d. Die II. *Yellow-olive*		80·00	27·00
		da. *Olive-green*		80·00	27·00
		dw. Wmk inverted		£130	50·00
		e. Die IIB. *Light olive* (1.23)		35·00	10·00
38		6d. ultramarine (Die II) (15.12.15)		50·00	7·00
		a. Die IIA (substituted cliché) (Upper plate rt pane R. 10/6)		£900	£225
		b. *Dull blue* (6.18)		65·00	10·00
		ba. Die IIA (substituted cliché)		£1000	£275
		cw. Wmk inverted		85·00	18·00
		d. Die IIB. *Brt ultramarine* (23.7.21)		55·00	7·00
		da. Leg of kangaroo broken		£2250	£450
		dw. Wmk inverted		—	40·00
39		9d. violet (Die II) (29.7.16)		38·00	7·00
		aw. Wmk inverted		60·00	17·00
		b. Die IIB. *Violet* (16.4.19)		35·00	7·00
		bw. Wmk inverted		50·00	16·00
40		1s. blue-green (Die II) (6.16)		35·00	3·50
		aw. Wmk inverted		60·00	16·00
		b. Die IIB (9.12.20)		35·00	3·00
		ba. Wmk sideways (12.27)		60·00	£100
		bw. Wmk inverted		55·00	16·00
41		2s. brown (Die II) (6.16)		£150	11·00
		a. Imperf three sides (horiz pair)		£16000	
		b. *Red-brown* (aniline)		£425	75·00
		w. Wmk inverted		£225	75·00
42		5s. grey and yellow (Die II) (4.18)		£180	75·00
		a. *Grey and orange* (1920)		£190	80·00
		b. *Grey and deep yellow*		£180	75·00
		ba. Wmk sideways		†	£5500
		c. *Grey and pale yellow* (1928)		£180	75·00
		w. Wmk inverted		£250	£120
43		10s. grey and pink (Die II) (5.2.17)		£400	£190
		a. *Grey and bright aniline pink* (10.18)		£350	£150
		ab. Wmk sideways		£7500	£3750
		aw. Wmk inverted		£550	£225
		b. *Grey and pale aniline pink* (1922)		£425	£170
44		£1 chocolate & dull blue (Die II) (7.16)		£1300	£700
		a. *Chestnut and bright blue* (6.17)		£1400	£750
		ab. Wmk sideways		£11000	£4750
		aw. Wmk inverted		£1700	£900
		b. *Bistre-brown and bright blue* (7.19)		£1300	£700
45		£2 black and rose (Die II) (12.19)		£2250	£1300
		a. *Grey and crimson* (1920)		£2000	£1200
		b. *Purple-black and pale rose* (6.24)		£1800	£1100
35/45b			*Set of 11*	£3500	£1800
43/5		Optd "Specimen"	*Set of 3*	£500	

*The Die IIA of No. 35a is a substituted cliché introduced to replace a cracked plate which occurred on R. 10/1 of the Upper plate left pane. The Die IIA characteristics are more pronounced in this cliché than on the sheet stamps from this die. The break at left, for instance, extends to the outer, in addition to the inner, frame line.

One plate of the 3d. contained mixed Die I and Die II stamps as described.

All values were printed by both Cooke and Harrison, and the 9d., 1s. and 5s. were also printed by Mullett and Ash.

1916 (14 Dec)–**18**. *Rough, unsurfaced paper, locally gummed.* W 5. P 14.

47	5a	1d. scarlet (Die I)	..	18·00	2·25
	a.	*Deep red* (1917)	..	18·00	2·25
	b.	*Rose-red* (1918)	..	28·00	2·50
	ba.	Substituted cliché (Pl 2 rt pane R. 6/5)		£750	55·00
	c.	*Rosine* (1918)	..	90·00	12·00
	ca.	Substituted cliché (Pl 2 rt pane R. 6/5)		£1200	£140
	dw.	Wmk inverted	..	28·00	3·50
	e.	Die II. *Rose-red* (1918)		£275	20·00
	ea.	Substituted cliché (Pl 2 rt pane R. 6/4)		£750	55·00
	ew.	Wmk inverted	..	£400	30·00
	f.	Die II. *Rosine* (1918)		£375	55·00
	fa.	Substituted cliché (Pl 2 rt pane R. 6/4		£1200	£140

All examples of the 5d. on this paper were perforated "OS" and will be found listed as No. O60.

(Typo J. B. Cooke to May 1918 thereafter T. S. Harrison)

1918 (4 Jan)–**20**. W 6a (*Mult*). P 14.

51	5a	½d. green (*shades*)	..	5·00	2·25
	a.	Thin 1 in fraction at right (Pl 5 rt pane R. 8/1)		£100	50·00
	b.	Wmk sideways		†	£3500
	w.	Wmk inverted	..	15·00	9·00
52		1d. carmine-pink (Die I) (23.1.18)		£100	55·00
	a.	*Deep red* (1918)	..	£900	£300
	w.	Wmk inverted	..	†	£1200
53		1d. carmine (10.12.19)	..	35·00	55·00
	aw.	Wmk inverted	..	£275	£140
	b.	*Deep red (aniline)* (1920)		£200	60·00
54		1½d. black-brown (30.1.19)	..	5·00	2·75
	a.	Very thin paper (2.19)	..	25·00	13·00
	w.	Wmk inverted	..	18·00	8·00
55		1½d. red-brown (4.19)	..	12·00	2·00
	a.	*Chocolate* (1920)	..	11·00	2·00
	w.	Wmk inverted	..	28·00	9·00

No. 51 was printed by Cooke and Harrison, Nos. 52/a by Cooke only and Nos. 53/55a by Harrison only. Nos. 52/a have rather yellowish gum, that of No. 53 being pure white.

1d. Die III

1d. Die III. In 1918 a printing (in sheets of 120) was made on paper originally prepared for printing War Savings Stamps, with watermark T 5. A special plate was made for this printing, differing in detail from those previously used. The shading round the head is even; the solid background of the words "ONE PENNY" is bounded at each end by a white vertical line; and there is a horizontal white line cutting the vertical shading lines at left on the King's neck.

(Typo J. B. Cooke)

1918 (15 July). *Printed from a new Die III plate on white unsurfaced paper, locally gummed.* W 5. P 14.

55b	5a	1d. rose-red	..	55·00	28·00
	ba.	*Rose-carmine*	..	55·00	30·00
	bw.	Wmk inverted	..	75·00	35·00

(Typo T. S. Harrison or A. J. Mullett (1s. 4d. from March 1926))

1918 (9 Nov)–**23**. W 5. P 14.

56	5a	½d. orange (9.11.23)	..	2·50	2·75
	w.	Wmk inverted	..	5·00	5·50
57		1d. violet (*shades*) (12.2.22)	..	7·00	1·50
	a.	Imperf three sides (horiz pair)		£8500	
	b.	*Red-violet*	..	8·00	2·25
58		1½d. black-brown	..	8·50	1·25
	w.	Wmk inverted	..	12·00	3·00
59		1½d. deep red-brown (4.19)	..	6·50	70
	a.	*Chocolate* (1920)	..	6·50	60
	w.	Wmk inverted	..	14·00	4·00
60		1½d. bright red-brown (20.1.22)		12·00	3·25
61		1½d. green (7.3.23)	..	4·00	70
	a.	Coarse unsurfaced paper (1923)		£110	
	w.	Wmk inverted	..	†	£1000
62		2d. brown-orange (4.10.20)	..	15·00	90
	a.	*Dull orange* (1921)	..	18·00	90
	w.	Wmk inverted	..	†	£1000
63		2d. bright rose-scarlet (19.1.22)		9·00	1·25
	a.	*Dull rose-scarlet*	..	9·00	1·25
	w.	Wmk inverted	..	£1500	
64		4d. violet (21.6.21)	..	13·00	15·00
	a.	Line through "FOUR PENCE" (Pl 2 rt pane R. 2/6)		£6000	£2250
	b.	"FOUR PENCE" in thinner letters (Pl 2 rt pane R. 2/6)		£400	£225
65		4d. ultramarine (*shades*) (23.3.22)		48·00	8·00
	a.	"FOUR PENCE" in thinner letters (Pl 2 rt pane R. 2/6)		£400	£150
	b.	*Pale milky blue*	..	70·00	13·00
	w.	Wmk inverted	..	65·00	35·00
66		1s. 4d. pale blue (2.12.20)	..	55·00	23·00
	a.	*Dull greenish blue*	..	60·00	23·00
	b.	*Deep turquoise* (1922)		£850	£350
56/66			*Set of 11*	£160	50·00

In addition to a number of mint pairs from two sheets purchased at Gumeracha, South Australia, with the bottom row imperforate on three sides, a single used example of No. 57 imperforate on three sides is known.

No. 61a was printed on a batch of coarse unsurfaced paper during 1923. Mint examples can be identified by the yellowish gum and a mesh effect in the paper, but there is no conclusive method of identifying used stamps from this printing.

The 4d. ultramarine was originally printed from the Cooke plates but the plates were worn in mid-1923 and Harrison prepared a new pair of plates. Stamps from these plates can only be distinguished by the minor flaws which are peculiar to them.

The variety of Nos. 64 and 65 with "FOUR PENCE" thinner, was caused by the correction of the line through "FOUR PENCE" flaw early in the printing of No. 64.

(Typo T. S. Harrison (to February 1926), A. J. Mullett (to June 1927), thereafter J. Ash)

1923 (6 Dec)–**24**. W 6. P 12.

73	1	6d. chestnut (Die IIB)	..	24·00	1·50
	a.	Leg of kangaroo broken (Upper plate lt pane R. 1/6)		75·00	95·00
	w.	Wmk inverted	..	†	£1200
74		2s. maroon (Die II) (1.5.24)		50·00	24·00
	w.	Wmk inverted	..	£120	65·00
75		£1 grey (Die IIB) (1.5.24) (Optd S. £75)		£400	£225

The 6d. and 2s. were printed by all three printers, but the £1 only by Harrison.

No. 73a was corrected during the Ash printing.

(Typo T. S. Harrison (to February 1926), thereafter A. J. Mullett)

1924 (1 May–18 Aug). P 14. (*a*) W 5.

76	5a	1d. sage-green	..	3·00	1·25
	w.	Wmk inverted	..	11·00	5·50
77		1½d. scarlet (*shades*)	..	2·25	30
	a.	Very thin paper	..	40·00	17·00
	b.	"HALEPENCE" (Pl 22 left pane R. 4/4)		30·00	17·00
	c	"RAL" of "AUSTRALIA" thin (Pl 22 left pane R. 5/4)		30·00	17·00
	d.	Curved "1" and thin fraction at left (Pl 24 rt pane R. 7/5)		30·00	17·00
	w.	Wmk inverted	..	30·00	9·00
78		2d. red-brown	..	20·00	7·00
	a.	*Bright red-brown*	..	26·00	8·00
	w.	Wmk inverted	..	†	£1200
79		3d. dull ultramarine	..	24·00	1·50
	a.	Imperf three sides (horiz pair)		£6000	
80		4d. olive-yellow	..	28·00	5·00
	a.	*Olive-green*	..	28·00	5·50
	w.	Wmk inverted	..	†	£950
81		4½d. violet	..	23·00	3·25

(*b*) W 6a

82	5a	1d. sage-green (20 May)		8·00	8·00
	w.	Wmk inverted	..	†	£900

(*c*) No wmk

83	5a	1d. sage-green (18 August)		5·50	9·50
84		1½d. scarlet (14 August)	..	11·00	9·50
76/84			*Set of 9*	£110	40·00

Nos. 78/a and 82/4 were printed by Harrison only but the remainder were printed by both Harrison and Mullett.

In the semi-transparent paper of Nos. 54a and 77a the watermark is almost indistinguishable.

Nos. 77b, 77c and 77d are typical examples of retouching of which there are many others in these issues. In No. 77c the letters "RAL" differ markedly from the normal. There is a white stroke cutting the oval frame-line above the "L", and the right-hand outer line of the Crown does not cut the white frame-line above the "A".

It is believed that No. 79a occurs on the bottom row of at least four sheets purchased from post offices in Victoria during 1926.

7

I

II

New Dies

1d. For differences see note above No. 20.

1½d. From new steel plates made from a new die. Nos. 87a and 96a are the Ash printings, the ink of which is shiny.

2d. Die I. Height of frame 25.6 mm. Left-hand frame-line thick and uneven behind Kangaroo. Pearls in Crown vary in size.

Die II. Height of frame 25.6 mm. Left-hand frame-line thin and even. Pearls in Crown are all the same size.

Die III. Height 25.1 mm; lettering and figures of value bolder than Die I.

3d. Die II has bolder letters and figures than Die I, as illustrated above.

5d. Die II has a bolder figure "5" with flat top compared with Die I of the earlier issues.

(Typo A. J. Mullett or J. Ash (from June 1927))

1926–**30**. W 7. (*a*) P 14.

85	5a	½d. orange (10.3.27)	..	6·00	7·50
	w.	Wmk inverted	..	38·00	28·00
86		1d. sage-green (23.10.26)		3·25	85
	w.	Wmk inverted	..	11·00	3·50
87		1½d. scarlet (5.11.26)	..	7·50	1·75
	a.	*Golden scarlet* (1927)	..	11·00	2·25
	w.	Wmk inverted	..	14·00	4·50
89		2d. red-brown (Die I) (17.8.27)		28·00	30·00
90		3d. dull ultramarine (12.26)		23·00	5·00
	w.	Wmk inverted	..	†	£900
91		4d. yellow-olive (17.1.28)		48·00	30·00
92		4½d. violet (26.10.27)	..	18·00	3·75
93		1s. 4d. pale greenish blue (6.9.27)		90·00	75·00
	w.	Wmk inverted	..	†	£1100
85/93			*Set of 8*	£200	£140

(*b*) P 13½×12½

94	5a	½d. orange (21.11.28)		2·25	1·40
95		1d. sage-green (Die I) (23.12.26)		2·25	70
	aw.	Wmk inverted	..	10·00	4·50
	b.	Die II (6.28)	..	50·00	80·00
	bw.	Wmk inverted	..	£225	
96		1½d. scarlet (14.1.27)	..	2·25	1·00
	a.	*Golden scarlet* (1927)	..	2·25	1·00
	w.	Wmk inverted	..	6·00	2·50
97		1½d. red-brown (16.9.30)	..	5·50	5·50
98		2d. red-brown (Die II) (28.4.28)		8·00	8·50
99		2d. golden scarlet (Die II) (2.8.30)		11·00	1·60
	a.	Die III (9.9.30)	..	9·00	85
	ab.	No wmk	..	£600	£750
	ac.	*Tête-bêche* (pair)		£30000	
	aw.	Wmk inverted (*from booklets*)		9·00	1·40
100		3d. dull ultramarine (Die I) (28.2.28)		45·00	6·50
	aw.	Wmk inverted	..	£110	£150
	b.	Die II. *Deep ultramarine* (28.9.29)		23·00	1·40
	bw.	Wmk inverted	..	†	£1000
102		4d. yellow-olive (19.4.29)		23·00	3·25
	w.	Wmk inverted	..	†	£900
103		4½d. violet (11.28)	..	48·00	22·00
103a		5d. orange-brown (Die II) (27.8.30)		23·00	6·50
104		1s. 4d. turquoise (30.9.28)		80·00	25·00
	w.	Wmk inverted	..	†	£1200
94/104			*Set of 11*	£190	65·00

Owing to defective manufacture, part of a sheet of the 2d. (Die III), discovered in July 1931, escaped unwatermarked; while the watermark in other parts of the same sheet was faint or normal. Only one example of No. 99ac is known.

8 Parliament House, Canberra   9 "DH66" Biplane and Pastoral Scene

(Des R. A. Harrison. Die eng J. A. C. Harrison (Waterlow, London). Plates and printing by A. J. Mullett)

1927 (9 May). *Opening of Parliament House, Canberra.* No wmk. P 11.

105	8	1½d. brownish lake	..	50	50
	a.	Imperf between (vert pair)		£2250	
	b.	Imperf between (horiz pair)		£3250	£3250

(Eng H. W. Bell. Recess J. Ash)

1928 (29 Oct). *4th National Stamp Exhibition, Melbourne.* As T 4. No wmk. P 11.

106		3d. blue	..	4·25	4·75
	a.	Pane of four with margins		£120	£225
	ab.	Imperf (pane of four)		£18000	

No. 106a comes from special sheets of 60 stamps divided into 15 blocks of 4 (5 × 3) and separated by wide gutters perforated down the middle, printed and sold at the Exhibition.

(Typo J. Ash)

1929 (Feb)–**30**. W 7. P 12.

107	1	6d. chestnut (Die IIB) (25.9.29)		23·00	4·50
108		9d. violet (Die IIB)	..	30·00	14·00
109		1s. blue-green (Die IIB) (12.6.29)		35·00	5·50
	w.	Wmk inverted	..	†	£1200
110		2s. maroon (Die II) (3.29)		45·00	15·00
111		5s. grey and yellow (Die II) (30.11.29)		£190	80·00
112		10s. grey and pink (Die II)		£275	£400
114		£2 black and rose (Die II) (11.30)		£1900	£450
107/14			*Set of 7*	£2250	£850
112/14		Optd "Specimen"	*Set of 2*	£325	

(Des R. A. Harrison and H. Herbert. Eng A. Taylor. Recess J. Ash)

1929 (20 May). *Air.* No wmk. P 11.

115	9	3d. green (*shades*)	..	10·00	3·75

Variations of up to ¾ mm in the design size of No. 115 are due to paper shrinkage on the printings produced by the "wet" process. The last printing, in 1935, was printed by the "dry" method.

10 Black Swan   11 "Capt. Charles Sturt" (J. H. Crossland)

(Des G. Pitt Morrison. Eng F. D. Manley. Recess J. Ash)

1929 (28 Sept). *Centenary of Western Australia.* No wmk. P 11.

116	10	1½d. dull scarlet	..	1·25	1·60
	a.	Re-entry ("T" of "AUSTRALIA" clearly double) (Pl 2 R. 7/4)		55·00	60·00

(Des R. A. Harrison. Eng F. D. Manley. Recess J. Ash)

1930 (2 June). *Centenary of Exploration of River Murray by Capt. Sturt.* No wmk. P 11.

117	11	1½d. scarlet	..	1·00	75
118		3d. blue	..	3·25	6·00

No. 117 with manuscript surcharge of "2d. paid P M L H I" was issued by the Postmaster of Lord Howe Island during a shortage of 2d. stamps between 23 August and 17 October 1930. A few copies of the 1½d. value No. 96a were also endorsed. These provisionals are not recognized by the Australian postal authorities. (*Price £500 un. or us., either stamp*).

TWO

PENCE

(12)

13 Fokker F.VIIa/3m
Southern Cross above
Hemispheres

1930 (31 July–2 Aug). *T 5a surch as T 12. W 7. P* 13½×12½.
119 2d. on 1½d. golden scarlet .. .. 1·25 60
120 5d. on 4½d. violet (2 Aug) .. 5·50 8·00
No. 120 is from a redrawn die in which the words "FOURPENCE HALFPENNY" are noticeably thicker than in the original die and the figure "4" has square instead of tapering serifs.
Stamps from the redrawn die without the surcharge were printed, but not issued thus. Some stamps, *cancelled to order*, were then supplied by the post office. A few mint copies, which escaped, the cancellation were found and some may have been used postally (*Price £2000 unused, £45 used c.t.o.*).

(Des and eng F. D. Manley. Recess John Ash)
1931 (19 Mar). *Kingsford Smith's Flights. No wmk. P* 11.
(*a*) *Postage.*
121 **13** 2d. rose-red 75 75
122 3d. blue .. .. .. 4·50 4·50
(*b*) *Air. Inscr* "AIR MAIL SERVICE" *at sides*
123 **13** 6d. violet .. .. .. 7·00 11·00
a. Re-entry ("FO" and "LD" double) (Pl 1 R. 5/5) .. .. 50·00 70·00
121/3 .. .. .. *Set of 3* 11·00 14·50

15

17 Superb Lyrebird

(Typo John Ash)
1931–36. *W 15. (a) P* 13½×12½.
124 **5a** ½d. orange (2.33) .. .. 4·75 5·50
125 1d. green (Die I) (10.31) .. 1·75 10
w. Wmk inverted .. .. 9·00 3·00
x. Wmk reversed .. .. £150 60·00
y. Wmk inverted and reversed .. £225 90·00
126 1½d. red-brown (10.36) .. .. 6·00 9·00
127 2d. golden scarlet (Die III) (18.12.31) 1·75 10
w. Wmk inverted (*from booklets*) 2·25 50
128 3d. ultramarine (Die II) (30.9.32) .. 18·00 90
w. Wmk inverted £1200 £1000
129 4d. yellow-olive (2.33) .. 18·00 1·00
w. Wmk inverted .. .. † £1000
130 5d. orange-brown (Die II) (25.2.32) 15·00 15
w. Wmk inverted .. .. † £850
131 1s. 4d. turquoise (18.8.32) .. 55·00 3·50
w. Wmk inverted .. .. † £950
124/31 .. .. .. *Set of 8* £110 16·00
(*b*) *P* 12
132 **1** 6d. chestnut (Die IIB) (20.4.32) .. 22·00 25·00
133 9d. violet (Die IIB) (20.4.32) .. 26·00 1·00
134 2s. maroon (Die II) (6.8.35) .. 5·00 60
135 5s. grey and yellow (Die II) (12.32) £110 12·00
136 10s. grey and pink (Die II) (31.7.32) £250 £100
137 £1 grey (Die IIB) (11.35) .. £425 £150
138 £2 black and rose (Die II) (6.34) £1600 £325
132/38 .. .. .. *Set of 7* £2250 £550
136/138 Optd "Specimen" .. *Set of 3* 75·00
Stamps as No. 127, but without watermark and perforated 11, are forgeries made in 1932 to defraud the P.O.
For re-engraved type of No. 134, see No. 212.

(Des and eng F. D. Manley. Recess John Ash)
1931 (4 Nov). *Air Stamp. As T 13 but inscr* "AIR MAIL SERVICE" *in bottom tablet. No wmk. P* 11.
139 6d. sepia .. .. .. 16·00 12·00

1931 (17 Nov). *Air. No. 139 optd with Type O 4.*
139a 6d. sepia .. .. .. 35·00 48·00
This stamp was not restricted to official use but was on general sale to the public.

(Des and eng F. D. Manley. Recess John Ash)
1932 (15 Feb). *No wmk. P* 11.
140 **17** 1s. green .. .. 42·00 1·75
a. Yellow-green .. .. 48·00 2·50

18 Sydney Harbour Bridge

19 Laughing Kookaburra

(Des R. A. Harrison. Eng F. D. Manley. Printed John Ash)
1932 (14 Mar). *Opening of Sydney Harbour Bridge. (a) Recess. No wmk. P* 11.
141 **18** 2d. scarlet .. .. 2·25 2·50
142 3d. blue .. .. .. 4·25 7·00
143 5s. blue-green £375 £180
(*b*) *Typo. W* 15. *P* 10½.
144 **18** 2d. scarlet .. .. 2·00 1·40
141/4 .. .. .. *Set of 4* £375 £180
Stamps as No. 144 without wmk and perf 11 are forgeries made in 1932 to defraud the P.O.

(Des F. D. Manley. Die eng E. Broad. Typo John Ash)
1932 (1 June). *W* 15. *P* 13½×12½.
146 **19** 6d. red-brown .. .. 25·00 55
w. Wmk inverted .. .. † £750

20 Melbourne and R. Yarra

21 Merino Ram

(Des and eng F. D. Manley. Recess John Ash)
1934 (2 July). *Centenary of Victoria. W* 15. *P* 10½.
147 **20** 2d. orange-vermilion .. 2·50 1·75
a. Perf 11½ .. .. 4·50 1·50
148 3d. blue .. .. .. 5·00 5·50
a. Perf 11½ .. .. 5·00 8·00
149 1s. black .. .. 45·00 19·00
a. Perf 11½ .. .. 45·00 21·00
147/9 .. .. .. *Set of 3* 48·00 24·00
147a/9a .. .. *Set of 3* 50·00 27·00
Stamps were originally issued perforated 10½, but the gauge was subsequently changed to 11½ in August 1934 due to difficulties in separating stamps in the first perforation.

(Des and eng F. D. Manley. Recess John Ash)
1934 (1–26 Nov). *Death Centenary of Capt. John Macarthur (founder of Australian sheep farming). W* 15. *P* 11½.
150 **21** 2d. carmine-red (A) .. 4·00 1·50
150a 2d. carmine-red (B) (26 Nov) 25·00 3·25
151 3d. blue .. .. 10·00 8·50
152 9d. bright purple .. 38·00 40·00
150/2 .. .. .. *Set of 3* 48·00 45·00
Type A of the 2d. shows shading on the hill in the background varying from light to dark (as illustrated). Type B has the shading almost uniformly dark.

22 Hermes

23 Cenotaph, Whitehall

(Des F. D. Manley. Eng E. Broad and F. D. Manley. Recess John Ash until April 1940; W. C. G. McCracken thereafter)
1934 (1 Dec)–48. (*a*) *No wmk. P* 11.
153 **22** 1s. 6d. dull purple .. 32·00 1·00
(*b*) *W* 15. *Chalk-surfaced paper. P* 13½×14.
153a **22** 1s. 6d dull purple (22.10.37) .. 9·00 45
b. Thin rough ordinary paper (12.2.48) .. .. 3·00 1·25

(Des B. Cottier; adapted and eng F. D. Manley. Recess John Ash)
1935 (18 Mar). *20th Anniv of Gallipoli Landing. W* 15. *P* 13½×12½ *or* 11 (1s.).
154 **23** 2d. scarlet 80 30
155 1s. black (*chalk-surfaced*) 48·00 38·00
a. Perf 13½×12½ £1500

24 King George V on "Anzac"

25 Amphitrite and Telephone Cable

(Des and eng F. D. Manley. Recess John Ash)
1935 (2 May). *Silver Jubilee. Chalk-surfaced paper. W* 15 (*sideways*). *P* 11½.
156 **24** 2d. scarlet .. .. 1·50 30
157 3d. blue .. .. .. 6·00 7·50
158 2s. bright violet .. 40·00 40·00
156/8 .. .. .. *Set of 3* 42·00 42·00

(Des and eng F. D. Manley. Recess John Ash)
1936 (1 Apr). *Opening of Submarine Telephone Link to Tasmania. W* 15. *P* 11½.
159 **25** 2d. scarlet 75 50
160 3d. blue .. .. .. 2·75 2·75

26 Site of Adelaide, 1836; Old Gum Tree, Glenelg; King William St., Adelaide

(Des and eng F. D. Manley. Recess John Ash)
1936 (3 Aug). *Centenary of South Australia. W* 15. *P* 11½.
161 **26** 2d. carmine .. .. 1·25 40
162 3d. blue .. .. .. 4·00 3·50
163 1s. green .. .. 10·00 8·50
161/3 .. .. .. *Set of 3* 14·00 11·00

27 Wallaroo   **28** Queen Elizabeth **28a**

29   **30**   **30a**
King George VI

31 King   **32** Koala **33** Merino Ram
George VI

34 Laughing Kookaburra **35** Platypus **36** Superb Lyrebird

38 Queen Elizabeth **39** King George VI

40 King George VI and Queen Elizabeth

Dies of 3d.:

TA	TA	TA
Die I	Die Ia	Die II

Die I. The letters "TA" of "POSTAGE" at right are joined by a white flaw; the outline of the chin consists of separate strokes.
No. 168*a* is a preliminary printing made with unsuitable ink and may be detected by the absence of finer details; the King's face appears whitish and the wattles are blank. The greater part of this printing was distributed to the Press with advance notices of the issue.
Die Ia. As Die I, but "T" and "A" have been clearly separated by individual retouches made on the plates.
Die II. A completely new die. "T" and "A" are separate and a continuous line has been added to the chin. The outline of the cheek extends to about 1 mm above the lobe of the King's right ear.
Die III. Differs from Dies I and II in the King's left eyebrow which is shaded downwards from left to right instead of from right to left.

Line to Kangaroo's ear (Rt pane R. 6/8)

Medal flaw
(Right pane R. 2/5)

(Des R. A. Harrison (T **28/30**), F. D. Manley (T **27, 31/6**), H. Barr (T **38/9**), H. Barr and F. D. Manley (T **40**). Eng F. D. Manley and T. C Duffell (T **34**), T. C Duffell (revised lettering for T **28a, 30a**), F. D. Manley (others). All recess with John Ash, W. C. G. McCracken or "By Authority ..." imprints)

1937–49. W **15** (*sideways on 5d., 9d., 5s. and 10s.*). *Chalk-surfaced paper* (3d. (No. 168), 5s., 10s., £1).

(a) *P* 13½ × 14 (*vert designs*) *or* 14 × 13½ (*horiz*)

164	27	½d. orange (3.10.38)	..	2·50	45
165	28	1d. emerald-green (10.5.37)	..	40	10
166	29	1½d. maroon (20.4.38)	..	9·00	3·00
167	30	2d. scarlet (10.5.37)	..	40	10
168	31	3d. blue (Die I) (2.8.37)	..	60·00	9·50
		a. "White wattles" (from 1st ptg)		£120	70·00
		b. Die Ia	..	£140	6·50
		c. Die II (3.38)	..	60·00	3·50
		ca. *Bright blue (ordinary thin paper)* (20.12.38)		60·00	2·50
170	32	4d. green (1.2.38)	..	14·00	85
171	33	5d. purple (1.12.38)	..	2·00	10
172	34	6d. purple-brown (2.8.37)	..	23·00	90
173	35	9d. chocolate (1.9.38)	..	5·00	90
174	36	1s. grey-green (2.8.37)	..	48·00	2·25
175	31	1s. 4d. pale magenta (3.10.38)	..	1·50	1·50
		a. *Deep magenta* (1943)	..	3·25	2·00

(b) *P* 13½

176	38	5s. claret (1.4.38)	..	14·00	1·25
		a. Thin rough ordinary paper (4.2.48)		4·00	2·00
177	39	10s. dull purple (1.4.38) (Optd S. £30)	38·00	12·00
		a. Thin rough ordinary paper (11.48)		42·00	29·00
178	40	£1 bl-slate (1.11.38) (Optd S. £400)	65·00	30·00
		a. Thin rough ordinary paper (4.4.49) ..		65·00	60·00
164/78	..	..	*Set of 14*	£250	48·00

(c) *P* 15×14 (*vert designs*) *or* 14×15 (*horiz*) (1d. *and* 2d. *redrawn with background evenly shaded and lettering strengthened*)

179	27	½d. orange (28.1.42)	..	55	10
		a. Line to kangaroo's ear	..	12·00	
		b. Coil pair (1942)	..	15·00	17·00
		ba. Coil block of four (1943)	..	£250	
180	28a	1d. emerald-green (1.8.38)	..	2·50	10
181		1d. maroon (10.12.41)	..	1·25	10
		a. Coil pair (1942)	..	12·00	16·00
182	29	1½d. maroon (21.11.41)	..	4·00	7·50
183		1½d. emerald-green (10.12.41)	..	1·00	70
184	30a	2d. scarlet (11.7.38)	..	2·75	10
		a. Coil pair (10.41)	..	£325	£375
		b. Medal flaw	..	£100	
		w. Wmk inverted (*from booklets*)	4·00	50
185		2d. bright purple (10.12.41)	..	50	80
		a. Coil pair (1942)	..	42·00	48·00
		b. Medal flaw	..	40·00	
		w. Wmk inverted (*from coils*)	80·00	24·00
186	31	3d. bright blue (Die III) (11.40)	45·00	2·25
187		3d. purple-brown (Die III) (10.12.41)	30	10
188	32	4d. green (10.42)	..	1·00	10
		w. Wmk inverted	..	†	£650
189	33	5d. purple (17.12.45)	..	45	1·50
190	34	6d. red-brown (6.42)	..	2·00	10
		a. *Purple-brown* (1944)	..	1·75	10
191	35	9d. chocolate (12.9.43)	..	1·00	20
192	36	1s. grey-green (29.3.41)	..	1·00	10
		w. Wmk inverted	..	£650	£375
179/92	..	..	*Set of 14*	55·00	11·00

For unwmkd issue, see Nos. 228/30d.

Thin paper. Nos. 176a, 177a, 178a. In these varieties the watermark is more clearly visible on the back and the design is much less sharp. On early printings of No. 176a the paper appears tinted.

SPECIAL COIL PERFORATION. This special perforation of large and small holes on the narrow sides of the stamps was introduced after 1939 for stamps issued in coils and was intended to facilitate separation. Where they exist they are listed as "Coil pairs".

The following with "special coil" perforation were placed on sale in *sheets*: Nos. 179, 205, 222a (1952), 228, 230, 237, 262 (1953), 309, 311, and 314. These are listed as "Coil blocks of four".

Coils with "normal" perforations also exist for Nos. 180 and 184.

41 "Governor Phillip at Sydney Cove" (J. Alcott)

"Tail" flaw (Left pane R. 7/1. Later retouched)

(Des and eng E. Broad and F. D. Manley. Recess J. Ash)

1937 (1 Oct). *150th Anniv of Foundation of New South Wales.* W **15**. *P* 13½ × 14.

193	41	2d. scarlet	..	2·25	15
		a. "Tail" flaw	..	£250	60·00
194		3d. bright blue	..	6·00	2·25
195		9d. purple	..	16·00	10·00
193/5	..		*Set of 3*	22·00	11·00

42 A.I.F. and Nurse

(Des and eng F. D. Manley from drawing by Virgil Reilly. Recess W. C. G. McCracken)

1940 (15 July). *Australian Imperial Forces.* W **15** (*sideways*). *P* 14 × 13½.

196	42	1d. green	..	1·75	1·25
197		2d. scarlet	..	1·75	50
198		3d. blue	..	12·00	7·50
199		6d. brown-purple	..	22·00	13·00
196/9			*Set of 4*	35·00	20·00

 (43)   (44)   (45)

(Opts designed by F. D. Manley)

1941 (10 Dec). *Nos. 184, 186 and 171 surch with T* **43/5**.

200	40b	2½d. on 2d. scarlet (V.)	..	60	40
		a. Pair, one without surcharge	..	£3750	
		b. Medal flaw	..	95·00	
201	31	3½d. on 3d. bright blue (Y. on Black)	75	1·50
202	33	5½d. on 5d. purple (V.)	..	3·50	4·00
200/2			*Set of 3*	4·25	5·50

Nos 200/2 were prepared in connection with the imposition of a ½d. "war tax" increase on most postage rates.

One sheet of the 2½d. on 2d. was discovered showing the surcharge omitted on R.1/4 and R.1/5.

46 Queen Elizabeth   46a

47 King George VI

48 King George VI   49 King George VI   50 Emu

(Des F. D. Manley. Eng F. D. Manley and T. C. Duffell (T **46/a**) or F. D. Manley (others))

1942–50. *Recess.* W **15**. *P* 15×14.

203	46	1d. brown-purple (2.1.43)	..	50	10
		a. Coil pair (1944)	..	18·00	23·00
204	46a	1½d. green (1.12.42)	..	40	10
205	47	2d. bright purple (4.12.44)	..	55	60
		b. Coil pair (1.49)	..	90·00	95·00
		ba. Coil block of four (5.50)	..	£850	
206	48	2½d. scarlet (7.1.42)	..	30	10
		a. Imperf (pair)*	..	£2750	
		w. Wmk inverted (*from booklets*)	3·75	30

207	49	3½d. bright blue (3.42)	..	40	20
		a. *Deep blue*	..	50	20
208	50	5½d. slate-blue (12.2.42)	..	65	10
203/8			*Set of 6*	2·50	40

*No. 206a comes in horizontal pair with the right-hand stamp completely imperforate and the left-hand stamp imperforate at right only.

Coils with normal perforations exist for 1d.

For stamps as Nos. 204/5 but without watermark see Nos. 229/30.

The following items are understood to have been the subject of unauthorised leakages from the Commonwealth Note and Stamp Printing Branch and are therefore not listed by us.

It is certain that none of this material was distributed to post offices for issue to the public.

Imperforate all round. 1d. Princess Elizabeth; 1½d. Queen; 2½d. King; 4d. Koala; 6d. Kookaburra; 9d. Platypus; 1s. Lyrebird (small) (also imperf three sides); 1s. 6d. Air Mail (Type 22); 2½d. Mitchell; 2½d. Newcastle (also imperf three sides or imperf vertically).

Also 2½d. Peace, unwatermarked; 2½d. King, *tête-bêche*; 3½d. Newcastle, in dull ultramarine; 2½d. King on "toned" paper.

---

52 Duke and Duchess of Gloucester

(Des F. D. Manley. Eng F. D. Manley and T. C. Duffell. Recess)

1945 (19 Feb). *Arrival of Duke and Duchess of Gloucester in Australia.* W **15**. *P* 14½.

209	52	2½d. lake	..	10	10
210		3½d. ultramarine	..	15	55
211		5½d. indigo	..	20	55
209/11			*Set of 3*	40	1·10

A   B

1945 (24 Dec). *Kangaroo type, as No. 134, but re-engraved as* B. W **15**. *P* 12.

212	1	2s. maroon	..	3·50	4·25
		w. Wmk inverted	..	†	£1300

No. 134 has two background lines between the value circle and "TWO SHILLINGS"; No. 212 has only one line in this position. There are also differences in the shape of the letters.

53 Star and Wreath   56 Sir Thomas Mitchell and Queensland

(Des F. D. Manley (2½d.), F. D. Manley and G. Lissenden (3½d.), G. Lissenden (5½d.). Eng F. D. Manley. Recess)

1946 (18 Feb). *Victory Commemoration. T* **53** *and similar designs.* W **15** (*sideways on 5½d.*). *P* 14½.

213		2½d. scarlet	..	10	10
214		3½d. blue	..	25	75
215		5½d. green	..	30	50
213/15			*Set of 3*	60	1·25

Designs: Horiz—3½d. Flag and dove. Vert—5½d. Angel.

For these designs re-issued in 1995 with face values in decimal currency see Nos. 1542/4.

(Des F. D. Manley. Eng F. D. Manley and T. C. Duffell. Recess)

1946 (14 Oct). *Centenary of Mitchell's Exploration of Central Queensland.* W **15**. *P* 14½.

216	56	2½d. scarlet	..	10	10
217		3½d. blue	..	35	80
218		1s. grey-olive	..	35	30
216/18			*Set of 3*	70	1·10

57 Lt. John Shortland R.N.   58 Steel Foundry   59 Coal Carrier Cranes

(Des and eng G. Lissenden (5½d.), F. D. Manley (others). Recess)

1947 (8 Sept). *150th Anniv of City of Newcastle, New South Wales.* W **15** (*sideways on 3½d.*). *P* 14½ *or* 15×14 (2½d.).

219	57	2½d. lake	..	10	10
220	58	3½d. blue	..	40	65
221	59	5½d. green	..	40	45
219/21			*Set of 3*	80	1·10

60 Queen Elizabeth II when Princess

(Des R. A. Harrison. Eng. F. D. Manley. Recess)

1947 (20 Nov)–52. *Marriage of Princess Elizabeth. P* 14×15.

(a) *W* **15** (*sideways*)

222	**60**	1d. purple	..	15	10

(b) *No wmk*

222a	**60**	1d. purple (8.48)	..	10	10
		b. Coil pair (1.50)	..	2·25	4·50
		c. Coil block of four (9.52)	..	4·50	

61 Hereford Bull   **61a** Hermes and Globe

62 Aboriginal Art   **62a** Commonwealth Coat of Arms

(Des G. Sellheim (T **62**), F. D. Manley (others). Eng G. Lissenden (T **62**), F. D. Manley (1s. 3d., 1s. 6d., 5s.), F. D. Manley and R. J. Becker (10s., £1, £2). Recess)

1948 (16 Feb)–56. (a) *W* **15** (*sideways*). *P* 14½

223	**61**	1s. 3d. brown-purple	..	1·75	95
223a	**61a**	1s. 6d. blackish brown (1.9.49)	..	90	10
224	**62**	2s. chocolate	..	2·00	10

(b) *W* **15**. *P* 14½×13½

224a	**62a**	5s. claret (11.4.49)	..	2·75	20
		ab. Thin paper (1951)	..	27·00	11·00
224b		10s. purple (3.10.49)	..	14·00	70
224c		£1 blue (28.11.49)	..	30·00	3·50
224d		£2 green (16.1.50)	..	95·00	14·00
224b/d	Optd "Specimen"	*Set of* 3	£140	

(c) *No wmk. P* 14½

224e	**61a**	1s. 6d. blackish brown (2.12.56)	..	13·00	1·50
224f	**62**	2s. chocolate (27.6.56)	..	13·00	60
223/4f		*Set of* 9	£150	19·00

No. 224ab is an emergency printing on white Harrison paper instead of the toned paper used for No. 224a.

No. 224b exists with watermark inverted and overprinted "SPECIMEN".

63 William J. Farrer   **64** F. von Mueller   **65** Boy Scout

(Des and eng F. D. Manley. Recess)

1948 (12 July). *William J. Farrer (wheat research) Commemoration. W* **15**. *P* 15×14.

225	**63**	2½d. scarlet	..	10	10

(Des and eng F. D. Manley. Recess)

1948 (13 Sept). *Sir Ferdinand von Mueller (botanist) Commemoration. W* **15**. *P* 15×14.

226	**64**	2½d. lake	..	10	10

(Des and eng F. D. Manley. Recess)

1948 (15 Nov). *Pan-Pacific Scout Jamboree, Wonga Park. W* **15** (*sideways*). *P* 14 × 15.

227	**65**	2½d. lake	..	10	10

See also No. 254.

Sky retouch (normally unshaded near hill) (Rt pane R. 6/8) (No. 228a retouched in 1951)

"Green mist" retouch. A large area to the left of the bird's feathers is recut (upper plate left pane R. 9/3)

1948–56. *No wmk. P* 15×14 *or* 14×15 (9d.).

228	**27**	½d. orange (15.9.49)	..	20	10
		a. Line to kangaroo's ear	..	9·00	
		b. Sky retouch	..	21·00	
		c. Coil pair (1950)	..	75	2·25
		ca. Line to kangaroo's ear	..	32·00	
		cb. Sky retouch (in pair)	..	£110	
		d. Coil block of four (1953)	..	£250	
229	**46a**	1½d. green (17.8.49)	..	1·25	85
230	**47**	2d. bright purple (20.12.48)	..	80	80
		aa. Coil pair	..	3·00	5·50
230a	**32**	4d. green (18.8.56)	..	2·00	80
230b	**34**	6d. purple-brown (18.8.56)	..	4·75	70
230c	**35**	9d. chocolate (13.12.56)	..	22·00	2·75
230d	**36**	1s. grey green (13.12.56)	..	4·00	90
		da. "Green mist" retouch	..	£650	
228/30d		*Set of* 7	32·00	6·00

66 "Henry Lawson" (Sir Lionel Lindsay)   **67** Mounted Postman and Convair CV 240 Aircraft

(Des F. D. Manley. Eng. E. R. M. Jones. Recess)

1949 (17 June). *Henry Lawson (poet) Commemoration. P* 15×14.

231	**66**	2½d. maroon	..	15	10

(Des Sir Daryl Lindsay and F. D. Manley. Eng F. D. Manley. Recess)

1949 (10 Oct). *75th Anniv of Founding of U.P.U. P* 15 × 14.

232	**67**	3½d. ultramarine	..	30	40

68 John, Lord Forrest of Bunbury   **69** Queen Elizabeth   **70** King George VI

(Des and eng F. D. Manley. Recess)

1949 (28 Nov). *John, Lord Forrest of Bunbury (explorer and politician) Commemoration. W* **15**. *P* 15×14.

233	**68**	2½d. lake	..	15	10

(Des and eng F. D. Manley. Recess)

1950 (12 Apr)–52. *P* 15×14. (a) *W* **15**

234	**70**	2½d. scarlet (12.4.50)	..	10	10
235		3d. scarlet (28.2.51)	..	15	10
		aa. Coil pair (4.51)	..	17·00	20·00

(b) *No wmk*

236	**69**	1½d. green (19.6.50)	..	15	10
237		2d. yellow-green (28.3.51)	..	15	10
		a. Coil pair	..	5·00	7·50
		b. Coil block of four (11.52)	..	10·00	
237c	**70**	2½d. purple-brown (23.5.51)	..	15	15
237d		3d. grey-green (14.11.51)	..	15	10
		da. Coil pair (12.51)	..	24·00	30·00
234/7d		*Set of* 6	80	40

On 14 October 1951 No. 235 was placed on sale in sheets of 144 originally intended for use in stamp booklets. These sheets contain 3 panes of 48 (16×3) with horizontal gutter margin between.

71 Aborigine   **72**   **73** Reproductions of First Stamps of New South Wales and Victoria

---

(Des and eng F. D. Manley. Recess)

1950 (14 Aug). *W* **15**. *P* 15×14.

238	**71**	8½d. brown	..	15	45

For T **71** in a larger size, see Nos. 253/b.

(Des and eng G. Lissenden (T **72**), E. R. M. Jones (T **73**). Recess)

1950 (27 Sept). *Centenary of First Adhesive Postage Stamps in Australia. P* 15×14.

239	**72**	2½d. maroon	..	20	10
		a. Horiz pair. Nos. 239/40	..	40	55
240	**73**	2½d. maroon	..	20	10

Nos. 239/40 were printed alternately in vertical columns throughout the sheet.

74 Sir Edmund Barton   **75** Sir Henry Parkes

76 "Opening First Federal Parliament" (T. Roberts)   **77** Federal Parliament House, Canberra

(Des and eng F. D. Manley. Recess)

1951 (1 May). *50th Anniv of Commonwealth of Australia. P* 15×14.

241	**74**	3d. lake	..	30	10
		a. Horiz. pair. Nos. 241/2	..	1·75	2·25
242	**75**	3d. lake	..	30	10
243	**76**	5½d. blue	..	20	2·00
244	**77**	1s. 6d. purple-brown	..	35	50
241/4		*Set of* 4	2·00	2·50

Nos. 241/2 are printed alternately in vertical columns throughout the sheet.

78   **79** E. H. Hargraves   C. J. Latrobe

(Des and eng F. D. Manley. Recess)

1951 (2 July). *Centenaries of Discovery of Gold in Australia and of Responsible Government in Victoria. P* 15×14.

245	**78**	3d. maroon	..	30	10
		a. Horiz pair. Nos. 245/6	..	70	95
246	**79**	3d. maroon	..	30	10

Nos. 245/6 were printed alternately in vertical columns throughout the sheet.

80   **81**   **82** King George VI

(Des E. R. M. Jones (7½d.), F. D. Manley (others). Eng. F. D. Manley. Recess)

1951–52. *W* **15** (*sideways on 1s. 0½d.*). *P* 14½ (1s. 0½d.) *or* 15×14 (*others*).

247	**80**	3½d. brown-purple (28.11.51)	..	10	10
		a. Imperf between (horiz pair)	..	£5500	
248		4½d. scarlet (20.5.52)	..	15	70
249		6½d. brown (20.2.52)	..	15	60
250		6½d. emerald-green (9.4.52)	..	10	15
251	**81**	7½d. blue (31.10.51)	..	15	45
		a. Imperf three sides (vert pr)	..	£7500	
252	**82**	1s. 0½d. indigo (19.3.52)	..	35	30
247/52		*Set of* 6	90	2·00

No. 251a occurs on the left-hand vertical row of one sheet.

(Des F. D. Manley. Eng E. R. M. Jones. Recess)

1952 (19 Mar)–65. *P* 14½. (a) *W* **15** (*sideways**)

253		2s. 6d. deep green	..	1·50	35
		aw. Wmk Crown to left of C of A	..	†	£700

(b) *No wmk*

253b		2s. 6d. deep brown (30.1.57)	..	5·00	55
		ba. Sepia (10.65)	..	12·00	12·00

Design:—2s. 6d. As T **71** but larger (21×25½ mm).

*The normal sideways watermark on No. 253 shows Crown to right of C of A, *as seen from the back of the stamp.*

No. 253ba was an emergency printing and can easily be distinguished from No. 253b as it is on white Harrison paper, No. 253b being on toned paper.

(Des and eng F. D. Manley. Recess)

1952 (19 Nov). *Pan-Pacific Scout Jamboree, Greystanes. As T* **65**, *but inscr* "1952–53". *W* **15** (*sideways*). *P* 14 × 15.

254		3½d. brown-lake	..	10	10

83 Butter   84 Wheat   85 Beef

(Des P.O. artists; adapted G. Lissenden. Typo)

1953 (11 Feb). *Food Production.* P 14½.
255	83	3d. emerald		30	10
		a. Strip of 3. Nos. 255/7		2·00	
256	84	3d. emerald		30	10
257	85	3d. emerald		30	10
258	83	3½d. scarlet		30	10
		a. Strip of 3. Nos. 258/60		2·00	
259	84	3½d. scarlet		30	10
260	85	3½d. scarlet		30	10
255/60		*Set of 6*		3·75	40

The three designs in each denomination appear in rotation, both horizontally and vertically, throughout the sheet.

86 Queen   87 Queen Elizabeth II
Elizabeth II

(Des F. D. Manley from photograph by Dorothy Wilding Ltd. Eng D. Cameron. Recess)

1953–56. P 15×14. (a) *No wmk.*
261	86	1d. purple (19.8.53)		15	10
261a		2½d. blue (23.6.54)		20	10
262		3d. deep green (17.6.53)		20	10
		aa. Coil pair		5·00	7·50
		ab. Coil block of four (9.53)		13·00	
262a		3½d. brown-red (2.7.56)		1·25	20
262b		6½d. orange (9.56)		1·75	1·50

(b) *W 15*
263	86	3½d. brown-red (21.4.53)		20	10
263a		6½d. orange (23.6.54)		1·50	20
261/3a		*Set of 7*		4·75	1·75

(Des and eng F. D. Manley. Recess)

1953 (25 May). *Coronation.* P 15 × 14.
264	87	3½d. scarlet		35	10
265		7½d. violet		75	1·10
266		2s. dull bluish green		2·50	1·10
264/6		*Set of 3*		3·25	2·00

88 Young Farmers and Calf

(Des P.O. artist; adapted P. E. Morriss. Eng E. R. M. Jones. Recess)

1953 (3 Sept). *25th Anniv of Australian Young Farmers' Clubs.* P 14½.
| 267 | 88 | 3½d. red-brown and deep green | | 10 | 10 |

89 Lt.-Gov. D.   90 Lt.-Gov. W.
Collins   Paterson

91 Sullivan Cove, Hobart, 1804

(Des E. R. M. Jones, eng D. Cameron (T 89/90); des and eng G. Lissenden (T 91). Recess)

1953 (23 Sept). *150th Anniv of Settlement in Tasmania.* P 15 × 14.
268	89	3½d. brown-purple		30	10
		a. Horiz pair. Nos. 268/9		80	1·25
269	90	3½d. brown-purple		30	10
270	91	2s. green		1·50	2·75
268/70		*Set of 3*		2·10	2·75

Nos. 268/9 were printed alternately in vertical columns throughout the sheet.

NEW INFORMATION

The editor is always interested to correspond with people who have new information that will improve or correct the Catalogue.

92 Stamp of 1853

(Des R. L. Beck; eng G. Lissenden. Recess)

1953 (11 Nov). *Tasmanian Postage Stamp Centenary.* P 14½.
| 271 | 92 | 3d. rose-red | | 10 | 30 |

93 Queen Elizabeth II and Duke of Edinburgh

94 Queen Elizabeth II   Re-entry (lower plate
left pane R. 8/2)

(Des and eng F. D. Manley; border and lettering on 7½d. des by R. M. Warner. Recess)

1954 (2 Feb). *Royal Visit.* P 14.
272	93	3½d. scarlet		20	10
		a. Re-entry		38·00	13·00
273	94	7½d. purple		35	1·25
274	93	2s. dull bluish green		85	65
272/4		*Set of 3*		1·25	1·75

95 "Telegraphic   96 Red Cross and
Communications"   Globe

(Des R. M. Warner. Eng P. E. Morriss. Recess)

1954 (7 Apr). *Australian Telegraph System Centenary.* P 14.
| 275 | 95 | 3½d. brown-red | | 10 | 10 |

(Des B. Stewart. Eng P. E. Morriss. Design recess; cross typo)

1954 (9 June). *40th Anniv of Australian Red Cross Society.* P 14½.
| 276 | 96 | 3½d. ultramarine and scarlet | | 10 | 10 |

97 Mute Swan   98 Locomotives of 1854 and 1954

(Des R. L. Beck. Eng G. Lissenden. Recess)

1954 (2 Aug). *Western Australian Postage Stamp Centenary.* P 14½.
| 277 | 97 | 3½d. black | | 20 | 10 |

(Des R. M. Warner. Eng G. Lissenden. Recess)

1954 (13 Sept). *Australian Railways Centenary.* P 14.
| 278 | 98 | 3½d. purple-brown | | 30 | 10 |

99 Territory Badge   100 Olympic Games   101 Rotary Symbol,
Symbol   Globe and Flags

(Des F. D. Manley. Eng G. Lissenden. Recess)

1954 (17 Nov). *Australian Antarctic Research.* P 14½ × 13½.
| 279 | 99 | 3½d. grey-black | | 15 | 10 |

(Des R. L. Beck. Eng P. E. Morriss. Recess)

1954 (1 Dec)–**55.** *Olympic Games Propaganda.* P 14.
| 280 | 100 | 2s. deep bright blue | | 70 | 80 |
| 280a | | 2s. deep bluish green (30.11.55) | | 1·75 | 1·75 |

(Des and eng D. Cameron. Recess)

1955 (23 Feb). *50th Anniv of Rotary International.* P 14 × 14½.
| 281 | 101 | 3½d. carmine | | 10 | 10 |

101a Queen   101b Queen   102 Queen Elizabeth II
Elizabeth II   Elizabeth II

(Des F. D. Manley from bas-relief by W. L. Bowles. Eng D. Cameron (7½d.), G. Lissenden (others). Recess)

1955 (9 Mar)–**57.** P 15×14 (T 101a/b) or 14½ (T 102).
(a) *W 15 (sideways)*
| 282 | 102 | 1s. 0½d. deep blue | | 1·50 | 75 |

(b) *No wmk*
282a	101a	4d. lake (13.3.57)		20	10
		ab. Booklet pane of 6		7·50	
282b	101b	7½d. violet (13.11.57)		60	1·25
		ba. Double print		£1800	
282c	101a	10d. deep grey-blue (6.3.57)		60	75
282d	102	1s. 7d red-brown (13.3.57)		1·50	30
282/d		*Set of 5*		4·00	2·75

No. 282ab has the outer edges of the pane imperforate, producing single stamps with one or two adjacent sides imperforate.

103 American Memorial,   104 Cobb & Co. Coach (from
Canberra   dry-print by Sir Lionel Lindsay)

(Des R. L. Beck (head by F. D. Manley). Eng F. D. Manley. Recess)

1955 (4 May). *Australian–American Friendship.* P 14 × 14½.
| 283 | 103 | 3½d. violet-blue | | 10 | 10 |

(Design adapted and eng by F. D. Manley. Recess)

1955 (6 July). *Mail-coach Pioneers Commemoration.* P 14½ × 14.
| 284 | 104 | 3½d. blackish brown | | 25 | 10 |
| 285 | | 2s. reddish brown | | 75 | 1·40 |

105 Y.M.C.A. Emblem and Map   106 Florence Nightingale
of the World   and Young Nurse

(Des E. Thake. Eng P. E. Morriss. Design recess; emblem typo)

1955 (10 Aug). *World Centenary of Y.M.C.A.* P 14½ × 14.
| 286 | 105 | 3½d. deep bluish green and red | | 10 | 10 |
| | | a. Red (emblem) omitted | | £7000 | |

(Des and eng F.D. Manley. Recess)

1955 (21 Sept). *Nursing Profession Commem.* P 14×14½.
| 287 | 106 | 3½d. reddish violet | | 10 | 10 |

107 Queen Victoria   108 Badges of New South Wales,
Victoria and Tasmania

(Des and eng D. Cameron. Recess)

1955 (17 Oct). *Centenary of First South Australian Postage Stamps. P* 14½.
288 107 3½d. green 10 10

(Des and eng F. D. Manley. Recess)

1956 (26 Sept). *Centenary of Responsible Government in New South Wales, Victoria and Tasmania. P* 14½ × 14.
289 108 3½d. brown-lake 10 10

109 Arms of Melbourne   **110** Olympic Torch and Symbol

111 Collins Street, Melbourne   **112** Melbourne across R. Yarra

(Des P. E. Morriss; eng F. D. Manley (4d.). Des and eng F. D. Manley (7½d.). Recess. Des and photo Harrison from photographs by M. Murphy and sketches by L. Coles (1s.). Des and photo Courvoisier from photographs by M. Murphy (2s.))

1956 (31 Oct). *Olympic Games, Melbourne. P* 14½ (4d.), 14 × 14½ (7½d., 1s.) *or* 11½ (2s.).
290 109 4d. carmine-red 25 10
291 110 7½d. deep bright blue .. .. .. 50 1·25
292 111 1s. multicoloured 60 30
293 112 2s. multicoloured .. .. .. 85 1·25
290/3 .. .. *Set of 4* 2·00 2·50

115 South Australia Coat of Arms   **116** Map of Australia and Caduceus

(Des and eng P. E. Morriss. Recess)

1957 (17 Apr). *Centenary of Responsible Government in South Australia. P* 14½.
296 115 4d. red-brown 10 10

(Des J. E. Lyle; adapted B. Stewart. Eng D. Cameron. Recess)

1957 (21 Aug). *Flying Doctor Service. P* 14½ × 14.
297 116 7d. ultramarine 15 10

117 "The Spirit of Christmas"

Re-entry (upper plate left pane R. 10/1)

(Des and eng D. Cameron from a painting by Sir Joshua Reynolds. Recess)

1957 (6 Nov). *Christmas. P* 14½ × 14.
298 117 3½d. scarlet 10 20
      a. Re-entry .. .. .. 9·00 9·00
299   4d. purple 10 10

118 Lockheed L.1049 Super Constellation Airliner

(Des and eng P. E. Morriss. Recess)

1958 (6 Jan). *Inauguration of Australian "Round the World" Air Service. P* 14½ × 14.
301 118 2s. deep blue .. .. .. 75 1·00

119 Hall of Memory, Sailor and Airman   **120** Sir Charles Kingsford Smith and Fokker F.VIIa/3m *Southern Cross*

(Des and eng G. Lissenden. Recess)

1958 (10 Feb). *T* **119** *and similar horiz design. P* 14½ × 14.
302 119 5½d. brown-red 40 30
      a. Horiz pair. Nos. 302/3 .. .. 80 5·50
303 — 5½d. brown-red 40 30
    No. 303 shows a soldier and service-woman respectively in place of the sailor and airman. Nos. 302/3 are printed alternately in vertical columns throughout the sheet.

(Des J. E. Lyle. Eng F. D. Manley. Recess)

1958 (27 Aug). *30th Anniv of First Air Crossing of the Tasman Sea. P* 14 × 14½.
304 120 8d. deep ultramarine 60 95

121 Silver Mine, Broken Hill   **122** The Nativity

(Des R. H. Evans; adapted and eng F. D. Manley. Recess)

1958 (10 Sept). *75th Anniv of Founding of Broken Hill. P* 14½ × 14.
305 121 4d. chocolate 30 10

(Des D. Cameron. Eng P. E. Morriss. Recess)

1958 (5 Nov). *Christmas. P* 14½ × 15.
306 122 3½d. deep scarlet 20 10
307   4d. deep violet 20 10

123   **124**   **126**

127   **128**   **129**

Queen Elizabeth II

Type I   Type II
Short break in outer line   Line unbroken
to bottom right of "4"

Type A   Type B
Four short lines   Five short lines
inside "5"   inside "5"

(Des G. Lissenden from photographs by Baron Studios. Eng F. D. Manley (2d.), D. Cameron (3d.). P. E. Morriss (others). Recess)

1959–63. *P* 14×15 (*horiz*) *or* 15×14 (*vert*).
308 123 1d. deep slate-purple (2.2.59) .. 10 10
      a. Deep slate-lilac (1961) .. 85 20
309 124 2d. brown (21.3.62) 50 15
      a. Coil pair (1962) .. .. 4·00 4·25
      b. Coil block of four (1963) .. 8·00
311 126 3d. blue-green (20.5.59) .. 15 10
      a. Coil pair (8.59) .. .. 4·00 4·75
      b. Coil block of four (9.11.61) .. 10·00
312 127 3½d. deep green (18.3.59) .. 15 15
313 128 4d. carmine-lake (Type I) (2.2.59) .. 1·75 10
      a. Carmine-red .. .. 1·75 10
      ab. Booklet pane of 6 (18.3.59) .. 19·00
      b. Type II .. .. 1·75 10
      ba. Carmine-red .. .. 1·75 10
314 129 5d. deep blue (Type A or B) (1.10.59) 90 10
      a. Vert *se-tenant* pair (A and B) .. 1·75 2·50
      b. Coil pair (18.7.60) .. .. 8·00 10·00
      c. Coil block of four (7.61) .. 35·00
      d. Booklet pane of 6 (23.3.60) .. 10·00
308/14 .. .. *Set of 6* 3·00 30
    No. 313. Produced in printer's sheets, of 640 split into sheets of 160 for issue. Type I occurs on the two upper sheets from the printers' sheet and on ten positions from the left pane of the lower right sheet. Type II occurs on all stamps from the lower sheets except for ten positions from the left pane of lower right sheet.
    No. 314. Both types occur in alternate horizontal rows in the sheet (Type A in Row 1, Type B in Row 2, and so on), and their value is identical. Booklet pane No. 314d contains two Type A and four Type B.
    Nos. 309a/b, 311a/b and 314b/c have horizontal coil perforations as described after No. 191.
    Nos. 313ab and 314d have the outer edges of the panes imperforate, producing stamps with one or two adjacent sides imperforate.
    Printings of the 2d. (from March 1965) and of the 3d. (from April 1965), both including coils, were on Helecon paper.

131 Numbat   **137** Christmas Bells

142 Aboriginal Stockman

(Des Eileen Mayo (6d., 8d., 9d., 11d., 1s., 1s. 2d.), B. Stewart (5s.), Margaret Stones (others). Eng P. Morriss (11d.), F. D. Manley (1s.), B. Stewart (others).)

1959–64. *T* **131, 137, 142** *and similar designs. W* **15** (5s.), *no wmk (others). P* 14 × 15 (1s. 2d.), 15 × 14 (6d. *to* 1s.), 14½ × 14 (5s.) *or* 14½ (*others*).
316   6d. brown (30.9.60) .. .. 2·00 10
317   8d. red-brown (11.5.60) .. 75 10
      a. Pale red-brown (9.61) .. 75 10
318   9d. deep sepia (21.10.59) .. 1·75 55
319   11d. deep blue (3.5.61) .. 1·25 15
320   1s. deep green (9.9.59) .. 3·50 40
321   1s. 2d. deep purple (21.3.62) .. 1·25 15
322   1s. 6d. crimson/*yellow* (3.2.60) .. 2·50 80
323   2s. grey-blue (8.4.59) .. 1·25 10
324   2s. 3d. green/*maize* (9.9.59) .. 1·25 10
324a   2s. 3d. yellow-green (28.10.64) .. 5·00 1·50
325   2s. 5d. brown/*yellow* (16.3.60) .. 6·00 65
326   3s. scarlet (15.7.59) .. 1·50 20
327   5s. red-brown (26.7.61) .. 20·00 85
      a. White paper. *Brown-red* (17.6.64) .. £100 7·50
316/327 .. .. .. *Set of 13* 42·00 4·75
    Designs: (As *T* **131**) Vert—8d. Tiger Cat; 9d. Eastern Grey Kangaroos; 11d. Common Rabbit-Bandicoot; 1s. Platypus. *Horiz*—1s. 2d. Thylacine. (As *T* **137**) Vert—2s. Flannel Flower; 2s. 3d. Wattle; 2s. 5d. Banksia; 3s. Waratah.
    No. 327 is on toned paper. No. 327a was a late printing on the white paper referred to in the note below No. 360.
    An experimental printing of the 11d. was made on Helecon paper in December 1963. See note below No. 362.
    All printings of the 8d., 11d., 1s. 2d. and 2s. 3d. (No. 324a) were on Helecon paper from April 1965.

NEW INFORMATION

The editor is always interested to correspond with people who have new information that will improve or correct the Catalogue.

143 Postmaster Isaac Nichols boarding the brig *Experiment*

144 Parliament House, Brisbane, and Arms of Queensland

(Des R. Shackel; adapted and eng F. D. Manley. Recess)

1959 (22 Apr). *150th Anniv of the Australian Post Office.* P 14½ × 14.
331 143 4d. slate 15 10

(Des and eng G. Lissenden. Recess and typo)

1959 (5 June). *Centenary of Self-Government in Queensland.* P 14 × 14½.
332 144 4d. lilac and green .. 10 10

145 "The Approach of the Magi"

146 Girl Guide and Lord Baden-Powell

(Des and eng F. D. Manley. Recess)

1959 (4 Nov). *Christmas.* P 15 × 14.
333 145 5d. deep reddish violet .. 10 10

(Des and eng B. Stewart. Recess)

1960 (18 Aug). *50th Anniv of Girl Guide Movement.* P 14½×14.
334 146 5d. deep ultramarine .. 30 15

147 "The Overlanders" (Sir Daryl Lindsay)

148 "Archer" and Melbourne Cup

Two types:

I Mane rough   II Mane smooth

Type II occurs on Pane A, Row 2 Nos. 8 and 9, Row 4 Nos. 1 to 12, Row 5 Nos. 10 to 12, and on Pane C, Row 4 Nos. 5 to 12, Row 5 Nos. 1 to 9, and Rows 6 to 10 inclusive; the stamps in Row 4 Nos. 5 to 12 and Row 5 Nos. 1 to 9 are considered to be of an intermediate type with the mane as in Type II but the ear and rein being as in Type I. All the rest are Type I.

(Adapted and eng P. E. Morriss. Recess)

1960 (21 Sept). *Centenary of Northern Territory Exploration.* P 15 × 14½.
335 147 5d. magenta (I) 30 15
    a. Type II .. .. .. 1·75 55

(Des F. D. Manley. Eng G. Lissenden. Recess)

1960 (12 Oct). *100th Melbourne Cup Race Commemoration.* P 14½.
336 148 5d. sepia 20 10

149 Queen Victoria   **150** Open Bible and Candle

(Des F. D. Manley. Eng B. Stewart. Recess)

1960 (2 Nov). *Centenary of First Queensland Postage Stamp.* P 14½×15.
337 149 5d. deep myrtle-green .. 25 10

(Des K. McKay. Adapted and eng B. Stewart. Recess)

1960 (9 Nov). *Christmas.* P 15 × 14½.
338 150 5d. carmine-red 10 10

151 Colombo Plan Bureau Emblem

152 Melba (after bust by Sir Bertram Mackennal)

(Des and eng G. Lissenden. Recess)

1961 (30 June). *Colombo Plan.* P 14×14½.
339 151 1s. red-brown 10 10
    No. 339 was issued on Helecon paper in April 1965. See note after No. 362.

(Des and eng B. Stewart. Recess)

1961 (20 Sept). *Birth Centenary of Dame Nellie Melba* (singer). P 14½×15.
340 152 5d. blue 30 15

153 Open Prayer Book and Text

(Des G. Lissenden. Eng P. E. Morriss. Recess)

1961 (8 Nov). *Christmas.* P 14½ × 14.
341 153 5d. brown 10 10

154 J. M. Stuart   **155** Flynn's Grave and Nursing Sister

(Des W. Jardine. Eng P. E. Morriss. Recess)

1962 (25 July). *Centenary of Stuart's Crossing of Australia from South to North.* P 14½ × 15.
342 154 5d. brown-red 15 10

(Des F. D. Manley. Photo)

1962 (5 Sept). *50th Anniv of Australian Inland Mission.* P 13½.
343 155 5d. multicoloured .. 30 10
    a. Red omitted .. .. † £500
    The note below No. 372b also applies to No. 343a.

156 "Woman"   **157** "Madonna and Child"

(Des D. Dundas. Eng G. Lissenden. Recess)

1962 (26 Sept). *"Associated Country Women of the World" Conference, Melbourne.* P 14 × 14½.
344 156 5d. deep green 10 10

(Des and eng G. Lissenden. Recess)

1962 (17 Oct). *Christmas.* P 14½.
345 157 5d. violet 15 10

158 Perth and Kangaroo Paw (plant)

159 Arms of Perth and Running Track

(Des R. M. Warner (5d.), G. Hamori (2s. 3d.). Photo Harrison)

1962 (1 Nov). *Seventh British Empire and Commonwealth Games, Perth.* P 14 (5d.) or 14½ × 14 (2s. 3d.).
346 158 5d. multicoloured .. 40 10
    a. Red omitted £900
347 159 2s. 3d. black, red, blue and green 3·25 2·75

160 Queen Elizabeth II.

161 Queen Elizabeth II and Duke of Edinburgh

(Des and eng after portraits by Anthony Buckley, P. E. Morriss (5d.), B. Stewart (2s. 3d.). Recess)

1963 (18 Feb). *Royal Visit.* P 14½.
348 160 5d. deep green 35 10
349 161 2s. 3d. brown-lake .. 2·00 3·50

162 Arms of Canberra and W. B. Griffin (architect)

163 Centenary Emblem

(Des and eng B. Stewart. Recess)

1963 (8 Mar). *50th Anniv of Canberra.* P 14½ × 14.
350 162 5d. deep green 15 10

(Des G. Hamori. Photo)

1963 (8 May). *Red Cross Centenary.* P 13½ × 13.
351 163 5d. red, grey-brown and blue .. 30 10

164 Blaxland, Lawson and Wentworth on Mt. York

(Des T. Alban. Eng P. E. Morriss. Recess)

1963 (28 May). *150th Anniv of First Crossing of Blue Mountains.* P 14½ × 14.
352 164 5d. ultramarine 15 10

165 "Export"   **166** Queen Elizabeth II

(Des and eng B. Stewart. Recess)

1963 (28 Aug). *Export Campaign.* P 14½×14.
353 165 5d. red 10 10

(Des and eng P. E. Morriss from photograph by Anthony Buckley. Recess)

1963 (9 Oct)–**65**. P 15×14.
354 166 5d. deep green 65 10
    a. Booklet pane of 6 (17.6.64) 21·00
    b. Imperf between (horiz pair) (31.7.64) 1·25 2·50
354c 5d. red (30.6.65) 55 10
    ca. Coil pair .. .. 18·00 23·00
    cb. Booklet pane of 6 .. 21·00
    The 5d. deep green exists from both sheets and booklets on Helecon paper produced in error.
    The 5d. red was issued with or without Helecon added to the ink. All coil and booklet printings included Helecon in the ink, except for a small printing produced in error. Examples of the sheet and booklet printings with Helecon ink have been found on Helecon *paper.*
    Nos. 354a and 354cb have the outer edges of the panes imperforate producing single stamps with one or two adjacent sides imperforate.

PRICES OF SETS

Set prices are given for many issues, generally those containing three stamps or more. Definitive sets include one of each value or major colour change, but do not cover different perforations, die types or minor shades. Where a choice is possible the set prices are based on the cheapest versions of the stamps included in the listings.

No. 354b comes from sheets of uncut booklet panes containing 288 stamps (16×18) with wide margins intersecting the sheet horizontally below each third row, alternate rows of stamps imperforate between vertically and the outer left, right and bottom margins imperforate. This means that in each sheet there are 126 pairs of stamps imperf between vertically, plus a number with wide imperforate margins attached, as shown in the illustration.

A 5d. in a similar design, printed in blue and brown with vertical edges imperforate, was prepared, but not issued.

167 Tasman and *Heemskerk*   **168** Dampier and *Roebuck*

(Des W. Jardine. Eng B. Stewart (4s.), P. E. Morriss (others). Recess)

1963–65. *T 167/8 and similar designs. No wmk (4s.) or W 15 (others), (sideways on 5s., £1). P 14 or 14½ (5s., £1, £2).*
355	4s. ultramarine (9.10.63)	..	..	3·00	55
356	5s. red-brown (25.11.64)	..	..	4·00	1·25
357	7s. 6d. olive (26.8.64)	..	..	19·00	16·00
358	10s. brown-purple (26.2.64)	..	..	30·00	4·50
	a. White paper. *Deep brown-purple* (14.1.65)			30·00	7·50
359	£1 deep reddish violet (26.2.64)	..		35·00	15·00
	a. White paper. *Deep bluish violet* (16.11.64)			42·00	24·00
360	£2 sepia (26.8.64)	..	..	65·00	75·00
355/360	..	..	*Set of 6*	£130	£100
357/60 Optd "Specimen"			*Set of 4*	£450	

Designs: As *T 167*—7s. 6d. Captain Cook; 10s. Flinders and *Investigator*. As *T 168*—£1 Bass and *Tom Thumb* (whaleboat); £2 Admiral King and *Mermaid* (survey cutter).

Nos. 358 and 359 were printed on a toned paper but all the other values are on white paper, the 4s. being on rather thicker paper.

173 "Peace on Earth . . ."   **174** "Commonwealth Cable"

(Des R. M. Warner. Eng B. Stewart. Recess)

1963 (25 Oct). *Christmas. P 14½.*
361	**173**	5d. greenish blue	..	10	10

(Des P. E. Morriss. Photo)

1963 (3 Dec). *Opening of COMPAC (Trans-Pacific Telephone Cable). Chalk-surfaced paper. P 13½.*
362	**174**	2s. 3d. red, blue, black and pale blue	..	2·00	3·50

HELECON (PHOSPHOR) STAMPS. "Helecon", a chemical substance of the zinc sulphide group, has been incorporated in stamps in two different ways, either in the ink with which the stamps are printed, or included in the surface coating of the stamp paper.

Owing to the difficulty of identification without the use of a U.V. lamp we do not list the helecon stamps separately but when in stock can supply them after testing under the lamp.

The first stamp to be issued on helecon was the 11d. Bandicoot (No. 319) from an experimental printing of four million released to the public in December 1963. The next printing, on ordinary

paper, was released in September 1964. The experimental printing was coarse, showing a lot of white dots and the colour is slate-blue, differing from both the ordinary and the later helecon paper.

Further Helecon printings followed from March 1965. Almost all issues from No. 378 onwards were on Helecon paper or paper coated with Derby Luminescence.

175 Yellow-tailed Thornbill   **176** Black-backed Magpie

(Des Betty Temple-Watts. Photo)

1964 (11 Mar)–65. *Birds. T 175/6 and similar designs. Chalk-surfaced paper. P 13½.*
363	6d. brown, yellow, blk & bluish grn (19.8.64)		80	25
	a. *Brown, yellow, black & emer-grn* (6.65)		2·50	2·00
364	9d. black, grey and pale green	..	1·00	2·75
365	1s. 6d. pink, grey, dull purple and black	..	75	1·40
366	2s. yellow, black and pink (21.4.65)		1·75	50
367	2s. 5d. deep royal blue, light violet-blue, yellow-orange, grey and black		2·50	3·50
	a. Ordinary paper. *Deep blue, light blue, orange-brown, blue-grey and black* (7.65)		20·00	12·00
368	2s. 6d. black, red, grey and green (21.4.65)		1·00	3·25
	a. Red omitted (white breast)	..	£1600	
369	3s. black, red, buff & yellow-green (21.4.65)		5·00	1·75
363/9		*Set of 7*	15·00	12·00

Designs: *Vert*—1s. 6d. Galah; 2s. Golden Whistler; 2s. 5d. Blue Wren; 3s. Straw-necked Ibis. *Horiz*—2s. 6d. Scarlet Robin.

No. 367a was from a printing, made in 1962, on unsurfaced Wiggins Teape paper, the rest of the set being on chalk-surfaced Harrison paper. Apart from the differences in shade, the inscriptions, particularly "BLUE WREN", stand out very much more clearly on No. 367a. Although two colours are apparent in both stamps, the grey and black were printed from one cylinder.

The 6d. (No. 363) and 2s. 5d. were only issued on ordinary paper. The 9d. and 1s. 6d. exist on ordinary or Helecon paper. The 6d. (No. 363a), 1s., 2s. 6d. and 3s. were issued on Helecon paper only.

182 Bleriot XI Aircraft (type flown by M. Guillaux, 1914)   Re-entry (upper right plate, R. 4/4)

(Des K. McKay. Adapted and eng P. E. Morriss. Recess)

1964 (1 July). *50th Anniv of First Australian Airmail Flight. P 14½ × 14.*
370	**182**	5d. olive-green	40	10
		a. Re-entry	£180	90·00
371		2s. 3d. scarlet	3·50	2·75

183 Child looking at Nativity Scene   **184** "Simpson and his Donkey"

(Des P. E. Morriss and J. Mason. Photo)

1964 (21 Oct). *Christmas. Chalk-surfaced paper. P 13½.*
372	**183**	5d. red, blue, buff and black	10	10
		a. Red omitted	†	£550
		b. Black omitted	£750	

The red ink is soluble and can be removed by bleaching and it is therefore advisable to obtain a certificate from a recognised expert committee before purchasing No. 372a. The used price quoted is for an example on cover.

(Des C. Andrew (after statue, Shrine of Remembrance, Melbourne). Eng E. R. M. Jones. Recess)

1965 (14 Apr). *50th Anniv of Gallipoli Landing. P 14 × 14½.*
373	**184**	5d. drab	65	10
374		8d. blue	1·00	2·50
375		2s. 3d. reddish purple	1·75	2·50
373/5 ..		*Set of 3*	3·00	4·50

185 "Telecommunications"   **186** Sir Winston Churchill

(Des J. McMahon and G. Hamori. Photo)

1965 (10 May). *I.T.U. Centenary. Chalk-surfaced paper. P 13½.*
376	**185**	5d. black, brown, orange-brown & blue	40	10
		a. Black (value and pylon) omitted ..	£950	

(Des P. E. Morriss from photo by Karsh. Photo)

1965 (24 May). *Churchill Commemoration. Chalk-surfaced paper. P 13½.*
377	**186**	5d. black, pale grey, grey and light blue	15	10
		a. Pale grey (facial shading) omitted	£950	

No. 377a occurred on stamps from the bottom row of one sheet.

Two used examples are known showing the grey ("AUSTRALIA") omitted.

No. 377 exists on ordinary or Helecon paper in approximately equal quantities.

HELECON PAPER. All stamps from No. 378 were on Helecon paper, *unless otherwise stated.*

187 General Monash   **188** Hargrave and "Multiplane" Seaplane (1902)

(Des O. Foulkes and W. Walters. Photo)

1965 (23 June). *Birth Centenary of General Sir John Monash (engineer and soldier). P 13½.*
378	**187**	5d. multicoloured	..	15	10

(Des G. Hamori. Photo)

1965 (4 Aug). *50th Death Anniv of Lawrence Hargrave (aviation pioneer). P 13½.*
379	**188**	5d. purple-brown, blk, yell-ochre & pur	15	10
		a. Purple (value) omitted	£250	

189 I.C.Y. Emblem   **190** "Nativity Scene"

(Des H. Fallu from U.N. theme. Photo)

1965 (1 Sept). *International Co-operation Year. P 13½.*
380	**189**	2s. 3d. emerald and light blue	..	90	2·00

(Des J. Mason. Photo)

1965 (20 Oct). *Christmas. P 13½.*
381	**190**	5d. multicoloured	..	15	10
		a. Gold omitted	£1100	
		b. Blue omitted	£550	

No. 381a comes from the bottom row of a sheet in which the gold is completely omitted, the background appearing as black with "CHRISTMAS 1965" and "AUSTRALIA" omitted. The row above had the black missing from the lower two-fifths of the stamp.

(New Currency. 100 cents = 1 dollar)

191 Queen Elizabeth II   **192** Blue-faced Honeyeater   **193** White-tailed Dascyllus ("Humbug Fish")

Nos. 401 (top), 401a (centre) and 401b (bottom). No. 401b shows the final form of the variety with a plate crack visible in sky and across sail (Lower sheet left pane. R. 10/1)

(Des Betty Temple-Watts (6 c. (No. 387), 13 c., 24 c.), Eileen Mayo (7 c. (No. 388) to 10 c.). Recess (T **191**, 40 c. to $4). Photo (others))

1966 (14 Feb)–73. *Decimal currency.* T **191/3** *and similar designs, some reused from previous issues.* P 15×14 (T **191**), 14 (40 c., 75 c., $1), 14½ (50 c., $2, $4) *or* 13½ (*others*).

382	191	1 c. deep red-brown	.. ..	25	10
383		2 c. olive-green	.. ..	70	10
384		3 c. slate-green	.. ..	70	10
385		4 c. red	.. ..	20	10
		a. Booklet pane. Five stamps plus one printed label	..	22·00	
386	175	5 c. brown, yellow, black & emer-grn		25	10
		a. Brown (plumage) omitted	..	£1200	
		b. *Brown, yellow, blk & bl-grn* (1.67)	25	20
386c	191	5 c. deep blue (29.9.67)	..	70	10
		ca. Booklet pane. Five stamps plus one printed label	..	8·00	
		cb. Imperf in horiz strip of 3*	..	£1400	
387	192	6 c. olive-yellow, blk, blue & pale grey		80	45
		aa. Blue (eye markings) omitted	..	£275	
387a	191	6 c. orange (28.9.70)	..	55	10
388	193	7 c. black, grey, salmon and brown		85	10
388a	191	7 c. purple (1.10.71)	..	70	10
389	–	8 c. red, yell, bl-grn & blackish green	85	40
390	–	9 c. brown-red, purple-brown, black and light yellow-olive	..	85	15
391	–	10 c. orange, blackish brown, pale turquoise-blue and olive-brown	85	10
392	–	13 c. red, black, grey & light turq-green	1·75	25
		a. Red omitted	..	£1200	
		b. Grey (plumage and legs) omitted	£900	
393	–	15 c. rose-carmine, black, grey and light bluish green	..	1·50	90
		a. Rose-carmine omitted	..	£2750	
394	–	20 c. yellow, black and pink	..	3·00	15
		a. Yellow (plumage) omitted	..	£1000	
395	–	24 c. ultramarine, yellow, blk & lt brn	90	1·25
396	–	25 c. black, red, grey and green	..	3·75	30
		a. Red omitted	..	£1300	
397	–	30 c. black, red, buff & lt yellow-green	12·00	80
		a. Red omitted	..	£1100	
398	167	40 c. ultramarine	..	5·00	10
399	168	50 c. red-brown	..	7·00	10
400	–	75 c. olive	..	1·00	1·00
401	–	$1 brown-purple (*shades*)	..	1·75	15
		a. Recut lines in sky	..	55·00	
		b. Recut lines and plate crack	75·00	
		c. Perf 15×14¼ (9.73)	..	85·00	22·00
402	–	$2 deep reddish violet	..	7·50	65
403	–	$4 sepia	..	5·50	6·50
382/403			*Set of 25*	50·00	10·50
400/3 Optd "Specimen"			*Set of 4*	90·00	

Designs: *Vert* (as T **193**)—8 c. Copper-banded Butterflyfish ("Coral Fish"); 9 c. Hermit Crab; 10 c. Orange Clownfish ("Anemone Fish"). (As T **192**)—13 c. Red-necked Avocet; 15 c. Galah; 20 c. Golden Whistler; 30 c. Straw-necked Ibis. *Horiz* (as T **192**)—24 c. Azure Kingfisher; 25 c. Scarlet Robin. As T **167**—75 c. Captain Cook; $1 Flinders and *Investigator*. As T **168**—$2 Bass and whaleboat; $4 Admiral King and *Mermaid* (survey cutter).

*This shows two stamps imperforate all round and one imperforate at left only.

†The note below No. 553 also applies to No. 401c, its exact gauge being 14.8×14.1. No. 401 is 14.25×13.95.

Nos. 385a and 386ca have the outer edges of the pane imperforate producing single stamps with one or two adjacent sides imperforate.

No. 385 was normally printed in Helecon ink. Early in 1967 experimental printings on different kinds of paper coated with Helecon or Derby Luminescents phosphor were put on sale. These cannot be distinguished by the naked eye.

199 Queen Elizabeth II   200 "Saving Life"

1966 (14 Feb)–67. *Coil stamps.* Photo. P 15×imperf.

404	199	3 c. black, light brown and green	45	70
405		4 c. black, light brown & lt vermilion	35	30
405a		5 c. black, lt brown & new bl (1.10.67)	40	10
404/5a			*Set of 3*	1·10	1·00

(Des L. Mason. Photo.)

1966 (6 July). *75th Anniv of Royal Life Saving Society.* P 13½.

406	200	4 c. black, bright blue and blue	15	10

201 "Adoration of the Shepherds"   202 *Eendracht*

(Des L. Stirling, after medieval engraving. Photo)

1966 (19 Oct). *Christmas.* P 13½.

407	201	4 c. black and yellow-olive	..	10	10
		a. Value omitted	..	£2000	

No. 407a was caused by a shift of the yellow-olive which covered the white face value.

(Des F. Eidlitz. Photo)

1966 (24 Oct). *350th Anniv of Dirk Hartog's Landing in Australia.* P 13½.

408	202	4 c. multicoloured	..	10	10
		a. Red (sphere) omitted	..	£1700	

203 Open Bible   204 Ancient Keys and Modern Lock

(Des L. Stirling. Photo.)

1967 (7 Mar). *150th Anniv of British and Foreign Bible Society in Australia.* P 13½.

409	203	4 c. multicoloured	..	10	10

(Des G. Andrews. Photo.)

1967 (5 Apr). *150th Anniv of Australian Banking.* P 13½.

410	204	4 c. black, light blue and emerald	10	10

205 Lions Badge and 50 Stars   206 Y.W.C.A. Emblem

(Des M. Ripper. Photo.)

1967 (7 June). *50th Anniv of Lions International.* P 13½.

411	205	4 c. black, gold and blue	..	10	10

(Des H. Williamson. Photo.)

1967 (21 Aug). *World Y.M.C.A. Council Meeting, Monash University, Melbourne.* P 13½.

412	206	4 c. dp blue, ultramarine, lt pur & lt bl	10	10

207 Anatomical Figures   (208)

(Des R. Ingpen. Photo.)

1967 (20 Sept). *Fifth World Gynaecology and Obstetrics Congress, Sydney.* P 13½.

413	207	4 c. black, blue and light reddish violet	10	10

1967 (29 Sept). *No. 385 surch with T* **208**.

414	191	5 c. on 4 c. red	..	35	10
		a. Booklet pane. Five stamps plus one printed label	..	1·75	

No. 414 was only issued in 50 c. or $1 booklets with the outer edges of the pane imperforate so all stamps have one or two adjacent sides imperforate. It only exists printed in Helecon ink.

209 Christmas Bells and Gothic Arches   210 Religious Symbols

(Des M. Ripper (5 c.), Erica McGilchrist (25 c.). Photo)

1967. *Christmas.* P 13½.

415	209	5 c. multicoloured (18.10.67)	..	20	10
		a. Imperf three sides (vert pair)	£4500	
416	210	25 c. multicoloured (27.11.67)	..	1·40	2·00

No. 415a show the stamps perforated at left only.

MINIMUM PRICE

The minimum price quote is 10p which represents a handling charge rather than a basis for valuing common stamps. For further notes about prices see introductory pages.

---

211 Satellite in Orbit   212 World Weather Map

(Des J. Mason. Photo.)

1968 (20 Mar). *World Weather Watch.* P 13½.

417	211	5 c. orange-brown, pl blue, blk & ochre	30	10
418	212	20 c. orange-brown, blue and black	1·40	3·25
		a. White (radio waves) omitted	£700	
		b. Orange-brown (triangle) omitted	£1700	

213 Radar Antenna   214 Kangaroo Paw (Western Australia)

(Des R. Ingpen. Photo.)

1968 (20 Mar). *World Telecommunications via Intelsat II.* P 13½.

419	213	25 c. greenish blue, black & lt blue-green	1·75	3·00

(Des Nell Wilson (6c., 30 c.); R. and P. Warner (13 c., 25 c.); Dorothy Thornhill (15 c., 20 c.). Photo)

1968 (10 July)–71. *State Floral Emblems.* T **214** *and similar vert designs. Multicoloured.* P 13½.

420		6 c. Type 214	..	55	90
421		13 c. Pink Heath (Victoria)	..	65	60
422		15 c. Tasmanian Blue Gum (Tasmania)	..	90	20
423		20 c. Sturt's Desert Pea (South Australia)	2·50	60
424		25 c. Cooktown Orchid (Queensland)	..	1·75	60
425		30 c. Waratah (New South Wales) (Type I)	60	10
		a. Green (leaves) omitted	..	£1100	
		b. Type II (29.6.71)	..	4·75	1·50
420/5			*Set of 6*	6·00	2·50

The 30 c. was reprinted in 1971 from new cylinders so that Type II shows greater areas of white in the pink tones of the petals.

220 Soil Sample Analysis

(Des R. Ingpen. Photo.)

1968 (6 Aug). *International Soil Science Congress and World Medical Association Assembly.* T **220** *and similar horiz design.* P 13½.

426	220	5 c. orange-brn, stone, greenish bl & blk	10	10
		a. Nos. 426/7 se-tenant with gutter margin between	..	11·00	15·00
427	–	5 c. greenish blue, dull ol-yell, rose & blk	10	10

Design:—No. 427, Rubber-gloved hands, syringe and head of Hippocrates.

The above were printed in sheets of 100 containing a pane of 50 of each design.

The major shades formerly listed have been deleted as there is a range of intermediate shades.

222 Athlete carrying Torch, and Sunstone Symbol   223 Sunstone Symbol and Mexican Flag

(Des H. Williamson. Photo.)

1968 (2 Oct). *Olympic Games, Mexico City.* P 13½.

428	222	5 c. multicoloured	..	30	10
429	223	25 c. multicoloured	..	60	1·50

224 Houses and Dollar Signs

225 Church Window and View of Bethlehem

(Des Erica McGilchrist. Photo)

1968 (16 Oct). *Building and Savings Societies Congress.* P 13½.
430 224 5 c. multicoloured 10 40

(Des G. Hamori. Photo)

1968 (23 Oct). *Christmas.* P 13½.
431 225 5 c. multicoloured 10 10
  a. Green window (gold omitted) .. £500
  b. Red (inscr) omitted £800

226 Edgeworth David (geologist)

(Des Note Ptg Branch (Nos. 432, 434), A. Cook (others). Recess, background litho)

1968 (6 Nov). *Famous Australians (1st series). T* 226 *and similar vert portraits.* P 15 × 14.
432 5 c. myrtle-green/*pale green* .. 45 20
  a. Booklet pane. Five stamps plus one printed label .. .. 2·00
433 5 c. black/*pale blue* 45 20
  a. Booklet pane. Five stamps plus one printed label .. .. 2·00
434 5 c. blackish brown/*pale buff* .. 45 20
  a. Booklet pane. Five stamps plus one printed label .. .. 2·00
435 5 c. deep violet/*pale lilac* .. 45 20
  a. Booklet pane. Five stamps plus one printed label .. .. 2·00
432/5 .. .. .. *Set of 4* 1·60 70
Designs:—No. 432, Type 226; No. 433, A. B. Paterson (poet); No. 434, Albert Namatjira (artist); No. 435, Caroline Chisholm (social worker).
Nos. 432/5 were only issued in $1 booklets with the outer edges of the pane imperforate so all stamps have one or two adjacent sides imperforate.
See also Nos. 446/9, 479/82, 505/8, 537/40, 590/5, 602/7 and 637/40.

230 Macquarie Lighthouse

231 Pioneers and Modern Building, Darwin

(Des and eng Note Ptg Branch. Recess; background litho)

1968 (27 Nov). *150th Anniv of Macquarie Lighthouse.* P 14½ × 13½.
436 230 5 c. black and pale yellow .. 30 50
Used examples are known with the pale yellow background colour omitted.

(Des Marietta Lyon. Photo)

1969 (5 Feb). *Centenary of Northern Territory Settlement.* P 13½.
437 231 5 c. blackish brown, yellow-olive and yellow-ochre 10 10

232 Melbourne Harbour

233 Concentric Circles (symbolising Management, Labour and Government)

(Des J. Mason. Photo)

1969 (26 Feb). *Sixth Biennial Conference of International Association of Ports and Harbours, Melbourne.* P 13½.
438 232 5 c. multicoloured 15 10

(Des G. Hamori. Photo.)

1969 (4 June). *50th Anniv of International Labour Organisation.* P 13½.
439 233 5 c. multicoloured 15 10
  a. Gold (middle circle) omitted .. £1100

234 Sugar Cane

238 "The Nativity" (stained-glass window)

240 Edmund Barton

(Des R. Ingpen. Photo)

1969 (17 Sept). *Primary Industries. T* 234 *and similar vert designs. Multicoloured.* P 13½.
440 7 c. Type 234 .. .. 80 1·50
441 15 c. Timber .. .. 1·75 3·50
  a. Black ("Australia" and value) omitted .. £1000
442 20 c. Wheat 65 80
443 25 c. Wool .. .. 1·25 2·00
440/3 .. .. .. *Set of 4* 4·00 7·00

(Des G. Hamori (5 c.), J. Coburn (25 c.). Photo)

1969 (15 Oct). *Christmas. T* 238 *and similar multicoloured designs.* P 13½.
444 5 c. Type 238 .. .. 25 10
  a. Magenta (robe) omitted .. £650
  b. Yellow omitted £475
445 25 c. "Tree of Life", Christ in Crib and Christmas Star (abstract) .. 1·25 2·00

(Des from drawings by J. Santry. Recess, background litho)

1969 (22 Oct). *Famous Australians (2nd series). Prime Ministers. T* 240 *and similar vert designs each black on pale green.* P 15 × 14.
446 5 c. Type 240 .. .. 50 20
  a. Booklet pane. Five stamps plus one printed label .. .. 2·25
447 5 c. Alfred Deakin 50 20
  a. Booklet pane. Five stamps plus one printed label .. .. 2·25
448 5 c. J. C. Watson 50 20
  a. Booklet pane. Five stamps plus one printed label .. .. 2·25
449 5 c. G. H. Reid 50 20
  a. Booklet pane. Five stamps plus one printed label .. .. 2·25
446/9 .. .. .. *Set of 4* 1·75 70
Nos. 446/9 were only issued in $1 booklets with the outer edges of the pane imperforate so all stamps have one or two adjacent sides imperforate.

244 Capt. Ross Smith's Vickers Vimy, 1919

247 Symbolic Track and Diesel Locomotive

(Des E. Thake. Photo)

1969 (12 Nov). *50th Anniv of First England–Australia Flight. T* 244 *and similar horiz designs.* P 13½.
450 5 c. olive-green, pale blue, black and red .. 15 10
  a. Strip of 3. Nos. 450/2 .. 1·50
451 5 c. black, red and olive-green .. 15 10
452 5 c. olive-green, black, pale blue and red .. 15 10
450/2 .. .. .. *Set of 3* 1·50 25
Designs:—No. 450, Type 244; No. 451, Lt. H. Fysh and Lt. P. McGinness on 1919 survey with Ford car; No. 452, Capt. Wrigley and Sgt. Murphy in Royal Aircraft Factory B.E.2E taking off to meet the Smiths.
The three designs appear *se-tenant*, both horizontally and vertically, throughout the sheet.

(Des B. Sadgrove. Photo)

1970 (11 Feb). *Sydney–Perth Standard Gauge Railway Link.* P 13½.
453 247 5 c. multicoloured 15 10

248 Australian Pavilion, Osaka

251 Australian Flag

(Des J. Copeland (5 c.), A. Leydin (20 c.). Photo)

1970 (16 Mar). *World Fair, Osaka. T* 248 *and similar horiz design.* P 13½.
454 5 c. multicoloured 15 10
455 20 c. orange-red and black .. 35 65
Design:—20 c. "Southern Cross" and "from the Country of the South with warm feelings" (message).

(Des P.O. Artists (5 c.), J. Mason (30 c.). Photo)

1970 (31 Mar). *Royal Visit. T* 251 *and similar horiz design.* P 13½.
456 5 c. black and deep ochre 35 15
457 30 c. multicoloured .. .. 1·00 2·25
Design:—5 c. Queen Elizabeth II and Prince Philip.

252 Lucerne Plant, Bull and Sun

253 Captain Cook and H.M.S. *Endeavour*

(Des R. Ingpen. Photo)

1970 (13 Apr). *Eleventh International Grasslands Congress, Queensland.* P 13½.
458 252 5 c. multicoloured 10 40

(Des R. Ingpen and "Team" (T. Keneally, A. Leydin, J. R. Smith). Photo)

1970 (20 Apr). *Bicentenary of Captain Cook's Discovery of Australia's East Coast. T* 253 *and similar multicoloured designs.* P 13½.
459 5 c. Type 253 .. .. 50 10
  a. Strip of 5. Nos. 459/63 .. 2·25
460 5 c. Sextant and H.M.S. *Endeavour* .. 50 10
461 5 c. Landing at Botany Bay .. 50 10
462 5 c. Charting and exploring .. 50 10
463 5 c. Claiming possession .. 50 10
464 30 c. Captain Cook, H.M.S. *Endeavour*, sextant, aborigines and kangaroo (63 × 30 mm) .. .. 1·75 2·50
459/64 .. .. .. *Set of 6* 3·50 2·75
MS465 157 × 129 mm. Nos. 459/64. Imperf 9·00 9·00
The 5 c. stamps were issued horizontally *se-tenant* within the sheet, to form a composite design in the order listed.
50,000 miniature sheets were made available by the Post Office to the organisers of the Australian National Philatelic Exhibition which overprinted them in the white margin at each side of the 30 c. stamp with "Souvenir Sheet AUSTRALIAN NATIONAL PHILATELIC EXHIBITION" at left and "ANPEX 1970 SYDNEY 27 APRIL–1 MAY" at right in light red-brown and they were also serially numbered. These were put on sale at the exhibition on the basis of one sheet to each visitor paying 30 c. for admission. Although still valid for postage, since the stamps themselves had not been defaced, these sheets were not sold at post offices.
Subsequently further supplies were purchased and similarly overprinted and numbered by a private firm without the authority of the Post Office and ANPEX took successful legal action to stop their further sale to the public. This firm also had the unoverprinted sheets rouletted in colour between the stamps whilst further supplies of the normal sheets were overprinted with reproductions of old coins and others with an inscription commemorating the opening of Melbourne Airport on 1st July 1970, but all these are private productions. Further private productions have been reported.

259 Sturt's Desert Rose

AUSTRALIA AUSTRALIA
I. II.

Two types of 2 c.
I. "AUSTRALIA" thin; "2c" thin; flower name lightly printed.
II. Redrawn. "AUSTRALIA" thicker; "2c" much more heavily printed; flower name thicker and bolder.

(Des Note Ptg Branch. Photo)

1970–75. *Coil Stamps. Vert designs as T* 259. *Multicoloured White fluorescent paper (10 c.). Perf* 15×*imperf.*
465a 2 c. Type 259 (I) (1.10.71) .. 40 20
  ab. White fluorescent paper (6.73) 40
  b. Type II (white fluorescent paper) (11.73) 65 35
466 4 c. Type 259 (27.4.70) .. 70 1·25
467 5 c. Golden Wattle (27.4.70) .. 20 10
  a. White fluorescent paper (6.73) 20
468 6 c. Type 259 (28.9.70) .. 1·25 1·00
  a. Green (leaves) omitted .. £450
468b 7 c. Sturt's Desert Pea (1.10.71) 40 40
  ba. Black (berries, "7 c." and inscr) omitted £1000
  bb. Buff (shadows on flowers) omitted .. £200
  bc. Buff and green (leaves) omitted 75·00
  bd. White fluorescent paper (10.73) 40
468d 10 c. As 7 c. (15.1.75) 40 40
465a/8d .. .. .. *Set of 6* 3·00 3·00
Nos. 465a/8d have horizontal coil perforations described after No. 191.
Examples of No. 468bb also show the green colour displaced downwards.
For notes on white fluorescent paper see after No. 504.

264 Snowy Mountains Scheme   **265** Rising Flames

(Des L. Mason (7 c.), R. Ingpen (8 c., 9 c.), B. Sadgrove (10 c.). Photo)

1970 (31 Aug). *National Development (1st series). T* **264** *and similar horiz designs. Multicoloured.* P 13½.

469	7 c. Type **264**..				30	80
470	8 c. Ord River Scheme				15	15
471	9 c. Bauxite to aluminium				15	15
472	10 c. Oil and Natural Gas	..			40	10
469/72			*Set of 4*		90	1·10

See also Nos. 541/4.

(Des G. Hamori. Photo)

1970 (2 Oct). *16th Commonwealth Parliamentary Association Conference, Canberra.* P 13½.

473	**265**	6 c. multicoloured			10	10

266 Milk Analysis and Dairy Herd   **267** "The Nativity"

(Des R. Honisett. Photo)

1970 (7 Oct). *18th International Dairy Congress, Sydney.* P 13½.

474	**266**	6 c. multicoloured	..		10	10

(Des W. Beasley. Photo)

1970 (14 Oct). *Christmas.* P 13½.

475	**267**	6 c. multicoloured	..		10	10

268 U.N. "Plant"   **269** Boeing 707 and
and Dove of Peace   Avro 504

(Des Monad Design and Visual Graphics. Photo)

1970 (19 Oct). *25th Anniv of United Nations.* P 13½.

476	**268**	6 c. multicoloured	..		15	10

(Des G. Hamori. Photo)

1970 (2 Nov). *50th Anniv of QANTAS Airline. T* **269** *and similar horiz design. Multicoloured.* P 13½.

477	6 c. Type **269**			30	10
478	30 c. Avro 504 and Boeing 707			95	1·50

270 The Duigan Brothers   **271** "Theatre"
(Pioneer Aviators)

(Des A. Cook (No. 480), T. Adams (No. 482), Note Ptg Branch (others). Recess (background litho))

1970 (16 Nov). *Famous Australians (3rd series). T* **270** *and similar vert designs.* P 15×14.

479	6 c. blue		85	20
	a. Booklet pane. Five stamps plus one printed label		4·00	
480	6 c. black/*cinnamon*		85	20
	a. Booklet pane. Five stamps plus one printed label		4·00	
481	6 c. purple/*pale pink*		85	20
	a. Booklet pane. Five stamps plus one printed label ..		4·00	

482	6 c. brown-lake/*flesh*		85	20
	a. Booklet pane. Five stamps plus one printed label ..		4·00	
479/82	*Set of 4*		3·00	75

Designs:—No. 479 Type **270**; No. 480 Lachlan Macquarie (Governor of N.S.W.); No. 481 Adam Lindsay Gordon (poet); No. 482 E.J. Eyre (explorer).

Nos. 479/82 were only issued in 60 c. or $1.20 booklets with the outer edges of the pane imperforate so all stamps have one or two adjacent sides imperforate.

(Des D. Annand. Photo)

1971 (6 Jan). *"Australia-Asia". 28th International Congress of Orientalists, Canberra. T* **271** *and similar horiz designs. Multicoloured.* P 13½.

483	7 c. Type **271**		45	60
484	15 c. "Music"		70	1·00
485	20 c. "Sea Craft"		65	90
483/5	*Set of 3*		1·60	2·25

272 The Southern Cross   **273** Market "Graph

(Des R. Beck. Photo)

1971 (21 Apr). *Centenary of Australian Natives' Association.* P 13½.

486	**272**	6 c. black, vermilion and bright blue	10	10

(Des Monad Design and Visual Graphics Photo)

1971 (5 May). *Centenary of Sydney Stock Exchange.* P 13½.

487	**273**	6 c. multicoloured	10	10

274 Rotary Emblem   **275** Dassault Mirage
Jets and De Havilland
D.H.9A Biplane

(Des H. Williamson. Photo)

1971 (17 May). *50th Anniv of Rotary International in Australia.* P 13½.

488	**274**	6 c. multicoloured	..	15	10

(Des R. Honisett. Photo)

1971 (9 June). *50th Anniv of R.A.A.F.* P 13½.

489	**275**	6 c. multicoloured	30	10
		a. Black (face value and inscr) omitted £1400		

276 Draught-horse,   **277** Bark Painting
Cat and Dog

(Des R. Ingpen. Photo)

1971 (5 July). *Animals. T* **276** *and similar vert designs. Multicoloured.* P 13½.

490	6 c. Type **276**		20	10
491	12 c. Vet and lamb ("Animal Science")		45	35
492	18 c. Red Kangaroo ("Fauna Conservation") ..		80	55
493	24 c. Guide-dog ("Animals Aid to Man")		1·00	1·40
490/3 ..	*Set of 4*		2·25	2·25

The 6 c. commemorated the Centenary of the Australian R.S.P.C.A., and the others were short-term definitives.

(Des J. Mason. Photo)

1971 (29 Sept)–**74**. *Aboriginal Art. T* **277** *and similar multi-coloured designs.* P 13½.

494	20 c. Type **277**		20	20
	a. White fluorescent paper (12.73)		70	
495	25 c. Body decoration		20	50
	a. Black (face value and "AUSTRALIA") omitted		£750	
	b. White fluorescent paper (11.73)		70	
496	30 c. Cave painting (*vert*)		30	20
	a. White fluorescent paper (12.73)		1·00	
497	35 c. Grave posts (*vert*)		30	15
	a. White fluorescent paper (10.74)		75	
494/7	*Set of 4*		90	95

The 35 c. exists with both PVA gum and gum arabic.

278 The Three Kings and the Star   **279** Andrew Fisher

(Des J. Lee. Photo)

1971 (13 Oct). *Christmas. Colours of star and colour of "AUSTRALIA" given.* P 13½.

498	**278**	7 c. royal blue, pl mauve & pl lake-brn	50	15
		a. Block of 7. Nos. 498/504 ..	21·00	
		b. White fluorescent paper	70	
		ba. Block of 7. Nos. 498b/504b	24·00	
499		7 c. pale mauve, pl lake-brown & white	50	15
		b. White fluorescent paper	70	
500		7 c. pale mauve, white and black	3·75	80
		b. White fluorescent paper	4·75	
501		7 c. black, green and black	50	15
		b. White fluorescent paper	70	
502		7 c. lilac, green and lilac	50	15
		b. White fluorescent paper	70	
503		7 c. black, pale lake-brown and white	50	15
		b. White fluorescent paper	70	
504		7 c. royal blue, pale mauve and green	17·00	2·25
		b. White fluorescent paper	19·00	
498/504		*Set of 7*	21·00	3·50

Nos. 498/504, which also exist on fluorescent paper, were issued in sheets having two panes of 50 stamps. Each half pane had its stamps arranged thus:—

498	499	500	499	498
503	502	501	502	503
504	501	500	501	504
503	502	501	502	503
498	499	500	499	498

FLUORESCENT VERY WHITE CHALK-SURFACED PAPER. As an experiment 10% of the above issue was printed on very white paper which fluoresces back and front under an ultraviolet lamp; it also has a strong coating of chalk on the surface. Late in 1972 this paper began to be introduced more generally and a number of stamps exist on both types. The normal Helecon paper does not fluoresce under the lamp but does react to the chalky test to a lesser degree.

(Des J. Santry. Recess (off-white backgrounds Litho))

1972 (8 Mar). *Famous Australians (4th series). Prime Ministers. T* **279** *and similar vert designs.* P 15×14.

505	7 c. ultramarine (Type **279**)		30	20
	a. Booklet pane. Five stamps plus one printed label		1·75	
506	7 c. ultramarine. (W. M. Hughes)		30	20
	a. Booklet pane. Five stamps plus one printed label		1·75	
507	7 c. red (Joseph Cook)		30	20
	a. Booklet pane. Five stamps plus one printed label		1·75	
508	7 c. red (S. M. Bruce)..		30	20
	a. Booklet pane. Five stamps plus one printed label		1·75	
505/8	*Set of 4*		1·10	70

Nos. 505/8 were only issued in 70 c. or $1.40 booklets with the outer edges of the pane imperforate so all stamps have one or two adjacent sides imperforate.

280 Cameo Brooch   **281** Fruit

(Des Val Mason. Photo)

1972 (18 Apr). *50th Anniv of Country Women's Association.* P 13½.

509	**280**	7 c. multicoloured	20	10

(Des D. Annand. Photo)

1972 (14 June). *Primary Industries. T* **281** *and similar horiz designs. Multicoloured.* P 13½.

510	20 c. Type **281** ..		1·25	2·75
511	25 c. Rice		1·25	5·00
512	30 c. Fish		1·25	1·50
513	35 c. Beef		2·50	75
510/13	*Set of 4*		5·75	9·00

282 Worker in Wheelchair   **283** Telegraph Line

(Des from photographs by Barbara Ardizzone. Photo)
1972 (2 Aug)–73. *Rehabilitation of the Disabled. T 282 and similar designs. P 13½.*
514	12 c. yellow-brown and emerald	..	10	10
	a. White fluorescent paper (12.73)	..	10	
515	18 c. sage-green and yellow-orange	..	80	35
516	24 c. blue and yellow-brown	..	15	10
	a. White fluorescent paper (7.73)	..	15	
514/16		*Set of 3*	90	50

Designs: *Horiz*—18 c. Patient and teacher. *Vert*—24 c. Boy playing with ball.

(Des J. Copeland. Photo)
1972 (22 Aug). *Centenary of Overland Telegraph Line. P 13½.*
517	**283** 7 c. multicoloured	..	15	15

284 Athletics   **285** Numerals and Computer Circuit

(Des B. Sadgrove. Photo)
1972 (28 Aug). *Olympic Games, Munich. T 284 and similar vert designs. Multicoloured. P 13½.*
518	7 c. Type 284	..	25	25
519	7 c. Rowing	..	25	25
520	7 c. Swimming	..	25	25
521	35 c. Equestrian	..	1·50	3·50
518/21		*Set of 4*	2·00	3·75

(Des G. Andrews. Photo)
1972 (16 Oct). *Tenth International Congress of Accountants, Sydney. P 13½.*
522	**285** 7 c. multicoloured	..	15	15

286 Australian-built Harvester

(Des R. Ingpen. Photo)
1972 (15 Nov)–74. *Pioneer Life. T 286 and similar multicoloured designs. P 13½.*
523	5 c. Pioneer family (*vert*)	..	15	10
	a. White fluorescent paper (11.73)	..	15	
524	10 c. Water-pump (*vert*)	..	40	10
	a. White fluorescent paper (5.74)	..	70	
525	15 c. Type 286	..	15	10
	a. Black (face value and inscr) omitted		£750	
	b. White fluorescent paper (12.73)	..	40	
526	40 c. House	..	30	60
	a. White fluorescent paper (1974)	..	50	
527	50 c. Stage-coach	..	80	20
	a. White fluorescent paper (1974)	..	1·25	
528	60 c. Morse key (*vert*)	..	60	1·00
	a. White fluorescent paper (1974)	..	60	
529	80 c. Gem (paddle-steamer)	..	60	1·00
	a. White fluorescent paper (1974)	..	60	
	ab. Black (face value and inscr) omitted		£600	
523/9		*Set of 7*	2·50	2·50

287 Jesus with Children   **288** "Length"

(Des from drawing by Wendy Tamlyn (7 c.), L. Stirling (35 c.). Photo)
1972 (29 Nov). *Christmas. T 287 and similar vert design. Multicoloured. White fluorescent paper (7 c.). P 15×14 (7 c.) or 13½ (35 c.).*
530	7 c. Type 287	..	30	10
	a. Brown-red ("Australia 7c") omitted	..	£650	
	b. Red-brown (inscr) omitted	..	£500	
531	35 c. Dove and spectrum motif	..	4·00	6·00

(Des Weatherhead & Stitt Pty Ltd. Photo)
1973 (7 Mar). *Metric Conversion. T 288 and similar multicoloured designs. White fluorescent paper. P 15×14 (No. 535) or 14×15 (others).*
532	7 c. Type 288	..	40	50
533	7 c. "Volume"	..	40	50
	a. Yellow-olive omitted*		£800	
534	7 c. "Mass"	..	40	50
535	7 c. "Temperature" (*horiz*)	..	40	50
532/5		*Set of 4*	1·40	1·75

*This results in the man's drink and shorts appearing white, and the colour of the stool being the same as the background.

289 Caduceus and Laurel Wreath   **290** William Wentworth (statesman and explorer)

(Des H. Williamson. Photo)
1973 (4 Apr). *25th Anniv of W.H.O. White fluorescent paper. P 15×14.*
536	**289** 7 c. multicoloured	..	30	15

(Des J. Santry. Recess and litho)
1973 (16 May). *Famous Australians (5th series). T 290 and similar vert designs. P 15×14.*
537	7 c. yellow-bistre and black	..	35	35
	a. Block of 4. Nos. 537/40	..	1·25	
538	7 c. lilac and black	..	35	35
539	7 c. yellow-bistre and black	..	35	35
540	7 c. lilac and black	..	35	35
537/40		*Set of 4*	1·25	1·25

Designs:—No. 537, Type **290**; No. 538, Isaac Isaacs (first Australian-born Governor-General); No. 539, Mary Gilmore (writer); No. 540, Marcus Clarke (author).
Nos. 537/40 were printed in *se-tenant* blocks of four within the sheet.

291 Shipping   **292** Banded Coral Shrimp

(Des J. Copeland. Photo)
1973 (6 June). *National Development (2nd series). T 291 and similar vert designs. Multicoloured. P 13½.*
541	20 c. Type 291	..	1·50	2·75
542	25 c. Iron ore and steel	..	1·50	2·75
543	30 c. Beef roads	..	1·50	2·75
544	35 c. Mapping	..	2·00	2·75
541/4		*Set of 4*	6·00	10·00

(Des Printing Bureau artists (1 to 4 c.), J. Mason (others). Photo)
1973 (11 July)–74. *Marine Life and Gemstones. T 292 and similar multicoloured designs. White fluorescent paper. P 14×15 (1 to 4 c.) or 15×14 (others).*
545	1 c. Type 292	..	10	10
	a. Black (inscr and face value) omitted		£200	
	b. Yellow-brown omitted		£600	
546	2 c. Fiddler crab	..	10	10
547	3 c. Coral crab	..	10	10
	a. Black (inscr and value) omitted		£500	
548	4 c. Mauve stinger	..	30	55
	a. Black (face value and inscr) omitted		£450	
549	6 c. Chrysoprase (*vert*)	..	30	10
550	7 c. Agate (*vert*)	..	30	10
	a. Black (value and "agate") omitted		80·00	
551	8 c. Opal (*vert*)	..	30	10
	a. Black (face value and inscr) omitted		£200	
552	9 c. Rhodonite (*vert*)	..	60	15
552a	10 c. Star sapphire (*vert*) (16.10.74)	..	40	10
	ab. Black (value, inscr, etc.) omitted		£200	
	ac. Turquoise-blue omitted*		£100	
	ad. Printed on the gummed side		35·00	
545/52a		*Set of 9*	2·00	1·25

*The turquoise-blue occurs on the gemstones, and is normally partly covered by the black.
The 1, 3, 7 and 10 c. exist with PVA gum as well as gum arabic.

293 Children at Play   **294** John Baptising Jesus

(Des G. Hamori. Photo)
1973 (5 Sept). *50th Anniv of Legacy (Welfare Organisation). P 13½.*
553	**293** 7 c. cinnamon, deep claret and emerald	30	10

PERFORATIONS. From 1973 to 1975 two different perforating machines were used for some issues, giving gauges of 14½×14 or 15×14 (on horizontal stamps), the exact measurement being 14.4×14.1 or 14.8×14.1. The latter gauge was also used for a reprint of the $1 definitive (No. 401c).

(Des G. Hamori. Photo)
1973 (3 Oct). *Christmas. T 294 and similar vert design. Multicoloured. White fluorescent paper. P 14×14½ (7 c.) or 13½ (30 c.).*
554	7 c. Type 294	..	35	10
	a. Perf 14×15	..	3·50	80
	ab. Printed on the gummed side		55·00	
555	30 c. The Good Shepherd	..	1·75	2·00

295 Sydney Opera House   **296** Wireless Receiver and Speaker

(Des A. Leydin. Photo)
1973 (17 Oct). *Architecture. T 295 and similar designs. White fluorescent paper. P 14½×14 (7, 10 c.) or 13½ (40, 50 c.).*
556	7 c. pale turquoise-blue and new blue	..	30	15
	a. Perf 15×14	..	3·50	1·60
557	10 c. light ochre and sepia	..	80	70
558	40 c. black, drab and dull mauve	..	1·25	2·25
	a. Dull mauve (background) omitted		£1200	
559	50 c. multicoloured	..	1·25	2·50
556/9		*Set of 4*	3·25	5·00

Designs: *Horiz*—10 c. Buchanan's Hotel, Townsville; 40 c. Como House, Melbourne. *Vert*—50 c. St. James' Church, Sydney.

(Des E. Thake. Photo)
1973 (21 Nov). *50th Anniv of Regular Radio Broadcasting. P 13½.*
560	**296** 7 c. lt turquoise-blue, brown-red & blk	15	10

297 Common Wombat   **298** "Sergeant of Light Horse" (G. Lambert)

(Des R. Bates. Photo)
1974 (13 Feb)–76. *Animals. T 297 and similar vert designs. Multicoloured. White fluorescent paper. P 14×15 (20, 30 c.) or 13½ (others).*
561	20 c. Type 297	..	35	10
562	25 c. Short-nosed Echidna	..	75	60
563	30 c. Brush-tailed Possum	..	60	15
	a. Carmine-red (face-value, etc) omitted	..	£1100	
564	75 c. Pygmy Glider	..	1·00	85
561/4		*Set of 4*	2·40	1·50

The 20 c. exists with gum arabic as well as PVA gum.

(Des P.O. artists. Litho Asher & Co, Melbourne ($5, $10). Photo R.B.A. (others))
1974 (24 Apr)–79. *Paintings. T 298 and similar multicoloured designs. Ordinary paper ($1, $2, $4). P 13½ ($1, $2, $4) or 14½ (others).*
565	$1 Type 298	..	1·00	10
566	$2 "Red Gums of the Far North" (H. Heysen) (*horiz*)	..	1·50	25
566a	$4 "Shearing the Rams" (Tom Roberts) (*horiz*)	..	3·00	2·25
567	$5 "McMahon's Point" (Sir Arthur Streeton) (14.3.79)	..	6·00	2·25
567a	$10 "Coming South" (Tom Roberts) (19.10.77)	..	7·50	3·50
565/7a		*Set of 5*	17·00	7·50
567/a, 778 Optd "Specimen"		*Set of 3*	9·00	

The $1, $2 and $4 exist with PVA gum as well as gum arabic. Nos. 567/a and 778 optd "Specimen" come from a special "Ausipex 84" Presentation Pack issued on 9 February 1983.

299 Supreme Court Judge   **300** Rugby Football

(Des T. Thompson. Photo)
1974 (15 May). *150th Anniv of Australia's Third Charter of Justice. White fluorescent paper. P 14×15.*
568	**299** 7 c. multicoloured	..	20	10

(Des A. Leydin from drawings by D. O'Brien. Photo)
1974 (24 July). *Non-Olympic Sports. T 300 and similar multicoloured designs. White fluorescent paper. P 15×14 (Nos. 569/70) or 14×15 (others).*
569	7 c. Type 300	..	40	40
570	7 c. Bowls	..	40	40
571	7 c. Australian football (*vert*)	..	40	40
572	7 c. Cricket (*vert*)	..	40	40
573	7 c. Golf (*vert*)	..	40	40
	a. Black (face value and inscr) omitted			
574	7 c. Surfing (*vert*)	..	40	40
575	7 c. Tennis (*vert*)	..	40	40
569/75		*Set of 7*	2·50	2·50

301 "Transport of Mails"

302 Letter "A" and W. C. Wentworth (co-founder)

(Des J. Copeland. Photo)

1974 (9 Oct). *Centenary of Universal Postal Union. T* **301** *and similar vert design. Multicoloured. White fluorescent paper. P* 15×14 (7 c.) *or* 13½ (30 c.).

576	7 c. Type **301**.	..	..	40	20
	a. Perf 14½×14	..	..	60	30
577	30 c. Three-part version of Type **301**			85	1·90

Most examples of the 7 c. are on PVA gum; the 30c was on gum arabic.

(Des I. Dalton. Typo and litho)

1974 (9 Oct). *150th Anniv of First Independent Newspaper, "The Australian". White fluorescent paper. P* 14×15.

578	**302**	7 c. black/light cinnamon	..	30	30
	a. Perf 14×14½	..	..	1·25	50

(303)

304 "The Adoration of the Magi"

1974 (16 Oct). *No. 551 surch with T* **303**, *in red.*

579	9 c. on 8 c. Opal	15	15

(Des, recess and litho R.B.A.)

1974 (13 Nov). *Christmas. Woodcuts by Dürer. T* **304** *and similar horiz design. White fluorescent paper. P* 14×15.

580	10 c. black/cream	..	..	25	10
581	35 c. black/cream	..	..	80	1·00

Design:—35 c. "The Flight into Egypt".

PROCESS. All the following issues to No. 772 were printed in photogravure, *except where otherwise stated.*
PAPER. The following issues were on white fluorescent paper unless otherwise stated. The gum used changed from gum arabic to PVA.

305 "Pre-School Education"   **306** "Road Safety"

(Des Vivienne Binns (5 c.), Erica McGilchrist (11 c.), E. Tanner (15 c.), J. Meldrum (60 c.))

1974 (20 Nov). *Education in Australia. T* **305** *and similar multicoloured designs. P* 13½.

582	5 c. Type **305**	..	..	25	40
583	11 c. "Correspondence Schools"	..	25	25
584	15 c. "Science Education"	..	40	40
585	60 c. "Advanced Education" (*vert*)	..	50	1·75
582/5	..	..	..	*Set of* 4	1·25	2·50

(Des G. Andrews)

1975 (29 Jan). *Environment Dangers. T* **306** *and similar horiz designs. Multicoloured. P* 14×14½ (No. 586) *or* 14½×14 (*others*).

586	10 c. Type **306**	..	..	50	50
	a. Printed on the gummed side	..	30·00	
587	10 c. "Pollution"	..	..	50	50
	a. Perf 15×14	..	..	7·50	3·50
588	10 c. "Bush Fires"	..	..	50	50
	a. Perf 15×14	..	..	1·40	1·10
586/8	..	..	..	*Set of* 3	1·40	1·40

307 Australian Women's Year Emblem   **308** J. H. Scullin

(Des Leonora Howlett)

1975 (12 Mar). *International Women's Year. P* 14×15.

589	**307**	10 c. dp violet-blue, green & bluish violet	20	15

This stamp exists with either PVA gum or gum arabic.

(Des B. Dunlop)

1975 (26 Mar). *Famous Australians* (6th series). *Prime Ministers. T* **308** *and similar vert designs. Multicoloured. P* 14 × 15.

590	10 c. Type **308**	..	..	25	35
591	10 c. J. A. Lyons	..	..	25	35
	a. Printed on the gummed side	..	70·00	
592	10 c. Earle Page	..	..	25	35
593	10 c. Arthur Fadden	..	..	25	35
594	10 c. John Curtin	..	..	25	35
595	10 c. J. B. Chifley	..	..	25	35
590/5	..			*Set of* 6	1·40	1·90

Nos. 590/5 exist with either PVA gum or gum arabic.

309 Atomic Absorption Spectrophotometry

310 Logo of Australian Postal Commission

(Des Weatherhead & Stitt)

1975 (14 May). *Scientific Development. T* **309** *and similar horiz designs. Multicoloured. P* 13½.

596	11 c. Type **309**	..	..	60	40
597	24 c. Radio astronomy	..	..	1·25	1·90
598	33 c. Immunology	..	..	1·25	2·00
599	48 c. Oceanography	..	..	1·50	2·75
596/9	..			*Set of* 4	4·25	6·25

(Des P. Huveneers)

1975 (1 July). *Inauguration of Australian Postal and Telecommunications Commissions. T* **310** *and similar horiz design. P* 14½×14.

600	10 c. black, rosine and pale grey	..	25	10
	a. Pair. Nos. 600/1	..	..	1·10	1·40
	b. Perf 15×14	..	..	25	10
	ba. Pair. Nos. 600b/1b	..	1·25	1·50
601	10 c. black, orange-yellow and pale grey	25	10
	b. Perf 15×14	..	..	25	10

Design:—No. 601, Logo of Australian Telecommunications Commission.

Nos. 600/1 were printed together, *se-tenant* in horizontal and vertical pairs throughout the sheet.

311 Edith Cowan

312 *Helichrysum thomsonii*

313 "Tambaran" House and Sydney Opera House

(Des D. and J. O'Brien)

1975 (6 Aug). *Famous Australians* (7th series). *Australian Women. T* **311** *and similar vert designs. Multicoloured. P* 14×14½.

602	10 c. Type **311**	..	..	35	55
	a. Perf 14×15	..	..	35	65
	ab. Printed on the gummed side	..	70·00	
603	10 c. Louisa Lawson	..	..	35	55
	a. Perf 14×15	..	..	60	55
604	10 c. Ethel Richardson	..	..	35	55
	a. Perf 14×15	..	..	60	55
605	10 c. Catherine Spence	..	..	35	55
	a. Perf 14×15	..	..	45	55
606	10 c. Constance Stone	..	..	35	55
	a. Perf 14×15	..	..	35	55
607	10 c. Truganini	..	..	35	55
	a. Perf 14×15	..	..	40	55
602/7	..			*Set of* 6	2·00	3·00

No. 604 is inscribed with the *nom de plume* "Henry Handel Richardson".

(Des F. Knight)

1975 (27 Aug). *Wild Flowers. T* **312** *and similar multicoloured design. P* 15×14 (18 c.) *or* 14×15 (45 c.).

608	18 c. Type **312**.	..	..	25	10
	a. Black omitted	..	..	30·00	
	b. Grey (stem, etc) omitted	..	£120	
609	45 c. *Callistemon teretifolius* (*horiz*).	50	10
	a. Black (face value and inscr) omitted	..	£600	
	b. Yellow-green (twigs) omitted	..	£160	

The 18 c. exists with both PVA gum and gum arabic.

(Des D. Annand (18 c.) or G. Hamori (25 c.))

1975 (16 Sept). *Papua New Guinea Independence. T* **313** *and similar horiz design. Multicoloured. P* 13½.

610	18 c. Type **313**	..	..	20	10
611	25 c. "Freedom" (bird in flight)	..	50	1·25

---

314 Epiphany Scene   **315** Australian Coat of Arms

(Des D. O'Brien (15 c.) or J. Milne (45 c.))

1975 (29 Oct). *Christmas. T* **314** *and similar horiz design. P* 14×15 (15 c.) *or* 13½ (45 c.).

612	15 c. multicoloured	..	..	25	10
613	45 c. reddish violet, greenish blue and silver	75	2·40

Design:—45 c. "Shining Star".

I   II

Two types of No. 614:
  I. Emu's legs without toes.
  II. Emu showing toes.
Other minor differences also occur.

(Des J. Spatchurst)

1976 (5 Jan). *75th Anniv of Nationhood. P* 15×14.

614	**315**	18 c. multicoloured (I)	..	40	20
	a. Buff (supporters) omitted	..	£425	
	b. Gold (shield and star) omitted	..	£250	
	c. Type II	..	..	75	30
	cb. Gold (shield and star) omitted	..	£700	

316 Telephone-user, *circa* 1878   **317** John Oxley

(Des R. Ingpen)

1976 (10 Mar). *Telephone Centenary. P* 13½.

615	**316**	18 c. multicoloured	..	20	15

(Des B. Dunlop)

1976 (9 June). *19th Century Explorers. T* **317** *and similar horiz designs. Multicoloured. P* 13½.

616	18 c. Type **317**	..	..	35	40
617	18 c. Hume and Hovell	..	..	35	40
618	18 c. John Forrest	..	..	35	40
619	18 c. Ernest Giles	..	..	35	40
620	18 c. William Gosse	..	..	35	40
621	18 c. Peter Warburton.	..	..	35	40
616/21	..			*Set of* 6	1·90	2·25

318 Measuring Stick, Graph and Computer Tape   **319** Football

(Des R. Ingpen)

1976 (15 June). *50th Anniv of Commonwealth Scientific and Industrial Research Organisation. P* 15×14.

622	**318**	18 c. multicoloured	..	20	15

(Des A. Leydin)

1976 (14 July). *Olympic Games, Montreal. T* **319** *and similar multicoloured designs. P* 13½.

623	18 c. Type **319**	..	..	35	20
624	18 c. Gymnastics (*vert*)	..	..	35	20
625	25 c. Diving (*vert*)	..	..	60	80
626	40 c. Cycling	..	..	90	1·25
623/6	..			*Set of* 4	2·00	2·25

The 25 c. exists with gum arabic as well as PVA gum.

320 Richmond Bridge, Tasmania   **321** Blamire Young (designer of first Australian stamp)

(Des O. Borchert)

1976 (23 Aug). *Australian Scenes.* T **320** and similar designs.
Multicoloured. P 14 × 15 (50 c.) or 15 × 14 (others).

627	5 c. Type **320** ..	..	20	10
628	25 c. Broken Bay, N.S.W.	..	65	20
629	35 c. Wittenoom Gorge, W.A. ..		45	20
630	50 c. Mt. Buffalo, Victoria (vert)		90	30
631	70 c. Barrier Reef ..	..	1·25	1·25
632	85 c. Ayers Rock, N.T. ..	..	1·25	1·75
627/32		Set of 6	4·25	3·50

(Des R. Honisett)

1976 (27 Sept). *National Stamp Week.* P 13½.

633	**321** 18 c. multicoloured ..	..	15	15
MS634	101 × 112 mm. No. 633 × 4	..	75	2·00

MS634 contains one stamp coloured as No. 633; the others, showing the different colour separations used in the printing, are each differently coloured.

The miniature sheet exists with "AUSTRALIAN STAMP PROMOTION COUNCIL" overprinted in red on the margin from a privately produced booklet.

322 "Virgin and Child" (detail, Simone Cantarini)   **323** John Gould

(Des C. Medlycott (15 c.), Wendy Tamlyn (45 c.))

1976 (1 Nov). *Christmas.* T **322** and similar horiz design.
P 15 × 14 (15 c.) or 13½ (45 c.).

635	15 c. bright magenta and light azure ..		25	10
636	45 c. multicoloured	..	70	90

Design:—45 c. Toy koala bear and decorations.

(Des B. Weatherhead)

1976 (10 Nov). *Famous Australians (8th series).* T **323** and similar horiz designs. Multicoloured. P 15 × 14.

637	18 c. Type **323** ..	..	35	50
638	18 c. Thomas Laby ..	..	35	50
	a. Red-brown ("AUSTRALIA" etc.) omitted		£500	
639	18 c. Sir Baldwin Spencer ..		85	50
640	18 c. Griffith Taylor ..	..	35	50
637/40		Set of 4	1·25	1·75

324 "Music"   **325** Queen Elizabeth II

1977 (19 Jan). *Performing Arts.* T **324** and similar vert designs. Multicoloured. P 14 × 15.

641	20 c. Type **324** ..	..	25	25
642	30 c. Drama ..	..	40	35
643	40 c. Dance ..	..	55	40
	a. Black (inscr and face value) omitted		£1500	
644	60 c. Opera ..	..	1·25	1·75
641/4		Set of 4	2·25	2·50

(Des P.O. Artists. Litho Govt Printer, Sydney (2% of supplies) or by Norman J. Field, Melbourne)

1977 (2 Feb). *Silver Jubilee.* T **325** and similar vert design. Multicoloured. P 14 × 15.

645	18 c. Type **325** ..	..	20	10
646	45 c. The Queen and Prince Philip ..		50	80

326 Fielder and Wicket Keeper   **327** Parliament House

(Des B. Weatherhead)

1977 (9 Mar). *Australia–England Test Cricket Centenary.*
T **326** and similar vert designs. Multicoloured. P 13½.

647	18 c. Type **326** ..	..	55	65
	a. Horiz strip of 5. Nos. 647/51 ..		2·50	
	ab. Black (face value, inscr, etc) omitted			
648	18 c. Umpire, batsman and scoreboard		55	65
649	18 c. Fielders ..	..	55	65
650	18 c. Batsman and umpire ..		55	65

651	18 c. Bowler and fielder ..		55	65
652	45 c. Batsman awaiting delivery ..		1·00	1·50
647/52		Set of 6	3·25	4·00

Nos. 647/51 were printed together, se-tenant, in horizontal strips of 5 throughout the sheet, forming a composite design.

No. 647ab shows the black completely omitted from No. 647, but traces of it remain at the top of the other designs. The error occurs on the bottom row of a sheet.

(Des R.B.A.)

1977 (13 Apr). *50th Anniv of Opening of Parliament House, Canberra.* P 15 × 14.

653	**327** 18 c. multicoloured ..		15	10
	a. Yellow (foreground) omitted ..		£1100	

328 Trade Unions Workers   **329** Surfing Santa

(Des D. Lanyon; adapted B. Sadgrove)

1977 (9 May). *50th Anniv of Australian Council of Trade Unions.* P 13½.

654	**328** 18 c. multicoloured ..	..	15	10

(Des R. Roberts (15 c.), J. O'Brien (45 c.))

1977 (31 Oct). *Christmas.* T **329** and similar vert design. Multicoloured. P 14 × 15 (15 c.) or 13½ (45 c.).

655	15 c. Type **329** ..	..	25	10
656	45 c. Madonna and Child ..		75	1·25

330 National Flag   **331** Harry Hawker and Sopwith Atlantic

(Des Cato Hibberd Design)

1978 (26 Jan). *Australia Day.* P 13½.

657	**330** 18 c. multicoloured ..		20	15

(Litho Asher and Co, Melbourne)

1978 (19 Apr). *Early Australian Aviators.* T **331** and similar horiz designs. Multicoloured. P 15½.

658	18 c. Type **331** ..	..	40	50
	a. Imperf (horiz pair) ..	..	£650	
659	18 c. Bert Hinkler and Avro Type 581 Avian		40	50
	a. Imperf (horiz pair) ..	..	£600	
660	18 c. Sir Charles Kingsford Smith and Fokker F311a/3m *Southern Cross*		40	50
	a. Imperf (pair) ..	..	£110	
661	18 c. Charles Ulm and Fokker F311a/3m *Southern Cross*		40	50
658/61		Set of 4	1·50	1·75
MS662	100×112 mm.. Nos. 660/1×2. Imperf		75	1·75

Forgeries of No. **MS662** have been reported. These can be detected, under strong magnification, by the lack of magenta screen on the blue panel at right and by the presence of magenta dots in the yellow background to No. 661.

332 Piper PA-31 Navajo landing at Station Airstrip   **333** Illawarra Flame Tree

1978 (15 May). *50th Anniv of Royal Flying Doctor Service.* P 13½.

663	**332** 18 c. multicoloured ..	..	20	15

(Des D. Rose)

1978 (1 June). *Trees.* T **333** and similar vert designs. Multicoloured. P 14 × 15 (18 c.) or 13½ (others).

664	18 c. Type **333** ..	..	20	15
665	25 c. Ghost Gum ..	..	35	1·10
666	40 c. Grass Tree ..	..	45	1·75
667	45 c. Cootamundra Wattle ..		45	70
664/7		Set of 4	1·25	3·25

NEW INFORMATION

The editor is always interested to correspond with people who have new information that will improve or correct the Catalogue.

334 Sturt's Desert Rose and Map   **335** Hooded Plover

(Des D. Pitt. Litho Asher and Co, Melbourne)

1978 (19 June). *Establishment of State Government for the Northern Territory.* P 15½.

668	**334** 18 c. multicoloured	..	20	15

(Des Kay Breeden-Williams. Photo)

1978 (3 July)–**80.** *Birds (1st series).* Multicoloured designs as T **335**. P 15 × 14 (20 c. (both)), 14 × 15 (22 c.) or 13½ (others).

669	1 c. Spotted-sided Finch (17.9.79) ..		10	20
670	2 c. Crimson Finch (17.9.79) ..		10	20
671	5 c. Type **335** (17.7.78) ..		50	10
	a. Grey-brown (bird's back) omitted		£400	
672	15 c. Forest Kingfisher (vert) (17.9.79)		20	20
673	20 c. Australian Dabchick ("Little Grebe") ..		70	10
	a. Yellow (beak and eye) omitted ..		£170	
674	20 c. Eastern Yellow Robin (17.9.79) ..		20	10
675	22 c. White-tailed Kingfisher (22 × 29 mm) (31.3.80) ..		30	10
676	25 c. Masked Plover (17.7.78) ..		90	35
677	30 c. Oystercatcher (17.7.78) ..		1·00	25
678	40 c. Variegated Wren (vert) (17.9.79)		30	45
679	50 c. Flame Robin (vert) (17.9.79) ..		50	50
680	55 c. Comb-crested Jacana ("Lotus-bird") ..		85	60
669/80		Set of 12	5·00	2·75

See also Nos. 734/40.

336 1928 3d. "National Stamp Exhibition" Commemorative   **337** "The Madonna and Child" (after van Eyck)

(Des Cato Hibberd Design. Litho Asher and Co, Melbourne)

1978 (25 Sept). *National Stamp Week. 50th Anniv of National Stamp Exhibition, Melbourne.* P 15½.

694	**336** 20 c. multicoloured ..	..	15	15
MS695	78 × 113 mm. No. 694 × 4 ..		75	1·75

(Litho Asher and Co, Melbourne)

1978 (3 Oct–1 Nov). *Christmas Paintings.* T **337** and similar vert designs. Multicoloured. P 14½.

696	15 c. Type **337** (1.11) ..	..	30	10
697	25 c. "The Virgin and Child" (Marmion)		45	55
698	55 c. "The Holy Family" (del Vaga) (1.11) ..		70	90
696/8 ..		Set of 3	1·25	1·40

338 "Tulloch"   **339** Raising the Flag, Sydney Cove, 26 January 1788

(Des B. Clinton)

1978 (18 Oct). *Race-horses.* T **338** and similar multicoloured designs. P 15 × 14 (20 c.) or 13½ (others).

699	20 c. Type **338** ..	..	35	10
700	35 c. "Bernborough" (vert) ..		60	85
701	50 c. "Phar Lap" (vert) ..		85	1·25
702	55 c. "Peter Pan" ..	..	90	1·10
699/702		Set of 4	2·40	3·00

(Des B. Clinton. Litho Asher and Co, Melbourne)

1979 (26 Jan). *Australia Day.* P 15½.

703	**339** 20 c. multicoloured ..	..	15	15
	a. Yellow omitted ..	..		

AUSTRALIA — 1979

340 *Canberra* (paddle-steamer)   **341** Port Campbell, Victoria

(Des O. Borchert)

1979 (14 Feb). *Ferries and Murray River Steamers. T **340** and similar horiz designs. Multicoloured. P 15 × 14 (20 c.) or 13½ (others).*

704	20 c. Type **340**		35	10
705	35 c. *Lady Denman*		60	1·00
706	50 c. *Murray River Queen* (paddle-steamer)		80	1·40
707	55 c. *Curl Curl* (hydrofoil)		90	1·25
704/7		Set of 4	2·40	3·25

(Des M. Robinson. Litho Asher and Co. Melbourne)

1979 (9 Apr). *National Parks. T **341** and similar multicoloured designs. P 15½.*

708	20 c. Type **341**		25	25
	a. Horiz strip of 5. Nos. 708/12		1·10	
709	20 c. Uluru, Northern Territory		25	25
710	20 c. Royal, New South Wales		25	25
711	20 c. Flinders Ranges, South Australia		25	25
712	20 c. Nambung, Western Australia		25	25
713	20 c. Girraween, Queensland (*vert*)		25	25
	a. Horiz pair. Nos. 713/14		50	50
	ab. Imperf (horiz pair)*		£700	
714	20 c. Mount Field, Tasmania (*vert*)		25	25
708/14		Set of 7	1·40	1·40

Nos. 708/14 were printed together, *se-tenant*; Nos. 708/12 in horizontal strips of 5 and Nos. 713/14 in horizontal pairs, throughout separate sheets.

*The imperforate error, No. 713ab, involves the two right-hand vertical columns of the sheet only, the left-hand stamp having vertical perforations at left.

342 "Double Fairlie" Type Locomotive, Western Australia   **343** Symbolic Swan

(Des R. Honisett)

1979 (16 May). *Steam Railways. T **342** and similar horiz designs. Multicoloured. P 14 × 15 (20 c.) or 13½ (others).*

715	20 c. Type **342**		30	10
716	35 c. Locomotive, Puffing Billy Line, Victoria		60	70
717	50 c. Locomotive, Pichi Richi Line, South Australia		70	1·50
718	55 c. Locomotive, Zig Zag Railway, New South Wales		80	1·40
715/18		Set of 4	2·25	3·25

(Des B. Weatherhead)

1979 (6 June). *150th Anniv of Western Australia. P 13½.*
719 **343** 20 c. multicoloured   15 15

344 Children playing on Slide   **345** Letters and Parcels

(Des Wendy Tamlyn. Litho Asher and Co, Melbourne)

1979 (13 Aug). *International Year of the Child. P 13½ × 13.*
720 **344** 20 c. multicoloured   15 10

(Des A. Collins. Litho Asher and Co, Melbourne)

1979 (24 Sept–1 Nov). *Christmas. T **345** and similar vert designs. Multicoloured. P 13 × 13½.*

721	15 c. Christ's Nativity (Eastern European icon) (1.11.79)		15	10
722	25 c. Type **345**		25	50
723	55 c. "Madonna and Child" (Buglioni) (1.11.79)		40	75
721/3		Set of 3	70	1·25

346 Fly-fishing   **347** Matthew Flinders

(Des B. Clinton)

1979 (24 Oct). *Fishing. T **346** and similar vert designs. P 14 × 15 (20 c.) or 13½ (others).*

724	20 c. multicoloured		20	10
725	35 c. black, deep grey-blue and violet-blue		35	70
726	50 c. multicoloured		40	90
727	55 c. multicoloured		45	85
724/7		Set of 4	1·25	2·25

Designs:—35 c. Spinning; 50 c. Deep sea game-fishing; 55 c. Surf-fishing.

(Des B. Weatherhead. Litho Asher and Co, Melbourne)

1980 (23 Jan). *Australia Day. P 13½ × 13.*
728 **347** 20 c. multicoloured   20 10

348 Dingo   **349** Queen Elizabeth II

(Des Marg Towt. Litho Asher and Co, Melbourne)

1980 (20 Feb). *Dogs. T **348** and similar horiz designs. Multicoloured. P 13½ × 13.*

729	20 c. Type **348**		35	10
730	35 c. Border Collie		35	50
731	35 c. Australian Terrier		50	90
732	50 c. Australian Cattle Dog		1·10	1·75
733	55 c. Australian Kelpie		1·00	1·40
729/33		Set of 5	3·00	4·25

(Des Kay Breeden-Williams. Litho Asher and Co, Melbourne)

1980 (31 Mar)–**82**. *Birds (2nd series). Multicoloured designs as T **335**. P 12½.*

734	10 c. Golden-shouldered Parrot (*vert*) (1.7.80)		50	10
	a. Perf 14½ × 14 (1982)		1·50	55
734b	18 c. Spotted Catbird (*vert*) (17.11.80)		50	1·25
735	28 c. Australian Bee Eater ("Rainbow Bird") (*vert*)		50	20
736	35 c. Regent Bowerbird (*vert*) (1.7.80)		35	10
737	45 c. Masked Wood Swallow (*vert*)		40	10
	a. Perf 14 × 14½ (1982)		2·00	90
738	60 c. Australian King Parrot (*vert*)		50	15
739	80 c. Rainbow Pitta (1.7.80)		1·00	75
740	$1 Black-backed Magpie (*vert*) (1.7.80)		1·00	10
734/40		Set of 8	4·25	2·25

Designs of Nos. 734/40 measure 22 × 29 mm (vert) or 29 × 22 mm (horiz).

(Des B. Weatherhead. Litho Asher and Co, Melbourne)

1980 (21 Apr). *Queen Elizabeth II's Birthday. P 13 × 13½.*
741 **349** 22 c. multicoloured   30 20

350 "Once a jolly Swagman camp'd by a Billabong"   **351** High Court Buildings

(Des R. Roberts. Litho Asher and Co, Melbourne)

1980 (7 May). *Folklore. Scenes and Verses from the Folksong "Waltzing Matilda". T **350** and similar vert designs. Multicoloured. P 13 × 13½.*

742	22 c. Type **350**		30	20
	a. Horiz strip of 5. Nos. 742/6		1·40	
743	22 c. "And he sang as he shoved that Jumbuck in his Tuckerbag"		30	20
744	22 c. "Up rode the Squatter, mounted on his Thoroughbred"		30	20
745	22 c. "Down came the Troopers one, two, three"		30	20
746	22 c. "And his Ghost may be heard as you pass by that Billabong"		30	20
742/6		Set of 5	1·40	90

Nos. 742/6 were printed together, *se-tenant*, in horizontal strips of 5 throughout the sheet, forming a composite design.

(Des Cato Hibberd Design. Litho Asher and Co, Melbourne)

1980 (19 May). *Opening of High Court Building, Canberra. P 13 × 13½.*
747 **351** 22 c. multicoloured   20 20

STANLEY GIBBONS STAMP COLLECTING SERIES

Introductory booklets on *How to Start, How to Identify Stamps* and *Collecting by Theme*. A series of well illustrated guides at a low price.
Write for details.

352 Salvation Army   **353** Postbox, circa 1900

(Des J. Spatchurst. Litho Asher and Co, Melbourne)

1980 (11 Aug). *Community Welfare. T **352** and similar multicoloured designs. P 13½ × 13 (Nos. 748, 751) or 13 × 13½ (others).*

748	22 c. Type **352**		40	40
749	22 c. St. Vincent de Paul Society (*vert*)		40	40
750	22 c. Meals on Wheels (*vert*)		40	40
751	22 c. "Life. Be in it"		40	40
748/51		Set of 4	1·40	1·40

(Des B. Weatherhead. Litho Asher and Co, Melbourne)

1980 (29 Sept). *National Stamp Week. T **353** and similar vert designs showing postal history, circa 1900. Multicoloured. P 13 × 13½.*

752	22 c. Type **353**		30	20
	a. Horiz strip of 5. Nos. 752/6		1·40	
753	22 c. Postman (facing left)		30	20
754	22 c. Mail van		30	20
755	22 c. Postman and postbox		30	20
756	22 c. Postman (facing right)		30	20
752/6		Set of 5	1·40	1·40
MS757	95 × 130 mm. Nos. 752, 754 and 756		1·10	1·60
	a. Error. Imperf			

Nos. 752/6 were printed together, *se-tenant*, in horizontal strips of 5 throughout the sheet.
Stamps from No. MS757 have different backgrounds to the stamps from normal sheets.

354 "Holy Family" (painting, Prospero Fontana)   **355** Commonwealth Aircraft Factory CA-6 Wackett, 1941

(Des B. Weatherhead. Litho Asher and Co, Melbourne)

1980 (1 Oct–3 Nov). *Christmas. Works of Art. T **354** and similar vert designs. Multicoloured. P 13 × 13½.*

758	15 c. "The Virgin Enthroned" (detail of painting by Justin O'Brien) (3.11)		15	10
759	28 c. Type **354**		25	40
760	60 c. "Madonna and Child" (sculpture by School of M. Zuern) (3.11)		50	1·10
758/60		Set of 3	80	1·80

(Des O. Borchert. Litho Victorian Government Printer, Melbourne (22 c.), Asher and Co, Melbourne (others))

1980 (19 Nov). *Aircraft. T **355** and similar horiz designs. Multicoloured. P 13½ × 14 (22 c.) or 13½ × 13 (others).*

761	22 c. Type **355**		35	10
762	40 c. Commonwealth Aircraft Factory CA-25 Winjeel, 1955		70	90
763	45 c. Commonwealth Aircraft Factory CA-13 Boomerang, 1944		70	1·00
764	60 c. Government Aircraft Factory N22B Nomad, 1975		80	1·60
761/4		Set of 4	2·25	3·25

356 Flag in shape of Australia   **357** Caricature of Darby Munro (jockey)

(Des B. Weatherhead. Litho Asher and Co, Melbourne)

1981 (21 Jan). *Australia Day. P 13½ × 13.*
765 **356** 22 c. multicoloured   20 20

(Des T. Rafty. Litho Cambec Press, Melbourne)

1981 (18 Feb). *Sports Personalities. T **357** and similar vert designs showing caricatures. Multicoloured. P 14 × 13½.*

766	22 c. Type **357**		30	10
767	35 c. Victor Trumper (cricketer)		65	80
768	55 c. Sir Norman Brookes (tennis player)		85	1·25
769	60 c. Walter Lindrum (billiards player)		90	1·50
766/9		Set of 4	2·40	3·25

358 1931 Kingsford Smith's Flights 6d. Commemorative

359 Apex Emblem and Map of Australia

(Des Cato Hibberd Design. Litho Asher and Co, Melbourne)

1981 (25 Mar). *50th Anniv of Official Australia–U.K. Airmail Service. T* **358** *and similar horiz design showing 1931 Kingsford Smith's Flights 6d. commemorative. P* 13 × 13½ (22 c.) or 13½ × 13 (60 c.).
770 22 c. blackish lilac, rosine and bright blue .. 20 10
771 60 c. blackish lilac, rosine and ultramarine .. 60 90

(Dès P. Clark)

1981 (6 Apr). *50th Anniv of Apex* (young men's service club). *P* 13½.
772 **359** 22 c. multicoloured 20 20

ASHER AND CO. From April 1981 this firm was known as Leigh-Mardon Ltd, Melbourne.

360 Queen's Personal Standard for Australia

361 "Licence Inspected"

(Litho Leigh-Mardon Ltd, Melbourne)

1981 (21 Apr). *Queen Elizabeth II's Birthday. P* 13½ × 13.
773 **360** 22 c. multicoloured 20 20

(Des B. Weatherhead. Litho Leigh-Mardon Ltd, Melbourne)

1981 (20 May). *Gold Rush Era. Sketches by S. T. Gill. T* **361** *and similar vert designs. Multicoloured. P* 13 × 13½.
774 22 c. Type **361** 20 25
775 22 c. "Puddling" 20 25
776 22 c. "Quality of washing stuff" 20 25
777 22 c. "On route to deposit gold" 20 25
774/7 .. .. *Set of 4* 70 90

362 "On the Wallaby Track" (Fred McCubbin)

(Litho Leigh-Mardon Ltd, Melbourne)

1981 (17 June)–84. *Paintings. T* **362** *and similar horiz design. Multicoloured. P* 15 × 14½.
778 $2 Type **362** .. .. .. 1·50 30
779 $5 "A Holiday at Mentone, 1888" (Charles Conder) (4.4.84) (Optd S. £2·75) .. 4·75 1·25
For No. 778 overprinted "Specimen" see after No. 567a.

363 Thylacine

363a Blue Mountain Tree-Frog

363b *Papilio ulysses* (butterfly)

PRINTINGS OF THE 24 C. VALUE. (Nos. 788, 788b). Original printings of this stamp were produced by a combination of printing processes. The centre design was first printed in photogravure by the Note Printing Branch, Reserve Bank of Australia, and then the half-printed sheets were transferred to Leigh-Mardon Ltd for the inscriptions and face value to be added in lithography.

Further supplies of this value were required in late 1981, but these were printed by Leigh-Mardon Ltd entirely in lithography.

The work of the two printers can be identified by the usual differences exhibited by the processes concerned; the lithography version tending to be darker in appearance with much sharper outlines.

Other specific differences are as follows:

On the *photogravure* version the front legs show a diagonal pattern of screening dots which are replaced by vertical and horizontal lines on the *litho* stamp.

The animal's eye is highlighted on the *photogravure* stamp.

The fourth and sixth bands on the animal's back are much longer on the *litho* version.

The end of the right-hand twig is pointed on the *photogravure* and blunt on the *litho*.

Photogravure Centre

Lithography Centre

(Des C. McCubbin (4, 10, 20, 27 c. (No. 791), 30 c. (No. 792a), 35, 45, 60, 80 c., $1), F. Knight (5, 24, 25, 30 c. (No. 792), 50, 55 c.) or Beverley Bruen (others). Photo Note Ptg Branch, Reserve Bank of Australia and litho Leigh-Mardon (24 c. (No. 788)), litho Leigh-Mardon (3, 5, 15, 24 c. (No. 788b)), 25, 27 c. (both), 30 c. (both), 40, 50, 55, 65, 75, 90 c.), Cambec Press (others))

1981 (19 July)–83. *Wildlife. Multicoloured designs as T* **363** (5, 24, 25, 30, 50, 55 c.), *T* **363a** (1, 3, 5, 27 (No. 790), 40, 65, 70, 75, 85, 90, 95 c.) *or vert as T* **363b** *(others). P* 13½ (1, 4, 10, 20, 24, 35, 45, 60, 70, 80, 85, 95 c., $1), 14½×14 (27 c. (No. 791), 30 c. (No. 792a)) *or* 12½ *(others)*.
781 1 c. Lace Monitor (2.2.83) .. 10 20
782 3 c. Corroboree Frog (19.4.82) .. 10 10
   a. Perf 14×14½ (1983) 50 50
783 4 c. *Euschemon rafflesia* ("Regent Skipper") (butterfly) (vert) (15.6.83) .. 55 55
784 5 c. Queensland Hairy-nosed Wombat (vert) (15.7.81) 10 10
   a. Perf 14½×14 (12.83) .. .. 1·25 50
785 10 c. *Ornithoptera priamus* ("Cairns Bird-wing") (butterfly) (vert) (15.6.83) .. 60 10
786 15 c. Eastern Snake-necked Tortoise (16.6.82) 50 50
   a. Perf 14×14½ (12.83) .. .. 1·25 60
787 20 c. *Graphium macleayanus* ("MacLeay's Swallow Tail") (butterfly) (vert) (15.6.83) 80 35
788 24 c. Type **363** (centre photo, inscr litho) .. 45 10
   a. Imperf (pair) £200
   b. Centre and inscr litho (12.81) .. 65 75
789 25 c. Common Rabbit-Bandicoot (vert) (15.7.81) 35 40
   a. Perf 14×14½ (1982) 90 75
790 27 c. Type **363a** (19.4.82) .. 55 20
   a. Perf 14×14½ (6.82) 75 20
791 27 c. Type **363b** (15.6.83) .. 90 30
   a. Imperf (pair) £400
792 30 c. Bridle Nail-tailed Wallaby (vert) (15.7.81) 70 15
792a 30 c. *Pseudalmenus chlorinda* ("Chlorinda Hairstreak") (butterfly) (vert) (24.10.83) .. .. 1·00 20
793 35 c. *Danaus hamata* ("Blue Tiger") (butterfly) (vert) (15.6.83) .. 1·00 30
794 40 c. Smooth Knob-tailed Gecko (16.6.82) 45 30
   a. Perf 14×14½ (12.83) .. .. 2·50 75
795 45 c. *Cressida cressida* ("Big Greasy") (butterfly) (vert) (15.6.83) .. 1·00 30
796 50 c. Leadbeater's Possum (15.7.81) .. 50 10
   a. Perf 14×14½ (1983) .. .. 1·50 50
797 55 c. Stick-nest Rat (vert) (15.7.81) .. 50 30
798 60 c. *Delias aganippe* ("Wood White") (butterfly) (vert) (15.6.83) .. 1·10 30
799 65 c. Yellow-faced Whip Snake (19.4.82) .. 80 40
   a. Perf 14×14½ (1983) .. .. 1·50 1·00
800 70 c. Crucifix Toad (2.2.83) .. 65 1·00
801 75 c. Eastern Water Dragon (19.4.82) .. 1·25 40
   a. Perf 14×14½ (12.83) .. .. 1·75 1·50
802 80 c. *Ogyris amaryllis* ("Amaryllis Azure") (butterfly) (vert) (15.6.83) .. 1·40 1·50
803 85 c. Centralian Blue-tongued Lizard (2.2.83) .. .. 1·10 1·25
804 90 c. Freshwater Crocodile (16.6.82) .. 1·60 1·25
805 95 c. Thorny Devil (2.2.83) .. 1·25 1·60
806 $1 *Tisiphone abeona* ("Sword-grass Brown") (butterfly) (vert) (15.6.83) 1·40 30
781/806 .. .. .. *Set of 27* 18·00 10·50
A late printing of No. 781, issued July 1987, is on thicker paper with a creamier appearance.

364 Prince Charles and Lady Diana Spencer

365 *Cortinarius cinnabarinus*

(Des B. Clinton. Litho Leigh-Mardon Ltd, Melbourne)

1981 (29 July). *Royal Wedding. P* 13½ × 13.
821 **364** 24 c. multicoloured 20 10
822 60 c. multicoloured .. .. 55 1·00

(Des Celia Rosser. Litho Leigh-Mardon Ltd, Melbourne)

1981 (19 Aug). *Australian Fungi. T* **365** *and similar vert designs. Multicoloured. P* 13 × 13½.
823 24 c. Type **365** 35 10
824 35 c. *Coprinus comatus* .. .. 60 1·10
825 55 c. *Armillaria luteobubalina* .. 80 1·25
826 60 c. *Cortinarius austrovenetus* .. 90 1·40
823/6 .. .. *Set of 4* 2·40 3·50

366 Disabled People playing Basketball

367 "Christmas Bush for His Adorning"

(Des J. Spatchurst. Litho Cambec Press, Melbourne)

1981 (16 Sept). *International Year for Disabled Persons. P* 14 × 13½.
827 **366** 24 c. multicoloured 20 20

(Des F. Beck. Litho Leigh-Mardon Ltd, Melbourne)

1981 (28 Sept–2 Nov). *Christmas. Scenes and Verses from Carols by W. James and J. Wheeler. T* **367** *and similar vert designs. Multicoloured. P* 13 × 13½.
828 18 c. Type **367** (2 Nov) 25 10
829 30 c. "The Silver Stars are in the Sky" .. 35 25
830 60 c. "Noeltime" (2 Nov) 60 70
828/30 .. .. .. *Set of 3* 1·10 90

368 Globe depicting Australia

369 *Ragamuffin* (ocean racing yacht)

(Des B. Weatherhead. Litho Leigh-Mardon Ltd, Melbourne)

1981 (30 Sept). *Commonwealth Heads of Government Meeting, Melbourne. P* 13 × 13½.
831 **368** 24 c. black, pale blue and gold .. 20 10
832 60 c. black, pale blue and silver .. 65 75

(Des R. Fletcher. Litho Leigh-Mardon Ltd, Melbourne)

1981 (14 Oct). *Yachts. T* **369** *and similar vert designs. Multicoloured. P* 13 × 13½.
833 24 c. Type **369** 35 10
834 30 c. "Sharpie" 50 55
835 55 c. "12 Metre" .. .. .. 75 1·00
836 60 c. "Sabot" .. .. .. 1·00 1·25
833/6 .. .. *Set of 4* 2·40 2·50

370 Aborigine, Governor Phillip (founder of N.S.W., 1788) and Post World War II Migrant

371 Humpback Whale

(Des B. Clinton. Litho Cambec Press, Melbourne)

1982 (20 Jan). *Australia Day. "Three Great Waves of Migration". P* 13½ × 14.
837 **370** 24 c. multicoloured 35 25

(Des R. and Katrina Ingpen. Litho Cambec Press, Melbourne)

1982 (17 Feb). *Whales. T 371 and similar multicoloured designs. P 13½ × 14 (24, 60 c.) or 14 × 13½ (others).*

838	24 c. Sperm Whale	..	..	40	10
839	35 c. Black Right Whale (*vert*)	..		60	70
840	55 c. Blue Whale (*vert*)	..		1·10	1·75
841	60 c. Type 371 (new blue background)			1·25	1·75
	a. Solid greenish blue background			£250	£160
838/41			*Set of 4*	3·00	3·75

No. 841a comes from a small trial printing, some sheets of which were included amongst normal stock by mistake. The correct version of the 60 c. value shows the new blue background streaked with white at top left. On No. 841a the background is in greenish blue and is without the white streaks.

372 Queen Elizabeth II

373 "Marjorie Atherton"

(Des R. Honisett. Litho Cambec Press, Melbourne)

1982 (21 Apr). *Queen Elizabeth II's Birthday. P 14 × 13½.*

842	**372** 27 c. multicoloured	..	..	35	15

(Des Betty Conabere. Litho Leigh-Mardon Ltd, Melbourne)

1982 (19 May). *Roses. T 373 and similar vert designs. Multicoloured. P 13 × 13½.*

843	27 c. Type 373	..	..	40	15
844	40 c. "Imp"	..		75	75
845	65 c. "Minnie Watson"	..		1·25	2·00
846	75 c. "Satellite"	..		1·25	1·60
843/6	..		*Set of 4*	3·25	4·00

374 Radio Announcer and 1930-style Microphone

375 Forbes Post Office

(Des Cato Hibberd Design. Litho Leigh-Mardon Ltd, Melbourne)

1982 (16 June). *50th Anniv of ABC (Australian Broadcasting Commission). T 374 and similar horiz design. Multicoloured. P 13½ × 13.*

847	27 c. Type 374	..	..	40	50
	a. Pair. Nos. 847/8	..		80	1·00
848	27 c. ABC logo	..		40	50

Nos. 847/8 were printed together, *se-tenant*, in horizontal and vertical pairs throughout the sheet.

(Des F. Beck. Litho Cambec Press, Melbourne)

1982 (4 Aug). *Historic Australian Post Offices. T 375 and similar multicoloured designs. P 14 × 13½ (vert) or 13½ × 14 (horiz).*

849	27 c. Type 375	..	..	40	40
850	27 c. Flemington Post Office	..		40	40
851	27 c. Rockhampton Post Office	..		40	40
852	27 c. Kingston S.E. Post Office (*horiz*)			40	40
853	27 c. York Post Office (*horiz*)			40	40
854	27 c. Launceston Post Office	..		40	40
855	27 c. Old Post and Telegraph Station, Alice Springs (*horiz*)	..		40	40
849/55			*Set of 7*	2·50	2·50

376 Early Australian Christmas Card

377 Boxing

(Des B. Weatherhead. Litho Leigh-Mardon Ltd, Melbourne)

1982 (15 Sept–1 Nov). *Christmas. T 376 and similar multicoloured designs. P 14½.*

856	21 c. Bushman's Hotel, with Cobb's coach arriving (*horiz*) (1.11.82)		30	10
857	35 c. Type 376	..		50	60
858	75 c. Little girl offering Christmas pudding to swagman (1.11.82)		75	1·40
856/8	..		*Set of 3*	1·40	1·90

(Des R. Carnielye. Litho Leigh-Mardon Ltd, Melbourne)

1982 (22 Sept). *Commonwealth Games, Brisbane. T 377 and similar horiz designs. P 14½.*

859	27 c. stone, lemon and bright carmine		30	20
860	27 c. lemon, stone and emerald		30	20
861	27 c. stone, lemon and yellow-brown		30	20
862	75 c. multicoloured			90	90
859/62			*Set of 4*	1·60	1·40
MS863	130 × 95 mm. Nos. 859/61. P 13½ × 13		1·25	1·75

Designs:—No. 859, Type **377**; No. 860, Archery; No. 861, Weightlifting; No. 862, Pole-vaulting.

378 Sydney Harbour Bridge 5s. Stamp of 1932

379 "Yirawala" Bark Painting

(Des Cato Hibberd Design. Litho Cambec Press, Melbourne)

1982 (27 Sept). *National Stamp Week. P 13½ × 14.*

864	**378** 27 c. multicoloured	..		35	30

(Des Australia Post Graphic Design Section. Litho Leigh-Mardon Ltd, Melbourne)

1982 (12 Oct). *Opening of Australian National Gallery. P 14½.*

865	**379** 27 c. multicoloured	..		30	25

380 Mimi Spirits Dancing

381 Eucalyptus calophylla "Rosea"

(Des D. Milaybuma (27 c.), L. Nabardayal (40 c.), J. Galareya (65 c.), D. Nguleingulei-Murrumurru (75 c.). Litho Cambec Press, Melbourne)

1982 (17 Nov). *Aboriginal Culture. Music and Dance. T 380 and similar horiz designs depicting Aboriginal Bark Paintings of Mimi Spirits. P 13½ × 14.*

866	27 c. multicoloured	..	..	25	10
867	40 c. multicoloured	..		40	70
868	65 c. multicoloured	..		60	1·25
869	75 c. multicoloured	..		65	1·25
866/9			*Set of 4*	1·75	3·00

(Des Elizabeth Conabere. Photo Enschedé)

1982 (17 Nov). *Eucalyptus Flowers. T 381 and similar horiz designs. Multicoloured. P 12½×13½.*

870	1 c. Type 381	..		10	30
	a. Booklet pane. Nos. 870/1 and 874 each × 2	1·00	
	b. Booklet pane. Nos. 870/1 each × 2, 872/3 and 874 × 3	2·50	
871	2 c. Eucalyptus casia	..		10	30
872	3 c. Eucalyptus ficifolia	..		90	1·40
873	10 c. Eucalyptus globulus	..		90	1·40
874	27 c. Eucalyptus forrestiana	..		30	40
870/4			*Set of 5*	2·00	3·50

Nos. 870/4 only exist from 60 c. (pane No. 870a) and $1 (pane No. 870b) stamp booklets and the stamps have one or two adjacent sides imperforate. They were printed on Harrison paper which gives a bluish white reaction under U.V. light.

382 Shand Mason Steam Fire Engine, 1891

383 H.M.S. *Sirius*

(Des A. Puckett. Litho Cambec Press, Melbourne)

1983 (12 Jan). *Historic Fire Engines. T 382 and similar horiz designs. Multicoloured. P 13½ × 14.*

875	27 c. Type 382	..	..	40	10
876	40 c. Hotchkiss fire engine, 1914		60	75
877	65 c. Ahrens-Fox PS2 fire engine, 1929		1·00	1·50
878	75 c. Merryweather manual fire appliance, 1851		1·00	1·40
875/8			*Set of 4*	2·75	3·25

(Des J. Spatchurst. Litho Leigh-Mardon Ltd, Melbourne)

1983 (26 Jan). *Australia Day. T 383 and similar horiz design. Multicoloured. P 14½.*

879	27 c. Type 383	..		40	50
	a. Pair. Nos. 879/80	..		80	1·00
	ab. Printed on the gummed side		£150	
880	27 c. H.M.S. Supply	..		40	50

Nos. 879/80 were printed together, *se-tenant*, in horizontal and vertical pairs throughout the sheet.

384 Stylised Kangaroo and Kiwi

385 Equality and Dignity

(Des G. Emery. Litho Cambec Press, Melbourne)

1983 (2 Feb). *Closer Economic Relationship Agreement with New Zealand. P 14 × 13½.*

881	**384** 27 c. multicoloured	..		30	30

(Des G. Emery. Litho Leigh-Mardon Ltd, Melbourne)

1983 (9 Mar). *Commonwealth Day. T 385 and similar vert designs. Multicoloured. P 14½.*

882	27 c. Type 385	..	..	20	25
883	27 c. Liberty and Freedom	..		20	25
884	27 c. Social Justice and Co-operation		20	25
885	75 c. Peace and Harmony	..		50	1·50
882/5			*Set of 4*	1·00	2·00

386 R.Y. *Britannia* passing Sydney Opera House

387 "Postal and Telecommunications Services"

(Des J. Richards. Litho Leigh-Mardon Ltd, Melbourne)

1983 (20 Apr). *Queen Elizabeth II's Birthday. P 14½.*

886	**386** 27 c. multicoloured	..		45	30

(Des B. Sadgrove. Litho Cambec Press, Melbourne)

1983 (18 May). *World Communications Year. P 13 × 13½.*

887	**387** 27 c. multicoloured	..		30	30

388 Badge of the Order of St. John

389 Jaycee Members and Badge

(Des T. McCauley. Litho Cambec Press, Melbourne)

1983 (8 June). *Centenary of St. John Ambulance in Australia. P 14 × 13½.*

888	**388** 27 c. black and deep turquoise-blue		35	30

(Des B. Clinton. Litho Cambec Press, Melbourne)

1983 (8 June). *50th Anniv of Australian Jaycees. P 13½ × 14.*

889	**389** 27 c. multicoloured	..		30	30

390 "The Bloke"

391 Nativity Scene

(Des B. Clinton. Litho Leigh-Mardon Ltd, Melbourne)

1983 (8 Aug). *Folklore. "The Sentimental Bloke" (humorous poem by C. J. Dennis). T 390 and similar vert designs. Multicoloured. P 14½.*

890	27 c. Type 390	..		40	50
	a. Horiz strip of 5. Nos. 890/4		1·75	
891	27 c. "Doreen—The Intro"	..		40	50
892	27 c. "The Stror' at Coot"	..		40	50
893	27 c. "Hitched"	..		40	50
894	27 c. "The Mooch o'Life"	..		40	50
890/4			*Set of 5*	1·75	2·25

Nos. 890/4 were printed together, *se-tenant*, in horizontal strips of 5 throughout the sheet.

(Des Holly Alvarez (24 c.), Deanne Head (35 c.), Justine Jacobi (85 c.). Litho Cambec Press, Melbourne)

1983 (14 Sept–2 Nov). *Christmas. Children's Paintings. T 391 and similar horiz designs. Multicoloured. P 13½ × 14.*

895	24 c. Type 391 (2 November)	..		20	10
896	35 c. Kookaburra	..		35	45
897	85 c. Father Christmas in sleigh over beach (2 November)		90	1·40
895/7	..		*Set of 3*	1·25	1·75

392 Sir Paul Edmund
de Strzelecki

393 Cook Family Cottage,
Melbourne

(Des Dianne Quinn. Litho Leigh-Mardon Ltd, Melbourne)

1983 (26 Sept). *Explorers of Australia. T **392** and similar vert designs. Multicoloured. P 14½.*

898	30 c. Type **392**	35	40
899	30 c. Ludwig Leichardt	35	40
900	30 c. William John Wills and Robert O'Hara Burke	35	40
901	30 c. Alexander Forrest	35	40
898/901	Set of 4	1·25	1·40

(Des J. Quinn. Litho Cambec Press, Melbourne)

1984 (26 Jan). *Australia Day. P 13½ × 14.*

902	**393**	30 c. black and stone	30	35

MACHINE LABELS. From 22 February 1984 gummed labels in the above design, ranging in value from 1 c. to $9.99, were available from seven automatic machines. The postcode at the top of the label indicates the location of the machine from which it was issued; 2000, Sydney; 2601, Canberra (until 1 October 1998) (Canberra subsequently used labels without postcode or code letters); 3000, Melbourne; 4000, Brisbane; 5000, Adelaide; 5790, Darwin (from 29 July 1985 then 0800 from 1 June 1988 until 24 October 1998); 6000, Perth (until 2 November 1998); 7000, Hobart. Labels without postcode numbers appeared on 24 June 1985.

These were replaced by a further series, with a background pattern of kangaroos, on 22 October 1985. These exist with the same code numbers as before or without code.

On 25 August 1986 a further series, with a background pattern of platypuses, were issued. The design was again changed on 2 September 1987 to show Echidnas. These were followed by Ringtail Possums on 28 September 1988, Frilled-necked Lizards on 1 September 1989, Koalas on 3 September 1990, Emus on 2 January 1992 and the Waratah (flower) on 8 September 1994.

An overall pattern of geometric shapes, streamers and springs was introduced on 6 June 1996.

A new design using Tiwi aboriginal art was introduced at "Australia 99" where four machines operated producing labels incorporating a line of ship images. Labels in this design, but without the ships, were available nationally from 6 October 1999.

As the number of machines increased rapidly only those situated at the State, or Capital Territory, General Post Offices showed a postcode. Other machines eventually showed a code, letter followed by numbers at bottom left. Later machines had a top label value of either $10 or $20.

394 Charles Ulm, Avro Type 618
Ten *Faith in Australia* and
Trans-Tasman Cover

(Des G. Beck and J. Quinn. Litho Cambec Press, Melbourne)

1984 (22 Feb). *50th Anniv of First Official Airmail Flights, New Zealand–Australia and Australia–Papua New Guinea. T **394** and similar horiz design. Multicoloured. P 13½.*

903	45 c. Type **394**	1·00	1·25
	a. Horiz pair. Nos. 903/4	2·00	2·50
904	45 c. As Type **394** but showing flown cover to Papua New Guinea	1·00	1·25

Nos. 903/4 were printed together, *se-tenant*, in horizontal pairs throughout the sheet.

395 Thomson "Steamer", 1898

396 Queen Elizabeth II

(Des A. Puckett. Litho Leigh-Mardon Ltd, Melbourne)

1984 (14 Mar). *Veteran and Vintage Cars. T **395** and similar horiz designs. Multicoloured. P 14½.*

905	30 c. Type **395**	50	60
	a. Vert strip of 5. Nos. 905/9	2·25	
906	30 c. Tarrant, 1906	50	60
907	30 c. Gordon & Co "Australian Six", 1919	50	60

908	30 c. Summit, 1923	50	60
909	30 c. Chic, 1924	50	60
905/9	Set of 5	2·25	2·75

Nos. 905/9 were printed together, *se-tenant*, in vertical strips of 5 throughout the sheet.

(Des B. Weatherhead. Litho Leigh-Mardon Ltd, Melbourne)

1984 (18 Apr). *Queen Elizabeth II's Birthday. P 14½.*

910	**396**	30 c. multicoloured	30	35
	a. Dull mauve (background) omitted	£400	

397 Cutty Sark

398 Freestyle

(Des J. Earl and J. Quinn. Litho Cambec Press, Melbourne)

1984 (23 May). *Clipper Ships. T **397** and similar multicoloured designs. P 14 × 13½ (30 c., 85 c.) or 13½ × 14 (others).*

911	30 c. Type **397**	40	25
912	45 c. Orient (horiz)	70	80
913	75 c. Sobraon (horiz)	1·25	1·75
914	85 c. Thermopylae	1·25	1·50
911/14	Set of 4	3·25	3·75

(Des B. Clinton. Litho Leigh-Mardon Ltd, Melbourne)

1984 (6 June). *Skiing. T **398** and similar multicoloured designs. P 14½.*

915	30 c. Type **398**	40	45
916	30 c. Downhill racer	40	45
917	30 c. Slalom (horiz)	40	45
918	30 c. Nordic (horiz)	40	45
915/18	Set of 4	1·50	1·75

399 Coral Hopper

400 Before the Event

(Des G. Ryan and R. Fletcher (2, 25, 30, 50, 55, 85 c.) or G. Ryan (others). Litho Leigh-Mardon Ltd, Melbourne (30, 33 c.) or Cambec Press, Melbourne (others))

1984 (18 June)–*86. Marine Life. T **399** and similar horiz designs. Multicoloured. P 14×14½ (30 c., 33 c.) or 13½ (others).*

919	2 c. Type **399**	10	20
920	3 c. Jimble (11.6.86)	20	20
921	5 c. Tasselled Frogfish ("Anglerfish") (12.6.85)	15	10
922	10 c. Rough Stonefish (11.6.86)	20	10
923	20 c. Red Handfish (12.6.85)	65	30
924	25 c. Orange-lipped Cowrie	45	40
925	30 c. Choat's Wrasse	45	40
926	33 c. Leafy Seadragon (20.3.85)	60	10
927	40 c. Red Velvetfish (12.6.85)	85	75
928	45 c. Textile or Cloth of Gold Cone (11.6.86)	1·00	60
929	50 c. Clown Surgeonfish	80	50
930	55 c. Bennett's Nudibranch	80	50
	a. New blue ("BENNETT'S NUDI-BRANCH") omitted	†	—
931	60 c. Zebra Lionfish (11.6.86)	90	70
932	65 c. Banded Stingray (11.6.86)	1·25	1·00
933	70 c. Southern Blue-ringed Octopus (11.6.86)	1·25	1·00
934	80 c. Pineconefish ("Pineapple Fish") (12.6.85)	1·25	70
935	85 c. Royal Angelfish	90	70
936	90 c. Crab-eyed Goby (12.6.85)	1·60	75
937	$1 Crown of Thorns Starfish (11.6.86)	1·50	80
	(Optd S. 50p.)		
919/37	Set of 19	13·00	8·75

No. 930a only exists used on maximum card.

Used examples have been reported of both the 33 c. and $1 with the face value and inscriptions omitted. The colours involved were dull orange on the 33 c. and mauve on the $1.

(Des O. Schmidinger and Christine Stead. Litho Cambec Press, Melbourne)

1984 (25 July). *Olympic Games, Los Angeles. T **400** and similar multicoloured designs. P 14 × 13½ (No. 943) or 13½ × 14 (others).*

941	30 c. Type **400**	35	35
942	30 c. During the event	35	35
943	30 c. After the event (vert)	35	35
941/3	Set of 3	95	95

401 Australian 1913
1d. Kangaroo Stamp

402 "Angel"
(stained-glass window,
St. Francis' Church, Melbourne)

(Des Ken Cato Design Studio. Litho Cambec Press, Melbourne)

1984 (22 Aug–21 Sept). *"Ausipex" International Stamp Exhibition, Melbourne. T **401** and similar vert designs. Multicoloured. P 14½.*

944	30 c. Type **401**	35	30
MS945	126 × 175 mm. 30 c. × 7, Victoria 1850 3d. "Half Length"; New South Wales 1850 1d. "Sydney View"; Tasmania 1853 1d.; South Australia 1855 1d.; Western Australia 1854 1d. "Black Swan"; Queensland 1860 6d.; Type **401** (21 Sept.)	3·50	4·50

On No. MS945 the emblem and inscription on the sheet margin are embossed.

(Des Ken Cato Design Studio. Litho Cambec Press, Melbourne)

1984 (17 Sept–31 Oct). *Christmas. Stained-glass Windows. T **402** and similar vert designs. Multicoloured. P 13½.*

946	24 c. "Angel and Child" (Holy Trinity Church, Sydney) (31.10.84)	25	20
947	30 c. "Veiled Virgin and Child" (St. Mary's Catholic Church, Geelong) (31.10.84)	35	20
948	40 c. Type **402**	50	60
949	50 c. "Three Kings" (St. Mary's Cathedral, Sydney) (31.10.84)	65	80
950	85 c. "Madonna and Child" (St. Bartholomew's Church, Norwood) (31.10.84)	80	1·25
946/50	Set of 5	2·25	2·75

403 "Stick Figures"
(Cobar Region)

404 Yellow-tufted
Honeyeater

(Des Elizabeth Innes. Litho Leigh-Mardon Ltd, Melbourne)

1984 (7 Nov). *Bicentenary of Australian Settlement (1988) (1st issue). The First Australians. T **403** and similar square designs showing aborigine rock paintings. Multicoloured. P 14½.*

951	30 c. Type **403**	35	45
952	30 c. "Bunjil" (large figure), Grampians	35	45
953	30 c. "Quikans" (tall figures), Cape York	35	45
954	30 c. "Wandjina Spirit and Baby Snakes" (Gibb River)	35	45
955	30 c. "Rock Python" (Gibb River)	35	45
956	30 c. "Silver Barramundi" (fish) (Kakadu National Park)	35	45
957	30 c. Bicentenary emblem	35	45
958	85 c. "Rock Possum" (Kakadu National Park)	80	1·40
951/8	Set of 8	3·00	4·00

See also Nos. 972/6, 993/6, 1002/7, 1019/22, 1059/63, 1064/6, 1077/81, 1090/2, 1105/9, 1110, 1137/41, 1145/8 and 1149.

(Des. G. Emery. Litho Leigh-Mardon Ltd, Melbourne)

1984 (19 Nov). *150th Anniv of Victoria. T **404** and similar vert design. Multicoloured. P 14½.*

959	30 c. Type **404**	40	65
	a. Pair. Nos. 959/60	80	1·25
960	30 c. Leadbeater's Possum	40	65

Nos. 959/60 were printed together, *se-tenant*, in horizontal and vertical pairs throughout the sheet.

405 "Musgrave Ranges"
(Sir Sidney Nolan)

406 Young People of
Different Races, and Sun

(Des Sue Titcher. Litho Leigh-Mardon Ltd, Melbourne)

1985 (25 Jan). *Australia Day. Birth Centenary of Dorothea Mackellar (author of poem "My Country"). T **405** and similar horiz design. Multicoloured. P 14½.*

961	30 c. Type **405**	45	70
	a. Tête-bêche (vert pair)	1·50	1·40
	b. Vert pair. Nos. 961/2	90	1·40
962	30 c. "The Walls of China" (Russell Drysdale)	45	70
	a. Tête-bêche (vert pair)	1·50	2·25

Nos. 961/2 were printed together, *se-tenant*, within the sheet of 100 (2 panes 50 (5×10)). In each pane No. 961 occurs in horizontal rows 1, 4, 5, 8 and 9, and No. 962 in rows 2, 3, 6, 7 and 10. Horizontal rows 3/4 and 7/8 are inverted forming tête-bêche pairs of the same design in addition to the vertical *se-tenant* pairs containing both designs.

(Des Derryn Vogelnest. Litho Cambec Press, Melbourne)

1985 (13 Feb). *International Youth Year. P 14 × 13½.*

963	**406**	30 c. multicoloured	40	30

NEW INFORMATION

The editor is always interested to correspond with people who have new information that will improve or correct the Catalogue.

407 Royal Victorian Volunteer Artillery   **408** District Nurse of early 1900's

(Des Pam Andrews. Litho Leigh-Mardon Ltd, Melbourne)

1985 (25 Feb). *19th-Century Australian Military Uniforms. T* 407 *and similar vert designs. Multicoloured.* P 14½.

964	33 c. Type **407**		60	65
	a. Horiz strip of 5. Nos. 964/8		2·75	
965	33 c. Western Australian Pinjarrah Cavalry		60	65
966	33 c. New South Wales Lancers		60	65
967	33 c. New South Wales Contingent to the Sudan		60	65
968	33 c. Victorian Mounted Rifles		60	65
964/8		*Set of 5*	2·75	3·00

Nos. 964/8 were printed together, *se-tenant*, in horizontal strips of 5 throughout the sheet.

(Des Wendy Tamlyn. Litho Leigh-Mardon Ltd, Melbourne)

1985 (13 Mar). *Centenary of District Nursing Services.* P 14½.

969	**408**	33 c. multicoloured		45	35

409 Sulphur-crested Cockatoos

(Des R. Bevers. Litho Leigh-Mardon Ltd, Melbourne)

1985 (13 Mar). *Multicoloured, background colour given.* P 14½×*imperf.*

970	**409**	1 c. flesh		1·50	2·25
		a. Booklet pane. Nos. 970, and 971×3		2·75	
971		33 c. pale turquoise-green		45	55

Nos. 970/1 only exist from $1 stamp booklets. As stamps from these booklets have their outer edges imperforate, the end example of No. 971 is only perforated along one side.

410 Abel Tasman and Journal Entry   **411** Sovereign's Badge of Order of Australia

(Des G. Emery. Litho Cambec Press, Melbourne)

1985 (10 Apr). *Bicentenary of Australian Settlement* (1988) (*2nd issue*). *Navigators. T* 410 *and similar square designs. Multicoloured.* P 13.

972	33 c. Type **410**		60	35
973	33 c. Dirk Hartog's *Eendracht* (detail, Aert Anthonisz)		60	35
974	33 c. "William Dampier" (detail, T. Murray)		60	35
975	90 c. Globe and hand with extract from Dampier's journal		1·40	2·00
972/5		*Set of 4*	2·75	2·75
MS976	150×115 mm. As Nos. 972/5, but with cream-coloured margins		3·25	4·25

(Des Elizabeth Innes. Litho Cambec Press, Melbourne)

1985 (22 Apr). *Queen Elizabeth II's Birthday.* P 14×13½.

977	**411**	33 c. multicoloured		40	30

412 Tree, and Soil running through Hourglass ("Soil")   **413** *Elves and Fairies* (Annie Rentoul and Ida Rentoul Outhwaite)

(Des L. Whaite and G. Jorgensen. Litho Cambec Press, Melbourne)

1985 (15 May). *Conservation. T* 412 *and similar vert designs. Multicoloured.* P 14×13½.

978	33 c. Type **412**		45	20
979	50 c. Washing on line and smog ("air")		80	85
980	80 c. Tap and flower ("water")		1·25	1·50
981	90 c. Chain encircling flames ("energy")		1·40	2·00
978/81		*Set of 4*	3·50	4·00

(Des P. Leuver. Litho Leigh-Mardon Ltd, Melbourne)

1985 (17 July). *Classic Australian Children's Books. T* 413 *and similar vert designs. Multicoloured.* P 14½.

982	33 c. Type **413**		50	65
	a. Horiz strip of 5. Nos. 982/6		2·25	
983	33 c. *The Magic Pudding* (Norman Lindsay)		50	65
984	33 c. *Ginger Meggs* (James Charles Bancks)		50	65
985	33 c. *Blinky Bill* (Dorothy Wall)		50	65
986	33 c. *Snugglepot and Cuddlepie* (May Gibbs)		50	65
982/6		*Set of 5*	3·00	

Nos. 982/6 were printed together, *se-tenant*, in horizontal strips of 5 throughout the sheet.

414 Dish Aerials   **415** Angel in Sailing Ship

(Des J. Ostoja-Kotkowski. Litho Leigh-Mardon Ltd, Melbourne)

1985 (18 Sept). *Electronic Mail Service.* P 14½.

987	**414**	33 c. multicoloured		35	30

(Des S. Hartshorne. Litho Leigh-Mardon Ltd, Melbourne)

1985 (18 Sept–1 Nov). *Christmas. T* 415 *and similar horiz designs. Multicoloured.* P 14½.

988	27 c. Angel with holly wings (1.11)		35	15
989	33 c. Angel with bells (1.11)		40	15
990	45 c. Type **415**		60	50
991	55 c. Angel with star (1.11)		75	80
992	90 c. Angel with Christmas tree bauble (1.11)		1·40	1·50
988/92		*Set of 5*	3·25	2·75

416 Astrolabe (*Batavia*, 1629)   **417** Aboriginal Wandjina Spirit, Map of Australia and Egg

(Des G. Emery. Litho Cambec Press, Melbourne)

1985 (2 Oct). *Bicentenary of Australian Settlement* (1988) (*3rd issue*). *Relics from Early Shipwrecks. T* 416 *and similar square designs. Multicoloured.* P 13.

993	33 c. Type **416**		40	15
994	50 c. German beardman jug (*Vergulde Draeck*, 1656)		80	90
995	90 c. Wooden bobbins (*Batavia*, 1629) and encrusted scissors (*Zeewijk*, 1727)		1·75	2·25
996	$1 Silver and brass buckle (*Zeewijk*, 1727)		1·75	2·25
993/6		*Set of 4*	4·25	5·00

(Des R. Meeks. Litho Leigh-Mardon Ltd, Melbourne)

1986 (24 Jan). *Australia Day.* P 14½.

997	**417**	33 c. multicoloured		40	30

418 AUSSAT Satellite, Moon and Earth's Surface   **419** H.M.S. *Buffalo*

(Des O. Schmidinger and Christine Stead. Litho Leigh-Mardon Ltd, Melbourne)

1986 (24 Jan). *AUSSAT National Communications Satellite System. T* 418 *and similar vert design. Multicoloured.* P 14½.

998	33 c. Type **418**		50	15
999	80 c. AUSSAT satellite in orbit		1·50	2·25

(Des I. Kidd. Litho Cambec Press, Melbourne)

1986 (12 Feb). *150th Anniv of South Australia. T* 419 *and similar horiz design. Multicoloured.* P 13½×14.

1000	33 c. Type **419**		70	90
	a. Pair. Nos. 1000/1		1·40	1·75
1001	33 c. "City Sign" sculpture (Otto Hajek), Adelaide		70	90

Nos. 1000/1 were printed together, *se-tenant*, in horizontal and vertical pairs throughout the sheet, the background of each horizontal pair showing an extract from the colony's Letters Patent of 1836.

420 *Banksia serrata*   **421** Radio Telescope, Parkes, and Diagram of Comet's Orbit

(Des Sue Titcher. Litho Cambec Press, Melbourne)

1986 (12 Mar). *Bicentenary of Australian Settlement* (1988) (*4th issue*). *Cook's Voyage to New Holland. T* 420 *and similar horiz designs. Multicoloured.* P 13.

1002	33 c. Type **420**		60	35
1003	33 c. *Hibiscus meraukensis*		60	35
1004	50 c. *Dillenia alata*		90	1·10
1005	80 c. *Correa reflexa*		1·60	2·50
1006	90 c. "Joseph Banks" (botanist) (Reynolds) and Banks with Dr. Solander		2·00	2·00
1007	90 c. "Sydney Parkinson" (self-portrait) and Parkinson drawing		2·00	2·00
1002/7		*Set of 6*	7·00	7·50

(Des J. Passmore. Litho Cambec Press, Melbourne)

1986 (9 Apr). *Appearance of Halley's Comet.* P 14×13½.

1008	**421**	33 c. multicoloured		50	35

422 Queen Elizabeth II   **423** Brumbies (wild horses)

(Des Fay Plamka. Litho Leigh-Mardon Ltd, Melbourne)

1986 (21 Apr). *60th Birthday of Queen Elizabeth II.* P 14½.

1009	**422**	33 c. multicoloured		45	35

(Des R. Ingpen. Litho Leigh-Mardon Ltd, Melbourne)

1986 (21 May). *Australian Horses. T* 423 *and similar horiz designs. Multicoloured.* P 14½.

1010	33 c. Type **423**		60	15
1011	80 c. Mustering		1·50	2·00
1012	90 c. Show-jumping		1·50	2·25
1013	$1 Child on pony		1·75	2·25
1010/13		*Set of 4*	4·75	6·00

424 "The Old Shearer stands"   **425** "King George III" (A. Ramsay) and Convicts

(Des R. Ingpen. Litho Leigh-Mardon Ltd, Melbourne)

1986 (21 July). *Folklore. Scenes and Verses from the Folksong "Click go the Shears". T* 424 *and similar vert designs. Multicoloured.* P 14½.

1014	33 c. Type **424**		55	75
	a. Horiz strip of 5. Nos. 1014/18		2·50	
1015	33 c. "The ringer looks around"		55	75
1016	33 c. "The boss of the board"		55	75
1017	33 c. "The tar-boy is there"		55	75
1018	33 c. "Shearing is all over"		55	75
1014/18		*Set of 5*	2·50	3·50

Nos. 1014/18 were printed together, *se-tenant*, in horizontal strips of 5 throughout the sheet, forming a composite design.

(Des D. Lancashire. Litho Cambec Press, Melbourne)

1986 (6 Aug). *Bicentenary of Australian Settlement* (1988) (*5th issue*). *Convict Settlement in New South Wales.* T **425** *and similar horiz designs. Multicoloured.* P 13.

1019	33 c. Type 425	80	50
1020	33 c. "Lord Sydney" (Gilbert Stuart) and convicts	80	50
1021	33 c. "Captain Arthur Phillip" (F. Wheatley) and ship	80	50
1022	$1 "Captain John Hunter" (W. B. Bennett) and aborigines	3·25	4·25
1019/22	Set of 4	5·00	5·25

426 Red Kangaroo   **427** Royal Bluebell   **428** Pink Enamel Orchid

(Des D. Higgins. Litho Leigh-Mardon Ltd, Melbourne)

1986 (13 Aug). *Australian Wildlife* (*1st series*). T **426** *and similar vert designs. Multicoloured.* P 14½×14.

1023	36 c. Type 426	55	70
	a. Horiz strip of 5. Nos. 1023/7	2·50	
1024	36 c. Emu	55	70
1025	36 c. Koala	55	70
1026	36 c. Laughing Kookaburra	55	70
1027	36 c. Platypus	55	70
1023/7	Set of 5	2·50	3·25

Nos. 1023/7 were printed together, *se-tenant*, in horizontal strips of 5 throughout the sheet.
For 37 c. values see Nos. 1072/6.

(Des Betty Conabere. Litho Mercury-Walch Pty, Hobart)

1996 (25 Aug). *Alpine Wildflowers.* T **427** *and similar vert designs. Multicoloured.* Roul.

1028	3 c. Type 427	35	35
	a. Booklet pane. Nos. 1028, 1029 and 1031×2	2·50	
	b. Booklet pane. Nos. 1028, 1030 and 1031×2	2·50	
1029	5 c. Alpine Marsh Marigold	1·60	2·50
1030	25 c. Mount Buffalo Sunray	1·60	2·50
1031	36 c. Silver Snow Daisy	45	30
1028/31	Set of 4	3·50	5·00

Nos. 1028/31 only exist from 80 c. (pane No. 1028a) and $1 (pane No. 1028b) stamp booklets. The outer edges of the booklet panes are imperforate.

(Des O. Schmidinger and Christine Stead. Litho Leigh-Mardon Ltd, Melbourne)

1986 (18 Sept). *Native Australian Orchids.* T **428** *and similar vert designs. Multicoloured.* P 14½.

1032	36 c. Type 428	70	20
1033	55 c. Dendrobium nindii	1·25	1·00
1034	90 c. Duck Orchid	2·00	2·00
1035	$1 Queen of Sheba Orchid	2·00	2·00
1032/5	Set of 4	5·50	4·75

429 *Australia II crossing Finishing Line*   **430** Dove with Olive Branch and Sun

(Des J. Passmore and G. Rowan. Litho Cambec Press, Melbourne)

1986 (26 Sept). *Australian Victory in America's Cup, 1983.* T **429** *and similar vert designs. Multicoloured.* P 14×13½.

1036	36 c. Type 429	75	75
1037	36 c. Boxing kangaroo flag of winning syndicate	75	75
	a. Grey (inscr and face value) omitted	£130	
1038	36 c. America's Cup trophy	75	75
	a. Grey (inscr and face value) omitted	£130	
1036/8	Set of 3	2·00	2·00

(Des K. Cato. Litho Cambec Press, Melbourne)

1986 (22 Oct). *International Peace Year.* P 14×13½.

1039	**430** 36 c. multicoloured	65	40

Examples with the gutter margin overprinted to commemorate the Papal visit in November 1986 were not produced by the Australian Post Office.

NEW INFORMATION

The editor is always interested to correspond with people who have new information that will improve or correct the Catalogue.

---

431 Mary and Joseph   **432** Australian Flag on Printed Circuit Board

(Des B. Clinton. Litho Leigh-Mardon Ltd, Melbourne)

1986 (3 Nov–Dec). *Christmas.* T **431** *and similar multicoloured designs showing scenes from children's nativity play.* P 14½.

1040	30 c. Type 431	40	30
	a. Perf 14×13½ (12.86)	75	75
1041	36 c. Three Wise Men leaving gifts	50	45
1042	60 c. Angels (horiz)	90	1·50
1040/2	Set of 3	1·60	2·00
MS1043	147×70 mm. 30 c. Three angels and shepherd (horiz); 30 c. Kneeling shepherds (horiz); 30 c. Mary, Joseph and three angels; 30 c. Innkeeper and two angels; 30 c. Three Wise Men (horiz)	2·75	3·00

No. 1040a was printed by Cambec Press after stocks of the original printing by Leigh-Mardon Ltd ran short. It is believed that this Cambec Press printing was distributed in New South Wales, Tasmania, Victoria and Western Australia.

(Des J. Passmore. Litho CPE Australia Ltd, Melbourne)

1987 (23 Jan). *Australia Day.* T **432** *and similar horiz design. Multicoloured.* P 13½×14.

1044	36 c. Type 432	55	35
1045	36 c. "Australian Made" Campaign logos	55	35

433 Aerial View of Yacht   **434** Grapes and Melons

(Des O. Schmidinger and Christine Stead. Litho Leigh-Mardon Ltd, Melbourne)

1987 (28 Jan). *America's Cup Yachting Championship.* T **433** *and similar vert designs. Multicoloured.* P 14½.

1046	36 c. Type 433	40	20
1047	55 c. Two yachts tacking	90	1·00
1048	90 c. Two yachts beating	1·40	2·00
1049	$1 Two yachts under full sail	1·50	1·75
1046/9	Set of 4	3·75	4·50

(Des Susan Tilley. Litho CPE Australia Ltd, Melbourne)

1987 (11 Feb). *Australian Fruit.* T **434** *and similar vert designs. Multicoloured.* P 14×13½.

1050	36 c. Type 434	40	20
1051	65 c. Tropical and sub-tropical fruits	1·00	1·25
1052	90 c. Citrus fruit, apples and pears	1·40	1·90
1053	$1 Stone and berry fruits	1·40	1·60
1050/3	Set of 4	3·75	4·50

435 Livestock   **436** Queen Elizabeth in Australia, 1986

(Des D. Lancashire. Litho CPE Australia Ltd, Melbourne)

1987 (10 Apr). *Agricultural Shows.* T **435** *and similar vert designs. Multicoloured.* P 14×13½.

1054	36 c. Type 435	60	20
1055	65 c. Produce	1·25	1·75
1056	90 c. Sideshows	1·75	2·40
1057	$1 Competitions	1·90	2·40
1054/7	Set of 4	5·00	6·00

(Des Janet Boschen. Litho CPE Australia Ltd, Melbourne)

1987 (21 Apr). *Queen Elizabeth II's Birthday.* P 13½×14.

1058	**436** 36 c. multicoloured	55	50

---

437 Convicts on Quay   **438** "At the Station"

(Des Sue Passmore. Litho CPE Australia Ltd, Melbourne)

1987 (13 May). *Bicentenary of Australian Settlement* (1988) (*6th issue*). *Departure of the First Fleet.* T **437** *and similar square designs. Multicoloured.* P 13.

1059	36 c. Type 437	80	90
	a. Horiz strip of 5. Nos. 1059/63	3·50	
1060	36 c. Royal Marines officer and wife	80	90
1061	36 c. Sailors loading supplies	80	90
1062	36 c. Officers being ferried to ships	80	90
1063	36 c. Fleet in English Channel	80	90
1059/63	Set of 5	3·50	4·00

Nos. 1059/63 were printed together, *se-tenant*, in horizontal strips of 5 throughout the sheet.
See also Nos. 1064/6, 1077/81, 1090/2 and 1105/9.

(Des Sue Passmore. Litho CPE Australia Ltd, Melbourne)

1987 (3 June). *Bicentenary of Australian Settlement* (1988) (*7th issue*). *First Fleet at Tenerife. Square designs as* T **437**. *Multicoloured.* P 13.

1064	36 c. Ferrying supplies, Santa Cruz	70	90
	a. Horiz pair. Nos. 1064/5	1·40	1·75
1065	36 c. Canary Islands fishermen and departing fleet	70	90
1066	$1 Fleet arriving at Tenerife (Optd S. 50p)	1·75	2·00
1064/6	Set of 3	2·75	3·50

Nos. 1064/5 were printed together, *se-tenant*, in horizontal pairs throughout the sheet, forming a composite design.

(Des C. Lee. Litho CPE Australia Ltd, Melbourne)

1987 (24 June). *Folklore. Scenes and Verses from Poem "The Man from Snowy River".* T **438** *and similar vert designs. Multicoloured.* P 14×13½.

1067	36 c. Type 438	70	90
	a. Horiz strip of 5. Nos. 1067/71	3·25	
1068	36 c. "Mountain bred"	70	90
1069	36 c. "That terrible descent"	70	90
1070	36 c. "At their heels"	70	90
1071	36 c. "Brought them back"	70	90
1067/71	Set of 5	3·25	4·00

Nos. 1067/71 were printed together, *se-tenant*, in horizontal strips of five throughout the sheet, forming a composite background design of mountain scenery.

(Des D. Higgins. Litho Leigh-Mardon Ltd, Melbourne)

1987 (1 July). *Australian Wildlife* (*2nd series*). *Vert designs as* T **426**. *Multicoloured.* P 14½×14.

1072	37 c. Common Brushtail Possum	55	65
	a. Horiz strip of 5. Nos. 1072/6	2·50	
	ab. Pale orange (top panel) omitted	£1500	
1073	37 c. Sulphur-crested Cockatoo	55	65
1074	37 c. Common Wombat	55	65
1075	37 c. Crimson Rosella	55	65
1076	37 c. Echidna	55	65
1072/6	Set of 5	2·50	3·00

Nos. 1072/6 were printed together, *se-tenant*, in horizontal strips of 5 throughout the sheet.

(Des Sue Passmore. Litho CPE Australia Ltd, Melbourne)

1987 (6 Aug). *Bicentenary of Australian Settlement* (1988) (*8th issue*). *First Fleet at Rio de Janeiro. Square designs as* T **437**. *Multicoloured.* P 13.

1077	37 c. Sperm Whale and fleet	80	85
	a. Horiz strip of 5. Nos. 1077/81	3·50	
1078	37 c. Brazilian coast	80	85
1079	37 c. British officers in market	80	85
1080	37 c. Religious procession	80	85
1081	37 c. Fleet leaving Rio	80	85
1077/81	Set of 5	3·50	3·75

Nos. 1077/81 were printed together, *se-tenant*, in horizontal strips of 5, forming a composite design.

439 Bionic Ear   **440** Catching Crayfish

(Des. O. Schmidinger and Christine Stead. Litho Leigh-Mardon Ltd, Melbourne)

1987 (19 Aug). *Australian Achievements in Technology.* T **439** *and similar vert designs. Multicoloured.* P 14½.

1082	37 c. Type 439	40	35
1083	53 c. Microchips	75	60
1084	63 c. Robotics	85	70
1085	68 c. Ceramics	95	75
1082/5	Set of 4	2·75	2·25

(Des Elizabeth Honey. Litho Leigh-Mardon Ltd, Melbourne)

1987 (16 Sept). *"Aussie Kids". T 440 and similar horiz designs. Multicoloured.* P 14½.
1086	37 c.	Type **440**			40	35
1087	55 c.	Playing cat's cradle			1·00	75
1088	90 c.	Young football supporters			1·40	1·40
1089	$1	Children with kangaroo (Optd S. 50p)			1·60	1·40
1086/9				Set of 4	4·00	3·50

(Des Sue Passmore. Litho CPE Australia Ltd, Melbourne)

1987 (13 Oct). *Bicentenary of Australian Settlement (1988) (9th issue). First Fleet at Cape of Good Hope. Square designs as T 437. Multicoloured.* P 13.
1090	37 c.	Marine checking list of livestock			65	90
	a.	Horiz pair. Nos. 1090/1			1·25	1·75
1091	37 c.	Loading livestock			65	90
1092	$1	First Fleet at Cape Town (Optd S. 50p)			1·50	2·00
1090/2				Set of 3	2·50	3·50

Nos. 1090/1 were printed together, *se-tenant*, in horizontal and vertical pairs throughout the sheet, the former showing a composite design.

441 Detail of Spearthrower, Western Australia

442 Grandmother and Granddaughters with Candles

(Des J. Passmore. Litho Leigh-Mardon Ltd, Melbourne)

1987 (13 Oct). *Aboriginal Crafts. T 441 and similar horiz designs. Multicoloured.* P 15½×imperf.
1093	3 c.	Type **441**			1·00	1·50
	a.	Booklet pane. Nos. 1093 and 1095, each × 2			3·75	
1094	15 c.	Shield pattern, New South Wales			3·75	4·75
	a.	Booklet pane. Nos. 1094, 1096 × 3 and 1097 × 2			7·50	
1095	37 c.	Basket weave, Queensland			1·00	1·50
1096	37 c.	Bowl design, Central Australia			90	1·50
1097	37 c.	Belt pattern, Northern Territory			1·00	1·50
1093/7				Set of 5	7·00	9·50

Nos. 1093/7 only exist from 80 c. (pane No. 1093a) and $2 (pane No. 1094a) stamp booklets. The vertical edges of the booklet panes are imperforate.

(Des B. Clinton. Litho Leigh-Mardon Ltd, Melbourne (30 c.) or CPE Australia Ltd, Melbourne (37 c., 63 c.))

1987 (2 Nov). *Christmas. T 442 and similar multicoloured designs showing carol singing by candlelight.* P 14½ (30 c.) or 13½ × 14 (37 c., 63 c.).
1098	30 c.	Type **442**			45	55
	a.	Horiz strip of 5. Nos. 1098/102			2·00	
1099	30 c.	Father and daughters			45	55
1100	30 c.	Four children			45	55
1101	30 c.	Family			45	55
1102	30 c.	Six teenagers			45	55
1103	37 c.	Choir (*horiz*)			45	40
1104	63 c.	Father and two children (*horiz*)			75	1·00
1098/104				Set of 7	3·00	3·75

Nos. 1098/1102 were printed together, *se-tenant*, in horizontal strips of five throughout the sheet.

(Des Sue Passmore. Litho CPE Australia Ltd, Melbourne)

1988 (26 Jan). *Bicentenary of Australian Settlement (10th issue). Arrival of First Fleet. Square designs as T 437. Multicoloured.* P 13.
1105	37 c.	Aborigines watching arrival of Fleet, Botany Bay			65	85
	a.	Horiz strip of 5. Nos. 1105/9			3·00	
1106	37 c.	Aborigine family and anchored ships			65	85
1107	37 c.	Fleet arriving at Sydney Cove			65	85
1108	37 c.	Ship's boat			65	85
1109	37 c.	Raising the flag, Sydney Cove, 26 January 1788			65	85
1105/9				Set of 5	3·00	3·75

Nos. 1105/9 were printed together, *se-tenant*, in horizontal strips of five throughout the sheet, forming a composite design.

443 Koala with Stockman's Hat and Eagle dressed as Uncle Sam

444 "Religion" (A. Horner)

(Des R. Harvey. Litho CPE Australia Ltd, Melbourne)

1988 (26 Jan). *Bicentenary of Australian Settlement (11th issue). Joint issue with U.S.A.* P 13.
1110	443	37 c. multicoloured			60	35

NEW PRINTINGS. From the beginning of 1990 new printings of definitive stamps were identified by small koala or kangaroo symbols printed on the vertical sheet margins alongside alternate rows. One koala represented the first printing, two koalas the second and so on. The kangaroo symbol was used once four koalas had been reached.

(Litho Leigh-Mardon Ltd, Melbourne (4, 5, 20, 25, 30, 37, 39, 40, 50, 53, 70, 80, 90 c., $1) or CPE Australia Ltd, Melbourne (others))

1988 (17 Feb)–**95**. *"Living Together". T 444 and similar square designs showing cartoons. Multicoloured (except 30 c.).* P 14.
1111	1 c.	Type **444** (16.3.88)			50	30
1112	2 c.	"Industry" (P. Nicholson) (16.3.88)			50	30
1113	3 c.	"Local Government" (A. Collette) (16.3.88)			50	30
1114	4 c.	"Trade Unions" (Liz Honey)			10	10
1115	5 c.	"Parliament" (Bronwyn Halls) (16.3.88)			50	30
1116	10 c.	"Transport" (Meg Williams)			30	30
1117	15 c.	"Sport" (G. Cook)			50	40
1118	20 c.	"Commerce" (M. Atcherson)			70	30
1119	25 c.	"Housing" (C. Smith)			45	30
	a.	Perf 14½ (14.9.95)			1·50	1·50
1120	30 c.	"Welfare" (R. Tandberg) (black and pale rose-lilac) (16.3.88)			55	40
1121	37 c.	"Postal Services" (P. Viska)			60	50
	a.	Booklet pane. No. 1121×10 (1.7.88)			6·00	
1121*b*	39 c.	"Tourism" (J. Spooner) (28.9.88)			60	50
	ba.	Booklet pane. No. 1121*b*×10			7·00	
1122	40 c.	"Recreation" (R. Harvey) (16.3.88)			70	40
1123	45 c.	"Health" (Jenny Coopes)			70	50
1124	50 c.	"Mining" (G. Haddon)			70	50
1125	53 c.	"Primary Industry" (S. Leahy)			1·75	1·00
1126	55 c.	"Education" (Victoria Roberts) (16.3.88)			1·50	55
1127	60 c.	"Armed Forces" (B. Green) (16.3.88)			1·50	70
1128	63 c.	"Police" (J. Russell) (16.3.88)			2·00	85
1129	65 c.	"Telecommunications" (B. Petty) (16.3.88)			1·50	75
1130	68 c.	"The Media" (A. Langoulant) (16.3.88)			2·00	1·75
1131	70 c.	"Science and Technology" (J. Hook)			1·75	1·00
1132	75 c.	"Visual Arts" (G. Dazeley) (16.3.88)			1·00	1·00
1133	80 c.	"Performing Arts" (A. Stitt)			1·25	1·00
1134	90 c.	"Banking" (S. Billington)			1·50	90
1135	95 c.	"Law" (C. Aslanis) (16.3.88)			1·00	1·00
1136	$1	"Rescue and Emergency" (M. Leunig) (Optd S. 50p.)			1·10	90
1111/36				Set of 27	23·00	14·00

Although both Leigh-Mardon printed the 37 c. and 39 c. sheet stamps, and some of the 37 c. booklets, Nos. 1121a and 1121ba were produced by CPE with the upper and lower edges of the panes imperforate, so that stamps from them exist imperforate at top or bottom. These panes also show margins at both right and left.

Early in 1989 Leigh-Mardon Ltd, whose works were situated at Moorabbin, took over C.P.E Australia Ltd of Scoresby. Printings of the 45, 55, 60, 75, 80, 95 c. and $1 were made at both printing works.

No. 1119a comes from part of the 4 koala printing.

445 "Government House, Sydney, 1790" (George Raper)

446 Queen Elizabeth II (from photo by Tim Graham)

(Des J. Passmore. Litho CPE Australia Ltd, Melbourne)

1988 (13 Apr). *Bicentenary of Australian Settlement (12th issue). "The Early Years, 1788–1809". T 445 and similar square designs showing paintings. Multicoloured.* P 13.
1137	37 c.	Type **445**			75	80
	a.	Horiz strip of 5. Nos. 1137/41			1·25	
1138	37 c.	"Government Farm, Parramatta, 1791" ("The Port Jackson Painter")			75	80
1139	37 c.	"Parramatta Road, 1796" (attr Thomas Watling)			75	80
1140	37 c.	"View of Sydney Cove, c. 1800" (detail) (Edward Dayes)			75	80
1141	37 c.	"Sydney Hospital, 1803", (detail) (George William Evans)			75	80
1137/41				Set of 5	3·25	3·50

Nos. 1137/41 were printed together, *se-tenant*, in horizontal strips of 5 throughout the sheet, each strip forming a composite background design from the painting, "View of Sydney from the East Side of the Cove, c. 1808" by John Eyre.

(Des Sandra Baker. Litho Leigh-Mardon Ltd, Melbourne)

1988 (21 Apr). *Queen Elizabeth II's Birthday.* P 14½.
1142	446	37 c. multicoloured			50	40

447 Expo '88 Logo

448 New Parliament House

(Des G. Emery. Litho CPE Australia Ltd, Melbourne)

1988 (29 Apr). *"Expo '88" World Fair, Brisbane.* P 13.
1143	447	37 c. multicoloured			50	40

(Des B. Sadgrove. Litho Leigh-Mardon Ltd, Melbourne)

1988 (9 May). *Opening of New Parliament House, Canberra.* P 14½.
1144	448	37 c. multicoloured			50	40

449 Early Settler and Sailing Clipper

450 Kiwi and Koala at Campfire

(Des G. Emery. Litho CPE Australia Ltd, Melbourne)

1988 (21 June). *Bicentenary of Australian Settlement (13th issue). T 449 and similar square designs. Multicoloured.* P 13.
1145	37 c.	Type **449**			75	1·00
	a.	Pair. Nos. 1145/6			1·50	2·00
1146	37 c.	Queen Elizabeth II with British and Australian Parliament Buildings			75	1·00
1147	$1	W. G. Grace (cricketer) and tennis racquet			1·50	2·25
	a.	Pair. Nos. 1147/8			3·00	4·50
1148	$1	Shakespeare, John Lennon (entertainer) and Sydney Opera House			1·50	2·25
1145/8				Set of 4	4·00	6·00

Nos. 1145/6 and 1147/8 were printed together, *se-tenant*, in horizontal and vertical pairs throughout the sheets, each horizontal pair showing a background design of the Australian flag.

Stamps in similar designs were also issued by Great Britain.

(Des R. Harvey. Litho Leigh-Mardon Ltd, Melbourne)

1988 (21 June). *Bicentenary of Australian Settlement (14th issue).* P 14½.
1149	450	37 c. multicoloured			65	40

A stamp in a similar design was also issued by New Zealand.

451 "Bush Potato Country" (Turkey Tolsen Tjupurrula and David Corby Tjapaltjarri)

452 Basketball

(Des Janet Boschen. Litho CPE Australia Ltd, Melbourne)

1988 (1 Aug). *Art of the Desert. Aboriginal Paintings from Central Australia. T 451 and similar square designs. Multicoloured.* P 13.
1150	37 c.	Type **451**			40	40
1151	55 c.	"Courtship Rejected" (Limpi Puntungka Tjapangati)			80	60
1152	90 c.	"Medicine Story" (artist unknown)			1·00	1·75
1153	$1	"Ancestor Dreaming" (Tim Leura Tjapaltjarri)			1·25	1·40
1150/3				Set of 4	3·00	3·75

(Des Sue Passmore. Litho Leigh-Mardon Ltd, Melbourne)

1988 (14 Sept). *Olympic Games, Seoul. T 452 and similar horiz designs. Multicoloured.* P 14½.
1154	37 c.	Type **452**			40	40
1155	65 c.	Athlete crossing finish line			80	1·10
1156	$1	Gymnast with hoop			1·25	1·50
1154/6				Set of 3	2·25	2·75

453 Rod and Mace

(Des K. Christos. Litho Leigh-Mardon Ltd, Melbourne)

1988 (19 Sept). *34th Commonwealth Parliamentary Conference, Canberra.* P 14½.
1157	453	37 c. multicoloured			50	60

454 Necklace by Peter Tully

(Des K. Christos. Litho Mercury-Walch Pty, Hobart)

1988 (28 Sept). *Australian Crafts. T* **454** *and similar horiz designs. Multicoloured. Roul×imperf.*
1158	2 c. Type **454**		3·00	4·00
	a. Booklet pane. Nos. 1158 and 1160 × 2		3·50	
1159	5 c. Vase by Colin Levy		3·00	4·00
	a. Booklet pane. Nos. 1159 and 1160 × 5		5·00	
1160	39 c. Teapot by Frank Bauer		50	35
1158/60		*Set of 3*	6·00	7·50

Nos. 1158/60 only exist from 80 c. (pane No. 1158a) and $2 (pane No. 1159a) stamp booklets. The vertical edges of the booklet panes are imperforate.

455 Pinnacles Desert   **456** "The Nativity" (Danielle Hush)

(Des K. Christos. Litho CPE Australia Ltd, Melbourne)

1988 (17 Oct). *Panorama of Australia. T* **455** *and similar horiz designs. Multicoloured. P* 13.
1161	39 c. Type **455**		60	40
1162	55 c. Flooded landscape, Arnhem Land		85	1·00
1163	65 c. Twelve Apostles, Victoria		1·10	40
1164	70 c. Mountain Ash wood		1·25	1·75
1161/4		*Set of 4*	3·50	4·00

(Des Sandra Baker. Litho CPE Australia Ltd, Melbourne (32, 39 c.) or Leigh-Mardon Ltd, Melbourne (63 c.))

1988 (31 Oct). *Christmas. T* **456** *and similar square designs. Multicoloured. P* 14½ (63 c.) *or* 13 (*others*).
1165	32 c. Type **456**		50	35
1166	39 c. "Koala as Father Christmas" (Kylie Courtney)		55	40
1167	63 c. "Christmas Cockatoo" (Benjamin Stevenson)		1·10	1·40
1165/7		*Set of 3*	1·90	1·90

PRINTERS. On 1 April 1989 Leigh-Mardon Ltd took over CPE Australia Ltd. Stamp printing continued at both the Moorabbin (original Leigh-Mardon) and Scoresby (ex-CPE) works with some stamps being printed at one and then perforated at the other. The Scoresby works closed at the end of 1991.

457 Sir Henry Parkes   **458** Bowls

(Des R. Bevers. Litho CPE Australia Ltd, Melbourne)

1989 (25 Jan). *Australia Day. Centenary of Federation Speech by Sir Henry Parkes (N.S.W. Prime Minister). P* 14 × 13½.
1168	**457** 39 c. multicoloured		45	40

(Des Sue Passmore (5, 10, 20, 41, 43, 65 c., $1, $1.20), N. Stapleton (75, 80, 85, 90 c.), G. Cook (others). Litho Printset Cambec Pty Ltd (5 c., (No. 1172a), 65 c. (No. 1186a) and ptgs of 1 c. (No. 1169), 3 c., 75 c., 80 c. (No. 1189) and $1 (No. 1192) from 1993) or Leigh-Mardon Ltd, Melbourne (others))

1989 (13 Feb)–94. *Sports. T* **458** *and similar horiz designs. Multicoloured. P* 13½ (5, 10, 20, 65 c., $1.20) *or* 14×14½ (*others*).
1169	1 c. Type **458**		10	10
	a. Perf 13½ (4.90)		30	30
1170	2 c. Tenpin-bowling		10	10
	a. Perf 13½ (9.89)		10	10
1171	3 c. Australian football		10	10
1172	5 c. Kayaking and canoeing (17.1.90)		15	10
	a. Perf 14×14½ (3.94)		40	10
1174	10 c. Sailboarding (17.1.90)		15	15
	a. Perf 14×14½ (2.92)		60	10
1176	20 c. Tennis (17.1.90)		20	25
	a. Perf 14×14½ (7.93)		1·25	40
1179	39 c. Fishing		35	40
	a. Booklet pane. No. 1179×10		9·00	
	b. Perf 13½ (6.89)		1·00	1·00
	ba. Booklet pane. No. 1179b×10		10·00	
1180	41 c. Cycling (23.8.89)		40	35
	a. Booklet pane. No. 1180×10		6·00	
	b. Imperf horiz (vert pair)		£110	
1181	43 c. Skateboarding (27.8.90)		35	40
	a. Booklet pane. No. 1181×10		6·50	
1184	55 c. Kite-flying		40	45
1186	65 c. Rock-climbing (17.1.90)		70	60
	a. Perf 14×14½ (2.92)		75	65
1187	70 c. Cricket		85	80

1188	75 c. Netball (22.8.91)		55	60
1189	80 c. Squash (22.8.91)		60	65
1190	85 c. Diving (22.8.91)		1·75	80
1191	90 c. Soccer (22.8.91)		1·75	80
1192	$1 Fun-run (17.1.90)		1·00	95
	a. Perf 13½ (1.91)		3·50	3·00
1193	$1.10, Golf		1·00	90
1194	$1.20, Hang-gliding (27.8.90)		2·00	1·10
1169/94		*Set of 19*	11·00	8·00
1192/4 Optd "Specimen"		*Set of 3*	1·75	

The booklet panes have the upper and lower edges imperforate, so that the stamps from them are imperforate at top or bottom, and have margins at both left and right.

No. 1180b occurred in booklet panes, most of which were affixed to first day covers, but not postmarked. Price quoted is for unused pair, without gum. An example also exists used on postmarked cover, together with two mint in booklets.

Nos. 1169a (1 koala ptg), 1170a (all ptgs except the first), 1179b (1st new ptg) and 1192a (1 koala ptg) are Scoresby printings of values originally produced at Moorabbin. Nos. 1174a (2, 3, and 4 koala ptgs) and 1176a (2 and 3 koala) are Moorabbin printings of values originally produced at Scoresby.

No. 1186a (2 koala ptg) was printed by Printset Cambec Pty Ltd. instead of Leigh-Mardon Ltd. There are minor differences in the arrangement of the inscriptions. Further supplies of the 1 c. (No. 1169) (2 koala), 3 c. (3 and 4 koala), 75 c. (1, 2, 3, 4 koala, 1 kangaroo), 80 c. (2 koala) and $1 (No. 1192) (2 koala) were also produced by Printset Cambec from 1993.

No. 1172a (4 koala ptg) was printed by McPherson's as were additional supplies of the 65 c. (No. 1186a) (3 koala) and $1 (No. 1192) (1 kangaroo + 1 koala and 1 kangaroo + 2 koala ptgs). For self-adhesive versions of Nos. 1180/1 see Nos. 1259/60a.

WARNING. The coating on a batch of paper used during 1989-90 was defective so that stamps lose parts of their design if immersed in water.

459 Merino

(Des K. McEwan. Litho CPE Australia Ltd, Melbourne)

1989 (27 Feb). *Sheep in Australia. T* **459** *and similar horiz designs. Multicoloured. P* 13½ × 14.
1195	39 c. Type **459**		70	40
1196	39 c. Poll Dorset		70	40
1197	85 c. Polwarth		1·40	1·75
1198	$1 Corriedale (Optd S. 70p.)		1·40	1·40
1195/8		*Set of 4*	3·75	3·50

460 Adelaide Botanic Garden

(Des J. Passmore. Eng B. Stewart. Litho Leigh-Mardon Ltd and die-stamped Avon Graphics, both of Melbourne ($20), litho CPE Australia Ltd, Melbourne ($2 later by Leigh-Mardon Ltd) and recess Note Ptg Branch, Reserve Bank of Australia (others))

1989 (12 Apr)–90. *Botanic Gardens. T* **460** *and similar horiz designs. Multicoloured. P* 14 ($2 to $10) *or* 14½×14 ($20).
1199	$2 Nooroo, New South Wales (13.9.89)		1·50	60
	a. Perf 13½		4·00	1·00
1200	$5 Mawarra, Victoria (13.9.89)		4·25	85
	a. Perf 13½		6·00	3·25
1201	$10 Type **460**		7·50	1·75
1201a	$20 "A View of the Artist's House and Garden in Mills Plains, Van Diemen's Land" (John Glover) (15.8.90)		15·00	11·00
1199/1201a		*Set of 4*	25·00	13·00
1199a/1201a Optd "Specimen"		*Set of 4*	14·00	

461 "Queen Elizabeth II" (sculpture, John Dowie)   **462** Arrival of Immigrant Ship, 1830's

(Des Sandra Baker. Litho Leigh-Mardon Ltd, Melbourne)

1989 (21 Apr). *Queen Elizabeth II's Birthday. P* 14½.
1202	**461** 39 c. multicoloured		55	50

(Des D. Lancashire. Litho Leigh-Mardon Ltd, Melbourne)

1989 (10 May). *Colonial Development (1st issue). Pastoral Era 1810–1850. T* **462** *and similar square designs. Multicoloured. P* 14½.
1203	39 c. Type **462**		55	55
	a. Horiz strip of 5. Nos. 1203/7		2·50	
1204	39 c. Pioneer cottage and wool dray		55	55
1205	39 c. Squatter's homestead		55	55

1206	39 c. Shepherd with flock (from Joseph Lycett's "Views of Australia")		55	55
1207	39 c. Explorer in desert (after watercolour by Edward Frome)		55	55
1203/7		*Set of 5*	2·50	2·50

Nos. 1203/7 were printed together, *se-tenant*, in horizontal strips of five throughout the sheet.
See also Nos 1254/8 and 1264/8.

463 Gladys Moncrieff and Roy Rene   **464** "Impression" (Tom Roberts)

(Des Sue Passmore. Litho Leigh-Mardon Ltd, Melbourne)

1989 (12 July). *Australian Stage and Screen Personalities. T* **463** *and similar vert designs. Multicoloured. P* 14½.
1208	39 c. Type **463**		45	40
	a. Perf 14 × 13½		7·50	7·50
1209	85 c. Charles Chauvel and Chips Rafferty		1·25	1·40
1210	$1 Nellie Stewart and J. C. Williamson		1·25	1·10
1211	$1.10, Lottie Lyell and Raymond Longford		1·25	1·25
1208/11		*Set of 4*	3·75	3·75
1210/11 Optd "Specimen"		*Set of 2*	1·40	

No. 1208a was from a small first printing produced at the Scoresby (ex C.P.E.) plant and used in presentation packs or on first day covers. The rest of the 39 c. printing was perforated at the Moorabbin works.

(Des K. Christos. Litho Leigh-Mardon Ltd, Melbourne)

1989 (23 Aug). *Australian Impressionist Paintings. T* **464** *and similar multicoloured designs. P* 14 × 13½ (*No.* 1214) *or* 13½ × 14 (*others*).
1212	41 c. Type **464**		45	50
1213	41 c. "Impression for Golden Summer" (Sir Arthur Streeton)		45	50
1214	41 c. "All on a Summer's Day" (Charles Conder) (*vert*)		45	50
1215	41 c. "Petit Déjeuner" (Frederick McCubbin)		45	50
1212/15		*Set of 4*	1·60	1·75

465 Freeways

(Des Sally Newell and Carolyn Limonta. Litho Leigh-Mardon Ltd, Melbourne)

1989 (1 Sept). *The Urban Environment. T* **465** *and similar horiz designs. P* 15½×imperf.
1216	41 c. black, maroon and blue-green		65	90
	a. Booklet pane. Nos. 1216×2, 1217×3 and 1218×2		4·00	
1217	41 c. black, maroon and magenta		65	90
1218	41 c. black, maroon and bright blue		65	90
1216/18		*Set of 3*	1·75	2·40

Designs:—No. 1217, City buildings, Melbourne; No. 1218, Commuter train at platform.
Nos. 1216/18 only exist from $3 stamp booklets in which the vertical edges of the pane are imperforate.

466 Hikers outside Youth Hostel   **467** Horse Tram, Adelaide, 1878

(Des Priscilla Cutter. Litho Leigh-Mardon Ltd, Melbourne)

1989 (13 Sept). *50th Anniv of Australian Youth Hostels. P* 14½.
1219	**466** 41 c. multicoloured		55	50

(Des I. McKellar. Litho Leigh-Mardon Ltd, Melbourne)

1989 (11 Oct). *Historic Trams. T* **467** *and similar horiz designs. Multicoloured. P* 13½×14.
1220	41 c. Type **467**		60	60
1221	41 c. Steam tram, Sydney, 1884		60	60
1222	41 c. Cable tram, Melbourne, 1886		60	60
	a. Perf 14½		1·00	1·00
	ab. Booklet pane. No. 1222a×10		10·00	
1223	41 c. Double-deck electric tram, Hobart, 1893		60	60
1224	41 c. Combination electric tram, Brisbane, 1901		60	60
1220/4		*Set of 5*	2·75	2·75

The upper and lower edges of booklet pane No. 1222ab are imperforate. It was printed and perforated at the Moorabbin plant.

468 "Annunciation" (15th-century Book of Hours)

469 Radio Waves and Globe

(Des Lynette Brown. Litho Leigh-Mardon Ltd, Melbourne)

1989 (1 Nov). *Christmas. Illuminated Manuscripts. T* **468** *and similar vert designs. Multicoloured. P* 14×13½ (36 c.) *or* 14½ (*others*).

1225	36 c. Type **468**		40	40
	a. Booklet pane. No. 1225×10		4·00	
1226	41 c. "Annunciation to the Shepherds" (Wharncliffe Book of Hours, c. 1475)		50	45
1227	80 c. "Adoration of the Magi" (15th-century Parisian Book of Hours)		1·25	1·40
1225/7		*Set of 3*	1·90	2·00

The vertical sides of booklet pane No. 1225a are imperforate.

(Des B. Sadgrove. Litho Leigh-Mardon Ltd, Melbourne)

1989 (1 Nov). *50th Anniv of Radio Australia. P* 14×13½.

1228	**469** 41 c. multicoloured		55	50

470 Golden Wattle

471 Australian Wildflowers

(Des Celia Rosser. Litho Leigh-Mardon Ltd, Melbourne)

1990 (17 Jan). *Australia Day. P* 14½.

1229	**470** 41 c. multicoloured		55	50

(Des Beverley Graham and G. Rogers. Litho Leigh-Mardon Ltd, Melbourne)

1990 (7 Feb–3 Sept). *Greetings Stamps. P* 14×13½ (41 c.) *or* 14½ (43 c.).

1230	**471** 41 c. multicoloured		65	65
	a. Booklet pane. No. 1230×10		6·50	
	b. Perf 14½ (May)		1·00	1·00
	ba. Booklet pane. No. 1230b×10		10·00	
1231	43 c. multicoloured (3 Sept)		50	50
	a. Booklet pane. No. 1231×10		5·00	

The upper and lower edges of the booklet panes are imperforate.
No. 1230b is a Moorabbin (1 koala) printing which only exists from booklets. The remainder were printed at the Scoresby works.

472 Dr. Constance Stone (first Australian woman doctor), Modern Doctor and Nurses

473 Greater Glider

(Des Priscilla Cutter. Litho Leigh-Mardon Ltd, Melbourne)

1990 (7 Feb). *Centenary of Women in Medical Practice. P* 14½.

1232	**472** 41 c. multicoloured		50	45

(Des D. Higgins. Litho Leigh-Mardon Ltd, Melbourne)

1990 (21 Feb). *Animals of the High Country. T* **473** *and similar vert designs. Multicoloured. P* 14×13½.

1233	41 c. Type **473**		60	45
1234	65 c. Tiger Cat ("Spotted-tailed Quoll")		90	1·10
1235	70 c. Mountain Pygmy-possum		95	1·10
1236	80 c. Brush-tailed Rock-wallaby		1·10	1·10
1233/6		*Set of 4*	3·25	3·25

PRICES OF SETS

Set prices are given for many issues, generally those containing three stamps or more. Definitive sets include one of each value or major colour change, but do not cover different perforations, die types or minor shades. Where a choice is possible the set prices are based on the cheapest versions of the stamps included in the listings.

474 "Stop Smoking"

475 Soldiers from Two World Wars

(Des A. Stitt. Litho Leigh-Mardon Ltd, Melbourne)

1990 (14 Mar). *Community Health. T* **474** *and similar vert designs. Multicoloured. P* 14×13½.

1237	41 c. Type **474**		55	55
1238	41 c. "Drinking and driving don't mix"		55	55
1239	41 c. "No junk food, please"		55	55
1240	41 c. "Guess who's just had a checkup?"		55	55
1237/40		*Set of 4*	2·00	2·00

(Des O. Schmidinger and Christine Stead. Litho Leigh-Mardon Ltd, Melbourne)

1990 (12 Apr). *"The Anzac Tradition". T* **475** *and similar vert designs. Multicoloured. P* 14½.

1241	41 c. Type **475**		50	40
1242	41 c. Fighter pilots and munitions worker		50	40
1243	65 c. Veterans and Anzac Day parade		85	90
1244	$1 Casualty evacuation, Vietnam, and disabled veteran		1·25	1·40
1245	$1.10, Letters from home and returning troopships		1·40	1·50
1241/5		*Set of 5*	4·00	4·25
1244/5 Optd "Specimen"		*Set of 2*	1·10	

476 Queen at Australian Ballet Performance, London, 1988

477 New South Wales 1861 5s. Stamp

(Des Lynette Brown. Litho Leigh-Mardon Ltd, Melbourne)

1990 (19 Apr). *Queen Elizabeth II's Birthday. P* 14½.

1246	**476** 41 c. multicoloured		65	45

(Des J. Passmore. Litho Leigh-Mardon Ltd, Melbourne)

1990 (1 May). *150th Anniv of the Penny Black. T* **477** *and similar horiz designs showing stamps. Multicoloured. P* 13½×14.

1247	41 c. Type **477**		60	75
	a. Block of 6. Nos. 1247/52		3·25	
1248	41 c. South Australia 1855 unissued 1s.		60	75
1249	41 c. Tasmania 1853 4d.		60	75
1250	41 c. Victoria 1867 5s.		60	75
1251	41 c. Queensland 1897 unissued 6d.		60	75
1252	41 c. Western Australia 1855 4d. with inverted frame		60	75
1247/52		*Set of 6*	3·25	4·00
MS1253	122×85 mm. Nos. 1247/52		3·25	4·00

Nos. 1247/52 were printed together, *se-tenant*, throughout the sheet of 100 (two panes 5×10). The first and fifth vertical rows contained Nos. 1247 and 1250 alternately, the second and fourth rows Nos. 1248 and 1251, and the third row Nos. 1249 and 1252.
No. MS1253 also exists overprinted with the "Stamp World London 90" logo for sale at this international stamp exhibition.

478 Gold Miners on way to Diggings

479 Glaciology Research

(Des B. Weatherhead. Litho Leigh-Mardon Ltd, Melbourne)

1990 (16 May). *Colonial Development (2nd issue). Gold Fever. T* **478** *and similar square designs. Multicoloured. P* 13.

1254	41 c. Type **478**		65	70
	a. Horiz strip of 5. Nos. 1254/8		3·00	
1255	41 c. Mining camp		65	70
1256	41 c. Panning and washing for gold		65	70
1257	41 c. Gold Commissioner's tent		65	70
1258	41 c. Moving gold under escort		65	70
1254/8		*Set of 5*	3·00	3·25

Nos. 1254/8 were printed together, *se-tenant*, in horizontal strips of 5 throughout the sheet.

1990 (16 May)–91. *As Nos. 1180/1, but self-adhesive. P* 11½.

(a) Typo Pemara Labels, Victoria

1259	41 c. Cycling		65	1·00
1260	43 c. Skateboarding (27.8.90)		75	80

(b) Litho Printset-Cambec Pty Ltd, Melbourne

1260a	43 c. Skateboarding (26.6.91)		1·25	1·50

Nos. 1259/60a were only available in rolls of 100, No. 1260a also initially in rolls of 200, from major post offices or as strips of three from philatelic counters, each stamp, with die-cut perforations, being separate on the imperforate backing strip.
No. 1260a can be identified by its screened colours: on No. 1260 these are solid. The lithography printing also shows a kangaroo on the reverse and is on plain, rather than waxed, backing paper.
Due to the type of adhesive used examples should be retained on piece.

(Des Janet Boschen and Yu. Artsimenev. Litho Leigh-Mardon Ltd, Melbourne)

1990 (13 June). *Australian-Soviet Scientific Co-operation in Antarctica. T* **479** *and similar horiz design. Multicoloured. P* 14½.

1261	41 c. Type **479**		55	40
1262	$1.10, Krill (marine biology research) (Optd S. 55p)		1·40	1·50
MS1263	85 × 65 mm. Nos. 1261/2		1·90	1·90

Stamps in similar designs were also issued by Russia.
Examples of No. MS1263 imperforate originate from the Russian postal archives.
No. MS1263 also exists overprinted with the "New Zealand 1990" logo for sale at this international stamp exhibition in Auckland.

480 Auctioning Building Plots

481 "Salmon Gums" (Robert Juniper)

(Des B. Clinton. Litho Leigh-Mardon Ltd, Melbourne)

1990 (12 July). *Colonial Development (3rd series). Boomtime. T* **480** *and similar square designs. Multicoloured. P* 13.

1264	41 c. Type **480**		55	55
	a. Horiz strip of 5. Nos. 1264/8		2·50	
1265	41 c. Colonial mansion		55	55
1266	41 c. Stock exchange		55	55
1267	41 c. Fashionable society		55	55
1268	41 c. Factories		55	55
1264/8		*Set of 5*	2·50	2·50

Nos. 1264/8 were printed together, *se-tenant*, in horizontal strips of 5 throughout the sheet.

(Des Sandra Baker. Litho Leigh-Mardon Ltd, Melbourne)

1990 (3 Sept). *"Heidelberg and Heritage" Art Exhibition. T* **481** *and similar vert design. Multicoloured. Imperf × p* 14½.

1269	28 c. Type **481**		2·00	2·50
	a. Booklet pane. Nos. 1269 and 1270 × 4		3·50	
	b. Imperf × p 15½		4·00	5·00
	ba. Booklet pane. Nos. 1269b and 1270a × 4		7·50	
1270	43 c. "The Blue Dress" (Brian Dunlop)		40	45
	a. Imperf × p 15½		90	90

Nos. 1269/70 only exist from $2 stamp booklets in which the horizontal edges of the pane are imperforate.

482 "Adelaide Town Hall" (Edmund Gouldsmith)

483 Laughing Kookaburras and Gifts

(Des Janet Boschen. Litho Leigh-Mardon Ltd, Melbourne)

1990 (31 Oct). *150th Anniv of Local Government. P* 14½.

1271	**482** 43 c. multicoloured		65	50

(Des Marg Towt. Litho Leigh-Mardon Ltd, Melbourne)

1990 (31 Oct). *Christmas. T* **483** *and similar multicoloured designs. P* 14½.

1272	38 c. Type **483**		50	40
	a. Booklet pane. No. 1272 × 10		5·50	
1273	43 c. Baby Jesus with Koalas and Wallaby (vert)		50	40
1274	80 c. Possum on Christmas tree		1·50	1·75
1272/4		*Set of 3*	2·25	2·25

The upper and lower edges of booklet pane No. 1272a are imperforate, producing stamps imperforate top or bottom, and there are margins at left and right.

484 National Flag

485 Black-necked Stork

(Des Dianne Cook. Litho Leigh-Mardon Ltd, Melbourne)

1991 (10 Jan). *Australia Day. 90th Anniv of Australian Flag. T 484 and similar horiz designs. P 14¹/₂.*

275	43 c. deep ultramarine, brt scarlet & grey		50	40
276	90 c. multicoloured		1·10	1·25
277	$1 multicoloured		1·25	1·40
278	$1.20, brt scarlet, dp ultramarine & grey		1·60	1·75
275/8		*Set of 4*	4·00	4·25

Designs:—90 c. Royal Australian Navy ensign; $1 Royal Australian Air Force standard; $1.20, Australian merchant marine ensign.

(Des P. Margocsy. Litho Leigh-Mardon Ltd, Melbourne)

1991 (14 Feb). *Waterbirds. T 485 and similar multicoloured designs. P 14¹/₂.*

279	43 c. Type 485		75	40
280	43 c. Black Swan (*horiz*)		75	40
281	85 c. Cereopsis Goose ("Cape Barren Goose")		1·75	2·25
282	$1 Chestnut-breasted Teal (*horiz*) (Optd S. 55p)		1·90	1·75
279/82		*Set of 4*	4·75	4·25

486 Recruitment Poster (Women's Services)

487 Queen Elizabeth at Royal Albert Hall, London

(Des Dianne Cook. Litho Leigh-Mardon Ltd, Melbourne)

1991 (14 Mar). *Anzac Day. 50th Anniversaries. T 486 and similar horiz designs. P 14¹/₂.*

283	43 c. multicoloured		60	40
284	43 c. black, brown-olive & pale grey-brown		60	40
285	$1.20, multicoloured (Optd S. 55p)		2·25	2·00
283/5		*Set of 3*	3·00	2·50

Designs:—43 c. (No. 1284) Patrol (Defence of Tobruk); $1.20, "V-P Day Canberra" (Harold Abbot) (Australian War Memorial).

(Des R. Bulach. Litho Leigh-Mardon Ltd, Melbourne)

1991 (11 Apr). *Queen Elizabeth II's Birthday. P 14¹/₂.*

286	487	43 c. multicoloured	80	50

488 *Tectocoris diophthalmus* (bug)

489 "Bondi" (Max Dupain)

(Des D. Nelson. Litho Leigh-Mardon Ltd, Melbourne)

1991 (11 Apr). *Insects. T 488 and similar horiz designs. Multicoloured. P 14¹/₂.*

287	43 c. Type 488		75	45
288	43 c. *Cizara ardeniae* (hawk moth)		75	45
289	80 c. *Petasida ephippigera* (grasshopper)		2·00	2·00
290	$1 *Castiarina producta* (beetle)		2·00	1·50
287/90		*Set of 4*	5·00	4·00

(Des Janet Boschen. Litho Leigh-Mardon Ltd, Melbourne)

1991 (13 May). *150 Years of Photography in Australia. T 489 and similar vert designs. P 14¹/₂.*

291	43 c. black, chestnut and deep ultramarine		75	65
	a. Horiz pair. Nos. 1291/2		1·50	1·25
292	43 c. black, turquoise-green and chestnut		75	65
293	70 c. black, yellow-green and chestnut		1·25	1·10
294	$1.20, black, light brown and deep blue-green (Optd S. 55p)		1·75	1·50
291/4		*Set of 4*	4·00	3·50

Designs:—No. 1292, "Gears for the Mining Industry, Vickers Ruwolt, Melbourne" (Wolfgang Sievers); No. 1293, "The Wheel of Youth" (Harold Cazneaux); No. 1294, "Teacup Ballet" (Olive Cotton).

Nos. 1291/2 were printed together, *se-tenant*, in horizontal pairs throughout the sheet.

490 Singing Group

491 Puppy

(Des O. Schmidinger and Christine Stead. Litho Leigh-Mardon Ltd, Melbourne)

1991 (13 June). *Australian Radio Broadcasting. T 490 and similar vert designs showing listeners and scenes from radio programmes. Multicoloured. P 14¹/₂.*

295	43 c. Type 490		60	45
296	43 c. "Blue Hills" serial		60	45
297	85 c. "The Quiz Kids"		1·25	1·25
298	$1 "The Argonauts' Club" children's programme (Optd S. 55p.)		1·50	1·40
295/8		*Set of 4*	3·50	3·25

(Des Betina Ogden. Litho Leigh-Mardon Ltd, Melbourne)

1991 (25 July). *Domestic Pets. T 491 and similar vert designs. Multicoloured. P 14¹/₂.*

299	43 c. Type 491		70	45
300	43 c. Kitten		70	45
301	70 c. Pony		1·40	1·40
302	$1 Sulphur-crested Cockatoo		1·90	1·40
299/1302		*Set of 4*	4·25	3·25

492 George Vancouver (1791) and Edward Eyre (1841)

493 *Seven Little Australians* (Ethel Turner)

(Des D. Lancashire. Litho Leigh-Mardon Ltd, Melbourne)

1991 (25 Sept). *Exploration of Western Australia. P 14¹/₂.*

303	492 $1.05, multicoloured		1·00	1·10
MS1304	100 × 65 mm. No. 1303		1·25	1·40

No. MS1304 also exists overprinted with the "Philanippon '91" logo for sale at this international stamp exhibition in Tokyo.

(Des Dianne Cook. Litho Leigh-Mardon Ltd, Melbourne)

1991 (10 Oct). *Australian Writers of the 1890s. T 493 and similar multicoloured designs. P 14¹/₂.*

305	43 c. Type 493		50	45
306	75 c. *On Our Selection* (Steele Rudd)		80	75
307	$1 "Clancy of the Overflow" (poem, A. B. Paterson) (*vert*)		1·10	95
308	$1.20, "The Drover's Wife" (short story, Henry Lawson) (*vert*) (Optd S. 55p)		1·25	1·40
305/8		*Set of 4*	3·25	3·25

494 Shepherd

495 Parma Wallaby

(Des Sue Passmore. Litho Leigh-Mardon Ltd, Melbourne)

1991 (1 Nov). *Christmas. T 494 and similar horiz designs. Multicoloured. P 14¹/₂.*

309	38 c. Type 494		40	40
	a. Booklet pane. No. 1309 × 20		9·00	
310	43 c. Infant Jesus		45	45
311	90 c. Wise Man		1·50	1·25
309/11		*Set of 3*	2·10	1·90

The vertical edges of booklet pane No. 1309a are imperforate, producing stamps imperforate at right or left, and there are margins at top and bottom.

Variations in the shades of all three values were caused by changes in the production method during printing.

(Des Betina Ogden. Litho Leigh-Mardon Ltd, Melbourne)

1992 (2 Jan). *Threatened Species. T 495 and similar horiz designs. Multicoloured. P 14 × 14¹/₂.*

312	45 c. Type 495		65	60
	a. Block of 6. Nos. 1312/17		3·50	
313	45 c. Ghost Bat		65	60
314	45 c. Long-tailed Dunnart		65	60
315	45 c. Little Pygmy-possum		65	60
316	45 c. Dusky Hopping-mouse		65	60
317	45 c. Squirrel Glider		65	60
1312/17		*Set of 6*	3·50	3·25

Nos. 1312/17 were printed together, *se-tenant*, throughout the sheet of 100, giving fifteen blocks of 6 (3 × 2) and 10 single stamps.

For self-adhesive versions of these designs see Nos. 1321/32.

496 Basket of Wild Flowers

(Des Priscilla Cutter. Litho Leigh-Mardon Ltd, Melbourne)

1992 (2 Jan). *Greetings Stamp. P 14¹/₂.*

318	496	45 c. multicoloured	50	50
	a. Booklet pane. No. 1318×10		5·00	

The upper and lower edges of booklet pane No. 1318a are imperforate, producing stamps imperforate at top or bottom, and there are margins at left and right.

497 Noosa River, Queensland

(Des Sue Passmore. Litho Leigh-Mardon Ltd, Melbourne)

1992 (2 Jan)–94. *Wetlands and Waterways. T 497 and similar horiz design. P 14¹/₂×imperf.*

319	20 c. Type 497		1·75	2·00
	a. Booklet pane. Nos. 1319 and 1320×4		3·00	
	b. Perf 14×imperf (3.94)		2·50	3·50
	ba. Booklet pane. Nos. 1319b and 1320b×4		3·75	
320	45 c. Lake Eildon, Victoria		40	45
	b. Perf 14×imperf (3.94)		40	45

Nos. 1319/20 only exist from $2 stamp booklets in which the vertical edges of the pane are imperforate.

Nos. 1319b/ba and 1320b (2 koala ptg) were printed by McPherson's Ptg Group.

1992 (2 Jan–24 Dec). *As Nos. 1312/17, but self-adhesive.*

(a) Typo Pemara Labels, Victoria. Phosphorised paper. P 11

321	45 c. Type 495		60	70
	a. Black (inscr, etc) omitted		£130	
322	45 c. Squirrel Glider		60	70
	a. Black (inscr, etc) omitted		£130	
323	45 c. Dusky Hopping-mouse		60	70
	a. Black (inscr, etc) omitted		£130	
324	45 c. Little Pygmy-possum		60	70
	a. Black (inscr, etc) omitted		£130	
325	45 c. Long-tailed Dunnart		60	70
	a. Black (inscr, etc) omitted		£130	
326	45 c. Ghost Bat		60	70
	a. Black (inscr, etc) omitted		£130	
321/6		*Set of 6*	3·25	3·75

(b) Litho Printset Cambec Pty Ltd. Phosphorised paper. P 11¹/₂

327	45 c. Type 495		60	70
	p. Broad phosphor band at right		1·75	1·75
	pa. Booklet pane. Nos. 1327p×2, 1328p/9p and 1330p/2p×2		13·50	
	q. Horiz phosphor bands at top, bottom and on animal (22.4.92)		1·75	1·75
	qa. Booklet pane. Nos. 1327q×2, 1328q/9q and 1330q/2q×2		13·50	
	qb. Booklet pane. As No. 1327qa, but imperf		£300	
328	45 c. Squirrel Glider		60	70
	p. Broad phosphor band at right		1·40	1·75
	pa. Sheetlet of 5. Nos. 1328p/32p		6·50	
	q. Horiz phosphor bands at top, bottom and on animal (22.4.92)		1·40	1·75
	qa. Sheetlet of 5. Nos. 1328q/32q (24.12.92)		6·50	
329	45 c. Dusky Hopping-mouse		60	70
	p. Broad phosphor band at right		1·40	1·75
	q. Horiz phosphor bands at top, bottom and on animal (22.4.92)		1·40	1·75
330	45 c. Little Pygmy-possum		60	70
	p. Broad phosphor band at right		1·40	1·75
	q. Horiz phosphor bands at top, bottom and on animal (22.4.92)		1·40	1·75
331	45 c. Long-tailed Dunnart		60	70
	p. Broad phosphor band at right		1·40	1·75
	q. Horiz phosphor bands at top, bottom and on animal (22.4.92)		1·40	1·75
332	45 c. Ghost Bat		60	70
	p. Broad phosphor band at right		1·40	1·75
	q. Horiz phosphor bands at top, bottom and on animal (22.4.92)		1·40	1·75
1327/32		*Set of 6*	3·25	3·75
1327p/32p		*Set of 6*	8·00	9·50
1327q/32a		*Set of 6*	8·00	9·50

Nos. 1321/6 were only available in rolls of 100 with Nos. 1327/32 in rolls of 100 or 200, each stamp, with die-cut perforations, being separate on the imperforate backing strip.

Nos. 1321a/6a also show a horizontal red line across the stamp which normally occurs on the reverse. Examples are reported to have been purchased from Buxton, N.S.W., post office.

The booklet panes Nos. 1327pa and 1327qa are arranged as a block of eight and a separate vertical pair with backing card forming the booklet cover. Stamps from these panes and the sheetlet of 5, Nos. 1328pa and 1328qa, differ from the coil printing by retaining the surplus self-adhesive paper around the stamps.

Booklet pane No. 1327pa and sheetlet No. 1328pa have a broad phosphor band, which shows pink under U.V. light, over the right-hand half of each design. Nos. 1327qa and 1328pa show this phosphor as horizontal bands at the top and bottom of each design and also have the animal overprinted in phosphor ink.

No. 1328pa also exists overprinted with the "World Columbian Stamp Expo '92" logo for sale at this international stamp exhibition in Chicago.

498 *Young Endeavour* (cadet brigantine)   **499** Bombing of Darwin

(Des Sue Passmore. Litho Leigh-Mardon Ltd, Melbourne)

1992 (15 Jan). *Australia Day and 500th Anniv of Discovery of America by Columbus (No.* **MS1337**). *Sailing Ships. T* **498** *and similar multicoloured designs.* P 14½.

1333	45 c. Type **498**	80	50
1334	45 c. *Britannia* (yacht) (*vert*)	80	50
1335	$1.05, *Akarana* (cutter) (*vert*)	1·75	2·50
1336	$1.20, *John Louis* (pearling lugger) (Optd. S. 55p)	2·00	1·75
1333/6	*Set of 4*	4·75	4·75
MS1337	147×64 mm. Nos. 1333/6	4·75	4·75

No. **MS1337** also exists overprinted with either the "World Columbian Stamp Expo '92" or "Genova '92" logos for sale at these international stamp exhibitions in Chicago or Genoa.

(Des B. Clinton. Litho Leigh-Mardon Ltd, Melbourne)

1992 (19 Feb). *50th Anniv of Second World War Battles. T* **499** *and similar horiz designs. Multicoloured.* P 14½.

1338	45 c. Type **499**	70	45
1339	75 c. Anti-aircraft gun and fighters, Milne Bay	1·25	1·00
1340	75 c. Infantry on Kokoda Trail	1·25	1·00
1341	$1.05, H.M.A.S. *Australia* (cruiser) and U.S.S. *Yorktown* (aircraft carrier), Coral Sea	1·50	1·50
1342	$1.20, Australians advancing, El Alamein (Optd. S. 55p)	1·75	1·60
1338/42	*Set of 5*	5·75	5·00

500 Helix Nebula   **501** Hunter Valley, New South Wales

(Des Sandra Harman. Litho Leigh-Mardon Ltd, Melbourne)

1992 (19 Mar). *International Space Year. T* **500** *and similar horiz designs. Multicoloured.* P 14½.

1343	45 c. Type **500**	60	45
1344	$1.05, The Pleiades	1·50	1·25
1345	$1.20, Spiral Galaxy, NGC 2997 (Optd. S. 55p)	1·75	1·50
1343/5	*Set of 3*	3·50	3·00
MS1346	133×70 mm. Nos. 1343/5	3·50	3·00

No. **MS1346** also exists overprinted with the "World Columbian Stamp Expo '92" logo for sale at this international stamp exhibition in Chicago.

(Des P. Blizzard-Allen. Litho McPherson's Ptg Group, Mulgrave)

1992 (9 Apr). *Vineyard Regions. T* **501** *and similar horiz designs. Multicoloured.* P 14×14½.

1347	45 c. Type **501**	60	60
1348	45 c. North-east Victoria	60	60
1349	45 c. Barossa Valley, South Australia	60	60
1350	45 c. Coonawarra, South Australia	60	60
1351	45 c. Margaret River, Western Australia	60	60
1347/51	*Set of 5*	2·75	2·75

502 3½d. Stamp of 1953   **503** Salt Action

(Des Lynette Brown. Litho McPherson's Ptg Group, Mulgrave)

1992 (9 Apr). *Queen Elizabeth II's Birthday.* P 14×14½.

1352	**502** 45 c. multicoloured	70	50

(Des J. Wolseley. Litho McPherson's Ptg Group, Mulgrave)

1992 (11 June). *Land Conservation. T* **503** *and similar vert designs. Multicoloured.* P 14½×14.

1353	45 c. Type **503**	85	90
	a. Horiz strip of 5. Nos. 1353/7	3·75	
1354	45 c. Farm planning	85	90
1355	45 c. Erosion control	85	90
1356	45 c. Tree planting	85	90
1357	45 c. Dune care	85	90
1353/7	*Set of 5*	3·75	4·00

Nos. 1353/7 were printed together, *se-tenant*, in horizontal strips of 5 throughout the sheet.

504 Cycling   **505** Echidna

(Des G. Emery. Litho Leigh-Mardon Ltd, Melbourne)

1992 (2 July). *Olympic Games and Paralympic Games (No.* 1359), *Barcelona. T* **504** *and similar horiz designs. Multicoloured.* P 14½.

1358	45 c. Type **504**	60	45
1359	$1.20, High jumping	1·50	1·60
1360	$1.20, Weightlifting	1·50	1·60
1358/60	*Set of 3*	3·25	3·25
1359/60	Optd "Specimen" *Set of 2*	1·10	

(Des Marg Towt (30, 85 c., $1.35), Betina Ogden (35, 50, 60, 95 c.), S. Morrell (others). Litho McPherson's Ptg Group, Mulgrave)

1992 (13 Aug)–**98**. *Australian Wildlife (1st series). T* **505** *and similar horiz designs. Multicoloured.* P 14×14½.

1361	30 c. Saltwater Crocodile (10.3.94)	25	20
1362	35 c. Type **505**	25	20
1363	40 c. Platypus (12.8.93)	30	25
1364	50 c. Koala	40	35
1365	60 c. Common Bushtail Possum	50	55
1366	70 c. Laughing Kookaburra ("70 c" and "AUSTRALIA" in orange) (12.8.93)	1·00	1·00
	a. "70 c" and "AUSTRALIA" in orange-brown (3.96)	1·75	1·75
1367	85 c. Australian Pelican (10.3.94)	65	70
1368	90 c. Eastern Grey Kangaroo ("90 c" and "AUSTRALIA" in orange) (12.8.93)	1·25	1·25
	a. "90 c." and "AUSTRALIA" in orange-brown (4.98)	80	85
1369	95 c. Common Wombat	75	80
1370	$1.20, Major Mitchell's Cockatoo ("$1.20" and "AUSTRALIA" in orge) (12.8.93)	1·25	1·25
	a. "$1.20" and "AUSTRALIA" in orange-brown (12.98)	90	95
1371	$1.35, Emu (10.3.94)	1·00	1·10
1361/71	*Set of 11*	6·00	5·50

No. 1366a is from the 3 koala or 1 kangaroo + 1 koala printings, No. 1368a from the 2 koala printing, and No. 1370a from the 1 kangaroo printing.

506 Sydney Harbour Tunnel (value at left)   **507** Warden's Courthouse, Coolgardie

(Des Sandra Harman. Litho Leigh-Mardon Ltd, Melbourne)

1992 (28 Aug). *Opening of Sydney Harbour Tunnel. T* **506** *and similar vert design. Multicoloured.* P 14½.

1375	45 c. Type **506**	2·50	2·50
	a. Horiz pair. Nos. 1375/6	5·00	5·00
	b. Perf 15½	1·75	1·75
	ba. Horiz pair. Nos. 1375b/6b	3·50	3·50
1376	45 c. Sydney Harbour Tunnel (value at right)	2·50	2·50
	b. Perf 15½	1·75	1·75

Nos. 1375/6 were printed together, *se-tenant*, in horizontal pairs throughout the sheet, each pair forming a composite design.

(Des Janet Boschen. Litho Printset Cambec Pty Ltd)

1992 (17 Sept). *Centenary of Discovery of Gold at Coolgardie and Kalgoorlie. T* **507** *and similar horiz designs. Multicoloured.* P 14×14½.

1377	45 c. Type **507**	60	45
1378	45 c. Post Office, Kalgoorlie	60	45
1379	$1.05, York Hotel, Kalgoorlie	1·50	1·60
1380	$1.20, Town Hall, Kalgoorlie	1·75	1·90
1377/80	*Set of 4*	4·00	4·00

508 Bowler of 1892   **509** Children's Nativity Play

(Des Janet Boschen and M. Sofilas. Litho Leigh-Mardon Ltd, Melbourne)

1992 (15 Oct). *Centenary of Sheffield Shield Cricket Tournament. T* **508** *and similar vert design. Multicoloured.* P 14½.

1381	45 c. Type **508**	85	50
1382	$1.20, Batsman and wicket-keeper	1·90	2·50

(Des C. Smith. Litho McPherson's Ptg Group, Mulgrave)

1992 (30 Oct). *Christmas. T* **509** *and similar horiz designs. Multicoloured.* P 14×14½.

1383	40 c. Type **509**	55	40
	a. Booklet pane. No. 1383×20	9·00	
1384	45 c. Child waking on Christmas Day	60	45
1385	$1 Children carol singing	1·90	1·60
1383/5	*Set of 3*	2·75	2·25

The vertical edges of booklet pane No. 1383a are imperforate and there are margins at top and bottom.

510 "Ghost Gum, Central Australia" (Namatjira)   **511** "Wild Onion Dreaming" (Pauline Nakamarra Woods)

(Des Janet Boschen. Litho McPherson's Ptg Group, Mulgrave)

1993 (14 Jan). *Australia Day. Paintings by Albert Namatjira. T* **510** *and similar horiz design. Multicoloured.* P 14×14½.

1386	45 c. Type **510**	75	75
	a. Pair. Nos. 1386/7	1·50	2·25
1387	45 c. "Across the Plain to Mount Giles"	75	1·25

Nos. 1386/7 were printed together, *se-tenant*, in horizontal and vertical pairs throughout the sheet.

(Des C. Atkinson. Litho Printset Cambec Pty Ltd)

1993 (4 Feb). *"Dreamings". Paintings by Aboriginal Artists. T* **511** *and similar multicoloured designs.* P 14×14½ (*horiz*) or 14½×14 (*vert*).

1388	45 c. Type **511**	60	45
1389	75 c. "Yam Plants" (Jack Wunuwun) (*vert*)	1·10	95
1390	85 c. "Goose Egg Hunt" (George Milpurrurru) (*vert*)	1·25	1·25
1391	$1 "Kalumpiwarra-Ngulalintji" (Rover Thomas)	1·40	1·40
1388/91	*Set of 4*	4·00	3·50

512 Uluru (Ayers Rock) National Park   **513** Queen Elizabeth II on Royal Visit, 1992

(Des Lynette Brown. Litho McPherson's Ptg Group, Mulgrave)

1993 (4 Mar). *World Heritage Sites (1st series). T* **512** *and similar horiz designs. Multicoloured.* P 14½×14.

1392	45 c. Type **512**	70	45
1393	85 c. Rain forest, Fraser Island	1·75	1·60
1394	95 c. Beach, Shark Bay	1·75	1·60
1395	$2 Waterfall, Kakadu	2·00	1·90
1392/5	*Set of 4*	5·50	5·00

See also Nos. 1582/5.

(Des Dianne Cook. Litho Printset Cambec Pty Ltd)

1993 (7 Apr). *Queen Elizabeth II's Birthday.* P 14½×14.

1396	**513** 45 c. multicoloured	60	60

514 H.M.A.S. *Sydney* (cruiser, launched 1934) in Action   **515** "Work in the Home"

(Des R. Shardlow and Sue Passmore. Litho McPherson's Ptg Group, Mulgrave)

1993 (7 Apr). *Second World War Naval Vessels. T* **514** *and similar horiz designs. Multicoloured.* P 14×14½.

1397	45 c. Type **514**	80	45
1398	85 c. H.M.A.S. *Bathurst* (minesweeper)	1·60	1·75
1399	$1.05, H.M.A.S. *Arunta* (destroyer)	1·75	2·40
1400	$1.20, *Centaur* (hospital ship) and tug (Optd S. £2)	2·00	2·40
1397/1400	*Set of 4*	5·50	6·25

(Des G. Hogg. Litho McPherson's Ptg Group, Mulgrave)

1993 (7 May). *Working Life in the 1890s. T* **515** *and similar vert designs. Multicoloured.* P 14½×14.

1401	45 c. Type **515**	55	45
1402	45 c. "Work in the Cities"	55	45
1403	$1 "Work in the Country"	1·10	1·10
1404	$1.20, Trade Union banner	1·50	1·75
1401/4	*Set of 4*	3·25	3·25

516 "Centenary Special",
Tasmania, 1971

(Des Sue Passmore and J. Richards. Litho Prinset Cambec Pty Ltd)

1993 (1 June). *Australian Trains.* T **516** *and similar horiz designs.* (a) *Phosphorised paper.* P 14×14½.
1405	45 c. Type **516**	65	70
	a. Block of 6. Nos. 1405/10	3·50	
1406	45 c. "Spirit of Progress", Victoria	65	70
1407	45 c. "Western Endeavour", Western Australia, 1970	65	70
1408	45 c. "Silver City Comet", New South Wales	65	70
1409	45 c. Cairns–Kuranda tourist train, Queensland	65	70
1410	45 c. "The Ghan", Northern Territory	65	70
1405/10	*Set of 6*	3·50	3·75

(b) *Self-adhesive. Phosphor frame.* P 11½
1411	45 c. Type **516**	95	1·25
	a. Booklet pane. Nos. 1411/12×2, 1413, 1414/15×2 and 1416	7·50	
1412	45 c. "Spirit of Progress", Victoria	95	1·25
1413	45 c. "Western Endeavour", Western Australia, 1970	95	1·25
1414	45 c. "Silver City Comet", New South Wales	95	1·25
1415	45 c. Cairns–Kuranda tourist train, Queensland	95	1·25
1416	45 c. "The Ghan", Northern Territory	95	1·25
1411/16	*Set of 6*	5·00	6·50

Nos. 1405/10 were printed together, *se-tenant*, in sheets of 100 (2 panes of 50 5×10) each pane providing five blocks of 6 and twenty single stamps.

Nos. 1411/16 occur either in rolls of 100, on which the surplus self-adhesive paper around each stamp was removed, or in $4.50 booklets, containing No. 1411a, on which the surplus paper was retained.

The phosphor on both rolls and booklets, which shows pink under U.V. light, extends from the frame onto sections of the centre design.

COUNTER-PRINTED LABELS. Since 1960 the Australian Post Office used a number of different franking machines at post office counters issuing "POSTAGE PAID" labels. On 21 June 1993 a further type of self-adhesive label was introduced which incoported Threatened Species designs as Nos. 1312/17 with the machine-printed face value and code. Possible face values of these labels ranged from 45 c. to $9,999.99. This was subsequently restricted to a top value of $100.

The labels were initially available at the National Philatelic Centre, Melbourne showing code "NPCI" and were subsequently available from Canberra Parliament House post office ("ACT 93" and "CPH1") and Royal Exchange, Sydney ("RX1").

45 c. NPC1

517 "Black Cockatoo Feather" (Fiona Foley)

518 Conference Emblem

(Des Lynette Brown. Litho McPherson's Ptg Group, Mulgrave)

1993 (1 July). *International Year of Indigenous Peoples. Aboriginal Art.* T **517** *and similar multicoloured designs.* P 14½×14 (*vert*) *or* 14×14½ (*horiz*).
1417	45 c. Type **517**	55	45
1418	75 c. "Ngarrgooroon Country" (Hector Jandany) (*horiz*)	1·10	1·40
1419	$1 "Ngak Ngak" (Ginger Riley Mundawalawala) (*horiz*)	1·25	1·60
1420	$1.05, "Untitled" (Robert Cole) (Optd S. £2)	1·50	1·90
1417/20	*Set of 4*	4·00	4·75

(Des Dianne Cook. Litho Leigh-Mardon Ltd, Melbourne)

1993 (2 Sept). *Inter-Parliamentary Union Conference and 50th Anniv of Women in Federal Parliament.* T **518** *and similar square design. Multicoloured.* P 14½.
1421	45 c. Type **518**	1·00	1·90
	a. Pair. Nos. 1421/2	2·00	2·75
1422	45 c. Dame Enid Lyons and Senator Dorothy Tangney	1·00	1·40

Nos. 1421/2 were printed together, *se-tenant*, in sheets of 25 (5×5) with a block of nine examples of No. 1422 (R. 2/2-4, 3/2-4, 4/2-4) surrounded by sixteen examples of No. 1421 (R. 1/1-5, 2/1, 2/5, 3/1, 3/5, 4/1, 4/5, 5/1-5).

These stamps also exist in reverse format showing No. 1421 as the centre block of nine. Such panes were prepared for inclusion in the Eminent Women portfolio which was jointly produced by Note Printing Australia and Australia Post. Examples from the portfolio were numbered in red or black with unnumbered panes also available by mail order.

519 Ornithocheirus

520 "Goodwill"

(Des P. Trusler and Sue Passmore)

1993 (1 Oct). *Prehistoric Animals.* T **519** *and similar multicoloured designs.* (a) *Litho McPherson's Ptg Group, Mulgrave. Phosphorised paper.* P 14×14½ (Nos. 1423, 1427) *or* 14½×14 (Nos. 1424/6, 1428).
1423	45 c. Type **519**	60	50
1424	45 c. Leaellynasaura (25×30 mm)	60	50
1425	45 c. Timimus (26×33 mm)	60	50
1426	45 c. Allosaurus (26×33 mm)	60	50
1427	75 c. Muttaburrasaurus (30×50 mm)	1·00	90
1428	$1.05, Minmi (50×30 mm)	1·50	1·50
1423/8	*Set of 6*	4·50	4·00
MS1429	166×73 mm. Nos. 1423/8. P 14½	5·50	6·50

(b) *Litho Printset Cambec Pty Ltd. Self-adhesive. Phosphor background.* P 11½.
1430	45 c. Type **519**	65	80
	a. Booklet pane. Nos. 1430/1, each × 5	6·00	
1431	45 c. Leaellynasaura (25×30 mm)	65	80

No. **MS**1429 exists overprinted with the logos of "Bangkok '93" or Sydney Stamp and Coin Fair, 1993, for sale at these exhibitions.

Nos. 1430/1 occur either in rolls of 100 and 200, on which the surplus self-adhesive paper around each stamp was removed, or in $4.50 booklets, containing No. 1430a, on which the surplus paper was retained.

The phosphor on both rolls and booklets, which shows pink under U.V. light, covers much of the background of each design.

(Des Sandra Harman. Litho McPherson's Ptg Group, Mulgrave)

1993 (1 Nov). *Christmas.* T **520** *and similar vert designs. Multicoloured.* P 14½×14.
1432	40 c. Type **520**	50	45
	a. Booklet pane. No. 1432×20	8·50	
1433	45 c. "Joy"	55	45
1434	$1 "Peace"	1·90	1·60
1432/4	*Set of 3*	2·75	2·25

The horizontal edges of booklet pane No. 1432a are imperforate and there are margins at right and left.

521 "Shoalhaven River Bank – Dawn" (Arthur Boyd)

(Des Lynette Brown. Litho McPherson's Ptg Group, Mulgrave)

1994 (13 Jan). *Australia Day. Landscape Paintings.* T **521** *and similar multicoloured designs.* P 14×14½ ($2) *or* 14½×14 (*others*).
1435	45 c. Type **521**	60	45
1436	85 c. "Wimmera" (Sir Sidney Nolan)	1·40	1·40
1437	$1.05, "Lagoon, Wimmera" (Nolan)	1·60	1·60
1438	$2 "White Cockatoos with Flame Trees" (Boyd) (*vert*)	2·50	2·50
1435/8	*Set of 4*	5·50	5·50

522 Teaching Lifesaving Techniques

523 Rose

(Des O. Schmidinger, Christine Stead and Lynette Brown. Litho Printset Cambec Pty Ltd)

1994 (20 Jan). *Centenary of Organised Life Saving in Australia.* T **522** *and similar horiz designs. Multicoloured.*
(a) *Phosphorised paper.* P 14×14½.
1439	45 c. Type **522**	60	45
1440	45 c. Lifeguard on watch	60	45
1441	95 c. Lifeguard team	1·25	1·40
1442	$1.20, Lifeguards on surf boards	1·60	1·75
1439/42	*Set of 4*	3·75	3·75

(b) *Self-adhesive. Phosphor frame.* P 11½.
1443	45 c. Type **522**	65	1·00
	a. Booklet pane. Nos. 1443/4, each × 5	6·00	
1444	45 c. Lifeguard on watch	65	1·00

Nos. 1443/4 occur either in rolls of 100, on which the surplus self-adhesive paper around each stamp was removed, or in $4.50 booklets containing No. 1443a, on which the surplus paper was retained.

The phosphor on the rolls and booklets, which shows pink under U.V. light, extends onto the left or right corner of the centre designs.

(Des Sandra Harman. Litho McPherson's Ptg Group, Mulgrave)

1994 (3 Feb). *Greetings Stamps. Flower photographs by Lariane Fonseca.* T **523** *and similar vert designs. Multicoloured.* P 14½×14.
1445	45 c. Type **523**	40	45
1446	45 c. Tulips	40	45
	a. Horiz pair. Nos. 1446/7	80	90
	b. Booklet pane. Nos. 1446/7 each × 5	4·50	
1447	45 c. Poppies	40	45
1445/7	*Set of 3*	1·10	1·25

Nos. 1446/7 were printed together, *se-tenant*, in horizontal pairs throughout the sheet.

The vertical edges of booklet pane No. 1446b are imperforate, producing stamps imperforate at left (No. 1446) or right (No. 1447), and there are margins at top and bottom.

524 Bridge and National Flags

525 "Queen Elizabeth II" (Sir William Dargie)

(Des W. Crossett and Sue Passmore. Litho McPherson's Ptg Group, Mulgrave)

1994 (8 Apr). *Opening of Friendship Bridge between Thailand and Laos.* P 14½×14.
1448	524	95 c. multicoloured	1·25	1·40

(Des Sue Passmore. Litho Leigh-Mardon Ltd, Melbourne)

1994 (8 Apr). *Queen Elizabeth II's Birthday.* P 14½.
1449	525	45 c. multicoloured	70	70

526 "Family in Field" (Bobbie-Lea Blackmore)

527 Suffragettes

(Des Lynette Brown. Litho Leigh-Mardon Ltd, Melbourne)

1994 (14 Apr). *International Year of the Family. Children's Paintings.* T **526** *and similar horiz designs. Multicoloured.* P 14½.
1450	45 c. Type **526**	55	45
1451	75 c. "Family on Beach" (Kathryn Teoh)	1·00	1·10
1452	$1 "Family around Fire" (Maree McCarthy)	1·25	1·50
1450/2	*Set of 3*	2·50	2·75

Two types of inscr on Nos. 1453/5:

Type I. "KANGAROO" 9 mm long with spaces between letters.

Type II. "KANGAROO" 7 mm long without spaces between letters.

(Des Janet Boschen)

1994 (12 May)–**97**. *Australian Wildlife* (2nd series). *Horiz designs as* T **505**. *Multicoloured.* (a) *Litho Leigh-Mardon Ltd, Melbourne* (Nos. 1453/8) *or SNP Cambec* (Nos. 1453b/8b, 1453c/8c). *Phosphorised paper.* P 14×14½.
1453	45 c. Kangaroo (pale orange inscr) (I)	60	50
	a. Block of 6. Nos. 1453/8	3·25	
	b. Type II. Orange-brown inscr (1.96)	90	90
	ba. Block of 6. Nos. 1453b/8b	4·75	
	c. Type II. Pale orange inscr (8.97)	90	90
	ca. Block of 6. Nos. 1453c/5c and 1456/8	4·25	
1454	45 c. Female kangaroo with young (pale orange inscr) (I)	60	50
	b. Type II. Orange-brown inscr (1.96)	90	90
	c. Type II. Pale orange inscr (8.97)	90	90
1455	45 c. Two kangaroos (pale orange inscr) (I)	60	50
	b. Type II. Orange-brown inscr (1.96)	90	90
	c. Type II. Pale orange inscr (8.97)	90	90
1456	45 c. Family of koalas on branch (pale orange inscr)	60	50
	b. Orange-brown inscr (1.96)	90	90
1457	45 c. Koala on ground (pale orange inscr)	60	50
	b. Orange-brown inscr (1.96)	90	90
1458	45 c. Koala asleep in tree (pale orange inscr)	60	50
	b. Orange-brown inscr (1.96)	90	90
1453/8	*Set of 6*	3·25	3·00

(b) *Litho Printset Cambec Pty Ltd. Self-adhesive. Phosphor frame.* P 11½.
1459	45 c. Kangaroo	60	80
	a. Booklet pane. Nos. 1459/60×2, 1461, 1462/3×2 and 1464	5·50	
	ab. Imperf pane		
	b. Sheetlet of 5. Nos. 1459 and 1461/4 (15.2.95)	4·50	
1460	45 c. Female kangaroo with young	60	80
1461	45 c. Two kangaroos	60	80
1462	45 c. Family of koalas on branch	60	80
1463	45 c. Koala on ground	60	80
1464	45 c. Koala asleep in tree	60	80
1459/64	*Set of 6*	3·25	4·25

(c) Typo Pemara Labels, Victoria. Self-adhesive. Phosphor frame. P 11½.

1464a	45 c. Kangaroo (5.95)	6·00	6·00
	ap. Phosphorised mesh (9.95)	80	90
1464b	45 c. Female kangaroo with young (5.95)	6·00	6·00
	bp. Phosphorised mesh (9.95)	80	90
1464c	45 c. Two kangaroos (5.95)	6·00	6·00
	cp. Phosphorised mesh (9.95)	80	90
1464d	45 c. Family of koalas on branch (5.95)	6·00	6·00
	dp. Phosphorised mesh (9.95)	80	90
1464e	45 c. Koala on ground (5.95)	6·00	6·00
	ep. Phosphorised mesh (9.95)	80	90
1464f	45 c. Koala asleep in tree (5.95)	6·00	6·00
	fp. Phosphorised mesh (9.95)	80	90
1464a/f		Set of 6 32·00	32·00
1464ap/fp		Set of 6 4·25	4·75

Nos. 1453/8 were printed together, *se-tenant*, in sheets of 100 (2 panes of 50 5×10) each pane providing five blocks of 6 and twenty single stamps. They also exist as a *se-tenant* sheetlet of 6 with inscribed margins produced for sale at "Philakorea '94" Stamp Exhibition, Seoul.

The colour of the "AUSTRALIA" inscription and face value is repeated on a horizontal band at the foot of each design.

Nos. 1453b/8b are from the 2 koala printing and Nos. 1453c/5c from the 3 koala printing. Both show "1996" smaller than on the original printing.

Nos. 1459/64 occur either in rolls of 100, rolls of 200, booklets of 10 or sheetlets of 5. On all rolls the surplus self-adhesive paper around each stamp was removed, but this was retained on booklet pane No. 1459a and sheetlet No. 1459b.

The phosphor on Nos. 1459/64 and Nos. 1464a/f, which shows pink under U.V. light, extends from bars at top and bottom onto sections of the centre designs. On Nos. 1464ap/fp, which come from the 3 koala, 4 koala, 1 kangaroo and 1 kangaroo + 2 koala printings, the phosphor extends over the same area; but is broken up by a mesh pattern into small squares or diamonds.

The Pemara printings were produced in rolls only.

Counter-printed labels, as described beneath No. 1416, in designs as Nos. 1453/64, but 40×28 mm, were issued on 17 November 1994. Possible face values for these labels ranged from 45 c. to $100. Machines issuing the labels were located at National Philatelic Centre, Melbourne ("NPC"), Canberra Parliament House post office ("CPH"), Royal Exchange ("REX") and Haymarket ("HAYMKT") post offices, Sydney, and at the General Post Offices in Adelaide ("ADEL GPO"), Brisbane ("BRIS GPO"), Melbourne ("MELB GPO"), Perth ("PERTH GPO") (from 26 June 1995) and Bathurst Street, Hobart ("BTH ST HBT") (from 16 October 1995). Exhibition labels were issued for events both in Australia and overseas from 1994 onwards.

Very similar labels were produced from "Weigh & Pay" machines first used in the Perth area from 20 May 1996. Those from Perth itself are inscribed "GPO PERTH" or "PERTH GPO", but labels from other post offices are without inscription. Exhibition labels were issued at National Stamp Show, Fremantle, 1997 and at "Australia 99".

For Nos. 1453b, 1454b and 1455b in miniature sheet for "CHINA" '96 see No. **MS**1626.

(Des Maire Smith. Litho McPherson's Ptg Group, Mulgrave)

1994 (9 June). *Centenary of Women's Emancipation in South Australia.* P 14×14½.

1465	527	45 c. multicoloured	60	60

528 Bunyip from Aboriginal Legend

529 "Robert Menzies" (Sir Ivor Hele)

(Des J. Morrison (No. 1466), D. Lancashire (No. 1467), R. Brooks (No. 1468), Marg Towt (No. 1470). Litho Leigh-Mardon Ltd, Melbourne)

1994 (14 July). *The Bunyip (mythological monster).* T 528 and similar square designs. Multicoloured. P 14½.

1466	45 c. Type 528		60	60
	a. Pair. Nos. 1466/7		1·10	1·10
1467	45 c. Nature spirit bunyip		60	60
1468	90 c. "The Bunyip of Berkeley's Creek" (book illustration)		1·50	1·50
1469	$1.35, Bunyip as natural history		1·90	2·00
1466/9		Set of 4	4·00	4·00

Nos. 1466/7 were printed together, *se-tenant*, in horizontal or vertical pairs throughout the sheet.

(Des FHA Design. Litho McPherson's Ptg Group, Mulgrave)

1994 (11 Aug). *Wartime Prime Ministers.* T 529 and similar horiz designs. Multicoloured. P 14×14½.

1470	45 c. Type 529		85	85
	a. Horiz strip of 5. Nos. 1470/4		3·75	
1471	45 c. "Arthur Fadden" (William Dargie)		85	85
1472	45 c. "John Curtin" (Anthony Dattilo-Rubbo)		85	85
1473	45 c. "Francis Forde" (Joshua Smith)		85	85
1474	45 c. "Joseph Chifley" (A. D. Colquhoun)		85	85
1470/4		Set of 5	3·75	3·75

Nos. 1470/4 were printed together, *se-tenant*, in horizontal strips of 5 throughout the sheet.

530 Lawrence Hargrave and Box Kites

531 Scarlet Macaw

(Des Janet Boschen. Eng C. Slania. Recess Royal Swedish Stamp Ptg Office, Stockholm)

1994 (29 Aug). *Aviation Pioneers.* T 530 and similar vert designs. P 12½.

1475	45 c. red-brown, blackish olive & cinnamon		70	45
1476	45 c. red-brown, deep carmine and lavender		70	45
1477	$1.35, red-brown, dp violet & greenish bl		2·25	2·75
1478	$1.80, red-brown, slate-green & sage-grn		2·50	3·00
1475/8		Set of 4	5·50	6·00

Designs:—No. 1475, Type 530; No. 1476, Ross and Keith Smith with Vickers Vimy (first England-Australia flight); No. 1477, Ivor McIntyre, Stanley Goble and Fairey IIID seaplane (first aerial circumnavigation of Australia); No. 1478, Freda Thompson and De Havilland Moth Major *Christopher Robin* (first Australian woman to fly solo from England to Australia).

No. 1475 also exists as a pane of 25 numbered in red or black from a limited issue Hargrave portfolio.

Two types of phosphor on self-adhesive Type 531;
Type I. Leaf below second tail feather covered by phosphor
Type II. Leaf without phosphor

(Des G. Cook)

1994 (28 Sept). *Australian Zoos. Endangered Species.* T 531 and similar multicoloured designs. (a) Litho McPherson's Ptg Group, Mulgrave. Phosphorised paper. P 14×14½ (No. 1479) or 14½×14 (others).

1479	45 c. Type 531		65	55
1480	45 c. Cheetah (25×30 mm)		65	55
1481	45 c. Orang-Utan (26×37 mm)		65	55
1482	45 c. Fijian Crested Iguana (26×37 mm)		65	55
1483	$1 Asian Elephants (49×28 mm)		1·75	1·60
1479/83		Set of 5	4·00	4·00
MS1484	166×73 mm. Nos. 1479/83. P 14½		4·00	4·50

(b) Litho Printset Cambec Pty Ltd. Self-adhesive. Phosphor frame. P 11½.

1485	45 c. Type 531 (I)		1·50	1·50
	a. Type II		1·50	1·50
	b. Booklet pane. Nos. 1485×4, 1485a×2 and 1486×4		12·00	
1486	45 c. Cheetah		1·50	1·50

No. **MS**1484 exists overprinted with the logos of the Sydney Stamp and Coin Fair, Brisbane Stamp and Coin Fair, "Stampshow Melbourne '94" or "Swanpex '94" (including one with overprint inverted) for sale at these Australian exhibitions.

Nos. 1485/6 occur in $4.50 booklets, containing No. 1485b.

The phosphor on the booklets, which shows pink under U.V. light, appears as an irregular frame to each design.

532 "Madonna and Child" (detail, "The Adoration of the Magi") (Giovanni Toscani)

533 Yachts outside Sydney Harbour

(Des Lisa Christenson. Litho McPherson's Ptg Group, Mulgrave)

1994 (31 Oct). *Christmas.* T 532 and similar designs showing "The Adoration of the Magi" by Giovanni Toscani. Multicoloured. P 14½×14 (40 c., $1.80) or 14×14½ (45 c., $1).

1487	40 c. Type 532		60	40
	a. Booklet pane. No. 1487×20		8·50	
1488	45 c. "Wise Man and Horse" (detail) (horiz)		60	45
1489	$1 "Wise Man and St. Joseph" (detail) (horiz)		1·50	1·40
1490	$1.80, Complete painting (49×29 mm)		2·00	2·50
1487/90		Set of 4	4·25	4·25

The vertical edges of booklet pane No. 1487a are imperforate and there are margins at top and bottom.

(Des J. Spatchurst)

1994 (31 Oct). *50th Sydney to Hobart Yacht Race.* T 533 and similar horiz design. (a) Litho Leigh-Mardon Ltd, Melbourne. Phosphorised paper. P 14½.

1491	45 c. Type 533		70	70
	a. Pair. Nos. 1491/2		1·40	1·40
1492	45 c. Yachts passing Tasmania coastline		70	70

(b) Litho Printset Cambec Pty Ltd. Self-adhesive. Phosphor frame. P 11½.

1493	45 c. Type 533 (31×20 mm)		80	1·25
1494	45 c. Yachts passing Tasmania coastline (31×20 mm)		80	1·25

Nos. 1491/2 were printed together, *se-tenant*, in horizontal and vertical pairs throughout the sheet.

Nos. 1493/4 occur in rolls of 100. The phosphor, which shows pink under U.V. light, appears as an irregular frame to each design.

534 Symbolic Kangaroo

535 "Back Verandah" (Russell Drysdale)

(Des Sandra Harman and J. Passmore. Typo (gold die-stamped) Pemara Labels)

1994 (2 Nov)–96. *Self-adhesive. Automatic Cash Machine Stamps. Phosphorised paper.* P 16½.

1495	534	45 c. gold, emerald and dull blue-green	50	50
		a. Pane of 20. Nos. 1495/1502	9·00	
		ab. Pane of 20. Nos. 1495/7, 1498a, 1499/1501 and 1502a (11.4.96)	9·00	
1496		45 c. gold, emerald and cobalt	50	50
1497		45 c. gold, emerald and bright lilac	50	50
1498		45 c. gold, emerald and apple-green (grey-brown dots in background)	50	50
		a. Emerald dots in background (11.4.96)	50	50
1499		45 c. gold, emerald & pale yellow-green	50	50
1500		45 c. gold, emerald and pink	50	50
1501		45 c. gold, emerald and rose	50	50
1502		45 c. gold, emerald and yellow-ochre (grey-brown dots in background)	50	50
		a. Emerald dots in background (11.4.96)	50	50
1495/1502		Set of 8	4·00	4·00

Nos. 1495/1502 were issued in panes of 20 from automatic cash machines at Advance Bank branches in Australian Capital Territory, New South Wales and Queensland, and from the National Philatelic Centre, Melbourne. The stamps were arranged, *tête-bêche*, in horizontal rows of 3 or 4 with the pane containing two examples of Nos. 1495, 1497, 1499 and 1501 and three of Nos. 1496, 1498, 1500 and 1502. As originally issued the backing paper carried advertising for the Advance Bank. A second version advertising Postpak packaging was introduced on 11 April 1996 and contained Nos. 1495/7, 1498a, 1499/1501 and 1502a.

St. George Bank took over Advance Bank on 1 April 1998 and the sale of Nos. 1495/1502 through automatic cash machines was discontinued from 11 September 1998.

(Des Allnutt Graphics. Litho Leigh-Mardon Ltd, Melbourne)

1995 (12 Jan). *Australia Day. Paintings.* T 535 and similar horiz designs. Multicoloured. P 15×14½.

1503	45 c. Type 535		50	45
1504	45 c. "Skull Springs Country" (Guy Grey-Smith)		50	45
1505	$1.05, "Outcamp" (Robert Juniper)		1·40	1·50
1506	$1.20, "Kite Flying" (Ian Fairweather)		1·50	1·50
1503/6		Set of 4	3·50	3·50

536 Red Heart and Rose

537 *Endeavour* Replica at Sea

(Des Kim Roberts. Litho Printset Cambec Pty Ltd, (gold die-stamped Avon Graphics))

1995 (30 Jan). *St. Valentine's Day.* T 536 and similar vert designs. Multicoloured. P 14½×14.

1507	45 c. Type 536		55	55
	a. Horiz strip of 5. Nos. 1507/8×2 and 1509		2·40	
1508	45 c. Gold and red heart with rose		55	55
1509	45 c. Gold heart and roses		55	55
1507/9		Set of 3	1·50	1·50

Nos. 1507/9 were printed together, *se-tenant*, in horizontal strips of 5 throughout the sheet each containing two examples of Nos. 1507/8 and one of No. 1509.

(Des Michelle Gauci. Litho McPherson's Ptg Group, Mulgrave)

1995 (9 Feb). *Completion of Endeavour Replica.* T 537 and similar horiz design. Multicoloured. (a) Sheet stamps, 38×26 mm. P 14×14½.

1510	45 c. Type 537		90	90
	a. Pair. Nos. 1510/11		1·75	1·75
1511	45 c. "Captain Cook's Endeavour" (detail) (Oswald Brett)		90	90

(b) Booklet stamps, 44×26 mm. P 14×imperf

1512	20 c. Type 537		1·00	1·25
	a. Booklet pane. Nos. 1512 and 1513×4		2·50	
1513	45 c. As No. 1511		45	50

Nos. 1510/11 are printed together, *se-tenant*, in horizontal and vertical pairs throughout the sheet.

The 20 c. value was only available from $2 stamp booklets. The vertical edges of pane No. 1512a are imperforate and there are margins at top and bottom.

538 Coalport Plate and
Bracket Clock, Old
Government House,
Parramatta

(Des Janet Boschen. Recess Note Ptg Branch, Reserve Bank of
Australia)

1995 (16 Mar). *50th Anniv of Australian National Trusts.
T 538 and similar horiz designs.* P 14×14½.
1514 45 c. deep violet-blue and purple-brown .. 45 45
a. Pair. Nos. 1514/15 .. .. .. 90 90
1515 45 c. deep blue-green and purple-brown .. 45 45
1516 $1 brown-red and royal blue .. .. 1·00 95
1517 $2 blackish olive and royal blue .. 1·90 1·90
1514/17 .. .. .. *Set of 4* 3·50 3·75
Designs:—No. 1515, Steiner doll and Italian-style chair,
Ayers House, Adelaide; No. 1516, "Advance Australia" teapot
and parian-ware statuette, Victoria; No. 1517, Silver bowl and
china urn, Old Observatory, Perth.
Nos. 1514/15 were printed together, *se-tenant*, in horizontal
and vertical pairs throughout the sheet.

539 Light Opal

(Des Sue Passmore. Litho Printset Cambec Pty Ltd (exelgrams
by Avon Graphics))

1995 (5 Apr). *Opals. T 539 and similar horiz design.
Multicoloured.* P 14½×14.
1518 $1.20, Type 539 .. .. .. 1·75 1·25
1519 $2.50, Black opal .. .. .. 3·25 3·25
The opals depicted on Nos. 1518/19 are produced as exelgrams
(holographic printing on an ultra thin plastic film) embossed
onto the stamps.

540 Queen Elizabeth   **541** Sir Edward
II at Gala Concert,   Dunlop and P.O.W.
1992   Association Badge

(Des Nuttshell Graphics. Litho Leigh-Mardon Ltd, Melbourne)
1995 (20 Apr). *Queen Elizabeth II's Birthday.* P 14½.
1520 **540** 45 c. multicoloured 65 75

Two types of phosphor on Nos. 1527/8:
Type I. Phosphor at right ends level with hat or cap (coils)
Type II. Phosphor at right extends to the ear (No. 1527a) or
shoulder (No. 1528a) (booklets)

(Des Sue Passmore)
1995 (20 Apr). *Australian Second World War Heroes (1st
series). T 541 and similar vert designs. Multicoloured.* (a)
Litho McPherson's Ptg Group, Mulgrave. Phosphorised paper.
P 14½×14.
1521 45 c. Type 541 .. .. 60 60
a. Block of 4. Nos. 1521/4 .. 2·25
1522 45 c. Mrs. Jessie Vasey and War Widows'
Guild badge 60 60
1523 45 c. Sgt. Tom Derrick and Victoria Cross 60 60
1524 45 c. Flt. Sgt. Rawdon Middleton and
Victoria Cross 60 60
1521/4 .. .. .. *Set of 4* 2·25 2·25
(b) *Litho Printset Cambec Pty Ltd. Self-adhesive. Designs
21×32½ mm. Phosphor frame.* P 11½
1525 45 c. Type 541 (I) 85 95
a. Booklet pane. Nos. 1525×4 and 1526,
1527a/8a, each × 2 .. .. 6·50
1526 45 c. Mrs. Jessie Vasey and War Widows'
Guild badge 85 95
1527 45 c. Sgt. Tom Derrick and Victoria Cross
(I) 85 95
a. Type II .. .. .. 1·25 1·40
1528 45 c. Flt. Sgt. Rawdon Middleton and
Victoria Cross (I) 85 95
a. Type II .. .. .. 1·25 1·40
1525/8 .. .. .. *Set of 4* 3·00 3·50
Nos. 1521/4 were printed together, *se-tenant*, in sheets of 100
(2 panes of 50 10×5) each pane providing ten blocks of 4 and ten
single stamps.

Nos. 1525/8 occur either in rolls of 100, on which the surplus
self-adhesive paper around each stamp was removed, or in $4.50
booklets, containing No. 1525a, on which the surplus paper was
retained.
The phosphor, which shows pink under U.V. light, covers the
designs, with the exception of the portraits and emblems, and
the backing paper on both the booklets and the rolls.
See also Nos. 1545/8.

542 Children and Globe of   **543** The Story of
Flags   the Kelly Gang

(Des FHA Design. Litho McPherson's Ptg Group, Mulgrave)
1995 (11 May). *50th Anniv of United Nations.* P 14×14½.
1529 **542** 45 c. multicoloured 75 75
No. 1529 was printed in sheets with *se-tenant* 10×26 mm
labels. In rows 1, 3, 5, 7 and 9 these labels occur on the right of
each stamp and commemorate the 50th anniversary or
the F.A.O. alternately. On rows 2, 4, 6, 8 and 10 the labels occur
on the left of each stamp and are inscribed for either
U.N.E.S.C.O. or U.N.I.C.E.F.

(Des J. Spatchurst)
1995 (8 June). *Centenary of Cinema. T 543 and similar vert
designs showing scenes from films. Multicoloured.* (a) *Litho
McPherson's Ptg Group, Mulgrave. Phosphorised paper.*
P 14½×14.
1530 45 c. Type 543 .. .. .. 70 80
a. Horiz strip of 5. Nos. 1530/4 .. 3·25
1531 45 c. On Our Selection 70 80
1532 45 c. Jedda 70 80
1533 45 c. Picnic at Hanging Rock .. 70 80
1534 45 c. Strictly Ballroom 70 80
1530/4 .. .. .. *Set of 5* 3·25 3·50
(b) *Litho Printset Cambec Pty Ltd. Self-adhesive. Designs
19×30½ mm. Phosphor frame.* P 11½.
1535 45 c. Type 543 .. .. .. 90 90
a. Booklet pane. Nos. 1535/9 each × 2 5·50
1536 45 c. On Our Selection 90 90
1537 45 c. Jedda 90 90
1538 45 c. Picnic at Hanging Rock .. 90 90
1539 45 c. Strictly Ballroom 90 90
1535/9 .. .. .. *Set of 5* 4·00 4·00
Nos. 1530/4 were printed together, *se-tenant*, in horizontal
strips of 5 throughout the sheet.
Nos. 1535/9 occur either in rolls of 100, on which the surplus
self-adhesive paper around each stamp was removed, or in $4.50
booklets, containing No. 1535a, on which the surplus paper was
retained.

544 Man in   **545** Koala with Cub
Wheelchair flying
Kite

(Des Tracie Grimwood. Litho McPherson's Ptg Group,
Mulgrave)
1995 (13 July). *People with Disabilities. T 544 and similar vert
design. Multicoloured.* P 14½×14.
1540 45 c. Type 544 .. .. .. 65 65
a. Horiz pair. Nos. 1540/1 .. 1·25 1·25
1541 45 c. Blind woman playing violin .. 65 65
Nos. 1540/1 were printed together, *se-tenant*, in horizontal
pairs throughout the sheet.

(Adapted L. Dolan. Recess Note Ptg Branch, Reserve Bank of
Australia)
1995 (10 Aug). *50th Anniv of Peace in the Pacific. Designs as
1946 Victory Commemoration (Nos. 213/15) redrawn with
new face values.* P 14×14½ (horiz) or 14½×14 (vert).
1542 53 45 c. scarlet 75 60
1543 — 45 c. green 75 60
1544 — $1.50, blue .. .. .. 1·90 2·25
1542/4 .. .. .. *Set of 3* 3·00 3·00
Designs: Vert—No. 1543, Angel. Horiz—No. 1544, Flag and
dove.

(Des Sue Passmore. Litho McPherson's Ptg Group, Mulgrave)
1995 (10 Aug). *Australian Second World War Heroes (2nd
series). Vert designs as T 541. Multicoloured.* P 14½×14.
1545 45 c. Sister Ellen Savage and George Medal 60 70
a. Block of 4. Nos. 1545/8 .. 2·25
1546 45 c. Chief Petty Officer Percy Collins and
Distinguished Service Medal and Bar 60 70
1547 45 c. Lt-Comm. Leon Goldsworthy and
George Cross 60 70
1548 45 c. Warrant Officer Len Waters and
R.A.A.F. wings 60 70
1545/8 .. .. .. *Set of 4* 2·25 2·50
Nos. 1545/8 were printed together, *se-tenant*, in sheets of 100
(2 panes of 50 10×5) each pane providing ten blocks of 4 and ten
single stamps.

PRINTERS. Leigh-Mardon Ltd ceased printing Australian
stamps in May 1995. On 10 July 1995 Singapore National
Printer Pty Ltd took over Printset Cambec and the firm was
then known as SNP Cambec.

(Des Xu Yanbo and Lisa Christensen. Litho SNP Cambec (Nos.
1549/50) or Postage Stamp Ptg Works, Peking (No. MS1551))
1995 (1 Sept). *Australia–China Joint Issue. Endangered
Species. T 545 and similar horiz design. Multicoloured.*
P 14½×14.
1549 45 c. Type 545 .. .. .. 70 90
a. Pair. Nos. 1549/50 .. .. 1·40 1·75
1550 45 c. Giant Panda with cubs .. 70 90
MS1551 Two sheets, each 106×70 mm. (a) No.
1549. (b) No. 1550. P 11×11½ .. *Set of 2 sheets* 1·60 1·60
Nos. 1549/50 were printed together, *se-tenant*, in horizontal
and vertical pairs throughout the sheet.
No. MS1551a also exists overprinted "AUSTRALIAN
STAMP EXHIBITION" and No. MS1551b "INTERNATIONAL
STAMP & COIN EXPO BEIJING" for sale at these exhibitions
in China.

546 Father Joseph   **547** Flatback Turtle
Slattery, Thomas Lyle
and Walter Filmer
(Radiology)

(Des O. Schmidinger, Christine Stead and Melinda
Whitechurch. Litho McPherson's Ptg Group, Mulgrave)
1995 (7 Sept). *Medical Scientists. T 546 and similar
multicoloured designs.* P 14×14½ (horiz) or 14½×14 (vert).
1552 45 c. Type 546 .. .. .. 60 70
a. Pair. Nos. 1552/3 .. .. 1·10 1·40
1553 45 c. Dame Jean Macnamara and Sir
Macfarlane Burnet (viruses) .. 60 70
1554 45 c. Fred Hollows (ophthalmology) (vert) 60 60
1555 $2.50, Sir Howard Florey (antibiotics)
(vert) .. .. .. 3·75 4·50
1552/5 .. .. .. *Set of 4* 5·00 6·00
Nos. 1552/3 were printed together, *se-tenant*, in horizontal
and vertical pairs throughout the sheet.
It was intended that 45 c. gutter blocks for philatelic sale
would be produced in special sheets, but these were withdrawn
just prior to issue when it was found that the gutter pairs
contained two examples of the same design, instead of one of
each.
No. 1555 also exists as a pane of 10 numbered in red or black
from a limited issue Howard Florey portfolio.

Two types of phosphor on self-adhesive Type 547:
Type I. Outcrop at bottom left completely covered by
phosphor (coils)
Type II. Only part of outcrop covered by phosphor (booklets)

(Des G. Ryan. Litho SNP Cambec)
1995 (3 Oct). *Marine Life. T 547 and similar horiz designs.* (a)
Phosphorised paper. P 14×14½.
1556 45 c. Type 547 .. .. .. 55 55
a. Vert pair. Nos. 1556/7 .. 1·10 1·10
1557 45 c. Flame Angelfish and Nudibranch 55 55
1558 45 c. Potato Grouper ("Potato Cod") and
Hump-headed Wrasse ("Maori
Wrasse") 55 55
a. Vert pair. Nos. 1558/9 .. 1·10 1·10
1559 45 c. Giant Trevally 55 55
1560 45 c. Black Marlin 55 55
a. Vert pair. Nos. 1560/1 .. 1·10 1·10
1561 45 c. Mako and Tiger Sharks .. 55 55
1556/61 .. .. .. *Set of 6* 3·00 3·00
MS1562 166×73 mm. As Nos. 1556/61, but
without lighter frame .. .. 3·00 3·00
(b) *Self-adhesive. Phosphor frame on three sides.* P 11½
1563 45 c. Type 547 (I) 50 65
a. Type II 50 65
ab. Booklet pane Nos. 1563a/6, each × 2,
and Nos. 1567/8 .. .. 4·25
1564 45 c. Flame Angelfish and Nudibranch .. 50 65
1565 45 c. Potato Cod and Maori Wrasse .. 50 65
1566 45 c. Giant Trevally 50 65
1567 45 c. Black Marlin 50 65
1568 45 c. Mako and Tiger Sharks .. 50 65
1563/8 .. .. .. *Set of 6* 2·75 3·50
Nos. 1556/7, 1558/9 and 1560/1 were printed together,
se-tenant, in vertical pairs throughout the sheets. Parts of No.
MS1562 are printed in luminescent ink.
No. MS1562 also exists overprinted with the logos of the
Adelaide Stamp and Collectables Fair, Sydney Centrepoint 95
National Stamp Exhibition, Brisbane Stamp Show, Melbourne
Stamp and Coin Fair and "Swanpex WA", Perth, for sale at
these Australian exhibitions.
Nos. 1563/8 occur either in rolls of 100, on which the surplus
self-adhesive paper around each stamp was removed, or in $4.50
booklets, containing No. 1563ab, on which the surplus paper
was retained.
The phosphor on both rolls and booklets shows pink under
U.V. light.

MINIMUM PRICE

The minimum price quote is 10p which represents
a handling charge rather than a basis for valuing
common stamps. For further notes about prices
see introductory pages.

548 "Madonna and Child"   **549** "West Australian Banksia" (Margaret Preston)

(Des Dianne Cook. Litho SNP Cambec)

1995 (1 Nov). *Christmas. Stained-glass Windows from Our Lady Help of Christians Church, Melbourne.* T **548** and *similar vert designs.* (a) *Phosphorised paper.* P 14½×14.

1569	40 c. Type **548**		45	45
1570	45 c. "Angel carrying the Gloria banner"		45	45
1571	$1 "Rejoicing Angels"	..	1·10	1·50
1569/71		Set of 3	1·75	2·25

(b) *Self-adhesive. Phosphor frame.* P 11½

1572	40 c. Type **548**		50	45
	a. Booklet pane. No. 1572×20		8·50	

No. 1572, on which the phosphor shows pink under U.V. light, was only issued in $8 booklets, on which the surplus self-adhesive paper was retained.

(Des Susan Horvath. Litho McPherson's Ptg Group, Mulgrave)

1996 (16 Jan). *Australia Day. Paintings.* T **549** and *similar multicoloured designs.* P 14×14½ (*vert*) or 14½×14 (*horiz*).

1573	45 c. Type **549**		60	45
1574	85 c. "The Babe is Wise" (Lina Bryans)		1·40	1·25
1575	$1 "The Bridge in Curve" (Grace Cossington Smith) (*horiz*)		1·50	1·25
1576	$1.20, "Beach Umbrellas" (Vida Lahey) (*horiz*)		1·75	1·50
1573/6	..	Set of 4	4·75	4·00

550 Gold Heart and Rose   **551** Bristol Type 156 Beaufighter and Curtiss P-40E Kittyhawk I

(Des Kim Roberts and Sandra Harman. Litho SNP Cambec (gold die-stamped Avon Graphics))

1996 (30 Jan). *St. Valentine's Day.* P 14×14½.

1577	**550** 45 c. multicoloured	..	50	50

(Des Melinda Whitechurch and N. Clifford. Litho SNP Cambec)

1996 (26 Feb). *Military Aviation.* T **551** and *similar horiz designs. Multicoloured.* P 14×14½.

1578	45 c. Type **551**		75	90
	a. Block of 4. Nos. 1578/81		2·75	
1579	45 c. Hawker Sea Fury and Fairey Firefly		75	90
1580	45 c. Bell Kiowa helicopters		75	90
1581	45 c. Government Aircraft Factory Hornets		75	90
1578/81		Set of 4	2·75	3·25

Nos. 1578/81 were printed together, *se-tenant*, in different combinations throughout the pane of 25, giving four blocks of 4 and nine single stamps.

552 Tasmanian Wilderness   **553** Australian Spotted Cuscus

(Des Dianne Cook. Litho SNP Cambec)

1996 (14 Mar). *World Heritage Sites (2nd series).* T **552** and *similar horiz designs. Multicoloured.* P 14½×14.

1582	45 c. Type **552**		50	45
1583	75 c. Willandra Lakes		90	90
1584	95 c. Naracoorte Fossil Cave		1·25	1·25
1585	$1 Lord Howe Island		1·50	1·60
1582/5	..	Set of 4	3·75	3·75

(Des Rosemary Ganf and Josephine Mure. Litho SNP Cambec)

1996 (22 Mar). *Australia–Indonesia Joint Issue.* T **553** and *similar vert design. Multicoloured.* P 14½×14.

1586	45 c. Type **553**		70	70
	a. Horiz pair. Nos. 1586/7	..	1·40	1·40
1587	45 c. Indonesian Bear Cuscus		70	70
MS1588	106×70 mm. Nos. 1586/7	..	1·60	1·60

Nos. 1586/7 were printed together, *se-tenant*, in horizontal pairs throughout the sheet.

No. **MS1588** also exists overprinted "WORLD PHILATELIC YOUTH EXHIBITION PAMERAN FILATELI REMAJA DUNIA INDONESIA '96" and emblem for sale at this exhibition.

554 Head of Queen Elizabeth II   **555** North Melbourne Players

(Des Pendulum Design. Recess and litho Note Ptg Branch, Reserve Bank of Australia and SNP Cambec)

1996 (11 Apr). *Queen Elizabeth II's Birthday.* P 14×14½.

1589	**554** 45 c. multicoloured	..	55	55

Numbered gutter strips of ten, overprinted to commemorate the 30th anniversary of decimal currency in Australia, come from a limited issue Queen Elizabeth II portfolio.

(Des Rankin Bevers Design and B. Clinton. Litho SNP Cambec)

1996 (23 Apr). *Centenary of Australian Football League.* T **555** and *similar designs each showing players from a different team. Multicoloured.* (a) *Phosphorised paper.* P 14½×14.

1590	45 c. Type **555**		60	65
	a. Sheetlet. Nos. 1590/1605		8·75	
1591	45 c. Brisbane (red and yellow shirt)		60	65
1592	45 c. Sydney (red and white shirt)		60	65
1593	45 c. Carlton (black shirt with white emblem)		60	65
1594	45 c. Adelaide (black, red and yellow shirt)		60	65
1595	45 c. Fitzroy (yellow, red and blue shirt)		60	65
1596	45 c. Richmond (black shirt with yellow diagonal stripe)		60	65
1597	45 c. St. Kilda (red, white and black shirt)		60	65
1598	45 c. Melbourne (black shirt with red top)		60	65
1599	45 c. Collingwood (black and white vertical striped shirt)		60	65
1600	45 c. Fremantle (green, red, white and blue shirt)		60	65
1601	45 c. Footscray (blue, white and red shirt)		60	65
1602	45 c. West Coast (deep blue shirt with yellow stripes)		60	65
1603	45 c. Essendon (black shirt with red stripe)		60	65
1604	45 c. Geelong (black and white horizontal striped shirt)		60	65
1605	45 c. Hawthorn (black and yellow vertical striped shirt)		60	65
1590/1605		Set of 16	8·75	9·50

(b) *Self-adhesive. Phosphor frame at top and left.* P 11½

1606	45 c. Type **555**		70	75
	a. Booklet pane. No. 1606×10		6·00	
1607	45 c. Brisbane		70	75
	a. Booklet pane. No. 1607×10		6·00	
1608	45 c. Sydney		70	75
	a. Booklet pane. No. 1608×10		6·00	
1609	45 c. Carlton		70	75
	a. Booklet pane. No. 1609×10		6·00	
1610	45 c. Adelaide		70	75
	a. Booklet pane. No. 1610×10		6·00	
1611	45 c. Fitzroy		70	75
	a. Booklet pane. No. 1611×10		6·00	
1612	45 c. Richmond		70	75
	a. Booklet pane. No. 1612×10		6·00	
1613	45 c. St. Kilda		70	75
	a. Booklet pane. No. 1613×10		6·00	
1614	45 c. Melbourne		70	75
	a. Booklet pane. No. 1614×10		6·00	
1615	45 c. Collingwood		70	75
	a. Booklet pane. No. 1615×10		6·00	
1616	45 c. Fremantle		70	75
	a. Booklet pane. No. 1616×10		6·00	
1617	45 c. Footscray		70	75
	a. Booklet pane. No. 1617×10		6·00	
1618	45 c. West Coast		70	75
	a. Booklet pane. No. 1618×10		6·00	
1619	45 c. Essendon		70	75
	a. Booklet pane. No. 1619×10		6·00	
1620	45 c. Geelong		70	75
	a. Booklet pane. No. 1620×10		6·00	
1621	45 c. Hawthorn		70	75
	a. Booklet pane. No. 1621×10		6·00	
1606/21		Set of 16	10·00	10·50

Nos. 1590/1605 were printed together, *se-tenant*, in sheetlets of 16.

Nos. 1606/21 were only available in $4.50 booklets. The phosphor shows pink under U.V. light.

556 Leadbeater's Possum   **557** Edwin Flack (800 and 1500 metres gold medal winner, 1896)

(Des Rankin Bevers Design. Litho McPherson's Ptg Group, Mulgrave)

1996 (9 May). *Fauna and Flora (1st series). Central Highlands Forest, Victoria.* T **556** and *similar multicoloured designs. Phosphorised paper.* P 14×14½.

1622	5 c. Type **556**		10	10
1623	10 c. Powerful Owl		10	10
1624	$2 Blackwood Wattle		1·60	1·75
1625	$5 Soft Tree Fern and Mountain Ash (30×50 mm)		4·00	4·25
1622/5		Set of 4	5·25	5·75

See also Nos. 1679/90 and 1854/66.

(Des Janet Boschen. Litho McPherson's Ptg Group, Mulgrave)

1996 (18 May). *"CHINA '96" 9th Asian International Stamp Exhibition, Peking. Sheet* 120×65 *mm, containing Nos.* 1453b, 1454b *and* 1455b. *Multicoloured.* P 14×14½.

MS1626	45 c. Kangaroo; 45 c. Female kangaroo with young; 45 c. Two kangaroos	..	1·75	1·90

(Des Pendulum Design. Eng L. Dolan. Recess and litho Note Ptg Branch, Reserve Bank of Australia and SNP Cambec)

1996 (6 June). *Centennial Olympic Games and 10th Para-lympic Games, Atlanta.* T **557** and *similar horiz designs. Multicoloured.* P 14×14½.

1627	45 c. Type **557**		70	70
	a. Pair. Nos. 1627/8		1·40	1·40
1628	45 c. Fanny Durack (100 metres freestyle swimming gold medal winner, 1912)		70	70
1629	$1.05, Wheelchair athletes		1·60	1·60
1627/9		Set of 3	2·75	2·75

Nos. 1627/8 were printed together, *se-tenant*, in horizontal and vertical pairs throughout the sheet.

558 *Animalia* (Graeme Base)   **559** American Bald Eagle, Kangaroo and Olympic Flame

(Des Pendulum Design. Litho SNP Cambec)

1996 (4 July). *50th Anniv of Children's Book Council Awards.* T **558** and *similar horiz designs taken from book covers.*

(a) *Phosphorised paper.* P 14×14½

1630	45 c. Type **558**		60	60
	a. Block of 4. Nos. 1630/3		2·25	
1631	45 c. *Greetings from Sandy Beach* (Bob Graham)		60	60
1632	45 c. *Who Sank the Boat?* (Pamela Allen)		60	60
1633	45 c. *John Brown, Rose and the Midnight Cat* (Jenny Wagner, illustrated by Ron Brooks)		60	60
1630/3		Set of 4	2·25	2·25

(b) *Self-adhesive. Phosphor frame.* P 11½

1634	45 c. Type **558**		60	70
	a. Booklet pane. Nos. 1634×4 and 1635/7, each × 2		5·50	
1635	45 c. *Greetings from Sandy Beach* (Bob Graham)		60	70
1636	45 c. *Who Sank the Boat?* (Pamela Allen)		60	70
1637	45 c. *John Brown, Rose and the Midnight Cat* (Jenny Wagner, illustrated by Ron Brooks)		60	70
1634/7		Set of 4	2·25	2·50

Nos. 1630/3 were printed together, *se-tenant*, in sheets of 50 (2 panes of 25 5×5) providing ten blocks of 4 and ten single stamps.

Nos. 1634/7 occur either in rolls of 100, on which the surplus self-adhesive paper around each stamp was removed, or in $4.50 booklets, containing No. 1634a, on which the surplus paper was retained.

The phosphor on both rolls and booklets shows pink under U.V. light.

(Des C. Ellett. Litho SNP Cambec (gold die-stamped Avon Graphics))

1996 (22 July). *Passing of Olympic Flag to Sydney.* P 14×14½.

1638	**559** 45 c. multicoloured	..	55	50

560 Margaret Windeyer   **561** Pearl

(Des Mad House Design. Litho Canberra Press)

1996 (8 Aug). *Centenary of the National Council of Women.* T **560** and *similar vert design.* P 14½×14.

1639	45 c. deep reddish purple and lemon		50	50
1640	$1 blue and lemon		1·25	1·25

Design:—$1 Rose Scott.

(Des Janet Boschen. Litho SNP Cambec (exelgram (45c.) and hologram ($1.20) Avon Graphics))

1996 (5 Sept). *Pearls and Diamonds. T 561 and similar horiz designs. Multicoloured. P 14½×14.*
1641	45 c. Type 561		60	50
1642	$1.20, Diamond		1·40	1·50

The pearl on the 45 c. is shown as an exelgram (holographic printing on ultra thin plastic film) and the diamond on the $1.20 as a hologram, each embossed on to the stamp.

562 Silhouettes of Female Dancer and Musician on Rural Landscape

563 Ginger Cats

(Des A. Ashton. Litho McPherson's Ptg Group, Mulgrave)

1996 (12 Sept). *50th Anniv of Arts Councils. T 562 and similar horiz design. Multicoloured. P 14×imperf.*
1643	20 c. Type 562		60	1·00
	a. Booklet pane. Nos. 1643 and 1644×4		2·00	
1644	45 c. Silhouettes of musician and male dancer on landscape		35	40

Nos. 1643/4 only exist from $2 stamp booklets in which the vertical edges of the pane are imperforate.

(Des Dianne Cooke. Litho SNP Cambec)

1996 (1 Oct). *Australian Pets. T 563 and similar multicoloured designs. (a) Phosphorised paper. P 14×14½ (Nos. 1647, 1650) or 14½×14 (others).*
1645	45 c. Type 563		60	60
	a. Pair. Nos. 1645/6		1·10	1·10
1646	45 c. Blue Heeler dogs		60	60
1647	45 c. Cockatoo (30×25 mm)		60	60
1648	45 c. Duck with ducklings (25×30 mm)		60	60
	a. Horiz pair. Nos. 1648/9		1·10	1·10
1649	45 c. Dog and cat (25×30 mm)		60	60
1650	45 c. Ponies (30×50 mm)		60	60
1645/50		Set of 6	3·25	3·50
MS1651	166×73 mm. Nos. 1645/50. P 14½		3·25	3·50

(b) Self-adhesive. Phosphor band. P 11½
1652	45 c. Type 563		60	75
	a. Booklet pane. Nos. 1652×4 and 1653×6		5·50	
1653	45 c. Blue Heeler dogs		60	75

Nos. 1645/6 and 1648/9 were each printed together, se-tenant, either in vertical and horizontal pairs (Nos. 1645/6) or in horizontal pairs (Nos. 1648/9) throughout the sheets.

Nos. 1652/3 were printed either in rolls of 100 on which the surplus self-adhesive paper around each stamp was removed, or in $4.50 booklets containing No. 1652a, on which the surplus paper was retained.

The phosphor on both rolls and booklets shows orange-pink under U. V. light and appears as a bar at the top and on the cats for No. 1652 and as an L-shaped frame for No. 1653.

No. **MS**1651 also exists overprinted with the logos of the ASDA Centrepoint '96 Sydney, St. Peter's Stamp and Coin Fair, 'Melbourne '96", "TAIPEI '96", Queensland Stamp and Coin Expo, Stamp Show '96 Claremont and "HONG KONG '97" for sale at these exhibitions.

564 Ferdinand von Mueller

565 Willem de Vlamingh

(Des J. Sellitto and D. Blyth. Litho State Ptg Wks, Berlin)

1996 (9 Oct). *Australia–Germany Joint Issue. Death Centenary of Ferdinand von Mueller (botanist). P 14.*
1654	564	$1.20, multicoloured		1·25	1·40

(Des A. Donato. Litho McPherson's Ptg Group, Mulgrave)

1996 (1 Nov). *300th Anniv of the Visit of Willem de Vlamingh to Western Australia. P 14×14½.*
1655	565	45 c. multicoloured		75	75
	a. Horiz pair. No. 1655 and No. 433 of Christmas Island		1·50	1·50

No. 1655 and No. 433 of Christmas Island were printed together, se-tenant, in horizontal pairs throughout the sheet.

NEW INFORMATION

The editor is always interested to correspond with people who have new information that will improve or correct the Catalogue.

566 Madonna and Child

567 "Landscape '74" (Fred Williams)

(Des Vivienne Goodman. Litho SNP Cambec)

1996 (1 Nov). *Christmas. T 566 and similar vert designs. Multicoloured. (a) Phosphorised paper. P 14½×14.*
1656	40 c. Type 566		55	45
1657	45 c. Wise man with gift		55	50
1658	$1 Shepherd boy with lamb		1·25	1·40
1656/8		Set of 3	2·10	2·10

(b) Self-adhesive. Phosphor on inscr panel and central figures. P 11½
1659	40 c. Type 566		50	45
	a. Booklet pane. No. 1659×20		9·00	

No. 1659 on which the phosphor shows pink under U. V. light was only issued in $8 booklets, on which the surplus self-adhesive paper was retained.

(Des Karina Weston. Litho McPherson's Ptg Group, Mulgrave)

1997 (16 Jan). *Australia Day. Contemporary Paintings. T 567 and similar horiz designs. Multicoloured. P 14½×14.*
1660	85 c. Type 567		1·10	1·10
1661	90 c. "The Balcony 2" (Brett Whiteley)		1·10	1·10
1662	$1.20, "Fire Haze at Gerringong" (Lloyd Rees)		1·40	1·40
1660/2		Set of 3	3·25	3·25

568 Sir Donald Bradman

569 Red Roses

(Des Sophie Byass. Litho SNP Cambec)

1997 (23 Jan). *Australian Legends (1st series). Sir Donald Bradman (cricketer). T 568 and similar square design. Multicoloured. P 14½.*
1663	45 c. Type 568		55	55
	a. Horiz pair. Nos. 1663/4		1·10	1·10
1664	45 c. Bradman playing stroke		55	55

Nos. 1663/4 were printed together, se-tenant, in horizontal pairs throughout the sheet of 10.

See also Nos. 1731/54 and 1838/41.

(Des Kate Linton. Litho SNP Cambec)

1997 (29 Jan). *St. Valentine's Day. (a) Phosphorized paper. P 14½×14.*
1665	569	45 c. multicoloured		50	50

(b) Self-adhesive. Phosphor on inscr panel and background. P 11½
1666	569	45 c. multicoloured		70	75
	a. Booklet pane. No. 1666×10		6·00	

No. 1666, on which the phosphor shows pink under U. V. light, was only issued in $4.50 booklets on which the surplus self-adhesive paper was retained.

570 Ford Coupe Utility, 1934

571 May Wirth and Horse

(Des Sandra Harmon. Litho SNP Cambec)

1997 (27 Feb). *Classic Cars. T 570 and similar horiz designs. Multicoloured. (a) Phosphorised paper. P 14×14½.*
1667	45 c. Type 570		60	60
	a. Block of 4. Nos. 1667/70		2·25	
	b. Booklet pane. No. 1667×4 with margins all round		2·25	
1668	45 c. GMH Holden 48-215 (FX), 1948		60	60
	a. Booklet pane. No. 1668×4 with margins all round		2·25	
1669	45 c. Austin Lancer, 1958		60	60
	a. Booklet pane. No. 1669×4 with margins all round		2·25	
1670	45 c. Chrysler Valiant "R" Series, 1962		60	60
	a. Booklet pane. No. 1670×4 with margins all round		2·25	
1667/70		Set of 4	2·25	2·25

(b) Self-adhesive. Designs 32½×21 mm. Phosphor frames. P 11½
1671	45 c. Type 570		65	65
	a. Booklet pane. Nos. 1671, 1673 each × 2 and 1672, 1674 each × 3		5·00	
1672	45 c. GMH Holden 48-215 (FX), 1948		65	65
1673	45 c. Austin Lancer, 1958		65	65
1674	45 c. Chrysler Valiant "R" Series, 1962		65	65
1671/4			2·40	2·40

Nos. 1667/70 were printed together, se-tenant, in sheets of 50 (2 panes 5×5), each sheet providing ten blocks of 4 and ten single stamps.

Nos. 1671/4 occur either in rolls of 100, on which the surplus self-adhesive paper was removed, or in $4.50 booklets, containing No. 1671a, on which the surplus paper was retained. The phosphor on both rolls and booklets shows pink under U. V. light.

(Des Cathleen Bryant. Litho McPherson's Ptg Group, Mulgrave)

1997 (13 Mar). *150th Anniv of the Circus in Australia. T 571 and similar vert designs. Multicoloured. P 14½×14.*
1675	45 c. Type 571		55	55
	a. Block of 4. Nos. 1675/8		2·00	
1676	45 c. Con Colleano on tightrope		55	55
1677	45 c. Clowns		55	55
1678	45 c. Acrobats		55	55
1675/8		Set of 4	2·00	2·00

Nos. 1675/8 were printed together, se-tenant, in sheets of 50 (2 panes of 5×5), each sheet providing ten blocks of 4 and ten single stamps.

(Des Rankin Bevers Design)

1997 (10 Apr)–**98**. *Fauna and Flora (2nd series). Kakadu Wetlands, Northern Territory. Multicoloured designs as T 556.*

(a) Litho SNP Cambec (gold on $10 die-stamped Avon Graphics). Phosphorised paper. P 14½×14 ($10) or 14×14½ (others)
1679	20 c. Saltwater Crocodile		15	20
1680	25 c. Northern Dwarf Tree Frog		20	25
1681	45 c. Comb-crested Jacana (2.6.97)		35	40
	a. Block of 4. Nos. 1681/4		1·40	
1682	45 c. Little Kingfisher (2.6.97)		35	40
1683	45 c. Brolga (2.6.97)		35	40
1684	45 c. Black-necked Stork ("Jabiru") (2.6.97)		35	40
1685	$1 Cressida cressida (butterfly)		80	85
1686	$10 Kakadu Wetlands (50×30 mm)		8·75	9·00
1679/86		Set of 8	11·00	11·75
MS1686a	106×70 mm. No. 1686		10·50	10·50

Nos. 1681/4 were printed together, se-tenant, in sheets of 50 providing ten blocks of 4 and ten single stamps.

Supplies of No. 1685 printed at "Australia '99" showed the exhibition logo on the margin.

No. **MS**1686a was issued in connection with the "Australia 99" International Stamp Exhibition. It also exists overprinted with either the "Pacific '97" (San Francisco) or "Italia '98" (Milan) logos for sale at these international stamp exhibitions.

A further miniature sheet containing Nos. 1683/4 was sold at the "International Stamp and Coin Exposition Shanghai 97" and from philatelic outlets.

(b) Self-adhesive. Litho SNP Cambec (Nos. 1687/90) or Pemara (Nos. 1688/90). Phosphor frame. P 11½
1687	45 c. Comb-crested Jacana (2.6.97)		45	45
	a. Booklet pane. Nos. 1687 and 1689 each × 3, and Nos. 1688 and 1690, each × 2		4·50	
	b. Sheetlet. Nos. 1687×2 and 1688/90		2·00	
	c. Booklet pane. Nos. 1687/90, each × 5 (1.9.98)		20·00	
	d. Perf 12½×13 (13.11.97)		1·10	1·25
1688	45 c. Little Kingfisher (2.6.97)		45	45
	d. Perf 12½×13 (13.11.97)		1·10	1·25
1689	45 c. Brolga (2.6.97)		45	45
	d. Perf 12½×13 (13.11.97)		1·10	1·25
1690	45 c. Black-necked Stork (2.6.97)		45	45
	d. Perf 12½×13 (13.11.97)		1·10	1·25
1687/90		Set of 4	1·60	1·60

Nos. 1687/90 and 1687d/90d were printed in rolls of 100 or 200 (Nos. 1687/90 only) with the surplus paper around each stamp removed. Nos. 1687/90 also come in $4.50 and $9 booklets, and also sheetlets of 5, all of which have the surplus paper in place.

The phosphor shows orange-pink under U.V. light and appears as a broken frame around each stamp.

572 Royal Wedding 1d. Stamp of 1947

573 Hand holding Globe and Lions Emblem

(Des Cozzolino Ellett. Recess Note Ptg Branch, Reserve Bank of Australia)

1997 (17 Apr). *Queen Elizabeth II's Birthday. P 14×14½.*
1691	572	45 c. blackish purple		50	50

(Des Cozzolino Ellett. Recess Note Ptg Branch, Reserve Bank of Australia)

1997 (17 Apr). *50th Anniv of First Australian Lions Club. P 14½×14.*
1692	573	45 c. brt blue, chestnut & blackish pur		50	50

574 Doll holding
Teddy Bear (Kaye
Wiggs)

575 Police Rescue
Helicopter

(Des Cathleen Bryant. Litho McPherson's Ptg Group,
Mulgrave)

1997 (8 May). *Dolls and Teddy Bears.* T **574** *and similar vert
designs. Multicoloured.* P 14½×14.

1693	45 c. Type 574	45	50
	a. Horiz strip of 5. Nos. 1693/7	2·00	
1694	45 c. Teddy bear standing (Jennifer Laing)	45	50
1695	45 c. Doll wearing white dress with teddy bear (Susie McMahon)	45	50
1696	45 c. Doll in brown dress and bonnet (Lynda Jacobson)	45	50
1697	45 c. Teddy bear sitting (Helen Williams)	45	50
1693/7	*Set of 5*	2·00	2·25

Nos. 1693/7 were printed together in sheets of 10, containing
two *se-tenant* strips of 5. Sheets exist overprinted for the 1997
Brisbane Stamp and Coin Expo.

(Des B. Sadgrove. Litho McPherson's Ptg Group, Mulgrave)

1997 (10 July). *Emergency Services.* T **575** *and similar horiz
designs. Multicoloured.* P 14×14½.

1698	45 c. Type 575	45	50
	a. Horiz pair. Nos. 1698/9	90	1·00
1699	45 c. Emergency Service volunteers carrying victim	45	50
1700	$1.05, Fire service at fire	1·25	1·25
1701	$1.20, Loading casualty into ambulance	1·25	1·25
1698/1701	*Set of 4*	3·00	3·25

Nos. 1698/9 were printed together, *se-tenant*, in horizontal
pairs throughout the sheet.

Numbered gutter strips of ten of No. 1701, overprinted
"Emergency Services", come from a limited issue portfolio.

576 George Peppin Jnr
(breeder) and Merino
Sheep

577 Dumbi the Owl

(Des C. Shurey. Litho SNP Cambec)

1997 (7 Aug). *Bicentenary of Arrival of Merino Sheep in
Australia.* T **576** *and similar horiz design. Multicoloured.*
P 14×14½.

1702	45 c. Type 576	55	65
	a. Horiz pair. Nos. 1702/3	1·10	1·25
1703	45 c. Pepe chair, cloth and wool logo	55	65

Nos. 1702/3 were printed together, *se-tenant*, as horizontal
pairs in sheets of 10.

(Des Melinda Coombes. Litho SNP Cambec)

1997 (21 Aug). *"The Dreaming". Cartoons from Aboriginal
Stories.* T **577** *and similar square designs. Multicoloured.*
P 14½.

1704	45 c. Type 577	50	45
1705	$1 The Two Willy-Willies	1·00	95
1706	$1.20, How Brolga became a Bird	1·10	1·40
1707	$1.80, Tuggan-Tuggan	1·60	1·60
1704/7	*Set of 4*	3·75	4·00

578 *Rhoetosaurus
brownei*

579 Spotted-tailed
Quoll

(Des P. Schouten. Litho SNP Cambec)

1997 (4 Sept). *Prehistoric Animals.* T **578** *and similar vert
designs. Multicoloured.* P 14½×14.

1708	45 c. Type 578	45	50
	a. Horiz strip of 5. Nos. 1708/12	2·00	
1709	45 c. *Mcnamaraspis kaprios*	45	50
1710	45 c. *Ninjemys oweni*	45	50
1711	45 c. *Paracylotosaurus davidi*	45	50
1712	45 c. *Woolungasaurus glendowerensis*	45	50
1708/12	*Set of 5*	2·00	2·25

Nos. 1708/12 were printed together, *se-tenant*, as horizontal
strips of five in sheets of 10.

(Des P. Gouldthorpe. Litho SNP Cambec)

1997 (1 Oct). *Nocturnal Animals.* T **579** *and similar
multicoloured designs.*

(a) Phosphorised paper. P 14×14½ (Nos. 1715/17) or 14½×14
(others)

1713	45 c. Type 579	50	50
	a. Pair. Nos. 1713/14	1·00	1·00
1714	45 c. Barking Owl	50	50
1715	45 c. Platypus (30×25 mm)	50	50
	a. Horiz strip of 3. Nos. 1715/17	1·40	
1716	45 c. Brown Antechinus (30×25 mm)	50	50
1717	45 c. Dingo (30×25 mm)	50	50
1718	45 c. Yellow-bellied Glider (50×30 mm)	50	50
1713/18	*Set of 6*	2·75	2·75
MS1719	166×73 mm. Nos. 1713/18. P 14½	2·75	2·75

(b) Self-adhesive. Phosphor frame. P 11½

1720	45 c. Type 579 (25×32 mm)	55	65
	a. Vert pair. Nos. 1720/1	1·10	
	b. Booklet pane. Nos. 1720/1, each ×5	5·00	
1721	45 c. Barking Owl (25×32 mm)	55	65

Nos. 1713/14 were printed together, *se-tenant*, in horizontal or
vertical pairs and Nos. 1715/17 in horizontal strips of three
throughout the sheets.

No. **MS**1719 shows a spider and web printed in green
phosphor, visible under U.V. light, across much of the sheet.

Nos. 1720/1, on which the phosphor frame appears pink under
U.V. light, were printed either in rolls of 100 on which the
surplus self-adhesive paper around each stamp was removed or
in $4.50 booklets containing No. 1720b on which the surplus
paper was retained.

580 Woman

581 Two Angels

(Des Lynda Warner. Litho SNP Cambec)

1997 (27 Oct). *Breast Cancer Awareness Campaign.*
P 14×14½.

1722	**580** 45 c. multicoloured	40	45

(Des Cathleen Bryant. Litho SNP Cambec)

1997 (3 Nov). *Christmas. Children's Nativity Play.* T **581** *and
similar horiz designs. Multicoloured.*

(a) Phosphorised paper. P 14×14½

1723	40 c. Type 581	40	40
1724	45 c. Mary	45	45
1725	$1 Three Kings	90	1·10
1723/5	*Set of 3*	1·60	1·75

(b) Self-adhesive. Phosphor frame at right and foot. P 11½

1726	40 c. Type 581	35	40
	a. Booklet pane. No. 1726×20	7·00	

No. 1726, on which the phosphor shows pink under U.V. light,
was only issued in $8 booklets on which the surplus self-
adhesive paper was retained.

582 "*Flying Cloud*"
(clipper) (J. Scott)

583 Betty Cuthbert
(1956)

(Des B. Sadgrove. Litho McPherson's Ptg Group, Mulgrave)

1998 (15 Jan). *Ship Paintings.* T **582** *and similar square
designs. Multicoloured.* P 14½×14.

1727	45 c. Type 582	50	45
1728	85 c. "*Marco Polo*" (full-rigged ship) (T. Robertson)	85	90
1729	$1 "*Chusan I*" (steamship) (C. Gregory)	1·00	1·10
1730	$1.20, "*Heather Belle*" (clipper)	1·25	1·40
1727/30	*Set of 4*	3·25	3·50

No. 1727 was reissued on 17 June 1998 in sheets of 10 (2×5)
with inscribed margins publicising "Australia 99" International
Stamp Exhibition, Melbourne.

(Des Sophie Byass. Litho SNP Cambec)

1998 (21 Jan). *Australian Legends (2nd series).* Olympic Gold
Medal Winners. T **583** *and similar horiz designs.*

(a) Phosphorised paper. P 14×14½.

1731	45 c. Type 583	45	50
	a. Sheetlet. Nos. 1731/42	4·75	
1732	45 c. Betty Cuthbert running	45	50
1733	45 c. Herb Elliot (1960)	45	50
1734	45 c. Herb Elliot running	45	50
1735	45 c. Dawn Fraser (1956, 1960 and 1964)	45	50
1736	45 c. Dawn Fraser swimming	45	50
1737	45 c. Marjorie Jackson (1952)	45	50
1738	45 c. Marjorie Jackson running	45	50
1739	45 c. Murray Rose (1956)	45	50
1740	45 c. Murray Rose swimming	45	50
1741	45 c. Shirley Strickland (1952 and 1956)	45	50
1742	45 c. Shirley Strickland hurdling	45	50
1731/42	*Set of 12*	4·75	5·50

(b) Self-adhesive. Two vertical phosphor bands. P 11½

1743	45 c. Type 583	55	60
	b. Booklet pane. Nos. 1743/54	6·00	
1744	45 c. Betty Cuthbert running	55	60
1745	45 c. Herb Elliot	55	60
1746	45 c. Herb Elliot running	55	60
1747	45 c. Dawn Fraser	55	60
1748	45 c. Dawn Fraser swimming	55	60
1749	45 c. Marjorie Jackson	55	60
1750	45 c. Marjorie Jackson running	55	60
1751	45 c. Murray Rose	55	60
1752	45 c. Murray Rose swimming	55	60
1753	45 c. Shirley Strickland	55	60
1754	45 c. Shirley Strickland hurdling	55	60
1743/54	*Set of 12*	6·00	6·50

Nos. 1731/42 were printed together, *se-tenant*, in sheetlets of
12.

Nos. 1743/54, on which the phosphor bands appear pink under
U.V. light, were printed in $5.40 stamp booklets containing No.
1743b on which the surplus paper around each stamp was
retained.

584 Champagne Rose

585 Queen Elizabeth II

(Des Cathleen Bryant. Litho SNP Cambec)

1998 (12 Feb). *Greetings Stamp.* (a) P 14½×14.

1755	**584** 45 c. multicoloured	40	45

(b) Self-adhesive. Phosphor band. P 11½

1756	**584** 45 c. multicoloured	50	45
	a. Booklet pane. No. 1756×10	4·50	

No. 1756 was only issued in $4.50 booklets on which the
surplus self-adhesive paper was retained.

The phosphor, which shows pink under U.V. light, covers
most of the row of roses to the left of the design.

(Des Hannah Richardson. Litho McPherson's Ptg Group,
Mulgrave)

1998 (9 Apr). *Queen Elizabeth II's Birthday.* P 14×14½.

1757	**585** 45 c. multicoloured	40	45

586 Sea Hawk (helicopter)
landing on Frigate

587 Sheep Shearer and
Sheep

(Des Sandra Harman. Litho McPherson's Ptg Group, Mulgrave)

1998 (9 Apr). *50th Anniv of Royal Australian Navy Fleet Air
Arm.* P 14×14½.

1758	**586** 45 c. multicoloured	40	40

(Des C. Shurey. Litho SNP Cambec)

1998 (21 Apr). *Farming.* T **587** *and similar horiz designs.
Multicoloured.* (a) *Phosphorised paper.* P 14×14½.

1759	45 c. Type 587	45	45
	a. Horiz strip of 5. Nos. 1759/63	2·10	
1760	45 c. Barley and silo	45	45
1761	45 c. Farmers herding beef cattle	45	45
1762	45 c. Sugar cane harvesting	45	45
1763	45 c. Two dairy cows	45	45
1759/63	*Set of 5*	2·10	2·10

(b) Self-adhesive. Phosphor band. P 11½.

1764	45 c. Type 587	80	80
	a. Booklet pane. Nos. 1764/8, each × 2	7·00	
1765	45 c. Barley and silo	80	80
1766	45 c. Farmers herding beef cattle	80	80
1767	45 c. Sugar cane harvesting	80	80
1768	45 c. Two dairy cows	80	80
1764/8	*Set of 5*	3·50	3·50

Nos. 1759/63 were printed together, *se-tenant*, in horizontal
strips of 5 throughout the sheet.

On Nos. 1764/8 the phosphor, which shows pink under U. V.
light, appears as a horizontal band at the top with an irregular
extension to the foot of each design. They were printed in $4.50,
stamp booklets containing No. 1764a on which the surplus
paper around each stamp was retained.

588 Cardiograph Trace
and Heart

589 Johnny O'Keefe ("The
Wild One", 1958)

(Des Lynda Warner. Litho SNP Cambec)

1998 (4 May). *Heart Disease Awareness.* P 14×14½.

1769	**588** 45 c. multicoloured	40	45

(Des Cozzolino Ellett. Litho SNP Cambec)

1998 (26 May). *Australian Rock and Roll.* T **589** *and similar horiz designs. Multicoloured.* (a) *Phosphorised paper.* P 14×14½.

1770	45 c. Type **589**	..	45	45
	a. Sheetlet. Nos. 1770/81		4·75	
1771	45 c. Col Joye ("Oh Yeah Uh Huh", 1959)		45	45
1772	45 c. Little Pattie ("He's My Blonde Headed Stompie Wompie Real Gone Surfer Boy", 1963)	..	45	45
1773	45 c. Normie Rowe ("Shakin all Over", 1965)		45	45
1774	45 c. Easybeats ("She's so Fine", 1965)		45	45
1775	45 c. Russell Morris ("The Real Thing", 1969)		45	45
1776	45 c. Masters Apprentices ("Turn Up Your Radio", 1970)		45	45
1777	45 c. Daddy Cool ("Eagle Rock", 1971)		45	45
1778	45 c. Billy Thorpe and the Aztecs ("Most People I know think I'm Crazy", 1972)		45	45
1779	45 c. Skyhooks ("Horror Movie", 1974)		45	45
1780	45 c. AC/DC ("It's a Long Way to the Top", 1975)		45	45
1781	45 c. Sherbet ("Howzat", 1976)		45	45
1770/81		*Set of 12*	4·75	4·75

(b) *Self-adhesive. One side phosphor band.* P 11½.

1782	45 c. Sherbet ("Howzat", 1976)		45	50
	a. Horiz strip of 12. Nos. 1782/93		4·75	
1783	45 c. AC/DC ("It's a Long Way to the Top", 1975)		45	50
1784	45 c. Skyhooks ("Horror Movie", 1974)		45	50
1785	45 c. Billy Thorpe and the Aztecs ("Most People I Know Think I'm Crazy", 1972)		45	50
1786	45 c. Daddy Cool ("Eagle Rock", 1971)		45	50
1787	45 c. The Masters Apprentices ("Turn Up Your Radio", 1970)		45	50
1788	45 c. Russell Morris ("The Real Thing", 1969)		45	50
1789	45 c. Easybeats ("She's so Fine", 1965)		45	50
1790	45 c. Normie Rowe ("Shakin all Over", 1965)		45	50
1791	45 c. Little Pattie ("He's My Blonde Headed Stompie Wompie Real Gone Surfer Boy", 1963)		45	50
1792	45 c. Col Joye ("Oh Yeah Uh Huh", 1959)		45	50
1793	45 c. Type **589**		45	50
1782/93		*Set of 12*	4·75	5·50

Nos. 1770/81 were printed together, *se-tenant*, in sheetlets of 12.

Nos. 1782/93, on which the phosphor appears pale purple under U.V. light, shows the band alternating at left or right. They were issued in rolls of 100 on which the surplus paper around each stamp was removed.

590	Helmeted Honeyeater (Yellow-tufted Honeyeater subspecies)	**591** French Horn and Cello Players

(Des K. Stead and Melinda Coombes. Litho McPherson's Ptg Group, Mulgrave)

1998 (25 June). *Endangered Species. Birds.* T **590** *and similar horiz designs. Multicoloured. Ordinary paper (Nos. 1794/5).* P 14×14½.

1794	5 c. Type **590**	..	20	20
	a. Horiz pair. Nos. 1794/5		40	40
1795	5 c. Orange-bellied Parrot		20	20
1796	45 c. Red-tailed Black-Cockatoo		45	45
	a. Horiz pair. Nos. 1796/7		90	90
1797	45 c. Gouldian Finch		45	45
1794/7		*Set of 4*	1·25	1·25

Nos. 1794/5 and 1796/7 were each printed together, *se-tenant*, in horizontal pairs throughout the sheets.

(Des Michelle Gauci. Litho SNP Cambec)

1998 (16 July). *Youth Arts, Australia.* T **591** *and similar horiz design. Multicoloured.* P 14×14½.

1798	45 c. Type **591**		50	50
	a. Horiz pair. Nos. 1798/9		1·00	1·00
1799	45 c. Dancers		50	50

Nos. 1798/9 were printed together, *se-tenant*, in horizontal pairs throughout the sheet.

SNP AUSPRINT. SNP Cambee was renamed SNP Ausprint on 1 August 1998

592	*Phalaenopsis rosenstromii*	**593** Flying Angel with Teapot (cartoon by Michael Leunig)

(Des Clare Kaegi and Cathleen Cram. Litho SNP Ausprint)

1998 (6 Aug). *Australia–Singapore Joint Issue. Orchids.* T **592** *and similar vert designs. Multicoloured.* P 14½×14.

1800	45 c. Type **592**		55	40
1801	85 c. *Arundina graminifolia*		1·00	1·00
1802	$1 *Grammatophyllum speciosum*		1·25	1·25
1803	$1.20, *Dendrobium phalaenopsis*		1·50	1·60
1800/3		*Set of 4*	3·75	3·75
MS1804	138×72 mm. Nos. 1800/3	..	3·75	3·75

(Des Sandra Harman. Litho SNP Ausprint)

1998 (13 Aug). *"The Teapot of Truth" (cartoons by Michael Leunig).* T **593** *and similar horiz designs. Multicoloured.* P 14×14½.

1805	45 c. Type **593**		50	55
	a. Booklet pane. No. 1805×4 with margins all round		1·75	
1806	45 c. Two birds in heart-shaped tree		50	55
	a. Booklet pane. No. 1806×4 with margins all round		1·75	
1807	45 c Pouring tea		50	55
	a. Booklet pane. No. 1807×4 with margins all round		1·75	
1808	$1 Mother and child (29×24 *mm*)		1·10	1·25
	a. Booklet pane. No. 1808×2 with margins all round		2·00	
1809	$1.20, Cat with smiling face (29×24 *mm*)		1·10	1·25
	a. Booklet pane. No. 1809×2 and stamp-size label with margins all round		2·00	
1805/9		*Set of 5*	3·25	3·75

Nos. 1805/9 were only issued in $9.95 stamp booklets.

594 Red Lacewing		**595** Flinders' Telescope and Map of Tasmania

(Des C. Shurey. Litho SNP Ausprint)

1998 (3 Sept). *Butterflies.* T **594** *and similar vert designs. Multicoloured. Phosphorised paper.* (a) P 14½×14

1810	45 c. Type **594**		45	45
	a. Horiz strip of 5. Nos. 1810/14		2·00	
1811	45 c. Dull Oakblue		45	45
1812	45 c. Meadow Argus		45	45
1813	45 c. Ulysses Butterfly		45	45
1814	45 c. Common Red-eye		45	45
1810/14		*Set of 5*	2·00	2·00

(b) *Self-adhesive.* P 11½.

1815	45 c. Type **594**		45	50
	a. Vert strip of 5. Nos. 1815/19		2·00	
1816	45 c. Dull Oakblue		45	50
1817	45 c. Meadow Argus		45	50
1818	45 c. Ulysses Butterfly		45	50
1819	45 c. Common Red-eye		45	50
1815/19		*Set of 5*	2·00	2·25

Nos. 1810/14 were printed together, *se-tenant*, as horizontal strips of five in sheets of 10.

Nos. 1815/19 come, *se-tenant*, in strips of 5 or rolls of 100 with the surplus self-adhesive paper around each stamp removed.

A miniature sheet containing Nos. 1810/14 was sold at "China '99" International Stamp Exhibition, Beijing, and from philatelic outlets.

(Des Lynda Warner. Litho McPherson's Ptg Group, Mulgrave)

1998 (10 Sept). *Bicentenary of the Circumnavigation of Tasmania by George Bass and Matthew Flinders.* T **595** *and similar vert design. Multicoloured.* P 14½×14.

1820	45 c. Type **595**		50	50
	a. Vert pair. Nos. 1820/1		1·00	1·00
1821	45 c. Sextant and letter from Bass		50	50

Nos. 1820/1 were printed together, *se-tenant*, in vertical pairs throughout the sheet.

596 Weedy Seadragon		**597** Rose of Freedom

(Des W. Rankin. Litho SNP Ausprint)

1998 (1 Oct). *International Year of the Ocean.* T **596** *and similar multicoloured designs.*

(a) *Phosphorised paper.* P 14×14½ (*Nos. 1825/6*) or 14½×14 (*others*)

1822	45 c. Type **596**		50	55
	a. Horiz pair. Nos. 1822/3		1·00	1·10
1823	45 c. Bottlenose Dolphin		50	55
1824	45 c. Fiery Squid (24×29 *mm*)		50	55
1825	45 c. Manta Ray (29×24 *mm*)		50	55
1826	45 c. White Pointer Shark (29×49 *mm*)		50	55
1827	45 c. Southern Right Whale (49×29 *mm*)		50	55
1822/7		*Set of 6*	2·75	3·00
MS1828	166×73 mm. Nos. 1822/7. P 14½		2·40	2·75

(b) *Self-adhesive. Phosphor frame.* P 11½.

1829	45 c. Type **596** (24×36 *mm*)		35	40
	a. Vert pair. Nos. 1829/30		70	
	b. Booklet pane. Nos. 1829/30, each × 5		3·50	
1830	45 c. Bottlenose Dolphin (24×36 *mm*)		35	40

Nos. 1822/3 were printed together, *se-tenant*, in horizontal or vertical pairs throughout the sheet.

Nos. 1829/30, on which the phosphor frame appears pink under U.V. light, were printed either in rolls of 100 on which the surplus self-adhesive paper around each stamp was removed or in $4.50 booklets containing No. 1829b on which the surplus paper was retained.

(Des Lynda Warner. Litho SNP Ausprint)

1998 (22 Oct). *50th Anniv of Universal Declaration of Human Rights.* P 14½×14.

1831	**597**	45 c. multicoloured	40	40

598 Three Kings

(Des Sophie Byass and K. Done. Litho SNP Ausprint)

1998 (2 Nov). *Christmas.* T **598** *and similar horiz designs. Multicoloured.* (a) *Phosphorised paper.* P 14×14½.

1832	40 c. Type **598**		40	35
1833	45 c. Nativity scene		40	40
1834	$1 Mary and Joseph		1·10	1·25
1832/4		*Set of 3*	1·75	1·75

(b) *Self-adhesive. Phosphor frame.* P 11½

1835	40 c. Type **598**		40	40
	a. Booklet pane. No. 1835×20		7·00	

On Nos. 1832/4 the yellow parts of the designs are printed in fluorescent ink.

No. 1835 was only issued in $8 booklets on which the surplus self-adhesive paper was retained.

599 Australian Coat of Arms		**600** Arthur Boyd

(Des B. Sadgrove. Litho SNP Ausprint)

1999 (14 Jan). *50th Anniv of Australian Citizenship.*

(a) *Phosphorised paper.* P 14×14½.

1836	**599**	45 c. multicoloured	40	40

(b) *Self-adhesive. Phosphor frame around central oval.* P 11½

1837	**599**	45 c. multicoloured	40	40

No. 1837, on which the phosphor shows pink under U.V. light, was printed in rolls of 100 on which the surplus self-adhesive paper around each stamp was removed.

(Des Lisa Christensen. Litho SNP Ausprint)

1999 (22 Jan). *Australian Legends (3rd series). Arthur Boyd (painter).* T **600** *and similar horiz design. Multicoloured.*

(a) *Phosphorised paper.* P 14×14½

1838	45 c. Type **600**		40	40
	a. Horiz pair. Nos. 1838/9		80	80
1839	45 c. "Neubuchadnezzer on fire falling over Waterfall" (Arthur Boyd)		40	40

(b) *Self-adhesive. Two phosphor bands over inscr panels.* P 11½

1840	45 c. Type **600**		40	40
	a. Booklet pane. Nos. 1840/1, each × 5		3·75	
1841	45 c. "Nebuchadnezzer on fire falling over Waterfall" (Arthur Boyd)		40	40

Nos. 1838/9 were printed together, *se-tenant*, in horizontal pairs throughout the sheet.

Nos. 1840/1, on which the phosphor shows pink under U.V. light, were only issued in $4.50 booklets on which the surplus self-adhesive paper was retained.

601 Red Roses		**602** Elderly Man and Grandmother with Boy

(Des Nicole Bryant. Litho SNP Ausprint)

1999 (4 Feb). *Greetings Stamp. Romance.* (a) *Phosphorised paper.* P 14×14½.

1842	**601**	45 c. multicoloured	40	40

(b) *Self-adhesive. Phosphor background.* P 11½.

1843	**601**	45 c. multicoloured	40	40
	a. Booklet pane. No. 1843×10		3·75	

No. 1843, on which the phosphor shows pink under U.V. light, was only issued in $4.50, booklets on which the surplus self-adhesive paper was retained.

(Des Lynda Warner. Litho McPherson's Ptg Group, Mulgrave)

1999 (11 Feb). *International Year of Older Persons.* T **602** *and similar horiz design. Multicoloured.* P 14×14½.

1844	45 c. Type **602**		40	40
	a. Horiz pair. Nos. 1844/5		80	80
1845	45 c. Elderly woman and grandfather with boy		40	40

Nos. 1844/5 were printed together, *se-tenant*, as horizontal pairs in sheets of 10.

603 *Polly Woodside*
(barque)

604 Olympic Torch
and 1956 7½d.
Stamp

(Des Beth McKinlay. Litho SNP Ausprint)

1999 (19 Mar). *Sailing Ships.* T **603** *and similar square designs. Multicoloured. Phosphor background* (45 c.) *or phosphorised paper* (others). P 14½×14.

1846	45 c. Type **603**	50	35
1847	85 c. *Alma Doepel* (topsail schooner)	90	90
1848	$1 *Enterprize* replica (topsail schooner)	1·10	1·10
1849	$1.05, *Lady Nelson* replica (topsail schooner)	1·25	1·40
1846/9	*Set of 4*	3·25	3·25

No. 1846, on which the phosphor appears pink under U.V. light, was printed in sheets with the stamps horizontally *se-tenant* with half stamp-size labels showing the "Australia '99" International Stamp Exhibition emblem. Examples available at the exhibition could be "personalised" by the addition of a portrait photograph in place of the logo on these labels for the cost of $10 per sheet of ten.

No. 1846 exists as half sheets of 10 numbered in red or black from a limited issue Maritime Heritage portfolio.

(Litho SNP Ausprint)

1999 (19 Mar). *Australia—Ireland Joint Issue. Polly Woodside* (*barque*). *Sheet* 137×72 *mm. Multicoloured. Phosphorised paper.* P 14×14½.

MS1850 45 c. Type **603**; 30p. Type **374** of Ireland (*No.* MS1850 *was sold at* $1.25 *in Australia*) . . 1·25 1·40

No. MS1850 includes the "Australia '99" emblem on the sheet margin and was postally valid in Australia to the value of 45 c. The same miniature sheet was also available in Ireland.

(Litho Ashton-Potter Canada)

1999 (19 Mar). *Australia—Canada Joint Issue.* Marco Polo (*emigrant ship*). *Sheet* 160×95 *mm. Multicoloured. Fluorescent frames.* P 13½ (85 c.) *or* 13 (46 c.).

MS1851 85 c. As No. 1728; 46 c. Type **701** of Canada (*No.* MS1851 *was sold at* $1.30 *in Australia*) . . 1·25 1·40

No. MS1851, on which the fluorescent frame appears green under U.V. light, includes the "Australia '99" emblem on the sheet margin and was postally valid in Australia to the value of 85 c. The same miniature sheet was also available in Canada.

(Litho SNP Ausprint)

1999 (19 Mar). *"Australia '99" International Stamp Exhibition, Melbourne.* Two sheets, each 142×76 mm, containing designs as Nos. 398/403, but printed litho and all with face value of 45 c. P 14×14⅓ (No. MS1852a) or 14½×14 (No. MS1852b).

MS1852 (a) 45 c. deep ultramarine (Type **167**); 45 c. grey-olive (Captain Cook); 45 c. purple-brown (Flinders). (b) 45 c. Indian red (Type **168**); 45 c. deep olive-brown (Bass); 45 c. deep reddish purple (King) . . *Set of 2 sheets* 2·50 2·75
c. Imperf . . *Set of 2 sheets* 2·50 2·75

Designs in No. MS1852a are 37×25 mm and those in No. MS1852b 24×29 mm.

The imperforate miniature sheets, No. MS1852c, could be perforated on machinery at the exhibition which also applied an "A99" perfin. Examples showing the perforations inverted, or other perforation varieties, exist from unauthorised use of this machinery.

(Des FHA Image Design. Litho SNP Ausprint)

1999 (22 Mar). *Olympic Torch Commemoration.* P 14½×14.
1853 **604** $1.20, multicoloured . . . . 1·10 1·10

605 *Correa reflexa* (Native
Fuschia)

606 Queen Elizabeth II
with Queen Mother

(Des W. Rankin)

1999 (8 Apr–8 July). *Fauna and Flora* (3rd series). *Coastal Environment.* T **605** *and similar horiz designs. Multicoloured.*

(a) *Litho SNP Ausprint. Phosphorised paper.* P 14×14½

1854	45 c. Type **605**	35	40
	a. Block of 4. Nos. 1854/7	1·40	
1855	45 c. *Hibbertia scandens* (Guinea Flower)	35	40
1856	45 c. *Ipomoea pre-caprae* (Beach Morning Glory)	35	40
1857	45 c. *Wahlenbergia stricta* (Australian Bluebells)	35	40
1858	70 c. Humpback Whales and Zebra Volute shell (29×24 *mm*) (8.7.99)	55	60
1859	90 c. Brahminy Kite and Checkerboard Helmet shell (29×24 *mm*) (8.7.99)	70	75
	a. Horiz pair. Nos. 1859/60	1·40	
1860	90 c. Fraser Island and Chambered Nautilus (29×24 *mm*) (8.7.99)	70	75

1861	$1.05, Loggerhead Turtle and Melon shell (29×24 *mm*) (8.7.99)	80	85
1862	$1.20, White-bellied Sea Eagle and Campbell's Stromb shell (29×24 *mm*) (8.7.99)	90	95
1854/62	*Set of 9*	5·00	5·50

(b) *Self-adhesive. Litho SNP Ausprint* (Nos. 1863/6) *or Pemara* (Nos. 1863c/6c). *Phosphor frame.* P 11½

1863	45 c. Type **605**	35	40
	a. Booklet pane. Nos. 1863 and 1865, each × 3, and Nos. 1864 and 1866, each × 2	3·50	
	b. Sheetlet of 5. Nos. 1858, 1859×2 and 1860/1	1·75	
	c. Perf 12½×13	35	40
	ca. Booklet pane. Nos. 1863c and 1865c, each × 3, and Nos. 1864c and 1866c, each × 2	3·50	
1864	45 c. *Hibbertia scandens* (Guinea Flower)	35	40
	c. Perf 12½×13	35	40
1865	45 c. *Ipomoea pre-caprae* (Beach Morning Glory)	35	40
	c. Perf 12½×13	35	40
1866	45 c. *Wahlenbergia stricta* (Australian Bluebells)	35	40
	c. Perf 12½×13	35	40
1863/6	*Set of 4*	1·40	1·60
1863c/6c	*Set of 4*	1·40	1·60

Nos. 1854/7 were printed together, *se-tenant*, in sheets of 50 containing ten blocks of 4 and ten single stamps.

Nos. 1859/60 were printed together, *se-tenant*, in horizontal pairs throughout the sheet, each pair forming a composite design.

Nos. 1863/6 and 1863c/6c, on which the phosphor appears pink under U.V. light, were printed in rolls of 100 with the surplus paper around each stamp removed. They also come in $4.50 booklets or sheetlets of 5, containing Nos. 1863a/b or 1863ca, on which the surplus paper was retained.

(Des A. Christensen. Litho SNP Ausprint)

1999 (15 Apr). *Queen Elizabeth II's Birthday.* P 14×14½.
1870 **606** 45 c. multicoloured 35 40

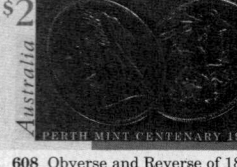

607 *Here's
Humphrey*

608 Obverse and Reverse of 1899
Sovereign

(Des P. Ellett. Litho SNP Ausprint)

1999 (6 May). *Children's Television Programmes.* T **607** *and similar vert designs. Multicoloured.* (a) *Phosphorised paper.* P 14½×14.

1871	45 c. Type **607**	35	40
	a. Horiz strip of 5. Nos. 1871/5	1·75	
1872	45 c. *Bananas in Pyjamas*	35	40
1873	45 c. *Mr. Squiggle*	35	40
1874	45 c. *Play School* (teddy bears)	35	40
1875	45 c. *Play School* (clock, toy dog and doll)	35	40
1871/5	*Set of 5*	1·75	2·00

(b) *Self-adhesive. Phosphor three-sided frame.* P 11½×11

1876	45 c. Type **607**	35	40
	a. Booklet pane. Nos. 1876/80, each × 2	3·50	
1877	45 c. *Bananas in Pyjamas*	35	40
1878	45 c. *Mr. Squiggle*	35	40
1879	45 c. *Play School* (teddy bears)	35	40
1880	45 c. *Play School* (clock, toy dog and doll)	35	40
1876/80	*Set of 5*	1·75	2·00

Nos. 1871/5 were printed together, *se-tenant*, as horizontal strips of 5 in sheets of 10.

Nos. 1876/80, on which the phosphor appears pink under U.V. light, were only available in $4.50 booklets on which the surplus self-adhesive paper was retained.

(Des Janet Boschen. Litho SNP Ausprint (gold embossed Avon Graphics))

1999 (13 May). *Centenary of the Perth Mint.* P 14½×14.
1881 **608** $2 gold, ultramarine and grey-green 1·60 1·75

609 Lineout against
New Zealand

610 Drilling at Burn's
Creek and Rock Bolting
in Tumut 2 Power
Station Hall

(Des M. Sofilas. Litho SNP Ausprint)

1999 (8 June). *Centenary of Australian Test Rugby.* T **609** *and similar multicoloured designs.* (a) *Phosphorised paper.* P 14½×14 (45 c.) *or* 14×14½ (others).

1882	45 c. Type **609**	35	40
	a. Pair. Nos. 1882/3	70	
1883	45 c. Kicking the ball against England	35	40
1884	$1 Try against South Africa (*horiz*)	80	85
1885	$1.20, Passing the ball against Wales (*horiz*)	90	95
1882/5	*Set of 4*	2·40	2·50

(b) *Self-adhesive. Phosphor background.* P 11½

1886	45 c. Type **609**	35	40
	a. Vert pair. Nos. 1886/7	70	
1887	45 c. Kicking the ball against England	35	40

Nos. 1882/3 were printed together, *se-tenant*, in horizontal or vertical pairs throughout the sheet.

Nos. 1886/7, on which the phosphor appears pink under U.V. light, were only available in rolls of 100 on which the surplus paper around each stamp was removed.

(Des Fragile Design. Litho SNP Ausprint)

1999 (12 Aug). *50th Anniv of Snowy Mountain Scheme* (*hydro-electric project*). T **610** *and similar horiz designs. Multicoloured.* (a) *Phosphorised paper.* P 14×14½.

1888	45 c. Type **610**	35	40
	a. Block of 4. Nos. 1888/91	1·40	
1889	45 c. English class for migrant workers, Cooma	35	40
1890	45 c. Tumut 2 Tailwater Tunnel and Eucumbene Dam	35	40
1891	45 c. German carpenters and Island Bend Dam	35	40
1888/91	*Set of 4*	1·40	1·50

(b) *Self-adhesive. Phosphor frame.* P 11½

1892	45 c. Type **610**	35	40
	a. Horiz strip of 4. Nos. 1892/5	1·40	
1893	45 c. English class for migrant workers, Cooma	35	40
1894	45 c. Tumut 2 Tailwater Tunnel and Eucumbene Dam	35	40
1895	45 c. German carpenters and Island Bend Dam	35	40
1892/5	*Set of 4*	1·40	1·50

Nos. 1888/91 were printed together, *se-tenant*, in sheets of 50 (2 panes of 5×5), each sheet providing ten blocks of 4 and ten single stamps.

Nos. 1892/5, on which the phosphor shows pink under U.V. light, were printed in rolls of 100 on which the surplus self-adhesive paper around each stamp was removed.

611 Calligraphy Pen
and Letter

612 Sydney Olympic
Emblem

(Des C. Shurey. Litho SNP Ausprint)

1999 (1 Sept). *Greetings Stamps.* T **611** *and similar square designs. Multicoloured. Phosphorised paper* ($1) *or phosphor background* (others). P 14½×14.

1896	45 c. Type **611**	35	40
1897	45 c. Wedding rings	35	40
1898	45 c. Birthday cake	35	40
1899	45 c. Christmas decoration	35	40
1900	45 c. Teddy bear	35	40
1901	$1 Koala	80	85
1896/1901	*Set of 6*	2·50	2·75

Nos. 1896/1901 were each printed in sheets of 20 stamps and 20 *se-tenant* labels inscribed with greetings messages. Labels measure 23×30 mm (No. 1899), or 16×30 mm (others).

No. 1846 was reissued at the same time in a similar format. This printing differs from previous examples of this stamp by being on phosphorised paper instead of having a phosphor background.

Nos. 1896/1901, together with the new printing of No. 1846, were also available with the inscriptions on the *se-tenant* labels replaced by personal photographs. This service was only available by mail order.

See also No. 1921.

(Des FHA Image Design. Litho McPherson's Ptg Group, Mulgrave)

1999 (14 Sept). *Olympic Games, Sydney* (2000) (1st issue). P 14½×14.
1902 **612** 45 c. multicoloured . . 35 40

613 Australia Post
Symbol, 1975

614 Magnificent
Tree Frog

(Des Lynda Warner. Litho SNP Ausprint)

1999 (16 Sept). *"Sydney Design '99" International Congress and Exhibition.* T **613** *and similar horiz designs. Multicoloured.* P 14×14½.

1903	45 c. Type **613**	35	40
1904	90 c. Embryo chair, 1988	70	75
1905	$1.35, Possum skin textile, c. 1985	1·00	1·10
1906	$1.50, Storey Hall, R.M.I.T. University, 1995	1·10	1·25
1903/6	*Set of 4*	3·00	3·50

(Des Cathleen Cram and K. Stead. Litho SNP Ausprint)

1999 (1 Oct). *National Stamp Collecting Month, Small Pond Life. T **614** and similar multicoloured designs.*

(a) *Phosphorised paper. P* 14×14½ *(Nos. 1909/10) or* 14½×14 *(others)*

1907	45 c. Type **614**	..	..	35	40
	a. Pair. Nos. 1907/8	..	..	70	80
1908	45 c. Sacred Kingfisher	..	..	35	40
1909	45 c. Roth's Tree Frog (29×24 *mm*)			35	40
	a. Pair. Nos. 1909/10	..	..	70	80
1910	45 c. Dragonfly (29×24 *mm*)	..		35	40
1911	50 c. Javelin Frog (24×29 *mm*)	..		40	45
	a. Pair. Nos. 1911/12	..	..	80	90
1912	50 c. Northern Dwarf Tree Frog (24×29 *mm*)..			40	45
1907/12			*Set of* 6	2·20	2·25
MS1913	166×73 mm. Nos. 1907/12. P 14½		..	2·25	2·50

(b) *Self-adhesive. Phosphor background. P* 11½

1914	45 c. Type **614**	..	..	35	40
	a. Pair. Nos. 1914/15	..	..	70	80
1915	45 c. Sacred Kingfisher	..	..	35	40
1916	50 c. Javelin Frog (24×29 *mm*)	..		40	45
	a. Booklet pane. Nos. 1916/17, each ×5			4·00	
1917	50 c. Northern Dwarf Tree Frog (24×29 *mm*)	..	..	40	45
1914/17			*Set of* 4	1·50	1·75

Nos. 1907/8, 1909/10 and 1911/12 were each printed together, *se-tenant*, in horizontal or vertical pairs throughout the sheets.

On No. **MS**1913 the wings of the dragonfly are printed by silver foil die stamping. The miniature sheet also exists overprinted with the "Adelaide Stampex 99" logo for sale at this national exhibition.

Nos. 1914/15 were printed in rolls of 100 on which the surplus self-adhesive paper around each stamp was removed. Nos. 1916/17 were printed in $4.50 booklets containing No. 1916a on which the surplus paper was retained. All four self-adhesive stamps show large parts of the background optd with phosphor which appears pink under U.V. light.

615 Madonna and Child

616 Fireworks amd Hologram

(Des J. Coburn. Litho SNP Ausprint)

1999 (1 Nov). *Christmas. T **615** and similar multicoloured design. (a) Phosphorised paper. P* 14½×14 (40 c.) *or* 14×14½ ($1).

1918	40 c. Type **615**	..	..	30	35
1919	$1 Tree of Life (*horiz*)	..	..	80	85

(b) *Self-adhesive. Phosphor frame. P* 11½

1920	40 c. Type **615**	..	..	30	35
	a. Booklet pane. No. 1925×20		..	6·00	

No. 1920 was printed in $8 booklets containing No. 1920a on which the surplus self-adhesive paper around each stamp was retained.

(Des C. Shurey. Litho SNP Ausprint)

1999 (1 Nov). *Millennium Greetings Stamp. P* 14½×14.

1921	**616** 45 c. multicoloured	..	..	35	40

No. 1921 was printed in a similar format to Nos. 1896/1901 and was also available with the greetings label (16×30 mm) replaced by a personal photograph.

617 Rachael Thomson

618 Walter Parker

(Des Jo Mure. Litho McPherson's Ptg Group, Mulgrave)

2000 (1 Jan). *New Millennium. "Face of Australia". T **617** and similar vert designs. Multicoloured. P* 14½×14.

1922	45 c. Nicholle and Meghan Triandis (twin babies)			35	40
	a. Sheetlet. Nos. 1922/46	..	..	8·75	
1923	45 c. David Willis (cattleman)	..		35	40
1924	45 c. Natasha Bramley (scuba diver)	..		35	40
1925	45 c. Cyril Watson (Aborigine boy)	..		35	40
1926	45 c. Mollie Dowdall (wearing red hat)	..		35	40
1927	45 c. Robin Dicks (flying instructor)	..		35	40
1928	45 c. Mary Simons (elderly woman)	..		35	40
1929	45 c. Peta and Samantha Nieuwerth (mother and baby)			35	40
1930	45 c. John Matthews (doctor)	..		35	40
1931	45 c. Edith Dizon-Fitzimmons (wearing drop earrings)			35	40
1932	45 c. Philippa Weir (wearing brown hat)		35	40
1933	45 c. John Thurgar (in bush hat and jacket)		35	40
1934	45 c. Miguel Alzona (with face painted)	..	35	40
1935	45 c. Type **617**	..	..	35	40
1936	45 c. Necip Akarsu (wearing blue shirt)	..	35	40
1937	45 c. Justin Allan (R.A.N. sailor)	..	35	40

1938	45 c. Wadad Dennaoui (wearing checked shirt)			35	40
1939	45 c. Jack Laity (bushman)	..	..	35	40
1940	45 c. Kelsey Stubbin (wearing cricket cap)		35	40
1941	45 c. Gianna Rossi (resting chin on hand)		35	40
1942	45 c. Paris Hansch (young girl)	..		35	40
1943	45 c. Donald George Whatham (in blue shirt and tie)			35	40
1944	45 c. Stacey Coull (wearing pendant)	..		35	40
1945	45 c. Alex Payne (wearing cycle helmet)	..	35	40
1946	45 c. John Lodge (Salvation Army officer)		35	40
1922/46			*Set of* 25	8·75	10·00

Nos. 1922/46 were printed together, *se-tenant*, in sheetlets of 25.

(Des Cathleen Cram. Litho SNP Ausprint)

2000 (25 Jan). *Australian Legends (4th series). Australia Day. "The Last Anzacs". T **618** and similar horiz designs. Multicoloured. (a) Phosphorised paper. P* 14×14½.

1947	45 c. Type **618**	..	..	35	40
	a. Block of 4. Nos. 1947/50	..		1·40	
1948	45 c. Roy Longmore	..	..	35	40
1949	45 c. Alec Campbell	..	..	35	40
1950	45 c. 1914–15 Star (medal)	..		35	40
1947/50			*Set of* 4	1·40	1·60

(b) *Self-adhesive. Two phosphor bands over inscr panels. P* 11½

1951	45 c. Type **618**	..	..	35	40
	a. Booklet pane. Nos. 1951/3×2 and No. 1954×4			3·50	
1952	45 c. Roy Longmore	..	..	35	40
1953	45 c. Alec Campbell	..	..	35	40
1954	45 c. 1914–15 Star (medal)	..		35	40
1951/4			*Set of* 4	1·40	1·60

Nos. 1947/50 were printed together, *se-tenant*, in sheets of 50 (2 panes of 5×5), each sheet providing ten blocks of 4 and ten single stamps.

Nos. 1951/4, on which the phosphor shows pink under U.V. light, were only issued in $4.50 booklets on which the surplus self-adhesive paper was retained.

Index to Australian Stamp Designs from 1942

The following index is intended to facilitate the identification of all Australian stamps from 1942 onwards. Portrait stamps are usually listed under surnames only, views under the name of the town or city and other issues under the main subject or a prominent word and date chosen from the inscription. Simple abbreviations have occasionally been resorted to and when the same design or subject appears on more than one stamp, only the first of each series is indicated.

Index to Australian Stamp Designs from 1942—*Continued*

STAMP BOOKLETS

Illustrations of booklet covers are reduced to ½ size, *unless otherwise stated.*
All booklets from 1913 to 1949 were stapled.

1913 (17 Jan). *Red on pink cover (SB1) or blue on pink cover with map of Australia on front and picture of State G.P.O. on back (SB2)*
SB1 2s. booklet containing twelve ½d. and eighteen 1d. (Nos. 1/2) in blocks of 6 .. .. ..£1000
SB2 £1 booklet containing two hundred and forty 1d. (No. 2) in blocks of 30 .. .. ..£5000

1914 (6 Oct)–**18**. *Red on pink cover (Nos. SB2a/3), black on red cover (No. SB4) or blue on pink cover with map of Australia on front and picture of State G.P.O. on back (No. SB5).*
SB2a 2s. booklet containing twelve ½d. and eighteen 1d. (Nos. 1, 21c) in blocks of 6 .. ..£1500
SB3 2s. booklet containing twelve ½d. and eighteen 1d. (Nos. 20, 21c) in blocks of 6 (1915) ..£1500
SB4 2s. booklet containing twenty-four 1d. (No. 21c) in blocks of 6 (10.5.17) £1800
 a. Black on green cover £1800
 b. Red on green cover £1800
SB5 £1 booklet containing two hundred and forty 1d. (No. 21c) in blocks of 30 .. ..£5000
 a. Back cover without G.P.O. picture (1918) ..£5000
Records show that a £1 booklet containing one hundred and twenty 2d. stamps was issued in very limited quantities during 1914. No examples are known to have survived.

1919 (Jan–Apr). *Black on pink (Nos. SB6/7) or black on green (Nos. SB8/9c) covers.*
SB6 2s. booklet containing eighteen 1½d. (No. 58) in blocks of 6 .. ..£1300
 a. Black on green cover £1300
SB7 2s. 3d. booklet containing eighteen 1½d. (No. 54) in blocks of 6 .. ..£1300
 a. Black on green cover £1300
SB8 2s. 3d. booklet containing eighteen 1½d. (No. 59) in blocks of 6 (Apr) £1300
 a. Black on pink cover £1300
SB9 2s. 3d. booklet containing eighteen 1½d. (No. 55) in blocks of 6 (Apr) £1300
 a. Black on pink cover £1300
 b. Black on blue cover £1300
SB9c £1 booklet containing one hundred and sixty 1½d. (No. 55) in blocks of 20 (Apr) ..£5000

1920 (Dec)–**22**. *Black on blue (Nos. SB10, SB12), black on white (No. SB11) or black on brown (No. SB14) covers.*
SB10 2s. booklet containing twelve 2d. (No. 62) in blocks of 6 .. ..£1500
 a. Black on pink cover £1500
 b. Black on orange cover (3.22) £2000
SB11 2s. booklet containing twelve 2d. (No. 63) in blocks of 6 (3.22) £1500
 a. Black on orange cover (7.22) £2000
 b. Black on pink cover £1500
 c. Brown on buff cover £1500
 d. Black on pink cover £1500
SB12 £1 booklet containing one hundred and twenty 2d. (No. 62) in blocks of 15 (1.21) £5000
 a. Black on pink cover
SB13 £1 booklet containing ninety 2d. and fifteen 4d. (Nos. 63, 65) in blocks of 15 (3.22) ..
SB14 £1 booklet containing one hundred and twenty 2d. (No. 63) in blocks of 15 (8.22) ..£2000

1923 (Oct)–**24**. *Black on rose (No. SB15), or green on pale green (Nos. SB16/18) covers.*
SB15 2s. 3d. booklet containing eighteen 1½d. (No. 61) in blocks of 6 .. .. ..£1200
 a. Black on pale green cover £1200
 b. Green on pale green cover £1200
SB16 2s. 3d. booklet containing eighteen 1½d. (No. 77) in blocks of 6 (5.24) £1200
SB17 £1 booklet containing one hundred and sixty 1½d. (No. 61) in blocks of 20 (3.24) ..£4000
SB18 £1 booklet containing one hundred and sixty 1½d. (No. 77) in blocks of 20 (5.24) ..£4000

1927 (Jan–June). *Green on pale green covers.*
SB19 2s. 3d. booklet containing eighteen 1½d. (No. 87) in blocks of 6 .. .. ..£750
SB20 2s. 3d. booklet containing eighteen 1½d. (No. 96) in blocks of 6 .. .. ..£750
SB21 £1 booklet containing one hundred and sixty 1½d. (No. 96) in blocks of 20 (June) ..£3750

1927 (9 May). *Opening of Parliament House, Canberra. Green on pale green cover with picture of H.M.S. Renown on back (2s.).*
SB22 2s. booklet containing sixteen 1½d. (No. 105) in blocks of 8 .. .. ..80·00
SB22a 10s. booklet containing eighty 1½d. (No. 105) in blocks of 8
Surviving examples of No. SB22a are without front cover and have a blank back cover.

1928 (Nov). *Green on pale green cover.*
SB23 2s. 3d. booklet containing eighteen 1½d. (No. 96a or 96w) in blocks of 6 .. ..£325

1930 (July)–**35**. *Air. Black on blue cover inscr "AIR MAIL. SAVES TIME" and biplane.*
SB24 3s. booklet containing twelve 3d. (No. 115) in blocks of 4 plus two panes of air mail labels £650
 a. Cover inscr "USE THE AIR MAIL" and monoplane (5.35) £1200
 b. Black on pale green cover inscr "USE THE AIR MAIL" (5.35) £900

1930 (9 Sept)–**33**. *Green on pale green covers inscr "USE THE AIR MAIL" on the back (2s)*
SB25 2s. booklet containing twelve 2d. (No. 99a or 99aw) in blocks of 6 .. ..£300
SB25a 2s. booklet containing twelve 2d. (No. 127 or 127w) in blocks of 6 (1.32) £275
 ab. Cover with parcel rates on back (1933) ..£375
SB26 £1 booklet containing one hundred and twenty 2d. (No. 99) in blocks of 20 .. ..£3750
SB26a £1 booklet containing one hundred and twenty 2d. (No. 99a) in blocks of 20 .. ..£3750

1934 (June). *Black on cream cover inscr "Address your mail fully…" on front.*
SB26b 2s. booklet containing twelve 2d. (No. 127 or 127w) in blocks of 6 .. .. ..£400

1935–38. *Black on green cover with Commonwealth Savings Bank advertisement on front inscr "WHEREVER THERE IS A MONEY ORDER POST OFFICE".*
SB26c 2s. booklet containing twelve 2d. (No. 127 or 127w) in blocks of 6 .. .. ..£325
 ca. Front cover inscr "IN MOST MONEY ORDER OFFICES" (1936) £275
 cb. Ditto with waxed interleaves (1938) ..£325

1938 (Dec). *Black on green cover as No. SB26c. Postal rates on interleaves.*
SB27 2s. booklet containing twelve 2d. (No. 184 or 184w) in blocks of 6 .. .. ..£350
 a. With waxed interleaves. Postal rates on back cover £450
 b. Black on buff cover £400

1942 (Aug). *Black on buff cover, size 73×47½ mm. Postal rates on interleaves.*
SB28 2s. 6d. booklet containing twelve 2½d. (No. 206 or 206w) in blocks of 6, upright within the booklet £110
 a. With waxed interleaves. Postal rates on back cover £200

1949 (Sept). *Black on buff cover, size 79½×42½ mm including figure of Hermes.*
SB29 2s. 6d. booklet containing twelve 2½d. (No. 206) in blocks of 6, sideways within the booklet 80·00

All booklets from 1952 to 1972 were stitched and stapled booklets of this period are remakes of defective stitched booklets with new covers. All subsequent booklets have their panes attached by selvedge *unless otherwise stated.*

B 1

1952 (24 June). *Vermilion and deep blue on green cover as Type B 1.*
SB30 3s. 6d. booklet containing twelve 3½d. (No. 247) in blocks of 6 .. .. ..17·00
 a. With waxed interleaves .. .. ..90·00

B 1a

1953 (8 July)–**56**. *Vermilion and deep blue on green cover as Type B 1a.*
SB31 3s. 6d. booklet containing twelve 3½d. (No. 263) in blocks of 6 .. .. ..11·00
 a. With waxed interleaves .. .. ..22·00
SB32 3s. 6d. booklet containing twelve 3½d. (No. 262a) in blocks of 6 (7.56) .. ..23·00
 a. With waxed interleaves .. .. ..80·00

B 2

1957 (13 Mar)–**59**. *Vermilion and deep blue on green cover as Type B 2.*
SB33 4s. booklet containing two panes of 6 4d. (No. 282ab) .. ..15·00
 a. With waxed interleaves .. .. ..40·00
SB34 4s. booklet containing two panes of 6 4d. (No. 313ab) (18.3.59) .. .. ..38·00
 a. With waxed interleaves .. .. ..75·00

B 3

1960 (23 Mar). *Vermilion and deep blue on green cover as Type B 3.*
SB35 5s. booklet containing two panes of 6 5d. (No. 314d) .. ..20·00
 a. With waxed interleaves .. .. ..42·00

B 4

1962 (July)–**65**. *Rose and emerald on green cover as Type B 4.*
SB36 5s. booklet containing two panes of 6 5d. (No. 314d) .. ..45·00
 a. With waxed interleaves (1963) £100
SB37 5s. booklet containing two panes of 6 5d. (No. 354a) (17.6.64) .. .. ..45·00
 a. With waxed interleaves £100
SB38 5s. booklet containing two panes of 6 5d. (No. 354cb) (13.7.65) .. .. ..50·00
 a. With waxed interleaves £120

B 5

1966 (14 Feb). *Greenish blue and black on yellow-olive cover as Type B 5.*
SB39 60 c. booklet containing three panes of 5 4 c. and 1 label (No. 385a) .. .. ..60·00
 a. With waxed interleaves £130

1967 (29 Sept). *Greenish blue and black on yellow-olive covers as Type B 5. (a) Surcharged covers*
SB40 50 c. booklet containing two panes of 5 5 c. on 4 c. and 1 label (No. 414a) .. ..12·00
SB41 $1 booklet containing four panes of 5 5 c. on 4 c. and 1 label (No. 414a) .. ..11·00
 a. Normal cover as Type B 5 .. ..11·00
 ab. With waxed interleaves .. ..55·00
  (b) Normal covers
SB42 50 c. booklet containing two panes of 5 5 c. and 1 label (No. 386ca) .. .. ..15·00
SB43 $1 booklet containing four panes of 5 5 c. and 1 label (No. 386ca) .. .. ..30·00
 a. With waxed interleaves .. .. ..65·00
Booklets SB40/1ab were intended as provisional issues until supplies of the new 5 c. became available in booklet form, but in the event these were put on sale on the same date.

B 6

1968 (6 Nov). *Famous Australians (1st series). Black, red, white and blue cover as Type B 6.*
SB44 $1 booklet containing four panes of 5 5 c. and 1 label (Nos 432a, 433a, 434a, 435a) .. ..8·00
 a. With waxed interleaves .. .. ..50·00

B 7

1969 (22 Oct). *Famous Australians (2nd series). Olive-green, gold and black cover as Type B 7.*
SB45 $1 booklet containing four panes of 5 5 c. and 1 label (Nos. 446a, 447a, 448a, 449a) .. ..9·00
 a. With waxed interleaves .. .. ..60·00

B 8

1970 (16 Nov). *Famous Australians (3rd series). Multicoloured on white covers as Type* B **8**.

SB46 60 c. booklet containing two panes of 5 6 c. and 1
      label (Nos. 479a, 480a) .. .. .. 10·00
SB47 60 c. booklet containing two panes of 5 6 c. and 1
      label (Nos. 481a, 482a) .. .. .. 10·00
SB48 $1.20 booklet containing four panes of 5 6 c.
      and 1 label (Nos. 479a, 480a, 481a, 482a) 13·00
      a. With waxed interleaves .. .. .. 60·00

1972 (8 Mar). *Famous Australians (4th series). Covers in reddish violet (No.* SB49), *yellowish olive (No.* SB50) *or blue (No.* SB51), *each with inscr in yellow-brown and black as Type* B **7**.

SB49 70 c. booklet containing two panes of 5 7 c. and 1
      label (Nos. 505a, 506a) .. .. .. 3·75
SB50 70 c. booklet containing two panes of 5 7 c. and 1
      label (Nos. 507a, 508a) .. .. .. 3·75
SB51 $1.40, booklet containing four panes of 5 7 c.
      and 1 label (Nos. 505a, 506a, 507a, 508a) 5·50
      a. With waxed interleaves .. .. .. 50·00

The Australian Post Office discontinued the general use of stamp booklets in May 1973, but from 30 April 1979 tested two stamp-vending machines in Brisbane which issued 60 c. and 80 c. folders containing three or four examples of No. 673 taken from sheet stock. These folders were withdrawn on 30 January 1981.

During 1982 experimental stamp booklet vending machines were under test at the G.P.O.s in Melbourne and Sydney. These machines dispensed a cream card folder, without printing, containing two copies of Nos. 669/70 and 790a. The stamps, from normal sheets, were affixed to the folders by their selvedge. These 60 c. trial folders were replaced by booklets Nos. SB52/3 in November 1982.

From 1982 all booklets have folded covers with the stamps attached by their selvedge, *unless otherwise stated.*

B 9

1982 (17 Nov). *Eucalyptus Flowers. Covers in pale greenish yellow with olive-grey (60 c.) or rose-red ($1) as Type* B **9**.

SB52 60 c. booklet containing pane of 6 (No. 870a) .. 1·00
SB53 $1 booklet containing pane of 9 (No. 870b) .. 2·50
Nos. SB52/3 were sold from vending machines.

B 10

1985 (13 Mar). *Turquoise-green on white cover as Type* B **10**.

SB54 $1 booklet containing pane of 4 (No. 970a) .. 2·75
No. SB54 was sold from vending machines.

B 11

1986 (25 Aug). *Alpine Wildflowers. Apple-green (80 c.) or orange-yellow ($1) on white covers as Type* B **11**.

SB55 80 c. booklet containing pane of 4 (No. 1028a) 2·50
SB56 $1 booklet containing pane of 4 (No. 1028b) .. 2·50
Nos. SB55/6 were sold from vending machines.

B 12

1987 (13 Oct). *Aboriginal Crafts. Orange-brown (80 c.) or orange-yellow ($2) on white covers as Type* B **12**.

SB57 80 c. booklet containing pane of 4 (No. 1093a) .. 3·75
SB58 $2 booklet containing pane of 6 (No. 1094a) .. 7·50
Nos. SB57/8 were sold from vending machines
Trial versions of both booklets exist which differ considerably from the main supply. On the trial versions the outside back cover is headed "ABORIGINAL CRAFTS", there is no advertisement on the selvedge of the pane and the bottom stamp in each pane is imperforate at foot.

B 13

1988 (1 July–28 Sept). *Multicoloured covers as Type* B **13**.

SB59 $3.70, booklet containing 37 c. (No. 1121) in block
      of 10 (printed by Leigh-Mardon Ltd) 6·00
SB60 $3.70, booklet containing pane of 10 37 c. (No.
      1121a) (printed by CPE Australia Ltd) with
      upper and lower edges of the pane imperf and
      margins at left and right .. .. 6·00
SB61 $3.90, booklet containing pane of 10 39 c. (No.
      1121ba) (28 Sept) .. .. .. 7·00

B 14

1988 (28 Sept). *Australian Crafts. Orange-yellow (80 c.) or bright purple ($2) on white covers as Type* B **14**.

SB62 80 c. booklet containing pane of 3 (No. 1158a) .. 3·50
SB63 $2 booklet containing pane of 6 (No. 1159a) .. 5·00
Nos. SB62/3 were sold from vending machines.

B 15

1989 (13 Feb). *Multicoloured cover as Type* B **15**.

SB64 $3.90, booklet containing pane of 10 39 c. (No.
      1179a) .. .. 9·00
      a. Containing pane No. 1179ba .. .. 10·00

B 16

1989 (23 Aug). *Multicoloured cover as Type* B **16**.

SB65 $4.10, booklet containing pane of 10 41 c. (No.
      1180a) .. .. .. 6·00
No. SB65 also exists overprinted with the "Austamp 90" logo for sale at this exhibition.

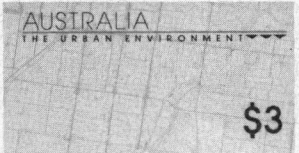

B 17

1989 (1 Sept). *Urban Environment. Black and grey-brown on white cover as Type* B **17**.

SB66 $3 booklet containing pane of 7 (No. 1216a) .. 4·00
No. SB66 was sold from vending machines and only contained stamps to a face value of $2.87. A refund of 13 c. could, however, be obtained by returning the empty booklet cover to a post office. No. SB66 also exists overprinted with the "New Zealand 1990" logo for sale at this exhibition.

B 18

(Illustration reduced. Actual size 132×54 mm)

1989 (11 Oct). *"Stampshow '89" National Stamp Exhibition, Melbourne. Multicoloured cover as Type* B **18**. *Stapled.*

SB67 $8 booklet containing pane of 10 41 c. (No.
      1222ab) .. .. .. 10·00
Booklet No. SB67 also contains a Melbourne Metro travel pass and entrance ticket to "Stampshow '89".

B 19

1989 (1 Nov). *Christmas. Reddish brown on toned cover as Type* B **19**.

SB68 $3.60, booklet containing pane of 10 36 c. (No.
      1225a) .. .. .. 4·00
No. SB68 was also overprinted with the Sydney Stamp and Coin Show, 1989, or "World Stamp Expo", Washington logos for sale at these exhibitions.

B 20

1990 (7 Feb–May). *Greetings Stamps. Maroon and dull mauve cover as Type* B **20**.

SB69 $4.10, booklet containing pane of 10 41 c. (No.
      1230a) and pane of 10 greetings labels .. 6·50
      a. Containing pane of 10 (No. 1230ba) and pane
      of 10 greetings labels (May) .. .. 10·00

For three months from May 1990 a series of provisional booklets was available from a vending machine at Sydney International Airport. These had plain covers, each handstamped with the airport post office's pictorial cancellation, and exist with the following contents:
70 c. (No. 1187) × 5 (lemon cover).
75 c. (No. 1132) × 5 (buff cover).
80 c. (No. 1133) × 5 (buff cover).
$1 (No. 1192) × 5 (buff cover).
$1.10 (No. 1193) × 5 (buff cover).

1990 (27 Aug)–**91**. *Multicoloured cover as Type* B **16**.

SB70 $4.30, booklet containing pane of 10 43 c. (No.
      1181a) .. .. .. 6·50
      a. Inscription changed and with additional
      slotted tab attached at right (2.91) .. .. 7·50

BARCODES. Barcodes appear on the back cover of booklet No. SB70 and later issues. From 1996 two different barcodes were used on self-adhesive booklets to identify operational from philatelic stock.

1990 (3 Sept). *Greetings Stamps. Maroon, brown-olive and pale olive cover as Type* B **20**.

SB71 $4.30, booklet containing pane of 10 43 c. (No.
      1231a) and pane of 10 greetings labels .. 5·00

NEW INFORMATION

The editor is always interested to correspond with people who have new information that will improve or correct the Catalogue.

$2.00

Heidelberg and Heritage *The Modern 9 x 5s*

B 21 "Wild Life is Fun" (David Larwill)

1990 (3 Sept). *"Heidelberg and Heritage" Art Exhibition. Multicoloured cover as Type B 21.*
SB72 $2 booklet containing pane of 5 (No. 1269a) .. 3·50
    a. Containing pane of 5 (No. 1269ba) .. .. 7·50
    Nos. SB72/a were sold from vending machines. Both also exist overprinted with the Norpex 91, Newcastle, logo for sale at this exhibition.

$3.80

10 x 38c Stamps

B 22 "Parrot unwrapping Parcel"

1990 (31 Oct). *Christmas. Multicoloured cover as Type B 22.*
SB73 $3.80, booklet containing pane of 10 38 c. (No. 1272a) .. .. 5·50
    No. SB73 also exists overprinted with the Sydney Stamp and Coin Show, 1990, logo for sale at this exhibition.

1991 (Jan). *Red-brown and brown-olive cover as Type B 20, but inscr "8 GREETINGS STICKERS".*
SB74 $4.30, booklet containing pane of 10 43 c. (No. 1231a) and 8 self-adhesive greetings labels affixed to the inside back cover .. .. 16·00

CHRISTMAS

20 x 38c stamps
20 card only stickers
$7.60

B 23

1991 (1 Nov). *Christmas. Multicoloured cover as Type B 23.*
SB75 $7.60, booklet containing pane of 20 38 c. (No. 1309a) and 20 self-adhesive "Card Only" stickers affixed to the inside back cover .. 9·00

$2.00

B 24

1992 (2 Jan)–**94**. *Wetlands and Waterways. Multicoloured cover as Type B 24.*
SB76 $2 booklet containing pane of 5 (No. 1319a) .. 3·00
    a. Containing pane No. 1319ba (3.94) .. 3·75
    Nos. SB76/a were sold from vending machines. No. SB76 was also overprinted with "N.P.C. Canberra 14–16 March 1992", "World Columbian Stamp Expo '92", Chicago, "Australian Stamp Exhibition 1993", Kaohsiung, and No. S76a with Queensland Stamp and Coin Show 94 logos for sale at these events.

1992 (2 Jan). *"Thinking of You". Orange-yellow, red-orange and grey-black cover as Type B 20, showing wild flowers.*
SB77 $4.50, booklet containing pane of 10 45 c. (No. 1318a) with 8 self-adhesive greetings labels affixed to the inside back cover .. .. 5·00
    No. SB77 was also overprinted with "Australian Stamp Exhibition 1993", Taichung, logo for sale at this exhibition.

ALTERED CATALOGUE NUMBERS

Any Catalogue numbers altered from the last edition are shown as a list in the introductory pages.

WIN a trip to the 1997 Olympics flying Qantas

AUSTRALIA 45c

$4.50

10 x 45c self adhesive stamps

Australia Post

B 25

1992 (2 Jan)–**94**. *Threatened Species. Multicoloured covers as Type B 25. Self-adhesive.*
SB78 $4.50, booklet containing pane of 10 45 c. (No. 1327pa) (cover showing No. 1329 on front and Olympic draw details on back) .. .. 12·00
    a. Containing pane No. 1327qa (cover as Type B 25, but without Olympic draw flash and with National Philatelic Centre advertisement on back) (22.4.92) .. .. 12·00
    b. Containing pane No. 1327qa (cover as No. SB78a, but Stamp Collecting Kit advertisement on back) (7.11.92) .. .. 12·00
    c. Containing pane No. 1327qa (cover as Type B 25, but showing larger illustration (46×39 *mm*) of Dusky Hopping-mouse instead of stamp) (1.93) .. .. 12·00
    d. Containing pane No. 1327qa (cover as No. SB78c, but illustration (46×32 *mm*) of Little Pygmy Possum) (7.93) .. .. 12·00
    e. Containing pane No. 1327qa (cover as No. SB78c, but illustration (46×32 *mm*) of Ghost Bat) (1.94) .. .. 12·00
    These booklets can also be identified by the new printing symbols (koalas or kangaroos) which appear in the margin of the pane. No. SB78a shows 1 or 2 koalas, No. SB78b 3 koalas, No. SB78c 4 koalas, No. SB78d 1 kangaroo and No. SB78e 1 kangaroo and 1 koala.
    An example of No. SB78e has been reported showing the printing of the stamps omitted.
    No. SB78a (1 koala) was also overprinted with "National Stamp Show '92" logo, No. SB78a (2 koalas) with "Kuala Lumpur '92" and No. SB78c with "Australian Stamp Exhibition 1993", Taipeh, logo for sale at these exhibitions.

Christmas 1992

$8.00

20 x 40c stamps 20 card only stickers

B 26

1992 (30 Oct). *Christmas. Multicoloured cover as Type B 26.*
SB79 $8 booklet containing pane of 20 40 c. (No. 1383a) and 20 self-adhesive "Card Only" stickers affixed to the inner cover .. .. 9·00
    No. SB79 was also overprinted with "Sydney Stamp and Coin Fair '92" logo for sale at this exhibition.

STAMPS

$4.50 10 x 45.

WIN A TRIP ON THE GHAN

B 27

1993 (1 June). *Trains of Australia. Multicoloured cover as Type B 27. Self-adhesive.*
SB80 $4.50, booklet containing pane of 10 45 c. (No. 1411a) .. .. 6·00
    No. SB80 was also overprinted with "Indopex '93", Surabaya, or "Queensland Stamp and Coin Show" logos for sale at these exhibitions.

SELF-ADHESIVE STAMPS

$4.50
10 x 45c

OCTOBER IS STAMP COLLECTING MONTH

B 28

1993 (1 Oct). *Prehistoric Animals. Multicoloured cover as Type B 28. Self-adhesive.*
SB81 $4.50, booklet containing pane of 10 45 c. (No. 1430a) .. .. 6·00
    No. SB81 was also overprinted with the "Sydney Stamp and Coin Show 93" logo for sale at this exhibition.

$8.00
20 x 40c STAMPS
20 CARD ONLY STICKERS

B 29

1993 (1 Nov). *Christmas. Multicoloured cover as Type B 29.*
SB82 $8 booklet containing pane of 20 40 c. (No. 1432a) with 20 self-adhesive "Card only" stickers affixed to the inner cover .. .. 8·50

SELF-ADHESIVE STAMPS

LIFESAVING 1894 - 1994

$4.50
10 x 45c

B 30

THINKING OF YOU

10 x 45c Stamps

8 Greeting Stickers

B 31

1994 (20 Jan). *Centenary of Organised Life Saving in Australia. Multicoloured cover as Type B 30. Self-adhesive.*
SB83 $4.50, booklet containing pane of 10 45 c. (No. 1443a) .. .. 6·00
    No. SB83 was also overprinted with the "Newcastle Mini-National Exhibition" logo for sale at this event.

1994 (3 Feb). *"Thinking of You". Multicoloured cover as Type B 31.*
SB84 $4.50, booklet containing pane of 10 45 c. (No. 1446b) with 8 self-adhesive greetings stickers affixed to the inner cover .. .. 4·50
    No. SB84 was also overprinted with "Melbourne Stamp and Coin Show" or "Canberra Stamp Show 94" logos for sale at these exhibitions.

SELF-ADHESIVE STAMPS

AUSTRALIAN KOALAS & KANGAROO WILDLIFE

$4.50
10 x 45c

ZOOS ENDANGERED SPECIES

$4.50
10 x 45c

OCTOBER IS ZOOTOBER - STAMP COLLECTING MONTH

B 32   **B 33**

1994 (12 May)–**96.** *Australian Wildlife (2nd series). Multi-coloured cover as Type B 32. Self-adhesive.*
SB85 $4.50, booklet containing pane of 10 45 c. (No.
1459a)   . .   . .   5·50
   a. Cover with "BOOKABOUT" advert at foot
(1.96)   . .   . .   . .   5·50
   b. Cover with "WIN A TRIP FOR TWO TO
THE ATLANTA OLYMPICS" advert at foot
(16.3.96)   . .   . .   . .   5·50
  No. SB85a is from the 4 koala, 1 kangaroo + 1 koala,
1 kangaroo + 2 koala and 1 kangaroo + 3 koala printings.
  No. SB85b is from the 1 kangaroo printing and also exists
overprinted "CANBERRA STAMPSHOW 96 16–18 March
1996" in gold on the cover.

1994 (28 Sept). *Australian Zoos. Endangered Species.
Multicoloured cover as Type B 33. Self-adhesive.*
SB86 $4.50, booklet containing pane of 10 45 c. (No.
1485b)   . .   . .   12·00

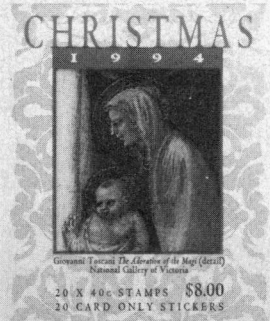

B 34

1994 (31 Oct). *Christmas. Multicoloured cover as Type B 34.*
SB87 $8 booklet containing pane of 20 40 c. (No.
1487a) and 20 self-adhesive "CARD ONLY"
stickers affixed to the inner cover   . .   8·50

B 35

1995 (9 Feb). *Completion of Endeavour Replica. Multicoloured
cover as Type B 35.*
SB88 $2 booklet containing pane of 5 (No. 1512a)   . .   2·50

B 36

1995 (20 Apr). *Australian Second World War Heroes.
Multicoloured cover as Type B 36. Self-adhesive.*
SB89 $4.50 booklet containing pane of 10 45 c. (No.
1525a)   . .   . .   6·50

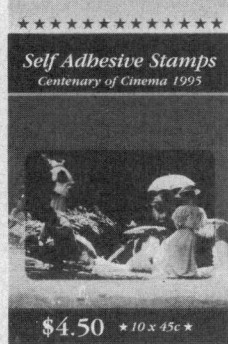

B 37

1995 (8 June). *Centenary of Cinema. Multicoloured cover as
Type B 37. Self-adhesive.*
SB90 $4.50, booklet containing pane of 10 45 c. (No.
1535a)   . .   . .   . .   5·50
  No. SB90 was also overprinted with the "Queensland Stamp
and Coin Show 1995" logo for sale at this exhibition.

B 38   B 39

1995 (3 Oct). *Marine Life. Multicoloured cover as Type B 38.
Self-adhesive.*
SB91 $4.50, booklet containing pane of 10 45 c. (No.
1563ab)   . .   . .   . .   4·25

1995 (1 Nov). *Christmas. Multicoloured cover as Type B 39.
Self-adhesive.*
SB92 $8 booklet containing pane of 20 40 c. (No.
1572a) and 20 self-adhesive "Card Only"
labels affixed to the inner cover   . .   8·50
  Booklet No. SB92 shows either an advertisement for B.P.
Australia or a selection of Christmas cards available from
Australia Post on the back cover.

B 40   North Melbourne

(Des Janet Boschen)

1996 (23 Apr). *Centenary of Australian Football League.
Multicoloured covers as Type B 40 showing team logos. Self-
adhesive.*
SB 93 $4.50, booklet containing pane of ten 45 c. (No.
1606a) (Type B 40)   . .   . .   6·00
SB 94 $4.50, booklet containing pane of ten 45 c. (No.
1607a) (Brisbane)   . .   . .   6·00
SB 95 $4.50, booklet containing pane of ten 45 c. (No.
1608a) (Sydney)   . .   . .   6·00
SB 96 $4.50, booklet containing pane of ten 45 c. (No.
1609a) (Carlton)   . .   . .   6·00
SB 97 $4.50, booklet containing pane of ten 45 c. (No.
1610a) (Adelaide)   . .   . .   6·00
SB 98 $4.50, booklet containing pane of ten 45 c. (No.
1611a) (Fitzroy)   . .   . .   6·00
SB 99 $4.50, booklet containing pane of ten 45 c. (No.
1612a) (Richmond)   . .   . .   6·00
SB100 $4.50, booklet containing pane of ten 45 c. (No.
1613a) (St. Kilda)   . .   . .   6·00
SB101 $4.50, booklet containing pane of ten 45 c. (No.
1614a) (Melbourne)   . .   . .   6·00
SB102 $4.50, booklet containing pane of ten 45 c. (No.
1615a) (Collingwood)   . .   . .   6·00
SB103 $4.50, booklet containing pane of ten 45 c. (No.
1616a) (Fremantle)   . .   . .   6·00
SB104 $4.50, booklet containing pane of ten 45 c. (No.
1617a) (Footscray)   . .   . .   6·00
SB105 $4.50, booklet containing pane of ten 45 c. (No.
1618a) (West Coast)   . .   . .   6·00
SB106 $4.50, booklet containing pane of ten 45 c. (No.
1619a) (Essendon)   . .   . .   6·00
SB107 $4.50, booklet containing pane of ten 45 c. (No.
1620a) (Geelong)   . .   . .   6·00
SB108 $4.50, booklet containing pane of ten 45 c. (No.
1621a) (Hawthorn)   . .   . .   6·00
  No. SB94 also exists overprinted with "Queensland Stamp &
Coin Expo 1996" for sale at this event.

B 41

1996 (4 July). *50th Anniv of Children's Book Council Awards.
Multicoloured cover as Type B 41. Self-adhesive.*
SB109 $4.50, booklet containing panes of 10 45 c. (No.
1634a)   . .   . .   . .   5·50

B 42   Silhouettes on Landscape

1996 (12 Sept). *50th Anniv of Arts Councils. Multicoloured
cover as Type B 42.*
SB110 $2 booklet containing pane of 5 (No. 1643a)   . .   2·00

B 43   Dog and Cat

1996 (1 Oct). *Australian Pets. Multicoloured cover as Type
B 43. Self-adhesive.*
SB111 $4.50, booklet containing pane of 10 45 c. (No.
1652a)   . .   . .   5·50

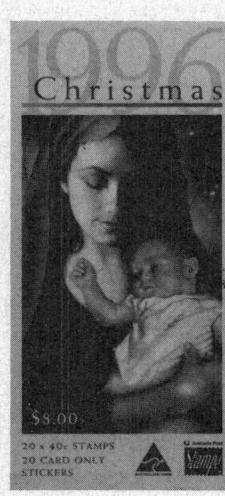

B 44   Madonna and Child

1996 (1 Nov). *Christmas. Multicoloured cover as Type B 44.
Self-adhesive.*
SB112 $8 booklet containing pane of 20 40 c. (No.
1659a) and 20 self-adhesive "Card Only"
labels affixed to the inner cover   . .   9·00

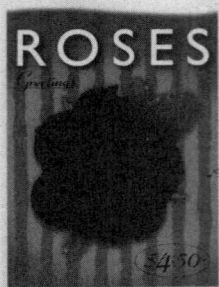

B 45 Rose

1997 (29 Jan). *St. Valentine's Day. Multicoloured cover as Type* B **45**. *Self-adhesive.*
SB113 $4.50, booklet containing pane of 10 45 c. (No. 1666a) and 12 self-adhesive greetings stickers affixed to the inner cover   ..   ..   6·00

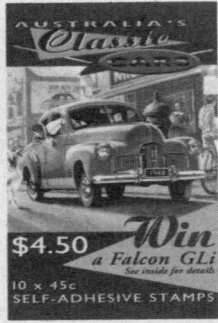

B 46 GMH Holden 48-215 (FX)

1997 (27 Feb). *Classic Cars. Multicoloured cover as Type* B **46**. *Self-adhesive.*
SB114 $4.50, booklet containing pane of 10 45 c. (Nos. 1671a)   ..   ..   5·00

B 47 Classic Cars
(Illustration reduced. Actual size 155×105 mm)

1997 (27 Feb). *Classic Cars Prestige Booklet. Multicoloured cover as Type* B **47**.
SB115 $9.95, booklet containing four panes of 4 45 c. (Nos. 1667b/70a), two pre-paid postcards and 16 self-adhesive labels   ..   ..   10·00

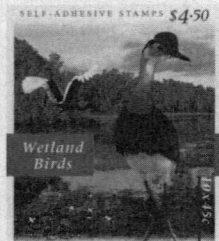

B 48 Wetland Birds

1997 (2 June). *Flora and Fauna. Multicoloured cover as Type* B **48**. *Self-adhesive.*
SB116 $4.50, booklet containing pane of 10 45 c. (No. 1687a)   ..   ..   4·50

COVER PRICES

Cover factors are quoted at the beginning of each country for most issues to 1945. An explanation of the system can be found on page x. The factors quoted do not, however, apply to philatelic covers.

B 49 Barking Owl   **B 50** Two Angels

1997 (1 Oct). *Nocturnal Animals. Multicoloured cover as Type* B **49**. *Self-adhesive.*
SB117 $4.50, booklet containing pane of 10 45 c. (No. 1720b)   ..   ..   ..   5·00

1997 (3 Nov). *Christmas. Children's Nativity Play. Multicoloured cover as Type* B **50**. *Self-adhesive.*
SB118 $8 booklet containing pane of 20 40 c. (No. 1726a) and 20 self-adhesive "Card Only" labels affixed to the inner cover   ..   ..   7·00

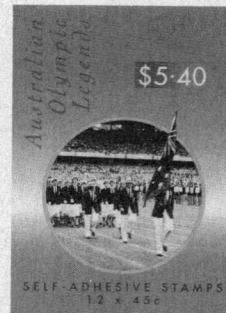

B 51 Australian Athletes

1998 (21 Jan). *Australian Legends (2nd series). Olympic Gold Medal Winners. Multicoloured cover as Type* B **51**. *Self-adhesive.*
SB119 $5.40, booklet containing pane of 12 45 c. (No. 1743b)   ..   ..   ..   4·75

B 52 Champagne Rose   **B 53** Brolga

1998 (12 Feb). *Greetings Stamp. Multicoloured cover as Type* B **52**. *Self-adhesive.*
SB120 $4.50, booklet containing pane of 10 45 c. (No. 1756a) and 12 self-adhesive greetings stickers affixed to the inner cover   ..   4·50
  No. SB120 also exists overprinted "Natstamp'98 Canberra 14–16 March 1998" for sale at this exhibition.

1998 (12 Feb). *Wetland Birds. Multicoloured cover as Type* B **53**. *Self-adhesive. Stamps loose within cover.*
SB121 $9 booklet containing 20×45 c. (Nos. 1687d/90d) 20·00
  No. SB121 was introduced as a trial product and was available at a number of Post Offices in Victoria and from Philatelic counters.

B 54 Farmhouse and Fields

1998 (21 Apr). *Farming. Multicoloured cover as Type* B **54**. *Self-adhesive.*
SB122 $4.50, booklet containing pane of 10 45 c. (No. 1764a)   ..   ..   7·00

B 55 Pouring Tea
(Illustration reduced. Actual size 145×103 mm)

1998 (13 Aug). *"The Teapot of Truth" Prestige Booklet. Multicoloured cover as Type* B **55**. *Stapled.*
SB123 $9.95, booklet containing three panes of 4 45 c. (Nos. 1805a/7a), panes of 2 $1 and $1.20 (Nos. 1808a/9a), pre-paid postcard and 16 self-adhesive labels   ..   ..   8·50

B 56

1998 (1 Sept). *Wetland Birds. Multicoloured cover as Type* B **56**. *Self-adhesive.*
SB124 $9 booklet containing pane of 20 45 c. (No. 1687c)   ..   ..   7·50

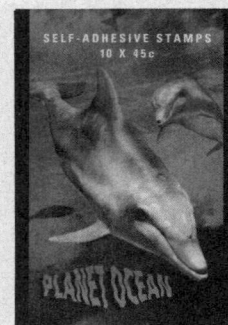

B 57 Bottlenose Dolphin

1998 (1 Oct). *International Year of the Ocean. Multicoloured cover as Type* B **57**. *Self-adhesive.*
SB125 $4.50, booklet containing pane of 10 45 c. (No. 1829b)   ..   ..   3·50

B 58 Christmas Star

1998 (2 Nov). *Christmas. Multicoloured cover as Type* B **58**. *Self-adhesive.*
SB126 $8 booklet containing pane of 20 40 c. (No. 1835a) and 20 self-adhesive "Card Only" labels affixed to the inner cover .. .. 7·00

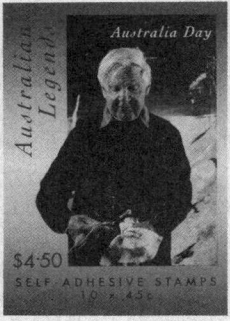

B 59

1999 (22 Jan). *Australian Legends (3rd series). Arthur Boyd (painter). Multicoloured cover as Type* B **59**. *Self-adhesive.*
SB127 $4.50, booklet containing pane of 10 45 c. (No. 1840a) .. .. 3·75

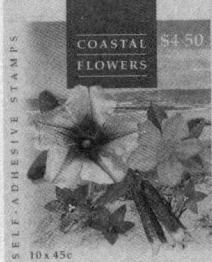

B 60 Red Roses   B 61 Flowers on Beach

1999 (4 Feb). *Greetings Stamp. Romance. Multicoloured cover as Type* B **60**. *Self-adhesive.*
SB128 $4.50, booklet containing pane of 10 45 c. (No. 1843a) .. .. 3·75

1999 (8 Apr). *Coastal Flowers. Multicoloured cover as Type* B **61**. *Self-adhesive.*
SB129 $4.50, booklet containing pane of 10 45 c. (No. 1863a) .. .. 3·50
        a. Containing booklet pane No. 1863ca .. 3·50

PRICES OF SETS

Set prices are given for many issues, generally those containing three stamps or more. Definitive sets include one of each value or major colour change, but do not cover different perforations, die types or minor shades. Where a choice is possible the set prices are based on the cheapest versions of the stamps included in the listings.

B 62 Bananas in Pyjamas   B 63 Northern Dwarf Tree Frog

1999 (6 May). *Children's Television Programmes. Multicoloured cover as Type* B **62**. *Self-adhesive.*
SB130 $4.50, booklet containing pane of 10 45 c. (No. 1876a) .. .. .. 3·50

1999 (1 Oct). *National Stamp Collecting Month. Small Pond Life. Multicoloured cover as Type* B **63**. *Self-adhesive.*
SB131 $5 booklet containing pane of 10 50 c. (No. 1916a) .. .. 4·00

B 64 Madonna and Child

1999 (1 Nov). *Christmas. Multicoloured cover as Type* B **64**. *Self-adhesive.*
SB132 $8 booklet containing pane of 20 40 c. (No. 1920a) and 20 "Card Only" labels affixed to the inner cover .. .. 6·00

B 65 Anzac Emblem

2000 (25 Jan). *Australian Legends (4th series). "The Last Anzacs". Multicoloured cover as Type* B **65**. *Self-adhesive.*
SB133 $4.50, booklet containing pane of 10 45 c. (No. 1951a) .. .. 3·50

Military Post Booklets

Issued for the use of Australian Forces in Vietnam.

AUSTRALIAN DEFENCE FORCES

Postage Stamps

TEN 5c STAMPS

MB 1

1967 (30 May–Sept). *Yellow-green and black on white cover as Type* MB **1**. *Pane attached by selvedge.*
MB1   50 c. booklet containing 5 c. (No. 386) in block of 10 .. .. 80·00
        a. Containing No. 386b (Sept) .. .. 80·00

1968 (Mar). *Yellow-green and black on white cover as Type* MB **1**. *Pane attached by selvedge.*
MB2   50 c. booklet containing 5 c. (No. 386c) in block of 10 .. .. 50·00

POSTAGE DUE STAMPS

POSTAGE DUE PRINTERS. Nos. D1/62 were typographed at the New South Wales Government Printing Office, Sydney. They were not used in Victoria.

INVERTED WATERMARKS. These occur frequently amongst Nos. D1/62. In some instances examples with inverted watermarks are more common than those showing the watermark upright.

    D 1   D 2   D 3

Type D 1 adapted from plates of New South Wales Type D 1. No letters at foot.

1902 (1 July). *Chalk-surfaced paper. Wmk Type D 2.*

(a) P 11½, 12

D 1	D 1	½d. emerald-green ..	..	3·25 4·00
D 2		1d. emerald-green ..	..	12·00 5·50
D 3		2d. emerald-green ..	..	28·00 6·50
D 4		3d. emerald-green ..	..	28·00 18·00
D 5		4d. emerald-green ..	..	42·00 11·00
D 6		6d. emerald-green ..	..	55·00 9·00
D 7		8d. emerald-green ..	..	95·00 75·00
D 8		5s. emerald-green ..	..	£180 70·00
D1/8			*Set of 8*	£400 £180
D1/7 Optd "Specimen"			*Set of 7*	£275

(b) P 11½, 12, compound with 11

D 9	D 1	1d. emerald-green		£200 £110
D 10		2d. emerald-green		£275 £110

(c) P 11

D 12	D 1	1d. emerald-green ..	..	£750 £325

The ½d., 6d. and 8d. exist in dull green.
Stamps may be found showing portions of the letters "N S W" at foot.

1902 (July)–**04.** *Type D 3, space at foot filled in. Chalk-surfaced paper. Wmk Type D 2.*

(a) P 11½, 12

D13	1d. emerald-green ..	..	£150 80·00
D14	2d. emerald-green ..	..	£150 65·00
D15	3d. emerald-green ..	..	£180 65·00
D17	5d. emerald-green ..	..	40·00 9·50
D18	10d. emerald-green ..	..	70·00 17·00
D19	1s. emerald-green ..	..	55·00 10·00
D20	2s. emerald-green ..	..	£100 16·00
D21	5s. emerald-green ..	..	£600 £160

(b) P 11½, 12, compound with 11

D22	½d. emerald-green ..	..	6·50 6·00
D23	1d. emerald-green ..	..	6·50 2·75
D24	2d. emerald-green ..	..	20·00 2·75
D25	3d. emerald-green ..	..	60·00 10·00
D26	4d. emerald-green ..	..	50·00 9·00
D27	5d. emerald-green ..	..	50·00 16·00
D28	6d. emerald-green ..	..	50·00 10·00
D29	8d. emerald-green ..	..	£120 45·00
D30	10d. emerald-green ..	..	90·00 18·00
D31	1s. emerald-green ..	..	85·00 18·00
D32	2s. emerald-green ..	..	£120 27·00
D33	5s. emerald-green ..	..	£180 21·00

(c) P 11

D34	½d. emerald-green ..	..	£190 £130
D35	1d. emerald-green ..	..	65·00 20·00
D36	2d. emerald-green ..	..	£100 23·00
D37	3d. emerald-green ..	..	65·00 27·00
D38	4d. emerald-green ..	..	£120 42·00
D39	5d. emerald-green ..	..	£170 30·00
D40	6d. emerald-green ..	..	85·00 15·00
D41	8d. emerald-green ..	..	£190 38·00
D42	5s. emerald-green ..	..	£475 95·00
D43	10s. emerald-green ..	..	£1600 £1300
D44	20s. emerald-green ..	..	£3250 £2250
D13/44		*Set of 14*	£5000 £3250
D13/44 Optd "Specimen"		*Set of 14*	£850

Most values exist in dull green.

    D 4   D 6

1906 (From Jan)–**08.** *Chalky paper. Wmk Type D 4.*

(a) P 11½, 12, compound with 11

D45	D 3	½d. green (1907) ..	..	9·00 7·00
D46		1d. green ..	..	12·00 2·25
D47		2d. green ..	..	28·00 4·00
D48		3d. green ..	..	£450 £190
D49		4d. green (1907) ..	..	60·00 20·00
D50		6d. green (1908) ..	..	£170 20·00
D45/50			*Set of 6*	£650 £225

(b) P 11

D51	D 3	1d. dull green ..	..	£750 £300
D52		4d. dull green ..	..	£1100 £475

Shades exist.

1907 (From July). *Chalky paper. Wmk Type w 11 (see Introduction). P 11½ × 11.*

D53	D 3	½d. dull green ..	..	20·00 55·00
D54		1d. dull green ..	..	60·00 30·00
D55		2d. dull green ..	..	£100 70·00
D56		4d. dull green ..	..	£170 80·00
D57		6d. dull green ..	..	£200 £100
D53/7			*Set of 5*	£500 £275

1908 (Sept)–**09.** *Stroke after figure of value. Chalky paper. Wmk Type D 4.*

(a) P 11½ × 11

D58	D 6	1s. dull green (1909)..	..	75·00 8·50
D59		5s. dull green ..	..	£200 48·00

(b) P 11

D60	D 6	2s. dull green (1909)		£850 £1200
D61		10s. dull green (1909)		£2000 £2250
D62		20s. dull green (1909)		£5000 £6000
D58/62			*Set of 5*	£7500 £8500

Nos. D61/2 were only issued in New South Wales.

D 7

Die I   Die II

1d.

Die I   Die II

2d.

(Typo J. B. Cooke, Melbourne)

1909 (July)–**10.** *Wmk Crown over A, Type w 11.*

(a) P 12×12½ (comb) or 12½ (line)

D63	D 7	½d. rosine and yellow-green ..	..	14·00 26·00
D64		1d. rosine and yellow-green (I)	..	14·00 4·00
	aw.	Wmk inverted ..	..	40·00 10·00
	b.	Die II (7.10) ..	..	17·00 1·75
	bw.	Wmk inverted ..	..	35·00 11·00
D65		2d. rosine and yellow-green (I)	..	24·00 3·50
	a.	Die II (7.10) ..	..	20·00 1·75
D66		3d. rosine and yellow-green (1910)		24·00 12·00
D67		4d. rosine and yellow-green		22·00 4·50
D68		6d. rosine and yellow-green		27·00 7·00
D69		1s. rosine and yellow-green		30·00 4·00
D70		2s. rosine and yellow-green		70·00 13·00
D71		5s. rosine and yellow-green		90·00 15·00
D72		10s. rosine and yellow-green		£250 £150
D73		£1 rosine and yellow-green		£475 £275
D63/73			*Set of 11*	£900 £450

(b) P 11

D74	D 7	1d. rose and yellow-green (II)		£1200 £500
D74a		2d. rose and yellow-green (II)		
D75		6d. rose and yellow-green ..	..	£5500 £2750

Only one unused example, without gum, and another pen-cancelled are known of No. D74a.

The 1d. of this printing is distinguishable from No. D78 by the colours, the green being very yellow and the rose having less of a carmine tone. The paper is thicker and slightly toned, that of No. D78 being pure white; the gum is thick and yellowish, No. D78 having thin white gum.

All later issues of the 1d. and 2d. are Die II.

(Typo J. B. Cooke and T. S. Harrison (from May 1918))

1912 (Dec)–**23.** *Thin paper. White gum. W w 11.* *(a) P 12½*

D76	D 7	½d. scarlet and pale yellow-green ..	..	23·00 26·00
	w.	Wmk inverted ..	..	28·00 32·00

(b) P 11

D77	D 7	½d. rosine & brt apple-green (10.14)		11·00 16·00
	a.	Wmk sideways ..	..	6·50 7·00
D78		1d. rosine & brt apple-green (10.14)		5·50 1·75
	a.	Wmk sideways ..	..	9·50 1·75
	w.	Wmk inverted ..	..	40·00 11·00

(c) P 14

D79	D 7	½d. rosine & brt apple-green (11.14)		80·00 £100
	a.	*Carmine & apple-green* (Harrison) (1920)		9·00 16·00
D80		1d. rosine & brt apple-green (10.14)		55·00 12·00
	a.	*Scarlet & pale yellow-green* (1918)		20·00 3·75
	b.	*Carmine & apple-green* (Harrison) (1919)		12·00 3·50
D81		2d. scarlet & pale yellow-green (4.18)		17·00 6·00
	a.	*Carmine & apple-green* (Harrison) (1920)		18·00 3·50
D82		3d. rosine and apple-green (5.16)		70·00 32·00
	a.	Wmk sideways ..	..	£1600 £1000
D83		4d. rosine and apple-green (Harrison) (26.4.21)		90·00 55·00
	a.	Wmk sideways ..	..	£475 £325
	b.	*Carmine & pale yell-grn* (26.4.21)		65·00 50·00
D85		1s. scarlet & pale yellow-green (7.23)		25·00 13·00
D86		10s. scarlet & pale yellow-green (5.21)		£850 £1100
D87		£1 scarlet & pale yellow-green (5.21)		£700 £900
D76/87			*Set of 8*	£1500 £1900

Although printed by Cooke, the three higher values were not issued until some years later.

(Typo T. S. Harrison (to Feb. 1926), A. J. Mullet (to June 1927) and J. Ash (later))

1922 (1 Mar)–**30.** *W 6. (a) P 14*

D91	D 7	½d. carmine & yellow-green (17.5.23)		2·50 4·75
D92		1d. carmine and yellow-green		4·00 1·00
D93		1½d. carmine and yellow-green (3.25)		1·50 9·00
D94		2d. carmine & yellow-green (20.3.22)		3·50 2·00
D95		3d. carmine and yellow-green		9·50 3·50
	w.	Wmk inverted ..	..	55·00 35·00
D96		4d. carmine & yellow-green (13.2.22)		35·00 20·00
D97		6d. carmine & yellow-green (8.22)		26·00 11·00

(b) P 11

D98	D 7	4d. carmine & yellow-green (8.30)		4·00 4·25
D91/8			*Set of 8*	75·00 42·00

All values perf 14 were printed by Harrison and all except the 4d. by Mullett and Ash. There is a wide variation of shades in this issue.

(Typo J. Ash)

1931 (Oct)–**36.** *W 15. (a) P 14*

D100	D 7	1d. carmine and yellow-green (10.31)		7·00 11·00
	a.	Imperf between (horiz pair)		† £5000
D102		2d. carmine & yellow-grn (19.10.31)		7·00 11·00

(b) P 11

D105	D 7	½d. carmine and yellow-green (4.34)		12·00 14·00
D106		1d. carmine & yellow-grn (21.11.32)		7·50 1·25
D107		2d. carmine & yellow-green (20.9.32)		8·50 60
D108		3d. carmine and yellow-green (5.36)		70·00 70·00
D109		4d. carmine & yellow-green (26.7.34)		4·50 2·25
D110		6d. carmine and yellow-green (8.36)		£300 £275
D111		1s. carmine and yellow-green (8.34)		48·00 32·00
D105/11			*Set of 7*	£375 £350

    D 8   D 9

    A   B   C

The differences are found in the middle of the "D"

    D   E

Type E. Larger "1" with only three background lines above; hyphen more upright.

(Frame recess. Value typo J. Ash)

1938 (May–Aug). *W 15. P 14½×14.*

D112	D 8	½d. carmine and green (A) (Aug)		3·75 2·50
D113		1d. carmine and green (A)		10·00 8·00
D114		2d. carmine and green (A)		10·00 1·25
D115		3d. carmine and green (B) (Aug) ..		30·00 13·00
D116		4d. carmine and green (A) (Aug)		12·00 60
D117		6d. carmine and green (A) (Aug)		70·00 42·00
D118		1s. carmine and green (D) (Aug)		50·00 12·00
D112/18			*Set of 7*	£170 65·00

Shades exist.

1946–57. *Redrawn as Type C and E (1s). W 15. P 14½×14.*

D119	D 9	½d. carmine and green (9.56)	..	85 3·00
D120		1d. carmine and green (1.11.47)	..	1·25 90
D121		2d. carmine and green (9.46)	..	4·50 1·25
D122		3d. carmine and green (25.9.46)	..	6·00 1·25
D123		4d. carmine and green (30.7.52)	..	9·00 1·75
D124		5d. carmine and green (16.12.48)	..	12·00 3·00
D125		6d. carmine and green (9.47)	..	11·00 1·75
D126		7d. carmine and green (26.8.53)	..	4·25 8·50
D127		8d. carmine and green (24.4.57)	..	10·00 25·00
D128		1s. carmine and green (9.47)	..	18·00 1·60
D119/28			*Set of 10*	65·00 42·00

There are many shades in this issue.

D 10

1953 (26 Aug)–**59.** *W 15. P 14½×14.*

D129	D 10	1s. carmine & yellow-green (17.2.54)		7·50 3·00
	a.	*Carmine and deep green*		11·00 8·00
D130		2s. carmine and yellow-green		18·00 12·00
	a.	*Carmine and deep green*		£170 60·00
D131		5s. carmine and green		18·00 6·00
	a.	*Carmine and deep green* (6.59)		18·00 7·00
D129/31			*Set of 3*	40·00 19·00
D129a/31a			*Set of 3*	£170 60·00

A new die was introduced for No. D131a. This differs from the original in having a distinct gap between the two arms of the "5" On No. D131 these two features are joined.

Type I. Numeral, "D" and stop, generally unoutlined.

Type II. Clear white line separates numeral, etc. from background.

1958–60. *No wmk.* P 14½×14.

D132	D 9	½d. carmine & dp grn (II) (27.2.58)	1·60	1·75
D133		1d. carmine & dp green (I) (25.2.58)	3·00	3·50
		a. Type II (6.59)	1·50	80
D134		3d. carmine & dp grn (II) (25.5.60)	1·75	3·00
D135		4d. carmine & dp green (I) (27.2.58)	4·00	9·00
		a. Type II (6.59)	3·00	8·50
D136		5d. carmine & dp grn (II) (27.2.58)	13·00	15·00
		a. Type II (6.59)	60·00	60·00
D137		6d. carmine & dp grn (II) (25.5.60)	2·75	3·25
D138		8d. carmine & dp grn (II) (25.2.58)	10·00	28·00
D139		10d. carmine & dp grn (II) (9.12.59)	4·50	3·25
D140	D 10	1s. carmine and deep green (6.5.58)	5·50	2·75
		a. Deep carmine & dp green (6.59)	6·50	4·00
D141		2s. dp carmine & dp green (8.3.60)	22·00	20·00
D132/41		Set of 10	55·00	80·00

Nos. D140a and D141. Value tablets are re-engraved and have thicker and sharper printed lines than before.

The use of Postage Due stamps ceased on 13 January 1963.

OFFICIAL STAMPS

From 1902 the departments of the Commonwealth government were issued with stamps of the various Australian States perforated "OS" to denote official use. These were replaced in 1913 by Commonwealth of Australia issues with similar perforated initials as listed below.

During the same period the administrations of the Australian States used their own stamps and those of the Commonwealth perforated with other initials for the same purpose. These States issues are outside the scope of this catalogue.

Most shades listed under the postage issues also exist perforated "OS". Only those which are worth more than the basic colours are included below.

(O 1)   (O 2)   (O 3)

1913 (Jan–Apr). *Nos. 1/16 punctured as Type O 1. W 2.* P 12.

O1	1	½d. green (Die I)		11·00	6·00
		w. Wmk inverted		†	50·00
O2		1d. red (Die I)		9·50	2·00
		cw. Wmk inverted		50·00	5·00
		d. Die II		14·00	4·00
		dw. Wmk inverted		50·00	5·00
O3		2d. grey (Die I)		23·00	7·00
O4		2½d. indigo (Die II)		£140	85·00
O5		3d. olive (Die I)		65·00	30·00
		ca. In pair with Die II		£475	
		dw. Wmk inverted		75·00	35·00
		e. Die II		£180	50·00
		ew. Wmk inverted		£225	60·00
O6		4d. orange (Die II)		£100	16·00
		a. Orange-yellow		£160	65·00
O7		5d. chestnut (Die II)		75·00	23·00
O8		6d. ultramarine (Die II)		65·00	13·00
		w. Wmk inverted		£100	35·00
O9		9d. violet (Die II)		70·00	12·00
		w. Wmk inverted		†	£750
O10		1s. emerald (Die II)		95·00	22·00
		w. Wmk inverted		£180	50·00
O11		2s. brown (Die II)		£170	80·00
		a. Double print		†£1000	
O12		5s. grey and yellow		£425	£225
O13		10s. grey and pink		£1200	£700
O14		£1 brown and ultramarine		£1900	£1300
O15		£2 black and rose		£3500	£2000
O1/15		Set of 15		£7000	£4000

1914. *Nos. 1/16 punctured as Type O 2. W 2.* P 12.

O16	1	½d. green (Die I)		8·00	4·00
		w. Wmk inverted		†	30·00
O17		1d. red (Die I)		10·00	3·50
		d. Die II		16·00	2·00
		e. Die IIA		12·00	2·25
O18		2d. grey (Die I)		40·00	4·50
		w. Wmk inverted		50·00	8·00
O19		2½d. indigo (Die II)		£120	65·00
O20		3d. olive (Die I)		50·00	6·00
		e. Die II		£130	40·00
		ew. Wmk inverted		£180	50·00
O21		4d. orange (Die II)		£110	50·00
		a. Orange-yellow		£160	70·00
O22		5d. chestnut (Die II)		90·00	32·00
O23		6d. ultramarine (Die II)		60·00	12·00
		w. Wmk inverted		90·00	30·00
O24		9d. violet (Die II)		60·00	17·00
O25		1s. emerald (Die II)		60·00	17·00
O26		2s. brown (Die II)		£150	65·00
O27		5s. grey and yellow		£450	£275
O28		10s. grey and pink		£1400	£900
O29		£1 brown and ultramarine		£2250	£1400
O30		£2 black and rose		£3750	£2250
O16/30		Set of 15		£7500	£4500

1915. *Nos. 24 and 26/30 punctured as Type O 2. W 5.* P 12.

O31	1	2d. grey (Die I)		55·00	11·00
O33		6d. ultramarine (Die II)		85·00	15·00
		b. Die IIA		£750	£170
O34		9d. violet (Die II)		£130	48·00
O35		1s. blue-green (Die II)		£120	32·00
O36		2s. brown (Die II)		£425	70·00
O37		5s. grey and yellow		£500	£100
		a. Yellow portion doubly printed		†£1500	
		w. Wmk inverted		£600	£130

1914–21. *Nos. 20/3 punctured as Type O 2. W 5.* P 14¼×14 (comb).

O38	5a	½d. bright green		8·50	2·50
		w. Wmk inverted		13·00	5·50
O39		1d. carmine-red (I) (No. 21c)		9·00	70
		gw. Wmk inverted		14·00	2·00
		h. Die II		£275	12·00
O41		4d. orange		38·00	3·50
		a. Yellow-orange		55·00	7·50
		b. Pale orange-yellow		90·00	13·00
		c. Lemon-yellow		£150	45·00
		w. Wmk inverted		50·00	15·00
O42		5d. brown (p 14¼ (line))		45·00	3·25
		aw. Wmk inverted		75·00	18·00
		b. Printed on the gummed side (wmk inverted)		£475	
		c. Perf 14¼×14 (comb)		45·00	3·25
		cw. Wmk inverted		75·00	15·00

1915–28. *Nos. 35/45 punctured as Type O 2. W 6.* P 12.

O43	1	2d. grey (Die I)		16·00	3·50
		bw. Wmk inverted		20·00	5·50
		d. Die II		25·00	12·00
O44		2½d. deep blue (Die II)		38·00	8·00
		w. Wmk inverted		†	20·00
O45		3d. yellow-olive (Die I)		20·00	3·25
		cw. Wmk inverted		24·00	6·00
		d. Die II		75·00	38·00
		dw. Wmk inverted		£100	50·00
		e. Die IIB		20·00	8·50
		ew. Wmk inverted		30·00	11·00
O46		6d. ultramarine (Die II)		30·00	3·75
		a. Die IIA		£450	£110
		d. Die IIB		40·00	8·50
		dw. Wmk inverted		50·00	15·00
O47		9d. violet (Die II)		22·00	7·50
		b. Die IIB		22·00	7·00
		bw. Wmk inverted		†	13·00
O48		1s. blue-green (Die II)		23·00	2·50
		aw. Wmk inverted		50·00	13·00
		b. Die IIB		23·00	3·50
O49		2s. brown (Die II)		£110	13·00
		b. Red-brown (aniline)		£225	40·00
		w. Wmk inverted		£180	60·00
O50		5s. grey and yellow		£150	40·00
		w. Wmk inverted		£225	75·00
O51		10s. grey and pink		£250	60·00
		w. Wmk inverted			
O52		£1 chocolate and dull blue		£1500	£950
		ab. Wmk sideways. *Chestnut & brt blue*		†£4250	
		aw. Wmk inverted		£1700	£1100
O53		£2 black and rose		£2000	£850
O43/53		Set of 11		£3250	£1600

1916–20. *Nos. 47/f and 5d. as No. 23 punctured as Type O 2. W 5. Rough paper.* P 14.

O54	5a	1d. scarlet (Die I)		16·00	4·00
		a. Deep red		16·00	4·00
		b. Rose-red		16·00	4·00
		c. Rosine		55·00	9·00
		dw. Wmk inverted		20·00	5·50
		e. Die II. Rose-red		£200	11·00
		f. Die II. Rose		£400	38·00
		fw. Wmk inverted			
O60		5d. bright chestnut (10.20)		£1200	£100

All examples of the 5d. on this paper were perforated "OS".

1918–20. *Nos. 51 and 53/5 punctured as Type O 2. W 6a.* P 14.

O61	5a	½d. green		13·00	2·00
		w. Wmk inverted		17·00	8·50
O63		1d. carmine (I)		50·00	26·00
O64		1½d. black-brown		17·00	2·50
		a. Very thin paper		32·00	12·00
		w. Wmk inverted		38·00	8·50
O65		1½d. red-brown		17·00	2·50
		w. Wmk inverted		32·00	8·50
O61/5		Set of 4		85·00	30·00

1918–23. *Nos. 56/9 and 61/6 punctured as Type O 2. W 5.* P 14.

O66	5a	½d. orange		13·00	8·00
O67		1d. violet		19·00	7·50
		w. Wmk inverted		†	£1500
O68		1½d. black-brown		20·00	2·50
		w. Wmk inverted		30·00	6·00
O69		1½d. deep red-brown		17·00	1·50
		w. Wmk inverted		28·00	6·00
O70		1½d. green		12·00	1·25
O71		2d. brown-orange		12·00	1·25
		w. Wmk inverted		26·00	8·00
O72		2d. bright rose-scarlet		13·00	4·00
		w. Wmk inverted		26·00	12·00
O73		4d. violet		35·00	13·00
O74		4d. ultramarine		60·00	9·00
O75		1s. 4d. pale blue		50·00	15·00
		b. Deep turquoise		£550	£325
O66/75		Set of 10		£225	55·00

1923–24. *Nos. 73/5 punctured as Type O 2. W 6.* P 12.

O76	1	6d. chestnut (Die IIB)		17·00	2·50
O77		2s. maroon (Die IIB)		55·00	12·00
O78		£1 grey (Die IIB)		£475	£275
O76/8		Set of 3		£500	£275

1924. *Nos. 76/84 punctured as Type O 2.* P 14. *(a)* W 5.

O79	5a	1d. sage-green		6·00	1·40
O80		1½d. scarlet		5·00	60
		w. Wmk inverted		40·00	10·00
		wa. Printed on the gummed side		£160	

O81	5a	2d. red-brown		20·00	13·00
		a. Bright red-brown		35·00	20·00
O82		3d. dull ultramarine		32·00	6·00
O83		4d. olive-yellow		35·00	5·00
O84		4½d. violet		70·00	12·00
		w. Wmk inverted		†	£1200

(b) W 6a

O85	5a	1d. sage-green		12·00	12·00

(c) No wmk

O86	5a	1d. sage-green		55·00	50·00
O87		1½d. scarlet		60·00	50·00
O79/87		Set of 9		£250	£130

1926–30. *Nos. 85/104 punctured as Type O 2. W 7. (a)* P 14

O88	5a	½d. orange		£150	65·00
O89		1d. sage-green		8·50	70
O90		1½d. scarlet		17·00	2·00
		a. Golden scarlet		19·00	4·50
		w. Wmk inverted		18·00	3·00
O92		2d. red-brown (Die I)		£100	38·00
O93		3d. dull ultramarine		42·00	12·00
		w. Wmk inverted		42·00	12·00
O94		4d. yellow-olive		£100	35·00
O95		4½d. violet		£100	32·00
O96		1s. 4d. pale greenish blue		£225	£110
O88/96		Set of 8		£650	£275

(b) P 13½×12½

O97	5a	½d. orange		2·50	60
O98		1d. sage-green (Die I)		2·50	60
		b. Die II		80·00	£100
O100		1½d. scarlet		5·00	1·25
		a. Golden scarlet		3·50	1·40
		w. Wmk inverted		5·00	2·50
O102		1½d. red-brown		14·00	3·75
O103		2d. red-brown (Die II)		21·00	11·00
O104		2d. golden scarlet (Die II)		13·00	3·00
		a. Die III		11·00	2·00
		aw. Wmk inverted		17·00	6·50
O106		3d. dull ultramarine (Die I)		28·00	5·00
		aw. Wmk inverted		28·00	12·00
		b. Die II. Deep ultramarine		14·00	1·50
		bw. Wmk inverted		£1400	£900
O108		4d. yellow-olive		18·00	3·75
O109		4½d. violet		60·00	60·00
O110		5d. orange-brown (Die II)		38·00	6·00
O111		1s. 4d. turquoise		£160	22·00
O97/111		Set of 11		£300	£100

1927 (9 May). *Opening of Parliament House, Canberra. No. 105 punctured as Type O 3.*

O112	8	1½d. brownish lake		13·00	7·50

1928 (29 Oct). *National Stamp Exhibition, Melbourne. No. 106 punctured as Type O 2.*

O113		3d. blue		13·00	9·00

1929–30. *Nos. 107/14 punctured as Type O 2. W 7.* P 12.

O114	1	6d. chestnut (Die IIB)		17·00	3·00
O115		9d. violet (Die IIB)		32·00	5·50
O116		1s. blue-green (Die IIB)		23·00	3·00
O117		2s. maroon (Die II)		65·00	8·00
O118		5s. grey and yellow		£160	40·00
O118a		10s. grey and pink			
O118b		£2 black and rose		£2000	

1929 (20 May). *Air. No. 115 punctured as Type O 3.*

O119	9	3d. green		20·00	12·00

1929 (28 Sept). *Centenary of Western Australia. No. 116 punctured as Type O 3.*

O120	10	1½d. dull scarlet		13·00	8·00

1930 (2 June). *Centenary of Exploration of River Murray by Capt. Sturt. Nos. 117/18 punctured as Type O 2.*

O121	11	1½d. scarlet		6·50	4·50
O122		3d. blue		13·00	7·50

(O 4)

1931 (4 May). *Nos. 121/2 optd with Type O 4.*

O123	13	2d. rose-red		55·00	16·00
O124		3d. blue		£200	32·00

For No. 139 overprinted with Type O 4, see No. 139a.

1932 (Feb)–**33.** *Optd as Type O 4. (a)* W 7. (i) P 13½×12½

O125	5a	2d. golden scarlet (Die III)		8·00	1·10
		a. Opt inverted		†£3000	
O126		4d. yellow-olive (3.32)		16·00	5·00
O126a		5d. orange-brown (3.32)		†	—

(ii) P 12

O127	1	6d. chestnut (3.32)		40·00	45·00

(b) W 15. (i) P 13½×12½

O128	5a	½d. orange (11.7.32)		4·75	1·50
		a. Opt inverted		£3500	£2000
O129		1d. green (3.32)		3·25	45
		w. Wmk inverted		75·00	35·00
		x. Wmk reversed		£225	80·00
O130		2d. golden scarlet (Die III)		6·50	55
		a. Opt inverted		†£3250	
O131		3d. ultramarine (Die II) (2.33)		7·50	4·00
O132		5d. orange-brown (7.32)		35·00	27·00

(ii) P 12

O133	1	6d. chestnut (9.32)		20·00	20·00
		a. Opt inverted		†£5000	

(c) Recess. No wmk. P 11

O134	18	2d. scarlet (3.32)		5·00	2·00
O135		3d. blue (3.32)		14·00	7·00
O136	17	1s. green (3.32)		40·00	35·00

A single used example of No. O126a is known. It is believed that it was used to "patch" a sheet of No. O132 before overprinting.

Issue of overprinted official stamps ceased in February 1933 and thereafter mail from the federal administration was carried free.

BRITISH COMMONWEALTH OCCUPATION FORCE (JAPAN)

Nos. J1/7 were used by the Australian forces occupying Japan after the Second World War. Initially their military post offices supplied unoverprinted Australian stamps, but it was decided to introduce the overprinted issue to prevent currency speculation.

B.C.O.F. JAPAN 1946 (1)	B.C.O.F. JAPAN 1946 (2)

Ɔ.F.Ɔ.F.

1946   **AN AN**

Wrong fount "6" (left pane R. 9/4)	Normal	Narrow "N" (right pane R. 1/8)

1946 (11 Oct)–48. *Stamps of Australia optd as T* **1** *(1d., 3d.) or T* **2** *(others) at Hiroshima Printing Co, Japan.*

J1	27	½d. orange (No. 179)	..	..	3·00	4·50
		a. Wrong fount "6"	..	..	65·00	75·00
		b. Narrow "N"	..	..	65·00	75·00
		c. Stop after "JAPAN" (right pane R.5/5)	65·00	75·00
J2	46	1d. brown-purple (No. 203)	..	..	2·50	1·75
		a. Blue-black overprint	..	55·00	95·00
J3	31	3d. purple-brown (No. 187)	..	2·00	2·00
		a. Opt double	..	..	£500	
J4	34	6d. purple-brown (No. 189a) (8.5.47)	15·00	9·00
		a. Wrong fount "6"	..	£180	£130
		b. Stop after "JAPAN" (right pane R. 5/5)	£180	£130
		c. Narrow "N"	..	£180	£130
J5	36	1s. grey-green (No. 191) (8.5.47)	15·00	11·00
		a. Wrong fount "6"	..	£190	£150
		b. Stop after "JAPAN" (right pane R. 5/5)	£190	£150
		c. Narrow "N"	..	£190	£150
J6	1	2s. maroon (No. 212) (8.5.47)	42·00	45·00
J7	38	5s. claret (No. 176) (8.5.47)	120	£130
		a. Thin rough paper (No. 176a) (1948)	£120	£140
J1/7			*Set of 7*	£180	£180

The ½d., 1d. and 3d. values were first issued on 11 October 1946, and withdrawn two days later, but were re-issued together with the other values on 8 May 1947.

The following values with T **2** in the colours given were from proof sheets which, however, were used for postage: ½d. (red), 1d. (red or black) and 3d. (gold, red or black). *(Prices for black opts £100, each, and for red or gold from £300 each, all un)*

The use of B.C.O.F. stamps ceased on 12 February 1949.

AUSTRALIAN ANTARCTIC TERRITORY

For use at the Antarctic bases of Casey (opened early 1969: used Wilkes postmark until early 1970), Davis (closed from 1965 until early 1969), Heard Island (seasonal occupation only), Macquarie Island, Mawson and Wilkes (closed January 1969). Stamps of Australia were used from the bases before the introduction of Australian Antarctic Territory issues.

The following are also valid for use in Australia, where they are put on sale for a limited period when first issued.

DATES OF ISSUE. The dates given refer to release dates in Australia. Local release dates are usually later and where known they are given in footnotes.

1 1954 Expedition at Vestfold Hills and Map

(Des. T. Lawrence: adapted by artist of the Printing Branch. Recess)

1957 (27 Mar). *P* 14½.

1	1	2s. ultramarine	..	..	1·25	50

Issued Macquarie Island 11.12.57, Davis 6.2.58, Mawson 18.2.58, Wilkes 1.2.59.

2 Members of Shackleton Expedition at South Magnetic Pole, 1909   **3** Weazel and Team

1959 (16 Dec). *T* **2** *and designs as T* **3**. *Recess; new values surch typo (5d., 8d.). P* 14½ *(5d.),* 14½ × 14 *(8d.) or* 14 × 14½ *(others).*

2		5d. on 4d. black and sepia	..	..	60	15
3		8d. on 7d. black and indigo	..	3·00	2·25
4		1s. deep green	..	..	3·00	2·00
5		2s. 3d. green	..	..	7·00	4·00
2/5			*Set of 4*		12·00	7·50

Designs: *Vert—*1s. Dog-team and iceberg; 2s. 3d. Map of Antarctica and Emperor Penguins. Issued Macquarie Island 26.12.59, Davis 30.1.60, Mawson 10.2.60, Wilkes 13.2.60.

---

6   **7** Sir Douglas Mawson (Expedition leader)

1961 (5 July). *Recess. P* 14½.

6	6	5d. deep blue	..	..	1·25	20

Issued Macquarie Island 6.12.61, Wilkes 10.1.62, Davis 20.1.62, Mawson 30.1.62.

1961 (18 Oct). *50th Anniv of 1911–14 Australasian Antarctic Expedition. Recess. P* 14½.

7	7	5d. myrtle-green	..	..	35	20

Issued Macquarie Island 6.12.61, Wilkes 10.1.62, Davis 20.1.62, Mawson 30.1.62.

(New Currency. 100 cents = 1 Australian dollar)

8 Aurora and Camera Dome   **9** Bell 47G Trooper Helicopter

(Des J. Mason. Photo)

1966 (28 Sept)–68. *Vert designs as T* **8** *(1 c. to 15 c.) or horiz as T* **9** *(20 c. to $1). Multicoloured. Helecon paper (5 c.). P* 13½.

8	1 c.	Type 8 *(shades)*	..	..	70	30
9	2 c.	Emperor Penguins *(shades)*	..	3·00	80
10	4 c.	Ship and iceberg	..	..	90	90
11	5 c.	Banding Elephant-seals (25.9.68)	2·75	1·75
12	7 c.	Measuring snow strata	..	80	80
13	10 c.	Wind gauges	..	..	1·00	90
14	15 c.	Weather balloon	..	..	5·00	2·00
15	20 c.	Type 9	..	..	6·00	2·50
16	25 c.	Radio operator	..	..	3·00	3·00
17	50 c.	Ice compression tests	..	4·50	5·50
18	$1	Parahelion ("mock sun")	..	26·00	14·00
8/18			*Set of 11*	48·00	29·00

Nos. 13/15 and 17 have parts of the designs printed in bright orange fluorescent ink.

Nos. 8/10 and 12/18 placed on sale locally at Macquarie Island on 11.12.66, Wilkes 9.2.67 and Mawson 16.2.67.

No. 11 issued Macquarie Island 4.12.68, Mawson 13.1.69, Wilkes/Casey 9.2.69 and Davis 20.2.69.

11 Sastrugi (Snow Ridges)   **12** Capt. Cook, Sextant and Compass

(Des J. Mason. Photo)

1971 (23 June). *Tenth Anniv of Antarctic Treaty. T* **11** *and similar horiz design. P* 13½.

19	6 c.	blue and black	..	..	75	1·00
20	30 c.	multicoloured (Pancake ice)	..	3·25	6·00

Issued Macquarie Island 23.11.71, Mawson 27.12.71, Davis 13.1.72 and Casey 17.1.72.

(Des J. Mason. Photo)

1972 (13 Sept). *Bicentenary of Cook's Circumnavigation of Antarctica. T* **12** *and similar horiz design. Multicoloured Helecon paper (7 c.). P* 13½.

21	7 c.	Type 12	..	..	1·00	75
22	35 c.	Chart and H.M.S. *Resolution*	..	4·00	5·00

Issued Macquarie Island 19.11.72, Mawson 24.12.72, Davis 3.1.73 and Casey 22.1.73.

13 Plankton   **14** Admiral Byrd (expedition leader), Ford 4-AT-B Trimotor *Floyd Bennett* and Map of South Pole

(Des G. Browning (1, 7, 9, 10, 20 c., $1), R. Honisett (others). Photo)

1973 (5 Aug). *T* **13** *and similar multicoloured designs. Helecon paper. P* 13½.

23	1 c.	Type 13	..	..	30	15
24	5 c.	Mawson's De Havilland D.H.60G Gipsy Moth, 1931	..	70	70
25	7 c.	Adélie Penguin	..	..	2·25	70

26	8 c.	Rymill's De Havilland D.H.83 Fox Moth, 1934–7	75	90
27	9 c.	Leopard Seal *(horiz)*	..	40	90
28	10 c.	Killer Whale *(horiz)*	..	5·50	2·00
		a. Buff (overlay on seals) omitted	£850	
29	20 c.	Wandering Albatross *(horiz)*	1·25	1·00
30	25 c.	Wilkins's Lockheed X-3903 *San Francisco*, 1928 *(horiz)*	90	1·00
31	30 c.	Ellsworth's Northrop Gamma *Polar Star*, 1935	90	1·00
32	35 c.	Christensen's Avro Type 581 Avian, 1934 *(horiz)*	90	1·00
33	50 c.	Byrd's Ford 4-AT-B Trimotor *Floyd Bennett*, 1929	90	1·00
34	$1	Sperm Whale	..	1·25	1·40
23/34			*Set of 12*	14·00	10·50

The red ink used on the 1 c. and $1 is fluorescent.
Issued Macquarie Island 29.11.73, Mawson 30.12.73, Davis 10.1.74 and Casey 31.1.74.

(Des R. Honisett. Litho Asher and Co, Melbourne)

1979 (20 June). *50th Anniv of First Flight over South Pole. T* **14** *and similar horiz design. Multicoloured. P* 15½.

35	20 c.	Type 14	..	..	30	50
36	55 c.	Admiral Byrd, Ford 4-AT-B Trimotor *Floyd Bennett* and Antarctic terrain	80	1·50

Issued Macquarie Island 24.10.79, Davis 3.1.80, Mawson 13.1.80 and Casey 9.2.80.

15 *Thala Dan* (supply ship)   **16** Sir Douglas Mawson in Antarctic Terrain

(Des R. Honisett, Litho Asher and Co, Melbourne)

1979 (29 Aug)–81. *Ships. Multicoloured designs as T* **15**. *P* 13½ × 13 *(horiz) or* 13 × 13½ *(vert).*

37	1 c.	*Aurora (horiz)* (21.5.80)	..	15	10
38	2 c.	*Penola* (Rymill) (9.9.81)	..	40	10
39	5 c.	Type 15	..	..	30	40
40	10 c.	H.M.S. *Challenger* (survey ship) *(horiz)* (9.9.81)	50	55
41	15 c.	*Morning** (bow view) (whaling ship) *(horiz)* (21.5.80)	2·00	3·00
42	15 c.	*Nimrod* (stern view) (Shackleton) *(horiz)* (9.9.81)	1·40	60
43	20 c.	*Discovery II* (supply ship) *(horiz)*	1·25	1·50
44	22 c.	*Terra Nova* (Scott) (21.5.80)	90	1·25
45	25 c.	*Endurance* (Shackleton)	..	60	1·00
46	30 c.	*Fram* (Amundsen) *(horiz)*	60	1·75
47	35 c.	*Nella Dan* (supply ship) *(horiz)* (21.5.80)	80	1·75
48	40 c.	*Kista Dan* (supply ship) (9.9.81)	1·25	1·00
49	45 c.	*L'Astrolabe* (D'Urville) (9.9.81)	70	70
50	50 c.	*Norvegia* (supply ship) *(horiz)* (9.9.81)	70	70
51	55 c.	*Discovery* (Scott)	..	85	2·00
52	$1	H.M.S. *Resolution* (Cook) (21.5.80)	1·75	2·50
37/52			*Set of 16*	12·00	16·00

*No. 41 is incorrectly inscribed "S.Y. *Nimrod*".
On No. 46 the S.S. *Fram* is shown flying the Icelandic ensign, instead of the Norwegian.
Nos. 37, 41, 44, 47 and 52 issued Macquarie Island 27.10.80, Casey 1.12.80, Mawson 5.12.80 and Davis 11.12.80.
Nos. 38, 40, 42 and 48/50 issued Macquarie Island 21.10.81, Mawson 25.11.81, Davis 11.1.82 and Casey 25.1.82.
Nos. 39, 43, 45/6 and 51 issued Macquarie Island 24.10.79, Davis 3.1.80, Mawson 13.1.80 and Casey 9.2.80.

(Des R. Honisett. Litho Cambec Press, Melbourne)

1982 (5 May). *Birth Centenary of Sir Douglas Mawson (Antarctic explorer). T* **16** *and similar vert design. Multicoloured. P* 14 × 13½.

53	27 c.	Type 16	..	..	35	30
54	75 c.	Sir Douglas Mawson and map of Australian Antarctic Territory	1·25	2·00

Issued Macquarie Island 26.10.82, Casey 16.1.83, Davis 10.2.83 and Mawson 2.3.83.

17 Light-mantled Sooty Albatross   **18** Antarctic Scientist

(Des R. Honisett. Litho Leigh-Mardon Ltd, Melbourne)

1983 (6 Apr). *Regional Wildlife. T* **17** *and similar vert designs. Multicoloured. P* 14½.

55	27 c.	Type 17	..	..	85	90
		a. Horiz strip of 5. Nos. 55/9	..	3·75	
56	27 c.	King Cormorant	..	..	85	90
57	27 c.	Southern Elephant-Seal	..	85	90
58	27 c.	Royal Penguin	..	..	85	90
59	27 c.	Dove Prion	..	..	85	90
55/9			*Set of 5*	3·75	4·00

Nos. 55/9 were issued together, *se-tenant*, in horizontal strips of five, forming a composite design.
Issued Macquarie Island 21.10.83, Mawson 9.12.83, Casey 1.1.84 and Davis 2.1.84.

(Des R. Honisett. Litho Leigh-Mardon Ltd, Melbourne)

1983 (7 Sept). *12th Antarctic Treaty Consultative Meeting, Canberra. P 14½.*
60	**18**	27 c. multicoloured			55	55

Issued Macquarie Island 21.10.83, Mawson 9.12.83, Casey 1.1.84 and Davis 2.1.84.

19 Prismatic Compass and Lloyd-Creak Dip Circle   **20** Dog Team pulling Sledge

(Des R. Fletcher. Litho Leigh-Mardon Ltd, Melbourne)

1984 (16 Jan). *75th Anniv of Magnetic Pole Expedition.* **T 19** *and similar horiz design. Multicoloured. P 14½.*
61	30 c. Type **19**			50	50
62	85 c. Aneroid barometer and theodolite		1·25	1·50

Issued Macquarie Island 23.10.84, Mawson 15.11.84, Casey 16.11.84 and Davis 1.2.85.

(Des G. Emery. Litho Leigh-Mardon Ltd (2, 10, 20, 36, 60 c.) or Cambec Press (others), both of Melbourne)

1984 (18 July)–**87**. *Antarctic Scenes.* **T 20** *and similar multicoloured designs. P 14½ (2 c., 10 c., 20 c., 36 c., 60 c.), 14 × 13½ (45 c., 90 c.) or 13½ × 14 (others).*
63	2 c. Summer afternoon, Mawson Station (11.3.87)		10	40
64	5 c. Type **20**		15	15
65	10 c. Late summer evening, MacRobertson Land (11.3.87)		15	15
66	15 c. Prince Charles Mountains (7.8.85)		15	20
67	20 c. Summer morning, Wilkes Land (11.3.87)		15	20
68	25 c. Sea-ice and iceberg		60	75
69	30 c. Mount Coates		25	30
70	33 c. "Iceberg Alley", Mawson (7.8.85)		25	40
71	36 c. Early winter evening, Casey Station (11.3.87)		30	35
72	45 c. Brash ice (*vert*) (7.8.85)		70	1·25
73	60 c. Midwinter shadows, Casey Station (11.3.87)		50	55
74	75 c. Coastline		2·25	2·75
75	85 c. Landing strip		2·50	3·00
76	90 c. Pancake ice (*vert*) (7.8.85)		75	80
77	$1 Emperor Penguins (7.8.85) (Optd S. 50p)	2·75	1·25
63/77		*Set of 15*	10·50	10·00

Nos. 63, 65, 67, 71 and 73 issued Macquarie Island 6.10.87, Davis 25.11.87, Mawson 1.1.88 and Casey 13.1.88.

Nos. 64, 68/9 and 74/5 issued Macquarie Island 23.10.84, Mawson 15.11.84, Casey 16.11.84 and Davis 1.2.85.

Nos. 66, 70, 72 and 76/7 issued Heard Island 1.11.85, Casey 31.11.85, Mawson 6.12.85, Macquarie Island 6.12.85 and Davis 11.12.85.

21 Prince Charles Mountains near Mawson Station   **22** Hourglass Dolphins and *Nella Dan*

(Des A. McGregor. Litho Cambec Press, Melbourne)

1986 (17 Sept). *25th Anniv of Antarctic Treaty. P 14 × 13½.*
78	**21**	36 c. multicoloured			1·25	85

Issued Mawson 9.11.86, Davis 15.11.86, Casey 23.11.86 and Macquarie Island 7.12.86.

(Des Trish Hart. Litho CPE Australia Ltd, Melbourne)

1988 (20 July). *Environment, Conservation and Technology.* **T 22** *and similar square designs. Multicoloured. P 13.*
79	37 c. Type **22**		1·10	1·10
	a. Horiz strip of 5. Nos. 79/83	5·00	
80	37 c. Emperor Penguins and Davis Station	1·10	1·10
81	37 c. Crabeater Seal and Hughes 500D helicopters		1·10	1·10
82	37 c. Adelie Penguins and tracked vehicle	1·10	1·10
83	37 c. Grey-headed Albatross and photographer		1·10	1·10
79/83		*Set of 5*	5·00	5·00

Nos. 79/83 were printed together, *se-tenant,* in horizontal strips of five throughout the sheet.

Issued Macquarie Island 29.10.88, Casey 14.12.88, Mawson 21.12.88 and Davis 29.12.88.

23 "Antarctica"   **24** Aurora Australis

(Des Janet Boschen. Litho CPE Australia Ltd, Melbourne)

1989 (14 June). *Antarctic Landscape Paintings by Sir Sidney Nolan.* **T 23** *and similar vert designs. Multicoloured. P 14 × 13½.*
84	39 c. Type **23**		1·00	70
85	39 c. "Iceberg Alley"		1·00	70
86	60 c. "Glacial Flow"		1·75	1·25
87	80 c. "Frozen Sea"		2·25	1·40
84/7		*Set of 4*	5·50	3·50

Issued Casey 28.10.89, Davis 29.10.89, Mawson 17.11 89 and Macquarie Island 24.11.89.

Supplies of Australia Nos. 1261/3 were sent to the Antarctic and were issued at Macquarie Island on 24.11.90, Mawson 10.12.90, Davis 14.12.90 and Casey 19.12.90

(Des Lynette Brown. Litho Leigh-Mardon Ltd, Melbourne)

1991 (20 June). *30th Anniv of Antarctic Treaty (43 c.) and Maiden Voyage of Aurora Australis (research ship) ($1.20).* **T 24** *and similar horiz design. Multicoloured. P 14½.*
88	43 c. Type **24**		75	50
89	$1.20, Aurora Australis off Heard Island (optd S. 55p.)		2·75	3·00

Issued Mawson 12.11.91, Casey 22.12.91, Macquarie Island 17.1.92 and Davis 9.2.92.

25 Adélie Penguin and Chick   **26** Head of Husky

(Des Janet Boschen. Litho McPherson's Ptg Group, Mulgrave ($1, $1.40, $1.50) or Printset Cambec Pty Ltd (others))

1992 (14 May)–**93**. *Antarctic Wildlife.* **T 25** *and similar multicoloured designs. P 14½×14 ($1.20, $1.50) or 14×14½ (others).*
90	45 c. Type **25**		35	40
91	75 c. Elephant Seal with pup		60	65
92	85 c. Hall's Giant Petrel on nest with fledgling		65	70
93	95 c. Weddell Seal and pup		80	85
94	$1 Royal Penguin (14.1.93)		80	85
95	$1.20, Emperor Penguins with chicks (*vert*) (Optd. S. 55p)		90	95
96	$1.40, Fur Seal (14.1.93)		1·10	1·25
97	$1.50, King Penguin (*vert*) (14.1.93)		1·10	1·25
90/7		*Set of 8*	6·25	7·00

Nos. 90/3 and 95 issued Mawson 2.11.92, Davis 11.11.92, Casey 27.11.92 and Macquarie Island 10.12.92.

Nos. 94 and 96/7 issued Mawson 28.10.93, Casey 13.11.93, Davis 2.12.93 and Macquarie Island 19.12.93.

(Des FHA Design. Litho Leigh-Mardon Ltd, Melbourne)

1994 (13 Jan). *Departure of Huskies from Antarctica.* **T 26** *and similar multicoloured designs. P 14½.*
104	45 c. Type **26**		60	50
105	75 c. Dogs pulling sledge (*horiz*)	1·00	1·25
106	85 c. Husky in harness		1·25	1·50
107	$1.05, Dogs on leads (*horiz*)		1·40	1·75
104/7		*Set of 4*	3·75	4·50

Issued Casey 31.10.94, Davis 11.11.94, Mawson 14.11.94 and Macquarie Island 4.12.94.

27 Humpback Whale with Calf   **28** "Rafting Sea Ice" (Christian Clare Robertson)

(Des D. Nelson. Litho Leigh-Mardon Ltd, Melbourne)

1995 (15 June). *Whales and Dolphins.* **T 27** *and similar multicoloured designs. P 14½.*
108	45 c. Type **27**		75	65
109	45 c. Pair of Hourglass Dolphins (*vert*)		75	65
	a. Horiz pair. Nos. 109/10		1·50	1·25
110	45 c. Pair of Minke Whales (*vert*)		75	65
111	$1 Killer Whale		1·50	1·50
108/11		*Set of 4*	3·25	3·00
MS112	146×64 mm. Nos. 108/11		3·25	3·00

Nos. 109/10 were printed together, *se-tenant,* in horizontal pairs throughout the sheet, with the background forming a composite design.

Issued Macquarie Island 18.11.95, Casey 5.12.95, Mawson 16.12.95 and Davis 20.12.95.

No. **MS**112 also exists overprinted "Singapore 95 World Stamp Exhibition", "Philately and Collections Fair, Hong Kong '95" or "CAPEX '96 WORLD PHILATELIC EXHIBITION EXPOSITION PHILATELIQUE MONDIALE" for sale at these exhibitions.

(Des Melinda Whitechurch. Litho McPherson's Ptg Group, Mulgrave)

1996 (16 May). *Paintings by Christian Clare Robertson.* **T 28** *and similar vert designs. Multicoloured. P 14½×14.*
113	45 c. Type **28**		80	70
	a. Horiz pair. Nos. 113/14		1·60	1·40
114	45 c. "Shadow on the Plateau"		80	70
115	$1 "Ice Cave"		1·75	1·40
116	$1.20, "Twelve Lake"		1·90	1·60
113/16		*Set of 4*	4·75	3·75

Nos. 113/14 were printed together, *se-tenant,* in horizontal pairs throughout the sheet.

Issued Macquarie Island 28.11.96, Mawson 23.12.96, Davis 29.12.96 and Casey 11.1.97.

29 Apple Huts   **30** Aurora Australis (research ship)

(Des Sophie Byass. Litho McPherson's Ptg Group, Mulgrave)

1997 (15 May). *50th Anniv of Australian National Antarctic Research Expeditions (A.N.A.R.E.).* **T 29** *and similar horiz designs. Multicoloured. P 14×14½.*
117	45 c. Type **29**		55	55
	a. Pair. Nos. 117/18		1·10	1·10
118	45 c. Tuning a radio receiver		55	55
119	95 c. Summer surveying		90	1·10
120	$1.05, Scientists in cage above sea ice	1·00	1·25
121	$1.20, Scientists and tents		1·25	1·40
117/21		*Set of 5*	4·25	

Nos. 117/18 were printed together, *se-tenant,* in horizontal and vertical pairs throughout the sheet.

Issued Macquarie Island 18.11.97, Davis 22.12.97, Mawson 26.12.97 and Casey 7.1.98.

(Des Sandra Harman. Litho McPherson's Ptg Group, Mulgrave)

1998 (5 Mar). *Antarctic Transport.* **T 30** *and similar multicoloured designs. P 14×14½ (45 c.) or 14½×14 (others).*
122	45 c. Type **30**		75	75
	a. Pair. Nos. 122/3		1·50	1·50
123	45 c. Skidoo		75	75
124	$1 Helicopter lifting quad-bike (*vert*)	1·75	1·75
125	$2 Hagglunds tractor and trailer (*vert*)	2·00	2·00
122/5		*Set of 4*	4·75	4·75

Nos. 122/3 were printed together, *se-tenant,* in horizontal and vertical pairs throughout the sheet.

Issued Davis 18.11.98, Macquarie Island 21.11.98, Casey and Mawson 1.12.98.

31 Sir Douglas Mawson (expedition leader, 1911–14) and *Aurora* (research ship)

(Des Janet Boschen. Litho SNP Ausprint)

1999 (13 May). *Restoration of Mawson's Huts, Cape Denison.* **T 31** *and similar horiz designs, each including a background drawing of a hut. Multicoloured. P 14×14½.*
126	45 c. Type **31**		50	50
	a. Pair. Nos. 126/7		1·00	1·00
127	45 c. Huts in blizzard		50	50
128	90 c. Husky team		95	95
129	$1.35, Conservation in progress		1·40	1·40
126/9		*Set of 4*	3·00	3·00

Nos. 126/7 were printed together, *se-tenant,* in horizontal or vertical pairs throughout the sheet.

Nos. 126/9 were spot-coated with U.V. varnish to simulate ice.

CHRISTMAS ISLAND

Formerly a part of the Straits Settlements and then of the Colony of Singapore, Christmas Island was occupied by the Japanese from 31 March, 1942, until September, 1945. It reverted to Singapore after liberation, but subsequently became an Australian territory on 15 October 1958.

Stamps of the STRAITS SETTLEMENTS were used on Christmas Island from 1901 until 1942. Following liberation issues of MALAYA (BRITISH MILITARY ADMINI-STRATION) and then SINGAPORE were used from 1946 to 1958.

(Currency. 100 cents = 1 Malayan dollar)

1 Queen Elizabeth II

(Des G. Lissenden. Recess with name and value typo in black. Note Printing Branch, Commonwealth Bank, Melbourne)

1958 (15 Oct). *No wmk. P* 14½.

1	1	2 c. yellow-orange			55	70
2		4 c. brown	..	..	60	30
3		5 c. deep mauve	..		60	30
4		6 c. grey-blue		..	1·00	30
5		8 c. black-brown		..	2·25	50
6		10 c. violet		..	1·50	30
7		12 c. carmine		..	2·75	1·75
8		20 c. blue	..	..	1·50	1·75
9		50 c. yellow-green		..	3·00	1·75
10		$1 deep bluish green			3·75	1·75
1/10	..	..	..	*Set of* 10	16·00	8·50

PRINTERS. Nos. 11/32 were printed by the Note Printing Branch, Reserve Bank of Australia, Melbourne. Nos. 33/82 were printed in photogravure by Harrison and Sons, Ltd, London.

2 Map   **11** White-tailed Tropic Bird

(Des G. Lissenden (2, 8c.), P. Morriss (4, 5, 10, 20 c.), B. Stewart (others). Recess)

1963 (28 Aug). *T* **2** *and similar designs and T* **11**. *P* 14½ × 14 ($1) *or* 14½ (*others*).

11		2 c. orange			90	55
12		4 c. red-brown	..	..	50	20
13		5 c. purple		..	50	30
14		6 c. indigo		..	40	50
15		8 c. black		..	3·25	60
16		10 c. violet		..	40	20
17		12 c. brown-red		..	40	40
18		20 c. blue		..	1·00	35
19		50 c. green		..	1·50	35
20		$1 yellow		..	3·50	60
11/20	..	..	..	*Set of* 10	11·00	3·50

Designs: *Vert*—4 c. Moonflower; 5 c. Robber Crab; 8 c. Phosphate train; 10 c. Raising phosphate. *Horiz*—6 c. Island scene; 12 c. Flying Fish Cove; 20 c. Loading cantilever; 50 c. Christmas Island Frigate Bird.

I Thick lettering

II Thinner lettering

1965. *50th Anniversary of Gallipoli Landing. As T* **184** *of Australia, but slightly larger* (22×34½ *mm*) *and colour changed. Photo. P* 13½.

21		10 c. sepia, black and emerald (I) (14.4)			45	80
		a. Black-brown, black and light emerald (II) (24.4)			2·00	2·00

(New Currency. 100 cents = 1 Australian dollar)

12 Golden-striped Grouper   **13** "Angel" (mosaic)

(Des G. Hamori. Photo)

1968 (6 May)–**70.** *Fishes. T* **12** *and similar horiz designs. Multicoloured. P* 13½.

22	1 c. Type **12**		45	45
23	2 c. Moorish Idol		60	20
24	3 c. Long-nosed Butterflyfish		60	30
25	4 c. Pink-tailed Triggerfish		60	20
	a. Deep blue (face value) omitted		£600	
26	5 c. Regal Angelfish		75	20
27	9 c. White-cheeked Surgeonfish		80	40
28	10 c. Lionfish		80	20
28a	15 c. Saddle Butterflyfish (14.12.70)		10·00	5·50
29	20 c. Ornate Butterflyfish		2·50	55
29a	30 c. Giant Ghost Pipefish (14.12.70)		10·00	5·50
30	50 c. Clown Surgeonfish		3·50	3·00
31	$1 Meyer's Butterflyfish		3·50	5·00
22/31		*Set of* 12	30·00	19·00

(Des G. Hamori. Photo)

1969 (10 Nov). *Christmas. P* 13½.

32	**13**	5 c. red, deep blue and gold	20	30

14 "The Ansidei Madonna" (Raphael)   **15** "The Adoration of the Shepherds" (ascr to the School of Seville)

(Des Harrison)

1970 (26 Oct). *Christmas. Paintings. T* **14** *and similar vert design. Multicoloured. P* 14 × 14½.

33		3 c. Type **14**	20	15
34		5 c. "The Virgin and Child, St. John the Baptist and an Angel" (Morando)	20	15

(Des Harrison)

1971 (4 Oct). *Christmas. T* **15** *and similar vert design. Multicoloured. W w* **12**. *P* 14.

35		6 c. Type **15**	30	50
36		20 c. "The Adoration of the Shepherds" (Reni)	70	1·00

16 H.M.S. *Flying Fish*, 1887   **17** Angel of Peace

(Des V. Whiteley)

1972 (7 Feb)–**73.** *Ships. Horiz designs as T* **16**. *Multicoloured. P* 14×13½.

37	1 c. *Eagle* (merchantman), 1714 (5.6.72)		25	60
38	2 c. H.M.S. *Redpole* (gunboat), 1890 (5.6.72)		30	70
39	3 c. *Hoi Houw* (freighter), 1959 (5.6.72)		30	70
40	4 c. *Pigot* (sailing ship), 1771 (6.2.73)		40	75
41	5 c. *Valetta* (cargo-liner), 1968 (6.2.73)		40	75
42	6 c. Type **16**		40	75
43	7 c. *Asia* (merchantman), 1805		40	75
44	8 c. *Islander* (freighter), 1929–60		45	80
45	9 c. H.M.S. *Imperieuse* (armoured cruiser), 1888 (6.2.73)		65	70
46	10 c. H.M.S. *Hecate* (coast defence turret ship), 1871 (4.6.73)		55	80
47	20 c. *Thomas* (galleon), 1615		70	90
48	25 c. Royal Navy sail sloop, 1864 (4.6.73)		80	1·50
49	30 c. *Cygnet* (flute), 1688 (4.6.73)		80	1·00
50	35 c. *Triadic* (freighter), 1958 (4.6.73)		80	1·00
51	50 c. H.M.S. *Amethyst* (frigate), 1857 (6.2.73)		80	1·50
52	$1 *Royal Mary* (warship), 1643 (5.6.72)		1·10	1·75
37/52		*Set of* 16	8·00	13·50

No. 45 is inscribed "H.M.S. *Imperious*", No. 46 "H.M.S. *Egeria*" and No. 48 "H.M.S. *Gordon*", all in error.

(Des Jennifer Toombs)

1972 (2 Oct). *Christmas. T* **17** *and similar vert design. Multicoloured. P* 14.

53	3 c. Type **17**		20	40
	a. Pair. Nos. 53/4		40	80
54	3 c. Angel of Joy		20	40
55	7 c. Type **17**		30	50
	a. Pair. Nos. 55/6		60	1·00
56	7 c. As No. 54		30	50
53/6		*Set of* 4	90	1·60

Nos. 53/4 and 55/6 have the two designs printed horizontally *se-tenant* within the sheet.

18 Virgin and Child, and Map   **19** Mary and Holy Child within Christmas Star

(Des P. Law)

1973 (2 Oct). *Christmas. P* 14 × 13.

57	**18**	7 c. multicoloured	25	35
58		25 c. multicoloured	1·25	1·00

(Des Jennifer Toombs)

1974 (2 Oct). *Christmas. P* 13 × 14½.

59	**19**	7 c. mauve and grey-black	25	60
60		30 c. light orange, bright yell & grey-blk	1·00	2·50

20 "The Flight into Egypt"   **21** Dove of Peace and Star of Bethlehem

(Des Jennifer Toombs)

1975 (2 Oct). *Christmas. P* 14 × 13.

61	**20**	10 c. light greenish yellow, agate and gold	30	35
62		35 c. bright rose, deep blue and gold	95	1·75

(Des R. Bates)

1976 (2 Oct). *Christmas. P* 13½.

63	**21**	10 c. cerise, lemon and bright mauve	20	45
		a. Pair. Nos. 63/4	40	90
64	—	10 c. cerise, lemon and bright mauve	20	45
65	**21**	35 c. reddish violet, light greenish blue and light yellow-green	25	55
		a. Pair. Nos. 65/6	50	1·10
66	—	35 c. reddish violet, light greenish blue and light yellow-green	25	55
63/6		*Set of* 4	80	1·75

Nos. 64 and 66 are "mirror-images" of T **21**, the two designs of each value being printed horizontally *se-tenant* throughout the sheet.

22 William Dampier (explorer)   **23** Australian Coat of Arms on Map of Christmas Island

(Des V. Whiteley Studio)

1977 (30 Apr)–**78.** *Famous Visitors. Horiz designs as T* **22** *in black, vermilion and greenish yellow* (45 c.) *or multicoloured* (*others*). *P* 14 × 13.

67	1 c. Type **22**		15	70
68	2 c. Capt. de Vlamingh (explorer) (22.2.78)		20	70
69	3 c. Vice-Admiral MacLear (22.2.78)		30	70
70	4 c. Sir John Murray (oceanographer) (22.2.78)		30	80
71	5 c. Admiral Aldrich (31.5.78)		30	40
72	6 c. Andrew Clunies Ross (first settler)		30	60
73	7 c. J. J. Lister (naturalist) (31.5.78)		30	40
74	8 c. Admiral of the Fleet Sir William May (1.9.78)		35	70
75	9 c. Henry Ridley (botanist)		40	1·00
76	10 c. George Clunies Ross (phosphate miner) (1.9.78)		35	55
77	20 c. Capt. Joshua Slocum (yachtsman) (1.9.78)		50	75
78	45 c. Charles Andrews (naturalist) (31.5.78)		85	45
79	50 c. Richard Hanitsch (biologist) (31.5.78)		95	80
80	75 c. Victor Purcell (scholar) (1.9.78)		85	1·25
81	$1 Fam Choo Beng (educator)		85	1·25
82	$2 Sir Harold Spencer-Jones (astronomer) (22.2.78)		1·00	2·25
67/82		*Set of* 16	7·00	12·00

(Des Mrs S. Muir. Litho Harrison)

1977 (2 June). *Silver Jubilee. P* 14½ × 13½.
83   23   45 c. multicoloured   45   55

24 "A Partridge in a   **25** Abbott's Booby
Pear Tree"

(Des Jennifer Toombs. Litho Questa)

1977 (20 Oct)–**78**. *Christmas. T* **24** *and similar vert designs depicting the carol "The Twelve Days of Christmas". Multicoloured. P* 14. **A**. *No wmk.*
84A   10 c. Type **24**   10   20
    a. Sheetlet. Nos. 84A/95A   1·10
85A   10 c. "Two turtle doves"   ..   10   20
86A   10 c. "Three French hens"   ..   10   20
87A   10 c. "Four calling birds"   10   20
88A   10 c. "Five gold rings"   10   20
89A   10 c. "Six geese a-laying"   ..   10   20
90A   10 c. "Seven swans a-swimming" ..   10   20
91A   10 c. "Eight maids a-milking" ..   10   20
92A   10 c. "Nine ladies dancing" ..   10   20
93A   10 c. "Ten lords a-leaping" ..   10   20
94A   10 c. "Eleven pipers piping" ..   10   20
95A   10 c. "Twelve drummers drumming" ..   10   20
84A/95A   .. .. ..   *Set of* 12   1·10   2·25

    B. *W w* **14** (27.1.78).
84B   10 c. Type **24**   ..   15   25
    a. Sheetlet. Nos. 84B/95B   1·60
85B   10 c. "Two turtle doves"   ..   15   25
86B   10 c. "Three French hens"   ..   15   25
87B   10 c. "Four calling birds"   15   25
88B   10 c. "Five gold rings"   15   25
89B   10 c. "Six geese a-laying"   ..   15   25
90B   10 c. "Seven swans a-swimming" ..   15   25
91B   10 c. "Eight maids a-milking" ..   15   25
92B   10 c. "Nine ladies dancing" ..   15   25
93B   10 c. "Ten lords a-leaping" ..   15   25
94B   10 c. "Eleven pipers piping" ..   15   25
95B   10 c. "Twelve drummers drumming"   15   25
84B/95B   .. .. ..   *Set of* 12   1·60   2·75
Nos. 84/95 were printed as a *se-tenant* block within a sheetlet 142 × 170 mm.

(Des Jennifer Toombs. Litho Questa)

1978 (21 Apr). *25th Anniv of Coronation. T* **25** *and similar vert designs. P* 15.
96   45 c. black and bright ultramarine   ..   45   75
    a. Sheetlet. Nos. 96/8 × 2   ..   2·50
97   45 c. multicoloured   45   75
98   45 c. black and bright ultramarine   ..   45   75
96/8   .. .. ..   *Set of* 3   1·25   2·00
Designs:—No. 96, White Swan of Bohun; No. 97, Queen Elizabeth II; No. 98, Type **25**.
Nos. 96/8 were printed together in small sheets of 6, containing two *se-tenant* strips of 3 with horizontal gutter margin between.

26 "Christ Child"   **27** Chinese Children

(Des Jennifer Toombs. Litho J.W.)

1978 (2 Oct). *Christmas. Scenes from "The Song of Christmas". T* **26** *and similar horiz designs. Multicoloured. P* 14.
99   10 c. Type **26**   15   20
    a. Sheetlet. Nos. 99/107   ..   1·25
100   10 c. "Herald Angels"   15   20
101   10 c. "Redeemer"   15   20
102   10 c. "Israel"   15   20
103   10 c. "Star"   15   20
104   10 c. "Three Wise Men"   ..   15   20
105   10 c. "Manger"   15   20
106   10 c. "All He Stands For"   ..   15   20
107   10 c. "Shepherds Came"   ..   15   20
99/107   .. ..   *Set of* 9   1·25   1·60
Nos. 99/107 were printed together, *se-tenant*, in a small sheet of 9.

(Des Jennifer Toombs. Litho Questa)

1979 (20 Apr). *International Year of the Child. T* **27** *and similar vert designs showing children of different races. Multicoloured, colour of inscr given. P* 14.
108   20 c. apple-green (Type **27**)   ..   30   45
    a. Horiz strip of 5. Nos. 108/12   1·25
109   20 c. turquoise-green (Malay children)   30   45
110   20 c. lilac (Indian children)   ..   30   45
111   20 c. rose (European children)   ..   30   45
112   20 c. orange-yellow ("Oranges and Lemons")   30   45
108/12   .. ..   *Set of* 5   1·25   2·00
Nos. 108/12 were printed together, *se-tenant*, in horizontal strips of 5 throughout the sheet, forming a composite design.

28 1958 2 c. Definitive   **29** Wise Men following Star

(Des J.W. Litho Questa)

1979 (27 Aug). *Death Centenary of Sir Rowland Hill. T* **28** *and similar horiz designs showing stamps and Sir Rowland Hill. Multicoloured. P* 13½.
113   20 c. Type **28**   25   40
    a. Horiz strip of 5. Nos. 113/17   1·10
114   20 c. 1963 2 c. Map definitive   ..   25   40
115   20 c. 1965 50th anniversary of Gallipoli Landing 10 c. commemorative   ..   25   40
116   20 c. 1968 4 c. Pink-tailed Triggerfish definitive   25   40
117   20 c. 1969 5 c. Christmas issue   ..   25   40
113/17   .. ..   *Set of* 5   1·10   1·75
Nos. 113/17 were printed together, *se-tenant*, in horizontal strips of 5 throughout the sheet.

(Des L. Curtis. Litho Walsall)

1979 (22 Oct). *Christmas. T* **29** *and similar horiz design. Multicoloured. P* 14 × 14½.
118   20 c. Type **29**   20   30
119   55 c. Virgin and Child. .   ..   45   70

30 9th Green   **31** Surveying

(Des R. Granger Barrett. Litho Format)

1980 (12 Feb). *25th Anniv of Christmas Island Golf Club. T* **30** *and similar horiz design. Multicoloured. P* 14½ × 14.
120   20 c. Type **30**   35   50
121   55 c. Clubhouse   40   1·00

(Des L. Curtis. Litho Walsall)

1980 (6 May). *Phosphate Industry (1st issue). T* **31** *and similar horiz designs. Multicoloured. P* 14.
122   15 c. Type **31**   15   25
123   22 c. Drilling for samples   ..   20   30
124   40 c. Sample analysis   ..   30   45
125   55 c. Mine planning   ..   40   55
122/5   .. ..   *Set of* 4   95   1·40
See also Nos. 126/9, 136/9 and 140/3.

(Des L. Curtis. Litho Walsall)

1980 (14 July). *Phosphate Industry (2nd issue). Horiz designs as T* **31**. *Multicoloured. P* 14.
126   15 c. Jungle clearing   15   15
127   22 c. Overburden removal   ..   20   20
128   40 c. Open cut mining   ..   30   25
129   55 c. Restoration   35   30
126/9   .. ..   *Set of* 4   90   80

32 Angel with Harp   **33** *Cryptoblepharus egeriae*

(Des Jennifer Toombs. Litho Walsall)

1980 (6 Oct). *Christmas. T* **32** *and similar vert designs. Multicoloured. P* 13½ × 13.
130   15 c. Type **32**   10   25
    a. Sheetlet. Nos. 130/5   ..   75
131   15 c. Angel with wounded soldier   ..   10   30
132   22 c. Virgin and Child   ..   15   30
133   22 c. Kneeling couple   ..   15   30
134   60 c. Angel with harp (*different*)   ..   20   30
135   60 c. Angel with children   ..   20   30
130/5   .. ..   *Set of* 6   75   1·50
Nos. 130/5 were printed together in small sheets of 6, containing two *se-tenant* strips of 3 (Nos. 130, 132, 134 and 131, 133, 135) with horizontal gutter margin between.

(Des L..Curtis. Litho Walsall)

1981 (9 Feb). *Phosphate Industry (3rd issue). Horiz designs as T* **31**. *Multicoloured. P* 14.
136   22 c. Screening and stockpiling   ..   20   20
137   28 c. Train loading   ..   25   25
138   40 c. Railing   40   40
139   60 c. Drying   55   55
136/9   .. ..   *Set of* 4   1·25   1·25

(Des L. Curtis. Litho Walsall)

1981 (4 May). *Phosphate Industry (4th issue). Horiz designs as T* **31**. *Multicoloured. P* 14.
140   22 c. Crushing   30   20
141   28 c. Conveying   40   25
142   40 c. Bulk storage   60   40
143   60 c. Consolidated Venture (bulk carrier) loading   70   55
140/3   .. ..   *Set of* 4   1·75   1·25

(Des L. Curtis. Litho Walsall)

1981 (10 Aug). *Reptiles. T* **33** *and similar horiz designs. Multicoloured. P* 13.
144   24 c. Type **33**   25   25
145   30 c. *Emoia nativitata*   ..   30   30
146   40 c. *Lepidodactylus listeri*   ..   45   45
147   60 c. *Cyrtodactylus sp. nov.*   ..   65   65
144/7   .. ..   *Set of* 4   1·50   1·50

34 Scene from Carol   **35** Eastern Reef Heron
"Away in a Manger"

(Des Jennifer Toombs. Litho Questa)

1981 (19 Oct). *Christmas. T* **34** *and similar horiz designs showing scenes from carol "Away in a Manger". P* 14½ × 14.
148   18 c. silver, deep blue and turquoise-blue   30   50
    a. Sheetlet. Nos. 148/51   1·25
149   24 c. multicoloured   30   55
150   40 c. multicoloured   35   65
151   60 c. multicoloured   40   75
148/51   .. ..   *Set of* 4   1·25   2·25
Nos. 148/51 were printed together, *se-tenant*, in sheetlets of 4.

(Des N. Arlott. Litho Questa)

1982 (8 Mar)–**83**. *Birds. Multicoloured designs as T* **35**. *P* 14.
152   1 c. Type **35**   70   30
153   2 c. Common Noddy   70   30
154   3 c. White-bellied Swiftlet (14.6.82)   70   70
155   4 c. Christmas Island Imperial Pigeon (14.6.82)   70   70
156   5 c. Christmas Island White Eye (21.2.83)   80   70
157   10 c. Island Thrush (14.6.82)   ..   70   70
158   25 c. Red-tailed Tropic Bird   ..   1·25   60
159   30 c. Emerald Dove (21.2.83)   ..   80   70
160   40 c. Brown Booby (23.8.82)   ..   80   55
161   50 c. Red-footed Booby (23.8.82)   ..   80   55
162   65 c. Christmas Island Frigate Bird (23.8.82)   80   55
163   75 c. White-tailed Tropic Bird (23.8.82)   90   65
164   80 c. Australian Kestrel (*vert*) (21.2.83)   1·25   1·75
165   $1 Indonesian Hawk Owl (*vert*) (21.2.83)   2·50   2·00
166   $2 Australian Goshawk (*vert*) (14.6.82)   1·75   4·00
167   $4 Abbott's Booby (*vert*)   ..   3·00   3·25
152/67   ..   *Set of* 16   16·00   16·00

36 Joseph   **37** "Mirror" Dinghy
and Club House

(Des Jennifer Toombs. Litho and embossed Walsall)

1982 (18 Oct). *Christmas. Origami Paper Sculptures. T* **36** *and similar vert designs. Multicoloured. P* 14½ × 14.
168   27 c. Type **36**   30   30
    a. Horiz strip of 3. Nos. 168/70   1·25
169   50 c. Angel   45   45
170   75 c. Mary and baby Jesus   ..   65   65
168/70   .. ..   *Set of* 3   1·25   1·25
Nos. 168/70 were printed together, *se-tenant*, in horiz strips of 3 throughout the sheet.

(Des L. McCombie. Litho Format)

1983 (2 May). *25th Anniv of Christmas Island Boat Club. T* **37** *and similar multicoloured designs. P* 14 × 14½ (27, 35 c.) *or* 14½ × 14 (*others*).
171   27 c. Type **37**   30   35
172   35 c. Ocean-going yachts   ..   30   40
173   50 c. Fishing launch and cargo ship (*horiz*)   35   50
174   75 c. Dinghy-racing and cantilever (*horiz*)   40   70
171/4   .. ..   *Set of* 4   1·25   1·75

38 Maps of Christmas Island and   **39** Candle and Holly
Australia, Eastern Grey Kangaroo
and White-tailed Tropic Bird

(Des A. Theobald. Litho Questa)

1983 (1 Oct). *25th Anniv of Christmas Island as an Australian Territory.* T **38** *and similar horiz designs. Multicoloured. P* 14.

175	24 c. Type **38**		40	25
176	30 c. Christmas Island and Australian flag		45	45
177	85 c. Maps of Christmas Island and Australia, with Boeing 727 ..		1·25	1·25
175/7		*Set of* 3	1·90	1·75

(Des J.W. Litho Walsall)

1983 (31 Oct). *Christmas. Candles.* T **39** *and similar vert designs. Multicoloured. P* 13.

178	24 c. Type **39**		20	20
179	30 c. Six gold candles ..		30	40
180	85 c. Candles ..		70	1·00
178/80		*Set of* 3	1·10	1·40

40 Feeding on Leaf

41 *Leucocoprinus fragilissimus*

(Des L. Curtis. Litho Questa)

1984 (20 Feb). *Red Land Crab.* T **40** *and similar horiz designs showing various aspects of crab's life. Multicoloured. P* 14 × 14½.

181	30 c. Type **40**		30	30
182	40 c. Migration		35	40
183	55 c. Development stages		40	50
184	85 c. Adult female and young..		60	70
181/4		*Set of* 4	1·50	1·75

(Des I. Loe. Litho Format)

1984 (30 Apr). *Fungi.* T **41** *and similar vert designs. Multicoloured. P* 14 × 14½.

185	30 c. Type **41**		65	55
186	40 c. *Microporus xanthopus*		75	70
187	45 c. *Hydropus anthidepas* ("*Trogia anthidepas*")		85	80
188	55 c. *Haddowia longipes*		85	90
189	85 c. *Phillipsia domingensis*		1·10	1·25
185/9		*Set of* 5	3·75	3·75

42 Run-out

43 Arrival of Father Christmas

(Des A. Theobald. Litho J.W.)

1984 (23 July). *25th Anniversary of Cricket on Christmas Island.* T **42** *and similar horiz designs. Multicoloured. P* 14.

190	30 c. Type **42**		75	85
191	40 c. Bowled-out		85	1·10
192	55 c. Batsman in action		1·10	1·50
193	85 c. Fielder diving for catch		1·25	1·75
190/3 ..		*Set of* 4	3·50	4·75

(Des D. Slater. Litho B.D.T.)

1984 (21 Sept). *Christmas and "Ausipex" International Stamp Exhibition, Melbourne. Sheet* 100 × 100 *mm containing* T **43** *and similar horiz designs. Multicoloured. P* 13½.

MS194 30 c. Type **43**; 55 c. Distribution of presents; 85 c. Departure of Father Christmas .. 2·25 2·25
No. **MS**194 also contains three labels horizontally *se-tenant* with the stamps and forming composite designs with them.

44 Robber Crab

45 "Once in Royal David's City"

(Des L. Curtis. Litho Walsall)

1985 (30 Jan). *Crabs (1st series).* T **44** *and similar horiz designs. Multicoloured. P* 13 × 13½.

195	30 c. Type **44**		1·00	70
196	40 c. Horn-eyed Ghost Crab		1·10	1·10
197	55 c. Purple Hermit Crab		1·50	1·60
198	85 c. Little Nipper		2·00	2·00
195/8 ..		*Set of* 4	5·50	5·50

See also Nos. 199/202 and 203/6.

(Des L. Curtis. Litho Walsall)

1985 (29 Apr). *Crabs (2nd series). Horiz designs as* T **44**. *Multicoloured. P* 13 × 13½.

199	33 c. Blue Crab		1·00	55
200	45 c. Tawny Hermit Crab		1·10	1·10
201	60 c. Red Nipper		1·60	1·75
202	90 c. Smooth-handed Ghost Crab		2·25	2·50
199/202		*Set of* 4	5·50	5·50

(Des L. Curtis. Litho Walsall)

1985 (22 July). *Crabs (3rd series). Horiz designs as* T **44**. *Multicoloured. P* 13 × 13½.

203	33 c. Red Crab		1·10	60
204	45 c. Mottled Crab		1·50	1·40
205	60 c. Rock Hopper Crab		2·25	2·50
206	90 c. Yellow Nipper		2·75	3·50
203/6		*Set of* 4	7·00	7·25

(Des Jennifer Toombs. Litho Harrison)

1985 (28 Oct). *Christmas. Carols.* T **45** *and similar vert designs. Multicoloured. P* 14 × 14½.

207	27 c. Type **45**		1·00	1·25
	a. Horiz strip of 5. Nos. 207/11		6·00	
208	33 c. "While Shepherds Watched Their Flocks by Night"		1·10	1·40
209	45 c. "Away in a Manger"		1·40	1·60
210	60 c. "We Three Kings of Orient Are"		1·50	1·75
211	90 c. "Hark the Herald Angels Sing"		1·60	1·90
207/11		*Set of* 5	7·00	7·00

Nos. 207/11 were printed together, *se-tenant* in horizontal strips of 5 throughout the sheet.

46 Halley's Comet over Christmas Island

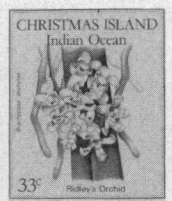
47 Ridley's Orchid

(Des L. Curtis. Litho Format)

1986 (30 Apr). *Appearance of Halley's Comet.* T **46** *and similar horiz designs. Multicoloured. P* 14.

212	33 c. Type **46**		65	80
213	45 c. Edmond Halley ..		80	1·10
214	60 c. Comet and *Consolidated Venture* (bulk carrier) loading phosphate		1·00	2·25
215	90 c. Comet over Flying Fish Cove		1·50	2·50
212/15		*Set of* 4	3·50	6·00

(Des I. Loe. Litho Format)

1986 (30 June). *Native Flowers.* T **47** *and similar vert designs. Multicoloured. P* 14.

216	33 c. Type **47** ..		70	55
217	45 c. Hanging Flower		55	85
218	60 c. Hoya		60	1·50
219	90 c. Sea Hibiscus		65	2·00
216/19		*Set of* 4	2·25	4·50

(Des D. Miller. Litho Walsall)

1986 (23 July). *Royal Wedding. Square designs as* T **112** *of Ascension. Multicoloured. P* 14½ × 14.

220	33 c. Prince Andrew and Miss Sarah Ferguson		45	50
221	90 c. Prince Andrew piloting helicopter, Digby, Canada, 1985		95	1·75

48 Father Christmas and Reindeer in Speed Boat

(Des G. Vasarhelyi. Litho Walsall)

1986 (30 Sept). *Christmas.* T **48** *and similar horiz designs. Multicoloured. P* 13 × 13½.

222	30 c. Type **48**		75	50
223	36 c. Father Christmas and reindeer on beach		85	60
224	55 c. Father Christmas fishing		1·50	1·50
225	70 c. Playing golf		2·25	2·75
226	$1 Sleeping in hammock		2·50	3·50
222/6		*Set of* 5	7·00	8·00

49 H.M.S. *Flying Fish* and Outline Map of Christmas Island

(Des L. Curtis. Litho Format)

1987 (21 Jan). *Centenary of Visits by H.M.S. "Flying Fish" and H.M.S. "Egeria".* T **49** *and similar horiz design. Multicoloured. P* 14½.

227	36 c. Type **49**		60	75
228	90 c. H.M.S. *Egeria* and outline map		1·00	2·50

50 Blind Snake
51 Children watching Father Christmas in Sleigh

(Des G. Drummond. Litho Questa)

1987 (25 Mar)–**89**. *Wildlife.* T **50** *and similar horiz designs. Multicoloured. P* 14.

229	1 c. Type **50**		40	90
	a. Sheetlet of 16. Nos. 229/37 and 238/44 (1.3.88)		28·00	
230	2 c. Blue-tailed Skink		40	90
231	3 c. Insectivorous Bat (24.6.87)		90	90
232	5 c. Grasshopper (1.3.88)		90	90
233	10 c. Christmas Island Fruit Bat (24.6.87)		90	90
234	25 c. Gecko		1·00	1·00
235	30 c. *Mantis religiosa* (mantid) (1.3.88)		1·25	1·25
236	36 c. Indonesian Hawk Owl (24.6.87)		3·00	1·75
237	40 c. Bull-mouth Helmet (*Cypraecassis rufa*) (26.8.87)		1·75	1·00
237a	41 c. Nudibranch (*Phidiana* sp) (1.9.89)		1·25	70
238	50 c. Textile or Cloth of Gold Cone (*Conus textile*) (26.8.87)		1·75	1·25
239	65 c. Brittle Stars (26.8.87)		1·40	1·25
240	75 c. Regal Angelfish (26.8.87)		1·40	1·25
241	90 c. *Appias paulina* (butterfly) (1.3.88)		3·75	2·75
242	$1 *Hypolimnas misippus* (butterfly) (1.3.88)		3·75	2·75
243	$2 Shrew (*Crocidura attenuata trichura*) (24.6.87)		3·75	6·00
244	$5 Green Turtle		4·50	7·00
229/44		*Set of* 17	28·00	28·00

No. 229a was originally only available from a presentation pack, but was, subsequently, sold separately by the Christmas Island Post Office. Stamps from it show "1988" imprint date. Examples from the ordinary sheets are without imprint date.

(Des D. Miller. Litho CPE Australia Ltd, Melbourne)

1987 (7 Oct). *Christmas. Sheet,* 165 × 65 *mm, containing* T **51** *and similar multicoloured designs. P* 13½.

MS245 30 c. Type **51**; 37 c. Father Christmas distributing gifts (48 × 22 *mm*); 90 c. Children with presents (48 × 22 *mm*); $1 Singing carols 4·00 4·00
a. Imperf between 37 c. and 90 c.
The stamps within No. **MS**245 form a composite design of a beach scene.

(Des Sue Passmore. Litho CPE Australia Ltd, Melbourne)

1988 (26 Jan). *Bicentenary of Australian Settlement. Arrival of First Fleet. Square designs as Nos.* 1105/9 *of Australia, but each inscribed* "CHRISTMAS ISLAND Indian Ocean" *and* "AUSTRALIA BICENTENARY".

246	37 c. Aborigines watching arrival of Fleet, Botany Bay		1·50	1·75
	a. Horiz strip of 5. Nos. 246/50		6·75	
247	37 c. Aboriginal family and anchored ships ..		1·50	1·75
248	37 c. Fleet arriving at Sydney Cove..		1·50	1·75
249	37 c. Ship's boat		1·50	1·75
250	37 c. Raising the flag, Sydney Cove, 26 January 1788 ..		1·50	1·75
246/50		*Set of* 5	6·75	8·00

Nos. 246/50 were printed together, *se-tenant*, in horizontal strips of five throughout the sheet, forming a composite design.

52 Captain William May
53 Pony and Trap, 1910

(Des Josephine Martin. Litho Questa)

1988 (8 June). *Centenary of British Annexation.* T **52** *and similar vert designs. Multicoloured. P* 14½ × 14.

251	37 c. Type **52**		35	40
252	53 c. Annexation ceremony		50	55
253	95 c. H.M.S. *Imperieuse* (armoured cruiser) firing salute		90	95
254	$1.50, Building commemorative cairn		1·40	1·50
251/4		*Set of* 4	2·75	3·00

(Des L. Curtis. Litho Walsall)

1988 (24 Aug). *Centenary of Permanent Settlement.* T **53** *and similar horiz designs. Multicoloured. P* 14 × 14½.

255	37 c. Type **53**		60	40
256	55 c. Phosphate mining, 1910		85	55
257	70 c. Steam locomotive, 1914		1·25	85
258	$1 Arrival of first aircraft, 1957		1·50	1·25
255/8		*Set of* 4	3·75	2·75

54 Beach Toys | **55** Food on Table ("Good Harvesting")

(Des N. Shewring. Litho Format)

1988 (15 Nov). *Christmas. Toys and Gifts. T* **54** *and similar vert designs. Multicoloured. P* 14.
259	32 c. Type **54**	40	35
260	39 c. Flippers, snorkel and mask	50	40
261	90 c. Model soldier, doll and soft toys	1·10	1·10
262	$1 Models of racing car, lorry and jet aircraft	1·25	1·25
259/62	Set of 4	3·00	2·75

(Des D. Miller. Litho Questa)

1989 (31 Jan). *Chinese New Year. T* **55** *and similar horiz designs. Multicoloured. P* 14 × 14½.
263	39 c. Type **55**	45	40
264	70 c. Decorations ("Prosperity")	80	70
265	90 c. Chinese girls ("Good Fortune")	1·10	90
266	$1 Lion dance ("Progress Every Year")	1·25	1·00
263/6	Set of 4	3·25	2·75

56 Sir John Murray | **57** Four Children

(Des S. Noon. Litho Walsall)

1989 (16 Mar). *75th Death Anniv of Sir John Murray (oceanographer). T* **56** *and similar horiz designs. Multicoloured. P* 14 × 14½.
267	39 c. Type **56**	50	50
268	80 c. Map of Christmas Island showing Murray Hill	1·25	95
269	$1 Oceanographic equipment	1·50	1·25
270	$1.10, H.M.S. *Challenger* (survey ship), 1872	1·75	1·50
267/70	Set of 4	4·50	3·75

(Des C. Burke. Litho Questa)

1989 (31 May). *Malay Hari Raya Festival. T* **57** *and similar vert designs. Multicoloured. P* 14.
271	39 c. Type **57**	55	50
272	55 c. Man playing tambourine	80	70
273	80 c. Girl in festival costume	1·25	1·00
274	$1.10, Christmas Island Mosque	1·60	1·40
271/4	Set of 4	3·75	3·25

58 *Huperzia phlegmaria* | **59** Virgin Mary and Star

(Des Kerrie Rockett. Litho Walsall)

1989 (16 Aug). *Ferns. T* **58** *and similar vert designs. Multicoloured. P* 14.
275	41 c. Type **58**	75	60
276	65 c. *Asplenium polydon*	1·10	85
277	80 c. Common Bracken	1·40	1·00
278	$1.10, Birds-nest Fern	1·60	1·40
275/8	Set of 4	4·25	3·50

(Des G. Maynard. Litho Leigh-Mardon Ltd, Melbourne)

1989 (4 Oct). *Christmas. T* **59** *and similar vert designs. Multicoloured. P* 14½.
279	36 c. Type **59**	60	40
280	41 c. Christ Child in manger	60	45
281	80 c. Shepherds and Star	1·50	80
282	$1.10, Three Wise Men following Star	1·60	1·10
279/82	Set of 4	3·75	2·50

COVER PRICES

Cover factors are quoted at the beginning of each country for most issues to 1945. An explanation of the system can be found on page x. The factors quoted do not, however, apply to philatelic covers.

(60) | **61** First Sighting, 1615

1989 (18 Oct). *"Melbourne Stampshow '89". No. 237a and as No. 242, but with imprint date, optd with T* **60**.
283	41 c. Nudibranch (*Phidiana* sp)	75	45
284	$1 *Hypolimnas misippus*	1·75	1·00

(Des R. Honisett. Litho Note Ptg Branch, Reserve Bank of Australia)

1990 (31 Jan). *375th Anniv of Discovery of Christmas Island. T* **61** *and similar vert design. Multicoloured. P* 14×15.
285	41 c. Type **61**	1·00	50
286	$1.10, Second sighting and naming, 1643	2·25	1·40

62 Miniature Tractor pulling Phosphate | **63** Male Abbott's Booby

(Des C. Lee. Litho Leigh-Mardon Ltd, Melbourne)

1990 (18 Apr–22 Aug). *Christmas Island Transport. T* **62** *and similar multicoloured designs. P* 13½×14 (*horiz*) or 14×13½ (*vert*).
287	1 c. Type **62**	15	20
288	2 c. Phosphate train (22 Aug)	40	40
289	3 c. Diesel railcar No. 8802 (*vert*)	20	20
290	5 c. Loading Road train (22 Aug)	40	40
291	10 c. Trishaw (*vert*)	30	30
292	15 c. Terex truck (22 Aug)	65	65
293	25 c. Articulated bus	30	30
294	30 c. Cable passenger carriage (*vert*)	30	35
295	40 c. Passenger barge (*vert*)	35	40
296	50 c. Kolek (outrigger canoe)	55	55
297	65 c. Flying Doctor aircraft and ambulance (22 Aug)	3·75	1·50
298	75 c. Commercial van (22 Aug)	1·50	1·50
299	90 c. Vintage lorry (22 Aug)	1·75	1·75
300	$1 Water tanker (22 Aug)	1·75	1·75
301	$2 Traction engine (22 Aug)	3·25	3·25
302	$5 Steam locomotive No. 1	4·50	4·75
287/302	Set of 16	18·00	17·00

(Des N. Shewring. Litho Questa)

1990 (6 June). *Abbott's Booby. T* **63** *and similar vert designs. Multicoloured. P* 13½×14.
303	10 c. Type **63**	85	30
304	20 c. Juvenile male	1·40	50
305	29 c. Female with egg	1·60	55
306	41 c. Pair with chick	2·25	70
303/6	Set of 4	5·50	1·90
MS307	122×68 mm. 41 c. Male with wings spread; 41 c. Male on branch; 41 c. Female with fledgling. P 14½	4·00	2·75

The three stamps within No. **MS**307 form a composite design and are without the W.W.F. logo.

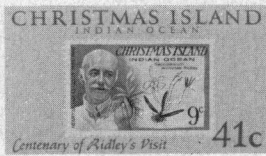

64 1977 Famous Visitors 9 c. Stamp

(Des Elizabeth Innes. Litho Leigh-Mardon Ltd, Melbourne)

1990 (11 July). *Centenary of Henry Ridley's Visit. T* **64** *and similar multicoloured design. P* 15×14½ (41 c.) *or* 14½×15 (75 c.).
308	41 c. Type **64**	55	65
309	75 c. Ridley (botanist) in rainforest (*vert*)	85	1·75

1990 (24 Aug). *"New Zealand 1990" International Stamp Exhibition, Auckland. No.* **MS**307 *optd "NZ 1990 WORLD STAMP EXHIBITION AUCKLAND, NEW ZEALAND, 24 AUGUST – 2 SEPTEMBER 1990" in purple on the sheet margins.*
MS310	122×68 mm. 41 c. Male with wings spread; 41 c. Male on branch; 41 c. Female with fledgling	5·00	5·50
	a. Error. Imperf	£1000	

65 *Corymborkus veratrifolia* | **66** *Islander* (freighter), 1898

(Litho Leigh-Mardon Ltd, Melbourne)

1990 (3 Oct). *Christmas. Flowers. T* **65** *and similar horiz designs. Multicoloured. P* 14½.
311	38 c. Type **65**	1·10	70
312	43 c. *Hoya aldrichii*	1·25	75
313	80 c. *Quisqualis indica*	2·25	2·75
314	$1.20, *Barringtonia racemosa*	2·75	3·50
311/14	Set of 4	6·50	7·00

1990 (6 Dec). *"Birdpex '90" Stamp Exhibition, Christchurch. No.* **MS**307 *optd "BIRDPEX '90 NATIONAL PHILATELIC EXHIBITION UNIVERSITY OF CANTERBURY CHRISTCHURCH NZ 6–9 DEC 1990 IN CONJUNCTION WITH THE 20th INTERNATIONAL ORNITHOLOGICAL CONGRESS" in green on the sheet margins.*
MS315	122×68 mm. 41 c. Male with wings spread; 41 c. Male on branch; 41 c. Female with fledgling	6·00	6·50

(Des C. Lee. Litho Leigh-Mardon Ltd, Melbourne)

1991 (13 Feb). *Centenary of First Phosphate Mining Lease. T* **66** *and similar vert designs. Multicoloured. P* 14½.
316	43 c. Type **66**	1·00	90
	a. Horiz strip of 5. Nos. 316/20	6·50	
317	43 c. Miners loading tipper wagons, 1908	1·00	90
318	85 c. Shay steam locomotive No. 4, 1925	1·40	1·25
319	$1.20, Extracting phosphate, 1951	1·75	1·60
320	$1.70, Land reclamation, 1990	2·00	1·90
316/20	Set of 5	6·50	6·00

Nos. 316/20 were printed together, *se-tenant*, in horizontal strips of 5 throughout the sheet, the background forming a composite forest design.

67 Teaching Children Road Safety | **68** Map of Christmas Island, 1991

(Des R. Honisett. Litho Leigh-Mardon Ltd, Melbourne)

1991 (17 Apr). *Christmas Island Police Force. T* **67** *and similar horiz designs. Multicoloured. P* 14½.
321	43 c. Type **67**	1·50	75
322	43 c. Traffic control	1·50	75
323	90 c. Airport customs	2·25	2·25
324	$1.20, Police launch *Fregata Andrews* towing rescued boat	3·00	3·00
321/4	Set of 4	7·50	6·00
MS325	135×88 mm. Nos. 321/4	7·50	6·00

(Des D. Miller. Litho Questa)

1991 (19 June). *Maps of Christmas Island. T* **68** *and similar vert designs. Multicoloured. P* 14×13½.
326	43 c. Type **68**	1·00	65
327	75 c. Goos Atlas, 1666	1·75	1·10
328	$1.10, De Manevillette, 1745	2·25	1·60
329	$1.20, Comberford, 1667	2·25	1·90
326/9	Set of 4	6·50	4·75

69 *Bruguiera gymnorrhiza* | **70** "Family round Christmas Tree", (S'ng Yen Luiw)

(Des Jane Moore. Litho Leigh-Mardon Ltd, Melbourne)

1991 (21 Aug). *Local Trees. T* **69** *and similar horiz designs. Multicoloured. P* 14.
330	43 c. Type **69**	1·00	65
331	70 c. *Syzygium operculatum*	1·50	1·00
332	85 c. *Ficus microcarpa*	1·75	1·25
333	$1.20, *Arenga listeri*	2·00	1·60
330/3	Set of 4	5·75	4·00

(Des Liz Innes. Litho Leigh-Mardon Ltd, Melbourne)

1991 (2 Oct). *Christmas. Children's Paintings. T* **70** *and similar horiz designs. Multicoloured. P* 14½.

334	38 c. Type **70**		75	55
	a. Horiz strip of 5. Nos 334/8		3·25	
335	38 c. "Opening Presents" (Liew Ann Nee)		75	55
336	38 c. "Beach Party" (Foo Pang Chuan)		75	55
337	38 c. "Christmas Walk" (Too Lai Peng)		75	55
338	38 c. "Santa Claus and Christmas Tree" (Jesamine Wheeler)		75	55
339	43 c. "Santa Claus fishing" (Ho Puay Ha)		75	60
340	$1 "Santa Claus in Boat" (Ng Hooi Hua)		1·50	1·25
341	$1.20, "Santa Claus surfing" (Yani Kawi)		1·75	1·50
334/41		*Set of* 8	7·00	5·50

Nos. 334/8 were printed together, *se-tenant*, in horizontal strips of 5 throughout the sheet.

71 Discussing Evacuation, 1942

72 Snake's-head Cowrie (*Cypraea caputserpentis*)

(Des C. Lee. Litho Leigh-Mardon Ltd, Melbourne)

1992 (19 Feb). *50th Anniv of Partial Evacuation. T* **71** *and similar vert designs. Multicoloured. P* 14½.

342	45 c. Type **71**		1·00	1·00
343	45 c. Families waiting to embark		1·00	1·00
344	$1.05, Ferrying evacuees to *Islander*		2·50	2·50
345	$1.20, Departure of *Islander* (freighter)		2·75	2·75
342/5		*Set of* 4	6·50	6·50

(Des G. Ryan. Litho Leigh-Mardon Ltd, Melbourne)

1992 (15 Apr–19 Aug). *Shells. T* **72** *and similar vert designs. Multicoloured. P* 14½.

346	5 c. Tiger Cowrie (*Cypraea tigris*) (19 Aug)		50	40
347	10 c. Type **72**		60	50
348	15 c. Scorpion Conch (*Lambis scorpius*) (19 Aug)		75	50
349	20 c. Royal Oak Scallop (*Cryptopecten pallium*)		85	50
350	25 c. Striped Engina (*Engina mendicaria*) (19 Aug)		85	50
351	30 c. Prickly Pacific Drupe (*Drupa ricinus*)		1·00	50
352	40 c. Reticulate Distorsio (*Distorsio recticulata*) (19 Aug)		1·00	55
353	45 c. Tapestry Turban (*Turbo petholatus*)		1·25	60
354	50 c. Beautiful Goblet (*Pollia puchra*) (19 Aug)		1·25	55
355	60 c. Captain Cone (*Conus capitaneus*)		1·50	65
356	70 c. Lajonkaire's Turban (*Turbo lajonkairii*) (19 Aug)		1·50	75
357	80 c. Chiragra Spider Conch (*Lambis chiragra chiragra*)		1·75	85
358	90 c. Common Delphina (*Angaria delphinus*) (19 Aug)		1·75	1·10
359	$1 Ceramic Vase (*Vasum ceramicum*)		1·75	1·25
360	$2 Pacific Partridge Tun (*Tonna perdix*)		2·00	2·10
361	$5 Strawberry Drupe (*Drupa rubusidaeus*) (19 Aug)		5·00	5·25
346/61		*Set of* 16	21·00	14·00

73 Torpedoing of *Eidsvold*

(74)

(Des R. Watton. Litho Enschedé)

1992 (17 June). *50th Anniv of Sinkings of* Eidsvold *and* Nissa Maru. *T* **73** *and similar horiz designs. Multicoloured. P* 14×13½.

362	45 c. Type **73**		1·25	75
363	80 c. *Eidsvold* sinking		2·00	1·75
364	$1.05, *Nissa Maru* under attack		2·50	2·75
365	$1.20, *Nissa Maru* beached		2·50	3·00
362/5		*Set of* 4	7·50	7·50

1992 (1 Sept). *"Kuala Lumpur '92" International Philatelic Exhibition. No.* 361 *optd with T* **74** *in red.*

366	$5 Strawberry Drupe (*Drupa rubusidaeus*)		9·00	7·00

75 Jungle

76 Abbott's Booby

(Des Jane Moore and Elizabeth Innes. Litho Leigh-Mardon Ltd, Melbourne)

1992 (7 Oct). *Christmas. T* **75** *and similar vert designs. Multicoloured. P* 14½.

367	40 c. Type **75**		90	1·00
	a. Horiz strip of 5. Nos. 367/71		5·50	
368	40 c. Seabirds over rock		90	1·00
369	45 c. Brown Boobies on headland		90	1·00
370	$1.05, Seabirds and cliffs		1·60	1·75
371	$1.20, Cliffs		1·60	1·75
367/71		*Set of* 5	5·50	6·00

Nos. 367/71 were printed together, *se-tenant*, in horizontal strips of 5 throughout the sheet, each strip forming a composite coastal design.

On 2 March 1993 responsibility for the Christmas Island postal service passed from the territorial administration to Australia Post. In consequence Nos. 372/7 and all subsequent issues are valid for postal purposes in both Christmas Island and Australia.

(Des D. Nelson and Janet Boschen. Litho McPherson's Ptg Group, Mulgrave)

1993 (4 Mar). *Seabirds. T* **76** *and similar vert designs. Multicoloured. P* 14½×14.

372	45 c. Type **76**		60	80
	a. Horiz strip of 5. Nos. 372/6		2·75	
373	45 c. Christmas Island Frigate Bird		60	80
374	45 c. Common Noddy		60	80
375	45 c. White-tailed Tropic Bird ("Golden Bosunbird")		60	80
376	45 c. Brown Booby		60	80
372/6		*Set of* 5	2·75	3·50
MS377	140×70 mm. Nos. 372/6		2·75	3·50

Nos. 372/6 were printed together, *se-tenant*, in horizontal strips of 5 throughout the sheet, forming a composite design.

No. MS377 also exists overprinted with the "Indopex '93" or "Taipei '93" logos for sale at these stamp exhibitions in Surabaya, Indonesia, and Taiwan.

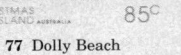

77 Dolly Beach

78 Turtle on Beach

(Des Jane Moore and Janet Boschen. Litho McPherson's Ptg Group, Mulgrave)

1993 (1 June). *Scenic Views of Christmas Island. T* **77** *and similar horiz designs. Multicoloured. P* 14×14½.

378	85 c. Type **77**		1·25	1·50
379	95 c. Blow Holes		1·50	1·75
380	$1.05, Merrial Beach		1·60	1·90
381	$1.20, Rainforest		1·75	2·00
378/81		*Set of* 4	5·50	6·50

(Des B. Wood and Sandra Harman. Litho McPherson's Ptg Group, Mulgrave)

1993 (2 Sept). *Christmas. T* **78** *and similar vert designs. Multicoloured. P* 14½×14.

382	40 c. Type **78**		1·00	60
383	45 c. Crabs and wave		1·00	60
384	$1 Christmas Island Frigate Bird and rainforest		2·25	3·00
382/4		*Set of* 3	3·75	3·75

79 Map of Christmas Island

80 Pekingese

(Des Betina Ogden. Litho McPherson's Ptg Group, Mulgrave)

1993 (1 Dec). *350th Anniv of Naming of Christmas Island. P* 14½×14½.

385	79 $2 multicoloured		3·00	3·25

(Des Yen Lau. Litho McPherson's Ptg Group, Mulgrave)

1994 (20 Jan). *Chinese New Year ("Year of the Dog"). T* **80** *and similar horiz design. P* 14×14½.

386	45 c. Type **80**		1·00	1·25
	a. Pair. Nos. 386/7		2·00	2·50
387	45 c. Mickey (Christmas Island dog)		1·00	1·25
MS388	106×70 mm. Nos. 386/7		2·50	3·00

Nos. 386/7 were printed together, *se-tenant*, in horizontal or vertical pairs throughout the sheet.

No. MS388 also exists overprinted with "Melbourne Stamp & Coin Show 11–13 February 1994", "Hong Kong '94 Stamp Exhibition", "Canberra Stamp Show 94" or "Queensland Stamp and Coin Show 94" logos for sale at these exhibitions.

81 Shay Locomotive No. 4

82 *Brachypeza archytas*

(Des J. Richards. Litho McPherson's Ptg Group, Mulgrave)

1994 (19 May). *Steam Locomotives. T* **81** *and similar horiz designs. Multicoloured. P* 14×14½.

389	85 c. Type **81**		1·75	1·75
390	95 c. Locomotive No. 9		1·75	1·75
391	$1.20, Locomotive No. 1		2·00	2·25
389/91		*Set of* 3	5·00	5·25

(Des Celia Rosser. Litho McPherson's Ptg Group, Mulgrave)

1994 (16 Aug). *Orchids. T* **82** *and similar vert designs. Multicoloured. P* 14½×14.

392	45 c. Type **82**		1·10	1·25
	a. Horiz strip of 5. Nos. 392/6		5·00	
393	45 c. *Thelasis capitata*		1·10	1·25
394	45 c. *Corymborkis veratrifolia*		1·10	1·25
395	45 c. *Flickingeria nativitatis*		1·10	1·25
396	45 c. *Dendrobium crumenatum*		1·10	1·25
392/6		*Set of* 5	5·00	5·50

Nos. 392/6 were printed together, *se-tenant*, in horizontal strips of 5 throughout the sheet.

83 Angel blowing Trumpet

84 Pig

(Des Tracie Grimwood. Litho McPherson's Ptg Group, Mulgrave)

1994 (8 Sept). *Christmas. T* **83** *and similar horiz designs. Multicoloured. P* 14×14½.

397	40 c. Type **83**		80	50
398	45 c. Wise Man holding gift		80	50
399	80 c. Star over Bethlehem		1·75	2·50
397/9		*Set of* 3	3·00	3·25

(Des J. Chan. Litho McPherson's Ptg Group, Mulgrave)

1995 (12 Jan). *Chinese New Year ("Year of the Pig"). T* **84** *and similar horiz design showing a different pig. P* 14×14½.

400	45 c. multicoloured		75	50
401	85 c. multicoloured		1·25	1·60
MS402	106×71 mm. Nos. 400/1		2·00	2·50

No. MS402 also exists overprinted with "Melbourne Stamp & Coin Show 10–12 February 1995" logo for sale at this exhibition.

85 Golfer playing Shot

86 Father Christmas with Map on Christmas Island Frigate Bird

(Des N. Buchanan. Litho McPherson's Ptg Group, Mulgrave)

1995 (11 May). *40th Anniv of Christmas Island Golf Course. P* 14×14½.

403	85 $2.50, multicoloured		4·25	4·00

(Des B. Wood and Sophie Newman. Litho McPherson's Ptg Group, Mulgrave)

1995 (14 Sept). *Christmas. T* **86** *and similar horiz designs. Multicoloured. P* 14×14½.

404	40 c. Type **86**		80	50
405	45 c. Father Christmas distributing presents		80	50
406	80 c. Father Christmas waving goodbye		1·75	2·50
404/6		*Set of* 3	3·00	3·25

COVER PRICES

Cover factors are quoted at the beginning of each country for most issues to 1945. An explanation of the system can be found on page x. The factors quoted do not, however, apply to philatelic covers.

87 De Havilland D.H.98
Mosquito on
Reconnaissance Mission

88 Lemon-peel Angelfish

(Des B. Sadgrove. Recess and litho Note Ptg Branch, Reserve
Bank of Australia)

1995 (12 Oct). *50th Anniv of End of Second World War. T* **87**
and similar horiz design, each black, stone and vermilion.
P 14×14½.
407	45 c. Type **87**	..	..	95	95
	a. Pair. Nos. 407/8			1·90	1·90
408	45 c. H.M.S. *Rother* (frigate)	..	..	95	95

Nos. 407/8 were printed together, *se-tenant*, in horizontal and
vertical pairs throughout the sheet.

(Des Lisa Christensen (85 c., 95 c., $1.20), Josephine Mure
(others). Litho SNP Cambec (75 c., $1) or McPherson's Ptg
Group, Mulgrave (others))

1995 (12 Oct)–**97**. *Marine Life. T* **88** *and similar horiz designs.*
Multicoloured. P 14×14½.
412	20 c. Pink-tailed Triggerfish (18.4.96)		15	20
413	30 c. Japanese Inflator-filefish ("Longnose			
	Filefish") (18.4.96)			25	30
414	45 c. Princess Anthias (18.4.96)	..	35	40
415	75 c. Type **88**	..	..	60	65
416	85 c. Moon Wrasse (17.7.97)	..	65	70
417	90 c. Spotted Boxfish (18.4.96)	..	70	75
418	95 c. Moorish Idol (17.7.97)	..	75	80
419	$1 Emperor Angelfish	..	..	80	85
420	$1.20, Glass-eyed Snapper ("Glass			
	Bigeye") (17.7.97)	..	..	90	95
412/20		*Set of 9*	5·00	5·50

89 Rat with Drum

90 Christmas
Island White Eye

(Des L. Chiang. Litho SNP Cambec (gold die-stamped Avon
Graphics))

1996 (9 Jan). *Chinese New Year ("Year of the Rat"). T* **89** *and*
similar horiz design. Multicoloured. P 14×14½.
425	45 c. Type **89**	..	..	75	75
	a. Pair. Nos. 425/6			1·50	1·50
426	45 c. Rat with tambourine		75	75
MS427	106×70 mm. Nos. 425/6	..	2·00	2·25

Nos. 425/6 were printed together, *se-tenant*, in horizontal and
vertical pairs throughout the sheet.

No. MS427 also exists overprinted with the logo of the
Melbourne Stamp and Coin Fair for sale at this Australian
exhibition.

(Des T. Pridham and Susan Horvath. Litho McPherson's Ptg
Group, Mulgrave)

1996 (11 July). *Christmas Island Land Birds. T* **90** *and similar*
vert design. Multicoloured. P 14½×14.
428	45 c. Type **90**	..	..	75	50
429	85 c. Christmas Island Hawk Owl	..	1·75	2·00

91 Three Ships approaching Island

92 Ox facing Right

(Des P. Gifford. Litho McPherson's Ptg Group, Mulgrave)

1996 (12 Sept). *Christmas. "I saw Three Ships" (carol). T* **91**
and similar square designs. Multicoloured. P 14½.
430	40 c. Type **91**	..	..	75	60
431	45 c. Madonna and Child with ships at			
	anchor	..	..	75	60
432	80 c. Ships leaving	..	..	1·60	1·90
430/2		*Set of 3*	2·75	2·75

(Des A. Donato. Litho McPherson's Ptg Group, Mulgrave)

1996 (1 Nov). *300th Anniv of Willem de Vlamingh's Discovery*
of Christmas Island. As No. 1655 of Australia. P 14×14½.
433	45 c. multicoloured	..	..	75	75

No. 433 and No. 1655 of Australia were printed together,
se-tenant, in horizontal pairs throughout the sheet which are
listed as No. 1655a of Australia.

(Des L. Chiang. Litho SNP Cambec (gold die-stamped Avon
Graphics))

1997 (6 Jan). *Chinese New Year ("Year of the Ox"). T* **92** *and*
similar horiz design. Multicoloured. P 14×14½.
434	45 c. Type **92**	..	..	70	80
	a. Pair. Nos. 434/5	..	..	1·40	1·60
435	45 c. Ox facing left	..	..	70	80
MS436	106×70 mm. Nos. 434/5	..	1·75	2·00

Nos. 434/5 were printed together, *se-tenant*, in horizontal and
vertical pairs throughout the sheet.

93 Father Christmas
reading Letter

94 Tiger

(Des A. Hopgood. Litho McPherson's Ptg Group, Mulgrave)

1997 (11 Sept). *Christmas. T* **93** *and similar horiz designs.*
Multicoloured. P 14×14½.
437	40 c. Type **93**	..	..	55	45
438	45 c. Father Christmas carving wooden boat	55	45
439	80 c. Father Christmas in sleigh	..	1·10	1·40
437/9		*Set of 3*	2·00	2·10

(Des L. Chiang. Litho SNP Cambec)

1998 (5 Jan). *Chinese New Year ("Year of the Tiger"). T* **94** *and*
similar horiz design. Multicoloured. P 14×14½.
440	45 c. Type **94**	..	..	55	65
	a. Pair. Nos. 440/1	..	..	1·10	1·25
441	45 c. Tiger with head facing left	..	55	65
MS442	106×70 mm. Nos. 440/1	..	1·40	1·60

Nos. 440/1 were printed together, *se-tenant*, in horizontal and
vertical pairs throughout the sheet.

95 Christmas Island
Frigate Bird

96 Orchid Tree

(Des Lisa Christensen. Litho SNP Cambec)

1998 (12 Mar). *Marine Life. T* **95** *and similar horiz designs.*
Multicoloured. P 14×14½.
443	5 c. Type **95**	..	..	15	20
	a. Sheetlet. Nos. 443/62	..	4·50	
444	5 c. Four Ambon Chromis	..	15	20
445	5 c. Three Ambon Chromis	..	15	20
446	5 c. One Pink Anemonefish	..	15	20
447	5 c. Three Pink Anemonefish	..	15	20
448	10 c. Eastern Reef Egret	..	20	25
449	10 c. Whitelined Cod	..	..	20	25
450	10 c. Pyramid Butterflyfish	..	20	25
451	10 c. Dusky Parrotfish	..	20	25
452	10 c. Spotted Garden Eel	..	20	25
453	25 c. Sooty Tern	..	..	25	30
454	25 c. Stripe-tailed Damselfish ("Scissortail		
	Sergeant")	..	..	25	30
455	25 c. Thicklip Wrasse	..	..	25	30
456	25 c. Blackaxil Chromis	..	..	25	30
457	25 c. Orange Anthias	..	..	25	30
458	45 c. Brown Booby	..	..	35	40
459	45 c. Green Turtle ..	..	..	35	40
460	45 c. Pink Anemonefish	..	..	35	40
461	45 c. Blue Sea Star	..	..	35	40
462	45 c. Kunie's Chromodoris	..	35	40
443/62		*Set of 20*	4·50	5·00

Nos. 443/62 were printed together, *se-tenant*, in sheetlets of 20
with the backgrounds forming a composite design.

(Des Clare Kaegi. Litho McPherson's Ptg Group, Mulgrave)

1998 (3 Sept). *Christmas. Flowering Trees. T* **96** *and similar*
vert designs. Multicoloured. P 14½×14.
463	40 c. Type **96**	..	..	50	45
464	80 c. Flame Tree	..	..	1·00	1·10
465	95 c. Sea Hibiscus ..	..	..	1·10	1·25
463/5		*Set of 3*	2·40	2·50

COVER PRICES

Cover factors are quoted at the beginning of each
country for most issues to 1945. An explanation of
the system can be found on page x. The factors
quoted do not, however, apply to philatelic covers.

---

97 Leaping Rabbit

98 Carnival Dragon (Fong
Jason) (Community Arts
Festival)

(Des L. Chiang. Litho SNP Ausprint)

1999 (14 Jan). *Chinese New Year ("Year of the Rabbit"). T* **97**
and similar horiz design. Multicoloured. P 14×14½.
466	45 c. Type **97**	..	..	50	55
	a. Pair. Nos. 466/7	..	..	1·00	1·10
467	45 c. Rabbit with pestle and mortar	50	55
MS468	106×70 mm. Nos. 466/7	..	1·00	1·10

Nos. 466/7 were printed together, *se-tenant*, in horizontal and
vertical pairs throughout the sheet.

(Des A. Christensen. Litho McPherson's Ptg Group, Mulgrave)

1999 (15 July). *Festivals. Children's Paintings. T* **98** *and*
similar multicoloured designs. P 14×14½ (45 c.) *or* 14½×14
(*others*).
469	45 c. Type **98**	..	..	50	50
	a. Pair. Nos. 469/70	..	..	1·00	1·00
470	45 c. Red crab holding Easter egg		
	(Community Arts Festival, Siti		
	Zanariah Zainal)	..	..	50	50
471	85 c. Ghost and child (Tan Diana) (Hungry		
	Ghost Festival) (*vert*)	..	85	85
472	$1.20, Walls of Mecca (Anwar Ramlan)		
	(Hari Raya Haji Festival) (*vert*)	1·10	1·10
469/72		*Set of 4*	2·75	2·75

Nos. 469/70 were printed together, *se-tenant*, in horizontal
and vertical pairs throughout the sheet.

99 Santa Claus in Hammock

100 Chinese Dragon

(Des N. Buchanan and Jo Mure. Litho McPherson's Ptg Group,
Mulgrave)

1999 (9 Sept). *Christmas. T* **99** *and similar horiz designs.*
Multicoloured. P 14×14½.
473	40 c. Type **99**	..	..	30	35
474	45 c. Santa Claus with Christmas pudding	35	40
475	95 c. Santa Claus in sleigh pulled by		
	Abbott's Boobies	..	..	75	80
473/5		*Set of 3*	1·40	1·50

(Des L. Chiang. Litho SNP Ausprint)

2000 (13 Jan). *Chinese New Year ("Year of the Dragon"). T* **100**
and similar horiz design. Multicoloured. P 14×14½.
476	45 c. Type **100**	..	..	35	40
	a. Pair. Nos. 476/7	..	..	70	
477	45 c. Chinese dragon facing left	..	35	40
MS478	106×70 mm. Nos. 476/7	..	70	75

Nos. 476/7 were printed together, *se-tenant*, in horizontal and
vertical pairs throughout the sheet.

STAMP BOOKLETS

Between mid-1995 and 25 June 1996 the Christmas Island
Postmaster produced stamp booklets utilising card from surplus
Presentation Packs. These booklets contained blocks of ten 45 c.
stamps from whichever issue was currently available.

1996 (26 June). *Black on red cover, 95×150 mm, inscr*
"CHRISTMAS ISLAND POST OFFICE STAMP BOOKLET",
often with Christmas Island postmark on front. Stapled.
SB1 $4.50, booklet containing 45 c. (No. 414) in block
of 10 .. .. £150
 a. Containing 45 c. (No. 353) £550
All examples of No. SB1a are postmarked 23 June 1996.

COCOS (KEELING) ISLANDS

The Cocos (Keeling) Islands, which had been settled by the Clunies Ross family in the 1820s, were annexed by Great Britain in 1857. In 1878 the group was attached to Ceylon, but was transferred to the Straits Settlements on 7 February 1886. During the Second World War the islands were under British military control exercised from Ceylon. At the end of hostilities administration from Singapore was continued until the islands were transferred to Australia on 23 November 1955.

The stamps of the STRAITS SETTLEMENTS were used by a postal agency operating on Cocos (Keeling) Islands from 1 April 1933 until 1 March 1937. The postal agency reopened on 2 September 1952 and used the stamps of SINGAPORE until the islands were transferred to Australia in 1955. From 1955 until 1963 stamps of AUSTRALIA were in use.
Nos. 1/31 were also valid for use in Australia.

PRINTERS. All the following stamps to No. 31 were printed by the Note Printing Branch, Reserve Bank of Australia, Melbourne.

1 Copra Industry   **2** "Super Constellation"

(Des K. McKay and E. Jones (5d.), E. Jones (others). Eng E. Jones. Recess)

1963 (11 June). *T* **1/2** *and similar designs. P* 14½×14 (5d., 2s. 3d.) *or* 14½ (*others*).

1	3d. chocolate	1·00	1·50
2	5d. ultramarine	1·50	80
3	8d. scarlet	1·50	2·25
4	1s. green	1·00	55
5	2s. deep purple	11·00	3·25
6	2s. 3d. deep green	28·00	3·25
1/6	*Set of* 6	40·00	10·50

Designs: *Vert* (*as T* **1**)—8d. Map of islands; 2s. Jukong (sailboat). *Horiz* (*as T* **1**)—1s. Palms. (*as T* **2**)—2s. 3d. White Tern.

I Thick lettering
II Thinner lettering

1965 (14 Apr). *50th Anniv of Gallipoli Landing. As T* **184** *of Australia, but slightly larger* (22×34½ mm) *and colour changed. Photo. P* 13½.

7	5d. sepia, black and emerald (I)	60	45
	a. Black-brown, black and light emerald (II)	2·50	1·75

No. 7a comes from a second printing, using a new black cylinder, which was available from the end of April.

With the introduction of decimal currency on 14 February 1966, Australian stamps were used in Cocos Islands, until the appearance of the new definitives on 9 July 1969.

(New Currency. 100 cents = 1 Australian dollar)

7 Reef Clam   **8** Great Frigate Bird
(*Tridacna derasa*)

(Des L. Annois (1 c. to 6 c.), P. Jones (10 c. to $1). Photo)

1969 (9 July). *Decimal Currency. T* **8** *or designs as T* **7**. *Multicoloured. P* 13½.

8	1 c. Lajonkaines Turbo shell (*Turbo lajonkairii*) (*vert*)	30	60
9	2 c. Elongate or Small Giant Clam (*Tridacna maxima*) (*vert*)	1·00	80
10	3 c. Type **7**	40	20
11	4 c. Floral Blenny (fish)	30	50
	a. Salmon-pink omitted	£650	
12	5 c. *Porites cocosensis* (coral)	35	30
13	6 c. Atrisignis Flyingfish	75	75
14	10 c. Banded Rail	1·00	70
15	15 c. Java Sparrow	1·00	30
16	20 c. Red-tailed Tropic Bird	1·00	30
17	30 c. Sooty Tern	1·00	30
18	50 c. Eastern Reef Heron (*vert*)	1·00	30
19	$1 Type **8**	3·00	1·00
8/19	*Set of* 12	10·00	5·50

9 *Dragon*, 1609   **10** Map of Cocos (Keeling) Islands Union Flag, Stars and Trees

(Des R. Honisett. Photo)

1976 (29 Mar). *Ships. Multicoloured designs as T* **9**. *P* 13½.

20	1 c. Type **9**	30	40
21	2 c. H.M.S. *Juno*, 1857	30	40
22	5 c. H.M.S. *Beagle*, 1836	30	40
23	10 c. H.M.A.S. *Sydney*, 1914	35	40
24	15 c. S.M.S. *Emden*, 1914	75	55
25	20 c. *Ayesha*, 1907	75	65
26	25 c. T.S.S. *Islander*, 1927	75	1·00
27	30 c. M.V. *Cheshire*, 1951	75	1·00
28	35 c. Jukong (sailboat)	75	1·00
29	40 c. C.S. *Scotia*, 1900	75	1·00
30	50 c. R.M.S. *Orontes*, 1929	80	1·10
31	$1 Royal Yacht *Gothic*, 1954	1·40	1·40
20/31	*Set of* 12	7·00	8·50

The 2 c. to 20 c., 35 c. and 40 c. are horizontal designs.

(Des Marg Towt. Litho Asher and Co, Melbourne)

1979 (3 Sept). *Inauguration of Independent Postal Service* (20 c.) *and Establishment of First Statutory Council* (50 c.). *T* **10** *and similar horiz design. Multicoloured. P* 15½ × 15.

32	20 c. Type **10**	25	35
33	50 c. Council seal and jukong (sailboat)	35	65

11 Forceps Fish   **12** "Peace on Earth"

(Des Marg Towt. Litho Asher and Co, Melbourne)

1979 (3 Sept)–**80**. *Fishes. Horiz designs as T* **11**. *Multicoloured. P* 13½ × 13 (22 c., 28 c., 60 c.) *or* 15½ × 15 (*others*).

34	1 c. Type **11**	30	80
35	2 c. Ornate Butterflyfish (19.11.79)	30	30
36	5 c. Barbier	50	90
37	10 c. Meyer's Butterflyfish (18.2.80)	30	75
38	15 c. Pink Wrasse (19.11.79)	30	75
39	20 c. Clark's Anemonefish (19.11.79)	45	30
39a	22 c. Undulate Triggerfish (1.7.80)	45	30
40	25 c. Red-breasted Wrasse (18.2.80)	45	80
40a	28 c. Guineafowl Wrasse (1.7.80)	35	35
41	30 c. Madagascar Butterflyfish (19.11.79)	65	45
42	35 c. Cocos-Keeling Angelfish	65	1·60
43	40 c. Coral Hogfish (19.11.79)	70	60
44	50 c. Clown Wrasse (19.11.79)	85	75
45	55 c. Yellow-tailed Tamarin (18.2.80)	75	1·00
45a	60 c. Greasy Grouper (1.7.80)	75	75
46	$1 Palette Surgeonfish	1·75	3·50
47	$2 Melon Butterflyfish (18.2.80)	2·00	3·50
34/47	*Set of* 17	10·00	15·00

(Des D. Pitt. Litho Asher & Co, Melbourne)

1979 (22 Oct). *Christmas. T* **12** *and similar multicoloured design. P* 15 × 15½ (25 c.) *or* 15½ × 15 (55 c.).

48	25 c. Type **12**	25	40
49	55 c. "Goodwill Toward Men" (*horiz*)	40	70

13 Star, Map of Cocos (Keeling) Islands and Island Landscape   **14** "Administered by the British Government, 1857"

(Des P. Arnold. Litho Asher and Co, Melbourne)

1980 (22 Oct). *Christmas. T* **13** *and similar horiz designs. Multicoloured. P* 13.

50	15 c. Type **13**	10	10
51	28 c. Map and Wise Men following star	15	15
52	60 c. Map and Nativity scene	40	40
50/2	*Set of* 3	60	60

(Des Sue Wilson. Litho Asher and Co, Melbourne)

1980 (24 Nov). *25th Anniv of Cocos (Keeling) Islands as an Australian Territory. T* **14** *and similar horiz designs. Multicoloured. P* 13½ × 13.

53	22 c. Type **14**	15	15
	a. Horiz strip of 5. Nos. 53/7	70	
54	22 c. "Administered by the Government of Ceylon, 1878, 1942–6"	15	15
55	22 c. "Administered by the Straits Settlements, 1886"	15	15
56	22 c. "Administered by the Colony of Singapore, 1946"	15	15
57	22 c. "Administered by the Australian Government, 1955"	15	15
53/7	*Set of* 5	70	70

Nos. 53/7 were printed together, *se-tenant*, in horizontal strips of 5 throughout the sheet, forming a composite design.

15 *Eye of the Wind* and Map of Cocos (Keeling) Islands   **16** Aerial View of Animal Quarantine Station

(Des Sue Wilson. Litho Asher and Co, Melbourne)

1980 (18 Dec). *"Operation Drake" (round the world expedition) and 400th Anniv of Sir Francis Drake's Circumnavigation of the World. T* **15** *and similar multicoloured designs. P* 13.

58	22 c. Type **15**	25	15
59	28 c. Map showing voyage routes (*horiz*)	25	15
60	35 c. Sir Francis Drake and *Golden Hind*	25	15
61	60 c. Prince Charles and *Eye of the Wind* (brigantine)	45	30
58/61	*Set of* 4	1·10	65

(Des Cato Hibberd Design. Litho Leigh-Mardon Ltd, Melbourne)

1981 (12 May). *Opening of Animal Quarantine Station. T* **16** *and similar horiz designs. Multicoloured. P* 13½ × 13.

62	22 c. Type **16**	15	15
63	45 c. Unloading livestock	30	30
64	60 c. Livestock in pen	35	35
62/4	*Set of* 3	70	70

17 Consolidated "Catalina" *Guba II* Flying Boat   **18** Prince Charles and Lady Diana Spencer

(Des R. Honisett. Litho Leigh-Mardon Ltd, Melbourne)

1981 (23 June). *Aircraft. T* **17** *and similar horiz designs. Multicoloured. P* 13½ × 13.

65	22 c. Type **17**	25	25
	a. Horiz strip of 5. Nos. 65/9	1·10	
66	22 c. Consolidated "Liberator" and Avro "Lancastrian"	25	25
67	22 c. Douglas "DC4 (Skymaster)" and Lockheed "Constellation"	25	25
68	22 c. Lockheed "Electra"	25	25
69	22 c. Boeing "727" airliners	25	25
65/9	*Set of* 5	1·10	1·10

Nos. 65/9 were printed together, *se-tenant*, in horizontal strips of 5 throughout the sheet.

(Des B. Clinton. Litho Leigh-Mardon Ltd, Melbourne)

1981 (29 July). *Royal Wedding. P* 13½ × 13.

70	**18** 24 c. multicoloured	30	20
71	60 c. multicoloured	50	60

19 "Angels we have heard on High"   **20** *Pachyseris speciosa* and *Heliofungia actiniformis* (corals)

(Des B. Weatherhead. Litho Leigh-Mardon Ltd, Melbourne)

1981 (22 Oct). *Christmas. Scenes and Lines from Carol "Angels we have heard on High". T* **19** *and similar horiz designs. Multicoloured. P* 13½ × 13.

72	18 c. Type **19**	10	10
73	30 c. "Shepherds why this Jubilee?"	20	20
74	60 c. "Come to Bethlehem and see Him"	35	35
72/4	*Set of* 3	60	60

(Des B. Weatherhead. Litho Leigh-Mardon Ltd, Melbourne)

1981 (28 Dec). *150th Anniv of Charles Darwin's Voyage. T* **20** *and similar horiz designs. Multicoloured. P* 13½ × 13.

75	24 c. Type **20**	35	15
76	45 c. Charles Darwin in 1853 and *Pavona cactus* (coral)	55	30
77	60 c. H.M.S. *Beagle*, 1832, and *Lobophyllia hemprichii* (coral)	70	35
75/7	*Set of* 3	1·40	70
MS78	130 × 95 mm. 24 c. Cross-section of West Island; 24 c. Cross-section of Home Island	75	85

21 Queen Victoria   22 Lord Baden-Powell

(Des B. Weatherhead. Litho Cambec Press, Melbourne)

1982 (31 Mar). *125th Anniv of Annexation of Cocos (Keeling) Islands to British Empire. T* **21** *and similar horiz designs. Multicoloured. P* 13½ × 14.

79	24 c. Type 21		20	15
80	45 c. Union flag		35	25
81	60 c. Capt. S. Fremantle (annexation visit, 1857)		40	35
79/81		Set of 3	85	65

(Des B. Clinton. Litho Cambec Press, Melbourne)

1982 (21 July). *75th Anniv of Boy Scout Movement. T* **22** *and similar multicoloured design. P* 13½ × 14 (27 c.) *or* 14 × 13½ (75 c.).

82	27 c. Type 22		30	25
83	75 c. "75" and map of Cocos (Keeling) Islands (vert)		1·10	1·75

23 *Precis villida*   24 "Call His Name Immanuel"

(Des B. Hargreaves. Litho Harrison)

1982 (6 Sept)–**83**. *Butterflies and Moths. T* **23** *and similar multicoloured designs. P* 14.

84	1 c. Type 23		1·00	60
85	2 c. *Cephonodes picus* (horiz) (6.1.83)		40	40
86	5 c. *Macroglossum corythus* (horiz)		1·50	70
87	10 c. *Chasmina candida* (6.1.83)		40	40
88	20 c. *Nagia linteola* (horiz) (6.4.83)		40	65
89	25 c. *Eublemma rivula* (1.7.83)		40	75
90	30 c. *Eurrhyparodes tricoloralis* (6.4.83)		40	65
91	35 c. *Hippotion boerhaviae* (horiz)		1·50	75
92	40 c. *Euploea core* (6.4.83)		40	80
93	45 c. *Psara hipponalis* (horiz)		50	80
94	50 c. *Danaus chrysippus* (horiz) (1.7.83)		60	1·25
95	55 c. *Hypolimnas misippus* (6.1.83)		60	70
96	60 c. *Spodoptera litura* (1.7.83)		65	1·75
97	$1 *Achaea janata*		2·75	2·75
98	$2 *Panacra velox* (horiz) (1.7.83)		2·00	2·75
99	$3 *Utetheisa pulchelloides* (horiz) (6.1.83)		2·75	2·75
84/99		Set of 16	14·50	17·00

(Des G. Hamori. Litho Cambec Press, Melbourne)

1982 (25 Oct). *Christmas. T* **24** *and similar horiz designs. Multicoloured. P* 13½ × 14.

100	21 c. Type 24		25	30
101	35 c. "I bring you good tidings"		40	40
102	75 c. "Arise and flee into Egypt"		1·00	1·25
100/2		Set of 3	1·50	1·75

25 "God will look after us"   26 Hari Raya Celebrations
(Matt. 1:20)

(Des R. Roberts. Litho Cambec Press, Melbourne)

1983 (25 Oct). *Christmas. Extracts from the New Testament. T* **25** *and similar vert designs. Multicoloured. P* 14 × 13½.

103	24 c. Type 25		30	40
	a. Horiz strip of 5. Nos. 103/7		1·40	
104	24 c. "Our baby King, Jesus" (*Matthew* 2:2)		30	40
105	24 c. "Your Saviour is born" (*Luke* 2:11)		30	40
106	24 c. "Wise men followed the Star" (*Matthew* 2:9–10)		30	40
107	24 c. "And worship the Lord" (*Matthew* 2:11)		30	40
103/7		Set of 5	1·40	1·75

Nos. 103/7 were printed together, *se-tenant*, in horizontal strips of 5 throughout the sheet.

(Des Marg Towt. Litho Cambec Press, Melbourne)

1984 (24 Jan). *Cocos-Malay Culture. (1st series). Festivals. T* **26** *and similar vert designs. Multicoloured. P* 13½ × 13.

108	45 c. Type 26		45	35
109	75 c. Melenggok dancing		65	50
110	85 c. Cocos-Malay wedding		75	55
108/10		Set of 3	1·75	1·25

See also Nos. 126/8.

27 Unpacking Barrel   28 Captain William Keeling

(Des R. Honisett. Litho Cambec Press, Melbourne)

1984 (20 Apr). *75th Anniv of Cocos Barrel Mail. T* **27** *and similar horiz designs. Multicoloured. P* 13½ × 14.

111	35 c. Type 27		40	25
112	55 c. Jukong awaiting mail ship		75	50
113	70 c. P. & O. mail ship *Morea*		85	55
111/13		Set of 3	1·75	1·10
MS114	125 × 95 mm. $1 Retrieving barrel		90	1·25

(Des B. Clinton. Litho Cambec Press, Melbourne)

1984 (10 July). *375th Anniv of Discovery of Cocos (Keeling) Islands. T* **28** *and similar vert designs. Multicoloured. P* 14.

115	30 c. Type 28		60	40
116	65 c. Keeling's ship *Hector*		1·25	90
117	95 c. Mariner's astrolabe		1·50	1·25
118	$1. 10, Map *circa* 1666		1·60	1·50
115/18		Set of 4	4·50	3·50

29 Malay Settlement,   30 "Rainbow" Fish
Home Island

(Des E. Roberts. Litho Cambec Press, Melbourne)

1984 (21 Sept). *"Ausipex" International Stamp Exhibition, Melbourne. T* **29** *and similar horiz designs. Multicoloured. P* 13½ × 14.

119	45 c. Type 29		75	50
120	55 c. Airstrip, West Island		85	60
MS121	130 × 95 mm. $2 Jukongs (native craft) racing		2·75	2·50

(Des R. Roberts. Litho Cambec Press, Melbourne)

1984 (31 Oct). *Christmas. T* **30** *and similar horiz designs. Multicoloured. P* 13½ × 14.

122	24 c. Type 30		50	60
123	35 c. "Rainbow" butterfly		1·10	1·40
124	55 c. "Rainbow" bird		1·25	1·75
122/4		Set of 3	2·50	3·25

31 Cocos Islanders   32 Jukong building

(Des B. Weatherhead. Litho Cambec Press, Melbourne)

1984 (30 Nov). *Integration of Cocos (Keeling) Islands with Australia. Sheet* 90 × 52 mm. *containing T* **31** *and similar horiz design. Multicoloured. P* 13½ × 14.

MS125	30 c. Type 31: 30 c. Australian flag on island		1·50	1·25

(Des Marg Towt. Litho Cambec Press, Melbourne)

1985 (30 Jan). *Cocos-Malay Culture (2nd series). Handicrafts. T* **32** *and similar vert designs. Multicoloured. P* 14 × 13½.

126	30 c. Type 32		75	35
127	45 c. Blacksmithing		1·00	55
128	55 c. Woodcarving		1·25	65
126/8		Set of 3	2·75	1·40

33 C.S. *Scotia*   34 Red-footed Booby

(Des B. Clinton. Litho Cambec Press, Melbourne)

1985 (24 Apr). *Cable-laying Ships. T* **33** *and similar horiz designs. Multicoloured. P* 13½ × 14.

129	33 c. Type 33		1·25	40
130	65 c. C.S. *Anglia*		2·00	1·60
131	80 c. C.S. *Patrol*		2·25	2·25
129/31		Set of 3	5·00	3·75

(Des Marg Towt. Litho Cambec Press, Melbourne)

1985 (17 July). *Birds of Cocos (Keeling) Islands. T* **34** *and similar multicoloured designs. P* 13½.

132	33 c. Type 34		1·75	2·00
	a. Block of 3. Nos. 132/4		5·50	
	ab. Imperf vert (block of 3)		£600	
133	60 c. Rufous Night Heron (juvenile) (*horiz*)		2·00	2·25
134	$1 Banded Rail (*horiz*)		2·25	2·50
132/4		Set of 3	5·50	6·00

Nos. 132/4 were printed together, *se-tenant*, in blocks of 3 throughout the sheet, each block forming a composite design.

35 Mantled Top (*Trochus*   36 Night Sky and Palm
maculatus)   Trees

(Des G. Ryan. Litho Cambec Press, Melbourne)

1985 (18 Sept)–**86**. *Shells and Molluscs. T* **35** *and similar horiz designs. Multicoloured. P* 13½ × 14.

135	1 c. Type 35		45	60
136	2 c. Rang's Nerite (*Smaragdia rangiana*) (29.1.86)		55	65
137	3 c. Jewel Box (*Chama sp*) (29.1.86)		60	70
138	4 c. Money Cowrie (*Cypraea moneta*) (30.7.86)		60	70
139	5 c. Purple Pacific Drupe (*Drupa morum*)		60	70
140	10 c. Soldier Cone (*Conus miles*) (29.1.86)		70	75
141	15 c. Marlin-spike Auger (*Terebra maculata*) (30.4.86)		1·50	1·00
142	20 c. Pacific Strawberry Cockle (*Fragum fragum*) (30.4.86)		1·25	1·10
143	30 c. Lajonkaire's Turban (*Turbo lajonkairii*) (30.4.86)		1·25	1·25
144	33 c. Reticulate Mitre (*Scabricola fissurata*)		1·75	1·25
145	40 c. Common Spider Conch (*Lambis lambis*) (30.4.86)		1·75	1·40
146	50 c. Fluted Giant Clam or Scaled Tridacna (*Tridacna squamosa*) (30.7.86)		1·75	1·50
147	60 c. Minstrel Cowrie (*Cypraea histrio*) (30.7.86)		2·00	2·00
148	$1 Varicose Nudibranch (*Phyllidia varicosa*)		3·00	3·00
149	$2 Tesselated Nudibranch (*Halgerda tessellata*) (30.7.86)		3·50	4·00
150	$3 *Haminoea cymballum* (29.1.86)		4·25	4·75
135/50		Set of 16	23·00	23·00

(Des D. Goodwin. Litho Cambec Press, Melbourne)

1985 (30 Oct). *Christmas. Sheet* 121 × 88 mm, *containing T* **36** *and similar horiz designs. P* 13½ × 14.

MS151	27 c. × 4 multicoloured		2·00	2·75

The stamps within **MS151** show a composite design of the night sky seen through a grove of palm trees. The position of the face value on the four stamps varies. Type **36** shows the top left design. The top right stamp shows the face value at bottom right, the bottom left at top left and the bottom right at top right.

37 Charles Darwin, *c* 1840   38 Coconut Palm and
Holly Sprigs

(Des B. Clinton. Litho Cambec Press, Melbourne)

1986 (1 Apr). *150th Anniv of Charles Darwin's Visit. T* **37** *and similar vert designs. Multicoloured. P* 14 × 13½.

152	33 c. Type 37		70	50
153	60 c. Map of H.M.S. *Beagle*'s route Australia to Cocos Islands		1·25	2·00
154	$1 H.M.S. *Beagle*		1·75	2·50
152/4		Set of 3	3·25	4·50

(Des S. Hartshorne. Litho Cambec Press, Melbourne)

1986 (29 Oct). *Christmas. T* **38** *and similar horiz designs. Multicoloured. P* 13½ × 14.

155	30 c. Type 38		60	50
156	90 c. Nautilus shell and Christmas tree bauble		2·00	2·50
157	$1 Tropical fish and bell		2·00	2·50
155/7		Set of 3	4·25	5·00

39 Jukong   40 Beach, Direction Island

(Des J. Earl. Litho Cambec Press, Melbourne)

1987 (28 Jan). *Sailing Craft.* T **39** *and similar horiz designs. Multicoloured.* P 13½×14.

158	36 c. Type **39**	..	1·10	1·40
	a. Horiz strip of 4. Nos. 158/61	..	4·00	
159	36 c. Ocean racing yachts	..	1·10	1·40
160	36 c. *Sarimanok* (replica of early dhow)		1·10	1·40
161	36 c. *Ayesha* (schooner)	..	1·10	1·40
158/61		*Set of 4*	4·00	5·00

Nos. 158/61 were printed together, *se-tenant*, in horizontal strips of 5 throughout the sheet, each strip forming a composite background design.

(Des H. Missingham and R. Fletcher. Litho CPE Australia Ltd, Melbourne)

1987 (8 Apr). *Cocos Islands Scenes.* T **40** *and similar horiz designs. Multicoloured.* P 13½×14.

162	70 c. Type **40**	..	1·40	1·40
163	90 c. Palm forest, West Island		1·75	2·00
164	$1 Golf course	..	2·75	3·00
162/4		*Set of 3*	5·50	5·75

41 Radio Transmitter and Palm Trees at Sunset   42 Batik Printing

(Des R. Fletcher. Litho CPE Australia Ltd, Melbourne)

1987 (29 July). *Communications.* T **41** *and similar horiz designs. Multicoloured.* P 13½×14.

165	70 c. Type **41**	..	1·25	1·50
166	70 c. Air liner at terminal	..	1·50	1·75
167	90 c. "Intelsat 5" satellite	..	1·75	2·25
168	$1 Airmail letter and globe	..	2·00	2·25
165/8		*Set of 4*	6·00	7·00

(Des B. Clinton. Litho CPE Australia Ltd, Melbourne)

1987 (16 Sept). *Cocos (Keeling) Islands Malay Industries.* T **42** *and similar horiz designs. Multicoloured.* P 13½×14.

169	45 c. Type **42**	..	1·25	1·50
170	65 c. Jukong building	..	1·75	2·00
171	75 c. Copra production	..	2·00	2·25
169/71		*Set of 3*	4·50	5·25

43 Hands releasing Peace Dove and Map of Islands   44 Coconut Flower

(Des Marg Towt. Litho CPE Australia Ltd, Melbourne)

1987 (28 Oct). *Christmas.* T **43** *and similar vert designs. Multicoloured.* P 14×13½.

172	30 c. Type **43**	..	40	40
173	90 c. Local children at Christmas party	..	1·25	1·90
174	$1 Island family and Christmas star	..	1·50	1·90
172/4		*Set of 3*	2·75	3·75

(Des Sue Passmore. Litho CPE Australia Ltd, Melbourne)

1988 (26 Jan). *Bicentenary of Australian Settlement. Arrival of First Fleet. Square designs as Nos. 1105/9 of Australia but each inscribed* "COCOS (KEELING) ISLANDS" *and* "AUSTRALIA BICENTENARY".

175	37 c. Aborigines watching arrival of Fleet, Botany Bay	..	1·50	1·75
	a. Horiz strip of 5. Nos. 175/9		6·75	
176	37 c. Aboriginal family and anchored ships	..	1·50	1·75
177	37 c. Fleet arriving at Sydney Cove..		1·50	1·75
178	37 c. Ship's boat	..	1·50	1·75
179	37 c. Raising the flag, Sydney Cove, 26 January 1788..		1·50	1·75
175/9		*Set of 5*	6·75	8·00

Nos. 175/9 were printed together, *se-tenant*, in horizontal strips of five throughout the sheet, forming a composite design.

(Des Celia Rosser. Litho CPE Australia Ltd, Melbourne)

1988 (13 Apr). *Life Cycle of the Coconut.* T **44** *and similar vert designs. Multicoloured.* P 14×13½.

180	37 c. Type **44**	..	50	40
181	65 c. Immature nuts	..	75	1·00
182	90 c. Coconut palm and mature nuts		1·10	1·75
183	$1 Seedlings	..	1·25	1·75
180/3		*Set of 4*	3·25	4·50
MS184	102×91 mm. Nos. 180/3		4·00	4·50

MINIMUM PRICE

The minimum price quote is 10p which represents a handling charge rather than a basis for valuing common stamps. For further notes about prices see introductory pages.

45 Copra 3d. Stamp of 1963   46 Pisonia grandis

(Des R. Fletcher. Recess and litho Note Printing Branch, Reserve Bank of Australia, Melbourne)

1988 (15 June). *25th Anniv of First Cocos (Keeling) Islands Stamps.* T **45** *and similar vert designs, each showing stamp from 1963 definitive set.* P 15×14.

185	37 c. chocolate, black and azure	..	1·25	85
186	55 c. green, black and pale drab		1·75	1·50
187	65 c. ultramarine, black and pale grey-lilac	1·90	2·00
188	70 c. scarlet, black and bluish grey		1·90	2·00
189	90 c. deep purple, black and greenish grey	2·25	2·25
190	$1 deep green, black and light brown		2·25	2·25
185/90		*Set of 6*	10·00	9·75

Designs:—55 c. Palms 1s.; 65 c. "Super Constellation" 5d.; 70 c. Map 8d.; 90 c. Jukong (sailboat) 2s.; $1 White Tern 2s. 3d.

(Des R. Fletcher. Litho CPE Australia Ltd, Melbourne)

1988 (29 July)–89. *Flora.* T **46** *and similar vert designs. Multicoloured.* P 14×13½.

191	1 c. Type **46**	..	30	50
192	2 c. *Cocos nucifera* (18.1.89)	..	40	60
193	5 c. *Morinda citrifolia*		65	70
194	10 c. *Cordia subcordata* (18.1.89)	..	70	70
195	30 c. *Argusia argentea* (18.1.89)	..	1·00	90
196	37 c. *Calophyllum inophyllum*		1·00	1·00
197	40 c. *Barringtonia asiatica* (19.4.89)	1·00	1·25
198	50 c. *Caesalpinia bonduc* (19.4.89)	..	1·25	2·00
199	90 c. *Terminalia catappa* (19.4.89)		1·75	2·50
200	$1 *Pemphis acidula* (19.4.89)	..	1·75	2·50
201	$2 *Scaevola sericea* (18.1.89)	..	2·50	2·50
202	$3 *Hibiscus tiliaceus*	..	3·50	3·75
191/202		*Set of 12*	14·00	17·00

(Des R. Fletcher. Litho CPE Australia Ltd, Melbourne)

1988 (30 July). *"Sydpex '88" National Stamp Exhibition, Sydney. Sheet* 70×85 *mm. Multicoloured.* P 14×13½.

MS203	$3 As No. 202	..	4·25	5·00

47 Beach at Sunset   48 Capt. P. G. Taylor

(Des T. Bland. Litho CPE Australia Ltd, Melbourne)

1988 (12 Oct). *Christmas.* P 13½×14.

204	47 32 c. multicoloured	..	80	50
205	90 c. multicoloured	..	1·75	2·50
206	$1 multicoloured	..	2·00	2·50
204/6		*Set of 3*	4·00	5·00

(Des B. Clinton. Litho CPE Australia Ltd, Melbourne)

1989 (19 July). *50th Anniv of First Indian Ocean Aerial Survey.* T **48** *and similar vert designs.* P 14×13½.

207	40 c. multicoloured	..	80	65
208	70 c. multicoloured	..	1·75	2·00
209	$1 multicoloured	..	2·00	2·25
210	$1.10, deep ultramarine, pale lilac & black	2·25	2·50
207/10		*Set of 4*	6·00	6·50

Designs:—70 c. Consolidated Catalina "PBY2" *Guba II* and crew; $1 *Guba II* over Direction Island; $1.10, Unissued Australia 5s. stamp commemorating flight.

49 Jukong and Star   50 H.M.A.S. *Sydney* (cruiser)

(Des T. Bland. Litho Leigh-Mardon Ltd, Melbourne)

1989 (18 Oct). *Christmas.* P 14×13½.

211	49 35 c. multicoloured	..	85	60
212	80 c. multicoloured	..	2·50	2·75
213	$1.10, multicoloured	..	2·50	2·75
211/13		*Set of 3*	5·25	5·50

(Des PCS Studios. Litho Leigh-Mardon Ltd, Melbourne)

1989 (9 Nov). *75th Anniv of Destruction of German Cruiser* Emden. T **50** *and similar horiz designs. Multicoloured.* P 13½×14.

214	40 c. Type **50**	..	1·75	1·75
	a. Horiz strip of 4, Nos. 214/17, with central label		7·50	
215	70 c. *Emden* (German cruiser)	..	2·00	2·00
216	$1 *Emden*'s steam launch	..	2·25	2·25
217	$1.10, H.M.A.S. *Sydney*, (1914) and crest	2·25	2·25
214/17		*Set of 4*	7·50	7·50
MS218	145×90 mm. Nos. 214/17		7·50	7·50

Nos. 214/17 were printed together, *se-tenant*, in horizontal strips of four stamps and one label throughout the sheet.

51 Xanthid Crab   52 Captain Keeling and Hector, 1609

(Des Jill Ruse. Litho Leigh-Mardon Ltd, Melbourne)

1990 (31 May). *Cocos Islands Crabs.* T **51** *and similar multicoloured designs.* P 14½.

219	45 c. Type **51**	..	1·50	75
220	75 c. Ghost Crab	..	2·00	2·00
221	$1 Red-backed Mud Crab	..	2·25	2·25
222	$1.30, Coconut Crab (*vert*)	..	2·50	3·00
219/22		*Set of 4*	7·50	7·25

(Des Elizabeth and R. Innes. Litho Note Ptg Branch, Reserve Bank of Australia)

1990 (24 Aug). *Navigators of the Pacific.* T **52** *and similar horiz designs.* P 14½.

223	45 c. dull mauve	..	2·00	85
224	75 c. dull mauve and pale azure	..	2·25	2·50
225	$1 dull mauve and pale stone	..	2·75	3·00
226	$1.30, dull mauve and pale buff		3·50	4·25
223/6		*Set of 4*	9·50	9·50
MS227	120×95 mm. As Nos. 223/6, but imperf	7·50	8·50

Designs:—75 c. Captain Fitzroy and H.M.S. *Beagle*, 1836; $1 Captain Belcher and H.M.S. *Samarang*, 1846; $1.30, Captain Fremantle and H.M.S. *Juno*, 1857.

(53)   (54)

(Des Elizabeth Innes (No. **MS229**). Litho Western Australian Govt Ptg Division, Perth)

1990 (3 Sept). *"New Zealand 1990" International Stamp Exhibition, Auckland. No. 188 optd with T* **53** *in red and miniature sheet containing designs as Nos. 194, 199 and 201.*

228	70 c. scarlet, black and bluish grey		2·25	2·75
MS229	127×90 mm. As Nos. 194, 199 and 201, but self-adhesive. Roul 9		5·00	3·75

Nos. 228/9 were available at the Exhibition from 24 August 1990, but were not sold locally until 3 September.

1990 (11 Dec). *No. 187 surch with T* **54** *in deep ultramarine by Western Australian Govt Ptg Division, Perth.*

230	$5 on 65 c. ultram, black & pale grey-lilac	18·00	17·00

55 Cocos Atoll from West and Star

(Des Stylegraphics, Perth. Litho Scott Four-Colour Print, Perth)

1990 (12 Dec). *Christmas.* T **55** *and similar square designs. Multicoloured.* Roul 5.

231	40 c. Type **55**	..	70	90
	a. Booklet pane. No. 231×4 and No. 232×2 plus 6 labels		10·00	
	b. Booklet pane. No. 231×10 plus 2 labels	15·00	
232	70 c. Cocos atoll from south	..	1·50	2·50
233	$1.30, Cocos atoll from east	..	2·50	2·75
231/3		*Set of 3*	4·25	5·50

Booklet panes Nos. 231a/b have the upper and lower edges imperforate, producing stamps imperforate at top or bottom and there are margins at left and right.

MAINLAND POSTAGE PAID

(56)

LOCAL

POSTAGE PAID

(57)

1990 (12 Dec)–**91**. *Nos. 140/1, 143 and 146/7 surch by Western Australian Govt Ptg Division.*

(a) *With T 56 in blue*

234 (43 c.) on 10 c. Soldier Cone (*Conus miles*) .. 30·00 3·75

(b) *No. 234 with additional cross-hatching overprinted on the original face value in blue*

235 (43 c.) on 10 c. Soldier Cone (*Conus miles*) (7.3.91) .. .. 1·40 1·75

(c) *As T 57 with original face value obliterated*

236 (1 c.) on 30 c. Lajonkaire's Turban (*Turbo lajonkairii*) (Type 57) (B.) (21.1.91) 1·50 2·50
237 70 c. on 60 c. Minstrel Cowrie (*Cypraea histrio*) ("ZONE 1") (7.3.91) 1·50 2·50
238 80 c. on 50 c. Fluted Giant Clam or Scaled Tridacna (*Tridacna squamosa* ("ZONE 2") (7.3.91) .. 1·75 3·25
239 $1.20 on 15 c. Marlin-spike Auger (*Terebra maculata* ("ZONE 5") (7.3.91) .. .. 2·00 3·50
234/9 .. .. *Set of 6* 35·00 15·00

58 Beaded Sea Star   **59** Cocos Islands

(Des Jill Ruse. Litho Leigh-Mardon Ltd, Melbourne)

1991 (28 Feb). *Starfish and Sea Urchins. T 58 and similar horiz designs. Multicoloured. P 14½.*

240 45 c. Type **58** .. .. .. 1·00 65
241 75 c. Feather Star .. .. 1·90 2·00
242 $1 Slate Pencil Urchin .. 2·00 2·25
243 $1.30, Globose Sea Urchin .. 2·50 3·00
240/3 .. .. .. *Set of 4* 6·75 7·25

(Des P. Cunningham. Litho Leigh-Mardon Ltd, Melbourne)

1991 (16 Apr). *Malay Hari Raya Festival. T 59 and similar horiz designs. Multicoloured. P 14½.*

244 45 c. Type **59** .. .. 1·00 65
245 75 c. Island house .. .. 1·75 2·00
246 $1.30, Islands scene .. .. 2·50 3·00
244/6 .. .. .. *Set of 3* 4·75 5·00

60 Child praying   **61** *Lybia tessellata*

(Des R. Honisett. Litho Leigh-Mardon Ltd, Melbourne)

1991 (6 Nov). *Christmas. T 60 and similar vert designs. Multicoloured. P 15½.*

247 38 c. Type **60** 80 55
248 43 c. Child dreaming of Christmas Day .. 85 60
249 $1 Child singing .. .. .. 2·00 2·25
250 $1.20, Child fascinated by decorations .. 2·50 2·75
247/50 .. .. .. *Set of 4* 5·50 6·00
MS251 118×74 mm. 38 c., 43 c., $1, $1.20, Local children's choir .. .. 6·00 6·50
The four values in No. MS251 form a composite design.

(Des Jane Moore. Litho Leigh-Mardon Ltd, Melbourne)

1992 (28 Feb–11 Aug). *Crustaceans. T 61 and similar multicoloured designs. P 14½.*

252 5 c. Type **61** 50 50
253 10 c. Pilodius areolatus (11 Aug) .. 60 60
254 20 c. Trizopagurus strigatus .. 90 90
255 30 c. Lophozozymus pulchellus (11 Aug) 1·25 1·25
256 40 c. Thalamitoides quadridens .. 1·25 1·25
257 45 c. Calcinus elegans (vert) .. 1·25 1·25
258 50 c. Clibarius humilis (11 Aug) .. 1·50 1·50
259 60 c. Trapezia rufopunctata (vert) .. 1·75 1·75
260 80 c. Pylopaguropsis magnimanus (vert) (11 Aug) .. .. 2·00 2·00
261 $1 Trapezia ferruginea (vert) (11 Aug) .. 2·00 2·00
262 $2 Trapezia guttata (vert) (11 Aug) .. 3·00 3·75
263 $3 Trapezia cymodoce (vert) .. 3·50 3·75
252/63 .. .. .. *Set of 12* 17·00 18·00

OMNIBUS ISSUES

Details, together with prices for complete sets, of the various Omnibus issues from the 1935 Silver Jubilee series to date are included in a special section following Zimbabwe at the end of Volume 2.

62 Santa Maria   **63** Banded Rail searching for Food

(Des Philatelic Studios, Melbourne. Litho Leigh-Mardon Ltd, Melbourne)

1992 (22 May). *500th Anniv of Discovery of America by Columbus. P 14½.*

264 **62** $1.05, multicoloured .. .. 2·25 2·50

(Des G. Drummond. Litho Questa)

1992 (11 June). *Endangered Species. Banded Rail. T 63 and similar horiz designs. Multicoloured. P 14.*

265 10 c. Type **63** 50 60
a. Strip of 4. Nos. 265/8 .. 2·50
266 15 c. Banded Rail with chick .. 65 75
267 30 c. Two Rails drinking .. 80 90
268 45 c. Rail and nest .. .. 90 1·10
265/8 .. .. .. *Set of 4* 2·50 3·00
MS269 165×78 mm. 45 c. Two Rails by pool; 85 c. Chick hatching; $1.20, Head of Rail .. 4·50 5·00
Nos. 265/8 were printed together, *se-tenant*, in horizontal or vertical strips of 4 throughout the sheet.

64 R.A.F. Spitfires on Island Airstrip   **65** Waves breaking on Reef

(Des Philatelic Studios, Melbourne. Litho Leigh-Mardon Ltd, Melbourne)

1992 (13 Oct). *50th Anniv of Second World War. T 64 and similar horiz designs. Multicoloured. P 14½.*

270 40 c. Type **64** .. .. 1·50 1·00
271 85 c. Japanese aircraft bombing Kampong 2·25 2·75
272 $1.20, R.A.F. Sunderland (flying boat) 2·75 3·50
270/2 .. .. .. *Set of 3* 6·00 6·50

(Des Philatelic Studios, Melbourne. Litho Leigh-Mardon Ltd, Melbourne)

1992 (11 Nov). *Christmas. T 65 and similar vert designs. Multicoloured. P 14½.*

273 40 c. Type **65** 80 60
274 80 c. Direction Island .. 2·00 2·50
275 $1 Moorish Idols (fish) and coral .. 2·00 2·50
273/5 .. .. .. *Set of 3* 4·25 5·00

66 Lobophyllia hemprichii   **67** Plastic 5 r. Token

(Litho Leigh-Mardon Ltd, Melbourne)

1993 (28 Jan). *Corals. T 66 and similar vert designs. Multicoloured. P 14½.*

276 45 c. Type **66** 75 55
277 85 c. Pocillopora eydouxi .. 1·25 1·75
278 $1.05, Fungia scutaria .. 1·75 2·00
279 $1.20, Sarcophyton sp .. 1·75 2·25
276/9 .. .. .. *Set of 4* 5·00 6·00

(Des Sandra Harman. Litho Leigh-Mardon Ltd, Melbourne)

1993 (30 Mar). *Early Cocos (Keeling) Islands Currency. T 67 and similar vert designs. Multicoloured. P 14½.*

280 45 c. Type **67** .. .. 1·00 70
281 85 c. 1968 1 r. plastic token .. 1·50 2·00
282 $1.05, 1977 150 r. commemorative gold coin .. .. .. 2·00 2·25
283 $1.20, 1910 plastic token .. 2·00 2·50
280/3 .. .. .. *Set of 4* 6·00 6·75

68 Primary School Pupil   **69** Lifeboat and Crippled Yacht

(Des Philatelic Studios. Litho Leigh-Mardon Ltd, Melbourne)

1993 (1 June). *Education. T 68 and similar vert designs. Multicoloured. P 14½.*

284 5 c. Type **68** 40 60
285 45 c. Secondary school pupil .. 80 60
286 85 c. Learning traditional crafts .. 1·50 1·75
287 $1.05, Learning office skills .. 2·00 2·50
288 $1.20, Seaman training .. 2·50 2·75
284/8 .. .. .. *Set of 5* 6·50 7·50

(Des Philatelic Studios. Litho Leigh-Mardon Ltd, Melbourne)

1993 (17 Aug). *Air-Sea Rescue. T 69 and similar horiz designs. Multicoloured. P 14½.*

289 45 c. Type **69** .. .. 1·50 85
290 85 c. Westwind Seascan (aircraft) .. 2·50 2·75
291 $1.05, R.J. Hawke (ferry) .. 2·75 3·75
289/91 .. .. .. *Set of 3* 6·00 6·50
MS292 135×61 mm. Nos. 289/91 .. 6·00 7·00

70 Peace Doves   **71** Rectangle Triggerfish and Coral

(Des Philatelic Studios. Litho Leigh-Mardon Ltd, Melbourne)

1993 (26 Oct). *Christmas. P 14½.*

293 **70** 40 c. multicoloured .. 1·00 70
294 80 c. multicoloured .. 2·25 2·75
295 $1 multicoloured .. .. 2·25 2·75
293/5 .. .. .. *Set of 3* 5·00 5·50

On 1 January 1994 responsibility for the Cocos (Keeling) Islands postal service passed from the territorial administration to Australia Post. In consequence Nos. 296/315 and all subsequent issues are valid for postal purposes in both Cocos (Keeling) Islands and Australia.

(Des Sue Passmore. Litho McPherson's Ptg Group, Mulgrave)

1994 (17 Feb). *Transfer of Postal Service to Australia Post. T 71 and similar vert designs. Multicoloured. P 14½×14.*

296 5 c. Type **71** 25 30
a. Sheetlet. Nos. 296/315 6·00
297 5 c. Three Rectangle Triggerfish and map section 25 30
298 5 c. Two Rectangle Triggerfish and map section 25 30
299 5 c. Two Rectangle Triggerfish, map section and red coral .. 25 30
300 5 c. Rectangle Triggerfish with red and brown corals 25 30
301 10 c. Green Turtles on beach .. 25 30
302 10 c. Two Green Turtles .. 25 30
303 10 c. Crowd of young Green Turtles 25 30
304 10 c. Green Turtle and map section 25 30
305 10 c. Green Turtle, Pyramid Butterflyfish and map section .. 25 30
306 20 c. Three Pyramid Butterflyfish and map section 40 45
307 20 c. Pyramid Butterflyfish with brown coral 40 45
308 20 c. Two Pyramid Butterflyfish and coral 40 45
309 20 c. Three Pyramid Butterflyfish and coral 40 45
310 20 c. Coral, Pyramid Butterflyfish and map section 40 45
311 45 c. Jukongs with map of airport 50 55
a. Horiz strip of 5. Nos. 311/15 2·25
312 45 c. Two jukongs with red or blue sails and map section .. 50 55
313 45 c. Jukong in shallows .. 50 55
314 45 c. Two jukongs with red or yellow sails and map section .. 50 55
315 45 c. Two jukongs, one with blue jib, and map section .. 50 55
296/315 .. .. *Set of 20* 6·00 7·00
Nos. 296/315 were printed together, *se-tenant*, in sheetlets of 20 with inscriptions on the sheet margins and the backgrounds forming a composite map. Nos. 311/15 were also avaliable printed together, *se-tenant*, in horizontal strips of 5 in sheets of 100.

72 Prabu Abjasa Puppet   **73** Angel playing Harp

(Des Josephine Muré. Litho McPherson's Ptg Group, Mulgrave)

1994 (16 June). *Shadow Puppets. T 72 and similar vert designs. Multicoloured. P 14½×14.*

316 45 c. Type **72** 65 50
317 90 c. Prabu Pandu .. 1·25 1·50
318 $1 Judistra .. .. 1·40 1·50
319 $1.35, Abimanju .. .. 1·50 2·00
316/19 .. .. .. *Set of 4* 4·25 5·00

(Des Tracie Grimwood. Litho McPherson's Ptg Group, Mulgrave)

1994 (31 Oct). *Seasonal Festivals. T* **73** *and similar horiz designs. Multicoloured. P* 14×14½.

320	40 c. Type **73**		50	50
321	45 c. Wise Man holding gift		55	50
322	80 c. Mosque at night		1·00	1·75
320/2		Set of 3	1·90	2·50

74 White-tailed Tropic Bird and Blue-faced Booby

75 Yellow Crazy Ant

(Des Lisa Christensen and B. Wood. Litho McPherson's Ptg Group, Mulgrave)

1995 (16 Mar). *Sea-birds of North Keeling Island. T* **74** *and similar horiz designs. Multicoloured. P* 14×14½.

323	45 c. Type **74**		75	50
324	85 c. Great Frigate Bird and White Tern		1·00	1·50
MS325	106×70 mm. Nos. 323/4		1·75	2·00

No. **MS**325 also exists overprinted with the "JAKARTA 95" logo for sale at this exhibition.

(Des Sue Maddern. Litho McPherson's Ptg Group, Mulgrave)

1995 (13 July). *Insects. T* **75** *and similar vert designs. Multicoloured. P* 14½×14.

326	45 c. Type **75**		70	80
	a. Horiz strip of 5. Nos. 326/30		3·25	
327	45 c. Aedes Mosquito		70	80
328	45 c. Hawk Moth		70	80
329	45 c. Scarab Beetle		70	80
330	45 c. Lauxaniid Fly		70	80
331	$1.20, Common Eggfly (butterfly)		1·25	1·50
326/31		Set of 6	4·00	5·00

Nos. 326/30 were printed together, *se-tenant*, in horizontal strips of 5 throughout the sheet, with the backgrounds forming a composite design.

76 Saddle Butterflyfish

77 Members of Malay Community

(Des M. Baker and Sandra Harman (5 c., 75 c., 90 c., $1, $1.20), M. Baker and Dianne Cook (70 c., 95 c., $5), M. Baker and Sophie Byass (others). Litho SNP Cambec (40 c., 80 c., $1.05) or McPherson's Ptg Group, Mulgrave (others))

1995 (1 Nov)–**98**. *Marine Life. T* **76** *and similar horiz designs. Multicoloured. P* 14×14½.

332	5 c. Redspot Wrasse (14.8.97)		10	10
333	30 c. Blue-throated Triggerfish ("Gilded Triggerfish") (15.8.96)		25	30
334	40 c. Type **76**		30	35
335	45 c. Arc-eyed Hawkfish (15.8.96)		35	40
335a	70 c. Crowned Squirrelfish (13.8.98)		55	60
336	75 c. Orangespine Unicornfish (14.8.97)		60	65
337	80 c. Blue Tang		60	65
338	85 c. Juvenile Twin-spotted Wrasse ("Humphead Wrasse") (15.8.96)		65	70
339	90 c. Threadfin Butterflyfish (14.8.97)		70	75
339a	95 c. Sixstripe Wrasse (13.8.98)		75	80
340	$1 Bluestripe Snapper (14.8.97)		80	85
341	$1.05, Longnosed Butterflyfish		80	85
342	$1.20, Freckled Hawkfish (14.8.97)		90	95
343	$2 Powder-blue Surgeonfish (15.8.96)		1·60	1·75
343a	$5 Goldback Anthias (13.8.98)		4·00	4·25
332/43a		Set of 15	13·00	14·00

(Des Melinda Whitechurch and Jacqui Young. Litho McPherson's Ptg Group, Mulgrave)

1996 (19 Feb). *Hari Raya Puasa Festival. T* **77** *and similar square designs. Multicoloured. P* 14½.

344	45 c. Type **77**		55	50
345	75 c. Beating drums		1·00	1·25
346	85 c. Preparing festival meal		1·10	1·50
344/6		Set of 3	2·40	3·00

78 Black Rhinoceros with Calf

79 Dancers and Tambourine

(Des Kerry Argent and Lisa Christensen. Litho Canberra Press)

1996 (13 June). *Cocos Quarantine Station. T* **78** *and similar vert designs. Multicoloured. P* 14½×14.

347	45 c. Type **78**		70	70
348	50 c. Alpacas		70	75
349	$1.05, Boran cattle		1·25	1·50
350	$1.20, Ostrich with chicks		1·50	1·75
347/50		Set of 4	3·75	4·25

(Des MYD Graphic. Litho SNP Cambec)

1997 (6 Jan). *Hari Raya Puasa Festival. T* **79** *and similar square designs. Multicoloured. P* 14½.

351	45 c. Type **79**		55	50
352	75 c. Girl clapping and sailing dinghies		90	1·25
353	85 c. Dancers on beach and food		1·00	1·25
351/3		Set of 3	2·25	2·75

80 "Wrapped Present" (Lazina Brian)

81 Preparing Food on Beach

(Adapted Dianne Cook. Litho SNP Cambec)

1998 (22 Jan). *Hari Raya Puasa Festival. T* **80** *and similar vert designs showing paintings by children. Multicoloured. P* 14½×14.

354	45 c. Type **80**		50	55
	a. Horiz strip of 5. Nos. 354/8		2·25	
355	45 c. "Mosque" (Azran Jim)		50	55
356	45 c. "Cocos Malay Woman" (Kate Gossage)		50	55
357	45 c. "Yacht" (Matt Harber)		50	55
358	45 c. "People dancing" (Rakin Chongkin)		50	55
354/8		Set of 5	2·25	2·50

Nos. 354/8 were printed together, *se-tenant*, in horizontal strips of five throughout the sheet.

(Des Jacqui Young and Sandra Harman. Litho SNP Ausprint)

1999 (11 Feb). *Hari Raya Puasa Festival. T* **81** *and similar vert designs. Multicoloured. P* 14½×14.

359	45 c. Type **81**		45	50
	a. Horiz strip of 5. Nos. 359/63		2·00	
360	45 c. Woman with child and jukongs on beach		45	50
361	45 c. Jukongs and palm fronds		45	50
362	45 c. Two men watching jukongs		45	50
363	45 c. Jukong and white flowers		45	50
359/63		Set of 5	2·00	2·25

Nos. 359/63 were printed together, *se-tenant*, in horizontal strips of 5 throughout the sheet.

82 Jukong (Cocos sailing boat)

(Des Melinda Coombes. Litho SNP Ausprint)

1999 (17 June). *Island Wildlife. T* **82** *and similar horiz designs. Multicoloured. P* 14×14½.

364	5 c. Type **82**		10	10
	a. Sheetlet. Nos. 364/83		3·25	
365	5 c. Bennett's and Ornate Butterflyfish		10	10
366	5 c. Green and Hawksbill Turtles		10	10
367	5 c. Yellow-tailed Anemonefish and various Butterflyfish		10	10
368	5 c. Hump-headed Wrasse		10	10
369	10 c. Yacht, Direction Island		10	10
370	10 c. Black-backed Butterflyfish		10	10
371	10 c. Moorish Idols		10	10
372	10 c. *Pseudoanthias cooperi* (fish)		10	10
373	10 c. Red-tailed Tropic Birds		10	10
374	25 c. Blue-faced Booby		20	25
375	25 c. Lesser Wanderer (butterfly)		20	25
376	25 c. Lesser and Greater Frigatebirds		20	25
377	25 c. *Hippotion velox* (moth)		20	25
378	25 c. Common Eggfly (butterfly)		20	25
379	45 c. White Tern		35	40
380	45 c. Red-tailed Tropic Bird and Great Frigate Bird		35	40
381	45 c. Chinese Rose		35	40
382	45 c. Meadow Argus (butterfly)		35	40
383	45 c. Sea Hibiscus		35	40
364/83		Set of 20	3·25	4·00

Nos. 364/83 were printed together, *se-tenant*, in sheetlets of 20 with the backgrounds forming a composite design.

COVER PRICES

Cover factors are quoted at the beginning of each country for most issues to 1945. An explanation of the system can be found on page x. The factors quoted do not, however, apply to philatelic covers.

STAMP BOOKLETS

COCOS (KEELING) ISLANDS
INDIAN OCEAN

PHILATELIC BUREAU

B 1 Prison Island

1990 (12 Dec). *Christmas. Multicoloured cover as Type* **B 1**. *Panes attached by selvedge.*

SB1	$3 booklet containing *se-tenant* pane of 6 (No. 231a)		10·00
SB2	$4 booklet containing pane of 10 (No. 231b)		15·00

OFFICIAL STAMP

OFFICIAL PAID MAINLAND

(O 1)

1991 (25 Jan). *No. 182 surch with Type* O **1** *in deep violet-blue.*

O1	(43 c.) on 90 c. Coconut palm and mature nuts	†	90·00

No. O1 was only sold to the public cancelled-to-order and not in unused condition.

NORFOLK ISLAND

Norfolk Island, first settled in 1788 from New South Wales, was transferred to Tasmania on 29 September 1844. It became a separate settlement on 1 November 1856 under the control of the Governor of New South Wales. The island was declared an Australian Territory on 1 July 1914. Unlike the other External Territories it retains an independent postal administration.

The stamps of TASMANIA were used on Norfolk Island from mid-1854 until May 1855, such use being identified by the "72" numeral cancellation. Stamps of NEW SOUTH WALES were first used on the island in 1877, but were not regularly available until 1898. The first "NORFOLK ISLAND" cancellation was supplied in 1892, but not used until 1898. Stamps of AUSTRALIA were in use from 1913 to 1947.

PRINTERS. Nos. 1 to 42 were printed at the Note Printing Branch Reserve Bank of Australia (until 14 Jan 1960, known as the Note Printing Branch, Commonwealth Bank) by recess. See note at the beginning of Australia *re* imprints.

1 Ball Bay

(Des and eng F. Manley)

1947 (10 June)–59. *Toned paper.* P 14.

1	1	1/2d. orange	..	85	60
		a. White paper (11.56)	..	1·10	4·50
2		1d. bright violet	..	50	60
		a. White paper (8.57)	..	5·00	14·00
3		1 1/2d. emerald-green	..	50	70
		a. White paper (11.56)	..	7·50	20·00
4		2d. reddish violet	..	55	40
		a. White paper (11.56)	..	90·00	£130
5		2 1/2d. scarlet	..	80	30
6		3d. chestnut	..	70	70
6a		3d. emerald-green (*white paper*) (6.7.59)	16·00	7·00
7		4d. claret	..	1·25	40
8		5 1/2d. indigo	..	70	30
9		6d. purple-brown	..	70	30
10		9d. magenta	..	1·25	40
11		1s. grey-green	..	70	40
12		2s. yellow-bistre	..	1·00	1·00
12a		2s. deep blue (*white paper*) (6.7.59)	24·00	7·50
1/12a		*Set of 14*	45·00	18·00

Stamps as Type 1, some in different colours, perforated 11 were prepared in 1940, but never issued. Examples exist from sheets stolen prior to the destruction of these stocks.

2 Warder's Tower   3 Airfield

(Des B. Stewart, eng. G. Lissenden (3 1/2d.), D. Cameron (7 1/2d.). Des and eng D. Cameron (6 1/2d.), P. Morriss (8 1/2d., 10d.) or G. Lissenden (5s.))

1953 (10 June). *T 2/3 and similar designs.* P 14 1/2 × 15 (*vert*) or 15 × 14 1/2 (*horiz*).

13	3 1/2d. brown-lake	..	1·00	90
14	6 1/2d. deep green	..	2·25	3·00
15	7 1/2d. deep blue	..	1·50	3·00
16	8 1/2d. chocolate	..	1·75	4·50
17	10d. reddish violet	..	1·00	75
18	5s. sepia	..	42·00	10·00
13/18	..	*Set of 6*	45·00	20·00

Designs: *Horiz* (*as T 3*)—7 1/2d. Old Stores (Crankmill); 5s. Bloody Bridge. *Vert* (*as T 2*)—8 1/2d. Barracks entrance; 10d. Salt House.

8 Norfolk Island Seal and Pitcairners Landing

Two types of 2s.:

Type I   Type II

Alternate stamps on each horizontal row are with or without a dot in bottom right corner.

(Des and eng F. Manley)

1956 (8 June). *Centenary of Landing of Pitcairn Islanders on Norfolk Island.* P 15×14 1/2.

19	8	3d. deep bluish green	..	1·50	40
20		2s. violet (I)	..	2·00	75
		a. Type II	..	2·00	75
		b. Deep violet (I)	..	3·50	2·25
		ba. Type II	..	3·50	2·25

7d   **NORFOLK ISLAND**

8d   **5D**

(9)   (10)   (11)

1958 (1 July). *Nos. 15/16 surch with T 9/10.*

21	7d. on 7 1/2d. deep blue	..	75	1·00
22	8d. on 8 1/2d. chocolate	..	75	1·00

1959 (7 Dec). *150th Anniv of Australian Post Office. No. 331 of Australia surch with T 11.*

23	5d. on 4d. slate (R.)	..	35	30

12 Hibiscus insularis   14 White Tern

16 Red Hibiscus   17 Queen Elizabeth II and Cereus

21 Rose Apple   22 Red-tailed Tropic Bird

(Des G. Lissenden, eng P. Morriss (5s.). Des and eng G. Lissenden (10s.), P. Morriss (others). Recess and typo (2s. 8d.), recess (others))

1960–62. *T 12, 14, 16/17, 21/2 and similar designs.* P 14 1/2 or 14 1/2×14 (10s.).

24	1d. bluish green (23.5.60)	..	15	10
25	2d. rose and myrtle-green (23.5.60)	..	20	10
26	3d. green (1.5.61)	..	70	15
27	5d. bright purple (20.6.60)	..	55	20
28	8d. red (20.6.60)	..	80	50
29	9d. ultramarine (23.5.60)	..	80	45
30	10d. brown and reddish violet (as No. 17) (27.2.61)	..	2·00	1·25
31	1s. 1d. carmine-red (16.10.61)	..	80	35
32	2s. sepia (1.5.61)	..	6·00	90
33	2s. 5d. deep violet (5.2.62)	..	1·00	40
34	2s. 8d. cinnamon and deep green (9.4.62)	..	2·75	55
35	5s. sepia and deep green (as No. 18) (27.2.61)	6·50	75
36	10s. emerald-green (14.8.61) (Optd S. £48) ..	45·00	26·00
24/36		*Set of 13*	60·00	28·00

Designs: *Vert* (*as T 12*)—2d. *Lagunaria patersonii*; 5d. Lantana. (*As T 21*); 1s. 1d. Fringed Hibiscus; 2s. 5d. Passion-flower. (*As T 14*)—2s. Solander's Petrel.

Nos. 30 and 35 are redrawn.

The *Specimen* overprint on No. 36 is from sets sold by the Australian Post Office.

For Nos. 25 and 28 with face values in decimal currency see Nos. 600/1.

2/8

1/1   2/5

(23)   (24)   (25)

1960. *As Nos. 13/15 but colours changed, surch with T 23/5.*

37	1s. 1d. on 3 1/2d. deep ultramarine (26.9.60)	3·50	2·50
38	2s. 5d. on 6 1/2d. bluish green (26.9.60)	..	4·00	1·50
39	2s. 8d. on 7 1/2d. sepia (29.8.60)	..	10·00	6·00
37/9		*Set of 3*	16·00	9·00

26 Queen Elizabeth II and Map   27 Open Bible and Candle

(Des and eng P. Morriss.)

1960 (24 Oct). *Introduction of Local Government.* P 14.

40	26	2s. 8d. reddish purple	..	13·00	11·00

(Des K. McKay. Adapted and eng B. Stewart. Recess)

1960 (21 Nov). *Christmas.* P 15×14 1/2.

41	27	5d. bright purple	..	80	50

---

28 Open Prayer Book and Text   29 Stripey (Atypichthys latus)

(Des G. Lissenden. Eng P. Morriss. Recess)

1961 (20 Nov). *Christmas.* P 14 1/2×14.

42	28	5d. slate-blue	..	30	60

PRINTERS. All the following issues to No. 233 were printed in photogravure by Harrison and Sons, Ltd, London, *except where otherwise stated.*

1962–63. *Fishes. Horiz designs as T 29.* P 14 1/2×14.

43	6d. sepia, yellow & dp bluish green (16.7.62)	75	25
44	11d. red-orange, brown and blue (25.2.63)	2·00	80
45	1s. blue, pink and yellow-olive (17.9.62)	..	75	25
46	1s. 3d. blue, red-brown and green (15.7.63)	2·00	1·75
47	1s. 6d. sepia, violet and light blue (6.5.63) ..	2·75	80
48	2s. 3d. dp blue, red & greenish yell (23.9.63)	5·00	80
43/8		*Set of 6*	12·00	4·25

Designs:—11d. Gold-mouthed Emperor (*Lethrinus chrysostomus*); 1s. Surge Wrasse ("Po'ov"); 1s. 3d. Seachub ("Dreamfish"); 1s. 6d. Giant Grouper (*Promicrops lanceolatus*); 2s. 3d. White Trevally (*Carangidae*).

30 "Madonna and Child"   31 "Peace on Earth..."

(Des and eng G. Lissenden. Recess Note Ptg Branch, Reserve Bank of Australia)

1962 (19 Nov). *Christmas.* P 14 1/2.

49	30	5d. ultramarine	..	45	80

(Des R. Warner. Eng B. Stewart. Recess Note Ptg Branch, Reserve Bank of Australia)

1963 (11 Nov). *Christmas.* P 14 1/2.

50	31	5d. red	..	40	70

32 Overlooking Kingston   33 Norfolk Pine

(Photo Note Ptg Branch, Reserve Bank of Australia, Melbourne)

1964 (24 Feb–28 Sept). *Views. Horiz designs as T 32. Multicoloured.* P 14 1/2×14.

51	5d. Type 32	..	75	50
52	8d. Kingston	..	1·00	1·25
53	9d. The Arches (Bumboras) (11.5)	..	2·25	30
54	10d. Slaughter Bay (28.9)	..	2·25	30
51/4		*Set of 4*	5·50	2·10

(Photo Note Ptg Branch, Reserve Bank of Australia)

1964 (1 July). *50th Anniv of Norfolk Island as Australian Territory.* P 13 1/2.

55	33	5d. black, red and orange	..	40	15
56		8d. black, red and grey-green	..	40	1·10

34 Child looking at Nativity Scene   35 Nativity Scene

(Des P. Morriss and J. Mason. Photo Note Ptg Branch, Reserve Bank of Australia)

1964 (9 Nov). *Christmas.* P 13 1/2.

57	34	5d. green, blue, buff and violet	..	30	40

1965 (14 Apr). *50th Anniv of Gallipoli Landing. As T 22 of Nauru.* P 13 1/2.

58		5d. sepia, black and emerald	..	15	10

(Des J. Mason. Photo Note Ptg Branch, Reserve Bank of Australia)

1965 (25 Oct). *Christmas. Helecon paper.* P 13 1/2.

59	35	5d. multicoloured	..	15	10

(New Currency. 100 cents = 1 Australian dollar)

38 *Hibiscus insularis*   **39** Headstone Bridge

1966 (14 Feb). *Decimal currency. Various stamps surch in black on silver tablets, which vary slightly in size, obliterating old value as in T* **38**. *Surch typo.*

60	**38**	1 c. on 1d. bluish green (*value tablet* 4×5 *mm*)		20	10
		a. Value tablet larger, 5½×5½ mm		40	30
61	–	2 c. on 2d. rose & myrtle-green (No. 25)		20	10
62	**14**	3 c. on 3d. green		50	50
		a. Silver tablet omitted		£275	
63	–	4 c. on 5d. bright purple (No. 27)		25	10
64	**16**	5 c. on 8d. red		30	10
65	–	10 c. on 10d. brown & reddish vio (No. 30)		90	15
66	–	15 c. on 1s. 1d. carmine-red (No. 31)		45	50
67	–	20 c. on 2s. sepia (No. 32)		3·50	2·75
68	–	25 c. on 2s. 5d. deep violet (No. 33)		1·50	
69	**21**	30 c. on 2s. 8d. cinnamon and deep green		1·00	50
70	–	50 c. on 5s. sepia and deep green (No. 35)		3·50	75
71	**22**	$1 on 10s. emerald-green (*value tablet* 7×6½ *mm*)		3·00	2·50
		a. Value tablet smaller, 6½×4 mm		2·75	2·50
60/71		*Set of* 12		13·00	7·50

1966 (27 June). *Horiz designs as T* **39**. *Multicoloured. P* 14½ × 14.

72		7 c. Type **39**		40	15
73		9 c. Cemetery Road		40	15

41 St. Barnabas' Chapel   **42** St. Barnabas' Chapel
(interior)   (exterior)

1966 (23 Aug). *Centenary of Melanesian Mission. P* 14 × 14½.

74	**41**	4 c. multicoloured		10	10
75	**42**	25 c. multicoloured		20	20

43 Star over Philip Island   **44** H.M.S. *Resolution*, 1774

(Des B. G. W. McCoy)

1966 (24 Oct). *Christmas. P* 14½.

76	**43**	4 c. multicoloured		10	10

(Des V. Whiteley)

1967 (17 Apr)–**68**. *T* **44** *and similar horiz designs showing ships. Multicoloured. P* 14×14½.

77		1 c. Type **44**		10	10
78		2 c. *La Boussole* and *L'Astrolabe*, 1788		15	10
79		3 c. H.M.S. *Supply*, 1788		15	10
80		4 c. H.M.S. *Sirius*, 1790		50	10
81		5 c. *Norfolk* (sloop), 1798 (14.8.67)		20	10
82		7 c. H.M.S. *Mermaid* (survey cutter), 1825 (14.8.67)		20	10
83		9 c. *Lady Franklin*, 1853 (14.8.67)		20	10
84		10 c. *Morayshire*, 1856 (14.8.67)		20	30
85		15 c. *Southern Cross*, 1866 (18.3.68)		45	30
86		20 c. *Pitcairn*, 1891 (18.3.68)		60	40
87		25 c. *Black Billy* (Norfolk Island whaleboat), 1895 (18.3.68)		1·50	75
88		30 c. *Iris* (cable ship), 1907 (18.6.68)		1·50	2·00
89		50 c. *Resolution*, 1926 (18.6.68)		4·75	3·50
90		$1 *Morinda*, 1931 (18.6.68)		5·50	3·50
77/90		*Set of* 14		14·00	10·00

45 Lions Badge   **46** Prayer of John Adams and
and 50 Stars   Candle

(Des M. Ripper. Photo Note Ptg Branch, Reserve Bank of Australia)

1967 (7 June). *50th Anniv of Lions International. P* 13½.

91	**45**	4 c. black, bluish green and olive-yellow		10	10

(Des B. G. W. McCoy)

1967 (16 Oct). *Christmas. P* 14.

92	**46**	5 c. black, light yellow-olive and red		10	10

---

47 Queen
Elizabeth II

(Photo Note Ptg Branch, Reserve Bank of Australia)

1968 (5 Aug)–**71**. *Coil stamps. P* 15×*imperf.*

93	**47**	3 c. black, light brown and vermilion		10	10
94		4 c. black, light brown and blue-green		10	10
95		5 c. black, light brown and deep violet		10	10
95a		6 c. black, lt brown & lake-brn (25.8.71)		30	45
93/5a		*Set of* 4		45	55

59 Avro Type 691 Lancastrian   **60** Bethlehem Star
and Douglas DC-4 Aircraft   and Flowers

(Des Harrison)

1968 (25 Sept). *21st Anniv of QANTAS Air Service, Sydney–Norfolk Island. P* 14.

96	**59**	5 c. bluish black, carmine-red & lt blue		15	10
97		7 c. blackish brown, carmine-red & turq		15	10

(Des Betty Laing)

1968 (24 Oct). *Christmas. P* 14×14½.

98	**60**	5 c. multicoloured		10	10

 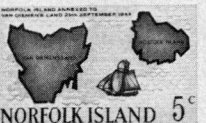

61 Captain Cook, Quadrant   **62** Van Diemen's Land, Norfolk
and Chart of Pacific Ocean   Island and Sailing Cutter

(Des V. Whiteley from sketch by J. Cowap)

1969 (3 June). *Captain Cook Bicentenary* (1st issue). *Observation of the transit of Venus across the Sun, from Tahiti. P* 14.

99	**61**	10 c. multicoloured		10	10

See also Nos. 118/19, 129, 152/5, 200/2 and 213/14.

(Des Mrs. A. Bathie and Mrs. M. J. McCoy)

1969 (29 Sept). *125th Anniv of the Annexation of Norfolk Island to Van Diemen's Land. P* 14 × 14½.

100	**62**	5 c. multicoloured		10	10
101		30 c. multicoloured		50	80
		a. Inscr "VAN DIFMEN'S LAND" (R. 8/5)		11·00	

63 "The Nativity" (carved   **64** New Zealand
mother-of-pearl plaque)   Grey Flyeater

(Des J. Cowap)

1969 (27 Oct). *Christmas. P* 14½ × 14.

102	**63**	5 c. multicoloured		10	10

(Des G. Mathews)

1970–71. *Birds. T* **64** *and similar multicoloured designs. Chalk-surfaced paper. P* 14.

103		1 c. Scarlet Robins (22.7.70)		30	10
104		2 c. Golden Whistler (24.2.71)		30	20
105		3 c. Type **64** (25.2.70)		30	10
106		4 c. Long-tailed Koels (25.2.70)		60	10
107		5 c. Red-fronted Parakeet (24.2.71)		1·50	60
108		7 c. Long-tailed Triller (22.7.70)		45	10
109		9 c. Island Thrush (25.2.70)		70	10
110		10 c. Boobook Owl (22.7.70)		1·75	1·50
111		15 c. Norfolk Island Pigeon (24.2.71)		1·50	65
112		20 c. White-chested White Eye (16.6.71)		7·00	3·25
113		25 c. New Zealand Parrots (22.7.70)		2·50	40
		a. Error. Glazed, ordinary paper		£375	
114		30 c. Collared Grey Fantail (16.6.71)		7·00	1·75
115		45 c. Norfolk Island Starlings (25.2.70)		3·00	80
116		50 c. Crimson Rosella (24.2.71)		3·50	1·75
117		$1 Sacred Kingfisher (16.6.71)		10·00	10·00
103/17		*Set of* 15		35·00	19·00

Nos. 105, 106, 109, 112, 114, 115 and 117 are horizontal, and the remainder vertical designs.
It is believed that only one sheet of No. 113a was issued.

---

65 Capt. Cook and Map of Australia   **66** First Christmas
Service, 1788

(Des R. Bates)

1970 (29 Apr). *Captain Cook Bicentenary* (2nd issue). *Discovery of Australia's East Coast. T* **65** *and similar horiz design. Multicoloured. P* 14.

118		5 c. Type **65**		15	10
119		10 c. H.M.S. *Endeavour* and aborigine		40	10

(Des R. Bates)

1970 (15 Oct). *Christmas. P* 14.

120	**66**	5 c. multicoloured		10	10

67 Bishop Patteson and Martyrdom   **68** Rose Window,
of St. Stephen   St. Barnabas Chapel,
      Kingston

(Des R. Bates)

1971 (20 Sept). *Death Centenary of Bishop Patteson. T* **67** *and similar horiz designs. Multicoloured. P* 14 × 14½.

121		6 c. Type **67**		10	25
		a. Pair. Nos. 121/2		15	50
122		6 c. Bible, Martyrdom of St. Stephen and knotted palm-frond		10	25
123		10 c. Bishop Patteson and stained-glass		10	25
		a. Pair. Nos. 123/4		20	50
124		10 c. Cross and Bishop's Arms		10	25
121/4		*Set of* 4		30	90

Nos. 121/2 and 123/4 were printed in *se-tenant* pairs throughout the sheet.

(Des G. Hitch. Photo Heraclio Fournier, Spain)

1971 (25 Oct). *Christmas. P* 14 × 13½.

125	**68**	6 c. multicoloured		10	10

69 Map and Flag   **70** "St. Mark" (stained-glass
window, All Saints, Norfolk Is)

(Des G. Hitch)

1972 (7 Feb). *25th Anniv of South Pacific Commission. P* 14 × 14½.

126	**69**	7 c. multicoloured		15	20

(Des Mrs. M. J. McCoy)

1972 (16 Oct). *Christmas. P* 14.

127	**70**	7 c. multicoloured		10	10

71 Cross and Pines   **72** H.M.S. *Resolution* in
(stained-glass window,   the Antarctic
All Saints Church)

(Des Harrison)

1972 (20 Nov). *Centenary of First Pitcairn-built Church. P* 14.

128	**71**	12 c. multicoloured		10	10
		a. Purple (background to dates) omitted		£600	

No. 128a occurred on the top row of one sheet.

(Des G. Hitch)

1973 (17 Jan). *Captain Cook Bicentenary (3rd issue). Crossing of the Antarctic Circle. P* 14.
129　**72**　35 c. multicoloured　..　..　..　..　2·50　2·25

73 Child and Christmas Tree　**74** Protestant Clergyman's Quarters

(Des B. G. W. McCoy (T **73**), R. Westwood (35 c.))

1973 (22 Oct). *Christmas. T* **73** *and similar vert design. Multicoloured. P* 14.
130　7 c. Type **73**　..　..　..　..　20　10
131　12 c. Type **73**　..　..　..　..　25　10
132　35 c. Fir trees and star　..　..　..　70　80
130/2 ..　..　..　..　Set of 3　1·00　90

(Des G. Hitch)

1973 (19 Nov)–**75**. *Historic Buildings. T* **74** *and similar horiz designs. Multicoloured. P* 14 × 14½.
133　1 c. Type **74**　..　..　..　..　10　10
134　2 c. Royal Engineers' Office (1.5.74)..　10　10
135　3 c. Double Quarters for Free Overseers (19.2.75)　..　..　..　25　30
136　4 c. Guard House (12.7.74)　..　..　20　20
137　5 c. Entrance to Pentagonal Gaol　..　25　15
138　7 c. Pentagonal Gaol (1.5.74)　..　35　35
139　8 c. Prisoners' Barracks (19.2.75)　..　1·25　1·75
140　10 c. Officers' Quarters, New Military Barracks　..　..　..　50　55
141　12 c. New Military Barracks (1.5.74)..　50　30
142　14 c. Beach Stores (12.7.74)　..　50　70
143　15 c. The Magazine (19.2.75)　..　1·25　50
144　20 c. Entrance, Old Military Barracks (12.7.74)　..　..　50　90
145　25 c. Old Military Barracks (19.2.75)..　1·25　1·00
146　30 c. Old Stores (Crankmill) (1.5.74)　..　50　60
147　50 c. Commissariat Stores　..　..　50　2·00
148　$1 Government House (12.7.74)　..　1·00　4·00
133/48 ..　..　..　..　Set of 16　8·00　11·00

75 Royal Couple and Map

(Des Harrison)

1974 (8 Feb). *Royal Visit. P* 14 × 14½.
149　**75**　7 c. multicoloured　..　..　40　15
150　25 c. multicoloured　..　..　1·00　75

76 Chichester's De Havilland D.H.60G Gipsy Moth Seaplane *Madame Elijah*

(Des B. G. W. McCoy. Litho State Bank Note Printing Works, Helsinki)

1974 (28 Mar). *First Aircraft Landing on Norfolk Island. P* 14.
151　**76**　14 c. multicoloured　..　..　75　70

77 "Captain Cook" (engraving by J. Basire)　**78** Nativity Scene (pearl-shell pew carving)

(Des C. I. Buffett. Litho Questa)

1974 (8 Oct). *Captain Cook Bicentenary (4th issue). Discovery of Norfolk Is. T* **77** *and similar vert designs. Multicoloured. P* 14.
152　7 c. Type **77**　..　..　..　75　75
153　10 c. "H.M.S. *Resolution*" (H. Roberts)　..　1·75　1·75
154　14 c. Norfolk Island Pine　..　1·50　2·25
155　25 c. "Norfolk Island flax" (G. Raper)　..　1·50　3·00
152/5 ..　..　..　Set of 4　5·00　7·00

(Des G. Hitch)

1974 (18 Oct). *Christmas. P* 14½.
156　**78**　7 c. multicoloured　..　..　15　10
157　30 c. multicoloured　..　..　60　75

79 Norfolk Pine

(Manufactured by Walsall)

1974 (16 Dec). *Centenary of Universal Postal Union. T* **79** *and similar "island"-shaped designs. Multicoloured. Imperf (backing-paper roll 20). Self-adhesive.*
158　10 c. Type **79**　..　..　..　25　50
159　15 c. Offshore islands　..　..　35　55
160　35 c. Crimson Rosella and Sacred Kingfisher　75　85
161　40 c. Pacific map　..　..　75　95
158/61 ..　..　..　Set of 4　1·90　2·50
MS162　106 × 101 mm. Map of Norfolk Is. cut-to-shape with reduced-size replicas of Nos. 158/61　20·00　24·00

80 H.M.S. *Mermaid* (survey cutter)

(Manufactured by Walsall)

1975 (18 Aug). *150th Anniv of Second Settlement. T* **80** *and similar "island"-shaped design. Multicoloured. Imperf (backing-paper roll 20). Self-adhesive.*
163　10 c. Type **80**　..　..　..　40　75
164　35 c. Kingston, 1835 (from painting by T. Seller)　..　..　..　60　1·00

81 Star on Norfolk Island Pine　**82** Memorial Cross

(Des Harrison)

1975 (6 Oct). *Christmas. P* 14.
165　**81**　10 c. multicoloured　..　..　15　10
166　15 c. multicoloured　..　..　20　10
167　35 c. multicoloured　..　..　30　35
165/7 ..　..　..　Set of 3　60　45

(Des Harrison)

1975 (24 Nov). *Centenary of St. Barnabas Chapel. T* **82** *and similar horiz design. Multicoloured. P* 14.
168　30 c. Type **82**　..　..　..　20　15
169　60 c. Laying foundation stone and Chapel in 1975　..　..　..　40　40

83 Launching of *Resolution*　**84** Whaleship *Charles W. Morgan*

(Des Harrison)

1975 (1 Dec). *50th Anniv of Launching of Schooner "Resolution". T* **83** *and similar horiz design. Multicoloured. P* 14.
170　25 c. Type **83**　..　..　..　25　40
171　45 c. *Resolution* at sea..　..　40　70

(Des Harrison)

1976 (5 July). *Bicentenary of American Revolution. T* **84** *and similar horiz designs. Multicoloured. P* 14.
172　18 c. Type **84**　..　..　..　30　30
173　25 c. Thanksgiving Service　..　40　30
174　40 c. Boeing B-17 Flying Fortress over Norfolk Is　..　..　75　65
175　45 c. California Quail　..　..　1·00　85
172/5 ..　..　..　Set of 4　2·25　1·90

85 Swallow-tailed Tern and Sun　**86** *Vanessa ita*

(Des Harrison)

1976 (4 Oct). *Christmas. P* 14.
176　**85**　18 c. multicoloured　..　..　30　15
177　25 c. multicoloured　..　..　55　20
178　45 c. multicoloured　..　..　90　50
176/8 ..　..　..　Set of 3　1·60　75

(Des B. Hargreaves)

1976 (17 Nov)–**77**. *Butterflies and Moths. T* **86** *and similar horiz designs. Multicoloured. P* 14.
179　1 c. Type **86**　..　..　10　40
180　2 c. *Utetheisa pulchelloides* (moth) (22.2.77)　..　..　10　40
181　3 c. *Agathia asterias* (moth) (5.7.77)　10　20
182　4 c. *Cynthia kershawi* (5.7.77)　..　10　25
183　5 c. *Leucania loreyimima* (moth)　..　15　40
184　10 c. *Hypolimnas bolina*　..　..　30　35
185　15 c. *Pyrrhorachis pyrrhogona* (moth) (22.2.77)　..　..　30　30
186　16 c. *Austrocarea iocephala* (moth)　..　30　30
187　17 c. *Pseudocoremia christiani* (moth) (10.5.77)　..　..　35　30
188　18 c. *Cleora idiocrossa* (moth)　..　35　30
189　19 c. *Simplicia caeneusalis* (moth) (10.5.77)　35　30
190　20 c. *Austrocidaria ralstonae* (moth) (10.5.77)　..　..　40　30
191　30 c. *Hippotion scrofa* (moth) (22.2.77)　50　60
192　40 c. *Papilio amynthor* (ilioneus) (10.5.77)　55　40
193　50 c. *Tiracola plagiata* (moth) (22.2.77)　70　75
194　$1 *Precis villida* ..　..　..　75　75
195　$2 *Cepora perimale* (5.7.77)　..　1·25　1·40
179/95 ..　..　..　Set of 17　5·75　7·00

87 Queen's View, Kingston

(Des Harrison)

1977 (10 June). *Silver Jubilee. P* 14.
196　**87**　25 c. multicoloured　..　..　35　30

88 Hibiscus Flowers and Oil Lamp　**89** Captain Cook (from a portrait by Nathaniel Dance)

(Des Marguerite M. J. McCoy)

1977 (4 Oct). *Christmas. P* 14 × 14½.
197　**88**　18 c. multicoloured　..　..　15　10
198　25 c. multicoloured　..　..　15　10
199　45 c. multicoloured　..　..　30　35
197/9 ..　..　..　Set of 3　55　50

(Des Harrison)

1978 (18 Jan). *Captain Cook Bicentenary (5th issue). Discovery of Hawaii. T* **89** *and similar horiz designs. Multicoloured. P* 14½.
200　18 c. Type **89**　..　..　30　20
201　25 c. Discovery of Northern Hawaiian islands　30　30
202　80 c. British flag against island background　60　70
200/2 ..　..　..　Set of 3　1·10　1·10

90 Guide Flag and Globe

(Manufactured by Walsall)

1978 (22 Feb). *50th Anniv of Girl Guides. T* **90** *and similar
"island"-shaped designs. Multicoloured. Imperf (backing paper
roul 20). Self-adhesive.*
203	18 c. Type **90**	..	..	25	35
204	25 c. Emblem and scarf badge			30	45
	a. Horiz roul omitted (vert pair)				
205	35 c. Emblem and Queen Elizabeth			45	70
	a. Horiz roul omitted (vert pair)				
206	45 c. Emblem and Lady Baden-Powell			55	70
203/6			*Set of* 4	1·40	2·00

Nos. 204a and 205a each come from sheets of 20 on which all
the horizontal roulettes were omitted.

91 St. Edward's Crown

(Des Harrison)

1978 (29 June). *25th Anniv of Coronation. T* **91** *and similar horiz
design. Multicoloured. P* 14½.
207	25 c. Type **91**	..	..	15	15
208	70 c. Coronation regalia	..	..	40	45

92 View of Duncombe Bay with Scout at Camp Fire

(Des S. Jensen. Manufactured by Walsall)

1978 (22 Aug). *50th Anniv of Boy Scouts. T* **92** *and similar
"island"-shaped designs. Multicoloured. Imperf (backing paper
roul 20). Self-adhesive.*
209	20 c. Type **92**	..	..	30	45
210	25 c. View from Kingston and emblem			35	55
211	35 c. View of Anson Bay and Link Badge			50	90
212	45 c. Sunset scene and Lord Baden-Powell			55	95
209/12			*Set of* 4	1·50	2·50

93 Chart showing Route of Arctic   **94** Poinsettia and
Voyage   Bible

(Des G. Hitch)

1978 (29 Aug). *Captain Cook Bicentenary (6th issue). Northern-
most Voyages. T* **93** *and similar horiz design. Multicoloured.
P* 14½.
213	25 c. Type **93**	..	..	30	30
214	90 c. "H.M.S. *Resolution* and H.M.S. *Dis-
covery* in Pack Ice" (painting by Web-
ber)			80	80

(Des Marie L. McCoy)

1978 (3 Oct). *Christmas. T* **94** *and similar vert designs. Multicoloured. P* 14½ × 14.
215	20 c. Type **94**	..	..	15	10
216	30 c. Native Oak and Bible	..	..	20	15
217	55 c. Hibiscus and Bible	..	..	30	30
215/17			*Set of* 3	60	50

95 Cook and Village of Staithes near Marton

(Des Harrison)

1978 (27 Oct). *250th Birth Anniv of Captain Cook. T* **95** *and
similar horiz design. Multicoloured. P* 14½.
218	20 c. Type **95**	..	..	30	25
219	80 c. Cook and Whitby Harbour	..	70	1·25

MINIMUM PRICE

The minimum price quote is 10p which represents
a handling charge rather than a basis for valuing
common stamps. For further notes about prices
see introductory pages.

---

96 H.M.S. *Resolution*   **97** Assembly Building

(Des G. Hitch)

1979 (14 Feb). *Death Bicentenary of Captain Cook. T* **96** *and
similar horiz designs. Multicoloured. P* 14.
220	20 c. Type **96**	..	..	30	30
	a. Pair. Nos. 220/1	..	..	60	60
221	20 c. Cook (statue)	..	..	30	30
222	40 c. Cook's death	..	..	40	50
	a. Pair. Nos. 222/3	..	..	80	1·00
223	40 c. Cook's death (*different*)	..	40	50
220/23			*Set of* 4	1·25	1·60

The 20 c. designs depict the *Resolution* and Cook's statue on a
map showing the last voyage. The 40 c. designs show Cook's death
from an aquatint by John Clevely.

Nos. 220/1 and 222/3 were each printed together, *se-tenant*, in
horizontal pairs throughout the sheets, forming composite designs.

1979 (10 Aug). *First Norfolk Island Legislative Assembly.
P* 14½ × 14.
224	**97**	$1 multicoloured	..	50	50

98 Tasmania 1853 1d. Stamp
and Sir Rowland Hill

1979 (27 Aug). *Death Centenary of Sir Rowland Hill. T* **98**
*and similar horiz designs showing stamps and Sir Rowland Hill.
P* 14 × 14½.
225	20 c. new blue and sepia	..	20	10
226	30 c. brown-red and olive-grey	..	25	15
227	55 c. violet and indigo ..	..	40	30
225/7			*Set of* 3	75	50
MS228	142 × 91 mm. No. 227. P 14			55	1·25

Designs:—30 c. Penny Red; 55 c. 1d. "Ball Bay".

99 I.Y.C. Emblem and Map of Pacific showing Norfolk Island as
Pine Tree

(Des Claire Walters. Litho Asher and Co, Melbourne)

1979 (25 Sept). *International Year of the Child. P* 15.
229	**99**	80 c. multicoloured	..	40	45

100 Emily Bay   **101** Lions International
Emblem

1979 (5 Nov).* *Christmas. T* **100** *and similar horiz designs
showing different aspects of Emily Bay. P* 12½ × 13.
230	15 c. multicoloured	..	..	15	15
	a. Horiz strip of 3. Nos. 230/2	..	40	
231	20 c. multicoloured	..	..	15	15
232	30 c. multicoloured	..	..	15	15
230/2			*Set of* 3	40	40
MS233	152 × 83 mm. Nos. 230/2. P 14 × 14½			1·00	1·60

Nos. 230/2 were printed together, *se-tenant*, in horizontal strips
of 3 throughout the sheet, forming a composite design.

*Although released by the Crown Agents in London on 2 October
the stamps were not released locally until 5 November.

(Des Norfolk Island Lions Club. Litho Asher and Co, Melbourne)

1980 (25 Jan). *Lions Convention. P* 15.
234	**101**	50 c. multicoloured	..	35	30

102 Rotary International Emblem

(Des E. Lenthall. Litho Asher and Co, Melbourne)

1980 (21 Feb). *75th Anniv of Rotary International. P* 15.
235	**102**	50 c. multicoloured	..	35	30
	a. Black (face value and "NORFOLK
ISLAND") omitted ..				

103 De Havilland D.H.60G
Gipsy Moth Seaplane *Madame
Elijah*

(Des G. Hitch and B. G. W. McCoy. Litho Harrison)

1980 (25 Mar)–81. *Airplanes. Horiz designs as T* **103**.
Multicoloured. P 14½ × 14.
236	1 c. Hawker Siddeley H.S.748 (3.3.81)	..	15	20
237	2 c. Type **103**	..	..	15	20
238	3 c. Curtiss P.40E Kittyhawk I	..	15	20
239	4 c. Chance Vought F4U-1 Corsair
(19.8.80)			15	30
240	5 c. Grumman TBF Avenger (19.8.80)	..	15	30
241	15 c. Douglas SBD-5 Dauntless (19.8.80)	..	30	30
242	20 c. Cessna 172D Skyhawk	..	30	30
243	25 c. Lockheed 414 Hudson (3.3.81)	..	30	35
244	30 c. Lockheed PV-1 Ventura (13.1.81)	..	40	90
245	40 c. Avro Type 685 York (3.3.81)	..	50	55
246	50 c. Douglas DC-3 (13.1.81)	..	65	65
247	60 c. Avro Type 691 Lancastrian (13.1.81)	..	75	75
248	80 c. Douglas DC-4 (13.1.81)	..	95	95
249	$1 Beech 200 Super King Air (3.3.81)	..	1·25	90
250	$2 Fokker F.27 Friendship (19.8.80)	..	2·50	2·25
251	$5 Lockheed C-130 Hercules	..	6·00	2·00
236/51			*Set of* 16	13·00	10·00

104 Queen Elizabeth the Queen Mother

(Des K. Williams. Litho Harrison)

1980 (4 Aug). *80th Birthday of Queen Elizabeth the Queen Mother.
P* 14.
252	**104**	22 c. multicoloured	..	20	20
253		60 c. multicoloured	..	35	40

105 Red-tailed Tropic Birds

(Des K. Williams. Litho Harrison)

1980 (28 Oct). *Christmas. Birds. T* **105** *and similar horiz designs.
Multicoloured. P* 14 × 14½.
254	15 c. Type **105**	..	..	30	25
	a. Horiz strip of 3. Nos. 254/6	..	80	
255	22 c. White Terns	..	..	30	25
256	35 c. White-capped Noddys	..	30	45
257	60 c. White Terns (*different*)	..	40	45
254/7			*Set of* 4	1·10	1·10

Nos. 254/6 were printed together, *se-tenant*, in horizontal strips
of 3 throughout the sheet.

106 *Morayshire* and View of   **107** Wedding Bouquet from
Norfolk Island   Norfolk Island

(Des Jennifer Toombs. Litho Harrison)

1981 (5 June). *125th Anniv of Pitcairn Islanders' Migration to
Norfolk Island. T* **106** *and similar horiz designs. Multicoloured.
P* 14½.
258	15 c. Type **106**	..	..	15	15
259	35 c. Islanders arriving ashore	..	40	30
260	60 c. View of new settlement ..	..	60	45
258/60			*Set of* 3	1·00	80
MS261	183 × 127 mm. Nos. 258/60			1·50	2·00

(Des J.W. Litho Harrison)

1981 (22 July). *Royal Wedding. T* **107** *and similar vert designs. Multicoloured. P* 14.

262	35 c. Type **107**	..	..	15	15
263	55 c. Prince Charles at horse trials	..	..	25	25
264	60 c. Prince Charles and Lady Diana Spencer		25	35
262/4	..	..	*Set of* 3	60	65

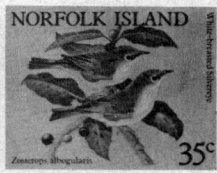

108 Uniting Church in Australia   **109** Pair of White-chested White Eyes

(Des K. Williams. Litho Harrison)

1981 (15 Sept). *Christmas. Churches. T* **108** *and similar horiz designs. Multicoloured. P* 14½ × 14.

265	18 c. Type **108**	..	..	15	10
266	24 c. Seventh Day Adventist Church	..	15	15
267	30 c. Church of the Sacred Heart	..	20	20
268	$1 St. Barnabas Chapel	..	..	50	70
265/8	..	..	*Set of* 4	90	1·00

(Des P. Slater. Litho Questa)

1981 (10 Nov). *White-chested White Eye ("Silvereye"). T* **109** *and similar horiz designs. Multicoloured. P* 14 × 14½.

269	35 c. Type **109**	..	..	35	40
	a. Horiz strip of 5. Nos. 269/73	..	1·50	
270	35 c. Bird on nest	..	..	35	40
271	35 c. Bird with egg	..	..	35	40
272	35 c. Parents with chicks	..	..	35	40
273	35 c. Fledgelings	..	..	35	40
269/73	..	..	*Set of* 5	1·50	2·00

Nos. 269/73 were printed together, *se-tenant*, in horizontal strips of 5 throughout the sheet.

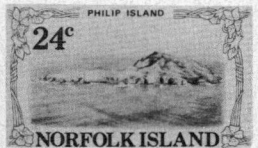

110 Aerial View of Philip Island

(Des local artist. Litho Harrison)

1982 (12 Jan). *Philip and Nepean Islands. T* **110** *and similar horiz designs. Multicoloured. P* 14 × 13½.

274	24 c. Type **110**	..	..	20	20
	a. Horiz strip of 5. Nos. 274/8	..	90	
275	24 c. Close-up view of Philip Island landscape		20	20
276	24 c. Gecko (*Phyllodactylus guentheri*), Philip Island		20	20
277	24 c. Sooty Tern (*Sterna fuscata*), Philip Island		20	20
278	24 c. Philip Island Hibiscus (*Hibiscus insularis*)		20	20
279	35 c. Aerial view of Nepean Island	..	25	25
	a. Horiz strip of 5. Nos. 279/83	..	1·10	
280	35 c. Close-up view of Nepean Island landscape		25	25
281	35 c. Gecko (*Phyllodactylus guentheri*), Nepean Island		25	25
282	35 c. Blue-faced Boobies (*Sula dactylatra*), Nepean Island		25	25
283	35 c. *Carpobrotus glaucescens* (flower), Nepean Island		25	25
274/83	..	..	*Set of* 10	2·00	2·00

The five designs of each value were printed together, *se-tenant*, in horizontal strips of 5 throughout the sheet.

111 Sperm Whale

(Des Jennifer Toombs. Litho Harrison)

1982 (23 Feb). *Whales. T* **111** *and similar horiz designs. P* 14½.

284	24 c. multicoloured	..	..	60	35
285	55 c. multicoloured	..	..	1·10	95
286	80 c. black, mauve and stone	..	1·40	2·00
284/6	..	..	*Set of* 3	2·75	3·00

Designs:—55 c. Black Right Whale; 80 c. Humpback Whale.

112 *Diocet*, Wrecked 20 April 1873

(Litho Harrison)

1982 (18 May–27 July). *Shipwrecks. T* **112** *and similar horiz designs. Multicoloured. P* 14½ × 14.

287	24 c. H.M.S. *Sirius*, wrecked 19 March 1790 (27 July)		50	50
288	27 c. Type **112**	..	..	50	50
289	35 c. *Friendship*, wrecked 17 May 1835 (27 July)		90	80
290	40 c. *Mary Hamilton*, wrecked 6 May 1873 (27 July)		90	1·25
291	55 c. *Fairlie*, wrecked 14 February 1840 (27 July)		1·25	1·25
292	65 c. *Warrigal*, wrecked 18 March 1918		1·25	1·75
287/92	..	..	*Set of* 6	4·75	5·50

C-KURITY PAPER. The following issues up to No. 342 were all printed on this type of security paper, *unless otherwise stated*. It shows a pattern of blue fluorescent markings, resembling rosettes, on the reverse beneath the gum.

113 R.N.Z.A.F. Lockheed 414 Hudson dropping Christmas Supplies, 1942   **114** 50th (Queen's Own) Regiment

(Des A. Theobald. Litho Walsall)

1982 (7 Sept). *Christmas. 40th Anniv of first Supply-plane Landings on Norfolk Island (Christmas Day* 1942*). T* **113** *and similar horiz designs. Multicoloured. P* 14.

293	27 c. Type **113**	..	..	55	35
294	40 c. Lockheed 414 Hudson landing Christmas supplies, 1942		75	65
295	75 c. Christmas, 1942	..	..	90	1·40
293/5	..	..	*Set of* 3	2·00	2·25

(Des W. Fenton. Litho Questa)

1982 (9 Nov). *Military Uniforms. T* **114** *and similar vert designs. Multicoloured. P* 14½ × 14.

296	27 c. Type **114**	..	..	30	35
297	40 c. 58th (Rutlandshire) Regiment	..	40	75
298	55 c. 80th (Staffordshire Volunteers) Battalion Company		50	95
299	65 c. 11th (North Devonshire) Regiment	..	60	1·25
296/9	..	..	*Set of* 4	1·60	3·00

115 *Panaeolus papilionaceus*   **116** Beech 18 Aircraft

(Des Jane Thatcher. Litho Enschedé)

1983 (29 Mar). *Fungi. T* **115** *and similar vert designs. Multicoloured. P* 13½ × 13.

300	27 c. Type **115**	..	..	40	35
301	40 c. *Coprinus domesticus*	..	..	60	50
302	55 c. *Marasmius niveus*	..	..	75	70
303	65 c. *Cymatoderma elegans* var *lamellatum*		1·00	85
300/3	..	..	*Set of* 4	2·50	2·25

(Des Walsall. Litho Format)

1983 (12 July). *Bicentenary of Manned Flight. T* **116** *and similar horiz designs. Multicoloured. P* 14½ × 14.

304	10 c. Type **116**	..	..	15	15
305	27 c. Fokker F.28 Fellowship	..	..	25	35
306	45 c. French military Douglas C-54	..	40	60
307	75 c. Sikorsky S-61N helicopter	..	60	95
304/7	..	..	*Set of* 4	1·25	1·90
MS308	105×100 mm. Nos. 304/7	..	1·75	2·75

117 St. Matthew   **118** Cable Ship *Chantik*

(Des McCombie-Skinner Studio. Litho Format)

1983 (13 Sept). *Christmas. 150th Birth Anniv of Sir Edward Burne-Jones. T* **117** *and similar vert designs showing stained-glass windows from St. Barnabas Chapel, Norfolk Island. Multicoloured. P* 14.

309	5 c. Type **117**	..	..	10	10
310	24 c. St. Mark	..	..	20	30
311	30 c. Jesus Christ	..	..	25	40
312	45 c. St. Luke	..	..	35	55
313	85 c. St. John	..	..	55	1·10
309/13	..	..	*Set of* 5	1·25	2·25

(Des G. Drummond. Litho Format)

1983 (15 Nov). *World Communications Year. ANZCAN Cable. T* **118** *and similar horiz designs. Multicoloured. Ordinary paper. P* 14½ × 14.

314	30 c. Type **118**	..	..	30	40
315	45 c. *Chantik* during in-shore operations		40	55
316	75 c. Cable ship *Mercury*	..	..	55	95
317	85 c. Diagram of cable route	..	55	1·10
314/17	..	..	*Set of* 4	1·60	2·75

119 Popwood   **120** Morwong

(Des I. Loe. Litho B.D.T.)

1984 (10 Jan–27 Mar). *Flowers. T* **119** *and similar vert designs. Multicoloured. P* 14.

318	1 c. Type **119** (27.3)	..	..	30	70
319	2 c. Strand Morning Glory	..	40	70
320	3 c. Native Phreatia	..	..	45	70
321	4 c. Philip Island Wisteria (27.3)	..	45	70
322	5 c. Norfolk Island Palm (27.3)	..	70	70
323	10 c. Evergreen	..	..	50	70
324	15 c. Bastard Oak (27.3)	..	..	60	70
325	20 c. Devil's Guts	..	..	60	70
326	25 c. White Oak	..	..	70	80
327	30 c. Ti (27.3)	..	..	70	90
328	35 c. Philip Island Hibiscus (27.3)	..	70	90
329	40 c. Native Wisteria	..	..	80	1·25
330	50 c. Native Jasmine	..	..	90	1·25
331	$1 Norfolk Island Hibiscus (27.3)	..	90	1·75
332	$3 Native Oberonia (27.3)	..	1·75	4·00
333	$5 Norfolk Island Pine	..	..	2·50	4·50
318/33	..	..	*Set of* 16	11·50	19·00

(Des Marg Towt. Litho Cambec Press, Melbourne)

1984 (17 Apr). *Reef Fishes. T* **120** *and similar horiz designs. Multicoloured. Ordinary paper. P* 13½ × 14.

334	30 c. Type **120**	..	..	40	45
335	45 c. Black-spotted Goatfish (*Pseudopeneus signatus*)		60	65
336	75 c. Surgeonfish (*Acanthuridae*)	..	1·00	1·10
337	85 c. Three-striped Butterflyfish (*Chaeton ancinetus*)		1·25	1·40
334/7	..	..	*Set of* 4	2·75	3·25

121 Owl with Eggs   **122** 1953 7½d. and 1974 Cook Bicent 10 c. Stamps

(Des P. Slater. Litho Questa)

1984 (17 July). *Boobook Owl. T* **121** *and similar vert designs. Multicoloured. P* 14.

338	30 c. Type **121**	..	..	75	70
	a. Horiz strip of 5. Nos. 338/42	..	3·25	
339	30 c. Fledgeling	..	..	75	70
340	30 c. Young owl on stump	..	75	70
341	30 c. Adult on branch	..	..	75	70
342	30 c. Owl in flight	..	..	75	70
338/42	..	..	*Set of* 5	3·25	3·00

Nos. 338/42 were printed together, *se-tenant*, in horizontal strips of 5 throughout the sheet.

(Des D. Miller. Litho Harrison)

1984 (18 Sept). *"Ausipex" International Stamp Exhibition, Melbourne. T* **122** *and similar horiz designs. Multicoloured. W w* 14 (*sideways*). *P* 14.

343	30 c. Type **122**	..	..	30	35
344	45 c. John Buffett commemorative postal stationery envelope		50	75
345	75 c. Design from Presentation Pack for 1982 Military Uniforms issue		90	1·75
343/5	..	..	*Set of* 3	1·50	2·50
MS346	151 × 93 mm. Nos. 343/5. P 14½.	..	4·00	4·50

123 Font, Kingston Methodist Church   **124** The Revd. Nobbs teaching Pitcairn Islanders

(Des R. Murphy. Litho Questa)

1984 (9 Oct). *Christmas. Centenary of Methodist Church on Norfolk Island. T* **123** *and similar vert designs. Multicoloured. W w* 14. *P* 14.

347	5 c. Type **123**		10	10
348	24 c. Church service in Old Barracks, Kingston, late 1800's		25	40
349	30 c. The Revd. & Mrs. A. H. Phelps and sailing ship		35	45
350	45 c. The Revd. A. H. Phelps and First Congregational Church, Chester, U.S.A.		40	65
351	85 c. Interior of Kingston Methodist Church ..		80	1·40
347/51	.. ..	*Set of* 5	1·60	2·50

(Des D. Hopkins. Litho B.D.T.)

1984 (6 Nov). *Death Centenary of the Revd. George Hunn Nobbs (leader of Pitcairn community). T* **124** *and similar vert designs. Multicoloured. W w* 14. *P* 14 × 15.

352	30 c. Type **124**		30	45
353	45 c. The Revd. Nobbs with sick islander		45	65
354	75 c. Baptising baby		75	1·10
355	85 c. Presented to Queen Victoria, 1852		80	1·40
352/5	.. .. ..	*Set of* 4	2·10	3·25

125 *Fanny Fisher*   **126** The Queen Mother (from photo by Norman Parkinson)

(Des D. Hopkins. Litho Cambec Press, Melbourne)

1985 (19 Feb). *19th-Century Whaling Ships (1st series). T* **125** *and similar horiz designs. Multicoloured. P* 13½ × 14.

356	5 c. Type **125** ..		40	25
357	33 c. Costa Rica Packet		75	55
358	50 c. Splendid ..		1·25	1·25
359	90 c. Onward ..		1·50	2·00
356/9	.. ..	*Set of* 4	3·50	3·50

See also Nos. 360/3.

(Des D. Hopkins. Litho Cambec Press, Melbourne)

1985 (30 Apr). *19th-Century Whaling Ships (2nd series). Horiz designs as T* **125**. *Multicoloured. P* 13½ × 14.

360	15 c. Waterwitch ..		60	70
361	20 c. Canton ..		70	80
362	60 c. Aladdin ..		1·25	1·75
363	80 c. California ..		1·40	2·25
360/3	.. ..	*Set of* 4	3·50	5·00

(Des A. Theobald ($1), C. Abbott (others). Litho Questa)

1985 (6 June). *Life and Times of Queen Elizabeth the Queen Mother. T* **126** *and similar vert designs. Multicoloured. W w* 16. *P* 14½ × 14.

364	5 c. The Queen Mother (from photo by Dorothy Wilding)		10	10
365	33 c. With Princess Anne at Trooping the Colour ..		25	25
366	50 c. Type **126**..		40	55
367	90 c. With Prince Henry at his christening (from photo by Lord Snowdon)..		60	1·00
364/7	.. ..	*Set of* 4	1·25	1·75
MS368	91 × 73 mm. $1 With Princess Anne at Ascot Races. Wmk sideways		1·10	1·25

127 "Swimming"   **128** Prize-winning Cow and Owner

(Des from children's paintings. Litho Cambec Press, Melbourne)

1985 (9 July). *International Youth Year. T* **127** *and similar horiz design. Multicoloured. P* 13½ × 14.

369	33 c. Type **127**..		40	40
370	50 c. "A Walk in the Country"		70	85

(Des Flett Henderson & Arnold. Litho Cambec Press, Melbourne)

1985 (10 Sept). *125th Anniv of Royal Norfolk Island Agricultural and Horticultural Show. T* **128** *and similar horiz design. Multicoloured. P* 13½ × 14.

371	80 c. Type **128**..		75	80
372	90 c. Show exhibits		85	90
MS373	132 × 85 mm. Nos. 371/2 ..		1·75	2·50

Christmas 1985 Norfolk Island 27c

129 Shepherds with Flock   **130** Long-spined Sea Urchin

(Des R. Murphy. Litho Cambec Press, Melbourne)

1985 (3 Oct). *Christmas. T* **129** *and similar vert designs. Multicoloured. P* 13½.

374	27 c. Type **129**..		40	30
375	33 c. Mary and Joseph with donkey..		50	40
376	50 c. The Three Wise Men		80	65
377	90 c. The Nativity ..		1·25	1·25
374/7	..	*Set of* 4	2·75	2·25

(Des L. Curtis. Litho Cambec Press, Melbourne)

1986 (14 Jan). *Marine Life. T* **130** *and similar horiz designs. Multicoloured. P* 13½ × 14.

378	5 c. Type **130** ..		10	10
379	33 c. Blue Starfish ..		30	35
380	55 c. Southern Eagle Ray ..		50	85
381	75 c. Snowflake Moray ..		70	1·25
378/81		*Set of* 4	1·40	2·25
MS382	100 × 95 mm. Nos. 378/81 ..		3·00	3·75

131 *Giotto* Spacecraft   **132** Isaac Robinson (U.S. Consul 1887–1908)

(Des G. Revell. Litho Leigh-Mardon Ltd, Melbourne)

1986 (11 Mar). *Appearance of Halley's Comet. T* **131** *and similar vert design. Multicoloured. P* 14½ × 15.

383	$1 Type **131**		75	1·50
	a. Horiz pair. Nos. 383/4		1·50	3·00
384	$1 Halley's Comet		75	1·50

Nos. 383/4 were printed together, *se-tenant*, in horizontal pairs throughout the sheet, each pair forming a composite design.

(Des G. Revell. Litho Cambec Press, Melbourne)

1986 (22 May). *"Ameripex '86" International Stamp Exhibition, Chicago. T* **132** *and similar multicoloured designs. P* 13½.

385	33 c. Type **132**..		30	35
386	50 c. Ford "Model T" (first vehicle on island) (*horiz*)		50	50
387	80 c. Statue of Liberty		55	80
385/7	..	*Set of* 3	1·25	1·50
MS388	125 × 100 mm. Nos. 385/7 ..		1·50	2·25

No. 387 also commemorates the Centenary of the Statue of Liberty.

133 Princess Elizabeth and Dog   **134** Stylized Dove and Norfolk Island

(Des Allison Ryves. Litho Cambec Press, Melbourne)

1986 (12 June). *60th Birthday of Queen Elizabeth II. T* **133** *and similar vert designs. Multicoloured. P* 13½.

389	5 c. Type **133**..		10	10
390	33 c. Queen Elizabeth II		40	35
391	80 c. Opening Norfolk Island Golf Club		1·60	1·40
392	90 c. With Duke of Edinburgh in carriage		1·25	1·60
389/92	..	*Set of* 4	3·00	3·00

(Des Lyn Studham. Litho Cambec Press, Melbourne)

1986 (23 Sept). *Christmas. P* 13½ × 14.

393	**134** 30 c. multicoloured		25	30
394	40 c. multicoloured		35	45
395	$1 multicoloured		1·00	1·50
393/5	..	*Set of* 3	1·40	2·00

135 British Convicts, 1787   **136** Stone Tools

(Des Josephine Martin. Litho Cambec Press, Melbourne)

1986 (14 Oct–16 Dec). *Bicentenary of Norfolk Island Settlement (1988) (1st issue). Governor Phillip's Commission. T* **135** *and similar vert designs. Multicoloured. P* 14 × 13½.

396	36 c. Type **135**..		80	35
397	55 c. Judge passing sentence of transportation		1·50	85
398	90 c. Governor Phillip meeting Home Secretary (inscr "Home Society")		2·50	3·50
399	90 c. As No. 398, but correctly inscr "Home Secretary" (16.12)		2·25	3·25
400	$1 Captain Arthur Phillip..		2·50	2·50
396/400		*Set of* 5	8·50	9·50

See also Nos. 401/4, 421/4, 433/5, 436/7 and 438/43.

(Des B. Clinton. Litho Cambec Press, Melbourne)

1986 (16 Dec). *Bicentenary of Norfolk Island Settlement (1988) (2nd issue). Pre-European Occupation. T* **136** *and similar horiz designs. Multicoloured. P* 13½.

401	36 c. Type **136**..		65	85
402	36 c. Bananas and taro ..		65	85
403	36 c. Polynesian outrigger canoe		65	85
404	36 c. Maori chief ..		65	85
401/4	..	*Set of* 4	2·40	3·00

137 Philip Island from Point Ross   **138** Male Red-fronted Parakeet

(Des C. Abbott. Litho CPE Australia Ltd, Melbourne)

1987 (17 Feb)–88. *Norfolk Island Scenes. T* **137** *and similar square designs. Multicoloured. P* 13½.

405	1 c. Cockpit Creek Bridge (17.5.88)		50	70
406	2 c. Cemetery Bay Beach (17.5.88)		50	70
407	3 c. Island guesthouse (17.5.88)		50	70
408	5 c. Type **137**..		30	50
409	15 c. Cattle in pasture (27.7.87)		80	1·25
410	30 c. Rock fishing (7.4.87)		30	1·00
411	37 c. Old Pitcairner-style house (27.7.87)		1·40	1·50
412	40 c. Shopping centre (7.4.87)		35	1·25
413	50 c. Emily Bay ..		45	1·25
414	60 c. Bloody Bridge (27.7.87)		2·00	2·25
415	80 c. Pitcairner-style shop (7.4.87)		1·75	2·50
416	90 c. Government House ..		1·25	2·00
417	$1 Melanesian Memorial Chapel ..		1·00	1·75
418	$2 Convict Settlement, Kingston (7.4.87)..		1·75	3·50
419	$3 Ball Bay (27.7.87) ..		5·00	6·00
420	$5 Northern cliffs (17.5.88) ..		7·00	8·50
405/20	..	*Set of* 16	22·00	32·00

(Des Josephine Martin. Litho CPE Australia Ltd, Melbourne)

1987 (13 May). *Bicentenary of Norfolk Island Settlement (1988) (3rd issue). The First Fleet. Vert designs as T* **135**. *Multicoloured. P* 14 × 13½.

421	5 c. Loading supplies, Deptford ..		50	75
422	55 c. Fleet leaving Spithead ..		1·75	2·25
	a. Horiz pair. Nos. 422/3		3·50	4·50
423	55 c. H.M.S. *Sirius* leaving Spithead		1·75	2·25
424	$1 Female convicts below decks		2·25	3·00
421/4	..	*Set of* 4	5·50	7·50

Nos. 422/3 were printed together, *se-tenant*, in horizontal pairs throughout the sheet, forming a composite design.

(Des P. Slater. Litho CPE Australia Ltd, Melbourne)

1987 (16 Sept). *Red-fronted Parakeet ("Green Parrot"). T* **138** *and similar vert designs. Multicoloured. P* 14 × 13½.

425	5 c. Type **138**..		2·00	1·75
	a. Horiz strip of 4. Nos. 425/8		11·00	
426	15 c. Adult with fledgeling and egg ..		2·50	2·25
427	36 c. Young parakeets		3·50	3·25
428	55 c. Female parakeet		4·50	3·50
425/8	..	*Set of* 4	11·00	10·00

Nos. 425/8 were printed together, *se-tenant*, in horizontal strips of four throughout the sheet.

139 Christmas Tree and **140** Airliner, Container Ship
Restored Garrison Barracks and Sydney Harbour Bridge

(Des T. Bland and Alison Ryves. Litho CPE Australia Ltd,
Melbourne)

1987 (13 Oct). *Christmas.* T **139** *and similar horiz designs.
Multicoloured. P* 14½ × 14.
429	30 c. Type **139**.		..	..	30	30
430	42 c. Children opening presents		..	45	55
431	58 c. Father Christmas with children		..	60	1·00
432	63 c. Children's party	..	..		70	1·25
429/32	..	..	..	*Set of 4*	1·90	2·75

(Des Josephine Martin. Litho CPE Australia Ltd, Melbourne)

1987 (8 Dec). *Bicentenary of Norfolk Island Settlement* (1988)
(*4th issue*). *Visit of La Perouse* (*navigator*). *Vert designs as
T* **135**. *Multicoloured. P* 14 × 13½.
433	37 c. La Perouse with King Louis XVI		95	55
434	90 c. *L'Astrolabe* and *La Boussole* off Norfolk Island		2·75	3·00
435	$1 *L'Astrolabe* wrecked in Solomon Islands		2·75	3·00
433/5	..	..	*Set of 3*	5·75	6·00

(Des Josephine Martin. Litho CPE Australia Ltd, Melbourne)

1988 (25 Jan). *Bicentenary of Norfolk Island Settlement* (*5th
issue*). *Arrival of First Fleet at Sydney. Vert designs as T* **135**.
Multicoloured. P 14 × 13½.
436	37 c. Ship's cutter approaching Port Jackson	1·25	75
437	$1 Landing at Sydney Cove	..	2·75	3·25

(Des Josephine Martin. Litho CPE Australia Ltd, Melbourne)

1988 (4 Mar). *Bicentenary of Norfolk Island Settlement* (*6th
issue*). *Foundation of First Settlement. Vert designs as T* **135**.
Multicoloured. P 14 × 13½.
438	5 c. Lt. Philip Gidley King	..	20	50
439	37 c. Raising the flag, March 1788	..	85	75
440	55 c. King exploring	..	..	1·75	1·50
441	70 c. Landing at Sydney Bay, Norfolk Island	2·00	2·50
442	90 c. H.M.S. *Supply* (brig)	..	2·25	2·75
443	$1 Sydney Bay settlement, 1788 ..		2·25	2·75
438/43	..	..	*Set of 6*	8·50	9·75

(Des Janet Boschen. Litho CPE Australia Ltd, Melbourne)

1988 (30 July). *"Sydpex '88" National Stamp Exhibition,
Sydney.* T **140** *and similar multicoloured designs. P* 14 × 13½
(*vert*) *or* 13½ × 14 (*horiz*).
444	37 c. Type **140**		95	1·25
445	37 c. Exhibition label under magnifying glass (*horiz*)		95	1·25
446	37 c. Telephone and dish aerial	..	95	1·25
444/6			*Set of 3*	2·50	3·25
MS447	118×84 mm. Nos. 444/6	..		4·00	4·75

In No. **MS**447 the horizontal design is perforated 14 at foot
and 13½ on the other three sides.

141 Flowers and **142** Pier Store and Boat
Decorations Shed

(Des Sue Pearson. Litho CPE Australia Ltd, Melbourne)

1988 (27 Sept). *Christmas.* T **141** *and similar vert designs.
Multicoloured. P* 14 × 13½.
448	30 c. Type **141**		..	..	50	40
449	42 c. Flowers	..	..	..	70	70
450	58 c. Fishes and beach	..	..	85	95
451	63 c. Norfolk Island	..	..	95	1·25
448/51	..	..	..	*Set of 4*	2·75	3·00

(Des R. Murphy. Litho CPE Australia Ltd, Melbourne)

1988 (6 Dec). *Restored Buildings from the Convict Era.* T **142**
and similar horiz designs. Multicoloured. P 13½ × 14.
452	39 c. Type **142**	..	..	45	40
453	55 c. Royal Engineers Building	..	60	60
454	90 c. Old Military Barracks	..	1·00	1·60
455	$1 Commissariat Store and New Military Barracks	..	1·10	1·60
452/5	..	..	*Set of 4*	2·75	3·75

ALTERED CATALOGUE NUMBERS

Any Catalogue numbers altered from the last
edition are shown as a list in the introductory
pages.

---

143 *Lamprima aenea* **144** H.M.S. *Bounty* off
Tasmania

(Des T. Nolan. Litho CPE Australia Ltd, Melbourne)

1989 (14 Feb). *Endemic Insects.* T **143** *and similar horiz
designs. Multicoloured. P* 13½ × 14.
456	39 c. Type **143**			65	40
457	55 c. *Insulascirtus nythos*	..		90	75
458	90 c. *Caedicia araucariae*	..	1·40	2·00
459	$1 *Thrincophora aridela*	..	1·60	2·00
456/9			*Set of 4*	4·00	4·75

(Des C. Abbott. Litho CPE Australia Ltd, Melbourne (Nos.
460/3), B.D.T. (No. **MS**464))

1989 (28 Apr). *Bicentenary of the Mutiny on the* Bounty. T **144**
and similar horiz designs. Multicoloured. P 13½.
460	5 c. Type **144**		60	60
461	39 c. Mutineers and Polynesian women, Pitcairn Island		1·75	1·25
462	55 c. Lake Windermere, Cumbria (Christian's home county)		2·25	2·25
463	$1.10, "Mutineers casting Bligh adrift" (Robert Dodd)		3·50	4·50
460/3			*Set of 4*	7·25	7·75
MS464	110×85 mm. 39 c. No. 461; 90 c. Isle of Man 1989 Mutiny 35p., No. 414; $1 Pitcairn Islands 1989 Settlement Bicent 90 c., No. 345. P 14			5·50	7·00

145 Norfolk Island **146** Red Cross
Flag

(Des R. Fletcher. Litho CPE Australia Ltd, Melbourne)

1989 (10 Aug). *10th Anniv of Internal Self-Government.* T **145**
and similar vert designs. Multicoloured. P 14 × 13½.
465	41 c. Type **145**	..	90	55
466	55 c. Old ballot box	..	95	65
467	$1 Norfolk Island Act, 1979	..	1·75	2·00
468	$1.10, Island crest	..	1·75	2·75
465/8	..	..	*Set of 4*	4·75	5·50

(Des E. Lenthall. Litho CPE Australia Ltd, Melbourne)

1989 (25 Sept). *75th Anniv of Red Cross on Norfolk Island.*
P 13½.
469 **146**	$1 bright rose-red and ultramarine	..	3·00	3·00

147 "Gethsemane" **148** John Royle (first
announcer)

(Des Sue Pearson. Litho CPE Australia Ltd, Melbourne)

1989 (9 Oct). *Christmas.* T **147** *and similar horiz designs
showing opening lines of hymns and local scenes.
Multicoloured. P* 13½×14.
470	36 c. Type **147**		90	40
471	60 c. "In the Sweet Bye and Bye"		1·75	2·00
472	75 c. "Let the Lower Lights Be Burning"		2·25	2·75
473	80 c. "The Beautiful Stream"		2·25	3·00
470/3			*Set of 4*	6·50	7·25

(Des Philatelic Studios. Litho Leigh-Mardon Ltd, Melbourne)

1989 (21 Nov). *50th Anniv of Radio Australia.* T **148** *and
similar vert designs each showing Kingston buildings.
Multicoloured. P* 14×13½.
474	41 c. Type **148**	..	95	55
475	65 c. Radio waves linking Australia and Norfolk Island		1·75	2·25
476	$1.10, Anniversary kookaburra logo		2·75	3·75
474/6			*Set of 3*	5·00	6·00

---

149 H.M.S. *Bounty* **150** H.M.S. *Sirius* striking Reef
on fire, Pitcairn
Island, 1790

(Des G. Hitch. Litho Leigh-Mardon Ltd, Melbourne)

1990 (23 Jan). *History of the Norfolk Islanders* (*1st series*).
Settlement on Pitcairn Island. T **149** *and similar vert design.
Multicoloured. P* 14½.
477	70 c. Type **149**	2·50	2·50
478	$1.10, Arms of Norfolk Island	..	2·75	3·00

See also Nos. 503/4 and 516/17.

(Des Maree Edmiston. Litho Leigh-Mardon Ltd, Melbourne)

1990 (19 Mar). *Bicentenary of Wreck of H.M.S. Sirius.* T **150**
and similar horiz designs. Multicoloured. P 13½.
479	41 c. Type **150**		1·75	2·00
	a. Horiz pair. No. 479/80		3·50	4·00
480	41 c. H.M.S. *Sirius* failing to clear bay	1·75	2·00
481	65 c. Divers at work on wreck		2·50	3·00
482	$1 Recovered artifacts and chart of site	2·75	3·25
479/82			*Set of 4*	8·00	9·25

Nos. 479/80 were printed together, *se-tenant*, in horizontal
pairs throughout the sheet, each pair forming a composite
design.

151 Unloading **152** *Ile de Lumiere*
Lighter, (*freighter*)
Kingston

(Des Philatelic Studios. Litho Leigh-Mardon Ltd, Melbourne)

1990 (17 July)–91. *Ships.* T **152** *and horiz designs as* T **152**.
P 14×14½ (5, 10 c.) *or* 14½ (*others*).
483	**151**	5 c. purple-brown	..	20	40
484		10 c. ochre		20	40
485	–	45 c. multicoloured (19.2.91)		80	60
486	–	50 c. multicoloured (19.2.91)		90	1·00
487	–	65 c. multicoloured (19.2.91)		1·00	1·25
488	**152**	70 c. multicoloured		90	1·00
489	–	75 c. multicoloured (13.8.91)		2·00	2·00
490	–	80 c. multicoloured (13.8.91)		2·00	2·25
491	–	90 c. multicoloured (13.8.91)		2·00	2·25
492	–	$1 multicoloured (13.8.91)		2·00	2·00
493	–	$2 multicoloured		2·25	3·00
494	–	$5 multicoloured (19.2.91)		5·00	7·00
483/94			*Set of 12*	17·00	21·00

Designs: *Horiz* (as T **152**)—45 c. *La Dunkerquoise* (French
patrol vessel); 50 c. *Dmitri Mendeleev* (Russian research vessel);
65 c. *Pacific Rover* (tanker); 75 c. *Norfolk Trader* (freighter);
80 c. *Roseville* (transport); 90 c. *Kalia* (container ship); $1
Bounty (replica); $2 H.M.A.S. *Success* (supply ship); $5 H.M.A.S.
Whyalla (patrol vessel).

153 Santa on **154** William
House Roof Charles
Wentworth

(Des G. Hitch, adapted Philatelic Studios. Litho Leigh-Mardon
Ltd, Melbourne)

1990 (25 Sept). *Christmas.* T **153** *and similar multicoloured
designs. P* 14½.
499	38 c. Type **153**		75	45
500	43 c. Santa at Kingston Post Office		80	50
501	65 c. Santa over Sydney Bay, Kingston (*horiz*)		1·75	2·25
502	85 c. Santa on Officers' Quarters (*horiz*)		2·00	2·75
499/502	..	..	*Set of 4*	4·75	5·50

(Des G. Hitch. Litho Leigh-Mardon Ltd, Melbourne)

1990 (11 Oct). *History of the Norfolk Islanders* (*2nd series*).
The First Generation. T **154** *and similar vert design. P* 14½.
503	70 c. reddish brown and pale cinnamon		1·25	1·50
504	$1.20, reddish brown and pale cinnamon		2·00	2·50

Designs:—$1.20, Thursday October Christian.

155 Adult Robin and Chicks in Nest

156 Map of Norfolk Island

(Des E. Monks. Litho Leigh-Mardon Ltd, Melbourne)

1990 (3 Dec). *"Birdpex '90" Stamp Exhibition, Christchurch, New Zealand. Scarlet Robin. T* **155** *and similar vert designs. Multicoloured. P* 14½.

505	65 c. Type **155**		1·25	1·50
506	$1 Hen on branch		1·75	2·00
507	$1.20, Cock on branch		1·75	2·25
505/7		Set of 3	4·25	5·25
MS508	70×90 mm. $1 Hen; $1 Cock and hen		4·00	4·50

(Des Philatelic Studios. Litho Leigh-Mardon Ltd, Melbourne)

1991 (9 Apr). *Ham Radio Network. T* **156** *and similar vert designs. Multicoloured. P* 14½.

509	43 c. Type **156**		1·25	70
510	$1 Globe showing Norfolk Island		2·75	3·00
511	$1.20, Map of South-west Pacific		2·75	4·00
509/11		Set of 3	6·00	7·00

157 Display in *Sirius* Museum

158 H.M.S. *Pandora* wrecked on Great Barrier Reef (1791)

(Des Philatelic Studios. Litho Leigh-Mardon Ltd, Melbourne)

1991 (16 May). *Norfolk Island Museums. T* **157** *and similar multicoloured designs. P* 14½

512	43 c. Type **157**		90	50
513	70 c. 19th-century sitting room, House Museum (*horiz*)		1·75	2·00
514	$1 Carronade, *Sirius* Museum (*horiz*)		2·50	2·75
515	$1.20, Reconstructed jug and beaker, Archaeological Museum		2·50	3·25
512/15		Set of 4	7·00	7·75

(Des Philatelic Studios. Litho Leigh-Mardon, Melbourne)

1991 (2 July). *History of the Norfolk Islanders (3rd series). Search for the Bounty. T* **158** *and similar horiz design. Multicoloured. P* 13½×14.

516	$1 Type **158**		2·75	2·50
517	$1.20, H.M.S. *Pandora* leaving bay		2·75	3·00

159 Hibiscus and Island Scene

160 Tank and Soldier in Jungle

(Des Philatelic Studios. Litho Leigh-Mardon Ltd, Melbourne)

1991 (23 Sept). *Christmas. P* 14½.

518	**159** 38 c. multicoloured		90	45
519	43 c. multicoloured		1·00	55
520	65 c. multicoloured		1·50	2·00
521	85 c. multicoloured		1·75	2·50
518/21		Set of 4	4·75	5·00

(Des Philatelic Studios. Litho Leigh-Mardon Ltd, Melbourne)

1991 (9 Dec). *50th Anniv of Outbreak of Pacific War. T* **160** *and similar horiz designs. Multicoloured. P* 14½.

522	43 c. Type **160**		1·25	65
523	70 c. Boeing B-17 Flying Fortress on jungle airstrip		2·25	2·75
524	$1 Warships		2·75	3·50
522/4		Set of 3	5·50	6·25

161 Coat of Arms

162 Deployment Map

(Des Philatelic Studios. Litho Leigh-Mardon Ltd, Melbourne)

1992 (11 Feb). *500th Anniv of Discovery of America by Columbus. T* **161** *and similar vert designs. Multicoloured. P* 14½.

525	45 c. Type **161**		85	55
526	$1.05, *Santa Maria*		2·00	2·75
527	$1.20, Columbus and globe		2·50	3·25
525/7		Set of 3	4·75	6·00

(Des Philatelic Studios. Litho Leigh-Mardon Ltd, Melbourne)

1992 (4 May). *50th Anniv of Battle of the Coral Sea. T* **162** *and similar vert designs. Multicoloured. P* 14½.

528	45 c. Type **162**		1·25	60
529	70 c. H.M.A.S. *Australia* (cruiser)		2·00	2·50
530	$1.05, U.S.S. *Yorktown* (aircraft carrier)		2·75	3·50
528/30		Set of 3	5·50	6·00

(Des Philatelic Studios. Litho Leigh-Mardon Ltd, Melbourne)

1992 (4 May). *50th Anniv of Battle of Midway. Vert designs as T* **162**. *Multicoloured. P* 14½.

531	45 c. Battle area		1·25	60
532	70 c. Consolidated PBY-5 Catalina flying boat over task force		2·00	2·50
533	$1.05, Douglas SBD Dauntless dive bomber and *Akagi* (Japanese aircraft carrier) burning		2·75	3·50
531/3		Set of 3	5·50	6·00

(Des Philatelic Studios. Litho Leigh-Mardon Ltd, Melbourne)

1992 (6 Aug). *50th Anniv of Battle of Guadalcanal. Multicoloured designs as T* **162**, *but horiz. P* 14½.

534	45 c. American troops landing		1·25	60
535	70 c. Machine-gun crew		2·00	2·50
536	$1.05, Map of Pacific with Japanese and American flags		2·75	3·50
534/6		Set of 3	5·50	6·00

163 Norfolk Pines above Ball Bay

164 Boat Shed and Flaghouses, Kingston

(Des Philatelic Studios. Litho Leigh-Mardon Ltd, Melbourne)

1992 (29 Oct). *Christmas. T* **163** *and similar vert designs. Multicoloured. P* 14½.

537	40 c. Type **163**		70	40
538	45 c. Headstone Creek		75	45
539	75 c. South side of Ball Bay		1·50	2·25
540	$1.20, Rocky Point Reserve		2·00	3·00
537/40		Set of 4	4·50	5·50

(Des Philatelic Studios. Litho Leigh-Mardon Ltd, Melbourne)

1993 (23 Feb). *Tourism. Historic Kingston. T* **164** *and similar horiz designs. Multicoloured. P* 14½.

541	45 c. Type **164**		80	1·00
	a. Horiz strip of 5. Nos. 541/5		3·50	
542	45 c. Old Military Barracks		80	1·00
543	45 c. All Saints Church		80	1·00
544	45 c. Officers' Quarters		80	1·00
545	45 c. Quality Row		80	1·00
541/5		Set of 5	3·50	4·50

Nos. 541/5 were printed together, *se-tenant*, in horizontal strips of 5 forming a composite design.

165 Fire Engine

166 Blue Sea Lizard (*Glaucus atlanticus*)

(Des Philatelic Studios, Melbourne. Litho Leigh-Mardon Ltd, Melbourne)

1993 (18 May). *Emergency Services. T* **165** *and similar horiz designs. Multicoloured. P* 14½.

546	45 c. Type **165**		1·00	60
547	70 c. Cliff rescue squad		1·10	1·75
548	75 c. Ambulance		1·40	1·90
549	$1.20, Police car		2·50	3·00
546/9		Set of 4	5·50	6·50

(Des Philatelic Studios. Litho Leigh-Mardon Ltd, Melbourne)

1993 (7 July). *Nudibranchs. T* **166** *and similar horiz designs. Multicoloured. P* 14½.

550	45 c. Type **166**		80	55
551	45 c. Ocellate Nudibranch (*Phyllidia ocellata*)		80	55
552	75 c. *Bornella* sp		1·50	1·75
553	85 c. *Glossodoris rubroannolata*		1·75	2·25
554	95 c. *Halgerda villeyi*		2·00	2·50
555	$1.05, *Ceratosoma amoena*		2·00	3·00
550/5		Set of 6	8·00	9·50

---

167 Christmas Wreath

168 Maori Stone Clubs

(Des Philatelic Studios. Litho Leigh-Mardon Ltd, Melbourne)

1993 (28 Oct). *Christmas. P* 14½.

556	**167** 40 c. multicoloured		60	45
557	45 c. multicoloured		60	45
558	75 c. multicoloured		1·00	1·50
559	$1.20, multicoloured		1·90	2·50
556/9		Set of 4	3·75	4·50

(Des Philatelic Studios. Litho Leigh-Mardon Ltd, Melbourne)

1993 (28 Oct). *Bicentenary of Contact with New Zealand. T* **168** *and similar vert design. Multicoloured. P* 14½.

560	70 c. Type **168**		1·25	1·50
561	$1.20, First Maori map of New Zealand, 1793		2·00	2·50

169 Alvaro de Saavedra, Route Map and *Florida*

170 Sooty Tern

(Des G. Hitch and Philatelic Consultative Services. Litho Leigh-Mardon Ltd, Melbourne)

1994 (8 Feb–26 July). *Pacific Explorers. T* **169** *and similar multicoloured designs. P* 14½.

562	5 c. Vasco Nunez de Balboa, map and *Barbara* (3 May)		55	55
563	10 c. Ferdinand Magellan, map and *Vitoria* (3 May)		55	55
564	20 c. Juan Sebastian del Cano, map and *Vitoria* (3 May)		75	75
565	50 c. Type **169**		95	95
566	70 c. Ruy Lopez de Villalobos, map and *San Juan*		1·25	1·25
567	75 c. Miguel Lopez de Legaspi, map and *San Lesmes*		1·25	1·25
568	80 c. Sir Francis Drake, map and *Golden Hind* (26 July)		1·25	1·25
569	85 c. Alvaro de Mendana, map and *Santiago* (26 July)		1·25	1·25
570	90 c. Pedro Fernandes de Quiros, map and *San Pedro y Pablo* (26 July)		1·25	1·25
571	$1 Luis Baez de Torres, map and *San Pedrico* (26 July)		1·40	1·40
572	$2 Abel Tasman, map and *Heemskerk*		2·00	2·25
573	$5 William Dampier, map and *Cygnet* (3 May)		4·25	5·00
562/73		Set of 12	15·00	16·00
MS574	100×80 mm. $1.20, *Golden Hind* (Drake) (32×52 mm). P 13		1·75	2·00

(Des Philatelic Studios. Litho Leigh-Mardon Ltd, Melbourne)

1994 (17 Aug). *Sea Birds. T* **170** *and similar vert designs. Multicoloured. P* 14½.

575	45 c. Type **170**		95	1·00
	a. Horiz strip of 5. Nos. 575/9		4·25	
576	45 c. Red-tailed Tropic Bird		95	1·00
577	45 c. Australian Gannet		95	1·00
578	45 c. Wedge-tailed Shearwater		95	1·00
579	45 c. Blue-faced Booby		95	1·00
575/9		Set of 5	4·25	4·50

Nos. 575/9 were printed together, *se-tenant*, in horizontal strips of 5 throughout the sheet with the backgrounds forming a composite design.

171 House and Star

172 Chevrolet, 1926

(Des Olive Gregory. Litho Walsall)

1994 (27 Oct). *Christmas. T 171 and similar vert designs. Multicoloured. Roul 9×imperf*. Self-adhesive.*
580	45 c. Type 171			80	55
581	75 c. Figures from stained-glass windows			1·50	2·00
582	$1.20, Rainbow and *The Church of God* (missionary sailing ship)			2·50	3·00
580/2			*Set of 3*	4·25	5·00

*Nos. 580/2 were separated horizontally by roulette and vertically by rotary knife cuts which produce straight edges with two teeth between stamps.

(Litho McPherson's Ptg Group, Mulgrave)

1995 (7 Feb). *Vintage Motor Vehicles. T 172 and similar horiz designs. Multicoloured. P 14×14½.*
583	45 c. Type 172			75	55
584	75 c. Ford Model "A", 1928			1·25	1·75
585	$1.05, Ford Model "A A/C", 1929			1·60	2·00
586	$1.20, Ford Model "A", 1930			1·75	2·25
583/6			*Set of 4*	4·75	6·00

173 Tail Flukes of Humpback Whale   **174** Dot-and-Dash Butterflyfish

(Des Mary Butterfield. Litho McPherson's Ptg Group, Mulgrave)

1995 (11 May). *Humpback Whale Conservation. T 173 and similar multicoloured designs. P 14½×14 ($1.05) or 14×14½ (others).*
587	45 c. Type 173			1·00	55
588	75 c. Mother and calf			1·50	2·00
589	$1.05, Whale breaching (*vert*)			1·75	2·50
587/9			*Set of 3*	3·75	4·50
MS590	107×84 mm. $1.20, Humpback Whale (29×49 mm). P 14×14½			2·25	2·50

(Des Mary Butterfield. Litho Leigh-Mardon Ltd, Melbourne)

1995 (15 June). *Butterflyfishes. T 174 and similar square designs. Multicoloured. P 14×14½.*
591	5 c. Type 174			30	50
592	45 c. Blue-spotted Butterflyfish (*Chaetodon plebeius*)			85	50
593	$1.20, Three-belted Butterflyfish (*Chaetodon tricinatus*)			2·25	2·75
594	$1.50, Thread-finned Butterflyfish (*Chaetodon auriga*)			2·50	3·00
591/4			*Set of 4*	5·50	6·00

1995 (19 July). *"JAKARTA '95" Stamp Exhibition, Indonesia. No. MS590 optd "Selamat Hari Merdeka" and emblem on sheet margin in gold.*
MS595	107×84 mm. $1.20, Humpback Whale		1·75	2·50

175 International 4×4 Refueller, 1942   **176** Servicing Fighter

(Des G. Douran. Litho Southern Colour Print, Dunedin)

1995 (8 Aug). *Second World War Vehicles. T 175 and similar horiz designs. Multicoloured. P 14×14½.*
596	5 c. Type 175			30	40
597	45 c. Ford Sedan, 1942			75	45
598	$1.20, Ford 3 ton tipper, 1942			2·00	2·50
599	$2 D8 caterpillar with scraper			3·00	3·50
596/9			*Set of 4*	5·50	6·25

NORFOLK ISLAND INTERNAL POSTAL SERVICE. Nos. 600/1 and subsequent locally-produced booklet stamps were primarily intended for use in the island postal service which collects mail from letter boxes and sorts it into boxes at the main post office for residents to pick up. Such issues are, however, also valid for postage on mail sent overseas.

(Litho Photopress International, Norfolk Island)

1995 (1 Sept). *Flower designs as 1960 issues, but with face values in decimal currency. Roul 7.*
600	5 c. bright rose & dp blue-green (as No. 25)		10	10
	a. Booklet pane. No. 600×18		1·40	
601	5 c. bright rose-red (as No. 28)		10	10
	a. Booklet pane. No. 601×18		1·40	

Nos. 600/1 were only issued in $1.80 stamp booklets containing panes of 18 (two blocks of 9 separated by a horizontal gutter and with margins all round).

The original printing of Nos. 600a/1a had black inscriptions beneath each pane. These were subsequently changed to deep blue-green (No. 600a) or bright rose-red (No. 601a).

(Des Mary Butterfield (Nos. 602/5). Litho and die-stamped ($10) or litho (others) Southern Colour Print, Dunedin)

1995 (18 Sept). *50th Anniv of End of Second World War in the Pacific. T 176 and similar multicoloured designs. P 12.*
602	5 c. Type 176			40	50
603	45 c. Sgt. Tom Derrick, V.C. (*vert*)			70	45
604	75 c. Gen. Douglas MacArthur (*vert*)			1·25	1·50
605	$1.05, Girls celebrating victory			1·75	2·00
606	$10 Pacific War medals (50×30 mm)			16·00	18·00
602/6			*Set of 5*	18·00	20·00

The $10 also includes the "Singapore '95" International stamp exhibition logo.

177 Peace Dove and Anniversary Emblem   **178** Skink on Bank

(Des Mary Butterfield. Litho SNP Cambec)

1995 (7 Nov). *Christmas. 50th Anniv of United Nations. T 177 and similar vert designs, each including U.N. anniversary emblem. P 14½×14.*
607	45 c. gold and new blue			60	45
608	75 c. gold and bright violet			1·00	1·25
609	$1.05, gold and bright rose-red			1·40	2·00
610	$1.20, gold and light green			1·60	2·25
607/10			*Set of 4*	4·25	5·50

Designs:—75 c. Star of Bethlehem; $1.05, Symbolic candles on cake; $1.20, Olive branch.

(Des Doreen McGuiness. Litho Questa)

1996 (6 Feb). *Endangered Species. Skinks and Geckos. T 178 and similar horiz designs. Multicoloured. P 14½×15.*
611	5 c. Type 178			55	65
	a. Strip of 4. Nos. 611/14			2·25	
612	5 c. Gecko on branch			55	65
613	45 c. Skink facing right			70	75
614	45 c. Gecko on flower			70	75
611/14			*Set of 4*	2·25	2·50

Nos. 611/14 were printed together, *se-tenant*, in horizontal and vertical strips of 4 throughout sheets of 16.

179 Sopwith Pup Biplane and Emblem

(Des B. McCoy and B. Klemke. Litho Southern Colour Print, Dunedin)

1996 (22 Apr). *75th Anniv of Royal Australian Air Force. T 179 and similar vert designs showing aircraft. Multicoloured. P 14.*
615	45 c. Type 179			60	60
616	45 c. Wirraway fighter			60	60
617	75 c. F-111C jet fighter			1·00	1·40
618	85 c. F/A-18 Hornet jet fighter			1·10	1·50
615/18			*Set of 4*	3·00	3·50

180 Rat

(Des G. Douran. Litho Southern Colour Print, Dunedin)

1996 (18 May). *Chinese New Year ("Year of the Rat"). Sheet 100×75 mm. P 12.*
MS619	180 $1 black, rosine and brown-ochre		1·50	2·00
	a. With "CHINA '96" 9th Asian International Stamp Exhibition logo on bottom margin		1·60	2·00

181 *Naticarlus oncus*   **182** Shopping

(Des Mary Butterfield. Litho Southern Colour Print, Dunedin)

1996 (2 July). *Shells. T 181 and similar square designs. Multicoloured. P 14.*
620	45 c. Type 181			70	85
621	45 c. *Janthina janthina*			70	85
622	45 c. *Cypraea caputserpentis*			70	85
623	45 c. *Argonauta nodosa*			70	85
620/3			*Set of 4*	2·50	3·00

(Des G. Douran. Litho Southern Colour Print, Dunedin)

1996 (17 Sept). *Tourism. T 182 and similar horiz designs. Multicoloured. P 13½×14.*
624	45 c. Type 182			50	50
625	75 c. Celebrating Bounty Day			1·00	1·00
626	$2.50, Horse riding			3·75	4·25
627	$3.70, Unloading lighter			4·50	5·25
624/7			*Set of 4*	8·75	10·00

MACHINE LABELS. A Hytech weighing and label printing machine was introduced by the Norfolk Island Post Office in 1996 for use on parcels. This machine produced adhesive labels as illustrated with face values of $1.40 or above to reflect current parcel rates. The earliest recorded date is 5 November 1996.

183 The Nativity   **184** Coat of Arms

(Des Mary Duke. Litho Questa)

1996 (5 Nov). *Christmas. T 183 and similar vert designs. Multicoloured. P 14½.*
628	45 c. Type 183			50	50
629	45 c. Star and boat sheds			50	50
630	75 c. Star, bungalow and ox			90	1·50
631	85 c. Star, fruit, flowers and ox			1·10	1·75
628/31			*Set of 4*	2·75	3·75

(Litho Photopress International, Norfolk Island)

1997 (22 Jan). *T 184 and similar vert design. Roul 7.*
632	184	5 c. turquoise-blue and pale lemon		20	30
		a. Booklet pane of 10 with margins all round		1·75	
633	—	5 c. orange-brown		20	30
		a. Booklet pane of 10 with margins all round		1·75	

Design:—No. 633, Great Seal of Norfolk Island. Nos. 632/3 were only issued in $2 stamp booklets.

185 Calf   **186** *Cepora perimale*

(Des G. Douran. Litho Southern Colour Print, Dunedin)

1997 (11 Feb). *Beef Cattle. Sheet 67×67 mm. P 13½×13.*
MS634	185 $1.20, multicoloured		1·75	2·00

1997 (12 Feb). *"HONG KONG '97" International Stamp Exhibition. As No. MS634, but with exhibition emblem on sheet margin.*
MS635	67×67 mm. 185 $1.20, multicoloured		1·75	2·00

(Des Tracey Yager. Litho and gold die-stamped Southern Colour Print, Dunedin)

1997 (28 Mar). *Butterflies. T 186 and similar horiz designs. Multicoloured. P 14½.*
636	75 c. Type 186			1·00	85
637	90 c. *Danaus chrysippus*			1·25	1·50
638	$1 *Danaus hamata*			1·40	1·50
639	$1.20, *Danaus plexippus*			1·50	2·00
636/9			*Set of 4*	4·50	5·25

187 Dusky Dolphins

(Des Mary Butterfield. Litho Southern Colour Print, Dunedin)

1997 (29 May). *Dolphins. T* **187** *and similar horiz designs. Multicoloured.* P 14.

640	45 c. Type **187**		75	60
641	75 c. Common dolphin and calf		1·25	1·40
MS642	106×80 mm. $1.05, Dolphin		1·50	1·75

1997 (29 May). *"Pacific '97" International Stamp Exhibition, San Francisco. As No.* **MS642**, *but with exhibition emblem on sheet margin.*

MS643	106×80 mm. $1.05, Dolphin		2·00	2·25

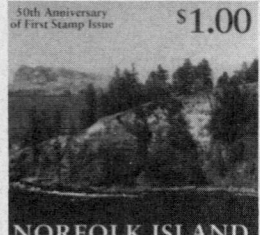

188 Ball Bay, Norfolk Island

(Litho Southern Colour Print, Dunedin)

1997 (30 June). *50th Anniv of Norfolk Island Stamps. T* **188** *and similar multicoloured designs.* P 12.

644	$1 Type **188**		80	85
	a. Horiz pair. Nos. 644/5		1·90	2·25
645	$1.50, 1947 2d. stamp		1·10	1·40
646	$8 Ball Bay and 1947 2s. yellow-bistre stamp (90×45 mm)		6·50	6·75
644/6		*Set of 3*	8·25	9·00

Nos. 644/5 were printed together, *se-tenant*, in horizontal pairs with the backgrounds forming a composite design.

(Des N. Shewring (No. **MS651**), D. Miller (others). Litho Questa)

1997 (12 Aug). *Golden Wedding of Queen Elizabeth and Prince Philip. Multicoloured designs as T* **173** *of Ascension.* P 14¹/₂×14.

647	20 c. Queen Elizabeth		30	40
	a. Horiz pair. Nos. 647/8		60	80
648	25 c. Prince Philip in carriage-driving trials		30	40
649	25 c. Prince Philip		30	40
	a. Horiz pair. Nos. 649/50		90	1·00
650	50 c. Queen in phaeton at Trooping the Colour		60	60
647/50		*Set of 4*	1·40	1·60
MS651	110×70 mm. $1.50, Queen Elizabeth and Prince Philip in landau (*horiz*). P 14×14¹/₂		1·75	2·25

Nos. 647/8 and 649/50 were each printed together, *se-tenant*, in horizontal pairs throughout the sheets with the backgrounds forming composite designs.

189 Royal Yacht *Britannia* leaving Hong Kong

190 Christmas Tree

1997 (16 Sept). *Return of Hong Kong to China. Sheet* 126×91 *mm. Litho.* P 14.

MS652	**189** 45 c. multicoloured		75	1·00

No. **MS652** is inscribed "Brittania" in error

(Des Sue Wickison. Litho Southern Colour Print, Dunedin)

1997 (4 Nov). *Annual Festivals. T* **190** *and similar vert designs. Multicoloured.* P 13¹/₂.

653	45 c. Type **190**		50	45
654	75 c. Fireworks (New Year's Eve)		80	1·00
655	$1.20, Rose (Valentine's Day)		1·25	1·50
653/5		*Set of 3*	2·25	2·75

191 Oriental Pearl T.V. Tower, Shanghai

192 Tiger Mask

(Litho Questa)

1997 (18 Nov). *"Shanghai '97" International Stamp and Coin Exhibition, Shanghai. Sheet* 103×138 *mm.* P 14¹/₂.

MS656	**191** 45 c. multicoloured		75	1·00

(Des Ren Yu. Litho Southern Colour Print, Dunedin)

1998 (12 Feb). *Chinese New Year ("Year of the Tiger"). Sheet* 75×95 *mm.* P 12.

MS657	**192** 45 c. multicoloured		75	1·00

193 "Pepper"

194 Entrance to Pentagonal Gaol

(Des Mary Butterfield. Litho Southern Colour Print, Dunedin)

1998 (26 Feb). *Cats. T* **193** *and similar vert designs. Multicoloured.* P 14¹/₂.

658	45 c. Type **193**		65	65
659	45 c. "Tabitha" at window		65	65
660	75 c. "Midnight"		85	1·00
661	$1.20, "Rainbow" with flower pot		1·25	1·50
658/61		*Set of 4*	3·00	3·50

(Des B. Hilder. Litho Photopress International, Norfolk Island)

1998 (27 Feb). *T* **194** *and similar horiz design. Roul* 7.

662	**194** 5 c. black and azure		10	15
	a. Booklet pane of 10 with margins all round		1·00	
663	– 5 c. black and turquoise-green		10	15
	a. Booklet pane of 10 with margins all round		1·00	

Design:—No. 663, Ruined First Settlement cottage. Nos. 662/3 were only issued in $2 stamp booklets.

(Des D. Miller. Litho Questa)

1998 (28 Apr). *Diana, Princess of Wales Commemoration. Vert designs as T* **177** *of Ascension. Multicoloured.* P 14¹/₂×14.

664	45 c. Princess Diana with bouquet, 1991		40	40
MS665	145×70 mm. 45 c. Wearing blue and white dress, 1989; 45 c. Wearing pearl earrings, 1990; 45 c. No. 664; 45 c. Wearing striped dress (*sold at* $1.80 + 45 c. charity premium)		1·60	2·00

195 Tweed Trousers

196 Hammer Throwing

(Des Mary Butterfield. Litho Questa)

1998 (5 May–29 June). *Reef Fishes. T* **195** *and similar multicoloured designs.* P 14¹/₂.

666	10 c. Type **195**		10	15
667	20 c. Conspicuous Angelfish (29 June)		15	20
668	30 c. Moon Wrasse		25	30
669	45 c. Wide-striped Clownfish (29 June)		35	40
670	50 c. Raccoon Butterflyfish		40	45
671	70 c. Artooti (juvenile) (29 June)		55	60
672	75 c. Splendid Hawkfish		60	65

673	85 c. Scorpion Fish (29 June)		65	70
674	90 c. Orange Fairy Basslet		70	75
675	$1 Sweetlips (29 June)		80	85
676	$3 Moorish Idol (29 June)		2·40	2·50
677	$4 Gold-ribbon Soapfish		3·25	3·50
666/77		*Set of 12*	10·00	10·25
MS678	110×85 mm. $1.20, Shark (29×39 *mm*). P 14×14¹/₂		90	95

Nos. 672 and 675 are incorrectly inscribed "Splendid Hawkefish" and "Sweetlip".

(Des Tracey Yager. Litho Southern Colour Print, Dunedin)

1998 (23 July). *16th Commonwealth Games, Kuala Lumpur. T* **196** *and similar designs.* P 14¹/₂.

679	75 c. orange-vermilion and black		85	1·00
680	95 c. bluish violet and black		1·00	1·25
681	$1.05, deep mauve and black		1·10	1·40
679/81		*Set of 3*	2·75	3·25
MS682	80×100 mm. 85 c. brt blue-green & black		90	1·25

Designs: Horiz—95 c. Trap shooting. Vert—85 c. Flag bearer; $1.05, Lawn bowls.

197 *Norfolk* (sloop)

(Des Mary Butterfield. Litho Cartor)

1998 (24 Sept). *Bicentenary of the Circumnavigation of Tasmania by George Bass and Matthew Flinders.* P 13.

683	**197** 45 c. multicoloured		65	65
MS684	101×69 mm. **197** $1.20, multicoloured		1·40	1·50

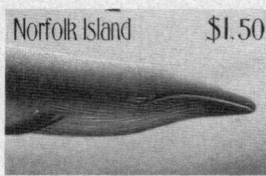

198 Blue Whale

(Des Mary Butterfield. Litho Questa)

1998 (23 Oct). *Whales of the Southern Oceans (joint issue with Namibia and South Africa). Sheet* 103×70 *mm.* P 13¹/₂×14.

MS685	**198** $1.50, multicoloured		1·60	1·75

199 "Peace on Earth"

200 Short S.23 Sandringham (flying boat)

(Des Mary Butterfield. Litho Cartor)

1998 (10 Nov). *Christmas. T* **199** *and similar horiz designs. Multicoloured.* P 13×13¹/₂.

686	45 c. Type **199**		35	40
687	75 c. "Joy to the World"		60	65
688	$1.05, "A Season of Love"		80	85
689	$1.20, "Light of the World"		90	95
686/9		*Set of 4*	2·50	2·75

(Des Mary Duke. Litho Photopress International, Norfolk Island)

1999 (28 Jan). *Booklet Stamps. Aircraft. T* **200** *and similar horiz design. Each brown-lake and deep grey-green. Roul* 7.

690	5 c. Type **200**		10	10
	a. Booklet pane of 10 with margins all round		40	
691	5 c. DC-4 *Norfolk Trader*		10	10
	a. Booklet pane of 10 with margins all round		40	

201 Soft Toy Rabbit

202 Hull of *Resolution* under Construction

(Des K. Partridge. Litho Questa)

1999 (9 Feb). *Chinese New Year ("Year of the Rabbit"). Sheet 80×100 mm. P 14.*
MS692 **201** 95 c. multicoloured   85   1·00

(Des R. Pennycuick. Litho Cartor)

1999 (19 Mar). *"Australia '99" International Stamp Exhibition, Melbourne. Schooner* Resolution. *T* **202** *and similar horiz designs. Multicoloured. P* 13×13½.
693   45 c. Type **202**   35   40
   a. Booklet pane. Nos. 693/7 plus printed
     label ..   ..   ..   1·75
694   45 c. After being launched   ..   35   40
695   45 c. In Emily Bay   35   40
696   45 c. Off Cascade   35   40
697   45 c. Alongside at Auckland   ..   35   40
693/7   ..   ..   ..   *Set of 5* 1·75   1·90
Nos. 693/7 were only available in stamp booklets sold for $2.50.

203 Pacific Black Duck   **204** Solander's
                                Petrel in Flight

(Des Tracey Yager. Litho Southern Colour Print, Dunedin)

1999 (27 Apr). *"iBRA '99" International Stamp Exhibition, Nuremberg. Sheet 80×100 mm. P* 14½.
MS698 **203** $2.50, multicoloured   ..   2·25   2·40

(Des Patricia Altman. Litho Southern Colour Print, Dunedin)

1999 (27 May). *Endangered Species. Solander's Petrel ("Providence Petrel"). T* **204** *and similar multicoloured designs. P* 14½.
699   75 c. Type **204**   60   65
700   $1.05, Head of Solander's Petrel (*horiz*)   80   85
701   $1.20, Adult and fledgling (*horiz*)   90   95
699/701   ..   ..   ..   *Set of 3* 2·25   2·40
MS702   130×90 mm. $4.50, Solander's Petrel in flight (35×51 *mm*). P 13   ..   4·25   4·50

205 "Cecile Brunner" Rose   **206** Pottery

(Litho Questa)

1999 (30 July). *Roses. T* **205** *and similar vert designs. Multicoloured. P* 14½×14.
703   45 c. Type **205**   35   40
704   75 c. Green rose   60   65
705   $1.05, "David Buffett" Rose   ..   80   85
703/5   ..   ..   ..   *Set of 3* 1·75   1·90
MS706   60×81 mm. $1.20, "A Country Woman"
Rose   90   95
No. MS706 also commemorates the 50th anniversary of the Country Women's Association on Norfolk Island.

(Des K. Partridge. Litho Questa)

1999 (23 Aug). *"China '99" International Stamp Exhibition, Beijing. No.* MS692 *with "China '99" logo optd on the margin in carmine. P* 14.
MS707   80×100 mm. 95 c. Type **201**   ..   75   80

(Des G. Douran. Litho B.D.T.)

1999 (16 Sept). *Handcrafts of Norfolk Island. T* **206** *and similar vert designs. Multicoloured. P* 14×15.
708   45 c. Type **206**   35   40
709   45 c. Woodcarving   35   40
710   75 c. Quilting   60   65
711   $1.05, Basket-weaving   ..   80   85
708/11   ..   ..   ..   *Set of 4* 2·10   2·25

STAMP BOOKLETS

A $4.10 booklet containing No. 465 in block of ten was prepared in 1989, but not issued.

B 1

1991 (9 Apr). *Ham Radio Network. Emerald on cinnamon cover as Type* B 1. *Stamps attached by selvedge.*
SB1 $4.30, booklet containing 43 c. (No. 509) in block
    of 10 ..   ..   8·00

B 2

1991 (Dec). *Ships. Emerald on bluish grey (No.* SB2) *or cinnamon (No.* SB3) *covers as Type* B 2. *Stamps attached by selvedge.*
SB2 $4.50, booklet containing 45 c. (No. 485) in block
    of 10 ..   ..   6·50
SB3 $7 booklet containing 70 c. (No. 488) in block of 10   7·00

B 3

1993 (23 Feb). *Tourism. Emerald on white cover as Type* B 3. *Stamps attached by selvedge.*
SB4 $4.50, booklet containing five different 45 c. (Nos.
    541/5) in block of 10 ..   ..   7·00

1993 (20 Aug). *Nudibranchs. Emerald on white cover as Type* B 3 *showing illustration of No.* 550. *Stamps attached by selvedge.*
SB5 $4.50, booklet containing 45 c. (No. 550) in block
    of 10 ..   ..   6·50

1994 (17 Aug). *Sea Birds. Emerald on white cover as Type* B 3, *but showing illustration of No.* 577. *Stamps attached by selvedge.*
SB6 $4.50, booklet containing horiz gutter strip of ten
    45 c. (No. 575a×2)   ..   ..   6·00

B 4

1995 (1 Sept). *Flowers. Rose and blue green cover as Type* B 4. *Stamps attached by selvedge.*
SB7 $1.80, booklet containing two different panes of
    eighteen 5 c. (Nos. 600a/1a)   ..   2·75
No. SB7 also exists with either the "Singapore '95" International Stamp Exhibition or Australian Stamp Dealers' Association logos shown on the front cover at bottom left.

B 5
(Illustration reduced. Actual size, 170×80 mm)

1997 (22 Jan). *Multicoloured cover as Type* B 5. *Stamps attached by selvedge.*
SB8 $2 booklet containing four panes of ten 5 c. (Nos
    632a/3a, each × 2)   ..   ..   6·00

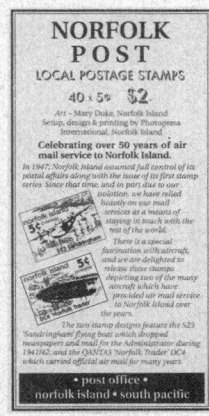

B 6
(Illustration reduced. Actual size 87×178 mm)

1998 (27 Feb). *Black and turquoise-green cover as Type* B 6. *Stamps attached by selvedge.*
SB9 $2 booklet containing four panes of ten 5 c. (Nos.
    662a/3a, each × 2)   ..   ..   1·50

B 7
(Illustration reduced. Actual size 90×177 mm)

1999 (28 Jan). *Aircraft. Brown-lake and deep grey-green on white cover as Type* B 7. *Stamps attached by selvedge.*
SB10 $2 booklet containing four panes of ten 5 c. (Nos.
    690a/1a, each × 2)   ..   ..   1·50

B 8 Emily Bay
(Illustration reduced. Actual size, 170×75 mm)

1999 (19 Mar). *"Australia '99" International Stamp Exhibition, Melbourne. Schooner* Resolution. *Multicoloured cover as Type* B 8. *Stamps attached by selvedge.*
SB11 $2.50, booklet containing pane of five 45 c. and
    label (No. 693a)   ..   ..   1·75

Baghdad
see Iraq

Bahamas

The British Post Office at Nassau was established during the early days of the West Indies packet system, and was certainly operating by 1733. The first known local postmark dates from 1802.

The crowned-circle handstamp No. CC1 was issued in 1846 and was generally replaced, for the public mails, by various stamps of Great Britain in 1858.

Local mail deliveries were rudimentary until 1859 when Nos. 1/2 were issued by the colonial authorities for interisland mails. Examples used for this purpose are usually cancelled in manuscript or with a "27" postmark. The "local" 1d. stamp became valid for overseas mails in May, 1860, when the colonial authorities took over this service from the British G.P.O.

For illustrations of the handstamp and postmark types see BRITISH POST OFFICES ABROAD notes, following GREAT BRITAIN.

NASSAU

CROWNED-CIRCLE HANDSTAMPS

CC1 CC 2 BAHAMAS (Nassau) (18.5.1846) (R.)
Price on cover £2250

No. CC1 was later struck in black and used as an Offical Paid mark between July 1899 and September 1935. Handstamps as Types CC 1 and CC 3 (only three known) struck in black were used for the same purpose from 1933 until 1953; but it is believed that these were never employed during the pre-stamp period. *Price on cover from £50.*

Stamps of GREAT BRITAIN cancelled "A 05" as Type **2**.

1858 *to* 1860.
Z1	1d. rose-red (1857), perf 14			£1800
Z2	2d. blue (1858) (Plate Nos. 7, 8)			£1300
Z3	4d. rose (1857)			£450
Z4	6d. lilac (1856)			£350
Z5	1s. green (1856)			£2250

PRICES FOR STAMPS ON COVER TO 1945
No. 1	*from* × 8
No. 2	
Nos. 3/6	*from* × 8
No. 7	
Nos. 8/11	*from* × 10
Nos. 12/15	*from* × 4
Nos. 16/19*a*	*from* × 6
Nos. 20/5	*from* × 15
Nos. 26/8	*from* × 4
No. 29	
Nos. 30/2	*from* × 15
No. 33	*from* × 30
Nos. 35/7	*from* × 6
Nos. 38/9	*from* × 10
No. 39*b*	*from* × 30
No. 40	*from* × 50
No. 41	*from* × 6
No. 42	*from* × 15
No. 43	*from* × 6
Nos. 44/*a*	*from* × 10
No. 45	*from* × 40
Nos. 47/57	*from* × 4
Nos. 58/89	*from* × 2
Nos. 90/130	*from* × 3
Nos. 131/2	*from* × 10
Nos. 141/5	*from* × 4
Nos. 146/8	*from* × 6
Nos. 149/57	*from* × 3
Nos. 158/60	*from* × 4
No. 161	*from* × 8
Nos. 162/75	*from* × 5
Nos. S1/3	*from* × 20

CROWN COLONY

1	**2**	**3**
ONE PENNY	FOUR PENCE	ONE SHILLING

(Eng and recess P.B.)

1859 (10 June)**–60.** *No wmk. Imperf.* (a) *Thick, opaque paper*
1	1	1d. reddish lake (*shades*)		£4500 £2250

(b) *Thin paper*
2	1	1d. dull lake (4.60)		50·00 £1500

No. 1, the printing on thick opaque paper, is very rare in unused condition. Unused remainders, on medium to thick, but slightly transparent, paper are worth about £250.

Collectors are warned against false postmarks upon the remainder stamps of 1d., imperf, on thin paper.

1860 (Oct). *No wmk. Clean-cut perf* 14 *to* 16.
3	1	1d. lake (H/S "CANCELLED" in oval £6000)		£3750	£700

For notes on "CANCELLED" examples see Catalogue Introduction. Examples with this handstamp on No. 3 are imperforate horizontally.

1861 (June)**–62.** *No wmk.* (a) *Rough perf* 14 *to* 16
4	1	1d. lake			£750 £300
5	2	4d. dull rose (Dec, 1861)			£1400 £375
		a. Imperf between (pair)			£22000
6		6d. grey-lilac (Dec, 1861)			£3500 £550
		a. Pale dull lilac			£3000 £500

(b) *P* 11 *to* 12½ (1862)
7	1	1d. lake			£2000

No. 7 was a perforation trial on a new machine at Perkins, Bacon. It was not sent out to the Colony and is also known part perforated.

(Recess D.L.R.)

1862. *No wmk.* (a) *P* 11½, 12.
8	1	1d. carmine-lake			£950 £170
9		1d. lake			£1100 £180
10	2	4d. dull rose			£3250 £400
11		6d. lavender-grey			£9500 £475

(b) *P* 11½, 12, *compound with* 11
12	1	1d. carmine-lake			£1900 £850
13		1d. lake			£2250 £950
14	2	4d. dull rose			£15000 £1800
15		6d. lavender-grey			£16000 £1800

(c) *P* 13
16	1	1d. lake			£850 £160
17		1d. brown-lake			£700 £130
18	2	4d. dull rose			£2750 £375
19		6d. lavender-grey			£3250 £475
		a. Lilac			£2750 £450

*Stamps exist with part of papermaker's sheet wmk ("T. H. SAUNDERS" and date).

1863–77. *Wmk Crown CC.* (a) *P* 12½
20	1	1d. brown-lake			90·00 55·00
		w. Wmk inverted			£140
21		1d. carmine-lake			£100 60·00
		w. Wmk inverted			£140
		x. Wmk reversed			£110 60·00
22		1d. carmine-lake (aniline)			£100 60·00
		w. Wmk inverted			£150
		x. Wmk reversed			
23		1d. rose-red			60·00 40·00
		w. Wmk inverted			£100
		x. Wmk reversed			60·00 40·00
24		1d. red			60·00 40·00
		w. Wmk inverted			
		x. Wmk reversed			— 40·00
25		1d. vermilion			65·00 40·00
		w. Wmk inverted			£100
		x. Wmk reversed			65·00 40·00
		y. Wmk inverted and reversed			£150
26	2	4d. bright rose			£275 60·00
		w. Wmk inverted			— £150
		x. Wmk reversed			
27		4d. dull rose			£400 60·00
		w. Wmk inverted			— £150
		x. Wmk reversed			£375 60·00
28		4d. brownish rose (*wmk reversed*)			£425 80·00
		w. Wmk inverted			
29		6d. rose-lilac			—£2250
		w. Wmk inverted			£6000
30		6d. lilac (*shades*)			£350 65·00
		w. Wmk inverted			
		x. Wmk reversed			
31		6d. deep violet			£160 60·00
		w. Wmk inverted			— £150
		x. Wmk reversed			£180 65·00
32		6d. violet (aniline)			£250 90·00

(b) *P* 14
33	1	1d. scarlet-vermilion (1877)			50·00 15·00
		x. Wmk reversed			60·00 22·00
34		1d. scarlet (or scarlet-vermilion) (aniline) £1000			
		x. Wmk reversed			
35	2	4d. bright rose (1876)			£350 40·00
		w. Wmk inverted			
36		4d. dull rose			£1500 40·00
		w. Wmk inverted			
37		4d. rose-lake			£425 40·00

No. 29 is believed to be the shade of the first printing only and should not be confused with other lilac shades of the 6d.

No. 34 is not known postally used, although manuscript fiscal cancellations on this shade do exist.

(Typo D.L.R.)

1863–80. *Wmk Crown CC.* (a) *P* 12½.
38	3	1s. green (1865)			£2500 £300

(b) *P* 14
39	3	1s. dark green			£180 35·00
		aw. Wmk inverted			
39*b*		1s. green (*thick paper*) (1880)			7·50 7·00
		bw. Wmk inverted			— £150

1882 (Mar). *Wmk Crown CA.* (a) *P* 12
40	1	1d. scarlet-vermilion			45·00 12·00
41	2	4d. rose			£550 45·00

(b) *P* 14
42	1	1d. scarlet-vermilion			£400 55·00
		x. Wmk reversed			
43	2	4d. rose			£800 60·00
		x. Wmk reversed			£850 60·00

1882 (Mar)**–98.** *Wmk Crown CA.* *P* 14.
44	3	1s. green			32·00 14·00
44*a*		1s. blue-green (1898)			35·00 22·00

5

FOURPENCE
(4)

1883. *No. 31 surch with T* 4.
45	2	4d. on 6d. deep violet			£550 £400
		a. Surch inverted			£12000 £8000
		x. Wmk reversed			£600 £450

Type 4 was applied by handstamp and occurs in various positions.

Caution is needed in buying Nos. 45 and 45a.

Sloping "2" (R. 10/6)   Malformed "E"

(Typo D.L.R.)

1884–90. *Wmk Crown CA. P* 14.
47	5	1d. pale rose			55·00 11·00
48		1d. carmine-rose			6·50 2·25
49		1d. bright carmine (aniline)			2·75 6·50
50		2½d. dull blue (1888)			60·00 17·00
51		2½d. blue			42·00 7·50
		a. Sloping "2"			£400 £120
52		2½d. ultramarine			9·00 2·25
		a. Sloping "2"			£130 70·00
		w. Wmk inverted			£140 75·00
53		4d. deep yellow			9·00 4·00
54		6d. mauve (1890)			5·50 26·00
		a. Malformed "E" (R. 6/6)			£180 £325
56		5s. sage-green			65·00 75·00
57		£1 Venetian red			£275 £225
47/57				*Set of* 6	£325 £300
50 & 54	Optd "Specimen"			*Set of* 2	£130

Examples of Nos. 54/7 are known showing a forged Bahamas postmark dated "AU 29 94".

6 Queen's Staircase, Nassau	7	8
1d ONE PENNY	ONE PENNY	HALF PENNY

(Recess D.L.R.)

1901 (23 Sept)**–03.** *Wmk Crown CC. P* 14.
58	6	1d. black and red			6·50 3·00
		w. Wmk inverted			80·00 80·00
59		5d. black and orange (1.03)			8·50 48·00
		y. Wmk inverted and reversed			90·00 £130
60		2s. black and blue (1.03)			26·00 50·00
61		3s. black and green (1.03)			32·00 60·00
		w. Wmk inverted			
		y. Wmk inverted and reversed			£100 £110
58/61				*Set of* 4	65·00 £140
58/61	Optd "Specimen"			*Set of* 4	£120

For stamps in this design, but with Mult Crown CA or Mult Script CA watermarks see Nos 75/80 and 111/14.

(Typo D.L.R.)

1902 (18 Dec)**–10.** *Wmk Crown CA. P* 14.
62	7	1d. carmine			1·50 2·50
63		2½d. ultramarine			6·50 1·25
64		4d. orange			15·00 50·00
65		4d. deep yellow (3.10)			20·00 60·00
66		6d. brown			3·50 17·00
		a. Malformed "E" (R.6/6)			£130 £180
67		1s. grey-black and carmine			20·00 48·00
68		1s. brownish grey and carmine (6.07)			21·00 48·00
69		5s. dull purple and blue			60·00 80·00
70		£1 green and black			£250 £325
62/70				*Set of* 7	£300 £425
62/70	Optd "Specimen"			*Set of* 7	£250

Examples of most values are known showing a forged Nassau postmark dated "2 MAR 10".

1906 (Apr)**–11.** *Wmk Mult Crown CA. P* 14.
71	7	½d. pale green (5.06) (Optd S. £50)			5·00 2·00
72		1d. carmine-rose			24·00 1·25
73		2½d. ultramarine (4.07)			24·00 26·00
		w. Wmk inverted			£100 £100
74		6d. bistre-brown (8.11)			17·00 48·00
		a. Malformed "E" (R. 6/6)			£275 £475
71/4				*Set of* 4	60·00 70·00

1911 (Feb)**–19.** *Wmk Mult Crown CA. P* 14.
75	6	1d. black and red			15·00 2·75
		a. Grey-black and scarlet (1916)			4·50 2·50
		b. Grey-black & deep carmine-red (1919)			5·50 5·50
76		3d. purple/yellow (thin paper) (18.5.17)			4·00 22·00
		a. Reddish purple/buff (thick paper) (1.19)			5·00 4·50
77		3d. black and brown (23.3.19)			1·75 2·25
		w. Wmk inverted			
78		5d. black and mauve (18.5.17)			2·75 5·50
79		2s. black and blue (11.16)			28·00 48·00
		w. Wmk inverted			
80		3s. black and green (8.17)			50·00 55·00
		w. Wmk inverted			£120 £120
		y. Wmk inverted and reversed			£110 £110
75/80				*Set of* 6	80·00 £140
76/8	Optd "Specimen"			*Set of* 3	£100

(Typo D.L.R.)

1912–19. *Wmk Mult Crown CA. Chalk-surfaced paper (1s. to £1). P 14.*

81	**8**	½d. green	..	..	80	6·50
		a. Yellow-green	..	..	2·50	9·00
82		1d. carmine (aniline)	..	..	3·00	30
		a. Deep rose	..	..	7·50	2·00
		b. Rose	..	..	11·00	2·25
		w. Wmk inverted	..	..	—	65·00
83		2d. grey (1919)	..	..	2·25	3·00
84		2½d. ultramarine	..	..	4·50	18·00
		a. Deep dull blue	..	..	14·00	27·00
85		4d. orange-yellow	..	..	5·50	18·00
		a. Yellow	..	..	2·25	12·00
86		6d. bistre-brown	..	..	1·75	4·00
		a. Malformed "E" (R. 6/6)	..	80·00	£110
87		1s. grey-black and carmine	..	1·75	9·00
		a. Jet-black and carmine	..	14·00	22·00
88		5s. dull purple and blue	..	40·00	65·00
		a. Pale dull purple and deep blue		50·00	65·00
89		£1 dull green and black	..	£150	£275
		a. Green and black	..	£190	£300
81/9				*Set of 9*	£170	£350
81/9		Optd "Specimen"	..	*Set of 9*	£325	

1.1.17.   WAR TAX
(9)   (10)

1917 (18 May). *No. 75b optd with T 9 in red by D.L.R.*

90	**6**	1d. grey-black and deep carmine-red (Optd S. £60)		40	1·75
		a. Long stroke to "7" (R.4/6)		40·00	75·00

It was originally intended to issue No. 90 on 1 January 1917, but the stamps were not received in the Bahamas until May. Half the proceeds from their sale were donated to the British Red Cross Society.

1918 (21 Feb–10 July). *Nos. 75/6, 81/2 and 87 optd at Nassau with T 10.*

91	**8**	½d. green		9·00	38·00
		a. Opt double			
		b. Opt inverted			
92		1d. carmine (aniline)		80	50
		a. Opt double			
		b. Opt inverted			
		w. Wmk inverted		£180	
		x. Wmk reversed		£180	
93	**6**	1d. black and red (10 July)		3·50	3·50
		a. Opt double, one inverted		£800	
		b. Opt double		£1600	£1700
		c. Opt inverted		£1400	£1500
		x. Wmk reversed		£150	
94		3d. purple/*yellow (thin paper)*		2·25	2·25
		a. Opt double		£1500	£1600
		b. Opt inverted		£1000	£1100
95	**8**	1s. grey-black and carmine		90·00	£130
		a. Opt double			
91/5			*Set of 5*	95·00	£150

No. 93 was only on sale for ten days.

WAR TAX   WAR TAX   WAR CHARITY 3.6.18.
(11)   (12)   (13)

1918 (1 June–20 July). *Optd by D.L.R. in London with T 11 or 12 (3d).*

96	**8**	½d. green		1·75	1·75
		w. Wmk inverted			
		x. Wmk reversed			
97		1d. carmine		70	35
		a. Wmk sideways		£350	
		w. Wmk inverted			
		y. Wmk inverted and reversed		£250	
98	**6**	3d. purple/*yellow* (20 July)		60	1·50
		w. Wmk inverted		70·00	
99	**8**	1s. grey-black and carmine (R.)		8·00	2·75
96/9			*Set of 4*	10·00	5·75
96/9		Optd "Specimen"	*Set of 4*	£130	

1919 (21 Mar). *No. 77 optd with T 12 by D.L.R.*

100	**6**	3d. black and brown (Optd S. £45)		45	4·00
		a. "C" and "A" missing from wmk		£1200	
		w. Wmk inverted		50·00	

No. 100a shows the "C" omitted from one impression and the "A" missing from the next one to the right (as seen from the front of the stamp). The "C" is badly distorted in the second watermark.

1919 (1 Jan). *No. 75b optd with T 13 by D.L.R.*

101	**6**	1d. grey-black and deep carmine-red (R.) (Optd S. £50)		30	2·50
		a. Opt double		£1400	
		w. Wmk inverted		50·00	
		x. Wmk reversed		50·00	
		y. Wmk inverted and reversed		75·00	

The date is that originally fixed for the issue of the stamp. The year 1918 was also the bicentenary of the appointment of the first Royal governor.

NEW INFORMATION

The editor is always interested to correspond with people who have new information that will improve or correct the Catalogue.

WAR   WAR

TAX   TAX
(14)   (15)

1919 (14 July). *(a) Optd with T 14 by D.L.R.*

102	**8**	½d. green (R.)		30	1·25
103		1d. carmine		1·25	1·50
104		1s. grey-black and carmine (R.)		11·00	27·00

(b) No. 77 optd with T 15

105	**6**	3d. black and brown		55	6·50
		w. Wmk inverted		50·00	
		x. Wmk reversed		60·00	
		y. Wmk inverted and reversed		50·00	
102/5			*Set of 4*	11·00	32·00
102/5		Optd "Specimen"	*Set of 4*	£120	

16   17 Great Seal of the Bahamas.

(Recess D.L.R.)

1920 (1 Mar). *Peace Celebration. Wmk Mult Crown CA (sideways*). P 14.*

106	**16**	½d. green		1·00	5·00
		x. Wmk sideways reversed		£275	£275
107		1d. carmine		2·75	1·00
		x. Wmk sideways reversed		£375	
		y. Wmk Crown to right of CA and reversed		£375	
108		2d. slate-grey		2·75	7·50
		a. "C" of "CA" missing from wmk		£800	
109		3d. deep brown		2·75	9·00
		w. Wmk Crown to right of CA			
110		1s. deep myrtle-green		12·00	35·00
		a. Substituted crown in wmk		£1100	
		x. Wmk sideways reversed		£500	
106/10			*Set of 5*	19·00	50·00
106/10		Optd "Specimen"	*Set of 5*	£150	

*The normal sideways watermark shows Crown to left of CA, as seen from the back of the stamp.
For illustration of the substituted watermark crown see Catalogue Introduction.

1921 (29 Mar)–29. *Wmk Script CA. P 14.*

111	**6**	1d. grey and rose-red		80	1·00
112		5d. black and purple (8.29)		3·75	38·00
113		2s. black and blue (11.22)		16·00	22·00
114		3s. black and green (9.24)		40·00	65·00
111/14			*Set of 4*	55·00	£110
111/14		Optd/Perf "Specimen"	*Set of 4*	£160	

F PENN

Elongated "E"
(left pane R. 9/6)

1921 (8 Sept)–37. *Wmk Mult Script CA. Chalk-surfaced paper (3d., 1s., 5s., £1). P 14.*

115	**8**	½d. green (1924)		45	40
		a. Elongated "E"		28·00	
116		1d. carmine		1·00	15
117		1½d. brown-red (1934)		2·50	1·00
118		2d. grey (1927)		1·10	2·75
119		2½d. ultramarine (1922)		80	2·75
120		3d. purple/*pale yellow* (1931)		6·00	16·00
		a. Purple/orange-yellow (1937)		6·00	15·00
121		4d. orange-yellow (1924)		1·25	5·00
122		6d. bistre-brown (1922)		70	1·25
		a. Malformed "E" (R.6/6)		75·00	£100
123		1s. black and carmine (1926)		2·50	5·50
124		5s. dull purple and blue (1924)		32·00	60·00
125		£1 green and black (1926)		£160	£300
115/25			*Set of 11*	£180	£350
115/25		Optd/Perf "Specimen"	*Set of 11*	£375	

(Recess B. W.)

1930 (2 Jan). *Tercentenary of Colony. Wmk Mult Script CA. P 12.*

126	**17**	1d. black and scarlet		2·00	2·75
127		3d. black and deep brown		4·00	15·00
128		5d. black and deep purple		4·00	15·00
129		2s. black and deep blue		18·00	45·00
130		3s. black and green		40·00	80·00
126/30			*Set of 5*	60·00	£140
126/30		Perf "Specimen"	*Set of 5*	£150	

18

(Recess B.W.)

1931 (14 July)–46. *Wmk Mult Script CA. P 12.*

131	**18**	2s. slate-purple and deep ultramarine	20·00	25·00
		a. Slate-purple and indigo (9.42)	65·00	38·00
		b. Brownish black and indigo (13.4.43)	6·50	2·75
		c. Brownish black and steel-blue (6.44)	10·00	1·25
132		3s. slate-purple and myrtle-green	28·00	26·00
		a. Brownish black and indigo (13.4.43)	7·00	2·00
		b. Brownish blk & myrtle-grn (1.10.46)	6·00	2·50
131/2		Perf "Specimen"	*Set of 2*	70·00	

Most of the stamps from the September 1942 printing (No. 131a and further stocks of the 3s. similar to No. 132) were used for the 1942 "LANDFALL" overprints.

1935 (6 May). *Silver Jubilee. As Nos. 91/4 of Antigua. P 13½ × 14.*

141		1½d. deep blue and carmine		1·00	2·25
		h. Dot by flagstaff		75·00	
		i. Dash by turret		£100	
142		2½d. brown and deep blue		5·00	8·00
		f. Diagonal line by turret		£110	
		g. Dot to left of chapel		£140	
143		6d. light blue and olive-green		7·00	11·00
		g. Dot to left of chapel		£180	
144		1s. slate and purple		7·00	8·00
		h. Dot by flagstaff		£180	
141/4			*Set of 4*	18·00	26·00
141/4		Perf "Specimen"	*Set of 4*	90·00	

For illustrations of plate varieties see Catalogue Introduction.

19 Greater Flamingos in flight   20 King George VI

(Recess Waterlow)

1935 (22 May). *Wmk Mult Script CA. P 12½.*

145	**19**	8d. ultramarine and scarlet		6·00	2·75
145		Perf "Specimen"		42·00	

1937 (12 May). *Coronation. As Nos. 95/7 of Antigua, but printed by D.L.R. P 14.*

146		½d. green		15	15
147		1½d. yellow-brown		30	75
148		2½d. bright blue		50	75
146/8			*Set of 3*	85	1·50
146/8		Perf "Specimen"	*Set of 3*	60·00	

Accent flaw (right pane R. 1/5) (1938 ptg only)   Short "T" in "TWO" (right pane R. 3/6) (Retouched on No. 152c, although bottom of letter is still pointed)

(Typo D.L.R.)

1938 (11 Mar)–52. *Wmk Mult Script CA. Chalk-surfaced paper (1s. to £1). P 14.*

149	**20**	½d. green		15	90
		a. Elongated "E"		45·00	
		b. Accent flaw		75·00	
		c. Bluish green (11.9.42)		1·75	1·25
		ca. Elongated "E"		95·00	
		d. Myrtle-green (11.12.46)		5·50	5·00
		da. Elongated "E"		£180	
149e		½d. brown-purple (18.2.52)		90	2·50
		ea. Error. Crown missing		£5500	
		eb. Error. St. Edward's Crown		£2250	
		ec. Elongated "E"		85·00	
150		1d. carmine		8·50	4·75
150a		1d. olive-grey (17.9.41)		3·25	3·25
		ab. Pale slate (11.9.42)		50	60
151		1½d. red-brown (19.4.38)		1·25	1·00
		a. Pale red-brown (19.4.48)		4·25	2·25
152		2d. pale slate (19.4.38)		18·00	6·00
		a. Short "T"		£475	
152b		2d. scarlet (17.9.41)		75	55
		ba. Short "T"		85·00	
		bb. "TWO PENCE" printed double	†£5000	
		bc. Dull rose-red (19.4.48)		2·75	2·75
152c		2d. green (1.5.51)		1·00	80
153		2½d. ultramarine		3·25	2·00
153a		2½d. violet (1.7.43)		1·25	70
		ab. "2½ PENNY" printed double	£2750	
154		3d. violet (19.4.38)		16·00	4·00
154a		3d. blue (4.43)		60	90
		ab. Bright ultramarine (19.4.48)	4·00	4·00
154b		3d. scarlet (1.2.52)		50	3·00
154c		10d. yellow-orange (18.11.46)		2·00	20
155		1s. grey-black and carmine (*thick paper*) (15.9.38)	16·00	5·50
		a. Brownish grey and scarlet (4.42)	£275	55·00
		b. Ordinary paper. Black and carmine (9.42)	17·00	6·50
		c. Ordinary paper. Grey-black and bright crimson (6.3.44)	9·00	65
		d. Pale brownish grey and crimson (19.4.48)	9·50	1·00
156		5s. lilac & blue (*thick paper*) (19.4.38)	£170	£100
		a. Reddish lilac and blue (4.42)	£1200	£400
		b. Ordinary paper. Purple & bl (9.42)	27·00	15·00
		c. Ordinary paper. Dull mauve and deep blue (11.46)	75·00	35·00
		d. Brown-purple & dp brt bl (19.4.48)	30·00	9·00
		e. Red-purple & dp bright blue (8.51)	23·00	12·00

157	**20**	£1 deep grey-green and black (*thick paper*) (15.9.38)			£250	£140
		a. Ordinary paper. *Blue-green and black* (13.4.43)			60·00	45·00
		b. Ordinary paper. *Grey-green and black* (3.44)			95·00	65·00
149/57a				Set of 17	£130	70·00
149/57 Perf "Specimen"				Set of 14	£425	

Nos. 149/50a exist in coils, constructed from normal sheets.
No. 149eb occurs on a row in the watermark in which the crowns and letters "CA" alternate.

The thick chalk-surfaced paper, used for the initial printing of the 1s., 5s. and £1, was usually toned and had streaky gum. The April 1942 printing for the 1s. and 5s., which was mostly used for the "LANDFALL" overprints, was on thin, white chalk-surfaced paper with clear gum. Printings of the three values between September 1942 and November 1946 were on a thick, smooth, opaque ordinary paper.

21 Sea Garden, Nassau

22 Fort Charlotte

23 Greater Flamingos in Flight

3d.
(24)

(Recess Waterlow)

1938 (1 July). *Wmk Mult Script CA. P 12½.*

158	**21**	4d. light blue and red-orange			1·00	90
159	**22**	6d. olive-green and light blue			60	90
160	**23**	8d. ultramarine and scarlet			6·00	2·00
158/60				Set of 3	7·00	3·50
158/60 Perf "Specimen"				Set of 3	£100	

1940 (28 Nov). *No. 153 surcharged with T 24 by The Nassau Guardian.*

161	**20**	3d. on 2½d. blue			90	60

1 4 9 2
LANDFALL
OF
COLUMBUS
1 9 4 2
(25)

"RENCE" flaw (Right pane R. 9/3. Later corrected so that it does not occur on No. 154a)

1942 (12 Oct). *450th Anniv of Landing of Columbus in New World. Optd as T 25 by The Nassau Guardian.*

162	**20**	½d. bluish green			30	60
		a. Elongated "E"			40·00	
		b. Opt double			£1000	
163		1d. pale slate			30	60
164		1½d. red-brown			40	60
165		2d. scarlet			30	65
		a. Short "T"			70·00	
166		2½d. ultramarine			30	65
167		3d. ultramarine			30	65
		a. "RENCE" flaw			95·00	
168	**21**	4d. light blue and red-orange			40	90
		a. "COIUMBUS" (R. 5/2)			£650	£650
169	**22**	6d. olive-green and light blue			40	1·75
		a. "COIUMBUS" (R. 5/2)			£650	£700
170	**23**	8d. ultramarine and scarlet			90	70
		a. "COIUMBUS" (R. 5/2)			£4750	£2250
171	**20**	1s. brownish grey and scarlet			4·50	3·50
		a. Ordinary paper. *Black and carmine*			4·50	4·00
		b. Ordinary paper. *Grey-black and bright crimson*			9·00	6·00
172	**18**	2s. slate-purple and indigo			15·00	17·00
		a. Brownish black and indigo			8·00	10·00
		b. Brownish black and steel-blue			22·00	22·00
		c. Stop after "COLUMBUS" (R. 2/12)			£3000	
173		3s. slate-purple and myrtle-green			5·00	6·50
		a. Brownish black and green			40·00	32·00
		b. Stop after "COLUMBUS" (R. 2/12)			£2000	
174	**20**	5s. reddish lilac and blue			30·00	15·00
		a. Ordinary paper. *Purple and blue*			18·00	14·00
175		£1 deep grey-green & blk (*thick paper*)			65·00	50·00
		a. Ordinary paper. *Grey-green & black*			30·00	25·00
162/75				Set of 14	60·00	60·00
162/75 Perf "Specimen"				Set of 14	£400	

These stamps replaced the definitive series for a period of six months. Initially stocks of existing printings were used, but when further supplies were required for overprinting a number of new printings were produced, some of which, including the new colour of the 3d., did not appear without overprint until much later.

1946 (11 Nov). *Victory. As Nos. 110/11 of Antigua.*

176		1½d. brown			10	40
177		3d. blue			10	40
176/7 Perf "Specimen"				Set of 2	55·00	

NEW INFORMATION

The editor is always interested to correspond with people who have new information that will improve or correct the Catalogue.

---

26 Infant Welfare Clinic

(Recess C.B.N.)

1948 (11 Oct). *Tercentenary of Settlement of Island of Eleuthera. T 26 and similar horiz designs. P 12.*

178		½d. orange			30	90
179		1d. sage-green			30	35
180		1½d. yellow			30	80
181		2d. scarlet			30	40
182		2½d. brown-lake			45	75
183		3d. ultramarine			85	85
184		4d. black			60	70
185		6d. emerald-green			1·75	80
186		8d. violet			60	70
187		10d. carmine			60	35
188		1s. sepia			1·00	50
189		2s. magenta			4·00	8·50
190		3s. blue			8·00	8·50
191		5s. mauve			8·50	4·50
192		10s. grey			9·50	9·00
193		£1 vermilion			11·00	14·00
178/93				Set of 16	40·00	45·00

Designs:—1d. Agriculture (combine harvester); 1½d. Sisal; 2d. Straw work; 2½d. Dairy farm; 3d. Fishing fleet; 4d. Island settlement; 6d. Tuna fishing; 8d. Paradise Beach; 10d. Modern hotels; 1s. Yacht racing; 2s. Water sports (skiing); 3s. Shipbuilding; 5s. Transportation; 10s. Salt production; £1, Parliament Buildings.

1948 (1 Dec). *Royal Silver Wedding. As Nos. 112/13 of Antigua.*

194		1½d. red-brown			20	25
195		£1 slate-green			32·00	32·00

1949 (10 Oct). *75th Anniv of Universal Postal Union. As Nos. 114/17 of Antigua.*

196		2½d. violet			35	40
197		3d. deep blue			2·25	2·25
198		6d. greenish blue			55	2·25
199		1s. carmine			55	75
196/9				Set of 4	3·25	5·00

1953 (3 June). *Coronation. As No. 120 of Antigua.*

200		6d. black and pale blue			40	35

42 Infant Welfare Clinic

43 Queen Elizabeth II

(Recess B.W.)

1954 (1 Jan)–**63**. *Designs previously used for King George VI issue, but with portrait of Queen Elizabeth II as in T 42, and commemorative inscr omitted. Wmk Mult Script CA. P 11 × 11½.*

201		½d. black and red-orange			10	1·50
202		1d. olive-green and brown			10	30
203		1½d. blue and black			15	60
204		2d. yellow-brown and myrtle-green			15	30
		a. *Yellow-brn & dp myrtle-grn* (23.1.62)			5·50	6·50
205		3d. black and carmine-red			65	75
206		4d. turquoise-green & deep reddish purple			30	30
		a. *Turq-blue & dp reddish pur* (23.1.62)			11·00	12·00
207		5d. red-brown and deep bright blue			1·40	2·25
208		6d. light blue and black			1·75	20
		w. Wmk inverted			—	£500
209		8d. black and reddish lilac			70	40
		a. *Black and deep reddish lilac* (21.11.56)			1·90	1·90
210		10d. black and ultramarine			30	10
		a. *Black and deep ultramarine* (8.1.63)			6·00	2·75
211		1s. ultramarine and olive-brown			70	10
		a. *Ultramarine & dp ol-sepia* (19.2.58)			2·25	30
212		2s. orange-brown and black			2·00	70
		a. *Chestnut and black* (19.2.58)			10·00	1·50
213		2s. 6d. black and deep blue			3·50	2·00
214		5s. bright emerald and orange			18·00	75
		a. *Brt emerald & reddish orange* (14.1.59)			45·00	5·50
215		10s. black and slate-black			20·00	2·50
216		£1 slate-black and violet			20·00	6·50
201/16				Set of 16	60·00	17·00

Designs:—1d. Agriculture (combine harvester); 1½d. Island settlement; 2d. Straw work; 3d. Fishing fleet; 4d. Water sports (skiing); 5d. Dairy farm; 6d. Transportation; 8d. Paradise Beach; 10d. Modern hotels; 1s. Yacht racing; 2s. Sisal; 2s. 6d. Shipbuilding; 5s. Tuna fishing; 10s. Salt production; £1 Parliament Buildings.

Nos. 201/2, 205, 208 and 211 exist in coils, constructed from normal sheets.

See also No. 246.

(Recess Waterlow)

1959 (10 June). *Centenary of First Bahamas Postage Stamp. W w 12. P 13½.*

217	**43**	1d. black and scarlet			35	20
218		2d. black and blue-green			35	1·00
219		6d. black and blue			45	40
220		10d. black and chocolate			50	1·00
217/20				Set of 4	1·50	2·40

---

44 Christ Church Cathedral

(Photo Enschedé)

1962 (30 Jan). *Nassau Centenary. T 44 and similar horiz design. P 14 × 13.*

221		8d. green			45	55
222		10d. bluish violet			45	25

Design:—10d. Nassau Public Library.

1963 (4 June). *Freedom from Hunger. As No. 146 of Antigua.*

223		8d. sepia			40	40
		a. Name and value omitted			£900	

BAHAMAS TALKS 1962	**NEW CONSTITUTION 1964**	
(46)	(47)	

1963 (15 July). *Bahamas Talks, 1962. Nos. 209/10 optd with T 46.*

224		8d. black and reddish lilac			40	75
225		10d. black and deep ultramarine			50	75

1963 (2 Sept). *Red Cross Centenary. As Nos. 147/8 of Antigua.*

226		1d. red and black			50	50
227		3d. red and blue			1·75	2·50

SELF GOVERNMENT

1964 (7 Jan). *New Constitution. As Nos. 201/16 but W w 12, optd with T 47, by B.W.*

228		½d. black and red-orange			15	1·00
229		1d. olive-green and brown			15	15
230		1½d. blue and black			70	1·00
231		2d. yellow-brown and deep myrtle-green			15	20
232		3d. black and carmine-red			1·50	1·25
233		4d. turquoise-blue and deep reddish purple			40	55
234		5d. red-brown and deep bright blue			40	1·50
235		6d. light blue and black			2·00	30
236		8d. black and reddish lilac			70	30
237		10d. black and deep ultramarine			30	15
238		1s. ultramarine and olive-brown			1·25	15
239		2s. chestnut and black			1·50	1·75
240		2s. 6d. black and deep blue			3·00	2·75
241		5s. bright emerald and orange			6·50	3·25
242		10s. black and slate black			7·00	5·50
243		£1 slate-black and violet			8·50	18·00
228/243				Set of 16	27·00	32·00

1964 (23 April). *400th Birth Anniv of William Shakespeare. As No. 164 of Antigua.*

244		6d. turquoise			20	10
		w. Wmk inverted			48·00	

8d.
(48)

1964 (1 Oct). *Olympic Games, Tokyo. As No. 211 but W w 12, surch with T 48.*

245		8d. on 1s. ultramarine and olive-brown			45	15

1964 (6 Oct). *As No. 204a, but wmk w 12.*

246		2d. yellow-brown and deep myrtle-green			45	30

½d.
BAHAMAS
49 Colony's Badge

9d.
(64)

(Queen's portrait by Anthony Buckley. Litho and recess (portrait and "BAHAMAS") B.W.)

1965 (7 Jan–14 Sept). *Horiz designs as T 49. W w 12. P 13½.*

247		½d. multicoloured			15	1·25
248		1d. slate, light blue and orange			30	65
249		1½d. rose-red, green and brown			15	1·00
250		2d. slate, green and turquoise-blue			15	10
251		3d. red, light blue and purple			1·75	20
252		4d. green, blue and orange-brown			2·25	1·60
253		6d. dull green, light blue and rose			30	10
254		8d. reddish purple, light blue & bronze-green			50	30
255		10d. orange-brown, green and violet			25	30
256		1s. red, yellow, turquoise-blue & deep emer			50	20
		a. *Red, yellow, dull blue & emer* (14.9.65)			30	15
257		2s. brown, light blue and emerald			1·00	1·25
258		2s. 6d. yellow-olive, blue and carmine			2·25	3·00
259		5s. orange-brown, ultramarine and green			2·25	1·00

260	10s. rose, blue and chocolate			15·00	3·00
261	£1 chestnut, blue and rose-red			15·00	8·50
247/261			Set of 15	38·00	20·00

Designs:—1d. Out Island regatta; 1½d. Hospital; 2d. High School; 3d. Greater Flamingo; 4d. R.M.S. *Queen Elizabeth*; 6d. "Development"; 8d. Yachting; 10d. Public square; 1s. Sea garden; 2s. Old cannons at Fort Charlotte; 2s. 6d. Sikorsky S-38 flying boat, 1929, and Boeing 707 airliner; 5s. Williamson film project, 1914, and Undersea Post Office, 1939; 10s. Queen or Pink Conch; £1, Columbus's flagship.

Nos. 247, 251, 253 and 256 exist in coils, constructed from normal sheets.

1965 (17 May). *I.T.U Centenary. As Nos. 166/7 of Antigua.*

262	1d. light emerald and orange			15	10
	w. Wmk inverted			55·00	
263	2s. purple and yellow-olive			65	40
	w. Wmk inverted			16·00	

1965 (12 July). *No. 254 surch with T 64.*

264	9d. on 8d. reddish purple, light blue and bronze-green			30	15

1965 (25 Oct). *International Co-operation Year. As Nos. 168/9 of Antigua.*

265	½d. reddish purple and turquoise-green			10	85
266	1s. deep bluish green and lavender	..		30	40

1966 (24 Jan). *Churchill Commemoration. As Nos. 170/3 of Antigua.*

267	½d. new blue			10	40
	w. Wmk inverted			30·00	
268	2d. deep green			40	30
269	10d. brown			75	85
270	1s. bluish violet			75	1·40
267/70			Set of 4	1·75	2·75

1966 (4 Feb). *Royal Visit. As Nos. 174/5 of Antigua, but inscr "to the Caribbean" omitted.*

271	6d. black and ultramarine			90	50
272	1s. black and magenta			1·60	1·25

(New Currency. 100 cents = 1 Bahamas dollar)

(65)	(66)

1966 (25 May). *Decimal Currency. Nos. 247/61 variously surch as T 65/6, by B.W.*

273	1 c. on ½d. multicoloured			10	30
274	2 c. on 1d. slate, light blue and orange			75	30
275	3 c. on 2d. slate, green and turquoise-blue			10	10
276	4 c. on 3d. red, light blue and purple	.		1·50	20
277	5 c. on 4d. green, blue and orange-brown			1·25	2·75
	a. Surch omitted (vert strip of 10)			£2250	
278	8 c. on 6d. dull green, light blue and rose			20	20
279	10 c. on 8d. reddish purple, light blue and bronze-green			30	75
280	11 c. on 1½d. rose-red, green and brown			15	30
281	12 c. on 10d. orange-brown, green and violet			15	10
282	15 c. on 1s. multicoloured			25	10
283	22 c. on 2s. brown, light blue and emerald			60	90
284	50 c. on 2s. 6d. yellow-olive, blue and carmine			90	1·40
285	$1 on 5s. orange-brown, ultram & green			1·75	1·50
286	$2 on 10s. rose, blue and chocolate			7·50	4·25
287	$3 on £1 chestnut, blue and rose-red			7·50	4·25
273/287			Set of 15	20·00	15·00

The above were made on new printings some of which vary slightly in shade and in No. 273 the shield appears as vermilion and green instead of carmine and blue-green due to a different combination of the printing colours.

No. 277a. One sheet exists and the stamp can be distinguished from No. 252 when in a vertical strip of ten as these were printed in sheets of 100 whereas No. 252 was printed in sheets of 60 (six rows of ten across).

1966 (1 July). *World Cup Football Championships. As Nos. 176/7 of Antigua.*

288	8 c. violet, yellow-green, lake & yell-brown			25	15
289	15 c. chocolate, blue-green, lake & yell-brown			30	25

1966 (20 Sept). *Inauguration of W.H.O. Headquarters, Geneva. As Nos. 178/9 of Antigua.*

290	11 c. black, yellow-green and light blue	..		50	50
291	15 c. black, light purple and yellow-brown			50	50

1966 (1 Dec). *20th Anniv of U.N.E.S.C.O. As Nos. 196/8 of Antigua.*

292	3 c. slate-violet, red, yellow and orange			10	10
293	15 c. orange-yellow, violet and deep olive			35	35
294	$1 black, bright purple and orange			1·50	2·50
292/4			Set of 3	1·75	2·75

67 *Oceanic*

68 Conch Shell

(Portrait by Anthony Buckley. Litho and recess (portrait, "BAHAMAS" and value), B.W.)

1967 (25 May)–**71**. *T 67/8 or designs as Nos. 247/51, 253/9 and 261 but values in decimal currency and colours changed. Toned paper. W w 12. P 13½.*

295	1 c. multicoloured (as ½d.)	..		10	2·25
	a. Whiter paper (1970)			45	3·25
296	2 c. slate, light blue & deep emerald (as 1d.)			20	60
	a. Whiter paper (1970)			1·40	4·00
297	3 c. slate, green and violet (as 2d.)	..		10	10
	a. Whiter paper (1970)			48·00	5·00
298	4 c. red, light blue and ultramarine (as 3d.)			4·25	50
	a. Whiter paper (9.70*)			12·00	18·00
299	5 c. black, greenish blue and purple			1·00	5·00
	a. Whiter paper (1970)			1·50	5·00
300	8 c. dull green, light blue and sepia (as 6d.)			25	10
	a. Whiter paper (1970)			£170	17·00
301	10 c. reddish pur, greenish bl & carm (as 8d.)			30	70
	a. Whiter paper (1970)			1·00	3·00
302	11 c. rose-red, green and blue (as 1½d.)			25	80
	a. Whiter paper (1970)			80	2·25
303	12 c. orange-brown, green and olive (as 10d.)			25	10
	a. Whiter paper (4.71)			12·00	26·00
304	15 c. red, yellow, turquoise-bl & carm (as 1s.)			55	10
	a. Whiter paper (1970)			£170	22·00
305	22 c. brown, new blue and rose-red (as 2s.)			70	65
	a. Whiter paper (1970)			1·50	5·50
306	50 c. yellow-olive, new bl & emer (as 2s. 6d.)			2·00	75
	a. Whiter paper (1970)			2·25	4·00
307	$1 orange-brown, ultram & slate-pur (as 5s.)			2·00	60
	a. Whiter paper (4.71)			19·00	50·00
308	$2 multicoloured			12·00	3·00
	a. Whiter paper (4.71)			30·00	60·00
309	$3 chestnut, new blue and purple (as £1)			3·75	2·00
	a. Whiter paper (4.71)			30·00	60·00
295/309			Set of 15	24·00	13·00
295a/309a			Set of 15 (whiter paper)	£450	£250

*This is the earliest known date recorded in the Bahamas.

The 3 c. has the value at right instead of at left as on No. 250.

The 1970–71 printings on whiter paper were released as needed, the 12 c., $1, $2 and $3 only a week or two before the issue was withdrawn. Due to the marked difference in paper and the use of some new plates there are marked differences in shade in nearly all values.

69 Bahamas Crest

(Des R. Granger Barrett. Photo Enschedé)

1967 (1 Sept). *Diamond Jubilee of World Scouting. T 69 and similar horiz design. Multicoloured. W w 12 (sideways*). P 14×13.*

310	3 c. Type 69			35	15
	w. Wmk Crown to left of CA	..		14·00	
311	15 c. Scout badge			40	15

*The normal sideways watermark shows Crown to right of CA, as seen from the back of the stamp.

71 Globe and Emblem	**74** Golf

(Des R. Granger Barrett, Litho D.L.R)

1968 (13 May). *Human Rights Year. T 71 and similar horiz designs. Multicoloured. W w 12 (sideways*). P 14×13½.*

312	3 c. Type 71			10	10
313	12 c. Scales of Justice and emblem			20	10
314	$1 Bahamas Crest and emblem			70	80
312/14			Set of 3	90	85

*The normal sideways watermark shows Crown to right of CA on the 12 c. and Crown to left of CA on the others, each when seen from the back of the stamp.

(Litho B.W.)

1968 (20 Aug). *Tourism. T 74 and similar vert designs. Multicoloured. P 13.*

315	5 c. Type 74			1·75	1·50
316	11 c. Yachting	..		1·25	40
317	15 c. Horse-racing			1·75	45
318	50 c. Water-skiing			2·50	6·00
315/18			Set of 4	6·50	7·50

ALTERED CATALOGUE NUMBERS

Any Catalogue numbers altered from the last edition are shown as a list in the introductory pages.

---

78 Racing Yacht and Olympic Monument

(Photo Harrison)

1968 (29 Sept). *Olympic Games, Mexico City. T 78 and similar horiz designs. No wmk. P 14½ × 13½.*

319	5 c. red-brown, orange-yellow & blue-green			40	60
320	11 c. multicoloured			55	25
321	50 c. multicoloured			80	1·50
322	$1 olive-grey, greenish blue and violet			2·25	3·75
319/22			Set of 4	3·50	5·50

Designs:—11 c. Long-jumping and Olympic Monument; 50 c. Running and Olympic Monument; $1, Type 78.

It is understood that the above were released by the Philatelic Agency in the U.S.A. on 1st September.

81 Legislative Building

(Des J. Cooter, Litho Format)

1968 (1 Nov). *14th Commonwealth Parliamentary Conference. T 81 and similar multicoloured designs. P 14.*

323	3 c. Type 81			10	30
324	10 c. Bahamas Mace and Westminster Clock-Tower (*vert*)			15	30
325	12 c. Local straw market (*vert*)			15	25
326	15 c. Horse-drawn Surrey			20	35
323/6	..		Set of 4	55	1·10

85 Obverse and reverse of $100 Gold Coin

(Recess D.L.R.)

1968 (2 Dec). *Gold Coins commemorating the first General Election under the New Constitution. T 85 and similar "boomerang" shaped designs. P 13½.*

327	3 c. red/*gold*			40	25
328	12 c. blue-green/*gold*			60	50
329	15 c. dull purple/*gold*			70	60
330	$1 black/*gold*			1·75	2·50
327/30			Set of 4	3·00	3·50

Designs:—12 c. Obverse and reverse of $50 gold coin; 15 c. Obverse and reverse of $20 gold coin; $1, Obverse and reverse of $10 gold coin.

89 First Flight Postcard of 1919

90 Sikorsky S-38 Flying Boat of 1929

(Des V. Whiteley. Litho Format)

1969 (30 Jan). *50th Anniv of Bahamas Airmail Service. P 14.*

331	89	12 c. multicoloured	..		50	50
332	90	15 c. multicoloured	..		60	1·50

91 Game-fishing Boats	**92** "The Adoration of the Shepherds" (Louis le Nain)

(Des J. Cooter. Litho Format)

1969 (26 Aug). *Tourism. One Millionth Visitor to Bahamas. T* **91** *and similar horiz designs. Multicoloured.* W w **12** (sideways). P 14½.

333	3 c. Type **91**	..	..	25	10
334	11 c. Paradise Beach	..	..	35	15
335	12 c. "Sunfish" sailing boats	..		35	15
336	15 c. Rawson Square and Parade	..		45	25
333/6			Set of 4	1·25	60
MS337	130 × 96 mm. Nos. 333/6	..		2·50	3·00

(Des G. Drummond. Litho D.L.R.)

1969 (15 Oct). *Christmas. T* **92** *and similar vert designs.* W w **12**. P 12.

338	3 c. Type **92**	..	..	10	10
339	11 c. "The Adoration of the Shepherds" (Poussin)			15	15
340	12 c. "The Adoration of the Kings" (Gerard David)			15	20
341	15 c. "The Adoration of the Kings" (Vincenzo Foppa)			20	40
338/41			Set of 4	55	75

93 Badge of Girl Guides

(Des Mrs. R. Sands. Litho Harrison)

1970 (23 Feb). *Girl Guides Diamond Jubilee. T* **93** *and similar designs. Multicoloured.* W w **12**. P 14½.

342	3 c. Type **93**	..	..	30	10
	w. Wmk inverted	..	..		
343	12 c. Badge of Brownies	..		45	20
344	15 c. Badge of Rangers	..		50	35
	w. Wmk inverted	..	..		
342/4			Set of 3	1·10	55

94 U.P.U. Headquarters and Emblem

(Des L. Curtis, Litho J.W.)

1970 (20 May). *New U.P.U. Headquarters Building.* W w **12** (sideways). P 14.

345	**94**	3 c. multicoloured	..	10	10
346		15 c. multicoloured	..	20	30

95 Coach and Globe

(Des G. Drummond. Litho B.W.)

1970 (14 July). *"Goodwill Caravan". T* **95** *and similar horiz designs. Multicoloured.* W w **12** (sideways*). P 13½×13.

347	3 c. Type **95**	..		75	20
	w. Wmk Crown to right of CA	..			
348	11 c. Diesel train and globe	..		2·00	40
349	12 c. *Canberra* (liner), yacht and globe	..		2·00	40
	w. Wmk Crown to right of CA	..		3·50	
350	15 c. B.A.C. One Eleven airliner and globe	..		2·00	1·40
347/50			Set of 4	6·00	2·25
MS351	165×125 mm. Nos. 347/50	..		9·50	15·00

*The normal sideways watermark shows Crown to left of CA, as seen from the back of the stamp.

96 Nurse, Patients and Greater Flamingo

97 "The Nativity" (detail, Pittoni)

(Photo Harrison)

1970 (1 Sept). *Centenary of British Red Cross. T* **96** *and similar horiz design. Multicoloured.* W w **12** (sideways*). P 14½.

352	3 c. Type **96**	..	..	1·00	50
	a. Gold ("EIIR", etc) omitted	..		£275	
	w. Wmk Crown to right of CA	..			
353	15 c. Hospital and Blue Marlin	..		1·00	1·50

*The normal sideways watermark shows Crown to left of CA, as seen from back of the stamp.

(Des G. Drummond. Litho D.L.R.)

1970 (3 Nov). *Christmas. T* **97** *and similar vert designs. Multicoloured.* W w **12**. P 13.

354	3 c. Type **97**	..		15	10
355	11 c. "The Holy Family" (detail, Anton Raphael Mengs)			20	20
356	12 c. "The Adoration of the Shepherds" (detail, Giorgione)			20	20
357	15 c. "The Adoration of the Shepherds" (detail, School of Seville)			30	55
354/7			Set of 4	75	95
MS358	114 × 140 mm. Nos. 354/7 plus two labels			1·40	3·00

98 International Airport

(Des Mrs. W. Wasile. Litho Format)

1971 (27 Apr–1 Sept). *Multicoloured designs as T* **98**. W w **12** (sideways on $1 to $3). P 14½×14 (1 to 50 c.) or 14×14½ ($1 to $3).

359	1 c. Type **98**	..		10	30
360	2 c. Breadfruit	..		15	35
361	3 c. Straw market	..		15	30
362	4 c. Hawksbill turtle	..		1·75	8·00
363	5 c. Nassau Grouper	..		60	60
364	6 c. As 4 c. (21.9.71)	..		45	1·25
365	7 c. Hibiscus (21.9.71)	..		2·00	3·50
366	8 c. Yellow Elder	..		60	1·50
	w. Wmk inverted	..			
367	10 c. Bahamian sponge boat	..		55	30
368	11 c. Greater Flamingos	..		2·50	2·50
	w. Wmk inverted	..		11·00	
369	12 c. As 7 c.	..		2·00	3·00
370	15 c. Bonefish	..		55	55
	w. Wmk inverted	..			
371	18 c. Royal Poinciana (21.9.71)	..		65	65
	w. Wmk inverted	..			
372	22 c. As 18 c.	..		2·75	12·00
373	50 c. Post Office, Nassau	..		1·40	2·25
374	$1 Pineapple (vert)	..		6·00	2·50
375	$2 Crawfish (vert)	..		4·50	5·00
376	$3 Junkanoo (vert)	..		4·50	10·00
359/76			Set of 18	27·00	48·00

See also Nos. 395/400, 460/73 and 518/25.

99 Snowflake

(Litho (15 c. additionally die-stamped in gold) Walsall)

1971 (19 Oct). *Christmas. T* **99** *and similar horiz designs.* W w **12**. P 14 × 14½.

377	3 c. deep reddish purple, orange and gold			10	10
378	11 c. light ultramarine and gold	..		20	15
	w. Wmk inverted	..		1·00	
379	15 c. multicoloured	..		20	20
380	18 c. bluish green, royal blue and gold			25	25
377/80			Set of 4	65	60
MS381	126×95 mm. Nos. 377/80. P 15			1·25	1·50

Designs:—11 c. "Peace on Earth" (doves); 15 c. Arms of Bahamas and holly; 18 c. Starlit lagoon.

100 High jumping

(Des J. W. Litho B.W.)

1972 (11 July). *Olympic Games, Munich. T* **100** *and similar horiz designs. Multicoloured.* W w **12**. P 13½.

382	10 c. Type **100**	..		35	60
383	11 c. Cycling	..		1·50	75
384	15 c. Running	..		60	75
385	18 c. Sailing	..		95	60
382/5			Set of 4	3·00	3·00
MS386	127 × 95 mm. Nos. 382/5	..		3·00	3·00

---

101 Shepherd   **102** Northerly Bahama Islands

(Des Jennifer Toombs. Litho (15 c. additionally embossed) J.W.)

1972 (3 Oct). *Christmas. T* **101** *and similar vert designs. Multi-coloured.* W w **12** (sideways on 6 and 20 c.) P 14.

387	3 c. Type **101**	..		10	10
388	6 c. Bells	..		10	10
389	15 c. Holly and Cross	..		15	20
390	20 c. Poinsettia	..		25	45
387/90			Set of 4	50	70
MS391	108 × 140 mm. Nos. 387/90 (wmk sideways)			80	1·75

(Des M. Shamir. Litho Format)

1972 (1 Nov). *Tourism Year of the Americas. Sheet* 133 × 105 *mm, containing T* **102** *and similar vert designs.* P 15.
MS392   11, 15, 18 and 50 c. multicoloured   2·50   3·25

The four designs are printed horizontally *se-tenant* in **MS**392, forming a composite map design of the Bahamas.

103 Mace and Galleon

(Des (from photograph by D. Groves) and photo Harrison)

1972 (13 Nov). *Royal Silver Wedding. Multicoloured; background colour given.* W w **12**. P 14 × 14½.

393	**103**	11 c. rose	..	15	15
		w. Wmk inverted	..	60·00	
394		18 c. bluish violet	..	15	20
		w. Wmk inverted	..	1·75	

1972 (23 Nov)–**73**. *As Nos.* 363, 366 *and* 373/6 *but* W w **12** *sideways* on 5 to 50 c. *and upright on* $1 *to* $3.

395	5 c. Nassau Grouper	..		9·00	3·00
396	8 c. Yellow Elder (25.7.73)	..		2·75	2·00
397	50 c. Post Office, Nassau (25.7.73)	..		2·00	2·50
	w. Wmk Crown to left of CA	..		3·50	
398	$1 Pineapple (25.7.73)	..		2·50	4·00
399	$2 Crawfish (25.7.73)	..		2·50	6·00
400	$3 Junkanoo (1973)	..		3·00	14·00
395/400			Set of 6	20·00	28·00

*The normal sideways watermark shows Crown to right of CA, as seen from the back of the stamp.
Nos. 401/9 vacant.

104 Weather Satellite

(Des C. Abbott. Litho Questa)

1973 (3 Apr). *I.M.O./W.M.O. Centenary. T* **104** *and similar horiz design. Multicoloured.* W w **12**. P 14.

410	15 c. Type **104**	..		50	25
411	18 c. Weather radar	..		60	35

INDEPENDENT

105 C. A. Bain (national hero)

106 "The Virgin in Prayer" (Sassoferrato)

(Des PAD Studio. Litho Questa)

1973 (10 July–1 Aug). *Independence. T* **105** *and similar vert designs. Multicoloured.* W w **12** (sideways). P 14½ × 14.

412	3 c. Type **105**	..		10	10
413	11 c. Coat of arms	..		15	10
414	15 c. Bahamas flag	..		20	15
415	$1 Governor-General, M. B. Butler (1 Aug)			65	1·00
412/15			Set of 4	1·00	1·10
MS416	86 × 121 mm. Nos. 412/15 (1 Aug)			1·75	1·75

(Des C. Abbott. Litho Format)

1973 (16 Oct). *Christmas. T **106** and similar vert designs. Multicoloured.* W w **12** (*sideways**). *P* 14.

417	3 c. Type **106**		10	10
418	11 c. "Virgin and Child with St. John" (Filippino Lippi)		15	15
419	15 c. "A Choir of Angels" (Simon Marmion)		15	15
420	18 c. "The Two Trinities" (Murillo)		25	25
417/20		*Set of 4*	60	55
MS421	120×99 mm. Nos. 417/20		90	1·40
	w. Wmk Crown to right of CA			2·75

*The normal sideways watermark shows Crown to left of CA, as seen from the back of the stamp.

107 "Agriculture and Sciences"

(Des C. Abbott. Litho Questa)

1974 (5 Feb). *25th Anniv of University of West Indies. T **107** and similar horiz design. Multicoloured.* W w **12**. *P* 13½.

422	15 c. Type **107**	20	25
423	18 c. "Arts, Engineering and General Studies"	25	30

108 U.P.U. Monument, Berne

(Des P. Powell. Litho Questa)

1974 (23 Apr). *Centenary of Universal Postal Union. Designs as T **108** showing different arrangements of the U.P.U. Monument.* W w **12** (*upright on 3 c., 14 c. and **MS**428; sideways on others*). *P* 14.

424	**108** 3 c. multicoloured		10	10
425	– 13 c. multicoloured (*vert*)		20	25
426	– 14 c. multicoloured		20	30
427	– 18 c. multicoloured (*vert*)		25	35
424/7		*Set of 4*	65	90
MS428	128×95 mm. Nos. 424/7		80	1·60
	w. Wmk inverted			£150

109 Roseate Spoonbills

(Des G. Drummond. Litho Questa)

1974 (10 Sept). *15th Anniv of Bahamas National Trust. T **109** and similar horiz designs. Multicoloured.* W w **12** (*sideways*). *P* 13½.

429	13 c. Type **109**		1·40	85
430	14 c. White-crowned Pigeon		1·40	75
431	21 c. White-tailed Tropic Birds		1·75	1·25
432	36 c. Cuban Amazon		2·25	4·50
429/32		*Set of 4*	6·00	6·50
MS433	123 × 120 mm. Nos. 429/32		8·00	11·00

110 "The Holy Family" (Jacques de Stella)

(Des J. W. Litho Enschedé)

1974 (29 Oct). *Christmas. T **110** and similar horiz designs. Multicoloured.* W w **12** (*sideways*). *P* 13 × 13½.

434	8 c. Type **110**		10	10
435	10 c. "Madonna and Child" (16th-cent Brescian School)		15	15
436	12 c. "Virgin and Child with St. John the Baptist and St. Catherine" (Previtali)		15	15
437	21 c. "Virgin and Child with Angels" (Previtali)		25	30
434/7		*Set of 4*	60	60
MS438	126 × 105 mm. Nos. 434/7		80	1·40

NEW INFORMATION

The editor is always interested to correspond with people who have new information that will improve or correct the Catalogue.

111 *Anteos maerula*

(Des PAD Studio. Litho D.L.R.)

1975 (4 Feb). *Butterflies. T **111** and similar horiz designs. Multicoloured.* W w **12**. *P* 14 × 13½.

439	3 c. Type **111**		25	15
440	14 c. *Eurema nicippe*		80	50
441	18 c. *Papilio andraemon*		95	65
442	21 c. *Euptoieta hegesia*		1·10	85
	w. Wmk inverted		45·00	
439/42		*Set of 4*	2·75	2·00
MS443	119×94 mm. Nos. 439/42		7·50	6·50

112 Sheep Husbandry   **113** Rowena Rand (evangelist)

(Des Daphne Padden. Litho Questa)

1975 (27 May). *Economic Diversification. T **112** and similar multicoloured designs. P* 14.

444	3 c. Type **112**		10	10
445	14 c. Electric-reel fishing (*vert*)		20	15
446	18 c. Farming		25	20
447	21 c. Oil Refinery (*vert*)		45	35
444/7		*Set of 4*	90	65
MS448	127 × 94 mm. Nos. 444/7		90	1·50

(Des Jennifer Toombs. Litho Questa)

1975 (22 July). *International Women's Year. T **113** and similar vert design.* W w **14**. *P* 14.

449	14 c. bistre-brown, lt turquoise-blue & ultram	20	40
450	18 c. lemon, bright yellow-green and sepia	25	45

Design:—18 c. I.W.Y. symbol and Harvest symbol.

114 "Adoration of the Shepherds" (Perugino)

(Des Jennifer Toombs. Litho J.W.)

1975 (2 Dec). *Christmas. T **114** and similar horiz design. Multicoloured.* W w **14** (*sideways*). *P* 13.

451	3 c. Type **114**		15	50
452	8 c. "Adoration of the Magi" (Ghirlandaio)		20	10
453	18 c. As 8 c.		55	80
454	21 c. Type **114**		60	85
451/4		*Set of 4*	1·40	2·00
MS455	142 × 107 mm. Nos. 451/4. P 13½		2·25	3·50

115 Telephones, 1876 and 1976

(Des G. Vasarhelyi. Litho D.L.R.)

1976 (23 Mar). *Telephone Centenary. T **115** and similar horiz designs. Multicoloured.* W w **14** (*sideways**). *P* 14.

456	3 c. Type **115**		20	40
	w. Wmk Crown to right of CA		2·25	
457	16 c. Radio-telephone link, Deleporte		40	50
	w. Wmk Crown to right of CA			
458	21 c. Alexander Graham Bell		50	65
	w. Wmk Crown to right of CA		60·00	
459	25 c. Satellite		60	80
	w. Wmk Crown to right of CA		2·75	
456/9		*Set of 4*	1·50	2·10

*The normal sideways watermark shows Crown to left of CA, as seen from the back of the stamp.

1976 (30 May)–**79**. *Designs as Nos. 359/63, 365/7 and 373/6 (some with new face values).* W w **14** (*sideways on $1 to $3*). *Ordinary paper.*

460	1 c. Type **98** (1.11.76)		1·75	2·50
	a. Chalk-surfaced paper (1979)		16·00	17·00
461	2 c. Breadfruit		2·00	30
462	3 c. Straw market (1.11.76)		2·25	3·25
	a. Chalk-surfaced paper (1979)		60	60

463	5 c. Nassau Grouper (1.11.76)		4·00	3·50
	a. Chalk-surfaced paper (1979)		70	70
464	8 c. Yellow Elder		5·00	30
465	10 c. Bahamian sponge boat		80	30
466	16 c. As 7 c. (2.11.76)		70	35
	a. Chalk-surfaced paper (1979)		70	80
	aw. Wmk inverted		18·00	
467	21 c. As 2 c. (2.11.76)		3·00	1·50
	a. Chalk-surfaced paper (1979)		80	1·25
	aw. Wmk inverted		18·00	
468	25 c. As 4 c. (2.11.76)		90	40
	a. Chalk-surfaced paper (1979)		90	2·00
	aw. Wmk inverted		18·00	
469	40 c. As 10 c. (2.11.76)		4·00	75
470	50 c. Post Office, Nassau		1·75	1·75
471	$1 Pineapple		2·00	2·50
472	$2 Crawfish (2.5.76)		3·00	7·00
	a. Chalk-surfaced paper (1979)		13·00	27·00
473	$3 Junkanoo (1.11.76)		3·00	9·00
460/73		*Set of 14*	30·00	30·00
460a/72a		*Set of 7*	29·00	45·00

No. 474 vacant.

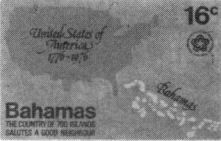

116 Map of North America

(Des and litho Walsall)

1976 (1 June). *Bicentenary of American Revolution. T **116** and similar horiz design. Multicoloured.* W w **14** (*sideways**). *P* 14.

475	16 c. Type **116**		30	30
476	$1 John Murray, Earl of Dunmore		1·50	1·75
MS477	127×100 mm. No. 476×4		6·00	7·50
	w. Wmk Crown to right of CA		18·00	

*The normal sideways watermark shows Crown to left of CA, as seen from the back of the stamp.

117 Cycling   **118** "Virgin and Child" (detail, Lippi)

(Des J.W. Litho Questa)

1976 (13 July). *Olympic Games, Montreal. T **117** and similar vert designs.* W w **14**. *P* 14.

478	8 c. magenta, blue and pale cobalt		90	20
479	16 c. orange, brown and pale cobalt		35	30
480	25 c. blue, deep magenta and pale cobalt		45	45
481	40 c. brown, orange and pale cobalt		55	1·25
478/81		*Set of 4*	2·00	2·00
MS482	100 × 126 mm. Nos. 478/81		2·50	2·50

Designs:—16 c. Jumping; 25 c. Sailing; 40 c. Boxing.

(Des G. Drummond. Litho Questa)

1976 (5 Oct). *Christmas. T **118** and similar vert designs. Multicoloured.* W w **14**. *P* 14.

483	3 c. Type **118**		10	10
484	21 c. "Adoration of the Shepherds" (School of Seville)		20	15
485	25 c. "Adoration of the Kings" (detail, Foppa)		20	20
486	40 c. "Virgin and Child" (detail, Vivarini)		35	40
483/6		*Set of 4*	75	75
MS487	107 × 127 mm. Nos. 483/6		1·00	2·00

119 Queen beneath Cloth of Gold Canopy

(Des G. Vasarhelyi. Litho Cartor)

1977 (7 Feb). *Silver Jubilee. T **119** and similar horiz designs. Multicoloured. No wmk. P* 12.

488	8 c. Type **119**		10	10
489	16 c. The Crowning		15	15
490	21 c. Taking the Oath		15	15
491	40 c. Queen with sceptre and orb		25	30
488/91		*Set of 4*	60	60
MS492	122 × 90 mm. Nos. 488/91		80	1·25

120 Featherduster

(Des BG Studio. Litho J.W.)

1977 (24 May). *Marine Life.* T **120** *and similar designs. Multicoloured.* W w 14 *(sideways).* P 13½.

493	3 c. Type **120**		30	15
494	8 c. Porkfish and cave		45	20
495	16 c. Elkhorn Coral		70	40
496	21 c. Soft Coral and sponge		80	55
493/6		*Set of* 4	2·00	1·10
MS497	119×93 mm. Nos. 493/6. P 14½		2·50	4·00

121 Scouts around Campfire and Home-made Shower

Royal Visit
October 1977

(**122**)

(Des Harrison. Litho J.W.)

1977 (27 Sept). *Sixth Caribbean Scout Jamboree.* T **121** *and similar horiz design. Multicoloured.* W w 14 *(sideways).* P 13½.

498	16 c. Type **121**		75	30
499	21 c. Boating scenes		85	35

One used example of No. 498 is known with the mauve (face value and inscription) omitted.

1977 (19 Oct). *Royal Visit. As Nos. 488/92, but* W w 14 *(sideways*), optd with* T **122**.

500	8 c. Type **119**		15	10
501	16 c. The Crowning		20	15
	w. Wmk Crown to right of CA		70	
502	21 c. Taking the Oath		25	20
503	40 c. Queen with sceptre and orb		30	40
500/3		*Set of* 4	80	75
MS504	122×90 mm. Nos. 500/3		1·00	2·00
	w. Wmk Crown to right of CA		2·00	

*The normal sideways watermark shows Crown to right of CA on 8, 21, 40 c.; to left on 16 c. and miniature sheet; *all as seen from the back of the stamp.*

123 Virgin and Child

124 Public Library, Nassau (Colonial)

(Des and litho J.W.)

1977 (25 Oct). *Christmas.* T **123** *and similar vert designs. Multicoloured.* W w 14. P 13½.

505	3 c. Type **123**		10	10
506	16 c. The Magi		20	25
507	21 c. Nativity scene		25	40
508	25 c. The Magi and star		30	45
505/8		*Set of* 4	75	1·10
MS509	136 × 74 mm. Nos. 505/8. P 14		75	1·75

(Des G. Drummond. Litho Questa)

1978 (28 Mar). *Architectural Heritage.* T **124** *and similar vert designs.* W w 14. P 14½ × 14.

510	3 c. black and apple-green		10	10
511	8 c. black and pale greenish blue		15	10
512	16 c. black and mauve		20	20
513	18 c. black and salmon-pink		25	30
510/13		*Set of* 4	60	65
MS514	91×91 mm. Nos. 510/13		70	1·60

Designs:—8 c. St. Matthew's Church (Gothic); 16 c. Government House (Colonial); 18 c. Hermitage, Cat Island (Spanish).

125 Sceptre, St. Edward's Crown and Orb

126 Coat of Arms within Wreath and Three Ships

(Des BG Studio. Litho Enschedé)

1978 (27 June). *25th Anniv of Coronation.* T **125** *and similar vert design. Multicoloured.* W w 14. P 14 × 13½.

515	16 c. Type **125**		15	10
516	$1 Queen in Coronation regalia		50	65
MS517	147×96 mm. Nos. 515/16		1·25	1·00
	w. Wmk inverted		9·00	

1978 (June). *As Nos. 359/76, but no wmk.*

518	1 c. Type **98**		65	2·50
519	5 c. Nassau Grouper		1·00	1·00
520	16 c. Hibiscus		1·25	1·75
521	25 c. Hawksbill Turtle		5·50	1·75
522	50 c. Post Office, Nassau		2·50	3·00
523	$1 Pineapple		2·50	3·00
524	$2 Crawfish		4·50	8·00
525	$3 Junkanoo		4·50	8·00
518/25		*Set of* 8	20·00	26·00

Nos. 526/31 vacant.

(Des Jennifer Toombs. Litho Questa)

1978 (14 Nov). *Christmas.* T **126** *and similar horiz design.* W w 14 *(sideways).* P 14 × 14½.

532	5 c. gold, bright crimson and bright rose		15	10
533	21 c. gold, deep ultramarine and violet-blue		30	25
MS534	95 × 95 mm. Nos. 532/3		2·75	5·00

Design:—21 c. Three angels with trumpets.

127 Child reaching for Adult

128 Sir Rowland Hill and Penny Black

(Litho J.W.)

1979 (15 May). *International Year of the Child.* T **127** *and similar vert designs. Multicoloured.* W w 14. P 13.

535	5 c. Type **127**		20	15
536	16 c. Boys playing leap-frog		40	45
537	21 c. Girls skipping		50	60
538	25 c. Bricks with I.Y.C. emblem		50	75
535/8		*Set of* 4	1·40	1·75
MS539	101 × 125 mm. Nos. 535/8. P 14		1·40	2·75

(Des J. Cooter. Litho Format)

1979 (14 Aug). *Death Centenary of Sir Rowland Hill.* T **128** *and similar horiz designs. Multicoloured.* W w 14 *(sideways).* P 13½×14.

540	10 c. Type **128**		30	10
541	21 c. Printing press, 1840 and 6d. stamp of 1862		40	30
542	25 c. Great Britain 6d. stamp of 1856 with "A 05" (Nassau) cancellation and Two-penny blue		40	50
543	40 c. Early mailboat and 1d. stamp of 1859		45	70
540/3		*Set of* 4	1·40	1·40
MS544	115 × 80 mm. Nos. 540/3		2·00	2·50

129 Commemorative Plaque and Map of Bahamas

130 Goombay Carnival Headdress

(Des G. Drummond. Litho Secura, Singapore)

1979 (27 Sept). *250th Anniv of Parliament.* T **129** *and similar horiz designs. Multicoloured.* W w 14 *(sideways*).* P 13½.

545	16 c. Type **129**		25	10
	w. Wmk Crown to right of CA		45	
546	21 c. Parliament Buildings		30	15
	w. Wmk Crown to right of CA		50	
547	25 c. Legislative Chamber		30	15
	w. Wmk Crown to right of CA		55	
548	$1 Senate Chamber		80	80
	w. Wmk Crown to right of CA		1·40	
545/8		*Set of* 4	1·50	1·00
MS549	116×89 mm. Nos. 545/8 (wmk upright)		2·50	3·50
	w. Wmk inverted		2·50	

*The normal sideways watermark shows Crown to left of CA, *as seen from the back of the stamp.*

(Des BG Studio. Litho J.W.)

1979 (6 Nov). *Christmas.* T **130** *and similar vert designs showing Goombay Carnival headdresses.* W w 14. P 13.

550	5 c. multicoloured		10	10
551	10 c. multicoloured		10	10
552	16 c. multicoloured		15	10
553	21 c. multicoloured		20	20
554	25 c. multicoloured		20	20
	w. Wmk inverted		2·50	
555	40 c. multicoloured		30	35
550/5		*Set of* 6	90	85
MS556	50×88 mm. Nos. 550/5 (wmk sideways)			
	P 13½		2·00	2·75

COVER PRICES

Cover factors are quoted at the beginning of each country for most issues to 1945. An explanation of the system can be found on page x. The factors quoted do not, however, apply to philatelic covers.

131 Landfall of Columbus, 1492

132 Virgin and Child

(Des J.W. Litho Format)

1980 (9 July). *Horiz designs as* T **131**. *Multicoloured.* W w 14. P 14½.

557	1 c. Type **131**		85	2·25
558	3 c. Blackbeard the Pirate, 1718		30	2·25
559	5 c. Eleutheran Adventurers (Articles and Orders, 1647)		30	80
560	10 c. Ceremonial mace		20	30
	w. Wmk inverted			†
561	12 c. The Loyalists, 1783–88 (Colonel Andrew Deveaux)		30	1·75
562	15 c. Slave trading, Vendue House		5·50	75
563	16 c. Wrecking in the 1800's		1·00	75
564	18 c. Blockade running (American Civil War)		1·25	2·00
565	21 c. Bootlegging, 1919–29		40	2·00
	a. "BAHAMAS" omitted			
566	25 c. Pineapple cultivation		40	2·00
567	40 c. Sponge clipping		70	1·50
568	50 c. Tourist development		75	1·50
569	$1 Modern agriculture		1·10	4·00
570	$2 Modern air and sea transport		4·00	4·50
571	$3 Banking in the Bahamas (Central Bank)		1·50	4·00
572	$5 Independence, 10 July 1973 (Prince of Wales and Prime Minister L. O. Pindling)		1·75	6·00
557/72		*Set of* 16	18·00	32·00

No. 565a comes from a sheet showing a major shift of the orange colour so that stamps in the bottom horizontal row are without "BAHAMAS".

See also Nos. 720/6 for stamps watermarked w **16**.

(Des B. Malone. Litho Walsall)

1980 (28 Oct). *Christmas. Straw-work.* T **132** *and similar vert designs. Multicoloured.* W w 14. P 14½ × 14.

573	5 c. Type **132**		10	10
574	21 c. Three Kings		25	10
575	25 c. Angel		25	15
576	$1 Christmas Tree		75	70
573/6		*Set of* 4	1·25	80
MS577	168 × 105 mm. Nos. 573/6		1·25	2·25

133 Disabled Person with Walking-stick

(Des and litho Walsall)

1981 (10 Feb). *International Year for Disabled Persons.* T **133** *and similar horiz design. Multicoloured.* W w 14 *(sideways).* P 14½ × 14.

578	5 c. Type **133**		10	10
579	$1 Disabled person in wheelchair		1·25	1·25
MS580	120 × 60 mm. Nos. 578/9		1·40	2·50

134 Grand Bahama Tracking Site

135 Prince Charles and Lady Diana Spencer

(Litho Enschedé)

1981 (21 Apr). *Space Exploration.* T **134** *and similar multicoloured designs.* W w 14 *(sideways* on 10 and 25 c.).* P 13½.

581	10 c. Type **134**		25	15
582	20 c. Satellite view of Bahamas (*vert*)		55	50
	w. Wmk inverted		20·00	
583	25 c. Satellite view of Eleuthera		60	60
	w. Wmk Crown to right of CA		1·60	
584	50 c. Satellite view of Andros and New Providence (*vert*)		85	1·25
581/4		*Set of* 4	2·00	2·25
MS585	115×99 mm. Nos. 581/4 (wmk sideways)		1·60	2·25

*The normal sideways watermark shows Crown to left of CA, *as seen from the back of the stamp.*

(Des C. Abbott. Litho Questa)

1981 (22 July). *Royal Wedding.* T **135** *and similar horiz design. Multicoloured.* W w 14 *(sideways*).* P 14×14½.

586	30 c. Type **135**		1·00	30
587	$2 Prince Charles and Prime Minister Pindling		1·50	1·25
MS588	142×120 mm. Nos. 586/7		5·00	1·25
	a. Upper stamp in miniature sheet imperf on 3 sides		£650	
	w. Wmk Crown to right of CA		30·00	

*The normal sideways watermark shows Crown to left of CA, *as seen from the back of the stamp.*

No. **MS588a** shows the upper stamp in the miniature sheet perforated at foot only.

136 Bahama Pintail

(Des Walsall. Litho Questa)

1981 (25 Aug). *Wildlife (1st series). Birds. T* **136** *and similar horiz designs. Multicoloured. W w* **14** *(sideways). P* 14.

589	5 c. Type **136**		1·00	30
590	20 c. Reddish Egret		1·90	50
591	25 c. Brown Booby		1·90	55
592	$1 Black-billed Whistling Duck		3·50	5·50
589/92		Set of 4	7·50	6·25
MS593	100 × 74 mm. Nos. 589/92		8·00	7·50

See also Nos. 626/30, 653/7 and 690/4.

COMMONWEALTH FINANCE MINISTERS' MEETING

(137)

1981 (21 Sept). *Commonwealth Finance Ministers' Meeting. Nos.* 559/60, 566 *and* 568 *optd with T* **137**.

594	5 c. Eleutheran Adventurers (Articles and Orders, 1647)		15	15
	a. Opt inverted		40·00	
595	10 c. Ceremonial mace		20	20
	w. Wmk inverted		5·00	
596	25 c. Pineapple cultivation		50	60
597	50 c. Tourist development		85	1·50
594/7		Set of 4	1·50	2·25

138 Poultry   **139** Father Christmas

(Des L. McCombie. Litho J.W.)

1981 (16 Oct). *World Food Day. T* **138** *and similar horiz designs. Multicoloured. W w* **14** *(sideways). P* 13.

598	5 c. Type **138**		10	10
599	20 c. Sheep		30	35
600	30 c. Lobsters		40	50
601	50 c. Pigs		75	1·50
598/601		Set of 4	1·40	2·25
MS602	115 × 63 mm. Nos. 598/601. P 14		1·50	3·25

(Des local artists. Litho Format)

1981 (24 Nov). *Christmas. T* **139** *and similar vert designs. Multicoloured. W w* **14**. *P* 13½ × 14.

603	5 c. Type **139**		45	60
	a. Sheetlet of 9. Nos. 603/11		4·75	
604	5 c. Mother and child		45	60
605	5 c. St. Nicholas, Holland		45	60
606	25 c. Lussibruden, Sweden		60	85
607	25 c. Mother and child (different)		60	85
608	25 c. King Wenceslas, Czechoslovakia		60	85
609	30 c. Mother with child on knee		60	85
610	30 c. Mother carrying child		60	85
611	$1 Christkindl Angel, Germany		1·00	1·50
603/11		Set of 9	4·75	6·75

Nos. 603/11 were printed together, *se-tenant*, in a sheetlet of 9.

140 Robert Koch   **141** Male Flamingo (*Phoenicopterus ruber*)

(Des A. Theobald. Litho Harrison)

1982 (3 Feb). *Centenary of Discovery of Tubercle Bacillus by Robert Koch. T* **140** *and similar horiz designs. W w* **14** *(sideways).*

612	5 c. black, red-brown and rose-lilac		70	40
613	16 c. black, drab and dull orange		1·25	50
614	21 c. multicoloured		1·40	55
615	$1 multicoloured		3·00	6·50
612/15		Set of 4	5·75	7·25
MS616	94 × 97 mm. Nos. 612/15. P 14½		6·00	7·50

Designs:—16 c. Stylised infected person; 21 c. Early and modern microscopes; $1 Mantoux test.

(Des N. Arlott. Litho Questa)

1982 (28 Apr). *Greater Flamingos. T* **141** *and similar vert designs. Multicoloured. W w* **14**. *P* 14 × 13½.

617	25 c. Type **141**		1·50	1·00
	a. Horiz strip of 5. Nos. 617/21		6·50	
618	25 c. Female		1·50	1·00
619	25 c. Female with nestling		1·50	1·00
620	25 c. Juvenile		1·50	1·00
621	25 c. Immature bird		1·50	1·00
617/21		Set of 5	6·50	4·50

Nos. 617/21 were printed together, *se-tenant*, in horizontal strips of 5 throughout the sheet, forming a composite design.

142 Lady Diana Spencer at Ascot, June 1981   **143** House of Assembly Plaque

(Des C. Abbott. Litho Format)

1982 (1 July). *21st Birthday of Princess of Wales. T* **142** *and similar vert designs. Multicoloured. W w* **14**. *P* 13½ × 14 (16 c., $1) *or* 13½ (*others*).

622	16 c. Bahamas coat of arms		20	10
	a. Perf 13½		1·00	1·25
623	25 c. Type **142**		45	15
624	40 c. Bride and Earl Spencer arriving at St. Paul's		60	20
	w. Wmk inverted		11·00	
625	$1 Formal portrait		1·00	1·25
622/5		Set of 4	2·00	1·40

(Des Walsall. Litho Questa)

1982 (18 Aug). *Wildlife (2nd series). Mammals. Horiz designs as T* **136**. *Multicoloured. W w* **14** *(sideways). P* 14.

626	10 c. Buffy Flower Bat		70	15
627	16 c. Bahaman Hutia		90	25
628	21 c. Common Racoon		1·10	35
629	$1 Common Dolphin		2·75	1·75
626/9		Set of 4	5·00	2·25
MS630	115 × 76 mm. Nos. 626/9		5·00	3·50

(Des and litho Walsall)

1982 (16 Oct). *28th Commonwealth Parliamentary Association Conference. T* **143** *and similar vert designs. Multicoloured. W w* **14**. *P* 14 × 13½.

631	5 c. Type **143**		15	10
632	25 c. Association coat of arms		50	35
633	40 c. Coat of arms		80	60
634	50 c. House of Assembly		1·10	75
631/4		Set of 4	2·25	1·60

144 Wesley Methodist Church, Baillou Hill Road

(Des Jennifer Toombs. Litho Format)

1982 (3 Nov). *Christmas. Churches. T* **144** *and similar horiz designs. Multicoloured. W w* **14** *(sideways). P* 14.

635	5 c. Type **144**		10	10
636	12 c. Centreville Seventh Day Adventist Church		15	20
637	15 c. The Church of God of Prophecy, East Street		20	30
638	21 c. Bethel Baptist Church, Meeting Street		25	30
639	25 c. St. Francis Xavier Catholic Church, Highbury Park		25	50
640	$1 Holy Cross Anglican Church, Highbury Park		75	2·75
635/40		Set of 6	1·50	3·75

145 Prime Minister Lynden O. Pindling

(Des Walsall. Litho Questa)

1983 (14 Mar). *Commonwealth Day T* **145** *and similar horiz designs. Multicoloured. W w* **14** *(sideways). P* 14.

641	5 c. Type **145**		10	10
642	25 c. Bahamian and Commonwealth flags		30	40
643	35 c. Map showing position of Bahamas		40	50
644	$1 Ocean liner		1·10	1·40
641/4		Set of 4	1·60	2·10

20c

(146)

1983 (5 Apr). *Nos.* 562/5 *surch as T* **146**.

645	20 c. on 15 c. Slave trading, Vendue House		50	35
646	31 c. on 21 c. Bootlegging, 1919–29		60	55
	w. Wmk inverted		2·00	
647	35 c. on 16 c. Wrecking in the 1800's		1·25	60
648	80 c. on 18 c. Blockade running (American Civil War)		1·50	1·40
	w. Wmk inverted		7·00	
645/8		Set of 4	3·50	2·50

147 Customs Officers and *Queen Elizabeth 2* (liner)   **148** Raising the National Flag

(Des Walsall. Litho Harrison)

1983 (31 May). *30th Anniv of Customs Co-operation Council. T* **147** *and similar vert design. Multicoloured. W w* **14**. *P* 13½ × 13.

649	31 c. Type **147**		1·50	45
650	$1 Customs officers and Lockheed Jet Star 1 airliner		3·50	2·75

(Des L. Curtis. Litho Questa)

1983 (6 July). *10th Anniv of Independence. W w* **14**. *P* 14.

651	**148** $1 multicoloured		1·00	1·40
MS652	105 × 65 mm. No. 651. P 12		1·00	1·40

(Des F. Solomon, adapted N. Arlott. Litho Harrison)

1983 (24 Aug). *Wildlife (3rd series). Butterflies. Horiz designs as T* **136**. *W w* **14** *(sideways). P* 14½ × 14.

653	5 c. multicoloured		90	20
654	25 c. multicoloured		1·60	40
655	31 c. black, bistre-yellow and bright rose-red		1·60	55
656	50 c. multicoloured		2·00	85
653/6		Set of 4	5·50	1·75
MS657	120 × 80 mm. Nos. 653/6		5·00	5·00
	a. Perf 14		4·25	6·00

Designs:—5 c. *Atalopedes carteri*; 25 c. *Ascia monuste*; 31 c. *Phoebis agarithe*; 50 c. *Dryas julia*.

No. MS657a was perforated by Questa, the remainder of the issue by Harrison.

149 "Loyalist Dreams"   **150** Consolidated PBY-5 Catalina

(Des A. Lowe; adapted C. Abbott. Litho Questa)

1983 (28 Sept). *Bicentenary of Arrival of American Loyalists in the Bahamas. T* **149** *and similar multicoloured designs. W w* **14** *(sideways on* 31 c., 35 c.). *P* 14.

658	5 c. Type **149**		10	10
659	31 c. New Plymouth, Abaco (*horiz*)		45	50
660	35 c. New Plymouth Hotel (*horiz*)		50	70
661	50 c. "Island Hope"		65	90
658/61		Set of 4	1·50	2·00
MS662	111 × 76 mm. Nos. 658/61. Wmk sideways		1·50	2·50

(Des and litho Harrison)

1983 (13 Oct). *Air Bicentenary of Manned Flight. T* **150** *and similar horiz designs. Multicoloured. W w* **14** *(sideways). P* 14.

663	10 c. Type **150**		55	15
664	25 c. Avro Type 688 Tudor IV		75	40
665	31 c. Avro Type 691 Lancastrian		85	45
666	35 c. Consolidated Commodore		1·00	60
663/6		Set of 4	2·75	1·40

For these stamps without the Manned Flight logo see Nos. 699/702 (W w **14** (sideways) and 752/3 (W w **16** (sideways)).

151 "Christmas Bells"   **152** 1861 4d. Stamp
(Monica Pinder)

(Des local children, adapted G. Vasarhelyi. Litho Walsall)

1983 (1 Nov). *Christmas. Children's Paintings.* T **151** *and similar multicoloured designs.* W w 14 *(sideways on 31 c. and 50 c.).* P 14.

667	5 c. Type **151**				10	10
668	20 c. "Flamingo" (Cory Bullard)				30	30
669	25 c. "Yellow Hibiscus with Christmas Candle" (Monique Bailey)				40	40
670	31 c. "Santa goes a Sailing" (Sabrina Seiler) (horiz)				45	45
671	35 c. "Silhouette scene with Palm Trees" (James Blake)				50	50
672	50 c. "Silhouette scene with Pelicans" (Erik Russell) (horiz)				70	70
667/72				Set of 6	2·25	2·25

(Des D. Miller. Litho Format)

1984 (22 Feb). *125th Anniv of First Bahamas Postage Stamp.* T **152** *and similar vert design. Multicoloured.* W w 14. P 14.

673	5 c. Type **152**				25	10
674	$1 1859 1d. stamp				1·75	1·50

153 *Trent I* (paddle   **154** Running
steamer)

(Des L. Curtis. Litho Questa)

1984 (25 Apr). *250th Anniv of "Lloyd's List" (newspaper).* T **153** *and similar vert designs. Multicoloured.* W w 14. P 14½ × 14.

675	5 c. Type **153**				40	40
676	31 c. *Orinoco II* (mailship), 1886				90	60
677	35 c. Cruise liners in Nassau harbour				1·00	1·00
678	50 c. *Oropesa* (container ship)				1·40	1·60
675/8				Set of 4	3·25	2·75

(Des McCombie Skinner Studio. Litho Questa)

1984 (20 June). *Olympic Games, Los Angeles.* T **154** *and similar horiz designs.* W w 14 *(sideways).* P 14 × 14½.

679	5 c. green, black and gold				15	15
680	25 c. new blue, black and gold				50	50
681	31 c. brown-lake, black and gold				55	60
682	$1 sepia, black and gold				4·25	4·25
679/82				Set of 4	5·00	5·00
MS683	115 × 80 mm. Nos. 679/82				5·00	6·00

Designs:— 25 c. Shot-putting; 31 c. Boxing; $1 Basketball.

155 Bahamas and Caribbean   **156** Bahama Woodstar
Community Flags

(Des McCombie Skinner Studio. Litho Questa)

1984 (4 July). *5th Conference of Caribbean Community Heads of Government.* W w 14. P 14.

684	**155** 50 c. multicoloured				90	95

(Des N. Arlott. Litho Questa)

1984 (15 Aug). *25th Anniv of National Trust.* T **156** *and similar vert designs. Multicoloured.* W w 14. P 14.

685	31 c. Type **156**				3·00	3·00
	a. Horiz strip of 5. Nos. 685/9				13·00	
686	31 c. Belted Kingfishers, Greater Flamingos and *Eleutherodactylus planirostris* (frog)				3·00	3·00
687	31 c. Black-necked Stilts, Greater Flamingos and *Phoebis sennae* (butterfly)				3·00	3·00
688	31 c. *Urbanus proteus* (butterfly) and *Chelonia mydas* (turtle)				3·00	3·00
689	31 c. Osprey and Greater Flamingos				3·00	3·00
685/9				Set of 5	13·00	13·00

Nos. 685/9 were printed together, *se-tenant*, in horizontal strips of 5 throughout the sheet, forming a composite design.

(Des N. Arlott. Litho Questa)

1984 (18 Sept). *Wildlife (4th series). Reptiles and Amphibians.* *Horiz designs as* T **136**. W w 14 *(sideways).* P 14.

690	5 c. Allen's Cay Iguana				40	20
691	25 c. Curly-tailed Lizard				1·00	60
692	35 c. Greenhouse Frog				1·25	85
693	50 c. Atlantic Green Turtle				1·75	2·50
690/3				Set of 4	4·00	3·75
MS694	112 × 82 mm. Nos. 690/3				4·75	6·50

157 "The Holy Virgin with   **158** Brownie Emblem and
Jesus and Johannes"   Queen or Pink Conch
(19th-century porcelain
plaque after Titian)

(Des D. Slater. Litho J.W.)

1984 (7 Nov). *Christmas. Religious Paintings.* T **157** *and similar vert designs. Multicoloured,* W w 14. P 13½.

695	5 c. Type **157**				20	10
696	31 c. "Madonna with Child in Tropical Landscape" (aquarelle, Anaïs Colin)				75	60
	w. Wmk inverted				1·00	
697	35 c. "The Holy Virgin with the Child" (miniature on ivory, Elena Caula)				80	65
695/7				Set of 3	1·60	1·25
MS698	116×76 mm. Nos. 695/7. P 14				1·60	3·25

1985 (2 Jan). *Air. As Nos. 663/6, but without Manned Flight logo.* W w 14 *(sideways*).* P 14.

699	10 c. Type **150**				70	30
700	25 c. Avro Type 688 Tudor IV				85	40
701	31 c. Avro Type 691 Lancastrian				85	55
	w. Wmk Crown to right of CA				18·00	
702	35 c. Consolidated Commodore				1·25	85
699/702				Set of 4	3·25	1·90

*The normal sideways watermark shows Crown to left of CA, as seen from the back of the stamp.
See also Nos. 752/3 for stamps watermarked w **16** (sideways).

(Des Berta Dallen Sands. Litho Walsall)

1985 (22 Feb). *International Youth Year. 75th Anniv of Girl Guide Movement.* T **158** *and similar horiz designs. Multicoloured.* W w 14 *(sideways).* P 14.

703	5 c. Type **158**				50	40
704	25 c. Tents and coconut palm				1·25	90
705	31 c. Guide salute and Greater Flamingos				1·50	1·25
706	35 c. Ranger emblem and marlin				1·75	1·50
703/6				Set of 4	4·50	3·50
MS707	95 × 74 mm. Nos. 703/6				4·75	6·50

159 Killdeer   **160** The Queen Mother
at the Christening of
Peter Phillips, 1977

(Des Josephine Martin. Litho Walsall)

1985 (24 Apr). *Birth Bicentenary of John J. Audubon (ornithologist).* T **159** *and similar multicoloured designs.* W w 14 *(sideways on 5 c.,* $1).* P 14.

708	5 c. Type **159**				1·00	30
709	31 c. Mourning Dove (vert)				2·25	55
710	35 c. "Mourning Dove" (John J. Audubon) (vert)				2·25	60
711	$1 "Killdeer" (John J. Audubon)				4·00	3·75
708/11				Set of 4	8·50	4·75

(Des A. Theobald ($1.25), C. Abbott (others). Litho Questa)

1985 (7 June). *Life and Times of Queen Elizabeth the Queen Mother.* T **160** *and similar vert designs. Multicoloured.* W w 16. P 14½ × 14.

712	5 c. Visiting Auckland, New Zealand, 1927				15	15
713	25 c. Type **160**				55	40
714	35 c. The Queen Mother attending church				60	55
	w. Wmk inverted				80	
715	50 c. With Prince Henry at his christening (from photo by Lord Snowdon)				85	1·00
712/15				Set of 4	1·90	1·90
MS716	91×73 mm. $1.25, In horse-drawn carriage, Sark. Wmk sideways				1·75	1·90

---

161 Ears of Wheat and Emblems   **162** Queen Elizabeth II

(Des A. Theobald. Litho Questa)

1985 (26 Aug). *40th Anniv of United Nations and F.A.O. (Food and Agriculture Organization).* W w 16 *(sideways).* P 14.

717	**161** 25 c. multicoloured				85	60

(Des L. Curtis. Litho Walsall)

1985 (16 Oct). *Commonwealth Heads of Government Meeting, Nassau.* T **162** *and similar vert design. Multicoloured.* W w 16. P 14½.

718	31 c. Type **162**				2·00	2·25
	w. Wmk inverted				16·00	
719	35 c. Bahamas Prime Minister's flag and Commonwealth emblem				2·00	2·75
	w. Wmk inverted				16·00	

1985 (6 Nov). *As Nos. 557/8, 560 and 566, but* W w 16. P 14½.

720	1 c. Type **131**				1·75	4·50
721	3 c. Blackbeard the Pirate, 1718				2·25	5·00
723	10 c. Ceremonial mace				3·00	1·75
726	25 c. Pineapple cultivation				6·50	6·50
720/6				Set of 4	12·00	16·00

163 "Grandma's Christmas Bouquet"
(Alton Roland Lowe)

(Des D. Miller. Litho J.W.)

1985 (12 Nov). *Christmas. Paintings by Alton Roland Lowe.* T **163** *and similar multicoloured designs.* W w 16 *(sideways on 5, 35 c.).* P 13 × 13½ (5, 35 c.) *or* 13½ × 13 (others).

736	5 c. Type **163**				30	10
737	25 c. "Junkanoo Romeo and Juliet" (vert)				1·00	75
738	31 c. "Bunce Gal" (vert)				1·25	1·50
739	35 c. "Home for Christmas"				1·50	1·75
736/9				Set of 4	3·50	3·50
MS740	110 × 68 mm. Nos. 736/9. Wmk sideways. P 14				2·25	3·00

(Des A. Theobald. Litho Harrison)

1986 (21 Apr). *60th Birthday of Queen Elizabeth II. Vert designs as* T **110** *of Ascension. Multicoloured.* W w 16. P 14½×14.

741	10 c. Princess Elizabeth aged one, 1927				15	15
742	25 c. The Coronation, 1953				30	30
	w. Wmk inverted					
743	35 c. Queen making speech at Commonwealth Banquet, Bahamas, 1985				35	40
744	40 c. In Djakova, Yugoslavia, 1972				35	45
	w. Wmk inverted				8·00	
745	$1 At Crown Agents Head Office, London 1983				80	1·40
741/5				Set of 5	1·75	2·40

164 1980 1 c. and 18 c.
Definitive Stamps

(Des G. Drummond. Litho Walsall)

1986 (19 May). *"Ameripex '86" International Stamp Exhibition, Chicago.* T **164** *and similar designs.* W w 16 *(sideways on 5 to 50 c.).* P 14.

746	5 c. multicoloured				50	40
747	25 c. multicoloured				1·25	50
748	31 c. multicoloured				1·50	60
749	50 c. multicoloured				2·00	3·00
750	$1 black, emerald and pale blue				2·25	3·75
746/50				Set of 5	6·75	7·50
MS751	80×80 mm. No. 750				3·50	3·75

Designs: *Horiz* (showing Bahamas stamps)—25 c. 1969 50th Anniversary of Bahamas Airmail Service pair; 31 c. 1976 Bicentenary of American Revolution 16 c.; 50 c. 1981 Space Exploration miniature sheet. *Vert*—$1 Statue of Liberty.
Nos. 750/1 also commemorate the Centenary of the Statue of Liberty.

1986 (17 June). *Air. As Nos. 699/700, but* W w 16 *(sideways).* P 14.

752	10 c. Type **150**				1·75	50
753	25 c. Avro Type 688 Tudor IV				2·00	1·50

(Des D. Miller. Litho Walsall)

1986 (23 July). *Royal Wedding. Square designs as T 112 of Ascension. Multicoloured. W w 16. P 14½×14.*
756 10 c. Prince Andrew and Miss Sarah Ferguson 20 20
757 $1 Prince Andrew .. .. 1·25 2·10

165 Rock Beauty (juvenile)   166 Christ Church Cathedral, Nassau, 1861

(Des Harrison Studio. Litho Questa)

1986 (5 Aug)–90. *Fishes. T 165 and similar horiz designs. Multicoloured. W w 16. P 14. A. Without imprint date at foot.*
758A 5 c. Type 165 .. .. .. 75 75
759A 10 c. Stoplight Parrotfish .. .. 80 1·00
760A 15 c. Jackknife-fish .. .. 1·50 1·50
761A 20 c. Flamefish .. .. 1·25 1·25
762A 25 c. Peppermint Basslet ("Swissguard Basslet") .. .. .. 1·50 1·50
763A 30 c. Spot-finned Butterflyfish .. 1·10 1·50
764A 35 c. Queen Triggerfish .. 1·10 1·50
765A 40 c. Four-eyed Butterflyfish .. 1·50 1·25
766A 45 c. Royal Gramma ("Fairy Basslet") .. 1·50 1·25
767A 50 c. Queen Angelfish .. .. 2·00 2·00
768A 60 c. Blue Chromis .. .. 3·50 4·00
769A $1 Spanish Hogfish .. .. 3·50 4·00
770A $2 Harlequin Bass .. .. 8·00 9·00
771A $3 Black-barred Soldierfish .. 6·00 7·00
772A $5 Cherub Angelfish ("Pygmy Angelfish") .. .. .. 6·50 8·00
773A $10 Red Hind (2.1.87) .. .. 15·00 20·00
758A/73A *Set of 16* 48·00 60·00

B. With imprint date
759B 10 c. Stoplight Parrotfish (8.90) .. 1·00 2·25
762B 25 c. Peppermint Basslet ("Swissguard Basslet") (8.90) .. 1·00 2·50
765B 40 c. Four-eyed Butterflyfish (15.8.88) .. 1·10 1·60
766B 45 c. Royal Gramma ("Fairy Basslet") (8.90) .. .. 1·60 2·75
767B 50 c. Queen Angelfish (8.90) .. 1·60 2·75
769B $1 Spanish Hogfish (15.8.88) .. 2·75 3·00
770B $2 Harlequin Bass (15.8.88) .. 13·00 9·50
771B $3 Black-barred Soldierfish (8.90) .. 5·00 12·00
772B $5 Cherub Angelfish ("Pygmy Angelfish") (8.90) .. 6·50 13·00
759B/72B *Set of 9* 30·00 45·00
Imprint dates: "1988", Nos. 765B, 769B/70B; "1990", Nos. 759B, 762B, 765B/7B, 769B, 771B/2B.
For those designs watermarked w 14 see Nos. 791/9.

(Des L. Curtis. Litho Walsall)

1986 (16 Sept). *125th Anniv of City of Nassau, Diocese and Cathedral. T 166 and similar vert design. Multicoloured. W w 16. P 14½×14.*
774 10 c. Type 166 .. .. .. 20 20
775 40 c. Christ Church Cathedral, 1986 .. 65 80
MS776 75×100 mm. Nos. 774/5 .. 2·50 4·25

167 Man and Boy looking at Crib   168 Great Isaac Lighthouse

(Des Jennifer Toombs. Litho Questa)

1986 (4 Nov). *Christmas. International Peace Year. T 167 and similar horiz designs. Multicoloured. W w 16 (sideways). P 14.*
777 10 c. Type 167 .. .. .. 35 20
778 40 c. Mary and Joseph journeying to Bethlehem 85 75
779 45 c. Children praying and Star of Bethlehem .. .. 95 1·00
780 50 c. Children exchanging gifts .. 1·00 2·00
777/80 *Set of 4* 2·75 3·50
MS781 95×90 mm. Nos. 777/80 .. 7·00 9·50

(Des A. Lowe, adapted L. Curtis. Litho Walsall)

1987 (31 Mar). *Lighthouses. T 168 and similar horiz designs. Multicoloured. W w 16 (sideways). P 14×14½.*
782 10 c. Type 168 .. .. .. 1·75 70
783 40 c. Bird Rock Lighthouse .. 3·75 1·75
784 45 c. Castle Island Lighthouse .. 3·75 1·75
785 $1 "Hole in the Wall" Lighthouse .. 5·50 9·00
782/5 *Set of 4* 13·00 12·00

MINIMUM PRICE

The minimum price quote is 10p which represents a handling charge rather than a basis for valuing common stamps. For further notes about prices see introductory pages.

169 Anne Bonney   170 Boeing 737

(Des D. and Jane Hartley. Litho Questa)

1987 (2 June). *Pirates and Privateers of the Caribbean. T 169 and similar vert designs. Multicoloured. W w 16. P 14½.*
786 10 c. Type 169 .. .. .. 1·75 85
787 40 c. Edward Teach ("Blackbeard") .. 3·75 2·75
788 45 c. Captain Edward England .. 3·75 2·75
789 50 c. Captain Woodes Rogers .. 4·25 3·75
786/9 *Set of 4* 12·00 9·00
MS790 75×95 mm. $1.25, Map of Bahamas and colonial coat of arms .. .. 6·50 3·50

1987 (25 June). *As Nos. 758/60 and 765/70, but W w 14. With imprint date. P 14.*
791 5 c. Type 165 .. .. .. 1·25 2·00
792 10 c. Stoplight Parrotfish .. 1·25 90
793 15 c. Jackknife-fish .. .. 2·00 2·50
794 40 c. Four-eyed Butterflyfish .. 2·00 2·50
795 45 c. Royal Gramma .. .. 2·25 2·50
796 50 c. Queen Angelfish .. 2·25 3·00
797 60 c. Blue Chromis .. .. 2·25 4·50
798 $1 Spanish Hogfish .. .. 2·50 4·50
799 $2 Harlequin Bass .. .. 3·00 7·00
791/9 *Set of 9* 17·00 26·00
Imprint dates: "1987", Nos. 791/9; "1988", No. 792; "1989", No. 791.

(Des A. Theobald. Litho Questa)

1987 (7 July). *Air. Aircraft. T 170 and similar horiz designs. Multicoloured. W w 16. P 14.*
800 15 c. Type 170 .. .. .. 1·50 80
801 40 c. Boeing 757-200 .. .. 2·25 1·50
802 45 c. Airbus Industrie A300B4-200 .. 2·25 1·50
803 50 c. Boeing 747-200 .. .. 2·25 2·25
800/3 *Set of 4* 7·50 5·50

171 Norway (liner) and Catamaran   172 Cattleyopsis lindenii

(Des A. Theobald. Litho Questa)

1987 (26 Aug). *Tourist Transport. T 171 and similar vert designs. Multicoloured. W w 16. P 14.*
804 40 c. Type 171 .. .. .. 1·60 1·60
    a. Horiz strip of 5. Nos. 804/8 .. 7·25
805 40 c. Liners and speedboat .. 1·60 1·60
806 40 c. Game fishing boat and cruising yacht .. 1·60 1·60
807 40 c. Game fishing boat and racing yachts .. 1·60 1·60
808 40 c. Fishing boat and schooner .. 1·60 1·60
809 40 c. Hawker Siddeley H.S.748 airliner .. 1·60 1·60
    a. Horiz strip of 5. Nos. 809/13 .. 7·25
810 40 c. Boeing 737 and Boeing 727-200 airliners .. .. .. 1·60 1·60
811 40 c. Beech 200 Super King Air aircraft and radio beacon .. .. 1·60 1·60
812 40 c. Aircraft and Nassau control tower .. 1·60 1·60
813 40 c. Helicopter and parked aircraft .. 1·60 1·60
804/13 *Set of 10* 14·50 14·50
Nos. 804/8 and 809/13 were each printed together, *se-tenant*, in horizontal strips of 5 throughout the sheets, each strip forming a composite design.

(Des A. Lowe; adapted L. Curtis. Litho Questa)

1987 (20 Oct). *Christmas. Orchids. T 172 and similar horiz designs. Multicoloured. W w 16 (sideways). P 14×14½.*
814 10 c. Type 172 .. .. .. 1·25 40
815 40 c. *Encyclia lucayana* .. .. 2·50 1·25
816 45 c. *Encyclia hodgeana* .. .. 2·50 1·25
817 50 c. *Encyclia lleidae* .. .. 2·50 1·75
814/17 *Set of 4* 8·00 5·00
MS818 120×92 mm. Nos. 814/17 .. 8·00 5·00

173 King Ferdinand and Queen Isabella of Spain   174 Whistling Ducks in Flight

(Des L. Curtis. Litho Format)

1988 (24 Feb). *500th Anniv of Discovery of America by Columbus (1992) (1st issue). T 173 and similar vert designs. Multicoloured. W w 14. P 14×14½.*
819 10 c. Type 173 .. .. .. 85 40
820 40 c. Columbus before Talavera Committee. 1·75 1·75
821 45 c. Lucayan village .. .. 1·90 1·90
822 50 c. Lucayan potters .. .. 2·00 2·50
819/22 *Set of 4* 6·00 6·00
MS823 65×50 mm. $1.50, Map of Antilles, c. 1500. Wmk sideways .. .. 6·00 3·75
See also Nos. 844/8, 870/4, 908/12, 933/7 and MS946.

(Des W. Oliver. Litho Walsall)

1988 (29 Apr). *Black-billed Whistling Duck. T 174 and similar horiz designs. Multicoloured. W w 14 (sideways). P 14×14½.*
824 5 c. Type 174 .. .. .. 2·25 1·00
825 10 c. Whistling Duck in reeds .. 2·25 1·00
826 20 c. Pair with brood .. .. 4·00 2·00
827 45 c. Pair wading .. .. 6·00 2·50
824/7 *Set of 4* 13·00 6·00

175 Grantstown Cabin, c. 1820   176 Olympic Flame, High Jumping, Hammer throwing, Basketball and Gymnastics

(Des N. Shewring. Litho B.D.T.)

1988 (9 Aug). *150th Anniv of Abolition of Slavery. T 175 and similar horiz design. Multicoloured. W w 14 (sideways). P 13½.*
828 10 c. Type 175 .. .. .. 50 30
829 40 c. Basket-making, Grantstown .. 1·25 95

(Des D. Miller. Litho Walsall)

1988 (30 Aug). *Olympic Games, Seoul. T 176 and similar horiz designs taken from painting by James Martin. Multicoloured. W w 16 (sideways). P 14.*
830 10 c. Type 176 .. .. .. 65 30
831 40 c. Athletics, archery, swimming, long jumping, weightlifting and boxing .. 80 60
832 45 c. Javelin throwing, gymnastics, hurdling and shot put 80 60
833 $1 Athletics, hurdling, gymnastics and cycling .. .. .. 2·75 3·50
830/3 *Set of 4* 4·50 4·50
MS834 113×85 mm. Nos. 830/3. W w 14 (sideways) .. .. .. 3·00 2·75

(Des O. Bell and D. Miller (40 c.), E. Nisbet and D. Miller ($1), D. Miller (others). Litho Format)

1988 (4 Oct). *300th Anniv of Lloyd's of London. Multicoloured designs as T 123 of Ascension. W w 14 (sideways on 40, 45 c.). P 14.*
835 10 c. Lloyd's List of 1740 .. .. 30 15
836 40 c. Freeport Harbour (horiz) .. 1·50 60
837 45 c. Space shuttle over Bahamas (horiz) .. 1·50 60
838 $1 Yarmouth Castle (freighter) on fire .. 2·25 1·90
835/8 *Set of 4* 5·00 3·00

177 "Oh Little Town of Bethlehem"   178 Cuban Emerald

(Des Josephine Martin. Litho Questa)

1988 (21 Nov). *Christmas. Carols. T 177 and similar vert designs. Multicoloured. W w 16. P 14½×14.*
839 10 c. Type 177 .. .. .. 45 30
840 40 c. "Little Donkey" .. .. 1·25 75
841 45 c. "Silent Night" .. .. 1·25 90
842 50 c. "Hark the Herald Angels Sing" .. 1·40 1·75
839/42 *Set of 4* 4·00 3·25
MS843 88×108 mm. Nos. 839/42. W w 14 .. 2·50 2·50

(Des A. Lowe (50 c.), L. Curtis (others). Litho Questa)

1989 (25 Jan). *500th Anniv of Discovery of America by Columbus (1992) (2nd issue). Vert designs as T 173. Multicoloured. W w 16. P 14½×14.*
844 10 c. Columbus drawing chart .. 1·25 50
845 40 c. Types of caravel .. .. 2·75 1·25
846 45 c. Early navigational instruments .. 2·75 1·25
847 50 c. Arawak artefacts .. .. 2·75 3·25
844/7 *Set of 4* 8·50 5·50
MS848 64×64 mm. $1.50, Caravel under construction (from 15th-cent *Nuremburg Chronicles*) .. .. .. 2·50 2·50

(Des N. Shewring. Litho Questa)

1989 (29 Mar). *Hummingbirds. T* **178** *and similar vert designs. Multicoloured. W w* **16**. *P* 14½ × 14.

849	10 c. Type 178		1·75	85
850	40 c. Ruby-throated Hummingbird		3·00	2·00
851	45 c. Bahama Woodstar		3·00	2·00
852	50 c. Rufous Hummingbird		3·25	3·50
849/52		*Set of 4*	10·00	7·50

179 Teaching Water Safety

180 Church of the Nativity, Bethlehem

(Des S. Noon. Litho Questa)

1989 (31 May). *125th Anniv of International Red Cross. T* **179** *and similar horiz design. Multicoloured. W w* **16** *(sideways). P* 14×14½.

853	10 c. Type 179		90	30
854	$1 Henri Dunant (founder) and Battle of Solferino		3·25	3·25

(Des A. Theobald ($2), D. Miller (others). Litho Questa)

1989 (20 July). *20th Anniv of First Manned Landing on Moon. Multicoloured designs as T* **126** *of Ascension. W w* **16** *(sideways on 40, 45 c.). P* 14×13½ (10 c., $1) *or* 14 *(others)*.

855	10 c. "Apollo 8" Communications Station, Grand Bahama		50	40
856	40 c. Crew of "Apollo 8" (30×30 mm)		1·00	70
857	45 c. "Apollo 8" emblem (30×30 mm)		1·00	70
858	$1 The Earth seen from "Apollo 8"		1·75	3·00
855/8		*Set of 4*	3·75	4·25
MS859	100×83 mm. $2 "Apollo 11" astronauts in training, Manned Spacecraft Centre, Houston. P 14×13½		3·25	3·75

(Des E. Weishoff. Litho Questa)

1989 (16 Oct). *Christmas. Churches of the Holy Land. T* **180** *and similar vert designs. Multicoloured. W w* **14**. *P* 14½×14.

860	10 c. Type 180		50	30
861	40 c. Basilica of the Annunciation, Nazareth		1·25	60
862	45 c. Tabgha Church, Galilee		1·25	60
863	$1 Church of the Holy Sepulchre, Jerusalem		2·50	3·50
860/3		*Set of 4*	5·00	4·50
MS864	92×109 mm. Nos. 860/3. Wmk sideways		4·50	6·50

181 1974 U.P.U. Centenary 13 c. Stamp and Globe

(Des J. Sayer. Litho Questa)

1989 (17 Nov). *"World Stamp Expo '89" International Stamp Exhibition, Washington. T* **181** *and similar multicoloured designs. W w* **16** *(sideways). P* 14.

865	10 c. Type 181		70	40
866	40 c. 1970 New U.P.U. Headquarters Building 3 c. and building		1·40	85
867	45 c. 1986 "Ameripex '86" $1 and Capitol, Washington		1·40	90
868	$1 1949 75th anniversary of U.P.U. 2½d. and Boeing 737 airliner		4·75	6·00
865/8		*Set of 4*	7·50	7·50
MS869	107×80 mm. $2 Map showing route of Columbus, 1492 (30×38 mm). P 14½		9·00	11·00

(Des A. Lowe (50 c.), L. Curtis (others). Litho Questa)

1990 (24 Jan). *500th Anniversary of Discovery of America by Columbus (1992) (3rd issue). Vert designs as T* **173**. *Multicoloured. W w* **14**. *P* 14½×14.

870	10 c. Launching caravel		1·50	70
871	40 c. Provisioning ship		2·50	2·00
872	45 c. Shortening sail		2·50	2·00
873	50 c. Lucayan fishermen		2·50	3·50
870/3		*Set of 4*	8·00	7·50
MS874	70×61 mm. $1.50, Departure of Columbus, 1492		5·50	7·00

182 Bahamas Flag, O.A.S. Headquarters and Centenary Logo

(Des O. Bell. Litho Questa)

1990 (14 Mar). *Centenary of Organization of American States. W w* **16** *(sideways). P* 14.

875	**182** 40 c. multicoloured		1·75	1·75

183 Supermarine Spitfire Mk I
Bahamas I

(Des A. Theobald. Litho Questa)

1990 (3 May). *"Stamp World London 90" International Stamp Exhibition, London. Presentation Fighter Aircraft. Sheet* 107×78 *mm. containing T* **183** *and similar horiz design. Multicoloured. W w* **16** *(sideways). P* 14.

MS876	$1 Type 183; $1 Hawker Hurricane Mk IIc *Bahamas V*		6·50	6·50

184 Teacher with Boy

185 Cuban Amazon preening

(Des G. Vasarhelyi. Litho Questa)

1990 (27 June). *International Literacy Year. T* **184** *and similar horiz designs. Multicoloured. W w* **16** *(sideways). P* 14.

877	10 c. Type 184		75	50
878	40 c. Three boys in class		1·75	1·25
879	50 c. Teacher and children with books		1·75	2·50
877/9		*Set of 3*	3·75	3·75

(Des D. Miller. Litho Questa)

1990 (4 Aug). *90th Birthday of Queen Elizabeth the Queen Mother. Vert designs as T* **134** (40 c.) *or* **135** ($1.50) *of Ascension. W w* **16**. *P* 14×15 (40 c.) *or* 14½ ($1.50).

880	40 c. multicoloured		1·00	50
881	$1.50, brownish black and ochre		2·50	3·25

Designs:—40 c. "Queen Elizabeth, 1938" (Sir Gerald Kelly); $1.50, Queen Elizabeth at garden party, France, 1938.

(Des N. Arlott. Litho Questa)

1990 (26 Sept). *Cuban Amazon (Bahamian Parrot). T* **185** *and similar vert designs. Multicoloured. W w* **14**. *P* 14.

882	10 c. Type 185		1·25	65
883	40 c. Pair in flight		2·25	1·25
884	45 c. Cuban Amazon's head		2·25	1·25
885	50 c. Perched on branch		2·50	3·00
882/5		*Set of 4*	7·50	5·50
MS886	73×63 mm. $1.50, Feeding on berries		7·00	8·00

186 The Annunciation

187 Green Heron

(Des Jennifer Toombs. Litho B.D.T.)

1990 (5 Nov). *Christmas. T* **186** *and similar vert designs. Multicoloured. W w* **14**. *P* 14×13½.

887	10 c. Type 186		50	30
888	40 c. The Nativity		1·00	60
889	45 c. Angel appearing to Shepherds		1·00	70
890	$1 The three Kings		2·75	4·00
887/90		*Set of 4*	4·75	5·00
MS891	94×110 mm. Nos. 887/90.		6·00	7·00

(Des N. Arlott. Litho Questa)

1991 (4 Feb–1 July). *Birds. T* **187** *and similar vert designs. Multicoloured. W w* **16** *(sideways). "1991" imprint date. P* 14.

892	5 c. Type 187		80	75
893	10 c. Turkey Vulture		90	75
894	15 c. Osprey		2·50	80
895	20 c. Clapper Rail		1·00	80
896	25 c. Royal Tern		1·50	90
897	30 c. Key West Quail Dove		1·50	90
898	40 c. Smooth-billed Ani		1·75	55
899	45 c. Burrowing Owl		2·50	80
900	50 c. Hairy Woodpecker		2·25	80
901	55 c. Mangrove Cuckoo		2·50	85
902	60 c. Bahama Mockingbird		2·00	1·75
903	70 c. Red-winged Blackbird		2·00	1·75
904	$1 Thick-billed Vireo		2·50	1·50

905	$2 Bahama Yellowthroat		5·50	5·00
906	$5 Stripe-headed Tanager		11·00	12·00
907	$10 Greater Antillean Bullfinch (1 July)		13·00	15·00
892/907		*Set of 16*	48·00	40·00

For these designs watermarked w **14** (sideways) see Nos. 975/88.

(Des A. Lowe (55 c.), L. Curtis (others). Litho Questa)

1991 (9 Apr). *500th Anniv of Discovery of America by Columbus (1992) (4th issue). Vert designs as T* **173**. *Multicoloured. W w* **16**. *P* 14½ × 14.

908	15 c. Columbus navigating by stars		1·50	75
909	40 c. Fleet in mid-Atlantic		2·25	2·00
910	55 c. Lucayan family worshipping at night		2·25	2·25
911	60 c. Map of First Voyage		2·75	4·00
908/11		*Set of 4*	8·00	8·00
MS912	56 × 61 mm. $1.50, *Pinta's* look-out sighting land		5·25	6·50

(Des D. Miller. Litho Questa)

1991 (17 June). *65th Birthday of Queen Elizabeth II and 70th Birthday of Prince Philip. Vert designs as T* **139** *of Ascension. Multicoloured. W w* **16** *(sideways). P* 14½ × 14.

913	15 c. Prince Philip		1·00	1·50
	a. Horiz pair. Nos. 913/14 separated by label		2·75	3·50
914	$1 Queen Elizabeth II		1·75	2·00

Nos. 913/14 were printed in the same sheet format as Nos. 539/40 of Ascension.

188 Radar Plot of Hurricane Hugo
189 The Annunciation

(Des A. Theobald. Litho B.D.T)

1991 (28 Aug). *International Decade for Natural Disaster Reduction. T* **188** *and similar horiz designs. Multicoloured. W w* **16** *(sideways). P* 14.

915	15 c. Type 188		1·00	40
916	40 c. Diagram of hurricane		1·50	1·10
917	55 c. Flooding caused by Hurricane David, 1979		1·75	1·75
918	60 c. U.S. Dept of Commerce weather reconnaissance Lockheed WP-3D Orion		2·50	3·50
915/18		*Set of 4*	6·00	6·00

(Des Jennifer Toombs. Litho B.D.T.)

1991 (28 Oct). *Christmas. T* **189** *and similar vert designs. Multicoloured. W w* **14**. *P* 14.

919	15 c. Type 189		40	25
920	55 c. Mary and Joseph travelling to Bethlehem		1·00	1·00
921	60 c. Angel appearing to the shepherds		1·10	1·40
922	$1 Adoration of the Kings		2·00	3·25
919/22		*Set of 4*	4·00	5·50
MS923	92 × 108 mm. Nos. 919/22		6·50	8·00

190 First Progressive Liberal Party Cabinet

(Des G. Vasarhelyi. Litho B.D.T.)

1992 (10 Jan). *25th Anniv of Majority Rule. T* **190** *and similar multicoloured designs. W w* **14** *(sideways on 15 c. and 40 c.). P* 14.

924	15 c. Type 190		60	40
925	40 c. Signing of Independence Constitution		1·40	1·10
926	55 c. Prince of Wales handing over Constitutional Instrument (*vert*)		1·50	1·50
927	60 c. First Bahamian Governor-General, Sir Milo Butler (*vert*)		1·75	3·00
924/7		*Set of 4*	4·75	5·50

(Des D. Miller. Litho Questa ($1), B.D.T. (others))

1992 (6 Feb). *40th Anniv of Queen Elizabeth II's Accession. Horiz designs as T* **143** *of Ascension. Multicoloured. W w* **14** *(sideways). P* 14.

928	15 c. Queen Elizabeth with bouquet		60	30
929	40 c. Queen Elizabeth with flags		1·10	70
930	55 c. Queen Elizabeth at display		1·10	90
931	60 c. Three portraits of Queen Elizabeth		1·25	1·50
932	$1 Queen Elizabeth II		1·50	2·50
928/32		*Set of 5*	5·00	5·50

(Des A. Lowe and L. Curtis. Litho Questa)

1992 (17 Mar). *500th Anniv. of Discovery of America by Columbus (5th issue). Vert designs as T* **173**. *Multicoloured. W w* **16**. *P* 14½×14.

933	15 c. Lucayans sighting fleet		1·25	70
934	40 c. *Santa Maria* and dolphins		2·00	1·50
935	55 c. Lucayan canoes approaching ships		2·00	2·00
936	60 c. Columbus giving thanks for landfall		2·50	3·50
933/6		*Set of 4*	7·00	7·00
MS937	61×57 mm. $1.50, Children at Columbus Monument		3·50	5·00

191 Templeton, Galbraith and Hansberger Ltd Building

192 Pole Vaulting

(Des O. Bell. Litho Questa)

1992 (22 Apr). *20th Anniv of Templeton Prize for Religion.* W w **16** (*sideways*). P 14½.
938	191	55 c. multicoloured	..	..	1·50	1·50

(Des O. Bell. Litho Questa)

1992 (2 June). *Olympic Games, Barcelona.* T **192** and similar vert designs. Multicoloured. W w **14**. P 14½.
939	15 c. Type 192	..	..	..	60	40
940	40 c. Javelin	..	..	..	1·00	90
941	55 c. Hurdling	..	..		1·10	1·25
942	60 c. Basketball	..	..		4·00	4·00
939/42			*Set of 4*		6·00	6·00
MS943	70×50 mm. $2 Sailing	..			6·50	7·50

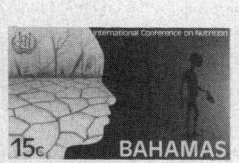

193 Arid Landscape and Starving Child

194 Mary visiting Elizabeth

(Des Jennifer Toombs. Litho Enschedé)

1992 (11 Aug). *International Conference on Nutrition.* T **193** and similar horiz design. Multicoloured. W w **14** (*sideways*). P 14½×13½.
944	15 c. Type 193	..	..		75	50
945	55 c. Seedling, cornfield and child	..		1·75	2·00

(Des L. Curtis. Litho B.D.T.)

1992 (12 Oct). *500th Anniv of Discovery of America by Columbus* (6th issue). *Sheet*, 65×65 mm, containing vert design as T **173**. Multicoloured. W w **16**. P 13½.
MS946	$2 Columbus landing in Bahamas			6·00	7·00

(Des Jennifer Toombs. Litho B.D.T.)

1992 (2 Nov). *Christmas.* T **194** and similar vert designs. Multicoloured. W w **14**. P 14×13½.
947	15 c. Type 194	..	..		40	20
948	55 c. The Nativity	..	..		1·10	1·00
949	60 c. Angel and Shepherds	..		1·25	1·50
950	70 c. Wise Men and star	..		1·40	2·00
947/50			*Set of 4*		3·75	4·75
MS951	95×110 mm. Nos. 947/50			6·00	7·00

HURRICANE RELIEF +$1

(195)

196 Flags of Bahamas and U.S.A. with Agricultural Worker

1992 (16 Nov). *Hurricane Relief. No.* MS876 *showing each stamp with* T **195**.
MS952	$1 + $1 Type 183; $1 + $1 Hawker Hurricane MkIIc *Bahamas V* ..	.. ..	9·00	12·00

(Des Lorraine Cox, adapted D. Miller. Litho Questa)

1993 (16 Mar). *50th Anniv of The Contract* (U.S.A.–Bahamas farm labour programme). T **196** and similar horiz designs, each including national flags. Multicoloured. W w **16** (*sideways*). P 14×14½.
953	15 c. Type 196	..	..		85	70
954	55 c. Onions	..	..		2·00	1·50
955	60 c. Citrus fruit	..	..		2·00	2·25
956	70 c. Apples	..	..		2·50	2·75
953/6			*Set of 4*		6·50	6·50

(Des A. Theobald. Litho Questa)

1993 (1 Apr). *75th Anniv of Royal Air Force. Horiz designs as* T **149** *of Ascension.* Multicoloured. W w **14** (*sideways*). P 14.
957	15 c. Westland Wapiti IIA	..	..	1·00	75
958	40 c. Gloster Gladiator I	..		1·75	1·00
959	55 c. De Havilland D.H.100 Vampire F.3		2·00	1·75
960	70 c. English Electric Lightning F.3		2·50	3·25
957/60			*Set of 4*		6·50	6·00
MS961	110×77 mm. 60 c. Avro Shackleton M.R.2; 60 c. Fairey Battle; 60 c. Douglas Boston III; 60 c. De Havilland D.H.9a		6·00	7·00

197 1978 Coronation Anniversary Stamps

198 Lignum vitae (national tree)

(Des D. Miller. Litho Enschedé)

1993 (2 June). *40th Anniv of Coronation.* T **197** and similar horiz designs. Multicoloured. W w **14** (*sideways*). P 13½.
962	15 c. Type 197	..	..		70	50
963	55 c. Two examples of 1953 Coronation stamp		1·75	1·75
964	60 c. 1977 Silver Jubilee 8 c. and 16 c. stamps		1·75	2·00
965	70 c. 1977 Silver Jubilee 21 c. and 40 c. stamps		2·00	2·75
962/5			*Set of 4*		5·50	6·25

(Des N. Shewring. Litho B.D.T.)

1993 (8 July). *20th Anniv of Independence.* T **198** and similar vert designs. Multicoloured. W w **14**. P 14.
966	15 c. Type 198	..	..		20	20
967	55 c. Yellow Elder (national flower)		90	90
968	60 c. Blue Marlin (national fish)		1·00	1·25
969	70 c. Greater Flamingo (national bird)		1·40	1·90
966/9			*Set of 4*		3·25	3·75

199 Cordia

200 The Annunciation

(Des D. Miller and A. Lowe. Litho B.D.T.)

1993 (8 Sept). *Environment Protection* (1st series). *Wildflowers.* T **199** and similar vert designs. Multicoloured. W w **14**. P 13½.
970	15 c. Type 199	..	..		65	50
971	55 c. Seaside Morning Glory	..		1·75	1·25
972	60 c. Poinciana	..	..		2·00	2·00
973	70 c. Spider Lily	..	..		2·50	3·00
970/3			*Set of 4*		6·00	6·00

See also Nos. 1017/22, 1035/9, 1084/8, 1121/4, 1149/54 and 1193/7.

1993 (23 Sept)–**95**. *As Nos. 893/4, 896/8, 901 and 906, but* W w **14** (*sideways*). *With imprint date.* P 14.
975	10 c. Turkey Vulture	..		1·25	90
976	15 c. Osprey (4.95)	..		80	70
978	25 c. Royal Tern	..	..		60	70
979	30 c. Key West Quail Dove		1·50	90
980	40 c. Smooth-billed Ani (31.12.93)		1·25	1·50
983	55 c. Mangrove Cuckoo	..		2·00	80
988	$5 Stripe-headed Tanager		6·50	8·50
975/88			*Set of 7*		12·50	12·50

Imprint dates: "1993", Nos. 975, 978/80, 983, 988; "1995", Nos. 976, 978, 980, 983, 988.

(Des Jennifer Toombs. Litho B.D.T.)

1993 (1 Nov). *Christmas.* T **200** and similar vert designs. Multicoloured. W w **14**. P 13½.
990	15 c. Type 200	..	..		65	40
991	55 c. Angel and shepherds	..		2·00	1·75
992	60 c. Holy family	..	..		2·00	2·00
993	70 c. Three Kings	..	..		2·50	3·00
990/3			*Set of 4*		6·50	6·50
MS994	86×106 mm. $1 Virgin Mary with Child		4·50	6·00

201 Family

202 Flags of Bahamas and Great Britain

(Des Jennifer Toombs. Litho B.D.T.)

1994 (18 Feb). *"Hong Kong '94" International Stamp Exhibition. International Year of the Family.* T **201** and similar horiz designs. Multicoloured. W w **16** (*sideways*). P 13½.
995	15 c. Type 201	..	..		60	40
996	55 c. Children doing homework		1·50	1·25
997	60 c. Grandfather and grandson fishing		1·60	1·60
998	70 c. Grandmother teaching grandchildren the Lord's Prayer		2·25	3·00
995/8			*Set of 4*		5·50	5·50

(Des D. Miller. Litho B.D.T.)

1994 (7 Mar). *Royal Visit.* T **202** and similar vert designs. Multicoloured. W w **14**. P 13½.
999	15 c. Type 202	..	..		70	45
1000	55 c. Royal Yacht *Britannia*	..		2·00	1·50
1001	60 c. Queen Elizabeth II	..		2·00	1·75
1002	70 c. Queen Elizabeth and Prince Philip		2·00	3·00
999/1002			*Set of 4*		6·00	6·00

203 Yachts

204 Logo and Bahamas 1968 Olympic Games Stamps

(Des D. Miller and A. Lowe. Litho B.D.T.)

1994 (27 Apr). *40th Anniv of National Family Island Regatta.* T **203** and similar multicoloured designs. W w **14** (*sideways*). P 13½.
1003	15 c. Type 203	..	..		60	40
1004	55 c. Dinghies racing	..		1·40	1·10
1005	60 c. Working boats	..		1·50	1·75
1006	70 c. Sailing sloop	..		2·00	3·50
1003/6			*Set of 4*		5·00	6·00
MS1007	76×54 mm. $2 Launching sloop (*vert*). Wmk upright	..	6·00	7·00

(Des D. Miller. Litho Enschedé)

1994 (31 May). *Centenary of International Olympic Committee.* T **204** and similar multicoloured designs. W w **14** (*sideways on* 55 c. *and* 70 c.). P 13½.
1008	15 c. Type 204	..	..		1·00	50
1009	55 c. 1976 Olympic Games stamps (*vert*)		2·00	1·25
1010	60 c. 1984 Olympic Games stamps		2·00	2·25
1011	70 c. 1992 Olympic Games stamps (*vert*)		2·25	3·00
1008/11			*Set of 4*		6·50	6·00

205 Star of Order

206 Calpodes ethlius and Canna

(Des D. Miller. Litho Enschedé)

1994 (5 July). *First Recipients of Order of the Caribbean Community. Sheet* 90×69 mm. W w **14**. P 13×14.
MS1012	205 $2 multicoloured	..	..	4·00	5·00

(Des R. Watton. Litho Walsall)

1994 (16 Aug). *Butterflies and Flowers.* T **206** and similar vert designs. Multicoloured. W w **14**. P 14.
1013	15 c. Type 206	..	..		1·10	55
1014	55 c. *Phoebis sennae* and Cassia		2·00	1·50
1015	60 c. *Anartia jatrophae* and Passion Flower	2·25	2·25
1016	70 c. *Battus devilliersi* and Calico Flower	2·25	2·75
1013/16			*Set of 4*		7·00	6·25

207 Spot-finned Hogfish and Spanish Hogfish

208 Angel

(Des A. Robinson. Litho Enschedé)

1994 (13 Sept). *Environment Protection* (2nd series). *Marine Life.* T **207** and similar vert designs. Multicoloured. W w **14**. P 13×14½.
1017	40 c. Type 207	..	..		1·00	1·25
	a. Horiz strip of 5. Nos. 1017/21			4·50	
1018	40 c. Tomate and Long-spined Squirrelfish		1·00	1·25
1019	40 c. French Angelfish	..		1·00	1·25
1020	40 c. Queen Angelfish	..		1·00	1·25
1021	40 c. Rock Beauty	..		1·00	1·25
1017/21			*Set of 5*		4·50	5·50
MS1022	57×55 mm. $2 Rock Beauty, Queen Angelfish and windsurfer		4·50	5·50

Nos. 1017/21 were printed together, *se-tenant*, in horizontal strips of 5 throughout the sheet with the backgrounds forming a composite design.

(Des Jennifer Toombs. Litho B.D.T.)

1994 (31 Oct). *Christmas. T **208** and similar multicoloured designs. W w **16** (sideways). P 14.*

1023	15 c. Type 208	30	30
1024	55 c. Holy Family	90	1·10
1025	60 c. Shepherds	1·10	1·40
1026	70 c. Wise Men	1·25	2·00
1023/6	*Set of 4*	3·25	4·25
MS1027	73×85 mm. $2 Jesus in manger. Wmk upright	3·25	4·50

209 Lion and Emblem   210 Kirtland's Warbler on Nest

(Des D. Miller. Litho Enschedé)

1995 (8 Feb). *20th Anniv of the College of the Bahamas. T **209** and similar vert design. Multicoloured. W w **14**. P 14×13½.*

1028	15 c. Type 209	30	30
1029	70 c. Queen Elizabeth II and College building	1·25	1·75

(Des R. Watton. Litho Cartor (Nos. 1030/3) or Questa (No. MS1034))

1995 (8 May). *50th Anniv of End of Second World War. Multicoloured designs as T **161** of Ascension. W w **14** (sideways). P 13½.*

1030	15 c. Bahamian infantry drilling	75	50
1031	55 c. Consolidated PBY-5A Catalina flying boat	2·00	1·25
1032	60 c. Bahamian women in naval operations room	2·00	2·00
1033	70 c. Consolidated B-24 Liberator bomber	2·50	3·00
1030/3	*Set of 4*	6·50	6·00
MS1034	75×85 mm. $2 Reverse of 1939–45 War Medal (vert). Wmk upright. P 14	3·00	4·00

(Des N. Arlott. Litho Cartor)

1995 (7 June). *Environment Protection (3rd series). Endangered Species. Kirtland's Warbler. T **210** and similar vert designs. Multicoloured. W w **14**. P 13½.*

1035	15 c. Type 210	55	60
	w. Wmk inverted	55	60
	wa. Strip of 4. Nos. 1035/8	2·00	
1036	15 c. Singing on branch	55	60
	w. Wmk inverted	55	60
1037	25 c. Feeding chicks	55	60
	w. Wmk inverted	55	60
1038	25 c. Catching insects	55	60
	w. Wmk inverted	55	60
1035/8	*Set of 4*	2·00	2·25
MS1039	73×67 mm. $2 On branch. Wmk sideways. P 13	6·50	7·50

Nos. 1035/8 were issued in sheets of 50 of each design and Nos. 1035w/8w in sheets of 16 (4×4) containing horizontal and vertical *se-tenant* strips.

No. MS1039 does not show the W.W.F. Panda emblem.

211 Eleuthera Cliffs

(Des D. Miller. Litho Questa)

1995 (18 July). *Tourism. T **211** and similar horiz designs. Multicoloured. W w **16** (sideways). P 14½.*

1040	15 c. Type 211	65	50
1041	55 c. Clarence Town, Long Island	1·60	1·25
1042	60 c. Albert Lowe Museum	1·75	1·90
1043	70 c. Yachts	2·00	2·50
1040/3	*Set of 4*	5·50	5·50

212 Pigs and Chick

(Des Jennifer Toombs. Litho Cartor)

1995 (5 Sept). *50th Anniv of Food and Agriculture Organization. T **212** and similar horiz designs. Multicoloured. W w **14** (sideways). P 13½×13.*

1044	15 c. Type 212	60	45
1045	55 c. Seedling and hand holding seed	1·40	1·10
1046	60 c. Family with fruit and vegetables	1·60	1·60
1047	70 c. Fishes and crustaceans	2·00	2·50
1044/7	*Set of 4*	5·00	5·00

213 Sikorsky S-55 Helicopter, Sinai, 1957

(Des A. Theobald. Litho B.D.T.)

1995 (24 Oct). *50th Anniv of United Nations. T **213** and similar horiz designs. Multicoloured. W w **16** (sideways). P 14.*

1048	15 c. Type 213	70	50
1049	55 c. Ferret armoured car, Sinai, 1957	1·25	1·25
1050	60 c. Fokker F.27 Friendship (airliner), Cambodia, 1991–93	1·50	1·75
1051	70 c. Lockheed C-130 Hercules (transport)	1·60	2·25
1048/51	*Set of 4*	4·50	5·25

214 St. Agnes Anglican Church

(Des R. Watton. Litho B.D.T.)

1995 (17 Nov). *Christmas. Churches. T **214** and similar horiz designs. Multicoloured. W w **16** (sideways). P 14.*

1052	15 c. Type 214	30	25
1053	55 c. Church of God, East Street	90	90
1054	60 c. Sacred Heart Roman Catholic Church	95	1·25
1055	70 c. Salem Union Baptist Church	1·10	1·75
1052/5	*Set of 4*	3·00	3·75

215 Microscopic View of AIDS Virus

(Des N. Shewring. Litho B.D.T.)

1995 (1 Dec). *World AIDS Day. T **215** and similar horiz design. Multicoloured. W w **14** (sideways). P 14.*

1056	25 c. Type 215	60	50
1057	70 c. Research into AIDS	1·00	1·50

216 Sunrise Tellin

(Des D. Miller. Litho Questa)

1996 (2 Jan–1 July). *Sea Shells. T **216** and similar horiz designs. Multicoloured. "1996" imprint date. W w **14** (sideways). P 14.*

1058	5 c. Type 216	25	50
1059	10 c. Queen Conch	35	50
1060	15 c. Angular Triton	55	40
1061	20 c. True Tulip	70	40
1062	25 c. Reticulated Cowrie-helmet	70	45
1063	30 c. Sand Dollar	80	55
1064	40 c. Lace Short-frond Murex	1·00	60
1065	45 c. Inflated Sea Biscuit	1·00	60
1066	50 c. West Indian Top Shell	1·10	70
1067	55 c. Spiny Oyster	1·25	75
1068	60 c. King Helmet	1·50	80
1069	70 c. Lion's Paw	1·60	1·00
1070	$1 Crown Cone	2·25	1·75
1071	$2 Atlantic Partridge Tun	3·50	4·00
1072	$5 Wide-mouthed Purpura	8·00	8·50
1073	$10 Atlantic Trumpet Triton (1 July)	14·00	17·00
1058/73	*Set of 16*	35·00	35·00

For 70 c. in miniature sheet with "1997" imprint date see No. MS1097 and for the $1 with inverted watermark and "1997" imprint date No. MS1096.

For these designs with watermark w **14** (upright) and "1997" imprint date see Nos. 1098/1113.

---

217 East Goodwin Lightship with Marconi Apparatus on Mast   218 Swimming

(Des N. Shewring. Litho B.D.T.)

1996 (2 Apr). *Centenary of Radio. T **217** and similar horiz designs. W w **14** (sideways). P 13½×14.*

1074	15 c. Type 217	75	55
1075	55 c. Newspaper headline concerning Dr. Crippen	1·60	1·25
1076	60 c. *Philadelphia* (liner) and first readable transatlantic message	1·75	2·00
1077	70 c. Guglielmo Marconi and *Elettra* (yacht)	2·00	2·50
1074/7	*Set of 4*	5·50	5·75
MS1078	80×47 mm. $2 *Titanic* and *Carpathia* (liners)	4·25	5·00

(Des S. Noon. Litho B.D.T.)

1996 (25 June). *Centenary of Modern Olympic Games. T **218** and similar vert designs. Multicoloured. W w **16**. P 14×13½.*

1079	15 c. Type 218	40	35
1080	55 c. Running	90	90
1081	60 c. Basketball	1·75	1·75
1082	70 c. Long jumping	1·40	2·25
1079/82	*Set of 4*	4·00	4·75
MS1083	73×68 mm. $2 Javelin throwing	3·00	4·00

219 Green Anole   220 The Annunciation

(Des Doreen McGuiness. Litho Questa)

1996 (3 Sept). *Environment Protection (4th series). Reptiles. T **219** and similar vert designs. Multicoloured. W w **16**. P 14.*

1084	15 c. Type 219	55	50
1085	55 c. Little Bahama Bank Boa	1·10	1·00
1086	60 c. Inagua Freshwater Turtle	1·50	1·75
1087	70 c. Acklins Rock Iguana	1·75	2·75
1084/7	*Set of 4*	4·50	5·50
MS1088	85×105 mm. Nos. 1084/7	4·50	5·50

(Des Jennifer Toombs. Litho B.D.T.)

1996 (4 Nov). *Christmas. T **220** and similar vert designs. Multicoloured. W w **14**. P 14.*

1089	15 c. Type 220	50	30
1090	55 c. Joseph and Mary travelling to Bethlehem	1·25	85
1091	60 c. Shepherds and Angel	1·40	1·50
1092	70 c. Adoration of the Magi	1·50	2·25
1089/92	*Set of 4*	4·25	4·50
MS1093	70×87 mm. $2 Presentation in the Temple	3·00	3·75

221 Department of Archives Building   222 Underwater Scene

(Des N. Shewring. Litho Questa)

1996 (9 Dec). *25th Anniv of Archives Department. T **221** and similar horiz design showing Archives Building. W w **16**. P 14½×14.*

1094	221 55 c. multicoloured	1·25	1·00
MS1095	83×54 mm. $2 multicoloured. Wmk sideways. P 14	3·75	4·50

(Des D. Miller. Litho Questa)

1997 (3 Feb). *"HONG KONG '97" International Stamp Exhibition. Sheet 130×90 mm, containing design as No. 1070, but with "1997" imprint date. Multicoloured. W w **14** (inverted).*

MS1096	$1 Crown Cone	1·50	2·00

(Des D. Miller. Litho Walsall)

1997 (20 June). *Return of Hong Kong to China. Sheet 130×90 mm containing design as No. 1069, but with "1997" imprint date.*
MS1097 70 c. Lion's Paw .. .. .. 2·00 2·50

1997 (1 July)–99. *As Nos. 1058/73, but W w 14 (upright). With imprint date. P 14.*
1098 5 c. Type **216** (22.9.97) 10 10
1099 10 c. Queen Conch (22.9.97) .. 10 10
1100 15 c. Angular Triton (22.9.97) .. 20 25
1101 20 c. True Tulip (22.9.97) .. 25 30
1102 25 c. Reticulated Cowrie-helmet (22.9.97) 30 35
1103 30 c. Sand Dollar (22.9.97) .. 35 40
1103a 35 c. As 30 c. (29.7.99) .. 40 45
1104 40 c. Lace Short-frond Murex (22.9.97) .. 50 55
1105 45 c. Inflated Sea Biscuit (22.9.97) 55 60
1106 50 c. West Indian Top Shell (22.9.97) 60 65
1107 55 c. Spiny Oyster (22.9.97) .. 65 70
1108 60 c. King Helmet (22.9.97) .. 70 75
1108a 65 c. As 45 c. (29.7.99) .. 80 85
1109 70 c. Lion's Paw (22.9.97) .. 85 90
1109a 80 c. As 55 c. (29.7.99) .. 1·00 1·10
1110 $1 Crown Cone .. .. 1·25 1·40
1111 $2 Atlantic Partridge Tun .. 2·40 2·50
1112 $5 Wide-mouthed Purpura .. 6·00 6·25
1113 $10 Atlantic Trumpet Triton .. 12·00 12·50
1098/113 .. .. *Set of 19* 28·00 29·00
Imprint dates: "1997", Nos. 1098/103, 1104/8, 1110/13; "1999", Nos. 1098/102, 1103a/4, 1106, 1108/a, 1109a/13.

(Des N. Shewring (No. MS1120), D. Miller (others). Litho Questa (No. MS1120) or Cartor (others))

1997 (9 July). *Golden Wedding of Queen Elizabeth and Prince Philip. Multicoloured designs as T **173** of Ascension. W w 14. P 13.*
1114 50 c. Queen Elizabeth II in Bonn, 1992 1·00 1·10
    a. Horiz pair. Nos. 1114/15 .. 2·00 2·10
1115 50 c. Prince Philip and Prince Charles at Trooping the Colour .. 1·00 1·10
1116 60 c. Prince Philip .. .. 1·10 1·25
    a. Horiz pair. Nos. 1116/17 .. 2·10 2·50
1117 60 c. Queen at Trooping the Colour 1·10 1·25
1118 70 c. Queen Elizabeth and Prince Philip at polo, 1970 .. .. 1·40 1·50
    a. Horiz pair. Nos. 1118/19 .. 2·75 3·00
1119 70 c. Prince Charles playing polo 1·40 1·50
1114/19 .. .. *Set of 6* 6·25 7·00
MS1120 110×70 mm. $2 Queen Elizabeth and Prince Philip in landau (*horiz*). W w 14 (sideways). P 14×14¹⁄₂ .. .. 3·50 4·00
Nos. 1114/15, 1116/17 and 1118/19 were each printed together, *se-tenant*, in horizontal pairs throughout the sheets with the backgrounds forming composite designs.

(Des D. Miller. Litho Questa)

1997 (3 Sept). *Environment Protection (5th series). International Year of the Reefs. T **222** and similar horiz designs showing different children's paintings of underwater scenes. W w 16 (sideways). P 14¹⁄₂.*
1121 15 c. multicoloured 45 30
1122 55 c. multicoloured .. .. 1·10 1·00
1123 60 c. multicoloured .. .. 1·25 1·40
1124 70 c. multicoloured .. .. 1·50 2·00
1121/4 .. .. .. *Set of 4* 3·75 4·25

223 Angel   224 Newsletters

(Des Jennifer Toombs. Litho Cartor)

1997 (4 Nov). *Christmas. T **223** and similar vert designs. Multicoloured. W w 14 (inverted). P 13×13¹⁄₂.*
1125 15 c. Type **223** 40 30
1126 55 c. Mary and Baby Jesus .. 90 70
1127 60 c. Shepherd .. .. 1·00 90
1128 70 c. King .. .. 1·10 1·50
1125/8 .. .. *Set of 4* 3·00 3·00
MS1129 74×94 mm. $2 Baby Jesus wrapped in swaddling-bands. Wmk upright .. 3·50 4·00

(Des D. Miller. Litho Questa)

1998 (31 Mar). *Diana, Princess of Wales Commemoration. Vert designs as T **177** of Ascension. W w 16 (No. 1130). P 14¹⁄₂×14.*
1130 15 c. Wearing grey jacket, 1988 .. 40 40
MS1131 145×70 mm. 15 c. As No. 1130; 55 c. Wearing striped jacket, 1983; 60 c. In evening dress, 1983; 70 c. Meeting crowds, 1993. W w 14 (sideways) .. .. .. 2·50 2·75

(Des A. Theobald. Litho Enschedé)

1998 (1 Apr). *80th Anniv of the Royal Air Force. Horiz designs as T **178** of Ascension. Multicoloured. W w 14 (sideways*). P 13¹⁄₂×14.*
1132 15 c. Handley Page Hyderabad .. 55 40
1133 55 c. Hawker Demon .. .. 1·00 85
1134 60 c. Gloster Meteor F.8 .. 1·10 1·40
1135 70 c. Lockheed Neptune MR.1 .. 1·40 1·75
1132/5 .. .. *Set of 5* 3·50 3·50
MS1136 110×76 mm. 50 c. Sopwith Camel; 50 c. Short 184 (seaplane); 50 c. Supermarine Spitfire PR.19; 50 c. North American Mitchell III 3·00 3·50

---

*The normal sideways watermark shows Crown to left of CA on Nos. 1132/5 and Crown to right of CA on No. MS1136, both as seen from the back of the stamp.

(Des D. Miller. Litho Questa)

1998 (15 Apr). *50th Anniv of Organisation of American States. T **224** and similar horiz design. Multicoloured. W w 14 (sideways). P 13¹⁄₂×14.*
1137 15 c. Type **224** 30 30
1138 55 c. Headquarters building and flags, Washington 70 80

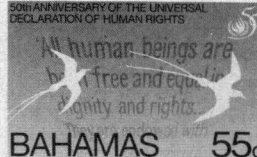

225 Start of Declaration and Birds

(Des D. Miller. Litho Questa)

1998 (15 Apr). *50th Anniv of Universal Declaration of Human Rights. W w 14 (sideways). P 13¹⁄₂×14.*
1139 **225** 55 c. bright blue and black .. 80 80

226 University Arms and Graduates

(Des D. Miller. Litho Questa)

1998 (15 Apr). *50th Anniv of University of the West Indies. W w 14 (sideways). P 13¹⁄₂×14.*
1140 **226** 55 c. multicoloured .. 80 80

227 Supreme Court Building

(Des D. Miller. Litho Questa)

1998 (9 July). *25th Anniv of Independence. T **227** and similar horiz designs. Multicoloured. W w 14 (sideways). P 13¹⁄₂.*
1141 15 c. Type **227** 40 30
1142 55 c. Nassau Library 90 80
1143 60 c. Government House .. 1·00 1·00
1144 70 c. Gregory Arch .. .. 1·10 1·40
1141/4 .. .. *Set of 4* 3·00 3·00
MS1145 70×55 mm. $2 Island Regatta, George Town .. .. .. 3·00 3·50

228 Disney Magic (cruise liner) at Night

(Des N. Shewring. Litho Questa)

1998 (1 Aug). *Disney Cruise Line's Castaway Cay Holiday Development. T **228** and similar horiz design. Multicoloured. W w 14 (sideways). P 14.*
1146 55 c. Type **228** .. .. 90 1·00
    a. Pair. Nos. 1146/7 .. .. 1·75 2·00
    b. Booklet pane. Nos. 1146/7, each ×5 with margins all round .. 9·00
1147 55 c. Disney Magic by day .. 90 1·00
Nos. 1146/7 were printed together, *se-tenant*, in horizontal and vertical pairs throughout the sheet.

229 Ryndam (cruise liner)

(Des N. Shewring. Litho Cartor)

1998 (19 Aug). *Holland America Line's Half Moon Cay Holiday Development. W w 14 (sideways). P 13¹⁄₂×13.*
1148 **229** 55 c. multicoloured .. 1·00 80

---

230 Barrel Pink Rose   231 The Annunciation

(Des D. Miller. Litho B.D.T.)

1998 (8 Sept). *Environment Protection (6th series). Roses. T **230** and similar horiz designs. Multicoloured. W w 14 (sideways). P 14.*
1149 55 c. Type **230** 65 70
    a. Booklet pane. Nos. 1149/53, each × 2 with margins all round .. 6·50
1150 55 c. Yellow Cream 65 70
1151 55 c. Seven Sisters 65 70
1152 55 c. Big Red 65 70
1153 55 c. Island Beauty 65 70
1149/53 .. .. *Set of 5* 3·25 3·50
MS1154 100×70 mm. No. 1153 .. 65 70

(Des Jennifer Toombs. Litho Questa)

1998 (10 Nov). *Christmas. T **231** and similar horiz designs. Multicoloured. W w 16 (sideways). P 14¹⁄₂.*
1155 15 c. Type **231** 30 25
1156 55 c. Shepherds 75 70
1157 60 c. Three Kings 85 85
1158 70 c. The Flight into Egypt .. 1·10 1·25
1155/8 .. .. *Set of 4* 2·75 2·75
MS1159 87×67 mm. $2 The Nativity .. 2·40 2·75

232 Killer Whale and other Marine Life

(Des B. Dare. Litho Questa)

1998 (24 Nov). *International Year of the Ocean. T **232** and similar horiz design. Multicoloured. W w 14 (sideways). P 13¹⁄₂×14.*
1160 15 c. Type **232** 50 40
1161 55 c. Tropical fish 75 80

233 Timothy Gibson (composer)   234 Head of Greater Flamingo and Chick

(Des D. Miller. Litho Cartor)

1998 (10 Dec). *25th Anniv of "March on Bahamaland" (national anthem). W w 14 (sideways). P 13¹⁄₂.*
1162 **233** 60 c. multicoloured 85 85

(Des A. Robinson. Litho Questa)

1999 (9 Feb). *40th Anniv of National Trust (1st issue). Inagua National Park. T **234** and similar vert designs. Multicoloured. W w 16. P 14.*
1163 55 c. Type **234** 85 90
    a. Horiz strip of 5. Nos. 1163/7 .. 3·75
1164 55 c. Pair with two chicks .. 85 90
1165 55 c. Greater Flamingos asleep or stretching wings .. 85 90
1166 55 c. Greater Flamingos feeding .. 85 90
1167 55 c. Greater Flamingos in flight .. 85 90
1163/7 .. .. *Set of 5* 3·75 4·00
Nos. 1163/7 were printed together, *se-tenant*, in horizontal strips of 5 throughout the sheet with the backgrounds forming a composite design.
See also Nos. 1173/7, 1198/1202 and 1207/11.

235 Arawak Indian Canoe   236 Society Headquarters Building

BAHAMAS — 1999

(Des D. Miller. Litho Questa)

1999 (9 Mar). *"Australia '99" World Stamp Exhibition, Melbourne. Maritime History. T 235 and similar horiz designs. Multicoloured. W w 14 (sideways). P 14½.*
1168	15 c. Type **235**	30	25
1169	55 c. *Santa Maria* (Columbus), 1492	90	80
1170	60 c. *Queen Anne's Revenge* (Blackbeard), 1716	1·00	1·00
1171	70 c. *The Banshee* (Confederate paddle-steamer) running blockade	1·25	1·40
1168/71	*Set of 4*	3·00	3·00
MS1172	110×66 mm. $2 Firing on American ships, 1776	3·00	3·25

(Des A. Robinson. Litho Questa)

1999 (6 Apr). *40th Anniv of National Trust (2nd issue). Exuma Cays Land and Sea Park. Vert designs as T 234. Multicoloured. W w 16. P 14.*
1173	55 c. Dolphin	85	90
	a. Horiz strip of 5. Nos. 1173/7	3·75	
1174	55 c. Angelfish and Parrotfish	85	90
1175	55 c. Queen Triggerfish	85	90
1176	55 c. Turtle	85	90
1177	55 c. Lobster	85	90
1173/7	*Set of 5*	3·75	4·00

Nos. 1173/7 were printed together, *se-tenant*, in horizontal strips of 5 throughout the sheet, with the backgrounds forming a composite design.

(Des N. Shewring. Litho Cartor)

1999 (9 June). *40th Anniv of Bahamas Historical Society. W w 14 (sideways). P 13.*
1178	**236** $1 multicoloured	1·25	1·40

(Des J. Batchelor (65 c.), N. Shewring (others). Litho Walsall)

1999 (20 July). *30th Anniv of First Manned Landing on Moon. Multicoloured designs as T 186 of Ascension. W w 16. P 14×13½.*
1179	15 c. Constructing ascent module	30	25
1180	65 c. Diagram of command and service module	1·00	90
1181	70 c. Lunar module descending	1·00	1·00
1182	80 c. Lunar module preparing to dock with service module	1·10	1·25
1179/82	*Set of 4*	3·00	3·00
MS1183	90×80 mm. $2 Earth as seen from Moon (*circular, 40 mm diam.*). Wmk sideways. P 14	3·00	3·25

(Des D. Miller. Litho Cartor)

1999 (24 Aug). *"Queen Elizabeth the Queen Mother's Century". Horiz designs as T 187 of Ascension. Multicoloured. W w 14 (sideways). P 13½.*
1184	15 c. Visiting Herts Hospital, 1940	30	25
1185	65 c. With Princess Elizabeth, Hyde Park, 1944	1·10	90
1186	70 c. With Prince Andrew, 1997	1·10	1·10
1187	80 c. With Irish Guards' mascot, 1997	1·25	1·40
1184/7	*Set of 4*	3·25	3·25
MS1188	145×70 mm. $2 Lady Elizabeth Bowes-Lyon with her brother David, 1904, and England World Cup team celebrating, 1966. W w 16 (sideways)	3·00	3·25

237 *Delaware* (American mail ship), 1880

(Des J. Batchelor. Litho Cartor)

1999 (7 Sept). *125th Anniv of Universal Postal Union. Ships. T 237 and similar horiz designs. Multicoloured. W w 16 (sideways). P 13½.*
1189	15 c. Type **237**	30	25
1190	65 c. *Atlantis* (liner), 1923	1·10	90
1191	70 c. *Queen of Bermuda* (liner), 1937	1·10	1·10
1192	80 c. *U.S.S. Saufley* (destroyer), 1943	1·25	1·40
1189/92	*Set of 4*	3·25	3·25

238 "Turtle Pond" (Green Turtle) **239** Man on Elephant Float

(Des D. Miller. Litho B.D.T.)

1999 (21 Sept). *Environment Protection (7th series). Marine Life Paintings by Ricardo Knowles. T 238 and similar horiz designs. Multicoloured. W w 14 (sideways). P 13½×14.*
1193	15 c. Type **238**	20	25
1194	65 c. "Turtle Cliff" (Loggerhead Turtle)	80	85
1195	70 c. "Barracuda"	85	90
1196	80 c. "Coral Reef"	1·00	1·25
1193/6	*Set of 4*	2·75	3·00
MS1197	90×75 mm. $2 "Atlantic Bottle-nosed Dolphins"	2·40	3·50

The 65 c. is inscribed "GREEN TURTLES" in error.

(Des A. Robinson. Litho Walsall)

1999 (8 Oct). *40th Anniv of National Trust (3rd issue). Birds. Vert designs as T 234. Multicoloured. W w 16. P 14.*
1198	65 c. Gull	80	85
	a. Horiz strip of 5. Nos. 1198/1202	4·00	
1199	65 c. Heron	80	85
1200	65 c. Hummingbird	80	85
1201	65 c. Duck	80	85
1202	65 c. Parrot	80	85
1198/1202	*Set of 5*	4·00	4·50

Nos. 1198/1202 were printed together, *se-tenant*, in horizontal strips of 5 throughout the sheet with the backgrounds forming a composite design.

(Des C. Fernander, adapted D. Miller. Litho Walsall)

1999 (25 Oct). *Christmas. Junkanoo Festival. T 239 and similar vert designs. Multicoloured. W w 14. P 14½×14.*
1203	15 c. Type **239**	20	25
1204	65 c. Man in winged costume	70	80
1205	70 c. Man in feathered mask	85	90
1206	80 c. Man blowing conch shell	1·00	1·25
1203/6	*Set of 4*	2·75	3·00

(Des A. Robinson. Litho Walsall)

1999 (30 Nov). *40th Anniv of National Trust (4th issue). Flora and Fauna. Vert designs as T 234. Multicoloured. W w 16. P 14.*
1207	65 c. Foxglove	80	85
	a. Horiz strip of 5. Nos. 1207/11	4·00	
1208	65 c. Vole	80	85
1209	65 c. Hummingbird	80	85
1210	65 c. Lizard	80	85
1211	65 c. Red Hibiscus	80	85
1207/11	*Set of 5*	4·00	4·50

Nos. 1207/11 were printed together, *se-tenant*, in horizontal strips of 5 throughout the sheet with the backgrounds forming a composite design.

240 New Plymouth

(Des D. Miller. Litho Cartor)

2000 (25 Jan). *Historic Fishing Villages. T 240 and similar horiz designs. Multicoloured. W w 14 (sideways). P 13½×13.*
1212	15 c. Type **240**	20	25
1213	65 c. Cherokee Sound	80	85
1214	70 c. Hope Town	85	90
1215	80 c. Spanish Wells	1·00	1·10
1212/15	*Set of 4*	2·75	3·00

STAMP BOOKLETS

1938. *Black on pink cover with map and "BAHAMAS ISLES OF JUNE" on reverse. Stapled.*
SB1	2s. booklet containing twelve 1d. (No. 150) in blocks of 6 and eight 1½d. (No. 151) in folded block of 8	£5000

1961 (15 Aug). *Brown-purple cover (3s.) or green cover (6s.). Stitched.*
SB2	3s. booklet containing eight each of 1d. 1½d. and 2d. (Nos. 202/4) in blocks of 4	25·00
SB3	6s. booklet containing four each of 4d., 6d. and 8d. (Nos. 206, 208/9) in blocks of 4	32·00

1965 (23 Mar). *Pink cover (3s.) or green cover (6s.). Stapled.*
SB4	3s. booklet containing eight each of 1d., 1½d. and 2d. (Nos. 248/50) in blocks of 4	19·00
SB5	6s. booklet containing four each of 4d., 6d. and 8d. (Nos. 252/4) in blocks of 4	19·00

B 1

1998 (1 Aug). *Disney Cruise Line's Castaway Cay Holiday Development. Folded card cover as Type B 1. Pane attached by selvedge.*
SB6	$5.50, booklet containing pane No. 1146b	9·00

B 2
(*Illustration reduced. Actual size 137×70 mm*)

1998 (8 Sept). *Environment Protection (6th issue). Roses. Folded card cover as Type B 2. Pane attached by selvedge.*
SB7	$5.50, booklet containing pane No. 1149a	6·50

SPECIAL DELIVERY STAMPS

SPECIAL DELIVERY

(S 1)

1916 (1 May). *No. 59 optd with Type S 1 by The Nassau Guardian.*
S1	**6** 5d. black and orange	5·00	30·00
	a. Opt double	£800	£1200
	b. Opt double, one inverted	£950	£1300
	c. Opt inverted	£1300	£1400
	d. Pair, one without opt	£20000	£30000
	x. Wmk reversed		

There were three printings from similar settings of 30, and each sheet had to pass through the press twice. The first printing of 600 was on sale from 1 May 1916 in Canada at Ottawa, Toronto, Westmount (Montreal) and Winnipeg; and under an agreement with the Canadian P.O. were used in combination with Canadian stamps and were cancelled in Canada. The second printing (number unknown) was made about the beginning of December 1916, and the third of 6000, issued probably on 1 March 1917, were on sale only in the Bahamas. These printings caused the revocation, in mid-December 1916, of the agreement by Canada, which no longer accepted the stamps as payment of the special delivery fee and left them to be cancelled in the Bahamas.

It is not possible to identify the printings of the normal stamps without plating both the basic stamp and the overprint, though, in general, the word "SPECIAL" is further to the right in relation to "DELIVERY" in the third printing than in the first or second. Our prices for No. S1 are for the third printing and any stamps which can be positively identified as being from the first or second printings would be worth about eight times as much unused, and any on cover are very rare. All the errors appear to be from the third printing.

SPECIAL DELIVERY	SPECIAL DELIVERY
(S 2)	(S 3)

1917 (2 July). *As No. 59, but Wmk Mult Crown CA. Optd with Type S 2 by D.L.R.*
S2	**6** 5d. black and orange (Optd S. £65)	45	5·50

1918. *No. 78 optd with Type S 3 by D.L.R.*
S3	**6** 5d. black and mauve (R.) (Optd S. £65)	30	2·00

Nos. S2/3 were only on sale in the Bahamas.

Bahrain

An independent shaikhdom, with an Indian postal administration from 1884. A British postal administration operated from 1 April 1948 to 31 December 1965.

The first, and for 62 years the only, post office in Bahrain opened at the capital, Manama, on 1 August 1884 as a sub-office of the Indian Post Office at Bushire (Iran), both being part of the Bombay Postal Circle.

Unoverprinted postage stamps of India were supplied to the new office, continuing on sale there until 1933. Examples of the lower values can sometimes be found postmarked at Bahrain, but such cancellations on values over 4 a. are decidedly scarce. The occasional Official stamp can also be discovered, possibly used by the office of the Indian Political Agent.

The initial cancellation supplied showed a "B" against a circular background of horizontal lines, this being used in conjunction with a single ring date-stamp without any indication of the year of use.

1884 Cancellation and Date-stamp

This was followed by a squared-circle type, first seen in 1886, which was used into the early years of the 20th century. Its replacement was a single ring date-stamp, succeeded in turn by the first of a considerable number of Indian-style double-circle postmarks, all inscribed "BAHRAIN".

1886 Squared-circle

PRICES FOR STAMPS ON COVER TO 1945	
Nos. 1/14	from × 5
Nos. 15/19	from × 6
Nos. 20/37	from × 2
Nos. 38/50	from × 6

(Currency. 12 pies = 1 anna;
16 annas = 1 rupee)

BAHRAIN (1)   **BAHRAIN** (2)

Stamps of India overprinted with T 1 or T 2 (rupee values)

1933 (10 Aug–Nov). *King George V. Wmk Mult Star, T 69.*

1	55	3 p. slate (Nov)			3·25	45
2	56	½ a. green			7·50	3·25
		w. Wmk inverted			—	20·00
3	80	9 p. deep green			3·75	1·00
4	57	1 a. chocolate			7·00	2·50
		w. Wmk inverted				
5	82	1 a. 3 p. mauve			4·50	90
		w. Wmk inverted			4·50	90
6	70	2 a. vermilion			10·00	8·50
		w. Wmk inverted			10·00	8·50
7	62	3 a. blue			19·00	40·00
8	83	3 a. 6 p. ultramarine			3·75	30
		w. Wmk inverted			5·50	30
9	71	4 a. sage-green			18·00	40·00
10	65	8 a. reddish purple			6·00	30
		w. Wmk inverted				
11	66	12 a. claret			7·50	1·00
		w. Wmk inverted			—	40·00
12	67	1 r. chocolate and green			16·00	7·50
13		2 r. carmine and orange			32·00	38·00
14		5 r. ultramarine and purple			90·00	£120
		w. Wmk inverted			90·00	£120
1/14				*Set of 14*	£200	£225

The 9 p. exists both offset-litho and typo.

1934–37. *King George V. Wmk Mult Star, T 69.*

15	79	½ a. green (1935)			4·50	55
		w. Wmk inverted			6·50	55
16	81	1 a. chocolate			9·50	40
		w. Wmk inverted			25·00	15·00
17	59	2 a. vermilion (1935)			38·00	7·50
17a		2 a. vermilion (*small die*) (1937)			50·00	25
18	62	3 a. carmine			4·75	40
19	63	4 a. sage-green (1935)			4·00	40
15/19				*Set of 6*	£100	8·50

1938–41. *King George VI.*

20	91	3 p. slate (5.38)			8·00	3·25
21		½ a. red-brown (5.38)			4·25	10
22		9 p. green (5.38)			3·50	3·75
23		1 a. carmine (5.38)			2·75	10
24	92	2 a. vermilion (1939)			6·50	1·50
26	—	3 a. yellow-green (1941)			10·00	5·00
27	—	3 a. 6 p. bright blue (7.38)			4·25	3·00
28	—	4 a. brown (1941)			£120	65·00
30	—	8 a. slate-violet (1940)			£140	35·00
31	—	12 a. lake (1940)			£100	45·00

32	93	1 r. grey and red-brown (1940)			2·75	1·75
33		2 r. purple and brown (1940)			13·00	2·75
34		5 r. green and blue (1940)			15·00	13·00
35		10 r. purple and claret (1941)			65·00	30·00
36		15 r. brown and green (1941)			48·00	48·00
		w. Wmk inverted			48·00	48·00
37		25 r. slate-violet and purple (1941)			95·00	85·00
20/37				*Set of 16*	£550	£300

1942–45. *King George VI on white background.*

38	100a	3 p. slate			1·75	60
39		½ a. purple			4·00	90
40		9 p. green			12·00	12·00
41		1 a. carmine			3·50	50
42	101	1 a. 3 p. bistre			8·00	14·00
43		1½ a. dull violet			4·75	4·25
44		2 a. vermilion			4·50	1·50
45		3 a. bright violet			15·00	4·00
46		3½ a. bright blue			3·50	13·00
47	102	4 a. brown			2·00	1·50
48		6 a. turquoise-green			9·50	9·00
49		8 a. slate-violet			3·25	2·50
50		12 a. lake			5·50	4·00
38/50				*Set of 13*	70·00	60·00

Stamps of Great Britain surcharged

For similar surcharges without the name of the country, see BRITISH POSTAL AGENCIES IN EASTERN ARABIA.

BAHRAIN
1 ANNA (3)

BAHRAIN
5 RUPEES (4)

1948 (1 Apr)–**49.** *Surch as T 3, 4 (2 r. and 5 r.) or similar surch with bars at foot (10 r.).*

51	128	½ a. on ½d. pale green			40	85
52		1 a. on 1d. pale scarlet			40	1·25
53		1½ a. on 1½d. pale red-brown			40	1·25
54		2 a. on 2d. pale orange			40	20
55		2½ a. on 2½d. light ultramarine			50	2·25
56		3 a. on 3d. pale violet			40	10
57	129	6 a. on 6d. purple			40	10
58	130	1 r. on 1s. bistre-brown			1·25	10
59	131	2 r. on 2s. 6d. yellow-green			5·00	4·50
60		5 r. on 5s. red			5·50	4·00
60a	132	10 r. on 10s. ultramarine (4.7.49)			60·00	42·00
51/60a				*Set of 11*	65·00	50·00

BAHRAIN 2½ ANNAS (5)

BAHRAIN 15 RUPEES (6)

1948 (26 Apr). *Silver Wedding, surch as T 5 or 6.*

61	137	2½ a. on 2½d. ultramarine			1·00	30
62	138	15 r. on £1 blue			40·00	48·00

1948 (29 July). *Olympic Games, surch as T 5, but in one line (6 a.) or two lines (others); the 1 r. also has a square of dots as T 7.*

63	139	2½ a. on 2½d. ultramarine			55	1·25
		a. Surch double			£800	£1400
64	140	3 a. on 3d. violet			55	2·00
65	141	6 a. on 6d. bright purple			1·50	2·50
66	142	1 r. on 1s. brown			1·50	2·50
63/6				*Set of 4*	3·75	7·50

Fourteen used examples of No. 63a are known, of which twelve were postmarked at Experimental P.O. K-121 (Muharraq), one at F.P.O. 756 (Shaibah) and one apparently cancelled-to-order at Bahrain on 10 October 1949.

BAHRAIN 3 ANNAS (7)

1949 (10 Oct). *75th Anniv of U.P.U., surch as T 7, in one line (2½ a.) or in two lines (others).*

67	143	2½ a. on 2½d. ultramarine			55	2·25
68	144	3 a. on 3d. violet			85	2·75
69	145	6 a. on 6d. bright purple			75	3·00
70	146	1 r. on 1s. brown			1·60	2·00
67/70				*Set of 4*	3·25	9·00

BAHRAIN   **BAHRAIN**

2 RUPEES (7a)   **2 RUPEES** Type II

BAHRAIN

Extra bar (R. 6/1)

Three Types of 2 r.:

Type I. As Type 7a showing "2" level with "RUPEES" and "BAHRAIN" sharp.
Type II. "2" raised. "BAHRAIN" worn. 15 mm between "BAHRAIN" and "2 RUPEES".
Type III. As Type II, but 16 mm between "BAHRAIN" and "2 RUPEES". Value is set more to the left of "BAHRAIN".

1950 (2 Oct)–**55.** *Surch as T 3 or 7a (rupee values).*

71	128	½ a. on ½d. pale orange (3.5.51)			1·00	1·25
72		1 a. on 1d. light ultramarine (3.5.51)			2·00	10
73		1½ a. on 1½d. pale green (3.5.51)			2·00	9·50
74		2 a. on 2d. pale red-brown (3.5.51)			80	30
75		2½ a. on 2½d. pale scarlet (3.5.51)			2·00	9·50
76	129	4 a. on 6d. light ultramarine			2·00	1·50
77	147	2 r. on 2s. 6d. yellow-green (3.5.51)			21·00	6·00
		a. Surch Type II (1953)			65·00	32·00
		b. Surch Type III (1955)			£700	80·00
		ba. "I" inverted and raised (R.2/1)			£2500	£600
78	148	5 r. on 5s. red (3.5.51)			13·00	3·75
		a. Extra bar			£250	
79	149	10 r. on 10s. ultramarine (3.5.51)			26·00	7·00
71/79				*Set of 9*	60·00	32·00

1952 (5 Dec)–**54.** *Q.E. II (W 153), surch as T 3 (in two lines on 2½ and 6 a.).*

80	154	½ a. on ½d. orange-red (31.8.53)			10	75
		a. Fraction "½" omitted			£110	£150
81		1 a. on 1d. ultramarine (31.8.53)			10	10
82		1½ a. on 1½d. green (31.8.53)			10	10
83		2 a. on 2d. red-brown (31.8.53)			20	10
84	155	2½ a. on 2½d. carmine-red			20	1·50
85		3 a. on 3d. deep lilac (B.) (18.1.54)			1·50	10
86	156	4 a. on 4d. ultramarine (2.11.53)			8·00	30
87	157	6 a. on 6d. reddish purple (18.1.54)			3·25	10
88	160	12 a. on 1s. 3d. green (2.11.53)			3·25	20
89	159	1 r. on 1s. 6d. grey-blue (2.11.53)			3·25	10
80/89				*Set of 10*	18·00	2·50

The word BAHRAIN is in taller letters on the 1½ a., 2½ a., 3 a. and 6 a.

2½ BAHRAIN ANNAS (8)

1953 (3 June). *Coronation. Surch as T 8, or similarly.*

90	161	2½ a. on 2½d. carmine-red			1·25	75
91	162	4 a. on 4d. ultramarine			2·25	3·50
92	163	12 a. on 1s. 3d. deep yellow-green			3·25	1·50
93	164	1 r. on 1s. 6d. deep grey-blue			7·50	50
90/3				*Set of 4*	13·00	7·50

BAHRAIN 2 RUPEES I
BAHRAIN 2 RUPEES II
BAHRAIN 2 RUPEES III (9)
BAHRAIN 5 RUPEES I
BAHRAIN 5 RUPEES II (10)
BAHRAIN 10 RUPEES I
BAHRAIN 10 RUPEES II (11)

TYPE I (T 9/11). Type-set surch by Waterlow. Bold thick letters with sharp corners and straight edges.
TYPE II (T 9/11). Plate-printed surch by Harrison. Thinner letters, rounded corners and rough edges. Bars wider apart.
TYPE III (T 9). Plate-printed surch by Harrison. Similar to Type II as regards the position of the bars on all 40 stamps of the sheet, but the letters are thinner and with more rounded corners than in II, while the ink of the surcharge is less black.

The general characteristics of Type II of the 2 r. are less pronounced than in the other values, but a distinguishing test is in the relative position of the bars and the "U" of "RUPEES". In Type II (except for the 1st stamp, 5th row) the bars start immediately beneath the left-hand edge of the "U". In Type I they start more to the right.

In the 10 r. the "1" and the "0" are spaced 0.9 mm in Type I and only 0.6 mm in Type II.

1955 (23 Sept)–**60.** *T 166/8 (Waterlow ptgs) surch as T 9/11.*

94	166	2 r. on 2s. 6d. black-brown (Type I)			5·50	1·60
		a. Type II (13.5.58)			11·00	9·00
		b. Type III (No. 536a, D.L.R.) (29.1.60)			25·00	45·00
95	167	5 r. on 5s. rose-red (Type I)			12·00	2·75
		a. Type II (19.8.57)			11·00	8·00
96	168	10 r. on 10s. ultramarine (Type I)			20·00	2·75
		a. Type II (13.5.58)			90·00	95·00
		ab. Type II. Surch on No. 538a (D.L.R. ptg) (1960)			£100	
94/6				*Set of 3*	32·00	6·25
94a/6a				*Set of 3*	65·00	£100

1956–7. *Q.E. II (W 165), surch as T 3 (in two lines on 6 a.).*

97	154	½ a. on ½d. orange-red (1.57)			10	15
98	156	4 a. on 4d. ultramarine (8.6.56)			5·50	17·00
99	157	6 a. on 6d. reddish purple (5.12.56)			50	50
100	160	12 a. on 1s. 3d. green (2.8.56)			7·50	11·00
101	159	1 r. on 1s. 6d. grey-blue (4.3.57)			8·50	1·00
		a. Surch double			†	£1800
97/101				*Set of 5*	20·00	26·00

(New Currency. 100 naye paise = 1 rupee)

BAHRAIN BAHRAIN BAHRAIN

NP 1	NP	3 NP	75 NP
(12)	(13)		(14)

1957 (1 Apr)–59. *Q.E. II* (W 165), *surch as* T 12 (1 n.p., 15 n.p., 25 n.p., 40 n.p., *and* 50 n.p.), T 14 (75 n.p.) *or* T 13 (*others*).

102	157	1 n.p. on 5d. brown	..	..	10	10
103	154	3 n.p. on ½d. orange-red	..	..	30	1·75
104		6 n.p. on 1d. ultramarine	..	..	30	1·75
105		9 n.p. on 1½d. green	..	..	30	1·75
106		12 n.p. on 2d. light red-brown	..		30	60
107	155	15 n.p. on 2½d. carmine-red (Type I)	..	30	15
	a.	Type II (1959)	..	..	1·00	2·00
108		20 n.p. on 3d. deep lilac (B.)	..	30	10
109	156	25 n.p. on 4d. ultramarine	..	..	75	2·00
110	157	40 n.p. on 6d. reddish purple	..	40	10
	a.	Deep claret (1959)	..	..	55	10
111	158	50 n.p. on 9d. bronze-green	..	3·75	4·50
112	160	75 n.p. on 1s. 3d. green	..	2·25	50
102/112			Set of 11	8·00	11·50

BAHRAIN
15 NP

(15)

1957 (1 Aug). *World Scout Jubilee Jamboree. Surch in two lines as* T 15 (15 n.p.), *or in three lines* (*others*).

113	170	15 n.p. on 2½d. carmine-red	..	25	35
114	171	25 n.p. on 4d. ultramarine	..	30	35
115	172	75 n.p. on 1s. 3d. green	..	40	45
113/15			Set of 3	85	1·00

1960 (24 May). *Q.E. II* (W 179), *surch as* T 12.

116	155	15 n.p. on 2½d. carmine-red (Type II)	..	2·25	8·00

16	17

Shaikh Sulman bin Hamed al-Khalifa

(Des M. Farrar Bell. Photo Harrison (T 16). Des O. C. Meronti. Recess D.L.R. (T 17))

1960 (1 July). *P* 15 × 14 (T **16**) *or* 13½ × 13 (T **17**).

117	16	5 n.p. × bright blue	..	..	10	10
118		15 n.p. red-orange	..	..	10	10
119		20 n.p. reddish violet	..	..	10	10
120		30 n.p. bistre-brown	..	..	10	10
121		40 n.p. grey	..	..	15	10
122		50 n.p. emerald-green	..	..	15	10
123		75 n.p. chocolate	..	..	30	15
124	17	1 r. black	..	..	1·50	30
125		2 r. rose-red	..	..	2·75	1·75
126		5 r. deep blue	..	..	4·50	2·50
127		10 r. bronze-green	..	..	12·00	3·75
117/127			Set of 11	19·00	8·00

18 Shaikh Isa bin Sulman al-Khalifa   **19** Air Terminal, Muharraq

20 Deep Water Harbour

(Des M. Farrar Bell. Photo Harrison (5 to 75 n.p.). Des D. C. Rivett. Recess B.W. (others))

1964 (22 Feb). *P* 15 × 14 (T **18**) *or* 13½ × 13 (T **19/20**).

128	18	5 n.p. bright blue	..	..	10	10
129		15 n.p. orange red	..	..	10	10

130	18	20 n.p. reddish violet	..	..	10	10
131		30 n.p. olive-brown	..	..	10	10
132		40 n.p. slate	..	..	15	10
133		50 n.p. emerald-green	..	..	15	20
134		75 n.p. brown	..	..	25	10
135	19	1 r. black	..	..	6·50	1·50
136		2 r. carmine-red	..	..	8·50	1·50
137	20	5 r. ultramarine	..	..	11·00	9·50
138		10 r. myrtle-green	..	..	13·00	9·50
128/138		..	Set of 11	35·00	20·00

LOCAL STAMPS

The following stamps were issued primarily for postage within Bahrain, but apparently also had franking value when used on external mail.

L 1 Shaikh Sulman bin Hamed L 2 al-Khalifa

(Types L 1/2. Recess D.L.R.)

1953–56. *P* 12 × 12½.

L1	L 1	½ a. deep green (1.10.56)	..	..	3·75	75
L2		1 a. deep blue (1.10.56)	..	..	3·75	45
L3		1½ a. carmine (15.2.53)	..	..	50	4·00
L1/3		..	Set of 3	7·25	4·75

1957 (16 Oct). *As Nos.* L 1/3 *but values in new currency.*

L4		3 p. deep green	..	..	4·25	1·25
L5		6 p. carmine	..	..	4·25	1·25
L6		9 p. deep blue	..	..	4·25	1·25
L4/6			Set of 3	11·50	3·25

1961 (20 Mar). *P* 12 × 12½.

L 7	L 2	5 p. green	..	..	1·25	30
L 8		10 p. carmine-red	..	..	1·60	30
L 9		15 p. grey	..	..	1·25	25
L10		20 p. blue	..	..	1·50	25
L11		30 p. sepia	..	..	1·25	25
L12		40 p. ultramarine	..	..	2·00	30
L7/12			Set of 6	8·00	1·50

STAMP BOOKLETS

1934. *Red and black on tan cover. Mysore Sandal Soap advertisement on front.*

SB1	16 a. booklet containing sixteen 1 a. (No. 16w) in blocks of 4	..	..	..	£850

The Bahrain Post Department took over the postal services on 1 January 1966. Later stamp issues will be found in Part 19 (*Middle East*) of the Stanley Gibbons catalogue.

Bangkok
see British Post Office in Siam

Bangladesh

In elections during December 1970 the Awami League party won all but two of the seats in the East Pakistan province and, in consequence, held a majority in the National Assembly. On 1 March 1971 the Federal Government postponed the sitting of the Assembly with the result that unrest spread throughout the eastern province. Pakistan army operations against the dissidents forced the leaders of the League to flee to India from where East Pakistan was proclaimed independent as Bangladesh. In early December the Indian army moved against Pakistan troops in Bangladesh and civilian government was re-established on 22 December 1971.

From 20 December 1971 various Pakistan issues were overprinted by local postmasters, mainly using handstamps. Their use was permitted until 30 April 1973. These are of philatelic interest, but are outside the scope of the catalogue.

(Currency. 100 paisa = 1 rupee)

1 Map of Bangladesh   (2)

(Des B. Mullick. Litho Format)

1971 (29 July). *Vert designs as* T 1. *P* 14 × 14½.

1		10 p. indigo-blue, red-orange and pale blue	..	10	10
2		20 p. multicoloured	..	..	10	10
3		50 p. multicoloured	..	..	10	10
4		1 r. multicoloured	..	..	10	10
5		2 r. deep greenish blue, light new blue and rose-magenta	..	25	35
6		3 r. apple-green, dull yellowish green and greenish blue	..	30	55
7		5 r. multicoloured	..	..	50	90
8		10 r. gold, rose-magenta & deep greenish blue	1·00	1·75
1/8			Set of 8	2·00	3·50

Designs:—20 p. "Dacca University Massacre"; 50 p. "75 Million People"; 1 r. Flag of Independence; 2 r. Ballot box; 3 r. Broken chain; 5 r. Shaikh Mujibur Rahman; 10 r. "Support Bangla Desh" and map.

Nos. 1/8 exist imperforate from stock dispersed by the liquidator of Format International Security Printers Ltd.

1971 (20 Dec). *Liberation. Nos.* 1 *and* 7/8 *optd with* T **2**.

9		10 p. indigo-blue, red-orange and pale blue	..	10	10
10		5 r. multicoloured (O.)	..	..	1·50	1·75
11		10 r. gold, rose-magenta & deep greenish blue	2·00	2·50
9/11			Set of 3	3·25	3·75

The remaining values of the original issue were also overprinted and placed on sale in Great Britain but were not issued in Bangladesh. (*Price for the complete set £4 un*.)

On 1 February 1972 the Agency placed on sale a further issue in the flag, map and Shaikh Mujibur designs in new colours and new currency (100 paisas = 1 taka). This issue proved to be unacceptable to the Bangladesh authorities who declared them to be invalid for postal purposes, no supplies being sold within Bangladesh. The values comprise 1, 2, 3, 5, 7, 10, 15, 20, 25, 40, 50, 75 p., 1, 2 and 5 t. (*Price for set of 15 un*., £1.)

(New Currency. 100 paisa = 1 taka)

3 "Martyrdom"   **4** Flames of Independence

(Des and photo Indian Security Printing Press, Nasik)

1972 (21 Feb). *In Memory of the Martyrs. P* 13.

12	3	20 p. dull green and rose-red	..	30	50

(Des N. Kundu. Photo Indian Security Printing Press, Nasik)

1972 (26 Mar). *First Anniv of Independence. P* 13.

13	4	20 p. brown-lake and red	..	..	20	10
14		60 p. dull ultramarine and red	..	25	45
15		75 p. reddish violet and red	..	30	55
13/15			Set of 3	65	1·00

5 Doves of Peace   **6** "Homage to Martyrs"

(Litho B.W.)

1972 (16 Dec). *Victory Day. P* 13½.

16	5	20 p. multicoloured	..	..	15	10
17		60 p. multicoloured	..	..	20	55
18		75 p. multicoloured	..	..	20	55
16/18			Set of 3	50	1·10

(Des K. Mustafa. Litho B.W.)

1973 (25 Mar). *In Memory of the Martyrs. P* 13½.

19	6	20 p. multicoloured	..	..	15	10
20		60 p. multicoloured	..	..	30	40
21		1 t. 35, multicoloured	..	..	65	1·75
19/21		..	Set of 3	1·10	2·00

7 Embroidered Quilt   **8** Court of Justice

(Litho B.W.)

1973 (30 Apr). T **7/8** *and similar designs. P* 14½ × 14 (50 p., 1 t., 5 t., 10 t.) *or* 14 × 14½ (*others*).

22		2 p. black	..	..	10	40
23		3 p. blue-green	..	..	20	30
	a.	Imperf (pair)	..	..		

24		5 p. light brown			20	10
25		10 p. slate-black			20	10
26		20 p. yellow-green			50	10
27		25 p. bright reddish mauve			2·75	15
28		50 p. bright purple			1·50	30
29		60 p. greenish slate			75	50
30		75 p. yellow-orange			80	50
31		90 p. orange-brown			90	70
32		1 t. light violet			4·00	30
33		2 t. olive-green			4·00	55
34		5 t. grey-blue			5·50	1·50
35		10 t. rose			5·50	3·25
22/35			*Set of 14*		24·00	7·50

Designs: *As T 7*—3 p. Jute field; 5 p. Jack fruit; 10 p. Bullocks ploughing; 20 p. Rakta jaba (flower); 25 p. Tiger; 60 p. Bamboo grove; 75 p. Plucking tea; 90 p. Handicrafts. *Horiz (28×22 mm)*—50 p. Hilsa (fish). *Horiz as T 8*—5 t. Fishing boat; 10 t. Sixty-dome mosque, Bagerhat. *Vert as T 8*—2 t. Date tree.
See also Nos. 49/51a, 64/75 and 711.

9 Flame Emblem   10 Family, Map and Graph

(Des A. Karim. Litho B.W.)

1973 (10 Dec). *5th Anniv of Declaration of Human Rights.* P 13½.

36	**9**	10 p. multicoloured			10	10
37		1 t. 25, multicoloured			20	20

(Des A. Karim. Litho B.W.)

1974 (10 Feb). *First Population Census.* P 13½.

38	**10**	20 p. multicoloured			10	10
39		25 p. multicoloured			10	10
40		75 p. multicoloured			20	20
38/40			*Set of 3*		30	30

11 Copernicus and Heliocentric   12 U.N. H.Q. and System   Bangladesh Flag

(Des K. Mustafa. Litho B.W.)

1974 (22 July). *500th Birth Anniv of Copernicus.* P 13½.

41	**11**	25 p. yellow-orange, bluish violet & blk		10	10
		a. Imperf (pair)			26·00	
42		75 p. orange, yellow-green and black		25	50

(Des A. Karim. Litho B.W.)

1974 (25 Sept). *Bangladesh's Admission to the U.N. Multicoloured; frame colour given.* P 13½.

43	**12**	25 p. light lilac			10	10
44		1 t. light greenish blue			35	40

13 U.P.U. Emblem   14 Courts of Justice

(Des K. Mustafa. Litho B.W.)

1974 (9 Oct). *Centenary of Universal Postal Union. T 13 and similar vert designs. Multicoloured; country name on a yellow background (Nos. 45/6) or a blue background (Nos. 47/8).* P 13½.

45		25 p. Type 13			10	10
46		1 t. 25, Mail runner			20	15
47		1 t. 75, Type 13			25	25
48		5 t. As 1 t. 25			80	1·60
45/8			*Set of 4*		1·25	1·75

The above exist imperforate in a miniature sheet from a restricted printing.

1974–76. *Nos. 32/5 redrawn with revised value inscriptions as T 14.*

49		1 t. light violet			1·50	10
50		2 t. olive			2·00	90
51		5 t. grey-blue (1975)			5·50	70
51a		10 t. rose (1976)			12·00	9·00
49/51a			*Set of 4*		19·00	9·50

For these designs redrawn to 32×20 or 20×32 mm and perforated 14½ see Nos. 72/5, and for the 10 t. size 35×22 mm with the same perforation see No. 711.

15 Royal Bengal Tiger   16 Symbolic Family

(Des and litho B.W.)

1974 (4 Nov). *Wildlife Preservation. T 15 and similar vert designs. Multicoloured.* P 13½.

52		25 p. Type 15			70	10
53		50 p. Tiger whelp			1·25	70
54		2 t. Tiger in stream			2·75	3·50
52/4			*Set of 3*		4·25	3·75

(Des A. Karim. Litho B.W.)

1974 (30 Dec). *World Population Year. "Family Planning for All". T 16 and similar multicoloured designs.* P 14.

55		25 p. Type 16			15	10
56		70 p. Village family			25	50
57		1 t. 25, Heads of family (*horiz*)		40	1·10
55/7			*Set of 3*		70	1·50

The Bengali numerals on the 70 p. resemble "90".

17 Radar Antenna   18 Woman's Head

(Des and litho B.W.)

1975 (14 June). *Inauguration of Betbunia Satellite Earth Station.* P 13½.

58	**17**	25 p. black, silver and dull red		10	10
59		1 t. black, silver and ultramarine		20	60

(Des A. Karim. Litho Asher & Co, Melbourne)

1975 (31 Dec). *International Women's Year.* P 15.

60	**18**	50 p. multicoloured			10	10
61		2 t. multicoloured			25	85
		a. Vert pair, bottom stamp imperf		75·00	

(Litho Asher & Co., Melbourne)

1976 (15 Jan)–**77.** *As Nos. 24/31 and 49/51a but redrawn in smaller size and colours changed (5, 75p.).* P 14½×15 (50 p.), 14½ (1 to 10 t.) or 15×14½ (others). *(a) 23×18 mm (50 p.) or 18×23 mm (others).*

64		5 p. deep yellow-green (11.2.76)		20	10
		a. Imperf (pair)			10·00	
65		10 p. slate-black (28.4.76)			20	10
66		20 p. yellow-green			70	10
		a. Imperf (pair)			10·00	
67		25 p. bright reddish mauve			2·50	10
		a. Imperf (pair)			10·00	
68		50 p. light purple (8.6.76)			2·25	10
69		60 p. greenish slate (10.11.76)		40	20
70		75 p. yellow-olive (10.11.76)		1·25	2·00
71		90 p. orange-brown (10.11.76)		40	20

(b) 20×32 mm (2 t.) or 32×20 mm (others)

72		1 t. light violet			2·00	10
73		2 t. olive-green (8.6.76)			6·50	10
		a. Imperf (pair)			35·00	
74		5 t. grey-blue (10.11.76)			3·25	2·00
75		10 t. rose (25.2.77)			8·50	2·00
64/75			*Set of 12*		25·00	6·00

For the 10 t. in this perforation, but redrawn to 35×22 mm see No. 711.

19 Telephones, 1876 and 1976   20 Eye and Nutriments

(Des A. Karim. Litho Asher & Co, Melbourne)

1976 (10 Mar). *Telephone Centenary. T 19 and similar vert design.* P 15.

76		2 t. 25, multicoloured			25	20
77		5 t. dull vermilion, apple-green and black		55	65

Design:— 5 t. Alexander Graham Bell.

(Des A. Karim. Litho Asher & Co, Melbourne)

1976 (17 Apr). *Prevention of Blindness.* P 15.

78	**20**	30 p. multicoloured			50	10
79		2 t. 25, multicoloured			1·40	2·25

21 Liberty Bell   22 Industry, Science, Agriculture and Education

(Des E. Roberts. Photo Heraclio Fournier)

1976 (29 May). *Bicentenary of American Revolution. T 21 and similar horiz designs. Multicoloured.* P 14.

80		30 p. Type 21			10	10
81		2 t. 25, Statue of Liberty			30	25
82		5 t. Mayflower			80	50
83		10 t. Mount Rushmore			80	80
80/3			*Set of 4*		1·75	1·40
MS84		167 × 95 mm. Nos. 80/3			2·50	3·00

No. **MS84** also exists imperforate from a restricted printing.

(Des K. Mustafa. Litho Asher & Co, Melbourne)

1976 (29 July). *25th Anniv of the Colombo Plan.* P 15.

85	**22**	30 p. multicoloured			15	10
86		2 t. 25, multicoloured			35	35

23 Hurdling   24 The Blessing

(Des K. Mustafa. Litho Asher & Co, Melbourne)

1976 (29 Nov). *Olympic Games, Montreal. T 23 and similar multicoloured designs.* P 14½.

87		25 p. Type 23			10	10
88		30 p. Running (*horiz*)			10	10
		a. Imperf (pair)				
89		1 t. Pole vault			15	10
90		2 t. 25, Swimming (*horiz*)			40	45
91		3 t. 50, Gymnastics			75	1·25
92		5 t. Football			1·40	2·00
87/92			*Set of 6*		2·50	3·50

(Des and litho Harrison)

1977 (7–17 Feb). *Silver Jubilee. T 24 and similar vert designs. Multicoloured.* P 14 × 14½.

93		30 p. Type 24			10	10
94		2 t. 25, Queen Elizabeth II			20	25
95		10 t. Queen Elizabeth and Prince Philip		70	85
93/5			*Set of 3*		80	1·00
MS96		114 × 127 mm. Nos. 93/5. P 14½ (17 Feb)		80	1·50

25 Qazi Nazrul Islam (poet)

(Des K. Mustafa. Litho Harrison)

1977 (29 Aug). *Qazi Nazrul Islam Commemoration. T 25 and similar design.* P 14.

97		40 p. blue-green and black			10	10
98		2 t. 25, sepia, stone and chestnut		30	30

Design: *Horiz*—2 t. 25, Head and shoulders portrait.

26 Bird with Letter

(Des A. Karim. Litho Harrison)

1977 (29 Sept). *15th Anniv of Asian-Oceanic Postal Union.* P 14.

| 99 | 26 | 30 p. light rose, new blue and dull green | 10 | 10 |
| 100 | | 2 t. 25, light rose, new blue and light grey .. | 20 | 25 |

27 Sloth Bear   **28** Campfire and Tent

(Des K. Mustafa. Litho Harrison)

1977 (9 Nov). *Animals. T* **27** *and similar multicoloured designs.* P 13.

101	40 p. Type 27	..	..	..	20	10
102	1 t. Spotted Deer	..	..	..	30	10
103	2 t. 25, Leopard (*horiz*)	..	..	85	20
104	3 t. 50, Gaur (*horiz*)..	..	..	90	35
105	4 t. Indian Elephant (*horiz*)	..	..	1·75	40
106	5 t. Tiger (*horiz*)	..	..	2·00	75
101/6 ..				*Set of 6*	5·50	1·75

The Bengali numerals on the 40 p. resemble "80", and that on the 4 t. resembles "8".

(Des A. Karim. Litho Harrison)

1978 (22 Jan). *First National Scout Jamboree. T* **28** *and similar designs.* P 13.

107	40 p. red, deep blue and light blue	30	10
108	3 t. 50, carmine, deep blue and green ..	1·25	30
109	5 t. reddish lilac, deep blue and bright green	1·40	45
107/9 ..		*Set of 3*	2·75	70

Designs: *Horiz*—3 t. 50, Scout stretcher-team. *Vert*—5 t. Scout salute.

29 *Michelia champaca*

(Des and litho Harrison)

1978 (29 Apr). *Flowers. T* **29** *and similar horiz designs. Multicoloured.* P 14.

110	40 p. Type 29	..	..	..	30	10
111	1 t. *Cassia fistula*	..	..	55	15
112	2 t. 25, *Delonix regia* ..	..	..	85	30
113	3 t. 50, *Nymphaea nouchali*	..	1·00	60
114	4 t. *Butea monosperma*	..	..	1·10	80
115	5 t. *Anthocephalus indicus*	..	1·40	80
110/15				*Set of 6*	4·50	2·40

30 St. Edward's Crown and Sceptres   **31** Sir Alan Cobham's De Havilland D.H.50J

(Des and litho Harrison)

1978 (20 May). *25th Anniv of Coronation. T* **30** *and similar vert designs. Multicoloured.* P 14.

116	40 p. Type 30	..	..	..	10	10
117	3 t. 50, Balcony scene	..	..	15	30
118	5 t. Queen Elizabeth and Prince Philip ..	25	50
119	10 t. Coronation portrait by Cecil Beaton ..	45	80
116/19				*Set of 4*	80	1·50
MS120	89 × 121 mm. Nos. 116/19. P 14½ ..	1·10	1·50

(Des and litho Harrison)

1978 (15 June). *75th Anniv of Powered Flight. T* **31** *and similar horiz designs.* P 13.

121	40 p. multicoloured	..	..	15	10
122	2 t. 25, blackish brown and light new blue ..	50	45
123	3 t. 50, blackish brown and yellow ..	65	65
124	5 t. multicoloured	..	..	4·00	3·50
121/4 ..				*Set of 4*	4·75	4·25

Designs:—2 t. 25, Captain Hans Bertram's Junkers W.33 seaplane *Atlantis*; 3 t. 50, Wright brothers' Flyer III; 5 t. Concorde.

32 Fenchuganj Fertilizer Factory   **33** Tawaf-E-Ka'aba, Mecca

(Des P. Mandal (5 p.), A. Karim (10 p.), Harrison (30, 50 p., 1 t.). Photo Harrison)

1978 (6 Nov)–*82. Designs as T* **32**. P 14½.

125	5 p. deep brown (25.3.79)	..	..	10	10
126	10 p. turquoise-blue	..	..	10	10
127	15 p. orange (1.8.80)	..	..	10	10
128	20 p. brown-red (15.12.79)	..	..	10	10
129	25 p. grey-blue (1982)	..	..	15	10
130	30 p. deep green (10.12.80)	..	1·50	10
131	40 p. maroon (15.12.79)	..	30	10
132	50 p. black (1981)	..	..	3·25	1·50
134	80 p. brown (1.8.80)	..	..	20	10
136	1 t. reddish violet (6.81)	..	4·25	10
137	2 t. dull ultramarine (21.10.81)	..	50	2·00
125/37			*Set of 11*	9·50	3·50

Designs: *Horiz*—5 p. Lalbag Fort; 25 p. Jute on a boat; 40 p., 50 p. Baitul Mukarram Mosque; 1 t. Dotara (musical instrument); 2 t. Karnaphuli Dam. *Vert*—15 p. Pineapple; 20 p. Bangladesh gas; 30 p. Banana Tree; 80 p. Mohastan Garh.

(Des A. Karim. Litho J.W.)

1978 (9 Nov). *Holy Pilgrimage to Mecca. T* **33** *and similar multicoloured design.* P 13.

| 140 | 40 p. Type 33 | .. | .. | .. | 20 | 10 |
| 141 | 3 t. 50, Pilgrims in Wuquf, Arafat (*horiz*) .. | 60 | 45 |

34 Jasim Uddin

(Des P. Mandal. Litho J.W.)

1979 (14 Mar). *3rd Death Anniv of Jasim Uddin (poet).* P 14.

| 142 | **34** | 40 p. multicoloured | .. | .. | 20 | 50 |

35 Moulana Abdul Hamid Khan Bhashani   **36** Sir Rowland Hill

(Des P. Mandal. Litho Harrison)

1979 (17 Nov). *3rd Death Anniv of Moulana Abdul Hamid Khan Bhashani (national leader).* P 12½.

| 143 | **35** | 40 p. multicoloured | .. | .. | 40 | 30 |

(Des A. Karim. Litho Harrison)

1979 (26 Nov). *Death Centenary of Sir Rowland Hill. T* **36** *and similar designs.* P 14.

144	40 p. turquoise-blue, Venetian red and pale turquoise-blue	10	10
145	3 t. 50, multicoloured	..	..	35	30
146	10 t. multicoloured	..	..	80	1·00
144/6 ..			*Set of 3*	1·10	1·25
MS147	176 × 96 mm. Nos. 144/6 ..	2·00	2·75

Designs: *Horiz*—3 t. 50, 1971 10 p. definitive stamp and Sir Rowland Hill; 10 t. 1974 1 t. 25, Centenary of U.P.U. commemorative stamp and Sir Rowland Hill.

37 Children with Hoops   **38** Rotary International Emblem

(Des P. Mandal. Litho Harrison)

1979 (17 Dec). *International Year of the Child. T* **37** *and similar vert designs. Multicoloured.* P 14 × 14½.

148	40 p. Type 37	..	..	10	10
149	3 t. 50, Child with kite	..	..	35	35
150	5 t. Children playing	..	..	50	50
148/50			*Set of 3*	80	80
MS151	170×120 mm. Nos. 148/50. P 14½	1·50	2·75

(Des P. Mandal. Litho Rosenbaum Bros, Vienna)

1980 (23 Feb). *75th Anniv of Rotary International. T* **38** *and similar vert design showing club emblem.* P 13½×14.

| 152 | 40 p. black, vermilion and bistre-yellow | 20 | 10 |
| 153 | 5 t. gold and bright blue | .. | .. | 65 | 45 |

39 Canal Digging   **40** A. K. Fazlul Huq

(Des A. Karim. Litho Rosenbaum Bros, Vienna)

1980 (27 Mar). *Mass Participation in Canal Digging.* P 14×13½.

| 154 | **39** | 40 p. multicoloured | .. | .. | 40 | 30 |

(Des P. Mandal. Litho Rosenbaum Bros, Vienna)

1980 (27 Apr). *18th Death Anniv of A. K. Fazlul Huq (national leader).* P 13½×14.

| 155 | **40** | 40 p. multicoloured | .. | .. | 30 | 30 |

On the face value the Bengali numerals resemble "80".

41 Early forms of Mail Transport   **42** Dome of the Rock

(Des A. Karim. Litho Rosenbaum Bros, Vienna)

1980 (5 May). *"London 1980" International Stamp Exhibition. T* **41** *and similar horiz design. Multicoloured.* P 14×13½.

156	1 t. Type 41	..	..	15	10
157	10 t. Modern forms of mail transport ..	1·25	85
MS158	140 × 95 mm. Nos. 156/7 ..	1·40	2·00

(Des A. Karim. Litho Harrison)

1980 (21 Aug). *Palestinian Welfare.* P 14½.

| 159 | **42** | 50 p. deep mauve | .. | .. | 70 | 30 |

A similar stamp in grey, showing a Palestinian guerilla and the Dome of the Rock, printed by the State Printing Works, Moscow, was prepared in 1980, but not issued due to errors in the Arabic inscription. Quantities of the stamp were subsequently reported stolen. Examples were also issued by Comilla and Kotbari post offices on 27 September 1992 without authority.

43 Outdoor Class

(Des P. Mandal. Litho Rosenbaum Bros, Vienna)

1980 (23 Aug). *Education.* P 13½×14.

| 160 | **43** | 50 p. multicoloured | .. | .. | 40 | 30 |

44 Beach Scene   **45** Mecca

(Des A. Karim. Litho Rosenbaum Bros, Vienna)

1980 (27 Sept). *World Tourism Conference, Manila. T* **44** *and similar horiz design showing different beach scene. P* 14.

161	50 p. multicoloured	..	..	30	30
	a. Horiz pair. Nos. 161/2	..	..	90	1·00
162	5 t. multicoloured	..	..	60	70
MS163	140 × 88 mm. Nos. 161/2	..	..	90	1·50

Nos. 161/2 were printed together, *se-tenant*, in horizontal pairs throughout the sheet.

(Des A. Karim. Litho Rosenbaum Bros, Vienna)

1980 (11 Nov). *Moslem Year 1400 A.H. Commemoration.* P 14×13½.

164	**45**	50 p. multicoloured	..	20	20

46 Begum Roquiah

47 Spotted Deer and Scout Emblem

(Des A. Karim. Litho Rosenbaum Bros, Vienna)

1980 (9 Dec). *Birth Centenary of Begum Roquiah (campaigner for women's rights). P* 14.

165	**45**	50 p. multicoloured	..	..	10	10
166		2 t. multicoloured	..	..	35	20

(Des A. Karim. Litho Rosenbaum Bros, Vienna)

1981 (1 Jan). *5th Asia-Pacific/2nd Bangladesh Scout Jamboree. P* 13½×14.

167	**47**	50 p. multicoloured	..	..	40	15
168		5 t. multicoloured	..	..	1·25	2·00

2nd. CENSUS 1981

(48)

49 Queen Elizabeth the Queen Mother

1981 (6 Mar). *Second Population Census. Nos.* 38/40 *optd with T* **48**.

169	**10**	20 p. multicoloured	..	..	10	10
170		25 p. multicoloured	..	..	10	10
171		75 p. multicoloured	..	..	20	30
169/71				Set of 3	30	40

(Des R. Granger Barrett. Litho Rosenbaum Bros, Vienna)

1981 (16 Mar). *80th Birthday of Queen Elizabeth the Queen Mother. P* 13½×14.

172	**49**	1 t. multicoloured	..		15	15
173		15 t. multicoloured	..		1·75	2·50
MS174		95 × 73 mm. Nos. 172/3	..		2·40	2·50

50 Revolutionary with Flag and Sub-machine-gun

51 Bangladesh Village and Farm Scenes

(Des P. Mandal. Litho Rosenbaum Bros, Vienna)

1981 (26 Mar). *Tenth Anniv of Independence. T* **50** *and similar vert design. Multicolourd. P* 13½×14.

175	**50**	50 p. Type **50**	..		15	10
176		2 t. Figures on map symbolising Bangladesh life-style	..		25	45

(Des A. Karim. Litho Rosenbaum Bros, Vienna)

1981 (1 Sept). *U.N. Conference on Least Developed Countries, Paris. P* 14×13½.

177	**51**	50 p. multicoloured	..		35	15

52 Kemal Atatürk in Civilian Dress

53 Deaf People using Sign Language

(Des F. Karim and P. Mandal. Litho Rosenbaum Bros, Vienna)

1981 (10 Nov). *Birth Centenary of Kemal Atatürk (Turkish statesman). T* **52** *and similar vert design. Multicoloured.*

178	**50** p. Type **52**		..	..	45	30
179	1 t. Kemal Atatürk in uniform		..	..	80	80

(Des F. Karim. Litho Ueberreuter, Austria)

1981 (26 Dec). *International Year for Disabled Persons. T* **53** *and similar multicoloured design. P* 13½ × 14 (50 p.) *or* 14 × 13½ (2 t.).

180	**50** p. Type **53**	..			40	20
181	2 t. Disabled person writing (*horiz*)	..		1·25	2·00

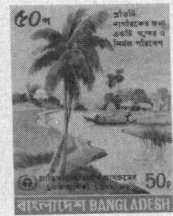

54 Farm Scene and Wheat Ear

55 River Scene

(Des F. Karim. Litho Ueberreuter, Austria)

1981 (31 Dec). *World Food Day. P* 13½ × 14.

182	**54**	50 p. multicoloured	..	..	50	80

(Des P. Mandal. Litho Ueberreuter, Vienna)

1982 (22 May). *10th Anniv of Human Environment Conference. P* 13½×14.

183	**55**	50 p. multicoloured	..	..	50	80

56 Dr. M. Hussain

57 Knotted Rope surrounding Bengali "75"

(Des F. Karim. Litho Ueberreuter, Vienna)

1982 (9 Oct). *First Death Anniv of Dr. Motahar Hussain (educationist). P* 13½.

184	**56**	50 p. multicoloured	..	..	50	80

(Des F. Karim and P. Mandal. Litho Ueberreuter, Vienna)

1982 (21 Oct). *75th Anniv of Boy Scout Movement and 125th Birth Anniv of Lord Baden-Powell. T* **57** *and similar multicoloured design. P* 14×13½ (50 p.) *or* 13½×14 (2 t.).

185	**57**	50 p. Type **57**	..		75	30
186		2 t. Lord Baden-Powell (*vert*)	..		2·75	4·00

(58)

59 Capt. Mohiuddin Jahangir

1982 (21 Nov). *Armed Forces' Day. No.* 175 *optd with T* **58**.

187	**50** p. Type **50**	..			2·25	2·25

(Litho Ueberreuter, Vienna)

1982 (16 Dec). *Heroes and Martyrs of the Liberation. T* **59** *and similar horiz designs. Multicoloured: background colours of commemorative plaque given. P* 14×13½.

188	**50** p. Type **59** (pale orange)		30	45
	a. Horiz strip of 7. Nos. 188/94		1·90	
189	50 p. Sepoy Hamidur Rahman (apple-green)		30	45

190	50 p. Sepoy Mohammed Mustafa Kamal (dull claret)		30	45
191	50 p. Muhammed Ruhul Amin (bistre-yellow)		30	45
192	50 p. Flt. Lt. M. Matiur Rahman (olive-bistre)		30	45
193	50 p. Lance-Naik Munshi Abdur Rob (chestnut)		30	45
194	50 p. Lance-Naik Nur Muhammad (bright green)		30	45
188/94		Set of 7	1·90	2·75

Nos. ·188/94 were printed together, *se-tenant*, in horizontal strips of 7 throughout the sheet.

60 Metric Scales

61 Dr. Robert Koch

(Des F. Karim. Litho Ueberreuter, Vienna)

1983 (10 Jan). *Introduction of Metric Weights and Measures. T* **60** *and similar multicoloured design. P* 13½×14 (50 p.) *or* 14×13½ (2 t.).

195	**50** p. Type **60**	..		40	30
196	2 t. Weights, jug and tap measure (*horiz*)	..	1·75	2·50

(Des F. Karim. Litho Ueberreuter, Vienna)

1983 (20 Feb). *Centenary (1982) of Robert Koch's Discovery of Tubercle Bacillus. T* **61** *and similar vert design. Multicoloured. P* 13½×14.

197	**50** p. Type **61**	..		1·00	40
198	1 t. Microscope, slide and X-ray	..	2·25	3·25

62 Open Stage Theatre

63 Dr. Muhammed Shahidulla

(Des F. Karim and P. Mandal. Litho Ueberreuter, Vienna)

1983 (14 Mar). *Commonwealth Day. T* **62** *and similar horiz designs. Multicoloured. P* 14.

199	**62**	1 t. Type **62**	..		10	15
200		3 t. Boat race	..		20	30
201		10 t. Snake dance	..		50	90
202		15 t. Picking tea	..		60	1·50
199/202			Set of 4	1·25	2·50

(Litho Ueberreuter, Vienna)

1983 (10 July). *Dr. Muhammed Shahidulla (Bengali scholar) Commemoration. P* 13½×14.

203	**63**	50 p. multicoloured	..	75	1·00

64 Magpie Robin

(Des F. Karim and P. Mandal. Litho Ueberreuter, Vienna)

1983 (17 Aug). *Birds of Bangladesh. T* **64** *and similar multicoloured designs. P* 14×13½ (50 p., 5 t.) *or* 13½×14 (2 t., 3 t. 75).

204	**50** p. Type **64**			1·25	40
205	2 t. White-brested Kingfisher (*vert*)	..	2·25	2·25
206	3 t. 75 Lesser Golden-backed Woodpecker (*vert*)		3·00	3·00
207	5 t. White-winged Wood Duck		3·50	3·50
204/7		Set of 4	9·00	8·25
MS208	165×110 mm. Nos. 204/7 (sold at 13 t.)	..	11·00	14·00

65 *Macrobrachium rosenbergii*

Visit of Queen Nov. '83

(66)

(Litho Ueberreuter, Vienna)

1983 (31 Oct). *Marine Life. T* **65** *and similar horiz designs. Multicoloured. P* 14×13½.
209	50 p. Type **65**	..	..	80	30
210	2 t. White Pomfret	..	..	2·00	1·60
211	3 t. 75, Rohu	..	..	2·50	2·00
212	5 t. Climbing Perch	..	..	3·00	2·75
209/12			*Set of 4*	7·50	6·00
MS213	119×98 mm. Nos. 209/12. Imperf *(sold at 13 t.)*			5·00	6·00

1983 (14 Nov). *Visit of Queen Elizabeth II. No. 95 optd with T* **66** *in red.*
214	10 t. Queen Elizabeth and Prince Philip	..		3·00	4·00
	a. Optd "Nov '83" (R. 3/10)				

67 Conference Hall, Dhaka   **68** Early Mail Runner

(Des M. Begum and M. Shamim. Litho Ueberreuter, Vienna)

1983 (5 Dec). *14th Islamic Foreign Ministers' Conference, Dhaka. T* **67** *and similar horiz design. Multicoloured. P* 14×13½.
215	50 p. Type **67**	..	..	50	30
216	5 t. Old Fort, Dhaka	..	..	1·75	2·75

(Litho Ueberreuter, Vienna)

1983 (21 Dec). *World Communications Year. T* **68** *and similar multicoloured designs. P* 14×13½ (10 t.) *or* 13½×14 (*others*).
217	50 p. Type **68**	..	..	30	15
218	5 t. Sailing ship, steam train and Boeing 707 airliner	..	..	2·00	1·50
219	10 t. Mail runner and dish aerial (*horiz*)	..	2·75	2·50
	a. Gold (on dish aerial) omitted			£100	
217/19			*Set of 3*	4·50	3·75

69 Carrying Mail   **(70)**
by Boat

(Des M. Akond, P. Mandal and M. Shamim. Litho State Ptg Wks, Moscow)

1983 (21 Dec)–**86**. *Postal Communications. T* **69** *and similar designs. P* 11½×12½ (5, 25 p.), 12×11½ (1, 2, 3, 5 t.) *or* 12½×11½ (*others*).
220	5 p. turquoise-blue	..	..	10	10
221	10 p. purple	..	..	10	10
222	15 p. new blue	..	..	30	10
223	20 p. grey-black	..	..	45	10
224	25 p. slate	..	..	15	10
225	30 p. brown	..	..	15	10
226	50 p. light brown	..	..	30	10
227	1 t. dull ultramarine	..	..	50	10
228	2 t. deep bluish green	..	..	50	10
228a	3 t. bistre (11.1.86)	..	..	85	50
229	5 t. bright purple	..	..	90	60
220/9			*Set of 11*	3·75	1·40

Designs: *Horiz* (22 × 17 *mm*)—10 p. Counter, Dhaka G.P.O.; 15 p. I.W.T.A. Terminal, Dhaka; 20 p. Inside railway travelling post office; 30 p. Emptying pillar box; 50 p. Mobile post office van. (30 × 19 *mm*)—1 t. Kamalapur Railway Station, Dhaka; 2 t. Zia International Airport; 3 t. Sorting mail by machine; 5 t. Khulna G.P.O. *Vert* (17×22 *mm*)—25 p. Delivering a letter.

1984 (1 Feb). *1st National Stamp Exhibition (1st issue). Nos. 161/2 optd with T* **70** (5 t.) *or* "First Bangladesh National Philatelic Exhibition—1984" (50 p.), *both in red.*
230	44	50 p. multicoloured	..	1·00	1·00
		a. Horiz pair. Nos. 230/1		2·25	2·75
231		5 t. multicoloured	..	1·25	1·75

71 Girl with Stamp Album

(Des P. Mandal. Litho Harrison)

1984 (12 May). *1st National Stamp Exhibition (2nd issue). T* **71** *and similar triangular design. Multicoloured. P* 14.
232	50 p. Type **71**	..	..	65	1·25
	a. Pair. Nos. 232/3.			1·75	2·75
233	7 t. 50, Boy with stamp album	..	1·10	1·60
MS234	98×117 mm. Nos. 232/3 *(sold at 10 t.)*		3·00	4·00

Nos. 232/3 were printed together, *se-tenant*, in pairs throughout the sheet.

72 Sarus Crane and Gavial   **73** Eagle attacking
Hen with Chicks

(Des P. Mandal and M. Akond. Litho Ueberreuter, Vienna)

1984 (17 July). *Dhaka Zoo. T* **72** *and similar vert design. Multicoloured. P* 13½×14.
235	1 t. Type **72**	..	..	1·75	85
236	2 t. Common Peafowl and Tiger	..	2·50	3·50

(Des K. Mustafa. Litho Harrison)

1984 (3 Dec). *Centenary of Postal Life Insurance. T* **73** *and similar vert design. Multicoloured. P* 14.
237	1 t. Type **73**	..	..	50	20
238	5 t. Bangladesh family and postman's hand with insurance cheque	..	1·50	1·50

74 Abbasuddin Ahmad   **(75)**

(Des K. Mustafa. Litho Harrison)

1984 (24 Dec). *Abbasuddin Ahmad (singer) Commemoration. P* 14.
239	**74**	3 t. multicoloured	..	70	40

1984 (27 Dec). *"Khulnapex-84" Stamp Exhibition. No. 86 optd with T* **75**.
240	**22**	2 t. 25, multicoloured	..	70	60

76 Cycling

(Des M. Shamim. Litho Harrison)

1984 (31 Dec). *Olympic Games, Los Angeles. T* **76** *and similar horiz designs. Multicoloured. P* 14.
241	1 t. Type **76**	..	..	1·25	30
242	5 t. Hockey	..	..	2·50	2·25
243	10 t. Volleyball	..	..	3·00	3·00
241/3			*Set of 3*	6·00	5·00

77 Farmer with Rice and Sickle   **78** Mother and Baby

(Des M. Shamim. Litho Harrison)

1985 (2 Feb). *9th Annual Meeting of Islamic Development Bank, Dhaka. T* **77** *and similar horiz design. Multicoloured. P* 14.
244	1 t. Type **77**	..	..	35	15
245	5 t. Citizens of four races	..	1·25	1·25

(Des M. Akond. Litho Harrison)

1985 (14 Mar). *Child Survival Campaign. T* **78** *and similar vert design. Multicoloured. P* 14.
246	1 t. Type **78**	..	..	30	10
247	10 t. Young child and growth graph	..	2·50	2·00

উপজেলা নির্বাচন ১৯৮৫

(79)

1985 (16 May). *Local Elections. Nos. 110/15 optd with T* **79**.
248	40 p. Type **29**	..	..	15	15
249	1 t. Cassia fistula	..	..	15	20
250	2 t. 25, Delonix regia	..	..	20	35
251	3 t. 50, Nymphaea nouchali	..	30	55
252	4 t. Butea monosperma	..	30	55
253	5 t. Anthocephalus indicus	..	35	65
248/53			*Set of 6*	1·25	2·25

80 Women working at   **81** U.N. Building, New York,
Traditional Crafts   Peace Doves and Flags

(Des M. Akond. Litho Harrison)

1985 (18 July). *United Nations Decade for Women. T* **80** *and similar vert design. Multicoloured. P* 14.
254	1 t. Type **80**	..	..	25	10
255	10 t. Women with microscope, computer terminal and in classroom.	..	1·25	85

(Des M. Akond. Litho Harrison)

1985 (14 Sept). *40th Anniv of United Nations Organization and 11th Anniv of Bangladesh Membership. T* **81** *and similar horiz design. Multicoloured. P* 14.
256	1 t. Type **81**	..	..	10	10
257	10 t. Map of world and Bangladesh flag	..	80	90

82 Head of Youth,   **83** Emblem and Seven Doves
Flowers and Symbols
of Commerce and
Agriculture

(Des M. Shamim. Litho Harrison)

1985 (2 Nov). *International Youth Year. T* **82** *and similar vert design. Multicoloured. P* 14.
258	1 t. Type **82**	..	..	10	10
259	5 t. Head of youth, flowers and symbols of industry	..	40	60

(Des M. Akond. Litho Harrison)

1985 (8 Dec). *1st Summit Meeting of South Asian Association for Regional Co-operation, Dhaka. T* **83** *and similar vert design. Multicoloured. P* 14.
260	1 t. Type **83**	..	..	10	10
261	5 t. Flags of member nations and lotus blossom	..	40	60

84 Zainul Abedin   **(85)**

(Des P. Mandal. Litho Harrison)

1985 (28 Dec). *10th Death Anniv of Zainul Abedin (artist). P* 14.
262	**84**	3 t. multicoloured	..	75	30
		a. Red-brown ("BANGLADESH" and face value) omitted			

1985 (29 Dec). *3rd National Scout Jamboree. No. 109 optd with T* **85**.
263	5 t. reddish lilac, deep blue and bright green	2·25	1·75

OMNIBUS ISSUES

Details, together with prices for complete sets, of the various Omnibus issues from the 1935 Silver Jubilee series to date are included in a special section following Zimbabwe at the end of Volume 2.

86 "Fishing Net" (Safiuddin Ahmed)

(Litho Harrison)

1986 (6 Apr). *Bangladesh Paintings. T* **86** *and similar horiz designs. Multicoloured. P* 14.
264   1 t. Type **86**   15   10
265   5 t. "Happy Return" (Quamrul Hassan) ..   40   50
266   10 t. "Levelling the Ploughed Field" (Zainul Abedin)   70   80
264/6 ..   ..   *Set of* 3   1·10   1·25

87 Two Players competing for Ball

88 General M. A. G. Osmani

(Des K. Mustafa. Litho Harrison)

1986 (29 June). *World Cup Football Championship, Mexico. T* **87** *and similar horiz design. Multicoloured. P* 15 × 14.
267   1 t. Type **87**   50   10
268   10 t. Goalkeeper and ball in net ..   2·25   2·75
MS269   105 × 75   mm. 20 t. Four players (60 × 44 *mm*). Imperf. ..   ..   ..   5·00   5·00

(Des P. Mandal. Litho Harrison)

1986 (18 Sept). *General M. A. G. Osmani* (*army commander-in-chief*) *Commemoration. P* 14.
270   **88**   3 t. multicoloured ..   ..   ..   1·00   75

SAARC SEMINAR '86

(89)

90 Butterflies and Nuclear Explosion

1986 (3 Dec). *South Asian Association for Regional Co-operation Seminar. No.* 183 *optd with T* **89**.
271   **55**   50 p. multicoloured ..   ..   1·75   2·50

(Des M. Shamim. Litho State Ptg Wks, Moscow)

1986 (29 Dec). *International Peace Year. T* **90** *and similar vert designs. Multicoloured. P* 12 × 12½.
272   1 t. Type **90**   50   25
273   10 t. Flowers and ruined buildings ..   2·75   3·00
MS274   109 × 80 mm. 20 t. Peace dove and soldier   1·50   2·00

TK. 1.00

CONFERENCE FOR DEVELOPMENT '87

(91)

1987 (12 Jan). *Conference for Development. Nos.* 152/3 *surch or optd as T* **91**.
275   **38**   1 t. on 40 p. black, vermilion & bistre-yell   10   15
    a. Surch double ..   ..   ..
    b. Surch triple ..   ..   ..
    c. Surch sideways ..   ..   ..
    d. Surch inverted ..   ..   ..
276   5 t. gold and bright blue   30   60
    a. Opt double ..   ..   ..
    b. Opt double, one inverted ..   ..
    c. Opt inverted..   ..   ..

Stamp booklets containing Nos. 275/6 in strips of three are private productions and were not sold by the Bangladesh Post Office.

92 Demonstrators with Placards   **93** Nurse giving Injection

(Des B. Sardar. Litho State Ptg Wks, Moscow)

1987 (21 Feb). *35th Anniv of Bangla Language Movement. T* **92** *and similar horiz design. Multicoloured. P* 12½ × 12.
277   3 t. Type **92** ..   ..   ..   1·00   1·50
    a. Horiz pair. Nos. 277/8 ..   ..   2·00   3·00
278   3 t. Martyrs' Memorial ..   ..   1·00   1·50
Nos. 277/8 were printed together, *se-tenant*, in horizontal pairs throughout the sheet, each pair forming a composite design.

(Litho State Ptg Wks, Moscow)

1987 (7 Apr). *World Health Day. P* 11½ × 12.
279   **93**   1 t. blue-black and deep blue ..   1·75   1·50
See also No. 295.

94 Pattern and Bengali Script   **95** Jute Shika

(Des M. Akond. Litho State Ptg Wks, Moscow)

1987 (16 Apr). *Bengali New Year. T* **94** *and similar vert design. Multicoloured. P* 12 × 12½.
280   1 t. Type **94**   10   10
281   10 t. Bengali woman   40   60

(Des P. Mandal, K. Mustafa and M. Akond. Photo State Ptg Wks, Moscow)

1987 (18 May). *Export Products. T* **95** *and similar multicoloured designs. P* 12½ × 12 (5 *t.*) *or* 12 × 12½ (*others*).
282   1 t. Type **95**   10   10
283   5 t. Jute carpet (*horiz*)   30   35
284   10 t. Cane table lamp   45   70
282/4 ..   ..   *Set of* 3   70   1·00

96 Ustad Ayet Ali Khan and Surbahar   **97** Palanquin

(Litho State Ptg Wks, Moscow)

1987 (2 Sept). *20th Death Anniv of Ustad Ayet Ali Khan* (*musician and composer*). *P* 12 × 12½.
285   **96**   5 t. multicoloured   55   40

(Litho State Ptg Wks, Moscow)

1987 (24 Oct). *Transport. T* **97** *and similar horiz designs. Multicoloured. P* 12½ × 12.
286   2 t. Type **97**   20   15
287   3 t. Bicycle rickshaw   30   20
288   5 t. River steamer   70   35
289   7 t. Express diesel train ..   ..   1·60   50
290   10 t. Bullock cart   50   75
286/90 ..   ..   *Set of* 5   3·00   1·75

98 H. S. Suhrawardy   **99** Villagers fleeing from Typhoon

(Des P. Mandal. Litho State Ptg Wks, Moscow)

1987 (5 Dec). *Hossain Shahid Suhrawardy* (*politician*) *Commem. P* 12 × 12½.
291   **98**   3 t. multicoloured   20   30

(Des M. Akond. Litho State Ptg Wks, Moscow)

1987 (15 Dec). *International Year of Shelter for the Homeless. T* **99** *and similar horiz design. Multicoloured. P* 12½ × 12.
292   5 t. Type **99**   20   30
    a. Horiz pair. Nos. 292/3   40   60
293   5 t. Villagers and modern houses ..   20   30
Nos. 292/3 were printed together, *se-tenant*, in horizontal pairs throughout the sheet.

100 President Ershad addressing Parliament

(Des K. Mustafa. Litho State Ptg Wks, Moscow)

1987 (31 Dec). *1st Anniv of Return to Democracy. P* 12½ × 12.
294   **100**   10 t. multicoloured   40   60

(Litho State Ptg Wks, Moscow)

1988 (16 Jan). *World Health Day. Vert design as T* **93**. *P* 11½ × 12.
295   25 p. brown   30   20
Design:—25 p. Oral rehydration.

101 Woman Planting Palm Saplings

(Des K. Mustafa. Litho State Ptg Wks, Moscow)

1988 (26 Jan). *I.F.A.D. Seminar on Agricultural Loans for Rural Women. T* **101** *and similar horiz design. Multicoloured. P* 12½ × 12.
296   3 t. Type **101**   15   20
297   5 t. Village woman milking cow ..   20   40

102 Basketball

(Litho State Ptg Wks, Moscow)

1988 (20 Sept). *Olympic Games, Seoul. T* **102** *and similar diamond-shaped designs. Multicoloured. P* 11½.
298   5 t. Type **102**   55   40
    a. Strip of 5. Nos. 298/302 ..   ..   2·50
299   5 t. Weightlifting   55   40
300   5 t. Tennis   55   40
301   5 t. Rifle-shooting   55   40
302   5 t. Boxing   55   40
298/302 ..   ..   ..   *Set of* 5   2·50   1·75
Nos. 298/302 were printed together, *se-tenant*, in horizontal and vertical strips of five throughout the sheet.

103 Interior of Shait Gumbaz Mosque, Bagerhat   **104** Henri Dunant (founder), Red Cross and Crescent

(Litho State Ptg Wks, Moscow)

1988 (9 Oct). *Historical Buildings.* T **103** *and similar horiz designs. Multicoloured.* P 12½×12.
303   1 t. Type **103** 10   10
304   4 t. Paharpur Monastery 20   10
305   5 t. Kantanagar Temple, Dinajpur .. 20   10
306   10 t. Lalbag Fort, Dhaka 30   15
303/6 .. .. *Set of 4* 65   30

(Litho State Ptg Wks, Moscow)

1988 (26 Oct). *125th Anniv of International Red Cross and Red Crescent.* T **104** *and similar vert design. Multicoloured.* P 12 × 12½.
307   5 t. Type **104** 50   25
308   10 t. Red Cross workers with patient .. 90   65

105 Dr. Qudrat-i-   **106** Wicket-keeper
Khuda in Laboratory

(Litho State Ptg Wks, Moscow)

1988 (3 Nov). *Dr. Qudrat-i-Khuda (scientist) Commemoration.* P 12 × 12½.
309 **105** 5 t. multicoloured 30   30

(Litho State Ptg Wks, Moscow)

1988 (27 Nov). *Asia Cup Cricket.* T **106** *and similar vert designs. Multicoloured.* P 12 × 12½.
310   1 t. Type **106** 80   90
     a. Horiz strip of 3. Nos. 310/12 .. 2·75
311   5 t. Batsman .. .. .. 1·00 1·00
312   10 t. Bowler .. .. .. 1·25 1·40
310/12 .. .. .. *Set of 3* 2·75 3·00
   Nos. 310/12 were printed together, *se-tenant*, in horizontal strips of three throughout the sheet.

107 Labourers,
Factory and
Technician

(Litho State Ptg Wks, Moscow)

1988 (29 Nov). *32nd Meeting of Colombo Plan Consultative Committee, Dhaka.* P 12×12½.
313 **107** 3 t. multicoloured 10   10
314   10 t. multicoloured 40   45

108 Dhaka G.P.O. Building

(Litho State Ptg Wks, Moscow)

1988 (6 Dec). *25th Anniv of Dhaka G.P.O. Building.* T **108** *and similar horiz design. Multicoloured.* P 12.
315   1 t. Type **108** 15   10
316   5 t. Post Office counter 30   30

(**109**)

110 Bangladesh Airport

1988 (29 Dec). *5th National Rover Scout Moot.* No. 168 optd with T **109**.
317 **47** 5 t. multicoloured .. .. 1·25 1·25
     a. Opt inverted

(Des K. Mustafa (3, 10 t.), N. Islam (5 t.), M. Akond (20 t.). Litho State Ptg Wks, Moscow)

1989 (1 Jan)–92. *Bangladesh Landmarks.* T **110** *and similar designs.* P 12×11½ (3 t.), 12×12½ (4, 20 t.), 12½×12 (5 t.) or 11½×12 (10 t.).
318   3 t. black and light blue 10   10
318a   4 t. steel blue (15.7.92) 15   20
319   5 t. black and orange-brown (31.3.89) .. 30   20
320   10 t. rosine (1.7.89) 50   35
321   20 t. multicoloured (1.7.89) .. 65   70
318/21 .. .. *Set of 5* 1·50 1·50
   Designs: *Vert* (22×33 *mm*)—5 t. Curzon Hall. (19½×31½ *mm*) 10 t. Fertiliser factory, Chittagong. *Horiz* (33×23 *mm*)— 4 t. Chittagong port. 20 t. Postal Academy, Rajshahi.
   For the 5 t. redrawn and perforated 14½ see No. 710.

**চতুর্থ দ্বিবার্ষিক এশীয়
চারুকলা প্রদর্শনী
বাংলাদেশ ১৯৮৯**

(**111**)

112 Irrigation
Methods and Student
with Telescope

1989 (1 Mar). *4th Biennial Asian Art Exhibition.* No. 266 optd with T **111**.
322   10 t. "Levelling the Ploughed Field" (Zainul Abedin) 40   45

(Litho State Ptg Wks, Moscow)

1989 (7 Mar). *12th National Science and Technology Week.* P 12×12½.
323 **112** 10 t. multicoloured 40   45

113 Academy Logo   **114** Rejoicing Crowds, Paris, 1789

(Litho State Ptg Wks, Moscow)

1989 (13 Mar). *75th Anniv of Police Academy, Sardah.* P 12×12½.
324 **113** 10 t. multicoloured 50   45

(Des K. Mustafa (Nos. MS327/8). Litho Harrison)

1989 (12 July). *Bicentenary of French Revolution.* T **114** *and similar horiz design. Multicoloured.* P 14×14½.
325   17 t. Type **114** 70   75
     a. Horiz pair. Nos. 325/6 plus label 1·40 1·50
326   17 t. Storming the Bastille, 1789 .. 70   75
MS327   125×125 mm. 5 t. Men with pickaxes; 10 t. "Liberty guiding the People" (detail) (Delacroix); 10 t. Crowd with cannon. P 14 .. 2·00 2·75
MS328   152×88 mm. 25 t. Storming the Bastille. Imperf .. .. .. 2·00 2·75
   Nos. 325/6 were printed in sheets of 30 (6×5) with No. 325 in vertical columns one and four, labels showing the Bicentenary emblem in columns two and five, and No. 326 in columns three and six.
   The design of No. **MS**328 incorporates the three scenes featured on No. **MS**327.

115 Sowing and Harvesting

(Litho State Ptg Wks, Moscow)

1989 (10 Aug). *10th Anniv of Asia-Pacific Integrated Rural Development Centre.* T **115** *and similar horiz design. Multicoloured.* P 12½×12.
329   5 t. Type **115** 45   45
     a. Horiz pair. Nos. 329/30 .. 95   95
330   10 t. Rural activities 50   50
   Nos. 329/30 were printed together, *se-tenant*, in horizontal pairs throughout the sheet, each pair forming a composite design.

**STANLEY GIBBONS
STAMP COLLECTING SERIES**

Introductory booklets on *How to Start, How to Identify Stamps* and *Collecting by Theme.* A series of well illustrated guides at a low price.
Write for details.

---

116 Helper and Child playing   **117** U.N. Soldier on
with Baby   Watch

1989 (22 Aug). *40th Anniv of S.O.S. International Children's Village.* T **116** *and similar horiz design. Multicoloured.* P 12½ × 12.
331   1 t. Type **116** 15   10
332   10 t. Foster mother with children .. 55   55

(Litho State Ptg Wks, Moscow)

1989 (12 Sept). *1st Anniv of Bangladesh Participation in U.N. Peace-keeping Force.* T **117** *and similar vert design. Multicoloured.* P 12×12½.
333   4 t. Type **117** 50   30
334   10 t. Two soldiers checking positions .. 1·00 70

118 Festival Emblem   **119** State Security Printing
Press

(Litho State Ptg Wks, Moscow)

1989 (17 Nov). *2nd Asian Poetry Festival, Dhaka.* T **118** *and similar vert design.* P 12×12½.
335   2 t. brt scarlet, dp carmine & myrtle-green .. 15   10
336   10 t. multicoloured 60   65
   Design:—10 t. Festival emblem and hall.

(Litho State Security Ptg Press, Gazipur)

1989 (7 Dec). *Inauguration of State Security Printing Press, Gazipur.* P 13½.
337 **119** 10 t. multicoloured 65   65

120 Water Lilies and T.V.
Emblem

(Litho State Ptg Wks, Moscow (5 t.), State Security Ptg Press, Gazipur (10 t.))

1989 (25 Dec). *25th Anniv of Bangladesh Television.* T **120** *and similar horiz design. Multicoloured.* P 12½×12 (5 t.) or 13½ (10 t.).
338   5 t. Type **120** 30   30
339   10 t. Central emblem and water lilies .. 65   80

121 Gharial in Shallow Water   **122** Symbolic Family

(Des K. Mustafa. Litho Harrison)

1990 (31 Jan). *Endangered Wildlife. Gharial.* T **121** *and similar horiz designs. Multicoloured.* P 14.
340   50 p. Type **121** 80   45
     a. Block of 4. Nos. 340/3 .. 4·50
341   2 t. Gharial feeding .. .. 1·00 60
342   4 t. Gharials basking on sand bank .. 1·40 70
343   10 t. Two gharials resting .. 1·75 95
340/3 .. .. *Set of 4* 4·50 2·40
   Nos. 340/3 were printed together, *se-tenant*, in blocks of four throughout the sheet.

(Litho State Ptg Press, Gazipur)

1990 (10 Feb). *Population Day.* P 13½.
344 **122** 6 t. multicoloured 55   35

sandafayre.com

The World's Largest Postal Auction Company

Classics to **thematics**

Errors to **Airmails**

Fine and **scarce**

Cartons and box lots

And **Always** the **Unusual**

Albums albums albums

SANDAFAYRE

Knutsford. Cheshire. UK WA16 8XN. Tel: +44 (0)1565 653214 Fax: +44 (0)1565 651637 E-mail: stamp@sandafayre.com

---

Complete this card for your <u>FREE</u> Catalogue

Name
_____

Address
_____

_____

Country
_____

Area of Special Interest
_____

Also please send a <u>FREE</u> Catalogue to my friend

Name
_____

Address
_____

_____

Country
_____

Area of Special Interest
_____

123 Justice S.M. Murshed   **124** Boy learning Alphabet

(Des P. Mandal. Litho State Ptg Wks, Moscow)

1990 (3 Apr). *10th Death Anniv of Justice Syed Mahbub Murshed.* P 12½×12.
345 **123** 5 t. multicoloured .. .. .. 1·25 35

(Litho State Ptg Wks, Moscow)

1990 (10 Apr). *International Literacy Year. T* **124** *and similar vert design. Multicoloured.* P 12×12½.
346 6 t. Type **124** .. .. .. 1·00 50
347 10 t. Boy teaching girl to write .. 1·50 1·00

125 Penny Black with "Stamp World London 90" Exhibition Emblem   **126** Goalkeeper and Ball

(Des K. Mustafa. Litho State Security Ptg Press, Gazipur)

1990 (6 May). *150th Anniv of the Penny Black. T* **125** *and similar vert design. Multicoloured.* P 13½.
348 7 t. Type **125** .. .. 1·50 60
349 10 t. Penny Black, 1983 World Communications Year stamp and Bengali mail runner .. .. 1·75 1·00

(Des M. Shamim. Litho State Security Ptg Press, Gazipur)

1990 (12 June). *World Cup Football Championship, Italy. T* **126** *and similar horiz designs. Multicoloured.* P 13½.
350 8 t. Type **126** .. .. 1·75 90
351 10 t. Footballer with ball .. 2·00 1·00
MS352 104×79 mm. 25 t. Colosseum, Rome, with football. Imperf .. 6·00 6·50
    a. Country and commemorative inscrs inverted
On No. MS352a "BANGLADESH WORLD CUP FOOTBALL ITALY 1990" at the foot of the design is in white with the same inscriptions in blue inverted at the top of the miniature sheet.

127 Mango   **128** Man gathering Wheat

(Des M. Shamim (1, 2t.), N. Islam (3, 4 t.), P. Mandal (5, 10 t.). Litho State Ptg Wks, Moscow)

1990 (16 July). *Fruit. T* **127** *and similar vert designs. Multicoloured.* P 12×12½.
353 1 t. Type **127** 30 10
354 2 t. Guava 30 10
355 3 t. Water-melon 35 15
356 4 t. Papaya 40 25
357 5 t. Bread fruit 65 50
358 10 t. Carambola .. .. 1·25 1·25
353/8 .. .. .. *Set of 6* 3·00 2·00

PRINTERS. The following issues were printed in lithography by the State Security Printing Press, Gazipur, *unless otherwise stated.*

(Des M. Akond)

1990 (3 Sept). *U.N. Conference on Least Developed Countries, Paris.* P 14.
359 **128** 10 t. multicoloured .. .. 1·25 90
    a. Blue (U.N. emblem and inscr) inverted
On the evidence of the sheet marginal markings it would appear that the blue on No. 359a may be printed correctly and the remainder of the colours inverted. Unequal margins at top and bottom of the sheet also cause the country name and face value, in green, to be displaced.

129 Map of Asia with Stream of Letters   **130** Canoe Racing

(Des K. Mustafa)

1990 (10 Sept). *20th Anniv of Asia–Pacific Postal Training Centre. T* **129** *and similar vert design. Multicoloured.* P 13½×14.
360 2 t. Type **129** 90 65
    a. Horiz pair. Nos. 360/1 .. 1·75 1·25
361 6 t. Map of Pacific with stream of letters 90 65
Nos. 360/1 were printed together, *se-tenant,* in horizontal pairs throughout the sheet, forming a composite map design.

(Des K. Mustafa)

1990 (22 Sept). *Asian Games, Beijing. T* **130** *and similar horiz designs. Multicoloured.* P 14×13½.
362 2 t. Type **130** 70 20
363 4 t. Kabaddi 85 25
364 8 t. Wrestling .. .. 1·40 1·00
365 10 t. Badminton .. .. 2·25 1·50
362/5 .. .. *Set of 4* 4·75 2·75

131 Lalan Shah   **132** U.N. Logo and "40"

(Des K. Mustafa)

1990 (17 Oct). *1st Death Anniv of Lalan Shah (poet).* P 13½×14.
366 **131** 6 t. multicoloured .. .. 1·00 35

(Des M. Akond)

1990 (24 Oct). *40th Anniv of United Nations Development Programme.* P 14×13½.
367 **132** 6 t. multicoloured 80 35

133 Baby   **134** *Danaus chrysippus*

(Des M. Akond)

1990 (29 Nov). *Immunization.* P 14½×14.
368 **133** 1 t. emerald 25 25
369 2 t. brown 25 15

(Des M. Shamim)

1990 (3 Dec). *Butterflies. T* **134** *and similar square designs. Multicoloured.* P 13½×12.
370 6 t. Type **134** .. .. 1·60 1·60
    a. Block of 4. Nos. 370/3 .. 6·00
    ab. Deep blue and chestnut inscr inverted (block of 4) .. ..
371 6 t. *Precis almana* .. .. 1·60 1·60
372 10 t. *Ixias pyrene* .. .. 1·75 1·75
373 10 t. *Danaus plexippus* .. 1·75 1·75
370/3 .. .. *Set of 4* 6·00 6·00
Nos. 370/3 were printed together, *se-tenant,* in blocks of four throughout the sheet.
On No. 370ab the printing of "BANGLADESH", in deep blue on No. 371 and in chestnut on No. 372, is inverted so that the inscription does not occur on these two designs. The inverted deep blue "BANGLADESH" appears on the left sheet margin of No. 373 and the chestnut on No. 370.

135 Drugs attacking Bangladesh   **136** Salimullah Hall

(Des F. Karim (2 t.), M. Akond (4 t.))

1991 (1 Jan). *United Nations Anti-Drugs Decade. T* **135** *and similar horiz design. Multicoloured.* P 14.
374 2 t. Type **135** .. .. 1·00 50
375 4 t. "Drug" snake around globe .. 1·25 1·25

(Des P. Mandal)

1991 (30 Jan). P 14½×14.
376 **136** 6 t. slate-blue and greenish yellow 20 25

137 Silhouetted People on Map   **138** "Invincible Bangla" (statue)

(Des P. Mandal)

1991 (12 Mar). *Third National Census.* P 14.
382 **137** 4 t. multicoloured 65 60

(Des M. Akond)

1991 (26 Mar). *20th Anniv of Independence. T* **138** *and similar square designs. Multicoloured.* P 13½.
383 4 t. Type **138** 55 65
    a. Horiz strip of 5. Nos. 383/7 .. 2·50
384 4 t. "Freedom Fighter" (statue) .. 55 65
385 4 t. Mujibnagar Memorial .. 55 65
386 4 t. Eternal Flame .. 55 65
387 4 t. National Martyrs' Memorial .. 55 65
383/7 .. .. *Set of 5* 2·50 3·00
Nos. 383/7 were printed together, *se-tenant,* in horizontal strips of five throughout the sheet, with the backgrounds forming a composite design.

139 Pres. Rahman Seated   **140** Red Giant Flying Squirrel

(Des P. Mandal. Litho Ueberreuter, Austria)

1991 (30 May). *10th Death Anniv of President Ziaur Rahman. T* **139** *and similar vert design. Multicoloured.* P 13½×14.
388 50 p. Type **139** 20 15
389 2 t. President Rahman's head in circular decoration 65 85
MS390 146 × 75 mm. Nos. 388/9 (*sold at* 10 t.) .. 1·25 1·75

(Des K. Mustafa)

1991 (16 June). *Endangered Species. T* **140** *and similar multicoloured designs.* P 12.
391 2 t. Type **140** .. .. 1·10 1·40
    a. Vert pair. Nos. 391 and 394 .. 2·10 2·75
392 4 t. Black-faced Monkey (*vert*) .. 1·10 1·40
    a. Horiz pair. Nos. 392/3 .. 2·10 2·75
393 6 t. Great Indian Hornbill (*vert*) .. 1·10 1·40
394 10 t. Armoured Pangolin .. 1·10 1·40
391/4 .. .. *Set of 4* 4·00 5·00
Nos. 391 and 394, and 392/3 were printed together, *se-tenant,* in vertical (Nos. 391 and 394) or horizontal (Nos. 392/3) pairs throughout separate sheets.

141 Kaikobad   **142** Rabindranath Tagore and Temple

(Des K. Mustafa)

1991 (21 July). *40th Death Anniv of Kaikobad (poet).* P 14.
395 **141** 6 t. multicoloured 80 60

(Des A. Karim)

1991 (7 Aug). *50th Death Anniv of Rabindranath Tagore (poet).* P 14.
396 **142** 4 t. multicoloured 70 55

143 Voluntary Blood Donation Programme

144 Shahid Naziruddin and Crowd

(Des P. Mandal)

1991 (19 Sept). *14th Anniv of "Sandhani" (medical students' association). T* **143** *and similar vert design. P* 14.

397	3 t. black and bright carmine	..	75	50
398	5 t. multicoloured	..	1·25	1·50

Design:—5 t. Blind man and eye

1991 (10 Oct). *1st Death Anniv of Shahid Naziruddin Jahad (democrat). P* 14.

399	**144** 2 t. black, emerald and cinnamon		55	50
	a. Emerald ("BANGLADESH" and face value) omitted		£100	

145 Shaheed Noor Hossain with Slogan on Chest

146 Bronze Stupa

(Des K. Mustafa)

1991 (10 Nov). *4th Death Anniv of Shaheed Noor Hossain (democrat). P* 14.

400	**145** 2 t. multicoloured	..	45	40

(Des M. Akond)

1991 (26 Nov). *Archaeological Relics from Mainamati. T* **146** *and similar horiz designs. Multicoloured. P* 13½.

401	4 t. Type **146**		1·00	1·10
	a. Horiz strip of 5. Nos. 401/5		4·50	
402	4 t. Earthenware and bronze pitchers		1·00	1·10
403	4 t. Remains of Salban Vihara Monastery		1·00	1·10
404	4 t. Gold coins		1·00	1·10
405	4 t. Terracotta plaque		1·00	1·10
401/5		*Set of 5*	4·50	5·00

Nos. 401/5 were printed together, *se-tenant*, in horizontal strips of 5 throughout the sheet.

147 Demonstrators

148 Munier Chowdhury

(Des. M. Muniruzzaman)

1991 (6 Dec). *1st Anniv of Mass Uprising. P* 13½.

406	**147** 4 t. multicoloured	..	75	50

1991 (14 Dec). *20th Anniv of Independence. Martyred Intellectuals* (1st series). *T* **148** *and similar vert designs. Each grey-black and reddish brown. P* 13½.

407	2 t. Type **148**	..	30	30
	a. Sheetlet. Nos. 407/16		2·75	
408	2 t. Ghyasuddin Ahmad	..	30	30
409	2 t. Rashidul Hasan	..	30	30
410	2 t. Muhammad Anwar Pasha	..	30	30
411	2 t. Dr. Muhammad Mortaza	..	30	30
412	2 t. Shahid Saber	..	30	30
413	2 t. Fazlur Rahman Khan	..	30	30
414	2 t. Ranada Prasad Saha	..	30	30
415	2 t. Adhyaksha Joges Chandra Ghose		30	30
416	2 t. Santosh Chandra Bhattacharyya		30	30
417	2 t. Dr. Gobinda Chandra Deb	..	30	30
	a. Sheetlet. Nos. 417/26		2·75	
418	2 t. A. Muniruzzaman	..	30	30
419	2 t. Mufazzal Haider Chaudhury	..	30	30
420	2 t. Dr. Abdul Alim Choudhury	..	30	30
421	2 t. Sirajuddin Hossain	..	30	30
422	2 t. Shahidulla Kaiser	..	30	30

423	2 t. Altaf Mahmud	..	30	30
424	2 t. Dr. Jyotirmay Guha Thakurta	..	30	30
425	2 t. Dr. Muhammad Abul Khair	..	30	30
426	2 t. Dr. Serajul Haque Khan	..	30	30
427	2 t. Dr. Mohammad Fazle Rabbi	..	30	30
	a. Sheetlet. Nos. 427/36		2·75	
428	2 t. Mir Abdul Quyyum	..	30	30
429	2 t. Golam Mostafa	..	30	30
430	2 t. Dhirendranath Dutta	..	30	30
431	2 t. S. Mannan	..	30	30
432	2 t. Nizamuddin Ahmad	..	30	30
433	2 t. Abul Bashar Chowdhury	..	30	30
434	2 t. Selina Parveen	..	30	30
435	2 t. Dr. Abul Kalam Azad	..	30	30
436	2 t. Saidul Hassan	..	30	30
407/36		*Set of 30*	8·00	8·00

Nos. 407/16, 417/26 and 427/36 were printed together, *se-tenant*, in sheetlets of 10, the two horizontal rows in each sheetlet being separated by a row of inscribed labels.

See also Nos. 483/92, 525/40, 568/83, 620/35, 656/71 and 691/706.

149 *Penaeus monodon*

1991 (31 Dec). *Shrimps. T* **149** *and similar horiz design. Multicoloured. P* 14×13½.

437	6 t. Type **149**	..	1·25	1·50
	a. Horiz pair. Nos. 437/8		2·50	3·00
438	6 t. *Metapenaeus monoceros*		1·25	1·50

Nos. 437/8 were printed together, *se-tenant*, in horizontal pairs throughout the sheet.

150 Death of Raihan Jaglu

151 Rural and Urban Scenes

(Des M. Muniruzzaman)

1992 (8 Feb). *5th Death Anniv of Shaheed Mirze Abu Raihan Jaglu. P* 14×13½.

439	**150** 2 t. multicoloured	..	60	50

(Des K. Mustafa (4 t.), A. Karim (10 t.))

1992 (5 June). *World Environment Day. T* **151** *and similar multicoloured design. P* 14.

440	4 t. Type **151**		50	15
441	10 t. World Environment Day logo (*horiz*)	1·25	1·75

152 Nawab Sirajuddaulah

153 Syed Ismail Hossain Sirajee

(Des K. Mustafa)

1992 (2 July). *235th Death Anniv of Nawab Sirajuddaulah of Bengal. P* 13½.

442	**152** 10 t. multicoloured		80	80
	a. Emerald ("BANGLADESH" inscr) omitted		£100	

1992 (17 July). *61st Death Anniv of Syed Ismail Hossain Sirajee. P* 14.

443	**153** 4 t. multicoloured	..	60	40

154 Couple planting Seedling

(Des M. Huq and M. Muniruzzaman)

1992 (19 July). *Plant Week. T* **154** *and similar multicoloured design. P* 14.

444	2 t. Type **154**	..	85	70
445	4 t. Birds on tree (*vert*)	..	85	70

155 Canoe Racing

Banglapex '92
(156)

(Des M. Akond, M. Mia and S. Datta)

1992 (25 July). *Olympic Games, Barcelona. T* **155** *and similar horiz designs. Multicoloured. P* 14.

446	4 t. Type **155**		90	1·00
	a. Block of 4. Nos. 446/9		3·25	
447	6 t. Hands holding torch with Olympic rings		90	1·00
448	10 t. Olympic rings and doves		90	1·00
449	10 t. Olympic rings and multiracial hand-shake		90	1·00
446/9		*Set of 4*	3·25	3·50

Nos. 446/9 were printed together, *se-tenant*, in blocks of four throughout the sheet of 100 with the two 10 t. values occurring in the first, third, fifth, seventh and ninth horizontal rows.

1992 (18 Aug). *"Banglapex '92", National Philatelic Exhibition* (1st issue). *No.* 290 *optd with T* **156**.

450	10 t. Bullock cart	..	1·00	1·25

157 Masnad-e-Ala Isa Khan

158 Ceremonial Elephant (19th-century ivory carving)

1992 (15 Sept). *393rd Death Anniv of Masnad-e-Ala Isa Khan. P* 14.

451	**157** 4 t. multicoloured	..	60	40

(Des M. Begum)

1992 (26 Sept). *"Banglapex '92", National Philatelic Exhibition* (2nd issue). *T* **158** *and similar horiz design. Multicoloured. P* 14.

452	10 t. Type **158**		1·00	1·25
	a. Horiz pair. Nos. 452/3 plus label		2·00	2·50
453	10 t. Victorian pillarbox between early and modern postmen		1·00	1·25
MS454	145×92 mm. Nos. 452/3 plus label. Imperf (*sold at* 25 t.)		2·50	3·00

Nos. 452/3 were printed together, *se-tenant*, in sheets with No. 452 in vertical columns one and four, labels showing the exhibition emblem in columns two and five, and No. 453 in columns three and six.

159 Star Mosque

(Des Md. Jasimuddin)

1992 (29 Oct). *Star Mosque, Dhaka. P* 14½×13½.

455	**159** 10 t. multicoloured	..	90	90

160 Meer Nisar Ali Titumeer and Fort

(Des M. Akond)

1992 (19 Nov). *161st Death Anniv of Meer Nisar Ali Titumeer. P* 14½×13½.

456	**160** 10 t. multicoloured	..	90	90

161 Terracotta Head and Seal

(Des M. Akond, M. Begum and M. Mia)

1992 (30 Nov). *Archaeological Relics from Mahasthangarh.*
T **161** *and similar horiz designs. Multicoloured. P* 14½×13½.

457	10 t. Type **161**	..	1·10	1·25
	a. Horiz strip of 4. Nos. 457/60	..	4·00	
458	10 t. Terracotta panel showing swan	..	1·10	1·25
459	10 t. Terracotta statue of Surya	..	1·10	1·25
460	10 t. Gupta stone column	..	1·10	1·25
457/60		*Set of* 4	4·00	4·50

Nos. 457/60 were printed together, *se-tenant*, in horizontal
strips of 4 throughout the sheet.

162 Young Child and Food   163 National Flags

(Des M. Muniruzzaman)

1992 (5 Dec). *International Conference on Nutrition, Rome.*
P 14½×13½.

461	**162**	4 t. multicoloured	..	60	40

(Des N. Islam (6 t.), M. Akond (10 t.))

1992 (5 Dec). *7th South Asian Association for Regional*
Co-operation Summit Conference, Dhaka. T **163** *and similar*
vert design. Multicoloured. P 13½×14½.

462		6 t. Type **163**	..	60	60
463		10 t. S.A.A.R.C. emblem	..	80	90

164 Syed Abdus Samad   165 Haji Shariat Ullah

(Des P. Mandal)

1993 (2 Feb). *Syed Abdus Samad (footballer) Commemoration.*
P 14.

464	**164**	2 t. multicoloured	..	70	50

(Des M. Rahman)

1993 (10 Mar). *Haji Shariat Ullah Commemoration. P* 14½.

465	**165**	2 t. multicoloured	..	60	40

166 People digging Canal

(Des M. Rahman)

1993 (31 Mar). *Irrigation Canals Construction Project. T* **166**
and similar horiz design. Multicoloured. P 14.

466		2 t. Type **166**	..	45	55
		a. Horiz pair. Nos. 466/7	..	90	1·10
467		2 t. Completed canal and paddy-fields	..	45	55

Nos. 466/7 were printed together, *se-tenant*, in horizontal
pairs throughout the sheet.

MINIMUM PRICE

The minimum price quote is 10p which represents
a handling charge rather than a basis for valuing
common stamps. For further notes about prices
see introductory pages.

---

167 Accident Prevention   168 National Images

(Des A. Hussain (6 t.), N. Islam (10 t.))

1993 (7 Apr). *World Health Day. T* **167** *and similar*
multicoloured design. P 14.

468		6 t. Type **167**	..	1·25	75
469		10 t. Satellite photograph and symbols of			
		trauma (*vert*)	..	1·50	1·75

(Des Md. Shamsuzzoha)

1993 (14 Apr). *1400th Year of Bengali Solar Calendar. P* 14.

470	**168**	2 t. multicoloured	..	55	40

169 Schoolchildren   170 Nawab Sir Salimullah and
and Bengali Script   Palace

(Des M. Huq (No. 471), M. Mia (No. 472))

1993 (26 May). *Compulsory Primary Education. T* **169** *and*
similar multicoloured design. P 14×14½ (*No.* 471) *or*
14½×14 (*No.* 472).

471		2 t. Type **169**	..	40	50
472		2 t. Books and slate (*horiz*)	..	40	50

(Des S. Shaheen)

1993 (7 June). *122nd Birth Anniv of Nawab Sir Salimullah.*
P 14½×14.

473	**170**	4 t. multicoloured	..	55	40

171 Fish Production

(Des M. Rahman)

1993 (15 Aug). *Fish Fortnight. P* 14½×14.

474	**171**	2 t. multicoloured	..	30	30

172 Sunderban   173 Exhibition Emblem

(Des M. Mia, M. Rahman and B. Biswas)

1993 (30 Oct). *Natural Beauty of Bangladesh. T* **172** *and*
similar multicoloured designs. P 14½×14 (*horiz*) *or* 14×14½
(*vert*).

475		10 t. Type **172**	..	70	90
476		10 t. Kuakata beach	..	70	90
477		10 t. Madhabkunda waterfall (*vert*)	..	70	90
478		10 t. River Piyain, Jaflang (*vert*)	..	70	90
475/8			*Set of* 4	2·50	3·25
MS479	174×102 mm. Nos. 475/8. Imperf. (*sold at*				
	50 t.)			2·75	3·25

No. 476 and the same design in No. **MS**479 also exist with
smaller country name and inscr "TOURISM MONTH '93" in
English and Bengali. This version was not issued.

(Des Q. Chowdhury)

1993 (2 Nov). *6th Asian Art Biennale. P* 14×14½.

480	**173**	10 t. multicoloured	..	60	80

---

174 Foy's Lake   175 Burdwan
House

(Des A. Hussain)

1993 (6 Nov). *Tourism Month. P* 14½×14.

481	**174**	10 t. multicoloured	..	70	90

(Des N. Islam)

1993 (3 Dec). *Foundation Day, Bangla Academy. P* 14×14½.

482	**175**	2 t. deep brown and emerald	..	30	20

1993 (14 Dec). *Martyred Intellectuals (2nd series). Vert designs*
as T **148**. *Each grey-black and reddish brown. P* 14½.

483	2 t. Lt. Cdr. Moazzam Hussain	..	15	20
	a. Sheetlet. Nos. 483/92	..	1·25	
484	2 t. Muhammad Habibur Rahman	..	15	20
485	2 t. Khandoker Abu Taleb	..	15	20
486	2 t. Moshiur Rahman	..	15	20
487	2 t. Md Abdul Muktadir	..	15	20
488	2 t. Nutan Chandra Sinha	..	15	20
489	2 t. Syed Nazmul Haque	..	15	20
490	2 t. Dr. Mohammed Amin Uddin	..	15	20
491	2 t. Dr. Faizul Mohee	..	15	20
492	2 t. Sukha Ranjan Somaddar	..	15	20
483/92		*Set of* 10	1·25	1·75

Nos. 483/92 were printed together, *se-tenant*, as a sheetlet of
10, the two horizontal rows being separated by a row of inscribed
labels.

176 Throwing the Discus

1993 (19 Dec). *6th South Asian Federation Games, Dhaka.*
T **176** *and similar multicoloured design. P* 14½×14 (2 t.) *or*
14×14½ (4 t.).

493	2 t. Type **176**	..	15	15
	a. Rose-lilac, yellow-brown and orange			
	(parts of logo) omitted			
494	4 t. Running (*vert*)	..	25	25
	a. Yellow-brown (part of logo) omitted	£100	

177 Tomb of Sultan   178 Scouting Activities
Ghiyasuddin Azam Shah   and Jamboree Emblem

(Des Md. Shamsuzzoha)

1993 (30 Dec). *Muslim Monuments. P* 14½×14.

495	**177**	10 t. multicoloured	..	60	70

(Des A. Hussain)

1994 (5 Jan). *14th Asian-Pacific and 5th Bangladesh National*
Scout Jamboree. P 14×14½.

496	**178**	2 t. multicoloured	..	30	30

179 Emblem and Mother   180 Interior of Chhota Sona
giving Solution to Child   Mosque, Nawabgonj

(Des Md. Shamsuzzoha)

1994 (5 Feb). *25th Anniv of Oral Rehydration Solution.*
P 14×14½.

497	**179**	2 t. multicoloured	..	30	30

BANGLADESH — 1994

(Des A. Hussain, M. Huq and M. Rahman)

1994 (30 Mar). *Ancient Mosques. T 180 and similar horiz designs. Multicoloured. P 14½×14.*
498	4 t. Type 180		15	15
499	6 t. Exterior of Chhota Sona Mosque		30	40
500	6 t. Exterior of Baba Adam's Mosque, Munshigonj		30	40
498/500		Set of 3	65	85

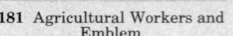

181 Agricultural Workers and Emblem

182 Priest releasing Peace Doves

(Des R. Hussain and M. Huq)

1994 (11 Apr). *75th Anniv of International Labour Organization. T 181 and similar multicoloured design. P 14½×14 (4 t.) or 14×14½ (10 t.).*
501	4 t. Type 181		15	15
	a. Bright blue ("BANGLADESH" inscr) omitted		£150	
502	10 t. Worker turning cog (vert)		60	85

(Des A. Hussain)

1994 (14 Apr). *1500th Year of Bengali Solar Calendar. P 14×14½.*
503	**182** 2 t. multicoloured		15	15

183 Scenes from Baishakhi Festival

184 Family, Globe and Logo

(Des A. Hussain)

1994 (12 May). *Folk Festivals. T 183 and similar horiz design. Multicoloured. P 14½×14.*
504	4 t. Type 183		25	25
505	4 t. Scenes from Nabanna and Paush Parvana Festivals		25	25

(Des M. Huq)

1994 (15 May). *International Year of the Family. P 14×14½.*
506	**184** 10 t. multicoloured		80	1·00

185 People planting Saplings

186 Player kicking Ball

(Des M. Mia and R. Hussain)

1994 (15 June). *Tree Planting Campaign. T 185 and similar vert design. Multicoloured. P 14×14½.*
507	4 t. Type 185		25	15
508	6 t. Hands holding saplings		40	50

(Des M. Shamim)

1994 (17 June). *World Cup Football Championship, U.S.A. T 186 and similar vert design. Multicoloured. P 14½.*
509	20 t. Type 186		1·75	2·25
	a. Horiz strip of 3. Nos. 509/10 and label		3·50	
510	20 t. Player heading ball		1·75	2·25

Nos. 509/10 were printed together, *se-tenant,* in sheets of 15 (3×5) with each horizontal row containing one of each design separated by a label showing the championship mascot.

NEW INFORMATION

The editor is always interested to correspond with people who have new information that will improve or correct the Catalogue.

196

187 Traffic on Bridge

188 Asian Black-headed Oriole

(Des A. Rouf)

1994 (24 July). *Inauguration of Jamuna Multi-purpose Bridge Project. P 14½×14.*
511	**187** 4 t. multicoloured		40	30

(Des A. Hussain)

1994 (31 Aug). *Birds. T 188 and similar vert designs. Multicoloured. P 14×14½.*
512	4 t. Type 188		40	40
513	6 t. Greater Racquet-tailed Drongo (Dicrurus paradiseus)		60	80
514	6 t. Indian Tree Pie (Dendrocitta vagabunda)		60	80
515	6 t. Red Junglefowl (Gallus gallus)		60	80
512/15		Set of 4	2·00	2·50
MS516	165×110 mm. Nos. 512/15 (sold at 25 t.)		2·00	2·75

189 Dr. Mohammad Ibrahim and Hospital

190 Nawab Faizunnessa Chowdhurani

(Des M. Shamim)

1994 (6 Sept). *5th Death Anniv of Dr. Mohammad Ibrahim (diabetes treatment pioneer). P 14½×14.*
517	**189** 2 t. multicoloured		30	20

(Des M. Rahman)

1994 (23 Sept). *160th Birth Anniv of Nawab Faizunnessa Chowdhurani (social reformer). P 14×14½.*
518	**190** 2 t. multicoloured		20	20

191 Boxing

(Des A. Hussain)

1994 (2 Oct). *Asian Games, Hiroshima, Japan. P 14½×14.*
519	**191** 4 t. multicoloured		60	30

192 Pink and White Pearls with Windowpane Oysters

(Des M. Mia, M. Rahman and Md. Shamsuzzoha)

1994 (30 Oct). *Sea Shells. T 192 and similar multicoloured designs. P 14×14½ (No. 523) or 14½×14 (others).*
520	6 t. Type 192		60	70
521	6 t. Tranquelous Scallop and other shells		60	70
522	6 t. Lister's Conch, Asiatic Arabian Cowrie, Bladder Moon and Woodcock Murex		60	70
523	6 t. Spotted Tun, Spiny Frog Shell, Spiral Melongena and Gibbous Olive		60	70
520/3		Set of 4	2·25	2·50

193 Dr. Milon and Demonstrators

194 *Diplazium esculentum*

(Des M. Akond)

1994 (27 Nov). *4th Death Anniv of Dr. Shamsul Alam Khan Milon (medical reformer). P 14½×14.*
524	**193** 2 t. multicoloured		15	15

(Des M. Huq, A. Hussain, M. Mia, A. Moniruzzaman, M. Rahman and Md. Shamsuzzoha)

1994 (14 Dec). *Martyred Intellectuals (3rd series). Vert designs as T 148. Each grey-black and reddish brown. P 14×14½.*
525	2 t. Dr. Harinath Dey		15	15
	a. Sheetlet. Nos. 525/32		1·10	
526	2 t. Dr. A. F. Ziaur Rahman		15	15
527	2 t. Mamun Mahmud		15	15
528	2 t. Mohsin Ali Dewan		15	15
529	2 t. Dr. N. A. M. Jahangir		15	15
530	2 t. Shah Abdul Majid		15	15
531	2 t. Muhammad Akhter		15	15
532	2 t. Meherunnesa		15	15
533	2 t. Dr. Kasiruddin Talukder		15	15
	a. Sheetlet. Nos. 533/40		1·10	
534	2 t. Fazlul Haque Choudhury		15	15
535	2 t. Md. Shamsuzzaman		15	15
536	2 t. A. K. M. Shamsuddin		15	15
537	2 t. Lt. Mohammad Anwarul Azim		15	15
538	2 t. Nurul Amin Khan		15	15
539	2 t. Mohammad Sadeque		15	15
540	2 t. Md. Araz Ali		15	15
525/40		Set of 16	2·00	2·00

Nos. 525/32 and 533/40 were printed together, *se-tenant,* in sheetlets of 8, the two horizontal rows in each sheetlet being separated by a row of inscribed labels.

(Des A. Hussain, N. Islam and Md. Shamsuzzoha)

1994 (24 Dec). *Vegetables. T 194 and similar multicoloured designs. P 14½×14 (No. 546) or 14×14½ (others).*
541	4 t. Type 194		30	20
542	4 t. Momordica charantia		30	20
543	6 t. Lagenaria siceraria		50	40
544	6 t. Trichosanthes dioica		50	40
545	10 t. Solanum melongena		80	1·10
546	10 t. Cucurbita maxima (horiz)		80	1·10
541/6		Set of 6	2·75	3·00

195 Sonargaon

(Des A. Hussain)

1995 (2 Jan). *20th Anniv of World Tourism Organization. P 14½.*
547	**195** 10 t. multicoloured		75	80

196 Exports

(Des M. Huq)

1995 (7 Jan). *Dhaka International Trade Fair '95. T 196 and similar horiz design. Multicoloured. P 14½.*
548	4 t. Type 196		20	20
549	6 t. Symbols of industry		45	55

197 Soldiers of Ramgarh Battalion (1795) and of Bangladesh Rifles (1995)

(Des M. Rahman and Md. Shamsuzzoha)

1995 (10 Jan). *Bicentenary of Bangladesh Rifles. T* **197** *and similar horiz design. Multicoloured. P* 14½.
550 2 t. Type **197** 25 25
551 4 t. Riflemen on patrol 45 45

198 Surgical Equipment and Lightning attacking Crab (cancer)

199 Fresh Food and Boy injecting Insulin

(Des M. Rohana)

1995 (7 Apr). *Campaign against Cancer. P* 14×14½.
552 **198** 2 t. multicoloured 30 20

(Des N. Islam)

1995 (28 Feb). *National Diabetes Awareness Day. P* 14.
553 **199** 2 t. multicoloured 30 20

200 Munshi Mohammad Meherullah

রাজশাহীপেক্স-৯৫ (201)

(Des M. Huq)

1995 (7 June). *Munshi Mohammad Meherullah (Islamic educator) Commemoration. P* 14×14½.
554 **200** 2 t. multicoloured 20 20

1995 (23 Aug). *"Rajshahipex '95" National Philatelic Exhibition. No.* 499 *optd with T* **201** *in red.*
555 6 t. Exterior of Chhota Sona Mosque 75 75

202 Lagerstroemia speciosa

203 Aspects of Farming

(Des A. Hussain, Md. Shamsuzzoha, Md. Jasimuddin, M. Muniruzzaman)

1995 (9 Oct). *Flowers. T* **202** *and similar multicoloured designs. P* 14½.
556 6 t. Type **202** 60 60
557 6 t. Bombax ceiba (horiz) .. 60 60
558 10 t. Passiflora incarnata .. 80 80
559 10 t. Bauhina purpurea .. 80 80
560 10 t. Canna indica 80 80
561 10 t. Gloriosa superba .. 80 80
556/61 .. .. .. Set of 6 4·00 4·00

(Des A. Hussain)

1995 (16 Oct). *50th Anniv of Food and Agriculture Organization. P* 14×14½.
562 **203** 10 t. multicoloured 45 55

A 2 t. stamp, in a vertical design, commemorating Shaheed Khandaker Mosharraf Hossain was due for release on 21 October 1995, but was withdrawn on day of issue although the instructions may not have reached some offices in time to prevent sale of these stamps. Some used examples are known.

COVER PRICES

Cover factors are quoted at the beginning of each country for most issues back to 1945. An explanation of the system can be found on page x. The factors quoted do not, however, apply to philatelic covers.

204 Anniversary Emblem, Peace Dove and U.N. Headquarters

(Des A. Hussain)

1995 (24 Oct). *50th Anniv of United Nations. T* **204** *and similar horiz designs. Multicoloured. P* 14½×14.
563 2 t. Type **204** 15 15
564 10 t. Peace doves circling dates and Globe 65 75
565 10 t. Clasped hands and U.N. Headquarters 65 75
563/5 .. .. .. Set of 3 1·25 1·50

205 Diseased Lungs, Microscope, Family and Map

206 Peace Doves, Emblem and National Flags

(Des A. Hussain)

1995 (29 Oct). *18th Eastern Regional Conference on Tuberculosis, Dhaka. P* 14½×14.
566 **205** 6 t. multicoloured 50 40

(Des A. Hussain)

1995 (8 Dec). *10th Anniv of South Asian Association for Regional Co-operation. P* 14×14½.
567 **206** 2 t. multicoloured 30 15

1995 (14 Dec). *Martyred Intellectuals (4th series). Vert designs as T* **148**. *Each grey-black and reddish brown. P* 14×14½.
568 2 t. Abdul Ahad 15 15
  a. Sheetlet. Nos. 568/75 .. 1·10
569 2 t. Lt. Col. Mohammad Qadir .. 15 15
570 2 t. Mozammel Hoque Chowdhury 15 15
571 2 t. Rafiqul Haider Chowdhury 15 15
572 2 t. Dr. Azharul Haque .. 15 15
573 2 t. A. K. Shamsuddin .. 15 15
574 2 t. Anudwaipayan Bhattacharjee 15 15
575 2 t. Lutfunnahar Helena .. 15 15
576 2 t. Shaikh Habibur Rahman 15 15
  a. Sheetlet. Nos. 576/83 .. 1·10
577 2 t. Major Naimul Islam .. 15 15
578 2 t. Md. Shahidullah .. 15 15
579 2 t. Ataur Rahman Khan Khadim 15 15
580 2 t. A. B. M. Ashraful Islam Bhuiyan 15 15
581 2 t. Dr. Md. Sadat Ali .. 15 15
582 2 t. Sarafat Ali 15 15
583 2 t. M. A. Sayeed 15 15
568/83 .. .. Set of 16 2·00 2·00

Nos. 568/75 and 576/83 were printed together, *se-tenant*, in sheetlets of 8, the two horizontal rows in each sheetlet being separated by a row of inscribed labels.

207 Aspects of COMDECA Projects

208 Volleyball Players

(Des Md. Shamsuzzoha)

1995 (18 Dec). *2nd Asia-Pacific Community Development Scout Camp. P* 14×14½.
584 **207** 2 t. multicoloured 15 15

(Des A. Hussain)

1995 (25 Dec). *Centenary of Volleyball. P* 14×14½.
585 **208** 6 t. multicoloured 40 40

209 Man in Punjabi and Lungi

210 Shaheed Amanullah Mohammad Asaduzzaman

(Des M. Huq, A. Hussain, Md. Shamsuzzoha and M. Rahman)

1995 (25 Dec). *Traditional Costumes. T* **209** *and similar multicoloured designs. P* 14½.
586 6 t. Type **209** 40 40
587 6 t. Woman in sari 40 40
588 10 t. Christian bride and groom .. 75 75
589 10 t. Muslim bride and groom .. 75 75
590 10 t. Buddhist bride and groom (horiz) 75 75
591 10 t. Hindu bride and groom (horiz) 75 75
586/91 .. .. .. Set of 6 3·50 3·50

(Des A. Hussain)

1996 (20 Jan). *27th Death Anniv of Shaheed Amanullah Mohammad Asaduzzaman (student leader). P* 14×14½.
592 **210** 2 t. multicoloured 20 20

211 Bowler and Map

(Des M. Huq, A. Hussain and Md. Shamsuzzoha)

1996 (14 Feb). *World Cup Cricket Championship. T* **211** *and similar multicoloured designs. P* 14½×14 (10 t.) *or* 14×14½ (others).
593 4 t. Type **211** 60 30
594 6 t. Batsman and wicket keeper .. 75 50
595 10 t. Match in progress (horiz) 1·10 1·40
593/5 .. .. .. Set of 3 2·25 2·00

212 Liberation Struggle, 1971

(Des A. Hussain, M. Huq, M. Rahman and Md. Shamsuzzoha)

1996 (26 Mar). *25th Anniv of Independence. T* **212** *and similar horiz designs. Multicoloured. P* 14½.
596 4 t. Type **212** 15 20
597 4 t. National Martyrs Memorial .. 15 20
598 4 t. Education 15 20
599 4 t. Health 15 20
600 4 t. Communications .. 15 20
601 4 t. Industry 15 20
596/601 .. .. Set of 6 90 1·10

213 Michael Madhusudan Dutt

214 Gymnastics

(Des M. Huq)

1996 (29 June). *Michael Madhusudan Dutt (poet) Commemoration. P* 14×14½.
602 **213** 4 t. multicoloured 15 15

(Des M. Huq, Md. Shamsuzzoha and M. Rahman)

1996 (19 July). *Olympic Games, Atlanta.* T **214** *and similar multicoloured designs.* P 14×14½ (*vert*) or 14½×14 (*horiz*).

603	4 t. Type **214**	20	20
604	6 t. Judo	25	25
605	10 t. Athletics (*horiz*)	35	35
606	10 t. High jumping (*horiz*)	35	35
603/6	*Set of 4*	1·25	1·25
MS607	165×110 mm. Nos. 603/6. P 14×14½		
	(*sold at 40 t.*)	1·25	1·40

1996 (29 July). *25th Anniv of Bangladesh Stamps. No.* **MS**234 *optd* "Silver Jubilee Bangladesh Postage Stamps 1971–96" *on sheet margin.*

MS608	98×117 mm. Nos. 232/3 (*sold at 10 t.*)	30	35

215 Bangabandhu
Sheikh Mujibur
Rahman

216 Maulana Mohammad
Akrum Khan

(Des M. Rahman)

1996 (15 Aug). *21st Death Anniv of Bangabandhu Sheikh Mujibur Rahman.* P 14×14½.

609	**215** 4 t. multicoloured	20	20

(Des Md. Muniruzzaman)

1996 (18 Aug). *28th Death Anniv of Maulana Mohammad Akrum Khan.* P 14×14½.

610	**216** 4 t. multicoloured	20	20

217 Ustad Alauddin
Khan

218 "Kingfisher"
(Mayeesha Robbani)

(Des A. Hussain)

1996 (6 Sept). *24th Death Anniv of Ustad Alauddin Khan* (*musician*). P 14×14½.

611	**217** 4 t. multicoloured	40	20

1996 (9 Oct). *Children's Paintings.* T **218** *and similar multicoloured design.* P 13½×14½ (2 t.) or 14½×13½ (4 t.).

612	2 t. Type **218**	15	10
613	4 t. "River Crossing" (Iffat Panchlais)	15	20
	(*horiz*)		

219 Syed Nazrul Islam

220 Children receiving
Medicine

(Des M. Rahman)

1996 (3 Nov). *21st Death Anniv of Jail Martyrs.* T **219** *and similar vert designs. Multicoloured.* P 14×14½.

614	4 t. Type **219**	20	25
	a. Block of 4. Nos. 614/17	70	
615	4 t. Tajuddin Ahmad	20	25
616	4 t. M. Monsoor Ali	20	25
617	4 t. A. H. M. Quamaruzzaman	20	25
614/17	*Set of 4*	70	90

Nos. 614/17 were printed together, *se-tenant*, in blocks of four throughout the sheet.

(Des A. Hussain)

1996 (11 Dec). *50th Anniv of U.N.I.C.E.F.* T **220** *and similar vert design. Multicoloured.* P 14×14½.

618	4 t. Type **220**	25	20
619	10 t. Mother and child	45	45

(Des A. Hussain (Nos. 620/1, 625, 632/3), M. Huq (Nos. 622, 624, 627/9, 631) M. Rahman (Nos. 623, 630, 634), T. Hussain (No. 626), N. Islam (No. 635))

1996 (14 Dec). *Martyred Intellectuals* (5th series). *Vert designs as* T **148**. *Each grey-black and reddish brown.* P 14×14½.

620	2 t. Dr. Jekrul Haque	15	15
	a. Sheetlet. Nos. 620/7	1·10	
621	2 t. Munshi Kabiruddin Ahmed	15	15
622	2 t. Md. Abdul Jabbar	15	15
623	2 t. Mohammad Amir	15	15
624	2 t. A. K. M. Shamsul Huq Khan	15	15
625	2 t. Dr. Siddique Ahmed	15	15
626	2 t. Dr. Soleman Khan	15	15
627	2 t. S. B. M. Mizanur Rahman	15	15
628	2 t. Aminuddin	15	15
	a. Sheetlet. Nos. 628/35	1·10	
629	2 t. Md. Nazrul Islam	15	15
630	2 t. Zahirul Islam	15	15
631	2 t. A. K. Lutfor Rahman	15	15
632	2 t. Afsar Hossain	15	15
633	2 t. Abul Hashem Mian	15	15
634	2 t. A. T. M. Alamgir	15	15
635	2 t. Baser Ali	15	15
620/35	*Set of 16*	2·00	2·00

Nos. 620/7 and 628/35 were each printed together, *se-tenant*, in sheetlets of 8, the two horizontal rows in each sheetlet being separated by a row of inscribed labels.

221 Celebrating Crowds

222 Paul P. Harris

(Des Md. Shamsuzzoha)

1996 (16 Dec). *25th Anniv of Victory Day.* T **221** *and similar multicoloured design.* P 14½×14 (4 t.) or 14×14½ (6 t.).

636	4 t. Type **221**	25	25
637	6 t. Soldiers and statue (*vert*)	40	40

(Des M. Huq)

1997 (18 Feb). *50th Death Anniv of Paul Harris* (*founder of Rotary*). P 14×14½.

638	**224** 4 t. multicoloured	20	20
	a. Rotary emblem printed twice		

No. 638a shows the blue and gold Rotary emblem at bottom right printed twice.

223 Shaikh Mujibur Rahman
making Speech

(Des A. Hussain)

1997 (7 Mar). *25th Anniv of Shaikh Mujibur's Speech of 7 March* (1996). P 12½.

639	**223** 4 t. multicoloured	20	20

224 Sheikh Mujibur
Rahman

225 Sheikh Mujibur Rahman
and Crowd with Banners

(Des M. Mozammel)

1997 (17 Mar). *77th Birth Anniv of Sheikh Mujibur Rahman* (*first President*). P 14×14½.

640	**224** 4 t. multicoloured	30	20

(Des M. Rahman)

1997 (26 Mar). *25th Anniv* (1996) *of Independence.* P 12½.

641	**225** 4 t. multicoloured	20	20

---

226 Heinrich von
Stephan

227 Sheep

(Des A. Hussain)

1997 (8 Apr). *Death Centenary of Heinrich von Stephan* (*founder of U.P.U.*). P 14×14½.

642	**226** 4 t. multicoloured	20	20

(Des A. Hussain)

1997 (10 Apr). *Livestock.* T **227** *and similar horiz designs. Multicoloured.* P 14½×14.

643	4 t. Type **227**	20	25
644	4 t. Goat	20	25
645	6 t. Buffalo bull	30	35
646	6 t. Cow	30	35
643/6	*Set of 4*	1·00	1·10

228 "Tilling the Field – 2" (S. Sultan)

(Des A. Hussain)

1997 (26 June). *Bangladesh Paintings.* T **228** *and similar horiz design. Multicoloured.* P 12½.

647	6 t. Type **228**	30	30
648	10 t. "Three Women" (Quamrul Hassan)	50	60

229 Trophy, Flag and Cricket Ball

(Des A. Hussain)

1997 (4 Sept). *6th International Cricket Council Trophy Championship, Malaysia.* P 12½.

649	**229** 10 t. multicoloured	85	70

230 Kusumba Mosque,
Naogaon

231 Adul Karim
Sahitya Vishard

(Des Md. Shamsuzzoha)

1997 (4 Sept). *Historic Mosques.* T **230** *and similar horiz designs. Multicoloured.* P 14½×14.

650	4 t. Type **230**	20	20
651	6 t. Atiya Mosque, Tangail	30	30
652	10 t. Bagha Mosque, Rajshahi	45	55
650/2	*Set of 3*	85	95

(Des M. Rahman)

1997 (11 Oct). *126th Birth Anniv of Abdul Karim Sahitya Vishard* (*scholar*). P 14×14½.

653	**231** 4 t. multicoloured	20	20

OMNIBUS ISSUES

Details, together with prices for complete sets, of the various Omnibus issues from the 1935 Silver Jubilee series to date are included in a special section following Zimbabwe at the end of Volume 2.

232 Rover Moot
Emblem and Scouts
standing on top of
World

233 Officers and Flag

(Des M. Rahman)

1997 (25 Oct). *9th Asia-Pacific and 7th Bangladesh Rover Moot, Lakkatura.* P 14×14¹/₂.
654 **232** 2 t. multicoloured 30 20

(Des Md. Jasimuddin)

1997 (21 Nov). *25th Anniv of Armed Forces.* P 14¹/₂×14.
655 **233** 2 t. multicoloured 40 20

1997 (14 Dec). *Martyred Intellectuals (6th series). Vert designs as T 148. Each grey-black and reddish brown.* P 14×14¹/₂.
656   2 t. Dr. Shamsuddin Ahmed 15 15
     a. Sheetlet. Nos. 656/63 .. 1·10
657   2 t. Mohammad Salimullah 15 15
658   2 t. Mohiuddin Haider 15 15
659   2 t. Abdur Rahin 15 15
660   2 t. Nitya Nanda Paul 15 15
661   2 t. Abdel Jabber 15 15
662   2 t. Dr. Humayun Kabir 15 15
663   2 t. Khaja Nizamuddin Bhuiyan .. 15 15
664   2 t. Gulam Hossain 15 15
     a. Sheetlet. Nos. 664/71 .. 1·10
665   2 t. Ali Karim 15 15
666   2 t. Md. Moazzem Hossain 15 15
667   2 t. Rafiqul Islam 15 15
668   2 t. M. Nur Husain 15 15
669   2 t. Captain Mahmood Hossain Akonda .. 15 15
670   2 t. Abdul Wahab Talukder .. 15 15
671   2 t. Dr. Hasimoy Hazra .. 15 15
656/71   *Set of* 16 2·00 2·00
Nos. 656/63 and 664/71 were printed together, *se-tenant*, in sheetlets of 8, the two horizontal rows in each sheetlet being separated by a row of inscribed labels.

234 Mohammad
Mansooruddin

235 Standard-bearer and
Soldiers

(Des P. Mandal)

1998 (4 Feb). *Professor Mohammad Mansooruddin (folklorist) Commemoration.* P 14×14¹/₂.
672 **234** 4 t. multicoloured 30 30

(Des M. Rahman)

1998 (15 Feb). *50th Anniv of East Bengal Regiment.* P 14¹/₂×14.
673 **235** 2 t. multicoloured 40 20

236 Bulbul Chowdhury

237 World Cup Trophy

(Des A. Hussain)

1998 (17 May). *Bulbul Chowdhury (traditional dancer) Commemoration.* P 14×14¹/₂.
674 **236** 4 t. multicoloured 30 20

(Des A. Hussain)

1998 (10 June). *World Cup Football Championship, France. T* **237** *and similar vert design. Multicoloured.* P 14×14¹/₂.
675   6 t. Type **237** 40 30
676   18 t. Footballer and trophy .. 1·00 1·10

238 Eastern Approach Road,
Bangabandhu Bridge

239 Diana, Princess
of Wales

(Des Md. Mia and Md. Shamsuzzoha)

1998 (23 June). *Opening of Bangabandhu Bridge. T* **238** *and similar horiz designs. Multicoloured.* P 14¹/₂×14.
677   4 t. Type **238** 25 20
678   6 t. Western approach road .. 35 25
679   8 t. Embankment 45 50
680   10 t. Main span, Bangabandhu Bridge 50 55
677/80 .. .. .. *Set of* 4 1·40 1·40

(Des Md. Miah and A. Hussain)

1998 (6 Sept). *Diana, Princess of Wales Commemoration. T* **239** *and similar vert designs. Multicoloured.* P 14.
681   8 t. Type **239** 40 40
     a. Horiz strip of 3. Nos. 681/3 .. 1·90
682   18 t. Wearing pearl choker .. 80 80
683   22 t. Wearing pendant necklace .. 90 90
681/3   *Set of* 3 1·90 1·90
Nos. 681/3 were printed together, *se-tenant*, in horizontal strips of 3 throughout the sheet.

240 Means of collecting
Solar Energy

241 World Habitat Day
Emblem and City Scene

(Des A. Hussain)

1998 (24 Sept). *World Solar Energy Programme Summit.* P 14×14¹/₂.
684 **240** 10 t. multicoloured 50 50

(Des A. Hussain)

1998 (5 Oct). *World Habitat Day.* P 14×14¹/₂.
685 **241** 4 t. multicoloured 30 20
     a. Logo at top left in green ..
No. 685 normally shows the logo at top left in white.

242 Farmworkers,
Sunflower and "20"

243 Batsman

(Des. A. Hussain)

1998 (17 Oct). *20th Anniv of International Fund for Agricultural Development. T* **242** *and similar vert design. Multicoloured.* P 14×14¹/₂.
686   6 t. Type **242** 30 25
687   10 t. Farmworker with baskets and harvested crops 45 50

(Des A. Hussain)

1998 (24 Oct). *Wills International Cricket Cup, Dhaka.* P 14×14¹/₂.
688 **243** 6 t. multicoloured 50 35

244 Begum Rokeya

245 Anniversary Logo

(Des A. Hussain)

1998 (9 Dec). *Begum Rokeya (campaigner for women's education) Commemoration.* P 14¹/₂×14.
689 **244** 4 t. multicoloured 15 20

(Des A. Hussain)

1998 (10 Dec). *50th Anniv of Universal Declaration of Human Rights.* P 14×14¹/₂.
690 **245** 10 t. multicoloured 30 35

1998 (14 Dec). *Martyred Intellectuals (7th series). Vert designs as T* **148**. *Each grey-black and reddish brown.* P 14×14¹/₂.
691   2 t. Md. Khorshed Ali Sarker 15 20
     a. Sheetlet. Nos. 691/8 .. 1·10
692   2 t. Abu Yakub Mahfuz Ali .. 15 20
693   2 t. S. M. Nural Huda 15 20
694   2 t. Nazmul Hoque Sarker .. 15 20
695   2 t. Md. Taslim Uddin 15 20
696   2 t. Gulam Mostafa 15 20
697   2 t. A. H. Nural Alam 15 20
698   2 t. Timir Kanti Dev 15 20
699   2 t. Altaf Hossain 15 20
     a. Sheetlet. Nos. 699/706 .. 1·10
700   2 t. Aminul Hoque 15 20
701   2 t. S. M. Fazlul Hoque .. 15 20
702   2 t. Mozammel Ali 15 20
703   2 t. Syed Akbar Hossain .. 15 20
704   2 t. Sk. Abdus Salam 15 20
705   2 t. Abdur Rahman 15 20
706   2 t. Dr. Shyamal Kanti Lala .. 15 20
691/706   *Set of* 16 2·00 2·50
Nos. 691/8 and 699/706 were each printed together, *se-tenant*, in sheetlets of 8, the horizontal rows in each sheetlet being separated by a row of inscribed labels.

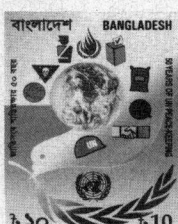

246 Dove of Peace and
U.N. Symbols

(Des A. Hussain)

1998 (30 Dec). *50th Anniv of U.N. Peace-keeping Operations.* P 14×14¹/₂.
707 **246** 10 t. multicoloured 40 50

247 Kazi Nazrul Islam

(Des A. Hussain)

1998 (31 Dec). *Birth Centenary (1999) of Kazi Nazrul Islam (poet).* P 14¹/₂.
708 **247** 6 t. multicoloured 30 30

248 Jamboree Emblem
and Scout Activities

249 Surjya Sen and
Demonstrators

(Des A. Hussain)

1999 (6 Feb). *6th Bangladesh National Scout Jamboree.* P 14×14¹/₂.
709 **248** 2 t. multicoloured 20 15

1999 (18 Mar–31 Aug). *As Nos. 75 and 319, but now printed litho by State Security Ptg Press, Gazipur. P 14½.*
710   5 t. black & brn-red (*as No. 319*) (31 Aug)   15   20
711   10 t. bright rose (*as No. 75, but 35×22 mm*)   35   40
No. 711 has been redrawn so that "SIXTY-DOME MOSQUE" appears above the face value at bottom right instead of below the main inscription at top left.

(Des A. Hussain)

1999 (22 Mar). *Surjya Sen (revolutionary) Commemoration. P 14½×14.*
715 249 4 t. multicoloured   ..   30   20

250 Dr. Fazlur Rahman Khan and Sears Tower   251 National Team Badges

(Des A. Hussain)

1999 (3 Apr). *70th Birth Anniv of Dr. Fazlur Rahman Khan (architect). P 14×14½.*
716 250 4 t. multicoloured   ..   30   20

(Des M. Rahman)

1999 (13 May). *Cricket World Cup, England. T 251 and similar vert design. Multicoloured. P 14×14½.*
717   8 t. Type 251   ..   30   25
718   10 t. Bangladesh cricket team badge and flag   ..   35   30
MS719 139×89 mm. Nos. 717/18 (*sold at 30 t.*)   95   1·00

252 Mother Theresa   253 Sheikh Mujibur Rahman, New York Skyline and Dove

(Des A. Hussain)

1999 (5 Sept). *Mother Theresa Commemoration. P 14×14½.*
720 252 4 t. multicoloured   ..   15   10

(Des A. Hussain)

1999 (13 Sept). *25th Anniv of Bangladesh's Admission to U.N. P 14×14½.*
721 253 6 t. multicoloured   ..   20   15

254 Shaheed Mohammad Maizuddin   255 Faces in Tree

(Des M. Rahman)

1999 (27 Sept). *15th Death Anniv of Shaheed Mohammad Maizuddin (politician). P 14×14½.*
722 254 2 t. multicoloured   ..   10   10

(Des A. Hussain)

1999 (1 Oct). *International Year of the Elderly. P 14×14½.*
723 255 6 t. multicoloured   ..   20   15

OMNIBUS ISSUES

Details, together with prices for complete sets, of the various Omnibus issues from the 1935 Silver Jubilee series to date are included in a special section following Zimbabwe at the end of Volume 2.

---

256 Shanty Town and Modern Buildings between Hands

(Des A. Hussain)

1999 (4 Oct). *World Habitat Day. P 14½×14.*
724 256 4 t. multicoloured   15   10

257 Mobile Post Office

(Des M. Rahman, A. Hussain and Md. Shamsuzzoha)

1999 (9 Oct). *125th Anniv of Universal Postal Union. T 257 and similar horiz designs. Multicoloured. P 14½×14.*
725   4 t. Type 257   15   10
726   4 t. Postman on motorcycle   15   10
727   6 t. Postal motor launch   20   15
728   6 t. Two Bangladesh airliners   ..   20   15
725/8   Set of 4   70   50
MS729 141×90 mm. Nos. 725/8 (*sold at 25 t.*)   80   85

OFFICIAL STAMPS

SERVICE (O 1)	SERVICE (O 2)	SERVICE (O 3)

1973 (30 Apr). *Nos. 22/7, 29/30, 32 and 34 optd with Type O 1.*

O 1	7	2 p. black (R.)	..	10	60
O 2	–	3 p. blue-green	..	10	60
O 3	–	5 p. light brown	..	20	10
O 4	–	10 p. slate-black (R.)	..	20	10
O 5	–	20 p. yellow-green	..	1·25	10
O 6	–	25 p. bright reddish mauve	..	3·25	10
O 7	–	60 p. greenish slate (R.)	..	3·25	1·50
O 8	–	75 p. yellow-orange	..	1·25	30
O 9	8	1 t. light violet	..	11·00	4·25
O10		5 t. grey-blue	..	5·00	7·50
O1/10			*Set of 10*	23·00	13·50

1974–75. *Nos. 49/51 optd with Type O 1.*

O11	14	1 t. light violet	..	4·00	30
O12		2 t. olive	..	5·00	1·75
O13		5 t. grey-blue (1975)	..	10·00	9·00
O11/13			*Set of 3*	17·00	10·00

1976. *Nos. 64/70 and 73 optd with Type O 2 and Nos. 72 and 74 optd with Type O 3.*

O14	5 p. deep yellow-green (11.2.76)		1·50	50
O15	10 p. slate-black (R.) (28.4.76)	..	1·75	50
O16	20 p. yellow-green (1.76)		2·00	50
O17	25 p. bright reddish mauve (1.76)		3·25	50
O18	50 p. light purple (8.6.76)		3·25	50
O19	60 p. greenish slate (R.) (10.11.76)		30	1·75
O20	75 p. yellow-olive (10.11.76)		30	2·50
O21	1 t. ultramarine (1.76)		2·75	50
O22	2 t. olive-green (8.6.76)		35	1·50
O23	5 t. grey-blue (10.11.76)		30	1·50
O14/23		*Set of 10*	14·00	9·00

1979–82. *Nos. 125/37 optd with Type O 1.*

O24	5 p. deep brown		1·00	1·50
O25	10 p. turquoise-blue		1·00	1·50
O26	15 p. orange (1980)		1·00	1·75
O27	20 p. brown-red		1·00	1·25
O28	25 p. grey-blue (1982)		80	2·00
O29	30 p. deep green		2·00	2·00
O30	40 p. maroon		2·00	50
O31	50 p. black (24.9.81)		30	10
O32	80 p. brown		1·00	15
O33	1 t. reddish violet (24.9.81)		30	10
O34	2 t. dull ultramarine (21.10.81)		35	2·00
O24/34		*Set of 11*	9·50	11·50

Service (O 4)	সার্ভিস (O 5)	সার্ভিস (O 6)

1983 (21 Dec)–94. *Nos. 220/9 and 318/a optd as Type O 4 in red, diagonally on 1 t. to 5 t.*

O35	5 p. turquoise-blue	..	10	10
O36	10 p. purple	..	10	10
O37	15 p. new blue	..	10	10
O38	20 p. grey-black	..	10	10
O39	25 p. slate	..	10	10
O40	30 p. brown	..	10	10
O41	50 p. light brown (opt horiz)	..	10	10
	a. Opt diagonal (1993)	..	10	10
O42	1 t. dull ultramarine	..	75	10
O43	2 t. deep bluish green	..	75	10
O44	3 t. black and light blue (16.7.94)	..	10	10
O45	4 t. slate-blue (28.6.90)	..	15	20
O46	5 t. bright purple (27.7.92)	..	15	20
O35/46		*Set of 12*	2·00	1·00

1989 (31 Mar)–92. *Nos. 227 and 319 optd with Type O 5.*

O47	1 t. ultramarine (R.) (16.9.92)	..	10	10
	a. Opt double			
	b. Opt double, one inverted			
O48	5 t. black and orange-brown (B.) (vert opt)	15	20
	Nos. O47a/b show attempts to remove the errors using an eraser.			

1990 (29 Nov). *Nos. 368/9 (Immunization) optd with Type O 6 in red.*

O49	133	1 t. emerald	..	10	10
O50		2 t. brown	..	10	10

1992 (22 Nov). *No. 376 optd as Type O 6, but horiz in red.*

O51	136	6 t. slate-blue and greenish yellow	20	25

1995 (28 Feb). *No. 553 (National Diabetes Awareness Day) optd as Type O 6, but horiz in red.*

O52	199	2 t. multicoloured	..	15	15

সার্ভিস (O 7)	সার্ভিস (O 8)

1996 (23 Aug). *Nos. 221 and 223 optd with Types O 7 (nylon block) or O 8 (typo) by Postal Printing Press, Tongi.*

O53	O 7	10 p. purple (Blk.)	..	10	10
		a. Opt inverted	..		
		b. Opt double	..		
		c. Opt double (Types O 8+O 7)	..		
		d. Red opt	..		
O54		20 p. grey-black (R.)	..	10	10
		a. Opt inverted	..		
		b. Opt double	..		
		c. Black opt	..		
O55	O 8	20 p. grey-black (R.)	..		

Similar overprints as Type O 7 in red or black on the 5 p. and 50 p. (Nos. 220 and 226) were prepared, but not issued.

1999 (31 Aug). *No. 710 optd on Type O 5, but vert in blue.*

O56		5 t. black and brown-red	..	15	20

Barbados

Regular mails between Barbados and Great Britain were established at an early date in the island's development and it is believed that the British Mail Packet Agency at Bridgetown was opened in 1688 as part of the considerable expansion of the Packet Service in that year.

From 1 August 1851 the colonial authorities were responsible for the internal post system, but the British G.P.O. did not relinquish control of the overseas post until 1858.

For illustrations of the handstamp types see BRITISH POST OFFICES ABROAD notes, following GREAT BRITAIN.

CROWNED-CIRCLE HANDSTAMPS

CC1 CC 1 BARBADOES (3.10.1849) (R). *Price on cover* £450
Combination covers exist with the local postage paid by a Barbados 1d. stamp and the overseas fee by an example of No. CC1. During shortages of ¹/₂d. stamps in 1893 (17 February to 15 March) and of the ¹/₄d. in 1896 (23 January to 4 May) No. CC1 was utilised, struck in black, on local mail. *Price on cover from* £85.

PRICES FOR STAMPS ON COVER TO 1945

Nos. 1/35	*from* × 5
Nos. 43/63	*from* × 4
Nos. 64/6	*from* × 10
Nos. 67/83	*from* × 5
Nos. 86/8	*from* × 3
Nos. 89/103	*from* × 4
No. 104	*from* × 20
Nos. 105/15	*from* × 4
Nos. 116/24	*from* × 8
Nos. 125/33	*from* × 5
Nos. 135/44	*from* × 4
Nos. 145/52	*from* × 6
No. 153	*from* × 8
Nos. 158/62	*from* × 5
Nos. 163/9	*from* × 3
Nos. 170/96	*from* × 4
Nos. 197/8	*from* × 10
Nos. 199/212	*from* × 6
Nos. 213/39	*from* × 3
No. 240	*from* × 10
Nos. 241/4	*from* × 5
Nos. 245/7	*from* × 6
Nos. 248/56a	*from* × 4
Nos. 257/61	*from* × 5
Nos. D1/3	*from* × 25

PERKINS BACON "CANCELLED". For notes on these handstamps, showing "CANCELLED" between horizontal bars forming an oval, see Catalogue Introduction.

CROWN COLONY

1　　Britannia　　2

(Recess Perkins, Bacon & Co)

1852 (15 April)**–55.** *Paper blued. No wmk. Imperf.*
1	1	(¹/₂d.) yellow-green	—	£550
2		(¹/₂d.) deep green	80·00	£300
3		(1d.) blue	28·00	£190
4		(1d.) deep blue	18·00	65·00
4a		(2d.) greyish slate	£200	£1100
		b. Bisected (1d.) (on cover) (1854)	†	£5500
5		(4d.) brownish red (1855)	70·00	£275

The bisect, No. 4b, was authorised for use between 4 August and 21 September 1854 during a shortage of 1d. stamps.

Nos. 5a/b were never sent to Barbados and come from the Perkins Bacon remainders sold in the 1880's.

Apart from the shade, which is distinctly paler, No. 4a can be distinguished from No. 5b by the smooth even gum, the gum of No. 5b being yellow and patchy, giving a mottled appearance to the back of the stamp. No. 5a also has the latter gum.

Prepared for use but not issued
5a	1	(No value), slate-blue (*shades*)	17·00
5b		(No value), deep slate	£200

1855–58. *White paper. No wmk. Imperf.*
7	1	(¹/₂d.) yellow-green (1857)	£375	£110
8		(¹/₂d.) green (1858)	95·00	£200
9		(1d.) pale blue	70·00	65·00
10		(1d.) deep blue (H/S "CANCELLED" in oval £5000)	23·00	55·00

1858 (10 Nov). *No wmk. Imperf.*
11	2	6d. pale rose-red	£700	£110
11a		6d. deep rose-red	£700	£180
12		1s. brown-black	£250	£110
12a		1s. black	£170	70·00

1860. *No wmk.* (a) *Pin-perf* 14.
13	1	(¹/₂d.) yellow-green	£1500	£375
14		(1d.) pale blue	£1500	£150
15		(1d.) deep blue	£1500	£600

(b) *Pin-perf* 12¹/₂
16	1	(¹/₂d.) yellow-green	£5000	£700
16a		(1d.) blue	—	£1200

(c) *Pin-perf* 14 × 12¹/₂
16b	1	(¹/₂d.) yellow-green	—	£5500

Two examples of No. 15 are known bisected and used on separate pieces.

1861. *No wmk. Clean-cut perf* 14 to 16.
17	1	(¹/₂d.) deep green (H/S "CANCELLED" in oval £5000)	70·00	8·00
18		(1d.) pale blue	£550	50·00
19		(1d.) blue	£650	50·00
		a. Bisected (¹/₂d.) (on cover)	†	£2750

1861–70. *No wmk.* (a) *Rough perf* 14 to 16.
20	1	(¹/₂d.) deep green	17·00	15·00
21		(¹/₂d.) green	12·00	9·00
21a		(¹/₂d.) blue-green	55·00	75·00
		b. Imperf (pair)	£475	
22		(¹/₂d.) grass-green	22·00	15·00
		a. Imperf (pair)	£550	
23		(1d.) blue (1861)	32·00	2·25
		a. Imperf (pair)	£475	
24		(1d.) deep blue	24·00	3·25
		a. Bisected diag (¹/₂d.) (on cover) (1863)	†	£1800
25		(4d.) dull rose-red (1861)	70·00	30·00
		a. Imperf (pair)	£650	
26		(4d.) dull brown-red (1865)	90·00	40·00
		a. Imperf (pair)	£900	
27		(4d.) lake-rose (1868)	75·00	55·00
		a. Imperf (pair)	£950	
28		(4d.) dull vermilion (1869)	£180	60·00
		a. Imperf (pair)	£900	
29	2	6d. rose-red (1861) (Handstamped "CANCELLED" in oval £5000)	£200	11·00
30		6d. orange-red (1864)	75·00	17·00
31		6d. bright orange-vermilion (1868)	60·00	17·00
32		6d. dull orange-vermilion (1870)	75·00	11·00
		a. Imperf (pair)	£425	
33		6d. orange (1870)	85·00	24·00
34		1s. brown-black (1863)	48·00	4·00
		a. Error. Blue	£12000	
35		1s. black (1866)	42·00	6·00
		a. Imperf between (horiz pair)	£5000	

(b) *Prepared for use, but not issued. P* 11 to 12
36	1	(¹/₂d.) grass-green	£6500
37		(1d.) blue	£2000

November 1866 during shortages of ¹/₂d. stamps.

No. 34a was an error on the part of the printer who supplied the first requisition of the 1s. value in the colour of the 1d. The 1s. blue stamps were never placed on sale, but the Barbados Colonial Secretary circulated some samples which were defaced by a manuscript corner-to-corner cross. A number of these samples subsequently had the cross removed.

Nos. 36/7 were never sent to Barbados and come from the Perkins Bacon remainders. It is believed that the imperforate pairs came from the same source.

1870. *Wmk Large Star, Type* w 1. *Rough perf* 14 to 16.
43	1	(¹/₂d.) green	80·00	5·50
		a. Imperf (pair)	£700	
43b		(¹/₂d.) yellow-green	£110	42·00
44		(1d.) blue	£1000	42·00
		a. Blue paper	£2750	80·00
45		(4d.) dull vermilion	£700	80·00
46	2	6d. orange-vermilion	£650	50·00
47		1s. black	£250	17·00

1871. *Wmk Small Star, Type* w 2. *Rough perf* 14 to 16.
48	1	(1d.) blue	90·00	1·25
49		(4d.) dull rose-red	£700	24·00
50	2	6d. orange-vermilion	£300	11·00
51		1s. black	£120	7·50

1872. *Wmk Small Star, Type* w 2. (a) *Clean-cut perf* 14¹/₂ to 15¹/₂.
52	1	(1d.) blue	£190	1·75
		a. Bisected diag (¹/₂d.) (on cover)	†	£1600
53	2	6d. orange-vermilion	£600	55·00
54		1s. black	£110	6·00

(b) *P* 11 to 13 × 14¹/₂ to 15¹/₂
56	1	(¹/₂d.) green	£225	27·00
57		(4d.) dull vermilion	£450	80·00

1873. *Wmk Large Star, Type* w 1. (a) *Clean-cut perf* 14¹/₂ to 15¹/₂.
58	1	(¹/₂d.) green	£190	11·00
59		(4d.) dull rose-red	£800	£130
60	2	6d. orange-vermilion	£550	50·00
		a. Imperf between (horiz pair)	£4500	
		b. Imperf (pair)	75·00	
61		1s. black	£100	7·00
		a. Imperf between (horiz pair)	£4500	

(b) *Prepared for use, but not issued. P* 11 to 12
62	2	6d. orange-vermilion	£4250

Only eight mint examples, in two strips of four, are known of No. 62.

Two used singles of No. 60b have been seen.

1873 (June). *Wmk Small Star, Type* w 2 (*sideways = two points upwards*). *P* 14.
63	2	3d. brown-purple	£325	£110

3

1873 (June). *Wmk Small Star, Type* w 2 (*sideways*). *P* 15¹/₂ × 15.
64	3	5s. dull rose (H/S S. £300)	£950	£300

1874 (May). *Wmk Large Star, Type* w 1. (a) *Perf* 14.
65	2	¹/₂d. deep green	22·00	6·00
66		1d. deep blue	65·00	1·75

(b) *Clean-cut perf* 14¹/₂ to 15¹/₂
66a	2	1d. deep blue	†	£8000
		b. Imperf (pair)		

(Recess D.L.R.)

1875–80. *Wmk Crown CC (sideways* on* 6d., 1s.). (a) *P* 12¹/₂.
67	2	¹/₂d. bright green	35·00	2·75
		x. Wmk reversed		
68		4d. deep red	£170	8·00
		w. Wmk inverted	£225	25·00
		x. Wmk reversed	£170	10·00
69		6d. bright yellow (aniline)	£850	75·00
70		6d. chrome-yellow	£500	65·00
		a. Wmk upright	†	£1500
71		1s. violet (aniline)	£450	3·00
		x. Wmk sideways reversed	£450	3·00
		y. Wmk sideways inverted and reversed	—	10·00

(b) *P* 14
72	2	¹/₂d. bright green (1876)	8·00	50
		w. Wmk inverted		
		x. Wmk reversed	8·00	75
73		1d. dull blue	45·00	70
		a. Bisected (¹/₂d.) (on cover) (1877)	†	£1400
		x. Wmk reversed		
74		1d. grey-blue	45·00	50
		a. Wmk sideways	—	£850
		w. Wmk inverted	80·00	20·00
		x. Wmk reversed	55·00	75
		y. Wmk inverted and reversed	—	30·00
75		3d. mauve-lilac (1878)	85·00	4·75
76		4d. red (1878)	85·00	7·50
		x. Wmk reversed		
77		4d. carmine	£140	1·75
		w. Wmk inverted		
78		4d. crimson-lake	£475	2·50
79		6d. chrome-yellow (1876)	95·00	1·00
		w. Wmk Crown to right of CA	—	2·00
		x. Wmk sideways reversed		2·00
80		6d. yellow	£300	5·00
		w. Wmk Crown to right of CA		
81		1s. purple (1876)	£110	3·00
		w. Wmk Crown to right of CA	—	3·00
		x. Wmk sideways reversed		
82		1s. violet (aniline)	£2750	32·00
		w. Wmk Crown to right of CA	—	32·00
		x. Wmk sideways reversed		
83		1s. dull mauve	£375	2·50
		a. Bisected (6d.) (on cover) (1.80)	†	£4000
		x. Wmk sideways reversed		

(c) *P* 14×12¹/₂
84	2	4d. red		£5000

72/3 (in red), 75/6, 79, 81 (in red)
H/S "Specimen" ... *Set of* 6 £500
72/3 (in black) H/S "Specimen" ... *Set of* 2 £150
*The normal sideways watermark shows Crown to left of CA as seen from the back of the stamp.

Only two examples, both used, of No. 70a have been reported. Very few examples of No. 84 have been found unused and only one used specimen is known.

1^{D.}　　1^{D.}　　1^{D.}

(3a)　　(3b)　　(3c)

1878 (28 Mar). No. 64 surch by West Indian Press with T 3a/c sideways twice on each stamp and then divided vertically by 11¹/₂ to 13 perforations. The lower label, showing the original face value, was removed before use.

(a) With T 3a. *Large numeral "1", 7 mm high with curved serif, and large letter "D",* 2³/₄ *mm high.*
86	3	1d. on half 5s. dull rose	£3750	£600
		a. No stop after "D"	£10000	£1600
		b. Unsevered pair (both No. 86)	£15000	£1800
		c. Ditto, Nos. 86 and 87	—	£3500
		ca. Pair without dividing perf	†	£21000
		d. Ditto, Nos. 86 and 88	£23000	£5500

(b) With T 3b. *As last, but numeral with straight serif*
87	3	1d. on half 5s. dull rose	£4250	£700
		a. Unsevered pair	†	£2500

(c) With T 3c. *Smaller numeral "1", 6 mm high and smaller "D",* 2¹/₂ *mm high.*
88	3	1d. on half 5s dull rose	£5000	£850
		a. Unsevered pair	£17000	£3500

All types of the surcharge are found reading upwards as well as downwards, and there are minor varieties of the type.

4

HALF-PENNY

(5)

(Typo D.L.R.)

1882 (28 Aug)**–86.** *Wmk Crown CA. P* 14.
89	4	¹/₂d. dull green (1882)	11·00	1·25
		w. Wmk inverted		
90		¹/₂d. green	11·00	1·25
91		1d. rose (1882)	50·00	2·00
		a. Bisected (¹/₂d.) (on cover)	†	£900
		w. Wmk inverted		
92		1d. carmine	11·00	70
93		2¹/₂d. ultramarine (1882)	75·00	1·25
		w. Wmk inverted		
94		2¹/₂d. deep blue	80·00	1·25
95		3d. deep purple (1885)	90·00	26·00
96		3d. reddish purple	4·00	13·00
97		4d. grey (1882)	£200	2·50

98	4	4d. pale brown (1885)	..	..	7·00	2·75
		w. Wmk inverted		..	—	50·00
		x. Wmk reversed				
		y. Wmk inverted and reversed			†	£150
99		4d. deep brown	..	..	4·50	1·25
100		6d. olive-black (1886)	..	..	70·00	35·00
102		1s. chestnut (1886)	..	..	25·00	21·00
103		5s. bistre (1886)	..	..	£140	£180
89/103			Set of 9	£475	£225	
95/103, except 97, Optd "Specimen"			Set of 5	£375		

1892 (July). *No. 99 surch with T 5 by West Indian Press.*

104	4	½d. on 4d. deep brown	..	..	1·75	3·00
		a. No hyphen		..	9·00	17·00
		b. Surch double (R.+Bk.)		..	£450	£700
		ba. Surch double (R.+Bk.) both without hyphen		..	£1300	£1300
		c. Surch double, one albino	..			
		d. Surch "PENNY HALF"	..	..	—	£200

Nos. 104b/ba come from a sheet with a trial surcharge in red which was subsequently surcharged again in black and put back into stock.

No. 104c is known in a horizontal pair with the left hand stamp showing the first two letters of the second impression inked. The right hand stamp shows a complete albino surcharge.

6 Seal of Colony

7

(Typo D.L.R.)

1892 (July)**–1903.** *Wmk Crown CA. P 14.*

105	6	¼d. slate-grey and carmine (5.5.96)		2·00	10	
106		½d. dull green	..		2·00	10
		w. Wmk inverted	..	..		
107		1d. carmine	..	..	4·25	10
108		2d. slate-black and orange (5.99)		7·50	65	
109		2½d. ultramarine	..	..	16·00	20
110		5d. grey-olive	..	..	6·50	4·50
111		6d. mauve and carmine		..	11·00	2·00
112		8d. orange and ultramarine		..	3·50	20·00
113		10d. dull blue-green and carmine		7·50	6·50	
114		2s. 6d. blue-black and orange		48·00	48·00	
		w. Wmk inverted	..	..	85·00	95·00
115		2s. 6d. violet and green (29.5.03)		75·00	£120	
105/15			Set of 11	£160	£180	
105/15 Optd "Specimen"			Set of 11	£170		

See also Nos. 135/44 and 163/9.

(Typo D.L.R.)

1897 (Dec)**–98.** *Diamond Jubilee. T 7. Wmk Crown CC. P 14.*

(a) White paper

116		¼d. grey and carmine	..	..	3·00	60
117		½d. dull green	..	..	3·00	60
118		1d. rose	..	..	3·00	60
119		2½d. ultramarine	..	..	6·00	85
		w. Wmk inverted	..	..		
120		5d. olive-brown	..	..	14·00	14·00
121		6d. mauve and carmine	..	..	18·00	19·00
122		8d. orange and ultramarine		..	7·00	22·00
123		10d. blue-green and carmine		..	48·00	55·00
124		2s. 6d. blue-black and orange		55·00	55·00	
		w. Wmk inverted	..	..		
116/24			Set of 9	£140	£150	
116/24 Optd "Specimen"			Set of 9	£150		

(b) Paper blued

125		¼d. grey and carmine	..	..	26·00	30·00
126		½d. dull green	..	..	27·00	30·00
127		1d. carmine	..	..	35·00	40·00
128		2½d. ultramarine	..	..	38·00	45·00
129		5d. olive-brown	..	..	£225	£250
130		6d. mauve and carmine	..	..	£130	£140
131		8d. orange and ultramarine		..	£140	£150
132		10d. dull green and carmine		..	£190	£225
133		2s. 6d. blue-black and orange		£110	£120	

1905. *Wmk Mult Crown CA. P 14.*

135	6	¼d. slate-grey and carmine		7·50	2·25	
136		½d. dull green	..	..	12·00	10
137		1d. carmine	..	..	12·00	10
139		2½d. blue	..	..	8·00	15
141		6d. mauve and carmine	..		11·00	12·00
142		8d. orange and ultramarine	..	35·00	70·00	
144		2s. 6d. violet and green	..	35·00	80·00	
135/144			Set of 7	£110	£150	

See also Nos. 163/9.

8 Nelson Monument

(Des Mrs. G. Goodman. Recess D.L.R.)

1906 (1 Mar). *Nelson Centenary. Wmk Crown CC. P 14.*

145	8	¼d. black and grey	..	..	7·00	1·50
		w. Wmk inverted	..	..	30·00	
146		½d. black and pale green	..	8·50	15	
		w. Wmk inverted	..	..		
		x. Wmk reversed	..	..		
147		1d. black and red	..	..	9·50	15
		w. Wmk inverted	..	..	30·00	
		x. Wmk reversed	..	..		

148	8	2d. black and yellow	..	..	1·75	4·50
149		2½d. black and bright blue	..	3·75	1·25	
		w. Wmk inverted	..	..		
150		6d. black and mauve	..	..	18·00	25·00
151		1s. black and rose	..	..	19·00	48·00
145/51			Set of 7	60·00	70·00	
145/51 Optd "Specimen"			Set of 7	£130		

Two sets may be made of the above: one on thick, opaque, creamy white paper; the other on thin, rather transparent, bluish white paper.

See also Nos. 158/62a.

9 Olive Blossom, 1605

Kingston Relief Fund. 1d.

(10)

(Des Lady Carter. Recess D.L.R.)

1906 (15 Aug). *Tercentenary of Annexation. Wmk Multiple Crown CA (sideways). P 14.*

152	9	1d. black, blue and green		10·00	25
152 Optd "Specimen"		..	..	65·00	

1907 (25 Jan–25 Feb). *Kingston Relief Fund. No. 108 surch with T 10 by T. E. King & Co., Barbados.*

153	6	1d. on 2d. slate-black and orange (R.)		2·00	4·50
		a. Surch inverted (25.2.07)		1·50	6·50
		b. Surch double	..	£550	£600
		c. Surch double, both inverted		£550	
		d. Surch *tête-bêche* (pair)		£700	
		e. No stop after "1d."		32·00	55·00
		ea. Do., surch inverted (25.2.07)		32·00	70·00
		eb. Do., surch double		—	£950
		f. Vert pair, one normal, one surch double		—	£750

The above stamp was sold for 2d. of which 1d. was retained for the postal revenue, and the other 1d. given to a fund for the relief of the sufferers by the earthquake in Jamaica.

An entire printing as No. 153a was created after a sheet of inverted surcharges was found in the initial supply.

1907 (6 July). *Nelson Centenary. Wmk Mult Crown CA. P 14.*

158	8	¼d. black and grey	..	..	5·00	3·00
161		2d. black and yellow	..	..	18·00	23·00
162		2½d. black and bright blue	..	10·00	19·00	
		a. Black and indigo	..	..	£700	£800
158/62			Set of 3	30·00	40·00	

1909 (July)**–10.** *Wmk Mult Crown CA. P 14.*

163	6	¼d. brown	..	..	3·50	30
164		½d. blue-green	..	..	17·00	75
165		1d. red	..	..	9·50	10
166		2d. greyish slate (8.10)	..	6·50	9·50	
167		2½d. bright blue (1910)	..	40·00	6·00	
168		6d. dull and bright purple (1910)		8·00	14·00	
169		1s. black/*green* (8.10)	..	8·50	14·00	
163/9			Set of 7	85·00	40·00	
163, 165/6, 168/9 Optd "Specimen"		Set of 5	£100			

11 **12** **13**

(Typo D.L.R.)

1912 (23 July)**–16.** *Wmk Mult Crown CA. P 14.*

170	11	¼d. brown	..	..	1·25	1·50
		a. Pale brown (1916)	..	..	65	2·50
		aw. Wmk inverted	..	..		
171		½d. green	..	..	2·75	10
		a. Wmk sideways	..	..	†	—
172		1d. red (13.8.12)	..	..	5·50	10
		a. Scarlet (1915)	..	..	18·00	2·75
173		2d. greyish slate (13.8.12)		2·00	13·00	
174		2½d. bright blue (13.8.12)		1·25	30	
175	12	3d. purple/*yellow* (13.8.12)		1·25	12·00	
176		4d. red and black/*yellow* (13.8.12)		1·25	16·00	
177		6d. purple and dull purple (13.8.12)		10·00	12·00	
178	13	1s. black/*green* (13.8.12)		8·00	10·00	
179		2s. blue and purple/*blue* (13.8.12)		40·00	45·00	
180		3s. violet and green (13.8.12)		75·00	85·00	
170/80			Set of 11	£130	£170	
170/80 Optd "Specimen"			Set of 11	£140		

14

WAR TAX

(15)

(Recess D.L.R.)

1916 (16 June)**–19.** *Wmk Mult Crown CA. P 14.*

181	14	¼d. deep brown	..	..	75	40
		a. Chestnut-brown (9.17)	..	1·50	35	
		b. Sepia-brown (4.18)	..	3·75	2·75	
		w. Wmk inverted	..	..	16·00	16·00
		y. Wmk inverted and reversed		27·00		

182	14	½d. green	..	..	1·10	15
		a. Deep green (9.17)	..	..	1·40	15
		b. Pale green (4.18)	..	..	1·90	80
		w. Wmk inverted	..	..	22·00	
		y. Wmk inverted and reversed				
183		1d. deep red	..	..	17·00	6·00
		a. Bright carmine-red (4.17)		2·50	15	
		b. Pale carmine-red (9.17)		6·00	65	
		w. Wmk inverted	..	..	22·00	
		x. Wmk reversed	..	..		
		y. Wmk inverted and reversed		22·00		
184		2d. grey	..	..	3·50	17·00
		a. Grey-black (9.19)	..	..	27·00	65·00
		w. Wmk inverted and reversed				
185		2½d. deep ultramarine	..	2·75	1·75	
		a. Royal blue (11.17)	..	..	2·75	1·75
		w. Wmk inverted	..	..		
		y. Wmk inverted and reversed		27·00	27·00	
186		3d. purple/*yellow* (thin paper)		1·75	4·50	
		a. Dp purple/*yell* (thick paper) (9.19)		28·00	32·00	
187		4d. red/*yellow*	..	..	70	14·00
188		6d. purple	..	..	2·50	3·50
189		1s. black/*green*	..	..	7·00	8·00
190		2s. purple/*blue*	..	..	16·00	7·50
		w. Wmk inverted and reversed		40·00		
191		3s. deep violet	..	..	45·00	90·00
		w. Wmk inverted	..	..		
		y. Wmk inverted and reversed				
181/91			Set of 11	75·00	£130	
181/91 Optd "Specimen"			Set of 11	£180		

Dates quoted for shades are those of despatch from Great Britain.

Examples of the ½d. and 1d. values can be found perforated either by line or by comb machines.

See also Nos. 199/200a.

1917 (10 Oct)**–18.** *War Tax. Optd in London with T 15.*

197	11	1d. bright red (Optd S. £55)		15	15	
		w. Wmk inverted	..	..		
198		1d. pale red (*thicker bluish paper*) (4.18)		2·75	40	

1918 (18 Feb)**–20.** *Colours changed. Wmk Mult Crown CA. P 14.*

199	14	4d. black and red	..	..	80	3·50
		x. Wmk reversed	..	..	£100	
200		3s. green and deep violet	..	16·00	48·00	
		a. Green and bright violet (1920)		£190	£275	
199/200 Optd "Specimen"			Set of 2	£120		

The centres of these are from a new die having no circular border line.

16 Winged Victory from the Louvre.

17 Victory from Victoria Memorial, London

(Recess D.L.R.)

1920 (9 Sept)**–21.** *Victory. P 14.*

(a) Wmk Mult Crown CA (sideways* on T 17)

201	16	¼d. black and bistre-brown	..	30	70	
		a. "C" of "CA" missing from wmk	..	£225		
		c. Substituted crown in wmk				
		w. Wmk inverted	..	..		
		x. Wmk reversed	..	..	30·00	
		y. Wmk inverted and reversed		38·00		
202		½d. black and bright yellow-green		90	15	
		a. "C" of "CA" missing from wmk	..	£250		
		b. "A" of "CA" missing from wmk	..	£250		
		c. Substituted crown in wmk				
		w. Wmk inverted	..	..		
		x. Wmk reversed	..	..		
		y. Wmk inverted and reversed				
203		1d. black and vermilion	..	3·00	10	
		a. "A" of "CA" missing from wmk	..	†	£275	
		w. Wmk inverted	..	..	32·00	
		y. Wmk inverted and reversed				
204		2d. black and grey	..	..	2·00	6·50
		a. "C" of "CA" missing from wmk	..	£300		
205		2½d. indigo and ultramarine	..	2·75	12·00	
		a. "C" of "CA" missing from wmk	..	£300		
		w. Wmk inverted	..	..		
		y. Wmk inverted and reversed		75·00		
206		3d. black and purple	..	..	2·75	5·50
		w. Wmk inverted	..	..	27·00	27·00
207		4d. black and blue-green	..	2·75	6·00	
208		6d. black and brown-orange	..	3·50	12·00	
		w. Wmk inverted	..	..	48·00	
		wa. "C" of "CA" missing from wmk		£750		
209	17	1s. black and bright green	..	9·00	24·00	
		w. Wmk Crown to left of CA				
		w. Wmk sideways reversed	..	£100		
		y. Wmk sideways inverted and reversed				
210		2s. black and brown	..	..	23·00	30·00
		w. Wmk Crown to left of CA		65·00		
		x. Wmk sideways reversed				
		y. Wmk sideways inverted and reversed				
211		3s. black and dull orange	..	27·00	38·00	
		a. "C" of "CA" missing from wmk	..	£600		
		w. Wmk Crown to left of CA		65·00		
		x. Wmk sideways reversed				

(b) Wmk Mult Script CA

212	16	1d. black and vermilion (22.8.21)		17·00	30	
201/12			Set of 12	85·00	£120	
201/12 Optd "Specimen"			Set of 12	£200		

*The normal sideways watermark on Nos. 209/11 shows Crown to right of CA, as seen from the back of the stamp.

For illustration of the substituted watermark crown see Catalogue Introduction.

18   19

(Recess D.L.R.)

1921 (14 Nov)–24. *P* 14. (a) *Wmk Mult Crown CA.*

213	18	3d. purple/*pale yellow*	..	2·00	6·00
		x. Wmk reversed			
214		4d. red/*pale yellow*	..	1·75	12·00
215		1s. black/*emerald*	..	4·75	11·00
		w. Wmk inverted	..		

(b) *Wmk Mult Script CA*

217	18	¼d. brown	..	15	10
		x. Wmk reversed	..	22·00	
		y. Wmk inverted and reversed	27·00		
219		½d. green	..	1·00	10
220		1d. red		80	10
		aw. Wmk inverted	..	22·00	
		ax. Wmk reversed			
		ay. Wmk inverted and reversed			
		b. Bright rose-carmine	..	6·50	1·00
		bw. Wmk inverted	..	20·00	
221		2d. grey	..	1·60	20
		y. Wmk inverted and reversed			
222		2½d. ultramarine	..	1·50	6·00
225		6d. reddish purple	..	3·50	5·50
226		1s. black/*emerald* (18.9.24)	..	48·00	80·00
227		2s. purple/*blue*	..	10·00	19·00
228		3s. deep violet	..	13·00	48·00
		y. Wmk inverted and reversed			
213/28			Set of 12	75·00	£170
213/28	Optd "Specimen" ..	..	Set of 12	£160	

1925 (1 Apr)–35. *Wmk Mult Script CA. P* 14.

229	19	¼d. brown	..	15	10
230		½d. green	..	30	10
		a. Perf 13½×12½ (2.32)	..	6·00	10
231		1d. scarlet	..	50	10
		a. Perf 13½×12½ (2.32)	..	5·00	30
231b		1½d. orange (1933)	..	10·00	2·50
		ba. Perf 13½×12½ (15.8.32)	2·00	1·00
232		2d. grey	..	50	3·00
233		2½d. blue	..	50	80
		a. Bright ultramarine (1933)	13·00	1·50
		ab. Perf 13½×12½ (2.32)	..	5·00	2·50
234		3d. purple/*pale yellow*	..	80	45
		a. Reddish purple/yellow (1935)	5·50	5·50
235		4d. red/*pale yellow*	..	75	95
236		6d. purple	..	75	90
237		1s. black/*emerald*	..	1·50	6·00
		a. Perf 13½×12½ (8.32)	..	42·00	14·00
		b. Brownish black/*bright yellow-green* (1934)	4·50	10·00
238		2s. purple/*blue*	..	7·00	6·50
238a		2s. 6d. carmine/*blue* (1.9.32)	22·00	24·00
239		3s. deep violet	..	11·00	13·00
229/39			Set of 13	42·00	50·00
229/39	Optd/Perf "Specimen"	Set of 13	£170	

Nos. 230/1 exist in coils constructed from normal sheets.

20 King Charles I and King George V   21 Badge of the Colony

(Recess B.W.)

1927 (17 Feb). *Tercentenary of Settlement of Barbados. Wmk Mult Script CA. P* 12½.

240	20	1d. carmine (Optd S. £40)	..	75	75

1935 (6 May). *Silver Jubilee. As Nos. 91/4 of Antigua, but ptd by Waterlow. P* 11 × 12.

241		1d. deep blue and scarlet	..	30	20
		j. Damaged turret	..	80·00	
242		1½d. ultramarine and grey	..	3·25	5·50
		j. Damaged turret	..	£110	
243		2½d. brown and deep blue	..	2·25	3·50
244		1s. slate and purple	..	15·00	16·00
		l. Kite and horizontal log	£225	
241/4			Set of 4	19·00	23·00
241/4	Perf "Specimen"		Set of 4	65·00	

For illustrations of plate varieties see Catalogue Introduction.

1937 (14 May). *Coronation. As Nos. 95/7 of Antigua, but printed by D.L.R. P* 14.

245		1d. scarlet	..	30	15
246		1½d. yellow-brown	..	40	60
247		2½d. bright blue	..	70	45
245/7			Set of 3	1·25	1·10
245/7	Perf "Specimen"		Set of 3	50·00	

NEW INFORMATION

The editor is always interested to correspond with people who have new information that will improve or correct the Catalogue.

Recut line (R. 10/6)   Extra frame line (R. 11/9)

Mark on central ornament (R. 1/3, 2/3, 3/3)   Vertical line over horse's head (R. 4/10) (corrected on Dec 1947 ptg)   "Flying mane" (R. 4/1) (corrected on Dec 1947 ptg)

Curved line at top right (R. 7/8)   Cracked plate (extends to top right ornament) (R. 6/10))

(Recess D.L.R.)

1938 (3 Jan)–47. *Wmk Mult Script CA. P* 13½×13.

248	21	½d. green	..	6·00	15
		a. Recut line	..	£110	
		b. Perf 14 (8.42)	..	70·00	1·25
		ba. Recut line	..	£300	
248c		½d. yellow-bistre (16.10.42)	15	30
		ca. "A" of "CA" missing from wmk	£1100	
		cb. Recut line	..	16·00	
249		1d. scarlet (1941)	..	£275	4·00
		a. Perf 14 (3.1.38)	..	16·00	10
249b		1d. blue-green (1943)	..	2·50	80
		c. Perf 14 (16.10.42)	..	15	10
		ca. "A" of "CA" missing from wmk	£1100	
250		1½d. orange	..	15	40
		a. "A" of "CA" missing from wmk	£1100	
		b. Perf 14 (11.41)	..	4·75	65
250c		2d. claret (3.6.41)	..	40	2·00
		ca. Extra frame line	..	28·00	
250d		2d. carmine (20.9.43)	..	15	60
		da. Extra frame line	..	17·00	
		e. Perf 14 (11.9.44)	..	15	1·40
		ea. Extra frame line	..	17·00	
251		2½d. ultramarine	..	50	40
		a. Mark on central ornament	32·00	
		b. Blue (17.2.44)	..	1·10	4·25
		ba. "A" of "CA" missing from wmk	£1000	
		bb. Mark on central ornament	42·00	
252		3d. brown	..	20	1·90
		a. Vertical line over horse's head	75·00	
		b. Perf 14 (4.41)	..	20	55
		ba. Vertical line over horse's head	75·00	
252c		3d. blue (1.4.47)	..	20	1·50
		ca. Vertical line over horse's head	75·00	
253		4d. black	..	20	10
		a. Flying mane	..	80·00	
		b. Curved line at top right	..	70·00	
		c. Cracked plate	..	70·00	
		d. Perf 14 (11.9.44)	..	20	3·50
		da. Flying mane	..	80·00	
		db. Curved line at top right	..	70·00	
		dc. Cracked plate	..	70·00	
254		6d. violet	..	80	10
254a		8d. magenta (9.12.46)	..	55	2·00
255		1s. olive-green	..	16·00	2·50
		a. Deep brown-olive (19.11.45)	1·00	10
256		2s. 6d. purple	..	6·50	1·50
256a		5s. indigo (3.6.41)	..	3·25	5·50
		ab. "A" of "CA" missing from wmk	£1300	
248/56a			Set of 16	32·00	13·00
248/56a	Perf "Specimen"		Set of 16	£190	

No. 249a was perforated by two machines, one gauging 13.8×14.1 (1938), the other 14.1 (1939).

Nos. 248/c and 249/c exist in coils constructed from normal sheets.

22 Kings Charles I, George VI, Assembly Chamber and Mace

(Recess D.L.R.)

1939 (27 June). *Tercentenary of General Assembly. Wmk Mult Script CA. P* 13½ × 14.

257	22	½d. green	..	2·25	30
258		1d. scarlet	..	2·25	30
259		1½d. orange	..	2·25	60
260		2½d. bright ultramarine	..	2·25	3·75
261		3d. brown	..	2·25	2·25
257/61			Set of 5	10·00	6·50
257/61	Perf "Specimen"		Set of 5	£140	

Two flags on tug (R. 5/2)

1946 (18 Sept). *Victory. As Nos. 110/11 of Antigua.*

262		1½d. red-orange	..	15	15
		a. Two flags on tug	..	20·00	
263		3d. brown	..	15	15
262/3	Perf "Specimen"		Set of 2	48·00	

ONE PENNY
(23)

NY PEN

Short "Y" (R. 6/2)   Broken "E" (R. 7/4 and 11/4)

(Surch by Barbados Advocate Co)

1947 (21 Apr). *Surch with T 23.* (a) *P* 14.

264	21	1d. on 2d. carmine (No. 250e)	..	1·25	2·25
		a. Extra frame line	..	50·00	
		b. Short "Y"	..	50·00	
		c. Broken "E"	..	26·00	

(b) *P* 13½×13

264d	21	1d. on 2d. carmine (No. 250d)	4·50	5·00
		da. Extra frame line	..	£150	
		db. Short "Y"	..	£150	
		dc. Broken "E"	..	90·00	

The relationship of the two words in the surcharge differs on each position of the sheet.

1948 (24 Nov). *Royal Silver Wedding. As Nos. 112/13 of Antigua.*

265		1½d. orange	..	30	10
266		5s. indigo	..	10·00	6·50

1949 (10 Oct). *75th Anniv of Universal Postal Union. As Nos. 114/17 of Antigua.*

267		1½d. red-orange	..	30	35
268		3d. deep blue	..	1·50	1·50
269		4d. grey	..	35	2·00
270		1s. olive	..	35	60
267/70			Set of 4	2·25	4·00

(New Currency. 100 cents = 1 West Indian, later Barbados, dollar)

24 Dover Fort   27 Statue of Nelson

(Recess B.W.)

1950 (1 May). *T* 24, 27 *and similar designs. Wmk Mult Script CA. P* 11 × 11½ (horiz), 13½ (vert).

271		1 c. indigo	..	15	2·00
272		2 c. emerald-green	..	15	2·00
273		3 c. reddish brown and blue-green	..	1·00	2·25
274		4 c. carmine	..	15	40
275		6 c. light blue	..	15	2·00
276		8 c. bright blue and purple-brown	..	1·00	2·00
277		12 c. greenish blue and brown-olive	..	90	1·00
278		24 c. scarlet and black	..	90	40
279		48 c. violet	..	8·00	6·00
280		60 c. green and claret	..	7·00	8·50
281		$1.20, carmine and olive-green	..	8·50	3·75
282		$2.40, black	..	15·00	14·00
271/282			Set of 12	38·00	40·00

Designs: Horiz—2 c. Sugar cane breeding; 3 c. Public buildings; 6 c. Casting net; 8 c. *Frances W. Smith* (schooner); 12 c. Four-winged Flyingfish; 24 c. Old Main Guard Garrison; 60 c. Careenage; $2.40, Seal of Barbados. Vert—48 c. St. Michael's Cathedral; $1.20, Map of Barbados and wireless mast.

1951 (16 Feb). *Inauguration of B.W.I. University College. As Nos. 118/19 of Antigua.*

283		3 c. brown and blue-green	..	30	30
284		12 c. blue-green and brown-olive	..	55	1·40

36 King George VI and Stamp of 1852

(Recess Waterlow)

1952 (15 Apr). *Barbados Stamp Centenary. Wmk Mult Script CA.*
P 13½.

285	**36**	3 c. green and slate-green	..	15	40
286		4 c. blue and carmine	..	15	1·00
287		12 c. slate-green and bright green	..	15	1·00
288		24 c. red-brown and brownish black	..	15	55
285/8	..		*Set of 4*	55	2·75

37 Harbour Police

(Recess B.W.)

1953 (13 Apr)–**61**. *Designs previously used for King George VI*
issue, but with portrait or cypher ($2.40) of Queen Elizabeth II,
as in T **37**. *Wmk Mult Script CA. P* 11×11½ (*horiz*) *or* 13½
(*vert*).

289	1 c. indigo		10	70
290	2 c. orange and deep turquoise (15.4.54)		15	40
291	3 c. black and emerald (15.4.54)	..	1·00	50
292	4 c. black and orange (15.4.54)	..	20	20
	a. Black and reddish brown (18.3.59)		2·50	1·25
293	5 c. blue and deep carmine-red (4.1.54)		90	40
294	6 c. red-brown (15.4.54)	..	50	40
	w. Wmk inverted			
295	8 c. black and blue (15.4.54)	..	40	40
296	12 c. turquoise-blue & brown-olive (15.4.54)		1·00	10
	a. Turquoise-grn & brown-olive (18.3.59)		13·00	3·00
	b. Turquoise-blue & bronze-grn (13.6.61)		13·00	2·00
297	24 c. rose-red and black (2.3.56)		45	10
298	48 c. deep violet (2.3.56)	..	5·00	1·00
299	60 c. blue-green and brown-purple (3.4.56)		20·00	5·00
	a. Blue-green and pale maroon (17.5.60)		30·00	8·00
300	$1.20, carmine and bronze-green (3.4.56)		19·00	2·50
301	$2.40, black (1.2.57)		7·50	1·25
289/301		*Set of 13*	50·00	11·50

Designs: *Horiz*—1 c. Dover Fort; 2 c. Sugar cane breeding; 3 c.
Public buildings; 6 c. Casting net; 8 c. *Frances W. Smith*
(schooner); 12 c. Flying fish; 24 c. Old Main Guard Garrison; 60 c.
Careenage; $2.40, Seal of Barbados. *Vert*—4 c. Statue of Nelson;
48 c. St. Michael's Cathedral; $1.20, Map of Barbados and
wireless mast.
See also Nos. 312/19.

1953 (4 June). *Coronation. As No. 120 of Antigua.*

302	4 c. black and red-orange	..	40	10

1958 (23 Apr). *Inauguration of British Caribbean Federation. As*
Nos. 135/7 *of Antigua.*

303	3 c. deep green	..	35	20
304	6 c. blue	..	50	2·25
305	12 c. scarlet	..	50	30
303/5	..	*Set of 3*	1·25	2·50

38 Deep Water Harbour, Bridgetown

(Recess B.W.)

1961 (6 May). *Opening of Deep Water Harbour, Bridgetown.*
W w **12**. *P* 11 × 12.

306	**38**	4 c. black and red-orange	..	25	50
307		8 c. black and blue	..	25	60
308		24 c. carmine-red and black	..	25	60
306/8			*Set of 3*	65	1·50

SELF-GOVERNMENT

39 Scout Badge and Map of   **40** Deep Sea Coral
Barbados

(Recess B.W.)

1962 (9 Mar). *Golden Jubilee of Barbados Boy Scout Association.*
W w **12**. *P* 11½ × 11.

309	**39**	4 c. black and orange	..	40	10
310		12 c. blue and olive-brown	..	80	15
311		$1.20, carmine and olive-green	..	1·25	3·25
309/11	..		*Set of 3*	2·25	3·25

1964 (14 Jan)–**65**. *As Nos.* 289, *etc., but wmk w* **12**.

312	1 c. indigo (6.10.64)		..	50	2·00
313	4 c. black and orange		..	40	50
314	8 c. black and blue (29.6.65)		..	60	35
315	12 c. turquoise-blue and brown-olive (29.6.65)			90	50
316	24 c. rose-red and black (6.10.64)			70	50
317	48 c. deep violet		..	4·00	2·00
318	60 c. blue-green and brown-purple (6.10.64)			12·00	4·00
319	$2.40, black (29.6.65)		..	1·75	2·25
312/19			*Set of 8*	19·00	11·00

The above dates are for Crown Agents releases. The 14.1.64
printings were not released in Barbados until April 1964, the
6.10.64 printings until December 1964 and of the stamps
released in London on 29 June 1965 the 8 c. and $2.40 were
released from about 15 June 1965, but the 12 c. value was never
put on sale in Barbados.

1965 (17 May). *I.T.U. Centenary. As Nos.* 166/7 *of Antigua.*

320	2 c. lilac and red	..	20	40
321	48 c. yellow and grey-brown	..	70	1·50

(Des V. Whiteley, from drawings by Mrs. J. Walker. Photo
Harrison)

1965 (15 July). *Marine Life. Horiz designs as T* **40**. W w **12**
(*upright*). *P* 14×13½.

322	1 c. black, pink and blue	..	20	30
323	2 c. olive-brown, yellow and magenta	..	20	15
324	3 c. olive-brown and orange	..	45	60
325	4 c. deep blue and olive-green	..	15	10
	a. Imperf (pair)		£225	£150
	w. Wmk inverted		—	15·00
326	5 c. sepia, rose and lilac	..	30	20
327	6 c. multicoloured	..	45	20
	w. Wmk inverted		1·25	
328	8 c. multicoloured	..	25	10
	w. Wmk inverted		2·75	
329	12 c. multicoloured	..	35	10
	a. Grey printing double		45·00	
	w. Wmk inverted			
330	15 c. black, greenish yellow and red		80	50
331	25 c. ultramarine and yellow-ochre		95	50
332	35 c. brown-red and deep green	..	1·50	15
	w. Wmk inverted			
333	50 c. bright blue and apple-green	..	2·00	40
334	$1 multicoloured	..	2·75	1·25
335	$2.50, multicoloured	..	2·75	2·25
322/35		*Set of 14*	12·00	6·00

Designs:—2 c. Lobster; 3 c. Lined Seahorse; 4 c. Sea Urchin;
5 c. Staghorn Coral; 6 c. Spot-finned Butterflyfish; 8 c. Rough
File shell; 12 c. Porcupinefish ("Balloon Fish"); 15 c. Grey
Angelfish; 25 c. Brain Coral; 35 c. Brittle Star; 50 c. Four-winged
Flyingfish; $1 Queen or Pink Conch shell; $2.50 Fiddler Crab.
The 3 c. value is wrongly inscribed "Hippocampus", the correct
spelling "Hippocampus" was used for subsequent printings, see
No. 344.
See also Nos. 342, etc.

1966 (24 Jan). *Churchill Commemoration. As Nos.* 170/3 *of*
Antigua.

336	1 c. new blue	..	10	1·75
	w. Wmk inverted		17·00	
337	4 c. deep green	..	30	10
338	25 c. brown	..	70	50
339	35 c. bluish violet	..	80	60
336/9		*Set of 4*	1·75	2·75

1966 (4 Feb). *Royal Visit. As Nos.* 174/5 *of Antigua.*

340	3 c. black and ultramarine	..	35	25
341	35 c. black and magenta	..	1·40	80

41 Dolphin   **54** Arms of Barbados

1966 (15 Mar)–**69**. *As Nos.* 322/35 *but wmk w* **12** (*sideways**).
New value and design (as T **41**).

342	1 c. black, pink and blue		..	10	20
	w. Wmk Crown to right of CA				
343	2 c. olive-brn, yellow & magenta (16.5.67)			30	80
344	3 c. olive-brown and orange (4.12.67)		..	30	2·50
345	4 c. deep blue and olive-green		..	50	10
	w. Wmk Crown to right of CA			45·00	
346	5 c. sepia, rose and lilac (23.8.66)			45	10
347	6 c. multicoloured (31.1.67)		..	70	10
348	8 c. multicoloured (19.9.67)		..	75	10
349	12 c. multicoloured (31.1.67)		..	45	10
350	15 c. black, greenish yellow and red			2·25	10
351	25 c. ultramarine and yellow-ochre			2·25	40
	aw. Wmk Crown to right of CA			7·00	
	b. Deep ultram & yellow-ochre (26.9.66)			8·50	2·25
352	35 c. brown-red and deep green (23.8.66)			2·50	65
	a. Chestnut and deep green (26.11.68)			6·50	3·00
353	50 c. bright blue and apple-green			1·75	3·00
	w. Wmk Crown to right of CA			50·00	
354	$1 multicoloured (23.8.66)			6·00	1·00
355	$2.50, multicoloured (23.8.66)			12·00	3·00
355a	$5 multicoloured (9.1.69)			12·00	7·00
342/55a			*Set of 15*	32·00	17·00

*The normal sideways watermark shows Crown to left of CA,
as seen from the back of the stamp.
The 3 c. value is correctly inscribed "Hippocampus".
All values except the 50 c. exist with PVA gum as well as gum
arabic but the 50 c. exists with PVA gum only.
The $5 was released by the Crown Agents on 6 January but was
not put on sale locally until 9 January.

INDEPENDENT

(Des. V. Whiteley. Photo Harrison)

1966 (2 Dec). *Independence. T* **54** *and similar multicoloured*
designs. P 14.

356	4 c. Type **54**		10	10
357	25 c. Hilton Hotel (*horiz*)		15	10
358	35 c. G. Sobers (Test cricketer)		1·50	65
359	50 c. Pine Hill Dairy (*horiz*)		70	1·10
356/9		*Set of 4*	2·00	1·75

1967 (6 Jan). *20th Anniv of U.N.E.S.C.O. As Nos.* 196/8 *of*
Antigua.

360	4 c. slate-violet, red, yellow and orange		30	10
361	12 c. orange-yellow, violet and deep olive		70	65
362	25 c. black, bright purple and orange		1·00	1·50
360/2	..	*Set of 3*	1·75	2·00

58 Policeman and   **62** Governor-General Sir Winston
Anchor   Scott, G.C.M.G.

(Des V. Whiteley. Litho D.L.R.)

1967 (16 Oct). *Centenary of Harbour Police. T* **58** *and similar*
multicoloured designs. P 14.

363	4 c. Type **58**		25	10
364	12 c. Policeman with telescope		40	15
365	35 c. *BPI* (police launch) (*horiz*)		45	15
366	50 c. Policeman outside H.Q.		60	1·60
363/6		*Set of 4*	1·50	1·75

(Des V. Whiteley. Photo Harrison)

1967 (4 Dec). *First Anniv of Independence. T* **62** *and similar*
multicoloured designs. P 14½ × 14 (4 c.) *or* 14 × 14½ (*others*).

367	4 c. Type **62**		10	10
368	25 c. Independence Arch (*horiz*)		20	10
369	35 c. Treasury Building (*horiz*)		25	10
370	50 c. Parliament Building (*horiz*)		35	90
367/70		*Set of 4*	75	1·00

66 U.N. Building, Santiago, Chile   **67** Radar Antenna

(Des G. Vasarhelyi. Photo Harrison)

1968 (27 Feb). *20th Anniv of the Economic Commission for Latin*
America. P 14½.

371	**66** 15 c. multicoloured	..	10	10

(Des G. Vasarhelyi. Photo Harrison)

1968 (4 June). *World Meteorological Day. T* **67** *and similar multi-*
coloured designs. P 14 × 14½ (25 c.) *or* 14½ × 14 (*others*).

372	**67** 10 c. Type **67**		10	10
373	25 c. Meteorological Institute (*horiz*)		25	10
374	50 c. Harp Gun and coat of arms		30	90
372/4		*Set of 3*	55	1·00

70 Lady Baden-Powell, and Guide at Camp Fire

(Des V. Whiteley (from local designs). Photo Harrison)

1968 (29 Aug). *50th Anniv of Girl Guiding in Barbados. T* **70** *and*
similar horiz designs. P 14.

375	3 c. ultramarine, black and gold	..	25	60
376	25 c. turquoise-blue, black and gold	..	50	60
377	35 c. orange-yellow, black and gold	..	65	60
375/7		*Set of 3*	1·25	1·60

Designs:—25 c. Lady Baden-Powell and Pax Hill; 35 c. Lady
Baden-Powell and Guide badge.

73 Hands breaking Chain, and Human Rights Emblem

(Des V. Whiteley. Litho B.W.)

1968 (10 Dec).* *Human Rights Year. T* **73** *and similar horiz designs.* P 11 × 12.
378	4 c. violet, brown and light green	..		10	20
379	25 c. black, blue and orange-yellow	..		15	25
380	35 c. multicoloured	..		15	25
378/80			Set of 3	30	60

Designs:—25 c. Human Rights emblem and family enchained; 35 c. Shadows of refugees beyond opening fence.
* This was the local release date but the Crown Agents issued the stamps on 29 October.

76 Racehorses in the Paddock

(Des J. Cooter. Litho Format)

1969 (20 Mar).* *Horse-Racing. T* **76** *and similar horiz designs. Multicoloured.* P 14.
381	4 c. Type 76			20	15
382	25 c. Starting-gate	..		25	15
383	35 c. On the flat	..		25	15
384	50 c. Winning post	..		35	2·00
381/4			Set of 4	95	2·25
MS385	117 × 85 mm. Nos. 381/4			2·00	2·75

*This was the local release date but the Crown Agents issued the stamps on 15 March.

80 Map showing "CARIFTA" Countries   **81** "Strength in Unity"

(Des J. Cooter. Photo Harrison)

1969 (6 May). *First Anniv of CARIFTA (Caribbean Free Trade Area).* W w **12** (*sideways on T* **80**). P 14.
386	80	5 c. multicoloured	..	10	10
387	81	12 c. multicoloured	..	10	10
388	80	25 c. multicoloured	..	10	10
389	81	50 c. multicoloured	..	15	20
386/9			Set of 4	30	30

82 I.L.O. Emblem and "1919-1969".   **ONE CENT** (**83**)

(Des Sylvia Goaman. Litho Enschedé)

1969 (12 Aug). *50th Anniv of International Labour Organisation.* P 14 × 13.
390	82	4 c. black, emerald and turquoise-blue	10	10
391		25 c. black, cerise and brown-red	..	20	10

Although released by the Crown Agents on 5 August, the above were not put on sale in Barbados until 12 August.

1969 (30 Aug). *No. 363 surch with T* **83**.
392	1 c. on 4 c. Type 58	..	..	10	10
	a. Surch double	..	..	65·00	

84 National Scout Badge

(Des J. Cooter. Litho Enschedé)

1969 (16 Dec). *Independence of Barbados Boy Scouts Association and 50th Anniv of Barbados Sea Scouts. T* **84** *and similar horiz designs. Multicoloured.* P 13 × 13½.
393	5 c. Type 84	..		15	10
394	25 c. Sea Scouts rowing	..		45	10
395	35 c. Scouts around camp fire	..		55	10
396	50 c. Scouts and National Scout Headquarters	80	1·25
393/6			Set of 4	1·75	1·40
MS397	155 × 115 mm. Nos. 393/6	..		11·00	12·00

4 x (**88**)   **89** Lion at Gun Hill

1970 (11 Mar). *No. 346 surch locally with T* **88**.
398	4 c. on 5 c. sepia, rose and lilac	..		10	10
	a. Vert pair, one without surch	..		35·00	
	b. Surch double	..		25·00	
	c. Vert pair, one normal, one surch double	50·00	
	d. Surch triple	..		—	£100
	e. Surch normal on front, inverted on back	12·00	
	f. Surch omitted on front, inverted on back	16·00	

(Des J.W. Photo D.L.R.)

1970 (4 May)–**71**. *Multicoloured designs as T* **89**. W w **12** (*sideways on 12 c. to $5*). *Chalk-surfaced paper.* P 12½.
399	1 c. Type 89	..	10	50
	a. Glazed, ordinary paper (15.3.71)	10	1·00
400	2 c. Trafalgar Fountain	..	30	60
	a. Glazed, ordinary paper (15.3.71)	10	1·50
401	3 c. Montefiore Drinking Fountain	10	60
	a. Glazed, ordinary paper (15.3.71)	10	1·50
	aw. Wmk inverted		6·50	
402	4 c. St. James' Monument	..	85	15
	a. Glazed, ordinary paper (15.3.71)	10	10
403	5 c. St. Anne's Fort	..	10	10
	a. Glazed, ordinary paper (15.3.71)	10	10
404	6 c. Old Sugar Mill, Morgan Lewis	35	2·75
405	8 c. Cenotaph	..	10	10
	a. Glazed, ordinary paper (15.3.71)	10	10
406	10 c. South Point Lighthouse	..	2·75	50
	a. Glazed, ordinary paper (15.3.71)	85	15
407	12 c. Barbados Museum (*horiz*)	..	80	10
	a. Glazed, ordinary paper (13.12.71)	2·75	30
408	15 c. Sharon Moravian Church (*horiz*)	30	15
	a. Glazed, ordinary paper (15.3.71)	60	30
409	25 c. George Washington House (*horiz*)	25	15
	a. Glazed, ordinary paper (15.3.71)	50	35
410	35 c. Nicholas Abbey (*horiz*)	..	30	85
	a. Glazed, ordinary paper (15.3.71)	45	70
411	50 c. Bowmanston Pumping Station (*horiz*)	40	95
	a. Glazed, ordinary paper (15.3.71)	70	4·00
412	$1 Queen Elizabeth Hospital (*horiz*)	70	2·50
	a. Glazed, ordinary paper (15.3.71)	4·00	8·50
413	$2.50, Modern sugar factory (*horiz*)	1·50	4·00
	a. Glazed, ordinary paper (13.12.71)	27·00	16·00
414	$5 Seawell International Airport (*horiz*)	6·00	11·00
	a. Glazed, ordinary paper (15.3.71)	13·00	15·00
399/414		Set of 16	12·00	22·00

See also Nos. 455/67.

105 Primary Schoolgirl

(Des V. Whiteley. Litho J.W.)

1970 (26 June). *25th Anniv of United Nations. T* **105** *and similar horiz designs. Multicoloured.* W w **12**. P 14.
415	4 c. Type 106	..		10	10
416	5 c. Secondary Schoolboy	..		10	10
417	25 c. Technical Student	..		35	10
418	50 c. University Buildings	..		55	1·50
415/18			Set of 4	90	1·60

106 Minnie Root

(Des and litho J.W.)

1970 (24 Aug). *Flowers of Barbados. T* **106** *and similar designs. Multicoloured.* W w **12** (*sideways on horiz designs*). P 14½.
419	1 c. Barbados Easter Lily (*vert*)	..	10	1·75
420	5 c. Type 106	..		40	10
421	10 c. Eyelash Orchid	..		1·75	20
422	25 c. Pride of Barbados (*vert*)	..	1·25	75
423	35 c. Christmas Hope	..		1·25	85
419/23			Set of 5	4·25	3·25
MS424	162 × 101 mm. Nos. 419/23. Imperf	2·00	5·50

107 "Via Dolorosa" (Window, St. Margaret's Church, St. John)   **108** "Sailfish" Dinghy

(Des Jennifer Toombs. Litho J.W.)

1971 (7 Apr). *Easter. T* **107** *and similar vert design. Multicoloured.* W w **12**. P 14.
425	4 c. Type 107	..	10	10
426	10 c. "The Resurrection" (Benjamin West)	10	10
427	35 c. Type 107	..	15	10
428	50 c. As 10 c.	..	30	1·25
425/8		Set of 4	45	1·40

(Des and litho Harrison)

1971 (17 Aug). *Tourism. T* **108** *and similar horiz designs. Multicoloured.* W w **12** (*sideways on 5 c. and 25 c.*). P 14.
429	1 c. Type 108	..	10	20
	w. Wmk inverted		50	45
430	5 c. Tennis	..	40	10
431	12 c. Horse-riding	..	60	10
	w. Wmk inverted		1·25	1·25
432	25 c. Water-skiing	..	40	20
433	50 c. Scuba-diving	..	50	80
	w. Wmk inverted		80	80
429/33		Set of 5	1·75	1·25

109 S. J. Prescod (politician)   **110** Arms of Barbados

(Des J.W. Litho Questa)

1971 (28 Sept).* *Death Centenary of Samuel Jackman Prescod.* W w **12**. P 14.
434	109	3 c. multicoloured	10	15
435		35 c. multicoloured	15	15

*This is the local date but the Crown Agents released the stamps two days earlier.

(Des G. Drummond. Litho Questa)

1971 (23 Nov). *Fifth Anniv of Independence. T* **110** *and similar horiz design. Multicoloured.* W w **12** (*sideways*). P 14.
436	4 c. Type 110	..	20	10
437	15 c. National flag and map	45	10
438	25 c. Type 110	..	45	10
439	50 c. As 15 c.	..	90	1·60
436/9		Set of 4	1·75	1·75

111 Transmitting "Then and Now"   **112** Map and Badge

(Des Cable & Wireless Ltd. Litho J.W.)

1972 (28 Mar). *Cable Link Centenary. T* **111** *and similar horiz designs. Multicoloured.* W w **12** (*sideways*). P 14.
440	4 c. Type 111	..	10	10
441	10 c. Stanley Angwin (cable ship)	15	10
442	35 c. Barbados Earth Station and "Intelsat 4"	35	20
443	50 c. Mt. Misery and Tropospheric Scatter Station	50	1·10
440/3		Set of 4	95	1·25

(Des Mrs. C. Barrow (50 c.), Major L. Quintyne (others) and adapted by G. Drummond. Litho Questa)

1972 (1 Aug). *Diamond Jubilee of Scouts. T* **112** *and similar horiz designs. Multicoloured.* W w **12** (*sideways* on 5 c.). P 14.
444	5 c. Type 112	..	10	10
	w. Wmk Crown to right of CA		
445	15 c. Pioneers of scouting	15	10
446	25 c. Scouts	..	30	15
447	50 c. Flags	..	50	1·00
444/7		Set of 4	90	1·25

*The normal sideways watermark shows Crown to left of CA, as seen from the back of the stamp.

113 Mobile Library

(Des PAD Studio. Litho Harrison)

1972 (31 Oct). *International Book Year. T* **113** *and similar horiz designs. Multicoloured.* W w **12**. P 14.

448	4 c. Type 113			20	10
449	15 c. Visual-aids van			25	10
450	25 c. Public library			30	10
451	$1 Codrington College			1·25	1·50
448/51			*Set of 4*	1·75	1·50

1972 (17 Nov)–**74**. *As Nos. 402/14, but* W w **12** (*sideways on 4 to 10 c; upright on 12 c. to $5*). *Glazed, ordinary paper.* P 12½.

455	4 c. St. James' Monument			1·50	1·50
456	5 c. St. Anne's Fort			1·25	1·50
457	6 c. Old Sugar Mill, Morgan Lewis			3·75	10·00
458	8 c. Cenotaph			1·50	1·25
459	10 c. South Point Lighthouse (21.1.74)			3·50	6·00
460	12 c. Barbados Museum			2·25	3·50
461	15 c. Sharon Moravian Church			75	1·25
462	25 c. George Washington House			2·75	2·50
463	35 c. Nicholas Abbey			2·50	70
464	50 c. Bowmanston Pumping Station			4·25	1·50
465	$1 Queen Elizabeth Hospital			7·00	2·75
466	$2.50, Modern sugar factory (2.10.73)			4·00	7·00
467	$5 Seawell International Airport (2.10.73)			4·00	5·50
	w. Wmk inverted			6·50	
455/67			*Set of 13*	35·00	40·00

114 Potter's Wheel

(Des PAD Studio. Litho Questa)

1973 (1 Mar). *Pottery in Barbados. T* **114** *and similar horiz designs. Multicoloured.* W w **12**. P 14.

468	5 c. Type 114			10	10
469	15 c. Kilns			20	10
470	25 c. Finished products			25	10
471	$1 Market scene			90	1·10
	w. Wmk inverted			25·00	
468/71			*Set of 4*	1·25	1·25

115 First Flight, 1911

(Des C. Abbott. Litho Enschedé)

1973 (25 July). *Aviation. T* **115** *and similar horiz designs.* W w **12** (*sideways*). P 12½ × 12.

472	5 c. multicoloured			30	10
473	15 c. multicoloured			90	10
474	25 c. grey-blue, black and cobalt			1·25	20
475	50 c. multicoloured			2·00	1·90
472/5			*Set of 4*	4·00	2·00

Designs:—15 c. De Havilland D.H.60 Cirrus Moth on first flight to Barbados, 1928; 25 c. Lockheed 14 Super Electra, 1939; 50 c. Vickers Super VC-10 airliner, 1973.

116 University Chancellor   (117)

(Des J. W. Litho Enschedé)

1973 (11 Dec). *25th Anniv of University of West Indies. T* **116** *and similar horiz designs. Multicoloured.* W w **12**. P 13 × 14.

476	5 c. Type 116			10	10
	w. Wmk inverted			24·00	
477	25 c. Sherlock Hall			25	15
478	35 c. Cave Hill Campus			30	25
476/8			*Set of 3*	55	40

1974 (30 Apr). *No.* 462 *surch with T* **117**.

479	4 c. on 25 c. George Washington House			15	15
	a. "4c." omitted			16·00	

No. 479a occurs on R. 10/1, the overprint being applied to sheets consisting of two horizontal panes, 5 × 5. The variety occurs on plate 1A, and shows a clear albino impression of the "4c." on the reverse.

118 Old Sail Boat

(Des J. Cooter. Litho Questa)

1974 (11 June). *Fishing Boats of Barbados. T* **118** *and similar diamond-shaped designs. Multicoloured.* W w **12**. P 14.

480	15 c. Type 118			30	15
481	35 c. Rowing-boat			55	25
482	50 c. Motor fishing-boat			70	70
483	$1 *Calamar* (fishing boat)			1·10	1·40
480/3			*Set of 4*	2·40	2·25
MS484	140 × 140 mm. Nos. 480/3			3·25	3·00

119 *Cattleya Gaskelliana Alba*

(Des PAD Studio. Photo Harrison)

1974 (16 Sept)–**77**. *Orchids. T* **119** *and similar multicoloured designs.* W w **12** (*upright on 1, 20, 25 c., $1 and $10; sideways* on others*). P 14½×14 ($1, $10), 14×14½ ($2.50, $5) *or* 14 (*others*).

485	1 c. Type 119			15	1·75
486	2 c. *Renanthera storiei*			20	1·75
487	3 c. *Dendrobium* "Rose Marie"			30	1·50
488	4 c. *Epidendrum ibaguense*			1·75	90
	w. Wmk Crown to right of CA			50·00	
489	5 c. *Schomburgkia humboldtii*			35	15
490	8 c. *Oncidium ampliatum*			1·00	90
	w. Wmk Crown to right of CA				
491	10 c. *Arachnis maggie oei*			55	20
492	12 c. *Dendrobium aggregatum*			45	2·25
	w. Wmk Crown to right of CA				
493	15 c. *Paphiopedilum puddle*			45	1·00
	aw. Wmk Crown to right of CA			4·50	
493b	20 c. *Spathoglottis* "The Gold" (3.5.77)			4·75	4·75
494	25 c. *Epidendrum ciliare* (Eyelash)			55	60
	w. Wmk inverted			75·00	
495	35 c. *Bletia patula*			2·00	1·75
	aw. Wmk Crown to right of CA			2·50	1·75
495b	45 c. *Phalaenopsis schilleriana* "Sunset Glow" (3.5.77)			4·75	4·50
496	50 c. As 45 c.			4·50	3·50
	w. Wmk Crown to left of CA			4·50	
497	$1 *Ascocenda* "Red Gem"			7·50	3·25
498	$2.50, *Brassolaeliocattleya* "Nugget"			3·50	6·50
499	$5 *Caularthron bicornutum*			3·50	6·00
500	$10 *Vanda* "Josephine Black"			9·00	13·00
485/500			*Set of 18*	35·00	48·00

The 1 c., 20 c., 25 c., $2.50 and $5 are horiz designs and the remainder are vert.

*The normal sideways watermark shows Crown to right of CA on the 50 c. and to left of CA on the others, *as seen from the back of the stamp.*

See also Nos. 510/24 and 543/51.

120 4d. Stamp of 1882, and U.P.U. Emblem

(Des Harrison. Litho Questa)

1974 (9 Oct). *Centenary of Universal Postal Union. T* **120** *and similar horiz designs.* W w **12** (*sideways**). P 14.

501	8 c. magenta, light orange & lt grey-green			10	10
502	35 c. dp rose-red, dull orange & bistre-brown			20	10
503	50 c. ultramarine, cobalt and silver			25	30
504	$1 bright blue, dull brown and grey-black			55	80
	w. Wmk Crown to right of CA				
501/4			*Set of 4*	1·00	1·10
MS505	126×101 mm. Nos. 501/4			1·50	2·25

Designs:—35 c. Letters encircling the globe; 50 c. U.P.U. emblem and arms of Barbados; $1 Map of Barbados, sailing ship and Boeing 747 airliner.

*The normal sideways watermark shows Crown to left of CA, *as seen from the back of the stamp.*

121 Royal Yacht *Britannia*

(Des Jennifer Toombs. Litho Harrison)

1975 (18 Feb). *Royal Visit. T* **121** *and similar horiz design. Multicoloured.* W w **12** (*sideways on 8 and 25 c.*) P 14.

506	8 c. Type 121			75	20
507	25 c. Type 121			1·10	30
508	35 c. Sunset and palms			60	35
509	$1 As 35 c.			1·75	2·75
506/9			*Set of 4*	3·75	3·25

1975 (30 Apr)–**79**. *As Nos. 485/9, 491/3, 494 and 495b/500 but* W w **14** (*sideways** on 1, 25 c., $1 and $10*).

510	1 c. Type 119			15	1·00
511	2 c. *Renanthera storiei*			15	1·00
512	3 c. *Dendrobium* "Rose Marie"			15	1·00
513	4 c. *Epidendrum ibaguense*			50	2·50
514	5 c. *Schomburgkia humboldtii* (19.10.77)			35	15
515	10 c. *Arachnis maggie oei* (19.10.77)			35	10
	w. Wmk inverted				
516	12 c. *Dendrobium aggregatum* (19.10.77)			7·50	15
517	15 c. *Paphiopedilum puddle*			70	15
518	25 c. *Epidendrum ciliare* (Eyelash) (27.3.79)			70	10
519	45 c. *Phalaenopsis schilleriana* "Sunset Glow" (25.5.78)			60	15
520	50 c. As 45 c. (23.8.79)			7·50	7·50
	w. Wmk Crown to right of CA			18·00	
521	$1 *Ascocenda* "Red Gem"			8·50	11·00
522	$2.50, *Brassolaeliocattleya* "Nugget"			8·50	3·75
523	$5 *Caularthron bicornutum*			8·50	6·00
524	$10 *Vanda* "Josephine Black"			11·00	11·00
	a. Dull green (stems) omitted			£120	
510/24			*Set of 15*	50·00	40·00

*The normal sideways watermark shows Crown to left of CA, *as seen from the back of the stamp.*

No. 525 vacant.

122 St. Michael's Cathedral   **123** Pony Float

(Des R. Granger Barrett. Litho Questa)

1975 (29 July). *150th Anniv of Anglican Diocese. T* **122** *and similar square designs. Multicoloured.* W w **12** (*sideways*). P 13½.

526	5 c. Type 122			10	10
527	15 c. Bishop Coleridge			15	10
528	50 c. All Saints' Church			45	50
529	$1 "Archangel Michael and Satan" (stained-glass window, St. Michael's Cathedral, Bridgetown)			70	80
526/9			*Set of 4*	1·25	1·25
MS530	95 × 96 mm. Nos. 526/9 (wmk upright)			1·40	2·00

(Des R. Granger Barrett. Litho Questa)

1975 (18 Nov). *Crop-over Festival. T* **123** *and similar horiz designs. Multicoloured.* W w **14** (*sideways*). P 14.

531	8 c. Type 123			10	10
532	25 c. Man on stilts			10	10
533	35 c. Maypole dancing			15	10
534	50 c. Cuban dancers			30	45
531/4			*Set of 4*	55	60
MS535	127 × 85 mm. Nos. 531/4			90	1·60

124 Barbados Coat   **125** 17th-Century
of Arms   Sailing Ship

(Des and litho Harrison)

1975 (15 Dec). *Coil Definitives.* W w **12** P 15 × 14.

536	**124** 5 c. greenish blue			15	80
537	25 c. bluish violet			25	1·10

For 5 c. in this design, but watermarked W w **14**, see No. 743.

(Des PAD Studio. Litho J.W.)

1975 (17 Dec). *350th Anniv of First Settlement. T* **125** *and similar vert designs. Multicoloured.* W w **14**. P 13½.

538	4 c. Type 125			50	10
539	10 c. Bearded fig tree and fruit			40	15
540	25 c. Ogilvy's 17th-century map			1·00	30
541	$1 Captain John Powell			2·00	5·00
538/41			*Set of 4*	3·50	5·00
MS542	105 × 115 mm. Nos. 538/41.			3·50	7·00

1976 (20 Feb). *As Nos. 485 etc., but* W w **12** (*sideways on 1 c., 25 c., $1*) *or upright* (*others*).

543	1 c. Type 119			45	3·00
544	2 c. *Renanthera storiei*			60	3·00
545	3 c. *Dendrobium* "Rose Marie"			65	3·25
546	4 c. *Epidendrum ibaguense*			45	3·25
547	10 c. *Arachnis maggie oei*			85	3·25
548	15 c. *Paphiopedilum puddle*			75	1·25
549	25 c. *Epidendrum ciliare* "Eyelash"			1·50	1·25
550	35 c. *Bletia patula*			2·00	1·75
551	$1 *Ascocenda* "Red Gem"			5·00	5·50
543/51			*Set of 9*	11·00	23·00

Nos. 552/8 vacant.

126 Map of the Caribbean

(Des PAD Studio. Litho Questa)

1976 (7 July). *West Indian Victory in World Cricket Cup. T* **126** *and similar design. No wmk. P* 14.
559	25 c. multicoloured	1·25	1·00
560	45 c. black and magenta	1·25	2·00

Design: *Vert*—45 c. The Prudential Cup.

127 Flag and Map of S. Carolina

(Des G. Vasarhelyi. Litho Walsall)

1976 (17 Aug). *Bicentenary of American Revolution. T* **127** *and similar horiz designs. Multicoloured. W* w **14** *(sideways). P* 13½.
561	15 c. Type **127**	55	15
562	25 c. George Washington and map of Bridgetown	55	15
563	50 c. Independence Declaration	70	1·00
564	$1 Prince Hall	1·00	3·00
561/4	*Set of* 4	2·50	3·75

128 Early Postman

(Des Jennifer Toombs. Litho Questa)

1976 (19 Oct). *125th Anniv of Post Office Act. T* **128** *and similar horiz designs. Multicoloured. W* w **14** *(sideways) P* 14.
565	8 c. Type **128**	10	10
566	35 c. Modern postman	25	10
567	50 c. Early letter	30	50
568	$1 Delivery van	50	1·40
565/8	*Set of* 4	1·00	1·90

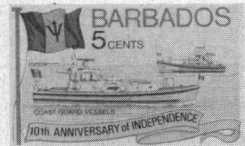

129 *Commander Marshall* and *T. T. Lewis* (coastguard launches)

(Des PAD Studio. Litho J.W.)

1976 (1 Dec).* *Tenth Anniv of Independence. T* **129** *and similar horiz designs. Multicoloured. W* w **14** *(sideways). P* 13 × 13½.
569	5 c. Type **129**	30	10
570	15 c. Reverse of currency note	30	10
571	25 c. National anthem	30	20
572	$1 Independence Day parade	1·10	2·50
569/72	*Set of* 4	1·75	2·50
MS573	90 × 125 mm. Nos. 569/72. P 14	1·75	3·00

*This is the local date of issue; the Crown Agents released the stamps a day earlier.

130 Arrival of Coronation Coach   **131** Underwater Park
at Westminster Abbey

(Des C. Abbott. Litho Walsall)

1977 (7 Feb). *Silver Jubilee. T* **130** *and similar vert designs. Multicoloured W* w **14**. *P* 13½.
574	15 c. Garfield Sobers being knighted, 1975	30	25
575	50 c. Type **130**	30	40
576	$1 Queen entering abbey	30	70
574/6	*Set of* 3	80	1·25

For the above with different inscription, see Nos. 590/2.

(Des R. Granger Barrett. Litho Questa)

1977 (3 May). *Natural Beauty of Barbados. T* **131** *and similar multicoloured designs. W* w **14** *(sideways on Nos. 577 and 579). P* 14.
577	5 c. Type **131**	15	10
578	35 c. Royal Palms (*vert*)	30	10
579	50 c. Underwater caves	40	50
580	$1 Stalagmite in Harrison's Cave (*vert*)	70	1·10
577/80	*Set of* 4	1·40	1·60
MS581	138 × 92 mm. Nos. 577/80 (wmk sideways)	2·25	2·75

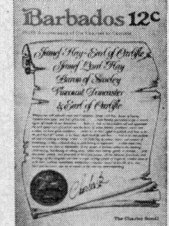

132 Maces of the House of   **133** The Charter Scroll
Commons

(Des C. Abbott. Litho J. W.)

1977 (2 Aug). *13th Regional Conference of the Commonwealth Parliamentary Association. T* **132** *and similar designs. W* w **14** *(sideways on* $1). *P* 13½.
582	10 c. pale orange, yellow and lake-brown	10	10
583	25 c. apple-green, orange and deep green	10	10
584	50 c. multicoloured	20	20
	w. Wmk inverted	12·00	
585	$1 pale blue, orange and deep violet-blue	55	75
582/5	*Set of* 4	80	95

Designs: *Vert*—25 c. Speaker's Chair, 50 c. Senate Chamber. *Horiz*—$1 Sam Lord's Castle.

(Des Walsall. Litho J.W.)

1977 (11 Oct). *350th Anniv of Granting of Charter to Earl of Carlisle. T* **133** *and similar multicoloured designs. W* w **14** *(sideways on* 45 c. *and* $1). *P* 13.
586	12 c. Type **133**	15	10
587	25 c. The earl receiving charter	15	10
588	45 c. The earl and Charles I (*horiz*)	30	35
589	$1 Ligon's map, 1657 (*horiz*)	50	1·00
586/9	*Set of* 4	1·00	1·40

(Des C. Abbott. Litho Walsall)

1977 (31 Oct). *Royal Visit. As Nos.* 574/6 *but inscr at top "*SILVER JUBILEE ROYAL VISIT*". W* w **14**. *Roul* 5. *Self-adhesive.*
590	15 c. Garfield Sobers being knighted, 1975	30	40
	w. Wmk inverted	9·00	
591	50 c. Type **130**	35	75
	w. Wmk inverted	16·00	
592	$1 Queen entering abbey	45	1·10
	w. Wmk inverted	6·50	
590/2	*Set of* 3	1·00	2·00

134 Gibson's Map of Bridgetown, 1766   **135** Brown Pelican

(Des J. W. Litho Questa)

1978 (1 Mar). *350th Anniv of Founding of Bridgetown. T* **134** *and similar horiz designs. W* w **14** *(sideways). P* 14.
593	12 c. multicoloured	15	10
594	25 c. black, light green and gold	20	10
595	45 c. multicoloured	25	15
596	$1 multicoloured	40	60
593/6	*Set of* 4	90	80

Designs:—25 c. "A Prospect of Bridgetown in Barbados" (engraving by S. Copens, 1695); 45 c. "Trafalgar Square, Bridgetown" (drawing by J. M. Carter, 1835); $1 The Bridges, 1978.

(Des C. Abbott. Litho Questa)

1978 (21 Apr). *25th Anniv of Coronation. T* **135** *and similar vert designs. P* 15.
597	50 c. yellow-olive, black and blue	25	50
	a. Sheetlet. Nos. 597/9 × 2	1·25	
598	50 c. multicoloured	25	50
599	50 c. yellow-olive, black and blue	25	50
597/9	*Set of* 3	65	1·40

Designs:—No. 597, Griffin of Edward III; No. 598, Queen Elizabeth II; No. 599, Type **135**.

Nos. 597/9 were printed together in small sheets of 6 containing two *se-tenant* strips of 3, with horizontal gutter margin between.

136 Barbados Bridge League Logo

(Des J.W. Litho Questa)

1978 (6 June). *7th Regional Bridge Tournament, Barbados. T* **136** *and similar horiz designs. Multicoloured. W* w **14** *(sideways*). *P* 14½.
600	5 c. Type **136**	10	10
601	10 c. Emblem of World Bridge Federation	15	10
602	45 c. Central American and Caribbean Bridge Federation emblem	25	10
603	$1 Playing cards on map of Caribbean	40	60
600/3	*Set of* 4	80	75
MS604	134×83 mm. Nos. 600/3	1·50	2·50
	w. Wmk Crown to right of CA	45·00	

*The normal sideways watermark shows Crown to left of CA, as seen from the back of the stamp.

137 Camp Scene

(Des and litho Harrison)

1978 (1 Aug). *Diamond Jubilee of Guiding. T* **137** *and similar diamond-shaped designs. Multicoloured. W* w **14** *(sideways on* 12, 28 c.). *P* 13½.
605	12 c. Type **137**	25	15
606	28 c. Community work	40	15
607	50 c. Badge and "60" (*vert*)	55	30
608	$1 Guide badge (*vert*)	75	1·00
605/8	*Set of* 4	1·75	1·40

138 Garment Industry

(Des Walsall. Litho Harrison)

1978 (14 Nov). *Industries. T* **138** *and similar multicoloured designs. W* w **14** *(sideways on* 12 *and* 50 c.). *P* 14.
609	12 c. Type **138**	15	10
610	28 c. Cooper (*vert*)	25	25
611	45 c. Blacksmith (*vert*)	35	95
612	50 c. Wrought iron working	40	95
609/12	*Set of* 4	1·00	2·00

139 *Forth* (early mail steamer)

(Des J. Cooter. Litho J. W.)

1979 (8 Feb). *Ships. T* **139** *and similar horiz designs. Multicoloured. W* w **14** *(sideways). P* 13.
613	12 c. Type **139**	35	10
614	25 c. *Queen Elizabeth 2* in Deep Water Harbour	55	15
615	50 c. *Ra II* nearing Barbados	75	1·00
616	$1 *Dee* (early mail steamer)	1·00	2·50
613/16	*Set of* 4	2·40	3·25

140 1953 1 c. Definitive Stamp

(Des J.W. Litho Format)

1979 (8 May). *Death Centenary of Sir Rowland Hill. T* **140** *and similar multicoloured designs showing stamps. W* w **14** *(sideways* on 12 c.). *P* 14.
617	12 c. Type **140**	15	15
618	28 c. 1975 35th anniv of first settlement 25 c. commemorative (*vert*)	20	30
	a. Ultramarine (face value) omitted	£130	
619	50 c. Penny Black with Maltese Cross postmark (*vert*)	30	45
617/19	*Set of* 3	60	80
MS620	137×90 mm 50 c. Unissued "Britannia" blue (wmk sideways)	55	40
	w. Wmk Crown to left of CA		

*The normal sideways watermark on No. **MS**620 shows Crown to right of CA, *as seen from the back of the stamp.*

All examples of No. 618 show anniversary spelt as "anniveary".

28c + .4c

ST. VINCENT RELIEF FUND
(141)

142 Grassland Yellow Finch

1979 (29 May). *St. Vincent Relief Fund. No. 495 surch with T 141.*
621   28 c. + 4 c. on 35 c. *Bletia patula* ..   50   60

(Des J.W. Photo Harrison)

1979 (7 Aug)–83. *Birds. Vert designs as T 142. Multicoloured. W w 14 (sideways* on 1, 5, 10, 12, 15, 20, 25, 28, 40, 50, 55, 60, 70 c. and $1). P 14.*
622   1 c. Type 142 10   70
    w. Wmk Crown to right of CA .. 1·40
623   2 c. Grey Kingbird 10   70
624   5 c. Lesser Antillean Bullfinch .. 10   70
625   8 c. Magnificent Frigate Bird .. 10   1·50
    w. Wmk inverted .. .. 32·00
626   10 c. Cattle Egret (deep slate inscr) 10   40
    a. Slate-blue inscr 20   40
    w. Wmk Crown to right of CA .. 6·00
627   12 c. Green Heron 50   85
627a   15 c. Carib Grackle (1.3.82) .. 4·50   5·00
628   20 c. Antillean Crested Hummingbird 20   55
    w. Wmk Crown to right of CA (14.3.83) 20   55
629   25 c. Scaly-breasted Ground Dove 20   60
630   28 c. As 15 c. .. .. 1·25   1·50
631   35 c. Green-throated Carib .. 30   70
    a. Yellow omitted £250
631b   40 c. Red-necked Pigeon (1.3.82) .. 4·50   5·50
632   45 c. Zenaida Dove .. .. 1·00   70
    w. Wmk inverted .. .. 12·00
633   50 c. As 40 c. .. .. 1·00   1·00
633a   55 c. American Golden Plover (1.9.81) 4·00   3·50
    aw. Wmk Crown to right of CA .. 10·00
633b   60 c. Bananaquit (1.3.82) .. 4·50   6·00
634   70 c. As 60 c. .. .. 1·25   2·75
635   $1 Caribbean Elaenia .. 1·50   1·50
636   $2.50, American Redstart .. 2·00   6·00
637   $5 Belted Kingfisher .. 3·25   9·00
    w. Wmk inverted .. .. 8·00
638   $10 Moorhen .. .. 6·50   14·00
    w. Wmk inverted .. .. 16·00
622/38 .. .. .. *Set of 21* 32·00   55·00
*The normal sideways watermark shows Crown to left of CA, as seen from the back of the stamp.
No. 626a occurred in the initial supply sent to Barbados.
No. 631a shows the birds' plumage in blue instead of green and has the background flowers omitted.

143 Gun aboard Landing Craft at Foul Bay   144 Family

(Des G. Vasarhelyi. Litho Format)

1979 (9 Oct). *Space Project Commemorations. T 143 and similar multicoloured designs. W w 14 (sideways on 10, 28 and 45 c.). P 14.*
639   10 c. Type 143 15   10
640   12 c. Transporting launcher through Barbados (*vert*) .. 15   15
641   20 c. Firing of 16" launcher in daylight (*vert*) 15   20
642   28 c. Bath Earth Station and "Intelsat IV A" 15   30
643   45 c. "Intelsat V" over the Caribbean .. 25   50
644   50 c. "Intelsat IV A" over Atlantic (*vert*) 25   60
639/44 .. .. .. *Set of 6* 1·00   1·60
MS645   118 × 90 mm. $1 Lunar module descending on to Moon (wmk sideways) .. 80   80
Commemorations:—10 to 20 c. H.A.R.P. Gun experiment: 28 to 50 c. First use of "Intelsat" satellites; $1, 10th anniversary of Moon landing.

(Des R. Granger Barrett. Litho Questa)

1979 (27 Nov). *International Year of the Child. T 144 and similar vert designs. Multicoloured. W w 14. P 14.*
646   12 c. Type 144 10   10
647   28 c. Ring of children and map of Barbados 15   15
648   45 c. Child with teacher 20   20
649   50 c. Children playing 20   20
650   $1 Children and kite 35   45
646/50 .. .. .. *Set of 5* 80   90

ALTERED CATALOGUE NUMBERS

Any Catalogue numbers altered from the last edition are shown as a list in the introductory pages.

145 Map of Barbados   146 Private, Artillery Company, Barbados Volunteer Force, *circa* 1909

(Des G. Hutchins. Litho Security Printers (M), Malaysia)

1980 (19 Feb). *75th Anniv of Rotary International. T 145 and similar horiz designs. Multicoloured. W w 14 (sideways). P 13.*
651   12 c. Type 145 15   10
652   28 c. Map of Caribbean .. 20   15
653   50 c. Rotary anniversary emblem .. 25   35
654   $1 Paul P. Harris (founder) .. 40   95
651/4 .. .. .. *Set of 4* 90   1·40

(Des J.W. Litho Questa)

1980 (8 Apr). *Barbados Regiment. T 146 and similar vert designs. Multicoloured. W w 14. P 14×14½.*
655   12 c. Type 146 25   10
656   35 c. Drum Major, Zouave uniform .. 35   15
657   50 c. Sovereign's and Regimental colours 40   30
    w. Wmk inverted .. .. 10·00
658   $1 Barbados Regiment Women's Corps 55   70
655/8 .. .. .. *Set of 4* 1·40   1·10

147 Early Postman   148 Yellow-tailed Snapper and other Fishes

(Des. V. Whiteley Studio. Litho Walsall)

1980 (6 May). *"London 1980" International Stamp Exhibition. Two sheets each 122 × 125 mm containing T 147 or similar vert design. Multicoloured. W w 14. P 14 × 13½.*
MS659   (a) 28 c. × 6, Type 147. (b) 50 c. × 6, Modern Postwoman and Inspector *Set of 2 sheets* 1·40   2·25
The two sheets each contain the stamp in full colour and in five different colour separations.

(Des G. Drummond. Litho Security Printers (M), Malaysia)

1980 (30 Sept). *Underwater Scenery. T 148 and similar horiz designs. Multicoloured. W w 14 (sideways*). P 13½.*
660   12 c. Type 148 20   10
661   28 c. Banded Butterflyfish .. 35   15
    w. Wmk Crown to right of CA .. 32·00
662   50 c. Male and female Blue-headed Wrasse and Princess Parrotfish .. 45   25
663   $1 French Grunt and French Angelfish 70   70
    w. Wmk Crown to right of CA .. 32·00
660/3 .. .. .. *Set of 4* 1·50   1·00
MS664   136×110 mm. Nos. 660/3 (wmk upright) 2·50   3·25
*The normal sideways watermark shows Crown to left of CA, as seen from the back of the stamp.

149 Bathsheba Railway Station

(Des J. W. Litho Questa)

1981 (13 Jan). *Early Transport. T 149 and similar horiz designs. Multicoloured. W w 14 (sideways). P 14½ × 14.*
665   12 c. Type 149 30   10
666   28 c. Cab stand at The Green .. 20   15
667   45 c. Animal-drawn tram .. 30   30
668   70 c. Horse-drawn bus 45   60
669   $1 Railway station in Fairchild Street 70   95
665/9 .. .. .. *Set of 5* 1·75   1·90

150 "The Blind at Work"   151 Prince Charles dressed for Polo

(Des BG Studio. Litho Walsall)

1981 (19 May). *International Year for Disabled Persons. T 150 and similar multicoloured designs. W w 14 (sideways on 10 c. and $2.50). P 14.*
670   10 c. Type 150 20   10
671   25 c. Sign language (*vert*) .. 25   15
672   45 c. "Be alert to the white cane" (*vert*) 40   25
673   $2.50, Children at play .. 1·25   3·00
670/3 .. .. .. *Set of 4* 1·90   3·00

(Des and litho J.W.)

1981 (22 July). *Royal Wedding. T 151 and similar vert designs. Multicoloured. W w 14. P 13½ × 13.*
674   28 c. Wedding bouquet from Barbados 15   10
675   50 c. Type 151 20   15
676   $2.50, Prince Charles and Lady Diana Spencer 55   1·25
674/6 .. .. .. *Set of 3* 80   1·25

152 Landship Manoeuvre   (153)

(Des C. Abbott. Litho Harrison)

1981 (11 Aug). *Carifesta (Caribbean Festival of Arts), Barbados. T 152 and similar vert designs. Multicoloured. W w 14. P 14½ × 14.*
677   15 c. Type 152 15   15
678   20 c. Yoruba dancers 15   15
679   40 c. Tuk band 20   25
680   55 c. Sculpture of Frank Collymore .. 25   35
    w. Wmk inverted .. .. 25·00
681   $1 Harbour scene 50   75
677/81 .. .. .. *Set of 5* 1·10   1·50

1981 (1 Sept). *Nos. 630, 632 and 634 surch as T 153.*
682   15 c. on 28 c. Carib Grackle .. 30   15
683   40 c. on 45 c. Zenaida Dove .. 30   35
684   60 c. on 70 c. Bananaquit .. 30   45
682/4 .. .. .. *Set of 3* 80   85

154 Satellite view of Hurricane

(Des A. Theobald. Litho Walsall)

1981 (29 Sept). *Hurricane Season. T 154 and similar horiz designs. W w 14 (sideways*). P 14.*
685   35 c. black and blue 35   20
    w. Wmk Crown to right of CA .. 28·00
686   50 c. multicoloured 45   35
    w. Wmk Crown to right of CA .. 28·00
687   60 c. multicoloured 70   50
    w. Wmk Crown to right of CA .. 6·00
688   $1 multicoloured 85   90
685/8 .. .. .. *Set of 4* 2·10   1·75
Designs:—50 c. Hurricane "Gladys" from "Apollo 7"; 60 c. Police Department on hurricane watch; $1 McDonnell F2H-2P Banshee "hurricane chaser" aircraft.
*The normal sideways watermark shows Crown to left of CA, as seen from the back of the stamp.

155 Twin Falls   156 Black Belly Ram

(Des. L. Curtis. Litho Format)

1981 (1 Dec.) *Harrison's Cave. T 155 and similar vert designs. Multicoloured. W w 14. P 14 × 14½.*
689   10 c. Type 155 10   10
690   20 c. Stream in Rotunda Room .. 20   15
691   55 c. Formations in Rotunda Room .. 30   50
692   $2.50, Cascade Pool 80   2·25
689/92 .. .. .. *Set of 4* 1·25   2·75

(Des BG Studio. Litho Format)

1982 (9 Feb). *Black Belly Sheep. T 156 and similar horiz designs. Multicoloured. W w 14 (sideways). P 14.*
693   40 c. Type 156 20   30
694   50 c. Black Belly ewe 20   35
695   60 c. Ewe with lambs 30   60
696   $1 Ram and ewe, with map of Barbados 50   1·50
693/6 .. .. .. *Set of 4* 1·10   2·50

157 Barbados Coat of Arms and Flag

(Des Harrison. Litho Format)

1982 (8 Apr). *President Reagan's Visit. T* **157** *and similar horiz design. Multicoloured. W* w **14** (*sideways*). *P* 14.

697	20 c. Type 157	..	..	40	1·25
	a. Pair. Nos. 697/8	..	..	80	2·50
698	20 c. U.S.A. coat of arms and flag		..	40	1·25
699	55 c. Type 157	..	..	50	1·50
	a. Pair. Nos. 699/700	..	..	1·00	3·00
700	55 c. As No. 698	..	..	50	1·50
697/700			*Set of 4*	1·60	5·00

The two designs of each value were printed together, *se-tenant*, in horizontal and vertical pairs within small sheets of 8 stamps.

158 Lighter   **159** Bride and Earl Spencer proceeding up Aisle

(Des J.W. Litho Harrison)

1982 (4 May). *Early Marine Transport. T* **158** *and similar horiz designs. Multicoloured. W* w **14** (*sideways*). *P* 14½.

701	20 c. Type 158	..	..	20	15
702	35 c. Rowing boat	..	..	35	25
703	55 c. Speightstown schooner	..		50	40
704	$2.50, Inter-colonial schooner	..		1·75	2·50
701/4			*Set of 4*	2·50	3·00

(Des Jennifer Toombs. Litho Questa)

1982 (1 July). *21st Birthday of Princess of Wales. T* **159** *and similar vert designs. Multicoloured W* w **14**. *P* 14½ × 14.

705	20 c. Barbados coat of arms	..		20	15
706	60 c. Princess at Llanelwedd, October 1981	..		45	50
707	$1.20, Type 159	..	..	75	1·10
708	$2.50, Formal portrait	..	..	1·25	1·90
705/8			*Set of 4*	2·40	3·25

160 "To Help other People"   **161** Arms of George Washington

(Des G. Drummond. Litho Format)

1982 (7 Sept). *75th Anniv of Boy Scout Movement. T* **160** *and similar multicoloured designs. W* w **14** (*sideways on Nos.* 710/11). *P* 14.

709	15 c. Type 160	..	..	50	10
710	40 c. "I Promise to do my Best" (*horiz*)		..	80	30
711	55 c. "To do my Duty to God, the Queen and my Country" (*horiz*)			90	65
712	$1 National and Troop flags		..	1·40	1·75
709/12			*Set of 4*	3·25	2·50
MS713	119 × 93 mm. $1.50, The Scout Law		..	3·50	3·00

(Des and litho J.W.)

1982 (2 Nov). *250th Birth Anniv of George Washington. T* **161** *and similar vert designs. Multicoloured. W* w **14**. *P* 13½ × 13.

714	10 c. Type 161	..		10	10
715	55 c. Washington House, Barbados	..		45	45
716	60 c. Washington with troops	..		50	50
717	$2.50, Washington taking Oath	..		1·60	1·60
714/17			*Set of 4*	2·40	2·40

162 *Agraulis vanillae*

(Des I. Loe. Litho J.W.)

1983 (8 Feb). *Butterflies. T* **162** *and similar horiz designs. Multicoloured. W* w **14** (*sideways*). *P* 13 × 13½.

718	20 c. Type 162	..	..	1·00	30
719	40 c. *Danaus plexippus*	..		1·50	40
720	55 c. *Hypolimnas misippus*	..		1·50	45
721	$2.50, *Hemiargus hanno*	..		3·25	3·50
718/21			*Set of 4*	6·50	4·25

163 Map of Barbados and Satellite View

(Des D. Bowen. Litho J.W.)

1983 (14 Mar). *Commonwealth Day. T* **163** *and similar horiz designs. Multicoloured. W* w **14** (*sideways*). *P* 13.

722	15 c. Type 163	..	..	20	10
723	40 c. Tourist beach	..		25	20
724	60 c. Sugar cane harvesting	..		35	40
725	$1 Cricket match	..	..	1·25	1·10
722/5			*Set of 4*	1·75	1·60

164 U.S. Navy "M" Class Airship M-20

(Des L. Curtis. Litho Format)

1983 (14 June). *Bicentenary of Manned Flight. T* **164** *and similar horiz designs. Multicoloured. W* w **14** (*sideways*). *P* 14.

726	20 c. Type 164	..	..	60	15
727	40 c. Douglas DC-3	..	..	80	40
728	55 c. Vickers Viscount 837	..		90	80
729	$1 Lockheed L-1011 TriStar 500	..		1·50	2·50
726/9			*Set of 4*	3·50	3·50

165 Nash "600", 1941   **166** Game in Progress

(Des and litho Harrison)

1983 (9 Aug). *Classic Cars. T* **165** *and similar horiz designs. Multicoloured. W* w **14** (*sideways*). *P* 14.

730	25 c. Type 165	..	..	60	20
731	45 c. Dodge, 1938	..	..	75	30
732	75 c. Ford "Model AA", 1930	..		95	1·50
733	$2.50, Dodge "Four", 1918	..		2·50	4·50
730/3			*Set of 4*	4·25	6·00

(Des L. Curtis. Litho Questa)

1983 (30 Aug). *Table Tennis World Cup Competition. T* **166** *and similar vert designs. Multicoloured. W* w **14**. *P* 14.

734	20 c. Type 166	..	..	25	20
735	65 c. Map of Barbados	..	..	50	55
736	$1 World Table Tennis Cup	..		75	1·00
734/6			*Set of 3*	1·40	1·60

167 Angel playing Lute (detail "The Virgin and Child") (Masaccio)   **168** Track and Field Events

(Des D. Miller. Litho Questa)

1983 (1 Nov). *Christmas. 50th Anniv of Barbados Museum. T* **167** *and similar multicoloured designs. W* w **14** (*sideways on 45 c., 75 c. and* $2.50). *P* 14.

737	10 c. multicoloured	..	..	30	10
738	25 c. multicoloured	..	..	60	20
739	45 c. multicoloured	..	..	90	40
740	75 c. black and gold	..		1·40	1·60
741	$2.50, multicoloured	..		4·50	5·50
737/41			*Set of 5*	7·00	7·00
MS742	59 × 98 mm. $2 multicoloured			1·75	2·00

Designs: *Horiz*—45 c. "The Barbados Museum" (Richard Day); 75 c. "St. Ann's Garrison" (W. S. Hedges); $2.50, Needham's Point, Carlisle Bay. *Vert*—25 c., $2 Different details from "The Virgin and Child" (Masaccio).

1983 (Dec). *Coil Definitive. As No.* 536 *but W* w **14**.

743	**124**	5 c. greenish blue	..	1·25	2·00

No. 743 was also available from sheets.

(Des McCombie Skinner Studio. Litho Walsall)

1984 (28 Mar). *Olympic Games, Los Angeles. T* **168** *and similar horiz designs. W* w **14** (*sideways*). *P* 14.

745	50 c. bright green, black and olive-sepia		60	45
746	65 c. dull orange, black and drab	..	80	60
747	75 c. greenish blue, black and deep cobalt		1·00	85
748	$1 light brown, black and yellow-ochre		2·50	1·75
745/8			*Set of 4*	4·50	3·25
MS749	115 × 97 mm. Nos. 745/8			6·50	8·00

Designs:—65 c. Shooting; 75 c. Sailing; $1 Cycling.

169 Global Coverage   **170** U.P.U. 1943 3d. Stamp and Logo

(Des C. Abbott. Litho Questa)

1984 (25 Apr). *250th Anniv of Lloyd's List (newspaper). T* **169** *and similar vert designs. Multicoloured. W* w **14**. *P* 14½ × 14.

750	45 c. Type 169	..	..	80	40
751	50 c. Bridgetown harbour	..		90	50
752	75 c. *Philosopher* (full-rigged ship), 1857		1·40	90
753	$1 *Sea Princess* (liner), 1984	..		1·40	1·25
750/3			*Set of 4*	4·00	2·75

(Des McCombie Skinner Studio. Litho J.W.)

1984 (6 June). *Universal Postal Union Congress, Hamburg. Sheet* 90 × 75 *mm. W* w **14** (*sideways*). *P* 13½.

MS754	**170** $2 multicoloured	..		2·50	2·50

171 Local Junior Match   **172** Poinsettia

(Des L. Curtis. Litho Walsall)

1984 (8 Aug). *60th Anniv of World Chess Federation. T* **171** *and similar horiz designs. Multicoloured. W* w **14** (*sideways*). *P* 14½.

755	25 c. Type 171	..	..	1·25	30
756	45 c. Staunton and 19th-century Knights		1·60	60
757	65 c. Staunton Queen and 18th-century Queen from Macao		1·75	1·60
758	$2 Staunton and 17th-century Rooks	..	3·50	5·50
755/8			*Set of 4*	7·25	7·25

(Des I. Loe. Litho Questa)

1984 (24 Oct). *Christmas. Flowers. T* **172** *and similar vert designs. Multicoloured. W* w **14**. *P* 14.

759	50 c. Type 172	..	..	1·50	80
760	65 c. Snow-on-the-Mountain	..		1·75	1·50
761	75 c. Christmas Candle	..		2·00	3·00
762	$1 Christmas Hope	..	..	2·25	3·50
759/62			*Set of 4*	6·75	8·00

173 Pink-tipped Anemone   **174** The Queen Mother at the Docks

(Des I. Loe. Litho Questa)

1985 (26 Feb)–**87**. *Marine Life. T* **173** *and similar horiz designs. Multicoloured. W* w **14** (*sideways*). *P* 14. A. *Without imprint date at foot.*

763A	1 c. Bristle Worm (7.5.85)	..		1·00	1·25
764A	2 c. Spotted Trunkfish (7.5.85)	..		1·00	1·25
765A	5 c. Coney (9.4.85)	..	..	3·00	75
766A	10 c. Type 173	..	..	80	75
767A	20 c. Christmas Tree Worm	..		2·00	2·00
768A	25 c. Hermit Crab	..	..	1·50	70
769A	35 c. Animal Flower (9.4.85)	..		4·00	75
770A	40 c. Vase Sponge (9.4.85)	..		4·00	80
771A	45 c. Spotted Moray (7.5.85)	..		1·50	90
772A	50 c. Ghost Crab	..	..	2·50	3·00
773A	65 c. Flamingo Tongue Snail (9.4.85)		3·75	1·00
774A	75 c. Sergeant Major (7.5.85)	..		2·50	2·00
775A	$1 Caribbean Warty Anemone (7.5.85)		3·75	1·25

776A	$2.50, Green Turtle			7·00	8·00
777A	$5 Rock Beauty (fish)			8·00	9·00
778A	$10 Elkhorn Coral (9.4.85)			8·50	9·00
763A/78A			Set of 16	45·00	38·00

B. *With imprint date ("1987") (15.9.87)*

763B	1 c. Bristle Worm			3·50	4·00
764B	2 c. Spotted Trunkfish			3·50	4·00
767B	20 c. Christmas Tree Worm			5·50	5·00
772B	50 c. Ghost Crab			7·00	8·00
774B	75 c. Sergeant Major			8·00	9·50
776B	$2.50, Green Turtle			12·00	17·00
777B	$5 Rock Beauty (fish)			16·00	21·00
763B/77B			Set of 7	50·00	60·00

For these designs watermarked w **16** (sideways) see Nos. 794/809.

(Des A. Theobald ($2), C. Abbott (others). Litho Questa)

1985 (7 June). *Life and Times of Queen Elizabeth the Queen Mother. T* **174** *and similar vert designs. Multicoloured. W* w **16**. *P* 14½ × 14.

779	25 c. In the White Drawing Room, Buckingham Palace, 1930s			20	20
780	65 c. With Lady Diana Spencer at Trooping the Colour, 1981			1·00	50
781	75 c. Type **174**			60	60
782	$1 With Prince Henry at his christening (from photo by Lord Snowdon)			75	75
779/82			Set of 4	2·25	1·90
MS783	91 × 73 mm. $2 In Land Rover opening Syon House Garden Centre. Wmk sideways			1·40	1·50

175 Peregrine Falcon

(Des D. Miller. Litho Walsall)

1985 (6 Aug). *Birth Bicentenary of John J. Audubon (ornithologist). T* **175** *and similar multicoloured designs showing original paintings. W* w **14** (sideways on 45 c.). *P* 14.

784	45 c. Type **175**			2·25	80
785	65 c. Prairie Warbler (vert)			2·50	2·25
786	75 c. Great Blue Heron (vert)			2·75	3·00
787	$1 Yellow Warbler (vert)			3·00	4·00
784/7			Set of 4	9·50	9·00

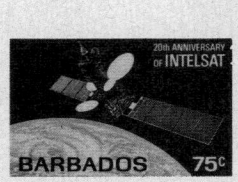

176 Intelsat Satellite orbitting Earth

177 Traffic Policeman

(Des L. Curtis. Litho Harrison)

1985 (10 Sept). *20th Anniv of Intelsat Satellite System. W* w **14** (sideways). *P* 14.

788	**176**	75 c. multicoloured		75	60

(Des L. Curtis. Litho Format)

1985 (19 Nov). *150th Anniv of Royal Barbados Police. T* **177** *and similar multicoloured designs. W* w **16**. *P* 14.

789	25 c. Type **177**			80	20
790	50 c. Police Band on bandstand			1·40	80
791	65 c. Dog handler			1·60	1·40
792	$1 Mounted policeman in ceremonial uniform			1·75	2·00
789/92			Set of 4	5·00	4·00
MS793	85 × 60 mm. $2 Police Band on parade (horiz). Wmk sideways			2·00	2·75

1986 (6 Jan)–87. *As Nos. 763/78 but W* w **16** (sideways). *P* 14.

A. *Without imprint date at foot*

796A	5 c. Coney			65	1·00
797A	10 c. Type **173**			65	1·00
798A	20 c. Christmas Tree Worm			90	1·25
799A	25 c. Hermit Crab			1·50	90
800A	35 c. Animal Flower			1·00	1·25
803A	50 c. Ghost Crab			2·00	1·50
807A	$2.50, Green Turtle			3·50	3·50
808A	$5 Rock Beauty (fish)			7·00	7·00
809A	$10 Elkhorn Coral			10·00	10·00
796A/809A			Set of 9	24·00	25·00

B. *With imprint date*

794B	1 c. Bristle Worm (23.7.86)			20	1·50
795B	2 c. Spotted Trunkfish (23.7.86)			20	1·50
796B	5 c. Coney (15.9.87)			15·00	8·00
797B	10 c. Type **173** (18.8.86)			30	30
798B	20 c. Christmas Tree Worm (18.8.86)			30	40
799B	25 c. Hermit Crab (18.8.86)			40	40
800B	35 c. Animal Flower (15.9.87)			15·00	8·00
801B	40 c. Vase Sponge (23.7.86)			50	50
802B	45 c. Spotted Moray (23.7.86)			60	50
803B	50 c. Ghost Crab (18.8.86)			60	60
804B	65 c. Flamingo Tongue Snail (18.8.86)			65	70
805B	75 c. Sergeant Major (18.8.86)			70	75
806B	$1 Caribbean Warty Anemone (18.8.86)			85	85

807B	$2.50, Green Turtle (18.8.86)			2·00	5·00
808B	$5 Rock Beauty (fish) (18.8.86)			2·50	6·50
809B	$10 Elkhorn Coral (18.8.86)			4·25	8·00
794B/809B			Set of 16	40·00	38·00

Imprint dates: "1986", Nos. 794B/5B, 797B/9B, 801B/9B; "1987", Nos. 796B/7B, 799B/802B, 804B, 806B, 809B; "1988", No. 797B.

(Des A. Theobald. Litho Format)

1986 (21 Apr). *60th Birthday of Queen Elizabeth II. Vert designs as T* **110** *of Ascension. Multicoloured. W* w **16**. *P* 14 × 14½.

810	25 c. Princess Elizabeth aged two, 1928			15	20
811	50 c. At University College of West Indies, Jamaica, 1953			30	40
812	65 c. With Duke of Edinburgh, Barbados, 1985			40	50
	a. Silver (logo) omitted			£300	
813	75 c. At banquet in Sao Paulo, Brazil, 1968			45	60
814	$2 At Crown Agents Head Office, London, 1983			1·00	1·50
810/14			Set of 5	2·10	3·00

178 Canadair DC-4M2 North Star of Trans-Canada Airlines

(Des L. Curtis. Litho Format)

1986 (2 May). *"Expo '86" World Fair, Vancouver. T* **178** *and similar horiz design. Multicoloured. W* w **16** (sideways). *P* 14.

815	50 c. Type **178**			75	50
816	$2.50, Lady Nelson (cargo liner)			2·00	2·50

(Des D. Miller. Litho Walsall)

1986 (22 May). *"Ameripex '86" International Stamp Exhibition, Chicago. Horiz designs as T* **164** *of Bahamas, showing Barbados stamps (Nos. 817/20). Multicoloured. W* w **16** (sideways). *P* 14.

817	45 c. 1976 Bicentenary of American Revolution 25 c.			70	35
818	50 c. 1976 Bicentenary of American Revolution 50 c.			80	55
819	65 c. 1981 Hurricane Season $1			90	1·00
820	$1 1982 Visit of President Reagan 55 c. pair			1·00	1·75
817/20			Set of 4	3·00	3·25
MS821	90 × 80 mm. $2 Statue of Liberty and liner Queen Elizabeth 2			5·50	8·00

No. **MS**821 also commemorates the Centenary of the Statue of Liberty.

(Des D. Miller. Litho Walsall)

1986 (23 July). *Royal Wedding. Square designs as T* **112** *of Ascension. Multicoloured. W* w **16**. *P* 14½ × 14.

822	45 c. Prince Andrew and Miss Sarah Ferguson			75	35
823	$1 Prince Andrew in Midshipman's uniform			1·25	75
	w. Wmk inverted			9·00	

179 Transporting Electricity Poles, 1923

180 Alpinia purpurata and Church Window

(Des A. Theobald. Litho B.D.T.)

1986 (16 Sept). *75th Anniv of Electricity in Barbados. T* **179** *and similar multicoloured designs. W* w **16** (sideways on 10, 65 c.). *P* 13½.

824	10 c. Type **179**			15	10
825	25 c. Heathman Ladder, 1935 (vert)			25	20
826	65 c. Transport fleet, 1941			60	60
827	$2 Bucket truck, 1986 (vert)			1·60	2·00
824/7			Set of 4	2·40	2·50

(Des A. Atkinson. Litho Questa)

1986 (28 Oct). *Christmas. T* **180** *and similar vert designs showing flowers and church windows. Multicoloured. W* w **14**. *P* 14.

828	25 c. Type **180**			20	20
829	50 c. Anthurium andraeanum			45	45
830	75 c. Heliconia rostrata			70	80
831	$2 Heliconia x psittacorum			1·50	3·00
828/31			Set of 4	2·50	4·00

181 Shot Putting

182 Barn Swallow

(Des G. Vasarhelyi. Litho Format)

1987 (27 Mar). *10th Anniv of Special Olympics. T* **181** *and similar horiz designs. Multicoloured. W* w **14** (sideways). *P* 14.

832	15 c. Type **181**			25	15
833	45 c. Wheelchair racing			45	30
834	65 c. Long jumping			60	65
835	$2 Logo and slogan			1·25	2·50
832/5			Set of 4	2·25	3·25

(Des P. Broadbent. Litho Walsall)

1987 (12 June). *"Capex '87" International Stamp Exhibition, Toronto. Birds. T* **182** *and similar vert designs. Multicoloured. W* w **16**. *P* 14.

836	25 c. Type **182**			2·00	50
	w. Wmk inverted			9·00	
837	50 c. Yellow Warbler			2·25	1·75
838	65 c. Audubon's Shearwater			2·25	2·75
839	75 c. Black-whiskered Vireo			2·50	3·25
840	$1 Scarlet Tanager			2·75	4·00
836/40			Set of 5	10·50	11·00

183 Sea Scout saluting

184 Bridgetown Synagogue

(Des L. Curtis. Litho Format)

1987 (24 July). *75th Anniv of Scouting in Barbados. T* **183** *and similar vert designs. Multicoloured. W* w **16**. *P* 14.

841	10 c. Type **183**			20	10
842	45 c. Scout jamboree			30	20
843	65 c. Scout badges			65	45
844	$2 Scout band			1·60	1·75
841/4			Set of 4	2·50	2·25

The 10 c. and $2 exist imperforate from stock dispersed by the liquidator of Format International Security Printers Ltd.

(Des R. Edge. Litho Questa)

1987 (6 Oct). *Restoration of Bridgetown Synagogue. T* **184** *and similar multicoloured designs. W* w **16** (sideways on 50, 65 c.). *P* 14 × 14½ (horiz) or 14½ × 14 (vert).

845	50 c. Type **184**			1·40	1·40
846	65 c. Interior of Synagogue			1·60	1·60
847	75 c. Ten Commandments (vert)			1·90	1·90
848	$1 Marble laver (vert)			2·25	2·75
845/8			Set of 4	6·50	7·00

185 Arms and Colonial Seal

(Des D. Hartley. Litho Walsall)

1987 (24 Nov). *21st Anniv of Independence. T* **185** *and similar multicoloured designs. W* w **16** (sideways). *P* 14 × 14½.

849	25 c. Type **185**			30	20
850	45 c. Flags of Barbados and Great Britain			55	30
851	65 c. Silver dollar and one penny coins			80	45
852	$2 Colours of Barbados Regiment			1·75	1·75
849/52			Set of 4	3·00	2·40
MS853	94 × 56 mm. $1.50, Prime Minister E. W. Barrow (vert). Wmk upright. P 14½ × 14			1·00	1·25

186 Herman C. Griffith

186a

(Des D. Hartley. Litho Walsall)

1988 (6 June–11 July). *West Indian Cricket. T **186** and similar horiz designs, each showing portrait, cricket equipment and early belt buckle. Multicoloured. W w 14 (sideways). P 14.*

854	15 c. E. A. (Manny) Martindale	..	..	2·00	65
855	45 c. George Challenor	..	..	2·75	75
856	50 c. Type **186** (11.7)	..	..	3·00	2·25
	a. Error. Portrait as Type **186***a*			£150	
857	75 c. Harold Austin	..	..	3·50	3·25
858	$2 Frank Worrell	..	..	4·25	8·50
854/8			*Set of 5*	14·00	14·00

As originally prepared the 50 c., inscribed "Herman C. Griffith", showed the portrait of another Barbadian cricketer, E. Lawson Bartlett, in error. The mistake was noticed two days prior to issue and the 50 c. was delayed until 11 July while supplies showing the correct portrait were printed. The instructions to withdraw the stamps with the Bartlett portrait, No. 856*a*, failed to reach the Parcel Post Department in time and, it is reported, 101 examples were sold in the normal course of business before the, belated, notification was received.

187 *Kentropyx borckianus*

188 Cycling

(Des Doreen McGuinness. Litho B.D.T.)

1988 (13 June). *Lizards of Barbados. T **187** and similar vert designs. Multicoloured. W w 14. P 14.*

859	10 c. Type **187**	..	..	1·25	45
860	50 c. Hemidactylus mabouia	..	..	2·50	70
861	65 c. Anolis extremus	..	..	2·50	1·00
862	$2 Gymnophthalmus underwoodii	..	..	5·00	7·50
859/62			*Set of 4*	10·00	8·50

(Des A. Edmonston. Litho Walsall)

1988 (2 Aug). *Olympic Games, Seoul. T **188** and similar vert designs. Multicoloured. W w 14. P 14¹/₂×14.*

863	25 c. Type **188**	..	..	75	20
864	45 c. Athletics	..	..	50	30
865	75 c. Relay swimming	..	..	65	55
866	$2 Yachting	..	..	1·50	1·75
863/6			*Set of 4*	3·00	2·50
MS867	144×63 mm. Nos. 863/6. W w 16			4·00	3·00

(Des S. Noon and D. Miller (50, 65 c.), D. Miller (others). Litho Questa)

1988 (18 Oct). *300th Anniv of Lloyd's of London. Designs as T **123** of Ascension. W w 14 (sideways on 50, 65 c.). P 14.*

868	40 c. multicoloured	..	..	55	30
869	50 c. multicoloured	..	..	65	35
870	65 c. multicoloured	..	..	1·25	45
871	$2 steel-blue and brown-lake	..	..	2·50	2·00
868/71			*Set of 4*	4·50	2·75

Designs:—Vert—40 c. Royal Exchange, 1774; $2 Sinking of *Titanic*, 1912. *Horiz*—50 c. Early sugar mill; 65 c. *Author* (container ship).

189 Harry Bayley and Observatory

190 L.I.A.T. Hawker Siddeley H.S.748

(Des Josephine Martin. Litho Walsall)

1988 (28 Nov). *25th Anniv of Harry Bayley Observatory. T **189** and similar horiz designs. Multicoloured. W w 16 (sideways). P 14×14¹/₂.*

872	25 c. Type **189**	..	..	60	20
873	65 c. Observatory with North Star and Southern Cross constellations	..		1·25	65
874	75 c. Andromeda galaxy	..	..	1·50	80
875	$2 Orion constellation	..	..	2·75	4·00
872/5			*Set of 4*	5·50	5·00

(Des A. Theobald. Litho Walsall)

1989 (20 Mar). *50th Anniv of Commercial Aviation in Barbados. T **190** and similar horiz designs. Multicoloured. W w 16 (sideways). P 14.*

876	25 c. Type **190**	..	..	1·75	40
877	65 c. Pan Am Douglas D.C.8-62	..	..	2·75	1·00
878	75 c. British Airways Concorde at Grantley Adams Airport	..		2·75	1·00
879	$2 Caribbean Air Cargo Boeing 707-351C	..		4·25	5·00
876/9			*Set of 4*	10·50	6·75

MINIMUM PRICE

The minimum price quote is 10p which represents a handling charge rather than a basis for valuing common stamps. For further notes about prices see introductory pages.

---

191 Assembly Chamber

192 Brown Hare

(Des A. Edmonston. Litho B.D.T.)

1989 (19 July). *350th Anniv of Parliament. T **191** and similar square designs. W w 16. P 13¹/₂.*

880	25 c. multicoloured	..	..	40	20
881	50 c. multicoloured	..	..	60	35
882	75 c. deep slate-blue and brownish black	..		1·00	50
883	$2.50, multicoloured	..	..	2·50	2·00
880/3			*Set of 4*	4·00	2·75

Designs:—50 c. The Speaker; 75 c. Parliament Buildings, c. 1882; $2.50, Queen Elizabeth II and Prince Philip in Parliament.

(Des R. Suffolk. Litho Questa)

1989 (1 Aug). *Wildlife Preservation. T **192** and similar multicoloured designs. W w 16 (sideways on 50 c., $2). P 14×13¹/₂ (vert) or 13¹/₂×14 (horiz).*

884	10 c. Type **192**	..	..	70	30
885	25 c. Red-footed Tortoise (horiz)	..		1·50	70
886	65 c. Savanna ("Green") Monkey	..		1·75	1·25
887	$2 Bufo marinus (toad) (horiz)	..		3·25	5·00
884/7			*Set of 4*	6·50	6·50
MS888	87×97 mm. $1 Small Indian Mongoose		1·00	1·25

(Des A. Edmonston. Litho B.D.T.)

1989 (9 Oct). *35th Commonwealth Parliamentary Conference. Square design as T **191**. Multicoloured. W w 14. P 13¹/₂.*

MS889	108×69 mm. $1 Barbados Mace	90	1·25

193 Bread 'n Cheese

194 Water Skiing

(Des Rosanne Sanders. Litho Questa)

1989 (1 Nov)–**92**. *Wild Plants. T **193** and similar vert designs. Multicoloured. W w 14. P 14¹/₂.*

890	2 c. Type **193**	..	..	50	1·25
891	5 c. Scarlet Cordia	..	..	30	50
892	10 c. Columnar Cactus	..	..	30	30
893	20 c. Spiderlily	..	..	40	30
894	25 c. Rock Balsam	..	..	70	1·00
895	30 c. Hollyhock	..	..	50	25
895a	35 c. Red Sage (9.6.92)	..	..	1·00	1·00
896	45 c. Yellow Shak-shak	..	..	85	1·00
897	50 c. Whitewood	..	..	85	1·00
898	55 c. Bluebell	..	..	70	55
899	65 c. Prickly Sage	..	..	1·00	1·50
900	70 c. Seaside Samphire	..	..	80	70
901	80 c. Flat-hand Dildo	..	..	90	80
901a	90 c. Herringbone (9.6.92)	..	..	1·50	2·00
902	$1.10, Lent Tree	..	..	1·25	2·00
903	$2.50, Rodwood	..	..	3·75	7·50
904	$5 Cowitch	..	..	6·50	11·00
905	$10 Maypole	..	..	11·00	17·00
890/905			*Set of 18*	29·00	45·00

Imprint dates: "1989", Nos. 890/5, 896/901, 902/5; "1991", Nos. 891/3, 895a, 900, 901a, 902.

For similar stamps but watermarked w 16, see Nos. 921/36.

(Des C. Burke. Litho Harrison)

1989 (17 Nov). *"World Stamp Expo '89" International Stamp Exhibition, Washington. Watersports. T **194** and similar vert designs. Multicoloured. W w 16. P 14.*

906	25 c. Type **194**	..	..	90	40
907	50 c. Yachting	..	..	1·75	1·00
908	65 c. Scuba diving	..	..	1·75	1·60
909	$2.50, Surfing	..	..	5·00	7·50
906/9			*Set of 4*	8·50	9·50

195 Barbados 1852 1d. Stamp

196 Bugler and Jockeys

(Des D. Miller. Litho B.D.T.)

1990 (3 May). *150th Anniv of the Penny Black and "Stamp World London 90" International Stamp Exhibition. T **195** and similar vert designs showing stamps. W w 14. P 14.*

910	25 c. dp bluish green, blk & pale yell-ochre		1·25	40
911	50 c. multicoloured	..	..	1·75	1·00
912	65 c. multicoloured	..	..	1·75	1·25
913	$2.50, multicoloured	..	..	4·00	6·50
910/13			*Set of 4*	8·00	8·25
MS914	90×86 mm. 50 c. multicoloured; 50 c. multicoloured	..		1·75	2·25

Designs:—50 c. 1882 1d. Queen Victoria; 65 c. 1899 2d.; $2.50, 1912 3d.; miniature sheet, 50 c. Great Britain Penny Black, 50 c. Barbados 1906 Nelson Centenary 1s.

(Adapted G. Vasarhelyi. Litho B.D.T.)

1990 (3 May). *Horse Racing. T **196** and similar multicoloured designs. W w 14 (sideways on 25, 45 and 75 c.). P 14.*

915	25 c. Type **196**	..	..	45	30
916	45 c. Horse and jockey in parade ring	..		70	50
917	75 c. At the finish	..	..	90	85
918	$2 Leading in the winner (vert)	..		2·50	4·50
915/18			*Set of 4*	4·00	5·50

(Des D. Miller. Litho Questa)

1990 (8 Aug). *90th Birthday of Queen Elizabeth the Queen Mother. Vert designs as T **134** (75 c.) or **135** ($2.50) of Ascension. W w 16. P 14×15 (75 c.) or 14¹/₂ ($2.50).*

919	75 c. multicoloured	..	..	75	60
920	$2.50, black and bronze-green	..		2·25	2·75

Designs:—75 c. Lady Elizabeth Bowes-Lyon, April 1923 (from painting by John Lander); $2.50, Lady Elizabeth Bowes-Lyon on her engagement, January 1923.

1990 (Sept). *As Nos. 890/4, 896/7, 903/5, but W w 16. "1990" imprint date. P 14¹/₂.*

921	2 c. Type **193**	..	..	20	90
922	5 c. Scarlet Cordia	..	..	70	1·40
923	10 c. Columnar Cactus	..	..	70	1·40
924	20 c. Spiderlily	..	..	90	1·50
925	25 c. Rock Balsam	..	..	30	20
927	45 c. Yellow Shak-shak	..	..	45	35
928	50 c. Whitewood	..	..	50	40
930	65 c. Prickly Sage	..	..	60	55
934	$2.50, Rodwood	..	..	1·90	4·00
935	$5 Cowitch	..	..	3·25	6·00
936	$10 Maypole	..	..	6·50	9·00
921/36			*Set of 11*	14·50	23·00

197 *Orthemis ferruginea* (dragonfly)

VISIT OF
HRH THE
PRINCESS ROYAL
OCTOBER 1990
(**198**)

(Des I. Loe. Litho Harrison)

1990 (16 Oct). *Insects. T **197** and similar horiz designs. Multicoloured. P 14.*

937	50 c. Type **197**	..	..	1·50	80
938	65 c. Ligyrus tumulosus (beetle)	..		1·75	1·00
939	75 c. Neoconocephalus sp (grasshopper)	..		2·00	1·25
940	$2 Bostra maxwelli (stick-insect)	..		3·50	5·00
937/40			*Set of 4*	8·00	7·25

1990 (21 Nov). *Visit of the Princess Royal. Nos. 894, 901 and 903 optd with T **198**.*

941	25 c. Rock Balsam	..	..	75	30
942	80 c. Flat-hand Dildo	..	..	1·75	1·75
943	$2.50, Rodwood	..	..	4·00	5·50
941/3			*Set of 3*	6·00	6·75

199 Star

200 Adult Male Yellow Warbler

(Des D. Miller. Litho B.D.T.)

1990 (4 Dec). *Christmas. T **199** and similar vert designs. Multicoloured. W w 14. P 14.*

944	20 c. Type **199**	..	..	65	20
945	50 c. Figures from crib	..	..	1·00	50
946	$1 Stained glass window	..	..	2·00	1·50
947	$2 Angel (statue)	..	..	3·00	5·00
944/7			*Set of 4*	6·00	6·50

(Des G. Drummond. Litho B.D.T.)

1991 (4 Mar). *Endangered Species. Yellow Warbler. T **200** and similar horiz designs. Multicoloured. W w 14 (sideways). P 14.*

948	10 c. Type **200**	..	..	1·40	70
949	20 c. Pair feeding chicks in nest	..		2·00	70
950	45 c. Female feeding chicks in nest	..		2·50	70
951	$1 Male with fledgeling	..	..	4·00	5·25
948/51			*Set of 4*	9·00	6·50

201 Sorting Daily Catch   **202** Masonic Building, Bridgetown

(Des M. Maynard, adapted G. Vasarhelyi. Litho Cartor)

1991 (18 June). *Fishing in Barbados. T* **201** *and similar multicoloured designs.* W w **14** *(sideways on* 50, 75 c.). P 13½×14 (5 c., $2.50) or 14×13½ *(others).*

952	5 c. Type **201**		50	50
953	50 c. Line fishing (*horiz*)		1·75	90
954	75 c. Fish cleaning (*horiz*)		2·25	1·25
955	$2.50, Game fishing		4·50	6·50
952/5		*Set of 4*	8·00	8·25

(Des N. Shewring. Litho B.D.T.)

1991 (17 Sept). *250th Anniv of Freemasonry in Barbados* (1990). *T* **202** *and similar vert designs.* W w **14.** *P* 14.

956	25 c. multicoloured		1·25	50
957	65 c. multicoloured		2·00	1·25
958	75 c. black, greenish yellow & yellow-brown	2·00	1·25
959	$2.50, multicoloured		4·75	7·00
956/9		*Set of 4*	9·00	9·00

Designs:—65 c. Compass and Square (masonic symbols); 75 c. Royal Arch Jewel; $2.50, Ceremonial apron, columns and badge.

203 *Battus polydamus*

(Des I. Loe. Litho B.D.T.)

1991 (15 Nov). *"Phila Nippon '91" International Stamp Exhibition, Tokyo. Butterflies. T* **203** *and similar multicoloured designs.* W w **16** *(sideways on* 20 c., 65 c.). P 14.

960	20 c. Type **203**		1·00	40
961	50 c. *Urbanus proteus* (*vert*)		1·50	65
962	65 c. *Phoebis sennae*		1·60	95
963	$2.50, *Junonia evarete* (*vert*)		4·00	6·00
960/3		*Set of 4*	7·25	7·25
MS964	87×86 mm. $4 *Vanessa cardui.* Wmk sideways		8·00	9·00

204 School Class   **205** Jesus carrying Cross

(Des G. Vasarhelyi. Litho B.D.T.)

1991 (20 Nov). *25th Anniv of Independence. T* **204** *and similar multicoloured designs.* W w **14** *(sideways).* P 14.

965	10 c. Type **204**		20	20
966	25 c. Barbados Workers' Union Labour College		30	30
967	65 c. Building a house		70	90
968	75 c. Sugar cane harvesting		80	1·00
969	$1 Health clinic		1·00	2·00
965/9		*Set of 5*	2·75	4·00
MS970	123 × 97 mm. $2.50, Gordon Greenidge and Desmond Haynes (cricketers) (*vert*). Wmk upright		6·00	7·00

(Des P. Argent. Litho B.D.T.)

1992 (7 Apr). *Easter. T* **205** *and similar vert designs. Multicoloured.* W w **16.** P 14.

971	35 c. Type **205**		70	30
972	70 c. Crucifixion		1·25	90
973	90 c. Descent from the Cross		1·40	1·25
974	$3 Risen Christ		3·75	6·00
971/4		*Set of 4*	6·50	7·50

206 Cannon Ball   **207** *Epidendrum "Costa Rica"*

(Des Jennifer Toombs. Litho Cartor)

1992 (9 June). *Conservation. Flowering Trees. T* **206** *and similar horiz designs. Multicoloured.* W w **14** *(sideways).* P 14×13½.

975	10 c. Type **206**		60	40
976	30 c. Golden Shower Tree		1·00	50
977	80 c. Frangipani		2·25	2·50
978	$1.10, Flamboyant		2·75	2·50
975/8		*Set of 4*	6·00	5·50

(Des Annette Robinson. Litho B.D.T.)

1992 (8 Sept). *Orchids. T* **207** *and similar horiz designs. Multicoloured.* W w **14** *(sideways).* P 13½×14.

979	55 c. Type **207**		85	65
980	65 c. *Cattleya guttaca*		1·00	1·00
981	70 c. *Laeliacattleya* "Splashing Around"		1·00	1·00
982	$1.40, *Phalaenopsis* "Kathy Saegert"		1·60	3·00
979/82		*Set of 4*	4·00	5·00

208 Mini Moke and Gun Hill Signal Station, St. George   **209** Barbados Gooseberry

(Des D. Miller. Litho Questa)

1992 (15 Dec). *Transport and Tourism. T* **208** *and similar horiz designs. Multicoloured.* W w **14** *(sideways).* P 14×14½.

983	5 c. Type **208**		50	50
984	35 c. Tour bus and Bathsheba Beach, St. Joseph		1·00	30
985	90 c. B.W.I.A. McDonnell Douglas MD-83 over Grantley Adams Airport		2·50	2·25
986	$2 *Festivale* (liner) and Bridgetown harbour		3·75	5·00
983/6		*Set of 4*	7·00	7·25

(Des I. Loe. Litho B.D.T.)

1993 (9 Feb). *Cacti and Succulents. T* **209** *and similar vert designs. Multicoloured.* W w **14.** P 14.

987	10 c. Type **209**		55	30
988	35 c. Night-blooming Cereus		1·25	35
989	$1.40, Aloe		3·00	3·50
990	$2 Scrunchineel		3·50	4·75
987/90		*Set of 4*	7·50	8·00

(Des A. Theobald. Litho Questa)

1993 (1 Apr). *75th Anniv of Royal Air Force. Horiz designs as T* **149** *of Ascension. Multicoloured.* W w **14** *(sideways).* P 14.

991	10 c. Hawker Hunter F.6		65	40
992	30 c. Handley Page H.P.80 Victor K2		1·00	40
993	70 c. Hawker Typhoon 1B		1·50	1·50
994	$3 Hawker Hurricane Mk 1		3·50	4·75
991/4		*Set of 4*	6·00	6·25
MS995	110×77 mm. 50 c. Armstrong Whitworth Siskin IIIA; 50 c. Supermarine S6B; 50 c. Supermarine Walrus Mk1; 50 c. Hawker Hart		2·25	2·75

(210)   **211** 18 pdr Culverin of 1625, Denmark Fort

1993 (1 Apr). *14th World Orchid Conference, Glasgow. Nos.* 979/82 *optd as T* **210**.

996	55 c. Type **207**		1·25	1·25
997	65 c. *Cattleya guttaca*		1·40	1·40
998	70 c. *Laeliacattleya* "Splashing Around"		1·40	1·40
999	$1.40, *Phalaenopsis* "Kathy Saegert"		2·25	3·00
996/9		*Set of 4*	5·50	6·25

The overprints on the 70 c. and $1.40 are in two lines.

(Des J. Batchelor. Litho Cartor)

1993 (8 June). *17th-century English Cannon. T* **211** *and similar horiz designs. Multicoloured.* W w **14** *(sideways).* P 13.

1000	5 c. Type **211**		30	50
1001	45 c. 6 pdr of 1649–60, St. Ann's Fort		85	50
1002	$1 9 pdr demi-culverin of 1691, The Main Guard		1·75	2·00
1003	$2.50, 32 pdr demi-cannon of 1693–94, Charles Fort		2·75	4·25
1000/3		*Set of 4*	5·00	6·50

COVER PRICES

Cover factors are quoted at the beginning of each country for most issues to 1945. An explanation of the system can be found on page x. The factors quoted do not, however, apply to philatelic covers.

212 Sailor's Shell-work Valentine and Carved Amerindian   **213** Plesiosaurus

(Des D. Miller. Litho B.D.T.)

1993 (14 Sept). *60th Anniv of Barbados Museum. T* **212** *and similar vert designs. Multicoloured.* W w **14.** P 13½.

1004	10 c. Type **212**		40	40
1005	75 c. "Barbados Mulatto Girl" (Agostino Brunias)		1·50	1·50
1006	90 c. Morris Cup and soldier of West India Regiment, 1858		1·75	1·90
1007	$1.10, Ogilby's map of Barbados, 1679, and Ashanti gold weights		2·00	2·50
1004/7		*Set of 4*	5·00	5·50

(Des N. Shewring. Litho Cartor)

1993 (28 Oct). *Prehistoric Aquatic Reptiles. T* **213** *and similar vert designs. Multicoloured.* W w **14.** P 13.

1008	90 c. Type **213**		1·50	1·75
	a. Horiz strip of 5. Nos. 1008/12		6·75	
1009	90 c. Ichthyosaurus		1·50	1·75
1010	90 c. Elasmosaurus		1·50	1·75
1011	90 c. Mosasaurus		1·50	1·75
1012	90 c. Archelon		1·50	1·75
1008/12		*Set of 5*	6·75	8·00

Nos. 1008/12 were printed together, *se-tenant*, in horizontal strips of 5 throughout the sheet with the background forming a composite design.

214 Cricket   **215** Whimbrel

(Des S. Noon. Litho B.D.T.)

1994 (11 Jan). *Sports and Tourism. T* **214** *and similar vert designs. Multicoloured.* W w **16.** P 14.

1013	10 c. Type **214**		1·00	60
1014	35 c. Rally driving		1·25	40
1015	50 c. Golf		2·00	1·25
1016	70 c. Long distance running		1·50	2·00
1017	$1.40, Swimming		1·75	3·00
1013/17		*Set of 5*	6·75	6·50

(Des N. Arlott. Litho B.D.T.)

1994 (18 Feb). *"Hong Kong '94" International Stamp Exhibition. Migratory Birds. T* **215** *and similar horiz designs. Multicoloured.* W w **14** *(sideways).* P 14.

1018	10 c. Type **215**		50	50
1019	35 c. American Golden Plover		1·00	50
1020	70 c. Turnstone		1·50	1·50
1021	$3 Louisiana Heron ("Tricoloured Heron")		3·50	5·00
1018/21		*Set of 4*	6·00	6·75

216 Bathsheba Beach and Logo   **217** William Demas

(Des D. Miller. Litho B.D.T.)

1994 (25 Apr). *First United Nations Conference of Small Island Developing States. T* **216** *and similar horiz designs showing scenery. Multicoloured.* W w **16** *(sideways).* P 14×15.

1022	10 c. Type **216**		15	15
1023	65 c. Pico Tenneriffe		60	60
1024	90 c. Ragged Point Lighthouse		1·25	1·90
1025	$2.50, Consett Bay		2·25	3·50
1022/5		*Set of 4*	3·75	4·90

(Des D. Miller. Litho Cot Printery Ltd)

1994 (4 July). *First Recipients of Order of the Caribbean Community. T* **217** *and similar vert designs. Multicoloured.* W w **14.** P 14.

1026	70 c. Type **217**		70	95
1027	70 c. Sir Shridath Ramphal		70	95
1028	70 c. Derek Walcott		70	95
1026/8		*Set of 3*	1·90	2·50

218 Dutch Flyut, 1695

219 Private, 2nd West India Regt, 1860

(Des A. Theobald. Litho B.D.T.)

1994 (16 Aug)–98. *Ships.* T **218** *and similar horiz designs. Multicoloured.* W w **14** *(sideways).* P 14. A. *Without imprint date*

1029A	5 c. Type 218			50	90
1030A	10 c. *Geestport* (freighter), 1994			50	90
1031A	25 c. H.M.S. *Victory* (ship of the line), 1805			50	30
1032A	30 c. *Royal Viking Queen* (liner), 1994			1·10	40
1033A	35 c. H.M.S. *Barbados* (frigate), 1945			1·10	45
1034A	45 c. *Faraday* (cable ship), 1924			1·25	65
1035A	50 c. U.S.C.G. *Hamilton* (coastguard cutter), 1974			1·25	75
1036A	65 c. H.M.C.S. *Saguenay* (destroyer), 1939			1·50	1·50
1037A	70 c. *Inanda* (cargo liner), 1928			1·50	1·50
1038A	80 c. H.M.S. *Rodney* (battleship), 1944			1·50	2·00
1039A	90 c. U.S.S. *John F. Kennedy* (aircraft carrier), 1982			1·75	1·75
1040A	$1.10, *William and John* (immigrant ship), 1627			2·00	2·25
1041A	$5 U.S.C.G. *Champlain* (coastguard cutter), 1931			6·00	7·00
1042A	$10 *Artist* (full-rigged ship), 1877			6·00	8·00
1029A/42A			Set of 14	24·00	25·00

B. *With imprint date*

1029B	5 c. Type 218 (20.1.98)			30	30
1030B	10 c. *Geestport* (freighter), 1994 (20.1.98)			30	30
1031B	25 c. H.M.S. *Victory* (ship of the line), 1805 (20.1.98)			15	20
1032B	30 c. *Royal Viking Queen* (liner), 1994 (20.1.98)			55	30
1033B	35 c. H.M.S. *Barbados* (frigate), 1945 (20.1.98)			55	30
1034B	45 c. *Faraday* (cable ship), 1924 (20.1.98)			60	35
1037B	70 c. *Inanda* (cargo liner), 1928 (20.1.98)			75	75
1039B	90 c. U.S.S. *John F. Kennedy* (aircraft carrier), 1982 (20.1.98)			90	90
1042B	$10 *Artist* (full-rigged ship), 1877 (20.1.98)			6·25	6·50
1029B/42B			Set of 9	9·25	9·00

Imprint dates: "1997", Nos. 1029B/34B, 1037B, 1039B, 1042B; "1998", Nos. 1029B/30B, 1034B, 1037B; "1999", Nos. 1030B, 1034B, 1042B.

For these designs watermarked W w **16** (sideways) and with imprint date see Nos. 1075/88.

(Des D. Cribbs. Litho Enschedé)

1995 (21 Feb). *Bicentenary of Formation of West India Regiment.* T **219** *and similar vert designs. Multicoloured.* W w **14**. P 15×14.

1043	30 c. Type 219			45	35
1044	50 c. Light Company private, 4th West India Regt, 1795			60	55
1045	70 c. Drum Major, 3rd West India Regt, 1860			75	95
1046	$1 Privates in undress and working dress, 5th West India Regt, 1815			1·00	1·40
	w. Wmk inverted			1·00	
1047	$1.10 Troops from 1st and 2nd West India Regts in Review Order, 1874			1·25	1·60
1043/7			Set of 5	3·50	4·25

(Des R. Watton. Litho Cot Printery Ltd)

1995 (8 May). *50th Anniv of End of Second World War. Multicoloured designs as* T **161** *of Ascension.* W w **14** *(sideways).* P 14.

1048	10 c. Barbadian Bren gun crew			60	50
1049	35 c. Avro Type 683 Lancaster bomber			90	50
1050	55 c. Supermarine Spitfire			1·25	75
1051	$2.50, *Davisian* (cargo liner)			3·00	4·00
1048/51			Set of 4	5·25	5·25
MS1052	75×85 mm. $2 Reverse of 1939–45 War Medal (*vert*). Wmk upright			1·50	2·25

221 Blue Beauty

220 Member of 1st Barbados Combermere Scout Troop, 1912

(Des S. Noon. Litho Cot Printery Ltd)

1995 (25 July). *300th Anniv of Combermere School.* T **220** *and similar multicoloured designs.* W w **14** *(sideways on horiz designs).* P 14.

1053	5 c. Type 220			20	30
1054	20 c. Violin and sheet of music			30	30
1055	35 c. Sir Frank Worrell (cricketer) (*vert*)			90	55
1056	$3 Painting by pupil			2·25	3·50
1053/6			Set of 4	3·25	4·25
MS1057	174×105 mm. Nos. 1053/6 and 90 c. 1981 Carifesta 55 c. stamp. Wmk sideways			4·00	4·75
	a. All four horiz stamps imperforate				

(Des A. Theobald. Litho Cot Printery Ltd)

1995 (24 Oct). *50th Anniv of United Nations. Horiz designs as* T **213** *of Bahamas. Multicoloured.* W w **14** *(sideways).* P 14.

1058	30 c. Douglas C-124 Globemaster (transport), Korea, 1950–53			60	40
1059	45 c. Royal Navy Sea King helicopter			80	50
1060	$1.40, Westland Wessex helicopter, Cyprus, 1964			1·25	2·00
1061	$2 Sud Aviation SA 341 Gazelle helicopter, Cyprus, 1964			1·50	2·50
1058/61			Set of 4	3·75	4·75

(Des I. Loe. Litho Cot Printery Ltd)

1995 (19 Dec). *Water Lilies.* T **221** *and similar vert designs. Multicoloured.* W w **14** *(inverted).* P 14.

1062	10 c. Type 221			30	30
1063	65 c. White Water Lily			75	60
1064	70 c. Sacred Lotus			75	60
1065	$3 Water Hyacinth			2·50	3·75
1062/5			Set of 4	3·75	4·75

222 Magnifying Glass, Tweezers and 1896 Colony Seal ¼d. Stamp

223 Football

(Des D. Miller. Litho Cot Printery Ltd)

1996 (30 Jan). *Centenary of Barbados Philatelic Society.* T **222** *and similar horiz designs, each showing magnifying glass, tweezers and stamp. Multicoloured.* W w **14** *(sideways).* P 14.

1066	10 c. Type 222			30	30
1067	55 c. 1906 Tercentenary of Annexation 1d.			55	45
1068	$1.10, 1920 Victory 1s.			1·10	1·25
1069	$1.40, 1937 Coronation 2½d.			1·40	2·00
1066/9			Set of 4	3·00	3·50

(Des S. Noon (Nos. 1070/3), G. Vasarhelyi (No. MS1074). Litho Cot Printery Ltd)

1996 (2 Apr). *Centenary of Modern Olympic Games.* T **223** *and similar vert designs. Multicoloured.* W w **14**. P 14.

1070	20 c. Type 223			30	30
1071	30 c. Relay running			35	30
1072	55 c. Basketball			1·10	60
1073	$3 Rhythmic gymnastics			2·25	3·50
1070/3			Set of 4	3·50	4·25
MS1074	68×89 mm. $2.50, "The Discus Thrower" (Myron). Wmk inverted			2·00	2·75

1996 (May–1 Sept). *As Nos. 1029/30 and 1032/41, but* W w **16** *(sideways) and with imprint date.* P 14.

1075	5 c. Type 218			10	15
1076	10 c. *Geestport* (freighter), 1994			10	15
1078	30 c. *Royal Viking Queen* (liner), 1994 (1 Sept)			20	25
1079	35 c. H.M.S. *Barbados* (frigate), 1945 (1 Sept)			20	25
1080	45 c. *Faraday* (cable ship), 1996 (1 Sept)			30	35
1081	50 c. U.S.C.G. *Hamilton* (coastguard cutter), 1974			30	35
1082	65 c. H.M.C.S. *Saguenay* (destroyer), 1939 (1 Sept)			40	45
1083	70 c. *Inanda* (cargo liner), 1928 (1 Sept)			40	45
1084	80 c. H.M.S. *Rodney* (battleship), 1944 (1 Sept)			50	55
1085	90 c. U.S.S. *John F. Kennedy* (aircraft carrier), 1982 (1 Sept)			55	60
1086	$1.10, *William and John* (immigrant ship), 1627			65	70
1087	$5 U.S.C.G. *Champlain* (coastguard cutter), 1931			3·00	3·25
1075/87			Set of 12	6·00	6·75

Imprint date: "1996", Nos. 1075/6 and 1078/87.

224 Douglas DC-10 of Canadian Airlines

(Des N. Shewring. Litho Cot Printery Ltd)

1996 (7 June). *"CAPEX '96" International Stamp Exhibition, Toronto. Aircraft.* T **224** *and similar horiz designs. Multicoloured.* W w **14** *(sideways).* P 14.

1089	10 c. Type 224			40	30
1090	90 c. Boeing 767 of Air Canada			90	80
1091	$1 Airbus Industrie A320 of Air Canada			95	95
1092	$1.40, Boeing 767 of Canadian Airlines			1·25	2·00
1089/92			Set of 4	3·25	3·50

225 Chattel House

(Des G. Vasarhelyi. Litho Cot Printery Ltd)

1996 (7 June). *Chattel Houses.* T **225** *and similar horiz designs showing different houses.* W w **14** *(sideways).* P 14.

1093	35 c. multicoloured			30	25
1094	70 c. multicoloured			55	60
1095	$1.10, multicoloured			80	1·10
1096	$2 multicoloured			1·60	2·50
1093/6			Set of 4	3·00	4·00

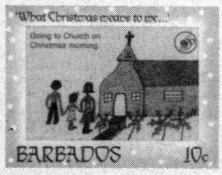
226 "Going to Church"   227 Doberman Pinscher

(Des Jennifer Toombs. Litho Cot Printery Ltd)

1996 (12 Nov). *Christmas. 50th Anniv of U.N.I.C.E.F. Children's Paintings.* T **226** *and similar horiz designs. Multicoloured.* W w **14** *(sideways).* P 14×14½.

1097	10 c. Type 226			20	15
1098	30 c. "The Tuk Band"			35	25
1099	55 c. "Singing carols"			50	40
1100	$2.50, "Decorated house"			1·75	2·50
1097/1100			Set of 4	2·50	3·00

(Des N. Shewring. Litho Cot Printery Ltd)

1997 (12 Feb). *"HONG KONG '97" International Stamp Exhibition. Dogs.* T **227** *and similar horiz designs. Multicoloured.* W w **14** *(sideways).* P 14×14½.

1101	10 c. Type 227			40	30
1102	30 c. German Shepherd			65	35
1103	90 c. Japanese Akita			1·25	1·25
1104	$3 Irish Red Setter			3·25	4·00
1101/4			Set of 4	5·00	5·50

228 Barbados Flag and State Arms   229 Measled Cowrie

(Des A. Theobald. Litho Cot Printery Ltd)

1997 (9 May). *Visit of President Clinton of U.S.A.* T **228** *and similar horiz design. Multicoloured.* W w **14** *(sideways).* P 14.

1105	35 c. Type 228			50	65
	a. Sheetlet. Nos. 1105/6 each × 4 and 2 labels			4·25	
1106	90 c. American flag and arms			70	85

Nos. 1105/6 were printed together, both horizontally and vertically se-tenant, in sheetlets of 8 with the blocks of four separated horizontally by two different stamp-sized illustrated labels.

Sheetlet No. 1105a was re-issued on 29 May 1997 with the bottom margin overprinted with two examples of the "PACIFIC '97" International Stamp Exhibition logo.

(Des N. Shewring. Litho Cot Printery Ltd)

1997 (29 July). *Shells.* T **229** *and similar vert designs. Multicoloured.* W w **14**. P 14.

1107	5 c. Type 229			20	30
1108	35 c. Trumpet Triton			45	25
1109	90 c. Scotch Bonnet			1·00	90
1110	$2 West Indian Murex			1·75	2·50
1107/10			Set of 4	3·00	3·50
MS1111	71×76 mm. $2.50, Underwater scene. Wmk inverted			1·90	2·50

NEW INFORMATION

The editor is always interested to correspond with people who have new information that will improve or correct the Catalogue.

230 Lucas Manuscripts	231 Barbados Cherry

(Des O. Bell. Litho Cot Printery Ltd)

1997 (1 Oct). *150th Anniv of the Public Library Service. T* **230** *and similar horiz designs. Multicoloured.* W w **14** (*sideways*). *P* 14×14¹/₂.

1112	10 c. Type **230**			15	15
1113	30 c. Librarian reading to children			30	25
1114	70 c. Mobile library van			60	60
1115	$3 Man using computer			2·25	3·00
1112/15			Set of 4	3·00	3·50

(Des I. Loe. Litho Cot Printery Ltd)

1997 (16 Dec). *Local Fruits. T* **231** *and similar horiz designs. Multicoloured.* W w **14** (*sideways*). *P* 14×14¹/₂.

1116	35 c. Type **231**			30	25
1117	40 c. Sugar Apple			35	30
1118	$1.15, Soursop			85	1·00
1119	$1.70, Pawpaw			1·25	1·75
1116/19			Set of 4	2·50	3·00

232 Arms of former British Caribbean Federation	233 Environment Regeneration

(Des B. Dare. Litho Cartor)

1998 (27 Apr). *Birth Centenary of Sir Grantley Adams* (*statesman*). *Sheet,* 118×74 *mm, containing T* **232** *and similar vert designs. Multicoloured.* W w **14**. *P* 13.

MS1120	$1 Type **232**; $1 Sir Grantley Adams; $1 Flag of former British Caribbean Federation		2·40	2·75

(Des D. Miller. Litho Questa)

1998 (18 May). *Diana, Princess of Wales Commemoration. Sheet* 145×70 *mm, containing vert designs as T* **177** *of Ascension. Multicoloured.* W w **14** (*sideways*). *P* 14¹/₂×14.

MS1121	$1.15, Wearing blue hat, 1985; $1.15, Wearing red jacket, 1981; $1.15, Wearing tiara, 1987; $1.15, Wearing black jacket, 1993		3·25	3·50

(Des N. Shewring. Litho Cot Printery Ltd)

1998 (30 June). *50th Anniv of Organization of American States. T* **233** *and similar horiz designs. Multicoloured.* W w **14** (*sideways*). *P* 14.

1122	15 c. Type **233**			10	10
1123	$1 Stilt dancing			60	70
1124	$2.50, Judge and figure of Justice			1·50	2·00
1122/4			Set of 3	2·10	2·50

234 Frank Worrell Hall	235 Catamaran

(Des N. Shewring. Litho Cot Printery Ltd)

1998 (22 July). *50th Anniv of University of West Indies. T* **234** *and similar horiz designs. Multicoloured.* W w **14** (*sideways*). *P* 14.

1125	40 c. Type **234**			30	30
1126	$1.15, Student graduating			1·00	1·10
1127	$1.40, 50th anniversary plaque			1·25	1·50
1128	$1.75, Quadrangle			2·50	2·75
1125/8			Set of 4	4·50	5·00

(Des N. Shewring. Litho Cot Printery Ltd)

1998 (1 Dec). *Tourism. T* **235** *and similar multicoloured designs.* W w **14** (*sideways on* 45, 70 c.). *P* 14.

1129	10 c. Type **235**			15	15
1130	45 c. Jolly Roger (tourist schooner) (*horiz*)		45	35
1131	70 c. Atlantis (tourist submarine) (*horiz*)		65	65
1132	$2 Harbour Master (ferry)			1·75	2·25
1129/32			Set of 4	2·75	3·00

236 Racing Yacht	237 Juvenile Piping Plover in Shallow Water

(Des D. Miller. Litho Cot Printery Ltd)

1999 (19 Mar). *"Australia '99" World Stamp Exhibition, Melbourne. Sheet* 90×90 *mm.* W w **14** (*sideways*). *P* 14.

MS1133	**236** $4 multicoloured			2·75	3·00

(Des J. Pointer. Litho Cot Printery Ltd)

1999 (27 Apr). *Endangered Species. Piping Plover. T* **237** *and similar horiz designs. Multicoloured.* W w **14** (*sideways*). *P* 14.

1134	10 c. Type **237**			20	20
1135	45 c. Female with eggs			55	55
1136	50 c. Male and female with fledglings		55	55
1137	70 c. Male in shallow water			65	75
1134/7			Set of 4	1·75	1·90

(Des J. Batchelor ($1.15), N. Shewring (others). Litho Walsall)

1999 (20 July). *30th Anniv of First Manned Landing on Moon. Multicoloured designs as T* **186** *of Ascension.* W w **16**. *P* 14×13¹/₂.

1138	40 c. Astronaut in training			30	30
1139	45 c. 1st stage separation			35	35
1140	$1.15, Lunar landing module			90	90
1141	$1.40, Docking with service module		1·10	1·10
1138/41			Set of 4	2·40	2·40
MS1142	90×80 mm. $2.50, Earth as seen from Moon (*circular*, 40 *mm diam*). Wmk sideways. P 14			1·90	2·00

238 Hare running

(Des O. Bell. Litho Cot Printery Ltd)

1999 (20 Aug). *"China '99" International Stamp Exhibition, Beijing. Hares. T* **238** *and similar horiz designs. Multicoloured.* W w **14** (*sideways*). *P* 14×14¹/₂.

1143	70 c. Type **238**			55	60
	a. Horiz strip of 5. Nos. 1143/7			2·50	
1144	70 c. Head of hare			55	60
1145	70 c. Baby hares suckling			55	60
1146	70 c. Hares boxing			55	60
1147	70 c. Two leverets			55	60
1143/7			Set of 5	2·50	2·75

Nos. 1143/7 were printed together, *se-tenant*, in horizontal strips of 5 throughout the sheet, each strip forming a composite background design.

239 Horse-drawn Mail Cart

(Des E. Nisbet. Litho Cot Printery Ltd)

1999 (12 Oct). *125th Anniv of Universal Postal Union. T* **239** *and similar horiz designs. Multicoloured.* W w **14** (*sideways*). *P* 14.

1148	10 c. Type **239**			10	10
1149	45 c. Mail van			30	35
1150	$1.75, Sikorsky S42 flying boat		1·00	1·10
1151	$2 Computer and fax machine		1·25	1·40
1148/51			Set of 4	2·50	2·75

STAMP BOOKLETS

1906 (Feb).

SB1	2s. ¹/₂d. booklet containing twenty-four 1d. (No. 137) in blocks of 6			

1909. *Black on red cover. Stapled.*

SB1a	1s. 6d. booklet containing eighteen 1d. (No. 165) in blocks of 6			

1913 (June). *Black on red cover. Stapled.*

SB2	2s. booklet containing twelve ¹/₂d. and eighteen 1d. (Nos. 171/2) in blocks of 6			

1916 (16 June). *Black on red cover. Stapled.*

SB3	2s. booklet containing twelve ¹/₂d. and eighteen 1d. (Nos. 182/3) in pairs			£650

1920 (Sept). *Black on red cover. Stapled.*

SB4	2s. booklet containing twelve ¹/₂d. and eighteen 1d. (Nos. 202/3) in pairs			

1932 (12 Nov). *Black on pale green cover. Austin Cars and Post Office Guide advertisements on front.*

SB5	2s. booklet containing ¹/₂d. and 1d. (Nos. 230a, 231a) each in block of 10 and 1¹/₂d. (No. 231ba) in block of 6			

1933 (4 Dec). *Black on pale green cover. Advocate Co. Ltd. advertisement on front. Stapled.*

SB6	2s. booklet containing ¹/₂d. and 1d. (Nos. 230/1) each in block of 10 and 1¹/₂d. (No. 231b) in block of 6			

1938 (3 Jan). *Black on light blue cover. Advocate Co. Ltd. advertisement on front. Stapled.*

SB7	2s. booklet containing ¹/₂d. and 1d. (Nos. 248, 249a) each in block of 10 and 1¹/₂d. (No. 250) in block of 6			£1300

POSTAGE DUE STAMPS

D 1	D 2

(Typo D.L.R.)

1934 (2 Jan)**–47**. *Wmk Mult Script CA. P* 14.

D1	D **1**	¹/₂d. green (10.2.35)		1·25	7·00
D2		1d. black		1·25	1·25
		a. Bisected (¹/₂d.) (on cover)		†	£800
D3		3d. carmine (13.3.47)		20·00	18·00
D1/3			Set of 3	20·00	24·00
D1/3 Perf "Specimen"			Set of 3	65·00	

The bisected 1d. was officially authorised for use between March 1934 and February 1935. Some specimens had the value "¹/₂d." written across the half stamp in red or black ink (*Price on cover* £900).

(Typo D.L.R.)

1950 (8 Dec)**–53**. *Values in cents. Wmk Mult Script CA. Ordinary paper. P* 14.

D4	D **1**	1 c. green		3·75	18·00
		a. Chalk-surfaced paper. *Deep green* (29.11.51)		30	3·00
D5		2 c. black		7·00	10·00
		a. Chalk-surfaced paper (20.1.53)		60	5·00
		ac. Error. St. Edward's Crown, W 9b		£300	
D6		6 c. carmine		16·00	17·00
		a. Chalk-surfaced paper (20.1.53)		1·00	8·50
		ab. Error. Crown missing, W 9a		£170	
		ac. Error. St. Edward's Crown, W 9b		£130	
D4/6			Set of 3	24·00	40·00
D4a/6a			Set of 3	1·75	15·00

The 1 c. has no dot below "c".

1965 (3 Aug)**–68**. *As Nos.* D4/6 *but wmk w* **12** (*upright*). *Chalk-surfaced paper.*

D7	D **1**	1 c. deep green		30	3·75
		a. Missing top serif on "C" (R. 2/4)		6·00	
		b. Green		1·75	5·50
		c. Centre inverted		£2000	
D8		2 c. black		30	4·00
D9		6 c. carmine		50	6·00
		a. Carmine-red (14.5.68)		1·40	11·00
D7/9			Set of 3	1·00	12·00

1974 (4 Feb). *As No.* D9 *but W w* **12** (*sideways*). *Glazed, ordinary paper. P* 14 × 13¹/₂.

D10	D **1**	6 c. carmine		9·50	18·00

1974 (4 Dec). *W w* **12** (*sideways*). *P* 13.

D12	D **1**	2 c. black		4·00	17·00
D13		6 c. carmine		4·00	17·00

(Des Jennifer Toombs. Litho Questa)

1976 (12 May)**–85**. *Different floral backgrounds as Type D* **2**. *W w* **14**. *P* 14.

D14	1 c. deep mauve and light pink		30	1·00
	a. Perf 15×14 (7.85)		10	10
D15	2 c. ultramarine and light cobalt		30	1·00
	a. Perf 15×14 (7.85)		10	10
D16	5 c. reddish brown and yellow		30	1·00
	a. Perf 15×14 (7.85)		10	15
D17	10 c. royal blue and light lilac		45	1·00
	a. Perf 15×14 (7.85)		15	20
D18	25 c. deep green and bright yellow-green		70	1·10
	a. Perf 15×14 (7.85)		20	30
D19	$1 rose-carmine and rose		75	1·25
D14/19		Set of 6	2·50	5·75
D14a/18a		Set of 5	50	70

Barbuda
(*see after* Antigua)

Basutoland
see Lesotho

Batum

Batum, the outlet port on the Black Sea for the Russian Transcaucasian oilfields, was occupied by the Turks on 15 April 1918.

Under the terms of the armistice signed at Mudros on 30 October 1918 the Turks were to withdraw and be replaced by an Allied occupation of Batum, the Baku oilfields and the connecting Transcaucasia Railway. British forces arrived off Batum in early December and the oblast, or district, was declared a British military governorship on 25 December 1918. The Turkish withdrawal was completed five days later.

The provision of a civilian postal service was initially the responsibility of the Batum Town Council. Some form of mail service was in operation by February 1919 with the postage prepaid in cash. Letters are known showing a framed oblong handstamp, in Russian, to this effect. The Town Council was responsible for the production of the first issue, Nos. 1/6, but shortly after these stamps were placed on sale a strike by Council employees against the British military governor led to the postal service being placed under British Army control.

SURCHARGES. Types **2** and **4/8** were all applied by handstamp. Most values from No. 19 onwards are known showing the surcharge inverted, surcharge double or in pairs with surcharge *tête-bêche*.

BRITISH OCCUPATION

(Currency. 100 kopeks = 1 rouble)

PRICES FOR STAMPS ON COVER	
Nos. 1/6	*from* × 60
Nos. 7/10	*from* × 15
Nos. 11/18	*from* × 60
Nos. 19/20	*from* × 15
Nos. 21/44	—
Nos. 45/53	*from* × 200

БАТУМ. ОБ.

Руб 10 Руб

1 Aloe Tree   (2)

1919 (4 Apr). *Litho. Imperf.*
1	1	5 k. green	..	5·50	8·00
2		10 k. ultramarine	..	5·50	8·00
3		50 k. yellow	..	2·00	2·50
4		1 r. chocolate	..	2·75	3·00
5		3 r. violet	..	8·50	11·00
6		5 r. brown	..	9·50	13·00
1/6			*Set of 6*	30·00	42·00

Nos. 1/6 were printed in sheets of 198 (18×11).

1919 (13 Apr). *Russian stamps (Arms types) handstamped with T* **2**.
7	10 r. on 1 k. orange (*imperf*)	..	32·00	35·00
8	10 r. on 3 k. carmine-red (*imperf*)	..	16·00	18·00
9	10 r. on 5 k. brown-lilac (*perf*)..		£300	£300
10	10 r. on 10 on 7 k. deep blue (*perf*)		£250	£250

A similar handstamped surcharge, showing the capital letters without serifs, is bogus.

BRITISH OCCUPATION

(3)

1919 (10 Nov.) *Colours changed and new values. Optd with T* **3**.
11	1	5 k. yellow-green	..	8·00	9·00
12		10 k. bright blue ..	..	8·00	9·00
13		25 k. orange-yellow	..	8·00	9·00
14		1 r. pale blue	..	3·25	7·00
15		2 r. pink	..	1·00	1·50
16		3 r. bright violet	..	1·00	1·50
17		5 r. brown	..	1·25	1·75
		a. "CCUPATION" (R.5/1)		£300	
18		7 r. brownish red	..	2·75	4·50
11/18			*Set of 8*	30·00	38·00

Nos. 11/18 were printed in sheets of 432 (18×24).

---

(4)   (5)

1919 (27 Nov)–**20**. *Russian stamps (Arms types) handstamped with T* **4** *or* **5**. *Imperf.*
19	10 r. on 3 k. carmine-red	..		12·00	14·00
20	15 r. on 1 k. orange	..		40·00	40·00
	a. Red surch	..		32·00	32·00
	b. Violet surch (10.3.20)	..		42·00	42·00

Nos. 20a/b have the handstamp in soluble ink.

1920 (12 Jan). *Russian stamps (Arms types) handstamped as T* **4**.
(a) Imperf
21	50 r. on 1 k. orange	..	£300	£300
22	50 r. on 2 k. yellow-green (R.)		£400	£400

(b) Perf
23	50 r. on 2 k. yellow-green	..	£400	£400
24	50 r. on 3 k. carmine-red	..	£900	£900
25	50 r. on 4 k. red	..	£650	£650
26	50 r. on 5 k. brown-lilac	..	£375	£375
27	50 r. on 10 k. deep blue (R.)	..	£1000	£1000
28	50 r. on 15 k. blue and red-brown	..	£400	£400

(6)

1920 (30 Jan–21 Feb). *Russian stamps (Arms types) handstamped as T* **6**. *(a) Perf*
29	25 r. on 5 k. brown-lilac (21 Feb)	..	32·00	32·00
	a. Blue surch	..	32·00	32·00
30	25 r. on 10 on 7 k. blue (21 Feb)	..	90·00	90·00
	a. Blue surch	..	50·00	50·00
31	25 r. on 20 on 14 k. dp carmine & bl (21 Feb)	55·00	55·00
	a. Blue surch	..	50·00	50·00
32	25 r. on 25 k. deep violet & lt green (21 Feb)	90·00	90·00
	a. Blue surch	..	75·00	75·00
33	25 r. on 50 k. green and copper-red (21 Feb)	50·00	50·00
	a. Blue surch	..	55·00	55·00
34	50 r. on 2 k. yellow-green	..	80·00	80·00
35	50 r. on 3 k. carmine-red	..	80·00	80·00
36	50 r. on 4 k. red	..	70·00	70·00
37	50 r. on 5 k. brown-lilac	..	50·00	50·00

(b) Imperf
38	50 r. on 2 k. yellow-green	..	£275	£275
39	50 r. on 3 k. carmine-red	..	£350	£350
40	50 r. on 5 k. brown-lilac	..	£1000	£1000

1920 (10 Mar). *Romanov issue, as T* **25** *of Russia, handstamped with T* **6**.
41	50 r. on 4 k. rose-carmine (B.)	..	40·00	45·00

РУБ 25 ЛЕЙ   R. 50 R. BRITISH OCCUPATION

25 РУБ. 25   РУБ.

(7)   (8)

1920 (1 Apr). *Nos.* 3, 11 *and* 13 *handstamped with T* **7** *(Nos.* 42/3) *or* **8** *(No.* 44).
42	25 r. on 5 k. yellow-green	..	24·00	24·00
	a. Blue surch	..	26·00	26·00
43	25 r. on 25 k. orange-yellow	..	19·00	19·00
	a. Blue surch	..	70·00	70·00
44	50 r. on 50 k. yellow	..	14·00	14·00
	a. "50" cut	..	11·00	11·00
	b. Blue surch	..	75·00	75·00
	ba. "50" cut	..	£130	£130

Nos. 44a and 44ba show the figures broken by intentional file cuts applied as a protection against forgery. The "5" is cut at the base and on the right side of the loop. The "0" is chipped at top and foot, and has both vertical lines severed.

1920 (19 June). *Colours changed and new values. Optd with T* **3**. *Imperf.*
45	1	1 r. chestnut	..	60	3·50
		a. "BPITISH"	..	45·00	
46		2 r. pale blue	..	70	3·50
		a. "BPITISH"	..	55·00	
47		3 r. pink	..	85	3·50
		a. "BPITISH"	..	55·00	
48		5 r. black-brown	..	70	3·50
		a. "BPITISH"	..	55·00	
49		7 r. yellow	..	70	3·50
		a. "BPITISH"	..	55·00	
50		10 r. myrtle-green	..	60	3·50
		a. "BPITISH"	..	55·00	
51		15 r. violet	..	90	4·75
		a. "BPITISH"	..	£110	

52	1	25 r. scarlet	..	80	4·25
		a. "BPITISH"	..	£100	
53		50 r. deep blue	..	1·00	7·00
		a. "BPITISH"	..	£170	
45/53			*Set of 9*	6·00	32·00

Nos. 45/53 were printed in sheets of 308 (22×14). The "BPITISH" error occurs on R. 1/19 of the overprint.

POSTCARD STAMPS

When Nos. 7/10 were issued on 13 April 1919 a similar 35 k. surcharge was applied to stocks of various Russian postcards held by the post office. The majority of these had stamp impressions printed directly on to the card, but there were also a few cards, originally intended for overseas mail, on which Russia 4 k. stamps had been affixed.

PRICES. Those in the left-hand column are for unused examples on complete postcard; those on the right for used examples off card. Examples used on postcard are worth more.

1919 (13 Apr). *Russian stamps handstamped as T* **2**.
P1	35 k. on 4 k. red (Arms type)		£2750	£3250
P2	35 k. on 4 k. carmine-red (Romanov issue)	£7500	£8500

Batum was handed over to the National Republic of Georgia on 7 July 1920.

Bechuanaland
see Botswana

Belize
(*formerly* British Honduras)

BRITISH HONDURAS

It is recorded that the first local post office was established by the inhabitants in 1809, but Belize did not become a regular packet port of call until 1829. A branch office of the British G.P.O. was established in 1857 and the stamps of Great Britain were supplied for use on overseas mail from 1858.

The colonial authorities took over the postal service on 1 April, 1860, the Great Britain stamps being withdrawn the following month. There was no inland postal service until 1862.

For illustrations of the handstamp and postmark types see BRITISH POST OFFICES ABROAD notes, following GREAT BRITAIN.

BELIZE

CROWNED-CIRCLE HANDSTAMPS

CC1	CC **1***b* BELIZE (R.)(13.11.1841)	..	*Price on cover* £4000

Stamps of GREAT BRITAIN *cancelled* "A 06" *as Type* **2**.

1858 to **1860**.
Z1	1d. rose-red (1857), *perf* 14 ..	..	..	£850
Z2	4d. rose (1857)	..	..	£350
Z3	6d. lilac (1856)	..	..	£350
Z4	1s. green (1856)	..	..	£1300

PRICES FOR STAMPS ON COVER TO 1945		
Nos. 1/4	*from* × 20	
Nos. 5/16	*from* × 25	
Nos. 17/22	*from* × 20	
Nos. 23/6	*from* × 10	
Nos. 27/30	*from* × 15	
Nos. 35/42	*from* × 20	
Nos. 43/4	*from* × 30	
Nos. 49/50	*from* × 25	
Nos. 51/69	*from* × 15	
Nos. 80/100	*from* × 6	
Nos. 101/10	*from* × 5	
Nos. 111/20	*from* × 15	
Nos. 121/2	*from* × 8	
No. 123	*from* × 10	
Nos. 124/37	*from* × 6	
Nos. 138/42	*from* × 10	
Nos. 143/9	*from* × 8	
Nos. 150/61	*from* × 5	
Nos. D1/3	*from* × 30	

CROWN COLONY

1

(Typo D.L.R.)

1865 (1 Dec). *No wmk. P 14.*

1	1	1d. pale blue	60·00	48·00
		a. Imperf between (pair)		
2		1d. blue ..	65·00	48·00
3		6d. rose ..	£275	£120
4		1s. green ..	£300	£110
		a. In horiz pair with 6d.	£16000	
		b. In vert pair with 1d.	£23000	

In the first printing all three values were printed in the same sheet separated by horizontal and vertical gutter margins. The sheet comprised two panes of 60 of the 1d. at the top with a pane of 60 of the 1s. at bottom left and another of 6d. at bottom right. Copies of 1d. *se-tenant* with the 6d. are not known. There were two later printings of the 1d. but they were in sheets without the 6d. and 1s.

1872–79. *Wmk Crown CC.* (a) *P 12½.*

5	1	1d. pale blue	60·00	16·00
		w. Wmk inverted		£150
		y. Wmk inverted and reversed		
6		1d. deep blue (1874)	70·00	16·00
7		3d. red-brown	£100	65·00
8		3d. chocolate (1874)	£120	80·00
9		6d. rose	£200	28·00
9a		6d. bright rose-carmine (1874)	£325	38·00
10		1s. green	£325	28·00
10a		1s. deep green (1874)	£275	20·00
		b. Imperf between (horiz pair)	†	£13000
		w. Wmk inverted		

(b) *P 14 (1877–79).*

11	1	1d. pale blue (1878)	55·00	15·00
12		1d. blue	50·00	10·00
		a. Imperf between (horiz pair)	£4000	
13		3d. chestnut	£100	16·00
14		4d. mauve (1879)	£150	8·00
		x. Wmk reversed		
15		6d. rose (1878)	£300	£160
		w. Wmk inverted	—	£250
16		1s. green	£170	11·00
		a. Imperf between (pair)		

1882–87. *Wmk Crown CA. P 14.*

17	1	1d. blue (4.84)	38·00	13·00
18		1d. rose (1884)	22·00	12·00
		a. Bisected (½d.) (on cover)		
19		1d. carmine (1887)	50·00	16·00
20		4d. mauve (7.82)	70·00	4·75
		w. Wmk inverted		
21		6d. yellow (1885)	£275	£180
22		1s. grey (1.87)	£250	£150
18,22		Optd "Specimen" .. Set of 2	£200	

(New Currency. 100 cents = 1 British Honduras (later Belize) dollar)

CENTS (2)   TWO (3)   CENTS (4)

1888 (1 Jan). *Stamps of 1872–79 (wmk Crown CC), surch locally as T 2.* (a) *P 12½.*

23	1	2 c. on 6d. rose	£160	£100
24		3 c. on 3d. chocolate	£10000	£4750

(b) *P 14*

25	1	2 c. on 6d. rose	90·00	80·00
		a. Surch double	£1500	
		b. Bisected (1 c.) (on cover)	†	£200
		c. Slanting "2" with curved foot	£1000	
		w. Wmk inverted	—	£250
26		3 c. on 3d. chestnut	70·00	70·00

There are very dangerous forgeries of these surcharges.

1888. *Stamps of 1882–87 (wmk Crown CA), surch locally as T 2, P 14.*

27	1	2 c. on 1d. rose	8·50	20·00
		a. Surch inverted	£1700	£1600
		b. Surch double	£900	£900
		c. Bisected (1 c.) (on cover)	†	£180
28		10 c. on 4d. mauve	45·00	16·00
29		20 c. on 6d. yellow	27·00	35·00
30		50 c. on 1s. grey	£325	£450
		a. Error. "5" for "50"	£7500	

Various settings were used for the surcharges on Nos. 23/30, the most common of which was of 36 (6 × 6) impressions. For No. 29 this setting was so applied that an albino surcharge occurs in the margin above each stamp in the first horizontal row.

The same setting was subsequently amended, by altering the "2" to "1", to surcharge the 4d. value. As this was in sheets of 30 it was only necessary to alter the values on the bottom five rows of the setting. Albino surcharges once again occur in the top margin of the sheet, but, as the type in the first horizontal row remained unaltered, these read "20 CENTS" rather than the "10 CENTS" on the actual stamps.

1888 (Mar). *No. 30 further surch locally with T 3.*

35	1	"TWO" on 50c. on 1s. grey (R.)	45·00	85·00
		a. Bisected (1 c.) (on cover)	†	£200
		b. Surch in black	£8000	£7000
		c. Surch double (R. + Blk.)	£8000	£7000

1888 (July)–91. *Surch in London as T 4. Wmk Crown CA. P 14.*

36	1	1 c. on 1d. dull green (?12.91)	60	1·50
37		2 c. on 1d. carmine	40	1·75
		a. Bisected (1 c.) (on cover)	†	90·00
		w. Wmk inverted		
38		3 c. on 3d. red-brown	2·50	1·40
39		6 c. on 3d. ultramarine (?4.91)	2·50	11·00
40		10 c. on 4d. mauve	6·00	40
		a. Surch double	£1600	
41		20 c. on 6d. yellow (2.89)	12·00	14·00
42		50 c. on 1s. grey (11.88)	28·00	75·00
36/42		.. Set of 7	48·00	95·00
36/42		Optd "Specimen" .. Set of 7	£350	

6 / 10 CENTS (5)

FIVE (6)   **15** (7)

1891. *Stamps of 1888–9 surch locally.* (a) *With T 5* (May).

43	1	6 c. on 10 c. on 4d. mauve (R.)	1·00	2·00
		a. "6" and bar inverted	£375	£375
		b. "6" only inverted	—	£2250
44		6 c. on 10 c. on 4d. mauve (Blk.)	80	1·50
		a. "6" and bar inverted	£2250	£700
		b. "6" only inverted	†	£2250

Of variety (b) only six copies of each can exist, as one of each of these errors came in the first six sheets, and the mistake was then corrected. Of variety (a) more copies exist.

Essays are known with "SIX" in place of "6", both with and without bars (*price £75 and £375 respectively*). Although not issued we mention them, as three contemporary covers franked with them are known.

(b) *With T 6/7* (23 Oct)

49	1	5 c. on 3 c. on 3d. red-brown	1·00	1·40
		a. Wide space between "I" and "V"	45·00	65·00
		b. "FIVE" and bar double	£275	£300
50		15 c. on 6 c. on 3d. ultramarine (R.)	11·00	24·00
		a. Surch double		

8   9

10   11

(Typo D.L.R.)

1891 (July)–**1901.** *Wmk Crown CA. P 14.*

51	8	1 c. dull green (4.95)	2·00	1·25
		a. Malformed "S"	£100	55·00
		w. Wmk inverted		
52		2 c. carmine-rose	1·75	20
		a. Malformed "S"	95·00	29·00
		b. Repaired "S"	80·00	29·00
53		3 c. brown	5·50	3·50
		w. Wmk inverted		
54		5 c. ultramarine (4.95)	12·00	65
		a. Malformed "S"	£250	55·00
55	11	5 c. grey-black & ultram/blue (10.00)	14·00	2·50
56	8	6 c. ultramarine	5·50	2·00
57	9	10 c. mauve and green (4.95)	8·50	8·50
58	10	10 c. dull purple and green (1901)	9·00	7·50
59	9	12 c. pale mauve and green	23·00	7·00
		a. Violet and green	2·50	2·00
60		24 c. yellow and blue	5·50	14·00
		a. Orange and blue	29·00	50·00
61		25 c. red-brown and green (4.95)	55·00	95·00
62	10	50 c. green and carmine (3.98)	22·00	55·00
63	11	$1 green and carmine (12.99)	60·00	£100
64		$2 green and ultramarine (12.99)	80·00	£120
65		$5 green and black (12.99)	£250	£300
51/65		.. Set of 15	£475	£650
51/65		Optd "Specimen" .. Set of 15	£300	

For illustrations of Nos. 51a, 52a/b and 54a see above Gambia No. 37.

1899 (1 July). *Optd "REVENUE" 12 mm long.*

66	8	5 c. ultramarine	9·00	2·50
		a. "BEVENUE"	80·00	85·00
		b. Malformed "S" at right	—	£200
		c. Repaired "S" at right	£180	
		d. Opt 11 mm long	19·00	7·50
67	9	10 c. mauve and green	3·00	13·00
		a. "BEVENUE"	£180	£250
		b. "REVENU"	£400	
		c. Opt 11 mm long	18·00	42·00
		cb. "REVENU"	£425	£475
68		25 c. red-brown and green	2·75	32·00
		a. "BEVENUE"	£120	£300
		b. "REVE UE"		
		c. Opt 11 mm long	4·00	50·00
69	1	50 c. on 1s. grey	£120	£275
		a. "BEVENUE"	£2750	
		c. Opt 11 mm long	£200	£375

Two minor varieties, a small "U" and a tall, narrow "U" are found in the word "REVENUE".

The overprint setting of 60 (6 × 10) contained 43 examples of the 12 mm size and 17 of the 11 mm. The smaller size overprints occur on R.8/1, R8/3 to 6 and on all positions in Rows 9 and 10.

The "BEVENUE" error appears on R. 6/4 and, it is believed, "REVE UE" comes from R. 6/6. Both occur on parts of the printing only. The missing "E" developed during the overprinting and damage to this letter can be observed on at least eight positions in the setting.

14   15

(Typo D.L.R.)

1902 (10 Oct)–04. *Wmk Crown CA. P 14.*

80	14	1 c. grey-green and green (28.4.04)	1·25	21·00
81		2 c. purple and black/red (18.3.03)	75	25
		w. Wmk inverted	—	50·00
82		5 c. grey-black and blue/blue	5·00	30
		w. Wmk inverted		
83	15	20 c. dull and bright purple (28.4.04)	4·75	17·00
80/3		.. Set of 4	10·50	35·00
80/3		Optd "Specimen" .. Set of 4	55·00	

1904 (Dec)–07. *Wmk Mult Crown CA. Ordinary paper* (1, 2 c.) *or chalk-surfaced paper* (others). *P 14.*

84	14	1 c. grey-green and green (8.05)	7·00	8·00
		a. Chalk-surfaced paper (1906)	65	1·75
85		2 c. purple and black/red	2·75	20
		a. Chalk-surfaced paper (1906)	65	10
86		5 c. grey-black and blue/blue (5.2.06)	1·75	20
87	15	10 c. dull purple & emerald-green (20.9.07)	5·00	11·00
89		25 c. dull purple and orange (20.9.07)	7·00	42·00
90		50 c. grey-green and carmine (20.9.07)	15·00	70·00
91	14	$1 grey-green and carmine (20.9.07)	48·00	70·00
92		$2 grey-green and blue (20.9.07)	85·00	£150
93		$5 grey-green and black (20.9.07)	£180	£250
84/93		.. Set of 9	£300	£550
87/93		Optd "Specimen" .. Set of 6	£225	

Examples of most values are known showing a forged Belize postmark dated "OC 23 09".

1908 (7 Dec)–11. *Colours changed. Wmk Mult Crown CA. Chalk-surfaced paper* (25 c.). *P 14.*

95	14	1 c. blue-green (1.7.10)	8·50	30
96		2 c. carmine	9·50	10
		w. Wmk inverted		
97		5 c. ultramarine (1.6.09)	1·75	10
100	15	25 c. black/green (14.10.11)	2·75	45·00
95/100		.. Set of 4	20·00	45·00
96/100		Optd "Specimen" .. Set of 3	70·00	

16   17   (18)

1913–21. *Wmk Mult Crown CA. Chalk-surfaced paper* (10 c. to $5). *P 14.*

101	16	1 c. blue-green	3·00	1·00
		a. Yellow-green (13.3.17)	4·50	1·75
		w. Wmk inverted		
102		2 c. red	3·00	1·00
		a. Bright scarlet (1915)	4·50	1·00
		b. Dull scarlet (8.17)	3·00	1·50
		c. Red/bluish	10·00	8·00
		w. Wmk inverted		
103		3 c. orange (16.4.17)	50	20
104		5 c. bright blue	2·00	60
105	17	10 c. dull purple and yellow-green	2·75	6·50
		a. Dull purple and bright green (1917)	11·00	23·00
106		25 c. black/green	1·25	12·00
		a. On blue-green, olive back (8.17)	4·00	11·00
		b. On emerald back (1921)	1·75	26·00
107		50 c. purple and blue/blue	9·00	13·00
108	16	$1 black and carmine	17·00	40·00
109		$2 purple and green	65·00	75·00
110		$5 purple and black/red	£190	£225
101/10		.. Set of 10	£250	£325
101/10		Optd "Specimen" .. Set of 10	£225	

1915–16. *Optd with T 18, in violet.*

111	16	1 c. green (30.12.15)	2·50	16·00
		a. Yellow-green (6.6.16)	30	11·00
112		2 c. scarlet (3.11.15)	2·25	50
113		5 c. bright blue (29.7.15)	30	5·00
111/13		Optd "Specimen" .. Set of 3	90·00	

These stamps were shipped early in the 1914–18 war, and were thus overprinted, so that if seized by the enemy, they could be distinguished and rendered invalid.

WAR (19)   WAR (20)   21

1916 (23 Aug). *No. 111 optd locally with T 19.*

114	16	1 c. green	10	75
		a. Opt inverted	£180	£200

1917. *Nos. 101 and 103 optd with T 19.*

116	16	1 c. blue-green	1·25	3·00
		aw. Wmk inverted		
		ax. Wmk reversed		
		b. Yellow-green	20	1·25
118		3 c. orange	2·75	4·00
		a. Opt double	£300	

1918. *Nos. 101 and 103 optd with T 20.*

119	16	1 c. blue-green	..	..	10	25
		a. *Yellow-green*	..	..	3·50	4·50
120		3 c. orange	..	..	40	1·25
		y. Wmk inverted and reversed				
119/20 Optd "Specimen"				*Set of 2* £100		

(Recess D.L.R.)

1921 (28 Apr). *Peace Commemoration. Wmk Mult Crown CA (sideways). P 14.*

121	21	2 c. rose-red (Optd S. £45)	..	..	2·50	30
		a. "C" of "CA" missing from wmk	..	£225		

1921 (26 Nov). *Wmk Mult Script CA. P 14.*

122	16	1 c. green (Optd S. £45)	..	..	3·00	10·00

1922 (4 Jan). *As T 21 but with words "PEACE" omitted. Wmk Mult Script CA (sideways). P 14.*

123		4 c. slate (Optd S. £45)	..	..	5·50	30

BELIZE RELIEF FUND PLUS 3 CENTS

22 (23)

(Typo D.L.R.)

1922 (1 Aug)–**33.** *Ordinary paper (1 c. to 5 c.) or chalk-surfaced paper (others). P 14 (a) Wmk Mult Crown CA.*

124	22	25 c. black/*emerald*	..	..	6·00	30·00
125		$5 purple and black/*red* (1.10.24)	..	£180	£200	

(b) *Wmk Mult Script CA*

126	22	1 c. green (2.1.29)	..	..	2·75	5·50
127		2 c. brown (1.3.23)	..	..	1·25	1·25
128		2 c. rose-carmine (10.12.26)	..	..	1·75	55
129		3 c. orange (1933)	..	..	12·00	4·00
130		4 c. grey (1.10.29)	..	..	3·50	85
131		5 c. ultramarine	..	..	1·25	55
		a. *Milky blue* (1923)	..	..	4·50	3·75
132		10 c. dull purple and sage-green (1.12.22)		1·00	30	
133		25 c. black/*emerald* (1.10.24)	..	..	1·00	8·50
134		50 c. purple and blue/*blue* (1.11.23)	..	4·75	15·00	
136		$1 black and scarlet (2.1.25)	..	..	6·50	24·00
137		$2 yellow-green and bright purple	..	32·00	30·00	
124/37					*Set of 13* £225	£325
124/37 Opted/Perf "Specimen"				*Set of 13* £250		

1932 (2 May). *Belize Relief Fund. Surch as T 23. Wmk Mult Script CA. P 14.*

138	22	1 c. + 1 c. green	..	..	70	6·50
139		2 c. + 2 c. rose-carmine	..	..	75	6·50
140		3 c. + 3 c. orange	..	..	85	14·00
141		4 c. + 4 c. grey (R.)	..	..	8·00	19·00
142		5 c. + 5 c. ultramarine	..	..	6·50	14·00
138/42					*Set of 5* 15·00	55·00
138/42 Perf "Specimen"				*Set of 5* £110		

1935 (6 May). *Silver Jubilee. As Nos. 91/4 of Antigua, but ptd by B. W. & Co. P 11 × 12.*

143		3 c. ultramarine and grey-black	..	..	1·00	45
		a. Extra flagstaff	..	..	50·00	
		b. Short extra flagstaff	..	..	60·00	
		c. Lightning conductor	..	..	50·00	
		d. Flagstaff on right-hand turret..	..	90·00		
144		4 c. green and indigo	..	..	1·50	3·00
		a. Extra flagstaff	..	..	£180	
		c. Lightning conductor	..	..	£180	
		d. Flagstaff on right-hand turret..	..	£180		
		e. Double flagstaff	..	..	£180	
145		5 c. brown and deep blue	..	..	1·50	60
146		25 c. slate and purple	..	..	2·75	3·25
		a. Extra flagstaff	..	..	£250	
		b. Short extra flagstaff	..	..	£250	
		c. Lightning conductor	..	..	£200	
		d. Flagstaff on right-hand turret..	..	£275		
		e. Double flagstaff..	..	..	£275	
143/6					*Set of 4* 6·00	6·50
143/6 Perf "Specimen"				*Set of 4* 75·00		

For illustrations of plate varieties see Catalogue Introduction.

1937 (12 May). *Coronation. As Nos. 95/7 of Antigua, but printed by D.L.R. P 14.*

147		3 c. orange	..	..	30	30
148		4 c. grey-black	..	..	70	30
149		5 c. bright blue	..	..	80	1·40
147/9					*Set of 3* 1·60	1·75
147/9 Perf "Specimen"				*Set of 3* 50·00		

24 Maya Figures   **25** Chicle Tapping

(Recess B.W.)

1938 (10 Jan)–**47.** *T 24/5 and similar designs. Wmk Mult Script CA (sideways on horizontal stamps). P 11½ × 11 (horiz designs) or 11 × 11½ (vert designs).*

150		1 c. bright magenta and green (14.2.38)	..	10	1·50	
151		2 c. black and scarlet (14.2.38)	..	20	90	
		a. Perf 12 (1947)	..	..	1·90	
152		3 c. purple and brown	..	..	30	70
153		4 c. black and green	..	..	30	70

154		5 c. mauve and dull blue	..	..	75	60
155		10 c. green and reddish brown (14.2.38)	..	75	60	
156		15 c. brown and light blue (14.2.38)	..	2·00	70	
157		25 c. blue and green (14.2.38)	..	..	2·00	1·25
158		50 c. black and purple (14.2.38)	..	11·00	3·00	
159		$1 scarlet and olive (28.2.38)	..	20·00	10·00	
160		$2 deep blue and maroon (28.2.38)	..	26·00	16·00	
161		$5 scarlet and brown (28.2.38)	..	26·00	23·00	
150/61					*Set of 12* 80·00	55·00
150/61 Perf "Specimen"				*Set of 12* £160		

Designs: *Vert*—3 c. Cohune palm; $1 Court House, Belize. $2 Mahogany felling; $5 Arms of Colony. *Horiz*—4 c. Local products; 5 c. Grapefruit; 10 c. Mahogany logs in river; 15 c. Sergeant's Cay; 25 c. Dorey; 50 c. Chicle industry.

1946 (9 Sept). *Victory. As Nos. 110/11 of Antigua.*

162		3 c. brown	..	..	10	10
163		5 c. blue	..	..	10	10
162/3 Perf "Specimen"				*Set of 2* 50·00		

1948 (1 Oct). *Royal Silver Wedding. As Nos. 112/13 of Antigua.*

164		4 c. green	..	..	15	50
165		$5 brown	..	..	16·00	38·00

36 Island of St George's Cay   **37** H.M.S. *Merlin*

(Recess Waterlow)

1949 (10 Jan). *150th Anniv of Battle of St. George's Cay. Wmk Mult Script CA. P 12½.*

166	36	1 c. ultramarine and green	..	10	50	
167		3 c. blue and yellow-brown	..	10	1·25	
168		4 c. olive and violet	..	..	10	50
169	37	5 c. brown and deep blue	..	80	20	
170		10 c. green and red-brown	..	..	70	30
171		15 c. emerald and ultramarine	..	70	30	
166/71					*Set of 6* 2·00	2·75

1949 (10 Oct). *75th Anniv of U.P.U. As Nos. 114/17 of Antigua.*

172		4 c. blue-green	..	..	40	30
173		5 c. deep blue	..	..	1·50	50
174		10 c. red-brown	..	..	50	2·25
175		25 c. blue	..	..	60	50
172/5					*Set of 4* 2·75	3·25

1951 (16 Feb). *Inauguration of B.W.I. University College. As Nos. 118/19 of Antigua.*

176		3 c. reddish violet and brown	..	45	1·25	
177		10 c. green and brown	..	..	45	30

1953 (2 June). *Coronation. As No. 120 of Antigua.*

178		4 c. black and green	..	..	40	30

38 Arms of British Honduras   **46** Maya Indian

(Recess Waterlow (until 20.6.1961), then D.L.R.)

1953 (2 Sept)–**62.** *T 38, 46 and similar designs. Wmk Mult Script CA. P 13½.*

179		1 c. green and black	..	..	10	40
		a. Perf 13½×13 (3.10.61)	..	20	1·00	
180		2 c. yellow-brown and black	..	..	20	1·75
		a. Perf 14 (18.9.57)	..	..	50	10
		b. Perf 13½×13 (20.6.61)	..	10	50	
181		3 c. reddish violet and bright purple	..	30	10	
		a. Perf 14 (18.9.57)	..	..	10	10
		b. Perf 13½×13 (20.6.61)	..	4·25	9·00	
		ba. *Reddish lilac and pale magenta* (19.1.62)	..	45	70	
182		4 c. brown and green	..	..	40	30
183		5 c. deep olive-green and scarlet	..	10	10	
		a. Perf 14 (15.5.57)	..	..	20	10
		ab. D.L.R. ptg (3.10.61)	..	4·00	7·00	
184		10 c. slate and bright blue	..	..	10	10
		a. Perf 13½×13 (19.1.62)	..	10	10	
185		15 c. green and violet	..	..	15	10
186		25 c. bright blue and yellow-brown	..	6·00	2·00	
187		50 c. yellow-brown and reddish purple	..	6·00	1·75	
		a. *Pale yellow-brown & pale pur* (22.3.60)	17·00	6·50	
188		$1 slate-blue and red-brown	..	5·50	5·00	
189		$2 scarlet and grey	..	..	6·50	4·50
190		$5 purple and slate	..	..	48·00	17·00
179/90					*Set of 12* 65·00	28·00

Designs: *Horiz*—2 c. Baird's Tapir ("Mountain Cow"); 3 c. Mace and Legislative Council Chamber, 4 c. Pine industry; 5 c. Spiny Lobster; 10 c. Stanley Field Airport; 15 c. Maya frieze; 25 c. *Morpho peleides* (butterfly); $1 Nine-banded Armadillo; $2 Hawksworth Bridge. *Vert*—$5 Mountain Orchid.

Nos. 179/90 were released a day earlier by the Crown Agents in London.

Stamps from the Waterlow printings perforated 13½ × 13 or 14 have a very fine perforation tooth at the *top* of each vertical side. On the De La Rue printings this tooth is at the *bottom*.

50 "Belize from Fort George, 1842" (C. J. Hullmandel)   **51** Public Seals, 1860 and 1960.

52 Tamarind Tree, Newtown Barracks.

(Recess B.W.)

1960 (1 July). *Post Office Centenary. W w 12. P 11½ × 11.*

191		2 c. green	..	..	30	1·25
192	51	10 c. deep carmine	..	..	30	10
193	52	15 c. blue ..	..	..	35	35
191/3					*Set of 3* 85	1·50

NEW CONSTITUTION 1960 (53)   **HURRICANE HATTIE** (54)

1961 (1 Mar). *New Constitution. Nos. 180a, 181a and 184/5 optd with T 53 by Waterlow.*

194		2 c. yellow-brown and black	..	25	20	
195		3 c. reddish violet and bright purple	..	30	20	
196		10 c. slate and bright blue	..	..	30	10
197		15 c. green and violet	..	..	30	20
194/7					*Set of 4* 1·00	60

1962 (15 Jan). *Hurricane Hattie Relief Fund. Nos. 179a, 184a, 186 and 187 optd with T 54 by D.L.R.*

198		1 c. green and black	..	..	10	65
199		10 c. slate and bright blue	..	..	30	10
200		25 c. bright blue and yellow-brown	..	1·40	80	
201		50 c. yellow-brown and reddish purple	..	50	1·00	
198/201					*Set of 4* 2·00	2·25

55 Great Curassow

(Des D. R. Eckelberry. Photo Harrison)

1962 (2 Apr). *Horiz designs on T 55. Multicoloured. W w 12 (upright). P 14 × 14½.*

202		1 c. Type **55**	..	..	1·50	75
		a. Orange-yellow (knob) omitted	..	£250		
		w. Wmk inverted				
203		2 c. Red-legged Honey-creeper	..	2·00	10	
		a. Turquoise-blue (bird's head) omitted	£225		
204		3 c. Northern Jacana	..	..	2·50	2·25
		a. Blue-green (legs) omitted	..	£300		
205		4 c. Great Kiskadee	..	..	3·75	2·75
206		5 c. Scarlet-rumped Tanager	..	2·50	10	
		w. Wmk inverted				
207		10 c. Scarlet Macaw	..	..	4·00	10
		a. Blue omitted	..	..	£275	
		w. Wmk inverted				†
208		15 c. Slaty-tailed Trogon	..	..	1·50	10
		w. Wmk inverted	..	..	20·00	
209		25 c. Red-footed Booby	..	..	4·50	30
		w. Wmk inverted				
210		50 c. Keel-billed Toucan	..	..	6·00	35
		a. Pale blue (claw and beak) omitted				
211		$1 Magnificent Frigate Bird	..	9·00	75	
212		$2 Rufous-tailed Jacamar	..	14·00	3·00	
		a. *Shade**	..	..	42·00	16·00
		w. Wmk inverted	..	..	60·00	
213		$5 Montezuma Oropendola	..	25·00	14·00	
202/13					*Set of 12* 65·00	22·00

**On No. 212a, the bird is myrtle-green and red-brown instead of yellow-green and orange-brown.
See also Nos. 239/45.

1963 (4 June). *Freedom from Hunger. As No. 146 of Antigua.*

214	22	22 c. bluish green	..	..	30	15

1963 (2 Sept). *Red Cross Centenary. As Nos. 147/8 of Antigua.*

215		4 c. red and black	..	..	20	40
216		22 c. red and blue	..	..	40	85

SELF-GOVERNMENT

SELF GOVERNMENT 1964 (56)   **DEDICATION OF SITE NEW CAPITAL 9th OCTOBER 1965** (57)

1964. *New Constitution. Nos. 202, 204/5, 207 and 209 optd with T 56.*

217		1 c. Type **55** (20.4)	..	..	10	30
		a. Opt inverted	..	..	£250	
		b. Orange-yellow (knob) omitted..	..	80·00		
218		3 c. Northern Jacana (20.4)	..	45	30	
219		4 c. Great Kiskadee (3.2)	..	..	45	30
220		10 c. Scarlet Macaw (20.4)	..	45	10	
221		25 c. Red-footed Booby (3.2)	..	55	30	
217/21					*Set of 5* 1·75	1·10

1965 (17 May). *I.T.U. Centenary. As Nos. 166/7 of Antigua.*
222	2 c. orange-red and light green		10	10
223	50 c. yellow and light purple	..	35	25

1965 (25 Oct). *International Co-operation Year. As Nos. 168/9 of Antigua.*
224	1 c. reddish purple and turquoise-green		10	15
225	22 c. deep bluish green and lavender ..		20	15

1966 (24 Jan). *Churchill Commemoration. As Nos. 170/3 of Antigua.*
226	1 c. new blue	..	10	10
227	4 c. deep green	..	15	10
228	22 c. brown		40	10
229	25 c. bluish violet	..	50	45
226/9 ..		Set of 4	95	60

1966 (1 July). *Dedication of New Capital Site. As Nos. 202, 204/5, 207 and 209, but wmk sideways*, optd with T 57 by Harrison.*
230	1 c. Type 55	..	10	40
	a. Orange-yellow (knob) omitted	..	£110	
	w. Wmk Crown to right of CA		70	
231	3 c. Northern Jacana	..	45	40
232	4 c. Great Kiskadee	..	45	10
233	10 c. Scarlet Macaw	..	45	10
234	25 c. Red-footed Booby	..	55	35
230/4		Set of 5	1·75	1·50

*The normal sideways watermark shows Crown to left of CA, as seen from the back of the stamp.

58 Citrus Grove

(Des V. Whiteley. Photo Harrison)

1966 (1 Oct). *Stamp Centenary. T 58 and similar horiz designs. Multicoloured. W w 12. P 14 × 14½.*
235	5 c. Type 58	..	10	10
236	10 c. Half Moon Cay	..	10	10
237	22 c. Hidden Valley Falls	..	10	10
238	25 c. Maya Ruins, Xunantunich	..	15	45
235/8 ..		Set of 4	30	65

1967. *As Nos. 202, etc, but W w 12 (sideways).*
239	1 c. Type 55 (16.2)		10	30
240	2 c. Red-legged Honey-creeper (28.11)		30	50
241	4 c. Great Kiskadee (16.2)		1·75	85
242	5 c. Scarlet-rumped Tanager (16.2)		40	10
243	10 c. Scarlet Macaw (28.11)		50	10
244	15 c. Slaty-tailed Trogon (28.11)		60	10
245	50 c. Keel-billed Toucan (16.2)		3·00	3·50
239/45		Set of 7	6·00	4·75

The 15 c. value exists with PVA gum as well as gum arabic.

59 Sailfish   **60** *Schomburgkia tibicinis*

(Des R. Granger Barrett. Photo Harrison)

1967 (1 Dec). *International Tourist Year. T 59 and similar horiz designs. W w 12. P 12½.*
246	5 c. deep violet-blue, black and light yellow		15	20
247	10 c. brown, black and orange-red		15	10
248	22 c. yellow-orange, black and bright green ..		30	10
249	25 c. lt greenish blue, black & greenish yellow		30	45
246/9		Set of 4	80	75

Designs:—10 c. Red Brocket; 22 c. Jaguar; 25 c. Atlantic Tarpon.

(Des Sylvia Goaman. Photo Harrison)

1968 (16 Apr). *20th Anniv of Economic Commission for Latin America. T 60 and similar vert designs showing orchids. Multicoloured. W w 12 (sideways). P 14½×14.*
250	5 c. Type 60	..	20	15
251	10 c. *Maxillaria tenuifolia*	..	25	10
252	22 c. *Bletia purpurea*	..	30	10
253	25 c. *Sobralia macrantha*	..	40	20
250/3 ..		Set of 4	1·10	40

61 Monument to Belizean Patriots   **62** Monument at Site of New Capital

(Des G. Vasarhelyi. Litho B.W.)

1968 (15 July). *Human Rights Year. W w 12. P 13½.*
254	**61** 22 c. multicoloured	..	15	10
255	**62** 50 c. multicoloured	..	15	20

63 Spotted Jewfish

(Des J. W. Litho D.L.R.)

1968 (15 Oct). *Wildlife. Horiz designs as T 63. Multicoloured. No wmk. P 13 × 12½.*
256	1 c. Type 63		20	10
257	2 c. White-lipped Peccary ("Warree")		10	10
258	3 c. Misty Grouper		20	10
259	4 c. Collared Anteater		10	85
260	5 c. Bonefish		10	85
261	10 c. Paca ("Gibnut")	..	15	10
262	15 c. Dolphin	..	75	20
263	25 c. Kinkajou ("Night Walker")	..	30	20
264	50 c. Mutton Snapper	..	70	1·25
265	$1 Tayra ("Bush Dog")	..	2·50	1·25
266	$2 Great Barracuda	..	2·50	2·00
267	$5 Puma	..	13·00	6·50
256/67		Set of 12	18·00	12·00

See also Nos. 276/8 and 338/40

64 *Rhyncholaelia digbyana*   **65** Ziricote Tree

(Des Sylvia Goaman. Photo Harrison)

1969 (9 Apr). *Orchids of Belize (1st series). T 64 and similar vert designs. Multicoloured. W w 12 (sideways). P 14½ × 14.*
268	5 c. Type 64	..	50	20
269	10 c. *Cattleya bowringiana*	..	55	15
270	22 c. *Lycaste cochleatum*	..	85	15
271	25 c. *Coryanthes speciosum*	..	1·10	1·10
268/71		Set of 4	2·75	1·40

See also Nos. 287/90.

(Des V. Whiteley. Litho D.L.R.)

1969 (1 Sept). *Indigenous Hardwoods (1st series). T 65 and similar vert designs. Multicoloured. W w 12. P 14.*
272	5 c. Type 65	..	10	20
273	10 c. Rosewood ..	..	10	10
274	22 c. Mayflower	..	20	10
275	25 c. Mahogany	..	20	45
272/5 ..		Set of 4	45	70

See also Nos. 291/4, 315/18 and 333/7.

1969–72. *As Nos. 257/8, 261, 267 and new value and design (½ c.), but W w 12 (sideways*).*
276	½ c. Mozambique Mouthbrooder ("Crana") (ultramarine background) (1.9.69)		10	10
277	½ c. Mozambique Mouthbrooder ("Crana") (yellow-olive background) (1.2.71)		2·00	1·00
	a. Black (inscr and value) omitted		£225	
	bw. Wmk Crown to right of CA		2·75	
277c	2 c. White-lipped Peccary (5.5.72)		3·75	3·75
277d	3 c. Misty Grouper (5.5.72)		3·75	3·75
277e	10 c. Paca (5.5.72)		3·75	3·75
278	$5 Puma (12.5.70)		6·50	12·00
276/8		Set of 6	17·00	22·00

*The normal sideways watermark shows Crown to left of CA, as seen from the back of the stamp.

66 "The Virgin and Child" (Bellini)   (68

(Des adapted by G. Drummond. Litho Format)

1969 (1 Nov). *Christmas. Paintings. T 66 and similar vert design. Multicoloured. W w 12. P 14× 14½.*
279	5 c. Type 66	..	10	10
280	15 c. Type 66	..	10	10
281	22 c. "The Adoration of the Kings" (Veronese)		10	10
282	25 c. As 22 c.		10	20
279/82		Set of 4	30	30

Although released by the Crown Agents on 1 October this issue was not put on sale locally until 1 November.

1970 (2 Feb). *Population Census. As Nos. 260 and 262/3 but W w 12 (sideways) and No. 277e optd with T 68.*
283	5 c. Bonefish ..		10	10
284	10 c. Paca	..	15	10
285	15 c. Dolphin	..	20	10
286	25 c. Kinkajou	..	20	15
283/6 ..		Set of 4	55	30

(Des G. Drummond. Litho Format)

1970 (2 Apr). *Orchids of Belize (2nd series). As T 64. Multicoloured. W w 12. P 14.*
287	5 c. Black Orchid	..	35	15
288	15 c. White Butterfly Orchid ..		50	10
289	22 c. Swan Orchid	..	70	10
290	25 c. Butterfly Orchid	..	70	40
287/90		Set of 4	2·00	60

69 Santa Maria   **70** "The Nativity" (A. Hughes).

(Des Jennifer Toombs, Litho Questa)

1970 (7 Sept). *Indigenous Hardwoods (2nd series). T 69 and similar vert designs. Multicoloured. W w 12 (sideways). P 14 × 14½.*
291	5 c. Type 69	..	25	10
292	15 c. Nargusta	..	35	10
293	22 c. Cedar	..	40	10
294	25 c. Sapodilla	..	40	35
291/4 ..		Set of 4	1·25	55

(Des J. Cooter Litho J.W.)

1970 (7 Nov*). *Christmas. T 70 and similar vert design. Multicoloured. W w 12. P 14.*
295	½ c. Type 70	..	10	10
296	5 c. "The Mystic Nativity" (Botticelli)		10	10
297	10 c. Type 70	..	20	10
298	15 c. As 5 c.		25	10
299	22 c. Type 70	..	25	10
300	50 c. As 5 c.		40	85
295/300		Set of 6	1·10	1·10

*These stamps were released by the Crown Agents in London on 2 November.

71 Legislative Assembly House

(Des G. Drummond. Litho Enschedé)

1971 (30 Jan). *Establishment of New Capital, Belmopan. T 71 and similar horiz designs. Multicoloured. W w 12 upright (5 c., 10 c.) or sideways (others). P 13 × 13½.*
301	5 c. Old Capital, Belize	..	10	10
302	10 c. Government Plaza	..	10	10
303	15 c. Type 71	..	10	10
304	22 c. Magistrates' Court	..	15	10
305	25 c. Police H.Q.	..	15	15
306	50 c. New G.P.O.	..	25	40
301/6 ..		Set of 6	70	75

The 5 c. and 10 c. are larger, 60 × 22 mm.

72 Tabebuia chrysantha

(Des Sylvia Goaman. Litho Questa)

1971 (27 Mar). *Easter. T 72 and similar horiz designs showing flowers. Multicoloured. W w 12 (sideways). P 14.*
307	½ c. Type 72	..	10	10
308	5 c. *Hymenocallis littorallis*		10	10
309	10 c. *Hippeastrum equestre*		10	10
310	15 c. Type 72	..	20	10
311	22 c. As 5 c.		20	10
312	25 c. As 10 c.		20	30
307/12		Set of 6	65	50

(73)   **74** Tubroos

1971 (14 June). *Racial Equality Year. As No. 264, but W w* **12** *(sideways*) and No. 277e optd with T* **73**.
313	10 c. Paca	..	25	10
314	50 c. Mutton Snapper	..	55	20
	w. Wmk Crown to left of CA	..	7·50	

*The normal sideways watermark shows Crown to left of CA on the 10 c. and to the right on the 50 c., *both as seen from the back of the stamp.*

(Des Jennifer Toombs, Litho Questa)

1971 (16 Aug). *Indigenous Hardwoods (3rd series).* T **74** *and similar vert designs. Multicoloured. W w* **12**. P 13½.
315	5 c. Type **74**	..	50	10
	w. Wmk inverted	..	2·50	
316	15 c. Yemeri	..	70	30
317	26 c. Billywebb	..	95	35
318	50 c. Logwood	..	1·75	3·50
315/18		*Set of 4*	3·50	3·75
MS319	96×171 mm. Nos. 315/18		3·50	6·50
	a. Silver (Queen's head) omitted		£1600	

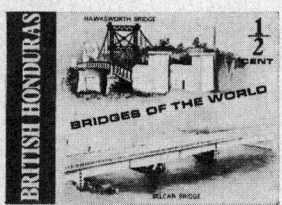

75 Hawksworth and Belcan Bridges

(Des and litho J.W.)

1971 (23 Sept). *Bridges of the World.* T **75** *and similar horiz designs. Multicoloured. W w* **12** *(sideways).* P 13½.
320	½ c. Type **75**	..	10	20
321	5 c. Narrows Bridge, N.Y. and Quebec Bridge		30	15
322	26 c. London Bridge (1871) and reconstructed, Arizona (1971)		70	15
323	50 c. Belize Mexican Bridge and Swing Bridge		90	1·25
320/3	..	*Set of 4*	1·75	1·60

76 *Petrae volubis*   77 Seated Figure

(Des G. Drummond. Litho Format)

1972 (28 Feb). *Easter.* T **76** *and similar vert designs showing wild flowers. Multicoloured. W w* **12**. P 14½.
324	6 c. Type **76**	..	15	10
325	15 c. Yemeri	..	35	30
326	26 c. Mayflower	..	50	45
327	50 c. Tiger's Claw	..	80	1·40
324/7		*Set of 4*	1·60	2·00

(Des Jennifer Toombs. Litho Questa)

1972 (22 May). *Mayan Artefacts.* T **77** *and similar multicoloured designs. W w* **12** *(sideways except* 16 c.). P 13½ × 13 (16 c.) or 13 × 13½ (others).
328	3 c. Type **77**	..	15	10
329	6 c. Priest in "dancing" pose	..	20	10
330	16 c. Sun God's head (*horiz*)	..	35	15
331	26 c. Priest and Sun God	..	50	20
332	50 c. Full-front figure	..	1·00	2·75
328/32		*Set of 5*	2·00	3·00

Nos. 328/32 are inscribed on the reverse with information about the artefacts depicted.

78 Banak   79 Orchids of Belize

(Des Jennifer Toombs. Litho Questa)

1972 (21 Aug). *Indigenous Hardwoods (4th series).* T **78** *and similar vert designs. Multicoloured. W w* **12** *(sideways).* P 14½.
333	3 c. Type **78**	..	15	10
334	5 c. Quamwood	..	15	10
335	16 c. Waika Chewstick	..	35	15
336	26 c. Mamee-Apple	..	50	25
337	50 c. My Lady	..	1·25	3·25
333/7	..	*Set of 5*	2·25	3·50

1972 (17 Nov). *As Nos. 258 and 260/1, but W w* **12** *(upright).*
338	3 c. Misty Grouper	..	1·75	2·25
339	5 c. Bonefish	..	1·75	2·25
340	10 c. Paca	..	1·75	2·25
	w. Wmk inverted	..	6·00	
338/40		*Set of 3*	4·75	6·00

(Des (from photograph by D. Groves) and photo Harrison)

1972 (20 Nov). *Royal Silver Wedding. Multicoloured; background colour given. W w* **12**. P 14 × 14½.
341	79	26 c. deep myrtle-green	..	25	10
		w. Wmk inverted	..	48·00	
342		50 c. bright bluish violet	..	40	65
		w. Wmk inverted	..	38·00	

80 Baron Bliss Day

(Des J.W. Litho Questa)

1973 (9 Mar). *Festivals of Belize.* T **80** *and similar horiz designs. Multicoloured. W w* **12**. P 14½ × 14.
343	3 c. Type **80**	..	15	10
344	10 c. Labour Day	..	15	10
345	26 c. Carib Settlement Day	..	30	15
346	50 c. Pan American Day	..	50	70
343/6	..	*Set of 4*	1·00	85

BELIZE

British Honduras was renamed Belize on 1 June 1973.

❋ BELIZE ❋

(81)

1973 (11 June*). *Designs as Nos. 256/7, 259, 262/7 and 277, but W w* **12** *(upright), and Nos. 338/40 optd with T* **81** *in black on silver by D.L.R.* P 13×12½.
347	½ c. Mozambique Mouthbreeder ("Crana")		10	20
348	1 c. Spotted Jewfish	..	10	20
349	2 c. White-lipped Peccary ("Waree")	..	10	20
350	3 c. Misty Grouper	..	10	10
	a. Silver background to opt omitted	..	†	—
351	4 c. Collared Anteater	..	10	20
352	5 c. Bonefish	..	10	20
353	10 c. Paca ("Gibnut")	..	15	15
	a. Black (value etc.) omitted	..	£225	
354	15 c. Dolphin	..	20	20
355	25 c. Kinkajou ("Night Walker")	..	35	35
356	50 c. Mutton Snapper	..	65	75
357	$1 Tayra ("Bush Dog")	..	1·10	1·50
358	$2 Great Barracuda	..	2·00	2·75
359	$5 Puma	..	2·50	4·75
347/59		*Set of 13*	6·50	10·50

*This is the local date of issue: the Crown Agents released the stamps on 1 June.

No. 350a shows the silver background to the overprint omitted. Traces of the adhesive used to apply the silver are visible.

1973 (14 Nov). *Royal Wedding. As Nos. 165/6 of Anguilla. Centre multicoloured. W w* **12** *(sideways).* P 13½.
360	26 c. light turquoise-blue	..	15	10
361	50 c. ochre	..	15	20

82 Mozambique
Mouthbrooder

1974 (1 Jan). *Designs as Nos. 256/67 and 277, but inscr "BELIZE" as in T* **82**. W w **12**. P 13½.
362	½ c. Type **82**	..	10	20
363	1 c. Spotted Jewfish	..	10	20
364	2 c. White-lipped Peccary ("Waree")	..	10	20
365	3 c. Misty Grouper	..	10	10
366	4 c. Collared Anteater	..	10	20
367	5 c. Bonefish	..	10	20
368	10 c. Paca ("Gibnut")	..	15	15
369	15 c. Dolphin	..	20	20
370	25 c. Kinkajou ("Night Walker")	..	35	35
371	50 c. Mutton Snapper	..	60	70
372	$1 Tayra ("Bush Dog")	..	1·00	1·50
373	$2 Great Barracuda	..	1·50	2·25
374	$5 Puma	..	3·50	5·50
362/74		*Set of 13*	7·00	10·50

83 Deer

(Des Mrs. Hosek; adapted PAD Studio, Litho Questa)

1974 (1 May). *Mayan Artefacts (1st series).* T **83** *and similar horiz designs showing pottery motifs. Multicoloured. W w* **12**. P 14½.
375	3 c. Type **83**	..	10	10
376	6 c. Jaguar deity	..	10	10
377	16 c. Sea monster	..	15	10
378	26 c. Cormorant	..	25	10
379	50 c. Scarlet macaw	..	40	40
375/9		*Set of 5*	85	65

See also Nos. 398/402.

84 *Parides arcas*

(Des J. Cooter from the collection of P.T. Hill. Litho Harrison)

1974 (2 Sept)–**76**. *Butterflies. Horiz designs as T* **84**. *Multicoloured. W w* **12** *(sideways*).* P 14 (½, 1, 2, 3, 4, 5, 10, 26 c.) or 14×14½ (others).
380	½ c. Type **84**	..	90	3·00
381	1 c. *Evenus regalis*	..	90	1·75
382	2 c. *Colobura dirce*	..	1·25	2·50
383	3 c. *Catonephele numilia*	..	1·40	2·00
384	4 c. *Battus belus*	..	1·75	2·75
385	5 c. *Callicore patelina*	..	2·00	2·75
386	10 c. *Diaethria astala*	..	1·50	70
387	15 c. *Nessaea aglaura*	..	4·00	3·00
	w. Wmk Crown to right of CA		4·00	
388	16 c. *Prepona pseudojoiceyi*	..	4·00	5·50
389	25 c. *Papilio thoas*	..	4·00	80
	w. Wmk Crown to right of CA		45·00	
390	26 c. *Hamadryas arethusa*	..	2·50	4·25
391	50 c. *Panthiades bathildis*	..	2·75	65
392	$1 *Caligo uranus*	..	6·50	4·50
	w. Wmk Crown to right of CA		45·00	
393	$2 *Heliconius sapho*	..	4·00	1·25
394	$5 *Eurytides philolaus*	..	4·75	5·00
395	$10 *Philaethria dido* (2.1.75)	..	10·00	4·00
	w. Wmk Crown to left of CA (2.8.76)		12·00	9·00
380/95		*Set of 16*	48·00	38·00

*The normal sideways watermark shows Crown to right of CA on the 16 c. and $10 and to left on the others, *as seen from the back of the stamp.*

See also Nos. 403/13 and 426/33.

85 Churchill when Prime Minister,   86 The Actun Balam
and Coronation Scene   Vase

(Des J.W. Litho Questa)

1974 (30 Nov). *Birth Centenary of Sir Winston Churchill.* T **85** *and similar horiz design. Multicoloured. W w* **14** *(sideways).* P 14.
396	50 c. Type **85**	..	20	20
397	$1 Churchill in stetson, and Williamsburg Liberty Bell		30	30

(Des Mrs. Hosek; adapted P. Powell. Litho Questa)

1975 (2 June). *Mayan Artefacts (2nd series).* T **86** *and similar vert designs showing decorated vessels. Multicoloured. W w* **14**. P 14.
398	3 c. Type **86**	..	10	10
399	6 c. Seated figure	..	10	10
400	16 c. Costumed priest	..	25	15
401	26 c. Head with headdress	..	35	20
402	50 c. Layman and priest	..	45	1·75
398/402		*Set of 5*	1·10	2·00

1975–78. *As Nos. 380, 382/7 and 389 and new value (35 c.), but W w* **14** *(sideways on* ½, 2, 3, 4, 5, 10 *and* 35 c.). P 14 × 14½ (15, 25 c.) or 14 (others).
403	½ c. Type **84** (11.6.75)		2·00	7·50
405	2 c. *Colobura dirce* (17.5.77)		50	75
406	3 c. *Catonephele numilia* (17.5.77)		1·25	70
407	4 c. *Battus belus* (7.3.77)		3·00	30
408	5 c. *Callicore patelina* (11.2.77)		3·25	30
409	10 c. *Diaethria astala* (11.2.77)		3·25	30
410	15 c. *Nessaea aglaura* (17.5.77)		75	70
412	25 c. *Papilio thoas* (27.1.78)		3·75	40
413	35 c. Type **84** (25.7.77)		11·00	4·50
403/13		*Set of 9*	26·00	14·00

1975–77. *As Nos. 387, 389, 391 and 394 but W w* **12** *upright.*
426	15 c. *Nessaea aglaura* (20.10.75)		1·00	2·25
428	25 c. *Papilio thoas* (7.3.77)		5·00	1·75
429	50 c. *Panthiades bathildis* (7.3.77)		5·50	1·75
433	$5 *Eurytides philolaus* (20.10.75)		5·50	9·00
	w. Wmk inverted		38·00	
426/33		*Set of 4*	15·00	13·50

87 Musicians

(Des PAD Studio. Litho Harrison)

1975 (17 Nov). *Christmas.* T **87** *and similar multicoloured designs. W w* **12** *(upright on* 6 c. 26 c.) or sideways (others). P 14 × 14½ (horiz) or 14½ × 14 (vert).
435	6 c. Type **87**	..	10	10
436	26 c. Children and "crib"	..	20	10
	w. Wmk inverted	..	5·00	3·00
437	50 c. Dancer and drummers (*vert*)	..	30	55
	a. Imperf (pair)	..	£100	
438	$1 Family and map (*vert*)	..	55	1·60
435/8		*Set of 4*	1·00	2·00

88 William Wrigley Jr. and Chicle Tapping

(Des PAD Studio. Litho Questa)

1976 (29 Mar). *Bicentenary of American Revolution. T 88 and similar horiz designs. Multicoloured. W w 14 (sideways). P 14.*

439	10 c. Type 88	10	10
440	35 c. Charles Lindbergh and *Spirit of St. Louis*	20	40
441	$1 J. L. Stephens (archaeologist)	50	1·25
439/41	*Set of 3*	70	1·60

89 Cycling

(Des J.W. Litho Walsall)

1976 (17 July). *Olympic Games. Montreal. T 89 and similar horiz designs. Multicoloured. W w 14 (sideways). P 14.*

442	35 c. Type 89	15	10
443	45 c. Running	20	15
444	$1 Shooting	35	1·10
442/4	*Set of 3*	65	1·25

20c

5c

(90)   (91)

1976 (30 Aug). *No. 390 surch with T 90 by Harrison.*

445	20 c. on 26 c. *Hamadryas arethusa*	1·10	80

1976 (18 Oct). *West Indian Victory in World Cricket Cup. As Nos. 559/60 of Barbados.*

446	35 c. Map of the Caribbean	50	50
447	$1 The Prudential Cup	1·10	2·00

1976 (2 Dec). *No. 426 surch with T 91 by the Govt Printery, Belize.*

448	5 c. on 15 c. *Nessaea aglaura*	1·10	2·25

92 Queen and Bishops

(Des R. Granger Barrett. Litho Enschedé)

1977 (7 Feb). *Silver Jubilee. T 92 and similar horiz designs. Multicoloured. W w 14 (sideways*). P 13×13½.*

449	10 c. Royal Visit, 1975	10	10
450	35 c. Queen and Rose Window	15	15
	w. Wmk Crown to right of CA	80·00	
451	$2 Type 92	45	90
	w. Wmk Crown to right of CA	42·00	
449/51	*Set of 3*	60	1·00

*The normal sideways watermark shows Crown to left of CA, as seen from the back of the stamp.

93 Red-capped Manakin

94 Laboratory Workers

(Des and litho J.W.)

1977 (3 Sept). *Birds (1st series). T 93 and similar vert designs. Multicoloured. W w 14. P 14.*

452	8 c. Type 93	75	55
453	10 c. Hooded Oriole	90	30
454	25 c. Blue-crowned Motmot	1·25	55
455	35 c. Slaty-breasted Tinamou	1·50	75
456	45 c. Ocellated Turkey	1·75	1·25
457	$1 White Hawk	3·00	5·50
452/7	*Set of 6*	8·25	8·00
MS458	110 × 133 mm. Nos. 452/7	8·25	11·00

See also Nos. 467/73, 488/94 and 561/7.

(Des G. Hutchins. Litho J.W.)

1977 (2 Dec). *75th Anniv of Pan-American Health Organisation. T 94 and similar horiz design. Multicoloured. W w 14 (sideways). P 13½.*

459	35 c. Type 94	20	20
460	$1 Mobile medical unit	40	65
MS461	126 × 95 mm. Nos. 459/60. P 13	85	1·25

BELIZE DEFENCE FORCE
1ST JANUARY 1978
(95)

1978 (15 Feb). *Establishment of Belize Defence Force. Nos. 409 and 413 optd with T 95 in gold by Govt Printery, Belize.*

462	10 c. *Diaethria astala*	75	75
463	35 c. *Parides arcas*	1·50	2·00

96 White Lion of Mortimer   **97** *Russelia sarmentosa*

(Des. C. Abbott. Litho Questa)

1978 (21 Apr). *25th Anniv of Coronation (1st issue). T 96 and similar vert designs. P 15.*

464	75 c. bistre, carmine and silver	20	30
	a. Sheetlet. Nos. 464/6 × 2	1·10	
465	75 c. multicoloured	20	30
466	75 c. bistre, carmine and silver	20	30
464/6	*Set of 3*	55	80

Designs:—No. 464, Type 96; No. 465, Queen Elizabeth II; No 466, Jaguar (Maya god of Day and Night).

Nos. 464/6 were printed together in small sheets of 6, containing two *se-tenant* strips of 3 with horizontal gutter margin between.

See also Nos. 495/503.

(Des. J.W. Litho Questa)

1978 (31 July). *Birds (2nd series). Vert designs as T 93. Multicoloured. W w 14. P 14 as Type 93.*

467	10 c. White-capped Parrot	55	30
468	25 c. Crimson-collared Tanager	1·00	45
469	35 c. Citreoline Trogon	1·40	55
470	45 c. American Finfoot	1·60	1·75
471	50 c. Muscovy Duck	1·75	2·50
472	$1 King Vulture	2·50	5·50
467/72	*Set of 6*	8·00	10·00
MS473	111 × 133 mm. Nos. 467/72	8·00	10·00

(Des J. Cooter. Litho Questa)

1978 (16 Oct). *Christmas. Wild Flowers and Ferns. T 97 and similar vert designs. Multicoloured. W w 14. P 14 × 13½.*

474	10 c. Type 97	15	10
475	15 c. *Lygodium polymorphum*	20	15
476	35 c. *Heliconia aurantiaca*	25	20
477	45 c. *Adiantum tetraphyllum*	30	40
478	50 c. *Angelonia ciliaris*	30	50
479	$1 *Thelypteris obliterata*	50	1·25
474/79	*Set of 6*	1·50	2·25

98 Fairchild Monoplane of Internal Airmail Service, 1937

(Des D. Bowen. Litho Questa)

1979 (15 Jan). *Centenary of U.P.U. Membership. T 98 and similar horiz designs. Multicoloured. W w 14 (sideways). P 13½ × 14.*

480	5 c. Type 98	25	30
481	10 c. *Heron H* (mail boat), 1949	25	10
482	35 c. Internal mail service, 1920 (canoe)	30	20
483	45 c. Stann Creek Railway mail, 1910	60	55
484	50 c. Mounted mail courier, 1882	60	60
485	$2 *Eagle* (mail boat), 1856	1·10	2·50
480/5	*Set of 6*	2·75	3·75

15¢

(99)   (100)

1979. *No. 413 surch. (a) By typography, locally, with T 99.*

486	15 c. on 35 c. Type 84 (March)	45·00	

(b) By lithography, in Great Britain, with T 100

487	15 c. on 35 c. Type 84 (June)	1·50	1·75
	w. Wmk Crown to right of CA	22·00	

*The normal sideways watermark shows Crown to left of CA, as seen from the back of the stamp.

(Des J.W. Litho Questa)

1979 (16 Apr). *Birds (3rd series). Vert designs as T 93. Multicoloured. P 14.*

488	10 c. Boat-billed Heron	50	20
489	25 c. Grey-necked Wood Rail	75	30
490	35 c. Lineated Woodpecker	85	55
491	45 c. Blue-grey Tanager	90	70
492	50 c. Laughing Falcon	90	1·25
493	$1 Long-tailed Hermit	1·40	3·00
488/93	*Set of 6*	4·75	5·50
MS494	113 × 136 mm. Nos. 488/93	4·75	6·00

PRINTER. The following issues to No. 742 were printed in lithography by Lito Nacional, Porto, Portugal.

AVAILABILITY. Certain values of some issues to No. 742 were only available in restricted quantities in Belize.

101 Paslow Building, Belize G.P.O.

(Des A. Medina)

1979 (31 May). *25th Anniv of Coronation (2nd issue). T 101 and similar multicoloured designs. P 14.*

495	25 c. Type 101	1·00	10
496	50 c. Houses of Parliament	1·50	10
497	75 c. Coronation State Coach	2·00	15
498	$1 Queen on horseback (vert)	2·50	15
499	$2 Prince of Wales (vert)	2·75	25
500	$3 Queen and Duke of Edinburgh (vert)	2·75	25
501	$4 Portrait of Queen (vert)	3·00	30
502	$5 St. Edward's Crown (vert)	3·50	30
495/502	*Set of 8*	17·00	1·40
MS503	Two sheets, both 126 × 95 mm: (a) $5 Princess Anne at Montreal Olympics (vert), $10 Queen at Montreal Olympics (vert); (b) $15 As Type 101 *Set of 2 sheets*	18·00	

Nos. 495/502 also exist imperforate from a restricted printing (price for set of 8 £15 mint).

102 Mortimer and Vaughan "Safety" Airplane, 1910

(Des A. Medina)

1979 (30 July). *Death Centenary of Sir Rowland Hill and 60th Anniv of I.C.A.O. (International Civil Aviation Organization, previously International Commission for Air Navigation). T 102 and similar horiz designs. Multicoloured. P 14.*

504	4 c. Type 102	40	10
505	25 c. Boeing 720	1·25	20
506	50 c. Concorde	3·00	30
507	75 c. Handley Page H.P.18 W8b (1922)	1·75	30
508	$1 Avro Type F (1912)	1·75	30
509	$1.50, Samuel Cody's biplane (1910)	2·50	30
510	$2 A. V. Roe Triplane I (1909)	2·50	40
511	$3 Santos Dumont's biplane *14 bis*	2·50	45
512	$4 Wright Type A	3·00	65
504/12	*Set of 9*	16·00	2·75
MS513	Two sheets: (a) 115×95 mm. $5 Dunne D-5 (1910), $5 G.B. 1969 Concorde stamp; (b) 130×95 mm. $10 Boeing 720 (different) *Set of 2 sheets*	20·00	

Nos. 504/12 also exist imperforate from a restricted printing (price for set of 9 £55 mint).

103 Handball   **104** Olympic torch

(Des A. Medina)

1979 (10 Oct). *Olympic Games. Moscow* (1980). *T* **103** *and similar vert designs. Multicoloured. P* 14.

514	25 c. Type **103**	..	45	10
515	50 c. Weightlifting	..	65	10
516	75 c. Athletics	..	90	15
517	$1 Football	..	1·25	20
518	$2 Yachting	..	1·75	25
519	$3 Swimming	..	2·00	30
520	$4 Boxing	..	2·50	30
521	$5 Cycling	..	5·00	50
514/21		*Set of 8*	13·00	1·60

MS522 Two sheets: (a) 126 × 92 mm. $5 Athletics (*different*), $10 Boxing (*different*); (b) 92 × 126 mm. $15 As $5 .. .. .. *Set of 2 sheets* 16·00

Nos. 514/21 also exist imperforate from a restricted printing (*price for set of 8 £55 mint*).

(Des A. Medina)

1979 (4 Dec). *Winter Olympic Games. Lake Placid* (1980). *T* **104** *and similar vert designs. Multicoloured. P* 14.

523	25 c. Type **104**	..	20	10
524	50 c. Giant slalom	..	45	15
525	75 c. Figure-skating	..	65	15
526	$1 Slalom skiing	..	80	15
527	$2 Speed-skating	..	1·60	20
528	$3 Cross-country skiing	..	2·50	30
529	$4 Shooting	..	3·00	40
530	$5 Gold, Silver and Bronze medals ..		3·50	45
523/30		*Set of 8*	11·50	1·60

MS531 Two sheets: (a) 127 × 90 mm. $5 Lighting the Olympic Flame, $10 Gold, Silver and Bronze medals (*different*); (b) 90 × 127 mm. $15 Olympic Torch (*different*) .. .. *Set of 2 sheets* 20·00

Nos. 523/30 also exist imperforate from a restricted printing (*price for set of 8 £55 mint*).

105 Measled Cowrie
(*Cypraea zebra*)

106 Girl and Flower
Arrangement

(Des C. Abbott)

1980 (7 Jan). *Shells. Multicoloured designs as* **105**. *P* 14.

532	1 c. Type **105**	..	55	10
533	2 c. Callico Clam (*Macrocallista maculata*)		70	10
534	3 c. Atlantic Turkey Wing (*Arca zebra*) (*vert*)		80	10
535	4 c. Leafy Jewel Box (*Chama macerophylla*) (*vert*)		80	10
536	5 c. Trochlear Latirus (*Latirus cariniferus*)		80	10
537	10 c. Alphabet Cone (*Conus spurius*) (*vert*)		1·00	10
538	15 c. Cabrit's Murex (*Murex cabritii*) (*vert*)		1·40	10
539	20 c. Stiff Pen Shell (*Atrina rigida*)		1·50	10
540	25 c. Little Knobbed Scallop (*Chlamys imbricata*) (*vert*)		1·50	10
541	35 c. Glory of the Atlantic Cone (*Conus granulatus*)		1·75	10
542	45 c. Sunrise Tellin (*Tellina radiata*) (*vert*)		2·00	10
543	50 c. *Leucozonia nassa leucozonalis*		2·00	10
544	85 c. Triangular Typhis (*Tripterotyphis triangularis*)		3·00	10
545	$1 Queen or Pink Conch (*Strombus gigas*) (*vert*)		3·25	10
546	$2 Rooster-tail Conch (*Strombus gallus*)		5·00	30
547	$5 True Tulip (*Fasciolaris tulipa*)		7·50	75
548	$10 Star Arene (*Arene cruentata*)		9·50	1·25
532/48		*Set of 17*	38·00	6·00

MS549 Two sheets, each 125×90 mm. (a) Nos. 544 and 547; (b) Nos. 546 and 548 .. *Set of 2 sheets* 27·00 15·00

Imprint dates: "1980" Nos. 532/49; "1981" Nos. 537, 543/5.

(Des A. Medina ($5), C. Mullin (others))

1980 (15 Mar). *International Year of the Child* (1st issue). *T* **106** *and similar vert designs. Multicoloured. P* 14.

550	25 c. Type **106**	..	45	10
551	50 c. Boy holding football	..	70	10
552	75 c. Boy with butterfly	..	1·00	10
553	$1 Girl holding doll	..	1·00	10
554	$1·50, Boy carrying basket of fruit	..	1·50	15
555	$2 Boy holding Reticulated Cowrie-Helmet shell ..		1·75	20
556	$3 Girl holding posy	..	2·25	25
557	$4 Boy and girl wrapped in blanket	..	2·50	30
550/7		*Set of 8*	10·00	1·00

MS558 130×95 mm. $5 Three children of different cultures. $5 "Madonna with Cat" (A. Dürer) (*each 35×53 mm*). *P* 13 .. 8·00

MS559 111×151 mm. $10 Children and Christmas tree (73×110 *mm*). *P* 13 .. 8·00

Nos. 550/7 also exist imperforate from a restricted printing (*price for set of 8 £35 mint*).

See also Nos. 583/91.

NEW INFORMATION

The editor is always interested to correspond with people who have new information that will improve or correct the Catalogue.

10¢

(107)

108 Jabiru

1980 (10 Apr*). *No.* 412 *surch with T* **107**.

560	10 c. on 25 c. *Papilio thoas*	..	75	1·00
	a. Surch inverted	..		60·00

* Earliest known date of use.

(Des J.W. Litho Questa)

1980 (16 June). *Birds* (4th series). *T* **108** *and similar vert designs. Multicoloured. P* 13.

561	10 c. Type **108**	..	5·50	2·75
	a. Sheetlet. Nos. 561/6			35·00
562	25 c. Barred Antshrike	..	6·00	2·75
563	35 c. Northern Royal Flycatcher	..	6·00	2·75
564	45 c. White-necked Puffbird	..	6·50	3·00
565	50 c. Ornate Hawk-eagle	..	6·50	3·00
566	$1 Golden-masked Tanager	..	7·00	3·75
561/6		*Set of 6*	35·00	16·00

MS567 85×90 mm. $2 Type **108**, $3 As $1 .. 26·00 17·00

Nos. 561/6 were printed together, *se-tenant* in sheetlets of 6 or in "double" sheetlets of 12. Stamps from the "double" sheetlets have a red frame and red imprint at foot.

109 Speed Skating

(110)

1980 (20 Aug). *Medal Winners, Winter Olympic Games, Lake Placid. T* **109** *and similar vert designs. Multicoloured. P* 14.

568	25 c. Type **109**	..	30	15
569	50 c. Ice hockey	..	50	15
570	75 c. Figure-skating	..	60	15
571	$1 Alpine skiing	..	85	15
572	$1·50, Giant slalom (women)	..	1·25	25
573	$2 Speed-skating (women)	..	1·50	30
574	$3 Cross-country skiing	..	2·25	40
575	$5 Giant slalom	..	3·50	55
568/75		*Set of 8*	9·75	1·90

MS576 Two sheets: (a) 126 × 91 mm. $5 Type **109**; $10 Type **109**; (b) 91 × 126 mm. $10 As 75 c. .. .. *Set of 2 sheets* 15·00

Nos. 568/75 were each printed in sheets of 30 (6×5) containing stamps in vertical rows 1, 3/4 and 6, and stamp-sized labels in rows 2 and 5.

Nos. 568/75 also exist imperforate from a restricted printing (*price for set of 8 £55 mint*).

1980 (3 Oct). "ESPAMER" *International Stamp Exhibition. Madrid. Nos.* 561/6 *optd* (Nos. 577/9) *or surch as T* **110**.

577	10 c. Type **107**	..	5·50	2·50
	a. Sheetlet. Nos. 577/82			32·00
578	25 c. Barred Antshrike	..	6·00	2·75
579	35 c. Northern Royal Flycatcher	..	6·00	2·75
580	40 c. on 45 c. White-necked Puffbird	..	6·50	3·00
581	40 c. on 50 c. Ornate Hawk-eagle	..	6·50	3·00
582	40 c. on $1 Golden-masked Tanager ..		6·50	3·00
577/82		*Set of 6*	32·00	15·00

111 Witch in Sky

112 Queen Elizabeth
The Queen Mother

(Des C. Mullin)

1980 (24 Nov). *International Year of the Child* (2nd issue). *Sleeping Beauty. T* **111** *and similar vert designs illustrating the story. P* 14.

583	35 c. multicoloured	..	1·00	15
584	40 c. multicoloured	..	1·25	15
585	50 c. multicoloured	..	1·50	15
586	75 c. multicoloured	..	1·60	15
587	$1 multicoloured	..	1·75	20

588	$1·50, multicoloured	..	2·50	30
589	$3 multicoloured	..	3·50	35
590	$4 multicoloured	..	3·50	45
583/90		*Set of 8*	15·00	1·60

MS591 Two sheets: (a) 82 × 110 mm. $8 "Paumgartner Altar-piece" (Dürer); (b) 110 × 82 mm. $5 Marriage ceremony, $5 Sleeping Beauty and Prince on horseback .. *Set of 2 sheets* 17·00

Nos. 583/90 were printed in a similar sheet format to Nos. 568/75.

Nos. 583/90 also exist imperforate from a restricted printing (*price for set of 8 £55 mint*).

(Des C. Mullen)

1980 (12 Dec). *80th Birthday of Queen Elizabeth the Queen Mother. P* 13.

592	**112** $1 multicoloured	..	1·25	40

MS593 82 × 110 mm, $5 As Type **112** (41 × 32 *mm*) 10·00 4·00

No. 592 exists imperforate from a restricted printing (*price £5·50 mint*).

$1

113 The Annunciation

(114)

(Des C. Mullin)

1980 (30 Dec). *Christmas. T* **113** *and similar vert designs. Multicoloured. P* 14.

594	25 c. Type **113**	..	45	10
595	50 c. Bethlehem	..	75	10
596	75 c. The Holy Family	..	1·00	10
597	$1 The Nativity	..	1·10	10
598	$1·50, The flight into Egypt	..	1·50	15
599	$2 Shepherds following the Star	..	1·75	20
600	$3 Virgin, Child and Angel	..	2·25	25
601	$4 Adoration of the Kings	..	2·25	30
594/601		*Set of 8*	10·00	1·00

MS602 Two sheets, each 82 × 111 mm: (a) $5 As $1; (b) $10 As $3 .. *Set of 2 sheets* 14·00

Nos. 594/601 were printed in a similar sheet format to Nos. 568/75.

1981 (22 May). "WIPA" *International Stamp Exhibition. Vienna. Nos.* 598 *and* 601/2b *surch with T* **114**.

603	$1 on $1·50, The flight into Egypt	..	3·00	80
604	$2 on $4 Adoration of the Kings	..	3·50	1·60

MS605 82 × 111 mm. $2 on $10 Virgin, Child and Angel .. .. 5·50 3·25

115 Paul Harris (founder)

116 Prince of Wales Coat of Arms

1981 (26 May). *75th Anniv of Rotary International. T* **115** *and similar multicoloured designs. P* 14.

606	25 c. Type **115**	..	80	25
607	50 c. Emblems of Rotary activities	..	1·25	35
608	$1 75th Anniversary emblem	..	1·75	65
609	$1·50, Educational scholarship programme (*horiz*)		2·50	1·00
610	$2 "Project Hippocrates"	..	3·00	1·40
611	$3 Emblems (*horiz*)	..	3·50	2·00
612	$5 Emblem and handshake (*horiz*) ..		4·50	3·25
606/12		*Set of 7*	15·00	8·00

MS613 Two sheets: (a) 95 × 130 mm. $10 As 50 c.; (b) 130 × 95 mm, $5 As $1, $10 As $2 .. .. *Set of 2 sheets* 27·00

*Nos. 606/13, together with a 75 c. value showing a map, were originally issued on 30 March 1981, but were withdrawn from sale after two hours as there were objections to the colours used on the map. The stamps, without the offending 75 c., were reissued on 26 May. First Day covers carry the later date and there are no reports of examples used before 26 May.

(Des C. Mullin)

1981 (16 July). *Royal Wedding. T* **116** *and similar vert designs. Multicoloured.* (a) *Size* 22 × 38 *mm* (*from sheets of* 27). *P* 13½ × 14.

614	50 c. Type **116**	..	35	40
	a. Horiz pair. Nos. 614/15		1·10	
615	$1 Prince Charles in military uniform	..	70	75
	a. Horiz pair. Nos. 615/16		1·90	
616	$1·50, Royal couple	..	1·10	1·25

(b) Size 25 × 42 mm with gold borders (sheets of 6 stamps and 3 labels). P 13.

617	50 c. Type **116**	..	35	15
618	$1 As No. 615	..	70	35
619	$1.50, As No. 616	..	1·10	45
614/19		*Set of 6*	3·75	3·00
MS620	145 × 85 mm. $3 × 3 As Nos 614/16, but 30 × 47 mm. P 14		2·50	4·25

Nos. 614/16 were each printed in blocks of 9 (3 × 3), the blocks se-tenant within the sheet.

Nos. 614/16 also exist imperforate from a restricted printing (price for set of 3 £4 mint).

10c

(117)

1981 (22 Aug). No. 538 surch with T **117**.

621	10 c. on 15 c. Cabrit's Murex (*Murex cabritii*)		2·25	2·25
	a. Surch double		†	—

For a similar surcharge, but with rectangular obliterating panel see No. 728.

118 Athletics

(Des C. Mullin)

1981 (14 Sept). History of the Olympic Games. T **118** and similar vert designs. Multicoloured. P 14.

622	85 c. Type **118**	.. ..	1·75	20
623	$1 Cycling	..	4·00	30
624	$1.50, Boxing	..	2·75	30
625	$2 1984 Games–Los Angeles and Sarajevo		3·25	30
626	$3 Baron Pierre de Coubertin	..	4·00	45
627	$5 Olympic Flame	..	4·75	60
622/7		*Set of 6*	18·00	1·75
MS628	Two sheets, each 175 × 123 mm: (a) $5 As $3, $10 As $5 (each 35 × 53 mm). P 13½; (b) $15 As $2 (45 × 67 mm). P 14½	*Set of 2 sheets*		35·00

The two miniature sheets of No. MS628 also exist with the stamps and borders printed in gold from a restricted printing.

INDEPENDENCE

Independence
21 Sept.,1981 $1

(119)   (120)

1981 (21 Sept). Independence Commemoration (1st issue). Optd as T **119** by Benex Press, Belize City. (a) On Nos. 532/44 and 546/9.

629	1 c. Type **119**		60	10
630	2 c. Callico Clam (*Macrocallista maculata*)		60	10
631	3 c. Atlantic Turkey Wing (*Arca zebra*) (vert)		70	10
632	4 c. Leafy Jewel Box (*Chama macrophylla*) (vert)		70	10
	a. Opt inverted			
633	5 c. Trochlear Latirus (*Latirus cariniferus*)		70	10
634	10 c. Alphabet Cone (*Conus spurius*) (vert)		85	10
	a. Opt inverted			
635	15 c. Cabrit's Murex (*Murex cabritii*) (vert)		1·50	10
636	20 c. Stiff Pen Shell (*Atrina rigida*) (vert)		1·60	15
637	25 c. Little Knobbed Scallop (*Chlamys imbricata*) (vert)		1·75	25
638	35 c. Glory of the Atlantic Cone (*Conus granulatus*)		1·75	30
639	45 c. Sunrise Tellin (*Tellina radiata*) (vert)		2·25	40
640	50 c. *Leucozonia nassa leucozonalis*		2·25	40
641	85 c. Triangular Typhis (*Tripterotyphis triangularis*)		3·50	90
	a. Opt inverted			
642	$2 Rooster-tail Conch (*Strombus gallus*) (vert)		6·00	2·50
643	$5 True Tulip (*Fasciolaria tulipa*)		8·00	5·50
	a. Opt inverted		†	—
644	$10 Star Arene (*Arene cruentata*)		12·00	9·50
629/44		*Set of 16*	40·00	18·00
MS645	Two sheets, each 126 × 91 mm: (a) Nos. 641 and 643; (b) Nos. 642 and 644	*Set of 2 sheets*		29·00

On the vertical designs and the miniature sheets the overprint is in roman type.

The 10 c. exists with either "1980" or "1981" imprint date.

Examples of the miniature sheets have been seen showing forged overprints apparently applied by rubber handstamp.

(b) On Nos. 606/13

646	25 c. Type **115** (Gold)		1·25	25
	a. Opt double			
647	50 c. Emblems of Rotary activities		1·75	35
648	$1 75th Anniversary emblem		2·00	65

649	$1.50, Educational scholarship programme		2·75	1·25
650	$2 "Project Hippocrates" (Gold)		3·50	1·60
651	$3 Emblems		4·25	2·50
652	$5 Emblems and handshake		5·50	3·75
646/52		*Set of 7*	19·00	9·25
MS653	Two sheets: (a) 95 × 130 mm. $10 As 50 c.; (b) 130 × 95 mm. $5 As $1, $10 As $2 (Gold)	*Set of 2 sheets*		27·00

See also Nos. 657/63.

1981 (13 Nov). "ESPAMER" International Stamp Exhibition, Buenos Aires. Nos. 609 and MS613b surch with T **120**

654	$1 on $1.50, Educational scholarship programme		4·25	2·00
MS655	95 × 130 mm. $1 on $5 75th anniversary emblem, $1 on $10 "Project Hippocrates".		7·50	4·75

 $1

14 · 18 · XI · 1981

(121)

1981 (14 Nov). "Philatelia 81" International Stamp Exhibition, Frankfurt. No. MS549 surch with T **121** in red.

MS656	Two sheets, each 125 × 90 mm: (a) $1 on 85 c. *Tripterotyphis triangularis*, $1 on $5 *Fasciolaria tulipa*; (b) $1 on $2 *Strombus gallus*. $1 on $10 *Arene cruentata* ... *Set of 2 sheets*	35·00

122 Black Orchid   123 Uruguayan Footballer

(Des C. Mullin)

1981 (18 Dec)–**82**. Independence Commemoration (2nd issue). T **122** and similar multicoloured designs. P 14.

657	10 c. Belize Coat of Arms (*horiz*) (10.2.82)	..	85	10
658	35 c. Map of Belize (10.2.82)	..	2·25	30
659	50 c. Type **122**	..	6·00	1·00
660	85 c. Baird's Tapir (*horiz*)		2·25	1·00
661	$1 Mahogany Tree		2·25	1·10
662	$2 Keel-billed Toucan (*horiz*)		8·00	3·25
657/62		*Set of 6*	19·00	6·00
MS663	130 × 98 mm. $5 As 10 c. P 14½ (10.2.82)		8·00	4·25

(Des C. Mullin)

1981 (28 Dec). World Cup Football Championship, Spain (1st issue). T **123** and similar vert designs. Multicoloured. P 14.

664	10 c. Type **123**		1·75	20
665	25 c. Italian footballer		2·75	20
666	50 c. German footballer		3·50	40
667	$1 Brazilian footballer		4·50	50
668	$1.50, Argentinian footballer		5·50	90
669	$2 English footballer		6·00	1·10
664/9		*Set of 6*	22·00	3·00
MS670	Two sheets: (a) 145 × 115 mm. $2 "SPAIN '82" logo; (b) 155 × 115 mm. $3 Footballer (46 × 76 mm)	*Set of 2 sheets*	20·00	5·50

See also Nos. 721/7.

124 H.M.S. *Centurion* (frigate)

(Des C. Mullin)

1982 (15 Mar). Sailing Ships. T **124** and similar horiz designs. Multicoloured. P 14.

671	10 c. Type **124**	..	2·25	35
672	25 c. *Madagascar* (1837)	..	3·50	45
673	35 c. Brig *Whitby* (1838)	..	4·00	50
674	50 c. *China* (1838)	..	4·50	85
675	85 c. *Swiftsure* (1850)		5·50	1·25
676	$2 *Windsor Castle* (1857)		8·00	5·50
671/6		*Set of 6*	25·00	5·50
MS677	110 × 87 mm. $5 Ships in battle		24·00	7·00

NEW INFORMATION

The editor is always interested to correspond with people who have new information that will improve or correct the Catalogue.

(125)   126 Princess Diana

1982 (28 Apr). "ESSEN '82" International Stamp Exhibition, West Germany. Nos. 662 and 669 surch with T **125**.

678	$1 on $2 Keel-billed Toucan		4·50	1·25
679	$1 on $2 English footballer	..	4·50	1·25

(Des C. Mullin)

1982 (20 May). 21st Birthday of Princess of Wales. T **126** and similar vert designs showing portrait of Princess of Wales with different backgrounds. (a) Size 22 × 38 mm (from sheets of 25). P 13½ × 14.

680	50 c. multicoloured		70	45
	a. Tête-bêche (pair)		1·40	
681	$1 multicoloured		80	75
	a. Tête-bêche (pair)		1·60	
682	$1.50, multicoloured		1·00	1·25
	a. Tête-bêche (pair)		2·00	

(b) Size 25 × 43 mm (from sheets of 6 stamps and 3 labels). P 13

683	50 c. multicoloured		70	30
684	$1 multicoloured		80	50
685	$1.50, multicoloured		1·00	75
680/5		*Set of 6*	4·50	3·50
MS686	145 × 85 mm. $3 × 3 As Nos. 680/2, but 30 × 47 mm. P 14		2·75	3·00

Stamps as Nos. 680/2, size 30×47 mm and perforated 14, exist from a limited printing. These have gold backgrounds to the central ovals and gold frames. In addition the Queen's head and the centre oval are embossed (Price per set of 3 £9 mint).

127 Lighting Camp-fire

(Des C. Mullin)

1982 (31 Aug). 125th Birth Anniv of Lord Baden-Powell. T **127** and similar horiz designs. Multicoloured. P 14.

687	10 c. Type **127**	..	1·50	20
688	25 c. Bird watching		2·25	30
689	35 c. Three scouts, one playing guitar		2·25	30
690	50 c. Hiking	..	2·50	55
691	85 c. Scouts with flag		3·00	1·00
692	$2 Saluting	..	4·00	2·50
687/92		*Set of 6*	14·00	4·25
MS693	Two sheets: each 85 × 115 mm: (a) $2 Scout with flag; (b) $3 Portrait of Lord Baden-Powell	*Set of 2 sheets*	20·00	9·00

128 *Gorgonia ventalina*

(Des C. Mullin)

1982 (20 Sept). First Anniv of Independence. Marine Life. T **128** and similar horiz designs. P 14.

694	10 c. Type **128**		1·75	20
695	35 c. *Carpiuis corallinus*		3·00	20
696	50 c. *Plexaura flexuasa*		3·50	45
697	85 c. *Candylactis gigantea*		3·75	60
698	$1 *Stenopus hispidus*		4·50	90
699	$2 Sergeant Major ("*Abudefduf saxatilis*")		5·50	1·60
694/9		*Set of 6*	20·00	3·50
MS700	130×98 mm. $5 *Schyllarides aequino-clialis*. P 14½		24·00	8·50

(129)

1982 (1 Oct). *"BELGICA 82" International Stamp Exhibition, Brussels. Nos 687/92 optd as T 129 in gold.*

701	10 c. Type 127	1·50	30
702	25 c. Bird watching	2·50	75
703	35 c. Three scouts, one playing guitar	2·50	1·50
704	50 c. Hiking	3·00	1·50
705	85 c. Scouts with flag	4·50	2·50
706	$2 Saluting	9·00	6·50
701/6	*Set of 6*	21·00	11·50

BIRTH OF H.R.H.

PRINCE
WILLIAM ARTHUR
PHILIP LOUIS
21ST JUNE 1982

(130) 131 Scotland v New Zealand

1982 (21 Oct). *Birth of Prince William of Wales (1st issue). Nos. 680/6 optd as T 130 in silver.* (a) *Size 22 × 38 mm.*

707	50 c. multicoloured	35	35
	a. *Tête-bêche* (pair)	70	
	b. Opt double	55·00	
708	$1 multicoloured	45	50
	a. *Tête-bêche* (pair)	90	
709	$1.50, multicoloured	65	75
	a. *Tête-beche* (pair)	1·25	

(b) *Size 25 × 43 mm*

710	50 c. multicoloured	35	35
	a. Opt double		
711	$1 multicoloured	45	50
712	$1.50, multicoloured	65	75
707/12	*Set of 6*	2·50	2·75
MS713	145 × 85 mm. $3 × 3 As Nos. 707/9, but 30 × 47 mm.	3·25	3·50

A similar overprint exists on the stamps from the limited printing described beneath No. **MS**686 (*Price per set of 3 £4 mint*).

1982 (25 Oct). *Birth of Prince William of Wales (2nd issue). Nos 614/20 optd as T 130 in gold* (a) *Size 22 × 38 mm.*

714	50 c. Type 116	2·50	1·00
	a. Horiz pair. Nos. 714/15	7·50	
715	$1 Prince Charles in military uniform	5·00	2·00
	a. Horiz pair. Nos. 715/16	12·50	
716	$1.50, Royal couple	7·50	3·00

(b) *Size 25 × 42 mm*

717	50 c. Type 116	35	35
718	$1 As No. 715	70	70
719	$1.50, As No. 716	1·10	1·10
714/9	*Set of 6*	16·00	7·25
MS720	145 × 85 mm. $3 × 3 As Nos. 714/16 but 30 × 47 mm	7·00	7·00

No. **MS**720 occurs with two different sizes of overprint. On the normal version the top line of the overprint, "BIRTH OF H.R.H." measures 19½ mm in length. On examples with the larger overprint this measures 22 mm. (*Price for miniature sheet with larger overprint £30 mint*).

(Des Baumann)

1982 (10 Dec). *World Cup Football Championship, Spain (2nd issue). T 131 and similar horiz designs. Multicoloured. P 14.*

721	20 c. + 10 c. Type 131	1·50	80
722	30 c. + 15 c. Scotland v New Zealand (*different*)	1·50	80
723	40 c. + 20 c. Kuwait v France	1·75	80
724	60 c. + 30 c. Italy v Brazil	2·25	1·00
725	$1 + 50 c. France v Northern Ireland	2·75	1·25
726	$1.50 + 75 c. Austria v Chile	3·50	1·60
721/6	*Set of 6*	12·00	5·50
MS727	Two sheets: (a) 91 × 137 mm. $1 + 50 c. Germany v Italy (50 × 70 *mm*); (b) 122 × 116 mm. $2 + $1 England v France (50 × 70 *mm*) *Set of 2 sheets*	12·00	7·00

10c

(132) 133 Belize Cathedral

1983 (28 Jan). *No. 538 surch with T 132.*

728	10 c. on 15 c. *Murex cabritii*		

No. 728 differs from the previous provisional, No. 621, in the size of the obliterating panel over the original face value. On No. 621 this measures 4½ × 4½ mm, but No. 728 shows it larger, 7 × 5½ mm.

1983 (7 March). *Visit of Pope John Paul II. P 13½.*

729	133 50 c. multicoloured	2·25	90
MS730	135 × 110 mm. $2.50, Pope John Paul II (30 × 47 *mm*). P 14	11·00	4·75

STANLEY GIBBONS STAMP COLLECTING SERIES

Introductory booklets on *How to Start, How to Identify Stamps* and *Collecting by Theme*. A series of well illustrated guides at a low price.
Write for details.

10c
35c

134 Map of Belize (135)

1983 (14 Mar). *Commonwealth Day. T 134 and similar multi-coloured designs. P 13.*

731	35 c. Type 134	35	35
732	50 c. "Maya Stella" from Lamanai Indian church (*horiz*)	50	50
733	85 c. Supreme Court Building (*horiz*)	60	75
734	$2 University Centre, Belize (*horiz*)	1·25	2·00
731/4	*Set of 4*	2·40	3·25

1983 (15 Apr). *No. 658 surch with T 135.*

735	10 c. on 35 c. Map of Belize		

136 De Lana-Terzi's "Aerial Ship", 1670

(Des C. Mullin)

1983 (16 May). *Bicentenary of Manned Flight. T 136 and similar horiz designs. Multicoloured. P 14.*

736	10 c. Type 136	2·00	40
737	25 c. De Gusmao's *La Passarola*, 1709	2·75	45
738	50 c. Guyton de Morveau's balloon with oars, 1784	3·00	80
739	85 c. Early airship	3·75	1·25
740	$1 Airship *Clement Bayard*	4·00	1·60
741	$1.50, Beardmore airship R-34	4·50	2·50
736/41	*Set of 6*	18·00	6·25
MS742	Two sheets: (a) 125×84 mm. $3 Charles Green's balloon *Royal Vauxhall*; (b) 115×128 mm. $3 Montgolfier balloon, 1783 (*vert*) *Set of 2 sheets*	16·00	4·50

$1.25

$1.25

(137) (138)

1983 (9 June). *Nos. 662 and 699 surch with T 137/8.*

743	$1.25 on $2 Keel-billed Toucan (surch T 137)	7·00	7·00
	a. Surch double		†
744	$1.25 on $2 Sergeant Major (surch T 138)	6·00	8·00

10C

10C

(139) (140)

1983 (28 Sept). *No. 541 surch with T 139/40.*

745	10 c. on 35 c. Glory of the Atlantic Cone (*Conus granulatus*) (surch T 139)	32·00	
	a. Surch inverted	38·00	
	b. Vert pair, lower stamp without "10 c"		
	c. Surch double		
746	10 c. on 35 c. Glory of the Atlantic Cone (*Conus granulatus*) (surch T 140)	28·00	
	a. Surch triple	25·00	

141 Altun Ha

(Des G. Vasarhelyi. Litho Format)

1983 (14 Nov). *Maya Monuments. T 141 and similar horiz designs. Multicoloured. P 13½ × 14.*

747	10 c. Type 141	10	10
748	15 c. Xunantunich	10	10
749	75 c. Cerros	30	40
750	$2 Lamanai	70	1·25
747/50	*Set of 4*	1·00	1·75
MS751	102 × 72 mm. $3 Xunantunich (*different*)	1·00	1·75

Nos. 747/50 exist imperforate from stock dispersed by the liquidator of Format International Security Printers Ltd.

142 Belmopan Earth Station

(Des G. Vasarhelyi. Litho Format)

1983 (28 Nov). *World Communications Year. T 142 and similar horiz designs. Multicoloured. P 14.*

752	10 c. Type 142	30	10
753	15 c. Telstar 2	40	25
754	75 c. U.P.U. logo	90	1·75
755	$2 M.V. *Heron H* mail service	2·25	4·50
752/5	*Set of 4*	3·50	6·00
MS756			

Nos. 752/5 exist imperforate from stock dispersed by the liquidator of Format International Security Printers Ltd.

143 Jaguar Cub

(Des G. Vasarhelyi. Litho Format)

1983 (9 Dec). *The Jaguar. T 143 and similar horiz designs. Multicoloured. P 14.*

756	5 c. Type 143	30	40
757	10 c. Adult Jaguar	35	30
758	85 c. Jaguar in river	1·75	2·50
759	$1 Jaguar on rock	2·00	2·75
756/9	*Set of 4*	4·00	5·50
MS760	102×72 mm. $3 Jaguar in tree (44×28 mm). P 13½×14	2·00	2·50

Nos. 756/9 exist imperforate from stock dispersed by the liquidator of Format International Security Printers Ltd.

144 Pope John Paul II

(Des G. Vasarhelyi. Litho Format)

1983 (22 Dec). *Christmas. T 144 and similar designs showing Pope John Paul II at Papal Mass on 11 March 1983 in Belize. P 13½ × 14.*

761	10 c. multicoloured	25	10
762	15 c. multicoloured	25	10
763	75 c. multicoloured	60	60
764	$2 multicoloured	1·25	1·40
761/4	*Set of 4*	2·10	2·00
MS765	102 × 72 mm. $3 multicoloured	2·75	3·75

145 Four-eyed Butterflyfish

(Des G. Drummond, Litho Format)

1984 (27 Feb)–88. *Marine Life from the Belize Coral Reef. T 145 and similar horiz designs. Multicoloured. P 15.*

766	1 c. Type 145	15	40
767	2 c. Cushion Star	20	50
	a. Perf 13½ (7.88)	3·50	4·00
768	3 c. Flower Coral	25	50
769	4 c. Royal Gramma ("Fairy Basslet")	25	50
770	5 c. Spanish Hogfish	30	50
771	6 c. Star-eyed Hermit Crab	30	50
772	10 c. Sea Fans and Fire Sponge	70	40
	a. Perf 13½ (7.88)	35	35
773	15 c. Blue-headed Wrasse	80	70
	a. Perf 13½ (7.88)	50	60
774	25 c. Blue-striped Grunt	1·00	80
	a. Perf 13½ (7.88)	70	80
775	50 c. Coral Crab	2·00	1·75
	a. Perf 13½ (7.88)	1·25	1·25
776	60 c. Tube Sponge	2·00	2·00
	a. Perf 13½ (7.88)	1·25	1·75
777	75 c. Brain Coral	1·00	1·50
778	$1 Yellow-tailed Snapper	1·00	1·25
	a. Perf 13½ (7.88)	1·50	1·50

779	$2 Common Lettuce Slug	..	..	1·25	90
780	$5 Three-spotted Damselfish	..	..	1·50	1·25
781	$10 Rock Beauty	..	..	2·00	2·75
766/81			Set of 16	13·00	14·00

Nos. 766/81 exist imperforate from stock dispersed by the liquidator of Format International Security Printers Ltd. Other values exist perforated 13½, but there is no evidence for their contemporary postal use.

Nos. 776 and 778 exist overprinted to commemorate the anniversary of Hurricane Hattie. These stamps were not issued, but exist from stock dispersed by the liquidator.

VISIT OF THE LORD ARCHBISHOP OF CANTERBURY 8th-11th MARCH 1984
(146)

1984 (8 Mar). *Visit of the Archbishop of Canterbury. Nos. 772A and 775A optd with T 146.*

782	10 c. Sea Fans and Fire Sponge	..	..	75	40
783	50 c. Coral Crab	..	..	1·50	1·00

147 Shooting

(Des G. Vasarhelyi. Litho Format)

1984 (30 Apr). *Olympic Games, Los Angeles, (a) Sheet stamps. T 147 and similar horiz designs. Multicoloured. P 13½ × 14.*

784	25 c. Type 147	..	..	..	30	25
785	75 c. Boxing	..	..	..	50	70
786	$1 Marathon	..	..	..	60	90
787	$2 Cycling	..	..	..	1·75	2·00
784/7	..			Set of 4	2·75	3·50
MS788	101 × 72 mm. $3 Statue of Discus-thrower				2·10	2·75

(b) *Booklet stamps. Similar designs to T 147 but Royal cypher replaced by Queen's head. P 14½.*

789	5 c. 1896 Marathon	..	..	15	50
	a. Booklet pane. No. 789 × 4	..		55	
790	20 c. Sprinting	..	..	25	60
	a. Booklet pane. No. 790 × 4	..		90	
791	25 c. Shot-putting	..	..	25	60
	a. Booklet pane. No. 791 × 4	..		90	
792	$2 Olympic torch	..	..	35	80
	a. Booklet pane. No. 792 × 4	..		1·25	
789/92	..	..	Set of 4	90	2·25

148 British Honduras 1866 1s.
    Stamp

149 Prince Albert

(Des G. Vasarhelyi. Litho Format)

1984 (26 Sept). *"Ausipex" International Stamp Exhibition, Melbourne. T 148 and similar horiz designs. Multicoloured. P 14 × 13½ ($2) or 15 (others).*

793	15 c. Type 148	..	..	..	15	15
794	30 c. Bath mail coach, 1784	..	..	25	25
795	65 c. Sir Rowland Hill and Penny Black	..	55	65
796	75 c. British Honduras railway locomotive, 1910			60	75
797	$2 Royal Exhibition Buildings, Melbourne (46 × 28 mm)			1·00	2·00
793/7	..			Set of 5	2·25	3·50
MS798	103 × 73 mm. $3 Australia 1932 Sydney Harbour Bridge 5s. and British Honduras 1866 1s. stamps (44 × 28 mm). P 13½ × 14				1·10	2·00

(Des G. Vasarhelyi. Litho Format)

1984 (15 Oct). *500th Anniv of British Royal House of Tudor (1985). T 149 and similar vert designs showing members of the Royal Family. Multicoloured. P 14.*

799	50 c. Type 149	..	..	..	25	35
	a. Sheetlet. Nos. 799/800 × 2	..		90	
800	50 c. Queen Victoria	..	..	25	35
801	75 c. King George VI	..	..	30	45
	a. Sheetlet. Nos. 801/2 × 2	..		1·00	
802	75 c. Queen Elizabeth the Queen Mother		30	45
803	$1 Princess of Wales	..	..	40	70
	a. Sheetlet. Nos. 803/4 × 2	..		1·40	
804	$1 Prince of Wales	..	..	40	70
799/804			Set of 6	1·75	2·75
MS805	147 × 97 mm. $1.50, Prince Philip; $1.50, Queen Elizabeth II				1·25	2·00

Nos. 799/804 were only issued in sheetlets of four stamps of one value, two of each design, with an illustrated vertical gutter margin

---

150 White-fronted Amazon

151 Effigy Censer, 1450 (Santa Rita Site)

(Des. G. Vasarhelyi. Litho Format)

1984 (1 Nov). *Parrots. T 150 and similar multicoloured designs. P 11.*

806	$1 Type 150	..	..	1·50	1·50
	a. Block of 4. Nos. 806/9	..		5·50	
807	$1 White-capped Parrot (horiz)	..	1·50	1·50
808	$1 Mealy Amazon (horiz)	..	1·50	1·50
809	$1 Red-lored Amazon	..	..	1·50	1·50
806/9			Set of 4	5·50	5·50
MS810	102 × 73 mm. $3 Scarlet Macaw. P 13½ × 14		3·25	3·75

Nos. 806/9 were issued together, *se-tenant*, in blocks of 4 throughout the sheet, each block forming a composite design.

Nos. 806/9 exist imperforate from stock dispersed by the liquidator of Format International Security Printers Ltd.

(Des G. Vasarhelyi. Litho Format)

1984 (30 Nov). *Maya Artefacts. T 151 and similar vert designs. Multicoloured. P 15.*

811	25 c. Type 151	..	..	25	25
812	75 c. Vase, 675 (Actun Chapat)	..	50	70
813	$1 Tripod Vase, 500 (Santa Rita site)	55	90
814	$2 Sun god Kinich Ahau, 600 (Altun Ha site)	90	2·25
811/14			Set of 4	2·00	3·75

152 Governor-General inspecting Girl Guides

153 White-tailed Kite

(Des R. Granger Barrett. Litho Format)

1985 (15 Mar). *International Youth Year and 75th Anniv of Girl Guide Movement. T 152 and similar horiz designs. Multicoloured. P 15.*

815	25 c. Type 152	..	..	..	30	15
816	50 c. Girl Guides camping	..	..	45	30
817	90 c. Checking map on hike	..	..	60	45
818	$1.25, Students in laboratory	..	..	70	60
819	$2 Lady Baden-Powell (founder)	..	90	75
815/19			Set of 5	2·75	2·00

(Des G. Vasarhelyi. Litho Format ($1, $5) Questa (others))

1985 (30 May)–88. *Birth Bicentenary of John J. Audubon (ornithologist). T 153 and similar multicoloured designs showing original paintings. P 15 ($1) or 14 (others).*

820	10 c. Type 153	..	..	..	70	60
821	15 c. Ruby-crowned Kinglet (horiz)	..	90	60
822	25 c. Painted Bunting	..	..	1·25	60
822a	60 c. As 25 c. (1988)	..	..	11·00	6·00
823	75 c. Belted Kingfisher	..	..	1·75	1·40
824	$1 Common Cardinal	..	..	1·75	2·25
825	$3 Long-billed Curlew (horiz)	..	2·50	4·00
820/5			Set of 7	18·00	14·00
MS826	139 × 99 mm. $5 "John James Audubon" (John Syme). P 13½ × 14			2·50	2·00

154 The Queen Mother with Princess Elizabeth, 1928

INAUGURATION OF NEW GOVERNMENT – 21st. DECEMBER 1984
(155)

(Des G. Vasarhelyi. Litho Format)

1985 (20 June). *Life and Times of Queen Elizabeth the Queen Mother. T 154 and similar multicoloured designs. P 13½ × 14.*

827	10 c. Type 154	..	..	10	10
828	15 c. The Queen Mother, 1980	..	10	10
829	75 c. Waving to the crowd, 1982	..	40	40
830	$5 Four generations of Royal Family at Prince William's Christening		1·50	2·75
827/30			Set of 4	1·75	3·00
MS831	Two sheets, each 138 × 98 mm. (a) $2 The Queen Mother with Prince Henry (from photo by Lord Snowdon) (38 × 50 mm): (b) $5 The Queen Mother, 1984 (38 × 50 mm)		Set of 2 sheets	3·75	4·50

1985 (24 June). *Inauguration of New Government. Nos. 772A/3A and 775A optd with T 155.*

832	10 c. Sea Fans and Fire Sponge	..	75	40
833	15 c. Blue-headed Wrasse	..	..	95	45
834	50 c. Coral Crab	..	..	1·60	2·50
832/4			Set of 3	3·00	3·00

156 British Honduras 1935 Silver Jubilee 25 c. stamp and King George V with Queen Mary in Carriage

(Des Harrison. Litho Format)

1985 (25 July). *50th Anniv of First Commonwealth Omnibus Issue. T 156 and similar horiz designs showing British Honduras/Belize stamps. Multicoloured. P 14.*

835	50 c. Type 156	..	..	40	55
	a. Sheetlet. Nos. 835/44	..		3·50	
836	50 c. 1937 Coronation 3 c., and King George VI and Queen Elizabeth in Coronation robes			40	55
837	50 c. 1946 Victory 3 c., and Victory celebrations			40	55
838	50 c. 1948 Royal Silver Wedding 4 c., and King George VI and Queen Elizabeth at Westminster Abbey service			40	55
839	50 c. 1953 Coronation 4 c., and Queen Elizabeth II in Coronation robes			40	55
840	50 c. 1966 Churchill 25 c., Sir Winston Churchill and fighter aircraft			40	55
841	50 c. 1972 Royal Silver Wedding 50 c., and 1948 Wedding photograph			40	55
842	50 c. 1973 Royal Wedding 50 c., and Princess Anne and Capt. Mark Phillips at their Wedding			40	55
843	50 c. 1977 Silver Jubilee $2, and Queen Elizabeth II during tour			40	55
844	50 c. 1978 25th anniv of Coronation 75 c. and Imperial Crown			40	55
835/44			Set of 10	3·50	5·00
MS845	138 × 98 mm. $5 Queen Elizabeth II in Coronation robes (38 × 50 mm). P 13½ × 14			4·00	4·00

Nos. 835/44 were printed together, *se-tenant*, in sheetlets of 10.

157 Mounted Postboy and Early Letter to Belize

COMMONWEALTH SUMMIT CONFERENCE, BAHAMAS 16th-22nd OCTOBER 1985
(158)

(Des G. Drummond. Litho Format)

1985 (1 Aug). *350th Anniv of the British Post Office. T 157 and similar horiz designs. Multicoloured. P 15.*

846	10 c. Type 157	..	..	40	15
847	15 c. *Hinchinbrook II* (sailing packet) engaging *Grand Turk* (American privateer)			55	25
848	25 c. *Duke of Marlborough II* (sailing packet)		70	30
849	75 c. *Diana* (packet)	..	..	1·25	1·50
850	$1 Falmouth packet ship	..	..	1·25	1·75
851	$3 *Conway* (mail paddle-steamer)	..	2·25	4·50
846/51			Set of 6	5·75	7·75

A $5 miniature sheet was prepared, but not issued. Examples exist from stock dispersed by the liquidator of Format International Security Printers Ltd.

1985 (5 Sept). *Commonwealth Heads of Government Meeting, Nassau, Bahamas. Nos. 827/31 optd with T 158 in silver.*

852	10 c. Type 154	..	..	30	30
853	15 c. The Queen Mother, 1980	..	40	35
854	75 c. Waving to the crowd, 1980	..	80	80
855	$5 Four generations of Royal Family at Prince William's christening		2·00	3·75
852/5			Set of 4	3·25	4·75
MS856	Two sheets, each 138 × 98 mm. (a) $2 The Queen Mother with Prince Henry (from photo by Lord Snowdon) (38 × 50 mm): (b) $5 The Queen Mother, 1984 (38 × 50 mm)		Set of 2 sheets	2·75	3·50

80TH ANNIVERSARY OF ROTARY INTERNATIONAL
(159)

160 Royal Standard and Belize Flag

1985 (25 Sept). *80th Anniv of Rotary International. Nos. 815/19 optd with T 159.*

857	25 c. Type 152..	50	30
858	50 c. Girl Guides camping ..	80	75
859	90 c. Checking map on hike ..	1·25	1·60
860	$1.25, Students in laboratory	1·75	2·25
861	$2 Lady Baden-Powell (founder) ..	2·25	2·75
857/61	*Set of 5*	6·00	7·00

(Des G. Vasarhelyi. Litho Format)

1985 (9 Oct). *Royal Visit. T 160 and similar multicoloured designs. P 15 × 14½.*

862	25 c. Type 160..	55	95
	a. Horiz strip of 3. Nos. 862/4	4·25	
863	75 c. Queen Elizabeth II	1·25	2·00
864	$4 Royal Yacht *Britannia* (81 × 39 *mm*) ..	3·00	3·25
862/4	*Set of 3*	4·25	5·50
MS865	138×98 mm. $5 Queen Elizabeth II (38×50 *mm*). P 13½×14	4·00	4·75

Nos. 862/4 were printed together, *se-tenant*, in horizontal strips of 3 within small sheets of 9 stamps.

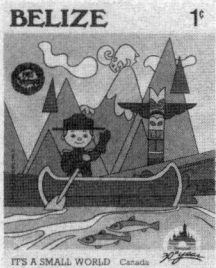

161 Mountie in Canoe (Canada)

(Des Walt Disney Productions. Litho Format)

1985 (1 Nov). *Christmas. 30th Anniv of Disneyland, U.S.A. T 161 and similar vert designs showing dolls from "It's a Small World" exhibition. Multicoloured. P 11.*

866	1 c. Type 161..	10	10
867	2 c. Indian chief and squaw (U.S.A.)	10	10
868	3 c. Incas climbing Andes (South America)	10	10
869	4 c. Africans beating drums (Africa) ..	10	10
870	5 c. Snake-charmer and dancer (India and Far East)	10	10
871	6 c. Boy and girl with donkey (Belize) ..	10	10
872	50 c. Musician and dancer (Balkans)	1·00	1·25
873	$1.50, Boys with camel (Egypt and Saudi Arabia)	2·25	2·75
874	$3 Woman and girls playing with kite (Japan)	3·25	4·25
866/74	*Set of 9*	6·00	7·50
MS875	127×102 mm. $4 Beefeater and castle (Great Britain). P 13½×14	4·50	5·50

PRE"WORLD CUP FOOTBALL" MEXICO 1986

(162)

163 Indian Costume

1985 (20 Dec). *World Cup Football Championship, Mexico (1986) (1st issue). Nos. 835/45 optd with T 162.*

876	50 c. Type 156..	65	65
	a. Sheetlet. Nos. 876/85 ..	6·00	
877	50 c. 1937 Coronation 3 c., and King George VI and Queen Elizabeth in Coronation robes	65	65
878	50 c. 1946 Victory 3 c., and Victory celebrations	65	65
879	50 c. 1948 Royal Silver Wedding 4 c., and King George VI and Queen Elizabeth at Westminster Abbey service	65	65
880	50 c. 1953 Coronation 4 c., and Queen Elizabeth II in Coronation robes	65	65
881	50 c. 1966 Churchill 25 c., Sir Winston Churchill and fighter aircraft ..	65	65
882	50 c. 1972 Royal Silver Wedding 50 c., and 1948 Wedding photograph	65	65
883	50 c. 1973 Royal Wedding 50 c., and Princess Anne and Capt. Mark Phillips at their Wedding..	65	65
884	50 c. 1977 Silver Jubilee $2, and Queen Elizabeth II during tour	65	65
885	50 c. 1978 25th anniv of Coronation 75 c., and Imperial Crown	65	65
876/85	*Set of 10*	6·00	6·00
MS886	138×98 mm. $5 Queen Elizabeth II in Coronation robes ..	4·25	4·25

See also Nos. 936/40.

(Des Jane Clark. Litho Format)

1986 (15 Jan). *Costumes of Belize. T 163 and similar vert designs. Multicoloured. P 15.*

887	5 c. Type 163..	75	30
888	10 c. Maya	80	30
889	15 c. Garifuna..	1·00	35
890	25 c. Creole ..	1·25	35

891	50 c. Chinese ..	1·75	1·25
892	75 c. Lebanese	2·00	2·00
893	$1 European *c* 1900	2·00	2·50
894	$2 Latin	2·75	3·75
887/94	*Set of 8*	11·00	9·75
MS895	139×98 mm. $5 Amerindian (38×50 *mm*). P 13½×14	6·00	7·50

164 Pope Pius X   **165** Princess Elizabeth aged Three

(Des G. Vasarhelyi. Litho Format)

1986 (15 Apr). *Easter. 20th-century Popes. T 164 and similar multicoloured designs. P 11.*

896	50 c. Type 164..	80	1·10
	a. Sheetlet. Nos. 896/903 ..	5·50	
897	50 c. Benedict XV	80	1·10
898	50 c. Pius XI ..	80	1·10
899	50 c. Pius XII ..	80	1·10
900	50 c. John XXIII	80	1·10
901	50 c. Paul VI ..	80	1·10
902	50 c. John Paul I	80	1·10
903	50 c. John Paul II	80	1·10
896/903	*Set of 8*	5·50	8·00
MS904	147×92 mm. $4 Pope John Paul II preaching (*vert*). P 13½×14	8·50	8·50

Nos. 896/903 were printed together, *se-tenant*, in sheetlets of eight stamps and one stamp-size label.

(Des G. Vasarhelyi. Litho Format)

1986 (21 Apr). *60th Birthday of Queen Elizabeth II. T 165 and similar vert designs. Multicoloured. P 14×13½.*

905	25 c. Type 165..	15	20
	a. Sheetlet. Nos. 905/8, each×2 ..	4·00	
906	50 c. Queen wearing Imperial State Crown ..	35	40
907	75 c. At Trooping the Colour	50	55
908	$3 Queen wearing diadem	1·25	2·25
905/8	*Set of 4*	2·00	3·00
MS909	147×93 mm. $4 Queen Elizabeth II (37×50 *mm*). P 13½×14	2·50	3·25

Nos. 905/8 were printed together, *se-tenant*, in sheetlets of eight stamps, two of each value, and one stamp-size label.

166 Halley's Comet and Japanese *Planet A* Spacecraft

(Des G. Vasarhelyi. Litho Format)

1986 (30 Apr). *Appearance of Halley's Comet. T 166 and similar multicoloured designs. P 13½×14.*

910	10 c. Type 166..	35	45
	a. Sheetlet. Nos. 910/12, each×3 ..	3·25	
911	15 c. Halley's Comet, 1910 ..	40	60
912	50 c. Comet and European *Giotto* spacecraft	50	75
913	75 c. Belize Weather Bureau	70	80
	a. Sheetlet. Nos. 913/15, each×3 ..	8·50	
914	$1 Comet and U.S.A. space telescope ..	95	1·10
915	$2 Edmond Halley..	1·50	1·60
910/15	*Set of 6*	4·00	4·75
MS916	147×93 mm. $4 Computer enhanced photograph of Comet (37×50 *mm*)	5·00	6·00

Nos. 910/12 and 913/15 were each printed together, *se-tenant*, in horizontal and vertical strips of 3, within the two sheetlets of nine.

Both sheetlets exist with the black printing omitted from stock dispersed by the liquidator of Format International Security Printers Ltd.

167 George Washington

(Des G. Vasarhelyi. Litho Format)

1986 (7 May). *United States Presidents. T 167 and similar vert designs. Multicoloured. P 11.*

917	10 c. Type 167..	35	45
	a. Sheetlet. Nos. 917/22 ..	3·00	
918	20 c. John Adams ..	35	55
919	30 c. Thomas Jefferson ..	40	60
920	50 c. James Madison ..	50	60
921	$1.50, James Monroe ..	80	1·25
922	$2 John Quincy Adams ..	1·00	1·50
917/22	*Set of 6*	3·00	4·50
MS923	147×93 mm. $4 George Washington (*different*). P 13½×14	3·50	4·75

Nos. 917/19 and 920/2 were printed together, *se-tenant*, in horizontal strips of 3, separated by three stamp-size labels, within the sheetlet of six stamps.

168 Auguste Bartholdi (sculptor) and Statue's Head

(Des G. Vasarhelyi. Litho Format)

1986 (15 May). *Centenary of Statue of Liberty. T 168 and similar multicoloured designs. P 13½×14.*

924	25 c. Type 168..	40	65
	a. Sheetlet. Nos. 924/7, each×2 ..	4·50	
925	50 c. Statue's head at U.S. Centennial Celebration, Philadelphia, 1876 ..	50	85
926	75 c. Unveiling Ceremony, 1886 ..	55	90
927	$3 Statue of Liberty and flags of Belize and U.S.A.	1·00	2·00
924/7	*Set of 4*	2·25	4·00
MS928	147×92 mm. $4 Statue of Liberty and New York skyline (37×50 *mm*)..	3·75	5·00

Nos. 924/7 were printed together, *se-tenant*, in sheetlets of eight stamps, two of each value, and one stamp-size label.

No. 924a exists with the gold omitted from stock dispersed by the liquidator of Format International Security Printers Ltd.

169 British Honduras 1866 1s. Stamp

(Des G. Vasarhelyi. Litho Format)

1986 (22 May). *"Ameripex" International Stamp Exhibition, Chicago. T 169 and similar multicoloured designs. P 13½×14.*

929	10 c. Type 169..	40	55
	a. Sheetlet. Nos. 929/31, each×3	4·50	
930	15 c. 1981 Royal Wedding $1.50 stamp	55	75
931	50 c. U.S.A. 1918 24 c. airmail inverted centre error	75	80
932	75 c. U.S.S. *Constitution* (frigate) ..	75	1·10
	a. Sheetlet. Nos. 932/4, each×3 ..	6·00	
933	$1 Liberty Bell ..	80	1·40
934	$2 White House ..	1·00	1·60
929/34	*Set of 6*	3·75	5·50
MS935	147×93 mm. $4 Capitol, Washington (37×50 *mm*)	3·25	4·00

Nos. 929/31 and 932/4 were each printed together, *se-tenant*, in horizontal and vertical strips of 3, within the two sheetlets of nine.

Nos. 929/34 exist imperforate and Nos. 929a and 932a with the gold omitted, all from stock dispersed by the liquidator of Format International Security Printers Ltd.

170 English and Brazilian Players

(Des G. Vasarhelyi. Litho Format)

1986 (16 June) *World Cup Football Championship, Mexico (2nd issue). T 170 and similar multicoloured designs. P 11.*

936	25 c. Type 170..	..	1·00 1·25
	a. Sheetlet. Nos. 936/9, each×2 ..		11·00
937	50 c. Mexican player and Maya statues ..	..	11·00
938	75 c. Two Belizean players ..		1·40 1·60
939	$3 Aztec stone calendar ..		1·50 2·00
936/9	*Set of 4*		2·25 3·50
MS940	147×92 mm. $4 Flags of competing nations on two footballs (37×50 *mm*). P 13½×14		5·00 7·00

Nos. 936/9 were printed together, *se-tenant*, in sheetlets of eight stamps, two of each value, and one stamp-size label.

No. 936a exists imperforate from stock dispersed by the liquidator of Format International Security Printers Ltd.

ARGENTINA-WINNERS 1986

171 Miss Sarah Ferguson   **(172)**

(Des G. Vasarhelyi. Litho Format)

1986 (23 July). *Royal Wedding. T 171 and similar multicoloured designs. P 14½.*

941	25 c. Type 171		40	40
	a. Horiz strip of 3. Nos. 941/3		2·25	
942	75 c. Prince Andrew		70	90
943	$3 Prince Andrew and Miss Sarah Ferguson (92×41 *mm*)		1·40	2·25
941/3		*Set of 3*	2·25	3·25
MS944	155×106 mm. $1 Miss Sarah Ferguson (*different*), $3 Prince Andrew (*different*)		3·25	5·00

Nos. 941/3 were printed together, *se-tenant*, in horizontal strips of 3 within small sheets of nine stamps.

No. MS944 exists imperforate from stock dispersed by the liquidator of Format International Security Printers Ltd.

1986 (15 Aug). *World Cup Football Championship Winners, Mexico. Nos. 936/40 optd with T 172.*

945	25 c. Type 170		1·00	1·00
	a. Sheetlet. Nos. 945/8, each ×2		13·00	
946	50 c. Mexican player and Maya statues		1·40	1·40
947	75 c. Two Belizean players		1·75	1·75
948	$3 Aztec stone calendar		3·00	3·00
945/8		*Set of 4*	6·50	6·50
MS949	147×92 mm. $4 Flags of competing nations on two footballs (37×50 *mm*)		5·00	6·50

(173)   **174** Amerindian Girl

1986 (28 Aug). *"Stockholmia '86" International Stamp Exhibition, Sweden. Nos. 929/35 optd with T 173.*

950	10 c. Type 169		40	50
	a. Sheetlet. Nos. 950/2, each ×3		4·75	
951	15 c. 1981 Royal Wedding $1.50 stamp		50	60
952	50 c. U.S.A. 1918 24 c. airmail inverted centre error		70	80
953	75 c. U.S.S. *Constitution*		90	1·10
	a. Sheetlet. Nos. 953/5, each ×3		10·50	
954	$1 Liberty Bell		1·10	1·25
955	$2 White House		1·60	1·60
950/5		*Set of 6*	4·75	5·25
MS956	147×93 mm. $4 Capitol, Washington (37×50 *mm*)		4·50	6·00

(Des G. Vasarhelyi. Litho Format)

1986 (3 Oct). *International Peace Year. T 174 and similar multicoloured designs. P 13½×14.*

957	25 c. Type 174		45	60
	a. Sheetlet. Nos. 957/60, each ×2		6·00	
958	50 c. European boy and girl		60	85
959	75 c. Japanese girl		80	1·25
960	$3 Indian boy and European girl		1·50	2·25
957/60		*Set of 4*	3·00	4·50
MS961	132 × 106 mm. $4 As 25 c. but vert (35 × 47 *mm*)		4·00	5·00

Nos. 957/60 were printed together, *se-tenant*, in sheetlets of eight stamps, two of each value, and one stamp-size label.

No. 957a exists with the gold omitted and No. MS961 imperforate, both from stock dispersed by the liquidator of Format International Security Printers Ltd.

175 *Amanita lilloi*   **176** Jose Carioca

(Des G. Drummond. Litho Format)

1986 (30 Oct). *Fungi and Toucans. T 175 and similar vert designs. Multicoloured. P 14×13½.*

962	5 c. Type 175		75	75
	a. Sheetlet. Nos. 962, 964, 966 and 969, each × 2		11·00	

963	10 c. Keel-billed Toucan		90	90
	a. Sheetlet. Nos. 963, 965 and 967/8, each × 2		10·00	
964	20 c. *Boletellus cubensis*		1·25	1·25
965	25 c. Collared Aracari		1·25	1·25
966	75 c. *Psilocybe caerulescens*		1·50	1·50
967	$1 Emerald Toucanet		1·50	1·50
968	$1.25, Crimson-rumped Toucanet		1·50	1·50
969	$2 *Russula puiggarii*		2·00	2·00
962/9		*Set of 8*	9·50	9·50

Nos. 962, 964, 966 and 969, and Nos. 963, 965 and 967/8, were each printed together, *se-tenant*, in sheetlets of eight stamps, two of each value, and one stamp-size label.

No. 962a exists imperforate and Nos. 962a/3a with the gold omitted, all from stock dispersed by the liquidator of Format International Security Printers Ltd.

(Des Walt Disney Productions. Litho Format)

1986 (14 Nov). *Christmas. T 176 and similar vert designs showing Walt Disney cartoon characters in scenes from "Saludos Amigos". Multicoloured. P 11.*

970	2 c. Type 176		20	10
	a. Sheetlet. Nos. 970/8		7·25	
971	3 c. Jose Carioca, Panchito and Donald Duck		20	10
972	4 c. Daisy Duck as Rio Carnival dancer		20	10
973	5 c. Mickey and Minnie Mouse as musician and dancer		20	10
974	6 c. Jose Carioca using umbrella as flute		20	10
975	50 c. Donald Duck and Panchito		1·00	1·25
976	65 c. Jose Carioca and Donald Duck playing hide and seek		1·25	1·50
977	$1.35, Donald Duck playing maracas		2·00	3·00
978	$2 Goofy as matador		2·75	3·50
970/8		*Set of 9*	7·25	8·50
MS979	131 × 111 mm. $4 Donald Duck. P 13½×14		6·50	8·50

Nos. 970/8 were printed together, *se-tenant*, in sheetlets of nine.

177 Princess Elizabeth in Wedding Dress, 1947   **178** *America II*

(Des G. Vasarhelyi. Litho Format)

1987 (7 Oct). *Royal Ruby Wedding. T 177 and similar vert designs. Multicoloured. P 15.*

980	25 c. Type 177		20	20
981	75 c. Queen and Duke of Edinburgh, 1972		35	40
982	$1 Queen on her 60th birthday		40	50
983	$4 In Garter robes		1·00	1·50
980/3		*Set of 4*	1·75	2·40
MS984	171×112 mm. $6 Queen and Duke of Edinburgh (44×50 *mm*). P 13½×14		4·00	6·00

(Des G. Vasarhelyi. Litho Format)

1987 (21 Oct). *America's Cup Yachting Championship. T 178 and similar multicoloured designs. P 15.*

985	25 c. Type 178		20	25
986	75 c. Stars and Stripes		35	50
987	$1 *Australia II*, 1983		40	60
988	$4 *White Crusader*		1·00	1·60
985/8		*Set of 4*	1·75	2·75
MS989	171×112 mm. $6 Sails of *Australia II* (44×50 *mm*). P 13½×14		4·50	7·00

179 "Mother and Child"   **180** Black-handed Spider Monkey

(Des G. Vasarhelyi. Litho Format)

1987 (4 Nov). *Wood Carvings by George Gabb. T 179 and similar vert designs. Multicoloured. P 15.*

990	25 c. Type 179		15	25
991	75 c. "Standing Form"		35	50
992	$1 "Love-doves"		40	60
993	$4 "Depiction of Music"		1·10	1·60
990/3		*Set of 4*	1·75	2·75
MS994	173×114 mm. $6 "African Heritage" (44×50 *mm*). P 13½×14		3·50	5·00

(Des G. Drummond. Litho Format)

1987 (11 Nov). *Primates. T 180 and similar vert designs. Multicoloured. P 15.*

995	25 c. Type 180		25	20
996	75 c. Black Howler Monkey		40	55
997	$1 Spider Monkeys with baby		45	65
998	$4 Two Black Howler Monkeys		1·10	2·00
995/8		*Set of 4*	2·00	3·00
MS999	171×112 mm. $6 Young Spider Monkey (41×48 *mm*). P 13½×14		4·50	6·50

181 Guides on Parade

(Des G. Vasarhelyi. Litho Format)

1987 (25 Nov). *50th Anniv of Girl Guide Movement in Belize. T 181 and similar multicoloured designs. P 15.*

1000	25 c. Type 181		45	20
1001	75 c. Brownie camp		80	1·00
1002	$1 Guide camp		1·00	1·25
1003	$4 Olave, Lady Baden-Powell		3·00	4·75
1000/3		*Set of 4*	4·75	6·50
MS1004	173×114 mm. $6 As $4, but vert (44×50 *mm*). P 13½×14		4·00	6·50

Nos. 1000/4 exist imperforate from stock dispersed by the liquidator of Format International Security Printers Ltd.

182 Indian Refugee Camp   **183** *Laelia euspatha*

(Des G. Vasarhelyi. Litho Format)

1987 (3 Dec). *International Year of Shelter for the Homeless. T 182 and similar horiz designs. Multicoloured. P 15.*

1005	25 c. Type 182		50	25
1006	75 c. Filipino family and slum		90	90
1007	$1 Family in Middle East shanty town		1·10	1·25
1008	$4 Building modern house in Belize		2·00	4·25
1005/8		*Set of 4*	4·00	6·00

(Des G. Drummond. Litho Format)

1987 (16 Dec). *Christmas. Orchids. T 183 and similar vert designs showing illustrations from Sanders' Reichenbachia. Multicoloured. P 13½×14.*

1009	1 c. Type 183		60	50
	a. Sheetlet. Nos. 1009/15, each × 2		7·50	
1010	2 c. *Cattleya citrina*		60	50
1011	3 c. *Masdevallia backhousiana*		60	50
1012	4 c. *Cypripedium tautzianum*		60	50
1013	5 c. *Trichopilia suavis alba*		60	50
1014	6 c. *Odontoglossum hebraicum*		60	50
1015	7 c. *Cattleya trianaei schroederiana*		60	50
1016	10 c. *Saccolabium giganteum*		75	65
	a. Sheetlet. Nos. 1016/22, each × 2		17·00	
1017	30 c. *Cattleya warscewiczii*		90	80
1018	50 c. *Chysis bractescens*		1·25	1·00
1019	70 c. *Cattleya rochellensis*		1·40	1·10
1020	$1 *Laelia elegans schilleriana*		1·50	1·10
1021	$1.50, *Laelia anceps percivaliana*		1·60	1·40
1022	$3 *Laelia gouldiana*		2·25	1·90
1009/22		*Set of 14*	12·50	10·50
MS1023	Two sheets, each 171×112 mm. (a) $3 *Odontoglossum roezlii* (40×47 *mm*). (b) $5 *Cattleya dowiana aurea* (40×47 *mm*)			
		Set of 2 sheets	7·50	10·00

Nos. 1009/1015 and 1016/22 were each printed together, *se-tenant*, in sheetlets of fourteen stamps, containing two of each value and one stamp-size label.

Examples of No. MS1023 with the orchid name on the $3 incorrectly spelt or the sheet imperforate are from stock dispersed by the liquidator of Format International Printers Ltd.

184 Christ condemned to Death   **185** Basketball

(Des G. Vasarhelyi. Litho Format)

1988 (21 Mar). *Easter. The Stations of the Cross. T 184 and similar vert designs. Multicoloured. P 13½×14.*

1024	40 c. Type 184		30	45
	a. Sheetlet. Nos. 1024/37		3·75	
1025	40 c. Christ carrying the Cross		30	45
1026	40 c. Falling for the first time		30	45
1027	40 c. Christ meets Mary		30	45
1028	40 c. Simon of Cyrene helping to carry the Cross		30	45
1029	40 c. Veronica wiping the face of Christ		30	45
1030	40 c. Christ falling a second time		30	45

1031	40 c.	Consoling the women of Jerusalem	30	45
1032	40 c.	Falling for the third time	30	45
1033	40 c.	Christ being stripped	30	45
1034	40 c.	Christ nailed to the Cross ..	30	45
1035	40 c.	Dying on the Cross	30	45
1036	40 c.	Christ taken down from the Cross ..	30	45
1037	40 c.	Christ being laid in the sepulchre ..	30	45
1024/37		*Set of 14*	3·75	5·50

Nos. 1024/37 were printed together, *se-tenant*, in a sheetlet of 14 stamps and one stamp-size label which appears in the central position.

No. 1024a exists imperforate from stock dispersed by the liquidator of Format International Security Printers Ltd.

A $6 miniature sheet was prepared, but not issued. Examples exist from stock dispersed by the liquidator.

(Des J. McDaniel. Litho Questa)

1988 (15 Aug). *Olympic Games, Seoul. T 185 and similar vert designs. Multicoloured. P 14.*

1038	10 c.	Type 185	90	40
1039	25 c.	Volleyball	90	30
1040	60 c.	Table tennis	90	60
1041	75 c.	Diving	90	70
1042	$1	Judo	1·00	1·00
1043	$2	Hockey	3·25	3·50
1038/43		*Set of 6*	7·00	6·00
MS1044		76×106 mm. $3 Gymnastics	3·50	4·50

186 Public Health Nurse, c. 1912

187 Collared Anteater ("Ants Bear")

(Des O. Fernandez. Litho Questa)

1988 (18 Nov). *125th Anniv of International Red Cross. T 186 and similar horiz designs. Multicoloured. P 14.*

1045	60 c.	Type 186	1·75	1·25
1046	75 c.	Aleda E. Lutz (hospital ship) and ambulance launch, 1937 ..	2·00	1·50
1047	$1	Ambulance at hospital tent, 1956 ..	2·50	1·75
1048	$2	Auster ambulance plane, 1940 ..	3·25	4·00
1045/8		*Set of 4*	8·50	7·75

(Des J. Barberis. Litho Questa)

1989 (24 Feb)–**90**. *Small Animals of Belize. T 187 and similar multicoloured designs. P 14. (a) W w 16 (sideways on 25 c.).*

1049	10 c.	Paca ("Gibnut") (30.6.89) ..	1·75	1·75
1049a	25 c.	Four-eyed Opossum (*vert*) (1.90) ..	2·00	2·00

(b) No wmk

1050	25 c.	Four-eyed Opossum (*vert*) ..	1·75	1·50
1051	50 c.	Type 187	2·25	2·00
1052	60 c.	As 10 c.	2·25	2·25
1053	75 c.	Red Brocket	2·25	2·25
1054	$2	Collared Peccary	3·75	5·00
1049/54		*Set of 7*	14·50	15·00

(Des A. Theobald ($5), D. Miller (others). Litho Questa)

1989 (20 July). *20th Anniv of First Manned Landing on Moon. Multicoloured designs as T 126 of Ascension. W w 16 (sideways on 50, 75 c.). P 14×13½ (25 c., $1) or 14 (others).*

1055	25 c.	Docking of "Apollo 9" modules ..	55	25
1056	50 c.	"Apollo 9" command service module in space (30×30 mm) ..	75	65
1057	75 c.	"Apollo 9" emblem (30×30 mm) ..	1·00	1·10
1058	$1	"Apollo 9" lunar module in space ..	1·25	1·60
1055/8		*Set of 4*	3·25	3·25
MS1059		83×100 mm. $5 "Apollo 11" command service module undergoing tests. P 14×13½. ..	6·00	6·50

WORLD STAMP EXPO '89™
United States Postal Service
Nov. 17 – 20 and
Nov. 24 – Dec. 3, 1989
Washington Convention Center
Washington, DC

5c

(188)   **(189)**

1989 (15 Nov). *No. 771A surch with T 188 by Govt Printer, Belize.*

1060	5 c. on 6 c. Star-eyed Hermit Crab	..	13·00	1·50

1989 (17 Nov). *"World Stamp Expo '89" International Stamp Exhibition, Washington. No. MS1059 optd with T 189.*

MS1061	83×100 mm. $5 "Apollo 11" command service module undergoing tests	..	5·50	6·50

STANLEY GIBBONS
STAMP COLLECTING SERIES

Introductory booklets on *How to Start, How to Identify Stamps* and *Collecting by Theme.* A series of well illustrated guides at a low price.
Write for details.

---

190 Wesley Church

191 White-winged Tanager and *Catonephele numilia*

(Des Jennifer Toombs. Litho B.D.T.)

1989 (13 Dec). *Christmas. Belize Churches. T 190 and similar vert designs. W w 16. P 13½.*

1062	10 c.	black, rose-pink and cinnamon ..	20	10
1063	25 c.	black, reddish lilac and rose-lilac ..	25	20
1064	60 c.	black, pale turquoise-blue and cobalt	50	70
1065	75 c.	black, pale blue-green and sage-green	65	90
1066	$1	blk, pale greenish yell & chrome-yell	80	1·25
1062/6		*Set of 5*	2·25	2·75

Designs:—25 c. Baptist Church; 60 c. St. John's Anglican Cathedral; 75 c. St. Andrew's Presbyterian Church; $1 Holy Redeemer Roman Catholic Cathedral.

(Des I. Loe. Litho Questa)

1990 (1 Mar)–**93**. *Birds and Butterflies. T 191 and similar vert designs. Multicoloured. W w 14. P 14. A. Without imprint date.*

1067A	5 c.	Type 191	60	60
1068A	10 c.	Keel-billed Toucan and *Nessaea aglaura* ..	80	70
1069A	15 c.	Magnificent Frigate Bird and *Eurytides philolaus* ..	80	40
1070A	25 c.	Jabiru and *Heliconius sapho* ..	80	40
1071A	30 c.	Great Blue Heron and *Colobura dirce* ..	80	50
1072A	50 c.	Northern Oriole and *Hamadryas arethusia* ..	1·00	60
1073A	60 c.	Scarlet Macaw and *Evenus regalis*	1·25	70
1074A	75 c.	Red-legged Honeycreeper and *Callicore patelina* ..	1·25	75
1075A	$1	Spectacled Owl and *Caligo uranus*	2·25	1·60
1076A	$2	Green Jay and *Philaethria dido* ..	2·75	3·50
1077A	$5	Turkey Vulture and *Battus belus*	4·50	6·00
1078A	$10	Osprey and *Papilio thoas* ..	8·50	10·00
1067A/78A		*Set of 12*	23·00	23·00

B. With imprint date ("1993") (5.7.93)

1068B	10 c.	Keel-billed Toucan and *Nessaea aglaura* ..	70	70

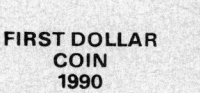

FIRST DOLLAR COIN 1990

(192)

193 Green Turtle

1990 (1 Mar). *First Belize Dollar Coin. No. 1075A optd with T 192 in gold.*

1079	$1 Spectacled Owl and *Caligo uranus*	..	4·25	2·75

(Des G. Drummond. Litho B.D.T.)

1990 (8 Aug). *Turtles. T 193 and similar horiz designs. Multicoloured. W w 14 (sideways). P 14.*

1080	10 c.	Type 193	65	40
1081	25 c.	Hawksbill Turtle	1·00	40
1082	60 c.	Saltwater Loggerhead Turtle ..	1·50	1·50
1083	75 c.	Freshwater Loggerhead Turtle ..	1·60	1·60
1084	$1	Bocatora Turtle	2·00	2·00
1085	$2	Hicatee Turtle	2·75	4·50
1080/5		*Set of 6*	8·50	9·50

194 Fairey Battle

195 *Cattleya bowringiana*

(Des A. Theobald. Litho B.D.T)

1990 (15 Sept). *50th Anniv of the Battle of Britain. T 194 and similar horiz designs. Multicoloured. W w 16 (sideways). P 13½.*

1086	10 c.	Type 194	80	50
1087	25 c.	Bristol Type 152 Beaufort ..	1·40	50
1088	60 c.	Bristol Type 142 Blenheim Mk IV ..	2·00	2·00
1089	75 c.	Armstrong-Whitworth Whitley ..	2·00	2·00
1090	$1	Vickers-Armstrong Wellington Mk 1c	2·00	2·00
1091	$2	Handley-Page Hampden ..	2·50	3·50
1086/91		*Set of 6*	9·50	9·50

(Des Lynn Chadwick. Litho Questa)

1990 (1 Nov). *Christmas. Orchids. T 195 and similar vert designs. Multicoloured. W w 14. P 14.*

1092	25 c.	Type 195	85	20
1093	50 c.	*Rhyncholaelia digbyana* ..	1·25	50
1094	60 c.	*Sobralia macrantha* ..	1·50	1·00
1095	75 c.	*Chysis bractescens* ..	1·50	1·00
1096	$1	*Vanilla planifolia* ..	1·75	1·75
1097	$2	*Epidendrum polyanthum* ..	2·50	4·00
1092/7		*Set of 6*	8·50	7·50

196 Common Iguana

(Des G. Drummond. Litho B.D.T.)

1991 (10 Apr). *Reptiles and Mammals. T 196 and similar horiz designs. Multicoloured. W w 14 (sideways). P 14.*

1098	25 c.	Type 196	80	35
1099	50 c.	Morelet's Crocodile ..	1·25	90
1100	60 c.	American Manatee ..	1·50	1·50
1101	75 c.	Boa Constrictor ..	1·75	1·75
1102	$1	Baird's Tapir	2·00	2·00
1103	$2	Jaguar	2·75	3·75
1098/1103		*Set of 6*	9·00	9·00

(Des D. Miller. Litho Questa)

1991 (17 June). *65th Birthday of Queen Elizabeth II and 70th Birthday of Prince Philip. Vert designs as T 139 of Ascension. Multicoloured. W w 16 (sideways). P 14½×14.*

1104	$1	Queen Elizabeth II wearing tiara ..	1·00	1·25
		a. Horiz pair. Nos. 1104/5 separated by label	2·00	2·50
1105	$1	Prince Philip wearing panama ..	1·00	1·25

Nos. 1104/5 were printed in a similar sheet format to Nos. 539/40 of Ascension.

197 Weather Radar

(Des D. Miller. Litho Walsall)

1991 (31 July). *International Decade for Natural Disaster Reduction. T 197 and similar horiz designs. W w 14 (sideways). P 14.*

1106	60 c.	multicoloured ..	1·50	1·50
1107	75 c.	multicoloured ..	1·60	1·40
1108	$1	greenish blue and grey-black ..	1·75	1·75
1109	$2	multicoloured ..	2·50	3·25
1106/9		*Set of 4*	6·50	7·00

Designs:—75 c. Weather station; $1 Floods in Belize after Hurricane Hattie, 1961; $2 Satellite image of Hurricane Gilbert.

198 Thomas Ramos and Demonstration

(Des G. Vasarhelyi. Litho Questa)

1991 (4 Sept). *10th Anniv of Independence. Famous Belizians (1st series). T 198 and similar horiz designs. Multicoloured. W w 16 (sideways). P 14.*

1110	25 c.	Type 198	60	30
1111	60 c.	Sir Isaiah Morter and palm trees ..	1·25	1·25
1112	75 c.	Antonio Soberanis and political meeting	1·25	1·50
1113	$1	Santiago Ricalde and cutting sugar-cane	1·50	1·75
1110/13		*Set of 4*	4·25	4·25

See also Nos. 1126/9 and 1148/51.

199 "Anansi the Spider"

200 *Gongora quinquenervis*

(Des G. Vasarhelyi. Litho B.D.T.)

1991 (6 Nov). *Christmas. Folklore. T* **199** *and similar multicoloured designs. W w* **14** *(sideways on horiz designs). P* **14.**

1114	25 c.	Type 199	80	20
1115	50 c.	"Jack-o'-Lantern"	1·25	55
1116	60 c.	"Tata Duende" (vert)	1·50	1·25
1117	75 c.	"Xtabai"	1·50	1·25
1118	$1	"Warrie Massa" (vert)	1·75	1·75
1119	$2	"Old Heg"	2·75	4·00
1114/19		*Set of 6*	8·50	8·00

(Des Lynn Chadwick. Litho B.D.T.)

1992 (1 Apr). *Easter. Orchids. T* **200** *and similar vert designs. W w* **14.** *P* 14×13½.

1120	25 c.	Type 200	90	20
1121	50 c.	Oncidium sphacelatum	1·50	75
1122	60 c.	Encyclia bratescens	1·75	1·75
1123	75 c.	Epidendrum ciliare	1·75	1·75
1124	$1	Psygmorchis pusilla	2·00	2·00
1125	$2	Galeandra batemanii	2·75	4·00
1120/5		*Set of 6*	9·50	9·50

(Des G. Vasarhelyi. Litho Enschedé)

1992 (26 Aug). *Famous Belizeans (2nd series). Horiz designs as T* **198**, *but inscr* "EMINENT BELIZEANS" *at top. Multicoloured. W w* **14** *(sideways). P* 13×12½.

1126	25 c.	Gwendolyn Lizarraga (politician) and High School	55	30
1127	60 c.	Rafael Fonseca (civil servant) and Government Offices, Belize	90	1·00
1128	75 c.	Vivian Seay (health worker) and nurses	1·10	1·25
1129	$1	Samuel Haynes (U.N.I.A. worker) and words of National Anthem	1·40	1·75
1126/9		*Set of 4*	3·50	3·75

201 Xunantunich and National Assembly

(Des D. Miller. Litho Questa)

1992 (1 Oct). *500th Anniv of Discovery of America by Columbus. T* **201** *and similar horiz designs showing Mayan sites and modern buildings. Multicoloured. W w* **16** *(sideways). P* 14.

1130	25 c.	Type 201	70	25
1131	60 c.	Altun Ha and Supreme Court	1·00	1·00
1132	75 c.	Santa Rita and Tower Hill Sugar Factory	1·25	1·25
1133	$5	Lamanai and Citrus Company works	6·50	8·50
1130/3		*Set of 4*	8·50	10·00

202 Hashishi Pampi   203 Lycaste aromatica

(Des G. Vasarhelyi. Litho Enschedé)

1992 (16 Nov). *Christmas. Folklore. T* **202** *and similar multicoloured designs. W w* **14** *(sideways on 25, 60 c., $5). P* 12½×13 ($1) *or* 13×12½ *(others).*

1134	25 c.	Type 202	30	20
1135	60 c.	Cadejo	60	60
1136	$1	La Sucia (vert)	90	1·00
1137	$5	Sisimito	4·00	6·00
1134/7		*Set of 4*	5·25	7·00

(Des A. Theobald. Litho Questa)

1993 (1 Apr). *75th Anniv of Royal Air Force. Horiz designs as T* **149** *of Ascension. Multicoloured. W w* **14** *(sideways). P* 14.

1138	25 c.	Sud Aviation SA 330L Puma helicopter	80	50
1139	50 c.	Hawker Siddeley Harrier GR3	1·10	65
1140	60 c.	De Havilland DH98 Mosquito Mk XVIII	1·25	1·10
1141	75 c.	Avro Type 683 Lancaster	1·25	1·10
1142	$1	Consolidated Liberator I	1·40	1·40
1143	$3	Short Stirling Mk I	3·00	5·00
1138/43		*Set of 6*	8·00	8·75

(Des Annette Robinson. Litho Walsall)

1993 (23 Apr). *14th World Orchid Conference, Glasgow. T* **203** *and similar vert designs. Multicoloured. W w* **16.** *P* 14½×14.

1144	25 c.	Type 203	40	25
1145	60 c.	Sobralia decora	75	80
1146	$1	Maxillaria alba	1·00	1·10
1147	$2	Brassavola nodosa	1·75	2·50
1144/7		*Set of 4*	3·50	4·25

(Des G. Vasarhelyi. Litho Questa)

1993 (11 Aug). *Famous Belizeans (3rd series). Horiz designs as T* **198**, *but inscr* "EMINENT BELIZEANS" *at top. Multicoloured. W w* **16** *(sideways). P* 14.

1148	25 c.	Herbert Watkin Beaumont, Post Office and postmark	40	25
1149	60 c.	Dr. Selwyn Walford Young and score of National Anthem	75	85
1150	75 c.	Cleopatra White and health centre	90	1·25
1151	$1	Dr. Karl Heusner and early car	1·10	1·40
1148/51		*Set of 4*	2·75	3·25

204 Boom and Chime Band

(Des Jennifer Toombs. Litho B.D.T.)

1993 (3 Nov). *Christmas. Local Customs. T* **204** *and similar horiz designs. Multicoloured. W w* **14** *(sideways). P* 14.

1152	25 c.	Type 204	40	20
1153	60 c.	John Canoe dance	80	70
1154	75 c.	Cortez dance	90	80
1155	$2	Maya musical group	2·25	3·50
1152/5		*Set of 4*	4·00	4·75

1994 (18 Feb). *"Hong Kong '94" International Stamp Exhibition. No. 1075A optd as T* **154** *of Ascension.*

1156	$1	Spectacled Owl and Caligo uranus	2·00	2·25

(Des D. Miller. Litho Questa)

1994 (22 Feb). *Royal Visit. Vert designs as T* **202** *of Bahamas. Multicoloured. W w* **16.** *P* 14½.

1157	25 c.	Flags of Belize and Great Britain	50	20
1158	60 c.	Queen Elizabeth II in yellow coat and hat	80	75
1159	75 c.	Queen Elizabeth in evening dress	1·00	90
1160	$1	Queen Elizabeth, Prince Philip and Yeomen of the Guard	1·50	1·60
1157/60		*Set of 4*	3·50	3·00

10c

205 Lonchorhina aurita (bat)   (206)

(Des N. Arlott. Litho B.D.T.)·

1994 (30 May). *Bats. T* **205** *and similar horiz designs. Multicoloured. W w* **16** *(sideways). P* 14.

1161	25 c.	Type 205	35	20
1162	60 c.	Vampyrodes caraccioli	65	65
1163	75 c.	Noctilio leporinus	80	80
1164	$2	Desmodus rotundus	2·00	3·00
1161/4		*Set of 4*	3·50	4·25

1994 (18 Aug). *75th Anniv of International Labour Organization. No. 1074A surch with T* **206.**

1165	10 c. on 75 c.	Red-legged Honey-creeper and Callicore patelina	70	70

207 Cycnoches chlorochilon   208 Ground Beetle

(Des N. Shewring. Litho B.D.T.)

1994 (7 Nov). *Christmas. Orchids. T* **207** *and similar vert designs. Multicoloured. W w* **16.** *P* 14×13½.

1166	25 c.	Type 207	45	20
1167	60 c.	Brassavola cucullata	75	70
1168	75 c.	Sobralia mucronata	90	90
1169	$1	Nidema boothii	1·10	1·25
1166/9		*Set of 4*	2·75	2·75

(Des I. Loe and D. Miller. Litho B.D.T.)

1995 (11 Jan)–96. *Insects. T* **208** *and similar horiz designs. Multicoloured. W w* **14** *(sideways*). P* 14. A. *Without imprint date at foot.*

1170A	5 c.	Type 208	30	50
1171A	10 c.	Harlequin Beetle	30	50
		w. Wmk Crown to right of CA		
1172A	15 c.	Giant Water Bug	40	60
1173A	25 c.	Peanut-head Bug	50	20
1174A	30 c.	Coconut Weevil	55	25
1175A	50 c.	Mantis	70	40
1176A	60 c.	Tarantula Wasp	90	50
1177A	75 c.	Rhinoceros Beetle	1·00	60
1178A	$1	Metallic Wood Borer	1·40	90
1179A	$2	Dobson Fly	3·00	4·00
1180A	$5	Click Beetle	5·50	7·00
1181A	$10	Long-horned Beetle	8·50	10·00
1070A/81A		*Set of 12*	21·00	23·00

B. *With imprint date* "1996" *at bottom right* (10.96)

1170B	5 c.	Type 208	10	10
1171B	10 c.	Harlequin Beetle	10	10
1172B	15 c.	Giant Water Bug	10	10
1173B	25 c.	Peanut-head Bug	15	20
1174B	30 c.	Coconut Weevil	20	25
1175B	50 c.	Mantis	30	35
1176B	60 c.	Tarantula Wasp	40	45
1177B	75 c.	Rhinoceros Beetle	45	50
1178B	$1	Metallic Wood Borer	60	65
1179B	$2	Dobson Fly	1·25	1·40
1180B	$5	Click Beetle	3·00	3·25
1181B	$10	Long-horned Beetle	6·25	6·50
1170B/81B		*Set of 12*	13·50	14·00

*The normal sideways watermark shows Crown to left of CA, as seen from the back of the stamp.

(Des R. Watton. Litho Cartor)

1995 (8 May). *50th Anniv of End of Second World War. Horiz designs as T* **161** *of Ascension. W w* **14** *(sideways). P* 13½.

1182	25 c.	War memorial	30	25
1183	60 c.	Remembrance Day parade	75	70
1184	75 c.	British Honduras forestry unit	90	90
1185	$1	Vickers-Armstrong Wellington bomber	1·10	1·25
1182/5		*Set of 4*	2·75	2·75

(209)   210 Male and Female Blue Ground Dove

1995 (1 Sept). *"Singapore '95" International Stamp Exhibition. Nos. 1166/9 optd with T* **209** *in blue.*

1186	25 c.	Type 207	40	25
1187	60 c.	Brassavola cucullata	75	80
1188	75 c.	Sobralia mucronata	90	95
1189	$1	Nidema boothii	1·10	1·40
1186/9		*Set of 4*	2·75	3·25

(Des A. Theobald. Litho B.D.T.)

1995 (24 Oct). *50th Anniv of United Nations. Horiz designs as T* **213** *of Bahamas. W w* **16** *(sideways). P* 14.

1190	25 c.	M113-light reconnaisance vehicle	25	20
1191	60 c.	Sultan armoured command vehicle	60	65
1192	75 c.	Leyland-Daf 8×4 drops lorry	75	80
1193	$2	Warrior infantry combat vehicle	1·50	2·25
1190/3		*Set of 4*	2·75	3·50

(Des N. Arlott. Litho B.D.T.)

1995 (6 Nov). *Christmas. Doves. T* **210** *and similar vert designs. Multicoloured. W w* **14.** *P* 14.

1194	25 c.	Type 210	35	20
1195	60 c.	White-fronted Doves	70	70
1196	75 c.	Pair of Ruddy Ground Doves	85	90
1197	$1	White-winged Doves	1·25	1·25
1194/7		*Set of 4*	2·75	2·75

(211)   212 Unloading Banana Train, Commerce Bight Pier

1996 (17 May). *"CHINA '96" 9th Asian International Stamp Exhibition, Peking. Nos. 1172A, 1174A/5A and 1179A optd with T* **211.**

1198	15 c.	Giant Water Bug	15	15
1199	30 c.	Coconut Weevil	30	30
1200	50 c.	Mantis	45	50
1201	$2	Dobson Fly	1·60	2·00
1198/1201		*Set of 4*	2·25	2·75

(Des A. Theobald. Litho Cartor)

1996 (7 June). *"CAPEX '96" International Stamp Exhibition, Toronto. Railways. T* **212** *and similar horiz designs. Multicoloured. W w* **14** *(sideways). P* 13½×13.
1202   25 c. Type 212 50   25
1203   60 c. Locomotive No. 1, Stann Creek
       station 80   70
1204   75 c. Locomotive No. 4 pulling mahogany
       log train 90   80
1205 $3 L.M.S. No. 5602 *British Honduras*
       locomotive .. .. .. 2·75 4·00
                          Set of 4 4·50 5·25

213 *Epidendrum*
stamfordianum

214 Red Poll

(Des Lynn Chadwick. Litho Cot Printery Ltd, Barbados)

1996 (6 Nov). *Christmas. Orchids. T* **213** *and similar vert designs. Multicoloured. W w* **14**. *P* 14.
1206   25 c. Type 213 40   20
1207   60 c. *Oncidium carthagenense* .. 70   70
1208   75 c. *Oerstedella verrucosa* .. 80   90
1209 $1 *Coryanthes speciosa* .. 1·10 1·25
1206/9   *Set of 4* 2·75 2·75

(Des G. Vasarhelyi. Litho Cot Printery Ltd, Barbados)

1997 (12 Feb). *"HONG KONG '97" International Stamp Exhibition. Chinese New Year ("Year of the Ox"). T* **214** *and similar horiz designs showing cattle breeds. Multicoloured. W w* **14** *(sideways). P* 14.
1210   25 c. Type 214 30   20
1211   60 c. Brahman 60   70
1212   75 c. Longhorn 70   80
1213 $1 Charbray .. .. .. 95 1·10
1210/13   *Set of 4* 2·25 2·50

215 Coral Snake

216 Adult Male
Howler Monkey

(Des Doreen McGuiness. Litho Cot Printery, Barbados)

1997 (28 May). *Snakes. T* **215** *and similar vert designs. Multicoloured. W w* **14**. *P* 14.
1214   25 c. Type 215 35   20
1215   60 c. Green Vine Snake 60   60
1216   75 c. Yellow-jawed Tommygoff .. 70   70
1217 $1 Speckled Racer .. .. 85 1·00
1214/17   *Set of 4* 2·25 2·25

(Des N. Shewring. Litho Walsall)

1997 (13 Aug). *Endangered Species. Howler Monkey. T* **216** *and similar vert designs. Multicoloured. W w* **14**. *P* 14.
1218   10 c. Type 216 20   15
1219   25 c. Female feeding 30   20
1220   60 c. Female with young 65   65
1221   75 c. Juvenile monkey feeding .. 80   95
1218/21   *Set of 4* 1·75 1·75

217 *Maxillaria elatior*

218 School Children
using the Internet

(Des Lynn Chadwick. Litho B.D.T.)

1997 (21 Nov). *Christmas. Orchids. T* **217** *and similar vert designs. Multicoloured. W w* **16**. *P* 13½.
1222   25 c. Type 217 25   20
1223   60 c. *Dimerandra emarginata* .. 50   50
1224   75 c. *Macradenia brassavolae* .. 60   60
1225 $1 *Ornithocephalus gladiatus* .. 75   80
1222/5   *Set of 4* 1·90 1·90

(Des D. Miller. Litho Questa)

1998 (31 Mar). *Diana, Princess of Wales Commemoration. Sheet, 145×70 mm, containing vert designs as T* **177** *of Ascension. Multicoloured. W w* **14** *(sideways). P* 14½×14.
MS1226 $1 Wearing floral dress, 1988; $1 In
       evening dress, 1981; $1 Wearing pearl drop
       earrings, 1988; $1 Carrying bouquet, 1983   3·00 3·50

(Des N. Shewring. Litho Cartor)

1998 (22 July). *50th Anniv of Organization of American States. T* **218** *and similar horiz design. Multicoloured. W w* **14** *(sideways). P* 13.
1227   25 c. Type 218 25   20
1228 $1 Map of Central America .. 75   80

219 University Arms

220 Baymen Gun Flats

(Des N. Shewring. Litho Cartor)

1998 (22 July). *50th Anniv of University of West Indies. W w* **14** *(sideways). P* 13.
1229   **219** $1 multicoloured 75   75

(Des A. Theobald. Litho Cartor)

1998 (5 Aug). *Bicentenary of Battle of St. George's Cay. T* **220** *and similar multicoloured designs. W w* **14** *(sideways on 25 c. to $2). P* 13½.
1230   10 c. Boat moored at quayside (*vert*) .. 20   20
       a. Horiz strip of 3. Nos. 1230/2   55
1231   10 c. Three sentries and cannon (*vert*) .. 20   20
1232   10 c. Cannon and rowing boats (*vert*) .. 20   20
1233   25 c. Type 220 30   20
1234   60 c. Baymen sloops 50   50
1235   75 c. British schooners 55   55
1236 $1 H.M.S. *Merlin* (sloop) .. 70   70
1237 $2 Spanish flagship .. .. 1·25 1·60
1230/7   *Set of 8* 3·50 3·75
Nos. 1230/2 were printed together, *se-tenant*, in horizontal strips of 3 throughout the sheet, showing a composite view of Belize from Fort George.

221 *Brassia maculata*

222 *Eucharis grandiflora*

(Des Lynn Chadwick. Litho Cot Printery Ltd, Barbados)

1998 (4 Nov). *Christmas. Orchids. T* **221** *and similar vert designs. Multicoloured. W w* **14**. *P* 14½×14.
1238   25 c. Type 221 25   20
1239   60 c. *Encyclia radiata* 40   40
1240   75 c. *Stanhopea ecornuta* .. 45   55
1241 $1 *Isochilus carnosiflorus* .. 60   80
1238/41   *Set of 4* 1·50 1·75

(Des Jennifer Toombs. Litho Cartor)

1999 (17 Mar). *Easter. Flowers. T* **222** *and similar vert designs. Multicoloured. W w* **14**. *P* 13.
1242   10 c. Type 222 10   10
1243   25 c. *Hippeastrum puniceum* .. 15   20
1244   60 c. *Zephyranthes citrina* .. 35   40
1245 $1 *Hymenocallis littoralis* .. 60   65
1242/5   *Set of 4* 1·10 1·25

223 Postman on Bicycle

(Des J. Batchelor. Litho Cartor)

1999 (18 Oct). *125th Anniv of Universal Postal Union. T* **223** *and similar horiz designs. Multicoloured. W w* **14** *(sideways). P* 13½.
1246   25 c. Type 223 15   20
1247   60 c. Postal truck 40   40
1248   75 c. *Dee* (mail ship) 45   50
1249 $1 Modern airliner 60   65
1246/9   *Set of 4* 1·60 1·75

STAMP BOOKLETS

1920. *Black on pink cover inscr "British Honduras–100–Two Cent Stamps". Stapled.*
SB1 $2 booklet containing one hundred 2 c. (No. 102*b*)
      in blocks of 10 (5×2) ..

1920. *Grey-blue cover inscr "British Honduras–100–Three Cent Stamps". Stapled.*
SB2 $3 booklet containing one hundred 3 c. (No. 103)
      in blocks of 10 (5×2)

1923. *Black on pink cover inscr "British Honduras–100–Two Cent Stamps". Stapled.*
SB3 $2 booklet containing one hundred 2 c. brown (No.
      127) in blocks of 10 (5×2) ..

1927. *Black on pink cover inscr "British Honduras–100–Two Cent Stamps". Stapled.*
SB4 $2 booklet containing one hundred 2 c. rose-
      carmine (No. 128) in blocks of 10 (5×2)

1984 (30 Apr). *Olympic Games, Los Angeles. Multicoloured cover, 155×102 mm, showing athlete and chariot. Stitched.*
SB5 $10 booklet containing 5 c., 20 c., 25 c. and $2, each
      in pane of 4 (Nos. 789a, 790a, 791a, 792a)   3·25

POSTAGE DUE STAMPS

D 1

D 2

(Typo D.L.R.)

1923–64. *Wmk Mult Script CA. Ordinary paper. P* 14.
D1   D 1   1 c. black .. .. .. 2·25 13·00
       a. Chalk-surfaced paper (25.9.56) .. 50 17·00
       b. White uncoated paper (9.4.64) .. 14·00 27·00
D2   2 c. black .. .. .. 2·25   7·50
       a. Chalk-surfaced paper (25.9.56) .. 50 17·00
D3   4 c. black .. .. .. 1·25   6·00
       a. Missing top serif on "C" (R. 6/6) .. 12·00
       b. Chalk-surfaced paper (25.9.56) .. 90 11·00
       ba. Missing top serif on "C" (R. 6/6) .. 11·00
       w. Wmk inverted £150
D1/3   *Set of 3* 5·25 24·00
D1a/3b   *Set of 3* 1·75 40·00
D1/3 Optd "Specimen" .. .. *Set of 3* 50·00
The early ordinary paper printings were yellowish and quite distinct from No. D1b.

1965 (3 Aug)–**72.** *As Nos. D2a and D3b, but Wmk w* **12** *(sideways on 2 c.). P* 13½×13 (2 c.) or 13½×14 (4 c.).
D4   D 1   2 c. black (10.1.72) .. .. 2·75   5·50
D5   4 c. black 90   6·00
The missing top serif on "C" variety of R. 6/6 was corrected before No. D5 was printed.

(Des P. Powell. Litho Questa)

1976 (1 July). *Type D* **2** *and similar vert designs, but with different frames. W w* **14** *(sideways). P* 13½×14.
D6   D 2   1 c. red and dull green .. .. 10 1·00
D7   — 2 c. light magenta and bluish violet .. 10 1·00
D8   — 5 c. dull green and orange-brown .. 15 1·25
D9   — 15 c. apple-green and dull vermilion .. 25 1·50
D10   — 25 c. orange and olive-green .. 40 1·75
D6/10 ..   *Set of 5* 85 6·00

CAYES OF BELIZE

A chain of several hundred islands, coral atolls, reefs and sand-banks stretching along the eastern seaboard of Belize.

Appendix

The following issues for the Cayes of Belize fall outside the criteria for full listing as detailed on page xi.

1984

Marine Life, Map and Views. 1, 2, 5, 10, 15, 25, 75 c., $3, $5
250th Anniv of Lloyd's List (newspaper). 25, 75 c., $1, $2.
Olympic Games, Los Angeles. 10, 15, 75 c., $2
90th Anniv of "Caye Service" Local Stamps. 10, 15, 75 c., $2

1985

Birth Bicentenary of John J. Audubon (ornithologist). 25, 75 c., $1, $3
Shipwrecks. $1 × 4

Issues for the Cayes of Belize were discontinued after June 1985. It is reported that remainders, probably the 1984 definitive stamps, were later issued to other Belize post offices for postal purposes.

Bermuda

The first internal postal system for Bermuda was organised by Joseph Stockdale, the proprietor of the *Bermuda Gazette*, in January 1784. This service competed with that of the colonial post office, set up in May 1812, until 1818.

Control of the overseas postal services passed to the British G.P.O. in 1818. The internal delivery system was discontinued between 1821 and 1830. The overseas posts became a colonial responsibility in September 1859.

For illustrations of the handstamp types see BRITISH POST OFFICES ABROAD notes, following GREAT BRITAIN.

CROWNED-CIRCLE HANDSTAMPS

CC1 CC1	ST. GEORGES BERMUDA (R.) (1.8.1845)	
		Price on cover £7000
CC2	IRELAND ISLE BERMUDA (R.) (1.8.1845)	
		Price on cover £7000
CC3	HAMILTON BERMUDA (R.) (13.11.1846)	
		Price on cover £3750

For Nos. CC1 and CC3 used as adhesive Postmasters' Stamps see Nos. O7 and O6.

PRICES FOR STAMPS ON COVER TO 1945

Nos. 1/11	*from* × 5
Nos. 12/17	*from* × 10
Nos. 19/29a	*from* × 8
Nos. 30/a	*from* × 10
Nos. 31/4	*from* × 4
Nos. 34a/55	*from* × 3
Nos. 56/8	*from* × 10
Nos. 59/76	*from* × 4
Nos. 76a/93	*from* × 3
Nos. 94/7	*from* × 4
Nos. 98/106	*from* × 3
Nos. 107/15	*from* × 4
Nos. 116/21	*from* × 5
No. 122	*from* × 20

COLONY

O 1

O 2

1848–61. *Postmasters' Stamps. Adhesives prepared and issued by the postmasters at Hamilton and St. Georges. Dated as given in brackets.*

(a) By W. B. Perot at Hamilton

O1	O 1	1d. black/*bluish grey* (1848)	—	£110000
O2		1d. black/*bluish grey* (1849)	—	£120000
O3		1d. red/*thick white* (1853)	—	£90000
O4		1d. red/*bluish wove* (1854)	—	£275000
O5		1d. red/*bluish wove* (1856)	—	£170000
O6	O 2	(1d.) carmine-red/*bluish laid* (1861)	—	£75000

*(b) By J. H. Thies at St. Georges
As Type O 2 but inscr "ST. GEORGES"*

O7	—	(1d.) carmine-red/*buff* (1860)	†	£65000

Stamps of Type O 1 bear manuscript value and signature, the dates being those shown on the eleven known examples. The stamps are distributed between the dates as follows: 1848 three examples, 1849 two examples, 1853 three examples, 1854 two examples, 1856 one example.

It is believed that the franking value of Nos. O6/7 was 1d., although this is not shown on the actual stamps. Four examples are known of this type used from Hamilton, from March 1861 (and one unused), and five used from St. Georges between July 1860 and January 1863, both issues being cancelled by pen.

Prices shown reflect our estimation of value based on known copies. For instance of the two copies known of No. O4, one is in the Royal collection and the other is on entire.

It is possible that a fourth postmaster's provisional was used by Robert Ward at Hamilton in late 1862 when two examples of Type O 2 on laid paper are known cancelled by blue crayon.

1   2   3

4   5

(Typo D.L.R.)

1865–1903. *Wmk Crown CC. (a) P 14*

1	1	1d. rose-red (25.9.65)		90·00	1·25
		a. Imperf		£25000	£15000
		w. Wmk inverted		£200	85·00
2		1d. pale rose		£120	6·50
		w. Wmk inverted		£225	95·00
3	2	2d. dull blue (14.3.66)		£250	20·00
		w. Wmk inverted		—	£225
4		2d. bright blue (1877)		£275	14·00
		w. Wmk inverted		—	£225

5	3	3d. yellow-buff (10.3.73)		£475	65·00
		aw. Wmk inverted		£800	£150
		ax. Wmk reversed			
5b		3d. orange (1875)		£1500	£120
6	4	6d. dull purple (25.9.65)		£850	75·00
		w. Wmk inverted		—	£550
7		6d. dull mauve (2.7.74)		23·00	12·00
		w. Wmk inverted		85·00	85·00
8	5	1s. green (25.9.65)		£275	48·00
		w. Wmk inverted		£425	£200

(b) P 14×12½

10	3	3d. yellow-buff (12.81)		£170	60·00
10a	4	6d. bright mauve (1903)		13·00	22·00
		aw. Wmk inverted		£350	
11	5	1s. green (11.93)		11·00	£120
		a. Imperf between (vert strip of 3)	£12000	

No. 11a occurs from Rows 8, 9, and 10 of four panes, possibly from a single sheet. Some of the stamps have become partially separated. One *used* vertical pair is known (*Price* £12000).

Although they arrived in Bermuda in March 1880, stamps perforated 14×12½ were not issued until the dates given above.

THREE PENCE	THREE PENCE
(6)	(6a)

THREE PENCE	One Penny.
(7)	(8)

1874 (12 Mar–19 May). *Nos. 1 and 8 surch diagonally.*

(a) With T 6 ("P" and "R" different type)

12	1	3d. on 1d. rose-red		£14000	
13	5	3d. on 1s. green		£2500	£850

(b) With T 6a ("P" same type as "R")

13b	5	3d. on 1s. green		£2000	£800

(c) With T 7 (19 May)

14	5	3d. on 1s. green		£1300	£650

The 3d. on 1d. was a trial surcharge which was not regularly issued, though a few specimens were postally used before 1879. Nos. 13, 13b and 14, being handstamped, are found with double or partial double surcharges.

(Surch by Queen's Printer, Donald McPhee Lee)

1875 (March–May). *Surch with T 8.*

15	2	1d. on 2d. (No. 4) (23 Apr)		£700	£375
		a. No stop after "Penny"		£12000	£7500
16	3	1d. on 3d. (No. 5) (8 May)		£450	£350
17	5	1d. on 1s. (No. 8) (11 Mar)		£500	£250
		a. Surch inverted		† £20000	
		b. No stop after "Penny"		£15000	£10000

It is emphasised that the prices quoted for Nos. 12/17 are for fine examples. The many stamps from these provisional issues which are in inferior conditio.. are worth much less.

| 9 | 10 | 11 |

(Typo D.L.R.)

1880 (25 Mar). Wmk Crown CC. P 14.
19	9	½d. stone	..	..	2·75	3·75
		w. Wmk inverted	..	..	60·00	£100
		y. Wmk inverted and reversed				
20	10	4d. orange-red	..	..	17·00	1·75
		w. Wmk inverted				
		x. Wmk reversed	..			

(Typo D.L.R.)

1883–1904. Wmk Crown CA. P 14.
21	9	½d. dull green (10.92)	..	2·75	2·75
21a		½d. deep grey-green (1893)		2·50	80
22	1	1d. dull rose (12.83)	..	£140	4·00
		w. Wmk inverted	..	—	£120
23		1d. rose-red	..	80·00	3·25
		w. Wmk inverted	..	—	£120
24		1d. carmine-rose (3.86)	..	48·00	70
24a		1d. aniline carmine (1889)		8·50	20
		aw. Wmk inverted	..	£110	60·00
25	2	2d. blue (12.86)	..	55·00	3·50
26		2d. aniline purple (7.93)		12·00	3·75
26a		2d. brown-purple (1898)		3·25	1·50
27	11	2½d. deep ultramarine (10.11.84)		13·00	2·25
		aw. Wmk inverted	..	£225	80·00
27b		2½d. pale ultramarine	..	5·00	40
		bw. Wmk inverted	..	—	80·00
28	3	3d. grey (20.1.86)	..	22·00	6·00
28a	10	4d. orange-brown (18.1.04)		27·00	48·00
		ax. Wmk reversed	..	£300	
29	5	1s. yellow-brown (1893)		15·00	17·00
		ax. Wmk reversed	..		£375
29b		1s. olive-brown	..	13·00	16·00
		bx. Wmk reversed	..		
21/9b		..	.. Set of 8	£120	70·00
21, 26 & 29 Optd "Specimen"			Set of 3	£375	

1893 PROVISIONAL POSTCARD. Following the reduction of the overseas postcard rate to 1d. in 1893 existing stocks of postal stationery postcards, including some from the September 1880 issue franked with Nos. 19 and 22, were surcharged "One Penny". This surcharge was applied by the *Royal Gazette* press. It is generally believed that an individual in the Post Office acquired all the examples showing Nos. 19 and 22, but provisional postcards are known used to Europe or locally. *Price from £550 unused, £1400 used.*

ONE FARTHING

| (12) | 13 Dry Dock | 14 |

1901. *As Nos. 29/a but colour changed, surch with T 12 by D.L.R.*
30	5	¼d. on 1s. dull grey (11.1.01) (Optd S. £75)	90	50
30a		¼d. on 1s. bluish grey (18.3.01)	1·25	85
		ab. "F" of "FARTHING" inserted by handstamp	£6000	£7000

Seven examples of No. 30ab are known, five unused (one being in the Royal Collection) and two used (one on postcard). It would appear that the "F" in position one of an unspecified horizontal row was either weak or missing and an additional impression of the letter was then inserted by a separate handstamp.

(Typo D.L.R.)

1902 (Nov)–03. Wmk Crown CA. P 14.
31	13	½d. black and green (12.03)	..	9·50	1·25
32		1d. brown and carmine	..	8·00	10
33		3d. magenta and sage-green (9.03)	..	2·75	1·75
31/3			Set of 3	18·00	2·75
31/3 Optd "Specimen"		..	Set of 3	£130	

1906–10. Wmk Mult Crown CA. P 14.
34	13	¼d. brown and violet (9.08)	..	1·50	1·50
35		½d. black and green (12.06)	..	18·00	65
36		½d. green (3.09)	..	11·00	2·50
37		1d. brown and carmine (4.06)	..	22·00	20
		w. Wmk inverted	..	£300	£190
38		1d. red (5.08)	..	18·00	10
39		2d. grey and orange (10.07)		7·50	11·00
40		2½d. brown and ultramarine (12.06)		14·00	7·00
41		2½d. blue (14.2.10)	..	12·00	5·75
42		4d. blue and chocolate (11.09)	..	3·00	16·00
34/42			Set of 9	95·00	40·00
34, 36, 38/42 Optd "Specimen"		Set of 7	£350	

(Recess D.L.R.)

1910–25. Wmk Mult Crown CA. P 14.
44	14	¼d. brown (26.3.12)	..	1·50	2·50
		a. Pale brown	..	60	1·50
45		½d. green (4.6.10)	..	1·25	25
		a. Deep green (1918)	..	6·50	90
		w. Wmk inverted			
		x. Wmk reversed	..	—	£170
		y. Wmk inverted and reversed			
46		1d. red (I) (15.10.10)	..	14·00	30
		a. Rose-red (1916)	..	18·00	30
		b. Carmine (12.19)	..	48·00	8·00
		w. Wmk inverted	..	£350	
		y. Wmk inverted and reversed	£250	
47		2d. grey (1.13)	..	..	3·00	8·00
		x. Wmk reversed			

48	14	2½d. blue (27.3.12)	..	..	3·50	60
		w. Wmk inverted	..			
		x. Wmk reversed	..		—	£170
		y. Wmk inverted and reversed		£130	90·00
49		3d. purple/yellow (1.13)	..	1·75	6·00
49a		4d. red/yellow (1.9.19)	..	4·75	11·00
50		6d. purple (26.3.12)	..	16·00	20·00
		a. Pale claret (2.6.24)	..	11·00	8·00
51		1s. black/green (26.3.12)		3·75	4·00
		a. Jet black/olive (1925)		4·50	13·00
44/51		..	Set of 9	40·00	35·00
44/51 Optd "Specimen"			Set of 9	£400	

Nos. 44 to 51a are comb-perforated 13.8×14 or 14. No. 45 exists also line-perforated 14, probably from the printing dispatched to Bermuda on 13 March 1911.
See also Nos. 76b/87a.

15

HIGH VALUE KEY TYPES. The reign of King Edward VII saw the appearance of the first in a new series of "key type" designs, initially on the issues of Malaya — Straits Settlements and Nyasaland, to be used for high value denominations where a smaller design was felt to be inappropriate. The system was extended during the reign of King George V, using the portrait as Bermuda Type 15, to cover Bermuda, Ceylon, Leeward Islands, Malaya — Straits Settlements, Malta and Nyasaland. A number of these territories continued to use the key type concept for high value King George VI stamps and one, Leeward Islands, for stamps of Queen Elizabeth II.

In each instance the King George V issues were printed in sheets of 60 (12×5) on various coloured papers. The system utilised a common "head" plate used with individual "duty" plates which printed the territory name and face value.

Two major plate flaws occur on the King George V head plate: the break in scroll on R.1/12 and the broken crown and scroll on R.2/12. Both of these occur in different states, having been repaired and then damaged once again, perhaps on several occasions. Later printings of R. 1/12 show additional damage to the crown and upper scrolls. The prices quoted in the listings are for examples approximately as illustrated.

Break in scroll (R. 1/12)

Broken crown and scroll (R. 2/12)

Break through scroll (R. 1/9. Ptgs from June 1929. Some show attempts at repair)

(Typo D.L.R.)

1918 (1 Apr)–22. Wmk Mult Crown CA. Chalk-surfaced paper. P 14.
51b	15	2s. purple and blue/blue (19.6.20)	18·00	48·00
		ba. Break in scroll	..	£200
		bb. Broken crown and scroll	£180	
		bx. Wmk reversed	..	£1600
52		2s. 6d. black and red/blue	..	27·00	70·00
		a. Break in scroll	..	£250	
52b		4s. black and carmine (19.6.20)	60·00	£140
		a. Break in scroll	..	£275	
		bb. Broken crown and scroll	£275	
53		5s. deep green and deep red/yellow	50·00	£100
		a. Break in scroll	..	£350	
		c. Green & carmine-red/pale yell (1920)	42·00	85·00
		ca. Break in scroll	..	£300	
		cb. Broken crown and scroll	£300	
		cw. Wmk inverted	..	£275	
		cx. Wmk reversed	..	£1800	
		cy. Wmk inverted and reversed	£1800	
54		10s. green and carmine/pale bluish green	160	£325
		a. Break in scroll	..	£550	
		c. Green & red/pale bluish green (10.22)	200	£350
		ca. Break in scroll	..	£600	
		cb. Broken crown and scroll	£600	
		cw. Wmk inverted	..		
55		£1 purple and black/red	..	£350	£550
		a. Break in scroll	..	£800	
		b. Broken crown and scroll	£950	
		c. Break through scroll	..	£1300	
		w. Wmk inverted	..	£1500	
51b/5		..	..	Set of 6	£550	£1000
51b/5 Optd "Specimen"		..	Set of 6	£800	

Beware of cleaned copies of the 10s. with faked postmarks. Examples of Nos. 51b/5 are known showing a forged Hamilton double ring postmark dated "22 JAN 13".
See also Nos. 88/93.

WAR TAX   **WAR TAX**
(16)   (17)

1918 (4 May). *Nos. 46 and 46a optd with T 16 by the Bermuda Press.*
56	14	1d. red	..	..	45	60
		a. Rose-red	..	..	45	1·00

1920 (5 Feb). *No. 46b optd with T 17 by the Bermuda Press.*
58	14	1d. carmine	..	..	75	1·75

The War Tax stamps represented a compulsory levy in addition to normal postal fees until 31 Dec 1920. Subsequently they were valid for ordinary postage.

| 18 | 19 |

(Des by the Governor (Gen. Sir James Willcocks). Typo D.L.R.)

1920 (11 Nov)–21. *Tercentenary of Representative Institutions (1st issue). Chalk-surfaced paper (3d. to 1s.). P 14.*
(a) Wmk Mult Crown CA (sideways*) (19.1.21)
59	18	¼d. brown	..	..	3·00	15·00
		a. "C" of "CA" missing from wmk	..	£375	
		b. "A" of "CA" missing from wmk	..	£375	
		w. Wmk Crown to right of CA	£130	
		x. Wmk sideways reversed	..	£160	
60		½d. green	..	..	3·00	8·00
		w. Wmk Crown to right of CA	£190	
		x. Wmk sideways reversed	£160	
		y. Wmk sideways inverted and reversed		
61		2d. grey	..	..	11·00	32·00
		a. "C" of "CA" missing from wmk	..	£550	
		w. Wmk Crown to right of CA	£275	
		y. Wmk sideways inverted and reversed	£350	
62		3d. dull and deep purple/pale yellow	..	10·00	28·00
		w. Wmk Crown to right of CA		
		x. Wmk sideways reversed		
63		4d. black and red/pale yellow	..	11·00	28·00
		a. "C" of "CA" missing from wmk	..	£850	
64		1s. black/blue-green	..	16·00	48·00

(b) Wmk Mult Script CA (sideways)
65	18	1d. carmine	..	..	3·00	30
66		2½d. bright blue	..	..	9·50	10·00
67		6d. dull and bright purple (19.1.21)	23·00	65·00
59/67			Set of 9	80·00	£200
59/67 Optd "Specimen"		Set of 9	£350	

*The normal sideways watermark shows Crown to left of CA as seen from the back of the stamp.

(Des H. J. Dale. Recess D.L.R.)

1921 (12 May). *Tercentenary of Representative Institutions (2nd issue). P 14. (a) Wmk Mult Crown CA (sideways*).*
68	19	2d. slate-grey	..	..	4·50	26·00
		a. "C" of "CA" missing from wmk		
		w. Wmk Crown to left of CA	..	£350	
69		2½d. bright ultramarine	..	9·00	3·00
		a. "C" of "CA" missing from wmk	..	£550	
		b. "A" of "CA" missing from wmk	..	£550	
		x. Wmk sideways reversed	..	—	£300
70		3d. purple/pale yellow	..	5·00	15·00
71		4d. red/pale yellow	..	15·00	20·00
		x. Wmk sideways reversed	£190	
72		6d. purple	..	..	10·00	42·00
		a. "C" of "CA" missing from wmk	..	£700	
		b. "A" of "CA" missing from wmk	..	£750	
		c. Substituted crown in wmk	†	£1100
73		1s. black/green	..	..	22·00	48·00
		(b) Wmk Mult Script CA (sideways*)		
74	19	¼d. brown	..	..	80	2·75
		w. Wmk Crown to left of CA		
		x. Wmk sideways reversed	..		

75	19	½d. green		2·75	6·00
		w. Wmk Crown left of CA		£110	£130
		y. Wmk sideways inverted and reversed			£225
76		1d. deep carmine		2·50	35
		a. "C" of "CA" missing from wmk			
68/76			Set of 9	65·00	£150
68/76 Optd "Specimen"			Set of 9	£325	

*The normal sideways watermark shows Crown to right of CA, as seen from the back of the stamp.
For illustration of the substituted watermark crown see Catalogue Introduction.

Three Types of the 1d.
I. Scroll at top left very weak and figure "1" has pointed serifs.
II. Scroll weak. "1" has square serifs and "1d" is heavy.
III. Redrawn. Scroll is completed by a strong line and "1" is thinner with long square serifs.

Two Types of the 2½d.
I. Short, thick figures, especially of the "1", small "d".
II. Figures taller and thinner, "d" larger.

1922–34. *Wmk Mult Script CA.* P 14.

76b	14	¼d. brown (7.28)		1·50	2·50
77		½d. green (11.22)		90	15
		w. Wmk inverted			
		x. Wmk reversed			
78		1d. scarlet (I) (11.22)		16·00	60
		a. Carmine (7.24)		18·00	60
		bx. Wmk reversed			
78c		1d. carmine (II) (12.25)		32·00	4·75
		cx. Wmk reversed			
		d. Scarlet (8.27)		10·00	80
79		1d. scarlet (III) (10.28)		12·00	30
		a. Carmine-lake (1934)		22·00	1·75
79b		1½d. red-brown (27.3.34)		9·00	35
80		2d. grey (12.23)		1·50	1·50
		x. Wmk reversed		55·00	
81		2½d. pale sage-green (12.22)		2·00	1·50
		a. Deep sage-green (1924)		1·50	1·50
		aw. Wmk inverted			
		ax. Wmk reversed			
		ay. Wmk inverted and reversed			
82		2½d. ultramarine (I) (1.12.26)		2·50	50
		aw. Wmk inverted		90·00	
82b		2½d. ultramarine (II) (3.32)		1·75	50
83		3d. ultramarine (12.24)		16·00	26·00
		w. Wmk inverted		£100	
84		3d. purple/yellow (10.26)		3·50	1·00
85		4d. red/yellow (8.24)		1·75	1·00
		x. Wmk reversed			
86		6d. purple (8.24)		1·00	80
87		1s. black/emerald (10.27)		4·75	9·00
		a. Brownish black/yellow-green (1934)		35·00	50·00
76b/87			Set of 13	48·00	40·00
76b/87 Optd/Perf "Specimen"			Set of 13	£500	

Both comb and line perforations occur on Nos. 76b/87a.
Detailed gauges are as follows:
13.7×13.9 comb — Nos. 77, 78/a, 80, 81/a, 83, 84, 85, 86, 87
13.75 line — Nos. 76b, 77, 78c/d, 79/a, 79b, 80, 82, 82b, 84, 85, 86, 87/a
13.75×14 line — Nos. 77, 78c/d, 79b, 80, 82b, 86, 87a
14×13.75 line — Nos. 79/a
14 line — Nos. 81/a

Breaks in scrolls at right (R. 1/3. Ptgs of 12s. 6d. from July 1932)

1924–32. *Wmk Mult Script CA. Chalk-surfaced paper.* P 14.

88	15	2s. purple and brt blue/pale blue (1.9.27)		42·00	70·00
		a. Break in scroll		£190	
		b. Broken crown and scroll		£190	
		c. Purple and blue/grey-blue (1931)		50·00	75·00
		ca. Break in scroll		£225	
		cb. Broken crown and scroll		£225	
		cc. Break through scroll		£275	

89	15	2s. 6d. black and carmine/pale blue (4.27)		55·00	£110
		a. Break in scroll		£225	
		b. Broken crown and scroll		£225	
		c. Black and red/blue to deep blue (6.29)		65·00	£110
		ca. Break in scroll		£300	
		cb. Broken crown and scroll		£300	
		cc. Break through scroll		£350	
		d. Grey-black and pale orange-vermilion/grey-blue (3.30)		£2750	£2750
		da. Break in scroll		£4250	
		db. Broken crown and scroll		£4250	
		dc. Break through scroll		£4250	
		e. Black and carmine-red/deep grey-blue (8.30)		70·00	£110
		ea. Break in scroll		£325	
		eb. Broken crown and scroll		£325	
		ec. Break through scroll		£375	
		f. Black & scarlet-vermilion/dp bl (9.31)		75·00	£110
		fa. Break in scroll		£325	
		fb. Broken crown and scroll		£325	
		fc. Break through scroll		£375	
		g. Black & brt orge-verm/dp blue (8.32)		£3000	£2750
		ga. Broken crown and scroll		£4500	
		gb. Broken crown and scroll		£4500	
92		10s. green and red/pale emerald (12.24)		£120	£250
		a. Break in scroll		£500	
		b. Broken crown and scroll		£450	
		c. Break through scroll		£500	
		d. Green and red/deep emerald (1932)		£130	£275
		da. Break in scroll		£500	
		db. Broken crown and scroll		£475	
		dc. Break through scroll		£550	
93		12s. 6d. grey and orange (8.32)		£250	£350
		a. Break in scroll		£650	
		b. Broken crown and scroll		£700	
		c. Break through scroll		£800	
		d. Breaks in scrolls at right		£800	
		e. Error. Ordinary paper			
88/93			Set of 4	£425	£700
88/93 Optd/Perf "Specimen"			Set of 4	£500	

The true No. 89d is the only stamp on grey-blue paper, other deeper orange-vermilion shades exist on different papers. No. 89g was despatched to Bermuda in July/August 1932, but is not known used before 1937.
Beware of fiscally used 2s. 6d. 10s. and 12s. 6d. stamps cleaned and bearing faked postmarks. Large quantities were used for a "head tax" levied on travellers leaving the country.
For 12s. 6d. design inscribed "Revenue" at both sides see No. F1 under POSTAL FISCAL.

1935 (6 May). *Silver Jubilee. As Nos. 91/4 of Antigua, but ptd by Waterlow.* P 11×12.

94		1d. deep blue and scarlet		45	55
		j. Damaged turret		90·00	
		m. "Bird" by turret		85·00	
95		1½d. ultramarine and grey		70	2·00
		m. "Bird" by turret		95·00	
96		2½d. brown and deep blue		1·40	90
		m. "Bird" by turret		£130	
97		1s. slate and purple		14·00	23·00
		k. Kite and vertical log		£140	
		l. Kite and horizontal log		£225	
94/7			Set of 4	15·00	24·00
94/7 Perf "Specimen"			Set of 4	£160	

For illustrations of plate varieties see Catalogue Introduction.

20 Red Hole, Paget   21 South Shore

22 Lucie (yacht)   23 Grape Bay, Paget Parish

24 Point House, Warwick Parish   25 Gardener's Cottage, Par-la-Ville, Hamilton

(Recess B.W.)

1936 (14 Apr)–*47. Wmk Mult Script CA (sideways on horiz designs).* P 12.

98	20	½d. bright green		10	10
99	21	1d. black and scarlet		30	20
100		1½d. black and chocolate		90	40
101	22	2d. black and pale blue		5·00	2·00
102	23	2½d. light and deep blue		80	25
103	24	3d. black and scarlet		2·75	90
104	25	6d. carmine-lake and violet		80	10
		a. Claret and dull violet (6.47)		3·25	1·00
105	23	1s. green		4·25	7·00
106	20	1s. 6d. brown		50	50
98/106			Set of 9	14·00	9·50
98/106 Perf "Specimen"			Set of 9	£250	

All are line-perf 11.9, except printings of the 6d. from July 1951 onwards, which are comb-perf 11.9 × 11.75.

1937 (14 May). *Coronation. As Nos. 95/7 of Antigua, but printed by D.L.R.* P 14.

107		1d. scarlet		50	50
108		1½d. yellow-brown		60	1·50
109		2½d. bright blue		70	1·50
107/9			Set of 3	1·60	3·25
107/9 Perf "Specimen"			Set of 3	£110	

26 Ships in Hamilton Harbour   27 St. David's Lighthouse

28 White-tailed Tropic Bird, Arms of Bermuda and Native Flower

(Des Miss Higginbotham (T 28). Recess B.W.)

1938 (20 Jan)–**1952.** *T 22, T 23 (but with portrait of King George VI) and T 26 to 28. Wmk Mult Script CA.* P 12.

110	26	1d. black and red (a) (b)		65	20
111		1½d. deep blue and purple-brown (a) (b)		6·00	1·00
		a. Blue and brown (a) (3.43)		5·50	2·50
		b. Lt blue & purple-brn (a) (b) (9.45)		2·25	35
		ba. "A" of "CA" missing from wmk			
112	22	2d. light blue and sepia (a)		45·00	8·50
112a		2d. ultramarine and scarlet (a) (b) (8.11.40)		1·50	80
113	23	2½d. light and deep blue (a)		11·00	1·50
113a		2½d. lt blue & sepia-black (a) (18.12.41)		3·00	1·50
		b. Pale blue & sepia-black (a) (3.43)		2·75	1·25
		c. Bright blue and deep sepia-black (b) (23.9.52)		5·00	4·00
114	27	3d. black and rose-red (a)		17·00	2·00
114a		3d. black & deep blue (a) (b) (16.7.41)		1·75	40
114b	28	7½d. black, blue & brt grn (a) (b) (18.12.41)		6·50	2·00
		c. Black, blue & yellow-grn (a) (3.43)		4·50	2·25
115	23	1s. green (a) (b)		2·00	50
		a. Bluish green (b) (20.6.52)		6·50	6·00

Perforations. Two different perforating machines were used on the various printings of these stamps: (a) the original 11.9 line perforation; (b) 11.9 × 11.75 comb perforation, introduced in July 1950. These perforations occur as indicated above.

29 King George VI

Shading omitted from top right scroll (R. 1/1. March 1943 ptgs of 2s. and £1)   Lower right scroll with broken tail (R. 2/10. Line perforated printings only)

Broken top right scroll (R. 5/11. Line perforated ptgs only. A retouched state of the flaw is visible in later ptgs up to March 1943)   Broken lower right scroll (R. 5/12. Occurs on printings made between May 1941 and March 1943)

Gash in chin (R.2/5.
Ptgs between May
1941 and March 1943

Missing pearl
(R.5/1, Nov 1945
ptg of 5s. only)

"ER" joined (R. 1/2. Occurs in its complete state on
1938 ptg only. Subsequent ptgs show it incomplete)

Damaged left value tablet
(R. 1/11. Part of 1951 ptg
only)

(Typo D.L.R.)

1938 (20 Jan)–53. *T* **29.** *Wmk Mult Crown CA* (£1) *or Mult
Script CA* (others). *Chalk-surfaced paper. P* 14 (comb).

116	2s. deep purple and ultramarine/grey-blue		£110	10·00
	a. *Deep reddish purple and ultram/grey-blue* (21.11.40)*		£275	22·00
	b. *Perf 14¼ line. Deep purple and ultram/grey-blue* (14.11.41)*		£300	85·00
	bc. Lower right scroll with broken tail		£1300	£550
	bd. Broken top right scroll		£1100	£450
	be. Broken lower right scroll		£1100	£450
	bf. Gash in chin		£1200	£500
	c. *Ordinary paper. Pur & bl /dp bl* (7.6.42)		7·00	1·50
	ce. Broken lower right scroll		£200	80·00
	cf. Gash in chin		£225	85·00
	d. *Ordinary paper. Purple and deep blue/pale blue* (5.3.43)		11·00	1·50
	db. Shading omitted from top right scroll		£900	£475
	de. Broken lower right scroll		£550	£300
	df. Gash in chin		£600	£325
	e. *Perf 13. Ordinary paper. Dull purple and blue/pale blue* (15.2.50)		17·00	14·00
	f. *Perf 13. Ordinary paper. Reddish purple and blue/pale blue* (10.10.50)		8·50	14·00
117	2s. 6d. black and red/grey-blue		70·00	8·50
	a. *Perf 14¼ line. Black and red/grey-blue* (21.2.42)*		£475	£110
	ac. Lower right scroll with broken tail		£1500	£600
	ad. Broken top right scroll		£1300	£500
	ae. Broken lower right scroll		£1300	£500
	af. Gash in chin		£1400	£550
	b. *Ordinary paper. Black and red/pale blue* (5.3.43)		19·00	6·50
	be. Broken lower right scroll		£450	£200
	bf. Gash in chin		£475	£225
	c. *Perf 13. Ordinary paper. Black and orange-red/pale blue* (10.10.50)		19·00	11·00
	d. *Perf 13. Ordinary paper. Black and red/pale blue* (18.6.52)		16·00	12·00
118	5s. green and red/*yellow*		£140	26·00
	a. *Pale green and red/yellow* (14.3.39)*		£300	65·00
	b. *Perf 14¼ line. Dull yellow-green and red/yellow* (5.1.43)*		£225	29·00
	bc. Lower right scroll with broken tail		£950	£375
	bd. Broken top right scroll		£800	£275
	be. Broken lower right scroll		£800	£275
	bf. Gash in chin		£850	£325
	c. *Ordinary paper. Dull yellow-green and carmine-red/pale yellow* (5.42)*		£450	95·00
	ce. Broken lower right scroll		£3000	£1000
	cf. Gash in chin		£3000	£1000
	d. *Ordinary paper. Pale bluish green and carmine-red/pale yellow* (5.3.43)		£100	50·00
	de. Broken lower right scroll		£750	£425
	df. Gash in chin		£750	£425
	e. *Ordinary paper. Green and red/pale yellow* (11.45)*		50·00	20·00
	ea. Missing pearl		£750	
	f. *Perf 13. Ordinary paper. Yellow-green and red/pale yellow* (15.2.50)		22·00	18·00
	g. *Perf 13. Green and scarlet/yellow* (chalk-surfaced) (10.10.50)		35·00	35·00
119	10s. green and deep lake/pale emerald		£450	£275
	a. *Bluish green and deep red/green* (8.39)*		£200	£130
	b. *Perf 14¼ line. Ordinary paper. Yellow-green and carmine/green* (1942)*		£400	£120
	bc. Lower right scroll with broken tail		£1400	£750
	bd. Broken top right scroll		£1200	£600
	be. Broken lower right scroll		£1200	£600
	bf. Gash in chin		£1300	£650

(119)	c. *Ordinary paper. Yellowish green and deep carmine-red/green* (5.3.43)		80·00	60·00
	ce. Broken lower right scroll		£2250	
	cf. Gash in chin		£2250	
	d. *Ordinary paper. Deep green and dull red/green* (emerald back) (11.12.46)		85·00	60·00
	e. *Perf 13. Ordinary paper. Green and vermilion/green* (19.9.51)		35·00	42·00
	f. *Perf 13. Ordinary paper. Green and dull red/green* (16.4.53)		35·00	48·00
120	12s. 6d. deep grey and brownish orange		£475	£425
	a. *Grey and brownish orange* (shades)		£180	65·00
	b. *Grey and pale orange* (9.11.40)*		95·00	50·00
	c. *Ordinary paper* (2.3.44)*		£100	60·00
	ce. Broken lower right scroll		£1700	£1800
	cf. Gash in chin		£1700	
	d. *Ordinary paper. Grey & yell†* (17.9.47)*		£600	£475
	e. *Perf 13. Grey and pale orange* (chalk-surfaced) (10.10.50)		95·00	75·00
121	£1 purple and black/*red*		£275	£100
	a. "ER" joined		£650	
	b. *Pale purple & black/pale red* (13.5.43)*		80·00	60·00
	bb. Shading omitted from top right scroll		£1600	
	be. Broken lower right scroll		£1100	£800
	bf. Gash in chin		£1100	£800
	c. *Dp reddish pur & blk/pale red* (5.3.43)*		70·00	48·00
	ce. Broken lower right scroll		£1100	
	cf. Gash in chin		£1100	
	d. *Perf 13. Violet & black/scarlet* (7.12.51)		48·00	75·00
	da. Damaged left value tablet		£1500	
	e. *Perf 13. Brt violet & blk/scar* (10.12.52)		£160	£150
110/21d			Set of 16	£275	£160
110/21 Perf "Specimen"		Set of 16	£1500	

Following extensive damage to their printing works on 29
December 1940 much of De La Rue's work was transferred to
other firms operating under their supervision. It is understood
that Williams Lea & Co produced those new printings ordered
for the Bermuda high value stamps during 1941. The first batch
of these printings showed the emergency use, by Williams Lea,
of a 14¼ line perforating machine (exact gauge 14.15) instead of
the comb perforation (exact gauge 13.9 × 13.8).

Dates marked * are those of earliest known use.

In No. 116c the coloured surfacing of the paper is mottled with
white specks sometimes accompanied by very close horizontal
lines. In Nos. 116d, 117b and 118c/d the surfacing is the same
colour as the back, sometimes applied in widely spaced
horizontal lines giving the appearance of laid paper.
†No. 120d is the so-called "lemon" shade.

HALF PENNY

X X

(30)

31 Postmaster Perot's Stamp

1940 (20 Dec). *No.* 110 *surch with T* **30** *by Royal Gazette,
Hamilton.*

122	26	½d. on 1d. black and red (shades)	40	45

The spacing between "PENNY" and "X" varies from 12½ mm
to 14 mm.

1946 (6 Nov). *Victory. As Nos.* 110/11 *of Antigua.*

123	1½d. brown		15	15
124	3d. blue		15	15
123/4 Perf "Specimen"		Set of 2	75·00	

1948 (1 Dec). *Royal Silver Wedding. As Nos.* 112/13 *of
Antigua.*

125	1½d. red-brown		30	50
126	£1 carmine		40·00	48·00

(Recess B.W.)

1949 (11 Apr). *Centenary of Postmaster Perot's Stamp. Wmk Mult
Script CA. P* 13½.

127	31	2½d. blue and brown	15	15
128		3d. black and blue	15	15
129		6d. violet and green	15	15
127/9		Set of 3	40	40

1949 (10 Oct). *75th Anniv of Universal Postal Union. As Nos.
114/17 of Antigua.*

130	2½d. blue-black		60	75
131	3d. deep blue		1·75	1·25
132	6d. purple		60	75
133	1s. blue-green		60	75
130/3		Set of 4	3·25	3·25

1953 (4 June). *Coronation. As No.* 120 *of Antigia, but ptd by
B.W.*

134	1½d. black and blue		60	15

32 Easter Lilies

34 Easter Lily

37 Map of Bermuda

Die I
"Sandy's"

Die II
"Sandys"

(Des C. Deakins (½d., 3d., 1s. 3d., 5s.), J. Berry (1d., 1½d., 2½d.,
4d., 1s.). B. Brown (2d., 6d., 8d.), D. Haig (4½d., 9d.), Pamela
Braley-Smith (2s. 6d.) and E. C. Leslie (10s.) Recess (except £1,
centre typo), B.W.)

1953 (9 Nov)–**62.** *T* **32, 34, 37,** *and similar designs. Wmk Mult
Script CA. P* 13½.

135	32	½d. olive-green	45	2·50
		a. *Yellow-olive* (19.5.54)	40	50
136		1d. black and red	1·50	50
		a. *Black and deep red* (19.5.54)	1·75	40
137	34	1½d. green	30	10
138		2d. ultramarine and brown-red	50	40
139		2½d. rose-red	2·00	50
140	37	3d. deep purple (I)	30	10
140a		3d. deep purple (II) (2.1.57)	1·00	20
141		4d. black and bright blue	30	40
142		4½d. emerald	45	1·00
143		6d. black and deep turquoise	5·50	60
143a		8d. black and red (16.5.55)	2·50	30
143b		9d. violet (6.1.58)	7·50	2·50
144		1s. orange	50	15
145	37	1s. 3d. blue (I)	3·50	30
		a. *Greenish blue* (21.9.54)	8·00	1·25
145b		1s. 3d. blue (II) (2.1.57)	7·00	50
		bc. *Bright blue* (14.8.62)	11·00	3·50
146		2s. brown	4·00	85
147		2s. 6d. scarlet	4·50	45
148		5s. carmine	19·00	85
149		10s. deep ultramarine	13·00	5·00
		a. *Ultramarine* (13.2.57)	42·00	14·00
150		£1 brown, blue, red, grn & bronze-grn	25·00	27·00
135/150		Set of 18	75·00	32·00

Designs: *Horiz*—1d., 4d. Postmaster Perot's stamps; 2d.
Victory II (racing dinghy); 2½d. Sir George Somers and *Sea
Venture*; 4½d., 9d. *Sea Venture* (galleon), coin and Perot design;
6d., 8d. White-tailed Tropic Bird; 1s. Early Bermudian coinage;
2s. Arms of St. Georges; 5s. Hog coin; 10s. Obverse and reverse
of hog coin; £1 Arms of Bermuda. *Vert*—2s. 6d. Warwick Fort.

Nos. 136, 138 and 143 exist in coils, constructed from normal
sheets.

1953 (26 Nov). *Royal Visit. As No.* 143 *but inscr* "ROYAL VISIT
1953" *in top left corner.*

151	6d. black and deep turquoise		30	20

Three Power Talks
December, 1953.

(46)

Three Power Talks
December, 1953.

(46a)

First setting (Type 46). First line 24½ mm long.
Second setting (Type 46a). First line 25¼ mm long.

1953 (8 Dec). *Three Power Talks. Nos.* 140 *and* 145 *optd with
T* 46.

152	37	3d. deep purple (Type 46) (B.)	10	10
		a. Optd with Type 46a	45	15
153		1s. 3d. blue (Type 46) (R.)	20	20
		a. Optd with Type 46a	1·75	1·75

50TH ANNIVERSARY
U S – BERMUDA
OCEAN RACE 1956

(47)

48 Perot's Post Office

1956 (22 June). *50th Anniv of United States–Bermuda Yacht
Race. Nos.* 143a *and* 145a *optd with T* **47** *by the Bermuda
Press.*

154	8d. black and red (Bk.)		20	40
155	1s. 3d. greenish blue (R.)		20	55

(Des W. Harrington. Recess B.W.)

1959 (1 Jan.) *Wmk Mult Script CA. P* 13½.

156	48	6d. black and deep mauve		70	15

49 Arms of King James I and Queen Elizabeth II

(Des W. Harrington. Recess; arms litho D.L.R.)

1959 (29 July). *350th Anniv of First Settlement. Arms, red, yellow and blue; frame colours below.* W w **12**. P 13.

157	**49**	1½d. grey-blue	..		25	10
158		3d. drab-grey	..	..	30	50
159		4d. reddish purple	..	..	35	55
160		8d. slate-violet	..	..	35	15
161		9d. olive-green	..	..	35	1·25
162		1s. 3d. brown	..	..	35	30
157/162				*Set of 6*	1·75	2·50

50 The Old Rectory, St. George's, circa 1730

67 *Tsotsi in the Bundu* (Finn class dinghy)

(Des W. Harrington. Photo Harrison)

1962 (26 Oct)–**68**. *Horiz designs as T* **50**. W w **12** *(upright)*. P 12½.

163	1d. reddish purple, black and orange	..	10	60
	w. Wmk inverted	..	†	—
164	2d. lilac, indigo, yellow and green	..	10	15
	a. Lilac omitted ..	..	£900	£700
	b. Green omitted	..	† £3750	
	c. Imperf (pair)	..	£1300	
	d. *Pale lilac, indigo, yell & grn* (22.10.68)	85	15
	w. Wmk inverted	..	—	£150
165	3d. yellow-brown and light blue ..	..	10	10
166	4d. red-brown and magenta	..	20	40
167	5d. grey-blue and rose	..	1·50	2·75
168	6d. grey-blue, emerald and light blue	..	20	30
	w. Wmk inverted	..	85·00	
169	8d. bright blue, bright green and orange	30	35
170	9d. light blue and brown	..	25	30
170a	10d. violet and ochre (8.2.65)	..	8·00	1·00
	aw. Wmk inverted	..		
171	1s. black, emerald, bright blue & orange	20	10
172	1s. 3d. lake, grey and bistre	..	75	15
173	1s. 6d. violet and ochre	..	1·75	1·75
174	2s. red-brown and orange	..	3·00	1·25
175	2s. 3d. bistre-brown and yellow-green	..	2·00	6·50
176	2s. 6d. bistre-brn, bluish grn & olive-yell	55	50
177	5s. brown-purple and blue-green	..	1·25	1·50
	w. Wmk inverted	..	70·00	
178	10s. magenta, deep bluish green and buff	4·00	5·00
	w. Wmk inverted	..	£275	£325
179	£1 black, yellow-olive and yellow-orange	14·00	14·00
163/79	.. .. .. *Set of 18*	35·00	32·00

Designs:—2d. Church of St. Peter, St. Georges; 3d. Government House, 1892; 4d. The Cathedral, Hamilton, 1894; 5d. H.M. Dockyard, 1811; 6d. Perot's Post Office, 1848; 8d. G.P.O. Hamilton, 1869; 9d. Library, Par-la-Ville; 10d., 1s. 6d. Bermuda cottage, *circa* 1705; 1s. Christ Church, Warwick, 1719; 1s. 3d. City Hall, Hamilton, 1960; 2s. Town of St. George; 2s. 3d. Bermuda house, *circa* 1710; 2s. 6d. Bermuda house, early 18th-century; 5s. Colonial Secretariat, 1833; 10s. Old Post Office, Somerset, 1890; £1 The House of Assembly, 1815.

Three examples of No. 164b are known, all used on piece.
The 3d. value with the yellow-brown omitted, previously No. 165a, is no longer listed as this is believed to be a dry print. All reported examples show traces of the yellow-brown.
See also Nos. 195/200 and 246a.

1963 (4 June). *Freedom from Hunger. As No.* 146 *of Antigua.*

180	1s. 3d. sepia	..	..	..	80	40

1963 (2 Sept). *Red Cross Centenary. As Nos.* 147/8 *of Antigua.*

181	3d. red and black	..	..	75	25
182	1s. 3d. red and blue	..	..	2·25	3·00

(Des V. Whiteley. Photo D.L.R.)

1964 (28 Sept). *Olympic Games, Tokyo.* W w **12**. P 14 × 13½.

183	**67**	3d. red, violet and blue..	..	10	10

1965 (17 May). *I.T.U. Centenary. As Nos.* 166/7 *of Antigua.*

184	3d. light blue and emerald	..	50	25
185	2s. yellow and ultramarine	..	1·00	1·50

68 Scout Badge and St. Edward's Crown

(Des W. Harrington. Photo Harrison)

1965 (24 July). *50th Anniv of Bermuda Boy Scouts Association.* W w **12**. P 12½.

186	**68**	2s. multicoloured	..	..	50	50
		w. Wmk inverted	..	..	35·00	

1965 (25 Oct). *International Co-operation Year. As Nos.* 168/9 *of Antigua.*

187	4d. reddish purple and turquoise-green	..	65	20
188	2s. 6d. deep bluish green and lavender	..	1·25	80

1966 (24 Jan). *Churchill Commemoration. As Nos.* 170/3 *of Antigua.*

189	3d. new blue ..	..	45	20
190	6d. deep green	..	70	60
191	10d. brown	..	90	75
192	1s. 3d. bluish violet	..	1·25	2·25
189/92		*Set of 4*	3·00	3·50

1966 (1 July). *World Cup Football Championships. As Nos.* 176/7 *of Antigua.*

193	10d. violet, yellow-green, lake & yellow-brn ..	60	15
194	2s. 6d. chocolate, blue-grn, lake & yell-brn ..	90	1·00

1966 (25 Oct)–**69**. *Designs as Nos.* 164, 167 (1s. 6d.), 169, 170a/1 *and* 174 *but* W w **12** *(sideways*).*

195	2d. lilac, indigo, yellow and green (20.5.69)	4·25	5·50
196	8d. brt blue, brt green & orange (14.2.67)	50	1·25
197	10d. violet and ochre (1.11.66)	75	60
	w. Wmk Crown to right of CA ..	†	£700
198	1s. black, emerald, brt bl & orge (14.2.67)	70	1·40
199	1s. 6d. grey-blue and rose (1.11.66)	2·75	75
	w. Wmk Crown to right of CA ..	50·00	
200	2s. red-brown and orange	2·75	1·50
195/200	*Set of 6*	10·50	10·00

*The normal sideways watermark shows Crown to left of CA, as seen from the back of the stamp.
The 2d. value exists with PVA gum only, and the 8d. exists with PVA gum as well as gum arabic.

1966 (1 Dec). *20th Anniv of U.N.E.S.C.O. As Nos.* 196/8 *of Antigua.*

201	4d. slate-violet, red, yellow and orange	60	15
202	1s. 3d. orange-yellow, violet and deep olive	1·40	50
203	2s. black, bright purple and orange..	1·60	1·25
201/3	..	*Set of 3*	3·25	1·75

69 G.P.O. Building

(Des G. Vasarhelyi. Photo Harrison)

1967 (23 June). *Opening of New General Post Office. Hamilton.* W w **12**. P 14½.

204	**69**	3d. multicoloured	..	..	10	10
205		1s. multicoloured	..		10	10
206		1s. 6d. multicoloured	..		15	25
207		2s. 6d. multicoloured	..		15	50
204/7				*Set of 4*	45	80

70 *Mercury* (cable ship) and Chain Links

(Des V. Whiteley. Photo Harrison)

1967 (14 Sept). *Inauguration of Bermuda–Tortola Telephone Service. T* **70** *and similar horiz designs. Multicoloured.* W w **12**. P 14½ × 14.

208	3d. Type **70**	..	15	10
209	1s. Map, telephone and microphone..	20	10
210	1s. 6d. Telecommunications media ..	25	25
211	2s. 6d. *Mercury* (cable ship) and marine fauna	35	60
208/11	.. .. .. *Set of 4*	85	90

74 Human Rights Emblem and Doves

(Des M. Farrar Bell. Litho Harrison)

1968 (1 Feb). *Human Rights Year.* W w **12**. P 14 × 14½.

212	**74**	3d. indigo, blue and dull green.	..	10	10
213		1s. yellow-brown, blue and light blue	..	10	10
214		1s. 6d. black, blue and rose	..	10	15
215		2s. 6d. grey-green, blue and yellow	15	25
212/15		.. .. .. *Set of 4*	30	50

REPRESENTATIVE GOVERNMENT

75 Mace and Queen's Profile

(Des R. Granger Barrett. Photo Harrison)

1968 (1 July). *New Constitution. T* **75** *and similar horiz design.* W w **12**. P 14.

216	**75**	3d. multicoloured	..	..	10	10
217		1s. multicoloured	..		10	10
218	—	1s. 6d. greenish yellow, black & turq-bl	10	20
219	—	2s. 6d. lilac, black and orange-yellow	15	50
216/19				*Set of 4*	30	75

Design:—1s. 6d., 2s. 6d. Houses of Parliament and House of Assembly, Bermuda.

77 Football, Athletics and Yachting

(Des V. Whiteley. Photo Harrison)

1968 (24 Sept). *Olympic Games, Mexico.* W w **12**. P 12½.

220	**77**	3d. multicoloured	..	15	10
		a. Red-brown ("BERMUDA" and value) omitted ..	£2500	
221		1s. multicoloured	..	25	10
222		1s. 6d. multicoloured	..	50	30
223		2s. 6d. multicoloured	..	50	1·40
220/3 ..		.. .. *Set of 4*	1·25	1·75

78 Brownie and Guide
80 Emerald-studded Gold Cross and Seaweed

(Des Harrison. Litho Format)

1969 (17 Feb). *50th Anniv of Bermuda Girl Guides.* P 14.

224	**78**	3d. multicoloured	..	..	10	10
225		1s. multicoloured	..		20	10
226	—	1s. 6d. multicoloured	..		25	40
227	—	2s. 6d. multicoloured	..		35	1·40
224/7				*Set of 4*	80	1·75

Design:—1s. 6d., 2s. 6d. Guides and badge.

(Des K. Giles adapted by V. Whiteley. Photo Harrison)

1969 (29 Sept). *Underwater Treasure. T* **80** *and similar vert design. Multicoloured.* W w **12** *(sideways).* P 14½ × 14.

228	**80**	4d. Type **80**	..	20	10
229		1s. 3d. Emerald-studded gold cross and seabed	..	35	15
230		2s. Type **80**	..	45	90
231		2s. 6d. As 1s. 3d.	..	45	1·75
228/31		.. .. .. *Set of 4*	1·25	2·50

(New Currency. 100 cents = 1 Bermuda dollar)

1c

(**82**)
Tall "2" (Pl 1A. R.2/2)

2c

1970 (6 Feb). *Decimal Currency. As Nos.* 163, 165/6, 168, 170, 172, 175/9 *and* 195/200 *surch as T* **82**. W w **12** *(sideways* on* 2, 5, 10, 12, 15, 18, 24, 30, 60 c., $1.20 *and* $2.40).

232	1 c. on 1d. reddish purple, black and orange	10	1·75
	w. Wmk inverted	..	80·00	25·00
233	2 c. on 2d. lilac, indigo, yellow and green	10	10
	a. Lilac omitted ..	..	£800	
	b. Vert pair, one without surch	£3750	
	c. Tall "2"	..	4·75	
	dw. Wmk Crown to right of CA	55·00	
	e. Wmk upright (No. 164)	1·00	2·50
	ea. Tall "2"	12·00	
	f. Wmk upright (No. 164d)	1·10	2·75
	fa. Tall "2"	13·00	
234	3 c. on 3d. yellow-brown and light blue ..	10	10
235	4 c. on 4d. red-brown and magenta (Br.)	10	10
236	5 c. on 8d. bright blue, brt green & orange	15	1·75
237	6 c. on 6d. grey-blue, emerald & light blue	15	70
	a. Horiz pair, one with albino surch, the other with albino bar		
	w. Wmk inverted	..	†	£150
238	9 c. on 9d. light blue and brown (Br.)	30	2·00
239	10 c. on 10d. violet and ochre	30	25
240	12 c. on 1s. black, emerald, brt blue & orge	30	50
241	15 c. on 1s. 3d. lake, grey and bistre	1·50	1·00
242	18 c. on 1s. 6d. grey-blue and rose	80	65
243	24 c. on 2s. red-brown and orange	85	85
	w. Wmk Crown to right of CA	75·00	

244	30 c. on 2s. 6d. bistre-brown, bluish green			
	and olive-yellow	..	..	1·00	2·50
245	36 c. on 2s. 3d. bistre-brown & yellow-green			1·75	6·00
246	60 c. on 5s. brown-purple and blue-green			2·25	3·00
	a. Surch omitted†			£800	
247	$1.20, on 10s. mag, dp bluish green & buff			5·00	15·00
248	$2.40, on £1 black, yellow-olive & yell-orge			7·50	19·00
232/48			Set of 17	19·00	50·00

*The normal sideways watermark shows Crown to left of CA, as seen from the back of the stamp.

†No. 246a differs from the normal No. 177 by its watermark, which is sideways, and its gum, which is PVA.

83 Spathiphyllum

(Des W. Harrington. Photo D.L.R.)

1970 (6 July)–75. *Flowers. Multicoloured designs as T 83. W w 12 (sideways on horiz designs). P 14.*

249	1 c. Type 83	..	..	..	10	20
250	2 c. Bottlebrush	..	..	..	20	25
251	3 c. Oleander (vert)	..	..	15	10
252	4 c. Bermudiana	..	..	15	10
253	5 c. Poinsettia	..	..	30	20
254	6 c. Hibiscus	..	..	30	30
255	9 c. Cereus	..	..	20	45
256	10 c. Bougainvillea (vert)	..	20	15
257	12 c. Jacaranda	..	..	80	60
258	15 c. Passion-Flower	..	90	1·40
258a	17 c. As 15 c. (2.6.75)	..	2·75	3·50
259	18 c. Coralita	..	..	2·25	2·50
259a	20 c. As 18 c. (2.6.75)	..	2·75	3·50
260	24 c. Morning Glory	..	1·50	3·50
260a	25 c. As 24 c. (2.6.75)	..	2·75	4·50
261	30 c. Tecoma	..	..	1·00	1·25
262	36 c. Angel's Trumpet	..	1·25	2·25
262a	40 c. As 36 c. (2.6.75)	..	2·75	5·50
263	60 c. Plumbago	..	..	1·75	2·75
263a	$1 As 60 c. (2.6.75)	..	3·25	6·50
264	$1.20, Bird of Paradise flower	..	2·75	3·00
264a	$2 As $1.20 (2.6.75)	..	5·50	8·50
265	$2.40, Chalice Cup.	..	5·50	6·00
265a	$3 As $2.40 (2.6.75)	..	10·00	11·00
249/65a		Set of 24	45·00	55·00

See also Nos. 303/6 and 340/1.

84 The State House, St. George's

(Des G. Drummond. Litho Questa)

1970 (12 Oct). *350th Anniv of Bermuda Parliament. T 84 and similar horiz designs. Multicoloured. W w 12 (sideways).*

266	4 c. Type 84	..	..	10	10
267	15 c. The Sessions House, Hamilton	..	25	15
268	18 c. St. Peter's Church, St George's	..	25	20
269	24 c. Town Hall, Hamilton	..	35	45
266/9	..	..	Set of 4	85	75
MS270	131 × 95 mm. Nos. 266/9	..	1·40	4·25

85 Street Scene, St. George's

(Des G. Drummond. Litho Questa)

1971 (8 Feb). *"Keep Bermuda Beautiful". T 85 and similar horiz designs. Multicoloured. W w 12 (sideways). P 14.*

271	4 c. Type 85	..	..	20	10
272	15 c. Horseshoe Bay	..	65	55
273	18 c. Gibb's Hill Lighthouse	..	1·50	2·00
274	24 c. Hamilton Harbour	..	1·25	2·50
271/4	..	..	Set of 4	3·25	4·50

86 Building of the *Deliverance*

(Des E. Amos. Adapted C. Abbott. Litho Questa)

1971 (10 May). *Voyage of the "Deliverance". T 86 and similar multicoloured designs. W w 12 (sideways on 4 c. and 24 c.). P 14.*

275	4 c. Type 86	..	..	60	20
276	15 c. Deliverance and Patience at Jamestown	1·75	1·75
277	18 c. Wreck of the Sea Venture	..	2·00	2·25
278	24 c. Deliverance and Patience on the high seas	2·25	2·50
275/8	..	..	Set of 4	6·00	6·00

The 15 c. and 18 c. are vert designs.

87 Green overlooking Ocean View

(Des G. Drummond. Litho D.L.R.)

1971 (1 Nov). *Golfing in Bermuda. T 87 and similar horiz designs. Multicoloured. W w 12 (sideways*). P 13.*

279	4 c. Type 87	..	..	85	10
	w. Wmk Crown to right of CA	..	80·00	50·00
280	15 c. Golfers at Port Royal	..	1·75	80
281	18 c. Castle Harbour	..	1·75	1·50
	w. Wmk Crown to right of CA	..	3·50	
282	24 c. Belmont	..	..	2·00	2·00
279/82		Set of 4	5·75	4·00

*The normal sideways watermark shows Crown to left of CA, as seen from the back of the stamp.

HEATH - NIXON
DECEMBER 1971

(88)

1971 (20 Dec). *Anglo-American Talks. Nos. 252, 258, 259 and 260 optd with T 88 by Format.*

283	4 c. Bermudiana	..	..	10	10
284	15 c. Passion Glory	..	10	20
285	18 c. Coralita	..	..	15	65
286	24 c. Morning Glory	..	20	80
283/6	..	..	Set of 4	50	1·60

89 Bonefish

(Des Maynard Reece. Litho B.W.)

1972 (21 Aug). *World Fishing Records. T 89 and similar horiz designs. Multicoloured. W w 12. P 13½ × 14.*

287	4 c. Type 89	..	..	35	10
288	15 c. Wahoo	..	..	40	50
289	18 c. Yellow-finned Tuna	..	45	75
290	24 c. Greater Amberjack	..	60	1·25
287/90	..	..	Set of 4	1·60	2·25

90 "Admiralty Oar" and Mace

(Des (from photograph by D. Groves) and photo Harrison)

1972 (20 Nov). *Royal Silver Wedding. Multicoloured; background colour given. W w 12. P 14 × 14½.*

291	**90**	4 c. bright bluish violet	..	15	10
292		15 c. rose-carmine	..	15	50
		w. Wmk inverted	..	2·00	

91 Palmetto   **92** Bernard Park, Pembroke, 1973

(Des Jennifer Toombs. Litho J.W.)

1973 (3 Sept). *Tree Planting Year. T 91 and similar vert designs. Multicoloured. W w 12 (sideways). P 14.*

293	4 c. Type 91	..	..	30	10
294	15 c. Olivewood Bark	..	90	75
	a. Brown (Queen's head and value) omitted	£900	
295	18 c. Bermuda Cedar	..	1·00	1·25
296	24 c. Mahogany	..	..	1·10	1·60
293/6	..	..	Set of 4	3·00	3·25

1973 (21 Nov*). *Royal Wedding. As Nos. 165/6 of Anguilla. Centre multicoloured. W w 12 (sideways). P 13½.*

| 297 | 15 c. bright mauve | .. | .. | 15 | 15 |
| 298 | 18 c. steel blue | .. | .. | 15 | 15 |

*This is the local date of issue. The Crown Agents released the stamps on the 14 November.

(Des J.W. Litho Questa)

1973 (17 Dec). *Lawn Tennis Centenary. T 92 and similar horiz designs. Multicoloured. W w 12. P 14.*

299	4 c. Type 92	..	..	30	10
300	15 c. Clermont Court, 1873	..	60	65
301	18 c. Leamington Spa Court, 1872	..	70	1·50
302	24 c. Staten Island Courts, 1874	..	85	2·00
299/302	..	..	Set of 4	2·25	3·75

1974 (13 June)–76. *As Nos. 253/4, 257 and 261, but W w 12 (upright).*

303	5 c. Poinsettia	..	..	90	1·75
304	6 c. Hibiscus	..	..	9·50	14·00
305	12 c. Jacaranda	..	..	1·75	5·00
	w. Wmk inverted	..	..	60·00	
306	30 c. Tecoma (11.6.76)	..	7·00	8·00
303/6		Set of 4	17·00	26·00

Nos. 307/19 vacant.

93 Weather Vane, City Hall   **94** Jack of Clubs and "good bridge hand"

(Des G. Drummond. Litho Questa)

1974 (24 June). *50th Anniv of Rotary in Bermuda. T 93 and similar horiz designs. Multicoloured. W w 12 (sideways). P 14.*

320	5 c. Type 93	..	..	15	10
321	17 c. St. Peter's Church, St George's	..	45	35
322	20 c. Somerset Bridge	..	50	1·50
323	25 c. Map of Bermuda, 1626	..	60	2·25
320/3	..	..	Set of 4	1·50	3·75

(Des J.W. Litho Format)

1975 (27 Jan). *World Bridge Championships, Bermuda. T 94 and similar vert designs. Multicoloured. W w 12. P 14.*

324	5 c. Type 94	..	..	20	10
325	17 c. Queen of Diamonds and Bermuda Bowl	35	50
326	20 c. King of Hearts and Bermuda Bowl	40	1·75
327	25 c. Ace of Spades and Bermuda Bowl	40	2·25
324/7	..	..	Set of 4	1·25	4·00

95 Queen Elizabeth II and the Duke of Edinburgh

(Des and photo Harrison)

1975 (17 Feb). *Royal Visit. W w 14. P 14 × 14½.*

| 328 | **95** | 17 c. multicoloured | .. | 60 | 65 |
| 329 | | 20 c. multicoloured | .. | 65 | 2·10 |

96 Short S.23 Flying Boat *Cavalier*, 1937

(Des R. Granger Barrett. Litho Questa)

1975 (28 Apr). *50th Anniv of Air-mail Service to Bermuda. T 96 and similar horiz designs. Multicoloured. W w 14 (sideways). P 14.*

330	5 c. Type 96	..	..	40	10
331	17 c. U.S.N. airship Los Angeles, 1925	1·25	85
332	20 c. Lockheed L.049 Constellation, 1946	1·40	2·75
333	25 c. Boeing 747-100, 1970	..	1·50	3·50
330/3	..	..	Set of 4	4·00	6·50
MS334	128 × 85 mm. Nos. 330/3	..	11·00	15·00

97 Supporters of American Army raiding Royal Magazine   **98** Launching *Ready* (bathysphere)

(Des J. Cooter. Litho J.W.)

1975 (27 Oct). *Bicentenary of Gunpowder Plot, St George's. T* **97** *and similar horiz designs. Multicoloured. W w* **14** *(sideways*). P* 13×13½.

335	5 c. Type **97**	20	10
336	17 c. Setting off for raid	40	40
337	20 c. Loading gunpowder aboard American ship	45	1·40
338	25 c. Gunpowder on beach	50	1·50
	w. Wmk Crown to left of CA	65·00	
335/8	*Set of 4*	1·40	3·00
MS339	165×138 mm. Nos. 335/8. P 14 *(sold for 75 c.)*	2·75	7·00

*The normal sideways watermark shows Crown to right of CA, as seen from the back of the stamp.

1975 (8 Dec)–76. *As Nos.* 250 *and* 254 *but W w* **14** *(sideways).*

340	2 c. Bottlebrush	85	4·00
341	6 c. Hibiscus (11.6.76)	6·00	8·50

Nos. 342/56 vacant.

(Des G. Drummond. Litho Questa)

1976 (29 Mar). *50th Anniv of Bermuda Biological Station. T* **98** *and similar multicoloured designs. W w* **14** *(sideways on 17 and 20 c.). P* 14.

357	5 c. Type **98**	30	10
358	17 c. View from the sea (*horiz*)	60	60
359	20 c. H.M.S. *Challenger*, 1873 (*horiz*)	65	2·25
360	25 c. Beebe's bathysphere descent, 1934	70	2·75
357/60	*Set of 4*	2·00	5·00

99 *Christian Radich* (cadet ship)

(Des R. Granger Barrett. Litho J.W.)

1976 (15 June). *Tall Ships Race, 1976. T* **99** *and similar horiz designs. Multicoloured. W w* **12** *(sideways). P* 13.

361	5 c. Type **99**	75	20
362	12 c. *Juan Sebastian de Elcano* (Spanish cadet schooner)	90	2·00
363	17 c. *Eagle* (U.S. coastguard cadet ship)	1·00	1·75
364	20 c. *Sir Winston Churchill* (cadet schooner)	1·00	2·50
365	40 c. *Kruzenshtern* (Russian cadet barque)	1·25	3·25
366	$1 *Cutty Sark* trophy	1·75	8·00
361/6	*Set of 6*	6·00	16·00

100 Silver Trophy and Club Flags

(Des C. Abbott. Litho Questa)

1976 (16 Aug). *75th Anniv of the St. George's v. Somerset Cricket Cup Match. T* **100** *and similar horiz designs. Multicoloured. W w* **14** *(sideways*). P* 14½×14.

367	5 c. Type **100**	35	10
	w. Wmk Crown to right of CA		
368	17 c. Badge and Pavilion, St. George's Club	60	65
369	20 c. Badge and Pavilion, Somerset Club	80	2·75
370	25 c. Somerset playing field	1·25	3·75
367/70	*Set of 4*	2·75	6·50

*The normal sideways watermark shows Crown to left of CA, as seen from the back of the stamp.

101 Royal Visit, 1975   **102** Stockdale House, St. George's 1784–1812

(Des Harrison. Litho Walsall)

1977 (7 Feb). *Silver Jubilee. T* **101** *and similar vert designs. Multicoloured. W w* 14. *P* 13½.

371	5 c. Type **101**	10	10
	w. Wmk inverted	£110	75·00
372	20 c. St. Edward's Crown	15	20
373	$1 Queen in Chair of Estate	40	1·25
371/3	*Set of 3*	55	1·40

(Des G. Drummond. Litho J.W.)

1977 (20 June). *Centenary of U.P.U. Membership. T* **102** *and similar horiz designs. Multicoloured. W w* 14 *(sideways). P* 13.

374	5 c. Type **102**	15	10
375	15 c. Perot Post Office and stamp	30	50
376	17 c. St. George's P.O. *circa* 1860	30	50
377	20 c. Old G.P.O., Hamilton, *circa* 1935	35	60
378	40 c. New G.P.O., Hamilton, 1967	60	1·10
374/8	*Set of 5*	1·50	2·50

103 17th-Century Ship approaching Castle Island   **104** Great Seal of Queen Elizabeth I

(Des R. Granger-Barrett. Litho Questa)

1977 (26 Sept). *Piloting. T* **103** *and similar horiz designs. Multicoloured. W w* 14 *(sideways). P* 13½.

379	5 c. Type **103**	40	10
380	15 c. Pilot leaving ship, 1795	70	60
381	17 c. Pilots rowing out to paddle-steamer	80	60
382	20 c. Pilot gigs and brig *Harvest Queen*	85	2·25
383	40 c. Modern pilot cutter and R.M.S. *Queen Elizabeth 2*	1·40	3·75
379/83	*Set of 5*	3·75	6·50

(Des BG Studio. Litho Questa)

1978 (28 Aug). *25th Anniv of Coronation. T* **104** *and similar vert designs. Multicoloured. W w* 14. *P* 14 × 13½.

384	8 c. Type **104**	10	10
385	50 c. Great Seal of Queen Elizabeth II	30	30
386	$1 Queen Elizabeth II	60	75
384/6	*Set of 3*	80	1·00

105 White-tailed Tropic Bird

(Des G. Drummond. Photo Harrison)

1978 (15 Nov)–83. *Wildlife. Horiz designs as* T **105**. *Multicoloured. W w* 14 *(sideways* on* 8, 15, 20, 40 *c. and* $1). *P* 14×14½ (4, 5 *c.*, $2, $3, $5) *or* 14 *(others).*

387	3 c. Type **105**	2·25	2·00
	aw. Wmk inverted	17·00	
	b. Perf 14×14½ (3.8.83)†	2·75	2·50
	bw. Wmk inverted		
388	4 c. White-eyed Vireo	1·75	2·00
	w. Wmk inverted	65·00	
389	5 c. Eastern Bluebird	1·25	1·75
	w. Wmk inverted	60·00	30·00
390	7 c. Whistling Frog (19.2.79)	50	1·50
391	8 c. Common Cardinal	1·25	55
392	10 c. Spiny Lobster (19.2.79)	20	10
393	12 c. Land Crab (19.2.79)	30	70
394	15 c. Lizard (Skink) (19.2.79)	30	15
395	20 c. Four-eyed Butterflyfish (12.3.79)	30	30
	w. Wmk Crown to right of CA	1·00	
396	25 c. Red Hind (12.3.79)	30	20
	a. Greenish blue omitted	£3000	
397	30 c. *Danaus plexippus* (butterfly) (19.2.79)	2·25	2·50
398	40 c. Rock Beauty (12.3.79)	45	1·50
399	50 c. Banded Butterflyfish (12.3.79)	55	85
400	$1 Blue Angelfish (12.3.79)	1·75	1·75
	w. Wmk Crown to right of CA	£275	
401	$2 Humpback Whale (12.3.79)	2·00	2·75
402	$3 Green Turtle (19.2.79)	2·75	3·00
403	$5 Cahow	6·50	6·00
387/403	*Set of 17*	22·00	25·00

*The normal sideways watermark shows Crown to left of CA, as seen from the back of the stamp.
†*Earliest known postmark date.*

ALTERED CATALOGUE NUMBERS

Any Catalogue numbers altered from the last edition are shown as a list in the introductory pages.

---

106 Map by Sir George Somers, 1609   **107** Policeman and Policewoman

(Des J. Cooter. Litho Questa)

1979 (14 May). *Antique Maps. T* **106** *and similar multicoloured designs. W w* 14 *(sideways on* 8, 15, 25 *and* 50 *c.) P* 14 × 13½ (20 *c.*) *or* 13½ × 14 *(others).*

404	8 c. Type **106**	15	10
405	15 c. Map by John Seller, 1685	20	15
406	20 c. Map by H. Moll, 1729–40 (*vert*)	25	25
407	25 c. Map by Desbruslins, 1740	30	30
408	50 c. Map by Speed, 1626	45	80
404/8	*Set of 5*	1·25	1·40

(Des L. Curtis. Litho Questa)

1979 (26 Nov). *Centenary of Police Force. T* **107** *and similar multicoloured designs. W w* 14 *(sideways on* 20 *and* 25 *c.). P* 14.

409	8 c. Type **107**	40	10
	w. Wmk inverted	12·00	
410	20 c. Policeman directing traffic (*horiz*)	65	55
411	25 c. *Blue Heron* (police launch) (*horiz*)	75	65
412	50 c. Police car and motorcycle	1·00	1·50
409/12	*Set of 4*	2·50	2·50

108 1848 1d. "Perot" and Penny Black Stamps

(Des J.W. Litho Enschedé)

1980 (25 Feb). *Death Centenary of Sir Rowland Hill* (1979). *T* **108** *and similar horiz designs. Multicoloured. W w* 14 *(sideways). P* 13 × 13½.

413	8 c. Type **108**	15	10
414	20 c. 1848 1d. "Perot" stamp and Sir Rowland Hill	25	25
415	25 c. 1848 1d. "Perot" stamp and early letter	25	30
416	50 c. 1848 1d. "Perot" stamp and "Paid 1" cancellation	35	70
413/16	*Set of 4*	90	1·25

109 Lockheed L-1011 TriStar 500 Airliner approaching Bermuda   **110** Gina Swainson with Rose

(Des R. Granger Barrett. Litho Harrison)

1980 (6 May). *"London 1980" International Stamp Exhibition. Mail-carrying Transport. T* **109** *and similar horiz designs. Multicoloured. W w* 14 *(sideways*). P* 13 × 13½.

417	25 c. Type **109**	30	15
418	50 c. *Orduna I* (liner) in Grassy Bay	45	35
	w. Wmk Crown to right of CA	45·00	
419	$1 *Delta* (screw steamer) at St. George's Harbour	85	1·00
420	$2 *Lord Sidmouth* (sailing packet) in Old Ship Channel, St. George's	1·40	2·00
417/20	*Set of 4*	2·75	3·25

*The normal sideways watermark shows Crown to left of CA, as seen from the back of the stamp.

(Des Walsall. Litho Questa)

1980 (8 May). *"Miss World 1979–80" (Gina Swainson) Commemoration. T* **110** *and similar vert designs. Multicoloured. W w* 14. *P* 14 × 13½.

421	8 c. Type **110**	15	10
422	20 c. After crowning ceremony	20	20
423	50 c. On Peacock Throne at "Welcome Home" party	35	35
424	$1 In Bermuda carriage	70	90
421/4	*Set of 4*	1·25	1·40

111 Queen Elizabeth the Queen Mother

(Des and litho Harrison)

1980 (4 Aug).   *80th Birthday of Queen Elizabeth the Queen Mother.*
W w 14 (*sideways*). P 14.

425	111	25 c. multicoloured		..	..	30	85

112 Bermuda from Satellite   113 Kitchen, 18th-century

(Des L. Curtis. Litho Questa)

1980 (24 Sept).   *Commonwealth Finance Ministers Meeting.*
T 112 and similar horiz designs. Multicoloured. W w 14
(*sideways*). P 14.

426	8 c. Type 112	..	..	..	10	10
427	20 c. "Camden"	..	..	20	40
428	25 c. Princess Hotel, Hamilton	..	20	50
	w. Wmk Crown to right of CA	..	75·00	
429	50 c. Government House	..	..	35	1·25
426/9			Set of 4	75	2·00

*The normal sideways watermark shows Crown to left of CA,
as seen from the back of the stamp.

(Des J.W. Litho Questa)

1981 (21 May).   *Heritage Week. T 113 and similar horiz*
designs. Multicoloured. W w 14 (*sideways**). P 14.

430	8 c. Type 113	..	..	..	15	10
	w. Wmk Crown to right of CA	..	8·00	
431	25 c. Gathering Easter lilies, 20th-century	40	50
432	30 c. Fishing, 20th-century	..	60	70
433	40 c. Stone cutting, 19th-century	..	60	1·00
	w. Wmk Crown to right of CA	..	1·10	
434	50 c. Onion shipping, 19th-century	..	90	1·25
435	$1 Privateering, 17th-century	..	1·60	2·75
430/5			Set of 6	3·75	5·50

*The normal sideways watermark shows Crown to left of CA,
as seen from the back of the stamp.

114 Wedding Bouquet   115 "Service", Hamilton
from Bermuda

(Des J.W. Litho Questa)

1981 (22 July).   *Royal Wedding. T 114 and similar vert designs.*
Multicoloured. W w 14. P 14.

436	30 c. Type 114	..	..	..	20	20
437	50 c. Prince Charles as Royal Navy Commander	..	35	40
438	$1 Prince Charles and Lady Diana Spencer	55	80
436/8	..		Set of 3	1·00	1·25

(Des L. Curtis. Litho Questa)

1981 (28 Sept).   *25th Anniv of Duke of Edinburgh Award Scheme.*
T 115 and similar vert designs. Multicoloured. W w 14. P 14.

439	10 c. Type 115	..	..	..	15	10
440	25 c. "Outward Bound", Paget Island	..	20	20
441	30 c. "Expedition", St. David's Island	..	20	30
442	$1 Duke of Edinburgh	..	..	55	1·25
439/42	..		Set of 4	1·00	1·75

116 Lightbourne's Cone
(*Conus lightbourni*)

(Des Walsall. Litho Questa)

1982 (22 Apr).   *Sea-shells. T 116 and similar horiz designs. Multi-*
coloured. W w 14 (*sideways*). P 14.

443	10 c. Type 116	..	..	..	40	10
444	25 c. Finlay's Frog Shell (*Bursa finlayi*)	..	80	75
445	30 c. Royal Bonnet (*Sconsia striata*)	..	85	85
446	$1 Lightbourne's Murex (*Murex light-* *bourni*)	..	..	2·25	3·25
443/6			Set of 4	3·75	4·50

117 Regimental Colours and   118 Charles Fort
Colour Party

(Des G. Drummond. Litho Questa)

1982 (17 June).   *Bermuda Regiment. T 117 and similar horiz*
designs. Multicoloured. W w 14 (*sideways*). P 14.

447	10 c. Type 117	..	..	..	55	10
448	25 c. Queen's Birthday Parade	..	1·00	80
449	30 c. Governor inspecting Guard of Honour	..	1·25	1·40
450	40 c. Beating the Retreat	..	1·40	1·75
451	50 c. Ceremonial gunners	..	1·40	2·00
452	$1 Guard of Honour, Royal visit, 1975	..	2·25	3·50
447/52			Set of 6	7·00	8·50

(Des L. Curtis. Litho Questa)

1982 (18 Nov).   *Historic Bermuda Forts. T 118 and similar multi-*
coloured designs. W w 14 (*sideways on 30 c. and $1*). P 14.

453	10 c. Type 118	..	..	..	20	20
454	25 c. Pembroks Fort	..	..	50	85
455	30 c. Southampton Fort (*horiz*)	..	60	1·25
456	$1 Smiths Fort and Pagets Fort (*horiz*)	..	1·75	4·25
453/6			Set of 4	2·75	6·00

119 Arms of Sir Edwin Sandys   120 Early Fitted Dinghy

(Des Harrison. Litho J.W.)

1983 (14 Apr).   *Coats of Arms (1st series). T 119 and similar vert*
designs. Multicoloured. W w 14. P 13.

457	10 c. Type 119	..	..	..	45	15
458	25 c. Arms of the Bermuda Company.	..	1·40	1·00
459	50 c. Arms of William Herbert, Earl of Pembroke	..	2·25	3·25
460	$1 Arms of Sir George Somers	..	3·00	5·50
457/60			Set of 4	6·50	9·00

See also Nos. 482/5 and 499/502.

(Des L. Curtis. Litho Harrison)

1983 (23 June).   *Fitted Dinghies. T 120 and similar vert designs.*
Multicoloured. W w 14 (*sideways*). P 14.

461	12 c. Type 120	..	..	..	45	15
462	30 c. Modern dinghy inshore	..	75	75
463	40 c. Early dinghy (*different*)	..	90	90
464	$1 Modern dinghy with red and white spinnaker	..	1·75	3·25
461/4	..		Set of 4	3·50	4·50

121 Curtiss N-9 Seaplane   122 Joseph Stockdale
(first flight over Bermuda)

(Des A. Theobald. Litho Walsall)

1983 (13 Oct).   *Bicentenary of Manned Flight. T 121 and similar*
horiz designs. Multicoloured. W w 14 (*sideways*). P 14.

465	12 c. Type 121	..	..	60	20
466	30 c. Stinson Pilot Radio seaplane (First completed flight between U.S.A. and Bermuda)	1·25	1·25
467	40 c. Short S.23 flying boat *Cavalier* (First scheduled passenger flight)	1·50	1·75
468	$1 U.S.N. *Los Angeles* (airship) moored to U.S.S. *Patoka*	..	2·50	5·00
465/8		Set of 4	5·25	7·50

(Des L. Curtis. Litho Harrison)

1984 (26 Jan).   *Bicentenary of Bermuda's First Newspaper and*
Postal Service. T 122 and similar multicoloured designs.
W w 14 (*sideways* on 40 c. and $1). P 14.

469	12 c. Type 122	..	..	30	15
470	30 c. *The Bermuda Gazette*	..	60	80
471	40 c. Stockdale's postal service (*horiz*)	80	1·10
	w. Wmk Crown to right of CA	..	£200	
472	$1 *Lady Hammond* (mail boat) (*horiz*)	2·75	3·25
469/72		Set of 4	4·00	4·75

*The normal sideways watermark shows Crown to left of CA,
as seen from the back of the stamp.

123 Sir Thomas Gates and Sir   124 Swimming
George Somers

(Des R. Granger Barrett. Litho Walsall)

1984 (3 May).   *375th Anniv of First Settlement. T 123 and similar*
horiz designs. Multicoloured. W w 14 (*sideways*). P 14.

473	12 c. Type 123	..	..	20	15
474	30 c. Jamestown, Virginia	..	50	1·25
475	40 c. Wreck of *Sea Venture*	..	90	1·25
476	$1 Fleet leaving Plymouth, Devon	2·00	5·00
473/6		Set of 4	3·25	7·00
MS477	130×73 mm. Nos. 474 and 476	..	3·75	8·50

(Des C. Collins. Litho J.W.)

1984 (19 July).   *Olympic Games, Los Angeles. T 124 and similar*
multicoloured designs. W w 14 (*sideways on 30 c., $1*). P 14.

478	12 c. Type 124	..	..	40	15
479	30 c. Track and field events (*horiz*)	..	70	85
480	40 c. Equestrian competition	..	1·25	1·25
481	$1 Sailing (*horiz*)	..	..	2·50	5·50
478/81		Set of 4	4·25	7·00

(Des Harrison. Litho J.W.)

1984 (27 Sept).   *Coats of Arms (2nd series). Vert designs as T 119.*
Multicoloured. W w 14. P 13.

482	12 c. Arms of Henry Wriothesley, Earl of Southampton	..	..	50	15
483	30 c. Arms of Sir Thomas Smith	..	1·00	85
	w. Wmk inverted	..	1·25	
484	40 c. Arms of William Cavendish, Earl of Devonshire	..	1·25	1·50
485	$1 Town arms of St. George	..	2·75	4·00
482/5		Set of 4	5·00	6·00

125 Buttery   126 Osprey

(Des D. Miller. Litho Walsall)

1985 (24 Jan).   *Bermuda Architecture. T 125 and similar multi-*
coloured designs. W w 14 (*inverted on 12 c., $1.50, sideways on*
30 c., 40 c.). P 13½ × 13 (12 c., $1.50) or 13 × 13½ (30 c., 40 c.).

486	12 c. Type 125	..	..	35	15
487	30 c. Limestone rooftops (*horiz*)	..	80	70
488	40 c. Chimneys (*horiz*)	..	95	1·00
489	$1.50, Entrance archway	..	3·00	3·75
486/9		Set of 4	4·75	5·00

(Des D. Miller. Litho Walsall)

1985 (28 Mar).   *Birth Bicentenary of John J. Audubon (orni-*
thologist). T 126 and similar multicoloured designs showing
original drawings. W w 14 (*sideways on 40 c.*). P 14.

490	12 c. Type 126	..	..	2·00	65
491	30 c. Yellow-crowned Night Heron	..	2·00	95
492	40 c. Great Egret (*horiz*)	..	2·25	1·25
493	$1.50, Eastern Bluebird	..	3·75	6·50
490/3		Set of 4	9·00	8·50

127 The Queen Mother with Grandchildren, 1980   **128** Halley's Comet and Bermuda Archipelago

(Des A. Theobald ($1), C. Abbott (others). Litho Questa)

1985 (7 June). *Life and Times of Queen Elizabeth the Queen Mother. T* **127** *and similar vert designs. Multicoloured.* W w **16**. *P* 14½×14.

494	12 c. Queen Consort, 1937	..	25	15
	w. Wmk inverted	..	†	
495	30 c. Type **127**	..	40	50
	w. Wmk inverted	..	1·50	
496	40 c. At Clarence House on 83rd birthday		50	60
497	$1.50, With Prince Henry at his christening (from photo by Lord Snowdon)		2·00	2·75
494/7		*Set of 4*	2·75	3·50
MS498	91×73 mm. $1 With Prince Charles at 80th birthday celebrations. Wmk sideways		2·00	2·25

(Des Harrison. Litho J.W.)

1985 (19 Sept). *Coats of Arms (3rd series). Vert designs as T* **119**. *Multicoloured.* W w **14**. *P* 13×13½.

499	12 c. Hamilton	..	75	15
500	30 c. Paget	..	1·40	80
501	40 c. Warwick	..	1·60	1·40
502	$1.50, City of Hamilton	..	3·75	4·25
499/502		*Set of 4*	6·75	6·00

(Des Jennifer Toombs. Litho Walsall)

1985 (21 Nov). *Appearance of Halley's Comet. T* **128** *and similar horiz designs. Multicoloured.* W w **16** *(sideways). P* 14×14½.

503	15 c. Type **128**.	..	85	25
504	40 c. Halley's Comet, A.D. 684 (from Nuremberg Chronicles, 1493)		1·60	1·75
505	50 c. "Halley's Comet, 1531" (from Peter Apian woodcut, 1532)		1·90	2·50
506	$1.50, "Halley's Comet, 1759" (Samuel Scott)		3·50	5·00
503/6		*Set of 4*	7·00	8·50

129 *Constellation* (schooner), 1943

(Des L. Curtis. Litho Questa)

1986 (16 Jan)–90. *Ships Wrecked on Bermuda. T* **129** *and similar horiz designs. Multicoloured.* W w **16** *(sideways*). P* 14. A. *Without imprint date at foot*

507A	3 c. Type **129**	..	70	1·00
508A	5 c. *Early Riser* (pilot boat), 1876		20	20
509A	7 c. *Madiana* (steamer), 1903 (20.3.86)		65	85
510A	10 c. *Curlew* (sail/steamer), 1856		30	30
511A	12 c. *Warwick* (galleon), 1619		60	80
	w. Wmk Crown to right of CA			
512A	15 c. H.M.S. *Vixen* (gunboat), 1890 (18.9.86)		40	60
512cA	18 c. As 7 c. (22.9.88)		5·00	2·75
513A	20 c. *San Pedro* (Spanish galleon), 1594 (20.3.86)		1·10	80
514A	25 c. *Alert* (fishing sloop), 1877 (18.9.86)		60	1·75
515A	40 c. *North Carolina* (barque), 1880 (18.9.86)		65	1·25
516A	50 c. *Mark Antonie* (Spanish privateer), 1777 (18.9.86)		1·50	2·00
517A	60 c. *Mary Celestia* (Confederate paddle-steamer), 1864 (20.3.86)		1·50	1·75
517cA	70 c. *Caesar* (brig), 1818 (27.10.88)		5·50	4·50
518A	$1 *L'Herminie* (French frigate), 1839 (18.9.86)		4·00	4·50
519A	$1.50, As 70 c. (20.3.86)		4·50	4·50
520A	$2 *Lord Amherst* (transport), 1778 (20.3.86)		7·00	8·00
521A	$3 *Minerva* (sailing ship), 1849 (20.3.86)		7·50	9·00
522A	$5 *Caraquet* (cargo liner), 1923 (18.9.86)		6·50	11·00
523A	$8 H.M.S. *Pallas* (frigate), 1783		8·00	12·00
507A/23A		*Set of 19*	48·00	55·00

B. *With imprint date*

507B	3 c. Type **129** (1.8.90)		1·75	2·75
513B	20 c. *San Pedro* (Spanish galleon), 1594 (1.8.90)		3·00	3·25
518B	$1 *L'Herminie* (French frigate), 1839 (7.89)		1·50	1·60
520B	$2 *Lord Amherst* (transport), 1778 (7.89)		2·50	3·50
521B	$3 *Minerva* (sailing ship), 1849 (7.89)		4·25	5·00
507B/21B		*Set of 5*	11·50	15·00

*The normal sideways watermark shows Crown to left of CA, *as seen from the back of the stamp.*

It is reported that the vessel depicted on the 70 c. is the *Wolf* and not the *Caesar.*

Imprint dates: "1989", Nos. 518B, 520B/1/B; "1990", Nos. 507B, 513B.

No. 523A shows "BERMUDA" printed in yellow fluorescent ink as a security marking.

For some of these designs watermarked w **14** (sideways) see Nos. 664/78.

(Des A. Theobald. Litho Harrison)

1986 (21 Apr). *60th Birthday of Queen Elizabeth II. Vert designs as T* **110** *of Ascension. Multicoloured.* W w **16**. *P* 14½×14.

524	15 c. Princess Elizabeth aged three, 1929	..	35	30
	w. Wmk inverted		19·00	
525	40 c. With Earl of Rosebery at Oaks May Meeting, Epsom, 1954		70	60
526	50 c. With Duke of Edinburgh, Bermuda, 1975		70	75
527	60 c. At British Embassy, Paris, 1972		80	90
528	$1.50, At Crown Agents Head Office, London, 1983		2·00	2·50
524/8		*Set of 5*	4·00	4·50

(Des G. Drummond. Litho Walsall)

1986 (22 May). *"Ameripex '86" International Stamp Exhibition, Chicago. Horiz designs as T* **164** *of Bahamas, showing Bermuda stamps (Nos. 529/32). Multicoloured.* W w **16** *(sideways). P* 14.

529	15 c. 1984 375th Anniv of Settlement miniature sheet.		1·00	30
530	40 c. 1973 Lawn Tennis Centenary 24 c.		1·75	70
531	50 c. 1983 Bicentenary of Manned Flight 12 c.		1·75	1·00
532	$1 1976 Tall Ships Race 17 c.		3·25	3·00
529/32		*Set of 4*	7·00	4·50
MS533	80×80 mm. $1.50, Statue of Liberty and *Monarch of Bermuda*		6·00	5·00

No. MS533 also commemorates the Centenary of the Statue of Liberty.

(130)

1986 (4 Dec). *25th Anniv of World Wildlife Fund. No. 402 surch with T* **130** *by J. W. Dunn Printers Ltd, Sutton, Surrey.*

534	90 c. on $3 Green Turtle	..	2·25	3·50
	a. Surch double	..	90·00	
	b. Surch double, one inverted	..	£425	
	c. "90 c" omitted			

131 Train in Front Street, Hamilton, 1940

(Des A. Theobald. Litho Walsall)

1987 (22 Jan). *Transport (1st series). Bermuda Railway. T* **131** *and similar horiz designs. Multicoloured.* W w **16** *(sideways). P* 14.

535	15 c. Type **131**.	..	1·50	25
536	40 c. Train crossing Springfield Trestle		2·00	90
537	50 c. "St. George Special" at Bailey's Bay Station		2·00	1·50
538	$1 50, Boat train at St. George		3·50	4·00
535/8		*Set of 4*	8·00	6·00

See also Nos. 557/60, 574/7 and 624/9.

132 "Bermuda Settlers", 1901

(Des L. Curtis. Litho Walsall)

1987 (30 Apr). *Bermuda Paintings (1st series). Works by Winslow Homer. T* **132** *and similar horiz designs. Multicoloured.* W w **16** *(sideways). P* 14×14½.

(a) *Sheet stamps (No. 541 with a buff frame).*

539	15 c. Type **132**.		60	25
540	30 c. "Bermuda", 1900		85	45
541	40 c. "Bermuda Landscape", 1901		95	55
542	50 c. "Inland Water", 1901		1·10	70
543	$1.50, "Salt Kettle", 1899	..	2·50	2·50
539/43		*Set of 5*	5·50	4·00

(b) *Booklet stamps, each with grey frame*

544	40 c. Type **132**.		90	1·60
	a. Booklet pane. Nos. 544/8, each × 2		8·00	
545	40 c. As No. 540		90	1·60
546	40 c. As No. 541		90	1·60
547	40 c. As No. 542		90	1·60
548	40 c. As No. 543		90	1·60
544/8		*Set of 5*	4·00	7·00

See also Nos. 607/10 and 630/3.

NEW INFORMATION

The editor is always interested to correspond with people who have new information that will improve or correct the Catalogue.

---

133 Sikorsky S-42B Flying Boat *Bermuda Clipper* of Pan Am

(Des A. Theobald. Litho Walsall)

1987 (18 June). *50th Anniv of Inauguration of Bermuda – U.S.A. Air Service. T* **133** *and similar horiz designs. Multicoloured.* W w **16** *(sideways). P* 14.

549	15 c. Type **133**		1·25	15
550	40 c. Short S.23 flying boat *Cavalier* of Imperial Airways		2·25	70
551	50 c. *Bermuda Clipper* in flight over signpost		2·50	80
552	$1.50, *Cavalier* on apron and *Bermuda Clipper* in flight		5·00	3·50
549/52		*Set of 4*	10·00	4·75

134 19th-century Wagon carrying Telephone Poles   **135** Mail Wagon, c. 1869

(Des L. Curtis. Litho B.D.T.)

1987 (1 Oct). *Centenary of Bermuda Telephone Company. T* **134** *and similar horiz designs. Multicoloured.* W w **16** *(sideways). P* 14×13½.

553	15 c. Type **134**.		75	15
554	40 c. Early telephone exchange		1·40	60
555	50 c. Early and modern telephones		1·75	70
556	$1.50, Communications satellite orbiting Earth		2·75	3·50
553/6		*Set of 4*	6·00	4·50

(Des O. Bell. Litho Questa)

1988 (3 Mar). *Transport (2nd series). Horse-drawn Carts and Wagons. T* **135** *and similar horiz designs. Multicoloured.* W w **16** *(sideways). P* 14.

557	15 c. Type **135**.		25	15
558	40 c. Open cart, c. 1823		55	55
559	50 c. Closed cart, c. 1823		65	65
560	$1.50, Two-wheeled wagon, c. 1930		2·00	2·50
557/60		*Set of 4*	3·00	3·50

136 "Old Blush"   **137** Devonshire Parish Militia, 1812

(Des R. Gorringe. Litho B.D.T.)

1988 (21 Apr). *Old Garden Roses (1st series). T* **136** *and similar multicoloured designs.* W w **14** *(sideways on horiz designs). P* 14×13½ *(vert) or* 13½×14 *(horiz).*

561	15 c. Type **136**		55	25
562	30 c. "Anna Olivier"		75	45
563	40 c. *Rosa chinensis semperflorens* (vert)		85	75
564	50 c. "Archduke Charles"		95	1·00
565	$1.50, *Rosa chinensis viridiflora* (vert)		2·50	3·50
561/5		*Set of 5*	5·00	5·50

See also Nos. 584/8 and, for these designs with the royal cypher instead of the Queen's head, Nos. 589/98, and 683/6.

(Des D. Miller (18 c.), E. Nisbet and D. Miller (others). Litho Questa)

1988 (13 Oct). *300th Anniv of Lloyd's of London. Multicoloured designs as T* **123** *of Ascension.* W w **16** *(sideways* on* 50, 60 c.). *P* 14.

566	18 c. Loss of H.M.S. *Lutine* (frigate), 1799		45	25
	w. Wmk inverted		10·00	
567	50 c. *Sentinel* (cable ship) (horiz)		1·00	65
	w. Wmk Crown to right of CA		15·00	
568	60 c. *Bermuda* (liner), Hamilton, 1931 (horiz)		1·10	75
	w. Wmk Crown to right of CA		12·00	
569	$2 Loss of H.M.S. *Valerian* (sloop) in hurricane, 1926		3·00	3·25
566/9		*Set of 4*	5·00	4·50

*The normal sideways watermark shows Crown to left of CA, *as seen from the back of the stamp.*

(Des A. Barbosa. Litho Harrison)

1988 (10 Nov). *Military Uniforms. T* **137** *and similar vert designs. Multicoloured. W* w **14**. *P* 14½.

570	18 c. Type **137**	1·00	25
571	50 c. 71st (Highland) Regiment, 1831-34	1·60	95
572	60 c. Cameron Highlanders, 1942	1·75	1·10
573	$2 Troop of horse, 1774	4·50	5·50
570/3	Set of 4	8·00	7·00

138 *Corona* (ferry)

139 Morgan's Island

(Des C. Abbott, adapted L. Curtis. Litho Questa)

1989 (16 Feb). *Transport (3rd series). Ferry Services. T* **138** *and similar horiz designs. Multicoloured. W* w **16** *(sideways). P* 14.

574	18 c. Type **138**	35	25
575	50 c. Rowing boat ferry	75	65
576	60 c. St. George's barge ferry	85	75
577	$2 *Laconia*	2·50	3·00
574/7	Set of 4	4·00	4·25

(Des A. Theobald. Litho Questa)

1989 (11 May). *150 Years of Photography. T* **139** *and similar horiz designs. Multicoloured. W* w **14** *(sideways). P* 14 × 14½.

578	18 c. Type **139**	55	25
579	30 c. Front Street, Hamilton	75	45
580	50 c. Waterfront, Front Street, Hamilton	1·10	1·00
581	60 c. Crow Lane from Hamilton Harbour	1·25	1·25
582	70 c. Shipbuilding, Hamilton Harbour	1·40	1·75
583	$1 Dockyard	2·00	2·50
578/83	Set of 6	6·25	6·50

(Des R. Gorringe. Litho B.D.T.)

1989 (13 July). *Old Garden Roses (2nd series). Multicoloured designs as T* **136**. *W* w **14** *(sideways on 50, 60 c. and $1.50). P* 14×13½ (18, 30 c.) or 13½×14 (others).

584	18 c. "Agrippina" (vert)	50	25
585	30 c. "Smith's Parish" (vert)	65	60
586	50 c. "Champney's Pink Cluster"	1·00	1·25
587	60 c. "Rosette Delizy"	1·10	1·60
588	$1.50, *Rosa bracteata*	2·00	3·50
584/8	Set of 5	4·75	6·50

For these designs with the royal cypher instead of the Queen's head, see Nos. 589/98.

1989 (13 July). *Old Garden Roses (3rd series). Designs as Nos.* **561/5** *and* **584/8**, *but with royal cypher at top left instead of Queen's head. Multicoloured. W* w **14** *(sideways on horiz, inverted on vert designs). P* 13½.

589	50 c. As No. 565 (vert)	1·40	1·60
	a. Booklet pane. Nos. 589/98	12·00	
590	50 c. As No. 563 (vert)	1·40	1·60
591	50 c. Type **136**	1·40	1·60
592	50 c. As No. 562	1·40	1·60
593	50 c. As No. 564	1·40	1·60
594	50 c. As No. 585 (vert)	1·40	1·60
595	50 c. As No. 584 (vert)	1·40	1·60
596	50 c. As No. 586	1·40	1·60
597	50 c. As No. 587	1·40	1·60
598	50 c. As No. 588	1·40	1·60
589/98	Set of 10	12·00	14·00

Nos. 589/98 were only issued in $5 stamp booklets in which the pane has margins on three sides.

140 Main Library, Hamilton

141 1865 1d. Rose

(Des O. Bell. Litho B.D.T.)

1989 (5 Oct). *150th Anniv of Bermuda Library. T* **140** *and similar horiz designs. Multicoloured. W* w **14** *(sideways). P* 13½×14.

599	18 c. Type **140**	30	25
600	50 c. The Old Rectory, St. George's	70	65
601	60 c. Somerset Library, Springfield	80	75
602	$2 Cabinet Building, Hamilton	2·75	3·00
599/602	Set of 4	4·00	4·25

(Des D. Miller. Litho Questa)

1989 (3 Nov). *Commonwealth Postal Conference. T* **141** *and similar vert designs. Multicoloured. W* w **16**. *P* 14.

603	18 c. brownish grey, brown-rose & brt scar	85	25
604	50 c. brownish grey, slate-bl & pale grey-bl	1·50	75
605	60 c. brownish grey, dull purple and purple	1·60	1·25
606	$2 brownish grey, dull green & brt emer	3·00	4·50
603/6	Set of 4	6·25	6·00

Designs:—50 c. 1866 2d. blue; 60 c. 1865 6d purple; $2 1865 1s. green.

142 "Fairylands, *c.* 1890" (Ross Turner)

(143)

(Des L. Curtis. Litho B.D.T.)

1990 (19 Apr). *Bermuda Paintings (2nd series). T* **142** *and similar horiz designs. Multicoloured. W* w **16** *(sideways). P* 13½.

607	18 c. Type **142**	60	25
608	50 c. "Shinebone Alley, *c.* 1953" (Ogden Pleissner)	1·10	1·10
609	60 c. "Salt Kettle, 1916" (Prosper Senat)	1·25	1·50
610	$2 "St. George's, 1934" (Jack Bush)	3·00	5·50
607/10	Set of 4	5·50	7·50

1990 (3 May). *"Stamp World London 90" International Stamp Exhibition, London. Nos.* 603/6 *optd with T* **143**.

611	18 c. brownish grey, brown-rose & brt scar	85	25
612	50 c. brownish grey, slate-bl & pale grey-bl	1·50	1·50
613	60 c. brownish grey, dull purple and purple	1·60	1·75
614	$2 brownish grey, dull green & brt emer	3·25	5·50
611/14	Set of 4	6·50	8·00

(144)

145 The Halifax and Bermudas Cable Company Office, Hamilton

1990 (13 Aug). *Nos.* 511A, 516A *and* 519A *surch as T* **144**.

615	30 c. on 12 c. *Warwick* (galleon), 1619	1·00	80
616	55 c. on 50 c. *Mark Antonie* (Spanish privateer), 1777	1·50	1·50
617	80 c. on $1.50 *Caesar* (brig), 1818	2·00	3·25
615/17	Set of 3	4·00	5·00

(Des C. Abbott. Litho Harrison)

1990 (18 Oct). *Centenary of Cable and Wireless in Bermuda. T* **145** *and similar horiz designs. P* 14.

618	20 c. light brown and black	70	25
619	55 c. light brown and black	2·00	1·25
620	70 c. multicoloured	2·00	2·25
621	$2 multicoloured	4·75	6·00
618/21	Set of 4	8·50	8·75

Designs:—55 c. *Westmeath* (cable ship), 1890; 70 c. Wireless transmitter station, St. George's, 1928; $2 *Sir Eric Sharp* (cable ship).

BUSH - MAJOR
16 MARCH 1991
(146)

147 Two-seater Pony Cart, 1805

1991 (16 Mar). *President Bush – Prime Minister Major Talks, Bermuda. Nos.* 618/19 *optd with T* **146** *by Island Press.*

622	**145**	20 c. light brown and black	1·50	75
623	—	55 c. light brown and black	2·50	3·00

(Des N. Shering. Litho Walsall)

1991 (21 Mar). *Transport (4th series). Horse-drawn Carriages. T* **147** *and similar horiz designs. Multicoloured. W* w **14** *(sideways). P* 14½.

624	20 c. Type **147**	80	30
625	30 c. Varnished rockaway, 1830	90	60
626	55 c. Vis-a-Vis victoria, 1895	1·60	1·10
627	70 c. Semi-formal phaeton, 1900	2·25	2·25
628	80 c. Pony runabout, 1905	2·50	2·75
629	$1 Ladies phaeton, 1910	2·75	3·50
624/9	Set of 6	9·75	9·50

148 "Bermuda, 1916" (Prosper Senat)

149 H.M.S. *Argonaut* (cruiser) in Floating Dock

(Des L. Curtis. Litho Questa)

1991 (16 May). *Bermuda Paintings (3rd series). T* **148** *and similar multicoloured designs. W* w **14** *(sideways on 55 c., $2). P* 13½×14 (20, 70 c.) or 14×13½ (55 c., $2).

630	20 c. Type **148**	1·00	30
631	55 c. "Bermuda Cottage", 1930 (Frank Allison) (horiz)	2·00	1·40
632	70 c. "Old Maid's Lane", 1934 (Jack Bush)	2·50	3·00
633	$2 "St. George's", 1953 (Ogden Pleissner) (horiz)	5·00	7·00
630/3	Set of 4	9·50	10·50

(Des D. Miller. Litho Questa)

1991 (20 June). *65th Birthday of Queen Elizabeth II and 70th Birthday of Prince Philip. Vert designs as T* **139** *of Ascension. Multicoloured. W* w **16** *(sideways). P* 14½×14.

634	55 c. Prince Philip in tropical naval uniform	1·25	1·50
	a. Horiz pair. Nos. 634/5 separated by label	2·50	3·00
635	70 c. Queen Elizabeth II in Bermuda	1·25	1·50

Nos. 634/5 were printed together in a similar sheet format to Nos. 539/40 of Ascension.

(Des N. Shewring. Litho Walsall)

1991 (19 Sept). *50th Anniv of Second World War. T* **149** *and similar horiz designs. Multicoloured. W* w **14** *(sideways). P* 14.

636	20 c. Type **149**	1·50	40
637	55 c. Kindley Airfield	2·25	1·40
638	70 c. Boeing 314A flying boat and map of Atlantic route	2·75	3·00
639	$2 Censored trans-Atlantic mail	4·50	7·00
636/9	Set of 4	10·00	10·50

(Des D. Miller. Litho Questa ($1), B.D.T. (others))

1992 (6 Feb). *40th Anniv of Queen Elizabeth II's Accession. Horiz designs as T* **143** *of Ascension. Multicoloured. W* w **14** *(sideways). P* 14.

640	20 c. Old fort on beach	60	30
641	30 c. Public gardens	75	55
642	55 c. Cottage garden	1·25	90
643	70 c. Beach and hotels	1·60	2·00
644	$1 Queen Elizabeth II	1·90	2·50
640/4	Set of 5	5·50	5·50

150 Rings and Medallion

(Des N. Shewring. Litho Enschedé)

1992 (23 July). *500th Anniv of Discovery of America by Columbus. Spanish Artifacts. T* **150** *and similar horiz designs. Multicoloured. W* w **14** *(sideways). P* 13½.

645	25 c. Type **150**	1·00	35
646	35 c. Ink wells	1·10	75
647	60 c. Gold ornaments	2·00	2·00
648	75 c. Bishop buttons and crucifix	2·25	3·00
649	85 c. Earrings and pearl buttons	2·50	3·25
650	$1 Jug and bowls	2·75	4·00
645/50	Set of 6	10·50	12·00

151 "Wreck of *Sea Venture*"

(Des D. Miller. Litho Questa)

1992 (24 Sept). *Stained Glass Windows. T* **151** *and similar horiz designs. Multicoloured. W* w **14** *(sideways). P* 13½×14.

651	25 c. Type **151**	1·00	40
652	60 c. "Birds in tree"	2·25	2·25
653	75 c. "St. Francis feeding bird"	2·75	3·00
654	$2 "Shells"	6·00	7·00
651/4	Set of 4	11·00	11·00

152 German Shepherd

153 Policeman, Cyclist and Liner

(Des Jacqueline Murray-Hall, adapted D. Miller. Litho Enschedé)

1992 (12 Nov). *7th World Congress of Kennel Clubs.* T **152** and similar multicoloured designs. W w **14** (sideways on 25, 35 c.). P 13½.

655	25 c. Type **152**			1·25	40
656	35 c. Irish Setter			1·50	70
657	60 c. Whippet (vert)			2·25	2·25
658	75 c. Border Terrier (vert)			2·25	3·00
659	85 c. Pomeranian (vert)			2·50	3·50
660	$1 Schipperke (vert)			2·50	4·00
655/60			Set of 6	11·00	12·50

1993 (25 Feb). As Nos. 510, 512, 513/14, 517 and 522/3, but W w **14** (sideways). With "1992" imprint date. P 14.

664	10 c. Curlew (sail/steamer), 1856		1·25	1·50
665	15 c. H.M.S. Vixen (gunboat), 1890		1·75	1·50
667	20 c. San Pedro (Spanish galleon), 1594		1·75	1·50
668	25 c. Alert (fishing sloop), 1877		1·75	60
672	60 c. Mary Celestia (Confederate paddle-steamer), 1864		3·00	1·75
677	$5 Caraquet (cargo liner), 1923		9·00	9·00
678	$8 H.M.S. Pallas (frigate), 1788		15·00	16·00
664/78		Set of 7	30·00	28·00

No. 678 does not have the fluorescent security marking present on the previous printing, No. 523A.

(Des adapted D. Miller. Litho Questa)

1993 (25 Feb). *Tourism Posters by Adolph Treidler.* T **153** and similar vert designs. Multicoloured. W w **14**. P 14.

679	25 c. Type **153**			1·50	70
680	60 c. Seaside golf course			2·25	2·25
681	75 c. Deserted beach			2·25	2·75
682	$2 Dancers in evening dress and liner		4·00	6·00
679/82			Set of 4	9·00	10·50

154 "Duchesse de Brabant" and Bee

(Des D. Miller. Litho Questa)

1993 (1 Apr). *Garden Roses* (4th series). W w **16** (sideways). P 14.

683	**154** 10 c. multicoloured		50	75
	a. Booklet pane. Nos. 683×2 and 685×3 with margins all round		3·50	
	b. Pane. No. 683×10 with margins all round		4·50	
684	25 c. multicoloured		40	40
	a. Booklet pane. No. 684×5 with margins all round		1·75	
685	50 c. multicoloured		1·00	1·75
686	60 c. multicoloured		75	1·10
	a. Booklet pane. No. 686×5 with margins all round		3·75	
683/6		Set of 4	2·40	3·50

The 10 c. was available as a loose pane of 10 and from $2·95 stamp booklets which also contained the 25 c. and 50 c. values. The 25 c. was also issued, together with the 60 c., in $4·25 booklets.

(Des A. Theobald. Litho Questa)

1993 (1 Apr). *75th Anniv of Royal Air Force.* Horiz designs as T **149** of Ascension. Multicoloured. W w **14** (sideways). P 14.

687	25 c. Consolidated PBY-5 Catalina		75	35
688	60 c. Supermarine Spitfire Mk IX		1·75	2·00
689	75 c. Bristol Type 156 Beaufighter Mk X		1·90	2·25
690	$2 Handley Page Halifax Mk III		3·50	4·50
687/90		Set of 4	7·00	8·00

155 Hamilton from the Sea

(Des R. Baxter and Sheila Semos (25 c.), N. Shewring and Sheila Semos (others). Litho Questa)

1993 (16 Sept). *Bicentenary of Hamilton.* T **155** and similar horiz designs. Multicoloured. W w **14** (sideways). P 14½.

691	25 c. Type **155**		75	35
692	60 c. Waterfront		1·75	2·00
693	75 c. Barrel warehouse		2·00	2·00
694	$2 Sailing ships off Hamilton		4·00	5·00
691/4		Set of 4	7·75	8·75

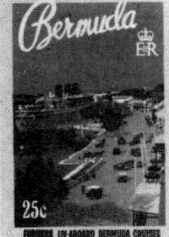

156 Queen of Bermuda (liner) at Hamilton

157 Queen Elizabeth II in Bermuda

(Des adapted D. Miller. Litho B.D.T.)

1994 (20 Jan). *75th Anniv of Furness Line's Bermuda Cruises.* T **156** and similar multicoloured designs showing Adolph Treidler posters. W w **16** (sideways on 60 c. and 75 c.). P 15×14 (vert) or 14×15 (horiz).

695	25 c. Type **156**		60	35
696	60 c. Monarch of Bermuda entering port (horiz)		1·50	1·60
697	75 c. Queen of Bermuda and Ocean Monarch (liners) (horiz)		1·60	1·75
698	$2 Passengers on promenade deck at night		3·50	5·00
695/8		Set of 4	6·50	8·00

The vessel depicted on the 60 c. was incorrectly identified as the Queen of Bermuda on the original, 1930s, travel poster.

(Des D. Miller. Litho Enschedé)

1994 (9 Mar). *Royal Visit.* T **157** and similar vert designs. Multicoloured. W w **14**. P 14.

699	25 c. Type **157**		65	35
700	60 c. Queen Elizabeth and Prince Philip in open carriage		1·50	1·75
701	75 c. Royal Yacht Britannia		3·00	2·75
699/701		Set of 3	4·75	4·25

158 Peach

159 Nurse with Mother and Baby

(Des Christine Phillips-Watlington and D. Miller. Litho Questa)

1994 (14 July)–**96**. *Flowering Fruits.* T **158** and similar multicoloured designs. W w **14** (sideways on horiz designs). P 14. A. Without imprint date

702A	5 c. Type **158**			30	30
703A	7 c. Fig			10	10
704A	10 c. Calabash (vert) (6.10.94)		10	15
705A	15 c. Natal Plum			40	40
706A	18 c. Locust and Wild Honey (23.3.95)	45	45
707A	20 c. Pomegranate			50	50
708A	25 c. Mulberry (vert) (6.10.94)		60	35
709A	35 c. Grape (vert) (6.10.94)		40	45
710A	55 c. Orange (vert) (6.10.94)		65	70
711A	60 c. Surinam Cherry (23.3.95)		70	75
712A	75 c. Loquat (23.3.95)		1·50	1·50
713A	90 c. Sugar Apple (23.3.95)		1·75	1·75
714A	$1 Prickly Pear (vert) (6.10.94)		1·75	1·75
715A	$2 Paw Paw (23.3.95)		2·40	2·50
716A	$3 Bay Grape (23.3.95)		3·50	3·75
717A	$5 Banana (vert) (6.10.94)		6·00	6·25
718A	$8 Lemon			10·00	10·50
702A/18A		Set of 17	28·00	29·00

B. *Imprint date* ("1996") at foot (1.9.96)

706B	18 c. Locust and Wild Honey		25	30

For some of these designs watermarked w **16** (sideways on horiz designs) and with imprint date see Nos. 792/804.

(Des S. Noon. Litho Enschedé)

1994 (15 Sept). *Centenary of Hospital Care.* T **159** and similar vert designs. Multicoloured. W w **14**. P 15×14.

719	25 c. Type **159**		80	35
720	60 c. Patient on dialysis machine		1·75	1·90
721	75 c. Casualty on emergency trolley		2·00	2·25
722	$2 Elderly patient in wheelchair with physiotherapists		4·25	5·50
719/22		Set of 4	8·00	9·50

160 Gombey Dancers

(Des Jennifer Toombs. Litho Enschedé)

1994 (10 Nov). *Cultural Heritage* (1st series). T **160** and similar horiz designs. Multicoloured. W w **14** (sideways). P 14×15.

723	25 c. Type **160**		55	35
724	60 c. Christmas carol singers		1·10	1·25
725	75 c. Marching band		1·40	2·00
726	$2 National Dance Group performers		3·50	4·75
723/6		Set of 4	6·00	7·50

See also Nos. 731/4.

161 Bermuda 1970 Flower 1 c. Stamps and 1 c. Coin

162 Bermuda Coat of Arms

(Des D. Miller. Litho Enschedé)

1995 (6 Feb). *25th Anniv of Decimal Currency.* T **161** and similar horiz designs. Multicoloured. W w **14** (sideways). P 13½×14.

727	25 c. Type **161**		45	35
728	60 c. 1970 5 c. stamps and coin		1·00	1·25
729	75 c. 1970 10 c. stamps and coin		1·25	1·75
730	$2 1970 25 c. stamps and coin		3·50	4·25
727/30		Set of 4	5·75	7·00

(Des Jennifer Toombs. Litho Enschedé)

1995 (30 May). *Cultural Heritage* (2nd series). Horiz designs as T **160**. Multicoloured. W w **14** (sideways). P 14×15.

731	25 c. Kite flying		55	35
732	60 c. Majorettes		1·50	1·50
733	75 c. Portuguese dancers		1·75	2·00
734	$2 Floral float		3·75	4·75
731/4		Set of 4	6·75	7·75

(Des Sheila Semas. Litho Enschedé)

1995 (3 Nov). *375th Anniv of Bermuda Parliament.* W w **14**. P 14×13½.

735	**162** 25 c. multicoloured		50	35
736	$1 multicoloured		1·75	2·25

For design as No. 736, but inscr "Commonwealth Finance Ministers Meeting" see No. 765.

163 U.S. Navy Ordnance Island Submarine Base

164 Triple Jump

(Des R. Watton. Litho Walsall)

1995 (4 Dec). *Military Bases.* T **163** and similar horiz designs. Multicoloured. W w **14** (sideways). P 14.

737	20 c. Type **163**		50	30
738	25 c. Royal Naval Dockyard		60	35
739	60 c. U.S.A.F. Fort Bell and Kindley Field	1·25	1·25
740	75 c. R.A.F. Darrell's Island flying boat base	1·50	1·75
741	90 c. U.S. Navy operating base		1·50	2·25
742	$1 Canadian Forces Communications Station, Daniel's Head		1·60	2·25
737/42		Set of 6	6·25	7·25

(Des S. Noon. Litho B.D.T.)

1996 (21 May). *Olympic Games, Atlanta.* T **164** and similar vert designs. Multicoloured. W w **16**. P 14.

743	25 c. Type **164**		45	35
744	30 c. Cycling		1·00	60
745	65 c. Yachting		1·40	1·60
746	80 c. Show jumping		1·60	1·90
743/6		Set of 4	4·00	4·00

165 Jetty and Islets, Hamilton

(Des D. Miller. Litho Walsall)

1996 (21 May). *Panoramic Paintings of Hamilton* (Nos. 747/51) and St. George's (Nos. 752/6) by E. J. Holland. T **165** and similar horiz designs. Multicoloured. W w **14** (sideways). P 14×14½.

747	60 c. Type **165**		70	75
	a. Booklet pane. Nos. 747/56, with margins all round		7·00	
748	60 c. End of island and buildings		70	75
749	60 c. Yachts and hotel		70	75
750	60 c. Islet, hotel and cathedral		70	75

751	60 c.	Cliff and houses by shore	.. ..	70	75
752	60 c.	Islet and end of main island	..	70	75
753	60 c.	Yacht and houses on hillside	..	70	75
754	60 c.	Yacht and St. George's Hotel on hilltop		70	75
755	60 c.	Shoreline and fishing boats	..	70	75
756	60 c.	Entrance to harbour channel	..	70	75
747/56			Set of 10	7·00	7·25

Nos. 747/56 were only available from $6 stamp booklets containing a pane of 10 (5×2) (No. 747a) showing the Hamilton panorama above that of St. George's.

166 Somerset Express Mail Cart, c. 1900

167 Hog Fish Beacon

(Des B. Dare. Litho Enschedé)

1996 (7 June). *"CAPEX '96" International Stamp Exhibition, Toronto. Local Transport. T **166** and similar horiz designs. Multicoloured. W w 14 (sideways). P 13½×14.*

757	25 c.	Type **166**		70	35
758	60 c.	Victoria carriage and railcar, 1930s	..	1·75	1·75
759	75 c.	First bus, 1946		1·75	2·00
760	$2	Sightseeing bus, c. 1947		4·00	4·50
757/60			Set of 4	7·50	7·75

(Des N. Shewring. Litho Enschedé)

1996 (15 Aug). *Lighthouses. T **167** and similar vert designs. Multicoloured. W w 14 (inverted on $2). P 14×13½.*

761	30 c.	Type **167**		80	45
762	65 c.	Gibbs Hill Lighthouse	..	1·40	1·25
763	80 c.	St. David's Lighthouse	..	2·00	2·00
764	$2	North Rock Beacon	..	3·50	4·50
761/4			Set of 4	7·00	7·50

(Litho Enschedé)

1996 (24 Sept). *Commonwealth Finance Ministers' Meeting. As No. 736, but inscr "Commonwealth Finance Ministers Meeting" at top and with wider gold frame. W w 14. P 14×13½.*

765	$1	multicoloured	.. .. ..	1·50	2·00

168 Waterville

(Des D. Miller. Litho Walsall)

1996 (28 Nov). *Architectural Heritage. T **168** and similar horiz designs. Multicoloured. W w 16 (sideways). P 14.*

766	30 c.	Type **168**		70	45
767	65 c.	Bridge House	..	1·25	1·25
768	80 c.	Fannie Fox's Cottage	..	1·60	2·00
769	$2.50	Palmetto House	..	3·75	5·00
766/9			Set of 4	6·50	8·00

(Des N. Shewring. Litho Walsall)

1997 (12 Feb). *"HONG KONG '97" International Stamp Exhibition. Designs as Nos. 761/4, but incorporating "HONG KONG '97" logo and with one value changed. W w 14. P 14.*

770	30 c.	As Type **167**	..	80	45
771	65 c.	Gibbs Hill Lighthouse	..	1·50	1·25
772	80 c.	St David's Lighthouse	..	1·75	1·75
773	$2.50	North Rock Beacon	..	4·25	5·50
770/3			Set of 4	7·50	8·00

The 65 c. and 80 c. also show "c. 1900" added to the inscription at foot.

169 White-tailed Tropic Bird

(Des N. Arlott. Litho B.D.T.)

1997 (17 Apr). *Birds Conservation. T **169** and similar multicoloured designs. W w 16 (sideways on 30 c., $2.50). P 14.*

774	30 c.	Type **169**		60	45
775	60 c.	White-tailed Tropic Bird and chick (vert)	..	1·25	1·25
776	80 c.	Cahow and chick (vert)	..	1·75	2·00
777	$2.50	Cahow	..	4·00	4·50
774/7			Set of 4	7·00	7·50

170 Queen Elizabeth II with Crowd

171 Father playing with Children

(Des D. Miller. Litho Questa)

1997 (9 Oct). *Golden Wedding of Queen Elizabeth and Prince Philip. T **170** and similar horiz design. Multicoloured. W w 14 (sideways). P 14½.*

778	30 c.	Type **170**		50	40
779	$2	Queen Elizabeth and Prince Philip	..	2·75	3·25
MS780		90×56 mm. Nos. 778/9	..	3·25	4·00

(Litho Questa)

1997 (18 Dec). *Education. T **171** and similar horiz designs. Multicoloured. W w 14 (sideways). P 14.*

781	30 c.	Type **171**		50	40
782	40 c.	Teacher and children with map		60	55
		a. Imperf (pair)			
783	60 c.	Boys holding sports trophy	..	85	1·00
784	65 c.	Pupils outside Berkeley Institute		90	1·10
785	80 c.	Scientific experiments	..	1·25	1·60
786	90 c.	New graduates	..	1·40	1·75
781/6			Set of 6	5·00	5·75

(Des D. Miller. Litho Questa)

1998 (31 Mar). *Diana, Princess of Wales Commemoration. Sheet, 145×70 mm, containing vert designs as T **177** of Ascension. Multicoloured. W w 14 (sideways). P 14½×14.*

MS787		30 c. Wearing black hat, 1983; 40 c. Wearing floral dress; 65 c. Wearing blue evening dress, 1996; 80 c. Carrying bouquets, 1993 (sold at $2.15 + 25 c. charity premium)	..	3·50	4·00

172 "Fox's Cottage, St. David's" (Ethel Tucker)

(Litho Enschedé)

1998 (4 June). *Paintings by Catherine and Ethel Tucker. T **172** and similar horiz designs. Multicoloured. W w 14 (sideways). P 13½×14.*

788	30 c.	Type **172**	..	55	40
789	40 c.	"East Side, Somerset"	..	75	60
790	65 c.	"Long Bay Road, Somerset"	..	1·25	1·10
791	$2	"Flatts Village"	..	3·00	3·75
788/91			Set of 4	5·00	5·25

1998 (9 July). *As Nos. 702/18, but with W w 16 (sideways on horiz designs) and with imprint date ("1998"). P 14.*

792	5 c.	Peach	..	10	10
795	15 c.	Natal Plum	..	20	25
796	18 c.	Locust and Wild Honey	..	25	30
797	20 c.	Pomegranate	..	25	30
798	25 c.	Mulberry (vert)	..	30	35
802	75 c.	Loquat	..	90	95
803	90 c.	Sugar Apple	..	1·25	1·40
804	$1	Prickly Pear (vert)	..	1·25	1·40
792/804			Set of 8	4·25	4·75

173 Horse and Carriage

(Des J. Semos. Litho Walsall)

1998 (24 Sept). *Hospitality in Bermuda. T **173** and similar horiz designs. Multicoloured. W w 16 (sideways). P 14½.*

809	25 c.	Type **173**	..	45	35
810	30 c.	Golf club desk	..	60	50
811	65 c.	Chambermaid preparing room	..	1·00	1·00
812	75 c.	Kitchen staff under training	..	1·10	1·10
813	80 c.	Waiter at beach hotel	..	1·25	1·40
814	90 c.	Nightclub bar	..	1·25	1·50
809/14			Set of 6	5·00	5·25

OMNIBUS ISSUES

Details, together with prices for complete sets, of the various Omnibus issues from the 1935 Silver Jubilee series to date are included in a special section following Zimbabwe at the end of Volume 2.

174 Agave attenuata

175 "Lizard with Fairy Lights" (Claire Critchley)

(Des Harris and Mitchell Associates. Litho Questa)

1998 (15 Oct). *Centenary of Botanical Gardens. T **174** and similar horiz designs. W w 14 (sideways). P 14.*

815	30 c.	Type **174**	..	50	40
816	65 c.	Bermuda Palmetto Tree	..	1·00	90
817	$1	Banyan Tree	..	1·50	1·60
818	$2	Cedar Tree	..	2·75	3·50
815/18			Set of 4	5·25	5·75

(Litho B.D.T.)

1998 (26 Nov). *Christmas. Children's Paintings. T **175** and similar multicoloured design. W w 14 (sideways on 40 c.). P 14.*

819	25 c.	Type **175**		40	35
820	40 c.	"Christmas stairway" (Cameron Rowling) (horiz)		60	65

176 Shelly Bay

(Des Sheila Semos. Litho Walsall)

1999 (29 Apr). *Bermuda Beaches. T **176** and similar horiz designs. Multicoloured. W w 14 (sideways). P 13×13½.*

821	30 c.	Type **176**		50	40
822	60 c.	Catherine's Bay	..	80	90
823	65 c.	Jobson's Cove	..	90	1·00
824	$2	Warwick Long Bay	..	2·75	3·25
821/4			Set of 4	4·50	5·00

177 Tracking Station

(Des D. Miller. Litho Walsall (No. MS829), Cartor (others))

1999 (21 July). *30th Anniv of First Manned Landing on Moon. T **177** and similar multicoloured designs. W w 14 (sideways on 30 c., 75 c.). P 13.*

825	30 c.	Type **177**		55	40
826	60 c.	Mission launch (vert)		90	90
827	75 c.	Aerial view of tracking station, Bermuda		1·10	1·10
828	$2	Astronaut on Moon (vert)		3·00	3·25
825/8			Set of 4	5·00	5·00
MS829		90×80 mm. 65 c. Earth as seen from Moon (circular, 40 mm diam). W w 16 (sideways). P 14	..	1·25	1·40

178 Theodolite and Map, 1901

(Litho Questa)

1999 (26 Aug). *20th-century Maps of Bermuda. T **178** and similar multicoloured designs. W w 14 (sideways). P 14.*

830	30 c.	multicoloured		50	40
831	65 c.	black, stone and silver	..	1·00	1·00
832	80 c.	multicoloured		1·40	1·40
833	$1	multicoloured		1·50	1·60
830/3			Set of 4	4·00	4·00

Designs:— 65 c. Street map, 1901; 80 c. Street plan and aerial photograph, 1999; $1 Satellite and Bermuda from Space, 1999.

179 Victorian Pillar Box and
Bermuda 1865 1s. Stamp

(Litho Questa)

1999 (5 Oct). *Bermuda Postal History. T* **179** *and similar vert designs. W w* **14.** *Multicoloured. P* 14.

834	30 c. Type **179**	35	40
835	75 c. King George V pillar box and 1920 2s. stamp	90	1·00
836	95 c. King George VI wall box and 1938 3d. stamp	1·10	1·25
837	$1 Queen Elizabeth II pillar box and 1953 Coronation 1½d. stamp	1·25	1·40
834/7	Set of 4	3·50	3·75

STAMP BOOKLETS

1948 (5 Apr–10 May). *Pink (No.* SB1), *or light blue (No.* SB2) *covers. Stapled.*

SB1   5s. booklet containing six 1d., 1½d., 2d., 2½d. and 3d. (Nos. 110, 111*b*, 112*a*, 113*b*, 114*a*) in blocks of 6 (10 May) ..   £130

SB2   10s. 6d. booklet containing six 3d. and eighteen 6d. (Nos. 114*a*, 104) in blocks of 6 with twelve air mail labels ..   £150

B 1 "Window" Design (*Illustration reduced. Actual size 125×91 mm*)

1987 (30 Apr). *Paintings by Winslow Homer. Folded card covers, printed in gold. Pane attached by selvedge.*

SB3 $4 containing booklet pane of 10 40 c. (No. 544a)   8·50

1989 (13 July). *Old Garden Roses. Folded card cover, 125×91 mm, as Type B* **1**, *printed in grey. Pane attached by selvedge.*

SB4 $5 containing booklet pane of 10 50 c. (No. 589a)   12·00

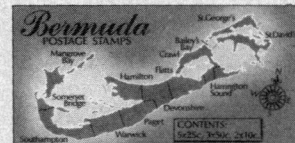

B 2 Map of Bermuda

1993 (1 Apr). *Folded card covers as Type B* **2** *printed in Venetian red, new blue and black. Panes attached by selvedge.*

SB5 $2.95, booklet containing panes Nos. 683a and 684a ..   4·75

SB6 $4.25, booklet containing panes Nos. 684a and 686a ..   5·25

B 3 Coats of Arms of Hamilton and St. George's

1996 (21 May). *Panoramic Paintings of Hamilton and St. George's. Pane attached by selvedge.*

SB7 $6 booklet containing pane No. 747a ..   7·00

EXPRESS LETTER STAMPS

E 1 Queen Elizabeth II

(Des D. Miller. Litho Enschedé)

1996 (7 Nov). *W w* **14.** *P* 14×13½.

E1   **E 1** $22 orange and royal blue   25·00 26·00

No. E1 shows the face value, all other inscriptions, the Crown and much of both the inner and the outer frames printed in yellow fluorescent ink as a security marking.

POSTAL FISCAL

1937 (1 Feb). *As T* **15**, *but inscr* "REVENUE" *at each side. Wmk Mult Script CA. Chalk-surfaced paper. P* 14.

F1	12s. 6d. grey and orange	£1000	£1100
	a. Break in scroll (R. 1/12)		£3000
	b. Broken crown and scroll (R. 2/12)		£3000
	c. Breaks in scrolls at right (R. 1/3)		£3000

No. F1 was issued for fiscal purposes towards the end of 1936. Its use as a postage stamp was authorised from 1 February to April 1937. The used price quoted above is for examples postmarked during this period. Later in the same year postmarks with other dates were obtained by favour.

For illustration of No. F1a/c see above Nos. 51*b* and 88.

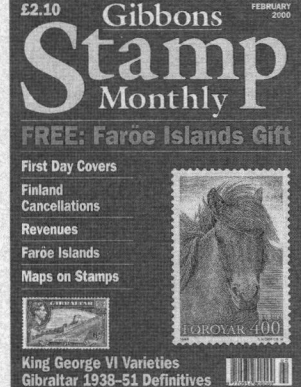

Botswana

(formerly Bechuanaland)

Before the 1880s the only Europeans in the area which became Bechuanaland were scattered hunters and traders, together with the missionaries who were established at Kuruman as early as 1816.

Tribal conflicts in the early years of the decade led to the intervention of Boers from the Transvaal who established the independent republics of Goshen and Stellaland.

STELLALAND

The Boer republic of Stellaland was proclaimed towards the end of 1882. A postal service was organised from the capital, Vryburg, and stamps were ordered from a firm in Cape Town. These were only valid within the republic. Until June 1885 mail to other parts of South Africa was sent through Christiana, in the Transvaal, and was franked with both Stellaland and Transvaal stamps.

No date stamps or obliterators were used by the Stellaland Post Office. Stamps were pen-cancelled with the initials of a postal official and the date.

```
PRICES FOR STAMPS ON COVER
The issues of Stellaland are very rare on cover.
```

1 Arms of the Republic

(Litho by Van der Sandt, de Villiers & Co., Cape Town)

1884 (29 Feb). *P* 12.

1	1	1d. red	£180	£300
		a. Imperf between (horiz pair)	£3750	
		b. Imperf between (vert pair)	£3750	
2		3d. orange	21·00	£300
		a. Imperf between (horiz pair)	£650	
		b. Imperf between (vert pair)	£900	
		c. Imperf vert (horiz pair)	£900	
3		4d. olive-grey	21·00	£325
		a. Imperf between (horiz pair)	£650	
		b. Imperf between (vert pair)	£1400	
4		6d. lilac-mauve	21·00	£325
		a. Imperf between (horiz pair)	£900	
		b. Imperf between (vert pair)	£1200	
5		1s. green	42·00	£550

In 1884 the British Government, following appeals from local chiefs for protection, decided to annex both Goshen and Stellaland. A force under Sir Charles Warren from the Cape reached Vryburg on 7 February 1885 and continued to Mafeking, the principal town of Goshen.

On 30 September 1885 Stellaland and other territory to the south of the Molopo River was constituted the Crown Colony of British Bechuanaland. A protectorate was also proclaimed over a vast tract of land to the north of the Molopo.

Stellaland stamps continued to be used until 2 December 1885 with external mail, franked with Stellaland and Cape of Good Hope stamps, postmarked at Barkly West and Kimberley in Griqualand West.

1885 (Oct). *Handstamped* "**Ttott**" *sideways in violet-lake.*

6	1	2d. on 4d. olive-grey	£3500

On 2 December 1885 Cape of Good Hope stamps overprinted "British Bechuanaland" were placed on sale at the Vryburg post office.

BRITISH BECHUANALAND

CROWN COLONY

```
PRICES FOR STAMPS ON COVER
Nos. 1/8      from × 12
No. 9         from × 80
Nos. 10/21    from × 8
Nos. 22/8     from × 10
No. 29        from × 10
No. 30        from × 10
Nos. 31/2     from × 12
Nos. 33/7     from × 20
Nos. 38/9     from × 25
```

British

Bechuanaland

(1)

BECHUANALAND

(2)

1885 (2 Dec)–87. *Stamps of Cape of Good Hope* ("*Hope*" *seated*) *optd with T* 1, *by W. A. Richards & Sons, Cape Town.*

(a) Wmk Crown CC (No. 3) or Crown CA (others)

1		½d. grey-black (No. 40a) (R.)	11·00	16·00
		a. Opt in lake	£3000	
		b. Opt double (Lake+Black)	£600	
2		3d. pale claret (No. 43)	32·00	38·00
3		4d. dull blue (No. 30) (12.86?)	55·00	65·00

(b) Wmk Anchor (*Cape of Good Hope. Type* 13)

4		½d. grey-black (No. 48a) (3.87)	7·00	11·00
		a. Error. "ritish"	£1700	
		b. Opt double	£2750	
5		1d. rose-red (No. 49)	9·00	9·00
		a. Error. "ritish"	£2250	£1800
		b. Opt double	† £1800	
6		2d. pale bistre (No. 50)	30·00	8·00
		a. Error. "ritish"	£4500	£3250
		b. Opt double	£1500	
7		6d. reddish purple (No. 52)	80·00	38·00
8		1s. green (No. 53) (11.86?)	£225	£150
		a. Error. "ritish"	£13000	£9500

Nos. 1/8 were overprinted from settings of 120. The missing "B" errors are believed to have occurred on one position for one of these settings only.

Overprints with stop after "Bechuanaland" are forged.

1887 (1 Nov). *No. 197 of Great Britain optd with T* 2, *by D.L.R.*

9		½d. vermilion (H/S S. £80)	1·25	1·25
		a. Opt double	£2250	

3

4

5

(Typo D.L.R.)

1887 (1 Nov). *(a) Wmk Orb* (*Great Britain Type* 48). *P* 14.

10	3	1d. lilac and black	14·00	1·75
11		2d. lilac and black	65·00	1·75
		a. *Pale dull lilac and black*	40·00	23·00
12		3d. lilac and black	3·50	5·50
		a. *Pale reddish lilac and black*	55·00	15·00
13		4d. lilac and black	40·00	2·25
14		6d. lilac and black	50·00	2·50

(b) Wmk Script "*V R*" (*sideways, reading up*). *P* 13½.

15	4	1s. green and black	29·00	5·50
16		2s. green and black	48·00	35·00
17		2s. 6d. green and black	60·00	45·00
18		5s. green and black	80·00	£150
19		10s. green and black	£170	£350

(c) Two Orbs (*sideways*). *P* 14×13½

20	5	£1 lilac and black	£900	£800
21		£5 lilac and black	£2750	£1300
10/21 H/S "Specimen"			Set of 12	£900

Nos. 10/21 were produced by overprinting a series of "Unappropriated Die" designs originally produced by the Board of Inland Revenue for use as Great Britain fiscal stamps.

Several values are known on blued paper. No. 11a is the first printing of the 2d. (on safety paper?) and has a faded appearance.

When purchasing Nos. 20/21 in used condition beware of copies with fiscal cancellations cleaned off and bearing forged postmarks. For No. 15 surcharged "£5" see No. F2.

1d.

(6)

1s.

(7)

One Half-Penny

(8)

1888 (7 Aug). *Nos.* 10/11 *and* 13/15 *surch as T* 6 *or* 7, *by P. Townshend & Co, Vryburg.*

22	3	1d. on 1d. lilac and black	7·50	6·00
23		2d. on 2d. lilac and black (R.)	17·00	2·75
		a. *Pale dull lilac and black* (No. 11a)	80·00	48·00
		b. Curved foot to "2"	£200	£150
		c. Surch in green	† £2500	
25		4d. on 4d. lilac and black (R.)	£190	£250
26		6d. on 6d. lilac and black	80·00	10·00
		a. Surch in blue	† £6500	
28	4	1s. on 1s. green and black	£110	70·00

Nos. 23c and 26a are from two sheets of surcharge trials subsequently put into stock and used at Vryburg (2d.) or Mafeking (6d.) during 1888–89.

1888 (Dec). *No.* 12a *surch with T* 8, *by P. Townshend & Co, Vryburg.*

29	3	½d. on 3d. pale reddish lilac and black	£130	£140
		a. Broken "f" in "Half"	£4250	

No. 29 was produced from a setting of 60 (12×5).

No. 29a shows the letter "f" almost completely missing and occurs on R. 5/11 of the setting. Five examples are known, one being in the Royal Collection.

Errors of spelling on this surcharge are bogus.

British

Bechuanaland.

(9)

British Bechuanaland.

(10)

BRITISH BECHUANALAND

(11)

1889 (Jan). *No.* 48a *of Cape of Good Hope* (*wmk Anchor*) *optd with T* 9, *by P. Townshend & Co, Vryburg.*

30		½d. grey-black (G.)	3·25	20·00
		b. Opt double, one inverted	£1000	
		c. Opt double, one vertical	£500	
		ca. *Se-tenant* with stamp without opt	£3000	
		e. "British" omitted	£2000	

No. 30 was produced using a setting of 30 (6×5). No. 30e occurred on R. 5/1 of the setting on some sheets only.

1891 (Nov). *Nos.* 49/50 *of Cape of Good Hope* (*wmk Anchor*), *optd with T* 10, *reading upwards.*

31		1d. rose-red	10·00	8·00
		a. Horiz pair, one without opt	£2000	
		b. "British" omitted	—£1100	
		c. "Bechuanaland" omitted	£1100	
32		2d. pale bistre	3·25	2·25
		a. No stop after "Bechuanaland"	£225	£275
31/2 H/S "Specimen"			Set of 2	£130

Nos. 31/2 were produced from separate settings of 120 (12×10). No. 32a occurs on R. 3/3.

See also Nos. 38 and 39.

1891 (1 Dec)–**1904**. *Nos.* 172, 200, 205, 208 *and* 211 *of Great Britain optd with T* 11, *by D.L.R.*

33		1d. lilac	6·00	1·10
34		2d. grey-green and carmine	5·50	3·75
35		4d. green and purple-brown	2·50	50
		a. Bisected (2d.) (on cover) (11.99)	† £2000	
36		6d. purple/rose-red	3·00	2·00
37		1s. dull green (7.94)	13·00	16·00
		a. Bisected (6d.) (on cover) (12.04)	† —	
33/7			Set of 5	27·00	21·00
33/6 H/S "Specimen"			Set of 4	£170

No. 35a was used at Palapye Station and No. 37a at Kanye, both in the Protectorate.

1893 (Dec)–**95**. *As Nos.* 31/2, *but T* 10 *reads downwards.*

38		1d. rose-red	2·25	2·25
		a. Pair, one without opt	£1100	
		b. "British" omitted	£1100	
		c. Optd "Bechuanaland. British"	£800	£900
		d. No dots to "i" of "British" (R. 1/10)	85·00	85·00
		e. Opt reading up, no dots to "i" of "British"	£1400	
39		2d. pale bistre (15.3.95)	4·50	2·25
		a. Opt double	£900	£550
		b. "British" omitted	£475	£475
		c. Optd "Bechuanaland. British"	£325	£200
		d. No dots to "i" of "British" (R. 1/10)	£100	£100
		e. Opt reading up, no dots to "i" of "British"		

A common setting of 120 (12×10) was used for Nos. 38/9. Some sheets of both values were overprinted the wrong way up, resulting in Nos. 38e and 39e.

On 16 November 1895 British Bechuanaland was annexed to the Cape of Good Hope and ceased to have its own stamps, but they remained in use in the Protectorate until superseded in 1897. The Postmaster-General of Cape Colony had assumed control of the Bechuanaland postal service on 1 April 1893 and the Cape, and subsequently the South African, postal authorities continued to be responsible for the postal affairs of the Bechuanaland Protectorate until 1963.

BECHUANALAND PROTECTORATE

```
PRICES FOR STAMPS ON COVER TO 1945
Nos. 40/51     from × 10
Nos. 52/71     from × 6
Nos. 72/82     from × 5
Nos. 83/98     from × 4
Nos. 99/110    from × 6
Nos. 111/17    from × 10
Nos. 118/28    from × 4
Nos. 129/31    from × 10

Nos. D1/3      from × 50
Nos. D4/6      from × 60

No. F1         from × 5
No. F2         —
No. F3         from × 5
```

This large area north of the Molopo River was proclaimed a British Protectorate on 30 September 1885 at the request of the native chiefs.

A postal service using runners was inaugurated on 9 August 1888 and Nos. 40 to 55 were issued as a temporary measure with the object of assessing the cost of this service.

Protectorate

(12) 15½ mm

Protectorate 1d

(13)

1888 (7 Aug). *No.* 9 *optd with T* 12 *and Nos.* 10/19 *surch or optd only as T* 13 *by P. Townshend & Co. Vryburg.*

40	—	½d. vermilion (H/S S. £75)	3·25	23·00
		a. "Protectorate" double	£300	
41	3	1d. on 1d. lilac and black	7·00	13·00
		a. Small figure "1" (R. 5/4, 7/2, 10/2)	£300	£325
42		2d. on 2d. lilac and black	21·00	17·00
		a. Curved foot to "2"	£425	£375
43		3d. on 3d. pale reddish lilac and black	£100	£150
44		4d. on 4d. lilac and black	£250	£250
		a. Small figure "4"	£2750	£2750
45		6d. on 6d. lilac and black	65·00	40·00
46	4	1s. green and black (H/S S. £100)	65·00	50·00
		a. First "o" omitted	£3500	£3000
47		2s. green and black	£550	£800
		a. First "o" omitted	£8500	
48		2s. 6d. green and black	£550	£700
		a. First "o" omitted	£8500	
49		5s. green and black	£1100	£1800
		a. First "o" omitted	£11000	
50		10s. green and black	£3000	£4750
		a. First "o" omitted	£16000	

Nos. 40/5 were produced from a basic setting of 120 (12×10) on which a faulty first "o" in "Protectorate" occurred on R.5/12. For Nos. 46/50 the setting was reduced to 84 (12×7) and on many sheets the first "o" on R.5/12 failed to print.

See also Nos. 54/5.

1888 (Dec). *No.* 25 *optd with T* 12 *by P. Townshend & Co, Vryburg.*

51	3	4d. on 4d. lilac and black	65·00	32·00

Bechuanaland

Protectorate

Protectorate.	Fourpence
(14)	(15)

1889 (Jan). *No. 48a of Cape of Good Hope (wmk Anchor), optd with T 14 by P. Townshend & Co., Vryburg.*

52	½d. grey-black (G.)	..	..	2·75	30·00
	a. Opt double	..	..	£425	£550
	ab. Ditto, one reading "Protectorate Bechuanaland"				£800
	b. "Bechuanaland" omitted				£800
	c. Optd "Protectorate Bechuanaland"			£400	£475

1889 (Aug). *No. 9 surch with T 15 by P. Townshend & Co., Vryburg.*

53	4d. on ½d. vermilion (H/S S. £120)		16·00	3·50
	a. "rpence" omitted (R. 9/2)	..	†	£6000
	b. "ourpence" omitted (R. 9/2)	..	£10000
	c. Surch (T 15) inverted	..	†	£4000
	cb. Ditto. "ourpence" omitted		†	£11000

Examples of No. 53c are postmarked "679" (Tati).

Protectorate	Protectorate
(16) 15 mm	(17)

1890. *No. 9 optd.*

54	16	½d. vermilion	..	£130	£140
		a. Type 16 inverted		70·00	90·00
		b. Type 16 double		85·00	£120
		c. Type 16 double and inverted	£550	£550
		d. Optd "Portectorate" inverted	£3000	
		w. Wmk inverted			
55	17	½d. vermilion ..		£150	£225
		a. Type 17 double		£800	
		b. Optd "Protectorrte"			
		c. Optd "Protectorrte" double	£12000	

These were trial printings made in 1888 which were subsequently issued.

In June 1890 the Bechuanaland Protectorate and the Colony of British Bechuanaland came under one postal administration and the stamps of British Bechuanaland were used in the Protectorate until 1897.

BRITISH

BECHUANALAND	BECHUANALAND PROTECTORATE
(18)	(19)

1897. *No. 61 of Cape of Good Hope (wmk Anchor), optd as T 18.*

(a) *Lines 13 mm apart, bottom line 16 mm long, by Taylor & Marshall, Cape Town*

56	½d. yellow-green (July?)	..	..	2·50	8·00

(b) *Lines 13½ mm apart, bottom line 15 mm long, by P. Townshend & Co, Vryburg*

57	½d. yellow-green (April)	..	18·00	65·00
	a. Opt double, one albino inverted			

(c) *Lines 10½ mm apart, bottom line 15 mm long, by W. A. Richards & Sons, Cape Govt Printers*

58	½d. yellow-green (July?)	..	8·00	38·00

Although issued only in the Protectorate, the above were presumably overprinted "BRITISH BECHUANALAND" because stamps bearing this inscription were in use there at the time.

1897 (Oct)–**1902.** *Nos. 172, 197, 200, 202, 205 and 208 of Great Britain (Queen Victoria) optd with T 19 by D.L.R.*

59	½d. vermilion	..	1·00	2·25
60	½d. blue-green (25.2.02)		1·40	3·00
61	1d. lilac	..	4·00	55
62	2d. grey-green and carmine	3·00	4·50
63	3d. purple/yellow (12.97)	5·50	8·50
64	4d. green and purple-brown	13·00	11·00
65	6d. purple/rose-red	22·00	11·00
59/65			Set of 7	45·00	38·00
59/65	Optd/H.S. (No. 60) "Specimen"	Set of 7	£225

BECHUANALAND	PROTECTORATE	BECHUANALAND PROTECTORATE
(20)		(21)

1904 (29 Nov)–**13.** *Nos. 216, 218/19, 230 and 313/14 (Somerset House ptgs) of Great Britain (King Edward VII) optd with T 20, by D.L.R.*

66	½d. blue-green (3.06)	..	1·75	1·75
67	½d. yellowish green (11.08)		3·50	3·50
68	1d. scarlet (4.05) (S. £60)		6·50	30
69	2½d. ultramarine		6·00	5·00
	a. Stop after "P" in "PROTECTORATE"	£800	£1200
70	1s. deep green and scarlet (10.12)	35·00	95·00
71	1s. green and carmine (1913) (S. £80)	35·00	95·00

No. 69a occurs on R.5/9 of the lower pane.

1912 (Sept)–**14.** *No. 342 of Great Britain (King George V, wmk Crown) optd with T 20.*

72	1d. scarlet	..	1·25	60
	a. No cross on crown	—	75·00
	b. Aniline scarlet (No. 343) (1914)	£120	80·00

1913 (July)–**24.** *Stamps of Great Britain (King George V) optd.*

(a) *Nos. 351, 357, 362, 367, 370/1, 376, 379, 385 and 395 (wmk Simple Cypher, T 100) optd with T 20*

73	½d. green (shades)	..	..	1·25	1·75
74	1d. scarlet (shades) (4.15)	..	2·75	60
	a. Carmine-red (1922)	..	13·00	1·75
75	1½d. red-brown (12.20)	..	2·25	3·00
76	2d. reddish orange (Die I)	..	2·50	4·25
	a. Orange (Die I) (1921)	..	13·00	4·50
	aw. Wmk inverted	..		
77	2d. orange (Die II) (1924)	..	35·00	5·00
78	2½d. cobalt-blue	..	3·50	17·00
	a. Blue (1915)	..	6·00	18·00
79	3d. bluish violet	..	6·00	12·00
80	4d. grey-green	..	6·50	14·00
81	6d. reddish purple (shades)	..	7·00	16·00
	a. Opt double, one albino		
82	1s. bistre (S. £75)	..	9·50	18·00
	a. Bistre-brown (1923)	..	20·00	32·00
73/82		Set of 9	38·00	75·00

(b) *With T 21*

(i) *Waterlow printings (Nos. 399 and 401) (1914–15)*

83	2s. 6d. deep sepia-brown (1.15)	£110	£225
	a. Re-entry (R.2/1)	£1000	£1400
	b. Opt double, one albino	£250	
84	5s. rose-carmine (1914)	£140	£350
	a. Opt double, one albino	£325	
83/4	Optd "Specimen"	Set of 2	£275

(ii) *D.L.R. printings (Nos. 407/8 and 409) (1916–19)*

85	2s. 6d. pale brown (7.16)	£100	£225
	a. Re-entry (R. 2/1)	£1100	
86	2s. 6d. sepia (1917)	£120	£200
	b. Re-entry (R. 2/1)		
87	5s. bright carmine (8.19)	£275	£400
	a. Opt double, one albino	£400	

(iii) *B.W. printings (Nos. 414 and 416) (1920–23)*

88	2s. 6d. chocolate-brown (7.23)	80·00	£150
	a. Major re-entry (R.1/2)	£1900	
	b. Opt double, one albino		
89	5s. rose-red (7.20)	£110	£250
	a. Opt treble, two albino		
	b. Opt double, one albino	£325	

1925 (July)–**27.** *Nos. 418/19, 421, 423/4, 426/a and 429 of Great Britain (wmk Block Cypher, T 111) optd with T 20.*

91	½d. green (1927)	..	..	1·50	1·75
92	1d. scarlet (8.25)	..	..	2·00	70
	w. Wmk inverted				
93	2d. orange (Die II)	..	..	1·75	1·00
94	3d. violet (10.26)	..	..	4·75	15·00
	a. Opt double, one albino		£250	
	w. Wmk inverted		£160	
95	4d. grey-green (10.26)	..	4·75	29·00
	a. Printed on the gummed side		
96	6d. reddish purple (chalk-surfaced paper) (12.25)	..	28·00	48·00
97	6d. purple (ordinary paper) (1926)	48·00	48·00
98	1s. bistre-brown (10.26)	..	9·00	24·00
	w. Wmk inverted		—	£300
91/8		..	Set of 8	90·00	£150

22 King George V, Baobab Tree and Cattle drinking	23 King George VI, Baobab Tree and Cattle drinking

(Des from photo by Resident Commissioner, Ngamiland, Recess Waterlow)

1932 (12 Dec). *Wmk Mult Script CA. P 12½.*

99	22	½d. green	1·00	30
		a. Imperf between (horiz pair)	£13000	
100		1d. scarlet	1·00	25
101		2d. brown	1·00	30
102		3d. ultramarine	1·00	1·00
103		4d. orange	1·25	5·00
104		6d. purple	2·50	2·75
105		1s. black and olive-green	3·00	7·00
106		2s. black and orange	24·00	38·00
107		2s.6d. black and scarlet	19·00	30·00
108		3s. black and purple	35·00	42·00
109		5s. black and ultramarine	50·00	55·00
110		10s. black and brown	£110	£120
99/110			Set of 12	£225	£275
99/110	Perf "Specimen"		Set of 12	£250

1935 (4 May). *Silver Jubilee. As Nos. 91/4 of Antigua but ptd by B.W. P 11 × 12.*

111	1d. deep blue and scarlet	..	30	2·25
	a. Extra flagstaff		£225	
	b. Short extra flagstaff		£275	
	c. Lightning conductor		£225	
	d. Flagstaff on right-hand turret	£225	
	e. Double flagstaff		£225	
112	2d. ultramarine and grey-black	..	1·00	2·25
	a. Extra flagstaff		95·00	
	b. Short extra flagstaff		85·00	
	c. Lightning conductor		75·00	
113	3d. brown and deep blue	..	2·25	2·25
	a. Extra flagstaff		£130	
	b. Short extra flagstaff		£110	
	c. Lightning conductor		£110	
114	6d. slate and purple	..	3·75	2·25
	a. Extra flagstaff		£120	
	b. Short extra flagstaff		£100	
	c. Lightning conductor		£110	
111/14		Set of 4	6·50	8·00
111/14	Perf "Specimen"	Set of 4	80·00

For illustrations of plate varieties see Catalogue Introduction.

1937 (12 May). *Coronation. As Nos. 95/7 of Antigua, but printed by D.L.R. P 14.*

115	1d. scarlet	..	..	45	40
116	2d. yellow-brown	..	60	1·00
117	3d. bright blue	..	60	1·25
115/17		Set of 3	1·50	2·40
115/17	Perf "Specimen"	Set of 3	55·00

(Recess Waterlow)

1938 (1 Apr)–**52.** *Wmk Mult Script CA. P 12½.*

118	23	½d. green		2·00	2·25
		a. Light yellowish green (1941)	5·00	6·00
		b. Yellowish green (4.43)	3·50	3·50
		c. Deep green (4.49)	2·50	6·00
119		1d. scarlet		60	50
120		1½d. dull blue		8·50	2·00
		a. Light blue (4.43)		60	1·00
121		2d. chocolate-brown	60	50
122		3d. deep ultramarine	60	2·00
123		4d. orange		1·75	3·00
124		6d. reddish purple	4·00	3·00
		a. Purple (1944)		3·50	2·50
125		1s. black and brown-olive	3·50	3·00
		a. Grey-black and olive-green (21.5.52)	13·00	15·00
126		2s.6d. black and scarlet	14·00	12·00
127		5s. black and deep ultramarine	30·00	12·00
		a. Grey-black & dp ultramarine (10.46)	65·00	35·00
128		10s. black and red-brown	14·00	18·00
118/28			Set of 11	65·00	50·00
118/28	Perf "Specimen"		Set of 11	£170

(24)	24a King George VI and Queen Elizabeth

1945 (3 Dec). *Victory. Stamps of South Africa optd with T 24. Inscr alternately in English and Afrikaans.*

			Un. pair	Used pair	Used single
129	55	1d. brown and carmine	50	55	10
130	56	2d. slate-blue and violet	50	1·00	10
131	57	3d. deep blue and blue	50	1·00	10
		a. Opt omitted (in vert pair with normal)	£6500		
129/31			Set of 3	1·40	2·25	25

No. 131a comes from a sheet on which the overprint was displaced downwards so that it is omitted from stamps in the top row and shown on the sheet margin at foot.

(Recess Waterlow)

1947 (17 Feb). *Royal Visit. T 24a and similar designs. Wmk Mult Script CA. P 12½.*

132	1d. scarlet	..	10	10
133	2d. green	..	10	10
134	3d. ultramarine	..	10	10
135	1s. mauve	..	10	10
132/5		Set of 4	35	30
132/5	Perf "Specimen"	Set of 4	80·00

Designs: *Vert*—1d. King George VI. *Horiz*—3d. Princess Elizabeth and Princess Margaret; 1s. The Royal Family.

1948 (1 Dec). *Royal Silver Wedding. As Nos. 112/13 of Antigua.*

136	1½d. ultramarine	..	30	10
137	10s. black	..	27·00	35·00

1949 (10 Oct). *75th Anniv of Universal Postal Union. As Nos. 114/17 of Antigua.*

138	1½d. blue	..	45	75
139	3d. deep blue	..	1·25	2·00
140	6d. magenta	..	90	1·00
141	1s. olive	..	95	1·00
138/41		Set of 4	3·25	4·25

1953 (3 June). *Coronation. As No. 120 of Antigua.*

142	2d. black and brown	..	30	30

25 Queen Elizabeth II, Baobab Tree and Cattle drinking	26 Queen Victoria, Queen Elizabeth II and Landscape

(Des from photo by Resident Commissioner, Ngamiland. Recess Waterlow)

1955 (3 Jan)–**58.** *Wmk Mult Script CA. P 13½ × 14.*

143	25	½d. green		50	30
144		1d. rose-red		80	10
145		2d. red-brown		1·25	30
146		3d. ultramarine		3·00	70
		a. Bright ultramarine (16.1.57)	7·00	2·75
146b		4d. red-orange (1.12.58)	6·50	7·00
147		4½d. blackish blue	1·50	35
148		6d. purple		1·25	60
149		1s. black and brown-olive	1·25	80
150		1s. 3d. black and lilac	14·00	9·50
151		2s. 6d. black and rose-red	10·00	9·50
152		5s. black and violet-blue	15·00	6·50
153		10s. black and red-brown	22·00	15·00
143/53			Set of 12	70·00	45·00

(Photo Harrison)

1960 (21 Jan). *75th Anniv of Bechuanaland Protectorate.* W w **12**. P 14½ × 14.

154	**26**	1d. sepia and black	..	40	50
155		3d. magenta and black	..	40	30
156		6d. bright blue and black	..	40	50
154/6	..		*Set of 3*	1·10	1·10

(New Currency. 100 cents = 1 rand)

1c   1c 1c   2½c 2½c
(27)   (I) (II)   (I) (II)

3 3 3   5c 5c   R1 R1
(I) (II) (III)   (I) (II)   (I) (II)
(3½ c. on 4d.)

2½c
Spaced "c"
(R. 10/3)

1961 (14 Feb–June). *Nos. 144/6a and 148/53 surch as T* **27** *by South African Govt Printer, Pretoria.*

157	**25**	1 c. on 1d. rose-red (Type I)	..	30	10
		a. Type II (6 June)	..	40	10
158		2 c. on 2d. red-brown	..	20	10
159		2½ c. on 2d. red-brown (Type I)	..	30	10
		a. Type II (26 July)	..	85	65
		b. Vert pair, one without surch	..	£2500	
160		2½ c. on 3d. bright ultramarine	..	2·00	3·25
		a. Spaced "c" (R.10/3)	..	42·00	
161		3½ c. on 4d. red-orange (Type I)	..	50	20
		a. Type II	..	2·00	3·25
		b. Wide surch (I)	..	14·00	21·00
		c. Wide surch (II)	..	50·00	65·00
		d. Type III (6 June)	..	20	40
162		5 c. on 6d. purple (Type I)	..	65	30
		a. Type II (12 May)	..	20	10
163		10 c. on 1s. black and brown-olive	..	20	10
		a. Horiz pair, one without surch	..	£1600	
164		12½ c. on 1s. 3d. black and lilac	..	65	20
165		25 c. on 2s. 6d. black and rose-red	..	2·00	50
166		50 c. on 5s. black and violet-blue	..	3·00	2·00
167		1 r. on 10s. black & red-brown (Type I)	..	£275	90·00
		a. Type II (surch at bottom left) (17 Mar)	..	8·50	8·50
		b. Type II (surch at foot, either to right or central) (Apr)	..	7·00	2·25
157/67b	..		*Set of 11*	14·50	7·50

Nos. 161/c occur from the same printing each sheet containing thirty-three examples of Type I, five of Type I with wide spacing, nineteen of Type II and three of Type II with wide spacing. The wide surcharge measures 9½ mm overall (with "C" spaced 1½ mm from "½") and comes on 8 of the 10 stamps in the last vertical row. The surcharge on the remainder of the sheet varies between 8½ and 9½ mm.

A later printing of the 12½ c. on 1s. 3d. was from a fresh setting of type, but is insufficiently different for separate listing. Later printings of the 10 c. and 25 c. were identical with the originals.

28 African Golden Oriole

39 Bechuana Ox

(Des P. Jones (1 c. to 12½ c.). Photo Harrison)

1961 (2 Oct). *T* **28, 39** *and similar designs.* W w **12**. P 14½ × 14 (25, 50 c.) or 14 × 14½ (*others*).

168		1 c. yellow, red, black and lilac	..	1·25	40
169		2 c. orange, black and yellow-olive	..	1·50	2·50
170		2½ c. carmine, green, black and bistre	..	1·50	10
171		3½ c. yellow, black, sepia and pink	..	1·75	1·25
172		5 c. yellow, blue, black and buff	..	3·00	1·00
173		7½ c. brown, red, black and apple-green	..	1·75	2·00
174		10 c. red, yellow, sepia & turquoise-green	..	1·75	60
175		12½ c. buff, blue, red and grey-black	..	18·00	5·50
176		20 c. yellow-brown and drab	..	80	70
177		25 c. deep brown and lemon	..	1·00	85
178		35 c. deep blue and orange	..	1·00	2·00
179		50 c. sepia and olive	..	1·00	2·25
180		1 r. black and cinnamon	..	3·00	2·50
181		2 r. brown and turquoise-blue	..	18·00	9·00
168/81	..		*Set of 14*	50·00	27·00

Designs: *Vert*—2 c. Hoopoe; 2½ c. Scarlet-chested Sunbird; 3½ c. Yellow-rumped Bishop; 5 c. Swallow-tailed Bee Eater; 7½ c. African Grey Hornbill; 10 c. Red-headed Weaver; 12½ c. Brown-hooded Kingfisher; 20 c. Woman musician; 35 c. Woman grinding maize; 1 r. Lion; 2 r. Police camel patrol. *Horiz*—25 c. Baobab Tree.

1963 (4 June). *Freedom from Hunger. As No. 146 of Antigua.*

182		12½ c. bluish green	..	30	15

1963 (2 Sept). *Red Cross Centenary. As Nos. 147/8 of Antigua.*

183		2½ c. red and black	..	20	10
184		12½ c. red and blue	..	40	50

1964 (23 April). *400th Birth Anniv of William Shakespeare. As No. 164 of Antigua.*

185		12½ c. light brown	..	15	15

BECHUANALAND

INTERNAL SELF-GOVERNMENT

42 Map and Gaberones Dam

(Des Mrs. M. Townsend, adapted V. Whiteley. Photo Harrison)

1965 (1 Mar). *New Constitution.* W w **12**. P 14½ × 14.

186	**42**	2½ c. red and gold	..	10	10
		w. Wmk inverted	..	14·00	3·75
187		5 c. ultramarine and gold	..	15	40
188		12½ c. brown and gold	..	20	40
189		25 c. green and gold	..	20	55
186/9			*Set of 4*	55	1·25

1965 (17 May). *I.T.U. Centenary. As Nos. 166/7 of Antigua.*

190		2½ c. red and bistre-yellow	..	20	10
191		12½ c. mauve and brown	..	45	30

1965 (25 Oct). *International Co-operation Year. As Nos. 168/9 of Antigua.*

192		1 c. reddish purple and turquoise-green	..	10	10
193		12½ c. deep bluish green and lavender	..	60	55

1966 (24 Jan). *Churchill Commemoration. As Nos. 170/3 of Antigua.*

194		1 c. new blue	..	15	30
195		2½ c. deep green	..	35	10
196		12½ c. brown	..	70	30
197		20 c. bluish violet	..	75	40
194/7	..		*Set of 4*	1·75	90

43 Haslar Smoke Generator

(Des V. Whiteley. Photo Harrison)

1966 (1 June). *Bechuanaland Royal Pioneer Corps. T* **43** *and similar horiz designs.* W w **12**. P 14½.

198		2½ c. Prussian blue, red and light emerald	..	20	10
199		5 c. brown and light blue	..	20	20
200		15 c. Prussian blue, rosine and emerald	..	30	25
201		35 c. buff, blackish brown, red and green	..	30	80
198/201			*Set of 4*	90	1·25

Designs:—5 c. Bugler; 15 c. Gun-site; 35 c. Regimental cap badge.

BOTSWANA

INDEPENDENCE

Bechuanaland became the independent republic of Botswana, within the Commonwealth, on 30 September 1966.

47 National Assembly Building

(Des R. Granger Barrett. Photo Harrison)

1966 (30 Sept). *Independence. T* **47** *and similar horiz designs. Multicoloured.* P 14½.

202		2½ c. Type 47	..	15	10
		a. Imperf (pair)	..	£250	
203		5 c. Abattoir, Lobatsi	..	20	10
204		15 c. National Airways Douglas DC-3	..	65	20
205		35 c. State House, Gaberones	..	40	30
202/5			*Set of 4*	1·25	55

REPUBLIC OF BOTSWANA
(51)

52 Golden Oriole

1966 (30 Sept). *Nos. 168/81 optd as T* **51**.

206		1 c. yellow, red, black and lilac	..	25	10
207		2 c. orange, black and yellow-olive	..	30	65
208		2½ c. carmine, green, black and bistre	..	30	10
209		3½ c. yellow, black, sepia and pink	..	40	15
		a. Yellow, black, sepia and flesh	..	1·25	1·00

210		5 c. yellow, blue, black and buff	..	40	1·25
211		7½ c. brown, red, black and apple-green	..	40	1·50
		a. Blue-green omitted			
212		10 c. red, yellow, sepia & turquoise-green	..	60	20
213		12½ c. buff, blue, red and grey-black	..	2·75	2·75
214		20 c. yellow-brown and drab	..	50	1·00
215		25 c. deep brown and lemon	..	50	1·75
216		35 c. deep blue and orange	..	60	2·00
217		50 c. sepia and olive	..	50	70
218		1 r. black and cinnamon	..	55	1·25
219		2 r. brown and turquoise-blue	..	1·00	2·50
206/19			*Set of 14*	8·00	14·00

No. 209a was a special printing produced to make up quantities. It does not exist without the overprint.

No. 211a shows the background in yellow instead of apple-green, the blue-green overlay being omitted.

(Des D. M. Reid-Henry. Photo Harrison)

1967 (3 Jan). *Birds. Vert designs as T* **52**. *Multicoloured.* P 14 × 14½.

220		1 c. Type 52	..	30	15
		a. Error. Wmk **105** of Malta	..	†	£700
221		2 c. Hoopoe	..	40	70
222		3 c. Groundscraper Thrush	..	55	10
223		4 c. Cordon-bleu ("Blue Waxbill")	..	55	10
224		5 c. Secretary Bird	..	55	10
225		7 c. Yellow-billed Hornbill	..	60	90
226		10 c. Burchell's Gonolek ("Crimson-breasted Shrike")	..	60	15
227		15 c. Malachite Kingfisher	..	8·50	3·00
228		20 c. African Fish Eagle	..	8·50	2·00
229		25 c. Go-away Bird ("Grey Loerie")	..	5·00	1·50
230		35 c. Scimitar-bill	..	7·00	2·25
231		50 c. Comb Duck	..	3·25	2·75
232		1 r. Levaillant's Barbet	..	8·00	3·50
233		2 r. Didric Cuckoo	..	9·50	16·00
220/33			*Set of 14*	45·00	29·00

A used copy of the 20 c. has been seen with the pale brown colour missing, resulting in the value (normally shown in white) being omitted.

The 1, 2, 4, 7 and 10 c. values exist with PVA gum as well as gum arabic.

66 Students and University

(Des V. Whiteley. Photo Harrison)

1967 (7 Apr). *First Conferment of University Degrees.* P 14 × 14½.

234	**66**	3 c. sepia, ultramarine & lt orange-yell	..	10	10
235		7 c. sepia, ultram & lt greenish bl	..	10	10
236		15 c. sepia, ultramarine and rose	..	10	10
237		35 c. sepia, ultramarine and light violet	..	20	20
234/7	..		*Set of 4*	30	30

67 Bushbuck

(Des G. Vasarhelyi. Photo Harrison)

1967 (2 Oct). *Chobe Game Reserve. T* **67** *and similar horiz designs. Multicoloured.* P 14.

238		3 c. Type 67	..	10	20
239		7 c. Sable Antelope	..	15	30
240		35 c. Fishing on Chobe River	..	80	1·10
238/40	..		*Set of 3*	90	1·40

70 Arms of Botswana and Human Rights Emblem

(Litho D.L.R.)

1968 (8 Apr). *Human Rights Year. T* **70** *and similar horiz designs showing Arms of Botswana and Human Rights emblem arranged differently.* P 13½ × 13.

241		3 c. multicoloured	..	10	10
242		15 c. multicoloured	..	25	40
243		25 c. multicoloured	..	25	50
241/3	..		*Set of 3*	50	85

73 Eland and Giraffe Rock Paintings, Tsodilo Hills

75 "Baobab Trees" (Thomas Baines)

76 National Museum and Art Gallery

(Litho D.L.R.)

1968 (30 Sept). *Opening of National Museum and Art Gallery. T 73/6 and similar multicoloured design. P 12½ (7 c.), 12½ × 13½ (15 c.), or 13 × 13½ (others).*
244	3 c. Type 73	..	..	..	20	20
245	7 c. Girl wearing ceremonial beads (30 × 48 mm)				35	20
246	10 c. Type 75	..	..	..	35	30
247	15 c. Type 76	..	..	..	50	1·40
244/7		..	..	*Set of* 4	1·25	1·90
MS248	132 × 82 mm. Nos. 244/7. P 13				1·25	2·00

77 African Family, and Star over Village

(Des Mrs M. E. Townsend, adapted J. Cooter. Litho Enschedé)

1968 (11 Nov). *Christmas. P 13 × 14.*
249	77	1 c. multicoloured	..	..	10	10
250		2 c. multicoloured	..	..	10	10
251		5 c. multicoloured	..	..	10	10
252		25 c. multicoloured	..	..	15	50
249/52		..	..	*Set of* 4	30	70

78 Scout, Lion and Badge in Frame

(Des D.L.R. Litho Format)

1969 (21 Aug). *22nd World Scout Conference, Helsinki. T 78 and similar multicoloured designs. P 13½.*
253	3 c. Type 78	..	..	..	50	30
254	15 c. Scouts cooking over open fire (*vert*)	..			75	1·25
255	25 c. Scouts around camp fire	..	..		75	1·25
253/5		..	..	*Set of* 3	1·75	2·50

81 Woman, Child and Christmas Star   82 Diamond Treatment Plant, Orapa

(Des A. Vale, adapted V. Whiteley. Litho Harrison)

1969 (6 Nov). *Christmas. P 14½ × 14.*
256	81	1 c. pale blue and chocolate	..	..	10	10
257		2 c. pale yellow-olive and chocolate	..		10	10
258		4 c. yellow and chocolate	..	..	10	10
259		35 c. chocolate and bluish violet..	..		20	20
256/9		..	..	*Set of* 4	30	30
MS260	86 × 128 mm. Nos. 256/9. P 14½ (*shades*)				70	1·10

(Des J.W. Litho Harrison)

1970 (23 Mar). *Developing Botswana. T 82 and similar designs. Multicoloured. P 14½ × 14 (3 c., 7 c.) or 14 × 14½ (others).*
261	3 c. Type 82	..	..	..	70	20
262	7 c. Copper-nickel mining	..	..		95	20
263	10 c. Copper-nickel mine, Selebi-Pikwe (*horiz*)			1·25	25
264	35 c. Orapa diamond mine, and diamonds (*horiz*)			2·75	1·60
261/4	..	..	..	*Set of* 4	5·00	2·00

83 Mr. Micawber (*David Copperfield*)

(Des V. Whiteley. Litho Walsall)

1970 (6 July). *Death Centenary of Charles Dickens. T 83 and similar horiz designs. Multicoloured. P 11.*
265	3 c. Type 83	..	..	..	25	10
266	7 c. Scrooge (*A Christmas Carol*)	..		35	10
267	15 c. Fagin (*Oliver Twist*)	..	..		60	40
268	25 c. Bill Sykes (*Oliver Twist*) ..			90	60
265/8		..	..	*Set of* 4	1·90	1·00
MS269	114 × 81 mm. Nos. 265/8	..			3·25	3·50

84 U.N. Building and Emblem

(Des J. Cooter. Litho Walsall)

1970 (24 Oct). *25th Anniv of United Nations. P 11.*
270	84	15 c. bright blue, chestnut and silver	..	70	30

85 Crocodile

(Des A. Vale. Litho Questa)

1970 (3 Nov). *Christmas. T 85 and similar horiz designs. Multi-coloured. P 14.*
271	1 c. Type 85	..	..	..	10	10
272	2 c. Giraffe	..	..	..	10	10
273	7 c. Elephant ..	..	..		15	10
274	25 c. Rhinoceros	..	..		60	80
271/4		..	..	*Set of* 4	80	95
MS275	128 × 90 mm. Nos. 271/4	..			1·25	2·75

86 Sorghum

(Des J.W. Litho Questa)

1971 (6 April). *Important Crops. T 86 and similar horiz designs. Multicoloured. P 14.*
276	3 c. Type 86	..	..	..	15	10
277	7 c. Millet	..	..	..	20	10
278	10 c. Maize	..	..	..	20	10
279	35 c. Groundnuts	..	..		70	40
276/9		..	..	*Set of* 4	1·10	50

87 Map and Head of Cow   88 King bringing Gift of Gold

(Des A. Vale, adapted L. Curtis. Litho Harrison)

1971 (30 Sept). *Fifth Anniv of Independence. T 87 and similar vert designs inscr "PULA" (local greeting). P 14½ × 14.*
280	3 c. black, brown and apple-green	..		10	10
281	4 c. black, new blue and pale blue	..		10	10
282	7 c. black and red-orange	..	..		20	15
283	10 c. multicoloured	..	..		25	15
284	20 c. multicoloured	..	..		80	2·00
280/4		..	..	*Set of* 5	1·25	2·25

Designs:—4 c. Map and cogs; 7 c. Map and zebra; 10 c. Map and sorghum stalk crossed by tusk; 20 c. Arms and map of Botswana.

(Des A. Vale. Litho Questa)

1971 (11 Nov). *Christmas. T 88 and similar vert designs. Multi-coloured. P 14.*
285	2 c. Type 88	..	..	..	10	10
286	3 c. King bearing frankincense	..		10	10
287	7 c. King bearing myrrh	..	..		10	10
288	20 c. Three Kings behold the star	..		35	65
285/8		..	..	*Set of* 4	40	75
MS289	85 × 128 mm. Nos. 285/8 ..				1·00	3·00

ALTERED CATALOGUE NUMBERS

Any Catalogue numbers altered from the last edition are shown as a list in the introductory pages.

89 Orion   90 Postmark and Map

(Des R. Granger Barrett. Litho Questa)

1972 (24 Apr). *"Night Sky". T 89 and similar vert designs. P 14.*
290	3 c. turquoise-blue, black and red	..		75	30
291	7 c. dull blue, black and yellow	..		1·10	60
292	10 c. dull green, black and orange	..		1·25	85
293	20 c. deep violet-blue, black and blue-green	..	1·75	3·00
290/3		..	..	*Set of* 4	4·25	4·25

Constellations:—7 c. The Scorpion; 10 c. The Centaur; 20 c. The Cross.

(Des M. Bryan. Litho A. & M.)

1972 (21 Aug). *Mafeking-Gubulawayo Runner Post. T 90 and similar vert designs. Multicoloured. P 13½ × 13.*
294	3 c. Type 90	..	..	..	30	10
	a. Imperf (vert pair)	..	..		£425	
295	4 c. Bechuanaland stamp and map	..		30	35
296	7 c. Runners and map	..	..		45	50
297	20 c. Mafeking postmark and map	..		1·10	1·25
294/7		..	..	*Set of* 4	2·00	2·00
MS298	84×216 mm. Nos. 294/7 vertically se-tenant, forming a composite map design		11·00	15·00

For these designs redrawn smaller with changed inscriptions see Nos. 652/6.

91 Cross, Map and Bells   92 Thor

(Des M. Bryan. Litho Questa)

1972 (6 Nov). *Christmas. Vert designs each with Cross and Map as T 91. Multicoloured. P 14.*
299	2 c. Type 91	..	..	..	10	75
300	3 c. Cross, map and candle	..	..	10	10
301	7 c. Cross, map and Christmas tree ..		15	25
302	20 c. Cross, map, star and holly	..		40	85
299/302		..	..	*Set of* 4	60	1·75
MS303	96 × 119 mm. Nos. 299/302			1·25	3·00

(Des Edna Elphick. Litho Questa)

1973 (23 Mar). *I.M.O./W.M.O. Centenary. T 92 and similar designs showing Norse myths. Multicoloured. P 14.*
304	3 c. Type 92	..	..	..	20	10
305	4 c. Sun God's chariot (*horiz*)..	..		25	15
306	7 c. Ymir, the frost giant	..	..		30	15
307	20 c. Odin and Sleipnir (*horiz*)	..		75	70
304/7		..	..	*Set of* 4	1·40	1·00

93 Livingstone and River Scene

(Des G. Vasarhelyi. Litho Walsall)

1973 (10 Sept). *Death Centenary of Dr. Livingstone. T 93 and similar horiz designs. Multicoloured. P 13½.*
308	3 c. Type 93	..	..	..	20	10
309	20 c. Livingstone meeting Stanley	..		90	80

94 Donkey and Foal at Village Trough   95 Gaborone Campus

(Des M. Bryan. Litho Questa)

1973 (3 Dec). *Christmas. T 94 and similar multicoloured designs. P 14.*

310	3 c. Type **94**			10	10
311	4 c. Shepherd and flock (*horiz*)			10	10
312	7 c. Mother and child			10	10
313	20 c. Kgotla meeting (*horiz*)			40	80
310/13			*Set of 4*	55	90

(Des. M. Bryan, adapted P. Powell. Litho Questa)

1974 (8 May). *Tenth Anniv of University of Botswana, Lesotho and Swaziland. T 95 and similar horiz designs. Multicoloured. P 14.*

314	3 c. Type **95**			10	10
315	7 c. Kwaluseni Campus			10	10
316	20 c. Roma Campus			15	20
317	35 c. Map and flags of the three countries			20	35
314/17			*Set of 4*	35	55

96 Methods of Mail Transport

(Des. M. Bryan. Litho J.W.)

1974 (29 May). *Centenary of Universal Postal Union. T 96 and similar horiz designs. Multicoloured. P 14.*

318	2 c. Type **96**			55	35
319	3 c. Post Office, Palapye, *circa* 1889			55	35
320	7 c. Bechuanaland Police Camel Post, *circa* 1900			95	70
321	20 c. Hawker Siddeley H.S.748 and De Havilland D.H.9 mail planes of 1920 and 1974			2·75	2·50
318/21			*Set of 4*	4·25	3·50

97 Amethyst **98** *Stapelia variegata*

(Des M. Bayliss, adapted PAD Studio. Photo Enschedé)

1974 (1 July). *Botswana Minerals. T 97 and similar horiz designs. Multicoloured. P 14×13.*

322	1 c. Type **97**			60	80
323	2 c. Agate—"Botswana Pink"			60	80
324	3 c. Quartz			65	80
325	4 c. Copper nickel			70	60
326	5 c. Moss agate			70	1·00
327	7 c. Agate			80	60
328	10 c. Stilbite			1·60	65
329	15 c. Moshaneng Banded Marble			2·00	3·25
330	20 c. Gem diamonds			4·00	3·50
331	25 c. Chrysotile			5·00	2·50
332	35 c. Jasper			5·00	4·00
333	50 c. Moss quartz			4·50	7·00
334	1 r. Citrine			7·50	10·00
335	2 r. Chalcopyrite			20·00	20·00
322/35			*Set of 14*	48·00	48·00

(Des M. Bryan. Litho Questa)

1974 (4 Nov). *Christmas. T 98 and similar vert designs showing flowers. Multicoloured. P 14.*

336	2 c. Type **98**			20	40
337	7 c. *Hibiscus lunarifolius*			50	20
338	15 c. *Ceratotheca triloba*			80	1·50
339	20 c. *Nerine laticoma*			90	1·75
336/9			*Set of 4*	2·25	3·50
MS340	85 × 130 mm. Nos. 336/9			3·00	4·25

99 President Sir Seretse Khama **100** Ostrich

(Des M. Bryan, adapted G. Vasarhelyi. Photo Enschedé)

1975 (24 Mar). *Tenth Anniv of Self-Government. P 13½×13.*

341	**99** 4 c. multicoloured			10	10
342	10 c. multicoloured			15	10
343	20 c. multicoloured			25	25
344	35 c. multicoloured			45	50
341/4			*Set of 4*	85	85
MS345	93×130 mm. Nos. 341/4			1·00	1·50

(Des M. Bryan. Litho Questa)

1975 (23 June). *Rock Paintings, Tsodilo Hills. T 100 and similar horiz designs. Multicoloured. P 14.*

346	4 c. Type **100**			80	10
347	10 c. White Rhinoceros			1·40	10
348	25 c. Spotted Hyena			2·75	55
349	35 c. Scorpion			2·75	1·10
346/9			*Set of 4*	7·00	1·60
MS350	150 × 150 mm. Nos. 346/9			11·00	7·50

101 Map of British Bechuanaland, 1885 **102** *Aloe marlothii*

(Des M. Bryan, adapted G. Vasarhelyi. Litho Harrison)

1975 (13 Oct). *Anniversaries. T 101 and similar multicoloured designs. P 14 × 14½ (25 c.) or 14½ × 14 (others).*

351	6 c. Type **101**			30	20
352	10 c. Chief Khama, 1875			40	15
353	25 c. Chiefs Sebele, Bathoen and Khama, 1895 (*horiz*)			80	75
351/3			*Set of 3*	1·40	1·00

Events:—6 c. 90th Anniv of Protectorate; 10 c. Centenary of Khama's Accession; 25 c. 80th Anniv of Chiefs' visit to London.

(Des M. Bryan. Litho Questa)

1975 (3 Nov). *Christmas. T 102 and similar vert designs showing aloes. Multicoloured. P 14½.*

354	3 c. Type **102**			30	10
355	10 c. *Aloe lutescens*			75	20
356	15 c. *Aloe zebrina*			1·10	1·75
357	25 c. *Aloe littoralis*			1·25	3·00
354/7			*Set of 4*	3·00	4·50

103 Drum

(Des M. Bryan. Litho Questa)

1976 (1 Mar). *Traditional Musical Instruments. T 103 and similar horiz designs. Multicoloured. P 14.*

358	4 c. Type **103**			15	10
359	10 c. Hand Piano			20	10
360	15 c. Segankuru (violin)			25	50
361	25 c. Kudu Signal Horn			30	1·25
358/61			*Set of 4*	80	1·75

104 One Pula Note

(Des M. Bryan from banknotes by D.L.R. Litho Questa)

1976 (28 June). *First National Currency. T 104 and similar horiz designs. Multicoloured. P 14.*

362	4 c. Type **104**			15	10
363	10 c. Two pula note			20	10
364	15 c. Five pula note			35	20
365	25 c. Ten pula note			45	45
362/5			*Set of 4*	1·00	70
MS366	163 × 107 mm. Nos. 362/5			1·50	3·50

(New Currency. 100 thebe = 1 pula)

1t	**1t**	**2t**	**2t**
(105)	(105)	(I)	(II)
(Type I)	(Type II)		

4t	**4t**	**5t**	**5t**
(I)	(II)	(I)	(II)

15t	**15t**	**20t**	**20t**
(I)	(II)	(I)	(II)

(Surch in letterpress by Govt Printer, Pretoria (Type I), or in lithography by Enschedé (Type II))

1976 (23 Aug)—77. *Nos. 322/35 surch as T 105.*

367	1 t. on 1 c. Type **97** (I)			2·00	70
	a. Type II Surch (15.7.77)			2·50	80
368	2 t. on 2 c. Agate—"Botswana Pink" (I)			2·00	80
	a. Type II Surch (15.7.77)			2·50	80
369	3 t. on 3 c. Quartz (surch at top right) (Gold)			1·50	60
	a. Surch at bottom right (17.10.77)			50·00	

370	4 t. on 4 c. Copper nickel (I)			2·50	40
	a. Type II Surch (15.7.77)			2·75	80
371	5 t. on 5 c. Moss agate (I)			2·50	40
	a. Type II Surch (15.7.77)			2·75	70
372	7 t. on 7 c. Agate (surch at top right)			1·25	2·25
	a. Surch at bottom right (10.10.77)			60·00	
373	10 t. on 10 c. Stilbite			1·25	80
374	15 t. on 15 c. Moshaneng Banded Marble (I) (Gold)			4·25	2·00
	a. Type II Surch (15.7.77)			6·00	1·50
375	20 t. on 20 c. Gem diamonds (I)			7·50	80
	a. Type II Surch (15.7.77)			8·00	1·50
376	25 t. on 25 c. Chrysotile			5·00	1·25
377	35 t. on 35 c. Jasper			4·50	4·00
378	50 t. on 50 c. Moss quartz (surch at top right)			7·00	9·00
	a. Surch at bottom right (17.10.77)			£250	
379	1 p. on 1 r. Citrine (surch at top right)			8·00	9·50
	a. Surch at bottom left (10.10.77)			80·00	
380	2 p. on 2 r. Chalcopyrite (Gold)			11·00	11·00
367/80			*Set of 14*	50·00	40·00
367a/75a			*Set of 6*	22·00	5·50

Nos. 369a, 372a, 378a and 379a come from a second Pretoria printing on a small stock returned from the Crown Agents. By the time the stamps arrived in Pretoria the surcharge type for the 3 t., 7 t., 50 t. and 1 p. had been dispersed and when it was reset the position of the value figures was changed.

106 Botswanan Cattle **107** *Colophospermum mopane*

(Des M. Bryan. Litho Questa)

1976 (30 Sept). *Tenth Anniv of Independence. T 106 and similar multicoloured designs. P 14.*

381	4 t. Type **106**			15	10
382	10 t. Deer, Okavango Delta (*vert*)			30	10
383	15 t. Schools and pupils			30	40
384	25 t. Rural weaving (*vert*)			35	50
385	35 t. Miner (*vert*)			1·00	85
381/5			*Set of 5*	1·90	1·75

Nos. 381/5 were printed on sand-grained paper which has an uneven surface.

(Des M. Bryan. Litho J.W.)

1976 (1 Nov). *Christmas. T 107 and similar horiz designs showing trees. Multicoloured. P 13.*

386	3 t. Type **107**			15	10
387	4 t. *Baikiaea plurijuga*			15	10
388	10 t. *Sterculia rogersii*			30	15
389	25 t. *Acacia nilotica*			60	50
390	40 t. *Kigelia africana*			1·00	1·25
386/90			*Set of 5*	2·00	1·75

108 Coronation Coach

(Des M. Bryan, adapted G. Vasarhelyi. Litho Cartor)

1977 (7 Feb). *Silver Jubilee. T 108 and similar horiz designs. Multicoloured. P 12.*

391	4 t. Queen and Sir Seretse Khama			10	10
392	25 t. Type **108**			20	15
393	40 t. The Recognition			35	80
391/3			*Set of 3*	60	90

Nos. 391/3 have matt, almost invisible gum.

109 African Clawless Otter **110** Cwihaba Caves

(Des M. Bryan. Litho Questa)

1977 (7 June). *Diminishing Species. T 109 and similar horiz designs. Multicoloured. P 14.*

394	3 t. Type **109**			3·00	40
395	4 t. Serval			3·00	40
396	10 t. Bat-eared Fox			3·75	40
397	25 t. Temminck's Ground Pangolin			9·00	2·00
398	40 t. Brown Hyena			11·00	6·50
394/8			*Set of 5*	27·00	8·75

(Des M. Bryan. Litho J.W.)

1977 (22 Aug). *Historical Monuments. T 110 and similar horiz designs. Multicoloured. P 14.*

399	4 t. Type **110**			25	10
400	5 t. Khama Memorial			25	10
401	15 t. Green's Tree			40	40
402	20 t. Mmajojo Ruins			40	45
403	25 t. Ancient morabaraba board			40	40
404	35 t. Matsieng's footprint			55	40
399/404			*Set of 6*	2·00	2·00
MS405	154 × 105 mm. Nos. 399/404			2·50	3·25

111 *Hypoxis nitida*   112 Little Black Bustard

(Des M. Bryan. Litho Questa)

1977 (7 Nov). *Christmas. T **111** and similar vert designs showing lilies. Multicoloured. P 14.*

406	3 t.	Type 111		15	10
407	5 t.	*Haemanthus magnificus*		15	10
408	10 t.	*Boophane disticha*		20	10
409	25 t.	*Vellozia retinervis*		40	55
410	40 t.	*Ammocharis coranica*		55	1·25
406/10			*Set of 5*	1·40	1·75

(Des M. Bryan. Photo Harrison)

1978 (3 July). *Birds. Vert designs as T **112**. Multicoloured. P 14 × 14½ (1 to 20 t.) or 14 (25t to 5 p.).*

411	1 t.	Type 112		50	1·25
412	2 t.	Marabou Stork		50	1·25
413	3 t.	Green Wood Hoopoe		50	85
414	4 t.	Carmine Bee Eater		50	75
415	5 t.	African Jacana		50	40
416	7 t.	African Paradise Flycatcher		50	2·25
417	10 t.	Bennett's Woodpecker		1·75	60
418	15 t.	Red Bishop		70	2·25
419	20 t.	Crowned Plover		1·50	2·00
420	25 t.	Giant Kingfisher		70	2·25
421	30 t.	White-faced Whistling Duck		70	70
422	35 t.	Green Heron		70	2·75
423	45 t.	Black-headed Heron		70	2·50
424	50 t.	Spotted Eagle Owl		6·50	4·50
425	1 p.	Gabar Goshawk		3·25	4·50
426	2 p.	Martial Eagle		4·00	8·00
427	5 p.	Saddle-bill Stork		12·00	16·00
411/27			*Set of 17*	32·00	45·00

113 Tawana making Karos

(Des M. Bryan. Litho Questa)

1978 (11 Sept). *Okavango Delta. T **113** and similar horiz designs. Multicoloured. P 14.*

428	4 t.	Type 113		10	10
429	5 t.	Tribe localities		10	10
430	15 t.	Bushmen collecting roots		25	40
431	20 t.	Herero woman milking		35	55
432	25 t.	Yei poling "mokoro" (canoe)		40	60
433	35 t.	Mbukushu fishing		45	1·50
428/33			*Set of 6*	1·50	2·75
MS434		150 × 98 mm. Nos. 428/33		1·50	3·50

Nos. 428/34 were printed on sand-grained paper which has an uneven surface.

114 *Caralluma lutea*   115 Sip Well

(Des M. Bryan. Litho J.W.)

1978 (6 Nov). *Christmas. Flowers. T **114** and similar vert designs. Multicoloured. P 14.*

435	5 t.	Type 114		35	10
436	10 t.	*Hoodia lugardii*		50	15
437	15 t.	*Ipomoea transvaalensis*		90	55
438	25 t.	*Ansellia gigantea*		1·10	70
435/8			*Set of 4*	2·50	1·40

(Des M. Bryan. Litho Questa)

1979 (30 Mar). *Water Development. T **115** and similar vert designs. Multicoloured. P 14.*

439	3 t.	Type 115		10	10
440	5 t.	Watering pit		10	10
441	10 t.	Hand dug well		15	10
442	25 t.	Windmill		20	30
443	40 t.	Modern drilling rig		40	55
439/43			*Set of 5*	80	1·00

ALTERED CATALOGUE NUMBERS

Any Catalogue numbers altered from the last edition are shown as a list in the introductory pages.

116 Pottery   117 1885 British Bechuanaland 1d. Stamp and Sir Rowland Hill

(Des M. Bryan. Litho Questa)

1979 (11 June). *Handicrafts. T **116** and similar vert designs. Multicoloured. P 14½ × 14.*

444	5 t.	Type 116		10	10
445	10 t.	Clay modelling		15	10
446	25 t.	Basketry		30	25
447	40 t.	Beadwork		50	50
444/7			*Set of 4*	95	80
MS448		123 × 96 mm. Nos. 444/7		95	2·25

(Des M. Bryan. Litho Secura, Singapore)

1979 (27 Aug). *Death Centenary of Sir Rowland Hill. T **117** and similar horiz designs showing stamps and Sir Rowland Hill. Multicoloured. P 13½.*

449	5 t.	Type 117		20	10
450	25 t.	1932 Bechuanaland Protectorate 2d		45	50
451	45 t.	1967 2 c. definitive		55	1·10
449/51			*Set of 3*	1·10	1·50

118 Children Playing   119 *Ximenia caffra*

(Des K. Mosinyi (5 t.), M. Bryan (10 t.). Litho Questa)

1979 (24 Sept). *International Year of the Child. T **118** and similar multicoloured design. P 14.*

452	5 t.	Type 118		20	10
453	10 t.	Child playing with doll (*vert*)		30	20

(Des M. Bryan. Litho Questa)

1979 (12 Nov). *Christmas. Fruit. T **119** and similar vert designs. Multicoloured. P 14.*

454	5 t.	Type 119		10	10
455	10 t.	*Sclerocarya caffra*		20	20
456	15 t.	*Hexalobus monopetalus*		35	35
457	25 t.	*Ficus soldanella*		45	45
454/7			*Set of 4*	1·00	1·00

120 Flap-necked Chameleon   121 Rock Breaking

(Des M. Bryan. Litho Security Printers (M), Malaysia)

1980 (3 Mar). *Reptiles. T **120** and similar horiz designs. Multicoloured. P 13½.*

458	5 t.	Type 120		40	10
459	10 t.	Leopard Tortoise		40	15
460	25 t.	Puff Adder		1·10	65
461	40 t.	White-throated Monitor		1·25	2·50
458/61			*Set of 4*	2·75	3·00

(Des M. Bryan. Litho Secura, Singapore)

1980 (7 July). *Early Mining. T **121** and similar horiz designs. Multicoloured. P 13½.*

462	5 t.	Type 121		25	15
463	10 t.	Ore hoisting		30	15
464	15 t.	Ore transport		70	60
465	20 t.	Ore crushing		75	70
466	25 t.	Smelting		80	90
467	35 t.	Tools and products		1·00	1·40
462/7			*Set of 6*	3·50	3·50

122 "Chiwele and the Giant"

(Des W. Battiss. Litho Questa)

1980 (8 Sept). *Folktales. T **122** and similar multicoloured designs. P 14 (5 t.), 14 × 13½ (45 t.) or 14½ × 14 (others).*

468	5 t.	Type 122 (35 × 22 mm)		10	10
469	10 t.	"Kgori is not deceived" (28 × 37 mm)		15	10
470	30 t.	"Nyambi's wife and Crocodile" (28 × 37 mm)		45	45
471	45 t.	"Clever Hare" (44 × 27 mm)		60	60
468/71			*Set of 4*	1·10	1·10

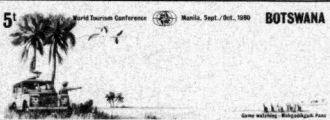

123 Game watching. Makgadikgadi Pans

(Des M. Bryan. Litho Govt Printer, Pretoria)

1980 (6 Oct). *World Tourism Conference, Manila. P 14.*

472	123	5 t. multicoloured		45	20

124 *Acacia gerrardii*   125 Heinrich von Stephan with Bechuanaland 1949 3d. and Botswana 1974 3 c. U.P.U. Anniversary Commemoratives

(Des M. Bryan. Litho Govt Printer, Pretoria)

1980 (3 Nov). *Christmas. Flora. T **124** and similar vert designs. Multicoloured. P 14 × 13½.*

473	5 t.	Type 124		10	10
474	10 t.	*Acacia nilotica*		20	10
475	25 t.	*Acacia erubescens*		45	30
476	40 t.	*Dichrostachys cinerea*		70	70
473/6			*Set of 4*	1·25	1·00

(Des M. Bryan. Litho Govt Printer, Pretoria)

1981 (7 Jan). *150th Birth Anniv of Heinrich von Stephan (founder of U.P.U.). T **125** and similar horiz design showing Von Stephan and U.P.U. anniversary commemoratives. Multicoloured. P 14.*

477	6 t.	Type 125		75	30
478	20 t.	Bechuanaland 1949 6d. and Botswana 1974 7 c.		1·75	2·25

126 *Anax imperator* (dragonfly)   127 Camphill Community Ramkoromane, Otse

(Des M. Bryan. Litho Govt Printer, Pretoria)

1981 (23 Feb). *Insects. T **126** and similar vert designs. Multicoloured. P 14.*

479	6 t.	Type 126		15	10
480	7 t.	*Sphodromantis gastrica* (mantid)		15	20
481	10 t.	*Zonocerus elegans* (grasshopper)		20	20
482	20 t.	*Kheper nigroaeneus* (beetle)		35	50
483	30 t.	*Papilio demodocus* (butterfly)		70	70
484	45 t.	*Acanthocampa belina* (moth larva)		80	1·10
479/84			*Set of 6*	2·10	2·50
MS485		180×89 mm. Nos. 479/84		4·75	7·50

(Des M. Bryan. Litho Govt Printer, Pretoria)

1981 (6 Apr). *International Year for Disabled Persons. T **127** and similar horiz designs. Multicoloured. P 14.*

486	6 t.	Type 127		20	10
487	20 t.	Resource Centre for the Blind, Mochudi		55	35
488	30 t.	Tlamelong Rehabilitation Centre, Tlokweng		75	45
486/8			*Set of 3*	1·40	80

128 Woman reading Letter   129 Sir Seretse Khama and Building

(Des Petra Rouendaal. Litho Govt Printer, Pretoria)

1981 (6 June). *Literacy Programme. T **128** and similar vert designs. Multicoloured. P 14.*

489	6 t.	Type 128		20	10
490	7 t.	Man filling in form		20	15
491	20 t.	Boy reading newspaper		60	35
492	30 t.	Child being taught to read		80	45
489/92			*Set of 4*	1·60	90

(Des G. Vasarhelyi. Litho Format)

1981 (13 July). *First Death Anniv of President Sir Seretse Khama.
T 129 and similar horiz designs. Multicoloured. P 14.*

493	6 t. Type 129		15	10
494	10 t. Seretse Khama and building (*different*)		25	15
495	30 t. Seretse Khama and Botswana flag		40	45
496	45 t. Seretse Khama and building (*different*)		55	70
493/6	..	*Set of 4*	1·25	1·25

25t
(130)
131 Traditional Ploughing

1981 (1 Sept). *Nos. 417 and 422 surch as T 130.*

497	25 t. on 35 t. Green Heron		3·00	2·00
498	30 t. on 10 t. Bennett's Woodpecker	..	3·00	2·00

(Des K. Mosinyi. Litho Format)

1981 (21 Sept). *Cattle Industry. T 131 and similar horiz designs.
Multicoloured. P 14½.*

499	6 t. Type 131		10	10
500	20 t. Agricultural show		30	50
501	30 t. Botswana Meat Commission		35	60
502	45 t. Vaccine Institute, Botswana		50	1·00
499/502	..	*Set of 4*	1·10	2·00

132 *Nymphaea caerulea*   **133** "Cattle Post Scene"
(Boitumelo Golaakwena)

(Des M. Bryan. Litho Govt Printer, Pretoria)

1981 (11 Nov). *Christmas. Flowers. T 132 and similar vert
designs. Multicoloured. P 14.*

503	6 t. Type 132		20	10
504	10 t. *Nymphoides indica*	..	25	10
505	25 t. *Nymphaea lotus*		60	90
506	40 t. *Ottelia kunenensis*		80	2·25
503/6	..	*Set of 4*	1·60	3·00

(Litho Govt Printer, Pretoria)

1982 (15 Feb). *Children's Art. T 133 and similar horiz designs.
Multicoloured. P 14.*

507	6 t. Type 133		40	10
508	10 t. "Kgotla Meeting" (Reginald Klinck)		50	15
509	30 t. "Village Water Supply" (Keromemang Matswiri)		1·75	1·25
510	45 t. "With the Crops" (Kennedy Balemoge)		1·75	2·75
507/10	..	*Set of 4*	4·00	3·75

134 Common Type   **135** African Masked
Weaver

(Des K. Mosinyi and V. Moremi. Litho Govt Printer, Pretoria)

1982 (3 May). *Traditional Houses. T 134 and similar horiz
designs. Multicoloured. P 14.*

511	6 t. Type 134		40	15
512	10 t. Kgatleng type		50	15
513	30 t. North Eastern type		2·00	1·10
514	45 t. Sarwa type		2·00	3·00
511/14	..	*Set of 4*	4·50	4·00

(Des M. Bryan. Photo Harrison)

1982 (2 Aug). *Birds. T 135 and similar multicoloured designs.
P 14×14½ (1 t. to 10 t.) or 14½×14 (others).*

515	1 t. Type 135		80	1·25
516	2 t. Lesser Double-collared Sunbird	..	90	1·40
517	3 t. Red-throated Bee Eater		1·00	1·40
518	4 t. Ostrich		1·00	1·40
519	5 t. Grey-headed Gull		1·00	1·40
520	6 t. African Pygmy Goose		1·00	40
521	7 t. Cattle Egret		1·00	15
522	8 t. Lanner Falcon		2·00	1·25
523	10 t. Yellow-billed Stork		1·00	20
524	15 t. Red-billed Pintail (*horiz*)		2·50	25
525	20 t. Barn Owl (*horiz*)		5·00	3·50
526	25 t. Hammerkop (*horiz*)		3·00	70
527	30 t. South African Stilt (*horiz*)		3·50	90
528	35 t. Blacksmith Plover (*horiz*)		3·50	80
529	45 t. Senegal Wattled Plover (*horiz*)		3·50	1·75
530	50 t. Helmet Guineafowl (*horiz*)		3·50	40
531	1 p. Cape Vulture (*horiz*)		8·50	12·00
532	2 p. Augur Buzzard (*horiz*)		10·00	16·00
515/32	..	*Set of 18*	48·00	42·00

136 *Coprinus comatus*   **137** President Quett Masire

(Des Gillian Condy. Litho Mardon Printers Ltd, Zimbabwe)

1982 (2 Nov). *Christmas. Fungi. T 136 and similar vert designs.
Multicoloured. P 14½.*

533	7 t. Type 136	..	1·50	20
534	15 t. *Lactarius deliciosus*	..	2·75	65
535	35 t. *Amanita pantherina*		4·50	2·00
536	50 t. *Boletus edulis*		5·50	6·50
533/6	..	*Set of 4*	13·00	8·50

(Des G. Vasarhelyi. Litho Questa)

1983 (14 Mar). *Commonwealth Day. T 137 and similar horiz
designs. Multicoloured. P 14.*

537	7 t. Type 137		10	10
538	15 t. Native dancers		15	20
539	30 t. Melbourne conference centre		45	55
540	45 t. Meeting of Heads of State, Melbourne		55	80
537/40	..	*Set of 4*	1·00	1·50

138 Wattled Crane   **139** Wooden Spoons

(Des Petra Rouendaal (50 t.), Gillian Condy (others). Litho
Mardon Printers Ltd, Zimbabwe)

1983 (19 Apr). *Endangered Species. T 138 and similar vert
designs. Multicoloured. P 14×14½.*

541	7 t. Type 138	..	3·00	55
542	15 t. *Aloe lutescens*	..	2·50	80
543	35 t. Roan Antelope	..	3·00	3·25
544	50 t. Ivory Palm (*Hyphaene ventricosa*)	..	3·50	6·00
541/4	..	*Set of 4*	11·00	9·50

(Des M. Bryan. Litho Mardon Printers Ltd, Zimbabwe)

1983 (20 July). *Traditional Artifacts. T 139 and similar vert
designs. Multicoloured. P 14½.*

545	7 t. Type 139		25	10
546	15 t. Personal ornaments		45	30
547	35 t. Ox-hide milk bag		75	65
548	50 t. Decorated knives		1·00	1·10
545/8	..	*Set of 4*	2·25	1·90
MS549	115 × 102 mm. Nos. 545/8	..	4·25	5·00

140 *Pantala flavescens*   **141** Sorting Diamonds

(Des Beverley Boudreau. Litho Mardon Printers Ltd, Zimbabwe)

1983 (7 Nov). *Christmas. Dragonflies. T 140 and similar horiz
designs. Multicoloured. P 14½×14.*

550	6 t. Type 140		85	10
551	15 t. *Anax imperator*		1·75	50
552	25 t. *Trithemis arteriosa*		2·00	85
553	45 t. *Chlorolestes elegans*		2·75	4·50
550/3	..	*Set of 4*	6·50	5·50

(Des M. Kahn. Litho Mardon Printers Ltd, Zimbabwe)

1984 (19 Mar). *Mining Industry. T 141 and similar multicoloured
designs. P 14½.*

554	7 t. Type 141		2·00	50
555	15 t. Lime kiln		2·00	75
556	35 t. Copper-nickel smelter plant (*vert*)		3·25	3·00
557	50 t. Stockpiled coal (*vert*)		3·75	7·00
554/7	..	*Set of 4*	10·00	10·00

142 Riding Cattle   **143** Avro 504 Aircraft

(Des S. Mogotsi. Litho Mardon Printers Ltd, Zimbabwe)

1984 (18 June). *Traditional Transport. T 142 and similar horiz
designs. Multicoloured. P 14½ × 14.*

558	7 t. Type 142		20	10
559	25 t. Sledge		65	50
560	35 t. Wagon		85	1·25
561	50 t. Two wheeled donkey cart		1·25	3·25
558/61	..	*Set of 4*	2·75	4·50

(Des V. Larsson. Litho Mardon Printers Ltd, Zimbabwe)

1984 (8 Oct). *40th Anniv of International Civil Aviation Organization. T 143 and similar horiz designs, each with I.C.A.O.
emblem. Multicoloured. P 14½ × 14.*

562	7 t. Type 143		60	15
563	10 t. Westland Wessex trimotor		75	20
564	15 t. Junkers Ju 52/3m		1·40	85
565	25 t. De Havilland D.H.89B Dominie		2·00	1·50
566	35 t. Douglas DC-3		2·25	3·00
567	50 t. Fokker F.27 Friendship		2·50	4·75
562/7	..	*Set of 6*	8·50	9·50

144 *Papilio demodocus*   **145** Seswaa (meat dish)

(Des M. Kahn. Litho Mardon Printers Ltd, Zimbabwe)

1984 (5 Nov). *Christmas. Butterflies. T 144 and similar horiz
designs. Multicoloured. P 14½ × 14.*

568	7 t. Type 144		2·00	30
569	25 t. *Byblia anvatara*		3·25	1·50
570	35 t. *Danaus chrysippus*		3·50	3·00
571	50 t. *Graphium taboranus*		4·75	8·00
568/71	..	*Set of 4*	12·00	11·50

No. 570 is incorrectly inscribed "Hypolimnas misisppus".

(Des K. Mosinyi. Litho Mardon Printers Ltd, Zimbabwe)

1985 (18 Mar). *5th Anniv of Southern African Development
Co-ordination Conference. Traditional Foods. T 145 and
similar vert designs. Multicoloured. P 14½.*

572	7 t. Type 145		25	10
573	15 t. Bogobe (cereal porridge)		45	35
574	25 t. Madila (soured coagulated cows milk)		70	55
575	50 t. Phane (caterpillars)		1·10	1·75
572/5	..	*Set of 4*	2·25	2·50
MS576	117×103 mm. Nos. 572/5	..	6·00	8·00

146 1885 British
Bechuanaland
Overprint on Cape
of Good Hope ½d.

147 Bechuanaland
Border Police,
1885–95

(Des D. Finlay and J. Hodgson. Litho Mardon Printers Ltd,
Zimbabwe)

1985 (24 June). *Centenary of First Bechuanaland Stamps.
T 146 and similar designs. P 14½.*

577	7 t. black, grey-black and orange-vermilion		80	20
578	15 t. black, deep brown and greenish yellow		1·40	50
579	25 t. black and bright scarlet		1·90	80
580	35 t. black, ultramarine and gold		2·25	2·00
581	50 t. multicoloured		2·50	3·25
577/81	..	*Set of 5*	8·00	6·00

Designs: *Vert*—15 t. 1897 Bechuanaland Protectorate overprint on G.B. 3d.; 25 t. Bechuanaland Protectorate 1932 1d.
definitive. *Horiz*—35 t. Bechuanaland 1965 Internal Self-
Government 5 c.; 50 t. Botswana 1966 Independence 2½ c.

(Des V. Larsson. Litho Mardon Printers Ltd, Zimbabwe)

1985 (5 Aug). *Centenary of Botswana Police. T 147 and similar
horiz designs. Multicoloured. P 14½ × 14.*

582	7 t. Type 147		2·00	50
583	10 t. Bechuanaland Mounted Police, 1895–1902		2·25	50
584	25 t. Bechuanaland Protectorate Police, 1903–66		3·25	2·00
585	50 t. Botswana Police, from 1966		4·50	6·00
582/5	..	*Set of 4*	11·00	11·00

MINIMUM PRICE

The minimum price quote is 10p which represents
a handling charge rather than a basis for valuing
common stamps. For further notes about prices
see introductory pages.

250

148 Cucumis metuliferus

149 Mr. Shippard and Chief Gaseitsiwe of the Bangwaketse

(Des Audrey Renew. Litho Mardon Printers Ltd, Zimbabwe)

1985 (4 Nov). *Christmas. Edible Wild Cucumbers. T* **148** *and similar horiz designs. Multicoloured. P* 14½ × 14.

586	7 t. Type 148	85	10
587	15 t. Acanthosicyos naudinianus	1·50	70
588	25 t. Coccinia sessifolia	2·25	1·10
589	50 t. Momordica balsamina	3·75	6·50
586/9	*Set of 4*	7·50	7·50

(Des A. Campbell. Litho Mardon Printers Ltd, Zimbabwe)

1985 (30 Dec). *Centenary of Declaration of Bechuanaland Protectorate. T* **149** *and similar vert designs. Multicoloured. P* 14 × 14½.

590	7 t. Type 149	35	10
591	15 t. Sir Charles Warren and Chief Sechele of the Bakwena	70	45
592	25 t. Revd. Mackenzie and Chief Khama of the Bamangwato	1·25	85
593	50 t. Map showing Protectorate	2·75	2·75
590/3	*Set of 4*	4·50	4·75
MS594	130×133 mm. Nos. 590/3	8·00	10·00

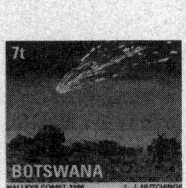
150 Halley's Comet over Serowe

151 Milk Bag

(Des L. Hutchings. Litho Mardon Printers Ltd, Zimbabwe)

1986 (24 Mar). *Appearance of Halley's Comet. T* **150** *and similar horiz designs. Multicoloured. P* 14½ × 14.

595	7 t. Type 150	80	15
596	15 t. Comet over Bobonong at sunset	1·50	70
597	35 t. Comet over Gomare at dawn	2·00	1·50
598	50 t. Comet over Thamaga and Letlhakeng	2·25	3·50
595/8	*Set of 4*	6·00	5·25

(Des B. Mazebedi. Litho Mardon Printers Ltd, Zimbabwe)

1986 (23 June). *Traditional Milk Containers. T* **151** *and similar vert designs. Multicoloured. P* 14½.

599	8 t. Type 151	15	10
600	15 t. Clay pot and calabashes	25	30
601	35 t. Wooden milk bucket	50	65
602	50 t. Milk churn	70	1·10
599/602	*Set of 4*	1·40	1·90

152 Map showing National Parks and Reserves

153 Ludwigia stogonifera

(Des K. Bogatsu, A. Campbell, I. Marshall and K. Mosinyi. Litho Govt Printer, Pretoria)

1986 (30 Sept). *20th Anniv of Independence. Sheet* 100 × 120 *mm, containing T* **152** *and similar vert designs. Multicoloured. P* 14.

MS603	20 t. Type 152; 20 t. Morupule Power Station; 20 t. Cattle breeding in Kgalagadi; 20 t. National Assembly Building	2·50	1·75

(Des Julia Cairns. Litho Mardon Printers Ltd, Zimbabwe)

1986 (3 Nov). *Christmas. Flowers of Okavango. T* **153** *and similar vert designs. Multicoloured. P* 14×14½.

604	8 t. Type 153	1·25	10
605	15 t. Sopubia mannii	2·25	1·10
606	35 t. Commelina diffusa	3·50	3·00
607	50 t. Hibiscus diversifolius	4·00	8·50
604/7	*Set of 4*	10·00	11·50

154 Divining

(155)

156 Oral Rehydration Therapy

(Des K. Mosinyi. Litho Mardon Printers Ltd, Zimbabwe)

1987 (2 Mar). *Traditional Medicine. T* **154** *and similar horiz designs. Multicoloured. P* 14½ × 14.

608	8 t. Type 154	80	10
609	15 t. Lightning prevention	1·50	80
610	35 t. Rain making	2·25	2·50
611	50 t. Blood letting	2·75	5·50
608/11	*Set of 4*	6·50	8·00

1987 (1 Apr). *Nos.* 520, 523 *and* 530 *surch as T* **155**.

612	3 t. on 6 t. African Pygmy Goose	1·50	60
613	5 t. on 10 t. Yellow-billed Stork	1·50	60
614	20 t. on 50 t. Helmet Guineafowl (horiz)	3·00	1·40
612/14	*Set of 3*	5·50	2·40

(Des A. Nunoo. Litho Govt Printer, Pretoria)

1987 (1 June). *U.N.I.C.E.F. Child Survival Campaign. T* **156** *and similar vert designs. Multicoloured. P* 14.

615	8 t. Type 156	35	10
616	15 t. Growth monitoring	60	55
617	35 t. Immunization	1·25	1·75
618	50 t. Breast feeding	1·50	3·75
615/18	*Set of 4*	3·25	5·50

157 Cape Fox

158 Cyperus articulatus

(Des P. Huebsch. Photo Harrison)

1987 (3 Aug). *Animals. T* **157** *and similar horiz designs. Multicoloured. P* 14.

619	1 t. Type 157	10	50
620	2 t. Lechwe	10	50
621	3 t. Zebra	15	50
622	4 t. Duiker	15	80
623	5 t. Banded Mongoose	20	80
624	6 t. Rusty-spotted Genet	20	80
625	8 t. Hedgehog	30	10
626	10 t. Scrub Hare	30	10
627	12 t. Hippopotamus	1·50	2·00
628	15 t. Suricate	90	40
629	20 t. Caracal	70	65
630	25 t. Steenbok	70	75
631	30 t. Gemsbok	1·25	60
632	35 t. Square-lipped Rhinoceros	1·50	60
633	40 t. Mountain Reedbuck	1·40	85
634	50 t. Rock Dassie	90	1·00
635	1 p. Giraffe	2·50	3·25
636	2 p. Tsessebe	2·50	4·00
637	3 p. Side-striped Jackal	3·75	7·00
638	5 p. Hartebeest	6·00	11·00
619/38	*Set of 20*	22·00	32·00

(Des Julia Cairns. Litho National Printing & Packaging, Zimbabwe)

1987 (26 Oct). *Christmas. Grasses and Sedges of Okavango. T* **158** *and similar vert designs. Multicoloured. P* 14 × 14½.

639	8 t. Type 158	40	10
640	15 t. Broomgrass	60	40
641	30 t. Cyperus alopurcides	1·25	75
642	1 p. Bulrush Sedge	2·50	4·00
639/42	*Set of 4*	4·25	4·75
MS643	88×99 mm. Nos. 639/42	4·25	4·75
	a. 30 t. value imperf vert	40·00	

159 Planting Seeds with Digging Stick

160 Red Lechwe at Water-hole

(Des K. Mosinyi. Litho National Printing & Packaging, Zimbabwe)

1988 (14 Mar). *Early Cultivation. T* **159** *and similar horiz designs. Multicoloured. P* 14½ × 14.

644	8 t. Type 159	40	10
645	15 t. Using iron hoe	60	35
646	35 t. Wooden ox-drawn plough	1·00	1·00
647	50 t. Villagers using lesotlas	1·40	2·00
644/7	*Set of 4*	3·00	3·00

(Des P. Augustinus. Litho National Printing & Packaging, Zimbabwe)

1988 (6 June). *Red Lechwe. T* **160** *and similar horiz designs. Multicoloured. P* 14½×14.

648	10 t. Type 160	75	15
649	15 t. Red Lechwe and early morning sun	1·50	65
650	35 t. Female and calf	2·25	1·75
651	75 t. Herd on the move	3·75	6·00
648/51	*Set of 4*	7·50	7·75

COVER PRICES

Cover factors are quoted at the beginning of each country for most issues to 1945. An explanation of the system can be found on page x. The factors quoted do not, however, apply to philatelic covers.

---

161 Gubulawayo Postmark and Route Southwards to Tati

162 Pope John Paul II and Outline Map of Botswana

(Des M. Bryan, adapted Lucy Phalayagae. Litho National Printing & Packaging, Zimbabwe)

1988 (22 Aug). *Centenary of Mafeking-Gubalawayo Runner Post. Designs as Nos.* 294/8, *but redrawn smaller with changed inscription as in T* **161**. *Multicoloured. P* 14½.

652	10 t. Type 161	35	10
653	15 t. Bechuanaland 1888 6d. on 6d. stamp and route from Tati southwards	55	30
654	30 t. Runners and twin routes south from Shoshong	95	75
655	60 t. Mafeking postmark and routes to Bechuanaland and Transvaal	1·60	2·75
652/5	*Set of 4*	3·00	3·50
MS656	81×151 mm. Nos. 652/5 vertically se-tenant, forming a composite map design	5·50	6·50

(Des P. Lodoen. Litho National Printing & Packaging, Zimbabwe)

1988 (13 Sept). *Visit of Pope John Paul II. T* **162** *and similar vert designs. Multicoloured. P* 14×14½.

657	10 t. Type 162	80	10
658	15 t. Pope John Paul II	1·00	30
659	30 t. Pope giving blessing and outline map	1·60	70
660	80 t. Pope John Paul II (different)	2·25	2·75
657/60	*Set of 4*	5·00	3·50

163 National Museum and Art Gallery

164 Grewia flava

(Des G. Mattsson and T. Sandberg (8 t.), A. Campbell (15 t.), K. Bogatsu (30 t.), T. Sandberg (60 t.). Litho National Printing & Packaging, Zimbabwe)

1988 (30 Sept). *20th Anniv of National Museum and Art Gallery, Gaborone. T* **163** *and similar vert designs. Multicoloured. P* 14½.

661	8 t. Type 163	15	10
662	15 t. Pottery	20	25
663	30 t. Blacksmith's buffalo bellows	35	40
664	60 t. Children and mobile museum van	70	1·00
661/4	*Set of 4*	1·25	1·60

(Des Verena Blomberg-Ermatinger. Litho National Printing & Packaging, Zimbabwe)

1988 (31 Oct). *Flowering Plants of South-eastern Botswana. T* **164** *and similar vert designs. Multicoloured. P* 14×14½.

665	8 t. Type 164	20	10
666	15 t. Cienfuegosia digitata	30	25
667	40 t. Solanum seaforthianum	60	55
668	75 t. Carissa bispinosa	1·00	1·40
665/8	*Set of 4*	1·90	2·00

165 Basket Granary

166 Female Red-throated Heron with Eggs

(Des K. Mosinyi. Litho National Printing & Packaging, Zimbabwe)

1989 (13 Mar). *Traditional Grain Storage. T* **165** *and similar vert designs. Multicoloured. P* 14 × 14½.

669	8 t. Type 165	40	10
670	15 t. Large letlole granary	75	40
671	30 t. Pot granary	1·25	60
672	60 t. Two types of serala	1·90	2·25
669/72	*Set of 4*	3·75	3·00

The use of different paper stocks led to a wide range of shades in this issue.

(Des P. Augustinus. Litho Harrison)

1989 (5 July). *Red-throated Heron ("Slaty Egret"). T* **166** *and similar horiz designs. Multicoloured. P* 15×14.

673	8 t. Type 166	55	15
674	15 t. Chicks in nest	75	40
675	30 t. Red-throated Heron in flight	1·00	95
676	60 t. Pair building nest	1·40	1·60
673/6	*Set of 4*	3·25	2·50
MS677	119×89 mm. Nos. 673/6	3·25	2·75

167 "My Work at Home" 168 *Eulophia*
(Ephraim Seeletso) *angolensis*

(Litho Govt Printer, Pretoria)

1989 (4 Sept). *Children's Paintings.* T **167** *and similar multicoloured designs.* P 14.
678	10 t. Type **167**	35	10
679	15 t. "My Favourite Game" (hopscotch) (Neelma Bhatia) (*vert*)	50	35
680	30 t. "My Favourite Toy" (clay animals) (Thabo Habana)	75	70
681	1 p. "My School Day" (Thabo Olesitse)	2·00	3·25
678/81	*Set of 4*	3·25	4·00

(Des Julia Cairns. Litho Govt Printer, Pretoria)

1989 (30 Oct). *Christmas. Orchids.* T **168** *and similar vert designs. Multicoloured.* P 14.
682	8 t. Type **168**	60	10
683	15 t. *Eulophia hereroensis*	1·10	50
684	30 t. *Eulophia speciosa*	1·60	1·00
685	60 t. *Eulophia petersii*	2·25	5·00
682/5	*Set of 4*	5·00	6·00

169 Bechuanaland 1965 New (**170**)
Constitution 25 c. Stamp
(25th anniv of Self
Government)

(Des K. Mosinyi. Litho National Printing & Packaging, Zimbabwe)

1990 (5 Mar). *Anniversaries.* T **169** *and similar horiz designs.* P 14½.
686	8 t. multicoloured	60	15
687	15 t. multicoloured	75	50
688	30 t. multicoloured	1·60	1·40
689	60 t. black, new blue and yellow-ochre	2·25	4·00
686/9	*Set of 4*	4·75	5·50

Designs:—15 t. Casting vote in ballot box (25th anniv of First Elections); 30 t. Outline map and flags of Southern African Development Coordination Conference countries (10th anniv); 60 t. Penny Black (150th anniv of first postage stamp).

1990 (27 Apr). *Nos. 619, 624 and 627 surch as* T **170**.
690	10 t. on 1 t. Type **157**	45	20
	a. Surch double	†	
691	20 t. on 6 t. Rusty-spotted Genet	60	70
692	50 t. on 12 t. Hippopotamus	2·00	2·75
690/2	*Set of 3*	2·75	3·25

171 Telephone 172 Young
Engineer Children

(Des M. Kahn. Litho National Printing & Packaging, Zimbabwe)

1990 (3 May). *"Stamp World London 90" International Stamp Exhibition.* T **171** *and similar vert designs. Multicoloured.* P 14½.
693	8 t. Type **171**	35	10
694	15 t. Transmission pylon	65	40
695	30 t. Public telephone	1·00	75
696	2 p. Testing circuit board	3·00	5·50
693/6	*Set of 4*	4·50	6·00

(Des K. Mosinyi. Litho National Printing & Packaging, Zimbabwe)

1990 (1 Aug). *Traditional Dress.* T **172** *and similar vert designs. Multicoloured.* P 14½.
697	8 t. Type **172**	35	10
698	15 t. Young woman	65	40
699	30 t. Adult man	1·00	70
700	2 p. Adult woman	3·00	5·50
697/700	*Set of 4*	4·50	6·00
MS701	104×150 mm. Nos. 697/700	4·50	6·50
	a. 30 t. and 2 p. imperf vert		

173 *Acacia nigrescens* 174 Children running in front
of Car

(Des Gillian Condy. Litho National Printing & Packaging, Zimbabwe)

1990 (30 Oct). *Christmas. Flowering Trees.* T **173** *and similar vert designs. Multicoloured.* P 14×14½.
702	8 t. Type **173**	50	10
703	15 t. *Peltophorum africanum*	85	30
704	30 t. *Burkea africana*	1·50	75
705	2 p. *Pterocarpus angolensis*	3·50	5·00
702/5	*Set of 4*	5·75	5·50

(Des B. Heman-Ackah. Litho National Printing & Packaging, Zimbabwe)

1990 (7 Dec). *First National Road Safety Day.* T **174** *and similar horiz designs. Multicoloured.* P 14½.
706	8 t. Type **174**	1·25	30
707	15 t. Careless overtaking	1·75	1·00
708	30 t. Cattle on road	2·25	2·25
706/8	*Set of 3*	4·75	3·25

175 Cattle 176 Children

(Des B. Mazebedi. Litho Questa)

1991 (4 Mar). *Rock Paintings.* T **175** *and similar horiz designs. Multicoloured.* P 14.
709	8 t. Type **175**	85	30
710	15 t. Cattle, drying frames and tree	1·50	75
711	30 t. Animal hides	2·00	1·25
712	2 p. Family herding cattle	4·00	6·00
709/12	*Set of 4*	7·50	7·50

Nos. 709/12 were printed on sand-grained paper which has an uneven surface.

(Des H. Methorst. Litho National Printing & Packaging, Zimbabwe)

1991 (3 June). *National Census.* T **176** *and similar vert designs. Multicoloured.* P 14.
713	8 t. Type **176**	50	10
	a. Perf 14½	4·00	10
714	15 t. Village	3·00	60
	a. Perf 14½	85	55
715	30 t. School	1·00	75
	a. Perf 14½	1·00	75
716	2 p. Hospital	4·50	6·00
	a. Perf 14½	4·50	6·00
713/16	*Set of 4*	6·00	6·50

177 Tourists viewing 178 *Harpagophytum*
Elephants *procumbens*

(Des P. Lodoen. Litho Govt Printer, Pretoria)

1991 (30 Sept). *African Tourism Year. Okavango Delta.* T **177** *and similar multicoloured designs.* P 14 (2 p.) or 14×14½ (others).
717	8 t. Type **177**	1·25	60
718	15 t. Crocodiles basking on river bank	1·75	90
719	35 t. African Fish Eagles and De Havilland D.H.C.7 Dash Seven aircraft	3·25	2·00
720	2 p. Okavango wildlife (26×44 mm)	5·00	7·00
717/20	*Set of 4*	10·00	9·50

(Des Gillian Condy. Litho Govt Printer, Pretoria)

1991 (4 Nov). *Christmas. Seed Pods.* T **178** *and similar vert designs. Multicoloured.* P 14.
721	8 t. Type **178**	60	10
722	15 t. *Tylosema esculentum*	1·00	40
723	30 t. *Abrus precatorius*	1·75	70
724	2 p. *Kigelia africana*	4·00	6·00
721/4	*Set of 4*	6·50	6·50

1992 (9 Mar). *Nos. 621, 624 and 627 surch as* T **170**.
725	8 t. on 12 t. Hippopotamus	1·00	50
726	10 t. on 12 t. Hippopotamus	1·00	50
727	25 t. on 6 t. Rusty-spotted Genet	1·25	1·25
728	40 t. on 3 t. Zebra	2·25	3·00
725/8	*Set of 4*	5·00	4·75

179 *Cacosternum* 180 Air-conditioned
boettgeri Carriages

(Des Julia Cairns. Litho Govt Printer, Pretoria)

1992 (23 Mar). *Climbing Frogs.* T **179** *and similar multicoloured designs.* P 14.
729	8 t. Type **179**	45	20
730	10 t. *Hyperolius marmoratus angolensis* (*vert*)	45	20
731	40 t. *Bufo fenoulheti*	1·40	1·25
732	1 p. *Hyperolius sp* (*vert*)	2·00	4·00
729/32	*Set of 4*	3·75	5·00

(Des P. Lodoen. Litho Harrison)

1992 (29 June). *Deluxe Railway Service.* T **180** *and similar multicoloured designs.* P 14.
733	10 t. Type **180**	85	30
734	25 t. Diesel locomotive No. BD001 (*vert*)	1·50	70
735	40 t. Carriage interior (*vert*)	2·00	1·00
736	2 p. Diesel locomotive No. BD028	3·50	5·50
733/6	*Set of 4*	7·00	6·75
MS737	127×127 mm. Nos. 733/6	7·00	8·00

181 Cheetah 182 Boxing

(Des Judith Penny. Photo Harrison)

1992 (3 Aug). *Animals.* T **181** *and similar horiz designs. Multicoloured.* P 14½×14.
738	1 t. Type **181**	20	60
739	2 t. Spring Hare	20	60
740	4 t. Blackfooted Cat	30	60
741	5 t. Striped Mouse	30	60
742	10 t. Oribi	30	10
743	12 t. Pangolin	55	75
744	15 t. Aardwolf	55	40
745	20 t. Warthog	55	40
746	25 t. Ground Squirrel	55	20
747	35 t. Honey Badger	60	30
748	40 t. Common Mole Rat	60	30
749	45 t. Wild Dog	60	30
750	50 t. Water Mongoose	75	35
751	80 t. Klipspringer	1·40	1·25
752	1 p. Lesser Bushbaby	1·50	1·25
753	2 p. Bushveld Elephant Shrew	2·25	2·75
754	5 p. Zorilla	4·00	5·50
755	10 p. Vervet Monkey	6·50	8·50
738/55	*Set of 18*	19·00	22·00

(Litho Harrison)

1992 (7 Aug). *Olympic Games, Barcelona.* T **182** *and similar vert designs. Multicoloured.* P 14×15.
756	10 t. Type **182**	40	10
757	50 t. Running	75	50
758	1 p. Boxing (*different*)	1·25	1·75
759	2 p. Running (*different*)	2·00	3·00
756/9	*Set of 4*	4·00	4·75
MS760	87×117 mm. Nos. 756/9	4·25	6·00

183 *Adiantum* 184 Helping
incisum Blind Person
(Lions Club
International)

(Des Gillian Condy. Litho National Printing & Packaging, Zimbabwe)

1992 (23 Nov). *Christmas. Ferns.* T **183** *and similar vert designs. Multicoloured.* P 14½.
761	10 t. Type **183**	40	10
762	25 t. *Actiniopteris radiata*	65	35
763	40 t. *Ceratopteris cornuta*	90	55
764	1 p. 50, *Pellaea calomelanos*	2·50	4·50
761/4	*Set of 4*	4·00	5·00

(Des Ann Nilsson. Litho National Printing & Packaging, Zimbabwe)

1993 (29 Mar). *Charitable Organizations in Botswana.* T **184** *and similar multicoloured designs.* P 14.
765	10 t. Type **184**	45	10
766	15 t. Nurse carrying child (Red Cross Society) (*horiz*)	55	35

767 25 t. Woman watering seedling (Ecumenical
Decade) 65 40
768 35 t. Deaf children (Round Table) (horiz) 80 90
769 40 t. Crowd of people (Rotary International) 90 1·25
770 50 t. Hands at prayer (Botswana Christian
Council) (horiz) .. .. 1·10 1·75
765/70 .. .. .. Set of 6 4·00 4·25

185 Bechuanaland Railways
Class "6" Locomotive No. 1

186 Long-crested
Eagle

(Des P. Lodoen. Litho Harrison)

1993 (24 May). *Railway Centenary. T 185 and similar horiz designs. Multicoloured. P 15×14.*
771 10 t. Type 185 .. .. 50 20
772 40 t. Class "19" locomotive No. 317 .. 90 60
773 50 t. Class "12" locomotive No. 256 .. 95 70
774 1 p. 50, Class "7" locomotive No. 71 .. 1·40 3·00
771/4 .. .. Set of 4 3·25 4·00
MS775 190×100 mm. Nos. 771/4 .. 3·25 4·25

(Des J. Leath. Litho National Printing & Packaging, Zimbabwe)

1993 (30 Aug). *Endangered Eagles. T 186 and similar vert designs. Multicoloured. P 14¹⁄₂.*
776 10 t. Type 186 .. .. 55 30
777 25 t. Short-toed Eagle .. .. 1·00 60
778 50 t. Bateleur .. .. 1·40 1·75
779 1 p. 50, Secretary Bird .. .. 2·50 4·00
776/9 .. .. Set of 4 4·75 6·00

187 *Aloe zebrina*

188 Boy with String Puppet

(Des Gillian Condy. Litho National Printing & Packaging, Zimbabwe)

1993 (25 Oct). *Christmas. Flora. T 187 and similar vert designs. Multicoloured. P 14×14¹⁄₂.*
780 12 t. Type 187 .. .. 30 10
781 25 t. Croton megalobotrys 50 25
782 50 t. Boophane disticha 75 70
783 1 p. Euphoria davyi .. .. 1·25 2·25
780/3 .. .. Set of 4 2·50 3·00

(Des K. Mosinyi. Litho National Printing & Packaging, Zimbabwe)

1994 (28 Mar). *Traditional Toys. T 188 and similar horiz designs. Multicoloured. P 14¹⁄₂.*
784 10 t. Type 188 .. .. 20 10
785 40 t. Boys with clay cattle 45 30
786 50 t. Boy with spinner 50 50
787 1 p. Girls playing in make-believe houses 1·10 2·00
784/7 .. .. Set of 4 2·00 2·50

 10t

189 Interior of Control Tower,
Gaborone Airport

(190)

(Des M. McArthur. Litho National Printing & Packaging, Zimbabwe)

1994 (30 June). *50th Anniv of International Civil Aviation Organization. T 189 and similar multicoloured designs. P 14¹⁄₂.*
788 10 t. Type 189 .. .. 30 10
789 25 t. Crash tender 45 25
790 40 t. Loading supplies onto airliner (vert) .. 65 70
791 50 t. Control tower, Gaborone (vert) .. 70 1·50
788/91 .. .. Set of 4 1·90 2·25

1994 (1 Aug). *No. 743 surch with T 190 by Govt Printer, Pretoria.*
792 10 t. on 12 t. Pangolin .. .. 1·75 50

MINIMUM PRICE

The minimum price quote is 10p which represents a handling charge rather than a basis for valuing common stamps. For further notes about prices see introductory pages.

191 Lesser Flamingos
at Sua Pan

192 *Ziziphus
mucronata*

(Des P. Lodoen. Litho National Printing & Packaging, Zimbabwe)

1994 (26 Sept). *Environment Protection. Makgadikgadi Pans. T 191 and similar multicoloured designs. P 14×14¹⁄₂ (vert) or 14¹⁄₂×14 (horiz).*
793 10 t. Type 191 .. .. 60 30
794 35 t. Baobab trees (horiz) 50 30
795 50 t. Zebra and palm trees 65 80
796 2 p. Map of area (horiz) .. .. 2·00 3·00
793/6 .. .. Set of 4 3·25 4·00

(Des Gillian Condy. Litho National Printing & Packaging, Zimbabwe)

1994 (24 Oct). *Christmas. Edible Fruits. T 192 and similar vert designs. Multicoloured. P 14×14¹⁄₂.*
797 10 t. Type 192 .. .. 25 10
798 25 t. Strychnos cocculoides 40 30
799 40 t. Bauhinia petersiana 60 70
800 50 t. Schinziphyton rautoneii .. .. 70 1·10
797/800 .. .. Set of 4 1·75 2·00

193 Fisherman with Bow and
Arrow

194 Boys watering
Horses (F.A.O.)

(Des B. Mazebedi. Litho National Printing & Packaging, Zimbabwe)

1995 (3 Apr). *Traditional Fishing. T 193 and similar horiz designs. Multicoloured. P 14¹⁄₂.*
801 15 t. Type 193 .. .. 35 20
802 40 t. Men in canoe and boy with fishing rod 60 40
803 65 t. Fisherman with net 80 75
804 80 t. Fisherman with basket fish trap .. 1·00 1·60
801/4 .. .. Set of 4 2·50 2·75

(Des M. McArthur. Litho National Printing & Packaging, Zimbabwe)

1995 (16 Oct). *50th Anniv of United Nations. T 194 and similar vert designs. Multicoloured. P 14¹⁄₂.*
805 20 t. Type 194 .. .. 20 10
806 50 t. Schoolchildren queuing for soup (W.F.P.) 35 30
807 80 t. Letters and postman delivering to village (U.N.D.P.) 60 80
808 1 p. Weighing baby (U.N.I.C.E.F.) .. 70 1·25
805/8 .. .. Set of 4 1·60 2·25

195 Brown Hyena

196 *Adenia
glauca*

(Des Judith Penny. Litho Questa)

1995 (6 Nov). *Endangered Species. Brown Hyena. T 195 and similar horiz designs. Multicoloured. P 14¹⁄₂.*
809 20 t. Type 195 .. .. 45 50
a. Strip of 4. Nos. 809/12 .. 2·75
810 50 t. Pair of Hyenas 65 65
811 80 t. Hyena stealing ostrich eggs .. 85 90
812 1 p. Adult Hyena and cubs .. .. 1·00 1·25
809/12 .. .. Set of 4 2·75 3·00
In addition to separate sheets of 50 Nos. 809/12 were also available in sheets of 16 (4×4) with the stamps arranged *se-tenant* both horizontally and vertically.

(Des Gillian Condy. Litho National Printing & Packaging, Zimbabwe)

1995 (27 Nov). *Christmas. Plants. T 196 and similar vert designs. Multicoloured. P 14.*
813 20 t. Type 196 .. .. 25 10
814 50 t. Pterodiscus ngamicus 45 30
815 80 t. Sesamothamnus lugardii .. 75 80
816 1 p. Fockea multiflora .. .. 80 1·25
813/16 .. .. Set of 4 2·00 2·25

 20t

(197)

Different "2"
(R. 7/5, 8/5, 9/5)

1996 (12 Feb). *Nos. 738/40 surch as T 197.*
817 20 t. on 2 t. Spring Hare 20 20
a. Different "2" .. .. 2·75
818 30 t. on 1 t. Type 181 .. .. 25 25
819 70 t. on 4 t. Blackfooted Cat .. 50 90
817/19 .. .. Set of 3 85 1·25

198 Spears

(Des B. Mazebedi. Litho National Printing & Packaging, Zimbabwe)

1996 (25 Mar). *Traditional Weapons. T 198 and similar horiz designs. Multicoloured. P 14¹⁄₂×14.*
820 20 t. Type 198 .. .. 20 10
821 50 t. Axes 35 30
822 80 t. Shield and knobkerries .. 55 65
823 1 p. Knives and sheaths 60 90
820/3 .. .. Set of 4 1·50 1·75

199 Child with
Basic Radio

200 Olympic Flame,
Rings and Wreath

(Des P. Lodoen. Litho National Printing & Packaging, Zimbabwe)

1996 (3 June). *Centenary of Radio. T 199 and similar vert designs. Multicoloured. P 14×14¹⁄₂.*
824 20 t. Type 199 .. .. 25 10
825 50 t. Radio Botswana's mobile transmitter 40 30
826 80 t. Police radio control 60 70
827 1 p. Listening to radio .. .. 70 1·10
824/7 .. .. Set of 4 1·75 2·00

(Des R. Andersson. Litho Govt Printer, Pretoria)

1996 (19 July). *Centenary of Modern Olympic Games. T 200 and similar vert designs. Multicoloured. P 14.*
828 20 t. Type 200 .. .. 25 10
829 50 t. Pierre de Coubertin (founder of modern Olympics) 40 30
830 80 t. Map of Botswana with flags and athletes 60 70
831 1 p. Ruins of ancient stadium at Olympia 70 1·10
828/31 .. .. Set of 4 1·75 2·00

201 Family Planning
Class (Botswana
Family Welfare
Association)

202 *Adansonia
digitata* Leaf and
Blossom

(Des K. Mosinyi. Litho National Printing and Packaging, Zimbabwe)

1996 (23 Sept). *Local Charities. T 201 and similar vert designs. Multicoloured. P 14½.*

832	20 t. Type 201		20	10
833	30 t. Blind workers (Pudulogong Rehabilitation Centre)		20	15
834	50 t. Collecting seeds (Forestry Association of Botswana)		30	30
835	70 t. Secretarial class (Y.W.C.A.)		40	60
836	80 t. Children's day centre (Botswana Council of Women)		50	70
837	1 p. Children's village, Tlokweng (S.O.S. Children's village)		60	90
832/7		*Set of* 6	2·00	2·40

(Des Gillian Condy. Litho National Printing and Packaging, Zimbabwe)

1996 (4 Nov). *Christmas. T 202 and similar vert designs showing parts of life cycle for Adansonia digitata. Multicoloured. P 14.*

838	20 t. Type 202		20	10
839	50 t. Fruit		35	25
840	80 t. Tree in leaf		55	60
841	1 p. Tree with bare branches		60	90
838/41		*Set of* 4	1·50	1·60

203 Tati Hotel

204 Steam Locomotive, Bechuanaland Railway, 1897

(Des M. Smith. Litho National Printing and Packaging, Zimbabwe)

1997 (21 Apr). *Francistown Centenary. T 203 and similar horiz designs. Multicoloured. P 14½×14.*

842	20 t. Type 203		15	10
843	50 t. Railway Station		45	35
844	80 t. Company Manager's House		55	60
845	1 p. Monarch Mine		65	90
842/5		*Set of* 4	1·60	1·75

(Des P. Lodoen. Litho National Printing and Packaging, Zimbabwe)

1997 (12 July). *Railway Centenary. T 204 and similar vert designs. Multicoloured. P 14×14½.*

846	35 t. Type 204		30	20
847	50 t. Elephants crossing railway line		50	35
848	80 t. First locomotive in Bechuanaland, 1897		60	45
849	1 p. Beyer-Garratt type steam locomotive No. 352		65	60
850	2 p. Diesel locomotive No. BD339		90	1·25
851	2 p. 50, Fantuzzi container stacker		1·00	1·50
846/51		*Set of* 6	3·50	4·00

205 Pel's Fishing Owl

206 *Combretum zeyheri*

(Des Helena Schüssel. Litho Enschedé)

1997 (4 Aug). *Birds. T 205 and similar multicoloured designs. P 13½×13 (vert) or 13×13½ (horiz).*

852	5 t. Type 205		10	10
853	10 t. Gymnogene (*horiz*)		10	10
854	15 t. Meyer's Parrot		10	10
855	20 t. Harlequin Quail (*horiz*)		10	10
856	25 t. Marico Sunbird (*horiz*)		10	10
857	30 t. Kurrichane Thrush (*horiz*)		10	10
858	40 t. Redheaded Finch		10	10
859	50 t. Buffalo Weaver		15	20
860	60 t. Sacred Ibis (*horiz*)		15	20
861	70 t. Cape Shoveler (*horiz*)		20	25
862	80 t. Greater Honeyguide (*horiz*)		20	25
863	1 p. Woodland Kingfisher (*horiz*)		25	30
864	1 p. 25, Purple Heron		25	30
865	1 p. 50, Yellow-billed Oxpecker (*horiz*)		25	30
866	2 p. Shaft-tailed Whydah (*horiz*)		55	60
867	2 p. 50, White Stork		55	60
868	5 p. Sparrowhawk		1·40	1·50
869	10 p. Spotted Crake		2·75	3·00
852/69		*Set of* 18	7·25	7·50

No. 861 is inscribed "Shoveller" in error.

(Des N. Shewring (No. **MS**876), D. Miller (others). Litho Questa (No. **MS**876), Cartor (others))

1997 (22 Sept). *Golden Wedding of Queen Elizabeth and Prince Philip. Multicoloured designs as T 173 of Ascension. W w 14. P 13.*

870	35 t. Prince Philip with carriage		20	30
	a. Horiz pair. Nos. 870/1		40	60
871	35 t. Queen Elizabeth with binoculars		20	30
872	2 p. Queen Elizabeth with horse team		90	1·25
	a. Horiz pair. Nos. 872/3		1·75	2·50
873	2 p. Prince Philip and horse		90	1·25
874	2 p. 50, Queen Elizabeth and Prince Philip		1·10	1·25
	a. Horiz pair. Nos. 874/5		2·10	2·50
875	2 p. 50, Princess Anne and Prince Edward		1·10	1·25
870/5		*Set of* 6	4·00	5·00
MS876	110×70 mm. 10 p. Queen Elizabeth and Prince Philip in landau (*horiz*). Wmk sideways. P 14×14½		4·00	5·00

Nos. 870/1, 872/3 and 874/5 were each printed together, *se-tenant*, in horizontal pairs throughout the sheets.

(Des Gillian Condy. Litho National Printing and Packaging, Zimbabwe)

1997 (10 Nov). *Christmas. Plants. T 206 and similar vert designs. Multicoloured. P 14.*

877	35 t. Type 206		25	10
878	1 p. Combretum apiculatum		65	35
879	2 p. Combretum molle		1·25	1·25
880	2 p. 50, Combretum imberbe		1·40	1·60
877/80		*Set of* 4	3·25	3·00

207 Baobab Trees

208 "Village Life" (tapestry)

(Des A. Campbell. Litho National Printing and Packaging, Zimbabwe)

1998 (23 Mar). *Tourism (1st series). T 207 and similar multicoloured designs. P 14½.*

881	35 t. Type 207		25	15
882	1 p. Crocodile		50	35
883	2 p. Stalactites (*vert*)		85	85
884	2 p. 50, Tourists and rock paintings (*vert*)		1·10	1·25
881/4		*Set of* 4	2·40	2·40

See also Nos. 899/902.

(Des D. Miller. Litho Cartor)

1998 (1 June). *Diana, Princess of Wales Commemoration. Vert designs as T 177 of Ascension. Multicoloured. W w 14. P 13.*

885	35 t. Princess Diana, 1990		25	15
886	1 p. In green hat, 1992		40	35
887	2 p. In white blouse, 1993		75	80
888	2 p. 50, With crowd, Cambridge, 1993		90	1·00
885/8		*Set of* 4	2·10	2·10
MS889	145×70 mm. As Nos. 885/8, but each with a face value of 2 p. 50		3·75	4·00

(Des M. McArthur. Litho Enschedé)

1998 (28 Sept). *Botswana Weavers. T 208 and similar multicoloured designs. P 14×13½.*

890	35 t. Type 208		20	15
891	55 t. Weaver dyeing threads		25	20
892	1 p. "African wildlife" (tapestry)		45	40
893	2 p. Weaver at loom		80	1·00
890/3		*Set of* 4	1·50	1·60
MS894	68×58 mm. 2 p. 50, "Elephants" (tapestry) (*horiz*). P 13½×14		1·00	1·25

209 *Ficus ingens*

210 Road Map

(Des Gillian Condy. Litho Oriental Press, Bahrain)

1998 (30 Nov). *Christmas. Plants. T 209 and similar vert designs. Multicoloured. P 13×13½.*

895	35 t. Type 209		15	10
896	55 t. Ficus pygmaea		25	20
897	1 p. Ficus abutilifolia		40	35
898	2 p. 50, Ficus sycomorus		85	1·10
895/8		*Set of* 4	1·50	1·50

(Des A. Campbell. Litho Enschedé)

1999 (26 Apr). *Tourism (2nd series). Multicoloured designs as T 207. P 13½×14 (horiz) or 14×13½ (vert).*

899	35 t. Rock painting of men and cattle		15	10
900	55 t. Expedition at salt pan		25	20
901	1 p. Rock painting of elephant and antelope (*vert*)		40	35
902	2 p. Tourists under Baobab tree (*vert*)		70	80
899/902		*Set of* 4	1·40	1·25

(Des K. Mosinyi. Litho)

1999 (17 Aug). *Southern African Development Community Day. Sheet 77×84 mm. P 14½.*

MS903	**210** 5 p. multicoloured	1·40	1·50

211 Modern Post Office   **212** Mpule Kwelagobe winning Contest

(Des K. Mosinyi. Litho National Printing and Packaging, Zimbabwe)

1999 (9 Oct). *125th Anniv of Universal Postal Union. P 14½.*

904	**211** 2 p. multicoloured		55	60

(Des Seasky Design Studio. Litho Southern Colour Print, Dunedin)

1999 (1 Dec). *Mpule Kwelagobe ("Miss Universe 1999"). T 212 and similar multicoloured designs. P 14½.*

905	35 t. Type 212		10	10
906	1 p. In traditional dress (*horiz*)		25	30
907	2 p. In traditional dancing costume with lion		55	60
908	2 p. 50, Wearing "Botswana" sash (*horiz*)		70	75
909	15 p. With leopard in background (*horiz*)		4·00	4·25
905/9		*Set of* 5	5·50	5·75
MS910	175×80 mm. Nos. 905/9		5·50	5·75

STAMP BOOKLETS

B 1

1989 (1 Dec)–**92**. *Covers as Type* B **1** *printed in blue on coloured card, each showing different stamp and postal logo. Stapled.*

SB1	20 t. booklet containing 2 t. (No. 620) in block of 10 (white cover)	50
SB2	40 t. booklet containing 2 t. (No. 620) in block of 20 (white cover)	75
SB3	50 t. booklet containing 5 t. (No. 623) in block of 10 (claret cover)	80
SB4	80 t. booklet containing 8 t. (No. 625) in block of 10 (grey cover)	1·10
	a. Containing 8 t. on 12 t. (No. 725) (1992)	
SB5	1 p. booklet containing 5 t. (No. 623) in block of 20 (claret cover)	1·25
SB6	1 p. booklet containing 10 t. (No. 626) in block of 10 (cinnamon cover)	1·25
	a. Containing 10 t. on 1 t. (No. 690) (1990)	
	b. Containing 10 t. on 12 t. (No. 726) (1992)	
SB7	1 p. 50, booklet containing 15 t. (No. 628) in block of 10 (pink cover)	2·00
SB8	1 p. 60, booklet containing 8 t. (No. 625) in block of 20 (grey cover)	2·00
	a. Containing 8 t. on 12 t. (No. 725) (1992)	
SB9	2 p. booklet containing 10 t. (No. 626) in block of 20 (cinnamon cover)	2·25
	a. Containing 10 t. on 1 t. (No. 690) (1990)	
	b. Containing 10 t. on 12 t. (No. 726) (1992)	
SB10	2 p. booklet containing 20 t. (No. 629) in block of 10 (pale blue cover)	2·25
	a. Containing 20 t. on 6 t. (No. 691) (1990)	
SB11	3 p. booklet containing 15 t. (No. 628) in block of 20 (pink cover)	3·25
SB12	3 p. booklet containing 30 t. (No. 631) in block of 10 (lemon cover)	3·25
SB13	4 p. booklet containing 20 t. (No. 629) in block of 20 (pale blue cover)	3·75
SB14	4 p. booklet containing 40 t. (No. 633) in block of 10 (pale green cover)	3·75
	a. Containing 40 t. on 3 t. (No. 728) (1992)	
	b. Error. Containing 50 t. on 12 t. (No. 692) (1990)	
SB15	6 p. booklet containing 30 t. (No. 631) in block of 20 (lemon cover)	5·50
SB16	8 p. booklet containing 40 t. (No. 633) in block of 20 (pale green cover)	7·00
	a. Containing 40 t. on 3 t. (No. 728) (1992)	

The booklets of twenty are larger, 81×69 mm.

No. SB14b, which was produced in error, has the face value of the booklet amended in manuscript.

B 2

1993 (4 Oct)–**94**. *Covers as Type* B **2** *printed in black on coloured card, each showing different stamp with postal logo. Stapled.*

SB17	1 p. booklet containing 10 t. (No. 742) in strip of 10 (yellow cover)	75
	a. Containing 10 t. on 12 t. (No. 792) (1994)	75
SB18	1 p. 20, booklet containing 12 t. (No. 743) in strip of 10 (pale orange cover)	90
SB19	1 p. 50, booklet containing 15 t. (No. 744) in strip of 10 (orange cover)	1·10
SB20	2 p. booklet containing 10 t. (No. 742) in block of 20 (yellow cover)	1·40
	a. Containing 10 t. on 12 t. (No. 792) (1994)	1·40
SB21	2 p. booklet containing 20 t. (No. 745) in strip of 10 (white cover)	1·40
SB22	2 p. 40, booklet containing 12 t. (No. 743) in block of 20 (pale orange cover)	1·75
SB23	2 p. 50, booklet containing 25 t. (No. 746) in strip of 10 (pink cover)	1·75
SB24	3 p. booklet containing 15 t. (No. 744) in block of 20 (orange cover)	1·90
SB25	3 p. 50, booklet containing 35 t. (No. 747) in strip of 10 (green cover)	2·00
SB26	4 p. booklet containing 20 t. (No. 745) in block of 20 (white cover)	2·50
SB27	4 p. booklet containing 40 t. (No. 748) in strip of 10 (blue cover)	2·50
SB28	4 p. 50, booklet containing 45 t. (No. 749) in strip of 10 (pale rose-lilac cover)	2·75
SB29	5 p. booklet containing 25 t. (No. 746) in block of 20 (pink cover)	3·00
SB30	5 p. booklet containing 50 t. (No. 750) in strip of 10 (grey cover)	3·00
SB31	7 p. booklet containing 35 t. (No. 747) in block of 20 (green cover)	3·75
SB32	8 p. booklet containing 40 t. (No. 748) in block of 20 (blue cover)	4·00
SB33	9 p. booklet containing 45 t. (No. 749) in block of 20 (pale rose-lilac cover)	4·50
SB34	10 p. booklet containing 50 t. (No. 750) in block of 20 (grey cover)	5·00

The booklets of twenty are larger, 75×80 mm.

1996. *Covers as Nos.* SB17 *and* SB21 *cut down to* 75×40 *mm. Stamps attached by selvedge.*

SB35	1 p. booklet containing 5 t. and 15 t. (Nos. 741 and 744) each in strip of 5 (yellow cover)	
SB36	1 p. booklet containing 20 t. (No. 809) in strip of 5 (white cover)	

Nos. SB35/6 were issued from machines at Gaborone and Francistown Main Post Offices. They were subsequently replaced by booklets with plain white covers containing 1 p. worth of current stamps attached by the selvedges.

POSTAGE DUE STAMPS

(D 1)   (D 2)

D 3   Normal   Large "d" (R. 9/6, 10/6)

Serif on "d" (R.1/6)

(Typo D.L.R.)

1926 (Jan). *Nos.* D9/10 *and* D13 *of Great Britain, optd. with Types* D **1** *or* D **2** (2*d.*).

D1	½d. emerald (No. D10)	..	..	..	3·75	65·00
D2	1d. carmine (No. D9).	..	..	..	3·75	48·00
D3	2d. agate (No. D13) ..	..	..	..	6·00	85·00
D1/3	..	..		Set of 3	12·00	£180

1932 (12 Dec)–**58**. *Wmk Mult Script CA. Ordinary paper. P* 14.

D4	D **3**	½d. sage-green	..	..	6·00	23·00
D5		1d. carmine	..	..	6·50	9·00
		a. Chalk-surfaced paper (27.11.58)	..	1·00	13·00
D6		2d. violet	..	..	9·00	38·00
		a. Large "d"	..	..	90·00	
		b. Chalk-surfaced paper (27.11.58)	..	1·50	18·00
		ba. Large "d"	..	..	24·00	
		bb. Serif on "d"	..	..	30·00	
D4/6b			..	Set of 3	7·75	55·00
D4/6	Perf "Specimen"		..	Set of 3	65·00	

No. D6a first occurred on the 1947 printing.

I (Small) II (Large)

1961 (14 Feb). *Surch as T* **27**. *Chalk-surfaced paper (Nos.* D7/8).

D7	D **3**	1 c. on 1d. (Type I)	..	..	25	50
		a. Type II (Apr)	..	..	15	1·75
		ab. Double surch	..	..	£160	
		ac. Ordinary paper	..	..	16·00	50·00
D8		2 c. on 2d. (Type I)	..	..	25	1·50
		a. Large "d"	..	..	6·50	
		b. Serif on "d"	..	..	9·00	
		c. Type II	..	..	15	2·00
		ca. Large "d"	..	..	4·50	
		cb. Serif on "d"	..	..	7·00	
		d. Ordinary paper. Type II	..	85·00	95·00
		da. Large "d"	..	..	£325	
D9		5 c. on ½d.	..	..	20	60
D7/9		..	..	Set of 3	45	2·40

1961 (15 Nov). *As Type* D **3** *but values in cents. Chalk-surfaced paper. Wmk Mult Script CA. P* 14.

D10	1 c. carmine	..	..	..	15	1·75
D11	2 c. violet	..	..	..	15	1·75
D12	5 c. green	..	..	..	30	2·00
D10/12		..	..	Set of 3	55	5·00

REPUBLIC OF

BOTSWANA

(D 4)   D **5** African Elephant   D **6** Common Zebra

1967 (1 Mar). *Nos.* D10/12 *optd with Type* D **4**.

D13	1 c. carmine	..	..	..	15	2·50
D14	2 c. violet	..	..	..	15	2·50
D15	5 c. green	..	..	..	20	2·75
D13/15		..	..	Set of 3	45	7·00

(Des and litho B.W.)

1971 (9 June). *P* 13½.

D16	D **5**	1 c. carmine	..	..	1·10	3·25
D17		2 c. bluish violet	..	..	1·40	3·50
D18		6 c. sepia	..	..	2·50	5·50
D19		14 c. blue-green	..	..	2·75	7·50
D16/19		..	..	Set of 4	7·00	18·00

BOTSWANA

(Des M. Bryan. Litho Govt Printer, Pretoria)

1977 (18 Apr)–**84.** *P* 12½.

D20	D 6	1 t. black and vermilion (1978)	..		70	2·50
		a. *Black and bright orange* (1980)	..		1·25	2·50
		b. Perf 14 (1982?)			70	2·00
D21		2 t. black and emerald			40	2·75
		a. Perf 14 (5.8.81*)	..		70	2·25
D22		4 t. black and red	..		40	2·75
		a. Perf 14 (28.9.81*)			70	2·25
D23		10 t. black and deep ultramarine			40	2·75
		a. Perf 14 (7.3.84)			70	2·25
D24		16 t. black and chestnut			65	3·25
		a. Perf 14 (7.3.84)			85	2·75
D20/24				Set of 5	2·25	12·50
D20b/24a				Set of 5	3·25	10·00

* First supplies of Nos. D20b, D21a and D22a were sent to Botswana in June 1981. The dates quoted for the 2 t. and 4 t. are earliest known dates of use. Early use of the 1 t. has yet to be identified.

Nos. D20b/4a are on white paper. A subsequent printing in September 1988 was on poorer grade paper. Stamps perforated 14 measure 24 mm across from perforation to perforation.

Type I

Type II

Two Types of Nos. D25/9 (Zimbabwe ptgs):—

Type I. Grass sparse. No shading dots on zebra. Zebra's right ear has right edge missing.
Type II. Grass thicker. Shading dots on zebra. Right ear almost complete.

(Litho National Printing & Packaging, Zimbabwe)

1989 (1 Apr)–**96.** *P* 14½.

D25	D 6	1 t. black and reddish orange (I)	..		30	70
		a. Type II. Perf 14 (1993)			30	40
		ab. Perf 14½ (1996)	..		10	10
D26		2 t. black and emerald (I)	..		30	70
		a. Type II. Perf 14 (1993)			30	40
		ab. Perf 14½ (1996)	..		10	10
D27		4 t. black and bright scarlet (I)	..		30	70
		a. Type II. Perf 14 (1993)			30	40
		ab. Perf 14½ (1996)	..		10	10
D28		10 t. black and deep ultramarine (I)			35	70
		a. Type II. Perf 14 (1993)			30	40
		ab. Perf 14½ (1996)	..		10	10
D29		16 t. black and reddish brown (I)	..		50	90
		a. Type II. Perf 14 (1993)			35	50
		ab. Perf 14½ (1996)	..		10	10
D25/9		..	..	Set of 5	1·60	3·25
D25a/9a		..	..	Set of 5	1·40	1·90

Nos. D25a/9a measure 26 mm across from perforation to perforation.

POSTAL FISCAL STAMPS

The following stamps issued for fiscal purposes were each allowed to be used for postal purposes for a short time. No. F2 was used by the public because the word "POSTAGE" had not been obliterated and No. F3 because the overprint did not include the words "Revenue only" as did the contemporary fiscal overprints for Basutoland and Swaziland.

Bechuanaland

Protectorate	£5	Bechuanaland Protectorate.
(F 1)	(F 2)	(F 3)

1910 (July). *No. 266a of Transvaal, optd with Type F 1 by Transvaal Govt Ptg Wks, Pretoria.*

F1 6d. black and brown-orange (Bl-Blk) .. £150 £300

No. F1 was supplied to Assistant Commissioners in January 1907 for revenue purposes. The "POSTAGE" inscription was not obliterated, however, and the stamp is known postally used for a period of a year from July 1910.

1918. *No. 15 surch with Type F 2 at top.*

F2 4 £5 on 1s. green and black £9500

1922. *No. 4b of South Africa optd with Type F 3, in varying positions.*

F3 1d. scarlet .. .. 42·00 £130
    a. Opt double, one albino £150

256

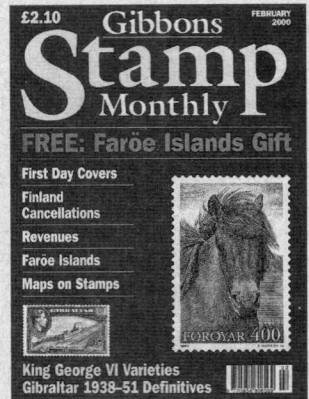

British Antarctic Territory

For use at the following bases:

Adelaide Island (Graham Land) (*closed 1977*)
Argentine Islands ("Faraday" *from 1981*), (Graham Land)
  (*closed 8 February 1996 and transferred to Ukraine*)
Brabant Island (Graham Land) (*opened 1984, closed 1985*)
Deception Island (South Shetlands) (*closed December 1967,
  opened 4 December 1968, closed 23 February 1969*)
Halley Bay (Coats Land)
Hope Bay (Graham Land) (*closed 12 February 1964*)
Port Lockroy (Graham Land) (*opened 21 November 1996*)
Rothera Point (Graham Land) (*opened 1977*)
Signy Island (South Orkneys)
Stonington Island (Graham Land) (*closed February 1975*)

1 M.V. *Kista Dan*

(Des B.W. (No. 15*a*), M. Goaman (others). Recess B.W.)

1963 (1 Feb)–**69.** *Horiz designs as T* **1**, *W w* **12**. *P* 11 × 11½.

1	½d. deep blue	90	1·40
2	1d. brown	1·25	80
3	1½d. orange-red and brown-purple	1·25	1·25
4	2d. purple	1·25	80
5	2½d. myrtle-green	3·00	1·25
6	3d. deep blue	3·75	1·25
7	4d. sepia	2·75	1·50
8	6d. olive and deep ultramarine	4·50	2·00
9	9d. olive-green	3·50	2·00
10	1s. deep turquoise-blue	3·75	70
11	2s. deep violet and orange-sepia	20·00	9·00
12	2s. 6d. blue	20·00	7·50
13	5s. red-orange and brown	21·00	13·00
14	10s. deep ultramarine and emerald	45·00	26·00
15	£1 black and light blue	55·00	48·00
15*a*	£1 red and brownish black (1.12.69)	£150	£120
1/15*a*	*Set of* 16	£300	£200

Designs:—1d. Manhauling; 1½d. Muskeg (tractor); 2d. Skiing; 2½d. De Havilland D.H.C.2 Beaver (aircraft); 3d. R.R.S. *John Biscoe II*; 4d. Camp scene; 6d. H.M.S. *Protector*; 9d. Sledging; 1s. De Havilland D.H.C.3 Otter (aircraft); 2s. Huskies; 2s. 6d. Westland Whirlwind helicopter; 5s. Snocat (tractor); 10s. R.R.S. *Shackleton*; £1 (No. 15) Antarctic map; £1 (No. 15*a*) H.M.S. *Endurance I*.

1966 (24 Jan). *Churchill Commemoration. As Nos.* 170/3 *of Antigua.*

16	½d. new blue	80	3·25
17	1d. deep green	3·00	3·25
18	1s. brown	21·00	6·50
19	2s. bluish violet	4·00	7·00
16/19	*Set of* 4	45·00	18·00

17 Lemaire Channel and Icebergs

(Des R. Granger Barrett. Litho Format)

1969 (6 Feb). *25th Anniv of Continuous Scientific Work. T* **17** *and similar horiz designs. W w* **12** (*sideways*). *P* 14.

20	3½d. black, pale blue and ultramarine	4·00	3·00
21	6d. multicoloured	2·00	2·50
22	1s. black, pale blue and vermilion	2·00	2·00
23	2s. black, orange and turquoise-blue	2·00	3·00
20/3	*Set of* 4	9·00	9·50

Designs:—6d. Radio Sonde balloon; 1s. Muskeg pulling tent equipment; 2s. Surveyors with theodolite.

(18)   19 Setting up Camp, Graham Land

1971 (15 Feb). *Decimal Currency. As Nos.* 1/14, *but glazed paper, colours changed and such as T* **18**.

24	½p. on ½d. blue	60	3·00
25	1p. on 1d. pale brown	1·00	90
26	1½p. on 1½d. red and pale brown-purple	1·25	75
27	2p. on 2d. bright purple	1·25	40
28	2½p. on 2½d. green	3·00	1·75
29	3p. on 3d. blue	2·50	75
	w. Wmk inverted	70·00	
30	4p. on 4d. bistre-brown	2·25	75
31	5p. on 6d. olive and ultramarine	4·75	2·00
32	6p. on 9d. dull green	16·00	8·00

33	7½p. on 1s. turquoise-blue	17·00	8·50
34	10p. on 2s. violet and orange-sepia	20·00	14·00
	w. Wmk inverted	£600	
35	15p. on 2s. 6d. pale blue	20·00	15·00
36	25p. on 5s. orange and pale rose-red	24·00	17·00
37	50p. on 10s. ultramarine and emerald	42·00	30·00
	w. Wmk inverted	£120	
24/37	*Set of* 14	£130	90·00

(Des M. Goaman. Recess and litho Enschedé)

1971 (23 June). *10th Anniv of Antarctic Treaty. Vert designs each including Antarctic Map and Queen Elizabeth, as T* **19**. *Multicoloured. W w* **12** (*sideways*). *P* 14 × 13.

38	1½p. Type **19**	6·00	5·50
39	4p. Snow Petrels	16·00	8·00
40	5p. Weddell Seals	9·50	8·00
41	10p. Adelie Penguins	22·00	9·00
38/41	*Set of* 4	48·00	27·00

20 Kerguelen Fur Seals and Emperor Penguins

21 James Cook and H.M.S. *Resolution*

(Des (from photograph by D. Groves) and photo Harrison)

1972 (13 Dec*). *Royal Silver Wedding. Multicoloured; background colour given. W w* **12**. *P* 14 × 14½.

42	**20** 5p. red-brown	3·00	3·00
	w. Wmk inverted	18·00	16·00
43	10p. brown-olive	3·00	3·00
	w. Wmk inverted	£180	

*This is the local release date; they were issued by the Crown Agents on 20 November.

(Des J.W. Litho Questa)

1973 (14 Feb). *T* **21** *and similar vert designs. Multicoloured. W w* **12** (*sideways*). *P* 14 × 14½.

44	½p. Type **21** (*shades*)	1·25	2·00
45	1p. Thaddeus von Bellingshausen and *Vostok*	2·50	3·25
46	1½p. James Weddell and *Jane*	11·00	4·50
47	2p. John Biscoe and *Tula*	2·25	1·75
48	2½p. J. S. C. Dumont d'Urville and *L'Astrolabe*	1·50	1·75
49	3p. James Clark Ross and H.M.S. *Erebus*	95	1·75
50	4p. C. A. Larsen and *Jason*	95	1·75
51	5p. Adrien de Gerlache and *Belgica*	1·00	1·75
52	6p. Otto Nordenskjöld and *Antarctic*	1·25	1·75
53	7½p. W. S. Bruce and *Scotia*	1·50	2·25
54	10p. Jean-Baptiste Charcot and *Pourquoi Pas?*	2·75	3·00
55	15p. Ernest Shackleton and *Endurance*	6·00	4·00
56	25p. Hubert Wilkins and Lockheed Vega *San Francisco*	3·00	4·00
57	50p. Lincoln Ellsworth and Northrop Gamma *Polar Star*	2·50	4·50
58	£1 John Rymill and *Penola*	2·00	6·00
44/58	*Set of* 15	35·00	42·00

The 25 and 50p. show aircraft; the rest show ships.
See also Nos. 64/78.

1973 (23 Dec*). *Royal Wedding. As Nos.* 165/6 *of Anguilla. Centre multicoloured. W w* **12** (*sideways*). *P* 13½.

59	5p. ochre	40	20
60	15p. light turquoise-blue	70	30

*This is the local date of issue: the Crown Agents released the stamps on 14 November.

22 Churchill and Churchill Peninsula, B.A.T.

(Des G. Vasarhelyi. Litho Format)

1974 (10 Dec*). *Birth Centenary of Sir Winston Churchill. T* **22** *and similar horiz design. Multicoloured. W w* **12** (*sideways on 5p*). *P* 14.

61	5p. Type **22**	1·50	1·75
62	15p. Churchill and *Trepassey* ("Operation Tabarin", 1943)	1·75	2·25
MS63	114 × 88 mm. Nos. 61/2. Wmk upright	11·00	8·00

*This is the local date of issue: the Crown Agents released the stamps on 30 November.

1975 (11 June)–**81.** *As Nos.* 44/58 *but W w* **14**. *Ordinary paper* (½, 2, 2½, 3, 5, 10, 15, 25, 50p.) *or chalk-surfaced paper* (1, 1½, 4, 6, 7½p., £1). *P* 12 (4, 6, 7½p.) *or* 14 × 14½ (*others*).

64	½p. Type **21**	3·00	3·25
	a. Chalk-surfaced paper (14.3.78)	75	2·50
65	1p. Thaddeus von Bellingshausen and *Vostok* (14.3.78)	60	2·25
	a. Ordinary paper (11.12.79)	80	3·00
66	1½p. James Weddell and *Jane* (14.3.78)	60	3·00
	a. Ordinary paper (11.12.79)	80	3·00
67	2p. John Biscoe and *Tula* (11.12.79)	1·50	2·50
68	2½p. J. S. C. Dumont d'Urville and *L'Astro-labe* (11.12.79)	1·50	2·50
69	3p. James Clark Ross and H.M.S. *Erebus* (11.12.79)	2·50	2·75

70	4p. C. A. Larsen and *Jason* (5.12.80)	55	3·00
71	5p. Adrien de Gerlache and *Belgica* (11.12.79)	2·75	3·25
72	6p. Otto Nordenskjöld and *Antarctic* (5.12.80)	80	3·00
73	7½p. W. S. Bruce and *Scotia* (5.12.80)	1·25	3·50
74	10p. Jean-Baptiste Charcot and *Pourquoi Pas?* (11.12.79)	1·75	3·25
	a. Perf 12. Chalk-surfaced paper (25.11.81)	85	3·00
75	15p. Ernest Shackleton and *Endurance* (11.12.79)	1·25	2·00
	a. Perf 12. Chalk-surfaced paper (25.11.81)	85	3·00
76	25p. Hubert Wilkins and Lockheed Vega *San Francisco* (11.12.79)	1·25	1·50
	a. Perf 12. Chalk-surfaced paper (25.11.81)	85	4·00
77	50p. Lincoln Ellsworth and Northrop Gamma *Polar Star* (11.12.79)	1·25	3·00
	aw. Wmk inverted	18·00	
	b. Perf 12. Chalk-surfaced paper (5.12.80)	85	2·75
78	£1 John Rymill and *Penola* (14.3.78)	3·25	2·00
	a. Perf 12 (5.12.80)	1·50	4·00
	aw. Wmk inverted	£450	
64*a*/78*a*	*Set of* 15	16·00	35·00

23 Sperm Whale

(Des J. Cooter. Litho Questa)

1977 (4 Jan). *Whale Conservation. T* **23** *and similar horiz designs. W w* **14** (*sideways*). *P* 13½.

79	2p. brownish black, slate and bright blue	6·50	4·00
80	8p. grey, brownish black and rosine	7·50	4·50
81	11p. multicoloured	8·00	4·50
82	25p. grey-blue, brownish blk & lt blue-green	8·50	6·00
79/82	*Set of* 4	27·00	17·00

Designs:—8p. Fin Whale; 11p. Humpback Whale; 25p. Blue Whale.

24 The Queen before Taking the Oath   25 Emperor Penguin

(Des J.W. Litho Questa)

1977 (7 Feb). *Silver Jubilee. T* **24** *and similar horiz designs. Multicoloured. W w* **14** (*sideways**). *P* 13½.

83	7p. Prince Philip's visit, 1956/7	70	40
84	11p. Coronation Oath	80	50
	w. Wmk Crown to right of CA	6·50	7·50
85	33p. Type **24**	1·25	65
	w. Wmk Crown to right of CA	£160	
83/5	*Set of* 3	2·50	1·40

*The normal sideways watermark shows Crown to left of CA, as seen from the back of the stamp.

(Des C. Abbott. Litho Questa)

1978 (2 June). *25th Anniv of Coronation. T* **25** *and similar vert designs. P* 15.

86	25p. green, deep bluish green and silver	80	1·00
	a. Sheetlet Nos. 86/8 × 2	4·50	
87	25p. multicoloured	80	1·00
88	25p. green, deep bluish green and silver	80	1·00
86/8	*Set of* 3	2·25	2·75

Designs:— No. 86. Black Bull of Clarence; No. 87, Queen Elizabeth II; No. 88, Type **25**.

Nos. 86/8 were printed together in small sheets of 6, containing two *se-tenant* strips of 3 with a horizontal gutter margin between.

26 Macaroni Penguins

(Des G. Drummond. Litho Walsall)

1979 (14 Jan). *Penguins. T* **26** *and similar horiz designs. Multicoloured. W w* **14** (*sideways**). *P* 13½.

89	3p. Type **26**	11·00	11·00
	w. Wmk Crown to right of CA	£350	
90	8p. Gentoo penguins	3·00	3·00
91	11p. Adelie penguins	3·50	3·50
92	25p. Emperor penguins	4·50	4·50
89/92	*Set of* 4	20·00	20·00

*The normal sideways watermark shows Crown to left of CA, as seen from the back of the stamp.

27 Sir John Barrow and *Tula*

(Des A. Theobald. Litho Secura, Singapore)

1980 (14 Dec*). *150th Anniv of Royal Geographical Society. Former Presidents.* T **27** *and similar horiz designs. Multi-coloured.* W w 14 (sideways†). P 13½.

93	3p. Type 27	..	..	20	15
94	7p. Sir Clement Markham and *Discovery*			25	25
	w. Wmk Crown to right of CA	..	..	4·00	
95	11p. Lord Curzon and whaleboat *James Caird*			30	30
	w. Wmk Crown to right of CA	..		3·00	
96	15p. Sir William Goodenough	..	..	35	35
97	22p. Sir James Wordie	..	..	50	55
	w. Wmk Crown to right of CA	..		85·00	
98	30p. Sir Raymond Priestley	..	..	60	65
93/8			*Set of 6*	2·00	2·00

*This is the local date of issue; the Crown Agents released the stamps on 1 December.

†The normal sideways watermark shows Crown to left of CA, as seen from the back of the stamp.

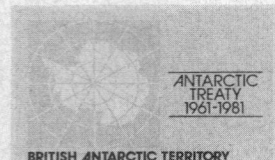

28 Map of Antarctic

(Des Walsall. Litho Questa)

1981 (1 Dec). *20th Anniv of Antarctic Treaty.* T **28** *and similar horiz designs.* W w 14 (sideways*). P 13½×14.

99	10p. black, new blue and azure			40	80
	w. Wmk Crown to right of CA	..		£200	
100	13p. black, new blue and apple-green			45	90
101	25p. black, new blue and mauve	..		55	1·00
102	26p. black, brown-ochre and rose-red			55	1·00
99/102			*Set of 4*	1·75	3·25

Designs:—13p. Conservation research ("scientific co-operation"); 25p. Satellite image mapping ("technical co-operation"); 26p. Global geophysics ("scientific co-operation").

*The normal sideways watermark shows Crown to left of CA, as seen from the back of the stamp.

29 Map of Gondwana showing position of Continents 280 million years ago, and Contemporary Landscape Scene

30 British Antarctic Territory Coat of Arms

(Des C. Abbott. Litho Walsall)

1982 (8 Mar). *Gondwana—Continental Drift and Climatic Change.* T **29** *and similar horiz designs depicting maps of Gondwana showing position of continents, and contemporary landscape scenes. Multicoloured.* W w 14 (sideways). P 13½ × 14.

103	3p. Type 29	..	..	25	40
104	6p. 260 million years ago	..		30	50
105	10p. 230 million years ago	..		35	60
106	13p. 175 million years ago	..		45	70
107	25p. 50 million years ago	..		55	75
108	26p. Present day	..	..	55	75
	a. Gold (royal cypher) omitted				
103/8	..	..	*Set of 6*	2·25	3·25

(Des Jennifer Toombs. Litho Questa)

1982 (1 July). *21st Birthday of Princess of Wales.* T **30** *and similar vert designs. Multicoloured.* W w 14. P 14½ × 14.

109	5p. Type 30	..	..	20	20
110	17p. Princess of Wales (detail of painting by Bryan Organ)			45	50
111	37p. Wedding ceremony	..		70	80
112	50p. Formal portrait	..	..	1·10	1·10
109/12			*Set of 4*	2·25	2·40

31 Leopard Seal

(Des R. Granger Barrett. Litho Walsall)

1983 (3 Jan). *10th Anniv (1982) of Antarctic Seal Conservation Convention.* T **31** *and similar horiz designs. Multicoloured.* W w 14 (sideways). P 11.

113	5p. Type 31	..	..	45	35
114	10p. Weddell Seals	..	..	50	40
115	13p. Southern Elephant Seals	..		55	45
116	17p. Kerguelen Fur Seals	..		65	55
117	25p. Ross Seal.	..	..	75	65
118	34p. Crabeater Seals	..		95	85
113/18	..	..	*Set of 6*	3·50	3·00

32 De Havilland D.H.C.6 Twin Otter 200/300

(Des Harrison. Litho Questa)

1983 (20 Dec). *Bicentenary of Manned Flight.* T **32** *and similar horiz designs. Multicoloured.* W w 14 (sideways). P 14.

119	5p. Type 32	..	..	25	30
120	13p. De Havilland D.H.C.3 Otter	..		40	45
121	17p. Consolidated PBY-5A Canso			55	60
122	50p. Lockheed Vega *San Francisco*			1·10	1·25
119/22			*Set of 4*	2·10	2·40

33 *Corethron criophilum*

(Des I. Loe. Litho Walsall)

1984 (15 Mar). *Marine Life.* T **33** *and similar horiz designs. Multicoloured.* W w 14 (sideways*). P 14.

123	1p. Type 33	..	..	60	1·40
124	2p. *Desmonema gaudichaudi*	..		65	1·40
125	3p. *Tomopteris carpenteri*	..		65	1·40
126	4p. *Pareuchaeta antarctica*	..		70	1·50
127	5p. *Antarctomysis maxima*	..		70	1·50
128	6p. *Antarcturus signiensis*	..		70	1·50
129	7p. *Serolis cornuta*	..		70	1·50
130	8p. *Parathemisto gaudichaudii*	..		70	1·50
131	9p. *Bovallia gigantea*	..		70	1·50
132	10p. *Euphausia superba*	..		70	1·50
133	15p. *Colossendeis australis*	..		70	1·75
134	20p. *Todarodes sagittatus*	..		75	1·75
	w. Wmk Crown to right of CA			80·00	
135	25p. Antarctic Rockcod ("*Notothenia neglecta*")			80	1·75
136	50p. Black-finned Icefish ("*Chaenocephalus aceratus*")			1·25	2·00
137	£1 Crabeater Seal	..		1·75	2·50
138	£3 Antarctic marine food chain			5·00	6·50
123/38			*Set of 16*	15·00	28·00

*The normal sideways watermark shows Crown to left of CA on 1, 3, 4, 6, 7, 8, 9, 10, 20p. and to right on 2, 5, 15, 25, 50p., £1, £3, all as seen from the back of the stamp.

34 M.Y. *Penola* in Stella Creek

35 Robert McCormick and McCormick's Skua

(Des A. Theobald. Litho Questa)

1985 (23 Mar). *50th Anniv of British Graham Land Expedition.* T **34** *and similar horiz designs. Multicoloured.* W w 14 (sideways). P 14½.

139	7p. Type 34	..	..	40	75
140	22p. Northern Base, Winter Island			70	1·40
141	27p. De Havilland D.H.83 Fox Moth at Southern Base, Barry Island			80	1·60
142	54p. Dog team near Ablation Point, George VI Sound			1·50	2·25
139/42			*Set of 4*	3·00	5·50

(Des I. Strange. Litho Questa)

1985 (4 Nov). *Early Naturalists.* T **35** *and similar vert designs. Multicoloured.* W w 14. P 14½×14.

143	7p. Type 35	..	..	1·25	1·50
144	22p. Sir Joseph Dalton Hooker and *Deschampsia antarctica*			1·75	2·75
145	27p. Jean René C. Quoy and Hourglass Dolphin			1·90	2·75
146	54p. James Weddell and Weddell Seal			2·75	4·00
143/6			*Set of 4*	7·00	10·00

NEW INFORMATION

The editor is always interested to correspond with people who have new information that will improve or correct the Catalogue.

36 Dr. Edmond Halley   **37** Snow Crystal

(Des A. Theobald. Litho Questa)

1986 (6 Jan). *Appearance of Halley's Comet.* T **36** *and similar vert designs. Multicoloured.* W w 14. P 14.

147	7p. Type 36	..	..	1·00	1·25
148	22p. Halley Station, Antarctica			1·75	2·25
149	27p. "Halley's Comet, 1531" (from Peter Apian woodcut, 1532)			2·00	2·50
150	54p. *Giotto* spacecraft	..		3·50	4·50
147/50			*Set of 4*	7·50	9·50

(Des C. Abbott. Litho Questa)

1986 (6 Dec). *50th Anniv of International Glaciological Society.* T **37** *and similar vert designs showing snow crystals.* W w 16. P 14½.

151	10p. cobalt and deep ultramarine	..		60	75
152	24p. pale turquoise-green & dp bluish green			90	1·40
153	29p. mauve and deep mauve.	..		1·00	1·50
154	58p. violet-blue and bright violet	..		1·40	2·50
151/4			*Set of 4*	3·50	5·50

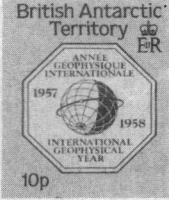

38 Captain Scott, 1904   **39** I.G.Y. Logo

(Des A. Theobald. Litho Questa)

1987 (19 Mar). *75th Anniv of Captain Scott's Arrival at South Pole.* T **38** *and similar horiz designs. Multicoloured.* W w 16 (sideways). P 14 × 14½.

155	10p. Type 38	..	..	85	95
156	24p. Hut Point and *Discovery*, Ross Island, 1902–4			1·40	2·00
157	29p. Cape Evans Hut, 1911–13	..		1·75	2·25
158	58p. Scott's Expedition at South Pole, 1912			2·25	3·00
155/8			*Set of 4*	5·50	7·50

(Des L. Curtis. Litho Questa)

1987 (25 Dec). *30th Anniv of International Geophysical Year.* T **39** *and similar vert designs.* W w 16. P 14½×14.

159	10p. black and pale green	..		30	75
160	24p. multicoloured	..		60	1·40
161	29p. multicoloured	..		75	1·75
162	58p. multicoloured	..		1·40	2·50
159/62			*Set of 4*	2·75	5·75

Designs:—24p. Port Lockroy; 29p. Argentine Islands; 58p. Halley Bay.

40 Aurora over South Ice Plateau Station

41 *Xanthoria elegans*

(Des D. Hartley. Litho Questa)

1988 (19 Mar). *30th Anniv of Commonwealth Trans-Antarctic Expedition.* T **40** *and similar vert designs. Multicoloured.* W w 16. P 14.

163	10p. Type 40	..	..	30	55
164	24p. "Otter" aircraft at Theron Mountains			60	90
165	29p. Seismic ice-depth sounding	..		70	1·10
166	58p. "Sno-cat" over crevasse.	..		1·25	1·75
163/6			*Set of 4*	2·50	3·75

(Des I. Loe. Litho Walsall)

1989 (25 Mar). *Lichens.* T **41** *and similar horiz designs. Multicoloured.* W w 14 (sideways). P 14.

167	10p Type 41	..	..	90	90
168	24p *Usnea aurantiaco-atra*	..		1·60	1·75
169	29p *Cladonia chlorophaea*	..		1·75	1·90
170	58p *Umbilicaria antarctica*	..		2·50	3·25
167/70			*Set of 4*	6·00	7·00

42 *Monocyathus*
(archaeocyath)

43 Late Cretaceous
Forest and Southern
Beech Fossil

(Des I. Loe. Litho Questa)

1990 (2 Apr). *Fossils. T* **42** *and similar horiz designs. Multicoloured. W* w **16** (*sideways*). *P* 14.

171	1p. Type **42**				75	1·00
172	2p. *Lingulella* (brachiopod)				75	1·00
173	3p. *Triplagnoslus* (trilobite)				90	1·00
174	4p. *Lyriaspis* (trilobite)				90	1·00
175	5p. *Glossopteris* leaf (gymnosperm)			90	1·00
176	6p. *Gonatosorus* (fern)				1·00	1·10
177	7p. *Belemnopsis aucklandica* (belemnite)		1·00	1·10
178	8p. *Samartinoceras africanum insignico-statum* (ammonite)		1·00	1·10
179	9p. *Pinna antarctica* (mussel)			1·00	1·10
180	10p. *Aucellina andina* (mussel)			1·00	1·10
181	20p. *Pterotrigonia malagninoi* (mussel)		1·50	1·60
182	25p. *Anchura* sp. (conch shell)			1·50	1·60
183	50p. *Ainoceras zinsmeisteri* (ammonite)		2·00	2·75
184	£1 *Gunnarites antarcticus* (ammonite)		3·50	4·25
185	£3 *Hoploparia* (crayfish)			7·00	8·00
171/85				*Set of* 15	22·00	26·00

(Des D. Miller. Litho Questa)

1990 (25 Dec*). *90th Birthday of Queen Elizabeth the Queen Mother. Vert designs as T* **134** (26p.) *or* **135** (£1) *of Ascension. W* w **16**. *P* 14×15 (26p.) *or* 14½ (£1);

186	26p. multicoloured				1·75	2·25
187	£1 brownish black and olive-bistre		3·75	4·25

Designs:—26p. Wedding of Prince Albert and Lady Elizabeth Bowes-Lyon, 1923; £1 The Royal Family, 1940.

*This is the local date of issue, the Crown Agents released the stamps on 4 August.

(Des N. Shewring. Litho Questa)

1991 (27 Mar). *Age of the Dinosaurs. T* **43** *and similar horiz designs. Multicoloured. W* w **14** (*sideways*). *P* 14×13½.

188	12p. Type **43**				1·25	1·25
189	26p. Hypsilophodont dinosaurs and skull		2·00	2·25
190	31p. Frilled Sharks and tooth			2·25	2·50
191	62p. Mosasaur, Plesiosaur, and Mosasaur vertebra			3·50	4·00
188/91				*Set of* 4	8·00	9·00

44 Launching
Meteorological Balloon,
Halley IV Station

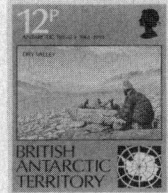

45 Researching Dry
Valley

(Des O. Bell. Litho Questa)

1991 (30 Mar). *Discovery of Antarctic Ozone Hole. T* **44** *and similar horiz designs. Multicoloured. W* w **16** (*sideways*). *P* 14×13½.

192	12p. Type **44**				90	90
193	26p. Measuring ozone with Dobson spectro-photometer			1·60	1·75
194	31p. Satellite map showing ozone hole		1·75	1·90
195	62p. Lockheed ER-2 aircraft and graph of chlorine monoxide and ozone levels		3·00	3·25
192/5				*Set of* 4	6·50	7·00

(Des O. Bell. Litho Questa)

1991 (2 Dec*). *30th Anniv of Antarctic Treaty. T* **45** *and similar vert designs. W* w **14**. *P* 13½×14 (31p.) *or* 14½×14 (*others*).

196	12p. multicoloured				90	90
197	26p. multicoloured				1·60	1·75
198	31p. black and blue-green			1·75	1·90
199	62p. multicoloured				3·00	3·25
196/9				*Set of* 4	6·50	7·00

Designs:—26p. Relief map of ice sheet; 31p. BIOMASS logo; 62p. Ross Seal.

*This is the local date of issue, the Crown Agents released the stamps on 24 June.

46 "H.M.S. *Erebus* and
H.M.S. *Terror* in the
Antarctic"
(J. Carmichael)

(Des R. Watton. Litho Walsall)

1991 (10 Dec). *Maiden Voyage of James Clark Ross* (*research ship*). *T* **46** *and similar horiz designs. Multicoloured. W* w **14** (*sideways*). *P* 14½.

200	12p. Type **46**				90	90
201	26p. Launch of *James Clark Ross*			1·60	1·75
202	31p. *James Clark Ross* in Antarctica		1·75	1·90
203	62p. Scientific research			3·00	3·25
200/3				*Set of* 4	6·50	7·00

1991 (24 Dec). *Birth Bicentenary of Michael Faraday* (*scientist*). *Nos.* 200/3 *additionally inscr* "200th Anniversary M. Faraday 1791–1867" *in blue.*

204	12p. Type **46**				90	90
205	26p. Launch of *James Clark Ross*			1·60	1·75
206	31p. *James Clark Ross* in Antarctica		1·75	1·90
207	62p. Scientific research			3·00	3·25
204/7				*Set of* 4	6·50	7·00

47 Ross Seals

(Des A. Robinson. Litho B.D.T.)

1992 (10 Dec*). *Endangered Species. Seals and Penguins. T* **47** *and similar horiz designs. Multicoloured. W* w **14** (*sideways*). *P* 13½.

208	4p. Type **47**				80	80
209	4p. Adelie Penguins				80	80
210	7p. Weddell Seal with pup			85	85
211	29p. Emperor Penguins with chicks		2·00	2·00
212	34p. Crabeater Seals with pup		1·75	2·00
213	68p. Chinstrap Penguins with young		2·25	2·40
208/13				*Set of* 6	7·50	8·00

*This is the local date of issue, the Crown Agents released the stamps in London, and at the "Genova 92" International Thematic Stamp Exhibition, on 20 October.

Nos. 212/13 do not carry the W.W.F. Panda emblem.

48 Sun Pillar at Faraday

49 *Fitzroy* (mail and supply
ship)

(Des N. Shewring. Litho Questa)

1992 (22 Dec). *Lower Atmospheric Phenomena. T* **48** *and similar horiz designs. Multicoloured. W* w **14** (*sideways*). *P* 14½.

214	14p. Type **48**				80	70
215	29p. Halo over iceberg			1·40	1·40
216	34p. Lee Wave Cloud			1·75	1·25
217	68p. Nacreous Clouds			2·75	2·00
214/17				*Set of* 4	6·00	4·50

(Des R. Watton. Litho Walsall)

1993 (13 Dec). *Antarctic Ships. T* **49** *and simlar horiz designs. Multicoloured. W* w **14** (*sideways*). *P* 14.

218	1p. Type **49**				35	50
219	2p. *William Scoresby* (research ship)		40	50
220	3p. *Eagle* (sealer)				45	50
221	4p. *Trepassey* (supply ship)			45	50
222	5p. *John Biscoe I* (research ship)		45	50
223	10p. *Norsel* (supply ship)			60	70
224	20p. H.M.S. *Protector* (ice patrol ship)		90	70
225	30p. *Oluf Sven* (supply ship)			1·10	1·25
226	50p. *John Biscoe II* and *Shackleton* (research ships)		1·60	1·60
227	£1 *Tottan* (supply ship)			2·50	2·75
228	£3 *Perla Dan* (supply ship)			6·00	6·50
229	£5 H.M.S. *Endurance I* (ice patrol ship)		10·00	11·00
218/29			*Set of* 12	22·00	24·00

For miniature sheets containing the 50p or £1 ("1997" imprint date) see Nos. **MS274/5**.

1994 (19 Mar*). "*Hong Kong '94*" *International Stamp Exhibition. Nos.* 240/5 *optd as T* **154** *of Ascension.*

230	15p. Type **51**				85	1·00
231	24p. De Havilland D.H.C.2 Turbo Beaver III aircraft			1·25	1·75
232	31p. De Havilland D.H.C.3 Otter aircraft and dog team			1·50	1·90
233	36p. De Havilland D.H.C.6 Twin Otter 200/300 aircraft and dog team		1·60	2·00
234	62p. De Havilland D.H.C.7 Dash Seven aircraft over landing strip, Rothera Point			2·25	2·75
235	72p. De Havilland D.H.C.7 Dash Seven aircraft on runway		2·25	2·75
230/5				*Set of* 6	8·75	11·00

*This is the local release date, the Crown Agents released the stamps in London and at the Exhibition on 18 February.

COVER PRICES

Cover factors are quoted at the beginning of each country for most issues to 1945. An explanation of the system can be found on page x. The factors quoted do not, however, apply to philatelic covers.

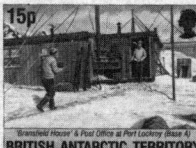

50 Bransfield House Post
Office, Port Lockroy

(Des R. Watton. Litho Walsall)

1994 (19 Mar). *50th Anniv of Operation Tabarin. T* **50** *and similar horiz designs. Multicoloured. W* w **16** (*sideways*). *P* 14×14½.

236	15p. Type **50**				65	75
237	31p. Survey team, Hope Bay			1·10	1·25
238	36p. Dog team, Hope Bay			1·40	1·60
239	72p. *Fitzroy* (supply ship) and H.M.S. *William Scoresby* (minesweeper)		2·25	2·75
236/9				*Set of* 4	4·75	5·50

51 Huskies and Sledge

(Des D. Miller. Litho Walsall)

1994 (21 Mar). *Forms of Transportation. T* **51** *and similar horiz designs. Multicoloured. W* w **14** (*sideways*). *P* 14½.

240	15p. Type **51**				60	70
241	24p. De Havilland D.H.C.2 Turbo Beaver III aircraft			80	90
242	31p. De Havilland D.H.C.3 Otter aircraft and dog team			90	1·00
243	36p. De Havilland D.H.C.6 Twin Otter 200/300 aircraft and dog team		1·00	1·25
244	62p. De Havilland D.H.C.7 Dash Seven aircraft over landing strip, Rothera Point			1·90	2·50
245	72p. De Havilland D.H.C.7 Dash Seven aircraft on runway			2·00	2·75
240/5				*Set of* 6	6·50	8·00

52 Capt. James Cook and
H.M.S. *Resolution*

(Des R. Watton. Litho Questa)

1994 (23 Nov). *Antarctic Heritage Fund. T* **52** *and similar horiz designs. Multicoloured. W* w **16** (*sideways*). *P* 14½×14.

246	17p. + 3p. Type **52**				1·50	1·60
247	35p. + 15p. Sir James Clark Ross with H.M.S. *Erebus* and H.M.S. *Terror*		1·75	1·90
248	40p. + 10p. Capt. Robert Falcon Scott and interior of hut			1·75	1·90
249	76p. + 4p. Sir Ernest Shackleton and *Endurance*			2·50	2·75
246/9				*Set of* 4	6·75	7·25

53 Pair of Crabeater Seals

54 Hauberg Mountains

(Des A. Robinson. Litho Questa)

1994 (29 Nov). *Antarctic Food Chain. T* **53** *and similar horiz designs. Multicoloured. W* w **14**. *P* 14×14½.

250	35p. Type **53**				1·25	1·50
	a. Sheetlet. Nos. 250/5				6·50	
251	35p. Blue Whale				1·25	1·50
252	35p. Wandering Albatross			1·25	1·50
253	35p. Mackerel Icefish			1·25	1·50
254	35p. Krill				1·25	1·50
255	35p. Seven Star Flying Squid (*Martialia hyadesi*)			1·25	1·50
250/5				*Set of* 6	6·50	8·00

Nos. 250/5 were printed together, *se-tenant*, in sheetlets of 6.

(Des N. Shewring. Litho Walsall)

1995 (28 Nov). *Geological Structures. T* **54** *and similar horiz designs. Multicoloured. W* w **14** (*sideways*). *P* 14×14½.

256	17p. Type **54**				75	75
257	35p. Arrowsmith Peninsula			1·50	1·50
258	40p. Colbert Mountains			1·75	1·75
259	76p. Succession Cliffs			2·50	2·50
256/9				*Set of* 4	6·00	6·00

55 World Map showing
Member Countries

(Des R. Watton. Litho Walsall)

1996 (23 Mar). *24th Meeting of Scientific Committee on
Antarctic Research, Cambridge. T **55** and similar horiz
designs. Multicoloured. W w **16** (sideways). P 14.*

260	17p. Type **55**		75	75
261	35p. Scientist analysing ice samples		1·50	1·50
262	40p. Releasing balloon		1·75	1·75
263	76p. Antarctic research ship catching marine life		2·50	2·50
260/3		Set of 4	6·00	6·00
MS264	100×90 mm. £1 S.C.A.R. logo. Wmk inverted		3·50	4·00

56 Killer Whales

57 Chinstrap
Penguins sledging

(Des Dafila Scott. Litho Questa)

1996 (25 Nov). *Whales. T **56** and similar horiz designs.
Multicoloured. W w **14** (sideways). P 14.*

265	17p. Type **56**		70	60
266	35p. Sperm Whales		1·25	1·10
267	40p. Minke Whales		1·50	1·40
268	76p. Blue Whale and calf		2·25	2·00
265/8		Set of 4	5·00	4·50
MS269	105×82 mm. £1 Humpback Whale		2·50	2·75

(Des D. Miller. Litho Walsall)

1996 (25 Nov). *70th Birthday of Queen Elizabeth II. Vert
designs as T **165** of Ascension, each incorporating a different
photograph of the Queen. Multicoloured. W w **16**. P 14½.*

270	17p. At premiere of *Chaplin*, Leicester Square, 1992		50	60
271	35p. At Buckingham Palace dinner, 1991		95	1·25
272	40p. In Aberdeen, 1993		1·25	1·50
273	76p. At Royal Military School of Music, 1990		1·75	2·25
270/3		Set of 4	4·00	5·00

(Des D. Miller. Litho Questa)

1997 (3 Feb). *"HONG KONG '97" International Stamp Exhibition. Sheet 130×90 mm, containing design as No. 226.
Multicoloured. W w **14**. P 14.*

MS274	50p. *John Biscoe II* and *Shackleton* (research ships)		1·40	1·40

(Des R. Watton. Litho Walsall)

1997 (20 June). *Return of Hong Kong to China. Sheet 130×90
mm containing design as No. 227, but with "1997" imprint date.*

MS275	£1 Tottan		2·75	3·00

(Des R. Watton. Litho Questa)

1997 (22 Dec). *Christmas. T **57** and similar vert designs.
Multicoloured. W w **16**. P 14½×14.*

276	17p. Type **57**		75	75
277	35p. Emperor Penguins carol singing		1·40	1·40
278	40p. Adelié Penguins throwing snowballs		1·60	1·60
279	76p. Gentoo Penguins ice-skating		2·25	2·75
276/9		Set of 4	5·50	6·00

(Des D. Miller. Litho Questa)

1998 (17 Mar). *Diana, Princess of Wales Commemoration.
Sheet, 145×70 mm, containing vert designs as T **177** of
Ascension. Multicoloured. W w **14** (sideways). P 14½×14.*

MS280	35p. Wearing sunglasses; 35p. Wearing round-necked white blouse, 1993; 35p. Wearing white blouse and jacket, 1990; 35p. Wearing green jacket, 1992 (*sold at £1.40 + 20p. charity premium*)		3·75	3·75

58 Chart of South Shetland
Islands (Swedish South
Polar Expedition, 1902–03)

59 Antarctic Explorer
and H.M.S. *Erebus*,
1843

(Des N. Shewring. Litho Walsall)

1998 (19 Mar). *History of Mapping in Antarctica. T **58** and
similar vert designs. Multicoloured. W w **14**. P 14.*

281	16p. Type **58**		75	75
282	30p. Map of Antarctic Peninsula (1949)		1·25	1·25
283	35p. Map of Antarctic Peninsula (1964)		1·40	1·40
284	40p. Map of Antarctic Peninsula from Landsat (1981)		1·50	1·50
285	65p. Map of Antarctic Peninsula from satellite (1995)		1·75	2·25
281/5		Set of 5	6·00	6·50

(Des V. Ambrus. Litho Walsall)

1998 (27 Nov). *Antarctic Clothing. T **59** and similar vert
designs. Multicoloured. W w **14**. P 14½×14.*

286	30p. Type **59**		80	80
287	35p. Explorer with dog and *Discovery I*, 1900		90	90
288	40p. Surveyor and *Fitzroy*, 1943		1·10	1·10
289	65p. Scientist with penguins and *James Clark Ross*, 1998		1·60	1·60
286/9		Set of 4	4·00	4·00

60 Snowy Sheathbill

(Des A. Robinson. Litho Walsall)

1998 (30 Nov). *Antarctic Birds. T **60** and similar horiz
designs. Multicoloured. W w **14** (sideways). P 14.*

290	1p. Type **60**		10	10
291	2p. Dove Prion ("Antarctic Prion")		10	10
292	5p. Adelié Penguin		10	10
293	10p. Emperor Penguin		20	25
294	20p. Swallow-tailed Tern ("Antarctic Tern")		40	45
295	30p. Black-bellied Storm Petrel		60	65
296	35p. Antarctic Fulmar		70	75
297	40p. Blue-eyed Shag		80	85
298	50p. McCormick's Skua		1·00	1·10
299	£1 Southern Black-backed Gull ("Kelp Gull")		2·00	2·10
300	£3 Wilson's Storm Petrel		6·00	6·25
301	£5 Brown Skua		10·00	10·50
290/301		Set of 12	21·00	22·00

61 Mackerel Icefish

(Des C. Austin. Litho Cartor)

1999 (14 Nov). *Fish of the Southern Ocean. T **61** and similar
horiz designs. Multicoloured. W w **14**. P 13½.*

302	10p. Type **61**		20	25
303	20p. Blenny Rockcod ("Toothfish")		40	45
304	25p. Borch		50	55
305	50p. Marbled Rockcod ("Marbled notothen")		1·00	1·10
306	80p. Bernacchi's Rockcod ("Bernach")		1·60	1·75
302/6		Set of 6	3·50	4·00

62 Map showing
Crustal Microplates
of West Antarctica

63 Wreck of *Endurance*

(Des N. Shewring. Litho Questa)

1999 (18 Dec). *British Antarctic Survey Discoveries. T **62** and
similar multicoloured designs. W w **14** (sideways on horiz
designs). P 14.*

307	15p. Type **62**		30	35
308	30p. Testing lead levels in ice		60	65
309	35p. Decolopodid sea spider (Gigantism in marine invertebrates) (*horiz*)		70	75
310	40p. Scientist operating Dobson Spectro-photometer for testing ozone layer (*horiz*)		80	85
311	70p. Radar antenna (aurora electric field research) (*horiz*)		1·40	1·50
307/11		Set of 5	3·75	4·00

(Des M. Skidmore. Litho Questa)

2000 (10 Feb). *Shackleton's Trans-Antarctic Expedition,
1914–17, Commemoration. T **63** and similar horiz designs.
Multicoloured. W w **14** (sideways). P 14.*

312	35p. Type **63**		70	75
313	40p. Ocean Camp on ice		80	85
314	65p. Launching *James Caird* from Elephant Island		1·25	1·40
312/14		Set of 3	2·75	3·00

British Central Africa
see Nyasaland Protectorate

British Columbia and Vancouver Island
see Canada

British East Africa
see Kenya, Uganda and Tanganyika

British Forces in Egypt
see Egypt

British Guiana
see Guyana

British Honduras
see Belize

British Indian Ocean Territory

This Crown Colony was created on 8 November 1965 when it comprised the Chagos Archipelago, previously administered by Mauritius, together with the islands of Aldabra, Farquhar and Desroches, previously administered by Seychelles.

(Currency. 100 cents=1 rupee)

B.I.O.T.
(1)

1968 (17 Jan). *As Nos. 196/200, 202/4 and 206/12 of Seychelles, optd with T 1. W w 12 (sideways* on 5, 10, 15, 20, 25, 50, 75 c. and 10 r.).*

1	5 c. multicoloured	..	1·00	60
	a. No stop after "I"	..	9·00	12·00
	b. No stop after "O"	..	6·00	8·50
	w. Wmk Crown to right of CA	..	29·00	
2	10 c. multicoloured	..	10	15
	a. No stop after "I"	..	9·00	12·00
	b. No stop after "O"	..	5·50	8·50
3	15 c. multicoloured	..	10	15
	a. No stop after "I"	..	9·00	12·00
	b. No stop after "O"	..	5·50	8·50
4	20 c. multicoloured	..	15	15
	a. No stop after "I"	..	9·00	12·00
	b. No stop after "O"	..	5·50	8·50
5	25 c. multicoloured	..	15	15
	a. No stop after "I"	..	9·50	13·00
	b. No stop after "O"	..	5·50	9·00

6	40 c. multicoloured	..	20	20
	a. No stop after "I"	..	13·00	17·00
	b. No stop after "O"	..	7·50	10·00
7	45 c. multicoloured	..	20	30
	a. No stop after "I"	..	13·00	17·00
	b. No stop after "B"	..	13·00	17·00
	c. No stop after "O"	..	13·00	17·00
8	50 c. multicoloured	..	20	30
	a. No stop after "I"	..	13·00	17·00
	b. No stop after "O"	..	7·00	9·50
9	75 c. multicoloured	..	20	35
10	1 r. multicoloured	..	40	35
	a. No stop after "I"	..	13·00	17·00
	b. No stop after "O"	..	7·00	9·50
11	1 r. 50, multicoloured	..	1·75	1·50
	a. No stop after "I"	..	27·00	30·00
	b. No stop after "O"	..	13·00	17·00
12	2 r. 25, multicoloured	..	3·00	3·75
	a. No stop after "I"	..	60·00	65·00
	b. No stop after "O"	..	28·00	35·00
13	3 r. 50, multicoloured	..	3·00	4·50
	a. No stop after "I"	..	60·00	65·00
	b. No stop after "O"	..	28·00	35·00
14	5 r. multicoloured	..	9·00	7·50
	a. No stop after "I"	..	85·00	90·00
	b. No stop after "O"	..	40·00	45·00
15	10 r. multicoloured	..	19·00	20·00
	a. No stop after "B"	..	£120	£130
	b. No stop after "I"	..	£120	£130
	c. No stop after "O"	..	70·00	80·00
1/15	..	*Set of 15*	35·00	35·00

*The normal sideways watermark shows Crown to left of CA, as seen from the back of the stamp.

These were issued by the Crown Agents on 15 January but owing to shipping delays they were not put on sale locally until 17 January.

The positions of the "no stop" varieties are as follows:
After "I": R. 2/4 on horiz stamps except 45 c. where it occurs on R. 3/3, and R. 8/5 on vert stamps except 10 r. where it occurs on R. 4/3.
After "O": R. 3/2 and 5/1 on vert stamps, R. 2/1 and 4/4 on horiz stamps (only occurs on R. 2/1 for 45 c.), and R. 2/7 and 5/9 on 10 r. value.
After "B": R. 10/4 (45 c.) or R. 1/8 (10 r.).
As sheets of all values from 5 c. to 50 c. are known with all stops in place the no stop varieties either developed during printing or their omission was discovered and replacements inserted.

2 Lascar

(Des G. Drummond, based on drawings by Mrs. W. Veevers-Carter. Litho D.L.R.)

1968 (23 Oct)–**70**. *Marine Life. Multicoloured designs as T 2. White paper (Nos. 20a, 23a, 24a) or cream paper (others). W w 12 (sideways on horiz, inverted on vert designs). P 14.*

16	5 c. Type 2	..	30	1·50
17	10 c. Smooth Hammerhead (vert)	..	30	1·25
18	15 c. Tiger Shark	..	30	1·50
19	20 c. Spotted Eagle Ray ("Bat Ray")	..	30	1·00
20	25 c. Yellow-finned Butterflyfish and Ear-spotted Angelfish (vert)	..	80	1·00
20a	30 c. Robber Crab (7.12.70)	..	3·50	2·75
21	40 c. Blue-finned Trevally ("Caranx")	..	40	40
22	45 c. Crocodile Needlefish ("Garfish") (vert)	..	2·25	2·50
23	50 c. Pickhandle Barracuda	..	45	30
23a	60 c. Spotted Pebble Crab (7.12.70)	..	3·50	3·25
24	75 c. Indian Ocean Steep-headed Parrotfish	..	2·50	2·75
24a	85 c. Rainbow Runner ("Dorade") (7.12.70)	..	6·00	3·50
25	1 r. Giant Hermit Crab	..	1·50	35
26	1 r. 50, Parrotfish ("Humphead")	..	2·50	2·50
27	2 r. 25, Yellow-edged Lyretail and Areolate Grouper ("Rock Cod")	..	8·00	8·50
28	3 r. 50, Black Marlin	..	4·00	3·75
29	5 r. black, blue-green and greenish blue (Whale Shark) (vert)	..	9·00	8·00
30	10 r. Lionfish	..	9·00	8·00
	a. Imperf (pair)	..	£600	
16/30	..	*Set of 18*	48·00	48·00

See also No. 52.

3 Sacred Ibis and Aldabra Coral Atoll

(Des and litho D.L.R.)

1969 (10 July). *Coral Atolls. W w 12 (sideways). P 13½ × 13.*

31	3	2 r. 25, multicoloured	1·75	1·00

4 Outrigger Canoe

(Des Mrs. M. Hayward adapted by V. Whiteley. Litho D.L.R.)

1969 (15 Dec). *Ships of the Islands. T 4 and similar horiz designs. Multicoloured. W w 12 (sideways). P 13½ × 14.*

32	45 c. Type 4	..	65	75
33	75 c. Pirogue	..	65	80
34	1 r. M. V. *Nordvaer*	..	70	90
35	1 r. 50, *Isle of Farquhar*	..	80	1·00
32/5	..	*Set of 4*	2·50	3·00

5 Giant Land Tortoise

(Des G. Drummond. Litho Format)

1971 (1 Feb). *Aldabra Nature Reserve. T 5 and similar horiz designs. Multicoloured. W w 12 (sideways). P 13½.*

36	45 c. Type 5	..	2·50	2·50
37	75 c. Aldabra Lily	..	3·00	2·50
38	1 r. Aldabra Tree Snail (*Rhachis aldabrae*)	3·50	2·75
39	1 r. 50, Western Reef Herons	..	12·00	10·00
36/9	..	*Set of 4*	19·00	16·00

6 Arms of Royal Society and White-throated Rail

(Des V. Whiteley. Litho J.W.)

1971 (30 June). *Opening of Royal Society Research Station on Aldabra. W w 12 (sideways). P 13½.*

40	6	3 r. 50, multicoloured	15·00	8·50

7 Staghorn Coral

(Des V. Whiteley. Litho A. & M.)

1972 (1 Mar). *Coral. T 7 and similar horiz designs. Multicoloured. W w 12 (sideways*). P 13½.*

41	40 c. Type 7	..	3·50	4·00
	w. Wmk Crown to left of CA	..	16·00	
42	60 c. Brain coral	..	4·00	4·25
	w. Wmk Crown to left of CA	..	9·00	
43	1 r. Mushroom coral	..	4·00	4·25
	w. Wmk Crown to left of CA	..	5·00	
44	1 r. 75, Organ Pipe coral	..	5·00	6·50
	w. Wmk Crown to left of CA	..	12·00	
41/4	..	*Set of 4*	15·00	17·00

*The normal sideways watermark shows Crown to right of CA, as seen from the back of the stamp.
On some sheets of No. 43 the inks have been applied in a different order, resulting in an almost total absence of blue.

8 White-throated Rail and Sacred Ibis   **9** "Christ on the Cross"

(Des (from photograph by D. Groves) and photo Harrison)

1972 (20 Nov). *Royal Silver Wedding. Multicoloured; background colour given. W w 12. P 14 × 14½.*

45	8	95 c. deep dull green	75	40
	a. Silver (frame and inscr) ptd double	£450	
	b. Slate-green	2·00	2·00
46		1 r. 50, bright bluish violet	75	40

(Des Jennifer Toombs. Litho Questa)

1973 (9 Apr). *Easter. T 9 and similar vert design showing illustrations from 17th-century Ethiopian manuscript. Multicoloured. W w 12 (sideways). P 14.*

47	45 c. Type 9	..	25	40
48	75 c. Joseph and Nicodemus burying Jesus	35	55
49	1 r. Type 9	..	35	60
50	1 r. 50. As 75 c.	..	40	70
47/50	..	*Set of 4*	1·25	2·00
MS51	126 × 110 mm. Nos. 47/50	..	1·50	4·00

1973 (2 Oct). *As No. 16 but white paper and wmk upright.*
52   5 c. Type **2** . . . . 1·00 4·00
No. 52 differs in shade from No. 16 because of the change of paper.

10 Upsidedown Jellyfish   **11** M.V. *Nordvaer*

(Des G. Drummond. Litho Walsall)

1973 (12 Nov). *Wildlife (1st series). T **10** and similar vert designs. Multicoloured. W w 12 (sideways*). P 14.*
53   50 c. Type **10** . . . . . . 3·50 3·00
54   1 r. *Hypolimnas misippus and Belenois aldabrensis* (butterflies) . . 4·00 3·00
55   1 r. 50, *Nephila madagascariensis* (spider) 4·25 3·00
      w. Wmk Crown to right of CA . . 6·50
53/5 . . . . *Set of 3* 10·50 8·00
*The normal sideways watermark shows Crown to left of CA, as seen from the back of the stamp.
See also Nos. 58/61, 77/80 and 86/9.

(Des C. Abbott. Litho Walsall)

1974 (14 July). *Fifth Anniv of "Nordvaer" Travelling Post Office. T **11** and similar vert design. Multicoloured. W w 12 (sideways). P 14.*
56   85 c. Type **11** 85 75
57   2 r. 50, *Nordvaer* off shore . . 1·40 1·25

12 Red-cloud Auger (*Terebra nebulosa*) and Subulate Auger (*Terebra subulata*)

(Des PAD Studio. Litho J.W.)

1974 (12 Nov). *Wildlife (2nd series). T **12** and similar horiz designs showing shells. Multicoloured. W w 12. P 13½ × 14.*
58   45 c. Type **12** . . . . . . 2·25 1·25
59   75 c. Great Green Turbo (*Turbo marmoratus*) 2·50 1·50
60   1 r. Strawberry Drupe (*Drupa rubusidaeus*) 2·75 1·75
61   1 r. 50, Bull-mouth Helmet (*Cypraecassis rufa*) . . . . . . 3·00 2·00
58/61 . . . . *Set of 4* 9·50 6·00

13 Aldabra Drongo   **14** *Grewia salicifolia*

(Des R. Granger Barrett. Litho Questa)

1975 (28 Feb). *Birds. Multicoloured designs as T **13**. W w 12 (sideways* on horiz designs). P 14.*
62   5 c. Type **13** . . . . . . 1·25 2·75
63   10 c. Black Coucal . . . . 1·25 2·75
64   20 c. Mascarene Fody . . . . 1·25 2·75
      w. Wmk inverted £100
65   25 c. White Tern . . . . 1·25 2·75
66   30 c. Crested Tern . . . . 1·25 2·75
67   40 c. Brown Booby . . . . 1·25 3·00
68   50 c. Common Noddy (*horiz*) . . 1·25 3·00
69   60 c. Grey Heron . . . . 1·25 3·00
70   65 c. Blue-faced Booby (*horiz*) . . 1·25 3·00
71   95 c. Madagascar White Eye (*horiz*) . . 1·25 3·00
      w. Wmk Crown to right of CA . . 65·00
72   1 r. Green Heron (*horiz*) . . 1·25 3·00
73   1 r. 75, Lesser Frigate Bird (*horiz*) 2·00 4·75
74   3 r. 50, White-tailed Tropic Bird (*horiz*) 2·75 4·75
75   5 r. Souimanga Sunbird (*horiz*) . . 4·00 5·00
76   10 r. Madagascar Turtle Dove (*horiz*) 8·00 9·00
62/76 . . . . *Set of 15* 27·00 48·00
*The normal sideways watermark shows Crown to left of CA, as seen from the back of the stamp.

(Des Sylvia Goaman. Litho Questa)

1975 (10 July). *Wildlife (3rd series). T **14** and similar vert designs showing seashore plants. Multicoloured. W w 12 (sideways). P 14.*
77   50 c. Type **14** . . . . . . 60 1·25
78   65 c. *Cassia aldabrensis* . . . . 65 1·40
79   1 r. *Hypoestes aldabrensis* . . . . 80 1·50
80   1 r. 60, *Euphorbia pyrifolia* . . 1·10 1·60
77/80 . . . . *Set of 4* 2·75 5·25

---

15 Map of Aldabra

(Des L. Curtis. Litho Questa)

1975 (8 Nov). *10th Anniv of Territory. Maps. T **15** and similar horiz designs. Multicoloured. W w 12. P 13½.*
81   50 c. Type **15** 70 65
82   1 r. Desroches 85 85
83   1 r. 50, Farquhar . . . . 95 1·00
84   2 r. Diego Garcia . . . . 1·00 1·25
81/4 . . . . *Set of 4* 3·25 3·25
MS85   147 × 147 mm. Nos. 81/4 (wmk sideways) 7·00 14·00

16 *Utetheisa pulchella* (moth)

(Des PAD Studio. Litho Questa)

1976 (22 Mar). *Wildlife (4th series). T **16** and similar horiz designs. Multicoloured. W w 12 (sideways). P 13½.*
86   65 c. Type **16** . . . . 60 1·10
87   1 r. 20, *Dysdercus fasciatus* (bug) . . 75 1·25
88   1 r. 50, *Sphex torridus* (wasp) . . 80 1·40
89   2 r. *Oryctes rhinoceros* (beetle) . . 85 1·40
86/9 . . . . *Set of 4* 2·75 4·50

When the Seychelles achieved independence on 29 June 1976 the islands of Aldabra, Farquhar and Desroches reverted to its administration so that British Indian Ocean Territory from that date consisted of the Chagos Archipelago, an island group, the largest of whose five main atolls is Diego Garcia. The indigenous population was resettled on Mauritius and Diego Garcia was developed as a U.S. Navy base while remaining under British administration.
Nos. 62/76 were withdrawn in August 1979 and, until May 1990, base personnel used British and American forces mail facilities routed via the Philippines and San Francisco. From 1987 British mails were routed via Singapore. The growing number of civilian workers eventually led to the re-introduction of a public postal service in May 1990 using stamps with face values in sterling.

(New Currency. Sterling)

17 White-tailed Tropic Bird   **18** 1974 Wildlife 1 r. 50 Stamp

(Des N. Arlott. Litho Questa)

1990 (3 May). *Birds. T **17** and similar vert designs. Multicoloured. W w 16 (sideways). P 14.*
90   15p. Type **17** . . . . 1·10 2·00
91   20p. Madagascar Turtle Dove . . 1·25 2·00
92   24p. Great Frigate Bird . . 1·40 2·00
93   30p. Green Heron . . . . 1·50 2·25
94   34p. Great Sand Plover . . 1·60 2·25
95   41p. Crab Plover . . . . 1·75 2·50
96   45p. Crested Tern . . . . 2·00 2·50
97   54p. Lesser Crested Tern . . 2·25 2·75
98   62p. White Tern . . . . 2·25 2·75
99   71p. Red-footed Booby . . 2·25 3·00
100   80p. Common Mynah . . 2·50 3·25
101   £1 Madagascar Red Fody . . 2·50 3·50
90/101 . . . . *Set of 12* 20·00 27·00

(Des D. Miller. Litho Walsall)

1990 (3 May). *"Stamp World London 90" International Stamp Exhibition. T **18** and similar horiz designs showing stamps. Multicoloured. W w 14 (sideways). P 14.*
102   15p. Type **18** . . . . 2·75 2·75
103   20p. 1976 Wildlife 2 r. . . 3·00 3·00
104   34p. 1975 Diego Garcia map 2 r. . . 4·50 4·50
105   54p. 1969 *Nordvaer* 1 r. . . 6·50 6·50
102/5 . . . . *Set of 4* 15·00 15·00

(Des D. Miller. Litho Walsall)

1990 (4 Aug). *90th Birthday of Queen Elizabeth the Queen Mother. Vert designs as T **134** (24p.) or **135** (£1) of Ascension. W w 16. P 14×15 (24p.) or 14½ (£1).*
106   24p. multicoloured . . 3·50 3·50
107   £1 brownish black and purple-brown 6·50 6·50
Designs:—24p. Lady Elizabeth Bowes-Lyon, 1923; £1 Queen Elizabeth and her daughters, 1940.

---

19 Territory Flag   **20** Postman emptying Pillar Box

(Des D. Miller. Litho Questa)

1990 (8 Nov). *25th Anniv of British Indian Ocean Territory. T **19** and similar vert designs. Multicoloured. W w 14. P 14×13½.*
108   20p. Type **19** . . . . 4·00 4·50
109   24p. Coat of arms . . . . 4·00 4·50
MS110   63×99 mm. £1 Map of Chagos Archipelago . . . . . . 9·50 11·00

(Des O. Bell. Litho Walsall)

1991 (3 June). *British Indian Ocean Territory Administration. T **20** and similar horiz designs. Multicoloured. W w 14 (sideways). P 14.*
111   20p. Type **20** . . . . 2·00 2·50
112   24p. Commissioner inspecting guard of Royal Marines . . . . 2·25 2·50
113   34p. Policemen outside station . . 4·00 4·50
114   54p. Customs officers boarding yacht 5·50 6·00
111/14 . . . . *Set of 4* 12·50 14·00

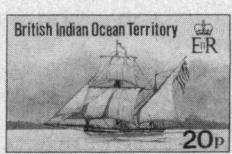

21 *Experiment* (E.I.C. survey brig), 1786

(Des E. Nisbet. Litho Walsall)

1991 (8 Nov). *Visiting Ships. T **21** and similar horiz designs. Multicoloured. W w 14 (sideways). P 14.*
115   20p. Type **21** . . . . 2·75 3·00
116   24p. *Pickering* (American brig), 1819 . . 3·00 3·25
117   34p. *Emden* (German cruiser), 1914 . . 4·00 4·25
118   54p. H.M.S. *Edinburgh* (destroyer), 1988 5·00 5·50
115/18 . . . . *Set of 4* 13·50 14·50

(Des D. Miller. Litho Questa (54p.), Walsall (others))

1992 (6 Feb). *40th Anniv of Queen Elizabeth II's Accession. Horiz designs as T **143** of Ascension. Multicoloured. W w 14 (sideways). P 14.*
119   15p. Catholic chapel, Diego Garcia . . 1·25 1·25
120   20p. Planter's house, Diego Garcia . . 1·40 1·40
121   24p. Railway tracks on wharf, Diego Garcia 2·50 2·00
122   34p. Three portraits of Queen Elizabeth . . 2·00 2·25
123   54p. Queen Elizabeth II . . . . 2·25 2·50
119/23 . . . . *Set of 5* 8·50 8·50

22 R.A.F. Consolidated PBY-5 Catalina (flying boat)   **23** "The Mystical Marriage of St. Catherine" (Correggio)

(Des A. Theobald. Litho Walsall)

1992 (23 Oct). *Visiting Aircraft. T **22** and similar horiz designs. Multicoloured. W w 16 (sideways). P 14.*
124   20p. Type **22** . . . . 2·00 2·50
125   24p. R.A.F. Hawker Siddeley H.S.801 Nimrod M.R.2 (maritime reconnaissance aircraft) . . . . 2·25 2·50
126   34p. Lockheed P-3 Orion (transport aircraft) 2·75 3·25
127   54p. U.S.A.A.F. Boeing B-52 Stratofortress (heavy bomber) . . . . 3·50 4·50
124/7 . . . . *Set of 4* 9·50 11·50

(Des D. Miller. Litho Walsall)

1992 (27 Nov). *Christmas. Religious Paintings. T **23** and similar vert designs. Multicoloured. W w 16. P 14½×14.*
128   5p. Type **23** 70 80
129   24p. "Madonna" (anon) . . 1·50 1·60
130   34p. "Madonna" (anon) (*different*) . . 1·75 2·00
131   54p. "The Birth of Jesus" (Kaspar Jele) 2·50 3·50
128/31 . . . . *Set of 4* 5·75 7·50

24 Coconut Crab and Rock

25 *Stachytarpheta urticifolia*

(Des G. Vasarhelyi. Litho Questa)

1993 (5 Mar). *Endangered Species. Coconut Crab. T* **24** *and similar horiz designs. Multicoloured. W* w **16** (*sideways*). *P* 14.

132	10p. Type 24	..	1·25	1·25
133	10p. Crab on beach	..	1·25	1·25
134	10p. Two crabs	..	1·25	1·25
135	15p. Crab climbing coconut tree		1·50	1·50
132/5		*Set of 4*	4·75	4·75

(Des A. Theobald. Litho Questa)

1993 (1 Apr). *75th Anniv of Royal Air Force. Horiz designs as T* **149** *of Ascension. Multicoloured. W* w **14** (*sideways*). *P* 14.

136	20p. Vickers Virginia Mk X		1·25	1·50
137	24p. Bristol Bulldog IIA		1·40	1·50
138	34p. Short S.25 Sunderland Mk III		1·75	2·00
139	54p. Bristol Type 142 Blenheim Mk IV		2·75	3·25
136/9		*Set of 4*	6·50	7·50

MS140 110×77 mm. 20p. Douglas DC-3 Dakota; 20p. Gloster G.41 Javelin; 20p. Blackburn Beverley C1; 20p. Vickers VC-10 .. .. 6·50 7·50

(Des N. Shewring. Litho Questa)

1993 (22 Nov). *Christmas. Flowers. T* **25** *and similar vert designs. Multicoloured. W* w **14**. *P* 14½.

141	20p. Type 25	..	1·25	1·50
142	24p. *Ipomea pes-caprae*	..	1·25	1·50
143	34p. *Sida pusilla*	..	1·50	2·25
144	54p. *Catharanthus roseus*	..	2·50	3·00
141/4		*Set of 4*	6·00	7·50

1994 (18 Feb). *"Hong Kong '94" International Stamp Exhibition. Nos. 92 and 101 optd as T* **154** *of Ascension.*

145	24p. Great Frigate Bird		1·50	1·50
146	£1 Madagascar Red Fody		3·00	4·50

26 Forrest's Map of Diego Garcia, 1778

27 *Junonia villida*

(Des D. Miller. Litho Questa)

1994 (1 June). *18th-century Maps. T* **26** *and similar vert designs. Each black and cobalt. W* w **14**. *P* 14½.

147	20p. Type 26	..	90	1·40
	a. Horiz strip of 5. Nos. 147/51		5·50	
148	24p. Blair's plan of Diego Garcia harbour, 1786–87		1·00	1·50
149	34p. Blair's chart of Chagos Archipelago, 1786–87		1·10	1·60
150	44p. Plan of part of Diego Garcia, 1774		1·40	1·75
151	54p. Fontaine's plan of Diego Garcia, 1770		1·60	1·90
147/51		*Set of 5*	5·50	7·25

Nos. 147/51 were printed together, *se-tenant*, in horizontal strips of 5 throughout the sheet.

(Des I. Loe. Litho Walsall)

1994 (16 Aug). *Butterflies. T* **27** *and similar vert designs. Multicoloured. W* w **16**. *P* 14½×14.

152	24p. Type 27	..	1·75	1·75
153	30p. *Petrelaea dana*	..	2·25	3·00
154	56p. *Hypolimnas misippus*	..	3·75	4·00
152/4		*Set of 3*	7·00	7·50

28 Short-tailed Nurse Sharks

(Des N. Shewring. Litho Walsall)

1994 (1 Nov). *Sharks. T* **28** *and similar horiz designs. Multicoloured. W* w **14** (*sideways*). *P* 14.

155	15p. Type 28	..	70	70
156	20p. Silver-tipped Sharks	..	80	80
157	24p. Black-finned Reef Shark		90	90
158	30p. Oceanic White-tipped Sharks		1·00	1·00

159	35p. Black-tipped Shark	..	1·25	1·25
160	41p. Smooth Hammerhead	..	1·40	1·40
161	46p. Sickle-finned Lemon Shark	..	1·40	1·40
162	55p. White-tipped Reef Shark	..	1·50	1·50
163	65p. Tiger Sharks	..	1·60	1·60
164	74p. Indian Sand Tiger	..	1·75	2·00
165	80p. Great Hammerhead	..	1·90	2·50
166	£1 Great White Shark	..	2·25	2·75
155/66		*Set of 12*	15·00	16·00

For miniature sheets containing the 65p. or 74p. (with "1997" imprint date) see Nos. **MS193/4**.

(Des R. Watton. Litho Walsall (Nos. 167/70) or Questa (No. **MS171**))

1995 (8 May). *50th Anniv of End of Second World War. Multicoloured designs as T* **161** *of Ascension. W* w **14** (*sideways*). *P* 14.

167	20p. Military cemetery		1·50	1·75
168	24p. Rusty 6-inch naval gun at Cannon Point		1·75	1·75
169	30p. Short S.25 Sunderland flying boat		2·00	2·25
170	56p. H.M.I.S. *Clive* (sloop)		3·00	3·75
167/70		*Set of 4*	7·50	8·50

MS171 75×85 mm. £1 Reverse of 1939–45 War Medal (*vert*). Wmk upright .. .. 2·50 3·00

29 Dolphin (fish)

30 *Terebra crenulata*

(Des K. McGee. Litho B.D.T.)

1995 (6 Oct). *Gamefish. T* **29** *and similar horiz designs. Multicoloured. W* w **16** (*sideways*). *P* 14.

172	20p. Type 29	..	1·25	1·50
173	24p. Sailfish	..	1·40	1·50
174	30p. Wahoo	..	2·00	2·25
175	56p. Striped Marlin	..	3·25	3·75
172/5		*Set of 4*	7·00	8·00

(Des G. Drummond. Litho Walsall)

1996 (8 Jan). *Sea Shells. T* **30** *and similar horiz designs. Multicoloured. W* w **14** (*sideways*). *P* 14½.

176	20p. Type 30	..	1·00	1·25
177	24p. *Bursa bufonia*	..	1·10	1·25
178	30p. *Nassarius papillosus*	..	1·75	1·90
179	56p. *Lopha cristagalli*	..	2·75	3·25
176/9		*Set of 4*	6·00	7·00

(Des D. Miller. Litho Walsall)

1996 (22 Apr). *70th Birthday of Queen Elizabeth II. Vert designs as T* **165** *of Ascension, each incorporating a different photograph of the Queen. Multicoloured. W* w **16**. *P* 14½.

180	20p. View of lagoon from south	..	60	80
181	24p. Manager's House, Peros Banhos		65	80
182	30p. Wireless Hut, Peros Banhos	..	80	1·25
183	56p. Sunset	..	1·25	1·75
180/3		*Set of 4*	3·00	4·25

MS184 64×66 mm. £1 Queen Elizabeth II 2·50 3·50

31 Loggerhead Turtle

32 Commissioner's Representative (naval officer)

(Des O. Bell. Litho Questa)

1996 (2 Sept). *Turtles. T* **31** *and similar horiz designs. Multicoloured. W* w **14** (*sideways*). *P* 14×14½.

185	20p. Type 31	..	80	90
186	24p. Leatherback Turtle	..	85	90
187	30p. Hawksbill Turtle	..	1·25	1·50
188	56p. Green Turtle	..	1·75	2·00
185/8		*Set of 4*	4·25	4·75

(Des R. Watton. Litho Questa)

1996 (16 Dec). *Uniforms. T* **32** *and similar vert designs. Multicoloured. W* w **14**. *P* 14.

189	20p. Type 32	..	90	1·00
190	24p. Royal Marine officer	..	95	1·00
191	30p. Royal Marine in battledress		1·40	1·60
192	56p. Police officers	..	2·00	2·25
189/92		*Set of 4*	4·75	5·25

(Des D. Miller. Litho Questa)

1997 (3 Feb). *"HONG KONG '97" International Stamp Exhibition. Sheet 130×90 mm, containing design as No. 163. Multicoloured. W* w **14**. *P* 14.

MS193 65p. Tiger Sharks .. .. 2·00 2·50

(Des N. Shewring. Litho Walsall)

1997 (20 June). *Return of Hong Kong to China. Sheet 130×90 mm containing design as No. 164, but with "1997" imprint date.*

MS194 74p. Indian Sand Tiger .. .. 2·75 3·50

(Des N. Shewring (No. MS201), D. Miller (others). Litho Questa)

1997 (10 July). *Golden Wedding of Queen Elizabeth and Prince Philip. Multicoloured designs as T* **173** *of Ascension. W* w **14**. *P* 14½.

195	20p. Queen Elizabeth at Bristol, 1994		80	1·00
	a. Horiz pair. Nos. 195/6		1·60	2·00
196	20p. Prince Philip competing in Royal Windsor Horse Show, 1996		80	1·00
197	24p. Queen Elizabeth in phaeton, Trooping the Colour, 1987		80	1·00
	a. Horiz pair. Nos. 197/8		1·60	2·00
198	24p. Prince Philip	..	80	1·00
199	30p. Queen Elizabeth and Prince Philip with Land Rover		90	1·25
	a. Horiz pair. Nos. 199/200		1·75	2·50
200	30p. Queen Elizabeth at Balmoral		90	1·25
195/200		*Set of 6*	4·50	6·00

MS201 110×71 mm. £1.50, Queen Elizabeth and Prince Philip in landau (*horiz*). Wmk sideways. P 14×14½ .. .. 4·00 5·00

Nos. 195/6, 197/8 and 199/200 were each printed together, *se-tenant*, in horizontal pairs throughout the sheets with the backgrounds forming composite designs.

33 H.M.S. *Richmond* (frigate) and H.M.S. *Beaver* (frigate)

(Litho Questa)

1997 (1 Dec). *Exercise Ocean Wave. T* **33** *and similar horiz designs. Multicoloured. W* w **14** (*sideways*). *P* 14×14½.

202	24p. Type 33	..	80	90
	a. Sheetlet. Nos. 202/13		8·50	
203	24p. H.M.S. *Illustrious* (aircraft carrier) launching aircraft		80	90
204	24p. H.M.S. *Beaver*	..	80	90
205	24p. Royal Yacht *Britannia*, R.F.A. *Sir Percival* and H.M.S. *Beaver*		80	90
206	24p. Royal Yacht *Britannia*		80	90
207	24p. H.M.S. *Richmond*, H.M.S. *Beaver* and H.M.S. *Gloucester* (destroyer)		80	90
208	24p. H.M.S. *Richmond*	..	80	90
209	24p. Aerial view of H.M.S. *Illustrious*		80	90
210	24p. H.M.S. *Gloucester*	..	80	90
211	24p. H.M.S. *Trenchant* (submarine) and R.F.A. *Diligence*		80	90
212	24p. R.F.A. *Fort George* replenishing H.M.S. *Illustrious* and H.M.S. *Gloucester*		80	90
213	24p. Aerial view of H.M.S. *Richmond*, H.M.S. *Beaver* and H.M.S. *Gloucester*		80	90
202/13		*Set of 12*	8·50	9·50

Nos. 202/13 were printed together, *se-tenant*, in sheetlets of 12.

No. 210 is inscribed "HMS Sheffield" in error.

(Des D. Miller. Litho Questa)

1998 (31 Mar). *Diana, Princess of Wales Commemoration. Sheet, 145×70 mm, containing vert designs as T* **177** *of Ascension. Multicoloured. W* w **14** (*sideways*). *P* 14½×14.

MS214 26p. Wearing patterned jacket, 1993; 26p. Wearing heart-shaped earrings, 1988; 34p. Wearing cream jacket, 1993; 60p. Wearing blue blouse, 1982 (*sold at £1.46 + 20p. charity premium*) .. .. 3·25 3·50

(Des A. Theobald. Litho Questa)

1998 (1 Apr). *80th Anniv of the Royal Air Force. Horiz designs as T* **178** *of Ascension. Multicoloured. W* w **16** (*sideways*). *P* 14.

215	26p. Blackburn Iris	..	1·00	1·10
216	34p. Gloster Gamecock	..	1·25	1·40
217	60p. North American Sabre F.4		2·25	2·50
218	80p. Avro Lincoln	..	2·75	3·00
215/18		*Set of 4*	6·50	7·25

MS219 110×77 mm. 34p. Sopwith Baby (seaplane); 34p. Martinsyde Elephant; 34p. De Havilland Tiger Moth; 34p. North American Mustang III .. .. 3·25 3·75

34 Bryde's Whale

(Des N. Shewring. Litho Walsall)

1998 (7 Dec). *International Year of the Ocean. T* **34** *and similar horiz designs. Multicoloured. W* w **14** (*sideways*). *P* 13½×14.

220	26p. Type 34	..	80	85
221	26p. Striped Dolphin	..	80	85
222	34p. Pilot Whale	..	90	95
223	34p. Spinner Dolphin	..	90	95
220/3		*Set of 4*	3·00	3·25

35 *Westminster* (East Indiaman), 1837

(Des J. Batchelor. Litho Walsall)

1999 (1 Feb). *Ships. T* **35** *and similar horiz designs. Multi-coloured. W w* **14** (*sideways*). *P* 13½×14.

224	2p. Type **35**	10	10
225	15p. *Sao Cristovao* (Spanish galleon), 1589	30	35
226	20p. *Sea Witch* (U.S. clipper), 1849	40	45
227	26p. H.M.S. *Royal George* (ship of the line), 1778	55	60
228	34p. *Cutty Sark* (clipper), 1883	70	75
229	60p. *Mentor* (East Indiaman), 1789	1·25	1·40
230	80p. H.M.S. *Trinculo* (brig), 1809	1·60	1·75
231	£1 *Enterprise* (paddle-steamer), 1825	2·00	2·10
232	£1.15, *Confiance* (French privateer), 1800	2·25	2·40
233	£2 *Kent* (East Indiaman), 1820	4·00	4·25
224/33	*Set of* 10	13·00	14·00

36 *Cutty Sark* (clipper)

(Des J. Batchelor. Litho Questa)

1999 (19 Mar). "*Australia '99*" *World Stamp Exhibition, Melbourne. Sheet* 150×75 *mm, containing T* **36** *and similar horiz design. Multicoloured. W w* **16** (*sideways*). *P* 13½×14.

MS234   60p. Type **36**; 60p. *Thermopylae* (clipper)   2·75   3·25

British Levant

The term "British Levant" is used by stamp collectors to describe the issues made by various British Post Offices within the former Turkish Empire.

Arrangements for the first such service were included amongst the terms of a commercial treaty between the two countries in 1832, but the system did not start operations until September 1857 when a post office for civilian use was opened in Constantinople, replacing the Army Post Office which had existed there since June 1854.

Eventually the number of British Post Offices grew to five:

Beyrout (Beirut, Lebanon). Opened 1873, closed 30 September 1914.

Constantinople (Istanbul). Opened 1 September 1857, closed 30 September 1914, re-opened 4 February 1919, finally closed 27 September 1923.

Salonica (Thessalonika, Greece). Opened 1 May 1900, closed October 1914. The city was captured by Greek troops on 7 November 1912 and incorporated into Greece by the Treaty of London (July 1913).

Smyrna (Izmir). Opened 1872, closed 30 September 1914, re-opened 1 March 1919, finally closed September 1922. Between 15 May 1919 and 8 September 1922 the city was under Greek occupation.

Stamboul (a sub-office of Constantinople). Opened 1 April 1884, closed 25 August 1896, re-opened 10 February 1908, finally closed 30 September 1914.

Stamps from the two British Post Offices in Egypt, still technically part of the Turkish Empire, are listed under EGYPT.

A. BRITISH POST OFFICES IN TURKISH EMPIRE, 1857–1914

For illustrations of the postmark types see BRITISH POST OFFICES ABROAD notes, following GREAT BRITAIN.

From 1 August 1885 letter and registered charges were prepaid with surcharged stamps (No. 1 onwards). Until 14 August 1905 postcards and parcels continued to be franked with unoverprinted Great Britain stamps. Only a limited range of values were stocked for this purpose and these are listed. Other values exist with Levant postmarks, but these stamps did not originate from the local post offices.

After 15 August 1905 the post offices were supplied with Great Britain stamps overprinted "LEVANT". Subsequent examples of unoverprinted stamps with Levant postmarks are omitted from the listing. The use of such stamps during 1919–22 at Constantinople and Smyrna is, however, covered by a later note.

BEYROUT (BEIRUT)

Between 1873 and 1876 much of the mail from the British Post Office in Beyrout sent to European addresses was forwarded through the French or Italian Post Offices at Alexandria. Such covers show Great Britain stamps used in combination with those of French or Italian P.O's in the Turkish Empire.

Stamps of GREAT BRITAIN cancelled "G 06" or circular postmark as in Types 8, 18 or 20.

1873.

Z 1	½d. rose-red (1870–79)				From	32·00
	Plate Nos. 12, 13, 14, 19, 20.					
Z 2	1d. rose-red (1864–79)				From	14·00
	Plate Nos. 107, 118, 130, 140, 145, 148, 155, 157, 162, 167, 177, 179, 180, 184, 185, 186, 187, 195, 198, 200, 203, 204, 211, 213, 215, 218, 220, 222.					
Z 3	1½d. lake-red (1870–74) (Plate 3)					£200
Z 4	2d. blue (1858–69)				From	19·00
	Plate Nos. 13, 14, 15.					
Z 5	2½d. rosy mauve (1875) (blued paper)					70·00
	Plate No. 1.					
Z 6	2½d. rosy mauve (1875–76)				From	30·00
	Plate Nos. 1, 2, 3.					
Z 7	2½d. rosy mauve (1876–79)				From	25·00
	Plate Nos. 3, 4, 5, 6, 7, 8, 9, 10, 11, 12, 13, 14, 15, 16, 17.					
Z 8	2½d. blue (1880)				From	15·00
	Plate Nos. 17, 18, 19, 20.					
Z 9	2½d. blue (1881)				From	11·00
	Plate Nos. 21, 22, 23.					
Z10	3d. rose (1867–73) (Plate No. 10)					
Z11	3d. rose (1873–76)					35·00
	Plate Nos. 12, 15, 16, 18, 19, 20.					
Z12	3d. rose (1881) (Plate Nos. 20, 21)					
Z13	4d. vermilion (1865–73)				From	35·00
	Plate Nos. 11, 12, 13, 14.					
Z14	4d. vermilion (1876) (Plate No. 15)					£180
Z15	4d. sage-green (1877)					£120
	Plate Nos. 15, 16.					
Z16	4d. grey-brown (1880) wmk Large Garter (Plate No. 17)					
Z17	4d. grey-brown (1880) wmk Crown					42·00
	Plate Nos. 17, 18.					
Z18	6d. mauve (1870) (Plate Nos. 8, 9)					
Z19	6d. buff (1872–79)				From	80·00
	Plate Nos. 11, 12.					
Z20	6d. chestnut (1872) (Plate No. 11)					40·00
Z21	6d. grey (1873) (Plate No. 12)					
Z22	6d. grey (1874–80)				From	28·00
	Plate Nos. 13, 14, 15, 16, 17.					
Z23	8d. orange (1876)					£300
Z24	10d. red-brown (1867)					£160
Z25	1s. green (1867–73)					27·00
	Plate Nos. 6, 7.					
Z26	1s. green (1873–77)				From	38·00
	Plate Nos. 8, 9, 10, 12, 13.					
Z27	1s. orange-brown (1880) (Plate No. 13)					
Z28	1s. orange-brown (1881)					50·00
	Plate Nos. 13, 14.					
Z29	2s. blue (1867)					£140
Z30	5s. rose (1867) (Plate Nos. 1, 2)				From	£600

1880.

Z31	½d. deep green					9·00
Z32	½d. pale green					10·00
Z33	1d. Venetian red					11·00
Z34	1½d. Venetian red					£140
Z35	2d. pale rose					42·00
Z36	2d. deep rose					42·00
Z37	5d. indigo					70·00

1881.

Z38	1d. lilac (14 dots)					
Z39	1d. lilac (16 dots)					5·50

1884.

Z40	½d. slate-blue					11·00
Z41	1½d. lilac					65·00
Z42	2d. lilac					60·00
Z43	2½d. lilac					11·00
Z44	4d. dull green					£150
Z45	5d. dull green					£100
Z46	1s. dull green					£200

1887–92.

Z47	½d. vermilion					5·50
Z54	6d. purple/rose-red					18·00
Z55	1s. dull green					£110

1900.

Z56	½d. blue-green					8·50
Z57	1s. green and carmine					£140

1902–04. De La Rue ptgs.

Z58	½d. blue-green					4·50
Z59	½d. yellowish green					5·00
Z60	1d. scarlet					4·00
Z64	1s. dull green and carmine					27·00

CONSTANTINOPLE

Stamps of GREAT BRITAIN cancelled "C" or circular postmark as in Types 1, 10, 18 or 19.

1857.

Z 68	½d. rose-red (1870–79)			From	22·00
	Plate Nos. 5, 6, 10, 11, 12, 13, 14, 15, 20.				
Z 69	1d. red-brown (1854), Die I, wmk Small Crown, perf 16				
Z 70	1d. red-brown (1855), Die II, wmk Small Crown, perf 14				
Z 71	1d. red-brown, (1855), Die II, wmk Large Crown, perf 14				17·00
Z 72	1d. rose-red (1857)				6·50
Z 73	1d. rose-red (1861) Alphabet IV				
Z 74	1d. rose-red (1864–79)			From	7·00
	Plate Nos. 71, 72, 73, 74, 76, 78, 79, 80, 81, 83, 85, 87, 89, 90, 92, 93, 94, 95, 96, 97, 99, 101, 102, 105, 106, 108, 109, 110, 113, 116, 118, 119, 120, 121, 122, 123, 124, 125, 127, 129, 130, 131, 134, 135, 136, 137, 138, 140, 141, 143, 144, 145, 146, 147, 148, 149, 150, 151, 152, 155, 156, 157, 158, 159, 160, 161, 162, 163, 164, 165, 166, 167, 170, 171, 172, 173, 174, 175, 176, 177, 178, 179, 180, 181, 183, 184, 186, 187, 188, 189, 190, 191, 192, 193, 194, 195, 196, 197, 198, 199, 201, 203, 204, 205, 206, 207, 208, 210, 212, 214, 215, 216, 220, 222, 224.				
Z 75	1½d. rose-red (1870) (Plate 1)				£180
Z 76	2d. blue (1855), wmk Large Crown, perf 14. (Plate Nos. 5, 6)				
Z 77	2d. blue (1858–69)			From	10·00
	Plate Nos. 7, 8, 9, 12, 13, 14, 15.				
Z 78	2½d. rosy mauve (1875–76) (blued paper) (Plate Nos. 1, 2)			From	50·00
Z 79	2½d. rosy mauve (1875–76)			From	27·00
	Plate Nos. 1, 2, 3.				
Z 80	2½d. rosy mauve (Error of Lettering)				
Z 81	2½d. rosy mauve (1876–79)			From	23·00
	Plate Nos. 3 to 17.				
Z 82	2½d. blue (1880–81)			From	11·00
	Plate Nos. 17, 18, 19, 20.				
Z 83	2½d. blue (1881) (Plate Nos. 21, 22, 23)				7·50
Z 84	3d. carmine-rose (1862) (Plate No. 2)				£110
Z 85	3d. rose (1865) (Plate No. 4)				65·00
Z 86	3d. rose (1867–73) (Plate Nos. 4 to 10)				65·00
Z 87	3d. rose (1873–76)				20·00
	Plates, 11, 12, 15, 16, 17, 18, 19.				
Z 88	3d. rose (1881) (Plate No. 21)				
Z 89	3d. on 3d. lilac (1883) (Plate No. 21)				
Z 90	4d. rose (1857)				40·00
	a. Rose-carmine				
Z 91	4d. red (1862) (Plate No. 3, 4)			From	35·00
Z 92	4d. vermilion (1865–73)			From	26·00
	Plate Nos. 7 to 14.				
Z 93	4d. vermilion (1876) (Plate No. 15)				£150
Z 94	4d. sage-green (1877)				90·00
	Plate Nos. 15, 16.				
Z 95	4d. grey-brown (1880) wmk Large Garter (Plate No. 17)				
Z 96	4d. grey-brown (1880) wmk Crown (Plate Nos. 17, 18)			From	30·00
Z 97	6d. lilac (1856)				50·00
Z 98	6d. lilac (1862) (Plate Nos. 3, 4)			From	35·00
Z 99	6d. lilac (1865–67)				32·00
	Plate Nos. 5, 6.				
Z100	6d. lilac (1867) (Plate No. 6)				40·00
Z101	6d. violet (1867–70)			From	32·00
	Plate Nos. 6, 8, 9.				
Z102	6d. buff (1872–79)				48·00
	Plate Nos. 11, 12.				
Z103	6d. chestnut (1872) (Plate No. 11)				28·00
Z104	6d. grey (1873) (Plate No. 12)				75·00
Z105	6d. grey (1874–76)			From	22·00
	Plate Nos. 13, 14, 15, 16.				
Z106	6d. grey (1881–82) (Plate Nos. 17, 18)				24·00
Z107	6d. on 6d. lilac (1883)				65·00
	a. Dots slanting (Letters MI or SJ)				£110

Z108	8d. orange (1876)					£275
Z109	10d. red-brown (1867), wmk Emblems					£13000
Z110	10d. red-brown (1867)					£160
Z111	1s. green (1856)					£100
Z112	1s. green (1862)					60·00
Z113	1s. green (1862) ("K" variety)					
Z114	1s. green (1862) (thick paper)					
Z115	1s. green (1865) (Plate No. 4)					60·00
Z116	1s. green (1867–73)				From	14·00
	Plate Nos. 4, 5, 6, 7.					
Z117	1s. green (1873–77)				From	26·00
	Plate Nos. 8, 9, 10, 11, 12, 13.					
Z118	1s. orange-brown (1880) (Plate No. 13)					£180
Z119	1s. orange-brown (1881)					42·00
	Plate Nos. 13, 14.					
Z120	2s. blue (1867)					85·00
Z121	5s. rose (1867–74)				From	£250
	Plate Nos. 1, 2.					
Z122	5s. rose (1882) (white paper)					£850
Z123	5s. rose (1882) (blued paper)					£1000

1880.

Z124	½d. deep green					6·00
Z125	½d. pale green					7·00
Z126	1d. Venetian red					6·00
Z127	2d. pale rose					35·00
Z128	2d. deep rose					35·00
Z129	5d. indigo					

1881.

Z130	1d. lilac (14 dots)					
Z131	1d. lilac (16 dots)					2·25

1883–84.

Z132	½d. slate-blue					6·00
Z133	1½d. lilac					
Z134	2d. lilac					50·00
Z135	2½d. lilac					7·00
Z136	3d. lilac					
Z137	4d. dull green					
Z138	5d. dull green					90·00
Z139	6d. dull green					
Z140	9d. dull green					
Z141	1s. dull green					£170
Z142	2s. 6d. lilac (blued paper)					£500
Z143	2s. 6d. lilac (white paper)					80·00
Z144	5s. rose (blued paper)					
Z145	5s. rose (white paper)					

1887–92.

Z146	½d. vermilion					2·50
Z154	6d. purple/rose-red					10·00
Z157	1s. dull green					70·00

1900.

Z158	½d. blue-green					4·00
Z159	1s. green and carmine					£130

1902–04. De La Rue ptgs.

Z160	½d. blue-green					3·00
Z161	½d. yellowish green					3·50
Z162	1d. scarlet					2·50
Z169	6d. purple					11·00
Z172	1s. green and carmine					17·00
Z173	2s. 6d. lilac					
Z174	5s. carmine					

POSTAL FISCALS

Z175	1d. purple (wmk Anchor) (1868)					
Z176	1d. purple (wmk Orb) (1881)					£600

SALONICA

Stamps of GREAT BRITAIN cancelled with circular postmark as in Type 18 or double-circle datestamp.

1900.

Z202	½d. vermilion (1887)					15·00
Z203	½d. blue-green (1900)					17·00
Z204	1d. lilac (1881)					17·00
Z205	6d. purple/red (1887)					22·00
Z206	1s. green and carmine (1900)					£140
Z207	5s. rose (white paper) (1883)					£700

1902.

Z208	½d. blue-green					21·00
Z209	½d. yellow-green					15·00
Z209a	1d. scarlet					15·00
Z209c	1s. green and carmine					38·00

SMYRNA (IZMIR)

Stamps of GREAT BRITAIN cancelled "F 87" or circular postmark as in Type 8, 16 or 18.

1872.

Z210	½d. rose-red (1870–79)				From	25·00
	Plates 11, 12, 13, 14, 15.					
Z211	1d. rose-red (1864–79)				From	11·00
	Plate Nos. 120, 124, 134, 137, 138, 139, 140, 142, 143, 145, 146, 148, 149, 150, 151, 152, 153, 155, 156, 157, 158, 159, 160, 161, 162, 163, 164, 166, 167, 168, 169, 170, 171, 172, 173, 174, 175, 176, 177, 178, 183, 184, 185, 186, 187, 188, 191, 193, 195, 196, 198, 200, 201, 204, 210, 212, 215, 217, 218.					
Z212	1½d. lake-red (1870–74) (Plate Nos. 1, 3)			From	£200
Z213	2d. blue (1858) wmk Large Crown, perf 16				
Z214	2d. blue (1858–69)				From	14·00
	Plate Nos. 13, 14, 15.					
Z215	2½d. rosy mauve (1875) (blued paper)					55·00
	Plate No. 1.					
Z216	2½d. rosy mauve (1875–76)				From	26·00
	Plate Nos. 1, 2, 3.					
Z217	2½d. rosy mauve (Error of lettering)					
Z218	2½d. rosy mauve (1876–79)				From	22·00
	Plate Nos. 3, 4, 5, 6, 7, 8, 9, 10, 11, 12, 13, 14, 15, 16, 17.					
Z219	2½d. blue (1880)				From	11·00
	Plate Nos. 17, 18, 19, 20.					

Z220	2½d. blue (1881) ..		9·00
	Plate Nos. 21, 22, 23.		
Z221	3d. rose (1867–73)		30·00
	Plate Nos. 5, 7, 9, 10.		
Z222	3d. rose (1873–76) (Plate No. 14)		
Z223	4d. vermilion (1865–73)		26·00
	Plate Nos. 12, 13, 14.		
Z224	4d. vermilion (1876) (Plate No. 15)		£150
Z225	4d. sage-green (1877)		90·00
	Plate Nos. 15, 16.		
Z226	4d. grey-brown (1880) wmk Large Garter		
	(Plate No. 17)		
Z227	4d. grey-brown (1880) wmk Crown (Plate Nos.		
	17, 18)	From	28·00
Z228	6d. buff (1872–73)	From	70·00
	Plate Nos. 11, 12.		
Z229	6d. chestnut (1872) (Plate No. 11)		
Z230	6d. grey (1873) (Plate No. 12)		75·00
Z231	6d. grey (1874–80)	From	25·00
	Plate Nos. 13, 14, 15, 16, 17.		
Z232	6d. grey (1881–82) (Plate Nos. 17, 18)		50·00
Z233	6d. on 6d. lilac (1883)		75·00
Z234	8d. orange (1876)		
Z235	9d. straw (1867)		£190
Z236	10d. red-brown (1867)		£130
Z237	1s. green (1867–73) (Plate Nos. 6, 7)		
Z238	1s. green (1873–77)	From	28·00
	Plate Nos. 8, 9, 10, 11, 12, 13.		
Z239	1s. orange-brown (1880) (Plate No. 13)		£160
Z240	1s. orange-brown (1881) (Plate Nos. 13, 14)		42·00
Z241	5s. rose (1867–74) (Plate No. 2)		

1880.

Z242	½d. deep green ..		6·50
Z243	½d. pale green ..		7·50
Z244	1d. Venetian red		10·00
Z245	1½d. Venetian red		70·00
Z246	2d. pale rose		32·00
Z247	2d. deep rose		32·00
Z248	5d. indigo		50·00

1881.

Z249	1d. lilac (16 dots)		4·25

1884.

Z250	½d. slate-blue		9·00
Z251	2d. lilac		60·00
Z252	2½d. lilac		10·00
Z253	4d. dull green		
Z254	5d. dull green		£100
Z255	1s. dull green		£190

1887.

Z256	½d. vermilion		4·75
Z263	6d. purple/rose-red		16·00
Z264	1s. dull green		£100

1900.

Z265	½d. blue-green		7·00
Z266	1s. green and carmine		

1902–04. De La Rue ptgs.

Z267	½d. blue-green		4·25
Z268	½d. yellowish green		4·75
Z269	1d. scarlet		3·75
Z276	6d. purple		12·00
Z279	1s. green and carmine		22·00
Z280	2s. 6d. purple		
Z281	5s. carmine		

STAMBOUL (CONSTANTINOPLE)

Stamps of GREAT BRITAIN *cancelled* "S" *as Type* 10, *or circular postmarks inscribed either* "BRITISH POST OFFICE CONSTANTINOPLE S" *or* "BRITISH POST OFFICE STAMBOUL" *as Type* 18.

1884.

Z296	½d. slate-blue		17·00
Z297	1d. lilac		8·00
Z298	2d. lilac		
Z299	2½d. lilac		11·00
Z300	5d. dull green		£100

1887–92.

Z306	½d. vermilion		8·00
Z314	6d. purple/rose-red		25·00
Z317	1s. dull green		

The "S" cancellation was in use from 1885 to 1891 and the "Stamboul" mark from 1892 to 1896, when the office was closed, and from its reopening in 1908 to 1914. The "CONSTANTINOPLE S" handstamp was normally used as a back stamp, but can be found cancelling stamps in the period 1885 to 1892.

PRICES FOR STAMPS ON COVER	
Nos. 1/3a	from × 8
Nos. 4/6a	from × 5
Nos. 7/40	from × 3
Nos. L1/10	from × 6
Nos. L11/17	from × 3

I. TURKISH CURRENCY

(40 paras = 1 piastre)

Following the depreciation of the Turkish piastre against sterling it was decided to issue stamps surcharged in Turkish currency to avoid speculation. During the early period unsurcharged stamps of Great Britain remained on sale from the British Post Offices at the current rate of exchange until replaced by "LEVANT" overprints.

80 PARAS 4 PIASTRES 12 PIASTRES
(1)   (2)   (3)

PRINTERS. Nos. 1/24 were surcharged or overprinted by De La Rue, *unless otherwise stated.*

Stamps of Great Britain (Queen Victoria) surch as T 1 to 3

1885 (1 Aug)–88.

1	64	40 pa. on 2½d. lilac		85·00	1·25
2	62	80 pa. on 5d. green		£180	9·50
3	58	12 pi. on 2s. 6d. lilac/*bluish*		£275	£200
		a. On white paper (4.88)		42·00	22·00

1887 (June)–96.

4	74	40 pa. on 2½d. purple/*blue*		2·25	10
		a. Surch double		£1900	£2500
5	78	80 pa. on 5d. purple and blue (7.90)		12·00	30
		a. Small "0" in "80"		£150	85·00
		w. Wmk inverted		†	£500
6	81	4 pi. on 10d. dull purple & carm (10.10.96)		38·00	8·00
		a. Dull purple and deep bright carmine		38·00	11·00
		b. Large, wide "4" (R. 1/2, 1/4)		£120	55·00

No. 5a first appeared on the June 1895 printing when the size of the surcharge plate was increased from 60 to 120. On the Victorian stamp the variety comes on R. 4/1 and 4/7. The same setting was used for the first printing of the Edward VII surcharge, but here the sheet size was further increased to 240 so that No. 9a occurs on R. 4/1, 4/7, 14/1 and 14/7.

1893 (25 Feb). *Roughly handstamped at Constantinople, as T 1.*

7	71	40 pa. on ½d. vermilion		£425	£100

This provisional was in use for five days only at the Constantinople and Stamboul offices. As fraudulent copies were made with the original handstamp, and can be found "used" on piece cancelled by fraudulent use of the usual canceller, this stamp should only be purchased from undoubted sources.

The handstamp became damaged during use so that by 1 March the top of the "S" was broken. Used examples dated 25 or 26 February showing the broken "S" *must* be fraudulent. It is also known with genuine handstamp inverted (*Price £800 unused, £300 used*).

1902–5. *Stamps of King Edward VII surch as T 1 to 3.*

8	86	40 pa. on 2½d. ultramarine (3.02)		10·00	10
		a. Pale ultramarine		11·00	10
		ab. Surch double		†	£2000
9	89	80 pa. on 5d. dull purple & ultram (5.6.02)		3·75	2·50
		a. Small "0" in "80"		£180	£190
10	92	4 pi. on 10d. dull purple & carm (6.9.02)		9·00	4·00
		a. No cross on crown		90·00	90·00
		b. Chalk-surfaced paper		6·00	9·00
		ba. Chalk-surfaced paper. No cross on crown		85·00	£100
11	94	12 pi. on 2s. 6d. lilac (29.8.03)		35·00	35·00
		a. Chalk-surfaced paper. Pale dull pur		70·00	75·00
		b. Chalk-surfaced paper. Dull purple		35·00	35·00
12	95	24 pi. on 5s. bright carmine (15.8.05)		32·00	40·00
			Set of 5	75·00	70·00
8/12			*Set of 5*	75·00	70·00
9/11		Optd "Specimen"	*Set of 3*	£150	

No. 9a only occurs on the first printing of 80 pa. on 5d.

1 PIASTRE
(4)

1905–08. *Surch in* "PIASTRES" *instead of* "PARAS" *as T 4 and 2.*

13	86	1 pi. on 2½d. ultramarine (17.4.06)		9·00	10
		a. Surch double		†	£1300
14	89	2 pi. on 5d. dull purple & ultram (11.11.05)		21·00	2·50
		a. Chalk-surfaced paper (1.08)		18·00	1·75
		ab. Slate-purple and ultramarine		22·00	6·50

1 PIASTRE
1 PIASTRE 10 PARAS
(5)   (6)

1906 (2 July). *Issued at Beyrout. No. L4 surch with T 5 by American Press, Beyrout.*

15	85	1 pi. on 2d. grey-green and carmine		£1300	£600

1909 (16 Nov–Dec). *Stamps of King Edward VII surch as T 1 (30 pa.),* **6,** *and* **2** *(5 pi.). Ordinary paper (No. 19) or chalk-surfaced paper (others).*

16	84	30 pa. on 1½d. pale dull purple and green		9·00	1·25
		a. Surch double, one albino			
17	87	1 pi. 10 pa. on 3d. dull purple/*orange-yell*		12·00	12·00
18	88	1 pi. 30 pa. on 4d. green & chocolate-brn		5·00	17·00
19		1 pi. 30 pa. on 4d. pale orange (16.12.09)		15·00	42·00
20	83	2 pi. 20 pa. on 6d. dull purple		16·00	50·00
21	93	5 pi. on 1s. dull grn & carm (Optd S. £60)		3·75	8·00
16/21			*Set of 6*	55·00	£130

1¾ PIASTRE 4 4
(7)   Normal "4"   Pointed "4"

1910 (24 Jan). *Stamps of King Edward VII surch as T 7. Chalk-surfaced paper (Nos. 22 and 24).*

22	87	1¼ pi. on 3d. dull purple/*orange-yellow*		40	1·00
23	88	1¾ pi. on 4d. pale orange		40	60
		a. Orange-red		4·50	5·50
		b. Thin, pointed "4" in fraction		5·50	26·00
24	83	2½ pi. on 6d. dull purple		1·10	65
22/4			*Set of 3*	1·75	2·00

No. 23b occurs in the first and seventh vertical rows of the sheet. The variety also occurs on No. 38, but not on No. 38b.

1 PIASTRE 1 PIASTRE
(8)   (9)

TYPE DIFFERENCES. In T 4 the letters are tall and narrow and the space enclosed by the upper part of the "A" is small.

In T 8 the opening of the "A" is similar but the letters are shorter and broader, the "P" and the "E" being particularly noticeable.

In T 9 the letters are short and broad, but the "A" is thin and open.

1911–13. *Stamps of King Edward VII, Harrison or Somerset House ptgs, surch at Somerset House.*

(a) Surch with T 4 (20 July)

25	86	1 pi. on 2½d. bright blue (*perf 14*)		12·00	7·00
		a. Surch double, one albino		£200	
26		1 pi. on 2½d. bright blue (*perf 15×14*) (14.10.11)		9·00	2·50
		a. Dull blue		8·50	2·00

(b) Surch with T 8

27	86	1 pi. on 2½d. bright blue (*perf 15×14*) (3.12)		11·00	2·00
		a. Dull blue		18·00	3·25

(c) Surch with T 9 (7.12)

28	86	1 pi. on 2½d. bright blue (*perf 15×14*)		55·00	45
		a. Dull blue		55·00	45

(d) Surch with T 1 to 3 (1911–13)

29	84	30 pa. on 1½d. reddish purple and bright green (22.8.11)		5·00	55
		a. Slate-purple and green		9·00	2·25
		b. Surch double, one albino		50·00	
30	89	2 pi. on 5d. dull reddish purple and bright blue (13.5.12)		7·50	1·50
		a. Deep dull reddish purple and bright blue		8·50	2·00
31	92	4 pi. on 10d. dull purple & scar (26.6.12)		25·00	10·00
		a. Dull reddish purple & aniline pink		£150	70·00
		b. Dull reddish purple and carmine		10·00	11·00
		c. No cross on crown			
32	93	5 pi. on 1s. green and carmine (1913)		21·00	5·00
		a. Surch double, one albino		£200	
33	94	12 pi. on 2s. 6d. dull reddish pur (3.2.12)		50·00	35·00
		a. Dull greyish purple		50·00	35·00
34	95	24 pi. on 5s. carmine (1913)		55·00	75·00
		a. Surch double, one albino		£225	
29/34			*Set of 6*	£130	£110

1913 (Apr)–14. *Stamps of King George V, wmk Royal Cypher, surch as T 1 (30 pa.),* **9** *(1 pi.),* **7** *or* **2** *(4 and 5 pi.).*

35	105	30 pa. on 1½d. red-brown (4.13)		3·00	12·00
		a. Surch double, one albino		£100	
36	104	1 pi. on 2½d. cobalt-blue (6.13)		3·50	10
		a. Bright blue		2·00	15
37	106	1¼ pi. on 3d. dull reddish violet (9.13)		3·50	4·50
		a. Violet		4·00	5·50
		b. Surch double, one albino		£300	
38		1¾ pi. on 4d. deep grey-green (7.13)		3·00	6·00
		a. Thin, pointed "4" in fraction		45·00	80·00
		b. Grey-green		3·00	5·00
39	108	4 pi. on 10d. turquoise-blue (12.13)		7·00	15·00
40		5 pi. on 1s. bistre-brown (1.14)		35·00	50·00
35/40			*Set of 6*	48·00	75·00

II. BRITISH CURRENCY

Stamps overprinted "LEVANT" were for use on parcels, with the ½d. and 1d. principally used for printed paper and post cards. They replaced unoverprinted Great Britain stamps, Nos. Z58/64, Z160/74, Z208/9c and Z267/81, which had previously been used for these purposes.

From October 1907 the three lowest values were also used for certain other amended postal rates until Nos. 16/21 were introduced.

LEVANT
(L 1)

1905 (15 Aug)–12. *Stamps of King Edward VII optd with Type L 1.*

(a) De La Rue ptgs

L 1	83	½d. pale yellowish green		6·50	15
		a. Yellowish green		6·50	15
L 2		1d. scarlet		4·75	15
		a. Bright scarlet		4·75	90
L 3	84	1½d. dull purple and green		4·50	1·50
		a. Chalk-surfaced paper. Pale dull purple and green		12·00	2·50
L 4	85	2d. grey-green and carmine-red		3·00	20·00
		a. Chalk-surfaced paper. Pale grey-green and carmine-red		2·00	6·00
		ab. Dull blue-green and carmine		3·00	7·00
L 5	86	2½d. ultramarine		7·50	18·00
L 6	87	3d. dull purple/*orange-yellow*		5·50	11·00
L 7	88	4d. green and grey-brown		7·00	27·00
		a. Green and chocolate-brown		14·00	30·00
L 8	89	5d. dull purple and ultramarine		14·00	25·00
L 9	83	6d. pale dull purple		11·00	25·00
L10	93	1s. dull green and carmine		32·00	45·00
		a. Chalk-surfaced paper		32·00	45·00
L1/10			*Set of 10*	85·00	£140

(b) Harrison ptgs optd at Somerset House

L11	83	½d. dull yellow-green (p. 14) (2.12)		19·00	17·00
		a. Dull green		19·00	17·00
		b. Deep dull green		22·00	18·00

On 28 December 1909 all values, except for the ½d. and 1d. were withdrawn from sale. A further consignment of the 2d., No. L4ab, probably ordered in error was, however, received, and, as there was no requirement for this value, sold mainly to collectors. Subsequently dated cancellations on the withdrawn values are philatelic, being worth much less than the used prices quoted.

Distorted "N" (R. 2/10, 12/10)

1911–13. *Stamps of King George V optd with Type* L 1 *at Somerset House.* (a) *Die A. Wmk Crown.*

L12	98	½d. green (No. 322) (12.9.11)	..	40	90
		a. Distorted "N"	..	17·00	
L13	99	1d. carmine-red (No. 327) (1.1.12)		40	3·75
		a. No cross on crown	..	£150	
		b. Opt double, one albino	..	£100	
		c. Distorted "N"	..	17·00	

(b) *Redrawn types. Wmk Crown.*

L14	101	½d. green (No. 339) (19.3.12)	..	25	10
		a. Yellow-green	..	70	15
		b. Distorted "N"	..	13·00	
L15	102	1d. bright scarlet (No. 341) (24.2.12)		25	1·10
		a. Scarlet (No. 342)	..	1·50	1·10
		b. Opt triple, two albino	..	40·00	
		c. Distorted "N"	..	13·00	

(c) *New types. Wmk Royal Cypher* (7.13)

L16	105	½d. green (No. 351)	..	15	30
		a. Yellow-green	..	30	90
		b. Distorted "N"	..	11·00	
L17	104	1d. scarlet (No. 357)	..	15	3·75
		a. Vermilion	..	5·50	8·00
		b. Distorted "N"	..	11·00	

Similar overprints were issued when the British Post Offices reopened in 1919, and are listed below.

B. BRITISH POST OFFICES IN CONSTANTINOPLE AND SMYRNA, 1919–1923

CONSTANTINOPLE

Following the occupation of Constantinople by Allied forces a British Military Post Office was opened for civilian use on 4 February 1919. During the period of its existence stamps of Great Britain with face values to 10s. were available and such use can be identified by the following cancellations:

"FIELD POST OFFICE H12" (4 February 1919 to 18 March 1919)
"ARMY POST OFFICE Y" (20 March 1919 to May 1920)
"ARMY POST OFFICE S.X.3" (April 1919 to August 1920)
"BRITISH A.P.O. CONSTANTINOPLE" (5 July 1919 to 1 Sept 1920)
Of these four marks the first two types were also used for military mail.

The office reverted to civilian control in July 1920, Nos. 41/50 and L18/24 being intended for its use.

Z 1   Z 2

Z 3   Z 4

1919–20. *Used at the Army Post Office. Stamps of* GREAT BRITAIN *cancelled with Types* Z 1, Z 2, Z 3, Z 4.

Z176	½d. green	..	2·00
Z177	1d. scarlet	..	2·00
Z178	1½d. brown	..	3·25
Z179	2d. orange (Die I)	..	2·50
Z180	2½d. blue	..	4·00
Z181	3d. grey-green	..	8·50
Z182	6d. purple	..	4·50
Z183	9d. agate	..	22·00
Z184	1s. bistre	..	5·50
Z185	2s. 6d. brown	..	32·00
Z186	5s. rose-red	..	50·00
Z187	10s. dull grey-blue	..	90·00

1920–21. *Used at the Civilian Post Office. Stamps of* GREAT BRITAIN *cancelled with Type* 18 *or double-circle datestamp.*

Z188	½d. green	..	2·00
Z189	1d. scarlet	..	2·00
Z190	1½d. brown	..	3·25
Z191	2d. orange (Die I)	..	2·50
Z192	2½d. blue	..	4·00
Z193	3d. violet	..	6·50
Z194	4d. grey-green	..	8·50
Z195	5d. brown	..	13·00
Z196	6d. purple	..	4·50
Z197	10d. turquoise-blue	..	22·00
Z198	1s. bistre	..	5·50
Z199	2s. 6d. brown	..	32·00
Z200	5s. rose-red	..	50·00
Z201	10s. dull grey-blue	..	90·00

Stamps of Great Britain surch at Somerset House

I. TURKISH CURRENCY

1½ PIASTRES (10)   **15 PIASTRES** (11)

18¾

Short hyphen bar
(R. 4/12, 14/12.)

1921 (Aug). *Stamps of King George V, wmk Royal Cypher, surch as* T 1 (30 pa.), **10** (15 and 18¾ pi.).

41	105	30 pa. on ½d. green	..	60	9·00
		a. Yellow-green	..	2·50	11·00
42	104	1½ pi. on 1d. bright scarlet	..	1·50	50
		a. Vermilion	..	4·50	2·50
		b. Scarlet-vermilion	..	4·25	3·00
43		3¾ pi. on 2½d. blue	..	1·00	25
		a. Dull Prussian blue	..	20·00	2·75
44	106	4½ pi. on 3d. violet	..	2·00	3·75
		a. Bluish violet	..	2·50	3·00
45	107	7½ pi. on 5d. brown	..	30	10
		a. Yellow-brown	..	1·75	20
46	108	15 pi. on 10d. turquoise-blue	..	55	15
47		18¾ pi. on 1s. bistre-brown	..	3·75	3·75
		a. Short hyphen bar	..	50·00	
		b. Olive-bistre	..	5·00	4·50
		ba. Short hyphen bar	..	65·00	

45 PIASTRES (12)   **45** Joined figures (second stamp in each horiz row)

1921. *Stamps of King George V (Bradbury, Wilkinson printing) surch as* T **12**.

48	109	45 pi. on 2s. 6d. chocolate-brown	..	20·00	45·00
		a. Joined figures	..	32·00	60·00
		b. Olive-brown	..	48·00	60·00
		ba. Joined figures	..	65·00	80·00
49		90 pi. on 5s. rose-red	..	25·00	30·00
		a. Surch double, one albino	..	£225	
50		180 pi. on 10s. dull grey-blue	..	45·00	40·00
		a. Surch double, one albino	..	£225	
41/50			*Set of 10*	90·00	£120
47/50	Optd "Specimen"		*Set of 4*	£250	

II. BRITISH CURRENCY

1921. *Stamps of King George V optd as Type* L 1.

L18	106	2d. reddish orange (Die I)	..	1·25	25·00
		a. Bright orange	..	2·00	25·00
L19		3d. bluish violet	..	7·50	10·00
L20		4d. grey-green..	..	4·50	13·00
L21	107	5d. yellow-brown	..	11·00	26·00
L22		6d. dull purple (*chalk-surfaced paper*)		22·00	38·00
		a. Reddish purple	..	22·00	8·50
L23	108	1s. bistre-brown (Optd S. £65)		11·00	7·50
		a. Olive-bistre	..	11·00	7·50
L24	109	2s. 6d. chocolate-brown (Optd S. £130)		35·00	80·00
		a. Olive-brown	..	65·00	£120
L18/24			*Set of 7*	80·00	£150

On No. L24 the letters of the overprint are shorter, being only 3 mm high.

Nos. 41/50 and L18/24 were used at the Constantinople office only.

SMYRNA

When the office re-opened on 1 March 1919 existing stocks of surcharged or overprinted issues were utilised until they were exhausted in mid-1920. During this period examples of Nos. 24, 29a, 30a, 33b/7, 39/40, L4b, L14/17 are known with commercial postmarks. These stamps were supplemented and finally replaced in mid-1920 by ordinary stamps of Great Britain.

Stamps of GREAT BRITAIN *cancelled with circular postmark as Type* 18 *or with* "REGISTERED" *oval.*

Z282	½d. green	..	2·50
Z283	1d. scarlet	..	2·50
Z284	1½d. brown	..	3·50
Z285	2d. orange (Die I)	..	3·00
Z286	2d. orange (Die II)	..	25·00
Z287	2½d. blue (*shades*)	..	5·00
Z288	2½d. dull Prussian blue	..	£375
Z289	4d. grey-green	..	11·00
Z290	6d. purple	..	8·00
Z291	10d. turquoise-blue	..	29·00
Z292	1s. bistre	..	8·50
Z293	2s. 6d. brown	..	60·00
Z294	5s. rose-red	..	85·00
Z295	10s. dull grey-blue	..	£130

MINIMUM PRICE

The minimum price quote is 10p which represents a handling charge rather than a basis for valuing common stamps. For further notes about prices see introductory pages.

C. BRITISH FIELD OFFICE IN SALONICA

These overprints were originally prepared for use by a civilian post office to be set up on Mt Athos, Northern Greece. When the project was abandoned they were placed on sale at the Army Field Office in Salonica.

Levant
(S 1)

1916 (end Feb–9 Mar). *Stamps of Gt. Britain, optd with Type* S 1 *by Army Printing Office, Salonica.*

S 1	105	½d. green	..	32·00	£170
		a. Opt double	..	£1800	£2250
		b. Vert pair, one without opt	..	£900	£1200
S 2	104	1d. scarlet	..	32·00	£170
		a. Opt double	..	£1200	£1500
S 3	106	2d. reddish orange (Die I)		£120	£300
S 4		3d. bluish violet	..	90·00	£300
		a. Opt double	..		
S 5		4d. grey-green	..	£120	£300
S 6	107	6d. reddish pur (*chalk-surfaced paper*)		70·00	£250
		a. Vert pair, one without opt	..	£1000	£1400
S 7	108	9d. agate	..	£275	£500
		a. Opt double	..	£8000	£6500
S 8		1s. bistre-brown	..	£225	£450
S1/8			*Set of 8*	£850	£2000

There are numerous forgeries of this overprint.
All values can be found with an additional albino overprint, inverted on the gummed side.

British New Guinea
see Papua New Guinea

British Occupation of Iraq
see Iraq

British Occupation of Italian Colonies

MIDDLE EAST FORCES

For use in territory occupied by British Forces in Eritrea (1942), Italian Somaliland (from 13 April 1942), Cyrenaica (1943), Tripolitania (1943), and some of the Dodecanese Islands (1945).

PRICES. Our prices for used stamps with "M.E.F." overprints are for specimens with identifiable postmarks of the territories in which they were issued. These stamps were also used in the United Kingdom with official sanction, from the summer of 1950 onwards, and with U.K. postmarks are worth considerably less.

PRINTERS. Considerable research has been undertaken to discover the origins of Nos. M1/10. It is now suggested that Nos. M1/5, previously assigned to Harrison and Sons, were produced by the Army Printing Services, Cairo, and that the smaller printing, Nos. M6/10, previously identified as the work of the Army Printing Services, Cairo, was from an unidentified printer within the Middle East Forces area.

M.E.F. M.E.F.

(M 1)   (M 2)

Opt. 14 mm long. Regular lettering and upright oblong stops.

Opt. 13½ mm long. Regular lettering and square stops.

M.E.F.

(M 2a)

Opt. 13½ mm long. Rough lettering and round stops.

(Illustrations twice actual size)

M.E.F.

Sliced "M"
(R.6/10)

1942 (2 Mar). *Stamps of Great Britain optd. W 127. P 15 × 14.*

(a) With Type M 1

M 1	128	1d. scarlet (No. 463)	..	..	60	1·50
		a. Sliced "M"	..	..	48·00	
M 2		2d. orange (No. 465)	..		30	2·50
		a. Sliced "M"	..	..	32·00	
M 3		2½d. ultramarine (No. 466)	..		30	45
		a. Sliced "M"	..	..	32·00	
M 4		3d. violet (No. 467)	..		30	10
		a. Opt double	..	..	— £2000	
M 5	129	5d. brown	..	..	30	15
		a. Sliced "M"	..	..	32·00	

(b) With Type M 2

M 6	128	1d. scarlet (No. 463)	..	55·00	12·00	
		a. Optd. with Type M 2a	..	45·00	8·50	
		b. Nos. M6/a se-tenant vert	£200	80·00	
M 7		2d. orange (No. 465)	..	65·00	75·00	
		a. Optd with Type M 2a	..	55·00	65·00	
		b. Nos. M7/a se-tenant vert	£275	£200	
M 8		2½d. ultramarine (No. 466)	..	35·00	7·00	
		a. Optd with Type M 2a	..	32·00	5·50	
		b. Nos. M8/a se-tenant vert	£160	55·00	
M 9		3d. violet (No. 467)	..	95·00	28·00	
		a. Optd with Type M 2a	..	85·00	26·00	
		b. Nos. M9/a se-tenant vert	£375	£140	
M10	129	5d. brown	..	£375	90·00	
		a. Optd with Type M 2a	..	£350	80·00	
		b. Nos. M10/a se-tenant vert	£1200	£600	

See note after No. M21.

Nos. M6/10 were issued in panes of 60 (6 × 10), rows 2, 3, and 7 being overprinted with Type M 2 and the other seven rows with Type M 2a.

M.E.F.

(M 3)

Optd 13½ mm long. Regular lettering and upright oblong stops.

(Illustration twice actual size)

1943 (1 Jan)–1947. *Stamps of Great Britain optd with Type M 3 by Harrison & Sons. W 127, P 15 × 14 (1d. to 1s.); W 133, P 14 (others).*

M11	128	1d. pale scarlet (No. 486)	..		1·50	10
M12		2d. pale orange (No. 488)	..		1·50	1·25
M13		2½d. light ultramarine (No. 489)	..	45	10	
M14		3d. pale violet (No. 490)	..		1·50	10
M15	129	5d. brown	..	..	2·25	10
M16		6d. purple	..	..	40	10
M17	130	9d. deep olive-green	..		85	10
M18		1s. bistre-brown	..	..	50	10
M19	131	2s. 6d. yellow-green	..		7·00	1·00
M20		5s. red (1947)	..	..	11·00	17·00
M21	132	10s. ultramarine (1947)	..	14·00	10·00	
M11/21				Set of 11	35·00	27·00
M18/21 Optd "Specimen"			Set of 4	£500		

The overprint on No. M15 should not be confused with the other overprints on the 5d. value. It can be distinguished from No. M5 by the ½ mm difference in length; and from No. M10 by the more intense colour, thicker lettering and larger stops.

POSTAGE DUE STAMPS

M.E.F.

(MD 1)

1942. *Postage Due stamps of Great Britain Nos. D27/30 and D33 optd with Type MD 1, in blue-black.*

MD1	D 1	½d. emerald	..	..	30	9·50
MD2		1d. carmine	..	..	30	1·75
MD3		2d. agate	..	..	1·25	1·25
MD4		3d. violet	..	..	50	4·25
MD5		1s. deep blue (Optd S. £150)	..	3·25	10·00	
MD1/5				Set of 5	5·00	24·00

CYRENAICA

In June 1949 the British authorities recognised the leader of the Senussi, Amir Mohammed Idris Al-Senussi, as Amir of Cyrenaica with autonomy in internal affairs.

(Currency. 10 millièmes = 1 piastre, 100 piastres = 1 Egyptian pound)

24   Mounted Warrior   25

(Recess Waterlow)

1950 (16 Jan). *P* 12½.

136	24	1 m brown	..	..	70	2·00
137		2 m. carmine	..	..	90	2·00
138		3 m. orange-yellow	..	..	90	2·00
139		4 m. blue-green	..	..	1·25	2·50
140		5 m. grey-black	..	..	60	70
141		8 m. orange	..	..	75	65
142		10 m. violet	..	..	75	65
143		12 m. scarlet	..	..	75	65
144		20 m. blue	..	..	75	60
145	25	50 m. ultramarine and purple-brown	..	2·25	3·00	
146		100 m. carmine and black	..	..	6·00	9·00
147		200 m. violet and deep blue	..	11·00	25·00	
148		500 m. orange-yellow and green	..	42·00	65·00	
136/148				Set of 13	60·00	£100

POSTAGE DUE STAMPS

D 26

(Recess Waterlow)

1950 (16 Jan). *P* 12½

D149	D 26	2 m. brown	..	..	45·00	95·00
D150		4 m. blue-green	..	..	45·00	95·00
D151		8 m. scarlet	..	..	45·00	95·00
D152		10 m. orange	..	..	45·00	95·00
D153		20 m. orange-yellow	..	..	45·00	95·00
D154		40 m. blue	..	..	45·00	95·00
D155		100 m. grey-brown	..	..	45·00	95·00
D149/155				Set of 7	£275	£600

On 24 December 1951 Cyrenaica united with Tripolitania, Fezzan and Ghadames to form the independent Kingdom of Libya, whose issues are listed in Part 13 (*Africa since Independence F—M*) of this catalogue.

ERITREA

From early 1950 examples of Nos. E1/32 exist precancelled in manuscript by a black or blue horizontal line for use by British troops on concession rate mail.

BRITISH MILITARY ADMINISTRATION

(Currency. 100 cents = 1 shilling)

B.M.A. ERITREA   B.M.A. ERITREA

10 CENTS   5 SHILLINGS

(E 1)   (E 2)

SH. 50   SH .50

Normal   Misplaced Stop

1948–9. *Stamps of Great Britain surch as Types E 1 or E 2.*

E 1	128	5 c. on ½d. pale green	..	..	50	65
E 2		10 c. on 1d. pale scarlet	..	..	65	2·00
E 3		20 c. on 2d. pale orange	..	..	45	2·25
E 4		25 c. on 2½d. light ultramarine	..	40	60	
E 5		30 c. on 3d. pale violet	..	..	1·25	4·00
E 6	129	40 c. on 5d. brown	..	..	30	4·00
E 7		50 c. on 6d. purple	..	..	30	60
E 7a	130	65 c. on 8d. bright carmine (1.2.49)	..	7·00	2·00	
E 8		75 c. on 9d. deep olive-green	..	50	75	
E 9		1 s. on 1s. bistre-brown	..	..	50	50
E10	131	2 s. 50 c. on 2s. 6d. yellow-green	..	6·50	10·00	
		a. Misplaced stop (R. 4/7)	..	85·00	£120	
E11		5 s. on 5s. red	..	..	6·50	16·00
E12	132	10 s. on 10s. ultramarine	..	20·00	21·00	
E1/12				Set of 13	40·00	55·00

BRITISH ADMINISTRATION

1950 (6 Feb). *As Nos. E1/12, but surch "B.A. ERITREA" and new values instead of "B.M.A." etc.*

E13	128	5 c. on ½d. pale green	..	..	50	6·00
E14		10 c. on 1d. pale scarlet	..	..	30	2·75
E15		20 c. on 2d. pale orange	..	..	30	70
E16		25 c. on 2½d. light ultramarine	..	30	60	

E17	128	30 c. on 3d. pale violet	..	..	30	1·00
E18	129	40 c. on 5d. brown	..	..	40	90
E19		50 c. on 6d. purple	..	..	30	20
E20	130	65 c. on 8d. bright carmine	..	40	1·00	
E21		75 c. on 9d. deep olive-green	..	30	25	
E22		1 s. on 1s. bistre-brown	..	..	30	15
E23	131	2 s. 50 c. on 2s. 6d. yellow-green	..	3·50	4·50	
E24		5 s. on 5s. red	..	..	6·00	9·00
E25	132	10 s. on 10s. ultramarine	..	55·00	55·00	
E13/25				Set of 13	60·00	70·00

1951 (28 May*). *Nos. 503/4, 506/7 and 509/11 of Great Britain surch "B.A. ERITREA" and new values.*

E26	128	5 c. on ½d. pale orange	..	..	30	60
E27		10 c. on 1d. light ultramarine	..	30	60	
E28		20 c. on 2d. pale red-brown	..	30	30	
E29		25 c. on 2½d. pale scarlet	..	30	30	
E30	147	2 s. 50 c. on 2s. 6d. yellow-green	..	6·00	18·00	
E31	148	5 s. on 5s. red	..	..	20·00	18·00
E32		10 s. on 10s. ultramarine	..	20·00	18·00	
E26/32				Set of 7	42·00	50·00

*This is the local release date. The stamps were placed on sale in London on 3 May.

POSTAGE DUE STAMPS

B.M.A. ERITREA

10 CENTS

(ED 1)

1948. *Postage Due stamps of Great Britain Nos. D27/30 and D33 surch as Type ED 1.*

ED1	D 1	5 c. on ½d. emerald	..	..	9·50	18·00
ED2		10 c. on 1d. carmine	..	..	8·50	20·00
		a. No stop after "B"	..	..	£100	
ED3		20 c. on 2d. agate	..	..	7·00	15·00
		a. No stop after "A"	..	..	60·00	
		b. No stop after "B" (R. 1/9)	..	£120		
ED4		30 c. on 3d. violet	..	..	8·50	14·00
ED5		1 s. on 1s. deep blue	..	..	16·00	27·00
ED1/5.				Set of 5	45·00	85·00

1950 (6 Feb). *As Nos. ED1/5, but surch "B.A. ERITREA" and new values instead of "B.M.A." etc.*

ED6	D 1	5 c. on ½d. emerald	..	..	11·00	42·00
ED7		10 c. on 1d. carmine	..	..	9·00	15·00
		a. "C" of "CENTS" omitted	..	£1600		
		ab. "C" omitted and vertical oblong for "E" of "CENTS"	..	£2750		
ED8		20 c. on 2d. agate	..	..	9·50	13·00
ED9		30 c. on 3d. violet	..	..	9·50	13·00
		w. Wmk sideways-inverted*	..	—	50·00	
ED10		1 s. on 1s. deep blue	..	..	15·00	22·00
		a. Stop after "A" omitted (R. 2/13)	£275			
ED6/10				Set of 5	48·00	95·00

No. ED7a, and probably No. ED7ab, occurred on R.7/20, but the error was quickly corrected.

*No. ED9w shows the Crowns pointing to the left, *as seen from the back of the stamp.*

Stamps of Ethiopia were used in Eritrea after 15 September 1952 following federation with Ethiopia.

SOMALIA

BRITISH OCCUPATION

E.A.F.

(S 1. "East Africa Forces")

1943 (15 Jan)–46. *Stamps of Great Britain optd with Type S 1, in blue.*

S1	128	1d. pale scarlet	..	..	60	40
S2		2d. pale orange	..	..	1·50	1·25
S3		2½d. light ultramarine	..	30	3·50	
S4		3d. pale violet	..	..	50	15
S5	129	5d. brown	..	..	50	40
S6		6d. purple	..	..	30	90
S7	130	9d. deep olive-green	..	..	60	2·25
S8		1s. bistre-brown	..	..	1·25	15
S9	131	2s. 6d. yellow-green (1946)	..	6·00	6·50	
S1/9				Set of 9	10·50	14·00
S8/9 Optd "Specimen"			Set of 2	£250		

The note *re* used prices above Type M 1 of Middle East Forces also applies to the above issue.

BRITISH MILITARY ADMINISTRATION

(Currency. 100 cents = 1 shilling)

1948 (27 May). *Stamps of Great Britain surch "B.M.A./SOMALIA" and new values, as Types E 1 and E 2 of Eritrea.*

S10	128	5 c. on ½d. pale green	..	..	50	1·25
S11		15 c. on 1½d. pale red-brown	..	80	13·00	
S12		20 c. on 2d. pale orange	..	..	2·00	3·25
S13		25 c. on 2½d. light ultramarine	..	1·75	4·00	
S14		30 c. on 3d. pale violet	..	..	2·00	9·00
S15	129	40 c. on 5d. brown	..	..	40	20
S16		50 c. on 6d. purple	..	..	40	2·00
S17	130	75 c. on 9d. deep olive-green	..	2·00	15·00	
S18		1 s. on 1s. bistre-brown	..	..	1·25	20
S19	131	2 s. 50 c. on 2s. 6d. yellow-green	..	3·25	24·00	
		a. Misplaced stop (R. 4/7)	..	80·00	£225	
S20		5 s. on 5s. red	..	..	8·00	32·00
S10/20				Set of 11	20·00	90·00

For illustration of No. S19a, see previous column above No. E1 of Eritrea.

BRITISH ADMINISTRATION

1950 (2 Jan). *As Nos. S10/20, but surch "B.A./SOMALIA" and new values, instead of "B.M.A." etc.*

S21	128	5 c. on ½d. pale green	..	..	20	2·50
S22		15 c. on 1½d. pale red-brown	..	60	14·00	
S23		20 c. on 2d. pale orange	..	..	60	4·00
S24		25 c. on 2½d. light ultramarine	..	40	6·00	
S25		30 c. on 3d. pale violet	..	..	1·00	3·00
S26	129	40 c. on 5d. brown	..	..	55	85
S27		50 c. on 6d. purple	..	..	40	2·00
S28	130	75 c. on 9d. deep olive-green	..	1·00	5·50	
S29		1 s. on 1s. bistre-brown	..	..	60	1·50

S30	131	2 s. 50 c. on 2s. 6d. yellow-green	..	4·00	22·00
S31		5 s. on 5s. red	..	8·50	27·00
S21/31			Set of 11	16·00	80·00

Somalia reverted to Italian Administration on 1 April 1950 later becoming independent. Later issues will be found listed in Part 8 (*Italy and Switzerland*) of this catalogue.

TRIPOLITANIA

BRITISH MILITARY ADMINISTRATION

(Currency. 100 centesimi = 1 Military Administration lira)

4 4
M.A.L. M.A.L.

Normal	Misaligned surcharge (R.8/8, 18/8)

1948 (1 July).   *Stamps of Great Britain surch "B.M.A./TRIPOLI-TANIA" and new values, as Types E 1 and E 2 of Eritrea, but expressed in M(ilitary) A(dministration) L(ire).*

T 1	128	1 l. on ½d. pale green	..	30	80
T 2		2 l. on 1d. pale scarlet	..	20	15
T 3		3 l. on 1½d. pale red-brown	..	20	50
		a. Misaligned surch	..	20·00	
T 4		4 l. on 2d. pale orange	..	25	50
		a. Misaligned surch	..	23·00	
T 5		5 l. on 2½d. light ultramarine	..	30	20
T 6		6 l. on 3d. pale violet	..	20	40
T 7	129	10 l. on 5d. brown	..	20	15
T 8		12 l. on 6d. purple	..	30	20
T 9	130	18 l. on 9d. deep olive-green	..	50	65
T10		24 l. on 1s. bistre-brown	..	50	65
T11	131	60 l. on 2s. 6d. yellow-green	..	2·00	70·00
T12		120 l. on 5s. red	..	11·00	15·00
T13	132	240 l. on 10s. ultramarine	..	19·00	80·00
T1/13			Set of 13	32·00	95·00

BRITISH ADMINISTRATION

1950 (6 Feb).   *As Nos. T1/13, but surch. "B.A. TRIPOLITANIA" and new values, instead of "B.M.A." etc.*

T14	128	1 l. on ½d. pale green	..	90	10·00
T15		2 l. on 1d. pale scarlet	..	1·00	40
T16		3 l. on 1½d. pale red-brown	..	35	11·00
		a. Misaligned surch	..	30·00	
T17		4 l. on 2d. pale orange	..	25	4·50
		a. Misaligned surch	..	23·00	
T18		5 l. on 2½d. light ultramarine	..	25	70
T19		6 l. on 3d. pale violet	..	90	3·25
T20	129	10 l. on 5d. brown	..	30	4·00
T21		12 l. on 6d. purple	..	75	50
T22	130	18 l. on 9d. deep olive-green	..	75	2·50
T23		24 l. on 1s. bistre-brown	..	75	3·50
T24	131	60 l. on 2s. 6d. yellow-green	..	4·25	12·00
T25		120 l. on 5s. red	..	17·00	22·00
T26	132	240 l. on 10s. ultramarine	..	27·00	50·00
T14/26			Set of 13	48·00	£110

1951 (3 May).   *Nos. 503/7 and 509/11 of Great Britain surch "B.A. TRIPOLITANIA" and new values.*

T27	128	1 l. on ½d. pale orange	..	20	4·50
T28		2 l. on 1d. light ultramarine	..	20	90
T29		3 l. on 1½d. pale green	..	30	6·50
T30		4 l. on 2d. pale red-brown	..	20	1·25
T31		5 l. on 2½d. pale scarlet	..	30	6·50
T32	147	60 l. on 2s. 6d. yellow-green	..	3·50	19·00
T33	148	120 l. on 5s. red	..	7·50	23·00
T34	149	240 l. on 10s. ultramarine	..	30·00	38·00
T27/34			Set of 8	38·00	90·00

POSTAGE DUE STAMPS

1948.   *Postage Due stamps of Great Britain Nos. D27/30 and D33 surch. "B.M.A/TRIPOLITANIA" and new values, as Type ED 1 of Eritrea, but expressed in M(ilitary) A(dministration) L(ire).*

TD1	D 1	1 l. on ½d. emerald	..	4·50	42·00
		a. No stop after "A"	..	60·00	
TD2		2 l. on 1d. carmine	..	2·50	28·00
		a. No stop after "A"	..	42·00	
		b. No stop after "M" (R.1/17)	..	80·00	
TD3		4 l. on 2d. agate	..	7·00	26·00
		a. No stop after "A"	..	£120	
		b. No stop after "M"	..	£150	
TD4		6 l. on 3d. violet	..	7·50	20·00
TD5		24 l. on 1s. deep blue	..	28·00	£100
TD1/5			Set of 5	45·00	£190

1950 (6 Feb).   *As Nos. TD1/5, but surch "B.A. TRIPOLITANIA" and new values, instead of "B.M.A." etc.*

TD 6	D 1	1 l. on ½d. emerald	..	11·00	75·00
		a. No stop after "B"	..	£110	
TD 7		2 l. on 1d. carmine	..	2·50	26·00
		a. No stop after "B"	..	65·00	
TD 8		4 l. on 2d. agate	..	2·75	29·00
		a. No stop after "B"	..	70·00	
TD 9		6 l. on 3d. violet	..	17·00	60·00
		a. No stop after "B"	..	£170	
		w. Wmk sideways-inverted*	..	50·00	
TD10		24 l. on 1s. deep blue	..	42·00	£140
		a. No stop after "A"	..	£325	
		b. No stop after "B"	..	£325	
TD6/10			Set of 5	65·00	£300

*No. TD9w shows the Crowns pointing to the left, *as seen from the back of the stamp.*

Tripolitania became part of the independent kingdom of Libya on 24 December 1951.

British P.Os in Crete

BRITISH ADMINISTRATION OF CANDIA PROVINCE (HERAKLEION)

Crete, formerly part of the Turkish Empire, was made autonomous, under Turkish suzerainty, in November 1898 with British, French, Italian and Russian troops stationed in separate zones to keep the peace.

Overseas mail franked with Nos. B1/5 was forwarded through the Austrian post office at Canea, being additionally franked with stamps of the Austro-Hungarian Post Offices in the Turkish Empire.

(Currency. 40 paras = 1 piastre)

PRICES FOR STAMPS ON COVER
No. B1   *from* × 10
Nos. B2/5   —

B 1   B 2

1898 (25 Nov).   *Handstruck locally. Imperf.*
B1	B 1	20 pa. bright violet	..	£425	£225

1898 (3 Dec).   *Litho by M. Grundmann, Athens. P 11½.*
B2	B 2	10 pa. blue	..	8·00	16·00
		a. Imperf (pair)	..	£250	
B3		20 pa. green	..	12·00	14·00
		a. Imperf (pair)	..	£250	

1899.   *P 11½.*
B4	B 2	10 pa. brown	..	8·00	23·00
		a. Imperf (pair)	..	£250	
B5		20 pa. rose	..	17·00	15·00
		a. Imperf (pair)	..	£250	

The British postal service closed at the end of 1899.

British P.O. in Siam
(Bangkok)

An overseas postal service for foreign residents was operated by the British Consulate at Bangkok from 1858. Mail was despatched by steamer to Singapore and from 1876 onwards was increasingly franked with Straits Settlements stamps. These were initially cancelled on arrival at Singapore, but later an oval postmark inscribed "BRITISH CONSULATE BANGKOK" was used. In 1883 a circular "BANGKOK" datestamp was introduced for use with Nos. 1/23. Both cancellations can also be found used on Hong Kong stamps between 1881 and 1885.

(Currency. 100 cents = 1 Straits dollar)

Stamps of Straits Settlements (see Malaysia) cancelled with oval postmark inscribed "BRITISH CONSULATE BANGKOK" around Royal Arms.

1877 to **1882.**   *Wmk Crown CC (Nos. 11/15, 33 and 35).*
Z1	2 c. brown	..	£350
Z2	4 c. rose	..	£350
Z3	6 c. dull lilac	..	£400
Z4	8 c. orange-yellow	..	£350
Z5	10 c. on 30 c. claret (thin "0") (No. 33)	..	£1000
Z6	10 c. on 30 c. claret (thick "10") (No. 34)	..	£1000
Z7	10 c. on 30 c. claret (thin "1", thick "0".) (No. 35)	..	£1100
Z8	12 c. blue	..	£450

Subsequent Straits Settlements values to 8 c. watermarked Crown CA are known used at Bangkok in 1883 and 1884. During this period the stamps overprinted "B" were on sale at the British Post Office.

PRICES FOR STAMPS ON COVER
The issues of the British Post Offices in Siam are worth from × 100 the prices quoted for used stamps when on cover.

B
(1)

1882 (May)–85.   *Stamps of Straits Settlements optd with T 1.*

(a) On No. 9 of 1867
1	32 c. on 2 a. yellow (1885)	..	£35000

(b) On Nos. 11/13, 14a, 15/17 and 19 of 1867–72 and Nos. 48/9 of 1882. Wmk Crown CC
2	2 c. brown	..	£2750 £1400
3	4 c. rose	..	£2250 £1100
	a. Opt double	..	– £7500
4	5 c. purple-brown	..	£275 £300
5	6 c. lilac	..	£200 £110
6	8 c. orange	..	£1900 £200
7	10 c. slate	..	£350 £150
8	12 c. blue	..	£900 £475
9	24 c. green	..	£700 £150
10	30 c. claret	..	£30000 £20000
11	96 c. grey	..	£5000 £2750

(c) On Nos. 59/60 of April 1883
12	2 c. on 32 c. pale red (*Wide "S"*)	£2000 £2250
13	2 c. on 32 c. pale red (*Wide "E"*)	£2500 £2750

(d) On Nos. 50/3 of 1882 and Nos. 63/7 of 1883–84. Wmk Crown CA
14	2 c. brown	£475 £350
15	2 c. pale rose (1883)	55·00 45·00
	a. Opt inverted	— £9500
	b. Opt double	£2750 £2750
	c. Opt treble	£10000
16	4 c. rose (1883)	£500 £300
17	4 c. pale brown (1883)	75·00 70·00
	a. Opt double	£3500
	b. Broken oval	£950 £950
18	5 c. blue (1884)	£225 £160
19	6 c. lilac (1884)	£160 £110
20	8 c. orange (1883)	£140 65·00
	a. Opt inverted	£17000 £10000
21	10 c. slate (1883)	£150 85·00
22	12 c. brown-purple (1883)	£150 £100
23	24 c. yellow-green (1884?)	£4000 £2500

The prices quoted for the overprint double errors, Nos. 3a, 15b and 17a, are for stamps showing two clear impressions of the overprint. Examples showing partial doubling, on these and other values, are worth a small premium over the price quoted for normal stamps.

No. 17b shows the edge of the central oval broken above the "O" of "POSTAGE". It occurs on R. 10/5 of the lower right pane.

The use of these stamps ceased on 30 June 1885. Siam joined the Universal Postal Union on 1 July 1885.

British Postal Agencies in Eastern Arabia

Certain Arab States in Eastern Arabia, whilst remaining independent, had British postal administrations.

Bahrain and Kuwait (from 1948) and Qatar (from 1957) used British stamps overprinted and surcharged in local currency. Abu Dhabi (from 1964) and Trucial States (from 1961 and used only in Dubai) had definitive issues made under the auspices of the British Agencies.

In addition, British stamps were surcharged with value only for use in Muscat and certain other states. They were formerly listed under Muscat as they were first put on sale there, but in view of their more extended use, the list has been transferred here, retaining the same numbering.

The stamps were used in Muscat from 1 April 1948 to 29 April 1966; in Dubai from 1 April 1948 to 6 January 1961; in Qatar: Doha from August 1950, Umm Said from February 1956, to 31 March 1957; and in Abu Dhabi from 30 March 1963 (Das Island from December 1960) to 29 March 1964.

Nos. 21/2 were placed on sale in Kuwait Post Offices in April and May 1951 and from February to November 1953 due to shortages of stamps with "KUWAIT" overprint. Isolated examples of other values can be found commercially used from Bahrain or Kuwait.

(Currency. 12 pies = 1 anna; 16 annas = 1 rupee)

Stamps of Great Britain surcharged

1 ANNA	2 RUPEES
(3)	(4)

1½	1½
I	II

Two types of 1½ a. surcharge:
I. "1" 3¼ mm high and aligns with top of "2" in "½" (Rows 1 to 10).
II. "1" 3½ mm high with foot of figure below top of "2" (Rows 11 to 20).

1948 (1 Apr).   *Surch with T 3 (½ a. to 1 r.) or 4 (2 r.).*
16	128	½ a. on ½d. pale green	..	2·00	6·50
17		1 a. on 1d. pale scarlet	..	2·00	20
18		1½ a. on 1½d. pale red-brown (I)	..	5·00	1·50
		a. Type II	..	5·00	1·50
		b. Vert pair. Nos. 18/a	..	30·00	
19		2 a. on 2d. pale orange	..	1·50	1·25
20		2½ a. on 2½d. light ultramarine	..	2·50	4·50
21		3 a. on 3d. pale violet	..	2·50	10
22	129	6 a. on 6d. purple	..	2·50	10
23	130	1 r. on 1s. bistre-brown	..	3·00	50
24	131	2 r. on 2s. 6d. yellow-green	..	8·00	28·00
16/24			Set of 9	26·00	38·00

One example of No. 22 is known with the surcharge almost completely omitted from position R. 20/2 in the sheet.

2½ ANNAS	15 RUPEES
(5)	(6)

1948 (26 Apr).   *Royal Silver Wedding. Nos. 493/4 surch with T 5 or 6.*
25	137	2½ a. on 2½d. ultramarine	..	1·75	1·50
26	138	15 r. on £1 blue	..	23·00	35·00

1948 (29 July). *Olympic Games. Nos. 495/8 surch with new values in "ANNAS" or "1 RUPEE", as T 5/6, but in one line on 2½ a. (vert) or 6 a. and 1 r. (horiz) and grills obliterating former values of all except 2½ a.*

27	139	2½ a. on 2½d. ultramarine	.. ..	35	2·00
28	140	3 a. on 3d. violet	.. ..	45	2·00
29	141	6 a. on 6d. bright purple	.. ..	45	2·00
30	142	1 r. on 1s. brown	.. ..	1·25	2·25
		a. Surch double	.. ..		
27/30	..			Set of 4	2·25	7·50

1949 (10 Oct). *75th Anniv of Universal Postal Union. Nos. 499/502 surch with new values in "ANNAS" or "1 RUPEE" as T 3/4, but all in one line, with grills obliterating former values.*

31	143	2½ a. on 2½d. ultramarine	.. ..	60	2·50
32	144	3 a. on 3d. violet	.. ..	60	2·50
33	145	6 a. on 6d. bright purple	.. ..	60	1·75
34	146	1 r. on 1s. brown	.. ..	3·00	2·75
31/4	..		Set of 4	4·25	8·50

2 RUPEES ═ ═ 2 RUPEES

(6a)   (6b)

Type 6a. "2" and "RUPEES" level and in line with lower of the two bars.
Type 6b. "2" raised in relation to "RUPEES" and whole surcharge below the lower bar.

1950 (2 Oct)–**55**. *Nos. 503/8 surch as T 3 and No. 509 with T 6a.*

35	128	½ a. on ½d. pale orange (3.5.51)	..	30	9·00
36		1 a. on 1d. light ultramarine (3.5.51) ..		30	7·50
37		1½ a. on 1½d. pale green (I) (3.5.51)	..	5·00	21·00
		a. Type II	..	5·00	21·00
		b. Vert pair. No. 37/a	..	30·00	
38		2 a. on 2d. pale red-brown (3.5.51)	..	30	8·50
39		2½ a. on 2½d. pale scarlet (3.5.51)	..	30	16·00
40	129	4 a. on 4d. light ultramarine	..	30	3·00
41	147	2 r. on 2s. 6d. yellow-green (3.5.51)	..	23·00	6·50
		a. Surch with Type 6b (1955)	£130	65·00	
35/41	..	..	Set of 7	27·00	65·00

1952 (5 Dec)–**54**. *Stamps of Queen Elizabeth II wmk Tudor Crown, surch as T 3 (in one line on 2½ and 6 a.).*

42	154	½ a. on ½d. orange-red (31.8.53)	..	10	1·75
43		1 a. on 1d. ultramarine (31.8.53)	..	10	1·75
44		1½ a. on 1½d. green (31.8.53)	..	10	1·25
45		2 a. on 2d. red-brown (31.8.53)	..	10	10
46	155	2½ a. on 2½d. carmine-red	..	10	10
47		3 a. on 3d. deep lilac (B.) (18.1.54)	..	20	60
48	156	4 a. on 4d. ultramarine (2.11.53)	..	55	3·25
49	157	6 a. on 6d. reddish purple (18.1.54)	..	35	10
50	160	12 a. on 1s. 3d. green (2.11.53)	..	2·00	10
51	159	1 r. on 1s. 6d. grey-blue (2.11.53)	..	2·00	10
42/51	..	..	Set of 10	5·00	8·00

1953 (10 June). *Coronation. Nos. 532/5 surch with new values.*

52	161	2½ a. on 2½d. carmine-red	..	1·75	95
53	162	4 a. on 4d. ultramarine	..	1·75	95
54	163	12 a. on 1s. 3d. deep yellow-green	..	2·25	95
55	164	1 r. on 1s. 6d. deep grey-blue	..	2·50	45
52/5	..		Set of 4	7·50	3·00

2 RUPEES ═ I

2 RUPEES ═ II

2 RUPEES ═ III

(7)

5 RUPEES ═ I

5 RUPEES ═ II

(8)

Types of surcharges

2 rupees.
Type I. On *Waterlow ptg.* Top of "R" level with top of "2" and other letters of "RUPEES". Bars 7 mm long.
Type II. On *Waterlow ptg* by Harrison. "R" dropped out of alignment with "2" and other letters of "RUPEES". Bars 6½ mm long.
Type III. On *De La Rue ptg* by Harrison. Top of "R" below level of top of "2". Bars 7–7¼ mm long and with left sides aligned with "S".

5 rupees.
Type I. On *Waterlow ptg* by Harrison. Ends of letters square and sharp. There were two printings made in March and May 1957.
Type II. On *De La Rue ptg* by Harrison. Type is thicker and ends of letters are relatively rounded.

For differences between Waterlow and De La Rue printings of the basic stamps see notes in Great Britain after No. 539.

1955–60. *T 166/7 (Waterlow ptgs) (W 165, St. Edward's Crown) surch with T 7/8.*

56	166	2 r. on 2s. 6d. black-brown (Type I) (23.9.55)	..	4·25	70
		a. Type II (2.57)		7·00	3·50
		b. Type III (No. 536a D.L.R.) (6.60)		22·00	50·00

57	167	5 r. on 5s. rose-red (Type I) (1.3.57)		10·00	2·00
		a. Wide surcharge		£250	£200
		b. Type II (No. 537a D.L.R.) (27.1.60)		20·00	50·00

No. 57a ("5" and "R" spaced 2¼ mm instead of 1¼ mm) occurred on R. 8/4 of the first surcharging of No. 57 only.

1956–57. *Stamps of Queen Elizabeth II, W 165, St. Edward's Crown, surch as T 3 (in one line on 2½ and 6 a.).*

58	154	1 a. on 1d. ultramarine (4.3.57)		35	50
58a		1½ a. on 1½d. green (1956)	..	£3500	£600
59		2 a. on 2d. red-brown (8.6.56)	..	70	2·00
60	155	2½ a. on 2½d. carmine-red (8.6.56)		80	3·50
61		3 a. on 3d. deep lilac (B.) (3.2.57)		1·00	6·50
62	156	4 a. on 4d. ultramarine (9.12.56)		5·00	15·00
63	157	6 a. on 6d. red-purple (10.2.57)		1·10	6·50
64	159	1 r. on 1s. 6d. grey-blue (2.8.56)		3·25	15
58/64 (ex 58a)	..		Set of 7	11·00	30·00

No. 58a came from a few sheets of the St. Edward's Crown watermark included, in error, with a printing of No. 44. Most examples were used in Dubai, but two are known from Muscat, a pair on a cover from Bahrain and a single postmarked F.P.O. 936 (Sharjah). A single mint example also exists.

(New Currency. 100 naye paise = 1 rupee)

NP 1 NP (9)   3 NP NP (10)   75 NP (11)

1957 (1 Apr)–**59**. *Value in naye paise. Stamps of Queen Elizabeth II, W 165, St. Edward's Crown, surch as T 9 (1, 15, 25, 40, 50 n.p.), 11 (75 n.p.) or 10 (others).*

65	157	1 n.p. on 5d. brown	..	10	75
66	154	3 n.p. on ½d. orange-red	..	20	2·00
67		6 n.p. on 1d. ultramarine	..	20	2·00
68		9 n.p. on 1½d. green	..	20	1·25
69		12 n.p. on 2d. light red-brown	..	30	1·50
70	155	15 n.p. on 2½d. carmine-red (Type I)	..	30	10
		a. Type II (4.59)		30	3·50
71		20 n.p. on 3d. deep lilac (B.)	..	20	10
72	156	25 n.p. on 4d. ultramarine	..	70	3·00
73	157	40 n.p. on 6d. reddish purple	..	30	10
		a. Deep claret (3.59)	..	35	10
74	158	50 n.p. on 9d. bronze-green	..	1·25	2·75
75	160	75 n.p. on 1s. 3d. green	..	2·00	35
65/75	..		Set of 11	5·00	12·00

15 NP

(12)

1957 (1 Aug). *World Scout Jubilee Jamboree. Nos. 557/9 surch in one line as T 12 (15 n.p.), or in two lines (others).*

76		15 n.p. on 2½d. carmine-red	..	25	85
77		25 n.p. on 4d. ultramarine	..	30	85
78		75 n.p. on 1s. 3d. green	..	35	85
76/8			Set of 3	80	2·25

1960 (26 Apr)–**61**. *Stamps of Queen Elizabeth II, W 179, Mult Crown, surch as T 9 (1, 15, 30, 40, 50 n.p.), 11 (75 n.p.), 3 (1 r.), 7 (2 r., 5 r.) or 10 (others).*

79	157	1 n.p. on 5d. brown (30.8.60)	..	10	20
80	154	3 n.p. on ½d. orange-red (21.6.60)	..	55	80
81		5 n.p. on 1d. ultramarine (8.4.61)	..	1·00	75
82		6 n.p. on 1d. ultramarine (21.6.60)	..	1·25	90
83		10 n.p. on 1½d. green (8.4.61)	..	50	1·25
84		12 n.p. on 2d. light red-brown (21.6.60)		2·00	2·50
85	155	15 n.p. on 2½d. carmine-red (Type II)	..	25	10
86		20 n.p. on 3d. deep lilac (B.) (28.9.60)	..	25	10
87	156	30 n.p. on 4½d. chestnut (8.4.61)	..	40	40
88	157	40 n.p. on 6d. deep claret (28.9.60)	..	45	10
89	158	50 n.p. on 9d. bronze-green (8.4.61)	..	1·00	1·25
90		75 n.p. on 1s. 3d. green (8.4.61)	..	3·00	1·50
91	159	1 r. on 1s. 6d. grey-blue (8.4.61)	..	14·00	2·75
92	166	2 r. on 2s. 6d. black-brown (No. 595) (8.4.61)		11·00	28·00
93	167	5 r. on 5s. rose-red (No. 596) (8.4.61)		18·00	42·00
79/93	..		Set of 15	48·00	75·00

British Solomon Islands
see Solomon Islands

British Somaliland
see Somaliland Protectorate

British South Africa Company
see Rhodesia

British Virgin Islands

CROWN COLONY

Apart from the 1951 Legislative Council issue, the word "BRITISH" did not appear regularly on the stamps until 1968 when it was introduced to avoid confusion with the nearby Virgin Islands of the United States (the former Danish West Indies).

Most mail from the early years of the islands' history was sent via the Danish island of St. Thomas.

It is not known exactly when the first post office, or agency, was established on Tortola, but an entry in a G.P.O. account book suggest that it was operating by 1787 and the earliest letter postmarked "TORTOLA" dates from June of that year. The stamps of Great Britain were used from 1858 to May 1860, when the colonial authorities assumed responsibility for the overseas mails from the British G.P.O.

For illustrations of the handstamp and postmark types see BRITISH POST OFFICES ABROAD notes, following GREAT BRITAIN.

TORTOLA

CROWNED-CIRCLE HANDSTAMPS

CC1	CC 1	TORTOLA (R.) (15.12.1842)	*Price on cover* £4000
CC2	CC 5	TORTOLA (R.) (21.6.1854)	*Price on cover* £7000

No. CC2 is known used as an Official Paid mark during the years 1900 to 1918. *Price on cover* £1200.

Stamps of GREAT BRITAIN cancelled "A 13" as Type 2.

1858 *to* **1860.**

Z1	1d. rose-red (1857), perf 14 ..	.. ..	£3000
Z2	4d. rose (1857)	.. .. ..	£2750
Z3	6d. lilac (1856)	.. .. ..	£1100
Z4	1s. green (1856)	..	

PRICES FOR STAMPS ON COVER TO 1945

Nos. 1/7	*from* × 15
Nos. 8/22	*from* × 12
Nos. 24/31	*from* × 8
Nos. 32/41	*from* × 10
No. 42	*from* × 20
Nos. 43/50	*from* × 6
Nos. 54/77	*from* × 5
Nos. 78/81	*from* × 6
Nos. 82/101	*from* × 3
Nos. 103/6	*from* × 4
Nos. 107/9	*from* × 6
Nos. 110/21	*from* × 2

1   St. Ursula   2

(Litho Nissen & Parker from original dies by Waterlow)

1866 (Dec). *No wmk. P 12 (a) White wove paper.*

1	1	1d. green	.. ..	45·00	60·00
2		1d. deep green	.. ..	50·00	65·00
3	2	6d. rose ..	.. ..	90·00	£110
4		6d. deep rose	.. ..	£130	£140
		a. Large "V" in "VIRGIN"	..	£375	£475

(b) Toned paper

5	1	1d. green	.. ..	45·00	60·00
		a. Perf 15 × 12	..	£4250	£5500
6		1d. deep green	.. ..	£100	£120
7	2	6d. rose-red	.. ..	60·00	90·00
		a. Large "V" in "VIRGIN" (R. 2/1)	£275	£375

The above were printed in sheets of 25.
6d. stamps showing part of the papermaker's watermark ("A. Cowan & Sons Extra Superfine A. C. & S.") are worth 50% more.
Beware of fakes of No. 5a made from perf 12 stamps.

3   4

Normal Variety

1s. Long-tailed "S" in "ISLANDS" (R. 3/1)

(Litho Nissen and Parker from original dies by Waterlow)

1867–70. *No wmk. P 15. 1s. with double-lined frame.*

(a) White wove paper

8	1	1d. yellow-green (1868)		80·00	80·00
9		1d. blue-green (1870)		65·00	70·00
10	2	6d. pale rose		£475	£475
11	4	1s. black and rose-carmine		£225	£300
		a. Long-tailed "S"		£600	£650

(b) Toned paper

12	1	1d. yellow-green (1868)		85·00	80·00
13	2	6d. dull rose (1868)		£225	£275
14	4	1s. black and rose-carmine (*greyish paper*)		£225	£300
		aa. Long-tailed "S"		£600	£650
14a		1s. black and rose-carmine		£300	£325
		b. Long-tailed "S"		£650	£700

(c) Pale rose paper

15	3	4d. lake-red		50·00	70·00

(d) Buff paper

16	3	4d. lake-red		40·00	60·00
17		4d. lake-brown		40·00	60·00

The thin lines of the frame on the 1s. are close together and sometimes merge into one.

The 1d. from the 1868 printing was in sheets of 20 with narrow margins between the stamps. Later printings were in sheets of 12 with wider margins. The 4d. was in sheets of 25; and the remaining two values in sheets of 20.

In Type 4 the figure of the Virgin was printed by typography and the remainder of the design by lithography.

The greyish paper used for Nos. 14 and 20 often shows traces of blue.

1867. *As T 4, but with crimson frames superimposed with bands extending through margins. P 15.*

18	4	1s. black and rose-carmine (*white paper*)		48·00	60·00
		a. Long-tailed "S"		£160	£180
		b. Figure of Virgin omitted		£60000	
19		1s. black and rose-carmine (*toned paper*)		48·00	60·00
		a. Long-tailed "S"		£160	£180
20		1s. black and rose-carmine (*greyish paper*)		£700	£850
		a. Long-tailed "S"		£1600	£1600

1868. *Nos. 11 and 14a with frame lines retouched so as to make them single lines. Margins remain white. P 15.*

21	4	1s. black and rose-carmine (*white paper*)		£130	£160
		aa. Long-tailed "S"		£375	£450
21a		1s. black and rose-carmine (*toned paper*)		£130	£160
		b. Long-tailed "S"		£375	£450

(Litho D.L.R.)

1878. *Wmk Crown CC (sideways). P 14.*

22	1	1d. green		70·00	85·00
		a. Yellow-green		£170	£130
		ab. Wmk upright		90·00	£120

6 (Die I)   (7)

(Typo D.L.R.)

1879–80. *Wmk Crown CC. P 14.*

24	6	1d. emerald-green (1880)		65·00	85·00
25		2½d. red-brown		90·00	£120

1883 (June)**–84.** *Wmk Crown CA. P 14.*

26	6	1d. yellow-buff		80·00	80·00
27		½d. dull green (*shades*) (11.83)		3·75	8·00
		b. Top left triangle detached		95·00	
29		1d. pale rose (15.9.83)		24·00	27·00
		a. Deep rose (1884)		55·00	60·00
31		2½d. ultramarine (9.84)		2·50	14·00
		b. Top left triangle detached		95·00	
		w. Wmk inverted			

For illustration of "top left triangle detached" variety see above No. 21 of Antigua.

(Litho D.L.R.)

1887–89. *Wmk Crown CA. P 14.*

32	1	1d. red (5.89)		2·00	7·00
33		1d. rose-red		2·25	7·00
34		1d. rose		5·00	14·00
35	3	4d. chestnut		35·00	65·00
		x. Wmk reversed			
36		4d. pale chestnut		35·00	65·00
37		4d. brown-red		45·00	70·00
38	2	6d. dull violet		13·00	48·00
39		6d. deep violet		12·00	42·00
40	1	1s. sepia (2.89)		80·00	£100
41		1s. brown to deep brown		45·00	70·00
34/40		Optd "Specimen"		*Set of 4*	£300

The De La Rue transfers of T 1 to 4 are new transfers and differ from those of Messrs. Nissen and Parker, particularly T 4

1888 (July). *Nos. 18/19 surch with T 7, in violet, in Antigua.*

42	4	4d. on 1s. black and rose-carmine (*toned paper*)		£110	£150
		a. Surch double		£6500	
		b. Surch inverted (in pair with normal)		£40000	
		c. Long-tailed "S"		£400	£500
42d		4d. on 1s. black and rose-carmine (*white paper*)		£140	£180

The special issues for Virgin Islands were superseded on 31 October 1890, by the general issue for Leeward Islands. In 1899, however, a new special issue (given below) appeared; it did not supersede the general issue for Leeward Islands, but was used concurrently, as were all subsequent issues, until 1 July 1956, when the general Leeward Islands stamps were withdrawn.

8   9   10

(Recess D.L.R.)

1899 (Jan). *Wmk Crown CA. P 14.*

43	8	½d. yellow-green		75	55
		a. Error. "HALFPFNNY" (R. 10/1)		80·00	£120
		b. Error. "HALFPENNY" (R. 8/2)		80·00	£120
		c. Imperf between (horiz pair)		£7000	
44		1d. brick-red		2·75	3·00
45		2½d. ultramarine		12·00	4·00
46		4d. brown		4·00	18·00
		a. Error "FOURPENCF" (R.10/3)		£850	£1200
47		6d. dull violet		4·50	4·50
48		7d. deep green		7·00	8·00
49		1s. brown-yellow		22·00	35·00
50		5s. indigo		70·00	85·00
43/50				*Set of 8*	£110	£140
43/50		Optd "Specimen"		*Set of 8*	£160

Nos. 43a/b and 46a were corrected after the first printing.

(Typo D.L.R.)

1904 (1 June). *Wmk Mult Crown CA. P 14.*

54	9	½d. dull purple and green		60	40
55		1d. dull purple and scarlet		2·25	35
56	10	2d. dull purple and ochre		5·00	4·50
57	9	2½d. dull purple and ultramarine		1·75	2·00
58	10	3d. dull purple and black		3·25	3·00
59	9	6d. dull purple and brown		2·75	3·00
60	10	1s. green and scarlet		3·75	4·75
61		2s. 6d. green and black		23·00	55·00
62	9	5s. green and blue		48·00	65·00
54/62				*Set of 9*	80·00	£120
54/62		Optd "Specimen"		*Set of 9*	£140

11   12

(Typo D.L.R.)

1913 (Feb)**–19.** *Die I. Wmk Mult Crown CA. Chalk-surfaced paper (3d. to 5s.). P 14.*

69	11	½d. green		1·50	3·00
		a. Yellow-green (8.16)		2·25	9·50
		b. Blue-green and deep green (3.19)		1·25	5·50
70		1d. deep red		8·50	11·00
		a. Deep red and carmine (10.17)		2·25	13·00
		b. Scarlet (10.17)		2·25	14·00
		c. Carmine-red (3.19)		48·00	27·00
71	12	2d. grey		3·75	21·00
		a. Slate-grey		4·00	25·00
72	11	2½d. bright blue		5·00	8·00
73	12	3d. purple/yellow		2·75	6·00
74	11	6d. dull and bright purple		4·50	8·00
75	12	1s. black/blue-green		3·25	8·00
76		2s. 6d. black and red/blue		48·00	50·00
77	11	5s. green and red/yellow		32·00	£110
69/77				*Set of 9*	90·00	£200
69/77		Optd "Specimen"		*Set of 9*	£180

Stock of the original printing of the ½d., No. 69, was exhausted by January 1916 and Leeward Islands ½d. stamps were used until the yellow-green printing, No. 69a, arrived in August 1916.

WAR STAMP

(13)   14

1916 (20 Oct)**–19.** *Optd with T 13.*

78	11	1d. carmine		1·75	16·00
		a. Watermark sideways		£900	
		b. Pale red/bluish		30	6·00
		bw. Wmk inverted		50·00	
		by. Wmk inverted and reversed			
		c. Scarlet (1918)		30	3·75
		d. Short opt (right pane R. 10/1)		20·00	
79	12	3d. purple/yellow		1·10	12·00
		a. Purple/lemon		3·00	8·50
		b. Purple/buff-yellow (11.3.19)		1·50	17·00
		bw. Wmk inverted		10·00	
		by. Wmk inverted and reversed			
		c. Short opt (right pane R. 10/1)		30·00	
78/9		Optd "Specimen"		*Set of 2*	70·00

Nos. 78d and 79c show the overprint 2 mm high instead of 2½ mm.

1921 (18 Nov). *As 1913–19, but Die II and wmk Mult Script CA.*

80	11	½d. green		2·25	24·00
		w. Wmk inverted			
81		1d. scarlet and deep carmine		1·25	19·00
80/1		Optd "Specimen"		*Set of 2*	70·00

(Typo D.L.R.)

1922 (15 June)**–29.** *P 14. (a) Wmk Mult Crown CA. Chalk-surfaced paper.*

82	14	3d. purple/pale yellow		65	13·00
83		1s. black/emerald		75	12·00
84		2s. 6d. black and red/blue		4·50	9·00
85		5s. green and red/pale yellow		30·00	90·00
82/5				*Set of 4*	32·00	£110
82/5		Optd "Specimen"		*Set of 4*	90·00

(b) Wmk Mult Script CA. Chalk-surfaced paper (5d. to 5s.)

86	14	½d. dull green		85	2·75
87		1d. rose-carmine		60	60
88		1d. bright violet (1927)		1·00	3·50
89		1d. scarlet (1929)		13·00	14·00
90		1½d. carmine-red (1927)		1·50	2·50
91		1½d. Venetian red (1928)		1·75	2·00
92		2d. grey		60	5·50
93		2½d. pale bright blue		1·50	14·00
94		2½d. dull orange (1.9.23)		1·25	1·50
95		2½d. bright blue (1927)		1·75	3·50
96		3d. purple/pale yellow (1928)		2·00	5·00
97		5d. dull purple and olive		5·00	45·00
98		6d. dull and bright purple		1·25	6·50
99		1s. black/emerald (1928)		2·00	13·00
100		2s. 6d. black and red/blue (1928)		19·00	45·00
101		5s. green and red/yellow (1.9.23)		19·00	70·00
86/101				*Set of 16*	65·00	£225
86/101		Optd/Perf "Specimen"		*Set of 16*	£275

In the 1½d. stamps the value is in colour on a white ground.

1935 (6 May). *Silver Jubilee. As Nos. 91/4 of Antigua but printed by Waterlow. P 11 × 12.*

103		1d. deep blue and scarlet		95	2·75
		k. Kite and vertical log		55·00	
		l. Kite and horizontal log		60·00	
104		1½d. ultramarine and grey		95	2·75
		k. Kite and vertical log		60·00	
		l. Kite and horizontal log		65·00	
105		2½d. brown and deep blue		95	2·75
		k. Kite and vertical log		65·00	
		l. Kite and horizontal log		70·00	
106		1s. slate and purple		5·50	14·00
		k. Kite and vertical log		£140	
		l. Kite and horizontal log		£140	
103/6				*Set of 4*	7·50	20·00
103/6		Perf "Specimen"		*Set of 4*	85·00

For illustrations of plate varieties see Catalogue Introduction.

1937 (12 May). *Coronation. As Nos. 95/7 of Antigua. P 11×11½.*

107		1d. carmine		20	1·00
108		1½d. yellow-brown		40	2·50
109		2½d. blue		45	1·00
107/9				*Set of 3*	95	4·00
107/9		Perf "Specimen"		*Set of 3*	55·00

15 King George VI and   16 Map
Badge of Colony

(Photo Harrison)

1938 (1 Aug)**–47.** *Wmk Mult Script CA. Chalk-surfaced paper. P 14.*

110	15	½d. green		2·25	1·75
		a. Ordinary paper (10.43)		30	90
111		1d. scarlet		2·75	1·25
		a. Ordinary paper (10.43)		30	60
112		1½d. red-brown		4·00	4·50
		a. Ordinary paper (10.43)		65	95
		w. Wmk inverted		†£1000	
113		2d. grey		4·25	1·75
		a. Ordinary paper (10.43)		40	90
114		2½d. ultramarine		3·50	1·75
		a. Ordinary paper (10.43)		60	2·00
115		3d. orange		5·50	70
		a. Ordinary paper (10.43)		40	80
116		6d. mauve		4·00	90
		a. Ordinary paper (10.43)		1·50	80
117		1s. olive-brown		9·00	2·75
		a. Ordinary paper (8.42)		1·50	70
118		2s. 6d. sepia		24·00	4·50
		a. Ordinary paper (8.42)		14·00	3·00
119		5s. carmine		45·00	5·50
		a. Ordinary paper (8.42)		13·00	4·00
120		10s. blue (1.12 47)		7·00	8·00
121		£1 black (1.12.47)		11·00	20·00
110/21				*Set of 12*	45·00	38·00
110/21		Perf "Specimen"		*Set of 12*	£225

The ordinary paper, used as a substitute for the chalk-surfaced for printings between 1942 and 1945, is thick, smooth and opaque.

1946 (1 Nov). *Victory. As Nos. 110/11 of Antigua.*

122		1½d. lake-brown		10	10
123		3d. orange		10	10
122/3		Perf "Specimen"		*Set of 2*	55·00

1949 (3 Jan). *Royal Silver Wedding. As Nos. 112/13 of Antigua.*

124		2½d. ultramarine		10	10
125		£1 black		12·00	15·00

1949 (10 Oct). *75th Anniv of U.P.U. As Nos. 114/17 of Antigua.*

126		2½d. ultramarine		30	45
127		3d. orange		80	2·00
128		6d. magenta		50	40
129		1s. olive		50	40
126/9				*Set of 4*	1·90	3·00

(New Currency. 100 cents = 1 B.W.I. dollar)

1951. *Inauguration of B.W.I. University College. As Nos. 118/19 of Antigua.*

130	3 c. black and brown-red (10.4)	..	40	80
131	12 c. black and reddish violet (16.2)	..	60	80

(Recess Waterlow)

1951 (2 Apr). *Restoration of Legislative Council. Wmk Mult Script CA. P 14½ x 14.*

132	**16**	6 c. orange	..	20	90
133		12 c. purple	..	20	50
134		24 c. olive	..	20	50
135		$1.20 carmine	..	45	90
132/5			*Set of 4*	95	2·50

17 Sombrero Lighthouse   18 Map of Jost Van Dyke

(Recess D.L.R.)

1952 (15 Apr). *T 17/18 and similar designs. Wmk Mult Script CA. P 12½ × 13 (vert) or 13 × 12½ (horiz).*

136	1 c. black	..	60	90
137	2 c. deep green	..	35	30
138	3 c. black and brown	..	50	80
139	4 c. carmine-red	..	35	90
140	5 c. claret and black	..	1·25	50
141	8 c. bright blue	..	35	1·25
142	12 c. dull violet	..	45	1·40
143	24 c. deep brown	..	35	30
144	60 c. yellow-green and blue	..	2·50	11·00
145	$1.20, black and bright blue	..	3·75	12·00
146	$2.40, yellowish green and red-brown	..	10·00	14·00
147	$4.80, bright blue and carmine	..	11·00	14·00
136/47		*Set of 12*	27·00	50·00

Designs: *Horiz*—3 c. Sheep industry; 4 c. Map of Anegada; 5 c. Cattle industry; 8 c. Map of Virgin Gorda; 12 c. Map of Tortola; 60 c. Dead Man's Chest; $1.20, Sir Francis Drake Channel; $2.40, Road Town; $4.80, Map of Virgin Islands. *Vert*—24 c. Badge of the Presidency.

1953 (2 June). *Coronation. As No. 120 of Antigua.*

148	2 c. black and green	..	30	1·00

29 Map of Tortola   30 Brown Pelican

(Recess D.L.R.)

1956 (1 Nov)–**62**. *Designs as T 29/30. Wmk Mult Script CA. P 13×12½ (½ c. to $1.20) or 12×11½ ($2.40 and $4.80).*

149	½ c. black and reddish purple	..	40	20
	a. Black and deep reddish purple (19.4.60)		1·10	2·50
150	1 c. turquoise-blue and slate	..	1·50	75
	a. Turquoise and slate-violet (26.11.62)		14·00	7·00
151	2 c. vermilion and black	..	30	10
152	3 c. blue and deep olive	..	30	30
153	4 c. deep brown and turquoise-green	..	35	30
154	5 c. grey-black	..	45	10
155	8 c. yellow-orange and deep blue	..	60	40
156	12 c. ultramarine and rose-red	..	2·00	75
157	24 c. myrtle-green and brown-orange	..	1·00	65
158	60 c. indigo and yellow-orange	..	8·00	8·00
159	$1.20, deep yellow-green and carmine-red	..	2·00	7·00
160	$2.40, lemon and deep dull purple	..	35·00	13·00
161	$4.80, blackish brown and turquoise-blue	..	35·00	13·00
149/61		*Set of 13*	75·00	40·00

Designs: *Size as T 29*—1 c. Virgin Islands Sloop; 2 c. Nelthrop Red Poll Bull; 3 c. Road Harbour; 4 c. Mountain travel; 5 c. Badge of the Presidency; 8 c. Beach scene; 12 c. *New Idea* (sloop) under construction; 24 c. White Cedar tree; 60 c. Skipjack Tuna ("Bonito"); $1.20, Treasury Square. *Size as T 30*—$4.80, Magnificent Frigate Bird.

(New Currency. 100 cents = 1 U.S. dollar)

1¢

(42)

1962 (10 Dec). *As Nos. 149/53 and 155/61, but W w 12, surch in U.S. currency as T 42 by D.L.R.*

162	1 c. on ½ c. black and deep reddish purple	..	30	10
163	2 c. on 1 c. turquoise and slate-violet	..	1·50	10
164	3 c. on 2 c. vermilion and black	..	30	10
165	4 c. on 3 c. black and deep olive	..	30	10
166	5 c. on 4 c. deep brown and turquoise-green	..	30	10
167	8 c. on 8 c. yellow-orange and deep blue	..	30	10
168	10 c. on 12 c. ultramarine and rose-red	..	65	10
169	12 c. on 24 c. myrtle-green and brown-orange	..	30	10
170	25 c. on 60 c. indigo and yellow-orange	..	2·50	45
171	70 c. on $1.20, dp yellow-green & carmine-red	..	35	45
	a. Stop to right of C in surcharge instead of beneath it (in pair with normal)		9·50	7·50
172	$1.40 on $2.40, lemon and deep dull purple	..	9·00	3·75
173	$2.80 on $4.80, blackish brown and turquoise-blue	..	9·00	3·75
162/73		*Set of 12*	22·00	8·00

No. 171a occurs on the first stamp on Rows 1 to 10.

1963 (4 June). *Freedom from Hunger. As No. 146 of Antigua.*

174	25 c. reddish violet	..	20	10

1963 (2 Sept). *Red Cross Centenary. As Nos. 147/8 of Antigua.*

175	2 c. red and black	..	15	20
176	25 c. red and blue	..	50	20

1964 (23 Apr). *400th Birth Anniv of William Shakespeare. As No. 164 of Antigua.*

177	10 c. bright blue	..	20	10

43 Skipjack Tuna

44 Map of Tortola   45 Badge of the Colony

(Des and recess D.L.R.)

1964 (2 Nov)–**68**. *Designs as T 43/5. W w 12. P 11½×12 ($2.80), 13×13½ (70 c., $1, $1.40), or 13×12½ (others).*

178	1 c. blue and olive-green	..	30	1·25
179	2 c. yellow-olive and rose-red	..	15	30
180	3 c. sepia and turquoise-blue	..	3·00	1·25
181	4 c. black and carmine-red	..	80	1·50
182	5 c. black and deep bluish green	..	65	1·50
183	6 c. black and brown-orange	..	30	85
184	8 c. black and magenta	..	30	45
185	10 c. lake and deep lilac	..	30	30
	a. Bright lake and reddish lilac (26.11.68)		9·50	2·25
186	12 c. deep bluish green and deep violet-blue		2·00	2·00
187	15 c. yellow-green and grey-black	..	35	2·00
188	25 c. green and purple	..	11·00	1·75
189	70 c. black and yellow-brown	..	3·75	4·50
190	$1 yellow-green and chestnut	..	3·00	2·00
191	$1.40, light blue and rose	..	23·00	9·00
192	$2.80, black and bright purple	..	23·00	9·00
178/92		*Set of 15*	65·00	35·00

Designs: *Horiz as T 43*—2 c. Soper's Hole; 3 c. Brown Pelican; 4 c. Dead Man's Chest; 5 c. Road Harbour; 6 c. Fallen Jerusalem; 8 c. The Baths, Virgin Gorda; 10 c. Map of Virgin Islands; 12 c. Youth of Tortola (Tortola-St. Thomas ferry); 15 c. The Towers, Tortola; 25 c. Beef Island Airfield. *Vert as T 44*—$1 Virgin Gorda; $1.40, Yachts at anchor.

1965 (17 May). *I.T.U. Centenary. As Nos. 166/7 of Antigua.*

193	4 c. yellow and turquoise	..	20	10
194	25 c. light blue and orange-buff	..	45	20

1965 (25 Oct). *International Co-operation Year. As Nos. 168/9 of Antigua.*

195	1 c. reddish purple and turquoise-green	..	10	15
196	25 c. deep bluish green and lavender	..	30	15

1966 (24 Jan). *Churchill Commemoration. As Nos. 170/3 of Antigua.*

197	1 c. new blue	..	10	10
198	2 c. deep green	..	15	10
199	10 c. brown	..	30	10
200	25 c. bluish violet	..	60	25
197/200		*Set of 4*	1·00	40

1966 (22 Feb). *Royal Visit. As Nos. 174/5 of Antigua.*

201	4 c. black and ultramarine	..	40	10
202	70 c. black and magenta	..	1·40	45

58 Atrato I (paddle-steamer), 1866

(Des R. Granger Barrett. Litho B.W.)

1966 (25 Apr). *Stamp Centenary. T 58 and similar horiz designs. W w 12 (sideways). P 13.*

203	5 c. black, red, yellow and emerald	..	35	10
204	10 c. black, green and rose-red/cream	..	35	10
205	25 c. black, rose-red and blue/pale green	..	55	10
206	60 c. black, red and green/pale blue	..	1·00	2·50
203/6		*Set of 4*	2·00	2·50

Design:—10 c. 1d. and 6d. stamps of 1866; 25 c. Air mail transport, Beef Island, and 6d. stamp of 1866; 60 c. Landing mail at Roadtown, 1866 and 1d. stamp of 1866.

50c.

(62)

1966 (15 Sept). *As Nos. 189 and 191/2 but wmk sideways, surch as T 62.*

207	50 c. on 70 c. black and yellow-brown	..	1·25	90
208	$1.50 on $1.40, light blue and rose	..	3·00	2·00
209	$3 on $2.80, black and bright purple	..	3·00	2·75
207/9		*Set of 3*	6·50	5·00

1966 (1 Dec). *20th Anniv of U.N.E.S.C.O. As Nos. 196/8 of Antigua.*

210	2 c. slate-violet, red, yellow and orange	..	10	10
211	12 c. orange-yellow, violet and deep olive	..	20	10
212	60 c. black, bright purple and orange	..	50	45
210/12		*Set of 3*	65	60

63 Map of Virgin Islands

(Des G. Vasarhelyi. Photo Harrison)

1967 (18 Apr). *New Constitution. W w 12. P 14½.*

213	**63**	2 c. multicoloured	..	10	10
214		10 c. multicoloured	..	15	10
		w. Wmk inverted		15·00	
215		25 c. multicoloured	..	15	10
		w. Wmk inverted		9·00	
216		$1 multicoloured	..	55	40
213/16			*Set of 4*	75	55

64 Mercury (cable ship) and Bermuda-Tortola Link

(Des G. Drummond, Photo Harrison)

1967 (14 Sept). *Inauguration of Bermuda-Tortola Telephone Service. T 64 and similar horiz designs. Multicoloured. W w 12. P 14½.*

217	4 c. Type 64	..	20	10
218	10 c. Chalwell Telecommunications Station	..	20	10
219	50 c. Mercury (cable ship)	..	50	30
217/19		*Set of 3*	80	40

67 Blue Marlin

(Des V. Whiteley. Photo Enschedé)

1968 (2 Jan). *Game Fishing. T 67 and similar horiz designs. W w 12 (sideways). P 12½ × 12.*

220	2 c. multicoloured	..	10	55
221	10 c. multicoloured	..	25	10
222	25 c. black, blue and bright violet	..	55	10
223	40 c. multicoloured	..	85	70
220/3		*Set of 4*	1·60	1·25

Designs—10 c. Cobia; 25 c. Wahoo; 40 c. Fishing launch and map.

1968 INTERNATIONAL YEAR FOR HUMAN RIGHTS

(71)

72 Dr. Martin Luther King, Bible, Sword and Armour Gauntlet

1968 (29 July). *Human Rights Year. Nos. 185 and 188 optd with T 71.*

224	10 c. lake and deep lilac	..	20	10
225	25 c. green and purple	..	30	40

29 July was the date of issue in the islands. The Crown Agents supplies went on sale in London on 1 July, the local consignment being delayed in transit.

(Des V. Whiteley. Litho Format)

1968 (15 Oct). *Martin Luther King Commemoration. W w 12 (sideways). P 14.*

226	**72**	4 c. multicoloured	..	20	20
227		25 c. multicoloured	..	30	40

73 De Havilland D.H.C.6 Twin Otter 100

(Des R. Granger Barrett. Litho Format)

1968 (16 Dec). *Opening of Beef Island Airport Extension. T* **73** *and similar horiz designs. Multicoloured. P* 14.

228	2 c. Type **73**		15	60
229	10 c. Hawker Siddeley H.S.748 airliner		20	10
230	25 c. De Havilland D.H.114 Heron 2		40	10
231	$1 Royal Engineers cap badge		50	2·00
228/31		*Set of* 4	1·10	2·50

77 Long John Silver and Jim Hawkins

78 Jim Hawkins escaping from the Pirates

(Des Jennifer Toombs. Photo Enschedé)

1969 (18 Mar). *75th Death Anniv of Robert Louis Stevenson. Scenes from* Treasure Island. *T* **77/8** *and similar designs. W* w **12** *(sideways on* 10 c., $1). *P* 13½×13 (4 c., 40 c.) or 13×13½ *(others)*.

232	4 c. indigo, pale yellow and carmine-red		25	15
233	10 c. multicoloured		25	10
234	40 c. brown, black and blue		30	30
235	$1 multicoloured		60	1·40
232/5		*Set of* 4	1·25	1·75

Designs: *Vert*—40 c. The fight with Israel Hands. *Horiz*—$1 Treasure trove.

82 Yachts in Road Harbour, Tortola

(Des J. Cooter, Litho P.B.)

1969 (20 Oct). *Tourism. T* **82** *and similar multicoloured designs. W* w **12** *(sideways on* 2 c., $1). *P* 12½.

236	2 c. Tourist and Yellow-finned Grouper (fish) *(vert)*		15	50
237	10 c. Type **82**		30	10
238	20 c. Sun-bathing at Virgin Gorda National Park		40	20
239	$1 Tourist and Pipe Organ Cactus at Virgin Gorda *(vert)*		90	1·50
236/9		*Set of* 4	1·60	2·00

85 Carib Canoe

(Des and litho J.W.)

1970 (16 Feb)–**74.** *Horiz designs as T* **85**. *W* w **12** *(sideways*). P* 14.

240	½ c. buff, red-brown and sepia		10	85
241	1 c. new blue, apple-green and chalky blue		15	30
	a. Perf 13½ (12.11.74)		1·25	2·00
242	2 c. yellow-orange, red-brown and slate		40	1·00
243	3 c. orange-red, cobalt and sepia		30	1·25
244	4 c. greenish blue, chalky blue & bistre-brn		30	50
	w. Wmk Crown to right of CA			
245	5 c. emerald, pink and black		30	10
246	6 c. reddish violet mauve and myrtle-green		40	1·75
247	8 c. apple-green, greenish yellow and sepia		50	2·50
248	10 c. greenish blue, yellow-brown & red-brn		50	15
	a. Perf 13½ (12.11.74)		2·50	2·25
249	12 c. yellow, crimson and brown		65	1·00
	a. Perf 13½ (12.11.74)		2·50	3·25
250	15 c. turquoise-green, orange & bistre-brn		6·00	85
	a. Perf 13½ (12.11.74)		3·50	3·25
251	25 c. grey-green, steel-blue and plum		6·00	1·75
252	50 c. magenta, dull green and purple-brown		4·50	1·50
253	$1 salmon, olive-green and red-brown		5·00	4·75
254	$2 buff, slate and grey		8·50	9·00
255	$3 ochre, deep blue and sepia		5·00	6·50
256	$5 violet and grey		6·00	9·00
240/56		*Set of* 17	38·00	38·00

Designs:—1 c. *Santa Maria* (Columbus' flagship); 2 c. *Elizabeth Bonaventure* (Drake's flagship); 3 c. Dutch Buccaneer, *circa* 1660; 4 c. *Thetis*, 1827 (after etching by E. W. Cooke); 5 c. Henry Morgan's ship (17th century); 6 c. H.M.S. *Boreas* (Captain Nelson, 1784); 8 c. H.M.S. *Éclair*, 1804; 10 c. H.M.S. *Formidable*, 1782; 12 c. H.M.S. *Nymph*, 1778; 15 c. *Windsor Castle* (sailing packet) engaging *Jeune Richard* (French brig), 1807; 25 c. H.M.S. *Astrea*, 1808; 50 c. Wreck of R.M.S. *Rhone*, 1867; $1 Tortola sloop; $2 H.M.S. *Frobisher*; $3 *Booker Viking* (cargo liner), 1967; $5 Hydrofoil *Sun Arrow*.
*The normal sideways watermark shows Crown to left of CA, as seen from the back of the stamp.
See also Nos. 295/300.

---

102 *A Tale of Two Cities*

(Des W. G. Brown. Litho D.L.R.)

1970 (4 May). *Death Centenary of Charles Dickens. T* **102** *and similar horiz designs showing original book illustrations. W* w **12** *(sideways). P* 14.

257	5 c. black, light rose and grey		10	50
258	10 c. black, light blue and pale green		20	10
259	25 c. black, light green and pale yellow		30	40
257/9		*Set of* 3	55	90

Designs:—10 c. *Oliver Twist*; 25 c. *Great Expectations*.

103 Hospital Visit

(Des R. Granger Barrett. Litho Questa)

1970 (10 Aug). *Centenary of British Red Cross. T* **103** *and similar horiz designs. Multicoloured. W* w **12** *(sideways*). P* 14.

260	4 c. Type **103**		25	10
261	10 c. First Aid Class		35	10
262	25 c. Red Cross and Coat of Arms		80	55
	w. Wmk Crown to right of CA		40·00	
260/2		*Set of* 3	1·25	70

*The normal sideways watermark shows Crown to left of CA, as seen from the back of the stamp.

104 Mary Read

105 Children and "UNICEF"

(Des and litho J.W.)

1970 (16 Nov). *Pirates. T* **104** *and similar vert designs. Multicoloured. W* w **12**. *P* 14 × 14½.

263	½ c. Type **104**		10	15
264	10 c. George Lowther		35	10
265	30 c. Edward Teach (Blackbeard)		85	25
266	60 c. Henry Morgan		1·25	1·00
263/6		*Set of* 4	2·25	1·40

(Des L. Curtis. Litho Format)

1971 (13 Dec). *25th Anniv of UNICEF. W* w **12** *(sideways). P* 13½ × 14.

267	**105** 15 c. multicoloured		10	10
268	30 c. multicoloured		20	25

VISIT OF
H.R.H.
THE
PRINCESS MARGARET
1972   1972

(106)

1972 (7 Mar). *Royal Visit of Princess Margaret. Nos. 244 and 251 optd with T* **106**.

269	4 c. greenish blue, chalky blue & bistre-brn		20	15
270	25 c. grey-green, steel-blue and plum		30	45

107 Seaman of 1800

108 Sailfish and *Sir Winston Churchill* (cadet schooner)

(Des J.W. Litho Questa)

1972 (17 Mar). *"Interpex" Stamp Exhibition, New York. T* **107** *and similar vert designs showing Naval Uniforms. Multicoloured. W* w **12** *(sideways*). P* 13½.

271	½ c. Type **107**		10	40
	w. Wmk Crown to left of CA		1·75	
272	10 c. Boatswain, 1787–1807		35	10
273	30 c. Captain, 1795–1812		85	55
274	60 c. Admiral, 1787–95		1·50	2·50
271/4		*Set of* 4	2·50	3·00

*The normal sideways watermark shows Crown to right of CA, as seen from the back of the stamp.

(Des (from photograph by D. Groves) and photo Harrison)

1972 (24 Nov). *Royal Silver Wedding. Multicoloured; background colour given. W* w **12**. *P* 14 × 14½.

275	**108** 15 c. bright blue		20	15
276	25 c. turquoise-blue		20	15
	a. Blue omitted*		£325	
	w. Wmk inverted		30·00	

*The omission of the blue colour results in the Duke's suit appearing sepia instead of deep blue.

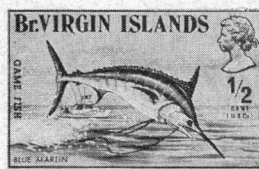

109 Blue Marlin

(Des G. Drummond. Litho Questa)

1972 (12 Dec). *Game Fish. T* **109** *and similar horiz designs. Multicoloured. W* w **12**. *P* 13½.

277	½ c. Type **109**		10	75
	a. Pair. Nos. 277/8		15	1·50
278	½ c. Wahoo		10	75
279	15 c. Yellow-finned Tuna ("Allison Tuna")		65	25
280	25 c. White Marlin		75	30
281	50 c. Sailfish		1·25	1·25
282	$1 Dolphin		2·00	2·75
277/82		*Set of* 6	4·25	5·50
MS283	194×158 mm. Nos. 277/82		8·50	8·50

Nos. 277/8 were printed horizontally and vertically *se-tenant* within the sheet.

110 J. C. Lettsom

111 Green-throated Carib and Antillean Crested Hummingbird

(Des J. Cooter. Litho Questa)

1973 (9 Mar). *"Interpex 1973" (Quakers). T* **110** *and similar multicoloured designs. W* w **12** *(sideways on* ½ c. and 15 c.). *P* 13½.

284	½ c. Type **110**		10	15
285	10 c. Lettsom House *(horiz)*		15	10
286	15 c. Dr. W. Thornton		20	10
287	30 c. Dr. Thornton and Capitol, Washington *(horiz)*		25	20
288	$1 William Penn *(horiz)*		1·00	1·10
284/8		*Set of* 5	1·50	1·40

(Des G. Drummond. Litho Questa)

1973 (30 June). *First Issue of Coinage. T* **111** *and similar horiz designs showing coins and local scenery. Multicoloured. W* w **12**. *P* 14.

289	1 c. Type **111**		10	30
290	5 c. Zenaida Dove		60	10
291	10 c. Ringed Kingfisher		75	10
292	25 c. Mangrove Cuckoo		95	15
293	50 c. Brown Pelican		1·10	1·00
294	$1 Magnificent Frigate Bird		1·40	2·00
289/94		*Set of* 6	4·50	3·25

1973 (17 Oct). *As Nos. 240, 243/5 and 248/9, but W* w **12** *upright.*

295	½ c. buff, red-brown and sepia		50	6·00
296	3 c. orange-red, cobalt and sepia		1·25	2·25
297	4 c. greenish blue, chalky blue & bistre-brn		1·25	4·50
298	5 c. emerald, pink and black		1·25	2·25
299	10 c. greenish blue, yellow-brown & red-brn		1·50	2·50
	w. Wmk inverted			
300	12 c. yellow, dull crimson and light brown		2·00	3·50
295/300		*Set of* 6	7·00	19·00

1973 (14 Nov). *Royal Wedding. As Nos. 165/6 of Anguilla. Centre multicoloured. W* w **12** *(sideways). P* 13½.

301	5 c. brown-ochre		10	10
302	50 c. light turquoise-blue		20	20

112 "The Virgin and Child" (Pintoricchio) 113 Crest of the *Canopus* (French)

(Des G. Drummond. Litho Questa)

1973 (7 Dec). *Christmas. T* **112** *and similar vert designs Multi coloured. W* w **12.** *P* 14.

303	½ c. Type 112		10	10
304	3 c. "Virgin and Child" (Lorenzo di Credi)		10	10
305	25 c. "Virgin and Child" (Crivelli)		15	10
306	50 c. "Virgin and Child with St. John" (Luini)		30	40
303/6		*Set of* 4	50	50

(Des J. Cooter. Litho Questa)

1974 (22 Mar). *"Interpex 1974" (Naval Crests). T* **113** *and similar vert designs. Multicoloured. W* w **12.** *P* 14.

307	5 c. Type 113		20	10
308	18 c. U.S.S. *Saginaw*		35	25
309	25 c. H.M.S. *Rothesay*		40	30
310	50 c. H.M.C.S. *Ottawa*		60	60
307/10		*Set of* 4	1.40	1.10
MS311	196 × 128 mm. Nos. 307/10		1.75	3.75

 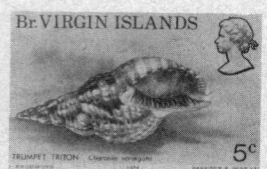

114 Christopher Columbus 115 Atlantic Trumpet Triton (*Charonia variegata*)

(Des J. W. Litho Format)

1974 (19 Aug). *Historical Figures. T* **114** *and similar vert designs. W* w **12.** *P* 14.

312	5 c. orange and black		20	10
	w. Wmk inverted		2.25	
313	10 c. greenish blue and black		30	10
314	25 c. reddish violet and black		35	25
315	40 c. yellow-brown and sepia		60	75
312/15		*Set of* 4	1.25	1.00
MS316	84×119 mm. Nos. 312/15		1.25	2.25

Portraits:—10 c. Sir Walter Raleigh; 25 c. Sir Martin Frobisher; 40 c. Sir Francis Drake.

(Des G. Drummond. Litho Harrison)

1974 (30 Sept). *Seashells. T* **115** *and similar horiz designs. Multicoloured. W* w **12.** *P* 13 × 13½.

317	5 c. Type 115		30	15
	a. Wmk T 53 of Lesotho (sideways)		£120	
	w. Wmk inverted		70.00	
318	18 c. West Indian Murex (*Murex brevifrons*)		60	30
319	25 c. Bleeding Tooth (*Nerita peloranta*)		75	35
320	75 c. Virgin Islands Latirus (*Latirus virginensis*)		1.75	2.00
317/20		*Set of* 4	3.00	2.50
MS321	146×95 mm. Nos. 317/20		3.00	5.50
	a. Printed on the gummed side		£500	
	w. Wmk inverted		32.00	

116 Churchill and St. Mary, Aldermanbury, London 117 H.M.S. *Boreas*

(Des J. W. Litho Questa)

1974 (30 Nov). *Birth Centenary of Sir Winston Churchill. T* **116** *and similar horiz design. Multicoloured. W* w **14** *(sideways*). *P* 14.

322	10 c. Type 116		15	10
	w. Wmk Crown to right of CA		3.75	
323	50 c. St. Mary, Fulton, Missouri		35	50
MS324	141×108 mm. Nos. 322/3		80	1.40

*The normal sideways watermark shows Crown to left of CA, as seen from the back of the stamp.

(Des J. Cooter. Litho J. W.)

1975 (14 Mar). *"Interpex 1975" Stamp Exhibition, New York. Ships' Figureheads. T* **117** *and similar vert designs. Multicoloured. W* w **12.** *P* 13.

325	5 c. Type 117		20	10
326	18 c. *Golden Hind*		50	15
327	40 c. H.M.S. *Superb*		70	25
328	85 c. H.M.S. *Formidable*		1.50	1.50
325/8		*Set of* 4	2.50	1.75
MS329	192×127 mm. Nos. 325/8 (Wmk inverted). P 14		1.75	7.00
	w. Wmk upright		80.00	

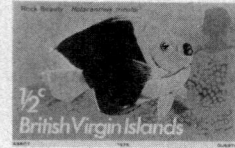

118 Rock Beauty

(Des C. Abbott. Litho Questa)

1975 (16 June–15 Aug). *Fishes. Horiz designs as T* **118.** *Multicoloured. W* w **14** *(sideways*). *P* 14.

330	½ c. Type 118		15	50
	w. Wmk Crown to right of CA		4.50	
331	1 c. Long-spined Squirrelfish		40	1.50
332	3 c. Queen Triggerfish		90	1.50
333	5 c. Blue Angelfish		30	20
334	8 c. Stoplight Parrotfish		30	25
335	10 c. Queen Angelfish		30	25
336	12 c. Nassau Grouper		40	30
337	13 c. Blue Tang		40	30
338	15 c. Sergeant Major		40	35
339	18 c. Spotted Jewfish		70	80
340	20 c. Bluehead Wrasse		60	80
	w. Wmk Crown to right of CA		55.00	
341	25 c. Grey Angelfish		1.00	60
342	60 c. Glass-eyed Snapper		1.25	2.25
343	$1 Blue Chromis		1.75	1.75
	w. Wmk Crown to right of CA		3.50	
344	$2.50, French Angelfish		3.50	5.00
345	$3 Queen Parrotfish		4.25	5.00
346	$5 Four-eyed Butterflyfish (15.8)		6.00	7.50
330/46		*Set of* 17	20.00	26.00

*The normal sideways watermark shows Crown to left of CA, as seen from the back of the stamp.

Imprint dates: "1975", Nos. 330/46; "1977", Nos. 330, 333/8, 340.

The imprints on all the stamps show the designer's name as "Abbot".

119 St. George's Parish School (First meeting-place, 1950)

(Des R. Granger Barrett. Litho Questa)

1975 (27 Nov). *25th Anniv of Restoration of Legislative Council. T* **119** *and similar horiz designs. Multicoloured. W* w **14** *(sideways*). *P* 14.

347	5 c. Type 119		10	10
348	25 c. Legislative Council Building		20	10
349	40 c. Mace and gavel		25	15
350	75 c. Commemorative scroll		35	65
347/50		*Set of* 4	75	80

120 Copper Mine Point

(Des PAD Studio. Litho Walsall)

1976 (12 Mar). *Historic Sites. T* **120** *and similar horiz designs. Multicoloured. W* w **14** *(sideways*). *P* 14½.

351	5 c. Type 120		10	10
352	18 c. Pleasant Valley		20	10
353	50 c. Callwood Distillery		40	30
354	75 c. The Dungeon		60	65
351/4		*Set of* 4	1.10	1.00

121 Massachusetts Brig *Hazard*

(Des J. W. Litho Questa)

1976 (29 May). *Bicentenary of American Revolution. T* **121** *and similar horiz designs. Multicoloured, W* w **14** *(sideways*). *P* 14.

355	8 c. Type 121		50	15
356	22 c. American Privateer *Spy*		70	45
357	40 c. *Raleigh* (American frigate)		1.10	1.00
358	75 c. Frigate *Alliance* and H.M.S. *Trepassy*		1.25	1.90
355/8		*Set of* 4	3.25	3.25
MS359	114×89 mm. Nos. 355/8		4.50	11.00

122 Government House, Tortola 123 Royal Visit, 1966

(Des Walsall. Litho Questa)

1976 (29 Oct). *Fifth Anniv of Friendship Day with U.S. Virgin Is. T* **122** *and similar multicoloured designs. W* w **14** *(sideways on 8 and 75 c.). P* 14.

360	8 c. Type 122		10	10
361	15 c. Government House, St. Croix (*vert*)		10	10
362	30 c. Flags (*vert*)		15	10
363	75 c. Government seals		30	40
360/3		*Set of* 4	50	55

(Des J. Cooter. Litho Walsall)

1977 (7 Feb). *Silver Jubilee. T* **123** *and similar vert designs (inscr "SILVER JUBILEE" at top). Multicoloured. W* w **14.** *P* 13½.

364	8 c. Type 123		10	10
365	30 c. The Holy Bible		15	15
366	60 c. Presentation of Holy Bible		25	40
364/6		*Set of* 3	40	50

For stamps with different inscription, see Nos. 371/3.

The imprint at the stamp's foot gives the designer (wrongly) as "Waddington Studio".

124 Chart of 1739

(Des J. Cooter. Litho Walsall)

1977 (13 June). *18th-Century Maps. T* **124** *and similar horiz designs. Multicoloured. W* w **14.** *P* 13½.

367	8 c. Type 124		40	10
368	22 c. French Map, 1758		65	30
369	30 c. Map from English and Danish surveys, 1775		80	65
370	75 c. Map of 1779		1.25	1.50
367/70		*Set of* 4	2.75	2.25

1977 (26 Oct). *Royal Visit. Designs as Nos.* **364/6** *but inscr. "SILVER JUBILEE ROYAL VISIT" at top, and face-values changed.*

371	5 c. Type 123		10	10
372	25 c. The Holy Bible		20	10
373	50 c. Presentation of Holy Bible		35	25
	w. Wmk inverted		5.50	
371/3		*Set of* 3	55	35

The above also differ from Nos. 364/6 in having the silver frame removed and the silver lettering replaced by white. The imprint at foot now has the designer's name correctly given as "J. E. Cooter".

125 Divers checking Equipment 126 Fire Coral

(Des J. W. Litho Rosenbaum Bros, Vienna)

1978 (10 Feb). *Tourism. T* **125** *and similar vert designs. Multicoloured. W* w **14.** *P* 13½.

374	½ c. Type 125		10	10
	w. Wmk inverted		8.50	
375	5 c. Cup coral on wreck of *Rhone*		20	10
	w. Wmk inverted		1.00	
376	8 c. Sponge formation on wreck of *Rhone*		25	10
	w. Wmk inverted		1.00	
377	22 c. Cup coral and sponges		60	15
	w. Wmk inverted		1.00	
378	30 c. Sponges inside cave		75	20
	w. Wmk inverted		1.25	
379	75 c. Marine life		1.25	85
	w. Wmk inverted		2.00	
374/9		*Set of* 6	2.75	1.25

(Des G. Drummond. Litho Harrison)

1978 (27 Feb). *Corals. T* **126** *and similar horiz designs. Multicoloured. W w* **14** (*sideways*). *P* 14.

380	8 c. Type **126**		25	15
381	15 c. Staghorn coral		40	30
382	40 c. Brain coral		75	85
383	75 c. Elkhorn coral		1·50	1·60
380/3		*Set of 4*	2·50	2·50

127 Iguana   **128** Lignum Vitae

(Des Jennifer Toombs. Litho Questa)

1978 (2 June). *25th Anniv of Coronation. T* **127** *and similar vert designs. P* 15.

384	50 c. brown-ochre, green and silver		20	40
	a. Sheetlet. Nos. 384/6 × 2		1·00	
385	50 c. multicoloured		20	40
386	50 c. brown-ochre, green and silver		20	40
384/6		*Set of 3*	55	1·10

Designs:—No. 384, Plantagenet Falcon; No. 385, Queen Elizabeth II; No. 386, Type **127**.

(Des and litho J.W.)

1978 (4 Sept). *Flowering Trees. T* **128** *and similar horiz designs. Multicoloured. W w* **14** (*sideways**). *P* 13.

387	8 c. Type **128**		15	10
388	22 c. Ginger Thomas		20	15
389	40 c. Dog Almond		30	20
390	75 c. White Cedar		45	70
387/90		*Set of 4*	1·00	1·00
MS391	131×95 mm. Nos. 387/90. P 14		1·25	3·00
	w. Wmk Crown to left of CA		60·00	

*The normal sideways watermark shows Crown to right of CA, *as seen from the back of the stamp.*

129 *Eurema lisa*

(Des G. Hutchins. Litho Questa)

1978 (4 Dec). *Butterflies. T* **129** *and similar horiz designs. Multicoloured. W w* **14** (*sideways*). *P* 14.

392	5 c. Type **129**		35	10
393	22 c. *Agraulis vanillae*		85	20
394	30 c. *Heliconius charithonia*		1·40	30
395	75 c. *Hemiargus hanno*		1·90	1·25
392/5		*Set of 4*	4·00	1·75
MS396	159×113 mm. No. 392×6 and 393×3		2·50	5·50

130 Spiny Lobster

(Des Picton Print. Litho Harrison)

1979 (10 Feb). *Wildlife Conservation. T* **130** *and similar multicoloured designs. W w* **14** (*sideways on 5 and 22 c.*). *P* 14.

397	5 c. Type **130**		15	10
398	15 c. Large Iguana (*vert*)		30	10
399	22 c. Hawksbill Turtle		50	15
400	75 c. Black Coral (*vert*)		1·10	90
397/400		*Set of 4*	1·90	1·10
MS401	130 × 153 mm. Nos. 397/400 (wmk sideways)		2·25	3·75

131 Strawberry Cactus   **132** West Indian Girl

(Des BG Studio. Litho Format)

1979 (7 May). *Cacti. T* **131** *and similar vert designs. Multicoloured. W w* **14**. *P* 14.

402	½ c. Type **131**		10	10
403	5 c. Snowy Cactus		15	10
404	13 c. Barrel Cactus		20	20
405	22 c. Tree Cactus		25	35
406	30 c. Prickly Pear		30	40
407	75 c. Dildo Cactus		40	1·00
402/7		*Set of 6*	1·10	1·90

(Des R. Granger Barrett. Litho Questa)

1979 (9 July). *International Year of the Child. T* **132** *and similar vert designs. Multicoloured. W w* **14** (*inverted*). *P* 14½ × 14.

408	5 c. Type **132**		10	10
409	10 c. African boy		10	10
410	13 c. Asian girl		10	10
411	$1 European boy		50	85
408/11		*Set of 4*	65	1·00
MS412	91 × 114 mm. Nos. 408/11.		70	1·50

133 1956 Road Harbour 3 c.   **134** Pencil Urchin
Definitive Stamp

(Des J. W. Photo Heraclio Fournier)

1979 (1 Oct). *Death Centenary of Sir Rowland Hill. T* **133** *and similar designs showing stamps. P* 13½.

413	5 c. deep blue, new blue and brown-olive		10	10
414	13 c. deep blue and claret		10	10
415	75 c. deep blue and bright purple		45	50
413/15		*Set of 3*	55	55
MS416	37 × 91 mm. $1 deep blue & carm-red. P 13		70	1·25

Designs: (39 × 27 *mm*)—13 c. 1889 2½d.; 75 c. Great Britain unissued 1910 2d. Tyrian plum. (40 × 28 *mm*)—$1. 1867 1s. "Missing Virgin" error.

(Des BG Studio. Litho Questa)

1979 (17 Dec)—**82.** *Marine Life. Vert designs as T* **134.** *Multicoloured. W w* **14.** *Ordinary paper. P* 14.

417	½ c. Calcified Algae (1.4.80)		40	1·75
418	1 c. Purple-tipped Sea Anemone (1.4.80)		55	1·75
419	3 c. Common Starfish (1.4.80)		60	1·75
420	5 c. Type **134**		60	1·25
	a. Chalk-surfaced paper (27.8.82)		75	60
421	8 c. Atlantic Trumpet Triton (*Charonia variegata*)		85	1·50
	a. Chalk-surfaced paper (27.8.82)		1·25	60
422	10 c. Christmas Tree Worms		30	1·00
423	13 c. Flamingo Tongue (*Cyphoma gibbosus*) (1.4.80)		1·50	2·50
	a. Chalk-surfaced paper (27.8.82)		1·50	75
424	15 c. Spider Crab		40	60
	a. Chalk-surfaced paper (27.8.82)		1·50	55
425	18 c. Sea Squirts (1.4.80)		2·00	3·00
426	20 c. True Tulip (*Fasciolaria tulipa*)		55	85
	a. Chalk-surfaced paper (27.8.82)		1·25	65
427	25 c. Rooster-tail Conch (*Strombus gallus*)		1·25	3·00
	w. Wmk inverted			
428	30 c. West Indian Fighting Conch (*Strombus pugilis*) (1.4.80)		1·75	1·25
	a. Chalk-surfaced paper (27.8.82)		2·00	1·00
429	60 c. Mangrove Crab (1.4.80)		1·75	2·50
430	$1 Coral Polyps (1.4.80)		2·00	3·50
431	$2.50, Peppermint Shrimp		2·50	5·00
432	$3 West Indian Murex (*Murex brevifrons*)		2·50	6·00
433	$5 Carpet Anemone (1.4.80)		3·25	7·50
417/33		*Set of 17*	20·00	35·00

Imprint dates: "1979", Nos. 420/2, 424, 426/7, 431/2; "1980", Nos. 417/19, 423, 425, 428/30, 433; "1982", Nos. 420a/1a, 423a/4a, 426a, 428a.

135 Rotary Athletics Meeting,   **136** Brown Booby
Tortola

(Des J. W. Litho Enschedé)

1980 (23 Feb). *75th Anniv of Rotary International. T* **135** *and similar horiz designs. Multicoloured. W w* **14** (*sideways*). *P* 13½ × 14.

434	13 c. Type **135**		10	10
435	22 c. Paul P. Harris (founder) and Rotary emblem		15	10
436	60 c. "Creation of a National Park", Mount Sage, Tortola		40	40
437	$1 Rotary anniversary emblem		70	75
434/7		*Set of 4*	1·25	1·25
MS438	149 × 148 mm. Nos. 434/7.		1·25	3·50

(Des K. Penny. Litho Secura, Singapore)

1980 (6 May). *"London 1980" International Stamp Exhibition. Birds. T* **136** *and similar horiz designs. Multicoloured. W w* **14** (*sideways**). *P* 13½.

439	20 c. Type **136**		20	20
	aw. Wmk Crown to right of CA			
	b. Wmk upright		40	50
	bw. Wmk inverted		50	60
440	25 c. Magnificent Frigate Bird		25	25
	b. Wmk upright		1·75	2·00
	bw. Wmk inverted		1·75	2·00
441	50 c. White-tailed Tropic Bird		40	40
	b. Wmk upright		65	75
	bw. Wmk inverted		80	90
442	75 c. Brown Pelican		55	55
	w. Wmk Crown to right of CA		5·00	
439/42		*Set of 4*	1·25	1·25
MS443	152×130 mm. Nos. 439/42		1·25	2·25
	w. Wmk Crown to left of CA		15·00	

*The normal sideways watermark shows Crown to left of CA on the sheet stamps and to right of CA on the miniature sheet; *both as seen from the back.* Singles of Nos. 439aw and 442w cannot be identified as the listed variety unless part of the sheet margin is attached to distinguish them from stamps originating in No. **MS443**.

CARIBBEAN
COMMONWEALTH
PARLIAMENTARY
ASSOCIATION
MEETING
TORTOLA   11-19 JULY 1980

(**137**)   **138** Sir Francis Drake

1980 (7 July). *Caribbean Commonwealth Parliamentary Association Meeting, Tortola.* Nos. 414/15 optd wth *T* **137**.

444	13 c. deep blue and claret		15	10
445	75 c. deep blue and bright blue		40	40

(Des Franklin Mint. Litho Questa)

1980 (26 Sept). *Sir Francis Drake Commemoration. T* **138** *and similar vert designs. W w* **14** (*inverted on 75 c.*). *P* 14 × 14½.

446	5 c. Type **138**		50	10
447	15 c. Queen Elizabeth I		70	15
448	30 c. Drake receiving knighthood		90	30
449	75 c. *Golden Hind* and coat of arms		1·75	1·25
446/9		*Set of 4*	3·50	1·60
MS450	171 × 121 mm. Nos. 446/9. Wmk inverted		3·50	6·00
	a. 75 c. value in miniature sheet imperf		£150	
	b. 30 c. value in miniature sheet imperf		£150	

139 Jost van Dyke

(Des Jennifer Toombs. Litho Rosenbaum Bros, Vienna)

1980 (1 Dec). *Island Profiles. T* **139** *and similar horiz designs. Multicoloured. W w* **14** (*sideways**). *P* 13½.

451	2 c. Type **139**		10	10
	w. Wmk Crown to right of CA		10	
452	5 c. Peter Island		10	10
	w. Wmk Crown to right of CA		10	
453	13 c. Virgin Gorda		15	10
	w. Wmk Crown to right of CA		20	
454	22 c. Anegada		20	10
	w. Wmk Crown to right of CA		30	
455	30 c. Norman Island		25	15
	w. Wmk Crown to right of CA		45	
456	$1 Tortola		70	1·00
	w. Wmk Crown to right of CA		45	
451/6		*Set of 6*	1·25	1·10
MS457	95×88 mm. No. 456 (wmk upright)		85	1·50
	a. Error. Imperf		£325	
	b. Gold and black omitted		£325	
	w. Wmk inverted		1·25	

*The normal sideways watermark shows Crown to left of CA, *as seen from the back of the stamp.*

140 Dancing Lady   **141** Wedding Bouquet from British Virgin Islands

(Des C. Abbott. Litho Walsall)

1981 (3 Mar). *Flowers. T* **140** *and similar vert designs. Multicoloured. W w* **14** *(sideways). P* 11.

458	5 c. Type 140		15	10
459	20 c. Love in the Mist		30	25
460	22 c. *Pitcairnia angustifolia*		30	25
461	75 c. Dutchman's Pipe		60	80
462	$1 Maiden Apple		70	1·00
458/62		*Set of 5*	1·90	2·25

(Des J. W. Litho Harrison)

1981 (22 July). *Royal Wedding. T* **141** *and similar vert designs. Multicoloured. W w* **14**. *P* 14.

463	10 c. Type 141		10	10
	w. Wmk inverted		2·50	
464	35 c. Prince Charles and Queen Elizabeth the Queen Mother in Garter robes		20	15
	w. Wmk inverted		3·00	
465	$1.25, Prince Charles and Lady Diana Spencer		60	80
463/5		*Set of 3*	80	90

 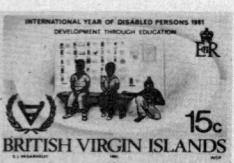

142 Stamp Collecting   **143** "Development through Education"

(Des BG Studio. Litho Questa)

1981 (10 Oct). *25th Anniv of Duke of Edinburgh Award Scheme. T* **142** *and similar vert designs. Multicoloured. W w* **14**. *P* 14.

466	10 c. Type 142		10	10
467	15 c. Athletics		10	10
468	50 c. Camping		25	25
469	$1 Duke of Edinburgh		40	45
466/9		*Set of 4*	65	80

(Des G. Vasarhelyi. Litho Walsall)

1981 (19 Oct). *International Year for Disabled Persons. T* **143** *and similar horiz designs. Multicoloured. W w* **14** *(sideways). P* 14.

470	15 c. Type 143		15	15
471	20 c. Fort Charlotte Children's Centre		20	20
472	30 c. "Developing cultural awareness"		30	30
473	$1 Fort Charlotte Children's Centre (different)		85	1·25
470/3		*Set of 4*	1·40	1·75

144 Detail from "The Adoration of the Shepherds" (Rubens)   **145** Green-throated Caribs and Erythrina

(Des J. W. Litho Questa)

1981 (30 Nov). *Christmas. T* **144** *and similar designs showing details from "The Adoration of the Shepherds" by Rubens. W w* **14**. *P* 14.

474	5 c. multicoloured		15	10
475	15 c. multicoloured		25	10
476	30 c. multicoloured		45	15
477	$1 multicoloured		1·10	1·10
474/7		*Set of 4*	1·75	1·25
MS478	117 × 90 mm. 50 c. multicoloured (*horiz*) (wmk sideways)		1·40	85

(Des Walsall. Litho Format)

1982 (5 Apr). *Hummingbirds. T* **145** *and similar vert designs. Multicoloured. W w* **14**. *P* 14 × 14½.

479	15 c. Type 145		50	15
480	30 c. Green-throated Carib and Bougainvillea		75	45
481	35 c. Antillean Crested Hummingbirds and *Granadilla passiflora*		85	55
482	$1.25, Antillean Crested Hummingbird and Hibiscus		2·50	3·00
479/82		*Set of 4*	4·25	3·75

146 "People caring for People"   **147** Princess at Victoria and Albert Museum, November 1981

(Des Harrison. Litho Format)

1982 (3 May). *Tenth Anniv of Lions Club of Tortola. T* **146** *and similar horiz designs. Multicoloured. W w* **14** *(sideways). P* 13½ × 14.

483	10 c. Type 146		20	15
484	20 c. Tortola Headquarters		30	15
485	30 c. "We Serve"		35	20
486	$1.50, "Lions" symbol		80	1·40
483/6		*Set of 4*	1·50	1·75
MS487	124 × 102 mm. Nos. 483/6		2·50	4·25

(Des C. Abbott. Litho Harrison)

1982 (2 July*). *21st Birthday of Princess of Wales. T* **147** *and similar vert designs. Multicoloured. W w* **14**. *P* 14½ × 14.

488	10 c. British Virgin Islands coat of arms		15	10
489	35 c. Type 147		30	15
490	50 c. Bride and groom proceeding into Vestry		45	35
491	$1.50, Formal portrait		1·10	1·10
488/91		*Set of 4*	1·75	1·50

*This is the local release date. The Crown Agents released the stamps on 1 July.

148 Douglas DC-3

(Des A. Theobald. Litho Questa)

1982 (10 Sept). *10th Anniv of Air BVI. T* **148** *and similar horiz designs. Multicoloured. W w* **14** *(sideways). P* 14.

492	10 c. Type 148		55	15
493	15 c. Britten Norman Islander		75	20
494	60 c. Hawker Siddeley H.S.748		1·40	75
495	75 c. Runway scene		1·50	90
492/5		*Set of 4*	3·75	1·75

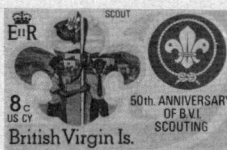

149 Scouts raising Flag

(Des R. Vigurs. Litho Questa)

1982 (18 Nov). *75th Anniv of Boy Scout Movement ($1) and 50th Anniv of Scouting in B.V.I. (others). T* **149** *and similar horiz designs. Multicoloured. W w* **14** *(sideways*). *P* 14.

496	8 c. Type 149		20	10
497	20 c. Cub Scout		45	25
498	50 c. Sea Scout		60	55
	w. Wmk Crown to right of CA		13·00	
499	$1 First camp, Brownsea Island, and portrait of Lord Baden-Powell		1·00	1·50
	w. Wmk Crown to right of CA		13·00	
496/9		*Set of 4*	2·00	2·25

*The normal sideways watermark shows Crown to left of CA, as seen from the back of the stamp.

150 Legislature in Session   **151** Florence Nightingale

(Des G. Vasarhelyi. Litho Enschedé)

1983 (10 Mar). *Commonwealth Day. T* **150** *and similar horiz designs. Multicoloured. W w* **14** *(sideways). P* 13 × 13½.

500	10 c. Type 150		10	10
501	30 c. Tourism		25	20
502	35 c. Satellite view of Earth showing Virgin Islands		25	25
503	75 c. B.V.I. and Commonwealth flags		70	90
500/3		*Set of 4*	1·10	1·25

(Des L. Curtis. Litho Questa)

1983 (9 May). *Nursing Week. T* **151** *and similar multicoloured designs. W w* **14** *(sideways on* 60 c. *and* 75 c.). *P* 14.

504	10 c. Type 151		50	15
505	30 c. Staff nurse and assistant nurse		90	45
506	60 c. Public Health nurses testing blood pressure (*horiz*)		1·75	1·25
507	75 c. Peebles Hospital (*horiz*)		1·90	1·75
504/7		*Set of 4*	4·50	3·25

---

152 Frame Construction

(Des R. Burnett. Litho Harrison)

1983 (25 July). *Traditional Boat-building. T* **152** *and similar horiz designs. Multicoloured. W w* **14** *(sideways). P* 14.

508	15 c. Type 152		35	25
509	25 c. Planking		50	45
510	50 c. Launching		80	80
511	$1 Maiden voyage		1·25	1·00
508/11		*Set of 4*	2·50	3·00
MS512	127 × 101 mm. Nos. 508/11		2·50	3·75

153 Grumman G-21 Goose Amphibian   **154** "Madonna and Child with the Infant Baptist"

(Des Walsall. Litho Questa)

1983 (15 Sept). *Bicentenary of Manned Flight. T* **153** *and similar horiz designs. Multicoloured. W w* **14** *(sideways). P* 14.

513	10 c. Type 153		20	15
514	30 c. Riley Turbo Skyliner		45	45
515	60 c. Embraer EMB-110 Bandeirante		85	85
516	$1.25, Hawker Siddeley H.S.748		1·50	1·60
513/16		*Set of 4*	2·75	2·75

(Des M. Joyce. Litho Questa)

1983 (7 Nov). *Christmas. 500th Birth Anniv of Raphael. T* **154** *and similar vert designs showing details of different paintings. Multicoloured. W w* **14**. *P* 14½ × 14.

517	8 c. Type 154		10	10
518	15 c. "La Belle Jardiniére"		20	25
519	50 c. "Madonna Del Granduca"		65	70
520	$1 "The Terranuova Madonna"		1·25	1·40
517/20		*Set of 4*	2·00	2·25
MS521	108 × 101 mm. Nos. 517/20		2·75	3·75

155 Local Tournament   **156** Port Purcell

(Des L. Curtis. Litho Questa)

1984 (20 Feb). *60th Anniv of World Chess Federation. T* **155** *and similar multicoloured designs. W w* **14** *(sideways on* 10 c. *and* $1, *inverted on* 35 c.). *P* 14.

522	10 c. Type 155		1·00	40
523	35 c. Staunton chess pieces (*vert*)		2·00	1·50
524	75 c. Karpov's winning position, 1980 Chess Olympiad (*vert*)		3·75	4·25
525	$1 B.V.I. Gold Medal won by Bill Hook at 1980 Chess Olympiad		4·25	5·50
522/5		*Set of 4*	10·00	10·50

(Des L. Curtis. Litho Questa)

1984 (16 Apr). *250th Anniv of "Lloyd's List" (newspaper). T* **156** *and similar vert designs. Multicoloured. W w* **14**. *P* 14½ × 14.

526	15 c. Type 156		25	30
527	25 c. Boeing 747-100		45	50
528	50 c. Wreck of *Rhone* (mail steamer), 1867		90	95
529	$1 *Booker Viking* (cargo liner)		1·50	1·60
526/9		*Set of 4*	2·75	3·00

157 Mail Ship *Boyne*, Boeing 747-100 and U.P.U. Logo

(Des L. Curtis. Litho Walsall)

1984 (16 May). *Universal Postal Union Congress, Hamburg. Sheet* 90 × 69 *mm. W w* **14** *(sideways). P* 14.

MS530	**157** $1 pale blue and black		2·25	2·50

158 Running   **159** Steel Band

(Des R. Granger Barrett. Litho Walsall)

1984 (3 July). *Olympic Games, Los Angeles. T* **158** *and similar horiz designs. Multicoloured. W w* **14** (*sideways**). P 14.

531	15 c. Type **158**	.. ..	40	40
	a. Pair. Nos. 531/2	..	80	80
	aw. Wmk Crown to right of CA		6·00	
532	15 c. Runner	.. ..	40	40
533	20 c. Wind-surfing ..	..	45	45
	a. Pair. Nos. 533/4		90	90
534	20 c. Surfer	.. ..	45	45
535	30 c. Sailing	.. ..	65	65
	a. Pair. Nos. 535/6		1·25	1·25
536	30 c. Yacht	.. ..	65	65
531/6		*Set of 6*	2·75	2·75
MS537	97×69 mm. $1 Torch bearer. Wmk upright		1·50	1·90

*The normal sideways watermark shows Crown to left of CA, *as seen from the back of the stamp.*

Nos. 531/2, 533/4 and 535/6 were printed together, *se-tenant*, in horizontal and vertical pairs throughout the sheets.

(Des D. Miller. Litho Format)

1984 (14 Aug). *150th Anniv of Abolition of Slavery. T* **159** *and similar vert designs showing various aspects of Emancipation Festival. Multicoloured. W w* **14**. P 14.

538	10 c. Type **159**	.. ..	30	35
	a. Horiz strip of 5. Nos. 538/42		1·40	
539	10 c. Dancing girls	..	30	35
540	10 c. Men in traditional costumes	..	30	35
541	10 c. Girl in traditional costume	..	30	35
542	10 c. Festival Queen	..	30	35
543	30 c. Green and yellow dinghies	..	45	50
	a. Horiz strip of 5. Nos. 543/7	..	2·00	
544	30 c. Blue and red dinghies	..	45	50
545	30 c. White and blue dinghies	..	45	50
546	30 c. Red and yellow dinghies	..	45	50
547	30 c. Blue and white dinghies	..	45	50
538/47		*Set of 10*	3·00	3·50

Nos. 538/42 and 543/7 were each printed together, *se-tenant*, in horizontal strips of 5 throughout the sheet, forming composite designs. On Nos. 543/7 the sail colours of the dinghies are described to assist identification.

160 Sloop

(Des R. Burnett. Litho J .W.)

1984 (15 Nov). *Boats. T* **160** *and similar horiz designs. Multicoloured. W w* **14** (*sideways*). P 13 × 13½.

548	10 c. Type **160** ..	..	40	40
549	35 c. Fishing boat	..	1·00	65
550	60 c. Schooner ..	..	1·40	1·25
551	75 c. Cargo boat	..	1·40	1·60
548/51		*Set of 4*	3·75	3·25
MS552	125 × 90 mm. Nos. 548/51. P 14	..	3·25	4·00

161 One Cent Coin and Aerial View   **162** Red-billed Tropic Bird

(Litho Walsall)

1985 (15 Jan). *New Coinage. T* **161** *and similar horiz designs showing coins and local scenery. Multicoloured. W w* **14** (*sideways*). P 14½.

553	1 c. Type **161**	..	10	10
554	5 c. Five cent coin and boulders on beach	..	10	10
555	10 c. Ten cent coin and scuba diving	..	20	20
556	25 c. Twenty-five cent coin and yachts	..	45	50
557	50 c. Fifty cent coin and jetty ..	..	90	1·25
558	$1 One dollar coin and beach at night	..	1·75	2·00
553/8		*Set of 6*	3·00	4·00
MS559	103 × 156 mm. Nos. 553/8 ..	..	3·00	6·50

A set of stamps, 55 c. and $1·50 each × 2, showing Michael Jackson the entertainer was prepared in 1985, but was never released for postal use. Samples of the $1·50 values were, however, distributed for publicity purposes and both values exist from stock dispersed by the liquidator of Format International Security Printers Ltd.

(Des N. Arlott. Litho Questa)

1985 (3 July). *Birds of the British Virgin Islands. T* **162** *and similar vert designs. Multicoloured. W w* **14**. "1985" imprint date. P 14.

560	1 c. Type **162**..	..	70	1·25
561	2 c. Yellow-crowned Night Heron ..	..	70	1·25
562	5 c. Mangrove Cuckoo	..	80	1·25
563	8 c. Northern Mockingbird ..	..	1·00	1·75
564	10 c. Grey Kingbird ..	..	1·00	40
565	12 c. Red-necked Pigeon	..	1·25	65
566	15 c. Least Bittern	..	1·50	65
567	18 c. Smooth-billed Ani	..	1·75	2·00
568	20 c. Clapper Rail	..	1·75	1·00
569	25 c. American Kestrel	..	1·75	2·00
570	30 c. Pearly-eyed Thrasher	..	1·75	1·10
571	35 c. Bridled Quail Dove	..	2·00	1·50
572	40 c. Green Heron	..	2·00	1·75
573	50 c. Scaly-breasted Ground Dove	..	2·25	2·50
574	60 c. Little Blue Heron	..	2·50	3·50
575	$1 Audubon's Shearwater ..	..	3·25	3·50
576	$2 Blue-faced Booby	..	4·00	7·00
577	$3 Cattle Egret	..	5·00	8·50
578	$5 Zenaida Dove	..	7·50	11·00
560/78		*Set of 19*	38·00	45·00

For these stamps watermarked w **16** see Nos. 647/60.

IMPERFORATES AND MISSING COLOURS. Various issues between Nos. 579 and 609 exist either imperforate or with colours omitted. Many originate from stock dispersed by the liquidator of Format International Security Printers Ltd. Such items are not listed as there is no evidence that they fulfil the criteria outlined on page xi of this catalogue.

163 The Queen Mother at Festival of Remembrance   **164** Seaside Sparrow

(Des Maxine Marsh. Litho Format)

1985 (26 Aug). *Life and Times of Queen Elizabeth the Queen Mother. Various vertical portraits as T* **163**. *Multicoloured.* P 12½. A. W w **15** (*sideways*)

579A	10 c. Type **163**	..	10	20
	a. Horiz pair. Nos. 579A/80A	..	20	40
580A	10 c. At Victoria Palace Theatre, 1984	..	10	20
581A	25 c. At the engagement of the Prince of Wales, 1981	..	15	40
	a. Horiz pair. Nos. 581A/2A	..	30	80
582A	25 c. Opening Celia Johnson Theatre, 1985	..	15	40
583A	50 c. The Queen Mother on her 82nd birthday	..	20	70
	a. Horiz pair. Nos. 583A/4A	..	40	1·40
584A	50 c. At the Tate Gallery, 1983	..	20	70
585A	75 c. At the Royal Smithfield Show, 1983	..	25	1·00
	a. Horiz pair. Nos. 585A/6A	..	50	2·00
586A	75 c. Unveiling Mountbatten statue, 1983	..	25	1·00
579A/86A		*Set of 8*	1·25	4·25
MS587A	85×114 mm. $1 At Columbia University; $1 At a Wedding, St. Margaret's Westminster, 1983	..	85	4·00

B. *No wmk*

579B	10 c. Type **163**	..	2·50	2·50
	a. Horiz pair. Nos. 579B/80B	..	5·00	5·00
580B	10 c. At Victoria Palace Theatre, 1984	..	2·50	2·50
581B	25 c. At the engagement of the Prince of Wales, 1981	..	2·50	2·50
	a. Horiz pair. Nos. 581B/2B	..	5·00	5·00
582B	25 c. Opening Celia Johnson Theatre, 1985	..	2·50	2·50
583B	50 c. The Queen Mother on her 82nd birthday	..	3·00	3·00
	a. Horiz pair. Nos. 583B/4B	..	6·00	6·00
584B	50 c. At the Tate Gallery, 1983 ..	..	3·00	3·00
585B	75 c. At the Royal Smithfield Show, 1983	..	3·00	3·00
	a. Horiz pair. Nos. 585B/6B ..	..	6·00	6·00
586B	75 c. Unveiling Mountbatten statue, 1983	..	3·00	3·00
579B/86B		*Set of 8*	20·00	20·00

The two designs of each value were issued, *se-tenant*, in horizontal pairs within the sheets.

Each *se-tenant* pair shows a floral pattern across the bottom of the portraits which stops short of the left-hand edge on the left-hand stamp and of the right-hand edge on the right-hand stamp.

Sets of four miniature sheets, containing the two designs of each value, were prepared, but not issued. Examples exist from stock dispersed by the liquidator of Format International Security Printers Ltd.

Designs as Nos. 583/4 and 585/6, but with face values of $2·50×2 and $1×2, also exist in additional miniature sheets from a restricted printing issued 18 December 1985.

(Des R. Vigurs. Litho Format)

1985 (17 Dec). *Birth Bicentenary of John J. Audubon* (ornithologist). *T* **164** *and similar vert designs. showing original paintings. Multicoloured. P* 15.

588	15 c. Type **164**	..	40	20
589	30 c. Passenger Pigeon	..	70	70
590	50 c. Yellow-breasted Chat	..	80	1·75
591	$1 American Kestrel	..	1·25	2·75
588/91		*Set of 4*	2·75	4·75

165 S.V. *Flying Cloud*   (**166**)

INAUGURAL FLIGHT

(Des G. Drummond. Litho Format)

1986 (27 Jan). *Visiting Cruise Ships. T* **165** *and similar horiz designs. Multicoloured. W w* **15**. P 15.

592	35 c. Type **165**	..	80	85
	w. Wmk inverted	..	10·00	
593	50 c. M.V. *Newport Clipper*	..	1·10	1·50
	w. Wmk inverted	..	9·00	
594	75 c. M.V. *Cunard Countess*	..	1·10	2·50
595	$1 M.V. *Sea Goddess*	..	1·25	3·00
	w. Wmk inverted	..	17·00	
592/5		*Set of 4*	3·75	7·00

1986 (17 Apr). *Inaugural Flight of Miami–Beef Island Air Service. Nos. 581/2 and 585/6 optd with T* **166**. A. W w **15** (*sideways*)

596A	25 c. At the engagement of the Prince of Wales, 1981	..	40	50
	a. Horiz pair. Nos. 596A/7A	..	80	1·00
597A	25 c. Opening Celia Johnson Theatre, 1985	..	40	50
598A	75 c. At the Royal Smithfield Show, 1983	..	1·25	1·50
	a. Horiz pair. Nos. 598A/9A	..	2·50	3·00
599A	75 c. Unveiling Mountbatten statue, 1983	..	1·25	1·50
596A/9A		*Set of 4*	3·00	3·50

B. *No wmk*

596B	25 c. At the engagement of the Prince of Wales, 1981	..	1·75	2·25
	a. Horiz pair. Nos. 596B/7B	..	3·50	4·50
597B	25 c. Opening Celia Johnson Theatre, 1985	..	1·75	2·25
598B	75 c. At the Royal Smithfield Show, 1983	..	1·75	2·25
	a. Horiz pair. Nos. 598B/9B	..	3·50	4·50
599B	75 c. Unveiling Mountbatten statue, 1983	..	1·75	2·25
596B/9B		*Set of 4*	6·00	8·00

167 Queen Elizabeth II in 1958

(Des Court House Studio. Litho Format)

1986 (21 Apr). *60th Birthday of Queen Elizabeth II. T* **167** *and similar multicoloured designs.* P 12½.

600	12 c. Type **167**..	..	15	20
601	35 c. At a Maundy Service	..	20	45
	a. Wmk w **15** (sideways)	..	2·00	
602	$1.50. Queen Elizabeth	..	45	1·75
	a. Wmk w **15** (sideways)	..	3·25	
603	$2 During a visit to Canberra, 1982 (vert)	..	60	2·25
600/3		*Set of 4*	1·25	4·25
MS604	85×115 mm $3 Queen with bouquet	..	3·50	5·50

Examples of the 12 c., 35 c. and $1.50 values with the blue (ribbons and frame) omitted are from stock dispersed by the liquidator of Format International Security Printers Ltd.

Unissued sets of five miniature sheets, each containing one value, come from the same source.

168 Miss Sarah Ferguson   **169** Harvesting Sugar Cane

(Des Court House Studio. Litho Format)

1986 (23 July–15 Oct). *Royal Wedding. T* **168** *and similar multicoloured designs.* P 12½.

605	35 c. Type **168**..	..	25	55
	a. Pair. Nos. 605/6..	..	50	1·10
	b. Wmk w **15**	..	2·00	
	ba. Pair. Nos. 605b/6b	..	4·00	
606	35 c. Prince Andrew and Miss Sarah Ferguson	..	25	55
	b. Wmk w **15**	..	2·00	
607	$1 Prince Andrew in morning dress (*horiz*)	..	40	1·25
	a. Pair. Nos. 607/8..	..	80	2·50

608	$1 Miss Sarah Ferguson (different) (horiz)		40	1·25
605/8	.. .. Set of 4		1·10	3·25
MS609	115×85 mm. $4 Duke and Duchess of			
	York in carriage after wedding (horiz) (15.10.86)		2·50	5·50

Nos. 605/6 and 607/8 were each printed together, se-tenant, in horizontal and vertical pairs throughout the sheets.
Nos. 605/8 imperforate come from souvenir stamp booklets.
Nos. 605/8 overprinted "Congratulations to T.R.H. The Duke & Duchess of York" were not issued.

(Des Toni Lance. Litho Questa)

1986 (30 July). *History of Rum Making.* T **169** and similar horiz designs. Multicoloured. W w 15. P 14.

610	12 c. Type 169..		80	40
611	40 c. Bringing sugar cane to mill		1·50	1·25
612	60 c. Rum distillery		2·00	3·25
613	$1 Delivering barrels of rum to ship		3·25	4·00
610/13	Set of 4		6·75	8·00
MS614	115×84 mm. $2 Royal Navy rum issue.			
	Wmk sideways		6·50	8·50

170 C.S. *Sentinel*   **171** Statue of Liberty at Sunset

(Des Court House Studio. Litho Format)

1986 (28 Oct). *20th Anniv of Cable and Wireless Caribbean Headquarters, Tortola.* T **170** and similar horiz designs. Multicoloured. W w 15. P 12½.

615	35 c. Type 170..		60	80
	a. Vert pair. Nos. 615/16		1·10	1·60
616	35 c. C.S. *Retriever* (1961)		60	80
617	60 c. C.S. *Cable Enterprise* (1964)		75	1·50
	a. Vert pair. Nos. 617/18		1·50	3·00
618	60 c. C.S. *Mercury* (1962)		75	1·50
619	75 c. C.S. *Recorder* (1955)		75	1·75
	a. Vert pair. Nos. 619/20		1·50	3·50
620	75 c. C.S. *Pacific Guardian* (1984)		75	1·75
621	$1 S.S. *Great Eastern* (1860's)		80	2·00
	a. Vert pair. Nos. 621/2		1·60	4·00
622	$1 C.S. *Cable Venture* (1977)		80	2·00
615/22	Set of 8		5·00	11·00
MS623	Four sheets, each 102×131 mm. (a) 40 c. × 2 As 35 c. (b) 50 c. × 2 As 60 c. (c) 80 c. × 2 As 75 c. (d) $1.50 × 2 As $1 Set of 4 sheets		5·00	12·00

The two designs of each value were printed, se-tenant, in vertical pairs throughout the sheets.

(Des Court House Studio. Litho Format)

1986 (15 Dec). *Centenary of Statue of Liberty.* T **171** and similar vert views of Statue in separate miniature sheets. Multicoloured. P 14×13½.

MS624	Nine sheets, each 85×115 mm. 50 c.; 75 c.; 90 c.; $1; $1.25; $1.50; $1.75; $2; $2.50		
	Set of 9 sheets	9·00	14·00

172 18th-century Spanish Galleon   **173** Outline Map and Flag of Montserrrat

(Des J. Batchelor. Litho Questa)

1987 (15 Apr). *Shipwrecks.* T **172** and similar horiz designs. Multicoloured. W w 15. P 14.

625	12 c. Type 172		1·50	55
626	35 c. H.M.S. *Astrea* (frigate), 1808		2·75	1·40
627	75 c. *Rhone* (mail steamer), 1867		4·25	4·25
628	$1.50 *Captain Rokos* (freighter), 1929		6·00	8·00
625/8	Set of 4		13·00	13·00
MS629	86×65 mm. $1.50, *Volvart*, 1819		13·00	13·00

(Des R. Burnett. Litho Walsall)

1987 (28 May). *11th Meeting of Organization of Eastern Caribbean States.* T **173** and similar vert designs, each showing outline map and flag. Multicoloured. W w 16. P 14.

630	10 c. Type 173..		70	70
631	15 c. Grenada		80	80
632	20 c. Dominica		85	80
633	25 c. St. Kitts–Nevis		90	1·00
634	35 c. St. Vincent and Grenadines		1·40	1·00
635	50 c. British Virgin Islands		2·00	2·50
636	75 c. Antigua and Barbuda		2·25	3·25
637	$1 St. Lucia..		2·75	3·50
630/7	Set of 8		10·50	12·00

174 Spider Lily   **175** Early Mail Packet and 1867 1s. Stamp

(Des Jennifer Toombs. Litho Questa)

1987 (20 Aug). *Opening of Botanical Gardens.* T **174** and similar vert designs. Multicoloured. W w 16. P 14.

638	12 c. Type 174..		80	35
639	35 c. Barrel Cactus		1·75	1·00
640	$1 Wild Plantain		2·75	3·25
641	$1.50, Little Butterfly Orchid		8·00	8·00
638/41	Set of 4		12·00	12·00
MS642	139×104 mm. $2.50, White Cedar		3·75	6·00

1987 (28 Oct). *As Nos. 564, 566, 568/9, 571, 575 and 577 but W w 16. "1987" imprint date. P 14.*

647	10 c. Grey Kingbird		70	90
649	15 c. Least Bittern		90	90
651	20 c. Clapper Rail		90	80
652	25 c. American Kestrel		1·25	1·00
654	35 c. Bridled Quail Dove		1·25	1·00
658	$1 Audubon's Shearwater..		2·25	3·50
660	$3 Cattle Egret		6·00	9·50
647/60	Set of 7		12·00	16·00

(Des and litho Walsall)

1987 (17 Dec). *Bicentenary of Postal Services.* T **175** and similar horiz designs, each including stamp and cancellation. Multicoloured. W w 16 (sideways). P 14½.

662	10 c. Type 175..		1·25	65
663	20 c. Map and 1899 1d.		1·75	1·10
664	35 c. Road Town Post Office and Customs House, 1913, and 1867 4d.		2·25	1·75
665	$1.50, Piper PA-23 Apache mail plane and 1964 25 c. definitive		6·50	9·50
662/5	Set of 4		10·50	11·50
MS666	70×60 mm. $2.50, Mail ship, 1880's, and 1880 1d.		6·00	9·00

176 De Havilland D.H.C.5 over Sir Francis Drake Channel and Staunton Pawn

(Des B. Bundock. Litho Questa)

1988 (25 Aug). *First British Virgin Islands Open Chess Tournament.* T **176** and similar horiz designs. Multicoloured. P 14.

676	35 c. Type 176		4·00	1·50
677	$1 Jose Capablanca (former World Champion) and Staunton king		8·00	8·50
MS678	109×81 mm. $2 Chess match		8·00	10·00

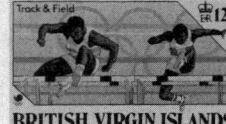

177 Hurdling

(Des L. Fried. Litho B.D.T.)

1988 (8 Sept). *Olympic Games, Seoul.* T **177** and similar horiz designs. Multicoloured. P 14.

679	12 c. Type 177		35	25
680	20 c. Windsurfing		60	45
681	75 c. Basketball		3·50	3·25
682	$1 Tennis		3·50	3·75
679/82	Set of 4		7·00	7·00
MS683	71 × 102 mm. $2 Athletics		3·00	4·50

178 Swimmer ("Don't Swim Alone")   **179** Princess Alexandra

(Des I. Arbell. Litho Questa)

1988 (26 Sept). *125th Anniv of International Red Cross.* T **178** and similar designs. P 14.

684	12 c. black, bright scarlet and cobalt		85	40
685	30 c. black, bright scarlet and cobalt		1·50	80
686	60 c. black, bright scarlet and cobalt		2·75	3·00
687	$1 black, bright scarlet and cobalt		3·25	4·00
684/7	Set of 4		7·50	7·50
MS688	68 × 96 mm. 50 c. × 4 black and bright scarlet		5·00	6·50

Designs: *Horiz*—30 c. Swimmers ("No swimming during electrical storms"); 60 c. Beach picnic ("Don't eat before swimming"); $1 Boat and equipment ("Proper equipment for boating"). *Vert*—50 c. × 4 Recovery position; clearing airway; mouth-to-mouth resuscitation; cardiac massage.

(Litho Questa)

1988 (9 Nov). *Visit of Princess Alexandra.* T **179** and similar vert designs showing different portraits. P 14.

689	40 c. multicoloured		1·75	75
690	$1.50, multicoloured		3·75	4·75
MS691	102 × 98 mm. $2 multicoloured		5·00	6·50

180 Brown Pelican in Flight   **181** Anegada Rock Iguana

(Des S. Barlowe. Litho Questa)

1988 (30 Nov). *Wildlife (1st series). Aquatic Birds.* T **180** and similar multicoloured designs. P 14.

692	10 c. Type 180		1·40	50
693	12 c. Brown Pelican perched on post		1·50	55
694	15 c. Brown Pelican		1·60	1·10
695	35 c. Brown Pelican swallowing fish		2·75	3·00
692/5	Set of 4		6·50	4·75
MS696	106×76 mm. $2 Common Shoveler (horiz)		7·50	9·00

No. MS696 is without the WWF logo.

(Des S. Barlowe. Litho Questa)

1988 (15 Dec). *Wildlife (2nd series). Endangered Species.* T **181** and similar multicoloured designs. P 14.

697	20 c. Type 181		1·25	75
698	40 c. Virgin Gorda Dwarf Gecko		1·50	1·40
699	60 c. Hawksbill Turtle		2·50	3·50
700	$1 Humpback Whale		7·00	8·00
697/700	Set of 4		11·00	12·00
MS701	106 × 77 mm. $2 Trunk Turtle (vert)		5·00	7·00

182 Yachts at Start   **183** "Apollo 11" Emblem

(Des D. Miller. Litho Questa)

1989 (7 Apr). *Spring Regatta.* T **182** and similar multicoloured designs. P 14.

702	12 c. Type 182		45	40
703	40 c. Yacht tacking (horiz)		1·00	1·00
704	75 c. Yachts at sunset		1·60	2·50
705	$1 Yachts rounding buoy (horiz)		2·00	2·75
702/5	Set of 4		4·50	6·00
MS706	83×69 mm. $2 Yacht under full sail		5·50	6·50

(Des D. Miller. Litho Questa)

1989 (8 May). *500th Anniv of Discovery of America by Columbus (1992) (1st issue). Pre-Columbian Arawak Society.* Multicoloured designs as T **247** of Antigua, but horiz. P 14.

707	10 c. Arawak in hammock		60	45
708	20 c. Making fire		85	50
709	25 c. Making implements		90	60
710	$1.50, Arawak family		4·25	7·00
707/10	Set of 4		6·00	7·75
MS711	85×70 mm. $2 Religious ceremony		6·00	8·00

See also Nos. 741/5, 793/7 and 818/26.

(Des W. Hanson. Litho Questa)

1989 (28 Sept). *20th Anniv of First Manned Landing on Moon. T **183** and similar multicoloured designs. P 14.*

712	15 c. Type **183**	1·00	60
713	30 c. Edwin Aldrin deploying scientific experiments	2·00	1·00
714	65 c. Aldrin and U.S. flag on Moon	2·75	3·75
715	$1 "Apollo 11" capsule after splashdown	3·75	4·00
712/15	*Set of 4*	8·50	8·50
MS716	102×77 mm. $2 Neil Armstrong (38×50 *mm*). P 13½×14	5·50	7·50

184 Black Harry and Nathaniel Gilbert preaching to Slaves

185 Player tackling

(Des R. Vigurs. Litho Questa)

1989 (24 Oct). *Bicentenary of Methodist Church in British Virgin Islands. T **184** and similar multicoloured designs. P 14.*

717	12 c. Type **184**	85	50
718	25 c. Methodist school exercise book	1·25	75
719	35 c. East End Methodist Church, 1810	1·40	85
720	$1.25, Revd. John Wesley (founder of Methodism) and church youth choir	3·25	6·00
717/20	*Set of 4*	6·00	7·25
MS721	100×69 mm. $2 Dr. Thomas Coke	4·50	7·00

(Des R. Vigurs. Litho Questa)

1989 (6 Nov). *World Cup Football Championship, Italy, 1990. T **185** and similar vert designs. Multicoloured. P 14.*

722	5 c. Type **185**	80	80
723	10 c. Player dribbling ball	80	80
724	20 c. Two players chasing ball	1·50	80
725	$1.75, Goalkeeper diving for ball	6·50	7·00
722/5	*Set of 4*	8·50	9·00
MS726	100×70 mm. $2 British Virgin Islands team captain	7·00	9·00

186 Princess Alexandra and Sunset House

(Litho Questa)

1990 (3 May). *"Stamp World London 90" International Stamp Exhibition. Royal Visitors. T **186** and similar horiz designs. Multicoloured. P 14.*

727	50 c. Type **186**	2·00	2·25
	a. Sheetlet. Nos. 727/30	7·00	
728	50 c. Princess Margaret and Government House	2·00	2·25
729	50 c. Hon. Angus Ogilvy and Little Dix Bay Hotel	2·00	2·25
730	50 c. Princess Diana with Princes William and Harry and Necker Island Resort	2·00	2·25
727/30	*Set of 4*	7·00	8·00
MS731	89×80 mm. $2 Royal Yacht *Britannia*	6·50	7·00

Nos. 727/30 were printed together, *se-tenant*, in sheetlets of four.

187 Audubon's Shearwater

188 Queen Elizabeth the Queen Mother

(Litho Questa)

1990 (15 May). *Birds. T **187** and similar multicoloured designs showing birds and eggs. P 14.*

732	5 c. Type **187**	55	70
733	12 c. Red-necked Pigeon	80	40
734	20 c. Moorhen ("Common Gallinule")	1·00	50
735	25 c. Green Heron	1·00	50
736	40 c. Yellow Warbler	1·50	1·25
737	60 c. Smooth-billed Ani	1·50	2·50
738	$1 Antillean Crested Hummingbird	1·75	2·50
739	$1.25, Black-faced Grassquit	2·00	3·00
732/9	*Set of 8*	9·00	10·00
MS740	Two sheets, each 98×70 mm. (a) $2 Royal Tern egg (*vert*). (b) $2 Red-billed Tropicbird egg (*vert*)		
	Set of 2 sheets	8·00	7·00

(Des Mary Walters. Litho Questa)

1990 (18 June). *500th Anniv of Discovery of America by Columbus (1992) (2nd issue). New World Natural History– Fishes. Multicoloured designs as T **260** of Antigua, but horiz. P 14.*

741	10 c. Blue Tang	75	60
742	35 c. Glass-eyed Snapper	1·50	70
743	50 c. Slippery Dick	2·00	2·50
744	$1 Porkfish	3·00	3·25
741/4	*Set of 4*	6·50	6·25
MS745	100×70 mm. $2 Yellow-tailed Snapper	4·25	5·00

(Litho Questa)

1990 (30 Aug). *90th Birthday of Queen Elizabeth the Queen Mother. T **188** and similar vert designs showing recent photographs. P 14.*

746	12 c. multicoloured	50	25
747	25 c. multicoloured	90	55
748	60 c. multicoloured	1·75	2·25
749	$1 multicoloured	2·00	2·50
746/9	*Set of 4*	4·75	5·00
MS750	75×75 mm. $2 multicoloured	2·75	2·75

189 Footballers

190 Judo

(Litho Questa)

1990 (10 Dec). *World Cup Football Championship, Italy. T **189** and similar vert designs showing footballers. P 14.*

751	12 c. multicoloured	60	40
752	20 c. multicoloured	90	50
753	50 c. multicoloured	1·75	2·00
754	$1.25, multicoloured	2·50	3·50
751/4	*Set of 4*	5·25	5·75
MS755	91×76 mm. $2 multicoloured	4·00	4·00

(Litho Questa)

1990 (20 Dec). *Olympic Games, Barcelona (1992). T **190** and similar horiz designs. Multicoloured. P 14.*

756	12 c. Type **190**	80	35
757	40 c. Yachting	1·60	1·40
758	60 c. Hurdling	2·25	3·00
759	$1 Show jumping	2·75	3·25
756/9	*Set of 4*	6·75	7·25
MS760	78×105 mm. $2 Windsurfing	4·00	4·00

191 Tree-fern, Sage Mountain National Park

192 Haiti Haiti

(Litho Questa)

1991 (1 Mar). *30th Anniv of National Parks Trust. T **191** and similar multicoloured designs. P 14.*

761	10 c. Type **191**	60	60
762	25 c. Coppermine ruins, Virgin Gorda (*horiz*)	85	60
763	35 c. Ruined windmill, Mount Healthy	1·00	60
764	$2 The Baths (rock formation), Virgin Gorda (*horiz*)	6·00	8·00
761/4	*Set of 4*	7·50	9·00

(Des Wendy Smith-Griswold. Litho Questa)

1991 (1 May)**–95**. *Flowers. T **192** and similar vert designs. Multicoloured. Without imprint date. P 14.*

765	1 c. Type **192**	20	60
766	2 c. Lobster Claw	20	60
767	5 c. Frangipani	20	60
768	10 c. Autograph Tree	60	80
769	12 c. Yellow Allamanda	40	30
770	15 c. Lantana	70	80
771	20 c. Jerusalem Thorn	50	30
772	25 c. Turk's Cap	55	40
773	30 c. Swamp Immortelle	80	80
774	35 c. White Cedar	90	90
775	40 c. Mahoe Tree	75	65
776	45 c. Pinguin	2·50	1·25
777	50 c. Christmas Orchid	2·50	1·75
	a. Perf 12 (8.95)	2·75	2·50
778	70 c. Lignum Vitae	1·10	2·00
779	$1 African Tulip Tree	1·25	2·00
	a. Perf 12 (8.95)	2·50	2·50
780	$2 Beach Morning Glory	4·00	6·00
	a. Perf 12 (8.95)	5·50	6·00
781	$3 Organ Pipe Cactus	4·00	6·00
	a. Perf 12½×11½ (8.95)	5·50	6·00
782	$5 Tall Ground Orchid	11·00	14·00
783	$10 Ground Orchid (1.5.92)	14·00	16·00
765/83	*Set of 19*	40·00	48·00

No. 781a shows a larger hole on every sixth perforation, both vertically and horizontally.

Nos. 777a, 779a and 780a/1a are known to have been sold for postal purposes by the B.V.I. post offices.

For some of these designs watermarked w **14** (sideways) and with imprint date see Nos. 887/901.

193 Phoebis sennae

194 Agaricus bisporus

(Litho Questa)

1991 (28 June). *Butterflies. T **193** and similar multicoloured designs. P 14.*

784	5 c. Type **193**	70	90
785	10 c. *Dryas iulia*	80	90
786	15 c. *Junonia evarete*	1·00	75
787	20 c. *Dione vanillae*	1·10	80
788	25 c. *Battus polydamus*	1·25	1·00
789	30 c. *Eurema lisa*	1·40	1·00
790	35 c. *Heliconius charitonius*	1·50	1·10
791	$1.50, *Siproeta stelenes*	3·50	5·50
784/91	*Set of 8*	10·00	10·50
MS792	Two sheets. (a) 77×117 mm. $2 *Danaus plexippus* (*horiz*). (b) 117×77 mm. $2 *Biblis hyperia* (*horiz*)		
	Set of 2 sheets	13·00	14·00

(Des T. Agans. Litho Questa)

1991 (20 Sept). *500th Anniv of Discovery of America by Columbus (1992) (3rd issue). History of Exploration. Designs as T **277** of Antigua. P 14.*

793	12 c. multicoloured	90	50
794	50 c. multicoloured	2·00	2·00
795	75 c. multicoloured	2·50	2·75
796	$1 multicoloured	3·00	3·50
793/6	*Set of 4*	8·00	8·00
MS797	105×76 mm. $2 black and red-orange	4·50	6·00

Designs: *Horiz*—12 c. *Vitoria* in Pacific (Magellan, 1519–21); 50 c. La Salle on the Mississippi, 1682, 75 c. John Cabot landing in Nova Scotia, 1497–98; $1 Cartier discovering the St. Lawrence, 1534. *Vert*—$2 *Santa Maria* (woodcut).

(Litho B.D.T.)

1991 (1 Nov). *Death Centenary of Vincent van Gogh (artist) (1990). Multicoloured designs as T **278** of Antigua. P 13.*

798	15 c. "Cottage with Decrepit Barn and Stooping Woman" (*horiz*)	80	50
799	30 c. "Paul Gauguin's Armchair"	1·40	80
800	75 c. "Breton Women" (*horiz*)	2·50	3·00
801	$1 "Vase with Red Gladioli"	2·75	3·50
798/801	*Set of 4*	6·75	7·00
MS802	103×81 mm. $2 "Dance Hall in Arles" (detail) (*horiz*)	7·00	9·00

(Litho Walsall)

1991 (12 Dec). *Christmas. Religious Paintings by Quinten Massys. Vert designs as T **291** of Antigua. Multicoloured. P 12.*

803	15 c. "The Virgin and Child Enthroned" (detail)	80	25
804	30 c. "The Virgin and Child Enthroned" (different detail)	1·50	50
805	60 c. "Adoration of the Magi" (detail)	3·00	3·75
806	$1 "Virgin in Adoration"	3·50	4·00
803/6	*Set of 4*	8·00	7·75
MS807	Two sheets, each 102×127 mm. (a) $2 "The Virgin standing with Angels"; (b) $2 "The Adoration of the Magi". P 14×14½.		
	Set of 2 sheets	10·00	12·00

(Litho Questa)

1992 (15 Jan). *Fungi. T **194** and similar multicoloured designs. P 14.*

808	12 c. Type **194**	1·25	55
809	30 c. *Lentinula edodes* (*horiz*)	1·90	85
810	45 c. *Hygrocybe acutoconica*	2·00	1·00
811	$1 *Gymnopilus chrysopellus* (*horiz*)	3·75	5·50
808/11	*Set of 4*	8·00	7·00
MS812	94×68 mm. $2 *Pleurotus ostreatus* (*horiz*)	7·00	9·00

(Des D. Miller. Litho Questa)

1992 (12 Mar). *40th Anniv of Queen Elizabeth II's Accession. Horiz designs as T **288** of Antigua. Multicoloured. P 14.*

813	12 c. Little Dix Bay, Virgin Gorda	60	30
814	45 c. Deadchest Bay, Peter Island	1·40	90
815	60 c. Pond Bay, Virgin Gorda	1·60	2·25
816	$1 Cane Garden Bay, Tortola	2·00	2·75
813/16	*Set of 4*	5·00	5·50
MS817	75×97 mm. $2 Long Bay, Beef Island	5·00	6·00

195 Queen Isabella of Spain

196 Basketball

(Des W. Hanson. Litho B.D.T.)

1992 (26 May). *500th Anniv of Discovery of America by Columbus (4th issue).* T **195** *and similar multicoloured designs.* P 14.

818	10 c. Type 195	70	70
819	15 c. Fleet of Columbus (*horiz*)	1·10	80
820	20 c. Arms awarded to Columbus	1·10	80
821	30 c. Landing Monument, Watling Island and Columbus' signature (*horiz*)	1·10	80
822	45 c. Christopher Columbus	1·60	1·40
823	50 c. Landing in New World and Spanish royal standard (*horiz*)	1·60	1·60
824	70 c. Convent at La Rabida	2·25	3·25
825	$1.50, Replica of *Santa Maria* and Caribbean Pavilion, New York World's Fair (*horiz*)	3·50	4·50
818/25	*Set of 8*	11·50	12·50

MS826 Two sheets. (a) 116× 86 mm. $2 Ships of second voyage at Virgin Gorda (*horiz*). (b) 86×116 mm. $2 De la Cosa's map of New World (*horiz*) . . *Set of 2 sheets* 8·00 11·00

(Litho Questa)

1992 (26 Oct). *Olympic Games, Barcelona.* T **196** *and similar vert designs. Multicoloured.* P 14.

827	15 c. Type 196	1·75	65
828	30 c. Tennis	2·00	90
829	60 c. Volleyball	2·50	3·00
830	$1 Football	2·75	3·75
827/30	*Set of 4*	8·00	7·50

MS831 100×70 mm. $2 Olympic flame 6·50 8·50

197 Issuing Social Security Cheque

(Litho Questa)

1993 (14 May). *25th Anniv of Ministerial Government.* T **197** *and similar horiz designs. Multicoloured.* P 14.

832	12 c. Type 197	35	25
833	15 c. Map of British Virgin Islands	75	50
834	45 c. Administration building	80	70
835	$1.30, International currency abbreviations	2·00	3·50
832/5	*Set of 4*	3·50	4·50

198 Cruising Yacht and Swimmers, The Baths, Virgin Gorda

(Litho Questa)

1993 (23 July). *Tourism.* T **198** *and similar multicoloured designs.* P 14.

836	15 c. Type 198	75	40
837	30 c. Cruising yacht under sail (*vert*)	1·00	60
838	60 c. Scuba diving	1·75	2·50
839	$1 Cruising yacht at anchor and snorklers (*vert*)	2·00	2·75
836/9	*Set of 4*	5·00	5·50

MS840 79×108 mm. $1 *Promenade* (trimaran) (*vert*); $1 Scuba diving (*different*) (*vert*) 5·00 6·50

(Des Kerri Schiff. Litho Questa)

1993 (27 Aug). *40th Anniv of Coronation. Vert designs as* T **307** *of Antigua.* P 13½×14.

841	12 c. multicoloured	90	1·25
	a. Sheetlet. Nos. 841/4×2	9·50	
842	45 c. multicoloured	1·25	1·50
843	60 c. bluish grey and black	1·40	1·75
844	$1 multicoloured	1·60	1·90
841/4	*Set of 4*	4·75	5·75

Designs:—12 c. Queen Elizabeth II at Coronation (photograph by Cecil Beaton); 45 c. Orb; 60 c. Queen with Prince Philip, Queen Mother and Princess Margaret, 1953; $1 Queen Elizabeth II on official visit.

Nos. 841/4 were printed in sheetlets of 8, containing two *se-tenant* blocks of 4.

A $2 miniature sheet showing "Queen Elizabeth II" (Sir Herbert James) was prepared, but not issued in British Virgin Islands.

200 Columbus with King Ferdinand and Queen Isabella

(Des G. Vasarhelyi. Litho Questa)

1993 (24 Sept). *500th Anniv of Discovery of Virgin Islands by Columbus.* T **200** *and similar horiz designs. Multicoloured.* P 14.

846	3 c. Type 200	15	40
847	12 c. Columbus's ship leaving port	40	40
848	15 c. Blessing the fleet	45	45
849	25 c. Arms and flag of B.V.I.	60	60
850	30 c. Columbus and *Santa Maria*	70	70
851	45 c. Ships of second voyage	95	95
852	60 c. Columbus in ship's boat	1·50	2·25
853	$1 Landing of Columbus	2·00	2·50
846/53	*Set of 8*	6·00	7·50

MS854 Two sheets, each 120×80 mm. (a) $2 Amerindians sighting fleet. (b) $2 Christopher Columbus and ships . . *Set of 2 sheets* 6·00 8·00

201 Library Services Publications   202 Anegada Ground Iguana

1993 (20 Dec). *50th Anniv of Secondary Education and Library Services.* T **201** *and similar multicoloured designs. Litho.* P 14×13½ (*horiz*) or 13½×14 (*vert*).

855	5 c. Type 201	50	70
856	10 c. Secondary school sports	60	70
857	15 c. Stanley Nibbs (school teacher) (*vert*)	70	60
858	20 c. Mobile library	80	60
859	30 c. Dr. Norwell Harrigan (adminstrator and lecturer) (*vert*)	1·00	65
860	35 c. Children in library	1·10	70
861	70 c. Commemorative inscription on book	2·00	3·00
862	$1 B.V.I. High School	2·25	3·00
855/62	*Set of 8*	8·00	9·00

(Litho Questa)

1994 (18 Mar). *Endangered Species. Anegada Ground Iguana.* T **202** *and similar vert designs showing iguanas.* P 14.

863	5 c. multicoloured	60	70
864	10 c. multicoloured	60	70
865	15 c. multicoloured	70	60
866	45 c. multicoloured	1·25	1·25
863/6	*Set of 4*	2·75	3·00

MS867 106×77 mm. $2 multicoloured 3·00 4·00
No. **MS**867 does not carry the W.W.F. Panda emblem.

203 Loading Disaster Relief Aircraft   204 Argentina v. Netherlands, 1978

(Litho Questa)

1994 (3 June). *Centenary of Rotary International in B.V.I.* T **203** *and similar horiz designs. Multicoloured.* P 14.

868	15 c. Type 203	35	35
869	45 c. Training children in marine safety	85	85
870	50 c. Donated operating table	90	1·00
871	90 c. Paul Harris (founder) and emblem	1·60	2·25
868/71	*Set of 4*	3·25	4·00

(Des W. Hanson. Litho Questa)

1994 (30 Sept). *25th Anniv of First Moon Landing. Horiz designs as* T **326** *of Antigua. Multicoloured.* P 14.

872	50 c. Anniversary logo	2·00	2·25
	a. Sheetlet. Nos. 872/7	11·00	
873	50 c. Lunar landing training vehicle	2·00	2·25
874	50 c. Launch of "Apollo 11"	2·00	2·25
875	50 c. Lunar module *Eagle* in flight	2·00	2·25
876	50 c. Moon's surface	2·00	2·25
877	50 c. Neil Armstrong (astronaut) taking first step	2·00	2·25
872/7	*Set of 6*	11·00	12·00

MS878 106×76 mm. $2 Signatures and mission logo 6·50 7·50
Nos. 872/7 were printed together, *se-tenant*, in sheetlets of 6.

(Des J. Iskowitz. Litho Questa)

1994 (16 Dec). *World Cup Football Championship, U.S.A. Previous Winners.* T **204** *and similar multicoloured designs.* P 14.

879	15 c. Type 204	85	50
880	35 c. Italy v. West Germany, 1982	1·50	70
881	50 c. Argentina v. West Germany, 1986	2·25	2·00
882	$1.30, West Germany v. Argentina, 1990	4·25	5·50
879/82	*Set of 4*	8·00	8·00

MS883 74×101 mm. $2 U.S. flag and World Cup trophy (*horiz*) . . 6·00 7·00

1995 (June). *As Nos. 768, 770, 773/4, 776/7, 780 and 782, but* W w **14** (*sideways*) *and with* "1995" *imprint date.* P 14.

887	10 c. Autograph Tree	50	70
889	15 c. Lantana	65	40
892	30 c. Swamp Immortelle	80	50
893	35 c. White Cedar	85	55
895	45 c. Pinguin	95	80
896	50 c. Christmas Orchid	2·25	1·75
899	$2 Beach Morning Glory	3·00	4·50
901	$5 Tall Ground Orchid	8·50	11·00
887/901	*Set of 8*	16·00	18·00

(Des A. Theobald. Litho Questa)

1995 (24 Oct). *50th Anniv of United Nations. Horiz designs as* T **213** *of Bahamas. Multicoloured.* W w **16** (*sideways*). P 14.

903	15 c. Peugeot P4 all-purpose field cars	45	40
904	30 c. Foden medium road tanker	75	60
905	45 c. SISU all-terrain vehicle	1·00	90
906	$2 Westland Lynx AH7 helicopter	3·75	5·00
903/6	*Set of 4*	5·50	6·25

205 Pair of Juvenile Flamingos   206 "Tortola House with Christmas Tree" (Maureen Walters)

(Des N. Arlott. Litho Cartor)

1995 (15 Nov). *Anegada Flamingos Restoration Project.* T **205** *and similar vert designs. Multicoloured.* W w **14**. P 13×13½.

907	15 c. Type 205	60	40
908	20 c. Pair of adults	65	45
909	60 c. Adult feeding	1·25	1·75
910	$1.45, Adult feeding chick	2·25	3·25
907/10	*Set of 4*	4·25	5·25

MS911 80×70 mm. $2 Chicks. P 13 3·25 4·50

(Adapted G. Vasarhelyi. Litho Walsall)

1995 (1 Dec). *Christmas. Children's Paintings.* T **206** *and similar horiz designs. Multicoloured.* W w **16** (*sideways*). P 13½×14.

912	12 c. Type 206	85	30
913	50 c. "Father Christmas in Rowing Boat" (Collin Collins)	2·00	1·40
914	70 c. "Christmas Tree and Gifts" (Clare Wassell)	2·25	2·50
915	$1.30, "Peace Dove" (Nicholas Scott)	3·25	4·00
912/15	*Set of 4*	7·50	7·50

207 Seine Fishing

(Des G. Vasarhelyi. Litho Cartor)

1996 (14 Feb). *Island Profiles (1st series). Jost Van Dyke.* T **207** *and similar horiz designs. Multicoloured.* W w **14** (*sideways*). P 13½×13.

916	15 c. Type 207	70	40
917	35 c. Sandy Spit	1·00	55
918	90 c. Map	2·75	2·75
919	$1.50, Foxy's Regatta	3·00	4·00
916/19	*Set of 4*	6·75	7·00

See also Nos. 1003/7.

(Des D. Miller. Litho Cartor)

1996 (22 Apr). *70th Birthday of Queen Elizabeth II. Vert designs as* T **165** *of Ascension, each incorporating a different photograph of the Queen. Multicoloured.* W w **14**. P 13½×14.

920	10 c. Government House, Tortola	20	20
921	30 c. Legislative Council Building	55	55
922	45 c. Liner in Road Harbour	1·00	70
923	$1.50, Map of British Virgin Islands	2·75	4·00
920/3	*Set of 4*	4·00	5·00

MS924 63×65 mm. $2 Queen Elizabeth II. P 13×13½ 3·00 3·50

208 Hurdling

(Des S. Noon. Litho Cartor)

1996 (22 May). *Centenary of Modern Olympic Games.* T **208** *and similar horiz designs. Multicoloured.* W w **14** *(sideways).* P 13.

925	20 c. Type **208**	.. .. ..	35	30
926	35 c. Volleyball	.. ..	60	60
927	50 c. Swimming	.. ..	90	1·50
928	$1 Yachting	.. ..	1·75	2·50
925/8	.. ..	*Set of* 4	3·25	4·50

209 Mercedes-Benz "500 K A", 1934

(Des R. Watton. Litho B.D.T.)

1996 (8 June). *"CAPEX '96" International Stamp Exhibition, Toronto. Early Motor Cars.* T **209** *and similar horiz designs. Multicoloured.* W w **14** *(sideways*).* P 13½.

929	15 c. Type **209**	.. ..	30	30
930	40 c. Citroën "12", 1934	..	70	70
931	60 c. Cadillac "V-8 Sport Phaeton", 1932		1·00	1·50
	w. Wmk Crown to right of CA		2·75	
932	$1.35, Rolls Royce "Phantom II", 1934	..	2·25	3·00
	w. Wmk Crown to right of CA		2·75	
929/32		*Set of* 4	3·75	5·00
MS933	79×62 mm. $2 Ford "Sport Coupé", 1932		3·00	4·00

*The normal sideways watermark shows Crown to left of CA, as seen from the back of the stamp.

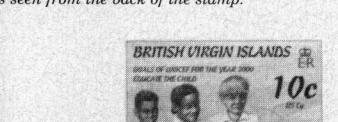

210 Children with Computer

(Des R. Watton. Litho Cot Printery Ltd, Barbados)

1996 (16 Sept). *50th Anniv of U.N.I.C.E.F.* T **210** *and similar horiz designs. Multicoloured.* W w **14** *(sideways).* P 14×14½.

934	10 c. Type **210**	.. ..	40	40
935	15 c. Carnival costume	..	50	50
936	30 c. Children on Scales of Justice	..	80	80
937	45 c. Children on beach	..	1·25	1·25
934/7		*Set of* 4	2·75	2·75

211 Young Rainbows in Art Class

(Des G. Vasarhelyi. Litho Cartor)

1996 (30 Dec). *75th Anniv of Guiding in the British Virgin Islands.* T **211** *and similar horiz designs. Multicoloured.* W w **14** *(sideways).* P 13½.

938	10 c. Type **211**	.. ..	20	20
939	15 c. Brownies serving meals	..	30	25
940	30 c. Guides around campfire	..	50	45
941	45 c. Rangers on parade	..	65	60
942	$2 Lady Baden-Powell	..	2·75	3·50
938/42		*Set of* 5	4·00	4·50

212 Spanish Mackerel

(Des A. Robinson. Litho Walsall)

1997 (6 Jan). *Game Fishes.* T **212** *and similar horiz designs. Multicoloured.* W w **16** *(sideways).* P 14.

943	1 c. Type **212**	.. ..	10	10
944	10 c. Wahoo	.. ..	10	15
945	15 c. Great Barracuda	..	20	25
946	20 c. Tarpon	..	25	30
947	25 c. Tiger Shark	..	30	35
948	35 c. Sailfish	..	40	45
949	40 c. Dolphin	..	50	55
950	50 c. Black-finned Tuna	..	60	65
951	60 c. Yellow-finned Tuna	..	70	75
952	75 c. King Mackerel ("Kingfish")	..	90	95
953	$1.50, White Marlin	..	1·75	1·90
954	$1.85, Amberjack	..	2·25	2·40
955	$2 Atlantic Bonito	..	2·40	2·50
956	$5 Bonefish	..	6·00	6·25
957	$10 Blue Marlin	..	12·00	12·50
943/57		*Set of* 15	28·00	29·00

(Des D. Miller. Litho Questa)

1997 (3 Feb). *"HONG KONG '97" International Stamp Exhibition. Sheet* 130×90 *mm, containing design as No.* 953, *but with "1997" imprint date. Multicoloured.* W w **14** *(inverted).* P 14.

MS958	$1.50, White Marlin	..	2·25	2·75

(Des N. Shewring (No. **MS965**), D. Miller (others). Litho Questa (No. **MS965**), Cartor (others))

1997 (10 July). *Golden Wedding of Queen Elizabeth and Prince Philip. Multicoloured designs as* T **173** *of Ascension.* W w **14**. P 13.

959	30 c. Prince Philip with horse		60	65
	a. Horiz pair. Nos. 959/60		1·10	1·25
960	30 c. Queen Elizabeth at Windsor, 1989		60	65
961	45 c. Queen in phaeton, Trooping the Colour		80	90
	a. Horiz pair. Nos. 961/2		1·60	1·75
962	45 c. Prince Philip in Scots Guards uniform		80	90
963	70 c. Queen Elizabeth and Prince Philip at the Derby, 1993		1·10	1·25
	a. Horiz pair. Nos. 963/4		2·10	2·50
964	70 c. Prince Charles playing polo, Mexico 1993		1·10	1·25
959/64		*Set of* 6	4·50	5·00
MS965	110×70 mm. $2 Queen Elizabeth and Prince Philip in landau *(horiz).* Wmk sideways. P 14×14½		2·75	3·25

Nos. 959/60, 961/2 and 963/4 were each printed together, *se-tenant,* in horizontal pairs throughout the sheets with the backgrounds forming composite designs.

213 Fiddler Crab

(Des Jennifer Toombs. Litho Cartor)

1997 (11 Sept). *Crabs.* T **213** *and similar horiz designs. Multicoloured.* W w **14** *(sideways).* P 13.

966	12 c. Type **213**	.. ..	40	40
967	15 c. Coral Crab	..	45	40
968	35 c. Blue Crab	..	85	60
969	$1 Giant Hermit Crab	..	1·75	2·50
966/9		*Set of* 4	3·00	3·50
MS970	76×67 mm. $2 Arrow Crab		3·50	4·25

214 *Psychilis macconnelliae*

(Des I. Loe. Litho Cot Printery Ltd, Barbados)

1997 (26 Nov). *Orchids of the World.* T **214** *and similar multicoloured designs.* W w **14** *(sideways).* P 14.

971	20 c. Type **214**	..	60	75
	a. Horiz strip of 4. Nos. 971/4		3·00	
972	50 c. *Tolumnia prionochila*	..	90	1·00
973	60 c. *Tetramicra canaliculata*	..	95	1·10
974	75 c. *Liparis elata*	..	1·00	1·25
971/4		*Set of* 4	3·00	3·50
MS975	59×79 mm. $2 *Dendrobium crumenatum (vert).* Wmk upright		3·25	4·00

Nos. 971/4 were printed together, *se-tenant,* in horizontal strips of four throughout the sheet.

215 Sir Francis Drake and Signature

(Des E. Nisbet. Litho Questa)

1997 (13 Dec). *420th Anniv of Drake's Circumnavigation of the World.* T **215** *and similar horiz designs. Multicoloured.* W w **14** *(sideways).* P 14½.

976	40 c. Type **215**	..	70	80
	a. Sheetlet. Nos. 976/87		7·50	
977	40 c. Drake's coat of arms	..	70	80
978	40 c. Queen Elizabeth I and signature		70	80
979	40 c. *Christopher* and *Marigold*		70	80
980	40 c. *Golden Hind*	..	70	80
981	40 c. *Swan*	..	70	80
982	40 c. *Cacafuego* (Spanish galleon)	..	70	80
983	40 c. *Elizabeth*	..	70	80
984	40 c. *Maria* (Spanish merchant ship)	..	70	80
985	40 c. Drake's astrolabe	..	70	80
986	40 c. *Golden Hind*'s figurehead	..	70	80
987	40 c. Compass rose	..	70	80
976/87		*Set of* 12	7·50	8·50
MS988	96×76 mm. $2 *Sir Francis Drake* (ketch)		3·25	4·00

Nos. 976/87 were printed together, *se-tenant,* in sheetlets of 12 with the backgrounds forming a composite map of Drake's route.

(Des D. Miller. Litho Questa)

1998 (31 Mar). *Diana, Princess of Wales Commemoration. Sheet,* 145×70 *mm, containing vert designs as* T **177** *of Ascension. Multicoloured.* W w **14** *(sideways).* P 14½×14.

MS989	15 c. Wearing pink jacket, 1992; 45 c. Holding child, 1991; 70 c. Laughing, 1991; $1 Wearing high-collared blouse, 1986 *(sold at* $2.30 + 20 c. *charity premium)*	3·50	4·00

(Des A. Theobald. Litho Enschedé)

1998 (1 Apr). *80th Anniv of Royal Air Force. Horiz designs as* T **178** *of Ascension. Multicoloured.* W w **14** *(sideways).* P 13½×14.

990	20 c. Fairey IIIF (seaplane)	..	60	40
991	35 c. Supermarine Scapa (flying boat)		85	50
992	50 c. Westland Sea King H.A.R.3 (helicopter)		1·40	1·10
993	$1.50, BAe Harrier GR7	..	2·50	3·00
990/3		*Set of* 4	4·75	4·50
MS994	110×77 mm. 75 c. Curtiss H.16 (flying boat); 75 c. Curtiss JN-4A; 75 c. Bell Airacobra; 75 c. Boulton-Paul Defiant		4·75	5·50

216 Fingerprint Cyphoma   **217** "Carnival Reveller" (Rebecca Peck)

(Des Odile and J. Scheiner. Litho Questa)

1998 (20 May). *Marine Life.* T **216** *and similar horiz designs. Multicoloured.* W w **16** *(sideways).* P 14×14½.

995	15 c. Type **216**	..	50	30
996	30 c. Long-spined Sea Urchin	..	70	45
997	45 c. Split Crown Feather Duster Worm		90	65
998	$1 Upside Down Jelly	..	1·60	2·25
995/8		*Set of* 4	3·25	3·25
MS999	77×56 mm. $2 Giant Anemone		3·50	4·00

(Adapted G. Vasarhelyi. Litho Cot Printery, Barbados)

1998 (25 Aug). *Festival. Children's Paintings.* T **217** *and similar multicoloured designs.* W w **14** *(sideways on $1.30, inverted on others).* P 14.

1000	30 c. Type **217**	..	50	50
1001	45 c. "Leader of a Troupe" (Jehiah Maduro)		65	65
1002	$1.30, "Steel Pans" (Rebecca McKenzie) *(horiz)*		1·90	2·25
1000/2		*Set of* 3	2·75	3·00

218 Salt Pond

(Des G. Vasarhelyi. Litho Cot Printery Ltd, Barbados)

1998 (28 Oct). *Island Profiles (2nd series). Salt Island.* T **218** *and similar horiz designs. Multicoloured.* W w **14** *(sideways).* P 14.

1003	12 c. Type **218**	..	45	30
1004	30 c. Wreck of *Rhone* (mail steamer)	..	60	45
1005	70 c. Traditional house	..	1·10	1·25
1006	$1.45, Salt Island from the air	..	2·25	2·40
1003/6		*Set of* 4	4·00	4·00
MS1007	119×78 mm. $2 Collecting salt	..	3·00	3·25

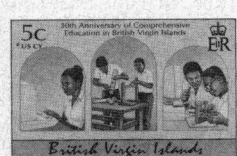

219 Business Studies, Woodwork and Technology Students

(Des N. Shewring. Litho Questa)

1998 (14 Dec). *Anniversaries.* T **219** *and similar horiz designs. Multicoloured.* W w **16** *(sideways).* P 14.

1008	5 c. Type **219**	..	15	20
1009	15 c. Comprehensive school band	..	30	25
1010	30 c. Chapel, Mona Campus, Jamaica	..	50	40
1011	45 c. Anniversary plaque and University arms		65	60
1012	50 c. Dr. John Coakley Lettsom and map of Little Jost Van Dyke		75	75
1013	$1 The Medical Society of London building and arms		1·40	1·75
1008/13		*Set of* 6	3·25	3·50

Events:—5, 15 c. 30th anniv of Comprehensive Education in B.V.I.; 30, 45 c. 50th anniv of University of West Indies; 50 c., $1 250th anniv of Medical Society of London

220 Rock Iguana

(Des R. Watton. Litho Enschedé)

1999 (30 Apr). *Lizards. T* **220** *and similar horiz designs. Multicoloured. W w* 14 *(sideways). P* 15×14.

1014	5 c. Type **220**		15	20
1015	35 c. Pygmy Gecko		55	45
1016	60 c. Slippery Back Skink		1·00	1·00
1017	$1.50, Wood Slave Gecko		2·00	2·25
1014/17		*Set of 4*	3·25	3·50
MS1018	100×70 mm. 75 c. Doctor Lizard; 75 c. Yellow-bellied Lizard; 75 c. Man Lizard; 75 c. Ground Lizard ..		4·25	4·75

(Des D. Miller. Litho Walsall)

1999 (15 June). *Royal Wedding. Vert designs as T* **185** *of Ascension. Multicoloured. W w* 16. *P* 14.

1019	20 c. Photographs of Prince Edward and Miss Sophie Rhys-Jones		35	30
1020	$3 Engagement photograph		4·00	4·25

(Des N. Shewring. Litho Walsall)

1999 (20 July). *30th Anniv of First Manned Landing on Moon. Multicoloured designs as T* **186** *of Ascension. W w* 16. *P* 14×13½.

1021	10 c. "Apollo 11" on launch pad		20	20
1022	40 c. Firing of second stage rockets		65	65
1023	50 c. Lunar module on Moon		75	75
1024	$2 Astronauts transferring to command module		3·00	3·25
1021/4		*Set of 4*	4·25	4·25
MS1025	90×80 mm. $2.50, Earth as seen from Moon (*circular, 40 mm diam*). Wmk sideways. P 14		3·50	3·75

221 Sunrise Tellin **222** Zion Hill Methodist Church

(Litho Questa)

1999 (1 Nov). *Sea Shells. T* **221** *and similar vert designs. W w* 14 *(sideways). Multicoloured. P* 14½. A. *Without imprint date at bottom right (from se-tenant sheets of 60)*

1026A	5 c. Type **221**		10	10
	a. Horiz strip of 5. Nos. 1026/31		3·00	
1027A	10 c. King Helmet		10	15
1028A	25 c. Measle Cowrie		30	35
1029A	35 c. West Indian Top Shell		40	45
1030A	75 c. Zigzag Scallop		90	95
1031A	$1 West Indian Fighting Conch		1·25	1·40
1026A/31A		*Set of 6*	3·00	3·25

B. *With "1999" imprint date at bottom right (from individual sheets of 100)*

1028B	25 c. Measle Cowrie		30	35
1029B	35 c. West Indian Top Shell		40	45
1030B	75 c. Zigzag Scallop		90	95
1031B	$1 West Indian Fighting Conch		1·25	1·40
1028B/31B		*Set of 4*	2·75	3·00

Nos. 1026A/31A were printed together, *se-tenant*, in horizontal strips of 5 throughout the sheet with the backgrounds forming a composite design.

(Des Jennifer Toombs. Litho Cartor)

1999 (16 Dec). *Christmas. Church Buildings. T* **222** *and similar horiz designs. Multicoloured. W w* 14 *(sideways). P* 13½×13.

1032	20 c. Type **222**		25	30
1033	35 c. Seventh Day Adventist Church, Fat Hogs Bay, 1982		40	45
1034	50 c. Ruins of St. Phillip's Anglican Church, Kingstown		60	65
1035	$1 St. William's Catholic Church, Road Town		1·25	1·40
1032/5		*Set of 4*	2·50	2·75

STAMP BOOKLETS

1981 (22 July). *Royal Wedding. Gold on blue cover, 75×50 mm, showing Royal coat of arms on front and St. Paul's Cathedral on back. Stapled.*

SB1	$3.50, booklet containing 10 c., 35 c., $1.25 (Nos. 463/5), in pairs		2·25

No. SB1 was sold at a 10 c. premium above the total face value of the stamps it contained.

1986 (23 July). *Royal Wedding. Gold (No. SB2) or silver (No. SB3) on new blue covers. Stapled.*

SB2	$4.20, booklet (Westminster Abbey cover) containing twelve 35 c. (Nos. 605/6) in blocks of four		5·50
SB3	$5.40, booklet (State Coach cover) containing four 35 c. (Nos. 605/6) and four $1 (Nos. 607/8), each in block of four		5·50

The stamps from No. SB3 are imperforate.

OFFICIAL STAMPS

OFFICIAL

(O 1)

Two varieties of overprint:
Type I. Foot of "OFFICIAL" 15–16 mm from top of design. Light impression with little or no black outline to letters.
Type II. Foot of "OFFICIAL" 20 mm from top of design. Heavy impression with thick black outline to letters.

1985 (Feb). *Nos.* 418/19, 420a/1a, 423a/4a, 425, 426a, 427, 428a *and* 429/33 *optd as Type O* 1 *in silver by Questa.*

O 1	1 c. Purple-tipped Sea Anemone (I)		30	1·00
	a. Opt Type II		50·00	60·00
O 2	3 c. Common Starfish (I)		45	1·00
	a. Opt Type II		55·00	65·00
O 3	5 c. Type 134 (II)		45	45
O 4	8 c. Atlantic Trumpet Triton (*Charonia variegata*) (I)		55	60
	a. Opt Type II		£100	
O 5	13 c. Flamingo Tongue (*Cyphoma gibbosus*) (II)		80	75
O 6	15 c. Spider Crab (I)		85	70
O 7	18 c. Sea Squirts (I)		90	1·50
	a. Opt Type II		£110	
O 8	20 c. True Tulip (*Fasciolaria tulipa*) (I)		90	80
O 9	25 c. Rooster-tail Conch (*Strombus gallus*) (I)		1·25	1·50
	w. Wmk inverted		15·00	
O10	30 c. West Indian Fighting Conch (*Strombus pugilis*) (I)		1·40	1·00
	a. Optd on No. 428		5·00	11·00
O11	60 c. Mangrove Crab (I)		2·00	2·50
O12	$1 Coral Polyps (I)		3·00	3·75
O13	$2.50, Peppermint Shrimp (I)		4·50	9·00
O14	$3 West Indian Murex (*Murex brevifrons*) (I)		5·50	10·00
	a. Opt inverted		£100	£120
O15	$5 Carpet Anemone (I)		7·50	10·00
O1/15		*Set of 15*	27·00	40·00

Examples of the ½ c. and 10 c. overprinted in silver and of all seventeen values overprinted in gold also exist, but were not issued in British Virgin Islands.

OFFICIAL **OFFICIAL**

(O 2) (O 3)

1986 (10 Feb–Sept). *Nos.* 560/78 *optd with Type O* 2 *by Questa.*

O16	1 c. Type 162 (9.86)		30	70
O17	2 c. Yellow-crowned Night Heron		30	70
O18	5 c. Mangrove Cuckoo (9.86)		40	75
O19	8 c. Northern Mockingbird		40	1·00
O20	10 c. Grey Kingbird (9.86)		50	85
O21	12 c. Red-necked Pigeon		50	40
O22	15 c. Least Bittern (9.86)		50	40
O23	18 c. Smooth-billed Ani		55	60
O24	20 c. Clapper Rail (9.86)		85	70
O25	25 c. American Kestrel (9.86)		85	85
O26	30 c. Pearly-eyed Thrasher (9.86)		1·25	1·00
O27	35 c. Bridled Quail Dove (9.86)		1·25	1·00
O28	40 c. Green Heron		1·25	1·00
O29	50 c. Scaly-breasted Ground Dove		1·40	1·75
O30	60 c. Little Blue Heron		1·50	2·50
O31	$1 Audubon's Shearwater		2·25	3·00
O32	$2 Blue-faced Booby		2·50	4·00
O33	$3 Cattle Egret		6·00	7·00
O34	$5 Zenaida Dove (9.86)		6·50	7·50
O16/34		*Set of 19*	26·00	32·00

1991 (Sept). *Nos.* 767/8, 771, 773/9 *and* 781 *optd with Type O* 3.

O35	5 c. Frangipani		45	60
O36	10 c. Autograph Tree		45	60
O37	20 c. Jerusalem Thorn		55	55
O38	30 c. Swamp Immortelle		70	55
O39	35 c. White Cedar		70	55
O40	40 c. Mahoe Tree		80	70
O41	45 c. Pinguin		80	75
O42	50 c. Christmas Orchid		1·50	90
O43	70 c. Lignum Vitae		1·50	2·25
O44	$1 African Tulip Tree		1·50	2·50
O45	$3 Organ Pipe Cactus		4·00	5·50
O35/45		*Set of 11*	11·50	14·00

The same stamps, except for the 30 c., exist overprinted with Type O 2, but such overprints were not placed on sale in British Virgin Islands.

Brunei

Sultan Hashim Jalil-ul-alam Akamudin, 1885–1906

(Currency. 100 cents = 1 Straits, later Malayan and Brunei, dollar)

For many years the status of the 1895 issue remained uncertain to such an extent that the 1906 provisionals on Labuan were taken to be the first issue of Brunei.

The 1895 "Star and Crescent" design stamps were, from their first appearance, considered bogus or, at best, as an issue made purely for philatelic purposes. Research into the background of the events surrounding the set led to the publication, in 1933, of the original agreement between Sultan Hashim and J. C. Robertson dated 20 August 1894 which made clear that the stamps fulfilled a genuine postal purpose. Although Robertson and his partners intended to exploit the philatelic sales for their own benefit the agreement testifies, as does other evidence, to the use of the stamps by the Sultan for his postal service. As Brunei did not, at that time, belong to any local or international postal union the stamps were only valid within the state or on mail to Labuan or Sarawak. Items for further afield required franking with Labuan stamps in addition. Although most covers surviving are addressed to Robertson's associates enough commercial covers and cards exist to show that there was, indeed, a postal service.

> **PRICES FOR STAMPS ON COVER TO 1945**
> Nos. 1/10 are rare used on cover.
> Nos. 11/22 *from* × 30
> Nos. 23/33 *from* × 25
> Nos. 34/50 *from* × 10
> Nos. 51/9 *from* × 12
> Nos. 60/78 *from* × 8

The Sarawak Government maintained a post office at the coal mining centre of Brooketon, and the stamps of SARAWAK were used there from 1893 until the office was handed over to Brunei in February 1907.

1 Star and Local Scene

(Litho in Glasgow)

1895 (22 July). *P* 13–13½.
1	1	1½ c. brown		2·50	19·00
2		1 c. brown-lake		3·00	14·00
3		2 c. black		4·00	14·00
4		3 c. deep blue		3·50	13·00
5		5 c. deep blue-green		6·50	15·00
6		8 c. plum		6·50	24·00
7		10 c. orange-red		8·00	24·00
		a. Imperf (pair)		£1200	
8		25 c. turquoise-green		48·00	70·00
9		50 c. yellow-green		18·00	85·00
10		$1 yellow-olive		20·00	£100
1/10			*Set of 10*	£110	£350

BRUNEI. **BRUNEI.**
(2)

BRUNEI. **TWO CENTS.** **25 CENTS.**
(2) (3) (4)

Line through "B" (R.5/10)

(Optd by Govt Printer, Singapore)

1906 (1 Oct). *Nos. 117/26 of Labuan (see Malaysia), optd with T* **2**, *or surch as T* **3** *or* **4** *(25 c.), in red. P* 13½ *or* 14 *(1 c.).*
11	1 c. black and purple			26·00	50·00
	a. Error. Opt in black			£1800	£2500
	b. Line through "B"			£300	
12	2 c. on 3 c. black and sepia			2·25	8·00
	a. "BRUNEI" double			£3750	£2500
	b. "TWO CENTS" double			£9000	
	c. Line through "B"			90·00	
13	2 c. on 8 c. black and vermilion			26·00	75·00
	a. "TWO CENTS" double			£8000	
	b. "TWO CENTS" omitted (in vert pair with normal)			£9000	
	c. Line through "B"			£300	
14	3 c. black and sepia			27·00	80·00
	a. Line through "B"			£300	

15	4 c. on 12 c. black and yellow		3·00	5·00
	a. Line through "B"		£100	
16	5 c. on 16 c. green and brown		42·00	70·00
	a. Line through "B"		£325	
17	8 c. black and vermilion		8·50	30·00
	a. Line through "B"		£180	
18	10 c. on 16 c. green and brown		6·50	21·00
	a. Line through "B"		£160	
19	25 c. on 16 c. green and brown		95·00	£130
	a. Line through "B"		£600	
20	30 c. on 16 c. green and brown		90·00	£120
	a. Line through "B"		£600	
21	50 c. on 16 c. green and brown		90·00	£120
	a. Line through "B"		£600	
22	$1 on 8 c. black and vermilion		90·00	£120
	a. Line through "B"		£600	
11/22		*Set of 12*	£450	£750

Only one sheet of the 1 c. received the black overprint.
The surcharges were applied in settings of 50. Nos. 13a/b occur from one sheet on which the surcharge from the second impression of the setting was misplaced to give two surcharges on row five and none on row ten.
Examples of all values are known showing a forged Brunei postmark dated "13 JUL".

Sultan Mohamed Jemal-ul-Alam, 1906–1924

PRINTERS. All Brunei stamps from Nos. 23 to 113 were recess-printed by De La Rue.

5 View on Brunei River

1907 (26 Feb)–**10**. *Wmk Mult Crown CA. P* 14.
23	5	1 c. grey-black and pale green		2·25	10·00
		x. Wmk reversed		15·00	
24		2 c. grey-black and scarlet		2·50	4·50
		x. Wmk reversed		30·00	
25		3 c. grey-black and chocolate		10·00	21·00
		x. Wmk reversed		30·00	
26		4 c. grey-black and mauve		7·50	10·00
		a. Grey-black and reddish purple (1910)		70·00	60·00
		w. Wmk inverted			
		x. Wmk reversed		50·00	
27		5 c. grey-black and blue		50·00	90·00
		x. Wmk reversed		90·00	
28		8 c. grey-black and orange		7·50	23·00
29		10 c. grey-black and deep green		4·50	7·00
30		25 c. pale blue and ochre-brown		30·00	48·00
31		30 c. violet and black		22·00	22·00
32		50 c. green and deep brown		15·00	22·00
33		$1 red and grey		60·00	90·00
23/33			*Set of 11*	£190	£300
23/33		Optd "Specimen"	*Set of 11*	£275	

I

II

I Double plate. Lowest line of shading on water is dotted.
II Single plate. Dotted line of shading removed.

Stamps printed in two colours are as I.

1908 (12 June)–**22**. *Colours changed. Double or single plates. Wmk Mult Crown CA. P* 14.
34	5	1 c. green (I)		80	2·25
35		1 c. green (II) (1911)		60	2·00
		a. "A" missing from wmk		£200	
		b. "C" missing from wmk		£200	
36		2 c. black and brown (5.4.11)		3·00	1·25
		w. Wmk inverted		45·00	
37		3 c. scarlet (I)		2·75	1·25
38		3 c. scarlet (II) (1916)		70·00	35·00
39		4 c. claret (II) (17.4.12)		3·00	75
40		5 c. black and orange (1916)		7·00	7·00
41		8 c. blue and indigo-blue (10.08)		7·00	11·00
42		10 c. purple/yellow (II) (11.12)		1·50	1·50
		a. On pale yellow (1922) (Optd S. £38)		1·25	4·00
		w. Wmk inverted		80·00	
		x. Wmk reversed		55·00	
43		25 c. deep lilac (II) (30.5.12)		3·75	14·00
		a. Deep dull purple (1920)			
44		30 c. purple and orange-yellow (18.3.12)		9·00	12·00
45		50 c. black/green (II) (1912)		27·00	65·00
		a. On blue-green (1920)		8·50	32·00
46		$1 black and red/blue (18.3.12)		20·00	48·00
47		$5 carmine/green (I) (1910)		95·00	£160
48		$25 black/red (I) (1910)		£450	£850
34/47			*Set of 12*	£140	£250
34/48		Optd "Specimen"	*Set of 13*	£500	

The used price for No. 48 is for a cancelled-by-favour example, dated before December 1941; there being no actual postal rate for which this value could be used. Examples dated after 1945 are worth much less.

Retouch   Normal   (6)

RETOUCHES. We list the very distinctive 5 c. Retouch (top left value tablet, 1st row, 8th stamp) but there are others of interest, notably in the clouds.

1916. *Colours changed. Single plates. Wmk Mult Crown CA. P* 14.
49	5	5 c. orange		14·00	14·00
		a. "5 c." retouch		£350	£350
50		8 c. ultramarine		5·50	22·00
49/50		Optd "Specimen"	*Set of 2*	£100	

MALAYA-BORNEO EXHIBITION OVERPRINTS. These were produced from a setting of 30 examples, applied twice to overprint the complete sheet of 60 stamps. Three prominent overprint flaws exist, each occurring on all the stamps in two vertical rows of the sheet.

HI **EX** **NE**

Short "I" Broken "E" Broken "N"
(all stamps in 2nd (all stamps in 4th and (all stamps in 6th and
and 8th vertical rows) 10th vertical rows) 12th vertical rows)

(Optd by Govt Printer, Singapore)

1922 (31 Mar). *Optd with T* **6**, *in black.*
51	5	1 c. green (II)		3·00	24·00
		a. Short "I"		6·00	35·00
		b. Broken "E"		6·00	35·00
		c. Broken "N"		6·00	35·00
52		2 c. black and brown		3·75	29·00
		a. Short "I"		10·00	40·00
		b. Broken "E"		10·00	40·00
		c. Broken "N"		10·00	40·00
53		3 c. scarlet (II)		6·00	35·00
		a. Short "I"		12·00	48·00
		b. Broken "E"		12·00	48·00
		c. Broken "N"		12·00	48·00
54		4 c. claret (II)		6·50	42·00
		a. Short "I"		12·00	60·00
		b. Broken "E"		12·00	60·00
		c. Broken "N"		12·00	60·00
55		5 c. orange (II)		10·00	55·00
		a. "5 c." retouch (and short "I")		£300	£650
		b. Short "I"		16·00	80·00
		c. Broken "E"		16·00	80·00
		d. Broken "N"		16·00	80·00
56		10 c. purple/yellow (II)		6·50	55·00
		a. Short "I"		14·00	80·00
		b. Broken "E"		14·00	80·00
		c. Broken "N"		14·00	80·00
57		25 c. deep dull purple (II)		14·00	80·00
		a. Short "I"		30·00	£120
		b. Broken "E"		30·00	£120
		c. Broken "N"		30·00	£120
		x. Wmk reversed			
58		50 c. black/blue-green (II)		45·00	£150
		a. Short "I"		80·00	£200
		b. Broken "E"		80·00	£200
		c. Broken "N"		80·00	£200
59		$1 black and red/blue		70·00	£190
		a. Short "I"		£120	£250
		b. Broken "E"		£120	£250
		c. Broken "N"		£120	£250
51/9			*Set of 9*	£140	£550

Examples of all values are known showing a forged Brunei postmark dated "13 JUL".

Sultan Ahmed Tajudin Akhazul Khairi Wadin, 1924–1950

7 Native houses, Water Village

1924 (Feb)–**37**. *Printed from single plates as Type* II, *except 30 c. and $1 as Type* I. *Wmk Mult Script CA. P* 14.
60	5	1 c. black (9.26)		80	60
61		2 c. brown (3.24)		90	5·50
62		2 c. green (3.33)		60	50
63		3 c. green (3.24)		80	6·00
64		4 c. maroon (3.24)		1·50	75
65		4 c. orange (1929)		1·00	60
66		5 c. orange-yellow* (3.24)		4·25	1·25
		a. "5 c." retouch		£160	£120
67		5 c. grey (1931)		9·50	9·50
		a. "5 c." retouch		£350	£350
68		5 c. chocolate (1933)		8·50	40
		a. "5 c." retouch		£170	50·00
69	7	6 c. intense black** (3.24)		14·00	10·00
		x. Wmk reversed			
70		6 c. scarlet (1931)		3·75	11·00
71	5	8 c. ultramarine (9.27)		6·00	5·00
72		8 c. grey-black (1933)		8·50	55
73		10 c. purple/yellow (3.37)		13·00	26·00
74	7	12 c. blue		4·50	9·00
		a. Pale greenish blue (1927)		£130	£200
75	5	25 c. slate-purple (1931)		5·50	12·00
76		30 c. purple and orange-yellow (1931)		8·50	16·00
77		50 c. black/emerald (1931)		7·00	15·00
78		$1 black and red/blue (1931)		24·00	70·00
60/78			*Set of 19*	£110	£180
60/72, 74/8		Optd/Perf "Specimen"	*Set of 18*	£350	

*For 5 c. orange, see No. 82. No. 66 is a "Wet" printing and No. 82 a "Dry".
**For 6 c. black, see No. 83. Apart from the difference in shade there is a variation in size, No. 69 being 37¾ mm long and No. 83 39 mm.

The 2 c. orange and 3 c. blue-green in Type 5, and the 6 c. greenish grey, 8 c. red and 15 c. ultramarine in Type 7 were not issued without the Japanese Occupation overprint although unoverprinted examples exist. It is believed that these 1941 printings were produced and possibly perforated, by other firms in Great Britain following bomb damage to the De La Rue works at the end of 1940 (*Price for set of 5, £450 un*).

During the life of this issue De La Rue changed the method of production from a "Wet" to a "Dry" process. Initially the stamps were printed on ungummed paper which was dampened before being put on the press. Once the paper had dried, and contracted in the process, the gum was then applied. "Dry" printings, introduced around 1934, were on pre-gummed paper. The contraction of the "Wet" printings was considerable and usually involves a difference of between 0.5 mm and 1 mm when compared with the larger "Dry" printings. The following stamps occur from both "Wet" and "Dry" versions: 1 c., 2 c. green, 4 c. orange, 5 c. chocolate, 6 c. scarlet, 8 c. grey-black, 10 c. and 25 c.

Stamps of this issue can be found either line or comb perforated.

Brunei was occupied by the Japanese Army in January 1942 and remained under Japanese administration until liberated by the 9th Australian Division in June 1945.

After the cessation of hostilities with the Japanese postal services were re-introduced by the British Military Administration. Post offices under B.M.A. control were opened at Brunei Town and Kuala Belait on 17 December 1945 where B.M.A. overprints on the stamps of NORTH BORNEO and SARAWAK were used until the reappearance of Brunei issues on 2 January 1947.

Redrawn clouds (R. 1/1
of No. 80ab only)

1947 (2 Jan)–**51**. *Colours changed and new values. Wmk Mult Script CA. P 14.*

79	5	1 c. chocolate			50	1·75
		a. "A" of "CA" missing from wmk			£1100	
80		2 c. grey			90	2·50
		a. Perf 14½×13½ (25.9.50)			1·50	4·25
		ab. Black (27.6.51)			2·00	6·00
		ac. Redrawn clouds			65·00	
81	7	3 c. green			1·00	4·00
82	5	5 c. orange*			80	1·25
		a. "5 c." retouch			55·00	75·00
		b. Perf 14½×13½ (25.9.50)			4·00	12·00
		c. Ditto "5 c." retouch			£120	£180
83	7	6 c. black*			1·00	3·75
84	5	8 c. scarlet			40	80
		a. Perf 13 (25.1.51)			55	8·50
85		10 c. violet			70	30
		a. Perf 14½×13½ (25.9.50)			2·00	4·75
86		15 c. ultramarine			50	60
87		25 c. deep claret			1·50	80
		a. Perf 14½×13½ (25.1.51)			1·50	7·00
88		30 c. black and orange			1·25	1·00
		a. Perf 14½×13½ (25.1.51)			1·50	11·00
89		50 c. black			2·50	55
		a. Perf 13 (25.9.50)			1·75	14·00
90		$1 black and scarlet			5·50	75
91		$5 green and red-orange (2.2.48)			16·00	17·00
92		$10 black and purple (2.2.48)			48·00	30·00
79/92				Set of 14	70·00	55·00
79/92 Perf "Specimen"				Set of 14	£200	

*See also Nos. 66 and 69.

The 1, 2, 3, 5, 6, 10 and 25 c. values utilised the plates of the pre-war issue and were line perforated until the introduction of the 14½×13½ comb machine for some values in 1950–51. The 8, 15, 50 c., $1, $5 and $10 were from new plates with the sheets comb perforated. The 30 c. was initially a pre-war plate, but it is believed that a new plate was introduced in 1951.

8 Sultan Ahmed Tajudin and Water Village

1949 (22 Sept). *Sultan's Silver Jubilee. Wmk Mult Script CA. P 13.*

93	8	8 c. black and carmine			70	80
94		25 c. purple and red-orange			70	1·40
95		50 c. black and blue			70	1·40
93/5				Set of 3	1·90	3·25

1949 (10 Oct). *75th Anniv of Universal Postal Union. As Nos. 114/17 of Antigua.*

96	8 c. carmine			1·25	1·25
97	15 c. deep blue			3·50	1·50
98	25 c. magenta			1·25	1·50
99	50 c. blue-black			1·75	1·25
96/9			Set of 4	7·00	5·00

Sultan Sir Omar Ali Saifuddin-Wasa'adul Khairi Wadin, 1950–1967

9 Sultan Omar Ali   10 Native houses, Water Village
Saifuddin

1952 (1 Mar)–**58**. *Wmk Mult Script CA. P 13.*

100	9	1 c. black		10	50
101		2 c. black and orange		10	50
102		3 c. black and lake-brown		10	30
103		4 c. black and green		10	20
104		6 c. black and grey		10	10
105		8 c. black and crimson		50	60
		a. Black and crimson-lake (15.2.56)		5·50	20
106		10 c. black and sepia		15	10
107		12 c. black and violet		4·50	10
108		15 c. black and pale blue		3·25	10
109		25 c. black and purple		2·50	10
		a. Black and reddish purple (8.10.53)		4·50	90
110		50 c. black and ultramarine		1·50	10
		a. Black and blue (22.6.55)		4·50	10
111	10	$1 black and green		1·50	1·40
		a. Black and bronze-green (23.7.58)		3·50	3·00
112		$2 black and scarlet		4·50	2·50
113		$5 black and maroon		13·00	7·00
		a. Black and brown-purple (15.2.56)		17·00	6·00
100/13			Set of 14	28·00	10·50

No. 106 exists in coils constructed from normal sheets.
See also Nos. 118/31 and 202/9.

11 Brunei Mosque and Sultan Omar

(Recess B.W.)

1958 (24 Sept). *Opening of Brunei Mosque. W w 12. P 13½.*

114	11	8 c. black and myrtle-green		20	65
115		15 c. black and carmine		25	15
116		35 c. black and deep lilac		30	90
114/16			Set of 3	65	1·50

12 "Protein Foods"

(Des M. Goaman. Photo Harrison)

1963 (4 June). *Freedom from Hunger. W w 12. P 14 × 14½.*

117	12	12 c. sepia		2·75	90

1964–72. *As Nos. 100/13, but W w 12. Glazed paper ($2, 5) or ordinary paper (others).*

118	9	1 c. black (17.3.64)		50	70
		a. Glazed paper. Grey (28.11.69)		1·10	2·50
		ab. Slate-grey (30.6.72)		15	2·00
119		2 c. black and orange (17.3.64)		1·50	20
		a. Glazed paper (27.5.70)		2·00	10
120		3 c. black and lake-brown (10.11.64)		1·50	30
		a. Glazed paper (27.5.70)		2·00	10
121		4 c. black and green (12.5.64)		30	10
		a. Glazed paper (22.4.70)		50	10
		ab. Black and emerald (19.11.71)		60	3·50
122		6 c. black and grey (12.5.64)		2·00	10
		a. Black (28.11.69)		5·50	6·00
		b. Glazed paper (28.11.69)		35	30
		ba. Light grey (19.11.71)		2·00	3·75
123		8 c. black and crimson-lake (12.5.64)		60	10
		a. Glazed paper (27.5.70)		75	15
		ab. Black and brown-red (19.11.71)		2·50	4·00
124		10 c. black and sepia (12.5.64)		50	10
		a. Glazed paper (31.3.70)		2·75	10
		ab. Grey and pale brown (coil) (11.10.71)		3·50	3·50
125		12 c. black and violet (12.5.64)		1·50	10
		a. Glazed paper (5.11.70)		11·00	1·00
126		15 c. black and pale blue (12.5.64)		55	10
		a. Glazed paper (28.11.69)		65	20
127		25 c. black and purple (12.5.64)		6·50	10
		a. Glazed paper (18.5.70)		11·00	5·00
		ab. Glazed paper. Black and reddish violet (30.4.71)		13·00	1·00
128		50 c. black and ultramarine (10.11.64)		2·50	10
		a. Black & brt ultramarine (17.3.69)		5·50	90
		b. Glazed paper (5.11.70)		11·00	3·50
		ba. Grey and indigo (21.12.71)		11·00	3·50
129	10	$1 black and bronze-green (14.5.68)		3·00	6·00
		a. Glazed paper (5.11.70)		7·00	6·00
130		$2 black and scarlet (5.11.70)		35·00	20·00
131		$5 black and maroon (5.11.70)		42·00	32·00
118/29			Set of 12	18·00	6·50
118a/29a, 130/1			Set of 14	£110	60·00

Printings of the 6 and 15 c. issued on 28 November 1969 were on both ordinary and glazed paper, the 6 c. on ordinary producing a distinct shade.

No. 124a exists in coils constructed from normal sheets.

13 I.T.U. Emblem

(Des M. Goaman. Litho Enschedé)

1965 (17 May). *I.T.U. Centenary. W w 12. P 11 × 11½.*

132	13	4 c. mauve and orange-brown		35	10
133		75 c. orange-yellow and light emerald		1·00	75

14 I.C.Y. Emblem

(Des V. Whiteley. Litho Harrison)

1965 (25 Oct). *International Co-operation Year. W w 12. P 14.*

134	14	4 c. reddish purple and turquoise-green		20	10
135		15 c. deep bluish green and lavender		55	35

15 Sir Winston Churchill and St. Paul's Cathedral in Wartime

(Des Jennifer Toombs. Photo Harrison)

1966 (24 Jan). *Churchill Commemoration. W w 12. P 14.*

136	15	3 c. black, cerise, gold and new blue		30	20
137		10 c. black, cerise, gold and deep green		1·50	20
138		15 c. black, cerise, gold and brown		1·75	35
139		75 c. black, cerise, gold and bluish violet		4·25	2·25
136/9			Set of 4	7·00	2·75

16 Footballer's Legs, Ball and Jules Rimet Cup

(Des V. Whiteley. Litho Harrison)

1966 (4 July). *World Cup Football Championships. W w 12 (sideways). P 14.*

140	16	4 c. violet, yellow-green, lake & yell-brn		20	15
141		75 c. chocolate, blue-grn, lake & yell-brn		75	60

17 W.H.O. Building

(Des M. Goaman. Litho Harrison)

1966 (20 Sept). *Inauguration of W.H.O. Headquarters, Geneva. W w 12 (sideways). P 14.*

142	17	12 c. black, yellow-green and light blue		35	50
143		25 c. black, light purple and yellow-brown		55	1·10

18 "Education"

19 "Science"

20 "Culture"

(Des Jennifer Toombs. Litho Harrison)

1966 (1 Dec). *20th Anniv of U.N.E.S.C.O.* W w **12** (*sideways*). P 14.
144	18	4 c. slate-violet, red, yellow and orange		35	10
145	19	15 c. orange-yellow, violet and deep olive		75	50
146	20	75 c. black, bright purple and orange	··	2·50	5·50
144/6			*Set of 3*	3·25	5·50

Sultan Sir Hassanal Bolkiah Mu'izzadin Waddaulah, 1967

21 Religious Headquarters Building

(Des and photo Harrison)

1967 (19 Dec). *1400th Anniv of Revelation of the Koran.* W w **12** (*sideways*). P 12½.
147	21	4 c. multicoloured	··	10	10
148		10 c. multicoloured	·· ··	15	10
149	—	25 c. multicoloured		20	30
150	—	50 c. multicoloured		35	1·50
147/50			*Set of 4*	70	1·75

Nos. 149/50 are as T **21** but have sprigs of laurel flanking the main design (which has a smaller circle) in place of flagpoles.

22 Sultan of Brunei, Mosque and Flags

(Des V. Whiteley. Photo Enschedé)

1968 (9 July). *Installation of Y.T.M. Seri Paduka Duli Pengiran Temenggong. T* **22** *and similar multicoloured design.* P 14 × 13 (12 c.) or 13 × 14 (*others*).
151		4 c. Type **22**	··	15	30
152		12 c. Sultan of Brunei, Mosque and Flags (*horiz*)		40	75
153		25 c. Type **22**	··	50	1·25
151/3			*Set of 3*	95	2·10

23 Sultan of Brunei   24 Sultan of Brunei

(Des V. Whiteley. Litho D.L.R.)

1968 (15 July). *Sultan's Birthday.* W w **12** (*sideways*). P 12.
154	23	4 c. multicoloured	·· ··	10	25
155		12 c. multicoloured	··	20	50
156		25 c. multicoloured		30	90
154/6	··		*Set of 3*	55	1·50

(Des V. Whiteley. Photo Harrison)

1968 (1 Aug). *Coronation of the Sultan of Brunei.* W w **12** (*sideways*). P 14½ × 14.
157	24	4 c. multicoloured		15	25
158		12 c. multicoloured		25	50
159		25 c. multicoloured		40	75
157/9	··		*Set of 3*	70	1·40

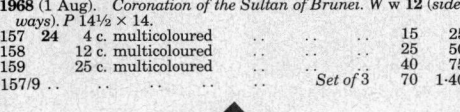

25 New Building and Sultan's Portrait

26 New Building and Sultan's Portrait

(Photo Enschedé)

1968 (29 Sept). *Opening of Language and Literature Bureau.* W w **12** (*sideways*). P 13½ (10 c.) or 12½ × 13½ (*others*).
160	25	10 c. multicoloured	··	20	1·75
		a. Tête-bêche (pair)		40	3·50
161	26	15 c. multicoloured	··	20	35
162		30 c. multicoloured	··	45	90
160/2			*Set of 3*	75	2·75

The above were scheduled for release in 1967, and when finally issued had the year altered by overprinting.

27 Human Rights   28 Sultan of Brunei and W.H.O. Emblem and struggling Man   Emblem

(Des V. Whiteley. Litho Harrison)

1968 (16 Dec). *Human Rights Year.* W w **12**. P 14.
163	27	12 c. black, yellow and green	··	10	20
164		25 c. black, yellow and blue	··	15	25
165		75 c. black, yellow and dull purple		45	1·75
163/5	··		*Set of 3*	65	2·00

(Des V. Whiteley. Litho Format)

1968 (19 Dec). *20th Anniv of World Health Organization.* P 14.
166	28	4 c. yellow, black and cobalt		30	30
167		15 c. yellow, black and deep bluish violet		55	65
168		25 c. yellow, black and pale yellow-olive		65	1·25
166/8			*Set of 3*	1·40	2·00

29 Deep Sea Oil-Rig, Sultan of Brunei and inset portrait of Pengiran Di-Gadong

(Des adapted by V. Whiteley. Photo Enschedé)

1969 (10 July). *Installation (9th May, 1968) of Pengiran Shah-bandar as Y.T.M. Seri Paduka Duli Pengiran Di-Gadong Sahibol Mal.* W w **12**. P 14 × 13.
169	29	12 c. multicoloured	··	85	50
170		40 c. multicoloured	··	1·25	2·00
171		50 c. multicoloured	··	1·25	2·00
169/71	··		*Set of 3*	3·00	4·00

30 Aerial View of Parliament Buildings

(Des Harrison. Litho D.L.R.)

1969 (23 Sept). *Opening of Royal Audience Hall and Legislative Council Chamber.* P 15.
172	30	12 c. multicoloured	··	20	25
173		25 c. multicoloured	··	30	45
174	—	50 c. rose-red and bluish violet		60	1·50
172/4	··		*Set of 3*	1·00	2·00

Design:—50 c. Elevation of new buildings.

32 Youth Centre and Sultan's Portrait

(Des V. Whiteley. Litho D.L.R.)

1969 (20 Dec). *Opening of the New Youth Centre.* W w **12**. P 15 × 14½.
175	32	6 c. flesh, slate-lilac and black	··	20	1·00
176		10 c. olive-yellow, grey-green and blackish brown		25	10
177		30 c. yellow-olive, yellow-brown & black		70	1·00
175/7	··		*Set of 3*	1·00	1·90

33 Soldier, Sultan and   34 Badge, and Officer in Badge   Full-dress Uniform

(Des Maj. M. A. Bowman. Adapted V. Whiteley. Litho Questa)

1971 (3 May). *Tenth Anniv of Royal Brunei Malay Regiment. Multicoloured designs, each with Badge and Sultan's portrait as T* **33**. W w **12** (*sideways on 15 and 75 c.*). P 14½.
178		10 c. Type **33**		80	30
179		15 c. Bell 205 UH-1H Iroquois helicopter (*horiz*)		1·40	90
180		75 c. *Pahlawan* (patrol boat) (*horiz*)		3·00	6·00
178/80			*Set of 3*	4·75	6·50

(Des Supt. T. Swan. Litho Format)

1971 (14 Aug). *50th Anniv of Royal Brunei Police Force. T* **34** *and similar vert designs. Multicoloured.* W w **12** (*sideways*). P 14½.
181		10 c. Type **34**		50	30
182		15 c. Badge and Patrol Constable		60	90
183		50 c. Badge and Traffic Constable		1·75	6·00
181/3	··		*Set of 3*	2·50	6·50

35 Perdana Wazir, Sultan of Brunei and view of Water Village

(Des and litho Harrison)

1971 (27 Aug). *Installation of the Yang Teramat Mulia as the Perdana Wazir (1970). T* **35** *and similar horiz designs showing different views of Brunei Town.* W w **12**. P 14.
184	35	15 c. multicoloured	··	40	50
185	—	25 c. multicoloured	··	70	1·00
186	—	50 c. multicoloured	··	1·40	5·00
184/6	··		*Set of 3*	2·25	6·00

36 Pottery

(Des C. Abbott. Litho Questa)

1972 (29 Feb). *Opening of Brunei Museum. T* **36** *and similar horiz designs. Multicoloured.* W w **12** (*sideways*). P 13½.
187		10 c. Type **36**	··	30	10
188		12 c. Straw-work	··	40	20
189		15 c. Leather-work	··	45	20
190		25 c. Gold-work	··	1·25	1·25
191		50 c. Museum Building (58 × 21 *mm*)	··	2·25	4·00
187/91			*Set of 5*	4·25	5·00

37 Brunei Museum, Queen Elizabeth and Sultan of Brunei

(Des locally. Photo Enschedé)

1972 (29 Feb). *Royal Visit. T* **37** *and similar horiz designs each with portraits of Queen and Sultan. Multicoloured.* W w **12** (*sideways*). P 13 × 13½.
192		10 c. Type **37**	··	70	20
193		15 c. Native houses	··	95	55
		w. Wmk Crown to right of CA			
194		25 c. Mosque	··	2·00	1·60
195		50 c. Royal Assembly Hall		3·75	7·00
192/5	··		*Set of 4*	6·75	8·50

*The normal sideways watermark shows Crown to left of CA, as seen from the back of the stamp.

38 Secretariat Building

(Des Harrison. Litho J.W.)

1972 (4 Oct). *Renaming of Brunei Town as Bandar Seri Begawan. T* **38** *and similar horiz designs.* W w **12** *(sideways).* P 13½.

196	10 c. multicoloured	30	15
197	15 c. green, light yellow and black	35	15
198	25 c. ultramarine, lemon and black	60	50
199	50 c. rosine, pale turquoise-blue and black	95	2·25
196/9	*Set of 4*	2·00	2·75

Views:—15 c. Darul Hana Palace; 25 c. Old Brunei Town; 50 c. Town and Water Village.

39 Blackburn Beverley
C1 parachuting Supplies

(Des Trident Artists. Litho Questa)

1972 (15 Nov). *Opening of R.A.F. Museum, Hendon. T* **39** *and similar horiz design.* Multicoloured. W w **12** *(sideways on 75 c.).* P 14 × 13½ (25 c.) *or* 13½ × 14 (75 c.).

200	25 c. Type **39**	1·75	1·25
201	75 c. Blackburn Beverley C1 landing	3·25	3·75

1972 (17 Nov)–**74**. *As Nos. 119/26, but* W w **12** *(sideways*).* Glazed paper.

202	**9**	2 c. black and orange (9.5.73)	2·25	7·00
203		3 c. black and lake-brown	1·75	40
204		4 c. black and green	50	1·00
205		6 c. black and grey	2·75	30
206		8 c. black and brown-red (9.5.73)	2·75	5·50
207		10 c. black and sepia	80	30
		a. Black and bistre-brown (24.7.74)	80	3·50
		aw. Wmk Crown to right of CA	5·00	
208		12 c. black and violet	1·50	2·25
209		15 c. black and pale blue	1·75	2·25
202/9		*Set of 8*	12·50	17·00

*The normal sideways watermark shows Crown to left of CA, as seen from the back of the stamp.

40 Girl with Traditional Flower-pot, and Boy with Bowl and Pipe

(Des (from photograph by D. Groves) and photo Harrison)

1972 (20 Nov). *Royal Silver Wedding.* Multicoloured; background colour given. W w **12**. P 14 × 14½.

210	**40**	12 c. carmine-red	10	10
		w. Wmk inverted	23·00	
211		75 c. deep myrtle-green	20	50

41 Interpol H.Q., Paris

(Des Shamir Bros. Litho Harrison)

1973 (7 Sept). *50th Anniv of Interpol. T* **41** *and similar horiz design.* W w **12** *(inverted on 50 c.).* P 14 × 14½.

212	25 c. bright green, purple and dull blue-black	1·50	1·25
213	50 c. pale greenish blue, ultramarine & carm	1·50	1·25

The 50 c. shows a different view of the H.Q.

42 Sultan, Princess Anne and Capt. Phillips

(Des PAD Studio. Litho Format)

1973 (14 Nov). *Royal Wedding.* W w **12**. P 14.

214	**42**	25 c. multicoloured	15	10
215		50 c. multicoloured	15	25

43 Churchill Painting

44 Sultan Sir Hassanal Bolkiah Mu'izzaddin Waddaulah

(Des C. Abbott. Litho Questa)

1973 (31 Dec). *Opening of Churchill Memorial Building. T* **43** *and similar vert design.* Multicoloured. W w **12** *(sideways).* P 14 × 13½.

216	12 c. Type **43**	10	20
217	50 c. Churchill Statue	30	1·40

(Des Staff Artists, Dept of Language and Literature. Photo Harrison)

1974 (15 July*). *Multicoloured; background colour given.* W w **12** *(sideways†).* P 13½ × 14½.

218	**44**	4 c. turquoise-green	20	20
219		5 c. pale blue	20	30
220		6 c. olive	1·50	2·50
221		10 c. lavender	30	10
222		15 c. light brown	1·00	10
223		20 c. stone	30	20
		w. Wmk Crown to right of CA	1·40	
224		25 c. sage-green	40	15
225		30 c. bright blue	40	15
226		35 c. grey	40	20
227		40 c. bright purple	40	20
228		50 c. cinnamon	40	20
229		75 c. light yellow-green	60	2·75
230		$1 pale salmon	1·50	4·25
231		$2 greenish yellow	2·25	9·50
232		$5 silver	4·00	17·00
233		$10 gold	6·00	30·00
218/33		*Set of 16*	17·00	60·00

*This was the London release date. The stamps were not put on sale locally until 29 August 1974, but First Day Covers were cancelled with the 15 July date.

†The normal sideways watermark shows Crown to left of CA, as seen from the back of the stamp.

See also Nos. 244/59 and 260/2.

45 Aerial View of Airport

(Des Harrison. Litho B.W.)

1974 (18 July). *Inauguration of Brunei International Airport. T* **45** *and similar horiz design.* Multicoloured. W w **12** *(sideways on 75 c.).* P 14 × 14½ (50 c.) *or* 12½ × 13 (75 c.).

234	50 c. Type **45**	1·25	1·00
235	75 c. Sultan in Army uniform, and airport (48 × 36 mm)	1·50	1·50

46 U.P.U. Emblem and Sultan

(Des J.W. Litho Harrison)

1974 (28 Oct). *Centenary of Universal Postal Union.* W w **12** *(sideways).* P 14½.

236	**46**	12 c. multicoloured	20	20
237		50 c. multicoloured	40	1·40
238		75 c. multicoloured	50	1·75
236/8		*Set of 3*	1·00	3·00

47 Sir Winston Churchill

(Des C. Abbott. Litho Questa)

1974 (30 Nov). *Birth Centenary of Sir Winston Churchill. T* **47** *and similar horiz design.* Multicoloured. W w **14** *(sideways).* P 14½.

239	12 c. Type **47**	25	20
240	75 c. Churchill smoking cigar (profile)	45	1·25

A set of four, 12, 20, 25 and 75 c., was prepared during this period to mark the opening of new port facilities at Muara, but these stamps were never issued.

48 Boeing 737 and R.B.A. Crest

(Des PAD Studio. Litho Enschedé)

1975 (14 May). *Inauguration of Royal Brunei Airlines. T* **48** *and similar horiz designs.* Multicoloured. No wmk. P 12½ × 12.

241	12 c. Type **48**	1·00	25
242	35 c. Boeing 737 over Bandar Seri Begawan Mosque	1·75	1·75
243	75 c. Boeing 737 in flight	2·50	2·50
241/3	*Set of 3*	4·75	3·50

1975 (13 Aug)–**78**. *As Nos. 218/33, but* W w **14** *(sideways*).*

244	**44**	4 c. turquoise-green	30	2·00
245		5 c. pale blue	30	2·00
246		6 c. olive	3·50	4·25
247		10 c. lavender	30	10
		a. Pale bluish violet (19.4.77)	30	10
248		15 c. light brown	60	1·25
249		20 c. stone	60	85
250		25 c. sage-green	70	1·00
		a. Grey-olive (25.5.78)	30	1·25
251		30 c. bright blue	35	1·50
		w. Wmk Crown to right of CA	1·25	
252		35 c. grey	45	1·50
253		40 c. bright purple	55	1·75
254		50 c. cinnamon	90	50
		a. Blue omitted†	60·00	
255		75 c. light yellow-green	80	3·00
256		$1 pale salmon	1·50	3·00
		w. Wmk Crown to right of CA	2·50	3·75
257		$2 greenish yellow	4·00	8·50
258		$5 silver	5·50	17·00
259		$10 gold	25·00	29·00
244/59		*Set of 16*	40·00	70·00

*The normal sideways watermark shows Crown to left of CA, as seen from the back of the stamp.

†The blue colour on the 50 c. value is only evident in the bluish green stripes of the sash and on several of the medal ribbons.

1976 (12 Apr). *As Nos. 221 and 223/4 but* W w **12** *(upright).*

260	**44**	10 c. lavender	3·50	1·50
261		20 c. stone	3·50	3·50
262		25 c. sage-green	3·50	5·00
260/2		*Set of 3*	9·50	9·00

(49)

50 Royal Coat of Arms

(Surchd by Govt Printer, Brunei)

1976 (16 Aug). *No. 246 surch with T* **49** *in silver.*

263	**44**	10 c. on 6 c. olive	1·75	1·00
		a. Surch on No. 220	2·25	1·10

(Des C. Abbott. Litho D.L.R.)

1977 (7 June). *Silver Jubilee. T* **50** *and similar vert designs.* Multicoloured. W w **14**. P 13½ × 14.

264	10 c. Type **50**	15	15
265	20 c. Imperial State Crown	20	20
	a. Silver omitted	£200	
266	75 c. Queen Elizabeth (portrait by Annigoni)	45	60
264/6	*Set of 3*	70	85

51 The Moment of Crowning

52 Royal Crest

(Des J. Cooter. Litho Enschedé)

1978 (2 June). *25th Anniv of Coronation. T* **51** *and similar vert designs.* Multicoloured. W w **14**. P 13½ × 13.

267	10 c. Type **51**	15	10
268	20 c. Queen in Coronation regalia	20	20
	w. Wmk inverted	75·00	
269	75 c. Queen's departure from Abbey	55	80
267/9	*Set of 3*	80	1·00

(Des local artist; adapted BG Studio. Litho Cartor)

1978 (1 Aug). *10th Anniv of Sultan's Coronation. T **52** and similar vert designs. W w **14** (inverted). P 12.*
270	10 c. black, scarlet and greenish yellow		20	10
271	20 c. multicoloured		40	25
272	75 c. multicoloured		1·10	2·25
270/2		Set of 3	1·50	2·25
MS273	182 × 77 mm. Nos. 270/2		12·00	16·00

Designs:—20 c. Coronation ceremony; 75 c. Royal Crown.

53 Human Rights Emblem and struggling Man

54 Smiling Children

(Des V. Whiteley; adapted L. McCombie. Litho Questa)

1978 (10 Dec). *Human Rights Year. W w **14**. P 14½.*
274	**53**	10 c. black, yellow and scarlet	15	10
275		20 c. black, yellow and violet	25	35
276		75 c. black, yellow and bistre	60	2·00
274/6		Set of 3	90	2·25

Type **53** is similar to the design used for the 1968 Human Rights Year issue.

(Des L. Curtis. Litho Harrison)

1979 (30 June). *International Year of the Child. T **54** and similar horiz design. W w **14** (sideways). P 14.*
277	10 c. multicoloured	20	10
278	$1 black and dull green	1·25	2·50

Design:—$1 I.Y.C. emblem.

55 Earth Satellite Station

56 Hegira Symbol

(Des A. Theobald. Litho Questa)

1979 (23 Sept). *Telisai Earth Satellite Station. T **55** and similar horiz designs. Multicoloured. W w **14** (sideways). P 14.*
279	10 c. Type **55**	25	15
280	20 c. Satellite and antenna	45	35
281	75 c. Television camera, telex machine and telephone	85	2·50
279/81	Set of 3	1·40	2·75

(Litho Secura, Singapore)

1979 (21 Nov). *Moslem Year 1400 AH Commemoration. W w **14**. P 13 × 13½.*
282	**56**	10 c. black, yellow and emerald	10	15
283		20 c. black, yellow and light blue	15	30
284		75 c. black, yellow and violet	45	2·00
282/4		Set of 3	60	2·25
MS285	178×200 mm. Nos. 282/4		4·00	6·50
	w. Wmk inverted		4·00	

57 Installation Ceremony

58 Royal Umbrella and Sash

(Des BG Studio. Litho Questa)

1980 (8 Nov). *1st Anniv of Prince Sufri Bolkiah's Installation as First Wazir. T **57** and similar vert design. Multicoloured. W w **14**. P 13½.*
286	10 c. Type **57**	15	10
287	75 c. Prince Sufri	85	2·00

Nos. 286/7 have blue borders.

(Des BG Studio. Litho Secura, Singapore)

1980 (6 Dec). *1st Anniv of Prince Jefri Bolkiah's Installation as Second Wazir. Vert designs as T **57**. Multicoloured. W w **14**. P 13½.*
288	10 c. Installation ceremony	15	10
	w. Wmk inverted	26·00	
289	75 c. Prince Jefri	55	2·00

Nos. 288/9 have green borders.

(Des BG Studio. Litho Security Printers (M), Malaysia)

1981 (18 Jan*). *Royal Regalia (1st series). T **58** and similar multicoloured designs. P 13½ × 13 (50 c.) or 12 × 11½ (others).*
290	10 c. Type **58**		20	15
291	15 c. Sword and Shield		35	25
292	20 c. Lance and Sheath		40	35
293	30 c. Betel-leaf Container		60	1·00
294	50 c. Coronation Crown (23 × 40 mm)		1·25	3·75
290/4		Set of 5	2·50	5·00
MS295	98 × 142 mm. Nos. 290/4		3·75	5·50

*This is the local release date. The Crown Agents released the stamps on 19 January.

See also Nos. 298/303, 314/19 and 320/5.

59 I.T.U. and W.H.O. Emblems

60 Shield and Broadsword

(Litho Security Printers (M), Malaysia)

1981 (17 May). *World Telecommunications and Health Day. P 13 × 13½.*
296	**59**	10 c. black and bright crimson	50	25
297		75 c. black, chalky blue & pale violet-bl	2·25	4·25

(Des BG Studio. Litho Security Printers (M), Malaysia)

1981 (15 July). *Royal Regalia (2nd series). T **60** and similar multicoloured designs. P 12.*
298	10 c. Type **60**		10	10
299	15 c. Blunderbuss and Pouch		20	30
300	20 c. Crossed Lances and Sash		30	30
301	30 c. Sword, Shield and Sash		40	65
302	50 c. Forked Lance		60	2·00
303	75 c. Royal Drum (29 × 45 mm)		80	3·25
298/303		Set of 6	2·10	6·00

61 Prince Charles as Colonel of the Welsh Guards

62 Fishing

(Des J.W. Litho Format)

1981 (29 July). *Royal Wedding. T **61** and similar vert designs. Multicoloured. W w **14**. P 14.*
304	10 c. Wedding bouquet from Brunei		15	15
305	$1 Type **61**		50	1·50
306	$2 Prince Charles and Lady Diana Spencer		70	2·50
	w. Wmk inverted		30·00	
304/6		Set of 3	1·25	3·75

(Des local artist. Litho Secura, Singapore)

1981 (16 Oct). *World Food Day. T **62** and similar vert design. Multicoloured. P 12 × 11½.*
307	10 c. Type **62**	50	15
308	$1 Farm produce and machinery	4·50	6·00

63 Blind Man and Braille Alphabet

64 Drawing of Infected Lungs

(Des local artist. Litho Security Printers (M), Malaysia)

1981 (16 Dec). *International Year for Disabled Persons. T **63** and similar vert designs. Multicoloured. W w **14**. P 12.*
309	10 c. Type **63**		65	20
	w. Wmk inverted		14·00	
310	20 c. Deaf people and sign language		1·50	80
	a. Wmk sideways		1·75	1·75
311	75 c. Disabled person and wheelchairs		3·00	6·25
309/11		Set of 3	4·75	6·50

(Des local artist. Litho Security Printers (M), Malaysia)

1982 (24 May). *Centenary of Robert Koch's Discovery of Tubercle Bacillus. T **64** and similar horiz design. Multicoloured. W w **14**. P 12 (10 c.) or 13½ (75 c.).*
312	10 c. Type **64**	50	25
313	75 c. Magnified tubercle bacillus and microscope	3·00	4·50

(Des PAD Studio. Litho Security Printers (M), Malaysia)

1982 (31 May). *Royal Regalia (3rd series). Multicoloured designs as T **60**. W w **14** (sideways). P 13½ (75 c.) or 12 × 11½ (others).*
314	10 c. Ceremonial Ornament		10	10
315	15 c. Silver Betel Caddy		20	20
316	20 c. Traditional Flower-pot		25	25
317	30 c. Solitary Candle		50	70
318	50 c. Golden Pipe		70	2·00
319	75 c. Royal Chin Support (28 × 45 mm)		90	3·25
314/19		Set of 6	2·40	5·75

(Des BG Studio. Litho Security Printers (M), Malaysia)

1982 (15 July). *Royal Regalia (4th series). Multicoloured designs as T **60**. W w **14** (sideways*). P 12 (75 c.) or 12×11½ (others).*
320	10 c. Royal Mace		25	10
321	15 c. Ceremonial Shield and Spears		35	20
322	20 c. Embroidered Ornament		45	30
323	30 c. Golden-tasselled Cushion		75	1·25
324	50 c. Ceremonial Dagger and Sheath		1·25	3·00
325	75 c. Religious Mace (28×45 mm)		1·60	4·00
	w. Wmk Crown to left of CA		20·00	
320/5		Set of 6	4·25	8·00

*The normal sideways watermark shows Crown to right of CA, as seen from the back of the stamp.

65 Brunei Flag

(Des Siti Zaleha Haji Kaprawi. Litho Secura, Singapore)

1983 (14 Mar). *Commonwealth Day. T **65** and similar horiz designs. P 13 × 13½.*
326	10 c. multicoloured		15	45
	a. Horiz strip of 4. Nos. 326/9		1·75	
327	20 c. bright blue, black and buff		20	55
328	75 c. bright blue, black and bright green		45	85
329	$2 bright blue, black and lemon		1·10	1·75
326/9		Set of 4	1·75	3·25

Designs:—20 c. Brunei Mosque; 75 c. Machinery; $2 Sultan of Brunei.

Nos. 326/9 were printed together, *se-tenant*, in horizontal strips of four throughout the sheet.

66 "Postal Service"

67 Football

(Litho Secura, Singapore)

1983 (15 Aug). *World Communications Year. T **66** and similar horiz designs. P 13½.*
330	10 c. multicoloured		15	10
331	75 c. yellow, orange-brown and black		60	75
332	$2 multicoloured		1·75	2·25
330/2		Set of 3	2·25	2·75

Designs:—75 c. "Telephone Service"; $2 "Communications".

(Litho Security Printers (M), Malaysia)

1983 (23 Sept). *Official Opening of Hassanal Bolkiah National Stadium. T **67** and similar multicoloured designs. P 12.*
333	10 c. Type **67**		55	15
334	75 c. Athletics		2·25	1·50
335	$1 View of stadium (44 × 27 mm)		2·75	4·00
333/5		Set of 3	5·00	5·00

68 Fishermen and Crustacea

(Litho Secura, Singapore)

1983 (23 Sept). *Fishery Resources. T **68** and similar horiz designs. Multicoloured. P 13½ × 14.*
336	10 c. Type **68**		80	15
337	50 c. Fishermen with net		2·25	1·50
338	75 c. Fishing trawler		2·50	2·50
339	$1 Fishing with hook and tackle		2·75	3·25
336/9		Set of 4	7·50	6·50

INDEPENDENCE

From No. 349 onwards issues are inscribed "BRUNEI DARUSSALAM".

69 Royal Assembly Hall

(Des Haji Salleh bin Haji Ibrahim (No. 346), Pengiran Haji Muhammed bin Pengiran Duraman (No. MS348) or Siti Zaleha Haji Kaprawi (others). Litho Cartor)

1984 (1 Jan). *Independence. T* **69** *and similar designs. P* 13.

340	10 c.	pale stone and bright orange		20	10
341	20 c.	flesh and brown-red		30	20
342	35 c.	rose-pink and plum		60	60
343	50 c.	pale blue and new blue		1·75	1·25
344	75 c.	bright yellow-green and emerald		1·75	2·00
345	$1	light brownish grey and light brown		2·00	2·50
346	$3	multicoloured		6·00	9·00
340/6			*Set of 7*	11·50	14·00

MS347 150 × 120 mm. Nos. 340/6 .. .. 9·50 14·00

MS348 Two sheets each 150 × 120 mm. containing 4 stamps (34 × 69 mm.). (a) 25 c. × 4 grey-black and new blue (Signing of the Brunei Constitution). (b) 25 c. × 4 multicoloured (Signing of Brunei-U.K. Friendship Agreement) .. .. *Set of 2 sheets* 1·75 3·25
Designs:—34×25 *mm.* 20 c. Government Secretariat Building; 35 c. New Supreme Court; 50 c. Natural gas well; 75 c. Omar Ali Saifuddin Mosque; $1 Sultan's Palace; 68×24 *mm.* $3 Brunei flag and map of South-East Asia.

70 Natural Forests and Enrichment Planting

(Des Awang Nor Ariffin bin Md. Yassin. Litho Secura, Singapore)

1984 (21 Apr). *Forestry Resources. T* **70** *and similar horiz designs. Multicoloured. P* 13½ × 14.

349	10 c.	Type **70**		90	25
350	50 c.	Forests and water resources		2·00	2·25
351	75 c.	Recreation forests		2·75	3·50
352	$1	Forests and wildlife		4·00	4·50
349/52			*Set of 4*	8·75	9·50

71 Sultan Omar Saifuddin 50 c. Stamp of 1952

(Recess and litho D.L.R.)

1984 (22 Oct). *"Philakorea" International Stamp Exhibition, Seoul. T* **71** *and similar vert designs. Multicoloured. P* 13.

353	10 c.	Type **71**		60	15
354	75 c.	Brunei River view 10 c. stamp of 1907		2·00	2·25
355	$2	Star and view ½ c. stamp of 1895		3·00	6·00
353/5			*Set of 3*	5·00	7·50

MS356 Three sheets, 117×100 mm, each containing one stamp as Nos. 353/5 .. *Set of 3 sheets* 4·25 6·50
a. Line perf 14 at left .. *Set of 3 sheets* 4·50 8·00
The stamps within the miniature sheets were perforated by means of a three-sided comb gauging 13 and completed by a line perforation at left. Normally this line perforation is also 13, but on MS356a it measures 14.

72 United Nations Emblem
73 Young People and Brunei Flag

(Des Awang Nor Ariffin bin Md. Yassin (No. 357, 359), Haji Salleh bin Haji Ibrahim (358) or Siti Zaleha Haji Kaprawi (360). Litho Cartor)

1985 (23 Sept). *Admission of Brunei to World Organizations (1st issue). T* **72** *and similar horiz designs. W w* **17** *(sideways*). *P* 13.

357	50 c.	black, gold and pale greenish blue		50	70
358	50 c.	multicoloured		50	70
359	50 c.	multicoloured		50	70
360	50 c.	multicoloured		50	70
357/60			*Set of 4*	1·75	2·50

MS361 110×151 mm. Nos. 357/60 .. .. 2·00 3·00
w. Wmk reading upwards .. .. 2·00 3·00
Designs:—No. 357, Type **72**; No. 358, Islamic Conference Organization logo; No. 359, Commonwealth logo; No. 360 A.S.E.A.N. emblem.
*The normal sideways version of the watermark shows the words reading downwards.
See also Nos. 383/7.

(Des Siti Zaleha Haji Kaprawi. Litho Security Printers (M), Malaysia)

1985 (17 Oct). *International Youth Year. T* **73** *and similar horiz designs. Multicoloured. P* 12.

362	10 c.	Type **73**		1·00	20
363	75 c.	Young people at work		4·50	5·50
364	$1	Young people serving the community		5·00	6·00
362/4			*Set of 3*	9·50	10·50

74 Palestinian Emblem
75 Early and Modern Scout Uniforms

(Des Haji Salleh bin Haji Ibrahim. Litho Secura, Singapore)

1985 (29 Nov). *International Palestinian Solidarity Day. P* 12×12½.

365	**74**	10 c. multicoloured		1·00	20
366		50 c. multicoloured		3·25	1·50
367		$1 multicoloured		4·00	3·00
365/7			*Set of 3*	7·50	4·25

(Des Awang Nor Ariffin bin Md. Yassin. Litho Secura, Singapore)

1985 (14 Dec). *National Scout Jamboree. T* **75** *and similar vert designs. Multicoloured. P* 13½.

368	10 c.	Type **75**		60	10
369	20 c.	Scout on tower signalling with flag		90	40
370	$2	Jamboree emblem		2·75	3·25
368/70			*Set of 3*	3·75	3·25

76 Sultan Sir Hassanal Bolkiah Mu'izzaddin Waddaulah

77

(Des Awang Nor Ariffin bin Md. Yassin. Photo Harrison)

1985 (23 Dec)—**86**. *W* **77**. *P* 13½×14½ (10 *to* 75 c.) *or* 14 ($1 *to* $10).

371	**76**	10 c. multicoloured		30	10
372		15 c. multicoloured		30	10
373		20 c. multicoloured		40	10
374		25 c. multicoloured		40	15
375		35 c. multicoloured (15.1.86)		55	20
376		40 c. multicoloured (15.1.86)		60	25
377		50 c. multicoloured (15.1.86)		70	35
378		75 c. multicoloured (15.1.86)		90	50
379		$1 multicoloured (23.2.86)		1·25	70
		a. Wmk sideways			
380		$2 multicoloured (23.2.86)		2·25	1·50
		a. Wmk sideways			
381		$5 multicoloured (23.2.86)		4·25	4·50
		a. Wmk sideways			
382		$10 multicoloured (29.3.86)		8·00	9·50
		a. Wmk sideways			
371/82			*Set of 12*	18·00	16·00

Nos. 379/82 are larger, size 32×39 mm.
The sideways watermark printings of the dollar values, which are only known used, may date from around 1995.

(Des Awang Nor Ariffin bin Md. Yassin. Litho Cartor)

1986 (30 Apr). *Admission of Brunei to World Organizations (2nd issue). Horiz designs as T* **72**. *W w* **17** *(sideways). P* 13.

383	50 c.	black, gold and bright yellow-green		40	60
384	50 c.	black, gold and bright pinkish mauve		40	60
385	50 c.	black, gold and orange-red		40	60
386	50 c.	black, gold and dull ultramarine		40	60
383/6			*Set of 4*	1·40	2·25

MS387 105×155 mm. Nos. 383/6. Wmk upright 1·50 3·25
Designs:—No. 383, World Meteorological Organization emblem; 384, International Telecommunication Union emblem; 385, Universal Postal Union emblem; 386, International Civil Aviation Organization emblem.

78 Soldiers on Assault Course and Bell 205 UH-1H Iroquois Helicopter
79 Tunggul Charok Buritan, Alam Bernaga (Alam Besar), Pisang-Pisang and Sandaran

(Des Awang Nor Ariffin bin Md. Yassin. Litho Secura, Singapore)

1986 (31 May). *25th Anniv of Brunei Armed Forces. T* **78** *and similar horiz designs. Multicoloured. P* 13½.

388	10 c.	Type **78**		2·75	2·75
		a. Horiz strip of 4. Nos. 388/91		12·50	
389	20 c.	Operating computer		3·00	3·00
390	50 c.	Anti-aircraft missile, MBB-Bolkow Bo 105L helicopter and missile boat		4·00	4·00
391	75 c.	Army commanders and parade		4·25	4·25
388/91			*Set of 4*	12·50	12·50

Nos. 388/91 were printed together, *se-tenant*, in horizontal strips of 4 throughout the sheet, forming a composite design.

(Des Awang Nor Ariffin bin Md. Yassin. Litho Secura, Singapore)

1986 (15 July). *Royal Ensigns (1st series). T* **79** *and similar vert designs. P* 12.

392	10 c.	black, greenish yellow and red		30	10
393	75 c.	multicoloured		1·10	1·10
394	$2	black, greenish yellow and green		2·25	2·75
392/4			*Set of 3*	3·25	3·25

Designs:—75 c. Ula-Ula Besar, Sumbu Layang and Payong Haram; $2 Panji-Panji, Chogan Istiadat (Chogan Di-Raja) and Chogan Ugama.

(Des Awang Nor Ariffin bin Md. Yassin. Litho Secura, Singapore)

1986 (30 Sept). *Royal Ensigns (2nd series). Vert designs as T* **79**. *P* 12.

395	10 c.	multicoloured		30	10
396	75 c.	black, red and greenish yellow		1·10	1·10
397	$2	multicoloured		2·25	2·75
395/7			*Set of 3*	3·25	3·50

Designs:—10 c. Dadap, Tunggul Kawan, Ambal, Payong Ubor-Ubor, Sapu-Sapu Ayeng and Rawai Lidah; 75 c. Payong Tinggi and Payong Ubor-Ubor Tiga Ringkat; $2 Lambang Duli Yang Maha Mulia and Mahligai.

80 Stylised Peace Doves
81 Drug Addict in Cage and Syringe (poster by Othman bin Ramboh)

(Des Zainal Abidin Haji Ibrahim. Litho Security Printers (M), Malaysia)

1986 (24 Oct). *International Peace Year. T* **80** *and similar horiz designs. Multicoloured. P* 12.

398	50 c.	Type **80**		75	75
399	75 c.	Stylised hands and "1986"		1·00	1·10
400	$1	International Peace Year emblem and arms of Brunei		1·25	1·50
398/400			*Set of 3*	2·75	3·00

(Litho Security Printers (M), Malaysia)

1987 (15 Mar). *National Anti-drug Campaign. Children's Posters. T* **81** *and similar vert designs. Multicoloured. P* 12.

401	10 c.	Type **81**		1·00	25
402	75 c.	Drug addict and noose (Arman bin Mohd. Zaman)		2·50	3·50
403	$1	Blindfolded drug addict and noose (Abidin bin Hj. Rashid)		3·00	4·50
401/3			*Set of 3*	6·00	7·50

82 Cannon ("badil")
83 Map showing Member Countries

(Des Haji Salleh bin Haji Ibrahim. Litho Security Printers (M), Malaysia)

1987 (15 July). *Brassware (1st series). T 82 and similar vert designs. Multicoloured. P 12.*

404	50 c. Type 82	.. ..	50	50
405	50 c. Lamp ("pelita") ..	.. ..	50	50
406	50 c. Betel container ("langguai") ..		50	50
407	50 c. Water jug ("kiri")	.. ..	50	50
404/7	..	*Set of 4*	1·75	1·75

See also Nos. 434/7.

(Des Zainal Abidin bin Haji Ibrahim. Litho Security Printers (M), Malaysia)

1987 (8 Aug). *20th Anniv of Association of South East Asian Nations. T 83 and similar horiz designs. Multicoloured. P 14×13½.*

408	20 c. Type 83	.. ..	35	20
409	50 c. Dates and figures "20" ..	.. ..	60	50
410	$1 Flags of member states. .		1·25	1·25
408/10	..	*Set of 3*	2·00	1·75

84 Brunei Citizens

(Des Pengiran Haji Muhammad bin Pengiran Duraman. Litho Secura, Singapore)

1987 (29 Sept). *25th Anniv of Language and Literature Bureau (1986). T 84 and similar horiz designs. Multicoloured. P 13×12½.*

411	10 c. Type 84 ..	.. ..	10	10
	a. Horiz strip of 3. Nos. 411/13	..	2·00	
412	50 c. Flame emblem and hands holding open book	..	40	40
413	$2 Scenes of village life	.. ..	1·50	1·50
411/13	..	*Set of 3*	2·00	2·00

Nos. 411/13 were printed together, *se-tenant*, in horizontal strips of three throughout the sheet, each strip forming a composite design taken from a mural.

85 *Artocarpus odoratissima*

(Litho Security Printers (M), Malaysia)

1987 (31 Oct). *Local Fruits (1st series). T 85 and similar horiz designs. Multicoloured. P 12.*

414	50 c. Type 85 ..	.. ..	45	55
	a. Horiz strip of 4. Nos. 414/17	..	1·60	
415	50 c. *Canarium odontophyllum mig.* .		45	55
416	50 c. *Litsea garciae* ..	..	45	55
417	50 c. *Mangifera foetida lour* ..	..	45	55
414/17	..	*Set of 4*	1·60	2·00

Nos. 414/17 were printed together, *se-tenant*, in horizontal strips of 4 throughout the sheet.
See also Nos. 421/4, 459/62, 480/2 and 525/8.

86 Modern House   87 Wooden Lathe

(Litho Security Printers (M), Malaysia)

1987 (28 Nov). *International Year of Shelter for the Homeless. T 86 and similar horiz designs, each showing modern Brunei housing. P 13×12½.*

418	50 c. multicoloured	.. ..	40	50
419	75 c. multicoloured	.. ..	55	65
420	$1 multicoloured	.. ..	80	90
418/20	.. ..	*Set of 3*	1·60	1·90

(Des Awang Nor Ariffin bin Md. Yassin. Litho Security Printers (M), Malaysia)

1988 (30 Jan). *Local Fruits (2nd series). Horiz designs as T 85. Multicoloured. P 12.*

421	50 c. *Durio spp*		60	70
	a. Horiz strip of 4. Nos. 421/4	..	2·25	
422	50 c. *Durio oxleyanus.* .		60	70
423	50 c. *Durio graveolens* (blue background)		60	70
424	50 c. *Durio graveolens* (white background)		60	70
421/4	..	*Set of 4*	2·25	2·50

Nos. 421/4 were printed together, *se-tenant*, in horizontal strips of four throughout the sheet.

(Des Awang Padzil bin Haji Ahmad. Litho Security Printers (M), Malaysia)

1988 (29 Feb). *Opening of Malay Technology Museum. T 87 and similar vert designs. Multicoloured. P 12.*

425	10 c. Type 87 ..	.. ..	15	10
426	75 c. Crushing sugar cane	.. ..	55	70
427	$1 Bird scarer	.. ..	70	85
425/7	..	*Set of 3*	1·25	1·50

88 Beragi Bunga Sakah-Sakah   89 Sultan reading
dan Bunga Cengkih Cloth   Proclamation

(Des Awang Nor Ariffin bin Md. Yassin. Litho Security Printers (M), Malaysia)

1988 (30 Apr). *Handwoven Material (1st series). T 88 and similar horiz designs showing different patterns. Multicoloured. P 12.*

428	10 c. Type 88	.. ..	10	10
429	20 c. Jong Sarat cloth	.. ..	15	15
430	25 c. Si Pugut cloth	.. ..	20	25
431	40 c. Si Pugut Bunga Berlapis cloth	..	30	35
432	75 c. Si Lobang Bangsi Bunga Belitang Kipas cloth		55	80
428/32	..	*Set of 5*	1·10	1·50
MS433	150×204 mm. Nos. 428/32	..	2·25	3·00

See also Nos. 442/7.

(Des Haji Salleh bin Haji Ibrahim. Litho Security Printers (M), Malaysia)

1988 (30 June). *Brassware (2nd series). Vert designs as T 82. Multicoloured. P 12.*

434	50 c. Lidded two-handled pot ("periok")	..	40	50
435	50 c. Candlestick ("lampong")	..	40	50
436	50 c. Shallow circular dish with stand ("gangsa")		40	50
437	50 c. Repousse box with lid ("celapa")	..	40	50
434/7	.. ..	*Set of 4*	1·40	1·75

(Des Awang Nor Ariffin bin Md. Yassin. Litho Security Printers (M), Malaysia)

1988 (1 Aug). *20th Anniv of Sultan's Coronation. T 89 and similar vert designs. Multicoloured. P 14 (20, 75 c.) or 12½×13 ($2).*

438	20 c. Type 89	.. ..	15	15
439	75 c. Sultan reading from Koran	..	55	60
440	$2 In Coronation robes (26×63 mm)	..	1·50	1·60
438/40		*Set of 3*	2·10	2·25
MS441	164×125 mm. Nos. 438/40	..	2·10	2·25

In No. MS441 the perforations of the stamps are as Nos. 438/40 except for the 75 c. which is perforated 13 at right.

(Des Awang Nor Ariffin bin Md. Yassin. Litho Security Printers (M), Malaysia)

1988 (29 Sept). *Handwoven Material (2nd series). Horiz designs as T 88. Multicoloured. P 12.*

442	10 c. Beragi cloth	.. ..	15	10
443	20 c. Bertabur cloth	.. ..	20	20
444	25 c. Sukma Indra cloth	.. ..	25	25
445	40 c. Si Pugut Bunga cloth	.. ..	40	55
446	75 c. Beragi Si Lobang Bangsi Bunga Cendera Kesuma cloth		75	90
442/6		*Set of 5*	1·60	1·75
MS447	150×204 mm. Nos. 442/6	..	2·50	3·25

90 Malaria-carrying Mosquito

(Litho Cartor)

1988 (17 Dec). *40th Anniv of World Health Organization. T 90 and similar horiz designs. Multicoloured. P 14×13½.*

448	25 c. Type 90	.. ..	70	30
449	35 c. Man with insecticide spray and sample on slide		80	45
450	$2 Microscope and magnified malaria cells	2·50	2·00
448/50	..	*Set of 3*	3·50	2·50

91 Sultan and Council of   92 Dove escaping from
Ministers   Cage

(Des Awang Nor Ariffin bin Md Yassin. Litho Security Printers (M), Malaysia)

1989 (23 Feb). *5th Anniv of National Day. T 91 and similar multicoloured designs. P 12.*

451	20 c. Type 91	.. ..	15	10
452	30 c. Guard of honour	.. ..	20	15
453	60 c. Firework display (27 × 55 mm)	..	45	40
454	$2 Congregation in mosque	..	1·50	1·75
451/4	..	*Set of 4*	2·25	2·25
MS455	164 × 124 mm. Nos. 451/4	..	2·25	2·75

(Des Haji Salleh bin Haji Ibrahim. Litho Secura, Singapore)

1989 (1 Apr). *"Freedom of Palestine". T 92 and similar horiz designs. Multicoloured. P 13½.*

456	20 c. Type 92	..	30	20
457	75 c. Map and Palestinian flag	..	90	85
458	$1 Dome of the Rock, Jerusalem ..		1·10	1·25
456/8	..	*Set of 3*	2·10	2·10

(Des Awang Nor Ariffin bin Md. Yassin. Litho Secura, Singapore)

1989 (31 Oct). *Local Fruits (3rd series). Horiz designs as T 85. Multicoloured. P 12.*

459	60 c. *Daemonorops fissa*	..	1·75	2·00
	a. Horiz strip of 4. Nos. 459/62		6·00	
460	60 c. *Eleiodoxa conferta*	..	1·75	2·00
461	60 c. *Salacca zalacca*	..	1·75	2·00
462	60 c. *Calamus ornatus*	..	1·75	2·00
459/62		*Set of 4*	6·00	7·00

Nos. 459/62 were printed together, *se-tenant*, in horizontal strips of four throughout the sheet.

93 Oil Pump

(Des Brunei Shell Petroleum Co. Litho Secura, Singapore)

1989 (28 Dec). *60th Anniv of Brunei Oil and Gas Industry. T 93 and similar horiz designs. Multicoloured. P 13½.*

463	20 c. Type 93	..	1·25	30
464	60 c. Loading tanker	..	2·25	2·25
465	90 c. Oil well at sunset	..	2·50	2·75
466	$1 Pipe laying	..	2·75	2·75
467	$2 Oil terminal	..	5·00	6·50
463/7	..	*Set of 5*	12·50	13·00

94 Museum Building and
Exhibits

(Des Awang Padzil bin Haji Ahmad ($1), Mohd Yamin bin Haji Abd. Momin (others). Litho Security Printers (M), Malaysia)

1990 (1 Jan). *25th Anniv of Brunei Museum. T 94 and similar horiz designs. Multicoloured. P 12.*

468	30 c. Type 94	.. ..	1·25	60
469	60 c. Official opening, 1965	..	2·00	2·25
470	$1 Brunei Museum	..	2·75	3·25
468/70	..	*Set of 3*	5·50	5·50

95 Letters from Malay   96 Tarsier in Tree
Alphabet

(Des Pengiran Haji Muhammad bin Pengiran Duraman. Litho Security Printers (M), Malaysia)

1990 (15 July). *International Literacy Year. T 95 and similar horiz designs. Multicoloured. P 12.*

471	15 c. Type 95	..	75	30
472	90 c. English alphabet	..	2·75	3·25
473	$1 Literacy Year emblem and letters	..	2·75	3·50
471/3	..	*Set of 3*	5·50	6·50

(Des Haji Salleh bin Haji Ibrahim. Litho Security Printers (M), Malaysia)

1990 (29 Sept). *Endangered Species. Western Tarsier. T 96 and similar vert designs. Multicoloured. P 12 (20 c.) or 12½×13 (others).*

474	20 c. Western Tarsier on branch	..	1·25	45
475	60 c. Western Tarsier feeding	..	2·50	2·75
476	90 c. Type 96	..	3·50	4·00
474/6	..	*Set of 3*	6·50	6·50

97 Symbolic Family

98 Proboscis Monkey on Ground

(Litho Security Printers (M), Malaysia)

1990 (1 Dec). *Worldwide Campaign against AIDS. T* **97** *and similar vert designs. Multicoloured. P* 12½.

477	20 c.	Type **97**		1·25	60
478	30 c.	Sources of infection		2·00	1·50
479	90 c.	"AIDS" headstone surrounded by skulls		5·00	6·25
477/9			*Set of 3*	7·50	7·50

(Litho Security Printers (M), Malaysia)

1990 (31 Dec). *Local Fruits (4th series). Horiz designs as T* **85**. *Multicoloured. P* 12.

480	60 c.	*Willoughbea* sp. (brown fruit)		2·75	3·00
		a. Horiz strip of three. Nos. 480/2		7·50	
481	60 c.	Ripe *Willoughbea* sp. (yellow fruit)		2·75	3·00
482	60 c.	*Willoughbea angustifolia*		2·75	3·00
480/2			*Set of 3*	7·50	8·00

Nos. 480/2 were printed together, *se-tenant*, in horizontal strips of three throughout the sheet.

(Des Haji Salleh bin Haji Ibrahim. Litho Cartor)

1991 (30 Mar). *Endangered Species. Proboscis Monkey. T* **98** *and similar vert designs. Multicoloured. P* 13½×14.

483	15 c.	Type **98**		1·60	60
484	20 c.	Head of monkey		1·60	70
485	50 c.	Monkey sitting on branch		3·00	3·25
486	60 c.	Female monkey with baby climbing tree		3·25	3·75
483/6			*Set of 4*	8·50	7·50

99 Junior School Classes

100 Young Brunei Beauty

(Des Awang Nor Ariffin bin Md Yassin. Litho, Secura Singapore)

1991 (29 Sept). *Teachers' Day. T* **99** *and similar horiz design. Multicoloured. P* 13½×14.

487	60 c.	Type **99**		2·25	2·50
488	90 c.	Secondary school class		2·75	3·50

(Des Awang Padzil bin Haji Ahmad. Litho Security Printers (M), Malaysia)

1991 (1 Oct). *Fishes. Brunei Beauty. T* **100** *and similar horiz designs. Multicoloured. P* 12½.

489	30 c.	Type **100**		1·50	85
490	60 c.	Female fish		2·50	3·25
491	$1	Male fish		3·00	3·75
489/91			*Set of 3*	6·25	7·00

101 Graduate with Family

102 Symbolic Heart and Trace

(Des A. Mansur. Litho Cartor)

1991 (30 Nov). *Happy Family Campaign. T* **101** *and similar vert designs. Multicoloured. P* 13.

492	20 c.	Type **101**		70	50
493	60 c.	Mothers with children		1·75	2·00
494	90 c.	Family		2·50	3·25
492/4			*Set of 3*	4·50	5·25

(Des Siti Zaleha Haji Kaprawi. Litho Cartor)

1992 (7 Apr). *World Health Day. T* **102** *and similar horiz designs showing heart and heartbeat trace. P* 13.

495	20 c.	multicoloured		80	50
496	50 c.	multicoloured		2·00	2·00
497	75 c.	multicoloured		2·75	3·50
495/7			*Set of 3*	5·00	5·50

The 75 c. is larger, 48 × 27 mm.

103 Map of Cable System

(Des Awang Nor Ariffin bin Md. Yassin. Litho Security Printers (M), Malaysia)

1992 (28 Apr). *Launching of Singapore–Borneo–Philippines Fibre Optic Submarine Cable System. T* **103** *and similar horiz designs. P* 12.

498	20 c.	Type **103**		1·00	50
499	30 c.	Diagram of Brunei connection		1·40	1·10
500	90 c.	Submarine cable		3·00	3·75
498/500			*Set of 3*	4·75	5·00

104 Modern Sculptures

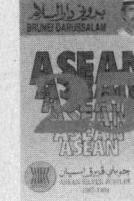
105 "A.S.E.A.N. 25" and Logo

(Des Awang Nor Ariffin bin Md. Yassin. Litho Enschedé)

1992 (30 June). *Visit A.S.E.A.N. Year. T* **104** *and similar horiz designs. Multicoloured. P* 13½×14.

501	20 c.	Type **104**		1·40	1·50
		a. Horiz strip of 3. Nos. 501/3		4·75	
502	60 c.	Traditional martial arts		1·75	2·00
503	$1	Modern sculptures (*different*)		2·00	2·25
501/3			*Set of 3*	4·75	5·25

Nos. 501/3 were printed together, *se-tenant*, in horizontal strips of 3 throughout the sheet with the backgrounds forming a composite design.

(Des Mohd. Yamin bin Haji Abd. Momin. Litho Questa)

1992 (8 Aug). *25th Anniv of A.S.E.A.N (Association of South East Asian Nations). T* **105** *and similar vert designs. Multicoloured. P* 14.

504	20 c.	Type **105**		1·00	65
505	60 c.	Headquarters building		2·25	2·75
506	90 c.	National landmarks		3·00	3·75
504/6			*Set of 3*	5·50	6·50

106 Sultan in Procession

107 Crested Wood Partridge

(Des Awang Padzil bin Haji Ahmad. Litho Enschedé)

1992 (5 Oct). *25th Anniv of Sultan's Accession. T* **106** *and similar vert designs. Multicoloured. P* 14×13½.

507	25 c.	Type **106**		85	1·00
		a. Horiz strip of 5. Nos. 507/11		3·75	
508	25 c.	Brunei International Airport		85	1·00
509	25 c.	Sultan's Palace		85	1·00
510	25 c.	Docks and Brunei University		85	1·00
511	25 c.	Mosque		85	1·00
507/11			*Set of 5*	3·75	4·50

Nos. 507/11 were printed together, *se-tenant*, in horizontal strips of 5 throughout the sheet, each strip forming a composite design.

(Des Awang Padzil bin Haji Ahmad. Litho Enschedé)

1992 (30 Dec). *Birds (1st series). T* **107** *and similar vert designs. Multicoloured. P* 14×13½.

512	30 c.	Type **107**		75	50
513	60 c.	Asiatic Paradise Flycatcher		1·60	2·25
514	$1	Great Argus Pheasant		1·90	3·00
512/14			*Set of 3*	3·75	5·25

(Des Awang Padzil bin Haji Ahmad (60 c.), Kassim bin Haji Ismail (others). Litho Enschedé)

1993 (2 Jan). *Birds (2nd series). Vert designs as T* **107**. *Multicoloured. P* 14×13½.

515	30 c.	Long-tailed Parakeet		1·00	50
516	60 c.	Magpie Robin		2·00	2·25
517	$1	Blue-crowned Hanging Parrot		2·50	3·00
515/17			*Set of 3*	5·00	5·25

(Des Kassim bin Haji Ismail. Litho Enschedé)

1993 (3 May). *Birds (3rd series). Multicoloured designs as T* **107**. *P* 13½×14 (*horiz*) *or* 14×13½ (*vert*).

518	30 c.	Chestnut-breasted Malkoha		1·25	50
519	60 c.	White-rumped Shama		2·25	2·50
520	$1	Black and Red Broadbill (*vert*)		3·00	3·50
518/20			*Set of 3*	6·00	6·00

108 National Flag and "10"

109 Cigarette burning Heart and Deformed Baby in Womb

(Des Awang Nor Ariffin bin Md. Yassin. Litho Cartor)

1994 (16 June). *10th Anniv of National Day. T* **108** *and similar vert designs. Multicoloured. P* 13.

521	10 c.	Type **108**		30	50
		a. Horiz strip of 4. Nos. 521/4		1·75	
522	20 c.	Symbolic hands		40	60
523	30 c.	Previous National Day symbols		55	80
524	60 c.	Coat of arms		75	1·00
521/4			*Set of 4*	1·75	2·50

Nos. 521/4 were printed together, *se-tenant*, in horizontal strips of 4 throughout the sheet.

(Des Ali bin Haji Abd Rahim. Litho Cartor)

1994 (8 Aug). *Local Fruits (5th issue). Horiz designs as T* **85**, *but each* 36×26 *mm. Multicoloured. P* 13½.

525	60 c.	*Nephelium mutabile*		85	1·10
526	60 c.	*Nephelium xerospermoides*		85	1·10
527	60 c.	*Nephelium* spp		85	1·10
528	60 c.	*Nephelium macrophyllum*		85	1·10
525/8			*Set of 4*	3·00	4·00

(Litho Enschedé)

1994 (1 Sept). *World No Tobacco Day. T* **109** *and similar vert designs. Multicoloured. P* 14×13½.

529	10 c.	Type **109**		15	10
530	15 c.	Symbols of smoking over crowd of people		15	10
531	$2	Globe crushing cigarettes		2·75	3·50
529/31			*Set of 3*	2·75	3·50

110 Raja Isteri (wife of Sultan) in Guide Uniform

111 Turbo-prop Airliner on Runway

(Des Awang Nor Ariffin bin Md. Yassin. Litho Enschedé)

1994 (7 Oct). *40th Anniv of Brunei Girl Guides' Association. T* **110** *and similar vert designs. Multicoloured. P* 14×13½.

532	40 c.	Type **110**		80	90
		a. Horiz strip of 5. Nos. 532/6		3·50	
533	40 c.	Guide receiving award		80	90
534	40 c.	Guide reading		80	90
535	40 c.	Group of guides		80	90
536	40 c.	Guides erecting tent		80	90
532/6			*Set of 5*	3·50	4·00

Nos. 532/6 were printed together, *se-tenant*, in horizontal strips of 5 throughout the sheet.

(Des Mohd Yamin bin Haji Abd Momin. Litho Cartor)

1994 (18 Nov). *20th Anniv of Royal Brunei Airlines. T* **111** *and similar horiz designs. Multicoloured. P* 13½.

537	10 c.	Type **111**		40	20
538	20 c.	Jet airliner on runway		70	35
539	$1	Jet airliner in the air		2·00	2·50
537/9			*Set of 3*	2·75	3·50

112 Malay Family

113 Aerial View of City, 1970

(Des Awang Padzil bin Haji Ahmad. Litho Cartor)

1994 (30 Dec). *International Day against Drug Abuse and Trafficking. T **112** and similar vert designs. P 13½×14.*
540	20 c. Type **112**	..	60	70
	a. Horiz strip of 3. Nos. 540/2	..	2·50	
541	60 c. Chinese family	..	1·00	1·25
542	$1 Doctor, police officers and members of youth organizations	..	1·25	1·50
540/2		Set of 3	2·50	3·00

Nos. 540/2 were printed together, *se-tenant*, in horizontal strips of 3 throughout the sheet, each strip forming a composite design.

(Des Awang Padzil bin Haji Ahmad. Litho Cartor)

1995 (4 Oct). *25th Anniv of Bandar Seri Begawan. T **113** and similar horiz designs. Multicoloured. P 13½.*
543	30 c. Type **113**	..	55	45
544	50 c. City in 1980	..	80	85
545	$1 City in 1990	..	1·50	2·00
543/5		Set of 3	2·50	3·00

114 United Nations General Assembly | **115** Students in Laboratory

(Des Mohd Yamin bin Haji Abd Momin. Litho Walsall)

1995 (24 Oct). *50th Anniv of United Nations. T **114** and similar vert designs. Multicoloured. P 14½×14.*
546	20 c. Type **114**	..	40	25
547	60 c. Security Council in session	..	75	80
548	90 c. United Nations Building, New York (27×44 mm)	..	1·25	1·75
546/8		Set of 3	2·25	2·50

(Des Mahadi bin Haji Matzain. Litho Cartor)

1995 (28 Oct). *10th Anniv of University of Brunei. T **115** and similar vert designs. Multicoloured. P 13×13½.*
549	30 c. Type **115**	..	35	35
550	50 c. University building	..	55	65
551	90 c. Sultan visiting University	..	1·10	1·75
549/51		Set of 3	1·75	2·50

116 Police Officers | **117** Telephones

(Des Awang Nor Ariffin bin Md. Yassin. Litho Enschedé)

1996 (10 Feb). *75th Anniv of Royal Brunei Police Force. T **116** and similar vert designs. Multicoloured. P 13½×13.*
552	25 c. Type **116**	..	60	30
553	50 c. Aspects of police work	..	90	90
554	75 c. Sultan inspecting parade	..	1·50	1·75
552/4		Set of 3	2·75	2·75

(Litho Cartor)

1996 (17 May). *World Telecommunications Day. Children's Paintings. T **117** and similar vert designs. Multicoloured. P 13½.*
555	20 c. Type **117**	..	40	25
556	35 c. Telephone dial and aspects of telecommunications	..	55	45
557	$1 Globe and aspects of telecommunications	..	1·75	2·00
555/7		Set of 3	2·40	2·40

118 Sultan and Crowd | **119** Sultan Hassanal Bolkiah Mu'izzaddin Waddaulah

120

(Des Awang Nor Ariffin bin Md. Yassin. Litho Cartor)

1996 (15 July). *50th Birthday of Sultan Hassanal Bolkiah Mu'izzaddin Waddaulah. T **118** and similar vert designs. Multicoloured. P 13×13½.*
558	50 c. Type **118**	..	75	85
559	50 c. Sultan in ceremonial dress	..	75	85
560	50 c. Sultan receiving dignitaries at mosque	..	75	85
561	50 c. Sultan with subjects	..	75	85
558/61		Set of 4	2·75	3·00
MS562	152×100 mm. $1 Sultan in ceremonial dress (*different*). P 13	..	1·50	2·00

A larger miniature sheet, 176×128 mm, containing five vertical $50 values was produced in a limited printing for presentation purposes.

FLUORESCENT SECURITY MARKING. All issues from No. 563 onwards carry a fluorescent security marking, *unless otherwise stated*. This takes the form of a single impression of the Postal Service logo only visible under U.V. light. The size and the colour of the fluorescent ink varies according to the printer involved.

(Litho Enschedé)

1996 (9 Oct). *T **119** and similar vert design. W **120**. P 14×13½.*
563	**119**	10 c. multicoloured	..	10	15
564		15 c. multicoloured	..	10	15
565		20 c. multicoloured	..	15	20
566		30 c. multicoloured	..	20	25
567		50 c. multicoloured	..	40	45
568		60 c. multicoloured	..	45	50
569		75 c. multicoloured	..	55	60
570		90 c. multicoloured	..	70	75
571	—	$1 multicoloured	..	75	80
572	—	$2 multicoloured	..	1·50	1·60
573	—	$5 multicoloured	..	3·75	4·00
574	—	$10 multicoloured	..	7·50	8·00
563/74			Set of 12	16·00	17·00

Design: (27×39 mm)—$1 to $10 Sultan in ceremonial robes.

121 Black-naped Tern | **122** *Acanthus ebracteatus*

(Des Siti Zaleha Haji Kaprawi. Litho Enschedé)

1996 (11 Nov). *Birds (4th series). Sea Birds. T **121** and similar vert designs. Multicoloured. P 14×13½.*
575	20 c. Type **121**	..	35	30
576	30 c. Roseate Tern	..	45	40
577	$1 Bridled Tern	..	1·25	1·60
575/7		Set of 3	1·90	2·10

No. 576 is inscribed "ROSLATE TERN" in error.

(Des J. Esther Lee. Litho Security Printers (M), Malaysia)

1997 (29 May). *Mangrove Flowers. T **22** and similar horiz designs. Multicoloured. P 12.*
578	20 c. Type **122**	..	25	20
579	30 c. *Lumnitzera littorea*	..	35	30
580	$1 *Nypa fruticans*	..	1·10	1·25
578/80		Set of 3	1·50	1·60

123 *Heterocentrotus mammillatus*

(Des J. Esther Lee. Litho Southern Colour Print, Dunedin)

1997 (15 Dec). *Marine Life. T **123** and similar horiz designs. Multicoloured. P 12.*
581	60 c. Type **123**	..	50	60
582	60 c. *Linckia laevigata* (starfish)	..	50	60
583	60 c. *Oxycomanthus bennetti* (plant)	..	50	60
584	60 c. *Bohadschia argus* (sea slug)	..	50	60
581/4		Set of 4	1·75	2·25

124 Children and Sign Language

(Des Padzil bin Haj Ahmed. Litho Cartor)

1998 (31 May). *Asian and Pacific Decade of Disabled Persons, 1993–2002. T **124** and similar horiz designs. Multicoloured. P 13×13½.*
585	20 c. Type **124**	..	20	20
586	50 c. Woman typing and firework display	..	40	50
587	$1 Disabled athletes	..	75	1·00
585/7		Set of 3	1·25	1·50

125 Sultan performing Ceremonial Duties | **126** A.S.E.A.N. Architecture and Transport

(Des Awang Nor Ariffin bin Md. Yassin. Litho Security Printers (M), Malaysia)

1998 (1 Aug). *30th Anniv of Coronation of Sultan Hassanal Bolkiah Mu'izzaddin Waddaulah. T **125** and similar horiz designs. Multicoloured. P 12.*
588	60 c. Type **125**	..	50	50
589	90 c. Sultan on Coronation throne	..	80	1·00
590	$1 Coronation parade	..	85	1·00
588/90		Set of 3	1·90	2·25
MS591	150×180 mm. Nos. 588/90	..	2·50	2·75

(Des Siti Zaleha Haji Kaprawi. Litho Enschedé)

1998 (8 Aug). *30th Anniv of Association of South-east Asian Nations. T **126** and similar vert designs. Multicoloured. P 13½.*
592	30 c. Type **126**	..	30	40
593	30 c. Map of Brunei and city scenes	..	30	40
594	30 c. Flags of member nations	..	30	40
592/4		Set of 3	80	1·10

127 Crown Prince at Desk | **128** Koran, Civil Servants and Handshake

(Des Mohd Yamin bin Haji Abd Momin. Litho Security Printers (M), Malaysia)

1998 (10 Aug). *Proclamation of Prince Al-Muhtadee Billah as Crown Prince. T **127** and similar vert designs. Multicoloured. P 12.*
595	$1 Type **127**	..	1·00	90
596	$2 Crown Prince in military uniform	..	1·75	2·00
597	$3 Crown Prince's emblem	..	2·25	3·00
595/7		Set of 3	4·50	5·50
MS598	175×153 mm. Nos. 595/7	..	5·00	5·50

(Des Awang Nor Ariffin bin Md Yassin. Litho Cartor)

1998 (29 Sept). *Fifth Anniv of Civil Service Day. T **128** and similar vert designs. Multicoloured. P 13×13½.*
599	30 c. Type **128**	..	30	25
600	60 c. Symbols of progress	..	50	60
601	90 c. Civil servants at work	..	80	1·00
599/601		Set of 3	1·40	1·75

129 Blue-eared Kingfisher | **130** Water Village, Bandar Seri Begawan

(Des J. Esther Lee. Litho Cartor)

1998 (11 Nov). *Birds (5th series). Kingfishers.* T **129** *and similar vert designs. Multicoloured.* P 13½×13.

602	20 c. Type **129**	30	25
603	30 c. Common Kingfisher	35	30
604	60 c. White-collared Kingfisher	60	70
605	$1 Stork-billed Kingfisher	90	1·25
602/5	*Set of* 4	1·90	2·25

(Des Siti Zaleha Haji Kaprawi. Litho Cartor)

1999 (23 Feb). *15th Anniv of National Day.* T **130** *and similar vert designs. Multicoloured.* P 13.

606	20 c. Type **130**	20	20
607	60 c. Modern telecommunications and air travel	60	65
608	90 c. Aspects of modern Brunei	90	95
606/8	*Set of* 3	1·50	1·60
MS609	118×85 mm. Nos. 606/8	1·50	1·75

131 Rifle-shooting   **132** Clasped Hands and Globe

(Litho Southern Colour Print, Dunedin)

1999 (7 Aug). *20th South-east Asia Games, Brunei.* T **131** *and similar square designs. Multicoloured.* P 14½.

610	20 c. Type **131**	25	25
	a. Horiz strip of 5. Nos. 610/14	1·10	
611	20 c. Golf and tennis	25	25
612	20 c. Boxing and judo	25	25
613	20 c. Squash and table tennis	25	25
614	20 c. Swimming and canoe racing	25	25
615	20 c. Hockey and cycling	25	25
	a. Horiz strip of 5. Nos. 615/19	1·10	
616	20 c. Basketball and football	25	25
617	20 c. High jumping, shot putting and running	25	25
618	20 c. Snooker	25	25
619	20 c. Bowling	25	25
610/19	*Set of* 10	2·10	2·10
MS620	110×73 mm. $1 Various sports	1·10	1·25

Nos. 610/14 and 615/19 were each printed together, *se-tenant*, in horizontal strips of 5 throughout separate sheets.

(Des Awang Nor Ariffin bin Md. Yassin. Litho Southern Colour Print, Dunedin)

1999 (9 Oct). *125th Anniv of Universal Postal Union.* T **132** *and similar vert designs. Multicoloured.* P 14.

621	20 s. Type **132**	15	15
622	30 s. "125" and logos	20	20
623	75 s. Aspects of postal service	55	55
621/3	*Set of* 3	90	90

STAMP BOOKLETS

1976 (23 Feb). *Buff card cover showing Sultan's arms. Stitched.*

SB1	$1 booklet containing four 5 c. and eight 10 c. (Nos. 245, 247) in blocks of 4	3·50

1986. *Black and bright scarlet printed cover showing Post Office emblem. Stitched.*

SB2	$1 booklet containing four 10 c. and four 15 c. (Nos. 371/2) in blocks of 4	1·75

JAPANESE OCCUPATION OF BRUNEI

Japanese forces landed in Northern Borneo on 15 December 1941 and the whole of Brunei had been occupied by 6 January 1942.

Brunei, North Borneo, Sarawak and, after a short period, Labuan, were administered as a single territory by the Japanese. Until September–October 1942, previous stamp issues, without overprint, continued to be used in conjunction with existing postmarks. From the Autumn of 1942 onwards unoverprinted stamps of Japan were made available and examples can be found used from the area for much of the remainder of the War. Japanese Occupation issues for Brunei, North Borneo and Sarawak were equally valid throughout the combined territory but not, in practice, equally available.

PRICES FOR STAMPS ON COVER	
Nos. J1/16	*from* × 8
Nos. J17/20	—

(1)	(2)
("Imperial Japanese Government")	("Imperial Japanese Postal Service $3")

1942 (Oct)–**44.** *Stamps of Brunei handstamped with* T **1** *in violet to blue. Wmk Mult Script CA (except Nos. J18/19, Mult Crown CA).* P 14.

J 1	5	1 c. black		6·00	23·00
		a. Red opt		50·00	70·00
J 2		2 c. green		48·00	£100
J 3		2 c. orange (1943)		3·00	9·00
J 4		3 c. blue-green		28·00	75·00
		a. Opt omitted (in pair with normal)	£1500	
J 5		4 c. orange		3·00	13·00
J 6		5 c. chocolate		3·00	13·00
		a. "5 c." retouch		£150	£375
J 7	7	6 c. greenish grey (*p* 14×11½) (1944)	50·00	£200
J 8		6 c. scarlet		£550	£550
J 9	5	8 c. grey-black		£650	£850
J10	7	8 c. red		3·75	12·00
		a. Opt omitted (in pair with normal)	£1100	
J11	5	10 c. purple/*yellow*		8·50	26·00
J12	7	12 c. blue		22·00	26·00
		a. Red opt		£140	£200
J13		15 c. ultramarine (1944)		13·00	26·00
J14	5	25 c. slate-purple		23·00	50·00
		a. Red opt		£225	£300
J15		30 c. purple and orange-yellow	95·00	£180
J16		50 c. black/*emerald*		38·00	60·00
		a. Red opt		£250	
J17		$1 black and red/*blue* (1944)	55·00	70·00
		a. Red opt		—	£550
J18		$5 carmine/*green* (1944)		£800	£1700
J19		$25 black/*red* (1944)		£850	£1700

The overprint varies in shade from violet to blue, and being handstamped, exists double, double one inverted and treble.

Nos. J3, J7, J10 and J13 were not issued without the overprint.

1944 (11 May). *No. J1 surch with* T **2** *in orange-red.*

J20	5	$3 on 1 c. black		£6000	£5500
		a. Surch on No. 60 of Brunei	£7000	

Three separate handstamps were used to apply Type **2**, one for the top line, one for the bottom and the third for the two central characters.

Burma

(Currency. 12 pies = 1 anna; 16 annas = 1 rupee)

Stamps of India were used in Burma from 1854 and, after 1856, individual examples can be identified by the use of the concentric octagonal postmarks of the Bengal Postal Circle of which the following were supplied to Burmese post offices:

Type A	Type B
No. B 156	No. B 5
(Rangoon)	(Akyab)

B5	Akyab	B146	Pegu
B12*	Bassein	B150	Prome
B22	Nga Thine Khyoung	B156*	Rangoon
B56	Amherst	B159	Sandoway
B108	Kyouk Phyoo	B165	Sarawah (to 1860)
B111	Meeaday	B165	Henzada (from 1861)
B112	Mengyee	B171	Shoay Gyeen
B127	Moulmein	B173	Sittang
B128	Mergui	B179	Thayetmyo
B129	Tavoy	B181	Toungoo
B133	Myanoung	B227	Port Blair
B136	Namayan		

*Exists in black or blue. Remainder in black only.

Akyab, Moulmein and Rangoon used postmarks as both Type A and Type B, Port Blair as Type B only and the remainder as Type A only.

From 1860 various types of duplex cancellations were introduced and Burmese examples can be identified when sufficient of the left-hand portion is visible on the stamp. Such marks were issued for the following offices:

Akyab	Rangoon
Bassein	Rangoon C.R.H.
Mandalay	(Cantonment Receiving House)
Moulmein	Thayetmyo
Port Blair	Toungoo
Prome	

1862 Duplex from Toungoo

1865 Duplex from Akyab

During 1875, a further series of duplex marks was introduced in which the right-hand portion of the cancellation included the office code number, prefixed by the letter "R" for Rangoon:

R–1	Rangoon	R–9	Myanoung
R–1/1	Rangoon Cantonment	R–10	Port Blair
R–2	Akyab	1/R–10	Nancowry
R–3	Bassein	R–11	Prome
R–4	Henzada	R–12	Sandoway
R–5	Kyouk Phyoo	R–13	Shwegyeen
R–6	Mandalay	R–14	Tavoy
R–7	Mergui	R–15	Thayetmyo
R–8	Moulmein	R–16	Tounghoo
1/R–8	Amherst		

1875 type from Rangoon

1875 type from Rangoon Cantonment Receiving House

From 1886 the whole of Burma was united under the Crown and the post offices were supplied with circular date stamps giving the name of the town.

Most Indian stamps, both postage and official, issued during the period were supplied to post offices in Burma. None of the imperforates printed by De La Rue have been seen however, and from the later issues the following have not been recorded with Burma postmarks:

Nos. 39a, 66a, 68, 85a, 92a, 110a/b, 148a, 155a, 165, 192a/c, 195a/b, O15, O38, O40b, O50a/b, O76a, O101a, O102, O103/a, O104/5 and O142.

The value of most India stamps used in Burma coincides proportionally with the used prices quoted for India, but some, especially the provisional surcharges, are extremely rare with Burmese postmarks. Stamps of the face value of 2 r. and above from the reigns of Victoria and Edward VII are more common with telegraph cancellations than with those of the postal service.

PRICES FOR STAMPS ON COVER TO 1945

Nos. 1/18	from × 6
Nos. 18a/33	from × 4
No. 34	from × 5
Nos. 35/50	from × 8
Nos. O1/27	from × 15

BRITISH ADMINISTRATION

From 1 January 1886 Burma was a province of the Indian Empire but was separated from India and came under direct British administration on 1 April 1937.

BURMA   BURMA
(1)   (1a)

1937 (1 Apr). *Stamps of India (King George V inscr "INDIA POSTAGE") optd with T* **1** *or* **1a** *(rupee values).* W 69. P 14.

1	3 p. slate	30	10
	w. Wmk inverted	1·00	50
2	½ a. green	60	10
	w. Wmk inverted	1·50	50
3	9 p. deep green	75	10
	w. Wmk inverted	1·00	50
4	1 a. chocolate	40	10
	w. Wmk inverted	1·25	
5	2 a. vermilion (small die)	40	10
6	2½ a. orange	30	10
	w. Wmk inverted	1·25	50
7	3 a. carmine	75	30
	w. Wmk inverted	2·50	1·00
8	3½ a. deep blue	65	10
	aw. Wmk inverted	1·00	20
	b. Dull blue	6·50	6·00
	bw. Wmk inverted	4·25	4·00
9	4 a. sage-green	70	10
	w. Wmk inverted	—	24·00
10	6 a. bistre	60	35
	w. Wmk inverted	—	24·00
11	8 a. reddish purple	1·50	10
12	12 a. claret	2·50	85
	w. Wmk inverted	6·00	1·75
13	1 r. chocolate and green	16·00	2·25
14	2 r. carmine and orange	25·00	9·00
	w. Wmk inverted	35·00	13·00
15	5 r. ultramarine and purple	35·00	15·00
16	10 r. green and scarlet	70·00	50·00
17	15 r. blue and olive (wmk inverted)	£225	95·00
18	25 r. orange and blue	£450	£225
	w. Wmk inverted	£500	£275
1/18	Set of 18	£750	£350

The opt is at top on all values except the 3 a.
The 1 a. has been seen used from Yenangyaung on 22 Mar 1937.

2 King George VI and "Chinthes"   3 King George VI and "Nagas"

4 Karaweik (royal barge)   8 King George VI and Peacock

10 Elephants' Heads

Extra trees flaw (R. 11/8)

(Des Maung Kyi (2 a. 6 p.), Maung Hline (3 a.), Maung Ohn Pe (3 a. 6 p.) and N. K. D. Naigamwalla (8 a.). Litho Security Ptg Press, Nasik)

1938 (15 Nov)–**40.** *T* **2/4**, **8** *and similar designs.* W **10**. P 14 *(vert) or* 13½×13 *(horiz).*

18a	2	1 p. red-orange (1.8.40)	3·00	80
19		3 p. bright violet	20	30
20		6 p. bright blue	20	10
21		9 p. yellow-green	1·00	80
22	3	1 a. purple-brown	20	10
23		1½ a. turquoise-green	20	60
24		2 a. carmine	45	10
25	4	2 a. 6 p. claret	14·00	90
26		3 a. dull violet	14·00	1·50
27	—	3 a. 6 p. light blue and blue	1·25	3·75
		a. Extra trees flaw	40·00	
28	3	4 a. greenish blue	60	10
29		8 a. myrtle-green	5·00	30
30	8	1 r. purple and blue	7·50	20
31		2 r. brown and purple	16·00	1·75
32	—	5 r. violet and scarlet	48·00	22·00
33		10 r. brown and myrtle	55·00	45·00
18a/33		Set of 16	£150	70·00

Designs: *Horiz (as T* **4**)—3 a. Burma teak; 3 a. 6 p. Burma rice; 8 a. River Irrawaddy. *Vert (as T* **8**)—5 r., 10 r. King George VI and "Nats".

The 1 a. exists lithographed or typographed, the latter having a "Jubilee" line in the sheet margin.

COMMEMORATION POSTAGE STAMP 6th MAY 1840

(11)

1940 (6 May) *Centenary of First Adhesive Postage Stamps. No. 25 surch with T* **11.**

34	4	1 a. on 2 a. 6 p. claret	3·75	1·50

For stamps issued in 1942–45 see under Japanese Occupation.

CHIN HILLS DISTRICT. This area, in the far north-west of the country, remained in British hands when the Japanese overran Burma in May 1942.

During the period July to December 1942 the local officials were authorised to produce provisional stamps and the letters "OHMS" are known overprinted by typewriter on Nos. 3, 20, 22/4, 28/9 and 31 of Burma or handstamped, in violet, on Nos. 25, 27 and 29. The two types can also occur together or in combination with a handstamped "SERVICE".

From early in 1943 ordinary postage stamps of India were used from the Chin Hills post offices of Falam, Haka, Fort White and Tiddim, this expedient continuing until the fall of Falam to the Japanese on 7 November 1943.

The provisional stamps should only be collected on Official cover where dates and the sender's handwriting can be authenticated.

BRITISH MILITARY ADMINISTRATION

Preparations for the liberation of Burma commenced in February 1943 when the Civil Affairs Service (Burma) (CAS(B)) was set up at Delhi as part of the proposed military administration structure. One of the specific tasks assigned to CAS(B) was the operation of a postal service for the civilian population.

Operations against the Japanese intensified during the second half of 1944. The port of Akyab in the Arakan was reoccupied in January 1945. The 14th Army took Mandalay on 29 March and Rangoon was liberated from the sea on 3 May.

Postal services for the civilian population started in Akyab on 13 April 1945 while post offices in the Magwe Division around Meiktila were operating from 4 March. Mandalay post offices opened on 8 June and those in Rangoon on 16 June, but the full network was only completed in December 1945, just before the military administration was wound-up.

MILY ADMN   MILY ADMN
(12)   (13)

1945 (from 11 Apr). *Nos. 18a to 33 optd with T* **12** (*small stamps*) *or* **13** (*others*) *by Security Printing Press, Nasik.*

35	2	1 p. red-orange	..	..	10	10
		a. Opt omitted (in pair with normal)			£1600	
36		3 p. bright violet	..	..	10	40
37		6 p. bright blue	..	..	10	30
38		9 p. yellow-green	..	..	30	40
39	3	1 a. purple-brown (16.6)	..	..	10	15
40		1½ a. turquoise-green (16.6)	..	..	10	15
41		2 a. carmine	..	..	10	15
42	4	2 a. 6 p. claret	..	..	2·00	60
43	–	3 a. dull violet	..	..	1·50	20
44	–	3 a. 6 p. light blue and blue	..	..	10	70
		a. Extra trees flaw			15·00	
45	3	4 a. greenish blue	..	..	10	25
46	–	8 a. myrtle-green	..	..	10	50
47	8	1 r. purple and blue	..	..	40	50
48		2 r. brown and purple	..	..	40	1·00
49	–	5 r. violet and scarlet	..	..	40	1·00
50	–	10 r. brown and myrtle	..	..	40	1·00
35/50				*Set of* 16	4·75	6·50

Only the typographed version of the 1 a., No. 22, received this overprint.

The exact dates of issue for Nos. 35/50 are difficult to establish.

The initial stock of overprints is known to have reached CAS(B) headquarters, Imphal, at the beginning of April 1945. Postal directives issued on 11 April refer to the use of the overprints in Akyab and in the Magwe Division where surcharged pre-war postal stationery envelopes had previously been in use. The 6 p., 1 a., 1½ a. and 2 a. values were placed on sale at Mandalay on 8 June and the 1 a. and 2 a. at Rangoon on 16 June. It has been suggested that only a limited service was initially available in Rangoon. All values were on sale by 9 August 1945.

BRITISH CIVIL ADMINISTRATION

1946 (1 Jan). *As Nos. 19/33, but colours changed.*

51	2	3 p. brown	..	..	10	1·25
52		6 p. deep violet	..	..	10	30
53		9 p. green	..	..	15	1·60
54	3	1 a. blue	..	..	15	20
55		1½ a. orange	..	..	15	10
56		2 a. claret	..	..	15	40
57	4	2 a. 6 p. greenish blue	..	..	2·00	3·50
57a	–	3 a. blue-violet	..	..	6·50	3·00
57b	–	3 a. 6 p. black and ultramarine	..	..	30	1·50
		ba. Extra trees flaw			29·00	
58	3	4 a. purple	..	..	30	30
59	–	8 a. maroon	..	..	1·75	2·00
60	8	1 r. violet and maroon	..	..	1·00	40
61		2 r. brown and orange	..	..	6·00	2·25
62	–	5 r. green and brown	..	..	6·00	11·00
63	–	10 r. claret and violet	..	..	6·50	17·00
51/63				*Set of* 15	28·00	40·00

No. 54 was printed in typography only.

14 Burman

(Des A. G. I. McGeogh. Litho Nasik)

1946 (2 May). *Victory. T* **14** *and similar vert designs. W* **10** (*sideways*). *P* 13.

64		9 p. turquoise-green	..	..	20	20
65		1½ a. violet	..	..	20	10
66		2 a. carmine	..	..	20	10
67		3 a. 6 p. ultramarine	..	..	50	20
64/7				*Set of* 4	1·00	50

Designs:—1½ a. Burmese woman; 2 a. Chinthe; 3 a. 6 p. Elephant.

INTERIM BURMESE GOVERNMENT

ကြားဖြတ်   ၁းဖြတ်ကြ   တ်ကြား၁း
အစိုးရ။   အစိုးရ။   အစိုးရ။

(18 Trans.   18a   18b
"Interim Government")

Type **18a** shows the first character transposed to the end of the top line (R. 6/15).

Type **18b** shows the last two characters transposed to the front of the top line (R. 14/14).

Some sheets of the 3 p. show both errors corrected by a handstamp as Type **18**.

1947 (1 Oct). *Stamps of 1946 optd with T* **18** (*small stamps*) *or larger opt* (*others*).

68	2	3 p. brown	..	..	70	70
		a. Opt Type 18a	..	..	20·00	
		ab. Corrected by handstamp as Type 18				
		b. Opt Type 18b	..	..	20·00	
		ba. Corrected by handstamp as Type 18				
69		6 p. deep violet	..	..	10	30
		a. Opt Type 18a	..	..	11·00	
70		9 p. green	..	..	10	30
		a. Opt inverted	..	..	19·00	22·00

71	3	1 a. blue	..	..	10	30
		a. Vert pair, one with opt omitted				
72		1½ a. orange	..	..	90	10
73		2 a. claret	..	..	30	15
		a. Horiz pair, one with opt omitted				
		b. Opt Type 18a	..	..	22·00	
74	4	2 a. 6 p. greenish blue	..	..	1·75	95
75	–	3 a. blue-violet	..	..	2·50	1·50
76	–	3 a. 6 p. black and ultramarine	..		45	2·00
		a. Extra trees flaw			26·00	
77	3	4 a. purple	..	..	1·75	30
78	–	8 a. maroon	..	..	1·75	90
79	8	1 r. violet and maroon	..	..	2·75	30
80		2 r. brown and orange	..	..	3·75	2·50
81	–	5 r. green and brown	..	..	3·75	3·25
82	–	10 r. claret and violet	..	..	3·25	3·25
68/82				*Set of* 15	21·00	15·00

The 3 p., 6 p., 2 a., 2 a. 6 p., 3 a. 6 p. and 1 r. are also known with overprint inverted.

OFFICIAL STAMPS

BURMA   **BURMA**

SERVICE   **SERVICE**
(O 1)   (O 1a)

1937 (Apr–June). *Stamps of India* (*King George V inscr* "INDIA POSTAGE") *optd with Type* O **1** *or* O **1a** (*rupee values*). *W* **69**. *P* 14.

O 1		3 p. slate	..	..	1·00	10
		w. Wmk inverted	..	..	—	12·00
O 2		½ a. green	..	..	6·00	10
O 3		9 p. deep green	..	..	3·50	30
O 4		1 a. chocolate	..	..	4·00	10
O 5		2 a. vermilion (*small die*)	..	..	7·00	35
		w. Wmk inverted	..	..	—	12·00
O 6		2½ a. orange	..	..	4·00	1·75
O 7		4 a. sage-green	..	..	4·25	10
O 8		6 a. bistre	..	..	4·00	6·50
O 9		8 a. reddish purple (1.4.37)	..		3·25	80
O10		12 a. claret (1.4.37)	..	..	3·25	3·25
O11		1 r. chocolate and green (1.4.37)	..		20·00	3·75
O12		2 r. carmine and orange	..	..	45·00	30·00
		w. Wmk inverted	..	..	55·00	38·00
O13		5 r. ultramarine and purple	..		90·00	42·00
O14		10 r. green and scarlet	..	..	£250	£120
O1/14				*Set of* 14	£400	£180

For the above issue the stamps were either overprinted 'BURMA' and 'SERVICE' at one operation or had the two words applied separately. Research has yet to establish if all values exist with both forms of overprinting.

SERVICE   **SERVICE**
(O 2)   (O 3)

1939. *Nos. 19/24 and 28 optd with Type* O **2** (*typo*) *and Nos. 25 and 29/33 optd with Type* O **3** (*litho*).

O15	2	3 p. bright violet	..	..	15	20
O16		6 p. bright blue	..	..	15	20
O17		9 p. yellow-green	..	..	5·00	2·50
O18	3	1 a. purple-brown	..	..	15	15
O19		1½ a. turquoise-green	..	..	4·50	1·50
O20		2 a. carmine	..	..	1·25	20
O21	4	2 a. 6 p. claret	..	..	25·00	10·00
O22	3	4 a. greenish blue	..	..	5·50	45
O23	–	8 a. myrtle-green	..	..	25·00	3·75
O24	8	1 r. purple and blue	..	..	38·00	5·00
O25		2 r. brown and purple	..	..	45·00	11·00
O26	–	5 r. violet and scarlet	..	..	42·00	28·00
O27	–	10 r. brown and myrtle	..	..	£120	38·00
O15/27				*Set of* 13	£275	90·00

Both versions of the 1 a. value exist with this overprint.

1946. *British Civil Administration. Nos. 51/6 and 58 optd with Type* O **2** (*typo*) *and Nos. 57 and 59/63 optd with Type* O **3** (*litho*).

O28	2	3 p. brown	..	..	90	2·50
O29		6 p. deep violet	..	..	90	2·00
O30		9 p. green	..	..	20	2·75
O31	3	1 a. blue	..	..	20	1·75
O32		1½ a. orange	..	..	20	20
O33		2 a. claret	..	..	20	1·75
O34	4	2 a. 6 p. greenish blue	..	..	1·40	4·50
O35	3	4 a. purple	..	..	20	70
O36	–	8 a. maroon	..	..	1·50	3·00
O37	8	1 r. violet and maroon	..	..	60	3·00
O38		2 r. brown and orange	..	..	7·00	35·00
O39	–	5 r. green and brown	..	..	9·00	40·00
O40	–	10 r. claret and violet	..	..	17·00	48·00
O28/40				*Set of* 13	35·00	£130

1947. *Interim Burmese Government. Nos.* O28/40 *optd with T* **18** (*small stamps*) *or larger opt* (*others*).

O41	2	3 p. brown	..	..	15	40
O42		6 p. deep violet	..	..	80	10
O43		9 p. green	..	..	1·40	90
O44	3	1 a. blue	..	..	1·75	80
O45		1½ a. orange	..	..	3·50	30
O46		2 a. claret	..	..	1·75	15
O47	4	2 a. 6 p. greenish blue	..	..	22·00	8·50
O48	3	4 a. purple	..	..	7·00	40
O49	–	8 a. maroon	..	..	6·50	3·75
O50	8	1 r. violet and maroon	..	..	14·00	2·25
O51		2 r. brown and orange	..	..	14·00	18·00
O52	–	5 r. green and brown	..	..	14·00	19·00
O53	–	10 r. claret and violet	..	..	14·00	30·00
O41/53				*Set of* 13	90·00	75·00

Later stamp issues will be found listed in Part 21 (*South-East Asia*) of this catalogue.

JAPANESE OCCUPATION OF BURMA

PRICES FOR STAMPS ON COVER

Nos. J1/44		—
Nos. J45/6	*from* × 6	
Nos. J47/56	*from* × 8	
No. J56g		—
Nos. J57/72	*from* × 6	
Nos. J73/5	*from* × 25	
No. J76	*from* × 8	
No. J77	*from* × 20	
Nos. J78/81	*from* × 25	
Nos. J82/4	*from* × 10	
Nos. J85/7	*from* × 40	
No. J88	*from* × 12	
Nos. J89/97	*from* × 30	
Nos. J98/104	*from* × 50	
Nos. J105/111	*from* × 30	

BURMA INDEPENDENCE ARMY ADMINISTRATION

The Burma Independence Army, formed by Aung San in 1941, took control of the Delta area of the Irrawaddy in May 1942. They reopened a postal service in the area and were authorised by the Japanese to overprint local stocks of stamps with the Burmese emblem of a peacock.

Postage and Official stamps with the peacock overprints or hand-stamps were used for ordinary postal purposes with the probable exception of No. J44.

DISTINGUISHING FEATURES. Type 1. Body and head of Peacock always clearly outlined by broad uncoloured band. There are four slightly different sub-types of overprint Type 1.

Type 2. Peacock with slender neck and more delicately detailed tail. Clear spur on leg at right. Heavy fist-shaped blob of ink below and parallel to beak and neck.

Type 4. No basic curve. Each feather separately outlined. Straight, short legs.

Type 5. Much fine detail in wings and tail in clearly printed overprints. Thin, long legs ending in claws which, with the basic arc, enclose clear white spaces in well-printed copies. Blob of colour below beak shows shaded detail and never has the heavy fist-like appearance of this portion in Type 2.

Two sub-types may be distinguished in Type 5, the basic arc of one having a chord of 14–15 mm and the other 12½–13 mm.

Type 6. Similar to Type 5, but with arc deeply curved and reaching nearly to the top of the wings. Single diagonal line parallel to neck below beak.

Collectors are warned against forgeries of these overprints, often in the wrong colours or on the wrong values.

(1)   (2)

(3)

1942 (May). *Stamps of Burma overprinted with the national device of a Peacock.*

I. *Overprinted at Myaungmya*

A. *With Type* 1 *in black*

On Postage Stamps of King George V

J 1		9 p. deep green (No. 3)	..	..	£110
J 2		3½ a. deep blue (No. 8)	..	..	50·00

On Official Stamp of King George V

J 3		6 a. bistre (No. O8)	..	..	70·00

On Postage Stamps of King George VI

J 4	2	9 p. yellow-green	..	..	£150
J 5	3	1 a. purple-brown	..	..	£500
J 6		4 a. greenish blue (opt black on red)	..		£160
		a. Triple opt, black on double red			£425

On Official Stamps of King George VI

J 7	2	3 p. bright violet	..	22·00	75·00
J 8		6 p. bright blue	..	15·00	50·00
J 9	3	1 a. purple-brown	..	14·00	42·00
J 9a		1½ a. turquoise-green	..	£650	
J10		2 a. carmine	..	22·00	80·00
J11		4 a. greenish blue	..	20·00	65·00

The overprint on No. J6 was apparently first done in red in error, and then corrected in black. Some stamps have the black overprint so accurately superimposed that the red hardly shows. These are rare.

Nos. J5 and J9 exist with the Peacock overprint on both the typographed and the litho printings of the original stamps.

B. *With Types* 2 *or* 3 (*rupee values*), *in black*

On Postage Stamps of King George VI

J12	2	3 p. bright violet	..	17·00	60·00
J13		6 p. bright blue	..	48·00	85·00
J14		9 p. yellow-green	..	17·00	55·00
J15	3	1 a. purple-brown	..	14·00	50·00
J16		2 a. carmine	..	17·00	65·00

J17	3	4 a. greenish blue	..	..	32·00 85·00
		a. Opt double			
		b. Opt inverted			£550
		c. Opt double, one inverted	..	..	£400
		d. Opt double, both inverted	..	..	£550
J18		1 r. purple and blue			£250
J19		2 r. brown and purple			£150

The Myaungmya overprints (including No. J44) are usually clearly printed.

(4)   (5)   (6)

Type 5 generally shows the details of the peacock much less clearly and, due to heavy inking, or careless impression, sometimes appears as almost solid colour.

Type 6 was officially applied only to postal stationery. However, the handstamp remained in the possession of a postal official who used it on postage stamps after the war. These stamps are no longer listed.

II. *Handstamped (at Pyapon?) with T 4, in black (so-called experimental type)*

On Postage Stamps of King George VI

J19*a*	2	6 p. bright blue	..	..	£120
J19*b*	3	1 a. purple-brown	..	..	95·00 £250
J20		2 a. carmine	..	..	£110 £250
J21		4 a. greenish blue	..	..	£650 £650

Unused specimens of Nos. J20/1 are usually in poor condition.

III. *Overprinted at Henzada with T 5 in blue, or blue-black*

On Postage Stamps of King George V

J22		3 p. slate (No. 1)	..	..	3·00 17·00
		a. Opt double			10·00 48·00
J23		9 p. deep green (No. 3)	..	..	21·00 60·00
		a. Opt double			80·00
J24		2 a. vermilion (No. 5)	..		£100 £180

On Postage Stamps of King George VI

J25	2	1 p. red-orange	..	..	£180 £275
J26		3 p. bright violet	..	..	30·00 75·00
J27		6 p. bright blue	..	..	25·00 50·00
		a. Opt double			£100 £150
		b. Clear opt, on back and front			£275
J28		9 p. yellow-green			£750
J29	3	1 a. purple-brown	..	..	9·00 40·00
		a. Opt inverted			£500
J30		1½ a. turquoise-green	..	..	21·00 65·00
		a. Opt omitted (in pair with normal)			£1500
J31		2 a. carmine	..	..	21·00 65·00
		a. Opt double			£500
J32		4 a. greenish blue	..	..	42·00 95·00
		a. Opt double			£250
		b. Opt inverted			£950

On Official Stamps of King George VI

J33	2	3 p. bright violet	..	..	£100 £225
J34		6 p. bright blue	..	..	£140 £225
J35	3	1½ a. turquoise-green	..	..	£150 £250
J35*a*		2 a. carmine	..	..	£325 £400
J36		4 a. greenish blue	..	..	£950

(6a)

("Yon Thon" = "Office use")

V. *Official Stamp of King George VI optd at Myaungmya with Type 6a in black*

J44	7	8 a. myrtle-green	..	..	80·00

No. J44 was probably for official use.

There are two types of T 6*a*, one with base of peacock 8 mm long and the other with base about 5 mm long. The neck and other details also vary. The two types are found *se-tenant* in the sheet.

Stocks of the peacock types were withdrawn when the Japanese Directorate-General took control of the postal services in the Delta in August 1942.

JAPANESE ARMY ADMINISTRATION

7   8 Farmer

1942 (1 June). *Impressed by hand. Thick yellowish paper. P 12 × 11. No gum.*

J45	7	1 a.) red	..	..	38·00 65·00

This device was the personal seal of Yano Sitza, the Japanese official in charge of the Posts and Telegraphs department of the Japanese Army Administration. It was impressed on paper

already perforated by a line machine. Some stamps show part of the papermaker's watermark, either "ABSORBO DUPLICATOR" or "ELEPHANT BRAND", each with an elephant.

Other impressions of this seal on different papers, and showing signs of wear, were not valid for postal purposes.

(Des T. Kato. Typo *Rangoon Gazette* Press)

1942 (15 June). *Value in annas. P 11 or 11 × 11½. Laid bâtonné paper. No gum.*

J46	8	1 a. scarlet	..	..	15·00 15·00

Some stamps show part of the papermaker's watermark, either "ELEPHANT BRAND" or "TITAGHUR SUPERFINE", each with an elephant.

(9)   (10)

1942 (22 Sept.). *(a) Nos. 314/17, 320/2, 325, 327 and 396 of Japan surch as T 9/10.*

J47	9	¼ a. on 1 s. chestnut (Rice harvesting)		23·00 27·00
		a. Surch inverted		95·00 95·00
		b. Surch double, one inverted		£140
J48		½ a. on 2 s. bright scarlet (General Nogi)		24·00 28·00
		a. Surch inverted		85·00 90·00
		b. Surch double, one inverted		£140
J49		¾ a. on 3 s. green (Power station)		50·00 55·00
		a. Surch inverted		£110 £110
		b. Surch double, one inverted		— £160
J50		1 a. on 5 s. claret (Admiral Togo)		40·00 40·00
		a. Surch inverted		£150 £150
		b. Surch double, one inverted		£170 £170
		c. Surch omitted (in pair with normal)		— £200
J51		3 a. on 7 s. green (Diamond Mts)		80·00 90·00
		a. Surch inverted		£150
J52		4 a. on 4 s. emerald (Togo)		38·00 40·00
		a. Surch inverted		£150
J53		8 a. on 8 s. violet (Meiji Shrine)		£150 £150
		a. Surch inverted		£225 £225
		b. Surch double, one inverted		£350
		c. Surch in red		£225 £250
		d. Red surch inverted		£350
		e. Surch double (black and red)		£550
J54	10	1 r. on 10 s. deep carmine (Yomei Gate)		15·00 24·00
		a. Surch inverted		80·00 90·00
		b. Surch double		80·00 £100
		c. Surch double (black and red)		£400
		d. Surch omitted (in pair with normal)		£190 £190
		e. Surch omitted (in pair with inverted surch)		£300
J55		2 r. on 20 s. ultramarine (Mt Fuji)		45·00 45·00
		a. Surch inverted		£110 £110
		b. Surch double, one inverted		£130
		c. Surch omitted (in pair with normal black surch)		£160 £160
		d. Surch in red		42·00 42·00
		e. Red surch inverted		£110 £110
		f. Red surch double		£110 £110
		g. Surch omitted (in pair with normal red surch)		£200 £200
		ga. Surch omitted (in pair with double red surch)		
		h. Surch double (black and red)		£325
J56	9	5 r. on 30 s. turquoise (Torii Shrine)		12·00 27·00
		a. Surch inverted		85·00
		b. Surch double		£110
		c. Surch double, one inverted		£150
		d. Surch omitted (in pair with normal surch)		£180 £180
		e. Surch omitted (in pair with inverted black surch)		£275
		f. Surch in red		23·00 32·00
		fa. Red surch inverted		90·00 90·00
		fb. J56a and J56fa *se-tenant*		£400 £400
		fc. Surch omitted (in pair with normal red surch)		£180 £180

(b) No. 386 of Japan commemorating the fall of Singapore similarly surch

J56g	9	4 a. on 4 + 2 s. green and red		£150 £160
		h. Surch omitted (in pair with normal)		£500
		ha. Surch omitted (in pair with inverted surch)		£550
		i. Surch inverted		£350

(New Currency. 100 cents = 1 rupee)

15 C.   15 C.   15 C.

(11)   (12)   (13)

1942 (15 Oct). *Previous issues, with "anna" surcharges obliterated, handstamped with new value in cents, as T 11 and 12 (No. J57 handstamped with new value only).*

(a) On No. J46

J57		5 c. on 1 a. scarlet		11·00 15·00
		a. Surch omitted (in pair with normal)		£1000

(b) On Nos. J47/53

J58		1 c. on ¼ a. on 1 s. chestnut		40·00 40·00
		a. "1 c." omitted (in pair with normal)		£500
		b. "¼ a." inverted		£250
J59		2 c. on ½ a. on 2 s. bright scarlet		38·00 40·00
J60		3 c. on ¾ a. on 3 s. green		42·00 42·00
		a. Surch in blue		£170
J61		5 c. on 1 a. on 5 s. claret		65·00 65·00
J62		10 c. on 3 a. on 7 s. green		£100 95·00
J63		15 c. on 4 a. on 4 s. emerald		29·00 32·00
J64		20 c. on 8 a. on 8 s. violet		£375 £325
		a. Surch on No. J53c (surch in red)		£225 £150

The "anna" surcharges were obliterated by any means available, in some cases by a bar or bars, and in others by the butt of a pencil dipped in ink. In the case of the fractional surcharges, the letter "A" and one figure of the fraction, were sometimes barred out, leaving the remainder of the fraction to represent the new value, e.g. the "1" of "½" deleted to create the 2 c. surcharge or the "4" of "¾" to create the 3 c. surcharge.

1942. *Nos. 314/17, 320/1 and 396 of Japan surcharged in cents only as T 13.*

J65		1 c. on 1 s. chestnut (Rice harvesting)		19·00 20·00
		a. Surch inverted		£110 £110
J66		2 c. on 2 s. brt scarlet (General Nogi)		38·00 32·00
J67		3 c. on 3 s. green (Power station)		42·00 38·00
		a. Pair, with and without surch		— £200
		b. Surch inverted		£120
		c. Surch in blue		85·00 95·00
		d. Surch in blue inverted		£200 £225
J68		5 c. on 5 s. claret (Admiral Togo)		45·00 42·00
		a. Pair, with and without surch		£250
		b. Surch in violet		£130 £150
		ba. Surch inverted		— £225
J69		10 c. on 7 s. green (Diamond Mts)		55·00 55·00
J70		15 c. on 4 s. emerald (Togo)		14·00 20·00
		a. Surch inverted		£120 £130
		b. Pair, with and without surch		— £190
J71		20 c. on 8 s. violet (Meiji Shrine)		£130 85·00
		a. Surch inverted		£275

Nos. J67c and J68b were issued for use in the Shan States.

BURMESE GOVERNMENT

On 1 November 1942 the Japanese Army Administration handed over the control of the postal department to the Burmese Government. On 1 August 1943 Burma was declared by the Japanese to be independent.

14 Burma State Crest   15 Farmer

(Des U Tun Tin and Maung Tin from drawing by U Ba Than. Typo Rangoon)

1943 (15 Feb). *P 11. No gum.*

J72	14	5 c. scarlet	..	..	15·00 19·00
		a. Imperf			16·00 20·00
		ab. Printed on both sides			85·00

No. J72 was usually sold affixed to envelopes, particularly those with the embossed 1 a. King George VI stamp, which it covered. Unused specimens off cover are not often seen and blocks are rare.

1943. *Typo. No gum. P 11½.*

J73	15	1 c. orange (22 March)	..	..	1·40 3·50
		a. Brown-orange			70 3·50
J74		2 c. yellow-green (24 March)	..	..	60 1·00
		a. "3" for "2" in face value (R.2/10)			£150
		b. Blue-green			7·50
J75		3 c. light blue (25 March)	..	..	1·00 85
		a. On laid paper			18·00 26·00
		b. Imperf between (horiz pair)			— £250
J76		5 c. carmine (small "c") (17 March)			14·00 9·00
J77		5 c. carmine (large "C")	..	..	1·75 3·00
		a. Imperf (pair)			£120
		b. "G" for "C" (R.2/6)			£170
J78		10 c. grey-brown (25 March)	..	..	3·50 3·50
		a. Imperf (pair)			£120
		b. Imperf between (horiz pair)			— £250
J79		15 c. magenta (26 March)	..	..	30 90
		a. Imperf between (vert strip of 3)			
		b. On laid paper			6·00 16·00
		c. Inverted "C" in value (R.2/3)			£130
J80		20 c. grey-lilac (29 March)	..	..	30 65
J81		30 c. deep blue-green (29 March)	..	..	30 70

The 1 c., 2 c. and 3 c. have large "C" in value as illustrated. The 10 c. and higher values have small "c". Nos. J73/81 had the face values inserted individually into the plate used for No. J46 with the original face value removed. There were a number of printings for each value, often showing differences such as missing stops, various founts of figures or "c", etc., in the value tablets.

The face value error, No. J74a, was later corrected.

Some sheets of No. J75a show a sheet watermark of Britannia seated within a crowned oval spread across fifteen stamps in each sheet. This paper was manufactured by T. Edmonds and the other half of the sheet carried the watermark inscription "FOOLSCAP LEDGER". No stamps have been reported showing letters from this inscription, but a block of 25 is known on laid paper showing a different sheet watermark "HERTFORDSHIRE LEDGER MADE IN ENGLAND". Examples showing parts of these sheet watermarks are rare.

No. J79a shows the horizontal perforations omitted between rows 3/4 and 4/5.

There are marked varieties of shade in this issue.

16 Soldier carving word "Independence"   17 Rejoicing Peasant

18 Boy with National Flag

Normal   Skyline flaw (R. 5/6)

(Des Maung Ba Thit (**16**), Naung Ohn Maung (**17**), and Maung Soi Yi (**18**). Typo State Press, Rangoon)

1943 (1 Aug). *Independence Day.* (a) *P* 11.

J82	**16**	1 c. orange		7·50	13·00
J83	**17**	3 c. light blue		8·00	14·00
J84	**18**	5 c. carmine		15·00	8·00
		a. Skyline flaw		65·00	
J82/4			Set of 3	27·00	32·00

(b) *Rouletted*

J85	**16**	1 c. orange		1·00	1·50
		b. Perf×roul		95·00	95·00
		c. Imperf (pair)		45·00	55·00
J86	**17**	3 c. light blue		1·00	1·50
		b. Perf×roul		85·00	85·00
		c. Imperf (pair)		45·00	55·00
J87	**18**	5 c. carmine		1·00	1·50
		a. Horiz roulette omitted (vert pair)			
		b. Perf×roul		55·00	55·00
		c. Imperf (pair)		45·00	55·00
		d. Skyline flaw		7·00	
J85/7			Set of 3	2·75	4·00

The stamps perf × rouletted may have one, two or three sides perforated.

The rouletted stamps often appear to be roughly perforated owing to failure to make clean cuts. These apparent perforations are very small and quite unlike the large, clean holes of the stamps perforated 11.

A few imperforate sets, mounted on a special card folder and cancelled with the commemorative postmark were presented to officials. These are rare.

19 Burmese Woman   **20** Elephant carrying Log   **21** Watch Tower, Mandalay

(Litho G. Kolff & Co, Batavia)

1943 (1 Oct). *P* 12½.

J88	**19**	1 c. red-orange		22·00	15·00
J89		2 c. yellow-green		50	2·00
J90		3 c. deep violet		50	2·25
		a. Bright violet		80	2·75
J91	**20**	5 c. carmine		55	60
J92		10 c. blue		85	95
J93		15 c. red-orange		65	2·25
J94		20 c. yellow-green		65	1·75
J95		30 c. olive-brown		65	1·75
J96	**21**	1 r. red-orange		30	2·00
J97		2 r. bright violet		30	2·25
J88/97			Set of 10	24·00	27·00

ဗမာနိုင်ငံတော်

၂၀ ဆင့်။

22 Bullock Cart   **23** Shan Woman   (**24** "Burma State" and value)

(Litho G. Kolff & Co, Batavia)

1943 (1 Oct). *Issue for Shan States. P* 12½.

J 98	**22**	1 c. olive-brown		24·00	30·00
J 99		2 c. yellow-green		22·00	32·00
J100		3 c. bright violet		3·00	10·00
J101		5 c. ultramarine		2·00	5·50
J102	**23**	10 c. blue		8·50	17·00
J103		20 c. carmine		22·00	17·00
J104		30 c. olive-brown		22·00	17·00
J98/104			Set of 7	85·00	£130

The Shan States, except for the frontier area around Keng Tung which was ceded to Thailand, were placed under the administration of the Burmese Government on 24 December 1943, and these stamps were later overprinted as T **24** for use throughout Burma.

1944 (1 Nov). Optd as T **24** (*the lower characters differ for each value*).

J105	**22**	1 c. olive-brown		2·50	6·00
J106		2 c. yellow-green		40	1·75
		a. Opt inverted		£330	£550
J107		3 c. bright violet		1·50	7·00
J108		5 c. ultramarine		80	1·00
J109	**23**	10 c. blue		2·25	2·00
J110		20 c. carmine		40	1·50
J111		30 c. olive-brown		40	1·75
J105/11			Set of 7	7·50	19·00

Bushire

BRITISH OCCUPATION

(Currency. 20 chahis = 1 kran; 10 kran = 1 toman)

Bushire, a seaport town of Persia, was occupied by the British on 8 August 1915. The Persian postal authorities resumed control on 18 October 1915. British forces returned to Bushire during 1916, but mail from this period was carried by Indian Army F.P.O. No. 319.

> **PRICES FOR STAMPS ON COVER**
> Nos. 1/29   *from* × 5

Types of Iran (Persia) overprinted

57   **66**

67   **68**

BUSHIRE
Under British
Occupation.
(1)

1915 (15 Aug). *Nos. 361/3, 365, 367/70, 372, 374/6 and 378/9 of Iran optd with T* **1** *at the British Residency.*

1	**57**	1 ch. orange and green		32·00	35·00
2		a. No stop		85·00	90·00
2		2 ch. sepia and carmine		32·00	29·00
		a. No stop		85·00	85·00
3		3 ch. green and grey		38·00	45·00
		a. No stop		£110	£130
4		5 ch. carmine and brown		£250	£250
5		6 ch. brown-lake and green		30·00	22·00
		a. No stop		85·00	75·00
6		9 ch. indigo-lilac and brown		32·00	35·00
		a. No stop		95·00	£100
		b. Opt double			
7		10 ch. brown and carmine		35·00	35·00
		a. No stop		£100	£100
8		12 ch. blue and green		42·00	45·00
		a. No stop		£120	£130
9		24 ch. green and purple		60·00	45·00
		a. No stop		£170	£140
10		1 kr. carmine and blue		60·00	27·00
		a. Double overprint		£5000	
		b. No stop		£170	80·00
11		2 kr. claret and green		£180	£130
		a. No stop		£475	£350
12		3 kr. black and lilac		£150	£150
		a. No stop		£425	£425
13		5 kr. blue and red		95·00	85·00
		a. No stop		£300	£275
14		10 kr. rose and bistre-brown		85·00	80·00
		a. No stop		£275	£250

Nos. 1/3 and 5/14 were overprinted in horizontal strips of 10 and No. 4 in horizontal strips of 5. Eight different settings are recognized, with the "No stop" variety occurring on stamp 9 from the four settings with 3 mm between "Under" and "British" and on stamp 10 from one setting where the gap is 2 mm.

1915 (Sept). *Nos. 426/40 and 441 of Iran optd with T* **1**.

15	**66**	1 ch. deep blue and carmine		£300	£300
16		2 ch. carmine and deep blue		£5000	£5500
17		3 ch. deep green		£375	£400
18		5 ch. vermilion		£3750	£4000
19		6 ch. carmine and green		£3000	£3250
20		9 ch. deep violet and brown		£500	£550
21		10 ch. brown and deep green		£850	£900
22		12 ch. ultramarine		£950	£1000
23		24 ch. sepia and brown		£375	£400

24	**67**	1 kr. black, brown and silver		£375	£400
25		2 kr. carmine, slate and silver		£325	£350
26		3 kr. sepia, dull lilac and silver		£450	£475
27		5 kr. slate, sepia and silver		£425	£450
		a. Opt inverted		—	£9500
28	**68**	1 t. black, violet and gold		£375	£425
29		3 t. red, crimson and gold		£2500	£2750

Nos. 15/29 were overprinted in strips of 5

Examples of overprint Type 1 on Iran No. 414, 1 ch. on 5 ch. (previously No. 30), are now believed to be forged.

Cameroon

I. CAMEROONS EXPEDITIONARY FORCE

Allied operations against the German protectorate of Kamerun commenced in September 1914 and were completed on 18 February 1916. The territory was divided, under an Anglo-French agreement, on 31 March 1916 with the British administering the area in the west along the Nigerian border. League of Nations mandates were issued for the two sections of Cameroon, which were converted into United Nations trusteeships in 1946.

Supplies of Kamerun stamps were found on the German steamer *Professor Woermann* captured at Freetown and these were surcharged, probably in Sierra Leone, and issued by the Cameroons Expeditionary Force in July 1915.

A French Post Office opened in Duala on 10 November 1915 using stamps of Gabon overprinted "Corps Expeditionnaire Franco-Anglais Cameroun". Although under the overall control of the British combined force commander this office remained part of the French postal system.

> **PRICES FOR STAMPS ON COVER**
> The stamps of British Occupation of Cameroons are rare used on cover.

A   B

C.E.F.   **C.E.F.**

1d.   **1**s.
(1)   (2)

SETTINGS. Nos. B1/3 were surcharged from a setting of 100 (10×10) with the face value changed for the 1d.

Nos. B4 and B6/9 were surcharged from a common setting of 50 (5×10) with the face value amended.

No. B5 was surcharged from a setting of 10 in a vertical strip repeated across the sheet. The figures of the surcharge on this value are in a different style from the remainder of the pence stamps.

Nos. B10/13 were surcharged from a common setting of 20 (4×5) with the face value amended.

Different fount "d"	"1" with thin serifs
(R. 1/10, 6/9, 10/10)	(R. 5/1)

Large "3"	Short "4"
(R. 3/5, 3/10)	(R. 10/2, 10/7)

"s" inverted
(R. 3/4)

5ˢ

"s" broken at top (R. 3/1)

1915 (12 July). *Stamps of German Kamerun. Types A and B, surch as T* **1** (*Nos.* B1/9) *or* **2** (*Nos.* B10/13) *in black or blue.*

B1	A	½d. on 3 pf. (No. K7) (B.)		11·00	26·00
		a. Different fount "d"		95·00	£190
B2		½d. on 5 pf. (No. K21 *wmk lozenges*) (B.)		2·00	8·00
		a. Different fount "d"		25·00	75·00
		b. Surch double		—	£700
		ba. Surch double, one albino		£170	
B3		1d. on 10 pf. (No. K22 *wmk lozenges*) (B.)		1·25	8·50
		a. "1" with thin serifs		13·00	65·00
		b. Surch double		£250	
		ba. Surch double, one albino		85·00	
		c. "1d." only double		£1800	
		d. Surch triple, two albino		£190	
		e. Surch in black		14·00	55·00
		ea. "1" with thin serifs		£150	
		eb. "C.E.F." omitted		£2750	
B4		2d. on 20 pf. (No. K23 *wmk lozenges*)		3·50	18·00
		a. Surch double, one albino		£180	
B5		2½d. on 25 pf. (No. K11)		12·00	38·00
		a. Surch double		£6500	
		ab. Surch double, one albino			

B6	A	3d. on 30 pf. (No. K12)	..	..	12·00 38·00
		a. Large "3" ..	..	..	£650
		b. Surch triple, two albino	..	..	£200
B7		4d. on 40 pf. (No. K13)	..	..	12·00 38·00
		a. Short "4" ..	..	..	£500 £800
		b. Surch triple, two albino	..	..	£190
		c. Surch quadruple, three albino	..	£1500
B8 .		6d. on 50 pf. (No. K14)	..	..	12·00 38·00
		a. Surch double, one albino	..	..	£170
B9		8d. on 80 pf. (No. K15)	..	..	12·00 38·00
B10	B	1s. on 1 m. (No. K16) ..	..	..	£140 £550
		a. "s" inverted	..	..	£600 £1800
B11		2s. on 2 m. (No. K17)	..	..	£140 £550
		a. "s" inverted	..	..	£600 £1800
		b. Surch double, one albino	..	£1000
B12		3s. on 3 m. (No. K18) ..	..	..	£140 £550
		a. "s" inverted	..	..	£600 £1800
		b. "s" broken at top	..	..	£425
		c. Surch double	..	..	£6000
		ca. Surch double, one albino	..	£1000
B13		5s. on 5 m. (No. K25a *wmk lozenges*)		£170 £600
		a. "s" inverted	..	..	£700 £1900
		b. "s" broken at top	..	..	£475
B1/13		.. .. ..	Set of 13	£600 £2250

Examples of all values exist showing a forged Duala Kamerun postmark dated "11 10 15". Another forged cancel dated "16 11 15" is also known. This can be identified by the lack of a serif on the index letter "b".

The stamps of Nigeria were subsequently used in British Cameroons and the area was administered as part of Nigeria from February 1924.

For issues of Cameroun under French administration see *Part 6 (France)* and for the Cameroun Republic (1960–1995) *Part 12 (Africa since Independence A to E)*.

II. CAMEROONS TRUST TERRITORY

Following the independence of the French Trust Territory of Cameroun on 1 January 1960 the United Nations directed that a plebiscite should be held in the British Trust Territory whose postal service continued, for the time being, to be run by Nigeria. The northern area voted to join Nigeria, but the southern part of the territory decided to join the Cameroun Republic.

The following issue, although ordered by the Southern Cameroons authorities, was also on sale in Northern Cameroons, until the latter joined Nigeria on 1 June 1961. The stamps therefore can be found with Nigerian postmarks.

CAMEROONS
U.K.T.T.
(1)

1960 (1 Oct)–**61.** *Nos. 69/71, 72ca/cc and 73/80 of Nigeria optd with T 1, in red.*

T 1	18	½d. black and orange	..		10	1·00
T 2	–	1d. black and bronze-green	..	..	10	60
		a. *Grey-black and dull bronze-green*				
		(19.9.61)	..		60	1·75
T 3	–	1½d. blue-green	..	..	10	20
T 4	21	2d. grey (Type B)	..	..	10	50
		a. *Slate-blue* (Type A)	..		£800 £250	
		b. *Bluish grey* (Type B)	..		50·00 15·00	
		c. *Pale grey* (Type B) (19.9.61)	..	10	30	
T 5	–	3d. black and deep lilac	..	..	15	10
T 6	–	4d. black and blue	..	..	10	90
T 7	24	6d. orange-brown and black (*p* 14)	..	30	10
		a. Perf 13×13½ (19.9.61)	..	20	2·00	
T 8	–	1s. black and maroon	..	..	15	10
T 9	26	2s. 6d. black and green	..	..	1·10	80
T10	–	5s. black and red-orange	..	..	1·60	3·50
T11	–	10s. black and red-brown	..	..	2·50	6·00
T12	29	£1 black and violet	..	..	8·50	18·00
T1/12		.. .. ..	Set of 12	13·00 28·00		

Nos. T2 and T4/*b* were overprinted on stamps printed by Waterlows' subsidiary, Imprimerie Belge de Securité.

Nos. T2*a*, T4*c* and T7a were from new printings produced by De La Rue instead of Waterlow.

The above stamps were withdrawn on 30 September 1961, when Southern Cameroons became part of the Cameroun Republic.

III. REPUBLIC OF CAMEROON

COMMONWEALTH MEMBER

1 November 1995

The Republic of Cameroon joined the Commonwealth on 1 November 1995 and issues from that date will be listed below. A letter from the Ministry of Posts and Telecommunications, Yaoundé, dated January 2000 confirmed that no new stamps had appeared since 1 November 1995.

Canada

Separate stamp issues appeared for British Columbia and Vancouver Island, Canada, New Brunswick, Newfoundland, Nova Scotia and Prince Edward Island before these colonies joined the Dominion of Canada.

BRITISH COLUMBIA & VANCOUVER ISLAND

Vancouver Island was organised as a Crown Colony in 1849 and the mainland territory was proclaimed a separate colony as British Columbia, in 1858. The two colonies combined, as British Columbia, on 19 November 1866.

PRICES FOR STAMPS ON COVER	
Nos. 2/3	from × 6
Nos. 11/12	from × 2
Nos. 13/14	from × 6
Nos. 21/2	from × 10
Nos. 23/7	from × 6
Nos. 28/9	from × 10
No. 30	×
No. 31	from × 10
Nos. 32/3	—

(Typo D.L.R.)

1860. *No wmk. P 14.*
2	1	2½d. deep reddish rose	..	..	£275 £180
3		2½d. pale reddish rose	..	..	£275 £180

When Vancouver Island adopted the dollar currency in 1862 the 2½d. was sold at 5 c. From 18 May until 1 November 1865 examples of Nos. 2/3 were used to prepay mail from Vancouver Island to British Columbia at the price of 15 cents a pair.

From 20 June 1864 to 1 November 1865, the 2½d. was sold in British Columbia for 3d. and was subsequently used for the same purpose during a shortage of 3d. stamps in 1867.

Imperforate plate proofs exist in pale dull red (*Price* £2500 *un*).

VANCOUVER ISLAND
(New Currency. 100 cents = 1 dollar)

2 3

(Typo D.L.R.)

1865 (19 Sept). *Wmk Crown CC.* (a) *Imperf* (1866).
11	2	5 c. rose	..	..	£20000 £8000
12	3	10 c. blue	..	..	£1400 £850

(b) P 14
13	2	5 c. rose	..	..	£225 £140
		w. Wmk inverted	..	..	£950
14	3	10 c. blue	..	..	£200 £140
		w. Wmk inverted	..	..	£650 £450

Medium or poor copies of Nos. 11 and 12 can be supplied at much lower prices, when in stock.

After the two colonies combined Nos. 13/14 were also used in British Columbia.

BRITISH COLUMBIA

4

(Typo D.L.R.)

1865 (1 Nov)–67. *Wmk Crown CC. P 14.*
21	4	3d. deep blue	..	..	75·00 60·00
22		3d. pale blue (19.7.67)	..	..	75·00 60·00
		w. Wmk inverted	..	..	£200 £150

British Columbia changed to the dollar currency on 1 January 1866. Remaining stocks of No. 21 and the supply of No. 22, when it finally arrived, were sold at 12½ c. a pair.

(New Currency. 100 cents = 1 dollar)

TWO CENTS   5.CENTS.5
(5)   (6)

1868–71. *T* **4** *in various colours. Wmk Crown CC. Surch as T* **5** *or* **6.** (a) *P* 12½ (3.69).
23		5 c. red (Bk.)	..	..	£600 £550
24		10 c. lake (B.)	..	..	£450 £425

25		25 c. yellow (V.)	..	..	..	£350 £350
26		50 c. mauve (R.)	..	..	..	£425 £375
27		$1 green (G.)	..	..	..	£650 £700

(b) P 14
28		2 c. brown (Bk.) (1.68)	..	..	90·00 90·00
29		5 c. pale red (Bk.) (5.69)	..	..	£120 £120
30		10 c. lake (B.)	..	..	£650
31		25 c. yellow (V.) (21.7.69)	..	..	£120 £120
32		50 c. mauve (R.) (23.2.71)	..	..	£400 £750
		w. Wmk inverted	..	..	£500
33		$1 green (G.)	..	..	£600

Nos. 30 and 33 were not issued.

British Columbia joined the Dominion of Canada on 20 July 1871.

COLONY OF CANADA

The first British post offices in what was to become the colony of Canada were opened at Quebec, Montreal and Trois Rivières during 1763. These, and subsequent, offices remained part of the British G.P.O. system until 6 April 1851.

The two provinces of Upper Canada (Ontario) and Lower Canada (Quebec) were united in 1840.

For illustration of the handstamp types see BRITISH POST OFFICES ABROAD notes, following GREAT BRITAIN.

NEW CARLISLE, GASPÉ
POSTMASTER'S PROVISIONAL ENVELOPE

1

1851 (7 April).
1	1	3d. black	

Only one example is known, addressed to Toronto, with the impression cancelled by the signature of the postmaster, R. W. Kelly.

QUEBEC
CROWNED-CIRCLE HANDSTAMPS

CC1 CC 1*b* QUEBEC L.C. (R.) (13.1.1842)   *Price on cover* £150

PRICES FOR STAMPS ON COVER	
Nos. 1/23	from × 2
Nos. 25/8	from × 3
Nos. 29/43a	from × 3
Nos. 44/5	from × 8

1 American Beaver   2 Prince Albert   3
(Designed by
Sir Sandford Fleming)

Major re-entry: Line though "EE PEN" (Upper pane R. 5/7)

(T **1/6.** Eng and recess Rawdon, Wright, Hatch and Edson, New York)

1851. *Imperf. Laid paper.*
1	1	3d. red (23 April)	..	..	..	£11000 £650
1a		3d. orange-vermilion	..	..	..	£11000 £650
		b. Major re-entry	..	..		— £1600
2	2	6d. slate-violet (15 May)	..	..	£14000 £900
3		6d. brown-purple	..	..	..	£15000 £1200
		a. Bisected (3d.) on cover	..	..	†£20000
4	3	12d. black (14 June)	..	..	£60000 £40000

There are several re-entries on the plate of the 3d. in addition to the major re-entry listed. All re-entries occur in this stamp on all papers.

Forgeries of the 3d. are known without the full stop after "PENCE". They also omit the foliage in the corners, as do similar forgeries of the 6d.

4   5   6 Jacques Cartier

1852–57. *Imperf.*
A. *Handmade wove paper, varying in thickness* (1852–56)
5	1	3d. red	..	..	£1100 £160
		a. Bisected (1½d.) on cover (1856)	..	†£22000
6		3d. deep red	..	..	£1200 £160
7		3d. scarlet-vermilion	..	..	£1500 £170

8	1	3d. brown-red	..	..	£1200 £160
		a. Bisected (1½d.) on cover (1856)	..	†£22000
		b. Major re-entry (all shades)	from	£2500 £650
9	2	6d. slate-violet	..	..	£12000 £950
		a. Bisected (3d.) on cover	..	†£12000
10		6d. greenish grey	..	..	£12000 £950
11		6d. brownish grey	..	..	£13000 £1100
12	5	7½d. yellow-green (shades) (2.6.57)	£7000 £1500
13	6	10d. bright blue (1.55)	..	£7000 £1200
14		10d. dull blue	..	..	£6500 £1100
15		10d. blue to deep blue	..	£7000 £1200
		a. Major re-entry (all shades)	from	— £2000
16	3	12d. black	..	..	— £45000

B. *Machine-made medium to thick wove paper of a more even hard texture with more visible mesh. Clearer impressions* (1857)
17	4	½d. deep rose (1.8.57)	..	£700 £400
18	1	3d. red	..	..	£1600 £450
		a. Bisected (1½d.) on cover	..	†£20000
		b. Major re-entry	..	..	— £1200
19	2	6d. grey-lilac	..	..	£14000 £2000
20	6	10d. blue to deep blue	..	£7000 £2000
		a. Major re-entry	..	..	£11000 £2500

C. *Thin soft horizontally ribbed paper* (1857)
21	4	½d. deep rose	..	..	£5500 £1600
		a. Vertically ribbed paper	..	£6000 £2250
22	1	3d. red	..	..	£3000 £400
		a. Major re-entry	..	..	— £1100

D. *Very thick soft wove paper* (1857)
23	2	6d. reddish purple	..	£14000 £2500
		a. Bisected (3d.) on cover	..	†£18000

Bisected examples of the 3d. value were used to make up the 7½d. Canadian Packet rate to England from May 1856 until the introduction of the 7½d. value on 2 June 1857.

The 7½d. and 10d. values can be found in wide and narrow versions. These differences are due to shrinkage of the paper, which was wetted before printing and then contracted unevenly during drying. The width of these stamps varies between 17 and 18 mm.

The listed major re-entry on the 10d. occurs on R.3/5 and shows strong doubling of the top frame line and the left-hand "8d. stg." with a line through the lower parts of "ANAD" and "ENCE". Smaller re-entries occur on all values.

Examples of the 12d. on wove paper come from a proof sheet used for postal purposes by the postal authorities.

The 3d. is known perforated 14 and also *percé en scie* 13. Both are contemporary, but were unofficial.

1858–59. *P* 11¾. A. *Machine-made medium to thick wove paper with a more even hard texture.*
25	4	½d. deep rose (12.58)	..	£1700 £600
		a. Lilac-rose	..	..	£1900 £650
26	1	3d. red (1.59)	..	..	£2500 £300
		a. Major re-entry	..	..	— £1000
27	2	6d. brownish grey (1.59)	..	£6500 £2500
		a. Slate-violet	..	..	£6500 £2250

B. *Thin soft horizontally ribbed paper*
27b	4	½d. deep rose-red	..	— £3250
28	1	3d. red	..	..	— £1200
		a. Major re-entry	..		

(New Currency. 100 cents = 1 dollar)

7   8 American Beaver

9 Prince Albert   10   11 Jacques Cartier

(Recess A.B.N. Co)

(On 1 May 1858, Messrs. Rawdon, Wright, Hatch and Edson joined with eight other firms to form "The American Bank Note Co" and the "imprint" on sheets of the following stamps has the new title of the firm with "New York" added.)

1859 (1 July). *P* 12.
29	7	1 c. pale rose (to rose-red)	..	£225 27·00
30		1 c. deep rose (to carmine-rose)	..	£300 45·00
		a. Imperf (pair)	..	..	£2500
		b. Imperf × perf			
31	8	5 c. pale red	..	..	£250 11·00
32		5 c. deep red	..	..	£250 11·00
		a. Re-entry* (R.3/8)	..	..	£2500 £450
		b. Imperf (pair)	..	..	£7000
		c. Bisected (2½ c.) with 10 c. on cover	†£4000
33	9	10 c. black-brown	..	£6000 £1300
		a. Bisected (5 c.), on cover	..	†£5500
33b		10 c. deep red-purple	..	£2500 £500
		ba. Bisected (5 c.), on cover	..	†£3750
34		10 c. purple (shades)	..	£750 42·00
		a. Bisected (5 c.), on cover	..	†£3750
35		10 c. brownish purple	..	£700 42·00
36		10 c. brown (to pale)	..	£700 42·00
		a. Bisected (5 c.), on cover	..	†£4500
37		10 c. dull violet	..	..	£750 50·00
38		10 c. bright red-purple	..	£750 42·00
		a. Imperf (pair)	..	..	£6000
39	10	12½ c. deep yellow-green	..	£600 40·00
40		12½ c. pale yellow-green	..	£550 40·00
41		12½ c. blue-green	..	£650 48·00
		a. Imperf (pair)	..	..	£2500
		b. Imperf between (vert pair)		

CANADA / *Colony of Canada* New Brunswick, Newfoundland

42	11	17 c. deep blue	.. .. ..	£700	60·00
		a. Imperf (pair)	.. ..	£3000	
43		17 c. slate-blue	.. ..	£850	90·00
43a		17 c. indigo	.. ..	£750	65·00

*The price of No. 32a is for the very marked re-entry showing oval frame line doubled above "CANADA". Slighter re-entries are worth from £30 upwards in used condition.

As there were numerous P.O. Dept. orders for the 10 c., 12½ c. and 17 c. and some of these were executed by more than one separate printing, with no special care to ensure uniformity of colour, there is a wide range of shade, especially in the 10 c., and some shades recur at intervals after periods during which other shades predominated. The colour-names given in the above list therefore represent groups only.

It has been proved by leading Canadian specialists that the perforations may be an aid to the approximate dating of a particular stamp, the gauge used measuring 11¾ × 11¾ from mid-July, 1859 to mid 1863, 12 × 11¾ from March 1863 to mid 1865 and 12 × 12 from April 1865 to 1868. Exceptionally in the 5 c. value many sheets were perforated 12 × 12 between May and October, 1862, whilst the last printings of the 12½ c. and 17 c. perf 11¾ × 11¾ were in July 1863, the perf 12 × 11¾ starting towards the end of 1863.

12

(Recess A.B.N. Co)

1864 (1 Aug). *P* 12.

44	12	2 c. rose-red	.. ..	£400	£140
45		2 c. bright rose ..	.. ..	£400	£140
		a. Imperf (pair)	.. ..	£1600	

The Colony of Canada became part of the Dominion of Canada on 1 July 1867.

NEW BRUNSWICK

New Brunswick, previously part of Nova Scotia, became a separate colony in June 1784.

PRICES FOR STAMPS ON COVER

Nos. 1/4	*from* × 2
Nos. 5/6	*from* × 3
Nos. 7/9	*from* × 10
Nos. 10/12	*from* × 30
No. 13	—
Nos. 14/17	*from* × 2
No. 18	*from* × 5
No. 19	*from* × 100

1 Royal Crown and Heraldic Flowers
of the United Kingdom

(Recess P.B.)

1851 (5 Sept). *Blue paper. Imperf.*

1	1	3d. bright red ..	.. ..	£2000	£350
2		3d. dull red ..	.. ..	£2000	£325
		a. Bisected (1½d.) (on cover) ..	†	£2750	
2b		6d. mustard-yellow ..	..	£6000	£1500
3		6d. yellow ..	.. ..	£4500	£800
4		6d. olive-yellow..	..	£4500	£700
		a. Bisected (3d.) (on cover) ..	†	£3000	
		b. Quartered (1½d.) (on cover)	†	£35000	
5		1s. reddish mauve	..	£13000	£4000
6		1s. dull mauve ..	..	£14000	£4500
		a. Bisected (6d.) (on cover)	†	£20000	
		b. Quartered (3d.) (on cover) ..	†	£28000	

Reprints of all three values were made in 1890 on thin, hard, white paper. The 3d. is bright orange, the 6d. and 1s. violet-black.
Nos. 2a and 4b were to make up the 7½d. rate to Great Britain, introduced on 1 August 1854.

(New Currency. 100 cents = 1 dollar)

2 Locomotive   **3**   **3a** Charles Connell

4   **5**   **6** Paddle-steamer *Washington*

7 King Edward VII when Prince of Wales

(Recess A.B.N. Co)

1860 (15 May)–**63**. *No wmk. P* 12.

7	2	1 c. brown-purple	..	55·00	38·00
8		1 c. purple	..	32·00	32·00
9		1 c. dull claret	..	32·00	32·00
10	3	2 c. orange (1863)	..	15·00	15·00
11		2 c. orange-yellow	..	16·00	15·00
12		2 c. deep orange	..	19·00	15·00
		a. Imperf horiz (vert pair)	..	£450	
13	3a	5 c. brown ..	..	£4250	
14	4	5 c. yellow-green	..	13·00	13·00
15		5 c. deep green	..	13·00	13·00
16		5 c. sap-green (deep yellowish green)	..	£300	40·00
17	5	10 c. red	..	38·00	38·00
		a. Bisected (5 c.) (on cover) (1860)	†	£600	
18	6	12½ c. indigo	..	50·00	40·00
19	7	17 c. black	..	35·00	40·00

Beware of forged cancellations.

New Brunswick joined the Dominion of Canada on 1 July 1867 and its stamps were withdrawn in March of the following year.

NEWFOUNDLAND

Newfoundland became a self-governing colony in 1855 and a Dominion in 1917. In 1934 the adverse financial situation led to the suspension of the constitution.

The first local postmaster, at St. John's, was appointed in 1805, the overseas mails being routed via Halifax, Nova Scotia. A regular packet service was established between these two ports in 1840, the British G.P.O. assuming control of the overseas mails at the same time.

The responsibility for the overseas postal service reverted to the colonial administration on 1 July 1851.

For illustrations of the handstamp types see BRITISH POST OFFICES ABROAD notes, following GREAT BRITAIN.

ST. JOHN'S

CROWNED-CIRCLE HANDSTAMPS

CC1 CC 1a ST. JOHNS NEWFOUNDLAND (R.)
(27.6.1846) .. .. *Price on cover* £900

PRICES FOR STAMPS ON COVER TO 1945

No. 1	*from* × 30
Nos. 2/4	*from* × 3
No. 5	*from* × 20
No. 6	*from* × 10
No. 7	*from* × 3
No. 8	*from* × 30
No. 9	*from* × 8
No. 10	—
No. 11	*from* × 8
No. 12	*from* × 8
Nos. 13/14	*from* × 20
Nos. 15/17	—
Nos. 18/20	*from* × 20
No. 21	*from* × 15
Nos. 22/3	—
No. 25	*from* × 30
No. 26	*from* × 5
No. 27	*from* × 8
No. 28	*from* × 3
Nos. 29/30	*from* × 10
No. 31	*from* × 30
No. 32	*from* × 8
No. 33	*from* × 5
No. 33a	—
Nos. 34/9	*from* × 8
Nos. 40/1	*from* × 5
Nos. 42/3	*from* × 30
Nos. 44/8	*from* × 8
No. 49	*from* × 50
Nos. 50/3	*from* × 10
No. 54	*from* × 4
Nos. 55/8b	*from* × 10
No. 59	*from* × 100
No. 59a	*from* × 4
Nos. 60/1	*from* × 8
Nos. 62/5	*from* × 3
Nos. 65a/79	*from* × 3
Nos. 83/90	*from* × 10
Nos. 91/3	*from* × 2
No. 94	*from* × 50
Nos. 95/141	*from* × 3
Nos. 142/a	*from* × 1½
No. 143	*from* × 8
Nos. 144/8f	*from* × 2
Nos. 149/62	*from* × 3

No. 163	—		
Nos. 164/78	*from* × 2		
Nos. 179/90	*from* × 3		
No. 191	—		
Nos. 192/220	*from* × 2		
No. 221	—		
Nos. 222/9	*from* × 3		
Nos. 230/4	*from* × 2		
No. 235	—		
Nos. 236/91	*from* × 2		
Nos. D1/6	*from* × 10		

1   **2**   **4**

3   **5**

Royal Crown and Heraldic flowers of the United Kingdom

(Recess P.B.)

1857 (1 Jan)–**64**. *No wmk. Thick, machine-made paper with a distinct mesh. Imperf.*

1	1	1d. brown-purple	..	85·00	£150
		a. Bisected (½d.) (1864) (on cover)	†	£12000	
2	2	2d. scarlet-vermilion (15 Feb)		£9000	£4500
3	3	3d. yellowish green	..	£700	£400
4	4	4d. scarlet-vermilion	..	£6000	£2500
5	1	5d. brown-purple	..	£180	£350
6	4	6d. scarlet-vermilion	..	£12000	£3000
7	5	6½d. scarlet-vermilion	..	£2250	£2500
8	4	8d. scarlet-vermilion	..	£225	£325
		a. Bisected (4d.) (1859) (on cover)	†	£3750	
9	2	1s. scarlet-vermilion	..	£13000	£4750
		a. Bisected (6d.) (1860) (on cover)	†	£12000	

The 6d. and 8d. differ from the 4d. in many details, as does also the 1s. from the 2d.

PERKINS BACON "CANCELLED". For notes on these handstamps, showing "CANCELLED" between horizontal bars forming an oval, see Catalogue Introduction.

1860 (15 Aug–Dec). *Medium, hand-made paper without mesh. Imperf.*

10	2	2d. orange-vermilion	..	£300	£375
11	3	3d. grn *to* dp grn* (H/S "CANCELLED" in oval £5000)		70·00	£150
12	4	4d. orange-verm (H/S "CANCELLED" in oval £8000)		£2250	£800
		a. Bisected (2d.) (12.60) (on cover)	†	£13000	
13	1	5d. Venetian red (H/S "CANCELLED" in oval £6500)		90·00	£275
14	4	6d. orange-vermilion	..	£2750	£600
15	2	1s. orange-verm (H/S "CANCELLED" in oval £11000)		£19000	£8000
		a. Bisected (6d.) (12.60) (on cover)	†	£40000	

*No. 11 includes stamps from the July and November 1861 printings which are very difficult to distinguish.

The 1s. on horizontally or vertically *laid* paper is now considered to be a proof (*Price* £10000).

Stamps of this and the following issue may be found with part of the paper-maker's watermark "STACEY WISE 1858".

BISECTS. Collectors are warned against buying bisected stamps of these issues without a reliable guarantee.

1862–64. *New colours. Hand-made paper without mesh. Imperf.*

16	1	1d. chocolate-brown	..	£160	£250
		a. Red-brown	..	£4000	
17	2	2d. rose-lake	..	£150	£375
18	4	4d. rose-lake (H/S "CANCELLED" in oval £6000)		28·00	90·00
		a. Bisected (2d.) (1864) (on cover)	†	—	
19	1	5d. chocolate-brown	..	60·00	£300
		a. Red-brown	..	45·00	£190
20	4	6d. rose-lake (H/S "CANCELLED" in oval £6000)		21·00	£100
		a. Bisected (3d.) (1863) (on cover)	†	£9000	
21	5	6½d. rose-lake (H/S "CANCELLED" in oval £5000)		65·00	£425
22	4	8d. rose-lake	..	75·00	£500
23	2	1s. rose-lake ("H/S "CANCELLED" in oval £5000)		35·00	£300
		a. Bisected (6d.) (1863) (on cover)	†	£14000	

Nos. 16/23 come from printings made in July (2d., 4d., 6d., 6½d., and 1s. only) or November 1861 (all values). The paper used was from the same manufacturer as that for Nos. 11/15, but was of more variable thickness and texture, ranging from a relatively soft medium paper, which can be quite opaque, to a thin hard transparent paper. The rose-lake stamps also show a considerable variation in shade ranging from pale to deep. The extensive remainders of this issue were predominately in pale shades on thin hard paper, but it is not possible to distinguish between stamps from the two printings with any certainty. Deep shades of the 2d., 4d., 6d., 6½d. and 1s. on soft opaque paper do, however, command a considerable premium.

Beware of buying used specimens of the stamps which are worth much less in unused condition, as many unused stamps have been provided with faked postmarks. A guarantee should be obtained.

300

(New Currency. 100 cents = 1 dollar)

6 Atlantic Cod **7** Common Seal on Ice-floe

8 Prince Consort **9** Queen Victoria

10 Schooner **11** Queen Victoria

(Recess A.B.N. Co, New York)

1865 (15 Nov)–**71.** *P* 12. (*a*) *Thin yellowish paper.*

25	**6**	2 c. yellowish green	..	£100	38·00
		a. Bisected (1 c.) (on cover) (1870)		†	£3750
26	**7**	5 c. brown	..	£450	£170
		a. Bisected (2½ c.) (on cover)			
27	**8**	10 c. black	..	£250	70·00
		a. Bisected (5 c.) (on cover) (1869)		†	£2750
28	**9**	12 c. red-brown	..	£400	£150
		a. Bisected (6 c.) (on cover)		†	£2750
29	**10**	13 c. orange-yellow	..	90·00	65·00
30	**11**	24 c. blue	..	32·00	32·00

(*b*) *Medium white paper*

31	**6**	2 c. bluish green (*to* deep) (1870)		65·00	30·00
32	**8**	10 c. black (1871)	..	£160	38·00
33	**9**	12 c. chestnut (1870)	..	42·00	42·00
33*a*	**11**	24 c. blue (1870?)	..	£800	£275

The inland postage rate was reduced to 3 c. on 8 May, 1870. Until the 3 c. value became available examples of No. 25 were bisected to provide 1 c. stamps.

12 King Edward VII when Prince of Wales **14** Queen Victoria

I

II

In Type II the white oval frame line is unbroken by the scroll containing the words "ONE CENT", the letters "N.F." are smaller and closer to the scroll, and there are other minor differences.

(Recess National Bank Note Co, New York)

1868 (Nov). *P* 12.

34	**12**	1 c. dull purple (I)	..	50·00	48·00

(Recess A.B.N. Co)

1868 (Nov)–**73.** *P* 12.

35	**12**	1 c. brown-purple (II) (5.71)	..	80·00	55·00
36	**14**	3 c. vermilion (7.70)	..	£250	£100
37		3 c. blue (1.4.73)	..	£275	18·00
38	**7**	5 c. black	..	£225	£100
39	**14**	6 c. rose (7.70)	..	7·50	17·00

1876–79. *Rouletted.*

40	**12**	1 c. lake-purple (II) (1877)		90·00	40·00
41	**6**	2 c. bluish green (1879)		£120	45·00
42	**14**	3 c. blue (1877)		£250	4·00
43	**7**	5 c. blue	..	£170	3·25
		a. Imperf (pair)			

15 King Edward VII when Prince of Wales **16** Atlantic Cod

17 **18** Common Seal on Ice-floe

(Recess British American Bank Note Co, Montreal)

1880–82. *P* 12.

44	**15**	1 c. dull grey-brown	..	26·00	8·00
		a. *Dull brown* ..	..	24·00	8·00
		b. *Red-brown*	..	28·00	12·00
46	**16**	2 c. yellow-green (1882)	..	45·00	22·00
47	**17**	3 c. pale dull blue	..	65·00	5·00
		a. *Bright blue* ..	..	70·00	3·00
48	**18**	5 c. pale dull blue	..	£200	8·00

19 Newfoundland Dog **20** Atlantic Brigantine **21** Queen Victoria

(Recess British American Bank Note Co, Montreal)

1887 (15 Feb)–**88.** *New colours and values. P* 12.

49	**19**	½ c. rose-red	..	9·00	7·00
50	**15**	1 c. blue-green (1.88)	..	11·00	6·00
		a. *Green*	..	6·00	3·00
		b. *Yellow-green*	..	11·00	8·00
51	**16**	2 c. orange-vermilion (1.88)	..	14·00	4·50
52	**17**	3 c. deep brown (1.88)	..	55·00	1·50
53	**18**	5 c. deep blue (1.88)	..	95·00	4·50
54	**20**	10 c. black (1.88)	..	45·00	50·00
49/54			*Set of* 6	£200	65·00

For reissues of 1880/8 stamps in similar colours, see Nos. 62/5*a*.

(Recess B.A.B.N.)

1890 (Nov). *P* 12.

55	**21**	3 c. deep slate	..	25·00	1·25
		a. Imperf (pair)			
56		3 c. slate-grey (*to* grey)	..	26·00	1·25
		a. Imperf horiz (vert pair)		£400	
57		3 c. slate-violet	..	32·00	3·50
58		3 c. grey-lilac	..	32·00	1·25
58*a*		3 c. brown-grey	..	32·00	6·00
58*b*		3 c. purple-grey	..	38·00	5·50

There is a very wide range of shades in this stamp, and those given only cover the main groups.

Stamps on pink paper are from a consignment recovered from the sea and which were affected by the salt water.

(Recess British American Bank Note Co, Montreal)

1894 (Aug–Dec). *Changes of colour. P* 12.

59	**19**	½ c. black (11.94)	..	9·00	4·75
59*a*	**18**	5 c. bright blue (12.94)	..	55·00	3·00
60	**14**	6 c. crimson-lake (12.94)	..	14·00	16·00
61	**9**	12 c. deep brown	..	48·00	48·00

The 6 c. is printed from the old American Bank Note Company's plates.

1896 (Jan)–**98.** *Reissues. P* 12.

62	**19**	½ c. orange-vermilion	..	42·00	48·00
63	**15**	1 c. deep brown	..	55·00	50·00
63*a*		1 c. deep green (1898)	..	15·00	8·50
64	**16**	2 c. green	..	75·00	40·00
65	**17**	3 c. deep blue	..	65·00	12·00
65*a*		3 c. chocolate-brown	..	80·00	75·00
62/5*a*			*Set of* 6	£300	£200

The above were *reissued* for postal purposes. The colours were generally brighter than those of the original stamps.

22 Queen Victoria **23** John Cabot **24** Cape Bonavista

25 Caribou hunting **26** Mining

27 Logging **28** Fishing

29 *Matthew* (Cabot) **30** Willow Grouse

31 Group of Grey Seals **32** Salmon-fishing

33 Seal of the Colony **34** Iceberg off St. John's **35** Henry VII

(Des R. O. Smith. Recess A.B.N. Co)

1897 (24 June). *400th Anniv of Discovery of Newfoundland and 60th year of Queen Victoria's reign. P* 12.

66	**22**	1 c. green	..	2·25	4·50
67	**23**	2 c. bright rose	..	2·00	2·50
		a. Bisected (1 c.) on cover		†	£250
68	**24**	3 c. bright blue	..	3·25	75
		a. Bisected (1½ c.) on cover		†	£250
69	**25**	4 c. olive-green	..	9·50	3·00
70	**26**	5 c. violet..	..	13·00	3·00
71	**27**	6 c. red-brown	..	8·50	3·25
		a. Bisected (3 c.) on cover		†	£250
72	**28**	8 c. orange	..	18·00	8·00
73	**29**	10 c. sepia ..	..	40·00	6·00
74	**30**	12 c. deep blue	..	35·00	5·50
75	**31**	15 c. bright scarlet	..	20·00	17·00
76	**32**	24 c. dull violet-blue	..	24·00	19·00
77	**33**	30 c. slate-blue	..	45·00	60·00
78	**34**	35 c. red	..	60·00	60·00
79	**35**	60 c. black ..	..	17·00	12·00
66/79			*Set of* 14	£275	£180

The 60 c. surcharged "TWO—2—CENTS" in three lines is an essay made in December 1918 (*Price* £275).

ONE CENT

(36)

ONE CENT

(37)

ONE CENT

(38)

1897 (19 Oct). *T* **21** *surch with T* **36/8** *by Royal Gazette, St. Johns, on stamps of various shades.*

80	**36**	1 c. on 3 c. grey-purple	..	42·00	18·00
		a. Surch double, one diagonal		£1100	
		d. Vert pair, one without lower bar and "ONE CENT"		£3500	
81	**37**	1 c. on 3 c. grey-purple	..	95·00	85·00
82	**38**	1 c. on 3 c. grey-purple	..	£450	£375

Nos. 80/2 occur in the same setting of 50 (10×5) applied twice to each sheet. Type **36** appeared in the first four horizontal rows, Type **37** on R. 5/1–8 and Type **38** on R. 5/9 and 10.

Trial surcharges in red or red and black were not issued.

(*Price: Type* **36** *in red* £750, *in red and black* £750: *Type* **37** *in red* £2250, *in red and black* £2500: *Type* **38** *in red* £5000, *in red and black* £6000*).*

These surcharges exist on stamps of various shades, but those on brown-grey are clandestine forgeries, having been produced by one of the printers at the *Royal Gazette.*

39 Prince Edward later Duke of Windsor

40 Queen Victoria

41 King Edward VII when Prince of Wales

42 Queen Alexandra when Princess of Wales

43 Queen Mary when Duchess of York

44 King George V when Duke of York

(Recess A.B.N. Co)

1897 (4 Dec)–**1918.** P 12.

83	39	½ c. olive (8.98)	..	2·25	1·50
		a. Imperf (pair)		£275	
84	40	1 c. carmine	..	3·25	3·50
85		1 c. blue-green (6.98) ..		7·50	20
		a. Yellow-green		6·50	20
		b. Imperf horiz (vert pair)		£170	
86	41	2 c. orange	..	3·25	3·00
		a. Imperf (pair)			£300
87		2 c. scarlet (6.98)	..	14·00	40
		a. Imperf (pair)		£225	£225
		b. Imperf between (pair)		£300	
88	42	3 c. orange (6.98)	..	15·00	30
		a. Imperf horiz (vert pair)		£275	
		b. Imperf (pair)		£225	£225
		c. Red-orange/bluish (6.18)		30·00	2·75
89	43	4 c. violet (21.10.01)	..	23·00	4·00
		a. Imperf (pair)		£300	
90	44	5 c. blue (6.99)	..	38·00	3·00
83/90		*Set of 8*		95·00	14·00

No. 88c was an emergency war-time printing made by the American Bank Note Co from the old plate, pending receipt of the then current 3 c. from England.

The imperforate errors of this issue are found used, but only as philatelic "by favour" items. It is possible that No. 86a only exists in this condition.

45 Map of Newfoundland

(Recess A.B.N. Co)

1908 (31 Aug). P 12.

94	45	2 c. lake	..	27·00	80

46 King James I

47 Arms of Colonisation Co

48 John Guy

49 *Endeavour* (immigrant ship), 1610

50 Cupids

51 Sir Francis Bacon

52 View of Mosquito

53 Logging Camp, Red Indian Lake

54 Paper Mills, Grand Falls

55 King Edward VII

56 King George V

6 c. (A) "Z" in "COLONIZATION" reversed. (B) "Z" correct.

(Litho Whitehead, Morris & Co Ltd)

1910 (15 Aug). (*a*) P 12.

95	46	1 c. green	..	7·00	2·25
		a. "NFWFOUNDLAND" (Right pane R. 5/1)		50·00	80·00
		b. "JAMRS" (Right pane R. 5/2)		50·00	80·00
		c. Imperf between (horiz pair)		£275	£300
96	47	2 c. rose-carmine	..	10·00	1·75
97	48	3 c. olive	..	6·00	15·00
98	49	4 c. violet	..	14·00	13·00
99	50	5 c. bright blue	..	22·00	6·50
100	51	6 c. claret (A) ..		45·00	£120
100a		6 c. claret (B) ..		20·00	65·00
101	52	8 c. bistre-brown	..	48·00	90·00
102	53	9 c. olive-green	..	40·00	80·00
103	54	10 c. purple-slate	..	55·00	£100
104	55	12 c. pale red-brown	..	55·00	80·00
		a. Imperf (pair)		£300	
105	56	15 c. black	..	65·00	£100
95/105		*Set of 11*		£300	£500

(*b*) P 12×14

106	46	1 c. green	..	4·00	7·00
		a. "NFWFOUNDLAND"		45·00	£100
		b. "JAMRS"..		45·00	£100
		c. Imperf between (horiz pair)		£475	£500
107	47	2 c. rose-carmine	..	3·50	35
		a. Imperf between (horiz pair)		£450	
108	50	5 c. bright blue (p 14×12)		8·00	2·75

(*c*) P 12×11

109	46	1 c. green	..	1·25	30
		a. Imperf between (horiz pair)		£250	
		b. Imperf between (vert pair)		£300	
		c. "NFWFOUNDLAND"		23·00	42·00
		e. "JAMRS"..		23·00	42·00

(*d*) P 12×11½

110	47	2 c. rose-carmine	..	£200	£190

(Dies eng Macdonald & Sons. Recess A. Alexander & Sons, Ltd)

1911 (7 Feb). As T **51** to **56**, but recess printed. P 14.

111		6 c. claret (B) ..		17·00	42·00
112		8 c. yellow-brown	..	48·00	65·00
		a. Imperf between (horiz pair)		£425	
		b. Imperf (pair)		£300	
113		9 c. sage-green	..	45·00	90·00
		a. Imperf between (horiz pair)		£375	
114		10 c. purple-black	..	85·00	£120
		a. Imperf between (horiz pair)		£375	
		b. Imperf (pair)		£250	
115		12 c. red-brown	..	60·00	60·00
116		15 c. slate-green	..	60·00	£110
111/16		*Set of 6*		£275	£425

The 9 c. and 15 c. exist with papermaker's watermark "E. TOWGOOD FINE".

57 Queen Mary

58 King George V

59 Duke of Windsor when Prince of Wales

60 King George VI when Prince Albert

61 Princess Mary, the Princess Royal

62 Prince Henry Duke of Gloucester

63 Prince George, Duke of Kent

64 Prince John

65 Queen Alexandra

66 Duke of Connaught

67 Seal of Newfoundland

(1 c. to 5 c., 10 c. eng and recess D.L.R.; others eng Macdonald & Co, recess A. Alexander & Sons)

1911 (19 June)–**16.** *Coronation.* P 13½ × 14 (*comb*) (1 c. to 5 c., 10 c.) or 14 (*line*) (others).

117	57	1 c. yellow-green	..	6·00	30
		a. Blue-green (1915)	..	7·00	30
118	58	2 c. carmine	..	3·50	20
		a. Rose-red (blurred impression). Perf 14 (1916)		7·00	55
119	59	3 c. red-brown	..	19·00	27·00
120	60	4 c. purple	..	18·00	26·00
121	61	5 c. ultramarine	..	6·50	1·50
122	62	6 c. slate-grey	..	13·00	25·00
123	63	8 c. aniline blue..		50·00	75·00
		a. Greenish blue		60·00	90·00
124	64	9 c. violet-blue	..	16·00	40·00
125	65	10 c. deep green	..	28·00	40·00
126	66	12 c. plum	..	23·00	40·00
127	67	15 c. lake	..	18·00	45·00
117/27		*Set of 11*		£180	£275

The 2 c. rose-red, No. 118a is a poor war-time printing by Alexander & Sons.

Although No. 123 has a typical aniline appearance it is believed that the shade results from the thinning of non-aniline ink.

68 Reindeer

FIRST TRANS-ATLANTIC AIR POST April, 1919.

(**69**)

(Des J. H. Noonan. Recess D.L.R.)

1919 (2 Jan). *Newfoundland Contingent, 1914–1918.* P 14.

130	68	1 c. green (a) (b)..		3·50	20
131		2 c. scarlet (a) (b)	..	3·50	85
		a. Carmine-red (b)	..	9·50	45
132		3 c. brown (a) (b)	..	5·00	20
		a. Red-brown (b)	..	5·50	30
133		4 c. mauve (a)	..	5·00	60
		a. Purple (b)	..	9·50	30
134		5 c. ultramarine (a) (b)	..	5·50	1·25
135		6 c. slate-grey (a)	..	5·00	32·00
136		8 c. bright magenta (a)	..	9·00	40·00
137		10 c. deep grey-green (a)..		5·50	3·75
138		12 c. orange (a)	..	18·00	45·00
139		15 c. indigo (a)	..	15·00	55·00
		a. Prussian blue (a)	..	80·00	£140
140		24 c. bistre-brown (a)	..	22·00	28·00
141		36 c. sage-green (a)	..	13·00	25·00
130/41		*Set of 12*		£100	£200

Each value bears with "Trail of the Caribou" the name of a different action: 1 c. Suvla Bay; 3 c. Gueudecourt; 4 c. Beaumont Hamel; 6 c. Monchy; 10 c. Steenbeck; 15 c. Langemarck; 24 c. Cambrai; 36 c. Combles; 2 c., 5 c., 8 c., and 12 c. inscribed "Royal Naval Reserve-Ubique".

Perforations. Two perforating heads were used: (*a*) comb 14 × 13.9; (*b*) line 14.1 × 14.1.

1919 (12 Apr). *Air.* No. **132** optd with T **69**, by Robinson & Co Ltd, at the offices of the "Daily News".

142	68	3 c. brown	..	£15000	£8000

These stamps franked correspondence carried by Lieut. H. Hawker on his Atlantic flight. 18 were damaged and destroyed, 95 used on letters, 11 given as presentation copies, and the remaining 76 were sold in aid of the Marine Disasters Fund.

1919 (19 April). *Nos.* **132** *optd in MS.* "Aerial Atlantic Mail. J.A.R."

142a	68	3 c. brown	..	—	£20000

This provisional was made by W. C. Campbell, the Secretary of the Postal Department, and the initials are those of the Postmaster, J. A. Robinson, for use on correspondence intended to be carried on the abortive Morgan-Raynham Trans-Atlantic flight. The mail was eventually delivered by sea.

In addition to the 25 to 30 used examples, one unused, no gum, copy of No. 142a is known.

A single example of a similar overprint on the 2 c., No. 131, is known used on cover together with an unoverprinted example of the same value.

Trans-Atlantic AIR POST, 1919. ONE DOLLAR.

(**70**)

THREE CENTS

(**71**)

1919 (9 June). *Air.* No. **75** *surch with* T **70** *by Royal Gazette, St. Johns.*

143	31	$1 on 15 c. bright scarlet	..	£110	£110
		a. No comma after "AIR POST"		£140	£150
		b. As Var a and no stop after "1919"..		£350	£350
		c. As Var a and "A" of "AIR" under "a" of "Trans"		£350	£350

These stamps were issued for use on the mail carried on the first successful flight across the Atlantic by Capt. J. Alcock and Lieut. A. Brown, and on other projected Trans-Atlantic flights (Alcock flown cover, *Price* £3000).

The surcharge was applied in a setting of which 16 were normal, 7 as No. 143a, 1 as No. 143b and 1 as No. 143c.

1920 (Sept). *Nos. 75 and 77/8 surch as T **71**, by Royal Gazette* (2 c. with only one bar, at top of stamp).

A. *Bars of surch 10½ mm apart.* B. *Bars 13½ mm apart*

144	**33**	2 c. on 30 c. slate-blue (24 Sept)	3·50	16·00
		a. Surch inverted	£450	£475
145	**31**	3 c. on 15 c. bright scarlet (A) (13 Sept)	£150	£150
		a. Surch inverted		£950
146		3 c. on 15 c. bright scarlet (B) (13 Sept)	13·00	13·00
147	**34**	3 c. on 35 c. red (15 Sept)	6·00	10·00
		a. Surch inverted		£800
		b. Lower bar omitted	£120	£140
		c. "THREE" omitted		£1100

Our prices for Nos. 147b and 147c are for stamps with lower bar or "THREE" entirely missing. The bar may be found in all stages of incompleteness and stamps showing broken bar are not of much value.

On the other hand, stamps showing either only the top or bottom of the letters "THREE" are scarce, though not as rare as No. 147c.

The 6 c. T **27** surcharged "THREE CENTS", in red or black, is an essay (*Price £400*). The 2 c. on 30 c. with red surcharge is a colour trial (*Price £475*).

AIR MAIL
to Halifax, N.S.
1921.
(72)

1921 (16 Nov). *Air. No. 78 optd with T **72** by Royal Gazette.*

I. 2¾ *mm between "AIR" and "MAIL"*

148	**34**	35 c. red	90·00	90·00
		a. No stop after "1921"	80·00	80·00
		b. No stop and first "1" of "1921" below "f" of "Halifax"	£180	£180
		c. As No. 148, inverted	£4000	
		d. As No. 148a, inverted	£3750	
		e. As No. 148b, inverted	£8000	

II. 1½ *mm between "AIR" and "MAIL"*

148f	**34**	35 c. red	£100	£100
		g. No stop after "1921"	£120	£120
		h. No stop and first "1" of "1921" below "f" of "Halifax"	£180	£180
		i. As No. 148f, inverted	£4500	
		k. As No. 148g, inverted	£5500	
		l. As No. 148h, inverted	£8000	

Type **72** was applied as a setting of 25 which contained ten stamps as No. 148a, seven as No. 148, four as No. 148f, two as No. 148g, one as No. 148b and one as No. 148h.

73 Twin Hills, Tor's Cove

74 South-West Arm, Trinity

75 Statue of the Fighting Newfoundlander, St. John's

(Recess D.L.R.)

1923 (9 July)—**26**. *T **73/5** and similar designs. P 14 (comb or line).*

149		1 c. green	75	20
150		2 c. carmine	60	10
		a. Imperf (pair)	£160	
151		3 c. brown	70	10
152		4 c. deep purple	90	30
153		5 c. ultramarine	1·50	1·75
154		6 c. slate	2·75	7·50
155		8 c. purple	3·75	3·50
156		9 c. slate-green	17·00	28·00
157		10 c. violet	4·50	2·75
		a. Purple	5·50	2·75
158		11 c. sage-green	2·50	16·00
159		12 c. lake	2·75	9·00
160		15 c. Prussian blue	2·75	13·00
161		20 c. chestnut (28.4.24)	7·00	10·00
162		24 c. sepia (22.4.24)	45·00	75·00
149/62		Set of 14	80·00	£150

Designs: *Horiz (as T **73**)*—6 c. Upper Steadies, Humber River; 11 c. Shell Bird Island; 20 c. Placentia. (*As T **74**)*—8 c. Quidi Vidi, near St. John's; 9 c. Caribou crossing lake; 12 c. Mount Moriah, Bay of Islands. (*As T **75**)*—4 c. Humber River, 5 c. Coast at Trinity; 10 c. Humber River Canon; 15 c. Humber River near Little Rapids; 24 c. Topsail Falls.

Perforations. Three perforating heads were used: comb 13.8×14 (all values); line 13.7 and 14, and combinations of these two (for all except 6, 8, 9 and 11 c.).

Air Mail
DE PINEDO
1927
(87)

1927 (18 May). *Air. No. 79 optd with T **87**, by Robinson & Co, Ltd.*

163	**35**	60 c. black (R.)	£24000 £7500

For the mail carried by De Pinedo to Europe 300 stamps were overprinted, 230 used on correspondence, 66 presented to De Pinedo, Government Officials, etc., and 4 damaged and destroyed. Stamps without overprint were also used.

NEW INFORMATION

The editor is always interested to correspond with people who have new information that will improve or correct the Catalogue.

---

88 Newfoundland and Labrador

89 S.S. *Caribou*

90 King George V and Queen Mary

91 Duke of Windsor when Prince of Wales

92 Express Train

93 Newfoundland Hotel, St. John's

94 Heart's Content

95 Cabot Tower, St. John's

96 War Memorial, St. John's

97 G.P.O., St. John's

98 Vickers "Vimy" Aircraft

99 Parliament House, St. John's

100 Grand Falls, Labrador

(Recess D.L.R.)

1928 (3 Jan)—**29**. *Publicity issue. P 14 (1 c.), 13½×13 (2, 3, 5, 6, 10, 20 c.), 13×13½ (4 c.) (all comb), or 14—13½* (line) (others).*

164	**88**	1 c. deep green	2·25	1·25
165	**89**	2 c. carmine	3·00	40
166	**90**	3 c. brown	3·50	1·25
		a. Perf 14—13½ (line)	2·25	1·25
167	**91**	4 c. mauve	6·50	2·50
		a. Rose-purple (1929)	6·50	6·50
168	**92**	5 c. slate-grey	13·00	4·50
		a. Perf 14—13½ (line)	23·00	5·50
169	**93**	6 c. ultramarine	2·50	18·00
		a. Perf 14—13½ (line)	6·00	18·00
170	**94**	8 c. red-brown	2·50	24·00
171	**95**	9 c. deep green	2·00	11·00
172	**96**	10 c. deep violet	11·00	12·00
		a. Perf 14—13½ (line)	6·00	14·00
173	**97**	12 c. carmine-lake	2·00	18·00
174	**95**	14 c. brown-purple	10·00	11·00
		a. Perf 14—13½ (line)	5·00	8·00
175	**98**	15 c. deep blue	3·00	27·00
176	**99**	20 c. grey-black	10·00	11·00
		a. Perf 14—13½ (line)	2·50	6·50
177	**97**	28 c. deep green	28·00	48·00
178	**100**	30 c. sepia	6·00	16·00
164/78 (cheapest)		Set of 15	75·00	£180

*Exact gauges for the various perforations are: 14 comb = 14×13.9; 13½×13 comb = 13.5×12.75; 14—13½ line = 14—13.75.

See also Nos. 179/87 and 198/208.

D 1 c. P

D 2 c. P

D 3 c. P   D 4 c. P

D 5 c. P

D 6 c. P   D 10 c. P

D 15 c. P

D 20 c. P

D. De La Rue printing

P. Perkins, Bacon printing

1929 (10 Aug)—**31**. *Perkins, Bacon printing. Former types re-engraved. No wmk. P 14 (comb) (1 c.), 13½ (comb) (2, 6 c.), 14—13½ (line) (20 c.) or 13½×14 (comb) (others)*.*

179	**88**	1 c. green (26.9.29)	3·50	30
		a. Perf 14—13½ (line)	3·50	30
		b. Imperf between (vert pair)	£130	
		c. Imperf (pair)	£110	
180	**89**	2 c. scarlet	1·50	40
		a. Imperf (pair)	95·00	
		b. Perf 14—13½ (line)	3·00	90
181	**90**	3 c. red-brown	1·00	20
		a. Imperf (pair)	95·00	
182	**91**	4 c. reddish purple (26.8.29)	2·75	80
		a. Imperf (pair)	£110	
183	**92**	5 c. deep grey-green (14.9.29)	5·50	2·00
184	**93**	6 c. ultramarine (8.11.29)	6·50	12·00
		a. Perf 14—13½ (line)	2·25	12·00
185	**96**	10 c. violet (5.10.29)	4·00	3·00
186	**98**	15 c. blue (1.30)	17·00	80·00
187	**99**	20 c. black (1.1.31)	48·00	42·00
179/87		Set of 9	75·00	£130

*Exact gauges for the various perforations are: 14 comb = 14×13.9; 13½ comb = 13.6×13.5; 14—13½ line = 14—13.75; 13½×14 comb = 13.6×13.8.

Trans-Atlantic
AIR MAIL
By B. M.
"Columbia"
September
1930

THREE CENTS	Fifty Cents
(101)	(102)

(Surch by Messrs D. R. Thistle, St. John's)

1929 (23 Aug). *No. 154 surch with T **101**.*

188		3 c. on 6 c. slate (R.)	1·00	4·25
		a. Surch inverted	£600	£900
		b. Surch in black	£700	

1930 (25 Sept). *Air. No. 141 surch with T **102** by Messrs D. R. Thistle.*

191	**68**	50 c. on 36 c. sage-green	£4500 £4250

103 Aeroplane and Dog-team

104 Vickers-Vimy Biplane and early Sailing Packet

105 Routes of historic Transatlantic Flights

106

(Des A. B. Perlin. Recess P.B.)

1931. *Air.* P 14. (a) *Without wmk* (2.1.31)

192	103	15 c. chocolate	4·50	11·00
		a. Imperf between (horiz or vert pair) £600		
		b. Imperf (pair)	£375	
193	104	50 c. green	30·00	45·00
		a. Imperf between (horiz or vert pair) £650		£500
		b. Imperf (pair)	£500	
194	105	$1 deep blue	48·00	85·00
		a. Imperf between (horiz or vert pair) £600		
		b. Imperf (pair)	£500	
192/4		*Set of 3*	75·00	£130

(b) *Wmk* W **106**, *(sideways)* (13.3.31)

195	103	15 c. chocolate	5·50	16·00
		a. Pair, with and without wmk	30·00	
		b. Imperf between (horiz or vert pair) £550		
		ba. Ditto, one without wmk (vert pair) £800		
		c. Imperf (pair)	£375	
		d. Wmk Cross (pair)	85·00	
196	104	50 c. green	26·00	60·00
		a. Imperf between (horiz or vert pair) £600		
		c. Pair, with and without wmk	£170	
197	105	$1 deep blue	75·00	£130
		a. Imperf between (horiz or vert pair) £600		
		b. Imperf horiz (vert pair)	£475	
		c. Pair, with and without wmk	£300	
		d. Imperf (pair)	£400	
195/7		*Set of 3*	95·00	£180

"WITH AND WITHOUT WMK" PAIRS listed in the issues from No. 195a onwards must have one stamp *completely* without any trace of watermark.

1931 (25 March–July). *Perkins, Bacon printing (re-engraved types).* W **106** (sideways on 1 c., 4 c., 30 c.). P 13½ (1 c.) or 13½×14 (others), both comb*.

198	88	1 c. green (7.31)	6·00	3·00
		a. Imperf between (horiz pair)	£500	
199	89	2 c. scarlet (7.31)	6·00	3·25
		w. Wmk inverted	40·00	
200	90	3 c. red-brown (7.31)	2·00	1·50
		w. Wmk inverted	40·00	
201	91	4 c. reddish purple (7.31)	2·00	80
202	92	5 c. deep grey-green (7.31)	7·00	9·00
203	93	6 c. ultramarine	10·00	22·00
204	94	8 c. chestnut (1.4.31)	23·00	27·00
		w. Wmk inverted	55·00	
205	96	10 c. violet (1.4.31)	10·00	9·00
206	98	15 c. blue (1.7.31)	21·00	48·00
207	99	20 c. black (1.7.31)	55·00	14·00
208	100	30 c. sepia (1.7.31)	28·00	42·00
198/208		*Set of 11*	£150	£160

*Exact gauges for the two perforations are: 13½ = 13.6×13.5; 13½×14 = 13.6×13.8.

107 Atlantic Cod

108 King George V

109 Queen Mary

110 Duke of Windsor when Prince of Wales

111 Caribou

112 Queen Elizabeth II when Princess

113 Atlantic Salmon

114 Newfoundland Dog

115 Harp Seal

116 Cape Race

117 Sealing Fleet

118 Fishing Fleet

(Recess P.B.)

1932 (2 Jan). W **106** *(sideways* on vert designs). P 13½ *(comb).*

209	107	1 c. green	2·25	30
		a. Imperf (pair)	£100	
		b. Perf 13 (line)	15·00	25·00
		ba. Imperf between (vert pair) £110		
		w. Wmk top of shield to right	40·00	
210	108	2 c. carmine	1·50	20
		a. Imperf (pair)	£100	
		c. Perf 13 (line)	10·00	20·00
		w. Wmk top of shield to right	40·00	
211	109	3 c. orange-brown	1·50	20
		a. Imperf (pair)	£75·00	
		c. Perf 13 (line)	15·00	26·00
		d. Perf 14 (line). Small holes	18·00	22·00
		da. Imperf between (vert pair) £140		
		w. Wmk top of shield to right	40·00	
212	110	4 c. bright violet	5·50	2·00
		w. Wmk top of shield to right		
213	111	5 c. maroon	3·00	1·25
		a. Imperf (pair)	£150	
		w. Wmk top of shield to right		
214	112	6 c. light blue	4·00	13·00
215	113	10 c. black-brown	70	65
		a. Imperf (pair)	£70·00	
		w. Wmk inverted	10·00	
216	114	14 c. black	3·75	4·50
		a. Imperf (pair)	£120	
217	115	15 c. claret	1·25	2·00
		a. Imperf (pair)	£130	
		b. Perf 14 (line)	8·00	10·00
218	116	20 c. green	1·00	90
		a. Imperf (pair)	£120	
		b. Perf 14 (line)	60·00	55·00
		w. Wmk inverted	20·00	
219	117	25 c. slate	2·00	2·25
		a. Imperf (pair)	£130	
		b. Perf 14 (line)	30·00	45·00
		ba. Imperf between (vert pair) £275		
220	118	30 c. ultramarine	28·00	28·00
		a. Imperf (pair)	£325	
		b. Imperf between (vert pair) £600		
		c. Perf 14 (line)	£225	
209/20		*Set of 12*	48·00	48·00

*The normal sideways watermark shows the top of the shield to left, *as seen from the back of the stamp*.

Nos. 209b, 210c and 211c were only issued in stamp booklets. For similar stamps in different perforations see Nos. 222/8c and 276/89.

**TRANS-ATLANTIC
WEST TO EAST
Per Dornier DO-X
May, 1932.
One Dollar and Fifty Cents**

(119)

1932 (19 May). *Air. No.* 197 *surch as* T **119**, *by Messrs. D. R. Thistle.* P 14.

221	105	$1.50 on $1 deep blue (R.)	£180	£225
		a. Surch inverted	£10000	

120 Queen Mother, when Duchess of York

121 Corner Brook Paper Mills

122 Loading Iron Ore, Bell Island

(Recess P.B.)

1932 (15 Aug)–38. W **106** *(sideways* on vert designs). P 13½ *(comb).*

222	107	1 c. grey	90	10
		a. Imperf (pair)	40·00	
		c. Perf 14 (line)	6·00	9·00
		d. Perf 14 (line). Small holes	15·00	24·00
		e. Pair, with and without wmk	40·00	
		w. Wmk top of shield to right	50·00	

223	108	2 c. green	40	10
		a. Imperf (pair)	35·00	
		c. Perf 14 (line)	7·00	9·00
		ca. Imperf between (horiz pair) £250		
		d. Perf 14 (line). Small holes	18·00	24·00
		e. Pair, with and without wmk	42·00	
		w. Wmk top of shield to right	35·00	
224	110	4 c. carmine (21.7.34)	1·75	40
		a. Imperf (pair)	50·00	
		b. Perf 14 (line)	3·25	4·75
		ba. Imperf between (horiz or vert pair) £120		
		w. Wmk top of shield to right	50·00	
225	111	5 c. violet (Die I)	2·00	1·75
		a. Imperf (pair)	55·00	
		b. Perf 14 (line). Small holes	24·00	22·00
		c. Die II	70	30
		ca. Imperf (pair)	60·00	
		cb. Perf 14 (line)	22·00	19·00
		cbw. Wmk top of shield to right	£190	
		cc. Imperf between (horiz pair) £190		
		cd. Pair, with and without wmk	£120	
226	120	7 c. red-brown	2·75	3·25
		b. Perf 14 (line)	£130	
		ba. Imperf between (horiz pair) £450		
		c. Imperf (pair)	£140	
		w. Wmk top of shield to right		
227	121	8 c. brownish red	3·00	2·00
		a. Imperf (pair)	85·00	
		w. Wmk inverted		
228	122	24 c. bright blue	85	3·00
		a. Imperf (pair)	£180	
		b. Doubly printed	£750	
		w. Wmk inverted	25·00	
228c	118	48 c. red-brown (1.1.38)	5·00	10·00
		ca. Imperf (pair)	85·00	
222/8c		*Set of 8*	13·50	17·00

*The normal sideways watermark shows the top of the shield to left, *as seen from the back of the stamp*.

No. 223. Two dies exist of the 2 c. Die I was used for No. 210 and both dies for No. 223. The differences, though numerous, are very slight.

No. 225. There are also two dies of the 5 c., Die I only being used for No. 213 and both dies for the violet stamp. In Die II the antler pointing to the "T" of "POSTAGE" is taller than the one pointing to the "S" and the individual hairs on the underside of the caribou's tail are distinct.

For similar stamps in a slightly larger size and perforated 12½ or 13½ (5 c.) see Nos. 276/89.

(123) "L.&S."—Land and Sea

1933 (9 Feb). *No.* 195 *optd with* T **123** *for ordinary postal use, by Messrs D. R. Thistle.* W **106** *(sideways).* P 14.

229	103	15 c. chocolate	3·25	9·00
		a. Pair, one without wmk	23·00	
		b. Opt reading up	£1600	
		c. Vertical pair, one without surch	£2500	

124 Put to Flight

125 Land of Heart's Delight

(Des J. Scott. Recess P.B.)

1933 (31 May). *Air.* T **124/5** *and similar horiz designs.* W **106** *(sideways).* P 14 (5, 30, 75 c.) or 11½ (10, 60 c.).

230		5 c. red-brown	14·00	16·00
		a. Imperf (pair)	£160	
		b. Imperf between (horiz or vert pair) £900		
231		10 c. orange-yellow	10·00	26·00
		a. Imperf (pair)	£130	
232		30 c. light blue	28·00	40·00
		a. Imperf (pair)	£375	
233		60 c. green	45·00	80·00
		a. Imperf (pair)	£425	
234		75 c. yellow-brown	45·00	75·00
		a. Imperf (pair)	£375	
		b. Imperf between (horiz or vert pair) £1600		
230/4		*Set of 5*	£120	£200

Designs:—30 c. Spotting the herd; 60 c. News from home; 75 c. Labrador.

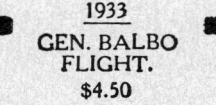

**1933
GEN. BALBO
FLIGHT.
$4.50**

(129)

(Surch by Robinson & Co, St. John's)

1933 (24 July). *Air. Balbo Transatlantic Mass Formation Flight. No.* 234 *surch with* T **129**. W **106**. P 14.

235		$4.50 on 75 c. yellow-brown	£250	£300
		a. Surch inverted	£30000	
		b. Surch on 10 c. (No. 231)	£30000	

No. 235a. When this error was discovered the stamps were ordered to be officially destroyed but four copies which had been torn were recovered and skilfully repaired. In addition four undamaged examples exist and the price quoted is for one of these.

130 Sir Humphrey Gilbert

131 Compton Castle, Devon

132 Gilbert Coat of Arms

(Recess P.B.)

1933 (3 Aug). *350th Anniv of the Annexation by Sir Humphrey Gilbert. T* **130/2** *and similar designs.* W **106** *(sideways* on vert designs).* P 13½ *(comb†).*

236	1 c. slate	..	..	70	1·25
	a. Imperf (pair)	..	..	45·00	
237	2 c. green	..	..	1·00	60
	a. Imperf (pair)	..	..	48·00	
	b. Doubly printed	..	..	£300	
238	3 c. chestnut	..	..	2·00	1·25
239	4 c. carmine	..	..	80	50
	a. Imperf (pair)	..	..	45·00	
240	5 c. violet	..	..	2·00	80
241	7 c. greenish blue	..	..	12·00	16·00
	a. Perf 14 (line)	..	..	10·00	35·00
242	8 c. vermilion	..	..	7·00	12·00
	a. *Brownish red*	..	..	£275	
	b. Bisected (4 c.) (on cover)	..	†	£375	
243	9 c. ultramarine	..	..	7·00	10·00
	a. Imperf (pair)	..	..	£200	
	b. Perf 14 (line)	..	..	42·00	50·00
244	10 c. brown-lake	..	..	4·00	7·50
	a. Imperf (pair)	..	..	£275	
	b. Perf 14 (line)	..	..	55·00	60·00
245	14 c. grey-black	..	..	12·00	30·00
	a. Perf 14 (line)	..	..	17·00	48·00
246	15 c. claret	..	..	10·00	
	w. Wmk top of shield to right	..	7·50	15·00	
247	20 c. grey-green	..	..	13·00	16·00
	a. Perf 14 (line)	..	..	20·00	32·00
	w. Wmk inverted	..	..	40·00	
248	24 c. maroon	..	..	13·00	22·00
	a. Imperf (pair)	..	..	£100	
	b. Perf 14 (line)	..	..	22·00	35·00
	w. Wmk top of shield to right	..	35·00		
249	32 c. olive-black	..	..	7·00	45·00
	a. Perf 14 (line)	..	..	22·00	60·00
	w. Wmk top of shield to right	..	20·00		
236/49			*Set of 14*	65·00	£160

Designs: *Horiz*—4 c. Eton College; 7 c. Gilbert commissioned by Elizabeth I; 8 c. Fleet leaving Plymouth, 1583; 9 c. Arrival at St. John's; 10 c. Annexation, 5 August 1583; 20 c. Map of Newfoundland, 1626. *Vert*—5 c. Anchor design; 14 c. Royal Arms; 15 c. Gilbert in the *Squirrel*; 24 c. Queen Elizabeth I. 32 c. Gilbert's statue at Truro.

*The normal sideways watermark shows the top of the shield to left, *as seen from the back of the stamp.*

†Exact gauges for the two perforations are: 13½ comb = 13.4; 14 line = 13.8.

1935 (6 May). *Silver Jubilee. As Nos.* 91/4 *of Antigua, but ptd by B.W.* P 11 × 12.

250	4 c. rosine	..	..	1·00	1·75
251	5 c. bright violet	..	..	1·25	1·75
252	7 c. blue	..	..	1·50	6·50
253	24 c. olive-green	..	..	5·00	7·50
250/3			*Set of 4*	8·00	16·00
250/3 Perf "Specimen"			*Set of 4*	£120	

1937 (12 May). *Coronation Issue. As Nos.* 95/7 *of Antigua, but name and value uncoloured on coloured background.* P 11×11½.

254	2 c. green	..	..	1·00	2·25
255	4 c. carmine	..	..	1·60	2·75
256	5 c. purple	..	..	3·00	2·75
254/6			*Set of 3*	5·00	7·00
254/6 Perf "Specimen"			*Set of 3*	75·00	

144 Atlantic Cod

Die I

Die II

No. 258. In Die II the shading of the King's face is heavier and dots have been added down the ridge of the nose. The top frame line is thicker and more uniform.

NEW INFORMATION

The editor is always interested to correspond with people who have new information that will improve or correct the Catalogue.

Fish-hook flaw (R. 1/7 or 3/3)

Re-entry to right of design (inscr oval, tree and value) (R.4/8)

Extra chimney (R. 6/5)

(Recess P.B.)

1937 (12 May). *Additional Coronation Issue. T* **144** *and similar horiz designs.* W **106**. P 14–13½ *(line)*.*

257	1 c. grey	..	2·25	20
	a. Pair, with and without wmk	..	22·00	
	b. Fish-hook flaw	..	21·00	
	c. Perf 13 (comb)	..	23·00	45·00
	ca. Pair, with and without wmk	..		
	cb. Fish-hook flaw	..	£170	
258	3 c. orange-brown (I)	..	6·00	3·00
	a. Pair, with and without wmk	..	55·00	
	b. Imperf between (horiz or vert pair)	..	£350	
	c. Perf 13 (comb)	..	4·25	3·00
	d. Die II	..	3·50	3·00
	da. Pair, with and without wmk	..	85·00	
	db. Imperf between (horiz or vert pair)	..	£450	
	dc. Perf 13 (comb)	..	5·00	2·50
	dca. Pair, with and without wmk	..	90·00	
259	7 c. bright ultramarine	..	2·25	90
	a. Pair, with and without wmk	..	45·00	
	b. Re-entry at right	..		
	c. Perf 13 (comb)	..	£275	£350
	cb. Re-entry at right	..	£1200	
260	8 c. scarlet	..	1·75	2·50
	a. Pair, with and without wmk	..	55·00	
	b. Imperf between (horiz or vert pair)	..	£550	
	c. Imperf (pair)	..	£275	
	d. Perf 13 (comb)	..	6·50	8·50
261	10 c. blackish brown	..	3·75	7·00
	a. Pair, with and without wmk	..	60·00	
	b. Perf 13 (comb)	..	3·25	9·50
	bw. Wmk inverted	..	75·00	
262	14 c. black	..	1·40	2·00
	a. Pair, with and without wmk	..	50·00	
	b. Perf 13 (comb)	..	£4750	£2750
263	15 c. claret	..	9·00	4·00
	a. Pair, with and without wmk	..	60·00	
	b. Imperf between (vert pair)	..	£375	
	cw. Wmk inverted	..	75·00	
	d. Perf 13 (comb)	..	17·00	19·00
	da. Pair, with and without wmk	..	95·00	
264	20 c. green	..	2·25	6·00
	a. Pair, with and without wmk	..	£120	
	b. Imperf between (vert pair)	..	£600	
	c. Extra chimney	..	40·00	
	dw. Wmk inverted	..	85·00	
	e. Perf 13 (comb)	..	2·50	7·00
	ec. Extra chimney	..	42·00	
265	24 c. light blue	..	2·25	2·50
	a. Pair, with and without wmk	..	£120	
	b. Imperf between (vert pair)	..	£600	
	c. Perf 13 (comb)	..	20·00	21·00
266	25 c. slate	..	2·75	1·75
	a. Pair, with and without wmk	..	£110	
	b. Perf 13 (comb)	..	22·00	42·00
267	48 c. slate-purple	..	8·50	4·50
	a. Pair, with and without wmk	..	£150	
	b. Imperf between (vert pair)	..	£600	
	c. Perf 13 (comb)	..	29·00	55·00
257/67		*Set of 11*	32·00	30·00

Designs:—3 c. Map of Newfoundland; 7 c. Reindeer; 8 c. Corner Brook paper mills; 10 c. Atlantic Salmon; 14 c. Newfoundland dog; 15 c. Harp Seal; 20 c. Cape Race; 24 c. Bell Island; 25 c. Sealing fleet; 48 c. The Banks fishing fleet.

*The line perforation was produced by two machines measuring respectively 13.7 and 14.1. The comb perforation measures 13.3×13.2.

Four used examples of No. 259c have now been identified on separate covers.

The paper used had the watermarks spaced for smaller format stamps. In consequence the individual watermarks are out of alignment so that stamps from the second vertical row were sometimes without watermark.

---

155 King George VI

156 Queen Mother

Damaged "A" (R. 5/9)

(Recess P.B.)

1938 (12 May). *T* **155/6** *and similar vert designs.* W **106** *(sideways).* P 13½ *(comb).*

268	2 c. green	..	1·50	60
	a. Pair, with and without wmk	..	£130	
	b. Imperf (pair)	..	75·00	
269	3 c. carmine	..	1·00	70
	a. Perf 14 (line)	..	£375	£225
	b. Pair, with and without wmk	..	£180	
	c. Imperf (pair)	..	75·00	
	d. Damaged "A"	..	38·00	
270	4 c. light blue	..	1·75	20
	a. Pair, with and without wmk	..	85·00	
	b. Imperf (pair)	..	70·00	
	w. Wmk inverted	..	65·00	
271	7 c. deep ultramarine	..	75	3·75
	a. Imperf (pair)	..	£100	
268/71		*Set of 4*	4·50	4·75

Designs:— 4 c. Queen Elizabeth II as princess; 7 c. Queen Mary. For similar designs, perf 12½, see Nos. 277/281.

159 King George VI and Queen Elizabeth

(Recess B.W.)

1939 (17 June). *Royal Visit. No wmk.* P 13½.

272	159	5 c. deep ultramarine	2·00	40

2

▲ **CENTS** ▲

(160)

1939 (20 Nov). *No.* 272 *surch as T* **160**, *at St. John's.*

273	159	2 c. on 5 c. deep ultramarine (Br.)	2·00	30
274		4 c. on 5 c. deep ultramarine (C.)	1·25	60

161 Grenfell on the *Strathcona* (after painting by Gribble)

162 Memorial University College

(Recess C.B.N.)

1941 (1 Dec). *50th Anniv of Sir Wilfred Grenfell's Labrador Mission.* P 12.

275	161	5 c. blue	30	55

(Recess Waterlow)

1941–44. W **106** *(sideways* on vert designs).* P 12½ *(line).*

276	107	1 c. grey	20	30
277	155	2 c. green	30	20
		w. Wmk top of shield to right	35·00	
278	156	3 c. carmine	30	10
		a. Pair, with and without wmk	75·00	
		w. Wmk top of shield to right	35·00	
279	–	4 c. blue (As No. 270)	2·25	20
		a. Pair, with and without wmk	£140	
		w. Wmk top of shield to right	35·00	
280	111	5 c. violet (Die I) (p 13½ comb)	90·00	
		a. Perf 12½ (line) (6.42)	2·75	30
		ab. Pair, with and without wmk	£120	
		ac. Printed double	£300	
		ad. Imperf vert (horiz pair)	£325	
		b. Imperf (pair)	£120	
281	–	7 c. deep ultramarine (As No. 271)	6·00	9·50
		a. Pair, with and without wmk	£150	
282	121	8 c. rose-red	1·50	1·75
		a. Pair, with and without wmk	£140	
283	113	10 c. black-brown	1·75	1·00
284	114	14 c. black	3·00	5·00
285	115	15 c. claret	5·50	7·50
286	116	20 c. green	5·50	5·50
287	122	24 c. blue	3·25	12·00
		w. Wmk top of shield to right	55·00	

288	117	25 c. slate	6·50	7·50
289	118	48 c. red-brown (1944)	3·00	5·50
276/89		*Set of 14*	35·00	50·00

*The normal sideways watermark shows the top of the shield to left, *as seen from the back of the stamp.*

Nos. 276/89 are redrawn versions of previous designs with slightly larger dimensions; the 5 c. for example, measures 21 mm in width as opposed to the 20.4 mm of the Perkins Bacon printings.

No. 280. For Die I see note relating to No. 225.

(Recess C.B.N.)

1943 (1 Jan). *P* 12.

290	162	30 c. carmine	1·00	1·60

TWO
CENTS

163 St. John's (164)

(Recess C.B.N.)

1943 (1 June). *Air. P* 12.

291	163	7 c. ultramarine	40	65

1946 (21 Mar). *No.* 290 *surch locally with T* **164**.

292	162	2 c. on 30 c. carmine	30	75

165 Queen Elizabeth II **166** Cabot off Cape Bonavista
when Princess

(Recess Waterlow)

1947 (21 Apr). *Princess Elizabeth's 21st Birthday. W* **106** *(sideways). P* 12½.

293	165	4 c. light blue	30	75
		a. Imperf vert (horiz pair)	£275	

(Recess Waterlow)

1947 (24 June). *450th Anniv of Cabot's Discovery of Newfoundland. W* **106** *(sideways). P* 12½.

294	166	5 c. mauve	20	80
		a. Imperf between (horiz pair)	£1200	

STAMP BOOKLETS

1926. *Black on pink cover with Ayre and Sons advertisement on front. Stapled.*

SB1 40 c. booklet containing eight 1 c. and sixteen 2 c. (Nos. 149/50) in blocks of 8 .. £1200

B 1

1932 (2 Jan). *Black on buff cover as Type B* **1**. *Stapled.*

SB2 40 c. booklet containing four 1 c., twelve 2 c. and four 3 c. (Nos. 209b, 210c, 211c) in blocks of 4 £350
a. Contents as No. SB2, but containing Nos. 209b, 210 and 211c .. £425
b. Contents as No. SB2, but containing Nos. 222d, 223d and 211d .. £400

B 2

1932. *Black on cream cover as Type B* **2**. *Stapled.*

SB3 40 c. booklet containing four 1 c., twelve 2 c. and four 3 c. (Nos. 222, 223, 211) in blocks of 4 £350

POSTAGE DUE STAMPS

D 1 D 6ac

(Litho John Dickinson & Co, Ltd)

1939 (1 May)—49. *P* 10.

D1	D 1	1 c. green	2·25	8·50
		a. Perf 11 (1949)	3·25	10·00
D2		2 c. vermilion	13·00	7·50
		a. Perf 11 × 9 (1946)	13·00	19·00
D3		3 c. ultramarine	5·00	19·00
		a. Perf 11 × 9 (1949)	11·00	30·00
		b. Perf 9	£500	
D4		4 c. orange	9·00	17·00
		a. Perf 11 × 9 (May 1948)	12·00	45·00
D5		5 c. brown	5·50	24·00
D6		10 c. violet	6·00	17·00
		a. Perf 11 (W 106) (1949)	22·00	75·00
		ab. Ditto. Imperf between (vert pair)	£650	
		ac. "POSTAGE LUE" (R 3/3 or 3/8)	£100	£275
D1/6		*Set of* 6	38·00	85·00

Newfoundland joined the Dominion of Canada on 31 March 1949.

NOVA SCOTIA

Organised postal services in Nova Scotia date from April 1754 when the first of a series of Deputy Postmasters was appointed, under the authority of the British G.P.O. This arrangement continued until 6 July 1851 when the colony assumed responsibility for its postal affairs.

For illustrations of the handstamp types see BRITISH POST OFFICES ABROAD notes, following GREAT BRITAIN.

AMHERST

CROWNED-CIRCLE HANDSTAMPS

CC1 CC 1 AMHERST. N.S.(R) (25.2.1845)
Price on cover £1000

ST. MARGARETS BAY

CROWNED-CIRCLE HANDSTAMPS

CC2 CC 1 ST. MARGARETS BAY. N.S.(R) (30.6.1845)
Price on cover £9000
Nos. CC1/2 were later used during temporary shortages of stamps, struck in red or black.

PRICES FOR STAMPS ON COVER		
No. 1	*from* × 5	
Nos. 2/4	*from* × 2	
Nos. 5/8	*from* × 4	
Nos. 9/10	*from* × 10	
Nos. 11/13	*from* × 2	
Nos. 14/15	—	
No. 16	*from* × 4	
Nos. 17/19	*from* × 10	
Nos. 20/5	*from* × 2	
No. 26	*from* × 50	
Nos. 27/8	*from* × 4	
No. 29	*from* × 10	

1 2

Crown and Heraldic Flowers of United Kingdom and Mayflower of Nova Scotia.

(Recess P.B.)

1851 (1 Sept)—57. *Bluish paper. Imperf.*

1	1	1d. red-brown (12.5.53)	£2000	£400
		a. Bisected (½d.) (on cover)	† £50000	
2	2	3d. deep blue	£1000	£160
		a. Bisected (1½d.) (on cover)	† £2250	
3		3d. bright blue	£900	£110
		a. Bisected (1½d.) (on cover)	† £2250	
4		3d. pale blue (1857)	£750	£130
		a. Bisected (1½d.) (on cover)	† £2250	
5		6d. yellow-green	£4000	£400
		a. Bisected (3d.) (on cover)	† £3000	
6		6d. deep green (1857)	£10000	£750
		a. Bisected (3d.) (on cover)	† £5000	
		b. Quartered (1½d.) (on cover)	† £38000	

7	2	1s. cold violet	£19000	£5000
		a. Bisected (6d.) (on cover)	† £42000	
		b. Quartered (3d.) (on cover)	† £55000	
7c		1s. deep purple (1851)	£15000	£3750
		d. Watermarked	£20000	£5000
8		1s. purple (1857)	£14000	£2500
		a. Bisected (6d.) (on cover)	† £32000	

The watermark on No. 7d consists of the whole or part of a letter from the name "P. H. SAUNDERS" (the papermakers).

The stamps formerly catalogued on almost white paper are probably some from which the bluish paper has been discharged.

Reprints of all four values were made in 1890 on thin, hard, white paper. The 1d. is brown, the 3d. blue, the 6d. deep green, and the 1s. violet-black.

The 3d. bisects are usually found used on cover to make up the 7½d. rate.

(New Currency. 100 cents = 1 dollar)

3 4 5

(Recess American Bank Note Co, New York)

1860—63. *P* 12. (a) *Yellowish paper.*

9	3	1 c. jet black	3·25	12·00
		a. Bisected (½ c.) (on cover)	† £10000	
10		1 c. grey-black	3·25	12·00
11		2 c. grey-purple	11·00	15·00
11a		2 c. purple	17·00	14·00
12		5 c. blue	£300	16·00
13		5 c. deep blue	£300	16·00
14	4	8½ c. deep green	2·50	
15		8½ c. yellow-green	2·50	
16		10 c. scarlet	12·00	23·00
17	5	12½ c. black	26·00	26·00
17a		12½ c. greyish black	—	26·00

(b) *White paper*

18	3	1 c. black	3·00	12·00
		a. Imperf vert (horiz pair)	£150	
19		1 c. grey	3·00	12·00
20		2 c. dull purple	3·25	14·00
21		2 c. purple	3·25	14·00
22		2 c. grey-purple	3·25	14·00
		a. Bisected (1 c.) (on cover)	† £4500	
23		2 c. slate-purple	3·25	12·00
24		5 c. blue	£325	16·00
25		5 c. deep blue	£325	16·00
26	4	8½ c. deep green	17·00	40·00
27		10 c. scarlet	4·00	20·00
28		10 c. vermilion	4·00	20·00
		a. Bisected (5 c.) (on cover)	† £750	
29	5	12½ c. black	38·00	30·00

Nova Scotia joined the Dominion of Canada on 1 July 1867.

PRINCE EDWARD ISLAND

Prince Edward Island, previously administered as part of Nova Scotia, became a separate colony in 1769.

PRICES FOR STAMPS ON COVER		
Nos. 1/4	*from* × 3	
Nos. 5/6	—	
Nos. 7/8	*from* × 5	
Nos. 9/20	*from* × 6	
Nos. 21/6	*from* × 3	
Nos. 27/31	*from* × 6	
Nos. 32/3	*from* × 50	
Nos. 34/7	*from* × 6	
Nos. 38/41	*from* × 20	
No. 42	*from* × 50	
Nos. 43/7	*from* × 5	

1 2 3

4 5 6

Two Dies of 2d:
Die I. Left-hand frame and circle merge at centre left (all stamps in the sheet of 60 (10×6) except R. 2/5.)
Die II. Left-hand frame and circle separate at centre left (R. 2/5). There is also a break in the top frame line.

(Typo Charles Whiting, London)

1861 (1 Jan). *Yellowish toned paper.* (a) *P* 9.

1	1	2d. rose (I)	£250	£120
		a. Imperf between (horiz pair)	£4250	
		b. Imperf horiz (vert pair)		
		c. Bisected (1d.) (on cover)	† £2750	
		d. Die II		

2	1	2d. rose-carmine (I)	£275	£130
		a. Die II	£500	£225
3	2	3d. blue	£500	£225
		a. Bisected (1½d.) (on cover)	†	£2750
		b. Double print	£1400	
4	3	6d. yellow-green	£750	£350

(b) Rouletted

5	1	2d. rose (I)	£2750	£2000

The 2d. and 3d., perf 9, were authorised to be bisected and used for half their normal value.

1862. *Yellowish toned paper. P 11.*

6	4	1d. brown-orange	30.00	55.00
7	6	9d. bluish lilac (29.3.62) ..	65.00	50.00
8		9d. dull mauve	65.00	50.00

1863–68. *Yellowish toned paper. (a) P 11½–12*

9	4	1d. yellow-orange	24.00	30.00
		a. Bisected (½d.) (on cover) ..	†	£1700
		b. Imperf between (horiz pair) ..	£275	
10		1d. orange-buff	25.00	30.00
11		1d. yellow	26.00	30.00
12	1	2d. rose (I)	8.50	9.00
		a. Imperf vert (horiz pair) ..		
		b. Bisected (1d.) (on cover)	†	£1500
		c. Die II	75.00	80.00
13		2d. deep rose (I)	9.00	12.00
		a. Die II	80.00	90.00
14	2	3d. blue	15.00	16.00
		a. Imperf horiz (vert pair) ..		
		b. Bisected (1½d.) (on cover) ..		
15		3d. deep blue	15.00	15.00
16	5	4d. black (1867)	15.00	21.00
		a. Imperf vert (horiz pair) ..	£200	
		b. Bisected (2d.) (on cover) ..	†	£1500
		c. Imperf between (horiz strip of 3)	£300	
17	3	6d. yellow-green (15.12.66) ..	80.00	70.00
		a. Bisected (3d.) (on cover) ..	†	£2500
18		6d. blue-green (1868) ..	70.00	75.00
19	6	9d. lilac	55.00	55.00
20		9d. reddish mauve	55.00	55.00
		a. Imperf vert (horiz pair) ..	£375	
		b. Bisected (4½d.) (on cover) ..	†	£2000

(b) Perf compound of 11 and 11½–12

21	4	1d. yellow-orange	38.00	45.00
22	1	2d. rose (I)	42.00	48.00
		a. Die II		
23	2	3d. blue	£170	65.00
24	5	4d. black	£190	£180
25	3	6d. yellow-green	£170	£180
26	6	9d. reddish mauve	£180	£180

1870. *Coarse, wove bluish white paper. P 11½–12.*

27	1	2d. rose (I)	9.50	11.00
		a. Die II	85.00	95.00
28		2d. rose-pink (I)	6.00	9.00
		a. Die II	65.00	75.00
		b. "TWC" (R. 6/4)	70.00	80.00
		c. Imperf between (horiz pair) ..	£130	
29	2	3d. pale blue	9.00	11.00
30		3d. blue	9.00	11.00
		a. Imperf between (horiz pair) ..	£275	
31	5	4d. black	4.50	27.00
		a. Imperf between (horiz pair) ..	£130	
		b. Bisected (2d.) (on cover) ..	†	£1600
		c. Perf compound 11 and 11½–12		

7

(Recess British-American Bank Note Co., Montreal and Ottawa)

1870 (1 June). *P 12.*

32	7	4½d. (3d. stg) yellow-brown ..	35.00	45.00
33		4½d. (3d. stg) deep brown ..	38.00	48.00

(New Currency. 100 cents = 1 dollar)

8 9 10

(Typo Charles Whiting, London)

1872 (1 Jan). *(a) P 11½–12.*

34	8	1c. orange	4.00	12.00
35		1c. yellow-orange	4.00	10.00
36		1c. brown-orange	4.50	13.00
37	10	3c. rose	14.00	18.00
		a. Stop between "PRINCE. EDWARD"	40.00	50.00
		b. Bisected (1½ c.) (on cover) ..	†	
		c. Imperf horiz (vert pair) ..	£325	

11 12 13

(b) Perf 12 to 12¼, large holes

38	9	2c. blue	11.00	32.00
		a. Bisected (1 c.) (on cover) ..	†	£2000
39	11	4c. yellow-green	4.50	16.00
40		4c. deep green	5.00	14.00
		a. Bisected (2 c.) (on cover) ..	†	£2000
41	12	6c. black	4.00	15.00
		a. Bisected (3 c.) (on cover) ..	†	£1100
		b. Imperf between (horiz pair)	£200	
		c. Imperf vert (horiz pair) ..		
42	13	12c. reddish mauve	3.75	26.00

(c) P 12½–13, smaller holes

43	8	1c. orange	13.00	
44		1c. brown-orange	4.50	12.00
45	10	3c. rose	14.00	22.00
		a. Stop between "PRINCE. EDWARD"	55.00	70.00
45b	12	6c. black	—	£250

(d) Perf compound of (a) and (c) 11½–12 × 12½–13

46	8	1c. orange	30.00	32.00
47	10	3c. rose	32.00	32.00
		a. Stop between "PRINCE. EDWARD"	£170	£180

Prince Edward Island joined the Dominion of Canada on 1 July 1873.

DOMINION OF CANADA

On July 1867, Canada, Nova Scotia and New Brunswick were united to form the Dominion of Canada.

The provinces of Manitoba (1870), British Columbia (1871), Prince Edward Island (1873), Alberta (1905), Saskatchewan (1905), and Newfoundland (1949) were subsequently added, as were the Northwest Territories (1870) and Yukon Territory (1898).

PRICES FOR STAMPS ON COVER TO 1945	
Nos. 46/67	*from* × 2
Nos. 68/71	*from* × 10
Nos. 72/89	*from* × 3
Nos. 90/100	*from* × 3
Nos. 101/2	*from* × 5
Nos. 103/11	*from* × 3
Nos. 115/20	*from* × 6
Nos. 121/49	*from* × 3
Nos. 150/65	*from* × 2
Nos. 166/72	*from* × 3
Nos. 173/87	*from* × 5
Nos. 188/95	*from* × 2
Nos. 196/215	*from* × 3
Nos. 219/224b	*from* × 4
Nos. 225/45	*from* × 2
Nos. 246/55	*from* × 8
Nos. 256/310	*from* × 2
No. 312	*from* × 20
No. 313	*from* × 10
Nos. 315/18	*from* × 2
Nos. 319/28	*from* × 3
Nos. 329/40	*from* × 2
Nos. 341/400	*from* × 1
Nos. R1/11	*from* × 5
Nos. S1/3	*from* × 8
No. S4	*from* × 6
No. S5	*from* × 5
Nos. S6/11	*from* × 3
Nos. S12/14	*from* × 5
Nos. D1/8	*from* × 4
Nos. D9/13	*from* × 5
Nos. D14/24	*from* × 4

13 14 15

Large types

PRINTERS. Nos. 46/120 were recess-printed by the British American Bank Note Co at Ottawa or Montreal.

1868 (1 Apr)–**90.** *As T 13/15 (various frames).*

I. Ottawa printings. P 12.

(a) Thin rather transparent crisp paper

46	13	½c. black (1.4.68) ..	65.00	55.00
47	14	1c. red-brown (1.4.68) ..	£325	50.00
48		2c. grass-green (1.4.68) ..	£350	40.00
49		3c. red-brown (1.4.68) ..	£600	20.00
50		6c. blackish brown (1.4.68) ..	£850	£150
51		12½c. bright blue (1.4.68) ..	£500	£110
52		15c. deep reddish purple ..	£750	£150

In these first printings the impression is generally blurred and the lines of the background are less clearly defined than in later printings.

(b) Medium to stout wove paper (1868–71)

53	13	½c. black	48.00	48.00
54		½c. grey-black	48.00	48.00
		a. Imperf between (pair) ..		
		b. Watermarked	£11000	£6000
55	14	1c. red-brown	£300	40.00
		a. Laid paper	£6500	£1600
		b. Watermarked (1868) ..	£1800	£190
56		1c. deep orange (Jan, 1869) ..	£700	80.00
56a		1c. orange-yellow (May (?), 1869)	£650	60.00
56b		1c. pale orange-yellow ..	£750	75.00
		ba. Imperf		

57	14	2c. deep green	£325	28.00
57a		2c. pale emerald-green (1871) ..	£400	40.00
		ab. Bisected (1 c. with 2 c. to make 3 c. rate) on cover	†	£4000
		ac. Laid paper	†	£60000
57d		2c. bluish green	£325	28.00
		da. Watermarked (1868) ..	£1500	£200
58		3c. brown-red	£650	15.00
		a. Laid paper	£6000	£300
		b. Watermarked (1868) ..	£2250	£160
59		6c. blackish brown (to chocolate)	£700	38.00
		a. Watermarked (1868) ..	£3000	£600
59b		6c. yellow-brown (1870) ..	£650	38.00
		ba. Bisected (3 c.), on cover ..	†	£2000
60		12½c. bright blue	£425	38.00
		a. Imperf horiz (vert pair) ..	†	£10000
		b. Watermarked (1868) ..	£1600	£225
60c		12½c. pale dull blue (milky) ..	£450	38.00
61		15c. deep reddish purple ..	£450	60.00
61a		15c. pale reddish purple ..	£400	60.00
		ab. Watermarked (1868) ..	—	£1200
61b		15c. dull violet-grey	£200	30.00
		ba. Watermarked (1868) ..	£3000	£500
61c		15c. dull grey-purple	£300	30.00

The official date of issue was 1 April 1868. Scattered examples of most values can be found used in the second half of March.

The watermark on the stout paper stamps consists of the words "E & G BOTHWELL CLUTHA MILLS," in large double-lined capitals. Portions of one or two letters only may be found on these stamps, which occur in the early printings of 1868.

The paper may, in most cases, be easily divided if the stamps are laid face downwards and carefully compared. The thin hard paper is more or less transparent and shows the design through the stamp; the thicker paper is softer to the feel and more opaque.

Of the 2 c. laid paper No. 57ac two examples only are known.

II. Montreal printings. Medium to stout wove paper.

(a) P 11½×12 or 11¾×12

62	13	½c. black (1873)	60.00	60.00
63	15	5c. olive-green (1.10.75) ..	£700	65.00
		a. Perf 12	£3500	£800
64	14	15c. dull grey-purple (1874) ..	£650	£150
65		15c. lilac-grey (3.77)	£850	£150
		a. Script watermark	£7000	£1800
		b. "BOTHWELL" watermark ..	†	£750
66		15c. slate	£850	£300

(b) P 12

67	14	15c. clear deep violet (1879) ..	£2250	£500
68		15c. deep slate (1881) ..	£130	28.00
69		15c. slaty blue (1887) ..	£130	28.00
70		15c. slate-purple (shades) (7.88–92)	60.00	17.00

No. 63a gauges 12 or above on all four sides.

The watermark on No. 65a is part of "Alex.Pirie & Sons" which appeared as script letters once per sheet in a small batch of the paper used for the 1877 printing. For a description of the sheet watermark on No. 65b see note after No. 61c.

Several used examples of the 12½ c. have been reported perforated 11½×12 or 11¾×12.

The last printing of the 15 c. slate-purple, No. 70, took place at Ottawa.

III. Ottawa printings. Thinnish paper of poor quality, often toned grey or yellowish. P 12

71	14	15c. slate-violet (shades) (5.90) ..	60.00	20.00
		a. Imperf (pair). Brown-purple ..	£1000	

Examples of No. 71 are generally found with yellowish streaky gum.

21

Small type

1870–91. *As T 21 (various frames). Ottawa (1870–73) and Montreal printings. P 12 (or slightly under).*

Papers (a) 1870–80. Medium to stout wove.
(b) 1870–72. Thin, soft, very white.
(c) 1878–97. Thinner and poorer quality.

72	21	1c. bright orange (a, b) (1870–73) ..	£120	22.00
		a. Thick soft paper (1871) ..	£350	£120
73		1c. orange-red (a) (1876–79) ..	45.00	1.50
74		1c. pale dull yellow (1877–79) ..	29.00	90
75		1c. bright yellow (a, c) (1878–97) ..	22.00	80
		a. Imperf (pair) (c)	£300	
		b. Bisected (½ c.) (on *Railway News*)	†	£3000
		c. Printed both sides	£1400	
76		1c. lemon-yellow (c) (1880) ..	75.00	15.00
77		2c. dp green (a, b) (1872–73 & 1876–78)	70.00	1.25
78		2c. grass-green (c) (1878–88) ..	42.00	80
		a. Imperf (pair) (1891–93?) ..	£350	
		b. Bisected (1 c. with 2 c. to make 3 c. rate) on cover	†	£1400
79		3c. Indian red (a) (1.70) ..	£850	50.00
		a. Perf 12½ (2.70) ..	£4250	£500
80		3c. pale rose-red (a) (9.70) ..	£275	9.00
81		3c. deep rose-red (a, b) (1870–73)	£300	8.50
		a. Thick soft paper (1.71) ..	—	£150
82		3c. dull red (a, c) (1876–88) ..	55.00	1.50
83		3c. orange-red (shades) (a, c) (1876–88)	45.00	90
84		3c. rose-carm (c) (10.88–4.89) ..	£350	11.00
85		5c. olive-green (a, c) (2.76–88) ..	£200	8.00
86		6c. yellowish brown (a, b, c) (1872–73 and 1876–90)	£180	11.00
		a. Bisected (3 c.) on cover ..	†	£1600
		b. Perf 12×11½ (1873) ..	†	—
87		10c. pale lilac-magenta (a) (1876–?) ..	£450	48.00
88		10c. deep lilac-magenta (a, c) (3.76–88)	£425	48.00
89		10c. lilac-pink (3.88)	£225	28.00

Nos. 75 and 78 were printed in the same shades during the second Ottawa period.

Examples of paper (a) can often be found showing traces of ribbing, especially on the 2 c. value.

No. 79a was issued in New Brunswick and Nova Scotia. One used copy of the 10 c. perf 12½ has been reported.

1873–79. *Montreal printings. Medium to stout wove paper.* P 11½×12 or 11¾×12.

90	21	1 c. bright orange		£180	26·00
91		1 c. orange-yellow (1873–79)		£150	10·00
92		1 c. pale dull yellow (1877–79)		£140	15·00
93		1 c. lemon-yellow (1879)		£170	15·00
94		2 c. deep green (1873–78)		£200	17·00
95		3 c. dull red (1875–79)		£200	13·00
96		3 c. orange-red (1873–79)		£200	13·00
97		5 c. olive-green (1.2.76–79)		£375	24·00
98		6 c. yellowish brown (1873–79)		£375	28·00
99		10 c. very pale lilac magenta (1874)		£850	£250
100		10 c. deep lilac-magenta (1876–79)		£550	£170

27

1882–97. *Montreal (to March 1889) and Ottawa printings. Thinnish paper of poor quality.* P 12.

101	27	½ c. black (7.82–97)		8·00	6·50
102		½ c. grey-black		8·00	6·50
		ab. Imperf (pair) (1891–93?)		£400	
		ac. Imperf between (pair)		£700	

1889–97. *Ottawa printings. Thinnish paper of poor quality, often toned grey or yellowish.* P 12.

103	21	2 c. dull sea-green		38·00	90
104		2 c. blue-green (7.89–91)		32·00	1·00
105		3 c. bright vermilion (4.89–97)		25·00	60
		a. Imperf (pair) (1891–93?)		£300	
106		5 c. brownish grey (5.89)		60·00	1·75
		a. Imperf (pair) (1891–93)		£400	
107		6 c. deep chestnut (10.90)		30·00	8·50
		a. "5 c." re-entry*		£2000	£1300
		b. Imperf (pair) (1891–93?)		£400	
108		6 c. pale chestnut		35·00	8·50
109		10 c. salmon-pink		£225	£110
110		10 c. carmine-pink (4.90)		£150	22·00
		ab. Imperf (pair) (1891–93?)		£450	
111		10 c. brownish red (1894?)		£150	22·00
		ba. Imperf (pair)		£400	

The 1 c. showed no change in the Ottawa printings, so is not included. The 2 c. reverted to its previous grass-green shade in 1891.

The 3 c. is known bisected and used as a ⅔ stamp for the 2 c. "drop letter" rate at Halifax in 1892.

28   29

(Recess B.A.B.N.)

1893 (17 Feb). P 12.

115	28	20 c. vermilion		£160	42·00
		a. Imperf (pair)		£1200	
116		50 c. blue		£225	24·00
		a. Imperf (Prussian blue) (pair)		£1200	

1893 (1 Aug). P 12.

117	29	8 c. pale bluish grey		85·00	3·75
		a. Imperf (pair)		£475	
118		8 c. bluish slate		£100	3·75
119		8 c. slate-purple		85·00	3·75
120		8 c. blackish purple		70·00	3·75
		a. Imperf (pair)		£500	

PRINTERS. The following stamps to No. 287 were recess-printed by the American Bank Note Co, Ottawa, which in 1923 became the Canadian Bank Note Co.

30

(Des L. Pereira and F. Brownell)

1897 (19 June). *Jubilee issue.* P 12.

121	30	½ c. black		48·00	48·00
122		1 c. orange		10·00	4·25
123		1 c. orange-yellow		10·00	4·25
		a. Bisected (½ c.) on cover		† £2500	
124		2 c. green		15·00	9·00
125		2 c. deep green		15·00	9·00
126		3 c. carmine		11·00	2·25
127		5 c. slate-blue		38·00	14·00
128		5 c. deep blue		38·00	14·00
129		6 c. brown		85·00	85·00
130		8 c. slate-violet		32·00	29·00
131		10 c. purple		50·00	42·00
132		15 c. slate		85·00	85·00
133		20 c. vermilion		85·00	85·00
134		50 c. pale ultramarine		£120	95·00
135		50 c. bright ultramarine		£120	£100
136		$1 lake		£400	£400
137		$2 deep violet		£700	£350

138	30	$3 bistre		£800	£650
139		$4 violet		£800	£600
140		$5 olive-green		£800	£600
121/40			Set of 16	£3500	£2500
133/40		Handstamped "Specimen"	Set of 7	£1800	

No 123a was used on issues of the *Railway News* of 5, 6 and 8 November 1897 and must be on a large part of the original newspaper with New Glasgow postmark.

31   32

(From photograph by W. & D. Downey, London)

1897–98. P 12.

141	31	½ c. grey-black (9.11.97)		6·00	4·75
142		½ c. black		7·50	5·00
		a. Imperf (pair)		£375	
143		1 c. blue-green (12.97)		18·00	90
		a. Imperf (pair)		£375	
144		2 c. violet (12.97)		18·00	1·50
		a. Imperf (pair)		£375	
145		3 c. carmine (1.98)		24·00	40
		a. Imperf (pair)		£700	
146		5 c. deep blue/*bluish* (12.97)		60·00	2·75
		a. Imperf (pair)		£375	
147		6 c. brown (12.97)		55·00	19·00
		a. Imperf (pair)		£700	
148		8 c. orange (12.97)		75·00	7·00
		a. Imperf (pair)		£400	
149		10 c. brownish purple (1.98)		£130	55·00
		a. Imperf (pair)		£425	
141/9			Set of 8	£350	80·00

BOOKLET PANES. Most definitive booklets issued from 1900 onwards had either the two horizontal sides or all three outer edges imperforate. Stamps from the panes show one side or two adjacent sides imperforate.

Two types of the 2 c.
Die Ia. Frame consists of four fine lines.
Die Ib. Frame has one thick line between two fine lines.

The die was retouched in 1900 for Plates 11 and 12 producing weak vertical frame lines and then retouched again in 1902 for Plates 15 to 20 resulting in much thicker frame lines. No. 155b covers both states of the retouching.

1898–1902. P 12.

150	32	½ c. black (9.98)		3·25	1·10
		a. Imperf (pair)		£375	
151		1 c. blue-green (6.98)		22·00	30
152		1 c. deep green/toned paper		22·00	30
		a. Imperf (pair)		£700	
153		2 c. dull purple (Die Ia) (9.98)		22·00	30
		a. Thick paper (6.99)		90·00	10·00
154		2 c. violet (Die Ia)		22·00	30
154a		2 c. reddish purple (Die Ia)		35·00	1·00
155		2 c. rose-carmine (Die Ia) (20.8.99)		30·00	30
		a. Imperf (pair)		£300	
155b		2 c. rose-carmine (Die Ib) (1900)		38·00	65
		ba. Booklet pane of 6 (11.6.00)		£750	
156		3 c. rose-carmine (6.98)		42·00	90
		a. Imperf (pair)		£750	
157		5 c. slate-blue/*bluish*		95·00	1·40
		a. Imperf (pair)		£750	
158		5 c. Prussian blue/*bluish*		£100	1·40
159		6 c. brown (9.98)		85·00	48·00
		a. Imperf (pair)		£650	
160		7 c. greenish yellow (23.12.02)		55·00	12·00
161		8 c. orange-yellow (10.98)		£110	24·00
162		8 c. brownish orange		£100	24·00
		a. Imperf (pair)		£650	
163		10 c. pale brownish purple (11.98)		£160	14·00
164		10 c. deep brownish purple		£160	14·00
		a. Imperf (pair)		£650	
165		20 c. olive-green (29.12.00)		£300	48·00
150/65			Set of 11	£750	£120

The 7 c. and 20 c. also exist imperforate, but unlike the values listed in this condition, they have no gum. (*Price*, 7 c. £350, 20 c. £1400 *pair, un*).

33

(Des R. Weir Crouch, G. Hahn, A. H. Howard and R. Holmes. Eng C. Skinner. Design recess, colours added by typo)

1898 (7 Dec). *Imperial Penny Postage. Design in black. British possessions in red. Oceans in colours given.* P 12.

166	33	2 c. lavender		29·00	5·50
167		2 c. greenish blue		25·00	5·00
168		2 c. blue		25·00	4·75

Forgeries of Type **33** are without horizontal lines across the continents and have a forged Montreal postmark of 24.12.98.

1899 (4 Jan). *Provisionals used at Port Hood, Nova Scotia. No. 156 divided vertically and handstamped.*

169	32	"1" in blue, on ⅓ of 3 c.		—	£3500
170		"2" in violet, on ⅔ of 3 c.		—	£3000

Nos. 169/70 were prepared by the local postmaster during a shortage of 2 c. stamps caused by a change in postage rates.

2 CENTS

(34)   35 King Edward VII

1899. *Surch with T 34, by Public Printing Office.*

171	31	2 c. on 3 c. carmine (8 Aug)		11·00	8·00
		a. Surch inverted		£275	
172	32	2 c. on 3 c. rose-carmine (28 July)		16·00	4·00
		a. Surch inverted		£275	

(Des King George V when Prince of Wales and J. A. Tilleard)

1903 (1 July)–12. P 12.

173	35	1 c. pale green		22·00	40
174		1 c. deep green		20·00	40
175		1 c. green		20·00	40
176		2 c. rose-carmine		20·00	40
		a. Booklet pane of 6		£750	
177		2 c. pale rose-carmine		20·00	40
		a. Imperf (pair) (18.7.09)		28·00	32·00
178		5 c. blue/*bluish*		70·00	2·50
179		5 c. indigo/*bluish*		70·00	2·75
180		7 c. yellow-olive		55·00	2·50
181		7 c. greenish bistre		65·00	2·50
181a		7 c. straw (1.12)		£110	35·00
182		10 c. brown-lilac		£110	8·00
183		10 c. pale dull purple		£110	8·00
184		10 c. dull purple		£110	8·00
185		20 c. pale olive-green (27.9.04)		£200	23·00
186		20 c. deep olive-green (H/S S £75)		£225	23·00
187		50 c. deep violet (19.11.08)		£350	80·00
173/87			Set of 7	£700	£100

The 1 c., 5 c., 7 c. and 10 c. exist imperforate but are believed to be proofs. (*Prices per pair,* 1 c. £400, 5 c. £600, 7 c. £400, 10 c. £600).

IMPERFORATE AND PART-PERFORATED SHEETS. Prior to 1946 many Canadian issues exist imperforate, or with other perforation varieties, in the colours of the issued stamps and, usually, with gum. In the years before 1927 such examples are believed to come from imprimatur sheets, removed from the Canadian Post Office archives. From 1927 until 1946 it is known that the printers involved in the production of the various issues submitted several imperforate plate proof sheets of each stamp to the Post Office authorities for approval. Some of these sheets or part sheets were retained for record purposes, but the remainder found their way onto the philatelic market.

Part-perforated sheets also occur from 1927–29 issues.

From 1908 until 1946 we now only list and price such varieties of this type which are known to be genuine errors, sold from post offices. Where other imperforate or similar varieties are known they are recorded in footnotes.

It is possible, and in some cases probable, that some imperforate varieties listed before 1908 may have also been removed from the archives as mentioned above, but it is far harder to be explicit over the status of this earlier material.

36 King George V and Queen   37 Jacques Cartier and
Mary when Prince and   Samuel Champlain
Princess of Wales

(Des Machado)

1908 (16 July). *Quebec Tercentenary T 36/7 and similar horiz designs.* P 12.

188		½ c. sepia		3·50	3·25
189		1 c. blue-green		12·00	2·75
190		2 c. carmine		18·00	90
191		5 c. indigo		45·00	18·00
192		7 c. olive-green		50·00	38·00
193		10 c. violet		55·00	45·00
194		15 c. brown-orange		75·00	65·00
195		20 c. dull brown		£100	80·00
188/95			Set of 8	£300	£225

Designs:—2 c. King Edward VII and Queen Alexandra; 5 c. Champlain's House in Quebec; 7 c. Generals Montcalm and Wolfe; 10 c. Quebec in 1700; 15 c. Champlain's departure for the West; 20 c. Cartier's arrival before Quebec.

Some values exist on both toned and white papers.

Nos. 188/95 exist imperforate. (*Price £325, un, for each pair*).

WET AND DRY PRINTINGS. Until the end of December 1922 all Canadian stamps were produced by the "wet" method of recess-printing in which the paper was dampened before printing, dried and then gummed.

In late December 1922 the Canadian Bank Note Co. began to use the "dry" process in which the paper was gummed before printing. Late printings of the 3 c. brown were the first stamps to be produced by this method, but the changeover was not completed until January 1926.

"Dry" printings have a sharper appearance and can often be found with a degree of embossing showing on the reverse. Stamps from "wet" printings shrink during drying and are narrower than "dry" examples. In many cases the difference can be as great as 0.5 mm. On some early booklet panes the difference is in the vertical, rather than the horizontal, measurement.

On Nos. 196/215 all values only exist from "wet" printings except the 3 c., 20 c. and 50 c. which come from both types of printing.

44

1911–22. P 12.

196	44	1 c. yellow-green (22.12.11) ..	5·50	30
		a. With fine horiz lines across stamp	35·00	8·50
197		1 c. bluish green ..	5·50	30
		a. Booklet pane of 6 (1.5.13) ..	50·00	
198		1 c. deep bluish green ..	6·00	30
199		1 c. deep yellow-green ..	6·00	45
		a. Booklet pane of 6	18·00	
200		2 c. rose-red (22.12.11) ..	4·50	30
201		2 c. deep rose-red ..	4·75	30
		a. Booklet pane of 6 (1.12)	32·00	
202		2 c. pale rose-red ..	4·50	30
		a. With fine horiz lines across stamp	25·00	8·00
203		2 c. carmine ..	5·50	30
204		3 c. brown (6.8.18) ..	6·00	30
205		3 c. deep brown ..	5·00	30
		a. Booklet pane of 4 + 2 labels (2.22)	50·00	
205b		5 c. deep blue (17.1.12) ..	60·00	65
206		5 c. indigo ..	85·00	2·25
206a		5 c. grey-blue ..	75·00	1·50
206b		7 c. straw (12.1.12) ..	75·00	13·00
207		7 c. pale sage-green (1914) ..	£180	30·00
208		7 c. olive-yellow (1915) ..	20·00	2·75
209		7 c. yellow-ochre (1916) ..	20·00	2·75
210		10 c. brownish purple (12.1.12) ..	90·00	2·25
211		10 c. reddish purple ..	£100	2·75
212		20 c. olive-green (23.1.12) ..	29·00	1·50
213		20 c. olive ..	29·00	1·75
214		50 c. grey-black (26.1.12) ..	£100	8·00
215		50 c. sepia ..	48·00	3·50
196/215		Set of 8	£225	10·00

The 20 c. and 50 c. values exist imperforate (*Price £1100 un, for each pair*).

1912 (Nov)–21. For use in coil-machines. (a) P 12×imperf.

216	44	1 c. yellow-green (1914) ..	3·50	9·50
217		1 c. blue-green ..	12·00	23·00
		a. Two large holes at top and bottom (vert pair) (7.18) ..	60·00	75·00
218		2 c. deep rose-red (1914) ..	25·00	17·00
218a		3 c. brown (1921) ..	3·50	5·50

No. 217a has two large holes about 3½ mm in diameter in the top and bottom margins. They were for experimental use in a vending machine at Toronto in July 1918 and were only in use for two days.

The 1 c. and 2 c. also exist with two small "V" shaped holes about 9.5 mm apart at top which are gripper marks due to modifications made in vending machines in 1917.

(b) Imperf × perf 8

219	44	1 c. yellow-green (9.12) ..	12·00	3·50
220		1 c. blue-green ..	15·00	3·75
		a. With fine horiz lines across stamp	55·00	
221		2 c. carmine (9.12) ..	11·00	1·00
222		2 c. rose-red ..	12·00	2·00
223		2 c. scarlet ..	32·00	4·75
224		3 c. brown (8.18) ..	5·00	1·50

(c) P 8 × imperf

224a	44	1 c. blue-green (15.2.13) ..	60·00	48·00
224b		2 c. carmine (15.2.13) ..	60·00	48·00

The stamps imperf × perf 8 were sold in coils over the counter; those perf 8 × imperf were on sale in automatic machines. Varieties showing perf 12 on 2 or 3 adjacent sides and 1 or 2 sides imperf are from booklets, or the margins of sheets.

(45)　　46　　47

1915 (12 Feb). Optd with T 45.

225	44	1 c. blue ..	£110	180
226		20 c. olive-green ..	55·00	90·00
227		50 c. sepia (R.) ..	£110	140
225/7		Set of 3	£250	£375

These stamps were intended for tax purposes, but owing to ambiguity in an official circular dated 16 April 1915, it was for a time believed that their use for postal purposes was authorised. The position was clarified by a further circular on 20 May 1916 which made clear that Nos. 225/7 were for fiscal use only.

1915. P 12.

228	46	1 c. green (15.4.15) ..	7·50	30
229		2 c. carmine-red (16.4.15) ..	10·00	40
230		2 c. rose-carmine ..	11·00	2·50

PRICES OF SETS

Set prices are given for many issues, generally those containing three stamps or more. Definitive sets include one of each value or major colour change, but do not cover different perforations, die types or minor shades. Where a choice is possible the set prices are based on the cheapest versions of the stamps included in the listings.

Die I　　Die II

In Die I there is a long horizontal coloured line under the foot of the "T", and a solid bar of colour runs upwards from the "1" to the "T".

In Die II this solid bar of colour is absent, and there is a short horizontal line under the left side of the "T", with two short vertical dashes and a number of dots under the right-hand side.

1916 (1 Jan). P 12.

231	47	2 c. + 1 c. rose-red (Die I) ..	22·00	1·00
232		2 c. + 1 c. bright carmine (Die I) ..	22·00	1·00
233		2 c. + 1 c. scarlet (Die I).. ..	19·00	1·00

1916 (Feb). Imperf × perf 8 (coils).

234	47	2 c. + 1 c. rose-red (Die I) ..	55·00	10·00

1916 (July). P 12 × 8.

235	47	2 c. + 1 c. carmine-red (Die I) ..	16·00	45·00
236		2 c. + 1 c. bright rose-red (Die I) ..	16·00	45·00

1916 (Aug). P 12.

237	47	2 c. + 1 c. carmine-red (Die II) ..	85·00	16·00

1916 (Aug). Colour changed. (a) P 12.

238	47	2 c. + 1 c. brown (Die I) ..	£180	20·00
239		2 c. + 1 c. yellow-brown (Die II) ..	4·00	30
		a. Imperf (pair)	£750	
240		2 c. + 1 c. deep brown (Die II) ..	10·00	30

(b) Imperf × perf 8

241	47	2 c. + 1 c. brown (Die I) ..	95·00	7·50
		a. Pair, 241 and 243	£325	
243		2 c. + 1 c. deep brown (Die II) ..	35·00	3·25

No. 239a, which is a genuine error, should not be confused with ungummed proofs of the Die I stamp, No. 238 (*Price per pair, £130*).

This value also exists p 12×imperf or imperf×p 12, but was not issued with these perforations (*Price, in either instance, £275, un, per pair*).

48 Quebec Conference, 1864, from painting "The Fathers of Confederation", by Robert Harris

1917 (15 Sept). 50th Anniv of Confederation. P 12.

244	48	3 c. bistre-brown ..	17·00	1·50
245		3 c. deep brown ..	19·00	1·75

No. 244 exists imperforate (*Price per pair, £275 un*).

I

II

Die I. Space between top of "N" and oval frame line and space between "CENT" and lower frame line.

Die II. "ONE CENT" appears larger so that "N" touches oval and "CENT" almost touches frame line. There are other differences but this is the most obvious one.

I

II

Die I. The lowest of the three horizontal lines of shading below the medals does not touch the three heavy diagonal lines; three complete white spaces over both "E's" of "THREE"; long centre bar to figures "3". Vertical spandrel lines fine.

Die II. The lowest horizontal line of shading touches the first of the three diagonal lines; two and a half spaces over first "E" and spaces over second "E" partly filled by stem of maple leaf; short centre bar to figures "3". Vertical spandrel lines thick. There are numerous other minor differences.

WET AND DRY PRINTINGS. See notes above No. 196.

On Nos. 246/63 all listed items occur from both "wet" and "dry" printings except Nos. 246aa/ab, 248aa, 256, 259, 260 and 262 which come "wet" only, and Nos. 246a, 248/a, 252/4a, 256b and 263 which are "dry" only.

1922–31. As T 44. (a) P 12.

246	44	1 c. chrome-yellow (Die I) (7.6.22) ..	2·50	20
		aa. Booklet pane of 4 + 2 labels (7.22)	48·00	
		ab. Booklet pane of 6 (12.22)	27·00	
247		2 c. deep green (6.6.22) ..	2·25	10
		aa. Booklet pane of 4 + 2 labels (7.22)	27·00	
		ab. Booklet pane of 6 (12.22)	£250	
		b. Thin paper (9.24) ..	2·75	3·75
248		3 c. carmine (Die I) (18.12.23) ..	3·75	10
		aa. Booklet pane of 4 + 2 labels (12.23)	28·00	
		a. Die II (11.24) ..	21·00	45
249		4 c. olive-yellow (7.7.22) ..	8·00	3·50
		a. Yellow-ochre ..	8·00	3·50
250		5 c. violet (2.2.22) ..	5·00	1·25
		a. Thin paper (9.24) ..	5·00	8·00
		b. Reddish violet (1925) ..	7·00	1·75
251		7 c. red-brown (12.12.24) ..	12·00	7·00
		a. Thin paper ..	£130	30·00
252		8 c. blue (1.9.25) ..	19·00	7·00
253		10 c. blue (20.2.22) ..	20·00	2·75
254		10 c. bistre-brown (1.8.25) ..	18·00	2·50
		a. Yellow-brown ..	18·00	2·50
255		$1 brown-orange (22.7.23) ..	50·00	7·00
246/55		Set of 10	£130	30·00

The $1 differs from T 44 in that the value tablets are oval.

Nos. 249/55 exist imperforate (*Prices per un pair 4 c. to 8 c. £850 each, 10 c. £900, $1 £1000*).

(b) Imperf × perf 8

256	44	1 c. chrome-yellow (Die I) (1922) ..	4·00	5·00
		a. Imperf horiz (vert pair) (1924) ..	£160	
		b. Die II (1925) ..	4·50	7·00
		c. Do. Imperf horiz (vert pair) (1927) ..	11·00	27·00
257		2 c. deep green (26.7.22) ..	9·00	2·00
		b. Imperf horiz (vert pair) (1927) ..	12·00	27·00
258		3 c. carmine (Die I) (9.4.24) ..	60·00	9·00
		a. Imperf horiz (vert pair) (1924) ..	£250	
		b. Die II (1925) ..	80·00	20·00
256/8		Set of 3	65·00	14·50

Nos. 256a, 256c, 257b and 258a come from coil printings sold in sheet form. Those issued in 1924 were from "wet" printings and those in 1927 from "dry". A "wet" printing of No. 257b, issued in 1924, also exists (*Price £160 mint*), but cannot be identified from that issued in 1927 except by the differences between "wet" and "dry" stamps.

(c) Imperf (pairs)

259	44	1 c. chrome-yellow (Die I) (6.10.24) ..	50·00	70·00
260		2 c. deep green (6.10.24) ..	50·00	70·00
261		3 c. carmine (Die I) (31.12.23)†.. ..	28·00	40·00

(d) P 12 × imperf

262	44	2 c. deep green (9.24) ..	65·00	60·00

(e) P 12 × 8

263	44	2 c. carmine (Die II) (24.6.31) ..	2·25	3·25

Nos. 259 to 261 were on sale only at the Philatelic Branch P.O. Dept, Ottawa.

†Earliest known postmark.

　2 **CENTS**

2 CENTS
(49)

2 CENTS
(50)

1926. No. 248 surch.

(a) With T 49, by the Govt Printing Bureau

264	44	2 c. on 3 c. carmine (12.10.26) ..	40·00	48·00
		a. Pair, one without surch	£300	
		b. On Die II	£350	

(b) With T 50, by the Canadian Bank Note Co

265	44	2 c. on 3 c. carmine (4.11.26) ..	15·00	20·00
		a. Surch double (partly treble) ..	£200	

51 Sir J. A. Macdonald　　52 "The Fathers of Confederation"

53 Parliament Buildings, Ottawa　　54 Sir W. Laurier

55 Canada, Map 1867–1927

1927 (29 June). 60th Anniv of Confederation. P 12. I. Commemorative Issue. Inscr "1867–1927 CANADA CONFEDERATION".

266	51	1 c. orange ..	2·50	1·25
267	52	2 c. green ..	2·25	20
268	53	3 c. carmine ..	7·00	5·00
269	54	5 c. violet ..	3·25	3·50
270	55	12 c. blue ..	22·00	5·00
266/70		Set of 5	32·00	13·50

Nos. 266/70 exist imperforate, imperf×perf or perf×imperf (*Prices from £65, un, per pair*).

56 Darcy McGee

57 Sir W. Laurier and Sir J. A. Macdonald

66

67 Parliamentary Library, Ottawa

72 Mercury and Western Hemisphere

73 Sir Georges Etienne Cartier

58 R. Baldwin and L. H. Lafontaine

II. Historical Issue

271	56	5 c. violet	..	3·00	2·50
272	57	12 c. green	..	15·00	4·50
273	58	20 c. carmine	..	17·00	12·00
271/3			Set of 3	32·00	17·00

Nos. 271/3 exist imperforate, imperf×perf or perf×imperf (Prices from £65, un, per pair).

68 The Old Citadel, Quebec

69 Harvesting with Tractor

59

(Des H. Schwartz)

1928 (21 Sept). Air. P 12.

274	59	5 c. olive-brown	..	5·50	3·00

No. 274 exists imperforate, imperf×perf or perf×imperf (Price per pair, £130, un).

60 King George V

61 Mt Hurd and Indian Totem Poles

62 Quebec Bridge

63 Harvesting with Horses

64 *Bluenose* (fishing schooner)

65 Parliament Buildings, Ottawa

1928–29. (a) P 12.

275	60	1 c. orange (25.10.28)	..	2·75	50
		a. Booklet pane of 6		18·00	
276		2 c. green (16.10.28)	..	1·25	10
		a. Booklet pane of 6		18·00	
277		3 c. lake (12.12.28)	..	17·00	14·00
278		4 c. olive-bistre (16.8.29)		13·00	6·00
279		5 c. violet (12.12.28)	..	6·50	3·00
		a. Booklet pane of 6 (6.1.29)		90·00	
280		8 c. blue (21.12.28)	..	7·50	4·50
281	61	10 c. green (5.12.28)	..	8·00	1·00
282	62	12 c. grey-black (8.1.29)		20·00	9·00
283	63	20 c. lake (8.1.29)	..	27·00	11·00
284	64	50 c. blue (8.1.29)	..	£100	38·00
285	65	$1 olive-green (8.1.29)		£110	60·00
		a. Brown-olive		£225	95·00
275/85			Set of 11	£275	£130

(b) Imperf × perf 8 (5.11.28)

286	60	1 c. orange		13·00	22·00
287		2 c. green		13·00	4·00

Slight differences in the size of many Canadian stamps, due to paper shrinkage, are to be found.

Nos. 275/85 exist imperforate, imperf×perf or perf×imperf (Prices per unused pair, 1 c. to 8 c., from £60, 10 c. to 20 c., from £100, 50 c. and $1, from £375). Tête-bêche horizontal pairs of the 1 c., 2 c. and 5 c. are also known from uncut booklet sheets (Prices per pair, £225, un).

PRINTERS. The following stamps to No. 334 were recess-printed by the British American Bank Note Co, Ottawa.

Die I 1 c.   Die II

 Die I 2 c.   Die II

1 c. Die I. Three thick coloured lines and one thin between "P" and ornament, at right. Curved line in ball-ornament short.
Die II. Four thick lines. Curved line longer.

2 c. Die I. Three thick coloured lines between "P" and ornament, at left. Short line in ball.
Die II. Four thick lines. Curved line longer.

1930–31. (a) P 11.

288	66	1 c. orange (I) (17.7.30)	..	1·75	90
289		2 c. green (I) (6.7.30)	..	1·25	10
		a. Booklet pane of 6 (17.6.30)		35·00	
290		4 c. yellow-bistre (5.11.30)		6·50	4·00
291		5 c. violet (18.6.30)	..	2·75	4·25
292		8 c. blue (13.8.30)	..	10·00	15·00
293	67	10 c. olive-green (15.9.30)		14·00	1·00
		a. Imperf (pair)		£900	
294	68	12 c. grey-black (4.12.30)		14·00	5·00
295	69	20 c. red (4.12.30)	..	22·00	75
296	70	50 c. blue (4.12.30)	..	80·00	17·00
297	71	$1 olive-green (4.12.30)		95·00	23·00
288/97			Set of 10	£200	60·00

Nos. 294/7 exist imperforate (Prices per unused pair, 12 c. £500, 20 c. £500, 50 c. £600, $1 £650).

(b) Imperf × perf 8½

298	66	1 c. orange (I)		10·00	14·00
299		2 c. green (I)		4·00	5·00

Colours changed and new value. (a) P 11

300	66	1 c. green (I) (6.12.30)		1·25	10
		b. Booklet pane of 6 (21.7.31)		25·00	
		d. Die II		1·25	10
		da. Imperf (pair)		£800	
		db. Booklet pane of 4 + 2 labels (13.11.31)		75·00	
301		2 c. scarlet (I) (17.11.30)		70	40
		a. Booklet pane of 6 (17.11.30)		23·00	
		b. Die II		90	10
302		2 c. deep brown (I) (4.7.31)		1·40	3·00
		a. Booklet pane of 6 (23.7.31)		35·00	
		b. Die II		1·00	10
		ba. Booklet pane of 4 + 2 labels (13.11.31)		£100	
303		3 c. sca·' (13.7.31)		90	10
		a. Booklet pane of 4 + 2 labels		35·00	
304		5 c. deep slate-blue (13.11.30)		5·00	20
		a. Dull blue		14·00	50
305		8 c. red-orange (5.11.30)		7·00	5·50
300/5			Set of 6	14·00	5·50

(b) Imperf × perf 8½

306	66	1 c. green (I)		6·00	7·00
307		2 c. scarlet (I)		4·50	4·00
308		2 c. deep brown (I) (4.7.31)		9·00	1·25
309		3 c. scarlet (13.7.31)		14·00	1·25
306/9			Set of 4	30·00	12·00

Some low values in the above and subsequent issues have been printed by both Rotary and "Flat plate" processes. The former can be distinguished by the gum, which has a striped appearance.
For 13 c. bright violet, T 68, see No. 325.

ALTERED CATALOGUE NUMBERS

Any Catalogue numbers altered from the last edition are shown as a list in the introductory pages.

(Des H. Schwartz)

1930 (4 Dec). Air. P 11.

310	72	5 c. deep brown	..	16·00	18·00

1931 (30 Sept). P 11.

312	73	10 c. olive-green	..	3·00	10

No. 312 exists imperforate (Price per pair, £300, un).

(74)

(75)

1932 (22 Feb). Air. No. 274 surch with T 74.

313	59	6 c. on 5 c. olive-brown	..	3·00	2·50

Examples of this stamp with surcharge inverted, surcharge double, surcharge triple or surcharge omitted in pair with normal are not now believed to have been regularly issued. Such "errors" have also been forged and collectors are warned against forged examples, some of which bear unauthorized markings which purport to be the guarantee of Stanley Gibbons Ltd.

1932 (21 June). Nos. 301/b surch with T 75.

314	66	3 c. on 2 c. scarlet (I)	..	2·00	2·50
		a. Die II		1·00	50

76 King George V

77 Duke of Windsor when Prince of Wales

78 Allegory of British Empire

OTTAWA CONFERENCE 1932

(79)

1932 (12 July). Ottawa Conference. P 11. (a) Postage stamps.

315	76	3 c. scarlet	..	70	60
316	77	5 c. blue	..	8·00	4·00
317	78	13 c. green	..	9·00	6·00

(b) Air. No. 310 surch with T 79

318	72	6 c. on 5 c. deep brown (B.)		10·00	12·00
315/18			Set of 4	25·00	20·00

80 King George V

"3" level Die I

"3" raised Die II

1932 (1 Dec)–33. (a) P 11.

319	80	1 c. green		60	10
		a. Booklet pane of 6 (28.12.33)		15·00	
		b. Booklet pane of 4 + 2 labels (19.9.33)		75·00	
320		2 c. sepia		70	10
		a. Booklet pane of 6 (7.9.33)		15·00	
		b. Booklet pane of 4 + 2 labels (19.9.33)		75·00	
321		3 c. scarlet (Die I)		70	10
		a. Booklet pane of 4 + 2 labels (22.8.33)		40·00	
		b. Die II (29.11.32)		85	10
		ba. Booklet pane of 4 + 2 labels (19.9.33)		30·00	
322		4 c. yellow-brown		35·00	8·50
323		5 c. blue		10·00	10
		a. Imperf vert (horiz pair)		£850	
324		8 c. red-orange		23·00	3·75
325	68	13 c. bright violet		32·00	2·25
319/25			Set of 7	90·00	13·00

A plate block of four from Plate 1 exists printed in varnish ink.
Nos. 319/25 exist imperforate (Prices per unused pair, 1 c. to 8 c. £140, 13 c. £425).

		(b) Imperf × perf 8½ (1933)		
326	80	1 c. green	13·00	3·25
327		2 c. sepia	19·00	2·25
328		3 c. scarlet (Die II)	12·00	1·25
326/8		*Set of 3*	40·00	6·00

81 Parliament Buildings, Ottawa

1933 (18 May). *U.P.U. Congress Preliminary Meeting. P* 11.
329	81	5 c. blue	5·50	2·75

No. 329 exists imperforate (*Price per pair £425, un*).

WORLD'S
GRAIN EXHIBITION &
CONFERENCE

REGINA 1933
(82)

1933 (24 July). *World's Grain Exhibition and Conference, Regina. No.* 295 *optd with T* **82** *in blue.*
330	69	20 c. red	16·00	7·00

No. 330 exists imperforate (*Price per pair £425, un*).

83 S.S. *Royal William* (after S. Skillett)   **84** Jacques Cartier approaching Land

1933 (17 Aug). *Centenary of First Trans-Atlantic Steamboat Crossing. P* 11.
331	83	5 c. blue	9·00	3·00

No. 331 exists imperforate (*Price per pair £450, un*).

1934 (1 July). *Fourth Centenary of Discovery of Canada. P* 11.
332	84	3 c. blue	2·25	1·50

No. 332 exists imperforate (*Price per pair £425, un*).

85 U.E.L. Statue, Hamilton   **86** Seal of New Brunswick

1934 (1 July). *150th Anniv of Arrival of United Empire Loyalists. P* 11.
333	85	10 c. olive-green	8·50	4·75

No. 333 exists imperforate (*Price per pair £750, un*).

1934 (16 Aug). *150th Anniv of Province of New Brunswick. P* 11.
334	86	2 c. red-brown	1·50	2·25

No. 334 exists imperforate (*Price per pair £400, un*).

PRINTERS. The following stamps were recess-printed (except where otherwise stated) by the Canadian Bank Note Co, Ottawa, until No. 616.

87 Queen Elizabeth II when Princess   **89** King George V and Queen Mary

1935 (4 May). *Silver Jubilee. T* **87**, **89** *and similar designs. P* 12.
335		1 c. green	55	50
336		2 c. brown	60	40
337		3 c. carmine-red	1·75	40
338		5 c. blue	5·50	4·50
339		10 c. green	3·25	3·50
340		13 c. blue	6·50	5·50
335/40		*Set of 6*	16·00	13·00

Designs: *Vert* (as *T* **87**)—2 c. King George VI when Duke of York; 5 c. King Edward VIII when Prince of Wales. *Horiz* (as *T* **89**)—10 c. Windsor Castle; 13 c. Royal Yacht *Britannia*.
Nos. 335/40 exist imperforate (*Price £160, un, for each pair*).

93 King George V   **94** Royal Canadian Mounted Policeman

99 Daedalus

1935 (1 June–5 Nov). *T* **93/4**, **99** *and similar designs. (a) Postage.*
(i) P 12.
341	93	1 c. green	30	10
		a. Booklet pane of 6 (19.8.35)	22·00	
		b. Booklet pane of 4+2 labels (22.7.35)	55·00	
342		2 c. brown	50	10
		a. Booklet pane of 6 (16.11.35)	26·00	
		b. Booklet pane of 4+2 labels (22.7.35)	55·00	
343		3 c. scarlet	70	10
		a. Booklet pane of 4+2 labels	28·00	
		b. Printed on the gummed side	£225	
344		4 c. yellow	2·75	1·25
345		5 c. blue	1·75	10
		a. Imperf vert (horiz pair)	£200	
346		8 c. orange	3·00	3·00
347	94	10 c. carmine	6·00	30
348	—	13 c. purple	5·50	45
349	—	20 c. olive-green	17·00	70
350	—	50 c. deep violet	25·00	4·50
351	—	$1 bright blue	40·00	11·00
341/51		*Set of 11*	90·00	19·00

(ii) Coil stamps. Imperf × perf 8
352	93	1 c. green (5.11.35)	13·00	3·75
353		2 c. brown (14.10.35)	9·50	3·25
354		3 c. scarlet (20.7.35)	9·00	1·25
352/4		*Set of 3*	28·00	7·50

(b) Air. P 12
355	99	6 c. red-brown	2·75	75
		a. Imperf vert (horiz pair)	£4500	

Designs: *Horiz* (as *T* **94**)—13 c. Confederation Conference, Charlottetown, 1864; 20 c. Niagara Falls; 50 c. Parliament Buildings, Victoria, British Columbia; $1 Champlain Monument, Quebec.
Nos. 341/51 (*Prices per pair*, 1 c. to 8 c. *each* £100, 10 c. *to* $1 *each* £190, *un.*) and 355 (*Price per pair* £375, *un*) exist imperforate.

100 King George VI and Queen Elizabeth

1937 (10 May). *Coronation. P* 12.
356	100	3 c. carmine	85	30

No. 356 exists imperforate (*Price per pair £425, un*).

101 King George VI   **102** Memorial Chamber Parliament Buildings, Ottawa

107 Fairchild 45-80 Sekani Seaplane over *Distributor* on River Mackenzie

(*T* **101**. Photograph by Bertram Park)

1937–38. *T* **101/2**, **107** *and similar designs. (a) Postage.*
(i) P 12.
357	101	1 c. green (1.4.37)	1·50	10
		a. Booklet pane of 4 + 2 labels (14.4.37)	28·00	
		b. Booklet pane of 6 (18.5.37)	3·50	
358		2 c. brown (1.4.37)	1·75	10
		a. Booklet pane of 4 + 2 labels (14.4.37)	55·00	
		b. Booklet pane of 6 (3.5.38)	11·00	
359	101	3 c. scarlet (1.4.37)	1·75	10
		a. Booklet pane of 4 + 2 labels (14.4.37)	4·25	
360		4 c. yellow (10.5.37)	3·75	1·75
361		5 c. blue (10.5.37)	4·00	10
362		8 c. orange (10.5.37)	3·75	1·75
363	102	10 c. rose-carmine (15.6.38)	5·00	10
		a. Red	5·00	10
364	—	13 c. blue (15.11.38)	14·00	90
365	—	20 c. red-brown (15.6.38)	22·00	50
366	—	50 c. green (15.6.38)	45·00	7·00
367	—	$1 violet (15.6.38)	60·00	8·50
		a. Imperf horiz (vert pair)	£2500	
357/67		*Set of 11*	£150	18·00

Nos. 357/67 exist imperforate (*Prices per pair* 1 c. *to* 8 c. *each* £160, 10 c. *to* 50 c. *each* £200, $1 £300 *un*).

(ii) Coil stamps. Imperf × perf 8
368	101	1 c. green (15.6.37)	3·50	2·25
369		2 c. brown (18.6.37)	3·50	2·50
370		3 c. scarlet (15.4.37)	17·00	75
368/70		*Set of 3*	22·00	5·00

(b) Air. P 12
371	107	6 c. blue (15.6.38)	11·00	60

Designs: *Horiz* (as *T* **107**)—13 c. Entrance to Halifax Harbour; 20 c. Fort Garry Gate, Winnipeg; 50 c. Entrance, Vancouver Harbour; $1 Chateau de Ramezay, Montreal.
No. 371 exists imperforate (*Price per pair £325, un*).

108 Queen Elizabeth II when Princess and Princess Margaret   **109** National War Memorial, Ottawa

110 King George VI and Queen Elizabeth

1939 (15 May). *Royal Visit. P* 12.
372	108	1 c. black and green	1·75	10
373	109	2 c. black and brown	60	50
374	110	3 c. black and carmine	60	10
372/4		*Set of 3*	2·75	60

Nos. 372/4 exist imperforate (*Price £300, un, for each pair*).

111
King George VI in Naval uniform   **112**
King George VI in Military uniform   **113**
King George VI in Air Force uniform

114 Grain Elevator   **116** Parliament Buildings

117 Ram Tank   **121** Air Training Camp

1942 (1 July)—48. *War Effort. T* **111/14**, **116/17**, **121** *and similar designs. (a) Postage. (i) P* 12.
375	111	1 c. green	1·50	10
		a. Booklet pane of 4 + 2 labels (12.9.42)	22·00	
		b. Booklet pane of 6 (24.11.42)	2·50	
376	112	2 c. brown	1·75	10
		a. Booklet pane of 4 + 2 labels (12.9.42)	26·00	
		b. Booklet pane of 6 (6.10.42)	18·00	
377	113	3 c. carmine-lake	1·25	60
		a. Booklet pane of 4 + 2 labels (20.8.42)	4·25	

378	113	3 c. purple (30.6.43)		90	10
		a. Booklet pane of 4 + 2 labels (28.8.43)		5·50	
		b. Booklet pane of 6 (24.11.47)		11·00	
379	114	4 c. slate		5·50	90
380	112	4 c. carmine-lake (9.4.43)		70	10
		a. Booklet pane of 6 (3.5.43)		3·50	
381	111	5 c. blue		3·00	10
382	—	8 c. red-brown		5·50	75
383	116	10 c. brown		5·50	10
384	117	13 c. dull green		6·50	6·50
385		14 c. dull green (16.4.43)		15·00	90
386	—	20 c. chocolate		14·00	20
387	—	50 c. violet		26·00	2·50
388	—	$1 blue		42·00	5·50
375/88			Set of 14	£110	16·00

Nos. 375/88 exist imperforate (Prices per pair 1 c. to 8 c. each £180, 10 c. to 20 c. each £250, 50 c. and $1 each £325, un).

(ii) Coil stamps. Imperf × perf 8

389	111	1 c. green (9.2.43)		1·00	1·50
390	112	2 c. brown (24.11.42)		2·25	1·50
391	113	3 c. carmine-lake (23.9.42)		2·00	5·00
392		3 c. purple (19.8.43)		5·50	3·00
393	112	4 c. carmine-lake (13.5.43)		6·00	1·50
389/93			Set of 5	15·00	11·00

(iii) Booklet stamps. Imperf × perf 12 (1.9.43)

394	111	1 c. green		3·00	1·25
		a. Booklet pane of 3		9·00	
395	113	3 c. purple		3·00	1·50
		a. Booklet pane of 3		9·00	
396	112	4 c. carmine-lake		3·00	1·75
		a. Booklet pane of 3		9·00	
394/6			Set of 3	8·00	4·00

Nos. 394/6 are from booklets in which the stamps are in strips of three, imperforate at top and bottom and right-hand end.

(iv) Coil stamps. Imperf × perf 9½

397	111	1 c. green (13.7.48)		3·00	4·00
397a	112	2 c. brown (1.10.48)		7·50	19·00
398	113	3 c. purple (2.7.48)		4·75	6·00
398a	112	4 c. carmine-lake (22.7.48)		7·00	3·50
397/8a			Set of 4	20·00	29·00

(b) Air. P 12

399	121	6 c. blue (1.7.42)		16·00	4·50
400		7 c. blue (16.4.43)		3·00	10

Designs: Horiz (as T 114)—8 c. Farm scene. (As T 117)—20 c. Launching of corvette H.M.C.S. *La Malbaie*, Sorel; 50 c. Munitions factory; $1 H.M.S. *Cossack* (destroyer).
Nos. 399/400 exist imperforate (Price £400, un, for each pair).

122 Ontario Farm Scene   **129** Alexander Graham Bell and "Fame"

1946 (16 Sept)–47. *Peace Re-conversion. T* **122** *and similar horiz designs. P* 12. *(a) Postage.*

401	8 c. brown		1·25	1·50
402	10 c. olive-green		1·75	10
403	14 c. sepia		4·00	80
404	20 c. slate		3·00	10
405	50 c. green		17·00	2·25
406	$1 purple		27·00	2·75

(b) Air

407	7 c. blue		4·00	10
	a. Booklet pane of 4 (24.11.47)		9·00	
401/7		Set of 7	50·00	6·50

Designs:—7 c. Canada Geese in flight; 10 c. Great Bear Lake; 14 c. St. Maurice River Power Station; 20 c. Combine Harvester; 50 c. Lumbering in British Columbia; $1 *Abegweit* (train ferry), Prince Edward Is.

1947 (3 Mar). *Birth Centenary of Bell (inventor of telephone). P* 12.

408	129	4 c. blue	15	10

(From photograph by Dorothy Wilding)

1948 (16 Feb). *Princess Elizabeth's Marriage. P* 12.

410	131	4 c. blue	10	10

130 "Canadian Citizenship".   **131** Queen Elizabeth II when Princess

1947 (1 July). *Advent of Canadian Citizenship and Eightieth Anniv of Confederation. P* 12.

409	130	4 c. blue	10	10

(From photograph by Dorothy Wilding)

NEW INFORMATION

The editor is always interested to correspond with people who have new information that will improve or correct the Catalogue.

---

132 Queen Victoria, Parliament Building, Ottawa, and King George VI   **133** Cabot's Ship *Matthew*

1948 (1 Oct). *One Hundred Years of Responsible Government. P* 12.

411	132	4 c. grey		10	10

1949 (1 Apr). *Entry of Newfoundland into Canadian Confederation. P* 12.

412	133	4 c. green		30	10

134 "Founding of Halifax, 1749" (C. W. Jefferys)

1949 (21 June). *Bicentenary of Halifax, Nova Scotia. P* 12.

413	134	4 c. violet		30	10

135   **136**   **137**

138 King George VI **139**

(From photographs by Dorothy Wilding)

1949 (15 Nov)–51. (i) *P* 12.

414	135	1 c. green			10	10
415	136	2 c. sepia			60	30
415a		2 c. olive-green (25.7.51)			30	10
416	137	3 c. purple			30	10
		a. Booklet pane of 4 + 2 labels (12.4.50)		2·25		
417	138	4 c. carmine-lake			20	10
		a. Booklet pane of 6 (5.5.50)		27·00		
417b		4 c. vermilion (2.6.51)			40	10
		ba. Booklet pane of 6		6·00		
418	139	5 c. blue			2·00	10
414/18			Set of 7		3·50	40

(ii) *Imperf × perf* 9½ (coil stamps)

419	135	1 c. green (18.5.50)			1·25	1·00
420	136	2 c. sepia (18.5.50)			5·50	5·50
420a		2 c. olive-green (9.10.51)			1·75	2·00
421	137	3 c. purple (18.5.50)			2·25	2·00
422	138	4 c. carmine-lake (20.4.50)			14·00	7·50
422a		4 c. vermilion (27.11.51)			2·00	2·50
419/22a			Set of 6		24·00	18·00

(iii) *Imperf × perf* 12 (booklets)

422b	135	1 c. green (18.5.50)			50	1·75
		ba. Booklet pane of 3		1·50		
423	137	3 c. purple (18.5.50)			1·25	1·00
		a. Booklet pane of 3		3·75		
423b	138	4 c. carmine-lake (18.5.50)			15·00	7·00
		ba. Booklet pane of 3		45·00		
423c		4 c. vermilion (25.10.51)			7·00	7·00
		ca. Booklet pane of 3		21·00		
422b/3c			Set of 4		21·00	15·00

These booklet panes are imperforate at top, bottom and right-hand end.

140 King George VI   **141** Oil Wells in Alberta

(From photograph by Dorothy Wilding)

1950 (19 Jan). *As T* 135/9 *but without* "POSTES POSTAGE", *as T* 140. (i) *P* 12.

424	1 c. green			10	50
425	2 c. sepia			10	1·00
426	3 c. purple			10	90
427	4 c. carmine-lake			10	20
428	5 c. blue			30	1·25
424/8			Set of 5	60	3·50

(ii) *Imperf × perf* 9½ (coil stamps)

429	1 c. green		30	1·00
430	3 c. purple		80	1·50

1950 (1 Mar). *P* 12.

431	141	50 c. green		7·50	1·00

142 Drying Furs   **143** Fisherman

1950 (2 Oct). *P* 12.

432	142	10 c. brown-purple	1·60	10

1951 (1 Feb). *P* 12.

433	143	$1 ultramarine	38·00	5·00

144 Sir R. L. Borden   **145** W. L. Mackenzie King

1951 (25 June). *Prime Ministers (1st issue). P* 12.

434	144	3 c. blue-green	10	50
435	145	4 c. rose-carmine	10	10

See also Nos. 444/5, 475/6 and 483/4.

146 Mail Trains, 1851 and 1951   **147** SS. *City of Toronto* and SS. *Prince George*

148 Mail Coach and DC-4M North Star   **149** Reproduction of 3d., 1851

1951 (24 Sept). *Canadian Stamp Centenary. P* 12.

436	146	4 c. black	35	10
437	147	5 c. violet	65	1·75
438	148	7 c. blue	35	1·00
439	149	15 c. scarlet	1·10	10
436/9			Set of 4	2·25	2·75

150 Queen Elizabeth II when Princess and Duke of Edinburgh   **151** Forestry Products

1951 (26 Oct). *Royal Visit. P* 12.

440	150	4 c. violet	10	10

(Des A. L. Pollock)

1952 (1 Apr). *P* 12.

441	151	20 c. grey	1·50	10

152 Red Cross Emblem

1952 (26 July). *18th International Red Cross Conference, Toronto. Design recess; cross litho. P* 12.

442	152	4 c. scarlet and blue	15	10

153 Canada Goose   **154** Pacific Coast Indian House and Totem Pole

(Des E. Hahn)

1952 (3 Nov). *P* 12.
443 153 7 c. blue   75   10

1952 (3 Nov). *Prime Ministers (2nd issue). Various portraits as* T 144. *P* 12.
444 3 c. reddish purple   ..   15   20
445 4 c. orange-red   ..   20   10
Portraits:—3 c. Sir John J. C. Abbott; 4 c. A. Mackenzie.

(Des E. Hahn)

1953 (2 Feb). *P* 12.
446 154 $1 black   ..   4·75   20

155 Polar Bear   156 Elk   157 American Bighorn

(Des J. Crosby (2 c.), E. Hahn (others))

1953 (1 Apr). *National Wild Life Week. P* 12.
447 155 2 c. blue   10   10
448 156 3 c. sepia   10   30
449 157 4 c. slate   15   10
447/9   *Set of 3*   30   30

158 Queen Elizabeth II 159

(From photograph by Karsh, Ottawa)

1953 (1 May–3 Sept). (*a*) *Sheet stamps. P* 12.
450 158 1 c. purple-brown   ..   10   10
451   2 c. green   ..   15   10
452   3 c. carmine   ..   15   15
    a. Booklet pane of 4+2 labels (17.7)   1·25
453   4 c. violet   ..   20   10
    a. Booklet pane of 6 (6.7)   3·00
454   5 c. ultramarine   ..   20   10
450/4   *Set of 5*   70   30

(*b*) *Coil stamps. Imperf × perf* 9½.
455 158 2 c. green (30.7)   ..   1·75   1·00
456   3 c. carmine (27.7)   ..   1·75   1·00
457   4 c. violet (3.9)   ..   1·50   1·00
455/7   *Set of 3*   4·50   2·75

(*c*) *Booklet stamps. Imperf × perf* 12.
458 158 1 c. purple-brown (12.8)   2·00   1·50
    a. Booklet pane of 3   5·50
459   3 c. carmine (17.7)   ..   2·00   1·50
    a. Booklet pane of 3   5·50
460   4 c. violet (6.7)   ..   2·00   1·50
    a. Booklet pane of 3   5·50
458/60   *Set of 3*   5·50   4·00
These booklet stamps have top and bottom or top, bottom and right-hand sides imperforate.

(Des E. Hahn)

1953 (1 June). *Coronation. P* 12
461 159 4 c. violet   10   10

160 Textile Industry   161 Queen Elizabeth II

(Des A. L. Pollock)

1953 (2 Nov). *P* 12.
462 160 50 c. deep bluish green   ..   1·25   10

(From photograph by Dorothy Wilding)

1954–62. (i) *P* 12.
463 161 1 c. purple-brown (10.6.54)   10   10
    a. Booklet pane. Five stamps plus printed label (1.6.56)   1·00
    p. Two phosphor bands (13.1.62)   80   3·00
464   2 c. green (10.6.54)   ..   20   10
    a. Pack. Two blocks of 25 (12.61)   6·00
    p. Two phosphor bands (13.1.62)   80   3·25
465   3 c. carmine (10.6.54)   ..   70   10
    a. Imperf vert (horiz pair)   £1300
    p. Two phosphor bands (13.1.62)   1·50   3·50
466   4 c. violet (10.6.54)   ..   30   10
    a. Booklet pane of 6 (7.7.55)   4·25
    b. Booklet pane. Five stamps plus printed label (1.6.56)   1·75
    p. One phosphor band (13.1.62)   2·00   8·00

---

467 161 5 c. bright blue (1.4.54)   ..   30   10
    a. Booklet pane. Five stamps plus printed label (14.7.54)   2·75
    b. Pack. One block of 20 (12.61)   5·00
    c. Imperf vert (horiz pair)
    p. Two phosphor bands (13.1.62)   2·00   8·00
468   6 c. red-orange (10.6.54)   ..   1·00   30
463/8   *Set of 6*   2·25   45
463p/7p   *Set of 5*   6·50   23·00

(ii) *Imperf × perf* 9½ (*coil stamps*)
469 161 2 c. green (9.9.54)   ..   55   75
470   4 c. violet (23.8.54)   ..   55   1·25
471   5 c. bright blue (6.7.54) ..   1·75   45
469/71   *Set of 3*   2·50   2·25
No. 467c is from the left side of a sheet and shows perforations between the stamps and the sheet margin.
Nos. 464a and 467b are blocks with the outer edges imperf. These come from "One Dollar Plastic Packages" sold at post offices.

WINNIPEG PHOSPHOR BANDS. In 1962 facer-cancelling machines were introduced in Winnipeg which were activated by phosphor bands on the stamps. Under long or short wave ultraviolet light the phosphor glows and there is also a short after-glow when the lamp is turned off. This should not be confused with the fluorescent bands introduced in Ottawa in 1971.

162 Walrus   163 American Beaver   164 Northern Gannet

(Des E. Hahn)

1954 (1 Apr). *National Wild Life Week. P* 12.
472 162 4 c. slate-black ..   35   10
473 163 5 c. ultramarine   ..   35   10
    a. Booklet pane. Five stamps plus one printed label   1·75

(Des L. Hyde)

1954 (1 Apr). *P* 12.
474 164 15 c. black   ..   80   10

1954 (1 Nov). *Prime Ministers (3rd issue). Various portraits as* T 144. *P* 12.
475 4 c. violet   ..   15   20
476 5 c. bright blue   ..   15   10
Portraits:—4 c. Sir John Thompson; 5 c. Sir Mackenzie Bowell.

165 Eskimo Hunter

(Des H. Beament)

1955 (21 Feb). *P* 12.
477 165 10 c. purple-brown   ..   30   10

166 Musk Ox   167 Whooping Cranes

(Des E. Hahn (4 c.), Dr. W. Rowan (5 c.))

1955 (4 Apr). *National Wild Life Week. P* 12.
478 166 4 c. violet   ..   30   10
479 167 5 c. ultramarine   ..   90   20

168 Dove and Torch   169 Pioneer Settlers

(Des W. Lohse)

1955 (1 June). *Tenth Anniv of International Civil Aviation Organisation. P* 12.
480 168 5 c. ultramarine   ..   20   20

(Des L. Hyde)

1955 (30 June). *50th Anniv of Alberta and Saskatchewan Provinces. P* 12.
481 169 5 c. ultramarine   ..   15   20

---

170 Scout Badge and Globe   173 Ice-hockey Players

(Des L. Hyde)

1955 (20 Aug). *Eighth World Scout Jamboree, Niagara-on-the-Lake. P* 12.
482 170 5 c. orange-brown and green   20   10

1955 (8 Nov). *Prime Ministers (4th issue). Various portraits as* T 144. *P* 12.
483 4 c. violet   10   20
484 5 c. bright blue   ..   10   10
Portraits:—4 c. R. B. Bennett; 5 c. Sir Charles Tupper.

(Des J. Simpkins)

1956 (23 Jan). *Ice-hockey Commemoration. P* 12.
485 173 5 c. ultramarine   ..   15   20

174 Reindeer   175 Mountain Goat

(Des E. Hahn)

1956 (12 Apr). *National Wild Life Week. P* 12.
486 174 4 c. violet   20   15
487 175 5 c. bright blue   ..   20   10

176 Pulp and Paper Industry   177 Chemical Industry

(Des A. J. Casson (20 c.), A. L. Pollock (25 c.))

1956 (7 June). *P* 12.
488 176 20 c. green   55   10
489 177 25 c. red   55   10

178

(Des A. Price)

1956 (9 Oct). *Fire Prevention Week. P* 12
490 178 5 c. red and black   ..   30   10

179 Fishing   180 Swimming

(Des L. Hyde)

1957 (7 Mar). *Outdoor Recreation.* T 179/180 *and similar horiz designs. P* 12.
491 179 5 c. ultramarine   ..   25   10
    a. Block of 4. Nos. 491/4   1·25
492 180 5 c. ultramarine   ..   25   10
493   5 c. ultramarine   ..   25   10
494   5 c. ultramarine   ..   25   10
491/4 ..   *Set of 4*   1·25   35
Designs:— No. 493, Hunting. No. 494, Skiing.
No. 491/4 are printed together in sheets of 50 (5 × 10). In the first, second, fourth and fifth vertical rows the four different designs are arranged in *se-tenant* blocks, whilst the central row is made up as follows (reading downwards):—Nos. 491/4, 491/2 (or 493/4), 491/4.

183 White-billed Diver **184** Thompson with Sextant, and North American Map

(Des L. Hyde)

1957 (10 Apr). *National Wild Life Week.* P 12.
495   183   5 c. black   50   20

(Des G. A. Gundersen)

1957 (5 June). *Death Centenary of David Thompson (explorer).* P 12.
496   184   5 c. ultramarine   15   30

185 Parliament Buildings, Ottawa **186** Globe within Posthorn

(Des Carl Mangold)

1957 (14 Aug). *14th U.P.U. Congress, Ottawa.* P 12.
497   185   5 c. grey-blue   15   10
498   186   15 c. blackish blue   55   1·75

187 Miner **188** Queen Elizabeth II and Duke of Edinburgh

(Des A. J. Casson)

1957 (5 Sept). *Mining Industry.* P 12.
499   187   5 c. black   35   10

(From photographs by Karsh, Ottawa)

1957 (10 Oct). *Royal Visit.* P 12.
500   188   5 c. black   30   10

189 "A Free Press" **190** Microscope

(Des A. L. Pollock)

1958 (22 Jan). *The Canadian Press.* P 12.
501   189   5 c. black   15   30

(Des A. L. Pollock)

1958 (5 Mar). *International Geophysical Year.* P 12.
502   190   5 c. blue   20   10

191 Miner panning for Gold **192** La Verendrye (statue)

(Des J. Harman)

1958 (8 May). *Centenary of British Columbia.* P 12.
503   191   5 c. deep turquoise-green   ..   20   10

(Des G. Trottier)

1958 (4 June). *La Verendrye (explorer) Commemoration.* P 12.
504   192   5 c. ultramarine   15   10

193 Samuel de Champlain and the Heights of Quebec **194** Nurse

(Des G. Trottier)

1958 (26 June). *350th Anniv of Founding of Quebec.* P 12.
505   193   5 c. brown-ochre and deep green   30   10

(Des G. Trottier)

1958 (30 July). *National Health.* P 12.
506   194   5 c. reddish purple   30   10

195 "Petroleum 1858–1958" **196** Speaker's Chair and Mace

(Des A. L. Pollock)

1958 (10 Sept). *Centenary of Canadian Oil Industry.* P 12.
507   195   5 c. scarlet and olive   ..   30   10

(Des G. Trottier and C. Dair)

1958 (2 Oct). *Bicentenary of First Elected Assembly.* P 12.
508   196   5 c. deep slate   30   10

197 John McCurdy's Silver Dart Biplane **198** Globe showing N.A.T.O. Countries

1959 (23 Feb). *50th Anniv of First Flight of the Silver Dart in Canada.* P 12.
509   197   5 c. black and ultramarine   ..   30   10

(Des P. Weiss)

1959 (2 Apr). *Tenth Anniv of North Atlantic Treaty Organisation.* P 12.
510   198   5 c. ultramarine   40   10

199 **200** Queen Elizabeth II

(Des Helen Fitzgerald)

1959 (13 May). *"Associated Country Women of the World" Commemoration.* P 12.
511   199   5 c. black and yellow-olive   ..   15   10

(Des after painting by Annigoni)

1959 (18 June). *Royal Visit.* P 12.
512   200   5 c. lake-red   30   10

201 Maple Leaf linked with American Eagle **202** Maple Leaves

(Des A. L. Pollock, G. Trottier (of Canada); W. H. Buckley, A. J. Copeland, E. Metzl (of the United States))

1959 (26 June). *Opening of St. Lawrence Seaway.* P 12.
513   201   5 c. ultramarine and red   ..   20   10
     a. Centre inverted £9000 £5000
   It is believed that No. 513a occurred on two printer's sheets, each of 200 stamps. About 230 examples have been discovered.

(Des P. Weiss)

1959 (10 Sept). *Bicentenary of Battle of Plains of Abraham (Quebec).* P 12.
514   202   5 c. deep green and red   30   10

203 **204** Dollard des Ormeaux

(Des Helen Fitzgerald)

1960 (20 Apr). *Golden Jubilee of Canadian Girl Guides Movement.* P 12.
515   203   5 c. ultramarine and orange-brown   ..   20   10

(Des P. Weiss)

1960 (19 May). *Tercentenary of Battle of the Long Sault.* P 12.
516   204   5 c. ultramarine and light brown   ..   20   10

205 Surveyor, Bulldozer and Compass Rose **206** E. Pauline Johnson

(Des B. J. Reddie)

1961 (8 Feb). *Northern Development.* P 12.
517   205   5 c. emerald and red   15   10

(Des B. J. Reddie)

1961 (10 Mar). *Birth Centenary of E. Pauline Johnson (Mohawk poetess).* P 12.
518   206   5 c. green and red   15   10

207 Arthur Meighen (statesman) **208** Engineers and Dam

1961 (19 Apr). *Arthur Meighen Commemoration.* P 12.
519   207   5 c. ultramarine   15   10

(Des B. J. Reddie)

1961 (28 June). *Tenth Anniv of Colombo Plan.* P 12.
520   208   5 c. blue and brown   30   10

209 "Resources for Tomorrow" **210** "Education"

(Des A. L. Pollock)

1961 (12 Oct). *Natural Resources.* P 12.
521   209   5 c. blue-green and brown   ..   15   10

(Des Helen Fitzgerald)

1962 (28 Feb). *Education Year.* P 12.
522   210   5 c. black and orange-brown   ..   15   10

211 Lord Selkirk and Farmer **212** Talon bestowing Gifts on Married Couple

(Des Phillips-Gutkin Ltd)

1962 (3 May). *150th Anniv of Red River Settlement.* P 12.
523   211   5 c. chocolate and green   ..   20   10

(Des P. Weiss)

1962 (13 June). *Jean Talon Commemoration.* P 12.
524   212   5 c. blue   20   10

213 Br Columbia & Vancouver Is 2½d. stamp of 1860, and Parliament Buildings, B.C. **214** Highway (map version) and Provincial Arms

(Des Helen Bacon)

1962 (22 Aug). *Centenary of Victoria, B.C. P* 12.
525 **213** 5 c. red and black 30 10

(Des A. L. Pollock)

1962 (31 Aug). *Opening of Trans-Canada Highway. P* 12.
526 **214** 5 c. black and orange-brown 15 10

215 Queen Elizabeth II and Wheat (agriculture) Symbol **216** Sir Casimir Gzowski

(From drawing by Ernst Roch)

1962–64. *Horiz designs as T* **215** *showing Queen Elizabeth II and industry symbols.* (i) *P* 12
527 1 c. chocolate (4.2.63) 10 10
  a. Booklet pane. Five stamps plus one printed label (15.5.63) .. 3·50
  p. Two phosphor bands (15.5.63) .. 15 45
528 2 c. green (2.5.63) 15 10
  a. Pack. Two blocks of 25 .. .. 8·50
  p. Two phosphor bands (15.5.63) .. 20 45
529 3 c. reddish violet† (2.5.63) .. 15 10
  p. Two phosphor bands (15.5.63) .. 30 80
530 4 c. carmine-red (4.2.63) 15 10
  a. Booklet pane. Five stamps plus one printed label (15.5.63) .. 3·50
  b. Pack. One block of 25 .. .. 4·25
  p. One centre phosphor band (*narrow*)* (2.63) .. .. 50 3·00
  pa. One centre phosphor band (*wide*) (8.64) 3·75 5·50
  pb. One side phosphor band (12.64) .. 40 2·50
531 5 c. ultramarine (3.10.62) 15 10
  a. Booklet pane. Five stamps plus one printed label (5.63) .. .. 3·00
  b. Pack. One block of 20 .. .. 4·75
  c. Imperf horiz (vert pair) £2000 £600
  p. Two phosphor bands (31.1.63?) .. 35 45
  pa. Pack. One block of 20 .. .. 14·00
  pb. Imperf (pair) ..
527/31 .. .. *Set of 5* 65 15
527p/31p .. .. *Set of 5* 1·25 4·25

(ii) *P* 9½×*imperf (coil stamps)*
532 2 c. green (1963) .. .. .. 6·50 8·50
532a 3 c. reddish violet (1964) .. .. 4·75 3·50
533 4 c. carmine-red (15.5.63) .. .. 1·75 3·50
534 5 c. ultramarine (15.5.63) .. .. 4·50 1·25
  a. Imperf (pair) ..
532/4 .. .. *Set of 4* 16·00 15·00

Symbols:–1 c. Crystals (Mining); 2 c. Tree (Forestry); 3 c. Fish (Fisheries); 4 c. Electricity pylon (Industrial power).

Nos. 528a, 530b, 531b and 531pa are blocks with the outer edges imperf. These come from "One Dollar Plastic Packages" sold at post offices.

†This is a fugitive colour which tends to become reddish on drying. In successive printings the violet colour became more and more reddish as the printer tried to match the shade of each previous printing instead of referring back to the original shade. A deep reddish violet is also known from Plate 3. As there is such a range of shades it is not practical to list them.

*On No. 530p the band is 4 mm wide as against 8 mm on No. 530pa. No. 530pb exists with the band at either left or right side of the stamp, the bands being applied across alternate vertical perforations.

Postal forgeries are known of the 4 c. showing a coarser background and lack of shading on the Queen's face.

(Des P. Weiss)

1963 (5 Mar). *150th Birth Anniv of Sir Casimir Gzowski (engineer). P* 12.
535 **216** 5 c. reddish purple 10 10

217 "Export Trade" **218** Frobisher and barque *Gabriel*

(Des A. L. Pollock)

1963 (14 June). *P* 12.
536 **217** $1 carmine .. .. .. 4·75 2·00

(Des P. Weiss)

1963 (21 Aug). *Sir Martin Frobisher Commemoration. P* 12.
537 **218** 5 c. ultramarine 20 10

219 Horseman and Map **220** Canada Geese

(Des B. J. Reddie)

1963 (25 Sept). *Bicentenary of Quebec–Trois-Rivieres–Montreal Postal Service. P* 12.
538 **219** 5 c. red-brown and deep green .. 15 10

(Des A. Short and P. Arthur)

1963 (30 Oct). *P* 12.
539 **220** 15 c. blue .. .. .. 1·50 10

221 Douglas DC-9 Airliner and Uplands Airport, Ottawa **222** "Peace on Earth"

1964. *P* 12.
540 **221** 7 c. blue (11 Mar) 35 70
540a 8 c. blue (18 Nov) 50 50

1964 (8 Apr). *"Peace". Litho and recess. P* 12.
541 **222** 5 c. ochre, blue and turquoise-blue .. 15 10

223 Maple Leaves

1964 (14 May). *"Canadian Unity". P* 12.
542 **223** 5 c. lake-red and light blue .. 10 10

224 White Trillium and Arms of Ontario **236** Maple Leaf and Arms of Canada

1964–66. *Provincial Emblems. T* **224**, **236** *and similar horiz designs. Recess (No.* 555) *or litho and recess (others). P* 12.
543 5 c. green, brown and orange (30.6.64) 40 20
544 5 c. green, orange-brown and yellow (30.6.64) 40 20
545 5 c. carmine-red, green and bluish violet (3.2.65) 30 20
546 5 c. blue, red and green (3.2.65) .. 30 20
547 5 c. purple, green and yellow-brown (28.4.65) 30 20
548 5 c. red-brown, deep bluish green and mauve (28.4.65) 30 20
549 5 c. slate-lilac, green and light reddish purple (21.7.65) 50 20
550 5 c. green, yellow and rose-red (19.1.66) 30 20
551 5 c. sepia, orange and green (19.1.66) 30 20
552 5 c. black, green and red (23.2.66) .. 30 20
553 5 c. drab, green and yellow (23.3.66).. 30 20
554 5 c. blue, green and rose-red (23.3.66) 30 20
555 5 c. red and blue (30.6.66) .. 30 20
543/55 .. .. *Set of 13* 4·00 2·40

Designs:—No. 543, Type **224**; No. 544, Madonna Lily and Arms of Quebec; No. 545, Purple Violet and Arms of New Brunswick; No. 546, Mayflower and Arms of Nova Scotia; No. 547, Dogwood and Arms of British Columbia; No. 548, Prairie Crocus and Arms of Manitoba; No. 549, Lady's Slipper and Arms of Prince Edward Island; No. 550, Wild Rose and Arms of Alberta; No. 551, Prairie Lily and Arms of Saskatchewan; No. 552, Pitcher Plant and Arms of Newfoundland; No. 553, Mountain Avens and Arms of Northwest Territories; No. 554, Fireweed and Arms of Yukon Territory; No. 555, Type **236**.

(237) **238** Fathers of the Confederation Memorial, Charlottetown

1964 (15 July). *No.* 540 *surch with T* **237**.
556 **221** 8 c. on 7 c. blue 15 15
  a. Surch omitted (left-hand stamp of horiz pair) £6000

(Des P. Weiss)

1964 (29 July). *Centenary of Charlottetown Conference. P* 12.
557 **238** 5 c. black 10 10

239 Maple Leaf and Hand with Quill Pen **240** Queen Elizabeth II

(Des P. Weiss)

1964 (9 Sept). *Centenary of Quebec Conference. P* 12.
558 **239** 5 c. light red and chocolate .. 15 10

(Portrait by Anthony Buckley)

1964 (5 Oct). *Royal Visit. P* 12.
559 **240** 5 c. reddish purple 15 10

241 "Canadian Family" **242** "Co-operation"

1964 (14 Oct). *Christmas. P* 12.
560 **241** 3 c. scarlet 10 10
  a. Pack. Two blocks of 25 .. 7·00
  p. Two phosphor bands .. 60 2·25
  pa. Pack. Two blocks of 25 .. 13·00
561 5 c. ultramarine 10 10
  p. Two phosphor bands .. 90 2·25

Nos. 560a and 560pa are blocks with the outer edges imperf. These come from "$1.50 Plastic Packages" sold at post offices.

1965 (3 Mar). *International Co-operation Year. P* 12.
562 **242** 5 c. grey-green 35 10

243 Sir W. Grenfell **244** National Flag

1965 (9 June). *Birth Centenary of Sir Wilfred Grenfell (missionary). P* 12.
563 **243** 5 c. deep bluish green 20 10

1965 (30 June). *Inauguration of National Flag. P* 12.
564 **244** 5 c. red and blue 15 10

245 Sir Winston Churchill **246** Peace Tower, Parliament Buildings, Ottawa

(Des P. Weiss from photo by Karsh. Litho)

1965 (12 Aug). *Churchill Commemoration. P* 12.
565 **245** 5 c. purple-brown 15 10

(Des Philips-Gutkin)

1965 (8 Sept). *Inter-Parliamentary Union Conference, Ottawa. P* 12.
566 **246** 5 c. deep green 10 10

247 Parliament Buildings, Ottawa, 1865 **248** "Gold, Frankincense and Myrrh"

(Des G. Trottier)

1965 (8 Sept). *Centenary of Proclamation of Ottawa as Capital. P* 12.
567 **247** 5 c. brown 10 10

(Des Helen Fitzgerald)

1965 (13 Oct). *Christmas. P* 12.
568 **248** 3 c. olive-green 10 10
  a. Pack. Two blocks of 25 .. 5·00
  p. Two phosphor bands .. 10 70
  pa. Pack. Two blocks of 25 .. 5·50
569 5 c. ultramarine 10 10
  p. Two phosphor bands .. 20 35

Nos. 568a and 568pa are blocks with the outer edges imperf. These come from "$1.50 Plastic Packages" sold at post offices.

249 "Alouette 2" over Canada **250** La Salle

1966 (5 Jan). *Launching of Canadian Satellite, "Alouette 2". P* 12.
570 **249** 5 c. ultramarine 15 10

(Des Brigdens Ltd., Toronto)

1966 (13 Apr). *300th Anniv of La Salle's Arrival in Canada.* P 12.
571 250 5 c. deep bluish green 15 10

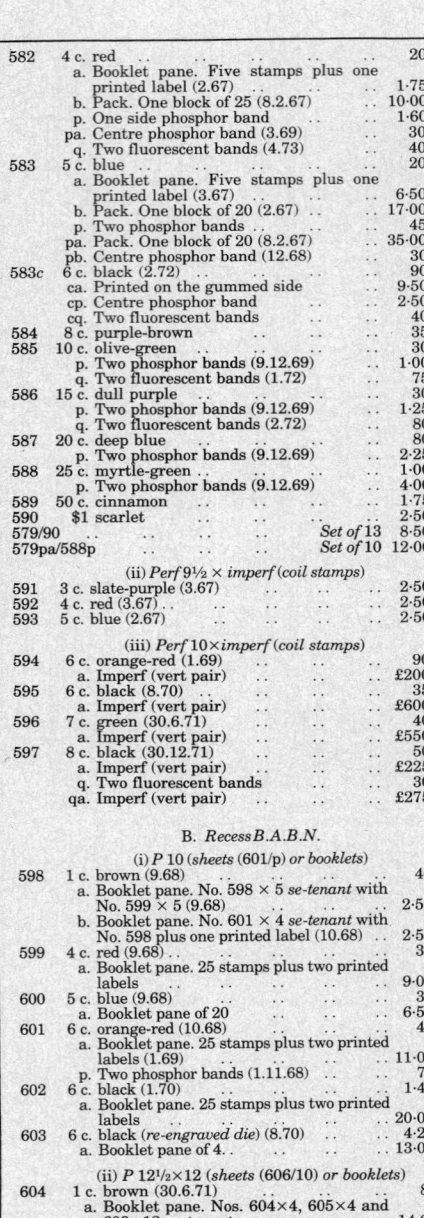

251 Road Signs   252 Canadian Delegation and Houses
                         of Parliament

(Des Helen Fitzgerald)

1966 (2 May). *Highway Safety. Invisible gum.* P 12.
572 251 5 c. yellow, blue and black 15 10

(Des P. Pederson (Brigdens Ltd))

1966 (26 May). *London Conference Centenary.* P 12.
573 252 5 c. red-brown 10 10

253 Douglas Point Nuclear Power   254 Parliamentary
        Station   Library, Ottawa

(Des A. L. Pollock)

1966 (27 July). *Peaceful Uses of Atomic Energy.* P 12.
574 253 5 c. ultramarine 10 10

(Des Brigdens Ltd)

1966 (8 Sept). *Commonwealth Parliamentary Association Conference, Ottawa.* P 12.
575 254 5 c. purple 10 10

255 "Praying Hands",   256 Flag and Canada or
    after Dürer   Globe

(Des G. Holloway)

1966 (12 Oct). *Christmas.* P 12.
576 255 3 c. carmine 10 10
        a. Pack. Two blocks of 25 .. .. 4·00
        p. Two phosphor bands 40 65
        pa. Pack. Two blocks of 25 .. 6·50
577   5 c. orange 10 10
        p. Two phosphor bands 40 95
Nos. 576a and 576pa are blocks with the outer edges imperf. These come from "$1.50 Plastic Packages" sold at post offices.

(Des Brigdens Ltd)

1967 (11 Jan). *Canadian Centennial. Invisible gum.* P 12.
578 256 5 c. scarlet and blue 10 10
        p. Two phosphor bands .. .. 30 1·00

257 Northern Lights   263 "The Jack Pine"
    and Dog-team   (T. Thomson)

1967 (8 Feb)–73. *T 257, 263 and similar horiz designs.*

A. Recess C.B.N.

(i) P 12
579 1 c. brown 10 10
        a. Booklet pane. Five stamps plus one
           printed label (2.67) 50
        b. Printed on the gummed side .. £450
        p. Two phosphor bands 30 80
        pa. Centre phosphor band (12.68) .. 30 70
        q. Two fluorescent bands (11.71) .. 30 10
580 2 c. green 10 10
        a. Booklet pane. No. 580×4 *se-tenant*
           with No. 581×4 with gutter margin
           between (26.10.70) .. .. 2·50
        p. Two phosphor bands 30 70
        pa. Centre phosphor band (12.68) .. 30 70
        q. Two fluorescent bands (12.72) .. 40 10
581 3 c. slate-purple 30 10
        p. Two phosphor bands .. .. 30 1·00
        q. Two fluorescent bands (1972?) ..

582 4 c. red 20 10
        a. Booklet pane. Five stamps plus one
           printed label (2.67) .. .. 1·75
        b. Pack. One block of 25 (8.2.67) .. 10·00
        o. One side phosphor band .. 1·60 2·25
        pa. Centre phosphor band (3.69) .. 30 70
        q. Two fluorescent bands (4.73) .. 40 10
583 5 c. blue 20 10
        a. Booklet pane. Five stamps plus one
           printed label (3.67) .. .. 6·50
        b. Pack. One block of 20 (2.67) .. 17·00
        p. Two phosphor bands 45 65
        pa. Pack. One block of 20 (8.2.67) .. 35·00
        pb. Centre phosphor band (12.68) .. 30 65
583c 6 c. black (2.72) 90 30
        ca. Printed on the gummed side .. 9·50
        cp. Centre phosphor band .. 2·50 2·25
        cq. Two fluorescent bands .. 40 30
584 8 c. purple-brown 35 30
585 10 c. olive-green 30 10
        p. Two phosphor bands (9.12.69) .. 1·00 1·75
        q. Two fluorescent bands (1.72) .. 75 50
586 15 c. dull purple 30 10
        p. Two phosphor bands (9.12.69) .. 1·25 2·75
        q. Two fluorescent bands (2.72) .. 80 1·00
587 20 c. deep blue 80 10
        p. Two phosphor bands (9.12.69) .. 2·25 2·75
588 25 c. myrtle-green .. .. .. 1·00 10
        p. Two phosphor bands (9.12.69) .. 4·00 5·50
589 50 c. cinnamon .. .. .. 1·75 10
590 $1 scarlet .. .. 2·50 65
579/90 .. .. *Set of 13* 8·50 1·60
579pa/588p .. .. .. *Set of 10* 12·00 16·00

(ii) *Perf 9½ × imperf (coil stamps)*
591 3 c. slate-purple (3.67) .. .. 2·50 3·00
592 4 c. red (3.67) .. .. .. 2·50 2·00
593 5 c. blue (2.67) .. .. .. 2·50 2·00

(iii) *Perf 10×imperf (coil stamps)*
594 6 c. orange-red (1.69) 90 35
        a. Imperf (vert pair) £200
595 6 c. black (8.70) 35 50
        a. Imperf (vert pair) £600
596 7 c. green (30.6.71) 40 70
        a. Imperf (vert pair) £550
597 8 c. black (30.12.71) 50 40
        a. Imperf (vert pair) £225
        q. Two fluorescent bands .. 30 30
        qa. Imperf (vert pair) £275

B. Recess B.A.B.N.

(i) *P 10 (sheets (601/p) or booklets)*
598 1 c. brown (9.68) .. .. .. 40 2·25
        a. Booklet pane. No. 598 × 5 *se-tenant* with
           No. 599 × 5 (9.68) .. .. 2·50
        b. Booklet pane. No. 601 × 4 *se-tenant* with
           No. 598 plus one printed label (10.68) .. 2·50
599 4 c. red (9.68) .. .. .. 30 1·25
        a. Booklet pane. 25 stamps plus two printed
           labels .. .. 9·00
600 5 c. blue (9.68) .. .. .. 30 1·25
        a. Booklet pane of 20 .. .. 6·50
601 6 c. orange-red (10.68) 45 10
        a. Booklet pane. 25 stamps plus two printed
           labels (1.69) .. .. .. 11·00
        p. Two phosphor bands (1.11.68) .. 75 85
602 6 c. black (1.70) .. .. .. 1·40 1·10
        a. Booklet pane. 25 stamps plus two printed
           labels .. .. 20·00
603 6 c. black (re-engraved die) (8.70) .. 4·25 3·00
        a. Booklet pane of 4. .. .. 13·00

(ii) *P 12½×12 (sheets (606/10) or booklets)*
604 1 c. brown (30.6.71) .. .. 80 1·60
        a. Booklet pane. Nos. 604×4, 605×4 and
           609×12 *se-tenant* .. .. 14·00
        b. Booklet pane. Nos. 604/5 and 609×3
           se-tenant plus one printed label .. 5·50
        c. Booklet pane. Nos. 604×3, 608 and
           610×2 *se-tenant* (30.12.71) .. 2·00
        d. Booklet pane. Nos. 604×6, 608 and
           610×11 *se-tenant* (30.12.71) .. 7·50
        e. Booklet pane. Nos. 604×4, 608 and
           610×5 *se-tenant* (8.72) .. 4·50
        q. Two fluorescent bands (30.12.71) .. 40 10
        qc. Booklet pane. Nos. 604q×3, 608q and
            610q×2 *se-tenant* .. .. 2·50
        qd. Booklet pane. Nos. 604q×6, 608q and
            610q×11 *se-tenant* .. .. 7·00
        qe. Booklet pane. Nos. 604q×4, 608q and
            610q×5 *se-tenant* (8.72) .. 4·50
605 3 c. slate-purple (30.6.71) .. 3·50 4·50
606 6 c. orange-red (3.69) .. .. 1·00 10
        p. Two phosphor bands .. .. 1·00 1·25
607 6 c. black (7.1.70) 30 10
        a. Booklet pane. 25 stamps plus two
           printed labels (8.70) .. 16·00
        p. Two phosphor bands .. .. 90 1·50
608 6 c. black (re-engraved die) (9.70) .. 80 10
        a. Booklet pane of 4 (11.70) .. 5·50
        p. One centre phosphor band (9.71) .. 1·75 2·50
        q. Two fluorescent bands (30.12.71) .. 75 10
609 7 c. myrtle-green (30.6.71) .. 30 10
        p. Two phosphor bands .. .. 60 1·75
610 8 c. slate-black (30.12.71) .. 30 10
        p. Two phosphor bands .. .. 60 1·00
        q. Two fluorescent bands (30.12.71) .. 45 15
Designs: (*as T 257*)—2 c. Totem pole; 3 c. Combine-harvester and oil derrick; 4 c. Ship in lock; 5 c. Harbour scene; 6 c., 7 c. "Transport"; 8 c. (Nos. 597, 610) Library of Parliament. (*as T 263*)—8 c. (No. 584) "Alaska Highway" (A. Y. Jackson); 15 c. "Bylot Island" (L. Harris); 20 c. "Quebec Ferry" (J. W. Morrice); 25 c. "The Solemn Land" (J. E. H. MacDonald); 50 c. "Summer's Stores" (grain elevators) (J. Ensor); $1 "Oilfield" (near Edmonton) (H. G. Glyde).
No. 581q only exists as a pre-cancel.
Nos. 582b, 583b and 583pa are blocks with the outer edges imperf. These come from "One Dollar Plastic Packages" sold at post offices.
No. 592p comes with the band to the left or right of the stamp, the phosphor having been applied across alternate vertical perforations.
Postal forgeries exist of the 6 c. orange printed in lithography and perforated 12½.

Normal

Re-engraved

When the basic postal rate was changed to 6 c. the C.B.N. lent their die to B.A.B.N. who made a duplicate die from it by transfer. Parts of this proved to be weak, but it was used for Nos. 601/2 and 606/7. B.A.B.N. later re-engraved their die to make fresh plates which were used for Nos. 603 and 608. No. 608 first appeared on sheets from Plate 4.
There are no records of dates of issue of the booklets, packs and coils, but supplies of these were distributed to depots in the months indicated.

IMPERF BETWEEN PAIRS FROM COIL STAMPS. Nos. 594/7 are known in blocks or horizontal pairs imperf between vertically. Coils are supplied to post offices in batches of ten coils held together by roulettes between every fourth stamp so that they can easily be split apart. If two or more unsplit coils are purchased it is possible to obtain blocks or pairs imperf between vertically.
Vertical coil stamps are also known imperf between horizontally or with some stamps apparently completely imperf. These can result from blind perforations identifiable by slight indentations.

WHITE FLUORESCENT PAPER. Different papers with varying degrees of whiteness have been used for Canadian stamps, but during 1968–70 a distinctive very white and highly fluorescent paper was used known as "hybrite"; this fluoresces on the back and front. This paper has also been employed for commemorative issues, some of which exist on more than one type of paper. The white fluorescent papers are recorded in the Stanley Gibbons *Elizabethan Catalogue*.

FLUORESCENT BANDS. During the second half of 1971 new sorting machines were installed in the Ottawa area which were activated by stamps bearing fluorescent bands. These differ from the Winnipeg phosphor bands in that they react green and have no after-glow. To the naked eye the fluorescent bands appear shiny when compared with the remainder of the stamp when looking along its surface. Winnipeg phosphor bands appear matt.
The experiments were successful and what was at first called "Ottawa tagging" has since come into more general use and the Winnipeg phosphor was phased out. However, the substance at first used (known as OP–4) was found to migrate to envelopes, documents, album pages, etc. as well as to adjoining stamps. Late in 1972 this fault was cured by using another substance (called OP–2). The migrating bands were used on early printings of Nos. 604q, 608q and 610q as well as certain stamps referred to in a footnote after No. 692. It is most advisable to use plastic mounts for housing stamps with migrating bands or else clear acetate should be affixed to the album leaves.

269 Canadian Pavilion   270 Allegory of
                             "Womanhood" on Ballot-box

(Des C.B.N.)

1967 (28 Apr). *World Fair, Montreal.* P 12.
611 269 5 c. blue and red 10 10

(Des Helen Fitzgerald. Litho)

1967 (24 May). *50th Anniv of Women's Franchise.* P 12.
612 270 5 c. reddish purple and black .. 10 10

271 Queen Elizabeth II and   272 Athlete
    Centennial Emblem

(Portrait from photo by Anthony Buckley)

1967 (30 June). *Royal Visit.* P 12.
613 271 5 c. plum and orange-brown .. 15 10

(Des Brigdens Ltd)

1967 (19 July). *Fifth Pan-American Games, Winnipeg.* P 12.
614 272 5 c. rose-red 10 10

273 "World News" 274 Governor-General Vanier

(Des W. McLauchlan)
1967 (31 Aug). *50th Anniv of the Canadian Press.* P 12.
615 273 5 c. blue 10 10

(Des from photo by Karsh)
1967 (15 Sept). *Vanier Commemoration.* P 12.
616 274 5 c. black 10 10

PRINTERS. The following were printed either by the Canadian Bank Note Co, Ottawa (C.B.N.) or the British American Bank Note Co, Ottawa (B.A.B.N.), *except where otherwise stated.*

275 People of 1867 and Toronto, 1967 276 Carol Singers

(Des and recess C.B.N.)
1967 (28 Sept). *Centenary of Toronto as Capital City of Ontario.* P 12.
617 275 5 c. myrtle-green and vermilion .. 10 10

(Des and recess B.A.B.N.)
1967 (11 Oct). *Christmas.* P 12.
618 276 3 c. scarlet 10 10
　　　a. Pack. Two blocks of 25 .. 3·25
　　　p. Two phosphor bands .. 15 50
　　　pa. Pack. Two blocks of 25 .. 3·25
619 　　5 c. emerald-green 10 10
　　　p. Two phosphor bands .. 30 50
Nos. 618a and 618pa are blocks with the outer edges imperf. These come from "$1.50 Plastic Packs" sold at post offices.

277 Grey Jays 278 Weather Map and Instruments

(Des M. G. Loates. Litho C.B.N.)
1968 (15 Feb). *Wild Life.* P 12.
620 277 5 c. multicoloured 30 10
See also Nos. 638/40.

(Des and litho B.A.B.N.)
1968 (13 Mar). *Bicentenary of First Meteorological Readings.* P 11.
621 278 5 c. multicoloured 15 10

279 Narwhal 280 Globe, Maple Leaf and Rain Gauge

(Des J. A. Crosby. Litho B.A.B.N.)
1968 (10 Apr). *Wildlife.* P 11.
622 279 5 c. multicoloured 15 10
No. 622 has a background of yellow-green and pale blue but copies are known with the yellow-green apparently missing. This "yellow-green" is produced by an overlay of yellow on the blue but we have not come across any copies where the yellow is completely missing and the wide range of colour variation is due to technical difficulties in maintaining an exact blend of the two colours.

(Des I. von Mosdossy. Litho B.A.B.N.)
1968 (8 May). *International Hydrological Decade.* P 11.
623 280 5 c. multicoloured 15 10

IMPERF EDGES. On Nos. 624/54, 657 and 659 (stamps printed by the B.A.B.N. Co.) the outer edges of the sheets were guillotined to remove the imprints for P.O. stock so that single stamps may, therefore, be found with either one, or two adjacent sides imperforate.

281 Nonsuch 282 Lacrosse Players

(Recess and photo B.A.B.N.)
1968 (5 June). *300th Anniv of Voyage of the "Nonsuch".* P 10.
624 281 5 c. multicoloured 20 10

(Des J. E. Aldridge. Recess and photo B.A.B.N.)
1968 (3 July). *Lacrosse.* P 10.
625 282 5 c. black, red and lemon .. 15 10

283 Front Page of The Globe, George Brown and Legislative Building 284 H. Bourassa

(Des N. Sabolotny. Recess and photo B.A.B.N.)
1968 (21 Aug). *150th Birth Anniv of George Brown (politician and journalist).* P 10.
626 283 5 c. multicoloured 10 10

(Des, recess and litho C.B.N.)
1968 (4 Sept). *Birth Centenary of Henri Bourassa (journalist and politician).* P 12.
627 284 5 c. black, red and pale cream .. 10 10

285 John McCrae, Battlefield and First Lines of "In Flanders Fields" 286 Armistice Monument, Vimy

(Des I. von Mosdossy. Litho C.B.N.)
1968 (15 Oct). *50th Death Anniv of John McCrae (soldier and poet).* P 12.
628 285 5 c. multicoloured 10 10

(Des and recess C.B.N.)
1968 (15 Oct). *50th Anniversary of 1918 Armistice.* P 12.
629 286 15 c. slate-black 30 40

287 Eskimo Family (carving) 288 "Mother and Child" (carving)

(Designs from Eskimo carvings by Munamee (6 c.) and unknown carver (5 c.). Photo C.B.N.)
1968. *Christmas.* P 12.
630 287 5 c. black and new blue (1.11.68) .. 10 10
　　　a. Booklet pane of 10 (15.11.68) .. 2·50
　　　p. One centre phosphor band .. 10 60
　　　pa. Booklet pane of 10 (15.11.68) .. 3·50
631 288 6 c. black and ochre (15.11.68) .. 10 10
　　　p. Two phosphor bands .. 20 60

289 Curling 290 Vincent Massey

(Des D. Eales. Recess and photo B.A.B.N.)
1969 (15 Jan). *Curling.* P 10.
632 289 6 c. black, new blue and scarlet .. 15 10

(Des I. von Mosdossy. Recess and litho C.B.N.)
1969 (20 Feb). *Vincent Massey, First Canadian-born Governor-General.* P 12.
633 290 6 c. sepia and yellow-ochre .. 10 10

291 "Return from the Harvest Field" (Suzor-Côté) 292 Globe and Tools

(Photo C.B.N.)
1969 (14 Mar). *Birth Centenary of Marc Aurèle de Foy Suzor-Côté (painter).* P 12.
634 291 50 c. multicoloured .. .. 70 2·00

(Des J. Hébert. Recess B.A.B.N.)
1969 (21 May). *50th Anniv of International Labour Organisation.* P 12½ × 12.
635 292 6 c. bronze-green 10 10

293 Vickers FB-27 Vimy Aircraft over Atlantic Ocean 294 "Sir William Osler" (J. S. Sargent)

(Des R. W. Bradford. Recess and photo B.A.B.N.)
1969 (13 June). *50th Anniv of First Non-stop Transatlantic Flight.* P 12 × 12½.
636 293 15 c. chocolate, bright green & pale blue 40 55

(Des, recess and photo B.A.B.N.)
1969 (23 June). *50th Death Anniv of Sir William Osler (physician).* P 12½ × 12.
637 294 6 c. deep blue, light blue and chestnut 20 10

295 White-throated Sparrows 298 Flags of Winter and Summer Games

(Des M. G. Loates. Litho C.B.N.)
1969 (23 July). *Birds.* T 295 and similar multicoloured designs. P 12.
638 　　6 c. Type 295 .. .. 25 10
639 　　10 c. Savannah Sparrow (horiz) .. 50 1·10
640 　　25 c. Hermit Thrush (horiz) .. 1·60 2·75
638/40 .. .. .. Set of 3 2·10 3·50

(Des C. McDiarmid. Recess and litho C.B.N.)
1969 (15 Aug). *Canadian Games.* P 12.
641 298 6 c. emerald, scarlet and blue .. 10 10

299 Outline of Prince Edward Island showing Charlottetown 300 Sir Isaac Brock and Memorial Column

(Des L. Fitzgerald. Recess and photo B.A.B.N.)
1969 (15 Aug). *Bicentenary of Charlottetown as Capital of Prince Edward Island.* P 12 × 12½.
642 299 6 c. yellow-brown, black and blue 20 10

(Des I. von Mosdossy. Recess and litho C.B.N.)
1969 (12 Sept). *Birth Bicentenary of Sir Isaac Brock.* P 12.
643 300 6 c. orange, bistre and bistre-brown 10 10

317

301 Children of the World in Prayer

302 Stephen Butler Leacock, Mask and "Mariposa"

(Des Rapid Grip and Batten Ltd. Litho C.B.N.)

1969 (8 Oct). *Christmas.* P 12.
644	301	5 c. multicoloured	..	..	10	10
		a. Booklet pane of 10	..	..	1·75	
		p. One centre phosphor band	..		10	70
		pa. Booklet pane of 10	..	..	2·50	
645		6 c. multicoloured	..	..	10	10
		a. Black (inscr, value and frame omitted			..£1200	
		p. Two phosphor bands ..	..	..	20	70

(Des, recess and photo B.A.B.N.)

1969 (12 Nov). *Birth Centenary of Stephen Butler Leacock (humorist).* P 12 × 12½.
646	302	6 c. multicoloured	..	..	10	10

303 Symbolic Cross-roads

304 "Enchanted Owl" (Kenojuak)

(Des K. C. Lochhead. Litho C.B.N.)

1970 (27 Jan). *Centenary of Manitoba.* P 12.
647	303	6 c. ultramarine, lemon and vermilion		15	10
		p. Two phosphor bands	..	..	15	70

(Des N. E. Hallendy and Miss S. Van Raalte. Recess C.B.N.)

1970 (27 Jan). *Centenary of Northwest Territories.* P 12.
648	304	6 c. carmine-red and black	..		10	10

305 Microscopic View of Inside of Leaf

306 Expo 67 Emblem and Stylized Cherry Blossom

(Des I. Charney. Recess and photo B.A.B.N.)

1970 (18 Feb). *International Biological Programme.* P 12 × 12½.
649	305	6 c. emerald, orange-yellow & ultram ..	15	10

(Des E. R. C. Bethune. Litho C.B.N.)

1970 (18 Mar). *World Fair, Osaka.* T **306** *and similar horiz designs. Multicoloured; colour of Cherry Blossom given.* P 12.
650	25 c. red	..	..	..	1·50	2·00
	a. Block of 4. Nos. 650/3	..	..	5·50	
	p. Two phosphor bands	..	..	1·50	2·25
	pa. Block of 4. Nos. 650p/3p	..	5·50	
651	25 c. violet	..	..	..	1·50	2·00
	p. Two phosphor bands	..	..	1·50	2·25
652	25 c. green	..	..	..	1·50	2·00
	p. Two phosphor bands	..	..	1·50	2·25
653	25 c. blue	..	..	..	1·50	2·00
	p. Two phosphor bands	..	..	1·50	2·25
650/3				*Set of* 4	5·50	7·00
650p/3p				*Set of* 4	5·50	8·00

Designs:—No. 650, Type **306**; No. 651, Dogwood and stylized cherry blossom; No. 652, White Trillium and stylized cherry blossom; No. 653, White Garden Lily and stylized cherry blossom.

Nos. 650/3 and 650p/3p are printed together in sheets of 50 (5 × 10). In the first, second, fourth and fifth vertical rows the four different designs are arranged in *se-tenant* blocks, whilst the centre row is composed as follows (reading downwards:—650(p)/3(p), 650(p) × 2, 653(p), 651(p), 652(p) and 650(p).

310 Henry Kelsey

311 "Towards Unification"

(Des D. Burton. Recess and photo B.A.B.N.)

1970 (15 Apr). *300th Birth Anniv of Henry Kelsey (explorer).* P 12 × 12½.
654	310	6 c. multicoloured	..	..	10	10

(Des B. Fisher. Litho B.A.B.N.)

1970 (13 May). *25th Anniv of United Nations.* P 11.
655	311	10 c. blue	..	..	40	30
		p. Two phosphor bands	..	60	2·00
656		15 c. magenta and bluish lilac	..	40	35
		p. Two phosphor bands	..	70	2·00

312 Louis Riel (Métis leader)

313 Mackenzie's Inscription, Dean Channel

(Des R. Derreth. Photo B.A.B.N.)

1970 (19 June). *Louis Riel Commemoration.* P 12½ × 12.
657	312	6 c. greenish blue and vermilion	10	10

(Design from Government Archives photo. Recess C.B.N.)

1970 (25 June). *Sir Alexander Mackenzie (explorer).* P 12 × 11½.
658	313	6 c. bistre-brown	..	..	15	10

314 Sir Oliver Mowat (statesman)

315 "Isles of Spruce" (A. Lismer)

(Des E. Roch. Recess and photo B.A.B.N.)

1970 (12 Aug). *Sir Oliver Mowat Commemoration.* P 12 × 12½.
659	314	6 c. vermilion and black	..	10	10

(Litho Ashton-Potter)

1970 (18 Sept). *50th Anniv of "Group of Seven" (artists).* P 11.
660	315	6 c. multicoloured	..	..	10	10

316 "Horse-drawn Sleigh" (D. Niskala)

317 "Christ in Manger" (C. Fortier)

(Des from children's drawings. Litho C.B.N.)

1970 (7 Oct). *Christmas. Horiz designs as* T **316/17**, *showing children's drawings. Multicoloured.* P 12.
661	5 c. Type **316**	..	..	50	20
	a. Strip of 5. Nos. 661/5	..	2·25	
	p. One centre phosphor band	..	90	1·25
	pa. Strip of 5. Nos. 661p/5p ..	4·00	
662	5 c. "Stable" and Star of Bethlehem" (L. Wilson) (26 × 21 *mm*)	..	50	20
	p. One centre phosphor band	..	90	1·25
663	5 c. "Snowmen" (M. Lecompte) (26 × 21 *mm*)		50	20
	p. One centre phosphor band	..	90	1·25
664	5 c. "Skiing" (D. Durham) (26 × 21 *mm*)		50	20
	p. One centre phosphor band	..	90	1·25
665	5 c. "Santa Claus" (A. Martin) (26 × 21 *mm*)		50	20
	p. One centre phosphor band	..	90	1·25
666	6 c. "Santa Claus" (E. Bhattacharya) (26 × 21 *mm*)	..	50	20
	a. Strip of 5. Nos. 666/70	..	2·25	
	p. Two phosphor bands	..	90	1·25
	pa. Strip of 5. Nos. 666p/70p..	4·00	
667	6 c. "Christ in Manger" (J. McKinney) (26 × 21 *mm*)	..	50	20
	p. Two phosphor bands	..	90	1·25
668	6 c. "Toy Shop" (N. Whateley) (26 × 21 *mm*)	..	50	20
	p. Two phosphor bands	..	90	1·25
669	6 c. "Christmas Tree" (J. Pomperleau) (26 × 21 *mm*)	..	50	20
	p. Two phosphor bands	..	90	1·25
670	6 c. "Church" (J. McMillan) (26 × 21 *mm*)	..	50	20
	p. Two phosphor bands	..	90	1·25
671	10 c. Type **317**	..	..	30	30
	p. Two phosphor bands	..	55	1·25
672	15 c. "Trees and Sledge" (J. Dojcak) (35 × 21 *mm*)	..	45	60
	p. Two phosphor bands	..	70	1·75
661/72			*Set of* 12	4·75	2·50
661p/672p			*Set of* 12	8·50	12·50

The designs of the 5 c. and 6 c. were each issued with the various designs *se-tenant* in a diamond shaped arrangement within the sheet. This generally results in *se-tenant* pairs both vert and horiz, but due to the sheet arrangement vert and horiz pairs of the same design exist from the two centre vert and horiz rows.

328 Sir Donald A. Smith

329 "Big Raven" (E. Carr)

(Des Dora de Pédery-Hunt. Litho C.B.N.)

1970 (4 Nov). *150th Birth Anniv of Sir Donald Alexander Smith.* P 12.
673	328	6 c. yellow, brown and bronze-green ..	15	10

(Litho C.B.N.)

1971 (12 Feb). *Birth Centenary of Emily Carr (painter).* P 12.
674	329	6 c. multicoloured	..	..	20	30

330 Laboratory Equipment

331 "The Atom"

(Des R. Webber. Litho B.A.B.N.)

1971 (3 Mar). *50th Anniv of Discovery of Insulin.* P 10½.
675	330	6 c. multicoloured	..	..	30	30

(Des R. Webber. Litho B.A.B.N.)

1971 (24 Mar). *Birth Centenary of Lord Rutherford (scientist).* P 11.
676	331	6 c. yellow, red and deep chocolate	20	20

332 Maple "Keys"

333 Louis Papineau

(Des Alma Duncan. Litho Ashton-Potter)

1971. *"The Maple Leaf in Four Seasons".* T **332** *and similar vert designs. Multicoloured.* P 11.
677	6 c. Type **332** (Spring) (14.4) ..	..	20	20
	a. Imperf (pair)	..	..	£600	
678	6 c. Green leaves (Summer) (16.6)	..	20	20
679	7 c. Autumn leaves (3.9)	..	..	20	20
	a. Grey (inscr and value) omitted ..	£2000	
680	7 c. Withered leaves and snow (Winter) (19.11)	..	..	20	20
677/80			*Set of* 4	70	70

(Des L. Marquart. Recess and photo B.A.B.N.)

1971 (7 May). *Death Centenary of Louis-Joseph Papineau (politician).* P 12½ × 12.
681	333	6 c. multicoloured	..	..	15	20

334 Chart of Coppermine River

335 "People" and Computer Tapes

(Des L. Marquart. Recess and photo B.A.B.N.)

1971 (7 May). *Bicentenary of Samuel Hearne's Expedition to Coppermine River.* P 12 × 12½.
682	334	6 c. red, sepia and pale buff		40	40

(Des H. Kleefeld. Litho C.B.N.)

1971 (1 June). *Centenary of First Canadian Census.* P 11½.
683	335	6 c. blue, red and black ..	..	30	20

336 Maple Leaves

(Des B. Kramer. Litho C.B.N.)

1971 (1 June). *Radio Canada International.* P 12.
684	336	15 c. red, yellow and black	..	50	1·25
		p. Two phosphor bands	..	1·75	3·50

337 "BC"

(Des E. R. C. Bethune. Litho C.B.N.)

1971 (20 July). *Centenary of British Columbia's Entry into the Confederation.* P 12.
685	337	7 c. multicoloured	..	..	15	10

338 "Indian Encampment on Lake Huron" (Kane)
339 "Snowflake"

(Des and litho B.A.B.N.)

1971 (11 Aug). *Death Centenary of Paul Kane (painter).* P 12½.
686 **338** 7 c. multicoloured 20 10

(Des Lisl Levinsohn. Recess (6 c., 7 c.) or recess and litho (others) C.B.N.)

1971 (6 Oct). *Christmas.* T **379** *and similar design.* P 12.
687 **339** 6 c. deep blue 10 10
  p. One centre phosphor band .. 30 60
688   7 c. deep emerald 15 10
  p. Two phosphor bands .. 40 65
689 – 10 c. silver and cerise .. .. 50 1·25
  p. Two phosphor bands .. 1·00 1·25
690 – 15 c. silver, brown-purple and lavender 65 1·50
  p. Two phosphor bands .. 1·00 2·75
687/90   Set of 4 1·25 2·75
687p/90p   Set of 4 2·40 5·50
Design:—10 c., 15 c. "Snowflake" design similar to Type **339**, but square (26×26 mm).

340 Pierre Laporte (Quebec Cabinet Minister)
341 Skaters

(Des G. Gundersen. Recess and litho B.A.B.N.)

1971 (20 Oct). *First Anniv of the Assassination of Pierre Laporte.* P 12½ × 12.
691 **340** 7 c. black/*pale buff* 15 10

(Des Design Workshop, Toronto. Litho C.B.N.)

1972 (1 Mar). *World Figure Skating Championships, Calgary.* P 12.
692 **341** 8 c. purple 15 10

MIGRATING FLUORESCENT BANDS. These are referred to in the notes after No. 610. In the following issues they exist on Nos. 719q/22q, 731q/2q and on early printings only of Nos. 702/6.

342 J. A. MacDonald
343 Forest, Central Canada

344 Vancouver

Type II

Two types of 10 c. (No. 702):
Type I. Light impression of green recess colour. Cross-hatching around "Canada" clearly visible (plate 1).
Type II. Green recess colour much more deeply etched. Cross-hatching around "Canada" entirely obscured (plates 2 and 3).

Type I

Type II

Two types of 15 c.:
Type I. Trees on hillside, shown in blue, clearly detailed (plate 1).
Type II. Trees shown in solid colour (plate 2).

Two types of 25 c.:
Type I. Bears' shadows evenly shaded.
Type II. Shadows have a solid central area.

(Des D. Annesley (1 to 10 c. (701)), R. Derreth (others))

1972–77. *Various designs as* T **342/4.**
(*a*) T **342** *and similar vert portraits. Recess C.B.N. (1 to 6 c. and last ptgs of 7 and 8 c. (No. 700), B.A.B.N. (7, 8, 10 c. and booklet panes). Two fluorescent bands. P 12 × 12½ (1 to 8 c.) or 13 (10 c.). (17.10.73)*
693   1 c. orange 10 10
  a. Booklet pane. Nos. 693×3, 698 and 700×2 (10.4.74) 65
  b. Booklet pane. Nos. 693×6, 698 and 700×11 (17.1.75) 2·25
  c. Booklet pane. Nos. 693×2, 694×4 and 701a×4 (1.9.76) 1·50
  d. Printed on the gummed side £150
694   2 c. deep green 10 10
695   3 c. agate 10 30
696   4 c. black 10 10
697   5 c. deep magenta 10 10
698   6 c. Indian red 10 10
  a. Printed on the gummed side .. 75·00
699   7 c. reddish brown (8.4.74) .. 20 30
700   8 c. dull ultramarine 15 10
  a. Perf 13 (12.76) .. .. 1·25 70
701   10 c. brown-lake (1.9.76) .. 50 10
  a. Perf 12×12½ (booklets) .. 90 90

(*b*) T **343** *and similar vert designs. Recess and photo B.A.B.N. Two fluorescent bands.* P 12½×12 (8.9.72)
702   10 c. dp green, blue-green & yellow-orge (I) 60 10
  a. Type II (7.74) 40 15
  b. Perf 13½ (2.76) 75 10
  p. Two phosphor bands .. 1·00 2·00
703   15 c. dull ultramarine and orange-brown (I) 90 15
  a. Type II (1975) .. .. 2·75 1·40
  b. Perf 13½ (2.76) 75 10
  p. Two phosphor bands .. 1·75 2·75
704   20 c. pale orange, reddish violet & ultram 75 10
  a. Perf 13½ (30.1.76) .. 30 10
  p. Two phosphor bands .. 2·00 3·00
705   25 c. deep ultramarine and pale blue (I) 1·25 10
  a. Type II (1975) .. .. 6·50 2·50
  b. Perf 13½ (2.76) .. .. 1·00 10
  p. Two phosphor bands .. 3·00 4·25
706   50 c. blue-green, royal blue and buff 60 30
  a. Blue-green, ultramarine and buff (8.74) 65 20
  b. Perf 13½ (2.76) .. .. 1·50 10

(*c*) T **344** *and similar horiz design. Recess B.A.B.N. and litho Ashton-Potter. No fluorescent bands.* P 11 (17.3.72)
707   $1 multicoloured .. .. 4·50 4·75
708   $2 multicoloured .. .. 1·50 2·00

(*d*) T **344.** *Recess and photo B.A.B.N. Two fluorescent bands.* P 12½ × 12 (24.10.73)
709   $1 multicoloured .. .. 2·75 1·00
  a. Perf 13½ (4.77) 85 70

(*e*) *As Nos.* 700/1. *Recess C.B.N. Imperf × perf 10 (coil stamps)*
710   8 c. dull ultramarine (10.4.74) 85 20
  a. Imperf (horiz pair) .. .. 80·00
711   10 c. brown-lake (1.9.76) .. 30 20
  a. Imperf (horiz pair) £100

Designs (1 to 7c. show Canadian Prime Ministers):—2 c. W. Laurier; 3 c. R. Borden; 4 c. W. L. Mackenzie King; 5 c. R. B. Bennett; 6 c. L. B. Pearson; 7 c. Louis St. Laurent; 8 and 10 c. (Nos. 701/a, 711), Queen Elizabeth II; 15 c. American Bighorn sheep; 20 c. Prairie landscape from the air; 25 c. Polar Bears; 50 c. Seashore, Eastern Canada; $2 Quebec.
Stamps from booklets exist with one or two adjacent sides imperforate.

345 Heart

(Des Joyce Wieland. Recess B.A.B.N.)

1972 (7 Apr). *Heart Disease (World Health Day).* P 12×12½.
719 **345** 8 c. carmine 30 10
  q. Two fluorescent bands .. 60 25
The chemical used on No. 719q migrates.

346 Frontenac and Fort Saint-Louis, Quebec

(Des L. Marquart. Recess and photo B.A.B.N.)

1972 (17 May). *300th Anniv of Governor Frontenac's Appointment to New France.* P 12 × 12½.
720 **346** 8 c. brown-red, orange-brn & dp ultram 15 15
  q. Two fluorescent bands .. 15 15
The chemical used on No. 720q migrates.

347 Plains Indians' Artefacts
347a Buffalo Chase

(Des G. Beaupré. Litho Ashton-Potter (721/2, 725/6 and 729/30), B.A.B.N. (723/4), C.B.N. (727/8))

1972–76. *Canadian Indians. Two fluorescent bands (Nos. 723/30 and 733/40).* P 12×12½ (721/2, 725/6), 12 (723/4), 13 (727/30), 12½×12 (731/6) or 12½ (737/40).
(*a*) *Horiz designs issued in se-tenant pairs, the first showing Artefacts as* T **347***, the second showing Scenes from Indian Life as* T **347a.**
721   8 c. multicoloured (6.7.72) 40 10
  a. Pair. Nos. 721/2 .. .. 85 1·00
  q. Two fluorescent bands .. 40 15
  qa. Pair. Nos. 721q/2q .. 85 1·00
722   8 c. dp brown, yellow & grey-black (6.7.72) 40 10
  q. Two fluorescent bands .. 40 15
723   8 c. multicoloured (21.2.73) .. 40 10
  a. Pair. Nos. 723/4 .. .. 85 1·00
724   8 c. multicoloured (21.2.73) .. 40 10
725   8 c. multicoloured (16.1.74) .. 40 10
  a. Pair. Nos. 725/6 .. .. 85 1·25
726   8 c. dp brown, yellow & grey-black (16.1.74) 40 10
727   8 c. multicoloured (4.4.75) .. 40 10
  a. Pair. Nos. 727/8 .. .. 85 1·25
728   8 c. multicoloured (4.4.75) .. 40 10
729   10 c. multicoloured (17.9.76) .. 40 20
  a. Pair. Nos. 729/30 .. .. 85 1·00
730   10 c. light stone and black (17.9.76) .. 40 20
Designs show the following tribes: Nos. 721/2 (T **347**/a), Plains Indians; 723/4, Algonkians; 725/6, Pacific Coast Indians; 727/8, Subarctic Indians; 729/30, Iroquoians.

348 Thunderbird and Tribal Pattern
348a Dancer in Ceremonial Costume

(Des G. Beaupré. Recess and photo B.A.B.N. (731/6). Litho and embossed Ashton-Potter (737, 739). Litho Ashton-Potter (738, 740))
(*b*) *Vert designs issued in se-tenant pairs, the first showing Thunderbird and pattern as* T **348***, the second Costumes as* T **348a.**
731   8 c. lt yellow-orge, rose-red & blk (4.10.72) 40 15
  a. Pair. Nos. 731/2 .. .. 85 1·00
  q. Two fluorescent bands .. 40 15
  qa. Pair. Nos. 731q/2q .. 85 1·00
732   8 c. multicoloured (4.10.72) .. 40 15
  q. Two fluorescent bands .. 40 15
733   8 c. light rose-red, violet & black (28.11.73) 40 10
  a. Pair. Nos. 733/4 .. .. 85 1·00
734   8 c. turq-green, lake-brn & blk (28.11.73) 40 10

735	8 c. rose-red and black (22.2.74)		40	10
	a. Pair. Nos. 735/6		85	1·00
736	8 c. multicoloured (22.2.74)		40	10
737	8 c. myrtle-green, grey-brn & blk (4.4.75)		40	10
	a. Pair. Nos. 737/8		85	1·25
738	8 c. multicoloured (4.4.75)		40	10
739	10 c. olive-bistre, reddish orange and black (17.9.76)		40	20
	a. Pair. Nos. 739/40		85	1·00
740	10 c. multicoloured (17.9.76)		40	20
721/40		Set of 20	7·50	2·10

Designs show the following tribes: Nos. 731/2 (T 348/a), Plains Indians; 733/4, Algonkians; 735/6, Pacific Coast Indians; 737/8, Subarctic Indians; 739/40, Iroquoians.
The fluorescent bands on Nos. 721q/2q and 731q/2q migrate.

349 Earth's Crust   350 Candles

(Des Gottschalk and Ash Ltd. Litho Ashton-Potter)

1972 (2 Aug). *Earth Sciences. T* **349** *and similar square designs.* P 12.

741	15 c. multicoloured		1·40	1·90
	a. Block of 4. Nos. 741/4		5·00	
	q. Two fluorescent bands		1·50	2·00
	qa. Block of 4. Nos. 741q/4q		5·50	
742	15 c. pale grey, dull ultramarine and black		1·40	1·90
	q. Two fluorescent bands		1·50	2·00
743	15 c. multicoloured		1·40	1·90
	q. Two fluorescent bands		1·50	2·00
744	15 c. light emerald, red-orange and black		1·40	1·90
	q. Two fluorescent bands		1·50	2·00
741/4		Set of 4	5·00	6·50
741q/4q		Set of 4	5·50	7·50

Designs and Events:—No. 741, Photogrammetric surveying (12th Congress of International Society of Photogrammetry); No. 742, "Siegfried" lines (6th Conference of International Cartographic Association); No. 743, Type **349** (24th International Geological Congress); No. 744, Diagram of village at road-intersection (22nd International Geographical Congress).
Nos. 741/4 were issued in sheets of 64, made up of 4 panes of 16, each pane having a marginal commemorative inscription. Within a pane are 4 copies of each design, arranged in *se-tenant* blocks of 4.

(Des R. Webber. Litho Ashton-Potter)

1972 (1 Nov). *Christmas. T* **350** *and similar designs.* P 12½ × 12 (6 *and* 8 c.) *or* 11 × 10½ (*others*).

745	350	6 c. multicoloured	15	10
		p. One centre phosphor band	35	60
		q. Two fluorescent bands	20	15
746		8 c. multicoloured	15	10
		p. Two phosphor bands	40	70
		q. Two fluorescent bands	25	15
747	—	10 c. multicoloured	50	1·00
		p. Two phosphor bands	1·25	1·75
		q. Two fluorescent bands	60	90
748	—	15 c. multicoloured	60	1·40
		p. Two phosphor bands	1·50	2·50
		q. Two fluorescent bands	90	1·50
745/8		Set of 4	1·25	2·25
745p/8p		Set of 4	3·25	5·00
745q/8q		Set of 4	1·75	2·40

Designs: *Horiz* (36 × 20 *mm*)—10 c. Candles with fruits and pine boughs; 15 c. Candles with prayer-book, caskets and vase.

351 "The Blacksmith's Shop"   352 François de
(Krieghoff)   Montmorency-Laval

(Des and litho B.A.B.N. and Saults & Pollard Ltd., Winnipeg)

1972 (29 Nov). *Death Centenary of Cornelius Krieghoff (painter).* P 12½.

749	351	8 c. multicoloured	30	15
		q. Two fluorescent bands	30	40

FLUORESCENT BANDS. Stamps from No. 750 onwards were issued only with two fluorescent bands, *unless otherwise stated.* Examples are known with the bands omitted in error, but such varieties are outside the scope of the catalogue.

(Des M. Fog and G. Lorange. Litho Ashton-Potter)

1973 (31 Jan). *350th Birth Anniv of Monsignor de Laval (First Bishop of Quebec).* P 11.

750	352	8 c. ultramarine, gold and silver	20	40

353 Commissioner French and Route of the March West

(Des Dallaire Morin DeVito Inc. Litho Ashton-Potter)

1973 (9 Mar). *Centenary of Royal Canadian Mounted Police.* T **353** *and similar horiz designs. Multicoloured (except 8 c.).* P 11.

751	8 c. Type **353** (deep reddish brown, dull orange and orange-vermilion)		35	20
752	10 c. Spectrograph		1·00	1·25
753	15 c. Mounted policeman		1·75	2·00
751/3		Set of 3	2·75	3·00

354 Jeanne Mance

(Des R. Bellemare. Litho Ashton-Potter)

1973 (18 Apr). *300th Death Anniv of Jeanne Mance (nurse).* P 11.

754	354	8 c. multicoloured	20	40

355 Joseph Howe   356 "Mist Fantasy"
                          (MacDonald)

(Des A. Fleming. Litho Ashton-Potter)

1973 (16 May). *Death Centenary of Joseph Howe (Nova Scotian politician).* P 11.

755	355	8 c. gold and black	20	40

(Des and litho Ashton-Potter)

1973 (8 June). *Birth Centenary of J. E. H. MacDonald (artist).* P 12½.

756	356	15 c. multicoloured	30	55

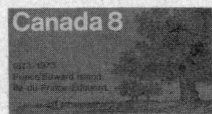

357 Oaks and Harbour

(Des A. Mann. Recess and photo B.A.B.N.)

1973 (22 June). *Centenary of Prince Edward Island's Entry into the Confederation.* P 12.

757	357	8 c. pale orange and brown-red	20	30

358 Scottish Settlers   359 Queen Elizabeth II

(Des P. Swan. Litho Ashton-Potter)

1973 (20 July). *Bicentennial of Arrival of Scottish Settlers at Pictou, Nova Scotia.* P 12 × 12½.

758	358	8 c. multicoloured	25	20

(Des A. Fleming from photograph by Anthony Buckley. Eng G. A. Gundersen. Recess and photo B.A.B.N.)

1973 (2 Aug). *Royal Visit and Commonwealth Heads of Government Meeting, Ottawa.* P 12 × 12½.

759	359	8 c. multicoloured	25	20
760		15 c. red, black and bright gold	80	1·50
		a. Red, black and pale dull gold	1·25	1·90

360 Nellie McClung   361 Emblem of 1976
                        Olympics

(Des S. Mennie. Litho Ashton-Potter)

1973 (29 Aug). *Birth Centenary of Nellie McClung (feminist).* P 10½ × 11.

761		8 c. multicoloured	20	50

(Des Wallis and Matanovic. Litho Ashton-Potter)

1973 (20 Sept). *Olympic Games, Montreal* (1976) (*1st issue*). P 12 × 12½.

762	361	8 c. multicoloured	25	15
763		15 c. multicoloured	45	1·25

See also Nos. 768/71, 772/4, 786/9, 798/802, 809/11, 814/16, 829/31, 833/7 and 842/4.

362 Ice-skate   363 Diving

(Des A. Maggs. Litho Ashton-Potter)

1973 (7 Nov). *Christmas. T* **362** *and similar vert designs. Multicoloured.* P 12½ × 12 (6, 8 c.) *or* 11 (*others*).

764	6 c. Type **362**		15	10
765	8 c. Bird decoration		20	10
766	10 c. Santa Claus (20 × 36 *mm*)		70	1·40
767	15 c. Shepherd (20 × 36 *mm*)		80	1·75
764/7		Set of 4	1·75	3·00

(Des Hunter, Straker, Templeton Ltd. Recess C.B.N.)

1974 (22 Mar). *Olympic Games, Montreal* (1976) (*2nd issue*). *"Summer Activities". T* **363** *and similar vert designs. Each deep blue.* P 12.

768	8 c. Type **363**		30	50
	a. Block of 4. Nos. 768/71		1·10	
769	8 c. "Jogging"		30	50
770	8 c. Cycling		30	50
771	8 c. Hiking		30	50
768/71		Set of 4	1·10	1·75

Nos. 768/71 were printed in *se-tenant* blocks of four throughout the sheet. Each design has a second (latent) image—the Canadian Olympic Games symbol—which appears when the stamp is viewed obliquely to the light.
See also Nos. 786/9.

(Des Wallis and Matanovic. Litho Ashton-Potter)

1974 (17 Apr). *Olympic Games, Montreal* (1976) (*3rd issue*). *As T* **361** *but smaller* (20 × 36½ *mm*). P 12½.

772	361	8 c. + 2 c. multicoloured	25	45
773		10 c. + 5 c. multicoloured	35	1·00
774		15 c. + 5 c. multicoloured	40	1·40
772/4		Set of 3	90	2·50

364 Winnipeg Signpost, 1872   365 Postmaster and Customer

(Des J. R. MacDonald. Litho and embossed Ashton-Potter)

1974 (3 May). *Winnipeg Centennial.* P 12½ × 12.

775	364	8 c. multicoloured	20	15

(Des S. Mennie. Litho Ashton-Potter)

1974 (11 June). *Centenary of Canadian Letter Carrier Delivery Service. T* **365** *and similar horiz designs. Multicoloured.* P 13½.

776	8 c. Type **365**		50	80
	a. Block of 6. Nos. 776/81		2·75	
777	8 c. Postman collecting mail		50	80
778	8 c. Mail handler		50	80
779	8 c. Mail sorters		50	80
780	8 c. Postman making delivery		50	80
781	8 c. Rural delivery by car		50	80
776/81		Set of 6	2·75	4·25

Nos. 776/81 were printed in *se-tenant* combinations throughout a sheet of 50, giving 6 blocks of 6 and 14 single stamps.

366 "Canada's Contribution   367 Telephone Development
to Agriculture"

(Des M. Brett, P. Cowley-Brown, and A. McAllister. Litho Ashton-Potter)

1974 (12 July). *"Agricultural Education". Centenary of Ontario Agricultural College.* P 12½ × 12.

782	366	8 c. multicoloured	20	20

(Des R. Webber. Litho Ashton-Potter)

1974 (26 July). *Centenary of Invention of Telephone by Alexander Graham Bell.* P 12½.

783	367	8 c. multicoloured	20	20

368 Bicycle Wheel

(Des Burns and Cooper. Recess and photo B.A.B.N.)

1974 (7 Aug). *World Cycling Championships, Montreal.*
P 12 × 12½.
784 **368** 8 c. black, rosine and silver 20 30

369 Mennonite Settlers

(Des W. Davies. Litho Ashton-Potter)

1974 (28 Aug). *Centenary of Arrival of Mennonites in Manitoba.*
P 12½.
785 **369** 8 c. multicoloured 20 20

(Des Hunter, Straker, Templeton Ltd. Recess C.B.N.)

1974 (23 Sept). *Olympic Games, Montreal (1976) (4th issue).*
"Winter Activities". Horiz designs as T 363, each rosine.
P 13½ × 13.
786 8 c. Snow-shoeing 50 60
a. Block of 4. Nos. 786/9 .. 1·75
ab. Printed on the gummed side (block of
four) £650
787 8 c. Skiing 50 60
788 8 c. Skating 50 60
789 8 c. Curling 50 60
786/9 .. .. .. *Set of 4* 1·75 2·25

370 Mercury, Winged Horses and U.P.U. Emblem

(Des G. Gundersen. Recess and photo B.A.B.N.)

1974 (9 Oct). *Centenary of Universal Postal Union. P* 12 × 12½.
790 **370** 8 c. violet, red-orange and cobalt .. 15 15
791 15 c. red-orange, violet and cobalt .. 50 1·50

371 "The Nativity"   372 Marconi and St. John's
(J. P. Lemieux)   Harbour, Newfoundland

(Des Wallis and Matanovic. Litho Ashton-Potter)

1974 (1 Nov). *Christmas. T 371 and similar horiz designs*
showing paintings. Multicoloured. P 13½.
792 6 c. Type 371 .. .. 10 10
793 8 c. "Skaters in Hull" (H. Masson) (34 × 31
mm) 10 10
794 10 c. "The Ice Cone, Montmorency Falls" (R. C.
Todd) 20 75
795 15 c. "Village in the Laurentian Mountains"
(C. A. Gagnon) .. .. .. 30 1·10
792/5 .. .. .. *Set of 4* 60 1·75

(Des J. Boyle. Litho Ashton-Potter)

1974 (15 Nov). *Birth Centenary of Guglielmo Marconi (radio*
pioneer). P 13.
796 **372** 8 c. multicoloured 20 20

373 Merritt and Welland Canal   374 Swimming

(Des W. Rueter. Recess (B.A.B.N.) and litho (C.B.N.))

1974 (29 Nov). *William Merritt Commemoration. P* 13 × 13½.
797 **373** 8 c. multicoloured 20 30

(Des Wallis and Matanovic. Litho C.B.N.)

1975 (5 Feb). *Olympic Games, Montreal (1976) (5th issue). T 374*
and similar horiz designs. Multicoloured.
798 8 c. + 2 c. Type 374 .. .. 30 50
799 10 c. + 5 c. Rowing 40 90
800 15 c. + 5 c. Sailing .. .. 45 1·00
798/800 .. .. .. *Set of 3* 1·00 2·25

375 "The Sprinter"   376 "Anne of Green Gables"
(Lucy Maud Montgomery)

(Des A. R. Fleming. Litho and embossed Ashton-Potter)

1975 (14 Mar). *Olympic Games, Montreal (1976) (6th issue).*
T 375 and similar multicoloured design showing sculpture by
R. T. McKenzie. P 12½ × 12 ($1) or 12 × 12½ ($2).
801 $1 Type 375 .. .. .. 2·00 2·75
802 $2 "The Diver" (*vert*) .. .. 2·75 4·75

(Des P. Swan (No. 803), C. Gagnon (No. 804). Litho Ashton-Potter)

1975 (15 May). *Canadian Writers (1st series). T 376 and similar*
vert design. Multicoloured. P 13½.
803 8 c. Type 376 .. .. .. 30 10
a. Pair. Nos. 803/4 .. .. 60 80
804 8 c. "Maria Chapdelaine" (Louis Hémon) .. 30 10
Nos. 803/4 were printed horizontally and vertically *se-tenant*
throughout the sheet.
See also Nos. 846/7, 940/1 and 1085/6.

377 Marguerite Bourgeoys   378 S. D. Chown
(founder of the Order   (founder of United Church
of Notre Dame)   of Canada)

(Des Design and Communication, Montreal. Litho Ashton-Potter
(Nos. 805/6). Des W. Southern. Eng G. Gundersen. Recess and
photo B.A.B.N. (Nos. 807/8))

1975 (30 May). *Canadian Celebrities. T 377/8 and similar vert*
designs.
(*a*) *As T 377. P* 12½ × 12
805 8 c. multicoloured 50 40
806 8 c. multicoloured 50 40
(*b*) *As T 378. P* 12 × 12½
807 8 c. sepia, flesh and light yellow .. 30 75
a. Pair. Nos. 807/8 .. .. 60 2·25
808 8 c. sepia, flesh and light yellow .. 30 75
805/8 .. .. .. *Set of 4* 1·40 2·25
Designs:—No. 805, Type 377; No. 806, Alphonse Desjardins
(leader of Credit Union movement); No. 807, Type 378; No. 808, Dr.
J. Cook (first moderator of Presbyterian Church in Canada).
Nos. 807/8 were printed together in the sheet horizontally and
vertically *se-tenant.*

379 Pole-vaulting   380 "Untamed"
(photo by Walt Petrigo)

(Des P. Swan. Litho Ashton-Potter)

1975 (11 June). *Olympic Games, Montreal (1976) (7th issue).*
T 379 and similar vert designs. Multicoloured. P 12 × 12½.
809 20 c. Type 379 .. .. .. 40 50
810 25 c. Marathon-running 55 80
811 50 c. Hurdling .. .. .. 70 1·25
809/11 .. .. .. *Set of 3* 1·50 2·25

(Des B. Reilander. Litho C.B.N.)

1975 (3 July). *Centenary of Calgary. P* 12 × 12½.
812 **380** 8 c. multicoloured 30 30

381 I.W.Y. Symbol   382 Fencing

(Des Susan McPhee. Recess and photo B.A.B.N.)

1975 (14 July). *International Women's Year. P* 13.
813 **381** 8 c. lt grey-brown, bistre-yellow & blk 30 30

(Des J. Hill. Litho C.B.N.)

1975 (6 Aug). *Olympic Games, Montreal (1976) (8th issue). T 382*
and similar vert designs showing combat sports. Multicoloured.
P 13.
814 8 c. + 2 c. Type 382 .. .. 30 55
815 10 c. + 5 c. Boxing .. .. 35 1·10
816 15 c. + 5 c. Judo .. .. .. 40 1·40
814/16 .. .. .. *Set of 3* 95 2·75

383 "Justice-Justitia"   384 William D. Lawrence
(statue by W. S. Allward)   (full-rigged ship)

(Des A. Fleming. Litho Ashton-Potter)

1975 (2 Sept). *Centenary of Canadian Supreme Court. P* 12½.
817 **383** 8 c. multicoloured 20 30

(Des T. Bjarnason. Recess and photo B.A.B.N.)

1975 (24 Sept). *Canadian Ships (1st series). T 384 and similar*
horiz designs showing coastal ships. P 13.
818 8 c. yellow-brown and black .. 60 75
a. Block of 4. Nos. 818/21 .. 2·25
819 8 c. blue-green and black .. 60 75
820 8 c. yellow-green and black .. 60 75
821 8 c. yellow-brown and black .. 60 75
818/21 .. .. .. *Set of 4* 2·25 2·75
Designs:—No. 819, *Neptune* (steamer). No. 820, *Beaver*
(paddle-steamer). No. 821, *Quadra* (steamer).
Nos. 818/21 were printed together, *se-tenant,* in different
combinations throughout the sheet, giving ten blocks of 4 and
ten single stamps.
See also Nos. 851/4, 902/5 and 931/4.

385 "Santa Claus"   386 Text, Badge and Bugle
(G. Kelly)

(Des B. Reilander from children's paintings. Litho Ashton-Potter)

1975 (22 Oct). *Christmas. T 385 and similar multicoloured*
designs. P 13.
822 6 c. Type 385 .. .. .. 15 10
a. Pair. Nos. 822/3 .. .. 30 40
823 6 c. "Skater" (Bill Cawsey) .. 15 10
824 8 c. "Child" (D. Hébert) .. 15 10
a. Pair. Nos. 824/5 .. .. 30 45
825 8 c. "Family" (L. Caldwell) .. 15 10
826 10 c. "Gift" (D. Lovely) 30 50
827 15 c. "Trees" (R. Kowalski) (*horiz*) .. 40 75
822/7 .. .. .. *Set of 6* 1·10 1·90
Nos. 822/3 and 824/5 were respectively issued together *se-tenant*
in an alternate arrangement within the sheet.

(Des R. Kavach. Recess and photo B.A.B.N.)

1975 (10 Nov). *50th Anniv of Royal Canadian Legion.*
P 12½ × 13.
828 **386** 8 c. multicoloured 20 20

387 Basketball

(Des J. Hill. Litho Ashton-Potter)

1976 (7 Jan). *Olympic Games, Montreal (1976) (9th issue). T 387 and*
similar vert designs. Multicoloured. P 13.
829 8 c. + 2 c. Type 387 .. .. 80 70
830 10 c. + 5 c. Gymnastics · .. 50 1·00
831 20 c. + 5 c. Soccer .. .. 65 1·40
829/31 .. .. .. *Set of 3* 1·75 2·75

388 Games Symbol and Snow Crystal   389 "Communications Arts"

(Des R. Harder. Litho Ashton-Potter)

1976 (6 Feb). *12th Winter Olympic Games, Innsbruck.* P 12½.
832 388 20 c. multicoloured 20 40

(Des R. Webber. Litho C.B.N.)

1976 (6 Feb). *Olympic Games, Montreal (10th issue).* T **389** *and similar vert designs. Multicoloured.* P 12 × 12½.
833 20 c. Type **389** 30 25
834 25 c. "Handicrafts" 55 75
835 50 c. "Performing Arts" .. 70 1·60
833/5 .. .. .. *Set of 3* 1·40 2·40

390 Place Ville Marie and Notre-Dame Church

(Des J. and P. Mercier. Recess and photo B.A.B.N.)

1976 (12 Mar). *Olympic Games, Montreal (11th issue).* T **390** *and similar horiz design. Multicoloured.* P 13.
836 $1 Type **390** .. .. 2·00 4·50
837 $2 Olympic Stadium and flags .. 2·50 5·50

391 Flower and Urban Sprawl   392 Benjamin Franklin and Map

(Des I. McLeod. Litho Ashton-Potter)

1976 (12 May). *U.N. Conference on Human Settlements (HABITAT), Vancouver.* P 12 × 12½.
838 391 20 c. multicoloured 20 30

(Des B. Reilander. Recess and photo B.A.B.N.)

1976 (1 June). *Bicentenary of American Revolution.* P 13.
839 392 10 c. multicoloured 20 35

393 Wing Parade before Mackenzie Building   394 Transfer of Olympic Flame by Satellite

(Des W. Davies. Litho C.B.N.)

1976 (1 June). *Royal Military College Centenary.* T **393** *and similar vert design. Multicoloured.* P 12 × 12½.
840 8 c. Colour party and Memorial Arch .. 15 20
    a. Pair. Nos. 840/1 .. 30 80
    ab. Printed double (pair)
841 8 c. Type **393** 15 20
Nos. 840/1 were printed horizontally and vertically *se-tenant* throughout the sheet.

(Des P. Swan. Litho Ashton-Potter)

1976 (18 June). *Olympic Games, Montreal (12th issue).* T **394** *and similar horiz designs. Multicoloured.* P 13½.
842 8 c. Type **394** 15 10
843 20 c. Carrying the Olympic flag .. 40 60
844 25 c. Athletes with medals .. 40 85
842/4 .. .. .. *Set of 3* 85 1·40

395 Archer

(Des T. Bjarnason. Litho C.B.N.)

1976 (3 Aug). *Olympiad for the Physically Disabled.* P 12 × 12½.
845 395 20 c. multicoloured 20 30

396 "Sam McGee" (Robert W. Service)   397 "Nativity" (F. Mayer)

(Des D. Bierk (No. 846), A. Dumas (No. 847). Litho Ashton-Potter)

1976 (17 Aug). *Canadian Writers (2nd series).* T **396** *and similar vert design. Multicoloured.* P 13.
846 8 c. Type **396** 15 30
    a. Pair. Nos. 846/7 .. 30 1·00
847 8 c. "Le Survenant" (Germaine Guèvremont) .. 15 30
Nos. 846/7 were printed horizontally and vertically *se-tenant* throughout the sheet.

(Des B. Reilander. Litho Ashton-Potter)

1976 (3 Nov). *Christmas.* T **397** *and similar vert designs showing stained-glass windows. Multicoloured.* P 13½.
848 8 c. Type **397** 10 10
849 10 c. "Nativity" (G. Maile & Son) .. 10 10
850 20 c. "Nativity" (Yvonne Williams) .. 20 60
848/50 .. .. *Set of 3* 30 60

398 *Northcote* (paddle-steamer)   399 Queen Elizabeth II

(Des T. Bjarnason. Recess and litho C.B.N.)

1976 (19 Nov). *Canadian Ships (2nd series).* T **398** *and similar horiz designs showing inland vessels.* P 12 × 12½.
851 10 c. ochre, chestnut and black .. 40 55
    a. Block of 4. Nos. 851/4 .. 1·40
852 10 c. violet-blue and black .. 40 55
853 10 c. bright blue and black .. 40 55
854 10 c. apple-green, olive-green and black .. 40 55
851/4 .. .. .. *Set of 4* 1·40 2·00
Designs:— No. 851, Type **398**; No. 852, *Passport* (paddle-steamer); No. 853, *Chicora* (paddle-steamer); No. 854, *Athabasca* (steamer).
Nos. 851/4 were printed together, *se-tenant*, in different combinations throughout the sheet, giving ten blocks of 4 and ten single stamps.

(Des K. Rodmell from photograph by P. Grugeon. Litho ("25" die-stamped) Ashton-Potter)

1977 (4 Feb). *Silver Jubilee.* P 12½ × 12.
855 399 25 c. multicoloured 30 50
    a. Silver (die-stamped "25") omitted .. £650 £325

400 Bottle Gentian   401 Queen Elizabeth II (bas-relief by J. Huta)   402 Houses of Parliament

403 Trembling Aspen   404 Prairie Town Main Street

405 Fundy National Park

(Des R. Derreth (Nos. 870/4). T. Bjarnason (880/3a), R. Bolt (884), B. Laycock and W. Tibbles (884b), B. Laycock (884c), A. Collier (885), W. Tibbles and G. Weber (No. 885a), W. Terry and W. Tibbles (885b), L. Marois and W. Tibbles (885c), Heather Cooper (others). Eng Y. Baril (880/3a))

1977 (1 Mar)–**86**. (a) *Vert designs as* T **400** *showing flowers. Multicoloured.* (i) *Recess and litho C.B.N. Sheet stamps.* P 12×12½.
856 1 c. Type **400** (22.4.77) .. 10 10
    a. Printed on the gummed side (pre-cancelled only) .. £500
857 2 c. Red Columbine (22.4.77) .. 10 10
    a. Printed on the gummed side .. £160
858 3 c. Canada Lily (22.4.77) .. 10 10
859 4 c. Hepatica (22.4.77) .. 10 10
    a. Printed on the gummed side .. £130
860 5 c. Shooting Star (22.4.77) .. 10 10
861 10 c. Franklin's Lady's Slipper Orchid (22.4.77) .. 15 10
    a. Perf 13×13½ (5.10.78) .. 40 30

(ii) *Recess and photo B.A.B.N. Booklet stamps (1, 2 c.) or sheet stamps (others). Chalk-surfaced paper.* P 12×12½ (1, 2 c.) or 13×13½ (others)
862 1 c. Type **400** (1.11.77) .. 65 2·50
    a. Booklet pane. Nos. 862×2 and 867a×4 .. 2·75
    b. Perf 13×13½ (from sheets) (16.6.79) 10 10
863 2 c. Red Columbine (1.4.78) .. 65 1·00
    a. Booklet pane. Nos. 863×4 and 868a×3 plus one printed label .. 3·25
    b. Perf 13×13½ (from sheets) (2.8.79) 10 10
864 3 c. Canada Lily (1.4.79) .. 20 10
864a 4 c. Hepatica (3.7.79) .. 20 10
865 5 c. Shooting Star (24.1.79) .. 20 10
865a 10 c. Franklin's Lady's Slipper Orchid (4.10.79) .. 60 10
866 12 c. Jewelweed (6.7.78) .. 15 50
866a 15 c. Canada Violet (16.8.79) .. 15 15

(b) T **401**. *Recess and photo B.A.B.N. Chalk-surfaced paper.* P 13×13½.
867 12 c. black, grey and cobalt (1.3.77) .. 15 10
    a. Perf 12×12½ (from booklets) (1.11.77) 70 1·00
868 14 c. black, grey and rose-red (7.3.78) .. 20 10
    a. Perf 12×12½ (from booklets) (1.4.78) 50 85
    ab. Booklet pane. No. 868a×25, plus two printed labels (13.11.78) .. 11·00
869 17 c. black, grey & yellowish green (8.3.79) 50 10
    a. Perf 12×12½ (from booklets) (28.3.79) 50 30
    ab. Booklet pane. No. 869a×25, plus two printed labels (3.7.79) .. 11·00
869b 30 c. maroon, grey & reddish pur (11.5.82) 70 70
    ba. Maroon, grey and bright mauve (9.83) 1·75 1·10
869c 32 c. black, grey and light blue (24.5.83) 45 60
    ca. Grey printed double .. †

(c) T **402**. (i) *Recess C.B.N.* (Nos. 872a, 873/4) or B.A.B.N. (others). *Booklet stamps* (Nos. 870/1) or sheet stamps (others). *Chalk-surfaced paper* (1, 5, 12 c.). P 12×12½ (1, 5, 12 c.) or 13×13½ (others)
870 1 c. indigo (28.3.79) .. 1·25 2·75
    a. Booklet pane. Nos. 869a×2, 870 and 871×3 .. 2·50
871 5 c. deep rose-lilac (28.3.79) .. 40 55
872 12 c. blue (chalk-surfaced paper) (3.5.77) 30 10
    a. New blue (ordinary paper) (4.78) 50 10
    ab. Printed on the gummed side .. £130
873 14 c. scarlet (7.3.78) .. 15 10
    a. Printed on the gummed side .. 18·00
874 17 c. deep green (8.3.79) .. 30 10
    a. Printed on the gummed side .. 19·00

(ii) *Recess C.B.N. Coil stamps. Imperf × perf 10*
874b 12 c. new blue (3.5.77) .. 40 30
    ba. Imperf (horiz pair) .. 90·00
874c 14 c. scarlet (7.3.78) .. 60 40
    ca. Imperf (horiz pair) .. 90·00
874d 17 c. deep green (8.3.79) .. 50 20
    da. Imperf (horiz pair) .. £100

(d) *Vert designs as* T **403** *showing leaves. Multicoloured. Recess and photo B.A.B.N. Chalk-surfaced paper.* P 13½.
875 15 c. Type **403** (8.8.77) .. 15 10
876 20 c. Douglas Fir (8.8.77) .. 15 10
877 25 c. Sugar Maple (8.8.77) .. 15 10
878 30 c. Red Oak (7.3.78) .. 20 10
879 35 c. White Pine (8.3.79) .. 25 10

(e) *Horiz designs at* T **404** *showing city streets. Multicoloured.* P 13½.
(i) *Recess and photo B.A.B.N. Chalk-surfaced paper. No fluorescent bands* (75, 80 c.). (6.7.78)
880 50 c. Type **404** .. 1·00 90
881 75 c. Eastern city street .. 85 1·00
882 80 c. Maritimes street .. 85 90

(ii) *Recess and litho C.B.N.*
883 50 c. Type **404** (13.12.78) .. 85 60
883a 60 c. Ontario city street (11.5.82) 65 50

(f) *Horiz designs as* T **405** *showing national parks. Multicoloured. Recess and litho C.B.N. or B.A.B.N.* (ptgs of Nos. 884ba, 885c and 885e from 26 Sept 1986). No. 884 *with or without fluorescent bands, others only exist without.* P 13½.
884 $1 Type **405** (fluorescent bands) (24.1.79) 90 50
    a. No fluorescent bands (4.3.81) 1·10 55
    ab. Black (inscr and value) ptd albino £400
884b $1 Glacier (chalk-surfaced paper) (15.8.84) 85 45
    ba. Ordinary paper (12.7.85) .. 1·50 80
884c $1·50, Waterton Lakes (18.6.82) .. 2·50 2·50

885	$2 Kluane (27.4.79)	..	..	1·50	45

885 $2 Kluane (27.4.79) .. .. 1·50 45
  a. Silver (inscr and value) omitted £250
  b. Chalk-surfaced paper (14.12.84) 4·00 2·00
885c $2 Banff (21.6.85) 3·75 1·25
  ca. Bottle-green (inscr and value) omitted £600
885d $5 Point Pelee (10.1.83) 5·50 2·25
  da. Chalk-surfaced paper (14.12.84) 7·00 3·50
885e $5 La Mauricie (14.3.86) 7·00 4·00

The main differences between No. 861a and No. 865a are in the background. On No. 865a this is toned and has the blurred edges typical of photogravure. No. 861a has a background of solid appearance with the edges clean. The B.A.B.N. version also has stronger lines on the recess part of the design.

No. 883 can be identified from 880 in that the brown printing from the recess plate of the former is deeper and the detail more defined; the registration plate of the car in the foreground can clearly be seen under a glass as "1978". The "hidden date" (1977) occurs alongside the grain elevator door on No. 880. Also the colours from the lithographic plates of No. 883 are much bolder than those from the photogravure cylinders of 880. In addition the paper of No. 883 has a shiny appearance.

No. 884ab shows an uninked impression of the recess-printed part of the design.

Stamps with one or two adjacent sides imperforate come from booklets.

406 Puma

407 "April in Algonquin Park"

(Des R. Bateman. Litho Ashton-Potter)

1977 (30 Mar). Endangered Wildlife (1st series). P 12½.
886 406 12 c. multicoloured .. 20 20
  See also Nos. 906, 936/7, 976/7 and 1006/7.

(Litho Ashton-Potter)

1977 (26 May). Birth Centenary of Tom Thomson (painter). T 407 and similar square design. Multicoloured. P 12.
887 12 c. Type 407 .. .. 15 10
  a. Pair. Nos. 887/8 .. 30 80
888 12 c. "Autumn Birches" .. 15 10
  Nos. 887/8 were printed horizontally and vertically se-tenant throughout the sheet.

408 Crown and Lion

409 Peace Bridge, Niagara River

(Des A. Hobbs. Litho (No. 890 also embossed) Ashton-Potter)

1977 (30 June). Anniversaries. T 408 and similar horiz design. Multicoloured. P 12½.
889 12 c. Type 408 .. .. 15 20
890 12 c. Order of Canada .. 15 20
  Events:—No. 889, 25th Anniv of first Canadian-born Governor-General; No. 890, Tenth Anniv of Order of Canada.

(Des R. Harder. Litho Ashton-Potter)

1977 (4 Aug). 50th Anniv of Opening of Peace Bridge. P 12½.
891 409 12 c. multicoloured 15 15

410 Sir Sandford Fleming (engineer)

(Des W. Davies. Recess B.A.B.N.)

1977 (16 Sept). Famous Canadians. T 410 and similar horiz design. P 13.
892 12 c. grey-blue 20 10
  a. Pair. Nos. 892/3 .. 40 80
893 12 c. reddish brown .. 20 10
Design:—No. 892, Joseph E. Bernier (explorer) and Arctic (survey ship).
The above were printed together, horizontally and vertically se-tenant throughout the sheet.

411 Peace Tower, Parliament Buildings, Ottawa

412 Hunter Braves following Star

(Des S. Ash. Litho Ashton-Potter)

1977 (19 Sept). 23rd Commonwealth Parliamentary Conference. P 12½.
894 411 25 c. multicoloured .. 20 30

(Des R. G. White. Litho C.B.N.)

1977 (26 Oct). Christmas. T 412 and similar horiz designs depicting Canada's first Christmas carol "Jesous Ahatonhia". Multicoloured. P 13½ × 13.
895 10 c. Type 412 .. 10 10
  a. Printed on the gummed side £200
  b. Imperf between (horiz pair) £600
896 12 c. Angelic choir and Northern Lights 10 10
  a. Imperf (vert pair) £500
897 25 c. Christ Child and chiefs 20 45
895/7 Set of 3 35 45
  No. 895b also shows both stamps partly imperforate at top and bottom.

413 Seal Hunter (soapstone sculpture)

414 Pinky (fishing boat)

(Des R. Derreth. Litho Ashton-Potter)

1977 (18 Nov). Canadian Eskimos ("Inuits") (1st series). Hunting. T 413 and similar horiz designs. Multicoloured. P 12 × 12½.
898 12 c. Type 413 .. 25 25
  a. Pair. Nos. 898/9 .. 50 80
899 12 c. Fishing with spear .. 25 25
900 12 c. Disguised archer .. 25 25
  a. Pair. Nos. 900/1 .. 50 80
901 12 c. Walrus hunting .. 25 25
898/901 Set of 4 90 90
  Nos. 898/9 and 900/1 were each printed together, se-tenant, in horizontal and vertical pairs throughout the sheet.
  See also Nos. 924/7, 958/61 and 989/92.

(Des T. Bjarnason. Recess and litho C.B.N.)

1977 (18 Nov). Canadian Ships (3rd series). T 414 and similar horiz designs, showing sailing craft. Multicoloured. P 12 × 12½.
902 12 c. Type 414 .. 20 30
  a. Block of 4. Nos. 902/5 .. 70
  ab. Imperf (block of 4)
903 12 c. Malahat (schooner) .. 20 30
904 12 c. Tern schooner .. 20 30
905 12 c. Mackinaw boat .. 20 30
902/5 Set of 4 70 1·10
  Nos. 902/5 were printed together, se-tenant, in different combinations throughout the sheet, giving ten blocks of 4 and ten single stamps.

415 Peregrine Falcon

416 Pair of 1851 12d. Black Stamps

(Des R. Bateman. Litho Ashton-Potter)

1978 (18 Jan). Endangered Wildlife (2nd series). P 12½.
906 415 12 c. multicoloured .. 30 20

(Des C. Brett. Recess and photo B.A.B.N.)

1978 (18 Jan). "CAPEX 78" International Stamp Exhibition, Toronto (1st issue). P 13.
907 416 12 c. black and brownish grey .. 10 10
  See also Nos. 914/17.

417 Games Emblem

418 "Captain Cook" (Nathaniel Dance)

(Des S. Ash. Litho Ashton-Potter)

1978 (31 Mar). Commonwealth Games. Edmonton (1st issue). T 417 and similar horiz design. Multicoloured. P 12½.
908 14 c. Type 417 .. 10 10
909 30 c. Badminton .. 20 60
  See also Nos. 918/21.

(Des W. Rueter. Litho Ashton-Potter)

1978 (26 Apr). Bicentenary of Cook's Third Voyage. T 418 and similar vert design. Multicoloured. P 13½.
910 14 c. Type 418 .. 20 20
  a. Pair. Nos. 910/11 .. 40 80
911 14 c. "Nootka Sound" (J. Webber) .. 20 20
  Nos. 910/11 were printed together, se-tenant, in horizontal and vertical pairs throughout the sheet.

419 Hardrock Silver Mine, Cobalt, Ontario

420 Princes' Gate (Exhibition entrance)

(Des W. Davies. Litho Ashton-Potter)

1978 (19 May). Resource Development. T 419 and similar horiz design. Multicoloured. P 12½.
912 14 c. Type 419 .. 15 20
  a. Pair. Nos. 912/13. .. 30 80
913 14 c. Giant excavators, Athabasca Tar Sands 15 20
  Nos. 912/13 were printed together, se-tenant, in horizontal and vertical pairs throughout the sheet.

(Des C. Brett. Eng R. Couture. Recess and photo B.A.B.N.)

1978 (1 June). "CAPEX 78" International Stamp Exhibition, Toronto (2nd issue). Horiz designs as T 416. Two fluorescent bands (none on $1.25 from miniature sheet). P 13.
914 14 c. Prussian blue, pale grey and brownish grey 15 10
915 30 c. deep rose, pale grey and brownish grey 25 35
916 $1.25, slate-violet, pale grey & brnish grey 70 1·40
914/16 Set of 3 1·25 1·60
MS917 101 × 76 mm. Nos. 914/16 .. 1·25 2·50
Designs:—14 c. Pair of 1855 10d. Cartier stamps; 30 c. Pair of 1857 ½d. deep rose stamps; $1.25, Pair of 1851 6d. Prince Albert stamps.

(Des S. Ash. Litho Ashton-Potter)

1978 (3 Aug). Commonwealth Games, Edmonton (2nd issue). Horiz designs as T 417. Multicoloured. P 12½.
918 14 c. Games stadium .. 20 20
  a. Pair. Nos. 918/19. .. 40 80
919 14 c. Running .. 20 20
920 30 c. Alberta Legislature building 50 50
  a. Pair. Nos. 920/1 .. 1·00 1·60
921 30 c. Bowls .. 50 50
918/21 Set of 4 1·25 1·10
  Nos. 918/19 and 920/1 were each printed together, se-tenant, in horizontal and vertical pairs throughout the sheet.

(Des T. Dimson. Litho Ashton-Potter)

1978 (16 Aug). Centenary of National Exhibition. P 12½.
922 420 14 c. multicoloured .. 15 30

421 Marguerite d'Youville

422 "Madonna of the Flowering Pea" (Cologne School)

(Des A. Dumas. Litho C.B.N.)

1978 (21 Sept). Marguerite d'Youville (founder of Grey Nuns) Commemoration. P 13.
923 421 14 c. multicoloured .. 15 30

(Des R. Derreth. Litho Ashton-Potter)

1978 (27 Sept). Canadian Eskimos ("Inuits") (2nd series). Travel. Horiz designs as T 413. Multicoloured. P 13½.
924 14 c. Woman on foot (painting by Pitseolak) .. 25 15
  a. Pair. Nos. 924/5 .. 50 80
925 14 c. "Migration" (soapstone sculpture of sailing umiak by Joe Talurinili) .. 25 15
926 14 c. Aeroplane (stencut and stencil print by Pudlo) .. 25 15
  a. Pair. Nos. 926/7 .. 50 80
927 14 c. Dogteam and dogsled (ivory sculpture by Abraham Kingmeatook). . 25 15
924/7 Set of 4 90 55
  Nos. 924/5 and 926/7 were each printed together, se-tenant, in horizontal and vertical pairs throughout the sheet.

(Des J. Morin. Litho Ashton-Potter)

1978 (20 Oct). Christmas. Paintings. T 422 and similar vert designs. Multicoloured. P 12½.
928 12 c. Type 422 .. 10 10
929 14 c. "The Virgin and Child with St. Anthony and Donor" (detail, Hans Memling) 10 10
930 30 c. "The Virgin and Child" (Jacopo di Cione) 25 90
928/30 Set of 3 35 1·00

423 Chief Justice Robinson (paddle-steamer)

424 Carnival Revellers

(Des T. Bjarnason. Recess and litho C.B.N.)

1978 (15 Nov). Canadian Ships (4th series). T 423 and similar horiz designs showing ice vessels. Multicoloured. P 13.
931 14 c. Type 423 .. 45 65
  a. Block of 4. Nos. 931/4 .. 1·60
932 14 c. St. Roch (steamer) .. 45 65
933 14 c. Northern Light (steamer) .. 45 65
934 14 c. Labrador (steamer) .. 45 65
931/4 Set of 4 1·60 2·40
  Nos. 931/4 were printed together, se-tenant, in different combinations throughout the sheet, giving ten block of 4 and ten single stamps.

(Des A. Dumas. Litho Ashton-Potter)

1979 (1 Feb). *Quebec Carnival. P* 13.
935 **424** 14 c. multicoloured 20 20

425 Eastern Spiny Soft-shelled
Turtle (*Trionyx spinifera*)

426 Knotted Ribbon round
Woman's Finger

(Des G. Lowe (17 c.), R. Bateman (35 c.). Litho Ashton-Potter)

1979 (10 Apr). *Endangered Wildlife* (3rd series). *T* **425** and
similar horiz design. Multicoloured. *P* 12½.
936 17 c. Type **425** 20 10
937 35 c. Bowhead Whale (*Balaena mysticetus*) .. 90 90

(Des D. Haws. Litho Ashton-Potter)

1979 (27 Apr). *Postal Code Publicity. T* **426** and similar vert
design. Multicoloured. *P* 13.
938 17 c. Type **426** 20 10
 a. Pair. Nos. 938/9 .. .. .. 40 1·00
939 17 c. Knotted string round man's finger 20 10
 Nos. 938/9 were printed together, *se-tenant*, in horizontal and
vertical pairs throughout the sheet.

427 Scene from "Fruits of the
Earth" by Frederick Philip
Grove

428 Charles-Michel de
Salaberry (military hero)

(Des Rosemary Kilbourne (No. 940), Monique Charbonneau (941).
Litho C.B.N.)

1979 (3 May). *Canadian Writers* (3rd series). *T* **427** and similar
horiz design. Multicoloured. *P* 13.
940 17 c. Type **427** 15 15
 a. Pair. Nos. 940/1 .. .. .. 30 1·00
 ab. Imperf (vert pair) ..
941 17 c. Scene from "Le Vaisseau d'Or" by
 Emile Nelligan 15 15
 Nos. 940/1 were printed together, *se-tenant*, in horizontal and
vertical pairs throughout the sheet.

(Des T. Dimson. Litho and embossed Ashton-Potter)

1979 (11 May). *Famous Canadians. T* **428** and similar vert
design. Multicoloured. *P* 13.
942 17 c. Type **428** 25 15
 a. Pair. Nos. 942/3 .. .. .. 50 1·00
943 17 c. John By (engineer) 25 15
 Nos. 942/3 were printed together, *se-tenant*, in horizontal and
vertical pairs throughout the sheet.

429 Ontario

430 Paddling Kayak

(Des R. Bellemare. Litho Ashton-Potter)

1979 (15 June). *Canada Day. Flags. Sheet* 128 × 140 *mm
containing T* **429** *and similar horiz designs. Multicoloured. P* 13.
MS944 17 c. × 12; Type **429**; Quebec; Nova Scotia;
New Brunswick; Manitoba; British Columbia;
Prince Edward Island; Saskatchewan; Alberta;
Newfoundland; Northwest Territories; Yukon
Territory .. .. 3·50 4·50

(Des J. Eby. Litho Ashton-Potter)

1979 (3 July). *Canoe-Kayak Championships. P* 12½.
956 **430** 17 c. multicoloured 15 30

431 Hockey Players

432 Toy Train

(Des J. Eby. Litho Ashton-Potter)

1979 (16 Aug). *Women's Field Hockey Championships,
Vancouver. P* 12½.
957 **431** 17 c. black, yellow and emerald .. 15 30

(Des R. Derreth. Litho Ashton-Potter)

1979 (13 Sept). *Canadian Eskimos* ("*Inuits*") (3rd series).
"*Shelter*" (*Nos.* 958/9) *and* "*Community*" (*Nos.* 960/1). *Horiz
designs as T* **413**. *Multicoloured. P* 13.
958 17 c. "Summer Tent" (print by Kiakshuk) .. 15 15
 a. Pair. Nos. 958/9 .. .. 30 80
959 17 c. "Five Eskimos building an Igloo" (soapstone sculpture by Abraham) .. 15 15
960 17 c. "The Dance" (print by Kalvak) .. 15 15
 a. Pair. Nos. 960/1 .. .. 30 80
961 17 c. "Inuit drum dance" (soapstone sculptures
 by Madeleine Isserkut and Jean
 Mapsalak) 15 15
958/61 .. .. .. *Set of 4* 60 55
 Nos. 958/9 and 960/1 were each printed together, *se-tenant*, in
horizontal and vertical pairs throughout the sheet.

(Des A. Maggs. Litho C.B.N.)

1979 (17 Oct). *Christmas. T* **432** *and similar multicoloured
designs showing toys. Fluorescent frame* (35 c.) *or two fluorescent
bands* (*others*). *P* 13.
962 15 c. Type **432** 10 10
963 17 c. Hobby-horse 10 10
964 35 c. Rag-doll (*vert*) 25 65
962/4 .. .. *Set of 3* 35 70

433 "Child watering Tree
of Life" (painting by
Marie-Annick Viatour)

434 Canadair CL-215

(Des J. Morin. Litho Ashton-Potter)

1979 (24 Oct). *International Year of the Child. P* 13.
965 **433** 17 c. multicoloured 15 30

(Des R. Bradford and J. Charette. Litho Ashton-Potter)

1979 (15 Nov). *Canadian Aircraft* (1st series). *Flying Boats. T* **434**
and similar horiz designs. Multicoloured. P 12½.
966 17 c. Type **434** 25 15
 a. Pair. Nos. 966/7 .. .. 50 70
967 17 c. Curtiss HS-2L 25 15
968 35 c. Vickers Vedette 65 55
 a. Pair. Nos. 968/9 .. .. 1·25 1·40
969 35 c. Consolidated PBY-5A Canso .. 65 55
966/9 .. .. .. *Set of 4* 1·60 1·10
 Nos. 966/7 and 968/9 were each printed together, *se-tenant*, in
horizontal and vertical pairs throughout the sheet.
 See also Nos. 996/9, 1026/9 and 1050/3.

435 Map of Arctic Islands

436 Skiing

(Des Gottschalk and Ash Ltd. Litho Ashton-Potter)

1980 (23 Jan). *Centenary of Arctic Islands Acquisition. P* 13.
970 **435** 17 c. multicoloured 15 30

(Des C. Malenfant. Litho C.B.N.)

1980 (23 Jan). *Winter Olympic Games, Lake Placid, U.S.A. P* 13.
971 **436** 35 c. multicoloured 55 85

437 "A Meeting of the School
Trustees"
(painting by Robert Harris)

438 Canadian Whitefish
(*Coregonus canadenis*)

(Des J. Morin. Litho Ashton-Potter)

1980 (6 Mar). *Centenary of Royal Canadian Academy of Arts.
T* **437** *and similar horiz designs. Multicoloured. P* 13.
972 17 c. Type **437** 25 15
 a. Pair. Nos. 972/3 .. .. 50 50
973 17 c. "Inspiration" (sculpture by Philippe
 Hébert) 25 15
974 35 c. "Sunrise on the Saguenay" (painting by
 Lucius O'Brien) 50 35
 a. Pair. Nos. 974/5 .. .. 1·00 1·50
975 35 c. Sketch of design for original Parliament
 Buildings by Thomas Fuller .. 50 35
972/5 .. .. .. *Set of 4* 1·40 90
 Nos. 972/3 and 974/5 were each printed together, *se-tenant*, in
horizontal and vertical pairs throughout the sheet.

(Des M. Dumas (No. 976), R. Bateman (No. 977). Litho Ashton-
Potter)

1980 (6 May). *Endangered Wildlife* (4th series). *T* **438** *and similar
horiz design. Multicoloured. P* 12½.
976 17 c. Type **438** 30 15
977 17 c. Prairie Chicken (*Tympanuchus cupido
 pinnatus*) 30 15

439 Garden Flowers

440 "Helping Hand"

(Des Heather Cooper. Litho Ashton-Potter)

1980 (29 May). *International Flower Show, Montreal. P* 13.
978 **439** 17 c. multicoloured 15 20

(Des R. Harder. Litho and embossed Ashton-Potter)

1980 (29 May). *Rehabilitation. P* 12½.
979 **440** 17 c. gold and ultramarine .. 15 20

441 Opening Bars of
"O Canada"

442 John G. Diefenbaker

(Des F. Peter. Litho Ashton-Potter)

1980 (6 June). *Centenary of "O Canada"* (national song). *T* **441**
and similar horiz design. Multicoloured. P 12½.
980 17 c. Type **441** 15 15
 a. Pair. Nos. 980/1 .. .. 30 40
981 17 c. Calixa Lavallee (composer), Adolphe-
 Basile Routhier (original writer) and
 Robert Stanley Weir (writer of English
 version) 15 15
 Nos. 980/1 were printed together, *se-tenant*, in horizontal and
vertical pairs throughout the sheet.

(Des B. Reilander. Eng Y. Baril. Recess C.B.N.)

1980 (20 June). *John G. Diefenbaker* (former Prime Minister)
Commemoration. P 13½ × 13.
982 **442** 17 c. deep ultramarine 15 20

443 Emma Albani
(singer)

444 Alberta

(Des C. Webster (No. 985), H. Brown (others). Litho Ashton-Potter)

1980 (4 July). *Famous Canadians. T* **443** *and similar multicoloured designs. P* 13.
983 17 c. Type **443** 15 25
 a. Pair. Nos. 983/4 .. .. 30 1·00
984 17 c. Healey Willan (composer) .. 15 25
985 17 c. Ned Hanlan (oarsman) (*horiz*) .. 15 15
983/5 .. .. .. *Set of 3* 40 60
 Nos. 983/4 were printed together, *se-tenant*, in horizontal and
vertical pairs throughout the sheet.

(Des G. Hunter and C. Yaneff. Litho Ashton-Potter)

1980 (27 Aug). *75th Anniv of Alberta and Saskatchewan Provinces. T* **444** *and similar horiz design. Multicoloured. P* 13.
986 17 c. Type **444** 15 15
987 17 c. Saskatchewan 15 15

445 Uraninite Molecular
Structure

446 "Christmas Morning"
(J. S. Hallam)

(Des J. Charette. Litho C.B.N.)

1980 (3 Sept). *Uranium Resources. P* 13.
988 **445** 35 c. multicoloured 30 30
 a. Printed on the gummed side .. £400

(Des R. Derreth. Litho C.B.N.)

1980 (25 Sept). *Canadian Eskimos* ("*Inuits*") (4th series). *Spirits.
Horiz designs as T* **413**. *Multicoloured. P* 13½.
989 17 c. "Return of the Sun" (print by Kenojouak) 20 15
 a. Pair. Nos. 989/90 .. .. 40 80
990 17 c. "Sedna" (sculpture by Ashoona Kiawak) 20 15
991 35 c. "Shaman" (print by Simon Tookoome) 35 30
 a. Pair. Nos. 991/2 .. .. 70 1·40
992 35 c. "Bird Spirit" (sculpture by Doris
 Hagiolok) 35 30
989/92 .. .. .. *Set of 4* 1·00 80
 Nos. 989/90 and 991/2 were each printed together, *se-tenant*, in
horizontal and vertical pairs throughout the sheet.

(Des Yvon Laroche. Litho Ashton-Potter)

1980 (22 Oct). *Christmas. Paintings. T 446 and similar vert designs. Multicoloured. P 12½ × 12.*
993	15 c. Type 446		10	10
994	17 c. "Sleigh Ride" (Frank Hennessy)		15	10
995	35 c. "McGill Cab Stand" (Kathleen Morris)		30	1·40
993/5		Set of 3	50	1·40

447 Avro (Canada) CF-100
Canuck Mk 5

(Des R. Bradford and J. Charette. Litho C.B.N.)

1980 (10 Nov). *Canadian Aircraft (2nd series). T 447 and similar horiz designs. Multicoloured. P 13.*
996	17 c. Type 447		15	15
	a. Pair. Nos. 996/7		30	60
997	17 c. Avro Type 683 Lancaster		15	15
998	35 c. Curtiss JN-4 Canuck		30	50
	a. Pair. Nos. 998/9		60	1·25
999	35 c. Hawker Hurricane Mk 1		30	50
996/9		Set of 4	80	1·10

Nos. 996/7 and 998/9 were each printed together, *se-tenant*, in horizontal and vertical pairs throughout the sheet.

448 Emmanuel-Persillier Lachapelle   **449** Mandora Instrument (18th-century)

(Des J. Morin. Litho Ashton-Potter)

1980 (5 Dec). *Dr. Emmanuel-Persillier Lachapelle (founder of Notre-Dame Hospital, Montreal) Commemoration. P 13½.*
1000	**448** 17 c. cobalt, chocolate and brown		15	15

(Des C. Webster. Litho Ashton-Potter)

1981 (19 Jan). *"The Look of Music" Exhibition, Vancouver. P 12½.*
1001	**449** 17 c. multicoloured		15	15

450 Henrietta Edwards   **451** Vancouver Marmot (*Marmota vancouverensis*)

(Des Muriel Wood and D. Goddard. Litho C.B.N.)

1981 (4 Mar). *Feminists. T 450 and similar horiz designs. Multicoloured. P 13.*
1002	17 c. Type 450		25	25
	a. Block of 4. Nos. 1002/5		90	
1003	17 c. Louise McKinney		25	25
1004	17 c. Idola Saint-Jean		25	25
1005	17 c. Emily Stowe		25	25
1002/5		Set of 4	90	90

Nos. 1002/5 were printed together, *se-tenant*, in different combinations throughout the sheet, giving ten blocks of 4 and ten single stamps.

(Des M. Dumas (17 c.), R. Bateman (35 c.). Litho C.B.N.)

1981 (6 Apr). *Endangered Wildlife (5th series). T 451 and similar horiz design. Multicoloured. P 13.*
1006	17 c. Type 451		15	10
1007	35 c. American Bison (*Bison bison athabascae*)		35	30

452 Kateri Tekakwitha   **453** "Self Portrait" (Frederick H. Varley)

(Des L. Marquart. Litho Ashton-Potter)

1981 (24 Apr). *17th-century Canadian Catholic Women. Statues by Emile Brunet. T 452 and similar vert design. P 12½.*
1008	17 c. red-brown and pale grey-olive		15	15
	a. Pair. Nos. 1008/9		30	40
1009	17 c. steel blue and new blue		15	15

Designs:—No. 1008, Type 452; No. 1009, Marie de l'Incarnation. Nos. 1008/9 were printed together, *se-tenant*, in horizontal and vertical pairs throughout the sheet.

(Des P. Fontaine. Litho Ashton-Potter (17 c. (both)), B.A.B.N. (35 c.))

1981 (22 May). *Canadian Paintings. T 453 and similar multicoloured designs. P 12½ (17 c. (both)) or 13 × 13½ (35 c.).*
1010	17 c. Type 453		20	10
1011	17 c. "At Baie Saint-Paul" (Marc-Aurele Fortin) (horiz)		20	10
1012	35 c. "Untitled No. 6" (Paul-Emile Borduas)		40	45
1010/12		Set of 3	70	60

454 Canada in 1867   **455** Frère Marie-Victorin

(Des R. Bellemare. Litho B.A.B.N.)

1981 (30 June). *Canada Day. Maps showing evolution of Canada from Confederation to present day. T 454 and similar horiz designs. Multicoloured. P 13½.*
1013	17 c. Type 454		15	20
	a. Horiz strip of 4. Nos. 1013/16		55	
1014	17 c. Canada in 1873		15	20
1015	17 c. Canada in 1905		15	20
1016	17 c. Canada since 1949		15	20
1013/16		Set of 4	55	70

Nos. 1013/16 were printed together, *se-tenant*, in horizontal strips of 4 throughout the sheet.

(Des R. Hill. Litho and embossed Ashton-Potter)

1981 (22 July). *Canadian Botanists. T 455 and similar vert design. Multicoloured. P 12½ × 12.*
1017	17 c. Type 455		20	20
	a. Pair. Nos. 1017/18		40	60
1018	17 c. John Macoun		20	20

Nos. 1017/18 were printed together, *se-tenant*, in horizontal and vertical pairs throughout the sheet.

456 The Montreal Rose   **457** Drawing of Niagara-on-the-Lake

(Des J.-P. Beaudin, J. Morin and T. Yakobina. Litho C.B.N.)

1981 (22 July). *Montreal Flower Show. P 13½.*
1019	**456** 17 c. multicoloured		15	20

(Des J. Mardon. Recess and litho B.A.B.N.)

1981 (31 July). *Bicentenary of Niagara-on-the-Lake (town). P 13 × 13½.*
1020	**457** 17 c. multicoloured		15	20

458 Acadian Community   **459** Aaron R. Mosher

(Des N. DeGrâce. Litho Ashton-Potter)

1981 (14 Aug). *Centenary of first Acadia (community) Convention. P 13½.*
1021	**458** 17 c. multicoloured		15	20

(Des R. Hill. Litho Ashton-Potter)

1981 (8 Sept). *Birth Centenary of Aaron R. Mosher (founder of Canadian Labour Congress). P 13½.*
1022	**459** 17 c. multicoloured		15	20

NEW INFORMATION

The editor is always interested to correspond with people who have new information that will improve or correct the Catalogue.

460 Christmas Tree, 1781   **461** De Havilland D.H.82C Tiger Moth

(Des Anita Kunz and W. Tibbles. Litho Ashton-Potter)

1981 (16 Nov). *Christmas. Bicentenary of First Illuminated Christmas Tree in Canada. T 460 and similar vert designs. Multicoloured. P 13½.*
1023	15 c. Type 460		20	15
1024	15 c. Christmas Tree, 1881		20	15
1025	15 c. Christmas Tree, 1981		20	15
1023/5		Set of 3	55	40

(Des R. Bradford and J. Charette. Litho Ashton-Potter)

1981 (24 Nov). *Canadian Aircraft (3rd series). T 461 and similar horiz designs. Multicoloured. P 12½.*
1026	17 c. Type 461		20	15
	a. Pair. Nos. 1026/7		40	40
1027	17 c. Canadair CL-41 Tutor		20	15
1028	35 c. Avro (Canada) CF-102 jet airliner		35	35
	a. Pair. Nos. 1028/9		70	70
1029	35 c. De Havilland D.H.C.7 Dash Seven		35	35
1026/9		Set of 4	1·10	90

The two designs of each value were printed together, *se-tenant*, in horizontal and vertical pairs throughout the sheet.

462 Canadian Maple Leaf Emblem   **463** 1851 3d. Stamp

(Des R. Bellemare, Recess B.A.B.N. (No. 1030a),C.B.N. (others))

1981 (29 Dec). *Ordinary paper. (a) Sheet stamp. P 13×13½.*
1030	**462** A (30 c.), bright scarlet		20	30
	a. Carmine-red, chalk-surfaced paper		20	25
	b. Printed on the gummed side		£300	

(b) Coil stamp, Imperf×perf 10
1031	**462** A (30 c.), bright scarlet		40	70
	a. Imperf (pair)		£250	£140

Nos. 1030/1 were printed before a new first class domestic letter rate had been agreed, "A" representing the face value of the stamp later decided at 30 c. Because of U.P.U. regulations these stamps were only intended for use within Canada.

(Recess, or recess and photo (Nos. 1032/b), B.A.B.N. (Nos. 1032/5b) or C.B.N. (Nos. 1036/b))

1982 (1 Mar)—**84.** *Designs as Nos. 1030/1 but including face values.*

(a) Sheet stamps (Nos. 1032, 1032b) or from booklets (Nos. 1032a, 1032ba). Chalk-surfaced paper. P 13×13½
1032	**462** 30 c. verm, slate-bl & azure (11.5.82)		30	40
	a. Perf 12×12½ (from booklets) (30.6.82)		70	1·25
	ab. Booklet pane. No. 1032a×20 plus one printed label		15·00	
1032b	32 c. verm, orge-brn & stone (10.2.83)		45	45
	ba. Perf 12×12½ (from booklets) (8.4.83)		60	1·25
	bb. Booklet pane. No. 1032ba×25 plus two printed labels		17·00	
	bc. Ordinary paper (15.2.84)		75	1·00
	bd. Booklet pane. No. 1032bc×25 plus two printed labels		19·00	

(b) Booklet stamps. Ordinary paper. P 12 × 12½*
1033	**462** 5 c. maroon		10	20
	a. Booklet pane. Nos. 1033 × 2, 1034 and 1035 plus two printed labels in bottom row		2·50	
	ab. Ditto. Printed labels in top row (10.82)		2·75	
	b. Chalk-surfaced paper (8.82)		40	50
	ba. Booklet pane. Nos. 1033b × 2, 1034a and 1035a plus two printed labels in bottom row		7·50	
	bb. Ditto. Printed labels in top row (10.82)		7·50	
	c. Booklet pane. Nos. 1033 × 2, 1033d and 1035b plus two printed labels (15.2.83)		3·00	
1033d	8 c. indigo (15.2.83)		1·25	1·75
1034	10 c. bottle green		1·25	1·75
	a. Chalk-surfaced paper		3·75	3·75
1035	30 c. carmine-red		1·50	2·25
	a. Chalk-surfaced paper		3·75	3·75
1035b	32 c. Indian red (15.2.83)		1·75	2·50

(c) Coil stamps. Ordinary paper. Imperf×perf 10
1036	**462** 30 c. bright scarlet (20.5.82)†		35	30
	a. Imperf (pair)		£180	
1036b	32 c. Indian red (10.2.83)		1·50	1·60
	ba. Imperf (pair)		90·00	

*The 30 c. and 32 c. values are perforated on two sides, the other values on three.

†The 30 c. coil stamp was originally intended for release on 11 May, but, due to production difficulties, it was not placed on sale until 20 May; F.D.C.s, however, carry the 11 May postmark.

(Des Gottschalk and Ash Ltd. Litho C.B.N.)

1982 (11 Mar–20 May). *"Canada 82" International Philatelic Youth Exhibition, Toronto. Stamps on Stamps.* T **463** *and similar horiz designs. Multicoloured.* P 13½.

1037	30 c. Type 463	..	30	25
1038	30 c. 1908 Centenary of Quebec 15 c. commemorative (20.5.82)		30	25
1039	35 c. 1935 10 c. R.C.M.P.		30	40
1040	35 c. 1928 10 c. (20.5.82)	..	30	40
1041	60 c. 1929 50 c. (20.5.82)	..	60	85
1037/41		*Set of 5*	1·60	2·00
MS1042	159×108 mm. Nos. 1037/41 (20.5.82)		2·25	3·25

464 Jules Léger   465 Stylised Drawing of Terry Fox

(Des P. Fontaine from photograph by M. Bedford. Litho Ashton-Potter)

1982 (2 Apr). *Jules Léger (politician) Commemoration.* P 13½.
1043 **464** 30 c. multicoloured   ..   20   20

(Des F. Peter. Litho Ashton-Potter)

1982 (13 Apr). *Cancer-victim Terry Fox's "Marathon of Hope" (Trans-Canada fund-raising run)·Commemoration.·Fluorescent frame.* P 12½.
1044 **465** 30 c. multicoloured   ..   20   20

466 Stylised Open Book

(Des F. Peter. Litho Ashton-Potter)

1982 (16 Apr). *Patriation of Constitution.* P 12 × 12½.
1045 **466** 30 c. multicoloured   20   20

467 1880's Male and Female Salvationists with Street Scene   468 "The Highway near Kluane Lake" (Yukon Territory) (Jackson)

(Des T. Dimson. Litho C.B.N.)

1982 (25 June). *Centenary of the Salvation Army in Canada.* P 13½.
1046 **467** 30 c. multicoloured   20   20

(Des J. Morin and P. Sasseville. Litho Ashton-Potter)

1982 (30 June). *Canada Day. Paintings of Canadian Landscapes. Sheet,* 139 × 139 *mm, containing* T **468** *and similar horiz designs. Multicoloured.* P 12½×12.
MS1047 30 c. × 12, Type 468; "Street Scene, Montreal" (Quebec) (Hébert); "Breakwater" (Newfoundland) (Pratt); "Along Great Slave Lake" (Northwest Territories) (Richard); "Till Hill" (Prince Edward Island) (Lamb); "Family and Rainstorm" (Nova Scotia) (Colville); "Brown Shadows" (Saskatchewan) (Knowles); "The Red Brick House" (Ontario) (Milne); "Campus Gates" (New Brunswick) (Bobak); "Prairie Town—Early Morning" (Alberta) (Kerr); "Totems at Ninstints" (British Columbia) (Plaskett); "Doc Snider's House" (Manitoba) (FitzGerald)   ..   4·25   4·75

469 Regina Legislature Building   470 Finish of Race

(Des Kim Martin and R. Russell. Litho Ashton-Potter)

1982 (3 Aug). *Regina Centenary.* P 13½ × 13.
1048 **469** 30 c. multicoloured   20   20

(Des B. Reilander. Litho Ashton-Potter)

1982 (4 Aug). *Centenary of Royal Canadian Henley Regatta.* P 12½.
1049 **470** 30 c. multicoloured   20   25

---

471 Fairchild FC-2W1   472 Decoy

(Des R. Bradford. Litho Ashton-Potter)

1982 (5 Oct). *Canadian Aircraft (4th series). Bush Aircraft.* T **471** *and similar horiz designs. Multicoloured.* P 12½.

1050	30 c. Type 471	..	35	20
	a. Pair. Nos. 1050/1		70	95
1051	30 c. De Havilland D.H.C.2 Beaver		35	20
1052	60 c. Fokker Super Universal	..	65	85
	a. Pair. Nos. 1052/3		1·25	2·00
1053	60 c. Noorduyn Norseman	..	65	85
1050/3		*Set of 4*	1·90	1·90

Nos. 1050/1 and 1052/3 were each printed together, se-tenant, in horiz and vert pairs throughout the sheet.

(Des J. P. Beaudin and J. Morin. Litho C.B.N. (Nos. 1054b/ba, 1055b/bc, 1056b, 1057b/ba, 1058b) or Ashton-Potter (others))

1982 (19 Oct)–**87**. *Heritage Artifacts.* T **472** *and similar designs. No fluorescent bands* (1 c. to 5 c.)*. Chalk-surfaced paper* (25, 42, 50, 72 c.)*.* P 12×12½ (37 c. to 72 c.) *or* 14×13½ (*others*).

1054	1 c. black, grey-brown and brown	..	10	10
	a. Chalk-surfaced paper (4.7.86)		10	10
	b. Perf 13×13½ (10.1.85)		30	30
	ba. Chalk-surfaced paper (6.8.85)		1·25	1·00
1055	2 c. black, pale turquoise-blue & dp bl-grn		10	10
	a. Chalk-surfaced paper (4.7.86)		20	20
	b. Perf 13×13½ (10.2.84)		30	30
	ba. Imperf (horiz pair)	..	£650	
	bb. Printed on the gummed side		35·00	
	bc. Ordinary paper (23.1.86)		10	10
1056	3 c. black, dull violet-blue and chalky blue		10	10
	a. Chalk-surfaced paper (4.7.86)		30	10
	b. Perf 13×13½ (10.1.85)		30	40
1057	5 c. black, flesh and chestnut		10	10
	a. Chalk-surfaced paper (15.8.86)		10	10
	b. Perf 13×13½ (chalk-surfaced paper) (6.7.84)		20	20
	ba. Ordinary paper (1.3.85)		20	30
1058	10 c. black, light blue & dp turquoise-blue		10	10
	a. Chalk-surfaced paper (22.8.86)		40	40
	b. Perf 13×13½ (15.3.85)		60	30
1059	20 c. black, brownish grey and sepia		20	10
	a. Chalk-surfaced paper (4.7.86)		50	50
1060	25 c. multicoloured (6.5.87)		35	10
1061	37 c. grey-black, deep yellow-green and sage-green (8.4.83)		50	40
	a. Chalk-surfaced paper (18.5.84)		1·00	90
1062	39 c. brownish black, violet-grey and slate-violet (1.8.85)		1·75	80
1063	42 c. multicoloured (6.5.87)		50	15
1064	48 c. blackish brown, red-brown and pale pink (8.4.83)		70	40
	a. Chalk-surfaced paper (19.12.83)		80	70
1065	50 c. black, dull turq-blue & turq-bl (1.8.85)		1·75	20
1066	55 c. multicoloured (6.5.87)		65	30
1067	64 c. grey-black, black & pale grey (8.4.83)		80	35
	a. Chalk-surfaced paper (29.6.84)		1·50	1·10
1068	68 c. black, pale brn & reddish brn (1.8.85)		1·75	50
1069	72 c. multicoloured (6.5.87)		85	35
1054/69		*Set of 16*	9·00	3·00

Designs: *Vert* (as T **472**)—2 c. Fishing spear; 3 c. Stable lantern; 5 c. Bucket; 10 c. Weathercock; 20 c. Skates; 25 c. Butter stamp. *Horiz* (26 × 20 *mm*)—37 c. Plough; 39 c. Settle-bed; 42 c. Linen chest; 48 c. Cradle; 50 c. Sleigh; 55 c. Iron kettle; 64 c. Kitchen stove; 68 c. Spinning wheel; 72 c. Hand-drawn cart.
No. 1058b has a fluorescent frame instead of bands.

475 Mary, Joseph and Baby Jesus   476 Globes forming Symbolic Designs

(Des J. Eby. Litho C.B.N.)

1982 (3 Nov). *Christmas. Nativity Scenes.* T **475** *and similar vert designs. Multicoloured.* P 13.

1080	30 c. Type 475	..	20	10
1081	35 c. The Shepherds	..	25	55
1082	60 c. The Three Wise Men	..	45	1·25
1080/2		*Set of 3*	80	1·75

(Des R. Bellemare. Litho Ashton-Potter)

1983 (10 Mar). *World Communications Year. Fluorescent frame.* P 12 × 12½.
1083 **476** 32 c. multicoloured   ..   30   30

STANLEY GIBBONS STAMP COLLECTING SERIES

Introductory booklets on *How to Start, How to Identify Stamps* and *Collecting by Theme.* A series of well illustrated guides at a low price.
Write for details.

---

477 Map of World showing Canada

(Des R. Harder. Litho Ashton-Potter)

1983 (14 Mar). *Commonwealth Day. Without fluorescent bands.* P 12½.
1084 **477** $2 multicoloured   2·00   3·25

478 Scene from Novel "Angéline de Montbrun" by Laure Conan (Félicité Angers)   479 St. John Ambulance Badge and "100"

(Des R. Milot (No. 1085), Claire Pratt (No. 1086), adapted W. Tibbles. Litho C.B.N.)

1983 (22 Apr). *Canadian Writers (4th series).* T **478** *and similar horiz design. Multicoloured.* P 13.

1085	32 c. Type 478	..	40	90
	a. Pair. Nos. 1085/6		80	1·75
1086	32 c. Woodcut illustrating "Sea-gulls" (poem by E. J. Pratt)		40	90

Nos. 1085/6 were printed together, se-tenant, in horizontal and vertical pairs throughout the sheet.

(Des L. Fishauf. Litho Ashton-Potter)

1983 (3 June). *Centenary of St. John Ambulance in Canada.* P 13.
1087 **479** 32 c. brt rose-red, gold & dp chocolate   30   30

480 Victory Pictogram   481 Fort William, Ontario

(Des Krista Huebner, D. Kilvert and P.-Y. Pelletier. Litho C.B.N.)

1983 (28 June). *"Universiade 83" World University Games, Edmonton.* P 13.

1088	**480**	32 c. multicoloured	25	15
		a. Printed on the gummed side	£400	
1089		64 c. multicoloured ..	50	70

(Des R. Harder. Litho Ashton-Potter)

1983 (30 June). *Canada Day. Forts (1st series).* T **481** *and similar horiz designs. Multicoloured.* P 12½×13.

1090	32 c. Fort Henry, Ontario (44 × 22 mm)		55	75
	a. Booklet pane. Nos. 1090/9		5·00	
1091	32 c. Type 481	..	55	75
1092	32 c. Fort Rodd Hill, British Columbia		55	75
1093	32 c. Fort Wellington, Ontario (28 × 22 mm)		55	75
1094	32 c. Fort Prince of Wales, Manitoba (28 × 22 mm)		55	75
1095	32 c. Halifax Citadel, Nova Scotia (44 × 22 mm)		55	75
1096	32 c. Fort Chambly, Quebec		55	75
1097	32 c. Fort No. 1, Point Levis, Quebec	..	55	75
1098	32 c. Coteau-du-Lac Fort, Quebec (28 × 22 mm)		55	75
1099	32 c. Fort Beauséjour, New Brunswick (28 × 22 mm)		55	75
1090/9		*Set of 10*	5·00	6·50

Nos. 1090/9 were only available from $3.20 stamp booklets containing the se-tenant pane, No. 1090a.
See also Nos. 1163/72.

482 Scouting Poster by Marc Fournier (aged 12)   483 Cross Symbol

(Des F. Dallaire. Litho Ashton-Potter)

1983 (6 July). *75th Anniv of Scouting in Canada and 15th World Scout Jamboree, Alberta.* P 13.
1100 **482** 32 c. multicoloured   30   30

(Des G. Tsetsekas. Recess and photo B.A.B.N.)

1983 (22 July). *6th Assembly of the World Council of Churches, Vancouver.* P 13.
1101 **483** 32 c. blue-green and grey-lilac 30   20

484 Sir Humphrey Gilbert (founder)   **485** "NICKEL" Deposits

(Des R. Hill. Litho C.B.N.)

1983 (3 Aug). *400th Anniv of Newfoundland.* P 13.
1102 **484** 32 c. multicoloured 30   20

(Des J. Capon. Litho ("NICKEL" die-stamped) C.B.N.)

1983 (12 Aug). *Centenary of Discovery of Sudbury Nickel Deposits.* P 13.
1103 **485** 32 c. multicoloured 30   20
    a. Silver ("NICKEL") omitted £650

486 Josiah Henson and Escaping Slaves   **487** Robert Stephenson's Locomotive *Dorchester*, 1836

(Des T. Kew and J. Hamel. Litho B.A.B.N.)

1983 (16 Sept). *Nineteenth-century Social Reformers.* T **486** and similar horiz design. Multicoloured. P 13 × 13½ (No. 1104) or 13 (No. 1105).
1104 32 c. Type **486** 35   25
1105 32 c. Father Antoine Labelle and rural village (32 × 26 mm) 35   25

(Des E. Roch. Litho Ashton-Potter)

1983 (3 Oct). *Railway Locomotives (1st series).* T **487** and similar horiz designs. Multicoloured. P 12½×13.
1106 32 c. Type **487** 90   1·00
    a. Pair. Nos. 1106/7 . . . . . . 1·75 2·00
1107 32 c. Locomotive *Toronto*, 1853 90   1·00
1108 37 c. Timothy Hackworth's locomotive *Samson*, 1838 90   1·00
1109 64 c. Western Canadian Railway locomotive *Adam Brown*, 1855 . . . . . . 1·40 2·00
1106/9 . . . . . . *Set of 4* 3·75 4·50
Nos. 1106/7 were printed together, *se-tenant*, in horizontal and vertical pairs throughout the sheet.
See also Nos. 1132/6, 1185/8 and 1223/6.

488 School Coat of Arms   **489** City Church

(Des Denise Saulnier. Litho C.B.N.)

1983 (28 Oct). *Centenary of Dalhousie Law School.* P 13.
1110 **488** 32 c. multicoloured 30   30

(Des C. Simard. Litho Ashton-Potter)

1983 (3 Nov). *Christmas. Churches.* T **489** and similar horiz designs. Multicoloured. P 13.
1111 32 c. Type **489** 40   10
1112 37 c. Family walking to church 55   90
1113 64 c. Country chapel . . . . . . 1·25 2·00
1111/13 . . . . . . *Set of 3* 2·00 2·75

490 Royal Canadian Regiment and British Columbia Regiment

(Des W. Southern and R. Tibbles. Litho C.B.N.)

1983 (10 Nov). *Canadian Army Regiments.* T **490** and similar vert design. Multicoloured. Fluorescent frame. P 13.
1114 32 c. Type **490** 75   1·25
    a. Pair. Nos. 1114/15 . . . . . . 1·50 2·50
1115 32 c. Royal Winnipeg Rifles and Royal Canadian Dragoons 75   1·25
Nos. 1114/15 were printed together, *se-tenant*, in horizontal and vertical pairs throughout the sheet.

(*Illustration reduced: actual size* 112 × 88 *mm*)

"STICK 'N TICK" POSTAGE LABELS. Prepaid labels in the above design, printed in a combination of red, green and black, were tested by the Canadian Post Office in Winnipeg, Manitoba, between 21 November and 17 December 1983. These self-adhesive labels were sold to the public in kits of 12 or 25, at a saving of 35 c. or $1.11 on the normal postage. They were primarily intended for use on Christmas cards and were only valid on mail posted to Canadian addresses.
    The label was affixed to normally addressed envelopes, but the user was then required to mark the postal code on the three lines at the foot. It was hoped that this incentive would increase the use of the postal codes and so speed automatic mail sorting.
    The system was extended to seven other cities in 1984. The second version had separate postage paid and Postal Code labels, being available from 5 November until 17 December 1984.

491 Gold Mine in Prospecting Pan   **492** Montreal Symphony Orchestra

(Des K. Hughes. Litho Ashton-Potter)

1984 (15 Mar). *50th Anniv of Yellowknife.* P 13½.
1116 **491** 32 c. multicoloured 30   30

(Des J. Delisle and P. Kohler. Litho Ashton-Potter)

1984 (24 Mar). *50th Anniv of Montreal Symphony Orchestra.* P 12½.
1117 **492** 32 c. multicoloured 35   30

493 Jacques Cartier   **494** *Eagle* (U.S. Coastguard cadet ship)

(Des Y. Paquin, Engraved C. Haley. Recess French Govt Ptg Wks, Perigueux)

1984 (20 Apr). *450th Anniv of Jacques Cartier's Voyage to Canada.* P 13.
1118 **493** 32 c. multicoloured 40   30

(Des O. Schenk. Litho Ashton-Potter)

1984 (18 May). *Tall Ships Visit. Fluorescent frame.* P 12×12½.
1119 **494** 32 c. multicoloured 35   30

495 Service Medal   **496** Oared Galleys

(Des W. Tibbles and C. Webster. Litho Ashton-Potter)

1984 (28 May). *75th Anniv of Canadian Red Cross Society.* P 13½.
1120 **495** 32 c. multicoloured 35   40

(Des P. Dorn. Photo and recess B.A.B.N.)

1984 (18 June). *Bicentenary of New Brunswick.* P 13½.
1121 **496** 32 c. multicoloured 35   30

497 St. Lawrence Seaway

(Des E. Barenscher. Litho C.B.N.)

1984 (26 June). *25th Anniv of St. Lawrence Seaway. Fluorescent frame.* P 13.
1122 **497** 32 c. multicoloured 45   30

498 New Brunswick   **499** Loyalists of 1784

(Des J. Morin and T. Yakobina. Litho C.B.N.)

1984 (29 June). *Canada Day. Paintings by Jean Paul Lemieux. Sheet,* 138 × 122 *mm, containing* T **498** *and similar multicoloured designs.* P 13.
MS1123 32 c. × 12, Type **498**; British Columbia; Northwest Territories; Quebec; Manitoba; Alberta; Prince Edward Island; Saskatchewan; Nova Scotia (*vert*); Yukon Territory, Newfoundland; Ontario (*vert*) . . . . . . 6·00 6·50
The captions on the Northwest Territories and Yukon Territory paintings were transposed at the design stage.

(Des W. Davies. Litho B.A.B.N.)

1984 (3 July). *Bicentenary of Arrival of United Empire Loyalists.* P 13 × 13½.
1124 **499** 32 c. multicoloured 30   30

500 St. John's Basilica   **501** Coat of Arms of Pope John Paul II

(Des J. Morin and R. Ethier. Litho C.B.N.)

1984 (17 Aug). *Bicentenary of Roman Catholic Church in Newfoundland.* P 13½.
1125 **500** 32 c. multicoloured 30   25

(Des L. Rivard. Litho Ashton-Potter)

1984 (31 Aug). *Papal Visit.* P 12½.
1126 **501** 32 c. multicoloured 40   20
1127 64 c. multicoloured 85   1·10

502 Louisbourg Lighthouse, 1734

(Des D. Noble and K. Rodmell. Litho Ashton-Potter)

1984 (21 Sept). *Canadian Lighthouses (1st series).* T **502** and similar horiz designs. Multicoloured. P 12½.
1128 32 c. Type **502** . . . . . . 1·25 1·40
    a. Block of 4. Nos. 1128/31 . . . . . . 4·50
1129 32 c. Fisgard Lighthouse, 1860 . . . . . . 1·25 1·40
1130 32 c. Ile Verte Lighthouse, 1809 . . . . . . 1·25 1·40
1131 32 c. Gibraltar Point Lighthouse, 1808 . . . . . . 1·25 1·40
1128/31 . . . . . . *Set of 4* 4·50 5·00
Nos. 1128/31 were printed together, *se-tenant*, in different combinations throughout the sheet, giving ten blocks of 4 and ten single stamps.
See also Nos. 1176/80.

503 Great Western Railway Locomotive, Scotia, 1860

(Des E. Roch. Litho Ashton-Potter)

1984 (25 Oct). *Railway Locomotives (2nd series).* T **503** and similar horiz designs. Multicoloured. P 12½×13.
1132 32 c. Type **503** 90   90
    a. Pair. Nos. 1132/3 . . . . . . 1·75 1·75
1133 32 c. Northern Pacific Railroad locomotive *Countess of Dufferin*, 1872 90   90
1134 37 c. Grand Trunk Railway Class E3 locomotive, 1886 90   1·40
1135 64 c. Canadian Pacific Class D10a steam locomotive . . . . . . 1·40 2·00
1132/5 . . . . . . *Set of 4* 3·75 4·75
MS1136 153×104 mm. As Nos. 1132/5, but with background colour changed from pale green to pale grey-blue . . . . . . 5·00 6·50
Nos. 1132/3 were issued together, *se-tenant*, in horizontal and vertical pairs throughout the sheet.
    No. **MS**1136 commemorates "CANADA 84" National Stamp Exhibition, Montreal.
    See also Nos. 1185/8 and 1223/6.

504 "The Annunciation"
(Jean Dallaire)

505 Pilots of 1914–18,
1939–45 and 1984

(Des J. Morin and T. Yakobina. Litho Ashton-Potter)

1984 (2 Nov). *Christmas. Religious Paintings.* T **504** *and similar horiz designs. Multicoloured.* P 13½.

1137	32 c. Type **504**		40	10
1138	37 c. "The Three Kings" (Simone Bouchard)		70	1·00
1139	64 c. "Snow in Bethlehem" (David Milne)		90	1·75
1137/9		*Set of 3*	1·75	2·50

(Des W. Southern and R. Tibbles. Litho Ashton-Potter)

1984 (9 Nov). *60th Anniv of Royal Canadian Air Force. Fluorescent frame.* P 12×12½.

1140	**505** 32 c. multicoloured	35	30

506 Treffle Berthiaume (editor)

507 Heart and Arrow

(Des P.-Y. Pelletier. Litho Ashton-Potter)

1984 (16 Nov). *Centenary of La Presse* (*newspaper*). *Fluorescent frame.* P 13×13½.

1141	**506** 32 c. agate, vermilion & pale grey-brn	35	30

(Des F. Dallaire. Litho Ashton-Potter)

1985 (8 Feb). *International Youth Year.* P 12½.

1142	**507** 32 c. multicoloured	30	30

508 Astronaut in Space,
and Planet Earth

509 Emily Murphy

(Des L. Holloway. Litho Ashton-Potter)

1985 (15 Mar). *Canadian Space Programme.* P 13½.

1143	**508** 32 c. multicoloured	40	30

(Des Muriel Wood and R. Tibbles. Litho Ashton-Potter)

1985 (17 Apr). *Women's Rights Activists.* T **509** *and similar horiz design. Multicoloured.* P 13½.

1144	32 c. Type **509**	40	70
	a. Horiz pair. Nos. 1144/5	80	1·40
1145	32 c. Therese Casgrain	40	70

Nos. 1144/5 were printed together, *se-tenant*, in horizontal pairs throughout the sheet.

510 Gabriel Dumont (Métis leader)
and Battle of Batoche, 1885

(Des R. Derreth. Litho Ashton-Potter)

1985 (6 May). *Centenary of the North-West Rebellion.* P 14×13½.

1146	**510** 32 c. blue, carmine and grey	30	30

511 Rear View,
Parliament Building,
Ottawa

512 Queen
Elizabeth II

512a Queen Elizabeth
II in 1984 (from photo
by Karsh)

(Des R. Bellemare. Eng R. Couture (Nos. 1161/2). Des T. Yakobina and C. Candlish (Nos. 1162a/h), R. Harder (others))

1985 (21 June)**–98.** *No fluorescent bands (1 c. to 6 c.) or fluorescent frame (34, 36, 39, 40, 42, 43, 45, 46 c.).*

(a) T **511** *and similar horiz designs*

(i) Booklet stamps. Recess B.A.B.N. Chalk-surfaced paper (6 c. (No. 1150b), 37 c., 38 c.) or ordinary paper (others). P 12½×12.

1147		1 c. grey-olive (30.3.87)	80	1·75
	a.	Booklet pane. Nos. 1147×2, 1150×2, 1152 and label	5·00	
	b.	Chalk-surfaced paper (1.10.87)	70	80
	ba.	Booklet pane. Nos. 1147b×2, 1150a×2, 1152a and label	4·50	
	bb.	Booklet pane. Nos. 1147b, 1150a×2, 1153 and two labels (3.2.88)	2·25	
1148		2 c. bottle green	20	55
	a.	Booklet pane. Nos. 1148×3, 1149×2 and 1151	2·25	
	b.	Chalk-surfaced paper (18.1.89)	30	40
	ba.	Booklet pane. Nos. 1148b×3, 1150b, 1154 and label	1·90	
1149		5 c. sepia	40	60
1150		6 c. chestnut (30.3.87)	1·00	1·25
	a.	Chalk-surfaced paper (1.10.87)	50	30
1150b		6 c. blackish purple (18.1.89)	85	95
1151	511	34 c. blue-black	1·25	1·75
1152		36 c. reddish purple (30.3.87)	2·50	3·00
	a.	Chalk-surfaced paper (1.10.87)	3·00	3·00
1153		37 c. dull ultramarine (3.2.88)	1·25	30
1154		38 c. deep blue (18.1.89)	1·25	1·25

(ii) Litho C.B.N. (Nos. 1155 (from sheets), 1156/7c), B.A.B.N. (No. 1155 (from booklets)) or Ashton-Potter (Nos. 1155b, 1156a, 1157a/ba, 1157ca/cb). Chalk-surfaced paper (Nos. 1155b/ba, 1156, 1156b/bb and 1157c/cb). P 13×13½ (No. 1157c) or 13½×13 (others).

1155	511	34 c. multicoloured	50	10
	a.	Booklet pane. No. 1155×25 (1.8.85)	11·50	
	b.	Perf 13½×14 (4.7.86)	1·25	1·75
	ba.	Booklet pane. No. 1155b×25	26·00	
1156		36 c. multicoloured (30.3.87)	40	30
	a.	Ordinary paper	30	45
	b.	Perf 13½×14	1·40	1·40
	ba.	Booklet pane. No. 1156a×10	10·00	
	bb.	Booklet pane. No. 1156a×25 (19.5.87)	22·00	
	c.	Imperf (vert pair)	£500	
1157		37 c. multicoloured (30.12.87)	85	10
	a.	Perf 13½×14 (5.1.88)	1·00	1·00
	ab.	Booklet pane. No. 1157a×10	12·00	
	ac.	Booklet pane. No. 1157a×25 (2.5.88)	15·00	
	ad.	Chalk-surfaced paper (5.1.88)	1·50	2·00
	ae.	Booklet pane. No. 1157ad×25	27·00	
1157c		38 c. multicoloured (29.12.88)	35	10
	ca.	Booklet pane. No. 1157c×10 and two labels	3·50	
	cb.	Booklet pane. No. 1157c×25 and two labels	12·00	
	cc.	Printed on the gummed side	35·00	

(iii) Coil stamps. Recess C.B.N. P 10×imperf

1158	511	34 c. purple-brown (1.8.85)	2·25	2·75
	a.	Imperf (pair)	£100	
1159		36 c. carmine-vermilion (19.5.87)	90	55
	a.	Imperf (pair)	£150	
1160		37 c. deep ultramarine (22.2.88)	60	40
	a.	Imperf (pair)	£100	
1160b		38 c. bottle green (1.2.89)	40	30
	ba.	Imperf (pair)	£200	

(b) Recess and photo B.A.B.N. P 13×13½

1161	512	34 c. black and cobalt (12.7.85)	45	30
1162		36 c. reddish purple (1.10.87)	2·75	1·10

(c) Litho B.A.B.N. (Nos. 1162a/c), Ashton-Potter (Nos. 1162bc, 1162ca, 1162d/e, 1162fa), C.B.N. (Nos. 1162f/g) or Ashton-Potter Canada (No. 1162h). Chalk-surfaced paper (40 c. to 46 c.). P 13½×13 (Nos. 1162a, 1162h), 13×12½ (No. 1162b) or 13×13½ (Nos. 1162c, 1162d/g).

1162a	512a	37 c. multicoloured (30.12.87)	2·00	10
1162b		38 c. multicoloured (29.12.88)	35	20
	ba.	Imperf (horiz pair)	£275	
	bb.	Imperf at top and sides (horiz pair)	£225	
	bc.	Perf 13×13½. Chalk-surfaced paper	45	65
	bd.	Booklet pane. No. 1162bc×10 and two labels	4·50	
	be.	Imperf between (horiz pair) (from pane No. 1162bd)	£500	
1162c		39 c. multicoloured (12.1.90)	1·00	20
	ca.	Chalk-surfaced paper	1·40	65
	cb.	Booklet pane. No. 1162ca×10 and two labels	13·00	
	cc.	Perf 13×12½ (2.90)	7·00	1·00
1162d		40 c. multicoloured (28.12.90)	80	20
	da.	Booklet pane. No. 1162d×10 and two labels	8·00	
	db.	Ordinary paper (24.5.91)	85	20
1162e		42 c. multicoloured (27.12.91)	90	40
	ea.	Booklet pane. No. 1162e×10	9·00	
1162f		43 c. multicoloured (30.12.92)	90	65
	fa.	Booklet pane. No. 1162f×10	9·00	
1162g		45 c. multicoloured (31.7.95)	45	60
	ga.	Booklet pane. No. 1162g×10	4·50	
1162h		46 c. multicoloured (28.12.98)	40	45

Designs:—1 c., 5 c., 6 c. (No. 1150b) East Block, Parliament Building; 2 c., 5 c. (No. 1150) West Block, Parliament Building; 37 c. (No. 1157) Front view, Parliament Building; 38 c. (No. 1157c) Side view, Parliament Building.

Stamps from booklet panes Nos. 1147a, 1147ba/bb and 1148a/b have one or two adjacent sides imperforate. Stamps from the first and last vertical columns of booklet panes Nos. 1155a, 1155ba, 1156ba/bb, 1157ab/ac, 1157ae, 1157ca/cb, 1162bd, 1162cb, 1162da, 1162ea, 1162fa and 1162ga are imperforate at left or right. Those from the bottom row of No. 1157ac are also imperforate at foot.

Nos. 1157c and 1162b/h have a slightly larger design image 21×17 mm.

Printings of booklet pane No. 1162fa from booklet No. SB164 were initially by Ashton-Potter. On 7 January 1994 the printer changed to C.B.N. and the booklet cover to Type B **37**. This booklet is listed as No. SB177. There were further printings by C.B.N. before production reverted to Ashton-Potter Canada for supplies released on 27 March 1995.

Nos. 1162g/ga were reissued on 6 October 1995 showing a change of printer to Ashton-Potter Canada. There are no listable differences between these stamps and the previous printings.

(Des R. Harder. Litho Ashton-Potter)

1985 (28 June). *Canada Day. Forts* (2nd series). *Horiz designs as* T **481.** *Multicoloured.* P 12½×13.

1163		34 c. Lower Fort Garry, Manitoba (44×22 mm)	50	60
	a.	Booklet pane. Nos. 1163/72	4·50	
1164		34 c. Fort Anne, Nova Scotia	50	60
1165		34 c. Fort York, Ontario	50	60
1166		34 c. Castle Hill, Newfoundland (28×22 mm)	50	60
1167		34 c. Fort Whoop Up, Alberta (28×22 mm)	50	60
1168		34 c. Fort Erie, Ontario (44×22 mm)	50	60
1169		34 c. Fort Walsh, Saskatchewan	50	60
1170		34 c. Fort Lennox, Quebec	50	60
1171		34 c. York Redoubt, Nova Scotia (28×22 mm)	50	60
1172		34 c. Fort Frederick, Ontario (28×22 mm)	50	60
1163/72		*Set of 10*	4·50	5·50

Nos. 1163/72 were only available from $3.40 stamp booklets containing the *se-tenant* pane, No. 1163a.

513 Louis Hébert
(apothecary)

514 Parliament
Buildings and Map
of World

515 Guide and
Brownie Saluting

(Des C. Malenfant. Litho Ashton-Potter)

1985 (30 Aug). *45th International Pharmaceutical Sciences Congress of Pharmaceutical Federation, Montreal. Fluorescent frame.* P 12½.

1173	**513** 34 c. multicoloured	45	35

(Des E. Barenscher. Litho Ashton-Potter)

1985 (3 Sept). *74th Conference of Inter-Parliamentary Union, Ottawa.* P 13½.

1174	**514** 34 c. multicoloured	45	35

(Des Barbara Griffin. Recess and photo B.A.B.N.)

1985 (12 Sept). *75th Anniv of Girl Guide Movement. Fluorescent frame.* P 13½×13.

1175	**515** 34 c. multicoloured	45	35

516 Sisters Islets
Lighthouse

517 Santa Claus in
Reindeer-drawn Sleigh

(Des B. Reilander (No. MS1180), L. Rivard (others). Litho Ashton-Potter)

1985 (3 Oct). *Canadian Lighthouses* (2nd series). T **516** *and similar horiz designs. Multicoloured.* P 13½.

1176		34 c. Type **516**	1·40	1·50
	a.	Block of 4. Nos. 1176/9	5·00	
1177		34 c. Pelee Passage Lighthouse	1·40	1·50
1178		34 c. Haut-fond Prince Lighthouse	1·40	1·50
1179		34 c. Rose Blanche Lighthouse, Cains Island	1·40	1·50
1176/9		*Set of 4*	5·00	5·50
MS1180		109×90 mm. Nos. 1176/9	6·00	7·00

Nos. 1176/9 were printed together, *se-tenant*, in different combinations throughout the sheet, giving ten blocks of 4 and ten single stamps.

No. **MS**1180 Publicises "Capex 87" International Stamp Exhibition, Toronto.

(Des Barbara Carroll and C. Yaneff. Litho Ashton-Potter)

1985 (23 Oct). *Christmas. Santa Claus Parade.* T **517** *and similar horiz designs. Multicoloured.* P 13½.

1181		32 c. Canada Post's parade float	70	1·00
	a.	Booklet pane. No. 1181×10	6·50	
1182		34 c. Type **517**	60	20
1183		39 c. Acrobats and horse-drawn carriage	70	1·00
1184		68 c. Christmas tree, pudding and goose on float	1·50	1·60
1181/4		*Set of 4*	3·25	4·50

No. 1181 was only available from $3.20 stamp booklets, which had the upper and lower edges of the pane imperforate. This value was intended for use on greeting cards posted on or before 31 January 1986, and represented a 2 c. saving of postage. After this date these stamps could be used for any postal purpose in conjunction with other values.

(Des E. Roch. Litho Ashton-Potter)

1985 (7 Nov). *Railway Locomotives (3rd series). Horiz designs as T 503. Multicoloured. P 12½×13.*
1185	34 c. Grand Trunk Railway Class K2 steam locomotive	80	90
	a. Pair. Nos. 1185/6	1·60	1·75
1186	34 c. Canadian Pacific Class P2a steam locomotive	80	90
1187	39 c. Canadian Northern Class O10a steam locomotive	95	1·25
1188	68 c. Canadian Govt Railway Class H4D steam locomotive	1·60	1·90
1185/8	*Set of 4*	3·75	4·50

Nos. 1185/6 were printed together, *se-tenant*, in horizontal and vertical pairs throughout the sheet.

518 Naval Personnel of 1910, 1939–45 and 1985

519 "The Old Holton House, Montreal" (James Wilson Morrice)

(Des W. Southern and R. Tibbles. Litho C.B.N.)

1985 (8 Nov). *75th Anniv of Royal Canadian Navy. Fluorescent frame. P 13½×13.*
1189	**518** 34 c. multicoloured	65	55

(Des L. Parent and J. Morin. Litho C.B.N.)

1985 (15 Nov). *125th Anniv of Montreal Museum of Fine Arts. P 13½.*
1190	**519** 34 c. multicoloured	40	35

520 Map of Alberta showing Olympic Sites

(Des P.-Y. Pelletier. Litho Ashton-Potter)

1986 (13 Feb). *Winter Olympic Games, Calgary (1988) (1st issue). Fluorescent frame. P 12½×13.*
1191	**520** 34 c. multicoloured	40	50

See also Nos. 1216/17, 1236/7, 1258/9 and 1281/4.

521 Canada Pavilion

522 Molly Brant

(Des Debbie Adams. Recess and photo B.A.B.N.)

1986 (7 Mar). *"Expo '86" World Fair, Vancouver (1st issue). T 521 and similar horiz design. Multicoloured. Fluorescent frame. P 13×13½.*
1192	**521** 34 c. Type 521	1·00	50
1193	39 c. Early telephone, dish aerial and satellite	1·25	2·00

See also Nos. 1196/7.

(Des Sara Tyson. Litho Ashton-Potter)

1986 (14 Apr). *'250th Birth Anniv of Molly Brant (Iroquois leader). P 13½.*
1194	**522** 34 c. multicoloured	40	40

523 Philippe Aubert de Gaspé and Scene from *Les Anciens Canadiens*

524 Canadian Field Post Office and Cancellation, 1944

(Des P. Fontaine and Y. Paquin. Litho Ashton-Potter)

1986 (14 Apr). *Birth Bicentenary of Philippe Aubert de Gaspé (author). Fluorescent frame. P 12½.*
1195	**523** 34 c. multicoloured	40	40

(Des Debbie Adams. Recess and photo B.A.B.N.)

1986 (28 Apr). *"Expo '86" World Fair, Vancouver (2nd issue). Multicoloured designs as T 521. Fluorescent frame. P 13½×13 (34 c.) or 13×13½ (68 c.).*
1196	34 c. Expo Centre, Vancouver (*vert*)	65	40
1197	68 c. Early and modern trains	1·25	2·00

(Des J. DesRosiers. Litho Ashton-Potter)

1986 (9 May). *75th Anniv of Canadian Forces Postal Service. P 13½.*
1198	**524** 34 c. multicoloured	75	40

525 Great Blue Heron

526 Railway Rotary Snowplough

(Des P. Fontaine and J.-L. Grondin. Litho Ashton-Potter)

1986 (22 May). *Birds of Canada. T 525 and similar horiz designs. Multicoloured. P 13½.*
1199	34 c. Type 525	1·50	1·75
	a. Block of 4. Nos. 1199/1202	5·50	
1200	34 c. Snow Goose	1·50	1·75
1201	34 c. Great Horned Owl	1·50	1·75
1202	34 c. Spruce Grouse	1·50	1·75
1199/1202	*Set of 4*	5·50	6·00

Nos. 1199/1202 were printed together, *se-tenant*, in different combinations throughout the sheet, giving ten blocks of 4 and ten single stamps.

(Des R. Hill. Litho C.B.N.)

1986 (27 June). *Canada Day. Science and Technology. Canadian Inventions (1st series). T 526 and similar vert designs. Multicoloured. P 13½.*
1203	34 c. Type 526	1·10	1·40
	a. Block of 4. Nos. 1203/6	4·00	
1204	34 c. Space shuttle *Challenger* launching satellite with Canadarm	1·10	1·40
1205	34 c. Pilot wearing anti-gravity flight suit and Supermarine Spitfire	1·10	1·40
1206	34 c. Variable-pitch propellor and Avro 504 airplane	1·10	1·40
1203/6	*Set of 4*	4·00	5·00

Nos. 1203/6 were printed together, *se-tenant*, in blocks of 4 throughout the sheet.
See also Nos. 1241/4 and 1292/5.

527 C.B.C. Logos over Map of Canada

528 Ice Age Artefacts, Tools and Settlement

(Des R. Mah and G. Tsetsekas. Litho Ashton-Potter)

1986 (23 July). *50th Anniv of Canadian Broadcasting Corporation. P 12½.*
1207	**527** 34 c. multicoloured	40	45

(Des F. Hagan. Litho Ashton-Potter)

1986 (29 Aug–1 Oct). *Exploration of Canada (1st series). Discoverers. T 528 and similar horiz designs. Multicoloured. P 12½×13.*
1208	34 c. Type 528	75	90
	a. Block of 4. Nos. 1208/11	2·75	
1209	34 c. Viking ships	75	90
1210	34 c. John Cabot's *Matthew*, 1497, compass and Arctic Char (fish)	75	90
1211	34 c. Henry Hudson cast adrift, 1611	75	90
1208/11	*Set of 4*	2·75	3·25
MS1212	119×84 mm. Nos. 1208/11 (1 Oct)	3·75	4·25

Nos. 1208/11 were printed together, *se-tenant*, in different combinations throughout the sheet, giving ten blocks of 4 and ten single stamps.
No. **MS**1212 publicises "Capex '87" International Stamp Exhibition, Toronto.
See also Nos. 1232/5, 1285/8 and 1319/22.

529 Crowfoot (Blackfoot Chief) and Indian Village

530 Peace Dove and Globe

(Des Wanda Lewicka and J. Morin. Litho C.B.N.)

1986 (5 Sept). *Founders of the Canadian West. T 529 and similar horiz design. Multicoloured. P 13×13½.*
1213	34 c. Type 529	35	55
	a. Pair. Nos. 1213/14	70	1·10
1214	34 c. James Macleod of the North West Mounted Police and Fort Macleod	35	55

Nos. 1213/4 were printed together, *se-tenant*, in horizontal and vertical pairs throughout the sheet.

(Des Carole Jeghers. Litho and embossed Ashton-Potter)

1986 (16 Sept). *International Peace Year. P 13½.*
1215	**530** 34 c. multicoloured	40	45

531 Ice Hockey

532 Angel with Crown

(Des P.-Y. Pelletier. Litho C.B.N.)

1986 (15 Oct). *Winter Olympic Games, Calgary (1988) (2nd issue). T 531 and similar vert design. Multicoloured. P 13½×13.*
1216	34 c. Type 531	1·25	1·40
	a. Pair. Nos. 1216/17	2·50	2·75
1217	34 c. Biathlon	1·25	1·40

Nos. 1216/17 were printed together, *se-tenant*, in horizontal and vertical pairs throughout the sheet.
See also Nos. 1236/7, 1258/9 and 1281/4.

(Des T. Dimson. Litho Ashton-Potter)

1986 (29 Oct). *Christmas. T 532 and similar multicoloured designs. Fluorescent frame (34 to 68 c.). P 13½×imperf (29 c.) or 12½ (others).*
1218	29 c. Angel singing carol (36×22 mm)	65	30
	a. Booklet pane. No. 1218×10	6·50	
	b. Perf 12½×imperf	5·00	30
	ba. Booklet pane. No. 1218b×10	50·00	
1219	34 c. Type 532	60	25
1220	39 c. Angel playing lute	1·00	90
1221	68 c. Angel with ribbon	1·25	2·25
1218/21	*Set of 4*	3·25	3·25

Nos. 1218/b were only available from $2.90 stamp booklets, which had the sides of the pane imperforate. In addition to the design each stamp in the pane included an integral horizontal label showing a bar code. This value was intended for use on greeting cards posted on or before 31 January 1987, and represented a 5 c. saving when used in conjunction with special postcoded envelopes. These stamps were valid for normal postal purposes after 31 January when used with other values.

533 John Molson with Theatre Royal, Montreal, *Accommodation* (paddle-steamer) and Railway Train

534 Toronto's First Post Office

(Des C. Malenfant. Litho Ashton-Potter)

1986 (4 Nov). *150th Death Anniv of John Molson (businessman). P 12½.*
1222	**533** 34 c. multicoloured	50	50

(Des E. Roch. Litho Ashton-Potter)

1986 (21 Nov). *Railway Locomotives (4th series). Horiz designs as T 503, but size 60×22 mm. Multicoloured. P 12½×13.*
1223	34 c. Canadian National Class V-1-a diesel locomotive No. 9000	1·50	1·50
	a. Pair. Nos. 1223/4	3·00	3·00
1224	34 c. Canadian Pacific Class T1a steam locomotive No. 9000	1·50	1·50
1225	39 c. Canadian National Class U-2-a steam locomotive	1·50	1·00
1226	68 c. Canadian Pacific Class H1c steam locomotive No. 2850	2·25	6·25
1223/6	*Set of 4*	6·00	6·25

Nos. 1223/4 were issued together, *se-tenant*, in horizontal and vertical pairs throughout the sheet.

(Des J. Mardon (stamps) and B. Reilander (sheet). Recess and litho B.A.B.N.)

1987 (16 Feb–12 June). *"Capex '87" International Stamp Exhibition, Toronto. T 534 and similar horiz designs showing Post Offices. Fluorescent frame. P 13×13½.*
1227	34 c. Type 534	60	20
1228	36 c. Nelson-Miramichi, New Brunswick (12.6)	65	45
1229	42 c. Saint-Ours, Quebec (12.6)	70	65
1230	72 c. Battleford, Saskatchewan (12.6)	1·00	1·25
1227/30	*Set of 4*	2·75	2·25
MS1231	155×92 mm. 36 c. As No. 1227 and Nos. 1228/30, but main inscr in brt green (12.6)	2·75	2·25

535 Étienne Brûlé exploring Lake Superior

(Des J. Britton and F. Hagan. Litho Ashton-Potter)

1987 (13 Mar). *Exploration of Canada (2nd series). Pioneers of New France. T 535 and similar horiz designs. Multicoloured. P 12½×13.*
1232	34 c. Type 535	90	1·10
	a. Block of 4. Nos. 1232/5	3·25	
1233	34 c. Radisson and des Groseilliers with British and French flags	90	1·10

1234	34 c. Jolliet and Father Marquette on the Mississippi	.. ..	90 1·10
1235	34 c. Jesuit missionary preaching to Indians..	.. ..	90 1·10
1232/5		Set of 4	3·25 4·00

Nos. 1232/5 were printed together, *se-tenant*, in different combinations throughout the sheet, giving ten blocks of 4 and ten single stamps.

(Des P.-Y. Pelletier. Litho C.B.N.)

1987 (3 Apr). *Winter Olympic Games, Calgary (1988) (3rd issue). Vert designs as T* 531. *Multicoloured.* P 13½×13.

1236	36 c. Speed skating	..	50	40
1237	42 c. Bobsleighing ..	..	75	60

536 Volunteer Activities   537 Canadian Coat of Arms

(Des W. Davies. Litho Ashton-Potter)

1987 (13 Apr). *National Volunteer Week.* P 12½×13.

1238	**536** 36 c. multicoloured	.. ..	30	35

(Des R. Tibbles. Litho Ashton-Potter)

1987 (15 Apr). *5th Anniv of Canadian Charter of Rights and Freedoms. Fluorescent frame.* P 14×13½.

1239	**537** 36 c. multicoloured	..	35	35

538 Steel Girder, Gear Wheel   539 R. A. Fessenden
and Microchip   (AM Radio)

(Des L. Holloway, R. Kerr and Nita Wallace. Litho Ashton-Potter)

1987 (19 May). *Centenary of Engineering Institute of Canada.* P 12½×13.

1240	**538** 36 c. multicoloured	.. ..	35	40

(Des R. Hill. Litho C.B.N.)

1987 (25 June). *Canada Day. Science and Technology. Canadian Inventors (2nd series). T* 539 *and similar vert designs. Multicoloured.* P 13½.

1241	36 c. Type 539	..	80	85
	a. Block of four. Nos. 1241/4	..	2·75	
1242	36 c. C. Fenerty (newsprint pulp) ..		80	85
1243	36 c. G.-E. Desbarats and W. Leggo (half-tone engraving)	..	80	85
1244	36 c. F. N. Gisborne (first North American undersea telegraph) ..	..	80	85
1241/4		Set of 4	2·75	3·00

Nos. 1241/4 were printed together, *se-tenant*, in blocks of four throughout the sheet.

540 *Segwun*   541 Figurehead from
                          Hamilton, 1813

(Des D. Champion. Litho C.B.N.)

1987 (20 July). *Canadian Steamships. T* 540 *and similar multicoloured design.* P 13.

1245	36 c. Type 540	.. ..	1·40	2·00
	a. Horiz pair. Nos. 1245/6	..	2·75	4·00
1246	36 c. *Princess Marguerite* (52×22 mm)	..	1·40	2·00

Nos. 1245/6 were printed together horizontally, *se-tenant*, throughout the sheet of 25, with No. 1245 occurring in columns 1, 3 and 5 and No. 1246 in columns 2 and 4.

(Des L.-A. Rivard. Litho Ashton-Potter)

1987 (7 Aug). *Historic Shipwrecks. T* 541 *and similar horiz designs. Multicoloured.* P 13½×13.

1247	36 c. Type 541	..	70	90
	a. Block of four. Nos. 1247/50	..	2·50	
1248	36 c. Hull of *San Juan,* 1565	..	70	90
1249	36 c. Wheel from *Breadalbane,* 1853	..	70	90
1250	36 c. Bell from *Ericsson,* 1892	..	70	90
1247/50		Set of 4	2·50	3·25

Nos. 1247/50 were printed together, *se-tenant*, in different combinations throughout the sheet, giving ten blocks of 4 and ten single stamps.

---

542 Air Canada Boeing   543 Summit Symbol
767-200 and Globe

(Des Debbie Adams and D. Carter. Litho C.B.N.)

1987 (1 Sept). *50th Anniv of Air Canada.* P 13½.

1251	**542** 36 c. multicoloured	.. .. ..	55	35

(Des C. Gaudreau. Litho Ashton-Potter)

1987 (2 Sept). *2nd International Francophone Summit, Quebec. Fluorescent frame.* P 13×12½.

1252	**543** 36 c. multicoloured	..	30	35

544 Commonwealth Symbol   545 Poinsettia

(Des G. Tsetsekas. Litho Ashton-Potter)

1987 (13 Oct). *Commonwealth Heads of Government Meeting, Vancouver. Fluorescent frame.* P 13×12½.

1253	**544** 36 c. multicoloured	..	35	40

(Des C. Simard. Litho Ashton-Potter)

1987 (2 Nov). *Christmas. Christmas Plants. T* 545 *and similar multicoloured designs. Fluorescent frame.* P 12½×13 (31 c.) or 13½ (others).

1254	31 c. Decorated Christmas tree and presents (36×20 mm)	..	50	35
	a. Booklet pane. No. 1254×10	5·00		
	b. Imperf between (horiz pair) (from booklet)			
1255	36 c. Type 545	..	35	40
1256	42 c. Holly wreath	..	40	45
1257	72 c. Mistletoe and decorated tree	..	65	70
1254/7		Set of 4	1·75	1·75

On No. 1254 the left-hand third of the design area is taken up by a bar code which has fluorescent bands between the bars. This value was only available from $3.10 stamp booklets which had the sides of the pane imperforate. This value was intended for use on greeting cards posted on or before 31 January 1988 and represented a 5 c. saving when used in conjunction with special postcoded envelopes.

(Des P.-Y. Pelletier. Litho C.B.N.)

1987 (13 Nov). *Winter Olympic Games, Calgary (1988) (4th issue). Vert designs as T* 531. *Multicoloured. Fluorescent frame.* P 13½×13.

1258	36 c. Cross-country skiing	.. ..	50	40
	a. Pair. Nos. 1258/9	..	1·00	80
1259	36 c. Ski-jumping	..	50	40

Nos. 1258/9 were printed together, *se-tenant*, in horizontal and vertical pairs throughout the sheet.

546 Football, Grey Cup
and Spectators

(Des L. Holloway. Litho Ashton-Potter)

1987 (20 Nov). *75th Grey Cup Final (Canadian football championship), Vancouver. Fluorescent frame.* P 12½.

1260	**546** 36 c. multicoloured	.. ..	35	40

547 Flying Squirrel   548 Lynx

548a Runnymede Library, Toronto

(Des Gottschalk & Ash International (1 c. to 25 c.), B. Tsang (43 c. to 80 c.), R. Bellemare ($1, $2, $5). Litho Ashton-Potter (1 c. to 80 c.), Recess and litho B.A.B.N. to June 1992, thereafter C.B.N. ($1, $2, $5))

1988 (18 Jan)–**93**. *Canadian Mammals and Architecture. Multicoloured. Fluorescent frame* (10 c. and 43 c. to 80 c.).

(a) Horiz designs as T 547. *Chalk-surfaced paper.* P 13×13½

1261	1 c. Type 547 (3.10.88)		10	10
	a. Perf 13×12½ (1.92)	..	2·75	1·25
1262	2 c. Porcupine (3.10.88)	..	10	10
1263	3 c. Muskrat (3.10.88)		10	10
1264	5 c. Varying Hare (3.10.88)		10	10
1265	6 c. Red Fox (3.10.88)		10	10
1266	10 c. Striped Skunk (3.10.88)		10	10
	a. Perf 13×12½ (2.91)	..	3·75	1·50
	b. No fluorescent frame (25.10.91)		45	10
1267	25 c. American Beaver (3.10.88)	..	30	15
	a. No fluorescent frame (22.4.92)		1·00	40

(b) Horiz designs as T 548. *Chalk-surfaced paper* (45, 46, 57, 61, 63, 78, 80 c.) *or ordinary paper* (others). P 12×12½ (43, 57, 74 c.) *or* 14½×14 (others)

1268	43 c. Type 548	..	1·40	30
1269	44 c. Walrus (18.1.89)	..	45	20
	a. Perf 12½×13. Chalk-surfaced paper	1·00	55
	ab. Booklet pane. No. 1269a×5 and label with margins all round	5·00	
	b. Chalk-surfaced paper (9.6.89)	3·00	1·25
	c. Perf 13½×13. Chalk-surfaced paper (1989)	£140	13·00
1270	45 c. Pronghorn (12.1.90)	..	35	40
	a. Perf 12½×13		1·75	40
	ab. Booklet pane. No. 1270a×5 and label with margins all round	7·00	
	b. Perf 13 (6.90)		11·00	50
1270c	46 c. Wolverine (28.12.90)		45	30
	ca. Perf 13		2·00	2·00
	cb. Perf 12½×13		1·25	45
	cc. Booklet pane. No. 1270cb×5 and label with margins all round	5·00	
1271	57 c. Killer Whale	..	2·00	55
	a. Ordinary paper (26.9.88)		3·25	1·75
1272	59 c. Musk Ox (18.1.89)	..	2·00	55
	a. Chalk-surfaced paper (1.11.89)	5·50	2·50
	b. Perf 13. Chalk-surfaced paper (1.11.89)	6·00	3·50
1273	61 c. Wolf (12.1.90)	..	60	85
	a. Perf 13 (7.90)		27·00	1·50
1273b	63 c. Harbour Porpoise (28.12.90)	65	60
	ba. Perf 13		5·50	3·00
1274	74 c. Wapiti	..	1·60	50
	a. Chalk-surfaced paper		£140	5·00
1275	76 c. Brown Bear (18.1.89)		90	50
	a. Perf 12½×13. Chalk-surfaced paper	1·75	70
	ab. Booklet pane. No. 1275a×5 and label with margins all round	8·50	
	b. Chalk-surfaced paper (25.8.89)	3·25	2·50
	c. Perf 13. Chalk-surfaced paper (1989)	17·00	7·50
1276	78 c. White Whale (12.1.90)		90	55
	a. Perf 12½×13		1·90	60
	ab. Booklet pane. No. 1276a×5 and label with margins all round	9·00	
	b. Perf 13 (4.90)		22·00	4·25
1276c	80 c. Peary Caribou (28.12.90)		1·00	60
	ca. Perf 13		2·50	80
	cb. Perf 12½×13		1·50	45
	cc. Booklet pane. No. 1276cb×5 and label with margins all round	8·00	

(c) Horiz designs as T 548a. *Chalk-surfaced paper* ($5) *or ordinary paper* (others). P 13½

1277	$1 Type 548a (brown roof) (5.5.89)	..	1·25	30
	a. Chalk-surfaced paper (28.8.92)	3·75	1·10
	ab. Black (recess inscr) inverted	£6000	
	ac. Imperf (pair)		£750	
	ad. Black roof (1993)		10·00	1·25
1278	$2 McAdam Railway Station, New Brunswick (5.5.89)	..	2·00	50
	a. Chalk-surfaced paper (29.7.92)	9·00	2·40
	ab. Imperf (pair)		£600	
1279	$5 Bonsecours Market, Montreal (28.5.90)	..	4·75	4·00
1261/79		Set of 22	18·00	10·00

The later issues of the mammal series are slightly larger than the original three, measuring 27×21 mm.

Nos. 1269a, 1270a, 1270cb, 1275a, 1276a and 1276cb were only issued in stamp booklets.

Nos. 1277a/ac and 1278a were printed by C.B.N. There was also a printing of the $5 by C.B.N. in September 1992, but this does not differ from the B.A.B.N. version. All C.B.N. printings are on thinner paper, less crisp than the initial printings.

No. 1277ad appears to be from new plates. In addition to the differences in the roof colour it shows a less solid blue background around the building.

For further designs as Type 548a, but in a changed format, see Nos. 1479/81.

(Des P.-Y. Pelletier. Litho Ashton-Potter)

1988 (12 Feb). *Winter Olympic Games, Calgary (5th issue). Vert designs as T* 531. *Multicoloured. Fluorescent frame.* P 12×12½ (37 c.) *or* 12½ (others).

1281	37 c. Slalom skiing ..	..	75	50
	a. Pair. Nos. 1281/2	..	1·50	1·00
1282	37 c. Curling..	..	75	50
1283	43 c. Figure skating..		75	45
1284	74 c. Luge	..	1·25	80
1281/4		Set of 4	3·25	2·00

Nos. 1281/2 were printed together, *se-tenant*, in horizontal and vertical pairs throughout the sheet.

549 Trade Goods, Blackfoot Encampment and Page from Anthony Henday's Journal

(Des F. Hagan. Litho Ashton-Potter)

1988 (17 Mar). *Exploration of Canada (3rd series). Explorers of the West.* T **549** *and similar horiz designs. Multicoloured. Fluorescent frame. P* 12½×13.

1285	37 c. Type **549**	65	50
	a. Block of 4. Nos. 1285/8	2·40	
1286	37 c. *Discovery* and map of George Vancouver's voyage	65	50
1287	37 c. Simon Fraser's expedition portaging canoes	65	50
1288	37 c. John Palliser's surveying equipment and view of prairie	65	50
1285/8	*Set of 4*	2·40	1·75

Nos. 1285/8 were printed together, *se-tenant*, in different combinations throughout the sheet, giving ten blocks of 4 and ten single stamps.

550 "The Young Reader" (Ozias Leduc)

551 Mallard landing on Marsh

(Des P.-Y. Pelletier. Eng G. Prosser. Recess and photo B.A.B.N.)

1988 (20 May). *Canadian Art (1st series). No fluorescent bands. P* 13×13½.

1289	**550** 50 c. multicoloured	70	70

No. 1289 was issued in sheets of 16 with descriptive texts on the margins.
See also Nos. 1327, 1384, 1421, 1504, 1539, 1589, 1629, 1681, 1721, 1825 and 1912.

(Des J. Gault and T. Telmet. Litho C.B.N.)

1988 (1 June). *Wildlife and Habitat Conservation.* T **551** *and similar horiz design. Multicoloured. Fluorescent frame. P* 13 × 13½.

1290	37 c. Type **551**	90	50
	a. Pair. Nos. 1290/1	1·75	1·00
1291	37 c. Moose feeding in marsh	90	50

Nos. 1290/1 were printed together, *se-tenant*, in horizontal and vertical pairs throughout the sheet.

552 Kerosene Lamp and Diagram of Distillation Plant

553 *Papilio brevicauda*

(Des R. Hill. Litho Ashton-Potter)

1988 (17 June). *Canada Day. Science and Technology. Canadian Inventions (3rd series).* T **552** *and similar vert designs. Multicoloured. Fluorescent frame. P* 12½×13.

1292	37 c. Type **552**	50	70
	a. Block of 4. Nos. 1292/5	1·75	
1293	37 c. Ears of Marquis wheat	50	70
1294	37 c. Electron microscope and magnified image	50	70
1295	37 c. Patient under "Cobalt 60" cancer therapy	50	70
1292/5	*Set of 4*	1·75	2·50

Nos. 1292/5 were printed together, *se-tenant*, in blocks of 4 throughout the sheet.

(Des Heather Cooper. Litho Ashton-Potter)

1988 (4 July). *Canadian Butterflies.* T **553** *and similar vert designs. Multicoloured. Fluorescent frame. P* 12×12½.

1296	37 c. Type **553**	70	70
	a. Block of four. Nos. 1296/9	2·50	
1297	37 c. *Lycaeides idas*	70	70
1298	37 c. *Oeneis macounii*	70	70
1299	37 c. *Papilio glaucus*	70	70
1296/9	*Set of 4*	2·50	2·50

Nos. 1296/9 were printed together, *se-tenant*, in different combinations throughout the sheet, giving ten blocks of 4 and ten single stamps.

554 St. John's Harbour Entrance and Skyline

555 Club Members working on Forestry Project and Rural Scene

(Des L.-A. Rivard. Litho Ashton-Potter)

1988 (22 July). *Centenary of Incorporation of St. John's, Newfoundland. Fluorescent frame. P* 13½×13.

1300	**554** 37 c. multicoloured	35	40

(Des Debbie Adams. Litho Ashton-Potter)

1988 (5 Aug). *75th Anniv of 4-H Clubs. Fluorescent frame. P* 13½×13.

1301	**555** 37 c. multicoloured	35	40

556 Saint-Maurice Ironworks

557 Tahltan Bear Dog

(Des Michèle Cayer and Hélène Racicot. Eng. Y. Baril. Recess and litho C.B.N.)

1988 (19 Aug). *250th Anniv of Saint-Maurice Ironworks, Québec. Fluorescent frame. P* 13½.

1302	**556** 37 c. black, pale orange and cinnamon	35	40

(Des Mia Lane and D. Nethercott. Litho Ashton-Potter)

1988 (26 Aug). *Canadian Dogs.* T **557** *and similar horiz designs. Multicoloured. Fluorescent frame. P* 12½×12.

1303	37 c. Type **557**	1·00	75
	a. Block of 4. Nos. 1303/6	3·50	
1304	37 c. Nova Scotia Duck Tolling Retriever	1·00	75
1305	37 c. Canadian Eskimo Dog	1·00	75
1306	37 c. Newfoundland	1·00	75
1303/6	*Set of 4*	3·50	2·75

Nos. 1303/6 were printed together, *se-tenant*, in different combinations throughout the sheet, giving ten blocks of 4 and ten single stamps.

558 Baseball, Glove and Pitch

559 Virgin with Inset of Holy Child

(Des L. Holloway. Litho C.B.N.)

1988 (14 Sept). *150th Anniv of Baseball in Canada. Fluorescent frame. P* 13½ × 13.

1307	**558** 37 c. multicoloured	35	40

(Des E. Roch and T. Yakobina. Litho Ashton-Potter)

1988 (27 Oct). *Christmas. Icons.* T **559** *and similar multicoloured designs. Fluorescent frame. P* 12½×13 (32 c.) *or* 13½×13 (*others*).

1308	32 c. Holy Family (36×21 *mm*)	35	35
	a. Booklet pane. No. 1308×10	3·50	
1309	37 c. Type **559**	35	40
1310	43 c. Virgin and Child	40	45
1311	74 c. Virgin and Child (*different*)	70	75
1308/11	*Set of 4*	1·60	1·75

On No. 1308 the left-hand third of the design area is taken up by a bar code which has fluorescent bands between the bars. This value was only available from $3.20 stamp booklets which had the sides and bottom of the pane imperforate. It was intended for use on greeting cards posted on or before 31 January 1989.
No. 1309 also commemorates the Millenium of Ukrainian Christianity.

560 Bishop Inglis and Nova Scotia Church

561 Frances Ann Hopkins and "Canoe manned by Voyageurs"

(Des S. Slipp and K. Sollows. Litho Ashton-Potter)

1988 (1 Nov). *Bicentenary of Consecration of Charles Inglis (first Canadian Anglican bishop) (1987). Fluorescent frame. P* 12½ × 12.

1312	**560** 37 c. multicoloured	35	40

(Des D. Nethercott. Litho Ashton-Potter)

1988 (18 Nov). *150th Birth Anniv of Frances Ann Hopkins (artist). Fluorescent frame. P* 13½ × 13.

1313	**561** 37 c. multicoloured	35	40

562 Angus Walters and *Bluenose* (yacht)

563 Chipewyan Canoe

(Des R. Hill. Litho Ashton-Potter)

1988 (18 Nov). *20th Death Anniv of Angus Walters (yachtsman). Fluorescent frame. P* 13½.

1314	**562** 37 c. multicoloured	35	40

(Des B. Leduc and L.-A. Rivard. Litho Ashton-Potter)

1989 (1 Feb). *Small Craft of Canada (1st series). Native Canoes.* T **563** *and similar horiz designs. Multicoloured. Fluorescent frame. P* 13½ × 13.

1315	38 c. Type **563**	85	60
	a. Block of 4. Nos. 1315/18	3·00	
1316	38 c. Haida canoe	85	60
1317	38 c. Inuit kayak	85	60
1318	38 c. Micmac canoe	85	60
1315/18	*Set of 4*	3·00	2·25

Nos. 1315/18 were printed together, *se-tenant*, throughout the sheet, giving ten blocks of 4 and ten single stamps.
See also Nos. 1377/80 and 1428/31.

564 Matonabbee and Hearne's Expedition

565 Construction of Victoria Bridge, Montreal and William Notman

(Des F. Hagan. Litho Ashton-Potter)

1989 (22 Mar). *Exploration of Canada (4th series). Explorers of the North.* T **564** *and similar horiz designs. Multicoloured. Fluorescent frame. P* 12½×13.

1319	38 c. Type **564**	65	65
	a. Block of 4. Nos. 1319/22	2·40	
1320	38 c. Relics of Franklin's expedition and White Ensign	65	65
1321	38 c. Joseph Tyrrell's compass, hammer and fossil	65	65
1322	38 c. Vilhjalmur Stefansson, camera on tripod and sledge dog team	65	65
1319/22	*Set of 4*	2·40	2·40

Nos. 1319/22 were printed together, *se-tenant*, in different combinations throughout the sheet, giving ten blocks of 4 and ten single stamps.

(Des J. Morin and T. Yakobina. Litho Ashton-Potter)

1989 (23 June). *Canada Day. "150 Years of Canadian Photography".* T **565** *and similar horiz designs, each showing early photograph and photographer. Multicoloured. P* 12½×12.

1323	38 c. Type **565**	50	50
	a. Block of 4. Nos. 1323/6	1·75	
1324	38 c. Plains Indian village and W. Hanson Boorne	50	50
1325	38 c. Horse-drawn sleigh and Alexander Henderson	50	50
1326	38 c. Quebec street scene and Jules-Ernest Livernois	50	50
1323/6	*Set of 4*	1·75	1·75

Nos. 1323/6 were printed together, *se-tenant*, in blocks of 4 throughout the sheet.

566 Tsimshian Ceremonial Frontlet, c 1900

567 Canadian Flag and Forest

(Des P.-Y. Pelletier. Litho and die-stamped Ashton-Potter)

1989 (29 June). *Canadian Art (2nd series). No fluorescent bands. P* 12½×13.

1327	**566** 50 c. multicoloured	55	60

No. 1327 was issued in a similar sheet format to No. 1289.

(Des Gottschalk & Ash International, Litho Ashton-Potter)

1989 (30 June)–93. *T* **567** *and similar horiz designs. Multicoloured. Fluorescent frame. Self-adhesive. Die-cut.*

1328	38 c. Type **567**	..	90	1·40
	a. Booklet pane. No. 1328×12	..	10·00	
1328*b*	39 c. Canadian flag and prairie (8.2.90)	1·00	1·50
	ba. Booklet pane. No. 1328*b*×12	..	11·00	
1328*c*	40 c. Canadian flag and sea (11.1.91)	1·00	1·25
	ca. Booklet pane. No. 1328*c*×12	..	11·00	
1328*d*	42 c. Canadian flag and mountains (28.1.92)		1·25	1·75
	da. Booklet pane. No. 1328*d*×12	..	12·00	
1328*e*	43 c. Canadian flag over lake (15.2.93)	80	1·10
	ea. Booklet pane. No. 1328*e*×12	..	9·00	
1328/*e*		*Set of 5*	4·50	6·25

Nos. 1328, 1328*b*, 1328*c*, 1328*d* and 1328*e* were only available from self-adhesive booklets in which the backing card forms the booklet cover.

568 Archibald Lampman

569 *Clavulinopsis fusiformis*

(Des R. Milot. Litho Ashton-Potter)

1989 (7 July). *Canadian Poets. T* **568** *and similar horiz design. Multicoloured. Fluorescent frame. P* 13½.

1329	38 c. Type **568**	..	40	45
	a. Pair. Nos. 1329/30	..	80	90
1330	38 c. Louis-Honoré Fréchette	..	40	45

Nos. 1329/30 were printed together, *se-tenant*, in horizontal and vertical pairs throughout the sheet.

(Des E. Roch. Litho Ashton-Potter)

1989 (4 Aug). *Mushrooms. T* **569** *and similar vert designs. Multicoloured. Fluorescent frame. P* 13½.

1331	38 c. Type **569**	..	70	60
	a. Block of 4. Nos. 1331/4	..	2·50	
1332	38 c. *Boletus mirabilis*	..	70	60
1333	38 c. *Cantharellus cinnabarinus*	..	70	60
1334	38 c. *Morchella esculenta*	..	70	60
1331/4		*Set of 4*	2·50	2·25

Nos. 1331/4 were printed together, *se-tenant*, in different combinations throughout the sheet, giving ten blocks of 4 and ten single stamps.

570 Night Patrol, Korea

571 Globe in Box

(Des N. Fontaine, J. Gault and T. Telmet. Eng Y. Baril. Recess and litho C.B.N.)

1989 (8 Sept). *75th Anniv of Canadian Regiments. T* **570** *and similar horiz design. Multicoloured. Fluorescent frame. P* 13.

1335	38 c. Type **570** (Princess Patricia's Canadian Light Infantry)	..	90	90
	a. Vert pair. Nos. 1335/6	..	1·75	1·75
1336	38 c. Trench raid, France, 1914-18 (Royal 22e Régiment)		90	90

Nos. 1335/6 were printed together, *se-tenant*, in vertical pairs throughout the sheet.

(Des L. Holloway and Nita Wallace. Litho Ashton-Potter)

1989 (2 Oct). *Canada Export Trade Month. Fluorescent frame. P* 13½×13.

1337	**571** 38 c. multicoloured	..	40	45

572 Film Director

573 "Snow II" (Lawren S. Harris)

(Des W. Tibbles from paper sculptures by J. Milne. Litho Ashton-Potter)

1989 (4 Oct). *Arts and Entertainment. T* **572** *and similar vert designs. Fluorescent frame. P* 13×13½.

1338	38 c. grey-brown, blackish brown and bright reddish violet		40	45
	a. Block of 4. Nos. 1338/41	..	1·50	
1339	38 c. grey-brown, blackish brown & brt grn	40	45
1340	38 c. grey-brn, blackish brn & brt magenta	40	45
1341	38 c. grey-brown, blackish brown & new bl	40	45
1338/41		*Set of 4*	1·50	1·60

Designs:—No. 1339, Actors; No. 1340, Dancers; No. 1341, Musicians.

Nos. 1338/41 were printed together, *se-tenant*, in different combinations throughout the sheet, giving ten blocks of 4 and ten single stamps.

(Des D. Nethercott and Viviane Warburton. Litho Ashton-Potter)

1989 (26 Oct). *Christmas. Paintings of Winter Landscapes. T* **573** *and similar multicoloured designs. Fluorescent frame. P* 12½×13 (33 c.), 13×13½ (38 c.) *or* 13½ (*others*).

1342	33 c. "Champ-de-Mars, Winter" (William Brymner) (35×21 *mm*)		90	55
	a. Booklet pane. No. 1342×10	..	9·00	
	b. Imperf between (horiz pair) (from booklet)			
1343	38 c. "Bend in the Gosselin River" (Marc-Aurèle Suzor-Coté) (21×35 *mm*)		40	35
	a. Perf 13×12½	..	3·25	3·50
	b. Booklet pane. No. 1343a×10	..	32·00	
1344	44 c. Type **573**	..	45	50
	a. Booklet pane. No. 1344×5 plus one printed label	..	13·00	
1345	76 c. "Ste. Agnès" (A. H. Robinson)	..	80	85
	a. Booklet pane. No. 1345×5 plus one printed label	..	22·00	
1342/5		*Set of 4*	2·25	2·00

On No. 1342 the left-hand third of the design area is taken up by a bar code which has fluorescent bands between the bars. This value was only available from $3.30 stamp booklets which had the sides and bottom of the pane imperforate. It was intended for use on greeting cards posted on or before 31 January 1990.

No. 1343a was only issued in $3.80 stamp booklets.

Booklet pane No. 1343ab has the outer edges of the pane imperforate while Nos. 1344a and 1345a have the vertical edges imperforate.

574 Canadians listening to Declaration of War, 1939

(Des J.-P. Armanville and P.-Y. Pelletier. Litho C.B.N.)

1989 (10 Nov). *50th Anniv of Second World War* (1st issue). *T* **574** *and similar horiz designs. Fluorescent frame. P* 13½.

1346	38 c. black, silver and slate-purple	85	65
	a. Block of 4. Nos. 1346/9	..	3·00	
1347	38 c. black, silver and olive-grey	..	85	65
1348	38 c. black, silver and grey-green	..	85	65
1349	38 c. black, silver and azure	..	85	65
1346/9		*Set of 4*	3·00	2·40

Designs:—No. 1347, Army mobilization; No. 1348, British Commonwealth air crew training; No. 1349, North Atlantic convoy.

Nos. 1346/9 were printed together, *se-tenant*, in different combinations throughout the sheet, giving four blocks of 4.

See also Nos. 1409/12, 1456/9, 1521/4, 1576/9, 1621/4 and 1625/8.

575 Canadian Flag

576

1989 (28 Dec)–98. *No fluorescent bands* (1, 5 c.) *or fluorescent frame* (39, 40, 42, 43, 45, 46 c.).

(a) *Booklet stamps. T* **575** *and similar horiz designs, each showing Canadian flag. Litho Ashton-Potter. Chalk-surfaced paper. P* 13½×14.

1350	**575** 1 c. multicoloured (12.1.90)	20	85
	a. Booklet pane. Nos. 1350, 1351×2 and 1352		1·40	
	b. Perf 12½×13	..	14·00	16·00
	ba. Booklet pane. Nos. 1350b, 1351a×2 and 1352a		35·00	
	c. Booklet pane. Nos. 1350×2, 1351 and 1353 (28.12.90)		2·00	
1351	5 c. multicoloured (12.1.90)	..	20	30
	a. Perf 12½×13	..	7·00	8·00
1352	39 c. multicoloured (12.1.90)	..	1·75	2·00
	a. Perf 12½×13	..	14·00	16·00
1353	40 c. multicoloured (28.12.90)	..	2·00	2·25

(b) *Litho* (for printers see below). *Chalk-surfaced paper. P* 14½ (45 c.), 13×13½ (46 c.) *or* 13½×13 (*others*).

1354	**576** 39 c. multicoloured	..	50	10
	a. Booklet pane. No. 1354×10 and two labels		8·00	
	b. Booklet pane. No. 1354×25 and two labels		17·00	
	c. Perf 12½×13 (2.90)	..	4·00	3·50
1355	40 c. multicoloured (28.12.90)	..	60	10
	a. Booklet pane. No. 1355×10 and two labels		8·00	
	b. Booklet pane. No. 1355×25 and two labels		18·00	
1356	42 c. multicoloured (27.12.91)	..	60	15
	a. Booklet pane. No. 1356×10	..	9·00	
	b. Booklet pane. No. 1356×25 and two labels		17·00	
	c. Booklet pane. No. 1356×50 and two labels		50·00	
1357	43 c. multicoloured (30.12.92)	..	60	60
	a. Booklet pane. No. 1357×10	..	8·50	
	b. Booklet pane. No. 1357×25 and two labels		18·00	
	c. Perf 14½ (18.1.94)	..	1·25	1·25
	ca. Booklet pane. No. 1357c×10	..	11·00	
	cb. Booklet pane. No. 1357c×25 and two labels		26·00	
	cc. Imperf between (vert pair)	..	£500	

1358	45 c. mult (17×21 *mm*) (31.7.95)	..	60	80
	a. Booklet pane. No. 1358×10	7·00	
	b. Booklet pane. No. 1358×25 and two labels		14·00	
	c. Perf 13½×13 (6.10.95)	..	45	55
	ca. Booklet pane. No. 1358c×10	4·50	
	cb. Booklet pane. No. 1358c×25 and two labels		17·00	
	d. Perf 13×13½ (16×20 *mm*) (2.2.98)		45	55
	da. Booklet pane. No. 1358d×10	..	4·50	
	db. Booklet pane. No. 1358d×30 (two blocks of 15 (5×3) separated by vertical gutter)		13·00	
1359	46 c. mult (16×20 *mm*) (28.12.98)	40	45
	a. Booklet pane. No. 1359×10	..	4·00	

(c) *Coil stamps. Designs as T* **575**, *but different folds in flag. Recess P* 10×*imperf*

1360	39 c. deep purple (8.2.90)	..	60	75
	a. Imperf (pair)	..	55·00	
1361	40 c. indigo (28.12.90)	..	40	45
	a. Imperf (pair)	..	£100	
1362	42 c. scarlet-vermilion (27.12.91)	..	40	45
	a. Imperf (pair)	..	55·00	
1363	43 c. deep olive (30.12.92)	..	55	80
	a. Imperf (pair)	..	55·00	
1364	45 c. bluish green (31.7.95)	..	55	40
	a. Imperf (pair)	..	55·00	
1365	46 c. carmine-red (28.12.98)	..	40	45

(d) *Self-adhesive booklet stamp. Litho Ashton-Potter Canada. Chalk-surfaced paper. Die-cut*

1366	46 c. multicoloured (28.12.98)	..	40	45
	a. Booklet pane. No. 1366×30	..	12·00	

Designs:—40 c. (No. 1355) Canadian flag over forest; 42 c. (No. 1356) Flag over mountains; 43 c. (No. 1357) Flag over prairie; 45 c. (No. 1358) Flag and skyscraper; 46 c. (Nos. 1359, 1366) Canadian flag and iceberg.

Booklet panes Nos. 1350a/b, 1356a/c, 1357ca/cb, 1358a/b, 1358ca/cb, 1358da/db and 1359a have the vertical edges of the panes imperforate and each shows a margin at foot. Booklet panes Nos. 1354a/b, 1355a/b and 1357a/b are imperforate at top and bottom.

Due to changes in the Canada Post contracts the printing history of Nos. 1354/9 is very complex. Details are provided below with Ashton-Potter Ltd. printings shown as AP, Canadian Bank Note Co as CBN, Leigh-Mardon Ltd as LM and Ashton-Potter Canada Ltd. as APC.

39 c. (No. 1354)	CBN (28.12.89), AP (14.2.90)
(No. 1354a/b)	AP (28.12.89)
(No. 1354c)	AP (2.90)
40 c. (No. 1355)	CBN (28.12.90)
(Nos. 1355a/b)	AP (28.12.90)
42 c. (Nos. 1356/c)	AP (27.12.91)
43 c. (No. 1357/b)	AP (30.12.92), CBN (14.11.94)
(Nos. 1357c/cb)	LM (18.1.94)
45 c. (Nos. 1358/b)	LM (31.7..95)
(Nos. 1358c/cb)	CBN (6.10.95)
(No. 1358d)	CBN (2.2.98), APC (2.2.98)
(No. 1358da)	CBN (2.2.98)
(No. 1358db)	APC (2.2.96)
(No. 1358db)	APC (2.2.98)
46 c. (No. 1359)	CBN (28.12.98)

The C.B.N. printings of the 45 c. (No. 1358c) show the copyright date on flag changed from "1990" to "1995".

Postal forgeries of Nos. 1359 and 1362 exist showing heavier printing across the foot of the design.

577 Norman Bethune in 1937, and performing Operation, Montreal

578 Maple Leaf Mosaic

(Des Wanda Lewicka, J. Morin and Liu Xiang Ping. Eng Hu Zhenyuan and Yan Bingwu. Recess and litho C.B.N.)

1990 (2 Mar). *Birth Centenary of Dr. Norman Bethune* (surgeon). *T* **577** *and similar horiz design. Multicoloured. Fluorescent frame. P* 13×13½.

1375	39 c. Type **577**	..	45	65
	a. Pair. Nos. 1375/6	..	90	1·25
1376	39 c. Bethune in 1939, and treating wounded Chinese soldiers		45	65

Nos. 1375/6 were printed together, *se-tenant*, in horizontal and vertical pairs throughout the sheet.

(Des B. Leduc and L.-A. Rivard. Litho Ashton-Potter)

1990 (15 Mar). *Small Craft of Canada* (2nd series). *Early Work Boats. Horiz designs as T* **563**. *Multicoloured. Fluorescent frame. P* 13½×13.

1377	39 c. Fishing dory	..	70	60
	a. Block of 4. Nos. 1377/80	..	2·50	
1378	39 c. Logging pointer	..	70	60
1379	39 c. York boat	..	70	60
1380	39 c. North canoe	..	70	60
1377/80		*Set of 4*	2·50	2·25

Nos. 1377/80 were printed together, *se-tenant*, throughout the sheet, giving ten blocks of 4 and ten single stamps.

(Des F. Peter. Recess and litho C.B.N.)

1990 (5 Apr). *Multiculturalism. P* 13.

1381	**578** 39 c. multicoloured	..	35	40

579 Mail Van
(facing left)

580 Amerindian and
Inuit Dolls

(Des J. Morin and A. Rochon. Litho Ashton-Potter)

1990 (3 May). *"Moving the Mail". T 579 and similar horiz design. Multicoloured. Fluorescent frame. P 13½.*

1382	39 c. Type 579		45	55
	a. Booklet pane. Nos. 1382/3, each × 4	4·50		
	b. Booklet pane. Nos. 1382×5, 1383×4 and 3 labels		12·00	
1383	39 c. Mail van (facing right)		45	55

Nos. 1382/3 were only issued in $9.75 stamp booklets.

(Des P.-Y. Pelletier. Litho and die-stamped Ashton-Potter)

1990 (3 May). *Canadian Art (3rd series). Vert design as T 550. Multicoloured. No fluorescent bands. P 12½×13.*

1384	50 c. "The West Wind" (Tom Thomson)		55	65

No. 1384 was issued in a similar sheet format to No. 1289.

(Des Nita Wallace. Litho Ashton-Potter)

1990 (8 June). *Dolls. T 580 and similar horiz designs. Multicoloured. Fluorescent frame. P 12½×12.*

1385	39 c. Type 580		65	60
	a. Block of 4. Nos. 1385/8	2·40		
1386	39 c. 19th-century settlers' dolls		65	60
1387	39 c. Commercial dolls, 1917–36		65	60
1388	39 c. Commercial dolls, 1940–60		65	60
1385/8		Set of 4	2·40	2·10

Nos. 1385/8 were printed together, *se-tenant*, in different combinations throughout the sheet, giving ten blocks of 4 and ten single stamps.

581 Canadian
Flag and
Fireworks

582 *Stromatolites* (fossil
algae)

(Des C. Malenfont. Litho Ashton-Potter)

1990 (1 July*). *Canada Day. Fluorescent frame. P 13×12½*
1389	581	39 c. multicoloured	45	50

No. 1389 was issued in sheets of 16 with descriptive texts on the coloured margins.

*First day covers of No. 1389 are postmarked 29 June 1990. The stamp was available from two temporary post offices in Ottawa on Sunday 1 July, but was not sold throughout Canada until 3 July.

(Des R. Harder. Eng Y. Baril. Recess and litho C.B.N.)

1990 (12 July). *Prehistoric Canada (1st series). Primitive Life. T 582 and similar horiz designs. Multicoloured. Fluorescent frame. P 13×13½.*

1390	39 c. Type 582		60	70
	a. Block of 4. Nos. 1390/3	2·25		
1391	39 c. *Opabinia regalis* (soft invertebrate)		60	70
1392	39 c. *Paradoxides davidis* (trilobite)		60	70
1393	39 c. *Eurypterus remipes* (sea scorpion)		60	70
1390/3		Set of 4	2·25	2·50

Nos. 1390/3 were printed together, *se-tenant*, in different combinations throughout the sheet, giving four blocks of 4 and four single stamps.

See also Nos. 1417/20, 1568/71 and 1613/16.

583 Acadian Forest

584 Clouds and Rainbow

(Des M. and Jan Waddell. Litho Ashton-Potter)

1990 (1 Aug). *Canadian Forests. T 583 and similar horiz designs. Multicoloured. Fluorescent frame. P 12½×13.*

1394	39 c. Type 583		60	70
	a. Block of 4. Nos. 1394/7	2·25		
1395	39 c. Great Lakes–St. Lawrence forest		60	70
1396	39 c. Pacific Coast forest		60	70
1397	39 c. Boreal forest		60	70
1394/7		Set of 4	2·25	2·50

Nos. 1394/7 were printed together, *se-tenant*, in different combinations throughout the sheet, giving four blocks of 4 and four single stamps.

Nos. 1394/7 also exist as blocks of four of the same design surrounded by margins. Such blocks were not available from post offices, but could be obtained for $1 each at Petro-Canada filling stations by using a previously-distributed voucher in conjunction with the purchase of 25 litres of petrol. They could also be obtained, at face value, from the Canadian Philatelic Service by post.

(Des D. L'Allier and Dominique Trudeau. Litho Ashton-Potter)

1990 (5 Sept). *150th Anniv of Weather Observing in Canada. Fluorescent frame. P 12½×13½.*
1398	584	39 c. multicoloured	40	50

No. 1398 has a break in the lower vertical sides of the fluorescent frame to allow the clouds to run on to the margins.

585 "Alphabet"
Bird

586 Sasquatch

(Des Debbie Adams. Recess and litho C.B.N.)

1990 (7 Sept). *International Literacy Year. Fluorescent frame. P 13½×13.*
1399	585	39 c. multicoloured	40	50

(Des A. Cormack, Deborah Drew-Brook and R. Tibbles. Litho Ashton-Potter)

1990 (1 Oct). *Legendary Creatures. T 586 and similar horiz designs. Multicoloured. Fluorescent frame. P 12½×12.*

1400	39 c. Type 586		70	80
	a. Block of 4. Nos. 1400/3	2·50		
	b. Perf 12½×12		6·00	6·00
	ba. Block of 4. Nos. 1400b/3b	22·00		
1401	39 c. Kraken		70	80
	b. Perf 12½×12		6·00	6·00
1402	39 c. Werewolf		70	80
	b. Perf 12½×12		6·00	6·00
1403	39 c. Ogopogo		70	80
	b. Perf 12½×12		6·00	6·00
1400/3		Set of 4	2·50	2·75

Nos. 1400/3 were printed together, *se-tenant*, in different combinations throughout the sheet, giving ten blocks of four and ten single stamps.

Stamps perforated 12½×12 come from a small percentage of the "non-philatelic" stock without imprints. Examples have also been found on official First Day Covers included in Presentation Packs.

587 Agnes
Macphail

588 "Virgin Mary
with Christ Child
and St. John the
Baptist" (Norval
Morrisseau)

(Des M. and Jan Waddell. Litho Ashton-Potter)

1990 (9 Oct). *Birth Centenary of Agnes Macphail (first woman elected to Parliament). Fluorescent frame. P 13×13½.*
1404	587	39 c. multicoloured	40	50

(Des C. Malenfant. Litho Ashton-Potter)

1990 (25 Oct). *Christmas. Native Art. T 588 and similar designs. Fluorescent frame. P 12½×13 (34 c.) or 13½ (others).*

1405	34 c. multicoloured (35×21 mm)		40	35
	a. Booklet pane. No. 1405×10	4·00		
1406	39 c. multicoloured		40	40
	a. Booklet pane. No. 1406×10	7·00		
1407	45 c. multicoloured		40	45
	a. Booklet pane. No. 1407×5 plus one printed label	4·00		
1408	78 c. black, bright scarlet and violet-grey		70	75
	a. Booklet pane. No. 1408×5 plus one printed label	7·00		
1405/8		Set of 4	1·75	1·75

Designs:—34 c. "Rebirth" (Jackson Beardy); 45 c. "Mother and Child" (Inuit sculpture, Cape Dorset); 78 c. "Children of the Raven" (Bill Reid).

On No. 1405 the left-hand third of the design area is taken up by a bar code which has fluorescent bands between the bars. This value was only available from $3.40 stamp booklets which had the sides and bottom of the pane imperforate. It was intended for use on greeting cards posted on or before 31 January 1991.

Booklet panes Nos. 1406a, 1407a and 1408a also have the side and bottom edges imperforate.

(Des J.-P. Armanville and P.-Y. Pelletier. Litho Ashton-Potter)

1990 (9 Nov). *50th Anniv of Second World War (2nd issue). Horiz designs as T 574. Fluorescent frame. P 12½×12.*

1409	39 c. black, silver and grey-olive		90	90
	a. Block of 4. Nos. 1409/12	3·25		
1410	39 c. black, silver and red-brown		90	90
1411	39 c. black, silver and bistre-brown		90	90
1412	39 c. black, silver and dull mauve		90	90
1409/12		Set of 4	3·25	3·25

Designs:—No. 1409, Canadian family at home, 1940; No. 1410, Packing parcels for the troops; No. 1411, Harvesting; No. 1412, Testing anti-gravity flying suit.

Nos. 1409/12 were printed together, *se-tenant*, in different combinations throughout the sheet, giving four blocks of 4.

589 Jennie Trout
(first woman
physician) and
Women's Medical
College, Kingston

590 Blue Poppies and
Butchart Gardens,
Victoria

(Des R. Milot. Litho Ashton-Potter)

1991 (15 Mar). *Medical Pioneers. T 589 and similar vert designs. Multicoloured. Fluorescent frame. P 13½.*

1413	40 c. Type 589		90	90
	a. Block of 4. Nos. 1413/16	3·25		
1414	40 c. Wilder Penfield (neurosurgeon) and Montreal Neurological Institute		90	90
1415	40 c. Frederick Banting (discoverer of insulin) and University of Toronto medical faculty		90	90
1416	40 c. Harold Griffith (anesthesiologist) and Queen Elizabeth Hospital, Montreal		90	90
1413/16		Set of 4	3·25	3·25

Nos. 1413/16 were printed together, *se-tenant*, in different combinations throughout the sheet, giving ten blocks of 4 and ten single stamps.

(Des R. Harder. Eng L. Bloss. Recess and litho Ashton-Potter)

1991 (5 Apr). *Prehistoric Canada (2nd series). Primitive Vertebrates. Horiz designs as T 582. Multicoloured. Fluorescent frame. P 12½×13½.*

1417	40 c. Foord's Crossopt (*Eusthenopteron foordi*) (fish fossil)		1·25	1·40
	a. Block of 4. Nos. 1417/20	4·50		
1418	40 c. *Hylonomus lyelli* (land reptile)		1·25	1·40
1419	40 c. Fossil Conodonts (fossil teeth)		1·25	1·40
1420	40 c. *Archaeopteris halliana* (early tree)		1·25	1·40
1417/20		Set of 4	4·50	5·00

Nos. 1417/20 were printed together, *se-tenant*, in different combinations throughout the sheet, giving four blocks of 4 and four single stamps.

(Des P.-Y. Pelletier. Litho and die-stamped Ashton-Potter)

1991 (7 May). *Canadian Art (4th series). Vert design as T 550. Multicoloured. No fluorescent bands. P 12½×13.*

1421	50 c. "Forest, British Columbia" (Emily Carr)		90	1·00

No. 1421 was issued in a similar sheet format to No. 1289.

(Des G. Gauci and D. Wyman. Litho Ashton-Potter)

1991 (22 May). *Public Gardens. T 590 and similar vert designs. Multicoloured. Fluorescent frame. P 13×12½.*

1422	40 c. Type 590		55	55
	a. Booklet pane. Nos. 1422/6, each × 2	5·50		
1423	40 c. Marigolds and International Peace Garden, Boissevain		55	55
1424	40 c. Lilac and Royal Botanical Gardens, Hamilton		55	55
1425	40 c. Roses and Montreal Botanical Gardens		55	55
1426	40 c. Rhododendrons and Halifax Public Gardens		55	55
1422/6		Set of 5	2·50	2·50

Nos. 1422/6 were only available from $4 stamp booklets containing No. 1422a, which is imperforate at top and bottom.

591 Maple Leaf

592 South Nahanni
River

(Des Lisa Miller, R. Séguin and J.-P. Veilleux. Litho C.B.N.)

1991 (28 June). *Canada Day. Fluorescent frame. P 13½×13.*
1427	591	40 c. multicoloured	50	60

No. 1427 was issued in sheets of 20 with inscribed and decorated margins.

(Des B. Leduc and L.-A. Rivard. Litho Ashton-Potter)

1991 (18 July). *Small Craft of Canada (3rd series). Horiz designs as T 563. Multicoloured. Fluorescent frame. P 13½×13.*

1428	40 c. Verchère rowboat		85	90
	a. Block of 4. Nos. 1428/31	3·00		
1429	40 c. Touring kayak		85	90
1430	40 c. Sailing dinghy		85	90
1431	40 c. Cedar strip canoe		85	90
1428/31		Set of 4	3·00	3·25

Nos. 1428/31 were printed together, *se-tenant*, throughout the sheet, giving ten blocks of 4 and ten single stamps.

(Des M. and Jan Waddell. Litho Ashton-Potter)

1991 (20 Aug). *Canadian Rivers* (1st series). *T 592 and similar vert designs. Multicoloured. Fluorescent frame.* P 13×12¹/₂.

1432	40 c. Type 592		80	90
	a. Booklet pane. Nos. 1432/6, each × 2 with margins all round		7·50	
1433	40 c. Athabasca River		80	90
1434	40 c. Boundary Waters, Voyageur Waterway		80	90
1435	40 c. Jacques-Cartier River		80	90
1436	40 c. Main River		80	90
1432/6	*Set of* 5		3·50	4·00

Nos. 1432/6 were only issued in $4 stamp booklets.
See also Nos. 1492/6, 1558/62 and 1584/8.

593 "Leaving Europe"

594 Ski Patrol rescuing Climber

(Des J. Gault and T. Telmet. Litho C.B.N.)

1991 (29 Aug). *Centenary of Ukrainian Immigration. Panels from "The Ukrainian Pioneer" by William Kurelek. T 593 and similar vert designs. Multicoloured. Fluorescent frame.* P 13¹/₂×13.

1437	40 c. Type 593		80	85
	a. Block of 4. Nos. 1437/40		2·75	
1438	40 c. "Canadian Winter"		80	85
1439	40 c. "Clearing the Land"		80	85
1440	40 c. "Harvest"		80	85
1437/40	*Set of* 4		2·75	3·00

Nos. 1437/40 were printed together, *se-tenant*, in different combinations throughout the sheet, giving four blocks of 4 and four single stamps.

(Des Suzanne Duranceau. Litho C.B.N.)

1991 (23 Sept). *Emergency Services. T 594 and similar vert designs. Multicoloured. Fluorescent frame.* P 13¹/₂.

1441	40 c. Type 594		1·25	1·25
	a. Block of 4. Nos 1441/4		4·50	
1442	40 c. Police at road traffic accident		1·25	1·25
1443	40 c. Firemen on extending ladder		1·25	1·25
1444	40 c. Boeing-Vertol CH-147 Chinook rescue helicopter and *Spindrift* (lifeboat)		1·25	1·25
1441/4	*Set of* 4		4·50	4·50

Nos. 1441/4 were printed together, *se-tenant*, in different combinations throughout the sheet, giving ten blocks of 4 and ten single stamps.

595 "The Witched Canoe"

596 Grant Hall Tower

(Des A. Cormack, Deborah Drew-Brook and R. Tibbles. Litho Ashton-Potter)

1991 (1 Oct). *Canadian Folktales. T 595 and similar vert designs. Multicoloured. Fluorescent frame.* P 13¹/₂×12¹/₂.

1445	40 c. Type 595		95	95
	a. Block of 4. Nos. 1445/8		3·50	
1446	40 c. "The Orphan Boy"		95	95
1447	40 c. "Chinook"		95	95
1448	40 c. "Buried Treasure"		95	95
1445/8	*Set of* 4		3·50	3·50

Nos. 1445/8 were printed together, *se-tenant*, in different combinations throughout the sheet, giving ten blocks of 4 and ten single stamps.

(Des L. Holloway and R. Kerr. Litho Ashton-Potter)

1991 (16 Oct). *150th Anniv of Queen's University, Kingston. Fluorescent frame.* P 13¹/₂×12¹/₂.

1449	596 40 c. multicoloured		80	1·00
	a. Booklet pane. No. 1449×10 plus two printed labels with margins all round		8·00	

No. 1449 was only issued in $4 stamp booklets.

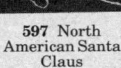

597 North American Santa Claus

598 Players jumping for Ball

(Des S. Slipp. Litho Ashton-Potter)

1991 (23 Oct). *Christmas. T 597 and similar multicoloured designs. Fluorescent frame.* P 12¹/₂×13 (35 c.) or 13¹/₂ (others).

1450	35 c. British Father Christmas (35×21 mm)		80	40
	a. Booklet pane. No. 1450×10		8·00	
1451	40 c. Type 597		70	20
	a. Booklet pane. No. 1451×10		9·00	
1452	46 c. French Bonhomme Noel		75	1·10
	a. Booklet pane. No. 1452×5 plus one printed label		4·50	
1453	80 c. Dutch Sinterklaas		1·40	2·25
	a. Booklet pane. No. 1453×5 plus one printed label		8·00	
1450/3	*Set of* 4		3·25	3·50

On No. 1450 the left-hand third of the design area is taken up by a bar code which has fluorescent bands between the bars. This value was only available from $3.50 stamp booklets which had the edges of the pane imperforate. It was intended for use on greeting cards posted on or before 31 January 1992.
Nos. 1451a, 1452a and 1453a also have the vertical edges of the panes imperforate.

(Des J. Gault, C. Reynolds and T. Telmet. Litho Ashton-Potter)

1991 (25 Oct). *Basketball Centenary. T 598 and similar vert designs. Multicoloured. Fluorescent frame.* P 13×13¹/₂.

1454	40 c. Type 598		90	75
MS1455	155×90 mm. 40 c. Type 598, but with shorter inscr below face value; 46 c. Player taking shot; 80 c. Player challenging opponent		5·50	5·50

(Des J.-P. Armanville and P.-Y. Pelletier. Litho C.B.N)

1991 (8 Nov). *50th Anniv of Second World War* (3rd issue). *Horiz designs as T 574. Fluorescent frame.* P 13¹/₂.

1456	40 c. black, silver and greenish blue		1·10	1·25
	a. Block of 4. Nos. 1456/9		4·00	
1457	40 c. black, silver and brown		1·10	1·25
1458	40 c. black, silver and lilac		1·10	1·25
1459	40 c. black, silver and ochre		1·10	1·25
1456/9	*Set of* 4		4·00	4·50

Designs:—No. 1456, Women's services, 1941; No. 1457, Armament factory; No. 1458, Cadets and veterans; No. 1459, Defence of Hong Kong.
Nos. 1456/9 were printed together, *se-tenant*, in different combinations throughout the sheet, giving four blocks of 4.

599 Blueberry

600 McIntosh Apple

600a Court House, Yorkton

(Des Tania Craan and D. Noble (1 c. to 25 c.), C. Malenfant (48 c. to 90 c.), R. Bellemare ($1, $2, $5))

1991 (27 Dec)–**96**. *Multicoloured. Chalk-surfaced paper.*

(a) *Edible Berries. Litho* (for printers see below). *T 599 and similar horiz designs. No fluorescent frame.* P 13×13¹/₂ (5.8.92).

1460	1 c. Type 599		10	10
1461	2 c. Wild Strawberry		10	10
1462	3 c. Black Crowberry		10	10
1463	5 c. Rose Hip		10	10
1464	6 c. Black Raspberry		10	10
1465	10 c. Kinnikinnick		10	10
	a. Imperf (horiz pair)			
1466	25 c. Saskatoon Berry		20	25

(b) *Fruit and Nut Trees. Litho* (for printers see below). *T 600 and similar horiz designs. Three fluorescent bands* (90 c.) or *fluorescent frame* (others). P 13.

1467	48 c. Type 600		50	35
	a. Perf 14¹/₂×14		1·25	1·00
	ab. Booklet pane. No. 1467a×5 and label		6·00	
1468	49 c. Delicious Apple (30.12.92)		1·00	1·00
	a. Booklet pane. No. 1468×5 and label (7.1.94)		6·00	
	b. Perf 14¹/₂×14		1·25	1·40
	ba. Booklet pane. No. 1468b×5 and label		6·00	
1469	50 c. Snow Apple (25.2.94)		1·00	1·00
	a. Booklet pane. No. 1469×5 and label		5·00	
	b. Perf 14¹/₂×14 (27.3.95)		1·25	1·75
	ba. Booklet pane. No. 1469b×5 and label		6·00	
1470	52 c. Gravenstein Apple (31.7.95)		50	50
	a. Booklet pane. No. 1470×5 and label		2·50	
	b. Perf 14¹/₂×14 (6.10.95)		60	45
	ba. Booklet pane. No. 1470b×5 and label		6·00	
1471	65 c. Black Walnut		70	50
1472	67 c. Beaked Hazelnut (30.12.92)		1·00	1·25
1473	69 c. Shagbark Hickory (25.2.94)		1·25	1·25
1474	71 c. American Chestnut (31.7.95)		80	1·00
	a. Perf 14¹/₂×14 (6.10.95)		2·50	1·10
1475	84 c. Stanley Plum		90	75
	a. Perf 14¹/₂×14		1·75	1·50
	ab. Booklet pane. No. 1475a×5 and label		9·00	
1476	86 c. Bartlett Pear (30.12.92)		85	1·00
	a. Booklet pane. No. 1476×5 and label (7.1.94)		8·00	
	b. Perf 14¹/₂×14		2·75	3·00
	ba. Booklet pane. No. 1476b×5 and label		13·00	
1477	88 c. Westcot Apricot (25.2.94)		1·60	1·60
	a. Booklet pane. No. 1477×5 and label		8·00	
	b. Three fluorescent bands (14.11.94)		1·75	2·25
	ba. Booklet pane. No. 1477b×5 and label		9·00	
	c. Perf 14¹/₂×14. Three fluorescent bands (27.3.95)		2·00	2·50
	ca. Booklet pane. No. 1477c×5 and label		10·00	
1478	90 c. Elberta Peach (31.7.95)		90	1·00
	a. Booklet pane. No. 1478×5 and label		4·50	
	b. Perf 14¹/₂×14 (6.10.95)		1·40	1·50
	ba. Booklet pane. No. 1478b×5 and label		7·00	

(c) *Architecture. Recess and litho Leigh-Mardon Ltd, Melbourne* (Nos. 1479/80) or *C.B.N.* (Nos. 1479a, 1480a, 1481). *T 600a and similar horiz designs.* P 14¹/₂×14 ($1, $2) or 13¹/₂×13 ($5)

1479	$1 Type 600a (21.2.94)		90	95
	a. Perf 13¹/₂×13 (20.2.95)		1·50	80
1480	$2 Provincial Normal School, Truro (21.2.94)		1·90	2·00
	a. Perf 13¹/₂×13 (20.2.95)		2·25	1·60
	ab. Deep turquoise-blue (recess inscr) omitted		£650	
	ac. Deep turquoise-blue (recess inscr) inverted			
1481	$5 Public Library, Victoria (29.2.96)		4·25	4·50
1460/81	*Set of* 22		16·00	16·00

Nos. 1460/6 were so printed that each horizontal row formed a composite design.
Nos. 1467a, 1468b, 1469b, 1475a, 1476b and 1477c were only issued in stamp booklets.
Booklet panes Nos. 1467ab, 1468a, 1468ba, 1475ab, 1476a, 1476ab, 1477a and 1477ba each have the vertical edges of the pane imperforate and margins at top and bottom.
Due to changes in the Canada Post contracts the printing history of Nos. 1460/80 is very complex. Details are provided below with Ashton-Potter Ltd printings shown as AP, Canadian Bank Note Co as CBN, Leigh-Mardon Ltd as LM and Ashton-Potter Canada Ltd as APC.

1 c. No. 1460 AP (5.8.92), CBN (19.8.94), APC (3.4.95)
2 c. No. 1461 AP (5.8.92), CBN (22.4.94), APC (1.8.95)
3 c. No. 1462 AP (5.8.92), CBN (22.4.94), APC (2.5.97)
5 c. No. 1463 AP (5.8.92), CBN (11.3.94), APC (20.9.95)
6 c. No. 1464 AP (5.8.92), CBN (11.3.94)
10 c. No. 1465 AP (5.8.92), CBN (11.3.94), APC (1.9.95)
25 c. No. 1466 AP (5.8.92), CBN (22.4.94), APC (1.5.96)
48 c. Nos. 1467/ab AP (27.12.91)
49 c. No. 1468 AP (30.12.92), CBN (7.1.94)
    No. 1468a CBN (7.1.94)
    Nos. 1468b/ba AP (30.12.92)
50 c. No. 1469 CBN (25.2.94), APC (10.4.95)
    No. 1469a CBN (25.2.94)
    Nos. 1469b/ba APC (27.3.95)
52 c. No. 1470 CBN (31.7.95), APC (6.10.95)
    No. 1470a CBN (31.7.95), APC (1997)
    Nos. 1470b/ba APC (6.10.95)
65 c. No. 1471 AP (27.12.91)
67 c. No. 1472 AP (30.12.92)
69 c. No. 1473 CBN (25.2.94), APC (10.4.95)
71 c. No. 1474 CBN (31.7.95), APC (6.10.95)
    No. 1474a APC (6.10.95)
84 c. Nos. 1475/ab AP (27.12.91)
86 c. No. 1476 AP (30.12.92), CBN (7.1.94)
    No. 1476a CBN (7.1.94)
    Nos. 1476b/ba AP (30.12.92)
88 c. Nos. 1477/a CBN (25.2.94)
    No. 1477b CBN (14.11.94), APC (10.4.95)
    No. 1477ba CBN (14.11.94)
    Nos. 1477c/ca APC (27.3.95)
90 c. No. 1478 CBN (31.7.95), APC (6.10.95)
    No. 1478a CBN (31.7.95), APC (1997)
    Nos. 1478b/ba APC (6.10.95)
$1 No. 1479 LM (21.2.94)
    No. 1479a CBN (20.2.95)
$2 No. 1480 LM (21.2.294)
    No. 1480a CBN (20.2.95)
$5 No. 1481 CBN (29.2.96)

601 Ski Jumping

(Des Gottschalk & Ash International. Litho Ashton-Potter)

1992 (7 Feb). *Winter Olympic Games, Albertville. T 601 and similar horiz designs. Multicoloured. Fluorescent frame.* P 12¹/₂×13.

1482	42 c. Type 601		80	90
	a. Booklet pane. Nos. 1482/6, each × 2 with margins all round		7·00	
1483	42 c. Figure skating		80	90
1484	42 c. Ice hockey		80	90
1485	42 c. Bobsleighing		80	90
1486	42 c. Alpine skiing		80	90
1482/6	*Set of* 5		3·50	4·00

Nos. 1482/6 were only available from $4.20 stamp booklets.

The Alaska Highway
La route de l'Alaska
1942-1992

602 Ville-Marie in 17th Century

603 Road Bed Construction and Route Map

(Des Suzanne Duranceau and P.-Y. Pelletier. Litho C.B.N.)

1992 (25 Mar). *"CANADA 92" International Youth Stamp Exhibition, Montreal. T **602** and similar horiz designs. Multicoloured. Fluorescent frame. P 13½.*

1487	42 c. Type **602**		80	1·00
	a. Pair. Nos. 1487/8		1·60	2·00
1488	42 c. Modern Montreal		80	1·00
1489	48 c. Compass rose, snow shoe and crow's nest of Cartier's ship *Grande Hermine*		1·25	90
1490	84 c. Atlantic map, Aztec "calendar stone" and navigational instrument		2·00	2·25
1487/90		*Set of 4*	4·25	4·75
MS1491	181×120 mm. Nos. 1487/90		4·75	5·50

Nos. 1487/8 were printed together, *se-tenant*, in horizontal and vertical pairs throughout the sheet.

Nos. MS1491 also exists showing the facsimile signature of Paul Chomedy de Maisonneuve printed at bottom right. These miniature sheets were prepared in connection with "CANADA '92", but were not sold by the Canadian Post Office.

(Des M. and Jan Waddell. Litho Ashton-Potter)

1992 (22 Apr). *Canadian Rivers (2nd series). Multicoloured designs as T **592**, but horiz. Fluorescent frame. P 12½×13.*

1492	42 c. Margaree River		95	1·00
	a. Booklet pane. Nos. 1492/6, each × 2		8·50	
1493	42 c. West (Eliot) River		95	1·00
1494	42 c. Ottawa River		95	1·00
1495	42 c. Niagara River		95	1·00
1496	42 c. South Saskatchewan River		95	1·00
1492/6		*Set of 5*	4·25	4·50

Nos. 1492/6 were only issued in $4.20 stamp booklets.
Booklet pane No. 1492a has the horizontal edges of the pane imperforate.

(Des J. Charette and Vivian Laliberté. Litho C.B.N.)

1992 (15 May). *50th Anniv of Alaska Highway. Fluorescent frame. P 13½.*

1497	**603** 42 c. multicoloured		70	70

(Des Gottschalk & Ash International. Litho Ashton-Potter)

1992 (15 June). *Olympic Games, Barcelona. Horiz designs as T **601**. Multicoloured. Fluorescent frame. P 12½×13.*

1498	42 c. Gymnastics		1·00	1·10
	a. Booklet pane. Nos. 1498/1502 each × 2 with margins all round		9·00	
1499	42 c. Athletics		1·00	1·10
1500	42 c. Diving		1·00	1·10
1501	42 c. Cycling		1·00	1·10
1502	42 c. Swimming		1·00	1·10
1498/1502		*Set of 5*	4·50	5·00

Nos. 1482/1502 were only available from $4.20 stamp booklets.

604 "Quebec, Patrimoine Mondial" (A. Dumas)   **605** Jerry Potts (scout)

(Des P.-Y. Pelletier. Litho Ashton-Potter)

1992 (29 June). *Canada Day. Paintings. Sheet, 190 × 256 mm, containing T **604** and similar diamond-shaped designs. Multicoloured. Fluorescent frame. P 13×12½.*

MS1503   42 c. Type **604**; 42 c. "Christie Passage, Hurst Island, British Columbia" (E. J. Hughes); 42 c. "Toronto, Landmarks of Time" (Ontario) (V. McIndoe); 42 c. "Near the Forks" (Manitoba) (S. Gouthro); 42 c. "Off Cape St. Francis" (Newfoundland) (R. Shepherd); 42 c. "Crowd at City Hall" (New Brunswick) (Molly Bobak); 42 c. "Across the Tracks to Shop" (Alberta) (Janet Mitchell); 42 c. "Cove Scene" (Nova Scotia) (J. Norris); 42 c. "Untitled" (Saskatchewan) (D. Thauberger); 42 c. "Town Life" (Yukon) (T. Harrison); 42 c. "Country Scene" (Prince Edward Island) (Erica Rutherford); 42 c. "Playing on an Igloo" (Northwest Territories) (Agnes Nanogak) .. .. 13·00 14·00

(Des P.-Y. Pelletier. Litho and die-stamped Ashton-Potter)

1992 (29 June). *Canadian Art (5th series). Vert design as T **550**. Multicoloured. No fluorescent bands. P 12½×13.*

1504	50 c. "Red Nasturtiums" (David Milne)		90	90

No. 1504 was issued in a similar sheet format to No. 1289

(Des A. Cormack, Deborah Cormack and R. Tibbles. Litho Ashton-Potter)

1992 (8 Sept). *Folk Heroes. T **605** and similar vert designs. Multicoloured. Fluorescent frame. P 12½.*

1505	42 c. Type **605**		90	1·10
	a. Block of 4. Nos. 1505/8		3·25	
1506	42 c. Capt. William Jackman and wreck of *Sea Clipper*, 1867		90	1·10
1507	42 c. Laura Secord (messenger)		90	1·10
1508	42 c. Jos Montferrand (lumberjack)		90	1·10
1505/8		*Set of 4*	3·25	4·00

Nos. 1505/8 were printed together, *se-tenant*, in different combinations throughout the sheet, giving ten blocks of 4 and ten single stamps.

606 Copper   **607** Satellite and Photographs from Space

(Des R. Bellamare. Litho Ashton-Potter)

1992 (21 Sept). *150th Anniv of Geological Survey of Canada. Minerals. T **606** and similar horiz designs. Multicoloured. Fluorescent frame. P 12½.*

1509	42 c. Type **606**		1·10	1·25
	a. Booklet pane. Nos. 1509/13, each × 2 with margins all round		10·00	
1510	42 c. Sodalite		1·10	1·25
1511	42 c. Gold		1·10	1·25
1512	42 c. Galena		1·10	1·25
1513	42 c. Grossular		1·10	1·25
1509/13		*Set of 5*	5·00	5·50

Nos. 1509/13 were only issued in $4.20 stamp booklets.

(Des Debbie Adams. Litho C.B.N.)

1992 (1 Oct). *Canadian Space Programme. T **607** and similar horiz design. Multicoloured. Fluorescent frame. P 13.*

1514	42 c. Type **607**		90	1·00
	a. Horiz pair. Nos. 1514/15		1·75	2·00
1515	42 c. Space Shuttle over Canada (hologram) (32×26 mm)		90	1·00
	a. Hologram omitted		£750	

Nos. 1514/15 were printed together, *se-tenant*, in horizontal pairs throughout the sheet of 20 with No. 1514 occurring on the first and fourth vertical rows and No. 1515 on the second and third.

608 Babe Siebert, Skates and Stick   **609** Companion of the Order of Canada Insignia

(Des L. Holloway and R. Kerr. Litho Ashton-Potter)

1992 (9 Oct). *75th Anniv of National Ice Hockey League. T **608** and similar horiz designs. Multicoloured. Fluorescent frame. P 13×12½.*

1516	42 c. Type **608**		95	1·25
	a. Booklet pane. No. 1516×8 plus one printed label with margins all round		6·50	
1517	42 c. Claude Provost, Terry Sawchuck and team badges		95	1·25
	a. Booklet pane. No. 1517×8 plus one printed label with margins all round		6·50	
1518	42 c. Hockey mask, gloves and modern player		95	1·25
	a. Booklet pane. No. 1518×9 with margins all round		6·50	
1516/18		*Set of 3*	2·50	3·25

Nos. 1516/18 were only issued in $10.50 stamp booklets.
Booklet pane Nos. 1516a/18a only exist folded between the first and second vertical rows.

(Des Tania Craan. Litho Ashton-Potter)

1992 (21 Oct). *25th Anniv of the Order of Canada and Daniel Roland Michener (former Governor-General) Commemoration. T **609** and similar vert design. Multicoloured. Fluorescent frame. P 12½.*

1519	42 c. Type **609**		90	1·00
	a. Pair. Nos. 1519/20		1·75	2·00
1520	42 c. Daniel Roland Michener		90	1·00

Nos. 1519/20 were printed together, *se-tenant*, within the sheet of 25 (5×5) with sixteen examples of No. 1519 (R. 1/1-5, 2/1, 2/5, 3/1, 3/5, 4/1, 4/5, 5/1-5) and nine of No. 1520 (R. 2/2-4, 3/2-4, 4/2-4).

(Des J.-P. Armanville and P.-Y. Pelletier. Litho C.B.N)

1992 (10 Nov). *50th Anniv of Second World War (4th issue). Horiz designs as T **574**. Fluorescent frame. P 13½.*

1521	42 c. black, silver and sepia		1·10	1·25
	a. Block of 4. Nos. 1521/4		4·00	
1522	42 c. black, silver and dull blue-green		1·10	1·25
1523	42 c. black, silver and brown		1·10	1·25
1524	42 c. black, silver and light blue		1·10	1·25
1521/4		*Set of 4*	4·00	4·50

Designs:—No. 1521, Reporters and soldiers, 1942; No. 1522, Consolidated Liberator bombers over Newfoundland; No. 1523, Dieppe raid; No. 1524, U-boat sinking merchant ship.

Nos. 1521/4 were printed together, *se-tenant*, in different combinations throughout the sheet, giving four blocks of 4.

610 Estonian Jouluvana   **611** Adelaide Hoodless (women's movement pioneer)

(Des R. MacDonald (37 c.), Anita Kunz (42 c.), J. Bennett (48 c.), S. Ng (84 c.), adapted L. Fishauf and Stephanie Power. Litho Ashton-Potter)

1992 (13 Nov). *Christmas. T **610** and similar multicoloured designs. Fluorescent frame. P 12½×imperf (37 c.), 12½ (42 c.) or 13½ (others).*

1525	37 c. North American Santa Claus (35×21 mm)		80	80
	a. Booklet pane. No. 1525×10		8·00	
1526	42 c. Type **610**		40	20
	a. Perf 13½		70	75
	ab. Booklet pane. No. 1526a×10		8·00	
1527	48 c. Italian La Befana		70	90
	a. Booklet pane. No. 1527×5 plus one printed label		5·00	
1528	84 c. German Weihnachtsmann		1·25	1·75
	a. Booklet pane. No. 1528×5 plus one printed label		8·00	
1525/8		*Set of 4*	2·75	3·25

On No. 1525 the left-hand third of the design area is taken up by a bar code which has fluorescent bands between the bars. This value was only available from $3.70 stamp booklets which had the vertical edges of the pane imperforate. It was intended for use on greeting cards posted on or before 31 January 1993.

No. 1526a was only issued in $4.20 stamp booklets. Nos. 1526ab, 1527a and 1528a have the vertical edges of the panes imperforate.

(Des Heather Cooper. Litho Ashton-Potter)

1993 (8 Mar). *Prominent Canadian Women. T **611** and similar vert designs. Multicoloured. Fluorescent frame. P 12½.*

1529	43 c. Type **611**		85	1·00
	a. Block of 4. Nos. 1529/32		3·00	
1530	43 c. Marie-Josephine Gérin-Lajoie (social reformer)		85	1·00
1531	43 c. Pitseolak Ashoona (Inuit artist)		85	1·00
1532	43 c. Helen Kinnear (lawyer)		85	1·00
1529/32		*Set of 4*	3·50	

Nos. 1529/32 were printed together, *se-tenant*, in different combinations throughout the sheet, giving ten blocks of 4 and ten single stamps.

612 Ice Hockey Players with Cup   **613** Coverlet, New Brunswick

(Des F. Dallaire and Lise Giguère. Litho C.B.N.)

1993 (16 Apr). *Centenary of Stanley Cup. Fluorescent frame. P 13½.*

1533	**612** 43 c. multicoloured		75	60

(Des P. Adam. Litho Ashton-Potter)

1993 (30 Apr). *Hand-crafted Textiles. T **613** and similar square designs. Multicoloured. Fluorescent frame. P 13×12½.*

1534	43 c. Type **613**		90	95
	a. Booklet pane. Nos. 1534/8, each × 2		8·00	
1535	43 c. Pieced quilt, Ontario		90	95
1536	43 c. Doukhobor bedcover, Saskatchewan		90	95
1537	43 c. Ceremonial robe, Kwakwaka'wakw		90	95
1538	43 c. Boutonné coverlet, Quebec		90	95
1534/8		*Set of 5*	4·00	4·25

Nos. 1534/8 were only available from $4.30 stamp booklets.
Booklet pane No. 1534a has the horizontal edges of the pane imperforate and margins at both left and right.

(Des P.-Y. Pelletier. Litho and die-stamped Ashton-Potter)

1993 (17 May). *Canadian Art (6th series). Vert design as T **550**. Multicoloured. Fluorescent frame. P 12½×13.*

1539	86 c. "The Owl" (Kenojuak Ashevak)		1·75	2·25

No. 1539 was issued in a similar sheet format to No. 1289.

614 Empress Hotel, Victoria   **615** Algonquin Park, Ontario

(Des G. Tsetsekas. Litho Ashton-Potter)

1993 (14 June). *Historic Hotels. T **614** and similar horiz designs. Multicoloured. Fluorescent frame. P 13½.*

1540	43 c. Type **614**		60	80
	a. Booklet pane. Nos. 1540/4, each × 2		6·00	
1541	43 c. Banff Springs Hotel		60	80
1542	43 c. Royal York Hotel, Toronto		60	80
1543	43 c. Le Chateau Frontenac, Quebec		60	80
1544	43 c. Algonquin Hotel, St. Andrews		60	80
1540/4		*Set of 5*	2·75	3·50

Nos. 1540/4 were only issued in $4.30 stamp booklets.
Booklet pane No. 1540a has the horizontal edges of the pane imperforate and margins at both left and right.

(Des M. and Jan Waddell. Litho C.B.N.)

1993 (30 June). *Canada Day. Provincial and Territorial Parks. T 615 and similar horiz designs. Multicoloured. Fluorescent frame. P 13.*
1545	43 c. Type 615	..	70	80
	a. Sheetlet. Nos. 1545/56		7·50	
1546	43 c. De La Gaspésie Park, Québec		70	80
1547	43 c. Cedar Dunes Park, Prince Edward Island		70	80
1548	43 c. Cape St. Mary's Seabird Reserve, Newfoundland		70	80
1549	43 c. Mount Robson Park, British Columbia		70	80
1550	43 c. Writing-on-Stone Park, Alberta		70	80
1551	43 c. Spruce Woods Park, Manitoba		70	80
1552	43 c. Herschel Island Park, Yukon		70	80
1553	43 c. Cypress Hills Park, Saskatchewan		70	80
1554	43 c. The Rocks Park, New Brunswick		70	80
1555	43 c. Blomidon Park, Nova Scotia		70	80
1556	43 c. Katannilik Park, Northwest Territories		70	80
1545/56		*Set of 12*	7·50	8·50

Nos. 1545/56 were printed together, *se-tenant*, in sheetlets of 12, which come with or without a large illustrated and inscribed margin at top.

616 Toronto Skyscrapers
617 Taylor's Steam Buggy, 1867

(Des R. Heeney and V. McIndoe. Litho C.B.N.)

1993 (6 Aug). *Bicentenary of Toronto. Fluorescent frame. P 13½×13.*
1557	**616** 43 c. multicoloured	.. ..	70	50

(Des M. and Jan Waddell. Litho Ashton-Potter.)

1993 (10 Aug). *Canadian Rivers (3rd series). Vert designs as T 592. Multicoloured. Fluorescent frame. P 13×12½.*
1558	43 c. Fraser River		60	80
	a. Booklet pane. Nos. 1558/62, each × 2		6·00	
1559	43 c. Yukon River		60	80
1560	43 c. Red River		60	80
1561	43 c. St. Lawrence River		60	80
1562	43 c. St. John River		60	80
1558/62		*Set of 5*	2·75	3·50

Nos. 1558/62 were only issued in $4.30 stamp booklets.

(Des J. Gault, T. Telmet and C. Wykes. Litho C.B.N.)

1993 (23 Aug). *Historic Automobiles (1st series). Sheet, 177×125 mm, containing T 617 and similar horiz designs. Multicoloured. Fluorescent frame. P 12½×13.*
MS1563	43 c. Type 617; 43 c. Russel "Model L" touring car, 1908; 49 c. Ford "Model T" touring car, 1914 (43×22 mm); 49 c. Studebaker "Champion Deluxe Starlight" coupe, 1950 (43×22 mm); 86 c. McLaughlin-Buick "28-496 special", 1928 (43×22 mm); 86 c. Gray-Dort "25 SM" luxury sedan, 1923 (43×22 mm)		6·50	7·00

See also Nos. MS1611, MS1636 and MS1683/4.

618 "The Alberta Homesteader"
619 Polish Swiety Mikolaj

(Des Deborah Cormack, A. Cormack and R. Tibbles. Litho Ashton-Potter)

1993 (7 Sept). *Folk Songs. T 618 and similar horiz designs. Multicoloured. Fluorescent frame. P 12½.*
1564	43 c. Type 618		70	90
	a. Block of 4. Nos. 1564/7		2·50	
1565	43 c. "Les Raftmans" (Quebec)		70	90
1566	43 c. "I'se the B'y that Builds the Boat" (Newfoundland)		70	90
1567	43 c. "Onkwá:ri Tenhanónniahkwe" (Mohawk Indian)		70	90
1564/7		*Set of 4*	2·50	3·25

Nos. 1564/7 were printed together, *se-tenant*, in different combinations throughout the sheet, giving ten blocks of 4 and ten single stamps.

(Des R. Harder. Litho Ashton-Potter)

1993 (1 Oct). *Prehistoric Canada (3rd series). Dinosaurs. Horiz designs as T 582, but 40×28 mm. Multicoloured. Fluorescent frame. P 13½.*
1568	43 c. Massospondylus		70	80
	a. Block of 4. Nos. 1568/71		2·50	
1569	43 c. Stryacosaurus		70	80
1570	43 c. Albertosaurus		70	80
1571	43 c. Platecarpus		70	80
1568/71		*Set of 4*	2·50	2·75

Nos. 1568/71 were printed together, *se-tenant*, in different combinations throughout the sheet, giving four blocks of 4 and four single stamps.

(Des J. Bennett (38 c.), J. Jackson (43 c.), B. Dawson (49 c.), B. Blitt (86 c.), adapted L. Fishauf and Stephanie Power. Litho C.B.N.)

1993 (4 Nov). *Christmas. T 619 and similar multicoloured designs. Fluorescent frame. P 13×imperf (38 c.) or 13½ (others).*
1572	38 c. North American Santa Claus (35×22 mm)		80	80
	a. Booklet pane. No. 1572×10		8·00	
1573	43 c. Type 619		50	20
	a. Booklet pane. No. 1573×10		9·00	
	b. Imperf between (horiz pair)		£750	
1574	49 c. Russian Ded Moroz		70	80
	a. Booklet pane. No. 1574×5 plus one printed label		5·00	
1575	86 c. Australian Father Christmas		1·10	2·00
	a. Booklet pane. No. 1575×5 plus one printed label		9·00	
1572/5		*Set of 4*	2·75	3·50

On No. 1572 the left-hand third of the design area is taken up by a barcode which has fluorescent bands between the bars. This value was only available from $3.80, stamp booklets which had the vertical edges of the pane imperforate. It was intended for use on greeting cards posted before 31 January 1994.

Nos. 1573a/5a have the vertical edges of the panes imperforate.

No. 1573b appears to originate from the incorrect use of the booklet pane perforation on ordinary sheet stock.

(Des J.-P. Armanville and P.-Y. Pelletier. Litho C.B.N.)

1993 (8 Nov). *50th Anniv of Second World War (5th issue). Horiz designs as T 574. Fluorescent frame. P 13½.*
1576	43 c. black, silver and brown-olive		1·10	1·10
	a. Block of 4. Nos. 1576/9		4·00	
1577	43 c. black, silver and slate-blue		1·10	1·10
1578	43 c. black, silver and dull-violet blue		1·10	1·10
1579	43 c. black, silver and chestnut		1·10	1·10
1576/9		*Set of 4*	4·00	4·00

Designs:—No. 1576, Loading munitions for Russia, 1943; No. 1577, Loading bombs on Avro Type 683 Lancaster; No. 1578, Escorts attacking U-boat; No. 1579, Infantry advancing, Italy. Nos. 1576/9 were printed together, *se-tenant*, in different combinations throughout the sheet, giving four blocks of 4.

620 (face value at right)

(Des Tarzan Communication Graphique. Litho Leigh-Mardon Ltd, Melbourne)

1994 (28 Jan). *Greetings stamps. T 620 and similar horiz design. Multicoloured. Inscriptions behind face value and "CANADA" show names of family events. Fluorescent outline. Self-adhesive. Die-cut.*
1580	43 c. Type 620		60	70
	a. Booklet pane. Nos. 1580/1, each × 5, and 35 circular greetings labels		5·50	
1581	43 c. As Type 620, but face value at left		60	70

Nos. 1580/1 were only available from $4.50 self-adhesive booklets in which the backing card formed the cover. It was intended that the sender should insert the appropriate greetings label into the circular space on each stamp before use.

For 45 c. values in this design see Nos. 1654/5.

621 Jeanne Sauvé
622 Timothy Eaton, Toronto Store of 1869 and Merchandise

(Des J. Morin and T. Yakobina. Litho C.B.N.)

1994 (8 Mar). *Jeanne Sauvé (former Governor-General) Commemoration. Fluorescent frame. P 12½×13.*
1582	**621** 43 c. multicoloured		60	60

No. 1582 was printed in sheets of 20 (4×5), the horizontal rows containing four stamps, each with a differently-inscribed 6×22½ mm *se-tenant* label. These are at the right of the stamps on rows 1, 3 and 5 and at left on rows 2 and 4.

(Des L. Fishauf. Litho C.B.N.)

1994 (17 Mar). *125th Anniv of T. Eaton Company Ltd (department store group). Fluorescent frame. P 13½×13.*
1583	**622** 43 c. multicoloured		55	75
	a. Booklet pane. No. 1583×10 and 2 labels with margins all round		5·50	

No. 1583 was only available from $4.30 stamp booklets.

(Des M. and Jan Waddell. Litho C.B.N.)

1994 (22 Apr). *Canadian Rivers (4th series). Horiz designs as T 592. Multicoloured. Fluorescent frame. P 13½×12½.*
1584	43 c. Saguenay River		60	75
	a. Booklet pane. Nos. 1584/8 each × 2		5·50	
1585	43 c. French River		60	75
1586	43 c. Mackenzie River		60	75
1587	43 c. Churchill River		60	75
1588	43 c. Columbia River		60	75
1584/8		*Set of 5*	2·75	3·25

Nos. 1584/8 were only issued in $4.30 stamp booklets. Booklet pane No. 1584a has the vertical edges of the pane imperforate.

(Des P.-Y. Pelletier. Litho and die-stamped Leigh-Mardon Ltd, Melbourne)

1994 (6 May). *Canadian Art (7th series). Vert design as T 550. Multicoloured. Fluorescent frame. P 14×14½.*
1589	88 c. "Vera" (detail) (Frederick Varley)		1·25	1·60

No. 1589 was issued in a similar sheet format to No. 1289.

623 Lawn Bowls
624 Mother and Baby

(Des D. Coates and R. Roodenburg. Litho and die-stamped Leigh-Mardon Ltd, Melbourne)

1994 (20 May–5 Aug). *15th Commonwealth Games, Victoria. T 623 and similar horiz designs. Multicoloured. Fluorescent frame. P 14.*
1590	43 c. Type 623		40	50
	a. Pair. Nos. 1590/1		80	1·00
1591	43 c. Lacrosse		40	50
1592	43 c. Wheelchair race (5 Aug)		40	50
	a. Pair. Nos. 1592/3		80	1·00
1593	43 c. High jumping (5 Aug)		40	50
1594	50 c. Diving (5 Aug)		45	60
1595	88 c. Cycling (5 Aug)		80	95
1590/5		*Set of 6*	2·75	3·25

Nos. 1590/1 and 1592/3 were printed together, *se-tenant*, in horizontal and vertical pairs throughout the sheets.

(Des Suzanne Duranceau. Litho Leigh-Mardon Ltd, Melbourne)

1994 (2 June). *International Year of the Family. Sheet 178×134 mm, containing T 624 and similar vert designs. Multicoloured. Fluorescent paper. P 14×14½.*
MS1596	43 c. Type 624; 43 c. Family outing; 43 c. Grandmother and granddaughter; 43 c. Computer class; 43 c. Play group, nurse with patient and female lawyer		3·00	3·50

625 Big Leaf Maple Tree
626 Billy Bishop (fighter ace) and Nieuport 17

(Des D. Noble. Litho C.B.N.)

1994 (30 June). *Canada Day. Maple Trees. T 625 and similar horiz designs. Multicoloured. Fluorescent frame. P 13×13½.*
1597	43 c. Type 625		60	65
	a. Sheetlet. Nos. 1597/1608		6·50	
1598	43 c. Sugar Maple		60	65
1599	43 c. Silver Maple		60	65
1600	43 c. Striped Maple		60	65
1601	43 c. Norway Maple		60	65
1602	43 c. Manitoba Maple		60	65
1603	43 c. Black Maple		60	65
1604	43 c. Douglas Maple		60	65
1605	43 c. Mountain Maple		60	65
1606	43 c. Vine Maple		60	65
1607	43 c. Hedge Maple		60	65
1608	43 c. Red Maple		60	65
1597/1608		*Set of 12*	6·50	7·00

Nos. 1597/1608 were printed together, *se-tenant*, in sheetlets of 12, which come with or without a large illustrated and inscribed margin at top.

(Des P. Fontaine and B. Leduc. Litho C.B.N.)

1994 (12 Aug). *Birth Centenaries. T 626 and similar horiz design. Multicoloured. Fluorescent frame. P 13½.*
1609	43 c. Type 626		75	90
	a. Pair. Nos. 1609/10		1·50	1·75
1610	43 c. Mary Travers ("La Bolduc") (singer) and musicians		75	90

Nos. 1609/10 were printed together, *se-tenant*, in horizontal and vertical pairs throughout the sheet.

(Des J. Gault, T. Telmet, and C. Wickes. Litho C.B.N.)

1994 (19 Aug). *Historic Automobiles (2nd issue). Sheet 177×125 mm, containing horiz designs as T 617. Multicoloured. Fluorescent frame. P 12½×13.*
MS1611	43 c. Ford "Model F60L-AMB" military ambulance, 1942–43; 43 c. Winnipeg police wagon, 1925; 50 c. Sicard snowblower, 1927 (43×22 mm); 50 c. Bickle "Chieftain" fire engine, 1936 (43×22 mm); 88 c. St. John Railway Company tramcar No. 40, 1894 (51×22 mm); 88 c. Motor Coach Industries "Courier 50 Skyview" coach, 1950 (51×22 mm)		7·00	7·50

No. MS1611 was sold in a protective pack.

627 Symbolic
Aircraft, Radar
Screen and Clouds

628 Carol Singing
around Christmas Tree

(Des Gottschalk & Ash International, Katalin Kovats and
S. Napoleone. Litho C.B.N.)

1994 (16 Sept). *50th Anniv of International Civil Aviation
Organization. Fluorescent frame. P 13.*
1612 627 43 c. multicoloured 60 60

(Des R. Harder. Litho C.B.N.)

1994 (26 Sept). *Prehistoric Canada (4th series). Mammals.
Multicoloured designs as T 582, but 40×28 mm. Fluorescent
frame. P 13½.*
1613 43 c. Coryphodon .. .. .. 90 1·00
    a. Block of 4. Nos. 1613/16 .. 3·25
1614 43 c. Megacerops .. .. .. 90 1·00
1615 43 c. Arctodus simus (bear) .. 90 1·00
1616 43 c. Mammuthus primigenius (mammoth) .. 90 1·00
1613/16 .. .. .. *Set of 4* 3·50 3·50
    Nos. 1613/16 were printed together, *se-tenant*, in different
combinations throughout the sheet, giving four blocks of 4 and
four single stamps.

(Des Nina Berkson, Diti Katona and J. Pylypczak. Litho C.B.N.)

1994 (3 Nov). *Christmas. T 628 and similar multicoloured
designs. Fluorescent frame. P 13×imperf (No. 1617) or 13½
(others).*
1617 (–) c. Carol singer (35×21 mm) .. 70 80
    a. Booklet pane. No. 1617×10 .. 7·00
1618 43 c. Type 628 .. .. .. 45 20
    a. Booklet pane. No. 1618×10 .. 8·00
1619 50 c. Choir (vert) 65 90
    a. Booklet pane. No. 1619×5 plus one
    printed label .. .. .. 4·25
1620 88 c. Couple carol singing in snow (vert) .. 1·60 2·25
    a. Booklet pane. No. 1620×5 plus one
    printed label .. .. .. 8·00
1617/20 .. .. .. *Set of 4* 3·00 3·75
    No. 1617 was only available from $3.80 stamp booklets with
the vertical edges of the pane imperforate. The stamp is without
face value, but was intended for use as a 38 c. on internal
greetings cards posted before 31 January 1995. The design
shows a barcode at left with fluorescent bands between the bars.
    Nos. 1617a/20a have the vertical edges of the panes
imperforate.
    Stamps as Nos. 1618/20, but with face values of 45 c., 50 c. and
90 c. were prepared, but not issued.

(Des J.-P. Armanville and P.-Y. Pelletier. Litho C.B.N.)

1994 (7 Nov). *50th Anniv of Second World War (6th issue).
Horiz designs as T 574. Fluorescent frame. P 13½.*
1621 43 c. black, silver and dull green .. 90 95
    a. Block of 4. Nos. 1621/4 .. 1·25
1622 43 c. black, silver and Venetian red .. 90 95
1623 43 c. black, silver and light blue .. 90 95
1624 43 c. black, silver and violet-grey .. 90 95
1621/4 .. .. .. *Set of 4* 3·25 3·50
    Designs:—No. 1621, D-Day landings, Normandy; No. 1622,
Canadian artillery, Normandy; No. 1623, Hawker Typhoons on
patrol; No. 1624, Canadian infantry and disabled German self-
propelled gun, Walcheren.
    Nos. 1621/4 were printed together, *se-tenant*, in different
combinations throughout the sheet, giving four blocks of 4.

(Des J.-P. Armanville and P.-Y. Pelletier. Litho C.B.N.)

1995 (20 Mar). *50th Anniv of Second World War (7th issue).
Horiz designs as T 574. Fluorescent frame. P 13½.*
1625 43 c. black, silver and reddish purple .. 90 95
    a. Block of 4. Nos. 1625/8 .. 3·25
1626 43 c. black, silver and yellow-brown .. 90 95
1627 43 c. black, silver and dull yellowish green 90 95
1628 43 c. black, silver and light greenish blue 90 95
1625/8 .. .. .. *Set of 4* 3·25 3·50
    Designs:—No. 1625, Returning troopship; No. 1626, Canadian
P.O.W's celebrating freedom; No. 1627, Canadian tank
liberating Dutch town; No. 1628, Parachute drop in support of
Rhine Crossing.
    Nos. 1625/8 were printed together, *se-tenant*, in different
combinations throughout the sheet, giving four blocks of 4.

(Des P.-Y. Pelletier. Litho and die-stamped C.B.N.)

1995 (21 Apr). *Canadian Art (8th series). Vert design as T 550.
Multicoloured. Fluorescent frame. P 13×13½.*
1629 88 c. "Floraison" (Alfred Pellan) .. 1·25 1·60
    No. 1629 was issued in a similar sheet format to No. 1289.

629 Flag and Lake

(Des Gottschalk & Ash International. Litho C.B.N.)

1995 (1 May). *30th Anniv of National Flag. Fluorescent frame.
P 13½×13.*
1630 629 (43 c.) multicoloured 50 50
    No. 1630 is without any indication of face value, but was sold
for 43 c.

PRINTER. Following a change in ownership, and the awarding
of a further Canada Post contract, the previous Ashton Potter
Ltd was known as Ashton Potter Canada Ltd from 1995.

630 Louisbourg Harbour

(Des R. Harder. Litho Ashton-Potter Canada)

1995 (5 May). *275th Anniv of Fortress of Louisbourg. T 630
and similar horiz designs. Multicoloured. "All-over"
fluorescent. P 12½×13.*
1631 (43 c.) Type 630 .. .. .. 40 55
    a. Booklet pane. Nos. 1631/5 each × 2
    with margins all round .. .. 4·00
1632 (43 c.) Barracks (32×29 mm) .. 40 55
1633 (43 c.) King's Bastion (40×29 mm) .. 40 55
1634 (43 c.) Site of King's Garden, convent and
    hospital (56×29 mm) 40 55
1635 (43 c.) Site of coastal fortifications .. 40 55
1631/5 .. .. .. *Set of 5* 2·00 2·50
    Nos. 1631/5 are without any indication of face value, but were
sold in booklets of 10 for $4.30.

(Des J. Gault, T. Telmet and C. Wykes. Litho C.B.N.)

1995 (26 May). *Historic Automobiles (3rd issue). Sheet 177×25
mm, containing horiz designs as T 617. Multicoloured.
Fluorescent frame. P 12½×13.*
MS1636 43 c. Cockshutt "30" farm tractor, 1950;
43 c. Bombardier "Ski-Doo Olympique 335"
snowmobile, 1970; 50 c. Bombardier "B-12 CS"
multi-passenger snowmobile, 1948 (43×22 mm);
50 c. Gotfredson "Model 20" farm truck, 1924
(43×22 mm); 88 c. Robin-Nodwell "RN 110"
tracked carrier, 1962 (43×22 mm); 88 c. Massey-
Harris "No. 21" self-propelled combine-
harvester, 1942 (43×22 mm) .. .. 6·00 6·50
    No. MS1636 was sold in a protective pack.

631 Banff Springs Golf
Club, Alberta

(Des P. Adam. Litho Ashton-Potter Canada)

1995 (6 June). *Centenaries of Canadian Amateur Golf
Championship and of the Royal Canadian Golf Association.
T 631 and similar horiz designs. Fluorescent frame.
P 13½×13.*
1637 43 c. Type 631 .. .. .. 50 60
    a. Booklet pane. Nos. 1637/41 each × 2 4·50
1638 43 c. Riverside Country Club, New
    Brunswick 50 60
1639 43 c. Glen Abbey Golf Club, Ontario .. 50 60
1640 43 c. Victoria Golf Club, British Columbia 50 60
1641 43 c. Royal Montreal Golf Club, Quebec .. 50 60
1637/41 .. .. .. *Set of 5* 2·25 2·75
    Nos. 1637/41 were only issued in $4.30 stamp booklets.
Booklet pane No. 1637a has the vertical edges of the pane
imperforate.

632 "October Gold" (Franklin
Carmichael)

633 Academy
Building and Ship
Plan

(Des A. Leduc. Litho C.B.N.)

1995 (29 June). *Canada Day. 75th Anniv of "Group of Seven"
(artists). Three sheets, each 180×80 mm, containing T 632
and similar square designs. Multicoloured. Fluorescent paper.
P 13.*
MS1642 (a) 43 c. Type 632; 43 c. "From the North
Shore, Lake Superior" (Lawren Harris); 43 c.
"Evening, Les Eboulements, Quebec" (A.
Jackson). (b) 43 c. "Serenity, Lake of the Woods"
(Frank Johnston); 43 c. "A September Gale,

Georgian Bay" (Arthur Lismer); 43 c. "Falls,
Montreal River" (J. E. H. MacDonald); 43 c.
"Open Window" (Frederick Varley). (c) 43 c. "Mill
Houses" (Alfred Casson); 43 c. "Pembina Valley"
(Lionel FitzGerald); 43 c. "The Lumberjack"
(Edwin Holgate) .. .. *Set of 3 sheets* 8·00 9·00
    The three sheets of No. MS1642 were sold together in an
envelope which also includes a small descriptive booklet.

(Des B. Mackay-Lyons and S. Slipp. Litho C.B.N.)

1995 (29 June). *Centenary of Lunenburg Academy.
Fluorescent frame. P 13.*
1643 633 43 c. multicoloured 40 45

634 Aspects of
Manitoba

635 Monarch
Butterfly

(Des T. Gallagher and S. Rosenberg. Litho Ashton-Potter
Canada)

1995 (14 July). *125th Anniv of Manitoba as Canadian
Province. Fluorescent frame. P 13½×13.*
1644 634 43 c. multicoloured 40 45

Two Types of Belted Kingfisher design:

    Type I. Inscr "aune migratrice" in error.
    Type II. Inscr corrected to "faune migratrice".

(Des Debbie Adams. Litho C.B.N.)

1995 (15 Aug–26 Sept). *Migratory Wildlife. T 635 and similar
vert designs. Fluorescent paper. P 13×12½.*
1645 45 c. Type 635 .. .. .. 65 80
    a. Block of 4. Nos. 1645/6, 1648/9 2·40
    b. Block of 4. Nos. 1645, 1647/9 (26 Sept) 2·40
1646 45 c. Belted Kingfisher (I) 65 80
1647 45 c. Belted Kingfisher (II) (26 Sept) .. 65 80
1648 45 c. Pintail 65 80
1649 45 c. Hoary Bat 65 80
1645/9 .. .. .. *Set of 5* 3·00 3·50
    The inscription error on No. 1646 was corrected in a new
printing issued 26 September 1995.
    The four different designs were printed together, *se-tenant*,
throughout the sheet, giving four blocks of 4 and four single
stamps, showing an overall background design of migration
routes.

636 Quebec Railway Bridge

(Des J. Gault, T. Telmet and C. Wykes. Litho Ashton-Potter
Canada)

1995 (1 Sept). *20th World Road Congress, Montreal. Bridges.
T 636 and similar horiz designs. Multicoloured. Fluorescent
paper. P 12½×13.*
1650 45 c. Type 636 .. .. .. 90 1·00
    a. Block of 4. Nos. 1650/3 .. 3·25
1651 45 c. 401-403-410 Interchange,
    Mississauga .. .. .. 90 1·00
1652 45 c. Hartland Bridge, New Brunswick .. 90 1·00
1653 45 c. Alex Fraser Bridge, British Columbia 90 1·00
1650/3 .. .. .. *Set of 4* 3·25 3·50
    Nos. 1650/3 were printed together, *se-tenant*, throughout the
sheet, giving four blocks of 4 and four single stamps.

Two Types of Background to Nos. 1654/5:

    Type I. Inscriptions behind face value and "CANADA" show
    names of Canadian Provinces.
    Type II. Inscription behind face value and "CANADA" show
    names of family events.

(Des Tarzan Communication Graphique. Litho Ashton-Potter
Canada (Nos. 1654/5) or Leigh-Mardon Ltd, Melbourne (Nos.
1654b/5b)).

1995 (1 Sept)–96. *Greetings stamps. Horiz designs as T 620.
Multicoloured. Fluorescent outline. Self-adhesive. Die-cut.*
1654 45 c. Face value at right (I) 40 45
    a. Booklet pane. Nos. 1654/5, each × 5 4·00
    b. Type II (15.1.96) 55 60
    ba. Booklet pane. Nos. 1654b and 1655b
    each × 5 .. .. .. 5·50
1655 45 c. Face value at left (I) 40 45
    b. Type II (15.1.96) 55 60
    Nos. 1654/5 were only available from $4.70 self-adhesive
booklets in which the backing card formed the cover. Booklets
containing Nos. 1654/5 also include a separate pane of 15
self-adhesive labels which it was intended the sender should
insert in the circular space on each stamp before use. Booklets
containing Nos. 1654b/5b included 35 circular greetings labels
on the same pane as the stamps.

637 Mountain, Baffin Island, Polar Bear and Caribou   **638** Superman

(Des Eskind Waddell. Litho C.B.N.)

1995 (15 Sept). *50th Anniv of Arctic Institute of North America. T* **637** *and similar horiz designs. Multicoloured. Fluorescent paper. P* 13×12½.

1656	45 c. Type **637**		80	90
	a. Booklet pane. Nos. 1656/60, each × 2, with margins all round		7·00	
1657	45 c. Arctic poppy, Auyuittuq National Park and cargo canoe		80	90
1658	45 c. Inuk man and igloo		80	90
1659	45 c. Ogilvie Mountains, dog team and ski-equipped airplane		80	90
1660	45 c. Inuit children		80	90
1656/60		*Set of 5*	3·50	4·00

Nos. 1656/60 were only issued in $4.50 stamp booklets.

(Des L. Fishauf. Litho Ashton-Potter Canada)

1995 (2 Oct). *Comic Book Superheroes. T* **638** *and similar vert designs. Multicoloured. Fluorescent frame. P* 13×12½.

1661	45 c. Type **638**		50	60
	a. Booklet pane. Nos. 1661/5, each × 2, with margins all round		4·75	
1662	45 c. Johnny Canuck		50	60
1663	45 c. Nelvana		50	60
1664	45 c. Captain Canuck		50	60
1665	45 c. Fleur de Lys		50	60
1661/5		*Set of 5*	2·25	2·75

Nos. 1661/5 were only issued in $4.50 stamp booklets.

639 Prime Minister MacKenzie King signing U.N. Charter, 1945   **640** "The Nativity"

(Des L. Holloway and R. Kerr. Litho and die-stamped C.B.N.)

1995 (24 Oct). *50th Anniv of United Nations. Fluorescent frame. P* 13½.

1666	**639** 45 c. multicoloured		50	50

No. 1666 was issued in sheets of 10 with a large illustrated and inscribed margin at top.

(Des F. Dallaire. Litho Ashton-Potter Canada (40 c.) or C.B.N. (others))

1995 (2 Nov). *Christmas. T* **640** *and similar multicoloured designs showing sculptured capitals from Ste.-Anne-de-Beaupré Basilica designed by Emilé Brunet (Nos. 1668/70). Fluorescent frames. P* 12½×13 (40 c.) *or* 13½ *(others)*.

1667	40 c. Sprig of holly (35×22 *mm*)		65	65
	a. Booklet pane. No. 1667×10		6·50	
1668	45 c. Type **640**		50	20
	a. Booklet pane. No. 1668×10		7·50	
1669	52 c. "The Annunciation"		75	1·00
	a. Booklet pane. No. 1669×5 plus one printed label		4·50	
1670	90 c. "The Flight to Egypt"		1·25	1·75
	a. Booklet pane. No. 1670×5 plus one printed label		8·50	
1667/70		*Set of 4*	2·50	3·00

On No. 1667 the left-hand third of the design area is taken up by a barcode which has fluorescent bands between the bars. This value was only available from $4 stamp booklets which had the vertical edges of the pane imperforate. It was intended for use on greetings cards posted before 31 January 1996.

Nos. 1668a/70a have the vertical edges of the panes imperforate.

641 World Map and Emblem

(Des A. Leduc. Litho Ashton-Potter Canada)

1995 (6 Nov). *25th Anniv of La Francophonie and The Agency for Cultural and Technical Co-operation. Fluorescent frame. P* 13×13½.

1671	**641** 45 c. multicoloured		50	50

642 Concentration Camp Victims, Uniform and Identity Card

(Des Q30 Design. Litho Ashton-Potter Canada)

1995 (9 Nov). *50th Anniv of the End of The Holocaust. Fluorescent frame. P* 12½×13.

1672	**642** 45 c. multicoloured		50	50

Horizontal strips of No. 1672 form a continuous design which is carried over onto the vertical sheet margins.

643 American Kestrel

(Des R. Bellemare and P. Leduc. Litho C.B.N.)

1996 (9 Jan). *Birds (1st issue). T* **643** *and similar horiz designs. Multicoloured. Fluorescent frame. P* 13½.

1673	45 c. Type **643**		85	85
	a. Horiz strip of 4. Nos. 1673/6		3·00	
1674	45 c. Atlantic Puffin		85	85
1675	45 c. Pileated Woodpecker		85	85
1676	45 c. Ruby-throated Hummingbird		85	85
1673/6		*Set of 4*	3·00	3·00

Nos. 1673/6 were printed together, *se-tenant*, in panes of 12 (4×3) containing three examples of No. 1673a. Those panes intended for philatelic sale had inscribed margins so arranged as to produce a diamond-shaped format.

See also Nos. 1717/20, 1779/82 and 1865/72.

644 *Louis R. Desmarais* (tanker), Three-dimensional Map and Radar Screen

(Des Q30 Design Inc. Litho C.B.N.)

1996 (15 Feb). *High Technology Industries. T* **644** *and similar horiz designs. Multicoloured. Fluorescent paper. P* 13½.

1677	45 c. Type **644**		65	70
	a. Booklet pane. Nos. 1677/80, each × 3		6·75	
1678	45 c. Canadair Challenger 601-3R, jet engine and navigational aid		65	70
1679	45 c. Map of North America and eye		65	70
1680	45 c. Genetic engineering experiment and Canola (plant)		65	70
1677/80		*Set of 4*	2·40	2·50

Nos. 1677/80 were only available from $5.40 stamp booklets which had the vertical edges of the pane imperforate.

(Des P.-Y. Pelletier. Litho and die-stamped Ashton-Potter Canada)

1996 (30 Apr). *Canadian Art (9th series). Vert design as T* 550. *Multicoloured. Fluorescent paper. P* 12½×13.

1681	90 c. "The Spirit of Haida Gwaii" (sculpture) (Bill Reid)		1·40	1·75

No. 1681 was issued in a similar sheet format to No. 1289.

645 "One World, One Hope" (Joe Average)

(Des G. Tsetsekas. Litho Ashton-Potter Canada)

1996 (8 May). *11th International Conference on AIDS, Vancouver. Fluorescent frame. P* 13½.

1682	**645** 45 c. multicoloured		70	70

ALTERED CATALOGUE NUMBERS

Any Catalogue numbers altered from the last edition are shown as a list in the introductory pages.

(Des J. Gault, T. Telmet and C. Wickes. Litho C.B.N.)

1996 (8 June). *Historic Automobiles (4th issue). Sheet* 177×125 *mm, containing horiz designs as T* 617. *Multicoloured. Fluorescent frame. P* 12½×13.

MS1683 45 c. Still Motor Co. electric van, 1899; 45 c. Waterous Engine Works steam roller, 1914; 52 c. International "D.35" delivery truck, 1938; 52 c. Champion road grader, 1936; 90 c. White "Model WA 122" articulated lorry, 1947 (51×22 *mm*); 90 c. Hayes "HDX 45-115" logging truck, 1975 (51×22 *mm*) .. .. .. 6·50   7·00

No. **MS1683** also includes the "CAPEX '96" International Stamp Exhibition logo on the sheet margin and was sold in a protective pack.

(Des J. Gault, T. Telmet and C. Wickes. Litho C.B.N.)

1996 (8 June). *"CAPEX '96" International Stamp Exhibition, Toronto. Sheet,* 368×182 *mm, containing horiz designs as Nos.* **MS1563**, **MS1611**, **MS1636**, **MS1683**, *but with different face values, and one new design (45 c.). Fluorescent frame* (45 c.). *P* 12½×13.

MS1684 5 c. Bombardier "Ski-Doo Olympique 335" snowmobile, 1970; 5 c. Cockshutt "30" farm tractor, 1950; 5 c. Type **617**; 5 c. Ford "Model F160L-AMB" military ambulance, 1942; 5 c. Still Motor Co electric van, 1895; 5 c. International "D.35" delivery truck, 1936; 5 c. Russel "Model L" touring car, 1908; 5 c. Winnipeg police wagon, 1925; 5 c. Waterous Engine Works steam roller, 1914; 5 c. Champion road grader, 1936; 10 c. White "Model WA 122" articulated lorry, 1947 (51×22 *mm*); 10 c. St. John Railway Company tramcar, 1894 (51×22 *mm*); 10 c. Hayes "HDX 45-115" logging truck, 1975 (51×22 *mm*); 10 c. Motor Coach Industries "Courier 50 Skyview" coach, 1950 (51×22 *mm*); 20 c. Ford "Model T" touring car, 1914 (43×22 *mm*); 20 c. McLaughlin-Buick "28-496 special", 1928 (43×22 *mm*); 20 c. Bombardier "B-12 CS" multi-passenger snowmobile, 1948 (43×22 *mm*); 20 c. Robin-Nodwell "RN 110" tracked carrier, 1962 (43×22 *mm*); 20 c. Studebaker "Champion Deluxe Starlight" coupe, 1950 (43×22 *mm*); 20 c. Gray-Dort "25 SM" luxury sedan, 1923 (43×22 *mm*); 20 c. Gotfredson "Model 20" farm truck, 1924 (43×22 *mm*); 20 c. Massey-Harris "No. 21" self-propelled combine-harvester, 1942 (43×22 *mm*); 20 c. Bickle "Chieftain" fire engine, 1936 (43×22 *mm*); 20 c. Sicard snowblower, 1927 (43×22 *mm*); 45 c. Bricklin "SV-1" sports car, 1975 (51×22 *mm*) .. .. 6·50   7·50

No. **MS1684** was sold folded within a special pack at $3.75, a premium of 40 c. over the face value. It was only possible to obtain an unfolded example by purchasing an uncut press sheet, containing three miniature sheets, of which only 25000 were made available. The price quoted for No. **MS1684** is for a folded example.

646 Skookum Jim Mason and Bonanza Creek   **647** Patchwork Quilt Maple Leaf

(Des S. Slipp. Litho and gold die-stamped Ashton-Potter Canada)

1996 (13 June). *Centenary of Yukon Gold Rush. T* **646** *and similar horiz designs. Multicoloured. Fluorescent paper. P* 12½.

1685	45 c. Type **646**		70	70
	a. Horiz strip of 5. Nos. 1685/9		3·25	
1686	45 c. Prospector and boats on Lake Laberge		70	70
1687	45 c. Superintendent Sam Steele (N.W.M.P.) and U.S.A.–Canada border		70	70
1688	45 c. Dawson saloon		70	70
1689	45 c. Miner with rocker box and sluice		70	70
1685/9		*Set of 5*	3·25	3·25

Nos. 1685/9 were printed together, *se-tenant*, in sheetlets of 10, containing two examples of No. 1685a.

(Des R. Bellemare. Litho Ashton-Potter Canada)

1996 (28 June). *Canada Day. Self-adhesive. Fluorescent frame. Die-cut.*

1690	**647** 45 c. multicoloured		50	50

No. 1690 was printed in sheets of 12 with each stamp separate on the backing paper.

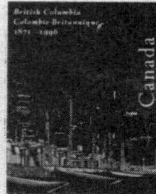

648 Ethel Catherwood (high jump), 1928   **649** Indian Totems, City Skyline, Forest and Mountains

(Des M. Koudys. Litho and die-stamped Ashton-Potter Canada)
1996 (8 July). *Canadian Olympic Gold Medal Winners. T 648 and similar vert designs. Multicoloured. Fluorescent paper.* P 13×12½.

1691	45 c. Type 648		80	85
	a. Booklet pane. Nos. 1691/5, each × 2 with margins all round		7·00	
1692	45 c. Etienne Desmarteau (56lb weight throw), 1904		80	85
1693	45 c. Fanny Rosenfeld (400 metres relay), 1928		80	85
1694	45 c. Gerald Ouellette (small bore rifle, prone), 1956		80	85
1695	45 c. Percy Williams (100 and 200 metres), 1928		80	85
1691/5		*Set of 5*	3·50	3·75

Nos. 1691/5 were only issued in $4.50 stamp booklets.

(Des M. Warburton. Litho Ashton-Potter Canada)
1996 (19 July). *125th Anniv of British Columbia. Fluorescent paper.* P 13×12½.

1696	**649** 45 c. multicoloured		50	50

650 Canadian Heraldic Symbols | **651** *L'Arrivee d'un Train en Gare* (1896)

(Des D. Sarty and R. Gaynor. Litho Ashton-Potter Canada)
1996 (19 Aug). *22nd International Congress of Genealogical and Heraldic Sciences, Ottawa. Fluorescent paper.* P 12½.

1697	**650** 45 c. multicoloured		50	50

(Des P.-Y. Pelletier. Litho C.B.N.)
1996 (22 Aug). *Centenary of Cinema. Two sheets, each 180×100 mm containing T 651 and similar vert designs. Multicoloured. Self-adhesive. Fluorescent paper. Die-cut.*

MS1698 Two sheets. (a) 45 c. Type **651**; 45 c. *Back to God's Country* (1919); 45 c. *Hen Hop!* (1942); 45 c. *Pour la Suite du Monde* (1963); 45 c. *Goin' Down the Road* (1970). (b) 45 c. *Mon Oncle Antoine* (1971); 45 c. *The Apprenticeship of Duddy Kravitz* (1974); 45 c. *Les Ordres* (1974); 45 c. *Les Bons Debarras* (1980); 45 c. *The Grey Fox* (1982) .. .. 7·50 8·00

The two sheets of No. MS1698 were sold together in an envelope with a descriptive booklet.

652 Interlocking Jigsaw Pieces and Hands | **653** Edouard Montpetit and Montreal University

(Des Debbie Adam. Litho Ashton-Potter Canada)
1996 (9 Sept). *Literacy Campaign. Fluorescent paper.* P 13×12½.

1699	**652** 45 c. + 5 c. multicoloured		60	65
	a. Booklet pane. No. 1699×10 with margins all round		5·50	

No. 1699 has one piece of the jigsaw removed by die-cutting and was only issued in $5 stamp booklet

(Des J. Beauchesne. Litho Ashton-Potter Canada)
1996 (26 Sept). *Edouard Montpetit (academic) Commemoration. Fluorescent frame.* P 12×12½.

1700	**653** 45 c. multicoloured		50	50

 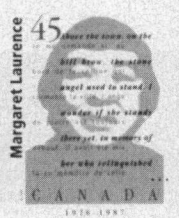

654 Winnie and Lt. Colebourn, 1914 | **655** Margaret Laurence

(Des Wai Poon. Litho Ashton-Potter Canada)
1996 (1 Oct). *Stamp Collecting Month. Winnie the Pooh. T 654 and similar horiz designs. Multicoloured. Fluorescent frame.* P 12½×13.

1701	45 c. Type 654		75	85
	a. Double sheetlet of 16. Nos. 1701/4 each × 4		10·00	
1702	45 c. Christopher Robin Milne and teddy bear, 1925		75	85
1703	45 c. Illustration from *Winnie the Pooh*, 1926		75	85
1704	45 c. Winnie the Pooh at Walt Disney World, 1996		75	85
1701/4		*Set of 4*	2·75	3·00
MS1705	152×112 mm. Nos. 1701/4		2·75	3·25

Nos. 1701/4 were printed together, *se-tenant*, as blocks of 4 in double sheetlets, used as a cover to "The True Story of Winnie the Pooh" booklet.

(Des A. Leduc. Recess and litho C.B.N.)
1996 (10 Oct). *Canadian Authors. T 655 and similar vert designs. Fluorescent paper.* P 13½×13.

1706	45 c. multicoloured		60	70
	a. Booklet pane. Nos. 1706/10 each × 2		5·25	
1707	45 c. black, greenish grey & scarlet-verm		60	70
1708	45 c. multicoloured		60	70
1709	45 c. multicoloured		60	70
1710	45 c. multicoloured		60	70
1706/10		*Set of 5*	2·75	3·25

Designs:—No. 1706, Type **655**; No. 1707, Donald G. Creighton; No. 1708, Gabrielle Roy; No. 1709, Felix-Antoine Savard; No. 1710, Thomas C. Haliburton.
Nos. 1706/10 were only issued in $4.50 stamp booklets with the horizontal edges of the pane imperforate and margins at left and right.

656 Children tobogganing | **657** Head of Ox

(Des T. Harrison (45 c.), Pauline Paquin (52 c.), Joan Bacquie (90 c.). Litho C.B.N. (45 c.) or Ashton-Potter Canada (others))
1996 (1 Nov). *Christmas. 50th Anniv of U.N.I.C.E.F. T 656 and similar vert designs. Multicoloured. Fluorescent frame.* P 13½ (45 c.) or 12½×12 (others).

1711	45 c. Type 656		50	20
	a. Booklet pane. No. 1711×10		4·75	
1712	52 c. Father Christmas skiing		60	80
	a. Perf 13½		60	80
	ab. Booklet pane. No. 1712a×5 plus one printed label		3·00	
1713	90 c. Couple ice-skating		90	1·25
	a. Perf 13½		95	1·40
	ab. Booklet pane. No. 1713a×5 plus one printed label		4·75	
1711/13		*Set of 3*	1·75	2·00

Nos. 1712a and 1713a were only issued in stamp booklets.
Nos. 1711a, 1712ab and 1713ab have the vertical edges of the panes imperforate and margins at top and bottom.

(Des Ivy Li and Liu Xiang-Ping. Litho Ashton-Potter Canada)
1997 (7 Jan). *Chinese New Year ("Year of the Ox"). Fluorescent frame.* P 13×12½.

1714	45 c. multicoloured		85	90
MS1715	155×75 mm*. No. 1714×2		2·00	2·50

No. MS1715 is an extended fan shape with overall measurements as quoted.
Two examples of No. 1714, taken from the miniature sheet, have been found with the gold ("Canada, 45", etc.) omitted.

1997 (7 Jan). *"HONG KONG '97" International Stamp Exhibition. As No. MS1715, but with exhibition logo added to the sheet margin in gold. Fluorescent frame.* P 13×12½.

MS1716 155×75 mm. No. 1714×2 .. 3·25 3·75

(Des R. Bellemare and P. Leduc. Litho Ashton-Potter, Canada)
1997 (10 Jan). *Birds (2nd series). Horiz designs as T 643. Multicoloured. Fluorescent frame.* P 12½×13.

1717	45 c. Mountain Bluebird		65	75
	a. Horiz strip of 4. Nos. 1717/20		2·40	
1718	45 c. Western Grebe		65	75
1719	45 c. Northern Gannet		65	75
1720	45 c. Scarlet Tanager		65	75
1717/20		*Set of 4*	2·40	2·75

Nos. 1717/20 printed together, *se-tenant*, in sheets of 20 (4×5) containing five examples of No. 1717a.

(Des P.-Y. Pelletier. Litho and die-stamped Ashton-Potter, Canada)
1997 (17 Feb). *Canadian Art (10th series). Vert design as T 550. Multicoloured. Fluorescent paper.* P 12½×13×13½.

1721 90 c. "York Boat on Lake Winnipeg, 1930" (Walter Phillips) .. .. 1·00 1·50
No. 1721 was issued in a similar sheet format to No. 1289

658 Man and Boy with Bike, and A. J. and J. W. Billes (company founders) | **659** Abbé Charles-Emile Gadbois

(Des Fuel Design. Litho Ashton-Potter Canada)
1997 (3 Mar). *75th Anniv of Canadian Tire Corporation. Fluorescent frame.* P 13×13½.

1722	**658** 45 c. multicoloured		50	50

No. 1722 was printed in sheets of 12 which were supplied in special envelopes each with a pamphlet on the history of the company.

(Des Marie Lessard. Litho C.B.N.)
1997 (20 Mar). *Abbé Charles-Emile Gadbois (musicologist) Commemoration. Fluorescent frame.* P 13½×13.

1723	**659** 45 c. multicoloured		50	50

660 Blue Poppy | **661** Nurse attending Patient

(Des C. Simard. Litho Ashton-Potter Canada)
1997 (4 Apr). *"Quebec in Bloom" International Floral Festival. Fluorescent frame.* P 13×12½.

1724	**660** 45 c. multicoloured		40	45
	a. Booklet pane. No. 1724×12		4·50	

No. 1724 was only issued in $5.40 booklets. No. 1724a has the horizontal edges of the pane imperforate and margins at left and right.

(Des Margaret Issenman. Litho Ashton-Potter Canada)
1997 (12 May). *Centenary of Victorian Order of Nurses. Fluorescent frame.* P 12½×13.

1725	**661** 45 c. multicoloured		50	50

662 Osgoode Hall and Seal of Law Society | **663** Great White Shark

(Des L. Holloway. Litho C.B.N.)
1997 (23 May). *Bicentenary of Law Society of Upper Canada. Fluorescent frame.* P 13½×13.

1726	**662** 45 c. multicoloured		50	50

(Des Q30 Design. Litho Ashton-Potter Canada)
1997 (30 May). *Ocean Fishes. T 663 and similar horiz designs. Multicoloured. Fluorescent paper.* P 12½×13.

1727	45 c. Type 663		75	75
	a. Block of 4. Nos. 1727/30		2·75	
1728	45 c. Pacific Halibut		75	75
1729	45 c. Common Sturgeon		75	75
1730	45 c. Blue-finned Tuna		75	75
1727/30		*Set of 4*	2·75	2·75

Nos. 1727/30 were printed together, *se-tenant*, throughout the sheet giving four blocks of 4 and four single stamps.

664 Lighthouse and Confederation Bridge

(Des C. Burke and J. Hudson. Litho C.B.N.)

1997 (31 May). *Opening of Confederation Bridge, Northumberland Strait. T* **664** *and similar horiz design. Multicoloured. Fluorescent frame.* P 12½×13.
1731	45 c. Type **664**		65	75
	a. Horiz pair. Nos. 1731/2 and centre label		1·25	1·50
1732	45 c. Confederation Bridge and Great Blue Heron		65	75

Nos. 1731/2 were printed together, horizontally *se-tenant*, in sheets of 20 (4×5) with labels measuring 16×23½ mm between vertical rows 1 and 2 and 3 and 4 which link the two designs.

665 Gilles Villeneuve in Ferrari T-3

(Des J. Gault and N. Skinner. Litho C.B.N.)

1997 (12 June). *15th Death Anniv of Gilles Villeneuve (racing car driver). T* **665** *and similar horiz design. Multicoloured. Fluorescent frame.* P 12½×13.
1733	45 c. Type **665**		60	60
1734	90 c. Villeneuve in Ferrari T-4		1·25	1·25
MS1735	203×115 mm. Nos. 1733/4 each × 4		7·00	7·50

No. **MS1735** was sold in an illustrated folder.

666 Globe and the *Matthew*

(Des Susan Warr. Litho Ashton-Potter Canada)

1997 (24 June). *500th Anniv of John Cabot's Discovery of North America. Fluorescent paper.* P 12½×13.
1736	**666** 45 c. multicoloured		50	50

667 Sea to Sky Highway, British Columbia, and Skier

(Des L. Cable. Litho C.B.N.)

1997 (30 June). *Scenic Highways (1st series). T* **667** *and similar horiz designs. Multicoloured. Fluorescent frame.* P 12½×13.
1737	45 c. Type **667**		75	75
	a. Block of 4. Nos. 1737/40		2·75	
1738	45 c. Cabot Trail, Nova Scotia, and rug-making		75	75
1739	45 c. Wine route, Ontario, and glasses of wine		75	75
1740	45 c. Highway 34, Saskatchewan, and cowboy		75	75
1737/40		*Set of 4*	2·75	2·75

Nos. 1737/40 were printed together, *se-tenant*, in sheets of 20 containing four blocks of 4 and four single stamps.
See also Nos. 1810/13 and 1876/9.

668 Kettle, Ski-bike, Lounger and Plastic Cases

(Des F. Dallaire. Litho C.B.N.)

1997 (23 July). *20th Congress of International Council of Societies for Industrial Design. Fluorescent frame.* P 12½×13.
1741	**668** 45 c. multicoloured		50	50

No. 1741 was printed in sheets of 24 (4×6), the horizontal rows containing four stamps each with a different 11½×24 mm *se-tenant* label showing examples of Canadian industrial design. These labels are on the right of the stamps in rows 1, 3 and 5 and to the left in rows 2, 4 and 6.

669 Caber Thrower, Bagpiper, Drummer and Highland Dancer

670 Knights of Columbus Emblem

(Des F. Ross. Litho C.B.N.)

1997 (1 Aug). *50th Anniv of Glengarry Highland Games, Ontario. Fluorescent frame.* P 12½×13.
1742	**669** 45 c. multicoloured		50	50

(Des A. Leduc. Litho C.B.N.)

1997 (5 Aug). *Centenary of Knights of Columbus (welfare charity) in Canada. Fluorescent frame.* P 13.
1743	**670** 45 c. multicoloured		50	50

671 Postal and Telephone Workers with P.T.T.I. Emblem

(Des Epicentre. Litho C.B.N.)

1997 (18 Aug). *28th World Congress of Postal, Telegraph and Telephone International Staff Federation, Montreal. Fluorescent frame.* P 13.
1744	**671** 45 c. multicoloured		50	50

672 C.Y.A.P. Logo

(Des K. Fung. Litho C.B.N.)

1997 (25 Aug). *Canada's Year of Asia Pacific. Fluorescent frame.* P 13½.
1745	**672** 45 c. multicoloured		50	50

673 Paul Henderson celebrating Goal

674 Martha Black

(Des C. Vinh. Litho Ashton-Potter Canada)

1997 (20 Sept). *25th Anniv of Canada–U.S.S.R. Ice Hockey Series. T* **673** *and similar horiz design. Multicoloured. Fluorescent frame.* P 12½×13.
1746	45 c. Type **673**		35	40
	a. Booklet pane. Nos. 1746/7, each × 5 with margins all round		3·75	
1747	45 c. Canadian team celebrating		35	40

Nos. 1746/7 were only issued in $4.50 stamp booklets with a partial fluorescent frame around each stamp.
Examples of the booklet pane, No. 1746a, exist overprinted "SERIES OF THE CENTURY 97-09-28 Anniversaire 25 Anniversary LA SERIE DU SIECLE" and player Paul Henderson's signature. These come from Collector Gift Sets which also included a sweatshirt, puck and print.

(Des S. Hepburn. Litho C.B.N.)

1997 (26 Sept). *Federal Politicians. T* **674** *and similar vert designs. Multicoloured. Fluorescent frame.* P 13½×13.
1748	45 c. Type **674**		50	60
	a. Block of 4. Nos. 1748/51		1·75	
1749	45 c. Lionel Chevrier		50	60
1750	45 c. Judy LaMarsh		50	60
1751	45 c. Réal Caouette		50	60
1748/51		*Set of 4*	1·75	2·25

The four different designs were printed together, *se-tenant*, throughout the sheet, giving four blocks of 4 and four single stamps.

675 Vampire and Bat

(Des L. Fishauf, J. Bennett, B. Drawson, T. Hunt, S. Ng. Litho Ashton-Potter Canada)

1997 (1 Oct). *The Supernatural. Centenary of Publication of Bram Stoker's Dracula. T* **675** *and similar square designs. Multicoloured. Fluorescent paper.* P 12½×13.
1752	45 c. Type **675**		60	65
	a. Block of 4. Nos. 1752/5		2·25	
1753	45 c. Werewolf		60	65
1754	45 c. Ghost		60	65
1755	45 c. Goblin		60	65
1752/5		*Set of 4*	2·25	2·40

Nos. 1752/5 were printed together, *se-tenant*, in blocks of 4 throughout the sheet.

676 Grizzly Bear

(Des R.-R. Carmichael and S. Slipp ($1), S. Slipp and B. Townsend ($2), A. Leduc ($8). Eng M. Morck ($2), J. Peral (others). Recess and litho C.B.N.)

1997 (15 Oct)–**98**. *Mammals . T* **676** *and similar horiz designs. Multicoloured.* P 12½×13 ($8) or 13½×13 (others).
1756	$1 Loon (47×39 mm) (27.10.98)		85	90
1757	$2 Polar Bear (47×39 mm) (27.10.98)		1·75	1·90
1758	$8 Type **676**		7·00	7·25
1756/8		*Set of 3*	9·50	10·00

No. 1758 was printed in sheets of 4.

677 "Our Lady of the Rosary" (detail, Holy Rosary Cathedral, Vancouver)

(Des G. Nincheri (45 c.), Ellen Simon (52 c.), C. Wallis (90 c.). Litho Ashton-Potter Canada)

1997 (3 Nov). *Christmas. Stained Glass Windows. T* **677** *and similar horiz designs. Multicoloured. Fluorescent frame.* P 12½×13.
1763	45 c. Type **677**		40	40
	a. Perf 12½×imperf		40	45
	ab. Booklet pane. No. 1763a×10		4·25	
1764	52 c. "Nativity" (detail, Leith United Church, Ontario)		45	55
	a. Perf 12½×imperf		50	60
	ab. Booklet pane. No. 1764a×5		2·50	
1765	90 c. "Life of the Blessed Virgin" (detail, St. Stephen's Ukrainian Catholic Church, Calgary)		80	90
	a. Perf 12½×imperf		85	1·00
	ab. Booklet pane. No. 1765a×5		4·25	
1736/5		*Set of 3*	1·50	1·75

Nos. 1763a/5a were only issued in stamp booklets with the vertical edges of the panes imperforate and margins at top and bottom.

678 Livestock and Produce

(Des Heather Lafleur and Shelagh Armstrong. Litho C.B.N.)

1997 (6 Nov). *75th Anniv of Royal Agricultural Winter Fair, Toronto. Fluorescent frame.* P 12½×13.
1766	**678** 45 c. multicoloured		50	50

679 Tiger

680 John Robarts (Ontario, 1961–71)

(Des R. Mah. Litho Ashton-Potter Canada)

1998 (8 Jan). *Chinese New Year ("Year of the Tiger"). Fluorescent frame. P 13½×12½.*

1767	**679**	45 c. multicoloured	50	50
MS1768		130×110 mm. As No. 1767×2.		
		P 13×12½	95	1·25

No. **MS**1768 is diamond-shaped with overall measurements as quoted.

As originally issued the miniature sheet was surrounded by a plain gold margin. Examples from the "Lunar New Year" pack issued on 28 January were additionally inscribed with design and printing information on this gold margin at foot.

(Des R. Bellemare. Litho C.B.N.)

1998 (18 Feb). *Canadian Provincial Premiers. T **680** and similar horiz designs. Multicoloured. Fluorescent frame. P 13½.*

1769	45 c. Type **680**	50	55
	a. Sheetlet. Nos.1769/78	4·50	
1770	45 c. Jean Lesage (Quebec, 1960–66) ..	50	55
1771	45 c. John McNair (New Brunswick, 1940–52) ..	50	55
1772	45 c. Tommy Douglas (Saskatchewan, 1944–61) ..	50	55
1773	45 c. Joseph Smallwood (Newfoundland, 1949–72) ..	50	55
1774	45 c. Angus MacDonald (Nova Scotia, 1933–40, 1945–54) ..	50	55
1775	45 c. W. A. C. Bennett (British Columbia, 1960–66) ..	50	55
1776	45 c. Ernest Manning (Alberta, 1943–68)	50	55
1777	45 c. John Bracken (Manitoba, 1922–43)	50	55
1778	45 c. J. Walter Jones (Prince Edward Island, 1943–53) ..	50	55
1769/78	*Set of 10*	4·50	5·00

Nos. 1769/78 were printed together, *se-tenant*, in sheetlets of 10 with illustrated margins.

(Des R. Bellemare and P. Leduc. Litho C.B.N.)

1998 (13 Mar). *Birds (3rd series). Horiz designs as T **643**. Multicoloured. Fluorescent frame. P 13×13½.*

1779	45 c. Hairy Woodpecker	60	65
	a. Horiz strip of 4. Nos. 1779/82	2·25	
1780	45 c. Great Crested Flycatcher ..	60	65
1781	45 c. Eastern Screech Owl ..	60	65
1782	45 c. Gray-crowned Rosy-finch ..	60	65
1779/82	*Set of 4*	2·25	2·40

Nos. 1779/82 were printed together, *se-tenant*, in sheets of 20 (4×5) containing five examples of No. 1779a.

681 Maple Leaf   **682** Coquihalla Orange Fly

(Des Gottschalk & Ash. Litho Avery Dennison, U.S.A.)

1998 (14 Apr). *Self-adhesive. Automatic Cash Machine Stamp. Fluorescent paper. Die-cut.*

1783	**681**	45 c. multicoloured	35	40

No. 1783 was issued, in sheets of 18 (3×6), from bank automatic cash machines and philatelic centres.

For stamps in this design, but without "POSTAGE POSTES" at top left see Nos. 1836/40.

(Des P. Brunelle. Litho Ashton Potter Canada)

1998 (16 Apr). *Fishing Flies. T **682** and similar horiz designs. Multicoloured. Fluorescent frame. P 12½×13.*

1784	45 c. Type **682**	55	60
	a. Booklet pane. Nos. 1784/9, each × 2	6·00	
1785	45 c. Steelhead Bee	55	60
1786	45 c. Dark Montréal	55	60
1787	45 c. Lady Amherst	55	60
1788	45 c. Coho Blue	55	60
1789	45 c. Cosseboom Special	55	60
1784/9	*Set of 6*	3·00	3·25

Nos. 1784/9 were only issued in stamp booklets containing pane No. 1784a which incorporates an inscribed margin at left.

683 Mineral and Petroleum Excavation and Pickaxe   **684** 1898 2 c. Imperial Penny Postage Stamp and Postmaster General Sir William Mulock

(Des Monique Dufour and Sophie Lafortune. Litho Ashton Potter Canada)

1998 (4 May). *Centenary of Canadian Institute of Mining, Metallurgy and Petroleum. Fluorescent frame. P 12½.*

1790	**683**	45 c. multicoloured	50	50

(Des F. Dallaire. Litho C.B.N.)

1998 (29 May). *Centenary of Imperial Penny Postage. Fluorescent frame. P 12½×13.*

1791	**684**	45 c. multicoloured	50	50

No. 1791 was printed in sheets of 14 stamps with a label showing the Imperial State Crown appearing in the centre of the sheet.

685 Two Sumo Wrestlers   **686** St. Peters Canal, Nova Scotia

(Des G. Takeuchi and S. Dittberner. Litho and embossed Ashton Potter Canada)

1998 (5 June). *First Canadian Sumo Basho (tournament), Vancouver. T **685** and similar horiz design. Multicoloured. Fluorescent frame. P 12½×13.*

1792	45 c. Type **685**	50	60
	a. Pair. Nos. 1792/3	1·00	1·10
1793	45 c. Sumo wrestler in ceremonial ritual	50	60
MS1794	84×152 mm. Nos. 1792/3	1·00	1·25

On Nos. 1792/4 the outlines of the wrestlers are embossed.

Nos. 1792/3 were printed together, *se-tenant*, both horizontally and vertically in sheets of 20 (4×5). The horizontal rows include labels, 7×30 mm, either side of each stamp with that on the left inscribed in English and that on the right in Japanese.

(Des V. McIndoe, G. George and D. Martin. Litho Ashton-Potter Canada)

1998 (17 June). *Canadian Canals. T **686** and similar vert designs. Multicoloured. Fluorescent frame. P 12½.*

1795	45 c. Type **686**	80	85
	a. Booklet pane. Nos. 1795/1804 and ten stamp-size labels ..	8·00	
1796	45 c. St. Ours Canal, Quebec ..	80	85
1797	45 c. Port Carling Lock, Ontario ..	80	85
1798	45 c. Lock on Rideau Canal, Ontario ..	80	85
1799	45 c. Towers and platform of Peterborough Lift Lock, Trent–Severn Waterway, Ontario ..	80	85
1800	45 c. Chambly Canal, Quebec ..	80	85
1801	45 c. Lachine Canal, Quebec ..	80	85
1802	45 c. Rideau Canal in winter, Ontario ..	80	85
1803	45 c. Boat on Big Chute incline railway, Trent–Severn Waterway, Ontario ..	80	85
1804	45 c. Sault Ste. Marie Canal, Ontario ..	80	85
1795/1804	*Set of 10*	8·00	8·50

Nos. 1795/1804 were only issued in $4.50 stamp booklets with the ten labels in the pane providing a location map for the canals depicted.

687 Staff of Aesculapius and Cross   **688** Policeman of 1873 and Visit to Indian Village

(Des P.-Y. Pelletier. Typo (embossed) and litho Ashton Potter Canada)

1998 (25 June). *Canadian Health Professionals. Fluorescent paper. P 12½.*

1805	**687**	45 c. multicoloured	50	50

(Des A. Valko and Circle Design. Litho (No. **MS**1808 also embossed) Ashton-Potter Canada)

1998 (3 July). *125th Anniv of Royal Canadian Mounted Police. T **688** and similar horiz design. Multicoloured. Fluorescent frame. P 12½×13.*

1806	45 c. Type **688**	50	60
	a. Horiz pair. No. 1806/7 with label ..	1·00	1·10
1807	45 c. Policewoman of 1998 and aspects of modern law enforcement ..	50	60
MS1808	160×102 mm. Nos. 1806/7	1·00	1·10

Nos. 1806/7 were printed together, *se-tenant*, in pairs both horizontally and vertically, throughout the sheet of 20 (4×5). The horizontal rows include labels, 15×26 mm, on either side of each stamp. There are two label designs, one showing the R.C.M.P. crest and the other the Musical Ride which continues the design shown on the two stamps.

No. **MS**1808 also exists from a limited printing with the facsimile signature of Lieut-Col. G. A. French, the first commissioner, added to the bottom margin.

No. **MS**1808 was also issued overprinted with the logos of "Portugal 98" or "Italia 98" for sale at these International Stamp Exhibitions.

689 William J. Roue (designer) and *Bluenose* (schooner)   **690** "Painting" (Jean-Paul Riopelle)

(Des L. Herbert. Recess and litho C.B.N.)

1998 (24 July). *William James Roue (naval architect) Commemoration. Fluorescent frame. P 13.*

1809	**689**	45 c. multicoloured	50	50

(Des L. Cable. Litho Ashton-Potter Canada)

1998 (28 July). *Scenic Highways (2nd series). Horiz designs as T **667**. Multicoloured. Fluorescent frame. P 12½×13.*

1810	45 c. Dempster Highway, Yukon, and caribou ..	55	60
	a. Block of 4. Nos. 1810/13	2·00	
1811	45 c. Dinosaur Trail, Alberta, and skeleton	55	60
1812	45 c. River Valley Drive, New Brunswick, and fern ..	55	60
1813	45 c. Blue Heron Route, Prince Edward Island, and lobster ..	55	60
1810/13	*Set of 4*	2·00	2·25

Nos. 1810/13 were printed together, *se-tenant*, in sheets of 20 containing four blocks of 4 and four single stamps.

(Des R. Bellemare. Litho C.B.N.)

1998 (7 Aug). *50th Anniv of Refus Global (manifesto of The Automatistes group of artists). T **690** and similar multicoloured designs. Self-adhesive. Fluorescent frame. Die-cut.*

1814	45 c. Type **690**	70	75
	a. Booklet pane. Nos. 1814/20	4·50	
1815	45 c. "La dernière campagne de Napoléon" (Fernand Leduc) (37×31½ mm)	70	75
1816	45 c. "Jet fuligineux sur noir torturé" (Jean-Paul Mousseau) ..	70	75
1817	45 c. "Le fond du garde-robe" (Pierre Gauvreau) (29½×42 mm) ..	70	75
1818	45 c. "Joie lacustre" (Paul-Émile Borduas)	70	75
1819	45 c. "Seafarers Union" (Marcelle Ferron) (36×34 mm) ..	70	75
1820	45 c. "Le tumulte à la mâchoire crispée" (Marcel Barbeau) (36×34 mm) ..	70	75
1814/20	*Set of 7*	4·50	4·75

Nos. 1814/20 were only available from $3.15 self-adhesive booklets in which the backing card formed the cover.

691 Napoléon-Alexandre Comeau (naturalist)   **692** Indian Wigwam

(Des Catherine Bradbury and D. Bartsch. Litho C.B.N.)

1998 (15 Aug). *Legendary Canadians. T **691** and similar vert designs. Multicoloured. Fluorescent frame. P 13½.*

1821	45 c. Type **691**	55	60
	a. Block of 4. Nos. 1821/4	2·00	
1822	45 c. Phyllis Munday (mountaineer) ..	55	60
1823	45 c. Bill Mason (film-maker) ..	55	60
1824	45 c. Harry Red Foster (sports commentator) ..	55	60
1821/4	*Set of 4*	2·00	2·25

Nos. 1821/4 were printed together, *se-tenant*, in sheets of 20 containing four blocks of 4 and four single stamps.

(Des P.-Y. Pelletier. Litho and die-stamped Ashton Potter Canada)

1998 (8 Sept). *Canadian Art (11th series). Vert design as T **550**. Multicoloured. Fluorescent frame. P 12½×13.*

1825	90 c. "The Farmer's Family" (Bruno Bobak)	80	1·00

No. 1825 was issued in a similar sheet format to No. 1289.

(Des C. Gibson and P. Scott. Litho Ashton Potter Canada)

1998 (23 Sept). *Canadian Houses. T **692** and similar horiz designs. Multicoloured. Fluorescent frame. P 12½×13.*

1826	45 c. Type **692**	50	55
	a. Sheetlet. Nos. 1826/34	4·00	
1827	45 c. Settler sod hut ..	50	55
1828	45 c. Maison Saint-Gabriel (17th-cent farmhouse), Quebec ..	50	55
1829	45 c. Queen Anne style brick house, Ontario	50	55

1830	45 c.	Terrace of town houses	.. ..	50	55
1831	45 c.	Prefabricated house	.. ..	50	55
1832	45 c.	Veterans' houses	.. ..	50	55
1833	45 c.	Modern bungalow	.. ..	50	55
1834	45 c.	Healthy House, Toronto	.. ..	50	55
1826/34			Set of 9	4·00	4·50

Nos. 1826/34 were printed together, *se-tenant*, in sheetlets of 9 with additional side margins carrying design descriptions.

693 University of Ottawa **694** Performing Animals

(Des Harris Design Associates. Litho C.B.N.)

1998 (25 Sept). *150th Anniv of University of Ottawa. Fluorescent frame.* P 13½.

1835	**693**	45 c. multicoloured	.. ..	50	50

1998 (30 Sept–28 Dec). *As T 681, but without "POSTAGE POSTES" at top left.*

(a) *Litho Ashton-Potter Canada. Fluorescent frame.* P 13×13½

1836	**681**	35 c. multicoloured (28 Dec)		45	50
		a. Booklet pane. No. 1836×5 plus printed label		2·25	
1837		73 c. multicoloured (28 Dec)		60	65
1838		95 c. multicoloured (28 Dec)		75	80
		a. Booklet pane. No. 1838×5 plus printed label		3·75	

(b) *Coil stamp. Litho and die-stamped (gold) Ashton-Potter Canada. Fluorescent frame.* P 13

1839	**681**	45 c. multicoloured		60	70

(c) *Self-adhesive automatic cash machine stamp. Litho Avery Dennison, U.S.A. Fluorescent paper. Die-cut.*

1840	**681**	46 c. multicoloured (28 Dec)		50	60

Booklet panes Nos. 1836a and 1838a have the vertical edges of the panes imperforate and margins at top and bottom.

No. 1839 was available in rolls of 100 on which the surplus self-adhesive paper around each stamp was removed.

No. 1840 was issued in sheets of 18 (3×6), from bank automatic cash machines and philatelic centres.

(Des Monique Dufour, Sophie Lafortune and Paule Thibault. Litho Ashton-Potter Canada)

1998 (1 Oct). *Canadian Circus. T 694 and similar vert designs, each incorporating a different clown. Multicoloured. Fluorescent frame.* P 13.

1851	**694**	45 c. Type 694		55	60
		a. Booklet pane. Nos. 1851/4, each × 3		6·00	
1852		45 c. Flying trapeze and acrobat on horseback		55	60
1853		45 c. Lion tamer		55	60
1854		45 c. Acrobats and trapeze artists		55	60
1851/4			Set of 4	2·00	2·25
MS1855	133×133 mm. Nos. 1851/4			2·00	2·25

Nos. 1851/4 only exist from $5.40 booklets in which the upper and lower edges of the pane are imperforate.

The fluorescent frames on Nos. 1851/4 are broken at various points where the designs encroach onto the margins.

695 John Peters Humphrey (author of original Declaration draft)

(Des J. Hudson. Litho C.B.N.)

1998 (7 Oct). *50th Anniv of Universal of Declaration of Human Rights. Fluorescent frame.* P 13×13½.

1856	**695**	45 c. multicoloured	.. ..	50	50

696 H.M.C.S. *Sackville* (corvette)

(Des T. Hawkins and D. Page. Litho C.B.N.)

1998 (4 Nov). *75th Anniv of Canadian Naval Reserve. T 696 and similar horiz design. Multicoloured. Fluorescent frame.* P 12½×13.

1857	**696**	45 c. Type 696		50	60
		a. Pair. Nos. 1857/8		1·00	1·10
1858		45 c. H.M.C.S. *Shawinigan* (coastal defence vessel)		50	60

Nos. 1857/8 were printed together, *se-tenant*, in horizontal and vertical pairs throughout the sheet.

697 Angel blowing Trumpet **698** Rabbit

(Des Anita Zeppetelli. Litho Ashton Potter Canada)

1998 (6 Nov). *Christmas. Statues of Angels. T 697 and similar vert designs. Multicoloured. Fluorescent frame.* P 13 (45 c.) or 13×13½ (others).

1859	45 c. Type 697			40	40
	a. Booklet pane. No. 1859×10	..	4·00		
	b. Perf 13×13½	..		40	40
	ba. Booklet pane. No. 1859b×10	..	4·00		
1860	52 c. Adoring Angel	..		40	50
	a. Booklet pane. No. 1860×5 plus one printed label		2·50		
	b. Perf 13	..		50	55
	ba. Booklet pane. No. 1860b×5 plus one printed label		2·50		
1861	90 c. Angel at prayer			70	85
	a. Booklet pane. No. 1861×5 plus one printed label		4·00		
	b. Perf 13	..		80	1·00
	ba. Booklet pane. No. 1861b×5 plus one printed label		4·00		
1859/61		Set of 3		1·40	1·60

Nos. 1860b and 1861b only come from stamp booklets. Sheets of the 45 c. are known in either perforation, but sheet stamps in the 13×13½ gauge are rare (*Price £40 mint for example with perforations on all four sides*).

The booklet panes show vertical edges of the panes imperforate and margins at top and bottom.

(Des K. Koo and K. Fung. Litho Ashton-Potter Canada)

1999 (8 Jan). *Chinese New Year. ("Year of the Rabbit"). Fluorescent frame.* P 13½.

1862	**698**	46 c. multicoloured		50	50
MS1863	Circular 100 mm diam. **698** 95 c. mult (40×40 mm). P 12½×13			90	1·00

No. MS1863 also exists with the "CHINA" '99 World Stamp Exhibition, Beijing, logo overprinted in gold on the top of the margin.

699 Stylised Mask and Curtain **700** "The Raven and the First Men" (B. Reid) and The Great Hall

(Des Y. Paquin and Marie Rouleau. Litho C.B.N.)

1999 (16 Feb). *50th Anniv of Le Théâtre du Rideau Vert. Fluorescent frame.* P 13×12½.

1864	**699**	46 c. multicoloured	.. ..	50	50

(Des R. Bellemare and P. Leduc. Litho Ashton-Potter Canada)

1999 (24 Feb). *Birds (4th series). Horiz designs as T 643. Multicoloured. Fluorescent frame.* (a) P 12½×13

1865	46 c. Northern Goshawk	..		50	60
	a. Horiz strip of 4. Nos. 1865/8		1·75		
1866	46 c. Red-winged Blackbird	..		50	60
1867	46 c. American Goldfinch	..		50	60
1868	46 c. Sandhill Crane	..		50	60
1865/8		Set of 4		1·75	2·25

(b) *Self-adhesive.* P 11½

1869	46 c. Northern Goshawk	..		50	60
	b. Booklet pane. Nos. 1869/72, each × 3 with margins all round		5·50		
1870	46 c. Red-winged Blackbird	..		50	60
1871	46 c. American Goldfinch	..		50	60
1872	46 c. Sandhill Crane	..		50	60
1869/72		Set of 4		1·75	2·25

Nos. 1865/8 were printed together, *se-tenant*, in sheets of 20 (4×5) containing five examples of No. 1865a.

Nos. 1869/72 were only issued in $5.52 stamp booklets on which the surplus self-adhesive paper was retained.

(Des Barbara Hodgson. Litho C.B.N.)

1999 (9 Mar). *50th Anniv of University of British Columbia Museum of Anthropology. Fluorescent frame.* P 13½.

1873	**700**	46 c. multicoloured	.. ..	50	50

OMNIBUS ISSUES

Details, together with prices for complete sets, of the various Omnibus issues from the 1935 Silver Jubilee series to date are included in a special section following Zimbabwe at the end of Volume 2.

701 *Marco Polo* (full-rigged **702** Inuit Children and Landscape ship)

(Des J. Franklin Wright. Litho Ashton-Potter Canada)

1999 (19 Mar). *Canada–Australia Joint Issue. Marco Polo (emigrant ship). Multicoloured. Fluorescent frame.* P 13×12½.

1874	46 c. Type 701			50	50
MS1875	160×95 mm. 85 c. As No. 1728 of Australia. P 13; 46 c. Type 701. P 13½ (No. MS1875 was sold at $1.25 in Canada)			1·25	1·40

No. MS1875 includes the "Australia '99" emblem on the sheet margin and was postally valid in Canada to the value of 46 c. The same miniature sheet was also available in Australia.

(Des L. Cable. Litho Ashton-Potter Canada)

1999 (31 Mar). *Scenic Highways (3rd series). Horiz designs as T 667. Multicoloured. Fluorescent frame.* P 12½×13.

1876	46 c. Route 132, Quebec, and hang-glider		50	55
	a. Block of 4. Nos. 1876/9		1·75		
1877	46 c. Yellowhead Highway, Manitoba, and Bison		50	55
1878	46 c. Dempster Highway, Northwest Territories, and Indian village elder		50	55
1879	46 c. The Discovery Trail, Newfoundland, and whale's tailfin		50	55
1876/9		Set of 4	1·75	2·00	

Nos. 1876/9 were printed together, *se-tenant*, in sheets of 20 comprising four blocks of 4 and four single stamps.

(Des Susan Point and Bonne Zabolotney. Litho Ashton-Potter Canada)

1999 (1 Apr). *Creation of Nunavut Territory. Fluorescent frame.* P 12½×13.

1880	**702**	46 c. multicoloured	.. ..	50	50

703 Elderly Couple on Country Path **704** Khanda (Sikh symbol)

(Des Sheila Armstrong-Hodgson, P. Hodgson and S. Peters. Litho C.B.N.)

1999 (12 Apr). *International Year of Older Persons. Fluorescent frame.* P 13½.

1881	**703**	46 c. multicoloured	.. ..	50	50

(Des S. Zabolotney. Litho C.B.N.)

1999 (19 Apr). *Centenary of Sikhs in Canada. Interrupted fluorescent frame.* P 13.

1882	**704**	46 c. multicoloured	.. ..	50	50

705 *Arethusa bulbosa* (orchid) **706** Bookbinding

(Des Marlene Wou, Poon Kuen Chow and Y. Lai. Litho Ashton-Potter Canada)

1999 (27 Apr). *16th World Orchid Conference, Vancouver. T 705 and similar vert designs. Multicoloured. Fluorescent frame.* P 13×12½.

1883	46 c. Type 705			55	55
	a. Booklet pane. Nos. 1883/6, each × 3, with margins all round		5·50		
1884	46 c. *Amerorchis rotundifolia*	..		55	55
1885	46 c. *Cypripedium pubescens*	..		55	55
1886	46 c. *Platanthera psycodes*	..		55	55
1883/6		Set of 4		2·00	2·00

Nos. 1883/6 were initially only issued in $5.52 stamp booklets, but later appeared in No. MS1917.

(Des Monique Dufour and Sophie Lafortune. Litho Ashton-Potter Canada)

1999 (29 Apr). *Traditional Trades. T* **706** *and similar vert designs. Multicoloured. No fluorescent frame.* P 13×13½.

1887	1 c. Type **706**	10	10
1888	2 c. Decorative ironwork	10	10
1889	3 c. Glass-blowing	10	10
1890	4 c. Oyster farming	10	10
1891	5 c. Weaving	10	10
1892	9 c. Quilting	10	10
1893	10 c. Wood carving	10	15
1894	25 c. Leatherworking	20	25
1887/94	*Set of 8*	50	55

707 "Northern Dancer" (racehorse)

708 Logo engraved on Limestone

(Des P.-Y. Pelletier. Litho Ashton-Potter Canada)

1999 (2 June). *Canadian Horses. T* **707** *and similar horiz designs. Multicoloured. Fluorescent frame.* (a) P 13×13½.

1903	46 c. Type **707**	55	55
	a. Block of 4. Nos. 1903/6	2·00	
1904	46 c. "Kingsway Skoal" (rodeo horse)	55	55
1905	46 c. "Big Ben" (show jumper)	55	55
1906	46 c. "Armbro Flight" (trotter)	55	55
1903/6	*Set of 4*	2·00	2·00

(b) *Self-adhesive.* P 11½×11

1907	46 c. Type **707**	55	55
	a. Booklet pane. Nos. 1907/10, each × 3 with margins all round	5·50	
1908	46 c. "Kingsway Skoal" (rodeo horse)	55	55
1909	46 c. "Big Ben" (show jumper)	55	55
1910	46 c. "Armbro Flight" (trotter)	55	55
1907/10	*Set of 4*	2·00	2·00

Nos. 1903/6 were printed together, *se-tenant*, in blocks of 4 throughout sheets of 16.

Nos. 1907/10 were only issued in $5.52 stamp booklets on which the surplus self-adhesive paper was retained.

(Des P. Fontaine. Litho C.B.N.)

1999 (3 June). *150th Anniv of Barreau du Québec* (*Quebec lawyers' association*). *Fluorescent frame.* P 13½.

1911	**708** 46 c. multicoloured	50	50

(Des P.-Y. Pelletier. Litho and die-stamped Ashton-Potter Canada)

1999 (3 July). *Canadian Art* (*12th series*). *Vert design as T* **550**. *Multicoloured. Fluorescent inner frame.* P 12½×13.

1912	95 c. "Coq licorne" (Jean Dallaire)	85	1·00

No. 1912 was issued in a similar sheet format to No. 1289.

709 Athletics

(Des Circle Design. Litho Ashton-Potter Canada)

1999 (12 July). *13th Pan-American Games, Winnipeg. T* **709** *and similar square designs. Multicoloured. Fluorescent frame.* P 13½.

1913	46 c. Type **709**	50	55
	a. Block of 4. Nos. 1913/16	1·75	
1914	46 c. Cycling	50	55
1915	46 c. Swimming	50	55
1916	46 c. Football	50	55
1913/16	*Set of 4*	1·75	2·00

Nos. 1913/16 were printed together, *se-tenant*, as blocks of 4 in sheets of 16.

(Des Chris Dahl Design, Poon Kuen Chow and Y. Lai. Litho Ashton-Potter Canada)

1999 (21 Aug). *"China '99" International Stamp Exhibition, Beijing. Sheet,* 78×133 *mm, containing Nos.* 1883/6. *Multicoloured. Fluorescent frame.* P 12½.

MS1917	46 c. Type **705**; 46 c. *Amerorchis rotundifolia*; 46 c. *Cypripedium pubescens*; 46 c. *Platanthera psycodes*	1·90	2·00

710 Female Rower

(Des P. Haslip and A. Lum. Litho Ashton-Potter Canada)

1999 (22 Aug). *23rd World Rowing Championships, St. Catharines. Fluorescent frame.* P 12½×13.

1918	**710** 46 c. multicoloured	50	50

711 U.P.U. Emblem and World Map

(Des P.-Y. Pelletier. Litho C.B.N.)

1999 (26 Aug). *125th Anniv of Universal Postal Union. Fluorescent frame.* P 12½×13.

1919	**711** 46 c. multicoloured	50	50

712 De Havilland Mosquito F.B. VI

(Des T. Telmet, M. Barac and G. Lay. Litho C.B.N.)

1999 (4 Sept). *75th Anniv of Canadian Air Force. T* **712** *and similar horiz designs. Multicoloured. Fluorescent frame.* P 12½×13.

1920	46 c. Type **712**	40	40
	a. Sheetlet. Nos. 1920/35	6·50	
1921	46 c. Sopwith F.1 Camel	40	40
1922	46 c. De Havilland Canada DHC-3 Otter	40	40
1923	46 c. De Havilland Canada CC-108 Caribou	40	40
1924	46 c. Canadair CL-28 Argus Mk 2	40	40
1925	46 c. Canadair (North American) F-86 Sabre 6	40	40
1926	46 c. McDonnell Douglas CF-18	40	40
1927	46 c. Sopwith 5.F.1 Dolphin	40	40
1928	46 c. Armstrong Whitworth Siskin IIIA	40	40
1929	46 c. Canadian Vickers (Northrop) Delta II	40	40
1930	46 c. Sikorsky CH-124A Sea King helicopter	40	40
1931	46 c. Vickers-Armstrong Wellington Mk II	40	40
1932	46 c. Avro Anson Mk I	40	40
1933	46 c. Canadair (Lockheed) CF-104G Starfighter	40	40
1934	46 c. Burgess-Dunne	40	40
1935	46 c. Avro 504K	40	40
1920/35	*Set of 16*	6·50	6·50

Nos. 1920/35 were printed together, *se-tenant*, in sheetlets of 16.

713 Fokker DR-1

(Des T. Telmet and M. Barac. Litho C.B.N)

1999 (4 Sept). *50th Anniv of Canadian International Air Show. T* **713** *and similar horiz designs. Multicoloured. Fluorescent frame.* P 12½×13.

1936	46 c. Type **713**	40	40
	a. Sheetlet. Nos. 1936/9	1·60	
1937	46 c. H101 Salto glider	40	40
1938	46 c. De Havilland DH100 Vampire Mk III	40	40
1939	46 c. Wing-walker on Stearman A-75	40	40
1936/9	*Set of 4*	1·60	1·75

Nos. 1936/9 were printed together, *se-tenant*, in sheetlets of 4 forming a composite design which includes a nine-plane "snowbird" formation of Canadair CT114 Tutor in the background.

714 N.A.T.O. Emblem and National Flags

(Des Bonnie Ross and F. Ross. Litho Ashton Potter Canada)

1999 (21 Sept). *50th Anniv of North Atlantic Treaty Organization. Fluorescent frame.* P 12½×13.

1940	**714** 46 c. multicoloured	40	40

NEW INFORMATION

The editor is always interested to correspond with people who have new information that will improve or correct the Catalogue.

715 Man ploughing on Book

(Des Q30 Design. Litho C.B.N)

1999 (24 Sept). *Centenary of Frontier College* (*workers' education organization*). *Fluorescent frame.* P 13×13½.

1941	**715** 46 c. multicoloured	40	40

The fluorescent frame on No. 1941 is incomplete as there are breaks at top right and at the lower left-hand corner.

716 Master Control Sports Kite

(Des Debbie Adams. Litho Ashton-Potter Canada)

1999 (1 Oct). *Stamp Collecting Month. Kites. T* **716** *and similar multicoloured designs. Die-cut perforations.*

1942	46 c. Type **716**	40	40
	a. Booklet pane. Nos. 1942/5×2	3·00	
1943	46 c. Indian Garden Flying Carpet (*irregular rectangle,* 35×32 *mm*)	40	40
1944	46 c. Gibson Girl box kite (*horiz,* 38½×25 *mm*)	40	40
1945	46 c. Dragon Centipede (*oval,* 39×29 *mm*)	40	40
1942/5	*Set of 4*	1·60	1·75

Nos. 1942/5 were only issued in stamp booklets containing pane No. 1942a.

717 Boy holding Dove

718 Angel playing Drum

(Des P.-Y. Pelletier (46 c.), Monique Dufour and Sophie Lafortune (55 c.), J. Peral (95 c.))

1999 (12 Oct). *New Millennium. Three sheets, each* 108×108 *mm, containing T* **717** *and similar square designs in blocks of* 4. (a) *Litho Ashton-Potter Canada* (*hologram by Crown Canada*). *Self-adhesive. Die-cut*

MS1946	46 c.×4 multicoloured	1·50	1·60

(b) *Litho Ashton-Potter Canada.* P 13½

MS1947	55 c.×4 multicoloured	1·90	2·00

(c) *Recess C.B.N.* P 13

MS1948	95 c.×4 red-brown	3·25	3·50

Designs:—46 c. Holographic image of dove in flight; 95 c. Dove with olive branch.

Designs as Nos. MS1946/8 also exist in similar-sized miniature sheets each containing one stamp. These were only available in the Canada Post "Official Millennium Keepsake" which presented them in a tin box, together with a certificate and a medallion, for $8.99.

(Des Tannis Hopkins, K. Tsetsekas and Bonne Zabolotney. Litho C.B.N.)

1999 (4 Nov). *Christmas. Victorian Angels. T* **718** *and similar vert designs. Multicoloured. Fluorescent frame.* P 13½.

1949	46 c. Type **718**	40	45
	a. Booklet pane. No. 1949×10	3·75	
1950	55 c. Angel with toys	45	50
	a. Booklet pane. No. 1950×5 plus one printed label	2·50	
1951	95 c. Angel with star	80	85
	a. Booklet pane. No. 1951×5 plus one printed label	4·00	
1949/51	*Set of 3*	1·60	1·75

Nos. 1949a/51a show the vertical edges of the panes imperforate and have margins at top and bottom.

Index to Canada Stamp Designs from 1942

The following index is intended to facilitate the identification of Canadian issues from 1942. Portrait stamps are usually listed under surnames only, views under the name of the town or city and other issues under the main subject or a prominent word and date chosen from the inscription. Simple abbreviations have occasionally been resorted to and when the same design or subject appears on more than one stamp, only the first of each series is indicated.

Index to Canada Stamp Designs from 1942—*Continued*

STAMP BOOKLETS

Booklet Nos. SB1/60 are stapled, all subsequent booklets have their panes attached by selvedge, *unless otherwise stated.*

All booklets up to and including No. SB41 contain panes consisting of two rows of three (3×2).

B 1

1900 (11 June). *Red on pink cover. Two panes of six 2 c. (No. 155ba).*
SB1   25 c. booklet. Cover as Type B **1** with English text £1700

1903 (1 July). *Red on pink cover. Two panes of six 2 c. (No. 176a).*
SB2   25 c. booklet. Cover as Type B **1** with English text £1800

1912 (Jan)–**16**. *Red on pink cover. Two panes of six 2 c. (No. 201a).*
SB3   25 c. booklet. Cover as Type B **1** with English text 60·00
    a. Cover handstamped "NOTICE Change in
      Postal Rates For New Rates See Postmaster" 60·00
    b. French text (4.16)   £100
    ba. Cover handstamped "AVIS Changement des
      tarifs Postaux Pour les nouveaux tarifs
      consulter le maitre de poste"   £100

1913 (1 May)–**16**. *Green on pale green cover. Four panes of six 1 c. (No. 197a).*
SB4   25 c. booklet. Cover as Type B **1** with English text £350
    a. Containing pane No. 199a   65·00
    ab. Cover handstamped "NOTICE Change in
      Postal Rates For New Rates See Postmaster" 65·00
    b. French text (28.4.16)   £500
    ba. Containing pane No. 199a   £130
    bb. Cover handstamped "AVIS Changement des
      tarifs Postaux Pour les nouveaux tarifs
      consulter le maitre de poste"   £275

1922 (Mar). *Black on brown cover. Two panes of four 3 c. and 2 labels (No. 205a).*
SB5   25 c. booklet. Cover as Type B **1** with English text £300
    a. French text   £600

1922 (July–Dec). *Black on blue cover. Panes of four 1 c., 2 c. and 3 c. (Nos. 246aa, 247aa, 205a) and 2 labels.*
SB6   25 c. booklet. Cover as Type B **1** with English text £300
    a. French text (Dec)   £475

1922 (Dec). *Black on orange cover. Four panes of six 1 c. (No. 246ab).*
SB7   25 c. booklet. Cover as Type B **1** with English text £100
    a. French text   £130

1922 (Dec). *Black on green cover. Two panes of six 2 c. (No. 247ab).*
SB8   25 c. booklet. Cover as Type B **1** with English text £600
    a. French text   £700

1923 (Dec). *Black on blue cover. Panes of four 1 c., 2 c. and 3 c. (Nos. 246aa, 247aa, 205a) and 2 labels.*
SB9   25 c. booklet. Cover as Type B **1** with English text £200
    a. French text   £325

1923 (Dec)–**24**. *Black on brown cover. Two panes of four 3 c. (No. 248aa) and 2 labels.*
SB10   25 c. booklet. Cover as Type B **1** with English text £180
    a. French text (5.24)   £275

B 2

1928 (16 Oct). *Black on green cover. Two panes of six 2 c. (No. 276a).*
SB11   25 c. booklet. Cover as Type B **2** with English text 55·00
    a. French text   75·00

1928 (25 Oct). *Black on orange cover. Four panes of six 1 c. (No. 275a).*
SB12   25 c. booklet. Cover as Type B **2** with English text £100
    a. French text   £190

1929 (6 June). *Plain manilla cover. Three panes of six 1 c., two panes of six 2 c. and one pane of six 5 c. (Nos. 275a, 276a, 279a).*
SB13   72 c. booklet. Plain cover   £300
    a. With "Philatelic Div., Fin. Br. P.O. Dept.,
      Ottawa" circular cachet on front cover   £800
    b. With code number in the centre of the
      circular cachet   £900

1930 (17 June). *Black on green cover. Two panes of six 2 c. (No. 289a).*
SB14   25 c. booklet. Cover as Type B **2** with English text 80·00
    a. French text   £110

1930 (17 Nov). *Black on red cover. Two panes of six 2 c. (No. 301a).*
SB15   25 c. booklet. Cover as Type B **2** with English text 55·00
    a. French text   75·00

1931 (13 July). *Black on red cover. Two panes of four 3 c. (No. 303a) and 2 labels.*
SB16   25 c. booklet. Cover as Type B **2** with English text 80·00
    a. French text   £110

1931 (21 July). *Black on green cover. Four panes of six 1 c. (No. 300b).*
SB17   25 c. booklet. Cover as Type B **2** with English text £120
    a. French text   £160

1931 (23 July). *Black on brown cover. Two panes of six 2 c. (No. 302a).*
SB18   25 c. booklet. Cover as Type B **2** with English text 80·00
    a. French text   £110

1931 (13 Nov). *Black on blue cover. Panes of four 1 c., 2 c. and 3 c. (Nos. 300db, 302ba, 303a) and 2 labels.*
SB19   25 c. booklet. Cover as Type B **2** with English text £250
    a. French text   £350

1933 (22 Aug–13 Nov). *Black on red cover. Two panes of four 3 c. (No. 321a) and 2 labels.*
SB20   25 c. booklet. Cover as Type B **2** with English text
      (13 Nov)   85·00
    a. French text (22 Aug)   £160

1933 (7 Sept). *Black on brown cover. Two panes of six 2 c. (No. 320a).*
SB21   25 c. booklet. Cover as Type B **2** with English text 60·00
    a. French text   £100

1933 (19 Sept–5 Dec). *Black on blue cover. Panes of four 1 c., 2 c. and 3 c. (Nos. 319b, 320b, 321ba) and 2 labels.*
SB22   25 c. booklet. Cover as Type B **2** with English text £200
    a. French text (5 Dec)   £300

1933 (28 Dec)–**34**. *Black on green cover. Four panes of six 1 c. (No. 319a).*
SB23   25 c. booklet. Cover as Type B **2** with English text 85·00
    a. French text (26.3.34)   £120

B 3

1935 (1 June–8 Aug). *Red on white cover. Two panes of four 3 c. (No. 343a) and 2 labels.*
SB24   25 c. booklet. Cover as Type B **3** with English text
      (8 Aug)   55·00
    a. French text (1 June)   70·00

1935 (22 July–1 Sept). *Blue on white cover. Panes of four 1 c., 2 c. and 3 c. (Nos. 341b, 342b, 343a) and 2 labels.*
SB25   25 c. booklet. Cover as Type B **3** with English text £140
    a. French text (1 Sept)   £180

1935 (19 Aug–18 Oct). *Green on white cover. Four panes of six 1 c. (No. 341a).*
SB26   25 c. booklet. Cover as Type B **3** with English text 90·00
    a. French text (18 Oct)   £130

1935 (16–18 Mar). *Brown on white cover. Two panes of six 2 c. (No. 342a).*
SB27   25 c. booklet. Cover as Type B **3** with English text 70·00
    a. French text (18 Mar)   £120

B 4

1937 (14 Apr)–**38**. *Blue and white cover. Panes of four 1 c., 2 c. and 3 c. (Nos. 357a, 358a, 359a) and 2 labels.*
SB28   25 c. booklet. Cover as Type B **3** with English text 85·00
    a. French text (4.1.38)   95·00
SB29   25 c. booklet. Cover as Type B **4** with English text
      57 mm wide   70·00
    a. English text 63 mm wide   85·00
    b. French text 57 mm wide (4.1.38)   90·00
    ba. French text 63 mm wide   £140

1937 (23–27 Apr). *Red and white cover. Two panes of four 3 c. (No. 359a) and 2 labels.*
SB30   25 c. booklet. Cover as Type B **3** with English text
      (27 Apr)   19·00
    a. French text (23 Apr)   30·00
SB31   25 c. booklet. Cover as Type B **4** with English text
      57 mm wide (27 Apr)   10·00
    a. English text 63 mm wide   35·00
    b. French text 57 mm wide (23 Apr)   13·00
    ba. French text 63 mm wide   £130

1937 (18 May)–**38**. *Green and white cover. Four panes of six 1 c. (No. 357b).*
SB32   25 c. booklet. Cover as Type B **3** with English text 30·00
    a. French text (14.10.38)   42·00
SB33   25 c. booklet. Cover as Type B **4** with English text
      57 mm wide   17·00
    a. English text 63 mm wide   55·00
    b. French text 57 mm wide (14.10.38)   18·00
    ba. French text 63 mm wide   £120

1938 (3 May)–**39**. *Brown and white cover. Two panes of six 2 c. (No. 358b).*
SB34   25 c. booklet. Cover as Type B **3** with English text 40·00
    a. French text (3.3.39)   50·00
SB35   25 c. booklet. Cover as Type B **4** with English text
      57 mm wide   23·00
    a. English text 63 mm wide   60·00
    b. French text 57 mm wide   42·00
    ba. French text 63 mm wide   85·00

1942 (20–29 Aug). *Red and white cover. Two panes of four 3 c. (No. 377a) and 2 labels.*
SB36   25 c. booklet. Cover as Type B **4** with English text 8·50
    a. French text (29 Aug)   12·00

1942 (12–14 Sept). *Violet and white cover. Panes of four 1 c., 2 c. and 3 c. (Nos. 375a, 376a, 377a), each with 2 labels.*
SB37   25 c. booklet. Cover as Type B **4** with English text
      (14 Sept)   48·00
    a. French text (12 Sept)   90·00

1942 (6 Oct)–**43**. *Brown and white cover. Two panes of six 2 c. (No. 376b).*
SB38   25 c. booklet. Cover as Type B **4** with English text 42·00
    a. French text (6.4.43)   70·00

1942 (24 Nov)–**46**. *Green and white cover. Four panes of six 1 c. (No. 375b).*
SB39   25 c. booklet. Cover as Type B **4** with English text 11·00
    a. French text (16.2.46)   17·00
    b. Bilingual text (8.1.46)   20·00

1943 (3 May)–**46**. *Orange and white cover. One pane of six 4 c. (No. 380a).*
SB40   25 c. booklet. Cover as Type B **4** with English text 4·00
    a. French text (12.5.43)   10·00
    b. Bilingual text (8.1.46)   13·00

1943 (28 Aug)–**46**. *Purple and white cover. Two panes of four 3 c. (No. 378a) and 2 labels.*
SB41   25 c. booklet. Cover as Type B **4** with English text 10·00
    a. French text (7.9.43)   25·00
    b. Bilingual text (8.1.46)   18·00

B 5

1943 (1 Sept)–**46**. *Black and white cover. Panes of three 1 c., 3 c. and 4 c. (Nos. 394a, 395a, 396a) (3×1).*
SB42   25 c. booklet. Cover as Type B **5** with English text 26·00
    a. French text (18.9.43)   32·00
    c. Bilingual text (23.1.46)   30·00

B 6

1947 (24 Nov). *Brown on orange cover. Panes of six 3 c. and 4 c. (3×2) and two panes of four 7 c. (2×2) (Nos. 378a, 380a, 407a).*
SB43 $1 booklet. Cover as Type B **6** with English text 25·00
    a. French text   40·00

1950 (12 Apr–18 May). *Purple and white cover. Two panes of four 3 c. (No. 416a) and 2 labels (3×2).*
SB44 25 c. booklet. Cover as Type B 4 with English text 5·00
    a. Bilingual text (18 May) .. .. 5·00

1950 (5–10 May). *Orange and white cover. One pane of six 4 c. (No. 417a) (3×2).*
SB45 25 c. booklet. Cover as Type B 4 with English text 28·00
    a. Stitched .. .. 60·00
    b. Bilingual text (10 May) .. .. 32·00

1950 (18 May). *Black and white cover. Panes of three 1 c., 3 c. and 4 c. (Nos. 422ba, 423a, 423ba) (3×1).*
SB46 25 c. booklet. Cover as Type B 5 with English text 50·00
    a. Bilingual text .. .. .. 55·00

1951 (2 June). *Orange and white cover. One pane of six 4 c. (No. 417ba) (3×2).*
SB47 25 c. booklet. Cover as Type B 4 with English text 6·00
    a. Stitched .. .. 12·00
    b. Bilingual text .. .. .. 8·50

1951 (25 Oct)–**52**. *Black and white cover. Panes of three 1 c., 3 c. and 4 c. (Nos. 422ba, 423a, 423ca) (3×1).*
SB48 25 c. booklet. Cover as Type B 5a with English text 26·00
    a. Bilingual text (9.7.52) .. .. 30·00

1953 (6 July–19 Aug). *Orange cover. One pane of six 4 c. (No. 453a) (3×2).*
SB49 25 c. booklet. Cover as Type B 4 with English text 3·50
    a. Bilingual text (19 Aug) .. .. 5·00

1953 (17 July–20 Oct). *Purple cover. Two panes of four 3 c. (No. 452a) and 2 labels (3×2).*
SB50 25 c. booklet. Cover as Type B 4 with English text 3·75
    a. Bilingual text (20 Oct) .. .. 8·50

1953 (12 Aug). *Grey cover. Panes of three 1 c., 3 c. and 4 c. (Nos. 458a, 459a, 460a) (3×1).*
SB51 25 c. booklet. Cover as Type B 5 with English text 16·00
    a. Bilingual text .. .. .. 19·00

All the following booklets are bilingual

1954 (1 Apr–Nov). *Blue cover as Type B 4.*
SB52 25 c. booklet containing pane of five 5 c. and 1 label (No. 473a) (3×2) .. .. 2·00
    a. Stitched (Nov) .. .. .. 3·25

1954 (14 July–Nov). *Blue cover as Type B 4.*
SB53 25 c. booklet containing pane of five 5 c. and 1 label (No. 467a) (3×2) .. .. 2·00
    a. Stitched (Nov) .. .. .. 3·25

1955 (7 July). *Violet cover as Type B 4.*
SB54 25 c. booklet containing pane of six 4 c. (No. 466a) (3×2) .. .. 4·75

B 7

1956 (1 June). *Red and white cover as Type B 7.*
SB55 25 c. booklet containing two panes of five 1 c. and five 4 c., each with 1 label (Nos. 463a, 466b) (3×2) .. .. 3·00

1956 (July). *Blue and white cover as Type B 7.*
SB56 25 c. booklet containing pane of five 5 c. and 1 label (No. 467a) (3×2) .. .. 2·75

B 8

1963 (May)–**67**. *Blue and white cover as Type B 7.*
SB57 25 c. booklet containing pane of five 5 c. and 1 label (No. 531a) (2×3) .. .. 3·50
    a. Cover Type B 8 (1.67) .. .. 32·00

1963 (15 May). *Red and white cover as Type B 7.*
SB58 25 c. booklet containing two panes of five 1 c. and five 4 c., each with 1 label (Nos. 527a, 530a) (2×3) .. .. 7·00

1967 (Feb). *Red cover as Type B 8.*
SB59 25 c. booklet containing two panes of five 1 c. and five 4 c., each with 1 label (Nos. 579a, 582a) (2×3) .. .. 2·50

1967 (Mar). *Blue cover as Type B 8.*
SB60 25 c. booklet containing pane of five 5 c. and 1 label (No. 583a) (2×3) .. .. 7·50

B 9

1968 (Sept). *Brown and cream cover, 70×48 mm, as Type B 9.*
SB61 25 c. booklet containing *se-tenant* pane of five 1 c. and five 4 c. (No. 598a) (2×5) .. 2·50

1968 (Sept). *Red and cream cover as Type B 9.*
SB62 $1 booklet containing pane of twenty-five 4 c. and 2 labels (No. 599a) (3×9) .. .. 9·00

1968 (Sept). *Blue and cream cover, 82×48 mm, as Type B 9.*
SB63 $1 booklet containing pane of twenty 5 c. (No. 600a) (2×10) .. .. .. 6·50

1968 (Oct). *Orange and cream cover, 70×48 mm, as Type B 9, but without border.*
SB64 25 c. booklet containing *se-tenant* pane of one 1 c., four 6 c. and 1 label (No. 598b) (2×3) .. 2·50

B 10 (*Illustration reduced. Actual size 128×60 mm*)

1968 (15 Nov). *Christmas. Red and green cover as Type B 10.*
SB65 $1 booklet containing two panes of ten 5 c. (No. 630a) (5×2) .. .. .. 6·00
    p. Phosphor (No. 630pa) .. .. 7·50
Nos. SB65/p exist with left or right opening (i.e. with selvedge at left or right of pane).

1969 (Jan). *Orange-red on cream cover as Type B 9, but without border.*
SB66 $1.50, booklet containing pane of twenty-five 6 c. and 2 labels (No. 601a) (3×9) .. 11·00

1969 (8 Oct). *Christmas. Red cover size as Type B 10.*
SB67 $1 booklet containing two panes of ten 5 c. (No. 644a) (5×2) .. .. .. 3·75
    p. Phosphor (No. 644pa) .. .. 6·00

1970 (Jan). *Black on cream cover as Type B 9, but without border.*
SB68 $1.50, booklet containing pane of twenty-five 6 c. and 2 labels (No. 602a) (3×9) .. 20·00

1970 (Aug). *Black on cream cover, 70×48 mm, as Type B 9, but without border.*
SB69 25 c. booklet containing pane of four 6 c. (No. 603a) (2×2) .. .. .. 13·00

1970 (Aug). *Black on cream cover as Type B 9, but without border.*
SB70 $1.50, booklet containing pane of twenty-five 6 c. and 2 labels (No. 607a) (3×9) .. 16·00

1970 (26 Oct). *Indigo on cream cover, 70×50 mm. Inscr* "CANADIAN POSTAGE STAMPS...MADE EXPRESSLY FOR OPAL MANUFACTURING CO. LIMITED".
SB71 25 c. booklet containing four 2 c. and four 3 c. (No. 580a) (2×2) with gutter margin between 2·50
No. SB71 was produced by the Canadian Bank Note Co for use in the private stamp-vending machines owned by the Opal Manufacturing Co Ltd, Toronto. To cover the cost of manufacture and installation these booklets were sold at 25 c. each. They were not available from the Canadian Post Office.

1970 (Nov). *Black on cream cover, 70×48 mm, as Type B 9, but without border.*
SB72 25 c. booklet containing pane of four 6 c. (No. 608a) (2×2) .. .. .. 5·50

1971 (30 June). *Green on cream cover, 70×48 mm, as Type B 9, but without border.*
SB73 25 c. booklet containing *se-tenant* pane of one 1 c., one 3 c., three 7 c. and 1 label (No. 604b) (2×3) .. .. 5·50
This exists with or without a black sealing strip inside the cover.

1971 (30 June). *Green and buff cover, 82×47 mm, as Type B 9, but without border.*
SB74 $1 booklet containing *se-tenant* pane of four 1 c., four 3 c. and twelve 7 c. (No. 604a) (2×10) 14·00

1971 (Aug). *Booklet No. SB73 with label affixed giving the new contents. Sold as an experiment in Toronto for 50 c.*
SB75 50 c. booklet. Contents as No. SB73, but containing two panes .. .. 11·00
The experiment was later continued by the use of machines which issued two 25 c. booklets for 50 c.

1971 (30 Dec). *Grey on cream cover, 70×48 mm, as Type B 9, but without border.*
SB76 25 c. booklet containing *se-tenant* pane of three 1 c., one 6 c. and two 8 c. (No. 604c) (2×3) 2·00
    q. With fluorescent bands (No. 604qc) .. 5·00

1971 (30 Dec). *Grey on cream cover, 77×48 mm, as Type B 9, but without border.*
SB77 $1 booklet containing *se-tenant* pane of six 1 c., one 6 c. and eleven 8 c. (No. 604d) (2×9) 7·50
    q. With fluorescent bands (No. 604qd) .. 7·00

B 11

1972 (Mar). *As No. SB76, but with brown on cream illustrated covers as Type B 11. Ten different designs showing Mail Transport:*
(a) Post Office, 1816   (b) Stage Coach, c 1820
(c) Paddle Steamer, 1855   (d) Rural postman, c 1900
(e) Motor car, 1910   (f) Ford Model "T", 1914
(g) Curtis "JN4", 1918   (h) Mail truck, 1921
(i) Motorcycle, 1923   (j) Horse-drawn mail wagon, 1926
SB78 25 c. booklet. Contents as No. SB76 (any cover) 2·00
    q. With fluorescent bands .. .. 2·50
    Set of 10 different cover designs .. 18·00
    Set of 10 different cover designs (fluorescent bands on stamps) .. .. 22·00

1972 (Aug). *Ten cover designs as No. SB78, but in blue on cream.*
SB79 50 c. booklet (any cover) containing *se-tenant* pane of one 6 c., four 1 c. and five 8 c. (No. 604e) (2×5) .. .. 4·50
    q. With fluorescent bands (No. 604qe) .. 4·50
    Set of 10 different cover designs .. 42·00
    Set of 10 different cover designs (fluorescent bands on stamps) .. .. 42·00
This exists with black or white sealing strip inside the cover.

1974 (10 Apr). *Red on cream covers as Type B 11. Ten different designs showing aircraft:*
(a) Gibson "Twin-plane"   (f) Fokker "Super Universal"
(b) Burgess Dunne seaplane   (g) "Mosquito"
(c) Nieuport "Scout"   (h) "Stranraer" flying-boat
(d) Curtiss "HS-2L"   (i) "CF-100 Canuck"
(e) Junkers "W-34"   (j) "Argus"
SB80 25 c. booklet (any cover) containing *se-tenant* pane of three 1 c., one 6 c. and two 8 c. (No. 693a) (3×2) 65
    Set of 10 different cover designs .. 6·00

B 12

1975 (17 Jan). *Violet on cream cover as Type B 12.*
SB81 $1 booklet containing *se-tenant* pane of six 1 c., one 6 c. and eleven 8 c. (No. 693b) (9×2) 2·25

1976 (1 Sept). *Violet on cream cover. Designs as No. SB80.*
SB82 50 c. booklet (any cover) containing *se-tenant* pane of two 1 c., four 2 c. and four 10 c. (No. 693c) (5×2) .. .. 1·50
    Set of 10 different cover designs .. 14·00

1977 (1 Nov). *Brown on cream covers, similar to Type B 11, but vert. Ten different designs showing flowers or trees:*
(a) Bottle Gentian   (g) Trembling Aspen
(b) Western Columbine   (h) Douglas Fir
(c) Canada Lily   (i) Sugar Maple
(d) Hepatica   (j) Rose, Thistle, Shamrock,
(e) Shooting Star   Lily and Maple leaf
(f) Lady's Slipper

SB83 50 c. booklet (*any cover*) containing *se-tenant*
pane of two 1 c. and four 12 c. (No. 862a)
(3×2) .. .. 2·75
Set of 10 different cover designs .. 25·00

1978 (17 May). *Green on cream covers. Designs as No. SB83.*
SB84 50 c. booklet (*any cover*) containing *se-tenant*
pane of four 2 c., three 14 c. and 1 label (No.
863a) (4×2) .. .. .. 3·25
Set of 10 different cover designs .. 30·00

B 13

1978 (13 Nov). *Black on cream covers as Type B 13. Five
different designs showing postcode publicity cartoons:*
  (a) Talking post box   (d) Letter running to post
  (b) Woman throwing letter   box
     to man   (e) Womam with letter and
  (c) Running letters   laughing post box
SB85 $3.50, booklet (*any cover*) containing pane of
twenty-five 14 c. and 2 labels (No. 868ab)
(9×3) .. .. .. 11·00
Set of 5 different cover designs .. 50·00

1979 (28 Mar). *Blue on cream covers. Designs as No. SB83.*
SB86 50 c. booklet (*any cover*) containing *se-tenant*
pane of one 1 c., three 5 c. and two 17 c. (No.
870a) (3×2) .. .. .. 2·50
Set of 10 different cover designs .. 23·00

1979 (3 July)–**81**. *Violet on cream covers. Designs as No. SB85.*
SB87 $4.25, booklet (*any cover*) containing pane of
twenty-five 17 c. and 2 labels (No. 869ab)
(9×3) (cover without wavy lines) .. 11·00
Set of 5 different cover designs .. 50·00
SB88 $4.25, booklet (*any cover*) containing No. 869ab
(horizontal wavy lines across cover) (4.2.81) 12·00
Set of 5 different cover designs .. 55·00

CANADA   Postage
    Postes

British Columbia/Colombie Britannique

B 14

1982 (1 Mar). *Black on cream covers as Type B 14. Ten
different designs showing provincial legislature buildings:*
  (a) Victoria, British   (e) Quebec
     Columbia   (f) Edmonton, Alberta
  (b) Fredericton, New   (g) Toronto, Ontario
     Brunswick   (h) Regina, Saskatchewan
  (c) Halifax, Nova Scotia   (i) Winnipeg, Manitoba
  (d) Charlottetown, Prince   (j) St. John's, Newfoundland
     Edward Island
SB89 50 c. booklet (*any cover*) containing *se-tenant*
pane of two 5 c., one 10 c., one 30 c. and 2
labels (No. 1033a) (3×2) .. .. 2·50
  a. Containing pane No. 1033ab .. .. 2·75
  b. Containing pane No. 1033ba .. .. 7·50
  c. Containing pane No. 1033bb .. .. 7·50
Set of 10 different cover designs (No. SB89) 22·00

CANADA   Postage
    Postes

Parliament Buildings/Hôtel du gouvernement

B 15 Parliament Buildings, Ottawa

1982 (30 June). *Black on cream cover as Type B 15.*
SB90 $6 booklet containing pane of twenty 30 c. and 1
label (No. 1032ab) (7×3) .. .. 15·00

1983 (15 Feb)–**85**. *Indian red on cream covers as Type B 14.
Designs as No. SB89.*
SB91 50 c. booklet (*any cover*) containing *se-tenant*
pane of two 5 c., one 8 c., one 32 c. and 2
labels (No. 1033c) (3×2) .. .. 3·00
Set of 10 different cover designs .. 27·00
  a. Indian red on surfaced yellow cover (3.4.85) 3·00
Set of 10 different cover designs .. 27·00

1983 (8 Apr). *Indian red on cream cover as Type B 15.*
SB92 $8 booklet containing pane of twenty-five 32 c.
and 2 labels (No. 1032bb) (9×3) .. 17·00

1983 (30 June). *Canada Day. Multicoloured cover, 100×78
mm, showing location map of various forts.*
SB93 $3.20, booklet containing *se-tenant* pane of ten
32 c. (No. 1090a) (5×2) .. .. 5·00

1984 (15 Feb). *Cover as Type B 15, but additionally inscribed
"1984" below "POSTES".*
SB94 $8 booklet containing pane of twenty-five 32 c.
and 2 labels (No. 1032bd) (9×3) .. 21·00

1985 (21 June). *Reddish brown on grey-brown covers similar
to Type B 14. Ten different designs showing architectural or
ornamental details from Parliament Buildings, Ottawa:*
  (a) Clock from Peace Tower
  (b) Library entrance
  (c) Gargoyle from Peace Tower
  (d) Indian mask sculpture
  (e) Stone carving at Memorial Chamber entrance
  (f) Door to House of Commons
  (g) Stone ornament at House of Commons main entrance
  (h) Carved head, Senate Chamber
  (i) Windows, Centre Block
  (j) Window and war memorial, Peace Tower
SB95 50 c. booklet (*any cover*) containing *se-tenant*
pane of three 2 c., two 5 c. and one 34 c.
(No. 1148a) (2×3) .. .. 2·25
Set of 10 different cover designs .. 20·00
  a. "R" on bottom left-hand corner of back cover 2·25
Set of 10 different cover designs .. 20·00

1985 (28 June). *Canada Day. Black, pale brown and pale
grey-brown cover, 100×78 mm, showing location map of
various forts.*
SB96 $3.40, booklet containing *se-tenant* pane of ten
34 c. (No. 1163a) (5×2) .. .. 4·50

Parliament Buildings   Hôtel du gouvernement

B 16 Parliament Buildings, Ottawa
(*Illustration reduced. Actual size 120×70 mm*)

1985 (1 Aug)–**86**. *White on agate cover as Type B 16.*
SB97 $8.50, booklet containing pane of twenty-five
34 c. (No. 1155a) (5×5) .. .. 11·50
  a. Containing pane No. 1155ba (4.7.86) .. 26·00

CHRISTMAS STAMP   TIMBRES DE NOËL
VALUE PACK   PAQUET ÉCONOMIQUE

B 17
(*Illustration reduced. Actual size 121×61 mm*)

1985 (23 Oct). *Christmas. Rosine and emerald cover as Type
B 17.*
SB98 $3.20, booklet containing pane of ten 32 c. (No.
1181a) (5×2) .. .. .. 6·50

C'EST FACILE, IL SUFFIT DE SUIVRE LES TROIS ÉTAPES SUIVANTES.

B 18
(*Illustration reduced. Actual size 150×72 mm*)

1986 (29 Oct). *Christmas. Black and brown-red cover as
Type B 18.*
SB99 $2.90, booklet containing pane of ten 29 c. (No.
1218a) (1×10) .. .. .. 6·50
  a. Containing pane No. 1218ba .. .. 50·00

1987 (30 Mar). *Ten cover designs as No. SB95 but in blackish
olive on grey-brown.*
SB100 50 c. booklet (*any cover*) containing *se-tenant*
pane of two 1 c., two 6 c., one 36 c. and 1
label (No. 1147a) (2×3) .. .. 5·00
Set of 10 different cover designs .. 45·00
  a. Containing pane No. 1147ba (1.10.87) .. 4·50
Set of 10 different cover designs .. 40·00

1987 (30 Mar). *Yellow-orange on agate cover similar to Type
B 16, but 48×74 mm.*
SB101 $3.60, booklet containing pane of ten 36 c. (No.
1156ba) (2×5) .. .. .. 10·00

1987 (19 May). *Yellow-orange on agate cover as Type B 16.*
SB102 $9 booklet containing pane of twenty-five 36 c.
(No. 1156bb) (5×5) .. .. .. 22·00

1987 (2 Nov). *Christmas. Christmas Plants. Black and
magenta cover as Type B 18, but 148×80 mm.*
SB103 $3.10, booklet containing pane of ten 31 c. (No.
1254a) (2×5) .. .. .. 5·00

STAMP PACK
10 X 37¢ STAMPS $3.70

CANADA POST
CORPORATION
Our commitment:
better service for you.

B 19

1988 (5 Jan). *White and black on bright green cover as Type
B 19.*
SB104 $3.70, booklet (49×73 mm) containing pane of
ten 37 c. (No. 1157ab) (2×5) .. .. 12·00
SB105 $9.25, booklet (120×73 mm) containing pane of
twenty-five 37 c. (No. 1157ae) (5×5) .. 27·00

1988 (15 Jan). *Covers as Type B 19, but inscribed "LUNCH
SAVER".*
SB106 $3.70, booklet (49×73 mm) containing pane of
ten 37 c. (No. 1157ab) (2×5) .. .. 12·00
SB107 $9.25, booklet (120×73 mm) containing pane of
twenty-five 37 c. (No. 1157ae) (5×5) .. 27·00

1988 (3 Feb). *Deep blue on grey-brown covers as Type B 14.
Ten different designs as No. SB95.*
SB108 50 c. booklet (*any cover*) containing *se-tenant*
pane of one 1 c., two 6 c., one 37 c. and 2
labels (No. 1147bb) (2×3) .. .. 2·25
Set of 10 different cover designs .. 20·00

1988 (27 Oct). *Christmas. Icons. Multicoloured cover as Type
B 18, but 150×80 mm, showing stamp illustration on the
front.*
SB109 $3.20, booklet containing pane of ten 32 c. (No.
1308a) (2×5) .. .. .. 3·50

B 20   **B 21**
(*Illustrations reduced. Actual size 79×152 mm*)

1988 (29 Dec)–**89**. *Multicoloured stamps on bright scarlet and
violet-blue covers (Type B 20) or on scarlet with white inscr
(Type B 21).*
SB110 $2.20, booklet containing pane of five 44 c. and
1 label (No. 1269ab) (2×3) (18.1.89) .. 5·00
  a. Cover Type B 21 (17.3.89) .. .. 5·00
SB111 $3.80, booklet containing pane of ten 38 c. and
2 labels (No. 1157ca) (3×4) .. .. 5·00
  a. Cover Type B 21 (17.3.89) .. .. 5·00
SB112 $3.80, booklet containing pane of ten 38 c. and
2 labels (No. 1162bd) (3×4) .. .. 4·50
  a. Cover Type B 21 (17.3.89) .. .. 4·50
SB113 $3.80, booklet containing pane of five 76 c. and
1 label (No. 1275ab) (2×3) (18.1.89) .. 8·50
  a. Cover Type B 21 (17.3.89) .. .. 8·50

SB114 $9.50, booklet containing pane of twenty-five
  38 c. and 2 labels (No. 1157cb) (3×9) .. 12·00
  a. Cover Type B 21 (17.3.89) .. .. .. 12·00
  Booklet Nos. SB110/14 each exist with either "Lunch Savers"
or "Would it be more convenient" advertisement on the reverse.
  Booklet Nos. SB110a/14a also exist with "Your "Rush"
Connection" advertisement on the reverse.

1989 (18 Jan). *Brown-purple on grey-brown covers as Type
B 14. Ten different designs as No. SB95.*
SB115 50 c. booklet (*any cover*) containing *se-tenant*
  pane of three 2 c., one 6 c., one 38 c. and 1
  label (No. 1148ba) (2×3) .. .. 1·90
  Set of 10 different cover designs .. 17·00

B 22
(Illustration reduced. Actual size 85 × 155 mm)

1989 (30 June). *Multicoloured cover as Type B 22.*
SB116 $5 booklet containing pane of twelve self-
  adhesive 38 c. (No. 1328ea) (6×2) .. 10·00
  Two types of cover exist for No. SB116 with one being the
mirror image of the other.

1989 (26 Oct). *Christmas. Paintings of Winter Landscapes.
Multicoloured covers as Type B 21.*
SB117 $2.20, booklet containing pane of five 44 c. and 1
  label (No. 1344a) (2×3) (*cover 60×155 mm*) 13·00
SB118 $3.30, booklet containing pane of ten 33 c. (No.
  1342a) (2×5) (80×155 mm) .. 9·00
SB119 $3.80, booklet containing pane of ten 38 c. (No.
  1343ab) (5×2) (80×155 mm) .. 32·00
SB120 $3.80, booklet containing pane of five 76 c. and 1
  label (No. 1345a) (2×3) (60×155 mm) .. 22·00

1989 (28 Dec). *Multicoloured covers as Type B 21.*
SB121 $3.90, booklet containing pane of ten 39 c. and 2
  labels (No. 1354a) (4×3) .. .. 8·00
SB122 $9.75, booklet containing pane of twenty-five
  39 c. and 2 labels (No. 1354b) (9×3) .. 17·00

B 23 Park Corner, Prince Edward Island

1990 (12 Jan). *Multicoloured cover as Type B 23.*
SB123 50 c. booklet containing *se-tenant* pane of one
  1 c., two 5 c. and one 39 c. (No. 1350a)
  (2×2) (*p* 13½×14) .. .. 1·40
  a. Containing pane No. 1350ba (*p* 12½×13) 35·00

1990 (12 Jan). *Multicoloured cover as Type B 21.*
SB124 $2.25, booklet containing pane of five 45 c. and 1
  label (No. 1270ab) (2×3) .. 7·00
SB125 $3.90, booklet containing pane of ten 39 c. and 2
  labels (No. 1162cb) (3×4) .. 13·00
SB126 $3.90, booklet containing pane of five 78 c. and 1
  label (No. 1276ab) (2×3) .. .. 9·00

1990 (8 Feb). *Multicoloured cover as Type B 22 showing
wheatfield.*
SB127 $5 booklet containing pane of twelve self-
  adhesive 39 c. (No. 1328ba) (2×6) .. 11·00
  Two types of cover exist for No. SB127 with one being the
mirror image of the other.

B 24
(Illustration reduced. Actual size 170 × 100 mm)

1990 (3 May). *"Moving the Mail". Multicoloured cover as Type
B 24. Booklet contains text and illustrations on labels attached
to the panes and on interleaving pages. Stitched.*
SB128 $9.75, booklet containing two panes of eight
  39 c. (No. 1382a) (2×4) and one pane of nine
  39 c. (No. 1382b) (3×4) .. .. 18·00

1990 (25 Oct). *Christmas. Native Art. Multicoloured covers as
Type B 21.*
SB129 $2.25, booklet containing pane of five 45 c. (No.
  1407a) (2×3) (*cover 60×155 mm*) .. 4·00
SB130 $3.40, booklet containing pane of ten 34 c. (No.
  1405a) (2×5) (80×155 mm) .. 4·00
SB131 $3.90, booklet containing pane of ten 39 c. (No.
  1406a) (2×5) (60×155 mm) .. 7·00
SB132 $3.90, booklet containing pane of five 78 c. (No.
  1408a) (2×3) (60×155 mm) .. 7·00

1990 (28 Dec). *Multicoloured cover as Type B 23, but showing
Point Atkinson, British Columbia.*
SB133 50 c. booklet containing *se-tenant* pane of two
  1 c., one 5 c. and one 40 c. (No. 1350c) (2×2) 2·00
  The face value of No. SB133 included 3 c. Goods and Service
Tax.

1990 (28 Dec). *Covers as Type B 21 showing multicoloured
stamps on scarlet background with white inscriptions.*
SB134 $2.30, booklet containing pane of five 46 c. and
  1 label (No. 1270cc) (2×3) .. 5·00
SB135 $4 booklet containing pane of ten 40 c. and 2
  labels (No. 1162da) (3×4) .. 8·00
SB136 $4 booklet containing pane of five 80 c. and 1
  label (No. 1276cc) (2×3) .. 8·00
SB137 $4 booklet containing pane of ten 40 c. and 2
  labels (No. 1355a) (4×3) .. 8·00
SB138 $10 booklet containing pane of twenty-five 40 c.
  and 2 labels (No. 1355b) (9×3) .. 18·00

1991 (11 Jan). *Multicoloured cover as Type B 22, but showing
coastal scene.*
SB139 $5.25, booklet containing pane of twelve self-
  adhesive 40 c. (No. 1328ca) (2×6) .. 11·00
  Two types of cover exist for No. SB139 with one being the
mirror image of the other.

B 25 *(Illustration reduced.*   B 26 *(Illustration*
Actual size 80×125 mm)   *reduced. Actual size*
                             64×156 mm)

1991 (22 May). *Public Gardens. Multicoloured cover as Type
B 25.*
SB140 $4 booklet containing *se-tenant* pane of ten 40 c.
  (No. 1422a) (5×2) .. .. .. 5·50

1991 (20 Aug). *Canadian Rivers (1st series). Multicoloured
cover as Type B 26.*
SB141 $4 booklet containing *se-tenant* pane of ten 40 c.
  (No. 1432a) (10×1) .. .. 7·50

B 27
(Illustration reduced. Actual size 150×81 mm)

1991 (16 Oct). *150th Anniv of Queen's University. Multicoloured cover as Type B 27. Booklet contains text and
illustrations on labels attached to the pane and on interleaving
pages. Stitched.*
SB142 $4 booklet containing pane of ten 40 c. and 2
  labels (No. 1449a) (4×3) .. .. 8·00

B 28 Christmas Tree   B 29

1991 (23 Oct). *Christmas. Multicoloured covers as Type B 28.*
SB143 $2.30, booklet containing pane of five 46 c. and
  1 label (No. 1452a) (2×3) .. 4·50
SB144 $3.50, booklet containing pane of ten 35 c. (No.
  1450a) (2×5) (punch bowl and candles cover
  design, 80×155 mm) .. 8·00
SB145 $4 booklet containing pane of ten 80 c. (No.
  1451a) (2×5) (Christmas stocking cover
  design) .. .. 9·00
SB146 $4 booklet containing pane of five 80 c. and 1
  label (No. 1453a) (2×3) (Christmas presents
  cover design) .. .. .. 9·00

1991 (27 Dec). *Covers as Type B 29 showing multicoloured
stamps on scarlet background with Olympic logo in black.*
SB147 $2.40, booklet containing pane of five 48 c. and
  1 label (No. 1467ab) (2×3) .. 6·00
SB148 $4.20, booklet containing pane of five 84 c. and
  1 label (No. 1475ab) (2×3) .. 9·00
SB149 $4.20, booklet containing pane of ten 42 c. (No.
  1162ea) (2×5) .. .. .. 9·00
SB150 $4.20, booklet containing pane of ten 42 c. (No.
  1356a) (2×5) .. .. .. 9·00
SB151 $10.50, booklet containing pane of twenty-five
  42 c. and 2 labels (No. 1356b) (3×9) .. 17·00
SB152 $21 booklet containing pane of fifty 42 c. and 2
  labels (No. 1356c) (4×13) .. 50·00
  The cover of booklet No. SB152 is made up of two $10.50
covers rouletted down the centre. It was issued in connection
with a Canada Post special offer of a $1 coupon towards the cost
of its purchase.

1992 (28 Jan). *Multicoloured cover as Type B 22, but showing
mountain peaks.*
SB153 $5.25, booklet containing pane of twelve self-
  adhesive 42 c. stamps (No. 1328da) (2×6) 12·00
  Two types of cover exist for No. SB153 with one being the
mirror image of the other.

B 30 Olympic Flame
(Illustration reduced. Actual size 83×151 mm)

1992 (7 Feb). *Winter Olympic Games, Albertville. Multicoloured cover as Type B 30.*
SB154 $4.20, booklet containing *se-tenant* pane of ten
  42 c. (No. 1482a) (5×2) .. 7·00
  Two types of cover exist for No. SB154 with one being the
mirror image of the other.

1992 (22 Apr). *Canadian Rivers (2nd series). Multicoloured
vert cover as Type B 26.*
SB155 $4.20, booklet containing *se-tenant* pane of ten
  42 c. (No. 1492a) (5×2) .. 8·50

1992 (15 June). *Olympic Games, Barcelona. Multicoloured
cover as Type B 30, but showing Olympic flag.*
SB156 $4.20, booklet containing *se-tenant* pane of ten
  42 c. (No. 1498a) (5×2) .. 9·00
  Two types of cover exist for No. SB156 with one being the
mirror image of the other.

B 31 Prospecting Equipment
(Illustration reduced. Actual size 90×151 mm)

1992 (21 Sept). *150th Anniv of Geological Survey of Canada. Multicoloured cover as Type* B **31**.
SB157 $4.20, booklet containing *se-tenant* pane of ten
     42 c. (No. 1509a) (5×2) .. .. .. 10·00

B 32 Hockey Players
(Illustration reduced. Actual size 171×105 mm)

1992 (9 Oct). *75th Anniv of National Ice Hockey League. Multicoloured cover as Type* B **32**. *Booklet contains text and illustrations on labels attached to the pane and on interleaving pages. Stitched.*
SB158 $10.50, booklet containing twenty-five 42 c.
     stamps in two panes of 8 and 1 label and one
     pane of 9 (Nos. 1516a, 1517a, 1518a) (each
     3×3) .. .. 19·00

B 33 Hand Bell

1992 (13 Nov). *Christmas. Multicoloured covers as Type* B **33**.
SB159 $2.40, booklet containing pane of five 48 c. and
     1 label (No. 1527a) (2×3) .. .. 5·00
SB160 $3.70, booklet containing pane of ten 37 c. (No.
     1525a) (2×5) (candle and cookies cover
     design, 80×156 mm) .. .. .. 8·00
SB161 $4.20, booklet containing pane of ten 42 c. (No.
     1526ab) (2×5) (hobby horse cover design) 8·00
SB162 $4.20, booklet containing pane of five 84 c. and
     1 label (No. 1528a) (2×3) (Christmas tree
     cover design) .. .. 8·00

1992 (30 Dec). *Multicoloured covers as Type* B **29**, *but without Olympic symbol at top right.*
SB163 $2.45, booklet containing pane of five 49 c. and
     1 label (No. 1468ba) (2×3) .. .. 6·00
SB164 $4.30, booklet containing pane of ten 43 c. (No.
     1162fa) (2×5) .. .. 9·00
SB165 $4.30, booklet containing pane of ten 43 c. (No.
     1357a) (2×5) .. .. 8·50
SB166 $4.30, booklet containing pane of five 86 c. and
     1 label (No. 1476ba) (2×3) .. .. 13·00
SB167 $10.75, booklet containing pane of twenty-five
     43 c. and 2 labels (No. 1357b) (3×9) .. 22·00

1993 (15 Feb). *Multicoloured cover as Type* B **22**, *but showing lake.*
SB168 $5.25, booklet containing pane of twelve
     self-adhesive 43 c. stamps (2×6) (No.
     1328ea) .. .. 9·00
   Two types of cover exist for No. SB168 with one being the mirror image of the other.

B 34 Hand-crafting
Techniques *(Illustration
reduced. Actual size
81×156 mm)*

B 35 Postcards and
Stamps *(Illustration
reduced. Actual size
60×155 mm)*

1993 (30 Apr). *Hand-crafted Textiles. Multicoloured cover as Type* B **34**.
SB169 $4.30, booklet containing *se-tenant* pane of ten
     43 c. (5×2) (No. 1534a) .. .. .. 8·00

1993 (14 June). *Historic Hotels. Multicoloured cover as Type* B **35**.
SB170 $4.30, booklet containing *se-tenant* pane of ten
     43 c. (5×2) (No. 1540a) .. .. .. 6·00

1993 (10 Aug). *Canadian Rivers (3rd series). Multicoloured vert cover as Type* B **26**.
SB171 $4.30, booklet containing *se-tenant* pane of ten
     43 c. (10×1) (No. 1558a) .. .. .. 6·00

B 36 Rabbit and Present

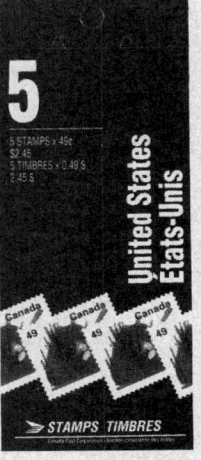

B 37

1993 (4 Nov). *Christmas. Multicoloured covers as Type* B **36**.
SB172 $2.45, booklet containing pane of five 49 c. and
     1 label (2×3) (No. 1574a) .. .. 5·00
SB173 $3.80, booklet containing pane of ten 38 c.
     (2×5) (No. 1572a) (wooden puppet cover
     design, 80×156 mm) .. .. .. 8·00
SB174 $4.30, booklet containing pane of ten 43 c.
     (2×5) (No. 1573a) (angel cover design) 9·00
SB175 $4.30, booklet containing pane of five 86 c. and
     1 label (2×3) (No. 1575a) (kangaroo cover
     design) .. .. 9·00

1994 (7 Jan–14 Nov). *Covers as Type* B **37**, *each showing multicoloured stamps in a continuous pattern on scarlet background.*
SB176 $2.45, booklet containing pane of five 49 c. and
     1 label (No. 1468a) (2×3) .. .. 6·00
SB177 $4.30, booklet containing pane of ten 43 c. (No.
     1162fa) (2×5) .. .. 9·00
SB178 $4.30, booklet containing pane of ten 43 c. (No.
     1357ca) (p 14½) (2×5) (18 Jan) .. 11·00
    a. Containing pane No. 1357a (p 13½×13)
     (14 Nov) .. .. 8·50
SB179 $4.30, booklet containing pane of five 86 c.
     (No. 1476a) and 1 label (2×3) .. 8·00
SB180 $10.75, booklet containing pane of twenty-five
     43 c. and 2 labels (No. 1357cb) (p 14½)
     (3×9) (18 Jan) .. .. 26·00
    a. Containing pane No. 1357b (p 13½×13)
     (14 Nov) .. .. 18·00

ALTERED CATALOGUE NUMBERS

Any Catalogue numbers altered from the last edition are shown as a list in the introductory pages.

B 38
*(Illustration reduced.
Actual size 106×157 mm)*

1994 (28 Jan). *Greetings. Multicoloured cover as Type* B **38**.
SB181 $4.50, booklet containing pane of ten self-
     adhesive 43 c. (No. 1580a) and 35 circular
     greetings labels .. .. 5·50

1994 (25 Feb)–**95**. *Covers as Type* B **37** *showing multicoloured stamps in a continuous pattern on scarlet backgrounds.*
SB182 $2.50, booklet containing pane of five 50 c. and 1
     label (No. 1469a) (p 13) (2×3) .. 5·00
    a. Containing pane No. 1469ba (p 14½×14)
     (27.3.95) .. .. 6·00
SB183 $4.40, booklet containing pane of five 88 c. and 1
     label (No. 1477a) (fluorescent frame) (p 13)
     (2×3) .. .. 8·00
    a. Containing pane No. 1477ba (three
     fluorescent bands) (p 13) (14.11.94) 9·00
    b. Containing pane No. 1477ca (three
     fluorescent bands) (p 14½×14) (27.3.95) .. 10·00

B 39 Images of T. Eaton Company Ltd
(Illustration reduced. Actual size 151×101 mm)

1994 (17 Mar). *125th Anniv of T. Eaton Company Ltd. Multicoloured cover as Type* B **39**. *Booklet containing text and illustrations on label attached to the pane and on interleaving pages. Stitched.*
SB184 $4.30, booklet containing ten 43 c. stamps and
     2 labels (No. 1583a) (6×2) .. .. 5·50

1994 (22 Apr). *Canadian Rivers (4th series). Multicoloured vert cover as Type* B **26**.
SB185 $4.30, booklet containing *se-tenant* pane of ten
     43 c. (No. 1584a) (2×5) .. .. 5·50

B 40 Carol Singer

1994 (3 Nov). *Christmas. Multicoloured covers as Type* B **40**.
SB186 $2.50, booklet containing pane of five 50 c. and
1 label (2×3) (No. 1619a) .. .. 4·25
SB187 $3.80, booklet containing pane of ten (38 c.)
(2×5) (No. 1617a) (chorister wearing ruff
cover design, 80×156 mm) .. .. .. 7·00
SB188 $4.30, booklet containing pane of ten 43 c. (2×5)
(No. 1618a) (pair of singers cover design) 8·00
SB189 $4.40, booklet containing pane of five 88 c. and
1 label (2×3) (No. 1620a) (singer in hat and
scarf cover design) .. .. 8·00

B **41** Fortress Gateway
(*Illustration reduced. Actual size*
96×157 *mm*)

1995 (5 May). *275th Anniv of Fortress of Louisbourg.*
Multicoloured cover as Type B **41**.
SB190 $4.30, booklet containing pane of ten (43 c.)
(5×2) (No. 1631a) .. .. 4·00

B **42** Player and Bunker   B **43** Fountain Pen
(*Illustration reduced.*   (*Illustration reduced.*
Actual size 52×156 *mm*)   *Actual size* 78×156 *mm*)

1995 (6 June). *Centenaries of Canadian Amateur Golf*
Championship and of the Royal Canadian Golf Association.
Multicoloured cover as Type B **42**.
SB191 $4.30, booklet containing *se-tenant* pane of ten
43 c. (5×2) (No. 1637a) .. .. 4·50

1995 (31 July–6 Oct). *Covers as Type* B **37**, *each showing*
multicoloured stamps in a continuous pattern on scarlet
background.
SB192 $2.60, booklet containing pane of five 52 c. and
1 label (No. 1470a) (*p* 13) (2×3) .. .. 2·50
a. Containing pane No. 1470ba (*p* 14½×14)
(6 Oct) .. .. 5·00
SB193 $4.50, booklet containing pane of ten 45 c. (No.
1162ga) (2×5) .. .. 4·50
SB194 $4.50, booklet containing pane of ten 45 c. (No.
1358a) (*p* 14½) (2×5) .. .. 7·00
a. Containing pane No. 1358ca (*p* 13½×13)
(6 Oct) .. .. 4·50
SB195 $4.50, booklet containing pane of five 90 c. and
1 label (No. 1478a) (*p* 13) (2×3) .. .. 4·50
a. Containing pane No. 1478ba (*p* 14½×14)
(6 Oct) .. .. 7·00
SB196 $11.25, booklet containing pane of twenty-five
45 c. and 2 labels (No. 1358b) (*p* 14½) (3×9) 14·00
a. Containing pane No. 1358cb (*p* 13½×13)
(6 Oct) .. .. 17·00
Nos. SB192a, SB194a, SB195a and SB196a, together with a
new printing of No. SB193 issued on the same date, show a
revised back cover layout including a customer service phone
number.

1995 (1 Sept). *Greetings. Multicoloured cover as Type* B **43**.
SB197 $4.70, booklet containing pane of ten self-
adhesive 45 c. (No. 1654a) and 15 circular
greetings labels .. .. 4·00

B **44** Aspects of Chiropractic
Healing (*Illustration reduced.*
Actual size 78×156 *mm*)

1995 (15 Sept). *Centenary of Chiropractic Healing in Canada.*
Multicoloured cover as Type B **44**.
SB198 $4.70, booklet containing pane of ten self-
adhesive 45 c. (No. 1654a) and 15 circular
commemorative labels .. .. 4·50

1995 (15 Sept). *50th Anniv of Arctic Institute of North*
America. Multicoloured cover as Type B **26**, *but showing Inuk*
woman and Arctic scene.
SB199 $4.50, booklet containing *se-tenant* pane of ten
45 c. (No. 1656a) (5×2) .. .. 7·00

B **45** Superman
(*Illustration reduced. Actual size*
105×169 *mm*)

1995 (2 Oct). *Comic Book Superheroes. Multicoloured cover as*
Type B **45**.
SB200 $4.50, booklet containing *se-tenant* pane of ten
45 c. (No. 1661a) (5×2) .. .. 4·75

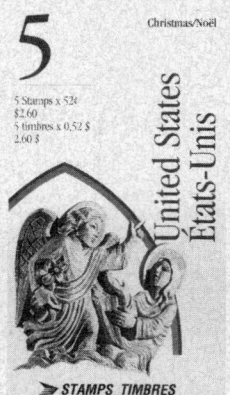

B **46** "The Annunciation"

1995 (2 Nov). *Christmas. Multicoloured covers as Type* B **46**.
SB201 $2.60, booklet containing pane of five 52 c. and
1 label (2×3) (No. 1669a) .. .. 4·50
SB202 $4 booklet containing pane of ten 40 c. (2×5)
(No. 1667a) (Sprig of holly cover design,
80×156 *mm*) .. .. 6·50
SB203 $4.50, booklet containing pane of ten 45 c. (2×5)
(No. 1668a) ("The Nativity" cover design) 7·50
SB204 $4.50, booklet containing pane of five 90 c. and
1 label (2×3) (No. 1670a) ("The Flight to
Egypt" cover design) .. .. 8·50

1996 (15 Jan). *Greetings. Multicoloured cover as Type* B **38**.
SB205 $4.70, booklet containing pane of ten self-
adhesive 45 c. (No. 1654ba) and 35 circular
greetings labels .. .. 5·50

B **47** Binary Codes and Globe
(*Illustration reduced. Actual size* 90×155 *mm*)

1996 (15 Feb). *High Technology Industries. Multicoloured*
cover as Type B **47**.
SB206 $5.40, booklet containing pane of twelve 45 c.
(No. 1677a) (2×6) .. .. 6·75

B **48** Ethel Catherwood
(*Illustration reduced. Actual*
size 95×155 *mm*)

1996 (8 July). *Canadian Olympic Gold Medal Winners. Multi-*
coloured cover as Type B **48**.
SB207 $4.50, booklet containing pane of ten 45 c. (No.
1691a) (5×2) .. .. 7·00

B **49** Father reading to Children
(*Illustration reduced. Actual size*
95×155 *mm*)

1996 (9 Sept). *Literacy Campaign. Multicoloured cover as Type*
B **49**.
SB208 $5 booklet containing pane of ten 45 + 5 c.
(5×2) (No. 1699a) .. .. 5·50

PRICES OF SETS

Set prices are given for many issues, generally
those containing three stamps or more. Definitive
sets include one of each value or major colour
change, but do not cover different perforations,
die types or minor shades. Where a choice is
possible the set prices are based on the cheapest
versions of the stamps included in the listings.

B 50 Canadian Authors
(Illustration reduced.
Actual size 80×155 mm)

1996 (10 Oct). *Canadian Authors. Multicoloured cover as Type* B 50.
SB209 $4.50, booklet containing pane of ten 45 c. (5×2)
(No. 1706a)   ..   ..   ..   5·25

B 51 Father Christmas

1996 (1 Nov). *Christmas. 50th Anniv of U.N.I.C.E.F. Multi-coloured covers as Type* B 51.
SB210 $2.60, booklet containing pane of five 52 c. and 1 label (2×3) (No. 1712ab) ..   ..   3·00
SB211 $4.50, booklet containing pane of ten 45 c. (2×5) (No. 1711a) (Child tobogganing design)   ..   4·75
SB212 $4.50, booklet containing pane of five 90 c. and 1 label (2×3) (No. 1713ab) (Couple ice-skating design)   ..   ..   ..   4·75

B 52 Blue Poppy

1997 (4 Apr). *"Quebec in Bloom" International Floral Festival. Multicoloured cover as Type* B 52.
SB213 $5.40, booklet containing pane of twelve 45 c. (6×2) (No. 1724a) ..   ..   ..   4·50

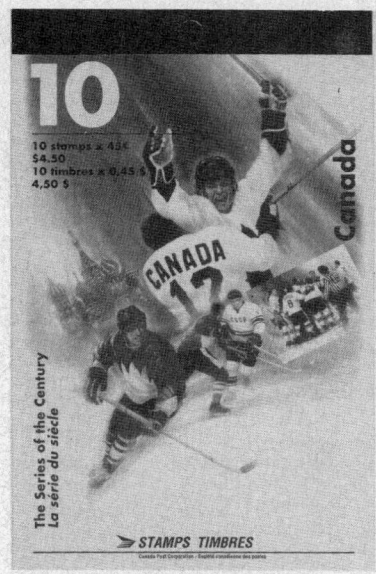

B 53 Paul Henderson celebrating

1997 (20 Sept). *25th Anniv of the Canada–U.S.S.R Ice Hockey Series. Multicoloured cover as Type* B 53.
SB214 $4.50, booklet containing pane of ten 45 c. (2×5) (No. 1746a)   ..   ..   ..   3·75

B 54 "The Holy Family"   **B 54a** Flags and Skyscrapers

1997 (3 Nov). *Christmas. Stained Glass Windows. Multi-coloured covers as Type* B 54.
SB215 $2.60, booklet containing pane of five 52 c. (No. 1764ab)   ..   ..   ..   2·50
SB216 $4.50, booklet containing pane of ten 45 c. (No. 1763ab) (cover showing "Regina SSi Rosarii")   4·25
SB217 $4.50, booklet containing pane of five 90 c. (No. 1765ab) (cover showing "Madonna and Child")   ..   ..   ..   4·25

1998 (2 Feb–July). *Covers as Type* B 37, *each showing multicoloured stamps in a continuous pattern on scarlet background.*
SB218 $4.50, booklet containing pane of 10 45 c. (5×2) (No. 1358da)   ..   ..   4·50
    a. Cover as Type B 54a (July)   ..   4·50
SB219 $13.50, booklet containing pane of 30 45 c. (two blocks of 15 (5×3) separated by vertical margin) (No. 1358db)   ..   13·00
    a. Cover as Type B 54a (July)   ..   13·00

PRICES OF SETS

Set prices are given for many issues, generally those containing three stamps or more. Definitive sets include one of each value or major colour change, but do not cover different perforations, die types or minor shades. Where a choice is possible the set prices are based on the cheapest versions of the stamps included in the listings.

B 55 Lady Amherst Fly

1998 (16 Apr). *Fishing Flies. Multicoloured cover as Type* B 55.
SB220 $5.40, booklet containing pane of twelve 45 c. (1×12) (No. 1784a)   ..   ..   6·00

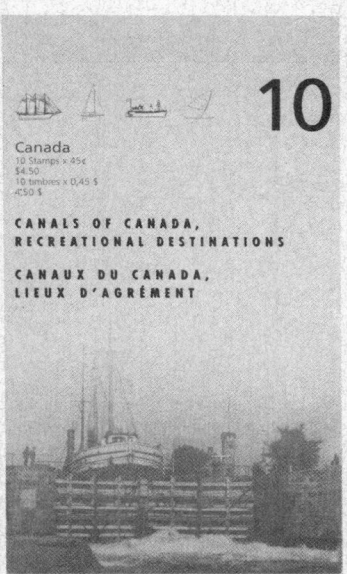

B 56 Ship in Canal Lock

1998 (17 June). *Canadian Canals. Multicoloured cover as Type* B 56.
SB221 $4.50, booklet containing pane of ten 45 c. and ten labels (No. 1795a) (10×2)   ..   8·00

B 57 "Joie Lacustre" (Paul-Emile Borduas)
(Illustration reduced. Actual size 130×115 mm)

1998 (7 Aug). *50th Anniv of Refus Global (manifesto of The Automatistes group of artists). Multicoloured cover as Type* B 57.
SB222 $3.15, booklet containing pane of seven self-adhesive 45 c. (No. 1814a)   ..   ..   4·50

B 58 Circus Scenes and VIA Rail Train
(Illustration reduced. Actual size 182×80 mm)

1998 (1 Oct). *Canadian Circus. Multicoloured cover as Type B* **58**.
SB223 $5.40, booklet containing *se-tenant* pane of twelve 45 c. (No. 1851a) (6×2)   ..   6·00

B 59 Adoring Angel   **B 60**

1998 (6 Nov). *Christmas. Statues of Angels. Multicoloured covers as Type B* **59**.
SB224 $2.60, booklet containing pane of five 52 c. and 1 label (2×3) (No. 1860a) (*p* 13×13½)   2·50
     a. Containing pane No. 1860ba (*p* 13)   2·50
SB225 $4.50, booklet containing pane of ten 45 c. (2×5) (No. 1859a) (*p* 13×13½) (cover showing Angel blowing trumpet)   4·00
     a. Containing pane No. 1859ba (*p* 13)   4·00
SB226 $4.50, booklet containing pane of five 90 c. and 1 label (2×3) (No. 1861a) (*p* 13×13½) (cover showing Angel at prayer)   ..   4·00
     a. Containing pane No. 1861ba (*p* 13)   4·00

1998 (28 Dec). *Multicoloured covers as Type B* **60**.
SB227 $4.60, booklet containing pane of ten 46 c. (2×5) (No. 1359a)   ..   4·00
SB228 $13.80, booklet containing pane of 30 self-adhesive 46 c. (3×10) (No. 1366a) (72×102 mm)   ..   ..   12·00

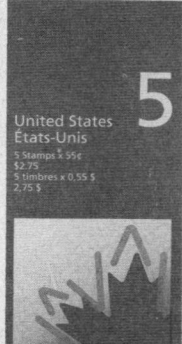

B 61

1998 (28 Dec). *Multicoloured covers as Type B* **61**.
SB229 $2.75, booklet containing pane of five 55 c. and 1 label (2×3) (No. 1836a)   ..   2·25
SB230 $4.75, booklet containing pane of five 95 c. and 1 label (2×3) (No. 1838a)   ..   3·75

COVER PRICES

Cover factors are quoted at the beginning of each country for most issues to 1945. An explanation of the system can be found on page x. The factors quoted do not, however, apply to philatelic covers.

B 62 Birds' Heads
(Illustration reduced. Actual size 110×157 mm)

1999 (24 Feb). *Birds (4th series). Multicoloured cover as Type B* **62**. *Self-adhesive.*
SB231 $5.52, booklet containing pane of 12 46 c. (No. 1869b)   ..   ..   5·50

B 63 *Platanthera psycodes*

1999 (27 Apr). *Orchids. Multicoloured cover as Type B* **63**.
SB232 $5.52, booklet containing *se-tenant* pane of twelve 46 c. (No. 1883a) (3×4)   ..   5·50

B 64 "Big Ben" (show jumper)

1999 (2 June). *Canadian Horses. Multicoloured cover as Type B* **64**.
SB233 $5.52, booklet containing pane of 12 self-adhesive 46 c. (No. 1907a)   ..   5·50

B 65 Kites

1999 (1 Oct). *Stamp Collecting Month. Kites. Multicoloured cover as Type B* **65**. *Self-adhesive.*
SB234 $3.68, booklet containing *se-tenant* pane of eight 46 c. (No. 1942a)   ..   3·00

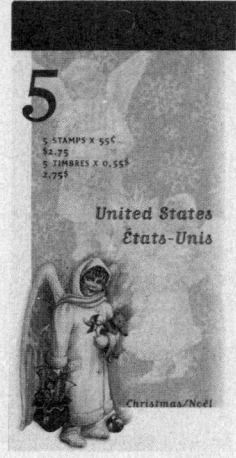

B 66 Angel with Toys

1999 (4 Nov). *Christmas. Victorian Angels. Multicoloured covers as Type B* **66**.
SB235 $2.75, booklet containing pane of five 55 c. and 1 label (2×3) (No. 1950a)   ..   2·50
SB236 $4.60, booklet containing pane of ten 46 c. (2×5) (No. 1949a) (cover showing Angel playing drum)   ..   3·75
SB237 $4.75, booklet containing pane of five 95 c. and 1 label (2×3) (No. 1951a) (cover showing Angel with star)   ..   4·00

REGISTRATION STAMPS

R 1

(Eng and recess – printed British-American Bank Note Co, Montreal and Ottawa)

1875 (15 Nov)–**92.** *White wove paper.* (*a*) *P* 12 (*or slightly under*).

R 1	R 1	2 c. orange		..	60·00	1·00
R 2		2 c. orange-red (1889)	..	..	70·00	6·00
R 3		2 c. vermilion		..	75·00	7·50
		a. Imperf (pair)	..	..	† £2500	
R 4		2 c. rose-carmine (1888)	..	..	£150	55·00
R 5		5 c. yellow-green (1878)	..	..	£100	1·50
R 6		5 c. deep green		..	80·00	1·25
		a. Imperf (pair)	..	..	£650	
R 7		5 c. blue-green (1888)	..	..	90·00	1·50
R 7a		5 c. dull sea-green (1892)	..	..	£130	3·25
R 8		8 c. bright blue	..	..	£325	£225
R 9		8 c. dull blue	..	..	£300	£200

(*b*) *P* 12 × 11½ or 12 × 11¾

R10	R 1	2 c. orange	..	£300	60·00
R11		5 c. green (*shades*)	..	£750	£150

SPECIAL DELIVERY STAMPS

PRINTERS. The following Special Delivery and Postage Due Stamps were recess-printed by the American Bank Note Co (to 1928), the British American Bank Note Co (to 1934), and the Canadian Bank Note Co (1935 onwards).

S 1

1898–1920. *P* 12.

S1	S 1	10 c. blue-green (28.6.98)	..	..	80·00	7·00
S2		10 c. deep green (12.13)	..	..	45·00	6·00
S3		10 c. yellowish green (8.20)	..	..	55·00	5·50

The differences between Types I and II (figures "10" with and without shading) formerly illustrated were due to wear of the plate. There was only one die.

S 2   S 3 Mail-carrying, 1867 and 1927

1922 (21 Aug). *P* 12.

S4	S 2	20 c. carmine-red	..	35·00	6·00

No. S4 exists in two slightly different sizes due to the use of "wet" or "dry" printing processes. See note below No. 195.

1927 (29 June). *60th Anniversary of Confederation. P* 12.

S5	S 3	20 c. orange	..	11·00	10·00

No. S5 exists imperforate, imperf×perf or perf×imperf (*Price, in each instance, £130 per pair, un*).

S 4

1930 (2 Sept). *P* 11.

S6	S 4	20 c. brown-red	..	42·00	7·00

1932 (24 Dec). *Type as* S 4, *but inscr* "CENTS" *in place of* "TWENTY CENTS". *P* 11.

S7	20 c. brown-red	..	45·00	13·00

No. S7 exists imperforate (*Price per pair £325, un*).

S 5 Allegory of Progress

(Des A. Foringer)

1935 (1 June). *P* 12.

S8	S 5	20 c. scarlet	..	3·50	2·75

No. S8 exists imperforate (*Price per pair £350, un*).

S 6 Canadian Coat of Arms

1938–39. *P* 12.

S 9	S 6	10 c. green (1.4.39)	..	..	18·00	3·00
S10		20 c. scarlet (15.6.38)	..	..	40·00	23·00

Nos. S9/10 exist imperforate (*Price £375, un, for each pair*).

≡10   10≡

(S 7)

1939 (1 Mar). *Surch with Type* S 7.

S11	S 6	10 c. on 20 c. scarlet	..	9·00	8·00

S 8 Coat of Arms and Flags

S 9 Lockheed L.18 Lodestar

1942 (1 July)–**1943.** *War Effort. P* 12. (*a*) *Postage.*

S12	S 8	10 c. green	..	4·50	30

(*b*) *Air*

S13	S 9	16 c. ultramarine	..	5·00	45
S14		17 c. ultramarine (1.4.43)	..	4·00	55

Nos. S12/14 exist imperforate (*Prices per un pair* 10 c. £350, 16 c. £400, 17 c. £400)

S 10 Arms of Canada and Peace Symbols

S 11 Canadair DC-4M North Star

1946 (16 Sept–5 Dec). *P* 12. (*a*) *Postage*

S15	S 10	10 c. green	..	2·75	30

(*b*) *Air.* (i) *Circumflex accent in* "EXPRÈS"

S16	S 11	17 c. ultramarine	4·50	3·50

(ii) *Grave accent in* "EXPRÈS"

S17	S 11	17 c. ultramarine (5.12.46)	..	5·00	4·00

POSTAGE DUE STAMPS

PRINTERS. See note under "Special Delivery Stamps".

D 1   D 2

1906 (1 July)–**28.** *P* 12.

D1	D 1	1 c. dull violet		..	8·50	2·75
D2		1 c. red violet (1916)	..	..	10·00	3·50
		a. Thin paper (10.24)	..	..	15·00	18·00
D3		2 c. dull violet	..	..	18·00	1·00
D4		2 c. red-violet (1917)	..	..	17·00	1·25
		a. Thin paper (10.24)	..	..	27·00	20·00
D5		4 c. violet (3.7.28)	..	..	45·00	50·00
D6		5 c. dull violet	..	..	24·00	3·00
D7		5 c. red-violet (1917)	..	..	24·00	3·00
		a. Thin paper (10.24)	..	..	17·00	26·00
D8		10 c. violet (3.7.28)	..	..	32·00	16·00
D1/8				*Set of 5*	£110	65·00

The 1 c., 2 c. and 5 c. values exist imperforate (*Price £250 for each un pair*).

Printings up to October 1924 used the "wet" method, those from mid 1925 onwards the "dry". For details of the differences between these two methods, see above No. 196.

1930–2. *P* 11.

D 9	D 2	1 c. bright violet (14.7.30)	..		8·50	10·00
D10		2 c. bright violet (21.8.30)	..		7·50	1·90
D11		4 c. bright violet (14.10.30)	..		15·00	6·50
D12		5 c. bright violet (12.12.31)	..		16·00	25·00
D13		10 c. bright violet (24.8.32)	..		65·00	26·00
D9/13				*Set of 5*	£100	60·00

Nos. D9/11 and D13 exist imperforate, No. D13 also exists imperf×perf (*Price for vertical pair £500, un*).

D 3   D 4   D 5

1933–4. *P* 11.

D14	D 3	1 c. violet (5.5.34)	..	..	9·50	14·00
D15		2 c. violet (20.12.33)	..	..	7·00	4·50
D16		4 c. violet (12.12.33)	..	..	12·00	14·00
D17		10 c. violet (20.12.33)	..	..	24·00	27·00
D14/17				*Set of 4*	48·00	55·00

No. D14 exists imperforate (*Price per pair £275, un*).

1935–65. *P* 12.

D18	D 4	1 c. violet (14.10.35)	..	..	70	10
D19		2 c. violet (9.9.35)	..	..	70	10
D20		3 c. violet (4.65)	..	..	3·75	5·00
D21		4 c. violet (2.7.35)	..	..	1·50	10
D22		5 c. violet (12.48)	..	..	3·00	90
D23		6 c. violet (1957)	..	..	1·50	3·00
D24		10 c. violet (16.9.35)	..	..	60	10
D18/24				*Set of 7*	10·50	8·25

The 1 c., 2 c., 4 c. and 10 c. exist imperforate (*Price £150 for each un pair*).

1967–78. *Litho. P* 12½ × 12 (20 c., 24 c., 50 c.) or 12 (*others*).

(*a*) *Size* 20 × 17½ mm

D25	D 5	1 c. scarlet (3.67)	..	..	1·75	3·75
D26		2 c. scarlet (3.67)	..	..	1·00	80
D27		3 c. scarlet (3.67)	..	..	1·00	4·00
D28		4 c. scarlet (2.67)	..	..	2·75	1·25
D29		5 c. scarlet (3.67)	..	..	4·25	3·75
D30		6 c. scarlet (2.67)	..	..	1·60	3·75
D31		10 c. scarlet (1.67)	..	..	30	45
D25/31				*Set of 7*	13·00	18·00

(*b*) *Size* 19½ × 16 mm

D32	D 5	1 c. scarlet (12.70)	..	..	30	30
		a. Perf 12½×12 (11.77)	..	..	15	90
D33		2 c. scarlet (1972)	..	..	75	2·00
D34		3 c. scarlet (1.74)	..	..	2·50	3·00
D35		4 c. scarlet (4.69)	..	..	30	40
		a. Printed on the gummed side		..	£325	
		b. Perf 12½×12 (11.77)	..	..	30	90
D36		5 c. scarlet (2.69)	..	..	22·00	35·00
		a. Perf 12½×12 (11.77)	..	..	30	1·50
D37		6 c. scarlet (1972)	..	..	2·75	3·50
D38		8 c. scarlet (1.69)	..	..	30	45
		a. Perf 12½×12 (28.6.78)	..	..	75	1·40
D39		10 c. scarlet (4.69)	..	..	30	45
		a. Perf 12½×12 (9.77)	..	..	40	50
D40		12 c. scarlet (1.69)	..	..	40	50
		a. Perf 12½×12 (9.77)	..	..	80	1·50
D41		16 c. scarlet (1.74)	..	..	90	3·00
D42		20 c. scarlet (10.77)	..	..	40	1·25
D43		24 c. scarlet (10.77)	..	..	40	1·75
D44		50 c. scarlet (10.77)	..	..	60	2·25
D32a/44				*Set of 13*	8·50	18·00

There are no records of dates of issue of the above but supplies were distributed to depots in the months indicated.

Both white and ordinary papers have been used for Nos. D32/41.

The last Postage Due stamps were withdrawn on 30 June 1982.

MINIMUM PRICE

The minimum price quote is 10p which represents a handling charge rather than a basis for valuing common stamps. For further notes about prices see introductory pages.

OFFICIAL STAMPS

Stamps perforated "O H M S" were introduced in May 1923 for use by the Receiver General's department in Ottawa and by the Assistant Receiver Generals' offices in provincial cities. From 1 July 1939 this use was extended to all departments of the federal government and such stamps continued to be produced until replaced by the "O.H.M.S." overprinted issue of 1949.

The perforated initials can appear either upright, inverted or sideways on individual stamps. The prices quoted are for the cheapest version. Stamps perforated with Type O 1 are only priced used. Only isolated examples are known mint and these are very rare.

A number of forged examples of the perforated "O.H.M.S." are known, in particular of Type O 1. Many of these forged perforated initials were applied to stamps which had already been used and this can aid their detection. Genuine examples, postmarked after the perforated initials were applied, often show the cancellation ink bleeding into the holes.

(O 1)	(O 2)
(Five holes in vertical bars of "H")	(Four holes in vertical bars of "H")

1923 (May). *Nos. 196/215 punctured as Type O 1.*
O1	44	1 c. yellow-green	..	—	20·00
O2		2 c. carmine	..	—	18·00
O3		3 c. deep brown	..	—	16·00
O4		5 c. deep blue	..	—	20·00
O5		7 c. yellow-ochre	..	—	35·00
O6		10 c. reddish purple	..	—	35·00
O7		20 c. olive	..	—	22·00
O8		50 c. sepia	..	—	35·00
O1/8			Set of 8	—	£180

1923 (May). *50th Anniv of Confederation. No. 244 punctured as Type O 1.*
O9	48	3 c. bistre-brown	..	—	£110

1923 (May)–31. *Nos. 246/55 and 263 punctured as Type O 1.*

(a) P 12
O10	44	1 c. chrome-yellow (Die I)	..	—	18·00
		a. Die II (1925)	..	—	18·00
O11		2 c. deep green	..	—	13·00
O12		3 c. carmine (Die I) (12.23)	..	—	13·00
		a. Die II (1924)	..	—	16·00
O13		4 c. olive-yellow	..	—	18·00
O14		5 c. violet	..	—	18·00
		a. Thin paper (1924)	..	—	22·00
O15		7 c. red-brown (1924)	..	—	27·00
O16		8 c. blue (1925)	..	—	32·00
O17		10 c. blue	..	—	22·00
O18		10 c. bistre-brown (1925)	..	—	13·00
O19		$1 brown-orange (7.23)	..	—	55·00
O10/19			Set of 10	—	£200

(b) P 12×8
O20	44	3 c. carmine (Die II) (1931)	..	—	42·00

1927 (29 June). *60th Anniv of Confederation. Nos. 266/73 punctured as Type O 1. (a) Commemorative issue.*
O21	51	1 c. orange	..	—	18·00
O22	52	2 c. green	..	—	25·00
O23	53	3 c. carmine	..	—	35·00
O24	54	5 c. violet	..	—	23·00
O25	55	12 c. blue	..	—	£140
O21/5			Set of 5	—	£225

(b) Historical issue
O26	56	5 c. violet	..	—	18·00
O27	57	12 c. green	..	—	£110
O28	58	20 c. carmine	..	—	70·00
O26/8			Set of 3	—	£180

1928 (21 Sept). *Air. No. 274 punctured as Type O 1.*
O29	59	5 c. olive-brown	..	—	90·00

1928–29. *Nos. 275/85 punctured as Type O 1.*
O30	60	1 c. orange	..	—	23·00
O31		2 c. green	..	—	15·00
O32		3 c. lake	..	—	40·00
O33		4 c. olive-bistre	..	—	48·00
O34		5 c. violet	..	—	16·00
O35		8 c. blue	..	—	45·00
O36	61	10 c. green	..	—	13·00
O37	62	12 c. grey-black	..	—	£120
O38	63	20 c. lake	..	—	38·00
O39	64	50 c. blue	..	—	£120
O40	65	$1 olive-green	..	—	£110
O30/40			Set of 11	—	£500

1930–31. *Nos. 288/97, and 300/5 punctured as Type O 1.*
O41	66	1 c. orange (Die I)	..	—	23·00
O42		1 c. green (Die I)	..	—	13·00
		a. Die II	..	—	11·00
O43		2 c. green (Die I)	..	—	35·00
O44		2 c. scarlet (Die I)	..	—	18·00
		a. Die II	..	—	16·00
O45		2 c. deep brown (Die I)	..	—	22·00
		a. Die II	..	—	18·00
O46		3 c. scarlet	..	—	13·00
O47		4 c. yellow-bistre	..	—	42·00
O48		5 c. violet	..	—	29·00
O49		5 c. deep slate-blue	..	—	23·00
O50		8 c. blue	..	—	55·00
O51		8 c. red-orange	..	—	40·00
O52	67	10 c. olive-green	..	—	75·00
O53	68	12 c. grey-black	..	—	75·00
O54	69	20 c. red	..	—	38·00

O55	70	50 c. blue	..	—	55·00
O56	71	$1 olive-green	..	—	£130
O41/56			Set of 15	—	£500

1930 (4 Dec). *Air. No. 310 punctured as Type O 1.*
O57	72	5 c. deep brown	..	—	£140

1931 (30 Sept). *No. 312 punctured as Type O 1.*
O58	73	10 c. olive-green	..	—	18·00

1932 (22 Feb). *Air. No. 313 punctured as Type O 1.*
O59	59	6 c. on 5 c. olive-brown	..	—	95·00

1932 (21 June). *Nos. 314/a punctured as Type O 1.*
O60	66	3 c. on 2 c. scarlet (Die I)	..	—	30·00
		a. Die II	..	—	23·00

1932 (12 July). *Ottawa Conference. Nos. 315/18 punctured as Type O 1. (a) Postage.*
O61	76	3 c. scarlet	..	—	15·00
O62	77	5 c. blue	..	—	27·00
O63	78	13 c. green	..	—	£160

(b) Air
O64	72	6 c. on 5 c. deep brown	..	—	£120
O61/4			Set of 4	—	£300

1932–33. *Nos. 319/25 punctured as Type O 1.*
O65	80	1 c. green	..	—	13·00
O66		2 c. sepia	..	—	13·00
O67		3 c. scarlet	..	—	13·00
O68		4 c. yellow-brown	..	—	45·00
O69		5 c. blue	..	—	20·00
O70		8 c. red-orange	..	—	45·00
O71	68	13 c. bright violet	..	—	45·00
O65/71			Set of 7	—	£180

1933 (18 May). *U.P.U. Congress Preliminary Meeting. No. 329 punctured as Type O 1.*
O72	81	5 c. blue	..	—	38·00

1933 (24 July). *World's Grain Exhibition and Conference, Regina. No. 330 punctured as Type O 1.*
O73	69	20 c. red	..	—	45·00

1933 (17 Aug). *Centenary of First Trans-Atlantic Steamboat Crossing. No. 331 punctured as Type O 1.*
O74	83	5 c. blue	..	—	40·00

1934 (1 July). *Fourth Centenary of Discovery of Canada. No. 332 punctured as Type O 1.*
O75	84	3 c. blue	..	—	45·00

1934 (1 July). *150th Anniv of Arrival of United Empire Loyalists. No. 333 punctured as Type O 1.*
O76	85	10 c. olive-green	..	—	48·00

1934 (16 Aug). *150th Anniv of Province of New Brunswick. No. 334 punctured as Type O 1.*
O77	86	2 c. red-brown	..	—	60·00

1935 (4 May). *Silver Jubilee. Nos. 335/40 punctured as Type O 1.*
O78	87	1 c. green	..	—	25·00
O79	–	2 c. brown	..	—	32·00
O80	89	3 c. carmine-red	..	—	40·00
O81	–	5 c. blue	..	—	38·00
O82	–	10 c. green	..	—	£110
O83	–	13 c. blue	..	—	£110
O78/83			Set of 6	—	£325

1935. *Nos. 341/51 and 355 punctured as Type O 1. (a) Postage*
O84	93	1 c. green	..	—	15·00
O85		2 c. brown	..	—	28·00
O86		3 c. scarlet	..	—	25·00
O87		4 c. yellow	..	—	45·00
O88		5 c. blue	..	—	25·00
O89		8 c. orange	..	—	45·00
O90	94	10 c. carmine	..	—	35·00
O91	–	13 c. purple	..	—	45·00
O92	–	20 c. olive-green	..	—	48·00
O93	–	50 c. deep violet	..	—	35·00
O94	–	$1 bright blue	..	—	95·00

(b) Air
O95	99	6 c. red-brown	..	—	75·00
O84/95			Set of 12	—	£475

1937 (10 May). *Coronation. No. 356 punctured as Type O 1.*
O96	100	3 c. carmine	..	—	40·00

1937–38. *Nos. 357/67, 370 and 371 punctured as Type O 1.*

(a) Postage
O 97	101	1 c. green	..	—	2·50
O 98		2 c. brown	..	—	2·75
O 99		3 c. scarlet	..	—	2·50
O100		4 c. yellow	..	—	8·00
O101		5 c. blue	..	—	6·50
O102		8 c. orange	..	—	13·00
O103	102	10 c. rose-carmine	..	—	20·00
		a. Red	..	—	23·00

O104	–	13 c. blue	..	—	28·00
O105	–	20 c. red-brown	..	—	28·00
O106	–	50 c. green	..	—	65·00
O107	–	$1 violet	..	—	95·00
O97/107			Set of 11	—	£250

(b) Coil stamp
O108	101	3 c. scarlet	..	—	65·00

(c) Air
O109	107	6 c. blue	..	—	28·00

1939 (15 May). *Royal Visit. Nos. 372/4 punctured as Type O 1.*
O110	108	1 c. black and green	..	—	32·00
O111	109	2 c. black and brown	..	—	42·00
O112	110	3 c. black and carmine	..	—	32·00
O110/12			Set of 3	—	95·00

1939 (1 July). *Air. No. 274 punctured as Type O 2.*
O113	59	5 c. olive-brown	..	20·00	14·00

1939 (1 July). *Nos. 347/50 and 355 punctured as Type O 2.*

(a) Postage
O114	94	10 c. carmine	..	55·00	38·00
O115	–	13 c. purple	..	60·00	38·00
O116	–	20 c. olive-green	..	75·00	48·00
O117	–	50 c. deep violet	..	60·00	38·00

(b) Air
O118	99	6 c. red-brown	..	50·00	42·00
O114/18			Set of 5	£275	£180

1939 (1 July). *Coronation. No. 356 punctured as Type O 2.*
O119	100	3 c. carmine	..	70·00	45·00

1939 (1 July). *Nos. 357/67, 369/70 and 371 punctured as Type O 2. (a) Postage*
O120	101	1 c. green	..	1·50	10
O121		2 c. brown	..	2·25	10
O122		3 c. scarlet	..	2·50	10
O123		4 c. yellow	..	5·00	2·25
O124		5 c. blue	..	3·50	20
O125		8 c. orange	..	13·00	4·25
O126	102	10 c. rose-carmine	..	50·00	3·25
		a. Red	..	8·00	30
O127	–	13 c. blue	..	13·00	1·50
O128	–	20 c. red-brown	..	35·00	2·00
O129	–	50 c. green	..	40·00	8·00
O130	–	$1 violet	..	£110	30·00
O120/30			Set of 11	£200	42·00

(b) Coil stamps
O131	101	2 c. brown	..	70·00	45·00
O132		3 c. scarlet	..	70·00	45·00

(c) Air
O133	107	6 c. blue	..	3·00	80

1939 (1 July). *Royal Visit. Nos. 372/4 punctured as Type O 2.*
O134	108	1 c. black and green	..	80·00	38·00
O135	109	2 c. black and brown	..	80·00	38·00
O136	110	3 c. black and carmine	..	80·00	38·00
O134/6			Set of 3	£225	£100

1942–43. *War Effort. Nos. 375/88 and 399/400 punctured as Type O 2. (a) Postage*
O137	111	1 c. green	..	40	10
O138	112	2 c. brown	..	50	10
O139	113	3 c. carmine-lake	..	1·10	40
O140		3 c. purple	..	60	10
O141	114	4 c. slate	..	2·75	75
O142	112	4 c. carmine-lake	..	55	10
O143	111	5 c. blue	..	1·25	15
O144	–	8 c. red-brown	..	7·50	2·00
O145	116	10 c. brown	..	4·50	20
O146	117	13 c. dull green	..	5·50	5·50
O147		14 c. dull green	..	9·00	85
O148	–	20 c. chocolate	..	12·00	70
O149	–	50 c. violet	..	35·00	5·50
O150	–	$1 blue	..	90·00	25·00

(b) Air
O151	121	6 c. blue	..	4·00	2·00
O152		7 c. blue	..	3·25	25
O137/52			Set of 16	£160	40·00

1946. *Peace Re-conversion. Nos. 401/7 punctured as Type O 2.*

(a) Postage
O153	122	8 c. brown	..	10·00	3·50
O154	–	10 c. olive-green	..	3·25	15
O155	–	14 c. sepia	..	4·25	65
O156	–	20 c. slate	..	4·50	50
O157	–	50 c. green	..	23·00	50
O158	–	$1 purple	..	60·00	15·00

(b) Air
O159	–	7 c. blue	..	3·00	40
O153/9			Set of 7	95·00	23·00

1949. *Nos. 415 and 416 punctured as Type O 2.*
O160	136	2 c. sepia	..	75	75
O161	137	3 c. purple	..	75	75

O.H.M.S.

(O 3)

1949. *Nos. 375/6, 378, 380 and 402/7 optd as Type O 3 by typography.*

(a) Postage

O162	111	1 c. green		1·75	2·00
		a. Missing stop after "S"		£150	50·00
O163	112	2 c. brown		12·00	12·00
		a. Missing stop after "S"		£150	85·00
O164	113	3 c. purple		1·25	1·10
O165	112	4 c. carmine-lake		2·00	80
O166	–	10 c. olive-green		3·75	15
		a. Missing stop after "S"		80·00	35·00
O167	–	14 c. sepia		4·50	1·75
		a. Missing stop after "S"		£100	48·00
O168	–	20 c. slate		12·00	60
		a. Missing stop after "S"		£140	50·00
O169	–	50 c. green		£160	£120
		a. Missing stop after "S"		£850	£550
O170	–	$1 purple		45·00	48·00
		a. Missing stop after "S"		£1500	

(b) Air

O171	–	7 c. blue		24·00	7·00
		a. Missing stop after "S"		£130	60·00
O162/71			*Set of 10*	£225	£140

Forgeries exist of this overprint. Genuine examples are 2.3×15 mm and show the tops of all letters aligned, as are the stops.
Only a few sheets of the $1 showed the variety, No. O170a.

MISSING STOP VARIETIES. These occur on R. 6/2 of the lower left pane (Nos. O162a, O163a and O176a) or R. 10/2 of the lower left pane (O166a, O167a, O168a, O169a, O170a and O171a). No. O176a also occurs on R. 8/8 of the upper left pane in addition to R. 6/2 of the lower left pane.

1949–50. *Nos. 414/15, 416/17, 418 and 431 optd as Type O 3 by typography.*

O172	135	1 c. green		85	85
O173	136	2 c. sepia		1·75	1·50
O174	137	3 c. purple		1·00	70
O175	138	4 c. carmine-lake		1·50	15
O176	139	5 c. blue (1949)		2·75	2·00
		a. Missing stop after "S"		85·00	38·00
O177	141	50 c. green (1950)		32·00	28·00
O172/7			*Set of 6*	35·00	30·00

G G G

(O 4) (O 5) (O 6)

Type O 6 differs from Type O 5 in having a thinner appearance and an upward sloping left serif to the lower arm. It results from a new plate introduced in 1961/62. Variations in thickness are known in Type O 4 but these are due to wear and subsequent cleaning of the plate. All are produced by typography. Examples showing the "G" applied by lithography are forgeries.

1950 (2 Oct)–52. *Nos. 402/4, 406/7, 414/18 and 431 optd with Type O 4 (1 to 5 c.) or O 5 (7 c. to $1). (a) Postage.*

O178	135	1 c. green		70	10
O179	136	2 c. sepia		1·50	1·60
O180		2 c. olive-green (11.51)		1·75	10
O181	137	3 c. purple		1·50	10
O182	138	4 c. carmine-lake		1·50	30
O183		4 c. vermilion (1.5.52)		1·90	10
O184	139	5 c. blue		2·50	30
O185	–	10 c. olive-green		3·00	10
O186	–	14 c. sepia		11·00	2·75
O187	–	20 c. slate		16·00	20
O188	141	50 c. green		11·00	9·00
O189	–	$1 purple		60·00	60·00

(b) Air

O190	–	7 c. blue		24·00	13·00
O178/90			*Set of 13*	£120	75·00

1950–51. *Nos. 432/3 optd with Type O 5.*

O191	142	10 c. brown-purple		2·25	10
		a. Opt omitted in pair with normal		£400	£350
O192	143	$1 ultramarine (1.2.51)		55·00	60·00

1952–53. *Nos. 441, 443 and 446 optd with Type O 5.*

O193	153	7 c. blue (3.11.52)		1·75	1·75
O194	151	20 c. grey (1.4.52)		2·00	10
O195	154	$1 black (2.2.53)		10·00	12·00
O193/5			*Set of 3*	12·50	12·50

1953 (1 Sept)–61. *Nos. 450/4 and 462 optd with Type O 4 (1 to 5 c.) or O 5 (50 c.).*

O196	158	1 c. purple-brown		15	10
O197		2 c. green		20	10
O198		3 c. carmine		20	10
O199		4 c. violet		30	10
O200		5 c. ultramarine		30	10
O201	160	50 c. deep bluish green (2.11.53)		3·00	2·00
		a. Opt Type O 6 (24.4.61*)		2·25	2·25
O196/201			*Set of 6*	3·00	2·10

*Earliest recorded date.

1955–56. *Nos. 463/4 and 466/7 optd with Type O 4.*

O202	161	1 c. purple-brown (12.11.56)		20	20
O203		2 c. green (19.1.56)		15	10
O204		4 c. violet (23.7.56)		40	10
O205		5 c. bright blue (11.1.55)		15	10
O202/5			*Set of 5*	80	30

1955–62. *Nos. 477 and 488 optd with Type O 5.*

O206	165	10 c. purple-brown (21.2.55)		40	10
		a. Opt Type O 6 (28.3.62*)		40	90
O207	176	20 c. green (4.12.56)		2·00	10
		a. Opt Type O 6 (10.4.62*)		5·00	40

*Earliest recorded date.

1963 (15 May). *Nos. 527/8 and 530/1 optd as Type O 4.*

O208		1 c. chocolate		40	3·75
O209		2 c. green		40	3·50
		a. Type O 4 omitted (vert pair with normal)		£600	
O210		4 c. carmine-red		40	2·00
O211		5 c. ultramarine		40	90
O208/11			*Set of 4*	1·40	9·00

No. O209a comes from the top row of an upper pane on which the overprint was misplaced downwards by one row. Owing to the margin between the panes the top row of the bottom pane had the overprint at the top of the stamp.

OFFICIAL SPECIAL DELIVERY STAMPS

1923 (May). *Nos. S3/4 punctured as Type O 1.*

OS1	S 1	10 c. yellowish green		—	85·00
OS2	S 2	20 c. carmine-red		—	70·00

1927 (29 June). *60th Anniv of Confederation. No. S5 punctured as Type O 1.*

OS3	S 3	20 c. orange		—	80·00

1930 (2 Sept). *Inscr "TWENTY CENTS" at foot. No. S6 punctured as Type O 1.*

OS4	S 4	20 c. brown-red		—	65·00

1932 (24 Dec). *Inscr "CENTS" at foot. No. S7 punctured as Type O 1.*

OS5	S 4	20 c. brown-red		—	65·00

1935 (1 June). *No. S8 punctured as Type O 1.*

OS6	S 5	20 c. scarlet		—	65·00

1938–39. *Nos. S9/10 punctured as Type O 1.*

OS7	S 6	10 c. green		—	38·00
OS8		20 c. scarlet		—	60·00

1939 (1 Mar). *No. S11 punctured as Type O 1.*

OS9	S 6	10 c. on 20 c. scarlet		—	60·00

1939 (1 July). *Inscr "CENTS" at foot. No. S7 punctured as Type O 2.*

OS10	S 4	20 c. brown-red		£150	80·00

1939 (1 July). *No. S8 punctured as Type O 2.*

OS11	S 5	20 c. scarlet		85·00	38·00

1939 (1 July). *No. S9 punctured as Type O 2.*

OS12	S 6	10 c. green		7·00	4·50

1939 (1 July). *No. S11 punctured as Type O 2.*

OS13	S 6	10 c. on 20 c. scarlet		£100	50·00

1942–43. *Nos. S12/14 punctured as Type O 2. (a) Postage*

OS14	S 8	10 c. green		9·00	6·50

(b) Air

OS15	S 9	16 c. ultramarine		17·00	13·00
OS16		17 c. ultramarine		10·00	8·00

1946–47. *Nos. S15/17 punctured as Type O 2. (a) Postage*

OS17	S 10	10 c. green		6·50	4·50

(b) Air

OS18	S 11	17 c. ultramarine (circumflex accent)	26·00	22·00
OS19		17 c. ultramarine (grave accent)		55·00	55·00

1950. *No. S15 optd as Type O 3, but larger.*

OS20	S 10	10 c. green		17·00	21·00

1950 (2 Oct). *No. S15 optd as Type O 4, but larger.*

OS21	S 10	10 c. green		26·00	27·00

The use of official stamps was discontinued on 31 December 1963.

Cape of Good Hope *see* South Africa

Cayman Islands

The first post office was opened at Georgetown in April 1889. The stamps of Jamaica with the following cancellations were used until 19 February 1901. At some stage, probably around 1891, a supply of the Jamaica 1889 1d., No. 27, was overprinted "CAYMAN ISLANDS", but these stamps were never issued. Two surviving examples are known, one unused and the other cancelled at Richmond in Jamaica.

Types of Jamaica

2	3	4

8	11

13

PRICES OF NOS. Z1/27. These are for a single stamp showing a clear impression of the postmark. Nos. Z1, 2, 6/8, 11/13, 18, 22 and Z25 are known used on cover and these are worth considerably more.

GEORGETOWN, GRAND CAYMAN

Z 1

Z 2   Z 3

Stamps of JAMAICA cancelled with Type Z 1 in purple.

1889 *to* **1894.**

Z1	8	½d. yellow-green (No. 16)			£400
Z2	11	1d. purple and mauve (No. 27)			£400
Z2a	2	2d. slate (No. 20a)			£3250
Z3	11	2d. green (No. 28)			£750
Z4		2½d. dull purple and blue (No. 29)			£900
Z5	4	4d. red-orange (No. 22)			£1800

Stamps of JAMAICA cancelled with Type Z 2 in purple or black.

1895 *to* **1898.**

Z6	8	½d. yellow-green (No. 16)			£450
Z7	11	1d. purple and mauve (No. 27)			£375
Z8		2½d. dull purple and blue (No. 29)			£650
Z9	3	3d. sage-green (No. 21)			£2500

Stamps of JAMAICA *cancelled with Type* **Z 3**.

1898 to 1901.

Z10	8	½d. yellow-green (No. 16)	..	..	£375	
		a. *Green* (No. 16a)			£375	
Z11	11	1d. purple and mauve (No. 27)	..	..	£375	
Z12	13	1d. red (No. 31) (1900)	..	..	£375	
Z13	11	2½d. dull purple and blue (No. 29)	..	£550	

OFFICIAL STAMPS

Stamps of JAMAICA *cancelled with Type* **Z 1** *in purple*.

1890 to 1894.

Z14	8	½d. green (No. O1) (*opt* 17–17½ *mm long*)	£750
Z15		½d. green (No. O3) (*opt* 16 *mm long*) (1893)	£1200
Z16	11	1d. rose (No. O4)	£900
Z17		2d. grey (No. O5)	£1800

Stamps of JAMAICA *cancelled with Type* **Z 2** *in purple or black*.

1895 to 1898.

Z18	8	½d. green (No. O3)	£1300
Z19	11	1d. rose (No. O4)	£2500
Z20		2d. grey (No. O5)	£2500

STAKE BAY, CAYMAN BRAC

Z 4   Z 5

Stamps of JAMAICA *cancelled with Type* **Z 4**.

1898 to 1900.

Z21	8	½d. yellow-green (No. 16)	..	£2250
Z22	11	1d. purple and mauve (No. 27)	..	£2500
Z23		2d. green (No. 28)	..	£3000
Z24		2½d. dull purple and blue (No. 29)	..	£2500

Stamps of JAMAICA *cancelled with Type* **Z 5**.

1900 to 1901.

Z25	8	½d. yellow-green (No. 16)	..	£2500
Z26	11	1d. purple and mauve (No. 27)	..	£2000
Z27	13	1d. red (No. 31)	..	£2000
Z28	11	2½d. dull purple and blue (No. 29)	..	£1800

PRICES FOR STAMPS ON COVER TO 1945

Nos. 1/2	*from* × 25
Nos. 3/12	*from* × 15
Nos. 13/16	*from* × 4
Nos. 17/19	*from* × 10
Nos. 25/34	*from* × 5
Nos. 35/52b	*from* × 4
Nos. 53/67	*from* × 5
Nos. 69/83	*from* × 4
Nos. 84/95	*from* × 6
Nos. 96/9	*from* × 5
Nos. 100/11	*from* × 4
Nos. 112/14	*from* × 6
Nos. 115/26	*from* × 2

DEPENDENCY OF JAMAICA

1   2   3

(T **1/3, 8/9** and **12/13** typo D.L.R.)

1900 (Nov). *Wmk Crown CA.* P 14.

1	1	½d. deep green	..	7·00	17·00
		a. *Pale green*	..	3·75	13·00
2		1d. rose-carmine	..	2·50	2·25
		a. *Pale carmine*	..	9·00	8·50
1/2 Optd "Specimen"		*Set of* 2	90·00	

Dented frame under "A" (R. 1/6
of left pane)

1902 (Jan)–03. *Wmk Crown CA.* P 14.

3	2	½d. green (15.9.02)	..	4·00	24·00
		a. *Dented frame*	..	80·00	
4		1d. carmine (6.3.03)	..	9·00	8·50
		a. *Dented frame*	..	£120	

5	2	2½d. bright blue		7·00	11·00
		a. *Dented frame*		£120	
6		6d. brown		27·00	60·00
		a. *Dented frame*		£250	
7	3	1s. orange		60·00	£110
		a. *Dented frame*		£350	
3/7			*Set of* 5	95·00	£190
3/7 Optd "Specimen"		*Set of* 5	£160	

1905 (Feb–18 Oct). *Wmk Mult Crown CA.* P 14.

8	2	½d. green		5·00	6·50
		a. *Dented frame*		80·00	
9		1d. carmine (18 Oct)		14·00	16·00
		a. *Dented frame*		£170	
10		2½d. bright blue		5·00	3·00
		a. *Dented frame*		90·00	
11		6d. brown		16·00	38·00
		a. *Dented frame*		£225	
12	3	1s. orange		32·00	48·00
		a. *Dented frame*		£300	
8/12			*Set of* 5	65·00	£100

1907 (13 Mar). *Wmk Mult Crown CA.* P 14.

13	3	4d. brown and blue		29·00	50·00
		a. *Dented frame*		£250	
14	2	6d. olive and rose		29·00	60·00
		a. *Dented frame*		£250	
15	3	1s. violet and green		50·00	70·00
		a. *Dented frame*		£325	
16		5s. salmon and green		£170	£275
		a. *Dented frame*		£1000	
13/16			*Set of* 4	£250	£400
13/16 Optd "Specimen"		*Set of* 4	£180	

One Halfpenny.   ½ D   1D

(4)   (5)   (6)

1907 (30 Aug). *No. 9 surch at Govt Printing Office, Kingston, with* T **4**.

17	2	½d. on 1d. carmine		38·00	55·00
		a. *Dented frame*		£325	

1907 (Nov). *No. 16 handstamped at Georgetown P.O. with* T **5** *or* **6**.

18	3	½d. on 5s. salmon and green (26 Nov)	£225	£325
		a. *Surch inverted*		£23000	
		b. *Surch double*		£9000	£9000
		c. *Surch double, one inverted*		£35000	
		d. *Surch omitted (in pair with normal)*	£35000	
		e. *Dented frame*		£950	
19		1d. on 5s. salmon and green (23 Nov)	£225	£300
		a. *Surch double*		£14000	
		b. *Surch inverted*		£38000	
		c. *Dented frame*		£8000	

The ½d. on 5s. may be found with the figures "1" or "2" omitted, owing to defective handstamping.

1 D   4 D   2½ D

8   9   (10)

1907 (27 Dec)–09. *Chalk-surfaced paper (3d. to 10s.).* P 14.

(a) Wmk Mult Crown CA

25	8	½d. green		1·75	4·00
26		1d. carmine		1·25	65
27		2½d. ultramarine (30.3.08)		3·00	3·50
28	9	3d. purple/*yellow* (30.3.08)		3·00	6·50
29		4d. black and red/*yellow* (30.3.08)	50·00	70·00
30	8	6d. dull and bright purple (2.10.08)	9·00	35·00
		a. *Dull purple and violet-purple*	30·00	48·00
31	9	1s. black/*green* (5.4.09)		7·00	22·00
32		5s. green and red/*yellow* (30.3.08)	38·00	60·00

(b) Wmk Crown CA (30.3.08)

33	9	1s. black/*green*		55·00	75·00
34	8	10s. green and red/*green*		£160	£225
25/34			*Set of* 10	£300	£450
25/34 (except 31) Optd "Specimen"		*Set of* 9	£275	

1908 (12 Feb). *No. 13 handstamped locally with* T **10**.

35	3	2½d. on 4d. brown and blue		£1500	£2250
		a. *Surch double*		£30000	£18000
		b. *Dented frame*		£8000	

No. 35 should only be purchased when accompanied by an expert committee's certificate or similar form of guarantee.

MANUSCRIPT PROVISIONALS. During May and June 1908 supplies of ½d. and 1d. stamps became exhausted, and the payment of postage was indicated by the Postmistress, Miss Gwendolyn Parsons, using a manuscript endorsement. Such endorsements were in use from 12 May to 1 June.

Price on cover

MP1	"(Postage Paid G.A.P.)" (12 May to 1 June)	£2500
MP1a	"(Postage Paid G.A.P.) ½ or 1d." (23 May)	£3750

In October of the same year there was a further shortage of ¼d. stamps and the manuscript endorsements were again applied by either the new Postmaster, William Graham McCausland, or by Miss Parsons who remained as his assistant.

MP2	"Pd ¼d. W.G. McC." (4 to 27 October)	£250
MP2a	"¼d Pd./W.G. McC" (14 October)	£1000
MP3	"Paid" (7 October)	£5500
MP4	"Pd ¼d" (8 October)	£4500
MP5	"(Paid ¼GAP. asst.)" (15 October)	£4000

No. MP2 exists in different inks and formats.

Manuscript endorsement for the 2½d. rate is also known, but this is thought to have been done by oversight.

A 1d. surcharge on 4d. (No. 29), issued in mid-May, was intended as a revenue stamp and was never authorised for postal use (*price* £225 *un.*). Used examples were either cancelled by favour or passed through the post in error. Exists with surcharge inverted (*price* £1600 *un.*), surcharge double (*price* £2500 *un.*) or surcharge double, both inverted (*price* £2500 *un.*).

11   12   13

1908 (30 June)–09. *Wmk Mult Crown CA. Litho.* P 14.

38	11	¼d. brown (Optd S. £65)		1·25	30
		a. *Grey-brown* (2.09)		2·00	75

1912 (24 Apr)–20. *Die I. Wmk Mult Crown CA. Chalk-surfaced paper (3d. to 10s.).* P 14.

40	13	¼d. brown (10.2.13)		75	30
41	12	½d. green		2·75	4·50
42		1d. red (25.2.13)		3·25	2·50
43	13	2d. pale grey		1·00	9·00
44	12	2½d. bright blue (26.8.14)		7·00	10·00
		a. *Deep bright blue* (9.11.17)		17·00	24·00
45	13	3d. purple/*yellow* (26.11.14)		13·00	35·00
		a. *White back* (19.11.13)		3·25	8·00
		b. *On lemon* (12.3.18) (Optd S. £50)	2·25	18·00
		c. *On orange-buff* (1920)		10·00	30·00
		d. *On buff* (1920)			
		e. *On pale yellow* (1920)		3·50	30·00
46		4d. black and red/*yellow* (25.2.13)		85	9·00
47	12	6d. dull and bright purple (25.2.13)		3·75	7·50
48	13	1s. black/*green* (15.5.16) (Optd S. £50)	3·50	24·00
		a. *White back* (19.11.13)		3·50	3·50
49		2s. purple and bright blue/*blue*		10·00	48·00
50		3s. green and violet		19·00	65·00
51		5s. green and red/*yellow* (26.8.14)		75·00	£150
52	12	10s. deep green and red/*green* (26.11.14) (Optd S. £80)		95·00	£170
		a. *White back* (19.11.13)		80·00	£140
		b. *On blue-green, olive back* (5.10.18)	80·00	£170
40/52b			*Set of* 13	£190	£425
40/4, 45a, 46/7, 48a, 49/51, 52a Optd "Specimen"		*Set of* 13	£325	

WAR   WAR
STAMP.   STAMP.

1½ d   1½ d   1½ d

(14)   (15)   Straight serif
                                (Left-hand pane R. 10/2)

1917 (26 Feb). T **12** *surch with* T **14** *or* **15** *at Kingston, Jamaica*.

53	14	1½d. on 2½d. deep blue		5·50	9·00
		a. *No fraction bar*		85·00	£140
		b. *Missing stop after "STAMP"* (R.1/4)	£325	
54	15	1½d. on 2½d. deep blue		1·75	5·00
		a. *No fraction bar*		55·00	£100
		b. *Straight serif*		65·00	£120

On No. 53 "WAR STAMP" and "1½d." were applied separately.

WAR STAMP   WAR STAMP   WAR STAMP

1½ d   1½ a   1½ d.

(16)   (17)   (18)

1917 (4 Sept). T **12** *surch with* T **16** *or* **17** *by D.L.R.*

55	16	1½d. on 2½d. deep blue		£650	£1800
56	17	1½d. on 2½d. deep blue (Optd S. £100)	30	50
		a. *Short opt* (right pane R. 10/1)	20·00	
		x. *Wmk reversed*		75·00	

De La Rue replaced surcharge Type **16** by Type **17** (which shows different figures) after only a few sheets as it did not adequately obliterate the original face value. A small quantity, said to be 3½ sheets, of Type **16** was included in the consignment in error.

1919–20. T **12** *and* **13** (2½d. *special printing*), *optd only, or surch in addition at Kingston* (No. 58) *or by D.L.R.* (*others*).

57	16	½d. green (4.2.19)		30	2·00
		a. *Short opt* (right pane R. 10/1)	20·00	
58	18	1½d. on 2d. grey (10.3.20)		1·25	7·00
59	17	1½d. on 2½d. orange (4.12.19)		70	90
		a. *Short opt* (right pane R. 10/1)		
57, 59 Optd "Specimen"		*Set of* 2	80·00	

The ½d. stamps on *buff* paper, and later consignments of the 2d. T **13** on *pinkish*, derived their colour from the paper in which they were packed for despatch from England.

Nos. 56a, 57a and 59a show the overprint 2 mm high instead of 2½ mm.

A further surcharge as No. 58, but in red, was prepared in Jamaica during April 1920, but these were not issued.

19   20 King William IV and
                        King George V

1921 (4 Apr)–26. P 14. (a) Wmk Mult Crown CA.

60	19	3d. purple/orange-buff	..	1·50	7·00
		aw. Wmk inverted	..	70·00	
		ay. Wmk inverted and reversed	..	60·00	
		b. Purple/pale yellow	..	45·00	60·00
		bw. Wmk inverted			
62		4d. red/yellow (1.4.22)	..	80	3·75
63		1s. black/green	..	1·25	8·50
		x. Wmk reversed			
64		5s. yellow-green/pale yellow	..	16·00	65·00
		a. Deep green/pale yellow	..	65·00	£100
		b. Blue-green/pale yellow	..	70·00	£120
		c. Deep green/orange-buff (19.11.21)		95·00	£160
67		10s. carmine/green (19.11.21)	..	55·00	95·00
60/7			Set of 5	70·00	£160
60/7 Optd "Specimen"			Set of 5	£180	

(b) Wmk Mult Script CA

69	19	¼d. yellow-brown (1.4.22)	..	40	1·50
		y. Wmk inverted and reversed	..	£150	
70		½d. pale grey-green (1.4.22)	..	50	30
		w. Wmk inverted			
		y. Wmk inverted and reversed			
71		1d. deep carmine-red (1.4.22)	..	1·10	85
72		1½d. orange-brown	..	1·75	30
73		2d. slate-grey (1.4.22)	..	1·75	3·75
74		2½d. bright blue (1.4.22)	..	50	45
		x. Wmk reversed	..	75·00	
75		3d. purple/yellow (29.6.23)	..	50	3·25
		y. Wmk inverted and reversed	..	60·00	
76		4½d. sage-green (29.6.23)	..	2·00	9·00
77		6d. claret (1.4.22)	..	5·50	29·00
		a. Deep claret	..	19·00	35·00
79		1s. black/green (15.5.25)	..	8·50	32·00
80		2s. violet/blue (1.4.22)	..	14·00	22·00
81		3s. violet (1.4.22)	..	23·00	16·00
82		5s. green/yellow (15.2.25)	..	24·00	45·00
83		10s. carmine/green (5.9.26)	..	60·00	85·00
69/83			Set of 14	£130	£225
69/53 Optd "Specimen"			Set of 14	£325	

An example of the 4d., No. 62, is known with the 'C' missing from the watermark in the top sheet margin.

"A.S.R." PROVISIONAL. On the night of 9/10 November 1932 the Cayman Brac Post Office at Stake Bay and its contents, was destroyed by a hurricane. Pending the arrival of replacement stamp stocks and cancellation the Postmaster, Mr. A. S. Rutty, initialled covers to indicate that postage had been paid. Those destined for overseas addresses additionally received a "Postage Paid" machine postmark in red when they passed through Kingston, Jamaica.

Price on cover

MP6 Endorsed "A.S.R." in manuscript £4000
MP7 Endorsed "A.S.R." in manuscript and "Postage Paid" machine postmark in red £6500
These emergency arrangements lasted until 19 December.

(Recess Waterlow)

1932 (5 Dec). Centenary of the "Assembly of Justices and Vestry". Wmk Mult Script CA. P 12½.

84	20	¼d. brown	..	1·50	1·00
		a. "A" of "CA" missing from wmk	£1000	£1000	
85		½d. green	..	2·75	7·50
		a. "A" of "CA" reversed in wmk	..	£1200	
86		1d. scarlet	..	2·75	6·00
87		1½d. red-orange	..	2·75	2·50
		a. "A" of "CA" missing from wmk			
88		2d. grey	..	2·25	3·25
89		2½d. ultramarine	..	2·50	1·50
90		3d. olive-green	..	2·75	4·50
91		6d. purple	..	9·00	20·00
92		1s. black and brown	..	17·00	30·00
93		2s. black and ultramarine	..	45·00	70·00
94		5s. black and green	..	80·00	£120
95		10s. black and scarlet	..	60·00	£350
84/95			Set of 12	£350	£500
84/95 Perf "Specimen"			Set of 12	£450	

No. 85a shows one "A" of the watermark reversed so that its head points to right when seen from the back. It is believed that this stamp may also exist with "A" missing.

Examples of all values are known showing a forged George Town postmark dated "DE 31 1932".

21 Cayman Islands   24 Queen or Pink Conch Shells

(Recess Waterlow)

1935 (1 May)–36. T 21, 24 and similar designs. Wmk Mult Script CA. P 12½.

96	21	¼d. black and brown	..	30	80
97		½d. ultramarine & yellow-green (1.1.36)	1·00	1·00	
98		1d. ultramarine and scarlet	..	3·50	2·25
99	24	1½d. black and orange	..	1·50	1·75
100		2d. ultramarine and purple	..	3·75	1·10
101		2½d. blue and black (1.1.36)	..	3·00	1·25
102	21	3d. black and olive-green	..	2·00	3·00
103		6d. bright purple and black (1.1.36)	..	8·50	4·00
104		1s. ultramarine and orange (1.1.36)	..	6·00	6·50
105		2s. ultramarine and black	..	45·00	50·00
106		5s. green and black	..	50·00	50·00
107	24	10s. black and scarlet	..	70·00	85·00
96/107			Set of 12	£170	£170
96/107 Perf "Specimen"			Set of 12	£250	

Designs: Horiz—½d., 2d., 1s. Cat boat; 1d., 2s. Red-footed Booby; 2½d., 6d. 5s. Hawksbill Turtles.

Examples of all values are known showing a forged George Town postmark dated "AU 23 1936"

1935 (6 May). Silver Jubilee. As Nos. 91/4 of Antigua.

108		½d. black and green	..	15	80
		f. Diagonal line by turret	..	30·00	
		h. Dot by flagstaff	..	45·00	
		i. Dash by turret	..	55·00	
109		2½d. brown and deep blue	..	1·00	1·00
110		6d. light blue and olive-green	..	1·00	3·25
		h. Dot by flagstaff	..	£140	
		i. Dash by turret	..	£140	
111		1s. slate and purple	..	7·00	7·00
		h. Dot by flagstaff	..	£200	
		i. Dash by turret	..	£225	
108/11			Set of 4	8·25	11·00
108/11 Perf "Specimen"			Set of 4	90·00	

For illustrations of plate varieties see Catalogue Introduction.

1937 (13 May). Coronation Issue. As Nos. 95/7 of Antigua. P 11×11½.

112		½d. green	..	30	75
113		1d. carmine	..	50	20
114		2½d. blue	..	95	40
112/14			Set of 3	1·60	1·25
112/14 Perf "Specimen"			Set of 3	75·00	

26 Beach View   27 Dolphin (fish)
(Coryphaena hippurus)

(Recess D.L.R. (½d., 2d., 6d., 1s., 10s.), Waterlow (others))

1938 (5 May)–48. T 26/7 and similar designs. Wmk Mult Script CA (sideways on ¼d., 1d., 1½d., 2½d., 3d., 2s., 5s.). Various perfs.

115	26	¼d. red-orange (p 12½)	..	40	55
		a. Perf 13½×12½ (16.7.43)	..	10	55
116	27	½d. green (p 13×11½)	..	75	55
		a. Perf 14 (16.7.43)	..	1·25	1·40
		ab. "A" of "CA" missing from wmk	£1000		
117	—	1d. scarlet (p 12½)	..	30	75
118	26	1½d. green (p 12½)	..	30	10
119	—	2d. violet (p 11½×13)	..	2·25	40
		a. Perf 14 (16.7.43)	..	60	30
120	—	2½d. bright blue (p 12½)	..	40	20
120a	—	2½d. orange (p 12½) (25.8.47)	..	2·25	50
121	—	3d. orange (p 12½)	..	40	15
121a	—	3d. bright blue (p 12½) (25.8.47)	..	2·25	30
122	—	6d. olive-green (p 11½×13)	..	9·00	4·00
		a. Perf 14 (16.7.43)	..	2·00	1·25
		b. Brownish (p 11½×13) (8.7.47)	3·00	1·50	
123	27	1s. red-brown (p 13×11½)	..	5·50	1·50
		a. Perf 14 (16.7.43)	..	4·00	2·00
		ab. "A" of "CA" missing from wmk	£1100		
124	26	2s. yellow-green (shades) (p 12½)	..	48·00	14·00
		a. Deep green (16.7.43)	..	25·00	9·00
125	—	5s. carmine-lake (p 12½)	..	32·00	15·00
		a. Crimson (1948)	..	60·00	22·00
126	—	10s. chocolate (p 11½×13)	..	23·00	9·00
		a. Perf 14 (16.7.43)	..	21·00	9·00
115/26a			Set of 14	80·00	35·00
115/26 Perf "Specimen"			Set of 14	£275	

Designs: Horiz (as T 26)—1d., 3d. Cayman Islands map; 2½d., 5s. Rembro (schooner). Vert (as T 27)—2d., 6d., 10s. Hawksbill Turtles.

Stop after "1946" (R.2/1)

1946 (26 Aug). Victory. As Nos. 110/11 of Antigua.

127		1½d. black	..	20	10
128		3d. orange-yellow	..	20	10
		a. Stop after "1946"	..	16·00	
127/8 Perf "Specimen"			Set of 2	65·00	

1948 (29 Nov). Royal Silver Wedding. As Nos. 112/13 of Antigua.

129		½d. green	..	10	10
130		10s. violet-blue	..	13·00	11·00

1949 (10 Oct). 75th Anniv of Universal Postal Union. As Nos. 114/17 of Antigua.

131		2½d. orange	..	30	30
132		3d. deep blue	..	1·50	1·40
133		6d. olive	..	60	1·40
134		1s. red-brown	..	60	30
131/4			Set of 4	2·75	3·00

31 Cat Boat   32 Coconut Grove, Cayman Brac

---

44 South Sound Lighthouse, Grand Cayman   45 Queen Elizabeth II

(Recess B.W.)

1950 (2 Oct). T 31/2 and similar horiz designs. Wmk Mult Script CA. P 11½ × 11.

135		¼d. bright blue and pale scarlet	..	15	60
136		½d. reddish violet and emerald-green	..	15	1·25
137		1d. olive-green and deep blue	..	60	75
138		1½d. green and brown	..	30	75
139		2d. reddish violet and rose-carmine	..	1·25	1·50
140		2½d. turquoise and black	..	70	60
141		3d. bright green and light blue	..	1·40	1·50
142		6d. red-brown and blue	..	2·00	1·25
143		9d. scarlet and grey-green	..	4·50	2·00
144		1s. brown and orange	..	3·25	2·75
145		2s. violet and reddish purple	..	8·00	9·00
146		5s. olive-green and violet	..	13·00	7·00
147		10s. black and scarlet	..	15·00	8·00
135/47			Set of 13	45·00	38·00

Designs:—1d. Green Turtle; 1½d. Thatch rope industry; 2d. Cayman seamen; 2½d. Map of Cayman Islands; 3d. Parrotfish; 6d. Bluff, Cayman Brac; 9d. Georgetown harbour; 1s. Turtle in "crawl"; 2s. Ziroma (schooner); 5s. Boat-building; 10s. Government Offices, Grand Cayman.

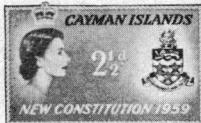

1953 (2 Mar)–62. Designs previously used for King George VI issue but with portrait of Queen Elizabeth II as in T 44/5. Wmk Mult Script CA. P 11½×11 or 11×11½ (4d., £1).

148		¼d. deep bright blue & rose-red (21.2.55)	85	50	
		a. Bright blue and bright rose-red (5.12.56)	2·00	90	
149		½d. purple and bright green (7.7.54)	40	50	
150		1d. brown-olive and indigo (7.7.54)	70	40	
151		1½d. deep green and red-brown (7.7.54)	50	20	
152		2d. reddish violet and cerise (2.6.54)	3·00	85	
153		2½d. turquoise-blue and black (2.6.54)	3·50	80	
154		3d. bright green and blue (21.2.55)	4·00	60	
155		4d. black and deep blue	..	2·00	40
		a. Black and greenish blue (13.10.54)	18·00	18·00	
		b. Black and deep bright blue (10.7.62)	14·00	14·00	
156		6d. lake-brown and deep blue (7.7.54)	1·75	30	
157		9d. scarlet and bluish green (2.6.54)	4·50	30	
158		1s. brown and red-orange (21.2.55)	3·25	20	
159		2s. slate-violet & reddish purple (21.2.55)	13·00	8·00	
160		5s. olive-green and slate-violet (21.2.55)	15·00	5·00	
161		10s. black and rose-red (21.2.55)	15·00	7·50	
161a		£1 blue (6.1.59) ..	..	30·00	10·00
148/61a			Set of 15	85·00	32·00

Designs: Horiz—¼d. Cat boat; ½d. Coconut grove, Cayman Brac; 1d. Green Turtle; 1½d. Thatch rope industry; 2d. Cayman seamen; 2½d. Map of Cayman Islands; 3d. Parrotfish; 6d. Bluff, Cayman Brac; 9d. Georgetown harbour; 1s. Turtle in "crawl"; 2s. Ziroma (schooner); 5s. Boat-building; 10s. Government Offices, Grand Cayman.

1953 (2 June). Coronation. As No. 120 of Antigua, but ptd by B.W.

162		1d. black and emerald	..	30	1·00

46 Arms of the Cayman Islands

(Photo D.L.R.)

1959 (4 July). New Constitution. Wmk Mult Script CA. P 12.

163	46	2½d. black and light blue	..	45	1·60
164		1s. black and orange	..	55	40

CROWN COLONY

47 Cuban Amazon   48 Cat Boat

(Recess B.W.)

1962 (28 Nov)–64. T 47/8 and similar designs. W w 12. P 11×11½ (vert) or 11½×11 (horiz).

165		¼d. emerald and red	..	45	70
		a. Emerald and rose (18.2.64)	..	2·50	2·75
166		1d. black and yellow-olive	..	70	20
167		1½d. yellow and purple	..	2·75	80
168		2d. blue and deep brown	..	75	30
169		2½d. violet and bluish green	..	85	80
170		3d. bright blue and carmine	..	30	10
171		4d. deep green and purple	..	80	60
172		6d. bluish green and sepia	..	3·25	30

173	9d. ultramarine and purple	.. ..	1·50	40
174	1s. sepia and rose-red	..	80	10
175	1s. 3d. bluish green and orange-brown	..	3·50	1·75
176	1s. 9d. deep turquoise and violet	..	14·00	1·25
177	5s. plum and deep green	.. ..	8·00	5·50
178	10s. olive and blue	.. ..	14·00	8·00
179	£1 carmine and black	.. ..	19·00	16·00
165/79		Set of 15	60·00	32·00

Designs: Horiz—1½d. *Schomburgkia thomsoniana* (orchid); 2d. Map of Cayman Islands; 2½d. Fisherman casting net; 3d. West Bay Beach; 4d. Green Turtle; 6d. *Lydia E. Wilson* (schooner); 1s. Iguana; 1s. 3d. Swimming Pool, Cayman Brac; 1s. 9d. Water sports; 5s. Fort George. *Vert*—9d. Angler with King Mackerel; 10s. Coat of Arms; £1 Queen Elizabeth II.

1963 (4 June). *Freedom from Hunger. As No. 146 of Antigua.*
180	1s. 9d. carmine	.. .. ..	30	15

1963 (2 Sept). *Red Cross Centenary. As Nos. 147/8 of Antigua.*
181	1d. red and black	.. ..	30	75
182	1s. 9d. red and blue	..	1·25	1·75

1964 (23 April). *400th Birth Anniv of William Shakespeare. As No. 164 of Antigua.*
183	6d. magenta	..	20	10

1965 (17 May). *I.T.U. Centenary. As Nos. 166/7 of Antigua.*
184	1d. blue and light purple	.. ..	15	10
185	1s. 3d. bright purple and green	..	55	45

1965 (25 Oct). *International Co-operation Year. As Nos. 168/9 of Antigua.*
186	1d. reddish purple and turquoise-green	..	15	10
187	1s. deep bluish green and lavender ..		50	25

1966 (24 Jan). *Churchill Commemoration. As Nos. 170/3 of Antigua.*
188	¼d. new blue	.. ..	10	1·25
	w. Wmk inverted	..	26·00	
189	1d. deep green	.. ..	25	10
190	1s. brown	.. ..	70	10
	w. Wmk inverted	..	4·50	5·00
191	1s. 9d. bluish violet	..	90	75
188/91	..	Set of 4	1·75	2·00

1966 (4 Feb). *Royal Visit. As Nos. 174/5 of Antigua.*
192	1d. black and ultramarine	..	60	20
193	1s. 9d. black and magenta	..	2·25	90

1966 (1 July). *World Cup Football Championships. As Nos. 176/7 of Antigua.*
194	1½d. violet, yellow-green, lake & yellow-brn	15	10
195	1s. 9d. chocolate, blue-grn, lake & yell-brn	50	25

1966 (20 Sept). *Inauguration of W.H.O. Headquarters, Geneva. As Nos. 178/9 of Antigua.*
196	2d. black, yellow-green and light blue	..	50	15
197	1s. 3d. black, light purple and yellow-brown	1·25	60

62 Telephone and Map

(Des V. Whiteley. Litho Harrison)

1966 (5 Dec). *International Telephone Links.* W w **12**. *P* 14½ × 14.
198	**62**	4d. red, black, greenish blue & ol-grn	20	20
199		9d. violet-blue, black, brown-red & lt grn	20	30

1966 (12 Dec*). *20th Anniv of U.N.E.S.C.O. As Nos. 196/8 of Antigua.*
200	1d. slate-violet, red, yellow and orange	..	15	10
201	1s. 9d. orange-yellow, violet and deep olive	..	60	10
202	5s. black, bright purple and orange	..	1·50	70
200/2		Set of 3	2·00	80

*This is the local date of issue; the Crown Agents released the stamps on 1 December.

63 B.A.C. One Eleven 200/400 Airliner over *Ziroma* (Cayman schooner)

(Des V. Whiteley. Photo Harrison)

1966 (17 Dec). *Opening of Cayman Jet Service.* W w **12**. *P* 14½.
203	**63**	1s. black, new blue and olive-green	..	60	30
204		1s. 9d. deep purple-brown, ultramarine and emerald	..	65	35

64 Water-skiing

(Des G. Vasarhelyi. Photo Harrison)

1967 (1 Dec). *International Tourist Year. T* **64** *and similar horiz designs. Multicoloured.* W w **12**. *P* 14½ × 14.
205	**64**	4d. Type **64**	.. ..	50	10
		a. Gold omitted	..	£200	
206		6d. Skin diving	.. ..	50	30
207		1s. Sport fishing	.. ..	50	30
208		1s. 9d. Sailing	.. ..	60	75
205/8			Set of 4	1·90	1·25

A used copy of No. 207 is known with yellow omitted.

68 Former Slaves and Emblem

(Des and photo Harrison)

1968 (3 June). *Human Rights Year.* W w **12**. *P* 14½ × 14.
209	**68**	3d. deep bluish green, black and gold	..	10	10
		w. Wmk inverted	..	60	80
210		9d. brown, gold and myrtle-green	..	10	10
211		5s. ultramarine, gold and myrtle-green	..	30	90
209/11			Set of 3	40	1·00

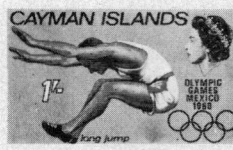

69 Long-jumping

(Des R. Granger Barrett. Litho P.B.)

1968 (1 Oct). *Olympic Games, Mexico. T* **69** *and similar multi-coloured designs.* W w **12**. *P* 13½.
212	Type **69**	.. ..	15	10
213	1s. 3d. High jumping	.. ..	20	25
214	2s. Pole vaulting (*vert*)	.. ..	20	60
212/14	.. ..	Set of 3	50	85

72 "The Adoration of the Shepherds" (Fabritius)

(Des and photo Harrison)

1968–69. *Christmas. T* **72** *and similar horiz design. Centres multicoloured; country name and frames in gold; value and background in colours given.* *P* 14 × 14½.

(a) W w **12**. (18.11.68)
215	**72**	¼d. brown	..	10	20
		a. Gold omitted	..	£190	
216	—	1d. bluish violet	..	10	10
217	**72**	6d. bright blue	..	15	10
218	—	8d. cerise	..	15	15
219	**72**	1s. 3d. bright green	..	20	25
220		2s. grey	..	25	35

(b) No wmk (8.1.69)
221	**72**	¼d. bright purple	..	10	20
215/21			Set of 7	80	1·10

Design:—1d., 8d., 2s. "The Adoration of the Shepherds" (Rembrandt).

74 Grand Cayman Thrush

76 Arms of the Cayman Islands

(Des G. Vasarhelyi. Litho Format)

1969 (5 June). *Designs as T* **74** *and T* **76** *in black, ochre and red (£1) or multicoloured (others). No wmk. P* 14.
222	¼d. Type **74**	..	10	75
223	1d. Brahmin Cattle (*horiz*)	..	10	10
224	2d. Blowholes on the coast (*horiz*)	..	10	10
225	2½d. Map of Grand Cayman (*horiz*)	..	15	10
226	3d. Georgetown scene (*horiz*)	..	15	10
227	4d. Royal Poinciana	..	30	10
228	6d. Cayman Brac and Little Cayman on Chart (*horiz*)	..	30	10
229	8d. Motor vessels at berth (*horiz*)	..	40	10
230	1s. Basket-making (*horiz*)	..	20	10
231	1s. 3d. Beach scene (*horiz*)	..	35	1·50
232	1s. 6d. Straw-rope making (*horiz*)	..	50	1·25
233	2s. Great Barracuda (*horiz*)	..	1·25	80
234	4s. Government House (*horiz*)	..	50	80
235	10s. Type **76**	..	1·00	2·25
236	£1 Queen Elizabeth II (*vert*)	..	1·75	2·50
222/36		Set of 15	6·00	9·00

1969 (11 Aug). *As No. 222, but wmk w* **12** *(sideways).*
237	**74**	¼d. multicoloured	.. ..	30	65

(New Currency. 100 cents = 1 dollar.)

C-DAY
8th September 1969   ¼c =

(89)

1969 (8 Sept). *Decimal Currency. No. 237, and as Nos. 223/36, but wmk w* **12** *(sideways on horiz designs), such as T* **89**.
238	¼ c. on ¼d. Type **74**	..	10	75
239	1 c. on 1d. Brahmin Cattle	..	10	10
240	2 c. on 2d. Blowholes on the coast	..	10	10
241	3 c. on 4d. Royal Poinciana	..	10	10
242	4 c. on 2½d. Map of Grand Cayman	..	10	10
243	5 c. on 6d. Cayman Brac and Little Cayman on Chart	..	10	10
244	7 c. on 8d. Motor vessels at berth	..	10	10
245	8 c. on 3d. Georgetown scene	..	15	10
246	10 c. on 1s. Basket-making	..	25	10
247	12 c. on 1s. 3d. Beach scene	..	35	1·25
248	15 c. on 1s. 6d. Straw-rope making	..	45	85
249	20 c. on 2s. Great Barracuda	..	1·25	1·50
250	40 c. on 4s. Government House	..	45	85
251	$1 on 10s. Type **76**	..	1·50	2·50
	w. Wmk inverted			
252	$2 on £1 Queen Elizabeth II	..	2·00	3·25
238/52		Set of 15	6·00	9·50

90 "Virgin and Child" (Vivarini)

92 "Noli me tangere" (Titian)

(Des adapted by G. Drummond. Photo Harrison)

1969 (14 Nov*). *Christmas. Multicoloured; background colours given.* W w **12** *(sideways on 1, 7 and 20 c.). P* 14½.
253	**90**	¼ c. orange-red	..	10	10
		w. Wmk inverted	..	2·75	5·00
254		¼ c. magenta	..	10	10
		w. Wmk inverted	..	2·75	5·00
255		¼ c. emerald	..	10	10
		a. Gold frame omitted	..	£150	
		w. Wmk inverted	..	1·00	1·75
256		¼ c. new blue	..	10	10
		w. Wmk inverted	..	2·75	5·00
257	—	1 c. ultramarine	..	10	10
258	**90**	5 c. orange-red	..	10	10
259	—	7 c. myrtle-green	..	10	10
260	**90**	12 c. emerald	..	15	15
261	—	20 c. brown-purple	..	20	25
253/61			Set of 9	45	45

Design:—1, 7, 20 c. "The Adoration of the Kings" (Gossaert).
*This is the local release date. The Crown Agents released the stamps on 4 November.

(Des L. Curtis. Litho D.L.R.)

1970 (23 Mar). *Easter. Paintings multicoloured; frame colours given. P* 14.
262	**92**	¼ c. carmine-red	.. ..	10	10
263		¼ c. deep green	.. ..	10	10
264		¼ c. yellow-brown	..	10	10
265		¼ c. pale violet	.. ..	10	10
266		10 c. chalky blue	.. ..	35	10
267		12 c. chestnut	.. ..	40	10
268		40 c. plum	.. ..	55	60
262/8	..	Set of 7	1·25	75

93 Barnaby (*Barnaby Rudge*)　　97 Grand Cayman Thrush

(Des Jennifer Toombs. Photo Harrison)

1970 (17 June). *Death Centenary of Charles Dickens. T **93** and similar vert designs. W w 12 (sideways*). P 14½×14.*

269	1 c. black, olive-green and greenish yellow	10	10
	w. Wmk Crown to right of CA	—	2·25
270	12 c. black, lake-brown and red	30	10
271	20 c. black, ochre-brown and gold	35	10
272	40 c. black, bright ultramarine and new blue	40	35
269/72	*Set of 4*	1·00	50

Designs:—12 c. Sairey Gamp (*Martin Chuzzlewit*); 20 c. Mr. Micawber and David (*David Copperfield*); 40 c. The "Marchioness" (*The Old Curiosity Shop*).
*The normal sideways watermark shows Crown to left of CA, as seen from the back of the stamp.

1970 (8 Sept). *Decimal Currency. Designs as Nos. 223/37, but with values inscr in decimal currency as T **97**. W w 12 (sideways* on cent values).*

273	¼ c. Type 97	10	10
274	1 c. Brahmin Cattle	10	10
275	2 c. Blowholes on the coast	10	10
276	3 c. Royal Poinciana	20	10
277	4 c. Map of Grand Cayman	20	10
278	5 c. Cayman Brac and Little Cayman on Chart	35	10
	w. Wmk Crown to right of CA	12·00	
279	7 c. Motor vessels at berth	30	10
280	8 c. Georgetown scene	30	10
281	10 c. Basket-making	30	10
282	12 c. Beach scene	90	45
283	15 c. Straw-rope making	1·25	3·00
284	20 c. Great Barracuda	2·50	1·25
285	40 c. Government House	85	75
286	$1 Type 76	1·25	4·75
	w. Wmk inverted	9·00	
287	$2 Queen Elizabeth II	2·00	4·75
273/87	*Set of 15*	9·50	14·00

*The normal sideways watermark shows Crown to left of CA, as seen from the back of the stamp.

98 The Three Wise Men

(Des G. Drummond. Litho Format)

1970 (8 Oct). *Christmas. T **98** and similar horiz design. W w 12 (sideways*). P 14.*

288	**98** ¼ c. apple-green, grey and emerald	10	10
	w. Wmk Crown to right of CA	5·00	5·00
289	– 1 c. black, lemon and turquoise-green	10	10
290	**98** 5 c. grey, red-orange and crimson	10	10
291	– 10 c. black, lemon and orange-red	10	10
292	**98** 12 c. grey, pale turquoise & ultramarine	15	10
293	– 20 c. black, lemon and green	20	15
288/93	*Set of 6*	55	30

Design:—1, 10, 20 c. Nativity scene and Globe.
*The normal sideways watermark shows Crown to left of CA, as seen from the back of the stamp.

100 Grand Cayman Terrapin

(Des V. Whiteley. Photo Harrison)

1971 (28 Jan). *Turtles. T **100** and similar diamond-shaped designs. W w 12 (sideways*, reading from inscr to "ISLANDS"). P 14½×14.*

294	5 c. Type 100	30	25
	w. Wmk Crown to right of CA	17·00	
295	7 c. Green Turtle	35	25
	w. Wmk Crown to right of CA	60·00	
296	12 c. Hawksbill Turtle	55	30
297	20 c. Turtle Farm	1·00	1·40
294/7	*Set of 4*	2·00	2·00

*The normal sideways watermark shows Crown to left of CA, as seen from the back of the stamp.

101 *Dendrophylax fawcettii*　　102 "Adoration of the Kings" (French, 15th Cent)

(Des Sylvia Goaman. Litho Questa)

1971 (7 Apr). *Orchids. T **101** and similar vert designs. Multicoloured. W w 12. P 14.*

298	¼ c. Type 101	10	90
299	2 c. *Schomburgkia thomsoniana*	50	70
300	10 c. *Vanilla claviculata*	1·25	50
301	40 c. *Oncidium variegatum*	3·25	3·50
298/301	*Set of 4*	4·50	5·00

(Des Jennifer Toombs. Litho Questa)

1971 (15 Oct*). *Christmas. T **102** and similar vert designs. Multicoloured. W w 12. P 14.*

302	¼ c. Type 102	10	10
	w. Wmk inverted	2·00	
303	1 c. "The Nativity" (Parisian, 14th Cent.)	10	10
304	5 c. "Adoration of the Magi" (Burgundian, 15th Cent.)	10	10
305	12 c. Type 102	20	15
306	15 c. As 1 c.	20	25
307	20 c. As 5 c.	25	35
302/7	*Set of 6*	70	80
MS308	113×115 mm. Nos. 302/7	1·25	2·25
	w. Wmk inverted	£225	

*This is the local date of issue. The Crown Agents released the stamps on 27 September.

103 Turtle and Telephone Cable

(Des Anglo Arts Associates. Litho Walsall)

1972 (10 Jan). *Co-Axial Telephone Cable. W w 12 (sideways*). P 14.*

309	**103** 2 c. multicoloured	10	10
310	10 c. multicoloured	15	10
	w. Wmk Crown to right of CA	8·00	
311	40 c. multicoloured	30	40
	w. Wmk Crown to right of CA	75	
309/11	*Set of 3*	45	45

*The normal sideways watermark shows Crown to left of CA, as seen from the back of the stamp.

104 Court House Building

(Des C. Abbott. Litho Questa)

1972 (15 Aug). *New Government Buildings. T **104** and similar horiz design. Multicoloured. W w 12. P 13½.*

312	5 c. Type 104	10	10
313	15 c. Legislative Assembly Building	10	10
314	25 c. Type 104	15	15
315	40 c. As 15 c.	20	30
312/15	*Set of 4*	35	45
MS316	121×108 mm. Nos. 312/15	70	2·00
	w. Wmk inverted	30·00	

105 Hawksbill Turtle and Queen or Pink Conch

(Des (from photograph by D. Groves) and photo Harrison)

1972 (20 Nov). *Royal Silver Wedding. Multicoloured; background colour given. W w 12. P 14 × 14½.*

317	**105** 12 c. deep slate-violet	15	10
318	30 c. yellow-olive	15	20
	a. Blue omitted*	£425	
	w. Wmk inverted	3·00	

*The omission of the blue colour results in the Duke's suit appearing sepia instead of deep blue.

106 $1 Coin and Note　　107 "The Way of Sorrow"

(Des and photo D.L.R.)

1973 (15 Jan). *First Issue of Currency. T **106** and similar horiz designs. Multicoloured. W w 12 (sideways*). P 13.*

319	3 c. Type 106	20	10
320	6 c. $5 Coin and note	20	20
321	15 c. $10 Coin and note	60	30
322	25 c. $25 Coin and note	80	45
319/22	*Set of 4*	1·60	95
MS323	128×107 mm. Nos. 319/22	3·25	3·25
	w. Wmk Crown to right of CA	70·00	

*The normal sideways watermark shows Crown to left of CA, as seen from the back of the stamp.

(Des G. Drummond. Litho Questa)

1973 (11 Apr*). *Easter. T **107** and similar multicoloured designs showing stained-glass windows. W w 12 (sideways on 10 and 12 c.). P 14½.*

324	10 c. Type 107	15	10
325	12 c. "Christ Resurrected"	20	10
326	20 c. "The Last Supper" (*horiz*)	25	15
327	30 c. "Christ on the Cross" (*horiz*)	30	25
324/7	*Set of 4*	80	45
MS328	122 × 105 mm. Nos. 324/7. Imperf	1·00	1·60

*This is the local date of issue; the Crown Agents released the stamps on 15 March.

108 "The Nativity" (Sforza Book of Hours)　　109 White-winged Dove

(Des J. Cooter. Litho Questa)

1973 (2 Oct). *Christmas. T **108** and similar vert design. W w 12 (sideways). P 14.*

329	**108** 3 c. multicoloured	10	10
330	– 5 c. multicoloured	10	10
331	**108** 9 c. multicoloured	15	10
332	– 12 c. multicoloured	15	10
333	**108** 15 c. multicoloured	15	15
334	– 25 c. multicoloured	20	25
329/34	*Set of 6*	65	50

Design:—5, 12, 25 c. "The Adoration of the Magi" (Breviary of Queen Isabella).

1973 (14 Nov). *Royal Wedding. As Nos. 165/6 of Anguilla. Centre multicoloured. W w 12 (sideways). P 13½.*

335	10 c. sage-green	10	10
336	30 c. bright mauve	15	10

(Des M. Goaman. Litho Walsall)

1974 (2 Jan). *Birds (1st series). T **109** and similar vert designs. Multicoloured. W w 12 (sideways). P 14.*

337	3 c. Type 109	2·00	30
338	10 c. Vitelline Warbler	2·75	30
339	12 c. Antillean Grackle	2·75	30
340	20 c. West Indian Red-bellied Woodpecker	4·25	80
341	30 c. Stripe-headed Tanager	5·50	1·50
342	50 c. Yucatan Vireo	7·00	4·50
337/42	*Set of 6*	22·00	7·00

See also Nos. 383/8.

110 Old School Building

(Des PAD Studio. Litho Questa)

1974 (1 May). *25th Anniv of University of West Indies. T **110** and similar horiz designs. Multicoloured. W w 12 (sideways). P 14.*

343	12 c. Type 110	10	10
344	20 c. New Comprehensive School	15	15
345	30 c. Creative Arts Centre, Mona	15	55
343/5	*Set of 3*	30	70

111 Hermit Crab and Staghorn Coral

(Des J.W. Litho Kynoch Press)

1974 (1 Aug). *Multicoloured designs as T 111 (size 41½ × 27 mm). W w 12 (sideways on $1 and $2). P* 14.

346	1 c. Type 111	..	3·50	1·25
347	3 c. Treasure-chest and Lion's Paw		3·50	75
348	4 c. Treasure and Spotted Scorpionfish		50	70
349	5 c. Flintlock pistol and Brain Coral		3·00	75
350	6 c. Blackbeard and Green Turtle	..	35	2·25
351	9 c. Jewelled pomander and Porkfish		3·50	7·00
352	10 c. Spiny Lobster and treasure	..	4·50	80
353	12 c. Jewelled sword and dagger, and Sea-fan		35	1·60
354	15 c. Cabrit's Murex (*Murex cabritii*) and treasure		45	1·25
355	20 c. Queen or Pink Conch (*Strombus gigas*) and treasure		10·00	1·75
356	25 c. Hogfish and Treasure	..	45	70
357	40 c. Gold chalice and sea-whip		4·00	1·25
358	$1 Coat of arms (*vert*)	..	2·75	3·25
359	$2 Queen Elizabeth II (*vert*)		4·00	15·00
346/59		*Set of* 14	35·00	35·00

See also Nos. 364/6, 412/19 and 445/52.

112 Sea Captain and Ship (Shipbuilding)

(Des G. Vasarhelyi. Litho D.L.R.)

1974 (7 Oct). *Local Industries. T 112 and similar horiz designs. Multicoloured. W w 12. P* 14×13½.

360	8 c. Type 112	..	20	10
	w. Wmk inverted	..	30	20
361	12 c. Thatcher and cottages	..	20	10
	w. Wmk inverted	..	30	30
362	20 c. Farmer and plantation	..	25	20
	w. Wmk inverted	..	40	40
360/2		*Set of* 3	60	35
MS363	92×132 mm. Nos. 360/2		1·50	2·75
	w. Wmk inverted	..	2·25	

1974–75. *As Nos. 346/7 and design of 351, but W w 12 (sideways*).*

364	1 c. Type 111 (29.9.75)	..	4·00	1·50
365	3 c. Treasure-chest and Lions-paw (12.11.74)		4·50	2·00
	w. Wmk Crown to right of CA		4·50	
366	8 c. Jewelled pomander and Porkfish (16.12.74)		2·50	8·50
364/6		*Set of* 3	10·00	11·00

*The normal sideways watermark shows Crown to left of CA, as seen from the back of the stamp.
Nos. 367/79 vacant.

113 Arms of Cinque Ports and Lord Warden's Flag   114 "The Crucifixion"

(Des P. Powell. Litho D.L.R.)

1974 (30 Nov). *Birth Centenary of Sir Winston Churchill. T 113 and similar vert design. Multicoloured. W w 12 (sideways*). P* 13½×14.

380	12 c. Type 113	..	15	10
381	50 c. Churchill's coat of arms		45	70
	w. Wmk Crown to right of CA (pair)		32·00	
MS382	98×86 mm. Nos. 380/1		60	1·60

*The normal sideways watermark shows Crown to left of CA on Nos. 380/1 or Crown to right of CA on MS382, as seen from the back of the stamp.

(Des M. Goaman. Litho Questa)

1975 (1 Jan). *Birds (2nd series). Multicoloured designs as T 109. W w 12 (sideways). P* 14.

383	3 c. Common Flicker	..	70	45
384	10 c. Black-billed Whistling Duck	..	1·25	45
385	12 c. Yellow Warbler	..	1·40	65
386	20 c. White-bellied Dove	..	2·00	2·00
387	30 c. Magnificent Frigate Bird	..	3·25	4·25
388	50 c. Cuban Amazon	..	3·75	11·00
	a. Error. Wmk Lesotho W 53 (inverted)		£600	
383/8		*Set of* 6	11·00	17·00

(Des PAD Studio. Litho D.L.R.)

1975 (24 Mar). *Easter. French Pastoral Staffs. T 114 and similar vert design showing "The Crucifixion" (different). Multicoloured. W w 12 (sideways). P* 13½ × 14.

389	114	15 c. multicoloured	10	15
390	–	35 c. multicoloured	20	30
MS391	128 × 98 mm. Nos. 389/90. W w 12 (*upright*)		65	2·50
	a. Error. Imperf	..		

See also Nos. 396/MS398.

115 Israel Hands

(Des J.W. Litho Harrison)

1975 (25 July). *Pirates. T 115 and similar horiz designs. Multicoloured. W w 12 (sideways*). P* 14.

392	10 c. Type 115	..	30	15
393	12 c. John Fenn	..	30	15
394	20 c. Thomas Anstis	..	50	40
	w. Wmk Crown to right of CA		60·00	
395	30 c. Edward Low	..	60	1·50
392/5		*Set of* 4	1·50	2·00

*The normal sideways watermark shows Crown to left of CA, as seen from the back of the stamp.

(Des PAD Studio. Litho Questa)

1975 (31 Oct). *Christmas. Vert designs as T 114 showing "Virgin and Child with Angels" (both different). W w 14. P* 14.

396	12 c. multicoloured	..	10	10
397	50 c. multicoloured	..	30	30
MS398	113 × 85 mm. Nos. 396/7	..	1·00	2·75

116 Registered Cover, Government House and Sub-Post Office

(Des J. Cooter. Litho Questa)

1976 (12 Mar). *75th Anniv of First Cayman Is. Postage Stamp. T 116 and similar horiz designs. Multicoloured. W w 14 (sideways). P* 13½.

399	10 c. Type 116	..	15	10
400	20 c. ½d. stamp and 1890–94 postmark		20	15
401	30 c. 1d. stamp and 1908 surcharge	..	30	25
402	50 c. ½d. and 1d. stamps	..	45	50
399/402		*Set of* 4	1·00	85
MS403	117 × 147 mm. Nos. 399/402		2·50	3·00

117 Seals of Georgia, Delaware and New Hampshire

(Des P. Powell. Litho J.W.)

1976 (29 May). *Bicentenary of American Revolution. T 117 and similar horiz designs showing seals of the States given. Multicoloured. W w 14 (sideways). P* 13½ × 14.

404	10 c. Type 117	..	50	15
405	15 c. S. Carolina, New Jersey and Maryland		65	20
406	20 c. Virginia, Rhode Is. and Massachusetts	..	75	25
407	25 c. New York, Connecticut and N. Carolina		75	35
408	30 c. Pennsylvania seal, Liberty Bell and U.S. Great Seal		90	40
404/8		*Set of* 5	3·25	1·25
MS409	166 × 124 mm. Nos. 404/8. P 14		5·00	8·00

118 "470" Dinghies   119 Queen Elizabeth II and Westminster Abbey

(Des C. Abbott. Litho D.L.R.)

1976 (16 Aug). *Olympic Games, Montreal. T 118 and similar vert design. Multicoloured. W w 14. P* 14.

410	20 c. Type 118	..	40	10
411	50 c. Racing dinghy	..	70	50

1976 (3 Sept)–78. *As Nos. 347/9, 352, 355, 358/9 and 366, but W w 14 (upright on $1, inverted on $2, sideways* on others). Chalk-surfaced paper (4, 5 c. and $1) or ordinary paper (others).*

412	3 c. Treasure-chest and Lion's Paw		1·00	4·00
	a. Chalk-surfaced paper (19.10.77)		4·50	4·50
413	4 c. Treasure and Spotted Scorpionfish (19.10.77)		1·25	4·50
414	5 c. Flintlock pistol and Brain Coral (19.10.77)		5·50	5·50
415	8 c. Jewelled pomander and Porkfish		8·50	4·00
	a. Chalk-surfaced paper (19.10.77)		10·00	4·75
416	10 c. Spiny Lobster and treasure		3·00	3·50
	a. Chalk-surfaced paper (27.1.78)		3·00	3·75
417	20 c. Queen or Pink Conch (*Strombus gigas*) and treasure		3·50	3·00
	a. Chalk-surfaced paper (27.1.78)		3·50	5·00
418	$1 Coat of arms (19.10.77)		6·50	9·00
419	$2 Queen Elizabeth II		7·50	6·50
	a. Chalk-surfaced paper (19.10.77)		11·00	17·00
412/19		*Set of* 8	32·00	35·00

*The normal sideways watermark shows Crown to right of CA on Nos. 416a and 417a, and Crown to left of CA on all other printings of horizontal designs, *all as seen from the back of the stamp.*

(Des BG Studio. Litho Questa)

1977 (7 Feb). *Silver Jubilee. T 119 and similar multicoloured designs. W w 14 (sideways on 50 c.). P* 13½.

427	8 c. Prince of Wales' visit, 1973	..	10	20
	w. Wmk inverted	..	8·00	
428	30 c. Type 119	..	15	40
	w. Wmk inverted	..	27·00	
429	50 c. Preparation for the Anointing (*horiz*)		30	75
427/9		*Set of* 3	50	1·25

120 Scuba Diving

(Des Jennifer Toombs. Litho J.W.)

1977 (25 July). *Tourism. T 120 and similar horiz designs. Multicoloured. W w 14 (sideways). P* 13½.

430	5 c. Type 120	..	10	10
431	10 c. Exploring a wreck	..	15	10
432	20 c. Royal Gramma ("Fairy Basslet") (fish)		45	20
433	25 c. Sergeant Major (fish)	..	55	35
430/3		*Set of* 4	1·10	60
MS434	146×89 mm. Nos. 430/3. P 14½		2·00	3·75

121 *Composia fidelissima* (moth)

(Des J. Cooter. Litho Enschedé)

1977 (2 Dec). *Butterflies and Moth. T 121 and similar horiz designs. Multicoloured. W w 14 (sideways). P* 14×13.

435	5 c. Type 121	..	75	20
436	8 c. *Heliconius charithonia*	..	85	20
437	10 c. *Danaus gilippus*	..	85	20
438	15 c. *Agraulis vanillae*	..	1·25	45
439	20 c. *Junonia evarete*	..	1·25	45
440	30 c. *Anartia jatrophae*	..	1·50	70
435/40		*Set of* 6	5·75	2·00

122 *Southward* (liner)   123 "The Crucifixion" (Dürer)

(Des G. Hutchins. Litho Questa)

1978 (23 Jan). *New Harbour and Cruise Ships. T 122 and similar multicoloured designs. W w 14 (sideways* on 3, 5 c.). P* 14×14½ (3, 5 c.) or 14½×14 (others).

441	3 c. Type 122	..	30	10
	w. Wmk Crown to right of CA	..	17·00	
442	5 c. *Renaissance* (liner)	..	30	10
443	30 c. New harbour (*vert*)	..	80	25
444	50 c. *Daphne* (liner) (*vert*)	..	1·10	55
441/4		*Set of* 4	2·25	85

*The normal sideways watermark shows Crown to left of CA, as seen from the back of the stamp.

(Litho Walsall)

1978 (16 Mar)–80. *Designs as Nos. 346/7, 349, 352, 355 and 357/9 but smaller, 40 × 26 or 26 × 40 mm. W w 14 (sideways on 1 to 40 c.). Chalk-surfaced paper.*

445	1 c. Type 111	1·00	1·25
446	3 c. Treasure-chest and Lion's Paw	80	50
447	5 c. Flintlock pistol and Brain Coral (11.12.79)	2·00	2·50
448	10 c. Spiny Lobster and treasure (25.5.78)	1·60	60
449	20 c. Queen or Pink Conch (*Strombus gigas*) and treasure (25.5.78)	3·25	1·25
450	40 c. Gold chalice and sea-whip (1979*)	13·00	15·00
451	$1 Coat of arms (30.7.80)	18·00	8·00
452	$2 Queen Elizabeth II (3.4.80)	6·00	26·00
445/52	*Set of 8*	42·00	50·00

*Supplies of No. 450 were sent to Cayman Islands on 7 May 1979. It is not known when these stamps were first placed on sale.
Nos. 453/8 vacant.

(Des Jennifer Toombs. Litho Cartor)

1978 (20 Mar). *Easter and 450th Death Anniv of Dürer. T 123 and similar vert designs. W w 14 (inverted on 20 c.). P 12.*

459	10 c. magenta and black	20	10
	w. Wmk inverted	18·00	
460	15 c. yellow and black	30	15
	w. Wmk inverted	16·00	
461	20 c. turquoise-green and black	40	20
	w. Wmk upright		
462	30 c. lilac and black	55	35
	w. Wmk inverted	2·25	
459/62	*Set of 4*	1·25	70
MS463	120×108 mm. Nos. 459/62	3·50	4·50
	w. Wmk inverted	4·50	

Designs:—15 c. "Christ at Emmaus"; 20 c. "The Entry into Jerusalem"; 30 c. "Christ washing Peter's Feet".

124 "Explorers" Singing Game 125 Yale of Beaufort

(Des Walsall. Litho Questa)

1978 (25 Apr). *3rd International Council Meeting of Girls' Brigade. T 124 and similar vert designs. Multicoloured. W w 14. P 14.*

464	3 c. Type 124	20	10
465	10 c. Colour party	30	10
466	20 c. Girls and Duke of Edinburgh Award interests	60	20
467	50 c. Girls using domestic skills	1·10	80
464/7	*Set of 4*	2·00	1·10

(Des C. Abbott. Litho Questa)

1978 (2 June). *25th Anniv of Coronation. T 125 and similar vert designs. P 15.*

468	30 c. apple-green, deep magenta and silver	20	25
	a. Sheetlet. Nos. 468/70 × 2	1·10	
469	30 c. multicoloured	20	25
470	30 c. apple-green, deep magenta and silver	20	25
468/70	*Set of 3*	55	65

Designs:—No. 468, Type 125; No. 469, Queen Elizabeth II; No. 470, Barn Owl.
Nos. 468/70 were printed together in small sheets of 6, containing two se-tenant strips of 3, with horizontal gutter margin between.

126 Four-eyed Butterflyfish

(Des G. Hutchins, Litho Walsall)

1978 (29 Aug). *Fish (1st series). T 126 and similar horiz designs. Multicoloured. W w 14 (sideways). P 14.*

471	3 c. Type 126	25	10
472	5 c. Grey Angelfish	30	10
473	10 c. Squirrelfish	45	10
474	15 c. Queen Parrotfish	60	30
475	20 c. Spanish Hogfish	70	35
476	30 c. Queen Angelfish	80	25
471/6	*Set of 6*	2·75	1·25

Examples of the 15 c. value inscribed "SERGEANT MAJOR FISH" and 20 c. inscribed "PARROT FISH" were prepared, but not issued for postal purposes.
See also Nos. 483/8.

127 Lockheed L.18 Lodestar

(Des A. Theobald. Litho Format)

1979 (5 Feb). *25th Anniv of Owen Roberts Airfield. T 127 and similar horiz designs. Multicoloured. W w 14 (sideways). P 14½ × 14.*

477	3 c. Type 127	30	15
478	5 c. Consolidated PBY-5A Catalina	30	15
479	10 c. Vickers Viking 1B	35	15
480	15 c. B.A.C. One Eleven 475 on tarmac	65	25
481	20 c. Piper PA-31 Cheyenne II, Bell 47G Trooper helicopter and Hawker Siddeley H.S.125	75	35
482	30 c. B.A.C. One Eleven 475 over airfield	1·00	50
477/82	*Set of 6*	3·00	1·40

128 Trumpetfish

(Des R. Granger Barrett. Litho Questa)

1979 (20 Apr). *Fish (2nd series). T 128 and similar horiz designs. Multicoloured. W w 14 (sideways*). P 14.*

483	1 c. Type 128	10	10
	w. Wmk Crown to right of CA	27·00	
484	3 c. Nassau Grouper	25	10
485	5 c. French Angelfish	25	10
	w. Wmk Crown to right of CA	3·50	
486	10 c. Schoolmaster Snapper	35	10
487	20 c. Banded Butterflyfish	55	25
488	50 c. Black-barred Soldierfish	1·00	70
483/8	*Set of 6*	2·25	1·25

*The normal sideways watermark shows Crown to left of CA, as seen from the back of the stamp.

129 1900 1d. Stamp

(Des J.W. Litho Walsall)

1979 (15 Aug). *Death Centenary of Sir Rowland Hill. T 129 and similar horiz designs showing stamps and Sir Rowland Hill. W w 14 (sideways). P 13½.*

489	5 c. black, rose-carmine and grey-blue	10	10
490	10 c. multicoloured	15	10
491	20 c. multicoloured	20	25
489/91	*Set of 3*	30	30
MS492	138 × 90 mm. 50 c. multicoloured	55	65

Designs:—10 c. Great Britain 1902 3d.; 20 c. 1955 £1 definitive; 50 c. 1908 2½d.

130 Holy Family and Angels

(Des G. Vasarhelyi. Litho Secura, Singapore)

1979 (20 Nov). *Christmas. T 130 and similar horiz designs. Multicoloured. W w 14 (sideways*). P 13½×13.*

493	10 c. Type 130	15	10
	w. Wmk Crown to right of CA	45	
494	20 c. Angels appearing before shepherds	20	10
	w. Wmk Crown to right of CA	55	
495	30 c. Nativity scene	30	20
	w. Wmk Crown to right of CA	75	
496	40 c. Wise men following star	40	30
	w. Wmk Crown to right of CA	1·00	
493/6	*Set of 4*	95	60

*The normal sideways watermark shows Crown to left of CA, as seen from the back of the stamp.

131 Local Rotary Project

(Des Walsall. Litho Secura, Singapore)

1980 (14 Feb). *75th Anniv of Rotary International. T 131 and similar designs in black, bistre-yellow and deep ultramarine. W w 14 (sideways on 20 c.). P 13½ × 13 (20 c.) or 13 × 13½ (others).*

497	20 c. Type 131	20	15
498	30 c. Paul P. Harris (founder) (*vert*)	25	20
499	50 c. Rotary anniversary emblem (*vert*)	35	40
	a. Black (Royal cypher, and face value) omitted	£750	
497/9	*Set of 3*	70	60

132 Walking Mail Carrier (late 19th-century)

(Des J.W. Litho Walsall)

1980 (6 May). *"London 1980" International Stamp Exhibition. T 132 and similar horiz designs. Multicoloured. W w 14 (sideways). P 14.*

500	5 c. Type 132	10	10
501	10 c. Delivering mail by cat boat (late 19th-century)	15	10
502	15 c. Mounted mail carrier (early 20th-century)	30	10
503	30 c. Horse-drawn waggonette (early 20th-century)	35	15
504	40 c. Postman on bicycle (mid 20th-century)	45	15
505	$1 Motor transport (late 20th-century)	65	55
500/5	*Set of 6*	1·75	1·00

133 Queen Elizabeth the Queen Mother at the Derby, 1976 134 American Thorny Oyster (*Spondylus americanus*)

(Des and litho Harrison)

1980 (4 Aug). *80th Birthday of Queen Elizabeth the Queen Mother. W w 14 (sideways). P 14.*

506	133 20 c. multicoloured	20	25

(Des J.W. Litho Walsall)

1980 (12 Aug). *Shells (1st series). T 134 and similar horiz designs. Multicoloured. W w 14 (sideways). P 14½ × 14.*

507	5 c. Type 134	50	10
508	10 c. West Indian Murex (*Murex brevifrons*)	50	10
509	30 c. Angular Triton (*Cymatium femorale*)	1·00	40
510	50 c. Caribbean Vase (*Vasum muricatum*)	1·10	80
507/10	*Set of 4*	2·75	1·25

See also Nos. 565/8 and 582/5.

135 Lantana 136 Juvenile Tarpon and Fire Sponge

(Des G. Hutchins. Litho Rosenbaum Bros, Vienna)

1980 (21 Oct). *Flowers (1st series). T 135 and similar horiz designs. Multicoloured. W w 14 (sideways). P 13½.*

511	5 c. Type 135	15	10
512	15 c. Bauhinia	35	10
513	30 c. Hibiscus Rosa	50	10
514	$1 Milk and Wine Lily	1·10	90
511/14	*Set of 4*	1·90	1·10

See also Nos. 541/4.

(Des G. Drummond. Litho J.W.)

1980 (9 Dec)–82. *Flora and Fauna of the Mangrove Swamp. Vert designs as T 136. Multicoloured. W w 14. P 13½×13.*

A. Without imprint date

515A	3 c. Type 136	50	1·50
516A	5 c. Flat Tree or Mangrove-root Oyster (*Isognomon alatus*)	90	1·50
517A	10 c. Mangrove Crab	40	80
518A	15 c. Lizard and *Phyciodes phaon* (butterfly)	1·00	1·50
519A	20 c. Louisiana Heron	1·50	2·00
520A	30 c. Red Mangrove flower	70	1·00
521A	40 c. Red Mangrove seeds	75	1·00
522A	50 c. Waterhouse's Leaf-nosed Bat	1·25	1·50
523A	$1 Black-crowned Night Heron	5·50	5·00
524A	$2 Cayman Islands coat of arms	1·50	3·75
525A	$4 Queen Elizabeth II	2·25	4·75
515A/25A	*Set of 11*	14·00	22·00

B. With imprint date at foot of designs (14.6.82)

515B	3 c. Type 136	5·50	4·00
516B	5 c. Flat Tree or Mangrove-root Oyster (*Isognomon alatus*)	1·00	70
517B	10 c. Mangrove Crab	1·25	80
518B	15 c. Lizard and *Phyciodes phaon* (butterfly)	4·50	1·50
519B	20 c. Louisiana Heron	2·50	2·00
520B	30 c. Red Mangrove flower	1·50	1·50

521B	40 c. Red Mangrove seeds	..	1·50	1·50
522B	50 c. Waterhouse's Leaf-nosed Bat	..	2·00	2·00
523B	$1 Black-crowned Night Heron	..	6·00	4·50
524B	$2 Cayman Islands coat of arms	..	3·75	4·00
525B	$4 Queen Elizabeth II	..	9·00	11·00
515B/25B		Set of 11	35·00	30·00

Imprint dates: "1982", Nos. 515B/25B; "1984", No. 516B; "1985", Nos. 516B/24B.

For stamps in these designs, but watermark **w 16**, see Nos. 626 and 631/2.

EASTER 1981

137 Eucharist   138 Wood Slave

(Des Jennifer Toombs. Litho Questa)

1981 (17 Mar). *Easter.* T **137** *and similar vert designs. Multicoloured.* W w **14**. P 14.

526	3 c. Type 137	..	10	10
527	10 c. Crown of thorns	..	10	10
528	20 c. Crucifix	..	20	10
529	$1 Lord Jesus Christ	..	70	80
526/9		Set of 4	90	90

(Des R. Granger Barrett. Litho Rosenbaum Bros, Vienna)

1981 (16 June). *Reptiles and Amphibians.* T **138** *and similar horiz designs. Multicoloured.* W w **14** (*sideways**). P 13½.

530	20 c. Type 138	..	30	20
	w. Wmk Crown to left of CA		70	
531	30 c. Cayman Iguana	..	45	35
	w. Wmk Crown to left of CA		90	
532	40 c. Lion Lizard	..	55	45
	w. Wmk Crown to left of CA		1·00	
533	50 c. Terrapin ("Hickatee")	..	65	55
	w. Wmk Crown to right of CA		1·25	
530/3		Set of 4	1·75	1·40

*The normal sideways watermark shows Crown to right of CA on Nos. 530/2 and to left on No. 533, *as seen from the back of the stamp.*

139 Prince Charles   140 Disabled Scuba Divers

(Des J.W. Litho Walsall)

1981 (22 July). *Royal Wedding.* T **139** *and similar vert designs. Multicoloured.* W w **14**. P 14.

534	20 c. Wedding bouquet from Cayman Islands		15	10
535	30 c. Type 139	..	20	10
536	$1 Prince Charles and Lady Diana Spencer		50	75
534/6		Set of 3	75	80

(Des J.W. Litho Walsall)

1981 (29 Sept). *International Year for Disabled Persons.* T **140** *and similar horiz designs. Multicoloured.* W w **14** (*sideways*). P 14.

537	5 c. Type 140	..	10	10
538	15 c. Old School for the Handicapped	..	25	20
539	20 c. New School for the Handicapped		30	25
540	$1 Disabled people in wheelchairs, by the sea	1·25	85
537/40		Set of 4	1·60	1·25

(Des G. Hutchins. Litho Questa)

1981 (20 Oct). *Flowers* (2nd series). *Horiz designs as* T **135**. *Multicoloured.* W w **14** (*sideways*). P 13½.

541	3 c. Bougainvillea	..	10	10
542	10 c. Morning Glory	..	20	10
543	20 c. Wild Amaryllis	..	45	25
544	$1 Cordia	..	1·75	1·75
541/4		Set of 4	2·25	2·00

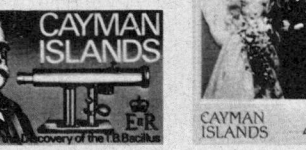

141 Dr. Robert Koch   142 Bride and Groom
and Microscope   walking down Aisle

(Des and litho Walsall)

1982 (24 Mar). *Centenary of Robert Koch's Discovery of Tubercle Bacillus.* T **141** *and similar multicoloured designs.* W w **14** (*sideways on 15 c, inverted on 30 c.*). P 14½.

545	15 c. Type 141	..	25	25
546	30 c. Koch looking through microscope (*vert*)	45	45
547	40 c. Microscope (*vert*)	..	70	70
548	50 c. Dr. Robert Koch (*vert*)	..	80	80
545/8		Set of 4	2·00	2·00

(Des Jennifer Toombs. Litho J.W.)

1982 (1 July). *21st Birthday of Princess of Wales.* T **142** *and similar vert designs. Multicoloured.* W w **14**. P 13.

549	20 c. Cayman Islands coat of arms	..	30	35
550	30 c. Lady Diana Spencer in London, June 1981	70	45
	w. Wmk inverted		3·00	
551	40 c. Type 142	..	70	65
552	50 c. Formal portrait	..	2·25	90
	w. Wmk inverted		5·00	
549/52		Set of 4	3·50	2·10

143 Pitching Tent   144 "Madonna and Child
with the Infant Baptist"

(Des L. Walker. Litho Questa)

1982 (24 Aug). *75th Anniv of Boy Scout Movement.* T **143** *and similar horiz designs. Multicoloured.* W w **14** (*sideways*). P 14.

553	3 c. Type 143	..	15	10
554	20 c. Scouts camping	..	55	40
555	30 c. Cub Scouts and Leaders	..	70	55
556	50 c. Boating skills	..	1·10	85
553/6		Set of 4	2·25	1·75

(Des PAD Studio. Litho Questa)

1982 (26 Oct). *Christmas. Raphael Paintings.* T **144** *and similar vert designs. Multicoloured.* W w **14**. P 14½ × 14.

557	3 c. Type 144	..	10	10
558	10 c. "Madonna of the Tower"	..	20	20
	w. Wmk inverted			
559	20 c. "Ansidei Madonna"	..	35	35
560	30 c. "Madonna and Child"	..	50	50
	w. Wmk inverted			
557/60		Set of 4	1·00	1·00

145 Mace

(Des and litho Walsall)

1982 (9 Nov). *150th Anniv of Representative Government.* T **145** *and similar horiz designs. Multicoloured.* W w **14** (*sideways*). P 14½ × 14.

561	3 c. Type 145	..	10	20
562	10 c. Old Courthouse	..	20	20
563	20 c. Commonwealth Parliamentary Association coat of arms	35	45
564	30 c. Legislative Assembly building	..	50	90
561/4		Set of 4	1·00	1·60

(Des J.W. Litho Format)

1983 (11 Jan). *Shells* (2nd series). *Horiz designs as* T **134**. *Multicoloured.* W w **14** (*sideways*). P 13½ × 13.

565	5 c. Colourful Atlantic Moon (*Natica canrena*)	15	20
566	10 c. King Helmet (*Cassis tuberosa*)	..	25	20
567	20 c. Rooster-tail Conch (*Strombus gallus*)	45	40
568	$1 Reticulated Cowrie-helmet (*Cypraecassis testiculus*)	1·75	3·75
565/8		Set of 4	2·40	4·00

146 Legislative Building, Cayman Brac

(Des C. Abbott. Litho Questa)

1983 (15 Feb). *Royal Visit.* T **146** *and similar multicoloured designs.* W w **14** (*sideways on 20 c., 30 c.*). P 14.

569	20 c. Type 146	..	45	35
570	30 c. Legislative Building, Grand Cayman	60	50
571	50 c. Duke of Edinburgh (*vert*)	..	1·25	90
572	$1 Queen Elizabeth II (*vert*)	..	1·75	1·50
569/72		Set of 4	4·00	3·25
MS573	113 × 94 mm. Nos. 569/72 (wmk sideways)	4·00	4·25

147 Satellite View of Earth

(Des J.W. Litho Questa)

1983 (14 Mar). *Commonwealth Day.* T **147** *and similar horiz designs. Multicoloured.* W w **14** (*sideways*). P 14.

574	3 c. Type 147	..	15	10
575	15 c. Cayman Islands and Commonwealth flags	35	30
576	20 c. Fishing	..	40	35
577	40 c. Portrait of Queen Elizabeth II	..	65	65
574/7		Set of 4	1·40	1·25

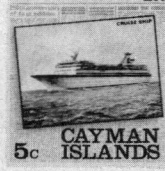

148 MRCU Cessna 188 Ag   149 Song of Norway
Wagon Aircraft   (cruise liner)

(Des Harrison. Litho Questa)

1983 (10 Oct). *Bicentenary of Manned Flight.* T **148** *and similar horiz designs. Multicoloured.* W w **14** (*sideways*). P 14.

578	3 c. Type 148	..	60	40
579	10 c. Consolidated PBY-5A Catalina	..	80	40
580	20 c. Boeing 727-200	..	1·60	1·50
581	40 c. Hawker Siddeley H.S. 748	..	2·25	3·25
578/81		Set of 4	4·75	5·00

(Des J.W. Litho Questa)

1984 (18 Jan). *Shells* (3rd series). *Horiz designs as* T **134**. *Multicoloured.* W w **14** (*sideways*). P 14 × 14½.

582	3 c. Florida Moon (*Natica floridana*)	..	80	35
583	10 c. Austin's Cone (*Conus atractus austini*)	1·10	35
584	30 c. Leaning Dwarf Triton (*Colubraria obscura*)	2·75	2·75
585	50 c. Filose or Threaded Turban (*Turbo cailletii*)	3·25	4·25
582/5		Set of 4	7·00	7·00

(Des G. Vasarhelyi and L. Curtis. Litho Questa)

1984 (18 June). *250th Anniv of "Lloyd's List"* (newspaper). T **149** *and similar vert designs. Multicoloured.* W w **14**. P 14½ × 14.

586	5 c. Type 149	..	35	20
587	10 c. View of old harbour	..	40	25
588	25 c. Wreck of *Ridgefield* (freighter)	..	1·00	1·00
589	50 c. *Goldfield* (schooner)	..	2·00	2·25
586/9		Set of 4	3·25	3·25
MS590	105×75 mm. $1 *Goldfield* (schooner) (*different*)	2·10	2·25

U.P.U. CONGRESS
HAMBURG 1984

(150)   151 Snowy Egret

1984 (18 June). *Universal Postal Union Congress, Hamburg. No. 589 optd with* T **150**.

591	50 c. Schooner *Goldfield*	..	1·00	1·50

(Des Josephine Martin. Litho Questa)

1984 (15 Aug). *Birds of the Cayman Islands* (1st series). T **151** *and similar horiz designs. Multicoloured.* W w **14** (*sideways*). P 14 × 14½.

592	5 c. Type 151	..	1·00	55
593	10 c. Bananaquit	..	1·00	55
594	35 c. Belted Kingfisher	..	3·25	2·50
595	$1 Brown Booby	..	6·00	8·50
592/5		Set of 4	10·00	11·00

See also Nos. 627/30.

152 Couple on Beach at Sunset   153 Schomburgkia
thomsoniana (var.
minor)

(Des G. Wilby. Litho Questa)

1984 (17 Oct). *Christmas. Local Festivities. T* **152** *and similar vert designs. Multicoloured. W w* **14** *(sideways). P* 14.

596 5 c. Type **152** .. 55 85
a. Horiz strip of 4. Nos. 596/9 .. 2·00
597 5 c. Family and schooner .. 55 85
598 5 c. Carol singers .. 55 85
599 5 c. East End bonfire .. 55 85
600 25 c. Yachts .. 75 95
a. Horiz strip of 4. Nos. 600/3 .. 2·75
601 25 c. Father Christmas in power-boat .. 75 95
602 25 c. Children on beach .. 75 95
603 25 c. Beach party .. 75 95
596/603 .. *Set of* 8 4·75 6·50
MS604 59×79 mm. $1 As No. 599, but larger, 27×41 mm .. 2·50 2·50

Nos. 596/9 and 600/3 were each printed together, *se-tenant*, in horizontal strips of 4 throughout the sheets, the four designs of each value forming a composite picture of a beach scene at night (5 c.) or in the daytime (25 c.).

(Des Liza Horstman. Litho J.W.)

1985 (13 Mar). *Orchids. T* **153** *and similar vert designs. Multicoloured. W w* **14**. *P* 14×13½.

605 5 c. Type **153** .. 1·00 30
606 10 c. *Schomburgkia thomsoniana* .. 1·00 30
607 25 c. *Encyclia plicata* .. 2·50 1·00
608 50 c. *Dendrophylax fawcettii* .. 3·75 3·00
605/8 .. *Set of* 4 7·50 4·25

154 Freighter Aground

155 Athletics

(Des Walsall. Litho J.W.)

1985 (22 May). *Shipwrecks. T* **154** *and similar horiz designs. Multicoloured. W w* **14** *(sideways). P* 14.

609 5 c. Type **154** .. 90 50
610 25 c. Submerged sailing ship .. 2·75 1·25
611 35 c. Wrecked trawler .. 3·00 2·50
612 40 c. Submerged wreck on its side .. 3·25 3·50
609/12 .. *Set of* 4 9·00 7·00

(Des Harrison. Litho Walsall)

1985 (14 Aug). *International Youth Year. T* **155** *and similar multicoloured designs. W w* **14** *(sideways on 5 c., 15 c.). P 14×14½ (5, 15 c.) or 14½×14 (others).*

613 5 c. Type **155** .. 20 20
614 15 c. Students in library .. 35 30
615 25 c. Football *(vert)* .. 65 55
616 50 c. Netball *(vert)* .. 1·25 2·00
613/16 .. *Set of* 4 2·25 2·75

156 Morse Key (1935)

157 Magnificent Frigate Bird

(Des G. Vasarhelyi. Litho Walsall)

1985 (25 Oct). *50th Anniv of Telecommunications System. T* **156** *and similar vert designs. Multicoloured. W w* **16**. *P* 14.

617 5 c. Type **156** .. 40 30
618 10 c. Hand cranked telephone .. 45 30
w. Wmk inverted .. £150
619 25 c. Tropospheric scatter dish (1966) .. 1·25 80
w. Wmk inverted
620 50 c. Earth station dish aerial (1979) .. 2·00 3·50
617/20 .. *Set of* 4 3·50 4·50

(Des A. Theobald. Litho Format)

1986 (21 Apr). *60th Birthday of Queen Elizabeth II. Vert designs as T* **110** *of Ascension. Multicoloured. W w* **16**. *P* 14×14½.

621 5 c. Princess Elizabeth at wedding of Lady May Cambridge, 1931 .. 10 20
622 10 c. In Norway, 1955 .. 15 20
623 25 c. Queen inspecting Royal Cayman Islands Police, 1983 .. 1·25 75
624 50 c. During Gulf tour, 1979 .. 75 1·50
625 $1 At Crown Agents Head Office, London, 1983 .. 1·10 2·25
621/5 .. *Set of* 5 3·00 4·50

(Litho J.W.)

1986 (Apr). *As No. 516B, but W w* **16**. *"1986" imprint date. P* 13½×13.

626 5 c. Mangrove Root Oyster .. 4·50 4·75

(Des Harrison. Litho Questa)

1986 (21 May). *Birds of the Cayman Islands (2nd series). T* **157** *and similar multicoloured designs. W w* **16** *(sideways on 10, 40 c.). P* 14.

627 10 c. Type **157** .. 1·50 60
628 25 c. Black-billed Whistling Duck *(vert)* .. 2·00 1·40
629 35 c. La Sagra's Flycatcher *(vert)* .. 2·25 2·50
630 40 c. Yellow-faced Grassquit .. 2·50 3·50
627/30 .. *Set of* 4 7·50 7·25

(Litho Questa)

1986 (June). *As Nos. 516B/17B, but different printer and W w* **16**. *"1986" imprint date. P* 14.

631 5 c. Mangrove Root Oyster .. 5·00 4·00
632 10 c. Mangrove Crab .. 5·00 4·00

(Des D. Miller. Litho Walsall)

1986 (23 July) *Royal Wedding. Square designs as T* **112** *of Ascension. Multicoloured. W w* **16**. *P* 14½×14.

633 5 c. Prince Andrew and Miss Sarah Ferguson .. 25 15
634 50 c. Prince Andrew aboard H.M.S. *Brazen* .. 1·25 1·75

158 Red Coral Shrimp

159 Golf

(Des D. Miller. Litho Walsall)

1986 (15 Sept). *Marine Life. T* **158** *and similar vert designs. Multicoloured. W w* **14**. *P* 13½×13.

635 5 c. Type **158** .. 40 50
636 10 c. Yellow Crinoid .. 40 50
637 15 c. *Calcinus tibicen* (hermit crab) .. 35 60
638 20 c. Tube dwelling Anemone .. 35 80
639 25 c. Christmas Tree Worm .. 45 2·00
640 35 c. Porcupinefish .. 70 2·25
641 50 c. Orangeball Anemone .. 80 3·75
642 60 c. *Astrophyton muricatum* (basket star-fish) .. 3·50 6·00
643 75 c. Flamingo Tongue (*Cyphoma gibbosus*) 7·00 7·50
644 $1 *Condylactis gigantea* (sea anemone) .. 1·40 2·50
645 $2 Diamond Blenny .. 2·25 4·25
646 $4 Rough File Shell (*Lima scabra*) .. 4·00 6·50
635/46 .. *Set of* 12 19·00 32·00

No. 644 is incorrectly inscribed "Conolylactis gigantea".

Imprint dates: "1986", Nos. 635/46; "1987", Nos. 635/8, 644/6; "1990", Nos. 635/41, 644/5.

For the 10 c. value with watermark w **16** see No. 696.

(Des L. Curtis. Litho Walsall)

1987 (26 Jan). *Tourism. T* **159** *and similar horiz designs. Multicoloured. W w* **16** *(sideways). P* 13×13½.

647 10 c. Type **159** .. 1·75 85
648 15 c. Sailing .. 2·00 95
649 25 c. Snorkelling .. 2·25 1·50
650 35 c. Paragliding .. 2·25 2·00
651 $1 Game fishing .. 4·00 7·00
647/51 .. *Set of* 5 11·00 11·00

160 Ackee

161 Lion Lizard

(Des Jennifer Toombs. Litho Questa)

1987 (20 May). *Cayman Islands Fruits. T* **160** *and similar vert designs. Multicoloured. W w* **16**. *P* 14½×14.

652 5 c. Type **160** .. 30 35
w. Wmk inverted
653 25 c. Breadfruit .. 75 55
w. Wmk inverted .. 8·50
654 35 c. Pawpaw .. 90 70
655 $1 Soursop .. 2·50 4·00
652/5 .. *Set of* 4 4·00 5·00

(Des I. Loe. Litho Questa)

1987 (26 Aug). *Lizards. T* **161** *and similar horiz designs. Multicoloured. W w* **16** *(sideways). P* 13½×14.

656 10 c. Type **161** .. 70 20
657 50 c. Iguana .. 1·75 1·75
658 $1 Anole .. 2·50 2·50
656/8 .. *Set of* 3 4·50 4·00

162 Poinsettia

163 *Hemiargus ammon* and *Strymon martialis*

(Des Annette Robinson. Litho Walsall)

1987 (18 Nov). *Flowers. T* **162** *and similar square designs. Multicoloured. W w* **16**. *P* 14½×14.

659 5 c. Type **162** .. 55 30
660 25 c. Periwinkle .. 1·50 75
661 35 c. Yellow Allamanda .. 1·75 1·10
662 75 c. Blood Lily .. 3·00 3·50
659/62 .. *Set of* 4 6·00 5·00

(Des Jane Thatcher. Litho Questa)

1988 (29 Mar). *Butterflies. T* **163** *and similar horiz designs. Multicoloured. W w* **16** *(sideways). P* 14.

663 5 c. Type **163** .. 1·25 65
664 25 c. *Phocides pigmalion* .. 2·50 85
665 50 c. *Anaea troglodyta* .. 4·00 3·75
666 $1 *Papilio andraemon* .. 5·00 5·00
663/6 .. *Set of* 4 11·50 9·25

164 Green Heron

165 Cycling

(Des Jane Thatcher. Litho Walsall)

1988 (27 July). *Herons. T* **164** *and similar vert designs. Multicoloured. W w* **16**. *P* 14.

667 5 c. Type **164** .. 1·25 65
668 25 c. Louisiana Heron .. 2·25 85
669 50 c. Yellow-crowned Night Heron .. 3·00 3·00
670 $1 Little Blue Heron .. 3·50 4·25
667/70 .. *Set of* 4 9·00 8·00

(Des L. Curtis. Litho Walsall)

1988 (21 Sept). *Olympic Games, Seoul. T* **165** *and similar horiz designs. Multicoloured. W w* **16** *(sideways). P* 14×14½.

671 10 c. Type **165** .. 1·25 55
672 50 c. Cayman Airways Boeing 727 airliner and national team .. 2·00 2·00
673 $1 "470" dinghy .. 2·25 2·75
671/3 .. *Set of* 3 5·00 4·75
MS674 53×60 mm. $1 Tennis. W w **14** (sideways) 4·00 3·00

166 Princess Alexandra

167 George Town Post Office and Cayman Postmark on Jamaica 1d., 1889

(Des N. Harvey. Litho B.D.T.)

1988 (1 Nov). *Visit of Princess Alexandra. T* **166** *and similar vert design. Multicoloured. W w* **14**. *P* 15×14.

675 5 c. Type **166** .. 1·00 65
676 $1 Princess Alexandra in evening dress .. 4·50 4·25

(Des L. Curtis. Litho Questa)

1989 (12 Apr). *Centenary of Cayman Islands Postal Service. T* **167** *and similar horiz designs. Multicoloured. W w* **16** *(sideways). P* 14×14½.

677 5 c. multicoloured .. 65 50
678 25 c. yellowish green, black and new blue 1·75 80
679 35 c. multicoloured .. 1·75 1·10
680 $1 multicoloured .. 5·50 6·00
677/80 .. *Set of* 4 8·75 7·50

Designs:—25 c. *Orinoco* (mail steamer) and 1900 ½d. stamp; 35 c. G.P.O., Grand Cayman and "London 1980" $1 stamp; $1 Cayman Airways B.A.C. One Eleven 200/400 and 1966 1s. Jet Service stamp.

168 Captain Bligh ashore in West Indies

169 Panton House

(Des Jane Hartley. Litho B.D.T.)

1989 (24 May). *Captain Bligh's Second Breadfruit Voyage, 1791-93. T* **168** *and similar vert designs. Multicoloured. W w* **16**. *P* 14.

681	50 c. Type **168**		3·00	3·50
	a. Horiz strip of 5. Nos. 681/5		13·50	
682	50 c. H.M.S. *Providence* (sloop) at anchor		3·00	3·50
683	50 c. Breadfruit in tubs and H.M.S. *Assistant* (transport)		3·00	3·50
684	50 c. Sailors moving tubs of breadfruit		3·00	3·50
685	50 c. Midshipman and stores		3·00	3·50
681/5		*Set of 5*	13·50	16·00

Nos. 681/5 were printed together, *se-tenant* as a composite design, in horizontal strips of five throughout the sheet.

(Des S. Conlin. Litho Walsall)

1989 (18 Oct). *Architecture. T* **169** *and similar square designs showing George Town buildings. Multicoloured. W w* **14**. *P* 14½×14.

686	5 c. Type **169**		35	35
687	10 c. Town Hall and Clock Tower		35	35
688	25 c. Old Court House		80	55
689	35 c. Elmslie Memorial Church		90	75
690	$1 Post Office		2·25	3·50
686/90		*Set of 5*	4·25	5·00

170 Map of Grand Cayman, 1773, and Surveying Instruments   **171** French Angelfish

(Des N. Shewring. Litho Walsall)

1989 (15 Nov). *Island Maps and Survey Ships. T* **170** *and similar horiz designs. Multicoloured. W w* **16** *(sideways). P* 14×14½.

691	5 c. Type **170**		80	80
692	25 c. Map of Cayman Islands, 1956, and surveying instruments		2·25	1·25
693	50 c. H.M.S. *Mutine*, 1914		3·50	3·50
694	$1 H.M.S. *Vidal*, 1956		5·50	6·50
691/4		*Set of 4*	11·00	11·00

1990 (Mar). *As No. 636, but W w* **16**. *"1990" imprint date. P* 13½×13.

696	10 c. Yellow Crinoid		1·75	2·25

(Des D. Miller. Litho Questa)

1990 (25 Apr). *Angelfishes. T* **171** *and similar horiz designs. Multicoloured. W w* **16** *(sideways). P* 14.

707	10 c. Type **171**		1·25	60
708	25 c. Grey Angelfish		2·25	90
709	50 c. Queen Angelfish		3·50	3·50
710	$1 Rock Beauty		5·50	6·50
707/10		*Set of 4*	11·00	10·50

(Des D. Miller. Litho Questa)

1990 (4 Aug). *90th Birthday of Queen Elizabeth the Queen Mother. Vert designs as T* **134** *(50 c.) or* **135** *($1) of Ascension. W w* **16**. *P* 14×15 *(50 c.) or* 14½ *($1).*

711	50 c. multicoloured		1·25	2·00
712	$1 black and blue		2·75	3·50

Designs:—50 c. Silver Wedding photograph, 1948; $1 King George VI and Queen Elizabeth with Winston Churchill, 1940.

172 *Danaus eresimus*   **173** Goes Weather Satellite

(Des G. Drummond. Litho Questa)

1990 (24 Oct). *"EXPO 90" International Garden and Greenery Exhibition, Osaka. Butterflies. T* **172** *and similar horiz designs. Multicoloured. W w* **16** *(sideways). P* 14.

713	5 c. Type **172**		65	50
714	25 c. *Brephidium exilis*		1·50	1·10
715	35 c. *Phyciodes phaon*		1·75	1·25
716	$1 *Agraulis vanillae*		4·00	6·00
713/16		*Set of 4*	7·00	8·00

(Des A. Theobald. Litho Questa)

1991 (8 Aug). *International Decade for Natural Disaster Reduction. T* **173** *and similar horiz designs. Multicoloured. W w* **16** *(sideways). P* 14.

717	5 c. Type **173**		80	60
718	30 c. Meteorologist tracking hurricane		2·00	1·10
719	40 c. Damaged buildings		2·25	1·25
720	$1 U.S. Dept of Commerce weather reconnaissance Lockheed WP-3D Orion		5·00	7·50
717/20		*Set of 4*	9·00	9·50

174 Angels and *Datura candida*   **175** Coconut Palm

(Des Jennifer Toombs. Litho Questa)

1991 (6 Nov). *Christmas. T* **174** *and similar horiz designs. Multicoloured. W w* **16** *(sideways). P* 14.

721	5 c. Type **174**		50	50
722	30 c. Mary and Joseph going to Bethlehem and *Allamanda cathartica*		1·40	60
723	40 c. Adoration of the Kings and *Euphorbia pulcherrima*		1·60	90
724	60 c. Holy Family and *Guaiacum officinale*		2·00	3·50
721/4		*Set of 4*	5·00	5·00

(Des D. Miller. Litho Enschede)

1991 (11 Dec). *Island Scenes. T* **175** *and similar multicoloured designs. W w* **14** *(sideways on horiz designs). P* 12½×13 *(vert)* or 13×12½ *(horiz).*

725	5 c. Type **175**		50	30
726	15 c. Beach scene (*horiz*)		1·00	30
727	20 c. Poincianas in bloom (*horiz*)		60	35
728	30 c. Blowholes (*horiz*)		70	50
	a. Silver (inscr and face value) omitted			
729	40 c. Police band (*horiz*)		2·50	1·40
730	50 c. *Song of Norway* (liner) at George Town		2·00	1·40
731	60 c. The Bluff, Cayman Brac (*horiz*)		1·75	2·00
732	80 c. Coat of arms		1·50	2·25
733	90 c. View of Hell (*horiz*)		1·60	2·25
734	$1 Game fishing (*horiz*)		2·00	2·25
735	$2 *Nieuw Amsterdam* (1983) and *Holiday* (liners) in harbour		4·25	4·50
736	$8 Queen Elizabeth II		13·00	15·00
725/36		*Set of 12*	28·00	29·00

Imprint dates: "1991", Nos. 725/36; "1994", No. 725.

(Des D. Miller. Litho Questa ($1), Leigh-Mardon Ltd, Melbourne (others))

1992 (6 Feb). *40th Anniv of Queen Elizabeth II's Accession. Horiz designs as T* **143** *of Ascension. W w* **16** *(sideways)* (30, 40 c.) *or* **14** *(sideways) (others). P* 14.

737	5 c. Caymans' house		30	30
738	20 c. Sunset over islands		1·00	50
739	30 c. Beach		1·10	65
740	40 c. Three portraits of Queen Elizabeth		1·10	1·00
741	$1 Queen Elizabeth II		2·00	3·50
737/41		*Set of 5*	5·00	5·50

176 Single Cyclist   **177** Woman and Donkey with Panniers

(Des G. Vasarhelyi. Litho Questa)

1992 (5 Aug). *Olympic Games, Barcelona. Cycling. T* **176** *and similar horiz designs. Multicoloured. W w* **14** *(sideways). P* 14.

742	15 c. Type **176**		1·25	65
743	40 c. Two cyclists		2·00	1·50
744	60 c. Cyclist's legs		2·50	3·00
745	$1 Two pursuit cyclists		3·25	4·00
742/5		*Set of 4*	8·00	8·25

(Des O. Ball. Litho Enschedé)

1992 (21 Oct). *Island Heritage. T* **177** *and similar vert designs. Multicoloured. W w* **14**. *P* 14×13½.

746	5 c. Type **177**		50	50
747	30 c. Fisherman weaving net		1·25	85
748	40 c. Maypole dancing		1·50	1·10
749	60 c. Basket making		2·50	3·25
750	$1 Cooking on caboose		3·00	4·00
746/50		*Set of 5*	8·00	8·75

178 Yellow Stingray   **179** Turtle and Sailing Dinghies

(Des G. Drummond. Litho Cartor)

1993 (16 June). *Rays. T* **178** *and similar horiz designs. Multicoloured. W w* **14** *(sideways). P* 13½.

751	5 c. Type **178**		70	60
752	30 c. Southern Stingray		1·75	1·25
753	40 c. Spotted Eagle-ray		2·00	1·50
754	$1 Manta		4·25	5·50
751/4		*Set of 4*	8·00	8·00

(Des D. Miller. Litho B.D.T.)

1993 (30 Sept). *Tourism. T* **179** *and similar vert designs. Multicoloured. W w* **14**. *P* 13½.

755	15 c. Type **179**		90	1·00
	a. Horiz strip of 5. Nos. 755/9		4·00	
	b. Booklet pane. Nos. 755/64		9·00	
756	15 c. Tourist boat, fishing launch and scuba diver		90	1·00
757	15 c. Golf		90	1·00
758	15 c. Tennis		90	1·00
759	15 c. Pirates and ship		90	1·00
760	30 c. Liner, tourist launch and yacht		1·10	1·25
	a. Horiz strip of 5. Nos. 760/4		5·00	
761	30 c. George Town street		1·10	1·25
762	30 c. Tourist submarine		1·10	1·25
763	30 c. Motor-scooter riders and cyclists		1·10	1·25
764	30 c. Cayman Airways Boeing 737 airliners		1·10	1·25
755/64		*Set of 10*	9·00	10·00

Nos. 755/9 and 760/4 were each printed together, *se-tenant*, in horizontal strips of 5 throughout the sheets. Booklet pane No. 755b contains both *se-tenant* strips as a block of 10 with the horizontal edges of the pane imperforate and margins at left and right.

180 Cuban Amazon with Wings spread   **181** *Ionopsis utricularioides* and Manger

(Des O. Ball. Litho Leigh-Mardon Ltd, Melbourne)

1993 (29 Oct). *Endangered Species. Cuban Amazon ("Grand Cayman Parrot"). T* **180** *and similar square designs. Multicoloured. W w* **14**. *P* 14.

765	5 c. Type **180**		75	75
766	15 c. On branch with wings folded		75	75
767	30 c. Head of parrot		1·90	2·00
768	30 c. Pair of parrots		1·90	2·00
765/8		*Set of 4*	4·75	4·00

(Des Jennifer Toombs. Litho B.D.T.)

1993 (6 Dec). *Christmas. Orchids. T* **181** *and similar horiz designs. Multicoloured. W w* **16** *(sideways). P* 13½×14.

769	5 c. Type **181**		70	55
770	40 c. *Encyclia cochleata* and shepherd		1·75	85
771	60 c. *Vanilla pompona* and wise men		2·50	3·25
772	$1 *Oncidium caymanense* and Virgin Mary		3·50	4·50
769/72		*Set of 4*	7·50	8·25

182 Queen Angelfish   **183** Flags of Great Britain and Cayman Islands

(Des D. Miller and A. Robinson. Litho Enschedé)

1994 (18 Feb). *"Hong Kong '94" International Stamp Exhibition. Reef Life. Sheet* 121×85 *mm containing T* **182** *and similar vert designs. Multicoloured. W w* **14** *(sideways). P* 14½×13.

MS773	60 c. Type **182**; 60 c. Diver with Porkfish and Spot-finned Hogfish; 60 c. Rock Beauty and Royal Gramma; 60 c. French Angelfish and Banded Butterflyfish		8·00	8·50

(Des D. Miller. Litho Questa)

1994 (22 Feb). *Royal Visit. T* **183** *and similar vert designs. Multicoloured. W w* **14**. *P* 14½×14.

774	5 c. Type **183**		60	45
775	15 c. Royal Yacht *Britannia*		1·50	85
776	30 c. Queen Elizabeth II		1·50	1·10
777	$2 Queen Elizabeth and Prince Philip disembarking		4·75	7·00
774/7		*Set of 4*	7·50	8·50

NEW INFORMATION

The editor is always interested to correspond with people who have new information that will improve or correct the Catalogue.

184 Black-billed
Whistling Duck

185 *Electrostrymon
angelia*

(Des Josephine Martin. Litho Walsall)

1994 (21 Apr). *Black-billed Whistling Duck ("West Indian Whistling Duck"). T **184** and similar multicoloured designs. W w 16 (sideways on 15 c., 20 c.). P 14½.*

778	5 c. Type **184**	70	65
779	15 c. Duck landing on water (*horiz*)	1·25	70
780	20 c. Duck preening (*horiz*)	1·25	80
781	80 c. Duck flapping wings	3·00	4·00
782	$1 Adult and duckling	3·50	4·25
778/82	*Set of 5*	8·75	9·50
MS783	71×45 mm. $1 As No. 782, but including Cayman Islands National Trust symbol	7·00	8·00

(Des K. McGee. Litho Enschedé)

1994 (16 Aug). *Butterflies. T **185** and simlar vert designs. Multicoloured. W w 14 (sideways). P 13½×14.*

784	10 c. Type **185**	70	90
	a. Vert pair. Nos. 784/5	1·40	1·75
785	10 c. *Eumaeus atala*	70	90
786	$1 *Eurema daira*	3·75	4·00
	a. Vert pair. Nos. 786/7	7·50	8·00
787	$1 *Urbanus dorantes*	3·75	4·00
784/7	*Set of 4*	8·00	8·75

Nos. 784/5 and 786/7 were printed together, *se-tenant*, in vertical pairs throughout the sheets.

186 H.M.S. *Convert*
(frigate)

187 Young Green Turtles

(Des B. Dare. Litho Enschedé)

1994 (12 Oct). *Bicentenary of Wreck of Ten Sail off Grand Cayman. T **186** and similar square designs. Multicoloured. W w 14 (sideways). P 13×14.*

788	10 c. Type **186**	45	45
789	10 c. Merchant brig and full-rigged ship	45	45
790	15 c. Full-rigged ship near rock	65	55
791	20 c. Long boat leaving full-rigged ship	75	55
792	$2 Merchant brig	4·25	6·75
788/92	*Set of 5*	6·00	8·00

(Des Doreen McGuiness. Litho Questa)

1995 (28 Feb). *Sea Turtles. T **187** and similer horiz designs. Multicoloured. W w 16 (sideways). P 14.*

793	10 c. Type **187**	55	45
794	20 c. Kemp's Ridley Turtle	80	55
795	25 c. Hawksbill Turtle	90	60
796	30 c. Leatherback Turtle	95	70
797	$1.30, Loggerhead Turtle	3·50	4·50
798	$2 Pacific Ridley Turtles	4·50	5·50
793/8	*Set of 6*	10·00	11·00
MS799	167×94 mm. Nos. 793/8	10·00	11·00

188 Running

189 Queen Elizabeth
the Queen Mother

(Des B. Dare. Litho Questa)

1995 (15 Apr). *C.A.R.I.F.T.A. and I.A.A.F. Games, George Town. T **188** and similar horiz designs. Multicoloured. W w 14 (sideways). P 14½.*

800	10 c. Type **188**	60	40
801	20 c. High jumping	90	70
802	30 c. Javelin throwing	1·25	80
803	$1.30, Yachting	4·25	6·00
800/3	*Set of 4*	6·25	7·00
MS804	100×70 $2 Athletes with medals	5·00	6·50

(Des R. Watton. Litho Cartor (Nos. 805/8) or Questa (No. MS809))

1995 (8 May). *50th Anniv of End of Second World War. Multicoloured designs as T **161** of Ascension. W w 14 (sideways). P 13½.*

805	10 c. Members of Cayman Home Guard	70	55
806	25 c. *Comayagua* (freighter)	1·75	85

807	40 c. U-boat *U125*	2·00	1·50
808	$1 U.S. Navy *L-3* airship	3·75	5·50
805/8	*Set of 4*	7·50	7·50
MS809	75×85 mm. $1.30, Reverse of 1939–45 War Medal (*vert*). Wmk upright. P 14	2·50	3·00

(Des N. Shewring. Litho Walsall)

1995 (25 Aug). *95th Birthday of Queen Elizabeth the Queen Mother. Sheet 70×90 mm. Multicoloured. W w 14 (sideways). P 14½.*

MS810	**189** $4 multicoloured	8·00	9·00

190 Ox and Christ
Child

191 Sea Grape

(Des Doreen McGuiness. Litho Walsall)

1995 (1 Nov). *Christmas. Nativity Animals. T **190** and similar vert designs. Multicoloured. W w 14. P 14×13½.*

811	10 c. Type **190**	55	30
812	20 c. Sheep and lamb	85	45
813	30 c. Donkey	1·25	60
814	$2 Camels	5·50	7·00
811/14	*Set of 4*	7·25	7·50
MS815	160×75 mm. Nos. 811/14	7·25	7·50

(Des I. Loe. Litho B.D.T.)

1996 (21 Mar). *Wild Fruit. T **191** and similar vert designs. Multicoloured. W w 16. P 14.*

816	10 c. Type **191**	35	30
817	25 c. Guava	75	50
818	40 c. West Indian Cherry	1·00	70
819	$1 Tamarind	2·25	3·50
816/19	*Set of 4*	4·00	4·50

192 "Laser" Dinghy

193 Guitar and Score
of National Song

(Des G. Vasarhelyi. Litho Walsall)

1996 (19 June). *Centenary of Modern Olympic Games. T **192** and similar vert designs. Multicoloured. W w 16. P 14×13½.*

820	10 c. Type **192**	35	30
821	20 c. Sailboarding	60	60
822	30 c. "Finn" dinghy	80	80
823	$2 Running	3·75	6·00
820/3	*Set of 4*	5·00	7·00

(Des N. Shewring. Litho Questa)

1996 (26 Sept). *National Identity. T **193** and similar square designs. Multicoloured. W w 14. P 14.*

824	10 c. Type **193**	15	30
825	20 c. Cayman Airways Boeing 737-200	30	35
826	25 c. Queen Elizabeth opening Legislative Assembly	40	45
827	30 c. Seven Mile Beach	45	50
828	40 c. Scuba diver and Stingrays	60	65
829	60 c. Children at turtle farm	90	95
830	80 c. Cuban Amazon ("Cayman Parrot") (national bird)	1·25	1·40
831	90 c. Silver Thatch Palm (national tree)	1·40	1·50
832	$1 Cayman Islands flag	1·50	1·60
833	$2 Wild Banana Orchid (national flower)	3·00	3·25
834	$4 Cayman Islands coat of arms	6·25	6·50
835	$6 Cayman Islands currency	9·25	9·50
824/35	*Set of 12*	25·00	27·00

Imprint dates: "1996", Nos. 824/35; "1997", No. 824.
For miniature sheet containing No. 830 with "1997" imprint date see No. MS840, and for values with watermark sideways Nos. 873/7.

OMNIBUS ISSUES

Details, together with prices for complete sets, of the various Omnibus issues from the 1935 Silver Jubilee series to date are included in a special section following Zimbabwe at the end of Volume 2.

194 "Christmas Time on
North Church Street"
(Joanne Sibley)

195 Children accessing
Internet

(Des D. Miller. Litho Questa)

1996 (12 Nov). *Christmas. Paintings. T **194** and similar square designs. Multicoloured. W w 14 (sideways). P 14.*

836	10 c. Type **194**	30	25
837	25 c. "Gone Fishing" (Lois Brezinsky)	60	50
838	30 c. "Claus Encounters" (John Doak)	70	70
839	$2 "A Caymanian Christmas" (Debbie van der Bol)	3·75	6·00
836/9	*Set of 4*	4·75	6·75

(Des D. Miller. Litho Questa)

1997 (3 Feb). *"HONG KONG '97" International Stamp Exhibition. Sheet 130×90 mm, containing design as No. 830 with "1997" imprint date. Multicoloured. W w 14 (inverted). P 14.*

MS840	80 c. Cuban Amazon ("Cayman Parrot")	1·50	2·00

(Des N. Shewring (No. MS847), D. Miller (others). Litho Questa (No. MS847), B.D.T.(others))

1997 (10 July). *Golden Wedding of Queen Elizabeth and Prince Philip. Multicoloured designs as T **173** of Ascension. W w 14. P 13½.*

841	10 c. Queen Elizabeth	45	55
	a. Horiz pair. Nos. 841/2	90	1·10
842	25 c. Prince Philip and Prince Charles at Trooping the Colour	45	55
843	30 c. Prince William horse riding, 1989	90	1·10
	a. Horiz pair. Nos. 843/4	1·75	2·10
844	30 c. Queen Elizabeth and Prince Philip at Royal Ascot	90	1·10
845	40 c. Prince Philip at the Brighton Driving Trials	95	1·25
	a. Horiz pair. Nos. 845/6	1·90	2·50
846	40 c. Queen Elizabeth at Windsor Horse Show, 1993	95	1·25
841/6	*Set of 6*	4·25	5·25
MS847	110×70 mm. $1 Queen Elizabeth and Prince Philip in landau (*horiz*). Wmk sideways. P 14×14½	2·25	2·75

Nos. 841/2, 843/4 and 845/6 were each printed together, *se-tenant*, in horizontal pairs throughout the sheets with the backgrounds forming a composite design.

(Des O. Bell. Litho Walsall)

1997 (10 Oct). *Telecommunications. T **195** and similar horiz designs. Multicoloured. W w 16 (sideways). P 14×14½.*

848	10 c. Type **195**	30	25
849	25 c. Cable & Wireless cable ship	60	45
850	30 c. New area code "345" on children's T-shirts	70	60
851	60 c. Satellite dish	1·25	2·00
848/51		2·50	3·00

196 Santa in Hammock

197 West Indian
Whistling Duck

(Des R. Watton. Litho Cartor)

1997 (3 Dec). *Christmas. T **196** and similar vert designs. Multicoloured. W w 14. P 13.*

852	10 c. Type **196**	25	20
853	30 c. Santa with children on the Bluff	50	45
854	40 c. Santa playing golf	1·00	80
855	$1 Santa scuba diving	1·60	2·25
852/5	*Set of 4*	3·00	3·25

(Des D. Miller. Litho Questa)

1998 (31 Mar). *Diana, Princess of Wales Commemoration. Vert designs as T **177** of Ascension. Multicoloured. W w 16 (Nos. 856/7). P 14½×14.*

856	10 c. Wearing gold earrings, 1997	25	25
857	20 c. Wearing black hat	45	45
MS858	145×70 mm. 10 c. As No. 856; 20 c. As No. 857; 40 c. With bouquet, 1995; $1 Wearing black and white blouse, 1983. W w 14 (sideways) (sold at $1.70 + 30 c. charity premium)	3·50	4·00

(Des A. Theobald. Litho B.D.T.)

1998 (1 Apr). *80th Anniv of the Royal Air Force. Horiz designs as T **178** of Ascension. Multicoloured. W w 14 (sideways). P 14.*

859	10 c. Hawker Horsley	40	40
860	20 c. Fairey Hendon	55	55
861	25 c. Hawker Siddeley Gnat	65	75
862	30 c. Hawker Siddeley Dominie	75	75
859/62	*Set of 4*	2·10	2·25
MS863	110×77 mm. 40 c. Airco D.H.9; 60 c. Spad 13 Scout; 80 c. Airspeed Oxford; $1 Martin Baltimore	5·00	6·00

(Des N. Shewring. Litho Cartor)

1998 (12 Oct). *Birds. T* **197** *and similar vert designs. Multicoloured. W w* 14. *P* 13½.

864	10 c. Type 197		30	30
865	20 c. Magnificent Frigate Bird		50	40
866	60 c. Red-footed Booby		1·40	1·50
867	$1 Grand Cayman Parrot		2·00	2·25
864/7		Set of 4	3·75	4·00

198 Santa at the Blowholes

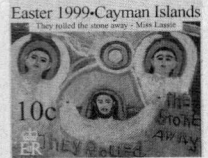

199 "They Rolled the Stone Away" (Miss Lassie)

(Des R. Watton. Litho Questa)

1998 (20 Nov). *Christmas. T* **198** *and similar horiz designs. Multicoloured. W w* 16 *(sideways). P* 14½.

868	10 c. Type 198		25	20
869	30 c. Santa diving on wreck of *Capt. Keith Tibbetts*		65	50
870	40 c. Santa at Pedro Castle		80	75
871	60 c. Santa arriving on Little Cayman		1·50	1·90
868/71		Set of 4	3·00	3·00

1999 (5 Feb). *As Nos.* 825, 827 *and* 829, *but W w* 14 *(sideways). P* 14.

873	20 c. Cayman Airways Boeing 737-200		30	35
875	30 c. Seven Mile Beach		45	50
877	60 c. Children at turtle farm		90	95
873/7		Set of 3	1·60	1·75

Imprint date: "1999", Nos. 873, 875, 877.

(Des D. Miller. Litho Cartor)

1999 (26 Mar). *Easter. Paintings by Miss Lassie (Gladwyn Bush). T* **199** *and similar multicoloured designs. W w* 14 *(sideways on horiz designs). P* 13.

884	10 c. Type 199		20	20
885	20 c. "Ascension" (*vert*)		40	35
886	30 c. "The World Praying for Peace"		55	55
887	40 c. "Calvary" (*vert*)		75	85
884/7		Set of 4	1·75	1·75

200 "Cayman House" (Jessica Cranston)

201 1969 Christmas ¼ c. Stamp

(Adapted D. Miller. Litho Cartor)

1999 (2 June). *Vision 2008 Project. Children's Paintings. T* **200** *and similar horiz designs. Multicoloured. W w* 14 *(sideways). P* 13½.

888	10 c. Type 200		20	20
889	30 c. "Coral Reef" (Sarah Hetley)		55	55
890	40 c. "Fisherman on North Sound" (Sarah Cuff)		70	70
891	$2 "Three Fish and a Turtle" (Ryan Martinez)		3·50	4·00
888/91		Set of 4	4·50	5·00

(Des D. Miller. Litho Walsall)

1999 (16 June). *Royal Wedding. Vert designs as T* **185** *of Ascension. Multicoloured. W w* 16. *P* 14.

892	10 c. Photographs of Prince Edward and Miss Sophie Rhys-Jones		25	20
893	$2 Engagement photograph		3·50	4·00

(Des J. Batchelor (10 c.), N. Shewring (others). Litho Walsall)

1999 (20 July). *30th Anniv of First Manned Landing on Moon. Multicoloured designs as T* **186** *of Ascension. W w* 16. *P* 14×13½.

894	10 c. Coastguard cutter on patrol during launch		25	20
895	25 c. Firing of third stage rockets		60	60
896	30 c. Buzz Aldrin descending to Moon's surface		65	65
897	60 c. Jettisoning of lunar module		1·10	1·25
894/7		Set of 4	2·40	2·40
MS898	90×80 mm. $1.50, Earth as seen from Moon (*circular,* 40 *mm diam*). Wmk sideways. P 14		2·75	3·00

(Des D. Miller. Litho Cartor)

1999 (18 Aug). "*Queen Elizabeth the Queen Mother's Century*". *Horiz designs as T* **187** *of Ascension. Multicoloured. W w* 16 *(sideways). P* 13½.

899	10 c. Visiting anti-aircraft battery, London, 1940		25	20
900	20 c. With children on her 94th birthday, 1994		45	45
901	30 c. With Prince Charles and Prince William, 1997		60	60
902	40 c. Reviewing Chelsea Pensioners, 1986		70	75
899/902		Set of 4	1·75	1·75
MS903	145×70 mm. $1.50, Duchess of York with Princess Elizabeth, 1926, and Royal Wedding, 1923		2·75	3·00

(Des D. Miller. Litho Cartor)

1999 (17 Nov). *Christmas. T* **201** *and similar multicoloured designs showing previous Christmas stamps. W w* 14 *(sideways on* $1). *P* 13½.

904	10 c. Type 201		20	25
905	30 c. 1984 Christmas 5 c.		45	50
906	40 c. 1997 Christmas 10 c.		60	65
907	$1 1979 Christmas 20 c. (*horiz*)		1·50	1·60
904/7		Set of 4	2·75	3·00
MS908	111×100 mm. Nos. 904/7. Wmk upright. P 12		2·75	3·00

(Des Crown Agents. Litho Walsall)

2000 (29 Feb). "*Stamp Show 2000*" *International Stamp Exhibition, London. Kings and Queens of England. Vert designs as T* **223** *of British Virgin Islands. Multicoloured. W w* 14. *P* 14.

909	40 c. King Henry VIII		60	65
	a. Sheetlet. Nos. 909/15		3·00	
910	40 c. Queen Mary I		60	65
911	40 c. King Charles II		60	65
912	40 c. Queen Anne		60	65
913	40 c. King George IV		60	65
914	40 c. King George V		60	65
909/14		Set of 6	3·00	3·75

Nos. 909/14 were printed together, *se-tenant,* in sheetlets of 6 with an enlarged illustrated right-hand margin.

STAMP BOOKLETS

B 1

1993 (30 Sept). *Tourism. Deep ultramarine and bright greenish blue cover as Type B* **1**. *Pane attached by selvedge.*

SB1	$2.25, booklet containing pane of five 15 c. and five 30 c. (No. 755b)		9·00

B 2

1994 (12 Oct). *Bicentenary of Wreck of Ten Sail off Grand Cayman. Multicoloured covers as Type B* **2**. *Stamps attached by selvedge.*

SB2	$1 booklet containing block of ten 10 c. stamps (No. 788)		4·00
SB3	$1.50, booklet containing block of ten 15 c. stamps (No. 790)		5·00
SB4	$2 booklet containing block of ten 20 c. stamps (No. 791)		6·00

PRICES OF SETS

Set prices are given for many issues, generally those containing three stamps or more. Definitive sets include one of each value or major colour change, but do not cover different perforations, die types or minor shades. Where a choice is possible the set prices are based on the cheapest versions of the stamps included in the listings.

B 3

1996 (26 Sept). *National Identity. Multicoloured covers as Type B* **3** *illustrating stamp design enclosed. Stamps attached by selvedge.*

SB5	$1 booklet containing block of ten 10 c. stamps (No. 824)		1·50
SB6	$3 booklet containing block of ten 30 c. stamps (No. 827)		4·50
SB7	$4 booklet containing block of ten 40 c. stamps (No. 828)		6·25

Ceylon see Sri Lanka

Channel Islands

These issues are now listed under GREAT BRITAIN after the Postal Fiscal Issues.

China—British Post Offices see after Hong Kong

Christmas Island see after Australia

Cocos (Keeling) Islands see after Australia

Cook Islands

(Rarotonga)

This group of fifteen islands was originally also known as the Hervey Islands. A British Protectorate was declared over the group by the local Vice-Consul on 20 September 1888.

Before the introduction of the Cook Islands Post Office mail was forwarded via Auckland, New Zealand.

PRICES FOR STAMPS ON COVER TO 1945

Nos. 1/4	from × 5
Nos. 5/74	from × 4
Nos. 75/145	from × 3

Watermarks of New Zealand used for Cook Islands (including Aitutaki and Penrhyn Island)

W 12b

W 38

W 43

W 98

Types of New Zealand Definitives overprinted or surcharged for Cook Islands (including Aitutaki and Penrhyn Island)

23

27

28

31

34

42

51

52

53

60

61

72

F 4

F 6

BRITISH PROTECTORATE

1

2 Queen Makea Takau

3 White Tern or Torea

(Des F. Moss. Typo Govt Printing Office, Wellington)

1892 (19 Apr). *No wmk. Toned paper.* P 12½.

1	1	1d. black		27·00	26·00
		b. White paper		26·00	26·00
		ba. Imperf between (vert pair)		£8500	
2		1½d. mauve		40·00	38·00
		a. Imperf (pair)		£9000	
		b. White paper		40·00	38·00
3		2½d. blue		40·00	38·00
		a. White paper		40·00	38·00
4		10d. carmine		£140	£130
		a. White paper		£160	£130
1/4			Set of 4	£200	£200

Nos. 1/4 were printed in sheets of 60 (6×10) from plates constructed from a matrix of 6 slightly different types.

(Eng A. E. Cousins. Typo Govt Printing Office, Wellington)

1893 (28 July)–**1900**. W 12b of New Zealand (N Z and Star wide apart) (sideways on T 3). (a) P 12 × 11½.

5	2	1d. brown		35·00	45·00
6		1d. blue (3.4.94)		7·50	2·00
		a. Perf 12×11½ and 12½ mixed		† £1000	
7		1½d. mauve		7·50	6·00
8		2½d. rose		38·00	23·00
		a. Rose-carmine		60·00	55·00
		ab. Perf 12×11½ and 12½ mixed		£1700	
9		5d. olive-black		15·00	13·00
10		10d. green		70·00	48·00
5/10			Set of 6	£150	£110

(b) P 11 (July 1896–1900)

11	3	½d. steel blue (1st setting) (11.99)		28·00	45·00
		a. Upper right "d" omitted		£1500	
		b. Second setting		18·00	22·00
		ba. Deep blue (1900)		4·00	4·75
12	2	1d. blue		4·50	4·50
13		1d. deep brown/cream (4.99)		14·00	14·00
		a. Wmk sideways			
		b. Bistre-brown (1900)		17·00	18·00
14		1½d. deep lilac		9·00	6·50
		a. Deep mauve (1900)		9·00	6·50
15	3	2d. brown/thin toned (7.98)		9·50	6·50
		a. Deep brown (1900)		8·00	6·50
16	2	2½d. pale rose		45·00	38·00
		a. Deep rose (1900)		14·00	9·00
17		5d. olive-black		24·00	17·00
18	3	6d. purple/thin toned (7.98)		24·00	28·00
		a. Bright purple (1900)		19·00	21·00
19	2	10d. green		18·00	45·00
20	3	1s. red/thin toned (7.98)		60·00	70·00
		a. Deep carmine (1900)		48·00	48·00
11/20a			Set of 10	£140	£160

Examples of the 1d., 1½d., 2½d. and 5d. perforated 11 and on laid paper are perforation trials.

On the 1st setting of the ½d. the face values are misplaced in each corner. As corrected in the second setting the face values are correctly positioned in each corner.

ONE
HALF
PENNY
(4)

(5)

1899 (24 Apr). No. 12 surch with T 4 by Govt Printer, Rarotonga.

21	2	½d. on 1d. blue		32·00	42·00
		a. Surch inverted		£850	£900
		b. Surch double		£1000	£850

NEW ZEALAND TERRITORY

On 8 and 9 October 1900 the chiefs of all the main islands, except Aitutaki, ceded their territory to the British Crown. On 11 June 1901 all the islands, including Aitutaki, were transferred by Great Britain to New Zealand control.

1901 (8 Oct). No. 13 optd with T 5 by Govt Printer, Rarotonga.

22	2	1d. brown		£180	£140
		a. Crown inverted		£1800	£1400
		c. Optd with crown twice		£1500	£1500

1902. No wmk. P 11.

(a) Medium white Cowan paper (Feb)

23	3	½d. blue-green		6·50	7·00
24	2	1d. dull rose		8·50	12·00

(b) Thick white Pirie paper (May)

25	3	½d. yellow-green		4·00	4·25
		a. Imperf horiz (vert pair)		£1100	
26	2	1d. rose-red		11·00	11·00
		a. Rose-lake		10·00	6·50
27		2½d. dull blue		11·00	21·00

NEW ZEALAND WATERMARKS. In W 43 the wmk units are in vertical columns widely spaced and the sheet margins are unwatermarked or wmkd "NEW ZEALAND POSTAGE" in large letters.

In W 98 the wmk units are arranged alternately in horizontal rows closely spaced and are continued into the sheet margins. Stamps with W 98 sideways show the star to the left of NZ, as seen from the back. Sideways inverted varieties have the star to the right, as seen from the back.

1902 (Sept). W 43 of New Zealand (single-lined NZ and Star, close together; sideways on T 2). P 11.

28	3	½d. yellow-green		2·75	3·25
		a. Grey-green		17·00	32·00
29	2	1d. rose-pink		4·00	3·00
30		1½d. deep mauve		3·50	8·50
31	3	2d. deep brown		4·50	10·00
		a. No figures of value		£1800	£2750
		b. Perf 11 × 14		£1200	
32	2	2½d. deep blue		3·75	7·00
33		5d. olive-black		35·00	48·00
34	3	6d. purple		32·00	28·00
35	2	10d. green		48·00	90·00
36	3	1s. carmine		48·00	70·00
		a. Perf 11 × 14		£1400	
28/36			Set of 9	£150	£225

Stamps in Type 3 were printed from a master plate with the value added by a series of separate duty plates. One sheet of the 2d. missed this second pass through the press and was issued without value.

1909–11. W 43 of New Zealand.

37	3	½d. green (p 14½×14) (1911)		6·00	8·00
38	2	1d. deep red (p 14)		28·00	26·00
		a. Wmk sideways (24.12.09)		11·00	9·00

1913–19. W 43 *of New Zealand (sideways on T 3). Chalk-surfaced paper.*

39	3	½d. deep green (*p* 14) (1915)	..	3·75	13·00
		a. Wmk upright	..	4·75	10·00
40	2	1d. red (*p* 14) (7.13)	..	4·00	4·00
41		1d. red (*p* 14 × 14½) (1914)	..	5·50	5·50
42		1½d. deep mauve (*p* 14) (1915)	..	85·00	45·00
43		1½d. deep mauve (*p* 14 × 15) (1916)	..	7·50	4·00
44	3	2d. deep brown (*p* 15 × 14) (1919)	..	5·00	45·00
45	2	10d. green (*p* 14 × 15) (1918)	..	13·00	80·00
46	3	1s. carmine (*p* 15 × 14) (1919)..		27·00	80·00
39/46	..		*Set of 6*	55·00	£200

RAROTONGA

APA PENE

(8)

1919 (Apr–July). *Stamps of New Zealand surch as T 8.*

(*a*) *T 53. W 43. De La Rue chalk-surfaced paper. P 14×15*

47		1d. carmine (No. 405) (B.) (June)	..	85	2·00

(*b*) *T 60 (recess). W 43. Cowan unsurfaced paper. P 14×13½.*

48		2½d. blue (No. 419) (R.) (June)	..	2·25	6·50
		a. Perf 14×14½	..	2·00	2·25
		b. Vert pair. Nos. 48/a	..	20·00	45·00
49		3d. chocolate (No. 420) (B.)	..	2·00	7·50
		a. Perf 14×14½	..	2·25	1·75
		b. Vert pair. Nos. 49/a	..	22·00	50·00
50		4d. bright violet (No. 422) (B.)	..	2·00	5·50
		a. Re-entry (Pl 20 R. 1/6)		60·00	
		b. Re-entry (Pl 20 R. 4/10)		60·00	
		c. Perf 14×14½	..	1·75	4·25
		d. Vert pair. Nos. 50 and 50c	..	20·00	55·00
51		4½d. deep green (No. 423) (B.)	..	2·00	7·00
		a. Perf 14×14½	..	1·75	7·00
		b. Vert pair. Nos. 51/a	..	20·00	65·00
52		6d. carmine (No. 425) (B.) (June)	..	3·00	8·50
		a. Perf 14×14½	..	1·75	5·50
		b. Vert pair. Nos. 52/a	..	38·00	80·00
53		7½d. red-brown (No. 426a) (B.)	..	1·50	5·50
54		9d. sage-green (No. 429) (B.)	..	3·25	13·00
		a. Perf 14×14½	..	2·00	13·00
		b. Vert pair. Nos. 54/a	..	38·00	95·00
55		1s. vermilion (No. 430) (B.) (June)	..	11·00	30·00
		a. Perf 14×14½	..	2·75	16·00
		b. Vert pair. Nos. 55/a	..	48·00	£110

(*c*) *T 61 (typo). W 43. De La Rue chalk-surfaced paper.*
P 14×15

56		½d. green (No. 435) (R.) (June)	..	40	90
57		1½d. orange-brown (No. 438) (R.) (June)	..	50	75
58		2d. yellow (No. 439) (R.)	..	1·50	1·50
59		3d. chocolate (No. 440) (B.) (July)	..	2·75	9·00
47/59			*Set of 13*	19·00	60·00

9 Capt. Cook landing

10 Wharf at Avarua

11 "Capt. Cook" (Dance)

12 Palm Tree

13 Huts at Arorangi

14 Avarua Harbour

R.2/8	R.3/6	R.5/2

Double derrick flaws

(Des, eng and recess Perkins, Bacon & Co)

1920 (23 Aug). *No wmk. P 14.*

70	9	½d. black and green	..	4·00	16·00
71	10	1d. black and carmine-red	..	4·75	15·00
		a. Double derrick flaw (R.2/8, 3/6 or 5/2)	..	22·00	
72	11	1½d. black and dull blue	..	8·50	8·50
73	12	3d. black and chocolate	..	2·25	5·50
74	13	6d. brown and yellow-orange	..	2·75	8·50
75	14	1s. black and violet	..	5·00	17·00
70/5			*Set of 6*	24·00	55·00

Examples of the 1d. and 1s. with centre inverted were not supplied to the Post Office.

RAROTONGA

(15)

RAROTONGA

Trimmed overprint (R. 1/6 and R. 3/7)

1921 (Oct)–**23.** *Postal Fiscal stamps as Type F 4 of New Zealand optd with T 15. W 43 (sideways). Chalk-surfaced "De La Rue" paper. P 14½×14.*

76		2s. deep blue (No. F111) (R.)	..	27·00	55·00
		a. Trimmed opt	..	95·00	
		b. Carmine opt (1923)	..	£150	£170
		ba. Trimmed opt	..	£425	
77		2s. 6d. grey-brown (No. F112) (B.)	..	18·00	50·00
		a. Trimmed opt	..	75·00	
78		5s. yellow-green (No. F115) (R.)	..	27·00	65·00
		a. Trimmed opt	..	95·00	
79		10s. maroon (No. F120) (B.)	..	50·00	90·00
		a. Trimmed opt	..	£160	
80		£1 rose-carmine (No. F123) (B.)	..	85·00	£150
		a. Trimmed opt	..	£275	
76/80			*Set of 5*	£190	£375

See also Nos. 85/9.

16 Te Po, Rarotongan Chief

17 Harbour, Rarotonga and Mt Ikurangi

(2½d. from a print; 4d. des A. H. Messenger. Plates by P.B. Recess Govt Ptg Office, Wellington)

1924–27. *W 43 of New Zealand. P 14.*

81	9	½d. black and green (13.5.26)	..	4·50	8·00
82	10	1d. black and deep carmine (10.11.24)	..	6·00	2·25
		a. Double derrick flaw (R.2/8, 3/6 or 5/2)		16·00	
83	16	2½d. red-brown and steel blue (15.10.27)	..	5·00	22·00
84	17	4d. green and violet (15.10.27)	..	8·00	16·00
81/4			*Set of 4*	21·00	42·00

1926 (Feb–May). *As Nos. 76/80, but on thick, opaque white chalk-surfaced "Cowan" paper.*

85		2s. blue (No. F131) (C.)	..	£110	£160
		a. Trimmed opt	..	£325	
86		2s. 6d. deep grey-brown (No. F132) (B.)	..	55·00	90·00
87		5s. yellow-green (No. F135) (R.) (May)	..	55·00	80·00
		a. Trimmed opt	..	£150	
88		10s. brown-red (No. F139) (B.) (May)	..	60·00	95·00
89		£1 rose-pink (No. F142) (B.) (May)	..	85·00	£140
85/9			*Set of 5*	£325	£500

1926 (Oct)–**28.** *T 72 of New Zealand, overprinted with T 15.*

(*a*) *Jones chalk-surfaced paper.*

90		2s. deep blue (No. 466) (R.)	..	10·00	40·00

(*b*) *Cowan thick, opaque chalk-surfaced paper*

91		2s. light blue (No. 469) (R.) (18.6.27)	..	15·00	40·00
92		3s. pale mauve (No. 470) (R.) (30.1.28)	..	16·00	42·00
90/2			*Set of 3*	38·00	£110

TWO PENCE COOK ISLANDS.

(18) (19)

1931 (Mar). *Surch with T 18. P 14.* (*a*) *No wmk.*

93	11	2d. on 1½d. black and blue (R.)	..	9·50	2·75

(*b*) *W 43 of New Zealand*

94	11	2d. on 1½d. black and blue (R.)	..	4·75	10·00

1931 (12 Nov)–**32.** *Postal Fiscal stamps as Type F 6 of New Zealand. W 43. Thick, opaque, white chalk-surfaced Cowan paper. P 14.*

(*a*) *Optd with T 15*

95		2s. 6d. deep brown (No. F147) (B.)	..	10·00	22·00
96		5s. green (No. F149) (R.)	..	17·00	50·00
97		10s. carmine-lake (No. F155) (B.)	..	35·00	80·00
98		£1 pink (No. F158) (B.)	..	80·00	£130

(*b*) *Optd with T 19 (3.32)*

98*a*		£3 green (No. F164) (R.)	..	£170	£350
98*b*		£5 indigo-blue (No. F168) (R.)	..	£170	£300

The £3 and £5 values were mainly used for fiscal purposes.

20 Capt. Cook landing

21 Capt. Cook

22 Double Maori Canoe

23 Natives working Cargo

---

24 Port of Avarua

25 R.M.S. *Monowai*

26 King George V

(Des L. C. Mitchell. Recess P.B.)

1932 (15 Mar–2 May). *No wmk. P 13.*

99	20	½d. black and deep green	..	3·50	16·00
		a. Perf 14	..	28·00	90·00
100	21	1d. black and lake	..	6·00	4·50
		a. Centre inverted	..	£2750	£2750
		b. Perf compound of 13 and 14	..	£180	£200
		c. Perf 14	..	15·00	20·00
101	22	2d. black and brown	..	3·00	5·50
		a. Perf 14	..	9·00	20·00
102	23	2½d. black and deep blue	..	7·00	48·00
		a. Perf 14	..	14·00	48·00
103	24	4d. black and bright blue	..	20·00	55·00
		a. Perf 14	..	10·00	48·00
		b. Perf 14×13	..	30·00	90·00
		c. Perf compound of 14 and 13	..	50·00	£100
104	25	6d. black and orange	..	24·00	48·00
		a. Perf 14	..	4·25	15·00
105	26	1s. black and violet (*p* 14) (2 May)	..	8·50	22·00
99/105			*Set of 7*	38·00	£140

Nos. 100b and 103c come from sheets reperforated 14 on arrival at Wellington. No. 100b comes from the first vertical column of a sheet and has 14 at left and No. 103c from the third or fourth vertical column with 13 at left or right.

Other major errors exist on this issue, but these are not listed as they originated from printer's waste which appeared on the market in 1935.

(Recess from P.B. plates at Govt Printing Office, Wellington)

1933–36. *W 43 of New Zealand (Single N Z and Star). P 14.*

106	20	½d. black and deep green	..	1·00	4·00
		w. Wmk inverted	..	—	75·00
107	21	1d. black and scarlet (1935)	..	1·25	2·00
		w. Wmk inverted and reversed			
108	22	2d. black and brown (1936)	..	1·50	50
109	23	2½d. black and deep blue	..	1·50	2·25
110	24	4d. black and bright blue	..	1·50	50
111	25	6d. black and orange-yellow (1936)	..	1·75	2·25
112	26	1s. black and violet (1936)	..	27·00	30·00
106/12			*Set of 7*	32·00	38·00

SILVER JUBILEE OF KING GEORGE V. 1910–1935.

Normal letters

B K E N

B K E N

Narrow letters

(27)

1935 (7 May). *Silver Jubilee. Optd with T 27 (wider vertical spacing on 6d.). Colours changed. W 43 of New Zealand. P 14.*

113	21	1d. red-brown and lake	..	60	1·40
		a. Narrow "K" in "KING"	..	2·75	
		b. Narrow "B" in "JUBILEE"	..	4·75	
114	23	2½d. dull and deep blue (R.)	..	1·00	2·50
		a. Narrow first "E" in "GEORGE"	..	3·50	6·00
115	25	6d. green and orange	..	3·50	6·00
		a. Narrow "N" in "KING"	..	16·00	
113/15			*Set of 3*	4·50	9·00

1936 (15 July)–**44.** *Stamps of New Zealand optd with T 19. W 43. P 14.*

(*a*) *T 72. Cowan thick, opaque chalk-surfaced paper*

116		2s. light blue (No. 469)	..	12·00	45·00
117		3s. pale mauve (No. 470)	..	13·00	65·00

(*b*) *Type F 6. Cowan thick, opaque chalk-surfaced paper*

118		2s. 6d. deep brown (No. F147)	..	17·00	60·00
119		5s. green (No. F149) (R.)	..	20·00	80·00
120		10s. carmine-lake (No. F155)	..	40·00	£130
121		£1 pink (No. F158)	..	60·00	£160
118/21			*Set of 4*	£120	£375

(*c*) *Type F 6. Thin, hard, chalk-surfaced Wiggins, Teape paper.*

122		2s. 6d. dull brown (No. F170) (12.40)	..	85·00	95·00
123		5s. green (No. F172) (10.40)	..	£325	£350
123*a*		10s. pale carmine-lake (No. F177) (11.44)	..	£120	£170
123*b*		£3 green (No. F183) (R.) (date?)	..	£325	£550
122/3b			*Set of 4*	£750	£1000

COOK IS'DS. COOK IS'DS.

(28)

Small second "S" (R. 1/2)

1937 (1 June). *Coronation. Nos. 599/601 of New Zealand (inscr "12th MAY 1937") optd with T 28.*

124		1d. carmine	..	40	30
		a. Small second "S"	..	11·00	
125		2½d. Prussian blue	..	80	30
		a. Small second "S"	..	20·00	
126		6d. red-orange	..	80	30
		a. Small second "S"	..	20·00	
124/6			*Set of 3*	1·75	80

29 King George VI

30 Native Village

31 Native Canoe

32 Tropical Landscape

(Des J. Berry (2s., 3s., and frame of 1s.). Eng B.W. Recess Govt Ptg. Office, Wellington)

1938 (2 May). *W 43 of New Zealand. P* 14.
127	**29**	1s. black and violet	..	8·00	10·00
128	**30**	2s. black and red-brown	..	18·00	11·00
		w. Wmk inverted			
129	**31**	3s. light blue and emerald-green		42·00	32·00
127/9			*Set of* 3	60·00	48·00

(Recess B.W.)

1940 (2 Sept). *Surch as in T* **32**. *W* **98** *of New Zealand. P* 13½ × 14.
130	**32**	3d. on 1½d. black and purple	..	50	50

Type **32** was not issued without surcharge.

1943–54. *Postal Fiscal stamps as Type F* **6** *of New Zealand optd with T* **19**. *W* **98**. *Wiggins, Teape chalk-surfaced paper. P* 14.
131	2s. 6d. dull brown (No. F193) (3.46)		38·00	50·00
	w. Wmk inverted (2.4.51)		14·00	18·00
132	5s. green (No. F195) (R.) (11.43)		8·50	18·00
	w. Wmk inverted (5.54)		17·00	30·00
133	10s. pale carmine-lake (No. F201) (10.48)		55·00	75·00
	w. Wmk inverted (10.51)		42·00	70·00
134	£1 pink (No. F203) (11.47)		50·00	75·00
	w. Wmk inverted (19.5.54)		48·00	75·00
135	£3 green (No. F208) (R.) (1946?)		£450	£650
	w. Wmk inverted (28.5.53)		55·00	£160
136	£5 indigo-blue (No. F211) (R.) (25.10.50)		£225	£350
	w. Wmk inverted (19.5.54)		£250	£375
131/6		*Set of* 6	£350	£600

The £3 and £5 were mainly used for fiscal purposes.

(Recess Govt Ptg Office, Wellington)

1944–46. *W* **98** *of New Zealand (sideways on ½d. 1d., 1s., and 2s.). P* 14.
137	**20**	½d. black and deep green (11.44)		1·50	3·50
		w. Wmk sideways inverted		7·00	
138	**21**	1d. black and scarlet (3.45)		2·00	35
		w. Wmk sideways inverted		10·00	
139	**22**	2d. black and brown (2.46)		1·25	4·25
140	**23**	2½d. black and deep blue (5.45)		65	1·75
141	**24**	4d. black and blue (4.44)		3·50	8·00
		y. Wmk inverted and reversed		40·00	40·00
142	**26**	6d. black and orange (6.44)		1·50	1·75
143	**29**	1s. black and violet (9.44)		1·50	2·25
144	**30**	2s. black and red-brown (8.45)		32·00	30·00
145	**31**	3s. light blue & emerald-green (6.45)		30·00	28·00
137/45			*Set of* 9	65·00	70·00

COOK ISLANDS
(33)

34 Ngatangiia Channel, Rarotonga

41 Map and Statue of Capt. Cook

(Des J. Berry. Recess Waterlow)

1949 (1 Aug)–**61.** *T* **34, 41** *and similar designs. W* **98** *of New Zealand (sideways on shilling values). P* 13½ × 13 *(horiz) or* 13 × 13½ *(vert).*
150		½d. violet and brown	..	10	1·00
151		1d. chestnut and green	..	3·50	2·00
152		2d. reddish brown and scarlet	..	1·25	2·00
153		3d. green and ultramarine	..	1·25	2·00
		aw. Wmk inverted	..	£100	
		b. Wmk sideways (white opaque paper) (22.5.61)		3·50	2·50
154		6d. emerald-green and violet	..	4·25	1·50
155		6d. black and carmine	..	4·50	2·75
156		8d. olive-green and orange	..	3·75	
		w. Wmk inverted	..	85·00	50·00
157		1s. light blue and chocolate	..	4·25	3·75

158		2s. yellow-brown and carmine	..	3·00	12·00
		w. Wmk sideways inverted			
159		3s. light blue and bluish green	..	8·50	19·00
150/9		.. ..	*Set of* 10	28·00	45·00

Designs: *Horiz*—1d. Capt. Cook and map of Hervey Islands; 2d. Rarotonga and Revd. John Williams; 3d. Aitutaki and palm trees; 5d. Rarotonga Airfield; 6d. Penrhyn village; 8d. Native hut. *Vert*—2s. Native hut and palms; 3s. *Matua* (inter-island freighter).

See note on white opaque paper below No. 736 of New Zealand.

42 Queen Elizabeth II

(Des J. Berry. Photo Harrison)

1953 (25 May). *Coronation. T* **42** *and similar vert design. W* **98**. *P* 14 × 14½.
160		3d. brown	..	1·00	85
161		6d. slate-grey	.. .. ..	1·25	1·40

Design:—6d. Westminster Abbey.

1/6

(44)

1960 (1 Apr). *No.* 154 *surch with T* **44**.
162		1s. 6d. on 5d. emerald-green and violet	..	30	30

45 Tiare Maori

48 White Tern

52 Queen Elizabeth II

53 Island Scene

(Des J. Berry. Recess (1s. 6d.), litho (others) B.W.)

1963 (4 June). *T* **45, 48, 52/3** *and similar designs. W* **98** *of New Zealand (sideways). P* 13½×13 (1d., 2d., 8d.), 13×13½ (3d., 5d., 6d., 1s.) *or* 13½ (others).
163		1d. emerald-green and yellow	..	45	40
164		2d. brown-red and yellow	..	20	40
165		3d. yellow, yellow-green & reddish violet	..	70	40
166		5d. blue and black	..	8·00	1·00
167		6d. red, yellow and green	..	1·00	40
168		8d. black and blue	..	4·00	1·50
169		1s. orange-yellow and yellow-green	..	40	40
170		1s. 6d. bluish violet	..	2·75	2·00
171		2s. bistre-brown and grey-blue	..	1·00	75
172		3s. black and yellow-green	..	1·25	1·00
173		5s. bistre-brown and blue	..	11·00	3·50
163/73			*Set of* 11	27·00	10·50

Designs: *Vert* (as *T* **45**)—2d. Fishing god; 8d. Long-tailed Tuna. *Horiz* (as *T* **48**)—3d. Frangipani; 6d. Hibiscus; 1s. Oranges. (As *T* **53**)—3s. Administration Centre, Mangaia; 5s. Rarotonga.

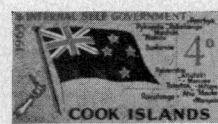

56 Eclipse and Palm

57 N.Z. Ensign and Map

(Des L. C. Mitchell. Litho B.W.)

1965 (31 May). *Solar Eclipse Observation, Manuae Island. W* **98** *of New Zealand. P* 13½.
174	**56**	6d. black, yellow and light blue	..	20	10

SELF-GOVERNMENT

(Des R. M. Conly (4d.), L. C. Mitchell (10d., 1s.), J. Berry (1s. 9d.). Litho B.W.)

1965 (16 Sept). *Internal Self-Government. T* **57** *and similar horiz designs. W* **98** *of New Zealand (sideways). P* 13½.
175		4d. red and blue	..	20	10
176		10d. multicoloured	..	20	15
177		1s. multicoloured	..	20	15
178		1s. 9d. multicoloured	..	50	1·25
175/8			*Set of* 4	1·00	1·50

Designs:—10d. London Missionary Society Church; 1s. Proclamation of Cession, 1900; 1s. 9d. Nikao School.

In Memoriam
Sir Winston Churchill
1874 - 1965
(61)

Airmail
(62)

1966 (24 Jan). *Churchill Commemoration. Nos.* 171/3 *and* 175/7 *optd with T* **61**, *in red.*
179		4d. red and blue	..	75	30
		a. "l" for "1" in "1874"		3·00	
180		10d. multicoloured	..	1·50	45
		a. Opt inverted		£160	
		b. "l" for "1" in "1874"		5·00	
181		1s. multicoloured	..	1·50	65
		a. Opt inverted		£100	
		b. "l" for "1" in "1874"		5·00	
182		2s. bistre-brown and grey-blue	..	1·50	1·25
		a. "l" for "1" in "1874"		5·00	
183		3s. black and yellow-green	..	1·50	1·25
		a. "l" for "1" in "1874"		5·00	
184		5s. bistre-brown and blue	..	2·00	1·75
		a. "l" for "1" in "1874"		10·00	
179/84			*Set of* 6	8·00	5·00

The lower case "l" for "1" in "1874" occurred on R. 6/5 for all values and additionally on R. 12/5 for the 2s., 3s. and 5s.

1966 (22 Apr). *Air. Various stamps optd with T* **62** *or surch also.*
185		6d. red, yellow and green (No. 167)	..	1·25	20
186		7d. on 8d. black and blue (No. 168)	..	2·00	25
187		10d. on 3d. yellow, yellow-green and reddish violet (No. 165)	..	1·00	15
188		1s. orange-yellow & yellow-green (No. 169)		1·00	15
189		1s. 6d. bluish violet (No. 170)	..	1·50	1·25
190		2s. 3d. on 3s. black & yellow-grn (No. 172)		1·00	65
191		5s. bistre-brown and blue (No. 173)	..	1·75	1·50
192		10s. on 2s. bistre-brown & grey-bl (No. 171)		1·75	1·00
193		£1 pink (No. 134)	..	12·00	17·00
		a. Aeroplane omitted		30·00	45·00
		w. Wmk inverted		12·00	16·00
185/93			*Set of* 9	20·00	28·00

No. 193a occurred in all stamps of the last vertical row as insufficient aeroplane symbols were available. There are also numerous other varieties on all values, notably aeroplanes of different sizes and broken first "i" with dot missing owing to damaged type.

PRINTERS. The following stamps were printed by Heraclio Fournier, Spain except *where otherwise stated*. The process used was photogravure until No. **MS1247** and lithography thereafter.

63 "Adoration of the Magi" (Fra Angelico)

1966 (28 Nov). *Christmas. T* **63** *and similar multicoloured designs. P* 13×12 (horiz) *or* 12×13 (vert).
194		1d. Type **63**	..	50	60
		a. Perf 13×14½		10	10
195		2d. "The Nativity" (Memling) (vert)	..	11·00	11·00
		a. Perf 14½×13		20	10
196		4d. "Adoration of the Magi" (Velazquez)		1·00	1·00
		a. Perf 13×14½		30	15
197		10d. "Adoration of the Magi" (Bosch)	..	2·00	4·50
		a. Perf 13×14½		30	20
198		1s. 6d. "Adoration of the Shepherds" (J. de Ribera) (vert)	..	22·00	6·50
		a. Perf 14½×13		40	35
194/8			*Set of* 5	32·00	21·00
194a/8a			*Set of* 5	1·10	70

68 Tennis, and Queen Elizabeth II

(Des V. Whiteley)

1967 (12 Jan). *2nd South Pacific Games, Nouméa. T* **68** *and similar horiz designs in orange-brown, black and new blue* (1d.) *or multicoloured* (others). P 13½. (a) Postage.

199	½d. Type **68**	10	10
200	1d. Netball and Games emblem	10	10
201	4d. Boxing and Cook Islands' team badge	10	10
202	7d. Football and Queen Elizabeth II	20	15

(b) Air

203	10d. Running and Games emblem	20	15
204	2s. 3d. Running and Cook Islands' team badge	25	45
199/204	Set of 6	70	80

(New Currency, 100 cents = 1 dollar)

1c	**2½c**	**2½c**
(74)	(I)	(II)

1967 (3 Apr–6 June). *Decimal Currency. Nos.* 134, 135w, 136, 163/70 *and* 172/5 *surch as T* **74** *by the Government Printer. Sterling values unobliterated except No.* 218.

205	1 c. on 1d. emerald-green and yellow (4.5)	45	1·50
206	2 c. on 2d. brown-red and yellow	10	10
207	2½ c. on 3d. yell, yellow-grn & reddish vio (I)	20	10
a. Horiz pair. Nos. 207/8	40	20
208	2½ c. on 3d. yellow, yellow-green & reddish violet (II)	20	10
209	3 c. on 4d. red and blue	15	10
210	4 c. on 5d. blue and black (4.5)	6·50	30
211	5 c. on 6d. red, yellow and green	15	10
212	5 c. on 6d. black, yellow and light blue	5·00	40
213	7 c. on 8d. black and blue	30	10
214	10 c. on 1s. orange-yellow and yellow-green	15	10
215	15 c. on 1s. 6d. bluish violet (R.) (4.5.67)	2·00	1·00
216	30 c. on 3s. black & yellow-green (R.) (4.5.67)	16·00	4·50
217	50 c. on 5s. bistre-brown & blue (R.) (4.5.67)	4·00	1·25
218	$1 and 10s. on 10d. mult (R.) (4.5.67)	15·00	6·50
219	$2 on £1 pink (R.) (6.6.67)	50·00	70·00
220	$6 on £3 green (R.) (6.6.67)	95·00	£110
221	$10 on £5 blue (R.) (6.6.67)	£150	£170
w. Wmk inverted	£150	£170
205/18	Set of 14	45·00	13·00

The two types of the 2½ c. occur on alternate vertical rows within the sheet.

The surcharge on No. 218 is $1 and its equivalent of 10s. in the old currency. The "10d." is obliterated by three bars.

A large number of minor varieties exist in these surcharges, such as wrong fount letter "C" and figures.

75 Village Scene. Cook Islands 1d. Stamp of 1892 and Queen Victoria (from "Penny Black")

(Des V. Whiteley)

1967 (3 July). *75th Anniv of First Cook Islands Stamps. T* **75** *and similar horiz designs. Multicoloured. P* 13½.

222	1 c. (1d.) Type **75**	10	10
223	3 c. (4d.) Post Office, Avarua, Rarotonga and Queen Elizabeth II	15	10
224	8 c. (10d.) Avarua, Rarotonga and Cook Islands 10d. stamp of 1892	30	10
225	18 c. (1s. 9d.) Moana Roa (inter-island ship), Douglas DC-3 aircraft, map and Captain Cook	1·40	25
222/5	Set of 4	1·75	40
MS226	134×109 mm. Nos. 222/5	1·75	2·75

The face values are expressed in decimal currency and in the sterling equivalent.

Each value was issued in sheets of 8 stamps and 1 label.

79 Hibiscus

80 Queen Elizabeth II

81 Queen Elizabeth and Flowers

Two types of $4

I. Value 32½ mm long. Coarse screen.
II. Value 33½ mm long. Finer screen.

(Floral designs from paintings by Kay Billings)

1967 (31 July)–**71**. *Multicoloured designs as T* **79/81**. *P* 14×13½.

A. Without fluorescent security markings

227A	½ c. Type **79**	10	10
228A	1 c. Hibiscus syriacus (27×37 mm)	10	10
229A	2 c. Frangipani (27×37 mm)	10	10
230A	2½ c. Clitoria ternatea (27×37 mm)	20	10
231A	3 c. "Suva Queen" (27×37 mm)	55	10
232A	4 c. Water Lily ("WALTER LILY") (27×37 mm)	70	1·00
233A	4 c. Water Lily (27×37 mm)	2·00	2·50
234A	5 c. Bauhinia bipinnata rosea (27×37 mm)	35	10
235A	6 c. Hibiscus (27×37 mm)	40	10
236A	8 c. Allamanda cathartica (27×37 mm)	40	10
237A	9 c. Stephanotis (27×37 mm)	40	10
238A	10 c. Poinciana regia flamboyant (27×37 mm)	40	10
239A	15 c. Frangipani (27×37 mm) (11.8.67)	40	10
240A	20 c. Thunbergia (27×37 mm) (11.8.67)	4·50	1·50
241A	25 c. Canna Lily (27×37 mm) (11.8.67)	80	30
242A	30 c. Euphorbia pulcherrima poinsettia (27×37 mm) (11.8.67)	65	50
243A	50 c. Gardinia taitensis (27×37 mm) (11.8.67)	1·00	55
244A	$1 Type **80** (31.8.67)	2·25	80
245A	$2 Type **80** (31.8.67)	4·75	1·50
246A	$4 Type **81** (I) (30.4.68)	2·00	4·00
247A	$6 Type **81** (30.4.68)	2·50	5·50
247cA	$8 Type **81** (21.4.69)	7·00	14·00
248A	$10 Type **81** (12.7.68)	4·50	12·00
227A/48A	Set of 22	30·00	38·00

B. With fluorescent security markings

227B	½ c. Type **79** (9.2.70)	20	10
228B	1 c. Hibiscus syriacus (27×37 mm) (9.2.70)	20	10
229B	2 c. Frangipani (27×37 mm) (9.2.70)	20	10
230B	2½ c. Clitoria ternatea (27×37 mm) (9.2.70)	20	10
231B	3 c. "Suva Queen" (27×37 mm) (9.2.70)	40	10
233B	4 c. Water Lily (27×37 mm) (9.2.70)	2·50	10
234B	5 c. Bauhinia bipinnata rosea (27×37 mm) (9.2.70)	30	10
235B	6 c. Hibiscus (27×37 mm) (9.2.70)	30	10
236B	8 c. Allamanda cathartica (27×37 mm) (9.2.70)	30	10
237B	9 c. Stephanotis (27×37 mm) (9.2.70)	30	10
238B	10 c. Poinciana regia flamboyant (27×37 mm) (9.2.70)	30	10
239B	15 c. Frangipani (27×37 mm) (9.2.70)	40	10
240B	20 c. Thunbergia (27×37 mm) (9.2.70)	3·50	95
241B	25 c. Canna Lily (27×37 mm) (9.2.70)	1·00	15
242B	30 c. Euphorbia pulcherrima poinsettia (27×37 mm) (9.2.70)	1·25	40
243B	50 c. Gardinia taitensis (27×37 mm) (9.2.70)	1·25	40
244B	$1 Type **80** (12.10.70)	1·25	80
245B	$2 Type **80** (12.10.70)	2·25	1·50
246B	$4 Type **81** (I) (11.11.70)	35·00	48·00
a. Type II (14.7.71)	5·50	8·50
247B	$6 Type **81** (12.2.71)	11·00	6·00
247cB	$8 Type **81** (3.5.71)	12·00	10·00
248B	$10 Type **81** (14.6.71)	16·00	12·00
227B/48B	Set of 22	55·00	35·00

The "WALTER" spelling error occurred on all stamps in one of the four post office sheets which went to make up the printing sheet and this was corrected in later supplies.

FLUORESCENT PAPER. This is on paper treated with fluorescent security markings, in the form of faint multiple coats of arms. Stamps exist with these markings inverted. In addition an invisible synthetic gum has been used which prevents curling and is suitable for use in the tropics without interleaving the sheets.

Some of the above are known with these markings omitted and can be distinguished when in unused condition from the original printings without markings by their synthetic invisible gum.

Gauguin - Ia Orana Maria
COOK ISLANDS
97 "Ia Orana Maria"

1967 (24 Oct). *Gauguin's Polynesian Paintings. T* **97** *and similar designs. Multicoloured. P* 13.

249	1 c. Type **97**	10	10
250	3 c. "Riders on the Beach"	15	10
251	5 c. "Still Life with Flowers"	20	10
252	8 c. "Whispered Words"	25	10
253	15 c. "Maternity"	50	15
254	22 c. "Why are you angry?"	65	20
249/54	Set of 6	1·60	55
MS255	156 × 132 mm. Nos. 249/54	1·75	1·25

The 5 c. includes an inset portrait of Queen Elizabeth.

MINIMUM PRICE

The minimum price quote is 10p which represents a handling charge rather than a basis for valuing common stamps. For further notes about prices see introductory pages.

COOK ISLANDS
98 "The Holy Family" (Rubens)

HURRICANE RELIEF PLUS 5c
(99)

1967 (4 Dec). *Christmas. Renaissance Paintings. T* **98** *and similar designs. Multicoloured. P* 12 × 13.

256	1 c. Type **98**	10	10
257	3 c. "Adoration of the Magi" (Dürer)	10	10
258	4 c. "The Lucca Madonna" (J. van Eyck)	10	10
259	8 c. "The Adoration of the Shepherds" (J. da Bassano)	15	15
260	15 c. "Adoration of the Shepherds" (El Greco)	30	15
261	25 c. "Madonna and Child" (Correggio)	35	15
256/61	Set of 6	90	50

1968 (12 Feb). *Hurricane Relief. Nos.* 231A, 233A, 251, 238A, 241A *and* 243/4A *surch as T* **99** *by Govt Printer, Rarotonga.*

262	3 c. + 1 c. "Suva Queen"	15	15
263	4 c. + 1 c. Water Lily	15	15
264	5 c. + 2 c. "Still Life with Flowers"	20	15
a. Black surch albino			
265	10 c. + 2 c. Poinciana regia flamboyant	20	15
266	25 c. + 5 c. Canna Lily	25	20
267	50 c. + 10 c. Gardinia taitensis	30	30
268	$1 + 10 c. Type **80**	1·50	1·25
262/8	Set of 7	1·60	1·40

The surcharge on No. 268 is as T **99**, but with seriffed letters. On No. 264 silver blocking obliterates the design area around the lettering.

100 "Matavai Bay, Tahiti" (J. Barralet)

101 "Resolution and Discovery" (J. Webber)

(Des J. Berry)

1968 (12 Sept). *Bicentenary of Captain Cook's First Voyage of Discovery. Multicoloured. Invisible gum. P* 13.

(a) Postage. Vert designs as T **100**

269	½ c. Type **100**	10	10
270	1 c. "Island of Huaheine" (John Cleveley)	15	10
271	2 c. "Town of St. Peter and St. Paul, Kamchatka" (J. Webber)	45	35
272	4 c. "The Ice Islands" (Antarctica: W. Hodges)	60	35

(b) Air. Horiz designs as T **101**

273	6 c. Type **101**	1·00	65
274	10 c. "The Island of Tahiti" (W. Hodges)	1·00	75
275	15 c. "Karakakooa, Hawaii" (J. Webber)	1·25	90
276	25 c. "The Landing at Middleburg" (J. Sherwin)	1·50	1·25
269/76	Set of 8	5·50	4·00

Each value was issued in sheets of 10 stamps and 2 labels.

FLUORESCENT PAPER. From No. 277, *unless otherwise stated*, all issues are printed on paper treated with fluorescent security markings with invisible synthetic gum. These markings may be inverted or omitted in error.

COOK ISLANDS
102 Dinghy-sailing

COOK ISLANDS
103 "Madonna and Child" (Titian)

1968 (21 Oct). *Olympic Games, Mexico. T 102 and similar horiz designs. Multicoloured. P 13.*

277	1 c. Type **102**	10	10
278	5 c. Gymnastics	10	10
279	15 c. High-jumping	25	10
280	20 c. High-diving	25	10
281	30 c. Cycling	60	20
282	50 c. Hurdling	50	25
277/82	*Set of 6*	1·50	60

Each value was issued in sheets of 10 stamps and 2 labels.

1968 (2 Dec). *Christmas. Paintings. T 103 and similar vert designs. Multicoloured. P 13½.*

283	1 c. Type **103**	10	10
284	4 c. "The Holy Family with Lamb" (Raphael)	15	10
285	10 c. "The Virgin of the Rosary" (Murillo)	25	10
286	20 c. "Adoration of the Kings" (Memling)	40	10
287	30 c. "Adoration of the Magi" (Ghirlandaio)	45	10
283/7	*Set of 5*	1·25	30
MS288	114 × 177 mm. Nos. 283/7 plus label	1·60	1·60

104 Camp-fire Cooking

1969 (6 Feb). *Diamond Jubilee of New Zealand Scout Movement and Fifth National (New Zealand) Jamboree. T 104 and similar square designs. Multicoloured. P 13½.*

289	½ c. Type **104**	10	10
290	1 c. Descent by rope	10	10
291	5 c. Semaphore	10	10
292	10 c. Tree-planting	15	10
293	20 c. Constructing a shelter	25	10
294	30 c. Lord Baden-Powell and island scene	40	15
289/94	*Set of 6*	90	35

Each value was issued in sheets of 10 stamps and 2 labels.

105 High Jumping

1969 (7 July). *Third South Pacific Games, Port Moresby. T 105 and similar triangular designs. Multicoloured. Without fluorescent security markings. P 13 × 13½.*

295	½ c. Type **105**	10	30
296	½ c. Footballer	10	30
297	1 c. Basketball	50	40
298	1 c. Weightlifter	50	40
299	4 c. Tennis-player	50	50
300	4 c. Hurdler	50	50
301	10 c. Javelin-thrower	55	50
302	10 c. Runner	55	50
303	15 c. Golfer	1·75	1·50
304	15 c. Boxer	1·75	1·50
295/304	*Set of 10*	6·00	6·00
MS305	174 × 129 mm. Nos. 295/304 plus two labels	6·50	6·00

Each value was issued in sheets containing 5 se-tenant pairs of both designs and 2 labels.

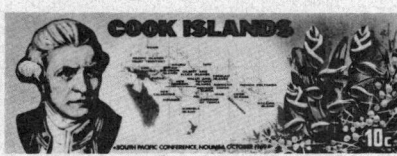

106 Flowers, Map and Captain Cook

1969 (8 Oct). *South Pacific Conference, Nouméa. T 106 and similar horiz designs. Multicoloured. Without fluorescent security markings. P 13.*

306	5 c. Flowers, map and Premier Albert Henry	40	20
307	10 c. Type **106**	1·00	75
308	25 c. Flowers, map and N.Z. arms	70	95
309	30 c. Queen Elizabeth II, map and flowers	70	1·10
306/9	*Set of 4*	2·50	2·75

PRICES OF SETS

Set prices are given for many issues, generally those containing three stamps or more. Definitive sets include one of each value or major colour change, but do not cover different perforations, die types or minor shades. Where a choice is possible the set prices are based on the cheapest versions of the stamps included in the listings.

107 "Virgin and Child with Saints Jerome and Dominic" (Lippi)

108 "The Resurrection of Christ" (Raphael)

1969 (21 Nov). *Christmas. Paintings. T 107 and similar designs. Multicoloured. Without fluorescent security markings. P 13.*

310	1 c. Type **107**	10	10
311	4 c. "The Holy Family" (Fra Bartolomeo)	10	10
312	10 c. "The Adoration of the Shepherds" (A. Mengs)	15	10
313	20 c. "Madonna and Child with Saints" (R. Campin)	25	20
314	30 c. "The Madonna of the Basket" (Correggio)	25	30
310/14	*Set of 5*	70	60
MS315	132 × 97 mm. Nos. 310/14	1·50	1·50

Each value was issued in sheets of 9 stamps and 1 label.

1970 (12 Mar). *Easter. Paintings. T 108 and similar vert designs showing "The Resurrection of Christ" by the artists named. Multicoloured. P 13.*

316	4 c. Type **108**	10	10
317	8 c. Dirk Bouts	10	10
318	20 c. Altdorfer	15	10
319	25 c. Murillo	20	10
316/19	*Set of 4*	50	30
MS320	132 × 162 mm. Nos. 316/19	1·25	1·25

Each value was issued in sheets of 8 stamps and 1 label.

KIA ORANA

APOLLO 13

ASTRONAUTS

Te Atua to

Tatou Irinakianga

(109)

1970 (17–30 Apr). *Apollo 13. Nos. 233, 236, 239/40, 242 and 245/6 optd with T 109 (4 c. to $2) or with first three lines only in larger type ($4), by Govt Printer. Without fluorescent security markings.*

321	4 c. Water Lily	10	10
	a. Opt albino	25·00	
322	8 c. Allamanda cathartica	10	10
323	15 c. Frangipani	10	10
324	20 c. Thunbergia	15	15
325	30 c. Euphorbia pulcherrima poinsettia	20	20
326	$2 Type **80**	60	90
327	$4 Type **81** (30.4)	28·00	45·00
	a. With fluorescent security markings	1·25	2·75
321/7a	*Set of 7*	2·00	3·75

110 The Royal Family

(Des V. Whiteley (5 c.), J. Berry ($1))

1970 (12 June). *Royal Visit to New Zealand. T 110 and similar horiz designs. Multicoloured. P 13.*

328	5 c. Type **110**	65	30
329	30 c. Captain Cook and H.M.S. *Endeavour*	2·75	1·75
330	$1 Royal Visit commemorative coin	4·00	3·00
328/30	*Set of 3*	6·75	4·50
MS331	145 × 97 mm. Nos. 328/30	9·00	9·50

Each value was issued in sheets of 8 stamps and 1 label.

FOUR

DOLLARS

FIFTH ANNIVERSARY
SELF-GOVERNMENT
AUGUST 1970

(113)

$4.00

(114)

1970 (27 Aug). *5th Anniv of Self-Government Nos. 328/30 optd with T 113 (30 c. and $1), or in single line in silver around frame of stamp (5 c.).*

332	5 c. Type **110**	40	15
333	30 c. Captain Cook and H.M.S. *Endeavour*	1·25	35
334	$1 Royal Visit commemorative coin	2·00	90
332/4	*Set of 3*	3·25	1·25

1970 (11 Nov). *Nos. 247c and 248 surch with T 114 by Govt Printer, Rarotonga. Without fluorescent security markings.*

335	81	$4 on $8 multicoloured	35·00	28·00
		a. With fluorescent security markings	1·50	2·00
336		$4 on $10 multicoloured	35·00	48·00
		a. With fluorescent security markings	1·50	1·50

There are variations in the setting of this surcharge and also in the rule.

PLUS 20c

UNITED KINGDOM

SPECIAL MAIL SERVICE

(116)

115 Mary, Joseph and Christ in Manger

(Des from De Lisle Psalter)

1970 (30 Nov). *Christmas. T 115 and similar square designs. Multicoloured. P 13.*

337	1 c. Type **115**	10	10
338	4 c. Shepherds and Apparition of the Angel	10	10
339	10 c. Mary showing Child to Joseph	15	10
340	20 c. The Wise Men bearing Gifts	20	10
341	30 c. Parents wrapping Child in swaddling clothes	25	15
337/41	*Set of 5*	65	35
MS342	100 × 139 mm. Nos. 337/41 plus label	90	1·50

Each value was issued in sheets of 5 stamps and 1 label. Stamps from the miniature sheet are smaller, since they do not have the buff parchment border as on the stamps from the sheets.

1971. *Nos. 242B and 243B surch as T 116.*

343	30 c. + 20 c. Euphorbia pulcherrima poinsettia (25.2)	30	50
344	50 c. + 20 c. Gardinia taitensis (8.3)	1·00	1·75

The premium of 20 c. was to prepay a private delivery service fee in Great Britain during the postal strike. The mail was sent by air to a forwarding address in the Netherlands. No. 343 was intended for ordinary airmail ½ oz letters, and No. 344 included registration fee.

The postal strike ended on 8 March and both stamps were withdrawn on 12 March.

117 Wedding of Princess Elizabeth and Prince Philip

(Des from photographs. Litho Format)

1971 (11 Mar). *Royal Visit of H.R.H. The Duke of Edinburgh. T 117 and similar horiz designs. Multicoloured. P 13½.*

345	1 c. Type **117**	20	50
346	4 c. Queen Elizabeth, Prince Philip, Princess Anne and Prince Charles at Windsor	60	1·10
347	10 c. Prince Philip sailing	80	1·25
348	15 c. Prince Philip in polo gear	80	1·25
349	25 c. Prince Philip in naval uniform, and the Royal Yacht *Britannia*	1·00	2·00
345/9	*Set of 5*	3·00	5·50
MS350	168 × 122 mm. Nos 345/9 plus printed labels in positions 1, 3, 4, and 6	4·25	8·00

Each value was issued in sheets of 7 stamps and 2 labels.

(118)

(119)

1971 (8 Sept). *Fourth South Pacific Games, Tahiti. Nos. 238B, 241B and 242B optd with T 118 in black, or surch as T 119 in blue.*

351	10 c. Poinciana regia flamboyant	10	10
352	10 c. + 1 c. Poinciana regia flamboyant	10	10
353	10 c. + 3 c. Poinciana regia flamboyant	10	10
354	25 c. Canna Lily	15	10
355	25 c. + 1 c. Canna Lily	15	10
356	25 c. + 3 c. Canna Lily	15	10

357	30 c. *Euphorbia pulcherrima poinsettia*	15	10
358	30 c. + 1 c. *Euphorbia pulcherrima poinsettia*	15	10
359	30 c. + 3 c. *Euphorbia pulcherrima poinsettia*	15	10
351/9	Set of 9	1·10	50

The stamps additionally surcharged 1 c. or 3 c. helped to finance the Cook Islands' team at the games.

10c ≡

(120)   121 "Virgin and Child" (Bellini)

1971 (20 Oct). *Nos. 230B, 233B, 236B/7B and 239B surch with T 120.*

360	10 c. on 2½ c. *Clitoria ternatea*	15	25
361	10 c. on 4 c. Water Lily	15	25
362	10 c. on 8 c. *Allamanda cathartica*	15	25
	a. Surch inverted	£140	
363	10 c. on 9 c. Stephanotis	15	25
364	10 c. on 15 c. Frangipani	15	25
	a. Surch double	95·00	
360/4	Set of 5	65	1·10

1971 (30 Nov). *Christmas. T 121 and similar vert designs showing different paintings of the "Virgin and Child", by Bellini. P 13.*

365	1 c. multicoloured	10	10
366	4 c. multicoloured	10	10
367	10 c. multicoloured	25	10
368	20 c. multicoloured	50	20
369	30 c. multicoloured	50	35
365/9	Set of 5	1·25	60
MS370	135 × 147 mm. Nos. 365/9	2·00	2·50
MS371	92 × 98 mm. 50 c. + 5 c. "The Holy Family in a Garland of Flowers (Jan Brueghel and Pieter van Avont) (41 × 41 mm)	75	1·40

Each value was issued in sheets of 8 stamps and 1 label.

(122)   123 St. John

1972 (17 Feb). *25th Anniv of South Pacific Commission. No. 244B optd with T 122.*

372	**80** $1 multicoloured	40	75

(Des from De Lisle Psalter)

1972 (6 Mar). *Easter. T 123 and similar vert designs. Multicoloured. P 13.*

373	5 c. Type **123**	10	10
374	10 c. Christ on the Cross	10	10
375	30 c. Mary, Mother of Jesus	25	40
373/5	Set of 3	35	50
MS376	79 × 112 mm. Nos. 373/5 forming triptych of "The Crucifixion"	80	2·25

Stamps from the miniature sheet do not have a border around the perforations, and are therefore smaller than stamps from sheets.

HURRICANE   **Hurricane**
RELIEF   **Relief**
PLUS 2c   **Plus 5c**
(124)   (125)

1972 (30 Mar). *Hurricane Relief. Nos. 373/5 surch as T 124, and Nos. 239B, 241B and 243B surch as T 125, by Govt Printer, Rarotonga.*

377	5 c. + 2 c. Type **123** (R.)	10	10
	a. Albino surch	50·00	
378	10 c. + 2 c. Christ on the Cross (R.)	15	15
379	15 c. + 5 c. Frangipani	20	20
380	25 c. + 5 c. Canna Lily	20	20
381	30 c. + 5 c. Mary, Mother of Jesus	20	20
	a. Albino surch		
382	50 c. + 10 c. *Gardinia taitensis*	25	25
377/82	Set of 6	90	90

126   Rocket heading for Moon   127

1972 (17 Apr). *Apollo Moon Exploration Flights. T 126/7 and similar horiz designs. Multicoloured. P 13.*

383	5 c. Type **126**	20	15
384	5 c. Type **127**	20	15
385	10 c. Lunar module and astronaut	20	15
386	10 c. Astronaut and experiment	20	15
387	25 c. Command capsule and Earth	25	20
388	25 c. Lunar Rover	25	20
389	30 c. Sikorsky S-61B SH-3 Sea King helicopter	60	20
390	30 c. Splashdown	60	20
383/90	Set of 8	2·25	1·25
MS391	83×205 mm. Nos. 383/90	3·50	4·75

These were issued in horizontal *se-tenant* pairs of each value, forming one composite design.

HURRICANE
RELIEF
Plus 2c
(128)   129 High-jumping

1972 (24 May). *Hurricane Relief. Nos. 383/91 surch as T 128.*

392	5 c. + 2 c. Type **126**	10	10
393	5 c. + 2 c. Type **127**	10	10
394	10 c. + 2 c. Lunar module and astronaut	10	10
395	10 c. + 2 c. Astronaut and experiment	10	10
396	25 c. + 2 c. Command capsule and Earth	15	15
397	25 c. + 2 c. Lunar Rover	15	15
398	30 c. + 2 c. Sikorsky S-61B SH-3 Sea King helicopter	25	15
399	30 c. + 2 c. Splashdown	25	15
392/9	Set of 8	1·00	75
MS400	83×205 mm. No. MS391 surch 3 c. on each stamp	2·50	3·50

1972 (26 June). *Olympic Games, Munich. T 129 and similar vert designs. Multicoloured. P 13½.*

401	10 c. Type **129**	20	10
402	25 c. Running	40	15
403	30 c. Boxing	40	20
401/3	Set of 3	90	40
MS404	88 × 78 mm. 50 c. + 5 c. Pierre de Coubertin	1·00	2·00
MS405	84 × 133 mm. Nos. 401/3 plus *se-tenant* label	1·25	2·00

Each value was issued in sheets of 8 stamps and 1 label.

130 "The Rest on the Flight into Egypt" (Caravaggio)   131 Marriage Ceremony

1972 (11 Oct). *Christmas T 130 and similar vert designs. Multicoloured. P 13.*

406	1 c. Type **130**	10	10
407	5 c. "Madonna of the Swallow" (Guercino)	25	10
408	10 c. "Madonna of the Green Cushion" (Solario)	35	10
409	20 c. "Madonna and Child" (di Credi)	55	20
410	30 c. "Madonna and Child" (Bellini)	85	30
406/10	Set of 5	1·90	60
MS411	141 × 152 mm. Nos. 406/10 plus *se-tenant* label in position 1	2·75	2·75
MS412	101 × 82 mm. 50 c + 5 c. "The Holy Night" (Correggio) (31 × 43 mm)	75	1·50

Each value was issued in sheets of 9 stamps and 1 label.

1972 (20 Nov). *Royal Silver Wedding. T 131 and similar black and silver designs. P 13.*

413	5 c. Type **131**	25	15
414	10 c. Leaving Westminster Abbey	35	40
415	15 c. Bride and Bridegroom (40 × 41 mm)	45	65
416	30 c. Family Group (67 × 40 mm)	55	90
413/16	Set of 4	1·40	1·90

The 5, 10 and 15 c. values were each issued in sheets of 8 stamps and 1 label.

132 Taro Leaf   133 "Noli me Tangere" (Titian)

1973 (15 Mar). *Silver Wedding Coinage. T 132 and similar designs showing coins. P 13.*

417	1 c. black, rosy carmine and gold	10	10
418	2 c. black, bright blue and gold	10	10
419	5 c. black, green and silver	10	10
420	10 c. black, royal blue and silver	20	10
421	20 c. black, deep blue-green and silver	30	10
422	50 c. black, carmine and silver	50	15
423	$1 black, bright blue and silver	75	30
417/23	Set of 7	1·75	60

Designs: *As T* **132**—2 c. Pineapple; 5 c. Hibiscus. 46×30 mm—10 c. Oranges; 20 c. White Tern; 50 c. Striped Bonito. 32×55 mm—$1 Tangaroa.

Each value was issued in sheets of 20 stamps and 1 label.

1973 (9 Apr). *Easter. T 133 and similar vert designs. Multicoloured. P 13.*

424	5 c. Type **133**	15	10
425	10 c. "The Descent from the Cross" (Rubens)	20	10
426	30 c. "The Lamentation of Christ" (Dürer)	25	10
424/6	Set of 3	55	50
MS427	132 × 67 mm. Nos. 424/6	55	1·25

Each value was issued in sheets of 15 stamps and 1 label.

1973 (30 Apr). *Easter. Children's Charity. Designs as Nos. 424/6 in separate Miniature Sheets 67 × 87 mm, each with a face value of 50 c. + 5 c. P 13 × 14.*

MS428	As Nos. 424/6	Set of 3 sheets	90	1·75

134 Queen Elizabeth II in Coronation Regalia   (135)

TENTH ANNIVERSARY
CESSATION OF
NUCLEAR TESTING
TREATY

1973 (1 June). *20th Anniv of Queen Elizabeth's Coronation. P 14 × 13½.*

429	**134** 10 c. multicoloured	50	90
MS430	64 × 89 mm. 50 c. as 10 c. P 13 × 14	2·50	2·25

The perforated portion of MS430 is similar to No. 429, but has no address.

No. 429 was issued in sheets of 5 stamps and 1 label.

1973 (25 July). *Tenth Anniv of Treaty Banning Nuclear Testing. Nos. 234B, 236B, 238B, and 240B/242B optd with T 135.*

431	5 c. *Bauhinia bi-pinnata rosea*	10	10
432	8 c. *Allamanda cathartica*	10	10
433	10 c. *Poinciana regia flamboyant*	10	10
434	20 c. Thunbergia	15	15
435	25 c. Canna Lily	20	15
436	30 c. *Euphorbia pulcherrima poinsettia*	20	15
431/6	Set of 6	70	65

136 Tipairua

1973 (17 Sept). *Maori Exploration of the Pacific. T 136 and similar horiz designs showing sailing craft. Multicoloured. P 13.*

437	½ c. Type **136**	10	10
438	1 c. Wa'a Kaulua	10	10
439	1½ c. Tainui	15	10
440	5 c. War canoe	50	15
441	10 c. Pahi	70	15
442	15 c. Amastasi	1·25	65
443	25 c. Vaka	1·50	80
437/443	Set of 7	3·75	1·75

137 The Annunciation

138 Princess Anne

1973 (30 Oct). *Christmas. T 137 and similar vert designs showing scenes from a 15th-century Flemish "Book of Hours". Multicoloured. P 13.*
444	1 c. Type **137**	..	..	..	10	10
445	5 c. The Visitation		..	..	10	10
446	10 c. Annunciation to the Shepherds	..	..	10	10
447	20 c. Epiphany		..	..	15	10
448	30 c. The Slaughter of the Innocents	..	20	15
444/8				*Set of 5*	40	30
MS449	121 × 128 mm. Nos. 444/8 plus *se-tenant*			
	label	..	..	..	55	1·40

Each value was issued in sheets of 14 stamps and 1 label.
See also No. MS454.

1973 (14 Nov). *Royal Wedding. T 138 and similar vert designs. Multicoloured. P 14 × 13½.*
450	25 c. Type **138**	..	..	..	20	10
451	30 c. Capt. Mark Phillips		..	25	10
452	50 c. Princess Anne and Capt. Phillips	30	15
450/2				*Set of 3*	65	30
MS453	119 × 100 mm. No. 450/2 plus *se-tenant*		
	label. P 13.	..	..	55	35

Each value was issued in sheets of 8 stamps and 1 label.

1973 (3 Dec). *Christmas. Children's Charity. Designs as Nos. 444/8 in separate Miniature Sheets 50 × 70 mm, each with a face value of 50 c. + 5 c.*
MS454	As Nos. 444/8	*Set of 5 sheets* 75	80

139 Running

140 "Jesus carrying the Cross" (Raphael)

1974 (24 Jan). *Commonwealth Games, Christchurch. T 139 and similar multicoloured designs. P 14 × 13½ (1 and 3 c.) or 13½ × 14 (others).*
455	1 c. Diving (*vert*)	..	..	..	10	10
456	3 c. Boxing (*vert*)	..	..	..	10	10
457	5 c. Type **139**	..	..	..	10	10
458	10 c. Weightlifting	..	..	..	10	10
459	30 c. Cycling	..	..	..	20	25
455/9				*Set of 5*	40	40
MS460	115 × 90 mm. 50 c. Discobolus	..	40	55

Each value was issued in sheets of 15 stamps and 1 label.

1974 (25 Mar). *Easter. T 140 and similar vert designs. Multicoloured. P 13½.*
461	5 c. Type **140**	..	..	..	10	10
462	10 c. "The Holy Trinity" (El Greco)	..	15	10
463	30 c. "The Deposition of Christ" (Caravaggio)	..	..	25	20
461/3				*Set of 3*	40	30
MS464	130 × 70 mm. Nos. 461/3	..	..	1·50	50

Each value was issued in sheets of 20 stamps and 1 label.

1974 (22 Apr). *Easter. Children's Charity. Designs as Nos. 461/3 in separate Miniature Sheets 59 × 87 mm, each with a face value of 50 c. + 5 c.*
MS465	As Nos. 461/3	*Set of 3 sheets* 70	1·40

141 Grey Bonnet (*Phalium glaucum*)

142 Queen Elizabeth II

1974 (17 May)–75. *Horiz designs as T 141 showing sea-shells (½ to 60 c.), T 142 or larger horiz design ($4 to $10). Multicoloured. P 14×13½ ($4 to $10) or 13½ (others).*
466	½ c. Type **141**		30	10
467	1 c. Common Pacific Vase (*Vasum turbinellum*)	30	10
468	1½ c. True Heart Cockle (*Corculum cardissa*)	30	10
469	2 c. Terebellum Conch (*Terebellum terebellum*)	30	10
470	3 c. Bat Volute (*Cymbiola vespertilio*)	45	10
471	4 c. Gibbose Conch (*Strombus gibberulus gibbosus*)	50	10
472	5 c. Common Hairy Triton (*Cymatium pileare*)	50	10
473	6 c. Serpent's-head Cowrie (*Cypraea caput-serpentis*)	50	90
474	8 c. Granulate Frog Shell (*Bursa granularis*)	60	10
475	10 c. Fly-spotted Auger (*Terebra areolata*)	60	10
476	15 c. Episcopan Mitre (*Mitra mitra*)	70	20
477	20 c. Butterfly Moon (*Natica alapapilionis*)	1·00	20
478	25 c. Royal Oak Scallop (*Cryptopecten pallium*)	1·00	60
479	30 c. Soldier Cone (*Conus miles*)	1·00	30
480	50 c. Textile or Cloth of Gold Cone (*Conus textile*) (26.8.74)	8·50	4·50
481	60 c. Red-mouth Olive (*Oliva miniacea miniacea*) (26.8.74)	8·50	4·50
482	$1 Type **142** (26.8.74)	3·00	4·50
483	$2 Type **142** (27.1.75)	1·75	2·25
484	$4 Queen Elizabeth II and seashells (17.3.75)	2·50	5·50
485	$6 As $4 (29.4.75)	14·00	7·00
486	$8 As $4 (30.5.75)	15·00	8·50
487	$10 As $4 (30.6.75)	18·00	9·00
466/87		*Set of 22*	70·00	42·00

Nos. 484/7 are larger, 60×39 mm.

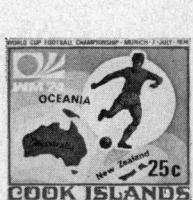

143 Footballer and Australasian Map

144 Obverse and Reverse of Commemorative $2·50 Silver Coin

1974 (5 July). *World Cup Football Championships, West Germany. T 143 and similar horiz designs. Multicoloured. P 13.*
488	25 c. Type **143**	..	20	10
489	50 c. Map and Munich Stadium	..	35	25
490	$1 Footballer, stadium and World Cup	55	45
488/90		*Set of 3*	1·00	70
MS491	89 × 100 mm. Nos. 488/90	..	1·00	2·75

Each value was issued in sheets of 8 stamps and 1 label.

1974 (22 July). *Bicentenary of Capt. Cook's Second Voyage of Discovery. T 144 and similar vert design. P 14.*
492	$2.50, silver, black and violet	..	12·00	7·00
493	$7.50, silver, black and deep turquoise-green	20·00	13·00
MS494	73 × 73 mm. Nos. 492/3	..	35·00	48·00

Design:—$7.50. As T **144** but showing $7.50 coin.
Each value was issued in sheets of 5 stamps and 1 label.

145 Early Stamps of Cook Islands

146 "Madonna of the Goldfinch" (Raphael)

1974 (16 Sept). *Centenary of Universal Postal Union. T 145 and similar horiz designs. Multicoloured. P 13½ × 14.*
495	10 c. Type **145**	..	20	15
496	25 c. Old landing strip, Rarotonga, and stamp of 1898	35	40
497	30 c. Post Office, Rarotonga, and stamp of 1920	40	40
498	50 c. U.P.U. emblem and stamps	45	65
495/8		*Set of 4*	1·25	1·40
MS499	118 × 79 mm. Nos. 495/8. P 13	1·25	1·75

Each value was issued in sheets of 8 stamps and 1 label.

1974 (15 Oct). *Christmas. T 146 and similar vert designs. Multicoloured. P 13.*
500	1 c. Type **146**		10	10
501	5 c. "The Sacred Family" (Andrea del Sarto)	20	10
502	10 c. "The Virgin adoring the Child" (Correggio)	25	10
503	20 c. "The Holy Family" (Rembrandt)	40	20
504	30 c. "The Virgin and Child" (Rogier Van Der Weyden)	50	30
500/504		*Set of 5*	1·25	60
MS505	114 × 133 mm. Nos. 500/4 plus *se-tenant* label	1·75	2·00

Each value was issued in sheets of 15 stamps and 1 label.
See also No. MS512.

147 Churchill and Blenheim Palace

1974 (20 Nov). *Birth Centenary of Sir Winston Churchill. T 147 and similar horiz designs. Multicoloured. P 13 × 14.*
506	5 c. Type **147**	..	20	10
507	10 c. Churchill and Houses of Parliament	20	10
508	25 c. Churchill and Chartwell	30	20
509	30 c. Churchill and Buckingham Palace	30	25
510	50 c. Churchill and St. Paul's Cathedral	40	50
506/10		*Set of 5*	1·25	1·00
MS511	108 × 114 mm. Nos. 506/10 plus *se-tenant* label	1·75	1·00

Each value was issued in sheets of 5 stamps and 1 label.

1974 (9 Dec). *Christmas. Children's Charity. Designs as Nos. 500/504 in separate miniature sheets 53 × 69 mm, each with a face value of 50 c. + 5 c.*
MS512	As Nos. 500/4	..	*Set of 5 sheets* 1·25 1·25

148 Vasco Nuñez de Balboa and Discovery of Pacific Ocean (1513).

1975 (3 Feb). *Pacific Explorers. T 148 and similar horiz designs. Multicoloured. P 13.*
513	1 c. Type **148**	..	15	10
514	5 c. Fernando de Magellanes and map (1520)	65	20
515	10 c. Juan Sebastian del Cano and *Vitoria* (1520)	1·25	20
516	25 c. Friar de Urdaneta and ship (1564–67)	2·25	75
517	30 c. Miguel Lopez de Legazpi and ship (1564–67)	2·25	80
513/17		*Set of 5*	6·00	1·90

149 "Apollo" Capsule

1975 (15 July). *"Apollo-Soyuz" Space Project. T 149 and similar horiz designs. Multicoloured. P 13½.*
518	25 c. Type **149**	..	35	15
519	25 c. "Soyuz" capsule	..	35	15
520	30 c. "Soyuz" crew	..	40	15
521	30 c. "Apollo" crew	..	40	15
522	50 c. Cosmonaut within "Soyuz"	45	25
523	50 c. Astronauts within "Apollo"	45	25
518/23		*Set of 6*	2·25	1·00
MS524	119 × 119 mm. Nos. 518/23. P 13 × 14	1·75	1·25

Each value was issued in sheets containing 9 horizontal *se-tenant* pairs of the two designs, together with 2 labels.

150 $100 Commemorative Gold Coin

1975 (8 Aug). *Bicentenary of Captain Cook's Second Voyage. P 13.*
525	**150** $2 brown, gold and bluish violet	3·25	1·25

No. 525 was issued in sheets of 5 stamps and 1 label.

151 Cook Islands' Flag and Map

1975 (8 Aug). *Tenth Anniv of Self-Government. T 151 and similar multicoloured designs. P 13.*

526	5 c. Type 151		40	10
527	10 c. Premier Sir Albert Henry and flag (*vert*)		45	10
528	25 c. Rarotonga and flag		80	30
526/8		*Set of 3*	1·50	45

152 "Madonna by the Fireside" (R. Campin)   **153** "Entombment of Christ" (Raphael)

1975 (1 Dec). *Christmas. T 152 and similar vert designs. Multicoloured. P 13½.*

529	6 c. Type 152		20	10
530	10 c. "Madonna in the Meadow" (Raphael)		20	10
531	15 c. "Madonna of the Oak" (attrib Raphael)		30	10
532	20 c. "Adoration of the Shepherds" (J. B. Maino)		35	15
533	35 c. "The Annunciation" (Murillo)		60	20
529/33		*Set of 5*	1·50	45
MS534	110 × 124 mm. Nos. 529/33		1·50	90

1975 (15 Dec). *Christmas. Children's Charity. Designs as Nos. 529/33 in separate miniature sheets 53 × 71 mm, each with a face value of 75 c. + 5 c.*

MS535	As Nos. 529/33	*Set of 5 sheets*	1·10 1·25
	a. Error. Miniature sheet as No. 531 imperf		£250

1976 (29 Mar). *Easter. T 153 and similar square designs. Multicoloured. P 13.*

536	7 c. Type 153		30	10
537	15 c. "Pietà" (Veronese)		50	15
538	35 c. "Pietà" (El Greco)		75	25
536/8		*Set of 3*	1·40	40
MS539	144 × 57 mm. Nos. 536/8		1·50	85

Each value was issued in sheets of 20 stamps and 1 label.

1976 (3 May). *Easter. Children's Charity. Designs as Nos. 536/8 in separate miniature sheets 69 × 69 mm. each with a face value of 60 c. + 5 c.*

MS540	As Nos. 536/8	*Set of 3 sheets*	1·10 1·40

154 Benjamin Franklin and H.M.S. *Resolution*

1976 (29 May). *Bicentenary of American Revolution. T 154 and similar horiz designs. Multicoloured. P 13.*

541	$1 Type 154		7·50	1·50
542	$2 Captain Cook and H.M.S. *Resolution*		9·50	2·50
MS543	118 × 58 mm. $3 Cook, Franklin and H.M.S. *Resolution* (74 × 31 mm)		15·00	6·50

Each value was issued in sheets of 5 stamps and 1 label.

Royal Visit July 1976

(155)

1976 (9 July). *Visit of Queen Elizabeth to the U.S.A. Nos. 541/3 optd with T 155.*

544	$1 Type 154		5·00 1·50
545	$2 Captain Cook and H.M.S. *Resolution*		7·00 2·50
MS546	$3 Cook, Franklin and H.M.S. *Resolution*		8·00 5·50

156 Hurdling   **157** "The Visitation"

1976 (22 July). *Olympic Games, Montreal. T 156 and similar square designs. Multicoloured. P 13.*

547	7 c.	} Type 156		20	10
548	7 c.			20	10
549	15 c.	} Hockey		40	15
550	15 c.			40	15
551	30 c.	} Fencing		40	15
552	30 c.			40	15
553	35 c.	} Football		40	20
554	35 c.			40	20
547/54			*Set of 8*	2·40	1·10
MS555	104 × 146 mm. Nos. 547/54			2·75	2·00

Each value was issued in sheets containing 5 horizontal *se-tenant* pairs and 2 labels. In each pair the first stamp has the face-value on the right, the second has it on the left. Illustrated is the left-hand stamp of the 7 c. design.

1976 (12 Oct). *Christmas. T 157 and similar vert designs showing Renaissance sculptures. Multicoloured. P 14 × 13½.*

556	6 c. Type 157		10	10
557	10 c. "Adoration of the Shepherds"		10	10
558	15 c. "Adoration of the Shepherds" (*different*)		15	10
559	20 c. "The Epiphany"		20	20
560	35 c. "The Holy Family"		25	25
556/60		*Set of 5*	70	60
MS561	116 × 110 mm. Nos. 556/60. P 13.		85	1·75

Each value was issued in sheets of 20 stamps and 1 label.

1976 (2 Nov.) *Christmas. Children's Charity. Designs as Nos. 556/60 in separate miniature sheets 66 × 80 mm, each with a face value of 75 c. + 5 c.*

MS562	As Nos. 556/60	*Set of 5 sheets*	1·10 1·10

158 Obverse and Reverse of $5 Mangaia Kingfisher Coin

1976 (15 Nov). *National Wildlife and Conservation Day. P 13.*

563	**158** $1 multicoloured		1·40 1·25

No. 563 was issued in sheets of 5 stamps and 1 label.

159 Imperial State Crown   **160** "Christ on the Cross"

1977 (7 Feb). *Silver Jubilee. T 159 and similar vert designs. Multicoloured. P 13.*

564	25 c. Type 159		40	40
565	25 c. Queen with regalia		40	40
566	50 c. Westminster Abbey		50	50
567	50 c. Coronation Coach		50	50
568	$1 Queen and Prince Philip		80	80
569	$1 Royal Visit, 1974		80	80
564/9		*Set of 6*	3·00	3·00
MS570	130 × 136 mm. As Nos. 564/9 (borders and "COOK ISLANDS" in a different colour)		2·25	2·00

The two designs of each value are printed horizontally *se-tenant* throughout the sheet, and stamps from **MS570** have borders and "COOK ISLANDS" in a different colour.

1977 (28 Mar). *Easter and 400th Birth Anniv of Rubens. T 160 and similar vert designs. Multicoloured. P 14 × 13½.*

571	7 c. Type 160		35	10
572	15 c. "Christ on the Cross"		55	15
573	35 c. "The Deposition of Christ"		1·10	30
571/3		*Set of 3*	1·75	50
MS574	118 × 65 mm. Nos. 571/3. P 13		1·75	1·60

Each value was issued in sheets of 24 stamps and 1 label.

1977 (18 Apr). *Easter. Children's Charity. Designs as Nos. 571/3 in separate miniature sheets 60 × 79 mm, each with a face value of 60 c. + 5 c. P 13 × 14.*

MS575	As Nos. 571/3	*Set of 3 sheets*	1·00 1·00

161 "Virgin and Child" (Memling)   **162** Obverse and Reverse of $5 Cook Islands Swiftlet Coin

---

1977 (3 Oct). *Christmas. T 161 and similar vert designs. Multicoloured. P 14.*

576	6 c. Type 161		20	10
577	10 c. "Madonna and Child with Saints and Donors" (Memling)		20	10
578	15 c. "Adoration of the Kings" (Geertgen)		30	10
579	20 c. "Virgin and Child with Saints" (Crivelli)		40	15
580	35 c. "Adoration of the Magi" (16th-cent Flemish School)		50	20
576/80		*Set of 5*	1·40	50
MS581	118 × 111 mm. Nos. 576/80. P 13½		1·40	1·75

Each value was issued in sheets of 24 stamps and 1 label.

1977 (31 Oct). *Christmas. Children's Charity. Designs as Nos. 576/80 in separate miniature sheets 69 × 69 mm, each with a face value of 75 c. + 5 c.*

MS582	As Nos. 576/80	*Set of 5 sheets*	1·00 1·25

1977 (15 Nov). *National Wildlife and Conservation Day. P 13.*

583	**162** $1 multicoloured		1·50 85

No. 583 was issued in sheets containing 10 stamps and 2 labels.

163 Captain Cook and H.M.S. *Resolution* (from paintings by N. Dance and H. Roberts)

1978 (20 Jan). *Bicentenary of Discovery of Hawaii. T 163 and similar horiz designs. Multicoloured. P 13½.*

584	50 c. Type 163		1·25	60
585	$1 Earl of Sandwich, and Cook landing at Owhyhee (from paintings by Thomas Gainsborough and J. Cleveley)		1·75	1·00
586	$2 Obverse and reverse of $200 coin and Cook monument, Hawaii		2·00	1·75
584/6		*Set of 3*	4·50	3·00
MS587	118 × 95 mm. Nos. 584/86		7·00	9·00

Each value was issued in sheets of 5 stamps and 1 label.

164 "Pieta" (Van der Weyden)   **165** Queen Elizabeth II

1978 (20 Mar). *Easter. Paintings from National Gallery, London. T 164 and similar horiz designs. Multicoloured. P 13.*

588	50 c. Type 164		40	15
589	35 c. "The Entombment" (Michelangelo)		50	30
590	75 c. "The Supper at Emmaus" (Caravaggio)		75	55
588/90		*Set of 3*	1·50	90
MS591	114 × 96 mm. Nos. 588/90		1·50	2·00

Each value was issued in sheets of 5 stamps and 1 label.

1978 (10 Apr). *Easter. Children's Charity. Designs as Nos. 588/90 in separate miniature sheets, 85 × 72 mm, each with a face value of 60 c. + 5 c. P 13½.*

MS592	As Nos. 588/90	*Set of 3 sheets*	1·10 1·10

1978 (6 June). *25th Anniv of Coronation. T 165 and similar vert designs. Multicoloured. P 13.*

593	50 c. Type 165		25	30
594	50 c. The Lion of England		25	30
595	50 c. Imperial State Crown		25	30
596	50 c. Statue of Tangaroa (god)		25	30
597	70 c. Type 165		25	30
598	70 c. Sceptre with Cross		25	30
599	70 c. St. Edward's Crown		25	30
600	70 c. Rarotongan staff god		25	30
593/600		*Set of 8*	1·75	2·00
MS601	103 × 142 mm. Nos. 593/600*		1·00	1·00

Each value was issued in sheets containing the 4 designs and 2 labels.

* In No MS601 the designs of Nos. 595 and 599 are transposed.

5c   ≡

(166)

1978 (10 Nov). *Nos. 466, 468, 473/4 and 478/81 surch as T 166.*

602	5 c. on 1½ c. True Heart Cockle (*Corculum cardissa*) (Silver)		40	10
603	7 c. on ½ c. Type 141		45	15
604	10 c. on 6 c. Serpent's-head Cowrie (*Cypraea caputserpentis*) (Gold)		50	15
605	10 c. on 8 c. Granulate Frog Shell (*Bursa granularis*) (Gold)		50	15
606	15 c. on ½ c. Type 141		50	20
607	15 c. on 25 c. Royal Oak Scallop (*Crypto-pecten pallium*) (Silver)		50	20
608	15 c. on 30 c. Soldier Cone (*Conus miles*)		50	20

609	15 c. on 50 c. Textile or Cloth of Gold Cone				
	(*Conus textile*) (Silver)			50	20
610	15 c. on 60 c. Red-mouth Olive (*Oliva miniacea miniacea*) (Gold)			50	20
611	17 c. on ½ c. Type **141**			80	25
612	17 c. on 50 c. Textile or Cloth of Gold Cone (*Conus textile*) (Silver)			80	25
602/12			*Set of 11*	5·50	1·75

7728 · 250th ANNIVERSARY OF COOK'S BIRTH · 1978

(167)

1978 (13 Nov). *250th Birth Anniv of Captain Cook. Nos. 584/7 optd with T **167** on silver.*

613	50 c. Type **163**			2·00	75
614	$1 Earl of Sandwich, and Cook landing at Owhyhee (from paintings by Thomas Gainsborough and J. Cleveley)			2·25	1·00
615	$2 Obverse and reverse of $200 coin and Cook monument, Hawaii			2·50	2·00
613/15			*Set of 3*	6·00	3·25
MS616	Nos. 613/15			17·00	17·00

168 Obverse and Reverse of $5 Pitcairn Warblers Coin

1978 (15 Nov). *National Wildlife and Conservation Day. P 13.*

617	**168**	$1 multicoloured		1·25	1·00

169 "The Virgin and Child" (Van der Weyden)   **170** Virgin with Body of Christ

1978 (8 Dec). *Christmas. Paintings. T **169** and similar vert designs. Multicoloured. P 13.*

618	15 c. Type **169**			45	15
619	17 c. "The Virgin and Child" (Crivelli)			45	20
620	35 c. "The Virgin and Child" (Murillo)			80	35
618/20			*Set of 3*	1·50	65
MS621	107 x 70 mm. Nos. 618/20			1·50	1·50

1979 (12 Jan). *Christmas. Children's Charity. Designs as Nos. 618/20 in separate miniature sheets 57 x 87 mm. each with a face value of 75 c. + 5 c. P 13½*

MS622	As Nos. 618/20		*Set of 3 sheets*	1·00	1·00

1979 (5 Apr). *Easter. Details of Painting "Descent" by Gaspar de Crayar. T **170** and similar vert designs. Multicoloured. P 13.*

623	10 c. Type **170**			25	10
624	12 c. St. John			30	20
625	15 c. Mary Magdalene			35	25
626	20 c. Weeping angels			45	30
623/6			*Set of 4*	1·25	75
MS627	83 × 100 mm. As Nos. 623/6, but each with charity premium of 2 c.			65	75

Stamps from No. MS627 are slightly smaller, 32 × 40 mm, and are without borders.

171 "Captain Cook" (James Weber)   **172** Post-Rider

1979 (23 July). *Death Bicentenary of Captain Cook. T **171** and similar vert designs. Multicoloured. P 14 × 13.*

628	20 c. Type **171**			40	20
629	30 c. H.M.S. *Resolution*			70	35
630	35 c. H.M.S. *Royal George* (ship of the line)			70	45
631	50 c. "Death of Captain Cook" (George Carter)			70	60
628/31			*Set of 4*	2·25	1·40
MS632	78×112 mm. Nos. 628/31			1·75	1·25

Stamps from No. MS632 have black borders.

1979 (10 Sept). *Death Centenary of Sir Rowland Hill. History of Mail Transport. T **172** and similar square designs. Multicoloured. P 14.*

633	30 c. Type **172**			25	20
634	30 c. Mail coach			25	20
635	30 c. Automobile			25	20
636	30 c. Diesel train			25	20
637	35 c. *Cap-Hornier* (full-rigged ship)			30	20
638	35 c. River steamer			30	20
639	35 c. *Deutschland* (liner)			30	20
640	35 c. *United States* (liner)			30	20
641	50 c. Balloon *Le Neptune*			40	25
642	50 c. Junkers F13 airplane			40	25
643	50 c. Airship LZ-127 *Graf Zeppelin*			40	25
644	50 c. Concorde			40	25
633/44			*Set of 12*	3·50	2·40
MS645	132×104 mm. Nos. 633/44			3·50	4·00

Nos. 633/6, 637/40 and 641/4 were each printed together, *se-tenant*, in blocks of 4 throughout the sheets.

6c   ≡

(173)

1979 (12 Sept). *Nos. 466, 468 and 481 surch as T **173**.*

646	6 c. on ½ c. Type **141** (Gold)			20	30
647	10 c. on 1½ c. Cockle shell (Silver)			25	20
	a. Surch inverted			90·00	
648	15 c. on 60 c. Olive shell (Gold)			40	40
646/8			*Set of 3*	75	80

174 Brother and Sister   **175** "Apollo 11" Emblem

1979 (10 Oct). *International Year of the Child. T **174** and similar horiz designs. Multicoloured. P 13.*

649	30 c. Type **174**			25	25
650	50 c. Boy with tree drum			40	40
651	65 c. Children dancing			50	50
649/51			*Set of 3*	1·00	1·00
MS652	102 × 75 mm. As Nos. 649/51, but each with charity premium of 5 c. P 13½ × 13			1·00	1·50

Designs for stamps from No. MS652 are as Nos. 649/51 but have I.Y.C. emblem in red.

1979 (7 Nov). *10th Anniv of Moon Landing. T **175** and similar vert designs. Multicoloured. P 14.*

653	30 c. Type **175**			40	50
654	50 c. Crew of "Apollo 11"			50	70
655	60 c. Astronaut on Moon			65	75
656	65 c. Command module after splashdown			70	85
653/6			*Set of 4*	2·00	2·50
MS657	119 × 105 mm. Nos. 653/6. P 13½			2·50	2·50

176 Obverse and Reverse of $5 Rarotongan Fruit Dove Coin   **177** Glass Christmas Tree Ornaments

1979 (15 Nov). *National Wildlife and Conservation Day. P 13 × 14.*

658	**176**	$1 multicoloured		1·60	2·50

1979 (14 Dec). *Christmas. T **177** and similar vert designs. Multicoloured. P 13½. (a) Postage.*

659	6 c. Type **177**			10	10
660	10 c. Hibiscus flower and star			10	10
661	12 c. Poinsettia flower, bells and candle			15	10
662	15 c. Poinsettia leaves and Tiki (god)			15	15

(b) Air

663	20 c. Type **177**			20	15
664	25 c. As 10 c.			25	20
665	30 c. As 12 c.			30	25
666	35 c. As 15 c.			35	30
659/66			*Set of 8*	1·40	1·10

1980 (15 Jan). *Christmas. Children's Charity. Designs as Nos. 659/66 with additional premiums. (a) Postage.*

667	6 + 2 c. Type **177**			10	10
668	10 c. + 2 c. Hibiscus flower and star			15	15
669	12 c. + 2 c. Poinsettia flower, bells and candle			15	20
670	15 c. + 2 c. Poinsettia leaves and Tiki (god)			15	20

(b) Air

671	20 c. + 4 c. Type **177**			15	25
672	25 c. + 4 c. As 10 c.			15	25
673	30 c. + 4 c. As 12 c.			20	30
674	35 c. + 4 c. As 15 c.			25	35
667/74			*Set of 8*	1·00	1·60

178 "Flagellation"   **179** Dove with Olive Twig

1980 (31 Mar). *Easter. Illustrations by Gustave Doré. T **178** and similar vert designs in sepia and gold. P 13.*

675	20 c. Type **178**			25	20
676	20 c. "Crown of Thorns"			25	20
677	30 c. "Jesus Insulted"			35	30
678	30 c. "Jesus Falls"			35	30
679	35 c. "The Crucifixion"			40	30
680	35 c. "The Descent from the Cross"			40	30
675/80			*Set of 6*	1·75	1·40
MS681	120 × 110 mm. As Nos. 675/80, but each with charity premium of 2 c.			1·10	1·50

Nos. 675/6, 677/8 and 679/80 were each printed together, *se-tenant*, in vertical pairs throughout the sheet.

1980 (23 Apr). *Easter. Children's Charity. Designs as Nos. 675/80 in separate miniature sheets 60 × 71 mm, each with a face value of 75 c. + 5 c. P 13.*

MS682	As Nos. 675/80		*Set of 6 sheets*	90	1·50

1980 (27 May). *75th Anniv of Rotary International. T **179** and similar horiz designs. Multicoloured. P 14.*

683	30 c. Type **179**			35	35
684	35 c. Hibiscus flower			40	40
685	50 c. Ribbons			50	50
683/5			*Set of 3*	1·10	1·10
MS686	72 × 113 mm. Nos. 683/5 but each with premium of 3 c. P 13½			1·10	1·50

(180)   **181** Queen Elizabeth the Queen Mother

1980 (22 Aug). *"Zeapex 80" International Stamp Exhibition, Auckland. Nos. 633/45 optd with T **180** in black on silver background.*

687	30 c. Type **172**			35	25
688	30 c. Mail coach			35	25
689	30 c. Automobile			35	25
690	30 c. Diesel train			35	25
691	35 c. *Cap-Hornier* (full-rigged ship)			40	30
692	35 c. River steamer			40	30
693	35 c. *Deutschland* (liner)			40	30
694	35 c. *United States* (liner)			40	30
695	50 c. Balloon *Le Neptune*			60	35
696	50 c. Junkers F13 airplane			60	35
697	50 c. Airship LZ-127 *Graf Zeppelin*			60	35
698	50 c. Concorde			60	35
687/98			*Set of 12*	4·75	3·25
MS699	132×104 mm. Nos. 687/98			6·00	6·00

1980 (22 Aug). *"Zeapex 80" International Stamp Exhibition, Auckland. As No. MS681 but containing stamps without charity premium of 2 c. optd "Zeapex '80 Auckland + 10 c" in black on gold background.*

MS700	120 × 110 mm. Nos. 675/80 (sold at $1.80)			80	1·75

Stamps from No. MS700 are unaffected by the overprint which appears on the sheet margin.

1980 (23 Sept). *80th Birthday of Queen Elizabeth the Queen Mother. P 13.*

701	**181**	50 c. multicoloured		80	90
MS702	64× 78 mm. 181 $2 multicoloured			1·25	1·75

182 Satellites orbiting Moon   **183** Scene from novel *From the Earth to the Moon*

1980 (7 Nov). *350th Death Anniv of Johannes Kepler (astronomer). T* **182** *and similar horiz designs. Multicoloured. P* 13.

703	12 c. Type **182**	50	35
704	12 c. Space-craft orbiting Moon	50	35
705	50 c. Space-craft orbiting Moon (*different*)	1·00	80
706	50 c. Astronaut and Moon vehicle	1·00	80
703/6	*Set of 4*	2·75	2·10
MS707	122 × 122 mm. Nos. 703/6	2·75	2·75

Nos. 703/4 and 705/6 were each printed together, *se-tenant*, in horizontal pairs throughout the sheet.

1980 (7 Nov). *75th Death Anniv of Jules Verne (author). T* **183** *and similar vert designs showing scenes from the novel "From the Earth to the Moon". P* 13.

708	20 c. multicoloured (green background)	45	35
709	20 c. multicoloured (brown background)	45	35
710	30 c. multicoloured (mauve background)	55	45
711	30 c. multicoloured (blue background)	55	45
708/11	*Set of 4*	1·75	1·40
MS712	121 × 122 mm. Nos. 708/11	2·25	2·25

Nos. 708/9 and 710/11 were each printed together, *se-tenant*, in horizontal pairs throughout the sheet.

184 *Siphonogorgia*

185 Annunciation

1980 (21 Nov)—82. *Corals (1st series). Multicoloured designs as T* **184**. *P* 13 (1 *c. to* $1) *or* 14 × 13½ ($2 *to* $10).

713	1 c. Type **184**	20	20
714	1 c. *Pavona praetorta*.	20	20
715	1 c. *Stylaster echinatus*	20	20
716	1 c. *Tubastraea*	20	20
717	3 c. *Millepora alicornis*	25	20
718	3 c. *Junceella gemmacea*	25	20
719	3 c. *Fungia fungites*	25	20
720	3 c. *Heliofungia actiniformis*	25	20
721	4 c. *Distichopora violacea*	25	20
722	4 c. *Stylaster*	25	20
723	4 c. *Goniopora* .	25	20
724	4 c. *Caulastraea echinulata*	25	20
725	5 c. *Ptilosarcus gurneyi*	25	20
726	5 c. *Stylophora pistillata*	25	20
727	5 c. *Melithaea squamata*	25	20
728	5 c. *Porites andrewsi* ..	25	20
729	6 c. *Lobophyllia bemprichii*	25	20
730	6 c. *Palauastrea ramosa*	25	20
731	6 c. *Bellonella indica*..	25	20
732	6 c. *Pectinia alcicornis*	25	20
733	8 c. *Sarcophyton digitatum*	25	20
734	8 c. *Melithaea albitincta*	25	20
735	8 c. *Plerogyra sinuosa*	25	20
736	8 c. *Dendrophyllia gracilis*	25	20
737	10 c. Type **184** (19.12.80)	30	20
738	10 c. As No. 714 (19.12.80)	30	20
739	10 c. As No. 715 (19.12.80)	30	20
740	10 c. As No. 716 (19.12.80)	30	20
741	12 c. As No. 717 (19.12.80)	30	20
742	12 c. As No. 718 (19.12.80)	30	20
743	12 c. As No. 719 (19.12.80)	30	20
744	12 c. As No. 720 (19.12.80)	30	20
745	15 c. As No. 721 (19.12.80)	30	20
746	15 c. As No. 722 (19.12.80)	30	20
747	15 c. As No. 723 (19.12.80)	30	20
748	15 c. As No. 724 (19.12.80)	30	20
749	20 c. As No. 725 (19.12.80)	35	30
750	20 c. As No. 726 (19.12.80)	35	30
751	20 c. As No. 727 (19.12.80)	35	30
752	20 c. As No. 728 (19.12.80)	35	30
753	25 c. As No. 729 (19.12.80)	35	30
754	25 c. As No. 730 (19.12.80)	35	30
755	25 c. As No. 731 (19.12.80)	35	30
756	25 c. As No. 732 (19.12.80)	35	30
757	30 c. As No. 733 (19.12.80)	40	30
758	30 c. As No. 734 (19.12.80)	40	30
759	30 c. As No. 735 (19.12.80)	40	30
760	30 c. As No. 736 (19.12.80)	40	30
761	35 c. Type **184** (16.3.81)	45	35
762	35 c. As No. 714 (16.3.81)	45	35
763	35 c. As No. 715 (16.3.81)	45	35
764	35 c. As No. 716 (16.3.81)	45	35
765	50 c. As No. 717 (16.3.81)	65	75
766	50 c. As No. 718 (16.3.81)	65	75
767	50 c. As No. 719 (16.3.81)	65	75
768	50 c. As No. 720 (16.3.81)	65	75
769	60 c. As No. 721 (16.3.81)	75	75
770	60 c. As No. 722 (16.3.81)	75	75
771	60 c. As No. 723 (16.3.81)	75	75
772	60 c. As No. 724 (16.3.81)	75	75
773	70 c. As No. 725 (13.4.81)	2·50	75
774	70 c. As No. 726 (13.4.81)	2·50	75
775	70 c. As No. 727 (13.4.81)	2·50	75
776	70 c. As No. 728 (13.4.81)	2·50	75
777	80 c. As No. 729 (13.4.81)	2·50	80
778	80 c. As No. 730 (13.4.81)	2·50	80
779	80 c. As No. 731 (13.4.81)	2·50	80
780	80 c. As No. 732 (13.4.81)	2·50	80
781	$1 As No. 733 (20.5.81)	3·75	1·00
782	$1 As No. 734 (20.5.81)	3·75	1·00
783	$1 As No. 735 (20.5.81)	3·75	1·00
784	$1 As No. 736 (20.5.81)	3·75	1·00
785	$2 As No. 723 (27.11.81)	12·00	3·00
786	$3 As No. 720 (27.11.81)	12·00	3·00

787	$4 As No. 726 (11.1.82)	4·50	11·00
788	$6 As No. 715 (11.1.82)	6·00	14·00
789	$10 As No. 734 (5.3.82)	27·00	32·00
713/89	*Set of 77*	£100	80·00

Nos. 761/84 are 30 × 40 mm and Nos. 785/9, which include a portrait of Queen Elizabeth II in each design, are 55 × 35 mm in size.

The four designs of each value to the $1 were printed together, *se-tenant*, in horizontal strips of 4 (Nos. 713/60) or in blocks of 4 (Nos. 761/84) throughout the sheet.

For similar designs with redrawn frames and inscriptions see Nos. 966/94.

1980 (1 Dec). *Christmas. Illustrations from 13th-century French Prayer Book. T* **185** *and similar vert designs. Multicoloured. P* 14 × 13½.

801	15 c. Type **185** ..	25	15
802	30 c. Visitation	35	25
803	40 c. Nativity	45	30
804	50 c. Epiphany	60	40
801/4	*Set of 4*	1·50	1·00
MS805	89 × 114 mm. Nos. 801/4. P 13½.	1·50	1·50

1981 (9 Jan). *Christmas. Children's Charity. Designs as Nos. 801/4 in separate miniature sheets 55 × 68 mm, each with a face value of 75 c. + 5 c. Imperf.*

MS806	As Nos. 801/4	*Set of 4 sheets*	1·50	1·50

186 "The Crucifixion" (from book of Saint-Amand)

187 Prince Charles

1981 (10 Apr). *Easter. Illustrations from 12th-century French Prayer Books. T* **186** *and similar horiz designs. Multicoloured. P* 13½ × 14.

807	15 c. Type **186** ..	20	20
808	25 c. "Placing in Tomb" (from book of Ingeburge)	30	30
809	40 c. "Mourning at the Sepulchre" (from book of Ingeburge)	40	40
807/9	*Set of 3*	80	80
MS810	72 × 116 mm. As Nos. 807/9 but each with charity premium of 2 c. P 13½	90	90

1981 (28 Apr). *Easter. Children's Charity. Designs as Nos. 807/9 in separate miniature sheets 64 × 53 mm, each with a face value of 75 c. +5 c. Imperf.*

MS811	As Nos. 807/9	*Set of 3 sheets*	1·10	1·10

1981 (29 July). *Royal Wedding. T* **187** *and similar vert design. Multicoloured. P* 14.

812	$1 Type **187**	50	1·10
813	$2 Prince Charles and Lady Diana Spencer	60	1·40
MS814	106 × 59 mm. Nos. 812/13. P 13½	1·40	2·50

Nos. 812/13 were each printed in small sheets of 4.

188 Footballers

(189)

1981 (20 Oct). *World Cup Football Championship, Spain (1982). T* **188** *and similar horiz designs showing footballers. Multicoloured. P* 13½ × 14.

815	20 c. Type **188**	40	20
816	20 c. Figures to right of stamp	40	20
817	30 c. Figures to left	50	30
818	30 c. Figures to right	50	30
819	35 c. Figures to left	50	35
820	35 c. Figures to right	50	35
821	50 c. Figures to left	65	45
822	50 c. Figures to right	65	45
815/22	*Set of 8*	3·75	2·40
MS823	180 × 94 mm. As Nos. 815/22, but each stamp with a charity premium of 3 c. P 13½	5·00	6·50

The two designs of each value were printed together, *se-tenant*, in horizontal pairs throughout the sheet, forming composite designs.

1981 (10 Nov). *International Year for Disabled Persons. Nos. 812/14 such as T* **189**.

824	$1 + 5 c. Type **187**	1·00	2·00
825	$2 + 5 c. Prince Charles and Lady Diana Spencer	1·40	3·00
MS826	106 × 59 mm. $1 + 10 c., $2 + 10 c. As Nos. 824/5	2·00	4·00

Nos. 824/6 have commemorative inscriptions overprinted on the sheet margins.

190 "Holy Virgin with Child"

191 Princess of Wales (inscr "21st Birthday")

1981 (14 Dec). *Christmas. Details from Paintings by Rubens. T* **190** *and similar vert designs. Multicoloured. P* 14 × 13½.

827	8 c. Type **190**	55	20
828	15 c. "Coronation of St. Catherine"	65	35
829	40 c. "Adoration of the Shepherds"	90	80
830	50 c. "Adoration of the Magi" ..	1·00	1·00
827/30	*Set of 4*	2·75	2·00
MS831	86 × 110 mm. As Nos. 827/30, but each with a charity premium of 3 c. P 13½ ..	3·00	3·50

1982 (18 Jan). *Christmas. Children's Charity. Designs as Nos. 827/30 in separate miniature sheets 62 × 78 mm, each with a face value of 75 c. + 5 c.*

MS832	As Nos. 827/30	*Set of 4 sheets*	3·50	4·00

1982 (21 June). *21st Birthday of Princess of Wales. T* **191** *and similar horiz designs. Multicoloured. P* 14.

833	$1.25, Type **191**	2·00	1·50
	a. Pair. Nos. 833/4	4·00	3·00
834	$1.25, As Type **191**, but inscr "1 July 1982"	2·00	1·50
835	$2.50, Princess (*different*) (inscr "21st Birthday")	2·75	2·25
	a. Pair. Nos. 835/6	5·50	4·50
836	$2.50, As No. 835, but inscr "1 July 1982"	2·75	2·25
833/6	*Set of 4*	8·50	6·50
MS837	92 × 72 mm. $1.25, Type **191**; $2.50, As No. 835. Both inscribed "21st Birthday 1 July 1982". P 13½	5·00	3·75

The two designs for each value were printed together, *se-tenant*, in small sheets of 4.

ROYAL BIRTH · 21 JUNE 1982

(192)

1982 (12 July). *Birth of Prince William of Wales (1st issue). Nos. 812/14 optd as T* **192**.

838	$1 Type **187** (optd with T **192**) ..	1·50	1·25
	a. Pair. Nos. 838/9	3·00	2·50
839	$1 Type **187** (optd "PRINCE WILLIAM OF WALES")	1·50	1·25
840	$2 Prince Charles and Lady Diana Spencer (optd with T **192**)	2·50	2·00
	a. Pair. Nos. 840/1	5·00	4·00
841	$2 Prince Charles and Lady Diana Spencer (optd. "PRINCE WILLIAM OF WALES")	2·50	2·00
838/41	*Set of 4*	7·00	6·00
MS842	106 × 59mm. Nos. 812/13 optd "21 JUNE 1982. ROYAL BIRTH"	4·00	4·00

1982 (3 Aug). *Birth of Prince William of Wales (2nd issue). Designs as Nos. 833/7 but with changed inscriptions. Multicoloured. P.*14.

843	$1.25, As Type **191** (inscr "Royal Birth") ..	1·40	1·00
	a. Pair. Nos. 843/4	2·75	2·00
844	$1.25, As Type **191** (inscr "21 June 1982")	1·40	1·00
845	$2.50, As No. 835 (inscr "Royal Birth")	2·00	1·50
	a. Pair. Nos. 845/6	4·00	3·00
846	$2.50, As No. 835 (inscr "21 June 1982")	2·00	1·50
843/6	*Set of 4*	6·00	4·50
MS847	92 × 73 mm. $1.25, As Type **191**; $2.50, As No. 835. Both inscribed "Royal Birth 21 June 1982". P 13½	4·50	2·75

193 "The Accordionist" (inscr "Serenade")

194 Franklin D. Roosevelt

(Litho Format)

1982 (10 Sept). *Norman Rockwell (painter) Commemoration. T* **193** *and similar vert designs. Multicoloured. P* 13½ × 14.

848	5 c. Type **193**	15	10
849	10 c. "Spring" (inscr "The Hikers")	20	15
850	20 c. "The Doctor and the Doll"	25	25
851	30 c. "Home from Camp"	25	30
848/51	*Set of 4*	75	70

1982 (30 Sept). *Air. American Anniversaries. T* **194** *and similar vert designs. Multicoloured. P* 14.

852	60 c. Type **194**	..	..	1·50	80
853	80 c. Benjamin Franklin	..	..	1·75	1·00
854	$1.40, George Washington..	..		2·00	1·50
852/4			*Set of* 3	4·75	3·00
MS855	116 × 60 mm. Nos. 852/4. P 13½			4·75	3·00

Anniversaries:—60 c. Roosevelt birth centenary; 80 c. "Articles of Peace" negotiations bicentenary; $1.40, Washington 250th birth anniv.

195 "Virgin with Garlands" (detail) (Rubens) and Princess Diana with Prince William

196 Princess Diana and Prince William

1982 (30 Nov). *Christmas. T* **195** *and similar horiz designs depicting different details from Rubens' painting "Virgin with Garlands". P* 13½ × 14.

856	35 c. multicoloured	..	..	1·25	60
857	48 c. multicoloured	..	..	1·75	1·25
858	60 c. multicoloured	..	..	2·00	1·75
859	$1.70, multicoloured	..	..	3·25	4·00
856/9			*Set of* 4	7·50	7·00
MS860	104 × 83 mm. 60 c × 4. Designs, each 27 × 32 mm, forming complete painting "Virgin with Garlands". P 13 × 13½			4·75	6·00

1982 (30 Nov). *Christmas. Birth of Prince William of Wales. Children's Charity. Sheet* 73 × 59 *mm. P* 13.

MS861	**196** 75 c. + 5 c. multicoloured	..		2·25	3·00

No. MS861 comes with 4 different background designs showing details from painting "Virgin with Garlands" (Rubens).

197 Statue of Tangaroa

198 Scouts using Map and Compass

1983 (14 Mar). *Commonwealth Day. T* **197** *and similar vert designs. Multicoloured. P* 14 × 13½.

862	60 c. Type **197**	..	..	55	60
863	60 c. Rarotonga oranges	..	..	55	60
864	60 c. Rarotonga Airport	..	..	55	60
865	60 c. Prime Minister Sir Thomas Davis	..		55	60
862/5			*Set of* 4	2·00	2·10

Nos. 862/5 were issued together, *se-tenant*, in blocks of four throughout the sheet.

1983 (5 Apr). *75th Anniv of Boy Scout Movement and 125th Birth Anniv of Lord Baden-Powell. T* **198** *and similar vert designs. Multicoloured. P* 13.

866	12 c. Type **198**	..	..	60	20
867	12 c. Hiking	..	..	60	20
868	36 c. Campfire cooking	..	..	90	40
869	36 c. Erecting tent	..	..	90	40
870	48 c. Hauling on rope	..	..	1·10	55
871	48 c. Using bos'n's chair	..	..	1·10	55
872	60 c. Digging hole for sapling..	..	1·25	70
873	60 c. Planting sapling..	..	..	1·25	70
866/73			*Set of* 8	7·00	3·25
MS874	161 × 132 mm. As Nos. 866/73, but each with a premium of 2 c.			4·50	5·50

The two designs of each value were printed together, *se-tenant*, in horizontal pairs throughout the sheets.

XV WORLD JAMBOREE
(199)

1983 (4 July). *15th World Scout Jamboree, Alberta, Canada. Nos.* 866/74 *optd with T* **199** (*Nos.* 875, 877, 879, 881) *or with* "ALBERTA, CANADA 1983" (*others*).

875	12 c. Type **198**	..	..	60	20
876	12 c. Hiking	..	..	60	20
877	36 c. Campfire cooking	..	..	90	40
878	36 c. Erecting tent	..	..	90	40
879	48 c. Hauling on rope	..	..	1·10	55
880	48 c. Using bos'n's chair	..	..	1·10	55
881	60 c. Digging hole for sapling..	..	1·25	70
882	60 c. Planting sapling..	..	..	1·25	70
875/82			*Set of* 8	7·00	3·25
MS883	161 × 132 mm. As Nos. 875/82, but each with a premium of 2 c.			2·75	3·25

The two designs of each value were printed together, *se-tenant*, in horizontal pairs throughout the sheet. In each such pair the left-hand design is overprinted with Type **199** and the right-hand with "ALBERTA, CANADA 1983".

204 "La Belle Jardinière"

205 Montgolfier Balloon 1783

18c **=** **$5.60**

(200)   (201)

1983 (12–30 Aug). *Various stamps surch.* (a) *Nos.* 733/6, 745/8, 753/64 *and* 773/6 *as T* **200**.

884	18 c. on 8 c. multicoloured (No. 733)	..	75	50
885	18 c. on 8 c. multicoloured (No. 734)	..	75	50
886	18 c. on 8 c. multicoloured (No. 735)	..	75	50
887	18 c. on 8 c. multicoloured (No. 736)	..	75	50
888	36 c. on 15 c. multicoloured (No. 745)	..	1·25	85
889	36 c. on 15 c. multicoloured (No. 746)	..	1·25	85
890	36 c. on 15 c. multicoloured (No. 747)	..	1·25	85
891	36 c. on 15 c. multicoloured (No. 748)	..	1·25	85
892	36 c. on 30 c. multicoloured (No. 757)	..	1·25	85
893	36 c. on 30 c. multicoloured (No. 758)	..	1·25	85
894	36 c. on 30 c. multicoloured (No. 759)	..	1·25	85
895	36 c. on 30 c. multicoloured (No. 760)	..	1·25	85
896	36 c. on 35 c. multicoloured (No. 761) (30.8.83)	1·25	85
897	36 c. on 35 c. multicoloured (No. 762) (30.8.83)	1·25	85
898	36 c. on 35 c. multicoloured (No. 763) (30.8.83)	1·25	85
899	36 c. on 35 c. multicoloured (No. 764) (30.8.83)	1·25	85
900	48 c. on 25 c. multicoloured (No. 753)	..	1·50	1·25
901	48 c. on 25 c. multicoloured (No. 754)	..	1·50	1·25
902	48 c. on 25 c. multicoloured (No. 755)	..	1·50	1·25
903	48 c. on 25 c. multicoloured (No. 756)	..	1·50	1·25
904	72 c. on 70 c. multicoloured (No. 773)	..	2·50	1·75
905	72 c. on 70 c. multicoloured (No. 774)	..	2·50	1·75
906	72 c. on 70 c. multicoloured (No. 775)	..	2·50	1·75
907	72 c. on 70 c. multicoloured (No. 776)	..	2·50	1·75

(b) *Nos.* 788/9, 813, 835/6 *and* 854, *as T* **201** *in gold*

908	96 c. on $1.40, George Washington	..	2·00	2·00
909	96 c. on $2 Prince Charles and Lady Diana Spencer	..	8·50	5·50
	a. Surch double	..	£130	
	b. Error. Surch on No. 840..	..	£16·00	
	ba. Pair, Nos. 909 b/c	..	£32·00	
	c. Error. Surch on No. 841..	..	£16·00	
910	96 c. on $2·50 Princess Diana (inscr "21st Birthday") (30.8.83)	..	3·00	3·00
911	96 c. on $2.50. As No. 910 but inscr "1 July 1982" (30.8.83)	..	3·00	3·00
912	$5.60 on $6 *Stylaster echinatus*	..	23·00	18·00
913	$5.60 on $10 *Melithaea albitincta* (30.8.83)	23·00	18·00
884/913		*Set of* 30	85·00	65·00

The surcharge on No. 908 is printed in gold on a black background, over the old value.

202 Union Flag

203 Dish Aerial, Satellite Earth Station

1983 (9 Sept). *Cook Islands Flags and Ensigns. T* **202** *and similar horiz designs. Multicoloured. P* 13½ × 14. (a) *Postage. Gold frames.*

914	6 c. Type **202**	..	..	45	30
915	6 c. Group Federal flag	..	..	45	30
916	12 c. Raratonga ensign	..	..	60	35
917	12 c. Flag of New Zealand	..	..	60	35
918	15 c. Cook Islands' flag (1973–79)	..	60	35
919	15 c. Cook Islands' National flag	..	60	35

(b) *Air. Silver frames and backgrounds changed*

920	20 c. Type **202**	..	..	70	50
921	20 c. Group Federal flag	..	..	70	50
922	30 c. Raratonga ensign	..	..	80	55
923	30 c. Flag of New Zealand	..	..	80	55
924	35 c. Cook Islands' flag (1973–79)	..	85	60
925	35 c. Cook Islands' National flag	..	85	60
914/25			*Set of* 12	7·00	4·75
MS926	Two sheets, each 132 × 120 mm. (a) Nos. 914/19; (b) Nos. 920/5. P 13			2·25	4·00

The two designs of each value were issued as *se-tenant* horizontal pairs within the sheets.

1983 (10 Oct). *World Communications Year. T* **203** *and similar vert designs showing satellites. P* 13.

927	36 c. multicoloured	..	..	60	60
928	48 c. multicoloured	..	..	75	75
929	60 c. multicoloured	..	..	1·00	1·25
930	96 c. multicoloured	..	..	1·60	2·25
927/30			*Set of* 4	3·50	4·25
MS931	90 × 65 mm. $2 multicoloured	..		2·25	3·50

1983 (14 Nov). *Christmas. 500th Birth Anniv of Raphael. T* **204** *and similar vert designs. Multicoloured. P* 14 × 13½.

932	12 c. Type **204**	..	..	70	40
933	18 c. "Madonna and Child with Five Saints"..	95	60
934	36 c. "Madonna and Child with St. John"..	1·60	1·60
935	48 c. "Madonna of the Fish"	..	2·00	2·00
936	60 c. "The Madonna of the Baldacchino"..	2·50	3·50
932/6			*Set of* 5	7·00	7·25
MS937	139 × 113 mm. As Nos. 932/6 but each with a premium of 3 c.			2·00	2·50

Nos. 932/6 were each printed in small sheets of 5 stamps and 1 label.

1983 (9 Dec). *Christmas. 500th Birth Anniv of Raphael. Children's Charity. Designs as Nos.* 932/6 *in separate miniature sheets* 66 × 82 *mm., each with a face value of* 85 c. + 5 c. *P* 13.

MS938	As Nos. 932/6	..	*Set of* 5 sheets	4·50	3·75

1984 (16 Jan). *Bicentenary of Manned Flight (1983). T* **205** *and similar vert designs. Multicoloured. P* 13.

939	36 c. Type **205**	..	..	50	50
940	48 c. Adorne's ascent, Strasbourg, 1784		60	60
941	60 c. Balloon driven by sails, 1785	..	75	90
942	72 c. Ascent of man on horse, 1798	..	90	1·10
943	96 c. Godard's aerial acrobatics, 1850		1·00	1·40
939/43			*Set of* 5	3·25	4·00
MS944	104 × 85 mm. $2.50, Blanchard and Jeffries crossing Channel, 1785			1·50	2·25
MS945	122 × 132 mm. As Nos. 939/43 but each with a premium of 5 c.			1·50	2·25

Nos. 939/43 were each printed in small sheets of 5 stamps and 1 label.

206 Cuvier's Beaked Whale

207 Athens, 1896

1984 (10 Feb). *Save the Whales. T* **206** *and similar horiz designs. Multicoloured. P* 13.

946	10 c. Type **206** ..	..	..	50	50
947	18 c. Risso's Dolphin	..	..	75	75
948	20 c. True's Beaked Whale	..	..	75	75
949	24 c. Long-finned Pilot Whale	..	80	80
950	30 c. Narwhal	..	..	90	90
951	36 c. White Whale (Beluga)	..	1·10	1·10
952	42 c. Common Dolphin	..	1·40	1·40
953	48 c. Commerson's Dolphin	..	1·60	1·60
954	60 c. Bottle-nosed Dolphin	..	1·90	1·90
955	72 c. Sowerby's Beaked Whale	..	2·00	2·00
956	96 c. Common Porpoise	..	2·50	2·50
957	$2 Boutu	..	..	3·25	3·25
946/57			*Set of* 12	16·00	16·00

1984 (8 Mar). *Olympic Games, Los Angeles. T* **207** *and similar vert designs showing official posters of earlier Games. Multicoloured. P* 13½.

958	18 c. Type **207**	..	..	50	40
959	24 c. Paris, 1900	..	..	55	45
960	36 c. St. Louis, 1904	..	..	65	55
961	48 c. London, 1948	..	..	75	65
962	60 c. Tokyo, 1964	..	..	85	75
963	72 c. Berlin, 1936	..	..	1·00	90
964	96 c. Rome, 1960	..	..	1·10	1·00
965	$1.20 Los Angeles, 1930	..	1·25	1·25
958/65			*Set of* 8	6·00	5·50

208 *Siphonogorgia*

$3.60

(209)

1984 (23 Mar–10 Aug). *Corals (2nd series). (a) Designs as No. 713 etc, but with redrawn frames and inscriptions as in T 208. Multicoloured. P 13.*

966	1 c. Type 208	30	10
967	2 c. *Millepora alcicornis*	30	10
968	3 c. *Distichopora violacea*	40	10
969	5 c. *Ptilosarcus gurneyi*	45	10
970	10 c. *Lobophyllia bemprichii*	50	10
971	12 c. *Sarcophyton digitatum*	60	15
972	14 c. *Pavona praetorta*	60	15
973	18 c. *Junceella gemmacea*	70	20
974	20 c. *Stylaster*	70	20
975	24 c. *Stylophora pistillata*	70	20
976	30 c. *Palauastrea ramosa*	1·00	25
977	36 c. *Melithaea albitincta*	1·25	30
978	40 c. *Stylaster echinatus*	1·25	30
979	42 c. *Fungia fungites*	1·25	35
980	48 c. *Gonipora*	1·25	35
981	50 c. *Melithaea squamata* (15 May)	1·75	45
982	52 c. *Bellonella indica* (15 May)	1·75	60
983	55 c. *Plerogyra sinuosa* (15 May)	1·75	65
984	60 c. *Tubastraea* (15 May)	1·90	70
985	70 c. *Heliofungia actiniformis* (15 May)	2·00	85
986	85 c. *Caulastraea echinulata* (15 May)	2·25	1·00
987	96 c. *Porites andrewsi* (15 May)	2·50	1·10
988	$1.10, *Pectinia alcicornis* (15 May)	2·50	1·40
989	$1.20, *Dendrophyllia gracilis* (15 May)	2·50	1·50

(b) Nos. 785/9 surch as T 209 in gold on black

990	$3.60 on $2 *Gonipora* (28 June)	5·50	4·00
991	$4.20 on $3 *Heliofungia actiniformis* (28 June)	6·00	5·00
992	$5 on $4 *Stylophora pistillata* (28 June)	6·50	5·50
993	$7.20 on $6 *Stylaster echinatus* (20 July)	8·50	8·50
994	$9.60 on $10 *Melithaea albitincta* (10 Aug)	10·00	10·00
966/94	*Set of 29*	60·00	40·00

Equestrian Team Dressage Germany

(210)

1984 (24 Aug). *Olympic Gold Medal Winners. Nos. 963/5 optd as T 210.*

995	72 c. Berlin, 1936 (optd T 210)	60	65
996	96 c. Rome, 1960 (optd "Decathlon Daley Thompson Great Britain")	80	85
997	$1.20 Los Angeles, 1930 (optd "Four Gold Medals Carl Lewis U.S.A.")	1·00	1·10
995/7	*Set of 3*	2·25	2·40

211 Capt. Cook's Cottage, Melbourne

1984 (20 Sept). *"Ausipex" International Stamp Exhibition, Melbourne. T 211 and similar horiz designs. Multicoloured. P 13.*

998	36 c. Type 211	1·50	1·25
999	48 c. "H.M.S. *Endeavour* careened for Repairs" (Sydney Parkinson)	2·50	2·25
1000	60 c. "Cook's landing at Botany Bay" (E. Phillips Fox)	3·00	3·00
1001	$2 "Capt. James Cook" (John Webber)	3·50	4·00
998/1001	*Set of 4*	9·50	9·50
MS1002	140 × 100 mm. As Nos. 998/1001, but each stamp with a face value of 90 c.	7·50	7·50

Commemorating- 15 Sept. 1984

(212)

213 "Virgin on Throne with Child" (Giovanni Bellini)

1984 (15 Oct). *Birth of Prince Henry. Nos. 812 and 833/6 optd or surch (No. 1007) as T 212.*

1003	$1.25, Type 191 (optd with T 212) (Gold)	1·50	1·10
	a. Pair. Nos. 1003/4.	3·00	2·25
1004	$1.25, As Type 191, but inscr "1 July 1982" (optd "Birth H.R.H. Prince Henry") (Gold)	1·50	1·10
1005	$2.50, Princess Diana (inscr "21st Birthday") (optd with T 212) (Gold)	2·25	2·00
	a. Pair. Nos. 1005/6.	4·50	4·00
1006	$2.50, As No. 835, but inscr "1 July 1982" (optd "Birth H.R.H. Prince Henry") (Gold)	2·25	2·00
1007	$3 on $1 Type 187 (surch "Royal Birth Prince Henry 15 Sept. 1984") (Sil.)	4·50	4·00
1003/7	*Set of 5*	11·00	9·25

1984 (21 Nov). *Christmas. T 213 and similar vert designs. Multicoloured. P 14.*

1008	36 c. Type 213	1·00	40
1009	48 c. "Virgin and Child" (anonymous, 15th century)	1·10	60
1010	60 c. "Virgin and Child with Saints" (Alvise Vivarini)	1·40	80
1011	96 c. "Virgin and Child with Angels" (H. Memling)	1·75	1·60
1012	$1.20, "Adoration of Magi" (G. Tiepolo)	2·00	2·00
1008/12	*Set of 5*	6·50	4·75
MS1013	120 × 113 mm. As Nos. 1008/12, but each with a premium of 5 c. P 13½.	3·00	3·25

1984 (10 Dec). *Christmas. Designs as Nos. 1008/12 in separate miniature sheets, 62 × 76 mm, each with a face value of 95 c. + 5 c. P 13½.*

MS1014	As Nos. 1008/12 *Set of 5 sheets*	4·50	4·75

214 Downy Woodpecker

1985 (23 Apr). *Birth Bicentenary of John J. Audubon (ornithologist). T 214 and similar vert designs showing original paintings. Multicoloured. P 13 × 13½.*

1015	30 c. Type 214	2·50	1·25
1016	55 c. Black-throated Blue Warbler	2·75	1·75
1017	65 c. Yellow-throated Warbler	3·00	2·25
1018	75 c. Chestnut-sided Warbler	3·25	2·75
1019	95 c. Dickcissel	3·25	3·00
1020	$1.15, White-crowned Sparrow	3·25	3·50
1015/20	*Set of 6*	16·00	13·00
MS1021	Three sheets, each 76 × 75 mm. (a) $1.30, Red-cockaded Woodpecker. (b) $2.80, Seaside Sparrow. (c) $5.30, Zenaida Dove *Set of 3 sheets*	13·00	8·50

215 "The Kingston Flyer" (New Zealand)

(Des and litho Format)

1985 (14 May). *Famous Trains. T 215 and similar horiz designs. Multicoloured. Ordinary paper. P 14 × 13½.*

1022	20 c. Type 215	40	50
1023	55 c. Class 625 locomotive (Italy)	55	85
1024	65 c. Gotthard electric locomotive (Switzerland)	60	90
1025	75 c. Union Pacific diesel locomotive No. 6900 (U.S.A.)	75	1·10
1026	95 c. Canadian National "Super Continental" type diesel locomotive (Canada)	75	1·25
1027	$1.15, TGV express train (France)	80	1·00
1028	$2.20, "The Flying Scotsman" (Great Britain)	85	2·50
1029	$3.40, "Orient Express"	90	3·75
1022/9	*Set of 8*	5·00	11·00

No. 1023 is inscribed "640" in error.
Nos. 1022/9 exist imperforate from stock dispersed by the liquidator of Format International Security Printers Ltd.

216 "Helena Fourment" (Peter Paul Rubens)

217 "Lady Elizabeth, 1908" (Mabel Hankey)

1985 (6 June). *International Youth Year. T 216 and similar vert designs. Multicoloured. P 13.*

1030	55 c. Type 216	2·75	2·50
1031	65 c. "Vigee-Lebrun and Daughter" (E. Vigee-Lebrun)	3·00	3·00
1032	75 c. "On the Terrace" (P. Renoir)	3·25	3·25
1033	$1.30, "Young Mother Sewing" (M. Cassatt)	4·25	4·50
1030/3	*Set of 4*	12·00	12·00
MS1034	103 × 106 mm. As Nos. 1030/3, but each with a premium of 10 c.	5·50	5·50

1985 (28 June). *Life and Times of Queen Elizabeth the Queen Mother. T 217 and similar vert designs showing paintings. Multicoloured. P 13.*

1035	65 c. Type 217	40	50
1036	75 c. "Duchess of York, 1923" (Savely Sorine)	45	60
1037	$1.15, "Duchess of York, 1925" (Philip de Laszlo)	55	85
1038	$2.80, "Queen Elizabeth, 1938" (Sir Gerald Kelly)	1·40	2·25
1035/8	*Set of 4*	2·50	3·75
MS1039	69 × 81 mm. $5.30, As $2.80	2·50	3·50

Nos. 1035/8 were each printed in small sheets of 4 stamps.
For these designs in a miniature sheet, each with a face value of 55 c., see No. MS1079.

218 Albert Henry (Prime Minister, 1965–78)

219 Golf

1985 (29 July). *20th Anniv of Self-Government. T 218 and similar vert designs. Multicoloured. P 13.*

1040	30 c. Type 218	80	60
1041	50 c. Sir Thomas Davis (Prime Minister, 1978–Apr 1983 and from Nov 1983)	1·25	1·25
1042	65 c. Geoffrey Henry (Prime Minister, Apr–Nov 1983)	1·50	1·75
1040/2	*Set of 3*	3·25	3·25
MS1043	134 × 70 mm. As Nos. 1040/2, but each stamp with a face value of 55 c.	1·75	2·00

1985 (29 July). *South Pacific Mini Games, Rarotonga. T 219 and similar vert designs. Multicoloured. P 14.*

1044	55 c. Type 219	4·00	3·50
1045	65 c. Rugby	4·00	4·00
1046	75 c. Tennis	5·50	6·00
1044/6	*Set of 3*	12·00	12·00
MS1047	126 × 70 mm. Nos. 1044/6, but each with a premium of 10 c. P 13½.	11·00	12·00

220 Sea Horse, Gearwheel and Leaves

221 "Madonna of the Magnificat"

1985 (29 July). *Pacific Conferences, Rarotonga. P 13.*

1048	**220** 55 c. black, gold and rosine	1·00	65
1049	65 c. black, gold and violet	1·10	80
1050	75 c. black, gold and blue-green	1·25	1·10
1048/50	*Set of 3*	3·00	2·25
MS1051	126 × 81 mm. As Nos. 1048/50, but each stamp with a face value of 50 c.	1·60	2·00

No. 1048 shows the South Pacific Bureau for Economic Co-operation logo and is inscribed "S.P.E.C. Meeting, 30 July–1 Aug 1985, Rarotonga". No. 1049 also shows the S.P.E.C. logo, but is inscribed "South Pacific Forum, 4–6 Aug 1985, Rarotonga". No. 1050 shows the Pacific Islands Conference logo and the inscription "Pacific Islands Conference, 7–10 Aug 1985, Rarotonga".

1985 (18 Nov). *Christmas. Virgin and Child Paintings by Botticelli. T 221 and similar vert designs. Multicoloured. P 14.*

1052	55 c. Type 221	1·75	60
1053	65 c. "Madonna with Pomegranate"	2·00	65
1054	75 c. "Madonna and Child with Six Angels"	2·25	1·00
1055	96 c. "Madonna and Child with St. John"	2·75	1·40
1052/5	*Set of 4*	8·00	3·25
MS1056	90 × 104 mm. As Nos. 1052/5, but each stamp with a face value of 50 c. P 13½.	4·00	3·75

1985 (9 Dec). *Christmas. Virgin and Child Paintings by Botticelli. Square designs (46 × 46 mm) as Nos. 1052/5 in separate miniature sheets, 50 × 51 mm, with face values of $1.20, $1.45, $2.20 and $2.75. Imperf.*

MS1057	As Nos. 1052/5 *Set of 4 sheets*	9·00	11·00

222 "The Eve of the Deluge" (John Martin)

223 Queen Elizabeth II

1986 (13 Mar). *Appearance of Halley's Comet. Paintings. T 222 and similar vert designs. Multicoloured. P 14.*

1058	55 c. Type 222		1·25	1·25
1059	65 c. "Lot and his Daughters" (Lucas van Leyden)		1·40	1·40
1060	75 c. "Auspicious Comet" (from treatise c 1587)		1·50	1·50
1061	$1.25, "Events following Charles I" (Herman Saftleven)		2·25	2·25
1062	$2 "Ossian receiving Napoleonic Officers" (Anne Louis Girodet-Trioson)		3·00	3·00
1058/62		Set of 5	8·50	8·50

MS1063 130 × 100 mm. As Nos. 1058/62, but each with a face value of 70 c. P 13½ .. 4·00 5·50

MS1064 84 × 63 mm. $4 "Halley's Comet of 1759 over the Thames" (Samuel Scott). P 13½ .. 5·50 7·00

1986 (21 Apr). *60th Birthday of Queen Elizabeth II. T 223 and similar vert designs showing formal portraits. P 13 × 13½.*

1065	95 c. multicoloured		1·10	1·50
1066	$1.25, multicoloured		1·40	1·75
1067	$1.50, multicoloured		1·50	2·00
1065/7		Set of 3	3·50	4·75

MS1068 Three sheets, each 44 × 75 mm. As Nos. 1065/7, but with face values of $1.10, $1.95 and $2.45 .. Set of 3 sheets 8·00 9·00

224 U.S.A. 1847 Franklin 5 c. Stamp and H.M.S. *Resolution* at Rarotonga

225 Head of Statue of Liberty

1986 (21 May). *"Ameripex '86" International Stamp Exhibition, Chicago. T 224 and similar horiz designs. Multicoloured. P 14.*

1069	$1 Type 224		5·00	3·75
1070	$1.50, Chicago		3·50	4·25
1071	$2 1975 definitive $2, Benjamin Franklin and H.M.S. *Resolution*		6·00	5·50
1069/71		Set of 3	13·00	12·00

1986 (4 July). *Centenary of Statue of Liberty. T 225 and similar vert designs. Multicoloured. P 14.*

1072	$1 Type 225		75	85
1073	$1.25, Hand and torch of Statue		90	1·10
1074	$2.75, Statue of Liberty		2·00	2·50
1072/4		Set of 3	3·25	4·00

226 Miss Sarah Ferguson

(227)

1986 (23 July). *Royal Wedding. T 226 and similar multicoloured designs. P 14 ($1, $2) or 13½ × 13 ($3).*

1075	$1 Type 226		1·25	1·25
1076	$2 Prince Andrew		2·00	2·50
1077	$3 Prince Andrew and Miss Sarah Ferguson (57 × 31 mm)		2·50	3·50
1075/7		Set of 3	5·25	6·50

Nos. 1075/7 were each printed in small sheets of 4 stamps.

1986 (4 Aug). *"Stampex '86" Stamp Exhibition, Adelaide. No. MS1002 optd with T 227 in gold (circle) and black (inscr) only on design as No. 1001.*

MS1078 90 c. × 4 multicoloured .. .. 6·00 6·50
The "Stampex '86" exhibition emblem is also overprinted on the sheet margin.

1986 (4 Aug). *86th Birthday of Queen Elizabeth the Queen Mother. Designs as Nos. 1035/8 in miniature sheet, 91 × 116 mm, each stamp with a face value of 55 c. Multicoloured. P 13 × 13½.*

MS1079 55 c. × 4. As Nos. 1035/8 .. .. 5·00 5·50

228 "The Holy Family with St. John the Baptist and St. Elizabeth"

(229)

1986 (17 Nov). *Christmas. Paintings by Rubens. T 228 and similar vert designs. Multicoloured. P 13½.*

1080	55 c. Type 228		1·50	90
1081	$1.30, "Virgin with the Garland"		2·50	2·25
1082	$2.75, "The Adoration of the Magi" (detail)		5·00	4·25
1080/2		Set of 3	8·00	6·75

MS1083 140 × 100 mm. As Nos. 1080/2, but each size 36 × 46 mm with a face value of $2.40 .. 12·00 13·00

MS1084 80 × 70 mm. $6.40, As No. 1081 but size 32 × 50 mm .. .. .. 12·00 13·00

1986 (21 Nov). *Visit of Pope John Paul II to South Pacific. Nos. 1080/4 surch as T 229 in silver.*

1085	55 c. + 10 c. Type 228		2·75	2·00
1086	$1.30 + 10 c. "Virgin with the Garland"		3·50	2·50
1087	$2.75 + 10 c. "The Adoration of the Magi" (detail)		6·00	3·75
1085/7		Set of 3	11·00	7·50

MS1088 140 × 100 mm. As Nos. 1085/7, but size 36 × 46 mm with a face value of $2.40 + 10 c. 12·00 13·00

MS1089 80 × 70 mm. $6.40 + 50 c. As No. 1086 but size 32 × 50 mm .. 12·00 13·00

═══

HURRICANE RELIEF

10c   **+ 50c**

(230)   **(231)**

1987 (10–12 Feb). *Various stamps surch as T 230 by N.Z. Govt Printer.*

(a) On Nos. 741/56, 761/76 and 787/8

1090	10 c. on 15 c. *Distichopora violacea* (11.2)		10	10
1091	10 c. on 15 c. *Stylaster* (11.2)		10	10
1092	10 c. on 15 c. *Gonipora* (11.2)		10	10
1093	10 c. on 15 c. *Caulastraea echinulata* (11.2)		10	10
1094	10 c. on 25 c. *Lobophyllia bemprichii* (11.2)		10	10
1095	10 c. on 25 c. *Palauastrea ramosa* (11.2)		10	10
1096	10 c. on 25 c. *Bellonella indica* (11.2)		10	10
1097	10 c. on 25 c. *Pectinia alcicornis* (11.2)		10	10
1098	18 c. on 12 c. *Millepora alcicornis* (11.2)		15	15
1099	18 c. on 12 c. *Junceella gemmacea* (11.2)		15	15
1100	18 c. on 12 c. *Fungia fungites* (11.2)		15	15
1101	18 c. on 12 c. *Heliofungia actiniformis* (11.2)		15	15
1102	18 c. on 20 c. *Ptilosarcus gurneyi* (11.2)		15	15
1103	18 c. on 20 c. *Stylophora pistillata* (11.2)		15	15
1104	18 c. on 20 c. *Melithaea squamata* (11.2)		15	15
1105	18 c. on 20 c. *Porites andrewsi* (11.2)		15	15
1106	55 c. on 35 c. Type 184 (11.2)		40	45
1107	55 c. on 35 c. *Pavona praetorta* (11.2)		40	45
1108	55 c. on 35 c. *Stylaster echinatus* (11.2)		40	45
1109	55 c. on 35 c. *Tubastraea* (11.2)		40	45
1110	65 c. on 50 c. As No. 1098 (11.2)		45	50
1111	65 c. on 50 c. As No. 1099 (11.2)		45	50
1112	65 c. on 50 c. As No. 1100 (11.2)		45	50
1113	65 c. on 50 c. As No. 1101 (11.2)		45	50
1114	65 c. on 60 c. As No. 1090 (11.2)		45	50
1115	65 c. on 60 c. As No. 1091 (11.2)		45	50
1116	65 c. on 60 c. As No. 1092 (11.2)		45	50
1117	65 c. on 60 c. As No. 1093 (11.2)		45	50
1118	75 c. on 70 c. As No. 1102 (11.2)		55	60
1119	75 c. on 70 c. As No. 1103 (11.2)		55	60
1120	75 c. on 70 c. As No. 1104 (11.2)		55	60
1121	75 c. on 70 c. As No. 1105 (11.2)		55	60
1122	$6.40 on $4 *Stylophora pistillata*		4·50	4·75
1123	$7.20 on $6 *Stylaster echinatus*		5·00	5·25

(b) On Nos. 812/13 in gold (12 Feb)

1124	$9.40 on $1 Type 187		15·00	16·00
1125	$9.40 on $2 Prince Charles and Lady Diana Spencer		15·00	16·00

(c) On Nos. 835/6 in gold (12 Feb)

1126	$9.40 on $2.50 Princess of Wales (inscr "21st Birthday")		15·00	16·00
1127	$9.40 on $2.50 As No. 1126, but inscr "1 July 1982"		15·00	16·00

(d) On Nos. 966/8, 971/2, 975, 979/80, 982 and 987/9

1128	5 c. on 1 c. Type 208		10	10
1129	5 c. on 2 c. *Millepora alcicornis*		10	10
1130	5 c. on 3 c. *Distichopora violacea*		10	10
1131	5 c. on 12 c. *Sarcophyton digitatum*		10	10
1132	5 c. on 14 c. *Pavona praetorta*		10	10
1133	18 c. on 24 c. *Stylophora pistillata*		15	15
1134	55 c. on 52 c. *Bellonella indica*		40	45
1135	65 c. on 42 c. *Fungia fungites*		45	50
1136	75 c. on 48 c. *Gonipora*		55	60
1137	95 c. on 96 c. *Porites andrewsi*		70	75
1138	95 c. on $1.10 *Pectinia alcicornis*		70	75
1139	95 c. on $1.20 *Dendrophyllia gracilis*		70	75

(e) On Nos. 998/1001 in gold (No. 1143) or gold (value) and black (bars) (others) (12 Feb)

1140	$1.30 on 36 c. Type 211		1·40	1·50
1141	$1.30 on 48 c. "The *Endeavour* careened for Repairs" (Sydney Parkinson)		1·40	1·50
1142	$1.30 on 60 c. "Cook's landing at Botany Bay" (E. Phillips Fox)		1·40	1·50
1143	$1.30 on $2 "Capt. James Cook" (John Webber)		1·40	1·50

(f) On Nos. 1065/7 in gold (12 Feb)

1144	223	$2.80 on 95 c. multicoloured		7·00	7·50
1145	–	$2.80 on $1.25 multicoloured		7·00	7·50
1146	–	$2.80 on $1.50 multicoloured		7·00	7·50

(g) On Nos. 1075/7 in gold (value) and black (bars) (12 Feb)

1147	$2.80 on $1 Type 226		6·00	6·50
	a. Black opt (bars) omitted			£110
1148	$2.80 on $2 Prince Andrew		6·00	6·50
1149	$2.80 on $3 Prince Andrew and Miss Sarah Ferguson (57 × 31 mm)		6·00	6·50
1090/149		Set of 60	£100	£120

1987 (17 June). *Various stamps surch as T 230.*

(a) On Nos. 785/6 and 789

1150	$2.80 on $2 *Gonipora*		2·10	2·25
1151	$5 on $3 *Heliofungia actiniformis*		4·00	4·25
1152	$9.40 on $10 *Melithaea albitincta*		7·50	7·75

(b) On Nos. 838/42 (in gold on Nos. 1153/6)

1153	$9.40 on $1 Type 187 (No. 838)		7·50	7·75
	a. Pair. Nos. 1153/4		15·00	16·00
1154	$9.40 on $1 Type 187 (No. 839)		7·50	7·75
1155	$9.40 on $2 Prince Charles and Lady Diana Spencer (No. 840)		7·50	7·75
	a. Pair. Nos. 1155/6		15·00	16·00
1156	$9.40 on $2 Prince Charles and Lady Diana Spencer (No. 841)		7·50	7·75
1150/6		Set of 7	40·00	40·00

MS1157 106 × 59 mm. $9.20 on $1 Type 187; $9.20 on $2 Prince Charles and Lady Diana Spencer .. .. 12·00 15·00

1987 (30 June–31 July). *Hurricane Relief Fund. Various stamps surch as T 231.*

(a) On Nos. 1035/9 in silver

1158	65 c. + 50 c. Type 217		80	85
1159	75 c. + 50 c. "Duchess of York, 1923" (Savely Sorine)		85	1·00
1160	$1.15 + 50 c. "Duchess of York, 1925" (Philip de Laszlo)		1·10	1·40
1161	$2.80 + 50 c. "Queen Elizabeth, 1938" (Sir Gerald Kelly)		2·25	3·00

MS1162 69 × 81 mm. $5.30 + 50 c. As $2.80 + 50 c. .. .. 5·00 6·50

(b) On Nos. 1058/62 (in silver on Nos. 1164/6)

1163	55 c. + 50 c. Type 222		75	80
1164	65 c. + 50 c. "Lot and his Daughters" (Lucas van Leyden)		80	85
1165	75 c. + 50 c. "Auspicious Comet" (from treatise c 1587)		85	90
1166	$1.25 + 50 c. "Events following Charles I" (Herman Saftleven)		1·25	1·40
1167	$2 + 50 c. "Ossian receiving Napoleonic Officers" (Anne Louis Girodet-Trioson)		1·75	2·25

(c) On Nos. 1065/8 (in silver on No. 1169) (31 July)

1168	223	95 c. + 50 c. multicoloured		1·00	1·10
1169	–	$1.25 + 50 c. multicoloured		1·25	1·40
1170	–	$1.50 + 50 c. multicoloured		1·40	1·50

MS1171 Three sheets, each 44 × 75 mm. As Nos. 1168/70, but with face values of $1.10 + 50 c., $1.95 + 50 c., $2.45 + 50 c. Set of 3 sheets 8·00 9·50

(d) On Nos. 1069/71 (in silver on No. 1172)

1172	$1 + 50 c. Type 224		3·00	3·00
1173	$1.50 + 50 c. Chicago		1·75	2·25
1174	$2 + 50 c. 1975 definitive $2, Benjamin Franklin and H.M.S. *Resolution*		3·50	3·50

(e) On Nos. 1072/4 (in silver on Nos. 1175 and 1177)

1175	$1 + 50 c. Type 225		1·00	1·25
1176	$1.25 + 50 c. Hand and torch of Statue		1·25	1·50
1177	$2.75 + 50 c. Statue of Liberty		2·25	3·00

(f) On Nos. 1075/7 in silver (31 July)

1178	$1 + 50 c. Type 226		1·00	1·25
1179	$2 + 50 c. Prince Andrew		1·75	2·00
1180	$3 + 50 c. Prince Andrew and Miss Sarah Ferguson (57 × 31 mm)		2·40	3·00

(g) On Nos. 1080/4 in silver

1181	55 c. + 50 c. Type 228		75	80
1182	$1.30 + 50 c. "Virgin with the Garland"		1·25	1·40
1183	$2.75 + 50 c. "The Adoration of the Magi" (detail)		2·25	2·75

MS1184 140 × 100 mm. As No. 1181/3, but each size 36 × 46 mm with a face value of $2.40 + 50 c. 8·00 9·50

MS1185 80 × 70 mm. $6.40 + 50 c. As No. 1182, but size 32 × 50 mm. .. 5·50 7·00

(h) On Nos. 1122, 1134/7 and 1150/1

1186	55 c. + 25 c. on 52 c. *Bellonella indica*		70	70
1187	65 c. + 25 c. on 42 c. *Fungia fungites*		80	80
1188	75 c. + 25 c. on 48 c. *Gonipora*		90	90
1189	95 c. + 25 c. on 96 c. *Porites andrewsi*		1·10	1·10
1190	$2.80 + 50 c. on $2 *Gonipora*		3·25	3·25
1191	$5 + 50 c. on $3 *Heliofungia actiniformis*		5·50	5·50
1192	$6.40 + 50 c. on $4 *Stylophora pistillata*		7·00	7·00
1158/92		Set of 31	48·00	50·00

ROYAL WEDDING FORTIETH ANNIVERSARY

(232)

1987 (20 Nov). *Royal Ruby Wedding. Nos. 484 and 787 optd with T 232 in black on gold.*

1193	$4 Queen Elizabeth II and seashells		4·50	4·50
1194	$4 Queen Elizabeth II and *Stylophora pistillata*		4·50	4·50

233 "The Holy Family" (Rembrandt)

1987 (7 Dec). *Christmas.* T **233** *and similar horiz designs showing different paintings of the Holy Family by Rembrandt.* P 13½.

1195	$1.25, multicoloured	..	2·25	2·00
1196	$1.50, multicoloured	..	2·75	2·25
1197	$1.95, multicoloured	..	4·00	3·50
1195/7		*Set of 3*	8·00	7·00

MS1198   100×140 mm. As Nos. 1195/7, but each size 47×36 mm with a face value of $1.15 .. 7·00 8·50
MS1199   70×80 mm. $6 As No. 1196, but size 40×31 mm. P 13×13½ .. .. 9·50 11·00

234 Olympic Commemorative $50 Coin

(Des G. Vasarhelyi)

1988 (26 Apr). *Olympic Games, Seoul.* T **234** *and similar vert designs. Multicoloured.* P 13½×14.

1200	$1.50, Type **234**	..	3·00	2·25
	a. Horiz strip of 3. Nos. 1200/2	8·00		
1201	$1.50, Olympic torch and Seoul Olympic Park..		3·00	2·25
1202	$1.50, Steffi Graf playing tennis and Olympic medal	..	3·00	2·25
1200/2		*Set of 3*	8·00	6·00

MS1203   131×81 mm. $10 Combined design as Nos. 1200/2, but measuring 114×47 mm. P 13½ 11·00 12·00
Nos. 1200/2 were printed together, *se-tenant*, in horizontal strips of 3 throughout the sheet, each strip forming a composite design.

MILOSLAV MECIR
ČECHOSLOVAKIA
GOLD MEDAL WINNER
MEN'S TENNIS
(235)

1988 (12 Oct). *Olympic Tennis Medal Winners, Seoul.* Nos. 1200/3 *optd as* T **235**.

1204	$1.50, Type **234** (optd with T **235**)	..	2·50	2·25
	a. Horiz strip of 3. Nos. 1204/6	6·75		
1205	$1.50, Olympic torch and Seoul Olympic Park (optd "TIM MAYOTTE UNITED STATES GABRIELA SABATINI ARGENTINA SILVER MEDAL WINNERS")		2·50	2·25
1206	$1.50, Steffi Graf playing tennis and Olympic medal (optd "GOLD MEDAL WINNER STEFFI GRAF WEST GERMANY")		2·50	2·25
1204/6		*Set of 3*	6·75	6·00

MS1207   131×81 mm. $10 Combined design as Nos. 1200/2, but measuring 114×47 mm. (optd "GOLD MEDAL WINNER SEOUL OLYMPIC GAMES STEFFI GRAF -WEST GERMANY") .. 11·00 11·00

236 "Virgin and Child"   **237** "Apollo II" leaving Earth

1988 (11 Nov). *Christmas.* T **236** *and similar vert designs showing paintings of "The Nativity"* ($6.40) *or different versions of "Virgin and Child" by Dürer.* P 13½.

1208	70 c. multicoloured	..	2·25	2·00
1209	85 c. multicoloured	..	2·50	2·25
1210	95 c. multicoloured	..	2·75	2·50
1211	$1.25, multicoloured	..	3·50	3·25
1208/11		*Set of 4*	10·00	9·00

MS1212   80 × 100 mm. $6.40, multicoloured (45 × 60 mm) .. .. .. 6·50 8·50

(Des G. Vasarhelyi)

1989 (14 July). *20th Anniv of First Manned Landing on Moon.* T **237** *and similar horiz designs.* P 13.

1213	40 c. Type **237**	..	1·50	1·50
	a. Horiz pair. Nos. 1213/14	3·00	3·00	
1214	40 c. Lunar module over Moon	..	1·50	1·50
1215	55 c. Armstrong stepping onto Moon	..	1·75	1·75
	a. Horiz pair. Nos. 1215/16	3·50	3·50	
1216	55 c. Astronaut on Moon	..	1·75	1·75

1217	65 c. Working on lunar surface	..	2·00	2·00
	a. Horiz pair. Nos. 1217/18	4·00	4·00	
1218	65 c. Conducting experiment		2·00	2·00
1219	75 c. "Apollo 11" leaving Moon		2·00	2·00
	a. Horiz pair. Nos. 1219/20	4·00	4·00	
1220	75 c. Splashdown in South Pacific		2·00	2·00
1213/20		*Set of 8*	13·00	13·00

MS1221   108×91 mm. $4.20, Astronauts on Moon .. .. 5·00 6·00
Nos. 1213/14, 1215/16, 1217/18 and 1219/20 were each printed together, horizontally *se-tenant*, in sheets of 12.

238 Rarotonga Flycatcher

(Des G. Drummond)

1989 (4 Oct). *Endangered Birds of the Cook Islands.* T **238** *and similar horiz designs. Multicoloured.* (a) *Postage.* P 13½×13

1222	15 c. Type **238**	..	2·00	2·00
1223	20 c. Pair of Rarotonga Flycatchers	..	2·00	2·00
1224	65 c. Pair of Rarotongan Fruit Doves	..	2·75	2·75
1225	70 c. Rarotongan Fruit Dove	..	2·75	2·75
1222/5		*Set of 4*	8·50	8·50

(b) *Air.* P 13½
MS1226   Four sheets, each 70×53 mm. As Nos. 1222/5, but with face values of $1, $1.25, $1.50, $1.75 and each size 50×32 mm. .. *Set of 4 sheets* 6·50 8·50

239 Villagers

1989 (24 Nov). *Christmas.* T **239** *and similar multicoloured designs showing details from "Adoration of the Magi" by Rubens.* P 13.

1227	70 c. Type **239**	..	1·40	1·40
1228	85 c. Virgin Mary	..	1·50	1·60
1229	95 c. Christ Child	..	1·75	2·00
1230	$1.50, Boy with gift	..	2·00	3·00
1227/30		*Set of 4*	6·00	7·25

MS1231   85×120 mm. $6.40, "Adoration of the Magi" (45×60 mm). P 13½ .. .. 10·00 11·00

240 Revd. John Williams   **241** "Woman writing and L.M.S. Church   Letter" (Terborch)

(Des Jennifer Toombs)

1990 (19 Feb). *Christianity in the Cook Islands.* T **240** *and similar square designs. Multicoloured.* P 13.

1232	70 c. Type **240**		75	80
1233	85 c. Mgr. Bernardine Castanié and Roman Catholic Church		90	1·10
1234	95 c. Elder Osborne Widstoe and Mormon Church		1·00	1·40
1235	$1.60, Dr. J. E. Caldwell and Seventh Day Adventist Church		1·75	2·00
1232/5		*Set of 4*	4·00	5·25

MS1236   90×90 mm. As Nos. 1232/5, but each with a face value of 90 c. P 13½ .. 4·75 6·00

1990 (2 May). *150th Anniv of the Penny Black.* T **241** *and similar vert designs showing paintings. Multicoloured.* P 13½.

1237	85 c. Type **241**	..	1·10	1·25
1238	$1.15, "George Gisze" (Holbein the Younger)	..	1·50	1·75
1239	$1.55, "Mrs. John Douglas" (Gainsborough)	..	1·90	2·25
1240	$1.85, "Portrait of a Gentleman" (Dürer)	..	2·25	2·50
1237/40		*Set of 4*	6·00	7·00

MS1241   82×150 mm. As Nos. 1237/40, but each with a face value of $1.05 .. .. 8·50 9·50

242 Sprinting   **243** Queen Elizabeth the Queen Mother

(Des G. Vasarhelyi)

1990 (15 June)–**91**. *Olympic Games, Barcelona, and Winter Olympic Games, Albertville* (1st issue) (1992). T **242** *and similar horiz designs. Multicoloured.* P 14.

1242	$1.85, Type **242**		4·50	4·75
	a. Horiz strip of 3. Nos. 1242/4	12·00		
1243	$1.85, Cook Islands $50 commemorative coin	..	4·50	4·75
1244	$1.85, Skiing		4·50	4·75
1242/4		*Set of 3*	12·00	13·00

MS1245   109×52 mm. $6.40, As Nos. 1242/4, but 80×26 mm. P 13½ (12.2.91) .. 12·00 13·00
Nos. 1242/4 were printed together, *se-tenant*, in horizontal strips of 3 throughout the sheet of 18.
See also Nos. 1304/10.

1990 (20 July). *90th Birthday of Queen Elizabeth the Queen Mother.* P 13½.

1246	**243** $1.85, multicoloured	..	4·00	4·50
MS1247	66×101 mm. **243** $6.40, multicoloured		9·00	11·00

244 "Adoration of the Magi"   (245)
(Memling)

(Litho Questa)

1990 (29 Nov). *Christmas. Religious Paintings.* T **244** *and similar multicoloured designs. Ordinary paper.* P 14.

1248	70 c. Type **244**	..	1·40	1·40
1249	85 c. "Holy Family" (Lotto)	..	1·50	1·50
1250	95 c. "Madonna and Child with Saints John and Catherine" (Titian)	..	1·75	2·00
1251	$1.50, "Holy Family" (Titian)	..	3·00	3·50
1248/51		*Set of 4*	7·00	7·50

MS1252   98×110 mm, $6.40, "Madonna and Child enthroned, surrounded by Saints" (Vivarini) (*vert*) .. .. 9·00 10·00

1990 (5 Dec). *"Birdpex '90" Stamp Exhibition, Christchurch, New Zealand. No.* **MS**1226 *optd with* T **245**.
MS1253   Four sheets, each 70×53 mm. As Nos. 1222/5, but with face values of $1, $1.25, $1.50, $1.75 and each size 50×32 mm .. *Set of 4 sheets* 12·00 13·00

246 Columbus   (247)
(engraving by
Theodoro de Bry)

1991 (14 Feb). *500th Anniv of Discovery of America by Columbus* (1992) (1st issue). P 13½×13.
1254   **246** $1 multicoloured .. .. 2·25 2·50
See also Nos. 1302/3.

1991 (22 Apr). *65th Birthday of Queen Elizabeth II. No.* 789 *optd with* T **247** *in gold.*
1255 $10 *Melithaea albitincta* .. .. 13·00 14·00

248 "Adoration of the Child"
(G. delle Notti)

(Des G. Vasarhelyi. Litho Questa)

1991 (12 Nov). *Christmas. Religious Paintings. T* **248** *and similar multicoloured designs. Ordinary paper.* P 14.
1256	70 c. Type **248**		1·50	1·50
1257	85 c. "The Birth of the Virgin" (B. Murillo)		1·75	1·75
1258	$1.15, "Adoration of the Shepherds" (Rembrandt)		2·25	2·25
1259	$1.50, "Adoration of the Shepherds" (L. le Nain)		3·25	3·75
1256/9		*Set of 4*	8·00	8·50
MS1260	79×103 mm. $6.40, "Madonna and Child" (Lippi) (*vert*)		10·00	11·00

249 Red-breasted Wrasse	**250** Tiger

(Litho Questa (5 c. to $2), Fournier ($3 to $15))

1992 (22 Jan)–**94**. *Reef Life* (1st series). T **249** *and similar horiz designs. Multicoloured with white borders. Ordinary paper* (5 c. to $2) *or fluorescent security markings* ($3 to $15). P 14 (5 c. to $2) *or* 14×13½ ($3 to $15).
1261	5 c. Type **249**		40	40
1262	10 c. Blue Sea Star		40	40
1263	15 c. Bicoloured Angelfish ("Black and Gold Angelfish")		55	55
1264	20 c. Spotted Pebble Crab		70	70
1265	25 c. Black-tipped Grouper ("Black-tipped Cod")		70	70
1266	30 c. Spanish Dancer		70	70
1267	50 c. Regal Angelfish		90	90
1268	80 c. Big-scaled Soldierfish ("Squirrel Fish")		1·25	1·25
1269	85 c. Red Pencil Sea Urchin (23.3.92)		2·75	2·75
1270	90 c. Red-spotted Rainbowfish (23.3.92)		2·75	2·75
1271	$1 Cheek-lined Wrasse (23.3.92)		2·75	2·75
1272	$2 Long-nosed Butterflyfish (23.3.92)		2·75	2·75
1273	$3 Red-spotted Rainbowfish (25.10.93)		2·50	3·00
1274	$5 Blue Sea Star (25.10.93)		3·75	4·50
1275	$7 *Pygoplites diacanthus* (6.12.93)		7·50	9·00
1276	$10 Spotted Pebble Crab (31.1.94)		9·00	10·00
1277	$15 Red Pencil Sea Urchin (9.9.94)		14·00	16·00
1261/77		*Set of 17*	48·00	50·00

The 25 c., 50 c., $1 and $2 include a silhouette of the Queen's head.
Nos. 1273/7 are larger, 55×34 mm, and show a portrait of Queen Elizabeth II at left.
For some of these designs in a larger size, 40×30 mm, and with light cinnamon borders, see Nos. 1342/52.

(Litho B.D.T.)

1992 (6 June)–**93**. *Endangered Wildlife. T* **250** *and similar horiz designs. Multicoloured. Ordinary paper.* P 14.
1279	$1.15, Type **250**		1·25	1·25
1280	$1.15, Indian Elephant (7.6.92)		1·25	1·25
1281	$1.15, Brown Bear (8.6.92)		1·25	1·25
1282	$1.15, Black Rhinoceros (9.6.92)		1·25	1·25
1283	$1.15, Chimpanzee (10.6.92)		1·25	1·25
1284	$1.15, Argali (11.6.92)		1·25	1·25
1285	$1.15, Heaviside's Dolphin (13.7.92)		1·25	1·25
1286	$1.15, Eagle Owl (14.7.92)		1·75	1·25
1287	$1.15, Bee Hummingbird (15.7.92)		1·75	1·25
1288	$1.15, Puma (16.7.92)		1·25	1·25
1289	$1.15, European Otter (17.7.92)		1·25	1·25
1290	$1.15, Red Kangaroo (18.7.92)		1·25	1·25
1291	$1.15, Jackass Penguin (2.11.92)		1·75	1·25
1292	$1.15, Asian Lion (3.11.92)		1·25	1·25
1293	$1.15, Peregrine Falcon (4.11.92)		1·75	1·25
1294	$1.15, Persian Fallow Deer (5.11.92)		1·25	1·25
1295	$1.15, Key Deer (6.11.92)		1·25	1·25
1296	$1.15, Alpine Ibex (7.11.92)		1·25	1·25
1297	$1.15, Mandrill (1.2.93)		1·25	1·25
1298	$1.15, Gorilla (2.2.93)		1·25	1·25
1299	$1.15, *Vanessa atalanta* (butterfly) (3.2.93)		1·25	1·25
1300	$1,15, Takin (4.2.93)		1·25	1·25
1301	$1.15, Ring-tailed Lemur (5.2.93)		1·25	1·25
1279/1301		*Set of 23*	28·00	26·00

251 Columbus and Landing in New World

(Des G. Vasarhelyi. Litho B.D.T.)

1992 (22 May–21 Sept). *500th Anniv of Discovery of America by Columbus* (2nd issue). *Ordinary paper.* P 14×14½.
1302 **251**	$6 multicoloured		6·50	7·50
MS1303	128×84 mm. $10 As T **251**, but detail of landing party only (40×29 *mm*). P 15×14 (21 Sept)		7·00	8·50

MINIMUM PRICE

The minimum price quote is 10p which represents a handling charge rather than a basis for valuing common stamps. For further notes about prices see introductory pages.

---

252 Football and $50 Commemorative Coin

(Des G. Vasarhelyi. Litho B.D.T.)

1992 (24 July). *Olympic Games, Barcelona* (2nd issue). T **252** *and similar horiz designs. Multicoloured. Ordinary paper.* P 13.
1304	$1.75, Type **252**		2·50	2·50
	a. Horiz strip of 3. Nos. 1304/06		6·75	
1305	$1.75, Olympic Gold medal		2·50	2·50
1306	$1.75, Basketball and $10 coin		2·50	2·50
1307	$2.25, Running		3·50	3·50
	a. Horiz strip of 3. Nos. 1307/09		9·50	
1308	$2.25, $10 and $50 coins		3·50	3·50
1309	$2.25, Cycling		3·50	3·50
1304/09		*Set of 6*	16·00	16·00
MS1310	155×91 mm. $6.40, Javelin throwing		10·00	11·00
Nos. 1304/06 and 1307/09 were each printed together, *se-tenant*, in horizontal strips of 3 throughout the sheets.

253 Festival Poster	**ROYAL VISIT** (**254**)

(Litho B.D.T.)

1992 (16 Oct). *6th Festival of Pacific Arts, Rarotonga. T* **253** *and similar vert designs. Multicoloured. Ordinary paper.* P 15×14.
1311	80 c. Type **253**		1·25	1·25
1312	85 c. Seated Tangaroa carving		1·25	1·25
1313	$1 Seated Tangaroa carving (*different*)		1·40	1·40
1314	$1.75, Standing Tangaroa carving		2·25	3·00
1311/14		*Set of 4*	5·50	6·25

1992 (16 Oct). *Royal Visit by Prince Edward. Nos.* 1311/14 *optd with T* **254**.
1315	80 c. Type **253**		1·50	1·50
1316	85 c. Seated Tangaroa carving		1·50	1·50
1317	$1 Seated Tangaroa carving (*different*)		1·60	1·60
1318	$1.75, Standing Tangaroa carving		3·00	3·50
1315/18		*Set of 4*	7·00	7·50

255 "Worship of Shepherds" (Parmigianino)	**256** Queen in Garter Robes

1992 (20 Nov). *Christmas. Religious Paintings by Parmigianino. T* **255** *and similar vert designs. Multicoloured. Ordinary paper.* P 13½.
1319	70 c. Type **255**		1·00	1·00
1320	85 c. "Virgin with Long Neck"		1·25	1·25
1321	$1.15, "Virgin with Rose"		1·50	1·75
1322	$1.90, "St. Margaret's Virgin"		2·75	3·75
1319/22		*Set of 4*	6·00	7·00
MS1323	86×102 mm. $6.40, As 85 c., but larger (36×46 *mm*)		9·00	10·00

(Litho B.D.T.)

1992 (10 Dec). *40th Anniv of Queen Elizabeth II's Accession. T* **256** *and similar vert designs. Multicoloured. Ordinary paper.* P 13½.
1324	80 c. Type **256**		1·75	1·50
1325	$1.15, Queen at Trooping the Colour		2·00	2·00
1326	$1.50, Queen in evening dress		2·75	3·00
1327	$1.95, Queen with bouquet		3·00	3·50
1324/7		*Set of 4*	8·50	9·00

---

257 Coronation Ceremony

(Des G. Vasarhelyi. Litho B.D.T.)

1993 (2 June). *40th Anniv of Coronation. T* **257** *and similar horiz designs. Multicoloured.* P 14.
1328	$1 Type **257**		2·00	1·75
1329	$2 Coronation photograph by Cecil Beaton		3·25	3·50
1330	$3 Royal family on balcony		4·25	4·75
1328/30		*Set of 3*	8·50	9·00

258 "Virgin with Child" (Filippo Lippi)

1993 (8 Nov). *Christmas. Religious Paintings. T* **258** *and similar vert designs. Multicoloured. Ordinary paper.* P 13½ ($4) *or* 14 (others).
1331	70 c. Type **258**		80	80
1332	85 c. "Bargellini Madonna" (Lodovico Carracci)		95	95
1333	$1.15, "Virgin of the Curtain" (Rafael Sanzio)		1·40	1·60
1334	$2.50, "Holy Family" (Agnolo Bronzino)		3·25	3·75
1335	$4 "Saint Zachary Virgin" (Parmigianino) (32×47 *mm*)		4·00	5·00
1331/5		*Set of 5*	9·50	11·00

259 Skiing, Flags and Ice Skating
(*illustration further reduced. Actual size* 94×28 *mm*)

(Litho Questa)

1994 (11 Feb). *Winter Olympic Games, Lillehammer.* P 13½×14.
1336 **259**	$5 multicoloured		6·50	7·50

260 Cup on Logo with German and Argentinian Players

(Des G. Vasarhelyi. Litho B.D.T.)

1994 (17 June). *World Cup Football Championship, U.S.A.* P 14×14½.
1337 **260**	$4.50, multicoloured		4·75	6·00

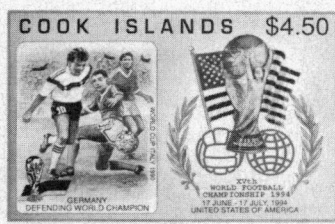

261 Neil Armstrong taking First Step on Moon

(Litho B.D.T.)

1994 (20 July). *25th Anniv of First Moon Landing. T 261 and similar horiz designs. Multicoloured.* P 14.
1338	$2.25, Type 261	3·75	3·75
	a. Sheetlet. Nos. 1338/41×2	26·00	
1339	$2.25, Astronaut on Moon and view of Earth	3·75	3·75
1340	$2.25, Astronaut and flag	3·75	3·75
1341	$2.25, Astronaut with reflection in helmet visor	3·75	3·75
1338/41	Set of 4	13·50	13·50

Nos. 1338/41 were printed together, *se-tenant*, in sheetlets of 8 (2×4), containing two of each design, with Nos. 1338/9 in the top two rows and Nos. 1340/1 in the bottom two. Each row shows two different designs with a half stamp-size *se-tenant* label in the centre.

(Litho B.D.T.)

1994 (24 Oct). *Reef Life (2nd series). As Nos. 1261 and 1263/71, but each 40×30 mm and with light cinnamon borders.* P 15×14.
1342	5 c. Type 249	40	40
1344	15 c. Bicoloured Angelfish	50	50
1345	20 c. Spotted Pebble Crab	55	55
1346	25 c. Black-tipped Grouper	60	60
1347	30 c. Spanish Dancer	60	60
1348	50 c. Regal Angelfish	75	75
1349	80 c. Big-scaled Soldierfish	1·00	1·00
1350	85 c. Red Pencil Sea Urchin	1·00	1·00
1351	90 c. Red-spotted Rainbowfish	1·10	1·10
1352	$1 Cheek-lined Wrasse	1·25	1·25
1342/52	Set of 10	7·00	7·00

Nos. 1261 and 1263/71, which were printed by Questa, are 35×27 mm and have white borders.

262 Actors in Outrigger Canoe

263 "The Virgin and Child" (Morales)

(Litho B.D.T.)

1994 (23 Nov)–**97**. *Release of The Return of Tommy Tricker (film shot in Cook Islands). T 262 and similar horiz designs showing scenes from film. Multicoloured.* P 14.
1359	85 c. Type 262	1·10	1·25
	a. Sheetlet. Nos. 1359/64	6·00	
1360	85 c. Male and female dancers	1·10	1·25
1361	85 c. European couple on beach	1·10	1·25
1362	85 c. Aerial view of island	1·10	1·25
1363	85 c. Two female dancers	1·10	1·25
1364	85 c. Cook Islands couple on beach	1·10	1·25
1364a	90 c. Type 262 (28.8.97)	65	70
	ab. Sheetlet. Nos. 1364a/f	4·00	
1364b	90 c. As No. 1360 (28.8.97)	65	70
1364c	90 c. As No. 1361 (28.8.97)	65	70
1364d	90 c. As No. 1362 (28.8.97)	65	70
1364e	90 c. As No. 1363 (28.8.97)	65	70
1364f	90 c. As No. 1364 (28.8.97)	65	70
1359/64f	Set of 12	10·00	11·50

Nos. 1359/64 and 1364a/f were each printed together, *se-tenant*, in sheetlets of 6.

(Litho B.D.T.)

1994 (30 Nov). *Christmas. Religious Paintings. T 263 and similar vert designs. Multicoloured.* P 14.
1365	85 c. Type 263	1·10	1·25
	a. Block of 4. Nos. 1365/8	4·00	
1366	85 c. "Adoration of the Kings" (Gerard David)	1·10	1·25
1367	85 c. "Adoration of the Kings" (Foppa)	1·10	1·25
1368	85 c. "The Madonna and Child with St. Joseph and Infant Baptist" (Baroccio)	1·10	1·25
1369	$1 "Madonna with Iris" (Dürer)	1·25	1·40
	a. Block of 4. Nos. 1369/72	4·50	
1370	$1 "Adoration of the Shepherds" (Le Nain)	1·25	1·40
1371	$1 "The Virgin and Child" (school of Leonardo)	1·25	1·40
1372	$1 "The Mystic Nativity" (Botticelli)	1·25	1·40
1365/72	Set of 8	8·50	9·50

Nos. 1365/8 and 1369/72 were printed together, *se-tenant*, in blocks of 4 throughout the sheets.

264 Pirates (Treasure Island)

(Des G. Vasarhelyi. Litho B.D.T.)

1994 (12 Dec). *Death Centenary of Robert Louis Stevenson (author). T 264 and similar horiz designs. Multicoloured.* P 14×15.
1373	$1.50, Type 264	1·90	2·25
	a. Block of 4. Nos. 1373/6	7·00	
1374	$1.50, Duel (David Balfour)	1·90	2·25
1375	$1.50, Mr. Hyde (Dr. Jekyll and Mr. Hyde)	1·90	2·25
1376	$1.50, Rowing boat and sailing ship (Kidnapped)	1·90	2·25
1373/6	Set of 4	7·00	8·00

Nos. 1373/6 were printed together, *se-tenant*, in blocks of 4 throughout the sheet.

265 U.N. and National Flags with Peace Doves

(Des G. Vasarhelyi. Litho B.D.T.)

1995 (17 July). *50th Anniv of United Nations.* P 13.
1377	265 $4.75, multicoloured	4·75	6·00

No. 1377 was printed in sheets of 4 with inscribed margins.

266 Queen Elizabeth the Queen Mother and Coat of Arms

(Des G. Vasarhelyi. Litho B.D.T.)

1995 (31 Aug). *95th Birthday of Queen Elizabeth the Queen Mother.* P 13.
1378	266 $5 multicoloured	7·00	7·50

No. 1378 was printed in sheets of 4 with inscribed margins.

267 German Delegation signing Unconditional Surrender at Rheims

(Litho B.D.T.)

1995 (4 Sept). *50th Anniv of End of Second World War. T 267 and similar horiz design. Multicoloured.* P 13.
1379	$3.50, Type 267	5·50	6·00
	a. Pair. Nos. 1379/80	11·00	12·00
1380	$3.50, Japanese delegation on U.S.S. Missouri, Tokyo Bay	5·50	6·00

Nos. 1379/80 were printed together, *se-tenant* horizontally and vertically, in sheets of 4.

(Des G. Vasarhelyi. Litho B.D.T.)

1995 (12 Oct). *50th Anniv of Food and Agriculture Organization. Horiz design as T 265. Multicoloured.* P 13×13½.
1381	$4.50, F.A.O. and U.N. emblems	4·75	6·00

No. 1381 was printed in sheets of 4 with inscribed margins.

268 Green Turtle

269 Emblem and Throwing the Discus

(Litho B.D.T.)

1995 (20 Nov). *Year of the Sea Turtle. T 268 and similar horiz designs. Multicoloured.* P 13½×14.
1382	85 c. Type 268	1·75	1·60
1383	$1 Hawksbill Turtle	2·00	1·75
1384	$1.75, Green Turtle on beach	3·00	3·25
1385	$2.25, Young Hawksbill Turtles hatching	3·75	4·00
1382/5	Set of 4	9·50	9·50

(Litho B.D.T.)

1996 (12 Jan). *Olympic Games, Atlanta. T 269 and similar horiz designs. Multicoloured.* P 14.
1386	85 c. Type 269	1·25	1·25
1387	$1 Athlete with Olympic Torch	1·50	1·50
1388	$1.50, Running	2·25	2·25
1389	$1.85, Gymnastics	2·50	2·50
1390	$2.10, Ancient archery	2·75	2·75
1391	$2.50, Throwing the javelin	3·00	3·00
1386/91	Set of 6	12·00	12·00

270 Queen Elizabeth II (271)

28th South Pacific Forum

(Des G. Vasarhelyi. Litho)

1996 (21 June). *70th Birthday of Queen Elizabeth II. T 270 and similar vert designs. Multicoloured.* P 14.
1392	$1.90, Type 270	2·25	2·25
1393	$2.25, Wearing tiara	2·75	2·75
1394	$2.75, In Garter robes	3·00	3·00
1392/4	Set of 3	7·25	7·25
MS1395	103×152 mm. Designs as Nos. 1392/4, but each with a face value of $2.50	11·00	12·00

Nos. 1392/4 were each printed in sheets of 4 with inscribed margins.

1997 (12 Sept). *28th South Pacific Forum. Nos. 1364a/f optd with T 271 (Nos. 1396, 1399/400) or "12–22 September 1997" (Nos. 1397/8 and 1401), all in silver.*
1396	90 c. Type 262	90	1·00
	a. Sheetlet. Nos. 1396/1401	4·75	
1397	90 c. As No. 1360	90	1·00
1398	90 c. As No. 1361	90	1·00
1399	90 c. As No. 1362	90	1·00
1400	90 c. As No. 1363	90	1·00
1401	90 c. As No. 1364	90	1·00
1396/1401	Set of 6	4·75	5·50

272 Lampides boeticus (female)

(Litho B.D.T.)

1997 (22 Oct)–**98**. *Butterflies. T 272 and similar horiz designs. Multicoloured.* P 13×13½ (5 c. to $1) or 13½ ($1.50 to $15).
1402	5 c. Type 272	10	10
1403	10 c. Vanessa atalanta	10	10
1404	15 c. Lampides boeticus (male)	10	15
1405	20 c. Papilio godeffroyi	15	20
1406	25 c. Danaus hamata	15	20
1407	30 c. Xois sesara	20	25
1408	50 c. Vagrans egista	30	35
1409	70 c. Parthenos sylvia	45	50
1410	80 c. Hyblaea sanguinea (12.11.97)	50	55
1411	85 c. Melanitis leda (12.11.97)	55	60
1412	90 c. Ascalapha odorata (12.11.97)	55	60
1413	$1 Precis villida (12.11.97)	65	70
1414	$1.50, Parthenos sylvia (11.3.98)	95	1·00
1415	$2 Lampides boeticus (female) (11.3.98)	1·25	1·40
1416	$3 Precis villida (11.3.98)	1·90	2·00
1417	$4 Melanitis leda (19.6.98)	2·50	2·75
1418	$5 Vagrans egista (19.6.98)	3·25	3·50
1419	$7 Hyblaea sanguinea (18.9.98)	4·50	4·75
1420	$10 Vanessa atalanta (18.9.98)	6·25	6·50
1421	$15 Papilio godeffroyi (13.11.98)	9·00	9·50
1402/21	Set of 19	33·00	35·00

The $1 includes an outline portrait of Queen Elizabeth II. Nos. 1414/21 are larger, 41×25 mm, with the Queen's portrait included on the $4 to $15.

273 Queen Elizabeth and Prince Philip

274 Diana, Princess of Wales

1997 (20 Nov). *Golden Wedding of Queen Elizabeth and Prince Philip.* P 14.
1424	273 $2 multicoloured	1·75	2·00
MS1425	76×102 mm. 273 $5 multicoloured	5·00	6·00

No. 1424 was printed in sheets of 4 with inscribed margins.

1998 (18 Mar). *Diana, Princess of Wales Commemoration. Litho.* P 14.
1426 $1.15, Type **274**   ..   ..   1·10   1·25
    a. Sheetlet. No. 1426×5 plus label   5·00
MS1427   70×100 mm. $3.50, Princess Diana and
    guard of honour   ..   ..   3·25   4·00
    No. 1426 was printed in sheetlets of 5 stamps with a label at
top left.

+ $1

CHILDREN'S CHARITIES

KIA ORANA THIRD MILLENNIUM

(275)   (276)

1998 (20 Nov). *Children's Charities.* No. MS1427 *surch with* T **275** *in silver.*
MS1428   70×100 mm. $3.50+$1 Princess Diana
    and guard of honour   ..   ..   3·50   4·00

1999 (31 Dec). *New Millennium.* Nos. 1311/14 *optd with* T **276**.
1429   80 c. Type **253**   50   55
1430   85 c. Seated Tangaroa carving   ..   55   60
1431 $1 Seated Tangaroa carving (*different*)   65   70
1432 $1.75, Standing Tangaroa carving   ..   1·10   1·25
1429/32   ..   ..   ..   *Set of* 4   2·75   3·00

STAMP BOOKLETS

1982 (June). *Royal Wedding. Multicoloured cover,* 130×74 *mm, showing Prince and Princess of Wales. Stitched.*
SB1 $6 booklet containing $1 and $2 (Nos. 812/13),
    each in pair   ..   ..   4·25

OFFICIAL STAMPS

O.H.M.S.	O.H.M.S.
(O **1**)	(O **2**)

1975 (17 Mar–19 May). Nos. 228/31, 233, 235/7, 239/40, 243/5 *and* 246c/7 *optd with* Type O **1** (5, 10, 18, 25 *and* 30 c. *surch also*), *in black and silver*
O   1   1 c. *Hibiscus syriacus*   ..   ..
O   2   2 c. Frangipani   ..   ..   ..
O   3   3 c. "Suva Queen"   ..   ..
O   4   4 c. Water Lily   ..   ..   ..
O   5   5 c. on 2½ c. *Clitoria ternatea*   ..   ..
O   6   8 c. *Allamanda cathartica*   ..   ..
O   7   10 c. on 6 c. Hibiscus   ..   ..
O   8   18 c. on 20 c. Thunbergia   ..   ..
O   9   25 c. on 9 c. Stephanotis   ..   ..
O10   30 c. on 15 c. Frangipani   ..   ..
O11   50 c. *Gardinia taitensis*   ..   ..
O12 $1 Type **80**   ..   ..   ..
O13 $2 Type **80**   ..   ..   ..
O14 $4 Type **81** (19 May)   ..   ..
O15 $6 Type **81** (19 May)   ..   ..
O1/15 ..   ..   ..   *Set of* 15   † 11·00
    These stamps were only sold to the public cancelled-to-order and
not in unused condition.

1978 (19 Oct)–**79**. Nos. 466/7, 474, 478/81, 484/5, 542 *and* 568/9 *optd or surch* (2, 5, 10, 15, 18 *and* 35 c.) *as Type* O **2**.
O16   1 c. Common Pacific Vase (*Vasum turbinellum*) (Silver)   ..   60   10
O17   2 c. on ½ c. Type **141**   60   10
O18   5 c. on ½ c. Type **141**   60   10
O19   10 c. on 8 c. Granulate Frog Shell (*Bursa granularis*) (Silver)   ..   65   10
O20   15 c. on 50 c. Textile or Cloth of Gold Cone (*Conus textile*) (Silver)   90   10
O21   18 c. on 60 c. Red-mouth Olive (*Oliva miniacea miniacea*) (Silver)   90   15
O22   25 c. Royal Oak Scallop (*Cryptopecten pallium*)   ..   ..   1·00   20
O23   30 c. Soldier Cone (*Conus miles*) (Silver)   1·00   25
O24   35 c. on 60 c. Red-mouth Olive (*Oliva miniacea miniacea*) (Silver)   ..   1·25   30
O25   50 c. Textile or Cloth of Gold Cone (*Conus textile*) (Silver)   ..   1·75   35
O26   60 c. Red-mouth Oliva (*Oliva miniacea miniacea*) (Silver)   ..   2·00   45
O27 $1 Queen and Prince Philip (Silver)   4·50   65
O28 $1 Royal Visit, 1974 (Silver)   ..   4·50   65
O29 $2 Captain Cook and H.M.S. *Resolution*   7·00   2·25
O30 $4 Queen Elizabeth II and seashells (15.2.79)   ..   ..   13·00   2·25
O31 $6 As $4 (15.2.79)   ..   ..   13·00   3·50
O16/31   ..   ..   *Set of* 16   48·00 10·00
    These stamps were originally only sold to the public cancelled-to-order and not in unused condition. They were made available to overseas collectors in mint condition during 1980.

75c	
O.H.M.S.	O.H.M.S.
(O **3**)	(O **4**)

O.H.M.S.

(O **5**)

1985 (10 July)–**90**. (a) Nos. 969/74, 976, 978, 981, 984/6 *and* 988/9 *optd or surch as Type* O **3** *by silver foil embossing.*
O32   5 c. *Ptilosarcus gurneyi*   50   50
O33   10 c. *Lobophyllia bemprichii*   ..   50   50
    a. Opt double, one albino ..   ..   50·00
O34   12 c. *Sarcophyton digitatum* (5.5.86)   ..   2·00   60
O35   14 c. *Pavona praetorta* (5.5.86)   ..   2·00   60
O36   18 c. *Junceella gemmacea* (5.5.86)   ..   2·00   60
O37   20 c. *Stylaster*   60   50
O38   30 c. *Palauastrea ramosa*   ..   60   50
O39   40 c. *Stylaster echinatus*   ..   60   50
O40   50 c. *Melithaea squamata* (5.5.86)   ..   2·75   70
O41   55 c. on 85 c. *Caulastraea echinulata*   70   50
    a. "O.H.M.S." albino   ..   ..   †
O42   60 c. *Tubastraea*   70   60
O43   70 c. *Heliofungia actiniformis* (5.5.86)   ..   3·00   85
O44 $1.10, *Pectinia alcicornis*   ..   1·10   90
O45 $2 on $1.20, *Dendrophyllia gracilis*   2·00   1·75

    (b) Nos. 862/5 *surch with* Type O **4** *by gold foil embossing*
O46   75 c. on 60 c. Type **197** (5.5.86)   ..   3·00   1·00
O47   75 c. on 60 c. Rarotonga oranges (5.5.86)   3·00   1·00
O48   75 c. on 60 c. Rarotonga Airport (5.5.86)   3·00   1·00
O49   75 c. on 60 c. Prime Minister Sir Thomas Davis (5.5.86)   ..   ..   3·00   1·00

    (c) Nos. 786/9 *surch as* T **209** *in silver and black further optd with Type* O **5** *by silver foil embossing.*
O50 $5 on $3 *Heliofungia actiniformis* (5.5.86)   7·00   4·75
O51 $9 on $4 *Stylophora pistillata* (30.5.89)   8·00   8·25
O52 $14 on $6 *Stylaster echinatus* (12.7.89)   12·50 13·00
O53 $18 on $10 *Melithaea albitincta* (4.6.90)   17·00 17·00
O32/53   ..   ..   *Set of* 22 65·00 50·00

O.H.M.S.

(O **6**)

1995 (24 Feb)–**98**. Nos. 1261/72 *optd with* Type O **3** *and Nos.* 1273/6 *with Type* O **6**, *both by silver foil embossing.*
O54   5 c. Type **249**   10   10
O55   10 c. Blue Sea Star   10   10
O56   15 c. Bicoloured Angelfish   ..   10   15
O57   20 c. Spotted Pebble Crab   ..   15   20
O58   25 c. Black-tipped Grouper   ..   15   20
O59   30 c. Spanish Dancer   20   25
O60   50 c. Regal Angelfish   30   35
O61   80 c. Big-scaled Soldierfish   ..   50   55
O62   85 c. Red Pencil Sea Urchin   ..   55   60
O63   90 c. Red-spotted Rainbowfish   ..   55   60
O64 $1 Cheek-lined Wrasse (15.5.95)   ..   65   70
O65 $2 Long-nosed Butterflyfish (15.5.95)   1·25   1·40
O66 $3 Red-spotted Rainbowfish (17.7.98)   1·90   2·00
O67 $5 Blue Sea Star (17.7.98)   ..   3·25   3·50
O68 $7 *Pygoplites diacanthus* (17.7.98)   4·50   4·75
O69 $10 Spotted Pebble Crab (12.11.98)   6·25   6·50
O54/69   ..   ..   *Set of* 16 20·00 21·00

AITUTAKI

Stamps of COOK ISLANDS were used in Aitutaki from 1892 until 1903.

PRICES FOR STAMPS ON COVER TO 1945	
Nos. 1/7	*from* × 4
Nos. 9/14	*from* × 3
Nos. 15/29	*from* × 4
Nos. 30/2	*from* × 6

A. NEW ZEALAND DEPENDENCY

The island of Aitutaki, under British protection from 1888, was annexed by New Zealand on 11 June 1901.

Stamps of New Zealand overprinted or surcharged. For illustrations of New Zealand watermarks and definitive types see the beginning of Cook Islands.

AITUTAKI.
(1)

Ava Pene.
(2) ½d.

Tai Pene.
(3) 1d.

Rua Pene Ma Te Ava.
(4) 2½d.

Toru Pene.
(5) 3d.

Ono Pene.
(6) 6d.

Tai Tiringi.
(7) 1s.

1903 (29 June)—11. *T* **23**, **27/8**, **31**, **34** *and* **42** *surch with T* **1** *at top and T* **2** *to* **7** *at foot. Thin, hard Cowan paper. W* **43**.

(a) P 14

1	½d. green (No. 302) (R.)	4·50	6·50
2	1d. carmine (No. 303) (B.)	4·75	5·50
3	2½d. deep blue (No. 320a) (R.) (9.11)	8·00	18·00
	a. "Ava" without stop	£130	£170
1/3	*Set of 3*	15·00	27·00

(b) P 11

4	2½d. blue (No. 308) (R.)	11·00	12·00
5	3d. yellow-brown (No. 309) (B.)	17·00	15·00
6	6d. rose-red (No. 312a) (B.)	29·00	25·00
7	1s. bright red (No. 315a) (B.)	55·00	85·00
	a. "Tiringi" without stop (R. 7/12)	£400	£550
	b. Orange-red	65·00	95·00
	ba. "Tiringi" without stop (R. 7/12)	£500	£650
	c. Orange-brown	£140	£160
	ca. "Tiringi" without stop (R. 7/12)	£1000	£1200
4/7	*Set of 4*	£100	£120

Nos. 1/2 and 4/7 were placed on sale in Auckland on 12 June 1903.

There were four states of the overprint used for No. 3. On the first the "no stop" variety (No. 3a) occurs on R. 6/8, on the second it appears on R. 1/4, 2/4 and 6/8, on the third on R. 5/8 and 6/8, and on the fourth all stops are present.

AITUTAKI.

Ono Pene.
(8)

1911–16. *T* **51** *and* **53** *surch with T* **1** *at top and T* **2** *or* **3** *at foot and T* **52** *surch as T* **8**. P 14×15 (½d., 1d.) *or* 14×14½ (*others*).

9	½d. green (No. 387) (R.) (9.11)	1·00	3·00
10	1d. carmine (No. 405) (B.) (2.13)	3·00	9·50
11	6d. carmine (No. 392) (B.) (23.5.16)	42·00	95·00
12	1s. vermilion (No. 394) (B.) (9.14)	55·00	£140
9/12	*Set of 4*	90·00	£225

1916–17. *T* **60** (recess) *surch as T* **8**. W **43**. P 14×13½.

13	6d. carmine (No. 425) (B.) (6.6.16)	14·00	50·00
	a. Perf 14×14½	7·50	26·00
	b. Vert pair. Nos. 13/13a	50·00	£150
14	1s. vermilion (No. 430) (B.) (3.17)	28·00	90·00
	a. Perf 14×14½	35·00	90·00
	ab. "Tai" without dot (R. 8/9, 9/12, 10/12)	£225	£425
	ac. "Tiringi" without dot on second "i" (R. 8/12, 10/7)	£275	£425
	ad. "Tiringi" without dot on third "i" (R. 8/11)	£350	£550
	b. Vert pair. Nos. 14/14a	£140	£350

1917–18. *T* **60** (recess) *optd* "AITUTAKI" *only, as in T* **8**. W **43**. P 14×13½.

15	2½d. blue (No. 419) (R.) (12.18)	2·00	15·00
	a. Perf 14×14½	1·75	15·00
	b. Vert pair. Nos. 15/15a	40·00	£130
16	3d. chocolate (No. 420) (B.) (1.18)	1·75	20·00
	a. Perf 14×14½	1·50	20·00
	b. Vert pair. Nos. 16/16a	38·00	£140
17	6d. carmine (No. 425) (B.) (11.17)	7·50	21·00
	a. Perf 14×14½	4·75	21·00
	b. Vert pair. Nos. 17/17a	50·00	£140
18	1s. vermilion (No. 430) (B.) (11.17)	17·00	38·00
	a. Perf 14×14½	12·00	28·00
	b. Vert pair. Nos. 18/18a	75·00	£180
15/18	*Set of 4*	18·00	75·00

1917–20. *T* **53** *and* **61** (typo) *optd* "AITUTAKI" *only, as in T* **8**. W **43**. P 14×15.

19	½d. green (No. 435) (R.) (2.20)	1·00	5·50
20	1d. carmine (No. 405) (B.) (5.20)	3·25	22·00

21	1½d. slate (No. 437) (R.) (11.17)	3·75	30·00
22	1½d. orange-brown (No. 438) (R.) (2.19)	80	7·00
23	3d. chocolate (No. 440) (B.) (6.19)	3·50	15·00
19/23	*Set of 5*	11·00	70·00

(Des and recess Perkins, Bacon & Co)

1920 (23 Aug). *T* **9/14** *of Cook Islands, but inscr* "AITUTAKI". *No wmk.* P 14.

24	½d. black and green	3·50	24·00
25	1d. black and dull carmine	3·50	17·00
	a. Double derrick flaw (R.2/8, 3/6 or 5/2)	11·00	
26	1½d. black and sepia	6·00	12·00
27	3d. black and deep blue	2·50	14·00
28	6d. red-brown and slate	5·50	14·00
29	1s. black and purple	9·50	16·00
24/9	*Set of 6*	27·00	85·00

(Recess Govt Printing Office, Wellington)

1924–27. *T* **9/10** *and* **16** *of Cook Islands, but inscr* "AITUTAKI". W **43** *of New Zealand.* P 14.

30	½d. black and green (5.27)	2·00	10·00
31	1d. black and deep carmine (10.24)	6·00	6·50
	a. Double derrick flaw (R.2/8, 3/6 or 5/2)	15·00	
32	2½d. black and dull blue (10.27)	7·50	50·00
30/2	*Set of 3*	14·00	60·00

Cook Islands stamps superseded those of Aitutaki on 15 March 1932. Separate issues were resumed in 1972.

B. PART OF COOK ISLANDS

On 9 August 1972, Aitutaki became a Port of Entry into the Cook Islands, and at the close of business on the previous day, Cook Islands stamps were withdrawn from sale there. Whilst remaining part of the Cook Islands, Aitutaki has a separate postal service.

(New Currency. 100 cents = 1 dollar)

PRINTERS. The following stamps, *unless otherwise stated*, were printed, in photogravure until No. **MS613** and in lithography thereafter, by Heraclio Fournier, Spain. All such issues are, *unless otherwise stated*, on paper treated with fluorescent security markings, and with synthetic gum. The fluorescent markings can be found inverted or omitted.

Aitutaki
(9)

Aitutaki
(10)

(Optd by Govt Printer, Wellington)

1972 (9 Aug). *Nos.* **227B** *etc. of Cook Is. optd with T* **9** (applied horizontally on $1), *by New Zealand Govt Printer.*

33	½ c. Type **79**	30	80
34	1 c. Hibiscus syriacus	70	1·40
35	2½ c. Clitoria ternatea	2·25	7·00
36	4 c. Water Lily (No. 233B)	70	85
37	5 c. Bauhinia bi-pinnata rosea	2·50	7·50
38	10 c. Poinciana regia flamboyant	2·50	5·50
39	20 c. Thunbergia	1·25	1·00
40	25 c. Canna Lily	70	1·00
41	50 c. Gardinia taitensis	2·75	2·75
42	$1 Type **80**	4·00	5·50
	a. Shade*	20·00	
33/42	*Set of 10*	16·00	30·00

* No. 42a has the border flowers predominantly in a carmine colour instead of scarlet, and may be due to a missing yellow colour.

1972 (27 Oct). *Christmas. Nos.* **406/8** *of Cook. Is. optd in silver with T* **10**.

43	**130** 1 c. multicoloured	10	10
44	— 5 c. multicoloured	15	15
45	— 10 c. multicoloured	15	25
43/5	*Set of 3*	30	40

1972 (20 Nov). *Royal Silver Wedding. As Nos.* **413** *and* **415** *of Cook Is., but inscr* "COOK ISLANDS Aitutaki".

46	**131** 5 c. black and silver	3·50	2·75
47	— 15 c. black and silver	1·50	1·50

AITUTAKI
(11)

AITUTAKI
(12)

1972 (24 Nov). *No.* **245B** *of Cook Is. optd with T* **11** *by Govt Printer, Rarotonga.*

48	**80** $2 multicoloured	50	75
	a. Optd "AJTUTAKI" for "AITUTAKI" (R. 2/4)	25·00	
	b. On No. 245A (gum arabic printing)	50·00	
	ba. Optd "AJTUTAKI" for "AITUTAKI" (R. 2/4)		

1972 (11 Dec). *Nos.* **227B** *etc of Cook Is. optd with T* **12**, *by Heraclio Fournier.*

49	½ c. Type **79**	15	10
50	1 c. Hibiscus syriacus	15	10
51	2½ c. Clitoria ternatea	20	10
52	4 c. Water Lily (No. 233B)	25	10
53	5 c. Bauhinia bi-pinnata rosea	25	15
54	10 c. Poinciana regia flamboyant	35	25
55	20 c. Thunbergia	1·00	50
56	25 c. Canna Lily	50	55
57	50 c. Gardinia taitensis	75	90
58	$1 Type **80**	1·25	1·75
49/58	*Set of 10*	4·25	4·00

13 "Christ Mocked"
(Grünewald)

AITUTAKI
(14)

1973 (6 Apr). *Easter. T* **13** *and similar vert designs. Multicoloured.* P 13.

59	1 c. Type **13**	15	10
60	1 c. "St. Veronica" (Van der Weyden)	15	10
61	1 c. "The Crucified Christ with Virgin Mary, Saints and Angels" (Raphael)	15	10
62	1 c. "Resurrection" (Piero della Francesca)	15	10
63	5 c. "The Last Supper" (Master of Amiens)	20	15
64	5 c. "Condemnation" (Holbein)	20	15
65	5 c. "Christ on the Cross" (Rubens)	20	15
66	5 c. "Resurrection" (El Greco)	20	15
67	10 c. "Disrobing of Christ" (El Greco)	25	15
68	10 c. "St. Veronica" (Van Oostsanen)	25	15
69	10 c. "Christ on the Cross" (Rubens)	25	15
70	10 c. "Resurrection" (Bouts)	25	15
59/70	*Set of 12*	2·25	1·25

Nos. 59/62, 63/6 and 67/70 were each printed together, *se-tenant*, in blocks of 4 throughout the sheet.

1973 (14 May). *Silver Wedding Coinage. Nos.* **417/23** *of Cook Is. optd in silver and black as T* **14**.

71	1 c. black, rosy carmine and gold	10	10
72	2 c. black, bright blue and gold	10	10
73	5 c. black, green and silver	15	10
74	10 c. black, royal blue and silver	20	10
75	20 c. black, deep blue-green and silver	30	15
76	50 c. black, carmine and silver	50	30
77	$1 black, bright blue and silver	70	45
71/7	*Set of 7*	1·90	1·00

TENTH ANNIVERSARY
CESSATION
OF
NUCLEAR TESTING
TREATY
(15)

16 Red Hibiscus and Princess Anne

1973 (13 Aug). *Tenth Anniv of Treaty Banning Nuclear Testing. Nos.* **236B**, **238B**, **240B** *and* **243B** *of Cook Is. optd with T* **15** *and T* **12** *together.*

78	8 c. Allamanda cathartica	15	15
79	10 c. Poinciana regia flamboyant	15	15
80	20 c. Thunbergia	30	20
81	50 c. Gardinia taitensis	70	50
78/81	*Set of 4*	1·10	90

1973 (14 Nov). *Royal Wedding. T* **16** *and similar horiz design. Multicoloured.* P 13½ × 14.

82	25 c. Type **16**	25	10
83	30 c. Capt. Phillips and Blue Hibiscus	25	10
MS84	114 × 65 mm. Nos. 82/3. P 13	50	40

17 "Virgin and Child"
(Montagna)

18 Rose-branch Murex
(*Murex ramosus*)

1973 (10 Dec). *Christmas. T* **17** *and similar vert designs showing* "The Virgin and Child" *by the artists listed. Multicoloured.* P 13½.

85	1 c. Type **17**	10	10
86	1 c. Crivelli	10	10
87	1 c. Van Dyck	10	10
88	1 c. Perugino	10	10
89	5 c. Veronese (child at shoulder)	25	15
90	5 c. Veronese (child on lap)	25	15
91	5 c. Cima	25	15
92	5 c. Memling	25	15
93	10 c. Memling	25	10
94	10 c. Del Colle	25	10
95	10 c. Raphael	25	10
96	10 c. Lotto	25	10
85/96	*Set of 12*	2·00	80

Nos. 85/8, 89/92 and 93/6 were each printed together, *se-tenant*, in blocks of 4 throughout the sheet.

1974 (31 Jan)—75. *T* **18** *and similar horiz designs showing seashells. Multicoloured.* P 13.

97	½ c. Type **18**	90	80
98	1 c. New Caledonia Nautilus (*Nautilus macromphallus*)	90	80

99	2 c.	Common or Major Harp (*Harpa major*)		90	80
100	3 c.	Striped Bonnet (*Phalium flammiferum*)		90	80
101	4 c.	Mole Cowrie (*Cypraea talpa*)	..	90	80
102	5 c.	Pontifical Mitre (*Mitra stictica*)		90	80
103	8 c.	Trumpet Triton (*Charonia tritonis*)		90	80
104	10 c.	Venus Comb Murex (*Murex pecten*)		90	80
105	20 c.	Red-mouth Olive (*Oliva miniacea marrati*)		1·25	80
106	25 c.	Ruddy Frog Shell (*Bursa rubeta*)		1·25	80
107	60 c.	Widest Pacific Conch (*Strombus latissimus*)		3·00	1·25
108	$1	Maple-leaf Triton or Winged Frog Shell (*Biplex perca*)		2·50	1·40
109	$2	Queen Elizabeth II and Marlin-spike Auger (*Terebra maculata*) (20.1.75)		6·00	9·00
110	$5	Queen Elizabeth II and Tiger Cowrie (*Cypraea tigris*) (28.2.75)		27·00	10·00
97/110			Set of 14	42·00	27·00

Nos. 109/110 are larger, 53×25 mm.

19 Bligh and H.M.S. *Bounty*

(Des G. Vasarhelyi)

1974 (11 Apr). *William Bligh's Discovery of Aitutaki. T* **19** *and similar horiz designs. Multicoloured. P* 13½.

114	1 c.	Type **19**	..	30	35
115	1 c.	H.M.S. *Bounty*		30	35
116	5 c.	Bligh, and H.M.S. *Bounty* at Aitutaki		65	50
117	5 c.	Aitutaki chart of 1856		65	50
118	8 c.	Capt. Cook and H.M.S. *Resolution*		95	70
119	8 c.	Map of Aitutaki and inset location map		95	70
114/19			Set of 6	3·50	2·75

Nos. 114/15, 116/17 and 118/19 were each printed together, *se-tenant*, in horizontal and vertical pairs throughout the sheet. See also Nos. 123/8.

20 Aitutaki Stamps of 1903, and Map

21 "Virgin and Child" (Hugo van der Goes)

1974 (15 July). *Centenary of Universal Postal Union. T* **20** *and similar horiz design. Multicoloured. P* 13½ × 14.

120	25 c.	Type **20**	..	65	50
121	50 c.	Stamps of 1903 and 1920, and map		85	75
MS122		66 × 75 mm. Nos. 120/1. P 13	..	1·50	2·50

Each value was issued in sheets of 5 stamps and 1 label.

1974 (9 Sept). *Air. As Nos.* 114/119, *but larger* (46 × 26 *mm*), *denominations changed, and inscr* "AIR MAIL".

123	10 c.	Type **19**	..	60	50
124	10 c.	H.M.S. *Bounty*		60	50
125	25 c.	Bligh, and H.M.S. *Bounty* at Aitutaki		70	60
126	25 c.	Aitutaki chart of 1856	..	70	60
127	30 c.	Capt. Cook and H.M.S. *Resolution*		80	60
128	30 c.	Map of Aitutaki and inset location map		80	60
123/8			Set of 6	3·75	3·00

Nos. 123/4, 125/6 and 127/8 were each printed together, *se-tenant*, in horizontal and vertical pairs throughout the sheet.

1974 (11 Oct). *Christmas. T* **21** *and similar vert designs showing "Virgin and Child" by the artists listed. Multicoloured. P* 13.

129	1 c.	Type **21**	..	10	10
130	5 c.	Bellini		10	10
131	8 c.	Gerard David		10	10
132	10 c.	Antonello da Messina		10	10
133	25 c.	Joos van Cleve		20	20
134	30 c.	Master of the Life of St. Catherine		20	20
129/34			Set of 6	65	65
MS135		127 × 134 mm. Nos. 129/34		1·40	1·60

Each value was issued in sheets of 15 stamps and 1 label.

22 Churchill as Schoolboy   (23)

1974 (29 Nov). *Birth Centenary of Sir Winston Churchill. T* **22** *and similar vert designs. Multicoloured. P* 13½.

136	1 c.	Type **22**	..	25	25
137	25 c.	Churchill as young man	..	30	40
138	30 c.	Churchill with troops		35	45
139	50 c.	Churchill painting		45	60
140	$1	Giving "V" sign		55	75
136/40			Set of 5	1·75	2·25
MS141		115 × 108 mm. Nos. 136/40 plus *se-tenant* label. P 13		1·75	1·50

Each value was issued in sheets of 5 stamps and 1 label.

1974 (2 Dec). *Children's Christmas Fund. Nos.* 129/34 *surch with T* **23**.

142	1 c. + 1 c.	multicoloured	..	10	10
143	5 c. + 1 c.	multicoloured		10	10
144	8 c. + 1 c.	multicoloured	..	10	10
145	10 c. + 1 c.	multicoloured		10	10
146	25 c. + 1 c.	multicoloured		20	20
147	30 c. + 1 c.	multicoloured		20	20
142/7			Set of 6	55	55

24 Soviet and U.S. Flags

25 "Madonna and Child with Saints Francis and John" (Lorenzetti)

1975 (24 July). *"Apollo-Soyuz" Space Project. T* **24** *and similar horiz design. Multicoloured. P* 13 × 14.

148	25 c.	Type **24**	..	30	20
149	50 c.	Daedalus and space capsule	..	40	30
MS150		123 × 61 mm. Nos. 148/9	..	1·25	1·10

Each value was issued in sheets of 8 stamps and 1 label.

1975 (24 Nov). *Christmas. T* **25** *and similar vert designs. Multicoloured. P* 13½.

151	6 c.	} Type **25**		10	10
152	6 c.		..	10	10
153	6 c.			10	10
154	7 c.	} "Adoration of the Kings" (Van der Weyden)		10	10
155	7 c.			10	10
156	7 c.			10	10
157	15 c.	} "Madonna and Child Enthroneth with Saints Onufrius and John the Baptist" (Montagna)		15	15
158	15 c.			15	15
159	15 c.			15	15
160	20 c.	} "Adoration of the Shepherds" (Reni)		20	15
161	20 c.			20	15
162	20 c.			20	15
151/62			Set of 12	1·50	1·40
MS163		104 × 201 mm. Nos. 151/62. P 13	..	2·25	2·50

Nos. 151/3, 154/6, 157/9 and 160/2 were each printed together, *se-tenant*, in horizontal strips of 3 throughout the sheet, forming composite designs. Type **25** shows the left-hand stamp of the 6 c. design.

1975 (19 Dec). *Children's Christmas Fund. Nos.* 151/62 *surch as T* **23**, *in silver*.

164	6 c. + 1 c.	} Type **25**		10	10
165	6 c. + 1 c.			10	10
166	6 c. + 1 c.			10	10
167	7 c. + 1 c.	} "Adoration of the Kings" (Van der Weyden)		10	10
168	7 c. + 1 c.			10	10
169	7 c. + 1 c.			10	10
170	15 c. + 1 c.	} "Madonna and Child" (Montagna)		15	15
171	15 c. + 1 c.			15	15
172	15 c. + 1 c.			15	15
173	20 c. + 1 c.	} "Adoration of the Shepherds" (Reni)		20	20
174	20 c. + 1 c.			20	20
175	20 c. + 1 c.			20	20
164/75			Set of 12	1·50	1·50

26 "The Descent" (detail, 15th-cent Flemish School)

27 "The Declaration of Independence" (detail)

1976 (5 Apr). *Easter. Various vert designs showing portions of "The Descent" as in T* **26**. *P* 13.

176	**26**	15 c. multicoloured	..	15	10
177	–	30 c. multicoloured	..	20	15
178	–	35 c. multicoloured	..	25	20
176/8			Set of 3	55	40
MS179		87 × 67 mm. Nos. 176/8 forming a complete picture of "The Descent". P 12½ × 13		1·00	1·25

Stamps from No. **MS179** have no borders and are therefore smaller than stamps from the sheets.

Each value was issued in sheets of 8 stamps and 1 label.

1976 (1 June). *Bicentenary of American Revolution. T* **27** *and similar vert designs showing paintings by John Trumbull. Multicoloured. P* 13.

180	30 c.			25	10
181	30 c.	} Type **27**		25	10
182	30 c.			25	10
183	35 c.			30	15
184	35 c.	} "The Surrender of Lord Cornwallis at Yorktown"		30	15
185	35 c.			30	15
186	50 c.			30	15
187	50 c.	} "The Resignation of General Washington"		30	15
188	50 c.			30	15
180/8			Set of 9	2·25	1·10
MS189		132 × 120 mm. Nos. 180/8. P 13	..	2·25	1·25

Nos. 180/2, 183/5 and 186/8 were each printed together, *se-tenant*, in horizontal strips of 3 throughout the sheet, forming composite designs. Each sheet includes 3 stamp-size labels. Type **27** shows the left-hand stamp of the 30 c. design.

Stamps from No. **MS189** have their borders in a different colour and come with a different inscription.

28 Cycling

1976 (15 July). *Olympic Games, Montreal. T* **28** *and similar horiz designs. Multicoloured. P* 13 × 14.

190	15 c.	Type **28**	..	30	15
191	35 c.	Sailing		45	20
192	60 c.	Hockey		70	25
193	70 c.	Sprinting		70	30
190/3			Set of 4	1·90	90
MS194		107 × 97 mm. Nos. 190/3		1·90	1·25

Stamps from No. **MS194** have borders of a different colour. Each value was issued in sheets of 5 stamps and 1 label.

ROYAL VISIT JULY 1976

(29)   30 "The Visitation"

1976 (30 July). *Visit of Queen Elizabeth to the U.S.A. Nos.* 190/**MS194** *optd with T* **29**.

195	15 c.	Type **28**	..	35	15
196	35 c.	Sailing		45	25
197	60 c.	Hockey		70	40
198	70 c.	Sprinting		70	45
195/8			Set of 4	2·00	1·10
MS199		107 × 97 mm. Nos. 195/8		2·00	1·25

1976 (18 Oct). *Christmas. T* **30** *and similar vert designs. Figures in gold; background colours given. P* 13.

200	6 c.	} deep bluish green		10	10
201	6 c.			10	10
202	7 c.	} dull brown-purple		10	10
203	7 c.			10	10
204	15 c.	} deep blue		10	10
205	15 c.			10	10
206	20 c.	} reddish violet		15	15
207	20 c.			15	15
200/207			Set of 8	60	60
MS208		128 × 96 mm. As Nos. 200/207 but with borders on three sides		1·00	1·40

Designs:—No. 201, Angel: No. 202, Angel; No. 203, Shepherds; No. 204, Joseph; No. 205, Mary and the Child; No. 206, Wise Man; No. 207, Two Wise Men.

Nos. 200/1, 202/3, 204/5 and 206/7 were each printed together, *se-tenant*, in horizontal pairs throughout the sheet, forming composite designs. Type **30** shows the left-hand stamp of the 6 c. design.

(31)   32 Alexander Graham Bell and First Telephone

1976 (19 Nov). *Children's Christmas Fund. Nos.* 200/**MS208** *surch in silver as T* **31**.

209	6 c. + 1 c.	} "The Visitation"		10	10
210	6 c. + 1 c.			10	10
211	7 c. + 1 c.	} "Angel and Shepherds"		10	10
212	7 c. + 1 c.			10	10
213	15 c. + 1 c.	} "The Holy Family"		15	15
214	15 c. + 1 c.			15	15
215	20 c. + 1 c.	} "The Magi"		15	15
216	20 c. + 1 c.			15	15
209/16			Set of 8	70	70
MS217		128 × 96 mm. As Nos. 209/216 but with a premium of "+ 2 c." and borders on three sides		80	1·40

1977 (3 Mar). *Telephone Centenary (1976). T 32 and similar horiz design. P 13.*

218	25 c. black, gold and dull scarlet	20	15
219	70 c. black, gold and lilac	40	40
MS220	116 × 59 mm. As Nos. 218/19 but with different colours	70	1·00

Design:—70 c. Earth Station and satellite.

33 "Christ on the Cross" (detail)

1977 (31 Mar). *Easter and 400th Birth Anniv of Rubens. T 33 and similar horiz designs. Multicoloured. P 13½ × 14.*

221	15 c. Type 33	45	15
222	20 c. "Lamentation for Christ"	60	20
223	35 c. "Christ with Straw"	75	25
221/3	Set of 3	1·60	55
MS224	115 × 57 mm. Nos. 221/3. P 13 × 12½	1·60	1·60

Each value was issued in sheets of 8 stamps and 1 label.

34 Capt. Bligh, George III and H.M.S. *Bounty*

1977 (21 Apr). *Silver Jubilee. T 34 and similar horiz designs. Multicoloured. P 13.*

225	25 c. Type 34	35	35
226	35 c. Rev. Williams, George IV and Aitutaki Church	40	40
227	50 c. Union Jack, Queen Victoria and island map	45	45
228	$1 Balcony scene, 1953	50	50
225/8	Set of 4	1·50	1·50
MS229	130 × 87 mm. Nos. 225/8 but with gold borders. P 13½ × 13	1·25	1·25

Each value was issued in sheets of 5 stamps and 1 label.

35 The Shepherds   (36) +1c

1977 (14 Oct). *Christmas. T 35 and similar vert designs. Multicoloured. P 13½ × 14.*

230	6 c. Type 35	10	10
231	6 c. Angel	10	10
232	7 c. Mary, Jesus and ox	10	10
233	7 c. Joseph and donkey	10	10
234	15 c. Three Kings	10	10
235	15 c. Virgin and Child	10	10
236	20 c. Joseph	10	10
237	20 c. Mary and Jesus on donkey	10	10
230/7	Set of 8	55	55
MS238	130 × 95 mm. Nos. 230/7	70	1·25

Each design covers two stamps; Type 35 shows the left-hand stamp of the 6 c. design.

1977 (15 Nov). *Children's Christmas Fund. Nos. 230/7 surch with T 36.*

239	6 c. + 1 c. } Type 35	10	10
240	6 c. + 1 c. }	10	10
241	7 c. + 1 c. } The Holy Family	10	10
242	7 c. + 1 c. }	10	10
243	15 c. + 1 c. } The Three Kings with Virgin and Child	15	10
244	15 c. + 1 c. }	15	10
245	20 c. + 1 c. } Flight into Egypt	15	10
246	20 c. + 1 c. }	15	10
239/46	Set of 8	75	55
MS247	130 × 95 mm. As Nos. 239/46 but each with premium of "+ 2 c."	70	85

37 Hawaiian Goddess

38 "Christ on the Way to Calvary" (Martini)

1978 (19 Jan). *Bicentenary of Discovery of Hawaii. T 37 and similar multicoloured designs. P 13½.*

248	35 c. Type 37	35	25
249	50 c. Figurehead of H.M.S. *Resolution (horiz)*	60	40
250	$1 Hawaiian temple figure	70	70
248/50	Set of 3	1·50	1·25
MS251	168 × 75 mm. Nos. 248/50	1·50	2·25

1978 (17 Mar). *Easter. Details of Paintings from Louvre, Paris. T 38 and similar horiz designs. Multicoloured. P 13½ × 14.*

252	15 c. Type 38	15	10
253	20 c. "Piéta of Avignon" (E. Quarton)	20	10
254	35 c. "Pilgrims at Emmaus" (Rembrandt)	25	15
252/4	Set of 3	55	30
MS255	108 × 83 mm. Nos. 252/4	75	75

Each value was printed in two panes of 9 within the sheet, both panes including one *se-tenant* stamp-size label.

1978 (17 Mar). *Easter. Children's Charity. Designs as Nos. 252/4, but smaller (34 × 26 mm) and without margins, in separate miniature sheets 75 × 58 mm, each with a face value of 50 c. + 5 c. P 14.*

MS256	As Nos. 252/4	Set of 3 sheets	1·40	1·00

39 Yale of Beaufort

40 "Adoration of the Infant Jesus"

1978 (15 June). *25th Anniv of Coronation. T 39 and similar vert designs. Multicoloured. P 13½ × 13.*

257	$1 Type 39	30	50
258	$1 Queen Elizabeth II	30	50
259	$1 Aitutaki ancestral statue	30	50
257/9	Set of 3	80	1·40
MS260	98 × 127 mm. Nos. 257/9 × 2	75	75

Stamps from No. MS260 have coloured borders, the upper row in lavender and the lower in apple-green.

Nos. 257/9 were printed together, *se-tenant*, in small sheets of 6, containing two horizontal strips of 3.

1978 (4 Dec). *Christmas. 450th Death Anniv of Dürer. T 40 and similar vert designs. Multicoloured. P 13 × 14.*

261	15 c. Type 40	35	15
262	17 c. "The Madonna with Child"	40	15
263	30 c. "The Madonna with the Iris"	55	20
264	35 c. "The Madonna of the Siskin"	60	25
261/4	Set of 4	1·75	65
MS265	101 × 109 mm. As Nos. 261/4 but each with premium of "+ 2 c."	1·50	1·00

Nos. 261/4 were each printed in small sheets of 6, including 1 *se-tenant* stamp-size label.

41 "Captain Cook" (Nathaniel Dance)

42 Girl with Flowers

1979 (20 July). *Death Bicentenary of Captain Cook. Paintings. T 41 and similar vert designs. Multicoloured. P 14 × 13½.*

266	50 c. Type 41	1·00	80
267	75 c. "H.M.S. *Resolution* and *Adventure* at Matavai Bay" (William Hodges)	1·75	95
MS268	94 × 58 mm. Nos. 266/7. P 13½	2·00	2·25

1979 (1 Oct). *International Year of the Child. T 42 and similar vert designs. Multicoloured. P 14 × 13½.*

269	30 c. Type 42	15	15
270	35 c. Boy playing guitar	20	20
271	65 c. Children in canoe	30	30
269/71	Set of 3	60	60
MS272	104 × 80 mm. As Nos. 269/71, but each with a premium of "+ 3 c."	70	1·00

43 "Man writing a Letter" (painting by G. Metsu)

44 "The Burial of Christ" (detail, Quentin Metsys)

1979 (14 Nov). *Death Centenary of Sir Rowland Hill. T 43 and similar horiz designs. Multicoloured. P 13.*

273	50 c. Type 43	45	45
274	50 c. Sir Rowland Hill with Penny Black, 1903 ½d. and 1911 1d. stamps	45	45
275	50 c. "Girl in Blue reading a Letter" (painting by J. Vermeer)	45	45
276	65 c. "Woman writing a Letter" (painting by G. Terborch)	50	50
277	65 c. Sir Rowland Hill with Penny Black, 1903 3d. and 1920 ½d. stamps	50	50
278	65 c. "Lady reading a Letter" (painting by J. Vermeer)	50	50
273/8	Set of 6	2·50	2·50
MS279	151 × 85 mm. 30 c. × 6. As Nos. 273/8	1·75	2·00

Nos. 273/5 and 276/8 were printed together, *se-tenant*, in horizontal strips of 3, the sheet having two panes separated by margin, one containing 273/5 × 3, the other containing 276/8 × 3.

1980 (3 Apr). *Easter. T 44 and similar vert designs showing different details of painting "The Burial of Christ" by Quentin Metsys. P 13.*

280	20 c. multicoloured	40	25
281	30 c. multicoloured	50	35
282	35 c. multicoloured	65	45
280/2	Set of 3	1·40	95
MS283	93 × 71 mm. As Nos. 280/2, but each with premium of "+ 2 c."	75	75

45 Einstein as Young Man

46 Ancestor Figure, Aitutaki

1980 (21 July). *25th Death Anniv of Albert Einstein (physicist). T 45 and similar vert designs. Multicoloured. P 14 × 13½.*

284	12 c. Type 45	50	50
285	12 c. Atom and "E=mc²" equation	50	50
286	12 c. Einstein as middle-aged man	55	55
287	15 c. Cross over nuclear explosion (Nuclear Test Ban Treaty, 1963)	55	55
288	20 c. Einstein as old man	65	65
289	20 c. Hand over bomb explosion (Nuclear Test Ban Treaty, 1963)	65	65
284/9	Set of 6	3·00	3·00
MS290	113 × 118 mm. Nos. 284/9. P 13½	3·00	3·00

Nos. 284/5, 286/7 and 288/9 were each printed together, *se-tenant*, in horizontal pairs throughout the sheet.

1980 (26 Sept). *South Pacific Festival of Arts. T 46 and similar vert designs. Multicoloured. P 13½.*

291	6 c. Type 46	10	10
292	6 c. Staff god image, Rarotonga	10	10
293	6 c. Trade adze, Mangaia	10	10
294	6 c. Carved image of Tangaroa, Rarotonga	10	10
295	12 c. Wooden image, Aitutaki	10	10
296	12 c. Hand club, Rarotonga	10	10
297	12 c. Carved mace "god", Mangaia	10	10
298	12 c. Fisherman's god, Rarotonga	10	10
299	15 c. Ti'i image, Aitutaki	15	15
300	15 c. Fisherman's god, Rarotonga (*different*)	15	15
301	15 c. Carved mace "god", Cook Islands	15	15
302	15 c. Carved image of Tangaroa, Rarotonga (*different*)	15	15
303	20 c. Chief's headdress, Aitutaki	15	15
304	20 c. Carved "mace" god, Cook Islands (*different*)	15	15
305	20 c. Staff god image, Rarotonga (*different*)	15	15
306	20 c. Carved image of Tangaroa, Rarotonga (*different*)	15	15
291/306	Set of 16	1·60	1·60
MS307	134 × 194 mm. Nos. 291/306	1·60	1·75

The four designs of each value were printed together, *se-tenant*, in blocks of 4 throughout the sheet.

47 Virgin and Child (13th-century)

48 "Mourning Virgin"

1980 (21 Nov). *Christmas. Sculptures. T 47 and similar vert designs showing various Virgin and Child works from the periods given. Multicoloured. P 13.*

308	15 c. Type 47	20	15
309	20 c. 14th-century	20	15
310	25 c. 15th-century	20	15
311	35 c. 15th-century (*different*)	30	20
308/11	Set of 4	80	60
MS312	82 × 120 mm. As Nos. 306/11 but each with premium of 2 c.	70	80

1981 (31 Mar). *Easter. Details of Sculpture "Burial of Christ" by Pedro Roldan. T **48** and similar vert designs. P 14.*

313	30 c. gold and myrtle-green	..	25	25
314	40 c. gold and deep reddish lilac	..	30	30
315	50 c. gold and Prussian blue	..	30	30
313/15		*Set of 3*	75	75
MS316	107 × 60 mm. As Nos. 313/15 but each with premium of 2 c.		75	85

Designs:—40 c. "Christ"; 50 c. "Saint John".

49 Gouldian Finch
(*Poephila gouldiae*)

50 Prince Charles

1981 (6 Apr)–**82**. *Birds (1st series). Multicoloured designs as T **49**. P 14 × 13½ (1 to 10 c.), 13½ × 14 (15 to 70 c.) or 13 ($1 to $4).*

317	1 c. Type **49**	..	45	30
318	1 c. Common Starling (*Sturnus vulgaris*)	..	45	30
319	2 c. Golden Whistler (*Pachycephala pectoralis*)	..	50	30
320	2 c. Scarlet Robin (*Petroica multicolor*)	..	50	30
321	3 c. Rufous Fantail (*Rhipidura rufifrous*)	..	60	30
322	3 c. Peregrine Falcon (*Falco peregrinus*)	..	60	30
323	4 c. Java Sparrow (*Padda oryzivora*)	..	70	30
324	4 c. Barn Owl (*Tyto alba*)	..	70	30
325	5 c. Tahitian Lory (*Vini peruviana*)	..	70	30
326	5 c. White-breasted Wood Swallow (*Artamus leucorhynchus*)		70	30
327	6 c. Purple Swamphen (*Porphyrio porphyrio*)		70	30
328	6 c. Rock Dove (*Columba livia*)		70	30
329	10 c. Chestnut-breasted Mannikin (*Lonchura castaneothorax*)		90	30
330	10 c. Zebra Dove (*Geopelia striata*)		90	30
331	12 c. Eastern Reef Heron (*Egretta sacra*)		1·00	40
332	12 c. Common Mynah (*Acridotheres tristis*)		1·00	40
333	15 c. Whimbrel (*Numenius phaeopus*) (*horiz*) (8.5.81)		1·25	40
334	15 c. Black-browed Albatross (*Diomeda melanophris*) (*horiz*) (8.5.81)		1·25	40
335	20 c. American Golden Plover (*Pluvialis dominica*) (*horiz*) (8.5.81)		1·50	55
336	20 c. White Tern (*Gygis alba*) (*horiz*) (8.5.81)		1·50	55
337	25 c. Spotbill Duck (*Anas superciliosa*) (*horiz*) (8.5.81)		1·75	70
338	25 c. Brown Booby (*Sula leucogaster*) (*horiz*) (8.5.81)		1·75	70
339	30 c. Great Frigate Bird (*Fregata minor*) (*horiz*) (8.5.81)		2·00	85
340	30 c. Pintail (*Anas acuta*) (*horiz*) (8.5.81)		2·00	85
341	35 c. Long-billed Reed Warbler (*Conopoderas caffra caffra*) (14.1.82)		2·25	1·00
342	35 c. Pomarine Skua (*Stercorarius pomarinus*) (14.1.82)		2·25	1·00
343	40 c. Banded Rail (*Gallirallus philippensis goodsoni*) (14.1.82)		2·75	1·25
344	40 c. Spotted Triller (*Lalage maculosa pumila*) (14.1.82)		2·75	1·25
345	50 c. Royal Albatross (*Diomedea epomophora*) (14.1.82)		3·00	1·50
346	50 c. Stephen's Lory (*Vini stepheni*) (14.1.82)		3·00	1·50
347	70 c. Red-headed Parrot Finch (*Erythrura cyaneovirens*) (14.1.82)		5·50	3·00
348	70 c. Orange Dove (*Ptilinopus victor victor*) (14.1.82)		5·50	3·00
349	$1 Blue-headed Flycatcher (*Myiagra azureocapilla whitneyi*) (15.2.82)		5·50	3·75
350	$2 Red-bellied Flycatcher (*Myiagra vanikorensis rufiventris*) (15.5.82)		8·00	8·00
351	$4 Red Munia (*Amandava amandava*) (19.3.82)		14·00	14·00
352	$5 Flat-billed Kingfisher (*Halcyon recurvirostris*) (19.3.82)		15·00	16·00
317/52		*Set of 36*	80·00	60·00

The two designs of each value (1 c. to 70 c.) were printed together, *se-tenant*, in horizontal and vertical pairs throughout the sheet.
Nos. 341/8 are 35 × 27 mm and Nos. 349/52, which include a portrait of Queen Elizabeth II, 35 × 48 mm in size.
See also Nos. 475/94 for redrawn designs as Type **65**.
Nos. 353/90 are vacant.

1981 (10 June). *Royal Wedding. T **50** and similar multicoloured designs. P 14 ($1.40) or 13 × 13½ (others).*

391	60 c. Type **50**	..	30	40
392	80 c. Lady Diana Spencer	..	40	55
393	$1.40, Prince Charles and Lady Diana (87 × 70 *mm*)	..	60	80
391/3	..	*Set of 3*	1·10	1·60

(51) **52** Footballers **53** "The Holy Family"

1981 (23 Nov). *International Year for Disabled Persons. Nos. 391/3 surch with T **51** on gold background.*

394	60 c. + 5 c. Type **50**	..	60	90
395	80 c. + 5 c. Lady Diana Spencer	..	70	1·10
396	$1. 40 + 5 c.Prince Charles and Lady Diana	..	90	1·60
394/6		*Set of 3*	2·00	3·25

Nos. 394/6 have commemorative inscriptions overprinted on the sheet margins.

1981 (30 Nov). *World Cup Football Championship, Spain (1982). T **52** and similar horiz designs showing footballers. Multicoloured. P 14.*

397	12 c. Ball to left of stamp	..	50	35
398	12 c. Ball to right	..	50	35
399	15 c. Ball to right	..	55	40
400	15 c. Ball to left	..	55	40
401	20 c. Ball to left	..	55	50
402	20 c. Ball to right	..	55	50
403	25 c. Type **52**	..	60	55
404	25 c. "ESPANA 82" inscr on printed background	..	60	55
397/404		*Set of 8*	4·00	3·25
MS405	100 × 137 mm. 12 c. + 2 c., 15 c. + 2 c., 20 c. + 2 c., 25 c. + 2 c., each × 2. As Nos. 397/404		3·50	3·00

The two designs of each value were printed together, *se-tenant*, in horizontal pairs throughout the sheet.

1981 (10 Dec). *Christmas. Details from Etchings by Rembrandt. T **53** and similar designs in purple-brown and gold. P 14.*

406	15 c. Type **53**	..	45	45
407	30 c. "Virgin with Child"	..	70	70
408	40 c. "Adoration of the Shepherds" (*horiz*)	..	95	95
409	50 c. "The Holy Family" (*horiz*)	..	1·25	1·25
406/9		*Set of 4*	3·00	3·00
MS410	Designs as Nos. 406/9 in separate miniature sheets, 65 × 82 mm or 82 × 65 mm, each with a face value of 80 c. + 5 c. P 14 × 13½			
		Set of 4 sheets	3·25	3·00

54 Princess of Wales **(55)**

1982 (24 June). *21st Birthday of Princess of Wales. T **54** and similar vert designs. Multicoloured. P 14.*

411	70 c. Type **54**	..	1·25	60
412	$1 Prince and Princess of Wales	..	1·50	75
413	$2 Princess Diana (*different*)	..	2·75	1·50
411/13		*Set of 3*	5·00	2·75
MS414	82 × 91 mm. Nos. 411/13	..	4·25	2·75

Nos. 411/13 were each printed in small sheets of 6 including two *se-tenant* stamp-size labels. The silver markings in the margins of the individual stamps differ for each position in the sheetlet.

1982 (13 July). *Birth of Prince William of Wales (1st issue). Nos. 391/3 optd as T **55**.*

415	60 c. Type **50** (optd with T **55**)	..	90	70
	a. Pair. Nos. 415/16	..	1·75	1·40
416	60 c. Type **50** (optd "COMMEMORATING THE ROYAL BIRTH")	..	90	70
417	80 c. Lady Diana Spencer (optd with T **55**)	..	1·10	80
	a. Pair. Nos. 417/18	..	2·10	1·60
418	80 c. Lady Diana Spencer (optd "COMMEMORATING THE ROYAL BIRTH")	..	1·10	80
419	$1.40, Prince Charles and Lady Diana (87 × 70 *mm*) (optd as T **55**)	..	1·25	1·00
	a. Pair. Nos. 419/20	..	2·50	2·00
420	$1.40, Prince Charles and Lady Diana (87 × 70 *mm*) (optd "COMMEMORATING THE ROYAL BIRTH")	..	1·25	1·00
415/20		*Set of 6*	5·50	4·50

Nos. 415/16, 417/18 and 419/20 were each printed together in *se-tenant* pairs, horiz and vert, throughout the sheets.

1982 (5 Aug). *Birth of Prince William of Wales (2nd issue). As Nos. 411/14, but inscr "ROYAL BIRTH 21 JUNE 1982 PRINCE WILLIAM OF WALES". Multicoloured. P 14.*

421	70 c. Type **54**	..	70	60
422	$1 Prince and Princess of Wales	..	80	75
423	$2 Princess Diana (*different*)	..	1·60	1·50
421/3	..	*Set of 3*	2·75	2·50
MS424	81 × 91 mm. Nos. 421/3	..	4·25	3·00

56 "Virgin and Child"
(12th-century sculpture)

57 Aitutaki Bananas

1982 (10 Dec). *Christmas. Religious Sculptures. T **56** and similar vert designs. Multicoloured. P 13.*

425	18 c. Type **56**	..	60	60
426	36 c. "Virgin and Child" (12th-century)		75	75
427	48 c. "Virgin and Child" (13th-century)		90	90
428	60 c. "Virgin and Child" (15th-century)		1·25	1·25
425/8		*Set of 4*	3·25	3·25
MS429	99 × 115 mm. As Nos. 425/8 but each with 2 c. charity premium		2·50	2·75

Nos. 425/8 were each printed in small sheets of 6 including one *se-tenant*, stamp size, label, depicting the Prince and Princess of Wales with Prince William.

1983 (14 Mar). *Commonwealth Day. T **57** and similar horiz designs. Multicoloured. P 13.*

430	48 c. Type **57**	..	95	50
431	48 c. Ancient Ti'i image	..	95	50
432	48 c. Tourist canoeing	..	95	50
433	48 c. Captain William Bligh and chart	..	95	50
430/3		*Set of 4*	3·50	1·75

Nos. 430/3 were issued together, *se-tenant*, in blocks of four throughout the sheet.

15th WORLD SCOUT JAMBOREE

58 Scouts around Campfire **(59)**

1983 (18 Apr). *75th Anniv of Boy Scout Movement, T **58** and similar horiz designs. Multicoloured. P 13½ × 14.*

434	36 c. Type **58**	..	55	55
435	48 c. Scout saluting	..	70	70
436	60 c. Scouts hiking	..	75	75
434/6		*Set of 3*	1·75	1·75
MS437	78 × 107 mm. As Nos. 434/6 but each with premium of 3 c. P 13		2·00	2·25

1983 (11 July). *15th World Scout Jamboree, Alberta, Canada. Nos. 434/7 optd with T **59**.*

438	36 c. Type **58**	..	80	45
439	48 c. Scout saluting	..	1·00	55
440	60 c. Scouts hiking	..	1·25	75
438/40		*Set of 3*	2·75	1·60
MS441	78 × 107 mm. As Nos. 438/40 but each with a premium of 3 c.		2·00	2·50

60 Modern Sport Balloon **(61)** **(62)**

1983 (22 July). *Bicentenary of Manned Flight. T **60** and similar vert designs showing different modern sport balloons. P 14 × 13.*

442	18 c. multicoloured	..	55	30
443	36 c. multicoloured	..	75	50
444	48 c. multicoloured	..	90	60
445	60 c. multicoloured	..	1·00	90
442/5		*Set of 4*	2·75	2·00
MS446	64 × 80 mm. $2.50, multicoloured (48½ × 28½ mm)		1·90	2·50

Nos. 442/5 were each issued in small sheets of 4 stamps.

1983 (22 Sept). *Various stamps surch.*

(a) Nos. 335/48 and 352 as T **61**

447	18 c. on 20 c. American Golden Plover (*Pluvialis dominica*)		2·50	1·00
448	18 c. on 20 c. White Tern (*Gygis alba*)		2·50	1·00
449	36 c. on 25 c. Spotbill Duck (*Anas superciliosa*)		3·50	1·25
450	36 c. on 25 c. Brown Booby (*Sula leucogaster*)		3·50	1·25
451	36 c. on 30 c. Great Frigate Bird (*Fregata minor*)		3·50	1·25
452	36 c. on 30 c. Pintail (*Anas acuta*)		3·50	1·25
453	36 c. on 35 c. Long-billed Reed Warbler (*Conopoderas caffra caffra*)		3·50	1·25
454	36 c. on 35 c. Pomarine Skua (*Stercorarius pomarinus*)		3·50	1·25
455	48 c. on 40 c. Banded Rail (*Gallirallus philippensis goodsoni*)		4·00	1·50
456	48 c. on 40 c. Spotted Triller (*Lalage maculosa pumila*)		4·00	1·50
457	48 c. on 50 c. Royal Albatross (*Diomedea epomophora*)		4·00	1·50
458	48 c. on 50 c. Stephen's Lory (*Vini stepheni*)		4·00	1·50
459	72 c. on 70 c. Red-headed Parrot Finch (*Erythrura cyaneovirens*)		7·00	2·50
460	72 c. on 70 c. Orange Dove (*Ptilinopus victor victor*)		7·00	2·50
461	$5.60 on $5 Flat-billed Kingfisher (*Halcyon recurvirostris*)		20·00	10·00

(b) Nos. 392/3 and 412/13 as T **62**

462	96 c. on 80 c. Lady Diana Spencer (Gold)		3·00	2·50
	a. Error. Surch on No. 417	..	12·00	
	ab. Pair. Nos. 462/a/b	..	25·00	
	b. Error. Surch on No. 418	..	12·00	

463	96 c. on $1 Prince and Princess of Wales	2·75	2·00
464	$1.20 on $1.40, Prince Charles and Lady Diana (Gold)	3·00	2·50
	a. Error. Surch on No. 419	12·00	
	ab. Pair. Nos. 464a/b	25·00	
	b. Error. Surch on No. 420	12·00	
465	$1.20 on $2, Princess Diana	2·75	2·00
447/65	Set of 19	75·00	35·00

On Nos. 462 and 464 the gold surcharge is printed on a black obliterating panel over the original face value.

63 International Mail

64 "Madonna of the Chair"

1983 (29 Sept). *World Communications Year. T* **63** *and similar vert designs. Multicoloured. P* 14 × 13½.

466	48 c. Type 63	65	50
467	60 c. Telecommunications	95	70
468	96 c. Space satellites	1·40	1·00
466/8	Set of 3	2·75	2·00
MS469	126 × 53 mm. Nos. 466/8. P 13	2·50	2·50

1983 (21 Nov). *Christmas. 500th Birth Anniv of Raphael. T* **64** *and similar horiz designs. Multicoloured. P* 13½ × 14.

470	36 c. Type 64	75	40
471	48 c. "The Alba Madonna"	90	50
472	60 c. "Conestabile Madonna"	1·25	70
470/2	Set of 3	2·50	1·40
MS473	95 × 116 mm. As Nos. 470/2, but each with a premium of 3 c. P 13	2·50	1·40

1983 (15 Dec). *Christmas. 500th Birth Anniv of Raphael. Children's Charity. Designs as Nos. 470/2 in separate miniature sheets* 46 × 47 mm, *but each with different frames and a face value of* 85 c. + 5 c. *Imperf.*

MS474	As Nos. 470/2	Set of 3 sheets 3·50	2·75

65 Gouldian Finch

66 Javelin-throwing

1984 (13 Feb–2 July). *Birds (2nd series). Designs as Nos. 317 etc. but with redrawn frames and inscriptions as in T* **65**. *Multicoloured. P* 13 × 13½ ($3 to $9.60) or 14 (others).

475	2 c. Type 65	1·75	1·00
476	3 c. Common Starling	1·75	1·00
477	5 c. Scarlet Robin	1·75	1·10
478	10 c. Golden Whistler	2·00	1·10
479	12 c. Rufous Fantail	2·00	1·10
480	18 c. Peregrine Falcon	2·25	1·50
481	24 c. Barn Owl	2·25	1·50
482	30 c. Java Sparrow	2·25	1·50
483	36 c. White-breasted Wood Swallow	2·25	1·50
484	48 c. Tahitian Lory	2·25	1·50
485	50 c. Rock Dove (26 Mar)	2·50	2·00
486	60 c. Purple Swamphen (26 Mar)	2·50	2·00
487	72 c. Zebra Dove (26 Mar)	3·00	2·00
488	96 c. Chestnut-breasted Mannikin (26 Mar)	3·00	2·00
489	$1.20, Common Mynah (26 Mar)	3·00	2·75
490	$2.10, Eastern Reef Heron (30 Apr)	4·00	3·75
491	$3 Blue-headed Flycatcher (30 × 42 mm) (30 Apr)	6·50	6·00
492	$4.20, Red-bellied Flycatcher (30 × 42 mm) (5 June)	3·75	6·00
493	$5.60, Red Munia (30 × 42 mm) (5 June)	4·50	7·00
494	$9.60, Flat-billed Kingfisher (30 × 42 mm) (2 July)	7·50	10·00
475/94	Set of 20	55·00	50·00

1984 (24 July). *Olympic Games, Los Angeles. T* **66** *and similar vert designs showing Memorial Coliseum and various events. Multicoloured. P* 13 × 13½.

495	36 c. Type 66	35	35
496	48 c. Shot-putting	40	45
497	60 c. Hurdling	45	55
498	$2 Basketball	1·75	1·50
495/8	Set of 4	2·75	2·50
MS499	88 × 117 mm. As Nos. 495/8, but each with a charity premium of 5 c.	3·50	3·50

1984 (21 Aug). *Olympic Gold Medal Winners. Nos. 495/8 optd as T* **209** *of Cook Islands in gold on black background.*

500	36 c. Type 66 (optd "Javelin Throw Tessa Sanderson Great Britain")	35	35
501	48 c. Shot-putting (optd "Shot Put Claudia Losch Germany")	40	45
502	60 c. Hurdling (optd "Heptathlon Glynis Nunn Australia")	45	55
503	$2 Basketball (optd "Team Basketball United States")	1·75	1·50
500/3	Set of 4	2·75	2·50

67 Capt. William Bligh and Chart

(68)

1984 (14 Sept). *"Ausipex" International Stamp Exhibition, Melbourne. T* **67** *and similar horiz designs. Multicoloured. P* 14.

504	60 c. Type 67	3·75	3·25
505	96 c. H.M.S. *Bounty* and map	3·75	3·50
506	$1.40, Aitutaki stamps of 1974, 1979 and 1981 with map	3·75	3·00
504/6	Set of 3	10·00	9·00
MS507	85 × 113 mm. As Nos. 504/6, but each with a premium of 5 c. P 13½.	6·50	4·00

1984 (10 Oct). *Birth of Prince Henry (1st issue). No. 391 surch with T* **68** *in gold.*

508	$3 on 60 c. Type 50	2·25	3·25

On No. 508 the gold surcharge is printed on a black obliterating panel over the original face value.

69 The Annunciation

70 Princess Diana with Prince Henry

1984 (16 Nov). *Christmas. Details from Altarpiece, St. Paul's Church, Palencia, Spain. T* **69** *and similar vert designs. Multicoloured. P* 13½ × 13.

509	36 c. Type 69	30	35
510	48 c. The Nativity	40	45
511	60 c. The Epiphany	45	50
512	96 c. The Flight into Egypt	75	80
509/12	Set of 4	1·75	1·90
MS513	Designs as Nos. 509/12 in separate miniature sheets, each 45 × 53 mm and with a face value of 90 c. + 7 c. Imperf.	Set of 4 sheets 2·50	3·25

1984 (10 Dec). *Birth of Prince Henry (2nd issue). T* **70** *and similar vert designs. Multicoloured. P* 14.

514	48 c. Type 70	1·75	1·50
515	60 c. Prince William with Prince Henry	1·75	1·75
516	$2.10, Prince and Princess of Wales with children	3·25	3·50
514/16	Set of 3	6·00	6·00
MS517	113 × 65 mm. As Nos. 514/16, but each with a face value of 96 c. + 7 c. P 13½.	5·50	3·25

71 Grey Kingbird

72 The Queen Mother, aged Seven

1985 (22 Mar). *Birth Bicentenary of John J. Audubon (ornithologist). T* **71** *and similar vert designs showing original paintings. Multicoloured. P* 13.

518	55 c. Type 71	1·10	1·10
519	65 c. Bohemian Waxwing	1·25	1·25
520	75 c. Summer Tanager	1·40	1·40
521	95 c. Common Cardinal	1·50	1·50
522	$1.15, White-winged Crossbill	1·90	1·90
518/22	Set of 5	6·50	6·50

1985 (14 June). *Life and Times of Queen Elizabeth the Queen Mother. T* **72** *and similar horiz designs. Multicoloured. P* 13.

523	55 c. Type 72	45	50
524	65 c. Engagement photograph, 1922	50	55
525	75 c. With young Princess Elizabeth	60	65
526	$1.30, With baby Prince Charles	1·00	1·10
523/6	Set of 4	2·25	2·50
MS527	75 × 49 mm. $3 Queen Mother on her 63rd birthday	2·25	2·40

Nos. 523/6 were each printed in sheetlets of 4.
For these stamps in a miniature sheet see No. MS550.

73 "The Calmady Children" (T. Lawrence)

1985 (16 Sept). *International Youth Year. T* **73** *and similar horiz designs. Multicoloured. P* 13.

528	75 c. Type 73	2·25	2·00
529	90 c. "Madame Charpentier's Children" (Renoir)	2·25	2·00
530	$1.40, "Young Girls at Piano" (Renoir)	3·00	3·25
528/30	Set of 3	6·75	6·50
MS531	103 × 104 mm. As Nos. 528/30, but each with a premium of 10 c.	4·75	3·75

74 "Adoration of the Magi" (Giotto) and *Giotto* Spacecraft

1985 (15 Nov). *Christmas. Appearance of Halley's Comet (1st issue). T* **74** *and similar multicoloured designs. P* 13.

532	95 c. Type 74	1·50	1·50
533	95 c. As Type 74 but showing *Planet A* spacecraft	1·50	1·50
534	$1.15, Type 74	1·50	1·50
535	$1.15, As No. 533	1·50	1·50
532/5	Set of 4	5·50	5·50
MS536	52 × 55 mm. $6.40, As Type 74 but without spacecraft (30 × 31 mm). Imperf	11·00	8·50

Nos. 532/3 and 534/5 were each printed together, *se-tenant*, in horizontal pairs throughout the sheets.

75 Halley's Comet, A.D. 684 (from "Nuremberg Chronicle")

76 Queen Elizabeth II on Coronation Day (from photo by Cecil Beaton)

1986 (25 Feb). *Appearance of Halley's Comet (2nd issue). T* **75** *and similar multicoloured designs. P* 13½ × 13.

537	90 c. Type 75	90	90
538	$1.25, Halley's Comet, 1066 (from Bayeux Tapestry)	1·10	1·10
539	$1.75, Halley's Comet, 1456 (from "Lucerne Chronicles")	1·50	1·50
537/9	Set of 3	3·25	3·25
MS540	107 × 82 mm. As Nos. 537/9, but each with a face value of 95 c.	3·25	2·50
MS541	65 × 80 mm. $4.20, "Melencolia I" (Albrecht Dürer woodcut) (61 × 76 mm). Imperf	4·50	3·50

1986 (21 Apr). *60th Birthday of Queen Elizabeth II. T* **76** *and similar vert design. Multicoloured. P* 14.

542	95 c. Type 76	1·25	1·25
MS543	58 × 68 mm. $4.20, As T **76**, but showing more of the portrait without oval frame. P 13½	5·50	5·50

No. 542 was printed in sheetlets of five stamps and one stamp-size label at top left.

77 Head of Statue of Liberty

78 Prince Andrew and Miss Sarah Ferguson

1986 (27 June). *Centenary of Statue of Liberty. T* **77** *and similar horiz design. Multicoloured. P* 14.

544	$1 Type 77	1·25	1·25
545	$2.75, Statue of Liberty at sunset	2·75	2·75
MS546	91 × 79 mm. As Nos. 544/5, but each with a face value of $1.25. P 13½	2·75	2·50

1986 (23 July). *Royal Wedding. P* 14.
547 **78** $2 multicoloured .. .. .. 2·00 2·00
MS548 85×70 mm. **78** $5 mult. P 13½ .. .. 6·50 8·00
No. 547 was printed in sheetlets of 5 stamps and one stamp-size label at top left.

1986 (4 Aug). *"Stampex '86" Stamp Exhibition, Adelaide. No. MS507 with "Ausipex" emblems obliterated in gold.*
MS549 As Nos. 504/6, but each with a premium of 5 c. .. .. 9·50 11·00
The "Stampex '86" exhibition emblem is overprinted on the sheet margin.

1986 (4 Aug). *86th Birthday of Queen Elizabeth the Queen Mother. Nos. 523/6 in miniature sheet, 132×82 mm. P* 13½×13.
MS550 Nos. 523/6 .. .. 8·50 9·00

+10c

79 "St. Anne with Virgin and Child" (80)

1986 (21 Nov). *Christmas. Paintings by Dürer. T* **79** *and similar vert designs. Multicoloured. P* 13½.
551 75 c. Type **79** .. .. .. 1·25 1·25
552 $1.35, "Virgin and Child" .. .. 1·75 1·75
553 $1.95, "The Adoration of the Magi" 2·25 2·25
554 $2.75, "Madonna of the Rosary" .. 3·00 3·00
551/4 .. .. .. *Set of 4* 7·50 7·50
MS555 88×125 mm. As Nos. 551/4, but each stamp with a face value of $1.65 .. 13·00 14·00

1986 (25 Nov). *Visit of Pope John Paul II to South Pacific. Nos. 551/5 surch with T* **80** *in silver.*
556 75 c. + 10 c. Type **79** .. .. 2·75 2·50
557 $1.35 + 10 c. "Virgin and Child" .. 3·25 3·00
558 $1.95 + 10 c. "The Adoration of the Magi" 4·00 3·50
559 $2.75 + 10 c. "Madonna of the Rosary" 5·00 5·00
556/9 .. .. .. *Set of 4* 13·50 12·50
MS560 88 × 125 mm. As Nos. 556/9, but each stamp with a face value of $1.65 + 10 c. .. 15·00 14·00

2.50

HURRICANE RELIEF
+50c

Royal Wedding 40th Anniv

(81) (82)

1987 (29 Apr). *Hurricane Relief Fund. Nos. 544/5, 547, 551/4 and 556/9 surch with T* **81** *in black (Nos. 563, 569) or silver (others).*
561 75 c. + 50 c. Type **79** .. .. 2·25 2·25
562 75 c. + 10 c. + 50 c. Type **79** .. 2·50 2·50
563 $1 + 50 c. Type **77** .. .. 2·75 2·75
564 $1.35 + 50 c. "Virgin and Child" (Dürer) .. 3·00 3·00
565 $1.35 + 10 c. + 50 c. "Virgin and Child" (Dürer) .. .. 3·00 3·00
566 $1.95 + 50 c. "The Adoration of the Magi" (Dürer) .. .. 3·50 3·50
567 $1.95 + 10 c. + 50 c. "The Adoration of the Magi" (Dürer) .. 3·50 3·50
568 $2 + 50 c. Type **78** .. .. 3·50 3·50
569 $2.75 + 50 c. Statue of Liberty at sunset .. 4·50 4·50
570 $2.75 + 50 c. "Madonna of the Rosary" (Dürer) .. .. 4·50 4·50
571 $2.75 + 10 c. + 50 c. "Madonna of the Rosary" (Dürer) .. 4·50 4·50
561/71 .. .. .. *Set of 11* 35·00 35·00

1987 (20 Nov). *Royal Ruby Wedding. Nos. 391/3 surch as T* **82**.
572 $2.50 on 60 c. Type **50** .. .. 2·00 2·50
573 $2.50 on 80 c. Lady Diana Spencer .. 2·00 2·50
574 $2.50 on $1.40, Prince Charles and Lady Diana (87×70 mm) .. .. 2·00 2·50
572/4 .. .. .. *Set of 3* 5·50 6·75
On Nos. 572/4 the original values are obliterated in gold.

83 "Angels" (detail from "Virgin with Garland")

1987 (10 Dec). *Christmas. T* **83** *and similar designs showing different details of angels from "Virgin with Garland" by Rubens. P* 13×13½.
575 70 c. multicoloured .. .. .. 1·75 1·75
576 85 c. multicoloured .. .. .. 1·75 1·75
577 $1.50, multicoloured .. .. .. 2·75 2·75
578 $1.85, multicoloured .. .. .. 3·25 3·25
575/8 .. .. .. *Set of 4* 8·50 8·50
MS579 92×120 mm. As Nos. 575/8, but each with a face value of 95 c. .. .. 9·00 10·00
MS580 96×85 mm. $6 "Virgin with Garland" (*diamond*, 56×56 *mm*). P 13 .. 10·00 11·00

84 Chariot Racing and Athletics

(Des G. Vasarhelyi. Litho Questa)

1988 (22 Aug). *Olympic Games, Seoul. T* **84** *and similar horiz designs showing ancient and modern Olympic sports. Multicoloured. P* 14½.
581 70 c. Type **84** .. .. .. 1·75 1·75
582 85 c. Greek runners and football .. 1·90 1·90
583 95 c. Greek wrestling and handball .. 2·00 2·00
584 $1.40, Greek hoplites and tennis .. 2·75 2·75
581/4 .. .. .. *Set of 4* 7·50 7·50
MS585 103×101 mm. As Nos. 581 and 584, but each with face value of $2 .. .. 7·00 8·00

1988 (10 Oct). *Olympic Medal Winners, Los Angeles. Nos. 581/4 optd as T* **235** *of Cook Islands.*
586 70 c. Type **84** (optd "FLORENCE GRIFFTH JOYNER UNITED STATES 100 M AND 200 M") .. .. .. 1·40 1·40
587 85 c. Greek runners and football (optd "GELINDO BORDIN ITALY MARA-THON") .. .. .. 1·50 1·50
588 95 c. Greek wrestling and handball (optd "HITOSHI SAITO JAPAN JUDO") .. 1·60 1·60
589 $1.40, Greek hoplites and tennis (optd "STEFFI GRAF WEST GERMANY WOMEN'S TENNIS") .. .. 2·75 2·75
586/9 .. .. .. *Set of 4* 6·50 6·50

85 "Adoration of the Shepherds" (detail)

1988 (2 Nov). *Christmas. T* **85** *and similar multicoloured designs showing paintings by Rembrandt. P* 13½.
590 55 c. Type **85** .. .. .. 1·40 1·40
591 70 c. "The Holy Family" .. .. 1·60 1·60
592 85 c. "Presentation in the Temple" .. 1·75 1·75
593 95 c. "The Holy Family" (*different*) .. 1·90 1·90
594 $1.15, "Presentation in the Temple" (*different*) .. .. .. 2·00 2·00
590/4 .. .. .. *Set of 5* 7·75 7·75
MS595 85 × 101 mm. $4.50, As Type **85** but 52 × 34 mm. P 14 .. .. 5·50 6·50

86 H.M.S. *Bounty* leaving Spithead and King George III

(Des Jennifer Toombs)
1989 (3 July). *Bicentenary of Discovery of Aitutaki by Capt. Bligh. T* **86** *and similar horiz designs. Multicoloured. P* 13½×13.
596 55 c. Type **86** .. .. .. 1·75 1·75
597 65 c. Breadfruit plants .. .. 2·00 2·00
598 75 c. Old chart showing Aitutaki and Capt. Bligh .. .. .. 2·25 2·25
599 95 c. Native outrigger and H.M.S. *Bounty* off Aitutaki .. .. .. 2·50 2·50
600 $1.65, Fletcher Christian confronting Bligh .. .. .. 3·00 3·00
596/600 .. .. .. *Set of 5* 10·50 10·50
MS601 94×72 mm. $4.20, "Mutineers casting Bligh adrift" (Robert Dodd) (60×45 *mm*). P 13½ 8·00 9·00

87 "Apollo 11" Astronaut on Moon   88 Virgin Mary

1989 (28 July). *20th Anniv of First Manned Landing on Moon. T* **87** *and similar horiz designs. Multicoloured. P* 13½×13.
602 75 c. Type **87** .. .. .. 1·75 1·75
603 $1.15, Conducting experiment on Moon .. 2·25 2·25
604 $1.80, Astronaut on Moon carrying equipment .. .. .. 3·25 3·25
602/4 .. .. .. *Set of 3* 6·50 6·50
MS605 105×86 mm. $6.40, Astronaut on Moon with U.S. flag (40×27 *mm*). P 13½ 8·00 9·00

1989 (20 Nov). *Christmas. T* **88** *and similar vert designs showing details from "Virgin in the Glory" by Titian. Multicoloured. P* 13½×13.
606 70 c. Type **88** .. .. .. 2·00 2·00
607 85 c. Christ Child .. .. .. 2·50 2·50
608 95 c. Angel .. .. .. 2·75 2·75
609 $1.25, Cherubs .. .. .. 3·25 3·25
606/9 .. .. .. *Set of 4* 9·50 9·50
MS610 80×100 mm. $6 "Virgin in the Glory" (45×60 *mm*). P 13½ .. 8·00 9·00

$1.75
Ninetieth Birthday

89 Human Comet striking Earth (90)

1990 (16 Feb). *Protection of the Environment. T* **89** *and similar horiz design. Multicoloured. P* 13½×13.
611 $1.75, Type **89** .. .. .. 2·25 2·25
a. Horiz pair. Nos. 611/12 .. 4·50 4·50
612 $1.75, Comet's tail .. .. .. 2·25 2·25
MS613 108×43 mm. $3 As Nos. 611/12 .. 3·50 4·50
Nos. 611/12 were printed together, *se-tenant*, in horizontal pairs throughout the sheet, each pair forming a composite design.

1990 (16 July). *90th Birthday of Queen Elizabeth the Queen Mother. No. MS550 optd with T* **90** *in black on gold on each stamp.*
MS614 132×82 mm. Nos. 523/6 .. .. 9·50 10·00

COMMEMORATING 65th BIRTHDAY OF H.M. QUEEN ELIZABETH II

91 "Madonna of the Basket" (Correggio)   (92)

(Litho Questa)
1990 (28 Nov). *Christmas. Religious Paintings. T* **91** *and similar multicoloured designs. Ordinary paper. P* 14.
615 70 c. Type **91** .. .. .. 1·25 1·25
616 85 c. "Virgin and Child" (Morando) .. 1·40 1·40
617 95 c. "Adoration of the Child" (Tiepolo) 1·50 1·50
618 $1.75, "Mystic Marriage of St. Catherine" (Memling) .. .. .. 2·25 2·25
615/18 .. .. .. *Set of 4* 5·75 5·75
MS619 165×93 mm. $6 "Donne Triptych" (Memling) (*horiz*) .. .. 9·00 10·00

1990 (5 Dec). *"Birdpex '90" Stamp Exhibition, Christchurch, New Zealand. Nos. 349/50 optd as T* **245** *of Cook Islands.*
620 $1 Blue-headed Flycatcher .. .. 3·50 3·50
621 $2 Red-bellied Flycatcher .. .. 4·50 4·50

1991 (22 Apr). *65th Birthday of Queen Elizabeth II. No. 352 optd with T* **92**.
622   $5 Flat-billed   Kingfisher   (*Halcyon recurvirostris*)   8·00   9·00

93 "The Holy Family"   **94** Hurdling
(A. Mengs)

(Des G. Vasarhelyi. Litho Questa)

1991 (13 Nov). *Christmas. Religious Paintings.* T **93** *and similar vert designs. Multicoloured. Ordinary paper.* P 14.
623   80 c. Type **93**   1·25   1·25
624   90 c. "Virgin and the Child" (Lippi)   1·40   1·40
625   $1.05, "Virgin and Child" (A. Dürer)   1·60   1·60
626   $1.75, "Adoration of the Shepherds" (G. de la Tour)   2·25   2·25
623/6   *Set of* 4   6·00   6·00
MS627   79×103 mm. $6 "The Holy Family" (Michelangelo) ..   10·00   11·00

(Des G. Vasarhelyi. Litho B.D.T.)

1992 (29 July). *Olympic Games, Barcelona.* T **94** *and similar horiz designs. Multicoloured. Ordinary paper.* P 14.
628   95 c. Type **94**   1·50   1·50
629   $1.25, Weightlifting   1·75   1·75
630   $1.50, Judo   2·25   2·25
631   $1.95, Football   2·75   2·75
628/31   *Set of* 4   7·50   7·50

95 Vaka Motu Canoe   **96** "Virgin's Nativity" (detail) (Reni)

(Litho B.D.T.)

1992 (16 Oct). *6th Festival of Pacific Arts, Rarotonga.* T **95** *and similar horiz designs showing sailing canoes. Multicoloured. Ordinary paper.* P 14×15.
632   30 c. Type **95**   65   65
633   50 c. Hamatafua   80   80
634   95 c. Alia Kalia Ndrua   1·50   1·50
635   $1.75, Hokule'a Hawaiian   2·25   2·50
636   $1.95, Tuamotu Pahi   2·50   2·75
632/6   *Set of* 5   7·00   7·50

1992 (16 Oct). *Royal Visit by Prince Edward. Nos. 632/6 optd with T* **254** *of Cook Islands.*
637   30 c. Type **95**   75   75
638   50 c. Hamatafua   1·00   1·00
639   95 c. Alia Kalia Ndrua   1·75   1·75
640   $1.75, Hokule'a Hawaiian   2·50   2·75
641   $1.95, Tuamotu Pahi   2·50   2·75
637/41   *Set of* 5   7·75   8·00

1992 (19 Nov). *Christmas. Different details from "Virgin's Nativity" by Guido Reni.* T **96** *and similar vert designs. Ordinary paper.* P 13½.
642   80 c. multicoloured   1·25   1·25
643   90 c. multicoloured   1·40   1·40
644   $1.05, multicoloured   1·60   1·60
645   $1.75, multicoloured   2·25   2·25
642/5   *Set of* 4   6·00   6·00
MS646   101×86 mm. $6 multicoloured (as $1.05, but larger (36×46 *mm*)   6·00   7·00

97 The Departure from Palos

(Litho B.D.T.)

1992 (11 Dec). *500th Anniv of Discovery of America by Columbus.* T **97** *and similar horiz designs. Multicoloured. Ordinary paper.* P 14×15.
647   $1.25, Type **97**   2·25   2·50
648   $1.75, Map of voyages   2·75   3·00
649   $1.95, Columbus and crew in New World ..   3·25   3·50
647/9   *Set of* 3   7·50   8·00

98 Queen Victoria and King Edward VII

(Litho B.D.T.)

1993 (4 June). *40th Anniv of Coronation.* T **98** *and similar horiz designs. Multicoloured.* P 14.
650   $1.75, Type **98**   2·50   2·50
   a. Horiz strip of 3. Nos. 650/2   6·75
651   $1.75, King George V and King George VI   2·50   2·50
652   $1.75, Queen Elizabeth II in 1953 and 1986   2·50   2·50
650/2   *Set of* 3   6·75   6·75
Nos. 650/2 were printed together, *se-tenant*, in horizontal strips of 3 throughout the sheet.

99 "Madonna and   **100** Ice Hockey
Child" (Nino Pisano)

1993 (29 Oct). *Christmas. Religious Sculptures.* T **99** *and similar vert designs. Multicoloured. Ordinary paper.* P 13½ ($3) or 14 (*others*).
653   80 c. Type **99**   80   80
654   90 c. "Virgin on Rosebush" (Luca della Robbia)   85   85
655   $1.15, "Virgin with Child and St. John" (Juan Francisco Rustici)   1·25   1·25
656   $1.95, "Virgin with Child" (Miguel Angel)   2·00   2·00
657   $3 "Madonna and Child" (Jacopo della Quercia) (32×47 *mm*)   3·00   3·00
653/7   *Set of* 7   7·00   7·00

(Litho B.D.T.)

1994 (11 Feb). *Winter Olympic Games, Lillehammer.* T **100** *and similar horiz designs. Multicoloured.* P 14.
658   $1.15, Type **100**   2·50   2·50
   a. Horiz strip of 3. Nos. 658/60   6·75
659   $1.15, Ski-jumping   2·50   2·50
660   $1.15, Cross-country skiing   2·50   2·50
658/60   *Set of* 3   6·75   6·75
Nos. 658/60 were printed together, *se-tenant*, in horizontal strips of 3 throughout the sheet.

101 *Ipomoea pes-caprae*   **102** Cook Islands and U.S.A. Flags with Astronauts Collins, Armstrong and Aldrin

(Des G. Drummond. Litho Questa ($3, $5, $8), B.D.T. (others))

1994 (17 Feb)—**97**. *Flowers.* T **101** *and similar vert designs. Multicoloured.* P 13½×14 ($3, $5, $8) or 13½ (*others*).
661   5 c. Type **101**   10   10
662   10 c. *Plumeria alba*   10   10
663   15 c. *Hibiscus rosa-sinensis*   10   15
664   20 c. *Allamanda cathartica*   15   20
665   25 c. *Delonix regia*   15   20
666   30 c. *Gardenia taitensis*   20   25
667   50 c. *Plumeria rubra*   30   35
668   80 c. *Ipomoea littoralis*   50   55
669   85 c. *Hibiscus tiliaceus*   55   60
670   90 c. *Erythrina variegata*   55   60
671   $1 *Solandra nitida* (29.4.94)   65   70
672   $2 *Cordia subcordata* (29.4.94)
673   $3 *Hibiscus rosa-sinensis* (*different*) (34×47 *mm*) (18.11.94)   1·25   1·40 / 1·90   2·00
674   $5 As $3 (34×47 *mm*) (18.11.94)   3·25   3·50
675   $8 As $3 (34×47 *mm*) (21.11.97)   5·00   5·25
661/75   *Set of* 15   14·50   15·50
Nos. 671/5 include a portrait of Queen Elizabeth II at top right.

(Des G. Vasarhelyi. Litho B.D.T.)

1994 (20 July). *25th Anniv of First Moon Landing.* T **102** *and similar horiz design. Multicoloured.* P 14.
676   $2 Type **102**   5·00   5·00
   a. Pair. Nos. 676/7   10·00   10·00
677   $2 "Apollo 11" re-entering atmosphere and landing in sea   5·00   5·00
Nos. 676/7 were printed together, *se-tenant*, in horizontal or vertical pairs throughout the sheet.

103 "The Madonna   **104** Battle of Britain
of the Basket"
(Correggio)

(Litho B.D.T.)

1994 (30 Nov). *Christmas. Religious Paintings.* T **103** *and similar vert designs. Multicoloured.* P 14.
678   85 c. Type **103**   1·00   1·10
   a. Block of 4. Nos. 678/81   3·50
679   85 c. "The Virgin and Child with Saints" (Memling)   1·00   1·10
680   85 c. "The Virgin and Child with Flowers" (Dolci)   1·00   1·10
681   85 c. "The Virgin and Child with Angels" (Bergognone)   1·00   1·10
682   90 c. "Adoration of the Kings" (Dosso)   1·00   1·10
   a. Block of 4. Nos. 682/5   3·50
683   90 c. "The Virgin and Child" (Bellini)   1·00   1·10
684   90 c. "The Virgin and Child" (Schiavone)   1·00   1·10
685   90 c. "Adoration of the Kings" (Dolci)   1·00   1·10
678/85   *Set of* 8   7·00   8·00
Nos. 678/81 and 682/5 were printed together, *se-tenant*, in blocks of 4 throughout the sheets.
No. 678 is inscribed "Corregio" in error.

(Litho B.D.T.)

1995 (4 Sept). *50th Anniv of End of Second World War.* T **104** *and similar horiz design. Multicoloured.* P 13.
686   $4 Type **104**   6·50   6·50
   a. Pair. Nos. 686/7   13·00   13·00
687   $4 Battle of Midway   6·50   6·50
Nos. 686/7 were printed together, *se-tenant* horizontally and vertically, in sheets of 4.

105 Queen Elizabeth the Queen Mother

(Des G. Vasarhelyi. Litho B.D.T.)

1995 (14 Sept). *95th Birthday of Queen Elizabeth the Queen Mother.* P 13.
688   **105** $4 multicoloured   6·50   7·00
No. 688 was printed in sheets of 4 with inscribed margins.

106 Globe, Doves, United Nations Emblem and Headquarters

(Des G. Vasarhelyi. Litho B.D.T.)

1995 (18 Oct). *50th Anniv of United Nations.* P 13×13½.
689   **106** $4.25, multicoloured   5·00   6·00
No. 689 was printed in sheets of 4 with inscribed margins.

107 Green Turtle

(Litho B.D.T.)

1995 (1 Dec). *Year of the Sea Turtle. T* **107** *and similar horiz designs. Multicoloured. P* 13½×14.
690	95 c. Type 107		1·75	1·75
691	$1.15, Leatherback Turtle		2·00	2·00
692	$1.50, Olive Ridley Turtle		2·25	2·25
693	$1.75, Loggerhead Turtle		2·50	2·50
690/3		Set of 4	7·75	7·75

108 Queen Elizabeth II

(Des G. Vasarhelyi. Litho)

1996 (24 June). *70th Birthday of Queen Elizabeth II. P* 14.
694	108	$4.50, multicoloured	6·00	7·00

109 Baron Pierre de Coubertin, Torch and Opening of 1896 Olympic Games

(Des G. Vasarhelyi. Litho)

1996 (11 July). *Centenary of Modern Olympic Games. T* **109** *and similar horiz design. Multicoloured. P* 14.
695	$2 Type 109		3·25	3·50
	a. Pair. Nos. 695/6		6·50	7·00
696	$2 Athletes and American flag, 1996		3·25	3·50

Nos. 695/6 were printed together, *se-tenant*, in horizontal and vertical pairs within sheets of four.

110 Princess Elizabeth and Lieut. Philip Mountbatten with King George VI and Queen Elizabeth, 1947

111 Diana, Princess of Wales

1997 (20 Nov). *Golden Wedding of Queen Elizabeth and Prince Philip. P* 14.
697	110	$2.50, multicoloured	2·75	2·75
MS698	76×102 mm. **110** $6 multicoloured		5·75	6·50

No. 697 was printed in sheets of 4 with inscribed margins.

1998 (15 Apr). *Diana, Princess of Wales Commemoration. Multicoloured. Litho. P* 14.
699	$1 Type 111		65	70
	a. Sheetlet. No. 699×5 plus label		3·25	
MS700	70×100 mm. $4 Diana, Princess of Wales		3·25	3·50

No. 699 was printed in sheetlets of 5 stamps with a label at top right.

1998 (19 Nov). *Children's Charities. No.* **MS700** *surch as T* **275** *of Cook Islands in silver.*
MS701	70×100 mm. $4+$1 Diana, Princess of Wales		3·75	4·00

KIA ORANA THIRD MILLENNIUM

(112)

1999 (31 Dec). *New Millennium. Nos.* 632/6 *optd with T* **112**.
702	30 c. Type 95		20	25
703	50 c. Hamatafua		30	35
704	95 c. Alia Kalia Ndrua		55	60
705	$1.75, Hokule'a Hawaiian		1·10	1·25
706	$1.95, Tuamotu Pahi		1·25	1·40
702/6		Set of 5	3·25	3·75

STAMP BOOKLETS

1982 (June). *Royal Wedding. Cover as No.* **SB1** *of Cook Islands, but inscr "Aitutaki".*
SB1	$5.60, booklet containing 60 c. and 80 c. (Nos. 391/2), each in block of 4	5·50

OFFICIAL STAMPS

O.H.M.S.

(O 1)

1978 (3 Nov)–**79**. *Nos.* 98/105, 107/10 *and* 227/8 *optd or surch (Nos.* O8/9 *and* O15) *as Type* O 1.
O 1	1 c. New Caledonia Nautilus (*Nautilus macromphallus*)	90	10
O 2	2 c. Common or Major Harp (*Harpa major*)	1·00	10
O 3	3 c. Striped Bonnet (*Phalium flammiferum*)	1·00	10
O 4	4 c. Mole Cowrie (*Cypraea talpa*) (Gold)	1·00	10
O 5	5 c. Pontifical Mitre (*Mitra stictica*)	1·00	10
O 6	8 c. Trumpet Triton (*Charonia tritonis*)	1·25	10
O 7	10 c. Venus Comb Murex (*Murex pecten*)	1·50	15
O 8	15 c. on 60 c. Widest Pacific Conch (*Strombus latissimus*)	2·75	20
O 9	18 c. on 60 c. Widest Pacific Conch (*Strombus latissimus*)	2·75	20
O10	20 c. Red-mouth Olive (*Oliva miniacea miniacea*) (Gold)	2·75	20
O11	50 c. Union Jack, Queen Victoria and island map	1·00	55
O12	60 c. Widest Pacific Conch (*Strombus latissimus*)	10·00	70
O13	$1 Maple-leaf Triton or Winged Frog Shell (*Biplex perca*)	10·00	70
O14	$2 Queen Elizabeth II and Marlin-spike Auger (*Terebra maculata*) (20.2.79)	9·00	75
O15	$4 on $1 Balcony scene, 1953 (Sil.) (20.2.79)	1·75	75
O16	$5 Queen Elizabeth II and Tiger Cowrie (*Cypraea tigris*) (20.2.79)	11·00	1·25
O1/16	Set of 16	50·00	5·00

These stamps were originally only sold to the public cancelled-to-order and not in unused condition.

They were made available to overseas collectors in mint condition during 1980.

75c ◼

O.H.M.S.   O.H.M.S.

(O 2)   (O 3)

1985 (9 Aug)–**90**. (*a*) *Nos.* 351/2, 475 *and* 477/94 *optd or surch as Type* O **2** *by foil embossing in blue ($14, $18) or emerald (others).*
O17	2 c. Type 65	35	35
O18	5 c. Scarlet Robin	45	45
O19	10 c. Golden Whistler	50	50
O20	12 c. Rufous Fantail	55	55
O21	18 c. Peregrine Falcon	1·00	1·00
O22	20 c. on 24 c. Barn Owl	1·00	1·00
O23	30 c. Java Sparrow	75	75
O24	40 c. on 36 c. White-breasted Wood Swallow	90	90
O25	50 c. Rock Dove	1·00	1·00
O26	55 c. on 48 c. Tahitian Lory	1·00	1·00
O27	60 c. Purple Swamphen	1·25	1·25
O28	65 c. on 72 c. Zebra Dove	1·25	1·25
O29	80 c. on 96 c. Chestnut-breasted Mannikin	1·25	1·25
O30	$1.20, Common Mynah (15.6.88)	1·75	1·75
O31	$2.10, Eastern Reef Heron (15.6.88)	2·75	2·75
O32	$3 Blue-headed Flycatcher (30×42 *mm*) (1.10.86)	3·50	3·50
O33	$4.20, Red-bellied Flycatcher (30×42 *mm*) (1.10.86)	5·00	5·00
O34	$5.60, Red Munia (30×42 *mm*) (1.10.86)	6·00	6·00
O35	$9.60, Flat-billed Kingfisher (30×42 *mm*) (1.10.86)	9·00	9·00
O36	$14 on $4 Red Munia (35×48 *mm*)	12·00	12·00
O37	$18 on $5 Flat-billed Kingfisher (35×48 *mm*) (2.7.90)	14·00	14·00

(*b*) *Nos.* 430/3 *surch as Type* O **3** *by gold foil embossing*
O38	75 c. on 48 c. Type 57	80	80
O39	75 c. on 48 c. Ancient Ti'i image	80	80
O40	75 c. on 48 c. Tourist canoeing	80	80
O41	75 c. on 48 c. Captain William Bligh and chart	80	80
O17/41	Set of 25	60·00	60·00

394

PENRHYN ISLAND

Stamps of COOK ISLANDS were used on Penrhyn Island from late 1901 until the issue of the surcharged stamps in May 1902.

PRICES FOR STAMPS ON COVER TO 1945	
No. 1	from ×25
No. 3	—
Nos. 4/5	from ×25
Nos. 6/8	—
Nos. 9/10	from ×50
Nos. 11/13	—
Nos. 14/18	from × 3
Nos. 19/23	from × 2
Nos. 24/37	from × 3
Nos. 38/40	from × 5

A. NEW ZEALAND DEPENDENCY

The island of Penrhyn, under British protection from 20 September 1888, was annexed by New Zealand on 11 June 1901.

Stamps of New Zealand overprinted or surcharged. For illustrations of New Zealand watermarks and definitive types see the beginning of Cook Islands.

PENRHYN ISLAND.

½ PENI.

(1)

PENRHYN ISLAND.

TAI PENI.

(2) 1d.

PENRHYN ISLAND.

2½ PENI.

(3)

1902 (5 May). *T 23, 27 and 42 surch with T 1, 2 and 3.*

(a) *Thick, soft Pirie paper. No wmk. P 11*
1	2½d. blue (No. 260) (R.)	..	..	2·50	7·00
	a. "½"and "P" spaced (all stamps in 8th vert row)		..	13·00	28·00

(b) *Thin, hard Basted Mills paper. W 38 of New Zealand.*

(i) *P 11*
3	1d. carmine (No. 286) (Br.)	..	..	£850	£900

(ii) *P 14*
4	½d. green (No. 287) (R.)	..	..	80	4·50
	a. No stop after "ISLAND"	..	..	£150	£200
5	1d. carmine (No. 288) (Br.)	..	..	3·25	14·00

(iii) *Perf compound of 11 and 14*
6	1d. carmine (No. 290) (Br.)	..	..	£750	£800

(iv) *Mixed perfs*
7	½d. green (No. 291) (R.)	..	..	..	£1000
8	1d. carmine (No. 292) (Br.)	..	..	..	£1200

(c) *Thin, hard Cowan paper. W 43 of New Zealand.* (i) *P 14*
9	½d. green (No. 302) (R.)	..	..	1·60	4·50
	a. No stop after "ISLAND" (R. 10/6)	..	£130	£170
10	1d. carmine (No. 303) (B.)	..	..	1·00	3·00
	a. No stop after "ISLAND" (R. 10/6)	..	48·00	80·00

(ii) *Perf compound of 11 and 14*
11	1d. carmine (No. 305) (B.)	..	..	..	£6000

(iii) *Mixed perfs*
12	½d. green (No. 306) (R.)	..	..	£1100	£1200
13	1d. carmine (No. 307) (B.)	..	..	£425	£475

PENRHYN ISLAND.

(4)

Toru Pene.

(5) 3d.

Ono Pene.

(6) 6d.

Tahi Silingi.

(7) 1s.

1903 (28 Feb). *T 28, 31 and 34 surch with name at top, T 4, and values at foot, T 5/7. Thin, hard Cowan paper. W 43 (sideways) of New Zealand. P 11.*
14	3d. yellow-brown (No. 309) (B.)	..	10·00	20·00
15	6d. rose-red (No. 312a) (B.)	..	15·00	32·00
16	1s. brown-red (No. 315) (B.)	..	50·00	55·00
	a. Bright red	..	..	48·00	48·00
	b. Orange-red	..	..	55·00	55·00
14/16			*Set of 3*	65·00	90·00

1914 (May)–**15**. *T 51/2 surch with T 1 (½d.) or optd with T 4 at top and surch with T 6/7 at foot.*
19	½d. yellow-green (No. 387) (C.) (5.14)	..	80	7·00
	a. No stop after "ISLAND"	..	30·00	70·00
	b. No stop after "PENI" (R. 3/17)	90·00	£160
	c. Vermilion opt (1.15)	..	80	7·00
	ca. No stop after "ISLAND"	..	10·00	42·00
	cb. No stop after "PENI" (R. 3/5, 3/17)	40·00	90·00
22	6d. carmine (No. 393) (B.) (8.14)	..	27·00	70·00
23	1s. vermilion (No. 394) (B.) (8.14)	48·00	95·00
19/23			*Set of 3*	65·00	£150

The "no stop after ISLAND" variety occurs on R. 1/4, 1/10, 1/16, 1/22, 6/4, 6/10, 6/16 and 6/22 of the carmine surcharge, No. 19, and on these positions plus R. 1/12, 1/24, 6/12 and 6/24 for the vermilion, No. 19c.

1917 (Nov)–**20**. *Optd as T 4.*

(a) *T 60 (recess). W 43 of New Zealand. P 14×13½.*
24	2½d. blue (No. 419) (R.) (10.20)	..	3·00	8·00
	a. Perf 14×14½	..	..	2·00	5·00
	ab. No stop after "ISLAND" (R. 10/8)	£150	£250
	b. Vert pair. Nos. 24/4a	..	50·00	80·00
25	3d. chocolate (No. 420) (B.) (6.18)	12·00	60·00
	a. Perf 14×14½	..	..	9·50	60·00
	b. Vert pair. Nos. 25/5a	..	70·00	£190
26	6d. carmine (No. 425) (B.) (1.18)	8·00	24·00
	a. Perf 14×14½	..	..	5·00	16·00
	ab. No stop after "ISLAND" (R. 10/8)	£350	£475
	b. Vert pair. Nos. 26/6a	..	55·00	£120
27	1s. vermilion (No. 430) (B.) (12.17)	15·00	40·00
	a. Perf 14×14½	..	..	12·00	30·00
	ab. No stop after "ISLAND" (R. 10/8)	£375	£500
	b. Vert pair. Nos. 27/7a	..	£110	£200
24/7			*Set of 4*	25·00	£100

(b) *T 61 (typo). W 43 of New Zealand. P 14×15*
28	½d. green (No. 435) (R.) (2.20)	..	1·00	2·00
	a. No stop after "ISLAND" (R. 2/24)	£100	£150
	b. Narrow spacing	..	..	6·00	8·50
29	1½d. slate (No. 437) (R.)	..	6·50	15·00
	a. Narrow spacing	..	..	18·00	35·00
30	1½d. orange-brown (No. 438) (R.) (2.19)	60	15·00
	a. Narrow spacing	..	..	5·00	35·00
31	3d. chocolate (No. 440) (B.) (6.19)	3·50	17·00
	a. Narrow spacing	..	..	15·00	45·00
28/31			*Set of 4*	10·50	45·00

The narrow spacing variety occurs on R. 1/5–8, 4/21–4, 7/5–8 and 9/21–4.

(Recess P.B.)

1920 (23 Aug). *As T 9/14 of Cook Islands, but inscr "PENRHYN". No wmk. P 14.*
32	½d. black and emerald	..	1·00	13·00
	a. Part imperf block of 4	..	£1200	
33	1d. black and deep red	..	1·50	13·00
	a. Double derrick flaw (R.2/8, 3/6 or 5/2)	5·50	
34	1½d. black and deep violet	..	6·50	17·00
35	3d. black and red	..	..	2·50	8·00
36	6d. red-brown and sepia	..	3·25	20·00
37	1s. black and slate-blue	..	10·00	24·00
32/7			*Set of 6*	22·00	85·00

No. 32a comes from sheets on which two rows were imperforate between horizontally and the second row additionally imperforate vertically.

Examples of the ½d. and 1d. with centre inverted were not supplied to the Post Office.

(Recess Govt Printing Office, Wellington)

1927–29. *As T 9/10 and 16 of Cook Islands, but inscr "PENRHYN". W 43. P 14.*
38	½d. black and green (5.29)	..	5·50	19·00
39	1d. black and deep carmine (14.3.28)	5·50	16·00
	a. Double derrick flaw (R.2/8, 3/6 or 5/2)	16·00	
40	2½d. red-brown and dull blue (10.27)	3·00	24·00
38/40			*Set of 3*	12·50	55·00

Cook Islands stamps superseded those of Penrhyn Islands on 15 March 1932. Separate issues were resumed in 1973.

B. PART OF COOK ISLANDS

The following issues are for use in all the islands of the Northern Cook Islands group.

(New Currency. 100 cents = 1 dollar)

PRINTERS. The notes above No. 33 of Aitutaki concerning printers and gum also apply here. Stamps printed by Fournier from No. 472 onwards are in lithography.

PENRHYN

PENRHYN NORTHERN

(8)

PENRHYN NORTHERN

(9)

1973 (24 Oct–14 Nov). *Nos. 228/45 of Cook Is optd with T 8 (without "NORTHERN" on $1, $2).*

A. *Without fluorescent security markings. Gum arabic*
41A	1 c. multicoloured	..	..	80	
42A	2 c. multicoloured	..	..	1·25	
43A	3 c. multicoloured	..	..	1·75	
44A	4 c. multicoloured (No. 233)	..	2·00	
	a. Optd on Cook Is No. 232	..	24·00	
45A	5 c. multicoloured	..	..	2·50	
46A	6 c. multicoloured	..	..	2·50	
47A	8 c. multicoloured	..	..	2·75	
48A	15 c. multicoloured	..	..	4·25	
50A	50 c. multicoloured	..	..	8·00	
51A	$1 multicoloured	..	..	9·00	
52A	$2 multicoloured (14.11)	..	10·00	
41A/52A			*Set of 11*	40·00	

B. *With fluorescent security markings. PVA gum.*
41B	1 c. multicoloured	..	..	10	10
42B	2 c. multicoloured	..	..	10	10
43B	3 c. multicoloured	..	..	20	10
44B	4 c. multicoloured (No. 233)	..	10	10
45B	5 c. multicoloured	..	..	10	10
46B	6 c. multicoloured	..	..	20	30
47B	8 c. multicoloured	..	..	30	40
48B	15 c. multicoloured	..	..	45	50
49B	20 c. multicoloured	..	..	1·50	80
50B	50 c. multicoloured	..	..	65	1·75
51B	$1 multicoloured	..	..	65	2·25
52B	$2 multicoloured (14.11)	..	65	2·50
41B/52B			*Set of 12*	4·25	7·50

1973 (14 Nov). *Royal Wedding. Nos. 450/2 of Cook Is optd as T 9, in silver.*
53	138	25 c. multicoloured	..	..	30	20
54	–	30 c. multicoloured	..	..	30	20
55	–	50 c. multicoloured	..	..	30	20
53/5		..	..	*Set of 3*	80	55

10 Yellow Boxfish   **11** Penrhyn Stamps of 1902

1974 (15 Aug)–**75**. *Multicoloured. (a) T 10 and similar horiz designs showing fishes. P 13½.*
56	½ c. Type 10	..	..	50	50
57	1 c. Diamond Fingerfish	..	70	50
58	2 c. Emperor Angelfish	..	80	50
59	3 c. Copper-banded Butterflyfish	80	50
60	4 c. Ornate Butterflyfish	..	80	50
61	5 c. Black-backed Butterflyfish	80	50
62	8 c. Latticed Butterflyfish	..	80	50
63	10 c. Saddle Butterflyfish	..	85	50
64	20 c. Regal Angelfish	..	1·75	50
65	25 c. Pennant Coralfish	..	1·75	50
66	60 c. Harlequin Sweetlips	..	2·50	90
67	$1 *Balistipus undulatus*	..	2·75	1·25

(b) *Larger designs, 63×25 mm. P 13×12½.*
68	$2 Birds-eye view of Penrhyn (12.2.75)	4·50	12·00
69	$5 Satellite view of Australasia (12.3.75)	4·50	6·00
56/69			*Set of 14*	21·00	23·00

1974 (27 Sept). *Centenary of Universal Postal Union. T 11 and similar vert design. Multicoloured. P 13.*
70	25 c. Type 11	..	..	20	40
71	50 c. Stamps of 1920	..	35	45

Each value was issued in sheets of 8 stamps and 1 label.

12 "Adoration of the Kings" (Memling)

1974 (30 Oct). *Christmas. T 12 and similar horiz designs. Multicoloured. P 13.*
72	5 c. Type 12	..	..	20	30
73	10 c. "Adoration of the Shepherds" (Hugo van der Goes)	25	30
74	25 c. "Adoration of the Magi" (Rubens)	40	45
75	30 c. "The Holy Family" (Borgianni)	45	65
72/5			*Set of 4*	1·10	1·50

13 Churchill giving "V" Sign   (14)

1974 (30 Nov). *Birth Centenary of Sir Winston Churchill. T 13 and similar vert design. P 13.*
76	30 c. agate and gold	..	..	35	85
77	50 c. myrtle-green and gold	..	45	90

Design:—50 c. Full-face portrait.

1975 (24 July). *"Apollo-Soyuz" Space Project. No. 69 optd with T 14.*
78	$5 Satellite view of Australasia	..	1·75	2·50

15 "Virgin and Child"   **16** "Pietà"
(Bouts)

1975 (21 Nov). *Christmas. T 15 and similar vert designs showing the "Virgin and Child". Multicoloured. P 14 × 13.*
79	7 c. Type 15	..	..	40	10
80	15 c. Leonardo da Vinci	..	70	20
81	35 c. Raphael	..	..	1·10	35
79/81			*Set of 3*	2·00	60

1976 (19 Mar). *Easter and 500th Birth Anniv of Michelangelo.* T **16** *and similar vert designs.* P 14 × 13.

82	15 c.	sepia and gold	..	25	15
83	20 c.	blackish purple and gold.	..	30	15
84	35 c.	myrtle-green and gold	..	40	20
82/4			*Set of 3*	85	45
MS85	112 × 72 mm. Nos. 82/4.			85	1·25

Each value was issued in sheets of 8 stamps and 1 label.

17 "Washington crossing the Delaware" (E. Leutze) **18** Running

1976 (20 May). *Bicentenary of American Revolution.* T **17** *and similar vert designs. Multicoloured.* P 13.

86	30 c.			30	15
87	30 c.	} Type **17**		30	15
88	30 c.			30	15
89	50 c.			40	20
90	50 c.	} "The Spirit of '76" (A. M. Willard)		40	20
91	50 c.			40	20
86/91			*Set of 6*	1·90	95
MS92	103 × 103 mm. Nos. 86/91. P 13			1·50	2·00

Nos. 86/8 and 89/91 were each printed together, *se-tenant*, in horizontal strips of 3 throughout the sheet, forming composite designs. Each sheet includes 3 stamp-size labels. Type **17** shows the left-hand stamp of the 30 c. design.

1976 (9 July). *Olympic Games, Montreal.* T **18** *and similar horiz designs. Multicoloured.* P 14.

93	25 c.	Type **18**		25	15
94	30 c.	Long Jumping	..	30	15
95	75 c.	Throwing the Javelin	..	55	25
93/5			*Set of 3*	1·00	50
MS96	86 × 128 mm. Nos. 93/5. P 14 × 13			1·10	2·00

19 "The Flight into Egypt"   **20** The Queen in Coronation Robes

1976 (20 Oct). *Christmas. Dürer Engravings.* T **19** *and similar horiz designs.* P 13.

97	7 c.	black and silver	..	15	10
98	15 c.	steel blue and silver	..	25	15
99	35 c.	violet and silver ..	..	35	25
97/9			*Set of 3*	65	45

Designs:—15 c. "Adoration of the Magi"; 35 c. "The Nativity".

1977 (24 Mar). *Silver Jubilee.* T **20** *and similar vert designs. Multicoloured.* P 13.

100	50 c.	Type **20**		25	60
101	$1	Queen and Prince Philip.	..	35	65
102	$2	Queen Elizabeth II	..	50	80
100/2			*Set of 3*	1·00	1·90
MS103	128 × 87 mm. Nos. 100/2. P 13			1·00	1·50

Stamps from the miniature sheet have silver borders.

21 "The Annunciation"   **22** Iiwi

1977 (23 Sept). *Christmas.* T **21** *and similar designs showing illustrations by J. S. von Carolsfeld.* P 13.

104	7 c.	light stone, purple-brown and gold		40	15
105	15 c.	pale rose, deep maroon and gold		60	15
106	35 c.	blackish green, pale green and gold		1·00	30
104/6			*Set of 3*	1·75	55

Designs:—15 c. "The Announcement to the Shepherds"; 35 c. "The Nativity".

1978 (19 Jan). *Bicentenary of Discovery of Hawaii.* T **22** *and similar vert designs showing Hawaiian birds or artefacts. Multicoloured.* P 13.

107	20 c.	Type **22**		80	30
108	20 c.	Elgin cloak	..	80	30
109	30 c.	Apapane	..	90	40
110	30 c.	Feather image of a god	..	90	40
111	35 c.	Moorhen	..	90	45

112	35 c.	Feather cape, helmet and staff		90	45
113	75 c.	Hawaii O-o	..	1·50	80
114	75 c.	Feather image and cloak	..	1·50	80
107/14			*Set of 8*	7·50	3·50
MS115	Two sheets each 78 × 119 mm containing (a) Nos. 107, 109, 111, 113; (b) Nos. 108, 110, 112, 114.			5·00	7·00

Nos. 107/8, 109/10, 111/12 and 113/14 were each printed together, *se-tenant*, in horizontal and vertical pairs throughout the sheet.

23 "The Road to Calvary"   **24** Royal Coat of Arms

1978 (10 Mar). *Easter and 400th Birth Anniv of Rubens.* T **23** *and similar vert designs. Multicoloured.* P 13.

116	10 c.	Type **23**		20	10
117	15 c.	"Christ on the Cross"	..	25	15
118	35 c.	"Christ with Straw"	..	45	25
116/18			*Set of 3*	80	45
MS119	87 × 138 mm. Nos. 116/18			1·00	1·60

Stamps from No. MS119 are slightly larger (28 × 36 mm.)

1978 (17 Apr). *Easter. Children's Charity. Designs as Nos. 116/18 in separate miniature sheets. 49 × 68 mm, each with a face value of 60 c. + 5 c.* P 12½–13.

MS120	As Nos. 116/18		*Set of 3 sheets*	90	1·50

1978 (24 May). *25th Anniv of Coronation.* T **24** *and similar vert designs.* P 13.

121	90 c.	black, gold and deep lilac		30	60
122	90 c.	multicoloured ..	..	30	60
123	90 c.	black, gold and deep bluish green		30	60
121/3			*Set of 3*	90	1·60
MS124	75 × 122 mm. Nos. 121/3 ..			1·10	2·00

Designs:—No. 122, Queen Elizabeth II; No. 123, New Zealand coat of arms.

Nos. 121/3 were printed together in small sheets of 6, containing two se-tenant strips of 3, with horizontal gutter margin between.

25 "Madonna of the Pear"   **26** Sir Rowland Hill and G.B. Penny Black Stamp

1978 (29 Nov). *Christmas. 450th Death Anniv of Dürer.* T **25** *and similar vert design. Multicoloured.* P 14.

125	30 c.	Type **25**		65	30
126	35 c.	"The Virgin and Child with St. Anne"		65	30
MS127	101 × 60 mm. Nos. 125/6. P 13½			1·50	1·75

Nos. 125/6 were each printed in small sheets of 6.

1979 (26 Sept). *Death Centenary of Sir Rowland Hill.* T **26** *and similar vert designs. Multicoloured.* P 13½ × 14.

128	75 c.	Type **26**		50	55
129	75 c.	1974 Centenary of Universal Postal Union 25 c. and 50 c. commemoratives ..		50	55
130	90 c.	Sir Rowland Hill ..	..	60	70
131	90 c.	1978 25th anniv of Coronation 90 c. (Queen Elizabeth II) commemorative		60	70
128/31			*Set of 4*	2·00	2·25
MS132	116 × 58 mm. Nos. 128/31.			1·50	1·75

Stamps from No. MS132 have cream backgrounds.

Nos. 128/9 and 130/1 were each printed together, *se-tenant*, in horizontal and vertical pairs throughout small sheets of 8.

27 Max and Moritz   **28** "Christ carrying Cross" (Book of Ferdinand II)

1979 (20 Nov). *International Year of the Child. Illustrations from Max and Moritz stories by Wilhelm Busch.* T **27** *and similar horiz designs. Multicoloured.* P 13.

133	12 c.	Type **27**		20	15
134	12 c.	Max and Moritz looking down chimney		20	15
135	12 c.	Max and Moritz making off with food		20	15
136	12 c.	Cook about to beat dog		20	15
137	15 c.	Max sawing through bridge		25	15

138	15 c.	Pursuer approaching bridge		25	15
139	15 c.	Bridge collapsing under pursuer		25	15
140	15 c.	Pursuer in river	..	25	15
141	20 c.	Baker locking shop	..	30	20
142	20 c.	Max and Moritz coming out of hiding		30	20
143	20 c.	Max and Moritz falling in dough		30	20
144	20 c.	Max and Moritz after being rolled into buns by baker		30	20
133/44			*Set of 12*	2·75	1·75

Nos. 133/6, 137/40 and 141/4 were each printed together, *se-tenant*, in sheets of 4, either with or without labels containing extracts from the books on the top and bottom selvedge.

1980 (28 Mar). *Easter. Scenes from 15th-century Prayer Books.* T **28** *and similar vert designs. Multicoloured.* P 13.

145	12 c.	Type **28**		15	20
146	20 c.	"The Crucifixion" (William Vrelant, Book of Duke of Burgundy)		20	25
147	35 c.	"Descent from the Cross" (Book of Ferdinand II)		30	45
145/7			*Set of 3*	55	80
MS148	111 × 65 mm. Nos. 145/7			55	1·00

Stamps from No. MS148 have cream borders.

1980 (28 Mar). *Easter. Children's Charity. Designs as Nos. 145/7 in separate miniature sheets 54 × 85 mm, each with a face value of 70 c. + 5 c.*

MS149	As Nos. 145/7		*Set of 3 sheets*	75	1·00

29 "Queen Elizabeth, 1937" (Sir Gerald Kelly)   **30** Falk Hoffman, D.D.R. (platform diving) (gold)

1980 (17 Sept). *80th Birthday of Queen Elizabeth the Queen Mother.* P 13.

150	**29**	$1 multicoloured	..	1·25	1·25
MS151	55 × 84 mm. **29** $2.50 multicoloured			1·60	1·60

1980 (14 Nov). *Olympic Games, Moscow. Medal Winners.* T **30** *and similar vert designs. Multicoloured.* P 13½.

152	10 c.	Type **30**		10	10
153	10 c.	Martina Jaschke, D.D.R. (platform diving) (gold)		10	10
154	20 c.	Tomi Polkolainen, Finland (archery) (gold)		15	15
155	20 c.	Kete Losaberidse, U.S.S.R. (archery) (gold)		15	15
156	30 c.	Czechoslovakia (football) (gold)		20	20
157	30 c.	D.D.R. (football) (silver) ..		20	20
158	50 c.	Barbel Wockel, D.D.R. (200-metre dash) (gold)		30	30
159	50 c.	Pietro Mennea, Italy (200-metre dash) (gold)		30	30
152/9			*Set of 8*	1·40	1·40
MS160	150 × 106 mm. Nos. 152/9. P 13			1·40	1·75

Stamps from No. MS160 have gold borders.

Nos. 152/3, 154/5, 156/7 and 158/9 were each printed together, *se-tenant*, in horizontal pairs throughout the sheet.

31 "The Virgin of Counsellors" (Luis Dalmau)   **32** Amatasi

1980 (5 Dec). *Christmas. Paintings.* T **31** *and similar vert designs. Multicoloured.* P 13.

161	20 c.	Type **31**		15	15
162	35 c.	"Virgin and Child" (Serra brothers)		20	20
163	50 c.	"The Virgin of Albocacer" (Master of the Porciuncula)		30	30
161/3			*Set of 3*	60	60
MS164	135 × 75 mm. Nos. 161/3 ..			1·50	1·50

1980 (5 Dec). *Christmas. Children's Charity. Designs as Nos. 161/3 in separate miniature sheets, 54 × 77 mm, each with a face value of 70 c. + 5 c.*

MS165	As Nos. 161/3		*Set of 3 sheets*	1·50	1·50

1981 (16 Feb–21 Sept). *Sailing Craft and Ships (1st series). Multicoloured designs as* T **32**. P 14 *(Nos. 166/85),* 13 × 14½ *(Nos. 186/205) or* 13½ *(Nos. 206/8).*

166	1 c.	Type **32**		20	15
167	1 c.	Ndrua	..	20	15
168	1 c.	Waka	..	20	15
169	1 c.	Tongiaki	..	20	15
170	3 c.	Va'a Teu'ua	..	40	15
171	3 c.	Vitoria, 1500	..	40	15
172	3 c.	Golden Hind, 1560	..	40	15
173	3 c.	Boudeuse, 1760	..	40	15
174	4 c.	H.M.S. Bounty, 1787	..	50	15
175	4 c.	L'Astrolabe, 1811	..	50	15

176	4 c. *Star of India*, 1861	50	15
177	4 c. *Great Republic*, 1853	50	15
178	6 c. *Balcutha*, 1886	50	20
179	6 c. *Coonatto*, 1863	50	20
180	6 c. *Antiope*, 1866	50	20
181	6 c. *Taeping*, 1863	50	20
182	10 c. *Preussen*, 1902	50	75
183	10 c. *Pamir*, 1921	50	75
184	10 c. *Cap Hornier*, 1910	50	75
185	10 c. *Patriarch*, 1869	50	75
186	15 c. As Type 32 (16 Mar)	50	85
187	15 c. As No. 167 (16 Mar)	50	85
188	15 c. As No. 168 (16 Mar)	50	85
189	15 c. As No. 169 (16 Mar)	50	85
190	20 c. As No. 170 (16 Mar)	50	85
191	20 c. As No. 171 (16 Mar)	50	85
192	20 c. As No. 172 (16 Mar)	50	85
193	20 c. As No. 173 (16 Mar)	50	85
194	30 c. As No. 174 (16 Mar)	50	95
195	30 c. As No. 175 (16 Mar)	50	95
196	30 c. As No. 176 (16 Mar)	50	95
197	30 c. As No. 177 (16 Mar)	50	95
198	50 c. As No. 178 (16 Mar)	1·00	1·75
199	50 c. As No. 179 (16 Mar)	1·00	1·75
200	50 c. As No. 180 (16 Mar)	1·00	1·75
201	50 c. As No. 181 (16 Mar)	1·00	1·75
202	$1 As No. 182 (15 May)	2·00	1·50
203	$1 As No. 183 (15 May)	2·00	1·50
204	$1 As No. 184 (15 May)	2·00	1·50
205	$1 As No. 185 (15 May)	2·00	1·50
206	$2 *Cutty Sark*, 1869 (26 June)	4·50	3·25
207	$4 *Mermerus*, 1872 (26 June)	9·00	5·00
208	$6 H.M.S. *Resolution* and *Discovery*, 1776– 80 (21 Sept)	15·00	12·00
166/208	*Set of 43*	48·00	42·00

Nos. 186/205 are 41×25 mm and Nos. 206/8 47×33 mm in size.

On Nos. 166/205 the four designs of each value were printed together, *se-tenant*, in blocks of 4 throughout the sheet.

Nos. 181 and 201 are wrongly inscribed "TEAPING".

For redrawn versions of these designs in other face values see Nos. 337/55.

33 "Jesus at the Grove" (Veronese)   **34** Prince Charles as Young Child

1981 (5 Apr). *Easter. Paintings. T* **33** *and similar vert designs. Multicoloured. P* 14.

218	30 c. Type 33	40	20
219	40 c. "Christ with Crown of Thorns" (Titian)	55	25
220	50 c. "Pietá" (Van Dyck)	60	30
218/20	*Set of 3*	1·40	65
MS221	110 × 68 mm. Nos. 218/20. P 13½	2·75	2·40

1981 (5 Apr). *Easter. Children's Charity. Designs as Nos.* 218/20 *in separate miniature sheets* 70 × 86 *mm., each with a face value of* 70 *c.* + 5 *c. P* 13½.

MS222	As Nos. 218/20 *Set of 3 sheets*	1·50	1·50

1981 (10 July). *Royal Wedding. T* **34** *and similar vert designs. Multicoloured. P* 14.

223	40 c. Type 34	15	35
224	50 c. Prince Charles as schoolboy	15	40
225	60 c. Prince Charles as young man	20	40
226	70 c. Prince Charles in ceremonial Naval uniform	20	45
227	80 c. Prince Charles as Colonel-in-Chief, Royal Regiment of Wales	20	45
223/7	*Set of 5*	80	1·90
MS228	99 × 89 mm. Nos. 223/7.	90	2·00

Nos. 223/7 were each printed in small sheets of 6 including one *se-tenant* stamp-size label.

1981 (30 Nov). *International Year for Disabled Persons. Nos.* 223/8 *surch as T* **51** *of Aitutaki.*

229	40 c.+ 5 c. Type 34	15	50
230	50 c.+ 5 c. Prince Charles as schoolboy	15	55
231	60 c.+ 5 c. Prince Charles as young man	20	55
232	70 c.+ 5 c. Prince Charles in ceremonial Naval uniform	20	60
233	80 c.+ 5 c. Prince Charles as Colonel-in-Chief, Royal Regiment of Wales	20	65
229/33	*Set of 5*	80	2·50
MS234	99 × 89 mm. As Nos. 229/33, but 10 c. premium on each stamp	80	2·50

Nos. 229/34 have commemorative inscriptions overprinted on the sheet margins.

35 Footballer   **36** "The Virgin on a Crescent"

1981 (7 Dec). *World Cup Football Championship, Spain* (1982). *T* **35** *and similar vert designs showing footballers. Multicoloured. P* 13.

235	15 c. Type 35	20	15
236	15 c. Footballer wearing orange jersey with black and mauve stripes	20	15
237	15 c. Player in blue jersey	20	15
238	35 c. Player in blue jersey	30	25
239	35 c. Player in red jersey	30	25
240	35 c. Player in yellow jersey with green stripes	30	25
241	50 c. Player in orange jersey	40	35
242	50 c. Player in mauve jersey	40	35
243	50 c. Player in black jersey	40	35
235/43	*Set of 9*	2·40	2·00
MS244	113 × 151 mm. As Nos. 235/43, but each stamp with a premium of 3 c.	4·75	2·75

The three designs of each value were printed together, *se-tenant*, in horizontal strips of 3 throughout the sheet.

1981 (15 Dec). *Christmas. Details from Engravings by Dürer. T* **36** *and similar vert designs in violet, deep reddish purple and stone. P* 13 × 13½.

245	30 c. Type 36	90	1·00
246	40 c. "The Virgin at the Fence"	1·25	1·40
247	50 c. "The Holy Virgin and Child"	1·50	1·75
245/7	*Set of 3*	3·25	3·75
MS248	134 × 75 mm. As Nos. 245/7, but each stamp with a premium of 2 c.	2·25	2·25
MS249	Designs as Nos. 245/7 in separate miniature sheets, 58 × 85 mm, each with a face value of 70 c. + 5 c. P 14 × 13½ *Set of 3 sheets*	1·75	1·75

37 Lady Diana Spencer as Baby   **(38)**

1982 (1 July). *21st Birthday of Princess of Wales. T* **37** *and similar vert designs. Multicoloured. P* 14.

250	30 c. Type 37	30	30
251	50 c. As young child	40	45
252	70 c. As schoolgirl	60	60
253	80 c. As teenager	70	80
254	$1.40, As young lady	1·10	1·25
250/4	*Set of 5*	2·75	3·00
MS255	87 × 110 mm. Nos. 250/4	5·00	3·50

1982 (30 July). *Birth of Prince William of Wales. Nos.* 223/8 *optd with T* **38**.

256	40 c. Type 34	30	35
257	50 c. Prince Charles as schoolboy	40	45
258	60 c. Prince Charles as young man	45	55
259	70 c. Prince Charles in ceremonial Naval uniform	50	60
260	80 c. Prince Charles as Colonel-in-Chief, Royal Regiment of Wales	50	65
256/60	*Set of 5*	1·90	2·25
MS261	99 × 89 mm. Nos. 256/60	6·00	7·00

1982 (6 Sept). *Birth of Prince William of Wales. As Nos.* 250/5 *but with changed inscriptions. Multicoloured. P* 13½ × 14.

262	30 c. As Type 37 (inscr "21 JUNE 1982. BIRTH OF PRINCE WILLIAM OF WALES")	30	30
263	30 c. As Type 37 (inscr "COMMEMORATING THE BIRTH OF PRINCE WILLIAM OF WALES")	30	30
264	50 c. As No. 251 (inscr. "21 JUNE 1982. BIRTH OF PRINCE WILLIAM OF WALES")	45	45
265	50 c. As No. 251 (inscr "COMMEMORATING THE BIRTH OF PRINCE WILLIAM OF WALES")	45	45
266	70 c. As No. 252 (inscr "21 JUNE 1982. BIRTH OF PRINCE WILLIAM OF WALES")	65	65
267	70 c. As No. 252 (inscr "COMMEMORATING THE BIRTH OF PRINCE WILLIAM OF WALES")	65	65
268	80 c. As No. 253 (inscr "21 JUNE 1982. BIRTH OF PRINCE WILLIAM OF WALES")	65	65
269	80 c. As No. 253 (inscr "COMMEMORATING THE BIRTH OF PRINCE WILLIAM OF WALES")	65	65
270	$1.40, As No. 254 (inscr "21 JUNE 1982. BIRTH OF PRINCE WILLIAM OF WALES")	1·25	1·25
271	$1.40, As No. 254 (inscr "COMMEMORATING THE BIRTH OF PRINCE WILLIAM OF WALES")	1·25	1·25
262/71	*Set of 10*	6·00	6·00
MS272	88 × 109 mm. As MS255 (stamps inscr "21 JUNE 1982. ROYAL BIRTH PRINCE WILLIAM OF WALES"	4·00	3·25

Nos. 262/3, 264/5, 266/7, 268/9 and 270/1 were printed together, *se-tenant*, in sheets of 5 stamps and 1 label, there being three examples of the "21 JUNE 1982..." and two of the "COMMEMORATING..." in each sheet.

ALTERED CATALOGUE NUMBERS

Any Catalogue numbers altered from the last edition are shown as a list in the introductory pages.

39 "Virgin and Child" (detail, Joos Van Cleve)   **40** Red Coral

1982 (10 Dec). *Christmas. Details from Renaissance Paintings of "Virgin and Child". T* **39** *and similar vert designs. Multicoloured. P* 14 × 13½.

273	35 c. Type 39	30	40
274	48 c. "Virgin and Child" (Filippino Lippi)	45	55
275	60 c. "Virgin and Child" (Cima da Conegliano)	60	70
273/5	*Set of 3*	1·25	1·50
MS276	134 × 73 mm. As Nos. 273/5 but each with 2 c. charity premium. P 13	1·00	2·00

Nos. 273/5 were each printed in small sheets of 6 including one *se-tenant*, stamp size, label, depicting the Prince and Princess of Wales with Prince William.

1982 (10 Dec). *Christmas. Children's Charity. Designs as Nos.* 273/5, *but without frames, in separate miniature sheets,* 60 × 85 *mm, each with a face value of* 70 *c.* + 5 *c. P* 13.

MS277	As Nos. 273/5 *Set of 3 sheets*	1·25	1·60

1983 (14 Mar). *Commonwealth Day. T* **40** *and similar vert designs. Multicoloured. P* 13.

278	60 c. Type 40	50	55
279	60 c. Aerial view of Penrhyn atoll	50	55
280	60 c. Eleanor Roosevelt on Penrhyn during Second World War	50	55
281	60 c. Map of South Pacific	50	55
278/81	*Set of 4*	1·75	2·00

Nos. 278/81 were issued together, *se-tenant*, in blocks of four throughout the sheet.

41 Scout Emblem and Blue Tropical Flower   **(42)**

1983 (5 Apr). *75th Anniv of Boy Scout Movement. T* **41** *and similar horiz designs. Multicoloured. P* 13 × 14.

282	36 c. Type 41	1·50	65
283	48 c. Emblem and pink flower	1·75	75
284	60 c. Emblem and orange flower	1·75	1·00
282/4	*Set of 3*	4·50	2·25
MS285	86 × 46 mm. $2 As 48 c., but with elements of design reversed	2·40	3·00

1983 (8 July). *15th World Scout Jamboree, Alberta, Canada. Nos.* 282/5 *optd with T* **42**.

286	36 c. Type 41	1·25	40
287	48 c. Emblem and pink flower	1·50	55
288	60 c. Emblem and orange flower	1·60	75
286/8	*Set of 3*	4·00	1·60
MS289	86 × 46 mm. $2 As 48 c., but with elements of design reversed	2·40	3·50

43 School of Sperm Whales   **44** *Mercury* (cable ship)

1983 (29 July). *Whale Conservation. T* **43** *and similar vert designs. Multicoloured. P* 13.

290	8 c. Type 43	1·00	70
291	15 c. Harpooner preparing to strike	1·40	95
292	35 c. Whale attacking boat	2·00	1·40
293	60 c. Dead whales marked with flags	3·00	2·00
294	$1 Dead whales on slipway	3·75	3·00
290/4	*Set of 5*	10·00	7·25

1983 (23 Sept). *World Communications Year. T* **44** *and similar horiz designs. Multicoloured. P* 13.

295	36 c. Type 44	80	35
296	48 c. Men watching cable being laid	85	45
297	60 c. *Mercury* (different)	1·10	60
295/7	*Set of 3*	2·50	1·25
MS298	115 × 90 mm. As Nos. 295/7 but each with charity premium of 3 c.	1·50	1·60

On No. MS298 the values are printed in black and have been transposed with the World Communications Year logo.

1983 (26 Sept). *Various stamps surch as T* **200** *of Cook Islands.*

(a) *Nos. 182/5, 190/7 and 206*

299	18 c. on 10 c. *Preussen*, 1902			20	20
300	18 c. on 10 c. *Pamir*, 1921			20	20
301	18 c. on 10 c. *Cap Hornier*, 1910			20	20
302	18 c. on 10 c. *Patriarch*, 1869			20	20
303	36 c. on 20 c. *Va'a Teu'ua*			35	35
304	36 c. on 20 c. *Vitoria*, 1500			35	35
305	36 c. on 20 c. *Golden Hind*, 1560			35	35
306	36 c. on 20 c. *Boudeuse*, 1760			35	35
307	36 c. on 30 c. H.M.S. *Bounty*, 1787			35	35
308	36 c. on 30 c. *L'Astrolabe*, 1811			35	35
309	36 c. on 30 c. *Star of India*, 1861			35	35
310	36 c. on 30 c. *Great Republic*, 1853			35	35
311	$1.20 on $2 *Cutty Sark*, 1869			1·40	1·40

(b) *Nos. 252/3*

312	72 c. on 70 c. Princess Diana as schoolgirl			2·00	1·50
313	96 c. on 80 c. Princess Diana as teenager			2·25	1·75
299/313			*Set of 15*	8·50	7·00

1983 (28 Oct). *Nos. 208, 225/6, 254 and 268/9 surch as T* **200** *of Cook Islands.*

314	48 c. on 60 c. Prince Charles as young man (Gold)			3·50	1·50
	a. Error. Surch on No. 258			4·50	5·00
315	72 c. on 70 c. Prince Charles in ceremonial Naval uniform			4·00	1·75
	a. Error. Surch on No. 259			5·00	5·00
316	96 c. on 80 c. As No. 253 (inscr "21 JUNE 1982...")			2·75	1·00
	a. Error. Surch on No. 260			6·00	5·50
317	96 c. on 80 c. As No. 253 (inscr "COMMEMORATING...")			1·75	1·00
318	$1.20 on $1.40, Princess Diana as young lady			3·25	1·50
319	$5.60 on $6, H.M.S. *Resolution* and *Discovery*, 1776–80			17·00	9·00
314/19			*Set of 6*	28·00	14·00

45 George Cayley's Airship Design, 1837

1983 (31 Oct). *Bicentenary of Manned Flight. T* **45** *and similar horiz designs. Multicoloured. P* 13.

A. *Inscr* "NORTHERN COOK ISLANS"

320A	36 c. Type **45**		1·00	80
321A	48 c. Dupuy de Lome's man-powered airship, 1872		1·25	90
322A	60 c. Santos Dumont's *Airship No. 6*, 1901		1·50	1·25
323A	96 c. Lebaudy-Juillot's practical airship No. 1 *La Jaune*, 1902		2·25	1·75
324A	$1.32, Airship LZ-127 *Graf Zeppelin*, 1929		3·00	2·50
320A/4A		*Set of 5*	8·00	6·50
MS325A	113×138 mm. Nos. 320A/4A		6·50	11·00

B. *Corrected spelling optd in black on silver over original inscription*

320B	36 c. Type **45**		30	35
321B	48 c. Dupuy de Lome's man-powered airship, 1872		40	45
322B	60 c. Santos Dumont's *Airship No. 6*, 1901		45	50
323B	96 c. Lebaudy-Juillot's practical airship No. 1 *La Jaune*, 1902		75	80
324B	$1.32, Airship LZ-127 *Graf Zeppelin*, 1929		1·00	1·10
320B/4B		*Set of 5*	2·75	3·00
MS325B	113×138 mm. Nos. 320B/4B		2·25	4·25

46 "Madonna in the Meadow"

47 Waka

1983 (30 Nov). *Christmas. 500th Birth Anniv of Raphael. T* **46** *and similar vert designs. Multicoloured. P* 13.

326	36 c. Type **46**		60	40
327	42 c. "Tempi Madonna"		60	40
328	48 c. "The Smaller Cowper Madonna"		80	50
329	60 c. "Madonna della Tenda"		95	60
326/9		*Set of 4*	2·75	1·75
MS330	87 × 115 mm. As Nos. 326/9 but each with a charity premium of 3 c.		3·00	2·50

1983 (1 Dec). *Nos. 266/7, 227 and 270/1 surch as T* **200** *of Cook Islands.*

331	72 c. on 70 c. As No. 252 (inscr "21 JUNE 1982...")		1·50	80
332	72 c. on 70 c. As No. 252 (inscr "COMMEMORATING...")		80	60
333	96 c. on 80 c. Prince Charles as Colonel-in-Chief, Royal Regiment of Wales.		1·50	65
334	$1.20 on $1.40, As No. 254 (inscr "21 JUNE 1982...")		1·75	70
335	$1.20 on $1.40, As No. 254 (inscr "COMMEMORATING...")		1·25	65
331/5		*Set of 5*	6·00	3·00

1983 (28 Dec). *Christmas. 500th Birth Anniv of Raphael. Children's Charity. Designs as Nos. 326/9 in separate miniature sheets, 65 × 84 mm, each with a face value of 75 c. + 5 c. P* 13.

MS336	As Nos. 326/9	*Set of 4 sheets*	2·00	3·00

1984 (8 Feb–15 June). *Sailing Craft and Ships* (2nd series). *Designs as Nos. 166, etc. but with redrawn frames, inscriptions and compass rose at top right as in T* **47**. *Multicoloured. P* 13 × 13½ ($9.60), 13 ($3, $5) or 11 (others).

337	2 c. Type **47**		20	50
338	4 c. *Amatasi*		30	50
339	5 c. *Ndrua*		30	50
340	8 c. *Tongiaki*		40	60
341	10 c. *Vitoria*		40	60
342	18 c. *Golden Hind*		50	70
343	20 c. *Boudeuse*		50	70
344	30 c. H.M.S. *Bounty*		60	70
345	36 c. *L'Astrolabe*		60	70
346	48 c. *Great Republic*		60	70
347	50 c. *Star of India* (21 Mar)		60	70
348	60 c. *Coonatto* (21 Mar)		60	70
349	72 c. *Antiope* (21 Mar)		60	70
350	80 c. *Balcutha* (21 Mar)		70	70
351	96 c. *Cap Hornier* (21 Mar)		85	85
352	$1.20, *Pamir* (21 Mar)		2·50	1·40
353	$3 *Mermerus* (41 × 31 mm) (4 May)		5·00	3·00
354	$5 *Cutty Sark* (41 × 31 mm) (4 May)		5·50	5·00
355	$9.60, H.M.S. *Resolution* and *Discovery* (41 × 31 mm) (15 June)		13·00	12·00
337/55		*Set of 19*	30·00	28·00

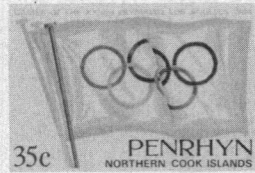

48 Olympic Flag

1984 (20 July). *Olympic Games, Los Angeles. T* **48** *and similar horiz designs. Multicoloured. P* 13½ × 13.

356	35 c. Type **48**		30	35
357	60 c. Olympic torch and flags		50	55
358	$1.80, Ancient athletes and Coliseum		1·50	1·60
356/8		*Set of 3*	2·10	2·25
MS359	103×86 mm. As Nos. 356/8 but each with a charity premium of 5 c.		2·40	2·50

49 Penrhyn Stamps of 1978, 1979 and 1981

1984 (20 Sept). *"Ausipex" International Stamp Exhibition, Melbourne. T* **49** *and similar horiz design. Multicoloured. P* 13½ × 13.

360	60 c. Type **49**		50	75
361	$1.20, Location map of Penrhyn		1·00	1·25
MS362	90 × 90 mm. As Nos. 360/1, but each with a face value of 96 c.		1·75	2·00

$2

Birth of Prince Henry 15 Sept. 1984

(50)

51 "Virgin and Child" (Giovanni Bellini)

1984 (18 Oct). *Birth of Prince Henry. Nos. 223/4 and 250/1 surch as T* **50**.

363	$2 on 30 c. Type **37**		1·40	1·50
364	$2 on 40 c. Type **34**		1·60	1·75
365	$2 on 50 c. Prince Charles as schoolboy		1·60	1·75
366	$2 on 50 c. Lady Diana as young child (Gold)		1·40	1·50
363/6		*Set of 4*	5·50	6·00

1984 (15 Nov). *Christmas. Paintings of the Virgin and Child by different artists. T* **51** *and similar vert designs. Multicoloured. P* 13 × 13½.

367	36 c. Type **51**		60	35
368	48 c. Lorenzo di Credi		75	45
369	60 c. Palma the Older		80	50
370	96 c. Raphael		1·00	80
367/70		*Set of 4*	2·75	1·90
MS371	93 ×118 mm. As Nos. 367/70, but each with a charity premium of 5 c.		2·50	3·00

1984 (10 Dec). *Christmas. Children's Charity. Designs as Nos. 367/70, but without frames, in separate miniature sheets 67 × 81 mm, each with a face value of 96 c. + 10 c. P* 13½.

MS372	As Nos. 367/70	*Set of 4 sheets*	3·75	3·50

52 Harlequin Duck

1985 (9 Apr). *Birth Bicentenary of John J. Audubon (ornithologist). T* **52** *and similar horiz designs showing original paintings. Multicoloured. P* 13.

373	20 c. Type **52**		2·00	1·75
374	55 c. Sage Grouse		2·75	2·75
375	65 c. Solitary Sandpiper		3·00	3·00
376	75 c. Dunlin		3·25	3·50
373/6		*Set of 4*	10·00	10·00
MS377	Four sheets, each 70×53 mm. As Nos. 373/6, but each with a face value of 95 c.		8·50	6·50

53 Lady Elizabeth Bowes-Lyon, 1921

54 "The House in the Wood"

1985 (24 June). *Life and Times of Queen Elizabeth the Queen Mother. T* **53** *and similar vert designs, each deep bluish violet, silver and yellow. P* 13.

378	75 c. Type **53**		40	65
379	95 c. With baby Princess Elizabeth, 1926		50	80
380	$1.20, Coronation Day, 1937		65	1·00
381	$2.80, On her 70th birthday		1·25	2·00
378/81		*Set of 4*	2·50	4·00
MS382	66×90 mm. $5 The Queen Mother		2·40	3·25

Nos. 378/81 were each printed in small sheets of 4 stamps. For these stamps in a miniature sheet see No. **MS403**.

1985 (10 Sept). *International Youth Year and Birth Centenary of Jacob Grimm (folklorist). T* **54** *and similar vert designs. Multicoloured. P* 13 × 13½.

383	75 c. Type **54**		2·00	2·00
384	95 c. "Snow-White and Rose-Red"		2·25	2·25
385	$1.15, "The Goose Girl"		2·50	2·50
383/5		*Set of 3*	6·00	6·00

55 "The Annunciation"

1985 (25 Nov). *Christmas. Paintings by Murillo. T* **55** *and similar horiz designs. Multicoloured. P* 14.

386	75 c. Type **55**		1·25	1·25
387	$1.15, "Adoration of the Shepherds"		1·75	1·75
388	$1.80, "The Holy Family"		2·50	2·50
386/8		*Set of 3*	5·00	5·00
MS389	66×131 mm. As Nos. 386/8, but each with a face value of 95 c. P 13½		2·75	3·00
MS390	Three sheets, each 66×72 mm. As Nos. 386/8, but with face values of $1.20, $1.45 and $2.75. P 13½	*Set of 3 sheets*	4·50	4·75

56 Halley's Comet

1986 (4 Feb). *Appearance of Halley's Comet. T* **56** *and similar horiz design showing details of the painting "Fire and Ice" by Camille Rendal. Multicoloured. P* 13½ × 13.

391	$1.50, Type **56**		1·75	1·50
392	$1.50, Stylised *Giotto* spacecraft		1·75	1·50
MS393	108×43 mm. $3 As Nos. 391/2 (104 × 39 mm). Imperf		2·25	4·00

Nos. 391/2 were printed together, *se-tenant*, in horizontal pairs throughout the sheet, forming a composite design of the complete painting.

57 Princess Elizabeth aged Three, 1929, and Bouquet

58 Statue of Liberty under Construction, Paris

1986 (21 Apr). *60th Birthday of Queen Elizabeth II. T* **57** *and similar horiz designs. Multicoloured. P* 13½ × 13 *($2.50) or* 14 *(others).*

394	95 c. Type **57**	..	1·00	80
395	$1.45, Profile of Queen Elizabeth and St. Edward's Crown		1·50	1·25
396	$2.50, Queen Elizabeth aged three and in profile with Imperial State Crown (56 × 30 *mm*)		2·25	2·00
394/6	.. .. ..	*Set of 3*	4·25	3·50

1986 (27 June). *Centenary of Statue of Liberty* (1st issue). *T* **58** *and similar vert designs, each black, gold and yellow-green. P* 13 × 13½.

397	95 c. Type **58**	..	65	70
398	$1.75, Erection of Statue, New York		1·10	1·25
399	$3 Artist's impression of Statue, 1876		2·10	2·25
397/9	.. ..	*Set of 3*	3·50	3·75

See also No. **MS412**.

59 Prince Andrew and Miss Sarah Ferguson

$2.00

(60)

1986 (23 July). *Royal Wedding. T* **59** *and similar vert design. Multicoloured. P* 13.

400	$2.50, Type **59**		3·50	3·50
401	$3.50, Profiles of Prince Andrew and Miss Sarah Ferguson		4·00	4·00

Nos. 400/1 were each printed in sheetlets of 4 stamps and 2 stamp-size labels.

1986 (4 Aug). *"Stampex '86" Stamp Exhibition, Adelaide. No.* **MS362** *surch with T* **60** *in black on gold.*

MS402	$2 on 96 c. × 2	6·00	7·00

The "Stampex '86" exhibition emblem is overprinted on the sheet margin.

1986 (4 Aug). *86th Birthday of Queen Elizabeth the Queen Mother. Nos.* 378/81 *in miniature sheet,* 90 × 120 *mm. P* 13 × 13½.

MS403	Nos. 378/81	9·50	9·50

 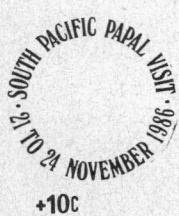

61 "The Adoration of the Shepherds"

+10c

(62)

1986 (20 Nov). *Christmas. Engravings by Rembrandt. T* **61** *and similar vert designs, each red-brown, yellow-ochre and gold. P* 13.

404	65 c. Type **61**		1·75	1·75
405	$1.75 "Virgin and Child"		3·00	3·00
406	$2.50 "The Holy Family"	..	4·25	4·25
404/6	..	*Set of 3*	8·00	8·00
MS407	120 × 87 mm. As Nos. 404/6, but each size 31 × 39 mm with a face value of $1.50. P 13½ × 13		9·50	9·00

1986 (24 Nov). *Visit of Pope John Paul II to South Pacific. Nos.* 404/7 *surch as T* **62** *in greenish blue.*

408	65 c. + 10 c. Type **61**		2·25	2·00
409	$1.75 + 10 c. "Virgin and Child"		3·75	3·50
410	$2.50 + 10 c. "The Holy Family"		4·50	4·00
408/10		*Set of 3*	9·50	8·50
MS411	120 × 87 mm. As Nos. 408/10, but each size 31 × 39 mm with a face value of $1.50 + 10 c.		11·00	9·00

63 Head and Torch of Statue of Liberty

1987 (15 Apr). *Centenary of Statue of Liberty* (1986) (2nd issue). *Two sheets, each* 122 × 122 *mm, containing T* **63** *and similar multicoloured designs. Litho. P* 14 × 13½ (vert) *or* 13½ × 14 (horiz).

MS412 Two sheets (a) 65 c. Type **63**; 65 c. Torch at sunset; 65 c. Restoration workers with flag; 65 c. Statue and Manhattan skyline; 65 c. Workers and scaffolding. (b) 65 c. Workers on Statue crown (*horiz*); 65 c. Aerial view of Ellis Island (*horiz*); 65 c. Ellis Island Immigration Centre (*horiz*); 65 c. View from Statue to Ellis Island and Manhattan (*horiz*); 65 c. Restoration workers (*horiz*)   *Set of 2 sheets*   9·00 11·00

Fortieth Royal Wedding Anniversary 1947-87

(64)

1987 (20 Nov). *Royal Ruby Wedding. Nos.* 68/9 *optd with T* **64** *in magenta.*

413	$2 Birds-eye view of Penrhyn	..	2·00	2·25
414	$5 Satellite view of Australasia	..	3·50	4·25

65 "The Garvagh Madonna"

66 Athletics

1987 (11 Dec). *Christmas. Religious Paintings by Raphael. T* **65** *and similar vert designs. Multicoloured. P* 13½.

415	95 c. Type **65**	..	1·50	1·50
416	$1.60, "The Alba Madonna"	..	2·00	2·00
417	$2.25, "The Madonna of the Fish"	..	3·00	3·00
415/17		*Set of 3*	6·00	6·00
MS418	91 × 126 mm. As Nos. 415/17, but each with a face value of $1.15		11·00	12·00
MS419	70 × 86 mm. $4.80, As No. 417, but size 36 × 39 mm		12·00	12·00

1988 (29 July). *Olympic Games, Seoul. T* **66** *and similar horiz designs. Multicoloured. P* 13½ × 13 (horiz) *or* 13 × 13½ (vert).

420	55 c. Type **66**		65	65
421	95 c. Pole vaulting (*vert*)		1·00	1·00
422	$1.25, Shotputting		1·40	1·40
423	$1.50, Lawn Tennis (*vert*)		2·25	1·75
421/3		*Set of 4*	4·75	4·25
MS424	110 × 70 mm. As Nos. 421 and 423, but each with a face value of $2.50		4·00	5·00

1988 (14 Oct). *Olympic Gold Medal Winners, Seoul. Nos.* 420/4 *optd as T* **235** *of Cook Islands.*

425	55 c. Type **66** (optd "CARL LEWIS UNITED STATES 100 METERS")		70	60
426	95 c. Pole vaulting (optd "LOUISE RITTER UNITED STATES HIGH JUMP")		1·00	90
427	$1.25, Shot putting (optd "ULF TIMMERMANN EAST GERMANY SHOT-PUT")		1·50	1·25
428	$1.50, Lawn Tennis (optd "STEFFI GRAF WEST GERMANY WOMEN'S TENNIS")		2·75	1·40
425/8		*Set of 4*	5·50	3·75
MS429	110 × 70 mm. $2.50, As No. 421 (optd "JACKIE JOYNER-KERSEE United States Heptathlon); $2.50, As No. 423 (optd "STEFFI GRAF West Germany Women's Tennis MILOSLAV MECIR Czechoslovakia Men's Tennis")		5·00	5·50

67 "Virgin and Child"

68 Neil Armstrong stepping onto Moon

1988 (9 Nov). *Christmas. T* **67** *and similar designs showing different "Virgin and Child" paintings by Titian. P* 13 × 13½.

430	70 c. multicoloured	..	90	90
431	85 c. multicoloured	..	1·00	1·00
432	95 c. multicoloured	..	1·25	1·25
433	$1.25, multicoloured		1·50	1·50
430/3		*Set of 4*	4·25	4·25
MS434	100 × 80 mm. $6.40, As Type **67**, but diamond-shaped (57 × 57 *mm*). P 13		6·00	7·00

(Des G. Vasarhelyi)

1989 (24 July). *20th Anniv of First Manned Landing on Moon. T* **68** *and similar horiz designs. Multicoloured. P* 14.

435	55 c. Type **68**		80	60
436	75 c. Astronaut on Moon carrying equipment		95	75
437	95 c. Conducting experiment on Moon		1·25	95
438	$1.25, Crew of "Apollo 11"		1·50	1·25
439	$1.75, Crew inside "Apollo 11"		1·90	1·60
435/9		*Set of 5*	5·75	4·75

69 Virgin Mary

1989 (17 Nov). *Christmas. T* **69** *and similar multicoloured designs showing details from "The Nativity" by Dürer. P* 13.

440	55 c. Type **69**		80	80
441	70 c. Christ Child and cherubs		90	90
442	85 c. Joseph		1·25	1·25
443	$1.25, Three women		1·60	1·60
440/3		*Set of 4*	4·00	4·00
MS444	88 × 95 mm. $6.40, "The Nativity" (31 × 50 *mm*)		6·50	7·50

70 Queen Elizabeth the Queen Mother

1990 (24 July). *90th Birthday of Queen Elizabeth the Queen Mother. P* 13½.

445	70 $2.25, multicoloured	..	2·50	2·50
MS446	85 × 73 mm. **70** $7.50, multicoloured	..	12·00	12·00

$1.50

71 "Adoration of the Magi" (Veronese)

(72)

(Litho Questa)

1990 (26 Nov). *Christmas. Religious Paintings. T* **71** *and similar vert designs. Multicoloured. Ordinary paper. P* 14.

447	55 c. Type **71**		1·00	1·00
448	70 c. "Virgin and Child" (Quentin Metsys)		1·40	1·40
449	85 c. "Virgin and Child Jesus" (Hugo van der Goes)		1·60	1·60
450	$1.50, "Adoration of the Kings" (Jan Gossaert)		2·50	2·50
447/50		*Set of 4*	6·00	6·00
MS451	108 × 132 mm. $6.40, "Virgin and Child with Saints, Francis, John the Baptist, Zenobius and Lucy" (Domenico Veneziano)		7·00	8·00

1990 (5 Dec). *"Birdpex '90" Stamp Exhibition, Christchurch, New Zealand. Nos.* 373/6 *surch as T* **72** *in red (Nos* 452, 455) *or black (others).*

452	$1.50 on 20 c. Type **52**		1·75	1·90
453	$1.50 on 55 c. Sage Grouse		1·75	1·90
454	$1.50 on 65 c. Solitary Sandpiper		1·75	1·90
455	$1.50 on 75 c. Dunlin		1·75	1·90
452/5		*Set of 4*	6·25	7·00

COMMEMORATING 65th BIRTHDAY OF H.M. QUEEN ELIZABETH II

(73)

1991 (22 Apr). *65th Birthday of Queen Elizabeth II. No. 208 optd with T* 73.
456	$6 H.M.S. *Resolution* and *Discovery*, 1776–80	..	9·00	10·00

74 "The Virgin and Child with Saints" (G. David)

(Des G. Vasarhelyi. Litho Questa)

1991 (11 Nov). *Christmas. Religious Paintings. T* 74 *and similar multicoloured designs. Ordinary paper. P* 14.
457	55 c. Type 74	..	1·00	1·00
458	85 c. "Nativity" (Tintoretto)	..	1·50	1·50
459	$1.15, "Mystic Nativity" (Botticelli)	..	1·75	1·75
460	$1.85, "Adoration of the Shepherds" (B. Murillo)	..	2·75	3·25
457/60		*Set of* 4	6·25	6·75
MS461	79×103 mm. $6.40, "The Madonna of the Chair" (Raphael) (*vert*)	..	11·00	11·00

(Des G. Vasarhelyi. Litho B.D.T.)

1992 (27 July). *Olympic Games, Barcelona. Horiz designs as T* 94 *of Aitutaki. Multicoloured. Ordinary paper. P* 14.
462	75 c. Running	..	1·40	1·40
463	95 c. Boxing	..	1·60	1·60
464	$1.15, Swimming	..	1·75	1·75
465	$1.50, Wrestling	..	1·90	1·90
462/5		*Set of* 4	6·00	6·00

75 Marquesan Canoe

(Litho B.D.T.)

1992 (16 Oct). *6th Festival of Pacific Arts, Rarotonga. T* 75 *and similar horiz designs. Multicoloured. Ordinary paper. P* 14×15.
466	$1.15, Type 75	..	1·40	1·40
467	$1.75, Tangaroa statue from Rarotonga	..	1·90	1·90
468	$1.95, Manihiki canoe	..	2·00	2·00
466/8		*Set of* 3	4·75	4·75

1992 (16 Oct). *Royal Visit by Prince Edward. Nos.* 466/8 *optd with T* 254 *of Cook Islands.*
469	$1.15, Type 75	..	1·75	1·75
470	$1.75, Tangaroa statue from Rarotonga	..	2·50	2·50
471	$1.95, Manihiki canoe	..	3·00	3·00
469/71		*Set of* 3	6·50	6·50

76 "Virgin with Child and Saints" (Borgognone) 77 Vincente Pinzon and *Nina*

1992 (18 Nov). *Christmas. Religious Paintings by Ambrogio Borgognone. T* 76 *and similar vert designs. Multicoloured. Ordinary paper. P* 13½.
472	55 c. Type 76	..	75	75
473	85 c. "Virgin on Throne"	..	1·10	1·10
474	$1.05, "Virgin on Carpet"	..	1·40	1·40
475	$1.85, "Virgin of the Milk"	..	2·25	2·25
472/5		*Set of* 4	5·00	5·00
MS476	101×86 mm. $6.40, As 55 c., but larger (36×46 *mm*)	..	7·00	8·00

(Litho B.D.T.)

1992 (4 Dec). *500th Anniv of Discovery of America by Columbus. T* 77 *and similar vert designs. Multicoloured. Ordinary paper. P* 15×14.
477	$1.15, Type 77	..	2·00	2·00
478	$1.35, Martin Pinzon and *Pinta*	..	2·25	2·25
479	$1.75, Christopher Columbus and *Santa Maria*	..	3·00	3·00
477/9		*Set of* 3	6·50	6·50

78 Queen Elizabeth II in 1953 79 Bull-mouth Helmet

(Des G. Vasarhelyi. Litho B.D.T.)

1993 (4 June). *40th Anniv of Coronation. P* 14.
480	78 $6 multicoloured	..	6·50	8·00

(Des G. Drummond. Litho Questa ($3 to $10), B.D.T. (others))

1993 (18 Oct)–**98**. *Marine Life. T* 79 *and similar horiz designs. Multicoloured. P* 14×13½ ($3 to $10) *or* 13½×14 (*others*).
481	5 c. Type 79	..	10	10
482	10 c. Daisy Coral	..	10	10
483	15 c. Hydroid Coral	..	10	15
484	20 c. Feather-star	..	15	20
485	25 c. Sea Star	..	15	20
486	30 c. Varicose Nudibranch	..	20	25
487	50 c. Smooth Sea Star	..	30	35
488	70 c. Black-lip Pearl Oyster	..	45	50
489	80 c. Four-coloured Nudibranch (3.12.93)	..	50	55
490	85 c. Prickly Sea Cucumber (3.12.93)	..	55	60
491	90 c. Organ Pipe Coral (3.12.93)	..	55	60
492	$1 Blue Sea Lizard (3.12.93)	..	65	70
493	$2 Textile Cone shell (3.12.93)	..	1·25	1·40
494	$3 Starfish (21.11.94)	..	1·90	2·00
495	$5 As $3 (21.11.94)	..	3·25	3·50
496	$8 As $3 (17.11.97)	..	5·00	5·25
497	$10 As $3 (1.10.98)	..	6·25	6·50
481/97		*Set of* 17	21·00	22·50

Nos. 494/7 are larger, 47×34 mm, and include a portrait of Queen Elizabeth II at top right.

80 "Virgin on Throne with Child" (detail) (Tura) 81 Neil Armstrong stepping onto Moon

1993 (2 Nov). *Christmas. T* 80 *and similar vert designs showing different details from "Virgin on Throne with Child" (Cosme Tura). Ordinary paper. P* 13½ ($4.50) *or* 14 (*others*).
499	55 c. multicoloured	..	1·00	1·00
500	85 c. multicoloured	..	1·50	1·50
501	$1.05, multicoloured	..	1·75	1·75
502	$1.95, multicoloured	..	2·75	3·00
503	$4.50, multicoloured (32×47 *mm*)	..	6·00	7·00
499/503		*Set of* 5	11·50	13·00

(Des G. Vasarhelyi. Litho B.D.T.)

1994 (20 July). *25th Anniv of First Moon Landing. P* 14.
504	81 $3.25, multicoloured	..	7·00	7·00

82 "The Virgin and Child with Sts. Paul and Jerome" (Vivarini)

(Litho B.D.T.)

1994 (30 Nov). *Christmas. Religious Paintings. T* 82 *and similar vert designs. Multicoloured. P* 14.
505	90 c. Type 82	..	1·10	1·25
	a. Block of 4. Nos. 505/8	..	4·00	
506	90 c. "The Virgin and Child with St. John" (Luini)	..	1·10	1·25
507	90 c. "The Virgin and Child with Sts. Jerome and Dominic" (Lippi)	..	1·10	1·25
508	90 c. "Adoration of the Shepherds" (Murillo)	..	1·10	1·25
509	$1 "Adoration of the Kings" (detail of angels) (Reni)	..	1·10	1·25
	a. Block of 4. Nos. 509/12	..	4·00	
510	$1 "Madonna and Child with the Infant Baptist" (Raphael)	..	1·10	1·25
511	$1 "Adoration of the Kings" (detail of manger) (Reni)	..	1·10	1·25
512	$1 "Virgin and Child" (Borgognone)	..	1·10	1·25
505/12		*Set of* 8	8·00	9·00

Nos. 505/8 and 509/12 were printed together, *se-tenant*, in blocks of 4 throughout the sheets.

83 Battleship Row burning, Pearl Harbor

(Litho B.D.T.)

1995 (4 Sept). *50th Anniv of End of Second World War. T* 83 *and similar horiz design. Multicoloured. P* 13.
513	$3.75, Type 83	..	5·00	5·00
	a. Pair. Nos. 686/7	..	10·00	10·00
514	$3.75, Boeing B-25 Superfortress *Enola Gay* over Hiroshima	..	5·00	5·00

Nos. 513/14 were printed together, *se-tenant* horizontally and vertically, in sheets of 4.

84 Queen Elizabeth the Queen Mother at Remembrance Day Ceremony

(Des G. Vasarhelyi. Litho B.D.T.)

1995 (14 Sept). *95th Birthday of Queen Elizabeth the Queen Mother. P* 13.
515	84 $4.50, multicoloured	..	6·00	7·00

No. 515 was printed in sheets of 4 with inscribed margins.

85 Anniversary Emblem, United Nations Flag and Headquarters

(Des G. Vasarhelyi. Litho B.D.T.)

1995 (20 Oct). *50th Anniv of United Nations. P* 13×13½.
516	85 $4 multicoloured	..	4·00	5·00

No. 516 was printed in sheets of 4 with inscribed margins.

86 Loggerhead Turtle 87 Queen Elizabeth II and Rose

(Litho B.D.T.)

1995 (7 Dec). *Year of the Sea Turtle. T* 86 *and similar vert designs. Multicoloured. P* 13½×14.
517	$1.15, Type 86	..	1·75	2·00
	a. Horiz pair. Nos. 517/18	..	3·50	4·00
518	$1.15, Hawksbill Turtle	..	1·75	2·00
519	$1.65, Olive Ridley Turtle	..	2·25	2·50
	a. Horiz pair. Nos. 519/20	..	4·50	5·00
520	$1.65, Green Turtle	..	2·25	2·50
517/20		*Set of* 4	7·25	8·00

Nos. 517/18 and 519/20 were printed together, *se-tenant*, in horizontal pairs throughout the sheets.

(Des G. Vasarhelyi. Litho)

1996 (20 June). *70th Birthday of Queen Elizabeth II.* P 14.
521 87 $4.25, multicoloured .. .. 4·75 5·50
No. 521 was printed in sheets of 4 with inscribed margins.

88 Olympic Flame, National Flags and Sports

(Des G. Vasarhelyi. Litho B.D.T.)

1996 (12 July). *Centenary of Modern Olympic Games.* P 14.
522 88 $5 multicoloured .. .. 6·50 7·00

89 Royal Wedding, 1947   90 Diana, Princess of Wales with Sons

1997 (20 Nov). *Golden Wedding of Queen Elizabeth and Prince Philip.* P 14.
523 89 $3 multicoloured .. .. 2·50 2·75
MS524 42×28 mm. 89 $4 multicoloured .. 3·50 4·00
No. 523 was printed in sheets of 4 with inscribed margins.

1998 (7 May). *Diana, Princess of Wales Commemoration.* Litho. P 14.
525 90 $1.50, multicoloured .. .. 1·25 1·50
 a. Sheetlet. No. 525×5 plus label .. 5·50
MS526 70×100 mm. 90 $3.75, multicoloured .. 3·50 4·00
No. 525 was printed in sheetlets of 5 stamps with a label at top left.

1998 (19 Nov). *Children's Charities. No.* **MS526** *surch as* T 275 *of Cook Islands in silver.*
MS527 70×100 mm. 90 $3.75+$1 multicoloured 3·00 3·50

1999 (31 Dec). *New Millennium. Nos. 466/8 optd with* T 112 *of Aitutaki.*
528 $1.15, Type 75 .. .. 75 80
529 $1.75, Tangaroa statue from Rarotonga 1·10 1·25
530 $1.95, Manihiki canoe .. .. 1·25 1·40
528/30 .. .. .. Set of 3 3·00 3·25

STAMP BOOKLETS

1982 (June). *Royal Wedding. Cover as No. SB1 of Cook Islands, but inscr* "Penrhyn".
SB1 $4.50, booklet containing 40 c. and 50 c. (Nos. 223/4), each in block of 5 and 1 label 4·75

OFFICIAL STAMPS

O.H.M.S.
(O 1)

1978 (14 Nov). *Nos. 57/66, 89/91 and 101/2 optd or surch (Nos. O8/9 and O12) as Type* O 1.
O 1   1 c. Diamond Fingerfish 15 10
O 2   2 c. Emperor Angelfish 15 10
O 3   3 c. Copper-banded Butterflyfish .. 25 10
O 4   4 c. Ornate Butterflyfish 25 10
O 5   5 c. Black-backed Butterflyfish .. 30 10
O 6   8 c. Latticed Butterflyfish 35 15
O 7 10 c. Saddle Butterflyfish 40 15
O 8 15 c. on 60 c. Harlequin Sweetlips 45 25
O 9 18 c. on 60 c. Harlequin Sweetlips 50 25
O10 20 c. Regal Angelfish 50 25
O11 25 c. Pennant Coralfish (Silver) .. 55 30
O12 30 c. on 60 c. Harlequin Sweetlips 55 35
O13 50 c. } 90 55
O14 50 c. } "The Spirit of '76" (A. M. Willard) (Gold) 90 55
O15 50 c. } 90 55
O16 $1 Queen and Prince Philip (Silver) 2·25 45
O17 $2 Queen Elizabeth II (Gold) .. 4·00 50
O1/17 .. .. .. Set of 17 12·00 4·00
These stamps were originally only sold to the public cancelled-to-order and not in unused condition. They were made available to overseas collectors in mint condition during 1980.

65c

O.H.M.S.   O.H.M.S.
(O 2)
       (O 3)

1985 (15 Aug)–87. (*a*) *Nos. 206/8, 337/47 and 349/55 optd or surch as Type* O 2 *by foil embossing in red* ($2, $4, $6) *or silver* (*others*)
O18   2 c. Type 47 .. .. .. 30 30
O19   4 c. Amatasi 30 30
O20   5 c. Ndrua 30 30
O21   8 c. Tongiaki 30 30
O22 10 c. Vitoria 30 30
O23 18 c. Golden Hind 65 50
O24 20 c. Boudeuse 65 50
O25 30 c. H.M.S. Bounty .. 65 50
O26 40 c. on 36 c. L'Astrolabe .. 70 50
O27 50 c. Star of India 80 50
O28 55 c. on 48 c. Great Republic .. 80 50
O29 75 c. on 72 c. Antiope (29.4.86) .. 1·50 70
O30 75 c. on 96 c. Cap Hornier (29.4.86) 1·50 70
O31 80 c. Balcutha (29.4.86) .. .. 1·50 70
O32 $1.20, Pamir (29.4.86) .. .. 1·75 1·00
O33 $2 Cutty Sark (29.4.86) .. .. 3·00 1·60
O34 $3 Mermerus (29.4.86) .. .. 3·00 2·40
O35 $4 Mermerus (29.4.86) .. .. 4·00 3·25
O36 $5 Cutty Sark (2.11.87) .. .. 5·00 4·00
O37 $6 H.M.S. *Resolution and Discovery* (2.11.87) .. .. .. 6·00 5·00
O38 $9.60, H.M.S. *Resolution and Discovery* (2.11.87) .. .. 9·50 7·25

(*b*) *Nos. 278/81 surch as Type* O 3 *by silver foil embossing*
O39 65 c. on 60 c. Type 40 .. .. 70 60
O40 65 c. on 60 c. Aerial view of Penrhyn atoll .. 70 60
O41 65 c. on 60 c. Eleanor Roosevelt on Penrhyn during Second World War .. 70 60
O42 65 c. on 60 c. Map of South Pacific .. 70 60
O18/42 .. .. .. Set of 25 38·00 30·00

O.H.M.S.
(O 4)

1998 (20 July–30 Sept). *Nos. 481/93 optd with Type* O 4 *in silver.*
O43   5 c. Type 79 .. .. .. 10 10
O44 10 c. Daisy Coral 10 10
O45 15 c. Hydroid Coral 10 15
O46 20 c. Feather-star 15 20
O47 25 c. Sea Star 15 20
O48 30 c. Varicose Nudibranch .. 20 25
O49 50 c. Smooth Sea Star 30 35
O50 70 c. Black-lip Pearl Oyster .. 45 50
O51 80 c. Four-coloured Nudibranch .. 50 55
O52 85 c. Prickly Sea Cucumber .. 55 60
O53 90 c. Organ Pipe Coral 55 60
O54 $1 Blue Sea Lizard 65 70
O55 $2 Textile Cone shell (30 Sept) .. 1·25 1·40
O43/55 .. .. .. Set of 13 4·75 5·50

Cyprus

Cyprus was part of the Turkish Ottoman Empire from 1571.
The first records of an organised postal service date from 1871 when a post office was opened at Nicosia (Lefkosa) under the jurisdiction of the Damascus Head Post Office. Various stamps of Turkey from the 1868 issue onwards are known used from this office, cancelled "KIBRIS", in Arabic, within a double-lined oblong. Manuscript cancellations have also been reported. The records report the opening of a further office at Larnaca (Tuzla) in 1873, but no cancellation for this office has been identified.

To provide an overseas postal service the Austrian Empire opened a post office in Larnaca during 1845. Stamps of the Austrian Post Offices in the Turkish Empire were placed on sale there from 1 June 1864 and were cancelled with an unframed straight-line mark or circular date stamp. This Austrian post office closed on 6 August 1878.

BRITISH ADMINISTRATION

Following the convention with Turkey, Great Britain assumed the administration of Cyprus on 11 July 1878 and the first post office, as part of the British G.P.O. system, was opened at Larnaca on 27 July 1878. Further offices as Famagusta, Kyrenia, Limassol, Nicosia and Paphos followed in September 1878.

The stamps of Great Britain were supplied to the various offices as they opened and continued to be used until the Cyprus Administration assumed responsibility for the postal service on 1 April 1880. With the exception of "969" (Nicosia) similar numeral cancellations had previously been used at offices in Great Britain.

Numeral postmarks for Headquarters Camp, Nicosia ("D48") and Polymedia (Polemidhia) Camp, Limassol ("D47") were supplied by the G.P.O. in London during January 1881. These cancellations had three bars above and three bars below the numeral. Similar marks, but with four bars above and below, had previously been used in London on newspapers and bulk mail.

Although both three bar cancellations subsequently occur on Cyprus issues only isolated examples have been found on loose Great Britain stamps and there are no known covers or pieces which confirm such usage in Cyprus.

For illustrations of the postmark types see BRITISH POST OFFICES ABROAD notes, following GREAT BRITAIN.

FAMAGUSTA

Stamps of GREAT BRITAIN *cancelled* "982" *as Type* **9**

1878 *to* **1880.**
Z1	½d. rose-red (1870–79) (Plate Nos. 11, 13)			£700
Z2	1d. rose-red (1864–79)			£475
	Plate Nos. 145, 174, 181, 193, 202, 204, 206, 215, 217.			
Z3	2d. blue (1858–69) (Plate Nos. 13, 14, 15)			£950
Z4	2½d. rosy mauve (1876) (Plate Nos. 13, 16)			£1100
Z5	6d. grey (1874–80) (Plate No. 15)			
Z6	1s. green (1873–77) (Plate No. 12)			£1900

KYRENIA

Stamps of GREAT BRITAIN *cancelled* "974" *as Type* **9**

1878 *to* **1880.**
Z 8	½d. rose-red (1870–79) (Plate No. 13)			
Z 9	1d. rose-red (1864–79)		*From*	£550
	Plate Nos. 168, 171, 193, 196, 206, 207, 209, 220.			
Z10	2d. blue (1858–69) (Plate Nos. 13, 15)		*From*	£850
Z11	2½d. rosy mauve (1876–79)		*From*	£1000
	Plate Nos. 12, 13, 14, 15.			
Z12	4d. sage-green (1877) (Plate No. 16)			
Z13	6d. grey (1874–80) (Plate No. 16)			

LARNACA

Stamps of GREAT BRITAIN *cancelled* "942" *as Type* **9**

1878 *to* **1880.**
Z14	½d. rose-red (1870–79)		*From*	£250
	Plate Nos. 11, 12, 13, 14, 15, 19, 20.			
Z15	1d. rose-red (1864–79)		*From*	£170
	Plate Nos. 129, 131, 146, 154, 170, 171, 174, 175, 176, 177, 178, 179, 181, 182, 183, 184, 187, 188, 190, 191, 192, 193, 194, 195, 196, 197, 198, 199, 200, 201, 202, 203, 204, 205, 206, 207, 208, 209, 210, 212, 213, 214, 215, 216, 217, 218, 220, 221, 222, 225.			
Z16	1½d. lake-red (1870) (Plate No. 3)			£1700
Z17	2d. blue (1858–69) (Plate Nos. 9, 13, 14, 15)			£225
Z18	2½d. rosy mauve (1876–79)		*From*	50·00
	Plate Nos. 4, 5, 6, 8, 9, 10, 11, 12, 13, 14, 15, 16, 17.			
Z19	2½d. blue (1880) (Plate Nos. 17, 18)			£500
Z21	4d. sage-green (1877) (Plate Nos. 15, 16)			£550
Z22	6d. grey (1874–76) (Plate Nos. 15, 16, 17)			£500
Z23	6d. pale buff (1872–73) (Plate No. 11)			£1900
Z24	8d. orange (1876)			£4250
Z25	1s. green (1873–77) (Plate Nos. 12, 13)			£900
Z27	5s. rose (1874) (Plate No. 2)			£4500

LIMASSOL

Stamps of GREAT BRITAIN *cancelled* "975" *as Type* **9**

1878 *to* **1880.**
Z28	½d. rose-red (1870–79) (Plate Nos. 11, 13, 15, 19)			£450
Z29	1d. rose-red (1864–79)		*From*	£275
	Plate Nos. 159, 160, 171, 173, 174, 177, 179, 184, 187, 190, 193, 195, 196, 197, 198, 200, 202, 206, 207, 208, 209, 210, 213, 215, 216, 218, 220, 221, 222, 225			

Z30	1½d. lake-red (1870–74) (Plate No. 3)			£1800
Z31	2d. blue (1858–69) (Plate Nos. 14, 15)		*From*	£400
Z32	2½d. rosy-mauve (1876–80)		*From*	£160
	Plate Nos. 11, 12, 13, 14, 15, 16.			
Z33	2½d. blue (1880) (Plate No. 17)			£1200
Z34	4d. sage-green (Plate No. 16)			£700

NICOSIA

Stamps of GREAT BRITAIN *cancelled* "969" *as Type* **9**

1878 *to* **1880.**
Z35	½d. rose-red (1870–79)			£450
	Plate Nos. 12, 13, 14, 15, 20.			
Z36	1d. rose-red (1864–79)		*From*	£275
	Plate Nos. 170, 171, 174, 189, 190, 192, 193, 195, 196, 198, 200, 202, 203, 205, 206, 207, 210, 212, 214, 215, 218, 221, 222, 225.			
Z37	2d. blue (1858–69) (Plate Nos. 14, 15)			£450
Z38	2½d. rosy mauve (1876–79)		*From*	£170
	Plate Nos. 10, 11, 12, 13, 14, 15, 16.			
Z42	4d. sage-green (1877) (Plate No. 16)			£800
Z43	6d. grey (1873) (Plate No. 16)			£800

PAPHOS

Stamps of GREAT BRITAIN *cancelled* "981" *as Type* **9**

1878 *to* **1880.**
Z44	½d. rose-red (1870–79) (Plate Nos. 13, 15)			
Z45	1d. rose-red (1864–79)		*From*	£500
	Plate Nos. 196, 201, 202, 204, 206, 213, 217.			
Z46	2d. blue (1858–69) (Plate No. 15)			£850
Z47	2½d. rosy mauve (1876–79)		*From*	£500
	Plate Nos. 13, 14, 15, 16.			

PRICES FOR STAMPS ON COVER TO 1945

No. 1	*from × 10*
No. 2	*from × 50*
No. 3	*from × 100*
No. 4	*from × 8*
Nos. 5/6	
Nos. 7/10	*from × 15*
Nos. 11/15	*from × 5*
No. 16	
Nos. 16a/24	*from × 10*
No. 25	*from × 40*
No. 26	
No. 27	*from × 10*
No. 28	
No. 29	*from × 30*
Nos. 31/5a	*from × 10*
No. 36/7	
Nos. 40/9	*from × 8*
Nos. 50/9	*from × 5*
Nos. 74/99	*from × 4*
No. 100/2	
Nos. 103/17	*from × 4*
No. 117a	
Nos. 118/31	*from × 5*
No. 132	
Nos. 133/43	*from × 5*
Nos. 144/7	*from × 6*
Nos. 148/63	*from × 5*

PERFORATION. Nos. 1/122 are perf 14.

Stamps of Great Britain overprinted

CYPRUS
(1)

CYPRUS
(2)

(Optd by D.L.R.)

1880 (1 Apr).
1	**1**	½d. rose	£100	£100
		a. Opt double (Plate 15)		£11000

Plate No.	Un.	Used.	Plate No.	Un. Used
12.	£170	£250	19.	£4250 £700
15.	£100	£100		

2	**2**	1d. red	9·50	28·00
		a. Opt double (Plate 208)		£13000
		aa. Opt double (Plate 218)		£4250
		b. Vert pair, top stamp without opt (Plate 208)		£15000

Plate No.	Un.	Used.	Plate No.	Un. Used
174.	£1200	£1200	208.	90·00 50·00
181.	£325	£170	215.	11·00 45·00
184.	£10000	£2250	216.	14·00 28·00
193.	£600	†	217.	9·50 48·00
196.	£550	†	218.	15·00 48·00
201.	10·00	48·00	220.	£350 £375
205.	45·00	45·00		

3	**2**	2½d. rosy mauve	2·25	7·00
		a. Large thin "C" (Plate 14) (BK, JK)	40·00	£160
		b. Large thin "C" (Plate 15) (BK, JK)	65·00	£375
		w. Wmk inverted (Plate 15)		£190

	14.		2·25 7·00	15.	3·25 20·00

4	**2**	4d. sage-green (Plate 16)	£120	£200
5		6d. grey (Plate 16)	£500	£650
6		1s. green (Plate 13)	£650	£450

No. 3 has been reported from Plate 9.

HALF-PENNY
(3) 18 mm

HALF-PENNY
(4) 16 or 16½ mm

HALF-PENNY
(5) 13 mm

30 PARAS
(6)

(Optd by Govt Ptg Office, Nicosia)

1881 (Feb–June). *No. 2 surch.*
7	**3**	½d. on 1d. red (Feb)	70·00	85·00
		a. "HALFPENN" (BG, LG) (*all plates*)	*From* £1700	£1700

Plate No.	Un.	Used.	Plate No.	Un.	Used
174.	£150	£300	215.	£600	£650
181.	£140	£160	216.	70·00	85·00
201.	85·00	£110	217.	£750	£650
205.	70·00	85·00	218.	£425	£550
208.	£160	£275	220.	£250	£300

8	**4**	½d. on 1d. red (Apr)	£120	£160
		a. Surch double (Plates 201 and 216)	£2250	£2250

201.	£120	£160	218.	—
216.	£350	£400		

9	**5**	½d. on 1d. red (1 June)	45·00	65·00
		aa. Surch double (Plate 205)		£650
		ab. Surch double (Plate 215)		£550
		b. Surch treble (Plate 205)		£3000
		ba. Surch treble (Plate 215)		£650
		bc. Surch treble (Plate 218)		£3000
		c. Surch quadruple (Plate 205)		£3500
		ca. Surch quadruple (Plate 215)		£3500

205.	£225	—	217.	£120 75·00
215.	45·00	65·00	218.	65·00 90·00

The surcharge on No. 8 was handstamped; the others were applied by lithography.

(New Currency: 40 paras = 1 piastre, 180 piastres = £1)

1881 (June). *No. 2 surch with T* **6** *by lithography.*
10	**6**	30 paras on 1d. red	£100	80·00
		a. Surch double, one invtd (Plate 216)		£3250
		aa. Surch double, one invtd (Plate 220)	£1300	£1000

201.	£120	85·00	217.	£170 £160
216.	£100	80·00	220.	£150 £160

7   **(8)**   **(9)**

(Typo D.L.R.)

1881 (1 July). *Die I. Wmk Crown CC.*
11	**7**	½ pi. emerald-green		£180 42·00
		w. Wmk inverted		£425
12		1 pi. rose		£375 30·00
13		2 pi. blue		£450 30·00
		w. Wmk inverted		£425
14		4 pi. pale olive-green		£900 £275
15		6 pi. olive-grey		£1400 £425

Stamps of Queen Victoria initialled "J.A.B." or overprinted "POSTAL SURCHARGE" with or without the same initials were employed for accounting purposes between the Chief Post Office and sub-offices, the initials are those of the then Postmaster, Mr. J. A. Bulmer.

"US" damaged at foot
(Left pane R. 5/5)

1882 (May)–86. *Die I*. Wmk Crown CA.*
16	**7**	½ pi. emerald-green (5.82)		£4250 £375
		a. *Dull green (4.83)*		11·00 90
		b. Top left triangle detached		— £110
17		30 pa. pale mauve (7.6.82)		55·00 18·00
		a. Top left triangle detached		£650 £275
		b. Damaged "US"		— £275
18		1 pi. rose (3.83)		75·00 1·50
		a. Top left triangle detached		— £130
19		2 pi. blue (4.83)		£100 1·50
		a. Top left triangle detached		— £130
20		4 pi. deep olive-green (10.83)		£500 29·00
		a. *Pale olive-green*		£350 22·00
		b. Top left triangle detached		— £375
21		6 pi. olive-grey (7.82)		40·00 17·00
		a. Top left triangle detached		— £300
22		12 pi. orange-brown (1886) (Optd S. £650)	£170	32·00
		a. Top left triangle detached		— £475
16a/22			*Set of 7*	£700 80·00

*For description and illustrations of Dies I and II see Introduction.

For illustration of "top left triangle detached" variety see above No. 21 of Antigua.

See also Nos. 31/7.

(Surch litho by Govt Ptg Office, Nicosia)

1882. *Surch with T* **8/9.** (*a*) *Wmk Crown CC.*
23	**7**	½ on ½ pi. emerald-green (6.82)		£500 75·00
24		30 pa. on 1 pi. rose (22.5.82)		£1400 £100

(*b*) *Wmk Crown CA*
25	**7**	½ on ½ pi. emerald-green (27.5.82)		£120 6·50
		a. Surch double		† £2750

NEW INFORMATION

The editor is always interested to correspond with people who have new information that will improve or correct the Catalogue.

$\frac{1}{2}$ $\frac{1}{2}$

(10)

11

Varieties of numerals:

1   1   1

Normal   Large   Small

2   2

Normal   Large

1886 (Apr). *Surch with T 10 (fractions approx 6 mm apart) in typography.*

(a) Wmk Crown CC

26	7	½ on ½ pi. emerald-green	..£13000	

(b) Wmk Crown CA

27	7	½ on ½ pi. emerald-green	£225	70·00
		a. Large "2" at right	—	£750

1886 (May–June). *Surch with T 10 (fractions approx 8 mm apart) in typography.*

(a) Wmk Crown CC

28	7	½ on ½ pi emerald-green	£7000	£425
		a. Large "1" at left	—	£1700
		b. Small "1" at right	£12000	£2250
		c. Large "2" at left	—	£2250
		d. Large "2" at right	†	£2250

(b) Wmk Crown CA

29	7	½ on ½ pi. emerald-green (June)	£325	8·50
		a. Large "1" at left	£2000	£200
		b. Small "1" at right	£2750	£275
		c. Large "2" at left	£2500	£275
		d. Large "2" at right	£2500	£275

Nos. 28/9 were surcharged in a setting of 60. The large "1" at left and large "2" at right both occur in the fourth vertical row, the large "2" at left in the fifth vertical row and the small "1" at right in the top horizontal row.

A third type of this surcharge is known with the fractions spaced approximately 10 mm apart on CA paper with postmarks from August 1886. This may be due to the shifting of type.

1892–94. *Die II. Wmk Crown CA.*

31	7	½ pi. dull green	3·50	50
32		30 pa. mauve	4·00	4·00
		a. Damaged "US"	£120	
33		1 pi. carmine	9·50	1·00
34		2 pi. ultramarine	12·00	1·25
35		4 pi. olive-green	50·00	26·00
		a. Pale olive-green	17·00	22·00
36		6 pi. olive-grey (1894)	£130	£500
37		12 pi. orange-brown (1893)	£120	£325
31/7			Set of 7 £275	£750

1894 (14 Aug)**–96.** *Colours changed and new values. Die II. Wmk Crown CA.*

40	7	½ pi. green and carmine (1896)	4·00	80
		w. Wmk inverted		
41		30 pa. bright mauve and green (1896)	2·00	85
		a. Damaged "US"	90·00	
42		1 pi. carmine and blue (1896)	4·50	90
43		2 pi. blue and purple (1896)	5·50	90
44		4 pi. sage-green and purple (1896)	13·00	4·00
45		6 pi. sepia and green (1896)	10·00	11·00
46		9 pi. brown and carmine	15·00	13·00
47		12 pi. orange-brown and black (1896)	16·00	50·00
48		18 pi. greyish slate and brown	42·00	45·00
49		45 pi. grey-purple and blue	90·00	£130
40/9			Set of 10 £180	£225
40/9 Optd "Specimen"			Set of 10 £300	

LIMASSOL FLOOD HANDSTAMP. Following a flood on 14 November 1894, which destroyed the local stamp stocks, the postmaster of Limassol produced a temporary handstamp showing "½C.P." which was applied to local letters with the usual c.d.s.

(Typo D.L.R.)

1902–04. *Wmk Crown CA.*

50	11	½ pi. green and carmine (12.02)	3·50	75
		w. Wmk inverted	65·00	40·00
51		30 pa. violet and green (2.03)	5·00	2·25
		a. Mauve and green	14·00	6·00
52		1 pi. carmine and blue (9.03)	13·00	2·50
53		2 pi. blue and purple (2.03)	42·00	8·00
54		4 pi. olive-green and purple (9.03)	28·00	17·00
55		6 pi. sepia and green (9.03)	40·00	£100
56		9 pi. brown and carmine (5.04)	95·00	£180
57		12 pi. chestnut and black (4.03)	13·00	45·00
58		18 pi. black and brown (5.04)	70·00	£130
59		45 pi. dull purple and ultramarine (10.03)	£200	£500
50/9			Set of 10 £450	£900
50w/9 Optd "Specimen"			Set of 10 £450	

The ½ pi "SPECIMEN" is only known with watermark inverted.

Broken top left triangle
(Left pane R.7/5)

1904–10. *Wmk Mult Crown CA.*

60	11	5 pa. bistre and black (14.1.08)	70	40
		a. Broken top left triangle	42·00	42·00
61		10 pa. orange and green (12.06)	2·25	40
		aw. Wmk inverted	—	65·00
		b. Yellow and green	32·00	5·50
		bw. Wmk inverted	—	75·00
		c. Broken top left triangle	55·00	35·00
62		½ pi. green and carmine (1.7.04)	4·00	15
		a. Broken top left triangle	75·00	25·00
		w. Wmk inverted	80·00	50·00
63		30 pa. purple and green (1.7.04)	11·00	1·25
		a. Violet and green (1910)	12·00	2·00
		b. Broken top left triangle	£140	50·00
		c. Damaged "US"	£140	50·00
64		1 pi. carmine and blue (11.04)	3·50	80
		a. Broken top left triangle	85·00	45·00
65		2 pi. blue and purple (11.04)	4·75	1·25
		a. Broken top left triangle	£110	60·00
66		4 pi. olive-green and purple (2.05)	9·50	6·50
		a. Broken top left triangle	£160	£140
67		6 pi. sepia and green (17.7.04)	11·00	12·00
		a. Broken top left triangle	£160	
68		9 pi. brown and carmine (30.5.04)	25·00	8·00
		a. Yellow-brown and carmine	20·00	20·00
		aw. Wmk inverted	95·00	65·00
		b. Broken top left triangle	£250	£180
69		12 pi. chestnut and black (4.06)	22·00	32·00
		a. Broken top left triangle	£250	
70		18 pi. black and brown (16.6.04)	28·00	10·00
		a. Broken top left triangle	£325	£225
71		45 pi. dull purple and ultram (15.6.04)	75·00	£140
60/71			Set of 12 £170	£190
60/1 Optd "Specimen"			Set of 2 £120	

12   13

Broken bottom left triangle (Right pane R.10/6)

(Typo D.L.R.)

1912 (July)**–15.** *Wmk Mult Crown CA.*

74	12	10 pa. orange and green (11.12)	3·00	1·90
		a. Wmk sideways	†	£2000
		b. Orange-yellow & brt green (8.15)	2·25	75
		ba. Broken bottom left triangle	60·00	40·00
75		½ pi. green and carmine	1·75	20
		a. Yellow-green and carmine	6·50	1·90
		ab. Broken bottom left triangle	80·00	50·00
		w. Wmk inverted	†	£750
76		30 pa. violet and green (3.13)	2·25	50
		a. Broken bottom left triangle	60·00	40·00
		w. Wmk inverted		
77		1 pi. rose-red and blue (9.12)	3·75	1·50
		a. Carmine and blue (1.15?)	12·00	4·00
		ab. Broken bottom left triangle	£120	60·00
78		2 pi. blue and purple (7.13)	6·50	1·50
		a. Broken bottom left triangle	95·00	50·00
79		4 pi. olive-green and purple	4·00	4·00
		a. Broken bottom left triangle	75·00	85·00
80		6 pi. sepia and green	3·25	8·00
		a. Broken bottom left triangle	75·00	
81		9 pi. brown and carmine (3.15)	22·00	24·00
		a. Yellow-brown and carmine	23·00	26·00
		b. Broken bottom left triangle	£250	
82		12 pi. chestnut and black (7.13)	10·00	25·00
		a. Broken bottom left triangle	£160	
83		18 pi. black and brown (3.15)	23·00	25·00
		a. Broken bottom left triangle	£225	
84		45 pi. dull purple and ultramarine (3.15)	65·00	£120
		a. Broken bottom left triangle	£450	
74/84			Set of 11 £130	£190
74/84 Optd "Specimen"			Set of 11 £350	

1921–23. *(a) Wmk Mult Script CA.*

85	12	10 pa. orange and green	3·00	4·00
		a. Broken bottom left triangle	70·00	80·00
86		10 pa. grey and yellow (1923)	11·00	6·50
		a. Broken bottom left triangle	£150	£120
87		30 pa. violet and green	2·50	40
		a. Broken bottom left triangle	65·00	35·00
		w. Wmk inverted		
		y. Wmk inverted and reversed	†	£600
88		30 pa. green (1923)	6·50	40
		a. Broken bottom left triangle	95·00	35·00
89		1 pi. carmine and blue	12·00	22·00
		a. Broken bottom left triangle	£130	
90		1 pi. violet and red (1922)	3·00	3·50
		a. Broken bottom left triangle	70·00	80·00
91		1½ pi. yellow and black (1922)	3·25	4·00
		a. Broken bottom left triangle	75·00	85·00
92		2 pi. blue and purple	14·00	8·50
		a. Broken bottom left triangle	£160	£130
93		2 pi. carmine and blue (1922)	9·00	22·00
		a. Broken bottom left triangle	£140	
94		2¾ pi. blue and purple (1922)	7·00	9·00
		a. Broken bottom left triangle	£130	£140
95		4 pi. olive-green and purple	4·00	13·00
		a. Broken bottom left triangle	£140	
		w. Wmk inverted	†	£600

96	12	6 pi. sepia and green (1923)	12·00	60·00
		a. Broken bottom left triangle	£160	
97		9 pi. brown and carmine (1922)	25·00	65·00
		a. Yellow-brown and carmine	65·00	95·00
		b. Broken bottom left triangle	£275	
98		18 pi. black and brown (1923)	60·00	£130
		a. Broken bottom left triangle	£375	
99		45 pi. dull purple and ultramarine (1923)	£150	£250
		a. Broken bottom left triangle	£700	
85/99			Set of 15 £275	£500
85/99 Optd "Specimen"			Set of 15 £475	

(b) Wmk Mult Crown CA (1923)

100	12	10s. green and red/pale yellow	£350	£650
		a. Broken bottom left triangle	£1700	
101		£1 purple and black/red	£1000	£1500
		a. Broken bottom left triangle	£3500	£6000
100/1 Optd "Specimen"			Set of 2 £500	

Examples of Nos. 96/101 are known showing a forged Limassol postmark dated "14 MR 25".

1924–28. *Chalk-surfaced paper. (a) Wmk Mult Crown CA.*

102	13	£1 purple and black/red	£300	£600

(b) Wmk Mult Script CA

103	13	¼ pi. grey and chestnut	1·00	15
		w. Wmk inverted	†	£750
104		½ pi. black	2·25	60
105		¾ pi. green	2·00	90
106		1 pi. purple and chestnut	1·75	60
107		1½ pi. orange and black	1·75	5·50
108		2 pi. carmine and green	1·75	9·00
109		2¾ pi. bright blue and purple	3·00	2·50
110		4 pi. sage-green and purple	3·00	2·25
111		4½ pi. black and orange/emerald	3·25	3·25
112		6 pi. olive-brown and green	3·50	5·00
113		9 pi. brown and purple	5·00	4·00
114		12 pi. chestnut and black	8·00	50·00
115		18 pi. black and orange	18·00	5·00
116		45 pi. purple and blue	32·00	38·00
117		90 pi. green and red/yellow	75·00	£160
117a		£5 blk/yellow (1928) (Optd S. £900)	£2750	£6000

Examples of No. 102 are known showing a forged Limassol postmark dated "14 MR 25" and of No. 117a showing a forged Registered Nicosia postmark dated "6 MAY 35".

CROWN COLONY

1925. *Wmk Mult Script CA. Chalk-surfaced paper (½, ¾ and 2 pi.)*

118	13	½ pi. green	1·75	85
119		¾ pi. brownish black	1·75	10
120		1½ pi. scarlet	2·25	30
121		2 pi. yellow and black	4·25	2·00
122		2½ pi. bright blue	2·00	30
102/122			Set of 21 to £1 £400	£700
102/22 Optd "Specimen"			Set of 21 £600	

In the above set the fraction bar in the value is horizontal. In Nos. 91, 94, 107 and 109 it is diagonal.

14 Silver Coin of   16 Map of Cyprus
Amathus, 6th-cent B.C.

(Recess B.W.)

1928 (1 Feb). *50th Anniv of British Rule. T 14, 16 and similar designs. Wmk Mult Script CA. P 12.*

123		¾ pi. deep dull purple	2·75	90
124		1 pi. black and greenish blue	3·00	1·25
125		1½ pi. scarlet	4·50	2·00
126		2½ pi. light blue	3·50	2·00
127		4 pi. deep brown	4·50	6·00
128		6 pi. blue	6·50	20·00
129		9 pi. maroon	7·50	11·00
130		18 pi. black and brown	17·00	17·00
131		45 pi. violet and blue	35·00	45·00
132		£1 blue and bistre-brown	£200	£300
123/132			Set of 10 £250	£350
123/32 Optd "Specimen"			Set of 10 £500	

Designs: Vert—1 pi. Zeno (philosopher); 2½ pi. Discovery of body of St Barnabas; 4 pi. Cloister, Abbey of Bella Paise; 9 pi. Tekke of Umm Haram; 18 pi. Statue of Richard I, Westminster; 45 pi. St. Nicholas Cathedral, Famagusta (now Lala Mustafa Pasha Mosque); £1 King George V. Horiz—6 pi. Badge of Cyprus.

24 Ruins of Vouni Palace   25 Small Marble Forum, Salamis

30 St. Sophia   31 Bayraktar Mosque,
Cathedral, Nicosia   Nicosia
(now Selimiye
Mosque)

CYPRUS — 1934

(Recess Waterlow)

1934 (1 Dec). *T* 24/5, 30/1 *and similar designs. Wmk Mult Script CA (sideways on* ½ pi., 1½ pi., 2½ pi., 4½ pi., 6 pi., 9 pi. and 18 pi.). *P* 12½.
133	¼ pi. ultramarine and orange-brown	..	85	50
	a. Imperf between (vert pair)	..	£19000	£15000
134	½ pi. green	..	1·00	1·00
	a. Imperf between (vert pair)	..	£10000	£11000
135	¾ pi. black and violet	..	90	10
	a. Imperf between (vert pair)	..	£21000	
136	1 pi. black and red-brown	..	80	80
	a. Imperf between (vert pair)	..	£12000	£12000
	b. Imperf between (horiz pair)	..	£10000	
137	1½ pi. carmine	..	1·25	55
138	2½ pi. ultramarine	..	1·25	1·75
139	4½ pi. black and crimson	..	3·00	3·50
140	6 pi. black and blue	..	7·50	12·00
141	9 pi. sepia and violet	..	5·50	4·25
142	18 pi. black and olive-green	..	40·00	27·00
143	45 pi. green and black	..	65·00	48·00
133/43		*Set of* 11	£110	90·00
133/43 Perf "Specimen"		*Set of* 11	£275	

Designs: *Horiz.*—¾ pi. Church of St. Barnabas and St. Hilarion, Peristerona; 1 pi. Roman theatre, Soli; 1½ pi. Kyrenia Harbour; 2½ pi. Kolossi Castle; 45 pi. Forest scene, Troodos. *Vert*—9 pi. Queen's Window, St. Hilarion Castle; 18 pi. Buyuk Khan, Nicosia.

1935 (6 May). *Silver Jubilee. As Nos. 91/4 of Antigua, but ptd by Waterlow & Sons. P* 11 × 12.
144	¾ pi. ultramarine and grey	..	1·75	40
145	1½ pi. deep blue and scarlet	..	3·50	2·50
	l. Kite and horizontal log	..	£170	
146	2½ pi. brown and deep blue	..	3·75	1·50
147	9 pi. slate and purple	..	13·00	12·00
144/7		*Set of* 4	20·00	15·00
144/7 Perf "Specimen"		*Set of* 4	£130	

For illustration of plate variety see Catalogue Introduction.

1937 (12 May). *Coronation. As Nos. 95/7 of Antigua. P* 11×11½.
148	¾ pi. grey	..	60	20
149	1½ pi. carmine	..	90	80
150	2½ pi. blue	..	2·00	1·25
148/50		*Set of* 3	3·25	2·00
148/50 Perf "Specimen"		*Set of* 3	£100	

35 Vouni Palace

36 Map of Cyprus

37 Othello's Tower, Famagusta

38 King George VI

(Recess Waterlow)

1938 (12 May)–1951. *T* 35 to 38 *and other designs as 1934, but with portrait of King George VI. Wmk Mult Script CA. P* 12½.
151	35	¼ pi. ultramarine and orange-brown	..	20	20
152	25	½ pi. green	..	30	10
152a	—	½ pi. violet (2.7.51)	..	1·75	20
153	—	¾ pi. black and violet	..	14·00	40
154	—	1 pi. orange	..	50	10
		a. Perf 13½ × 12½ (1944)	..	£375	27·00
155	—	1½ pi. carmine	..	5·00	1·50
155a	—	1½ pi. violet (15.3.43)	..	30	30
155ab	—	1½ pi. green (2.7.51)	..	2·25	40
155b	—	2 pi. black and carmine (2.2.42)	..	50	10
		c. Perf 12½ × 13½ (10.44)	..	2·00	6·00
156	—	2½ pi. ultramarine	..	18·00	2·50
156a	—	3 pi. ultramarine (2.2.42)	..	80	10
156b	—	4 pi. ultramarine (2.7.51)	..	3·00	30
157	36	4½ pi. grey	..	40	10
158	31	6 pi. black and blue	..	65	1·00
159	37	9 pi. black and purple	..	1·75	20
160	—	18 pi. black and olive-green	..	5·00	85
		a. Black and sage-green (19.8.47)	..	7·50	1·50
161	—	45 pi. green and black	..	14·00	2·50
162	38	90 pi. mauve and black	..	20·00	4·75
163	—	£1 scarlet and indigo	..	45·00	22·00
151/63		*Set of* 19	£110	32·00
151/63 Perf "Specimen"		*Set of* 16	£375	

Designs: *Horiz*—¾ pi., 2 pi. Peristerona Church; 1 pi. Soli Theatre; 1½ pi. Kyrenia Harbour; 2½ pi. 3 pi., 4 pi. Kolossi Castle; 45 pi. Forest scene. *Vert*—18 pi. Buyuk Khan, Nicosia.

1946 (21 Oct). *Victory. As Nos. 110/11 of Antigua.*
164	1½ pi. deep violet	..	15	10
165	3 pi. blue	..	15	15
164/5 Perf "Specimen"		*Set of* 2	90·00	

MINIMUM PRICE

The minimum price quote is 10p which represents a handling charge rather than a basis for valuing common stamps. For further notes about prices see introductory pages.

Extra decoration
(R. 3/5)

1948 (20 Dec). *Royal Silver Wedding. As Nos. 112/13 of Antigua.*
166	1½ pi. violet	..	50	20
	a. Extra decoration	..	30·00	
167	£1 indigo	..	42·00	48·00

1949 (10 Oct). *75th Anniv of Universal Postal Union. As Nos. 114/17 of Antigua but inscr* "CYPRUS" *(recess).*
168	1½ pi. violet	..	90	70
169	2 pi. carmine-red	..	2·00	1·50
170	3 pi. deep blue	..	1·25	1·00
171	9 pi. purple	..	1·50	1·10
168/71		*Set of* 4	5·00	3·75

1953 (2 June). *Coronation. As No. 120 of Antigua, but ptd by B.W.*
172	1½ pi. black and emerald	..	65	10

(New Currency. 1000 mils. = £1)

39 Carobs

42 Mavrovouni Copper Pyrites Mine

49 St. Hilarion Castle

52 Coins of Salamis, Paphos, Citium and Idalium

(Recess B.W.)

1955 (1 Aug)–60. *T* 39, 42, 49, 52 *and similar designs. Wmk Mult Script CA. P* 13½ *(Nos.* 183/5) *or* 11½ *(others).*
173	2 m. blackish brown	..	10	40
174	3 m. blue-violet	..	10	15
175	5 m. brown-orange	..	50	10
	a. Orange-brown (17.9.58)	..	2·75	30
176	10 m. deep brown and deep green	..	90	10
177	15 m. olive-green and indigo	..	2·50	45
	aa. Yellow-olive and indigo (17.9.58)	..	12·00	3·50
	a. Bistre and indigo (14.6.60)	..	19·00	7·50
178	20 m. brown and deep bright blue	..	80	15
179	25 m. deep turquoise-blue	..	1·50	60
	a. Greenish blue (17.9.58)	..	9·00	3·75
180	30 m. black and carmine-lake	..	1·25	10
181	35 m. orange-brown & deep turquoise-blue	..	55	40
182	40 m. deep green and sepia	..	1·00	60
183	50 m. turquoise-blue and reddish brown	..	85	30
184	100 m. mauve and bluish green	..	11·00	60
185	250 m. deep grey-blue and brown	..	9·00	7·00
186	500 m. slate and purple	..	24·00	11·00
187	£1 brown-lake and slate	..	24·00	30·00
173/87		*Set of* 15	70·00	48·00

Designs: *Vert* (as *T* 40)—3 m. Grapes; 5 m. Oranges. (as *T* 52)—£1 Arms of Byzantium, Lusignan, Ottoman Empire and Venice. *Horiz* (as *T* 42)—15 m. Troodos Forest; 20 m. Beach of Aphrodite; 25 m. 5th-century B.C. coin of Paphos; 30 m. Kyrenia; 35 m. Harvest in Mesaoria; 40 m. Famagusta Harbour. (as *T* 50)—100 m. Hala Sultan Tekke; 250 m. Kanakaria Church.

(54 "Cyprus Republic")   55 Map of Cyprus

1960 (16 Aug)–61. *Nos.* 173/87 *optd as T* 54, *in blue by B.W. Opt larger on Nos.* 191/7 *and in two lines on Nos.* 198/202.
188	2 m. blackish brown	..	20	60
189	3 m. blue-violet	..	20	15
190	5 m. brown-orange	..	1·00	10
	a. Orange-brown (15.8.61)	..	2·00	10
191	10 m. deep brown and deep green	..	70	10
192	15 m. yellow-bistre and indigo	..	75	10
	a. Olive-green and indigo	..	£110	38·00
	b. Brownish bis & dp ind (10.10.61)	..	4·25	2·75
193	20 m. brown and deep bright blue	..	40	70
	a. Opt double	..	†£9000	
194	25 m. deep turquoise-blue	..	1·25	70
	a. Greenish blue (7.2.61)	..	16·00	7·00

195	30 m. black and carmine-lake	..	1·75	10
	a. Opt double	..	†£15000	
196	35 m. orange-brown & dp turquoise-blue	1·75	30
197	40 m. deep green and sepia	..	2·00	1·50
198	50 m. turquoise-blue and reddish brown	2·00	50
199	100 m. mauve and bluish green	..	9·00	50
200	250 m. deep grey-blue and brown	..	25·00	2·50
201	500 m. slate and purple	..	40·00	16·00
202	£1 brown-lake and slate	..	50·00	48·00
188/202		*Set of* 15	£120	65·00

Only two used examples of No. 195a are known.

(Recess B.W.)

1960 (16 Aug). *Constitution of Republic. W w* 12. *P* 11½.
203	55	10 m. sepia and deep green	..	30	10
204		30 m. ultramarine and deep brown	..	65	10
205		100 m. purple and deep slate	..	2·00	2·00
203/5		*Set of* 3	2·75	2·00

PRINTERS. All the following stamps to No. 715 were designed by A. Tassos and lithographed by Aspioti-Elka, Athens, *unless otherwise stated.*

56 Doves

(Des T. Kurpershoek)

1962 (19 Mar). *Europa. P* 14 × 13.
206	56	10 m. purple and mauve	..	10	10
207		40 m. ultramarine and cobalt	..	20	15
208		100 m. emerald and pale green	..	20	20
206/8		*Set of* 3	40	40

57 Campaign Emblem

1962 (14 May). *Malaria Eradication. P* 14 × 13½.
209	57	10 m. black and olive-green	..	20	15
210		30 m. black and brown	..	40	15

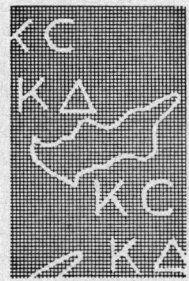
58 Mult K C K Δ and Map

WATERMARK VARIETIES. The issues printed by Aspioti-Elka with W 58 are known with the vertical stamps having the watermark normal or inverted and the horizontal stamps with the watermark reading upwards or downwards. Such varieties are not given separate listing.

62 Selimiye Mosque, Nicosia

63 St. Barnabas's Church

1962 (17 Sept). *T* 62/3 *and similar designs. W* 58 *(sideways on* 25, 30, 40, 50, 250 m., £1). *P* 13½ × 14 *(vert) or* 14 × 13½ *(horiz).*
211		3 m. deep brown and orange-brown	..	10	30
212		5 m. purple and grey-green	..	10	10
213		10 m. black and yellow-green	..	15	10
214		15 m. black and reddish purple	..	30	15
215		25 m. deep brown and chestnut	..	30	20
216		30 m. deep blue and light blue	..	20	10
217		35 m. light green and blue	..	35	10
218		40 m. black and violet-blue	..	1·25	1·50
219		50 m. bronze-green and bistre	..	50	10
220		100 m. deep brown and yellow-brown	..	3·50	30
221		250 m. black and cinnamon	..	8·50	2·25
222		500 m. deep brown and yellow-green	..	15·00	10·00
223		£1 bronze-green and grey	..	16·00	26·00
211/23		*Set of* 13	40·00	35·00

Designs: *Vert*—3 m. Iron Age jug; 5 m. Grapes; 10 m. Bronze head of Apollo; 35 m. Head of Aphrodite; 100 m. Hala Sultan Tekke; 500 m. Mouflon. *Horiz*—30 m. Temple of Apollo Hylates; 40 m. Skiing, Troodos; 50 m. Salamis Gymnasium; 250 m. Bella Paise Abbey; £1 St. Hilarion Castle.

72 Europa "Tree"

(Des L. Weyer)

1963 (28 Jan). *Europa.* W **58** (*sideways*). P 14 × 13½.
224	**72**	10 m. bright blue and black	..	75	20
225		40 m. carmine-red and black	..	3·00	2·00
226		150 m. emerald-green and black	..	12·00	6·00
224/6			*Set of 3*	14·00	7·50

73 Harvester 75 Wolf Cub in Camp

1963 (21 Mar). *Freedom from Hunger.* T **73** *and similar vert design.* W **58**. P 13½ × 14.
227		25 m. ochre, sepia and bright blue	..	30	25
228		75 m. grey, black and lake	..	1·75	1·00

Design:— 75 m. Demeter, Goddess of Corn.

1963 (21 Aug). *50th Anniv of Cyprus Scout Movement and Third Commonwealth Scout Conference, Platres.* T **75** *and similar vert designs. Multicoloured.* W **58**. P 13½ × 14.
229		3 m. Type **75**	..	10	20
230		20 m. Sea Scout	..	45	10
231		150 m. Scout with Mouflon	..	1·50	2·50
229/31			*Set of 3*	1·75	2·50
MS231*a*		110 × 90 mm. Nos. 229/31 (*sold at 250 m.*). Imperf		£100	£180

78 Nurse tending Child 79 Children's Centre, Kyrenia

1963 (9 Sept). *Centenary of Red Cross.* W **58** (*sideways on* 100 *m.*). P 13½ × 14 (10 *m.*) *or* 14 × 13½ (100 *m.*).
232	**78**	·10 m. red, blue, grey-bl, chestnut & blk		50	15
233	**79**	100 m. red, green, black and blue	..	2·00	3·50

80 "Co-operation" (emblem) (81)

(Des A. Holm)

1963 (4 Nov). *Europa.* W **58** (*sideways*). P 14 × 13½.
234	**80**	20 m. buff, blue and violet	..	1·25	40
235		30 m. grey, yellow and blue	..	1·75	40
236		150 m. buff, blue and orange-brown	..	8·00	9·00
234/6			*Set of 3*	10·00	9·00

1964 (5 May). *U.N. Security Council's Cyprus Resolutions. March, 1964, Nos. 213, 216, 218/20, optd with T **81** in blue by Govt Printing Office, Nicosia.*
237		10 m. black and yellow-green	..	20	10
238		30 m. deep blue and light blue	..	20	10
239		40 m. black and violet-blue	..	20	20
240		50 m. bronze-green and bistre	..	20	10
241		100 m. deep brown and yellow-brown	..	25	50
237/41			*Set of 5*	95	85

82 Soli Theatre

1964 (15 June). *400th Birth Anniv of Shakespeare.* T **82** *and similar horiz designs. Multicoloured.* W **58**. P 13½ × 13.
242		15 m. Type **82**	..	40	15
243		35 m. Curium Theatre	..	40	15
244		50 m. Salamis Theatre	..	40	15
245		100 m. Othello Tower and scene from *Othello*	1·00	2·25
242/5			*Set of 4*	2·00	2·50

86 Running 89 Europa "Flower"

1964 (6 July). *Olympic Games, Tokyo.* T **86** *and similar designs.* W **58** (*sideways,* 25 m. 75 m.). P 13½ × 14 (10 m.) *or* 14 × 13½ (*others*)
246		10 m. brown, black and yellow	..	15	10
247		25 m. brown, blue and blue-grey	..	35	10
248		75 m. brown, black and orange-red	..	50	65
246/8			*Set of 3*	90	75
MS248*a*		110 × 90 mm. Nos. 246/8 (*sold at 250 m.*). Imperf		6·00	14·00

Designs: *Horiz*—25 m. Boxing; 75 m. Charioteers.

1964 (14 Sept). *Europa.* W **58**. P 13½ × 14.
249	**89**	20 m. chestnut and light ochre	..	60	10
250		30 m. ultramarine and light blue	..	75	10
251		150 m. olive and light blue-green	..	5·25	8·00
249/51			*Set of 3*	6·00	8·00

90 Dionysus and Acme 91 Silenus (satyr)

1964 (26 Oct). *Cyprus Wines.* T **90**/1 *and similar multicoloured designs.* W **58** (*sideways,* 10 m., *or* 100 m.). P 14 × 13½ (*horiz*) 13½ × 14 (*vert*).
252		10 m. Type **90**	..	25	10
253		40 m. Type **91**	..	55	1·25
254		50 m. Commandaria Wine (*vert*)	..	60	10
255		100 m. Wine factory (*horiz*)	..	2·00	2·00
252/5			*Set of 4*	3·00	3·00

94 President Kennedy

1965 (15 Feb). *President Kennedy Commemoration.* W **58** (*sideways*). P 14 × 13½.
256	**94**	10 m. ultramarine	..	10	10
257		40 m. green	..	25	35
258		100 m. carmine-lake	..	30	35
256/8			*Set of 3*	55	70
MS258*a*		110 × 90 mm. Nos. 256/8 (*sold at 250 m.*). Imperf		3·00	6·50

95 "Old Age" 96 "Maternity"

1965 (12 Apr). *Introduction of Social Insurance Law.* T **95**/6 *and similar design.* W **58**. P 13½×12 (75 m.) *or* 13½×14 (*others*).
259		30 m. drab and dull green	..	20	10
260		45 m. light grey-green, blue & dp ultramarine	30	10
261		75 m. red-brown and flesh	..	1·75	2·50
259/61			*Set of 3*	2·00	2·50

Design: *Vert as* T **95**—45 m. "Accident".

98 I.T.U. Emblem and Symbols

1965 (17 May). *I.T.U. Centenary,* W **58** (*sideways*). P 14 × 13½.
262	**98**	15 m. black, brown and yellow	..	75	20
263		60 m. black, green and light green	..	5·50	2·75
264		75 m. black, indigo and light blue	..	6·00	4·75
262/4			*Set of 3*	11·00	7·00

99 I.C.Y. Emblem

1965 (17 May). *International Co-operation Year.* W **58** (*sideways*). P 14 × 13½.
265	**99**	50 m. brown, dp green & lt yellow-brown	75	10
266		100 m. purple, dp green & lt purple	..	1·25	70

100 Europa "Sprig"

U. N. Resolution on Cyprus 18 Dec. 1965 (101)

(Des H. Karlsson)

1965 (27 Sept). *Europa.* W **58** (*sideways*). P 14×13½.
267	**100**	5 m. black, orange-brown and orange	20	10
268		45 m. black, orange-brown & lt emer	1·25	1·50
269		150 m. black, orange-brown & lt grey	3·00	3·75
267/9			*Set of 3*	4·00	4·75

1966 (31 Jan). *U.N. General Assembly's Cyprus Resolution, 18 December 1965. Nos. 211, 213, 216 and 221 optd with* T **101**, *in blue by Govt Printing Office, Nicosia.*
270		3 m. deep brown and orange-brown	..	10	30
271		10 m. black and yellow-green	..	10	10
272		30 m. deep blue and light blue	..	10	15
273		250 m. black and cinnamon	..	55	2·00
270/3			*Set of 4*	70	2·25

102 Discovery of St. Barnabas's Body 104 St. Barnabas (icon)

103 St. Barnabas's Chapel

105 "Privileges of Cyprus Church"
(*Actual size* 102 × 82 *mm*)

1966 (25 Apr). *1900th Death Anniv of St. Barnabas.* W **58** (*sideways on* 15 m., 100 m., 250 m.). P 14 × 13 (25 m.) *or* 13 × 14 (*others*).
274	**102**	15 m. multicoloured	..	10	10
275	**103**	25 m. drab, black and blue	..	20	10
276	**104**	100 m. multicoloured	..	75	2·00
274/6			*Set of 3*	90	2·00
MS277		110 × 91 mm. **105** 250 m. mult. Imperf	..	4·25	13·00

NEW INFORMATION

The editor is always interested to correspond with people who have new information that will improve or correct the Catalogue.

5 M

(106)   **107** General K. S. Thimayya and U. N. Emblem

1966 (30 May). *No. 211 surch with T 106 by Govt Printing Office, Nicosia.*
278   5 m. on 3 m. deep brown & orange-brown   10   10

1966 (6 June) *General Thimayya Commemoration. W 58 (sideways). P 14 × 13.*
279   **107**   50 m. black and light orange-brown ..   30   10

108 Europa "Ship"

(Des G. and J. Bender)

1966 (26 Sept). *Europa. W 58. P 13½ × 14.*
280   **108**   20 m. green and blue ..   25   10
281   30 m. bright purple and blue ..   25   10
282   150 m. bistre and blue ..   1·75 3·00
280/2 .. .. *Set of 3*   2·00 3·00

110 Church of St. James, Trikomo

119 Vase of 7th Century B.C.

120 Bronze Ingot-stand

1966 (21 Nov)—**69**. *T 110, 119/20 and similar designs. W 58 (sideways on 3, 15, 25, 50, 250, 500 m., £1). P 12×13 (3 m.), 13×12 (5, 10 m.), 14×13½ (15, 25, 50 m.), 13½×14 (20, 30, 35, 40, 100 m.) or 13×14 (others).*
283   3 m. grey-green, buff, black & light blue   40   10
284   5 m. bistre, black and steel-blue   10   10
      a. Brownish bistre, black and steel-blue
          (18.4.69)   45   20
285   10 m. black and bistre   15   10
286   15 m. black, chestnut & light orange-brown   15   10
287   20 m. black, slate and brown .. ..   1·25   90
288   25 m. black, drab and lake-brown ..   30   10
289   30 m. black, yellow-ochre and turquoise .. 50   30
290   35 m. yellow, black and carmine-red ..   50   30
291   40 m. black, grey and new blue ..   70   30
      a. Grey (background) omitted ..
292   50 m. black, slate and brown ..   90   10
293   100 m. black, red, pale buff and grey ..   3·75   15
294   250 m. olive-green, black & lt yellow-ochre 1·50   40
295   500 m. multicoloured .. ..   2·25   70
296   £1 black, drab and slate .. ..   2·50 6·50
283/96 .. .. *Set of 14*   13·00 8·50
Designs: *Horiz (as T 110)*—3 m. Stavrovouni Monastery. (*As T 119*)—15 m. Minoan wine ship of 700 B.C. (painting); 25 m. Sleeping Eros (marble statue); 50 m. Silver coin of Alexander the Great. *Vert (as T 110)*—10 m. Zeno of Cibium (marble bust). (*As T 119*)—20 m. Silver coin of Evagoras I; 30 m. St. Nicholas Cathedral, Famagusta; 35 m. Gold sceptre from Curium; 40 m. Silver dish from 7th century. (*As T 120*)—500 m. "The Rape of Ganymede" (mosaic); £1 Aphrodite (marble statue).

OMNIBUS ISSUES

Details, together with prices for complete sets, of the various Omnibus issues from the 1935 Silver Jubilee series to date are included in a special section following Zimbabwe at the end of Volume 2.

---

123 Power Station, Limassol

124 Cogwheels

1967 (10 Apr). *First Development Programme. T 123 and similar designs but horiz. Multicoloured. W 58 (sideways on 15 to 100 m.). P 13½ × 14 (10 m.) or 14 × 13½ (others).*
297   10 m. Type 123   10   10
298   15 m. Arghaka-Maghounda Dam ..   15   10
299   35 m. Troodos Highway   20   10
300   50 m. Hilton Hotel, Nicosia ..   20   10
301   100 m. Famagusta Harbour   20   1·10
297/301 .. .. *Set of 5*   75   1·25

(Des O. Bonnevalle)

1967 (2 May). *Europa. W 58. P 13½ × 14.*
302   **124**   20 m. olive-green, green & pale yell-grn   25   10
303   30 m. reddish violet, lilac and pale lilac   25   10
304   150 m. brown, light reddish brown and
               pale yellow-brown   1·00 2·25
302/4 .. .. *Set of 3*   1·40 2·25

125 Throwing the Javelin

126 Running (amphora) and Map of Eastern Mediterranean
(*Actual size 97 × 77 mm*)

1967 (4 Sept). *Athletic Games, Nicosia. T 125 and similar designs and T 126. Multicoloured. W 58. P 13½ × 13.*
305   15 m. Type 125   20   10
306   35 m. Running   20   35
307   100 m. High-jumping   30   1·00
305/7 .. .. *Set of 3*   60   1·25
MS308 110×90 mm. 250 m. Type 126 (wmk sideways). Imperf   1·60 6·50

127 Ancient Monuments

128 St. Andrew Mosaic

1967 (16 Oct). *International Tourist Year. T 127 and similar horiz designs. Multicoloured. W 58. P 13 × 13½.*
309   10 m. Type 127   10   10
310   40 m. Famagusta Beach   15   90
311   50 m. Hawker Siddeley Comet 4 at Nicosia
           Airport   15   10
312   100 m. Skier and youth hostel .. 20   95
309/12 .. .. *Set of 4*   50   1·75

1967 (8 Nov). *Centenary of St. Andrew's Monastery. W 58 (sideways). P 13 × 13½.*
313   **128**   25 m. multicoloured   10   10

---

129 "The Crucifixion" (icon)   **130** The Three Magi

(Photo French Govt Ptg Wks, Paris)

1967 (8 Nov). *Cyprus Art Exhibition, Paris. P 12½ × 13½.*
314   **129**   50 m. multicoloured   10   10

1967 (8 Nov). *20th Anniv of U.N.E.S.C.O. W 58 (sideways). P 13 × 13½.*
315   **130**   75 m. multicoloured   20   20

131 Human Rights Emblem over Stars

132 Human Rights and U.N. Emblems

133 Scroll of Declaration
(*Actual size 95 × 75½ mm*)

1968 (18 Mar). *Human Rights Year. W 58. P 13 × 14.*
316   **131**   50 m. multicoloured   10   10
317   **132**   90 m. multicoloured   30   70
MS318 95 × 75½ mm. **133** 250 m. multicoloured.
       W 58 (sideways). Imperf. .. ..   1·00 4·75

134 Europa "Key"

(Des H. Schwarzenbach)

1968 (29 Apr). *Europa. W 58 (sideways). P 14 × 13.*
319   **134**   20 m. multicoloured   20   10
320   30 m. multicoloured   20   10
321   150 m. multicoloured   60   2·25
319/21 .. .. *Set of 3*   90   2·25

135 U.N. Children's Fund Symbol and Boy drinking Milk

136 Aesculapius

1968 (2 Sept). *21st Anniv of U.N.I.C.E.F. W 58 (sideways). P 14 × 13.*
322   **135**   35 m. yellow-brown, carmine-red & blk   10   10

1968 (2 Sept). *20th Anniv of W.H.O. W 58. P 13 × 14.*
323   **136**   50 m. black, green and light olive   10   10

137 Throwing the Discus   **138** I.L.O. Emblem

1968 (24 Oct). *Olympic Games, Mexico.* T **137** *and similar designs. Multicoloured.* W **58** (*sideways on* 100 *m.*). P 14 × 13 (100 *m.*) *or* 13 × 14 (*others*).

324	10 m. Type **137**	..	..	10	10
325	25 m. Sprint finish	..	..	10	10
326	100 m. Olympic Stadium (*horiz*)			20	1·25
324/6	..	..	*Set of* 3	30	1·25

1969 (3 Mar). *50th Anniv of International Labour Organization.* W **58**. P 12 × 13½.

327	**138**	50 m. yellow-brown, blue and light blue	15	10
328		90 m. yellow-brown, black and pale grey	15	55

139 Mercator's Map of Cyprus, 1554

140 Blaeu's Map of Cyprus, 1635

1969 (7 Apr). *First International Congress of Cypriot Studies.* W **58** (*sideways*). P 14 × 14½.

329	**139**	35 m. multicoloured	20	30
330	**140**	50 m. multicoloured	20	10
		a. Wmk upright	—	2·75
		ab. Grey (shading on boats and cartouche) omitted	£225	

141 Europa Emblem   **142** Common Roller

(Des L. Gasbarra and G. Belli)

1969 (28 Apr). *Europa.* W **58** (*sideways*). P 14 × 13½.

331	**141**	20 m. multicoloured	20	10
332		30 m. multicoloured	20	10
333		150 m. multicoloured	80	2·00
331/3	..	*Set of* 3	1·10	2·00

1969 (7 July). *Birds of Cyprus.* T **142** *and similar designs. Multicoloured.* W **58** (*sideways on horiz designs*). P 13½ × 12 (*horiz designs*) *or* 12 × 13½ (*vert designs*).

334	5 m. Type **142**	..		40	15
335	15 m. Audouin's Gull	..	60	15
336	20 m. Cyprus Warbler	..	60	15
337	30 m. Jay (*vert*)	..	60	15
338	40 m. Hoopoe (*vert*)	..	65	30
339	90 m. Eleanora's Falcon (*vert*)..		1·50	5·00
334/9	..	*Set of* 6	4·00	5·50

The above were printed on glazed Samuel Jones paper with very faint watermark.

143 "The Nativity" (12th-century Wall Painting)

145 "Virgin and Child between Archangels Michael and Gabriel" (6th–7th-century Mosaic) (*Actual size* 102 × 81 *mm*)

1969 (24 Nov). *Christmas.* T **143** *and similar horiz design, and* T **145**. *Multicoloured.* W **58** (*sideways*). P 13½ × 13.

340	20 m. Type **143**	..	15	10
341	45 m. "The Nativity" (14th-century wall painting)	..	15	20
MS342	110 × 90 mm. 250 m. Type **145**. Imperf	3·00	12·00
	a. Grey and light brown omitted ..	£1600	

146 Mahatma Gandhi

1970 (26 Jan). *Birth Centenary of Mahatma Gandhi.* W **58** (*sideways*). P 14 × 13½.

343	**146**	25 m. ultramarine, drab and black	15	10
344		75 m. yellow-brown, drab and black	20	65

147 "Flaming Sun"   **148** Gladioli

(Des L. le Brocquy)

1970 (4 May). *Europa.* W **58** (*sideways*). P 14 × 13.

345	**147**	20 m. brown, greenish yellow & orange	20	10
346		30 m. new blue, greenish yellow & orge	20	10
347		150 m. bright purple, greenish yell & orge	80	2·25
345/7		*Set of* 3	1·10	2·25

1970 (3 Aug). *European Conservation Year.* T **148** *and similar vert designs. Multicoloured.* W **58**. P 13 × 13½.

348	10 m. Type **148**	..	10	10
349	50 m. Poppies	..	15	10
350	90 m. Giant fennel	..	50	1·40
348/50	..	*Set of* 3	65	1·40

149 I.E.Y. Emblem   **150** Mosaic

151 Globe, Dove and U.N. Emblem

(Des G. Simonis (75 m.))

1970 (7 Sept). *Anniversaries and Events.* W **58** (*sideways on horiz designs*). P 13×14 (5 *m.*), *or* 14×13 (*others*).

351	**149**	5 m. black, red-brown & lt yellow-brn	10	10
352	**150**	15 m. multicoloured	10	10
353	**151**	75 m. multicoloured	15	75
351/3	..	*Set of* 3	30	80

Events:—5 m. International Education Year; 15 m. 50th General Assembly of International Vine and Wine Office; 75 m. 25th anniv of United Nations.

152 Virgin and Child   **153** Cotton Napkin

(Photo Harrison)

1970 (23 Nov). *Christmas. Wall-painting from Church of Panayia Podhythou, Galata.* T **152** *and similar multicoloured designs.* P 14 × 14½.

354	25 m. Archangel (facing right)	..	15	20
	a. Horiz strip of 3. Nos. 354/6		40	
355	25 m. Type **152**	..	15	20
356	25 m. Archangel (facing left)	..	15	20
357	75 m. Virgin and Child between Archangels	15	30
354/7		*Set of* 4	55	80

The 75 m. is horiz, size 42 × 30 mm, and the 25 m. values are vert, size as T **152**.

Nos. 354/6 were issued in *se-tenant* strips of three, throughout the sheet. The triptych thus formed is depicted in its entirety on the 75 m. value.

1971 (22 Feb). *Multicoloured designs as* T **153**. W **58** (*sideways on horiz designs*). (a) *Vert designs* 23 × 33 *mm*. P 12 × 13½.

358	3 m. Type **153**	..	30	55
359	5 m. St. George and Dragon (19th-cent bas-relief)	10	10

(b) *Vert* (10, 20, 25, 40, 50, 75 *m.*) *or horiz* (15, 30, 90 *m.*) *designs, each* 24 × 37 *or* 37 × 24 *mm*. P 13 × 14 (15, 30, 90 *m*) *or* 14 × 13 (*others*)

360	10 m. Woman in festival costume	..	15	30
361	15 m. Archaic Bichrome Kylix (cup)	..	20	10
	a. Vert laid paper		1·00	
362	20 m. A pair of donors (St. Mamas Church)	35	50
363	25 m. "The Creation" (6th-cent mosaic)	30	10
364	30 m. Athena and horse-drawn chariot (4th-cent B.C. terracotta) ..	30	10
365	40 m. Shepherd playing pipe (14th-cent fresco)	1·00	90
366	50 m. Hellenistic head (3rd cent B.C.)	80	10
367	75 m. "Angel" (mosaic detail), Kanakaria Church	1·75	1·00
368	90 m. Mycenaean silver bowl	..	2·00	1·50

(c) *Horiz* (250, 500 *m.*) *or vert* (£1) *designs, each* 41 × 28 *or* 28 × 41 *mm*. P 13½ × 13 (250, 500 *m.*) *or* 13 × 13½ (£1)

369	250 m. Moufflon (detail of 3rd-cent mosaic) (*shades*)	1·50	30
370	500 m. Ladies and sacred tree (detail, 6th-cent amphora)	80	40
371	£1 Horned god from Enkomi (12th-cent bronze statue)	1·50	60
358/71	..	*Set of* 14	10·00	5·50

154 Europa Chain   **155** Archbishop Kyprianos

(Des H. Haflidason)

1971 (3 May). *Europa.* W **58** (*sideways*). P 14 × 13

372	**154**	20 m. pale blue, ultramarine and black	20	10
373		30 m. apple green, myrtle-green & blk	20	10
374		150 m. lemon, bright green and black	90	2·25
372/4		*Set of* 3	1·10	2·25

The above were printed on glazed paper with very faint watermark.

1971 (9 July). *150th Anniv. of Greek War of Independence.* T **155** *and similar multicoloured designs.* W **58** (*sideways on* 30 *m.*). P 13½ × 12½ (30 *m.*) *or* 12½ × 13½ (*others*).

375	15 m. Type **155**	..	10	10
376	30 m. "Taking the Oath" (*horiz*)	..	10	10
377	100 m. Bishop Germanos, flag and freedom-fighters	20	50
375/7		*Set of* 3	30	55

156 Kyrenia Castle   **157** Madonna and Child in Stable

1971 (20 Sept). *Tourism. T 156 and similar multicoloured designs. W 58 (sideways on 15 and 100 m.). P 13½ × 13 (15 m., 100 m.) or 13 × 13½ (others).*

378	15 m. Type **156**	10	10
379	25 m. Gourd on sunny beach (*vert*)	10	10
380	60 m. Mountain scenery (*vert*)	20	60
381	100 m. Church of St. Evlalios, Lambousa	20	65
378/81	*Set of 4*	45	1·25

1971 (22 Nov). *Christmas. T 157 and similar vert designs. Multicoloured. W 58. P 13 × 14.*

382	10 m. Type **157**	10	10
	a. Horiz strip of 3. Nos. 382/4	35	
383	50 m. The Three Wise Men	15	35
384	100 m. The Shepherds	20	35
382/4	*Set of 3*	35	70

The 10 m. was issued in sheets of 100, and all three values were printed horizontally *se-tenant* in sheets of 36, the order being 50, 10 and 100 m.

158 Heart   159 "Communications"

1972 (11 Apr). *World Heart Month. W 58 (sideways). P 13½×12.*

385	**158** 15 m. multicoloured	10	10
386	50 m. multicoloured	20	45

(Des P. Huovinen)

1972 (22 May). *Europa. W 58. P 12½ × 13½.*

387	**159** 20 m. yellow-orge, sepia & pale grey-brn	25	15
388	30 m. yell-orge, brt dp ultram & cobalt	25	15
389	150 m. yellow-orange, myrtle-green and pale-turquoise-green	1·75	3·50
387/9	*Set of 3*	2·00	3·50

160 Archery

1972 (24 July). *Olympic Games, Munich. T 160 and similar horiz designs. Multicoloured. W 58 (sideways). P 14×13.*

390	10 m. Type **160**	10	10
391	40 m. Wrestling	20	15
392	100 m. Football	45	1·40
390/2	*Set of 3*	65	1·50

161 Stater of Marion   162 Bathing the Child Jesus

1972 (25 Sept). *Ancient Coins of Cyprus (1st series), T 161 and similar horiz designs. W 58 (sideways), P 14 × 13.*

393	20 m. pale turquoise-blue, black and silver	20	10
394	30 m. pale violet-blue, black and silver	20	10
395	40 m. brownish stone, black and silver	20	20
396	100 m. light salmon-pink, black and silver	60	1·00
393/6	*Set of 4*	1·10	1·25

Coins:—30 m. Stater of Paphos; 40 m. Stater of Lapithos, 100 m. Stater of Idalion.
See also Nos. 486/9.

1972 (20 Nov). *Christmas. T 162 and similar vert designs showing portions of a mural in the Church of the Holy Cross of Agiasmati. Multicoloured. W 58 (sideways on MS400). P 13 × 14.*

397	10 m. Type **162**	10	10
398	20 m. The Magi	10	10
399	100 m. The Nativity	15	30
397/9	*Set of 3*	30	35
MS400	100×90 mm. 250 m. Showing the mural in full. Imperf	1·10	4·50

163 Mount Olympus, Troodos

1973 (13 Mar). *29th Internation Ski Federation Congress. T 163 and similar horiz design. Multicoloured. W 58 (sideways). P 14 × 13.*

401	20 m. Type **163**	10	10
402	100 m. Congress emblem	25	35

164 Europa "Posthorn"

(Des I. Anisdahl)

1973 (7 May). *Europa. W 58 (sideways). P 14 × 13.*

403	**164** 20 m. multicoloured	15	10
404	30 m. multicoloured	15	10
405	150 m. multicoloured	1·10	3·00
403/5	*Set of 3*	1·25	3·00

165 Archbishop's Palace, Nicosia   (166)

1973 (23 July). *Traditional Architecture. T 165 and similar multicoloured designs. W 58 (sideways on 20 and 100 m.). P 14 × 13 (20 and 100 m.) or 13 × 14 (others).*

406	20 m. Type **165**	10	10
407	30 m. House of Hajigeorgajis Cornessios, Nicosia (*vert*)	10	10
408	50 m. House at Gourri, 1850 (*vert*)	15	10
409	100 n. House at Rizokarpaso, 1772	40	75
406/9	*Set of 4*	65	90

1973 (24 Sept). *No. 361 surch with T 166.*

410	20 m. on 15 m. Archaic Bichrome Kylix (cup)	15	15
	a. Vert laid paper	80	
	b. Surch inverted		

167 Scout Emblem   168 Archangel Gabriel

1973 (24 Sept). *Anniversaries and Events. T 167 and similar designs. W 58 (sideways on 25 and 35 m.). P 13×14 (10, 50 and 100 m.) or 14×13 (others).*

411	10 m. yellow-olive and deep brown	20	10
412	25 m. deep blue, and slate-lilac	20	10
413	35 m. light brown-olive, stone and sage-green	20	25
414	50 m. dull blue and indigo	20	10
415	100 m. brown and sepia	50	80
411/15	*Set of 5*	1·10	1·10

Designs and Events: *Vert*—10 m. Type **167** (60th anniv of Cyprus Boy Scouts); 50 m. Airline emblem (25th anniv of Cyprus Airways); 100 m. Interpol emblem (50th anniv of Interpol). *Horiz*—25 m. Outline of Cyprus and E.E.C. nations (Association of Cyprus with the E.E.C.); 35 m. F.A.O. emblem (Tenth anniv of F.A.O.).

1973 (26 Nov). *Christmas. Murals from Araka Church. T 168 and similar multicoloured designs. W 58 (sideways on 100 m.). P 14×13 (100 m.) or 13×14 (others).*

416	10 m. Type **168**	10	10
417	20 m. Madonna and Child	10	10
418	100 m. Araka Church (*horiz*)	40	75
416/18	*Set of 3*	45	75

169 Grapes   170 "The Rape of Europa" (Silver Stater of Marion)

1974 (18 Mar). *Products of Cyprus. T 169 and similar vert designs. Multicoloured. W 58. P 13 × 14.*

419	25 m. Type **169**	10	15
420	50 m. Grapefruit	20	60
	a. Horiz strip of 3, Nos. 420/2	55	
421	50 m. Oranges	20	60
422	50 m. Lemons	20	60
419/22	*Set of 4*	65	1·75

Nos. 420/2 were printed together, horizontally *se-tenant* throughout the sheet.

1974 (29 Apr). *Europa. W 58. P 13½ × 14.*

423	**170** 10 m. multicoloured	15	10
424	40 m. multicoloured	35	30
425	150 m. multicoloured	1·10	2·75
423/5	*Set of 3*	1·40	2·75

171 Title Page of A. Kyprianos' "History of Cyprus" (1788)   (172)

1974 (22 July*). *Second International Congress of Cypriot Studies. T 171 and similar multicoloured designs. W 58 (sideways on 25 m. and MS429). P 14 × 13½ (25 m.) or 13½ × 14 (others).*

426	10 m. Type **171**	10	10
427	25 m. Solon (philosopher) in mosaic (*horiz*)	15	10
428	100 m. "St. Neophytos" (wall painting)	60	75
426/8	*Set of 3*	70	80
MS429	111 × 90 mm. 250 m. Ortelius' map of Cyprus and Greek Islands, 1584. Imperf	1·75	6·00

*Although this is the date appearing on first day covers the stamps were not put on sale until the 24th.

1974 (1 Oct). *Obligatory Tax. Refugee Fund No. 359 surch with T 172.*

430	10 m. on 5 m. St. George and Dragon	10	10

174 "Refugees"

1974 (14 Oct). *U.N. Security Council Resolution 353. Nos. 360, 365, 366 and 369 optd as T 173.*

431	10 m. Woman in festival costume	20	10
432	40 m. Shepherd playing pipe	25	50
433	50 m. Hellenistic head	25	10
434	250 m. Moufflon (*shades*)	60	2·75
431/4	*Set of 4*	1·10	3·00

1974 (2 Dec). *Obligatory Tax. Refugee Fund. W 58 (sideways). P 12 × 12½.*

435	**174** 10 m. black and light grey	10	10

175 "Virgin and Child between Two Angels", Stavros Church

1974 (2 Dec). *Christmas. T 175 and similar multicoloured designs showing wall-paintings. W 58 (sideways on 10 m. and 100 m.). P 13 × 14 (50 m.) or 14 × 13 (others).*

436	10 m. Type **175**	10	10
437	50 m. "Adoration of the Magi", Ayios Neophytos Monastery (*vert*)	20	10
438	100 m. "Flight into Egypt", Ayios Neophytos Monastery	25	45
436/8	*Set of 3*	45	50

176 Larnaca–Nicosia Mail-coach, 1878   177 "The Distaff" (M. Kashalos)

(Photo Harrison)

1975 (17 Feb). *Anniversaries and Events. T 176 and similar designs. No wmk. P 14.*

439	**176** 20 m. multicoloured	25	10
440	30 m. ultramarine, slate-blk & dull orge	25	60
441	**176** 50 m. multicoloured	25	10
442	100 m. multicoloured	40	1·40
439/42	*Set of 4*	1·00	2·00

Designs and Events:—20 m., 50 m. Type **176** (Centenary of Universal Postal Union). *Vert*—30 m. "Disabled Persons" (Eighth European Meeting of International Society for the Rehabilitation of Disabled Persons); 100 m. Council flag (25th anniv of Council of Europe).

(Photo Harrison)

1975 (28 Apr). *Europa. T* **177** *and similar vert designs. Multi-coloured. P* 13½ × 14½.

443	20 m. Type **177**	..	25	40
	a. Horiz strip of 3. Nos. 443/5	..	80	
444	30 m. "Nature Morte" (C. Savva)	..	25	50
445	150 m. "Virgin and Child of Liopetri" (G. P. Georghiou)		40	80
443/5		*Set of 3*	80	1·50

Nos. 443/5 were printed horizontally *se-tenant* throughout the sheet.

178 Red Cross Flag over Map

179 Submarine Cable Links

1975 (4 Aug). *Anniversaries and Events. T* **178** *and similar horiz designs. P* 12½×13½ (25 m.) *or* 13½×12½ (*others*).

446	25 m. multicoloured	..	25	10
447	30 m. turquoise-green and greenish blue	..	25	10
448	75 m. red-brown, orge-brn & pale blue-grey		35	90
446/8		*Set of 3*	75	1·00

Designs and Events: *Vert*—25 m. Type **178** (25th anniversary of Cyprus Red Cross). *Horiz*—30 m. Nurse and lamp (International Nurses' Day); 75 m. Woman's Steatite Idol (International Women's Year).

1975 (13 Oct). *Telecommunications Achievements. T* **179** *and similar design. W* **58** (*sideways on* 100 m.). *P* 12 × 13½ (50 m.) *or* 13½ × 12 (100 m.).

449	50 m. multicoloured	..	40	10
450	100 m. orange-yellow, dull violet and lilac		50	90

Design: *Horiz*—100 m. International subscriber dialling.

(180)

181 Human-figured Vessel, 19th-Century

1976 (5 Jan). *No.* 358 *surch with T* **180**.

451	10 m. on 3 m. Cotton napkin	..	20	60

1976 (3 May). *Europa. Ceramics. T* **181** *and similar vert designs. Multicoloured. W* **58**. *P* 13×14.

452	20 m. Type **181**	..	20	10
453	60 m. Composite vessel, 2100–2000 B.C.	..	50	80
454	100 m. Byzantine goblet	..	90	1·75
452/4		*Set of 3*	1·40	2·40

182 Self-help Housing

183 Terracotta Statue of Youth

1976 (3 May). *Economic Reactivation. T* **182** *and similar horiz designs. Multicoloured. W* **58** (*sideways*). *P* 14 × 13.

455	10 m. Type **182**	..	10	10
456	25 m. Handicrafts	..	20	20
457	30 m. Reafforestation	..	20	20
458	60 m. Air Communications	..	35	55
455/8		*Set of 4*	75	90

1976 (7 June). *Cypriot Treasures. T* **183** *and similar designs. W* **58** (*sideways on horiz designs, upright on vert designs*). *Ordinary cream paper. P* 12 × 13½ (5, 10 m.), 13 × 14 (20, 25, 30 m.), 14×13 (40, 50, 60 m.), 13½×12 (100 m.) *or* 13 × 13½ (250 m. *to* £1).

459	5 m. multicoloured	..	10	60
460	10 m. multicoloured	..	15	40
461	20 m. red, yellow and black	..	30	40
462	25 m. multicoloured	..	30	10
463	30 m. multicoloured	..	30	10
464	40 m. grey-green, light olive-bistre and black	45	45
465	50 m. buff, brown and black	..	45	10
466	60 m. multicoloured	..	45	20
467	100 m. multicoloured	..	50	40
468	250 m. deep dull blue, grey and black	..	80	1·50
469	500 m. black, stone and deep blue-green		80	2·00
470	£1 multicoloured	..	1·25	2·25
459/70		*Set of 12*	5·25	7·50

Sizes:—23 × 34 *mm*, 5 m., 10 m.; 34 × 23 *mm*, 100 m.; 24 × 37 *mm*, 20, 25, 30 m.; 37 × 24 *mm*, 40, 50, 60 m.; 28 × 41 *mm*, others.
Designs:—10 m. Limestone head; 20 m. Gold necklace from Lambousa; 25 m. Terracotta warrior; 30 m. Statue of a priest of Aphrodite; 40 m. Bronze tablet; 50 m. Mycenaean crater; 60 m. Limestone sarcophagus; 100 m. Gold bracelet from Lambousa; 250 m. Silver dish from Lambousa; 500 m. Bronze stand; £1 Statue of Artemis.

184 Olympic Symbol

185 "George Washington" (G. Stuart)

(Litho Harrison)

1976 (5 July). *Olympic Games, Montreal. T* **184** *and similar designs. P* 14.

471	20 m. carmine-red, black and yellow	..	10	10
472	60 m. multicoloured	..	20	30
473	100 m. multicoloured	..	30	55
471/3		*Set of 3*	55	80

Designs: *Horiz*—60, 100 m. Olympic symbols (*different*).

1976 (5 July). *Bicentenary of American Revolution. W* **58**. *P* 13 × 13½.

474	**185**	100 m. multicoloured	..	40	30

186 Children in Library

187 Archangel Michael

1976 (27 Sept). *Anniversaries and Events. T* **186** *and similar vert designs. W* **58**. *P* 13½×12½ (50 m.) *or* 13½ (*others*).

475	40 m. multicoloured	..	20	15
476	50 m. yellow-brown and black	..	20	10
477	80 m. multicoloured	..	45	60
475/7		*Set of 3*	75	75

Designs and Events:—40 m. Type **186** (Promotion of Children's Books); 50 m. Low-cost housing (HABITAT Conference, Vancouver); 80 m. Eye protected by hands (World Health Day).

(Litho Harrison)

1976 (15 Nov). *Christmas. T* **187** *and similar vert designs, showing icons from Ayios Neophytis Monastery. Multicoloured. P* 12½.

478	10 m. Type **187**	..	15	10
479	15 m. Archangel Gabriel	..	15	10
480	150 m. The Nativity	..	60	80
478/80		*Set of 3*	80	80

188 "Cyprus 74" (wood-engraving by A. Tassos)

189 "View of Prodhromos" (A. Diamantis)

1977 (10 Jan)–82. *Obligatory Tax. Refugee Fund. W* **58**. *Ordinary cream paper. P* 13 × 12½.

481	**188**	10 m. grey-black	..	20	10
	a. Chalk-surfaced cream paper (3.5.82)*			

*Earliest known date of use.
For 1 c. value, see Nos. 634/b, 729 and 747.

1977 (2 May). *Europa. Paintings. T* **189** *and similar horiz designs. Multicoloured. No wmk. P* 13½×13.

482	20 m. Type **189**	..	15	10
483	60 m. "Springtime at Monagroulli" (T. Kanthos)	..	30	60
484	120 m. "Old Port, Limassol" (V. Ioannides) ..	60	1·50
482/4		*Set of 3*	95	2·00

190 Overprinted 500 m. Stamp of 1960

191 Bronze Coin of Emperor Trajan

1977 (13 June). *Silver Jubilee. W* **58**. *P* 13 × 13½.

485	**190**	120 m. multicoloured	..	30	30

(Litho Harrison)

1977 (13 June). *Ancient Coins of Cyprus* (2nd series). *T* **191** *and similar horiz designs. P* 14.

486	10 m. brownish black, gold and ultramarine	15	10
487	40 m. brownish black, silver and pale blue	30	30
488	60 m. brownish black, silver and dull orange	35	35
489	100 m. brownish black, gold and blue-green	50	95
486/9		*Set of 4*	1·10	1·50

Designs:—40 m. Silver tetradrachm of Demetrios Poliorcetes; 60 m. Silver tetradrachm of Ptolemy VIII; 100 m. Gold Octadrachm of Arsinoe II.

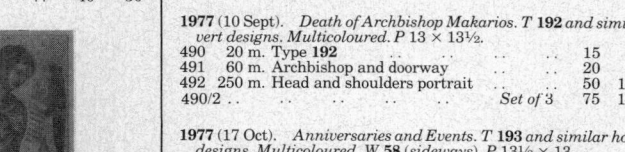

192 Archbishop Makarios in Ceremonial Robes

193 Embroidery, Pottery and Weaving

1977 (10 Sept). *Death of Archbishop Makarios. T* **192** *and similar vert designs. Multicoloured. P* 13 × 13½.

490	20 m. Type **192**	..	15	10
491	60 m. Archbishop and doorway	..	20	10
492	250 m. Head and shoulders portrait	..	50	1·10
490/2		*Set of 3*	75	1·10

1977 (17 Oct). *Anniversaries and Events. T* **193** *and similar horiz designs. Multicoloured. W* **58** (*sideways*). *P* 13½ × 13.

493	20 m. Type **193**	..	10	10
494	40 m. Map of Mediterranean	..	15	20
495	60 m. Gold medals	..	20	20
496	80 m. "Sputnik"	..	20	85
493/6		*Set of 4*	60	1·25

Events:—20 m. Revitalisation of handicrafts; 40 m. "Man and the Biosphere" Programme in the Mediterranean region; 60 m. Gold medals won by Cypriot students in the Orleans Gymnasiade; 80 m. 60th anniv of Russian October Revolution.

194 "Nativity"

(Litho Harrison)

1977 (21 Nov). *Christmas. T* **194** *and similar horiz designs showing children's paintings. Multicoloured. P* 14 × 13½.

497	10 m. Type **194**	..	10	10
498	40 m. "The Three Kings"	..	10	10
499	150 m. "Flight into Egypt"	..	25	80
497/9		*Set of 3*	35	90

195 Demetrios Libertis

196 Chrysorrhogiatissa Monastery Courtyard

(Des A. Ioannides)

1978 (6 Mar). *Cypriot Poets. T* **195** *and similar horiz design. W* **58** (*sideways*). *P* 14 × 13.

500	40 m. dull brown and olive-bistre	..	10	10
501	150 m. grey, grey-black and light red ..	..	30	80

Design:—150 m. Vasilis Michaelides.

(Litho Harrison)

1978 (24 Apr). *Europa. Architecture. T* **196** *and similar horiz designs. Multicoloured. P* 14 × 13½.

502	25 m. Type **196**	..	15	10
503	75 m. Kolossi Castle	..	25	35
504	125 m. Municipal Library, Paphos	..	45	1·50
502/4		*Set of 3*	75	1·75

197 Archbishop of Cyprus, 1950–77

198 Affected Blood Corpuscles (Prevention of Thalassaemia)

(Des A. Ioannides (300 m.). Photo Harrison)

1978 (3 Aug). *Archbishop Makarios Commemoration. T **197** and similar vert designs. Multicoloured. P* 14 × 15.
505	15 m. Type **197**			15	20
	a. Silver (inscr and emblem) omitted			†	—
	b. Horiz strip of 5. Nos. 505/9			85	
	ba. Imperf (horiz strip of 5)				
	bb. Silver omitted (horiz strip of 5)				
506	25 m. Exiled in Seychelles, 9 March 1956–				
	28 March 1957			15	20
507	50 m. President of the Republic, 1960–77			20	25
508	75 m. "Soldier of Christ"			20	30
509	100 m. "Fighter for Freedom"			25	35
	a. Silver (inscr and emblem) omitted				
505/9			*Set of* 5	85	1·10
MS510	110 × 80 mm. 300 m. "The Great Leader".				
	Imperf			1·00	2·50

Nos. 505/9 were printed together, *se-tenant*, in horizontal strips of 5 throughout the sheet.

Sheets of this issue are known with the silver omitted completely or only from the first or last vertical rows.

(Des A. Ioannides)

1978 (23 Oct). *Anniversaries and Events. T **198** and similar designs. P* 13½×14 (15, 35 m.) *or* 14×13½ (*others*).
511	15 m. multicoloured			10	10
512	35 m. multicoloured			15	10
513	75 m. black and grey			20	30
514	125 m. multicoloured			35	80
511/14			*Set of* 4	70	1·10

Designs and Events. *Vert*—35 m. Aristotle (sculpture) (2300th death anniversary). *Horiz*—75 m. "Heads" (Human Rights); 125 m. Wright brothers and Wright Flyer I (75th anniversary of powered flight).

199 Icon Stand

200 Aphrodite (statue from Soli)

(Litho Harrison)

1978 (4 Dec). *Christmas. T **199** and similar vert designs showing icon stands. P* 14 × 14½.
515	15 m. multicoloured			10	10
516	35 m. multicoloured			15	10
517	150 m. multicoloured			40	60
515/17			*Set of* 3	60	65

(Des G. Simonis. Litho Harrison)

1979 (12 Mar). *Aphrodite* (*Greek goddess of love and beauty*) *Commemoration* (1st issue). *T **200** and similar horiz design showing Aphrodite emerging from the sea at Paphos* (*legendary birthplace*). *Multicoloured. P* 14 × 13½.
518	75 m. Type **200**			25	10
519	125 m. Aphrodite on a shell (detail from				
	"Birth of Venus" by Botticelli)			35	25

See also Nos. 584/5.

201 Van, Larnaca–Nicosia Mail-coach and Envelope

202 Peacock Wrasse (*thalassoma pavo*)

(Des G. Simonis)

1979 (30 Apr). *Europa. Communications. T **201** and similar horiz designs. Multicoloured. W **58** (sideways). P* 14 × 13.
520	25 m. Type **201**			15	10
521	75 m. Radar, satellite and early telephone			30	20
522	125 m. Aircraft, ship and envelopes			65	80
520/2			*Set of* 3	1·00	1·00

1979 (25 June). *Flora and Fauna. T **202** and similar multicoloured designs. W **58** (sideways on 25 and 125 m.). P* 13½ × 12 (25, 125 m.) *or* 12 × 13½ (*others*).
523	25 m. Type **202**			15	10
524	50 m. Black Partridge (*Francolinus franco-*				
	linus) (*vert*)			70	60
525	75 m. Cedar (*Cedar brevifolia*) (*vert*)			45	30
526	125 m. Mule (*Equus mulus*)			50	1·25
523/6			*Set of* 4	1·60	2·00

203 I.B.E. and U.N.E.S.C.O. Emblems

204 "Jesus" (from Church of the Virgin Mary of Arakas, Lagoudhera)

1979 (1 Oct). *Anniversaries and Events. T **203** and similar designs in black, yellow-brown and yellow-ochre* (50 m.) *or multicoloured* (*others*). *P* 12½.
527	15 m. Type **203**			10	10
528	25 m. Graphic design of dove and stamp album				
	(*horiz*)			10	10
529	50 m. Lord Kitchener and map of Cyprus				
	(*horiz*)			20	15
530	75 m. Child's face (*horiz*)			25	10
531	100 m. Graphic design of footballers (*horiz*)			30	20
532	125 m. Rotary International emblem and "75"			30	75
527/32			*Set of* 6	1·10	1·25

Events:—15 m. 50th anniversary of International Bureau of Education; 25 m. 20th anniversary of Cyprus Philatelic Society; 50 m. Centenary of Cyprus Survey; 75 m. International Year of the Child; 100 m. 25th anniversary of U.E.F.A. (European Football Association); 125 m. 75th anniversary of Rotary International.

1979 (5 Nov). *Christmas. Icons. T **204** and similar vert designs. Multicoloured. W **58**. P* 13 × 13½ (35 m.) *or* 13½ × 14 (*others*).
533	15 m. Type **204**			10	10
534	35 m. "Nativity" (from the Iconostasis of the				
	Church of St. Nicholas, Famagusta				
	District) (29 × 44 mm)			10	10
535	150 m. "Holy Mary" (from Church of the Virgin				
	Mary of Arakas, Lagoudhera)			25	45
533/5			*Set of* 3	35	55

205 1880 ½d. Stamp with "969" (Nicosia) Postmark

206 St. Barnabas (Patron Saint of Cyprus)

1980 (17 Mar). *Cyprus Stamp Centenary. T **205** and similar horiz designs. Multicoloured. W **58** (sideways). P* 13½ × 13.
536	40 m. Type **205**			10	10
537	125 m. 1880 2½d. stamp with "974" (Kyrenia)				
	postmark			15	15
538	175 m. 1880 1s. stamp with "942" (Larnaca)				
	postmark			15	20
536/8			*Set of* 3	30	35
MS539	105 × 85 mm. 500 m. 1880 1d., ½d., 2½d.,				
	4d., 6d. and 1s. stamps (90 × 75 mm). Imperf			70	85

(Photo Harrison)

1980 (28 Apr). *Europa. Personalities. T **206** and similar vert design. Multicoloured. P* 12½.
540	40 m. Type **206**			15	10
541	125 m. Zeno of Citium (founder of the Stoic				
	philosophy)			30	20
	a. Pale Venetian red omitted			£110	

The pale Venetian red colour on No. 541 appears as an overlay on the bust. On No. 541a the bust is pure grey.

207 Sailing

208 Gold Necklace, Arsos (7th-century BC)

(Des A. Ioannides)

1980 (23 June). *Olympic Games, Moscow. T **207** and similar horiz designs. Multicoloured. W **58** (sideways). P* 13½ × 13.
542	40 m. Type **207**			10	10
543	125 m. Swimming			20	20
544	200 m. Gymnastics			25	25
542/4			*Set of* 3	50	50

1980 (15 Sept). *Archaeological Treasures. Multicoloured designs as T **208**. W **58** (sideways on 15, 40, 150 and 500 m.). Chalk-surfaced cream paper. P* 14 × 13 (15, 40, 150 and 500 m.) *or* 13 × 14 (*others*).
545	10 m. Type **208**			30	45
546	15 m. Bronze cow, Vouni Palace (5th-century				
	B.C.) (*horiz*)			30	45
547	25 m. Amphora, Salamis (6th-century B.C.)			30	10
548	40 m. Gold finger-ring, Enkomi (13th-century				
	B.C.) (*horiz*)			40	30
549	50 m. Bronze cauldron, Salamis (8th-century				
	B.C.)			40	10
550	75 m. Funerary stele, Marion (5th-century				
	B.C.)			1·25	1·00
551	100 m. Jug (15–14th-century B.C.)			85	15
552	125 m. Warrior (Terracotta) (6–5th-century				
	B.C.)			85	15
553	150 m. Lions attacking bull (bronze relief,				
	Vouni Palace (5th-century B.C.) (*horiz*)			1·50	15
554	175 m. Faience rhyton, Kition (13th-century				
	B.C.)			1·00	55

555	200 m. Bronze statue of Ingot God, Enkomi				
	(12th-century B.C.)			1·00	30
556	500 m. Stone bowl, Khirokitia (6th-millennium				
	B.C.) (*horiz*)			1·00	1·00
557	£1 Ivory plaque, Salamis (7th-century B.C.)			1·25	1·25
558	£2 "Leda and the Swan" (mosaic), Kouklia				
	(3rd-century A.D.)			2·50	2·00
545/58			*Set of* 14	11·00	6·50

209 Cyprus Flag

210 Peace Dove and Head Silhouettes

1980 (1 Oct). *20th Anniv of Republic. T **209** and similar multicoloured designs. P* 13½ × 13 (125 m.) *or* 13 × 14 (*others*).
559	40 m. Type **209**			10	10
560	125 m. Signing Treaty of Establishment				
	(41 × 29 mm)			20	15
561	175 m. Archbishop Makarios			35	25
559/61			*Set of* 3	60	45

(Des A. Ioannides)

1980 (29 Nov). *International Palestinian Solidarity Day. T **210** and similar horiz design showing Peace Dove and head silhouettes. W **58** (sideways). P* 13½ × 13.
562	40 m. grey and black			20	20
	a. Horiz pair. Nos. 562/3			55	55
563	125 m. grey and black			35	35

Nos. 562/3 were printed together, *se-tenant*, in horizontal pairs throughout the sheet.

211 Pulpit, Tripiotis Church, Nicosia

212 Folk-dancing

1980 (29 Nov). *Christmas. T **211** and similar vert designs. Multicoloured. W **58**. P* 13 × 14.
564	25 m. Type **211**			10	10
565	100 m. Holy Doors, Panayia Church, Para-				
	limni (24 × 37 mm)			15	20
566	125 m. Pulpit, Ayios Lazaros Church, Larnaca			15	20
564/6			*Set of* 3	30	40

(Litho Harrison)

1981 (4 May). *Europa. Folklore. T **212** and similar vert design showing folk-dancing from paintings by T. Photiades. P* 14.
567	40 m. multicoloured			30	30
568	175 m. multicoloured			60	50

213 Self-portrait

214 *Ophrys kotschyi*

1981 (15 June). *500th Anniv of Leonardo da Vinci's Visit. T **213** and similar multicoloured designs. W **58** (sideways on 125 m.). P* 12 × 14 (125 m.) *or* 13½ × 14 (*others*).
569	50 m. Type **213**			40	10
570	125 m. "The Last Supper" (50 × 25 mm)			70	40
571	175 m. Cyprus lace and Milan Cathedral			95	60
569/71			*Set of* 3	1·90	1·00

(Des A. Tassos)

1981 (6 July). *Cypriot Wild Orchids. T **214** and similar vert designs. Multicoloured. W **58**. P* 13½ × 14.
572	25 m. Type **214**			50	60
	a. Block of 4. Nos. 572/5			2·25	
573	50 m. *Orchis punctulata*			60	70
574	75 m. *Ophrys argolica elegans*			70	80
575	150 m. *Epipactis veratrifolia*			75	90
572/5			*Set of* 4	2·25	2·75

Nos. 572/5 were printed together, *se-tenant*, in blocks of 4 throughout the sheet.

215 Heinrich von Stephan

216 "The Lady of the Angels" (from Church of the Transfiguration of Christ, Palekhori)

(Des A. Tassos (200 m.), A. Ioannides (others))

1981 (28 Sept). *Anniversaries and Events. T* **215** *and similar horiz designs.* W **58** *(sideways).* P 13½×13.

576	25 m. brown-olive, dp yellow-green & brt bl	15	10
577	40 m. multicoloured	15	10
578	125 m. black, vermilion and deep yellow-green	30	25
579	150 m. multicoloured	35	30
580	200 m. multicoloured	40	25
576/80	*Set of 5*	1·25	95

Designs and Events:—25 m. Type 215 150th birth anniversary of Henrich von Stephan (founder of U.P.U.); 40 m. Stylised man holding dish of food (World Food Day); 125 m. Stylised hands (International Year for Disabled Persons); 150 m. Stylised building and flower (European Campaign for Urban Renaissance); 200 m. Prince Charles, Lady Diana Spencer and St. Paul's Cathedral (Royal Wedding).

1981 (16 Nov). *Christmas. Murals from Nicosia District Churches. T* **216** *and similar multicoloured designs.* W **58** *(sideways on 25 and 125 m.).* P 12½.

581	25 m. Type 216	20	10
582	100 m. "Christ Pantokrator" (from Church of Madonna of Arakas, Lagoudera) (*vert*)	60	20
583	125 m. "Baptism of Christ" (from Church of Our Lady of Assinou, Nikitari)	70	30
581/3	*Set of 3*	1·25	50

217 "Louomene" (statue of Aphrodite bathing, 250 B.C.)

218 Naval Battle with Greek Fire, 985 A.D.

1982 (12 Apr). *Aphrodite (Greek goddess of love and beauty) Commemoration (2nd issue). T* **217** *and similar vert design. Multicoloured.* W **58**. P 13½×14.

584	125 m. Type 217	80	45
585	175 m. "Anadyomene" (Aphrodite emerging from the waters) (Titian)	95	65

(Des G. Simonis. Photo Harrison)

1982 (3 May). *Europa. Historical Events. T* **218** *and similar horiz design. Multicoloured.* P 12½.

586	40 m. Type 218	60	10
587	175 m. Conversion of Roman Proconsul Sergius Paulus to Christianity, Paphos, 45 A.D.	1·00	2·50

219 Monogram of Christ (mosaic)

100 = (220)

1982 (5 July). *World Cultural Heritage. T* **219** *and similar multicoloured designs.* W **58** *(sideways on 50 and 225 m.).* P 13½×14 *(125 m.) or* 12½ *(others).*

588	50 m. Type 219	25	10
589	125 m. Head of priest-king of Paphos (sculpture) (24×37 *mm*)	50	25
590	225 m. Theseus (Greek god) (mosaic)	75	95
588/90	*Set of 3*	1·40	1·10

1982 (6 Sept). *No. 550 surch with T* **220** *by Govt Ptg Office, Nicosia.*

591	100 m. on 75 m. Funerary stele, Marion (5th-century B.C.)	50	50

221 Cyprus and Stylised "75"

222 Holy Communion— The Bread

1982 (8 Nov). *75th Anniv of Boy Scout Movement. T* **221** *and similar multicoloured designs.* W **58** *(sideways on 100 m. and* 175 *m.).* P 12½ × 13½ *(125 m.) or* 13½×12½ *(others).*

592	100 m. Type 221	40	20
593	125 m. Lord Baden-Powell (*vert*)	45	30
594	175 m. Camp-site	55	55
592/4	*Set of 3*	1·25	95

1982 (6 Dec). *Christmas. T* **222** *and similar designs.* W **58** *(sideways on 25 and 250 m.).* P 12½ × 12 *(25 and 250 m.) or* 13½ × 14 *(100 m.).*

595	25 m. multicoloured	10	10
596	100 m. gold and black	30	15
597	250 m. multicoloured	70	1·00
595/7	*Set of 3*	1·00	1·10

Designs: *Vert*—100 m. Holy Chalice. *Horiz*—250 m. Holy Communion—The Wine.

223 Cyprus Forest Industries' Sawmill

1983 (14 Mar). *Commonwealth Day. T* **223** *and similar horiz designs. Multicoloured.* W **58** *(sideways).* P 14 × 13½.

598	50 m. Type 223	10	10
599	125 m. "Ikarios and the Discovery of Wine" (3rd-cent mosaic)	20	25
600	150 m. Folk-dancers, Commonwealth Film and Television Festival, 1980	25	35
601	175 m. Royal Exhibition Building, Melbourne (Commonwealth Heads of Government Meeting, 1981)	25	40
598/601	*Set of 4*	70	1·00

224 Cyprosyllabic Inscription (6th-cent B.C.)

225 *Pararge aegeria*

(Des G. Simonis. Photo Harrison)

1983 (3 May). *Europa. T* **224** *and similar horiz design. Multicoloured.* P 14½ × 14.

602	50 m. Type 224	40	10
603	200 m. Copper ore, ingot (Enkomi 1400-1250 B.C.) and bronze jug (2nd-cent A.D.)	1·10	2·40

1983 (28 June). *Butterflies. T* **225** *and similar horiz designs. Multicoloured.* W w **58**. P 12½.

604	60 m. Type 225	25	20
605	130 m. *Aricia agestis*	45	25
606	250 m. *Glaucopsyche melanops*	85	2·00
604/6	*Set of 3*	1·40	2·25

(New Currency: 100 cents = £1 (Cyprus))

1c

=

(226)   227 View of Power Station

1983 (3 Oct). *Nos. 545/56 surch as T* **226** *by Govt Printing Office, Nicosia.*

607	1 c. on 10 m. Type 208	35	40
608	2 c. on 15 m. Bronze cow, Vouni Palace (5th-century B.C.)	35	40
609	3 c. on 25 m. Amphora, Salamis (6th-century B.C.)	35	20
610	4 c. on 40 m. Gold finger-ring, Enkomi (13th-century B.C.)	40	20
611	5 c. on 50 m. Bronze cauldron, Salamis (8th-century B.C.)	50	50
612	6 c. on 75 m. Funerary stele, Marion (5th-century B.C.)	50	20
613	10 c. on 100 m. Jug (15–14th-century B.C.)	50	40
614	13 c. on 125 m. Warrior (Terracotta) (6–5th-century B.C.)	60	50
615	15 c. on 150 m. Lions attacking bull (bronze relief), Vouni Palace (5th-century B.C.)	70	55
616	20 c. on 200 m. Bronze statue of Ingot God, Enkomi (12th-century B.C.)	70	65
617	25 c. on 175 m. Faience rhyton, Kition (13th-century B.C.)	80	1·10
618	50 c. on 500 m. Stone bowl, Khirokitia (6th-millennium B.C.)	1·00	2·00
607/18	*Set of 12*	6·00	6·50

1983 (27 Oct). *Anniversaries and Events. T* **227** *and similar vert designs. Multicoloured.* W **58**. P 13 × 14.

619	3 c. Type 227	10	20
620	6 c. W.C.Y. logo	20	15
621	13 c. *Sol Olympia* (liner) and *Polys* (tanker)	40	35
622	15 c. Human Rights emblem and map of Europe	40	25
623	20 c. Nicos Kazantzakis (poet)	45	75
624	25 c. Archbishop Makarios in church	50	75
619/24	*Set of 6*	1·75	2·25

Events:—3 c. 30th anniv of the Cyprus Electricity Authority; 6 c. World Communications Year; 13 c. 25th anniv of International Maritime Organization; 15 c. 35th anniv of Universal Declaration of Human Rights; 20 c. Birth centenary; 25 c. 70th birth anniv.

228 St. Lazaros Church, Larnaca

229 Waterside Cafe, Larnaca

1983 (12 Dec). *Christmas. Church Towers. T* **228** *and similar vert designs. Multicoloured.* W **58**. P 12×13½.

625	4 c. Type 228	15	10
626	13 c. St. Varvara Church, Kaimakli, Nicosia	40	35
627	20 c. St. Ioannis Church, Larnaca	70	1·50
625/7	*Set of 3*	1·10	1·75

(Litho Harrison)

1984 (6 Mar). *Old Engravings. T* **229** *and similar horiz designs. Each pale stone and black.* P 14½ × 14 (6 c.) or 14 (others).

628	6 c. Type 229	15	10
629	20 c. Bazaar at Larnaca (30 × 25 *mm*)	40	85
630	30 c. Famagusta Gate, Nicosia (30×25 *mm*)	65	1·50
628/30	*Set of 3*	1·10	2·25
MS631	110×85 mm. 75 c. "The Confession" (St. Lazarus Church, Larnaca)	1·60	2·00

230 C.E.P.T. 25th Anniversary Logo

(Des J. Larrivière. Litho Harrison)

1984 (30 Apr). *Europa.* W **58**. P 12½.

632	230	6 c. apple-green, deep bl-green & blk	50	10
633		15 c. light blue, dull ultram & blk	1·10	2·50

A. Waddington ptgs (Nos. 634/a)

B. Aspioti-Elka ptg (No. 634*b*)

(Des A. Tassos)

1984 (18 June)–**87**. *Obligatory Tax. Refugee Fund. Design as T* **188** *but new value and "1984" date.* P 13×12½.

(*a*) *Litho J.W.* W **58**. *Chalk-surfaced cream paper*

634	1 c. grey-black (A)	10	10
	a. Wmk sideways. Ordinary paper (21.2.87)*	70	70

(*b*) *Litho Aspioti-Elka.* W **58**. *Chalk-surfaced cream paper*

634*b*	1 c. grey-black (B) (3.11.87)*	65	65

*Earliest known date of use.

In addition to the redrawn inscriptions there are other minor differences between the work of the two printers.

For a further version of this design, showing "1974" at top right, see Nos. 729, 747 and 807.

231 Running

(Des K. Haine. Litho Harrison)

1984 (18 June). *Olympic Games. Los Angeles. T* **231** *and similar horiz designs. Multicoloured.* W **58** *(sideways).* P 14.

635	3 c. Type 231	20	10
636	4 c. Olympic column	20	20
637	13 c. Swimming	55	75
638	20 c. Gymnastics	80	1·50
635/8	*Set of 4*	1·60	2·25

232 Prisoners-of-War

233 Open Stamp Album (25th Anniv of Cyprus Philatelic Society)

1984 (20 July). *10th Anniv of Turkish Landings in Cyprus. T **232** and similar horiz design. Multicoloured. P 14 × 13½.*

639	15 c. Type **232**	40	45
640	20 c. Map and burning buildings ..	50	55

(Des P. St. Antoniades (6 c.), A. Ioannides (10 c.), Harrison (others). Litho Harrison)

1984 (15 Oct). *Anniversaries and Events. T **233** and similar multicoloured designs. W **58** (sideways on horiz designs). P 12½.*

641	6 c. Type **233**	30	20
642	10 c. Football in motion (*horiz*) (50th anniv of Cyprus Football Association) ..	45	30
643	15 c. "Dr. George Papanicolaou" (medical scientist – birth cent)	60	50
644	25 c. Antique map of Cyprus and ikon (*horiz*) (International Symposia on Cartography and Medieval Paleography) ..	1·00	2·00
641/4	.. .. *Set of 4*	2·10	2·75

234 St. Mark (miniature from 11th-century Gospel)

235 Autumn at Platania, Troodos Mountains

(Des and litho Harrison)

1984 (26 Nov). *Christmas. Illuminated Gospels. T **234** and similar vert designs. Multicoloured. W **58**. P 12½.*

645	4 c. Type **234**	30	10
646	13 c. Beginning of St. Mark's Gospel ..	60	50
647	20 c. St. Luke (miniature from 11th-century Gospel)	1·00	2·00
645/7	.. .. *Set of 3*	1·75	2·40

(Des and litho Harrison)

1985 (18 Mar.) *Cyprus Scenes and Landscapes. T **235** and similar multicoloured designs. Ordinary white paper. P 14 × 15 (6 c., 20 c., 25 c., £1, £5) or 15 × 14 (others).*

648	1 c. Type **235**.	20	40
649	2 c. Ayia Napa Monastery	20	40
650	3 c. Phini Village—panoramic view ..	20	30
651	4 c. Kykko Monastery	20	20
652	5 c. Beach at Makronissos, Ayia Napa	20	20
653	6 c. Village street, Omodhos (*vert*)..	30	20
654	10 c. Panoramic sea view	40	35
655	13 c. Windsurfing	55	25
656	15 c. Beach at Protaras	65	25
657	20 c. Forestry for development (*vert*)	80	50
658	25 c. Sunrise at Protaras (*vert*) ..	1·00	1·00
659	30 c. Village house, Pera	1·25	1·25
660	50 c. Apollo Hylates Sanctuary, Curium	2·00	1·75
661	£1 Snow on Troodos Mountains (*vert*)	3·50	3·00
662	£5 Personification of Autumn, House of Dionyssos, Paphos (*vert*) ..	13·00	15·00
648/62	.. .. *Set of 15*	22·00	23·00

236 Clay Idols of Musicians (7/6th Century B.C.)

237 Cyprus Coat of Arms (25th Anniv of Republic)

(Des and litho Harrison)

1985 (6 May). *Europa. European Music Year. T **236** and similar horiz design. Multicoloured. W **58** (sideways). P 12½.*

663	6 c. Type **236**.	65	35
664	15 c. Violin, lute, flute and score from the "Cyprus Suite"	1·10	2·00

(Des G. Simonis (4 c., 13 c.), Harrison (others). Litho Harrison)

1985 (23 Sept). *Anniversaries and Events. T **237** and similar designs. P 14½ (4, 20 c.) or 14 × 13½ (others).*

665	4 c. multicoloured	20	15
666	6 c. multicoloured	25	15
667	13 c. multicoloured	60	1·00
668	15 c. black, olive-black and yellow-orange ..	1·25	1·25
669	20 c. multicoloured	60	1·75
665/9	.. .. *Set of 5*	2·50	3·75

Designs and Events: *Horiz* (43×30 *mm*)—6 c. "Barn of Liopetri" (detail) (Pol. Georghiou) (30th anniv of EOKA Campaign); 13 c. Three profiles (International Youth Year); 15 c. Solon Michaelides (composer and conductor) (European Music Year). *Vert* (as T **237**)—20 c. U.N. Building, New York, and flags (40th anniv of United Nations Organization).

238 "The Visit of the Madonna to Elizabeth" (Lambadistis Monastery, Kalopanayiotis)

239 Figure from Hellenistic Spoon Handle

(Des and litho Harrison)

1985 (18 Nov). *Christmas. Frescoes from Cypriot Churches. T **238** and similar vert designs. Multicoloured. P 12½.*

670	4 c. Type **238**	25	10
671	13 c. "The Nativity" (Lambadistis Monastery, Kalopanayiotis)	60	65
672	20 c. "Candlemas-day" (Asinou Church) ..	1·00	2·00
670/2	.. .. *Set of 3*	1·75	2·50

(Des A. Ioannides. Litho Harrison)

1986 (17 Feb). *New Archaeological Museum Fund. T **239** and similar horiz designs. Multicoloured. P 15 × 14.*

673	15 c. Type **239**.	60	45
674	20 c. Pattern from early Ionian helmet and foot from statue	70	75
675	25 c. Roman statue of Eros and Psyche	80	95
676	30 c. Head of statue	1·00	1·10
673/6	.. .. *Set of 4*	2·75	3·00
MS677	111 × 90 *mm*. Nos. 673/6 (*sold at £1*) ..	12·00	16·00

Two-thirds of the amount received from sales of Nos. 673/7 was devoted to the construction of a new Archaeological Museum, Nicosia.

No. 676 also commemorates the 50th anniversary of the Department of Antiquities.

240 Cyprus Moufflon and Cedars

(Des G. Simonis)

1986 (28 Apr). *Europa. Protection of Nature and the Environment. T **240** and similar horiz design. Multicoloured. W **58** (sideways). P 14 × 13.*

678	7 c. Type **240**.	35	30
679	17 c. Greater Flamingos at Larnaca Salt Lake	1·40	2·50

=

241 Cat's-paw Scallop (242) (*Manupecten pesfelis*)

7c

(Des T. Katsoulides)

1986 (1 July). *Sea Shells. T **241** and similar horiz designs. Multicoloured. W **58** (sideways). P 14 × 13½.*

680	5 c. Type **241**	40	15
681	7 c. Atlantic Trumpet Triton (*Charonia variegata*)	45	15
682	18 c. Purple Dye Murex (*Murex brandaris*)	75	70
683	25 c. Yellow Cowrie (*Cypraea spurca*) ..	1·25	2·00
680/3	.. .. *Set of 4*	2·50	2·75

1986 (13 Oct). *Nos. 653 and 655 surch as T **242**.*

684	7 c. on 6 c. Village street, Omodhos (*vert*) ..	40	30
685	18 c. on 13 c. Windsurfing	1·10	60

For 15 c. on 4 c. see No. 730.

243 Globe, Outline Map of Cyprus and Barn Swallows (Overseas Cypriots' Year)

(Des T. Katsoulides)

1986 (13 Oct). *Anniversaries and Events. T **243** and similar horiz designs. Multicoloured. W **58** (sideways). P 13½ × 13.*

686	15 c. Type **243**.	1·00	45
687	18 c. Halley's Comet over Cyprus beach (40 × 23 *mm*)	1·25	2·00
	a. Horiz pair. Nos. 687/8	2·50	4·00
688	18 c. Comet's tail over sea and Edmond Halley (40 × 23 *mm*)	1·25	2·00
686/8	.. .. *Set of 3*	3·25	4·00

Nos. 687/8 were printed together, *se-tenant*, in horizontal pairs throughout the sheet, each pair forming a composite design.

244 Pedestrian Crossing

245 "The Nativity" (Church of Panayia tou Araka)

(Des A. Ioannides)

1986 (10 Nov). *Road Safety Campaign. T **244** and similar horiz designs. Multicoloured. W **58** (sideways). P 14 × 13.*

689	5 c. Type **244**.	1·00	30
690	7 c. Motor cycle crash helmet ..	1·10	30
691	18 c. Hands fastening car seat belt ..	2·25	3·00
689/91	.. .. *Set of 3*	4·00	3·25

(Des G. Simonis)

1986 (24 Nov). *Christmas. International Peace Year. T **245** and similar vert designs showing details of Nativity frescoes from Cypriot churches. Multicoloured. W **58** (inverted). P 13½ × 14.*

692	5 c. Type **245**.	30	15
693	15 c. Church of Panayia tou Moutoulla ..	80	30
694	17 c. Church of St. Nicholas tis Steyis ..	90	2·00
692/4	.. .. *Set of 3*	1·75	2·25

246 Church of Virgin Mary, Asinou

(Des and photo Harrison)

1987 (22 Apr). *Troodos Churches on the World Heritage List. T **246** and similar horiz designs. Multicoloured. P 12½.*

695	15 c. Type **246**.	80	1·10
	a. Sheetlet. Nos. 695/703	6·50	
696	15 c. Fresco of Virgin Mary, Moutoulla's Church	80	1·10
697	15 c. Church of Virgin Mary, Podithou	80	1·10
698	15 c. Fresco of Three Apostles, St. Ioannis Lampadistis Monastery ..	80	1·10
699	15 c. Annunciation fresco, Church of the Holy Cross, Pelentriou	80	1·10
700	15 c. Fresco of Saints, Church of the Cross, Ayiasmati	80	1·10
701	15 c. Fresco of Archangel Michael and Donor, Pedoula's Church of St. Michael	80	1·10
702	15 c. Church of St. Nicolaos, Steyis ..	80	1·10
703	15 c. Fresco of Prophets, Church of Virgin Mary, Araka	80	1·10
695/703	.. .. *Set of 9*	6·50	9·00

Nos. 695/703 were printed together, *se-tenant*, in sheetlets of nine.

247 Proposed Central Bank of Cyprus Building

(Des G. Simonis)

1987 (11 May). *Europa. Modern Architecture. T **247** and similar horiz design. Multicoloured. W **58** (sideways). P 14 × 13½.*

704	7 c. multicoloured	50	30
705	18 c. black, brownish grey and sage-green ..	1·10	2·00

Design:—18 c. Headquarters complex, Cyprus Telecommunications Authority.

248 Remains of Ancient Ship and Kyrenia Castle

(Des Y. Pantsopoulos)

1987 (3 Oct). *Voyage of "Kyrenia II" (replica of ancient ship). T **248** and similar horiz designs. Multicoloured. W **58** (sideways). P 14×13½.*

706	2 c. Type **248**		30	20
707	3 c. *Kyrenia II* under construction, 1982–5		30	90
708	5 c. *Kyrenia II* at Paphos, 1986		55	20
709	17 c. *Kyrenia II* at New York, 1986		1·40	90
706/9		*Set of 4*	2·25	2·00

249 Hands (from Michelangelo's *Creation*) and Emblem (10th anniv of Blood Donation Co-ordinating Committee)

250 Nativity Crib

(Des A. Ioannides)

1987 (2 Nov). *Anniversaries and Events. T **249** and similar horiz designs. Multicoloured. W **58** (sideways). P 14×13½.*

710	7 c. Type **249**		50	25
711	15 c. Snail with flowered shell and countryside (European Countryside Campaign)	1·10	40
712	20 c. Symbols of ocean bed and Earth's crust ("Troodos '87" Ophiolites and Oceanic Lithosphere Symposium)	1·40	3·00
710/12		*Set of 3*	2·75	3·25

(Des A. Ioannides)

1987 (30 Nov). *Christmas. Traditional Customs. T **250** and similar square designs. Multicoloured. W **58** (sideways). P 14.*

713	5 c. Type **250**		35	15
714	15 c. Door knocker decorated with foliage	1·10	35
715	17 c. Bowl of fruit and nuts	1·25	2·00
713/15		*Set of 3*	2·40	2·25

251 Flags of Cyprus and E.E.C.

(Des G. Simonis. Litho Alexandros Matsoukis, Athens)

1988 (11 Jan). *Cypriot–E.E.C. Customs Union. T **251** and similar horiz design. Multicoloured. W **58**. P 13×13½.*

716	15 c. Type **251**		80	1·50
717	18 c. Outline maps of Cyprus and E.E.C. countries	80	80

252 Intelpost Telefax Terminal

(Des A. Ioannides. Litho Alexandros Matsoukis, Athens)

1988 (9 May). *Europa. Transport and Communications. T **252** and similar horiz designs. Multicoloured. W **58**. P 14×14½.*

718	7 c. Type **252**		65	75
	a. Horiz pair. Nos. 718/19		1·25	1·50
719	7 c. Car driver using mobile telephone	65	75
720	18 c. Nose of Cyprus Airways airliner and Greater Flamingos	2·00	2·50
	a. Horiz pair. Nos. 720/1		4·00	
721	18 c. Boeing 737 airliner in flight and Greater Flamingos	2·00	2·50
718/21		*Set of 4*	4·75	6·00

The two designs of each value were printed together, se-tenant, in horizontal pairs throughout the sheet of ten.

253 Sailing

254 Conference Emblem

(Des A. Ioannides. Photo Courvoisier)

1988 (27 June). *Olympic Games, Seoul. T **253** and similar vert designs. Multicoloured. Granite paper. P 12.*

722	5 c. Type **253**		30	20
723	7 c. Athletes at start		35	40
724	10 c. Shooting		40	70
725	20 c. Judo		90	1·50
722/5		*Set of 4*	1·75	2·50

(Des A. Ioannides. Litho M. A. Moatsos, Athens)

1988 (5 Sept). *Non-Aligned Foreign Ministers' Conference, Nicosia. T **254** and similar horiz designs. W **58** (sideways). P 14×13½.*

726	1 c. black, pale blue and emerald		10	10
727	10 c. multicoloured		45	70
728	50 c. multicoloured		2·25	2·50
726/8		*Set of 3*	2·50	3·00

Designs:— 10 c. Emblem of Republic of Cyprus; 50 c. Nehru, Tito, Nasser and Makarios.

255 "Cyprus 74" (wood-engraving by A. Tassos)

256 "Presentation of Christ at the Temple" (Church of Holy Cross tou Agiasmati)

(Des A. Tassos. Litho M. A. Moatsos, Athens)

1988 (12 Sept). *Obligatory Tax. Refugee Fund. Design as Nos. 634/b, but with upper and lower inscriptions redrawn and "1974" added as in T **255**. W **58**. Chalk-surfaced paper. P 13×12½.*

729	**255** 1 c. brownish black and brownish grey		20	15

For this design printed in photogravure and perforated 11½ see No. 747, in lithography perforated 13 see No. 807 and in lithography perforated 14½×13½ see No. 892.

1988 (3 Oct). *No. 651 surch as T **242**.*

730	15 c. on 4 c. Kykko Monastery		1·00	70

(Des G. Simonis. Litho M. A. Moatsos, Athens)

1988 (28 Nov). *Christmas. T **256** and similar vert designs showing frescoes from Cypriot churches. Multicoloured. W **58**. P 13½ × 14.*

731	5 c. Type **256**		30	20
732	15 c. "Virgin and Child" (St. John Lampadistis Monastery)	70	25
733	17 c. "Adoration of the Magi" (St. John Lampadistis Monastery)	1·00	1·75
731/3		*Set of 3*	1·75	2·00

257 Human Rights Logo

258 Basketball

(Des G. Simonis. Litho M. A. Moatsos, Athens)

1988 (10 Dec). *40th Anniv of Universal Declaration of Human Rights. W **58** (inverted). P 13½ × 14.*

734	**257** 25 c. azure, dull violet-blue and cobalt		90	1·25

(Des A. Ioannides. Litho Alexandros Matsoukis, Athens)

1989 (10 Apr). *Third Small European States' Games, Nicosia. T **258** and similar horiz designs. Multicoloured. P 13½.*

735	1 c. Type **258**		10	15
736	5 c. Javelin		20	15
737	15 c. Wrestling		45	20
738	18 c. Athletics		60	1·00
735/8		*Set of 4*	1·25	1·40
MS739	109×80 mm. £1 Angel and laurel wreath (99×73 mm). Imperf		4·50	6·00

259 Lingri Stick Game

(Des S. Michael. Litho Alexandros Matsoukis, Athens)

1989 (8 May). *Europa. Children's Games. T **259** and similar horiz designs. Multicoloured. P 13×13½.*

740	7 c. Type **259**		75	90
	a. Horiz pair. Nos. 740/1		1·50	1·75
741	7 c. Ziziros		75	90
742	18 c. Sitsia		90	1·25
	a. Horiz pair. Nos. 742/3		1·75	2·50
743	18 c. Leapfrog		90	1·25
740/3		*Set of 4*	3·00	3·75

Nos. 740/1 and 742/3 were each printed together, se-tenant, in horizontal pairs throughout the sheets.

MACHINE LABELS. From 29 May 1989 gummed labels in the above design, ranging in value from 1 c. to £99.99, were available from machines at Eleftheria Square P.O., Nicosia ("001") (until 1991), District Post Office, Nicosia ("001") (1991 to January 1992) and District P.O., Limassol ("002") (until January 1999).

260 "Universal Man"

261 Stylized Human Figures

(Des A. Ioannides. Photo Courvoisier)

1989 (7 July). *Bicentenary of the French Revolution. Granite paper. P 11½.*

744	**260** 18 c. multicoloured		60	60

(Des A. Ioannides. Litho Alexandros Matsoukis, Athens)

1989 (4 Sept). *Centenary of Interparliamentary Union (15 c.) and 9th Non-Aligned Summit Conference, Belgrade (30 c.). T **261** and similar vert design. Multicoloured. P 13½.*

745	15 c. Type **261**		50	40
746	30 c. Conference logo		1·00	1·10

(Photo Courvoisier)

1989 (4 Sept). *Obligatory Tax. Refugee Fund. As T **255**, but inscr "1989" or "1990". Granite paper. P 11½.*

747	**255** 1 c. brownish black and brownish grey		45	30

262 Worker Bees tending Larvae

263 Outstretched Hand and Profile (aid for Armenian earthquake victims)

(Litho Alexandros Matsoukis, Athens)

1989 (16 Oct). *Bee-keeping. T **262** and similar vert designs. Multicoloured. P 13½.*

748	3 c. Type **262**		15	20
749	10 c. Bee on Rock-rose flower		40	50
750	15 c. Bee on Lemon flower		60	50
751	18 c. Queen and worker bees		65	90
748/51		*Set of 4*	1·60	1·90

(Des A. Ioannides. Litho Alexandros Matsoukis, Athens)

1989 (13 Nov). *Anniversaries and Events. T **263** and similar vert designs. Multicoloured. P 13½.*

752	3 c. Type **263**		20	55
753	5 c. Airmail envelope (Cyprus Philatelic Society F.I.P. membership)	30	10
754	7 c. Crab symbol and daisy (European Cancer Year)	55	1·10
755	17 c. Vegetables and fish (World Food Day)	90	1·10
752/5		*Set of 4*	1·75	2·50

264 Winter (detail from "Four Seasons")

265 Hands and Open Book (International Literacy Year)

(Litho Alexandros Matsoukis, Athens)

1989 (29 Dec). *Roman Mosaics from Paphos.* T **264** and similar multicoloured designs showing details. P 13 (1, 5, 7, 15 c.), 13×13½ (2, 4, 18, 40 c.), 13½×13 (3, 10, 20, 25 c.) or 14 (50 c., £1, £3).

756	1 c. Type **264**		10	10
757	2 c. Personification of Crete (32×24 mm)		10	10
758	3 c. Centaur and Maenad (24×32 mm)		10	10
759	4 c. Poseidon and Amymone (32×24 mm)		15	15
760	5 c. Leda		20	20
761	7 c. Apollon		25	25
762	10 c. Hermes and Dionysos (24×32 mm)		30	30
763	15 c. Cassiopeia		50	45
764	18 c. Orpheus (32×24 mm)		55	50
765	20 c. Nymphs (24×32 mm)		65	60
766	25 c. Amazon (24×32 mm)		75	70
767	40 c. Doris (32×24 mm)		1·40	1·25
768	50 c. Heracles and the Lion (39×27 mm)		1·60	1·50
769	£1 Apollon and Daphne (39×27 mm)		3·00	3·00
770	£3 Cupid (39×27 mm)		8·00	8·25
756/70		Set of 15	17·00	17·00

(Des A. Ioannides. Litho Alexandros Matsoukis, Athens)

1990 (3 Apr). *Anniversaries and Events.* T **265** and similar horiz designs. Multicoloured. P 13½.

771	15 c. Type **265**		55	50
772	17 c. Dove and profiles (83rd Inter-Parliamentary Conference, Nicosia)		65	90
773	18 c. Lions International emblem (Lions Europa Forum, Limassol)		75	90
771/3		Set of 3	1·75	2·10

266 District Post Office, Paphos

(Des A. Ioannides. Litho Alexandros Matsoukis, Athens)

1990 (10 May). *Europa. Post Office Buildings.* T **266** and similar horiz design. Multicoloured. P 13×13½.

774	7 c. Type **266**		80	25
775	18 c. City Centre Post Office, Limassol		1·10	1·75

267 Symbolic Lips (25th anniv of Hotel and Catering Institute)

(Des A. Ioannides. Litho Alexandros Matsoukis, Athens)

1990 (9 July). *European Tourism Year.* T **267** and similar horiz designs. Multicoloured. P 14.

776	5 c. Type **267**		25	20
777	7 c. Bell tower, St. Lazarus Church (1100th anniv)		30	25
778	15 c. Butterflies and woman		1·25	40
779	18 c. Birds and man		1·50	3·00
776/9		Set of 4	3·00	3·50

268 Sun (wood carving)

269 *Chionodoxa lochiae*

(Des A. Ioannides. Photo Courvoisier)

1990 (29 Sept). *30th Anniv of Republic.* T **268** and similar square designs. Multicoloured. Granite paper. P 11½.

780	5 c. Type **268**		55	45
781	17 c. Bulls (pottery design)		65	60
782	18 c. Fishes (pottery design)		75	70
783	40 c. Tree and birds (wood carving)		1·40	2·75
780/3		Set of 4	3·00	4·00
MS784	89×89 mm. £1 30th Anniversary emblem. Imperf			3·75	5·50

(Litho Alexandros Matsoukis, Athens)

1990 (5 Nov). *Endangered Wild Flowers.* T **269** and similar vert designs taken from book illustrations by Elektra Megaw. Multicoloured. P 13½×13.

785	2 c. Type **269**		30	60
786	3 c. *Pancratium maritimum*		30	60
787	5 c. *Paeonia mascula*		45	20
788	7 c. *Cyclamen cyprium*		50	25
789	15 c. *Tulipa cypria*		85	30
790	18 c. *Crocus cyprius*		1·10	2·50
785/90		Set of 6	3·25	4·00

270 "Nativity"

271 Archangel

(Litho Alexandros Matsoukis, Athens)

1990 (3 Dec). *Christmas. 16th-Century Icons.* T **270** and similar vert designs. Multicoloured. P 13½.

791	5 c. Type **270**		25	20
792	15 c. "Virgin Hodegetria"		80	30
793	17 c. "Nativity" (*different*)		1·00	2·50
791/3		Set of 3	1·90	2·75

(Des A. Ioannides. Photo Courvoisier)

1991 (28 Mar). *6th-century Mosaics from Kanakaria Church.* T **271** and similar vert designs. Multicoloured. Granite paper. P 12.

794	5 c. Type **271**		20	15
795	15 c. Christ Child		75	20
796	17 c. St. James		1·00	1·25
797	18 c. St. Matthew		1·00	1·75
794/7		Set of 4	2·75	3·00

272 *Ulysses* Spacecraft

273 Young Pied Wheatear

(Des G. Simonis. Litho Alexandros Matsoukis, Athens)

1991 (6 May). *Europa. Europe in Space.* T **272** and similar horiz design. Multicoloured. P 13×13½.

798	7 c. Type **272**		60	20
799	18 c. Giotto and Halley's Comet		1·25	2·00

(Des A. Ioannides. Litho Alexandros Matsoukis, Athens)

1991 (4 July). *Pied ("Cyprus") Wheatear.* T **273** and similar horiz designs. Multicoloured. P 13½.

800	5 c. Type **273**		35	30
801	7 c. Adult bird in autumn plumage		40	30
802	15 c. Adult male in breeding plumage		70	45
803	30 c. Adult female in breeding plumage		1·25	2·25
800/3		Set of 4	2·40	3·00

274 Mother and Child with Tents

275 The Nativity

(Des A. Ioannides. Litho Alexandros Matsoukis, Athens)

1991 (7 Oct). *40th Anniv of U.N. Commission for Refugees.* T **274** and similar horiz designs, each brown, orange-brown and silver. P 13½.

804	5 c. Type **274**		25	15
805	15 c. Three pairs of legs		90	65
806	18 c. Three children		1·10	2·00
804/6		Set of 3	2·00	2·50

(Litho Alexandros Matsoukis, Athens)

1991 (7 Oct). *Obligatory Tax. Refugee Fund. As* T **255**, *but inscr* "1991", "1992", "1993" *or* "1994". *Chalk-surfaced paper.* P 13.

807	255	1 c. brownish black and olive-grey		15	15

(Des Revd. D. Demosthenous. Litho Alexandros Matsoukis, Athens)

1991 (25 Nov). *Christmas.* T **275** and similar vert designs. Multicoloured. P 13½.

808	5 c. Type **275**		20	15
	a. Sheetlet of 9. Nos. 808/10×3		3·75	
809	15 c. Saint Basil		50	40
810	17 c. Baptism of Jesus		80	1·50
808/10		Set of 3	1·40	1·90

Nos. 808/10 were issued in separate sheets of 20 and in *se-tenant* sheetlets of 9.

276 Swimming

277 World Map and Emblem ("EXPO '92" Worlds Fair, Seville)

(Des A. Ioannides. Photo Courvoisier)

1992 (3 Apr). *Olympic Games, Barcelona.* T **276** and similar vert designs. Multicoloured. Granite paper. P 12.

811	10 c. Type **276**		50	35
812	20 c. Long jump		85	70
813	30 c. Running		1·25	1·25
814	35 c. Discus		1·40	2·25
811/14		Set of 4	3·50	4·00

(Des S. Karamallakis. Litho Alexandros Matsoukis, Athens)

1992 (20 Apr). *Anniversaries and Events.* T **277** and similar horiz designs. Multicoloured. P 14.

815	20 c. Type **277**		1·00	80
816	25 c. European map and football (10th Under-16 European Football Championship)		1·40	95
817	30 c. Symbols of Learning (inauguration of University of Cyprus)		1·40	2·75
815/17		Set of 3	3·50	4·00

278 Compass Rose and Map of Voyage

279 *Chamaeleo chamaeleon*

(Des G. Simonis. Litho Alexandros Matsoukis, Athens)

1992 (29 May). *Europa. 500th Anniv of Discovery of America by Columbus.* T **278** and similar horiz designs. Multicoloured. P 13×13½.

818	10 c. Type **278**		90	1·25
	a. Horiz pair. Nos. 818/19		1·75	2·50
819	10 c. "Departure from Palos" (R. Balaga)		90	1·25
820	30 c. Fleet of Columbus		1·40	1·75
	a. Horiz pair. Nos. 820/1		2·75	3·50
821	30 c. Christopher Columbus		1·40	1·75
818/21		Set of 4	4·00	5·50

Nos. 818/19 and 820/1 were printed together, *se-tenant*, in separate sheets, each horizontal pair forming a composite design.

(Litho Alexandros Matsoukis, Athens)

1992 (14 Sept). *Reptiles.* T **279** and similar horiz designs. Multicoloured. P 13½.

822	7 c. Type **279**		55	30
823	10 c. *Lacerta laevis troodica* (lizard)		65	45
824	15 c. *Mauremys caspica* (turtle)		90	80
825	20 c. *Coluber cypriensis* (snake)		1·00	2·00
822/5		Set of 4	2·75	3·25

280 Minoan Wine Ship of 7th-century B.C.

281 "Visitation of the Virgin Mary to Elizabeth", Church of the Holy Cross, Pelendri

(Des S. Vasiliou. Litho Alexandros Matsoukis, Athens)

1992 (9 Nov). *7th International Maritime and Shipping Conference, Nicosia.* P 14.

826	280	50 c. multicoloured		2·50	2·75

(Litho Alexandros Matsoukis, Athens)

1992 (9 Nov). *Christmas. Church Fresco Paintings.* T **281** and similar vert designs. Multicoloured. P 13½.

827	7 c. Type **281**		40	25
828	15 c. "Virgin and Child Enthroned", Church of Panayia tou Araka		75	65
829	20 c. "Virgin and Child", Ayios Nicolaos tis Stegis Church		1·10	1·90
827/9		Set of 3	2·00	2·50

NEW INFORMATION

The editor is always interested to correspond with people who have new information that will improve or correct the Catalogue.

282 School Building and Laurel Wreath   **283** "Motherhood" (bronze sculpture, Nicos Dymiotis)

(Des A. Ladommates. Litho Alexandros Matsoukis, Athens)

1993 (15 Feb). *Centenary of Pancyprian Gymnasium (secondary school).* P 14.

830	282	10 c. multicoloured	60	50

(Litho Alexandros Matsoukis, Athens)

1993 (5 Apr). *Europa. Contemporary Art. T 283 and similar multicoloured design.* P 13½.

831	10 c. Type 283		50	40
832	30 c. "Motherhood" (painting, Christoforos Savva) (horiz)		1·25	2·00

284 Women Athletes (13th European Cup for Women)   **285** Red Squirrelfish

Two types of 20 c.:
I. Incorrectly inscribed "MUFFLON ENCOURAGEMENT CUP"
II. Inscription corrected to "MOUFFLON ENCOURAGEMENT CUP"

(Des Maria Trillidou (10 c.), G. Simonis (25 c.), M. Christou (others). Litho Alexandros Matsoukis, Athens)

1993 (24 May–24 June). *Anniversaries and Events. T 284 and similar multicoloured designs.* P 14.

833	7 c. Type 234		40	30
834	10 c. Scout symbols (80th anniv of Scouting in Cyprus) (vert)		55	40
835	20 c. Water-skier, dolphin and gull (Moufflon Encouragement Cup) (I)	10·00	10·00	
	a. Type II (24 June)		95	95
836	25 c. Archbishop Makarios III and monastery (80th birth anniv)		1·40	2·00
833/6		Set of 4	3·00	3·25

No. 835 was withdrawn on 2 June 1993, after the spelling error had been spotted. No. 835a, with the spelling corrected, was placed on sale from 24 June.

(Des A. Ioannides. Litho Alexandros Matsoukis, Athens)

1993 (6 Sept). *Fishes. T 285 and similar horiz designs. Multicoloured.* P 13½.

837	7 c. Type 285		40	25
838	15 c. Red Scorpionfish		65	55
839	20 c. Painted Comber		75	85
840	30 c. Grey Triggerfish		1·40	2·25
837/40		Set of 4	2·75	3·50

286 Conference Emblem

(Des A. Ioannides. Litho Alexandros Matsoukis, Athens)

1993 (4 Oct). *12th Commonwealth Summit Conference.* P 13½.

841	286	35 c. orange-brown and pale ochre	1·60	1·90
842		40 c. bistre-brown and ochre	1·90	2·40

287 Ancient Sailing Ship and Modern Coaster   **288** Cross from Stavrovouni Monastery

(Des G. Simonis. Litho Alexandros Matsoukis, Athens)

1993 (4 Oct). *"Maritime Cyprus '93" International Shipping Conference, Nicosia.* P 13½×14.

843	287	25 c. multicoloured	1·40	1·40

(Litho Alexandros Matsoukis, Athens)

1993 (22 Nov). *Christmas. Church Crosses. T 288 and similar multicoloured designs.* P 13½.

844	7 c. Type 288		30	25
845	20 c. Cross from Lefkara		75	75
846	25 c. Cross from Pedoulas (horiz)		1·00	1·75
844/6		Set of 3	1·90	2·50

289 Copper Smelting   **290** Symbols of Disability (Persons with Special Needs Campaign)

(Des G. Simonis. Litho Alexandros Matsoukis, Athens)

1994 (1 Mar). *Europa. Discoveries. Ancient Copper Industry. T 289 and similar horiz design. Multicoloured.* P 13×13½.

847	10 c. Type 289		50	35
848	30 c. Ingot, ancient ship and map of Cyprus	1·25	1·75	

(Des E. Hadjimichael (7 c., 25 c.), S. Karamallakis (others). Litho Alexandros Matsoukis, Athens)

1994 (9 May). *Anniversaries and Events. T 290 and similar vert designs. Multicoloured.* P 13½.

849	7 c. Type 290		40	25
850	15 c. Olympic rings in flame (Centenary of International Olympic Committee)		65	55
851	20 c. Peace Doves (World Gymnasiade, Nicosia)		80	80
852	25 c. Adults and unborn baby in tulip (International Year of the Family)		1·10	1·75
849/52		Set of 4	2·75	3·00

291 Houses, Soldier and Family   **292** Black Pine

(Des A. Ioannides. Litho Alexandros Matsoukis, Athens)

1994 (27 June). *20th Anniv of Turkish Landings in Cyprus. T 291 and similar horiz designs. Multicoloured.* P 14.

853	10 c. Type 291		50	40
854	50 c. Soldier and ancient columns		2·00	3·00

(Des A. Ioannides. Litho Alexandros Matsoukis, Athens)

1994 (10 Oct). *Trees. T 292 and similar vert designs. Multicoloured.* P 13½×14.

855	7 c. Type 292		30	25
856	15 c. Cyprus Cedar		55	55
857	20 c. Golden Oak		70	80
858	30 c. Strawberry Tree		1·10	1·75
855/8		Set of 4	2·40	3·00

295 Woman from Paphos wearing Foustani   **296** "Hearth Room" Excavation, Alassa, and Frieze

(Des A. Ioannides. Litho Alexandros Matsoukis, Athens)

1994 (27 Dec). *Traditional Costumes. T 295 and similar vert designs. Multicoloured. Cream paper. With "1994" imprint date.* P 13½×13.

863	1 c. Type 295		10	10
864	2 c. Bride from Karpass		10	10
865	3 c. Woman from Paphos wearing sayia		10	10
866	5 c. Woman from Messaoria wearing foustani		10	10
867	7 c. Bridegroom		15	20
868	10 c. Shepherd from Messaoria		25	30
869	15 c. Woman from Nicosia in festive costume		35	40
870	20 c. Woman from Karpass wearing festive sayia		45	50
871	25 c. Woman from Pitsillia		55	60
872	30 c. Woman from Karpass wearing festive doupletti		65	70
873	35 c. Countryman		75	80
874	40 c. Man from Messaoria in festive costume		85	90
875	50 c. Townsman		1·10	1·25
876	£1 Townswoman wearing festive sarka		2·75	2·50
863/76		Set of 14	7·00	7·25

For £1 on white paper and perforated 14 see No. 958.

(Des A. Ladommatos. Litho Alexandros Matsoukis, Athens)

1995 (27 Feb). *3rd International Congress of Cypriot Studies, Nicosia. T 296 and similar multicoloured designs.* P 14.

877	20 c. Type 296		75	75
878	30 c. Hypostyle hall, Kalavasos, and Mycenaean amphora		1·00	1·50
MS879	110×80 mm. £1 Old Archbishop's Palace, Nicosia (107×71 mm). Imperf		3·50	4·50

297 Statue of Liberty, Nicosia (left detail)   **298** Nazi Heads on Peace Dove over Map of Europe

(Des G. Simonis. Litho Alexandros Matsoukis, Athens)

1995 (31 Mar). *40th Anniv of Start of E.O.K.A. Campaign. T 297 and similar vert designs showing different details of the statue. Multicoloured.* P 13×13½.

880	20 c. Type 297		90	1·10
	a. Horiz strip of 3. Nos. 880/2		2·40	
881	20 c. Centre detail (face value at top right)		90	1·10
882	20 c. Right detail (face value at bottom right)		90	1·10
880/2		Set of 3	2·40	3·00

Nos. 880/2 were printed together, se-tenant, in horizontal strips of 3 forming a composite design.

(Des Toulla Paphitis. Litho Alexandros Matsoukis, Athens)

1995 (8 May). *Europa. Peace and Freedom. T 298 and similar vert design. Multicoloured.* P 13½.

883	10 c. Type 298		75	35
884	30 c. Concentration camp prisoner and peace dove		1·50	2·25

299 Symbolic Figure holding Healthy Food   **300** European Union Flag and European Culture Month Logo

(Des Liza Petridou-Mala. Litho Alexandros Matsoukis, Athens)

1995 (26 June). *Healthy Living. T 299 and similar multicoloured designs.* P 13½.

885	7 c. Type 299		25	25
886	10 c. "AIDS" and patients (horiz)		50	50
887	15 c. Drug addict (horiz)		55	55
888	20 c. Smoker and barbed wire		75	1·00
885/8		Set of 4	1·75	2·10

293 Airliner, Route Map and Emblem   **294** "Virgin Mary" (detail) (Philip Goul)

(Des G. Simonis. Litho Alexandros Matsoukis, Athens)

1994 (21 Nov). *50th Anniv of International Civil Aviation Organization.* P 14.

859	293	30 c. multicoloured	1·50	1·50

(Litho Alexandros Matsoukis, Athens)

1994 (21 Nov). *Christmas. Church Paintings. T 294 and similar horiz designs. Multicoloured.* P 13½.

860	7 c. Type 294		35	25
861	20 c. "The Nativity" (detail) (Byzantine)		85	70
862	25 c. "Archangel Michael" (detail) (Goul)		1·10	1·90
860/2		Set of 3	2·10	2·50

(Des G. Simonis (Nos. 889/90), N. Rangos (No. **MS**891). Litho Oriental Press, Bahrain (Nos. 889/90) or Alexandros Matsoukis, Athens (No. **MS**891))

1995 (18 Sept). *European Culture Month and "Europhilex '95" International Stamp Exhibition, Nicosia.* T **300** *and similar horiz designs. Royal blue, orange-yellow and pale stone (No.* **MS**891*) or multicoloured (others).* P 13×13½.

889	20 c. Type **300**		55	60
890	25 c. Map of Europe and Cypriot church		70	90
MS891	95×86 mm. 50 c. Peace dove (42×30 mm); 50 c. European Cultural Month symbol (42×30 mm). P 14		4·50	5·00

A limited quantity of No. **MS**891 was surcharged "£5" on each stamp and sold at "Europhilex '95" on 27 and 28 October 1995.

(Litho Oriental Press, Bahrain)

1985 (24 Oct). *Obligatory Tax. Refugee Fund. As* T **255***, but inscr* "1995", "1996", "1997", "1998" *or* "1999". *Chalk-surfaced paper.* P 14½×13½.

892	**255** 1 c. brownish black and olive-grey		10	10

301 Peace Dove with Flags of Cyprus and United Nations

302 Reliquary from Kykko Monastery

(Des S. Hadjimichael (10, 25 c.), S. Karamallakis (15 c.), E. Georgiades (20 c.), Litho Oriental Press, Bahrain)

1995 (24 Oct). *Anniversaries and Events.* T **301** *and similar multicoloured designs.* P 13×13½ *(horiz) or* 13½×13 *(vert).*

893	10 c. Type **301** (50th anniv of United Nations)		30	35
894	15 c. Hand pushing ball over net (Centenary of volleyball) (vert)		55	50
895	20 c. Safety pin on leaf (European Nature Conservation Year) (vert)		65	70
896	25 c. Clay pigeon contestant (World Clay Target Shooting Championship)		75	1·40
893/6		Set of 4	2·00	2·75

(Des S. Karamallakis. Litho Oriental Press, Bahrain)

1995 (27 Nov). *Christmas.* T **302** *and similar vert designs showing different reliquaries of Virgin and Child from Kykko Monastery.* P 13½×13.

897	7 c. multicoloured		20	25
898	20 c. multicoloured		60	60
899	25 c. multicoloured		75	1·40
897/9		Set of 3	1·40	2·00

303 Family (25th anniv of Pancyprian Organisation of Large Families)

304 Maria Synglitiki

(Des Liza Petridou-Mala. Litho Oriental Press, Bahrain)

1996 (4 Jan). *Anniversaries and Events.* T **303** *and similar vert designs. Multicoloured.* P 13½×13.

900	10 c. Type **303**		45	35
901	20 c. Film camera (Centenary of cinema)		75	70
902	35 c. Silhouette of parent and child in globe (50th anniv of U.N.I.C.E.F.)		1·40	1·40
903	40 c. "13" and Commonwealth emblem (13th Conference of Commonwealth Speakers and Presiding Officers)		1·50	2·25
900/3		Set of 4	3·75	4·25

(Des G. Simonis. Litho Oriental Press, Bahrain)

1996 (8 Apr). *Europa. Famous Women.* T **304** *and similar vert design. Multicoloured.* P 14.

904	10 c. Type **304**		40	30
905	30 c. Queen Caterina Cornaro		1·00	1·50

305 High Jump

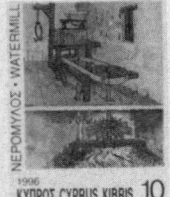
306 Watermill

(Des M. Christou. Litho Oriental Press, Bahrain)

1996 (10 June). *Centennial Olympic Games, Atlanta.* T **305** *and similar horiz designs. Multicoloured.* P 13×13½.

906	10 c. Type **305**		50	30
907	20 c. Javelin		85	65
908	25 c. Wrestling		95	1·00
909	30 c. Swimming		1·25	1·75
906/9		Set of 4	3·25	3·25

(Des E. Georgiades. Litho Oriental Press, Bahrain)

1996 (23 Sept). *Mills.* T **306** *and similar vert designs. Multicoloured.* P 13½×13.

910	10 c. Type **306**		40	40
911	15 c. Olivemill		55	50
912	20 c. Windmill		70	90
913	25 c. Handmill		80	1·25
910/13		Set of 4	2·25	2·75

307 Icon of Our Lady of Iberia, Moscow

308 "The Nativity" (detail)

(Des D. Komissarov (Nos. 914,917), G. Simonis (Nos. 915/16). Litho State Ptg Wks, Moscow)

1996 (13 Nov). *Cyprus–Russia Joint Issue. Orthodox Religion.* T **307** *and similar square designs. Multicoloured.* P 11½.

914	30 c. Type **307**		1·25	1·50
	a. Block of 4. Nos. 914/17		4·50	
915	30 c. Stravrovouni Monastery, Cyprus		1·25	1·50
916	30 c. Icon of St. Nicholas, Cyprus		1·25	1·50
917	30 c. Voskresenskie Gate, Moscow		1·25	1·50
914/17		Set of 4	4·50	5·50

Nos. 914/17 were printed together, *se-tenant*, in blocks of 4 throughout the sheet.
Stamps in similar designs were also issued by Russia.

(Litho Oriental Press, Bahrain)

1996 (2 Dec). *Christmas. Religious Murals from Church of the Virgin of Asinou.* T **308** *and similar multicoloured designs.* P 13½×13 (25 c.) *or* 13×13½ (others).

918	7 c. Type **308**		35	25
919	20 c. "Virgin Mary between the Archangels Gabriel and Michael"		85	60
920	25 c. "Christ bestowing Blessing" (vert)		1·25	1·75
918/20		Set of 3	2·25	2·40

309 Basketball

310 "The Last Supper"

(Des S. Karamallakis. Litho Oriental Press, Bahrain)

1997 (24 Mar). *Final of European Basketball Cup.* P 13½×13.

921	**309** 30 c. multicoloured		1·40	1·40

(Des G. Koumouros. Litho Oriental Press, Bahrain)

1997 (24 Mar). *Easter. Religious Frescoes from Monastery of St. John Lambadestis.* T **310** *and similar horiz design. Multicoloured.* P 13×13½.

922	15 c. Type **310**		50	50
923	25 c. "The Crucifixion"		75	1·00

311 Kori Kourelleni and Prince

312 Oedipoda miniata (grasshopper)

(Des Liza Petridou-Mala. Litho Oriental Press, Bahrain)

1997 (5 May). *Europa. Tales and Legends.* T **311** *and similar vert design. Multicoloured.* P 13½×13.

924	15 c. Type **311**		50	40
925	30 c. Digenis and Charon		1·00	1·50

(Des A. Ladommatos. Litho Oriental Press, Bahrain)

1997 (30 June). *Insects.* T **312** *and similar horiz designs. Multicoloured.* P 13×13½.

926	10 c. Type **312**		30	30
927	15 c. Acherontia atropos (hawk moth)		50	40
928	25 c. Daphnis nerii (hawk moth)		90	1·00
929	35 c. Ascalaphus macaronius (owl-fly)		1·10	1·75
926/9		Set of 4	2·50	3·00

313 Archbishop Makarios III and Chapel

314 The Nativity

(Des C. Sophocleous. Litho Oriental Press, Bahrain)

1997 (1 Aug). *20th Death Anniv of Archbishop Makarios III.* P 13×13½.

930	**313** 15 c. multicoloured		50	40

(Des G. Koumouros. Litho Oriental Press, Bahrain)

1997 (17 Nov). *Christmas. Byzantine Frescos from the Monastery of St. John Lambadestis.* T **314** *and similar vert designs. Multicoloured.* P 13½×13.

931	10 c. Type **314**		30	25
932	25 c. Three Kings following the star		90	65
933	30 c. Flight into Egypt		1·10	1·50
931/3		Set of 3	2·10	2·25

315 Green Jasper

316 Players competing for Ball

(Des A. Ladommatos. Litho Oriental Press, Bahrain)

1998 (9 Mar). *Minerals.* T **315** *and similar horiz designs. Multicoloured.* P 13.

934	10 c. Type **315**		40	30
935	15 c. Iron Pyrite		60	45
936	25 c. Gypsum		80	80
937	30 c. Chalcedony		1·00	1·40
934/7		Set of 4	2·50	2·75

(Des C. Sophocleous. Litho Oriental Press, Bahrain)

1998 (4 May). *World Cup Football Championship, France.* P 14.

938	**316** 35 c. multicoloured		1·40	1·40

317 Cataclysmos Festival, Larnaca

318 Mouflon Family Group

(Des S. Vassiliou (15 c.), A. Ladommatos (30 c.). Litho Oriental Press, Bahrain)

1998 (4 May). *Europa. Festivals.* T **317** *and similar horiz design. Multicoloured.* P 14.

939	15 c. Type **317**		50	40
940	30 c. House of Representatives, Nicosia (Declaration of Independence)		90	1·10

(Des S. Hadjimichael. Litho Oriental Press, Bahrain)

1998 (22 June). *Endangered Species. Cyprus Mouflon.* T **318** *and similar horiz designs. Multicoloured.* P 13×13½.

941	25 c. Type **318**		85	90
	a. Block of 4. Nos. 941/4		3·00	
942	25 c. Mouflon herd		85	90
943	25 c. Head of ram		85	90
944	25 c. Ram on guard		85	90
941/4		Set of 4	3·00	3·25

Nos. 941/4 were printed together, *se-tenant*, in blocks of 4 throughout the sheet.

(Litho Oriental Press, Bahrain)

1998 (22 June). *As No. 876, but different printer. White paper. With imprint date* ("1998"). P 14.

958	£1 Townswoman wearing festive sarka		2·10	2·25

319 Flames and Globe Emblem   **320** World "Stamp" and Magnifying Glass

(Des S. Vassiliou. Litho Oriental Press, Bahrain)

1998 (9 Oct). *50th Anniv of Universal Declaration of Human Rights. P 14.*
959 **319** 50 c. multicoloured .. .. .. 1·25 1·60

(Des T. Kakoullis. Litho Oriental Press, Bahrain)

1998 (9 Oct). *World Stamp Day. P 14.*
960 **320** 30 c. multicoloured .. .. .. 90 1·00
   a. Booklet pane of 8 .. .. .. 6·50
No. 960a has the horizontal edges of the pane imperforate and margins at left and right.

321 "The Annunciation"   **322** *Pleurotus eryngii*

(Des T. Kakoullis. Litho Oriental Press, Bahrain)

1998 (16 Nov). *Christmas. T 321 and similar vert designs showing religious murals. Multicoloured. P 14.*
961 **321** 10 c. Type **321** 35 30
962 25 c. "The Nativity" 80 65
963 30 c. "The Baptism of Christ" .. 1·00 1·25
961/3   *Set of 3* 1·90 2·00
MS964 102×75 mm. Nos. 961/3 .. .. 1·90 2·00

(Des S. Vassiliou. Litho Oriental Press, Bahrain)

1999 (4 Mar). *Mushrooms of Cyprus. T 322 and similar vert designs. Multicoloured. P 13½×13.*
965 10 c. Type **322** 20 15
966 15 c. *Lactarius deliciosus* 50 40
967 25 c. *Sparassis crispa* 80 80
968 30 c. *Morchella elata* .. .. 90 1·10
965/8   *Set of 4* 2·25 2·25

323 Pair of Moufflons at Tripylos Reserve

(Des Eleni Lambrou. Litho Oriental Press, Bahrain)

1999 (6 May). *Europa. Parks and Gardens. T 323 and similar horiz design. Multicoloured. P 14.*
969 15 c. Type **323** 35 40
   a. Booklet pane. Nos. 969/70, each × 4, with margins all round .. 4·00
970 30 c. Turtles on beach at Lara Reserve .. 65 70

324 Council of Europe Building, Emblem and Flags   **325** Temple of Hylates Apollo, Kourion

(Des Stella Symeonidou. Litho Oriental Press, Bahrain)

1999 (6 May). *50th Anniv of Council of Europe. P 14.*
971 **324** 30 c. multicoloured 65 70

(Des A. Ladommatos. Litho Alexandros Matsoukis, Athens)

1999 (28 June). *Cyprus–Greece Joint Issue. 4000 Years of Greek Culture. T 325 and similar vert designs. Multicoloured. P 13½×13.*
972 25 c. Type **325** 55 60
   a. Block of 4. Nos. 972/5 .. 2·25
973 25 c. Mycenaean pot depicting warriors 55 60
974 25 c. Mycenaean crater depicting horse .. 55 60
975 25 c. Temple of Apollo, Delphi .. 55 60
972/5   *Set of 4* 2·25 2·40
Nos. 972/5 were printed together, *se-tenant*, in blocks of four throughout the sheet.

326 Paper Aeroplane Letters and U.P.U. Emblem   **327** Container Ship and Cypriot Flag

(Des S. Vassiliou. Litho Oriental Press, Bahrain)

1999 (4 Oct). *125th Anniv of Universal Postal Union. T 326 and similar horiz design. Multicoloured. P 14.*
976 15 c. Type **326** 35 40
977 35 c. "125" and U.P.U emblem .. 75 80

(Des Thompson Communications. Litho Oriental Press, Bahrain)

1999 (4 Oct). *"Maritime Cyprus '99" Conference. Sheet, 103×80 mm, containing T 327 and similar horiz designs. Multicoloured. P 14*.
MS978 25 c. Type **327**; 25 c. Binoculars and chart; 25 c. Stern of container ship; 25 c. Tanker 2·25 2·40
*On No. MS978 the row of perforations across the foot of the lower pair gauges 13.

328 Cypriot Refugee Fund Stamps and Barbed Wire (*Illustration reduced. Actual size 110×75 mm*)

(Des G. Theofylactou. Litho Oriental Press, Bahrain)

1999 (11 Nov). *25th Anniv of Turkish Landings in Cyprus. Sheet 110×75 mm. Imperf.*
MS979 **328** 30 c. multicoloured 65 70

329 Angel

(Des G. Theofylactou. Litho Oriental Press, Bahrain)

1999 (11 Nov). *Christmas. T 329 and similar vert designs. Multicoloured. P 14.*
980 10 c. Type **329** 25 30
981 25 c. The Three Kings 50 60
982 30 c. Madonna and Child .. 65 70
980/2   *Set of 3* 1·40 1·50

PRICES OF SETS

Set prices are given for many issues, generally those containing three stamps or more. Definitive sets include one of each value or major colour change, but do not cover different perforations, die types or minor shades. Where a choice is possible the set prices are based on the cheapest versions of the stamps included in the listings.

STAMP BOOKLETS

Stamp-vending machines were introduced by the Cyprus Post Office in 1962. These were originally fitted to provide stamps to the value of 50 m., but in 1979 some were converted to accept 100 m. coins and, a year later, others were altered to supply 150, 200 or 300 m. worth of stamps.

The stamps contained in these booklets were a haphazard selection of low values to the required amount, attached by their sheet margins to the cardboard covers. From 1968 these covers carried commercial advertising and details of postage rates.

Following the change of currency in 1983 the machines were converted to supply 5, 10, 20 or 30 c. booklets.

B 1 World "Stamp" and Magnifying Glass

1998 (9 Oct). *World Stamp Day. Multicoloured cover as Type B 1. Pane attached by selvedge.*
SB1 £2.40, booklet containing pane of 8 30 c. (No. 960a) .. .. 6·50

B 2 Turtles on Beach at Lara Reserve

1999 (6 May). *Europa. Parks and Gardens. Multicoloured cover as Type B 2. Pane attached by selvedge.*
SB2 £1.80, booklet containing *se-tenant* pane of 8 (No. 969a) (4×2) .. .. 3·75

TURKISH CYPRIOT POSTS

After the inter-communal clashes during December 1963, a separate postal service was established on 6 January 1964 between some of the Turkish Cypriot areas, using handstamps inscribed "KIBRIS TURK POSTALARI". During 1964, however, an agreement was reached between representatives of the two communities for the restoration of postal services. This agreement, to which the United Nations representatives were a party, was ratified in November 1966 by the Republic's Council of Ministers. Under the scheme postal services were provided for the Turkish Cypriot communities in Famagusta, Larnaca, Limassol, Lefka, Nicosia and Paphos staffed by Turkish Cypriot employees of the Cypriot Department of Posts.

On 8 April 1970 5 m. and 15 m. locally-produced labels, originally designated "Social Aid Stamps", were issued by the Turkish Cypriot community and these can be found on commercial covers. These local stamps are outside the scope of this catalogue.

On 29 October 1973 Nos. 1/7 were placed on sale, but were used only on mail between the Turkish Cypriot areas.

Following the intervention by the Republic of Turkey on 20 July 1974 these stamps replaced issues of the Republic of Cyprus in that part of the island, north and east of the Attila Line, controlled by the Autonomous Turkish Cypriot Administration.

(Currency. 1000 mils = £1)

1 50th Anniversary Emblem   (2)

(Des F. Direkoglu Miss E. Ata and G. Pir. Litho Darbhane, Istanbul)

1974 (27 July*). *50th Anniv of Republic of Turkey. T 1 and similar designs in vermilion and black (15 m.) or multicoloured (others). P 12 × 11½ (vert) or 11½ × 12 (horiz).*
1	3 m. Woman sentry (vert)		30·00	30·00
2	5 m. Military Parade, Nicosia		60	40
3	10 m. Man and woman with Turkish flags (vert)		50	20
4	15 m. Type 1		2·50	1·50
5	20 m. Atatürk statue, Kyrenia Gate, Nicosia (vert)		70	20
6	50 m. "The Fallen" (vert)		2·00	1·50
7	70 m. Turkish flag and map of Cyprus		16·00	16·00
1/7		Set of 7	48·00	48·00

*This is the date on which Nos. 1/7 became valid for international mail.

On 13 February 1975 a Turkish Cypriot Federated State was proclaimed in that part of Cyprus under Turkish occupation and later 9,000 Turkish Cypriots were transferred from the South to the North of the island.

1975 (3 Mar). *Proclamation of the Turkish Federated State of Cyprus. Nos. 3 and 5 surch as T 2 by Halkin Sesi, Nicosia.*
8	30 m. on 20 m. Atatürk statue, Kyrenia Gate, Nicosia		75	1·00
9	100 m. on 10 m. Man and woman with Turkish flags		1·25	2·00

On No. 9 the surcharge appears at the top of the stamp and the inscription at the bottom.

3 Namik Kemal's Bust, Famagusta

4 Map of Cyprus

(Des I. Özişik. Litho Güzel Sanatlar Matbaasi, Ankara)

1975 (21 Apr). *Multicoloured designs as T 3. Imprint at foot with date "1975".*
10	3 m. Type 3		15	40
11	10 m. Atatürk Statue, Nicosia		15	10
12	15 m. St. Hilarion Castle		25	20
13	20 m. Atatürk Square, Nicosia		35	20
14	25 m. Famagusta Beach		35	30
15	30 m. Kyrenia Harbour		45	10
16	50 m. Lala Mustafa Pasha Mosque, Famagusta (vert)		50	10
17	100 m. Interior, Kyrenia Castle		80	90
18	250 m. Castle walls, Kyrenia		1·25	2·75
19	500 m. Othello Tower, Famagusta (vert)		2·25	5·00
10/19		Set of 10	6·00	9·00

See also Nos. 37/8.

(Des B. Erkmen (30 m.), S. Tuga (50 m.), N. Cüneş (150 m.). Litho Ajans-Türk Matbaasi, Ankara)

1975 (20 July). *"Peace in Cyprus". T 4 and similar multicoloured designs. P 13.*
20	30 m. Type 4		30	15
21	50 m. Map, laurel and broken chain		35	20
22	150 m. Map and laurel-sprig on globe (vert)		90	1·00
20/2		Set of 3	1·40	1·25

5 "Pomegranates" (I. V. Guney)

(Litho Güzel Sanatlar Matbaasi, Ankara)

1975 (29 Dec). *Europa. Paintings. T 5 and similar horiz design. Multicoloured. P 13.*
23	90 m. Type 5		80	60
24	100 m. "Harvest Time" (F. Direkoglu)		95	60

10 M ———
(6)

7 "Expectation"

1976 (28 Apr). *Nos. 16/17 surch as T 6 at Govt Printing House, Nicosia in horizontal clichés of 10.*
25	10 m. on 50 m. Lala Mustafa Pasha Mosque, Famagusta		50	70
26	30 m. on 100 m. Interior, Kyrenia Castle		50	80

(Litho Ajans-Türk Matbaasi, Ankara)

1976 (3 May). *Europa. T 7 and similar vert design showing ceramic statuette. Multicoloured. P 13.*
27	60 m. Type 7		40	80
28	120 m. "Man in Meditation"		60	90

8 Carob

9 Olympic Symbol "Flower"

(Des S. Atlihan. Litho Güzel Sanatlar Matbaasi, Ankara)

1976 (28 June). *Export Products—Fruits. T 8 and similar horiz designs. Multicoloured. P 13.*
29	10 m. Type 8		25	10
30	25 m. Mandarin		30	10
31	40 m. Strawberry		40	25
32	60 m. Orange		50	65
33	80 m. Lemon		55	1·75
29/33		Set of 5	1·75	2·50

(Des C. Mutver (60 m.), A. B. Kocamanoglu (100 m.). Litho Güzel Sanatlar Matbaasi, Ankara)

1976 (17 July). *Olympic Games. Montreal. T 9 and similar horiz design. Multicoloured. P 13.*
34	60 m. Type 9		25	20
35	100 m. Olympic symbol and doves		35	25

10 Kyrenia Harbour

11 Liberation Monument, Karaeglanoglu (Ay. Georghios)

(Des I. Özişik. Litho Ajans-Türk Matbaasi, Ankara)

1976 (2 Aug). *New design (5 m.) or as Nos. 12/13 but redrawn with lettering altered and new imprint at foot with date "1976". P 13.*
36	5 m. Type 10		40	15
37	15 m. St. Hilarion Castle		40	15
38	20 m. Atatürk Square, Nicosia		40	15
36/8		Set of 3	1·10	40

Nos. 39/46 vacant.

(Des D. Erimez and C. Gizer. Litho Ajans-Türk Matbaasi, Ankara)

1976 (1 Nov). *Liberation Monument. T 11 and similar vert design. P 13.*
47	11	30 m. lt turquoise-blue, lt flesh & black	15	20
48	—	150 m. light verm, light flesh & blk	35	45

No. 48 shows a different view of the Monument.

(Litho Türk Tarih Kurumu Basimevi, Ankara)

1977 (2 May). *Europa. T 12 and similar horiz design. Multicoloured. P 13.*
49	80 m. Type 12		65	80
50	100 m. Kyrenia Port		75	80

13 Pottery

14 Arap Ahmet Pasha Mosque, Nicosia

(Litho Güzel Sanatlar Matbaasi, Ankara)

1977 (27 June). *Handicrafts. T 13 and similar designs. Multicoloured. P 13.*
51	15 m. Type 13		10	10
52	30 m. Decorated gourds (vert)		10	10
53	125 m. Basketware		30	50
51/3		Set of 3	40	65

(Litho APA Ofset Basimevi, Istanbul)

1977 (2 Dec). *Turkish Buildings in Cyprus. T 14 and similar horiz designs. Multicoloured. P 13.*
54	20 m. Type 14		10	10
55	40 m. Paphos Castle		10	10
56	70 m. Bekir Pasha aqueduct		15	20
57	80 m. Sultan Mahmut library		15	25
54/7		Set of 4	45	60

15 Namik Kemal (bust) and House, Famagusta

16 Old Man and Woman

(Des B. Ozak. Litho Ticaret Matbaacilik TAS, Izmir)

1977 (21 Dec). *Namik Kemal (patriotic poet). T 15 and similar multicoloured design. P 12½ × 13 (30 m.) or 13 × 12½ (140 m.).*
58	30 m. Type 15		15	15
59	140 m. Namik Kemal (portrait) (vert)		35	60

(New Currency. 100 kurus = 1 lira)

(Des G. Pir. Litho Ajans-Türk Matbaasi, Ankara)

1978 (17 Apr). *Social Security. T 16 and similar vert designs. P 13 × 13½.*
60	150 k. black, yellow and blue		10	10
61	275 k. black, red-orange and green		15	15
62	375 k. black, blue and red-orange		25	20
60/2		Set of 3	45	40

Designs:—275 k. Injured man with crutch; 375 k. Woman with family.

17 Oratory in Büyük Han, Nicosia

18 Motorway Junction

(Des I. Özisik. Litho APA Ofset Basimevi, Istanbul)

1978 (2 May). *Europa. T 17 and similar horiz design. Multicoloured. P 13.*
63	225 k. Type 17		30	30
64	450 k. Cistern in Selimiye Mosque, Nicosia		60	70

(Litho APA Ofset Basimevi, Istanbul)

1978 (10 July). *Communications. T 18 and similar horiz designs. Multicoloured. P 13.*
65	75 k. Type 18		15	10
66	100 k. Hydrofoil		15	10
67	650 k. Boeing 720 at Ercan Airport		50	35
65/7		Set of 3	70	45

12 Hotel, Salamis Bay

19 Dove with Laurel Branch

20 Kemal Atatürk

(Des E. Kaya (725 k.), C. Kirkbesoglu (others). Litho APA Ofset Basimevi, Istanbul)

1978 (13 Sept). *National Oath.* T **19** *and similar designs.* P 13.
68	150 k. orange-yellow, violet and black			10	10
69	225 k. black, Indian red and orange-yellow			10	10
70	725 k. black, cobalt and orange-yellow			20	20
68/70			*Set of 3*	35	35

Designs: *Vert*—225 k. "Taking the Oath". *Horiz*—725 k. Symbolic dove.

(Des C. Mutver. Litho Türk Tarih Kurumu Basimevi, Ankara)

1978 (10 Nov). *Kemal Atatürk Commemoration.* P 13.
71	**20**	75 k. pale turquoise-grn & turq-grn		10	10
72		450 k. pale flesh and light brown		15	15
73		650 k. pale blue and light blue		20	25
71/3			*Set of 3*	40	40

(21)　　　　　**22** Gun Barrel with Olive Branch and Map of Cyprus

1979 (4 June). *Nos. 30/3 surch as* T **21**, *by Govt Printing Office, Lefkosa*
74	50 k. on 25 m. Mandarin			10	10
75	1 l. on 40 m. Strawberry			15	10
76	3 l. on 60 m. Orange			15	10
77	5 l. on 80 m. Lemon			35	15
74/7			*Set of 4*	65	30

(Des N. Dündar. Litho Ajans-Türk Matbaasi, Ankara)

1979 (20 July). *5th Anniv of Turkish Peace Operation in Cyprus. Sheet 72×52 mm. Imperf.*
MS78 **22**　15 l. black, deep turquoise-blue and pale green .. .. .. 80　1·25

23 Postage Stamp and Map of Cyprus　　**24** Symbolised Microwave Antenna

(Des S. Mumcu. Litho Ajans-Türk Matbaasi, Ankara)

1979 (20 Aug). *Europa. Communications.* T **23** *and similar horiz designs. Multicoloured.* P 13.
79	2 l. Type **23**			10	10
80	3 l. Postage stamps, building and map		10	10
81	8 l. Telephones, Earth and satellite		20	30
79/81			*Set of 3*	35	45

(Litho Ticaret Matbaacilik TAS, Izmir)

1979 (24 Sept). *50th Anniv of International Consultative Radio Committee.* P 13 × 12½.
82	**24**	2 l. multicoloured			20	10
83		5 l. multicoloured			20	10
84		6 l. multicoloured			25	15
82/4				*Set of 3*	60	30

25 School Children　　**26** Lala Mustafa Pasha Mosque, Magusa

(Des H. Hastürk (1½ l.), G. Akansel (4½ l.), P. Yalyali (6 l.). Litho APA Ofset Basimevi, Istanbul)

1979 (29 Oct). *International Year of the Child. Children's Drawings.* T **25** *and similar multicoloured designs.* P 13.
85	1½ l. Type **25**			25	15
86	4½ l. Children and globe (*horiz*)		40	20
87	6 l. College children			60	20
85/7			*Set of 3*	1·10	50

(Des S. Mumcu (20 l.), I. Özişik (others). Litho Ajans-Türk Matbaasi, Ankara)

1980 (23 Mar). *Islamic Commemorations.* T **26** *and similar vert designs. Multicoloured.* P 13.
88	2½ l. Type **26**			10	10
89	10 l. Arap Ahmet Pasha Mosque, Lefkosa		30	15
90	20 l. Mecca and Medina			50	20
88/90			*Set of 3*	80	40

Commemorations—2½ l. 1st Islamic Conference in Turkish Cyprus; 10 l. General Assembly of World Islam Congress; 20 l. Moslem Year 1400AH.

27 Ebu-Su'ud Efendi (philosopher)　　**28** Omer's Shrine, Kyrenia

(Litho Ajans-Türk Matbaasi, Ankara)

1980 (23 May). *Europa. Personalities.* T **27** *and similar vert design. Multicoloured.* P 13.
91	5 l. Type **27**			20	10
92	30 l. Sultan Selim II			70	40

(Litho Guzel Sanatlar Matbaasi, Ankara)

1980 (25 June). *Ancient Monuments,* T **28** *and similar horiz designs.* P 13.
93	2½ l. new blue and stone			10	10
94	3½ l. grey-green and pale rose-pink		10	10
95	5 l. lake and pale blue-green			15	10
96	10 l. deep mauve and pale green		30	10
97	20 l. dull ultramarine & pale greenish yellow	50	25
93/7			*Set of 5*	95	45

Designs:—3½ l. Entrance gate, Famagusta; 5 l. Funerary monuments (16th-century), Famagusta; 10 l. Bella Paise Abbey, Kyrenia; 20 l. Selimiye Mosque, Nicosia.

29 Cyprus 1880 6d.　**30** Dome of the Rock　**31** Extract from World Muslim Congress Statement in Turkish

(Des S. Mumcu. Litho Ajans-Türk Matbaasi, Ankara)

1980 (16 Aug). *Cyprus Stamp Centenary.* T **29** *and similar designs showing stamps.* P 14.
98	7½ l. black, drab and grey-olive		20	10
99	15 l. brown, grey-blue and blue		25	15
100	50 l. black, rose and grey			65	55
98/100			*Set of 3*	1·00	70

Designs: *Horiz*—15 l. Cyprus 1960 Constitution of the Republic 30 m. commemorative. *Vert*—50 l. Social Aid local, 1970.

(Litho Guzel Sanatlar Matbaasi, Ankara)

1980 (16 Oct). *Palestinian Solidarity.* T **30** *and similar multicoloured design.* P 13.
101	15 l. Type **30**			25	15
102	35 l. Dome of the Rock (*horiz*)		65	30

(Des S. Mumcu. Litho Turk Tarih Kurumu Basimevi, Ankara)

1981 (24 Mar). *Solidarity with Islamic Countries Day.* T **31** *and similar vert design showing extract from World Muslim Congress statement.* P 13.
103	1 l. rosine, stone and olive-sepia		15	15
104	35 l. black, pale blue-green and myrtle-green	55	85

Design:—35 l. Extract in English

32 "Atatürk" (F. Duran)　　**33** Folk-dancing

(Litho Ajans-Türk Matbaasi, Ankara)

1981 (19 May). *Atatürk Stamp Exhibition, Lefkosa.* P 13.
105 **32** 20 l. multicoloured 25 35
No. 105 was printed in sheets of 100, including 50 *se-tenant* stamp-size labels.

(Litho Ticaret Matbaacilik TAS, Izmir)

1981 (29 June). *Europa, Folklore.* T **33** *and similar horiz design showing folk-dancing.* P 12½ × 13.
106	10 l. multicoloured			35	15
107	30 l. multicoloured			60	35

MINIMUM PRICE

The minimum price quote is 10p which represents a handling charge rather than a basis for valuing common stamps. For further notes about prices see introductory pages.

34 "Kemal Atatürk" (I. Calli)　　**35** Wild Convolvulus

(Litho Basim Ofset, Ankara)

1981 (23 July). *Birth Centenary of Kemal Atatürk. Sheet 70 × 95 mm. Imperf.*
MS108 **34**　150 l. multicoloured .. .. 1·10　1·25

(Litho Turk Tarih Kurumu Basimevi, Ankara)

1981 (28 Sept)—82. *Flowers, Multicoloured designs as* T **35**. P 13.
109	1 l. Type **35**				10	10
110	5 l. Persian Cyclamen (*horiz*) (22.1.82)		10	10
111	10 l. Spring Mandrake (*horiz*)			10	10
112	25 l. Corn Poppy				15	10
113	30 l. Wild Arum (22.1.82)			20	10
114	50 l. Sage-leaved Rock Rose (*horiz*) (22.1.82)		30	20
115	100 l. *Cistus salviaefolius L.* (22.1.82)		55	30
116	150 l. Giant Fennel (*horiz*)			75	90
109/16			*Set of 8*	1·90	1·50

36 Stylized Disabled Person in Wheelchair　　**37** Turkish and Palestinian Flags

(Des H. Ulucam (7½ l.), N. Kozal (others). Litho Türk Tarih Kurumu Basimevi, Ankara)

1981 (16 Oct). *Commemorations.* T **36** *and similar multicoloured designs.* P 13.
117	7½ l. Type **36**			30	35
118	10 l. Heads of people of different races, peace dove and barbed wire (*vert*)	50	55
119	20 l. People of different races reaching out from globe, with dishes (*vert*)	75	85
117/19			*Set of 3*	1·40	1·60

Commemorations:—7½ l. International Year for Disabled Persons; 10 l. Anti-apartheid Publicity; 20 l. World Food Day.

(Des H. Ulucam. Litho Türk Tarih Kurumu Basimevi, Ankara)

1981 (29 Nov). *Palestinian Solidarity.* P 13.
120 **37** 10 l. multicoloured 30 40

38 Prince Charles and Lady Diana Spencer　　**39** Charter issued by Sultan Abdul Aziz to Archbishop Sophronios

(Des H. Ulucam. Litho Türk Tarih Kurumu Basimevi, Ankara)

1981 (30 Nov). *Royal Wedding.* P 13
121 **38** 50 l. multicoloured .. .. 1·00 85

(Des H. Ulucam, Litho Tezel Ofset, Lefkosa)

1982 (30 July). *Europa (CEPT). Sheet 83 × 124 mm containing* T **39** *and similar vert design. Multicoloured.* P 12½ × 13.
MS122　30 l. × 2. Type **39**; 70 l. × 2, Turkish forces landing at Tuzla, 1571 .. .. 4·50　5·00

40 Buffavento Castle　　**41** "Wedding" (A. Örek)

(Des H. Ulucac (Nos. 123/5). Litho Tezel Ofset, Lefkosa)

1982 (20 Aug). *Tourism. T* **40** *and similar multicoloured designs.*
P 12.
123	5 l.	Type **40**			10	10
124	10 l.	Windsurfing (*horiz*)			15	10
125	15 l.	Kantara Castle (*horiz*)			25	15
126	30 l.	Shipwreck (300 B.C.) (*horiz*)			50	40
123/6				Set of 4	90	65

(Litho Ajans-Türk Matbaasi, Ankara)

1982 (3 Dec). *Paintings* (1st series). *T* **41** *and similar multi-*
coloured design. P 13.
127	30 l.	Type **41**			15	30
128	50 l.	"Carob Pickers" (O. Naxim Selenge)			30	70

See also Nos. 132/3, 157/8, 176/7, 185/6, 208/9, 225/7, 248/50,
284/5, 315/16, 328/9, 369/70 and 436/7.

42 Cross of Lorraine, Koch
and Bacillus (Cent of Koch's
Discovery of Tubercle
Bacillus)

43 "Calloused Hands"
(Salih Oral)

(Des H. Ulucam. Litho Tezel Ofset, Lefkosa)

1982 (15 Dec). *Anniversaries and Events. T* **42** *and similar multi-*
coloured designs. P 12.
129	10 l.	Type **42**			1·00	40
130	30 l.	Spectrum on football pitch (World Cup Football Championships, Spain)			1·75	1·10
131	70 l.	"75" and Lord Baden-Powell (75th anniv of Boy Scout movement and 125th birth anniv) (*vert*)			2·25	4·00
129/31				Set of 3	4·50	5·00

(Litho Ajans-Türk Matbaasi, Ankara)

1983 (16 May). *Paintings* (2nd series). *T* **43** *and similar vert*
design. Multicoloured. P 13.
132	30 l.	Type **43**			90	1·40
133	35 l.	"Malya—Limassol Bus" (Emin Cizenel)			90	1·40

44 Old Map of Cyprus by
Piri Reis

45 First Turkish
Cypriot 10 m. Stamp

(Litho Türk Tarih Kurumu Basimevi, Ankara)

1983 (30 June). *Europa. Sheet* 82 × 78 *mm, containing T* **44** *and*
similar horiz design. Multicoloured. P 13.
MS134   100 l. Type **44**; 100 l. Cyprus as seen from
"Skylab" .. .. 2·50 3·50

(Des E. Ata (15 l.), A. Hasan (20 l.), G. Pir (25 l.), H. Ulucam
(others). Litho Ajans-Türk Matbaasi, Ankara)

1983 (1 Aug). *Anniversaries and Events. T* **45** *and similar*
multicoloured designs commemorating World Communi-
cations Year (30, 50 *l.*) *or 25th Anniv. of T.M.T. (Turkish*
Cypriot Resistance Organization). P 13.
135	15 l.	Type **45**			60	50
136	20 l.	"Turkish Achievements in Cyprus" (*horiz*)			70	60
137	25 l.	"Liberation Fighters"			80	80
138	30 l.	Dish aerial and telegraph pole (*horiz*)			95	1·00
139	50 l.	Dove and envelopes (*horiz*)			2·00	2·75
135/9				Set of 5	4·50	5·00

46 European Bee Eater

(**47**)

(Des E. Cizenel. Litho Ajans-Türk Matbaasi, Ankara)

1983 (10 Oct). *Birds of Cyprus. T* **46** *and similar horiz designs.*
Multicoloured. P 13.
140	10 l.	Type **46**			80	1·25
	a.	Block of 4. Nos. 140/3			4·00	
141	15 l.	Goldfinch			1·00	1·25
142	50 l.	European Robin			1·25	1·50
143	65 l.	Golden Oriole			1·40	1·50
140/3				Set of 4	4·00	5·00

Nos. 140/3 were printed together, *se-tenant*, in blocks of 4
throughout the sheet.

1983 (7 Dec). *Establishment of the Republic. Nos.* 109, 111/12 *and*
116 *surch as T* **47** (*No.* 145) *or optd only.*
144	10 l.	Spring Mandrake			20	15
145	15 l.	on 1 l. Type **35**			30	15
	a.	Surch inverted			75·00	
146	25 l.	Corn Poppy			40	25
147	150 l.	Giant Fennel			2·25	3·25
144/7				Set of 4	2·75	3·50

48 C.E.P.T. 25th Anniversary Logo.

49 Olympic Flame

(Des J. Larrivière. Litho Tezel Ofset, Lefkosa)

1984 (30 May). *Europa. P* 12 × 12½.
148	**48**	50 l. lemon, chestnut and black			2·25	3·00
		a. Pair. Nos. 148/9			4·50	6·00
149		100 l. pale blue, bright blue and black			2·25	3·00

Nos. 148/9 were printed together, *se-tenant*, in horizontal and
vertical pairs throughout the sheet.

(Des H. Ulucam. Litho Tezel Ofset, Lefkosa)

1984 (19 June). *Olympic Games, Los Angeles. T* **49** *and similar*
multicoloured designs. P 12½ × 12 (10 *l.*) *or* 12 × 12½ (*others*).
150	10 l.	Type **49**			15	10
151	20 l.	Olympic events within rings (*horiz*)			25	25
152	70 l.	Martial arts event (*horiz*)			50	1·50
150/2				Set of 3	80	1·60

50 Atatürk Cultural Centre

51

(Des H. Ulucam. Litho Tezel Ofset, Lefkosa)

1984 (20 July). *Opening of Atatürk Cultural Centre, Lefkosa.*
W **51**. *P* 12 × 12½.
153   **50**   120 l. stone, black and chestnut .. 1·25 1·75

52 Turkish Cypriot Flag and Map

(Des C. Guzeloglu (20 l.), M. Gozbebek (70 l.). Litho Tezel Ofset
Lefkosa)

1984 (20 July). *10th Anniv of Turkish Landings in Cyprus.*
T **52** *and similar horiz design. W* **51**. *Multicoloured. P* 12 × 12½.
154	20 l.	Type **52**			50	25
155	70 l.	Turkish Cypriot flag within book			1·00	2·00

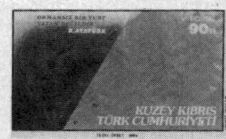

53 Burnt and Replanted Forests

(Des H. Ulucam. Litho Tezel Ofset, Lefkosa)

1984 (20 Aug). *World Forestry Resources. W* **51**. *P* 12 × 12½.
156   **53**   90 l. multicoloured .. .. .. 1·25 1·75

ALTERED CATALOGUE
NUMBERS

Any Catalogue numbers altered from the last
edition are shown as a list in the introductory
pages.

54 "Old Turkish Houses, Nicosia"
(Cevdet Cagdas)

55 Kemal Atatürk,
Flag and Crown

(Litho Tezel Ofset, Lefkosa)

1984 (21 Sept). *Paintings* (3rd series). *T* **54** *and similar horiz*
design. Multicoloured. W **51**. *P* 13 × 12½.
157	20 l.	Type **54**			50	40
158	70 l.	"Scenery" (Olga Rauf)			1·10	2·00

See also Nos. 176/7, 185/6, 208/9, 225/7, 248/50, 284/5, 315/16
and 328/9.

(Des H. Ulucam (20 l.), F. Isiman (70 l.). Litho Tezel Ofset,
Lefkosa)

1984 (15 Nov). *1st Anniv of Turkish Republic of Northern Cyprus.*
T **55** *and similar multicoloured design. W* **51** (*sideways on* 20 *l.,*
inverted on 70 *l.*). *P* 12½.
159	20 l.	Type **55**			50	40
160	70 l.	Legislative Assembly voting for Republic (*horiz*)			1·10	2·00

56 Taekwondo Bout

57 "Le Regard"
(Saulo Mercader)

(Des H. Ulucam. Litho Tezel Ofset, Lefkosa)

1984 (10 Dec). *International Taekwondo Championship, Girne.*
T **56** *and similar horiz design. W* **51** (*sideways on* 10 *l.*). *P* 12½.
161	10 l.	black, pale cinnamon and grey-black			40	25
162	70 l.	multicoloured			1·60	2·50

Design:—70 l. Emblem and flags of competing nations.

(Litho Tezel Ofset, Lefkosa)

1984 (10 Dec). *Exhibition by Saulo Mercader (artist). T* **57** *and*
similar multicoloured design. W **51** (*sideways on* 20 *l.*).
P 12½ × 13 (20 *l.*) *or* 13 × 12½ (70 *l.*).
163	20 l.	Type **57**			30	25
164	70 l.	"L'equilibre de L'esprit" (*horiz*)			1·10	2·25

58 Musical Instruments and Music

59 Dr. Fazil Kucuk
(politician)

(Des H. Ulucam. Litho Tezel Ofset, Lefkosa)

1984 (10 Dec). *Visit of Nurnberg Chamber Orchestra. W* **51** (*side-*
ways). *P* 12½.
165   **58**   70 l. multicoloured .. .. .. 1·50 2·25

(Des Y. Calli (20 l.), E. Cizenel (70 l.). Litho Tezel Ofset, Lefkosa)

1985 (15 Jan). *1st Death Anniv of Dr. Fazil Kucuk (politician).*
T **59** *and similar vert design. Multicoloured. W* **51** (*inverted on*
70 *l.*). *P* 12½ × 12.
166	20 l.	Type **59**			30	30
167	70 l.	Dr. Fazil Kucuk reading newspaper			95	2·00

60 Goat

61 George Frederick
Handel

(Des E. Cizenel. Litho Tezel Ofset, Lefkosa)

1985 (29 May). *Domestic Animals.* T **60** *and similar horiz designs. Multicoloured.* W **51**. P 12 × 12½.
168	100 l. Type **60**..	.. .. ..	55	30
169	200 l. Cow and calf	.. .. ..	90	80
170	300 l. Ram ..	.. .. ..	1·25	2·00
171	500 l. Donkey ..	.. .. ..	2·00	3·25
168/71		*Set of 4*	4·25	5·75

(Litho Tezel Ofset, Lefkosa)

1985 (26 June). *Europa. Composers.* T **61** *and similar vert designs.* W **51** *(sideways).* P 12½ × 12.
172	20 l. brown-purple, myrtle-green & pale grn		2·00	2·50
	a. Block of 4. Nos. 172/5 ..		8·00	
173	20 l. brown-purple, lake-brown & pale pink		2·00	2·50
174	100 l. brown-purple, steel blue & pale grey-bl		2·50	3·00
175	100 l. brown-purple, bistre-brown & pale cinn		2·50	3·00
172/5		*Set of 4*	8·00	10·00

Designs:—No. 172, Type **61**; 173, Guiseppe Domenico Scarlatti; 174, Johann Sebastian Bach; 175, Buhurizade Mustafa Itri Efendi.
Nos. 172/5 were printed together, *se-tenant*, in blocks of four throughout the sheet.

(Litho Tezel Ofset, Lefkosa)

1985 (15 Aug). *Paintings (4th series).* Vert designs as T **54**. *Multicoloured.* W **51**. P 12½ × 13.
176	20 l. "Village Life" (Ali Atakan)	..	60	50
177	50 l. "Woman carrying Water" (Ismet V. Güney)	.. .. ..	1·40	2·50

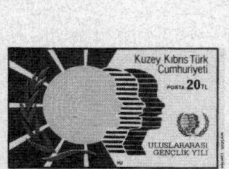

62 Heads of Three Youths   **63** Parachutist (Aviation League)

(Des H. Uluçam. Litho Tezel Ofset, Lefkosa)

1985 (29 Oct). *International Youth Year.* T **62** *and similar horiz design. Multicoloured.* W **51** *(sideways).* P 12 × 12½.
178	20 l. Type **62**..	.. .. ..	75	40
179	100 l. Dove and globe	.. .. ..	3·50	4·00

(Des H. Uluçam. Litho Tezel Ofset, Lefkosa)

1985 (29 Nov). *Anniversaries and Events.* T **63** *and similar designs.* W **51** *(inverted on Nos. 181/2, sideways on Nos. 183/4).* P 12 × 12½ *(Nos. 183/4)* or 12½ × 12 *(others).*
180	20 l. multicoloured	.. ..	1·25	45
181	50 l. grey-black, light brown and dull ultramarine	.. ..	1·75	1·25
182	100 l. light brown	.. ..	1·75	2·75
183	100 l. multicoloured	.. ..	1·75	2·75
184	100 l. multicoloured	.. ..	1·75	2·75
180/4		*Set of 5*	7·50	9·00

Designs: *Vert*—No. 181, Louis Pasteur (Centenary of Discovery of Rabies vaccine); 182, İsmet İnönü (Turkish statesman) (birth centenary (1984)). *Horiz*—183, "40" in figures and symbolic flower (40th anniv of United Nations Organization); 184, Patient receiving blood transfusion (Prevention of Thalassaemia).

(Litho Tezel Ofset, Lefkosa)

1986 (20 June). *Paintings (5th series).* Horiz designs as T **54**. *Multicoloured.* W **51** *(sideways).* P 13 × 12½.
185	20 l. "House with Arches" (Gönen Atakol)..		50	30
186	100 l. "Atatürk Square" (Yalkin Muhtaroğlu)	.. ..	1·75	1·75

64 Griffon Vulture   **65** Karagöz Show Puppets

(Des E. Çizenel (100 l.), H. Uluçam (200 l.). Litho Tezel Ofset, Lefkosa)

1986 (20 June). *Europa. Protection of Nature and the Environment. Sheet 82 × 76 mm. containing* T **64** *and similar horiz design. Multicoloured.* W **51** *(sideways).* P 12 × 12½.
MS187	100 l. Type **64**: 200 l. Litter on Cyprus landscape		7·00	6·00

(Des Y. Yazgin. Litho Tezel Ofset, Lefkosa)

1986 (25 July). *Karagöz Folk Puppets.* W **51** *(inverted).* P 12½ × 13.
188	**65** 100 l. multicoloured	.. ..	2·25	2·50

66 Old Bronze Age Composite Pottery   **67** Soldiers, Defence Force Badge and Atatürk (10th anniv of Defence Forces)

(Litho Tezel Ofset, Lefkosa)

1986 (15 Sept). *Archaeological Artifacts. Cultural Links with Anatolia.* T **66** *and similar multicoloured designs.* W **51** *(sideways on 10, 50 l., inverted on 20, 100 l.).* P 12 × 12½ (10, 50 l.) or 12½ × 12 (20, 100 l.).
189	10 l. Type **66**..	.. ..	55	30
190	20 l. Late Bronze Age bird jug *(vert)*	..	95	30
191	50 l. Neolithic earthenware pot	..	1·75	2·00
192	100 l. Roman statue of Artemis *(vert)*		2·25	3·50
189/92		*Set of 4*	5·00	5·50

(Des. H. Uluçam (No. 196). Litho Tezel Ofset, Lefkosa)

1986 (13 Oct). *Anniversaries and Events.* T **67** *and similar multicoloured designs.* W **51** *(inverted on 20, 50 l., sideways on others).* P 12½ × 12 *(vert)* or 12 × 12½ *(horiz).*
193	20 l. Type **67**..	.. ..	80	30
194	50 l. Woman and two children (40th anniv of Food and Agriculture Organization) ..		1·40	1·40
195	100 l. Football and world map (World Cup Football Championship, Mexico) *(horiz)*	.. ..	2·75	3·50
196	100 l. Orbit of Halley's Comet and *Giotto* spacecraft *(horiz)*	.. ..	2·75	3·50
193/6 ..		*Set of 4*	7·00	8·00

68 Güzelyurt Dam and Power Station   **69** Prince Andrew and Miss Sarah Ferguson

(Litho Tezel Ofset, Lefkosa)

1986 (17 Nov). *Modern Development (1st series).* T **68** *and similar horiz designs. Multicoloured.* W **51** *(sideways).* P 12 × 12½.
197	20 l. Type **68**..	.. ..	1·25	30
198	50 l. Low cost housing project, Lefkosa	..	1·40	1·40
199	100 l. Kyrenia Airport	.. ..	3·25	4·25
197/9 ..		*Set of 3*	5·50	5·50

See also Nos. 223/4 and 258/63.

(Litho Tezel Ofset, Lefkosa)

1986 (20 Nov). *60th Birthday of Queen Elizabeth II and Royal Wedding.* T **69** *and similar vert design. Multicoloured.* W **51** *(inverted).* P 12½ × 13.
200	100 l. Type **69**..	.. ..	1·75	2·25
	a. Pair. Nos. 200/1	..	3·50	4·50
201	100 l. Queen Elizabeth II	..	1·75	2·25

Nos. 200/1 were printed together, *se-tenant*, in horizontal and vertical pairs throughout the sheet.

70 Locomotive No. 11 and Trakhoni Station

(Des H. Uluçam (50 l.). Litho Tezel Ofset, Lefkosa)

1986 (31 Dec). *Cyprus Railway.* T **70** *and similar horiz design. Multicoloured.* W **51** *(sideways).* P 12 × 12½.
202	50 l. Type **70**..	.. ..	3·50	2·75
203	100 l. Locomotive No. 1	.. ..	4·00	4·25

Kuzey Kıbrıs Türk Cumhuriyeti

(**71**)

1987 (18 May). Nos. 94, 96/7 and 113 optd as T **71** or surch also.
204	10 l. deep mauve and pale green	.. ..	50	70
205	15 l. on 3½ l. grey-green and pale rose-pink		50	70
206	20 l. dull ultramarine & pale greenish yellow		55	75
207	30 l. multicoloured	.. ..	70	1·10
204/7 ..		*Set of 4*	2·00	3·00

(Litho Tezel Ofset, Lefkosa)

1987 (27 May). *Paintings (6th series).* Vert designs as T **54**. *Multicoloured.* W **51** *(inverted).* P 12½ × 13.
208	50 l. "Shepherd" (Feridun İşiman)..		1·25	1·25
209	125 l. "Pear Woman" (Mehmet Uluhan)		1·75	3·00

72 Modern House (architect   **73** Kneeling Folk Dancer A. Vural Behaeddin)

(Des H. Uluçam (50 l.). Litho Tezel Ofset, Lefkosa)

1987 (30 June). *Europa. Modern Architecture.* T **72** *and similar horiz design. Multicoloured.* W **51** *(sideways).* P 12 × 12½.
210	50 l. Type **72**..	.. ..	1·00	30
	a. Perf 12 × imperf		1·75	3·25
	ab. Booklet pane. Nos. 210a/11a, each × 2	7·00	
211	200 l. Modern house (architect Necdet Turgay)	..	1·75	3·25
	a. Perf 12 × imperf		1·75	3·25

Nos. 210a and 211a come from 500 l. stamp booklets containing *se-tenant* pane No. 210ab.

(Des B. Ruhi. Litho Tezel Ofset, Lefkosa)

1987 (20 Aug). *Folk Dancers.* T **73** *and similar vert designs. Multicoloured.* W **51** *(inverted).* P 12½ × 12.
212	20 l. Type **73**	.. ..	60	20
213	50 l. Standing male dancer	..	90	40
214	200 l. Standing female dancer	..	2·00	1·75
215	1000 l. Woman's headdress	..	4·75	6·50
212/15		*Set of 4*	7·50	8·00

74 Regimental Colour   **75** Ahmet Beliğ Pasha (1st Anniv of Infantry   (Egyptian judge) Regiment)

(Des H. Uluçam. Litho Tezel Ofset, Lefkosa)

1987 (30 Sept–2 Nov). *Anniversaries and Events.* T **74** *and similar multicoloured designs.* W **51** *(inverted on vert designs, sideways on horiz).* P 12½ × 12 *(vert)* or 12 × 12½ *(horiz).*
216	50 l. Type **74**..	.. ..	1·50	85
217	50 l. Pres. Denktash and Turgut Özal (1st anniv. of Turkish Prime Minister's visit) *(horiz)* (2.11)	..	1·50	85
218	200 l. Emblem and Crescent (5th Islamic Summit Conference, Kuwait)..		2·50	3·50
219	200 l. Emblem and laurel leaves (Membership of Pharmaceutical Federation) *(horiz)*	.. ..	2·50	3·50
216/19		*Set of 4*	7·25	8·00

(Des H. Uluçam. Litho Tezel Ofset, Lefkosa)

1987 (22 Oct). *Turkish Cypriot Personalities.* T **75** *and similar vert designs.* W **51** *(inverted).* P 12½ × 12.
220	75	50 l. brown and greenish yellow	..	65	40
221	—	50 l. multicoloured	..	65	40
222	—	125 l. multicoloured	..	1·50	3·00
220/2 ..			*Set of 3*	2·50	3·50

Designs:—50 l. (No. 221) Mehmet Emin Pasha (Ottoman Grand Vizier); 125 l. Mehmet Kâmil Pasha (Ottoman Grand Vizier).

76 Tourist Hotel, Girne   **77** Piyale Pasha (tug)

(Des A. Erduran. Litho Tezel Ofset, Lefkosa)

1987 (20 Nov). *Modern Development (2nd series).* T **76** *and similar horiz design. Multicoloured.* W **51** *(sideways).* P 12 × 12½.
223	150 l. Type **76**..	.. ..	1·50	1·50
224	200 l. Dogu Akdeniz University	..	1·75	2·25

(Litho Tezel Ofset, Lefkosa)

1988 (2 May). *Paintings (7th series). Multicoloured designs as T* **54**. W **51** (*inverted on* 20, 150 *l., sideways on* 50 *l.*). P 12¹⁄₂×13 (20, 150 *l.*) *or* 13×12¹⁄₂ (50 *l.*).

225	20 l. "Woman making Pastry" (Ayhan Mentes) (*vert*)	50	20
226	50 l. "Chair Weaver" (Osman Güvenir)	75	75
227	150 l. "Woman weaving a Rug" (Zekäi Yesiladali) (*vert*)	1·75	3·25
225/7	Set of 3	2·75	3·75

(Des H. Uluçam. Litho Tezel Ofset, Lefkosa)

1988 (31 May). *Europa. Transport and Communications. T* **77** *and similar multicoloured design.* W **51** (*sideways on* 200 *l., inverted on* 500 *l.*). P 12×12¹⁄₂ (200 *l.*) *or* 12¹⁄₂×12 (500 *l.*).

| 228 | 200 l. Type 77 | 1·75 | 75 |
| 229 | 500 l. Dish aerial and antenna tower, Selvilitepe (*vert*) | 2·50 | 4·00 |

No. 229 also commemorates the 25th anniversary of Bayrak Radio and Television Corporation.

78 Lefkosa

79 Bülent Ecevit

(Litho Tezel Ofset, Lefkosa)

1988 (17 June). *Tourism. T* **78** *and similar horiz designs. Multicoloured.* W **51** (*sideways*). P 12×12¹⁄₂.

230	150 l. Type 78	80	80
231	200 l. Gazi-Magusa	90	1·00
232	300 l. Girne	1·50	2·00
230/2	Set of 3	2·75	3·50

(Litho Tezel Ofset, Lefkosa)

1988 (20 July). *Turkish Prime Ministers. T* **79** *and similar vert designs. Multicoloured.* W **51**. P 12¹⁄₂×12.

233	50 l. Type 79	60	85
234	50 l. Bülent Ulusu	60	85
235	50 l. Turgut Ozal	60	85
233/5	Set of 3	1·60	2·25

80 Red Crescent Members on Exercise

81 Hodori the Tiger (Games mascot) and Fireworks

(Des N. Kozal. Litho Tezel Ofset, Lefkosa)

1988 (8 Aug). *Civil Defence.* W **51** (*sideways*). P 12×12¹⁄₂.

| 236 | 80 | 150 l. multicoloured | 1·25 | 1·50 |

(Des E. Cizenel (200 l.), N. Kozal (250 l.), H. Uluçam (400 l.). Litho Tezel Ofset, Lefkosa)

1988 (17 Sept). *Olympic Games, Seoul. T* **81** *and similar horiz designs. Multicoloured.* W **51** (*sideways*). P 12×12¹⁄₂.

237	200 l. Type 81	80	1·00
	a. Imperf (pair)	70·00	
238	250 l. Athletics	1·00	1·25
239	400 l. Shot and running track with letters spelling "SEOUL"	1·50	2·00
237/9	Set of 3	3·00	3·75

82 Sedat Simavi (journalist)

83 "Kemal Atatürk" (I. Calli)

(Des H. Uluçam (Nos. 241/3). Litho Tezel Ofset, Lefkosa)

1988 (17 Oct). *Anniversaries and Events. T* **82** *and similar designs.* W **51** (*inverted on Nos.* 240, 243 *and* 245, *sideways on Nos.* 241 *and* 244). P 12¹⁄₂×12 (*vert*) *or* 12×12¹⁄₂ (*horiz*).

240	50 l. olive-green	25	25
241	100 l. multicoloured	50	45
242	300 l. multicoloured	70	1·00
243	400 l. multicoloured	1·50	1·75
244	400 l. multicoloured	1·00	1·75
245	600 l. multicoloured	2·00	2·50
240/5	Set of 6	5·50	7·00

Designs: *Horiz*—No. 241, Stylised figures around table and flags of participating countries (International Girne Conferences); 244, Presidents Gorbachev and Reagan signing treaty (Summit Meeting). *Vert*—No. 242, Cogwheels as flowers (North Cyprus Industrial Fair); 243, Globe (125th anniv of International Red Cross); 245, "Medical Services" (40th anniv of W.H.O.).

(Litho Tezel Ofset, Lefkosa)

1988 (10 Nov). *50th Death Anniv of Kemal Atatürk. Sheet* 72 × 102 *mm containing T* **83** *and similar vert designs. Multicoloured.* W **51** (*inverted*). P 12¹⁄₂ × 12.

| MS246 | 250 l. Type 83; 250 l. "Kemal Atatürk" (N. Ismail); 250 l. In army uniform; 250 l. In profile | 2·50 | 2·50 |

84 Abstract Design

(Des E. Cizenel. Litho Tezel Ofset, Lefkosa)

1988 (15 Nov). *5th Anniv of Turkish Republic of Northern Cyprus. Sheet* 98 × 76 *mm.* W **51** (*sideways*). *Imperf.*

| MS247 | **84** | 500 l. multicoloured | 2·25 | 1·75 |

(Litho Tezel Ofset, Lefkosa)

1989 (28 Apr). *Paintings (8th series). Multicoloured designs as T* **54**. W **51** (*sideways on* 150, 400 *l., inverted on* 600 *l.*). P 12¹⁄₂×13 (600 *l.*) *or* 13×12¹⁄₂ (*others*).

248	150 l. "Dervis Pasa Mansion, Lefkosa" (Inci Kansu)	90	60
249	400 l. "Gamblers' Inn, Lefkosa" (Osman Güvenir)	1·75	2·25
250	600 l. "Mosque, Paphos" (Hikmet Ulucam) (*vert*)	2·50	3·00
248/50	Set of 3	4·75	5·25

85 Girl with Doll

86 Meeting of Presidents Vassiliou and Denktash

(Des N. Kozal. Litho Tezel Ofset, Lefkosa)

1989 (31 May). *Europa. Children's Games. T* **85** *and similar vert design. Multicoloured.* W **51**. P 12¹⁄₂×12.

251	600 l. Type 85	1·75	1·25
	a. Imperf × p 12	2·00	3·25
	ab. Booklet pane. Nos. 251a/2a, each ×2	7·50	
252	1000 l. Boy with kite	2·00	3·25
	a. Imperf × p 12	2·00	3·25

Nos. 251a and 252a come from 3200 l. stamp booklets containing *se-tenant* pane No. 251ab.

(Litho Tezel Ofset, Lefkosa)

1989 (30 June). *Cyprus Peace Summit, Geneva,* 1988. W **51** (*sideways*). P 12¹⁄₂×12.

| 253 | **86** | 500 l. deep rose-red and black | 1·25 | 1·25 |

87 Chukar Partridge

88 Road Construction

(Des E. Cizenel. Litho Tezel Ofset, Lefkosa)

1989 (31 July). *Wildlife. T* **87** *and similar horiz designs. Multicoloured.* W **51** (*sideways*). P 12×12¹⁄₂.

254	100 l. Type 87	65	25
255	200 l. Cyprus Hare	70	35
256	700 l. Black Partridge	2·50	2·00
257	2000 l. Red Fox	3·00	3·50
254/7	Set of 4	6·00	5·50

(Litho Tezel Ofset, Lefkosa)

1989 (29 Sept). *Modern Development (3rd series). T* **88** *and similar multicoloured designs.* W **51** (*sideways on* 100, 700 *l.*). P 12×12¹⁄₂ (100, 700 *l.*) *or* 12¹⁄₂×12 (*others*).

258	100 l. Type 88	15	10
259	150 l. Laying water pipeline (*vert*)	20	20
260	200 l. Seedling trees (*vert*)	30	30
261	450 l. Modern telephone exchange (*vert*)	75	1·00
262	650 l. Steam turbine power station (*vert*)	1·00	1·50
263	700 l. Irrigation reservoir	1·25	1·75
258/63	Set of 6	3·25	4·25

MINIMUM PRICE

The minimum price quote is 10p which represents a handling charge rather than a basis for valuing common stamps. For further notes about prices see introductory pages.

89 Unloading *Polly Pioneer* (freighter) at Quayside (15th anniv of Gazi Magusa Free Port)

90 Erdal Inonu

(Des E. Çizenel (450, 600 l.), Ö. Özünalp (500 l.), S. Oral (1000 l.). Litho Tezel Ofset, Lefkosa)

1989 (17 Nov). *Anniversaries. T* **89** *and similar designs.* W **51** (*inverted on* 450 *l., sideways on others*). P 12¹⁄₂×13 (450 *l.*) *or* 12×12¹⁄₂ (*others*).

264	100 l. multicoloured	45	20
265	450 l. black, dull ultramarine & scar- verm	80	80
266	500 l. black, yellow-ochre and olive-grey	80	80
267	600 l. black, vermilion and new blue	1·40	1·75
268	1000 l. multicoloured	2·50	3·25
264/8	Set of 5	5·50	6·00

Designs: *Vert* (26×47 *mm*)—450 l. Airmail letter and stylized bird (25th anniv of Turkish Cypriot postal service). *Horiz* (as *T* **89**)—500 l. Newspaper and printing press (centenary of *Saded* newspaper); 600 l. Statue of Aphrodite, lifebelt and seabird (30th anniv of International Maritime Organization); 1000 l. Soldiers (25th anniv of Turkish Cypriot resistance).

(Litho Tezel Ofset, Lefkosa)

1989 (15 Dec). *Visit of Professor Erdal Inonu (Turkish politician).* W **51** (*inverted*). P 12¹⁄₂×12.

| 269 | **90** | 700 l. multicoloured | 50 | 70 |

91 Mule-drawn Plough

92 Smoking Ashtray and Drinks

(Des N. Kozal. Litho Tezel Ofset, Lefkosa)

1989 (25 Dec). *Traditional Agricultural Implements. T* **91** *and similar multicoloured designs.* W **51** (*sideways on* 150, 450 *l.*). P 12¹⁄₂×12 (550 *l.*) *or* 12×12¹⁄₂ (*others*).

270	150 l. Type 91	15	20
271	450 l. Ox-drawn threshing sledge	50	65
272	550 l. Olive press (*vert*)	60	80
270/2	Set of 3	1·10	1·50

(Des O. Ozünalp (200 l.), H. Ulucam (700 l). Litho Tezel Ofset, Lefkosa)

1990 (19 Apr). *World Health Day. T* **92** *and similar horiz design. Multicoloured.* W **51** (*sideways*). P 12×12¹⁄₂.

| 273 | 200 l. Type 92 | 65 | 40 |
| 274 | 700 l. Smoking cigarette and heart | 1·25 | 2·00 |

93 Yenierenköy Post Office

94 Song Thrush

(Des H. Billur. Litho Tezel Ofset, Lefkosa)

1990 (31 May). *Europa. Post Office Buildings. T* **93** *and similar horiz design. Multicoloured.* W **51** (*sideways*). P 12×12¹⁄₂.

275	1000 t. Type 93	1·00	75
276	1500 t. Atatürk Meydani Post Office	1·75	2·50
MS277	105×72 mm. Nos. 275/6, each × 2	5·50	6·50

(Des H. Billur. Litho Tezel Ofset, Lefkosa)

1990 (5 June). *World Environment Day. T* **94** *and similar vert designs showing birds. Multicoloured.* W **51** (*inverted*). P 12¹⁄₂×12.

278	150 l. Type 94	1·50	65
279	300 l. Blackcap	2·25	90
280	900 l. Black Redstart	3·75	3·00
281	1000 l. Chiff-chaff	3·75	3·25
278/81	Set of 4	10·00	7·00

95 Two Football Teams

96 Amphitheatre, Soli

(Des H. Billur (1000 l.). Litho Tezel Ofset, Lefkosa)

1990 (8 June). *World Cup Football Championship, Italy. T **95** and similar horiz design. Multicoloured. W **51** (sideways). P 12×12½.*

| 282 | 300 l. Type **95** | 75 | 50 |
| 283 | 1000 l. Championship symbol, globe and ball | 2·50 | 3·00 |

(Litho Tezel Ofset, Lefkosa)

1990 (31 July). *Paintings (9th series). Multicoloured designs as T **54**. W **51** (sideways on 300 l.). P 13×12½ (300 l.) or 12½×13 (1000 l.).*

| 284 | 300 l. "Abstract" (Filiz Ankaçc) | 25 | 25 |
| 285 | 1000 l. Wooden sculpture (S. Tekman) (vert) | 85 | 1·50 |

(Litho Tezel Ofset, Lefkosa)

1990 (24 Aug). *Tourism. T **96** and similar vert design. Multicoloured. W **51**. P 12½.*

| 286 | 150 l. Type **96** | 40 | 20 |
| 287 | 1000 l. Swan mosaic, Soli | 1·75 | 2·50 |

97 Kenan Evren and Rauf Denktas

98 Road Signs and Heart wearing Seat Belt

(Litho Tezel Ofset, Lefkosa)

1990 (19 Sept). *Visit of President Kenan Evren of Turkey. W **51** (sideways). P 12½.*

| 288 | **97** 500 l. multicoloured | 1·00 | 1·00 |

(Des H. Billur. Litho Tezel Ofset, Lefkosa)

1990 (21 Sept). *Traffic Safety Campaign. T **98** and similar horiz designs. Multicoloured. W **51** (sideways). P 12½.*

289	150 l. Type **98**	65	30
290	300 l. Road signs, speeding car and spots of blood	90	50
291	1000 l. Traffic lights and road signs	2·75	3·50
289/91	Set of 3	3·75	3·75

99 Yildirim Akbulut

100 *Rosularia cypria*

(Litho Tezel Ofset, Lefkosa)

1990 (1 Oct). *Visit of Turkish Prime Minister Yildrim Akbulut. W **51** (inverted). P 12½.*

| 292 | **99** 1000 l. multicoloured | 1·10 | 1·10 |

(Des D. Viney and P. Jacobs (200, 1500 l.), D. Viney and C. Hessenberg (others). Litho Tezel Ofset, Lefkosa)

1990 (31 Oct). *Plants. T **100** and similar vert designs. Multicoloured. W **51**. P 12½.*

293	150 l. Type **100**	35	20
294	200 l. Silene fraudratrix	45	30
295	300 l. Scutellaria sibthorpii	50	35
296	600 l. Sedum lampusae	75	75
297	1000 l. Onosma caespitosum	1·00	1·50
298	1500 l. Arabis cypria	1·40	4·50
293/8	Set of 6	4·00	4·50

101 Kemal Atatürk at Easel (wood carving)

250 TL (**102**)

(Des M. Uzel (300 l.), H. Billur (750 l.). Litho Tezel Ofset, Lefkosa)

1990 (24 Nov). *International Literacy Year. T **101** and similar horiz design. Multicoloured. W **51** (sideways). P 12½.*

| 299 | 300 l. Type **101** | 50 | 35 |
| 300 | 750 l. Globe, letters and books | 1·25 | 1·75 |

1991 (3 June). *Nos. 189, 212 and 293 surch as T **102**.*

301	250 l. on 10 l. Type **66**	60	60
302	250 l. on 20 l. Type **73**	60	60
303	500 l. on 150 l. Type **100**	90	90
	a. Surch inverted	50·00	
301/3	Set of 3	1·90	1·90

PRINTER. Issues from Nos. 304/5 onwards were printed in lithography by the State Printing Works, Lefkosa, *unless otherwise stated.*

103 *Ophrys lapethica*

104 Hermes (projected shuttle)

1991 (8 July). *Orchids (1st series). T **103** and similar vert design. Multicoloured. W **51** (inverted). P 14.*

| 304 | 250 l. Type **103** | 1·25 | 60 |
| 305 | 500 l. Ophrys kotschyi | 2·25 | 2·50 |

See also Nos. 311/14.

1991 (29 July). *Europa. Europe in Space. Sheet 78×82 mm containing T **104** and similar vert design. Multicoloured. W **51**. P 12½.*

| MS306 | 2000 l. Type **104**; 2000 l. Ulysses (satellite) | 4·75 | 4·75 |

105 Kucuk Medrese Fountain, Lefkosa

106 Symbolic Roots (Year of Love to Yunus Emre)

(Des H. Billur)

1991 (9 Sept). *Fountains. T **105** and similar horiz designs. Multicoloured. W **51** (sideways). P 12½.*

307	250 l. Type **105**	35	15
308	500 l. Cafer Pasa Fountain, Magusa	50	30
309	1500 l. Sarayönü Square Fountain, Lefkosa	85	1·00
310	5000 l. Arabahmet Mosque Fountain, Lefkosa	2·25	3·00
307/10	Set of 4	3·50	4·00

1991 (10 Oct). *Orchids (2nd series). Vert designs as T **103**. Multicoloured. W **51**. P 14.*

311	100 l. Serapias levantina	45	20
312	500 l. Dactylorhiza romana	95	50
313	2000 l. Orchis simia	2·50	2·75
314	3000 l. Orchis sancta	3·00	3·50
311/14	Set of 4	6·25	6·25

1991 (5 Nov). *Paintings (10th series). Multicoloured designs as T **54**. W **51**. P 12½.*

| 315 | 250 l. "Hindiler" (S. Çizel) (vert) | 75 | 40 |
| 316 | 500 l. "Düsme" (A. Mene) (vert) | 1·25 | 1·50 |

(Des K. Sarikavak (250 l.), H. Billur (500, 1500 l.))

1991 (20 Nov). *Anniversaries and Events. T **106** and similar designs. W **51** (sideways on 1500 l., inverted on others). P 12×12½ (1500 l.) or 12½×12 (others).*

317	250 l. greenish yellow, black & brt mag	25	25
318	500 l. multicoloured	45	50
319	500 l. multicoloured	45	50

| 320 | 1500 l. multicoloured | 2·50 | 2·75 |
| 317/20 | Set of 4 | 3·25 | 3·50 |

Designs: *Vert*—No. 318, Mustafa Cagatay commemoration; No. 319, University building (5th anniv of Eastern Mediterranean University). *Horiz*—No. 320, Mozart (death bicent).

107 Four Sources of Infection

108 Lighthouse, Gazimagusa

1991 (13 Dec). *AIDS Day. W **51**. P 12×12½.*

| 321 | **107** 1000 l. multicoloured | 1·50 | 1·50 |

(Des H. Billur)

1991 (16 Dec). *Lighthouses. T **108** and similar horiz designs. Multicoloured. W **51** (sideways). P 12×12½.*

322	250 l. Type **108**	1·00	45
323	500 l. Ancient lighthouse, Girne harbour	1·40	1·10
324	1500 l. Modern lighthouse, Girne harbour	3·00	3·50
322/4	Set of 3	4·75	4·50

109 Elephant and Hippopotamus Fossils, Karaoglanoglu

1991 (27 Dec). *Tourism (1st series). T **109** and similar horiz designs. Multicoloured. W **51** (sideways). P 12.*

325	250 l. Type **109**	70	40
326	500 l. Roman fish ponds, Lambusa	90	65
327	1500 l. Roman remains, Lambusa	2·00	2·50
325/7	Set of 3	3·25	3·25

See also Nos. 330/3 and 351/2.

1992 (31 Mar). *Paintings (11th series). Multicoloured designs as T **54**, but 31×49 mm. W **51** (sideways). P 14.*

| 328 | 500 l. "Ebru" (A. Kandulu) | 40 | 20 |
| 329 | 3500 l. "Street in Lefkosa" (I. Tatar) | 2·00 | 2·75 |

1992 (21 Apr). *Tourism (2nd series). Multicoloured designs as T **109**. W **51** (sideways). P 14×13½ (1500 l.) or 13½×14 (others).*

330	500 l. Bugday Camii, Gazimagusa	40	30
331	500 l. Clay pigeon shooting	40	30
332	1000 l. Salamis Bay Hotel, Gazimagusa	75	90
333	1500 l. Casino, Girne (vert)	1·25	2·00
330/3	Set of 4	2·50	3·25

110 Fleet of Columbus and Early Map

(Des H. Billur)

1992 (29 May). *Europa. 500th Anniv of Discovery of America by Columbus. Sheet, 80×76 mm, containing T **110** and similar horiz design. Multicoloured. W **51** (sideways). P 13½×14.*

| MS334 | 1500 l. Type **110**; 3500 l. Christopher Columbus and signature | 2·00 | 2·50 |

111 Green Turtle

112 Gymnastics

(Des H. Billur)

1992 (30 June). *World Environment Day. Sea Turtles. Sheet, 105×75 mm, containing T **111** and similar horiz design. W **51** (sideways). P 13½×14.*

| MS335 | 1000 l. × 2, Type **111**: 1500 l. × 2, Loggerhead Turtle | 4·50 | 4·50 |

(Des H. Billur)

1992 (25 July). *Olympic Games, Barcelona. T 112 and similar multicoloured designs. W 51 (inverted on 500 l., sideways on 1000, 1500 l.). P 14×13½ (500 l.) or 13½×14 (others).*

336	500 l.	Type 112	..	..	65	75
	a. Horiz pair. Nos. 336/7	..	1·25	1·50
337	500 l.	Tennis	..	..	65	75
338	1000 l.	High jumping (horiz)	..	80	1·00
339	1500 l.	Cycling (horiz)	..	1·50	1·75
336/9			Set of 4	3·25	3·75

Nos. 336/7 were printed together, *se-tenant*, in horizontal pairs throughout the sheet.

113 New Generating Station, Girne

(Des H. Billur (Nos. 341/2), Therese Coustry (No. 343))

1992 (30 Sept). *Anniversaries and Events (1st series). T 113 and similar horiz designs. Multicoloured. W 51 (sideways). P 14.*

340	500 l.	Type 113		30	30
341	500 l.	Symbol of Housing Association (15th anniv)		30	30
342	1500 l.	Domestic animals and birds (30th anniv of Veterinary Service)		2·00	2·25
343	1500 l.	Cat (International Federation of Cat Societies Conference)		2·00	2·25
340/3		..	..	Set of 4	4·25	4·50

114 Airliner over Runway

(Des H. Billur)

1992 (20 Nov). *Anniversaries and Events (2nd series). T 114 and similar horiz designs. Multicoloured. W 51 (sideways). P 13½×14.*

344	1000 l.	Type 114 (17th anniv of civil aviation)	1·00	1·00
345	1000 l.	Meteorological instruments and weather (18th anniv of Meteorological Service)	1·00	1·00
346	1200 l.	Surveying equipment and map (14th anniv of Survey Department)	1·40	1·75
344/6		Set of 3	3·00	3·25

115 Zübiye   116 Painting by Turksal Ince

(Des A. Erduran)

1992 (14 Dec). *International Conference on Nutrition, Rome. Turkish Cypriot Cuisine. T 115 and similar horiz designs. W 51 (sideways). P 13½×14.*

347	2000 l.	Type 115	..	..	80	90
348	2500 l.	Çiçek Dolmasi	..	..	90	1·00
349	3000 l.	Tatar Böregi	..	..	1·00	1·10
350	4000 l.	Seftali Kebabi	..	..	1·25	1·50
347/50			Set of 4	3·50	4·00

1993 (1 Apr). *Tourism (3rd series). Horiz designs as T 109. Multicoloured. W 51 (sideways). P 13½×14.*

351	500 l.	Saint Barnabas Church and Monastery, Salamis	30	15
352	10000 l.	Ancient pot	..	2·50	3·00

(Des T. Ince and I. Onsoy)

1993 (5 May). *Europa. Contemporary Art. Sheet 79×69 mm containing T 116 and similar vert design. Multicoloured. W 51. P 14.*

MS353	2000 l. Type 116; 3000 l. Painting by Ilkay Onsoy	..	..	1·50	2·00

ALTERED CATALOGUE NUMBERS

Any Catalogue numbers altered from the last edition are shown as a list in the introductory pages.

117 Olive Tree, Girne   118 Traditional Houses

1993 (11 June). *Ancient Trees. T 117 and similar vert designs. Multicoloured. W 51 (inverted). P 14.*

354	500 l.	Type 117	..	..	15	15
355	1000 l.	River red gum, Kyrenia Gate, Lefkosa		25	25
356	3000 l.	Oriental plane, Lapta	..	70	1·00
357	4000 l.	Calabrian pine, Cinarli	..	85	1·40
354/7		..	..	Set of 4	1·75	2·50

(Des H. Billur)

1993 (20 Sept). *Arabahmet District Conservation Project, Lefkosa. T 118 and similar horiz design. Multicoloured. W 51 (sideways). P 13½×14.*

358	1000 l.	Type 118	..	..	75	40
359	3000 l.	Arabahmet street	..	1·75	2·25

119 National Flags turning into Doves   120 Kemal Atatürk

(Des H. Ulucam (5000 l.), H. Billur (others))

1993 (15 Nov). *10th Anniv of Proclamation of Turkish Republic of Northern Cyprus. T 119 and similar designs. W 51 (sideways on Nos. 361/3). P 14×13½ (No. 360) or 13½×14 (others).*

360	500 l.	carmine-red, black and new blue		20	15
361	500 l.	rosine and new blue	..	20	15
362	1000 l.	carmine-red, black and new blue		30	30
363	5000 l.	multicoloured	..	1·40	2·75
360/3			Set of 4	1·90	3·00

Designs: *Horiz*—No. 361, National flag forming figure "10"; No. 362, Dove carrying national flag; No. 363, Map of Cyprus and figure "10" wreath.

(Des H. Billur (Nos. 365/8))

1993 (27 Dec). *Anniversaries. T 120 and similar multicoloured designs. W 51 (inverted on No. 364 or sideways on others). P 14×13½ (No. 364) or 13½×14 (others).*

364	500 l.	Type 120 (55th death anniv)	20	20
365	500 l.	Stage and emblem (30th anniv of Turkish Cypriot theatre) (horiz)	20	20
366	1500 l.	Branch badges (35th anniv of T.M.T. organization) (horiz)	40	45
367	2000 l.	World map and computer (20th anniv of Turkish Cypriot news agency) (horiz)	55	65
368	5000 l.	Ballet dancers and Caykovski'nin (Death centenary) (horiz)	2·00	2·50
364/8		Set of 5	3·00	3·50

121 "Söyle Falci" (Göral Ozkan)

1994 (31 Mar). *Art (12th series). T 121 and similar vert design. Multicoloured. W 51. P 14.*

369	1000 l.	Type 121	..	..	15	20
370	6500 l.	"IV. Hareket" (sculpture) (Senol Ozdevrim)	..	85	1·40

See also Nos. 436/7.

122 Dr. Kucuk and Memorial

1994 (1 Apr). *10th Death Anniv of Dr. Fazil Kucuk (politician). W 51 (sideways). P 14.*

371	122	1500 l. multicoloured	..	50	50

123 Neolithic Village, Girne

(Des H. Billur)

1994 (16 May). *Europa. Archaeological Discoveries. Sheet 73×79 mm containing T 123 and similar horiz design. Multicoloured. W 51 (sideways). P 13½×14.*

MS372	8500 l. Type 123; 8500 l. Neolithic man and implements	..	..	4·50	4·50

124 Peace Doves and Letters over Pillar Box   125 World Cup Trophy

(Des H. Billur)

1994 (30 June). *30th Anniv of Turkish Cypriot Postal Service. W 51 (sideways). P 13½×14.*

373	124	50000 l. multicoloured	..	2·75	3·75

(Des H. Billur)

1994 (30 June). *World Cup Football Championship, U.S.A. T 125 and similar multicoloured design. W 51 (sideways on 10000 l.). P 14×13½ (2500 l.) or 13½×14 (10000 l.).*

374	2500 l.	Type 125	..	40	25
375	10000 l.	Footballs on map of U.S.A. (horiz)	1·50	1·75

126 Peace Emblem   127 Cyprus 1934 4½ pi. Stamp and Karpas Postmark

(Des H. Billur (2500, 8500 l.))

1994 (20 July). *20th Anniv of Turkish Landings in Cyprus. T 126 and similar designs. W 51 (sideways on horiz designs). P 14×13½ (2500 l.) or 13½×14 (others).*

376	2500 l.	greenish yellow, emerald and black	30	30
377	5000 l.	multicoloured	..	50	50
378	7000 l.	multicoloured	..	70	70
379	8500 l.	multicoloured	..	90	90
376/9		Set of 4	2·25	2·25

Designs: *Horiz*—5000 l. Memorial; 7000 l. Sculpture; 8500 l. Peace doves forming map of Cyprus and flame.

1994 (15 Aug). *Postal Centenary. T 127 and similar horiz designs. Multicoloured. W 51 (sideways). P 13½×14.*

380	1500 l.	Type 127	..	20	20
381	2500 l.	Turkish Cypriot Posts 1979 Europa 2 l. and Gazimagusa postmark	30	30
382	5000 l.	Cyprus 1938 6 pi. and Bey Keuy postmark	50	50
383	7000 l.	Cyprus 1955 100 m. and Aloa postmark	70	70
384	8500 l.	Cyprus 1938 18 pi. and Pyla postmark	90	90
380/4		Set of 5	2·40	2·40

128 Trumpet Triton   (129)
(*Charonia tritonis*)

***

1994 (15 Nov). *Sea Shells. T* **128** *and similar horiz designs. Multicoloured.* W **51** (*sideways*). P 13½×14.
385	2500 l. Type **128**	..	..	45	30
386	12500 l. Mole Cowrie (*Cypraea talpa*)	..	1·25	1·75
387	12500 l. Giant Tun (*Tonna galea*)	..	1·25	1·75
385/7			*Set of 3*	2·75	3·50

1994 (12 Dec)–**95**. *Nos.* 280, 295, 315 *and* 317 *surch as T* **129**.
388	1500 l. on 250 l. Type **106**	..	..	15	10
389	2000 l. on 900 l. Black Redstart (21.4.95)	..	75	60
390	2500 l. on 250 l. "Hindiler" (S. Çizel)	..	30	30
391	3500 l. on 300 l. *Scutellaria sibthorpii* (21.4.95)	..	75	75
388/91			*Set of 4*	1·75	1·60

Nos. 389/90 show the surcharge value horizontally.

130 Donkeys on Mountain   **131** Peace Dove and Globe

1995 (10 Feb). *European Conservation Year. T* **130** *and similar horiz designs.* W **51** (*sideways*). P 13½×14.
392	2000 l. Type **130**	..	..	30	20
393	3500 l. Coastline	..	..	30	30
394	15000 l. Donkeys in field	..	1·50	2·00
392/4			*Set of 3*	1·90	2·25

(Des H. Billur)

1995 (20 Apr). *Europa. Peace and Freedom. Sheet* 72×78 *mm containing T* **131** *and similar horiz design.* W **51** (*sideways*). P 13½×14.
MS395 15000 l. Type **131**; 15000 l. Peace doves over map of Europe .. .. 2·50 2·75

132 Sini Katmeri   **133** *Papilio machaon*

1995 (29 May). *Turkish Cypriot Cuisine. T* **132** *and similar horiz designs. Multicoloured.* W **51** (*sideways*). P 13½×14.
396	3500 l. Type **132**	..	..	20	20
397	10000 l. Kolokas musakka and bullez kizartma	..	55	60
398	14000 l. Enginar dolmasi	..	90	1·40
396/8			*Set of 3*	1·50	2·00

(Des H. Billur)

1995 (30 June). *Butterflies. T* **133** *and similar horiz designs. Multicoloured.* W **51** (*sideways*). P 13½×14.
399	3500 l. Type **133**	..	..	30	15
400	4500 l. *Charaxes jasius*	..	35	20
401	15000 l. *Cynthia cardui*	..	1·00	1·25
402	30000 l. *Vanessa atalanta*	..	1·75	2·25
399/402			*Set of 4*	3·00	3·50

134 Forest   **135** Beach, Girne

1995 (7 Aug). *Obligatory Tax. Forest Regeneration Fund.* P 14×13½.
403 **134** 1000 l. emerald and black .. 1·00 20
No. 403 was for compulsory use on all mail, in addition to the normal postage, between 7 August and 6 February 1996. It was intended to provide funds for the replanting of those forests destroyed by fire in June 1995. A similar 50000 l. stamp was issued for fiscal use only.

1995 (21 Aug). *Tourism. T* **135** *and similar multicoloured designs.* W **51** (*sideways on horiz designs*). P 13½×14 (*horiz*) or 14×13½ (*vert*).
404	3500 l. Type **135**	..	..	15	15
405	7500 l. Sail boards	..	35	35
406	15000 l. Ruins of Salamis (*vert*)	..	70	95
407	20000 l. St. George's Cathedral, Gazimagusa (*vert*)	..	90	1·25
404/7			*Set of 4*	1·90	2·40

136 Süleyman Demirel and   **137** Stamp Printing Press
Rauf Denktas

1995 (21 Aug). *Visit of President Süleyman Demirel of Turkey.* W **51** (*sideways*). P 14.
408 **136** 5000 l. multicoloured .. 30 30

(Des H. Billur (Nos. 410/14))

1995 (7 Nov). *Anniversaries. T* **137** *and similar designs.* W **51** (*sideways on horiz designs*). P 14×13½ (*No.* 414) *or* 13½×14 (*others*).
409	3000 l. multicoloured	..	..	40	40
410	3000 l. multicoloured	..	..	40	40
411	5000 l. multicoloured	..	..	70	70
412	22000 l. dull ultramarine, new blue & black	1·00	1·25
413	30000 l. multicoloured	..	1·40	1·75
414	30000 l. multicoloured	..	1·40	1·75
409/14			*Set of 6*	4·75	5·50

Designs: *Horiz*—No. 409, Type **137** (20th anniv od State Printing Works); No. 410, Map of Turkey (75th anniv of Turkish National Assembly); No. 411, Louis Pasteur (chemist) and microscope (Death centenary); No. 412, United Nations anniversary emblem (50th anniv); No. 413, Guglielmo Marconi (radio pioneer) and dial (Centenary of first radio transmissions). *Vert*—No. 414, Stars and reel of film (Centenary of cinema).

138 Kültegin   **139** "Bosnia"
Epitaph and   (sculpture)
Sculpture

(Des H. Billur)

1995 (28 Dec). *Centenary of Deciphering of Orhon Epitaphs. T* **138** *and similar vert design.* W **51**. P 14.
415	5000 l. Type **138**	..	..	45	40
416	10000 l. Epitaph and tombstone	..	80	1·00

(Des S. Ozdevrim)

1996 (31 Jan). *Support for Moslems in Bosnia and Herzegovina.* W **51** (*inverted*). P 14×13½.
417 **139** 10000 l. multicoloured 75 80

140 Striped Red Mullet   **141** Palm Trees

(Des H. Billur)

1996 (29 Mar). *Fishes. T* **140** *and similar horiz designs. Multicoloured.* W **51** (*sideways*). P 13½×14.
418	6000 l. Type **140**	..	..	50	30
419	10000 l. Peacock Wrasse	..	70	45
420	28000 l. Common Two-banded Seabream	1·25	1·40
421	40000 l. Dusky Grouper	..	1·75	2·00
418/21			*Set of 4*	3·75	3·75

1996 (26 Apr). *Tourism. T* **141** *and similar multicoloured designs.* W **51** (*sideways on horiz designs*). P 14×13½ (*vert*) or 13½×14 (*horiz*).
422	100000 l. Type **141**	..	..	50	45
423	150000 l. Pomegranate	..	55	65
424	250000 l. Ruins of Bella Paise Abbey (*horiz*)	1·25	1·10
425	500000 l. Traditional dancers (*horiz*)	2·25	2·10
422/5			*Set of 4*	4·25	4·25

142 Beria Remzi Ozoran   **143** Established Forest

(Des H. Billur)

1996 (31 May). *Europa. Famous Women. T* **142** *and similar horiz design. Multicoloured.* W **51** (*sideways*). P 13½×14.
426	15000 l. Type **142**	..	..	60	25
427	50000 l. Kadriye Hulusi Hacibulgur	..	1·50	2·00

1996 (28 June). *World Environment Day. Sheet* 72×78 *mm containing T* **143** *and similar horiz design. Multicoloured.* W **51** (*sideways*). P 13½×14.
MS428 50000 l. Type **143**; 50000 l. Conifer plantation .. .. .. 4·00 4·25

144 Basketball   **145** Symbolic Footballs

(Des H. Billur)

1996 (31 July). *Olympic Games, Atlanta. Sheet* 105×74 *mm containing T* **144** *and similar horiz designs. Multicoloured.* W **51** (*sideways*). P 13½×14.
MS429 15000 l. Type **144**; 15000 l. Discus throwing; 50000 l. Javelin throwing; 50000 l. Volleyball .. .. .. 3·25 3·75

(Des H. Billur)

1996 (31 Oct). *European Football Championship, England. T* **145** *and similar horiz design. Multicoloured.* W **51** (*sideways*). P 13½×14.
430	15000 l. Type **145**	..	..	65	65
	a. Pair. Nos. 430/1	..	1·75	1·75
431	35000 l. Football and flags of participating nations	..	1·10	1·10

In addition to separate sheets Nos. 430/1 were also available in pairs, *se-tenant* horizontally and vertically.

146 Houses on Fire   **147** *Amanita*
(Auxiliary Fire Service)   *phalloides*

(Des O. Oker (10000 l.), H. Billur (50000, 75000 l.))

1996 (23 Dec). *Anniversaries and Events. T* **146** *and similar multicoloured designs.* W **51** (*inverted on* 20000 l., *sideways on others*). P 14×13½ (20000 l.) *or* 13½×14 (*others*).
432	10000 l. Type **146**	..	..	30	30
433	20000 l. Colour party (20th anniv of Defence Forces) (*vert*)	..	40	40
434	50000 l. Children by lake (Nasreddin-Hoca Year)	..	85	85
435	75000 l. Flowers (Children's Rights)	..	1·25	1·50
432/5			*Set of 4*	2·50	2·75

1997 (31 Jan). *Arts (13th series). Multicoloured designs as T* **121**. W **51** (*sideways*). P 14.
436	25000 l. "City" (Lebibe Sonuc) (*horiz*)	..	50	35
437	70000 l. "Woman opening Letter" (Ruzen Atakan) (*horiz*)	..	1·40	1·90

(Des H. Billur)

1997 (31 Mar). *Fungi. T* **147** *and similar vert designs. Multicoloured.* W **51** (*inverted*). P 14×13½.
438	15000 l. Type **147**	..	..	40	30
439	25000 l. *Morchella esculenta*	..	55	45
440	25000 l. *Pleurotus eryngii*	..	55	45
441	70000 l. *Amanita muscaria*	..	1·25	1·75
438/41			*Set of 4*	2·50	2·75

148 Flag on   **149** Mother and Children
Hillside   playing Leapfrog

(Des H. Billur)

1997 (23 Apr). *Besparmak Mountains Flag Sculpture.* W **51** (*inverted*). P 14×13½.
442 **148** 60000 l. multicoloured .. .. 1·00 1·00

(Des H. Billur)

1997 (30 May). *Europa. Tales and Legends.* T **149** *and similar horiz design. Multicoloured.* W **51** (*sideways*). P 13½×14.
443   25000 l.   Type **149** 50   30
444   70000 l.   Apple tree and well .. 1·50   2·00

150 Prime Minister Necmettin Erbakan of Turkey

151 Golden Eagle

1997 (20 June). *Visit of the President and the Prime Minister of Turkey.* T **150** *and similar multicoloured design.* W **51** (*sideways on* 80000 l.). P 14×13½ (*vert*) or 13½×14 (*horiz*).
445   15000 l.   Type **150** 30   20
446   80000 l.   President Suleyman Demirel of Turkey (*horiz*) .. 1·25   1·75

(Des H. Billur)

1997 (31 July). *Birds of Prey.* T **151** *and similar vert designs. Multicoloured.* W **51**. P 14×13½.
447   40000 l.   Type **151** 70   70
448   40000 l.   Eleonora's Falcon .. 70   70
449   75000 l.   Common Kestrel .. 1·25   1·40
450   100000 l.   Honey Buzzard .. 1·40   1·60
447/50   .. .. .. *Set of 4*   3·50   4·00

152 Coin of Sultan Abdulaziz, 1861–76

153 Open Book and Emblem

1997 (28 Oct). *Rare Coins.* T **152** *and similar vert designs. Multicoloured.* W **51**. P 14×13½.
451   25000 l.   Type **152** .. 25   20
452   40000 l.   Coin of Sultan Mahmud II, 1808–39 35   30
453   75000 l.   Coin of Sultan Selim II, 1566–74 .. 55   60
454   100000 l.   Coin of Sultan Mehmed V, 1909–18 80   90
451/4   .. .. .. *Set of 4*   1·75   1·75

(Des H. Billur.)

1997 (22 Dec). *Anniversaries.* T **153** *and similar designs.* W **51** (*sideways on horiz designs*). P 13½×14 (*horiz*) or 14×13½ (*vert*).
455   25000 l.   multicoloured 25   20
456   40000 l.   multicoloured 35   30
457   100000 l.   black, brt scarlet & yellow ochre 90   95
458   150000 l.   multicoloured .. 1·40   1·60
455/8   .. .. .. *Set of 4*   2·50   2·75
Designs: *Horiz*—25000 l. Type **153** (Centenary of Turkish Cypriot Scouts); 40000 l. Guides working in field (90th anniv of Turkish Cypriot Guides); 150000 l. Rudolf Diesel and first oil engine (Centenary of the diesel engine). *Vert*—100000 l. Couple and symbols (AIDS prevention campaign).

154 Ahmet and Ismet Sevki

155 *Agrion splendens* (dragonfly)

1998 (28 Jan). *Ahmet and Ismet Sevki* (*photographers*) *Commemoration.* T **154** *and similar multicoloured design.* W **51** (*sideways on* 40000 l.). P 13½×14 (*horiz*) or 14×13½ (*vert*).
459   40000 l.   Type **154** .. 35   25
460   105000 l.   Ahmet Sevki (*vert*) .. 90   1·00

(Des H. Billur)

1998 (30 Mar). *Useful Insects.* T **155** *and similar horiz designs. Multicoloured.* W **51** (*sideways*). P 13½×14.
461   40000 l.   Type **155** .. 35   25
462   65000 l.   *Ascalaphus macaronius* (owl-fly) 50   40
463   125000 l.   *Podalonia hirsuta* .. 1·00   1·10
464   150000 l.   *Rhyssa persuasoria* .. 1·25   1·40
461/4   .. .. .. *Set of 4*   2·75   2·75

156 Wooden Double Door

157 Legislative Assembly Building (Republic Establishment Festival)

(Des H. Billur)

1998 (30 Apr). *Old Doors.* T **156** *and similar vert design showing different door.* W **51**. P 14×13½.
465   115000 l.   multicoloured .. 1·00   1·00
466   140000 l.   multicoloured .. 1·10   1·10

(Des H. Billur)

1998 (30 May). *Europa. Festivals.* T **157** *and similar multicoloured design.* W **51** (*sideways on* 40000 l., *inverted on* 150000 l.). P 13½×14 (*horiz*) or 14×13½ (*vert*).
467   40000 l.   Type **157** .. 40   25
468   150000 l.   Globe, flags and map (Int Children's Folk Dance Festival) (*vert*) 1·25   1·40

158 Marine Life

159 Prime Minister Mesut Yilmaz of Turkey

(Des H. Billur)

1998 (30 June). *International Year of the Ocean.* T **158** *and similar horiz design showing different underwater scene.* W **51** (*sideways*). P 13½×14.
469   40000 l.   multicoloured 40   30
470   90000 l.   multicoloured 85   95

1998 (20 July). *Prime Minister Yilmaz's Visit to Northern Cyprus.* W **51** (*sideways*). P 13½×14.
471   **159**   75000 l.   multicoloured .. 90   90

160 Pres. Suleyman Demirel of Turkey

161 Victorious French Team

1998 (25 July). *President Demirel's "Water for Peace" Project.* T **160** *and similar multicoloured design.* W **51** (*inverted on* 75000 l., *sideways on* 175000 l.). P 14×13½ (*vert*) or 13½×14 (*horiz*).
472   75000 l.   Type **160** 75   50
473   175000 l.   Turkish and Turkish Cypriot leaders with inflatable water tank (*horiz*) .. .. .. 1·50   1·75

1998 (31 July). *World Cup Football Championship, France.* T **161** *and similar multicoloured design.* W **51** (*sideways on* 75000 l., *inverted on* 175000 l.). P 13½×14 (*horiz*) or 14×13½ (*vert*).
474   75000 l.   Type **161** 75   50
475   175000 l.   World Cup trophy (*vert*) .. 1·50   1·75

162 Deputy Prime Minister Bulent Ecevit

163 Itinerant Tinsmiths

1998 (5 Sept). *Visit of the Deputy Prime Minister of Turkey.* W **51** (*inverted*). P 14×13½.
476   **162**   200000 l.   multicoloured .. 1·25   1·40

(Des H. Billur)

1998 (26 Oct). *Local Crafts.* T **163** *and similar multicoloured designs.* W **51** (*sideways on horiz designs, inverted on vert*). P 13½×14 (*horiz designs*) or 14×13½ (*others*).
477   50000 l.   Type **163** .. 25   25
478   75000 l.   Basket weaver (*vert*) .. 35   35
479   130000 l.   Grinder sharpening knife (*vert*) 70   75
480   400000 l.   Wood carver .. .. 2·00   2·50
477/80   .. .. .. *Set of 4*   3·00   3·50

164 Stylised Satellite Dish

165 Dr. Fazil Kucuk

(Des H. Billur and H. Ulucam)

1998 (15 Nov). *Anniversaries.* T **164** *and similar multicoloured designs* (*except No.* 483). W **51** (*inverted on* 175000 l., *sideways on others*). P 14×13½ (175000 l.) or 13½×14 (*others*).
481   50000 l.   Type **164** 30   25
482   75000 l.   Stylised birds and "15" .. 40   45
483   75000 l.   "75" and Turkish flag (rosine, black and dull orange) .. 40   45
484   175000 l.   Scroll, "50" and quill pen (*vert*) 90   1·25
481/4   .. .. .. *Set of 4*   1·75   2·25
MS485   72×78 mm. 75000 l. As No. 482; 75000 l. Map of Northern Cyprus 80   90
Anniversaries—No. 481, 35th anniv of Bayrak Radio and Television; Nos. 482, MS485, 15th anniv of Turkish Republic of Northern Cyprus; No. 483, 75th anniv of Turkish Republic; No. 484, 50th anniv of Universal Declaration of Human Rights.

1999 (15 Jan). *15th Death Anniv of Dr. Fazil Kucuk* (*politician*). W **51** (*inverted*). P 14×13½.
486   **165**   75000 l.   multicoloured .. 50   50

166 Otello

167 *Malpolon monspessulanus insignitus* (Montepellier)

1999 (30 Jan). *Performance of Verdi's Opera* Otello *in Cyprus. Sheet,* 78×74 mm, *containing* T **166** *and similar vert design. Multicoloured.* W **51** (*inverted*). P 14×13½.
MS487   200000 l. Type **166**; 200000 l. Desdemona dead in front of fireplace .. .. 2·00   2·25

(Des D. Basimevi)

1999 (26 Mar). *Snakes.* T **167** *and similar horiz designs. Multicoloured.* W **51** (*sideways*). P 13½×14.
488   50000 l.   Type **167** .. 15   15
489   75000 l.   *Hierophis jugularis* .. 25   25
490   195000 l.   *Vipera lebetina lebetina* (Levantine Viper) 65   70
491   220000 l.   *Natrix natrix* (Grass Snake) .. 75   80
488/91   .. .. .. *Set of 4*   1·60   1·75

168 Entrance to Cave

1999 (17 May). *Europa. Parks and Gardens. Incirli Cave.* T **168** *and similar multicoloured design.* W **51** (*sideways on* 75000 l., *inverted on* 200000 l.). P 13½×14 (*horiz*) or 14×13½ (*vert*).
492   75000 l.   Type **168** 25   20
493   200000 l.   Limestone rocks inside cave (*vert*) 70   75

169 Peace Dove and Map of Cyprus

170 Air Mail Envelope and Labels (35th anniv of Turkish Cypriot Posts)

(Des H. Billur)

1999 (20 July). *25th Anniv of Turkish Landings in Cyprus. T* **169** *and similar horiz designs. Multicoloured. W* **51** *(sideways). P* 13½×14.

494	150000 l. Type **169**	50	50
495	250000 l. Peace dove, map of Cyprus and Sun	75	75

(Des H. Billur)

1999 (12 Nov). *Anniversaries and Events. T* **170** *and similar horiz designs. Multicoloured. W* **51** *(sideways). P* 13½×14.

496	75000 l. Type **170**	15	20
497	125000 l. "125" and U.P.U emblem (125th anniv of U.P.U)	30	35
498	250000 l. Total eclipse of the Sun, August 1999	60	65
496/8	Set of 3	1·00	1·10

171 Turkish Gateway, Limassol

1999 (3 Dec). *Destruction of Turkish Buildings in Southern Cyprus. T* **171** *and similar grey-brown and orange-brown designs. W* **51** *(sideways on horiz designs). P* 14×13½ *(No.* 502) *or* 13½×14 *(others).*

499	75000 l. Type **171**	15	20
500	150000 l. Mosque, Evdim	35	40
501	210000 l. Bayraktar Mosque, Lefkosa	50	55
502	1000000 l. Kebir Mosque, Baf (*vert*)	2·50	2·75
499/502	Set of 4	3·50	3·75

STAMP BOOKLETS

Following the inauguration of the Turkish Cypriot postal service in 1974 several postmasters continued to use the covers previously supplied by the Cyprus Post Office in conjunction with Turkish Cypriot Posts issues.

1987 (30 June). *Europa. Modern Architecture. Black on bluish grey cover,* 61×50 *mm, showing Europa symbols. Pane attached by selvedge.*

SB1	500 l. booklet containing *se-tenant* pane of 4 (No. 210ab)	7·00

1989 (31 May). *Europa. Children's Games. Black on pale blue-green cover,* 62×48 *mm, showing Europa symbols. Pane attached by selvedge.*

SB2	3200 l. booklet containing *se-tenant* pane of 4 (No. 251ab)	7·50

Cyrenaica
see British Occupation of Italian Colonies

Dominica

CROWN COLONY

A British packet agency was operating on Dominica from about 1778, the date of the earliest known use of a postal marking. This was replaced by a branch office of the British G.P.O. which opened at Roseau on 8 May 1858. The stamps of Great Britain were used from that date until 1 May 1860, after which the colonial authorities assumed responsibility for the postal service. Until the introduction of Nos. 1/3 in 1874 No. CC1 and later handstamps were utilised.

For illustrations of handstamp and postmark types see BRITISH POST OFFICES ABROAD notes, following GREAT BRITAIN.

ROSEAU

CROWNED/CIRCLE HANDSTAMPS

CC1 CC **1** DOMINICA (Black or R.) (17.5.1845)
Price on cover £500
No. CC1 is also known struck in black on various adhesive stamps as late as 1883.

Stamps of GREAT BRITAIN cancelled "A 07" *as Type* **2**.

1858 to **1860**
Z1	1d. rose-red (1857), *perf* 14				£225
Z2	2d. blue (1858) (Plate No. 7)				£650
Z3	4d. rose (1857)				£275
Z4	6d. lilac (1856)				£275
Z5	1s. green				£1100

PRICES FOR STAMPS ON COVER TO 1945
Nos. 1/3	*from* × 25
No. 4	*from* × 40
No. 5	*from* × 100
No. 6	*from* × 40
Nos. 7/8	*from* × 100
No. 9	*from* × 40
Nos. 10/12	*from* × 15
Nos. 13/15	*from* × 100
No. 17	*from* × 50
Nos. 18/a	—
No. 19	*from* × 40
Nos. 20/5	*from* × 30
No. 26	—
Nos. 27/90	*from* × 5
No. 91	—
Nos. 92/8	*from* × 10
Nos. 99/109	*from* × 3
Nos. R1/3	*from* × 15
No. R4	*from* × 50
No. R6	*from* × 3

| 1 | | (2) | (3) | (4) |

(2) ½ (3) ½ (4) Half Penny

(Typo D.L.R.)

1874 (4 May). *Wmk Crown CC.* P 12½.
1	**1**	1d. lilac		£150	45.00
2		6d. green		£550	95.00
3		1s. dull magenta		£325	65.00

NCE NCE
Normal   Malformed "CE"
(R.10/6)

1877–79. *Wmk Crown CC.* P 14.
4	**1**	½d. olive-yellow (1879)		9.50	45.00
5		1d. lilac		4.50	2.00
		a. Bisected vert or diag (½d.) (on cover or card)		†	£1600
		w. Wmk inverted		55.00	
6		2½d. red-brown (1879)		£225	29.00
		w. Wmk inverted			
7		4d. blue (1879)		£110	2.50
		a. Malformed "CE" in "PENCE"		£1500	£225
8		6d. green (1879)		£150	20.00
9		1s. magenta		£120	48.00

1882 (25 Nov)–**83.** *No. 5 bisected vertically and surch.*
10	**2**	½ (d.), in *black*, on half 1d.		£150	35.00
		a. Surch inverted		£950	£800
		b. Surcharges *tête-bêche* (pair)		£1600	
11	**3**	½ (d.), in *red*, on half 1d. (12.82)		28.00	14.00
		a. Surch inverted		£950	£450
		c. Surch double		£1600	£650
12	**4**	½d., in *black*, on half 1d. (3.83)		50.00	20.00
		b. Surch double		£800	

Type **4** is found reading up or down.

1883–86. *Wmk Crown CA.* P 14.
13	**1**	½d. olive-yellow		2.00	9.00
14		1d. lilac (1886)		24.00	9.00
		a. Bisected (½d.) (on cover)		†	£1800
15		2½d. red-brown (1884)		£140	2.00
		w. Wmk inverted		£250	

Half   One
Penny   Penny

(5)   (6)

1886 (Mar). *Nos. 8 and 9 surch locally.*
17	**5**	½d. on 6d. green		4.00	3.50
18	**6**	1d. on 6d. green		£20000	£10000
		a. Thick bar (approx 1 mm)		†	£16000
19		1d. on 1s. magenta		14.00	16.00
		a. Surch double		£5000	£2750

It is believed that only two sheets of the 1d. on 6d. were surcharged. On one of these sheets the six stamps in the top row showed the thick bar variety, No. 18a.

1886–90. *Wmk Crown CA.* P 14.
20	**1**	½d. dull green		1.50	5.00
22		1d. rose (1887)		13.00	15.00
		a. *Deep carmine* (1889)		2.75	5.00
		aw. Wmk inverted		£110	
		b. Bisected (½d.) (on cover)		†	£1800
23		2½d. ultramarine (1888)		3.75	5.00
24		4d. grey		2.25	4.00
		a. Malformed "CE" in "PENCE"		£160	£200
25		6d. orange (1888)		6.00	35.00
26		1s. dull magenta (1890)		£150	£250
20/6			*Set of* 6	£150	£275
20/5 Optd "Specimen"			*Set of* 5	£225	

The stamps of Dominica were superseded by the general issue for Leeward Islands on 31 October 1890, but the sets following were in concurrent use with the stamps inscribed "LEEWARD ISLANDS" until 31 December 1939, when the island came under the administration of the Windward Islands.

9 "Roseau from the   **10**
Sea" (Lt. Caddy)

(T **9** to **11** typo D.L.R.)

1903 (1 Sept)–**07.** *Wmk Crown CC* (*sideways* on T* **9**). *Ordinary paper.* P 14.
27	**9**	½d. green and grey-green		3.75	2.25
		a. Chalk-surfaced paper (1906)		11.00	16.00
28		1d. grey and red		7.50	75
		a. Chalk-surfaced paper (1906)		25.00	6.00
29		2d. green and brown		2.50	4.50
		a. Chalk-surfaced paper (1906)		24.00	35.00
30		2½d. grey and bright blue		4.50	3.75
		a. Chalk-surfaced paper (3.9.07)		18.00	35.00
31		3d. dull purple and grey-black		8.00	3.25
		a. Chalk-surfaced paper (1906)		30.00	28.00
32		6d. grey and chestnut		4.25	17.00
33		1s. magenta and grey-green		25.00	38.00
		a. Chalk-surfaced paper (1906)		70.00	£140
34		2s. grey-black and purple		25.00	24.00
35		2s. 6d. grey-green and maize		17.00	75.00
36	**10**	5s. black and brown		90.00	£140
27/36			*Set of* 10	£170	£275
27/36 Optd "Specimen"			*Set of* 10	£130	

*The normal sideways watermark shows Crown to right of CC, *as seen from the back of the stamp.*

1907–08. *Wmk Mult Crown CA* (*sideways* on T* **9**). *Chalk-surfaced paper.* P 14.
37	**9**	½d. green		2.00	2.75
38		1d. grey and red		2.00	30
39		2d. green and brown		5.00	15.00
40		2½d. grey and bright blue		4.50	19.00
41		3d. dull purple and grey-black		4.00	13.00
42		6d. black and chestnut		48.00	80.00
43		1s. magenta and grey-green (1908)		3.75	50.00
44		2s. grey-black and purple (1908)		22.00	32.00
45		2s. 6d. grey-green and maize (1908)		22.00	60.00
46	**10**	5s. black and brown (1908)		60.00	60.00
37/46			*Set of* 10	£160	£300

*The normal sideways watermark shows Crown to right of CA, *as seen from the back of the stamp.*
Examples of Nos. 27/36 and 37/46 are known showing a forged Gen. Post Office Dominica postmark dated "JU 1 11".

WAR TAX

ONE HALFPENNY

11   (12)

1908–21. *Wmk Mult Crown CA* (*sideways* on T* **9**), *Chalk-surfaced paper* (3d., 6d., 1s.). P 14.
47	**9**	½d. blue-green		3.00	3.50
		aw. Wmk Crown to left of CA		2.50	2.75
		ay. Wmk sideways inverted and reversed			
		b. *Deep green* (wmk Crown to left of CA) (1918)		3.50	1.75
48		1d. carmine-red		3.00	30
		aw. Wmk Crown to left of CA		3.50	40
		b. *Scarlet* (1916)		1.50	40
		bw. Wmk Crown to left of CA		1.00	50

49	**9**	2d. grey (1909)		4.00	12.00
		aw. Wmk Crown to left of CA		3.50	16.00
		b. *Slate* (wmk Crown to left of CA) (1918)		3.50	12.00
50		2½d. blue		8.50	6.00
		aw. Wmk Crown to left of CA		—	9.00
		b. *Bright blue* (1918)		5.00	9.00
		bw. Wmk Crown to left of CA		6.00	13.00
51		3d. purple/*yellow* (1909)		3.00	4.25
		a. Ordinary paper (wmk Crown to left of CA) (1912)		3.00	4.50
		ab. *On pale yellow* (1920)		8.50	13.00
52		6d. dull and bright purple (1909)		10.00	15.00
		a. Ordinary paper. *Dull purple* (wmk Crown to left of CA) (1915)		3.50	18.00
53		1s. black/*green* (1910)		2.75	2.75
		a. Ordinary paper (wmk Crown to left of CA) (1912) (Optd S. (in red) £35)		3.00	4.00
53b		2s. purple and deep blue/*blue* (wmk Crown to left of CA) (1919)		25.00	75.00
53c		2s. 6d. black and red/*blue* (wmk Crown to left of CA) (1921)		25.00	85.00
54	**11**	5s. red and green/*yellow* (1914)		55.00	80.00
47/54			*Set of* 10	£110	£250
48/54 Optd "Specimen" (1s. optd in black)			*Set of* 9	£180	

*The normal sideways watermark shows Crown to right of CA, *as seen from the back of the stamp.*

1916 (Sept). *No. 47b surch with T* **12** *by De La Rue.*
55	**9**	½d. on ½d. deep green (R.)		10	75
		a. Small "O" in "ONE"		6.50	16.00

No. 55a occurs on ten stamps within each sheet of 60.

1918 (18 Mar). *No. 47b optd with T* **12** *locally, from D.L.R. plate, but with* "ONE HALF-PENNY" *blanked out.*
56	**9**	½d. deep green (Blk.)		2.00	5.50

The blanking out of the surcharge was not completely successful so that it almost always appears as an albino to a greater or lesser extent.

WAR TAX
(14)

1918 (June)–**19.** *Nos. 47b and 51a optd with T* **14** *by De La Rue.*
57	**9**	½d. deep green		10	30
		x. Wmk reversed			
58		3d. purple/*yellow* (R.) (1919)		65	3.75

WAR TAX   1½D.
=1½D.=

(15)   Short Fraction Bar (R.6/4)

1919. *As No. 50aw, but colour changed, surch with T* **15** *by De La Rue.*
59	**9**	1½d. on 2½d. orange (R.)		10	55
		a. Short fraction bar		7.50	32.00
		b. "C" and "A" missing from wmk			

No. 59b shows the "C" omitted from one impression with the "A" missing from the next one to the left (as seen from the back of the stamp). The "C" is badly distorted in the second watermark.

1920 (1 June). *As No. 59, but without* "WAR TAX".
60	**9**	1½d. on 2½d. orange (Blk.)		2.00	4.00
		a. Short fraction bar		55.00	70.00
55/60 Optd "Specimen"			*Set of* 6	£170	

1921–22. *Wmk Mult Script CA* (*sideways**). *Chalk-surfaced paper* (6d.). P 14.
62	**9**	½d. blue-green		2.00	13.00
63		1d. carmine-red		1.25	3.50
		w. Wmk Crown to right of CA		—	13.00
64		1½d. orange		2.75	10.00
65		2d. grey		2.75	3.25
66		2½d. bright blue		1.75	8.50
67		6d. purple		2.50	35.00
69		2s. purple and blue/*blue* (1922)		32.00	75.00
70		2s. 6d. black and red/*blue*		32.00	75.00
62/70			*Set of* 8	70.00	£200
62/70 Optd "Specimen"			*Set of* 8	£140	

*The normal sideways watermark shows Crown to left of CA, *as seen from the back of the stamp.*
The 1½d. has figures of value, in the lower corner and no ornamentation below words of value.

16

(Typo D.L.R.)

1923 (1 Mar)–**33.** *Chalk-surfaced paper.* P 14.
(a) *Wmk Mult Script CA* (*sideways**)
71	**16**	½d. black and green		1.50	30
72		1d. black and bright violet		1.75	1.40
73		1d. black and scarlet (1933)		9.00	90
74		1½d. black and scarlet		2.25	65
75		1½d. black and red-brown (1933)		9.00	60
76		2d. black and grey		1.75	40
77		2½d. black and orange-yellow		1.00	8.50
78		2½d. black and ultramarine (1927)		3.75	1.75
79		3d. black and ultramarine		1.00	11.00
80		3d. black and red/*yellow* (1927)		1.25	1.00
81		4d. black and brown		2.00	4.50
82		6d. black and bright magenta		3.50	6.00
83		1s. black/*emerald*		2.00	2.75
84		2s. black and blue/*blue*		8.00	15.00
85		2s. 6d. black and red/*blue*		18.00	17.00
86		3s. black and purple/*yellow* (1927)		9.00	18.00
87		4s. black and red/*emerald*		10.00	20.00
88		5s. black and green/*yellow* (1927)		22.00	42.00

(b) Wmk Mult Crown CA (sideways*)

89	16	3s. black and purple/yellow	..	..	4·00	60·00
90		5s. black and green/yellow			9·00	45·00
91		£1 black and purple/red			£225	£325
71/91				Set of 21	£300	£500
71/91 Optd/Perf "Specimen"				Set of 21	£350	

*The normal sideways watermark shows Crown to left of CA, as seen from the back of the stamp.

Examples of most values are known showing a forged G.P.O. Dominica postmark dated "MY 19 27".

1935 (6 May). *Silver Jubilee. As Nos. 91/4 of Antigua.*

92		1d. deep blue and carmine	..	..	75	20
	f.	Diagonal line by turret			35·00	
	h.	Dot by flagstaff			50·00	
93		1½d. ultramarine and grey	..	..	1·50	55
	f.	Diagonal line by turret			50·00	
	h.	Dot by flagstaff			75·00	
94		2½d. brown and deep blue			1·50	2·25
95		1s. slate and purple			1·50	3·25
	h.	Dot by flagstaff			£120	
	i.	Dash by turret			£120	
92/5				Set of 4	4·75	5·50
92/5 Perf "Specimen"				Set of 4	75·00	

For illustrations of plate varieties see Catalogue Introduction.

1937 (12 May). *Coronation. As Nos. 95/7 of Antigua.* P 11×11½.

96		1d. carmine	..	..	40	10
97		1½d. yellow-brown	..	..	40	10
98		2½d. blue			60	1·25
96/8				Set of 3	1·25	1·25
96/8 Perf "Specimen"				Set of 3	55·00	

17 Fresh Water Lake   **18** Layou River

(Recess Waterlow)

1938 (15 Aug)–**47**. T **17/18** *and similar horiz designs. Wmk Mult Script CA.* P 12½.

99	17	½d. brown and green	..	..	10	15
100	18	1d. grey and scarlet	..		20	20
101	–	1½d. green and purple	..		30	70
102	–	2d. carmine and grey-black	..		50	1·00
103	–	2½d. purple and bright blue	..		4·00	1·75
	a.	Purple & bright ultramarine (8.42)			20	1·25
104	18	3d. olive-green and brown			30	40
104a	–	3½d. ultramarine and purple (15.10.47)			1·75	1·25
105	17	6d. emerald-green and violet			1·75	1·00
105a	–	7d. green and yellow-brown (15.10.47)			1·75	1·25
106	–	1s. violet and olive-green			2·25	1·00
106a	18	2s. slate and purple (15.10.47)			4·50	8·00
107	17	2s. 6d. black and vermilion			12·00	4·75
108	18	5s. light blue and sepia			7·50	8·00
108a	–	10s. black and brown-orange (15.10.47)			12·00	14·00
99/108a				Set of 14	40·00	38·00

Designs:–1½d., 2½d., 3½d. Picking limes; 2d., 1s., 10s. Boiling Lake.

21 King George VI

(Photo Harrison)

1940 (15 Apr)–**42**. *Wmk Mult Script CA. Chalk-surfaced paper.* P 15×14.

109	21	¼d. chocolate	..	..	60	15
	a.	Ordinary paper (1942)			10	10
99/109 Perf "Specimen"				Set of 15	£225	

1946 (14 Oct). *Victory. As Nos. 110/11 of Antigua.*

110		1d. carmine	..	..	20	10
111		3½d. blue			20	10
110/11 Perf "Specimen"				Set of 2	48·00	

1948 (1 Dec). *Royal Silver Wedding. As Nos. 112/13 of Antigua.*

112		1d. scarlet	..	..	15	10
113		10s. red-brown			8·00	21·00

(New Currency. 100 cents = 1 B.W.I., later East Caribbean dollar)

1949 (10 Oct). *75th Anniv of Universal Postal Union. As Nos. 114/17 of Antigua.*

114		3c. blue	..	..	15	15
115		6c. brown	..	..	1·00	2·00
116		12c. purple	..	..	45	1·00
117		24c. olive	..	..	30	30
114/17				Set of 4	1·75	3·00

1951 (16 Feb). *Inauguration of B.W.I. University College. As Nos. 118/19 of Antigua.*

118		3c. yellow-green and reddish violet	..		50	45
119		12c. deep green and carmine	..		75	30

22 King George VI   **23** Drying Cocoa

(Photo Harrison (½ c.). Recess B.W. (others))

1951 (1 July). T **22** *and designs as* T **23**. *Wmk Mult Script CA. Chalk-surfaced paper* (½ c.). P 15×14 (½ c.), 13½×13 ($2.40), 13×13½ (others).

120		½ c. chocolate	..	..	10	15
121		1 c. black and vermilion	..	..	10	30
	b.	"A" of "CA" missing from wmk			£500	
	c.	"JA" for "CA" in wmk			£500	
122		2 c. red-brown and deep green			10	20
	a.	"C" of "CA" missing from wmk			†	—
	b.	"A" of "CA" missing from wmk			£600	
123		3 c. green and reddish violet			15	70
	a.	"C" of "CA" missing from wmk			£600	
	c.	"JA" for "CA" in wmk			£500	
124		4 c. brown-orange and sepia			30	80
	a.	"C" of "CA" missing from wmk			£600	
	b.	"A" of "CA" missing from wmk			£600	
125		5 c. black and carmine			85	30
	a.	"C" of "CA" missing from wmk			£800	
	b.	"A" of "CA" missing from wmk			£800	
126		6 c. olive and chestnut			90	30
	a.	"C" of "CA" missing from wmk			£1000	
	b.	"A" of "CA" missing from wmk			£1000	
127		8 c. blue-green and blue	..		60	60
	a.	"A" of "CA" missing from wmk			£1200	
128		12 c. black and bright green			45	1·25
	a.	"C" of "CA" missing from wmk			£1200	
129		14 c. blue and violet			95	1·25
	a.	"C" of "CA" missing from wmk			£1200	
	c.	"JA" for "CA" in wmk			†	—
130		24 c. reddish violet and rose-carmine			75	30
	c.	"C" of "CA" missing from wmk			£1200	
131		48 c. bright green and red-orange			3·00	6·50
	a.	"C" of "CA" missing from wmk			£1200	
	b.	"A" of "CA" missing from wmk			£1200	
	c.	"JA" for "CA" in wmk			£1200	
132		60 c. carmine and black	..		3·00	5·00
	a.	"JA" for "CA" in wmk			£800	
133		$1.20, emerald and black	..		4·00	6·00
	a.	"C" of "CA" missing from wmk			£1400	
	b.	"A" of "CA" missing from wmk			£1400	
134		$2.40, orange and black	..		3·00	29·00
120/34				Set of 15	30·00	45·00

Designs: *Horiz*—2 c., 60 c. Making Carib baskets; 3 c., 48 c. Lime plantation; 4 c. Picking oranges; 5 c. Bananas; 6 c. Botanical Gardens; 8 c. Drying vanilla beans; 12 c., $1.20, Fresh Water Lake; 14 c. Layou River; 24 c. Boiling Lake. *Vert*—$2.40, Picking oranges.

Examples of Nos. 121b, 122b, 124b, 125b, 126b, 129b, 131b and 133b show traces of the *left leg* of the "A", as seen from the back of the stamp.

Nos. 121c, 123c, 129c and 131c may represent an attempt to repair the missing "C" variety.

NEW CONSTITUTION 1951

(34)

1951 (15 Oct). *New Constitution. Nos. 123, 125, 127 and 129 optd with* T **34** *by B.W.*

135		3 c. emerald and reddish violet	..		15	70
136		5 c. black and carmine	..		15	70
	a.	"JA" for "CA" in wmk			£700	
137		8 c. blue-green and blue (R.)	..		15	15
	a.	"JA" for "CA" in wmk			£900	
138		14 c. blue and violet (R.)	..		15	20
	b.	"A" of "CA" missing from wmk			£900	
135/8				Set of 4	55	1·60

1953 (2 June). *Coronation. As No. 120 of Antigua.*

139		2 c. black and deep green	..		20	10

35 Queen Elizabeth II   **36** Mat Making

37 Picking Oranges   **38** Canoe Making

(Photo Harrison (½ c.). Recess B.W. (others))

1954 (1 Oct)–**62**. *Designs previously used for King George VI issue, but with portrait of Queen Elizabeth II as in* T **35/8**. *Wmk Mult Script CA.* P 15×14 (½ c.), 13½×13 ($2.40), 13×13½ (others).

140	35	½ c. brown	..	..	10	30
141	–	1 c. black and vermilion	..		10	10
142	–	2 c. chocolate and myrtle-green	..		55	1·00
	a.	Chocolate and grey-green (13.3.62)			6·50	7·00
143	–	3 c. green and purple	..		1·25	30
144	36	3 c. black and carmine (15.10.57)			3·25	2·00
145	37	4 c. brown-orange and sepia	..		20	10
146	–	5 c. black and carmine-red	..		1·25	50
147	38	5 c. light green & sepia-brown (15.10.57)			10·00	90
	a.	Blue and sepia (13.3.62)			18·00	6·00
148	–	6 c. bronze-green and red-brown			40	10
149	–	8 c. deep green and deep blue			30	10
150	–	10 c. green and brown (15.10.57)			5·00	2·00
	a.	Green and deep brown (17.7.62)			7·00	90
151	–	12 c. black and emerald			50	10
152	–	14 c. blue and purple	..		30	10
153	–	24 c. purple and carmine	..		40	10
154	–	48 c. green and red-orange	..		1·40	6·50

155	36	48 c. deep brown and violet (15.10.57)			1·25	1·00
156	–	60 c. rose-red and black	..		1·00	1·50
157	–	$1.20, emerald and black	..		16·00	6·50
158	–	$2.40, yellow-orange and black	..		16·00	14·00
140/58				Set of 19	55·00	30·00

Designs: *Horiz*—1 c. Drying cocoa; 2 c., 60 c. Making Carib baskets; 3 c. (No. 143), 48 c. (No. 154) Lime plantation; 5 c. (No. 146) Bananas; 6 c. Botanical Gardens; 8 c. Drying vanilla beans; 10 c. Bananas (different); 12 c., $1.20, Fresh Water Lake; 14 c. Layou River; 24 c. Boiling Lake. *Vert*—$2.40, Picking oranges.

1958 (22 Apr). *Inauguration of British Caribbean Federation. As Nos. 135/7 of Antigua.*

159		3 c. deep green	..	..	45	10
160		6 c. blue	..	..	60	1·25
161		12 c. scarlet	..	..	70	15
159/61				Set of 3	1·60	1·40

40 Seashore at Rosalie   **48** Traditional Costume

Two types of 14 c.

I. Eyes of model looking straight ahead.
II. Eyes looking to her right.

(Des S. Scott. Photo Harrison)

1963 (16 May)–**65**. T **40, 48** *and similar designs. W w* **12** (upright). P 14×14½ (vert) or 14½×14 (horiz).

162		1 c. green, blue and sepia	..	..	10	85
163		2 c. bright blue	..	..	30	10
	w.	Wmk inverted			—	10·00
164		3 c. blackish brown and blue	..		90	1·00
165		4 c. green, sepia and slate-violet			10	10
166		5 c. magenta	..		30	10
167		6 c. green, bistre and violet			10	20
168		8 c. green, sepia and black			30	10
169		10 c. sepia and pink			10	10
170		12 c. green, blue and blackish brown			60	10
171		14 c. multicoloured (I)			70	10
171a		14 c. multicoloured (II) (1.4.65)			2·50	2·25
172		15 c. yellow, green and brown			1·00	10
	w.	Wmk inverted			—	18·00
173		24 c. multicoloured			8·00	20
174		48 c. green, blue and black			75	40
175		60 c. orange, green and black			1·00	70
176		$1.20, multicoloured	..		6·50	90
177		$2.40, blue, turquoise and brown			3·25	2·50
178		$4.80, green, blue and brown			9·00	20·00
162/78				Set of 17	29·00	23·00

Designs: *Vert*—2 c., 5 c. Queen Elizabeth II; 24 c. Imperial Amazon; $2.40, Trafalgar Falls; $4.80, Coconut Palm. *Horiz*—3 c. Sailing canoe; 4 c. Sulphur springs; 6 c. Road making; 8 c. Dug-out canoe; 10 c. Crapaud (toad); 12 c. Scott's Head; 15 c. Bananas; 48 c. Goodwill; 60 c. Cocoa tree; $1.20, Coat of Arms. See also Nos. 200/4.

1963 (4 June). *Freedom from Hunger. As No. 146 of Antigua.*

179		15 c. reddish violet	..	..	15	10

1963 (2 Sept). *Red Cross Centenary. As Nos. 147/8 of Antigua.*

180		5 c. red and black	..	..	20	30
181		15 c. red and blue	..	..	40	55

1964 (23 April). *400th Birth Anniv of William Shakespeare. As No. 164 of Antigua.*

182		15 c. bright purple	..	..	10	10
	w.	Wmk inverted			1·50	

1965 (17 May). *I.T.U. Centenary. As Nos. 166/7 of Antigua.*

183		2 c. light emerald and blue	..		10	10
184		48 c. turquoise-blue and grey	..		45	20

1965 (25 Oct). *International Co-operation Year. As Nos. 168/9 of Antigua.*

185		1 c. reddish purple and turquoise-green	..		10	20
186		15 c. deep bluish green and lavender	..		35	10

1966 (24 Jan). *Churchill Commemoration. As Nos. 170/3 of Antigua.*

187		1 c. new blue	..	..	10	60
	a.	Gold omitted			£600	
188		5 c. deep green	..	..	15	10
189		15 c. brown	..	..	30	10
190		24 c. bluish violet	..	..	40	20
187/90				Set of 4	75	85

No. 187a occured on the bottom row of a sheet.
An example of the 1 c. is known showing the gold face value printed double.

1966 (4 Feb). *Royal Visit. As Nos. 174/5 of Antigua.*

191		5 c. black and ultramarine	..		1·00	30
192		15 c. black and magenta	..		1·50	30

1966 (1 July). *World Cup Football Championships. As Nos. 176/7 of Antigua.*

193		5 c. violet, yellow-green, lake & yellow-brown			25	15
194		24 c. chocolate, blue-green, lake & yell-brown			85	15

1966 (20 Sept). *Inauguration of W.H.O. Headquarters, Geneva. As Nos. 178/9 of Antigua.*

195		5 c. black, yellow-green and light blue			15	15
196		24 c. black, light purple and yellow-brown			30	15

1966 (1 Dec). *20th Anniv of U.N.E.S.C.O. As Nos. 196/8 of Antigua.*

197		5 c. slate-violet, red, yellow and orange	..		20	15
198		15 c. orange-yellow, violet and deep olive			50	10
199		24 c. black, bright purple and orange			60	15
197/9				Set of 3	1·10	30

1966 (30 Dec)–**67**. *As Nos. 165, 167/9 and 172 but wmk w 12 sideways.*
200	4 c. green, sepia and slate-violet (16.5.67)		1·25	90
201	6 c. green, bistre and violet		20	15
202	8 c. green, sepia and black		40	10
203	10 c. sepia and pink (16.5.67)		70	10
204	15 c. yellow, green and brown (16.5.67)		70	10
200/4		Set of 5	3·00	1·25

ASSOCIATED STATEHOOD

56 Children of Three Races

(Des and photo Harrison)

1967 (2 Nov). *National Day. T 56 and similar horiz designs. Multicoloured. W w 12. P 14½.*
205	5 c. Type 56		10	10
206	10 c. The *Santa Maria* and motto		40	15
207	15 c. Hands holding motto ribbon		15	15
208	24 c. Belaire dancing		15	20
205/8		Set of 4	70	45

57 John F. Kennedy

(Des G. Vasarhelyi. Litho D.L.R.)

1968 (20 Apr). *Human Rights Year. T 57 and similar horiz designs. Multicoloured. W w 12 (sideways). P 14 × 13½.*
209	1 c. Type 57		10	10
210	10 c. Cecil A. E. Rawle		10	10
211	a. Imperf (pair)		90·00	
211	12 c. Pope John XXIII		50	15
212	48 c. Florence Nightingale		35	25
213	60 c. Albert Schweitzer		35	25
209/13		Set of 5	1·25	75

ASSOCIATED STATEHOOD (58)   **NATIONAL DAY 3 NOVEMBER 1968** (59)

1968 (8 July). *Associated Statehood. As Nos. 162, 170 and 174, but wmk sideways, or Nos. 163/4, 166, 170, 171a, 173, 175/8 and 200/4 optd with T 58.*
214	1 c. green, blue and sepia (Sil.)		10	10
215	2 c. bright blue (Sil.)		10	10
216	3 c. blackish brown and blue (Sil.)		10	10
217	4 c. green, sepia and slate-violet (Sil.)		10	10
218	5 c. magenta (Sil.)		10	10
219	6 c. green, bistre and violet		10	10
220	8 c. green, sepia and black		10	10
221	10 c. sepia and pink (Sil.)		55	10
222	12 c. green, blue and blackish brown (Sil.) (wmk sideways)		10	10
	a. Wmk upright		10	10
224	14 c. multicoloured (II) (Sil.)		10	10
225	15 c. yellow, green and brown (Sil.)		10	10
226	24 c. multicoloured (Sil.)		3·50	10
227	48 c. green, bl & blk (Sil.) (wmk sideways)		55	1·25
	a. Wmk upright		40	75
228	60 c. orange, green and black		90	70
229	$1.20, multicoloured		1·00	2·25
230	$2.40, blue, turquoise and brown (Sil.)		1·25	2·25
231	$4.80, green, blue and brown (Sil.)		1·25	5·00
214/31		Set of 17	8·50	10·50

The 2, 5, 6, 8 and 10 c. values exist with PVA gum as well as gum arabic.

1968 (3 Nov). *National Day. Nos. 162/4, 171 and 176 optd with T 59.*
232	1 c. green, blue and sepia		10	10
	a. Opt inverted		45·00	
	b. Opt double			
233	2 c. bright blue		10	10
	a. Opt double		30·00	
234	3 c. blackish brown and blue		10	10
	a. Opt inverted		30·00	
235	14 c. multicoloured (I)		10	10
	a. Opt double		70·00	
236	$1.20, multicoloured		55	40
	a. Opt double		30·00	
	b. Vert pair, one opt omitted, other opt double		£150	
232/6		Set of 5	60	40

The above set was put on sale by the New York Agency on 1 November but not sold locally until the 3 November.

60 Forward shooting at Goal

(Des M. Shamir (1 c., 60 c.), K. Plowitz (5 c., 48 c.). Litho B.W.)

1968 (25 Nov). *Olympic Games, Mexico. T 60 and similar horiz designs. Multicoloured. P 11½ × 11.*
237	1 c. Type 60		10	10
	a. Horiz pair. Nos. 237/8			
238	1 c. Goalkeeper trying to save goal		10	10
239	5 c. Swimmers about to dive		10	10
	a. Horiz pair. Nos. 239/40			
240	5 c. Swimmers diving		10	10
241	48 c. Javelin-throwing		15	15
	a. Horiz pair. Nos. 241/2		30	30
242	48 c. Hurdling		15	15
243	60 c. Basketball		90	25
	a. Horiz pair. Nos. 243/4		1·75	50
244	60 c. Basketball players		90	25
237/44		Set of 8	2·00	85

Nos. 237/44 were issued in sheets of 40 containing two panes of *se-tenant* pairs.

61 "The Small Cowper Madonna" (Raphael)   **62** "Venus and Adonis" (Rubens)

(Photo Delrieu, Paris)

1968 (23 Dec). *Christmas. P 12½ × 12.*
245	61	5 c. multicoloured	10	10

Three other values were issued: 12 c. "Madonna of the Chair" (Raphael); 24 c. "Madonna and Child" (Italo-Byzantine, XVI century); $1.20 "Madonna and Child" (Byzantine, XIII century). Sizes as T 61.

These only come from miniature sheets, containing two *se-tenant* strips of each value.

(Litho D.L.R.)

1969 (30 Jan). *20th Anniv of World Health Organisation. Paintings. T 62 and similar vert designs. Multicoloured. W w 12. P 15.*
246	5 c. Type 62		20	10
247	15 c. "The Death of Socrates" (J.-L. David)		30	10
248	24 c. "Christ and the Pilgrims of Emmaus" (Velasquez)		30	10
249	50 c. "Pilate washing his Hands" (Rembrandt)		50	40
246/9		Set of 4	1·10	50

66 Picking Oranges   **67** "Strength in Unity" Emblem and Fruit Trees

(Des K. Plowitz. Litho Harrison)

1969 (10 Mar). *Tourism. T 66 and similar horiz designs. Multicoloured. W w 12. P 14½.*
250	10 c. Type 66		15	10
	a. Horiz pair. Nos. 250/1		30	15
251	10 c. Woman, child and ocean scene		15	10
252	12 c. Fort Yeoung Hotel		50	10
	a. Horiz pair. Nos. 252/3		1·00	20
253	12 c. Red-necked Amazons		50	10
254	24 c. Calypso band		30	15
	a. Horiz pair. Nos. 254/5		60	30
	w. Wmk inverted		30·00	
255	24 c. Women dancing		30	15
	w. Wmk inverted		30·00	
256	48 c. Underwater life		30	25
	a. Horiz pair. Nos. 256/7		60	50
257	48 c. Skin-diver and turtle		30	25
250/7		Set of 8	2·25	1·00

Each denomination was printed *se-tenant* throughout the sheet. The 12 c. values are on cream coloured paper.

(Litho B.W.)

1969 (July). *First Anniv of CARIFTA (Caribbean Free Trade Area). T 67 and similar horiz designs. Multicoloured. P 13½ × 13.*
258	5 c. Type 67		10	10
259	8 c. Hawker Siddeley H.S.748 aircraft, emblem and island		25	20
260	12 c. Chart of Caribbean Sea and emblem		25	25
261	24 c. Steamship unloading, tug and emblem		30	25
258/61		Set of 4	75	70

71 "Spinning"   **72** Mahatma Gandhi Weaving and Clock Tower, Westminster

(Litho B.W.)

1969 (10 July). *50th Anniv of International Labour Organisation. T 71 and similar vert designs showing paintings of people at work by J. Millet, bordered by flags of member-nations of the I.L.O. Multicoloured. No wmk. P 13 × 13½.*
262	15 c. Type 71		10	10
263	30 c. "Threshing"		15	15
264	38 c. "Flax-pulling"		15	15
262/4		Set of 3	30	30

(Des G. Vasarhelyi. Litho Format)

1969 (20 Oct). *Birth Centenary of Mahatma Gandhi. T 72 and similar horiz designs. Multicoloured. P 14½.*
265	6 c. Type 72		30	10
266	38 c. Gandhi, Nehru and Mausoleum		50	15
267	$1.20, Gandhi and Taj Mahal		60	75
265/7		Set of 3	1·25	90

Nos. 265/7 are incorrectly inscribed "Ghandi".

75 "Saint Joseph"

(Des G. Vasarhelyi. Litho Govt Printer, Jerusalem)

1969 (3 Nov). *National Day. Stained Glass Windows. T 75 and similar vert designs. Multicoloured. P 14.*
268	6 c. Type 75		10	10
269	8 c. "Saint John"		10	10
270	12 c. "Saint Peter"		10	10
271	60 c. "Saint Paul"		30	50
268/71		Set of 4	40	60

Nos. 268/71 were printed in sheets of 16 (4 × 4) containing 12 stamps and four printed labels in the top row. The labels each contain two lines of a patriotic poem by W. O. M. Pond, the first letter from each line spelling "DOMINICA".

79 Queen Elizabeth II   **80** Purple-throated Carib and Flower

81 Government Headquarters

82 Coat of Arms

(Photo D.L.R.)

1969 (26 Nov)–**72**. *T 79/82 and similar horiz designs. Multicoloured. W 41 of Singapore (Half-check Pattern) (60 c. to $4.80) or no wmk (others). Chalk-surfaced paper. P 13½×14 (½ c.), 14×13½ (1 to 50 c.) or 14 (60 c. to $4.80).*
272	½ c. Type 79		10	1·75
	a. Glazed paper (1972)		30	80
273	1 c. Type 80		30	1·75
	a. Glazed paper (1972)		1·50	90

274	2 c. Poinsettia	.. ..	15	10
	a. Glazed paper (1972)	.. ..	50	20
275	3 c. Red-necked Pigeon	..	2·25	2·25
	a. Glazed paper (1972)	..	2·00	90
276	4 c. Imperial Amazon	..	2·25	2·25
	a. Glazed paper (1972)	..	2·00	80
277	5 c. *Battus polydamas* (butterfly)		2·25	75
	a. Glazed paper (1972)	..	2·00	90
278	6 c. *Dryas julia* (butterfly)	..	2·25	2·50
	a. Glazed paper (1972)	..	2·00	2·50
279	8 c. Shipping Bananas	..	20	10
	a. Glazed paper (1972)	..	40	30
280	10 c. Portsmouth Harbour	..	20	10
	a. Glazed paper (1972)	..	35	20
281	12 c. Copra processing plant	..	20	10
	a. Glazed paper (1972)	..	35	20
282	15 c. Straw workers	..	20	10
	a. Glazed paper (1972)	..	35	25
283	25 c. Timber plant	..	30	10
	a. Glazed paper (1972)	..	40	25
284	30 c. Pumice mine	..	1·50	90
	a. Glazed paper (1972)	..	1·50	70
285	38 c. Grammar school and playing field		8·00	1·75
	a. Glazed paper (1972)	..	8·50	14·00
286	50 c. Roseau Cathedral	..	50	45
	a. Glazed paper (1972)	..	80	80
287	60 c. Type 81	..	55	1·50
288	$1.20, Melville Hall Airport (40×27 *mm*)		1·00	1·75
289	$2.40, Type 82	..	1·00	4·00
290	$4.80, Type 79 (26×39 *mm*)		1·75	7·00
272/90		Set of 19	21·00	25·00
272a/86a		Set of 15	21·00	21·00

99 "Virgin and Child with St. John" (Perugino)

101 Astronaut's First Step onto the Moon

(Des G. Vasarhelyi. Litho B.W.)

1969 (19 Dec). *Christmas. Paintings. T* **99** *and similar vert designs. Multicoloured. P* 14 × 14½.

291	6 c. "Virgin and Child with St. John" (Lippi)		10	10
292	10 c. "Holy Family with the Lamb" (Raphael)		10	10
293	15 c. Type **99**		10	10
294	$1.20, "Madonna of the Rose Hedge" (Botticelli)		35	40
291/4		Set of 4	35	40
MS295	89 × 76 mm. Nos. 293/4. Imperf		75	90

(Des G. Vasarhelyi. Photo Banknote Printing Office, Helsinki)

1970 (6 Feb*). *Moon Landing. T* **101** *and similar horiz designs. Multicoloured. P* 12½.

296	½ c. Type **101**		10	10
297	5 c. Scientific Experiment on the Moon, and Flag		15	10
298	8 c. Astronauts collecting Rocks		15	10
299	30 c. Module over the Moon		30	15
300	50 c. Moon Plaque		40	25
301	60 c. Astronauts		40	30
296/301		Set of 6	1·25	80
MS302	116 × 112 mm. Nos. 298/301. Imperf		2·00	2·00

*This is the date of release in Dominica, but the above were released by the Philatelic Agency in the U.S.A. on 2 February.

107 Giant Green Turtle

(Des G. Drummond. Litho Kyodo Printing Co, Tokyo)

1970 (7 Sept). *Flora and Fauna. T* **107** *and similar horiz designs. Multicoloured. P* 13.

303	6 c. Type **107**		50	20
304	24 c. Atlantic Flyingfish		60	40
305	38 c. Anthurium lily		70	65
306	60 c. Imperial and Red-necked Amazons		3·25	5·50
303/6		Set of 4	4·50	6·00
MS307	160×111 mm. Nos. 303/6		5·50	6·00

108 18th-Century National Costume

109 Scrooge and Marley's Ghost

(Des G. Drummond from local designs. Litho Questa)

1970 (30 Oct). *National Day. T* **108** *and similar horiz designs. Multicoloured. P* 14.

308	5 c. Type **108**		10	10
309	8 c. Carib Basketry		10	10
310	$1 Flag and Chart of Dominica		30	40
308/10		Set of 3	30	40
MS311	150 × 85 mm. Nos. 308/10 plus three labels		50	1·40

(Des R. Granger Barrett. Litho Questa)

1970 (23 Nov). *Christmas and Charles Dickens' Death Centenary. T* **109** *and similar vert designs showing scenes from "A Christmas Carol". Multicoloured. P* 14 × 14½.

312	2 c. Type **109**		10	10
313	15 c. Fezziwig's Ball		20	10
314	24 c. Scrooge and his Nephew's Party		20	10
315	$1.20, Scrooge and the Ghost of Christmas Present		65	60
312/15		Set of 4	1·00	70
MS316	142 × 87 mm. Nos. 312/15		1·00	3·25

110 "The Doctor" (Sir Luke Fildes)

(Des G. Vasarhelyi. Litho Questa)

1970 (28 Dec). *Centenary of British Red Cross. T* **110** *and similar horiz designs. Multicoloured. P* 14½ × 14.

317	8 c. Type **110**		10	10
318	10 c. Hands and Red Cross		10	10
319	15 c. Flag of Dominica and Red Cross Emblem		15	10
320	50 c. "The Sick Child" (E. Munch)		50	35
317/20		Set of 4	75	40
MS321	108 × 76 mm. Nos. 317/20		85	2·50

111 Marigot School

(Des G. Vasarhelyi. Litho Questa)

1971 (1 Mar). *International Education Year (1970). T* **111** *and similar horiz designs. Multicoloured. P* 13½.

322	5 c. Type **111**		10	10
323	8 c. Goodwill Junior High School		10	10
324	14 c. University of West Indies (Jamaica)		10	10
325	$1 Trinity College, Cambridge		35	30
322/5		Set of 4	45	30
MS326	85 × 85 mm. Nos. 324/5		50	1·00

112 Waterfall

(Des O. Bonnevalle. Litho Questa)

1971 (22 Mar). *Tourism. T* **112** *and similar horiz designs. Multicoloured. P* 13½.

327	5 c. Type **112**		15	10
328	10 c. Boat-building		15	10
329	30 c. Sailing		25	10
330	50 c. Yacht and motor launch		40	30
327/30		Set of 4	85	45
MS331	130 × 86 mm. Nos. 327/30		85	1·00

113 UNICEF Symbol in "D"

114 German Boy Scout

(Des G. Drummond. Litho Questa)

1971 (14 June). *25th Anniv of UNICEF. P* 14.

332	113	5 c. bluish violet, black and gold		10	10
333		10 c. yellow, black and gold		10	10
334		38 c. green, black and gold		10	10
335		$1.20 orange, black and gold		30	45
332/5			Set of 4	40	55
MS336	84 × 79 mm. Nos. 333 and 335			50	1·10

(Litho Format)

1971 (18 Oct). *World Scout Jamboree, Asagiri, Japan. T* **114** *and similar vert designs showing Boy Scouts from the nations listed. Multicoloured. W w* 12. *P* 11.

337	20 c. Type **114**		15	15
338	24 c. Great Britain		20	15
339	30 c. Japan		25	20
340	$1 Dominica		50	2·00
337/40		Set of 4	1·00	2·25
MS341	114 × 102 mm. Nos. 339/40		1·00	2·25

The above were printed on thick paper and the watermark is very faint.

Both No. 340 and the $1 value from the miniature sheet show the national flag of the Dominican Republic in error.

"Dominica" on the scout's shirt pocket is omitted on the $1 value from the miniature sheet.

115 Groine at Portsmouth

(Des V. Whiteley. Litho Format)

1971 (15 Nov). *National Day. T* **115** *and similar multicoloured designs. P* 13½.

342	8 c. Type **115**		10	10
343	15 c. Carnival scene		10	10
344	20 c. Carifta Queen (*vert*)		10	10
345	50 c. Rock of Atkinson (*vert*)		20	25
342/5		Set of 4	30	30
MS346	63 × 89 mm. $1.20, As 20 c. P 15		45	70

116 Eight Reals Piece, 1761

(Des G. Drummond. Litho Questa)

1972 (7 Feb). *Coins. T* **116** *and similar designs. P* 14.

347	10 c. black, silver and violet		10	10
348	30 c. black, silver and yellowish green		15	15
349	35 c. black, silver and bright blue		20	20
350	50 c. black, silver and vermilion		40	1·75
347/50		Set of 4	75	2·00
MS351	86 × 90 mm. Nos. 350/1		75	1·25

Designs: *Horiz*—30 c. Eleven and three bitt pieces, 1798. *Vert*—35 c. Two reals and two bitt pieces, 1770; 50 c. Mocos, Pieces-of-eight and eight reals-eleven bits piece, 1798.

117 Common Opossum

(Des R. Granger Barrett. Litho Questa)

1972 (3 June). *U.N. Conference on the Human Environment, Stockholm. T* **117** *and similar horiz designs. Multicoloured. W w* 12 (*sideways*). *P* 14.

352	½ c. Type **117**		10	10
353	35 c. Brazilian Agouti (rodent)		40	15
354	60 c. Orchid		2·50	50
355	$1.20, Hibiscus		2·50	1·60
352/5		Set of 4	5·00	2·00
MS356	139×94 mm. Nos. 352/5		7·00	9·00

118 Sprinter

(Des R. Granger Barrett. Litho Format)

1972 (16 Oct*). *Olympic Games, Munich. T* **118** *and similar multicoloured designs. P* 14.

357	30 c. Type **118**		10	10
358	35 c. Hurdler		15	15
359	58 c. Hammer-thrower (*vert*)		20	20
360	72 c. Long-jumper (*vert*)		40	40
357/60		Set of 4	75	75
MS361	98 × 96 mm. Nos. 359/60. P 15		75	90

*This is the local release date; the American philatelic agency released the stamps on 9 October.

119 General Post Office

(Des G. Vasarhelyi. Litho Format)

1972 (1 Nov). *National Day. T* **119** *and similar horiz designs. Multicoloured. P* 13½.

362	10 c. Type 119			10	10
363	20 c. Morne Diablotin			10	10
364	30 c. Rodney's Rock			15	15
362/4			Set of 3	30	30
MS365	83 × 96 mm. Nos. 363/4. P 15			50	70

120 Bananas and Imperial Amazon

(Des (from photograph by D. Groves) and photo Harrison)

1972 (20 Nov). *Royal Silver Wedding. Multicoloured; background colour given. W* w 12. *P* 14 × 14½.

366	120 5 c. yellow-olive			20	10
	a. Deep yellow-olive			50	25
367	$1 myrtle-green			60	40
	w. Wmk inverted			3·50	

121 "The Adoration of the Shepherds" (Caravaggio)   122 Launching of Weather Satellite

(Des G. Vasarhelyi. Litho Format)

1972 (4 Dec*). *Christmas. T* **121** *and similar vert designs. Multicoloured. P* 13½.

368	8 c. Type 121			10	10
369	14 c. "The Myosotis Virgin" (Rubens)			10	10
370	30 c. "Madonna and Child with St. Francesca Romana" (Gentileschi)			15	10
371	$1 "Adoration of the Kings" (Mostaert)			50	90
368/71			Set of 4	70	1·00
MS372	102 × 79 mm. Nos. 370/1. Imperf.			60	80

*This is the date of release in Dominica; the stamps were put on sale by the Philatelic agency in the U.S.A. on 27 November. No. 368 is wrongly attributed to Boccaccino in the design.

(Des G. Vasarhelyi. Litho Format)

1973 (16 July). *I.M.O./W.M.O. Centenary. T* **122** *and similar multicoloured designs. P* 14½.

373	½ c. Type 122			10	10
374	1 c. Nimbus satellite			10	10
375	2 c. Radiosonde balloon			10	10
376	30 c. Radarscope (horiz)			15	15
377	35 c. Diagram of pressure zones (horiz)			20	20
378	50 c. Hurricane shown by satellite (horiz)			30	35
379	$1 Computer weather-map (horiz)			60	65
373/9			Set of 7	1·25	1·40
MS380	90 × 105 mm. Nos. 378/9.			90	1·75

123 Going to Hospital   124 Cyrique Crab

(Des G. Vasarhelyi. Litho Format)

1973 (20 Aug). *25th Anniv of W.H.O. T* **123** *and similar horiz designs. Multicoloured. P* 14½.

381	½ c. Type 123			10	10
382	1 c. Maternity care			10	10
383	2 c. Smallpox inoculation			10	10
384	30 c. Emergency service			30	15
385	35 c. Waiting for the doctor			35	15
386	50 c. Medical examination			45	25
387	$1 Travelling doctor			65	60
381/7			Set of 7	1·75	1·10
MS388	112 × 110 mm. Nos. 386/7. P 14 × 14½			75	1·25
	a. Perf 14½			45·00	45·00

(Des G. Drummond. Litho Format)

1973 (15 Oct). *Flora and Fauna. T* **124** *and similar vert designs. Multicoloured. P* 14½.

389	½ c. Type 124			10	10
390	22 c. Blue Land-crab			35	10
391	25 c. Bread Fruit			35	15
392	$1.20, Sunflower			1·00	2·00
389/92			Set of 4	1·50	2·00
MS393	91 × 127 mm. Nos. 389/92.			2·50	4·00

125 Princess Anne and Captain Mark Phillips

(Des G. Drummond. Litho Format)

1973 (14 Nov). *Royal Wedding. P* 13½.

394	125 25 c. multicoloured			10	10
395	— $2 multicoloured			30	30
MS396	79 × 100 mm. 75 c. as 25 c. and $1.20 as $2			40	30

No. 395 is as T 125, but the portrait has a different frame.
Nos. 394/5 were each issued in small sheets of five stamps and one stamp-size label.

126 "Adoration of the Kings" (Brueghel)

(Des M. Shamir. Litho Format)

1973 (26 Nov). *Christmas. T* **126** *and similar horiz designs. Multicoloured. P* 14½.

397	½ c. Type 126			10	10
398	1 c. "Adoration of the Magi" (Botticelli)			10	10
399	2 c. "Adoration of the Magi" (Dürer)			10	10
400	12 c. "Mystic Nativity" (Botticelli)			20	10
401	22 c. "Adoration of the Magi" (Rubens)			25	10
402	35 c. "The Nativity" (Dürer)			25	10
403	$1 "Adoration of the Shepherds" (Giorgione)			60	55
397/403			Set of 7	1·10	80
MS404	122 × 98 mm. Nos. 402/3			85	1·10

127 Carib Basket-weaving

(Des G. Drummond. Litho Format)

1973 (17 Dec). *National Day. T* **127** *and similar multicoloured designs. P* 13½.

405	5 c. Type 127			10	10
406	10 c. Staircase of the Snake			10	10
407	50 c. Miss Caribbean Queen (vert)			15	15
408	60 c. Miss Carifta Queen (vert)			15	15
409	$1 Dance group			25	30
405/9			Set of 5	50	60
MS410	95×127 mm. Nos. 405/6 and 409			40	65

128 University Centre, Dominica

(Des G. Drummond. Litho Format)

1974 (21 Jan). *25th Anniv of West Indies University. T* **128** *and similar horiz designs. Multicoloured. P* 14½.

411	12 c. Type 128			10	10
412	30 c. Graduation ceremony			10	10
413	$1 University coat of arms			25	35
411/13			Set of 3	30	35
MS414	97 × 131 mm. Nos. 411/13			30	55

OMNIBUS ISSUES

Details, together with prices for complete sets, of the various Omnibus issues from the 1935 Silver Jubilee series to date are included in a special section following Zimbabwe at the end of Volume 2.

129 Dominicia 1d. Stamp of 1874 and Map   130 Footballer and Flag of Brazil

(Des G. Drummond. Litho Format)

1974 (27 May). *Stamp Centenary. T* **129** *and similar horiz designs. Multicoloured. P* 14½.

415	½ c. Type 129			10	10
416	1 c. 6d. stamp of 1874 and posthorn			10	10
417	2 c. 1s. stamp of 1874 and arms			10	10
418	10 c. Type 129			20	10
419	50 c. As 1 c.			40	30
420	$1.20, As 2 c.			50	70
415/20			Set of 6	1·10	1·00
MS421	105 × 121 mm. Nos. 418/20			1·00	1·50

(Des V. Whiteley. Litho Format)

1974 (12 Aug). *World Cup Football Championship, West Germany. T* **130** *and similar vert designs, showing footballers and flags of the countries given. Multicoloured. P* 14½.

422	½ c. Type 130			10	10
423	1 c. West Germany			10	10
424	2 c. Italy			10	10
425	30 c. Scotland			50	10
426	40 c. Sweden			50	10
427	50 c. Netherlands			55	35
428	$1 Yugoslavia			90	90
422/8			Set of 7	2·25	1·50
MS429	89 × 87 mm. Nos. 427/8			70	80

131 Indian Hole

(Des G. Vasarhelyi. Litho Format)

1974 (1 Nov). *National Day. T* **131** *and similar horiz designs. Multicoloured. P* 13½.

430	10 c. Type 131			10	10
431	40 c. Teachers' Training College			10	10
432	$1 Bay Oil distillery plant, Petite Savanne			50	45
430/2			Set of 3	60	45
MS433	96 × 143 mm. Nos. 430/2			60	65

132 Churchill with "Colonist"

(Des G. Drummond. Litho Format)

1974 (25 Nov). *Birth Centenary of Sir Winston Churchill. T* **132** *and similar horiz designs. Multicoloured. P* 14½.

434	½ c. Type 132			10	10
435	1 c. Churchill and Eisenhower			10	10
436	2 c. Churchill and Roosevelt			10	10
437	20 c. Churchill and troops on assault-course			15	10
438	45 c. Painting at Marrakesh			20	10
439	$2 Giving the "V" sign			50	1·00
434/9			Set of 6	75	1·10
MS440	126 × 100 mm. Nos. 438/9. P 13			70	1·50

133 Mailboats Orinoco (1851) and Geesthaven (1974)   134 "The Virgin and Child" (Tiso)

(Des G. Drummond. Litho Format)

1974 (4 Dec). *Centenary of Universal Postal Union. T* **133** *and similar horiz designs. Multicoloured. P* 13.

441	10 c. Type 133			20	10
442	$2 De Havilland D.H.4 (1918) and Boeing 747-100 (1974)			80	1·00
MS443	107×93 mm. $1.20 as 10 c. and $2.40 as $2			1·00	1·40

Nos. 442 and MS443 are inscr "De Haviland".
Nos. 441/2 were issued either in sheets of 50 or in sheets of five stamps and one inscribed label.

(Des M. Shamir. Litho Questa)

1974 (16 Dec). *Christmas. T 134 and similar vert designs. Multi-coloured. P 14.*

444	½ c. Type **134**		10	10
445	1 c. "Madonna and Child with Saints" (Costa)		10	10
446	2 c. "The Nativity" (School of Rimini, 14th-cent)		10	10
447	10 c. "The Rest on the Flight into Egypt" (Romanelli)		20	10
448	25 c. "Adoration of the Shepherds" (da Sermoneta)		35	10
449	45 c. "The Nativity" (Guido Reni)		45	10
450	$1 "The Adoration of the Magi" (Caselli)		65	40
444/50		Set of 7	1·60	60
MS451	114 × 78 mm. Nos. 449/50		60	1·00

135 Queen Triggerfish

(Des G. Vasarhelyi. Litho Format)

1975 (2 June). *Fishes. T 135 and similar horiz designs. Multi-coloured. P 14.*

452	½ c. Type **135**		10	10
453	1 c. Porkfish		10	10
454	2 c. Sailfish		10	10
455	3 c. Swordfish		10	10
456	20 c. Great Barracuda		1·00	60
457	$2 Nassau Grouper		3·25	2·75
452/7		Set of 6	3·75	3·25
MS458	104×80 mm. No. 457. P 13		2·75	6·00

136 *Myscelia antholia*

(Des J. W. Litho Format)

1975 (28 July). *Dominican Butterflies. T 136 and similar horiz designs. Multicoloured. P 14½.*

459	½ c. Type **136**		10	40
460	1 c. *Lycorea ceres*		10	40
461	2 c. *Anaea marthesia* ("*Siderone nemesis*")		15	40
462	6 c. *Battus polydamas*		60	55
463	30 c. *Anartia lytrea*		1·75	70
464	40 c. *Morpho peleides*		1·75	75
465	$2 *Dryas julia*		2·75	7·50
459/65		Set of 7	6·50	9·50
MS466	108 × 80 mm. No. 465. P 13		2·50	4·25

137 *Yare* (cargo liner)

(Des J. W. Litho Questa)

1975 (1 Sept). *"Ships Tied to Dominica's History". T 137 and similar horiz designs. Multicoloured. P 14.*

467	½ c. Type **137**		20	35
468	1 c. *Thames II* (liner), 1890		20	35
469	2 c. *Lady Nelson* (cargo liner)		20	35
470	20 c. *Lady Rodney* (cargo liner)		1·00	35
471	45 c. *Statesman* (freighter)		1·25	55
472	50 c. *Geestcape* (freighter)		1·25	80
473	$2 *Geeststar* (freighter)		3·25	4·50
467/73		Set of 7	6·50	6·50
MS474	78×103 mm. Nos. 472/3		3·00	5·00

138 "Women in Agriculture"

139 Miss Caribbean Queen, 1975

(Litho Questa)

1975 (20 Oct). *International Women's Year. T 138 and similar horiz designs. Multicoloured. P 14.*

475	10 c. Type **138**		10	10
476	$2 "Women in Industry and Commerce"		40	60

(Litho Format)

1975 (6 Nov). *National Day. T 139 and similar multicoloured designs. P 14 × 13½ (vert) or 13½ × 14 (horiz).*

477	5 c. Type **139**		10	10
478	10 c. Public Library (*horiz*)		10	10
479	30 c. Citrus Factory (*horiz*)		10	10
480	$1 National Day Trophy		25	50
477/80		Set of 4	35	60
MS481	130×98 mm. Nos. 478/80. Imperf		50	1·40

140 "Virgin and Child" (Mantegna) 141 Hibiscus

(Des M. Shamir. Litho Questa)

1975 (24 Nov). *Christmas. T 140 and similar vert designs showing "Virgin and Child". Multicoloured. P 14.*

482	½ c. Type **140**		10	10
483	1 c. Fra Filippo Lippi		10	10
484	2 c. Bellini		10	10
485	10 c. Botticelli		15	10
486	25 c. Bellini		25	10
487	45 c. Correggio		30	10
488	$1 Dürer		55	50
482/88		Set of 7	1·10	70
MS489	139 × 85 mm. Nos. 487/88		1·00	1·50

(Des J.W. Litho Format)

1975 (8 Dec)–**78**. *T 141 and similar multicoloured designs.*

(a) Size as T 141. P 14½

490	½ c. Type **141**		10	50
491	1 c. African Tulip		15	50
492	2 c. Castor Oil Tree		15	50
493	3 c. White Cedar Flower		15	50
494	4 c. Egg Plant		15	50
495	5 c. Needlefish ("Gare")		20	50
496	6 c. Ochro		20	60
497	8 c. Zenaida Dove		2·50	60
498	10 c. Screw Pine		20	15
	a. Perf 13½ (1978)		25·00	
499	20 c. Mango Longue		30	15
500	25 c. Crayfish		35	15
501	30 c. Common Opossum ("Manicou")		90	80

(b) Size 28 × 44 mm ($10) or 44 × 28 mm (others). P 13½

502	40 c. Bay Leaf Groves		90	80
503	50 c. Tomatoes		55	50
504	$1 Lime Factory		75	65
505	$2 Rum Distillery		1·25	3·50
506	$5 Bay Oil Distillery		1·75	5·00
507	$10 Queen Elizabeth II		2·50	15·00
490/507		Set of 18	11·50	27·00

Nos. 490/2, 494/9 and 501/7 exist imperforate from stock dispersed by the liquidator of Format International Security Printers Ltd.

142 American Infantry   143 Rowing

(Des J.W. Litho Format)

1976 (12 Apr). *Bicentenary of American Revolution. T 142 and similar vert designs. Multicoloured. P 14½.*

508	½ c. Type **142**		10	10
509	1 c. British three-decker, 1782		10	10
510	2 c. George Washington		10	10
511	45 c. British sailors		55	10
512	75 c. British ensign		80	40
513	$2 Admiral Hood		1·25	1·25
508/13		Set of 6	2·50	1·75
MS514	105 × 92 mm. Nos. 512/13. P 13		2·00	3·50

(Des J.W. Litho Format)

1976 (24 May). *Olympic Games, Montreal. T 143 and similar vert designs. Multicoloured. P 14½.*

515	½ c. Type **143**		10	10
516	1 c. Shot putting		10	10
517	2 c. Swimming		10	10
518	40 c. Relay		15	10
519	45 c. Gymnastics		15	10
520	60 c. Sailing		20	20
521	$2 Archery		55	80
515/21		Set of 7	1·10	1·10
MS522	90 × 104 mm. Nos. 520/1. P 13		1·50	1·75

Nos. 516/21 exist imperforate from stock dispersed by the liquidator of Format International Security Printers Ltd.

144 Ringed Kingfisher   145 Viking Spacecraft System

(Des G. Drummond. Litho Format)

1976 (28 June). *Wild Birds. T 144 and similar multicoloured designs. P 14½.*

523	½ c. Type **144**		10	50
524	1 c. Mourning Dove		15	50
525	2 c. Green Heron		15	50
526	15 c. Broad-winged Hawk		1·25	45
527	30 c. Blue-headed Hummingbird		1·75	80
528	45 c. Bananaquit		2·50	1·00
529	$2 Imperial Amazon		6·50	14·00
523/9		Set of 7	11·00	16·00
MS530	133 × 101 mm. Nos. 527/9. P 13		8·00	16·00

Nos. 523/5 exist imperforate from stock dispersed by the liquidator of Format International Security Printers Ltd.

1976 (26 July). *West Indian Victory in World Cricket Cup. As Nos. 559/60 of Barbados.*

531	15 c. Map of the Caribbean		75	1·25
532	25 c. Prudential Cup		75	1·75

(Des PAD Studio. Litho Format)

1976 (20 Sept). *Viking Space Mission. T 145 and similar multi-coloured designs. P 14½.*

533	½ c. Type **145**		10	10
534	1 c. Launching pad (*horiz*)		10	10
535	2 c. Titan IIID and Centaur DII		10	10
536	3 c. Orbiter and lander capsule		10	10
537	45 c. Capsule, parachute unopened		30	15
538	75 c. Capsule, parachute opened		40	50
539	$1 Lander descending (*horiz*)		45	60
540	$2 Space vehicle on Mars (*horiz*)		60	1·60
533/40		Set of 8	1·75	2·75
MS541	104 × 78 mm. Nos. 539/40. P 13		1·10	2·25

146 "Virgin and Child with Saints Anthony of Padua and Roch" (Giorgione)   147 Island Craft Co-operative

(Des M. Shamir. Litho Questa)

1976 (1 Nov). *Christmas. T 146 and similar vert designs showing "Virgin and Child" by the artists named. Multicoloured. P 14.*

542	½ c. Type **146**		10	10
543	1 c. Bellini		10	10
544	2 c. Mantegna		10	10
545	6 c. Mantegna (*different*)		10	10
546	25 c. Memling		15	10
547	45 c. Correggio		20	10
548	$3 Raphael		1·00	1·00
542/8		Set of 7	1·40	1·10
MS549	140 × 85 mm. 50 c. as No. 547 and $1 as No. 548		1·00	1·10

(Des G. Drummond. Litho Questa)

1976 (22 Nov). *National Day. T 147 and similar horiz designs. Multicoloured. P 13½.*

550	10 c. Type **147**		10	10
551	50 c. Harvesting bananas		15	10
552	$1 Boxing plant		30	35
550/2		Set of 3	45	45
MS553	96 × 122 mm. Nos. 550/2		50	90

148 American Giant Sundial (*Architectonica nobilis*)   149 The Queen Crowned and Enthroned

(Des J.W. Litho Questa)

1976 (20 Dec). *Shells. T* **148** *and similar vert designs. Multi-coloured. P* 14.

554	½ c.	Type **148**	..	10	10
555	1 c.	Flame Helmet (*Cassis flammea*)		10	10
556	2 c.	Mouse Cone (*Conus mus*)		10	10
557	20 c.	Caribbean Vase (*Vasum muricatum*)		45	10
558	40 c.	West Indian Fighting Conch (*Strombus pugilis*)		70	25
559	50 c.	Short Coral Shell (*Corralliophila abbreviata*)		70	25
560	$3	Apple Murex (*Murex pomum*)		3·00	3·25
554/60			*Set of* 7	4·50	3·50
MS561	101×55 mm. $2 Long-spined Star Shell				
(*Astraea phoebia*)		..	..	1·40	1·75

(Des J.W. Litho Questa)

1977 (7 Feb). *Silver Jubilee. T* **149** *and similar horiz designs. Multicoloured. P* 14 × 13½.

562	½ c.	Type **149**	..	10	10
563	1 c.	Imperial State Crown		10	10
564	45 c.	Queen Elizabeth and Princess Anne		15	10
565	$2	Coronation Ring		25	30
566	$2.50, Ampulla and Spoon		..	30	40
562/6			*Set of* 5	60	70
MS567	104 × 79 mm. $5 Queen Elizabeth and				
Prince Philip		..	..	75	1·25

Nos. 562/6 also exist perf 12×11½ (*Price for set of* 5 *50p mint or used*) from additional sheetlets of 5 stamps and one label. Stamps perforated 14×13½ are from normal sheets of 40. Stamps from the sheets of 5 have the arch at left in a different colour.

150 Joseph Haydn

151 Hiking

(Des J.W. Litho Questa)

1977 (25 Apr). *150th Death Anniv of Ludwig van Beethoven. T* **150** *and similar vert designs. Multicoloured. P* 14.

568	½ c.	Type **150**	..	10	10
569	1 c.	Scene from "Fidelio"		10	10
570	2 c.	Maria Casentini (dancer)		10	10
571	15 c.	Beethoven and pastoral scene		25	10
572	30 c.	"Wellington's Victory"		35	10
573	40 c.	Henriette Sontag (singer)		35	10
574	$2	The young Beethoven		1·10	2·00
568/74			*Set of* 7	1·75	2·25
MS575	138 × 93 mm. Nos. 572/4		..	1·50	3·25

(Des J.W. Litho Questa)

1977 (8 Aug). *Caribbean Scout Jamboree, Jamaica. T* **151** *and similar horiz designs. Multicoloured. P* 14.

576	½ c.	Type **151**	..	10	10
577	1 c.	First-aid		10	10
578	2 c.	Camping		10	10
579	45 c.	Rock climbing		35	15
580	50 c.	Canoeing		40	20
581	$3	Sailing		2·00	1·75
576/81			*Set of* 6	2·50	2·00
MS582	111 × 113 mm. 75 c. Map reading and $2				
Campfire singsong		..	..	1·25	1·25

152 Holy Family

ROYAL VISIT W.I. 1977

(153)

(Des G. Vasarhelyi. Litho Questa)

1977 (17 Nov). *Christmas. T* **152** *and similar horiz designs showing book miniatures from Foix Book of Hours* ($3) *or De Lisle Psalter* (*others*). *Multicoloured. P* 14.

583	½ c.	Type **152**	..	10	10
584	1 c.	Angel and Shepherds		10	10
585	2 c.	Holy Baptism		10	10
586	6 c.	Flight into Egypt		15	10
587	15 c.	Three Kings with gifts		15	10
588	45 c.	Holy Family in the Temple		30	10
589	$3	Flight into Egypt (*different*)		80	1·10
583/9			*Set of* 7	1·25	1·40
MS590	113 × 85 mm. 50 c. Virgin and Child; $2				
Flight into Egypt (*different*)		..	..	60	75

1977 (28 Nov). *Royal Visit. Nos.* 562/7 *optd with T* **153** *above "JUBILEE". P* 12×11½.

591	½ c.	Type **149**	..	10	10
592	1 c.	Imperial State Crown		10	10
593	45 c.	Queen Elizabeth and Princess Anne		15	10
	a. Opt in top left-hand corner (*p* 14×13½)			15	10
594	$2	Coronation Ring		45	55
	a. Opt in top left-hand corner (*p* 14×13½)			30	30
595	$2.50, Ampulla and Spoon			50	70
	a. Opt in top left-hand corner (*p* 14×13½)			35	35
591/5			*Set of* 5	1·00	1·40
MS596	104×79 mm. $5 Queen Elizabeth and				
Prince Philip (*opt to left of face value*)		..	1·00	1·50
	a. Optd "W.I. 1977" only on stamp		..	12·00	15·00

No. **MS**596a is overprinted "W.I. 1977" beneath "ROYAL VISIT" inscription to left of stamp design. Overprint as T **153**, but in one line, appears at top left of *miniature sheet*.

---

154 "Sousouelle Souris"

(Des L. Honychurch and J.W. Litho Questa)

1978 (9 Jan). *"History of Carnival". T* **154** *and similar horiz designs. Multicoloured. P* 14.

597	½ c.	Type **154**	..	10	10
598	1 c.	Sensay costume	..	10	10
599	2 c.	Street musicians	..	10	10
600	45 c.	Douiette band		15	10
601	50 c.	Pappy Show wedding		15	10
602	$2	Masquerade band		45	60
597/602			*Set of* 6	75	75
MS603	104 × 88 mm. $2.50 as No. 602		..	60	85

155 Col. Charles Lindbergh and Ryan NYP Special *Spirit of St. Louis*

156 Queen receiving Homage

(Des G. Drummond. Litho Format)

1978 (13 Mar). *Aviation Anniversaries. T* **155** *and similar horiz designs. Multicoloured. P* 14½.

604	6 c.	Type **155**	..	20	10
605	10 c.	Ryan NYP Special *Spirit of St. Louis*, New York, 20 May 1927		25	10
606	15 c.	Lindbergh and map of Atlantic		35	10
607	20 c.	Lindbergh reaches Paris, 21 May 1927		45	10
608	40 c.	Airship LZ-1, Lake Constance, 1900		55	20
609	60 c.	Count F. von Zeppelin and airship LZ-2, 1906		65	30
610	$3	Airship LZ-127 *Graf Zeppelin*, 1928		1·40	1·10
604/10			*Set of* 7	3·50	1·75
MS611	139×108 mm. 50 c. Ryan NYP Special *Spirit of St. Louis* in mid-Atlantic; $2 Airship LZ-127 *Graf Zeppelin*, 1928		..	1·40	1·10

The 6, 10, 15, 20 and 50 c. values commemorate the 50th anniversary of first solo transatlantic flight by Col. Charles Lindbergh; the other values commemorate anniversaries of various Zeppelin airships.

No. **MS**611 exists imperforate from stock dispersed by the liquidator of Format International Security Printers Ltd.

(Des J.W. Litho Questa)

1978 (2 June). *25th Anniv of Coronation. T* **156** *and similar vert designs. Multicoloured. P* 14.

612	45 c.	Type **156**	..	15	10
613	$2	Balcony scene		30	30
614	$2.50, Queen and Prince Philip			40	40
612/14			*Set of* 3	75	65
MS615	76 × 107 mm. $5 Queen Elizabeth II		75	75

Nos. 612/14 also exist perf 12 (*Price for set of* 3 *75p mint or used*) from additional sheetlets of 3 stamps and 1 label. Stamps perforated 14 come from sheets of 50. The stamps from sheetlets have changed background or inscription colours.

157 Wright Flyer III

158 "Two Apostles" (Rubens)

(Des G. Vasarhelyi. Litho Format)

1978 (10 July). *75th Anniv of Powered Flight. T* **157** *and similar horiz designs. Multicoloured. P* 14½.

616	30 c.	Type **157**	..	15	15
617	40 c.	Wright Type A, 1908		20	20
618	60 c.	Flyer I		25	25
619	$2	Flyer I (*different*)		85	85
616/19			*Set of* 4	1·25	1·25
MS620	116×89 mm. $3 Wilbur and Orville Wright		..	90	1·00

Nos. 616/20 exist imperforate from stock dispersed by the liquidator of Format International Security Printers Ltd.

(Des BG Studio. Litho Questa)

1978 (16 Oct). *Christmas. Paintings. T* **158** *and similar vert designs. Multicoloured. P* 14.

621	20 c.	Type **158**	..	10	10
622	45 c.	"The Descent from the Cross" (Rubens)		15	10
623	50 c.	"St Ildefonso receiving the Chasuble" (Rubens)		15	10

624	$3	"The Assumption of the Virgin" (Rubens)		35	80
621/4			*Set of* 4	60	90
MS625	113 × 83 mm. $2 "The Holy Family" (Sebastiano del Piombo*)		..	75	75

*This painting was incorrectly attributed to Rubens on the stamp.

INDEPENDENT

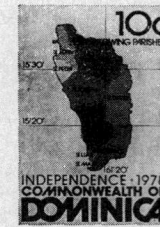

INDEPENDENCE 3rd NOVEMBER 1978

159 Map showing Parishes (160)

(Des J.W. Litho Questa)

1978 (3 Nov). *Independence. T* **159** *and similar vert designs. Multicoloured. P* 14.

626	10 c.	Type **159**	..	45	15
627	25 c.	*Sabinea carinalis* (National flower)		50	15
628	45 c.	New National flag		55	15
629	50 c.	Coat of arms		55	30
630	$2	Patrick John (Prime Minister)		70	1·75
626/30			*Set of* 5	2·50	2·25
MS631	113 × 90 mm. $2.50, Type **159**		1·00	1·25

1978 (3 Nov)–79. *Independence. Nos.* 490/507 (10 c. *now perf* 13½) *optd as T* **160** *by typography.*

632	½ c.	Type **141**	..	40	10
633	1 c.	African Tulip		45	10
634	2 c.	Castor Oil Tree		45	10
635	3 c.	White Cedar Flower		50	15
636	4 c.	Egg Plant		50	15
637	5 c.	Needlefish		50	15
638	6 c.	Ochro		50	15
639	8 c.	Zenaida Dove		2·25	20
640	10 c.	Screw Pine		50	15
	a. Perf 14½. Litho opt (7.79)			1·00	45
641	20 c.	Mango Longue		60	15
642	25 c.	Crayfish		70	20
643	30 c.	Common Opossum		70	20
644	40 c.	Bay Leaf Groves		70	25
	a. Litho opt (7.79)			70	40
645	50 c.	Tomatoes		80	30
646	$1	Lime Factory		80	65
647	$2	Rum Distillery		1·00	1·00
648	$5	Bay Oil Distillery		1·25	2·25
649	$10	Queen Elizabeth II		1·75	4·50
	a. Litho opt (7.79)			2·25	6·50
632/49			*Set of* 18	12·00	10·00

For History of Aviation gold foil stamps see Appendix at the end of the Dominica listing.

161 Sir Rowland Hill

162 Children and Canoe

(Des BG Studio. Litho Questa)

1979 (19 Mar). *Death Centenary of Sir Rowland Hill. T* **161** *and similar vert designs. P* 14.

650	25 c.	multicoloured		10	10
651	45 c.	multicoloured		15	10
652	50 c.	black, reddish violet and magenta		15	10
653	$2	black, magenta and yellow		35	65
650/3			*Set of* 4	65	80
MS654	186 × 96 mm. $5 black and vermilion		1·00	1·25

Designs:—45 c. Great Britain 1840 2d. blue; 50 c. 1874 1d. stamp; $2 Maltese Cross cancellations; $5 Penny Black.

Nos. 650/3 also exist perf 12 (*Price for set of* 4 *80p mint or used*) from additional sheetlets of 5 stamps and 1 label. Shades of these stamps differ from those perforated 14 which come from sheets of 40.

(Des BG Studio. Litho Questa)

1979 (23 Apr). *International Year of the Child. T* **162** *and similar horiz designs. Multicoloured. P* 14.

655	30 c.	Type **162**	..	25	15
656	40 c.	Children with bananas		25	25
657	50 c.	Children playing cricket	..	1·25	80
658	$3	Child feeding rabbits		1·75	2·00
655/8			*Set of* 4	3·25	2·75
MS659	117 × 85 mm. $5 Child with catch of fish	..	1·00	1·50

MINIMUM PRICE

The minimum price quote is 10p which represents a handling charge rather than a basis for valuing common stamps. For further notes about prices see introductory pages.

163 Nassau Grouper

(Des G. Drummond. Litho Questa)

1979 (21 May). *Marine Wildlife. T 163 and similar horiz designs. Multicoloured. P 14.*

660	10 c. Type 163		40	15
661	30 c. Striped Dolphin		70	35
662	50 c. White-tailed Tropic Bird		2·25	65
663	60 c. Brown Pelican		2·25	1·50
664	$1 Long-finned Pilot Whale		2·50	1·75
665	$2 Brown Booby		3·00	4·50
660/5		Set of 6	10·00	8·00
MS666	120 × 94 mm. $3 Elkhorn Coral		1·50	1·40

No. 661 is inscribed "SPOTTED DOLPHIN" in error.

164 H.M.S. *Endeavour*

(Des J.W. Litho Questa)

1979 (16 July). *Death Bicentenary of Captain Cook. T 164 and similar horiz designs. Multicoloured. P 14.*

667	10 c. Type 164		65	30
668	50 c. H.M.S. Resolution		1·10	1·00
669	60 c. H.M.S. Discovery		1·25	1·50
670	$2 Detail of Cook's chart of New Zealand, 1770		1·60	2·50
667/70		Set of 4	4·25	4·75
MS671	97 × 90 mm. $5 Captain Cook and signature		1·50	2·00

165 Cooking at Camp-fire   **166** Colvillea

(Des M. Diamond. Litho Questa)

1979 (30 July). *50th Anniv of Girl Guide Movement in Dominica. T 165 and similar horiz designs. Multicoloured. P 14.*

672	10 c. Type 165		20	10
673	20 c. Pitching emergency rain tent		25	10
674	50 c. Raising Dominican flag		35	10
675	$2.50, Singing and dancing to accordion		90	80
672/5		Set of 4	1·50	85
MS676	110 × 86 mm. $3 Guides of different age-groups		75	1·25

(Des J.W. Litho Questa)

1979 (3 Sept). *Flowering Trees. T 166 and similar vert designs. Multicoloured. P 14.*

677	20 c. Type 166		15	10
678	40 c. Lignum Vitae		20	15
679	60 c. Dwarf Poinciana		30	25
680	$2 Fern Tree		70	90
677/80		Set of 4	1·25	1·25
MS681	114 × 89 mm. $3 Perfume Tree		75	1·10

167 Cathedral of the Assumption, Roseau

(Des W. Grout. Litho Questa)

1979 (11 Oct). *Christmas. Cathedrals. T 167 and similar multi-coloured designs. P 14.*

682	6 c. Type 167		10	10
683	45 c. St. Paul's, London (vert)		15	10
684	60 c. St. Peter's, Rome (vert)		15	10
685	$3 Notre Dame, Paris (vert)		55	60
682/5		Set of 4	75	70
MS686	113 × 85 mm. 40 c. St. Patrick's, New York; $2 Cologne Cathedral (both vert)		50	80

HURRICANE RELIEF
(168)

169 Mickey Mouse and Octopus playing Xylophone

1979 (29 Oct). *Hurricane Relief. Nos. 495, 502 and 506/7 optd as T 168.*

687	5 c. Gare		10	10
688	40 c. Bay Leaf Groves		10	10
689	$5 Bay Oil Distillery		1·00	1·25
690	$10 Queen Elizabeth II		1·25	1·75
687/90		Set of 4	2·25	2·75

(Litho Format)

1979 (2 Nov). *International Year of the Child. Walt Disney Cartoon Characters. T 169 and similar vert designs showing characters playing musical instruments. Multicoloured. P 11.*

691	½ c. Type 169		10	10
692	1 c. Goofy playing guitar on rocking-horse		10	10
693	2 c. Mickey Mouse playing violin and Goofy playing bagpipes		10	10
694	3 c. Donald Duck playing drum with pneumatic drill		10	10
695	4 c. Minnie Mouse playing saxophone on roller-skates		10	10
696	5 c. Goofy as one-man-band		10	10
697	10 c. Dale being blown from French horn by Horace Horsecollar		10	10
698	$2 Huey, Dewey and Louie playing bass		2·00	2·00
699	$2.50, Donald Duck playing piano and Huey playing trumpet		2·00	2·25
691/9		Set of 9	4·00	4·25
MS700	127 × 102 mm. $3 Mickey Mouse playing piano. P 13½		2·50	3·00

170 Hospital Ward

(Des BG Studio. Litho Questa)

1980 (31 Mar). *75th Anniv of Rotary International. T 170 and similar horiz designs. Multicoloured. P 14.*

701	10 c. Type 170		10	10
702	20 c. Electric-cardiogram		15	10
703	40 c. Site for mental hospital		20	15
704	$2.50, Paul P. Harris (founder)		55	90
701/4		Set of 4	80	1·10
MS705	128 × 113 mm. $3 Interlocking cogs of Rotary emblem and globe		60	80

1980 (6 May). *"London 1980" International Stamp Exhibition. As Nos. 650/3 optd with T 262 of Grenada. P 12.*

706	25 c. multicoloured		25	10
707	45 c. multicoloured		30	15
708	50 c. olive-brown, blue and rose-red		30	15
709	$2 olive-brown, vermilion and yellow		80	60
706/9		Set of 4	1·50	80

171 Shot Putting

(Des J.W. Litho Questa)

1980 (27 May). *Olympic Games, Moscow. T 171 and similar horiz designs. Multicoloured. P 14.*

710	30 c. Type 171		15	10
711	40 c. Basketball		60	15
712	60 c. Swimming		35	20
713	$2 Gymnastics		60	65
710/13		Set of 4	1·50	90
MS714	114 × 86 mm. $3 The Marathon		70	90

172 "Supper at Emmaus" (Caravaggio)

(Des J.W. Litho Questa)

1980 (22 July). *Famous Paintings. T 172 and similar multi-coloured designs. P 13½.*

715	20 c. Type 172		20	10
716	25 c. "Portrait of Charles I Hunting" (Van Dyck) (vert)		20	10
717	30 c. "The Maids of Honour" (Velasquez) (vert)		25	10
718	45 c. "The Rape of the Sabine Women" (Poussin)		25	10
719	$1 "Embarkation for Cythera" (Watteau)		35	35
720	$5 "Girl before a Mirror" (Picasso) (vert)		1·00	1·50
715/20		Set of 6	2·00	2·00
MS721	114 × 111 mm. $3 "The Holy Family" (Rembrandt) (vert)		60	80

173 Scene from "Peter Pan"

(Litho Walsall)

1980 (1 Oct). *Christmas. Scenes from Walt Disney's Cartoon Film "Peter Pan". T 173 and similar horiz designs. P 11.*

722	½ c. multicoloured		10	10
723	1 c. multicoloured		10	10
724	2 c. multicoloured		10	10
725	3 c. multicoloured		10	10
726	4 c. multicoloured		10	10
727	5 c. multicoloured		10	10
728	10 c. multicoloured		10	10
729	$2 multicoloured		2·25	1·50
730	$2.50, multicoloured		2·25	1·75
722/30		Set of 9	4·50	3·25
MS731	124 × 98 mm. $4 multicoloured (vert)		3·50	3·50

174 Queen Elizabeth the Queen Mother in Doorway

(Litho Questa)

1980 (20 Oct). *80th Birthday of Queen Elizabeth the Queen Mother. P 12.*

732	174 40 c. multicoloured		25	15
	a. Perf 14		15	15
733	$2.50, multicoloured		65	60
	a. Perf 14		45	60
MS734	85 × 66 mm. 174 $3 multicoloured		75	2·00

Stamps perforated 12 are from normal sheets of 50. Those perforated 14 come either from similar sheets or from sheetlets of nine with inscribed sheet margins.

175 Douglas Bay

(Des G. Drummond. Litho Questa)

1981 (12 Feb). *Dominica Safari. T 175 and similar multicoloured designs. P 14.*

735	20 c. Type 175		10	10
736	30 c. Valley of Desolation		10	10
737	40 c. Emerald Pool (vert)		10	10
738	$3 Indian River (vert)		75	1·10
735/8		Set of 4	85	1·25
MS739	84 × 104 mm. $4 Trafalgar Falls (vert)		1·10	1·40

(Litho Format)

1981 (30 Apr). *50th Anniv of Walt Disney's Cartoon Character, Pluto. Vert designs as T 169. Multicoloured. P 13½ × 14.*

740	$2 Pluto and Fifi		1·25	1·50
MS741	128 × 102 mm. $4 Pluto in scene from film Pluto's Blue Note		2·00	2·00

176 Forest Thrush   **177** Windsor Castle

(Des P. Barrett. Litho Questa)

1981 (30 Apr). *Birds. T* **176** *and similar horiz designs. Multi-coloured. P* 14.

742	20 c.	Type **176**	55	30
743	30 c.	Wied's Crested Flycatcher	65	35
744	40 c.	Blue-hooded Euphonia	75	45
745	$5	Lesser Antillean Pewee	3·50	4·75
742/5		*Set of* 4	5·00	5·25
MS746	121 × 95 mm. $3 Imperial Amazon		2·75	1·75

(Des J.W. Litho Questa)

1981 (23 June). *Royal Wedding. T* **177** *and similar vert designs. Multicoloured. P* 14.

747	45 c.	Prince Charles and Lady Diana Spencer	10	10
	a.	Perf 12	25	35
748	60 c.	Type **177**	15	15
	a.	Perf 12	25	35
749	$4	Prince Charles as helicopter pilot	50	75
	a.	Perf 12	30	50
747/9		*Set of* 3	65	85
MS750	96×82 mm. $5 Westland HU Mk 5 Wessex helicopter of Queen's Flight		85	90

Nos. 747a/9a also exist from additional sheetlets of five stamps and one label with changed background colours.

178 Lady Diana Spencer

179 Ixora

(Manufactured by Walsall)

1981 (23 June). *Royal Wedding. T* **178** *and similar vert designs. Multicoloured. Roul* 5×*imperf**. *Self-adhesive.*

751	25 c.	Type **178**	20	35
	a.	Booklet pane. Nos. 751/2, each × 3	1·75	
752	$2	Prince Charles	50	1·00
753	$5	Prince Charles and Lady Diana Spencer	1·75	2·50
	a.	Booklet pane of 1.	1·75	
751/3		*Set of* 3	2·10	3·50

*The 25 c. and $2 values were separated by various combinations of rotary knife (giving a straight edge) and roulette. The $5 value exists only with straight edges. Nos. 751/3 were only issued in $11.75 stamp booklets.

(Litho Questa)

1981 (2 Nov). *Christmas. Horiz designs as T* **169** *showing scenes from Walt Disney's cartoon film "Santa's Workshop". P* 13½.

754	½ c.	multicoloured	10	10
755	1 c.	multicoloured	10	10
756	2 c.	multicoloured	10	10
757	3 c.	multicoloured	10	10
758	4 c.	multicoloured	15	10
759	5 c.	multicoloured	15	10
760	10 c.	multicoloured	20	10
761	45 c.	multicoloured	1·50	30
762	$5	multicoloured	4·25	5·50
754/62		*Set of* 9	5·75	5·50
MS763	129 × 103 mm. $4 multicoloured		4·00	3·50

(Des P. Barrett. Litho Questa)

1981 (1 Dec)–**85**. *Plant-Life. Horiz designs as T* **179**. *Multi-coloured.* A. *Without imprint date. P* 14

764A	1 c.	Type **179**	10	50
765A	2 c.	Flamboyant	10	50
766A	4 c.	Poinsettia	15	40
767A	5 c.	Bois Caribe (national flower of Dominica)	15	20
768A	8 c.	Annatto or Roucou	20	20
769A	10 c.	Passion Fruit	30	10
770A	15 c.	Breadfruit or Yampain	55	15
771A	20 c.	Allamanda or Buttercup	40	15
772A	25 c.	Cashew Nut	40	15
773A	35 c.	Soursop or Couassol	45	30
774A	40 c.	Bougainvillea	45	30
775A	45 c.	Anthurium	50	35
776A	60 c.	Cacao or Cocoa	1·25	70
777A	90 c.	Pawpaw Tree or Papay	70	1·00
778A	$1	Coconut Palm	1·50	1·00
779A	$2	Coffee Tree or Café	1·00	2·75
780A	$5	Heliconia or Lobster Claw	2·25	9·50
781A	$10	Banana/Fig	3·00	13·00
764A/81A		*Set of* 18	12·00	27·00

B. *With imprint date at foot of design. P* 14 (15, 60 c.) *or* 12 (*others*)

769B	10 c.	Passion Fruit (1984)	1·50	30
	a.	Perf 14 (7.85)	1·00	60
770B	15 c.	Breadfruit or Yampain (7.85)	3·50	1·50
776B	60 c.	Cacao or Cocoa (7.85)	5·00	3·00
778B	$1	Coconut Palm (1984)	2·25	2·50
780B	$5	Heliconia or Lobster Claw (1984)	3·25	5·50
781B	$10	Banana Fig (1984)	5·50	12·00
769B/81B		*Set of* 6	19·00	22·00

Imprint dates: "1984", Nos. 769B, 778B, 780B, 781B; "1985", Nos. 769Ba, 770B, 776B, 780B.

---

180 Curb slope for Wheelchairs

181 "Olga Picasso in an Armchair"

(Des BG Studio. Litho Format)

1981 (22 Dec). *International Year for Disabled Persons. T* **180** *and similar vert designs. Multicoloured. P* 14½.

782	45 c.	Type **180**	55	25
783	60 c.	Bus with invalid step	60	35
784	75 c.	Motor car controls adapted for handicapped	70	40
785	$4	Bus with wheelchair ramp	1·50	2·50
782/5		*Set of* 4	3·00	3·25
MS786	82 × 96 mm. $5 Specially designed elevator control panel		4·25	3·00

(Des J.W. Litho Format)

1981 (30 Dec). *Birth Centenary of Picasso. T* **181** *and similar vert designs. Multicoloured. P* 14½.

787	45 c.	Type **181**	45	15
788	60 c.	"Bathers"	50	35
789	75 c.	"Woman in Spanish Costume"	55	40
790	$4	"Detail of Dog and Cock"	1·25	2·50
787/90		*Set of* 4	2·50	3·00
MS791	140 × 115 mm. $5 "Sleeping Peasants" (detail)		4·00	3·50

(Litho Questa)

1982 (29 Jan). *World Cup Football Championship, Spain. Walt Disney Cartoon Characters. Horiz designs as T* **169**. *Multi-coloured. P* 14 × 13½.

792	½ c.	Goofy chasing ball with butterfly net	10	10
793	1 c.	Donald Duck with ball in beak	10	10
794	2 c.	Goofy as goalkeeper	10	10
795	3 c.	Goofy looking for ball	10	10
796	4 c.	Goofy as park attendant puncturing ball with litter spike	10	10
797	5 c.	Pete and Donald Duck playing	10	10
798	10 c.	Donald Duck after kicking rock instead of ball	15	10
799	60 c.	Donald Duck feeling effects of a hard game and Daisy Duck dusting ball	1·50	1·25
800		Goofy hiding ball under his jersey from Mickey Mouse	5·50	6·50
792/800		*Set of* 9	6·75	7·00
MS801	132 × 105 mm. $4 Dale making off with ball		4·00	3·25

182 "Gone Fishing"

183 Elma Napier (first woman elected to B.W.I. Legislative Council)

(Des M.B.I. Studios. Litho Questa)

1982 (10 Mar). *Norman Rockwell (painter) Commemoration. T* **182** *and similar vert designs. Multicoloured. P* 14 × 13½.

802	10 c.	Type **182**	10	10
803	25 c.	"Breakfast"	15	10
804	45 c.	"The Marbles Champ"	30	30
805	$1	"Speeding Along"	55	55
802/5		*Set of* 4	95	95

No. 802 is inscribed "Golden Days" and No. 803 "The Morning News".

(Des BG Studio. Litho Questa)

1982 (15 Apr). *Decade for Women. T* **183** *and similar horiz designs. Multicoloured. P* 14.

806	10 c.	Type **183**	10	10
807	45 c.	Margaret Mead (anthropologist)	30	30
808	$1	Mabel ("Cissy") Caudeiron (folk song composer and historian)	55	55
809	$4	Eleanor Roosevelt	2·25	2·25
806/9		*Set of* 4	2·75	2·75
MS810	92 × 63 mm. $3 Florence Nightingale		2·00	3·00

The new-issue supplement to this Catalogue appears each month in

**GIBBONS
STAMP MONTHLY**

—from your newsagent or by postal subscription—
sample copy and details on request.

15c

Commonwealth of Dominica

45c

184 George Washington and Independence Hall, Philadelphia

185 *Anaea dominicana*

(Des J.W. Litho Format)

1982 (1 May). *250th Birth Anniv of George Washington* (45, 90 c.) *and Birth Centenary of Franklin D. Roosevelt* (60 c., $2). *T* **184** *and similar horiz designs. Multicoloured. P* 14½.

811	45 c.	Type **184**	25	25
812	60 c.	Franklin D. Roosevelt and Capitol, Washington D.C.	30	35
813	90 c.	Washington at Yorktown (detail, "The Surrender of Cornwallis" by Trumbull)	40	55
814	$2	Construction of dam (from W. Gropper's mural commemorating Roosevelt's "New Deal")	70	1·60
811/14		*Set of* 4	1·50	2·50
MS815	115 × 90 mm. $5 Washington and Roosevelt with U.S.A. flags of 1777 and 1933		2·00	3·25

Nos. 811/15 exist imperforate from stock dispersed by the liquidator of Format International Security Printers Ltd.

(Des P. Barrett. Litho Questa)

1982 (1 June). *Butterflies. T* **185** *and similar vert designs. Multi-coloured. P* 14.

816	15 c.	Type **185**	1·50	35
817	45 c.	*Heliconius charithonia*	2·50	65
818	60 c.	*Hypolimnas misippus*	2·75	1·75
819	$3	*Biblis hyperia*	5·50	6·00
816/19		*Set of* 4	11·00	8·00
MS820	77×105 mm. $5 *Marpesia petreus*		7·00	5·00

186 Prince and Princess of Wales

187 Scouts around Campfire

(Des PAD Studio. Litho Questa)

1982 (1 July). *21st Birthday of Princess of Wales. T* **186** *and similar vert designs. Multicoloured. P* 14½ × 14.

821	45 c.	Buckingham Palace	20	10
822	$2	Type **186**	50	70
823	$4	Princess of Wales	80	1·25
821/3		*Set of* 3	1·40	1·75
MS824	103 × 75 mm. $5 Princess Diana (*different*)		2·25	2·25

Nos. 821/3 also exist in sheetlets of 5 stamps and 1 label.

(Des R. Sauber. Litho Questa)

1982 (3 Aug). *75th Anniv of Boy Scout Movement. T* **187** *and similar multicoloured designs. P* 14.

825	45 c.	Type **187**	1·25	50
826	60 c.	Temperature study, Valley of Desolation	1·75	1·25
827	75 c.	Learning about native birds	2·25	1·50
828	$3	Canoe trip along Indian River	4·25	5·50
825/8		*Set of* 4	8·50	8·00
MS829	99 × 70 mm. $5 Dominican scouts saluting the flag (*vert*)		2·25	3·25

1982 (30 Aug). *Birth of Prince William of Wales. Nos.* 821/4 *optd with T* **171** *of Antigua.*

830	45 c.	Buckingham Palace	30	30
831	$2	Type **186**	80	1·10
832	$4	Princess of Wales	1·40	1·90
830/2		*Set of* 3	2·25	3·00
MS833	103 × 75 mm. $5 Princess Diana (*different*)		2·00	2·75

Nos. 830/2 also exist in sheetlets of 5 stamps and 1 label.

188 "Holy Family of Francis I"

189 Cuvier's Beaked Whale

(Des Design Images. Litho Questa)

1982 (3 Nov). *Christmas. Raphael Paintings. T **188** and similar vert designs. Multicoloured. P 13½ × 14.*
834	25 c. Type **188** ..	15	10
835	30 c. "Holy Family of the Pearl"	15	10
836	90 c. "Canigiani Holy Family"	30	35
837	$4 "Holy Family of the Oak Tree"	1·25	1·50
834/7	*Set of 4*	1·60	1·75
MS838	95 × 125 mm. $5 "Holy Family of the Lamb" ..	1·75	2·00

(Des J. Cooter. Litho Questa)

1983 (15 Feb). *Save the Whales. T **189** and similar horiz designs. Multicoloured. P 14.*
839	45 c. Type **189** ..	2·00	65
840	60 c. Humpback Whale	2·25	1·75
841	75 c. Black Right Whale	2·25	2·25
842	$3 Melon-headed Whale	4·50	6·50
839/42	*Set of 4*	10·00	10·00
MS843	99 × 72 mm. $5 Pygmy Sperm Whale	4·00	4·00

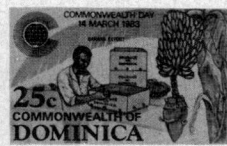

190 Banana Export

(Des R. Vigurs. Litho Questa)

1983 (14 Mar). *Commonwealth Day. T **190** and similar horiz designs. Multicoloured. P 14.*
844	25 c. Type **190** ..	15	15
845	30 c. Road building	15	20
846	90 c. Community nursing	30	45
847	$3 Tourism—handicrafts	75	1·50
844/7	*Set of 4*	1·25	2·10

191 Map and Satellite Picture of Hurricane

(Des G. Vasarhelyi. Litho Questa)

1983 (18 Apr). *World Communications Year. T **191** and similar horiz designs. Multicoloured. P 14.*
848	45 c. Type **191**	20	25
849	60 c. Aircraft-to-ship transmission	25	35
850	90 c. Satellite communications	30	45
851	$2 Shortwave radio	75	1·00
848/51	*Set of 4*	1·40	1·90
MS852	110 × 85 mm. $5 Communications satellite	2·00	2·75

192 Short-Mayo Composite

(Des W. Wright. Litho Format)

1983 (19 July). *Bicentenary of Manned Flight. T **192** and similar horiz designs. Multicoloured. P 14½.*
853	45 c. Type **192**	50	30
854	60 c. Macchi M.39 Schneider Trophy seaplane	75	85
855	90 c. Fairey Swordfish torpedo bomber	90	1·90
856	$4 Airship LZ-3 ..	2·25	4·75
853/6	*Set of 4*	4·00	6·50
MS857	105 × 79 mm. $5 *Double Eagle II* (balloon)	1·50	2·75

Nos. 853/7 exist imperforate from stock dispersed by the liquidator of Format International Security Printers Ltd.

193 Duesenberg "SJ", 1935

(Des R. Sauber. Litho Questa)

1983 (1 Sept). *Classic Motor Cars. T **193** and similar horiz designs. Multicoloured. P 14.*
858	10 c. Type **193** ..	30	15
859	45 c. Studebaker "Avanti", 1962	40	25
860	60 c. Cord "812", 1936	50	35
861	75 c. MG "TC", 1945	55	50
862	90 c. Camaro "350 SS", 1967	65	60
863	$3 Porsch "356", 1948	1·25	1·60
858/63	*Set of 6*	3·25	3·00
MS864	110 × 75 mm. $5 Ferrari "312 T", 1975	2·00	2·75

194 "Charity"

(Des Design Images. Litho Format)

1983 (4 Oct). *Christmas. 500th Birth Anniv of Raphael. T **194** and similar horiz designs. Multicoloured. P 13½.*
865	45 c. Type **194** ..	40	30
866	60 c. "Hope"	40	50
867	90 c. "Faith"	50	60
868	$4 "The Cardinal Virtues"	1·10	3·00
865/8	*Set of 4*	2·25	4·00
MS869	101 × 127 mm. $5 "Justice"	1·50	2·75

Nos. 867 and MS869 exist imperforate from stock dispersed by the liquidator of Format International Security Printers Ltd.

195 Plumbeous Warbler   **196** Donald Duck

(Des Jennifer Toombs. Litho Questa)

1984 (24 Apr). *Birds. T **195** and similar horiz designs. Multicoloured. P 14.*
870	5 c. Type **195** ..	2·25	1·10
871	45 c. Imperial Amazon	4·50	75
872	60 c. Blue-headed Hummingbird	5·00	3·25
873	90 c. Red-necked Amazon	6·00	6·00
870/3	*Set of 4*	16·00	10·00
MS874	72 × 72 mm. $5 Greater Flamingos	4·00	4·50

(Litho Format)

1984 (1 May). *Easter. T **196** and similar vert designs showing Disney cartoon characters and eggs. Multicoloured. P 11.*
875	½ c. Type **196** ..	10	10
876	1 c. Mickey Mouse	10	10
877	2 c. Tortoise and Hare	10	10
878	3 c. Brer Rabbit and Brer Bear	10	10
879	4 c. Donald Duck (*different*)	10	10
880	5 c. White Rabbit	10	10
881	10 c. Thumper	10	10
882	$2 Pluto	3·25	2·75
883	$4 Pluto (*different*)	4·50	4·00
875/83	*Set of 9*	7·50	6·50
MS884	126 × 100 mm. $5 Chip and Dale. P 13½ × 14	3·50	4·00

197 Gymnastics   **198** *Atlantic Star*

(Des R. Sauber. Litho Questa)

1984 (14 May). *Olympic Games, Los Angeles. T **197** and similar vert designs. Multicoloured. P 14.*
885	30 c. Type **197** ..	20	25
886	45 c. Javelin-throwing	30	35
887	60 c. High diving	40	45
888	$4 Fencing	2·00	2·50
885/8	*Set of 4*	2·50	3·25
MS889	104 × 85 mm. $5 Equestrian event	3·25	3·25

(Des W. Wright. Litho Questa)

1984 (14 June). *Shipping. T **198** and similar horiz designs. Multicoloured. P 14.*
890	45 c. Type **198**..	1·75	75
891	60 c. *Atlantic* (liner)	2·00	1·75
892	90 c. Carib fishing boat	2·50	2·50
893	$4 *Norway* (liner)	6·00	8·00
890/3	*Set of 4*	11·00	11·50
MS894	106 × 79 mm. $5 *Santa Maria*, 1492	3·75	5·50

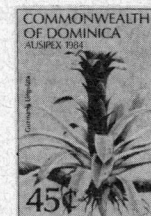

19th UPU CONGRESS HAMBURG

(199)   **200** *Guzmania lingulata*

1984 (19 June). *Universal Postal Union Congress, Hamburg. Nos. 769A and 780A optd with T **199**.*
895	10 c. Passion Fruit	10	10
896	$5 Heliconia or Lobster Claw	2·75	3·75

(Des P. Barrett. Litho Questa)

1984 (13 Aug). *"Ausipex" International Stamp Exhibition, Melbourne. Bromiliads. T **200** and similar vert designs. Multicoloured. P 14.*
897	45 c. Type **200** ..	30	35
898	60 c. Pitcairnia angustifolia	40	55
899	75 c. Tillandsia fasciculata	50	75
900	$3 Aechmea smithiorum	2·00	3·25
897/900	*Set of 4*	2·75	4·50
MS901	75 × 105 mm. $5 Tillandsia utriculata	2·75	4·25

201 "The Virgin and Child with Young St John" (Correggio)   **202** "Before the Start" (Edgar Degas)

(Litho Format)

1984 (30 Oct). *450th Death Anniv of Correggio (painter). T **201** and similar vert designs. Multicoloured. P 15.*
902	25 c. Type **201** ..	40	20
903	60 c. "Christ bids Farewell to the Virgin Mary"	50	40
904	90 c. "Do not Touch Me"	60	80
905	$4 "The Mystical Marriage of St Catherine"	1·10	3·25
902/5	*Set of 4*	2·40	4·25
MS906	89 × 60 mm. $5 "The Adoration of the Magi"	1·75	3·50

Nos. 902/6 exist imperforate from stock dispersed by the liquidator of Format International Security Printers Ltd.

(Litho Format)

1984 (30 Oct). *150th Birth Anniv of Edgar Degas (painter). T **202** and similar multicoloured designs. P 15.*
907	30 c. Type **202** ..	40	25
908	45 c. "Race on the Racecourse"	45	35
909	$1 "Jockeys at the Flagpole"	70	1·10
910	$3 "Racehorses at Longchamp"	1·25	3·50
907/10	*Set of 4*	2·50	4·75
MS911	89 × 60 mm. $5 "Self-portrait" (*vert*)	2·00	3·75

Nos. 907/11 exist imperforate from stock dispersed by the liquidator of Format International Security Printers Ltd.

203 Tabby   **204** Hawker Siddeley H.S.748

(Des I. MacLaury. Litho Format)

1984 (12 Nov). *Cats. T **203** and similar horiz designs. Multicoloured. P 15.*
912	10 c. Type **203** ..	20	15
913	15 c. Calico Shorthair ..	25	15
914	20 c. Siamese	35	15
915	25 c. Manx	40	20
916	45 c. Abyssinian	65	30
917	60 c. Tortoise-shell Longhair ..	80	65
918	$1 Cornish Rex	1·40	1·00
919	$2 Persian	2·00	3·00
920	$3 Himalayan	2·75	4·00
921	$5 Burmese	3·75	7·00
912/21	*Set of 10*	11·50	15·00
MS922	105 × 75 mm. $5 Grey Burmese, Persian and American Shorthair	3·50	6·50

Nos. 912/22 exist imperforate from stock dispersed by the liquidator of Format International Security Printers Ltd.

(Des Bonny Redecker. Litho Questa)

1984 (26 Nov). *40th Anniv of International Civil Aviation Organisation. T 204 and similar vert designs. Multicoloured. P 14.*

923	30 c. Type 204	1·25	35
924	60 c. De Havilland D.H.C.6 Twin Otter 100	2·00	80
925	$1 Britten Norman Islander	2·25	1·40
926	$3 De Havilland D.H.C.6 Twin Otter 100 (*different*)	4·00	4·50
923/6	*Set of 4*	8·50	6·25
MS927	102×75 mm. $5 Boeing 747-200	3·25	3·50

205 Donald Duck, Mickey Mouse and Goofy with Father Christmas

206 Mrs. M. Bascom presenting Trefoil to Chief Guide Lady Baden-Powell

(Litho Questa)

1984 (30 Nov). *Christmas. Walt Disney Cartoon Characters. T 205 and similar vert designs. Multicoloured. P 12 ($2) or 13½ × 14 (others).*

928	45 c. Type 205	1·25	30
929	60 c. Donald Duck as Father Christmas with toy train	1·50	70
930	90 c. Donald Duck as Father Christmas in sleigh	2·00	1·75
931	$2 Donald Duck and nephews in sledge	3·25	3·75
932	$4 Donald Duck in snow with Christmas tree	4·25	5·50
928/32	*Set of 5*	11·00	11·00
MS933	127 × 102 mm. $5 Donald Duck and nephews opening present	3·50	4·00

No. 931 was printed in sheetlets of 8 stamps.

(Des Marlise Najaka. Litho Questa)

1985 (28 Feb). *75th Anniv of Girl Guide Movement. T 206 and similar multicoloured designs. P 14.*

934	35 c. Type 206	60	30
935	45 c. Lady Baden-Powell inspecting Dominician Brownies	80	35
936	60 c. Lady Baden-Powell with Mrs. M. Bascom and Mrs. A. Robinson (Guide leaders)	1·00	65
937	$3 Lord and Lady Baden-Powell (*vert*)	2·50	3·50
934/7	*Set of 4*	4·50	4·25
MS938	77 × 105 mm. $5 Flags of Dominica and Girl Guide Movement	3·50	4·00

(Litho Questa)

1985 (4 Apr). *Birth Bicentenary of John J. Audubon (ornithologist) (1st issue). Multicoloured designs as T 198 of Antigua showing original paintings. P 14.*

939	45 c. Clapper Rail	1·10	30
940	$1 Black and White Warbler (*vert*)	2·00	1·25
941	$2 Broad-winged Hawk (*vert*)	2·75	2·75
942	$3 Ring-necked Duck	3·50	3·25
939/42	*Set of 4*	8·50	6·75
MS943	101×73 mm. $5 Reddish Egret	3·50	3·75

Nos. 939/42 were each printed in sheetlets of five stamps and one stamp-size label which appears in the centre of the bottom row.

See also Nos. 1013/17.

207 Student with Computer

208 The Queen Mother visiting Sadlers Wells Opera

(Des BG Studio. Litho Questa)

1985 (30 Apr). *Duke of Edinburgh's Award Scheme. T 207 and similar vert designs. Multicoloured. P 14.*

944	45 c. Type 207	35	30
945	60 c. Assisting doctor in hospital	75	40
946	90 c. Two youths hiking	90	80
947	$4 Family jogging	2·75	3·75
944/7	*Set of 4*	4·25	4·75
MS948	100×98 mm. $5 Duke of Edinburgh	2·75	3·00

(Des J.W. Litho Questa)

1985 (15 July). *Life and Times of Queen Elizabeth the Queen Mother. T 208 and similar multicoloured designs. P 14.*

949	60 c. Type 208	75	50
950	$1 Fishing in Scotland	80	60
951	$3 On her 84th birthday	1·90	2·25
949/51	*Set of 3*	3·00	3·00
MS952	56×85 mm. $5 Attending Garter ceremony, Windsor Castle	3·00	3·00

209 Cricket Match ("Sports")

210 Two Players competing for Ball

(Des S. Heinmann. Litho Questa)

1985 (22 July). *International Youth Year. T 209 and similar horiz designs. Multicoloured. P 14.*

953	45 c. Type 209	3·50	1·50
954	60 c. Bird-watching ("Environmental Study")	3·75	2·25
955	$1 Stamp collecting ("Education")	4·00	3·25
956	$3 Boating ("Leisure")	5·50	7·50
953/6	*Set of 4*	15·00	13·00
MS957	96×65 mm. $5 Young people linking hands	2·75	4·00

(Des Susan David. Litho Questa)

1985 (2 Sept). *300th Birth Anniv of Johann Sebastian Bach (composer). Vert designs as T 206 of Antigua showing antique musical instruments. P 14.*

958	45 c. multicoloured	1·50	40
959	60 c. multicoloured	1·75	60
960	$1 multicoloured	2·25	1·00
961	$3 multicoloured	4·00	3·50
958/61	*Set of 4*	8·50	5·00
MS962	109×75 mm. $5 black	4·00	4·50

Designs:—45 c. Cornett; 60 c. Coiled trumpet; $1 Piccolo; $3 Violoncello piccolo; $5 Johann Sebastian Bach.

(Litho Format)

1985 (25 Oct). *Royal Visit. Multicoloured designs as T 207 of Antigua. P 14½.*

963	60 c. Flags of Great Britain and Dominica	1·00	70
964	$1 Queen Elizabeth II (*vert*)	1·00	1·75
965	$4 Royal Yacht *Britannia*	2·25	5·50
963/5	*Set of 3*	3·75	7·00
MS966	111×83 mm. $5 Map of Dominica	3·50	4·00

(Litho Questa)

1985 (11 Nov). *150th Birth Anniv of Mark Twain (author). Horiz designs as T 118 of Anguilla showing Walt Disney cartoon characters in scenes from "Tom Sawyer". Multicoloured. P 14×13½.*

967	20 c. "The glorious whitewasher"	75	30
968	60 c. "Aunt Polly's home dentistry"	1·50	75
969	$1 "Aunt Polly's pain killer"	2·00	1·25
970	$1.50, Mickey Mouse balancing on fence	2·50	3·00
971	$2 "Lost in the cave with Becky"	2·75	3·50
967/71	*Set of 5*	8·50	8·00
MS972	126×101 mm. $5 Mickey Mouse as pirate	5·50	7·00

(Des Walt Disney Productions. Litho Questa)

1985 (11 Nov). *Birth Bicentenaries of Grimm Brothers (folklorists). Horiz designs as T 119 of Anguilla showing Walt Disney cartoon characters in scenes from "Little Red Cap". Multicoloured. P 14×13½.*

973	10 c. Little Red Cap (Daisy Duck) meeting the Wolf	30	20
974	45 c. The Wolf at the door	85	30
975	90 c. The Wolf in Grandmother's bed	1·75	1·75
976	$1 The Wolf lunging at Little Red Cap	2·00	1·75
977	$3 The Woodsman (Donald Duck) chasing the Wolf	3·75	5·00
973/7	*Set of 5*	7·75	8·00
MS978	126×101 mm. $5 The Wolf falling into cooking pot	5·00	5·50

(Litho Format)

1985 (27 Nov). *40th Anniv of United Nations Organization. Horiz designs as T 208 of Antigua showing United Nations (New York) stamps. Multicoloured. P 14½.*

979	45 c. Lord Baden-Powell and 1984 International Youth Year 35 c.	70	50
980	$2 Maimonides (physician) and 1966 W.H.O Building 11 c.	1·50	3·25
981	$3 Sir Rowland Hill (postal reformer) and 1976 25th anniv of U.N. Postal Administration 13 c.	1·50	3·50
979/81	*Set of 3*	3·25	6·50
MS982	110×85 mm. $5 "Apollo" spacecraft	2·75	3·25

(Des J. Iskowitz. Litho Questa)

1986 (26 Mar). *World Cup Football Championship, Mexico. T 210 and similar vert designs. Multicoloured. P 14.*

983	45 c. Type 210	1·75	40
984	60 c. Player heading ball	2·00	1·50
985	$1 Two players competing for ball (*different*)	2·25	1·75
986	$3 Player with ball	4·50	6·00
983/6	*Set of 4*	9·50	8·75
MS987	114×84 mm. $5 Three players	8·00	10·00

NEW INFORMATION

The editor is always interested to correspond with people who have new information that will improve or correct the Catalogue.

211 Police in Rowing Boat pursuing River Pirates, 1890

(Des J. Iskowitz. Litho Questa)

1986 (27 Mar). *Centenary of Statue of Liberty. T 211 and similar multicoloured designs. P 14.*

988	15 c. Type 211.	1·50	65
989	25 c. Police patrol launch, 1986	2·00	85
990	45 c. Hoboken Ferry Terminal, c 1890	2·00	85
991	$4 Holland Tunnel entrance and staff, 1986	4·50	6·00
988/91	*Set of 4*	9·00	7·50
MS992	104×76 mm. $5 Statue of Liberty (*vert*)	4·00	4·00

(Des W. Hanson. Litho Questa)

1986 (17 Apr). *Appearance of Halley's Comet (1st issue). Horiz designs as T 123 of Anguilla. Multicoloured. P 14.*

993	5 c. Nasir al Din al Tusi (Persian astronomer) and Jantal Mantar Observatory, Delhi	15	15
994	10 c. Bell XS-1 Rocket Plane breaking sound barrier for first time, 1947	20	15
995	45 c. Halley's Comet of 1531 (from "Astronomicum Caesareum", 1540)	55	30
996	$4 Mark Twain and quotation, 1910	2·75	3·75
993/6	*Set of 4*	3·25	4·00
MS997	104×71 mm. $5 Halley's Comet over Dominica	3·00	3·50

See also Nos. 1032/6.

(Des and litho Questa)

1986 (5 May). *60th Birthday of Queen Elizabeth II. Vert designs as T 125 of Anguilla. P 14.*

998	2 c. multicoloured	10	15
999	$1 multicoloured	70	80
1000	$5 multicoloured	2·00	3·00
998/1000	*Set of 3*	2·50	3·50
MS1001	120×85mm. $5 black and grey-brown	3·00	3·75

Designs:—2 c. Wedding photograph, 1947; $1 Queen meeting Pope John Paul II, 1982; $4 Queen on royal visit, 1971; $5 Princess Elizabeth with corgis, 1936.

212 Mickey Mouse and Pluto mounting Stamps in Album

213 William I

(Des Walt Disney Productions. Litho Format)

1986 (22 May). *"Ameripex" International Stamp Exhibition, Chicago. T 212 and similar horiz designs showing Walt Disney cartoon characters. Multicoloured. P 11.*

1002	25 c. Type 212	60	40
1003	45 c. Donald Duck examining stamp under magnifying glass	80	65
1004	60 c. Chip n'Dale soaking and drying stamps	1·10	1·50
1005	$4 Donald Duck as scoutmaster awarding merit badges to Nephews	3·50	6·00
1002/5	*Set of 4*	5·50	7·75
MS1006	127×101 mm. $5 Uncle Scrooge conducting stamp auction. P 14×13½	4·00	8·00

Nos. 1002/4 exist imperforate from stock dispersed by the liquidator of Format International Security Printers Ltd.

(Des Mary Walters. Litho Questa)

1986 (9 June). *500th Anniv of Succession of House of Tudor to English Throne (1985). T 213 and similar vert designs. Multicoloured. P 14.*

1007	10 c. Type 213	40	40
1008	40 c. Richard II	80	80
1009	50 c. Henry VIII	90	90
1010	$1 Charles II	1·25	1·75
1011	$2 Queen Anne	2·00	3·00
1012	$4 Queen Victoria	2·50	4·50
1007/12	*Set of 6*	7·00	10·00

Nos. 1007/12 were each issued in sheetlets of five stamps and one stamp-size label showing the monarch's consort.

(Litho Questa)

1986 (18 June). *Birth Bicentenary of John J. Audubon (ornithologist) (1985) (2nd issue). Multicoloured designs as T 198 of Antigua showing original paintings. P 12½×12 (25 c., $4) or 12×12½ (others).*

1013	25 c. Black-throated Diver	1·50	50
1014	60 c. Great Blue Heron (*vert*)	2·00	1·50
1015	90 c. Yellow-crowned Night Heron (*vert*)	2·00	2·25
1016	$4 Common Shoveler	4·50	6·50
1013/16	*Set of 4*	9·00	9·75
MS1017	73×103 mm. $5 Canada Goose. P 14	10·00	12·00

Nos. 1013/16 were each issued in sheetlets of five stamps and one stamp-size label, which appears in the centre of the bottom row.

(Litho Questa)

1986 (1 July). *Royal Wedding. Vert designs as T* **213** *of Antigua. Multicoloured. P* 14.

1018	45 c. Prince Andrew and Miss Sarah Ferguson		35	30
1019	60 c. Prince Andrew..		45	45
1020	$4 Prince Andrew climbing aboard aircraft		2·00	3·00
1018/20		*Set of 3*	2·50	3·25
MS1021	88 × 88 mm. $5 Prince Andrew and Miss Sarah Ferguson (*different*)		3·75	4·50

1986 (15 Sept). *World Cup Football Championship Winners, Mexico. Nos.* 983/7 optd with T **216** of Antigua in gold.

1022	45 c. Type **210**		1·50	55
1023	60 c. Player heading ball		1·75	1·50
1024	$1 Two players competing for ball		2·25	2·50
1025	$3 Player with ball		5·00	7·00
1022/5		*Set of 4*	9·50	10·50
MS1026	114 × 84 mm. $5 Three players..		8·50	11·00

214 "The Virgin at Prayer" 215 Broad-winged Hawk

(Litho Questa)

1986 (2 Dec). *Christmas. Paintings by Dürer. T* **214** *and similar vert designs. Multicoloured. P* 14.

1027	45 c. Type **214**		1·00	35
1028	60 c. "Madonna and Child"..		1·50	1·25
1029	$1 "The Madonna with the Pear"		2·00	2·25
1030	$3 "Madonna and Child with St. Anne"		5·50	8·50
1027/30		*Set of 4*	9·00	11·00
MS1031	76 × 102 mm. $5 "The Nativity"		8·00	11·00

1986 (16 Dec). *Appearance of Halley's Comet (2nd issue). Nos.* 993/7 optd as T **218** of Antigua (in silver on $5).

1032	5 c. Nasir al Din al Tusi (Persian astronomer) and Jantal Mantar Observatory, Delhi		15	15
1033	10 c. Bell XS-1 Rocket Plane breaking sound barrier for first time, 1947		20	15
1034	45 c. Halley's Comet of 1531 (from "Astronomicum Caesareum", 1540)		55	30
1035	$4 Mark Twain and quotation, 1910		2·75	3·50
1032/5		*Set of 4*	3·25	3·75
MS1036	104 × 71 mm. $5 Halley's Comet over Dominica		3·25	3·50

(Des S. Heinmann. Litho Format)

1987 (20 Jan). *Birds of Dominica. T* **215** *and similar vert designs. Multicoloured. Without imprint date. P* 15.

1037	1 c. Type **215**		20	40
1038	2 c. Ruddy Quail Dove		20	40
1039	5 c. Red-necked Pigeon		30	40
1040	10 c. Green Heron		30	15
1041	15 c. Moorhen		40	20
1042	20 c. Ringed Kingfisher		40	20
1043	25 c. Brown Pelican		40	20
1044	35 c. White-tailed Tropic Bird		40	30
1045	45 c. Red-legged Thrush		50	30
1046	60 c. Purple-throated Carib		65	45
1047	90 c. Magnificent Frigate Bird		70	70
1048	$1 Brown Trembler		80	80
1049	$2 Black-capped Petrel		1·25	4·00
1050	$5 Barn Owl		3·00	5·00
1051	$10 Imperial Amazon		5·00	9·50
1037/51		*Set of 15*	13·00	20·00

For similar stamps, with imprint date and perforated 14, 12 or 12½×11½ see Nos. 1241/54.

(Des J. Iskowitz. Litho Format)

1987 (16 Feb). *America's Cup Yachting Championship. Multicoloured designs as T* **222** *of Antigua. P* 15.

1052	45 c. *Reliance*, 1903 ..		50	30
1053	60 c. *Freedom*, 1980..		60	55
1054	$1 *Mischief*, 1881 ..		80	90
1055	$3 *Australia*, 1977		1·25	3·00
1052/5		*Set of 4*	2·75	4·25
MS1056	113 × 83 mm. $5 *Courageous*, 1977 (*horiz*)		3·00	5·00

Nos. 1052/6 exist imperforate from stock dispersed by the liquidator of Format International Security Printers Ltd.

(Litho Questa)

1987 (24 Mar). *Birth Centenary of Marc Chagall (artist). Multicoloured designs as T* **225** *of Antigua. P* 13½×14.

1057	25 c. "Artist and His Model"		10	10
1058	35 c. "Midsummer Night's Dream"		15	20
1059	45 c. "Joseph the Shepherd"		20	25
1060	60 c. "The Cellist"		25	30
1061	90 c. "Woman with Pigs"		40	45
1062	$1 "The Blue Circus"		45	50
1063	$3 "For Vava"		1·25	1·40
1064	$4 "The Rider"		1·75	1·90
1057/64		*Set of 8*	4·50	5·00
MS1065	Two sheets, each 110 × 95 mm. (a) $5 "Purim" (104 × 89 mm). (b) $5 "Firebird" (stage design) (104 × 89 mm) .. *Set of 2 sheets*		4·25	4·50

216 Poulsen's Triton 217 *Cantharellus cinnabarinus*

(Des L. Birmingham. Litho Format)

1987 (11 May). *Sea Shells. T* **216** *and similar designs. P* 15.

1066	35 c. multicoloured		20	20
1067	45 c. bluish violet, black and bright rose ..		25	25
1068	60 c. multicoloured		30	40
1069	$5 multicoloured		2·40	4·00
1066/9		*Set of 4*	2·75	4·25
MS1070	109 × 75 mm. $5 multicoloured.		3·25	5·50

Designs: *Vert*—45 c. Elongate Janthina; 60 c. Banded Tulip; $5 (No. 1069) Deltoid Rock Shell. *Horiz*—$5 (No. **MS**1070) Junonia Volute.

No. 1066 is inscribed "TIRITON" in error.

(Des BG Studio. Litho Questa)

1987 (15 June). *"Capex '87" International Stamp Exhibition, Toronto. Mushrooms of Dominica. T* **217** *and similar horiz designs. Multicoloured. P* 14.

1071	45 c. Type **217**		1·50	50
1072	60 c. *Boletellus cubensis*		2·00	1·25
1073	$2 *Eccilia cystiophorus*		4·25	4·50
1074	$3 *Xerocomus guadelupae*		4·50	5·00
1071/4		*Set of 4*	11·00	10·00
MS1075	85 × 85 mm. $5 *Gymnopilus chrysopellus*		9·00	11·00

218 Discovery of Dominica, 1493 219 "Virgin and Child with St. Anne" (Dürer)

(Des I. MacLaury. Litho Format)

1987 (27 July). *500th Anniv of Discovery of America (1992) (1st issue). T* **218** *and similar horiz designs. Multicoloured. P* 15.

1076	10 c. Type **218**		40	25
1077	15 c. Caribs greeting Columbus's fleet		50	30
1078	45 c. Claiming the New World for Spain ..		65	35
1079	60 c. Wreck of *Santa Maria*		80	60
1080	90 c. Fleet leaving Spain		1·00	1·00
1081	$1 Sighting the New World		1·10	1·10
1082	$3 Trading with Indians ..		2·25	3·00
1083	$5 Building settlement		3·25	4·00
1076/83		*Set of 8*	9·00	9·75
MS1084	Two sheets, each 109 × 79 mm. (a) $5 Fleet off Dominica, 1493. (b) $5 Map showing Columbus's route, 1493. *Set of 2 sheets*		5·50	8·00

See also Nos. 1221/5, 1355/63, 1406/14, 1547/53 and 1612/13.

(Des G. Welker. Litho Questa)

1987 (28 Sept). *Milestones of Transportation. Multicoloured designs as T* **226** *of Antigua. P* 14.

1085	10 c. H.M.S. *Warrior* (first ironclad warship), 1860		50	50
1086	15 c. MAGLEV-MLU 001 (fastest train), 1979		60	60
1087	25 c. *Flying Cloud* (fastest clipper passage New York–San Francisco) (*vert*)		70	70
1088	35 c. First elevated railway, New York, 1868 (*vert*)		80	80
1089	45 c. Peter Cooper's locomotive, *Tom Thumb* (first U.S. passenger locomotive), 1829		80	80
1090	60 c. *Spray* (Slocum's solo circumnavigation), 1895–8 (*vert*)		90	90
1091	90 c. *Sea-Land Commerce* (fastest Pacific passage), 1973 (*vert*)		1·25	1·25
1092	$1 First cable cars, San Francisco, 1873 ..		1·40	1·40
1093	$3 "Orient Express", 1883		3·00	3·00
1094	$4 *Clermont* (first commercial paddlesteamer), 1807		3·25	3·25
1085/94		*Set of 10*	12·00	12·00

(Litho Questa)

1987 (16 Nov). *Christmas. Religious Paintings. T* **219** *and similar vert designs. Multicoloured. P* 14.

1095	20 c. Type **219**		30	15
1096	25 c. "Virgin and Child" (Murillo) ..		30	15
1097	$2 "Madonna and Child" (Foppa)		1·50	2·25
1098	$4 "Madonna and Child" (Da Verona) ..		2·75	4·00
1095/8		*Set of 4*	4·25	6·00
MS1099	100 × 78 mm. $5 "Angel of the Annunciation" (anon, Renaissance period)		2·50	3·50

NEW INFORMATION

The editor is always interested to correspond with people who have new information that will improve or correct the Catalogue.

220 Three Little Pigs in People Mover, Walt Disney World 221 Kayak Canoeing

(Des Walt Disney Company. Litho Questa)

1987 (22 Dec). *60th Anniv of Mickey Mouse (Walt Disney cartoon character). T* **220** *and similar multicoloured designs showing cartoon characters in trains. P* 13½×14.

1100	20 c. Type **220**		45	35
1101	25 c. Goofy driving horse tram, Disneyland		45	35
1102	45 c. Donald Duck in *Roger E. Broggie*, Walt Disney World		75	65
1103	60 c. Goofy, Mickey Mouse, Donald Duck and Chip n'Dale aboard Big Thunder Mountain train, Disneyland		85	75
1104	90 c. Mickey Mouse in *Walter E. Disney*, Disneyland		1·40	1·25
1105	$1 Mickey and Minnie Mouse, Goofy, Donald and Daisy Duck in monorail, Walt Disney World		1·50	1·40
1106	$3 Dumbo flying over *Casey Jr* ..		3·25	3·75
1107	$4 Daisy Duck and Minnie Mouse in *Lilly Belle*, Walt Disney World		3·75	4·50
1100/7		*Set of 8*	11·00	11·50
MS1108	Two sheets, each 127 × 101 mm. (a) $5 Seven Dwarfs in Rainbow Caverns Mine train, Disneyland (*horiz*). (b) $5 Donald Duck and Chip n'Dale on toy train (from film *Out of Scale*) (*horiz*). P 14 × 13½ .. *Set of 2 sheets*		5·50	7·00

(Des and litho Questa)

1988 (15 Feb). *Royal Ruby Wedding. Vert designs as T* **234** *of Antigua. P* 14.

1109	45 c. multicoloured		85	30
1110	60 c. deep brown, black and light green		1·00	70
1111	$1 multicoloured		1·25	1·00
1112	$3 multicoloured		2·50	3·50
1109/12		*Set of 4*	5·00	5·00
MS1113	102 × 76 mm. $5 multicoloured		3·00	3·75

Designs:— 45 c. Wedding portrait with attendants, 1947; 60 c. Princess Elizabeth with Prince Charles, *c.* 1950; $1 Princess Elizabeth and Prince Philip with Prince Charles and Princess Anne, 1950; $3 Queen Elizabeth; $5 Princess Elizabeth in wedding dress, 1947.

(Des D. Miller. Litho Questa)

1988 (14 Mar). *Olympic Games, Seoul. T* **221** *and similar vert designs. Multicoloured. P* 14.

1114	45 c. Type **221**		75	35
1115	60 c. Taekwon-do ..		1·00	1·00
1116	$1 High diving		1·10	1·25
1117	$3 Gymnastics on bars ..		2·25	4·00
1114/17		*Set of 4*	4·50	6·00
MS1118	81 × 110 mm. $5 Football		2·50	3·50

222 Carib Indian 223 White-tailed Tropic Bird

(Des K. Gromell. Litho Questa)

1988 (13 Apr). *"Reunion '88" Tourism Programme. T* **222** *and similar multicoloured designs. P* 15.

1119	10 c. Type **222**		10	10
1120	25 c. Mountainous interior (*horiz*)		10	15
1121	35 c. Indian River ..		10	15
1122	60 c. Belaire dancer and tourists		15	30
1123	90 c. Boiling Lake		20	60
1124	$3 Coral reef (*horiz*)		60	2·00
1119/24		*Set of 6*	85	3·00
MS1125	112 × 82 mm. $5 Belaire dancer		1·75	4·00

1988 (1 June). *Stamp Exhibitions. Nos.* **MS**1084 *and* 1092/3 *optd as T* **241** *of Antigua showing various emblems.*

1126	$1 First cable cars, San Francisco, 1873 (optd "FINLANDIA 88", Helsinki)		1·00	75
1127	$3 "Orient Express", 1883 (optd "INDEPENDENCE 40", Israel)		2·00	2·25
	a. Opt albino			
MS1128	Two sheets, each 109 × 79 mm. (a) $5 Fleet off Dominica, 1493 (optd "OLYMPHILEX '88", Seoul). (b) $5 Map showing Columbus's route, 1493 (optd "Praga 88", Prague) *Set of 2 sheets*		4·25	5·50

(Des S. Barlow. Litho Questa)

1988 (25 July). *Dominica Rain Forest Flora and Fauna. T 223 and similar vert designs. Multicoloured. P 14½×14.*

1129	45 c. Type 223	..	50	50
	a. Sheetlet. Nos. 1129/48	..	9·00	
1130	45 c. Blue-hooded Euphonia	..	50	50
1131	45 c. Smooth-billed Ani	..	50	50
1132	45 c. Scaly-breasted Thrasher	..	50	50
1133	45 c. Purple-throated Carib	..	50	50
1134	45 c. *Marpesia petreus* and *Strymon maesites* (butterflies)		50	50
1135	45 c. Brown Trembler	..	50	50
1136	45 c. Imperial Amazon	..	50	50
1137	45 c. Mangrove Cuckoo	..	50	50
1138	45 c. *Dynastes hercules* (beetle)	..	50	50
1139	45 c. *Historis odius* (butterfly)	..	50	50
1140	45 c. Red-necked Amazon	..	50	50
1141	45 c. Tillandsia (plant)	..	50	50
1142	45 c. Bananaquit and *Polystacha luteola* (plant)		50	50
1143	45 c. False Chameleon	..	50	50
1144	45 c. Iguana	..	50	50
1145	45 c. *Hypolimnas misippus* (butterfly)	..	50	50
1146	45 c. Green-throated Carib	..	50	50
1147	45 c. Heliconia (plant)	..	50	50
1148	45 c. Agouti	..	50	50
1129/48		Set of 20	9·00	9·00

Nos. 1129/48 were printed together, *se-tenant*, in a sheetlet of 20 forming a composite design.

224 Battery Hens

225 Gary Cooper

(Des J. Martin. Litho Questa)

1988 (5 Sept). *10th Anniv of International Fund for Agricultural Development. T 224 and similar multicoloured designs. P 14.*

1149	45 c. Type 224	..	50	30
1150	60 c. Pig	..	70	65
1151	90 c. Cattle	..	95	1·25
1152	$3 Black Belly Sheep	..	2·25	4·00
1149/52		Set of 4	4·00	5·50
MS1153	95×68 mm. $5 Tropical fruits (vert)		2·25	3·50

(Des Lynda Bruscheni. Litho Questa)

1988 (8 Sept). *Entertainers. T 225 and similar vert designs. Multicoloured. P 14.*

1154	10 c. Type 225	..	10	10
1155	35 c. Josephine Baker	..	15	20
1156	45 c. Maurice Chevalier	..	20	25
1157	60 c. James Cagney	..	25	30
1158	$1 Clark Gable	..	45	50
1159	$2 Louis Armstrong	..	85	90
1160	$3 Liberace	..	1·25	1·40
1161	$4 Spencer Tracy	..	1·75	2·00
1154/61		Set of 8	5·00	5·50
MS1162	Two sheets, each 105×75 mm. (a) $5 Humphrey Bogart. (b) $5 Elvis Presley.			
		Set of 2 sheets	4·25	4·75

(Des Mary Walters. Litho Questa)

1988 (29 Sept). *Flowering Trees. Horiz designs as T 242 of Antigua. Multicoloured. P 14.*

1163	15 c. Sapodilla	..	10	10
1164	20 c. Tangerine	..	10	10
1165	25 c. Avocado Pear	..	10	10
1166	45 c. Amherstia	..	20	25
1167	90 c. Lipstick Tree	..	40	55
1168	$1 Cannonball Tree	..	45	55
1169	$3 Saman	..	1·25	1·75
1170	$4 Pineapple	..	1·60	2·00
1163/70		Set of 8	3·75	4·75
MS1171	Two sheets, each 96 × 66 mm. (a) $5 Lignum Vitae. (b) $5 Sea Grape	Set of 2 sheets	4·50	6·00

(Litho Questa)

1988 (10 Oct). *500th Birth Anniv of Titian (artist). Vert designs as T 238 of Antigua. Multicoloured. P 13½ × 14.*

1172	25 c. "Jacopo Strada"	..	15	15
1173	35 c. "Titian's Daughter Lavinia"	..	20	20
1174	45 c. "Andrea Navagero"	..	25	25
1175	60 c. "Judith with Head of Holoferenes"	..	30	30
1176	$1 "Emilia di Spilimbergo"	..	50	50
1177	$2 "Martyrdom of St. Lawrence"	..	80	1·25
1178	$3 "Salome"	..	1·25	2·00
1179	$4 "St. John the Baptist"	..	1·40	2·50
1172/9		Set of 8	4·25	6·50
MS1180	Two sheets, each 110 × 95 mm. (a) $5 "Self Portrait". (b) $5 "Sisyphus" Set of 2 sheets		4·25	6·00

PRICES OF SETS

Set prices are given for many issues, generally those containing three stamps or more. Definitive sets include one of each value or major colour change, but do not cover different perforations, die types or minor shades. Where a choice is possible the set prices are based on the cheapest versions of the stamps included in the listings.

226 Imperial Amazon

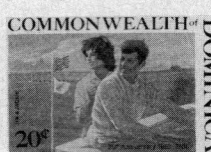

227 President and Mrs. Kennedy

(Des K. Gromell. Litho Questa)

1988 (31 Oct). *10th Anniv of Independence. T 226 and similar multicoloured designs. P 14.*

1181	20 c. Type 226		90	40
1182	45 c. Dominica 1874 1d. stamp and landscape (horiz)		90	30
1183	$2 1978 Independence 10 c. stamp and landscape (horiz)		1·50	2·75
1184	$3 Carib Wood (national flower)	..	1·75	3·25
1181/4		Set of 4	4·50	6·00
MS1185	116 × 85 mm. $5 Government Band (horiz) ..		2·25	3·50

(Des J. Martin. Litho Questa)

1988 (22 Nov). *25th Death Anniv of John F. Kennedy (American statesman). T 227 and similar multicoloured designs. P 14.*

1186	20 c. Type 227	..	10	10
1187	25 c. Kennedy sailing	..	10	10
1188	$2 Outside Hyannis Port house	..	80	1·50
1189	$4 Speaking in Berlin (vert)	..	1·60	2·50
1186/9		Set of 4	2·40	3·75
MS1190	100 × 71 mm. $5 President Kennedy (vert) ..		2·10	3·50

228 Donald Duck's Nephews decorating Christmas Tree

229 Raoul Wallenberg (diplomat) and Swedish Flag

(Des Walt Disney Co. Litho Questa)

1988 (1 Dec). *Christmas. "Mickey's Christmas Mall". T 228 and similar vert designs showing Walt Disney cartoon characters. Multicoloured. P 13½ × 14.*

1191	60 c. Type 228	..	55	65
	a. Sheetlet. Nos. 1191/8	..	4·00	
1192	60 c. Daisy Duck outside clothes shop	..	55	65
1193	60 c. Winnie the Pooh in shop window	..	55	65
1194	60 c. Goofy with parcels	..	55	65
1195	60 c. Donald Duck as Father Christmas	..	55	65
1196	60 c. Mickey Mouse contributing to collection		55	65
1197	60 c. Minnie Mouse	..	55	65
1198	60 c. Chip n' Dale with peanut	..	55	65
1191/8		Set of 8	4·00	4·75
MS1199	Two sheets, each 127 × 102 mm. (a) $6 Mordie Mouse with Father Christmas. (b) $6 Mickey Mouse at West Indian market			
		Set of 2 sheets	6·50	8·00

Nos. 1191/8 were printed together, *se-tenant* as a composite design, in sheetlets of eight.

(Des J. Genzo. Litho B.D.T.)

1988 (9 Dec). *40th Anniv of Universal Declaration of Human Rights. T 229 and similar multicoloured design. P 14.*

1200	$3 Type 229	..	2·00	2·50
MS1201	92 × 62 mm. $5 Human Rights Day logo (vert) ..		2·50	3·25

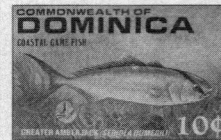

230 Greater Amberjack

(Des J. Iskowitz. Litho Questa)

1988 (22 Dec). *Game Fishes. T 230 and similar horiz designs. Multicoloured. P 14.*

1202	10 c. Type 230	..	20	15
1203	15 c. Blue Marlin	..	20	15
1204	35 c. Cobia	..	35	30
1205	45 c. Dolphin (fish)	..	45	30
1206	60 c. Cero	..	60	55
1207	90 c. Mahogany Snapper	..	85	95
1208	$3 Yellow-finned Tuna	..	2·50	3·25
1209	$4 Rainbow Parrotfish	..	3·00	3·75
1202/9		Set of 8	7·50	8·50
MS1210	Two sheets, each 104×74 mm. (a) $5 Manta. (b) $5 Tarpon	Set of 2 sheets	8·00	10·00

231 Leatherback Turtle (232)

(Des W. Wright. Litho Questa)

1988 (29 Dec). *Insects and Reptiles. T 231 and similar horiz designs. Multicoloured. P 14.*

1211	10 c. Type 231	..	45	35
1212	25 c. *Danaus plexippus* (butterfly)	..	1·25	75
1213	60 c. Green Anole (lizard)	..	1·60	1·25
1214	$3 *Mantis religiosa* (mantid)	..	4·00	6·50
1211/14		Set of 4	6·50	8·00
MS1215	119×90 mm. $5 *Dynastes hercules* (beetle) ..		3·00	4·50

1989 (20 Mar). *Olympic Medal Winners, Seoul. Nos. 1114/18 optd as T 232 (horizontally on No. MS1220).*

1216	45 c. Type 221 (optd with T 232)		20	25
1217	60 c. Taekwon-do (optd "Women's Flyweight N. Y. Choo S. Korea")		25	35
1218	$1 High diving (optd "Women's Platform Y. Xu China")		40	60
1219	$3 Gymnastics on bars (optd "V. Artemov USSR")		1·25	1·75
1216/19		Set of 4	1·90	2·75
MS1220	81×110 mm. $5 Football (optd "USSR defeated Brazil 3-2 on penalty kicks after a 1-1 tie") ..		3·25	4·00

(Des D. Miller. Litho Questa)

1989 (8 May). *500th Anniv of Discovery of America by Columbus (1992) (2nd issue). Pre-Columbian Carib Society. Designs as T 247 of Antigua, but horiz. Multicoloured. P 14.*

1221	20 c. Carib canoe	..	20	20
1222	35 c. Hunting with bows and arrows	..	30	20
1223	$1 Dugout canoe making	..	70	90
1224	$3 Shield contest	..	1·75	2·75
1221/4		Set of 4	2·75	3·50
MS1225	87×71 mm. $6 Ceremonial dance		2·75	4·00

233 Map of Dominica, 1766

234 *Papilio homerus*

(Des U. Purins. Litho B.D.T.)

1989 (17 July). *"Philexfrance 89" International Stamp Exhibition, Paris. T 233 and similar multicoloured designs. P 14.*

1226	10 c. Type 233	..	45	30
1227	35 c. French coin of 1653 (horiz)	..	65	40
1228	$1 French warship, 1720 (horiz)	..	1·40	1·25
1229	$4 Coffee plant (horiz)	..	2·00	3·00
1226/9		Set of 4	4·00	4·50
MS1230	98×98 mm. $5 Exhibition inscription (horiz) (black, grey and greenish yellow)		3·00	4·00

(Litho Questa)

1989 (31 Aug). *Japanese Art. Paintings by Taikan. Designs as T 250 of Antigua, but vert. Multicoloured. P 13½×14.*

1231	10 c. "Lao-tzu" (detail)		10	10
1232	20 c. "Red Maple Leaves" (panels 1 and 2)		10	10
1233	45 c. "King Wen Hui learns a Lesson from his Cook" (detail)		20	25
1234	60 c. "Red Maple Leaves" (panels 3 and 4)		25	35
1235	$1 "Wild Flowers" (detail)		45	50
1236	$2 "Red Maple Leaves" (panels 5 and 6)		85	90
1237	$3 "Red Maple Leaves" (panels 7 and 8)		1·25	1·50
1238	$4 "Indian Ceremony of Floating Lamps on the River" (detail)		1·75	1·90
1231/8		Set of 8	4·25	5·50
MS1239	Two sheets, each 78×102 mm. (a) $5 "Innocence" (detail). (b) 101×77 mm. $5 "Red Maple Leaves" (detail) .. Set of 2 sheets		5·50	5·75

Nos. 1231/8 were each printed in sheetlets of 10 containing two vertical strips of 5 stamps separated by printed labels commemorating Emperor Hirohito.

(Litho Questa)

1989 (31 Aug)–**91**. *As Nos. 1038/46 and 1048/51 but with "1989" imprint date. P 14.*

1241	2 c. Ruddy Quail Dove	..	40	60
	a. Perf 12 (1990)		40	60
	b. Perf 12½×11½ (1991)		55	60
1242	5 c. Red-necked Pigeon	..	50	40
	a. Perf 12 (1990)		50	40
	b. Perf 12½×11½ (1991)		70	40
1243	10 c. Green Heron	..	50	15
	a. Perf 12 (1990)		50	15
	b. Perf 12½×11½ (1991)		70	15
1244	15 c. Moorhen	..	60	30
	a. Perf 12 (1990)		60	30
	b. Perf 12½×11½ (1991)		80	30
1245	20 c. Ringed Kingfisher	..	65	40
	a. Perf 12 (1990)		65	40
	b. Perf 12½×11½ (1991)		85	40

1246	25 c. Brown Pelican		..	65	40
	a. Perf 12 (1990)	..	..	65	40
	b. Perf 12¹/₂×11¹/₂ (1991)	..		85	40
1247	35 c. White-tailed Tropic Bird		..	80	30
	a. Perf 12 (1990)		..	80	30
	b. Perf 12¹/₂×11¹/₂ (1991)	..		1·10	30
1248	45 c. Red-legged Thrush		..	1·00	30
	a. Perf 12 (1990)		..	1·00	30
	b. Perf 12¹/₂×11¹/₂ (1991)	..		1·25	30
1249	60 c. Purple-throated Carib		..	1·50	70
	a. Perf 12 (1990)		..	1·50	70
	b. Perf 12¹/₂×11¹/₂ (1991)	..		2·00	70
1251	$1 Brown Trembler		..	1·60	1·25
	a. Perf 12 (1990)		..	1·60	1·25
	b. Perf 12¹/₂×11¹/₂ (1991)	..		2·25	1·25
1252	$2 Black-capped Petrel		..	2·50	3·50
	a. Perf 12 (1990)		..	2·50	3·50
	b. Perf 12¹/₂×11¹/₂ (1991)	..		3·25	3·50
1253	$5 Barn Owl		..	5·50	7·00
	a. Perf 12 (1990)		..	5·50	7·00
	b. Perf 12¹/₂×11¹/₂ (1991)	..		6·50	7·00
1254	$10 Imperial Amazon		..	7·50	11·00
	a. Perf 12 (1989)		..	7·50	11·00
	b. Perf 12¹/₂×11¹/₂ (1991)	..		8·50	11·00
1241/54			Set of 13	21·00	23·00

Nos. 1241b/54b show a larger hole on every sixth perforation, both vertically and horizontally.

(Des W. Wright. Litho Questa)

1989 (11 Sept). *Butterflies. T* **234** *and similar horiz designs. Multicoloured. P* 14.

1255	10 c. Type **234**	..	40	30
1256	15 c. *Morpho peleides*	..	45	30
1257	25 c. *Dryas julia*	..	65	30
1258	35 c. *Parides gundlachianus*	..	70	30
1259	60 c. *Danaus plexippus*	..	1·00	75
1260	$1 *Agraulis vanillae*	..	1·25	1·25
1261	$3 *Phoebis avellaneda*	..	2·75	3·25
1262	$5 *Papilio andraemon*	..	3·75	5·00
1255/62		Set of 8	10·00	10·00

MS1263 Two sheets. (a) 105×74 mm. $6 *Adelpha cytherea*. (b) 105×79 mm. $6 *Adelpha iphicla*
Set of 2 sheets 8·00 9·00

235 *Oncidium pusillum*   236 "Apollo 11" Command Module in Lunar Orbit

(Des W. Hanson Studio. Litho Questa)

1989 (28 Sept). *Orchids. T* **235** *and similar vert designs. Multicoloured. P* 14.

1264	10 c. Type **235**	..	35	30
1265	35 c. *Epidendrum cochleata*	..	70	30
1266	45 c. *Epidendrum ciliare*	..	75	40
1267	60 c. *Cyrtopodium andersonii*	..	1·00	80
1268	$1 *Habenaria pauciflora*	..	1·25	1·25
1269	$2 *Maxillaria alba*	..	2·00	2·25
1270	$3 *Selenipedium palmifolium*	..	2·50	2·75
1271	$4 *Brassavola cucullata*	..	3·25	3·75
1264/71		Set of 8	10·50	10·50

MS1272 Two sheets, each 108×77 mm. (a) $5 *Oncidium lanceanum*. (b) $5 *Comparettia falcata*
Set of 2 sheets 8·00 9·00

(Litho Questa)

1989 (31 Oct). *20th Anniv of First Manned Landing on Moon. T* **236** *and similar multicoloured designs. P* 14.

1273	10 c. Type **236**	..	30	30
1274	60 c. Neil Armstrong leaving lunar module		70	70
1275	$2 Edwin Aldrin at Sea of Tranquility		1·60	2·00
1276	$3 Astronauts Armstrong and Aldrin with U.S. flag		2·00	2·50
1273/6		Set of 4	4·25	5·00

MS1277 62×77 mm. $6 Launch of "Apollo 11" (*vert*) .. 4·50 6·00

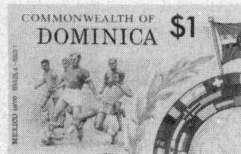

237 Brazil v Italy Final, 1970

(Des G. Vasarhelyi. Litho Questa)

1989 (8 Nov). *World Cup Football Championship, Italy* (1st issue). *T* **237** *and similar horiz designs. Multicoloured. P* 14.

1278	$1 Type **237**	..	1·75	2·00
	a. Sheetlet. Nos. 1278/81		6·00	
1279	$1 England v. West Germany, 1966		1·75	2·00
1280	$1 West Germany v. Holland, 1974		1·75	2·00
1281	$1 Italy v. West Germany, 1982		1·75	2·00
1278/81		Set of 4	6·00	7·00

MS1282 106×86 mm. $6 Two players competing for ball .. .. 4·00 4·75

Nos. 1278/81 were printed together, *se-tenant*, in a sheetlet of 4 stamps, forming a composite central design of a football surrounded by flags of competing nations.
See also Nos. 1383/7.

238 George Washington and Inauguration, 1789

(Des W. Hanson Studio. Litho Questa)

1989 (17 Nov). *"World Stamp Expo '89" International Stamp Exhibition, Washington* (1st issue). *Bicentenary of the U.S. Presidency. T* **238** *and similar horiz designs. Multicoloured. P* 14.

1283	60 c. Type **238**	..	60	60
	a. Sheetlet. Nos. 1283/8		3·25	
1284	60 c. John Adams and Presidential Mansion, 1800		60	60
1285	60 c. Thomas Jefferson, Graff House, Philadelphia and Declaration of Independence		60	60
1286	60 c. James Madison and U.S.S. *Constitution* defeating H.M.S. *Guerriere*, 1812		60	60
1287	60 c. James Monroe and freed slaves landing in Liberia		60	60
1288	60 c. John Quincy Adams and barge on Erie Canal		60	60
1289	60 c. Millard Fillmore and Perry's fleet off Japan		60	60
	a. Sheetlet. Nos. 1289/94		3·25	
1290	60 c. Franklin Pierce, Jefferson Davis and San Xavier Mission, Tucson		60	60
1291	60 c. James Buchanan, "Buffalo Bill" Cody carrying mail and Wells Fargo Pony Express stamp		60	60
1292	60 c. Abraham Lincoln and U.P.U. Monument, Berne		60	60
1293	60 c. Andrew Johnson, polar bear and Mt. McKinley, Alaska		60	60
1294	60 c. Ulysses S. Grant and Golden Spike Ceremony, 1869		60	60
1295	60 c. Theodore Roosevelt and steam shovel excavating Panama Canal		60	60
	a. Sheetlet. Nos. 1295/1300		3·25	
1296	60 c. William H. Taft and Admiral Peary at North Pole		60	60
1297	60 c. Woodrow Wilson and Curtiss JN-4 "Jenny" on first scheduled airmail flight, 1918		60	60
1298	60 c. Warren G. Harding and airship U.S.S. *Shenandoah* at Lakehurst		60	60
1299	60 c. Calvin Coolidge and Lindbergh's Ryan NYP Special *Spirit of St. Louis* on trans-Atlantic flight		60	60
1300	60 c. Mt. Rushmore National Monument		60	60
1301	60 c. Lyndon B. Johnson and Earth from Moon as seen by "Apollo 8" crew		60	60
	a. Sheetlet. Nos. 1301/6		3·25	
1302	60 c. Richard Nixon and visit to Great Wall of China		60	60
1303	60 c. Gerald Ford and *Gorch Fock* (German cadet barque) at Bicentenary of Revolution celebrations		60	60
1304	60 c. Jimmy Carter and Pres. Sadat of Egypt with Prime Minister Begin of Israel		60	60
1305	60 c. Ronald Reagan and space shuttle *Columbia*		60	60
1306	60 c. George Bush and Grumman TBF Avenger (fighter-bomber)		60	60
1283/1306		Set of 24	13·00	13·00

Nos. 1283/8, 1289/94, 1295/1300 and 1301/6 were printed together, *se-tenant*, in sheetlets of six stamps.

(Des Design Element. Litho Questa)

1989 (17 Nov). *"Expo '89" International Stamp Exhibition, Washington* (2nd issue). *Landmarks of Washington. Sheet* 77×62 mm. *containing horiz design as T* **257** *of Antigua. Multicoloured. P* 14.
MS1307 $4 The Capitol .. .. 2·50 3·25

(Des Walt Disney Co. Litho Questa)

1989 (30 Nov). *Mickey Mouse in Hollywood. Horiz designs as T* **267** *of Antigua showing Walt Disney cartoon characters. Multicoloured. P* 14×13¹/₂.

1308	20 c. Mickey Mouse reading script		40	40
1309	35 c. Mickey Mouse giving interview		55	55
1310	45 c. Mickey and Minnie Mouse with newspaper and magazines		65	65
1311	60 c. Mickey Mouse signing autographs		75	75
1312	$1 Trapped in dressing room		1·25	1·25
1313	$2 Mickey and Minnie Mouse with Pluto in limousine		2·00	2·50
1314	$3 Arriving at Awards ceremony		2·25	2·75
1315	$4 Mickey Mouse accepting award		2·40	2·75
1308/15		Set of 8	9·00	10·50

MS1316 Two sheets, each 127×102 mm. (a) $5 Mickey Mouse leaving footprints at cinema. (b) $5 Goofy interviewing .. *Set of 2 sheets* 7·50 8·50

(Litho Questa)

1989 (4 Dec). *Christmas. Paintings by Botticelli. Vert designs as T* **259** *of Antigua. Multicoloured. P* 14.

1317	20 c. "Madonna in Glory with Seraphim"		40	30
1318	25 c. "The Annunciation"		40	30
1319	35 c. "Madonna of the Pomegranate"		55	40
1320	45 c. "Madonna of the Rosegarden"		65	45
1321	60 c. "Madonna of the Book"		80	60
1322	$1 "Madonna under a Baldachin"		1·00	90
1323	$4 "Madonna and Child with Angels"		3·00	4·50
1324	$5 "Bardi Madonna"		3·50	4·75
1317/24		Set of 8	9·25	11·00

MS1325 Two sheets, each 71×96 mm. (a) $5 "The Mystic Nativity". (b) $5 "The Adoration of the Magi" .. *Set of 2 sheets* 7·00 9·00

240 Lady Olave Baden-Powell and Agatha Robinson   241 Jawaharlal Nehru

(Des A. Fagbohun. Litho Questa)

1989 (27 Dec). *60th Anniv of Girl Guides in Dominica. T* **240** *and similar multicoloured design showing Guide leaders. P* 14.
1326 60 c. Type **240** .. 1·00 1·00
MS1327 70×99 mm. $5 Dorris Stockmann and Judith Pestaina (*horiz*) .. 3·50 4·00

(Des A. Fagbohun. Litho Questa)

1989 (29 Dec). *Birth Centenary of Jawaharlal Nehru* (Indian statesman). *T* **241** *and similar multicoloured design. P* 14.
1328 60 c. Type **241** .. 1·50 1·25
MS1329 101×72 mm. $5 Parliament House, New Delhi (*horiz*) .. 3·50 4·00

242 Cocoa Damselfish

(Des P. Chinelli. Litho Questa)

1990 (21 May). *Tropical Fishes. T* **242** *and similar horiz designs. Multicoloured. P* 14.

1330	45 c. Type **242**	..	45	50
	a. Sheetlet. Nos. 1330/47		7·00	
1331	45 c. Stinging Jellyfish	..	45	50
1332	45 c. Dolphin (fish)	..	45	50
1333	45 c. Atlantic Spadefish and Queen Angelfish		45	50
1334	45 c. French Angelfish	..	45	50
1335	45 c. Blue-striped Grunt	..	45	50
1336	45 c. Porkfish	..	45	50
1337	45 c. Great Hammerhead	..	45	50
1338	45 c. Atlantic Spadefish	..	45	50
1339	45 c. Great Barracuda	..	45	50
1340	45 c. Southern Stingray	..	45	50
1341	45 c. Black Grunt	..	45	50
1342	45 c. Spot-finned Butterflyfish	..	45	50
1343	45 c. Dog Snapper	..	45	50
1344	45 c. Band-tailed Puffer	..	45	50
1345	45 c. Four-eyed Butterflyfish	..	45	50
1346	45 c. Lane Snapper	..	45	50
1347	45 c. Green Moray	..	45	50
1330/47		Set of 18	7·00	8·00

Nos. 1330/47 were printed together, *se-tenant*, in sheetlets of 18, forming a composite design.

243 St. Paul's Cathedral, London, c. 1840   244 Blue-headed Hummingbird

(Des M. Pollard. Litho B.D.T.)

1990 (18 June). *150th Anniv of the Penny Black and "Stamp World London 90" International Stamp Exhibition. T* **243** *and similar square designs. P* 13¹/₂.

1348	45 c. deep blue-green and black		50	25
1349	50 c. greenish blue and black		55	35
1350	60 c. greenish blue and black		65	45
1351	90 c. deep blue-green and black		85	85
1352	$3 deep ultramarine and black		2·25	3·00
1353	$4 deep ultramarine and black		2·75	3·50
1348/53		Set of 6	6·75	7·50

MS1354 Two sheets. (a) 103×79 mm. $5 brown-ochre and black. (b) 85×86 mm. $5 dull vermilion and blackish brown *Set of 2 sheets* 6·50 7·50
Designs:—50 c. British Post Office "accelerator" carriage, 1830; 60 c. St. Paul's and City of London; 90 c. Travelling post office, 1838; $3 "Hen and chickens" delivery cycle, 1883; $4 London skyline; $5 (a) As Type **243**; (b) Motor mail van, 1899.

(Des Mary Walters. Litho B.D.T.)

1990 (19 July). *500th Anniv of Discovery of America by Columbus (1992) (3rd issue). New World Natural History—Seashells. Vert designs as T 260 of Antigua. Multicoloured. P 14.*

1355	10 c.	Reticulated Cowrie-helmet (*Cyprae-cassis testiculus*)	30	30
1356	20 c.	West Indian Chank (*Turbinella angulata*)	40	40
1357	35 c.	West Indian Fighting Conch (*Strombus pugilis*)	50	35
1358	60 c.	True Tulip (*Fasciolaria tulipa*)	75	60
1359	$1	Sunrise Tellin (*Tellina radiata*)	1·00	1·00
1360	$2	Crown Cone (*Conus regius*)	1·75	2·50
1361	$3	Common Dove Shell (*Columbella mercatoria*)	2·50	3·25
1362	$4	Common or Atlantic Fig Shell (*Ficus communis*)	2·75	3·25
1355/62		*Set of 8*	9·00	10·50
MS1363		Two sheets, each 102×70 mm. (a) $5 King Helmet (*Cassis tuberosa*). (b) $5 Giant Tun (*Tonna galea*) .. *Set of 2 sheets*	6·50	8·00

(Des Mary Walters. Litho B.D.T.)

1990 (26 July). *Birds. T 244 and similar vert designs. Multicoloured. P 14.*

1364	10 c.	Type 244	35	35
1365	20 c.	Black-capped Petrel	45	45
1366	45 c.	Red-necked Amazon	65	40
1367	60 c.	Black Swift	80	70
1368	$1	Troupial	1·25	1·25
1369	$2	Common Noddy	2·00	2·50
1370	$4	Lesser Antillean Pewee	3·25	3·50
1371	$5	Little Blue Heron	3·75	4·25
1364/71		*Set of 8*	11·00	12·00
MS1372		Two sheets, each 103×70 mm. (a) $6 Imperial Amazon. (b) $6 House Wren .. *Set of 2 sheets*	7·00	8·00

(Litho Questa)

1990 (10 Sept). *90th Birthday of Queen Elizabeth the Queen Mother. Vert designs as T 266 of Antigua showing recent photographs of The Queen Mother. P 14.*

1373	20 c.	multicoloured	20	15
1374	45 c.	multicoloured	35	25
1375	60 c.	multicoloured	60	60
1376	$3	multicoloured	2·25	3·00
1373/6		*Set of 4*	3·00	3·50
MS1377		80×90 mm. $5 multicoloured	2·75	3·50

(Des B. Grout. Litho Questa)

1990 (6 Nov). *Olympic Games, Barcelona (1992) (1st issue). Vert designs as T 268 of Antigua. Multicoloured. P 14.*

1378	45 c.	Tennis	85	40
1379	60 c.	Fencing	85	50
1380	$2	Swimming	1·75	3·00
1381	$3	Yachting	2·40	3·25
1378/81		*Set of 4*	5·25	6·50
MS1382		100×70 mm. $5 Rowing	4·25	5·50

See also Nos. 1603/11.

245 Barnes, England

(Des Young Phillips Studio. Litho Questa)

1990 (6 Nov). *World Cup Football Championship, Italy (2nd issue). T 245 and similar multicoloured designs. P 14.*

1383	15 c.	Type 245	40	30
1384	45 c.	Romario, Brazil	70	30
1385	60 c.	Franz Beckenbauer, West Germany manager	85	70
1386	$4	Lindenberger, Austria	3·25	5·00
1383/6		*Set of 4*	4·75	5·75
MS1387		Two sheets, each 105×90 mm. (a) $6 McGrath, Ireland (*vert*). (b) $6 Litovchenko, Soviet Union (*vert*) .. *Set of 2 sheets*	7·50	9·00

246 Mickey Mouse riding Herschell-Spillman Frog

247 *Craterellus cornucopioides*

(Des Walt Disney Co. Litho Questa)

1990 (13 Dec). *Christmas. T 246 and similar multicoloured designs showing Walt Disney cartoon characters and American carousel animals. P 13½×14.*

1388	10 c.	Type 246	30	20
1389	15 c.	Huey, Duey and Louie on Allan Herschell elephant	35	25
1390	25 c.	Donald Duck on Allan Herschell polar bear	45	30
1391	45 c.	Goofy on Dentzel goat	70	30
1392	$1	Donald Duck on Zalar giraffe	1·00	1·00
1393	$2	Daisy Duck on Herschell-Spillman stork	1·75	2·25
1394	$4	Goofy on Dentzel lion	3·00	3·75
1395	$5	Daisy Duck on Stein and Goldstein palomino stander	3·50	4·00
1388/95		*Set of 8*	10·00	11·00
MS1396		Two sheets, each 127×101mm. (a) $6 Mickey, Morty and Ferdie Mouse on Philadelphia Toboggan Company swan chariot (*horiz*). P 14×13½. (b) $6 Mickey and Minnie Mouse with Goofy on Philadelphia Toboggan Company winged griffin chariot. P 13½×14 .. *Set of 2 sheets*	9·00	12·00

(Des W. Hanson Studio. Litho Walsall)

1991 (26 Mar). *Cog Railways. Multicoloured designs as T 275 of Antigua. P 14.*

1397	10 c.	Steam locomotive, Glion–Roches De Naye rack railway, 1890	10	10
1398	35 c.	Electric railcar, Mt Pilatus rack railway	15	20
1399	45 c.	Schynige Platte rack railway train	20	25
1400	60 c.	Steam train on Bugnli Viaduct, Furka–Oberalp rack railway (*vert*)	25	30
1401	$1	Jungfrau rack railway train, 1910	45	50
1402	$2	Testing Pike's Peak railcar, Switzerland, 1983	85	90
1403	$4	Brienz–Rothorn railway locomotive, 1991	1·75	1·90
1404	$5	Steam locomotive, Arth–Rigi, 1890	2·10	2·25
1397/404		*Set of 8*	5·75	6·50
MS1405		Two sheets. (a) 100×70 mm. $6 Swiss Europa stamps of 1983 showing Riggenbach's locomotive of 1871 (50×37 *mm*). (b) 90×68 mm. $6 Brunig line train and Sherlock Holmes (50×37 *mm*). P 13½ .. *Set of 2 sheets*	5·25	5·50

(Des T. Agans. Litho Questa)

1991 (8 Apr). *500th Anniv of Discovery of America by Columbus (1992) (4th issue). History of Exploration. Horiz designs as T 277 of Antigua. Multicoloured. P 14.*

1406	10 c.	Gil Eannes sailing south of Cape Bojador, 1433–34	25	25
1407	25 c.	Alfonso Baldaya sailing south to Cape Blanc, 1436	35	35
1408	45 c.	Bartolomeu Dias in Table Bay, 1487	45	35
1409	60 c.	Vasco da Gama on voyage to India, 1497–99	55	50
1410	$1	Vallarte the Dane off African coast	75	90
1411	$2	Aloisio Cadamosto in Cape Verde Islands, 1456–58	1·40	1·75
1412	$4	Diogo Gomes on River Gambia, 1457	2·75	3·50
1413	$5	Diogo Cao off African coast, 1482–85	3·25	3·75
1406/13		*Set of 8*	8·50	10·00
MS1414		Two sheets, each 105×71 mm. (a) $6 Green-winged Macaw and bow of Santa Maria. (b) $6 Blue and Yellow Macaw and caravel .. *Set of 2 sheets*	7·50	8·50

(Des Walt Disney Co. Litho Questa)

1991 (22 May). *"Phila Nippon '91" International Stamp Exhibition, Tokyo. Multicoloured designs as T 279 of Antigua showing Walt Disney cartoon characters in Japanese costumes. P 14×13½ (horiz) or 13½×14 (vert).*

1415	10 c.	Donald Duck as Shogun's guard (*horiz*)	20	20
1416	15 c.	Mickey Mouse as Kabuki actor (*horiz*)	25	25
1417	25 c.	Minnie and Mickey Mouse as bride and groom (*horiz*)	35	25
1418	45 c.	Daisy Duck as geisha	45	25
1419	$1	Mickey Mouse in Sokutai court dress	85	85
1420	$2	Goofy as Mino farmer	1·60	2·00
1421	$4	Pete as Shogun	2·75	3·25
1422	$5	Donald Duck as Samurai (*horiz*)	3·25	3·75
1415/22		*Set of 8*	8·75	9·75
MS1423		Two sheets, each 127×112 mm. (a) $6 Mickey Mouse as Noh actor. (b) $6 Goofy as Kabubei-jishi dancer .. *Set of 2 sheets*	9·00	11·00

(Litho Questa)

1991 (3 June). *Fungi. T 247 and similar vert designs. Multicoloured. P 14.*

1424	10 c.	Type 247	10	10
1425	15 c.	*Coprinus comatus*	10	10
1426	45 c.	*Morchella esculenta*	20	25
1427	60 c.	*Cantharellus cibarius*	25	30
1428	$1	*Lepista nuda*	45	50
1429	$2	*Suillus luteus*	85	90
1430	$4	*Russula emetica*	1·75	1·90
1431	$5	*Armillaria mellea*	2·10	2·25
1424/31		*Set of 8*	5·75	6·25
MS1432		Two sheets, each 100×70 mm. (a) $6 *Fistulina hepatica*. (b) $6 *Lactarius volemus* .. *Set of 2 sheets*	5·25	5·50

(Des D. Miller. Litho Walsall)

1991 (17 June). *65th Birthday of Queen Elizabeth II. Horiz designs as T 280 of Antigua. Multicoloured. P 14.*

1433	10 c.	Queen and Prince William on Buckingham Palace Balcony, 1990	30	20
1434	60 c.	The Queen at Westminster Abbey, 1988	75	50
1435	$2	Queen and Prince Philip in Italy, 1990	1·60	2·00
1436	$4	The Queen at Ascot, 1986	2·50	3·00
1433/6		*Set of 4*	4·75	5·00
MS1437		68×90 mm. $5 Separate portraits of Queen and Prince Philip	4·00	4·50

(Des D. Miller. Litho Walsall)

1991 (17 June). *10th Wedding Anniv of the Prince and Princess of Wales. Horiz designs as T 280 of Antigua. Multicoloured. P 14.*

1438	15 c.	Prince and Princess of Wales in West Germany, 1987	50	25
1439	40 c.	Separate photographs of Prince, Princess and sons	80	25
1440	$1	Separate photographs of Prince William and Prince Henry	1·10	95
1441	$5	Prince Charles at Caister and Princess Diana in Thailand	4·00	4·50
1438/41		*Set of 4*	5·75	5·50
MS1442		68×90 mm. $5 Prince Charles, and Princess Diana with sons on holiday	4·00	4·50

(Litho Walsall)

1991 (8 July). *Death Centenary of Vincent van Gogh (artist) (1990). Multicoloured designs as T 278 of Antigua. P 13½.*

1443	10 c.	"Thatched Cottages" (*horiz*)	10	10
1444	25 c.	"The House of Père Eloi" (*horiz*)	10	15
1445	45 c.	"The Midday Siesta" (*horiz*)	15	20
1446	60 c.	"Portrait of a Young Peasant"	25	30
1447	$1	"Still Life: Vase with Irises against a Yellow Background"	45	50
1448	$2	"Still Life: Vase with Irises" (*horiz*)	85	90
1449	$4	"Blossoming Almond Tree" (*horiz*)	1·75	2·00
1450	$5	"Irises" (*horiz*)	2·10	2·25
1443/50		*Set of 8*	5·75	6·50
MS1451		Two sheets, each 77×102 mm. (a) $6 "Doctor Gachet's Garden in Auvers". (b) 102×77 mm. $6 "A Meadow in the Mountains: Le Mas de Saint-Paul" (*horiz*). Imperf .. *Set of 2 sheets*	5·25	5·50

(Des Walt Disney Co. Litho Questa)

1991 (6 Aug). *International Literacy Year (1990). Multicoloured designs as T 269 of Antigua showing scenes from Disney cartoon film The Little Mermaid. P 14×13½.*

1452	10 c.	Ariel, Flounder and Sebastian (*horiz*)	30	25
1453	25 c.	King Triton (*horiz*)	45	30
1454	45 c.	Sebastian playing drums (*horiz*)	60	30
1455	60 c.	Flotsam and Jetsam taunting Ariel (*horiz*)	85	55
1456	$1	Scuttle, Flounder and Ariel with pipe (*horiz*)	1·25	1·00
1457	$2	Ariel and Flounder discovering book (*horiz*)	2·00	2·00
1458	$4	Prince Eric and crew (*horiz*)	3·25	3·50
1459	$5	Ursula the Sea Witch (*horiz*)	3·50	4·00
1452/9		*Set of 8*	11·00	11·00
MS1460		Two sheets, each 127×102 mm. (a) $6 Ariel without tail (*horiz*). P 14×13½. (b) $6 Ariel and Prince Eric dancing. P 13½×14 .. *Set of 2 sheets*	8·50	10·00

248 Empire State Building, New York

249 Japanese Aircraft leaving Carrier *Akagi*

(Des W. Wright. Litho Questa)

1991 (12 Aug). *World Landmarks. T 248 and similar multicoloured designs. P 14.*

1461	10 c.	Type 248	40	40
1462	25 c.	Kremlin, Moscow (*horiz*)	40	40
1463	45 c.	Buckingham Palace, London (*horiz*)	60	30
1464	60 c.	Eiffel Tower, Paris	75	60
1465	$1	Taj Mahal, Agra (*horiz*)	2·00	1·50
1466	$2	Opera House, Sydney (*horiz*)	3·00	3·00
1467	$4	Colosseum, Rome (*horiz*)	3·50	4·00
1468	$5	Pyramids, Giza (*horiz*)	3·50	4·00
1461/8		*Set of 8*	13·00	13·00
MS1469		Two sheets, each 100×68 mm. (a) $6 Galileo on Leaning Tower, Pisa (*horiz*). (b) $6 Emperor Shi Huang and Great Wall of China (*horiz*) .. *Set of 2 sheets*	12·00	13·00

(Des W. Wright. Litho Questa)

1991 (2 Sept). *50th Anniv of Japanese Attack on Pearl Harbor. T 249 and similar horiz designs. Multicoloured. P 14.*

1470	10 c.	Type 249	10	10
1471	15 c.	U.S.S. *Ward* (destroyer) and Consolidated PBY-5 Catalina flying boat attacking midget submarine	10	10
1472	45 c.	Second wave of Mitsubishi A6M Zero-Sen aircraft leaving carriers	15	20
1473	60 c.	Japanese Mitsubishi A6M Zero-Sen's attacking Kaneche naval airfield	25	30
1474	$1	U.S.S. *Breeze*, *Medusa* and *Curtiss* (destroyers) sinking midget submarine	45	50
1475	$2	U.S.S. *Nevada* (battleship) under attack	85	90
1476	$4	U.S.S. *Arizona* (battleship) sinking	1·75	1·90
1477	$5	Mitsubishi A6M Zero-Sen aircraft	2·10	2·25
1470/7		*Set of 8*	5·75	6·25
MS1478		Two sheets, each 118×78 mm. (a) $6 Mitsubishi A6M Zero-Sen over anchorage. (b) $6 Mitsubishi A6M Zero-Sen attacking Hickam airfield .. *Set of 2 sheets*	5·25	5·50

250 *Eurema venusta*

251 Symbolic Cheque

(Litho Cartor)

1991 (14 Oct)–**93**. *Butterflies. T 250 and similar vert designs. Multicoloured. P 13½.*

1479	1 c.	Type **250**		30	60
1480	2 c.	*Agraulis vanillae*		30	60
1481	5 c.	*Danaus plexippus*		40	60
1482	10 c.	*Biblis hyperia*		40	15
1483	15 c.	*Dryas julia*		50	15
1484	20 c.	*Phoebis agarithe*		50	20
1485	25 c.	*Junonia genoveva*		50	20
1486	35 c.	*Battus polydamas*		60	30
1487	45 c.	*Leptotes cassius*		60	30
1487*a*	55 c.	*Ascia monuste* (11.1.93)		75	55
1488	60 c.	*Anaea dominicana*		70	35
1488*a*	65 c.	*Hemiargus hanno* (11.1.93)		75	55
1489	90 c.	*Hypolimnas misippus*		80	55
1490	$1	*Urbanus proteus*		80	60
1490*a*	$1.20,	*Historis odius* (11.1.93)		1·00	1·25
1491	$2	*Phoebis sennae*		1·50	2·00
1492	$5	*Cynthia cardui* ("Vanessa cardui")		2·50	3·50
1493	$10	*Marpesia petreus*		4·75	6·00
1494	$20	*Anartia jatrophae*		9·50	12·00
1479/94			Set of 19	24·00	27·00

(Des J. Iskowitz. Litho Questa)

1991 (1 Nov). *Birth Centenary of Charles de Gaulle (French statesman) (1990). Designs as T 283 of Antigua showing De Gaulle in uniform. P 14.*

1495	45 c.	agate	1·00	75
MS1496	70×100 mm. $5 agate and deep ultramarine		4·00	4·50

No. 1495 is a vertical design.

(Litho Questa)

1991 (1 Nov). *40th Anniv of Credit Union Bank. T 251 and similar design. Multicoloured. P 14.*

1497	10 c.	grey-black and black	20	20
1498	60 c.	multicoloured	80	80

Design: *Horiz*—60 c. Credit Union symbol.

252 "18th-Century Creole Dress" (detail) (Agostino Brunias)

253 Island Beach

(Litho Questa)

1991 (1 Nov). *Creole Week. T 252 and similar multicoloured designs. P 14.*

1499	45 c.	Type **252**		50	25
1500	60 c.	Jing Ping band		70	60
1501	$1	Creole dancers		1·00	1·40
1499/501			Set of 3	2·00	2·00
MS1502	100×70 mm. $5 "18th-century Stick-fighting Match" (detail) (Agostino Brunias) (*horiz*)			4·25	5·50

(Litho Cartor)

1991 (18 Nov). *Year of Environment and Shelter. T 253 and similar horiz designs. Multicoloured. P 14.*

1503	15 c.	Type **253**	15	15
1504	60 c.	Imperial Amazon	2·25	1·25
MS1505	Two sheets. (a) 100×70 mm. $5 River estuary. (b) 70×100 mm. $5 As 60 c.			
		Set of 2 sheets	10·00	11·00

(Litho Walsall)

1991 (2 Dec). *Christmas. Religious Paintings by Jan van Eyck. Vert designs as T 287 of Antigua. Multicoloured. P 12.*

1506	10 c.	"Virgin Enthroned with Child" (detail)	40	20
1507	20 c.	"Madonna at the Fountain"	50	30
1508	35 c.	"Virgin in a Church"	60	30
1509	45 c.	"Madonna with Canon van der Paele"	70	30
1510	60 c.	"Madonna with Canon van der Paele" (detail)	1·00	60
1511	$1	"Madonna in an Interior"	1·25	1·00
1512	$3	"The Annunciation"	2·50	3·50
1513	$5	"The Annunciation" (*different*)	3·50	5·50
1506/13		Set of 8	9·50	10·50
MS1514	Two sheets, each 102×127 mm. (a) $5 "Virgin and Child with Saints and Donor". (b) $5 "Madonna with Chancellor Rolin". P 14			
		Set of 2 sheets	9·00	11·00

(Des D. Miller. Litho Questa)

1992 (13 Mar). *40th Anniv of Queen Elizabeth II's Accession. Horiz designs as T 288 of Antigua. Multicoloured. P 14.*

1515	10 c.	Coastline		10	10
1516	15 c.	Mountains overlooking small village		10	10
1517	$1	River estuary		55	60
1518	$5	Waterfall		2·75	3·25
1515/18			Set of 4	3·00	3·50
MS1519	Two sheets, each 74×97 mm. (a) $6 Roseau. (b) $6 Mountain stream		Set of 2 sheets	6·00	7·50

254 Cricket Match

255 Columbus and *Dynastes hercules* (beetle)

(Des Mary Walters. Litho B.D.T.)

1992 (30 Mar). *Centenary of Botanical Gardens (1991). T 254 and similar vert designs. Multicoloured. P 14.*

1520	10 c.	Type **254**		40	30
1521	15 c.	Scenic Entrance		30	20
1522	45 c.	Traveller's Tree		30	25
1523	60 c.	Bamboo House		45	30
1524	$1	The Old Pavilion		70	70
1525	$2	*Ficus benjamina*		1·25	1·75
1526	$4	Cricket match (*different*)		2·75	3·25
1527	$5	Thirty-five Steps		2·75	3·25
1520/7			Set of 8	8·00	9·00
MS1528	Two sheets, each 104×71 mm. (a) $6 Past and present members of national cricket team. (b) $6 The Fountain		Set of 2 sheets	6·50	7·50

(Litho Questa)

1992 (21 Apr). *Easter. Religious Paintings. Multicoloured designs as T 291 of Antigua. P 14×13½ (horiz) or 13½×14 (vert).*

1529	10 c.	"The Supper at Emmaus" (Van Honthorst)	20	20
1530	15 c.	"Christ before Caiaphas" (Van Honthorst) (*vert*)	25	25
1531	45 c.	"The Taking of Christ" (De Boulogne)	40	30
1532	60 c.	"Pilate washing his Hands" (Preti) (*vert*)	55	45
1533	$1	"The Last Supper" (detail) (Master of the Church of S. Francisco d'Evora)	75	75
1534	$2	"The Three Marys at the Tomb" (detail) (Bouguereau) (*vert*)	1·50	1·75
1535	$3	"Denial of St. Peter" (Terbrugghen)	1·75	2·25
1536	$5	"Doubting Thomas" (Strozzi)	2·75	3·50
1529/36		Set of 8	7·50	8·50
MS1537	Two sheets, each 72×102 mm. (a) $6 "The Crucifixion" (detail) (Grünewald) (*vert*). (b) $6 "The Resurrection" (detail) (Caravaggio) (*vert*)			
		Set of 2 sheets	7·00	8·50

(Litho B.D.T.)

1992 (4 May). *"Granada '92" International Stamp Exhibition, Spain. Art of Diego Rodriguez Velásquez. Multicoloured designs as T 292 of Antigua. P 13×13½.*

1538	10 c.	"Pope Innocent X" (detail)	10	10
1539	15 c.	"The Forge of Vulcan" (detail)	10	10
1540	45 c.	"The Forge of Vulcan" (different detail)	20	25
1541	60 c.	"Queen Mariana of Austria" (detail)	25	30
1542	$1	"Pablo de Valladolid"	45	50
1543	$2	"Sebastián de Morra"	85	90
1544	$3	"King Felipe IV" (detail)	1·25	1·40
1545	$4	"King Felipe IV"	1·75	1·90
1538/45		Set of 8	5·00	5·50
MS1546	Two sheets, each 120×95 mm. (a) $6 "The Drunkards" (110×81 *mm*). (b) $6 "Surrender of Breda" (110×81 *mm*). Imperf			
		Set of 2 sheets	5·25	5·50

(Des R. Brown. Litho Questa)

1992 (18 May). *500th Anniv of Discovery of America by Columbus (5th issue). World Columbian Stamp "Expo '92", Chicago. T 255 and similar multicoloured designs. P 14.*

1547	10 c.	Type **255**	30	20
1548	25 c.	Columbus and *Leptodactylus fallax* (frog)	40	20
1549	75 c.	Columbus and Red-necked Amazon (bird)	90	60
1550	$2	Columbus and *Ameiva fuscata* (lizard)	1·50	1·75
1551	$4	Columbus and Royal Gramma (fish)	2·50	3·00
1552	$5	Columbus and *Rosa sinensis* (flower)	2·50	3·25
1547/52		Set of 6	7·25	8·00
MS1553	Two sheets, each 100×67 mm. (a) $6 Ships of Columbus (*horiz*). (b) $6 *Mastophyllum scabricolle* (katydid) (*horiz*)		Set of 2 sheets	6·50	7·50

(Des R. Brown. Litho Questa)

1992 (28 May). *"Genova '92" International Thematic Stamp Exhibition. Hummingbirds. Horiz designs as T 295 of Antigua. Multicoloured. P 14.*

1554	10 c.	Female Purple-throated Carib	20	20
1555	15 c.	Female Rufous-breasted Hermit	20	20
1556	45 c.	Male Puerto Rican Emerald	50	30

1557	60 c.	Female Antillean Mango	60	45
1558	$1	Male Green-throated Carib	95	85
1559	$2	Male Blue-headed Hummingbird	1·50	1·75
1560	$4	Female Eastern Streamertail	2·50	2·75
1561	$5	Female Antillean Crested Hummingbird	2·75	3·00
1554/61		Set of 8	8·25	8·50
MS1562	Two sheets, each 105×72 mm. (a) $6 Jamaican Mango ("Green Mango"). (b) $6 Vervain Hummingbird	Set of 2 sheets	10·00	11·00

(Des D. Burkhart. Litho Questa)

1992 (23 June). *Prehistoric Animals. Multicoloured designs as T 290 of Antigua, but horiz. P 14.*

1563	10 c.	Head of Camptosaurus		10	10
1564	15 c.	Edmontosaurus		10	10
1565	25 c.	Corythosaurus		10	15
1566	60 c.	Stegosaurus		25	30
1567	$1	Torosaurus		45	50
1568	$3	Euoplocephalus		1·25	1·40
1569	$4	Tyrannosaurus		1·75	1·90
1570	$5	Parasaurolophus		2·10	2·25
1563/70			Set of 8	6·00	6·75
MS1571	Two sheets, each 100×70 mm. (a) $6 As 25 c. (b) $6 As $1		Set of 2 sheets	5·25	5·50

256 Trumpetfish and Blue Chromis

(Des I. MacLaury. Litho B.D.T.)

1992 (20 July). *Marine Life. T 256 and similar horiz designs. P 14.*

1572/1601	65 c.×30 multicoloured		12·00	13·00
MS1602	Two sheets, each 73×105 mm. (a) $6 multicoloured (Harlequin Bass). (b) $6 multicoloured (Flamefish)	Set of 2 sheets	9·00	10·00

Nos. 1572/86 and 1587/1601 were each issued in *se-tenant* sheetlets of 15 (3×5) showing reef marine life by day or by night.

(Litho Questa)

1992 (10 Aug). *Olympic Games, Barcelona (2nd issue). Vert designs as T 268 of Antigua. Multicoloured. P 14.*

1603	10 c.	Archery		15	15
1604	15 c.	Two-man canoeing		15	15
1605	25 c.	Men's 110 metres hurdles		20	15
1606	60 c.	Men's high jump		40	30
1607	$1	Greco-Roman wrestling		65	65
1608	$2	Men's gymnastics – rings		1·25	1·75
1609	$4	Men's gymnastics – parallel bars		2·50	3·00
1610	$5	Equestrian dressage		3·00	3·25
1603/10			Set of 8	7·50	8·50
MS1611	Two sheets, each 100×70 mm. (a) $6 Women's platform diving. (b) $6 Men's hockey		Set of 2 sheets	7·50	9·00

(Des F. Paul ($1), J. Esquino ($2). Litho Questa)

1992 (2 Sept). *500th Anniv of Discovery of America by Columbus (6th issue). Organization of East Caribbean States. Vert designs as Nos. 1670/1 of Antigua. Multicoloured. P 14½.*

1612	$1	Columbus meeting Amerindians	65	65
1613	$2	Ships approaching island	1·10	1·25

(Litho Questa)

1992 (2 Nov). *Hummel Figurines. Vert designs as T 302 of Antigua. Multicoloured. P 14.*

1614	20 c.	Angel playing violin	10	10
1615	25 c.	Angel playing recorder	10	15
1616	55 c.	Angel playing lute	25	30
1617	65 c.	Seated angel playing trumpet	30	35
1618	90 c.	Angel on cloud with lantern	40	45
1619	$1	Angel with candle	45	50
1620	$1.20,	Flying angel with Christmas tree	50	55
1621	$6	Angel on cloud with candle	2·50	2·75
1614/21		Set of 8	4·50	5·00
MS1622	Two sheets, each 97×127 mm. (a) Nos. 1614/17. (b) Nos. 1618/21	Set of 2 sheets	4·50	5·00

257 Brass *Reno* Locomotive, Japan (1963)

(Des W. Hanson. Litho B.D.T.)

1992 (11 Nov). *Toy Trains from Far Eastern Manufacturers. T 257 and similar multicoloured designs. P 14.*

1623	15 c.	Type **257**	10	10
1624	25 c.	Union Pacific *Golden Classic* locomotive, China (1992)	10	10
1625	55 c.	L.M.S. third class brake carriage, Hong Kong (1970s)	25	30
1626	65 c.	Brass Wabash locomotive, Japan (1958)	30	35
1627	75 c.	Pennsylvania "Duplex" type locomotive, Korea (1991)	35	40

1628	$1 Streamlined locomotive, Japan (post 1945)	45	50
1629	$3 Japanese National Railways Class "C62" locomotive, Japan (1960)	1·25	1·40
1630	$5 Tinplate friction driven trains, Japan (1960s)	2·10	2·25
1623/30	*Set of 8*	5·00	5·50

MS1631 Two sheets, each 119×87 mm. (a) $6 *Rocket*'s tender, Japan (1972) (multicoloured) (51½×40 *mm*). (b) $6 American model steam train presented to Emperor of Japan, 1854 (black, blackish olive and flesh) (40×51½ *mm*). P 13 *Set of 2 sheets* 5·25 5·50

258 Goofy in *Two Weeks Vacation*, 1952

(Des Walt Disney Co. Litho Questa)

1992 (17 Nov). *60th Anniv of Goofy* (*Disney cartoon character*). T **258** *and similar multicoloured designs showing sports from cartoon films.* P 14×13½.

1632	10 c. Type **258**	45	20
1633	15 c. *Aquamania*, 1961	55	20
1634	25 c. *Goofy Gymnastics*, 1949	60	20
1635	45 c. *How to Ride a Horse*, 1941	80	25
1636	$1 *Foul Hunting*, 1947	1·25	75
1637	$2 *For Whom the Bulls Toil*, 1953	2·00	2·25
1638	$4 *Tennis Racquet*, 1949	2·75	3·25
1639	$5 *Double Dribble*, 1946	2·75	3·25
1632/9	*Set of 8*	10·00	9·25

MS1640 Two sheets, each 128×102 mm. (a) $6 *The Goofy Sports Story*, 1956 (*vert*). (b) $6 *Aquamania*, 1961 (*different*) (*vert*). P 13½×14 *Set of 2 sheets* 10·00 11·00

259 Airship LZ-127 *Graf Zeppelin*, 1929

260 Elvis Presley

(Des W. Wright and W. Hanson (Nos. 1641, 1655, **MS**1656a), W. Wright and L. Fried (Nos. 1645, 1654, **MS**1656b), J. Genzo (Nos. 1649, **MS**1656d), W. Wright (others). Litho Questa)

1992 (30 Dec). *Anniversaries and Events.* T **259** *and similar vert designs. Multicoloured.* P 14.

1641	25 c. Type **259**	15	15
1642	45 c. Elderly man on bike	30	25
1643	45 c. Elderly man with seedling	30	25
1644	45 c. Elderly man and young boy fishing	30	25
1645	90 c. Space Shuttle *Atlantis*	60	60
1646	90 c. Konrad Adenauer (German states-man)	60	60
1647	$1.20, Sir Thomas Lipton and *Shamrock N* (yacht)	75	75
1648	$1.20, Snowy Egret (bird)	75	75
1649	$1.20, Wolfgang Amadeus Mozart	75	75
1650	$2 Pulling fishing net ashore	1·25	1·25
1651	$3 Helen Keller (lecturer)	1·75	1·75
1652	$4 Eland (antelope)	2·50	2·50
1653	$4 Map of Allied Zones of Occupation, Germany, 1949	2·50	2·50
1654	$4 Earth Resources satellite	2·50	2·50
1655	$5 Count von Zeppelin	2·75	3·00
1641/55	*Set of 15*	16·00	16·00

MS1656 Five sheets. (a) 100×70 mm. $6 Airship propeller. (b) 100×70 mm. $6 "Mir" Russian space station with "Soyuz". (c) 70×100 mm. $6 Cologne Cathedral. (d) 100×70 mm. $6 Rhinoceros Hornbill (bird). (e) 100×70 mm. $6 Monostatos from *The Magic Flute* ... *Set of 5 sheets* 15·00 16·00
Anniversaries and Events:—Nos. 1641, 1655, **MS**1656a, 75th death anniv of Count Ferdinand von Zeppelin; Nos. 1642/4, International Day of the Elderly; Nos. 1645, 1654, **MS**1656b, International Space Year; Nos. 1646, 1653, **MS**1656c, 25th death anniv of Konrad Adenauer; No. 1647, Americas Cup Yachting Championship; Nos. 1648, 1652, **MS**1656d, Earth Summit '92, Rio; No. 1649, **MS**1656e, Death bicent of Mozart; No. 1650, International Conference on Nutrition, Rome; No. 1651, 75th anniv of International Association of Lions Clubs.
No. **MS**1656b is inscribed "M.I.R." and No. **MS**1656d "Rhinocerus Hornbill", both in error.

(Litho Walsall)

1993 (24 Mar). *Bicentenary of the Louvre, Paris. Vert designs as* T **305** *of Antigua. Multicoloured.* P 12.

1657	$1 "Madonna and Child with St. Catherine and a Rabbit" (left detail) (Titian)	45	50
	a. Sheetlet. Nos. 1657/64	2·50	
1658	$1 "Madonna and Child with St. Catherine and a Rabbit" (right detail) (Titian)	45	50

1659	$1 "Women at her Toilet" (Titian)	45	50
1660	$1 "The Supper at Emmaus" (left detail) (Titian)	45	50
1661	$1 "The Supper at Emmaus" (right detail) (Titian)	45	50
1662	$1 "The Pastoral Concert" (Titian)	45	50
1663	$1 "An Allegory, perhaps of Marriage" (detail) (Titian)	45	50
1664	$1 "An Allegory, perhaps of Marriage" (different detail) (Titian)	45	50
1657/64	*Set of 8*	3·50	4·00

MS1665 70×100 mm. $6 "The Ship of Fools" (Bosch) (52×85 *mm*). P 14½ 2·50 2·75
Nos. 1657/64 were printed together, *se-tenant*, in sheetlets of 8 stamps and one centre label.

(Des A. Nahigian. Litho Walsall)

1993 (24 Mar). *15th Death Anniv of Elvis Presley* (*singer*). T **260** *and similar vert designs. Multicoloured.* P 14.

1666	$1 Type **260**	45	50
	a. Strip of 3. Nos. 1666/8	1·40	
1667	$1 Elvis with guitar	45	50
1668	$1 Elvis with microphone	45	50
1666/8	*Set of 4*	1·40	1·50

Nos. 1666/8 were printed together, horizontally and vertically *se-tenant*, in sheetlets of 9 (3×3).

261 Plumbeous Warbler

262 School Crest

(Des Tracy Pedersen. Litho Questa)

1993 (30 Apr). *Birds.* T **261** *and similar vert designs. Multicoloured.* P 14.

1669	90 c. Type **261**	80	90
	a. Sheetlet. Nos. 1669/80	8·50	
1670	90 c. Black Swift	80	90
1671	90 c. Blue-hooded Euphonia	80	90
1672	90 c. Rufous-throated Solitaire	80	90
1673	90 c. Ringed Kingfisher	80	90
1674	90 c. Blue-headed Hummingbird	80	90
1675	90 c. Bananaquit	80	90
1676	90 c. Brown Trembler	80	90
1677	90 c. Forest Thrush	80	90
1678	90 c. Purple-throated Carib	80	90
1679	90 c. Ruddy Quail Dove	80	90
1680	90 c. Least Bittern	80	90
1669/80	*Set of 12*	8·50	9·50

MS1681 Two sheets, each 100×70 mm. (a) $6 Imperial Amazon. (b) $6 Red-necked Amazon *Set of 2 sheets* 8·00 8·50
Nos. 1669/80 were printed together, *se-tenant*, in sheetlets of 12 forming a composite design.

(Litho Questa)

1993 (17 May). *Centenary of Dominica Grammar School.* T **262** *and similar horiz designs. Multicoloured.* P 14.

1682	25 c. Type **262**	20	15
1683	30 c. V. Archer (first West Indian headmaster)	25	20
1684	65 c. Hubert Charles (first Dominican headmaster)	45	50
1685	90 c. Present school buildings	65	80
1682/5	*Set of 4*	1·40	1·50

263 Leatherback Turtle on Beach

(Des S. Barlowe. Litho Walsall)

1993 (26 May). *Turtles.* T **263** *and similar horiz designs. Multicoloured.* P 14.

1686	25 c. Type **263**	50	15
1687	55 c. Hawksbill Turtle swimming	70	40
1688	65 c. Atlantic Ridley Turtle	80	50
1689	90 c. Green Turtle laying eggs	1·00	70
1690	$1 Green Turtle swimming	1·00	70
1691	$2 Hawksbill Turtle swimming (different)	1·50	2·00
1692	$4 Loggerhead Turtle	2·25	2·75
1693	$5 Leatherback Turtle swimming	2·25	2·75
1686/93	*Set of 8*	9·00	9·00

MS1694 Two sheets, each 99×70 mm. (a) $6 Green Turtle hatchling. (b) $6 Head of Hawksbill Turtle ... *Set of 2 sheets* 8·00 9·00

264 Ford "Model A", 1928

(Des W. Wright. Litho Walsall)

1993 (28 May). *Centenaries of Henry Ford's First Petrol Engine* (90 c., $5, $6) *and Karl Benz's First Four-wheeled Car* (*others*). T **264** *and similar horiz designs. Multicoloured.* P 14.

1695	90 c. Type **264**	40	45
1696	$1.20, Mercedes Benz car winning Swiss Grand Prix, 1936	50	55
1697	$4 Mercedes Benz car winning German Grand Prix, 1935	1·75	1·90
1698	$5 Ford "Model T", 1915	2·10	2·25
1695/8	*Set of 4*	4·75	5·00

MS1699 Two sheets, each 99×70 mm. (a) $3 Benz "Viktoria", 1893; $3 Mercedes Benz sports coupe, 1993. (b) $6 Ford "G.T.40", Le Mans, 1966 (57½×48 *mm*) ... *Set of 2 sheets* 2·50 2·75

(Des Kerri Schiff. Litho Questa)

1993 (10 June). *40th Anniv of Coronation. Vert designs as* T **307** *of Antigua.* P 13½×14.

1700	20 c. multicoloured	40	45
	a. Sheetlet. Nos. 1700/3×2	7·50	
1701	25 c. reddish brown and black	40	45
1702	65 c. multicoloured	60	65
1703	$5 multicoloured	2·75	3·00
1700/3	*Set of 4*	3·75	4·00

MS1704 71×101 mm. $6 multicoloured. P 14 4·50 5·00
Designs:—20 c. Queen Elizabeth II at Coronation (photograph by Cecil Beaton); 25 c. Queen wearing King Edward's Crown during Coronation ceremony; 65 c. Coronation coach; $5 Queen and Queen Mother in carriage. (28½×42½ *mm*)—$6 "Queen Elizabeth II, 1969" (detail) (Norman Hutchinson).
Nos. 1700/3 were printed together in sheetlets of 8 containing two *se-tenant* blocks of 4.

265 New G.P.O. and Duke of Edinburgh

(Des Kerri Schiff (Nos. 1712, 1719, **MS**1721f). Litho Questa)

1993 (30 July). *Anniversaries and Events.* T **265** *and similar designs. Each reddish brown, deep brown and black* (Nos. 1707, 1717, **MS**1721b) *or multicoloured* (*others*). P 14.

1705	25 c. Type **265**	10	10
1706	25 c. "Bather with Beach Ball" (Picasso) (*vert*)	10	10
1707	65 c. Willy Brandt and Pres. Eisenhower, 1959	30	35
1708	90 c. As Type **265**, but portrait of Queen Elizabeth II	40	45
1709	90 c. "Portrait of Leo Stein" (Picasso) (*vert*)	40	45
1710	90 c. Monika Holzner (Germany) (speed skating) (*vert*)	40	45
1711	90 c. "Self-portrait" (Marian Szczyrbula) (*vert*)	40	45
1712	90 c. Prince Naruhito and engagement photographs	40	45
1713	$1.20, 16th-century telescope (*vert*)	55	60
1714	$3 "Bruno Jasienski" (Tytus Czyzewski) (*vert*)	1·40	1·50
1715	$3 Modern observatory (*vert*)	1·40	1·50
1716	$4 Ray Leblanc and Tim Sweeney (U.S.A.) (ice hockey) (*vert*)	1·90	2·00
1717	$5 "Wilhelm Unde" (Picasso) (*vert*)	2·25	2·40
1718	$5 Willy Brandt and N.K. Winston at World's Fair, 1964	2·25	2·40
1719	$5 Masako Owada and engagement photographs	2·25	2·40
1720	$5 Pres. Clinton and wife applauding	2·25	2·40
1705/20	*Set of 16*	16·00	18·00

MS1721 Seven sheets, each 105×75 mm (a, c and f) or 75×105 mm (others). (a) $5 Copernicus (*vert*). (b) $6 "Man with Pipe" (detail) (Picasso) (*vert*). (c) $6 Willy Brandt, 1972. (d) $6 Toni Nieminen (Finland) (120 metre ski jump) (*vert*). (e) $6 "Miser" (detail) (Tadeusz Makowski) (*vert*). (f) $6 Masako Owada (*vert*). (g) $6 Pres. W. Clinton (*vert*) ... *Set of 7 sheets* 19·00 20·00
Anniversaries and Events:—Nos. 1705, 1708, Opening of New General Post Office Building; Nos. 1706, 1709, 1717, **MS**1721b, 20th death anniv of Picasso (artist); Nos. 1707, 1718, **MS**1721c, 80th birth anniv of Willy Brandt (German politician); Nos. 1710, 1716, **MS**1721d, Winter Olympic Games '94, Lillehammer; Nos. 1711, 1714, **MS**1721e, "Polska '93" International Stamp Exhibition, Poznan; Nos. 1712, 1719, **MS**1721a, 450th death anniv of Copernicus (astronomer); Nos. 1720, **MS**1721g, Inauguration of U.S. President William Clinton.
No. 1714 is inscribed "Tyrus" in error.

COVER PRICES

Cover factors are quoted at the beginning of each country for most issues to 1945. An explanation of the system can be found on page x. The factors quoted do not, however, apply to philatelic covers.

266 Hugo Eckener in New York Parade, 1928   **267** Maradona (Argentina) and Buchwald (Germany)

(Des W. Wright. Litho Walsall)

1993 (30 July). *Aviation Anniversaries. T **266** and similar multicoloured designs. P 14.*

1722	25 c. Type 266	30	15
1723	55 c. English Electric Lightning F.2 (fighter)	50	40
1724	65 c. Airship LZ-127 *Graf Zeppelin* over Egypt, 1929	60	55
1725	$1 Boeing 314A (flying boat) on trans-Atlantic mail flight	80	75
1726	$2 Astronaut carrying mail to the Moon	1·50	1·75
1727	$4 Airship LZ-11 *Viktoria Luise* over Kiel harbour, 1912	2·50	3·00
1728	$5 Supermarine Spitfire (*vert*)	2·50	3·00
1722/8	*Set of 7*	8·00	8·75

MS1729 Three sheets, each 99×70 mm. (a) $6 Hugo Eckener (42½×57 *mm*). (b) $6 Royal Air Force crest (42½×57 *mm*). (c) $6 Jean-Pierre Blanchard's hot air balloon, 1793 (*vert*)
     Set of 3 sheets 8·75 9·50

Anniversaries:—Nos. 1722, 1724, 1727, **MS**1729a, 125th birth anniv of Hugo Eckener (airship commander); Nos. 1723, 1728, **MS**1729b, 75th anniv of Royal Air Force; Nos. 1725/6, **MS**1729c, Bicentenary of First Airmail Flight.

(Des Rosemary DeFiglio. Litho Questa)

1993 (8 Sept). *World Cup Football Championship, U.S.A. (1994) (1st issue). T **267** and similar vert designs. Multicoloured. P 14.*

1730	25 c. Type 267	40	20
1731	55 c. Ruud Gullit (Netherlands)	60	40
1732	65 c. Chavarria (Costa Rica) and Bliss (U.S.A.)	65	45
1733	90 c. Diego Maradona (Argentina)	80	75
1734	90 c. Leonel Alvares (Colombia)	80	75
1735	$1 Altobelli (Italy) and Yong-hwang (South Korea)	85	80
1736	$2 Stopyra (France)	1·40	1·75
1737	$5 Renquin (Belgium) and Yaremtchuk (Russia)	2·50	3·25
1730/7	*Set of 8*	7·25	7·50

MS1738 Two sheets. (a) 73×103 mm. $6 Nestor Fabbri (Argentina). (b) 103×73 mm. $6 Andreas Brehme (Germany)   *Set of 2 sheets* 5·50 6·50
See also Nos. 1849/56.

268 Ornate Chedi, Wat Phra Boromathat Chaiya

(Des Kerri Schiff. Litho Questa)

1993 (4 Oct). *Asian International Stamp Exhibitons. T **268** and similar vert designs. Multicoloured. P 13½×14.*

(a) *"Indopex '93", Surabaya, Indonesia*

1739	25 c. Type 268	10	10
1740	55 c. Temple ruins, Sukhothai	25	30
1741	90 c. Prasat Hin Phimai, Thailand	40	45
1742	$1.65, Arjuna and Prabu Gilling Wesi puppets	70	75
	a. Sheetlet. Nos. 1742/7	4·25	
1743	$1.65, Loro Blonyo puppet	70	75
1744	$1.65, Yogyanese puppets	70	75
1745	$1.65, Wayang gedog puppet, Ng Setro	70	75
1746	$1.65, Wayang golek puppet	70	75
1747	$1.65, Wayang gedog puppet, Raden Damar Wulan	70	75
1748	$5 Main sanctuary, Prasat Phanom Rung, Thailand	2·10	2·25
1739/48	*Set of 10*	5·00	5·25

MS1749 105×136 mm. $6 Sculpture of Majaphit noble, Pura Sada   2·50 2·75

(b) *"Taipei '93", Taiwan*

1750	25 c. Aw Boon Haw Gardens, Causeway Bay	10	10
1751	65 c. Observation building, Kenting Park	25	30
1752	90 c. Tzu-en pagoda on lakeshore, Taiwan	40	45
1753	$1.65, Chang E kite	70	75
	a. Sheetlet. Nos. 1753/8	4·25	
1754	$1.65, Red Phoenix and Rising Sun kite	70	75
1755	$1.65, Heavenly Judge kite	70	75

1756	$1.65, Monkey King kite	70	75
1757	$1.65, Goddess of Luo River kite	70	75
1758	$1.65, Heavenly Maiden kite	70	75
1759	$5 Villa, Lantau Island	2·10	2·25
1750/9	*Set of 10*	5·00	5·50

MS1760 105×136 mm. $6 Jade sculpture of girl, Liao Dynasty   2·50 2·75

(c) *"Bangkok '93", Thailand*

1761	25 c. Tugu Monument, Java	10	10
1762	55 c. Candi Cangkuang mon, West Java	25	30
1763	90 c. Merus, Pura Taman Ayun, Mengwi	40	45
1764	$1.65, Hun Lek puppets of Rama and Sita	70	75
	a. Sheetlet. Nos. 1764/9	4·25	
1765	$1.65, Burmese puppet	70	75
1766	$1.65, Burmese puppets	70	75
1767	$1.65, Demon puppet at Wat Phra Kaew	70	75
1768	$1.65, Hun Lek puppet performing Khun Chang	70	75
1769	$1.65, Hun Lek puppets performing Ramakien	70	75
1770	$5 Stone mosaic, Ceto	2·10	2·25
1761/70	*Set of 10*	5·00	5·50

MS1771 105×136 mm. $6 Thai Stone carving 2·50 2·75
Nos. 1742/7, 1753/8 and 1764/9 were each printed together, *se-tenant*, in sheetlets of 6.
No. 1753 is inscribed "Chang E Rising Up th the Moon" in error.

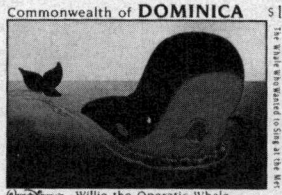

269 Willie

(Des Rosemary DeFiglio. Litho Questa)

1993 (1 Nov). *Willie the Operatic Whale. T **269** and similar multicoloured designs showing scenes from Walt Disney's cartoon film. P 14×13½.*

1772	$1 Type 269	85	90
	a. Sheetlet. Nos. 1772/80	7·00	
1773	$1 Willie's pelican friend	85	90
1774	$1 Willie singing to seals	85	90
1775	$1 Willie singing *Lucia*	85	90
1776	$1 Willie in *Pagliacci*	85	90
1777	$1 Willie as Mephistopheles	85	90
1778	$1 Tetti Tatti searching for Willie	85	90
1779	$1 Whalers listening to Willie	85	90
1780	$1 Tetti Tatti with harpoon gun	85	90
1772/80	*Set of 9*	7·00	7·50

MS1781 Two sheets. (a) 130×102 mm. $6 Seals listening to Willie. P 14×13½. (b) 97×118 mm. $6 Willie in Heaven (*vert*). P 13½×14.
     Set of 2 sheets 7·00 8·00
Nos. 1772/80 were printed together, *se-tenant*, in sheetlets of 9.

270 "Adoration of the Magi" (detail) (Dürer)

(Litho Cartor)

1993 (8 Nov). *Christmas. Religious Paintings. T **270** and similar multicoloured designs. Black, pale lemon and red (Nos. 1782/5, **MS**1790a) or multicoloured (others). P 13.*

1782	25 c. Type 270	35	10
1783	55 c. "Adoration of the Magi" (different detail) (Dürer)	55	30
1784	65 c. "Adoration of the Magi" (different detail) (Dürer)	65	35
1785	90 c. "Adoration of the Magi" (different detail) (Dürer)	80	50
1786	90 c. "Madonna of Foligno" (detail) (Raphael)	80	50
1787	$1 "Madonna of Foligno" (different detail) (Raphael)	90	60
1788	$3 "Madonna of Foligno" (different detail) (Raphael)	2·00	2·75
1789	$5 "Madonna of Foligno" (different detail) (Raphael)	2·75	3·75
1782/9	*Set of 8*	8·00	8·00

MS1790 Two sheets, each 105×130 mm. (a) $6 "Adoration of the Magi" (different detail) (Dürer) (*horiz*). (b) $6 "Madonna of Foligno" (different detail) (Raphael)   *Set of 2 sheets* 7·00 8·00

(Des W. Hanson. Litho Questa)

1994 (18 Feb). *"Hong Kong '94" International Stamp Exhibition (1st issue). Horiz designs as T **317** of Antigua. Multicoloured. P 14.*

1791	65 c. Hong Kong 1988 Peak Tramway 50 c. stamp and skyscrapers	30	35
	a. Horiz pair. Nos. 1791/2	60	70
1792	65 c. Dominica 1991 Cog Railways $5 stamp and Hong Kong Peak tram	30	35

Nos. 1791/2 were printed together, *se-tenant*, in horizontal pairs throughout the sheet with the centre part of each pair forming the composite design.

(Des Kerri Schiff. Litho Questa)

1994 (18 Feb). *"Hong Kong '94" International Stamp Exhibition (2nd issue). Tang Dynasty Jade. Multicoloured designs as T **318** of Antigua, but vert. P 14.*

1793	65 c. Horse	30	35
	a. Sheetlet. Nos. 1793/8	1·75	2·10
1794	65 c. Cup with handle	30	35
1795	65 c. Vase with birthday peaches	30	35
1796	65 c. Vase	30	35
1797	65 c. Fu Dog with puppy	30	35
1798	65 c. Drinking cup	30	35
1793/8	*Set of 6*	1·75	2·10

Nos. 1793/8 were printed together, *se-tenant*, in sheetlets of 6.

271 Male *Dynastes hercules* (beetle)   **272** *Laelio-cattleya*

(Litho Questa)

1994 (15 Mar). *Endangered Species. Birds and Insects. T **271** and similar horiz designs. Multicoloured. P 14.*

1799	20 c. Type 271	20	15
1800	25 c. Male *Dynastes hercules* (different)	20	15
1801	65 c. Male *Dynastes hercules* (different)	45	35
1802	90 c. Female *Dynastes hercules*	60	55
1803	$1 Imperial Amazon ("Imperial Parrot")	90	75
1804	$2 *Marpesia petreus* (butterfly)	1·50	2·00
1805	$3 *Hypolimnus misippus* (butterfly)	2·00	2·25
1806	$5 Purple-throated Carib	2·75	3·25
1799/1806	*Set of 8*	7·75	8·50

MS1807 Two sheets, each 98×70 mm. (a) $6 Blue-headed Hummingbird. (b) $6 *Libytheana fulvescens* (butterfly)   *Set of 2 sheets* 7·50 8·50
Nos. 1803/7 do not carry the W.W.F Panda emblem.
Nos. 1799/1802 were also available in vertical *se-tenant* strips of 4 from sheetlets of 12.

(Des Mary Walters. Litho Questa)

1994 (4 Apr). *Orchids. T **272** and similar vert designs. Multicoloured. P 14.*

1808	20 c. Type 272	35	15
1809	25 c. *Sophrolaelio cattleya*	35	15
1810	65 c. *Odontocidium*	70	45
1811	90 c. *Laelio-cattleya* (different)	90	75
1812	$1 *Cattleya*	1·00	75
1813	$2 *Odontocidium* (different)	1·50	2·00
1814	$3 *Epiphronitis*	2·00	2·50
1815	$4 *Oncidium*	2·00	2·50
1808/15	*Set of 8*	8·00	8·50

MS1816 Two sheets, each 100×70 mm. (a) $6 *Cattleya* (different). (b) $6 *Schombo cattleya*
     Set of 2 sheets 7·50 8·00

273 *Russula matoubenis*   **274** *Appias drusilla*

(Litho Questa)

1994 (18 Apr). *Fungi. T **273** and similar vert designs. Multicoloured. P 14.*

1817	20 c. Type 273	10	10
1818	25 c. *Leptonia caeruleocapitata*	10	15
1819	65 c. *Inocybe littoralis*	30	35
1820	90 c. *Russula hygrophytica*	40	45
1821	$1 *Pyrrhoglossum lilaceipes*	45	50
1822	$2 *Hygrocybe konradii*	85	90
1823	$3 *Inopilus magnificus*	1·25	1·40
1824	$5 *Boletellus cubensis*	2·10	2·25
1817/24	*Set of 8*	5·50	6·00

MS1825 Two sheets, each 110×85 mm. (a) $6 *Lentinus strigosus*. (b) $6 *Gerronema citrinum*
     Set of 2 sheets 5·25 5·50

(Litho Questa)

1994 (3 May). *Butterflies. T* **274** *and similar horiz designs. Multicoloured.* P 14.

1826	20 c. Type **274**		35	15
1827	25 c. *Didonis biblis*		35	15
1828	55 c. *Eurema daira*		70	45
1829	65 c. *Hypolimnas misippus*		75	45
1830	$1 *Phoebis agarithe*		1·00	75
1831	$2 *Marpesia petreus*		1·50	1·90
1832	$3 *Libytheana fulvescens*		1·75	2·50
1833	$5 *Precis evarete*		2·50	3·00
1826/33		Set of 8	8·00	8·50

MS1834 Two sheets, each 100×70 mm. (a) $6 *Chlorostrymon maesites.* (b) $6 *Vanessa cardui*
Set of 2 sheets 8·50 9·00

275 Dachshund

ROYAL VISIT
FEBRUARY 19, 1994

(276)

(Litho Questa)

1994 (17 May). *Chinese New Year ("Year of the Dog"). T* **275** *and similar vert designs. Multicoloured.* P 14.

1835	20 c. Type **275**		10	10
1836	25 c. Beagle		10	10
1837	55 c. Greyhound		25	30
1838	90 c. Jack Russell Terrier		40	45
1839	$1 Pekingese		45	50
1840	$2 Wire Fox Terrier		85	90
1841	$4 English Toy Spaniel		1·75	1·90
1842	$5 Irish Setter		2·10	2·25
1835/42		Set of 8	6·00	6·50

MS1843 Two sheets, each 102×72 mm. (a) $6 Welsh Corgi. (b) $6 Labrador Retriever
Set of 2 sheets 5·25 5·50

1994 (27 June). *Royal Visit. Nos.* 1700/4 *optd as T* **276** (*in three lines on No.* 1845 *and in silver on the sheet margin only of No.* MS1848).

1844	20 c. multicoloured		50	55
	a. Sheetlet. Nos. 1844/7×2		8·50	
1845	25 c. reddish brown and black		50	55
1846	65 c. multicoloured		80	90
1847	$5 multicoloured		3·00	3·25
1844/7		Set of 4	4·25	4·75

MS1848 71×101 mm. $6 multicoloured .. 4·25 4·75

277 Des Armstrong (U.S.A.)

(Litho Questa)

1994 (5 July–28 Dec). *World Cup Football Championship, U.S.A.* (2nd issue). *T* **277** *and similar horiz designs. Multicoloured.* P 14.

1849	25 c. Jefferey Edmund (Dominica) (28 Dec)		30	20
1850	$1 Type **277**		60	70
	a. Sheetlet. Nos. 1850/5		3·25	
1851	$1 Dennis Bergkamp (Netherlands)		60	70
1852	$1 Roberto Baggio (Italy)		60	70
1853	$1 Rai (Brazil)		60	70
1854	$1 Cafu (Brazil)		60	70
1855	$1 Marco van Basten (Netherlands)		60	70
1849/55		Set of 7	3·50	4·00

MS1856 Two sheets. (a) 70×100 mm. $6 Roberto Mancini (Italy). (b) 100×70 mm. $6 Player and Stanford Stadium, San Francisco Set of 2 sheets 8·00 9·00
Nos. 1850/5 were printed together, *se-tenant,* in sheetlets of 6.

278 Scout Backpacking

279 Pink Bird
and Red Flowers
Screen Painting

(Litho Questa)

1994 (18 July). *10th Caribbean Scout Jamboree. T* **278** *and similar multicoloured designs.* P 14.

1857	20 c. Type **278**		35	15
1858	25 c. Cooking over campfire		35	15
1859	55 c. Erecting tent		60	30
1860	65 c. Serving soup		70	45
1861	$1 Corps of drums		1·00	75
1862	$1 Planting tree		1·50	2·00
1863	$4 Sailing dinghy		2·25	2·50
1864	$5 Saluting		2·25	2·50
1857/64		Set of 8	8·00	8·00

MS1865 Two sheets, each 100×70 mm. (a) $6 Early scout troop. (b) $6 Pres. Crispin Sorhaindo (chief scout) (*vert*) .. Set of 2 sheets 8·50 9·00

(Des W. Hanson. Litho B.D.T.)

1994 (26 July). *25th Anniv of First Moon Landing. Horiz designs as T* **326** *of Antigua. Multicoloured.* P 14.

1866	$1 Crew of "Apollo 14"		45	50
	a. Sheetlet. Nos. 1866/71		2·75	
1867	$1 "Apollo 14" mission logo		45	50
1868	$1 Lunar module *Antares* on Moon		45	50
1869	$1 Crew of "Apollo 15"		45	50
1870	$1 "Apollo 15" mission logo		45	50
1871	$1 Lunar crater on Mt Hadley		45	50
1866/71		Set of 6	2·75	3·00

MS1872 99×106 mm. $6 "Apollo 11" logo and surface of Moon .. 2·50 2·75
Nos. 1866/71 were printed together, *se-tenant,* in sheetlets of 6.

(Des Kerri Schiff. Litho B.D.T.)

1994 (26 July). *Centenary of International Olympic Committee. Gold Medal Winners. Horiz designs as T* **327** *of Antigua. Multicoloured.* P 14.

1873	55 c. Urike Meyfarth (Germany) (high jump), 1984		25	30
1874	$1.45, Dieter Baumann (Germany) (5000 metres), 1992		60	65

MS1875 106×76 mm. $6 Ji Hoon Chae (South Korea) (500 metres speed skating), 1994 2·50 2·75

(Des A. Melville-Brown. Litho B.D.T.)

1994 (26 July). *Centenary of First English Cricket Tour to the West Indies* (1995). *Multicoloured designs as T* **329** *of Antigua.* P 14.

1876	55 c. David Gower (England) (*vert*)		40	30
1877	90 c. Curtly Ambrose (West Indies) and Wisden Trophy		60	60
1878	$1 Graham Gooch (England) (*vert*)		70	80
1876/8		Set of 3	1·50	1·50

MS1879 76×96 mm. $3 First English touring team, 1895 .. 2·40 2·40

(Des J. Batchelor. Litho B.D.T.)

1994 (26 July). *50th Anniv of D-Day. Horiz designs as T* **331** *of Antigua. Multicoloured.* P 14.

1880	65 c. American Waco gliders		30	35
1881	$2 British Horsa glider		85	90
1882	$3 British glider and troops attacking Pegasus Bridge		1·25	1·40
1880/2		Set of 3	2·40	2·75

MS1883 107×77 mm. $6 British Hadrian glider 2·50 2·75

(Des Kerri Schiff. Litho Questa (Nos. 1884/93), B.D.T. (Nos. 1894/7))

1994 (26 July). *"Philakorea '94" International Stamp Exhibition, Seoul. T* **279** *and similar multicoloured designs.* P 13 (*Nos.* 1884/93) *or* 14 (*others*).

1884	55 c. Type **279**		25	30
	a. Sheetlet. Nos. 1884/93		2·50	
1885	55 c. Bird with yellow, pink and red flowers		25	30
1886	55 c. Pair of birds and yellow flowers		25	30
1887	55 c. Chickens and flowers		25	30
1888	55 c. Pair of birds and pink flowers		25	30
1889	55 c. Ducks and flowers		25	30
1890	55 c. Blue bird and red flowers		25	30
1891	55 c. Pheasant and flowers		25	30
1892	55 c. Stork and flowers		25	30
1893	55 c. Deer and flowers		25	30
1894	65 c. P'alsang-jon Hall (38×24 *mm*)		30	35
1895	90 c. Popchu-sa Temple (38×24 *mm*)		35	40
1896	$2 Uhwajong Pavilion (38×24 *mm*)		85	90
1884/96		Set of 13	4·00	4·50

MS1897 100×70 mm. $4 Spirit Post Guardian (38×24 *mm*). P 14 .. 1·75 1·90
Nos. 1884/93 were printed together, *se-tenant,* in sheetlets of 10 and show screen paintings.

280 Dippy Dawg

281 Marilyn Monroe

(Des Alvin White Studio. Litho Questa)

1994 (3 Oct). *65th Anniv of Mickey Mouse* (1993). *T* **280** *and similar multicoloured designs showing Walt Disney cartoon characters.* P 13½×14.

1898	20 c. Type **280**		45	20
1899	25 c. Clarabelle Cow		45	20
1900	55 c. Horace Horsecollar		70	35
1901	65 c. Mortimer Mouse		80	45
1902	$1 Joe Piper		1·25	85
1903	$3 Mr. Casey		2·25	2·50
1904	$4 Chief O'Hara		2·50	3·00
1905	$5 Mickey and The Blot		2·50	3·00
1898/1905		Set of 8	9·75	9·50

MS1906 Two sheets, each 127×102 mm. (a) $6 Minnie Mouse with Tanglefoot. P 13½×14. (b) $6 Minnie and Pluto (*horiz*). P 14×13½
Set of 2 sheets 9·00 10·00

(Des R. Rundo. Litho B.D.T.)

1994 (1 Dec). *Entertainers. T* **281** *and similar vert designs. Multicoloured.* P 14.

1907	20 c. Sonia Lloyd (folk singer)		10	15
1908	25 c. Ophelia Marie (singer)		10	15
1909	55 c. Edney Francis (accordion player)		25	30
1910	65 c. Norman Letang (saxophonist)		30	35
1911	90 c. Edie André (steel-band player)		40	45
1912	90 c. Type **281**		40	45
	a. Sheetlet. Nos. 1912/20		3·50	
1913	90 c. Marilyn Monroe wearing necklace		40	45
1914	90 c. In yellow frilled dress		40	45
1915	90 c. In purple dress		40	45
1916	90 c. Looking over left shoulder		40	45
1917	90 c. Laughing		40	45
1918	90 c. In red dress		40	45
1919	90 c. Wearing gold cluster earrings		40	45
1920	90 c. In yellow dress		40	45
1907/20		Set of 14	4·50	5·50

MS1921 Two sheets, each 106×76 mm. (a) $6 Marilyn Monroe with top hat. (b) $6 With arms above head .. Set of 2 sheets 5·25 5·50
Nos. 1912/20 were printed together, *se-tenant,* in sheetlets of 9.

No. 1907 is inscribed "Llyod" in error.

(Litho Questa)

1994 (2 Dec). *Christmas. Religious Paintings. Vert designs as T* **336** *of Antigua. Multicoloured.* P 13½×14.

1922	20 c. "Madonna and Child" (Luis de Morales)		25	10
1923	25 c. "Madonna and Child with Yarn Winder" (De Morales)		25	10
1924	55 c. "Our Lady of the Rosary" (detail) (Zurbaran)		40	30
1925	65 c. "Dream of the Patrician" (detail) (Murillo)		50	35
1926	90 c. "Madonna of Charity" (El Greco)		70	45
1927	$1 "The Annunciation" (Zurbaran)		75	50
1928	$2 "Mystical Marriage of St. Catherine" (Jusepe de Ribera)		1·25	1·75
1929	$3 "The Holy Family with St. Bruno and Other Saints" (detail) (De Ribera)		1·50	2·00
1922/9		Set of 8	5·00	5·00

MS1930 Two sheets. (a) 136×97 mm. $6 "Adoration of the Shepherds" (detail) (Murillo). (b) 99×118 mm. $6 "Vision of the Virgin to St. Bernard" (detail) (Murillo) .. Set of 2 sheets 7·50 8·50

(Litho Questa)

1994 (16 Dec). *First Recipients of Order of the Caribbean Community. Horiz designs as Nos.* 2046/8 *of Antigua. Multicoloured.* P 14.

1931	25 c. Sir Shridath Ramphal		20	10
1932	65 c. William Demas		50	50
1933	90 c. Derek Walcott		70	80
1931/3		Set of 3	1·25	1·25

18th World Scout Jamboree
Mondial, Holland, May 6, 1995

(282)

283 Wood Duck

1995 (21 Mar). *18th World Scout Jamboree, Netherlands. Nos.* 1860, *and* 1863/5 *optd with T* **282** (*sideways, reading upwards on No.* MS1937b).

1934	65 c. Serving soup		30	35
1935	$4 Sailing dinghy		1·75	1·90
1936	$5 Saluting		2·10	2·25
1934/6		Set of 3	4·00	4·25

MS1937 Two sheets, each 100×70 mm. (a) $6 Early scout troop. (b) $6 Pres. Crispin Sorhaindo (chief scout) (*vert*) .. Set of 2 sheets 7·00 8·00

(Des R. Rundo. Litho Questa)

1995 (15 Apr). *Water Birds. T* **283** *and similar multicoloured designs.* P 14.

1938	25 c. Type **283**		40	30
1939	55 c. Mallard		50	40
1940	65 c. Blue-winged Teal		55	55
1941	65 c. Cattle Egret (*vert*)		55	65
	a. Sheetlet. Nos. 1941/52		6·00	
1942	65 c. Snow Goose (*vert*)		55	65
1943	65 c. Peregrine Falcon (*vert*)		55	65
1944	65 c. Barn Owl (*vert*)		55	65
1945	65 c. Black-crowned Night Heron (*vert*)		55	65
1946	65 c. Common Grackle (*vert*)		55	65
1947	65 c. Brown Pelican (*vert*)		55	65

1948	65 c.	Great Egret (*vert*)		55	65
1949	65 c.	Ruby-throated Hummingbird (*vert*)		55	65
1950	65 c.	Laughing Gull (*vert*)		55	65
1951	65 c.	Greater Flamingo (*vert*)		55	65
1952	65 c.	Moorhen (*vert*)		55	65
1953	$5	Red-eared Conure ("Blood Eared Parakeet")		2·50	3·00
1938/53			Set of 16	9·50	10·50

MS1954 Two sheets, each 105×75 mm. (a) $5 Trumpeter Swan (*vert*). (b) $6 White-eyed Vireo
Set of 2 sheets 7·00 7·50

Nos. 1941/52 were printed together, *se-tenant*, in sheetlets of 12 with the background forming a composite design.
No. 1946 is inscribed "Common Gralkle" in error.

284 Pig's Head facing Right

285 Paul Harris (founder) and Emblem

(Des Y. Lee. Litho Questa)

1995 (21 Apr). *Chinese New Year ("Year of the Pig"). T 284 and similar multicoloured designs.* P 14½.

1955	25 c.	Type **284**		10	10
		a. Horiz strip of 3. Nos. 1955/7		85	
1956	65 c.	Pig facing to the front		30	35
1957	$1	Pig facing left		45	50
1955/7			Set of 3	85	95

MS1958 101×50 mm. Nos. 1955/7 85 90
MS1959 105×77 mm. $2 Two pigs (*horiz*) 85 90

Nos. 1955/7 were printed together, *se-tenant*, in horizontal strips of 3 throughout the sheet.

(Litho Questa)

1995 (18 May). *50th Anniv of End of Second World War in Europe. Horiz designs as T 340 of Antigua. Multicoloured.* P 14.

1960	$2	German Panther tank in the Ardennes		85	90
		a. Sheetlet. Nos. 1960/7		6·75	
1961	$2	American fighter-bomber		85	90
1962	$2	American mechanized column crossing the Rhine		85	90
1963	$2	Messerschmitt Me 163B Komet and Allied bombers		85	90
1964	$2	V2 rocket on launcher		85	90
1965	$2	German U-boat surrendering		85	90
1966	$2	Heavy artillery in action		85	90
1967	$2	Soviet infantry in Berlin		85	90
1960/7			Set of 8	6·75	7·00

MS1968 106×76 mm. $6 Statue and devastated Dresden (56½×42½ mm) 2·50 2·75

Nos. 1960/7 were printed together, *se-tenant*, in sheetlets of 8 with the stamps arranged in two horizontal strips of 4 separated by a gutter showing liberation of Dachau.

(Litho Questa)

1995 (21 July). *90th Anniv of Rotary International. T 285 and similar horiz design.* P 14.

1969	$1	lake-brown, reddish purple and black		65	65

MS1970 70×100 mm. $6 vermilion and black 2·75 3·25
Design:—$6 Rotary emblems.

(Des J. Batchelor. Litho Questa)

1995 (21 July). *50th Anniv of End of Second World War in the Pacific. Horiz designs as T 340 of Antigua. Multicoloured.* P 14.

1971	$2	Mitsubishi A6M Zero-Sen torpedo-bomber		85	90
		a. Sheetlet. Nos. 1971/6		5·00	
1972	$2	Aichi D3A "Val" dive bomber		85	90
1973	$2	Nakajima B5N "Kate" bomber		85	90
1974	$2	Zuikaku (Japanese aircraft carrier)		85	90
1975	$2	Akagi (Japanese aircraft carrier)		85	90
1976	$2	Ryuho (Japanese aircraft carrier)		85	90
1971/6			Set of 6	5·00	5·25

MS1977 108×76 mm. $6 Japanese torpedo-bomber at Pearl Harbor 2·50 2·75

Nos. 1971/6 were printed together, *se-tenant*, in sheetlets of 6 with the stamps arranged in two horizontal strips of 3 separated by a gutter showing U.S. dive-bombers attacking Japanese aircraft carrier *Soryu*.

286 Boxing

287 Market Customers

(Des A. De Lorenzo. Litho Questa)

1995 (21 July). *Olympic Games, Atlanta (1st issue) (1996). T 286 and similar multicoloured designs.* P 14.

1978	15 c.	Type **286**		10	10
1979	20 c.	Wrestling		10	10
1980	25 c.	Judo		10	10
1981	55 c.	Fencing		25	30
1982	65 c.	Swimming		30	35
1983	$1	Gymnastics (*vert*)		45	50
1984	$2	Cycling (*vert*)		85	90
1985	$5	Volleyball		2·10	2·25
1978/85			Set of 8	4·50	4·75

MS1986 Two sheets, each 104×74 mm. (a) $6 Show jumping. (b) $6 Football (*vert*)
Set of 2 sheets 5·25 5·50

See also Nos. 2122/46 and 2213/14

(Des L. Fried. Litho Questa)

1995 (16 Aug). *50th Anniv of United Nations. Vert designs as T 341 of Antigua. Multicoloured.* P 14.

1987	65 c.	Signatures and U.S. delegate		30	35
		a. Horiz strip of 3. Nos. 1987/9		1·60	
1988	$1	U.S. delegate		45	50
1989	$2	Governor Stassen (U.S. delegate)		85	90
1987/9			Set of 3	1·60	1·75

MS1990 100×71 mm. $6 Winston Churchill 2·50 2·75

Nos. 1987/9 were printed together in sheets of 9 (3×3) containing three *se-tenant* horizontal strips, each forming a composite design.

(Des L. Fried. Litho Questa)

1995 (16 Aug). *50th Anniv of Food and Agriculture Organization. T 287 and similar multicoloured designs.* P 14.

MS1991 110×74 mm. 90 c., $1, $2 Panorama of Dominican market 1·60 1·75
MS1992 101×71 mm. $6 Women irrigating crops (*horiz*) 2·50 2·75

(Litho Questa)

1995 (16 Aug). *95th Birthday of Queen Elizabeth the Queen Mother. Vert designs as T 344 of Antigua.* P 13½×14.

1993	$1.65, orange-brown, pale brown and black			70	75
	a. Sheetlet. Nos. 1993/6, each × 2			5·50	
1994	$1.65, multicoloured			70	75
1995	$1.65, multicoloured			70	75
1996	$1.65, multicoloured			70	75
1993/6			Set of 4	2·75	3·00

MS1997 103×126 mm. $6 multicoloured 2·50 2·75
Designs:—No. 1993, Queen Elizabeth the Queen Mother (pastel drawing); No. 1994, Holding bouquet of flowers; No. 1995, At desk (oil painting); No. 1996, Wearing blue dress; No. **MS**1997, Wearing ruby and diamond tiara and necklace.
Nos. 1993/6 were printed together in sheetlets of 8, containing two *se-tenant* horizontal strips of 4.

288 Monoclonius

289 Oscar Sánchez (1987 Peace)

(Des B. Regal. Litho Questa)

1995 (8 Sept). *"Singapore '95" International Stamp Exhibition. Prehistoric Animals. T 288 and similar multicoloured designs.* P 14.

1998	20 c.	Type **288**		10	10
1999	25 c.	Euoplocephalus		10	10
2000	55 c.	Head of Coelophysis		25	30
2001	65 c.	Head of Compsognathus		30	35
2002	90 c.	Dimorphodon		40	45
		a. Horiz strip of 4. Nos. 2002/5		1·60	
2003	90 c.	Ramphorynchus		40	45
2004	90 c.	Head of Giant Alligator		40	45
2005	90 c.	Pentaceratops		40	45
2006	$1	Ceratosaurus (*vert*)		45	50
		a. Sheetlet. Nos. 2006/17		5·50	
2007	$1	Comptosaurus (*vert*)		45	50
2008	$1	Stegosaur (*vert*)		45	50
2009	$1	Camarasaurs (*vert*)		45	50
2010	$1	Baronyx (*vert*)		45	50
2011	$1	Dilophosaurus (*vert*)		45	50
2012	$1	Dromaeosaurids (*vert*)		45	50
2013	$1	Deinonychus (*vert*)		45	50
2014	$1	Dinicthys (Terror Fish) (*vert*)		45	50
2015	$1	Head of Carcharodon (Giant-toothed Shark) (*vert*)		45	50
2016	$1	Nautiloid (*vert*)		45	50
2017	$1	Trilobite (*vert*)		45	50
1998/2017			Set of 20	7·75	8·50

MS2018 Two sheets. (a) 95×65 mm. $5 Sauropelta. (b) 65×95 mm. $6 Triceratops (*vert*)
Set of 2 sheets 4·75 5·00

Nos. 2002/5 and 2006/17 were printed together, *se-tenant*, in horizontal strips of 4 (Nos. 2002/5) or sheetlets of 12 (Nos. 2006/17), each forming composite designs.
Nos. 2002/5 do not carry the "Singapore '95" exhibition logo.

(Des R. Rundo. Litho Questa)

1995 (27 Oct). *Centenary of Nobel Prize Trust Fund. T 289 and similar vert designs. Multicoloured.* P 14.

2019	$2	Type **289**		85	90
		a. Sheetlet. Nos. 2019/24		5·00	
2020	$2	Ernst Chain (1945 Medicine)		85	90
2021	$2	Aage Bohr (1975 Physics)		85	90
2022	$2	Jaroslav Seifert (1984 Literature)		85	90
2023	$2	Joseph Murray (1990 Medicine)		85	90
2024	$2	Jaroslav Heyrovsky (1959 Chemistry)		85	90
2025	$2	Adolf von Baeyer (1905 Chemistry)		85	90
		a. Sheetlet. Nos. 2025/30		5·00	
2026	$2	Eduard Buchner (1907 Chemistry)		85	90
2027	$2	Carl Bosch (1931 Chemistry)		85	90
2028	$2	Otto Hahn (1944 Chemistry)		85	90
2029	$2	Otto Diels (1950 Chemistry)		85	90
2030	$2	Kurt Alder (1950 Chemistry)		85	90
2019/30			Set of 12	10·00	10·50

MS2031 76×106 mm. $2 Emil von Behring (1901 Medicine) 85 90

Nos. 2019/24 and 2025/30 were printed together, *se-tenant*, in sheetlets of 6 with the backgrounds forming designs of the Nobel Medal.

(Litho Questa)

1995 (30 Nov). *Christmas. Religious Paintings. Vert designs as T 357 of Antigua. Multicoloured.* P 13½×14.

2032	20 c.	"Madonna and Child with St. John" (Pontormo)		15	15
2033	25 c.	"The Immaculate Conception" (Murillo)		15	15
2034	55 c.	"The Adoration of the Magi" (Filippino Lippi)		35	30
2035	65 c.	"Rest on the Flight into Egypt" (Van Dyck)		45	35
2036	90 c.	"The Holy Family" (Van Dyck)		65	50
2037	$5	"The Annunciation" (Van Eyck)		2·50	3·25
2032/7			Set of 6	3·75	4·25

MS2038 Two sheets, each 102×127 mm. (a) $5 "Madonna and Child Reading" (detail) (Van Eyck). (b) $6 "The Holy Family" (detail) (Ribera)
Set of 2 sheets 6·50 7·00

(Litho Questa)

1995 (10 Dec). *Centenary of Sierra Club (environmental protection society) (1992). Endangered Species. Multicoloured designs as T 320 of Antigua.* P 14.

2039	$1	Florida Panther		45	50
		a. Sheetlet. Nos. 2039/47		4·00	
2040	$1	Manatee (*horiz*)		45	50
2041	$1	Sockeye Salmon		45	50
2042	$1	Key Deer facing left		45	50
2043	$1	Key Deer doe		45	50
2044	$1	Key Deer stag		45	50
2045	$1	Wallaby with young in pouch		45	50
2046	$1	Wallaby feeding young		45	50
2047	$1	Wallaby and young feeding		45	50
2048	$1	Florida Panther showing teeth (*horiz*)		45	50
		a. Sheetlet. Nos. 2048/56		4·00	
2049	$1	Head of Florida Panther (*horiz*)		45	50
2050	$1	Manatee (*horiz*)		45	50
2051	$1	Pair of Manatees (*horiz*)		45	50
2052	$1	Pair of Sockeye Salmon (*horiz*)		45	50
2053	$1	Sockeye Salmon spawning (*horiz*)		45	50
2054	$1	Pair of Southern Sea Otters (*horiz*)		45	50
2055	$1	Southern Sea Otter with front paws together (*horiz*)		45	50
2056	$1	Southern Sea Otter with front paws apart (*horiz*)		45	50
2039/56			Set of 18	8·00	9·00

Nos. 2039/47 and 2048/56 were printed together, *se-tenant*, in sheetlets of 9.

290 Street Scene

1995 (27 Dec). *"A City of Cathay" (Chinese scroll painting). T 290 and similar multicoloured designs. Litho.* P 14½.

2057	90 c.	Type **290**		50	60
		a. Horiz strip of 5. Nos. 2057/61		2·25	
2058	90 c.	Street scene and city wall		50	60
2059	90 c.	City gate and bridge		50	60
2060	90 c.	Landing stage and junk		50	60
2061	90 c.	River bridge		50	60
2062	90 c.	Moored junks		50	60
		a. Horiz strip of 5. Nos. 2062/6		2·25	
2063	90 c.	Two rafts on river		50	60
2064	90 c.	Two junks on river		50	60
2065	90 c.	Roadside tea house		50	60
2066	90 c.	Wedding party on the road		50	60
2057/66			Set of 10	4·50	5·50

MS2067 Two sheets, each 106×77 mm. (a) $2 City street and sampan; $2 Footbridge. (b) $2 Stern of sampan (*vert*); $2 Bow of sampan (*vert*)
Set of 2 sheets 3·75 4·00

Nos. 2057/61 (showing inscriptions in black) and Nos. 2062/6 (showing inscriptions in chestnut) were each issued in sheets of 20 containing four *se-tenant* strips of 5, with each horizontal row separated by imperforate gutters incorporating inscribed labels.

NEW INFORMATION

The editor is always interested to correspond with people who have new information that will improve or correct the Catalogue.

291 "Bindo Altoviti"
(Raphael)

292 Rat

(Litho Questa)

1995 (27 Dec). *Paintings by Raphael. T* **291** *and similar vert designs. Multicoloured. P* 13½×14.

2068	$2 Type **291**	1·10	1·25
2069	$2 "Pope Leo with Nephews"	1·10	1·25
2070	$2 "Agony in the Garden"	1·10	1·25
2068/70	*Set of 3*	3·00	3·25

MS2071 110×80 mm. $6 "Pope Leo X with Cardinals Giulio de Medici and Luigi dei Rossi" (detail) .. .. .. 3·25 3·50

(Des Y. Lee. Litho Questa)

1996 (16 Jan). *Chinese New Year ("Year of the Rat"). T* **292** *and similar vert designs showing rats and Chinese symbols. Multicoloured. P* 14½.

2072	25 c. black, violet and chestnut	10	10
	a. Horiz strip of 3. Nos. 2072/4	85	
2073	65 c. black, orange-vermilion & deep green	30	35
2074	$1 black, magenta and blue	45	50
2072/4	*Set of 3*	85	95

MS2075 100×50 mm. Nos. 2072/4 .. 85 90
MS2076 105×77 mm. $2 black, grey-green and reddish violet (two rats) .. 85 90
Nos. 2072/4 were printed together, *se-tenant,* in horizontal strips of 3 throughout sheets of 12.

293 Mickey and Minnie Mouse
(Year of the Rat)

(Litho Questa)

1996 (16 Jan). *Chinese Lunar Calendar. T* **293** *and similar horiz designs showing Walt Disney cartoon characters. Multicoloured. P* 14×13½.

2077	55 c. Type **293**	40	45
	a. Sheetlet. Nos. 2077/88	4·25	
2078	55 c. Casey Jones (Year of the Ox)	40	45
2079	55 c. Tigger, Pooh and Piglet (Year of the Tiger)	40	45
2080	55 c. White Rabbit (Year of the Rabbit)	40	45
2081	55 c. Dragon playing flute (Year of the Dragon)	40	45
2082	55 c. Snake looking in mirror (Year of the Snake)	40	45
2083	55 c. Horace Horsecollar and Clarabelle Cow (Year of the Horse)	40	45
2084	55 c. Black Lamb and blue birds (Year of the Ram)	40	45
2085	55 c. King Louis reading book (Year of the Monkey)	40	45
2086	55 c. Cock playing lute (Year of the Cock)	40	45
2087	55 c. Mickey and Pluto (Year of the Dog)	40	45
2088	55 c. Pig building bridge (Year of the Pig)	40	45
2077/88	*Set of 12*	4·25	4·75

MS2089 Two sheets. (a) 127×102 mm. $3 Basil the Great Mouse Detective (Year of the Rat). (b) 102×127 mm. $6 Emblems for 1996, 1997 and 2007 .. .. .. *Set of 2 sheets* 6·00 6·50
Nos. 2077/88 were printed together, *se-tenant,* in sheetlets of 12.

294 Steam Locomotive *Dragon,*
Hawaii

(Des R. Sauber. Litho B.D.T.)

1996 (29 Jan). *Trains of the World. T* **294** *and similar horiz designs. Multicoloured. P* 14.

2090	$2 Type **294**	85	90
	a. Sheetlet. Nos. 2090/8	7·50	
2091	$2 Class 685 steam locomotive *Regina,* Italy	85	90
2092	$2 Class 745 steam locomotive, Calazo to Padua line, Italy	85	90

2093	$2 Mogul steam locomotive, Philippines	85	90
2094	$2 Class 23 and 24 steam locomotives, Germany	85	90
2095	$2 Class BB-15000 electric locomotive *Stanislaus,* France	85	90
2096	$2 Class "Black Five" steam locomotive, Scotland	85	90
2097	$2 Diesel-electric locomotive, France	85	90
2098	$2 L.N.E.R. Class A4 steam locomotive, *Sir Nigel Gresley,* England	85	90
2099	$2 Class 9600 steam locomotive, Japan	85	90
	a. Sheetlet. Nos. 2099/107	7·50	
2100	$2 "Peloponnese Express" train, Greece	85	90
2101	$2 Porter type steam locomotive, Hawaii	85	90
2102	$2 Steam locomotive *Holand,* Norway	85	90
2103	$2 Class 220 diesel-hydraulic locomotive, Germany	85	90
2104	$2 Steam locomotive, India	85	90
2105	$2 East African Railways Class 29 steam locomotive	85	90
2106	$2 Electric trains, Russia	85	90
2107	$2 Steam locomotive, Austria	85	90
2090/107	*Set of 18*	15·00	16·00

MS2108 Two sheets, each 103×73 mm. (a) $5 L.M.S. steam locomotive *Duchess of Hamilton,* England. (b) $6 Diesel locomotives, China .. .. .. *Set of 2 sheets* 4·75 5·00
Nos. 2090/8 and 2099/107 were each printed together, *se-tenant,* in sheetlets of 9 with enlarged illustrated top margins.

295 Horse-drawn Gig, 1965

(Des R. Sauber. Litho B.D.T.)

1996 (29 Jan). *Traditional Island Transport. T* **295** *and similar horiz designs. Multicoloured. P* 14.

2109	65 c. Type **295**	50	35
2110	90 c. Early automobile, 1910	60	55
2111	$2 Lorry, 1950	1·25	1·40
2112	$3 Bus, 1955	1·50	1·60
2109/12	*Set of 4*	3·25	3·50

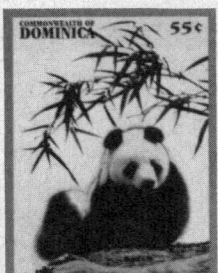

296 Giant Panda

1996 (15 May). *"CHINA '96" 9th Asian International Stamp Exhibition, Peking. Giant Pandas. T* **296** *and similar multicoloured designs. Litho. P* 13½×14.

2113	55 c. Type **296**	25	30
	a. Sheetlet. Nos. 2113/16 × 2	2·00	
2114	55 c. Panda on rock	25	30
2115	55 c. Panda eating bamboo shoots	25	30
2116	55 c. Panda on all fours	25	30
2113/16	*Set of 4*	1·00	1·10

MS2117 Two sheets. (a) 90×125 mm. $2 Huangshan Mountain, China (50×75 mm). P 12. (b) 160×125 mm. $3 Panda sitting (50×37 mm). P 14×13½ .. .. *Set of 2 sheets* 2·10 2·25
Nos. 2113/16 were printed together, *se-tenant,* in sheetlets of 8 containing two of each design.

(Litho Questa)

1996 (16 May). *70th Birthday of Queen Elizabeth II. Vert designs as T* **364** *of Antigua. Multicoloured. P* 13½×14.

2118	$2 As Type **364** of Antigua	85	90
	a. Strip of 3. Nos. 2118/20	2·50	
2119	$2 Queen in robes of Order of St. Michael and St. George	85	90
2120	$2 Queen in blue dress with floral brooch	85	90
2118/20	*Set of 3*	2·50	2·75

MS2121 103×125 mm. $6 Queen at Trooping the Colour. P 13½×14 .. .. 2·50 2·75
Nos. 2118/20 were printed together, *se-tenant,* in horizontal and vertical strips of 3 throughout the sheet.

297 Moscow Stadium, 1980

(Litho B.D.T.)

1996 (7 June). *Olympic Games, Atlanta (2nd issue). Previous Medal Winners. T* **297** *and similar multicoloured designs. P* 14.

2122	20 c. Type **297**	10	15
2123	25 c. Hermine Joseph (running) (*vert*)	10	15
2124	55 c. Zimbabwe women's hockey team, 1980	25	30
2125	90 c. Jerome Romain (long jump) (*vert*)	40	45
2126	90 c. Sammy Lee (diving), 1948 and 1952 (*vert*)	40	45
	a. Sheetlet. Nos. 2126/34	3·50	
2127	90 c. Bruce Jenner (decathlon), 1976 (*vert*)	40	45
2128	90 c. Olga Korbut (gymnastics), 1972 (*vert*)	40	45
2129	90 c. Steffi Graff (tennis), 1988 (*vert*)	40	45
2130	90 c. Florence Griffith-Joyner (track and field), 1988 (*vert*)	40	45
2131	90 c. Mark Spitz (swimming), 1968 and 1972 (*vert*)	40	45
2132	90 c. Li Ning (gymnastics), 1984 (*vert*)	40	45
2133	90 c. Erika Salumae (cycling), 1988 (*vert*)	40	45
2134	90 c. Abebe Bikila (marathon), 1960 and 1964 (*vert*)	40	45
2135	90 c. Ulrike Meyfarth (high jump), 1972 and 1984 (*vert*)	40	45
	a. Sheetlet. Nos. 2135/43	3·50	
2136	90 c. Pat McCormick (diving), 1952 and 1956 (*vert*)	40	45
2137	90 c. Takeichi Nishi (equestrian), 1932 (*vert*)	40	45
2138	90 c. Peter Farkas (Greco-Roman wrestling), 1992 (*vert*)	40	45
2139	90 c. Carl Lewis (track and field), 1984, 1988 and 1992 (*vert*)	40	45
2140	90 c. Agnes Keleti (gymnastics), 1952 and 1956 (*vert*)	40	45
2141	90 c. Yasuhiro Yamashita (judo), 1984 (*vert*)	40	45
2142	90 c. John Kelly (single sculls), 1920 (*vert*)	40	45
2143	90 c. Naim Suleymanoglu (weightlifting), 1988 and 1992 (*vert*)	40	45
2144	$1 Polo (*vert*)	45	50
2145	$2 Greg Louganis (diving), 1976, 1984 and 1988	85	90
2122/45	*Set of 24*	9·00	10·00

MS2146 Two sheets, each 105×75 mm. (a) $5 Joan Benoit (marathon), 1984 (*vert*). (b) $5 Milt Campbell (discus) .. *Set of 2 sheets* 4·25 4·50
Nos. 2126/34 and 2135/43 were each printed together, *se-tenant,* in sheetlets of 9, the backgrounds forming composite designs.

(Litho Questa)

1996 (31 July). *50th Anniv of U.N.I.C.E.F. Multicoloured designs as T* **366** *of Antigua. P* 14.

2147	20 c. Child and globe (*horiz*)	10	10
2148	55 c. Child with syringe and stethoscope (*horiz*)	25	30
2149	$5 Doctor and child (*horiz*)	2·10	2·25
2147/9	*Set of 3*	2·40	2·50

MS2150 74×104 mm. $5 African child .. 2·10 2·25

(Des R. Sauber. Litho Questa)

1996 (31 July). *3000th Anniv of Jerusalem. Vert designs as T* **367** *of Antigua. Multicoloured. P* 14.
MS2151 114×95 mm. 90 c. Shrine of the Book, Israel Museum; $1 Church of All Nations; $2 The Great Synagogue .. .. .. 1·60 1·75
MS2152 104×74 mm. $5 Hebrew University, Mount Scopus .. .. .. 2·10 2·25

(Des J. Iskowitz. Litho Questa)

1996 (31 July). *Centenary of Radio. Entertainers. Multicoloured designs as T* **368** *of Antigua. P* 13½×14.

2153	90 c. Artie Shaw	40	45
2154	$1 Benny Goodman	45	50
2155	$2 Duke Ellington	85	90
2156	$4 Harry James	1·75	1·90
2153/6	*Set of 4*	3·25	3·50

MS2157 70×99 mm. $6 Tommy and Jimmy Dorsey. P 14×13½ (*horiz*) .. .. 2·50 2·75

298 Irene Peltier in
National Dress

299 Humphrey Bogart as
Sam Spade

(Litho Questa)

1996 (31 July). *Local Entertainers. T* **298** *and similar vert designs. Multicoloured. P* 13½×14.

2158	25 c. Type **298**	10	15
2159	55 c. Rupert Bartley (steel-band player)	25	30
2160	65 c. Rosemary Cools-Lartigue (pianist)	30	35
2161	90 c. Celestine 'Orion' Theophile (singer)	40	45
2162	$1 Cecil Bellot (band master)	45	50
2158/62	*Set of 5*	1·50	1·75

1996 (31 July). *Centenary of Cinema. Screen Detectives.* T **299** *and similar vert designs. Multicoloured. Litho.* P 13¹⁄₂×14.

2163	$1 Type **299**		45	50
	a. Sheetlet. Nos. 2163/71		4·00	
2164	$1 Sean Connery as James Bond		45	50
2165	$1 Warren Beatty as Dick Tracy		45	50
2166	$1 Basil Rathbone as Sherlock Holmes	..	45	50
2167	$1 William Powell as the Thin Man		45	50
2168	$1 Sidney Toler as Charlie Chan		45	50
2169	$1 Peter Sellers as Inspector Clouseau	..	45	50
2170	$1 Robert Mitchum as Philip Marlowe	..	45	50
2171	$1 Peter Ustinov as Hercule Poirot	..	45	50
2163/71		*Set of 9*	4·00	4·50

MS2172 105×75 mm. $6 Margaret Rutherford as Miss Marple   2·50 2·75
Nos. 2163/71 were printed together, *se-tenant*, in sheetlets of 9.

300 Scribbled Filefish   301 Anthony Trollope and Postal Scenes

(Litho Questa)

1996 (1 Oct). *Fishes.* T **300** *and similar horiz designs. Multicoloured.* P 14¹⁄₂×13¹⁄₂.

2173	1 c. Type **300**		10	10
2174	2 c. Lionfish		10	10
2175	5 c. Porcupinefish		10	10
2176	10 c. Powder-blue Surgeonfish		10	10
2177	15 c. Red Hind		10	10
2178	20 c. Golden Butterflyfish		10	10
2179	25 c. Copper-banded Butterflyfish		10	15
2180	35 c. Pennant Coralfish		15	20
2181	45 c. Spotted Drum		20	25
2182	55 c. Blue-girdled Angelfish		25	30
2183	60 c. Scorpionfish		25	30
2184	65 c. Harlequin Sweetlips		30	35
2185	90 c. Flame Angelfish		40	45
2186	$1 Queen Triggerfish		45	50
2187	$1.20, Spotlight Parrotfish		50	55
2188	$1.45, Black Durgon		65	70
2189	$2 Glass-eyed Snapper		85	90
2190	$5 Balloonfish		2·10	2·25
2191	$10 Creole Wrasse		4·25	4·50
2192	$20 Sea Bass		8·75	9·00
2173/92		*Set of 20*	19·00	20·00

For these designs in a smaller format, 24×21 mm, see Nos. 2374/91.

(Litho Questa)

1996 (1 Oct). *World Post Day.* T **301** *and similar vert designs. Multicoloured.* P 14.

2193	10 c. Type **301**		10	10
2194	25 c. Anthony Trollope and Dominican Postmen		10	15
2195	55 c. *Yare* (mail steamer)		25	30
2196	65 c. Rural Post Office		30	35
2197	90 c. Postmen carrying mail		40	45
2198	$1 Grumman Goose (seaplane) and 1958 Caribbean Federation 12 c. stamp	..	45	50
2199	$2 Old and new Post Offices and 1978 Independence 10 c. stamp		85	90
2193/9		*Set of 7*	2·00	2·25

MS2200 74×104 mm. $5 18th-centenary naval officer   2·10 2·25

302 "Enthroned Madonna and Child" (S. Veneziano)   303 "Herdboy playing the Flute" (Li Keran)

(Litho Questa)

1996 (25 Nov). *Christmas. Religious Paintings.* T **302** *and similar multicoloured designs.* P 14.

2201	25 c. Type **302**		10	10
2202	55 c. "Noli Me Tangere" (Fra Angelico)		25	30
2203	65 c. "Madonna and Child Enthroned" (Angelico)		30	35
2204	90 c. "Madonna of Corneto Tarquinia" (F. Lippi)		40	45
2205	$2 "The Annunciation" and "Adoration of the Magi" (School of Angelico)		85	90
2206	$5 "Madonna and Child of the Shade" (Angelico)		2·10	2·25
2201/6		*Set of 6*	4·00	4·50

MS2207 Two sheets. (a) 76×106 mm. $6 "Coronation of the Virgin" (Angelico). (b) 106×76 mm. $6 "Holy Family with St. Barbara" (Veronese) (*horiz*)   *Set of 2 sheets* 5·25 5·50

(Des Y. Lee. Litho Questa)

1997 (10 Jan). *Lunar New Year ("Year of the Ox"). Paintings by Li Keran.* T **303** *and similar vert designs. Multicoloured.* P 14.

2208	90 c. Type **303**		40	45
	a. Sheetlet. Nos. 2208/11×2	..	3·00	
2209	90 c. "Playing Cricket in the Autumn"		40	45
2210	90 c. "Listening to the Summer Cicada"		40	45
2211	90 c. "Grazing in the Spring"		40	45
2208/11		*Set of 4*	1·60	1·75

MS2212 76×106 mm. $2 "Return in Wind and Rain" (34×51 mm). P 14¹⁄₂   85 90
MS2212a 135×80 mm. 55 c. × 4. Designs as Nos. 2208/11   95 1·00
Nos. 2208/11 were printed together *se-tenant*, in sheetlets of 8 containing two of each design.

304 Lee Lai-shan (Gold medal – Wind Surfing, 1996)

(Des Y. Lee. Litho)

1997 (12 Feb). *Olympic Games, Atlanta (3rd issue).* T **304** *and similar multicoloured design.* P 15×14.

2213	$2 Type **304**		85	95
	a. Sheetlet. No. 2213×3	..	2·50	

MS2214 97×67 mm. $5 Lee Lai-shan wearing Gold medal (37×50 mm). P 14   2·10 2·25
No. 2213 was printed in sheets of 3, with an enlarged illustrated left-hand margin.

305 *Meticella metis*

1997 (1 Apr). *Butterflies.* T **305** *and similar multicoloured designs. Litho.* P 14.

2215	55 c. Type **305**		25	30
	a. Sheetlet. Nos. 2215/23	..	2·25	
2216	55 c. *Coeliades forestan*		25	30
2217	55 c. *Papilio dardanus*		25	30
2218	55 c. *Mylothris chloris*		25	30
2219	55 c. *Poecilmitis thysbe*		25	30
2220	55 c. *Myrina silenus*		25	30
2221	55 c. *Bematistes aganice*		25	30
2222	55 c. *Euphaedra neophron*		25	30
2223	55 c. *Precis hierta*		25	30
2224	90 c. *Coeliadas forestan* (*vert*)		40	45
	a. Sheetlet. Nos. 2224/31	..	3·25	
2225	90 c. *Spialia spio* (*vert*)		40	45
2226	90 c. *Belenois aurota* (*vert*)		40	45
2227	90 c. *Dingana bowkom* (*vert*)		40	45
2228	90 c. *Charaxes jasius* (*vert*)		40	45
2229	90 c. *Catacroptera cloanthe* (*vert*)		40	45
2230	90 c. *Colias electo* (*vert*)		40	45
2231	90 c. *Junonia archesia* (*vert*)		40	45
2215/31		*Set of 17*	5·50	6·00

MS2232 Two sheets, each 102×71 mm. $6 *Eurytela dryope*. (b) $6 *Acraea natalica*   *Set of 2 sheets* 5·25 5·50
Nos. 2215/23 and 2224/31 were printed together, *se-tenant*, in sheetlets of 8 (Nos. 2224/31) or 9 (Nos. 2215/23) with the backgrounds forming composite designs.
No. 2230 is inscribed "*Collas electo*" in error.

(Des M. Freedman and Dena Rubin. Litho Questa)

1997 (7 Apr). *50th Anniv of U.N.E.S.C.O.* Multicoloured designs as T **374** of Antigua. P 14×13¹⁄₂ (*horiz*) or 13¹⁄₂×14 (*vert*).

2233	55 c. Temple roof, China		25	30
2234	65 c. The Palace of Diocletian, Split, Croatia		30	35
2235	90 c. St. Mary's Cathedral, Hildesheim, Germany		40	45
2236	$1 The Monastery of Rossanou, Mount Athos, Greece		45	50
2237	$1 Carved face, Copan, Honduras (*vert*)		45	50
	a. Sheetlet. Nos. 2237/44 and centre label		3·50	
2238	$1 Cuzco Cathedral, Peru (*vert*)	..	45	50
2239	$1 Church, Olinda, Brazil (*vert*)	..	45	50
2240	$1 Canaima National Park, Venezuela (*vert*)		45	50
2241	$1 Galapagos Islands National Park, Ecuador (*vert*)		45	50
2242	$1 Church ruins, La Santisima Jesuit Missions, Paraguay (*vert*)		45	50
2243	$1 San Lorenzo Fortress, Panama (*vert*)		45	50
2244	$1 Fortress, National Park, Haiti (*vert*)		45	50
2245	$2 Scandola Nature Reserve, France		85	90
2246	$4 Church of San Antao, Portugal		1·75	1·90
2233/46		*Set of 14*	7·50	7·25

MS2247 Two sheets, each 127×102 mm. (a) $6 Chengde Lakes, China. (b) $6 Pavilion, Kyoto, Japan   *Set of 2 sheets* 5·25 5·50
Nos. 2237/44 were printed together, *se-tenant*, in sheetlets of 8 with a centre label.
No. 2234 is inscribed "DICELECIAN" in error.

---

306 Tanglefoot and Minnie   307 Afghan Hound

(Litho Questa)

1997 (15 Apr)–98. *Disney Sweethearts.* T **306** *and similar multicoloured designs.* P 13¹⁄₂×14.

2248	25 c. Type **306**		20	20
2249	35 c. Mickey and Minnie kissing on ship's wheel		25	20
2250	55 c. Pluto and kitten		40	30
2251	65 c. Clarabelle Cow kissing Horace Horsecollar		45	35
2252	90 c. Elmer Elephant and tiger		60	45
2253	$1 Minnie kissing Mickey in period costume		65	60
2254	$2 Donald Duck and nephew	..	1·10	1·40
2255	$4 Dog kissing Pluto		2·00	2·50
2248/55		*Set of 8*	5·00	5·50

MS2256 Three sheets. (a) 126×100 mm. $5 Simba and Nala in *The Lion King*. P 13¹⁄₂×14 (16.6.98). (b) 133×104 mm. $6 Mickey covered in lipstick and Minnie (*horiz*). P 14×13¹⁄₂. (c) 104×124 mm. $6 Mickey and Pluto. P 13¹⁄₂×14   *Set of 3 sheets* 8·00 8·50

(Litho Questa)

1997 (24 Apr). *Cats and Dogs.* T **307** *and similar vert designs. Multicoloured.* P 14.

2257	20 c. Type **307**		10	15
2258	25 c. Cream Burmese		10	15
2259	55 c. Cocker Spaniel		25	30
2260	65 c. Smooth Fox Terrier		30	35
2261	90 c. West Highland White Terrier		40	45
2262	90 c. St. Bernard puppies		40	45
	a. Sheetlet. Nos. 2262/7	..	2·40	
2263	90 c. Boy with Grand Basset		40	45
2264	90 c. Rough Collie		40	45
2265	90 c. Golden Retriever		40	45
2266	90 c. Golden Retriever, Tibetan Spaniel and Smooth Fox Terrier		40	45
2267	90 c. Smooth Fox Terrier		40	45
2268	$1 Snowshoe		45	50
2269	$2 Sorrell Abyssinian		85	90
2270	$2 British Bicolour Shorthair		85	90
	a. Sheetlet. Nos. 2270/5		5·00	
2271	$2 Maine Coon and Somali kittens		85	90
2272	$2 Maine Coon kitten		85	90
2273	$2 Lynx Point Siamese		85	90
2274	$2 Blue Burmese kitten and White Persian		85	90
2275	$2 Persian kitten		85	90
2276	$5 Torbie Persian		2·10	2·25
2257/76		*Set of 20*	12·50	13·00

MS2277 Two sheets, each 106×76 mm. (a) $6 Silver Tabby. (b) $6 Shetland Sheepdog   *Set of 2 sheets* 5·25 5·50
Nos. 2262/7 and 2270/5 were each printed together, *se-tenant*, in sheetlets of 6 with the backgrounds forming composite design.

308 *Oncidium altissimum*   309 "Mary, Mary Quite Contrary"

(Litho Questa)

1997 (10 May). *Orchids of the Caribbean.* T **308** *and similar multicoloured designs.* P 14.

2278	20 c. Type **308**		10	10
2279	25 c. *Oncidium papilio*		10	15
2280	55 c. *Epidendrum fragrans*		25	30
2281	65 c. *Oncidium lanceanum*		30	35
2282	90 c. *Campylocentrum micranthum*		40	45
2283	$1 *Brassavola cucculata* (*horiz*)		45	50
	a. Sheetlet. Nos. 2283/8		2·75	
2284	$1 *Epidendrum ibaguense* (*horiz*)		45	50
2285	$1 *Ionopsis utricularioides* (*horiz*)		45	50
2286	$1 *Rodriguezia lanceolata* (*horiz*)		45	50
2287	$1 *Oncidium cebolleta* (*horiz*)		45	50
2288	$1 *Epidendrum ciliare* (*horiz*)		45	50
2289	$4 *Pogonia rosea*		1·75	1·90
2278/89		*Set of 12*	5·50	6·00

MS2290 Two sheets, each 106×76 mm. (a) $5 *Oncidium ampliatum* (*horiz*). (b) $5 *Starhopea grandiflora* (*horiz*)   4·25 4·50
Nos. 2283/8 were printed together, *se-tenant*, in sheetlets of 6 with the backgrounds forming a composite design.

(Des R. Rundo. Litho Questa)

1997 (29 May). *300th Anniv of Mother Goose Nursery Rhymes.*
Sheet 72×102 mm. P 14.
MS2291 **309** $6 multicoloured .. .. 2·50 2·75

(Litho Questa)

1997 (29 May). *10th Anniv of Chernobyl Nuclear Disaster.*
Vert designs as T 376 of Antigua. Multicoloured. P 13½.
2292 $2 As Type **376** of Antigua .. 85 90
2293 $2 As Type **376** of Antigua; but inscribed
"CHABAD'S CHILDREN OF CHERN-
OBYL" at foot 85 90

(Des J. Iskowitz. Litho Questa)

1997 (29 May). *50th Death Anniv of Paul Harris (founder of*
Rotary International). Horiz designs as T 377 of Antigua.
Multicoloured. P 14.
2294 $2 Paul Harris & irrigation project,
Honduras 85 90
MS2295 78×107 mm. $6 Paul Harris with
Rotary and World Community Service emblems 2·50 2·75

(Litho Questa)

1997 (29 May). *Golden Wedding of Queen Elizabeth and*
Prince Philip. Horiz designs as T 378 of Antigua. Multi-
coloured. P 14.
2296 $1 Queen Elizabeth II .. 45 50
a. Sheetlet. Nos. 2296/301 .. 2·75
2297 $1 Royal Coat of Arms .. 45 50
2298 $1 Queen Elizabeth and Prince Philip in
shirt sleeves 45 50
2299 $1 Queen Elizabeth and Prince Philip in
naval uniform 45 50
2300 $1 Buckingham Palace 45 50
2301 $1 Prince Philip 45 50
2296/301 .. .. *Set of 6* 2·75 3·00
MS2302 100×71 mm. $6 Queen Elizabeth and
Prince Philip with flower arrangement .. 2·50 2·75
Nos. 2296/301 were printed together, *se-tenant*, in sheetlets of
6.

(Des J. Iskowitz. Litho Questa)

1997 (29 May). *"Pacific '97" International Stamp Exhibition,*
San Francisco. Death Centenary of Heinrich von Stephan
(founder of the U.P.U.). Horiz designs as T 379 of Antigua.
P 14.
2303 $2 violet 85 90
a. Sheetlet. Nos. 2303/5 .. 2·50
2304 $2 chestnut 85 90
2305 $2 sepia 85 90
2303/5 .. .. *Set of 3* 2·50 2·75
MS2306 82×119 mm. $6 dull blue and grey-blue 2·50 2·75
Designs:—No. 2303, Kaiser Wilhelm II and Heinrich von
Stephan; No. 2304, Heinrich von Stephan and Mercury; No.
2305, Early Japanese postal messenger; No. MS2306, Heinrich
von Stephan and Russian postal dog team, 1859.
Nos. 2303/5 were printed together, *se-tenant*, in sheets of 3
with enlarged right-hand margin.

310 "Ichigaya Hachiman
Shrine"

311 Hong Kong
Skyline at Dusk

(Litho Questa)

1997 (29 May). *Birth Bicentenary of Hiroshige (Japanese*
painter). "One Hundred Famous Views of Edo". T 310 and
similar vert designs. Multicoloured. P 13½×14.
2307 $1.55, Type **310** 65 70
a. Sheetlet. Nos. 2307/12 .. 3·75
2308 $1.55, "Blossoms on the Tama River
Embankment" 65 70
2309 $1.55, "Kumano Junisha Shrine,
Tsunohazu" 65 70
2310 $1.55, "Benkei Moat from Soto-Sakurada
to Kojimachi" 65 70
2311 $1.55, "Kinokuni Hill and View of Akasak
Tameike" 65 70
2312 $1.55, "Naito Shinjuku, Yotsuya" .. 65 70
2307/12 .. .. *Set of 6* 3·75 4·00
MS2313 Two sheets, each 102×127 mm. (a) $6
"Sanno Festival Procession at Kojimachi
l-chome". (b) $6 "Kasumigaseki" *Set of 2 sheets* 5·25 5·50
Nos. 2307/12 were printed together, *se-tenant*, in sheetlets of
6.

(Des R. Sauber. Litho Questa)

1997 (29 May). *175th Anniv of Brothers Grimm's Third*
Collection of Fairy Tales. The Goose Girl. Multicoloured
designs as T 380 of Antigua. P 13½×14.
2314 $2 Goose Girl with horse .. 85 90
a. Sheetlet. Nos. 2314/16 .. 2·50
2315 $2 Geese in front of castle .. 85 90
2316 $2 Goose Girl 85 90
2314/16 .. .. *Set of 3* 2·50 2·75
MS2317 124×96 mm. $6 Goose Girl (*horiz*).
P 14×13½ .. .. .. 2·50 2·75
Nos. 2314/16 were printed together, *se-tenant*, in sheetlets of 3
with illustrated margins.

(Des Y. Lee. Litho Questa)

1997 (1 July). *Return of Hong Kong to China. T 311 and*
similar vert designs. Multicoloured. P 14×13½.
2318 65 c. Type **311** 30 35
a. Sheetlet. Nos. 2318/20 and 2324 .. 2·40
2319 90 c. Type **311** 40 45
2320 $1 Type **311** 45 50
2321 $1 Hong Kong at night .. 45 50
a. Sheetlet. No. 2321×4 .. 1·75
2322 $1.45, Hong Kong by day .. 65 70
a. Sheetlet. No. 2322×4 .. 2·50
2323 $2 Hong Kong at night (*different*) .. 85 90
a. Sheetlet. No. 2323×4 .. 3·25
2324 $3 Type **311** .. .. 1·25 1·40
2318/24 .. .. *Set of 7* 4·25 4·50
Nos. 2318/20 and 2324 were printed, *se-tenant*, in sheetlets of
4 with illustrated left-hand margin. Nos. 2321/3 were also
printed in sheetlets of 4, but containing stamps of one value
only.

312 Yukto Kasaya
(Japan) (ski jump),
1972

313 Joffre Robinson
(former Credit Union
President)

(Litho Questa)

1997 (15 July). *Winter Olympic Games, Nagano, Japan (1998).*
T 312 and similar vert designs. Multicoloured. P 14.
2325 20 c. Type **312** 10 15
2326 25 c. Jens Weissflog (Germany) (ski jump),
1994 .. .. .. 10 15
2327 55 c. Anton Maier (Norway) (100m men's
speed skating), 1968 .. 25 30
2328 55 c. Ljubov Egorova (Russia) (women's
5 km cross-country skiing), 1994 .. 25 30
2329 65 c. Swedish ice hockey team, 1994 .. 30 35
2330 90 c. Bernhard Glass (Germany) (men's
single luge), 1980 .. 40 45
2331 $1 Type **312** 45 50
a. Sheetlet. Nos. 2331/4, each × 2 .. 3·50
2332 $1 As No. 2326 .. .. 45 50
2333 $1 As No. 2327 .. .. 45 50
2334 $1 Christa Rethenburger (Germany)
(women's 100m speed skating), 1988 .. 45 50
2335 $4 Frank-Peter Roetsch (Germany)
(men's biathlon), 1988 .. 1·75 1·90
2325/35 .. .. *Set of 11* 6·50 6·75
MS2336 Two sheets, each 106×76 mm. (a) $5
Charles Jewtraw (U.S.A.) (men's 500m speed
skating), 1924. (b) $5 Jacob Tullin Thams
(Norway) (ski jumping), 1924 .. *Set of 2 sheets* 4·25 4·50
Nos. 2331/4 were printed together, *se-tenant*, in sheetlets of 8
containing two of each design.

(Litho Questa)

1997 (21 July). *World Cup Football Championship, France*
(1998). Designs as T 383 of Antigua. Multicoloured (except
Nos. 2343/4, 2348, 2350, 2353/4). P 13½×14.
2337 20 c. Klinsmann, Germany (*vert*) .. 10 10
2338 55 c. Bergkamp, Holland (*vert*) .. 25 30
2339 65 c. Ravanelli, Italy (*vert*) .. 30 35
2340 65 c. Wembley Stadium, England .. 30 35
a. Sheetlet. Nos. 2340/7 and central label 2·40
2341 65 c. Bernabeu Stadium, Spain .. 30 35
2342 65 c. Maracana Stadium, Brazil .. 30 35
2343 65 c. Stadio Torino, Italy (grey-black) .. 30 35
2344 65 c. Centenary Stadium, Uruguay (grey-
black) 30 35
2345 65 c. Olympiastadion, Germany .. 30 35
2346 65 c. Rose Bowl, U.S.A. .. 30 35
2347 65 c. Azteca Stadium, Mexico .. 30 35
2348 65 c. Meazza, Italy (grey-black) .. 30 35
a. Sheetlet. Nos. 2348/55 and label 2·40
2349 65 c. Matthaus, Germany .. 30 35
2350 65 c. Walter, West Germany (grey-black) .. 30 35
2351 65 c. Maradona, Argentina .. 30 35
2352 65 c. Beckenbauer, Germany .. 30 35
2353 65 c. Moore, England (grey-black) .. 30 35
2354 65 c. Dunga, Brazil (grey-black) .. 30 35
2355 65 c. Zoff, Italy 30 35
2356 90 c. Klinkladze, Georgia (*vert*) .. 40 45
2357 $2 Shearer, England (*vert*) .. 85 90
2358 $4 Dani, Portugal (*vert*) .. 1·75 1·90
2337/58 .. .. *Set of 22* 8·25 9·50
MS2359 Two sheets. (a) 102×126 mm. $5 Mario
Kempes, Argentina (*vert*). (b) 126×102 mm. $6
Ally McCoist, Scotland (*vert*) .. *Set of 2 sheets* 4·75 5·00
Nos. 2340/7 and 2348/55 were each printed together,
se-tenant, in sheetlets of 8 stamps and 1 label.

(Litho Questa)

1997 (15 Aug). *40th Anniv of Co-operative Credit Union*
League. T 313 and similar designs. P 14×13½.
2360 25 c. deep blue and black .. 10 10
2361 55 c. myrtle-green and black .. 25 30
2362 65 c. maroon and black .. 30 35
2363 90 c. multicoloured 40 45
2360/3 .. .. *Set of 4* 1·00 1·25
MS2364 94×106 mm. $5 multicoloured .. 2·10 2·25
Designs: *Horiz* (as T **313**)—55 c. Sister Alicia (*small*); 65 c.
Lorrel Bruce (first Credit Union President). *Vert* (30×60 *mm*)—
$5 Sister Alicia, Joffre Robinson and Lorrel Bruce.

314 Louis Pasteur

315 Diana, Princess
of Wales

(Des J. Iskowitz. Litho Questa)

1997 (1 Sept). *Medical Pioneers. T 314 and similar vert*
designs. P 14.
2365 20 c. purple-brown 10 10
2366 25 c. bright rose and orange-vermilion .. 10 15
2367 55 c. deep violet 25 30
2368 65 c. orange-red and yellow-brown .. 30 35
2369 90 c. greenish yellow and olive-yellow .. 40 45
2370 $1 bright blue and dull ultramarine .. 45 50
2371 $2 black 85 90
2372 $3 deep brown-red and yellow-brown .. 1·25 1·50
2365/72 .. .. *Set of 8* 3·50 3·75
MS2373 Two sheets, each 70×100 mm. (a) $5
multicoloured. (b) $6 multicoloured *Set of 2 sheets* 4·75 5·00
Designs:—25 c. Christiaan Barnard (first heart transplant);
55 c. Sir Alexander Fleming (discovery of penicillin); 65 c.
Camillo Golgi (neurologist); 90 c. Jonas Salk (discovery of polio
vaccine); $1 Har Gobind Khorana (genetics); $2 Elizabeth Black
(first woman doctor); $3 Sir Frank MacFarlane Burnet
(immunologist); $5 (No. MS2373a) Sir Alexander Fleming
(*different*); $6 (No. MS2373b), Louis Pasteur (*different*).

(Litho Questa)

1997 (Oct)–98. *Fishes. As Nos. 2175/92, but smaller, 24×21*
mm. P 13×13½.
2374 5 c. Porcupinefish 10 10
2375 10 c. Powder-blue Surgeonfish .. 10 10
2376 15 c. Red Hind 10 10
2377 20 c. Golden Butterflyfish .. 10 10
2378 25 c. Copper-banded Butterflyfish .. 10 15
2379 35 c. Pennant Coralfish .. 15 20
2380 45 c. Spotted Drum 20 25
2381 55 c. Blue-girdled Angelfish .. 25 30
2382 60 c. Scorpionfish 25 30
2383 65 c. Harlequin Sweetlips .. 30 35
2384 90 c. Flame Angelfish .. 40 45
2385 $1 Queen Triggerfish .. 45 50
2386 $1.20, Spotlight Parrotfish .. 50 55
2387 $1.45, Black Durgon .. 65 70
2388 $2 Glass-eyed Snapper .. 85 90
2389 $5 Balloonfish .. .. 2·10 2·25
2390 $10 Creole Wrasse (1998) .. 4·25 4·50
2391 $20 Sea Bass (1998) .. 8·75 9·00
2374/91 .. .. *Set of 18* 19·00 20·00

(Des J. Iskowitz. Litho Questa)

1997 (20 Oct). *Diana, Princess of Wales Commemoration.*
T 315 and similar vert designs. Multicoloured. P 14.
2392 $2 Type **315** 85 90
a. Sheetlet. No. 2392/5 .. 3·25
2393 $2 Wearing diamond-drop earrings .. 85 90
2394 $2 Resting head on hand .. 85 90
2395 $2 Wearing tiara 85 90
2392/5 .. .. *Set of 4* 3·25 3·50
MS2396 76×106 mm. $5 Diana, Princess of
Wales .. .. .. 2·10 2·25
Nos. 2392/5 were printed together, *se-tenant*, in sheetlets of 4
with enlarged illustrated margins.

316 "Echo et
Narcisse" (Toile)

317 "Tiger" (Gao
Qifeng)

(Litho Questa)

1997 (10 Nov). *Christmas. Paintings. T 316 and similar*
multicoloured designs. P 14.
2397 20 c. Type **316** 10 10
2398 55 c. "The Archangel Raphael leaving the
Family of Tobias" (Rembrandt) .. 25 30
2399 65 c. "Seated Nymphs with Flute" (Francois
Boucher) 30 35
2400 90 c. "Angel" (Rembrandt) .. 40 45
2401 $2 "Dispute" (Raphael) .. 85 90
2402 $4 "Holy Trinity" (Raphael) .. 1·75 1·90
2397/402 .. .. *Set of 6* 3·75 4·25
MS2403 Two sheets, each 114×104 mm. (a) $6
"Study Muse" (Raphael) (*horiz*). (b) "Christ on
the Mount of Olives" (El Greco) (*horiz*)
Set of 2 sheets 5·25 5·50

(Des Y. Lee. Litho Questa)

1998 (5 Jan). *Chinese New Year ("Year of the Tiger"). T* **317** *and similar multicoloured designs by different painters of the Ling-Nan School. P* 14½.

2404	55 c. Type **317**	..	25	30
	a. Sheetlet. Nos. 2404/7	..	1·40	
2405	65 c. "Tiger" (Zhao Shao'ang)	..	30	35
2406	90 c. "Tiger" (Gao Jianfu)	..	40	45
2407	$1.20, Tiger (*different*) (Gao Jianfu)	..	50	55
2404/7		*Set of 4*	1·40	1·75
MS2408	95×65 mm. $3 "Spirit of Kingship" (Gao Jianfu) (48×40 *mm*)	..	1·25	1·50

Nos. 2404/7 were printed together, *se-tenant*, in sheetlets of 4 with illustrated margins.

318 Akira Kurosawa   **319** *Omphalotus illudens*

(Des J. Iskowitz. Litho Questa)

1998 (9 Feb). *Millennium Series. Famous People of the Twentieth Century. T* **318** *and similar designs. Multicoloured (except Nos. 2411, 2414/15 and* **MS**2417*). P* 14.

(a) Japanese Cinema Stars

2409	$1 Type **318**	..	45	50
	a. Sheetlet. Nos. 2409/16	..	3·50	
2410	$1 *Rashomon* directed by Kurosawa (56×42 *mm*)	..	45	50
2411	$1 Toshiro Mifune in *Seven Samurai* (black and slate) (56×42 *mm*)	..	45	50
2412	$1 Toshiro Mifune	..	45	50
2413	$1 Yasujiro Ozu	..	45	50
2414	$1 *Late Spring* directed by Ozu (black and slate) (56×42 *mm*)	..	45	50
2415	$1 Sessue Hayakawa in *Bridge on the River Kwai* (orange-brown, red-brown and black) (56×42 *mm*)	..	45	50
2416	$1 Sessue Hayakawa	..	45	50
2409/16		*Set of 8*	3·50	4·00
MS2417	110×80 mm. $6 Akira Kurosawa (orange-brown, red-brown and black)	..	2·50	2·75

(b) Sporting Record Holders. Multicoloured.

2418	$1 Jesse Owens (winner of four Olympic gold medals, Berlin, 1936)	..	45	50
	a. Sheetlet. Nos. 2418/25	..	3·50	
2419	$1 Owens competing at Berlin (56×42 *mm*)	..	45	50
2420	$1 Isaac Berger competing (56×42 *mm*)	..	45	50
2421	$1 Isaac Berger (weightlifter)	..	45	50
2422	$1 Boris Becker (Wimbledon champion)	..	45	50
2423	$1 Boris Becker on court (56×42 *mm*)	..	45	50
2424	$1 Ashe with Wimbledon trophy (56×42 *mm*)	..	45	50
2425	$1 Arthur Ashe (1st African-American Wimbledon singles champion, 1975)	..	45	50
2418/25		*Set of 8*	3·50	4·00
MS2426	$6 Franz Beckenbauer (captain of German football team) (*horiz*)	..	2·50	2·75

Nos. 2409/16 and 2418/25 were each printed together, *se-tenant*, in sheetlets of 8 with illustrated margins.

(Des T. Wood. Litho Questa)

1998 (2 Mar). *Fungi of the World. T* **319** *and similar vert designs. Multicoloured. P* 14.

2427	10 c. Type **319**	..	10	15
2428	15 c. *Inocybe fastigiata*	..	10	15
2429	20 c. *Marasmius plicatulus*	..	10	15
2430	50 c. *Mycena lilacifolia*	..	20	25
2431	55 c. *Armillaria straminea* and *Calastrina argiolus* (butterfly)	..	25	30
2432	90 c. *Tricholomopsis rutilans* and *Melitaea didymna* (butterfly)	..	45	50
2433	$1 *Lepiota naucina*	..	45	50
	a. Sheetlet. Nos. 2433/41	..	4·50	
2434	$1 *Cortinarius violaceus*	..	45	50
2435	$1 *Boletus aereus*	..	45	50
2436	$1 *Tricholoma aurantium*	..	45	50
2437	$1 *Lepiota procera*	..	45	50
2438	$1 *Clitocybe geotropa*	..	45	50
2439	$1 *Lepiota acutesquamosa*	..	45	50
2440	$1 *Tricholoma saponaceum*	..	45	50
2441	$1 *Lycoperdon gemmatum*	..	45	50
2442	$1 *Boletus ornatipes*	..	45	50
	a. Sheetlet. Nos. 2442/50	..	4·50	
2443	$1 *Russula xerampelina*	..	45	50
2444	$1 *Cortinarius collinitus*	..	45	50
2445	$1 *Agaricus meleagris*	..	45	50
2446	$1 *Coprinus comatus*	..	45	50
2447	$1 *Amanita caesarea*	..	45	50
2448	$1 *Amanita brunnescens*	..	45	50
2449	$1 *Amanita muscaria*	..	45	50
2450	$1 *Morchella esculenta*	..	45	50
2427/50		*Set of 24*	10·50	12·00
MS2451	76×106 mm. $6 *Cortinarius violaceus*		2·50	2·75

Nos. 2433/41 and 2442/50 were each printed together, *se-tenant*, in sheetlets of 9 with composite background designs.

NEW INFORMATION

The editor is always interested to correspond with people who have new information that will improve or correct the Catalogue.

---

320 Topsail Schooner

(Des K. Gromoll. Litho Questa)

1998 (16 Mar). *History of Sailing Ships. T* **320** *and similar horiz designs. Multicoloured. P* 14.

2452	55 c. Type **320**	..	25	30
	a. Sheetlet. Nos. 2452/7, each × 2		3·00	
2453	55 c. *Golden Hind* (Drake)	..	25	30
2454	55 c. *Moshulu* (barque)	..	25	30
2455	55 c. *Bluenose* (schooner)	..	25	30
2456	55 c. Roman merchant ship	..	25	30
2457	55 c. *Gazela Primiero* (barquentine)	..	25	30
2458	65 c. Greek war galley	..	30	35
2459	90 c. Egyptian felucca	..	40	45
2460	$1 Viking longship	..	45	50
2461	$2 Chinese junk	..	85	90
2452/61		*Set of 10*	3·50	4·00
MS2462	Two sheets, each 106×76 mm. (a) $5 *Pinta* (Columbus). (b) $5 Chesapeake Bay skipjack	*Set of 2 sheets*	4·25	4·50

Nos. 2452/7 were printed together, *se-tenant*, in sheetlets of 12 containing two of each design.

No. 2457 is inscribed "GAZELA PRIMERIRO", and both Nos. 2458/9 "EGPYTIAN FELUCCA", all in error.

321 *Steamboat Willie*, 1928

(Litho Questa)

1998 (16 June). *70th Anniv of Mickey and Minnie Mouse. T* **321** *and similar multicoloured designs. P* 14×13½.

2463	25 c. Type **321**	..	40	40
	a. Sheetlet. Nos. 2463/9	..	5·75	
2464	55 c. *The Brave Little Tailor*, 1938	60	60
2465	65 c. *Nifty Nineties*, 1941	60	60
2466	90 c. *Mickey Mouse Club*, 1955	70	75
2467	$1 Mickey and Minnie at opening of Walt Disney World, 1971	75	80
2468	$1.45, *Mousercise Mickey and Minnie*, 1980	90	1·00
2469	$5 *Runaway Brain*, 1995 (97×110 *mm*)	2·40	2·75
2463/9		*Set of 7*	5·75	6·25
MS2470	Two sheets, each 130×104 mm. (a) $5 Walt Disney with Mickey and Minnie Mouse. (b) $5 Mickey and Minnie at 70th birthday party with Donald and Daisy Duck, Goofy and Pluto. Imperf	*Set of 2 sheets*	6·00	6·50

Nos. 2463/9 were printed together, *se-tenant*, in sheetlets of 7 in which No. 2469 is imperforate at top, right and foot.

322 Big-crested Penguin ("Erect Crested Penguin")

(Des D. Burkhart. Litho Questa)

1998 (4 Aug). *Sea Birds. T* **322** *and similar horiz designs. Multicoloured. P* 14.

2471	25 c. Type **322**	..	10	15
2472	65 c. Humboldt Penguin	..	30	35
2473	90 c. Knot	..	40	45
2474	90 c. Crested Tern	..	40	45
	a. Sheetlet. Nos. 2474/85	..	4·75	
2475	90 c. Franklin's Gull	..	40	45
2476	90 c. Australian Pelican	..	40	45
2477	90 c. Fairy Prion	..	40	45
2478	90 c. Andean Gull	..	40	45
2479	90 c. Blue-eyed Cormorant ("Imperial Shag")	..	40	45
2480	90 c. Grey Phalarope ("Red Phalarope")	..	40	45
2481	90 c. Hooded Grebe	..	40	45
2482	90 c. Least Auklet	..	40	45
2483	90 c. Little Grebe	..	40	45
2484	90 c. Pintado Petrel ("Cape Petrel")	..	40	45
2485	90 c. Slavonian Grebe ("Horned Grebe")	..	40	45
2486	$1 Audubon's Shearwater	..	45	50
2471/86		*Set of 16*	6·00	6·75
MS2487	Two sheets, each 100×70 mm. (a) $5 Blue-footed Booby. (b) $5 Fulmar	*Set of 2 sheets*	4·00	4·25

Nos. 2474/85 were printed together, *se-tenant*, in sheetlets of 12, with the backgrounds forming a composite design.

---

323 Jetstar II   **324** Mahatma Gandhi

(Des S. Gardner. Litho Questa)

1998 (17 Aug). *Modern Aircraft. T* **323** *and similar horiz designs. P* 14.

2488	20 c. Type **323**	..	10	10
2489	25 c. AN 225	..	10	15
2490	55 c. L.I.A.T. Dash-8	..	25	30
2491	65 c. Cardinal Airlines, Beech-99	30	35
2492	90 c. American Airlines Eagle	40	45
2493	$1 SR 71 "Blackbird" spy plane	45	50
	a. Sheetlet. Nos. 2493/500	..	3·50	
2494	$1 Stealth Bomber	..	45	50
2495	$1 Northrop YF23	..	45	50
2496	$1 F-14A Tomcat	..	45	50
2497	$1 F-15 Eagle S	..	45	50
2498	$1 MiG 29 Fulcrum	..	45	50
2499	$1 Europa X5	..	45	50
2500	$1 Camion	..	45	50
2501	$1 E 400	..	45	50
	a. Sheetlet. Nos. 2501/8	..	3·50	
2502	$1 CL-215 C-GKDN amphibian	45	50
2503	$1 Piper Jet	..	45	50
2504	$1 Beech Hawker	..	45	50
2505	$1 Lockheed YF22	..	45	50
2506	$1 Piper Seneca V	..	45	50
2507	$1 CL-215 amphibian	..	45	50
2508	$1 Vantase	..	45	50
2509	$2 Itansa HFB 320	..	85	90
2488/509		*Set of 22*	9·25	9·75
MS2510	Two sheets (a) 88×69 mm. $6 F1 Fighter. (b) 69×88 mm. $6 Sea Hopper seaplane	*Set of 2 sheets*	5·25	5·50

Nos. 2493/500 and 2501/8 were each printed together, *se-tenant*, in sheetlets of 8 with enlarged illustrated margins.

(Des M. Friedman. Litho Questa)

1998 (1 Sept). *50th Anniv of Organization of American States. Vert design as T* **399** *of Antigua. P* 13½×14.

2511	$1 multicoloured	..	45	50

(Des Diane Catherines. Litho Questa)

1998 (1 Sept). *25th Death Anniv of Pablo Picasso (painter). Multicoloured designs as T* **400** *of Antigua. P* 14½.

2512	90 c. "The Painter and his Model"	40	45
2513	$1 "The Crucifixion"	..	45	50
2514	$2 "Nude with Raised Arms" (*vert*)	85	90
2512/14		*Set of 3*	1·60	1·75
MS2515	122×102 mm. $6 "Cafe at Royan"	2·50	2·75

(Des F. Rivera. Litho Questa)

1998 (1 Sept). *Birth Centenary of Enzo Ferrari (car manufacturer). Horiz designs as T* **401** *of Antigua. Multicoloured. P* 14.

2516	55 c. 365 GT 2+2	..	25	30
2517	90 c. Boano/Ellena 250 GT	..	40	45
2518	$1 375 MM coupe	..	45	50
2516/18		*Set of 3*	1·10	1·25
MS2519	104×70 mm. $5 212 (91×34 *mm*). P 14×14½		2·10	2·25

(Des G. Bibby. Litho Questa)

1998 (1 Sept). *19th World Scout Jamboree, Chile. Multicoloured designs as T* **402** *of Antigua, but vert. P* 14.

2520	65 c. Scout saluting	..	30	35
2521	$1 Scout handshake	..	45	50
2522	$2 International Scout flag	..	85	90
2520/2		*Set of 3*	1·60	1·75
MS2523	76×106 mm. $5 Lord Baden-Powell	2·10	2·25

(Des J. Iskowitz. Litho Questa)

1998 (1 Sept). *50th Death Anniv of Mahatma Gandhi. T* **324** *and similar vert design. Multicoloured. P* 14.

2524	90 c. Type **324**	..	40	45
	a. Sheetlet of 4	..	1·60	
MS2525	106×75 mm. $6 Gandhi spinning thread	2·50	2·75

No. 2524 was issued in sheetlets of 4 with enlarged illustrated margins at top and right.

(Des D. Miller. Litho Questa)

1998 (1 Sept). *80th Anniv of Royal Air Force. Horiz designs as T* **404** *of Antigua. Multicoloured. P* 14.

2526	$2 H.S. 801 Nimrod MR2P (reconnaissance)	..	85	90
	a. Sheetlet. Nos. 2526/9	..	3·25	
2527	$2 Lockheed C-130 Hercules (transport)	85	90
2528	$2 Panavia Tornado GR1	..	85	90
2529	$2 Lockheed C-130 Hercules landing	85	90
2526/9		*Set of 4*	3·25	3·50
MS2530	Two sheets, each 90×68 mm. (a) $6 Bristol F2B fighter and Golden Eagle (bird). (b) $6 Hawker Hart and EF-2000 Euro-fighter	*Set of 2 sheets*	4·75	5·00

Nos. 2526/9 were printed together, *se-tenant*, in sheetlets of 4 with enlarged illustrated margins.

No. 2529 is inscribed "Panavia Tornado GR1" in error.

325 Fridman Fish   **(326)**

Save the Turtles

(Litho Questa)

1998 (7 Sept). *International Year of the Ocean. T* **325** *and similar horiz designs. Multicoloured. P* 14.

2531	25 c.	Type **325**	10	15
2532	55 c.	Hydrocoral	25	30
2533	65 c.	Feather-star	30	35
2534	90 c.	Royal Angelfish	40	45
2535	$1	Monk Seal	45	50
		a. Sheetlet. Nos. 2535/43	4·00	
2536	$1	Galapagos Penguin	45	50
2537	$1	Manta Ray	45	50
2538	$1	Hawksbill Turtle	45	50
2539	$1	Moorish Idols	45	50
2540	$1	Nautilus	45	50
2541	$1	Giant Clam	45	50
2542	$1	Tubeworms	45	50
2543	$1	Nudibranch	45	50
2544	$1	Spotted Dolphins	45	50
		a. Sheetlet. Nos. 2544/52	4·00	
2545	$1	Atlantic Sailfish	45	50
2546	$1	Sailfin Flying Fish	45	50
2547	$1	Fairy Basslet	45	50
2548	$1	Atlantic Spadefish	45	50
2549	$1	Leatherback Turtle	45	50
2550	$1	Blue Tang	45	50
2551	$1	Coral-banded Shrimp	45	50
2552	$1	Rock Beauty	45	50
2531/52		*Set of* 22	9·00	10·00

MS2553 Two sheets, each 110×85 mm. (a) $5 Humpback Whale and calf (56×41 mm). (b) $6 Leafy Sea-dragon (56×41 mm) .. *Set of* 2 *sheets* 4·75 5·00
Nos. 2535/43 and 2544/52 were each printed together, *se-tenant*, in sheetlets of 9, with the backgrounds forming composite designs.

1998 (14 Sept). *Save the Turtles Campaign. Nos.* 1686/7, 1689/90 *and* 1692 *optd with T* **326.**

2554	25 c.	Type **263**	10	15
2555	55 c.	Hawksbill Turtle swimming	25	30
2556	90 c.	Green Turtle laying eggs	40	45
2557	$1	Green Turtle swimming	45	50
2558	$4	Loggerhead Turtle	1·75	1·90
2554/8		*Set of* 5	2·75	3·25

327 Northern Cardinal   **328** "Magpies and Hare" (Ts'ui Pai)

(Litho B.D.T.)

1998 (1 Dec). *Christmas. Birds. T* **327** *and similar vert designs. Multicoloured. P* 14.

2559	25 c.	Type **327**	10	15
2560	55 c.	Eastern Bluebird	25	30
2561	65 c.	Carolina Wren	30	35
2562	90 c.	Blue Jay	40	45
2563	$1	Evening Grosbeak	45	50
2564	$2	Bohemian Waxwing	85	90
2559/64		*Set of* 6	2·25	2·50

MS2565 Two sheets, each 70×97 mm. (a) $5 Northern Parula. (b) $6 Painted Bunting
Set of 2 *sheets* 4·75 5·00

(Des Y. Lee. Litho Questa)

1999 (4 Jan). *Chinese New Year ("Year of the Rabbit"). Litho. P* 13¹⁄₂×14.

2566	**328**	$1.50, multicoloured	65	70
		a. Sheetlet of 4	2·50	

No. 2566 was printed in sheetlets of 4 with an enlarged illustrated right margin.

329 *Broughtonia sanguinea*   **330** County Donegal Petrol Rail Car No. 10, Ireland

---

(Des Zina Saunders. Litho Questa)

1999 (26 Apr). *Orchids of the Caribbean. T* **329** *and similar vert designs. Multicoloured. P* 14.

2567	55 c.	Type **329**	25	30
2568	65 c.	*Cattleyonia* Keith Roth "Roma"	30	35
2569	90 c.	*Comparettia falcata*	40	45
2570	$1	*Dracula erythiochaete*	45	50
		a. Sheetlet. Nos. 2570/7	3·50	
2571	$1	*Lycaste aromatica*	45	50
2572	$1	*Masdevallia marguerile*	45	50
2573	$1	*Encyclia marlae*	45	50
2574	$1	*Laelia gouldiana*	45	50
2575	$1	*Huntleya meleagris*	45	50
2576	$1	*Galeandria baueri*	45	50
2577	$1	*Lycale deppei*	45	50
2578	$1	*Anguloa clowesii*	45	50
		a. Sheetlet. Nos. 2578/85	3·50	
2579	$1	*Lemboglossum cervantesii*	45	50
2580	$1	*Oncidium cebolleta*	45	50
2581	$1	*Millonia*	45	50
2582	$1	*Pescatorea lehmannll*	45	50
2583	$1	*Sophronitis coccinea*	45	50
2584	$1	*Pescatorea cerina*	45	50
2585	$1	*Encyclia vitellina*	45	50
2586	$2	*Cochleanthes discolor*	85	90
2567/86		*Set of* 20	9·25	10·00

MS2587 Two sheets, each 76×89 mm. (a) $5 *Lepanthes ovalis.* (b) $5 *Encyclia cochleata*
Set of 2 *sheets* 4·25 4·50
Nos. 2570/7 and 2578/85 were each printed together, *se-tenant*, in sheetlets of 8.

1999 (10 May). *"Australia '99" International Stamp Exhibition, Melbourne. Diesel and Electric Trains. T* **330** *and similar multicoloured designs. Litho. P* 14.

2588	$1	Type **330**	45	50
		a. Sheetlet. Nos. 2588/95	3·50	
2589	$1	Canadian Pacific rail car, Canada	45	50
2590	$1	Class WDM locomotive, India	45	50
2591	$1	Bi-polar loomotive, No. E-2, U.S.A.	45	50
2592	$1	Class X locomotive, Australia	45	50
2593	$1	Class "Beijing" locomotive, China	45	50
2594	$1	Class E428 locomotive, Italy	45	50
2595	$1	Class 581 twelve-car train, Japan	45	50
2596	$1	Class 103.1 locomotive, West Germany	45	50
		a. Sheetlet. Nos. 2596/603	3·50	
2597	$1	Class 24 Trans-Pennine train, Great Britain	45	50
2598	$1	Amtrak Class GG1, No. 902, U.S.A.	45	50
2599	$1	Class LRC train, Canada	45	50
2600	$1	Class EW train, New Zealand	45	50
2601	$1	Class SS1 Shao-Shani, China	45	50
2602	$1	Gulf, Mobile and Ohio train, U.S.A.	45	50
2603	$1	Class 9100 locomotive, France	45	50
2588/2603		*Set of* 16	7·00	8·00

MS2604 Two sheets, each 106×76 mm. (a) $5 X-2000 tilting express train, Sweden (*vert*). (b) $6 Class 87 locomotive, Great Britain (*vert*)
Set of 2 *sheets* 4·75 5·00
Nos. 2588/95 and 2596/603 were each printed together, *se-tenant*, in sheetlets of 8.
No. 2589 is inscribed "USA - RDC Single Rail Car" in error.

331 Hypacrosaurus   **332** Miss Sophie Rhys-Jones

(Litho Questa)

1999 (1 June). *Prehistoric Animals. T* **331** *and similar multicoloured designs. P* 14.

2605	25 c.	Tyrannosaurus (*vert*)	10	15
2606	65 c.	Type **331**	30	35
2607	90 c.	Sauropelta	40	45
2608	$1	Barosaurus	45	50
		a. Sheetlet. Nos. 2608/16	4·00	
2609	$1	Rhamphorhynchus	45	50
2610	$1	Apatosaurus	45	50
2611	$1	Archaeopteryx	45	50
2612	$1	Diplodocus	45	50
2613	$1	Ceratosaurus	45	50
2614	$1	Stegosaurus	45	50
2615	$1	Elaphrosaurus	45	50
2616	$1	Vulcanodon	45	50
2617	$1	Psittacosaurus	45	50
		a. Sheetlet. Nos. 2617/25	4·00	
2618	$1	Pteranodon	45	50
2619	$1	Ichthyornis	45	50
2620	$1	Spinosaurus	45	50
2621	$1	Parasaurolophus	45	50
2622	$1	Ornithomimus	45	50
2623	$1	Anatosaurus	45	50
2624	$1	Triceratops	45	50
2625	$1	Baryonx	45	50
2626	$2	Zalambdalestes	85	90
2605/26		*Set of* 22	9·50	10·50

MS2627 Two sheets, each 106×80 mm. (a) $5 Yangchuanosaurus. (b) $6 Brachiosaurus
Set of 2 *sheets* 4·75 5·00
Nos. 2608/16 and 2617/25 were each printed together, *se-tenant*, in sheetlets of 9, with the backgrounds forming composite designs.

1999 (19 June). *Royal Wedding. T* **332** *and similar vert designs. Litho. P* 13¹⁄₂.

2628	$3	violet-blue and black	1·25	1·40
		a. Sheetlet. Nos. 2628/30	3·75	
2629	$3	multicoloured	1·25	1·40
2630	$3	violet-blue and black	1·25	1·40
2628/30		*Set of* 3	3·75	4·25

MS2631 78×108 mm. $6 multicoloured 2·50 2·75
Designs:—No. 2628, Type **332**; Nos. 2629 and **MS**2631, Miss Sophie Rhys-Jones and Prince Edward; No. 2630, Prince Edward.
Nos. 2628/30 were printed together, as a horizontal *se-tenant* strip of 3, in sheetlets with illustrated margins.

(Litho Questa)

1999 (22 June). *"iBRA '99" International Stamp Exhibition, Nuremberg. Horiz designs as T* **416** *of Antigua. Multicoloured. P* 14.

2632	65 c.	*Eendracht* (Dirk Hartog) with Cameroons Expeditionary Force 1915 2d. and 3d. surcharges	30	35
2633	90 c.	*Eendracht* with Kamerun 1900 10 pf. and 25 pf. stamps	40	45
2634	$1	Early German railway locomotive with Kamerun 1900 5 m. stamp	45	50
2635	$2	Early German railway locomotive with Kamerun 1890 overprinted 50 pf. stamp	85	90
2632/5		*Set of* 4	2·00	2·25

MS2636 138×109 mm. $6 Exhibition emblem and Kamerun 5 m. stamp postmarked 1913 2·50 2·75

1999 (22 June). *150th Death Anniv of Katsushika Hokusai (Japanese artist). Multicoloured designs as T* **417** *of Antigua but vert. Litho. P* 13¹⁄₂×14.

2637	$2	"Pilgrims at Kirifuri Waterfall"	85	90
		a. Sheetlet. Nos. 2637/42	5·00	
2638	$2	"Kakura-Sato" (rats pulling on rope)	85	90
2639	$2	"Travellers on the Bridge by Ono Waterfall"	85	90
2640	$2	"Fast Cargo Boat battling the Waves"	85	90
2641	$2	"Kakura-Sato" (rats with barrels)	85	90
2642	$2	"Buufinfinh and Weeping Cherry"	85	90
2643	$2	"Cuckoo and Azalea"	85	90
		a. Sheetlet. Nos. 2643/8	5·00	
2644	$2	"Soldiers" (with lamp)	85	90
2645	$2	"Lovers in the Snow"	85	90
2646	$2	"Ghost of Koheiji"	85	90
2647	$2	"Soldiers" (with hand on hip)	85	90
2648	$2	"Chinese Poet in Snow"	85	90
2637/48		*Set of* 12	10·00	11·00

MS2649 Two sheets, each 101×72 mm. (a) $5 "Empress Jito". (b) $6 "One Hundred Poems by One Hundred Poets" .. *Set of* 2 *sheets* 4·75 5·00
Nos. 2637/42 and 2643/8 were each printed together, *se-tenant*, in sheetlets of 6.

1999 (22 June). *10th Anniv of United Nations Rights of the Child Convention. Multicoloured designs as T* **419** *of Antigua. Litho. P* 14.

2650	$3	Small girl (*vert*)	1·25	1·40
		a. Sheetlet. Nos. 2650/2	3·75	
2651	$3	Small boy (*vert*)	1·25	1·40
2652	$3	Small boy and girl (*vert*)	1·25	1·40
2650/2		*Set of* 3	3·75	4·00

MS2653 85×110 mm. $6 Peace dove 2·50 2·75
Nos. 2650/2 were printed together, *se-tenant*, in sheetlets of 3, forming a composite design which continues onto the sheet margins.

1999 (22 June). *"PhilexFrance 99" International Stamp Exhibition, Paris. Railway Locomotives. Two sheets, each* 106×81 *mm, containing horiz designs as T* **420** *of Antigua. Multicoloured. Litho. P* 14×13¹⁄₂.
MS2654 Two sheets, each 106×80 mm. (a) $5 Steam locomotive *L'Aigle*, 1855. (b) $6 Mainline diesel locomotive, 1963 .. *Set of* 2 *sheets* 4·75 5·00

1999 (22 June). *250th Birth Anniv of Johann von Goethe (German writer). Designs as T* **421** *of Antigua. Litho. P* 14.

2655	$2	multicoloured	85	90
		a. Sheetlet. Nos. 2655/7	2·50	
2656	$2	blue, blackish purple and black	85	90
2657	$2	multicoloured	85	90
2655/7		*Set of* 3	2·75	

MS2658 76×106 mm. $6 grey-black, black & brn 2·50 2·75
Designs: *Horiz*—No. 2655, Faust and astrological sign; No. 2656, Von Goethe and Von Schiller; No. 2657, Faust tempted by Mephistopheles. *Vert*—No. **MS**2658, Johann von Goethe.
Nos. 2655/7 were printed together, *se-tenant*, in sheetlets of 3 with enlarged illustrated margins.

333 Command Module   **334** Queen Elizabeth, 1939

1999 (22 June). *30th Anniv of First Manned Landing on Moon. T* **333** *and similar horiz designs. Multicoloured. Litho. P* 14.

2659	$1.45,	Type **333**	65	70
		a. Sheetlet. Nos. 2659/64	4·00	
2660	$1.45,	Service module	65	70
2661	$1.45,	Booster separation	65	70

2662	$1.45, Lunar and Command modules	..	65	70
2663	$1.45, Tracking telescope	..	65	70
2664	$1.45, Goldstone Radio Telescope	..	65	70
2659/64		Set of 6	4·00	4·25
MS2665	106×76 mm. $6 "Apollo 11" after			
	splashdown	.. ..	2·50	2·75

Nos. 2659/64 were printed together, *se-tenant*, in sheetlets of 6.

(Litho Questa)

1999 (4 Aug). *"Queen Elizabeth the Queen Mother's Century". T* **334** *and similar vert designs. P* 14.

2666	$2 black and gold	..	85	90
	a. Sheetlet. Nos. 2666/9 ..	.. ..	3·25	
2667	$2 black and gold	..	85	90
2668	$2 multicoloured	..	85	90
2669	$2 multicoloured ..	..	85	90
2666/9		Set of 4	3·25	3·50
MS2670	153×157 mm. $6 mult. P 13½×14	..	2·50	2·75

Designs: (As Type **334**)—No. 2666, Type **334**; No. 2667, Queen Mother in Australia, 1958; No. 2668, Queen Mother in blue hat and coat, 1982; No. 2669, Queen Mother laughing, 1982. (37×50 mm)—No. **MS**2670, Queen Mother in 1953.

Nos. 2666/9 were printed together, *se-tenant*, as a sheetlet of 4 stamps and a central label with inscribed and embossed margins.

No. MS2670 also shows the Royal Arms embossed in gold. A $20 value embossed on gold foil also exists from a limited printing.

335 Female Dancer and "DOMFESTA" **336** Family

1999 (4 Oct). *21st Anniv of Dominica Festivals Commission. T* **335** *and similar multicoloured designs. Litho. P* 12½.

2671	25 c. Type **335**	..	10	15
2672	55 c. "21st BIRTHDAY" logo	..	25	30
2673	65 c. Carnival Development Committee			
	emblem	..	30	35
2674	90 c. World Creole Music Emblem	..	40	45
2671/4		Set of 4	1·00	1·25
MS2675	90×90 mm. $5 "21st BIRTHDAY" logo			
	(*different*) (33×48 mm). P 13½	..	2·10	2·25

1999 (4 Oct). *International Year of the Elderly. Sheet,* 90×50 mm, *containing T* **336** *and similar vert. designs. Multicoloured. Litho. P* 13½.

MS2676	25 c. Type **336**; 65 c. Parents and grandparents; 90 c. Family around elderly woman in chair	..	80	95

337 Helicona Lobster Claw **338** Yellow-crowned Parrot

(Litho B.D.T.)

1999 (9 Nov). *Flora and Fauna. T* **337** *and similar horiz designs. Multicoloured. P* 14.

2677	25 c. Type **337**	.. ..	10	15
2678	65 c. Broad-winged Hawk	..	30	35
2679	90 c. White-throated Sparrow	..	40	45
	a. Sheetlet. Nos. 2679/90	..	4·75	
2680	90 c. Blue-winged Teal	..	40	45
2681	90 c. Racoon	..	40	45
2682	90 c. Alfalfa Butterfly	..	40	45
2683	90 c. Foot bridge	..	40	45
2684	90 c. Whitetail Deer	..	40	45
2685	90 c. Grey Squirrel	..	40	45
2686	90 c. Banded-purple Butterfly	..	40	45
2687	90 c. Snowdrops	..	40	45
2688	90 c. Bullfrog	..	40	45
2689	90 c. Mushrooms ..	..	40	45
2690	90 c. Large-blotched Ensatina	..	40	45
2691	$1 Anthurium	..	45	50
2692	$1.55, Blue-headed Hummingbird	..	65	70
2693	$2 Bananaquit	..	85	90
2694	$4 Agouti	..	1·75	1·90
2677/94		Set of 18	8·75	9·75
MS2695	Two sheets, each 100×70 mm. (a) $5 Eastern Chipmunk. (b) $6 Black-footed Ferret			
		Set of 2 sheets	4·75	5·00

Nos. 2679/90 were printed together, *se-tenant*, in sheetlets of 12 with the background forming a composite design.

(Litho Questa)

1999 (7 Dec). *Christmas. Birds. T* **338** *and similar vert designs. Multicoloured (except No.* **MS**2702*). P* 14.

2696	25 c. Type **338**	..	..	..	10	15
2697	55 c. Red Bishop	..		..	25	30
2698	65 c. Troupial	..		..	30	35
2699	90 c. Puerto Rican Woodpecker		..	40	45
2700	$2 Mangrove Cuckoo	..		..	85	90
2701	$3 American Robin	..		..	1·25	1·40
2696/2701			Set of 6		3·00	3·50
MS2702	76×98 mm. $6 "Mary with Child beside the Wall" (Dürer) (drab, black and cream)				2·50	2·75

No. 2699 is inscribed "PUERTO RECAN WOODPECKER" and No. **MS**2702 "MARYWITH", both in error.

STAMP BOOKLETS

1981 (23 June). *Royal Wedding. Multicoloured cover,* 165×92 mm, *showing Prince Charles and Lady Diana Spencer on front and St. Paul's Cathedral on back. Stitched.*

SB1	$11.75, booklet containing *se-tenant* pane of 6 (No. 751a) and pane of 1 (No. 753a)	..	5·00	

POSTAL FISCALS

REVENUE	Revenue
(R 1)	(R 2)

1879–88. *Optd with Type* R **1** *by De La Rue. P* 14. (*a*) *Wmk Crown CC.*

R1	1	1d. lilac	..	..	75·00	8·00
		a. Bisected vert (½d.) on cover		†	—
R2		6d. green	..	..	3·00	22·00
		w. Wmk inverted	..	£100	
R3		1s. magenta	..	..	9·00	16·00
R1/3		..	Set of 3	80·00	42·00

(*b*) *Wmk Crown CA*

R4	1	1d. lilac (1888)	..	..	3·50	3·50

1888. *Optd with Type* R **2** *locally. Wmk Crown CA.*

R6	1	1d. rose	..	..	£250	65·00

Appendix

The following stamps have either been issued in excess of postal needs, or have not been made available to the public in reasonable quantities at face value. Miniature sheets, imperforate stamps etc., are excluded from this section.

1978–79
History of Aviation. $16 × 30, each embossed on gold foil.

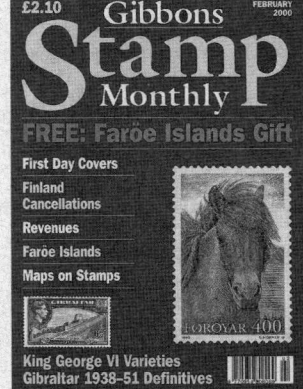

East Africa (G.E.A.)
see Tanzania

East Africa and Uganda Protectorates
see Kenya, Uganda and Tanzania

Egypt

TURKISH SUZERAINTY

In 1517 Sultan Selim I added Egypt to the Ottoman Empire, and it stayed more or less under Turkish rule until 1805, when Mohammed Ali became governor. He established a dynasty of governors owing nominal allegiance to the Sultan of Turkey until 1914.

Khedive Ismail
18 January 1863–26 June 1879

He obtained the honorific title of Khedive (viceroy) from the Sultan in 1867.

The operations of British Consular Post Offices in Egypt date from August 1839 when the first packet agency, at Alexandria, was opened. Further agencies at Suez (1 January 1847) and Cairo (1856) followed. Alexandria became a post office on 17 March 1858 with Cairo following on 23 February 1859 and Suez on 1 January 1861.

Great Britain stamps were issued to Alexandria in March 1858 and to the other two offices in August/September 1859. "B 01" cancellations as Type **2** were issued to both Alexandria and Cairo. Cancellations with this number as Types **8, 12** and **15** were only used at Alexandria.

Before 1 July 1873 combination covers showing Great Britain stamps and the first issue of Egypt exist with the latter paying the internal postage to the British Post Office at Alexandria.

The Cairo office closed on 30 June 1873 and the other two on 30 March 1878. Suez continued to function as a transit office for a number of years.

Stamps issued after 1877 can be found with the Egyptian cancellation "Port Said", but these are on letters posted from British ships.

For cancellations used during the 1882 and 1885 campaigns, see BRITISH FORCES IN EGYPT at the end of the listing.

For illustrations of the handstamp and postmark types see BRITISH POST OFFICES ABROAD notes, following GREAT BRITAIN.

ALEXANDRIA
CROWNED-CIRCLE HANDSTAMPS

CC1 CC1b ALEXANDRIA (R.) (13.5.1843)
Price on cover £1300

Stamps of GREAT BRITAIN *cancelled* "B 01" *as in Types* **2** (*also used at Cairo*), **8, 12,** *or* **15**.

1858 (Mar) *to* **1878**.

Z 1	½d. rose-red (1870–79)	*From*	18·00
	Plate Nos. 5, 6, 8, 10, 13, 14, 15, 19, 20.		
Z 2	1d. rose-red (1857)		6·50
Z 3	1d. rose-red (1861) (Alph IV)		
Z 4	1d. rose-red (1864–79)	*From*	9·00
	Plate Nos. 71, 72, 73, 74, 76, 78, 79, 80, 81, 82, 83, 84, 85, 86, 87, 88, 89, 90, 91, 92, 93, 94, 95, 96, 97, 98, 99, 101, 102, 103, 104, 106, 107, 108, 109, 110, 111, 112, 113, 114, 115, 117, 118, 119, 120, 121, 122, 123, 124, 125, 127, 129, 130, 131, 133, 134, 136, 137, 138, 139, 140, 142, 143, 144, 145, 146, 147, 148, 149, 150, 152, 154, 156, 157, 158, 159, 160, 162, 163, 165, 168, 169, 170, 171, 172, 174, 175, 177, 179, 180, 181, 182, 183, 185, 188, 190, 198, 200, 203, 206, 210, 220.		
Z 5	2d. blue (1858–69)	*From*	9·00
	Plate Nos. 8, 9, 9, 13, 14, 15.		
Z 6	2½d. rosy mauve (1875) (blued *paper*)	*From*	60·00
	Plate Nos. 1, 2.		
Z 7	2½d. rosy mauve (1875–6) (Plate Nos. 1, 2, 3)		27·00
Z 8	2½d. rosy mauve (*Error of Lettering*)		£1300
Z 9	2½d. rosy mauve (1876–79)	*From*	21·00
	Plate Nos. 3, 4, 5, 6, 7, 8, 9.		
Z10	3d. carmine-rose (1862)		£110
Z11	3d. rose (1865) (Plate No. 4)		55·00
Z12	3d. rose (1867–73) (Plate Nos. 4, 5, 6, 7, 8, 9)	*From*	21·00
Z13	3d. rose (1873–76)	*From*	21·00
	Plate Nos. 11, 12, 14, 15, 16, 18, 19.		
Z15	4d. rose (1857)		40·00
Z16	4d. red (1862) (Plate Nos. 3, 4)	*From*	40·00
Z17	4d. vermilion (1865–73)		23·00
	Plate Nos. 7, 8, 9, 10, 11, 12, 13, 14.		

Z18	4d. vermilion (1876) (Plate No. 15)		£140
Z19	4d. sage-green (1877) (Plate No. 15)		90·00
Z20	6d. lilac (1856)		45·00
Z21	6d. lilac (1862) (Plate Nos. 3, 4)	*From*	40·00
Z22	6d. lilac (1865–67) (Plate Nos. 5, 6)	*From*	32·00
Z23	6d. lilac (1867) (Plate No. 6)		42·00
Z24	6d. violet (1867–70) (Plate Nos. 6, 8, 9)	*From*	30·00
	a. Imperf (Plate No. 8)		£1200
Z25	6d. buff (1872–73) (Plate Nos. 11, 12)	*From*	55·00
Z26	6d. chestnut (1872) (Plate No. 11)		27·00
Z27	6d. grey (1873) (Plate No. 12)		70·00
Z28	6d. grey (1874–76) (Plate Nos. 13, 14, 15)	*From*	21·00
Z29	9d. straw (1862)		£140
Z30	9d. bistre (1862)		
Z31	9d. straw (1865)		
Z32	9d. straw (1867)		
Z33	10d. red-brown (1867)		£120
Z34	1s. green (1856)		£100
Z35	1s. green (1862)		60·00
Z36	1s. green (1862) ("K" *variety*)		
Z37	1s. green (1865) (Plate No. 4)		30·00
Z38	1s. green (1867–73) (Plate Nos. 4, 5, 6, 7)	*From*	12·00
Z39	1s. green (1873–77)	*From*	27·00
	Plate Nos. 8, 9, 10, 11, 12, 13.		
Z40	2s. blue (1867)		95·00
Z41	5s. rose (1867–74) (Plate Nos. 1, 2)	*From*	£250

CAIRO
CROWNED-CIRCLE HANDSTAMPS

CC2 CC **6** CAIRO (R. or Blk.) (23.3.1859) *Price on cover* £1800
Cancellation "B 01" as Type **2** (also issued at Alexandria) was used to cancel mail franked with Great Britain stamps between April 1859 and June 1873.

SUEZ
CROWNED-CIRCLE HANDSTAMPS

CC3 CC **1** SUEZ (B. *or* Black) (16.7.1847) *Price on cover* £2000

Stamps of GREAT BRITAIN *cancelled* "B 02" *as in Types* **2** *and* **8**, *or with circular date stamp as Type* **5**.

1859 (Aug) *to* **1878**.

Z42	½d. rose-red (1870–79)		27·00
	Plate Nos. 6, 10, 11, 12, 13, 14.		
Z43	1d. rose-red (1857)		8·50
Z44	1d. rose-red (1864–79)	*From*	10·00
	Plate Nos. 73, 74, 78, 79, 80, 81, 83, 84, 86, 87, 90, 91, 93, 94, 96, 97, 100, 101, 106, 107, 108, 110, 113, 118, 119, 120, 121, 122, 123, 124, 125, 129, 130, 131, 134, 136, 137, 138, 140, 142, 143, 144, 145, 147, 148, 149, 150, 151, 152, 153, 154, 156, 158, 159, 160, 161, 162, 163, 164, 165, 166, 167, 168, 170, 174, 176, 177, 178, 179, 180, 181, 182, 184, 185, 186, 187, 189, 190, 205.		
Z45	2d. blue (1858–69)	*From*	13·00
	Plate Nos. 8, 9, 13, 14, 15.		
Z46	2½d. rosy mauve (1875) (blued *paper*)	*From*	55·00
Z47	2½d. rosy mauve (1875–76) (Plate Nos. 1, 2, 3)	*From*	30·00
Z48	2½d. rosy mauve (*Error of Lettering*)		£1300
Z49	2½d. rosy mauve (1876–79)	*From*	24·00
	Plate Nos. 3, 4, 5, 6, 7, 8, 9, 10.		
Z50	3d. carmine-rose (1862)		£120
Z51	3d. rose (1865) (Plate No. 4)		60·00
Z52	3d. rose (1867–73) (Plate Nos. 5, 6, 7, 8, 10)		
Z53	3d. rose (1873–76) (Plate Nos. 12, 16)	*From*	24·00
Z54	3d. rose (1857)		50·00
Z55	4d. red (1862) (Plate Nos. 3, 4)	*From*	42·00
Z56	4d. vermilion (1865–73)	*From*	27·00
	Plate Nos. 7, 8, 9, 10, 11, 12, 13, 14.		
Z57	4d. vermilion (1876) (Plate No. 15)		
Z58	4d. sage-green (1877) (Plate No. 15)		95·00
Z59	6d. lilac (1856)		45·00
Z60	6d. lilac (1862) (Plate Nos. 3, 4)	*From*	40·00
Z61	6d. lilac (1865–67) (Plate Nos. 5, 6)	*From*	32·00
Z62	6d. lilac (1867) (Plate No. 6)		42·00
Z63	6d. violet (1867–70) (Plate Nos. 6, 8, 9)	*From*	32·00
Z64	6d. buff (1872–73) (Plate Nos. 11, 12)	*From*	60·00
Z65	6d. pale chestnut (Plate No. 12) (1872)		£2250
Z66	6d. chestnut (1872) (Plate No. 11)		27·00
Z67	6d. grey (1873) (Plate No. 12)		75·00
Z68	6d. grey (1874–76) (Plate Nos. 13, 14, 15, 16)	*From*	23·00
Z69	8d. orange (1876)		
Z70	9d. straw (1876)		£150
	a. Thick paper		
Z71	9d. bistre (1862)		
Z72	9d. straw (1867)		
Z73	10d. red-brown (1867)		£150
Z74	1s. green (1856)		£100
Z75	1s. green (1862)		65·00
Z76	1s. green (1862) ("K" *variety*)		
Z77	1s. green (1865) (Plate No. 4)		40·00
Z78	1s. green (1867–73) (Plate Nos. 4, 5, 6, 7)	*From*	12·00
Z79	1s. green (1873–77)	*From*	27·00
	Plate Nos. 8, 9, 10, 11, 12.		
Z80	2s. blue (1867)		£150
Z81	5s. rose (1867–74) (Plate Nos. 1, 2)	*From*	£275

PRICES FOR STAMPS ON COVER

Nos. 1/41	*from* × 8
Nos. 42/3	*from* × 30
Nos. 44/83	*from* × 5
Nos. 84/97	*from* × 2
Nos. D57/70	*from* × 12
Nos. D71/86	*from* × 5
Nos. D84/103	*from* × 2
Nos. O64/87	*from* × 5
Nos. O88/101	*from* × 2

(Currency: 40 paras = 1 piastre)

1   2   (3)

(Typo (1 pi) or litho (others)) Pellas Brothers, Genoa. Inscr (T **3**) applied typo (1, 2 pi.) or litho (others))

1866 (1 Jan). *Various designs as* T **1** *with black inscriptions as* T **3**. *The lowest group of characters indicates the value.* 1 pi. *no wmk, others* W **2** (*inverted*). P 12½.

1	5 pa. grey		35·00	25·00
	a. Greenish grey		35·00	25·00
	b. Imperf (pair)		£180	
	c. Imperf between (pair)		£300	
	d. Perf 12½×13 and compound		50·00	48·00
	e. Perf 13		£250	£300
	w. Wmk upright		£250	£200
2	10 pa. brown		55·00	28·00
	a. Imperf (pair)		£160	
	b. Imperf between (pair)		£350	
	c. Perf 12½×13 and compound		80·00	48·00
	d. Perf 12½×15		£250	£275
	e. Perf 13		£170	£190
	w. Wmk upright		65·00	28·00
3	20 pa. pale blue		70·00	28·00
	a. Greenish blue		70·00	28·00
	b. Imperf (pair)		£240	
	c. Imperf between (pair)		£400	
	d. Perf 12½×13 and compound		£100	80·00
	e. Perf 13		£425	£250
	w. Wmk upright		70·00	28·00
4	1 pi. claret		60·00	4·50
	a. Imperf (pair)		£100	
	b. Imperf between (pair)		£400	
	c. Perf 12½×13 and compound		90·00	20·00
	d. Perf 13		£300	£190
5	2 pi. yellow		90·00	40·00
	a. Orange-yellow		90·00	40·00
	b. Imperf (pair)			
	c. Imperf between (pair)		£350	£350
	d. Bisected diag (1 pi.) (on cover)		†	£2250
	e. Perf 12½×13 and compound		£120	45·00
	f. Perf 12½×15		£130	
	w. Wmk upright		90·00	40·00
6	5 pa. rose		£250	£170
	a. Imperf (pair)			
	b. Imperf between (pair)		£1000	
	c. Perf 12½×13 and compound		£275	
	d. Error. Inscr 10 pi., perf 12½×15		£900	£750
	da. Imperf		£500	
	w. Wmk upright		£250	£170
7	10 pi. slate		£275	£250
	a. Imperf (pair)		£2000	
	b. Imperf between (pair)			
	c. Perf 12½×13 and compound		£425	£425
	d. Perf 13		£1600	
	w. Wmk upright		£275	£250

The 2 pi. bisected was authorised for use between 16 and 31 July 1867 at Alexandria or Cairo.

Stamps perforated 12½, 12½×13 and compound, and 13 occur in the same sheets with the 13 gauge usually used on the top, left-hand, right-hand or bottom rows. Each sheet of 200 contained one stamp perforated 13 all round, two 13 on three sides, one 13 on two adjacent sides, eighteen 13×12½, eight 12½×13, eight 13 on one side and eighteen 13 at top or bottom. So many sheets were received imperforate or part-perforated that some stock was passed to V. Penasson of Alexandria who applied the 12½×15 gauge.

The two halves of each background differ in minor details of the ornamentation. All values can be found with either half at the top.

Proofs of all values exist on smooth paper, without watermark. Beware of forgeries.

All values also exist with the watermark reversed (*same price as upright*) or inverted and reversed (*same price as inverted*).

4   5

6

(Des F. Hoff. Litho V. Penasson, Alexandria)

1867 (1 Aug)–**71**. W **6** (*impressed on reverse*). P 15×12½.

11	**4**	5 pa. orange-yellow		25·00	8·00
		a. Imperf (pair)			
		b. Imperf between (horiz pair)		£170	
		w. Wmk inverted		£250	£200
12		10 pa. dull lilac		70·00	8·50
		b. Bright mauve (7.69)		50·00	9·00
		ba. Bisected diag (5 pa.) (on piece) (17.11.71)		†	£750
		w. Wmk inverted		£300	£200
13		20 pa. deep blue-green		£100	13·00
		a. Pale blue-green		£110	13·00
		b. Yellowish green (7.69)		£110	12·00
		w. Wmk inverted		£350	£200

14	5	1 pi. dull rose-red *to* rose	..	..	11·00	90
		a. *Lake*			£120	32·00
		b. Imperf (pair)			£100	
		c. Imperf between (horiz pair)			£170	
		d. Bisected diag (20 pa.) (on piece)			†	£750
		e. Rouletted			55·00	
		w. Wmk inverted			50·00	30·00
15		2 pi. bright blue			£110	15·00
		a. *Pale blue*			£110	15·00
		b. Imperf (pair)				
		c. Imperf between (pair) ..			£425	
		d. Bisected diag (1 pi.) (on cover)			†	—
		e. Perf 12½			£225	
		w. Wmk inverted			£400	£300
16		5 pi. brown			£300	£180
		w. Wmk inverted			£500	£300

Each value was engraved four times, the resulting blocks being used to form sheets of 200. There are therefore four types showing minor variations for each value.

No. 12*ba* was used on newspapers from Alexandria between 17 November 1871 and 20 January 1872.

Stamps printed both sides, both imperf and perf, come from printer's waste. The 1 pi. rose without watermark is a proof.

7   **8** (Side panels transposed and inverted)

8a (I)   **8a (II)**

WATERMARK 8a. There are two types of this watermark which, as they are not always easy to distinguish, we do not list separately. Type II is slightly wider and less deep and the crescent is flatter than in Type I. The width measurement for Type I is generally about 14 mm and for Type II about 15 mm, but there is some variation within the sheets for both types.

Nos. 26/43, 45/7a, 49/a, 50/1 and 57 come with Type I only. Nos. 44a, 48/a, 52, 54b, 73/7 and 78 exist with both types of watermark (but No. 83 and official overprints on these stamps still require research); our prices are generally for Type II. Other watermarked issues between 1888 and 1907 have Type II watermarks only.

1872 (1 Jan)–**75.** T **7** (the so-called "Penasson" printing*). *Thick opaque paper. W 8a. P 12½×13½.*

A. LITHOGRAPHED

26	7	20 pa. blue (*shades*)			£120	50·00
		a. Imperf (pair)			—	£2000
		b. Imperf between (pair) ..			£200	55·00
		c. Perf 13½			£200	75·00
		w. Wmk inverted			£200	75·00
27		1 pi. red (*shades*)			£225	8·00
		a. Perf 13½			£500	18·00
		w. Wmk inverted			£600	26·00

B. TYPOGRAPHED

28	7	5 pa. brown (*shades*)			7·00	4·50
		a. Perf 13½			24·00	9·00
		w. Wmk inverted			£100	60·00
29		10 pa. mauve			6·00	3·00
		a. Perf 13½			6·00	3·25
		w. Wmk inverted			40·00	25·00
30		20 pa. blue (*shades*)			50·00	3·75
		a. Perf 13½			80·00	20·00
		w. Wmk inverted			45·00	30·00
31		1 pi. rose-red			50·00	1·00
		a. Bisected (20 pa.) (on piece with No. 31) (7.75)			†	£600
		b. Perf 13½			80·00	3·50
		w. Wmk inverted			35·00	25·00
32		2 pi. chrome-yellow			85·00	4·00
		a. Bisected (1 pi.) (on piece) (7.74)			—	£650
		b. Perf 13½			18·00	4·00
		w. Wmk inverted				
33		2½ pi. violet			80·00	12·00
		a. Perf 13½			£700	£190
		w. Wmk inverted			90·00	30·00
34		5 pi. yellow-green			£180	32·00
		a. Tête-bêche (pair) ..				
		b. Perf 13½			£275	55·00
		w. Wmk inverted			£200	90·00

*It is now accepted that stamps in both processes were printed by the Government Printing Works at Bûlâq, Cairo, although Penasson may have been involved in the production of the dies.

The lithographed and typographed stamps each show the characteristic differences between these two processes:—

The typographed stamps show the coloured lines of the design impressed into the paper and an accumulation of ink along the margins of the lines.

The lithographed stamps are essentially flat in appearance, without the heaping of the ink. Many of the 20 pa. show evidence of retouching, particularly of the outer frame lines.

The 1 p. bisected was used at Gedda or Scio and the 2 pi. vertically bisected at Gallipoli or Scio.

See also the footnote below No. 41.

1874 (Nov)–**75.** *Typo from new stereos at Bûlâq, on thinner paper. W 8a. P 12½.*

35	8	5 pa. brown (3.75)			7·00	3·75
		a. Tête-bêche (vert pair) ..			35·00	35·00
		b. Tête-bêche (horiz pair) ..			£275	£300
		c. Imperf (pair)				
		d. Imperf between (pair) ..			£100	£120
		ew. Wmk inverted			7·00	3·75
		f. Perf 13½×12½ ..			10·00	3·75
		fa. Tête-bêche (vert pair) ..			60·00	60·00
		fb. Tête-bêche (horiz pair) ..			£325	£350
		fw. Wmk inverted			10·00	3·75

36	7	10 pa. grey-lilac (*shades*) (8.75) ..			8·00	2·75
		a. Tête-bêche (vert pair) ..			£140	£160
		b. Tête-bêche (horiz pair) ..				
		c. Imperf (pair)				
		dw. Wmk inverted				
		e. Perf 13½×12½ ..			15·00	3·25
		ea. Tête-bêche (vert pair) ..			£140	£160
		ew. Wmk inverted			16·00	3·50
37		20 pa. grey-blue (*shades*) (2.75) ..			90·00	3·00
		b. Bisected diag (10 pa.) (on cover)			†	—
		cw. Wmk inverted				
		d. Perf 13½×12½ ..			8·50	2·50
		da. Imperf between (pair) ..			£300	
38		1 pi. red (*shades*) (4.75) ..			5·00	65
		a. Tête-bêche (vert pair) ..			90·00	90·00
		b. Tête-bêche (horiz pair) ..			£300	£300
		c. Imperf (pair)				
		d. Imperf between (pair) ..			—	80·00
		ew. Wmk inverted			8·00	1·50
		f. Perf 13½×12½ ..			65·00	1·25
		fa. Tête-bêche (vert pair) ..			£350	£350
		fb. Tête-bêche (horiz pair) ..				
		fw. Wmk inverted			80·00	7·50
39		2 pi. yellow (12.74)			75·00	3·00
		a. Tête-bêche (pair) ..			£400	£400
		bw. Wmk inverted			90·00	7·50
		c. Perf 13½×12½ ..			5·50	6·00
		ca. Tête-bêche (pair) ..			£400	£400
		cb. Bisected diag (1 pi.) (on cover) (4.75)			†	£2500
		cw. Wmk inverted			7·50	6·50
		d. Perf 12½×13½ ..			65·00	12·00
		da. Tête-bêche (pair) ..			£850	
		dw. Wmk inverted			80·00	15·00
40		2½ pi. violet			8·50	5·00
		a. Tête-bêche (pair) ..			£350	
		bw. Wmk inverted			12·00	7·50
		c. Perf 12½×13½ ..			50·00	19·00
		ca. Tête-bêche (pair) ..			£1000	90·00
		cw. Wmk inverted			48·00	25·00
41		5 pi. green			55·00	19·00
		a. Imperf (pair)				
		bw. Wmk inverted			£100	50·00
		c. Perf 12½×13½ ..			£300	£275

The 2 pi. bisected was used at Gedda.

The 1872 printings have a thick line of colour in the top margin of the sheet and the other margins are all plain, an exception being the 5 pa., which on the majority of the sheets has the line at the righthand side of the sheet. The 1874–75 printings have a wide fancy border all round every sheet.

The 1872 printings are on thick opaque paper, with the impressions sharp and clear. The 1874–75 printings are on thinner paper, often semi-transparent and oily in appearance, and having the impressions very blurred and badly printed. These are only general distinctions and there are a number of exceptions.

The majority of the 1874–75 stamps have blind or defective perforations, while the 1872 stamps have clean-cut perfs.

The two printings of the 5 pa. to 1 pi. values can be identified by their perforation gauges, which are always different; the 5 pa. also differs in the side panels (Types **7** and **8**). Only the perf 12½×13½ varieties of the three higher values may need to be distinguished. As well as the general points noted above the following features are also helpful:

2 pi. In the 1872 issue the left-hand Arabic character in the top inscription is one complete shape, resembling an inverted "V" with a horizontal line on top. In the 1874 issue the character has three separate components, a line with two dots below.

2½ pi. There is a distinct thinning of the frame line in the top right-hand corner of the 1872 issue. This sometimes takes the form of a short white line within the frame.

5 pi. In the 1872 issue the top frame line is split for its entire length; in the 1874 issue the line is solid for all or most of its length. The 1872 printing always has a white dot above the "P" of "PIASTRE"; this dot appears on only a few positions of the 1874 printing.

There seem to be many different compositions of the sheets containing the *tête-bêche* varieties, settings being known with 1, 3, 9 and 10 inverted stamps in various sheets. Sheets of the 5 pa. are known with 9 of the 20 horizontal rows inverted, giving vertical *tête-bêche* pairs; four stamps were inverted within their row giving four horizontal *tête-bêche* pairs.

(9)

1878 (Dec). *No. 40 surch as T* **9** *at Bûlâq. P 12½.*

42	7	5 pa. on 2½ pi. violet ..			6·00	6·00
		a. Surch inverted ..			70·00	70·00
		b. Tête-bêche (pair) ..			£3500	
		dw. Wmk inverted ..			7·50	7·50
		e. Perf 12½×13½ ..			6·50	8·00
		ea. Surch inverted ..			£140	£140
		eb. Tête-bêche (pair) ..				
		ew. Wmk inverted ..			8·00	10·00
43		10 pa. on 2½ pi. violet ..			10·00	10·00
		a. Surch inverted ..			75·00	75·00
		b. Tête-bêche (pair) ..			£1500	
		dw. Wmk inverted ..			15·00	15·00
		e. Perf 12½×13½ ..			15·00	15·00
		ea. Surch inverted ..			£110	£110
		eb. Tête-bêche (pair) ..			£1500	
		ew. Wmk inverted ..			25·00	25·00

ALTERED CATALOGUE NUMBERS

Any Catalogue numbers altered from the last edition are shown as a list in the introductory pages.

10   **11**   **12**

13   **14**   **15**

(Typo De La Rue)

1879 (1 Apr). *Ordinary paper. W 8a* (*inverted on 10 pa.*). *P* 14.

44	10	5 pa. deep brown			1·00	30
		a. *Pale brown* ..			1·00	30
		w. Wmk inverted ..			£120	£100
45	11	10 pa. reddish lilac ..			50·00	30·00
46	12	20 pa. pale blue			60·00	1·75
		w. Wmk inverted ..			90·00	15·00
47	13	1 pi. rose			24·00	10
		a. *Pale rose* ..			24·00	10
		w. Wmk inverted ..			60·00	10·00
48	14	2 pi. orange			27·00	50
		a. *Orange-yellow* ..			24·00	80
		w. Wmk inverted ..			30·00	2·00
49	15	5 pi. green			55·00	9·00
		a. *Blue-green* ..			55·00	8·00
		w. Wmk inverted ..			50·00	9·50

See also Nos. 50/6.

Khedive Tewfik

26 June 1879–7 January 1892

British troops were landed in Egypt in 1882 to secure the Suez Canal against a nationalist movement led by Arabi Pasha. Arabi was defeated at Tel-el-Kebir and British troops remained in Egypt until 1954. A British resident and consul-general advised the Khedive. Holders of this post were Sir Evelyn Baring (Lord Cromer), 1883–1907; Sir Eldon Gorst, 1907–11; and Lord Kitchener, 1911–14.

1881–1902. *Colours changed. Ordinary paper. W 8a* (*inverted on No. 50*). *P* 14.

50	11	10 pa. claret (1.81)			50·00	6·00
51		10 pa. bluish grey (25.1.82) ..			7·50	1·75
		w. Wmk inverted ..			40·00	3·00
52		10 pa. green (15.12.84) ..			90	60
		w. Wmk inverted ..			20·00	3·00
53	12	20 pa. rose-carmine (15.12.84) ..			11·00	50
		a. *Bright rose* ..			11·00	50
		w. Wmk inverted ..			35·00	7·00
54	13	1 pi. blue (15.12.84) ..			5·00	20
		a. *Deep ultramarine* ..			6·00	20
		b. *Pale ultramarine* ..			3·50	20
		cw. Wmk inverted ..			26·00	10·00
		d. Chalk-surfaced paper. *Ultramarine* (1902) ..			2·50	10
		da. *Blue* ..			2·50	10
		dw. Wmk inverted ..			75·00	40·00
55	14	2 pi. orange-brown (1.8.93) ..			12·00	30
		aw. Wmk inverted ..			80·00	40·00
		b. Chalk-surfaced paper (1902) ..			12·00	10
		ba. *Orange* ..			22·00	1·00
		bw. Wmk inverted ..				
56	15	5 pi. pale grey (15.12.84) ..			13·00	50
		a. *Slate* ..			11·00	40
		bw. Wmk inverted ..				
		c. Chalk-surfaced paper. *Slate-grey* (1902) ..			16·00	15

(17)

1884 (1 Feb). *Surch with T* **17** *at Bûlâq.*

57	15	20 pa. on 5 pi. green			7·00	1·25
		a. Surch inverted ..			65·00	60·00
		w. Wmk inverted ..			50·00	30·00

(**New Currency:** 1000 milliemes = 100 piastres = £1 Egyptian)

18   **19**   **20**

21   **22**

1888 (1 Jan)–1909. *Ordinary paper.* W 8a. P 14.

58	18	1 m. pale brown	..	85	10
		a. *Deep brown*	..	1·75	10
		bw. *Wmk inverted*	..	25·00	4·00
		c. *Chalk-surfaced paper. Pale brown*			
		(1902)	..	80	10
		ca. *Deep brown*	..	90	10
		cw. *Wmk inverted*	..	40·00	5·00
59	19	2 m. blue-green ..	..	60	10
		a. *Green*	..	60	10
		bw. *Wmk inverted*	..	40·00	5·00
		c. *Chalk-surfaced paper. Green* (1902)	..	50	10
		cw. *Wmk inverted*	..	40·00	5·00
60	20	3 m. maroon (1.1.92)	..	2·25	1·00
61		3 m. yellow (1.8.93)	..	3·00	40
		a. *Orange-yellow*	..	2·25	15
		bw. *Wmk inverted*	..	45·00	15·00
		c. *Chalk-surfaced paper. Orange-yellow* (1902)	..	1·75	10
		cw. *Wmk inverted*	..	75·00	30·00
62	21	4 m. verm (*chalk-surfaced paper*) (1906)		1·50	10
		a. *Bisected (2 m.) (on cover)* (11.09) ..		†	—
63		5 m. rose-carmine	..	1·75	10
		a. *Bright rose*	..	1·75	10
		b. *Aniline rose*	..	3·00	10
		cw. *Wmk inverted*			
		d. *Chalk-surfaced paper. Rose* (1902)		1·50	10
		da. *Deep aniline rose*	..	3·50	20
64	22	10 p. mauve (1.1.89)	..	15·00	80
		a. *Aniline mauve*	..	18·00	80
		bw. *Wmk inverted*			
		c. *Chalk-surfaced paper. Mauve* (1902)	22·00	50

No. 62a was used at Gizira in conjunction with the 1 m. value and the Official, No. O64.

No. 63d exists in coils constructed from normal sheets.

Khedive Abbas Hilmi

7 January 1892–19 December 1914

A set of three values, in a common design showing Cleopatra and a Nile boat, was prepared in 1895 for the Nile Winter Fête, but not issued. Examples survive from the De La Rue archives.

29 Nile Feluccas	**30** Cleopatra from Temple of Dendera	**31** Ras-el-Tin Palace, Alexandria

35 Archway of Ptolemy III, Karnak	**37** Rock Temple of Abu Simbel

(Typo D.L.R.)

1914 (8 Jan). W 8a. P 13½×14 (1 m. to 10 m.) or 14 (20 m. to 200 m.).

73	29	1 m. sepia	..	70	40
74	30	2 m. green	..	1·00	20
		w. *Wmk inverted*			
75	31	3 m. yellow-orange	..	60	35
		a. *Double impression*			
		w. *Wmk inverted*		—	3·00
76	—	4 m. vermilion	..	1·50	65
		w. *Wmk inverted*		—	1·75
77	—	5 m. lake	..	1·50	10
		a. *Wmk sideways star to right* (booklets)	10·00	20·00
		aw. *Wmk sideways star to left*	10·00	20·00
		w. *Wmk inverted*		15·00	10·00
78	—	10 m. dull blue	..	3·00	10
		w. *Wmk inverted*		—	15·00
79	35	20 m. olive	..	6·50	30
		w. *Wmk inverted*		—	6·00
80	—	50 m. purple	..	11·00	40
		w. *Wmk inverted*		—	50·00
81	37	100 m. slate	..	12·00	60
82	—	200 m. maroon	..	26·00	3·00
73/82			*Set of 10*	55·00	6·00

Designs: As T **29**—4 m. Pyramids at Giza; 5 m. Sphinx; 10 m. Colossi of Amenophis III at Thebes. As T **35**—50 c. Cairo Citadel; 200 m. Aswân Dan.

*The normal sideways watermark shows the star to the right of the crescent, *as seen from the back of the stamp*.

All the above exist imperforate, but imperforate stamps without watermark are proofs.

See also Nos. 84/95.

BRITISH PROTECTORATE

On 18 December 1914, after war with Turkey had begun, Egypt was declared to be a British protectorate. Abbas Hilmi was deposed, and his uncle, Hussein Kamil, was proclaimed Sultan of Egypt.

Sultan Hussein Kamil

19 December 1914–9 October 1917

(39)

1915 (15 Oct). *No. 75 surch with T* **39**, *at Bûlâq.*

83	31	2 m. on 3 m. yellow-orange	..	55	1·25
		a. Surch inverted	..	£200	£200
		b. Surch double, one albino	..	£120	
		w. Wmk inverted			

Sultan Ahmed Fuad

9 October 1917–15 March 1922

40	(A)	(B)

41 Statue of Rameses II, **42** Luxor

(Typo Harrison)

1921–22. *As Nos. 73/82 and new designs (15 m.).* W **40.** P 14 (20, 50, 100 m.) *or* 13½×14 (*others*).

84	29	1 m. sepia (A) ..		1·00	1·50
		a. Two dots omitted (B) (R. 10/10)	..	35·00	45·00
		w. Wmk inverted	..	10·00	7·50
85	30	2 m. green	..	3·25	3·25
		a. Imperf between (pair)			
		w. Wmk inverted	..	15·00	10·00
86		2 m. vermilion (1922)	..	2·25	55
		w. Wmk inverted	..	15·00	10·00
87	31	3 m. yellow-orange	..	2·75	1·10
		w. Wmk inverted	..	16·00	10·00
88	—	4 m. green (1922)	..	4·00	5·00
		w. Wmk inverted		—	10·00
89	—	5 m. lake (1.21)	..	2·75	10
		a. Imperf between (pair)			
		w. Wmk inverted	..	15·00	10·00
90	—	5 m. pink (11.21)	..	2·75	10
		w. Wmk inverted	..	15·00	10·00
91	—	10 m. dull blue ..	..	2·75	20
		w. Wmk inverted		—	10·00
92	—	10 m. lake (9.22)	..	1·75	15
		w. Wmk inverted		—	10·00
93	41	15 m. indigo (3.22)	..	3·50	15
		w. Wmk inverted		—	8·00
94	42	15 m. indigo	..	20·00	3·00
		w. Wmk inverted	..	22·00	10·00
95	35	20 m. olive	..	7·50	30
		w. Wmk inverted	..	20·00	10·00
96	—	50 m. purple	..	10·00	65
		w. Wmk inverted	..	18·00	12·00
97	37	100 m. slate (1922)	..	70·00	6·50
84/97			*Set of 13*	95·00	16·00

Type **42** was printed first; but because the Arabic inscription at right was felt to be unsuitable the stamps were withheld and the corrected Type **41** printed and issued. Type **42** was released later.

STAMP BOOKLETS

1903 (1 Jan). *Black on pink cover inscr "Egyptian Post Office" in English and French. Stapled.*
SB1 121 m. booklet containing twenty-four 5 m. (No. 63c) in blocks of 6
    Price reduced to 120 m. from 1 July 1911.

1903 (1 July). *Black on blue cover inscr "Egyptian Post Office" in English and French. Stapled.*
SB2 73 m. booklet containing twenty-four 3 m. (No. 61ab) in blocks of 6

1911 (1 July). *Black on pink cover inscr "Egyptian Post Office" in English and Arabic. Stapled.*
SB3 120 m. Contents as No. SB1

1914 (8 Jan). *Black on pink cover inscr "Egyptian Post Office" in English and Arabic. Stapled.*
SB4 125 m. booklet containing twenty-four 5 m. (No. 77a) in blocks of 6

1919 (1 Jan). *Black on pink cover inscr "Egyptian Post Office" in English and Arabic. Stapled.*
SB5 120 m. Contents as No. SB4

1921 (12 June). *Deep blue on pink cover inscr "POST OFFICE" in English and Arabic. Stapled.*
SB6 120 m. booklet containing twenty-four 5 m. (No. 89) in blocks of 6
    a. Stitched

1921 (Nov). *Deep blue or pink cover inscr "POST OFFICE" in English and Arabic. Stapled.*
SB7 120 m. booklet containing twenty-four 5 m. (No. 90) in blocks of 6 .. .. ..

POSTAGE DUE STAMPS

D 16	D 23	D 24

(Des L. Barkhausen. Litho V. Penasson, Alexandria)

1884 (1 Jan). W **6** (*impressed on reverse*). P 10½.

D57	D 16	10 pa. red	..	42·00	9·00
		a. Imperf (pair)		£110	
		b. Imperf between (pair)		£110	
		w. Wmk inverted	..	75·00	15·00
D58		20 pa. red	..	£110	25·00
		w. Wmk inverted	..	£190	40·00
D59		1 pi. red	..	£130	40·00
		w. Wmk inverted	..	£200	£100
D60		2 pi. red	..	£225	10·00
		w. Wmk inverted	..	£325	20·00
D61		5 pi. red	..	14·00	38·00
		w. Wmk inverted	..	32·00	42·00

1886 (1 Aug)–87. *No wmk.* P 10½.

D62	D 16	10 pa. rose-red (1887)	..	55·00	8·50
		a. Imperf between (pair)		90·00	
D63		20 pa. rose-red	..	£225	35·00
		a. Imperf between (pair)			
D64		1 pi. rose-red	..	28·00	6·00
		a. Imperf between (pair)		£120	£120
D65		2 pi. rose-red	..	28·00	3·75
		a. Imperf between (pair)		£120	

Specialists distinguish four types of each value in both these issues.

(Litho V. Penasson, Alexandria)

1888 (1 Jan). *No wmk.* P 11½.

D66	D 23	2 m. green	..	11·00	16·00
		a. Imperf between (pair)		£170	£170
D67		5 m. rose-carmine	..	28·00	14·00
D68		1 p. blue	..	£130	35·00
		a. Imperf between (pair)		£170	
D69		2 p. orange ..		£150	12·00
D70		5 p. grey ..	..	£200	£180
		a. With stop after left-hand "PIASTRES"	..	£275	£225

Specialists distinguish four types of each value. No. D70a occurs on all examples of one of these types in the sheet except that on R. 2/1.

Beware of forgeries of the 5 p.

(Typo De La Rue)

1889 (Apr)–1907. *Ordinary paper.* W 8a. P 14.

D71	D 24	2 m. green	..	7·00	50
		a. Bisected (1 m.) (on cover with unbisected 2 m.) (2.98)	†	£250
		bw. Wmk inverted	..	8·00	50
		c. Chalk-surfaced paper (1906)	..	14·00	50
D72		4 m. maroon	..	2·25	50
		aw. Wmk inverted	..	4·00	1·00
		b. Chalk-surfaced paper (1906)	..	2·75	50
D73		1 p. ultramarine	..	5·50	50
		aw. Wmk inverted	..	7·50	50
		b. Chalk-surfaced paper (1906)	..	6·50	50
D74		2 p. orange	..	5·50	70
		a. Bisected diagonally (1 p.) (on cover)	†	—
		aw. Wmk inverted	..	5·00	70
		c. Chalk-surfaced paper (1907)	..	5·00	70

No. D71a was authorised for use on Egyptian Army letters from the Sudan campaign which were only charged 3 m. postage due.

See also Nos. 84/6 for stamps with watermark sideways.

(D 26)	(D 27)

Type D 26
The Arabic figure at right is less than 2 mm from the next character, which consists of a straight stroke only.

Type D 27
The distance is 3 mm and the straight character has a comma-like character above it. There are other minor differences.

1898 (7 May)–1907. *No. D74 surch at Bûlâq. Ordinary paper.*

    (*a*) *With Type D* 26

D75	D 24	3 m. on 2 p. orange	..	65	3·00
		a. Surch inverted	..	60·00	75·00
		b. Pair, one without surch			
		c. Arabic "2" for "3"			
		d. Arabic "3" over "2" ..	..	£100	

No. D75c occurred in the first printing on positions 10, 20, 30, 40, 50 and 60 of the pane of 60 (the Arabic figure is the right-hand character of the second line–see illustration on page xvii). In the second printing the correct figure was printed on top to form No. D75d. The error was corrected in subsequent printings.

    (*b*) *With Type D* 27 (11.04)

D76	D 24	3 m. on 2 p. orange	..	3·50	11·00
		a. Surch inverted	..	50·00	60·00
		b. Surch double	..	£200	
		c. Chalk-surfaced paper (1907)			

1914–15. As Nos. D71/3 but wmk sideways*.
D84	D 24	2 m. bright green (1915)	10·00	3·25
		w. Wmk star to left of crescent	17·00	11·00
D85		4 m. maroon	10·00	10·00
		w. Wmk star to left of crescent	20·00	
D86		1 p. dull ultramarine	18·00	8·50
		w. Wmk star to left of crescent	14·00	9·00

*The normal sideways watermark shows star to right of crescent, *as seen from the back of the stamp.*

D 43   D 44

(Typo Harrison)

1921 (Apr)–22. *Chalk-surfaced paper. W 40 (sideways*).* *P* 14×13½.
D 98	D 43	2 m. green	2·75	3·50
		w. Wmk stars below crescents	9·00	3·50
D 99		2 m. scarlet (1922)	1·00	1·50
		w. Wmk stars below crescents	7·50	4·00
D100		4 m. scarlet	5·00	13·00
D101		4 m. green (1922)	3·00	1·00
		w. Wmk stars below crescents	12·00	5·00
D102	D 44	10 m. deep slate-blue (11.21)	5·00	16·00
D103		10 m. lake (1922)	5·50	70
		w. Wmk stars below crescents	10·00	4·00
D98/103		Set of 6	20·00	32·00

*The normal sideways watermark shows the stars above the crescents.

OFFICIAL STAMPS

    O.H.H.S.   "O.H.H.S."
أميري   أميري

O 25   (O 28)   (O 29)

(Typo De La Rue)

1893 (1 Jan)–1914. *Ordinary paper. W 8a. P 14.*
O64	O 25	(–) chestnut	1·90	10
		a. Chalk-surfaced paper (1903)		
		bw. Wmk inverted		
		c. Wmk sideways star to right.		
		Chalk-surfaced paper (1914)	10·00	7·50
		cw. Wmk sideways star to left		

From January 1907 No. O64 was used on most official mail to addresses within Egypt. In 1907 it was replaced by Nos. O73/8, but the use of No. O64 for unregistered official mail to Egyptian addresses was resumed on 1 January 1909.

After No. O64c was withdrawn in 1915 the remaining stock was surcharged 1 p., 2 p., 3 p. or 5 p. for fiscal use.

1907 (1 Feb–Aug). *Nos. 54da, 56c, 58c, 59c, 61c and 63d optd with Type O 28 by De La Rue.*
O73	18	1 m. pale brown	1·75	30
O74	19	2 m. green	3·50	10
		a. Opt double		
O75	20	3 m. orange-yellow	2·75	1·25
O76	21	5 m. rose	4·50	10
O77	13	1 p. blue	2·00	20
O78	15	5 p. slate-grey (Aug)	16·00	1·50
O73/8		Set of 6	27·00	3·00

Nos. O73/8 were used on all official mail from February 1907 until 1 January 1909 after which their use was restricted to registered items and those sent to addresses overseas.

1913 (Nov). *No. 63d optd at Bûlâq.*

(a) *With Type O 29*
O79	21	5 m. rose	—	£300
		a. Opt inverted		

(b) *As Type O 29 but without inverted commas*
O80	21	5 m. rose	4·75	40
		a. No stop after "S" (R. 11/10)	50·00	16·00
		b. Opt inverted	£200	75·00

O.H.H.S.   O.H.H.S.   O.H.H.S.
أميري   أميري   أميري

(O 38)   (O 39)   (O 43)

1914 (Dec)–15. *Stamps of 1902–6 and 1914 optd with Type O 38 at Bûlâq.*
O83	29	1 m. sepia (1.15)	1·25	3·50
		a. No stop after "S" (R. 10/10)	12·00	25·00
O84	19	2 m. green (3.15)	3·00	4·00
		a. No stop after "S"	14·00	23·00
		b. Opt inverted	35·00	35·00
		c. Opt double	£325	
O85	31	3 m. yellow-orange (3.15)	2·00	3·50
		a. No stop after "S" (R. 10/10)	14·00	25·00
O86	21	4 m. vermilion (12.14)	3·50	1·75
		a. Opt inverted	£190	£140
		b. Pair, one without opt		
O87	–	5 m. lake (1.15)	3·50	80
		a. No stop after "S" (R. 10/10)	15·00	22·00
O83/7		Set of 5	12·00	12·00

No. O84a occurs on three positions from the first printing and on two different positions from the second.

1915 (Oct). *Nos. 59ab, 62 and 77 optd lithographically with Type O 39 at Bûlâq.*
O88	19	2 m. green	1·75	3·00
		a. Opt inverted	20·00	20·00
		b. Opt double	25·00	
O89	21	4 m. vermilion	3·75	4·75
O90	–	5 m. lake	4·50	1·25
		a. Pair, one without opt	£275	

1922. *Nos. 84, etc optd lithographically with Type O 43 at Bûlâq.*
O 98	29	1 m. sepia (A) (28.6)	3·50	8·50
		a. Two dots omitted (B)	£200	
		w. Wmk inverted		
O 99	30	2 m. vermilion (16.6)	7·00	12·00
O100	31	3 m. yellow-orange (28.6)	65·00	£130
O101	–	5 m. pink (13.3)	17·00	4·00

Egypt was declared to be an independent kingdom on 15 March 1922, and Sultan Ahmed Fuad became king.

Later stamp issues will be found listed in Part 19 (*Middle East*) of this catalogue.

EGYPTIAN POST OFFICES ABROAD

From 1865 Egypt operated various post offices in foreign countries. No special stamps were issued for these offices and use in them of unoverprinted Egyptian stamps can only be identified by the cancellation. Stamps with such cancellations are worth more than the used prices quoted in the Egypt listings.

Such offices operated in the following countries. An * indicates that details will be found under that heading elsewhere in the catalogue.

ETHIOPIA

A   B

C   D

MASSAWA. *Open Nov 1867 to 5 Dec 1885. Postmark types A (also without REGIE), B, C, D. An Arabic seal type is also known on stampless covers.*

SENHIT (near Keren). *Open 1878 to April 1885. Only one cover, cancelled "Mouderie Senhit" in 1879, is known, together with one showing a possible hand-drawn cancellation.*

A post office is also recorded at Harar in 1878, but no postal marking has so far been reported.

SOMALILAND*

Unoverprinted stamps of Egypt used from 1876 until 1884.

SUDAN*

Unoverprinted stamps of Egypt used from 1867 until 1897.

TURKISH EMPIRE

E   F

G   H

I   J

K   L

M   N

O

The offices are listed according to the spelling on the cancellation. The present-day name (if different) and country are given in brackets.

ALESSANDRETTA (Iskenderun, Turkey). *Open 14 July 1870 to Feb 1872. Postmark types E, I.*
BAIROUT (Beirut, Lebanon). *Open 14 July 1870 to Feb 1872. Postmark types E, J.*
CAVALA (Kavala, Greece). *Open 14 July 1870 to Feb 1872. Postmark type E.*
COSTANTINOPOLI (Istanbul, Turkey). *Open 13 June 1865 to 30 June 1881. Postmark types E, F, O.*
DARDANELLI (Canakkle, Turkey). *Open 10 June 1868 to 30 June 1881. Postmark types H, K.*
DJEDDAH, *see* GEDDA.
GALIPOLI (Gelibolu, Turkey). *Open 10 June 1868 to 30 June 1881. Postmark types E, L.*
GEDDA, DJEDDAH (Jeddah, Saudi Arabia). *Open 8 June 1865 to 30 June 1881. Postmark types F, G (also with year replacing solid half-circle), O (all spelt GEDDA), D (spelt DJEDDAH).*
IAFFA (Jaffa, Israel). *Open 14 July 1870 to Feb 1872. Postmark type E.*
LAGOS (Port Lago, Greece). *Open 14 July 1870 to Feb 1872. Postmark type E.*
LATAKIA (Syria). *Open 14 July 1870 to Feb 1872. Postmark type E.*
LEROS (Aegean Is). *Open July 1873 to January 1874 and May to October 1874. Postmark type E.*
MERSINA (Mersin, Turkey). *Open 14 July 1870 to Feb 1872. Postmark type E.*
METELINO (Lesbos, Greece). *Open 14 July 1870 to 30 June 1881. Postmark types E, M.*
RODI (Rhodes, Greece). *Open 13 Aug 1872 to 30 June 1881. Postmark type E.*
SALONNICCHI (Thessaloniki, Greece). *Open 14 July 1870 to Feb 1872. Postmark type E.*
SCIO (Chios, Aegean Is.). *Open 14 July 1870 to 30 June 1881. Postmark types E, N.*
SMIRNE (Izmir, Turkey). *Open 14 Nov 1865 to 30 June 1881. Postmark types E (also without "V. R."), F.*
TENEDOS (Bozcaada, Turkey). *Open 14 July 1870 to March 1871. Postmark type E.*
TRIPOLI (Lebanon). *Open 14 July 1870 to Feb 1872. Postmark type E.*
VOLO (Volos, Greece). *Open 14 July 1870 to Feb 1872. Postmark type E.*

BRITISH FORCES IN EGYPT

Following the rise of a nationalist movement led by Arabi Pasha, and serious disturbances in Alexandria, British troops landed at Ismalia in August 1882 and defeated the nationalists at Tel-el-Kebir on 13 September. A British Army Post Office detachment landed at Alexandria on 21 August and provided a postal service for the troops, using Great Britain stamps, from various locations until it was withdrawn on 7 October.

During the Gordon Relief Expedition of 1884–85 a postal detachment was sent to Suakin on the Red Sea. This operated between 25 March and 30 May 1885 using Great Britain stamps.

ZA 1

*Stamps of GREAT BRITAIN cancelled with Type ZA **1**.*

1882 (Aug–Oct).
ZA1	½d. rose-red (Plate No. 20)	..	..		
ZA2	½d. green (1880)	..	..	..	£300
ZA3	1d. Venetian red (1880)	..	..		
ZA4	1d. lilac (1881) ..	..	..	..	£175
ZA5	2½d. blue (1881) (Plate Nos. 21, 22, 23)	..	£100

1885. *Used at Suakin.*
ZA6	½d. slate-blue (1884)	..	..		
ZA7	1d. lilac (1881) ..	..	..	..	£300
ZA8	2½d. lilac (1884) ..	..	..	..	£225
ZA9	5d. dull green (1884)	..	..	..	£500

From 1 November 1932, to 29 February 1936 members of the British Forces in Egypt and their families were allowed to send letters to the British Isles at reduced rates. Special seals, which were on sale in booklets at N.A.A.F.I. Institutes and Canteens, were used instead of Egyptian stamps. These seals were stuck on the back of the envelopes, letters bearing the seals being franked on the front with a hand-stamp inscribed "EGYPT POSTAGE PREPAID" in a double circle surmounted by a crown.

PRICES FOR STAMPS ON COVER
Nos. A1/9	*from* × 5
No. A10	*from* × 2
No. A11	*from* × 5
No. A12	*from* × 100
No. A13	*from* × 20
No. A14	*from* × 200
No. A15	*from* × 20

A 1   A 2

(Des Lt-Col. C. Fraser. Typo Hanbury, Tomsett & Co. Ltd, London)

1932 (1 Nov)–33. *P* 11. (*a*) *Inscr* "POSTAL SEAL".
A1	A 1	1 p. deep blue and red ..	.. 70·00	3·25

(*b*) *Inscr* "LETTER SEAL".
A2	A 1	1 p. deep blue and red (8.33) ..	23·00	85

(Des Sgt. W. F. Lait. Litho Walker & Co, Amalgamated Press, Cairo)

1932 (26 Nov)–35. *Christmas Seals. P* 11½.
A3	A 2	3 m. black/*azure* ..	48·00	70·00
A4		3 m. brown-lake (13.11.33) ..	7·50	45·00
A5		3 m. deep blue (17.11.34) ..	7·00	23·00
A6		3 m. vermilion (23.11.35) ..	1·25	28·00
		a. Pale vermilion (19.12.35) ..	7·50	16·00

A 3

(Des Miss Waugh. Photo Harrison)

1934 (1 June)–35. (*a*) *P* 14½ × 14.
A7	A 3	1 p. carmine ..	35·00	85
A8		1 p. green (5.12.34) ..	4·00	4·00

(*b*) *P* 13½ × 14
A9	A 3	1 p. carmine (24.4.35) ..	2·00	2·25

(A 4)

1935 (6 May). *Silver Jubilee. As No. A9, but colour changed and optd with Type A 4, in red.*
A10	A 3	1 p. ultramarine	.. ..	£200 £180

Xmas 1935
3 Milliemes
(A 5)

1935 (16 Dec). *Provisional Christmas Seal. No. A9 surch with Type A **5**.*
A11	A 3	3 m. on 1 p. carmine	..	15·00 70·00

The seals and letter stamps were replaced by the following Army Post stamps issued by the Egyptian Postal Administration. No. A9 was accepted for postage until 15 March 1936.

A 6 King Fuad I   A 7 King Farouk

W 48 of Egypt

(Types A **6**/A **7**. Photo Survey Dept, Cairo)

1936. W **48** *of Egypt. P* 13½ × 14.
A12	A 6	3 m. green (9.11.36)	..	1·00	90
A13		10 m. carmine (1.3.36)	..	2·50	10
		w. Wmk inverted			

1939 (16 Dec). W **48** *of Egypt. P* 13 × 13½.
A14	A 7	3 m. green	..	1·75	3·50
A15		10 m. carmine	..	2·25	10
		w. Wmk inverted			

These stamps were withdrawn in April 1941 but the concession, without the use of special stamps, continued until October 1951 when the postal agreement was abrogated.

SUEZ CANAL COMPANY

PRICES FOR STAMPS ON COVER
Nos. 1/4	*from* × 20

100 Centimes = 1 Franc

On 30 November 1855 a concession to construct the Suez Canal was granted to Ferdinand de Lesseps and the Compagnie Universelle du Canal Maritime de Suez was formed. Work began in April 1859 and the canal was opened on 17 November 1869. In November 1875 the Khedive sold his shares in the company to the British Government, which then became the largest shareholder.

The company transported mail free of charge between Port Said and Suez from 1859 to 1867, when it was decided that payment should be made for the service and postage stamps were introduced in July 1868. Letters for destinations beyond Port Said or Suez required additional franking with Egyptian or French stamps.

The imposition of charges for the service was not welcomed by the public and in August the Egyptian Government agreed to take it over.

1

(Litho Chézaud, Ainé & Tavernier, Paris)

1868 (8 July). *Imperf.*
1	1	1 c. black ..	..	£250	£1000
2		5 c. green ..	..	85·00	£500
3		20 c. blue ..	..	75·00	£500
4		40 c. pink ..	..	£130	£750

Shades of all values exist.
Stamps can be found showing parts of the papermaker's watermark "LA+-F" (La Croix Frères).
These stamps were withdrawn from sale on 16 August 1868 and demonetised on 31 August.
Many forgeries exist, unused and cancelled. The vast majority of these forgeries show vertical lines, instead of cross-hatching, between "POSTES" and the central oval. It is believed that other forgeries, which do show cross-hatching, originate from the plate of the 40 c. value which is missing from the company's archives. These are, however, on thin, brittle paper with smooth shiny gum.

Falkland Islands

PRICES FOR STAMPS ON COVER TO 1945
No. 1	*from* × 70
No. 2	*from* × 50
Nos. 3/4	*from* × 10
No. 5	—
Nos. 6/10	*from* × 30
Nos. 11/12	*from* × 15
Nos. 13/17	*from* × 10
Nos. 17*b/c*	*from* × 100
Nos. 18/21	*from* × 10
Nos. 22/b	*from* × 30
Nos. 23/4	*from* × 100
Nos. 25/6	*from* × 30
No. 27	*from* × 20
No. 28	*from* × 40
No. 29	*from* × 5
Nos. 30/b	*from* × 50
No. 30c	*from* × 15
No. 31	*from* × 5
Nos. 32/8	*from* × 15
Nos. 41/2	—
Nos. 43/8	*from* × 12
Nos. 49/50	—
Nos. 60/5	*from* × 10
Nos. 66/9	—
Nos. 70/1	*from* × 10
Nos. 72/b	—
Nos. 73/9	*from* × 4
No. 80	—
No. 115	*from* × 2
Nos. 116/19	*from* × 20
Nos. 120/2	*from* × 6
Nos. 123/6	—
Nos. 127/34	*from* × 5
Nos. 135/8	—
Nos. 139/45	*from* × 50
Nos. 146/63	*from* × 5

CROWN COLONY

FALKLAND
PAID.
ISLANDS.

1   2

1869–76. *The Franks.*
FR1	1	In black, *on cover*	..	..	£6500
FR2	2	In red, *on cover* (1876)	..	..	£12000

On *piece*, No. FR1 on white or coloured paper £90; No. FR2 on white £130. The use of these franks ceased when the first stamps were issued.

The first recorded use of No. FR1 is on a cover to London datestamped 4 January 1869.

½d.

3   (4)

In the ½d., 2d., 2½d. and 9d. the figures of value in the lower corners are replaced by small rosettes and the words of value are in colour.

NOTE. Nos. 1, 2, 3, 4, 8, 10, 11 and 12 exist with one or two sides imperf from the margin of the sheets.

(Recess B.W.)

1878–79. *No wmk. P* 14, 14½.
1	3	1d. claret (19.6.78)	..	£550	£325
2		4d. grey-black (Sept 1879)	..	£1000	£150
		a. On wmkd paper	..	£2500	£500
3		6d. blue-green (19.6.78)	..	55·00	50·00
4		1s. bistre-brown (1878)	..	50·00	50·00

No. 2*a* shows portions of the papermaker's watermark—"R. TURNER, CHAFFORD MILLS"—in ornate double-lined capitals.

NOTES. The dates shown for Nos. 5/12 and 15/38 are those on which the printer delivered the various printings to the Crown Agents. Several months could elapse before the stamps went on sale in the Colony, depending on the availability of shipping

The plates used for these stamps did not fit the paper so that the watermark appears in all sorts of positions on the stamp. Well centred examples are scarce. Examples can also be found showing parts of the marginal watermarks, either CROWN AGENTS horizontally in letters 12 mm high or "CROWN AGENTS FOR THE COLONIES" vertically in 7 mm letters. Both are in double-lined capitals.

1882 (22 Nov). *Wmk Crown CA (upright).* P 14, 14½.

5	**3**	1d. dull claret	£325	£120
		a. Imperf vert (horiz pair)	£42000	
		y. Wmk inverted and reversed	£400	£225
6		4d. grey-black	£250	70·00
		w. Wmk inverted	£400	£160

1885 (23 Mar)–**87.** *Wmk Crown CA (sideways*).* P 14, 14½.

7	**3**	1d. pale claret	55·00	38·00
		w. Wmk Crown to right of CA	75·00	50·00
		x. Wmk sideways reversed	£150	90·00
		y. Wmk Crown to right of CA and reversed	£150	90·00
8		1d. brownish claret (3.10.87)	80·00	38·00
		a. Bisected (on cover) (1891) †		†£2000
		w. Wmk Crown to right of CA	90·00	42·00
		x. Wmk sideways reversed	£120	£100
		y. Wmk Crown to right of CA and reversed	£150	£120
9		4d. pale grey-black	£425	42·00
		w. Wmk Crown to right of CA	£450	50·00
		x. Wmk sideways reversed	£550	£150
		y. Wmk Crown to right of CA and reversed	£550	£100
10		4d. grey-black (3.10.87)	£325	35·00
		w. Wmk Crown to right of CA	£325	35·00
		x. Wmk sideways reversed	£550	90·00
		y. Wmk Crown to right of CA and reversed	£450	60·00

*The normal sideways watermark shows Crown to left of CA, as seen from the back of the stamp.

†See note below No. 14.

1889 (26 Sept)–**91.** *Wmk Crown CA (upright).* P 14, 14½.

11	**3**	1d. red-brown (21.5.91)	£140	65·00
		a. Bisected (on cover)*		† £2250
		x. Wmk reversed	£300	£160
12		4d. olive grey-black	£110	45·00
		w. Wmk inverted	£350	£225
		x. Wmk reversed	£275	£110

See note below No. 14.

1891 (Jan). *Nos. 8 and 11 bisected diagonally and each half handstamped with T 4.*

13	**3**	½d. on half of 1d. brownish claret (No. 8)	£500	£300
		a. Unsevered pair	£2250	£1000
		b. Unsevered pair se-tenant with unsurcharged whole stamp	£13000	
		c. Bisect se-tenant with unsurcharged whole stamp		† £1200
14		½d. on half 1d. red-brown (No. 11)	£550	£250
		a. Unsevered pair	£2500	£1200
		b. Bisect se-tenant with unsurcharged whole stamp		† £1100

1891 PROVISIONALS. In 1891 the postage to the United Kingdom and Colonies was reduced from 4d. to 2½d. per half ounce. As no ½d. or 2½d. stamps were available the bisection of the 1d. was authorised from 1 January 1891. This authorisation was withdrawn on 11 January 1892, although bisects were accepted for postage until July of that year. The ½d. and 2½d. stamps were placed on sale from 10 September 1891.

Cork Cancel used in 1891

The Type 4 surcharge was not used regularly; unsurcharged bisects being employed far more frequently. Genuine bisects should be cancelled with the cork cancel illustrated above. The use of any other postmark, including a different cork cancel, requires date evidence linked to known mail ship sailings to prove authenticity.

Posthumous strikes of the surcharge on "souvenir" bisects usually show a broken "2" and/or a large full stop. These are known on bisected examples of No. 18 and on varieties such as surcharge inverted, double or sideways. Forgeries exist of all these provisionals.

1891 (10 Sept*)–**1902.** *Wmk Crown CA (upright).* P 14, 14½.

15	**3**	½d. blue-green (Aug–Nov 1891)	20·00	26·00
		x. Wmk reversed	£225	£225
		y. Wmk inverted and reversed	£225	£225
16		½d. green (20.5.92)	16·00	15·00
		ax. Wmk reversed	£110	£110
		ay. Wmk inverted and reversed	£225	£225
		b. Deep dull green (15.4.96)	40·00	30·00
17		½d. deep yellow-green (1894–95)	17·00	21·00
		ay. Wmk inverted and reversed	£110	£110
		b. Yellow-green (19.6.99)	2·00	2·50
		c. Dull yellowish green (13.1.1902)	5·00	4·00
		cx. Wmk reversed	£225	£225
18		1d. orange red-brown (14.10.91)	60·00	48·00
		a. Brown	80·00	50·00
		w. Wmk inverted	£550	£275
		x. Wmk reversed	£150	£150
19		1d. reddish chestnut (20.4.92)	40·00	42·00
20		1d. orange-brn (wmk reversed) (18.1.94)	42·00	42·00
21		1d. claret (23.7.94)	80·00	80·00
		x. Wmk reversed	55·00	50·00
22		1d. Venetian red (pale to deep) (1895–96)	15·00	14·00
		ax. Wmk reversed	9·00	10·00
		b. Venetian claret (1898?)	28·00	12·00
23		1d. pale red (19.6.99)	5·00	2·00
		x. Wmk reversed	£160	£160
24		1d. orange-red (13.1.1902)	9·00	4·00
25		2d. purple (pale to deep) (1895–98)	6·50	12·00
		x. Wmk reversed	£250	£275
26		2d. reddish purple (15.4.96)	5·00	11·00
27		2½d. pale chalky ultramarine (8.91)	£120	38·00

28	**3**	2½d. dull blue (19.11.91)	£110	18·00
		x. Wmk reversed	£250	£225
29		2½d. Prussian blue (18.1.94)	£225	£130
30		2½d. ultramarine (1894–96)	20·00	9·00
		ax. Wmk reversed	35·00	10·00
		b. Pale ultramarine (10.6.98)	26·00	13·00
		bx. Wmk reversed	£100	75·00
		c. Deep ultramarine (18.9.1901)	30·00	30·00
		cx. Wmk reversed	£190	£190
31		4d. brownish black (wmk reversed) (18.1.94)	£600	£275
32		4d. olive-black (11.5.95)	10·00	21·00
33		6d. orange-yellow (19.11.91)	£150	£130
		x. Wmk reversed	45·00	38·00
34		6d. yellow (15.4.96)	27·00	35·00
35		9d. pale reddish orange (15.11.95)	30·00	55·00
		x. Wmk reversed	£200	£225
		y. Wmk inverted and reversed	£300	£300
36		9d. salmon (15.4.96)	35·00	48·00
		x. Wmk reversed	£200	£225
37		1s. grey-brown (15.11.95)	42·00	45·00
		x. Wmk reversed	£120	£120
38		1s. yellow-brown (15.4.96)	40·00	40·00
		x. Wmk reversed	£120	£120
		15/38	*Set of 8*	£120	£150
		15, 26, 28, 33, 35 Optd "Specimen"	*Set of 5*	£600	

*The ½d. and 2½d. were first placed on sale in the Falkland Islands on 10 September 1891. Such stamps came from the August 1891 printing. It is now believed that the stock of the May printings sent to the Falkland Islands was lost at sea.

The 2½d. ultramarine printing can sometimes be found in a violet shade, but the reason for this is unknown.

5 **6**

(Recess B.W.)

1898 (5 Oct). *Wmk Crown CC.* P 14, 14½.

41	**5**	2s. 6d. deep blue	£200	£250
42	**6**	5s. red	£170	£200
		41/2 Optd "Specimen"	*Set of 2*	£450	

7 **8**

(Recess D.L.R.)

1904 (16 July)–**12.** *Wmk Mult Crown CA.* P 14.

43	**7**	½d. yellow-green	4·25	1·50
		aw. Wmk inverted	£170	£120
		b. Pale yell-grn (on thick paper) (6.08)	13·00	9·00
		bw. Wmk inverted		
		c. Deep yellow-green (7.11)	9·00	3·00
44		1d. vermilion	9·50	1·50
		aw. Wmk inverted	£170	£130
		ax. Wmk reversed	£250	£225
		b. Wmk sideways (7.06)	1·00	2·50
		c. Thick paper (1908)	13·00	1·75
		cw. Wmk inverted	£275	£225
		cx. Wmk reversed	£350	£225
		d. Dull coppery red (on thick paper) (3.08)	£170	35·00
		dx. Wmk reversed	£500	£225
		e. Orange-vermilion (7.11)	11·00	2·50
		ex. Wmk reversed	£275	£275
45		2d. purple (27.12.04)	13·00	26·00
		ax. Wmk reversed	£110	£110
		b. Reddish purple (13.1.12)	£225	£275
46		2½d. ultramarine (shades)	29·00	7·50
		aw. Wmk inverted	£150	£140
		ay. Wmk inverted and reversed	—	£375
		b. Deep blue (13.1.12)	£225	£180
47		6d. orange (27.12.04)	38·00	48·00
48		1s. brown (27.12.04)	40·00	32·00
49	**8**	3s. green	£140	£130
		aw. Wmk inverted	£1000	
		b. Deep green (4.07)	£120	£120
		bx. Wmk reversed	£1000	£700
50		5s. red (27.12.04)	£150	£150
		43/50	*Set of 8*	£350	£350
		43/50 Optd "Specimen"	*Set of 8*	£475	

Examples of Nos. 41/50 and earlier issues are known with a forged Falkland Islands postmark dated "OCT 15 10".

For details of South Georgia underprint, South Georgia provisional handstamps and Port Foster handstamp see under FALKLAND ISLANDS DEPENDENCIES.

9 **10**

(Des B. MacKennal. Eng J. A. C. Harrison. Recess D.L.R.)

1912 (3 July)–**20.** *Wmk Mult Crown CA.* P 13¾×14 (*comb*) (½d. to 1s.) or 14 (*line*) (3s. to £1).

60	**9**	½d. yellow-green	2·75	3·50
		a. Perf 14 (line). Dp yell-green (1914)	18·00	35·00
		b. Perf 14 (line). Deep olive (1918)	24·00	85·00
		c. Deep olive (4.19)	3·50	25·00
		ca. Printed both sides		† £5500
		d. Deep yellowish green (on thick greyish paper) (1920)	4·50	27·00
61		1d. orange-red	5·50	2·50
		a. Perf 14 (line). Orange-vermilion (1914, 1916)	23·00	2·50
		b. Perf 14 (line). Vermilion (1918)	†	£600
		c. Orange-vermilion (4.19)	3·50	3·00
		d. Orange-vermilion (on thick greyish paper) (1920)	7·00	2·00
		dx. Wmk reversed	£140	
62		2d. maroon	23·00	23·00
		a. Perf 14 (line). Dp reddish pur (1914)	85·00	80·00
		b. Perf 14 (line). Maroon (4.18)	85·00	80·00
		c. Deep reddish purple (4.19)	7·00	16·00
63		2½d. deep bright blue	19·00	23·00
		a. Perf 14 (line). Dp bright blue (1914)	27·00	29·00
		b. Perf 14 (line). Deep blue (1916, 4.18)	27·00	29·00
		c. Deep blue (4.19)	7·00	17·00
64		6d. yellow-orange (6.7.12)	14·00	20·00
		aw. Wmk inverted	£300	£325
		b. Brown-orange (4.19)	12·00	38·00
65		1s. light bistre-brown (6.7.12)	30·00	30·00
		a. Pale bistre-brown (4.19)	48·00	85·00
		b. Brn (on thick greyish paper) (1920)	32·00	£130
66	**10**	3s. slate-green	75·00	80·00
67		5s. deep rose-red	75·00	95·00
		a. Reddish maroon (1914)	£180	£200
		b. Maroon (1916)	75·00	£100
		bx. Wmk reversed	£1900	£1200
68		10s. red/green (11.2.14)	£150	£250
69		£1 black/red (11.2.14)	£350	£400
		60/9 (inc 67b)	*Set of 11*	£700	£900
		60/9 (inc 67a) Optd "Specimen"	*Set of 11*	£1300	

The exact measurement of the comb perforation used for Type **9** is 13.7 × 13.9. The line perforation, used for the 1914, 1916 and 1918 printings and for all the high values in Type **10**, measured 14.1 × 14.1.

It was previously believed that all examples of the 1d. in vermilion with the line perforation were overprinted to form No. 71, but it has now been established that some unoverprinted sheets of No. 61b were used during 1919.

Many of the sheets showed sheets from the left-hand side in a lighter shade than those from the right. It is believed that this was due to the weight of the impression. Such differences are particularly noticeable on the 2½d. 1916 and 1918 printings where the lighter shades, approaching milky blue in appearance, are scarce.

All 1919 printings show weak impressions of the background either side of the head caused by the poor paper quality.

Examples of all values are known with forged postmarks, including one of Falkland Islands dated "5 SP 19" and another of South Shetlands dated "20 MR 27".

2½D

WAR STAMP **2½D**

(11) (12)

1918 (22 Oct*)–**20.** *Optd by Govt Printing Press, Stanley, with T 11.*

70	**9**	½d. deep olive (line perf) (No. 60b)	1·00	7·00
		a. Yellow-green (No. 60) (4.19)	14·00	
		ab. Albino opt	£1100	
		b. Deep olive (comb perf) (No. 60c) 4.19	50	6·50
		c. Dull yellowish green (on thick greyish paper) (No. 60d) (5.20)	12·00	65·00
		cx. Wmk reversed	£160	
71		1d. vermilion (line perf) (No. 61b)	2·00	18·00
		a. Opt double, one albino	£400	
		b. Orge-verm (line perf) (No. 61a) (4.19)	13·00	†
		c. Orge-verm (comb perf) (No. 61c)	50	3·50
		ca. Opt double	£1600	
		cx. Wmk reversed	£275	
		d. Orange-vermilion (on thick greyish paper) (No. 61d) (5.20)	75·00	£150
72		1s. light bistre-brown (No. 65)	30·00	70·00
		a. Pale bistre-brown (No. 65a) (4.19)	4·00	42·00
		ab. Opt double, one albino	£1200	
		ac. Opt omitted (in pair with normal)	£6000	
		b. Brown (on thick greyish paper) (No. 65b) (5.20)	7·00	42·00
		ba. Opt double, one albino	£1200	
		bw. Wmk inverted	£160	£225
		bx. Wmk reversed	£500	

*Earliest known postal use. Cancellations dated 8 October were applied much later.

There were five printings of the "WAR STAMP" overprint, but all, except that in May 1920, used the same setting. Composition of the five printings was as follows:

October 1918. Nos. 70, 71 and 72
January 1919. Nos. 70, 71 and 72
April 1919. Nos. 70/b, 71 and 72a
October 1919. Nos. 70b, 71c and 72a
May 1920. Nos. 70c, 71d and 72d

It is believed that the entire stock of No. 70a was sold to stamp dealers. Only a handful of used examples are known which may have subsequently been returned to the colony for cancellation.

No. 71ca exists in a block of 12 (6×2) from the bottom of a sheet on which the first stamp in the bottom row shows a single overprint, but the remainder have overprint double.

Examples of Nos. 70/2 are known with a forged Falkland Islands postmark dated "5 SP 19".

1921–28. *Wmk Mult Script CA.* P 14.

73	**9**	½d. yellowish green	3·00	4·00
		a. Green (1925)	3·00	4·00
74		1d. dull vermilion (1924)	5·00	1·25
		aw. Wmk inverted		† £1100
		ay. Wmk inverted and reversed	£200	
		b. Orange-vermilion (shades) (1925)	5·50	1·25

75	**9**	2d. deep brown-purple (8.23)		12·00	7·00
		aw. Wmk inverted		—	£950
		ax. Wmk reversed		£1000	
		b. Purple-brown (1927)		14·00	17·00
		c. Reddish maroon (1.28)		8·00	20·00
		cy. Wmk inverted and reversed			
76		2½d. deep blue		22·00	16·00
		a. Indigo (28.4.27)		16·00	20·00
		b. Deep steel-blue (1.28)		6·00	16·00
		c. Prussian blue (10.28)		£300	£450
77		2½d. deep purple/pale yellow (8.23)		4·50	32·00
		a. Pale purple/pale yellow (1925)		4·25	32·00
		y. Wmk inverted and reversed		£250	
78		6d. yellow-orange (1925)		8·00	38·00
		w. Wmk inverted		£170	
		x. Wmk reversed		£900	
79		1s. deep ochre		16·00	48·00
80	**10**	3s. slate-green (8.23)		80·00	£140
73/80			Set of 8	£120	£250
73/80	(incl 76a) Optd "Specimen"		Set of 9	£600	

Dates quoted above are those of despatch from Great Britain. No. 76c only occurred in part of the October 1928 printing. The remainder were in the deep steel-blue shade of the January 1928 despatch, No. 76b.

1928 (7 Feb). No. 75b surch with T **12**.

115	**9**	2½d. on 2d. purple-brown		£700	£750
		a. Surch double		£30000	

No. 115 was produced on South Georgia during a shortage of 2½d. stamps. The provisional was withdrawn on 22 February 1928.

13 Fin Whale and Gentoo Penguins **14**

(Recess P.B.)

1929 (2 Sept)–**36.** P 14 (comb). (a) Wmk Mult Script CA.

116	**13**	½d. green		90	3·00
		a. Line perf (1936)		4·00	8·00
117		1d. scarlet		3·25	80
		a. Line perf. Deep red (1936)		6·50	14·00
118		2d. grey		2·50	2·00
119		2½d. blue		2·75	2·25
120	**14**	4d. orange (line perf) (18.2.32)		14·00	13·00
		a. Deep orange (1936)		32·00	48·00
121	**13**	6d. purple		15·00	13·00
		a. Line perf. Reddish purple (1936)		38·00	25·00
122		1s. black/emerald		18·00	30·00
		a. Line perf. On bright emerald (1936)		23·00	27·00
123		2s. 6d carmine/blue		38·00	45·00
124		5s. green/yellow		60·00	80·00
125		10s. carmine/emerald		£110	£150

(b) Wmk Mult Crown CA

126	**13**	£1 black/red		£275	£375
116/26			Set of 11	£475	£650
116/26 Perf "Specimen"			Set of 11	£1000	

Two kinds of perforation exist:

A. Comb perf 13.9:—original values of 1929.

B. Line perf 13.9×14.2 or 14.2 (small holes)—4d. and 1936 printings of ½d., 1d., 6d. and 1s. On some sheets the last vertical row of perforations shows larger holes.

Examples of most values are known with forged postmarks, including one of Port Stanley dated "14 JY 31" and another of South Georgia dated "AU 30 31".

15 Romney Marsh Ram   **26** King George V

(Des (except 6d.) by G. Roberts. Eng and recess B.W.)

1933 (2 Jan–Apr). Centenary of British Administration. T **15, 26** and similar designs. Wmk Mult Script CA. P 12.

127		½d. black and green		1·50	5·00
128		1d. black and scarlet		3·50	2·25
129		1½d. black and blue		10·00	13·00
130		2d. black and brown		9·00	22·00
131		3d. black and violet		11·00	14·00
132		4d. black and orange		13·00	15·00
133		6d. black and slate		50·00	60·00
134		1s. black and olive-green		40·00	55·00
135		2s. 6d. black and violet		£140	£170
136		5s. black and yellow		£500	£650
		a. Black and yellow-orange (Apr)		£1100	£1300
137		10s. black and chestnut		£500	£750
138		£1 black and carmine		£1400	£1900
127/138			Set of 12	£2250	£3250
127/38 Perf "Specimen"			Set of 12	£2250	

Designs: Horiz—½d. Iceberg; 1½d. Whale-catcher Bransfield; 2d. Port Louis; 3d. Map of Falkland Islands; 4d. South Georgia; 6d. Fin Whale; 1s. Government House, Stanley. Vert—2s. 6d. Battle Memorial; 5s. King Penguin; 10s. Coat of Arms.

Examples of all values are known with forged Port Stanley postmarks dated "6 JA 33". Some values have also been seen with part strikes of the forged Falkland Islands postmark mentioned below Nos. 60/9 and 70/2.

1935 (7 May). Silver Jubilee. As Nos. 91/4 of Antigua, but printed by B.W. P 11 × 12.

139		1d. deep blue and scarlet		3·25	40
		b. Short extra flagstaff		£325	£200
		d. Flagstaff on right-hand turret		£200	£150
		e. Double flagstaff		£250	£180
140		2½d. brown and deep blue		9·00	1·75
		b. Short extra flagstaff		£750	£400
		d. Flagstaff on right-hand turret		£225	£160
		e. Double flagstaff		£350	£200
		l. Re-entry on value tablet (R. 8/1)		£200	£100
141		4d. green and indigo		11·00	4·50
		b. Short extra flagstaff		£500	£325
		d. Flagstaff on right-hand turret		£325	£200
		e. Double flagstaff		£375	£250
142		1s. slate and purple		8·00	3·50
		a. Extra flagstaff		£2750	£2250
		b. Short extra flagstaff		£550	£300
		c. Lightning conductor		£1300	£700
		d. Flagstaff on right-hand turret		£500	£325
		e. Double flagstaff		£550	£350
139/42			Set of 4	28·00	9·00
139/42 Perf "Specimen"			Set of 4	£300	

For illustrations of plate varieties see Catalogue Introduction.

27 Whales' Jaw Bones

(Des G. Roberts (Nos. 146, 148/9, 158 and 160/3), K. Lellman (No. 159). Recess B.W.)

1938 (3 Jan)–**50.** Horiz designs as T **27.** Wmk Mult Script CA. P 12.

146		½d. black and green (shades)		30	75
147		1d. black and carmine		27·00	80
		a. Black and scarlet		3·75	85
148		1d. black and violet (14.7.41)		2·50	1·75
		a. Black and purple-violet (1.43)		7·00	1·75
149		2d. black and deep violet		1·00	50
150		2d. black and carmine-red (14.7.41)		75	2·75
		a. Black and red (1.43)		2·75	1·00
151		2½d. black and bright blue		1·25	30
152		2½d. black and blue (15.6.49)		6·50	7·00
153		3d. black and blue (14.7.41)		6·50	2·50
		a. Black and deep blue (1.43)		9·00	2·50
154		4d. black and purple		2·75	50
155		6d. black and brown		3·25	1·50
156		6d. black (15.6.49)		5·00	3·75
157		9d. black and grey-blue		13·00	90
158		1s. pale blue		65·00	18·00
		a. Deep blue (1941)		16·00	2·50
159		1s. 3d. black and carmine-red (11.12.46)		2·50	1·40
160		2s. 6d. slate		55·00	10·00
161		5s. bright blue and pale brown		£110	60·00
		b. Indigo and yellow-brown (1942)		£600	£100
		c. Blue and buff-brown (9.2.50)		£140	£170
162		10s. black and orange		55·00	27·00
163		£1 black and violet		£110	48·00
146/63			Set of 18	£350	£140
146/63 (ex 152, 156) Perf "Specimen"			Set of 16	£950	

Designs:—Nos. 147 and 150, Black-necked Swan; Nos. 148/9, Battle Memorial; Nos. 151 and 153, Flock of sheep; Nos. 152 and 154, Magellan Goose; Nos. 155/6, Discovery II (polar supply vessel); No. 157, William Scoresby (research ship); No. 158, Mount Sugar Top; No. 159, Turkey Vultures; No. 160 Gentoo Penguins; No. 161, Southern Sealion; No. 162, Deception Island; No. 163, Arms of Falkland Islands.

1946 (7 Oct). Victory. As Nos. 110/11 of Antigua.

164		1d. dull violet		30	15
165		3d. blue		45	15
164/5 Perf "Specimen"			Set of 2	£140	

1948 (1 Nov). Royal Silver Wedding. As Nos. 112/13 of Antigua.

166		2½d. ultramarine		2·00	85
167		£1 mauve		90·00	55·00

1949 (10 Oct). 75th Anniv of Universal Postal Union. As Nos. 114/17 of Antigua.

168		1d. violet		1·50	75
169		3d. deep blue		5·00	2·00
170		1s. 3d. deep blue-green		4·00	2·25
171		2s. blue		4·00	7·50
168/71			Set of 4	13·00	11·00

39 Sheep   **43** Arms of the Colony

(Des from sketches by V. Spencer. Recess Waterlow)

1952 (2 Jan). T **39, 43** and similar designs. Wmk Mult Script CA. P 13×13½ (vert) or 13½×13 (horiz).

172		½d. green		70	70
173		1d. scarlet		1·50	40
174		2d. violet		3·50	2·50
175		2½d. black and light ultramarine		95	50
176		3d. deep ultramarine		1·00	1·00
177		4d. reddish purple		12·00	1·00
178		6d. bistre-brown		7·50	1·50
179		9d. orange-yellow		9·00	2·00
180		1s. black		22·00	80
181		1s. 3d. orange		13·00	5·00
182		2s. 6d. olive-green		16·00	10·00
183		5s. purple		10·00	7·00
184		10s. grey		23·00	15·00
185		£1 black		25·00	17·00
172/185			Set of 14	£130	55·00

Designs: Horiz—1d. Fitzroy (supply ship); 2d. Magellan Goose; 2½d. Map of Falkland Islands; 4d. Auster Autocrat aircraft; 6d. John Biscoe I (research ship); 9d. View of the Two Sisters; 1s. 3d. Kelp goose and gander; 10s. Southern Sealion and South American Fur Seal; £1 Hulk of Great Britain. Vert—1s. Gentoo Penguins; 2s. 6d. Sheep-shearing; 5s. Battle Memorial.

1953 (4 June). Coronation. As No. 120 of Antigua.

186		1d. black and scarlet		80	1·25

53 John Biscoe I (research ship)   **54** Austral Thrush

(Recess Waterlow)

1955–57. Designs previously used for King George VI issue but with portrait of Queen Elizabeth II as in T **53.** Wmk Mult Script CA. P 13 × 13½ (vert) or 13½ × 13 (horiz).

187		½d. green (2.9.57)		70	1·25
188		1d. scarlet (2.9.57)		1·25	1·00
189		2d. violet (3.9.56)		3·25	4·50
190		6d. deep yellow-brown (1.6.55)		6·50	60
191		9d. orange-yellow (2.9.57)		17·00	17·00
192		1s. black (15.7.55)		1·25	1·00
187/92			Set of 6	30·00	23·00

Designs: Horiz—1d. Sheep; 1d. Fitzroy (supply ship); 2d. Magellan Goose; 9d. View of Two Sisters. Vert—1s. Gentoo Penguins.

(Des from sketches by S. Scott. Recess Waterlow, then D.L.R. (from 9.1.62 onwards))

1960 (10 Feb)–**66.** T **54** and similar horiz designs. W w 12 (upright). P 13½.

193		½d. black and myrtle-green		4·50	50
		a. Black and green (DLR) (9.1.62)		13·00	4·50
		aw. Wmk inverted		£2250	£1100
194		1d. black and scarlet		1·75	80
		a. Black and carmine-red (DLR) (15.7.63)		10·00	3·75
195		2d. black and blue		4·00	1·00
		a. Black and deep blue (DLR) (25.10.66)		17·00	15·00
196		2½d. black and yellow-brown		1·50	30
197		3d. black and olive		80	30
198		4d. black and carmine		1·25	75
199		5½d. black and violet		2·25	2·00
200		6d. black and sepia		2·50	30
201		9d. black and orange-red		2·25	90
202		1s. black and maroon		80	30
203		1s. 3d. black and ultramarine		10·00	13·00
204		2s. black and brown-red		27·00	2·50
		a. Black and lake-brown (DLR) (25.10.66)		£120	42·00
205		5s. black and turquoise		27·00	11·00
206		10s. black and purple		48·00	13·00
207		£1 black and orange-yellow		48·00	27·00
193/207			Set of 15	£150	65·00

Designs:—1d. Southern Black-backed Gull; 2d. Gentoo Penguins; 2½d. Long-tailed Meadowlark; 3d. Magellan Geese; 4d. Falkland Islands Flightless Steamer Ducks; 5½d. Rockhopper Penguin; 6d. Black-browed Albatross; 9d. Silvery Grebe; 1s. Magellan Oystercatchers; 1s. 3d. Chilean Teal; 2s. Kelp Geese; 5s. King Cormorants; 10s. Common Caracara; £1 Black-necked Swan.

Waterlow   De La Rue

Waterlow printings were from Frame Plates 1 or 2. The De La Rue printings of the ½d., 1d., 2d. and 2s. are all from Frame Plate 2 and can be distinguished by the finer lines of shading on the Queen's face (appearing as a white face) and also the very faint cross hatching left of the face. Apart from this the shades differ in varying degrees. Frame Plate 1 was used by De La Rue to print initial supplies of the 6d. and these stamps have little to distinguish them from the original printing. Frame Plate 2 was subsequently used for this value which, although it shows the usual plate characteristics, does not differ in shade from the Waterlow printing.

For the ½d. with watermark sideways see No. 227.

69 Morse Key   **70 One-valve Receiver**

(Des M. Goaman. Photo Enschedé)

1962 (5 Oct). *50th Anniv of Establishment of Radio Communications. T* **69/70** *and similar vert design. W w* **12**. *P* 11½ × 11.

208	69	6d. carmine-lake and orange	..	1·00	30
209	70	1s. deep bluish green and yellow-olive		1·25	35
210	—	2s. deep violet and ultramarine	..	1·25	1·50
		w. Wmk inverted	..	55·00	
208/10			*Set of 3*	3·25	1·90

Design:—2s. Rotary Spark Transmitter.

1963 (4 June). *Freedom from Hunger. As No. 146 of Antigua.*
211   1s. ultramarine .. .. .. 13·00 1·50

1963 (2 Sept). *Red Cross Centenary. As Nos. 147/8 of Antigua.*
212   1d. red and black .. .. 5·00 50
213   1s. red and blue .. .. 20·00 6·00

1964 (23 April). *400th Birth Anniv of William Shakespeare. As No. 164 of Antigua.*
214   6d. black .. .. .. 1·25 50

72 H.M.S. Glasgow

(Recess D.L.R.)

1964 (8 Dec). *50th Anniv of the Battle of the Falkland Islands. T* **72** *and similar designs. W w* **12**. *P* 13 × 14 (2s.) *or* 13 (*others*).

215	2½d. black and red	..	10·00	3·25
216	6d. black and light blue	..	75	25
	a. Centre Type 72	..	£17000	
217	1s. black and carmine-red	..	75	1·00
	w. Wmk inverted	..	£1100	
218	2s. black and blue	..	50	75
215/18		*Set of 4*	11·00	4·75

Designs: *Horiz*—6d. H.M.S. *Kent*; 1s. H.M.S. *Invincible. Vert*—2s. Battle Memorial.

It is believed that No. 216a came from a sheet which was first printed with the centre of the 2½d. and then accidently included among the supply of the 6d. value and thus received the wrong frame. There have been seventeen reports of stamps showing the error, although it is believed that some of these *may* refer to the same example.

1965 (26 May). *I.T.U. Centenary. As Nos. 166/7 of Antigua.*
219   1d. light blue and deep blue .. 75 30
        w. Wmk inverted .. £550
220   2s. lilac and bistre-yellow .. 9·00 1·75

1965 (25 Oct). *International Co-operation Year. As Nos. 168/9 of Antigua.*
221   1d. reddish purple and turquoise-green 2·00 20
222   1s. deep bluish green and lavender .. 7·50 1·10

1966 (24 Jan). *Churchill Commemoration. As Nos. 170/3 of Antigua.*

223	½d. new blue	..	65	75
224	1d. deep green	..	2·25	15
	w. Wmk inverted	..	6·50	
225	1s. brown	..	7·00	2·00
	w. Wmk inverted	..	60·00	
226	2s. bluish violet	..	5·50	2·00
223/6		*Set of 4*	14·00	4·50

1966 (25 Oct). *As No. 193a, but wmk w* **12** *sideways.*
227 **54** ½d. black and green .. 30 40

76 Globe and Human Rights Emblem   **77 Dusty Miller**

(Des M. Farrar Bell. Photo Harrison)

1968 (4 July). *Human Rights Year. W w* **12**. *P* 14 × 14½.

228	76	2d. multicoloured	60	20
		a. Yellow omitted ("1968" white)	£950	
229		6d. multicoloured	70	20
230		1s. multicoloured	70	20
231		2s. multicoloured	70	30
228/31			*Set of 4* 2·40	80

(Des Sylvia Goaman)

1968 (9 Oct). *Flowers. Designs as T* **77**. *Chalk-surfaced paper. W w* **12** (*sideways on vert designs*). *P* 14.

232	½d. multicoloured	..	..	15	1·75
233	1½d. multicoloured	..	..	40	15
234	2d. multicoloured	..	..	50	15
235	3d. multicoloured	..	..	5·50	75
236	3½d. multicoloured	..	..	30	30
237	4½d. multicoloured	..	..	1·50	2·00
238	5½d. olive-green, brown and yellow-green		1·50	2·00
239	6d. carmine, black and yellow-green		75	20
240	1s. multicoloured	..	..	75	1·25
	w. Wmk inverted	..	..	85·00	
241	1s. 6d. multicoloured	..	..	4·50	12·00
242	2s. multicoloured	..	..	5·50	6·50
243	3s. multicoloured	..	..	8·00	8·00
244	5s. multicoloured	..	..	28·00	13·00
245	£1 multicoloured	..	..	13·00	2·00
232/45			*Set of 14*	65·00	45·00

Designs: *Horiz*—1½d. Pig Vine; 3½d. Sea Cabbage; 5½d. Arrowleaf Marigold; 6d. Diddle Dee; 1s. Scurvy Grass; 5s. Felton's Flower. *Vert*—2d. Pale Maiden; 3d. Dog Orchid; 4½d. Vanilla Daisy; 1s. 6d. Prickly Burr; 2s. Fachine; 3s. Lavender; £1 Yellow Orchid.

A further printing of the £1 took place with the decimal surcharges issued 15 February 1971. It was for some time believed that stamps from this printing could be identified by the brown shading which extended to the foot of the design, instead of stopping short as on the original printing, but this test has now been shown to be inconsistent.

For stamps inscribed in decimal currency see Nos. 276/88, 293/5 and 315.

91 De Havilland D.H.C.2 Beaver Seaplane

(Des V. Whiteley. Litho Format)

1969 (8 Apr). *21st Anniv of Government Air Services. T* **91** *and similar horiz designs. Multicoloured. W w* **12** (*sideways*). *P* 14.

246	2d. Type 91		35	30
247	6d. Noorduyn Norseman V		40	35
248	1s. Auster Autocrat		50	35
249	2s. Falkland Islands Arms		1·50	2·00
246/9		*Set of 4*	2·50	2·75

92 Holy Trinity Church, 1869

(Des G. Drummond. Litho Format)

1969 (30 Oct). *Centenary of Bishop Stirling's Consecration. T* **92** *and similar horiz designs. W w* **12** (*sideways*). *P* 14.

250	2d. black, grey and apple-green	..	50	60
251	6d. black, grey and orange-red		50	60
252	1s. black, grey and lilac		50	60
253	2s. multicoloured	..	70	75
250/3		*Set of 4*	2·00	2·25

Designs:—6d. Christ Church Cathedral, 1969; 1s. Bishop Stirling; 2s. Bishop's Mitre.

96 Mounted Volunteer   **97 S.S. Great Britain (1843)**

(Des R. Granger Barrett. Litho B.W.)

1970 (30 Apr). *Golden Jubilee of Defence Force. T* **96** *and similar designs. Multicoloured. W w* **12** (*sideways on 2d. and 1s.*). *P* 13.

254	2d. Type 96	..	1·90	70
255	6d. Defence Post (*horiz*)	..	2·00	70
256	1s. Corporal in Number One Dress Uniform	2·00	70
257	2s. Defence Force Badge (*horiz*)	..	3·00	75
254/7		*Set of 4*	8·00	2·50

(Des V. Whiteley. Litho J.W.)

1970 (30 Oct). *Restoration of S.S. "Great Britain". T* **97** *and views of the ship at different dates. Multicoloured. W w* **12** (*sideways**). *P* 14½×½.

258	2d. Type 97	..	1·75	40
259	4d. In 1845	..	2·00	1·00
	w. Wmk Crown to right of CA	..	15·00	
260	9d. In 1876	..	2·00	1·00
261	1s. In 1886	..	2·00	1·00
	w. Wmk Crown to right of CA	..	£700	
262	2s. In 1970	..	2·00	1·00
258/62		*Set of 5*	8·75	4·00

*The normal sideways watermark shows Crown to left of CA, as seen from the back of the stamp.

½p
(98)   **99 Dusty Miller**

1971 (15 Feb). *Decimal Currency. Nos. 232/44 surch as T* **98**. *W w* **12** (*sideways on vert designs*). *P* 14.

263	½p. on ½d. multicoloured		25	20
264	1p. on 1½d. multicoloured		30	15
	a. Error. Surch 5p.	..	£400	
	b. Do. but surch at right	..	£1000	
	c. Surch albino	..	£110	
	d. Surch albino in pair with normal	..	£3250	
265	1½p. on 2d. multicoloured		30	15
266	2p. on 3d. multicoloured		50	20
267	2½p. on 3½d. multicoloured		30	20
268	3p. on 4½d. multicoloured		30	20
269	4p. on 5½d. olive-yellow, brown & yell-grn	30	20
270	5p. on 6d. carmine, black and yellow-green	30	20
271	6p. on 1s. multicoloured		8·00	5·50
272	7½p. on 1s. 6d. multicoloured ..		8·00	6·50
273	10p. on 2s. multicoloured		8·50	3·00
274	15p. on 3s. multicoloured		6·50	2·75
275	25p. on 5s. multicoloured		7·00	3·25
263/75		*Set of 13*	35·00	20·00

1972 (1 June). *As Nos. 232/44, but Glazed, ordinary paper and with values inscr in decimal currency as T* **99**. *W w* **12** (*sideways on ½, 1½, 2, 3, 7½, 10 and 15p.*). *P* 14.

276	½p. multicoloured		35	4·25
277	1p. multicoloured (as 1½d.) ..		30	40
278	1½p. multicoloured (as 2d.) ..		30	3·75
279	2p. multicoloured (as 3d.)		13·00	1·25
280	2½p. multicoloured (as 3½d.) ..		35	3·75
281	3p. multicoloured (as 4½d.) ..		35	1·25
282	4p. olive-yellow, brown & yell-grn (as 5½d.)	40	50
283	5p. carmine, black and yellow-green (as 6d.)	40	55
284	6p. multicoloured (as 1s.) ..		20·00	9·50
285	7½p. multicoloured (as 1s. 6d.)		1·50	4·00
286	10p. multicoloured (as 2s.)		9·00	4·50
287	15p. multicoloured (as 3s.)		4·50	5·00
288	25p. multicoloured (as 5s.)		4·50	6·00
276/88		*Set of 13*	48·00	35·00

See also Nos. 293/5 and 315.

100 Romney Marsh Sheep and Southern Sealions

(Des (from photograph by D. Groves) and photo Harrison)

1972 (20 Nov). *Royal Silver Wedding. Multicoloured; background colour given. W w* **12**. *P* 14 × 14½.

289	100	1p. grey-green	40	40
290		10p. bright blue	85	85

1973 (14 Nov). *Royal Wedding. As Nos. 165/6 of Anguilla. Centre multicoloured. W w* **12** (*sideways*). *P* 13½.
291   5p. bright mauve .. 25 10
292   15p. brown-ochre .. 35 20

1974 (25 Feb–18 Oct). *As Nos. 276, 279 and 284, but wmk upright on ½p. and 2p. and sideways* on 6p. P* 14.

293	½p. multicoloured (18.10.74)	..	12·00	28·00
	w. Wmk inverted	..	£190	
294	2p. multicoloured	..	23·00	3·25
	w. Wmk inverted	..	£350	
295	6p. multicoloured (28.3.74)	..	1·50	2·25
	w. Wmk Crown to right of CA	..	£425	
293/5		*Set of 3*	32·00	30·00

*The normal sideways watermark shows Crown to left of CA, as seen from the back of the stamp.

101 South American Fur Seal   **102 19th-Century Mail-coach**

(Des J. Cooter. Litho Walsall)

1974 (6 Mar). *Tourism. T* **101** *and similar horiz designs. Multicoloured. W w* **12**. *P* 14.

296	2p. Type 101	..	2·25	1·25
297	4p. Trout-fishing	..	3·00	1·25
298	5p. Rockhopper penguins	..	9·50	2·50
299	15p. Long-tailed Meadowlark	..	12·00	4·50
296/9		*Set of 4*	24·00	8·50

(Des PAD Studio. Litho Questa)

1974 (31 July).   *Centenary of Universal Postal Union. T* **102** *and similar vert designs. Multicoloured. W* w **12** (*sideways*): P. 14.

300	2p. Type **102**		25	25
301	5p. Packet ship, 1841		35	45
302	8p. First U.K. aerial post, 1911		40	55
303	16p. Ship's catapult mail, 1920's		60	75
300/3		*Set of* 4	1·40	1·75

103 Churchill and Houses of Parliament

(Des G. Vasarhelyi. Litho Enschedé)

1974 (30 Nov).   *Birth Centenary of Sir Winston Churchill. T* **103** *and similar horiz design. Multicoloured. W* w **12**. *P.* 13½.

304	16p. Type **103**		1·40	1·60
305	20p. Churchill with H.M.S. *Inflexible* and H.M.S. *Invincible*, 1914		1·40	1·90
MS306	108×83 mm. Nos. 304/5		8·00	7·00
	w. Wmk inverted		£170	

104 H.M.S. *Exeter*   **105** Seal and Flag Badge

(Des J.W. Litho Harrison)

1974 (13 Dec).   *35th Anniv of the Battle of the River Plate. T* **104** *and similar horiz designs. Multicoloured. W* w **12** (*sideways**). *P.* 14.

307	2p. Type **104**		3·00	1·60
	w. Wmk Crown to right of CA		13·00	6·00
308	6p. H.M.N.Z.S. *Achilles*		4·50	3·50
	w. Wmk Crown to right of CA		8·50	3·50
309	8p. *Admiral Graf Spee*		5·00	4·50
	w. Wmk Crown to right of CA		95·00	50·00
310	16p. H.M.S. *Ajax*		8·50	15·00
	w. Wmk Crown to right of CA		27·00	17·00
307/10		*Set of* 4	19·00	22·00

*The normal sideways watermark shows Crown to left of CA, as seen from the back of the stamp.

(Des PAD Studio. Litho Walsall

1975 (28 Oct).   *50th Anniv of Heraldic Arms. T* **105** *and similar vert designs. Multicoloured. W* w **14** (*inverted*). *P.* 14.

311	2p. Type **105**		80	35
312	7½p. Coat of arms, 1925		1·60	1·40
313	10p. Coat of arms, 1948		1·75	1·60
314	16p. Arms of the Dependencies, 1952		2·50	3·25
311/14		*Set of* 4	6·00	6·00

1975 (8 Dec).   *As No. 276 but W* w **14** (*sideways*). *P.* 14.

315	**99** ½p. multicoloured		2·25	3·50

106 ½p. Coin and Brown Trout

(Des G. Drummond. Litho Questa)

1975 (31 Dec).   *New Coinage. T* **106** *and similar horiz designs each showing coin. Multicoloured. W* w **12** (*sideways**). *P.* 14.

316	2p. Type **106**		90	50
	w. Wmk Crown to right of CA		65·00	
317	5½p. Gentoo Penguin and 2p. coin		1·40	1·50
318	8p. Magellan Goose and 2p. coin		1·75	1·75
319	10p. Black-browed Albatross and 5p. coin		1·90	2·00
320	16p. Southern Sealion and 10p. coin		2·25	2·50
316/20		*Set of* 5	7·50	7·50

*The normal sideways watermark shows Crown to left of CA, as seen from the back of the stamp.

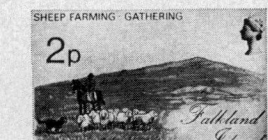

107 Gathering Sheep

(Des PAD Studio. Litho J.W.)

1976 (28 Apr).   *Sheep Farming Industry. T* **107** *and similar horiz designs. Multicoloured. W* w **14** (*sideways*). *P.* 13½.

321	2p. Type **107**		65	40
322	7½p. Shearing		1·40	1·50
323	10p. Dipping		1·75	1·60
324	20p. Shipping		2·25	3·00
321/4		*Set of* 4	5·50	6·00

108 The Queen awaiting Anointment

(Des M. and G. Shamir; adapted J.W. Litho Questa)

1977 (7 Feb–1 Nov).   *Silver Jubilee. T* **108** *and similar horiz designs. Multicoloured. P.* 13½. (*a*) *W* w **14** (*sideways*).

325	6p. Visit of Prince Philip, 1957		2·00	1·25
326	11p. Queen Elizabeth, ampulla and anointing spoon		30	75
	a. Booklet pane of 4 with blank margins (1.11.77)		75	
327	33p. Type **108**		40	1·25
	a. Booklet pane of 4 with blank margins (1.11.77)		1·00	

(*b*) *W* w **12** (*sideways*) (*from booklets only*) (1.11.77)

327*b*	6p. Visit of Prince Philip, 1957		2·75	4·00
	b*a*. Booklet pane of 4 with blank margins		10·00	
325/7*b*		*Set of* 4	5·00	6·50

109 Map of Falkland Islands

(Des K. Penny. Litho Questa)

1977 (24 Oct).   *Telecommunications. T* **109** *and similar horiz designs. Multicoloured. W* w **14** (*sideways**). *P.* 14½.

328	3p. Type **109**		75	15
329	11p. Ship to shore communications		1·25	40
	w. Wmk Crown to right of CA		£110	
330	40p. Telex and telephone service		2·75	1·75
328/30		*Set of* 3	4·25	2·10

*The normal sideways watermark shows Crown to left of CA, as seen from the back of the stamp.

110 *A.E.S.,* 1957–74

(Des J. Smith; adapted R. Granger Barrett. Litho Questa)

1978 (25 Jan)–**82**.   *Mail Ships. Horiz designs as T* **110**. *Multicoloured. W* w **14** (*sideways**). *P.* 14. A. *Without imprint date.*

331A	1p. Type **110**		20	30
332A	2p. *Darwin*, 1957–73		30	30
333A	3p. *Merak-N.*, 1951–2		25	90
	w. Wmk Crown to right of CA		£200	
334A	4p. *Fitzroy*, 1936–57		30	40
335A	5p. *Lafonia*, 1936–41		30	30
336A	6p. *Fleurus*, 1924–33		30	40
337A	7p. *Falkland*, 1914–34		30	1·50
338A	8p. *Oravia*, 1900–12		35	50
339A	9p. *Memphis*, 1890–97		35	50
340A	10p. *Black Hawk*, 1873–80		35	50
341A	20p. *Foam*, 1863–72		1·75	1·50
342A	25p. *Fairy*, 1857–61		2·00	3·00
343A	50p. *Amelia*, 1852–54		2·25	4·00
	w. Wmk Crown to right of CA		£275	
344A	£1 *Nautilus*, 1846–48		4·00	7·00
345A	£3 *Hebe*, 1842–46		11·00	16·00
331A/45A		*Set of* 15	21·00	32·00

B. *With imprint date* ("1982") *at foot* (1.12.82†)

331B	1p. Type **110**		45	1·50
332B	2p. *Darwin*, 1957–73		50	1·50
333B	3p. *Merak-N.*, 1951–2		65	1·50
334B	4p. *Fitzroy*, 1936–57		65	1·50
335B	5p. *Lafonia*, 1936–41		65	1·50
336B	6p. *Fleurus*, 1924–33		65	1·50
337B	7p. *Falkland*, 1914–34		70	1·50
338B	8p. *Oravia*, 1900–12		70	1·50
339B	9p. *Memphis*, 1890–97		70	1·50
340B	10p. *Black Hawk*, 1873–80		70	1·50
341B	20p. *Foam*, 1863–72		1·25	2·00
342B	25p. *Fairy*, 1857–61		1·25	2·50
343B	50p. *Amelia*, 1852–54		2·25	3·00
344B	£1 *Nautilus*, 1846–48		2·50	4·50
345B	£3 *Hebe*, 1842–46		5·50	9·50
331B/45B		*Set of* 15	17·00	32·00

*The normal sideways watermark shows Crown to left of CA, as seen from the back of the stamp.

†Nos. 331B/45B were available from the Crown Agents in London on 13 July 1982.

111 Short Hythe at Stanley

(Des L. McCombie. Litho Walsall)

1978 (28 Apr).   *26th Anniv of First Direct Flight, Southampton–Port Stanley. T* **111** *and similar horiz design. Multicoloured. W* w **14** (*sideways*). *P.* 14.

346	11p. Type **111**		3·00	2·50
347	33p. Route map and Short Hythe		3·50	3·00

112 Red Dragon of Wales   **113** First Fox Bay P.O. and 1d. Stamp of 1878

(Des C. Abbott. Litho Questa)

1978 (2 June).   *25th Anniv of Coronation. T* **112** *and similar vert designs. P.* 15.

348	25p. bistre, bright blue and silver		60	1·00
	a. Sheetlet. Nos. 348/50 × 2		3·00	
349	25p. multicoloured		60	1·00
350	25p. bistre, bright blue and silver		60	1·00
348/50		*Set of* 3	1·60	2·75

Designs:—No. 348, Type **112**; No. 349, Queen Elizabeth II; No. 350, Hornless Ram.

Nos. 348/50 were printed together in small sheets of 6, containing two *se-tenant* strips of 3, with horizontal gutter margin between.

(Des J. Cooter. Litho B.W.)

1978 (8 Aug).   *Centenary of First Falkland Is Postage Stamps. T* **113** *and similar vert designs. Multicoloured. W* w **14**. *P.* 13½ × 13.

351	3p. Type **113**		25	20
352	11p. Second Stanley P.O. and 4d. stamp of 1879		40	50
353	15p. New Island P.O. and 6d. stamp of 1878		50	60
	w. Wmk inverted		£700	
354	22p. First Stanley P.O. and 1s. stamp of 1878		80	1·00
351/4		*Set of* 4	1·75	2·10

114 *Macrocystis pyrifera*   **115** Britten Norman Islander over Falkland Islands

(Des I. Strange. Litho Questa)

1979 (19 Feb).   *Kelp and Seaweed. T* **114** *and similar multicoloured designs. W* w **14** (*sideways on* 11 *and* 15p.). *P.* 14.

355	3p. Type **114**		30	25
356	7p. *Durvillea* sp		50	45
357	11p. *Lessonia* sp (*horiz*)		65	60
358	15p. *Callophyllis* sp (*horiz*)		85	80
359	25p. *Iradaea* sp		1·00	1·40
355/9		*Set of* 5	3·00	3·25

(Des G. Hutchins. Litho Rosenbaum Bros, Vienna)

1979 (1 May).   *Opening of Stanley Airport. T* **115** *and similar horiz designs showing diagrammatic drawings. Multicoloured. W* w **14** (*sideways**). *P.* 13½.

360	3p. Type **115**		40	20
	w. Wmk Crown to right of CA		35·00	
361	11p. Fokker F.27 Friendship over South Atlantic		80	60
	w. Wmk Crown to left of CA		55·00	
362	15p. Fokker F.28 Fellowship over Airport		90	60
	w. Wmk Crown to left of CA		40·00	
363	25p. Cessna 172 Skyhawk, Britten Norman Islander, Fokker F.27 Friendship and Fokker F.28 Fellowship over runway		1·50	80
	w. Wmk Crown to left of CA		3·75	
360/3		*Set of* 4	3·25	2·00

*The normal sideways watermark shows Crown to left of CA on the 3p. and Crown to right of CA on the other values, *all as seen from the back of the stamp.*

COVER PRICES

Cover factors are quoted at the beginning of each country for most issues to 1945. An explanation of the system can be found on page x. The factors quoted do not, however, apply to philatelic covers.

116 Sir Rowland Hill and 1953 Coronation 1d.
Commemorative

(Des J.W. Litho Questa)

1979 (27 Aug). *Death Centenary of Sir Rowland Hill. T* **116** *and similar multicoloured designs showing stamps and portrait. W* w **14** *(sideways* on 3 and 25p.). P* 14.
364	3p. Type **116**		..	25	25
	w. Wmk Crown to left of CA		2·00		
365	11p. 1878 1d. stamp (*vert*)		..	40	70
366	25p. Penny Black		..	60	85
	w. Wmk Crown to left of CA		£200		
364/6			*Set of 3*	1·10	1·60
MS367	137×98 mm. 33p. 1916 5s. stamp (*vert*)			85	1·50

*The normal sideways watermark shows Crown to right of CA, *as seen from the back of the stamp.*

117 Mail Drop by De   **118** Peale's Dolphin
Havilland D.H.C.2 Beaver
Aircraft

(Des A. Peake; adapted J.W. Litho Questa)

1979 (26 Nov). *Centenary of U.P.U. Membership. T* **117** *and similar horiz designs. Multicoloured. W* w **14** *(sideways*). P* 14.
368	3p. Type **117**		..	20	20
	w. Wmk Crown to right of CA		2·00		
369	11p. Mail by horseback		..	45	55
370	25p. Mail by schooner *Gwendolin*		..	75	1·00
368/70			*Set of 3*	1·25	1·60

*The normal sideways watermark shows Crown to left of CA, *as seen from the back of the stamp.*

(Des I. Strange. Litho Harrison)

1980 (25 Feb). *Dolphins and Porpoises. T* **118** *and similar designs. W* w **14** *(sideways* on 6, 7, 15 and 25p.). P* 14.
371	3p. black, chestnut and blue		..	45	45
	w. Wmk inverted			£200	
372	6p. multicoloured		..	55	55
373	7p. multicoloured		..	55	55
374	11p. black, new blue and rose-red		..	80	90
375	15p. black, chestnut and greyish blue		..	90	1·10
	w. Wmk Crown to right of CA		60·00		
376	25p. multicoloured		..	1·00	1·75
371/6			*Set of 6*	3·75	4·75

Designs: *Horiz*—6p. Commerson's Dolphin; 7p. Hourglass Dolphin; 15p. Dusky Dolphin; 25p. Killer Whale. *Vert*—11p. Spectacled Porpoise.

*The normal sideways watermark shows Crown to left of CA, *as seen from the back of the stamp.*

119 1878 Falkland Islands Postmark

(Des G. Hutchins. Litho Walsall)

1980 (6 May). *"London 1980" International Stamp Exhibition. T* **119** *and similar horiz designs showing postmarks. W* w **14** *(sideways). P* 14.
377	11p. black, gold and light blue		..	30	30
	a. Block of 6. Nos. 377/82			1·50	
378	11p. black, gold and greenish yellow	..	..	30	30
379	11p. black, gold and blue-green		..	30	30
380	11p. black, gold and pale violet		..	30	30
381	11p. black, gold and claret		..	30	30
382	11p. black, gold and flesh		..	30	30
377/82			*Set of 6*	1·50	1·50

Designs:—No. 377, Type **119**; No. 378, 1915 New Island; No. 379, 1901 Falkland Islands; No. 380, 1935 Port Stanley; No. 381, 1952 Port Stanley first overseas airmail; No. 382, 1934 Fox Bay.

Nos. 377/82 were printed together, *se-tenant*, as a sheetlet, containing one of each design.

120 Queen Elizabeth the
Queen Mother at Ascot, 1971

(Des Harrison. Litho Questa)

1980 (4 Aug). *80th Birthday of Queen Elizabeth the Queen Mother. W* w **14** *(sideways). P* 14.
383	**120**	11p. multicoloured		40	30

121 Forster's Caracara

(Des I. Strange. Litho Secura, Singapore)

1980 (11 Aug). *Birds of Prey. T* **121** *and similar horiz designs. Multicoloured. W* w **14** *(sideways*). P* 13×13½.
384	3p. Type **121**		..	70	25
	w. Wmk Crown to left of CA		3·25		
385	11p. Red-backed Buzzard		..	90	60
	w. Wmk Crown to left of CA		£350		
386	15p. Common Caracara		..	1·10	75
	w. Wmk Crown to left of CA		£400		
387	25p. Peregrine Falcon		..	1·25	1·00
	w. Wmk Crown to left of CA		1·25		
384/7			*Set of 4*	3·50	2·40

*The normal sideways watermark shows Crown to right of CA, *as seen from the back of the stamp.*

122 Stanley

(Des C. Abbott. Litho Rosenbaum Bros, Vienna)

1981 (7 Jan). *Early Settlements. T* **122** *and similar horiz designs. Multicoloured. W* w **14** *(sideways*). P* 14.
388	3p. Type **122**		..	15	15
389	11p. Port Egmont		..	30	35
390	25p. Port Louis		..	60	65
	w. Wmk Crown to left of CA		£300		
391	33p. Mission House, Keppel Island		70	80
	w. Wmk Crown to left of CA		£250		
388/91			*Set of 4*	1·60	1·75

*The normal sideways watermark shows Crown to right of CA, *as seen from the back of the stamp.*

123 Sheep

(Des P. Oxenham. Litho Questa)

1981 (9 Jan). *Farm Animals. T* **123** *and similar horiz designs. Multicoloured. W* w **14** *(sideways*). P* 14.
392	3p. Type **123**		..	20	30
393	11p. Cattle		..	35	55
	w. Wmk Crown to right of CA		£140		
394	25p. Horse		..	70	1·25
	w. Wmk Crown to right of CA		80·00		
395	33p. Dogs		..	1·00	1·50
392/5			*Set of 4*	2·00	3·25

*The normal sideways watermark shows Crown to left of CA, *as seen from the back of the stamp.*

124 Bowles and Carver, 1779   **125** Wedding Bouquet
from Falkland Islands

(Des I. Strange. Litho Walsall)

1981 (22 May). *Early Maps. T* **124** *and similar horiz designs in black, dull rose and stone (26p.) or multicoloured (others). W* w **14** *(sideways*). P* 14.
396	3p. Type **124**		..	35	30
397	10p. J. Hawkesworth, 1773		..	55	55
	w. Wmk Crown to right of CA		£200		
398	13p. Eman. Bowen, 1747	..	..	60	75
399	15p. T. Boutflower, 1768		..	60	85
400	25p. Philippe de Pretot, 1771		..	65	90
401	26p. Bellin *Petite Atlas Maritime*, Paris, 1764			65	90
396/401			*Set of 6*	3·00	3·75

*The normal sideways watermark shows Crown to left of CA, *as seen from the back of the stamp.*

(Des and litho J.W.)

1981 (22 July). *Royal Wedding. T* **125** *and similar vert designs. Multicoloured. W* w **14**. *P* 13½ × 13.
402	10p. Type **125**		..	30	40
	w. Wmk inverted			65·00	
403	13p. Prince Charles riding		..	40	50
	w. Wmk inverted			35·00	
404	52p. Prince Charles and Lady Diana Spencer			70	1·00
402/4			*Set of 3*	1·25	1·75

126 "Handicrafts"   **127** "The Adoration
of the Holy Child"
(16th-century Dutch artist)

(Des BG Studio. Litho Questa)

1981 (28 Sept*). *25th Anniv of Duke of Edinburgh Award Scheme. T* **126** *and similar vert designs. Multicoloured. W* w **14**. *P* 14.
405	10p. Type **126**		..	15	20
406	13p. "Camping"		..	20	30
407	15p. "Canoeing"		..	30	40
408	26p. Duke of Edinburgh		..	35	60
405/8			*Set of 4*	90	1·40

*This is the local date of issue. The Crown Agents released the stamps in London on 14 September.

(Des BG Studio. Litho Walsall)

1981 (9 Nov*). *Christmas. Paintings. T* **127** *and similar vert designs. Multicoloured. W* w **14**. *P* 14.
409	3p. Type **127**		..	20	20
410	13p. "The Holy Family in an Italian Landscape" (17th-century Genoan artist)			35	45
411	26p. "The Holy Virgin" (Reni)		..	55	75
409/11			*Set of 3*	1·00	1·25

*This is the local date of issue. The Crown Agents released the stamps in London on 2 November.

128 Patagonian Sprat

(Des I. Strange. Litho Questa)

1981 (7 Dec). *Shelf Fishes. T* **128** *and similar multicoloured designs. W* w **14** *(sideways on 5, 15 and 25p.). P* 14 × 13½ (13, 26p.) or 13½ × 14 (others).
412	5p. Type **128**		..	20	20
413	13p. Gunther's Rockcod (*vert*)		..	35	35
414	15p. Argentine Hake		..	40	40
415	25p. Southern Blue Whiting		..	60	75
416	26p. Grey-tailed Skate (*vert*)		..	60	75
412/16			*Set of 5*	1·90	2·25

129 *Lady Elizabeth*, 1913

(Des J. Smith. Litho Questa)

1982 (15 Feb). *Shipwrecks. T* **129** *and similar horiz designs. Multicoloured. W* w **14** *(sideways). P* 14½.
417	5p. Type **129**		..	30	50
418	13p. *Capricorn*, 1882		..	35	70
419	15p. *Jhelum*, 1870		..	40	85
420	25p. *Snowsquall*, 1864		..	55	1·10
421	26p. *St. Mary*, 1890		..	55	1·10
417/21			*Set of 5*	1·90	3·75

PRICES OF SETS

Set prices are given for many issues, generally those containing three stamps or more. Definitive sets include one of each value or major colour change, but do not cover different perforations, die types or minor shades. Where a choice is possible the set prices are based on the cheapest versions of the stamps included in the listings.

ARGENTINE OCCUPATION
2 April to 15 June 1982

Following incidents, involving the illegal presence of Argentine scrap-metal workers on the dependency of South Georgia from 18 March 1982, Argentine forces attacked Port Stanley, the capital of the Falkland Islands early in the morning of 2 April. The small garrison of Royal Marines was overwhelmed and the Governor forced to agree to a cease-fire, before being deported.

South Georgia was occupied by the Argentines on the following day.

British forces, dispatched from the United Kingdom, recaptured South Georgia on 25 April, and, after landing at various points on East Falkland, forced the surrender of the Argentine troops throughout the islands on 15 June.

The last mail to be dispatched from the Falkland Islands prior to the invasion left on 31 March. The Port Stanley Post Office was closed on 2 April, when all current issues were withdrawn. From 5 April an Argentine post office operated in the town, initially accepting mail without stamps, which was then cancelled by a postmark inscribed "ISLAS MALVINAS". Any letters tendered franked with Falkland Islands issues had these cancelled by ballpoint pen. A limited range of Argentine stamps was placed on sale from 8 April. The Argentine definitive overprinted "LAS MALVINAS SON ARGENTINAS" for use throughout the country, was also available.

Following the Argentine surrender a rudimentary mail service was operating by 17 June, but the Port Stanley Post Office did not re-open until 24 June.

The last mail from South Georgia before the invasion was sent out on 16 March, although items remaining in the post office there were evacuated by the Deputy Postmaster when he was deported to the United Kingdom by the Argentines. The first mail left after recapture by the British on 2 May.

BRITISH ADMINISTRATION RESTORED

130 Charles Darwin   131 Falkland Islands Coat of Arms

(Des L. Curtis. Litho Questa)

1982 (5 July*). *150th Anniv of Charles Darwin's Voyage. T* **130** *and similar horiz designs. Multicoloured.* W w **14** (*sideways*). P 14.

422	5p. Type **130**	30	25
423	17p. Darwin's microscope	50	60
424	25p. Falkland Islands Wolf ("Warrah")	70	80
425	34p. H.M.S. *Beagle*	95	1·10
	a. Pale brown (background to side panels) omitted	£800	
422/5	*Set of 4*	2·25	2·50

*It was initially intended that these stamps were to be issued on 19 April. First Day covers were prepared, postmarked with this date, but, because of the Argentine invasion, the stamps were not actually released until 5 July. A postmark showing the actual date of issue was struck alongside the stamps on the First Day covers.

(Des C. Abbott. Litho J.W.)

1982 (16 Aug). *21st Birthday of Princess of Wales. T* **131** *and similar vert designs. Multicoloured.* W w **14**. P 13.

426	5p. Type **131**	15	20
427	17p. Princess at Royal Opera House, Covent Garden, November 1981	30	40
428	37p. Bride and groom in doorway of St Paul's	50	70
429	50p. Formal portrait	65	90
426/9	*Set of 4*	1·40	2·00

132 Map of Falkland Islands

(Des PAD Studio. Litho Format)

1982 (13 Sept). *Rebuilding Fund.* W w **14** (*sideways**). P 11.

430	**132**	£1 + £1 multicoloured	2·40	4·50
		w. Wmk Crown to right of CA	75·00	

*The normal sideways watermark shows Crown to left of CA, as seen from the back of the stamp.

1st PARTICIPATION COMMONWEALTH GAMES 1982

(133)   134 Blackish Cinclodes

1982 (7 Oct). *Commonwealth Games, Brisbane. Nos.* 335B *and* 342B *optd with T* **133**.

431	5p. *Lafonia*, 1936–41	15	30
432	25p. *Fairy*, 1857–61	60	1·10

(Des I. Strange. Litho W. S. Cowells Ltd)

1982 (6 Dec). *Birds of the Passerine Family. T* **134** *and similar vert designs. Multicoloured.* W w **14** (*inverted on 10p.*). P 15 × 14½.

433	5p. Type **134**	35	35
434	10p. Black-chinned Siskin	45	45
	w. Wmk upright	40·00	
435	13p. Short-billed Marsh Wren	50	55
436	17p. Black-throated Finch	55	65
437	25p. Correndera Pipit	65	85
438	34p. Dark-faced Ground Tyrant	75	1·10
433/8	*Set of 6*	2·75	3·50

Imperforate examples of all values, except the 34p., exist from printer's waste which escaped destruction. Some are known on unwatermarked paper with thick red lines across the face of the stamps.

135 Raising Flag, Port Louis, 1833   136 1933 British Administration Centenary 3d. Commemorative

(Des I. Strange and J. Sheridan. Litho Questa)

1983 (3 Jan). *150th Anniv of British Administration. T* **135** *and similar multicoloured designs.* W w **14** (*sideways on 2, 10, 15, 25 and 50p.*). P 14 × 13½ (1, 5, 20, 40p., £1, £2) or 13½ × 14 (*others*).

439	1p. Type **135**	20	30
440	2p. Chelsea pensioners and barracks, 1849 (*horiz*)	30	40
441	5p. Development of wool trade, 1874	30	40
442	10p. Ship-repairing trade, 1850–1890 (*horiz*)	60	70
443	15p. Government House, early 20th century (*horiz*)	70	80
444	20p. Battle of Falkland Islands, 1914	90	1·25
445	25p. Whalebone Arch, 1933 (*horiz*)	90	1·25
446	40p. Contribution to War effort, 1939–45	1·40	1·60
447	50p. Duke of Edinburgh's visit, 1957 (*horiz*)	1·50	2·00
448	£1 Royal Marine uniforms	2·00	3·00
449	£2 Queen Elizabeth II	2·75	4·50
439/49	*Set of 11*	10·00	14·50

(Des L. Curtis. Litho Questa)

1983 (28 Mar*). *Commonwealth Day. T* **136** *and similar multicoloured designs.* W w **14** (*sideways on 5p., 17p.*). P 14.

450	5p. Type **136**	15	15
451	17p. 1933 British Administration Centenary ½d. commemorative	30	35
452	34p. 1933 British Administration Centenary 10s. commemorative (*vert*)	60	80
453	50p. 1983 British Administration 150th anniversary £2 commemorative (*vert*)	75	1·00
450/3	*Set of 4*	1·60	2·10

*This is the local date of issue: the Crown Agents released the stamps on 14 March.

137 British Army advancing across East Falkland

(Des A. Theobald. Litho Questa)

1983 (14 June). *First Anniv of Liberation. T* **137** *and similar horiz designs. Multicoloured.* W w **14** (*sideways*). P 14.

454	5p. Type **137**	25	30
455	13p. S.S. *Canberra* and M.V. *Norland* at San Carlos	40	60
456	17p. R.A.F. Hawker Siddeley Harrier fighter	45	70
457	50p. H.M.S. *Hermes* (aircraft carrier)	1·00	1·40
454/7	*Set of 4*	1·90	2·75
MS458	169×130 mm. Nos. 454/7. P 12	2·25	3·50

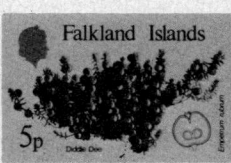

138 Diddle Dee

(Des A. Chater. Litho Questa)

1983 (10 Oct). *Native Fruits. T* **138** *and similar horiz designs. Multicoloured.* W w **14** (*sideways*). P 14.

459	5p. Type **138**	20	20
460	17p. Tea Berry	30	50
461	25p. Mountain Berry	45	65
462	34p. Native Strawberry	65	80
459/62	*Set of 4*	1·40	1·90

139 Britten Norman Islander

(Des Harrison. Litho Questa)

1983 (14 Nov). *Bicentenary of Manned Flight. T* **139** *and similar horiz designs. Multicoloured.* W w **14** (*sideways*). P 14.

463	5p. Type **139**	15	20
464	13p. De Havilland D.H.C.2 Beaver	35	45
465	17p. Noorduyn Norseman V	40	50
466	50p. Auster Autocrat	1·00	1·25
463/6	*Set of 4*	1·75	2·25

17 p

(140)	(140a)

17 p

1984 (3 Jan). Nos. 443 and 445 surch as T **140** by Govt Printer, Port Stanley.

467	17p. on 15p. Government House, early 20th century (figures as Type **140**)	60	45
	a. Surch figures as Type **140a**	1·00	1·25
468	22p. on 25p. Whalebone Arch, 1933	65	55

The surcharge setting used for the 17p. contained 27 examples as Type **140** and 23 as Type **140a**.

141 *Araneus cinnabarinus* (juvenile spider)   142 *Wavertree* (sail merchantman)

(Des I. Strange. Litho Questa)

1984 (3 Jan)–86. *Insects and Spiders. T* **141** *and similar horiz designs. Multicoloured.* W w **14** (*sideways*). P 14×14½.

A. Without imprint date

469A	1p. Type **141**	20	80
470A	2p. *Alopophion occidentalis* (fly)	40	80
471A	3p. *Pareuxoina falkandica* (moth)	30	80
472A	4p. *Lissopterus quadrinotatus* (beetle)	30	80
473A	5p. *Issoria cytheris* (butterfly)	30	80
474A	6p. *Araneus cinnabarinus* (adult spider)	30	65
475A	7p. *Trachysphyrus penai* (fly)	30	65
476A	8p. *Caphornia ochricraspia* (moth)	30	65
477A	9p. *Caneorhinus biangulatus* (weevil)	30	65
478A	10p. *Syrphus octomaculatus* (fly)	30	65
479A	20p. *Malvinius compressiventris* (weevil)	2·25	75
480A	25p. *Metius blandus* (beetle)	75	90
481A	50p. *Parudenus falkandicus* (cricket)	1·00	1·50
482A	£1 *Emmenomma beauchenieus* (spider)	1·75	2·25
483A	£3 *Cynthia carye* (butterfly)	4·00	6·00
469A/83A	*Set of 15*	13·00	18·00

B. With "1986" imprint date at foot of design

470B	2p. *Alopophion occidentalis* (fly) (19.5.86)	2·75	2·75

(Des A. Theobald. Litho Questa)

1984 (7 May). *250th Anniv of "Lloyd's List" (newspaper). T* **142** *and similar vert designs. Multicoloured.* W w **14**. P 14½ × 14.

484	6p. Type **142**	55	40
485	17p. *Bjerk* (whale catcher) at Port Stanley	1·10	60
486	22p. *Oravia* (liner) stranded	1·10	65
487	52p. *Cunard Countess* (liner)	1·60	2·00
484/7	*Set of 4*	3·75	3·25

OMNIBUS ISSUES

Details, together with prices for complete sets, of the various Omnibus issues from the 1935 Silver Jubilee series to date are included in a special section following Zimbabwe at the end of Volume 2.

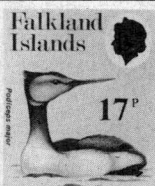

143 Ship, Lockheed C-130 Hercules Aircraft and U.P.U. Logo

144 Great Grebe

(Des E. Nisbet, adapted L. Curtis. Litho Questa)

1984 (25 June). *Universal Postal Union Congress, Hamburg.* W w **14** *(sideways). P* 14.

488	**143**	22p. multicoloured	.. .. ..	55	75

(Des I. Strange. Litho Questa)

1984 (6 Aug). *Grebes. T* **144** *and similar vert designs. Multicoloured. W w* 14½.

489	17p. Type **144**	1·40	1·25
490	22p. Silvery Grebe	1·60	1·40
491	52p. White-tufted Grebe	3·00	4·75
489/91	*Set of* 3	5·50	6·75

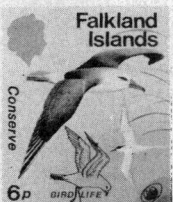

145 Black-browed Albatross

146 Technical Drawing of Class "Wren" Locomotive

(Des I. Strange. Litho Questa)

1984 (5 Nov). *Nature Conservation. T* **145** *and similar vert designs. Multicoloured. W w* 14*. P* 14½ × 14.

492	6p. Type **145**	1·25	80
493	17p. Tussock grass	1·25	1·10
494	22p. Dusky Dolphin and Southern Sealion	1·40	1·40
495	52p. Rockcod (fish) and krill ..	2·00	3·00
492/5	*Set of* 4	5·50	5·50
MS496	130×90 mm. Nos. 492/5	5·50	7·00

(Des C. Abbott. Litho Questa)

1985 (18 Feb). *70th Anniv of Camber Railway. T* **146** *and similar horiz designs, each black, deep brown and pale cinnamon. W w* 14 *(sideways). P* 14.

497	7p. Type **146**	35	30
498	22p. Sail-propelled trolley.. ..	60	90
499	27p. Class "Wren" locomotive at work	65	1·25
500	54p. "Falkland Islands Express" passenger train (75×25 *mm*)	1·10	2·00
497/500	*Set of* 4	2·40	4·00

147 Construction Workers' Camp

148 The Queen Mother on 84th Birthday

(Des N. Shewring. Litho Questa)

1985 (12 May). *Opening of Mount Pleasant Airport. T* **147** *and similar horiz designs. Multicoloured. W w* 16 *(sideways). P* 14½ × 14.

501	7p. Type **147**	75	40
502	22p. Building construction ..	1·40	90
503	27p. Completed airport	1·60	1·10
504	54p. Lockheed L-1011 TriStar 500 airliner over runway	2·00	2·50
501/4	*Set of* 4	5·25	4·50

(Des A. Theobald (£1), C. Abbott (others). Litho Questa)

1985 (7 June). *Life and Times of Queen Elizabeth the Queen Mother. T* **148** *and similar vert designs. Multicoloured. W w* 16*. P* 14½ × 14.

505	7p. Attending reception at Lancaster House	25	20
506	22p. With Prince Charles, Mark Phillips and Princess Anne at Falklands Memorial Service	60	50
	w. Wmk inverted	14·00	
507	27p. Type **148**	70	60
508	54p. With Prince Henry at his christening (from photo by Lord Snowdon) ..	1·25	1·25
505/8	*Set of* 4	2·50	2·25
MS509	91×73 mm £1 With Princess Diana at Trooping the Colour. Wmk sideways ..	2·50	2·25

149 Captain J. McBride and H.M.S. *Jason*, 1765

150 Painted Keyhole Limpet (*Fissurella picta*)

(Des O. Bell. Litho Questa)

1985 (30 Sept). *Early Cartographers. T* **149** *and similar horiz designs. Multicoloured. W w* 14 *(sideways). P* 14 × 14½.

510	7p. Type **149**	1·10	40
511	22p. Commodore J. Byron and H.M.S. *Dolphin* and *Tamar*, 1765 ..	1·60	80
512	27p. Vice-Admiral R. FitzRoy and H.M.S. *Beagle*, 1831	1·75	85
513	54p. Admiral Sir B. J. Sullivan and H.M.S. *Philomel*, 1842	2·50	1·75
510/13	*Set of* 4	6·25	3·50

(Des I. Strange. Litho Questa)

1985 (4 Nov). *Early Naturalists. Vert designs as T* **35** *of British Antarctic Territory. Multicoloured. W w* 14*. P* 14½ × 14.

514	7p. Philibert Commerson and Commerson's Dolphin	1·00	40
515	22p. René Primevère Lesson and *Lessonia sp.* (kelp).. ..	1·50	1·10
516	27p. Joseph Paul Gaimard and Common Diving Petrel	2·25	1·90
517	54p. Charles Darwin and *Calceolaria darwinii*	2·50	2·75
514/17	*Set of* 4	6·50	5·50

(Des I. Strange. Litho Questa)

1986 (10 Feb). *Seashells. T* **150** *and similar horiz designs. Multicoloured. W w* 16 *(sideways). P* 14 × 14½.

518	7p. Type **150**	85	60
519	22p. *Provocator palliata* (*Odontocymbiola magellanica*)	1·50	1·40
520	27p. Patagonian or Falkland Scallop (*Chlamys lischkei*)	1·75	2·25
521	54p. Rough Thorn Drupe (*Acanthina monodon imbricata*)	2·75	3·50
518/21	*Set of* 4	6·25	7·00

(Des A. Theobald. Litho Format)

1986 (21 Apr). *60th Birthday of Queen Elizabeth II. Vert designs as T* **110** *of Ascension. Multicoloured. W w* 16*. P* 14 × 14½.

522	10p. With Princess Margaret at St Paul's, Walden Bury, Welwyn, 1932 ..	20	25
523	24p. Queen making Christmas television broadcast, 1958	35	50
524	29p. In robes of Order of the Thistle, St. Giles Cathedral, Edinburgh, 1962 ..	35	60
525	45p. Aboard Royal Yacht *Britannia*, U.S.A., 1976	1·25	1·25
526	58p. At Crown Agents Head Office, London, 1983	80	1·50
522/6 ..	*Set of* 5	2·75	3·50

151 S.S. *Great Britain* crossing Atlantic, 1845

152 Head of Rockhopper Penguin

(Des O. Bell. Litho Format)

1986 (22 May). *"Ameripex '86" International Stamp Exhibition, Chicago. Centenary of Arrival of S.S. "Great Britain" in Falkland Islands. T* **151** *and similar horiz designs. Multicoloured. W w* 16 *(sideways*). P* 14.

527	10p. Type **151**	50	60
528	24p. Beached at Sparrow Cove, 1937	60	80
529	29p. Refloated on pontoon, 1970 ..	70	90
530	58p. Undergoing restoration, Bristol, 1986	80	2·25
	w. Wmk Crown to right of CA ..	70·00	
527/30	*Set of* 4	2·40	4·00
MS531	109×109 mm. Nos. 527/30. Wmk upright	2·00	3·25

The normal sideways watermark shows Crown to left of CA, as seen from the back of the stamp.

(Des I. Strange. Litho Questa)

1986 (25 Aug). *Rockhopper Penguins. T* **152** *and similar vert designs. Multicoloured. W w* 16*. P* 14½ × 14.

532	10p. Type **152**	1·00	70
533	24p. Rockhopper Penguins at sea ..	1·75	1·75
534	29p. Courtship display	2·00	2·00
535	58p. Adult with chick	2·50	4·50
532/5 ..	*Set of* 4	6·50	8·00

NEW INFORMATION

The editor is always interested to correspond with people who have new information that will improve or correct the Catalogue.

153 Prince Andrew and Miss Sarah Ferguson presenting Polo Trophy, Windsor

154 Survey Party, Sapper Hill

(Des D. Miller. Litho Questa)

1986 (10 Nov). *Royal Wedding. T* **153** *and similar vert designs. Multicoloured. W w* 16*. P* 14½ × 14.

536	17p. Type **153**	85	50
537	22p. Prince Andrew and Duchess of York on wedding day	95	65
538	29p. Prince Andrew in battledress at opening of Fox Bay Mill	1·25	90
536/8	*Set of* 3	2·75	1·90

(Des L. Curtis. Litho Questa)

1987 (9 Feb). *Bicentenary of Royal Engineers' Royal Warrant. T* **154** *and similar horiz designs. Multicoloured. W w* 16 *(sideways). P* 14 × 14½.

539	10p. Type **154**	1·25	80
540	24p. Mine clearance by robot ..	1·75	1·50
541	29p. Boxer Bridge, Stanley ..	2·00	2·50
542	58p. Unloading mail, Mount Pleasant Airport	2·75	4·00
539/42	*Set of* 4	7·00	8·00

155 Southern Sea Lion

156 *Suillus luteus*

(Des I. Strange. Litho Questa)

1987 (27 Apr). *Seals. T* **155** *and similar horiz designs. Multicoloured. W w* 16 *(sideways). P* 14½.

543	10p. Type **155**	85	55
544	24p. Falkland Fur Seal	1·75	90
545	29p. Southern Elephant Seal ..	1·90	1·50
546	58p. Leopard Seal	2·75	3·00
543/6	*Set of* 4	6·50	5·50

(Des I. Strange. Litho Questa)

1987 (14 Sept). *Fungi. T* **156** *and similar vert designs. Multicoloured. W w* 16*. P* 14½ × 14.

547	10p. Type **156**	1·75	85
548	24p. *Mycena sp.*	2·75	2·00
549	29p. *Hygrophorous adonis* ("*Camarophyllus adonis*")	3·00	3·00
550	58p. *Gerronema schusteri*	4·50	5·00
547/50	*Set of* 4	11·00	9·75

157 Victoria Cottage Home, c 1912

158 Morris Truck, Fitzroy, 1940

(Des D. Hartley. Litho Questa)

1987 (8 Dec). *Local Hospitals. T* **157** *and similar horiz designs. Multicoloured. W w* 16 *(sideways). P* 14.

551	10p. Type **157**	50	25
552	24p. King Edward VII Memorial Hospital, c 1914	85	55
553	29p. Churchill Wing, King Edward VII Memorial Hospital, c 1953 ..	95	60
554	58p. Prince Andrew Wing, New Hospital, 1987	1·50	1·25
551/4	*Set of* 4	3·50	2·40

(Des D. Hartley. Litho Questa)

1988 (11 Apr). *Early Vehicles. T* **158** *and similar horiz designs. Multicoloured. W w* 16 *(sideways). P* 14.

555	10p. Type **158**	50	25
556	24p. Citroen "Kegresse" half-track, San Carlos, 1929	85	55
557	29p. Ford one ton truck, Port Stanley, 1933	95	60
558	58p. Ford "Model T" car, Darwin, 1935 ..	1·50	1·25
555/8	*Set of* 4	3·50	2·40

159 Kelp Goose

(Des I. Strange. Litho Walsall)

1988 (25 July). *Falkland Islands Geese. T* **159** *and similar horiz designs. Multicoloured. W* w **16** *(sideways). P* 13½×14.

559	10p. Type **159**	2·00	55
560	24p. Magellan ("Upland") Goose	2·75	70
561	29p. Ruddy-headed Goose	3·00	90
562	58p. Ashy-headed Goose	4·50	2·00
559/62		*Set of* 4	11·00	3·75

(Des D. Miller (10, 24p.), E. Nesbit and D. Miller (29, 58p.). Litho Format)

1988 (14 Nov). *300th Anniv of Lloyd's of London. Multicoloured designs as T* **123** *of Ascension. W* w **14** *(sideways on* 24, 29p.*). P* 14.

563	10p. Silver from Lloyd's Nelson Collection	40	30
564	24p. Falkland Islands hydroponic market garden (*horiz*)	75	65
565	29p. *A.E.S.* (mail ship) (*horiz*)	1·25	75
566	58p. *Charles Cooper* (full-rigged ship), 1866	1·50	1·25
	w. Wmk inverted	28·00	
563/6		*Set of* 4	3·50	2·75

160 *Padua* (barque)

(Des A. Theobald. Litho Questa)

1989 (28 Feb)–90. *Cape Horn Sailing Ships. T* **160** *and similar multicoloured designs. W* w **14** *(sideways on horiz designs). P* 14.

567	1p. Type **160**	80	60
568	2p. *Priwall* (barque) (*vert*)	1·50	1·25
569	3p. *Passat* (barque)	1·50	1·25
570	4p. *Archibald Russell* (barque) (*vert*)	1·00	80
571	5p. *Pamir* (barque) (*vert*)	1·00	80
572	6p. *Mozart* (barquentine)	1·75	1·25
573	7p. *Pommern* (barque)	1·25	1·00
574	8p. *Preussen* (full-rigged ship)	1·25	1·00
575	9p. *Fennia* (barque)	1·75	1·25
576	10p. *Cassard* (barque)	1·25	1·00
577	20p. *Lawhill* (barque)	2·00	2·00
578	25p. *Garthpool* (barque)	2·00	2·00
579	50p. *Grace Harwar* (full-rigged ship)	3·00	3·00
580	£1 *Criccieth Castle* (full-rigged ship)	7·50	7·50
581	£3 *Cutty Sark* (full-rigged ship) (*vert*)	8·50	
582	£5 *Flying Cloud* (full-rigged ship) (2.1.90)	11·00	9·00
567/82		*Set of* 16	42·00	38·00

For 2, 3, 6, 9p. and £1 values watermarked w **16** and with imprint dates see Nos. 613/25.

161 Southern Right Whale

(Des I. Strange. Litho Questa)

1989 (15 May). *Baleen Whales. T* **161** *and similar horiz designs. Multicoloured. W* w **16** *(sideways). P* 13½×14.

583	10p. Type **161**	1·25	40
584	24p. Minke Whale	2·00	85
585	29p. Humpback Whale	2·25	1·25
586	58p. Blue Whale	3·50	2·50
583/6		*Set of* 4	8·00	4·50

162 "Gymkhana" (Sarah Gilding)

163 Vice-Admiral Sturdee and H.M.S. *Invincible* (battle cruiser)

(Adapted G. Vasarhelyi. Litho Walsall)

1989 (16 Sept). *Sports Associations' Activities. T* **162** *and similar horiz designs showing children's drawings. Multicoloured. W* w **16** *(sideways). P* 14.

587	5p. Type **162**	20	20
588	10p. "Steer Riding" (Karen Steen)	30	30
589	17p. "Sheep Shearing" (Colin Shepherd)	45	45
590	24p. "Sheepdog Trials" (Rebecca Edwards)	60	70
591	29p. "Horse Racing" (Dilys Blackley)	70	80
592	45p. "Sack Race" (Donna Newell)	1·00	1·10
587/92		*Set of* 6	3·00	3·25

(Des C. Collins. Litho B.D.T.)

1989 (8 Dec). *75th Anniv of Battle of the Falkland Islands and 50th Anniv of Battle of the River Plate. T* **163** *and similar vert designs. Multicoloured. W* w **16**. *P* 13½.

593	10p. Type **163**	40	30
594	24p. Vice-Admiral Graf von Spee and *Scharnhorst* (German cruiser)	80	75
595	29p. Commodore Harwood and H.M.S. *Ajax* (cruiser)	90	85
596	58p. Captain Langsdorff and *Admiral Graf Spee* (German pocket battleship)	1·75	2·00
593/6		*Set of* 4	3·50	3·50

164 Southern Sea Lions on Kidney Island

165 Supermarine Spitfire Mk 1 *Falkland Islands I*

(Des I. Strange. Litho Questa)

1990 (9 Apr). *Nature Reserves and Sanctuaries. T* **164** *and similar vert designs. Multicoloured. W* w **16**. *P* 14½.

597	12p. Type **164**	60	35
598	26p. Black-browed Albatrosses on Beauchene Island	1·40	70
599	31p. Penguin colony on Bird Island	1·40	90
600	62p. Tussock grass on Elephant Jason Island	1·50	1·75
597/600		*Set of* 4	4·50	3·25

(Des A. Theobald. Litho B.D.T.)

1990 (3 May). *"Stamp World London 90" International Stamp Exhibition, London. Presentation Spitfires. T* **165** *and similar horiz designs. Multicoloured. W* w **14** *(sideways). P* 14.

601	12p. Type **165**	65	35
602	26p. Supermarine Spitfire Mk 1 *Falkland Islands VII*	1·25	70
603	31p. Cockpit and wing of *Falkland Islands I*	1·25	1·00
604	62p. Squadron scramble, 1940	2·75	2·00
601/4		*Set of* 4	4·50	3·50
MS605	114×100 mm. £1 Supermarine Spitfire Mk 1 in action, 1940	4·00	2·50

For No. **MS**605 with additional inscription see No. **MS**628.

(Des D. Miller. Litho Questa)

1990 (4 Aug). *90th Birthday of Queen Elizabeth the Queen Mother. Vert designs as T* **134** (26p.) *or* **135** (£1) *of Ascension. W* w **16**. *P* 14×15 (26p.) *or* 14½ (£1).

606	26p. multicoloured	1·00	65
607	£1 brownish black and deep carmine-red	2·75	2·75

Designs:—26p. Queen Mother in Dover; £1 On bridge of liner *Queen Elizabeth*, 1946.

166 Black-browed Albatrosses

167 *Gavilea australis*

(Des I. Strange. Litho Questa)

1990 (3 Oct). *Black-browed Albatross. T* **166** *and similar vert designs. Multicoloured. W* w **16**. *P* 13½×14.

608	12p. Type **166**	75	50
609	26p. Female with egg	1·40	1·00
610	31p. Adult and chick	1·60	1·25
611	62p. Black-browed Albatross in flight	2·75	3·00
608/11		*Set of* 4	6·00	5·25

1991 (7 Jan). *As Nos.* 568/9, 572, 575 *and* 580, *but W* w **16** *(sideways on horiz designs) and with "1991" imprint date added at foot. P* 14.

613	2p. *Priwall* (barque) (*vert*)	60	80
614	3p. *Passat* (barque)	60	80
617	6p. *Mozart* (barquentine)	70	80
620	9p. *Fennia* (barque)	80	90
625	£1 *Criccieth Castle* (full-rigged ship)	2·75	3·50
613/25		*Set of* 5	5·00	6·00

(Des A. Theobald. Litho B.D.T.)

1991 (18 Mar). *Second Visit of H.R.H. The Duke of Edinburgh. As No.* **MS**605, *but with Exhibition emblem replaced by* "SECOND VISIT OF HRH THE DUKE OF EDINBURGH". *W* w **16** *(sideways). P* 14.

MS628	114×100 mm. £1 Spitfire Mk. I in action, 1940	5·50	7·00

The margin of No. **MS**628 also shows the Exhibition emblem omitted and has the same commemorative inscription added.

(Des I. Strange. Litho Questa)

1991 (18 Mar). *Orchids. T* **167** *and similar vert designs. Multicoloured. W* w **14**. *P* 14×13½.

629	12p. Type **167**	75	70
630	26p. Dog Orchid	1·25	1·00
631	31p. *Chlorea gaudichaudii*	1·40	1·50
632	62p. Yellow Orchid	2·50	3·75
629/32		*Set of* 4	5·50	6·25

168 Heads of Two King Penguins

169 ½d and 2½d Stamps of September 1891

(Des I. Strange. Litho Questa)

1991 (26 Aug). *Endangered Species. King Penguin. T* **168** *and similar vert designs. Multicoloured. W* w **16**. *P* 14.

633	2p. Type **168**	70	70
634	6p. Female incubating egg	90	90
635	12p. Female with two chicks	1·25	1·00
636	20p. Penguin underwater	1·50	1·25
637	31p. Parents feeding their chick	1·60	1·90
638	62p. Courtship dance	2·25	2·75
633/8		*Set of* 6	7·50	7·75

Nos. 637/8 do not include the W.W.F. panda emblem.

(Des D. Miller. Litho Questa)

1991 (10 Sept). *Centenary of Bisected Surcharges. T* **169** *and similar horiz designs. Multicoloured. W* w **16** *(sideways). P* 14½.

639	12p. Type **169**	60	50
640	26p. Cover of March 1891 franked with strip of five ½d bisects	1·00	1·00
641	31p. Unsevered pair of ½d. surcharge	1·25	1·50
642	62p. *Isis* (mail ship)	2·00	3·25
639/42		*Set of* 4	4·25	5·50

(Des R. Watton. Litho Walsall)

1991 (12 Dec). *500th Anniv of Discovery of America by Columbus and Re-enactment Voyages. Horiz designs as T* **144** *of Ascension. Multicoloured. W* w **14** *(sideways). P* 13½×14.

643	14p. Map of re-enactment voyages and *Eye of the Wind* (cadet brig)	60	60
644	29p. Compass rose and *Soren Larsen* (cadet brigantine)	1·25	1·40
645	34p. *Santa Maria*, *Pinta* and *Nina*	1·50	1·75
646	68p. Columbus and *Santa Maria*	2·50	4·00
643/6		*Set of* 4	5·25	7·00

(Des D. Miller. Litho Questa (68p.), Walsall (others))

1992 (6 Feb). *40th Anniv of Queen Elizabeth II's Accession. Horiz designs as T* **143** *of Ascension. Multicoloured. W* w **14** *(sideways). P* 14.

647	7p. "Stanley through the Narrows" (A. Asprey)	45	35
648	14p. "Hill Cove" (A. Asprey)	70	60
649	29p. "San Carlos Water" (A. Asprey)	1·10	95
650	34p. Three portraits of Queen Elizabeth	1·25	1·25
651	68p. Queen Elizabeth II	1·75	2·00
647/51		*Set of* 5	4·75	4·75

170 Laying Foundation Stone, 1890

171 Captain John Davis and Backstaff

(Des N. Shewring. Litho Questa)

1992 (21 Feb). *Centenary of Christ Church Cathedral, Stanley. T* **170** *and similar multicoloured designs. W* w **16** *(sideways on* 68p.*). P* 14½.

652	14p. Type **170**	75	55
653	29p. Interior of Cathedral, 1920	1·40	1·00
654	34p. Bishop's chair	1·60	1·25
655	68p. Cathedral in 1900 (*horiz*)	2·00	1·90
652/5		*Set of* 4	5·25	4·25

(Des N. Shewring. Litho Questa)

1992 (14 June). *10th Anniv of Liberation. Square designs as T **146** of Ascension. Multicoloured. W w **14** (sideways). P 14.*

656	14p. + 6p. San Carlos Cemetery		75	1·25
657	29p. + 11p. War Memorial, Port Stanley		1·40	1·75
658	34p. + 16p. South Atlantic medal		1·60	1·90
659	68p. + 32p. Government House, Port Stanley		2·75	3·00
656/9		*Set of 4*	6·00	7·00
MS660	115×115 mm. Nos. 656/9		6·00	7·00

The premiums on Nos. 656/60 were for the S.S.A.F.A.

(Des R. Watton. Litho Questa)

1992 (14 Aug). *400th Anniv of First Sighting of the Falkland Islands. T **171** and similar horiz designs. Multicoloured. W w **14** (sideways). P 14½.*

661	22p. Type **171**		1·25	80
662	29p. Capt. John Davis		1·50	1·10
663	34p. Queen Elizabeth I and Queen Elizabeth II		1·75	1·50
664	68p. *Desire* sighting Falkland Islands		2·75	3·00
661/4		*Set of 4*	6·50	5·75

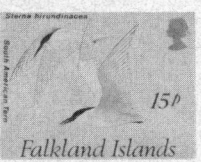

172 Private, Falkland Islands Volunteers, 1892

173 South American Tern

(Des C. Collins. Litho Questa)

1992 (1 Oct). *Centenary of Falkland Islands Defence Force and 50th Anniv of Affiliation to West Yorkshire Regiment. T **172** and similar vert designs. Multicoloured. W w **14**. P 14.*

665	7p. Type **172**		45	30
666	14p. Officer, Falkland Islands Defence Corps, 1914		70	50
667	22p. Officer, Falkland Islands Defence Force, 1920		90	70
668	29p. Private, Falkland Islands Defence Force, 1939–45		1·10	90
669	34p. Officer, West Yorkshire Regiment, 1942		1·40	1·25
670	68p. Private, West Yorkshire Regiment, 1942		2·40	2·10
665/70		*Set of 6*	6·25	5·25

(Des I. Strange. Litho Questa)

1993 (2 Jan). *Gulls and Terns. T **173** and similar horiz designs. Multicoloured. W w **16** (sideways). P 14×14½.*

671	15p. Type **173**		85	75
672	31p. Brown-hooded Gull ("Pink breasted Gull")		1·40	1·25
673	36p. Magellan Gull		1·60	1·75
674	72p. Southern Black-backed Gull ("Dominican Gull")		2·75	4·00
671/4		*Set of 4*	6·00	7·00

174 *Queen Elizabeth 2*

(Des N. Shewring. Litho Questa)

1993 (22 Jan). *Visit of the Queen Elizabeth 2 (cruise liner). Sheet 60×42 mm. W w **14** (sideways). P 14.*

MS675	**174** £2 multicoloured		5·25	5·50

(Des A. Theobald. Litho Questa)

1993 (1 Apr). *75th Anniv of Royal Air Force. Horiz designs as T **149** of Ascension. Multicoloured. W w **14** (sideways*). P 14.*

676	15p. Avro Vulcan B.1A		65	85
677	15p. Lockheed C-130K Hercules		65	85
678	15p. Boeing-Vertol CH-47 Chinook		65	85
679	15p. Lockheed L-1011 TriStar 500		65	85
676/9		*Set of 4*	2·40	3·00
MS680	110×77 mm. 36p. Hawker Siddeley Andover CC.2; 36p. Westland Wessex HC-2 helicopter; 36p. Panavia Tornado F Mk 3; 36p. McDonnell Douglas F-4M Phantom II		3·75	4·75
	w. Wmk Crown to right of CA			

*The normal sideways watermark shows Crown to left of CA, as seen from the back of the stamp.

175 Short-finned Squid

176 *Great Britain* in Dry Dock, Bristol

(Des O. Ball. Litho Questa)

1993 (1 July). *Fisheries. T **175** and similar horiz designs. Multicoloured. W w **16** (sideways). P 14.*

681	15p. Type **175**		60	60
682	31p. Catch of Whip-tailed Hake		1·25	1·40
683	36p. *Falklands Protector* (fisheries patrol vessel)		1·50	1·75
684	72p. Britten Norman Islander patrol aircraft and *Pomorze* (fish factory ship)		2·25	4·00
681/4		*Set of 4*	5·00	7·00

(Des O. Ball. Litho Questa)

1993 (19 July). *150th Anniv of Launch of Great Britain (liner). T **176** and similar vert design. Multicoloured. W w **16**. P 14×13½.*

685	8p. Type **176**		50	50
686	£1 *Great Britain* at sea		2·75	4·00

177 *Explorer* (liner)

178 Pony

(Des N. Shewring. Litho Questa)

1993 (1 Oct). *Tourism. T **177** and similar horiz designs. Multicoloured. W w **14** (sideways). P 14.*

687	16p. Type **177**		75	60
688	34p. Rockhopper Penguins		1·50	1·25
689	39p. *World Discoverer* (liner)		1·75	1·75
690	78p. *Columbus Caravelle* (liner)		2·25	2·75
687/90		*Set of 4*	5·50	5·75

(Des E. Tenney. Litho Walsall)

1993 (1 Dec). *Pets. T **178** and similar multicoloured designs. W w **16** (sideways on 8p., 16p., 34p.; inverted on 39p.). P 14×14½ (horiz) or 14½×14 (vert).*

691	8p. Type **178**		60	60
692	16p. Lamb		75	75
693	34p. Puppy and cat		1·75	1·75
694	39p. Kitten (*vert*)		2·00	2·00
695	78p. Collie dog (*vert*)		2·75	4·00
691/5		*Set of 5*	7·00	8·25

1994 (18 Feb). *"Hong Kong '94" International Stamp Exhibition. Nos. 691/5 additionally inscribed with the exhibition logo as T **154** of Ascension.*

696	8p. Type **178**		50	60
697	16p. Lamb		65	75
698	34p. Puppy and cat		1·50	1·75
699	39p. Kitten (*vert*)		1·60	2·00
700	78p. Collie dog (*vert*)		2·50	4·00
696/700		*Set of 5*	6·00	8·25

On the vertical designs "FALKLAND ISLANDS" ranges left instead of being centred as on Nos. 694/5.

179 Goose Barnacles

180 Dockyard Blacksmith's Shop and Sir James Clark Ross (explorer)

(Des T. Chater. Litho Walsall)

1994 (4 Apr). *Inshore Marine Life. T **179** and similar multicoloured designs. W w **16** (sideways on horiz designs). P 14.*

701	1p. Type **179**		40	50
702	2p. Painted Shrimp (*horiz*)		50	50
703	8p. Patagonian Copper Limpet (*horiz*)		75	75
704	9p. Eleginops ("Mullet") (*horiz*)		75	75
705	10p. Sea Anemones (*horiz*)		75	60
706	20p. Flathead Eelpout (*horiz*)		1·25	1·25
707	25p. Spider Crab (*horiz*)		1·25	90
708	50p. Lobster Krill (*horiz*)		2·25	2·00
709	80p. Falkland Skate (*horiz*)		2·50	2·50

710	£1 Centollón Crab (*horiz*)		2·50	2·50
711	£3 Wilton's Notothen ("Rock Cod") (*horiz*)		7·50	6·25
712	£5 Octopus		11·00	10·50
701/12		*Set of 12*	28·00	26·00

A similar 5p. value, showing a smelt and incorrectly inscribed "Austro Menidia Smithii", was withdrawn before issue.

For miniature sheet containing £1, wmk w **14** and with imprint date, see No. **MS784**.

(Des J. Peck. Litho Questa)

1994 (1 July). *150th Anniv of Founding of Stanley. T **180** and similar horiz designs. Multicoloured. W w **14** (sideways). P 14.*

713	9p. Type **180**		50	50
714	17p. 21 Fitzroy Road (home of Chaplain James Moody)		75	60
715	30p. Stanley Cottage (built by Dr. Henry Hamblin)		1·25	1·25
716	35p. Pioneer Row and Sgt-maj Henry Felton		1·50	1·75
717	40p. Government House (designed by Governor R. Moody)		1·60	1·90
718	65p. View of Stanley and Edward Stanley, Earl of Derby (Secretary of State for the Colonies)		2·25	3·00
713/18		*Set of 6*	7·00	8·00

181 Lockheed L-1011 TriStar over Gypsy Cove

(Des J. Peck. Litho Walsall)

1994 (24 Oct). *Falkland Beaches. T **181** and similar horiz designs. Multicoloured. W w **16** (sideways). P 14.*

719	17p. Type **181**		85	70
720	35p. *Explorer* (liner) off Sea Lion Island		1·60	1·40
721	40p. Britten Norman Islander aircraft at Pebble Island		2·00	2·00
722	65p. Landrover at Volunteer Beach		2·25	3·50
719/22		*Set of 4*	6·00	7·00

182 Mission House, Keppel Island

183 *Lupinus arboreus*

(Des G. Vasarhelyi. Litho Questa)

1994 (1 Dec). *150th Anniv of South American Missionary Society. T **182** and similar horiz designs. Multicoloured. W w **16** (sideways). P 14.*

723	5p. Type **182**		35	40
724	17p. Thomas Bridges (compiler of Yahgan dictionary)		65	65
725	40p. Fuegian Indians		1·40	1·75
726	65p. Capt. Allen Gardiner and *Allen Gardiner* (schooner)		1·75	2·50
723/6		*Set of 4*	3·75	4·75

(Des I. Strange. Litho Questa)

1995 (3 Jan). *Flowering Shrubs. T **183** and similar vert designs. Multicoloured. W w **16**. P 14½×14.*

727	9p. Type **183**		50	50
728	17p. *Hebe elliptica*		70	70
729	30p. *Fuschia magellanica*		95	95
730	35p. *Berberis ilicifolia*		1·10	1·10
731	40p. *Ulex europaeus*		1·25	1·25
732	65p. *Hebe x franciscana*		2·00	2·75
727/32		*Set of 6*	6·00	6·50

184 Magellanic Oystercatcher

(Des I. Strange. Litho B.D.T.)

1995 (1 Mar). *Shore Birds. T **184** and similar horiz designs. Multicoloured. W w **16** (sideways). P 13½.*

733	17p. Type **184**		1·00	70
734	35p. Rufous-chested Dotterel		1·60	1·40
735	40p. Blackish Oystercatcher		1·75	1·75
736	65p. Two-banded Plover		3·00	4·00
733/6		*Set of 4*	6·50	7·00

(Des R. Watton. Litho Questa)

1995 (8 May). *50th Anniv of End of Second World War. Multicoloured designs as T 161 of Ascension. W w 14 (sideways). P 14.*

737	17p.	Falkland Islands contingent in Victory Parade	75	75
738	35p.	Governor Sir Alan Cardinall on Bren gun-carrier	1·40	1·40
739	40p.	H.M.A.S. *Esperance Bay* (troopship)	1·50	1·75
740	65p.	H.M.S. *Exeter* (cruiser)	2·75	3·75
737/40		*Set of 4*	5·75	7·00
MS741	75×85 mm. £1 Reverse of 1939–45 War Medal (*vert*). Wmk upright		2·50	3·50

185 Ox and Cart   186 Kelp Geese

(Des N. Shewring. Litho B.D.T.)

1995 (1 Aug). *Transporting Peat. T 185 and similar horiz designs. Multicoloured. W w 16 (sideways). P 14.*

742	17p.	Type 185	60	50
743	35p.	Horse and cart	1·10	1·10
744	40p.	Caterpillar tractor pulling sleigh	1·25	1·25
745	65p.	Lorry	2·25	3·00
742/5		*Set of 4*	4·75	5·25

(Des Sonia Felton. Litho B.D.T.)

1995 (11 Sept). *Wildlife. T 186 and similar vert designs. Multicoloured. W w 16. P 13½.*

746	35p.	Type 186	1·10	1·10
		a. Sheetlet. Nos. 746/51	5·75	
747	35p.	Black-browed Albatross	1·10	1·10
748	35p.	Blue-eyed Cormorants	1·10	1·10
749	35p.	Magellanic Penguins	1·10	1·10
750	35p.	Fur Seals	1·10	1·10
751	35p.	Rockhopper Penguins	1·10	1·10
746/51		*Set of 6*	5·75	5·75

Nos. 746/51 were printed together, *se-tenant*, in sheetlets of 6, with the backgrounds forming a composite design.

187 Cottontail Rabbit

(Des A. Robinson. Litho Walsall)

1995 (6 Nov). *Introduced Wild Animals. T 187 and similar horiz designs. Multicoloured. W w 14 (sideways). P 14.*

752	9p.	Type 187	65	65
753	17p.	Brown Hare	90	75
754	35p.	Guanacos	1·40	1·25
755	40p.	Fox	1·60	1·40
756	65p.	Otter	2·50	2·50
752/6		*Set of 5*	6·25	5·50

188 Princess Anne and Government House

(Des D. Miller. Litho Walsall)

1996 (30 Jan). *Royal Visit. T 188 and similar horiz designs. Multicoloured. W w 14 (sideways). P 14½×14.*

757	9p.	Type 188	45	45
758	19p.	Falklands War Memorial, San Carlos Cemetery	75	65
759	30p.	Christ Church Cathedral	1·10	1·10
760	73p.	Helicopter over Goose Green	2·50	3·00
757/60		*Set of 4*	4·25	4·75

(Des D. Miller. Litho B.D.T.)

1996 (21 Apr). *70th Birthday of Queen Elizabeth II. Vert designs as T 165 of Ascension, each incorporating a different photograph of the Queen. W w 14. P 13½.*

761	17p.	Steeple Jason	60	50
762	40p.	*Tamar* (container ship)	1·50	1·25
763	45p.	New Island	1·50	1·40
764	65p.	Falkland Islands Community School	1·60	1·60
761/4		*Set of 4*	4·75	4·25
MS765	64×66 mm. £1 Queen Elizabeth II		2·40	3·00

189 Mounted Postman, *c.* 1890

(Des A. Theobald. Litho Walsall)

1996 (8 June). *"CAPEX '96" International Stamp Exhibition, Toronto. Mail Transport. T 189 and similar horiz designs. Multicoloured. W w 16 (sideways). P 14.*

766	9p.	Type 189	75	60
767	40p.	Noorduyn Norseman V seaplane	1·75	1·50
768	45p.	*Forrest* (freighter) at San Carlos	1·75	1·60
769	76p.	De Havilland D.H.C.2 Beaver seaplane	2·75	2·75
766/9		*Set of 4*	6·25	5·75
MS770	110×80 mm. £1 L.M.S. Class "Jubilee" steam locomotive No. 5606 *Falkland Islands* (47×31 *mm*). P 13½×14		2·40	3·25

190 Southern Bottlenose Whale

(Des E. King. Litho Walsall)

1996 (2 Sept). *Beaked Whales. T 190 and similar horiz designs. Multicoloured. W w 14 (sideways). P 13½×14.*

771	9p.	Type 190	45	45
772	30p.	Cuvier's Beaked Whale	1·10	1·10
773	35p.	Straptoothed Beaked Whale	1·25	1·25
774	75p.	Gray's Beaked Whale	2·40	2·40
771/4		*Set of 4*	4·75	4·75

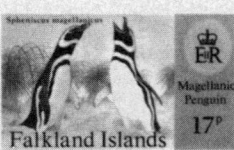

191 Magellanic Penguins performing Courtship Dance

(Des I. Strange. Litho Walsall)

1997 (2 Jan). *Magellanic Penguins. T 191 and similar horiz designs. Multicoloured. W w 14 (sideways). P 14½.*

775	17p.	Type 191	65	55
776	35p.	Penguin in burrow	1·25	1·00
777	40p.	Adult and chick	1·40	1·25
778	65p.	Group of Penguins swimming	1·75	1·75
775/8		*Set of 4*	4·50	4·00

192 Black Pejerry   193 Coral Fern

(Des T. Chater and D. Miller. Litho Questa)

1997 (3 Feb). *"HONG KONG '97" International Stamp Exhibition. Sheet 130×90 mm. W w 14 (sideways). P 14.*

MS779	192 £1 multicoloured	2·50	2·50

(Des I. Strange. Litho Walsall)

1997 (3 Mar). *Ferns. T 193 and similar vert designs. Multicoloured. W w 14. P 14½.*

780	17p.	Type 193	70	45
781	35p.	Adder's Tongue Fern	1·25	1·00
782	40p.	Fuegian Tall Fern	1·40	1·10
783	65p.	Small Fern	1·75	1·75
780/3		*Set of 4*	4·50	3·75

(Des T. Chater. Litho Walsall)

1997 (20 June). *Return of Hong Kong to China. Sheet 130×90 mm, containing design as No. 710. With imprint date. W w 14 (sideways). P 14.*

MS784	£1 Centollón Crab	2·50	2·50

COVER PRICES

Cover factors are quoted at the beginning of each country for most issues to 1945. An explanation of the system can be found on page x. The factors quoted do not, however, apply to philatelic covers.

(Des N. Shewring (No. MS791), D. Miller (others). Litho Questa)

1997 (10 July). *Golden Wedding of Queen Elizabeth and Prince Philip. Multicoloured designs as T 173 of Ascension. W w 16. P 14½.*

785	9p.	Queen Elizabeth holding bouquet, 1993	50	40
		a. Horiz pair. Nos. 785/6	1·00	80
786	9p.	Prince Philip and horse, 1985	50	40
787	17p.	Queen Elizabeth in phaeton at Trooping the Colour, 1996	80	65
		a. Horiz pair. Nos. 787/8	1·60	1·25
788	17p.	Prince Philip in R.A.F. uniform	80	65
789	40p.	Queen Elizabeth wearing red coat, 1986	1·00	1·00
		a. Horiz pair. Nos. 789/90	2·00	2·00
790	40p.	Prince William and Princess Beatrice on horseback	1·00	1·00
785/90		*Set of 6*	4·25	3·50
MS791	110×71 mm. £1.50, Queen Elizabeth and Prince Philip in landau (*horiz*). W w 14 (sideways). P 14×14½		3·50	3·50

Nos. 785/6, 787/8 and 789/90 were each printed together, *se-tenant*, in horizontal pairs throughout the sheets with the backgrounds forming composite designs.

194 Bull Point Lighthouse

(Des J. Peck. Litho Walsall)

1997 (4 Aug*). *Lighthouses. T 194 and similar horiz designs. Multicoloured. W w 14 (sideways). P 14.*

792	9p.	Type 194	60	40
793	30p.	Cape Pembroke Lighthouse	1·25	1·25
794	£1	Cape Meredith Lighthouse	2·75	3·00
792/4		*Set of 3*	4·25	4·25

*This is the local date of issue. The Crown Agents released the stamps in London on 4 July.

195 Forster's Caracara   196 Merryweather and Son Greenwich Gem Fire Engine

(Des Sonia Felton. Litho Questa)

1997 (6 Oct). *Endangered Species. T 195 and similar horiz designs. Multicoloured. W w 16 (sideways). P 14½.*

795	17p.	Type 195	90	65
796	19p.	Southern Sealion	90	75
797	40p.	Felton's Flower	1·50	1·50
798	73p.	Trout	2·50	3·00
795/8		*Set of 4*	5·25	5·50

(Des N. Shewring. Litho Questa)

1998 (26 Feb). *Centenary of Falkland Islands Fire Service. T 196 and similar vert designs. Multicoloured. W w 16. P 14½×14.*

799	9p.	Type 196	55	45
800	17p.	Merryweather's Hatfield trailer pump	80	60
801	40p.	Coventry Climax Godiva trailer pump	1·50	1·50
802	65p.	Carmichael Bedford "Type B" water tender	2·25	2·50
799/802		*Set of 4*	4·50	4·50

(Des D. Miller. Litho Questa)

1998 (31 Mar). *Diana, Princess of Wales Commemoration. Vert designs as T 177 of Ascension. W w 14 (sideways). P 14½×14.*

MS803	145×70 mm. 30p. Wearing black jacket, 1990; 30p. Wearing red dress, 1988; 30p. Resting head on hand, 1991; 30p. Wearing landmine protection clothing, Angola (*sold at £1.20 + 20p. charity premium*)	3·25	3·25

197 Tawny-throated Dotterel   198 *Penelope* (auxiliary ketch)

(Des A. Robinson. Litho Questa)

1998 (14 July). *Rare Visiting Birds. T 197 and similar horiz designs. Multicoloured. W w 14. P 14.*

(a) Designs 39½×23½ mm

804	1p.	Type 197	10	10
805	2p.	Hudsonian Godwit	10	10
806	5p.	Eared Dove	10	10
807	9p.	Great Grebe	20	25

808	10p.	Chilian Lapwing ("Southern Lapwing")	20	25
809	16p.	Buff-necked Ibis	30	35
810	30p.	Ashy-headed Goose	60	65
811	65p.	Red-legged Cormorant ("Red-legged Shag")	1·25	1·40
812	88p.	Argentine Shoveler ("Red Shoveler")	1·75	1·90
813	£1	Red-fronted Coot	2·00	2·10
814	£3	Chilian Flamingo	6·00	6·25
815	£5	Fork-tailed Flycatcher	10·00	10·50

(b) *Booklet stamps. Designs 35×22 mm*

816	9p.	Roseate Spoonbill	20	25
	a.	Booklet pane. Nos. 816×2, 817×8 and 2 stamp-size labels	3·00	
817	17p.	Austral Conure ("Austral Parakeet")	35	40
818	35p.	American Kestrel	70	75
	a.	Booklet pane. No. 818×6	4·00	
804/18		*Set of 15*	23·00	24·00

(Des R. Yssel. Litho Questa)

1998 (30 Sept). *Local Vessels. T* **198** *and similar multicoloured designs. W w* **14** *(sideways). P* 14.

819	17p.	Type **198**	65	55
820	35p.	*Ilen* (auxiliary ketch)	1·25	1·25
821	40p.	*Weddell* (schooner)	1·40	1·40
822	65p.	*Lively* (tug) (31×22 *mm*)	1·90	2·00
819/22		*Set of 4*	4·75	4·75

199 First Medivac Air Ambulance Service, 1948   **200** Marine at Port Egmont, Saunders Island, 1766

(Des N. Shewring. Litho Questa)

1998 (30 Oct). *50th Anniv of Falkland Islands Government Air Service. T* **199** *and similar horiz design. Multicoloured. W w* **14** *(sideways). P* 14.

823	17p.	Type **199**	60	50
824	£1	F.I.G.A.S. Beaver and Islander aircraft over map	2·50	2·50

(Des V. Ambrus. Litho Walsall)

1998 (8 Dec). *Royal Marine Uniforms. T* **200** *and similar vert designs. Multicoloured. W w* **14**. *P* 14½×14.

825	17p.	Type **200**	55	55
826	30p.	Officer at Port Louis, East Falklands, 1833	85	85
827	35p.	Corporal and H.M.S. *Kent* (cruiser), 1914	90	90
828	65p.	Bugler at Government House, 1976	1·75	2·00
825/8		*Set of 4*	3·50	3·75

201 Altar, St. Mary's Church

(Des J. Peck. Litho Walsall)

1999 (12 Feb). *Centenary of St. Mary's Roman Catholic Church, Stanley. T* **201** *and similar horiz designs. Multicoloured. W w* **16** *(sideways). P* 14.

829	17p.	Type **201**	45	45
830	40p.	St. Mary's Church	1·00	1·10
831	75p.	Laying of foundation stone, 1899	1·75	2·10
829/31		*Set of 3*	2·75	3·25

202 H.M.S. *Beagle* (Darwin)   **203** Prince of Wales (from photo by Clive Arrowsmith)

(Des R. Watton. Litho Walsall)

1999 (5 Mar). *"Australia '99" World Stamp Exhibition, Melbourne. Maritime History. T* **202** *and similar horiz designs. Multicoloured. W w* **16** *(sideways). P* 14.

832	25p.	Type **202**	70	70
833	35p.	H.M.A.S. *Australia* (battle cruiser)	90	90

834	40p.	*Canberra* (liner)	1·00	1·00
835	50p.	*Great Britain* (steam/sail)	1·25	1·50
	a.	Horiz pair. Nos. 835/6	2·50	3·00
836	50p.	All-England Cricket Team, 1861–62	1·25	1·50
832/6		*Set of 5*	4·50	5·00

Nos. 835/6 were printed together, *se-tenant*, in horizontal pairs throughout the sheet.

204 *Jeanne d'Arc* (French cruiser)   **205** Chiloe Wigeon

(Des and litho Walsall)

1999 (13 Mar). *Royal Visit. W w* **16**. *P* 14×13½.

837	**203**	£2 multicoloured	4·50	4·75

(Des D. Miller. Litho Walsall)

1999 (15 June). *Royal Wedding. Vert designs as T* **185** *of Ascension. Multicoloured. W w* **16**. *P* 14.

838	80p.	Photographs of Prince Edward and Miss Sophie Rhys-Jones	1·75	1·90
839	£1.20,	Engagement photograph	2·75	3·00

(Des J. Batchelor. Litho Questa)

1999 (21 June). *"PhilexFrance '99" International Stamp Exhibition, Paris. First Flight over Falkland Islands, 1931. T* **204** *and similar horiz designs. Multicoloured. W w* **14** *(sideways). P* 14.

840	35p.	Type **204**	90	90
841	40p.	CAMS 37 (flying boat) taking off	90	90
MS842		115×63 mm. £1 CAMS 37 over Port Stanley (47×31 *mm*). P 13½×14	2·25	2·25

(Des D. Miller. Litho Cartor)

1999 (18 Aug). *"Queen Elizabeth the Queen Mother's Century". Horiz designs as T* **187** *of Ascension. Multicoloured. W w* **16** *(sideways). P* 13½.

843	9p.	On board ship, Port of London, 1939	30	30
844	20p.	With Queen Elizabeth II, 1996	55	55
845	30p.	With Prince Charles and his sons, 1995	75	75
846	67p.	Presenting colours to Queen's Royal Hussars	1·75	1·75
843/6		*Set of 4*	3·00	3·00
MS847		145×70 mm. £1.40, Duchess of York, 1936, and Shackleton, Scott and Wilson in the Antarctic, 1902	3·50	3·75

(Des I. Strange. Litho Walsall)

1999 (9 Sept). *Waterfowl. T* **205** *and similar horiz designs. Multicoloured. W w* **16** *(sideways). P* 14×14½.

848	9p.	Type **205**	30	30
849	17p.	Crested Duck	55	55
850	30p.	Georgian Teal ("Brown Pintail")	75	75
851	35p.	Versicolor Teal ("Silver Teal")	80	80
852	40p.	Chilean Teal ("Yellow-billed Teal")	95	95
853	65p.	Falkland Islands Flightless Steamer Duck	1·60	1·60
848/53		*Set of 6*	4·50	4·50

206 Hulk of *Vicar of Bray*, 1999

(Litho Questa)

1999 (3 Nov). *150th Anniv of California Goldrush. T* **206** *and similar horiz designs. W w* **14** *(sideways). Multicoloured. P* 14.

854	9p.	Type **206**	40	40
855	35p.	Panning for gold, 1849	90	90
856	40p.	Gold rocking cradle, 1849	95	95
857	80p.	*Vicar of Bray* (barque) at sea, 1849	1·90	1·90
854/7		*Set of 4*	3·75	3·75
MS858		105×63 mm. £1 *Vicar of Bray* in San Francisco (47×31 *mm*). P 13½	2·00	2·10

207 Magellan Goose on Nest   **208** Princess Alexandra and Meadow

---

(Des A. Robinson. Litho Questa)

1999 (6 Dec). *New Millennium. T* **207** *and similar horiz designs. Multicoloured. W w* **14** *(sideways). P* 14½.

859	9p.	Type **207**	20	25
860	9p.	Kelp Gull at sunrise	20	25
861	9p.	Christ Church Cathedral, Stanley	20	25
862	30p.	Night Heron at sunset	60	65
863	30p.	Family and Christmas tree	60	65
864	30p.	King Penguins	60	65
859/64		*Set of 6*	2·40	2·75

(Des D. Miller. Litho Cartor)

2000 (1 Feb). *Visit of Princess Alexandra. T* **208** *and similar horiz design. Multicoloured. W w* **14** *(sideways). P* 13½.

865	9p.	Type **208**	20	25
866	$1	Princess Alexandra and plantation of saplings	2·00	2·10

(Des M. Skidmore. Litho Questa)

2000 (10 Feb). *Shackleton's Trans-Antarctic Expedition, 1914–17, Commemoration. Horiz designs as T* **63** *of British Antarctic Territory. W w* **14** *(sideways). P* 14.

867	17p.	multicoloured	35	40
868	45p.	grey-blue and black	90	95
869	75p.	multicoloured	1·50	1·75
867/9		*Set of 3*	2·75	3·00

Designs—17p., *Endurance* off Caird Coast; 45p., *Endurance* beset in the Weddell Sea pack-ice; 75p., Sir Ernest Shackleton and *Yelcho* (Chilean rescue tug).

(Des Crown Agents. Litho Walsall)

2000 (29 Feb). *"Stamp Show 2000" International Stamp Exhibition, London. Kings and Queens of England. Vert designs as T* **223** *of British Virgin Islands. Multicoloured. W w* **14**. *P* 14.

870	40p.	Queen Elizabeth I	80	85
	a.	Sheetlet. Nos. 870/5	4·75	
871	40p.	King James II	80	85
872	40p.	King George I	80	85
873	40p.	King William IV	80	85
874	40p.	King Edward VIII	80	85
875	40p.	Queen Elizabeth II	80	85
870/5		*Set of 6*	4·75	5·00

Nos. 870/5 were printed together, *se-tenant*, in sheetlets of 6 with an enlarged illustrated right-hand margin.

STAMP BOOKLETS

1977 (1 Nov). *Silver Jubilee. Multicoloured cover,* 117×79 *mm, showing* Norroy and Ulster King of Arms. *Stapled.*
SB1   £2 booklet containing 6p., 11p. and 33p., each in
     pane of 4 (Nos. 326a, 327a, 327ba)   ..   ..   10·00

1978 (27 Nov). *Mail Ships. Black and blue-green cover,* 99×57 *mm, showing* Hebe *on front and* Darwin *on back. Stapled.*
SB2   £1 booklet containing 1p., 3p., 5p., 6p., 10p. (Nos.
     331A, 333A, 335A/6A, 340A) each in block of 4   24·00

1979 (4 June). *Mail Ships. Black and bright new blue cover,* 99×57 *mm, showing* Nautilus *on front and* A.E.S. *on back. Stapled.*
SB3   £1 booklet. Contents as No. SB2   ..   ..   11·00

1980 (14 July). *Mail Ships. Black and red cover,* 100×59 *mm, showing* Amelia *on front and* Merak-N *on back. Stapled.*
SB4   £1 booklet. Contents as No. SB2   ..   5·50

1982 (23 Feb). *Mail Ships. Black and grey cover,* 99×58 *mm, showing* Fairy *on front and* Fitzroy *on back. Stapled.*
SB5   £1 booklet. Contents as No. SB2   ..   4·75

1985 (18 Feb). *Black and azure cover,* 95×64 *mm, with example of stamp No.* 471A *affixed. Stapled.*
SB6   £2.24, booklet containing eight 2p. and four each
     7p., 20p., 25p. (Nos. 470A, 475A, 479A, 480A)
     in blocks of 4   ..   ..   ..   21·00

1988 (2 Feb). *Black and greenish grey cover,* 95×64 *mm, with example of stamp No.* 470A *affixed. Stapled.*
SB7   £2.52, booklet containing eight 4p. and four each
     10p., 20p., 25p. (Nos. 472A, 478A/80A) in
     blocks of 4   ..   ..   ..   15·00

1988 (26 Sept). *Black and pale green cover,* 95×64 *mm, with example of stamp No.* 471A *affixed. Stapled.*
SB8   £2.52, booklet containing 1p., 4p., 6p., 8p., 9p.,
     10p., 25p. (Nos. 469A, 472A, 474A, 476A/8A,
     480A), each in block of 4   ..   7·00

1990 (29 Oct). *Cape Horn Sailing Ships. Black and greenish yellow showing No.* 575 *(No. SB9) or pale blue showing No.* 578 *(No. SB10) covers, each* 104×55 *mm. Panes attached by selvedge.*
SB9   60p. booklet containing 3p., 9p. (Nos. 569, 575),
     each in block of 5   ..   ..   7·50
SB10   £1.55, booklet containing 6p., 25p. (Nos. 572,
     578), each in block of 5   ..   ..   9·00

1998 (14 July). *Rare Visiting Birds. Multicoloured covers,* 86×52 *mm, showing* Roseate Spoonbill *(No. SB11) or* American Kestrel *(No. SB12). Panes attached by selvedge.*
SB11   £1.54, booklet containing pane of two 9p., eight
     17p. and 2 stamp-size labels (No. 816a)   3·00
SB12   £2.10, booklet containing pane of six 35p. (No.
     818a)   ..   ..   4·25

POSTAGE DUE STAMPS

D 1 King
Penguin

(Des O. Bell. Litho Questa)

1991 (7 Jan). *W w* 14 *(sideways). P* 15×14.
D1	D 1	1p. brown-lake and cerise	..	10	10
D2		2p. red-orange and pale orange	..	10	10
D3		3p. brown-ochre and chrome-yellow	..	10	10
D4		4p. deep blue-green & light blue-green		10	10
D5		5p. greenish blue & light greenish blue		10	15
D6		10p. deep violet-blue and cobalt	..	20	25
D7		20p. deep reddish violet and lilac	..	40	45
D8		50p. yellowish green and apple-green	..	1·00	1·10
D1/8	..	.. .. *Set of 8*		1·90	2·10

FALKLAND ISLANDS DEPENDENCIES

> **PRICES FOR STAMPS ON COVER TO 1945**
> Nos. A1/D8 *from* × 20

A. GRAHAM LAND

For use at Port Lockroy (established 16 February 1944) and Hope Bay (established 12 February 1945) bases.

Falkland Islands definitive stamps with face values of 1s. 3d. and above were valid for use from Graham Land in conjunction with Nos. A1/8 and subsequently Nos. G1/16.

Stamps of FALKLAND ISLANDS cancelled at Port Lockroy or Hope Bay with Graham Land circular datestamps between 16 February 1944 and 31 January 1954.

1938–50. *King George VI (Nos. 159/63).*

Z1	1s. 3d. black and carmine-red	..	..	75·00
Z2	2s. 6d. slate	..	..	30·00
Z3	5s. indigo and yellow-brown	..	..	£130
Z4	10s. black and orange	..	..	40·00
Z5	£1 black and violet	..	..	60·00

1952. *King George VI (Nos. 181/5).*

Z 6	1s. 3d. orange	..	..	
Z 7	2s. 6d. olive-green	..	..	
Z 8	5s. purple	..	..	
Z 9	10s. grey	..	..	
Z10	£1 black	..	..	

GRAHAM LAND

DEPENDENCY OF
(A 1)

1944 (12 Feb)–45. *Falkland Islands Nos. 146, 148, 150, 153/5, 157 and 158a optd with Type A 1, in red, by B.W.*

A1	½d. black and green		30	1·75
	a. *Blue-black and green*		£600	£375
A2	1d. black and violet		30	1·00
A3	2d. black and carmine-red		40	1·00
A4	3d. black and blue		30	1·00
A5	4d. black and purple		3·00	1·75
A6	6d. black and brown		14·00	2·25
	a. *Blue-black and brown* (24.9.45)		20·00	
A7	9d. black and grey-blue		1·00	1·25
A8	1s. deep blue		1·00	1·25
A1/8		*Set of 8*	18·00	10·00
A1/8 Perf "Specimen"		*Set of 8*	£325	

B. SOUTH GEORGIA

The stamps of Falkland Islands were used at the Grytviken whaling station on South Georgia from 3 December 1909.

Mr. J. Innes Wilson, the Stipendiary Magistrate whose duties included those of postmaster, was issued with a stock of stamps, values ½d. to 5s., together with an example of the current "FALKLAND ISLANDS" circular datestamp. This was used to cancel the stamps, but, as it gave no indication that mail had originated at South Georgia, a straight-line handstamp inscribed "SOUTH GEORGIA", or subsequently "South Georgia", was also supplied. It was intended that this should be struck directly on to each letter or card below the stamp, but it can sometimes be found struck across the stamp instead.

The use of the "South Georgia" handstamp continued after the introduction of the "SOUTH GEORGIA" circular datestamp in June 1910 apparently for philatelic purposes, but no example has been reported used after June 1912.

SOUTH GEORGIA.
Z 1

South Georgia.
Z 2

		On piece	On cover /card
ZU1	Example of Type Z 1 used in conjunction with "FALKLAND ISLANDS" postmark (22 Dec 1909 to 30 March 1910) *Price from*	£1000	£3750
ZU2	Example of Type Z 2 used in conjunction with "FALKLAND ISLANDS" postmark (May 1910) .. *Price from*	£750	£3000
ZU3	Example of Type Z 2 used in conjunction with "SOUTH GEORGIA" postmark (June 1910 to June 1912) .. *Price from*	£250	£900

Stamps of FALKLAND ISLANDS cancelled at Grytviken with South Georgia circular datestamps between June 1910 and 31 January 1954.

1891–1902. *Queen Victoria (Nos. 32, 36 and 38).*

Z11	4d. olive-black	..	..	£140
Z12	9d. salmon	..	..	£140
Z13	1s. yellow-brown	..	..	£150

1904–12. *King Edward VII (Nos. 43/50).*

Z14	½d. green	..	..	11·00
Z15	1d. vermilion	..	..	11·00
	d. *Dull coppery red (on thick paper)*			35·00
Z16	2d. purple	..	..	50·00
	b. *Reddish purple*	..	..	£275

Z17	2½d. ultramarine	..	..	20·00
	b. *Deep blue*	..	..	£180
Z18	6d. orange	..	..	£100
Z19	1s. brown	..	..	£100
Z20	3s. green	..	..	£200
Z21	5s. red	..	..	£250

SOUTH GEORGIA PROVISIONAL HANDSTAMPS. During October 1911 the arrival of the German South Polar Expedition at Grytviken, South Georgia, resulted in the local supply of stamps becoming exhausted. The Acting Magistrate, Mr. E. B. Binnie, who was also responsible for the postal facilities, produced a handstamp reading "Paid at (or At) SOUTH GEORGIA" which, together with a manuscript indication of the postage paid and his signature, was used on mail from 18 October 1911 to January 1912. Further examples, signed by John Innes Wilson, are known from February 1912, but these may be philatelic.

PH1	"Paid 1 at SOUTH GEORGIA EBB" *Price on cover*	£4250
PH1a	"Paid 1 At SOUTH GEORGIA EBB" (16 Dec)	
	Price on cover	£4500
PH2	"Paid 2½ at SOUTH GEORGIA EBB" *Price on cover*	£4750
PH2a	"Paid 2½ At SOUTH GEORGIA EBB" (16 Dec)	
	Price on cover	£5250

1912–23. *King George V. Wmk Mult Crown CA (Nos. 60/9).*

Z22	½d. green	..	..	15·00
	a. *Perf 14 (line). Deep yellow-green*			35·00
	d. *Dull yellowish green (on thick greyish paper)*			30·00
Z23	1d. orange-red	..	..	10·00
	a. *Perf 14 (line). Orange-vermilion*			10·00
	d. *Orange-vermilion*			10·00
Z24	2d. maroon	..	..	40·00
Z25	2½d. deep bright blue	..	..	25·00
	c. *Deep blue*	..	..	25·00
Z26	6d. yellow-orange	..	..	50·00
	b. *Brown-orange*	..	..	45·00
	ba. *Bisected (diag) (3d.) (on cover)* (3.23)			£11000
Z27	1s. bistre-brown	..	..	£100
	b. *Brown (on thick greyish paper)*			£150
Z28	3s. slate-green	..	..	£150
Z29	5s. deep rose-red	..	..	£180
	a. *Reddish maroon*	..	..	£275
	b. *Maroon*	..	..	£225
Z30	10s. red/*green*	..	..	£300
Z31	£1 black/*red*	..	..	£450

1918–20. "WAR STAMP" *ovpts (Nos. 70/2).*

Z32	½d. deep olive	..	..	15·00
Z33	1d. vermilion	..	..	15·00
Z34	1s. light bistre-brown	..	..	80·00

1921–28. *King George V. Wmk Mult Script CA (Nos. 73/80).*

Z35	½d. yellowish green	..	..	5·00
Z36	1d. dull vermilion	..	..	4·00
Z37	2d. deep brown-purple	..	..	25·00
Z38	2½d. deep blue	..	..	22·00
	a. *Bisected (diag) (1d.) (on cover)* (3.23)			£7000
	b. *Prussian blue*	..	..	£450
Z39	2½d. deep purple/*pale yellow*			45·00
Z40	6d. yellow-orange	..	..	50·00
Z41	1s. deep ochre	..	..	60·00
Z42	3s. slate-green	..	..	£160

1928 PROVISIONAL. For listing of the 2½d. on 2d. surcharge issued at Grytviken on 7 February 1928 see No. 115 of Falkland Islands.

1929–36. *King George V. Whale and Penguins design (Nos. 116/26).*

Z43	½d. green	..	..	5·00
Z44	1d. scarlet	..	..	4·00
Z45	2d. grey	..	..	10·00
Z46	2½d. blue	..	..	4·00
Z47	4d. orange	..	..	20·00
Z48	6d. purple	..	..	30·00
Z49	1s. black/*emerald*	..	..	35·00
Z50	2s. 6d. carmine/*blue*	..	..	75·00
Z51	5s. green/*yellow*	..	..	£110
Z52	10s. carmine/*emerald*	..	..	£200
Z53	£1 black/*red*	..	..	£500

Examples of most values are known with forged postmarks dated "Au 30" in 1928, 1930 and 1931.

1933. *Centenary of British Administration (Nos. 127/38).*

Z54	½d. black and green	..	..	7·00
Z55	1d. black and scarlet	..	..	4·00
Z56	1½d. black and blue	..	..	16·00
Z57	2d. black and brown	..	..	26·00
Z58	3d. black and violet	..	..	17·00
Z59	4d. black and orange	..	..	19·00
Z60	6d. black and slate	..	..	70·00
Z61	1s. black and olive-green	..	..	65·00
Z62	2s. 6d. black and violet	..	..	£200
Z63	5s. black and yellow	..	..	£750
	a. *Black and yellow-orange*			£1400
Z64	10s. black and chestnut	..	..	£850
Z65	£1 black and carmine	..	..	£2250

1935. *Silver Jubilee (Nos. 139/42).*

Z66	1d. deep blue and scarlet	..	..	3·00
Z67	2½d. brown and deep blue	..	..	4·00
Z68	4d. green and indigo	..	..	5·00
Z69	1s. slate and purple	..	..	5·00

1937. *Coronation (Nos. 143/5).*

Z70	½d. green	..	..	2·00
Z71	1d. carmine	..	..	2·00
Z72	2½d. blue	..	..	2·00

1938–50. *King George VI (Nos. 146/63).*

Z73	½d. black and green	..	..	3·00
Z74	1d. black and carmine	..	..	5·00
	a. *Black and scarlet*	..	..	2·00
Z75	1d. black and violet	..	..	4·50
Z76	2d. black and deep violet	..	..	6·00
Z77	2d. black and carmine-red	..	..	7·00
Z78	2½d. black and bright blue (No. 151)			2·00
Z79	3d. black and blue	..	..	6·00
Z80	4d. black and purple	..	..	6·00
Z81	6d. black and brown	..	..	8·00
Z82	9d. black and grey-blue	..	..	10·00

Z83	1s. pale blue	..	..	30·00
	a. *Deep blue*	..	..	30·00
Z84	1s. 3d. black and carmine-red	..	..	30·00
Z85	2s. 6d. slate	..	..	20·00
Z86	5s. bright blue and pale brown	..	..	£100
	a. *Indigo and yellow-brown*	..	..	£130
	b. *Blue and buff-brown*	..	..	£200
Z87	10s. black and orange	..	..	40·00
Z88	£1 black and violet	..	..	60·00

Falkland Islands definitive stamps with values of 1s. 3d. and above continued to be valid from South Georgia after the introduction of Nos. B1/8 and subsequently Nos. G1/16.

1952. *King George VI (Nos. 181/5).*

Z89	1s. 3d. orange	..	..	25·00
Z90	2s. 6d. olive-green	..	..	
Z91	5s. purple	..	..	
Z92	10s. grey	..	..	
Z93	£1 black	..	..	

1944 (24 Feb)–45. *Falkland Islands Nos. 146, 148, 150, 153/5, 157 and 158a optd "SOUTH GEORGIA/DEPENDENCY OF", in red, as Type A 1 of Graham Land.*

B1	½d. black and green		30	1·75
	a. *Wmk sideways*		£2750	
B2	1d. black and violet		30	1·00
B3	2d. black and carmine-red		40	1·00
B4	3d. black and blue		30	1·00
B5	4d. black and purple		3·00	1·75
B6	6d. black and brown		14·00	2·25
	a. *Blue-black and brown* (24.9.45)		20·00	
B7	9d. black and grey-blue		1·00	1·25
B8	1s. deep blue		1·00	1·25
B1/8		*Set of 8*	18·00	10·00
B1/8 Perf "Specimen"		*Set of 8*	£325	

For later issues, see after No. G44.

C. SOUTH ORKNEYS

Used from the *Fitzroy* in February 1944 and at Laurie Island (established January 1946).

Falkland Islands definitive stamps with face values of 1s. 3d. and above were valid for use from the South Orkneys in conjunction with Nos. C1/8 and subsequently Nos. G1/16.

Stamps of FALKLAND ISLANDS cancelled on the Fitzroy, at Laurie Island or at Signy Island with South Orkneys circular datestamps between 21 February 1944 and 31 January 1954.

1938–50. *King George VI (Nos. 160/3).*

Z95	2s. 6d. slate	..	..	30·00
Z96	5s. indigo and yellow-brown	..	..	£130
Z97	10s. black and orange	..	..	40·00
Z98	£1 black and violet	..	..	60·00

1952. *King George VI (Nos. 181/5).*

Z 99	1s. 3d. orange	..	..	
Z100	2s. 6d. olive-green	..	..	
Z101	5s. purple	..	..	
Z102	10s. grey	..	..	
Z103	£1 black	..	..	

1944 (21 Feb)–45. *Falkland Islands Nos. 146, 148, 150, 153/5, 157 and 158a optd "SOUTH ORKNEYS/DEPENDENCY OF", in red, as Type A 1 of Graham Land.*

C1	½d. black and green		30	1·75
C2	1d. black and violet		30	1·00
	w. *Wmk inverted*		£3750	
C3	2d. black and carmine-red		40	1·00
C4	3d. black and blue		30	1·00
C5	4d. black and purple		3·00	1·75
C6	6d. black and brown		14·00	2·25
	a. *Blue-black and brown* (24.9.45)		20·00	
C7	9d. black and grey-blue		1·00	1·25
C8	1s. deep blue		1·00	1·25
C1/8		*Set of 8*	18·00	10·00
C1/8 Perf "Specimen"		*Set of 8*	£325	

D. SOUTH SHETLANDS

Postal facilities were first provided at the Port Foster whaling station on Deception Island for the 1912–13 whaling season and were available each year between November and the following April until March 1931.

No postmark was provided for the 1912–13 season and the local postmaster was instructed to cancel stamps on cover with a straight-line "PORT FOSTER" handstamp. Most letters so cancelled subsequently received a "FALKLAND ISLANDS" circular postmark dated between 19 and 28 March 1913. It is known that only low value stamps were available at Port Foster. Higher values, often with other "FALKLAND ISLANDS" postmark dates, were, it is believed, subsequently "made to order".

Stamps of FALKLAND ISLANDS cancelled at Port Foster, Deception Island with part of "PORT FOSTER" straight-line handstamp.

1904–12. *King Edward VII (Nos. 43/4).*

Z104	½d. deep yellow-green	..	..	£1200
Z105	1d. orange-vermilion	..	..	£1200

1912. *King George V. Wmk Mult Crown CA (No. 60).*

Z106	½d. yellow-green	..	..	£1200

Stamps of FALKLAND ISLANDS cancelled at Port Foster with part of oval "DECEPTION ISLAND SOUTH SHETLANDS" postmark in black or violet between 1914 and 1927.

1904–12. *King Edward VII (No. 43c).*

Z108	½d. deep yellow-green	..	..	£200

1912–20. *King George V. Wmk Mult Crown CA (Nos. 60/9).*

Z110	½d. yellow-green	..	..	75·00
Z111	1d. orange-red	..	..	75·00
Z112	2d. maroon	..	..	£100
Z113	2½d. deep bright blue	..	..	£100

Z114	6d. yellow-orange			£120
Z115	1s. light bistre-brown			£140
Z116	3s. slate-green			£300
Z117	5s. deep rose-red			£350
Z118	10s. red/green			£450
Z119	£1 black/red			£600

1918–20. "WAR STAMP" *ovpts* (*Nos.* 70/2).

Z120	½d. deep olive		£100
Z121	1d. vermilion		£100
Z122	1s. light bistre-brown		£200

1921–28. *King George V. Wmk Mult Script CA* (*Nos.* 73/80).

Z123	½d. yellowish green		£100
Z126	2½d. deep blue		£130
Z129	1s. deep ochre		£150

Stamps of FALKLAND ISLANDS *cancelled at Port Foster with* "SOUTH SHETLANDS" *circular datestamp between 1923 and March 1931*

1912–20. *King George V. Wmk Mult Crown CA* (*Nos.* 60/9).

Z130	1d. orange-vermilion		50·00
Z131	2d. deep reddish purple		60·00
Z132	2½d. deep bright blue		
Z133	6d. brown-orange		80·00
Z134	1s. bistre-brown		
Z135	3s. slate-green		£160
Z136	5s. maroon		£180
Z137	10s. red/green		£325
Z138	£1 black/red		£550

Examples of all values are known with forged postmarks dated "20 MR 27".

1918–20. "WAR STAMP" *ovpts* (*Nos.* 70/2).

Z139	1d. vermilion		
Z140	1s. light bistre brown		

1921–28. *King George V. Wmk Mult Script CA* (*Nos.* 73/80).

Z141	½d. yellowish green		35·00
Z142	1d. dull vermilion		35·00
Z143	2d. deep brown-purple		50·00
Z144	2½d. deep blue		40·00
Z145	2½d. deep purple/pale yellow		75·00
Z146	6d. yellow-orange		60·00
Z147	1s. deep ochre		60·00
Z148	3s. slate-green		£170

1929. *King George V. Whale and Penguins design* (*Nos.* 116/26).

Z149	½d. green		50·00
Z150	1d. scarlet		50·00
Z151	2d. grey		70·00
Z152	2½d. blue		60·00
Z153	6d. purple		80·00
Z154	1s. black/emerald		80·00
Z155	2s. 6d. carmine/blue		£120
Z156	5s. green/yellow		£130
Z157	10s. carmine/emerald		£275
Z158	£1 black/red		£600

The whaling station at Port Foster was abandoned at the end of the 1930–31 season.

It was reoccupied as a Falkland Islands Dependencies Survey base on 3 February 1944.

Falkland Islands definitive stamps with face values of 1s. 3d. and above were valid for use from the South Shetlands in conjunction with Nos. D1/8 and subsequently Nos. G1/16.

Stamps of FALKLAND ISLANDS *cancelled at Port Foster or Admiralty Bay with South Shetlands circular datestamps between 5 February 1944 and 31 January 1954*

1938–50. *King George VI* (*Nos.* 160/3).

Z159	2s. 6d. slate		30·00
Z160	5s. indigo and yellow-brown		£130
Z161	10s. black and orange		40·00
Z162	£1 black and violet		60·00

1952. *King George VI* (*Nos.* 181/5).

Z163	1s. 3d. orange		
Z164	2s. 6d. olive-green		
Z165	5s. purple		
Z166	10s. grey		
Z167	£1 black		

1944 (5 Feb)–**45.** *Falkland Islands Nos.* 146, 148, 150, 153/5, 157 *and* 158a *optd* "SOUTH SHETLANDS/DEPENDENCY OF", *in red, as Type A* **1** *of Graham Land.*

D1	½d. black and green		30	1·75
D2	1d. black and violet		30	1·00
D3	2d. black and carmine-red		40	1·00
D4	3d. black and blue		30	1·00
D5	4d. black and purple		3·00	1·75
D6	6d. black and brown		14·00	2·25
	a. Blue-black and brown (24.9.45)		20·00	
D7	9d. black and grey-blue		1·00	1·25
D8	1s. deep blue		1·00	1·25
D1/8		*Set of* 8	18·00	10·00
D1/8 Perf "Specimen"		*Set of* 8	£325	

From 12 July 1946 to 16 July 1963, Graham Land, South Georgia, South Orkneys and South Shetlands used FALKLAND ISLANDS DEPENDENCIES stamps.

E. FALKLAND ISLANDS DEPENDENCIES

For use at the following bases:

Adelaide Island (Graham Land) (*opened* 1961)
Admiralty Bay (South Shetlands) (*opened* January 1948, *closed* January 1961)
Anvers Island (Graham Land) (*opened* February 1955, *closed* 10 January 1958)
Argentine Islands (Graham Land) (*opened* 1947)
Danco Coast ("Base O") (Graham Land) (*opened* 30 March 1956, *closed* 1958)
Deception Island (South Shetlands)
Grytviken (South Georgia)
Halley Bay (Coats Land) (*opened* 1956)
Hope Bay (Graham Land) (*closed* 4 February 1949, *opened* February 1952)
Laurie Island (South Orkneys) (*closed* 1947)
Loubet Coast ("Base W") (Graham Land) (*opened* 1955, *closed* 1959)
Marguerite Bay (Graham Land) (*opened* March 1955, *closed* 1960)
Port Lockroy (Graham Land) (*closed* 16 January 1962)
Prospect Point ("Base J") (Graham Land) (*opened* 1956, *closed* 1958)
Shackleton (Coats Land) (*opened* 1956, *closed* 1957)
Signy Island (South Orkneys) (*opened* 1946)
Stonington Island (Graham Land) (*opened* 1946, *closed* 1950, *opened* 1958, *closed* 1959, *opened* 1960)

G 1

Extra island (Plate 1 R. 3/9)   "SOUTH POKE" flaw (Plate 2 R. 6/8)

Missing "I" in "S. Shetland Is." (Plate 1 R. 1/2)

Nos. G1/8

Nos. G9/16

On Nos. G9 to G16 the map is redrawn; the "o°" meridian does not pass through the "S" of "COATS", the "n" of "Alexander" is not joined to the "L" of "Land" below, and the loops of letters "s" and "t" are generally more open.

(Map litho, frame recess D.L.R.)

1946 (12 July*)–**49.** *Wmk Mult Script CA (sideways).* P 12.

(a) Map thick and coarse

G 1	G **1**	½d. black and green		1·00	2·25
		a. Extra island		65·00	
		b. Missing "I"		65·00	
		c. "SOUTH POKE"		65·00	
G 2		1d. black and violet		1·25	1·75
		a. Extra island		65·00	
		b. Missing "I"		65·00	
G 3		2d. black and carmine		1·25	2·50
		a. Extra island		70·00	
		b. Missing "I"		70·00	
G 4		3d. black and blue		1·25	4·00
		a. Extra island		80·00	
		b. Missing "I"		80·00	
G 5		4d. black and claret		2·25	4·75
		c. "SOUTH POKE"		95·00	
G 6		6d. black and orange		3·25	4·75
		a. Extra island		£110	
		b. Missing "I"		£110	
		c. "SOUTH POKE"		£110	
		d. Black and ochre		48·00	90·00
		da. Extra island		£275	
		db. Missing "I"		£275	
		dc. "SOUTH POKE"		£275	
G 7		9d. black and brown		2·00	3·75
		c. "SOUTH POKE"		95·00	
G 8		1s. black and purple		2·00	4·25
		c. "SOUTH POKE"		95·00	
G1/8			*Set of* 8	13·00	25·00
G1/8 Perf "Specimen"			*Set of* 8	£450	

(b) Map thin and clear (16.2.48)

G 9	G **1**	½d. black and green		2·25	11·00
		a. Recess frame printed double, one albino and inverted		£900	
G10		1d. black and violet		1·50	14·00
G11		2d. black and carmine		3·75	19·00
G11a		2½d. black and deep blue (6.3.49)		7·50	7·00
G12		3d. black and blue		2·75	4·50
G13		4d. black and claret		16·00	20·00
G14		6d. black and orange		23·00	11·00
G15		9d. black and brown		23·00	10·00
G16		1s. black and purple		23·00	10·00
G9/16			*Set of* 9	90·00	95·00

*This is the date of issue for South Georgia. Nos. G1/8 were released in London on 11 February.

In Nos. G1/8 a variety with a gap in the 80th parallel occurs six times in each sheet of all values in positions R. 1/4, 1/9, 3/4, 3/9, 5/4 and 5/9 (*Price for set of 8 £40 mint, in pairs with normal*).

A constant variety, dot on "I" of "SOUTH", occurs on R. 5/2, 5/4, 5/6, 5/8 and 5/10 of all values of the "thin map" set with the exception of the 2½d.

1946 (4 Oct*). *Victory. As Nos.* 110/11 *of Antigua.*

G17	1d. deep violet		50	15
G18	3d. blue		75	15
G17/18 Perf "Specimen"		*Set of* 2	£120	

*This is the date of issue for South Georgia. The stamps were placed on sale from the South Orkneys on 17 January 1947, from the South Shetlands on 30 January 1947 and from Graham Land on 10 February 1947.

1948 (6 Dec). *Royal Silver Wedding. As Nos.* 112/13 *of Antigua, but 1s. in recess.*

G19	2½d. ultramarine		1·50 1·00
G20	1s. violet-blue		2·25 1·75

1949 (10 Oct). *75th Anniv of U.P.U. As Nos.* 114/17 *of Antigua.*

G21	1d. violet		1·50	1·50
G22	2d. carmine-red		5·00	2·50
G23	3d. deep blue		4·00	1·25
G24	6d. red-orange		7·00	3·00
G21/4		*Set of* 4	16·00	7·50

1953 (4 June). *Coronation. As No.* 120 *of Antigua.*

G25	1d. black and violet		1·10 1·25

G **2** *John Biscoe I,* 1947–52   G **3** *Trepassey,* 1945–47

(Recess Waterlow, then D.L.R. (from 27.3.62))

1954 (1 Feb)–**62.** *Types G* **2**/**3** *and similar designs showing ships. Wmk Mult Script CA.* P 12½.

G26	½d. black and bluish green		30	2·00
	a. Black and deep green (DLR) (17.4.62)		5·50	13·00
G27	1d. black and sepia-brown		1·75	1·50
	a. Black and sepia (DLR) (27.3.62)		14·00	18·00
G28	1½d. black and olive		2·00	1·50
	a. Black and yellow-olive (DLR) (21.9.62)		8·50	3·00
G29	2d. black and rose-red		1·25	20
G30	2½d. black and yellow-ochre		1·25	15
G31	3d. black and deep bright blue		1·25	15
G32	4d. black and bright reddish purple		3·25	55
G33	6d. black and deep lilac		3·50	45
G34	9d. black		3·50	1·00
G35	1s. black and brown		3·50	1·00
G36	2s. black and carmine		19·00	10·00
G37	2s. 6d. black and pale turquoise		20·00	6·00
G38	5s. black and violet		42·00	6·50

G39	10s. black and blue		55·00	18·00
G40	£1 black		90·00	48·00
G26/40		*Set of 15*	£200	85·00

Designs: *Horiz*—1½d. Wyatt Earp, 1934–36; 2d. Eagle, 1944–45; 2½d. *Penola*, 1934–37; 3d. *Discovery II*, 1929–37; 4d. *William Scoresby*, 1926–46; 1s. *Deutschland*, 1910–12; 2s. *Pourquoi-pas?*, 1908–10; 10s. *Antarctic*, 1901–03. *Vert*—6d. *Discovery*, 1925–27; 9d. *Endurance*, 1914–16; 2s. 6d. *Français*, 1903–05; 5s. *Scotia*, 1902–04; £1 *Belgica*, 1897–99.

TRANS-ANTARCTIC EXPEDITION 1955-1958
(G 4)

1956 (30 Jan). *Trans-Antarctic Expedition. Nos.* G27, G30/1 *and* G33 *optd with Type* G 4.

G41	1d. black and sepia-brown		10	30
G42	2½d. black and yellow-ochre		65	50
G43	3d. black and deep bright blue		65	30
G44	6d. black and deep lilac		65	30
G41/4		*Set of 4*	1·75	1·25

The stamps of Falkland Islands Dependencies were withdrawn on 16 July 1963 after Coats Land, Graham Land, South Orkneys and South Shetlands had become a separate colony, known as British Antarctic Territory.

F. SOUTH GEORGIA

From 17 July 1963 South Georgia and South Sandwich Islands used stamps inscribed "South Georgia".

1 Reindeer	**2** South Sandwich Islands

(Des D.L.R. (No. 16), M. Goaman (others). Recess D.L.R.)

1963 (17 July)–**69**. *T* **1**/2 *and similar designs. Ordinary or glazed paper* (No. 16). W w **12**. P 15.

1	½d. brown-red		50	75
	a. Perf 14 × 15 (13.2.67)		1·00	1·50
2	1d. violet-blue		70	60
3	2d. turquoise-blue		1·25	60
4	2½d. black		5·00	2·50
5	3d. bistre		2·75	40
6	4d. bronze-green		5·00	80
7	5½d. deep violet		2·50	90
8	6d. orange		75	30
9	9d. blue		5·00	2·00
10	1s. purple		75	30
11	2s. yellow-olive and light blue		19·00	4·50
12	2s. 6d. blue		22·00	4·00
13	5s. orange-brown		22·00	4·00
14	10s. magenta		42·00	10·00
15	£1 ultramarine		85·00	48·00
16	£1 grey-black (1.12.69)		10·00	16·00
1/16		*Set of 16*	£190	80·00

Designs: *Vert*—2d. Sperm Whale; 3d. South American Fur Seal; 6d. Light-mantled Sooty Albatross; 10s. Plankton and Krill; £1 (No. 16) King Penguins. *Horiz*—2½d. Chinstrap and King Penguins; 4d. Fin Whale; 5½d. Southern Elephant-Seal; 9d. *R2* (whale-catcher); 1s. Leopard Seal; 2s. Shackleton's Cross; 2s. 6d. Wandering Albatross; 5s. Southern Elephant-seal and South American Fur Seal; £1 (No. 15) Blue Whale.

1970 (22 Jan). *As No. 1, but wmk w* **12** *sideways and on glazed paper.*

17	½d. brown-red		2·50	2·25

(3)	(3a)
(4)	(4a)
(5)	(5a)

1971 (15 Feb)–**76**. *Decimal Currency. Nos.* 17 *and* 2/14 *surch as T* **3/4**. *Nos.* 18/a *wmk sideways, glazed paper. Others wmk upright, ordinary paper.*

18	½p. on ½d. brown-red (T **3**)		1·50	1·60
	a. Surch with T **3a** (16.6.72)		1·00	90
	b. Do. Wmk upright (24.8.73)		3·25	5·00
19	1p. on 1d. violet-blue		1·50	55
	a. Glazed paper (1.12.72)		2·25	1·50
	b. Do. but wmk sideways (9.3.76)		1·00	4·00
20	1½p. on 5½d. deep violet (T **4**)		3·00	2·25
	b. Surch with T **4a**. Glazed paper (24.8.73)		7·00	4·50
21	2p. on 2d. turquoise-blue		70	50
22	2½p. on 2½d. black		1·50	40

23	3p. on 3d. bistre		1·00	50
24	4p. on 4d. bronze-green		90	50
25	5p. on 6d. orange		90	30
26	6p. on 9d. blue		1·50	70
27	7½p. on 1s. purple		2·00	70
28	10p. on 2s. yellow-olive and light blue		32·00	15·00
29	15p. on 2s. 6d. blue		13·00	11·00
30	25p. on 5s. orange-brown		10·00	9·00
31	50p. on 10s. magenta (Type **5**)		35·00	16·00
	a. Surch with Type **5a**. Glazed paper (1.12.72)		10·00	21·00
	b. Do. but wmk sideways (9.3.76)		15·00	32·00
18/31a		*Set of 14*	70·00	50·00

The surcharge on No. 19b shows a larger "p". See also Nos. 53/66.

6 *Endurance* beset in Weddell Sea

(Des R. Granger Barrett. Litho A. & M.)

1972 (5 Jan). *50th Death Anniv of Sir Ernest Shackleton. T* **6** *and similar horiz designs. Multicoloured. W w* **12** (*sideways**). P 13½.

32	1½p. Type **6**		1·00	1·50
	w. Wmk Crown to right of CA		3·50	
33	5p. Launching the longboat *James Caird*		1·25	2·00
	w. Wmk Crown to right of CA		4·00	
34	10p. Route of the *James Caird*		1·75	2·25
	w. Wmk Crown to right of CA		4·25	
35	20p. Sir Ernest Shackleton and the *Quest*		2·00	2·50
	w. Wmk Crown to right of CA		4·50	
32/5		*Set of 4*	5·50	7·50

*The normal sideways watermark shows Crown to left of CA, as seen from the back of the stamp.

7 Southern Elephant-Seal and King Penguins

(Des (from photograph by D. Groves) and photo Harrison)

1972 (20 Nov). *Royal Silver Wedding. Multicoloured; background colour given. W w* **12**. P 14 × 14½.

36	**7** 5p. slate-green		75	35
	w. Wmk inverted		55·00	
37	10p. bluish violet		75	35

1973 (1 Dec*). *Royal Wedding. As Nos.* 165/6 *of Anguilla. Centre multicoloured. W w* **12** (*sideways*). P 13½.

38	5p. brown-ochre		25	10
39	5p. chalky blue		35	20

*This is the local date of issue: the Crown Agents released the stamps on 14 November.

8 Churchill and Westminster Skyline	**9** Captain Cook

(Des L. Curtis. Litho Questa)

1974 (14 Dec*). *Birth Centenary of Sir Winston Churchill. T* **8** *and similar horiz design. Multicoloured. W w* **12** (*sideways*). P 14½.

40	15p. Type **8**		1·50	1·25
41	25p. Churchill and warship		1·50	1·25
MS42	122 × 98 mm. Nos. 40/1		6·00	6·00

*This is the local date of issue: the Crown Agents released the stamps on 30 November.

(Des J. Cooter. Litho Questa)

1975 (26 Apr). *Bicentenary of Possession by Captain Cook. T* **9** *and similar horiz designs. Multicoloured. W w* **12** (*sideways on 8 and* 16p.). P 13.

43	2p. Type **9**		2·25	1·25
44	8p. H.M.S. *Resolution*		3·50	2·00
45	16p. Possession Bay		3·75	2·00
43/5		*Set of 3*	8·50	5·00

NEW INFORMATION

The editor is always interested to correspond with people who have new information that will improve or correct the Catalogue.

---

10 Discovery and Biological Laboratory	**11** Queen and Retinue after Coronation

(Des J. W. Litho Format)

1976 (21 Dec). *50th Anniv of "Discovery" Investigations. T* **10** *and similar vert designs. Multicoloured. W w* **14**. P 14.

46	2p. Type **10**		1·50	45
47	8p. William Scoresby and water-sampling bottles		1·75	60
48	11p. *Discovery II* and plankton net		2·00	65
49	25p. Biological Station and krill		2·50	95
46/9		*Set of 4*	7·00	2·40

(Des G. Drummond. Litho Questa)

1977 (7 Feb). *Silver Jubilee. T* **11** *and similar horiz designs. Multicoloured. W w* **14** (*sideways**). P 13½.

50	6p. Visit by Prince Philip, 1957		50	30
51	11p. Queen Elizabeth and Westminster Abbey		70	35
	w. Wmk Crown to right of CA		80·00	
52	33p. Type **11**		80	50
50/2		*Set of 3*	1·75	1·00

*The normal sideways watermark shows Crown to left of CA, as seen from the back of the stamp.

1977 (17 May)–**78**. *As Nos.* 18a *etc., but W w* **14** (*inverted on* 1p, 5p.; *upright on* 3p. *and* 50p.; *sideways* on *others*). *Glazed paper.*

53	½p. on ½d. brown-red		1·75	2·00
	w. Wmk Crown to right of CA		55·00	
54	1p. on 1d. violet-blue (16.8.77)		80	1·75
	w. Wmk upright		£325	
55	1½p. on 5½d. deep violet (16.8.77)		90	1·75
	w. Wmk Crown to right of CA		£475	
57	2½p. on 2½d. black (16.8.77)		12·00	3·50
58	3p. on 3d. bistre (16.8.77)		7·00	3·50
	w. Wmk inverted		£475	
59	4p. on 4d. bronze-green (16.8.77)		22·00	14·00
	w. Wmk Crown to right of CA		£650	
60	5p. on 6d. orange		2·50	2·75
	w. Wmk upright		2·50	2·75
62	7½p. on 1s. purple (16.8.77)		7·00	20·00
	w. Wmk Crown to right of CA (31.7.78)		1·25	8·00
63	10p. on 2s. yellow-olive & light blue (16.8.77)		5·00	9·00
	w. Wmk Crown to right of CA (31.7.78)		1·25	8·00
64	15p. on 2s. 6d. blue (16.8.77)		9·00	20·00
	w. Wmk Crown to right of CA (31.7.78)		2·00	8·00
65	25p. on 5s. orange-brown (16.8.77)		9·00	22·00
	w. Wmk Crown to right of CA (31.7.78)		1·25	8·00
66	50p. on 10s. pale magenta (12.78)		1·25	6·00
53/66		*Set of 12*	48·00	60·00

*The normal sideways watermark shows Crown to left of CA, as seen from the back of the stamp.

Surcharges on the above differ from those on Nos. 18a/30 by having straight outlines and being slightly more slender. The change in paper also results in the colours appearing brighter.

12 Fur Seal	**13** H.M.S. *Resolution*

(Des C. Abbott. Litho Questa)

1978 (2 June). *25th Anniv of Coronation. T* **12** *and similar vert designs. P* 15.

67	25p. indigo, ultramarine and silver		35	1·10
	a. Sheetlet. Nos. 67/9 × 2		1·75	
68	25p. multicoloured		35	1·10
69	25p. indigo, ultramarine and silver		35	1·10
67/9		*Set of 3*	90	3·00

Designs:—No. 67, Panther of Henry VI; No. 68, Queen Elizabeth II; No. 69, Type **12**.

Nos. 67/9 were printed together in small sheets of 6, containing two *se-tenant* strips of 3, with horizontal gutter margin between.

(Des and litho (25p. also embossed) Walsall)

1979 (14 Feb). *Bicentenary of Captain Cook's Voyages,* 1768–79. *T* **13** *and similar vert designs. Multicoloured. P* 11.

70	3p. Type **13**		1·50	1·25
71	6p. *Resolution* and map of South Georgia and S. Sandwich Isles showing route		1·50	1·00
72	11p. King Penguin (based on drawing by George Forster)		2·50	2·25
73	25p. Flaxman/Wedgwood medallion of Captain Cook		2·75	1·75
70/3		*Set of 4*	7·50	6·50

From 5 May 1980 South Georgia and South Sandwich Islands used stamps inscribed FALKLAND ISLANDS DEPENDENCIES.

G. FALKLAND ISLANDS DEPENDENCIES

For use in South Georgia and South Sandwich Islands.

14 Map of Falkland Islands Dependencies   **15** Magellanic Clubmoss

(Des and litho J.W.)

1980 (5 May)–84. *Horiz designs as T* **14**. *Multicoloured. W* w **14** *(sideways). P* 13½. A. *Without imprint date*

74A	1p. Type **14**		30	30
75A	2p. Shag Rocks		30	30
76A	3p. Bird and Willis Islands		30	30
77A	4p. Gulbrandsen Lake		30	30
78A	5p. King Edward Point		30	30
79A	6p. Sir Ernest Shackleton's Memorial Cross, Hope Point		60	30
80A	7p. Sir Ernest Shackleton's Grave, Grytviken		60	40
81A	8p. Grytviken Church		50	40
82A	9p. Coaling Hulk *Louise* at Grytviken		50	45
83A	10p. Clerke Rocks		50	45
84A	20p. Candlemas Island		2·75	1·75
85A	25p. Twitcher Rock and Cook Island, Southern Thule		2·75	1·75
86A	50p. R.R.S. *John Biscoe II* in Cumberland Bay		1·00	2·00
87A	£1 R.R.S. *Bransfield* in Cumberland Bay		1·25	2·75
88A	£3 H.M.S. *Endurance* in Cumberland Bay		3·00	6·50
74A/88A		*Set of 15*	13·00	16·00

B. *With imprint date* ("1984") *at foot* (3.5.84)

74B	1p. Type **14**		25	70
75B	2p. Shag Rocks		25	70
76B	3p. Bird and Willis Islands		25	70
77B	4p. Gulbrandsen Lake		25	80
78B	5p. King Edward Point		35	80
79B	6p. Sir Ernest Shackleton's Memorial Cross, Hope Point		30	70
80B	7p. Sir Ernest Shackleton's Grave, Grytviken		30	70
81B	8p. Grytviken Church		30	70
82B	9p. Coaling Hulk *Louise* at Grytviken		30	70
83B	10p. Clerke Rocks		50	70
84B	20p. Candlemas Island		2·00	1·50
85B	25p. Twitcher Rock and Cook Island, Southern Thule		2·00	2·50
86B	50p. R.R.S. *John Biscoe II* in Cumberland Bay		2·00	2·75
74B/86B		*Set of 13*	8·00	12·50

For some of these designs watermarked W **16** (sideways) see Nos. 148/52.

(Des L. McCombie. Litho Rosenbaum Bros, Vienna)

1981 (5 Feb). *Plants. T* **15** *and similar vert designs. Multicoloured. W* w **14** *(inverted on* 25p.*). P* 14.

89	3p. Type **15**		20	25
	w. Wmk inverted		7·50	
90	6p. Alpine Cat's-tail		20	30
91	7p. Greater Burnet		20	30
	w. Wmk inverted		£325	
92	11p. Antarctic Bedstraw		20	35
93	15p. Brown Rush		25	45
	a. Light brown (Queen's head and territory inscr) omitted		£1900	
94	25p. Antarctic Hair Grass		35	75
	w. Wmk upright		£300	
89/94		*Set of 6*	1·25	2·25

16 Wedding Bouquet from Falkland Islands Dependencies   **17** Introduced Reindeer during Calving, Spring

(Des J.W. Litho Format)

1981 (22 July). *Royal Wedding. T* **16** *and similar vert designs. Multicoloured. W* w **14**. *P* 14.

95	10p. Type **16**		15	30
96	13p. Prince Charles dressed for skiing		20	35
97	52p. Prince Charles and Lady Diana Spencer		65	85
95/7		*Set of 3*	90	1·40

(Des A. Theobald. Litho Format)

1982 (29 Jan). *Reindeer. T* **17** *and similar horiz designs. Multicoloured. W* w **14** *(sideways). P* 14.

98	5p. Type **17**		25	65
99	13p. Bull at rut, Autumn		30	85
100	25p. Reindeer and mountains, Winter		40	1·40
101	26p. Reindeer feeding on tussock grass, late Winter		40	1·40
98/101		*Set of 4*	1·25	3·75

18 *Gamasellus racovitzai* (tick)   **19** Lady Diana Spencer at Tidworth, Hampshire, July 1981

(Des I. Loe. Litho Questa)

1982 (16 Mar). *Insects. T* **18** *and similar vert designs. Multicoloured. W* w **14**. *P* 14.

102	5p. Type **18**		15	25
103	10p. *Alaskozetes antarcticus* (mite)		25	35
104	13p. *Cryptopygus antarcticus* (spring-tail)		25	40
105	15p. *Notiomaso australis* (spider)		30	45
106	25p. *Hydromedion sparsutum* (beetle)		50	70
107	26p. *Parochlus steinenii* (midge)		50	70
102/7		*Set of 6*	1·75	2·50

(Des C. Abbott. Litho Format)

1982 (7 Sept). *21st Birthday of Princess of Wales. T* **19** *and similar vert designs. Multicoloured. W* w **14**. *P* 13½ × 14.

108	5p. Falklands Islands Dependencies coat of arms		10	15
109	17p. Type **19**		40	35
	a. Perf 13½		2·00	4·50
110	37p. Bride and groom on steps of St Paul's		45	80
111	50p. Formal portrait		1·00	1·10
108/11		*Set of 4*	1·75	2·25

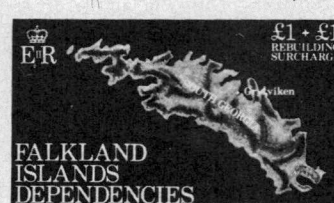

20 Map of South Georgia

(Des PAD Studio. Litho Format)

1982 (13 Sept). *Rebuilding Fund. W* w **14** *(sideways*). *P* 11.

112	**20** £1 + £1 multicoloured		2·40	4·00
	w. Wmk Crown to right of CA		80·00	

*The normal sideways watermark shows Crown to left of CA, as seen from the back of the stamp.

21 Westland Whirlwind   **22** *Euphausia superba*

(Des Harrison. Litho Questa)

1983 (23 Dec). *Bicentenary of Manned Flight. T* **21** *and similar horiz designs. Multicoloured. W* w **14** *(sideways). P* 14.

113	5p. Type **21**		30	35
114	13p. Westland AS.1 Wasp helicopter		55	70
115	17p. Vickers Supermarine Walrus II		60	75
116	50p. Auster Autocrat		1·40	1·60
113/16		*Set of 4*	2·50	3·00

(Des N. Weaver. Litho Questa)

1984 (23 Mar). *Crustacea. T* **22** *and similar vert designs. Multicoloured. W* w **14**. *P* 14½ × 14.

117	5p. Type **22**		40	20
118	17p. *Glyptonotus antarcticus*		70	50
119	25p. *Epimeria monodon*		85	60
120	34p. *Serolis pagenstecheri*		1·10	80
117/20		*Set of 4*	2·75	1·90

23 Zavodovski Island

(Des. J.W. Litho Questa)

1984 (8 Nov). *Volcanoes of South Sandwich Islands. T* **23** *and similar horiz designs. Multicoloured. W* w **14** *(sideways). P* 14 × 14½.

121	6p. Type **23**		80	80
122	17p. Mt Michael, Saunders Island		2·00	1·60
123	22p. Bellingshausen Island		2·00	1·75
124	52p. Bristol Island		2·50	3·25
121/4		*Set of 4*	6·50	6·75

24 Grey-headed Albatross   **25** The Queen Mother

(Des I. Loe. Litho Questa)

1985 (5 May). *Albatrosses. T* **24** *and similar horiz designs. Multicoloured. W* w **14** *(sideways). P* 14½.

125	7p. Type **24**		1·75	85
126	22p. Black-browed Albatross		2·50	1·40
127	27p. Wandering Albatross		2·75	1·60
128	54p. Light-mantled Sooty Albatross		3·50	2·50
125/8		*Set of 4*	9·50	5·50

(Des A. Theobald (£1), C. Abbott (others). Litho Questa)

1985 (23 June). *Life and Times of Queen Elizabeth the Queen Mother. T* **25** *and similar vert designs. Multicoloured. W* w **16**. *P* 14½ × 14.

129	7p. At Windsor Castle on Princess Elizabeth's 14th birthday, 1940		30	30
130	22p. With Princess Anne, Lady Sarah Armstrong-Jones and Prince Edward at Trooping the Colour		60	70
131	27p. Type **25**		70	80
	w. Wmk inverted		10·00	
132	54p. With Prince Henry at his christening (from photo by Lord Snowdon)		1·25	1·40
129/32		*Set of 4*	2·50	2·75
MS133	91×73 mm. £1 Disembarking from Royal Yacht *Britannia*. Wmk sideways		2·25	2·75

(Des I. Strange. Litho Questa)

1985 (4 Nov). *Early Naturalists. Vert designs as T* **35** *of British Antarctic Territory. Multicoloured. W* w **14**. *P* 14½ × 14.

134	7p. Dumont d'Urville and *Durvillea antarctica* (kelp)		1·25	1·00
135	22p. Johann Reinhold Forster and King Penguin		2·25	2·00
136	27p. Johann Georg Adam Forster and Tussock Grass		2·25	2·25
137	54p. Sir Joseph Banks and Dove Prion		3·00	3·50
134/7		*Set of 4*	8·00	8·00

1985 (18 Nov). *As Nos.* 84/8 *but W* w **16** *(sideways). With imprint date* ("1985"). *P* 13½.

148	20p. Candlemas Island		2·50	4·75
149	25p. Twitcher Rock and Cook Island, Southern Thule		3·00	4·75
150	50p. R.R.S. *John Biscoe* in Cumberland Bay		3·00	4·75
151	£1 R.R.S. *Bransfield* in Cumberland Bay		3·00	4·75
152	£3 H.M.S. *Endurance* in Cumberland Bay		8·00	8·00
148/52		*Set of 5*	17·00	24·00

Under the new constitution, effective 3 October 1985, South Georgia and South Sandwich Islands ceased to be dependencies of the Falkland Islands. Issues inscribed for the separate territory are listed under SOUTH GEORGIA AND SOUTH SANDWICH ISLANDS.

Fiji

PRICES FOR STAMPS ON COVER TO 1945		
Nos. 1/9	*from* × 6	
Nos. 10/34	*from* × 5	
Nos. 35/59	*from* × 8	
Nos. 60/3	—	
Nos. 64/9	*from* × 20	
Nos. 70/5	*from* × 5	
Nos. 76/103	*from* × 8	
Nos. 104/14	*from* × 5	
Nos. 115/24	*from* × 4	
Nos. 125/37	*from* × 3	
Nos. 138/241	*from* × 4	
Nos. 242/5	*from* × 3	
Nos. 246/8	*from* × 8	
Nos. 249/66b	*from* × 2	
No. 267	*from* × 8	
Nos. D1/5c	*from* × 4	
Nos. D6/10	*from* × 20	
Nos. D11/18	*from* × 15	

King Cakobau 1852–Oct 1874

Christian missionaries reached Fiji in 1835 and early letters are known to and from their mission stations, sent via Sydney, Hobart or Auckland.

In 1852 Cakobau, the chief of the island of Bau, declared himself King of Fiji and converted to Christianity two years later. Internal problems and difficulties with the American government led the king to offer to cede Fiji to Great Britain. The offer was refused, but resulted in the appointment of a British Consul in 1858. A Consular Post Office operated from September 1858 until 1872 and franked mail with New South Wales stamps from 1863.

The destruction of plantations in the Confederacy during the American Civil War led to an increased demand for Fijian cotton and this upsurge in commercial activity encouraged the *Fiji Times* newspaper on Levuka to establish a postal service on 1 November 1870.

1

(Type-set and printed at the office of *The Fiji Times*, Levuka, Ovalau, Fiji)

1870 (1 Nov)–**71**. *Rouletted in the printing.* (a) *Quadrillé paper.*

1	**1**	1d. black/*rose*	..	..	£3250 £3500
2		3d. black/*rose*	..	..	£3250 £3250
3		6d. black/*rose*	..	..	£2000 £2000
4		1s. black/*rose*	..	..	£1500 £1800

(b) *Laid bâtonné paper* (1871)

5	**1**	1d. black/*rose*	..	..	£900 £1800
		a. Vert strip of 4. Nos. 5, 7/9	..	£35000	
6		3d. black/*rose*	..	..	£1500 £2750
7		6d. black/*rose*	..	..	£1100 £1800
8		9d. black/*rose*	..	..	£1800 £2750
		a. Comma after "EXPRESS" (R.4/4)		£2500	
9		1s. black/*rose*	..	..	£1100 £1400

Nos. 1/4 were printed *se-tenant* as a sheet of 24 (6 × 4) with the 6d. stamps in the first horizontal row, the 1s. in the second, the 1d. in the third and the 3d. in the fourth. Nos. 5/9 were produced from the same plate on which three of the 3d. impressions had been replaced with three 9d. values.

The issued stamps showed the vertical frame lines continuous from top to bottom of the sheet with the horizontal rules broken and not touching the verticals. Used examples are cancelled in manuscript or by the star cancellation used at Bua.

There are no reprints of these stamps, but the 1d., 3d., 6d. and 1s. are known in the correct type on *yellow wove* paper and are believed to be proofs.

There are also three different sets of imitations made by the proprietors of *The Fiji Times* to meet the demands of collectors:—

The first was produced in 1876 on *white wove* or *vertically laid* paper, rouletted on dotted lines and arranged in sheets of 40 (5 rows of 8) comprising 1d., 3d., 6d., 9d. and 1s.; the horizontal frame lines are continuous and the vertical ones broken.

The second was produced before 1888 on *thick rosy mauve wove* paper, rouletted on dotted lines and arranged in sheets of 30 (5 rows of 6) comprising 1s., 9d., 6d., 3d. and 1d.; the vertical frame lines are continuous and the horizontal ones broken.

The third only came to light in the 1960s and is rare, only one complete sheet being recorded, which has since been destroyed. The sheet arrangement is the same as Nos. 1/4, which suggests that this was the first imitation to be produced. It is on *off-white wove* paper, rouletted on closely dotted or solid lines, with vertical frame lines continuous and the horizontal ones broken, as in the originals. These differ from the proofs mentioned above in that the lettering is slightly larger and the figures also differ.

King Cakobau established a formal government in June 1871 and stamps for the royal post office were ordered from Sydney. These arrived in October 1871 and the postal service was placed on a firm basis by the First Postal Act in December of that year. Under its terms the *Fiji Times* service closed on 17 January 1872 and the British Consular Post Office followed six months later.

Two

Cents

2	**3**	**(4)**

(Eng and electrotyped by A. L. Jackson. Typo Govt Printing Office, Sydney)

1871 (Oct). *Wove paper. Wmk "FIJI POSTAGE" in small sans-serif capitals across the middle row of stamps in the sheet.* P 12½.

10	**2**	1d. blue	..	..	50·00 £120
11		3d. pale yellow-green	..		£110 £350
12	**3**	6d. rose	..	..	£130 £275

The 3d. differs from T **2** in having a white circle containing square dots surrounding the centre.

All three values are known *imperf*, but were not issued in that condition.

See notes after No. 33b.

1872 (13 Jan). *Surch as T* **4**, *in local currency, by Govt Ptg Office, Sydney.*

13	**2**	2 c. on 1d. pale blue	..		50·00 65·00
		a. Deep blue	..	..	28·00 48·00
14		6 c. on 3d. yellow-green..			65·00 65·00
15	**3**	12 c. on 6d. carmine-rose..			90·00 75·00

CROWN COLONY

King Cakobau renewed his offer to cede Fiji to Great Britain and this took place on 12 October 1874.

V.R.   **V.R.**   **2d.**

(5)   (6)   (7)

Varieties:—

V.R.   **V.R.**

(*Enlarged*)

Cross pattée stop   Inverted "A"

Cross pattée stop after "R" (R. 3/6).
Round raised stop after "V" (R. 3/8).
Round raised stops after "V" and "R" (R. 3/9).
Inverted "A" for "V" (R. 3/10).
No stop after "R" (R. 2/3 on T **5**, R. 5/3 on T **6**).
Large stop after "R" (R. 5/10).

(Optd at *Polynesian Gazette* Office, Levuka)

1874 (10 Oct). *Nos. 13/15 optd.* (a) *With* T **5**.

16	**2**	2 c. on 1d. blue	..		£850 £225
		a. No stop after "R"	..		£2250 £1000
		b. Cross pattée stop after "R"..		£2250 £1000
		c. Round raised stop after "V"		£2250 £1000
		d. Round raised stops after "V" and "R"	£2250 £1000
		e. Inverted "A" for "V"	..		£2250 £1000
17		6 c. on 3d. green	..		£1300 £600
		a. No stop after "R"	..		£3500 £1600
		b. Cross pattée stop after "R"..		£3500 £1600
		c. Round raised stop after "V"		£3500 £1600
		d. Round raised stops after "V" and "R"	£3500 £1600
		e. Inverted "A" for "V"	..		£3500 £1600
18	**3**	12 c. on 6d. rose	..		£550 £180
		a. No stop after "R"	..		£2000 £1000
		b. Cross pattée stop after "R"..		£2000 £1000
		c. Round raised stop after "V"		£2000 £1000
		d. Round raised stops after "V" and "R"	£2000 £1000
		e. Inverted "A" for "V"	..		£2000 £1000
		f. Opt inverted	..	..	— £4000

(b) *With* T **6**

19	**2**	2 c. on 1d. blue	..		£950 £250
		a. No stop after "R"	..		£2250 £1000
		f. Large stop after "R"	..		
20		6 c. on 3d. green	..		£1700 £850
		a. No stop after "R"	..		£3500 £1600
21	**3**	12 c. on 6d. rose	..		£700 £190
		a. No stop after "R"	..		£2000 £1000
		b. Opt inverted	..	..	£4500

Nos. 16/21 were produced in sheets of 50 (10 × 5) of which the top three rows were overprinted with Type **5** and the lower two with Type **6**.

1875. *Stamps of 1874 surch at Polynesian Gazette Office, Levuka, with* T **7**.

(a) *In red* (May)

22	**2**	2d. on 6 c. on 3d. green (No. 17)		£450 £160
		a. No stop after "R"	..		£1500 £650
		b. Cross pattée stop after "R"..		£1500 £650
		c. Round raised stop after "V"		£1500 £650
		d. Round raised stops after "V" and "R"	£1500 £650
		e. Inverted "A" for "V"	..		£1500 £650
		f. No stop after "2d" (R. 1/2).		£1500 £650
23		2d. on 6 c. on 3d. green (No. 20)		£600 £250
		a. No stop after "R"	..		£1500 £650
		b. Stop between "2" and "d" (R. 5/7)	£1500 £650

(b) *In black* (30 Sept)

24	**2**	2d. on 6 c. on 3d. green (No. 17)	..	£1200 £425
		a. No stop after "R"	..		£3000 £1200
		b. Cross pattée stop after "R"		£3000 £1200
		c. Round raised stop after "V"		£3000 £1200
		d. Round raised stops after "V" and "R"	£3000 £1200
		e. Inverted "A" for "V"	..		£3000 £1200
		f. No stop after "2d" (R. 1/2).		£3000 £1200
		g. "V.R." double	..		
25		2d. on 6 c. on 3d. green (No. 20)	..	£1600 £600
		a. No stop after "R"	..		£3000 £1200
		b. Stop between "2" and "d" (R. 5/7)	£3000 £1200
		c. "V.R." double	..	..	—£3250

1875 (20 Nov). *No. 15 surch at Polynesian Gazette Office, Levuka, with* T **7** *and "V.R." at one operation.* (a) "V.R." T **5**.

26	**3**	2d. on 12 c. on 6d. rose	..	£1400 £600
		aa. Round raised stop after "R"		
		a. Inverted "A" for "V" (R. 1/3, 2/8, 4/4)	£1800 £750
		b. Do. and round raised stop after "V" (R. 3/3, 3/6, 3/8, 3/10)	£1600 £700
		c. As "a" and round raised stops after "R" and "V" (R. 3/2, 3/9)	£1900 £800
		d. Surch double	..	..	—£3250

(b) "V.R." T **6**

27	**3**	2d. on 12 c. on 6d. rose ..	..	£1400 £600
		a. Surch double	..	..	—£3500

The setting used for Nos. 26/7 was similar to that of Nos. 16/21, but the fourth stamp in the fourth row had a Type **5** "V.R." instead of a Type **6**.

The position of No. 26aa is not known.

(8)   **Two Pence**   **(9)**

(Typo Govt Printing Office, Sydney, from plates of 1871)

1876–77. *On paper previously lithographed "VR" as T* **8**, *the 3d. surch with T* **9**. P 12½. (a) *Wove paper* (31.1.76).

28	**2**	1d. grey-blue	..		50·00 48·00
		a. Dull blue	..	..	50·00 48·00
		b. Doubly printed	..		£550
		c. Void corner (R. 2/1)		£500 £300
		d. Imperf vert (horiz pair)		£850
29		2d. on 3d. pale green	..		40·00 50·00
		a. Deep green	..	..	38·00 50·00

30	**3**	6d. pale rose	..		60·00 60·00
		a. Dull rose	..	..	48·00 50·00
		b. Carmine-rose..	..		55·00 50·00
		c. Doubly printed	..		£2500

(b) *Laid paper* (5.1.77)

31	**2**	1d. blue	..		14·00 25·00
		a. Deep blue	..	..	15·00 25·00
		b. Void corner (R. 2/1)		£275 £200
		c. Imperf vert (horiz pair)		£700
32		2d. on 3d. yellow-green	..		55·00 65·00
		a. Deep yellow-green	..		55·00 65·00
		b. Imperf between (pair)		£850
		c. Perf 10	..		£300
		ca. Imperf vert (horiz pair)		
		d. Perf 11	..		£300
33	**3**	6d. rose	..		48·00 28·00
		a. Carmine-rose..	..		48·00 35·00
		b. Imperf vert (horiz pair)		£700

The 3d. *green* is known without the surcharge T **9** on wove paper and also without the surcharge and the monogram. In this latter condition it can only be distinguished from No. 11 by its colour, which is a fuller, deeper yellow-green.

Stamps on both wove and laid paper *imperf* are from printer's trial or waste sheets and were not issued.

All values are known on laid paper without the monogram "VR" and the 3d. stamp also without the surcharge but these are also believed to be from printer's trial sheets and were never issued. Being on laid paper they are easily distinguishable from Nos. 10/12.

1877 (12 Oct). *Optd with T* **8** *and surch as T* **9**. *Laid paper.* P 12½.

34	**2**	4d. on 3d. mauve	..		85·00 25·00
		a. Imperf vert (horiz pair)		£850

10   **11**

A **Four Pence**
B **Four Pence**

Type A: Length 12½ mm
Type B: Length 14 mm
Note also the different shape of the two "e"s.

(Typo from new plates made from original dies of 1871 with "CR" altered to "VR" at Govt Printing Office, Sydney. 2d. and 4d. made from old 3d. die.)

1878–99. *Surcharges as T* **9** *or as Types A or B for 4d. value. Wove paper with paper-maker's name "T. H. SAUNDERS" or "SANDERSON" in double-lined capitals extending over seven stamps in each full sheet.* (a) P 12½ (1878–80).

35	**10**	1d. pale ultramarine (19.2.79)		7·00 7·00
		a. Ultramarine	..		11·00 8·00
36		2d. on 3d. green (17.10.78)		4·75 15·00
37		2d. yellow-green (1.9.79)		13·00 8·00
		a. Blue-green..	..		24·00 13·00
		b. Error. Ultramarine		£25000
38	**11**	6d. rose (30.7.80)	..		£100 18·00

(b) P 10 (1881–90)

39	**10**	1d. dull blue (11.5.82)	..		45·00 3·00
		a. Ultramarine	..		14·00 2·75
		b. Cambridge blue (12.7.83)		45·00 3·25
40		2d. yellow-green (20.10.81)		11·00 1·00
		a. Blue-green..	..		20·00 4·50
41		4d. on 1d. mauve (29.1.90)		32·00 22·00
42		4d. on 2d. pale mauve (A) (23.5.83)	70·00 9·00
		a. Dull purple	..		70·00 9·00
43		4d. on 2d. dull purple (B) (7.11.88)	— £140
44		4d. mauve (13.9.90)	..		50·00
		a. Deep purple	..		50·00 55·00
45	**11**	6d. pale rose (11.3.85) ..		70·00 15·00
		a. Bright rose	..		14·00 14·00

(c) P 10 × 12½ (1881–82)

46	**10**	1d. ultramarine (11.5.82)		90·00 27·00
47		2d. green (20.10.81)	..		£160 50·00
48	**11**	6d. rose (20.10.81)	..		£325 45·00

(d) P 12½ × 10 (1888–90)

49	**10**	1d. ultramarine (1890)..	..	— £300
49a		2d. green (1888)	..		

(e) P 10 × *nearly* 12 (3.9.86)

50	**10**	1d. ultramarine ..	..		65·00 9·50
51		2d. yellow-green	..		60·00 7·50

(f) P *nearly* 12 × 10 (1886–88)

51a	**10**	1d. dull blue (7.11.88)	..	£225 35·00
51b		2d. yellow-green (3.9.86)		
52	**11**	6d. rose (1887)	..		

(g) P 11 × 12 (1892–93)

53	**10**	1d. ultramarine (18.8.92)		11·00 8·00
54		4d. pale mauve (18.8.92)		9·00 9·50
55	**11**	6d. pale rose (14.2.93)	..		6·50 16·00
		a. Rose..	..		11·00 19·00

(h) P 11 (1897–99)

56	**10**	4d. mauve (14.7.96)	..		11·00 7·50
57	**11**	6d. dull rose (14.7.96)	..		25·00 40·00
		a. Printed both sides (12.99)		£950 £800
		b. Bright rose	..		38·00 40·00

(i) P 11 × *nearly* 12 (1896)*

58	**10**	4d. deep purple (14.7.96)		30·00
		a. Bright purple	..		7·50 6·50
59	**11**	6d. rose (23.7.96)	..		32·00
		a. Bright rose	..		7·00 3·75

(j) *Imperf* (1882–90)

60	10	1d. ultramarine			
61		2d. yellow-green			
62		4d. on 2d. pale mauve			
63	11	6d. rose			

*Under this heading are included stamps from several perforating machines with a gauge varying between 11·6 and 12. No. 37b was printed in the colour of the 1d. in error. Only four examples have been reported, one of which was subsequently destroyed.

In the absence of detailed information on dates of issue printing dates are quoted for Nos. 35/63 and 76/103.

12

13

(Typo Govt Printing Office, Sydney)

1881–99. *Paper-maker's name wmkd as previous issue.*

(a) P 10 (19.10.81)

64	12	1s. pale brown		80·00	17·00
		a. Deep brown		80·00	19·00

(b) P 11 × 10 (1894)

65	12	1s. pale brown		38·00	38·00

(c) P 11 (1897)

66	12	1s. pale brown		38·00	14·00

(d) P 11 × nearly 12 (5.99)

67	12	1s. pale brown		32·00	9·00
		a. Brown		32·00	9·00
		b. Deep brown		45·00	45·00

(e) P nearly 12 × 11 (3.97)

68	12	1s. brown		48·00	42·00

Dates given of earliest known use.
Forgeries exist.

(Centre typo, frame litho Govt Printing Office, Sydney)

1882 (23 May). *Toned paper wmkd with paper-maker's name "Cowan" in old English outline type once in each sheet. P 10.*

69	13	5s. dull red and black		55·00	35·00

In July 1900, an electrotyped plate of a 5s. stamp was made and stamps were printed from it with pale orange-red centre and grey-black frame; these are known *perf 10, perf nearly 12,* and *imperf.* These stamps were sold as remainders with a special obliteration dated "15 Dec., 00," but were not issued for postal use. The design differs in many particulars from the issued stamp.

2½d.   2½d.
(14)   (15)

T 14. Fraction bar 1 mm from "2".
T 15. Fraction bar 2 mm from "2".

(Stamps typo in Sydney and surch at Govt Printing Office, Suva)

1891 (1 Jan). *T 10 surch. P 10.*

70	14	2½d. on 2d. green		40·00	48·00
71	15	2½d. on 2d. green		£130	£140

½d.   5ᵈ
(16)   (17)

FIVE   FIVE
PENCE   PENCE
(18) 2 mm spacing   (19) 3 mm spacing

1892 (1 Mar)–93. *P 10.* (a) *Surch on T 10.*

72	16	½d. on 1d. dull blue		48·00	70·00
		a. Ultramarine		40·00	65·00
73	17	5d. on 4d. deep purple (25.7.92)		48·00	65·00
		a. Dull purple		48·00	65·00

(b) *Surch on T 11.*

74	18	5d. on 6d. brownish rose (30.11.92)		55·00	65·00
		a. Bright rose		55·00	60·00
		b. Perf 10 × 12½			
75	19	5d. on 6d. rose (4.1.93)		70·00	80·00
		a. Deep rose		60·00	70·00
		b. Brownish rose		60·00	

20

21 Native Canoe

22

(Typo in Sydney)

1891–1902. *Wmk in sheet, either "SANDERSON" or "NEW SOUTH WALES GOVERNMENT" in outline capitals.*

(a) P 10 (1891–94)

76	20	½d. slate-grey (26.4.92)		4·50	3·75
77	21	1d. black (19.9.94)		8·00	4·00
78		2d. pale green (19.9.94)		90·00	10·00
79	22	2½d. chocolate (8.6.91)		38·00	12·00
80	21	5d. ultramarine (14.2.93)		75·00	48·00

(b) P 11 × 10 (1892–93)

81	20	½d. slate-grey (20.10.93)		4·75	13·00
82	21	1d. black (14.2.93)		4·75	2·50
83		2d. green (14.2.93)		10·00	3·75
84	22	2½d. chocolate (17.8.92)		19·00	19·00
		a. Brown		7·50	7·00
		b. Yellowish brown			
85	21	5d. ultramarine (14.2.93)		10·00	7·50

(c) P 11 (1893–96)

86	20	½d. slate-grey (2.6.96)		3·00	5·50
		a. Greenish slate		2·50	6·00
87	21	1d. black (31.10.95)		3·50	3·50
88		1d. pale mauve (2.6.96)		4·00	1·00
		a. Rosy mauve		4·75	1·00
89		2d. dull green (17.3.94)		4·75	80
		a. Emerald-green		6·00	2·00
90	22	2½d. brown (31.10.95)		18·00	8·00
		a. Yellowish brown		13·00	15·00
91	21	5d. ultramarine (14.2.93)		£200	

(d) P 10 × nearly 12 (1893–94)

92	20	½d. greenish slate			
93	21	1d. black (20.7.93)		14·00	5·50
94		2d. dull green (19.9.94)		£550	£275

(e) P nearly 12 × 10 (19.9.94)

94a	20	½d. pale grey			

(f) Perf nearly 12 (1894–98)

95	20	½d. greenish slate (19.9.94)		2·75	8·00
		a. Grey		27·00	
96	21	1d. black (19.9.94)		£180	24·00
97		1d. rosy mauve (4.5.98)		4·75	7·50
98		2d. dull green (19.9.94)		85·00	35·00

(g) P 11 × nearly 12 (1895–97)

99	20	½d. greenish slate (8.10.97)		1·00	2·75
100	21	1d. black (31.10.95)		£325	
101		1d. rosy mauve (14.7.96)		4·00	80
		a. Pale rosy mauve		4·00	2·00
102		2d. dull green (26.7.97)		30·00	4·00
103	22	2½d. brown (26.7.97)		11·00	17·00
		a. Yellow-brown		5·00	5·00

(h) P nearly 12 × 11 (1897–98)

103b	20	½d. greenish slate (8.10.97)		4·00	5·50
103c	21	1d. rosy mauve (10.2.97)		10·00	5·00
103d		2d. dull green (4.5.98)		£200	

The 2½d. brown is known *doubly printed,* but only occurs in the remainders and with the special obliteration (*Price* £100 *cancelled-to-order*). It was never issued for postal use.

23   24

(Typo D.L.R.)

1903 (1 Feb). *Wmk Crown CA. P 14.*

104	23	½d. green and pale green		2·25	2·00
105		1d. dull purple and black/red		13·00	55
106	24	2d. dull purple and orange		3·75	1·25
107	23	2½d. dull purple and blue/blue		14·00	8·00
108		3d. dull purple and purple		1·50	4·50
109	24	4d. dull purple and black		1·50	2·50
110	23	5d. dull purple and green		1·50	5·00
111	24	6d. dull purple and carmine		1·50	2·50
112	23	1s. green and carmine		11·00	50·00
113	24	5s. green and black		45·00	£100
114	23	£1 grey-black and ultramarine		£300	£375
104/14			Set of 11	£350	£475
104/14		Optd "Specimen"	Set of 11	£300	

1904–9. *Wmk Mult Crown CA. Chalk-surfaced paper* (1s.). *P 14.*

115	23	½d. green and pale green		10·00	3·00
116		1d. purple and black/red		23·00	10
117		1s. green and carmine (1909)		26·00	40·00
115/17			Set of 3	55·00	40·00

1906–12. *Colours changed. Wmk Mult Crown CA. Chalk-surfaced paper* (6d. to £1). *P 14.*

118	23	½d. green (1908)		10·00	3·25
119		1d. red (1906)		6·00	10
120		2½d. bright blue (1910)		6·50	7·50
121	24	6d. dull purple (1910)		9·50	23·00
122	23	1s. black/green (1911)		4·00	10·00
123	24	5s. green and red/yellow (1911)		48·00	55·00
124	23	£1 purple and black/red (1912)		£300	£300
118/24			Set of 7	£325	£350
119/24		Optd "Specimen"	Set of 6	£300	

Nos. 112/14, 117 and 120/4 are known with a forged registered postmark of Suva dated "10 DEC 1909".

25   26   WAR STAMP
(27)

(Typo D.L.R.)

1912 (Oct)–23. *Die I. Wmk Mult Crown CA. Chalk-surfaced paper* (5d. to £1). *P 14.*

125	26	¼d. brown (1.4.16)		2·25	30
		a. Deep brown (1917)		1·50	40
		y. Wmk inverted and reversed			
126	25	½d. green		1·50	95
		a. Yellow-green (1916)		8·50	8·50
		b. Blue-green (1917)		1·25	50
		w. Wmk inverted		80·00	
		y. Wmk inverted and reversed		80·00	
127	25	1d. carmine		2·00	10
		a. Bright scarlet (1916)		2·00	75
		b. Deep rose (1916)		9·00	1·75
128	26	2d. greyish slate (5.14)		1·75	10
129	25	2½d. bright blue (5.14)		3·50	3·50
130		3d. purple/yellow (5.14)		4·25	4·50
		a. Wmk sideways		£350	£425
		b. On lemon (1915)		2·00	8·50
		c. On pale yellow (1921)		1·75	13·00
		ca. "A" of "CA" missing from wmk			
		cw. Wmk inverted			
		d. Die II. On pale yellow (1922)		2·50	24·00
131	26	4d. black and red/yellow (5.14)		23·00	20·00
		a. On lemon		4·00	16·00
		b. On orange-buff (1920)		50·00	65·00
		c. On pale yellow (1921)		8·00	14·00
		cw. Wmk inverted			
		d. Die II. On pale yellow (1922) (Optd S. £38)			
132	25	5d. dull purple and olive-green (5.14)		5·50	10·00
133	26	6d. dull and bright purple (5.14)		2·00	5·50
134	25	1s. black/green (10.13)		1·25	14·00
		a. White back (4.14)		1·00	9·00
		b. On blue-green, olive back (1916)		4·75	10·00
		c. On emerald back (1921) (Optd S. £38)			
		d. Die II. On emerald back (1922)		3·50	22·00
135	26	2s. 6d. black and red/blue (19.1.16)		32·00	30·00
136		5s. green and red/yellow		32·00	40·00
137	25	£1 purple and black/red (5.14)		£250	£275
		a. Die II (1923)		£250	£275
125/37			Set of 13	£275	£325
125/37		Optd "Specimen"	Set of 13	£425	

1915 (1 Dec)–19. *Optd with T 27 by Govt Printer, Suva.*

138	25	½d. green		60	4·00
		a. Yellow-green (1916)		60	4·00
		b. Blue-green (1917)		60	2·50
		c. Opt inverted		£550	
		d. Opt double			
139		1d. carmine		23·00	23·00
		a. Bright scarlet		1·50	75
		ab. Horiz pair, one without opt		£5500	
		c. Opt inverted		£650	
		d. Deep rose (1919)		2·00	2·00
138/9 H/S "Specimen"			Set of 2	£120	

No. 139ab occurred on one pane of 120 only, the overprint being so misplaced that all the stamps of the last vertical row escaped it entirely.
Nos. 140/227 are no longer used.

1922–29. *Die II. Wmk Mult Script CA. Chalk-surfaced paper* (1s. to 5s.). *P 14.*

228	26	¼d. deep brown (1923)		2·50	23·00
229	25	½d. green (1923)		75	2·50
		w. Wmk inverted			
230		1d. carmine-red		2·50	2·00
231		1d. violet (6.1.27)		1·25	10
232	26	1½d. scarlet (6.1.27)		4·00	3·25
233		2d. grey		1·25	10
		a. Face value omitted		£7000	
234	25	3d. bright blue (1924)		2·75	1·50
235	26	4d. black and red/lemon (1924)		5·00	7·00
		a. On pale yellow (1929)		35·00	24·00
236	25	5d. dull purple and sage-green (1927)		1·50	2·00
237	26	6d. dull and bright purple		2·00	1·25
238	25	1s. black/emerald (1924)		4·00	6·00
		w. Wmk inverted			
239	23	2s. purple and blue/blue (6.1.27)		28·00	60·00
240		2s. 6d. black and red/blue (1925)		11·00	32·00
241		5s. green and red/pale yellow (1926)		30·00	65·00
228/41			Set of 14	85·00	£180
228/41		Optd "Specimen"	Set of 14	£300	

The 2d. imperforate with watermark Type 10 of Ireland came from a trial printing and was not issued.

Only one example of No. 233a is known. It was caused by an obstruction during the printing of the duty plate.

1935 (6 May). *Silver Jubilee. As Nos. 91/4 of Antigua.*

242		1½d. deep blue and carmine		80	6·00
		a. Deep blue and aniline red		6·50	17·00
		b. Frame printed double, one albino		£1000	
		f. Diagonal line by turret		45·00	
		h. Dot by flagstaff		85·00	
		i. Dash by turret		85·00	
243		2d. ultramarine and grey		1·50	35
		f. Diagonal line by turret		60·00	
		g. Dot to left of chapel		£110	
244		3d. brown and deep blue		2·50	3·00
		f. Diagonal line by turret		90·00	
		h. Dot by flagstaff		£150	
		i. Dash by turret		£150	
245		1s. slate and purple		4·50	5·00
		a. Frame printed double, one albino		£1500	
		f. Diagonal line by turret		£140	
		h. Dot by flagstaff		£190	
242/5			Set of 4	8·50	13·00
242/5		Perf "Specimen"	Set of 4	85·00	

For illustrations of plate varieties see Catalogue Introduction.

1937 (12 May). *Coronation. As Nos. 95/7 of Antigua. P 11×11½.*

246		1d. purple		60	45
247		2d. grey-black		60	1·25
248		3d. Prussian blue		60	1·25
246/8			Set of 3	1·60	2·75
246/8		Perf "Specimen"	Set of 3	55·00	

PRICES OF SETS

Set prices are given for many issues, generally those containing three stamps or more. Definitive sets include one of each value or major colour change, but do not cover different perforations, die types or minor shades. Where a choice is possible the set prices are based on the cheapest versions of the stamps included in the listings.

28 Native sailing Canoe

29 Native Village

30 Camakua (canoe)

31 Map of Fiji Islands

Two Dies of Type **30**:

Die I	Die II
Empty Canoe	Native in Canoe

Two Dies of Type **31**:

Die I	Die II
Without "180°"	With "180°"

Extra palm frond
(R. 5/8)

Levuka FIJI ISLANDS

Extra line (R. 2/1)

Spur on arms medallion (Pl 2
R. 4/2) (ptg of 26 Nov 1945)

(Des V. E. Ousey (½d., 1s., 2s. 6d.), Miss C. D. Lovejoy (1d., 1½d.,
5d.), Miss I. Stinson (3d., 5s.) and A. V. Guy (2d. (Nos. 253/4),
2½d., 6d., 2s.). Recess De La Rue (½d., 1½d., 2d., (Nos.
253/5a), 2½d., 6d., 8d., 1s. 5d., 1s. 6d.), Waterlow (others))

1938 (5 Apr)–**1955**. *T* **28/31** *and similar designs. Wmk Mult Script
CA. Various perfs.*
249	28	½d. green (*p* 13½)	..	20	75
		a. Perf 14 (5.41)	.. 20·00	3·50
		b. Perf 12 (8.48)	..	80	3·00
		ba. Extra palm frond		38·00	
250	29	1d. brown and blue (*p* 12½)		40	20
251	30	1½d. carmine (Die I) (*p* 13½)		15·00	35
252		1½d. carmine (Die II) (*p* 13½) (1.10.40)	1·40	3·00
		a. *Deep carmine* (10.42)	4·00	1·25
		b. Perf 14 (6.42)	.. 18·00	19·00
		c. Perf 12 (21.7.49)		90	1·25

253	31	2d. brown and green (Die I) (*p* 13½)	38·00	40
		a. Extra line	£275	42·00
254		2d. brown & green (Die II) (*p* 13½)		
		(1.10.40)	16·00	16·00
255	—	2d. grn & magenta (*p* 13½) (19.5.42)	40	60
		a. Perf 12 (27.5.46)	55	70
256	31	2½d. brown & grn (Die II) (*p* 14) (6.1.42)	60	1·00
		a. Perf 13½ (1.44)	70	80
		b. Perf 12 (19.1.48)	90	50
257		3d. blue (*p* 12½)	1·00	30
		a. Spur on arms medallion	£150	
258		5d. blue and scarlet (*p* 12½)	42·00	10·00
259		5d. yell-green & scar (*p* 12½) (1.10.40)	20	30
260	31	6d. black (Die I) (*p* 13×12)	60·00	12·00
261		6d. black (Die II) (*p* 13½) (1.10.40)	3·00	2·25
		a. *Violet-black* (1.44)	25·00	28·00
		b. Perf 12. *Black* (5.6.47)	1·50	1·50
261c		8d. carmine (*p* 14) (15.11.48)	1·00	1·75
		d. Perf 13 (7.6.50)	70	2·75
262		1s. black and yellow (*p* 12½)	75	70
263		1s. 5d. black & carm (*p* 14) (13.6.40)	20	10
263a		1s. 6d. ultramarine (*p* 14) (1.8.50)	3·50	2·75
		b. Perf 13 (16.2.55)	1·25	15·00
264		2s. violet and orange (*p* 12½)	2·50	40
265		2s. 6d. green and brown (*p* 12½)	2·50	1·50
266		5s. green and purple (*p* 12½)	2·50	1·75
266a		10s. orange & emer (*p* 12½) (13.3.50)	35·00	40·00
266b		£1 ultram & carm (*p* 12½) (13.3.50)	48·00	50·00
249/66b			Set of 22	£250	£120
249/66 excl 261c and 263a Perf				
"Specimen"			Set of 18	£450

Designs: *Horiz* (as *T* **30**)—2d. (Nos. 255/a) Government Offices.
(As *T* **29**)—3d. Canoe and arms of Fiji; 8d., 1s. 5d., 1s. 6d. Arms of
Fiji; 2s. Suva Harbour; 2s. 6d. River scene; 5s. Chief's hut. *Vert* (as
T **29**)—5d. Sugar cane; 1s. Spearing fish by torchlight; 10s. Paw-
paw Tree; £1 Police bugler.

2½d.

(42)

1941 (10 Feb). *No.* 254 *surch with T* **42** *by Govt Printer, Suva.*
267	31	2½d. on 2d. brown and green	..	65	20

1946 (17 Aug). *Victory. As Nos.* 110/11 *of Antigua.*
268		2½d. green	..	10	75
		a. Printed double, one albino	..	£275	
269		3d. blue	..	10	10
268/9 Perf "Specimen"			Set of 2	60·00	

1948 (17 Dec). *Royal Silver Wedding. As Nos.* 112/13 *of
Antigua.*
270		2½d. green	..	40	1·00
271		5s. violet-blue	..	14·00	7·00

1949 (10 Oct). *75th Anniv of U.P.U. As Nos.* 114/17 *of Antigua.*
272		2d. bright reddish purple	..	30	30
273		3d. deep blue	..	2·25	2·25
274		8d. carmine-red	..	45	1·25
275		1s. 6d. blue	..	45	1·00
272/5	..	..	Set of 4	3·00	4·25

43 Children Bathing   **44** Rugby Football

(Recess B.W.)

1951 (17 Sept). *Health Stamps. Wmk Mult Script CA. P* 13½.
276	43	1d. + 1d. brown	..	10	60
277	44	2d. + 1d. green	..	30	60

1953 (2 June). *Coronation. As No.* 120 *of Antigua.*
278		2½d. black and green	..	50	30

45 Arms of Fiji

(Recess D.L.R.)

1953 (16 Dec). *Royal Visit. Wmk Mult Script CA. P* 13.
279	45	8d. deep carmine-red	..	30	15

NEW INFORMATION

The editor is always interested to correspond with
people who have new information that will
improve or correct the Catalogue.

---

46 Queen Elizabeth II
(after Annigoni)

47 Government Offices

48 Loading Copra   **49** Sugar Cane Train

50 Preparing Bananas for Export   **51** Gold Industry

(Des V. E. Ousey (½d., 1s., 2s. 6d.), A. V. Guy (6d.). Recess D.L.R.
(½d., 2d., 6d., 8d.), Waterlow (1s., 2s. 6d., 10s., £1) B.W. (others))

1954 (1 Feb)–**59**. *T* **46/51** *and similar designs previously used
for King George VI issue (but with portrait of Queen Elizabeth
II as in T* **47**. *Wmk Mult Script CA. P* 12 (2d.), 13 (8d.), 12½
(6d., 1s., 2s. 6d., 10s., £1), 11½×11 (3d., 1s. 6d., 2s., 5s.) or
11½ (½d., 1d., 1½d., 2½d.).
280	—	½d. myrtle-green (1.7.54)		15	1·25
281	46	1d. turquoise-blue (1.6.56)		1·75	10
282		1½d. sepia (1.10.56)		1·00	40
283	47	2d. green and magenta		1·25	40
284	46	2½d. blue-violet (1.10.56)		1·75	10
285	48	3d. brown and reddish violet (1.10.56)	2·75	20
		a. *Brown & dp reddish vio* (10.11.59)	7·50	70
287	—	6d. black (1.7.54)		2·50	85
288	—	8d. deep carmine-red (1.7.54)		2·00	1·25
		a. *Carmine-lake* (6.3.58)		7·00	2·00
289	—	1s. black and yellow		2·25	10
290	49	1s. 6d. blue and myrtle-green (1.10.56)	19·00	90
291	50	2s. black and carmine (1.10.56)		5·50	50
292	—	2s. 6d. bluish green and brown		1·25	30
		a. *Bluish green & red-brown* (14.9.54)	1·25	10
293	51	5s. ochre and blue (1.10.56)		25·00	1·25
294	—	10s. orange and emerald (1.7.54)		12·00	20·00
295	—	£1 ultramarine and carmine (1.7.54)	42·00	19·00
280/95			Set of 15	£100	42·00

Designs: *Vert* (22½ × 36 *mm*)—½d. Fijians sailing canoe. (25
× 31 *mm*)—1s. Spearing fish by torchlight; 10s. Paw-paw tree; £1
Police bugler. *Horiz* (36 × 22½ *mm*)—6d. Map of Fiji. (31 × 25
mm)—8d. Arms of Fiji; 2s. 6d. River scene.

52 River Scene

53 Cross of Lorraine

(Recess B.W.)

1954 (1 Apr). *Health Stamps. Wmk Mult Script CA. P* 11 × 11½.
296	52	1½d. + ½d. bistre-brown and green	..	10	50
297	53	2½d. + ½d. orange and black	..	10	10

54
Queen Elizabeth II
(after Annigoni)

55 Fijian beating Lali

56 Hibiscus   **60** Red Shining Parrot

(Des M. Goaman: Photo Harrison (8d., 4s.). Recess. B.W. (others))

1959–63. T 54/6, 60 and similar designs. Wmk Mult Script CA. P 11½ (T 46 and 54), 11½ × 11 (T 46, 10d., 1s., 2s. 6d., 10s., £1), 14½ × 14 (8d.) or 14 × 14½ (4s)

298	46	½d. emerald-green (14.11.61)	..	15	1·25
299	54	1d. deep ultramarine (3.12.62)..		1·75	1·40
300		1½d. sepia (3.12.62)	..	1·25	30
301	46	2d. rose-red (14.11.61)	..	50	10
302		2½d. orange-brown (3.12.62)		1·50	2·50
303	55	6d. carmine and black (14.11.61)		1·25	10
304	56	8d. scarlet, yellow, green & blk (1.8.61)	50	25
305	—	10d. brown and carmine (1.4.63)		1·75	60
306	—	1s. light blue and blue (14.11.61)		1·50	
307	—	2s. 6d. black and purple (14.11.61)	12·00	10
308	60	4s. red, green, blue & slate-grn (13.7.59)	1·75	1·75
309	—	10s. emerald and deep sepia (14.11.61)..	6·50	3·00
310	—	£1 black and orange (14.11.61)		22·00	5·50
298/310			Set of 13	45·00	14·00

Designs: Horiz (as T 55)—10d. Yaqona ceremony; 1s. Location map; 2s. 6d. Nadi Airport; 10s. Cutting sugar-cane; £1 Arms of Fiji. Nos. 299 and 311 have turtles either side of "Fiji" instead of shells.

63 Queen Elizabeth II

64 International Dateline

65 White Orchid   **66** Orange Dove

(Des M. Goaman. Photo Harrison (3d., 9d. 1s. 6d., 2s., 4s., 5s.). Recess B.W. (others))

1962 (3 Dec)—**67.** W w 12 (upright). P 11½ (1d., 2d.), 12½ (3d.), 11½×11 (6d., 10d., 1s., 2s. 6d., 10s., £1), 14½×14 (9d., 2s.) or 14×14½ (1s. 6d., 4s., 5s.)

311	54	1d. deep ultramarine (14.1.64)	..	70	2·50
312	46	2d. rose-red (3.8.65)	..	45	10
313	63	3d. multicoloured	..	25	10
		w. Wmk inverted			
314	55	6d. carmine and black (9.6.64)		2·00	10
315	56	9d. scarlet, yellow, grn & ultram (1.4.63)	90	65
316	—	10d. brown and carmine (14.1.64)		60	50
317	—	1s. light blue and blue (24.1.66*)	2·00	45
318	64	1s. 6d. red, yellow, gold, black & blue	2·75	90
		a. Error. Wmk sideways		£750	
319	65	2s. yellow-green, green and copper ..	16·00	3·50
		a. Apple-green, grn & copper (16.5.67)	23·00	4·25
320	—	2s. black and purple (3.8.65)		2·50	90
		a. Black and deep purple (8.67)		2·50	
321	60	4s. red, yellow-green, blue & grn (1.4.64)	7·00	2·75
322		4s. red, green, blue & slate-grn (1.3.66)	4·50	3·50
323	66	5s. red, yellow and grey		14·00	35
		w. Wmk inverted		£120	
324	—	10s. emerald and deep sepia (14.1.64)	7·00	6·00
325	—	£1 black and orange (9.6.64)		18·00	11·00
311/25			Set of 15	65·00	29·00

Designs: Horiz (as T 55)—10d. Yaqona ceremony; 1s. Location map; 2s. 6d. Nadi Airport; 10s. Cutting sugar-cane; £1 Arms of Fiji.
*This is the earliest known used date in Fiji and it was not released by the Crown Agents until 1 November.
The 3d. value exists with PVA gum as well as gum arabic.
For 4s. with watermark sideways see No. 359.

ROYAL VISIT

1963

ROYAL VISIT 1963

     (67)   (68)

1963 (1 Feb). Royal Visit. Nos. 313 and 306 optd with T 67/8.

326	67	3d. multicoloured	..	30	10
327	68	1s. light blue and blue ..	..	30	10

1963 (4 June). Freedom from Hunger. As No. 146 of Antigua.

328		2s. ultramarine	2·50	70

69 Running   (**73** C.S. Retriever.)

(Des M. Goaman. Photo Harrison)

1963 (6 Aug). First South Pacific Games, Suva. T 69 and similar designs. W w 12. P 14½.

329		3d. red-brown, yellow and black		25	10
330		9d. red-brown, violet and black		35	1·75
331		1s. red-brown, green and black		35	10
332		2s. 6d. red-brown, light blue and black	90	1·00
329/32			Set of 4	1·75	2·50

Designs: Vert—9d. Throwing the discus; 1s. Hockey. Horiz—2s. 6d. High-jumping.

1963 (2 Sept). Red Cross Centenary. As Nos. 147/8 of Antigua.

333		2d. red and black		50	10
334		2s. red and blue		2·25	2·75

1963 (3 Dec). Opening of COMPAC (Trans-Pacific Telephone Cable). No. 317 optd with T 73 by B.W.

335		1s. light blue and blue		55	10

74 Jamborette   **75** Scouts of Three
Emblem   Races

(Des V. Whiteley assisted by Norman L. Joe, Asst. D.C., Fiji Scouts for Jamboree emblem. Photo Harrison)

1964 (4 Aug). 50th Anniv of Fijian Scout Movement. W w 12. P 12½.

336	74	3d. multicoloured	..	..	15	25
337	75	1s. violet and yellow-brown	..	15	30

76 Flying-boat   **78** Aotearoa and Map
Aotearoa

(Des V. Whiteley. Photo Harrison)

1964 (24 Oct). 25th Anniv of First Fiji-Tonga Airmail Service. T 76, 78 and similar design. W w 12. P 14½ × 14 (1s.) or 12½ (others).

338		3d. black and vermilion		40	10
339		6d. vermilion and bright blue		70	1·00
340		1s. black and turquoise-blue		70	1·00
338/40			Set of 3	1·60	1·75

Design: Vert (as T 76)—6d. De Havilland D.H.114 Heron 2.

1965 (17 May). I.T.U. Centenary. As Nos. 166/7 of Antigua.

341		3d. blue and rose-carmine		35	10
342		2s. orange-yellow and bistre		80	25

1965 (25 Oct). International Co-operation Year. As Nos. 168/9 of Antigua.

343		2d. reddish purple and turquoise-green		20	10
344		2s. 6d. deep bluish green and lavender		80	25

1966 (24 Jan). Churchill Commemoration. As Nos. 170/3 of Antigua.

345		3d. new blue ..	..	70	10
346		9d. deep green		90	70
347		1s. brown		90	10
348		2s. 6d. bluish violet		1·00	70
345/8			Set of 4	3·25	1·40

1966 (1 July). World Cup Football Championships. As Nos. 176/7 of Antigua.

349		2d. violet, yellow-green, lake & yellow-brn ..	20	10
350		2s. chocolate, blue-green, lake & yellow-brn	65	20

79 H.M.S. Pandora approaching
Split Island, Rotuma

(Des V. Whiteley. Photo Enschedé)

1966 (29 Aug). 175th Anniv of Discovery of Rotuma. T 79 and similar horiz designs. Multicoloured. W w 12 (sideways). P 14 × 13.

351		3d. Type 79		30	10
352		10d. Rotuma Chiefs		30	10
353		1s. 6d. Rotumans welcoming H.M.S. Pandora	40	30
351/3			Set of 3	90	40

1966 (20 Sept). Inauguration of W.H.O. Headquarters, Geneva. As Nos. 178/9 of Antigua.

354		6d. black, yellow-green and light blue		1·25	25
355		2s. 6d. black, light purple and yellow-brown	2·75	2·50

ALTERED CATALOGUE NUMBERS

Any Catalogue numbers altered from the last edition are shown as a list in the introductory pages.

LEGISLATIVE ASSEMBLY

82 Running

(Des V. Whiteley. Photo Harrison)

1966 (5 Dec*). 2nd South Pacific Games, Nouméa. T 82 and similar designs. W w 12 (sideways on 9d.). P 14½ × 14 (9d.) or 14 × 14½ (others).

356		3d. black, chestnut and yellow-olive		10	10
357		9d. black, chestnut and greenish blue		15	15
358		1s. multicoloured		15	15
356/8			Set of 3	30	30

Designs: Vert—9d. Putting the shot. Horiz—1s. Diving.
*These were not released in London until 8.12.66.

1967 (16 Feb). As No. 321 but wmk w 12 sideways.

359	60	4s. red, yellow-green, blue and green		3·25	1·25

85 Military Forces Band

(Des G. Vasarhelyi. Photo Enschedé)

1967 (20 Oct). International Tourist Year. T 85 and similar horiz designs. Multicoloured. W w 12 (sideways). P 14 × 13.

360		3d. Type 85		40	10
361		9d. Reef diving		20	10
362		1s. Beqa fire walkers		20	10
363		2s. Oriana (cruise liner) at Suva		55	15
360/3			Set of 4	1·25	30

89 Bligh (bust), H.M.S.   **91** Bligh's Tomb
Providence and Chart

90 "Bounty's longboat being chased in Fiji
waters"

(Des V. Whiteley. Photo Harrison)

1967 (11 Dec). 150th Death Anniv of Admiral Bligh. W w 12 (sideways on 1s.). P 12½ × 13 (1s.) or 15 × 14 (others).

364	89	4d. multicoloured		10	10
365	90	1s. multicoloured		10	10
366	91	2s. 6d. multicoloured		15	15
364/6			Set of 3	30	30

92 Simmonds Spartan
Seaplane

(Des V. Whiteley. Photo Harrison)

1968 (5 June). 40th Anniv of Kingsford Smith's Pacific Flight via Fiji. T 92 and similar horiz designs. W w 12. P 14 × 14½.

367		2d. black and green		15	10
368		6d. greenish blue, black and lake ..		15	10
369		1s. deep violet and turquoise-green..		20	10
370		2s. orange-brown and blue		30	15
367/70			Set of 4	70	30

Designs—6d. Hawker Siddeley H.S.748 and airline insignias; 1s. Fokker F.VIIa/3M Southern Cross and crew; 2s. Lockheed 8D Altair Lady Southern Cross monoplane.

96 Bure Huts   **97** Eastern Reef Heron
(after Belcher)

98 Sea Snake   **99** Queen Elizabeth and Arms of Fiji

(Des G. Hamori (½d., 1d., 9d.), W. O. Cernohorsky (2d., 4s.). H. S. Robinson (4d., 10d.), D. W. Blair (6d., 5s.), P. D. Clarke (1s.), G. Vasarhelyi (2s. 6d.), W. O. Cernohorsky and E. Jones (3s.), E. Jones and G. Hamori (10s.), E. Jones (£1). Adapted V. Whiteley. Photo D.L.R.)

1968 (15 July). *T* **96/9** *and similar designs. W w* **12** *(sideways on all vert designs). P* 14 × 13½ (2s., 2s. 6d., 5s., £1), 13½ × 14 (3d., 1s., 1s. 6d., 4s., 10s.) *or* 13½ × 13 *(others).*

371	½d. multicoloured		10	10
372	1d. deep greenish blue, red and yellow		10	10
373	2d. new blue, brown and ochre		10	10
374	3d. blackish green, blue and ochre		35	10
375	4d. multicoloured		80	75
376	6d. multicoloured		25	10
377	9d. multicoloured		15	75
378	10d. royal blue, orange and blackish brown		1·25	20
379	1s. Prussian blue and brown-red		20	10
380	1s. 6d. multicoloured		3·25	4·25
381	2s. turquoise, black and rosine		75	2·00
382	2s. 6d. multicoloured		75	75
383	3s. multicoloured		2·75	6·00
384	4s. yellow-ochre, black and olive		6·00	2·75
385	5s. multicoloured		3·00	2·50
386	10s. lake-brown, black and ochre		1·50	3·50
387	£1 multicoloured		1·50	6·00
371/87		*Set of* 17	14·00	26·00

Designs: *Horiz (as T* **96**)—1d. Passion Flowers; 2d. Chambered or Pearly Nautilus; 4d. *Psilogramma jordana* (moth); 6d. Pennant Coralfish; 9d. Bamboo raft; 10d. *Asota woodfordi* (moth); 3s. Golden Cowrie shell. *Vert (as T* **97**)—1s. Black Marlin; 1s. 6d. Orange-breasted Honeyeaters (after Belcher); 4s. Mining industry; 10s. Ceremonial whale's tooth. *Horiz (as T* **98**)—2s. 6d. Outrigger canoes; 5s. Bamboo Orchids.

113 Map of Fiji, W.H.O. Emblem and Nurses

(Des V. Whiteley. Litho D.L.R.)

1968 (9 Dec). *20th Anniv of World Health Organization. T* **113** *and similar horiz designs. Multicoloured. W w* **12** *(sideways). P* 14.

388	3d. Type **113**		15	10
389	9d. Transferring patient to Medical Ship *Vuniwai*		20	15
390	3s. Recreation		25	30
388/90		*Set of* 3	55	40

(New Currency. 100 cents = 1 dollar.)

116 Passion Flowers   **117** Fijian Soldiers overlooking the Solomon Islands

1969 (13 Jan)–**70**. *Decimal Currency. Designs as Nos.* 371/87, *but with values inscr in decimal currency as T* **116**. *W w* **12** *(sideways on vert designs) Chalk-surfaced paper. P* 14 × 13½ (20, 25, 50 c., $2) 13½ × 14 (3, 10, 15, 40 c., $1) *or* 13½ × 13 *(others).*

391	116	1 c. deep greenish blue, red and yellow		10	10
392	—	2 c. new blue, brown and ochre (as 2d.)		10	10
393	97	3 c. blackish green, blue and ochre		30	40
394	—	4 c. multicoloured (as 4d.)		1·50	40
395	—	5 c. multicoloured (as 6d.)		20	10
396	96	6 c. multicoloured		10	10
397	—	8 c. multicoloured (as 9d.)		10	10
398	—	9 c. royal blue, orange and blackish brown (as 10d.)		1·50	2·00
399	—	10 c. Prussian blue and brown-red (as 1s.)		20	10
400	—	15 c. multicoloured (as 1s. 6d.)		9·00	4·50
401	98	20 c. turquoise, black and rosine		1·00	80
402	—	25 c. multicoloured (as 2s. 6d.)		1·00	30
403	—	30 c. multicoloured (as 3s.)		6·50	1·75
404	—	40 c. yellow-ochre, black and olive (as 4s.)		7·50	4·00
405	—	50 c. multicoloured (as 5s.)		4·50	30
		a. Glazed, ordinary paper (3.9.70)		10·00	1·50
406	—	$1 lake-brown, black and ochre (as 10s.)		1·50	60
		a. Glazed, ordinary paper (3.9.70)		3·00	2·75
407	99	$2 multicoloured		1·50	4·00
391/407			*Set of* 17	25·00	16·00

(Des G. Drummond. Photo Harrison)

1969 (23 June). *25th Anniv of Fijian Military Forces' Solomons Campaign. T* **117** *and similar horiz designs. W w* **12**. *P* 14.

408	5 c. yellow-brown, black and bright emerald		20	10
409	10 c. multicoloured		25	10
410	25 c. multicoloured		35	20
408/10		*Set of* 3	70	30

Designs:—10 c. Regimental Flags and Soldiers in full dress and battledress; 25 c. Cpl. Sefanaia Sukanaivalu and Victoria Cross.

120 Javelin Thrower   **123** Map of South Pacific and "Mortar-board"

(Des L. Curtis. Photo Harrison)

1969 (18 Aug). *3rd South Pacific Games. Port Moresby. T* **120** *and similar designs. W w* **12** *(sideways*). P* 14½×14.

411	4 c. black, brown and vermilion		10	10
	w. Wmk Crown to right of CA		3·00	
412	8 c. black, grey and new blue		10	10
413	20 c. multicoloured		20	20
411/13		*Set of* 3	30	30

Designs:—8 c. Sailing dinghy; 20 c. Games medal and winners' rostrum.

*The normal sideways watermark shows Crown to left of CA, *as seen from the back of the stamp.*

(Des G. Drummond. Photo Harrison)

1969 (10 Nov). *Inauguration of University of the South Pacific. T* **123** *and similar horiz designs. Multicoloured. W w* **12**. *P* 14 × 15.

414	2 c. Type **123**		10	15
415	8 c. R.N.Z.A.F. badge and Short S.25 Sunderland flying boat over Laucala Bay (site of University)		15	10
416	25 c. Science students at work		25	15
	w. Wmk inverted		2·00	1·50
414/16		*Set of* 3	45	30

ROYAL VISIT 1970

(126)   **127** Chaulmugra Tree, Makogai

1970 (4 Mar). *Royal Visit. Nos.* 392, 399 *and* 402 *optd with T* **126**.

417	2 c. new blue, brown and ochre		10	20
418	10 c. Prussian blue and brown-red		10	10
419	25 c. multicoloured		20	10
417/19		*Set of* 3	35	30

(Des G. Drummond. Photo Harrison)

1970 (25 May). *Closing of Leprosy Hospital, Makogai. T* **127** *and similar designs. W w* **12** *(sideways* on 10 c.) P* 14×14½.

420	2 c. multicoloured		10	20
421	10 c. pale turquoise-green and black		20	10
	a. Pair. Nos. 421/2		40	20
	w. Wmk Crown to right of CA		5·00	
422	10 c. turquoise-blue, black and magenta		20	10
	w. Wmk Crown to right of CA		5·00	
423	30 c. multicoloured		35	50
420/3		*Set of* 4	70	80

Designs: *Vert*—No. 421, "Cascade" (Semisi Maya); No. 422, "Sea Urchins" (Semisi Maya). *Horiz*—No. 423, Makogai Hospital.

*The normal sideways watermark shows Crown to left of CA, *as seen from the back of the stamp.*

Nos. 421/2 were printed together, *se-tenant*, throughout the sheet.

131 Abel Tasman and Log, 1643

(Des V. Whiteley. Litho D.L.R.)

1970 (18 Aug). *Explorers and Discoverers. T* **131** *and similar horiz designs. W w* **12** *(sideways*). P* 13×12½.

424	2 c. black, brown and turquoise		40	25
	w. Wmk Crown to right of CA		50·00	
425	3 c. multicoloured		80	25
426	8 c. multicoloured		80	15
427	25 c. multicoloured		60	15
424/7		*Set of* 4	2·40	70

Designs:—3 c. Captain Cook and H.M.S. *Endeavour*, 1774; 8 c. Captain Bligh and longboat, 1789; 25 c. Fijian and ocean-going canoe.

*The normal sideways watermark shows Crown to left of CA, *as seen from the back of the stamp.*

INDEPENDENT

135 King Cakobau and Cession Stone   **139** 1d. and 6d. Stamps of 1870

(Des J.W. Litho Format)

1970 (10 Oct). *Independence. T* **135** *and similar horiz designs. Multicoloured. W w* **12** *(sideways). P* 14.

428	2 c. Type **135**		10	10
429	3 c. Children of the World		10	10
430	10 c. Prime Minister and Fijian flag		10	10
431	25 c. Dancers in costume		20	20
428/31		*Set of* 4	30	30

The design for the 10 c. value does not incorporate the Queen's head profile.

(Des V. Whiteley. Photo Harrison)

1970 (2 Nov). *Stamp Centenary. T* **139** *and similar horiz designs. Multicoloured. W w* **12** *(sideways on 15 c.) P* 14½ × 14.

432	4 c. Type **139**		15	10
433	15 c. Fijian stamps of all reigns (61×21 mm)		40	15
434	20 c. Fiji Times office and modern G.P.O.		40	15
	w. Wmk inverted		48·00	
432/4		*Set of* 3	85	35

140 Grey-backed White Eye   **141** Masked Shining Parrot

(Des G. Drummond. Litho Questa)

1971 (6 Aug)–**72**. *Birds and Flowers. Vert designs as T* **140/1**. *Multicoloured. W w* **12** *(upright).*

(a) Size as T **140**. *P* 13½×14.

435	1 c. *Cirrhopetalum umbellatum* (4.1.72)		15	30
436	2 c. Cardinal Honeyeater (22.11.71)		10	10
437	3 c. *Calanthe furcata* (23.6.72)		85	20
438	4 c. *Bulbophyllum sp nov* (23.6.72)		75	1·25
439	5 c. Type **140**		35	10
	w. Wmk inverted			5·00
440	6 c. *Phaius tancarvilliae* (23.6.72)		5·50	5·00
441	8 c. Blue-headed Flycatcher (22.11.71)		35	10
442	10 c. *Acanthephippium vitiense* (4.1.72)		40	10
443	15 c. *Dendrobium tokai* (23.6.72)		5·00	1·25
444	20 c. Slaty Flycatcher		2·00	30

(b) Size as T **141**. *P* 14

445	25 c. Yellow-faced Honeyeater (22.11.71)		3·75	20
446	30 c. *Dendrobium gordonii* (4.1.72)		10·00	90
447	40 c. Type **141**		4·50	50
448	50 c. White-throated Pigeon		3·50	50
449	$1 Collared Lory (22.11.71)		4·00	1·25
450	$2 *Dendrobium platygastrium* (4.1.72)		3·00	9·00
435/50		*Set of* 16	38·00	19·00

See also Nos. 459/73 and 505/20.

142 Women's Basketball   **143** Community Education

(Des R. Granger Barrett. Litho Questa)

1971 (6 Sept). *Fourth South Pacific Games, Tahiti. T* **142** *and similar horiz designs. W w* **12**. *P* 14.

451	8 c. multicoloured		10	10
452	10 c. cobalt, black and brown		10	10
453	25 c. pale turquoise-green, black and brown		30	25
451/3		*Set of* 3	45	30

Designs:—10c. Running; 25c. Weightlifting.

(Des V. Whiteley. Litho Questa)

1972 (7 Feb). *25th Anniv of South Pacific Commission. T* **143** *and similar vert designs. Multicoloured. W w* **12**. *P* 14.

454	2 c. Type **143**		10	10
455	4 c. Public Health		10	10
456	50 c. Economic Growth		35	65
454/6		*Set of* 3	40	70

144 "Native Canoe"   **145** Flowers, Conch and Ceremonial Whale's Tooth

(Des locally and adapted by A. B. New. Litho Questa)

1972 (10 Apr). *South Pacific Festival of Arts, Suva.* W w **12**. P 14.
457	144	10 c. black, orange and new blue		10	10

1972 (17 Nov)–**74.** *As Nos. 436/41, 443/5 and 447/50, but W w* **12** *(sideways*).*
459	2 c. Cardinal Honey-eater (12.12.73)	45	8·50
460	3 c. *Calanthe furcata* (8.3.73)	1·75	45
	w. Wmk Crown to left of CA (15.3.74)	1·75	80
461	4 c. *Bulbophyllum sp nov* (11.4.73)	6·00	45
462	5 c. Type **140** (8.3.73)	5·00	3·00
	w. Wmk Crown to right of CA	7·50	
463	6 c. *Phaius tancarvilliae* (11.4.73)	7·00	1·25
464	8 c. Blue-crested Broadbill (11.4.73)	3·75	75
466	15 c. *Dendrobium tokai* (11.4.73)	3·50	2·25
467	20 c. Slaty Flycatcher	13·00	2·00
468	25 c. Yellow-faced Honey-eater (11.4.73)	1·75	90
470	40 c. Type **141** (15.3.74)	3·00	6·50
471	50 c. White-throated Pigeon (15.3.74)	3·00	3·50
472	$1 Collared Lory	4·00	6·00
473	$2 *Dendrobium platygastrium*	5·50	6·00
459/73	*Set of 13*	50·00	38·00

**The normal sideways watermark shows Crown to right of CA on the 3 c. and Crown to left of CA on the remainder, as seen from the back of the stamp.*

(Des from photograph by D. Groves) and photo Harrison)

1972 (20 Nov). *Royal Silver Wedding. Multicoloured; background colour given.* W w **12**. P 14 × 14½.
474	10 c. slate-green	20	15
475	25 c. bright purple	30	15
	a. Blue printing omitted*	£200	

**The omission of the blue colour results in the Duke's suit appearing brown instead of deep blue.*

HURRICANE RELIEF +10 c

(146)   **147** Line Out

1972 (4 Dec). *Hurricane Relief. Nos. 400 and 403 surch as T* **146**, *by the Reserve Bank of Australia.*
476	15 c. + 5 c. multicoloured	15	15
477	30 c. + 10 c. multicoloured	15	15

(Des J.W. Litho Questa)

1973 (9 Mar). *Diamond Jubilee of Fiji Rugby Union. T* **147** *and similar vert designs. Multicoloured.* W w **12** *(sideways).* P 14.
478	2 c. Type **147**	30	1·60
479	8 c. Body tackle	45	10
480	25 c. Conversion	1·00	40
478/80	*Set of 3*	1·60	1·90

148 Forestry Development   **149** Christmas

(Des J.W. from local ideas. Litho Questa)

1973 (23 July). *Development Projects. T* **148** *and similar horiz designs. Multicoloured.* W w **12**. P 14.
481	5 c. Type **148**	10	10
482	8 c. Rice irrigation scheme	10	10
483	10 c. Low income housing	10	10
484	25 c. Highway construction	20	30
481/4	*Set of 4*	45	45

(Des L. Curtis. Litho Questa)

1973 (26 Oct). *Festivals of Joy. T* **149** *and similar vert designs. Multicoloured.* W w **12** *(sideways).* P 14.
485	3 c. Type **149**	10	10
486	10 c. Diwali	10	10
487	20 c. Id-ul-Fitar	15	15
488	25 c. Chinese New Year	15	15
485/8	*Set of 4*	35	40

150 Athletics   **151** Bowler

(Des G. Drummond. Litho Questa)

1974 (7 Jan). *Commonwealth Games, Christchurch. T* **150** *and similar vert designs. Multicoloured.* W w **12** *(sideways).* P 14.
489	3 c. Type **150**	15	10
490	8 c. Boxing	15	10
491	50 c. Bowling	50	75
489/91	*Set of 3*	70	80

(Des Hon. P. Snow. Adapted J.W. Litho Questa)

1974 (21 Feb). *Cricket Centenary. T* **151** *and similar multicoloured designs.* W w **12** *(sideways* on 3 and 25 c.).* P 14.
492	3 c. Type **151**	50	25
	w. Wmk Crown right of CA	5·00	
493	25 c. Batsman and wicketkeeper	90	35
	w. Wmk Crown to right of CA	3·00	
494	40 c. Fielder (*horiz*)	1·00	1·40
492/4	*Set of 3*	2·25	1·75

**The normal sideways watermark shows Crown to left of CA, as seen from the back of the stamp.*

152 Fijian Postman

(Des L. Curtis. Litho Format)

1974 (22 May). *Centenary of the Universal Postal Union. T* **152** *and similar horiz designs. Multicoloured.* W w **12**. P 14.
495	3 c. Type **152**	10	10
496	8 c. Loading mail onto *Fijian Princess*	10	10
497	30 c. Fijian post office and mail bus	20	25
498	50 c. B.A.C. One Eleven 200/400 modern aircraft	35	1·90
495/8	*Set of 4*	60	2·00

153 Cubs lighting Fire   **154** Cakobau Club and Flag

(Des E. W. Roberts. Litho Questa)

1974 (20 Aug). *First National Scout Jamboree, Lautoka. T* **153** *and similar multicoloured designs.* W w **12** *(sideways* on 40 c.).* P 14.
499	3 c. Type **153**	15	10
500	10 c. Scouts reading map	20	10
501	40 c. Scouts and Fijian flag (*vert*)	65	2·25
	w. Wmk Crown to right of CA	70·00	
499/501	*Set of 3*	90	2·25

**The normal sideways watermark shows Crown to left of CA, as seen from the back of the stamp.*

(Des J.W. Litho Enschedé)

1974 (9 Oct). *Centenary of Deed of Cession and Fourth Anniv of Independence. T* **154** *and similar horiz designs. Multicoloured.* W w **12** *(sideways on 8 and 50 c.).* P 13½ × 13 (3 c.) or 13 × 13½ (others).
502	3 c. Type **154**	10	10
503	8 c. King Cakobau and Queen Victoria	10	10
504	50 c. Raising the Royal Standard at Nasova Ovalau	30	1·10
502/4	*Set of 3*	40	1·10

1975 (9 Apr)–**77.** *As Nos. 435/44 and 446/50, but W w* **14** *(sideways on 1 and 10 c.).*
505	1 c. *Cirrhopetalum umbellatum*	75	3·50
506	2 c. Cardinal Honey-eater	75	3·50
507	3 c. *Calanthe furcata*	40	3·50
508	4 c. *Bulbophyllum sp nov* (3.9.76)	3·50	10
509	5 c. Type **140**	1·25	3·50
	w. Wmk inverted	5·00	
510	6 c. *Phaius tancarvilliae* (3.9.76)	2·75	20
511	8 c. Blue-crested Broadbill (3.9.76)	35	10
512	10 c. *Acanthephippium vitiense*	40	1·50
513	15 c. *Dendrobium tokai* (3.9.76)	2·50	60
514	20 c. Slaty Flycatcher (15.7.77)	3·00	55
516	30 c. *Dendrobium gordonii* (3.9.76)	5·00	95
517	40 c. Type **141** (3.9.76)	3·00	60
	w. Wmk inverted		
518	50 c. White-throated Pigeon (3.9.76)	3·00	65
519	$1 Collared Lory (3.9.76)	3·00	1·50
520	$2 *Dendrobium platygastrium* (3.9.76)	1·75	1·50
505/20	*Set of 15*	26·00	20·00

155 "Diwali" (Hindu Festival)   **156** Steam Locomotive No. 21

(Des Jennifer Toombs. Litho Walsall)

1975 (31 Oct). *Festivals of Joy. T* **155** *and similar vert designs. Multicoloured.* W w **14** *(inverted).* P 14.
521	3 c. Type **155**	10	10
522	15 c. "Id-Ul-Fitar" (Muslim Festival)	10	10
523	25 c. Chinese New Year	15	15
524	30 c. Christmas	20	1·10
521/4	*Set of 4*	40	1·25
MS525	121×101 mm. Nos. 521/4. W w **14** (sideways*)	1·25	6·00
	a. Imperf between (vert)	£1100	
	w. Wmk Crown to right of CA	30·00	

The normal sideways watermark on No.* **MS525 *shows Crown to left of CA, as seen from the back of the sheet.*

(Des R. Granger Barrett. Litho Questa)

1976 (26 Jan). *Sugar Trains. T* **156** *and similar horiz designs. Multicoloured.* W w **14** *(sideways).* P 14.
526	4 c. Type **156**	25	20
527	15 c. Diesel locomotive No. 8	75	40
528	20 c. Diesel locomotive No. 1	85	80
529	30 c. Free passenger train	1·10	2·25
526/9	*Set of 4*	2·75	3·25

157 Fiji Blind Society and Rotary Symbols

(Des V. Whiteley Studio. Litho J.W.)

1976 (26 Mar). *40th Anniv of Rotary in Fiji. T* **157** *and similar horiz design.* W w **14** *(sideways).* P 13.
530	10 c. ultramarine, pale sage-green and black	15	10
531	25 c. multicoloured	40	50

Design:—25 c. Ambulance and Rotary symbol.

158 De Havilland D.H.A.3 Drover 1

(Des P. Powell. Litho Questa)

1976 (1 Sept). *25th Anniv of Air Services. T* **158** *and similar horiz designs. Multicoloured.* W w **14**. P 13½ × 14.
532	4 c. Type **158**	40	20
533	15 c. B.A.C. One Eleven 200/400	1·00	1·50
534	25 c. Hawker Siddeley H.S.748	1·25	1·75
535	30 c. Britten Norman "long nose" Trislander	1·25	3·75
532/5	*Set of 4*	3·50	6·50

The new-issue supplement to this Catalogue appears each month in

GIBBONS STAMP MONTHLY

—from your newsagent or by postal subscription— sample copy and details on request.

159 The Queen's Visit to Fiji, 1970

160 Map of the World

(Des L. Curtis. Litho Questa)

1977 (7 Feb). *Silver Jubilee. T 159 and similar vert designs. Multicoloured. W w 14. P 13½.*

536	10 c. Type 159			10	10
537	25 c. King Edward's Chair			15	10
538	30 c. Queen wearing cloth-of-gold super-tunica			25	15
	w. Wmk inverted			3·50	
536/8			Set of 3	40	30

(Des J.W. Litho Walsall)

1977 (12 Apr). *E.E.C./A.C.P.* Council of Ministers Conference, Fiji. T 160 and similar horiz design. Multicoloured. W w 14 (sideways). P 14.*

539	4 c. Type 160			10	10
540	30 c. Map of Fiji group.			30	1·25

*A.C.P. = African, Caribbean, Pacific Group.

161 *Hibiscus rosa-sinensis*

(Des V. Whiteley Studio. Litho Walsall)

1977 (27 Aug). *21st Anniv of Fiji Hibiscus Festival. T 161 and similar horiz designs. W w 14 (sideways). P 14.*

541	161	4 c. multicoloured		10	10
542	—	15 c. multicoloured		15	15
543	—	30 c. multicoloured		25	25
544	—	35 c. multicoloured		40	50
541/4			Set of 4	80	90

Nos. 542/44 show different varieties of *H rosa-sinensis*.

162 Drua

163 White Hart of Richard II

(Des P. Powell. Litho Questa)

1977 (7 Nov). *Canoes. T 162 and similar horiz designs. Multicoloured. W w 14 (sideways). P 14.*

545	4 c. Type 162			15	10
546	15 c. Tabilai			30	20
547	25 c. Takai			35	25
548	40 c. Camakua			55	80
545/8			Set of 4	1·25	1·25

(Des C. Abbott. Litho Questa)

1978 (21 Apr). *25th Anniv of Coronation. T 163 and similar vert designs. P 15.*

549	25 c. bistre, blue-green and silver		15	20
	a. Sheetlet. Nos. 549/51 × 2		80	
550	25 c. multicoloured		15	20
551	25 c. bistre, blue-green and silver		15	20
549/51		Set of 3	40	55

Designs:—No. 549, Type 163; No. 550, Queen Elizabeth II; No. 551, Banded Iguana.
Nos. 549/51 were printed together in small sheets of 6, containing two se-tenant strips of 3, with horizontal gutter margin between.

164 Defence Force surrounding Fokker F.VIIa/3M *Southern Cross*, Suva

(Des A. Theobald. Litho Harrison)

1978 (26 June). *Aviation Anniversaries. T 164 and similar horiz designs. Multicoloured. W w 14 (sideways). P 14.*

552	4 c. Type 164			30	10
553	15 c. *Southern Cross* prior to leaving Naselai Beach		50	30
554	25 c. Wright Flyer 1			60	60
555	30 c. Bristol F2B "Brisfit"			60	85
552/5			Set of 4	1·75	1·60

Anniversaries—25 c. 75th of powered flight; 30 c. 60th of R.A.F.; others, 50th of first trans-Pacific flight by Kingsford-Smith.

165 Shallow Wooden Oil Dish in shape of Human Figure

166 Advent Crown with Candles (Christmas)

(Des J. Cooter. Litho Questa)

1978 (14 Aug). *Fijian Artifacts. T 165 and similar multicoloured designs. W w 14 (sideways on 15 and 25 c.). P 14.*

556	4 c. Type 165			10	10
557	15 c. Necklace of cachalot teeth (*horiz*)		10	10
558	25 c. Double water bottle (*horiz*)		15	10
559	30 c. Finely carved Ula or throwing club		15	15
556/9			Set of 4	35	35

(Des Jennifer Toombs. Litho Harrison)

1978 (30 Oct). *Festivals. T 166 and similar horiz designs. Multicoloured. W w 14 (sideways). P 14.*

560	4 c. Type 166			10	10
561	15 c. Lamps (Diwali)			15	10
562	25 c. Coffee pot, cups and fruit (Id-Ul-Fitr)	20	10
563	40 c. Lion (Chinese New Year)		35	40
560/3			Set of 4	65	60

167 Banded Iguana

(Des L. Curtis and G. Drummond. Litho Questa)

1979 (19 Mar). *Endangered Wildlife. T 167 and similar horiz designs. Multicoloured. W w 14 (sideways). P 14.*

564	4 c. Type 167			50	10
565	15 c. Tree Frog			1·00	15
566	25 c. Long-legged Warbler		4·00	40
567	30 c. Pink-billed Parrot Finch		4·00	2·40
564/7			Set of 4	8·50	2·75

168 Women with Dholak

(Des J.W. Litho Questa)

1979 (11 May). *Centenary of Arrival of Indians. T 168 and similar horiz designs. Multicoloured. W w 14 (sideways). P 14.*

568	4 c. Type 168			10	10
569	15 c. Men sitting round tanoa		10	10
570	30 c. Farmer and sugar cane plantation		15	10
571	40 c. Sailing ship *Leonidas*		40	45
568/71			Set of 4	60	45

169 Soccer

(Des BG Studio. Litho Questa)

1979 (2 July). *6th South Pacific Games. T 169 and similar horiz designs. Multicoloured. W w 14 (sideways). P 14.*

572	4 c. Type 169			20	10
573	15 c. Rugby Union			40	20
574	30 c. Lawn tennis			80	80
575	40 c. Weightlifting			80	1·40
572/5			Set of 4	2·00	2·25

170 Indian Child and Map of Fiji

(Des D. Bowen. Litho Walsall)

1979 (17 Sept). *International Year of the Child. T 170 and similar horiz designs showing children and map of Fiji. Multicoloured. W w 14 (sideways). P 14½ × 14.*

576	4 c. + 1 c. Type 170			10	10
577	15 c. + 2 c. European child		15	15
578	30 c. + 3 c. Chinese child		15	15
579	40 c. + 4 c. Fijian child		15	20
576/9			Set of 4	45	50

171 Old Town Hall, Suva

(Des J.W. Litho Questa (1, 2, 3, 4, 10, 15, 20, 30 c., \$5) or Harrison (others))

1979 (11 Nov)–**94**. *Architecture. Multicoloured designs as T 171. W w 14 (sideways* on horiz designs). Chalk-surfaced paper (1, 2, 3, 4, 10, 15, 20, 30 c., \$5). P 13½×13 (\$1), 13×13½ (\$2), 13×14 (\$5) or 14 (others).*

A. *Without imprint date at foot*

580A	1 c. Type 171		15	60
	c. Ordinary paper (13.6.80)		90	1·50
581A	2 c. Dudley Church, Suva		45	70
	c. Ordinary paper (13.6.80)		90	1·75
582A	3 c. Fiji International Telecommunications Building, Suva		35	80
	c. Ordinary paper (13.6.80)		1·00	1·75
583A	5 c. Lautoka Mosque (22.12.80)		15	10
	w. Wmk Crown to right of CA		†	—
584A	6 c. General Post Office, Suva (22.12.80)	15	70
585A	10 c. Fiji Visitors' Bureau, Suva		20	10
	c. Ordinary paper (13.6.80)		1·00	1·75
586A	12 c. Public School, Levuka (22.12.80)	20	1·40
587A	15 c. Colonial War Memorial Hospital, Suva		40	30
	c. Ordinary paper (13.6.80)		90	1·75
588A	18 c. Labasa Sugar Mill (22.12.80)		20	30
	w. Wmk Crown to right of CA		—	15·00
589A	20 c. Rewa Bridge, Nausori		55	30
	c. Ordinary paper (13.6.80)		1·25	2·00
590A	30 c. Sacred Heart Cathedral, Suva (*vert*)	65	50
	c. Ordinary paper (13.6.80)		30	1·75
591A	35 c. Grand Pacific Hotel, Suva (22.12.80)	30	1·00
592A	45 c. Shiva Temple, Suva (22.12.80)		40	45
593A	50 c. Serua Island Village (22.12.80)		40	40
594A	\$1 Solo Rock Lighthouse (30×46 mm) (22.12.80)		2·50	2·00
595A	\$2 Baker Memorial Hall, Nausori (46×30 mm) (22.12.80)		1·40	1·90
595cA	\$5 Government House, Suva (46×30 mm)		2·00	3·50
580A/95cA		Set of 17	9·00	13·00

B. *With imprint date*

580B	1 c. Type 171 (12.94)		70	1·50
581B	2 c. Dudley Church, Suva (19.11.86)	40	20
	c. Ordinary paper (2.84)		30	20
582B	3 c. Fiji International Telecommunications Building, Suva (11.93)	1·50	2·25
582dB	4 c. Lautoka Mosque (11.93)		2·00	3·00
	e. Ordinary paper (11.91)		2·00	3·00
583B	5 c. As 4 c. (1.84)		30	10
584B	6 c. General Post Office, Suva (15.6.83)	15	10
585B	10 c. Fiji Visitors' Bureau, Suva (*ordinary paper*) (11.91)	1·50	2·00
586B	12 c. Public School, Levuka (11.93)	80	1·75
587B	15 c. Colonial War Memorial Hospital, Suva (*ordinary paper*) (11.91)	1·50	1·75
589B	20 c. Rewa Bridge, Nausori (11.93)	1·75	2·00
593B	50 c. Serua Island Village (*chalk-surfaced paper*) (22.8.94)	2·00	2·25
580B/93B		Set of 11	11·00	15·00

*The normal sideways watermark show Crown to left of CA, as seen from the back of the stamp.
Imprint dates: "1983", Nos. 581Bc, 583B, 584B; "1986", No. 581B; "1991", Nos. 581Bc, 582Be, 585B, 587B; "1993", Nos. 581B, 582B, 582dB, 586B, 589B; "1994", Nos. 580B/1B, 582dB, 586B, 589B, 593B.

For these designs and similar 8 c. watermarked w 16 see Nos. 719/35.

172 *Southern Cross*, 1873

(Des L. Dunn. Litho Secura, Singapore)

1980 (28 Apr). *"London 1980" International Stamp Exhibition. Mail-carrying Ships. T 172 and similar horiz designs. Multicoloured. W w 14 (sideways*). P 13½.*

596	6 c. Type 172			30	10
	w. Wmk Crown to right of CA		18·00	
597	20 c. *Levuka*, 1910			40	10

598	45 c. *Matua*, 1936	55	50
599	50 c. *Oronsay*, 1951	55	70
	w. Wmk Crown to right of CA	18·00	
596/9	*Set of 4*	1·60	1·25

The normal sideways watermark shows Crown to left of CA, as seen from the back of the stamp.

173 Sovi Bay

(Des BG Studio. Litho Questa)

1980 (18 Aug). *Tourism. T 173 and similar horiz designs. Multicoloured. W w 14 (sideways). P 13½ × 14.*

600	6 c. Type 173	10	10
601	20 c. Evening scene, Yanuca Island	15	15
602	45 c. Dravuni Beach	20	40
603	50 c. Wakaya Island	20	45
600/3	*Set of 4*	50	95

174 Official Opening of Parliament, 1979

(Des J. Cooter. Litho J.W.)

1980 (6 Oct). *10th Anniv of Independence. T 174 and similar multicoloured designs. W w 14 (sideways on 6 and 45 c.). P 13.*

604	6 c. Type 174	10	10
605	20 c. Fiji coat of arms (*vert*)	15	10
606	45 c. Fiji flag	20	20
607	50 c. Queen Elizabeth II (*vert*)	25	35
604/7	*Set of 4*	55	60

175 "Coastal Scene" (painting, Semisi Maya)   176 Prince Charles Sailing

(Des J.W. Litho Questa)

1981 (21 Apr). *International Year for Disabled Persons. T 175 and similar multicoloured designs. W w 14 (sideways on 6 and 35 c.). P 14.*

608	6 c. Type 175	10	10
609	35 c. "Underwater Scene" (painting, Semisi Maya)	35	30
610	50 c. Semisi Maya (disabled artist) at work (*vert*)	40	40
611	60 c. "Peacock" (painting, Semisi Maya) (*vert*)	45	45
608/11	*Set of 4*	1·10	1·10

(Des J.W. Litho Questa)

1981 (22 July). *Royal Wedding. T 176 and similar vert designs. Multicoloured. W w 14. P 14.*

612	6 c. Wedding bouquet from Fiji	10	10
613	45 c. Type 176	30	15
614	$1 Prince Charles and Lady Diana Spencer	50	60
612/14	*Set of 3*	70	75

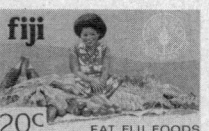

177 Operator Assistance Centre   178 "Eat Fiji Foods"

(Des A. Theobald. Litho Format)

1981 (17 Aug). *Telecommunications. T 177 and similar horiz designs. Multicoloured. W w 14 (sideways). P 14.*

615	6 c. Type 177	10	10
616	35 c. Microwave station	45	50
617	50 c. Satellite earth station	60	75
618	60 c. Cable ship *Retriever*	80	90
615/18	*Set of 4*	1·75	2·00

(Des J.W. Litho Format)

1981 (21 Sept). *World Food Day. W w 14. P 14½ × 14.*

619	178 20 c. multicoloured	30	10

179 Ratu Sir Lala Sukuna (first Speaker, Legislative Council)

(Des A. Theobald. Litho Format)

1981 (19 Oct). *Commonwealth Parliamentary Association Conference, Suva. T 179 and similar horiz designs. W w 14 (sideways). P 14.*

620	6 c. black, buff and orange-brown	10	10
621	35 c. multicoloured	30	30
622	50 c. multicoloured	45	45
620/2	*Set of 3*	75	75
MS623	73 × 53 mm. 60 c. multicoloured	70	1·00

Designs:—35 c. Mace of the House of Representatives; 50 c. Suva Civic Centre; 60 c. Flags of C.P.A. countries.

180 Bell P-39 Airacobra

(Des A. Theobald. Litho Walsall)

1981 (7 Dec). *World War II Aircraft. T 180 and similar horiz designs. Multicoloured. W w 14 (sideways). P 14.*

624	6 c. Type 180	1·00	10
625	18 c. Consolidated PBY-5 Catalina	1·75	40
626	35 c. Curtiss P-40E Warhawk	2·25	95
627	60 c. Short Singapore III	2·75	6·00
624/7	*Set of 4*	7·00	6·75

181 Scouts constructing Shelter

(Des B. Melton. Litho Questa)

1982 (22 Feb). *75th Anniv of Boy Scout Movement. T 181 and similar multicoloured designs. W w 14 (sideways on 6 and 45 c.). P 14½.*

628	6 c. Type 181	15	10
629	20 c. Scouts sailing (*vert*)	50	50
630	45 c. Scouts by campfire	85	50
631	60 c. Lord Baden-Powell (*vert*)	1·00	1·00
628/31	*Set of 4*	2·25	1·75

182 Fiji Soldiers at U.N. Checkpoint

(Des J.W. Litho Format)

1982 (10 May*). *Disciplined Forces. T 182 and similar horiz designs. Multicoloured. W w 14 (sideways). P 14.*

632	12 c. Type 182	30	10
633	30 c. Soldiers engaged in rural development	60	45
634	40 c. Police patrol	1·50	1·25
635	70 c. *Kiro* (minesweeper)	1·50	3·75
632/5	*Set of 4*	3·50	5·00

This is the local release date. The Crown Agents released the stamps in London on 3 May.

183 Footballers and Fiji Football Association Logo   184 Bride and Groom leaving St. Paul's

(Des A. Theobald. Litho Walsall)

1982 (15 June). *World Cup Football Championship, Spain. T 183 and similar horiz designs. W w 14 (sideways*). P 14.*

636	6 c. rosine, black and lemon	10	10
637	18 c. multicoloured	25	20
	w. Wmk Crown to right of CA	42·00	
638	50 c. multicoloured	70	70

639	90 c. multicoloured	1·10	2·00
	w. Wmk Crown to right of CA	3·50	
636/9	*Set of 4*	1·90	2·75

Designs:—18 c. Footballers and World Cup emblem; 50 c. Footballer and Bernabeu Stadium; 90 c. Footballers and Naranjito (mascot).

The normal sideways watermark shows Crown to left of CA, as seen from the back of the stamp.

(Des C. Abbott. Litho Harrison)

1982 (1 July). *21st Birthday of Princess of Wales. T 184 and similar vert designs. Multicoloured. W w 14. P 14½ × 14.*

640	20 c. Fiji coat of arms	20	15
641	35 c. Lady Diana Spencer at Broadlands, May 1981	35	25
642	45 c. Type 184	40	40
643	$1 Formal portrait	1·25	2·25
640/3	*Set of 4*	2·00	2·75

185 Prince Philip   186 Baby Jesus with Mary and Joseph

(Des C. Abbott. Litho Format)

1982 (1 Nov). *Royal Visit. T 185 and similar multicoloured designs. W w 14. P 14.*

644	6 c. Type 185	30	15
645	45 c. Queen Elizabeth II	80	2·50
MS646	128 × 88 mm. Nos. 644/5 and $1 Royal Yacht *Britannia* (*horiz*). Wmk sideways	2·50	3·00

(Des G. Wilby. Litho Questa)

1982 (22 Nov). *Christmas. T 186 and similar horiz designs. Multicoloured. W w 14 (sideways). P 14 × 14½.*

647	6 c. Type 186	10	10
648	20 c. Three Wise Men presenting gifts	30	20
649	35 c. Carol-singing	45	35
647/9	*Set of 3*	75	55
MS650	94 × 42 mm. $1 "Faith" (from the "Three Virtues" by Raphael)	1·25	1·50

187 Red-throated Lorikeet   188 Bure in Traditional Village

(Des N. Arlott. Litho Questa)

1983 (14 Feb). *Parrots. T 187 and similar vert designs. Multicoloured. W w 14. P 14.*

651	20 c. Type 187	1·50	20
652	40 c. Blue-crowned Lory	1·75	50
653	55 c. Masked Shining Parrot	2·00	1·25
654	70 c. Red Shining Parrot	2·50	3·25
651/4	*Set of 4*	7·00	4·75

(Des B. Melton. Litho Questa)

1983 (14 Mar). *Commonwealth Day. T 188 and similar horiz designs. Multicoloured. W w 14 (sideways). P 14.*

655	8 c. Type 188	10	10
656	25 c. Barefoot firewalkers	20	15
657	50 c. Sugar industry	30	35
658	80 c. Kava "Yagona" ceremony	55	70
655/8	*Set of 4*	1·00	1·10

189 First Manned Balloon Flight, 1783   190 Nawanawa

(Des Harrison. Litho Questa)

1983 (18 July). *Bicentenary of Manned Flight. T 189 and similar horiz designs. Multicoloured. W w 14 (sideways). P 14.*

659	8 c. Type 189	25	10
660	20 c. Wright brothers' Flyer 1	45	30
661	25 c. Douglas Super DC-3	50	40
662	40 c. De Havilland D.H.106 Comet 1	75	60
663	50 c. Boeing 747	90	70
664	58 c. Space Shuttle	1·00	80
659/64	*Set of 6*	3·50	2·50

(Des Harrison. Litho Format)

1983 (3 Oct*). *Flowers* (1st series). T **190** *and similar vert designs. Multicoloured.* W w **14**. P 14×14½.
665	8 c. Type **190**	.. ..	10	10
666	25 c. Rosawa	.. ..	30	30
667	40 c. Warerega	.. ..	40	50
668	$1 Saburo	.. ..	80	1·40
665/8		*Set of 4*	1·40	2·00

*This is the local release date. The Crown Agents issued the stamps in London on 26 September.
See also Nos. 680/3.

191 Fijian beating Lali and Earth Satellite Station

192 *Dacryopinax spathularia*

(Des Garden Studio. Litho Questa)

1983 (7 Nov). *World Communications Year.* W w **14**. P 13½.
669	**191** 50 c. multicoloured	.. ..	50	80

(Des Jennifer Toombs. Litho Enschedé)

1984 (9 Jan). *Fungi.* T **192** *and similar multicoloured designs.* W w **14** *(sideways on 50 c. and $1).* P 13½ × 13 (8 c. to 40 c.) or 13 × 13½ (others).
670	8 c. Type **192**	.. .. ..	85	15
	w. Wmk inverted	.. ..		
671	15 c. *Podoscypha involuta*	.. ..	1·25	25
672	40 c. *Lentinus squarrosulus*	..	2·25	1·00
673	50 c. *Scleroderma cepa* ("*Scleroderma flavidum*") (*horiz*)		2·25	1·25
674	$1 *Phillipsia domingensis* (*horiz*)		2·75	3·50
670/4		*Set of 5*	8·50	5·50

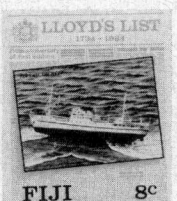

193 Tui Lau
(freighter) on Reef

(Des L. Curtis. Litho Questa)

1984 (7 May). *250th Anniv of "Lloyd's List" (newspaper).* T **193** *and similar multicoloured designs.* W w **14**. P 14½ × 14.
675	8 c. Type **193**	.. ..	55	10
676	40 c. *Tofua* (cargo liner)	..	1·25	80
677	55 c. *Canberra* (liner)	..	1·25	1·50
678	60 c. *NedLloyd Madras* (freighter) at Suva wharf	.. ..	1·40	1·75
675/8		*Set of 4*	4·00	3·75

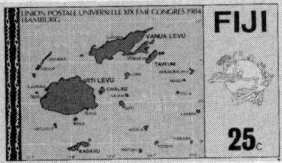

194 Map of Fijian Islands

(Des J. Cooter. Litho Questa)

1984 (14 June). *Universal Postal Union Congress, Hamburg. Sheet* 77 × 65 mm. W w **14** (sideways). P 14½.
MS679	**194** 25 c. multicoloured	..	1·75	1·25

(Des Harrison. Litho Format)

1984 (9 July). *Flowers* (2nd series). *Vert designs as* T **190**. W w **14**. P 14×14½.
680	15 c. Drividrivi	.. ..	25	25
681	20 c. Vesida	.. ..	35	40
682	50 c. Vuga	.. ..	50	90
683	70 c. Qaiqi	.. ..	60	1·40
680/3		*Set of 4*	1·50	2·75

195 Prize Bull, Yalavou Cattle Scheme

(Des D. Hartley-Marjoram. Litho Walsall)

1984 (17 Sept). *"Ausipex" International Stamp Exhibition, Melbourne.* T **195** *and similar multicoloured designs.* W w **14** (sideways* on 8, 40 c. and $1). P 14½×14 (25 c.) or 14×14½ (others).
684	8 c. Type **195**	.. ..	25	10
685	25 c. Wailoa Power Station (*vert*)	55	40
686	40 c. Air Pacific Boeing 737 airliner	1·75	1·25
687	$1 Container ship *Fua Kavenga*	1·40	3·00
	w. Wmk Crown to right of CA	1·40	
684/7		*Set of 4*	3·50	4·25

*The normal sideways watermark shows Crown to left of CA, as seen from the back of the stamp.

196 The Stable at Bethlehem

(Des G. Vasarhelyi. Litho Format)

1984 (5 Nov). *Christmas. Children's Paintings.* T **196** *and similar multicoloured designs.* W w **14** (sideways on horiz designs). P 14.
688	8 c. Type **196**	.. ..	10	10
689	20 c. Outrigger canoe	..	30	20
690	25 c. Father Christmas and Christmas tree	30	25
691	40 c. Going to church	..	40	70
692	$1 Decorating Christmas tree (*vert*)	70	1·75
688/92		*Set of 5*	1·50	2·75

197 *Danaus plexippus*

198 Outrigger Canoe off Toberua Island

(Des Annette Robinson. Litho Questa)

1985 (4 Feb). *Butterflies.* T **197** *and similar multicoloured designs.* W w **14** (sideways on 8 c. and 25 c.). P 14.
693	8 c. Type **197**	.. ..	1·50	15
694	25 c. *Hypolimnas bolina*	..	2·50	60
695	40 c. *Lampides boeticus* (*vert*)	3·25	2·25
696	$1 *Precis villida* (*vert*)	..	4·50	7·00
693/6		*Set of 4*	10·50	9·00

(Des D. Miller. Litho B.D.T.)

1985 (1 Apr). *"Expo '85" World Fair, Japan.* T **198** *and similar vert designs. Multicoloured.* W w **14**. P 14.
697	20 c. Type **198**	.. ..	55	30
698	25 c. Wainivula Falls	..	1·00	40
699	50 c. Mana Island	..	1·10	90
700	$1 Sawa-I-Lau Caves	..	1·40	2·25
697/700		*Set of 4*	3·50	3·50

199 With Prince Charles at Garter Ceremony

200 Horned Squirrelfish

(Des A. Theobald ($1), C. Abbott (others). Litho Questa)

1985 (7 June). *Life and Times of Queen Elizabeth the Queen Mother.* T **199** *and similar vert designs. Multicoloured.* W w **16**. P 14½ × 14.
701	8 c. With Prince Andrew on her 60th Birthday	.. ..	10	10
702	25 c. Type **199**	.. ..	35	40
703	40 c. The Queen Mother at Epsom Races	75	80
704	50 c. With Prince Henry at his christening (from photo by Lord Snowdon)	75	1·25
701/4		*Set of 4*	1·75	2·25
MS705	91×73 mm. $1 With Prince Andrew at Royal Wedding, 1981. Wmk sideways	1·90	2·00

(Des M. Raj. Litho Questa)

1985 (23 Sept). *Shallow Water Marine Fishes.* T **200** *and similar horiz designs. Multicoloured.* W w **14** (sideways). P 14½.
706	40 c. Type **200**	.. ..	1·50	55
707	50 c. Yellow-banded Goatfish	..	1·50	1·10
708	55 c. Yellow-edged Lyretail ("Fairy Cod")	1·75	1·75
709	$1 Peacock Hind	.. ..	2·75	5·00
706/9		*Set of 4*	7·00	7·50

201 Collared Petrel

202 Children and "Peace for Fiji and the World" Slogan

(Des Doreen McGuinness. Litho Walsall)

1985 (4 Nov). *Seabirds.* T **201** *and similar vert designs. Multicoloured.* W w **14**. P 14 × 13½.
710	15 c. Type **201**	.. ..	2·00	50
711	20 c. Lesser Frigate Bird	..	2·00	50
712	50 c. Brown Booby	.. ..	3·75	3·75
713	$1 Crested Tern	.. ..	5·50	8·00
710/13		*Set of 4*	12·00	11·50

(Des A. Theobald. Litho Format)

1986 (21 Apr). *60th Birthday of Queen Elizabeth II. Vert designs as* T **110** *of Ascension. Multicoloured.* W w **16**. P 14×14½.
714	20 c. With Duke of York at Royal Tournament, 1936	20	25
715	25 c. Royal Family on Palace balcony after Princess Margaret's wedding, 1960	20	25
716	40 c. Queen inspecting guard of honour, Suva, 1982	25	45
717	50 c. In Luxembourg, 1976	30	60
718	$1 At Crown Agents Head Office, London, 1983	45	1·60
714/18		*Set of 5*	1·25	2·75

(Litho Harrison (4 c. (1988 ptg), 8 c.) or Questa (others))

1986 (Apr)–**91**. *As Nos. 580/2, 582d, 585, 587, 589, 591, 593/4 and new value.* W w **16** (sideways on 1, 2, 3, 4, 8, 10, 15, 20, 35, 50 c.). *Chalk-surfaced paper* (2 c.). *With imprint date.* P 14×13½ ($1) or 14 (others).
719	1 c. Type **171** (11.3.91)	..	70	1·75
720	2 c. Dudley Church, Suva	..	40	30
	a. Ordinary paper (11.3.91)		30	30
721	3 c. Fiji International Telecommunications Building, Suva (1.6.88)	40	30
722	4 c. Lautoka Mosque (1.6.88)		30	30
724	8 c. Public School, Levuka (as No. 586) (1.12.86)	2·75	2·25
725	10 c. Fiji Visitors Bureau, Suva (1.3.90)	20	30
726	15 c. Colonial War Memorial Hospital, Suva (11.3.91)	30	20
730	20 c. Rewa Bridge, Nausori (1.6.88)	75	75
732	35 c. Grand Pacific Hotel, Suva (11.3.91)	1·10	1·50
734	50 c. Serua Island Village (11.3.91)	1·60	2·00
735	$1 Solo Rock Lighthouse (30×46 mm) (11.3.91)	4·00	5·00
719/35		*Set of 11*	11·00	13·00

From the 11 March 1991 printing all values were produced by Questa. The 4 c. (No. 722) was the only stamp in this issue to be printed by both Harrison and Questa.

Imprint dates: "1986", Nos. 720, 724; "1988", Nos. 720/2, 730; "1990", Nos. 725, 730; "1991", Nos. 719, 720a, 721/2, 725/6, 732, 734/5; "1992", Nos. 719, 721/2, 726, 730, 732, 734/5.

(Des G. Vasarhelyi. Litho Format)

1986 (23 June). *International Peace Year.* T **202** *and similar vert design. Multicoloured.* W w **16**. P 14½.
736	8 c. Type **202**	.. ..	25	10
737	40 c. Peace dove and houses	..	65	1·00

203 Halley's Comet in Centaurus Constellation and Newton's Reflector

204 Ground Frog

(Des D. Hartley. Litho B.D.T.)

1986 (7 July). *Appearance of Halley's Comet.* T **203** *and similar vert designs. Multicoloured.* W w **16**. P 13½.
738	25 c. Type **203**	.. ..	1·25	40
739	40 c. Halley's Comet over Lomaiviti	1·50	85
740	$1 *Giotto* spacecraft photographing Comet nucleus	2·50	5·50
738/40		*Set of 3*	4·75	6·00

(Litho Format)

1986 (1 Aug). *Reptiles and Amphibians.* T **204** *and similar horiz designs. Multicoloured.* W w **16** (sideways). P 14½.
741	8 c. Type **204**	.. ..	55	10
742	20 c. Burrowing Snake	..	1·00	30
743	25 c. Spotted Gecko	..	1·10	35
744	40 c. Crested Iguana	..	1·25	90
745	50 c. Blotched Skink	..	1·40	3·00
746	$1 Speckled Skink	..	1·75	5·50
741/6		*Set of 6*	6·25	9·00

205 Gatawaka

206 Weasel Cone
(*Conus mustelinus*)

(Des M. Raj. Litho Walsall)

1986 (10 Nov). *Ancient War Clubs. T* **205** *and similar vert designs. Multicoloured.* W w 16. *P* 14.

747	25 c. Type 205..					80	35
748	40 c. Siriti					1·00	60
749	50 c. Bulibuli					1·25	1·60
750	$1 Culacula..					2·25	3·00
747/50					*Set of 4*	4·75	5·00

(Des A. Riley. Litho Format)

1987 (26 Feb). *Cone Shells of Fiji. T* **206** *and similar vert designs. Multicoloured.* W w 16. *P* 14×14½.

751	15 c. Type 206..				80	25
752	20 c. Pertusus Cone (*Conus pertusus*)			90	35
753	25 c. Admiral Cone (*Conus ammiralis*)		1·00	40
754	40 c. Leaden Cone (*Conus scabriusculus*)	1·40	1·25
755	50 c. Imperial Cone (*Conus imperialis*)	1·50	2·50
	w. Wmk inverted					
756	$1 Geography Cone (*Conus geographus*)	2·00	4·75
	w. Wmk inverted					
751/6				*Set of 6*	7·00	8·50

207 Tagimoucia Flower   (**208**)

(Des M. Raj. Litho Format)

1987 (23 Apr). *Tagimoucia Flower. Sheet* 72×55 *mm.* W w 14 (*sideways*). *P* 14½.

MS757	**207** $1 multicoloured			2·75	2·00

1987 (13 June). *"Capex '87" International Stamp Exhibition, Toronto. No.* MS757 *optd with T* **208**.

MS758	72×55 mm. $1 Type **207**..			5·50	4·00

Stamps from Nos. **MS757** and **MS758** are identical as the overprint on **MS758** appears on the margin of the sheet.

209 Traditional Fijian House

(Des National Focal Point, adapted L. Curtis. Litho Format)

1987 (20 July). *International Year of Shelter for the Homeless. T* **209** *and similar horiz design. Multicoloured.* W w 16 (*sideways*). *P* 14.

759	55 c. Type 209..				45	50
760	70 c. Modern bungalows				55	60

210 *Bulbogaster ctenostomoides*
(stick insect)

(Des R. Lewington. Litho Walsall)

1987 (7 Sept). *Fijian Insects. T* **210** *and similar horiz designs. Multicoloured.* W w 16 (*sideways*). *P* 13½×14.

761	20 c. Type 210..				1·40	30
762	25 c. *Paracupta flaviventris* (beetle)		1·60	35
763	40 c. *Cerambyrhynchus schoenherri* (beetle)	2·00	1·50
764	50 c. *Rhinoscapha lagopyga* (weevil)		2·00	2·50
765	$1 *Xixuthrus heros* (beetle)			3·00	6·00
761/5				*Set of 5*	9·00	9·50

REPUBLIC

Following a military coup on 25 September 1987 Fiji was declared a republic on 7 October. The Governor-General resigned on 15 October 1987 and Fiji's Commonwealth membership lapsed until 1 October 1997 when the country was readmitted following further constitutional changes.

211 The
Nativity

212 Windsurfer
and Beach

(Des G. Vasarhelyi. Litho Walsall)

1987 (19 Nov). *Christmas. T* **211** *and similar multicoloured designs.* W w 16 (*sideways on* 40 c., 50 c.). *P* 14×13½ (*vert*) *or* 13½×14 (*horiz*).

766	8 c. Type 211..				40	10
767	40 c. The Shepherds (*horiz*)			1·25	40
768	50 c. The Three Kings (*horiz*)		1·75	90
769	$1 The Three Kings presenting gifts	2·25	2·50
766/9				*Set of 4*	5·00	3·50

(Des Ahgrafik. Litho Questa)

1988 (27 Apr). *"Expo '88" World Fair, Brisbane.* W w 16 (*sideways*). *P* 14.

770	**212** 30 c. multicoloured			1·00	50

213 Woman using Fiji
"Nouna" (stove)

214 Pottery Bowl

(Litho Questa)

1988 (14 June). *Centenary of International Council of Women.* W w 16 (*sideways*). *P* 14.

771	**213** 45 c. multicoloured			75	60

(Des N. Ahmed. Litho Questa)

1988 (29 Aug). *Ancient Fijian Pottery. T* **214** *and similar multicoloured designs.* W w 14 (*sideways*) (69 c.) *or* w **16** (*others, sideways on* 75 c.). *P* 14.

772	9 c. Type 214				15	10
773	23 c. Cooking pot				25	25
774	58 c. Priest's drinking vessel		50	1·00
775	63 c. Drinking vessel			55	1·25
776	69 c. Earthenware oil lamp		60	1·40
777	75 c. Cooking pot with relief pattern (*vert*)	70	1·50
772/7				*Set of 6*	2·50	5·00

215 Fiji Tree Frog

216 *Dendrobium
mohlianum*

(Des Doreen McGuinness. Litho Walsall)

1988 (3 Oct). *Fiji Tree Frog. T* **215** *and similar vert designs. Multicoloured.* W w 16. *P* 14×13½.

778	18 c. Type 215				1·75	85
779	23 c. Frog climbing grass stalks		2·00	1·25
780	30 c. On leaf				2·50	3·00
781	45 c. Moving from one leaf to another	3·00	4·00
778/81				*Set of 4*	8·25	8·25

(Des M. Raj. Litho Walsall)

1988 (21 Nov). *Native Flowers. T* **216** *and similar vert designs. Multicoloured.* W w 14. *P* 14.

782	9 c. Type 216				55	15
783	30 c. *Dendrobium cattilare*..		85	45
784	45 c. *Degeneria vitiensis*		85	70
785	$1 *Degeneria roseiflora*		1·25	2·40
782/5				*Set of 4*	3·25	3·25

217 Battle of Solferino, 1859

(Des L. Curtis. Litho Questa)

1989 (6 Feb). *125th Anniv of International Red Cross. T* **217** *and similar designs.* W w 16 (*sideways on* 58, 69 c.). *P* 13½ × 14 (*horiz*) *or* 14 × 13½ (*vert*).

786	58 c. multicoloured				1·10	80
787	63 c. multicoloured				1·10	1·00
788	69 c. multicoloured				1·40	1·25
789	$1 black and bright scarlet		1·50	1·50
786/9				*Set of 4*	4·50	4·00

Designs: *Vert*—63 c. Henri Dunant (founder); $1 Anniversary logo. *Horiz*—69 c. Fijian Red Cross worker with blood donor.

218 Plan of *Bounty*'s
Launch

219 *Platygyra daedalea*

(Des Jennifer Toombs. Litho Questa)

1989 (28 Apr). *Bicentenary of Captain Bligh's Boat Voyage. T* **218** *and similar horiz designs. Multicoloured.* W w 16 (*sideways*). *P* 14×14½.

790	45 c. Type 218				1·75	50
791	58 c. Cup, bowl and Bligh's journal		1·90	1·25
792	80 c. Bligh and extract from journal	2·25	2·75
793	$1 *Bounty*'s launch and map of Fiji	3·25	3·00
790/3				*Set of 4*	8·25	6·75

(Des M. Raj. Litho Harrison)

1989 (21 Aug). *Corals. T* **219** *and similar multicoloured designs.* W w 14 (*sideways on* 46, 60 c.). *P* 14.

794	46 c. Type 219				2·00	75
795	60 c. *Caulastrea furcata*		2·25	1·75
796	75 c. *Acropora echinata* (*vert*)		2·50	2·25
797	90 c. *Acropora humilis* (*vert*)		2·75	2·75
794/7				*Set of 4*	8·50	6·75

220 Goalkeeper

221 Congregation in
Church

(Des S. Noon. Litho Questa)

1989 (25 Sept). *World Cup Football Championship, Italy* (1990). *T* **220** *and similar horiz designs. Multicoloured.* W w 16 (*sideways*). *P* 14×14½.

798	35 c. Type 220				1·25	40
799	63 c. Goalkeeper catching ball		2·00	2·25
800	70 c. Player with ball			2·25	2·50
801	85 c. Tackling				2·25	3·00
798/801				*Set of 4*	7·00	7·25

(Des L. Curtis. Litho Questa)

1989 (1 Nov). *Christmas. T* **221** *and similar vert designs. Multicoloured.* W w 14. *P* 14½×14.

802	9 c. Type 221				25	10
803	45 c. *Delonix regia* (Christmas tree)		75	35
804	$1 The Nativity			1·50	2·00
805	$1.40, Fijian children under *Delonix regia* (tree)		1·75	3·00
802/5				*Set of 4*	3·75	5·00

222 River Snapper

223 1968 3d.
Eastern Reef Heron
Definitive

(Des M. Raj. Litho Questa)

1990 (23 Apr). *Freshwater Fishes. T 222 and similar horiz designs. Multicoloured. W w 16 (sideways). P 14½.*

806	50 c. Type 222		2·25	70
807	70 c. Kner's Grunter ("Orange-spotted Therapon")		2·75	3·00
808	85 c. Spotted Scat		3·25	3·50
809	$1 Rock Flagtail		3·50	4·00
806/9		*Set of 4*	10·50	10·00

(Des D. Miller. Litho Questa)

1990 (1 May). *"Stamp World London 90" International Stamp Exhibition, London. Sheet, 120×70 mm, containing T 223 and similar vert design. Multicoloured. W w 16 (sideways). P 14.*

MS810	$1 Type 223; $2 1968 1s. 6d. Orange-breasted Honeyeaters definitive		6·50	8·00

224 Vertiver Grass Contours

225 *Dacrydium nidulum*

(Des Ahgrafik. Litho Questa)

1990 (23 July). *Soil Conservation. T 224 and similar multicoloured designs. W w 14 (sideways on 50, 70, 90 c.). P 14.*

811	50 c. Type 224		1·00	50
812	70 c. Mulching		1·25	1·75
813	90 c. Hillside contour cultivation		1·50	2·25
814	$1 Land use rotation (*vert*)		1·50	2·50
811/14		*Set of 4*	4·75	6·25

(Des M. Raj. Litho Questa)

1990 (2 Oct). *Timber Trees. T 225 and similar vert designs. Multicoloured. W w 14. P 14.*

815	25 c. Type 225		75	20
816	35 c. Decussocarpus vitiensis		85	30
817	$1 Agathis vitiensis		2·50	3·00
818	$1.55, Santalum yasi		3·50	5·50
815/18		*Set of 4*	7·00	8·00

226 "Hark the Herald Angels sing"

227 Sigatoka Sand Dunes

(Des Jennifer Toombs. Litho Walsall)

1990 (26 Nov). *Christmas. Carols. T 226 and similar horiz designs. Multicoloured. W w 14 (sideways). P 14.*

819	10 c. Type 226		30	10
820	35 c. "Still the Night, Holy the Night"		75	30
821	65 c. "Joy to the World!"		1·25	1·75
822	$1 "The Race that long in Darkness pined"		2·00	2·75
819/22		*Set of 4*	3·75	4·50

(Des L. Curtis. Litho Leigh-Mardon Ltd, Melbourne)

1991 (25 Feb). *Environmental Protection. T 227 and similar square designs. Multicoloured. P 14.*

823	35 c. Type 227		1·00	30
824	50 c. Monu and Monuriki Islands		1·75	90
825	65 c. Ravilevu Nature Reserve, Taveuni		2·00	2·50
826	$1 Colo-I-Suva Forest Park		3·00	3·50
823/6		*Set of 4*	7·00	6·50

228 H.M.S. *Pandora* (frigate)

229 *Scylla serrata*

(Des D. Miller. Litho Questa)

1991 (8 Aug). *Bicentenary of Discovery of Rotuma Island. T 228 and similar horiz designs. Multicoloured. W w 14 (sideways). P 14.*

827	54 c. Type 228		2·00	90
828	70 c. Map of Rotuma		2·25	2·50
829	75 c. Natives welcoming H.M.S. *Pandora*		2·25	2·50
830	$1 Mount Soloroa and Uea Island		3·50	4·00
827/30		*Set of 4*	9·00	9·00

(Des Katrina Hindle. Litho Questa)

1991 (26 Sept). *Mangrove Crabs. T 229 and similar horiz designs. Multicoloured. W w 14 (sideways). P 14×14½.*

831	38 c. Type 229		90	35
832	54 c. Metopograpsus messor		1·25	85
833	96 c. Parasesarma erythrodactyla		2·25	3·00
834	$1.65, Cardisoma carnifex		3·25	4·50
831/4		*Set of 4*	7·00	8·00

230 Mary and Joseph travelling to Bethlehem

231 De Havilland D.H.89 Dragon Rapide of Fiji Airways

(Des A. Wheatcroft. Litho Leigh-Mardon Ltd, Melbourne)

1991 (31 Oct). *Christmas. T 230 and similar horiz designs. Multicoloured. W w 16. P 14.*

835	11 c. Type 230		40	10
	a. Error. Wmk w 14		†	—
836	75 c. Manger scene		1·50	1·25
837	96 c. Presentation in the Temple		1·75	2·75
838	$1 Infant Jesus with symbols		1·75	2·75
835/8		*Set of 4*	4·75	6·00

(Des D. Wood. Litho Questa)

1991 (18 Nov). *40th Anniv of Air Pacific. T 231 and similar horiz designs. Multicoloured. W w 16 (sideways). P 14½.*

839	54 c. Type 231		1·75	1·00
840	75 c. Douglas DC-3		2·25	2·25
841	96 c. Aerospatiale/Aeritalia ATR 42		2·50	3·25
842	$1.40, Boeing 767		3·50	4·00
839/42		*Set of 4*	9·00	9·50

232 Ethnic Dancers

(Des. W. Addison. Litho Leigh-Mardon Ltd, Melbourne)

1992 (23 Mar). *"Expo 92" World's Fair, Seville, Spain. T 232 and similar horiz designs. W w 14 (sideways). P 14½×14.*

843	27 c. Type 232		55	45
844	75 c. Peoples of Fiji		1·25	1·75
845	96 c. Gold bars and sugar cane train		4·00	4·25
846	$1.40, Queen Elizabeth 2 (cruise liner) at Suva		4·75	5·00
843/6		*Set of 4*	9·50	10·50

233 *Tabusoro*

234 Running

(Des O. Bell. Litho Walsall)

1992 (22 June). *Inter-Islands Shipping. T 233 and similar horiz designs. Multicoloured. W w 14 (sideways). P 13½×14.*

847	38 c. Type 233		1·50	55
848	54 c. Degei II		2·00	1·40
849	$1.40, Dausoko		3·25	3·75
850	$1.65, Nivanga		3·25	3·75
847/50		*Set of 4*	9·00	8·50

(Des M. Chandler. Litho Enschedé)

1992 (30 July). *Olympic Games, Barcelona. T 234 and similar vert designs. Multicoloured. W w 14. P 13½.*

851	20 c. Type 234		75	20
852	86 c. Dinghy sailing		2·50	2·50
853	$1.34, Swimming		3·00	3·50
854	$1.50, Judo		3·00	3·50
851/4		*Set of 4*	8·25	8·75

235 European War Memorial, Levuka

(Des L. Curtis. Litho Leigh-Mardon Ltd, Melbourne)

1992 (21 Sept). *Historic Levuka (former capital). T 235 and similar multicoloured designs. W w 14 (sideways on horiz designs).*

855	30 c. Type 235		30	30
856	42 c. Map of Fiji		45	55
857	59 c. Beach Street		65	1·00
858	77 c. Sacred Heart Church (*vert*)		80	1·50
859	$2 Deed of Cession site (*vert*)		1·75	3·25
855/9		*Set of 5*	3·50	6·00

236 The Nativity

(Des G. Vasarhelyi. Litho Leigh-Mardon Ltd, Melbourne)

1992 (17 Nov). *Christmas. T 236 and similar horiz designs. Multicoloured. W w 14 (sideways). P 15×14½.*

860	12 c. Type 236		50	10
861	77 c. Shepherds and family giving presents		1·75	1·60
862	83 c. Shepherds at manger and giving presents to pensioners		1·75	1·75
863	$2 Wise Men and collecting Fiji produce		3·50	5·00
860/3		*Set of 4*	6·75	7·50

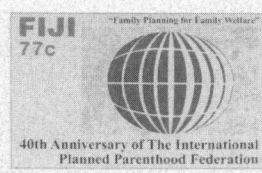

237 International Planned Parenthood Federation Logo

(Des D. Bowen. Litho Leigh-Mardon Ltd, Melbourne)

1992 (2 Dec). *40th Anniv of International Planned Parenthood Federation. T 237 and similar horiz design. Multicoloured. W w 14 (sideways). P 15×14½.*

864	77 c. Type 237		85	85
865	$2 Man weeping and pregnant mother with children		2·50	3·50

238 Dove and Peace Corps Emblem

239 Fijian Players performing Cibi (traditional dance)

(Des O. Bell. Litho Leigh-Mardon Ltd, Melbourne)

1993 (22 Feb). *25th Anniv of Peace Corps in Fiji. T 238 and similar horiz designs. Multicoloured. W w 14. P 14½.*

866	59 c. Type 238		1·10	75
867	77 c. Handshake		1·40	1·40
868	$1 Educational symbols		1·75	1·75
869	$2 Symbols of home businesses scheme		3·00	4·50
866/9		*Set of 4*	6·50	7·50

(Des R. Larson. Litho Questa)

1993 (26 Mar). *Hong Kong Rugby Sevens Competition. T 239 and similar vert designs. Multicoloured. W w 16. P 14×15.*

870	77 c. Type 239		1·50	1·40
871	$1.06, Players and map of Pacific		2·00	2·75
872	$2 Scrum and stadium		3·75	4·50
870/2		*Set of 3*	6·50	7·75

(Des A. Theobald. Litho Questa)

1993 (1 Apr). *75th Anniv of Royal Air Force. Horiz designs as T 149 of Ascension. Multicoloured. W w 14 (sideways). P 14.*

873	59 c. Gloster Gauntlet II		1·00	75
874	77 c. Armstrong Whitworth Whitley Mk V		1·25	1·40
875	83 c. Bristol F2b "Brisfit"		1·40	1·60
876	$2 Hawker Tempest Mk V		2·25	3·50
873/6		*Set of 4*	5·50	6·50
MS877	110×77 mm. $1 Vickers Vildebeest III; $1 Handley Page Hampden; $1 Vickers FB-27 Vimy; $1 British Aerospace Hawk T.1.		5·00	6·00

240 *Chromodoris fidelis*

241 Mango

(Des G. Drummond. Litho Leigh-Mardon Ltd, Melbourne)

1993 (27 July). *Nudibranchs. T 240 and similar horiz designs. Multicoloured. W w 14. P 14.*

878	12 c. Type 240	..	50	10
879	42 c. *Halgerda carlsoni*	..	1·10	55
880	53 c. *Chromodoris lochi*	..	1·40	1·25
881	83 c. Blue Sea Lizard (*Glaucus atlanticus*)		2·00	2·25
882	$1 *Phyllidia bourguini*	..	2·25	2·50
883	$2 Spanish Dancer (*Hexabranchus sanguineus*)		3·50	4·50
878/83		*Set of 6*	9·50	10·00

(Des Katrina Hindle. Litho Cartor)

1993 (25 Oct). *Tropical Fruits. T 241 and similar vert designs. Multicoloured. W w 14. P 13½.*

884	30 c. Type 241	..	1·00	45
885	42 c. Guava	..	1·25	80
886	$1 Lemon	..	2·50	2·50
887	$2 Soursop	..	4·50	5·50
884/7		*Set of 4*	8·25	8·25

242 *Anaphaesis java*　　　243 The Last Supper

(Des I. Loe and D. Miller. Litho Enschedé (No. MS889))

1994 (18 Feb). *"Hong Kong '94" International Stamp Exhibition.*

(a) No. MS877 optd as T 154 of Ascension on each stamp
MS888 110×77 mm. $1 Vickers Vildebeest III; $1 Handley Page Hampden; $1 Vickers FB-27 Vimy; $1 British Aerospace Hawk T.1 .. 4·50 6·00

(b) Sheet 122×85 mm containing T 242 and similar vert designs showing butterflies. Multicoloured. W w 14 (sideways). P 14½×13.
MS889 $1 Type 242; $1 *Euploea leucostictos*; $1 *Vagrans egista*; $1 *Acraea andromache* .. 4·50 6·00
No. MS888 also shows "HONG KONG '94 EXHIBITION" overprinted on the bottom margin.

(Des R. Larson. Litho Enschedé)

1994 (31 Mar). *Easter. T 243 and similar multicoloured designs. W w 14 (sideways on horiz designs). P 14×15 (horiz) or 15×14 (vert).*

890	59 c. Type 243	..	1·00	60
891	77 c. The Crucifixion (*vert*)	..	1·25	1·25
892	$1 The Resurrection	..	1·75	2·00
893	$2 Examining Christ's wounds (*vert*)		3·25	5·00
890/3		*Set of 4*	6·50	8·00

244 Sagati　　　245 White-collared Kingfisher on Branch

(Des I. Loe. Litho Walsall)

1994 (6 June). *Edible Seaweeds. T 244 and similar vert designs. Multicoloured. W w 16. P 14½×14.*

894	42 c. Type 244	..	90	45
895	83 c. Nama	..	1·75	2·00
896	$1 Lumicevata	..	2·00	2·50
897	$2 Lumiwawa	..	3·50	5·00
894/7		*Set of 4*	7·25	9·00

(Des Doreen McGuinness. Litho Questa)

1994 (16 Aug). *White-collared Kingfisher. Sheet 98×84 mm, containing T 245 and similar vert design. Multicoloured. W w 14. P 14×13½.*
MS898 $1.50, Type 245; $1.50, Kingfisher with crab in beak .. 7·50 8·00

---

246 *Neoveitchia storckii*　　　247 Father Ioane Batita

(Des N. Shewring. Litho Questa)

1994 (31 Aug). *"Singpex '94" International Stamp Exhibition. Endemic Palm. Sheet 97×69 mm, containing T 246 and similar vert design. Multicoloured. W w 16. P 14.*
MS899 $1.50, Type 246; $1.50, Palm flowers .. 6·50 7·50

(Des S. Noon. Litho Leigh-Mardon Ltd, Melbourne)

1994 (16 Dec). *150th Anniv of Arrival of Catholic Missionaries in Fiji. T 247 and similar vert designs. W w 14. P 14.*

900	23 c. Type 247	..	35	25
901	31 c. Local catechist	..	45	30
902	44 c. Sacred Heart Cathedral, Suva		60	70
903	63 c. Lomary Church	..	80	95
904	81 c. Pope Gregory XVI	..	1·25	1·40
905	$2 Pope John Paul II	..	2·75	3·50
900/5		*Set of 6*	5·50	6·25

248 Waterfall and Banded Iguana　　　249 Fiji ("Red-headed") Parrot Finch

(Des B. Dare. Litho Questa)

1995 (27 Mar). *Eco-Tourism in Fiji. Sheet 140×80 mm containing T 248 and similar square designs. Multicoloured. W w 16 (sideways). P 14.*
MS906 81 c. Type 248; 81 c. Mountain trekkers and Fiji Tree Frog; 81 c. Bilibili River trip and White-collared Kingfisher; 81 c. Historic sites and Flying Fox .. 4·50 5·50

(Des R. Watton. Litho Cartor (Nos. 907/10) or Questa (No. MS911))

1995 (8 May). *50th Anniv of End of Second World War. Multicoloured designs as T 161 of Ascension. W w 14 (sideways). P 13½.*

907	13 c. Fijian soldiers guarding crashed Japanese Mitsubishi A6M Zero-Sen aircraft		60	20
908	63 c. American spotter plane landing on Kameli Airstrip, Solomon Islands		1·75	1·50
909	87 c. Corporal Sukanaivalu and Victoria Cross ..		2·00	2·50
910	$1.12, H.M.S. *Fiji* (cruiser)	..	2·50	2·75
907/10		*Set of 4*	6·25	6·25
MS911	75×85 mm. $2 Reverse of 1939–45 War Medal (*vert*). Wmk upright. P 14		2·25	2·75

(Des A. Robinson. Litho Enschedé)

1995 (25 July–7 Nov). *Birds. T 249 and similar vert designs. Multicoloured. W w 14. P 13½×13.*

912	1 c. Type 249 (7 Nov)	..	10	10
913	2 c. Golden Whistler (7 Nov)		10	10
914	3 c. Versicoloured Flycatcher ("Ogea Flycatcher") (7 Nov)		10	10
915	4 c. Peale's Pigeon (7 Nov)		10	10
916	6 c. Blue-headed Flycatcher ("Blue-crested Broadbill") (7 Nov)		10	10
917	13 c. Island Thrush	..	10	10
918	23 c. Many-coloured Fruit Dove	..	15	20
919	31 c. Green Heron ("Mangrove Heron")		20	25
920	44 c. Purple Swamphen	..	30	35
921	63 c. Fiji Goshawk	..	40	45
922	81 c. Kandavu Fantail ("Kadavu Fantail")		50	55
923	87 c. Collared Lory (7 Nov)		55	60
924	$1 Scarlet Robin (7 Nov)	..	60	65
925	$2 Peregrine Falcon	..	1·25	1·40
926	$3 Barn Owl	..	1·90	2·00
927	$5 Masked Shining Parrot ("Yellow-breasted Musk Parrot") (7 Nov)		3·00	3·25
912/27		*Set of 16*	9·25	10·00

1995 (19 Aug). *"JAKARTA '95" Stamp Exhibition, Indonesia. No. MS898 optd "JAKARTA '95" and emblem on sheet margin.*
MS928 $1.50, Type 245; $1.50, Kingfisher with crab in beak .. 6·50 7·50

---

250 *Arundina graminifolia*　　　251 Pres. Ratu Sir Kamisese Mara, Parliament Building and National Flag

(Des I. Loe. Litho Questa)

1995 (1 Sept). *Orchids. Sheet 100×80 mm, containing T 250 and similar vert design. W w 16. P 14.*
MS929 $1 Type 250; $1 *Phaius tankervilliae* .. 4·00 4·50
No. MS929 also includes "Singapore '95" and emblem on the sheet margin.

(Des S. Noon. Litho B.D.T.)

1995 (4 Oct). *25th Anniv of Independence. T 251 and similar horiz designs. Multicoloured. W w 14 (sideways). P 13½.*

930	81 c. Type 251	..	1·00	1·00
931	87 c. Young citizens of Fiji	..	1·00	1·10
932	$1.06, Rugby players	..	1·50	1·75
933	$2 Boeing 747 *Island of Viti Levu*	..	3·00	4·00
930/3		*Set of 4*	6·00	7·00

252 "Praying Madonna with the Crown of Stars" (workshop of Correggio)　　　253 Trolling Lure

(Des D. Miller. Litho Cartor)

1995 (22 Nov). *Christmas. T 252 and similar vert designs. Multicoloured. W w 14. P 13×13½.*

934	10 c. Type 252	..	20	10
935	63 c. "Madonna and Child with Crowns" (on porcelain)		80	80
936	87 c. "The Holy Virgin with the Holy Child and St. John" (after Titian)		1·10	1·25
937	$2 "The Holy Family and St. John" (workshop of Rubens)		2·50	4·00
934/7		*Set of 4*	4·25	5·50

(Des B. Dare. Litho Walsall)

1996 (24 Jan). *50th Anniv of Resettlement of Banabans (inhabitants of Ocean Island) in Fiji. T 253 and similar multicoloured designs. W w 14 (sideways on horiz designs). P 14½.*

938	81 c. Type 253	..	1·00	1·00
939	87 c. Banaban fishing canoes	..	1·00	1·10
940	$1.12, Banaban warrior (*vert*)	..	1·40	2·00
941	$2 Great Frigate Bird (*vert*)	..	4·00	4·75
938/41		*Set of 4*	6·75	8·00

254 L2B Portable Tape Recorder　　　255 Winged Monster and Ring (bronze), c 450 B.C.

(Des N. Shewring. Litho Walsall)

1996 (11 Mar). *Centenary of Radio. T 254 and similar vert designs. Multicoloured. W w 14. P 14½×14.*

942	44 c. Type 254	..	65	45
943	63 c. Broadcasting House, Fiji	..	85	70
944	81 c. Communications satellite	..	1·10	1·25
945	$3 Guglielmo Marconi	..	3·75	5·50
942/5		*Set of 4*	5·75	7·00

(Des G. Vasarhelyi. Litho B.D.T.)

1996 (25 Apr). *"CHINA '96" 9th Asian International Stamp Exhibition, Peking. T* **255** *and similar vert designs. Multicoloured. W w* **16**. *P* 13½.

946	63 c. Type **255**		85	65
947	81 c. Archer (terracotta sculpture), 210 B.C.		1·10	1·10
948	$1 Dragon plate, 1426–35		1·40	1·50
949	$2 Central Asian horseman (sculpture), 706		2·75	4·00
946/9		*Set of 4*	5·50	6·50

MS950 81×127 mm. 30 c. "Yan Deng Mountains" (painting) (48½×76 *mm*). Wmk sideways. P 13 .. .. 80 1·00

256 Hurdling   **257** Computerised Telephone Exchange

(Des S. Noon. Litho Southern Colour Print, Dunedin, New Zealand)

1996 (18 June). *Centenary of Modern Olympic Games. T* **256** *and similar vert designs. Multicoloured. W w* **14**. *P* 14.

951	31 c. Type **256**		55	30
952	63 c. Judo		1·00	80
953	87 c. Sailboarding		1·25	1·40
954	$1.12, Swimming		1·40	2·00
951/4		*Set of 4*	3·75	4·00

MS955 59×99 mm. $2 Winning athlete, 1896. Wmk sideways .. .. 2·10 2·75

(Des G. Vasarhelyi. Litho Walsall)

1996 (1 July). *Inauguration of Independent Postal and Tele-communications Companies. T* **257** *and similar multicoloured designs. W w* **14** *(sideways on horiz designs). P* 14.

956	31 c. Type **257**		40	30
957	44 c. Unloading mail from aircraft		80	65
958	81 c. Manual telephone exchange (*vert*)		1·00	1·50
959	$1 Postman on motorbike (*vert*)		1·75	2·00
956/9		*Set of 4*	3·50	4·00

MS960 120×77 mm. $1.50, Fiji 1938 ½d. Sailing canoe stamp (*vert*); $1.50, Fiji 1985 20 c. "Expo '85" stamp (*vert*) .. .. *Set of 2 sheets* 4·25 5·00

258 "Our Children Our Future"

(Adapted Jennifer Toombs. Litho Questa)

1996 (13 Aug). *50th Anniv of U.N.I.C.E.F. Children's Paintings. T* **258** *and similar horiz designs. Multicoloured. W w* **16** *(sideways). P* 14½.

961	81 c. Type **258**		1·25	1·00
962	87 c. "Village Scene"		1·25	1·00
963	$1 "Living in Harmony the World over"		1·40	1·50
964	$2 "Their Future"		2·25	3·75
961/4		*Set of 4*	5·50	6·50

259 First Seaplane in Fiji, 1921

(Des N. Shewring. Litho Walsall)

1996 (1 Oct). *50th Anniv of Nadi International Airport. T* **259** *and similar horiz designs. Multicoloured. W w* **16** *(sideways). P* 14.

965	31 c. Type **259**		50	30
966	44 c. Nadi Airport in 1946		70	50
967	63 c. Arrival of first jet airliner, 1959		90	80
968	87 c. Airport entrance		1·25	1·50
969	$1 Control tower		1·50	1·75
970	$2 Diagram of Global Positioning System		2·50	4·00
965/70		*Set of 6*	6·50	8·00

260 The Annunciation and Fijian beating Lali (drum)

(Des M. Raj. Litho Questa)

1996 (20 Nov). *Christmas. T* **260** *and similar horiz designs. Multicoloured. W w* **14** *(sideways). P* 13½×14.

971	13 c. Type **260**		30	15
972	81 c. Shepherds with sheep, and canoe		1·25	85
973	$1 Wise men on camels, and people on cross		1·50	1·40
974	$3 The Nativity, and Fijian blowing conch		4·25	5·50
971/4		*Set of 4*	6·50	7·00

261 Brahman   **262** Black-throated Shrikebill

(Des G. Vasarhelyi. Litho B.D.T.)

1997 (12 Feb). *"HONG KONG '97" International Stamp Exhibition. Cattle. Sheet* 130×92 *mm, containing T* **261** *and similar horiz designs. Multicoloured. W w* **14** *(sideways). P* 14.

MS975 $1 Type **261**; $1 Friesian (Holstein); $1 Hereford; $1 Fiji draught bullock .. .. 4·50 5·00
No. **MS**975 is inscribed "FREISIAN" in error

(Des A. Robinson and Jennifer Toombs. Litho B.D.T.)

1997 (21 Feb). *"SINGPEX '97" Stamp Exhibition, Singapore. Sheet* 92×78 *mm. W w* **14**. *P* 14×15.

MS976 **262** $2 multicoloured .. .. 2·10 2·75

263 *Dendrobium biflorum*   **264** Hawksbill Turtle laying Eggs

(Des M. Raj. Litho B.D.T.)

1997 (22 Apr). *Orchids. T* **263** *and similar vert designs. Multicoloured. W w* **16**. *P* 14.

977	81 c. Type **263**		1·00	1·00
978	87 c. *Dendrobium dactylodes*		1·00	1·00
979	$1.06, *Spathoglottis pacifica*		1·25	1·60
980	$2 *Dendrobium macropus*		2·50	3·25
977/80		*Set of 4*	5·25	6·25

(Des Sue Wickison. Litho B.D.T.)

1997 (26 May). *Life Cycle of Hawksbill Turtle. Sheet* 140×85 *mm, containing T* **264** *and similar horiz designs. Multicoloured. W w* **14** *(sideways). P* 14.

MS981 63 c. Type **264**; 81 c. Turtles hatching; $1.06, Young turtles swimming; $2 Adult turtle 6·00 6·50

265 Branching Hard Coral   **266** Fijian Monkey-faced Bat

(Des M. Raj. Litho Walsall)

1997 (16 July). *Year of the Coral Reef. T* **265** *and similar horiz designs. Multicoloured. W w* **16** *(sideways). P* 14.

982	63 c. Type **265**		85	55
983	87 c. Massive Hard Coral		1·25	1·25
984	$1 White Soft Coral		1·50	1·50
985	$3 Pink Soft Coral		4·00	5·50
982/5		*Set of 4*	7·00	8·00

(Des Sue Wickison. Litho Enschedé)

1997 (15 Oct). *Endangered Species. Fijian Monkey-faced Bat. T* **266** *and similar vert designs showing bats. P* 13½.

986	44 c. multicoloured		60	40
987	63 c. multicoloured		80	60
988	81 c. multicoloured		1·10	1·10
989	$2 multicoloured		2·25	3·75
986/9		*Set of 4*	4·25	5·25

MS990 157×106 mm. Nos. 986/9, each × 2 8·00 10·00

267 Waisale Serevi (Captain)   **268** Shepherd and Angel

(Des G. Vasarhelyi. Litho Walsall)

1997 (31 Oct). *Fiji Rugby Club's Victory in Hong Kong Rugby Sevens Competition. T* **267** *and similar multicoloured designs. W w* **16** *(sideways). P* 14.

991	50 c. Type **267**		65	80
	a. Sheetlet. Nos. 991/1001		6·50	
992	50 c. Taniela Qauqau		65	80
993	50 c. Jope Tuikabe		65	80
994	50 c. Leveni Duvuduvukula		65	80
995	50 c. Inoke Maraiwai		65	80
996	50 c. Aminiasi Naituyaga		65	80
997	50 c. Lemki Koroi		65	80
998	50 c. Marika Vunibaka		65	80
999	50 c. Luke Erenavula		65	80
1000	50 c. Manasa Bari		65	80
1001	$1 Fijian rugby team (56×42 *mm*)		80	1·00
991/1001		*Set of 11*	6·50	8·00

Nos. 991/1001 were printed together, *se-tenant*, in sheetlets of 11 with the 50 c. stamps arranged in two rows of 5 above an illustrated margin containing the $1.

(Des Jennifer Toombs. Litho Questa)

1997 (18 Nov). *Christmas. T* **268** *and similar horiz designs. Multicoloured. W w* **14** *(sideways). P* 14½.

1002	13 c. Type **268**		20	10
1003	31 c. Mary, Joseph and baby Jesus		45	30
1004	87 c. The Three Kings		1·10	90
1005	$3 Mary and baby Jesus		3·25	4·50
1002/5		*Set of 4*	4·50	5·25

269 Chief in War Dress   **270** Man in Wheelchair using Computer

(Des M. Raj. Litho Questa)

1998 (20 Jan). *Traditional Chiefs' Costumes. T* **269** *and similar vert designs. Multicoloured. W w* **16**. *P* 14.

1006	81 c. Type **269**		75	75
1007	87 c. Formal dress		85	85
1008	$1.12, Presentation dress		1·25	1·40
1009	$2 War dress of Highland chief		1·75	2·50
1006/9		*Set of 4*	4·25	5·00

(Des G. Vasarhelyi. Litho Cartor)

1998 (13 Mar). *Asian and Pacific Decade of Disabled People. T* **270** *and similar horiz designs. Multicoloured. W w* **14** *(sideways). P* 13½×13.

1010	63 c. Type **270**		70	60
1011	87 c. Woman with child		90	80
1012	$1 Man at desk		1·10	1·10
1013	$2 Wheelchair race		1·75	2·50
1010/13		*Set of 4*	4·00	4·50

(Des D. Miller. Litho Questa)

1998 (31 Mar). *Diana, Princess of Wales Commemoration. Vert designs as T* **177** *of Ascension. Multicoloured. W w* **16**. *P* 14½×14.

1014	81 c. Wearing tartan jacket, 1990		1·00	1·00

MS1015 145×70 mm. 81 c. As No. 1014; 81 c. Wearing blue jacket, 1991; 81 c., Wearing high-necked blouse, 1990; 81 c. Carrying bouquet. W w **14** (sideways) (*sold at $3.24 + 50 c. charity premium*) .. .. .. 2·75 3·25

(Des A. Theobald. Litho Enschedé)

1998 (1 Apr). *80th Anniv of Royal Air Force. Horiz designs as T 178 of Ascension. Multicoloured.* W w 14 (*sideways*). P 13½×14.

1016	44 c. *R34* airship	..	55	30
1017	63 c. Handley Page Heyford	..	80	60
1018	87 c. Supermarine Swift FR.5	..	1·25	1·00
1019	$2 Westland Whirlwind	..	2·00	2·50
1016/19		Set of 4	4·25	4·00
MS1020	110×77 mm. $1 Sopwith Dolphin; $1 Avro 504K; $1 Vickers Warwick V; $1 Shorts Belfast ..		3·50	4·50

271 Pod of Sperm Whales Underwater   **272** Athletics

(Des Sue Wickison. Litho Walsall)

1998 (22 June). *Sperm Whales. T 271 and similar horiz designs. Multicoloured.* W w 14 (*sideways*). P 14.

1021	63 c. Type 271	..	75	55
1022	81 c. Female and calf	..	90	90
1023	87 c. Pod on surface	..	1·00	1·00
1024	$2 Ceremonial whale tooth	..	1·75	2·25
1021/4		Set of 4	4·00	4·25
MS1025	90×68 mm. No. 1024 ..	..	2·50	2·75

(Des S. Noon. Litho Questa)

1998 (11 Sept). *16th Commonwealth Games, Kuala Lumpur. T 272 and similar vert designs. Multicoloured.* W w 16. P 14.

1026	44 c. Type 272	..	35	30
1027	63 c. Lawn bowls	..	55	45
1028	81 c. Throwing the javelin	..	75	75
1029	$1.12, Weightlifting	..	95	1·10
1026/9		Set of 4	2·40	2·40
MS1030	63×77 mm. $2 Waisale Serevi (Fiji rugby captain) ..		2·00	2·50

273 Takia (traditional raft)

(Des J. Batchelor. Litho B.D.T.)

1998 (26 Oct). *Maritime Past and Present (1st series). T 273 and similar horiz designs. Multicoloured.* W w 16 (*sideways*). P 13½.

1031	13 c. Type 273	..	15	10
1032	44 c. Camakau (outrigger canoe)	..	35	30
1033	87 c. Drua (outrigger canoe)	..	70	70
1034	$3 *Pioneer* (inter-island ship)	..	2·50	2·75
1031/4		Set of 4	3·25	3·50
MS1035	105×75 mm. $1.50, Camakau (outrigger canoe) ..		1·50	1·75

No. MS1035 also includes the "World Stamp Expo Australia '99" emblem on the margin of the sheet.
See also Nos. 1044/8.

274 "Jesus in a Manger" (Grace Lee)

(Litho Cartor)

1998 (23 Nov). *Christmas. Children's Paintings. T 274 and similar multicoloured designs.* P 13½.

1036	13 c. Type 274	..	20	10
1037	50 c. "A Time with Family and Friends" (Brian Guevara)	..	50	35
1038	$1 "What Christmas Means to Me" (Naomi Tupou) (*vert*)	..	90	75
1039	$2 "The Joy of Christmas" (Lauretta Ah Sam) (*vert*)	..	1·75	2·25
1036/9		Set of 4	3·00	3·00

STANLEY GIBBONS STAMP COLLECTING SERIES

Introductory booklets on *How to Start, How to Identify Stamps* and *Collecting by Theme.* A series of well illustrated guides at a low price.
Write for details.

---

275 Women's Sitting Dance   **276** Wandering Whistling Duck

(Des T. Crilley. Litho Southern Colour Print, Dunedin)

1999 (20 Jan). *Traditional Fijian Dances. T 275 and similar horiz designs. Multicoloured.* P 14½.

1040	13 c. Type 275	..	15	10
1041	81 c. Club dance	..	75	70
1042	87 c. Women's fan dance	..	75	70
1043	$3 Kava-serving dance	..	2·50	3·00
1040/3		Set of 4	3·75	4·00

(Des J. Batchelor. Litho B.D.T.)

1999 (19 Mar). *Maritime Past and Present (2nd series). Horiz designs as T 273. Multicoloured.* W w 16 (*sideways*). P 13½.

1044	63 c. *Tofua I* (cargo liner)	..	55	45
1045	81 c. *Adi Beti* (government launch)	..	75	65
1046	$1 *Niagara* (liner)	..	85	85
1047	$2 *Royal Viking Sun* (liner)	..	1·60	2·00
1044/7		Set of 4	3·25	3·50
MS1048	105×75 mm. $1.50, *Makatea* (inter-island freighter)	..	1·50	1·75

No. MS1048 also includes the "Australia '99" emblem on the sheet margin.

(Des G. Tavelini. Litho B.D.T.)

1999 (27 Apr). *"iBRA '99" International Stamp Exhibition, Nuremberg. Sheet, 100×95 mm, containing T 276 and similar vert design. Multicoloured.* W w 14. P 13½.

MS1049	$2 Type 276; $2 Pacific Black Duck	..	2·75	3·25

277 *Calanthe ventilabrum*   **278** Sugar Mills Diesel Locomotive

(Litho Cartor)

1999 (28 June). *Orchids. T 277 and similar vert designs. Multicoloured.* W w 14. P 13½.

1050	44 c. Type 277	..	45	35
1051	63 c. *Dendrobium prasinum*	..	60	45
1052	81 c. *Dendrobium macrophyllum*	..	75	60
1053	$3 *Dendrobium tokai*	..	2·25	2·50
1050/3		Set of 4	3·50	3·50

(Des N. Shewring. Litho Walsall)

1999 (20 July). *30th Anniv of First Manned Landing on Moon. Multicoloured designs as T 186 of Ascension.* W w 16. P 14×13½.

1054	13 c. Astronaut preparing to enter module	..	15	10
1055	87 c. Third stage rockets firing near Moon	..	75	60
1056	$1 Buzz Aldrin on Moon's surface	..	85	70
1057	$2 Command module returning to Earth	..	1·60	1·75
1054/7		Set of 4	3·00	2·75
MS1058	90×80 mm. $2 Earth as seen from Moon (circular, 40 mm diam). Wmk sideways. P 14		1·50	1·75

(Des D. Miller. Litho Cartor)

1999 (18 Aug). *"Queen Elizabeth the Queen Mother's Century". Horiz designs as T 187 of Ascension. Multicoloured.* W w 16 (*sideways*). P 13½.

1059	13 c. Inspecting bomb damage, Hull, 1940	..	15	10
1060	63 c. With Prince Charles, 1950	..	55	45
1061	81 c. Meeting soldiers from the Light Infantry	..	70	60
1062	$3 Saying goodbye to Prince Charles, 1986	..	2·25	2·50
1059/62		Set of 4	3·25	3·25
MS1063	145×70 mm. $2 Lady Elizabeth Bowes-Lyon, 1923 and Armistice Day celebrations, 1918		1·50	1·60

(Litho Walsall)

1999 (26 Oct). *125th Anniv of Universal Postal Union. Sugar Mill Locomotives. T 278 and similar horiz designs. Multicoloured.* W w 14 (*sideways*). P 13½×14.

1064	50 c. Type 278	..	30	35
1065	87 c. Steam locomotive	..	55	60
1066	$1 Diesel locomotive *Hunsley*	..	60	65
1067	$2 Free passenger service	..	1·25	1·40
1064/7		Set of 4	2·75	3·00

---

279 Exchanging Gifts

(Litho Cartor)

1999 (29 Nov). *Christmas. T 279 and similar multicoloured designs.* W w 14 (*sideways on horiz designs*). P 13½×13 (*horiz*) or 13×13½ (*vert*).

1068	13 c. Type 279	..	10	15
1069	31 c. Two angels over Earth	..	20	25
1070	63 c. Open bible	..	40	45
1071	87 c. Joseph and Mary on donkey (*vert*)	..	55	60
1072	$1 The Nativity (*vert*)	..	60	65
1073	$2 Children and Father Christmas (*vert*)	..	1·25	1·40
1068/73		Set of 6	3·00	3·50

STAMP BOOKLETS

1909. *Black and red cover. Stapled.*

SB1	2s. booklet containing eleven ½d. (No. 118) in blocks of 5 and 6, and eighteen 1d. (No. 119) in blocks of 6	..	£2500

1914. *Black on red cover. Stapled.*

SB2	2s. booklet containing eleven ½d. (No. 126) in blocks of 5 and 6, and eighteen 1d. (No. 127) in blocks of 6	..	£2000

1939 (10 Mar)**–40.** *Black on green covers. No advertising pages. Stapled.*

SB3	3s. booklet containing eight ½d. and eight 1d. (Nos. 249/50) in blocks of 8 and twelve 2d. (No. 253) in blocks of 6	..	£700
a.	Including four advertising pages (black on buff cover) (1940)		
SB4	5s. 9d. booklet containing ten ½d. and ten 1d. (Nos. 249/50) in blocks of 10 and twenty-seven 2d. (No. 253) in blocks of 9	..	£2000
a.	Including four advertising pages (black on pink cover) (1940)		

Nos. SB3/4 were produced locally and Nos. SB3a/4a by De La Rue.

1967 (23 Jan). *Black on salmon cover. Stitched.*

SB5	2s. booklet containing eight 3d. (No. 313) in blocks of four	..	8·50

The first printing was not released by the Crown Agents, but a second printing was released in London on 30.6.67. The first printing had 4d. as the surface-rate for letters to the British Commonwealth on the inside back cover (*Price £12*); in the second printing this was corrected to 3d.

1969 (27 Feb). *Black on salmon cover. Stitched.*

SB6	20 c. booklet containing ten 2 c. (No. 392) in two blocks of 4 and a vert pair	..	4·50

1970 (27 Oct). *Black on salmon cover. Stitched.*

SB7	20 c. booklet containing four 1 c. and eight 2 c. (Nos. 391/2) in blocks of 4	..	5·50

1971 (22 Nov). *Black on blue cover. Stitched.*

SB8	20 c. booklet containing 2 c. (No. 436) in block of 10		5·50

1973 (7 Sept)**–74.** *Black on blue cover. Stitched.*

SB9	20 c. booklet containing 1 c. in block of 8 and 2 c. in block of 6 (Nos. 435/6)		9·50
a.	With 2 c. watermark sideways (No. 459) (28.3.74)	..	9·00

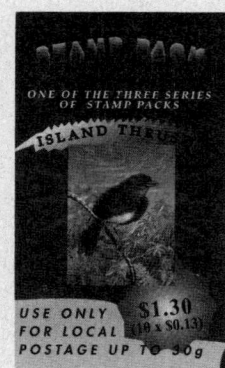

B 1 Island Thrush

1997 (13 June). *Multicoloured covers as Type B 1. Stamps attached by selvedge.*

SB10	$1.30, booklet containing 13 c. (No. 917) in block of 10	..	80
SB11	$3.10, booklet containing 31 c. (No. 919) in block of 10		1·75
SB12	$4.40, booklet containing 44 c. (No. 920) in block of 10	..	2·75

FIJI

POSTAGE DUE STAMPS

D 1   D 2

(Typo Govt Printer, Suva)

1917 (1 Jan). *Thick yellowish white laid paper. No gum. P 11.*

D1	D 1	½d. black	..	..	£700	£375
	a. *Se-tenant* strip of 8: 1d. (×3) + ½d. +					
		4d. + 3d. (×3)	..	..	£13000	
D2		1d. black	..	..	£300	75·00
D3		2d. black	..	..	£250	65·00
D4		3d. black	..	..	£300	80·00
D5		4d. black	..	..	£700	£375

Nos. D1/2 and D4/5 were printed, *se-tenant*, in sheets of 96 (8×12) with each horizontal row containing three 1d., one ½d., one 4d. and three 3d. in that order. Only thirty-one such sheets were issued. The 2d. was printed separately in sheets of 84 (7×12). On all these sheets marginal copies were imperforate on the outer edge.

1917 (21 April)–**18.** *Narrower setting, value in ½d. as Type* D 2.

D5a	½d. black	..	..	£475	£250
D5b	1d. black	..	..	£250	£120
D5c	2d. black (5.4.18)	..	..	£850	£500

1d. and 2d. stamps must have wide margins (3½ to 4 mm) on the vertical sides to be Nos. D2 or D3. Stamps with narrow margins of approximately the same width on all four sides are Nos. D5b or D5c.

Nos. D5a/c were printed in separate sheets of 84 (7 × 12). The marginal copies are perforated on all sides.

D 3   D 4

(Typo D.L.R.)

1918 (1 June). *Wmk Mult Crown CA. P 14.*

D 6	D 3	½d. black	..	..	3·00	16·00
D 7		1d. black	..	..	3·50	5·00
D 8		2d. black	..	..	3·25	7·50
D 9		3d. black	..	..	3·25	45·00
D10		4d. black	..	..	6·00	26·00
D6/10			Set of 5		17·00	90·00
D6/10 Optd "Specimen"			Set of 5		£150	

No postage due stamps were in use between 31 August 1931 and 3 July 1940.

(Typo Waterlow)

1940 (3 July). *Wmk Mult Script CA. P 12½.*

D11	D 4	1d. emerald-green	..	..	7·00	60·00
D12		2d. emerald-green	..	..	9·00	60·00
D13		3d. emerald-green	..	..	12·00	65·00
D14		4d. emerald-green	..	..	15·00	70·00
D15		5d. emerald-green	..	..	16·00	70·00
D16		6d. emerald-green	..	..	18·00	75·00
D17		1s. carmine-lake	..	..	22·00	£100
D18		1s. 6d. carmine-lake	..	..	23·00	£150
D11/18			Set of 8		£110	£600
D11/18 Perf "Specimen"			Set of 8		£180	

All values are known with forged postmarks, including one of Levuka dated "8 APR 41" and others of Suva dated "12 AUG 42", "14 AU 42" or "20 MR 45".

The use of postage due stamps was discontinued on 30 April 1946.

Gambia

WEST AFRICAN SETTLEMENT

British traders were active in the River Gambia area from the beginning of the 17th century, but it was not until 1808 that it was officially recognised as a Settlement. Administration passed from the merchants to the Governor of Freetown (Sierra Leone) in 1821 and in 1843 Gambia became a separate colony with a Protectorate declared over the banks of the river for 300 miles inland in 1857. A period of colonial retrenchment in 1865 saw a return to Settlement status under Sierra Leone, but Gambia once again became a Crown Colony in 1888.

There was no government postal service before 1858.

PRICES. The prices of Nos. 1 to 8 are for fine copies, with good margins and embossing. Brilliant or poor copies can be supplied at prices consistent with their condition.

DOUBLE EMBOSSING. The majority of the stamps of T 1 with so-called "double embossing" are merely specimens in which the printing and embossing do not register accurately and have no special value. We no longer list "twice embossed" or "twice embossed, once inverted" varieties as they are considered to be outside the scope of this catalogue.

1

(Typo and embossed by D.L.R.)

1869 (18 Mar)–**72.** *No wmk. Imperf.*

1	1	4d. brown		£475	£160
2		4d. pale brown (1871)		£400	£200
3		6d. deep blue		£425	£180
3a		6d. blue		£500	£150
4		6d. pale blue (17.2.72)		£2250	£1000

Our prices for the 6d. pale blue, No. 4, are for stamps which are pale by comparison with specimens of the "deep blue" and "blue" colour groups listed under Nos. 3 and 3a. The date given is the earliest known postmark. An exceptionally pale shade is recognized by specialists and this is rare.

1874 (Aug). *Wmk Crown CC. Imperf.*

5	1	4d. brown		£350	£180
		w. Wmk inverted		£425	£225
		x. Wmk reversed		£425	£225
		y. Wmk inverted and reversed		£475	£275
6		4d. pale brown		£350	£180
7		6d. deep blue		£300	£200
		w. Wmk inverted		£375	£250
		x. Wmk reversed		£400	£250
		y. Wmk inverted and reversed		£400	£250
8		6d. blue		£300	£180
		a. Sloping label		£500	£300
		b. Wmk sideways		†	
		w. Wmk inverted		£375	£250

SLOPING LABEL VARIETY. Traces of this flaw first occur in the 6d. imperforate on R.1/1 and R.1/5. In the perforated printings the variety on R.1/5 is much more pronounced and appears as illustrated above. Our listings are these examples from R.1/5, less noticeable varieties of this type from R.1/1, which slope from right to left, being worth less. These varieties continued to appear until the introduction of a new 6d. plate in 1893, used for No. 34.

1880–81. *Wmk Crown CC. P 14*. A. Wmk sideways†*

10A	1	½d. orange		£160	£130
		w. Wmk Crown to left of CC			
12A		1d. maroon		£275	£200
		w. Wmk Crown to left of CC			
		y. Wmk sideways inverted and reversed			
13A		2d. rose		85·00	48·00
		w. Wmk Crown to left of CC			
14A		3d. bright ultramarine		£325	£250
		w. Wmk Crown to left of CC			
15A		4d. brown		£325	55·00
		w Wmk Crown to left of CC		£300	48·00
16A		4d. pale brown		£300	48·00
		w. Wmk Crown to left of CC		£275	45·00
17A		6d. deep blue		£130	85·00
		c. Sloping label		£350	£225
18A		6d. blue		£130	85·00
		c. Sloping label		£350	£225
		w. Wmk Crown to left of CC			
19A		1s. green		£375	£250
20A		1s. deep green		£375	£250
		w. Wmk Crown to left of CC			
10A/20A			*Set of 7*	£1400	£900

B. *Wmk upright*

10B	1	½d. orange		6·50	12·00
11B		½d. dull orange		6·50	12·00
		w. Wmk inverted		38·00	
		x. Wmk reversed		32·00	
12B		1d. maroon		3·75	5·50
		w. Wmk inverted		80·00	80·00
13B		2d. rose		19·00	11·00
14B		3d. bright ultramarine		65·00	32·00
14cB		3d. pale dull ultramarine		48·00	26·00
		w. Wmk inverted		60·00	40·00
15B		4d. brown		£160	14·00
		w. Wmk inverted		†	—
16B		4d. pale brown		£150	15·00
17B		6d. deep blue		80·00	45·00
		c. Sloping label		£225	£150
18B		6d. blue		80·00	45·00
		c. Sloping label		£225	£150
19B		1s. green		£200	£120
		w. Wmk inverted		†	£325
20B		1s. deep green		£200	£120
10B/20B			*Set of 7*	£425	£200

*There were three different printings of these stamps. The original supply, sent in June 1880 and covering all seven values, had watermark sideways and was perforated by a line machine. In October of the same year a further printing of the lowest five values had the watermark changed to upright, but was still with line perforation. The final printing, sent May 1881 and containing all values, also had watermark upright, but was perforated on a comb machine.

†The normal sideways watermark shows Crown to right of CC, *as seen from the back of the stamp.*

1886–93. *Wmk Crown CA (sideways*). P 14.*

21	1	½d. myrtle-green (1887)		2·25	2·25
		w. Wmk Crown to right of CA		22·00	
		x. Wmk sideways reversed		32·00	
22		½d. grey-green		2·75	3·25
22b		1d. maroon		†	£15000
23		1d. crimson (1887)		4·00	5·50
23a		1d. aniline crimson		6·00	9·00
23b		1d. pale carmine		6·00	9·00
24		2d. orange (1887)		9·00	6·50
25		2d. deep orange		1·40	8·00
26		2½d. ultramarine (1887)		2·00	2·00
27		2½d. deep bright blue		1·75	1·25
		w. Wmk Crown to right of CA		80·00	
28		3d. slate-grey (1886)		4·00	13·00
29		3d. grey		2·50	14·00
30		4d. brown (1887)		3·00	2·00
31		4d. deep brown		3·00	2·00
		a. Wmk upright		†	£950
		w. Wmk Crown to right of CA		55·00	55·00
32		6d. yellowish olive-green (1886)		70·00	30·00
		a. Sloping label		£170	75·00
		bw. Wmk Crown to right of CA		£120	
32c		6d. olive-green (1887)		60·00	50·00
		ca. Sloping label		£160	£130
33		6d. bronze-green (1889)		24·00	50·00
		a. Sloping label		60·00	95·00
33b		6d. deep bronze-green (1889)		25·00	50·00
		ba. Sloping label		60·00	95·00
34		6d. slate-green (1893)		10·00	45·00
35		1s. violet (1887)		3·25	16·00
36		1s. deep violet		4·00	17·00
36b		1s. aniline violet		£1100	
21/36			*Set of 8*	25·00	80·00
21/4, 32 Optd "Specimen"			*Set of 4*	£400	

*The normal sideways watermark shows Crown to left of CA, *as seen from the back of the stamp.*

The above were printed in panes of 15 on paper intended for larger panes. Hence the watermark is sometimes misplaced or omitted and letters from "CROWN AGENTS FOR THE COLONIES" from the margin may appear on the stamps.

The ½d., 2d., 3d., 4d., 6d. (No. 32) and 1s. with watermark Crown CA are known imperforate (*price from* £1100, *unused*).

Only three examples, all used, are recorded of the 1d. maroon, No. 22b.

The previously listed 3d. "pearl-grey" shade has been deleted as it is impossible to distinguish from other 3d. shades when it occurs on a single stamp. Sheets from this late printing can be identified by three coloured dots in the left sheet margin and one in the right, this being the reverse of the normal arrangement.

Only three used examples are known of the 4d. with upright watermark, No. 31a.

NEW INFORMATION

The editor is always interested to correspond with people who have new information that will improve or correct the Catalogue.

CROWN COLONY

2

Normal	Malformed "S"	Repaired "S"

The Malformed "S" occurs on R. 7/3 of the left pane from Key Plate 2. This was used to print the initial supply all values. Printings of the ½d., 1d. and 2½d. despatched on 24 September 1898 had the "S" repaired as shown above. Subsequent printings of the ½d., 1d. and 3d. were from Key Plate 3.

(Typo D.L.R.)

1898 (2 May)–**1902.** *Wmk Crown CA. P 14.*

37	2	½d. dull green (*shades*)		2·50	1·75
		a. Malformed "S"		£170	
		b. Repaired "S"		£190	£160
38		1d. carmine (*shades*)		1·50	75
		a. Malformed "S"		£170	
		b. Repaired "S"		£190	
39		2d. orange and mauve		5·00	3·50
		a. Malformed "S"		£190	
40		2½d. ultramarine		1·50	2·00
		a. Malformed "S"		£170	
		b. Repaired "S"		£200	
41		3d. reddish purple and blue		14·00	12·00
		a. Malformed "S"		£250	
		b. Deep purple and ultramarine (1902)		85·00	£100
42		4d. brown and blue		8·50	27·00
		a. Malformed "S"		£225	
43		6d. olive-green and carmine		9·50	23·00
		a. Malformed "S"		£250	
44		1s. violet and green		26·00	55·00
		a. Malformed "S"		£350	
37/44			*Set of 8*	60·00	£110
37/44 Optd "Specimen"			*Set of 8*	£150	

3   4

Dented frame (R. 1/6 of left pane)

1902 (13 Mar)–**05.** *Wmk Crown CA. P 14.*

45	3	½d. green (19.4.02)		2·00	2·50
		a. Dented frame		50·00	
46		1d. carmine		2·00	85
		a. Dented frame		50·00	
47		2d. orange and mauve (14.6.02)		3·25	2·00
		a. Dented frame		85·00	
48		2½d. ultramarine (14.6.02)		25·00	18·00
		a. Dented frame		£190	
49		3d. purple and ultramarine (19.4.02)		12·00	3·50
		a. Dented frame		£160	
50		4d. brown and ultramarine (14.6.02)		3·00	23·00
		a. Dented frame		£120	
51		6d. pale sage-green & carmine (14.6.02)		3·25	11·00
		a. Dented frame		£120	
52		1s. violet and green (14.6.02)		48·00	85·00
		a. Dented frame		£300	
53	4	1s. 6d. green and carmine/*yellow* (6.4.05)		6·00	17·00
		a. Dented frame		£170	
54		2s. deep slate and orange (14.6.02)		48·00	60·00
		a. Dented frame		£275	
55		2s. 6d. purple and brown/*yellow* (6.4.05)		15·00	60·00
		a. Dented frame		£200	
56		3s. carmine and green/*yellow* (6.4.05)		20·00	60·00
		a. Dented frame		£200	
45/56			*Set of 12*	£170	£300
45/56 Optd "Specimen"			*Set of 12*	£180	

1904 (Aug)–06. *Wmk Mult Crown CA. P* 14.
57	3	½d. green (9.05)	..	..	..	4·00	30
		a. Dented frame	..	..	..	70·00	
58		1d. carmine	..	..	..	4·00	15
		a. Dented frame	..	..	..	80·00	
59		2d. orange and mauve (23.2.06)	..		11·00	2·25
		a. Dented frame	..	..	..	£160	
60		2½d. bright blue (8.05)	..	..	4·50	4·75
		a. *Bright blue and ultramarine*	..	12·00	25·00
		b. Dented frame	..	..	..	90·00	
61		3d. purple and ultramarine (9.05)	..	6·00	2·00
		a. Dented frame	..	..	..	£100	
62		4d. brown and ultramarine (23.2.06)	16·00	40·00
		a. Dented frame	..	..	..	£170	
63	4	5d. grey and black (6.4.05)	..	13·00	16·00
		a. Dented frame	..	..	..	£160	
64	3	6d. olive-green and carmine (23.2.06)	14·00	40·00
		a. Dented frame	..	..	..	£160	
65	4	7½d. green and carmine (6.4.05)	..	9·00	35·00
		a. Dented frame	..	..	..	£120	
66		10d. olive and carmine (6.4.05)	..	18·00	27·00
		a. Dented frame	..	..	..	£180	
67	3	1s. violet and green (9.05)	..	16·00	48·00
		a. Dented frame	..	..	..	£180	
68	4	2s. deep slate and orange (7.05)	..	65·00	75·00
		a. Dented frame	..	..	..	£300	
57/68			..		*Set of* 12	£160	£250
63, 65/6 Optd "Specimen"			*Set of* 3	70·00	

See also Nos. 72/85.

HALF PENNY

ONE PENNY

(5)   (6)

1906 (10 Apr). *Nos.* 55 *and* 56 *surch with T* 5 *or* 6 *by Govt Printer.*
69	½d. on 2s. 6d. purple and brown/*yellow*	..	45·00	65·00
	a. Dented frame	..	..		£350	
70	1d. on 3s. carmine and green/*yellow*	..	55·00	30·00
	a. Surch double	..	..	£1800	£5000
	b. Dented frame	..	..		£400	

No. 69 was surcharged in a setting of 30 (6 × 5), the spacing between the words and the bars being 5 mm on rows 1, 2 and 5; and 4 mm on rows 3 and 4. Constant varieties occur on R.2/1 (broken "E") and R.5/1 (dropped "Y") of the setting.

No. 70 was surcharged in a setting of 60 (6 × 10) and a similar dropped "Y" variety occurs on R.6/3 and R.8/5.

Both values were withdrawn on 24 April when fresh supplies of ½d. and 1d. definitives were received from London.

1909 (1 Oct). *Colours changed. Wmk Mult Crown CA. P* 14.
72	3	½d. blue-green	..	..	..	2·75	3·25
		a. Dented frame	..	..	..	65·00	
73		1d. red	..	..	..	4·25	15
		a. Dented frame	..	..	..	80·00	
74		2d. greyish slate	..	..		1·60	9·50
		a. Dented frame	..	..	..	85·00	
75		3d. purple/*yellow*	..	..		3·25	90
		a. *Purple/lemon-yellow*	..		5·50	1·75
		b. Dented frame	..	..	..	95·00	
76		4d. black and red/*yellow*	..		80	65
		a. Dented frame	..	..	..	95·00	
77	4	5d. orange and purple	..	..	1·50	1·25
		a. Dented frame	..	..	..	£100	
78	3	6d. dull and bright purple	..		2·00	2·25
		a. Dented frame	..	..	..	£110	
79	4	7½d. brown and blue	..	..	2·00	2·50
		a. Dented frame	..	..	..	£110	
80		10d. pale sage-green and carmine	..	2·50	6·50
		a. Dented frame	..	..	..	£120	
81	3	1s. black/*green*	..	..		3·00	17·00
		a. Dented frame	..	..	..	£120	
82	4	1s. 6d. violet and green	..		9·50	55·00
		a. Dented frame	..	..	..	£170	
83		2s. purple and bright blue/*blue*	..	14·00	20·00
		a. Dented frame	..	..	..	£170	
84		2s. 6d. black and red/*blue*	..	21·00	20·00
		a. Dented frame	..	..	..	£200	
85		3s. yellow and green	..	..	22·00	48·00
		a. Dented frame	..	..	..	£225	
72/85			..		*Set of* 14	80·00	£170
73/85 Optd "Specimen"			*Set of* 13	£225	

Most values between Nos. 45 and 85 are known with forged postmarks. These include circular types of Bathurst, dated "JA 2 97", and Macarthy Island, dated "FE 17 10", and an oval registered Gambia postmark dated "22 JU 10".

7   8

Split "A"
(R. 8/3 of
left pane)
(ptgs to
1918)

(Typo D.L.R.)

1912 (1 Sept)–22. *Wmk Mult Crown CA. Chalk-surfaced paper* (5s.). *P* 14.
86	7	½d. deep green	..	1·25	1·50
		a. *Green*	..	..	2·25	1·50
		b. *Pale green* (1916)	..	3·00	3·00
		c. Split "A"	..	..	55·00	
87		1d. red	..	..	2·50	70
		a. *Rose-red*	..	..	1·50	30
		b. *Scarlet* (1916)	..	2·50	90
		c. Split "A"	..	..	65·00	

88	8	1½d. olive-green and blue-green	..	30	30
		a. Split "A"	..	..	65·00	
89	7	2d. greyish slate	..	..	45	2·75
		a. Split "A"	..	..	65·00	
90		2½d. deep bright blue	..	..	4·00	3·00
		a. *Bright blue*	..	..	4·50	2·50
		b. Split "A"	..	..	£100	
91		3d. purple/*yellow*	..	..	40	30
		a. *On lemon* (1917)	..	14·00	18·00
		b. *On orange-buff* (1920)	..	10·00	8·50
		c. *On pale yellow*	..	1·00	75
		d. Split "A"	..	..	80·00	
92		4d. black and red/*yellow*	..	75	10·00
		a. *On lemon* (1917)	..	2·50	7·50
		b. *On orange-buff* (1920)	..	8·00	11·00
		c. *On pale yellow*	..	1·50	6·00
		d. Split "A"	..	..	90·00	
		w. Wmk inverted	..	..	80·00	
93	8	5d. orange and purple	..	70	1·75
		a. Split "A"	..	..	95·00	
94	7	6d. dull and bright purple	..	70	2·00
		a. Split "A"	..	..	95·00	
95	8	7½d. brown and blue	..	..	1·00	6·50
		a. Split "A"	..	..	£140	
96		10d. pale sage-green and carmine	..	2·00	17·00
		a. *Deep sage-green and carmine*	2·00	15·00
		b. Split "A"	..	..	£160	
97	7	1s. black/*green*	..	..	1·75	1·00
		a. *On emerald back* (1921)	..	80	16·00
		b. Split "A"	..	..	£110	
98	8	1s. 6d. violet and green	..	9·00	10·00
		a. Split "A"	..	..	£275	
99		2s. purple and blue/*blue*	..	2·50	6·00
		a. Split "A"	..	..	£225	
100		2s. 6d. black and red/*blue*	..	2·75	14·00
		a. Split "A"	..	..	£225	
101		3s. yellow and green	..	..	7·50	22·00
		a. Split "A"	..	..	£350	
102		5s. green and red/*pale yellow* (1922)	60·00	95·00
86/102			..	*Set of* 17	80·00	£170
86/102 Optd "Specimen"			*Set of* 17	£325	

1921–22. *Wmk Mult Script CA. Chalk-surfaced paper* (4s.). *P* 14.
108	7	½d. dull green	..	..	30	14·00
		x. Wmk reversed	..	..	75·00	
109		1d. carmine-red	..	..	1·00	4·00
		x. Wmk reversed	..	70·00	70·00
110	8	1½d. olive-green and blue-green	..	1·25	10·00
111	7	2d. grey	..	..	..	1·00	1·75
		x. Wmk reversed	..	..	60·00	
112		2½d. bright blue	..	..	50	4·75
113	8	5d. orange and purple	..	1·75	15·00
		x. Wmk reversed	..	..	35·00	
114	7	6d. dull and bright purple	..	1·75	15·00
		x. Wmk reversed	..	..	20·00	
115	8	7½d. brown and blue	..	..	2·00	26·00
		x. Wmk reversed	..	..	20·00	
116		10d. pale sage-green and carmine	..	7·00	15·00
		x. Wmk reversed	..	..	40·00	
117		4s. black and red (1922)	..	60·00	95·00
		w. Wmk inverted	..	..	55·00	£110
108/17			..	*Set of* 10	65·00	£180
108/17 Optd "Specimen"			*Set of* 10	£200	

Forged postmarks of the types mentioned below No. 85 have also been seen on various values between No. 86 and 117. Collectors should beware of partial strikes which do not show the year date.

9   10

(Recess D.L.R.)

1922 (1 Sept)–29. *Portrait and shield in black. P* 14*.
(a) Wmk Mult Crown CA
118	9	4d. red/*yellow* (*a*)	..	2·00	2·25
119		7½d. purple/*yellow* (*a*)	..	2·50	6·50
120	10	1s. purple/*yellow* (*a*)	..	6·00	19·00
		w. Wmk inverted	..	..	70·00	
121		5s. green/*yellow* (*c*)	..	32·00	90·00
		w. Wmk inverted	..	..	£110	
118/21			..	*Set of* 4	38·00	£100
118/21 Optd/H/S "Specimen"			*Set of* 4	£140	

(b) Wmk Mult Script CA
122	9	½d. green (*abd*)	..	..	55	40
123		½d. deep green (*bd*) (1925)	..	3·00	95
124		1d. brown (*abd*)	..	..	70	10
125		1½d. bright rose-scarlet (*abd*)	..	80	20
126		2d. grey (*abd*)	..	..	1·00	2·00
127		2½d. orange-yellow (*b*)	..	90	11·00
		w. Wmk inverted	..	..	70·00	
128		3d. bright blue (*abd*)	..	1·00	20
129		4d. red/*yellow* (*bd*) (1.3.27)	..	4·00	16·00
130		5d. sage-green (*a*)	..	..	2·00	10·00
131		6d. claret (*ad*)	..	..	1·25	30
132		7½d. purple/*yellow* (*ab*) (1927)	..	7·00	32·00
133		10d. blue (*a*)	..	..	4·50	18·00
134	10	1s. purple/*yellow* (*aef*) (9.24)	..	2·25	90
		a. *Blackish purple/yell-buff* (*c*) (1929)	32·00	42·00
135		1s. blue (*af*)	..	..	9·50	12·00
136		2s. purple/*blue* (*ac*)	..	3·75	4·00
137		2s. 6d. deep green (*a*)	..	4·25	9·50
138		3s. bright aniline violet (*a*)	..	11·00	40·00
139		3s. slate-purple (*c*) (1928)	..	£180	£350
140		4s. brown (*ace*)	..	..	4·75	16·00
141		5s. green/*yellow* (*acf*) (9.26)	..	12·00	35·00
142		10s. sage-green (*ce*)	..	70·00	£100
122/42			..	*Set of* 19	£120	£275
122/42 Optd "Specimen"			*Set of* 19	£400	

Perforations. A number of different perforating machines were used for the various printings of these stamps and the following varieties are known: (*a*) the original 14 line perforation; (*b*) 14 × 13.8 comb perforation used for Type 9; (*c*) 13.8 × 13.7 comb perforation used for Type 10; (*d*) 13.7 line perforation used for Type 9; (*e*) 14 × 13.8 compound line perforation used for Type 10; (*f*) 13.8 × 14 compound line perforation used for Type 10. The occurrence of these perforations on the individual values is indicated by the letters shown after the colour descriptions above.

No. 139 has been faked, but note that this stamp is comb perf 13.8 × 13.7 whereas No. 138 is line perf 14 exactly. There are also shades of the slate-purple.

Most values of the above issue are known with a forged oval registered Gambia postmark dated "22 JU 10", often with the year date not shown. Collectors should exercise particular caution in buying used examples of No. 139.

1935 (6 May). *Silver Jubilee. As T* 13 *of Antigua. Recess B.W. Wmk Mult Script CA. P* 11 × 12.
143		1½d. deep blue and scarlet	..	50	30
		a. Extra flagstaff	..	..	£250	
		b. Short extra flagstaff	..	£130	
		c. Lightning conductor	..	£250	
		d. Flagstaff on right-hand turret	£180	
		e. Double flagstaff	..	£180	
144		3d. brown and deep blue	..	55	70
		a. Extra flagstaff	..	..	£160	
		b. Short extra flagstaff	..	£160	
		c. Lightning conductor	..	£140	
145		6d. light blue and olive-green	..	90	2·00
		a. Extra flagstaff	..	..	£150	
		b. Short extra flagstaff	..	£150	
		c. Lightning conductor	..	£150	
		d. Flagstaff on right-hand turret	£275	
146		1s. slate and purple	..	2·75	5·50
		a. Extra flagstaff	..	..	£200	
		b. Short extra flagstaff	..	£225	
		c. Lightning conductor	..	£190	
		d. Flagstaff on right-hand turret	£350	
143/6			..	*Set of* 4	4·25	7·75
143/6 Perf "Specimen"			*Set of* 4	90·00	

For illustrations of plate varieties see Catalogue Introduction. Examples of Nos. 145a and 146a are known with the extra flagstaff erased from the stamp with a sharp point.

1937 (12 May). *Coronation. As Nos.* 95/7 *of Antigua. P* 11×11½
147		1d. yellow-brown	..	..	30	15
148		1½d. carmine	..	..	..	30	30
149		3d. blue	..	..	..	55	45
147/9			..	*Set of* 3	1·00	80
147/9 Perf "Specimen"			*Set of* 3	60·00	

11 Elephant (from Colony Badge)

(Recess B.W.)

1938 (1 Apr)–46. *Wmk Mult Script CA. P* 12.
150	11	½d. black and emerald-green	..	15	60
151		1d. purple and brown	..	20	50
152		1½d. brown-lake and bright carmine	£150	12·00
		a. *Brown-lake and scarlet*	..	2·50	2·25
		b. *Brown-lake and vermilion*	..	30	2·00
152c		1½d. blue and black (2.1.45)	..	30	1·25
153		2d. blue and black	..	2·75	3·00
153a		2d. lake and scarlet (1.10.43)	..	60	2·25
154		3d. light blue and grey-blue	..	30	10
154a		5d. sage-green & purple-brn (13.3.41)	45	45
155		6d. olive-green and claret	..	1·50	35
156		1s. slate-blue and violet	..	2·00	10
156a		1s. 3d. chocolate & lt blue (28.11.46)	2·75	2·50
157		2s. carmine and black	..	4·50	3·25
158		2s. 6d. sepia and dull green	..	12·00	2·00
159		4s. vermilion and purple	..	21·00	2·50
160		5s. blue and vermilion	..	21·00	4·00
161		10s. orange and black	..	21·00	7·00
150/61			..	*Set of* 16	80·00	28·00
150/61 Perf "Specimen"			*Set of* 16	£250	

1946 (6 Aug). *Victory. As Nos.* 110/11 *of Antigua.*
162		1½d. black	..	..	10	10
163		3d. blue	..	..	..	10	10
162/3 Perf "Specimen"			*Set of* 2	55·00	

1948 (24 Dec). *Royal Silver Wedding. As Nos.* 112/13 *of Antigua.*
164		1½d. black	..	..	25	10
165		£1 mauve	..	..	12·00	14·00

1949 (10 Oct). *75th Anniv of Universal Postal Union. As Nos.* 114/17 *of Antigua.*
166		1½d. blue-black	..	..	40	40
167		3d. deep blue	..	..	1·50	80
168		6d. magenta	..	..	60	40
169		1s. violet	..	..	60	30
166/9			..	*Set of* 4	2·75	1·75

1953 (2 June). *Coronation. As No.* 120 *of Antigua, but ptd by B.W.*
170		1½d. black and deep bright blue	..	50	40

12 Tapping for Palm Wine

13 Cutter

(Des Mrs O. W. Meronti. Recess D.L.R.)

1953 (2 Nov)–59. T 12/13 and similar horiz designs. Wmk Mult Script CA. P 13½.

171	12	½d. carmine-red and bluish green	30	20
		a. Carmine and bluish green (7.1.59)	1·50	2·00
172	13	1d. deep ultramarine and deep brown	40	30
		a. Deep ultramarine & choc (22.8.56)	2·50	1·75
173	–	1½d. deep brown and grey-black	20	50
174	–	2½d. black and carmine-red	45	70
175	–	3d. deep blue and slate-lilac	35	10
176	–	4d. black and deep blue	60	1·75
177	12	6d. brown and reddish purple	35	15
178	–	1s. yellow-brown and yellow-green	60	50
179	13	1s. 3d. ultramarine and pale blue	10·00	10·00
		a. Ultramarine and light blue (22.2.56)	14·00	55
180	–	2s. indigo and carmine	7·00	3·50
181	13	2s. 6d. deep bluish green and sepia	4·00	1·50
182	–	4s. grey-blue and Indian red	11·00	3·00
183	–	5s. chocolate and bright blue	2·50	1·50
184	–	10s. deep blue and myrtle-green	20·00	7·00
185	–	£1 green and black	15·00	9·00
171/85		Set of 15	65·00	26·00

Designs:—1½d., 5s. Wollof woman; 2½d., 2s. Barra canoe; 3d., 10s. S.S. Lady Wright; 4d., 4s. James Island; 1s., 2s. 6d. Woman hoeing; £1 Elephant and palm (from Colony Badge).

20 Queen Elizabeth II and Palm

21 Queen Elizabeth II and West African Map

(Des J. R. F. Ithier (T 20), A. W. Morley (T 21). Recess B.W.)

1961 (2 Dec). Royal Visit. W w 12. P 11½.

186	20	2d. green and purple	30	15
187	21	3d. turquoise-blue and sepia	75	15
188		6d. blue and cerise	75	65
189	20	1s. 3d. violet and myrtle-green	75	2·00
186/9		Set of 4	2·25	2·75

1963 (4 June). Freedom from Hunger. As No. 146 of Antigua.

190	1s. 3d. carmine	55	15

1963 (2 Sept). Red Cross Centenary. As Nos. 147/8 of Antigua.

191	2d. red and black	25	10
192	1s. 3d. red and blue	65	45

SELF-GOVERNMENT

22 Beautiful Sunbird

SELF GOVERNMENT 1963

(35)

(Des V. Whiteley. Photo Harrison)

1963 (4 Nov). Birds. Horiz designs as T 22. Multicoloured. W w 12. P 12½ × 13.

193		½d. Type 22	30	60
194		1d. Yellow-mantled Whydah	30	30
195		1½d. Cattle Egret	1·75	70
196		2d. Senegal Parrot	1·75	70
197		3d. Rose-ringed Parakeet	1·75	70
198		4d. Violet Starling	1·75	80
199		6d. Village Weaver	1·75	10
200		1s. Rufous-crowned Roller	1·25	10
201		1s. 3d. Red-eyed Dove	12·00	1·50
202		2s. 6d. Double-spurred Francolin	9·00	2·50
203		5s. Palm-nut Vulture	9·00	2·75
204		10s. Orange-cheeked Waxbill	13·00	7·00
205		£1 African Emerald Cuckoo	28·00	14·00
193/205		Set of 13	70·00	28·00

1963 (7 Nov). New Constitution. Nos. 194, 197, 200/1 optd with T 35.

206		1d. Yellow-mantled Whydah	10	40
207		3d. Rose-ringed Parakeet	25	20
208		1s. Rufous-crowned Roller	25	10
		a. Opt double		† £4000
209		1s. 3d. Red-eyed Dove	30	45
206/9		Set of 4	75	1·00

1964 (23 Apr). 400th Birth Anniv of William Shakespeare. As No. 164 of Antigua.

210		6d. bright blue	20	10
		w. Wmk inverted	35·00	35·00

INDEPENDENT

36 Gambia Flag and River

37 Arms

(Des V. Whiteley. Photo Harrison)

1965 (18 Feb). Independence. P 14½.

211	36	½d. multicoloured	10	40
212	37	2d. multicoloured	15	10
213	36	7½d. multicoloured	40	35
214	37	1s. 6d. multicoloured	50	10
211/14		Set of 4	1·00	1·00

INDEPENDENCE 1965

(38)

39 I.T.U. Emblem and Symbols

1965 (18 Feb). Nos. 193/205 optd with T 38 or with date centred (1d., 2d., 3d., 4d., 1s., 5s.).

215		½d. Type 22	30	70
216		1d. Yellow-mantled Whydah	30	20
217		1½d. Cattle Egret	60	70
218		2d. Senegal Parrot	70	30
219		3d. Rose-ringed Parakeet	70	15
220		4d. Violet Starling	70	90
221		6d. Village Weaver	70	10
222		1s. Rufous-crowned Roller	70	10
223		1s. 3d. Red-eyed Dove	70	10
224		2s. 6d. Double-spurred Francolin	70	60
225		5s. Palm-nut Vulture	70	75
226		10s. Orange-cheeked Waxbill	1·60	1·50
227		£1 African Emerald Cuckoo	6·00	7·50
215/27		Set of 13	13·00	12·00

(Des V. Whiteley. Photo Harrison)

1965 (17 May). I.T.U. Centenary. P 14½.

228	39	1d. silver and Prussian blue	25	10
229		1s. 6d. gold and bluish violet	1·00	40

THE GAMBIA. From this point onwards stamps are inscribed "The Gambia".

40 Sir Winston Churchill and Houses of Parliament

(Des Jennifer Toombs. Photo Harrison)

1966 (24 Jan). Churchill Commemoration. P 14 × 14½.

230	40	1d. multicoloured	10	10
231		6d. multicoloured	30	15
232		1s. 6d. multicoloured	50	75
230/2		Set of 3	80	85

41 Red-cheeked Cordon Bleu

42 Pin-tailed Whydah

(Des V. Whiteley. Photo Harrison)

1966 (18 Feb). Birds. Horiz designs as T 41, and T 42. Multicoloured. P 14 × 14½ (£1) or 12 × 13 (others).

233		½d. Type 41	90	40
234		1d. White-faced Whistling Duck	30	50
235		1½d. Red-throated Bee Eater	30	40
236		2d. Lesser Pied Kingfisher	4·25	50
237		3d. Golden Bishop	30	10
238		4d. African Fish Eagle	50	30
239		6d. Yellow-bellied Green Pigeon	40	10
240		1s. Blue-bellied Roller	40	10
241		1s. 6d. African Pygmy Kingfisher	75	30
242		2s. 6d. Spur-winged Goose	75	70
243		5s. Cardinal Woodpecker	75	75
244		10s. Violet Turaco	75	2·75
245		£1 Type 42	1·00	6·50
233/45		Set of 13	10·00	12·00

The ½d., 1d. and 2d. to 1s. values exist with PVA gum as well as gum arabic.

54 Arms, Early Settlement and Modern Buildings

(Photo, arms die-stamped Harrison)

1966 (24 June). 150th Anniv of Bathurst. P 14½ × 14.

246	54	1d. silver, brown and yellow-orange	10	10
247		2d. silver, brown and light blue	10	10
248		6d. silver, brown and light emerald	10	10
249		1s. 6d. silver, brown and light magenta	15	15
246/9		Set of 4	30	30

55 I.T.Y. Emblem and Hotels

(Des and photo (emblem die-stamped) Harrison)

1967 (20 Dec). International Tourist Year. P 14½ × 14.

250	55	2d. silver, brown and apple-green	10	10
251		1s. silver, brown and orange	10	10
252		1s. 6d. silver, brown and magenta	15	25
250/2		Set of 3	30	40

56 Handcuffs

(Des V. Whiteley. Photo Enschedé)

1968 (15 July). Human Rights Year. T 56 and similar horiz designs. Multicoloured. P 14 × 13.

253		1d. Type 56	10	10
254		1s. Fort Bullen	10	10
255		5s. Methodist Church	30	60
253/5		Set of 3	35	65

59 Queen Victoria, Queen Elizabeth II and 4d. Stamp of 1869

(Des G. Drummond. Photo and embossing (cameo head) Harrison)

1969 (20 Jan). Gambia Stamp Centenary. P 14½ × 13½.

256	59	4d. sepia and yellow-ochre	20	10
257		6d. Prussian blue and deep yellow-green	20	10
258		2s. 6d. multicoloured	70	1·40
256/8		Set of 3	1·00	1·40

Design:—2s. 6d. Queen Elizabeth II with 4d. and 6d. stamps of 1869.

In the 6d. value the stamp illustrated is the 6d. of 1869.

61 Catapult-Ship *Westfalen* launching Dornier Do-J II 10-t Wal

(Des L. Curtis. Litho Format)

1969 (15 Dec). 35th Anniv of Pioneer Air Services. T 61 and similar horiz designs showing various forms of transport, map of South Atlantic and Lufthansa emblem. Multicoloured. P 13½ × 14.

259		2d. Type 61	35	20
260		1s. Dornier Do-J II 10-t Wal *Boreas* flying boat	45	20
261		1s. 6d. Airship LZ-127 *Graf Zeppelin*	55	1·40
259/61		Set of 3	1·25	1·60

REPUBLIC

63 Athlete and Gambian Flag

(Des Jennifer Toombs. Litho Format)

1970 (16 July). *Ninth British Commonwealth Games, Edinburgh.* P 14.

262	63	1d. multicoloured			10	10
263		1s. multicoloured			10	10
264		5s. multicoloured			30	50
262/4				Set of 3	35	50

64 President Sir Dawda Kairaba Jawara and State House

(Des G. Vasarhelyi. Litho Questa)

1970 (2 Nov). *Republic Day. T 64 and similar multicoloured designs.* P 14.

265		2d. Type 64			10	10
266		1s. President Sir Dawda Jawara			15	10
267		1s. 6d. President and flag of Gambia			30	35
265/7				Set of 3	45	45

The 1s. and 1s. 6d. are both vertical designs.

65 Methodist Church, Georgetown

(Des J. Cooter. Litho Questa)

1971 (16 Apr). *150th Anniv of Establishment of Methodist Mission. T 65 and similar multicoloured designs.* P 14.

268		2d. Type 65			10	10
269		1s. Map of Africa and Gambian flag (vert)			15	10
270		1s. 6d. John Wesley and scroll (horiz)			15	35
268/70				Set of 3	30	45

(New Currency. 100 bututs = 1 dalasy)

66 Yellow-finned Tunny

(Des J.W. Litho Format)

1971 (1 July). *New Currency. Fishes. Horiz designs as T 66. Multicoloured.* P 14.

271		2 b. Type 66			10	50
272		4 b. Peter's Mormyrid			10	15
273		6 b. Four-winged Flyingfish			15	50
274		8 b. African Sleeper Goby			15	50
275		10 b. Yellow-tailed Snapper			20	15
276		13 b. Rock Hind			20	50
277		25 b. West African Eel Catfish			35	50
278		38 b. Tiger Shark			55	45
279		50 b. Electric Catfish			70	55
280		63 b. Black Swampeel			80	1·50
281		1 d. 25, Small-toothed Sawfish			1·40	2·50
282		2 d. 50, Great Barracuda			2·00	4·50
283		5 d. Brown Bullhead			2·25	7·00
271/83				Set of 13	8·00	17·00

67 Mungo Park in Scotland

(Des J.W. from ideas by P. J. Westwood. Litho Questa)

1971 (10 Sept). *Birth Bicentenary of Mungo Park (explorer). T 67 and similar horiz designs. Multicoloured. W w 12 (sideways).* P 13½ × 13.

284		4 b. Type 67			20	10
285		25 b. Dug-out canoe			45	35
286		37 b. Death of Mungo Park, Busa Rapids			75	1·50
284/6				Set of 3	1·25	1·75

68 Radio Gambia

(Des G. Drummond. Litho Questa)

1972 (1 July). *Tenth Anniv of Radio Gambia. T 68 and similar horiz design.* P 14.

287	68	4 b. orange-ochre and black			10	10
288	—	25 b. light new blue, red-orange and black			10	25
289	68	37 b. bright green and black			20	70
287/9				Set of 3	30	90

Design:—25 b. Broadcast-area map.

69 High Jumping   70 Manding Woman

(Des and litho D.L.R.)

1972 (31 Aug). *Olympic Games, Munich.* P 13.

290	69	4 b. multicoloured			10	10
291		25 b. multicoloured			20	15
292		37 b. multicoloured			25	20
290/2				Set of 3	50	30

(Des C. Abbott. Litho Questa)

1972 (16 Oct). *International Conference on Manding Studies, London. T 70 and similar vert designs. Multicoloured.* P 14 × 14½.

293		2 b. Type 70			10	10
294		25 b. Musician playing the Kora			15	15
295		37 b. Map of Mali Empire			25	25
293/5				Set of 3	40	40

71 Children carrying Fanal   72 Groundnuts

(Des L. Curtis. Litho Enschedé)

1972 (1 Dec). *Fanals (Model Boats). T 71 and similar horiz design. Multicoloured.* P 13 × 13½.

296		2 b. Type 71			10	10
297		1 d. 25, Fanal with lanterns			30	45

(Des locally; adapted G. Drummond. Litho Harrison)

1973 (31 Mar). *Freedom from Hunger Campaign.* P 14½ × 14.

298	72	2 b. multicoloured			10	10
299		25 b. multicoloured			15	10
300		37 b. multicoloured			25	20
298/300				Set of 3	40	30

73 Planting and Drying Rice   74 Oil Palm

(Des PAD Studio. Litho J.W.)

1973 (30 Apr). *Agriculture (1st series). T 73 and similar vert designs. Multicoloured.* P 14.

301		2 b. Type 73			10	10
302		25 b. Guinea Corn			20	15
303		37 b. Rice			25	25
301/3				Set of 3	45	40

(Des PAD Studio. Litho Format)

1973 (16 July). *Agriculture (2nd series). T 74 and similar vert designs. Multicoloured.* P 12.

304		2 b. Type 74			10	10
305		25 b. Limes			30	30
306		37 b. Oil palm (fruits)			40	40
304/6				Set of 3	65	65

---

75 Cassava

(Des PAD Studio. Litho Questa)

1973 (15 Oct). *Agriculture (3rd series). T 75 and similar horiz design. Multicoloured.* P 14.

307		2 b. Type 75			10	10
308		50 b. Cotton			40	25

76 O.A.U. Emblem

(Des and litho D.L.R.)

1973 (1 Nov). *Tenth Anniv of O.A.U.* P 13½ × 13.

309	76	4 b. multicoloured			10	10
310		25 b. multicoloured			15	10
311		37 b. multicoloured			15	20
309/11				Set of 3	30	30

77 Red Cross   78 Arms of Banjul

(Des J. Cooter. Litho Questa)

1973 (30 Nov). *25th Anniv of Gambian Red Cross.* P 14 × 14½.

312	77	4 b. dull orange-red, and black			10	10
313		25 b. dull orange-red, black and new blue			15	15
314		37 b. dull orange-red, black & lt yell-grn			20	20
312/14				Set of 3	35	35

(Des and litho D.L.R.)

1973 (17 Dec). *Change of Bathurst's Name to Banjul.* P 13½ × 13.

315	78	4 b. multicoloured			10	10
316		25 b. multicoloured			15	15
317		37 b. multicoloured			15	20
315/17				Set of 3	30	30

79 U.P.U. Emblem

(Des and litho D.L.R.)

1974 (24 Aug). *Centenary of Universal Postal Union.* P 13½.

318	79	4 b. multicoloured			10	10
319		37 b. multicoloured			20	30

80 Churchill as Harrow Schoolboy   81 "Different Races"

(Des and litho J.W.)

1974 (30 Nov). *Birth Centenary of Sir Winston Churchill. T 80 and similar vert designs. Multicoloured.* P 13½.

320		4 b. Type 80			10	10
321		37 b. Churchill as 4th Hussars officer			25	15
322		50 b. Churchill as Prime Minister			40	60
320/2				Set of 3	65	75

(Des G. Vasarhelyi. Litho Questa)

1974 (16 Dec). *World Population Year. T 81 and similar horiz designs. Multicoloured.* P 14.

323		4 b. Type 81			10	10
324		37 b. "Multiplication and Division of Races"			15	15
325		50 b. "World Population"			20	25
323/5				Set of 3	35	40

82 Dr. Schweitzer and River Scene

(Des G. Vasarhelyi. Litho Walsall)

1975 (14 Jan). *Birth Centenary of Dr. Albert Schweitzer. T* **82** *and similar horiz designs. Multicoloured. P* 14.

326	10 b.	Type 82	..	20	10
327	50 b.	Surgery scene	..	55	25
328	1 d. 25,	River journey..	..	1·00	55
326/8	..		Set of 3	1·60	75

83 Dove of Peace   **84 Development Graph**

(Des and litho D.L.R.)

1975 (18 Feb). *10th Anniv of Independence. T* **83** *and similar horiz designs. Multicoloured. P* 13.

329	4 b.	Type 83	..	10	10
330	10 b.	Gambian flag	..	10	10
331	50 b.	Gambian arms	..	15	10
332	1 d. 25,	Map of The Gambia	..	35	40
329/32	..		Set of 4	50	55

(Des PAD Studio. Litho Questa)

1975 (31 Mar). *Tenth Anniv of African Development Bank. T* **84** *and similar vert designs. Multicoloured. P* 14½.

333	10 b.	Type 84	..	10	10
334	50 b.	Symbolic plant	..	20	15
335	1 d. 25,	Bank emblem and symbols	..	55	60
333/5	..		Set of 3	70	75

85 Statue of "David"   **86 School Building**
(Michelangelo)

(Des C. Abbott. Litho Walsall)

1975 (14 Nov). *5Q0th Birth Anniv of Michelangelo. T* **85** *and similar multicoloured designs. P* 14½ × 14 (1 d. 25) or 14 × 14½ (others).

336	10 b.	Type 85	..	15	10
337	50 b.	"Madonna of the Steps"	..	30	15
338	1 d. 25,	"Battle of the Centaurs" (*horiz*)	..	50	1·25
336/8	..		Set of 3	85	1·40

(Des G. Vasarhelyi. Litho Format)

1975 (17 Nov). *Centenary of Gambia High School. T* **86** *and similar horiz designs. Multicoloured. P* 14½.

339	10 b.	Type 86	..	10	10
340	50 b.	Pupil with scientific apparatus	..	15	10
341	1 d. 50,	School crest	..	35	35
339/41	..		Set of 3	50	40

87 "Teaching"

(Des A. B. Oliver; adapted by Jennifer Toombs. Litho Questa)

1975 (15 Dec). *International Women's Year. T* **87** *and similar horiz designs. Multicoloured. P* 14½.

342	4 b.	Type 87	..	10	10
343	10 b.	"Planting rice"	..	10	10
344	50 b.	"Nursing"	..	35	15
345	1 d. 50,	"Directing traffic"	..	85	35
342/5	..		Set of 4	1·25	55

88 Woman playing Golf   **89 American Militiaman**

(Des R. Granger Barrett. Litho J.W.)

1976 (18 Feb). *11th Anniv of Independence. T* **88** *and similar horiz designs. Multicoloured. P* 14½ × 14.

346	10 b.	Type 88	..	55	10
347	50 b.	Man playing golf	..	1·50	20
348	1 d. 50,	President playing golf	..	2·25	70
346/8	..		Set of 3	3·75	90

(Des C. Abbott. Litho Questa)

1976 (15 May). *Bicentenary of American Revolution. T* **89** *and similar vert designs. Multicoloured. P* 14 × 13½.

349	25 b.	Type 89	..	20	10
350	50 b.	Soldier of the Continental Army	..	30	20
351	1 d. 25,	Independence Declaration	..	40	60
349/51	..		Set of 3	80	80
MS352	110 × 80 mm. Nos. 349/51	..		1·40	4·00

90 Mother and Child   **91 Serval**

(Des G. Vasarhelyi. Litho Questa)

1976 (28 Oct). *Christmas. P* 14.

353	**90**	10 b. multicoloured	..	10	10
354		50 b. multicoloured	..	15	10
355		1 d. 25, multicoloured	..	50	45
353/5	..		Set of 3	60	50

(Des G. Drummond. Litho Questa)

1976 (29 Nov). *Abuko Nature Reserve (1st series). T* **91** *and similar horiz designs. Multicoloured. P* 13½.

356	10 b.	Type 91	..	2·25	20
357	25 b.	Bushbuck	..	3·25	20
358	50 b.	Sitatunga	..	4·50	40
359	1 d. 25,	Leopard	..	10·00	2·00
356/9	..		Set of 4	18·00	2·50
MS360	137 × 110 mm. Nos. 356/9	..		26·00	9·00

See also Nos. 400/3, 431/5 and 460/3.

92 Festival Emblem and Gambian Weaver

(Des E. N. Sillah; adapted C. Abbott. Litho Walsall)

1977 (12 Jan). *Second World Black and African Festival of Arts and Culture, Nigeria. P* 14.

361	**92**	25 b. multicoloured	..	15	10
362		50 b. multicoloured	..	20	15
363		1 d. 25, multicoloured	..	50	70
361/3	..		Set of 3	75	85
MS364	118 × 114 mm. Nos. 361/3	..		1·75	3·75

93 The Spurs and Jewelled Sword

(Des PAD Studio. Litho Questa)

1977 (7 Feb). *Silver Jubilee. T* **93** *and similar horiz designs. Multicoloured. P* 13½.

365	25 b.	Queen's visit, 1961	..	25	30
366	50 b.	Type 93	..	20	25
367	1 d. 25,	Oblation of the sword	..	30	35
365/7	..		Set of 3	65	80

94 Stone Circles, Kuntaur

(Des J.W. Litho Questa)

1977 (18 Feb). *Tourism. T* **94** *and similar horiz designs. Multicoloured. P* 14.

368	25 b.	Type 94	..	10	10
369	50 b.	Ruined fort, James Island	..	20	20
370	1 d. 25,	Mungo Park Monument	..	70	70
368/70	..		Set of 3	90	90

95 Widow of Last Year   **96 Endangered Animals**

(Des PAD Studio. Litho Questa)

1977 (1 July)–**79**. *Flowers and Shrubs. Multicoloured designs as T* **95**. *Chalk-surfaced paper (No. 376a) or ordinary paper (others). P* 14.

371	2 b.	Type 95		10	15
		a. Chalk-surfaced paper (23.11.79)..		40	25
372	4 b.	White Water-lily		10	30
		a. Chalk-surfaced paper (23.11.79)..		40	30
373	6 b.	Fireball Lily		10	30
		a. Chalk-surfaced paper (22.6.79)..		40	30
374	8 b.	Cocks-comb		10	15
		a. Chalk-surfaced paper (23.11.79)..		30	15
375	10 b.	Broad Leaved Ground Orchid		2·00	30
		a. Chalk-surfaced paper (23.11.79)..		2·00	30
376	13 b.	Fibre Plant (pale yellow background)		15	40
376a	13 b.	Fibre Plant (pale olive-grey background)			
		(*chalk-surfaced paper*) (25.7.79)..		1·75	3·50
377	25 b.	False Kapok		15	15
		a. Chalk-surfaced paper (16.3.78)		55	35
378	38 b.	Baobab		25	55
		a. Chalk-surfaced paper (23.11.79)..		60	35
379	50 b.	Coral Tree		35	35
		a. Chalk-surfaced paper (16.3.78)		75	50
380	63 b.	Gloriosa Lily		40	70
		a. Chalk-surfaced paper (23.11.79)..		85	65
381	1 d. 25,	Bell-flowered Mimosa		45	1·25
		a. Chalk-surfaced paper (23.11.79)..		1·00	1·00
382	2 d. 50,	Kindin Dolo		50	1·25
383	5 d.	African Tulip Tree		60	2·00
371/83	..		Set of 14	6·00	9·75

The 6 to 38 b., 1 d. 25 and 2 d. 50 are vertical designs.

(Des N. Fortey (10, 50 b.), D. J. Thorp (25 b.), M. Langley (1 d. 25). Litho Questa)

1977 (15 Oct). *Banjul Declaration. T* **96** *and similar vert designs. P* 14.

384	10 b.	black and light new blue	..	25	10
385	25 b.	multicoloured	..	40	10
386	50 b.	multicoloured	..	65	20
387	1 d. 25,	black and light vermilion	..	1·75	75
384/7	..		Set of 4	2·75	1·00

Designs:—25 b. Extract from Declaration; 50 b. Declaration in full; 1 d. 25, Endangered insects and flowers.

97 "Flight into Egypt"   **98 Dome of the Rock, Jerusalem**

(Des BG Studio and Enschedé. Litho Enschedé)

1977 (15 Dec). *400th Birth Anniv of Rubens. T* **97** *and similar vert designs. Multicoloured. P* 13½ × 14.

388	10 b.	Type 97	..	15	10
389	25 b.	"The Education of the Virgin"	..	20	10
390	50 b.	"Clara Serena Rubens"	..	35	30
391	1 d.	"Madonna with Saints"	..	65	90
388/91	..		Set of 4	1·25	1·25

Nos. 388/91 were each printed in small sheets of 6 including 1 se-tenant stamp-size label.

(Des J. Cooter. Litho Questa)

1978 (3 Jan). *Palestinian Welfare.* P 14½ × 14.

392	**98**	8 b. multicoloured		50	15
393		25 b. multicoloured		2·00	85

99 Walking on a Greasy Pole   100 Lion

(Des J.W. Litho Harrison)

1978 (18 Feb). *13th Anniv of Independence.* T **99** and similar vert designs showing scenes from the Independence Regatta. Multicoloured. P 14.

394	10 b. Type **99**		10	10
395	50 b. Pillow fighting		20	10
396	1 d. 25, Long rowing boat		45	45
394/6		*Set of 3*	60	55

(Des Jennifer Toombs. Litho Questa)

1978 (15 Apr). *25th Anniv of Coronation.* T **100** and similar vert designs. P 15.

397	1 d. black, agate and orange-yellow		20	45
	a. Sheetlet. Nos. 397/9 × 2.		1·00	
398	1 d. multicoloured		20	45
399	1 d. black, agate and orange-yellow		20	45
397/9		*Set of 3*	50	1·25

Designs:—No. 397, White Greyhound of Richmond; No. 398, Queen Elizabeth II; No. 399, Type **100**.

Nos. 397/9 were printed together in small sheets of 6, containing two *se-tenant* strips of 3, with horizontal gutter margin between.

101 Verreaux's Eagle Owl   102 M.V. *Lady Wright* (previous vessel)

(Des M. Bryan. Litho Questa)

1978 (28 Oct). *Abuko Nature Reserve (2nd series).* T **101** and similar vert designs. Multicoloured. P 14 × 13½.

400	20 b. Type **101**		6·00	65
401	25 b. Lizard Buzzard		6·00	65
402	50 b. African Harrier Hawk		9·00	2·25
403	1 d. 25, Long-crested Eagle		13·00	9·00
400/3		*Set of 4*	30·00	11·00

(Des A. Theobald. Litho Questa)

1978 (1 Dec). *New River Vessel "Lady Chilel Jawara" Commemoration.* T **102** and similar horiz designs. Multicoloured. P 14.

404	8 b. Type **102**		15	10
405	25 b. Lady Chilel Jawara (sectional view)		40	25
406	1 d. *Lady Chilel Jawara*		1·25	1·40
404/6		*Set of 3*	1·60	1·50

103 Police Service   (104)

(Des G. Vasarhelyi. Litho Questa)

1979 (18 Feb). *14th Anniv of Independence.* T **103** and similar horiz designs. Multicoloured. P 14.

407	10 b. Type **103**		60	10
408	50 b. Fire service		1·10	25
409	1 d. 25, Ambulance service		1·40	80
407/9		*Set of 3*	2·75	1·00

1979 (5–26 Mar). Nos. 376 and 380/1 surch as T **104**.

410	25 b. on 13 b. Fibre Plant		20	35
411	25 b. on 63 b. Gloriosa Lily (26.3.79)		15	20
412	25 b. on 1 d. 25, Bell-flowered Mimosa (26.3.79)		15	20
410/12		*Set of 3*	45	65

105 "Ramsgate Sands" (detail showing Children playing on Beach)

(Des C. Abbott. Litho Questa)

1979 (25 May). *International Year of the Child.* T **105** and similar multicoloured designs showing the painting "Ramsgate Sands" by William Powell Frith. P 14 × 13½ (25 b.) or 13½ × 14 (others).

413	10 b. Type **105**		10	10
414	25 b. Detail showing child paddling (vert)		20	10
415	1 d. Complete painting (60 × 23 mm)		60	60
413/15		*Set of 3*	80	65

106 1883 2½d. Stamp

(Des J.W. Litho Questa)

1979 (16 Aug). *Death Centenary of Sir Rowland Hill.* T **106** and similar horiz designs showing stamps. Multicoloured. P 14.

416	10 b. Type **106**		10	10
417	25 b. 1869 4d.		15	10
418	50 b. 1965 7½d. Independence commemorative		20	20
419	1 d. 25, 1935 1½d. Silver Jubilee commemorative		40	50
416/19		*Set of 4*	75	80
MS420	109 × 83 mm. No. 419		65	1·00

107 Satellite Earth Station under Construction   108 "Apollo 11" leaving Launch Pad

(Des A. Theobald. Litho Questa)

1979 (20 Sept). *Abuko Satellite Earth Station.* T **107** and similar horiz designs. Multicoloured. P 14.

421	25 b. Type **107**		20	10
422	50 b. Satellite Earth Station (completed)		30	20
423	1 d. "Intelsat" satellites		65	60
421/3		*Set of 3*	1·00	80

(Des and litho Walsall)

1979 (17 Oct). *10th Anniv of Moon Landing.* T **108** and similar vert designs. Multicoloured. (a) Sheet stamps. P 14.

424	25 b. Type **108**		20	10
425	38 b. "Apollo 11" in Moon orbit		25	20
426	50 b. Splashdown		30	40
424/6		*Set of 3*	65	60

(b) Booklet stamps. Roul 5 × imperf.* Self-adhesive

427	25 b. Type **108**		25	55
	a. Booklet pane. Nos. 427/9, each × 2		1·60	
428	38 b. As No. 425		30	55
429	50 b. As No. 426		30	55
430	2 d. Lunar module on Moon		1·50	2·25
	a. Booklet pane of 1		1·50	

*Nos. 427/9 are separated by various combinations of rotary-knife (giving a straight edge) and roulette. No. 430 exists only with straight edges.

109 *Acraea zetes*

(Des J. Cooter. Litho Questa)

1980 (3 Jan). *Abuko Nature Reserve (3rd series). Butterflies.* T **109** and similar horiz designs. Multicoloured. P 13½.

431	25 b. Type **109**		2·50	20
432	50 b. *Precis hierta*		3·00	50
433	1 d. *Graphium leonidas*		5·00	1·00
434	1 d. 25, *Charaxes jasius*		5·00	1·10
431/4		*Set of 4*	14·00	2·50
MS435	145 × 122 mm. Nos. 431/4		23·00	4·50

110 Steam Launch *Vampire*

(Des C. Abbott. Litho Harrison)

1980 (6 May). *"London 1980" International Stamp Exhibition. Mail Boats.* T **110** and similar multicoloured designs. P 14 (10, 25 b.) or 13 × 14 (others).

436	10 b. Type **110**		25	10
437	25 b. T.S.S. Lady Denham		35	10
438	50 b. T.S.C.M.Y. Mansa Kila Ba (49 × 26 mm)		40	20
439	1 d. 25, T.S.S. Prince of Wales (49 × 26 mm)		65	60
436/9		*Set of 4*	1·50	85

111 Queen Elizabeth the Queen Mother

(Des and litho Harrison)

1980 (4 Aug). *80th Birthday of Queen Elizabeth the Queen Mother.* P 14.

440	**111**	67 b. multicoloured		30	35

112 Phoenician Trading Vessel   113 "Madonna and Child" (Francesco de Mura)

(Des A. Theobald. Litho Walsall)

1980 (2 Oct). *Early Sailing Vessels.* T **112** and similar horiz designs. Multicoloured. P 14½ × 14.

441	8 b. Type **112**		10	10
442	67 b. Egyptian sea-going vessel		40	20
443	75 b. Portuguese caravel		50	30
444	1 d. Spanish galleon		70	50
441/4		*Set of 4*	1·50	1·00

(Des BG Studio. Litho Questa)

1980 (23 Dec). *Christmas. Paintings.* T **113** and similar vert designs. Multicoloured. P 14.

445	8 b. Type **113**		10	10
446	67 b. "Praying Madonna with Crown of Stars" (workshop of Correggio)		25	25
447	75 b. "La Zingarella" (workshop replica of Correggio painting)		25	30
445/7		*Set of 3*	50	60

114 New Atlantic Hotel

(Des BG Studio. Litho Format)

1981 (18 Feb). *World Tourism Conference, Manila.* T **114** and similar horiz designs. Multicoloured. P 14.

448	25 b. Type **114**		15	10
449	75 b. Ancient stone circle		30	40
450	85 b. Conference emblem		40	50
448/50		*Set of 3*	75	90

115 1979 Abuko Satellite Earth Station 50 b. Commemorative   116 Prince Charles in Naval Uniform

497

(Des BG Studio. Litho Questa)

1981 (17 May). *World Telecommunications Day. T* **115** *and similar horiz designs.* P 14.

451	50 b. multicoloured	..	..	30	20
452	50 b. multicoloured	..	..	30	20
453	85 b. black and brown-ochre	..	..	50	45
451/3	..		*Set of 3*	1·00	75

Designs:—No. 452, 1975 Birth Centenary of Dr. Albert Schweitzer 50 b. commemorative; No. 453, I.T.U. and W.H.O. emblems.

(Des and litho J.W.)

1981 (22 July). *Royal Wedding. T* **116** *and similar vert designs. Multicoloured.* P 13½ × 13.

454	75 b. Wedding bouquet from Gambia	..	..	20	20
455	1 d. Type **116**	..	..	25	30
456	1 d. 25, Prince Charles and Lady Diana Spencer		..	30	35
454/6	..		*Set of 3*	65	75

117 Planting-out Seedlings

(Des Jennifer Toombs. Litho Format)

1981 (4 Sept). *10th Anniv of West African Rice Development Association. T* **117** *and similar horiz designs. Multicoloured.* P 14.

457	10 b. Type **117**	..	..	10	10
458	50 b. Care of the crops	..	..	25	35
459	85 b. Winnowing and drying	..	..	40	55
457/9	..		*Set of 3*	65	85

118 Bosc's Monitor

(Des J. Cooter. Litho Format)

1981 (17 Nov). *Abuko Nature Reserve (4th series). Reptiles. T* **118** *and similar horiz designs. Multicoloured.* P 14.

460	40 b. Type **118**	..	..	4·00	20
461	60 b. Dwarf Crocodile	..	..	4·50	60
462	80 b. Royal Python	..	..	5·50	1·00
463	85 b. Chameleon	..	..	5·50	1·00
460/3	..		*Set of 4*	18·00	2·50

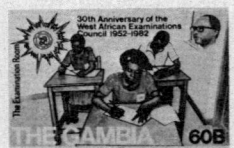

119 Examination Room   **(120)**

(Des PAD Studio. Litho Walsall)

1982 (16 Mar). *30th Anniv of West African Examinations Council. T* **119** *and similar horiz designs. Multicoloured.* P 14.

464	60 b. Type **119**	..	..	50	30
465	85 b. First High School	..	..	65	45
466	1 d. 10, Council's office	..	..	85	55
464/6	..		*Set of 3*	1·75	1·10

1982 (19 Apr). *No. 454 surch with T* **120**.

467	60 b. on 75 b. Wedding bouquet from Gambia	75	1·60

121 Tree-planting ("Conservation")

(Des L. Curtis. Litho Harrison)

1982 (16 May). *75th Anniv of Boy Scout Movement. T* **121** *and similar horiz designs. Multicoloured.* P 14.

468	85 b. Type **121**	..	..	2·00	1·25
469	1 d. 25, Woodworking	..	..	2·25	2·00
470	1 d. 27, Lord Baden-Powell	..	..	2·50	3·25
468/70	..		*Set of 3*	6·00	6·25

---

122 Gambia Football Team   **123** Gambia Coat of Arms

(Des A. Theobald. Litho Questa)

1982 (13 June). *World Cup Football Championship, Spain. T* **122** *and similar horiz designs. Multicoloured.* P 14.

471	10 b. Type **122**	..	..	20	10
472	1 d. 10, Gambian team practice	..	..	1·10	70
473	1 d. 25, Bernabéu Stadium, Madrid	..		1·10	75
474	1 d. 55, FIFA World Cup	..	..	1·25	80
471/4	..		*Set of 4*	3·25	2·10
MS475	114 × 85 mm. Nos. 471/4			4·00	4·50

(Des C. Abbott. Litho Walsall)

1982 (1 July). *21st Birthday of Princess of Wales. T* **123** *and similar vert designs. Multicoloured.* P 14½ × 14.

476	10 b. Type **123**	..	..	10	10
477	85 b. Princess at Cardiff City Hall, October 1981		..	30	20
478	1 d. 10, Bride and groom returning to Buckingham Palace		..	35	35
479	2 d. 50, Formal portrait	..	..	1·25	1·00
476/9	..		*Set of 4*	1·75	1·40

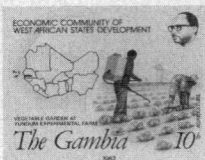

124 Vegetable Garden at Yundum Experimental Farm

(Des Harrison. Litho Questa)

1982 (5 Nov). *Economic Community of West African States Development. T* **124** *and similar horiz designs. Multicoloured.* P 14 × 14½.

480	10 b. Type **124**	..	..	30	15
481	60 b. Banjul/Kaolack microwave tower	..	2·00	2·25
482	90 b. Soap factory, Denton Bridge, Banjul		2·00	3·00
483	1 d. 25, Control tower, Yundum Airport		3·00	3·50
480/3	..		*Set of 4*	6·50	8·00

125 Kassina cassinoides

(Des PAD Studio. Litho Questa)

1982 (2 Dec). *Frogs. T* **125** *and similar horiz designs. Multicoloured.* P 14.

484	10 b. Type **125**	..	..	90	20
485	20 b. *Hylarana galamensis*	..	..	1·90	30
486	85 b. *Euphlyctis occipitalis*	..	3·00	2·00
487	2 d. *Kassina senegalensis*	..	4·25	8·00
484/7	..		*Set of 4*	9·00	9·50

126 Satellite View of Gambia   **127** Blessed Anne Marie Javouhey (foundress of the Order)

(Des Walsall. Litho Questa)

1983 (14 Mar). *Commonwealth Day. T* **126** *and similar horiz designs. Multicoloured.* P 14.

488	10 b. Type **126**	..	..	10	10
489	60 b. Batik cloth	..	..	20	45
490	1 d. 10, Bagging groundnuts	..		35	65
491	2 d. 10, Gambia flag	..	..	55	1·25
488/91	..		*Set of 4*	1·00	2·25

(Des G. Vasarhelyi. Litho Format)

1983 (8 Apr). *Centenary of Sisters of St. Joseph of Cluny's Work in Gambia. T* **127** *and similar multicoloured design.* P 13½.

492	10 b. Type **127**	..	..	10	10
493	85 b. Bathurst Hospital, nun and school-children (*horiz*)			45	50

---

128 Canoes

(Des A. Theobald. Litho Walsall)

1983 (11 July). *River Craft. T* **128** *and similar horiz designs. Multicoloured.* P 14.

494	1 b. Type **128**	..	..	15	40
495	2 b. Upstream ferry	..	..	20	40
496	3 b. Dredger	..	..	20	40
497	4 b. *Sir Dawda* (harbour launch)	..	30	40
498	5 b. Cargo liner	..	..	30	40
499	10 b. *Lady Dale* (60 ft launch)	..	30	10
500	20 b. *Shonga* (container ship)	..	45	40
501	30 b. Large sailing canoe	..	45	40
502	40 b. *Lady Wright* (river steamer)		65	55
503	50 b. Container ship (*different*)		65	55
504	75 b. Fishing boats	..	..	75	60
505	1 d. Tug with groundnut barges	..	90	80
506	1 d. 25, Groundnut canoe	..	1·00	1·25
507	2 d. 50, *Banjul* (car ferry)	..	1·75	2·50
508	5 d. *Bintang Bolong* (freighter)	..	2·50	4·00
509	10 d. *Lady Chilel Jawara* (river vessel)		4·00	6·50
494/509			*Set of 16*	13·00	18·00

Nos. 494/509 come with a pattern of blue fluorescent security markings, resembling rosettes, printed on the reverse beneath the gum.

129 Osprey in Tree

(Des N. Arlott. Litho Questa)

1983 (12 Sept). *The Osprey. T* **129** *and similar horiz designs. Multicoloured.* P 14.

510	10 b. Type **129**	..	..	1·50	50
511	60 b. Osprey	..	..	2·75	2·50
512	85 b. Osprey with catch	..	3·25	3·00
513	1 d. 10, In flight	..	..	3·50	5·00
510/13	..		*Set of 4*	10·00	10·00

130 Local Ferry

(Des L. Curtis. Litho Questa)

1983 (10 Oct). *World Communications Year. T* **130** *and similar horiz designs. Multicoloured.* P 14.

514	10 b. Type **130**	..	..	10	10
515	85 b. Telex operator	..	..	45	50
516	90 b. Radio Gambia	..	..	45	50
517	1 d. 10, Loading mail onto Douglas DC-9-80 Super Eighty aircraft			1·25	65
514/17	..		*Set of 4*	2·00	1·60

131 "St. Paul preaching at Athens" (detail) (Raphael)

(Des C. Abbott. Litho Questa)

1983 (1 Nov). *500th Birth Anniv of Raphael. T* **131** *and similar designs.* P 14.

518	60 b. multicoloured	..	..	35	40
519	85 b. multicoloured	..	..	45	50
520	1 d. multicoloured	..	..	50	55
518/20			*Set of 3*	1·10	1·25
MS521	105 × 83 mm. 2 d. multicoloured			1·50	1·25

Nos. 519/21 show different details of "St. Paul preaching at Athens", the 85 b. and 1 d. being horizontal and the 2 d. vertical.

MINIMUM PRICE

The minimum price quote is 10p which represents a handling charge rather than a basis for valuing common stamps. For further notes about prices see introductory pages.

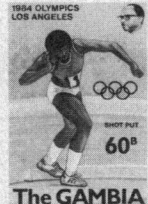

132 Montgolfier Balloon and Siege of Paris Cover   133 Shot-putting

(Des Harrison. Litho Questa)

1983 (12 Dec). *Bicentenary of Manned Flight.* T **132** and similar horiz designs. Multicoloured. P 14.
522	60 b. Type **132**	..	35	40
	a. Booklet pane. Nos. 522/3, each × 2		1·60	
523	85 b. Douglas DC-10 aircraft and flown cover		45	50
524	90 b. Junkers W.33 seaplane *Atlantis* and Hans Bertram cover		45	50
	a. Booklet pane. Nos. 524/5, each × 2		2·25	
525	1 d. 25, Lunar module and H. E. Sieger's space cover		65	70
526	4 d. Airship LZ-127 *Graf Zeppelin*		2·00	3·00
	a. Booklet pane of 1		2·00	
522/6		*Set of 5*	3·50	4·50

Nos. 522/6 come with a pattern of blue fluorescent security markings, resembling rosettes, printed on the reverse beneath the gum.

No. 526 only exists from booklets.

On 14 December 1983 four provisional surcharges, 1 d. 50 on 1 d. 25 (No. 439), 1 d. 50 on 1 d. 25 (No. 473), 2d. on 1 d. 25 (No. 456) and 2 d. on 1 d. 10 (No. 478), were issued in very limited quantities, there being, it is believed, no more than 600 complete sets (*Price for set of 4 £110 mint*).

(Des G. Vasarhelyi. Litho Questa)

1984 (30 Mar). *Olympic Games, Los Angeles* (1st issue). T **133** and similar multicoloured designs. P 11.
527	60 b. Type **133**	..	25	30
528	85 b. High jumping (*horiz*)	..	35	40
529	90 b. Wrestling	..	35	40
530	1 d. Gymnastics	..	40	45
531	1 d. 25, Swimming (*horiz*)	..	50	55
532	2 d. Diving	..	80	85
527/32		*Set of 6*	2·40	2·75
MS533	100 × 80 mm. 5 d. Yachting. P 13½ × 14		2·00	2·25

See also Nos. 555/8.

134 Goofy

(Litho Format)

1984 (27 Apr). *Easter.* T **134** and similar vert designs showing Walt Disney cartoon characters painting eggs. P 11.
534	1 b. Type **134**	..	10	10
535	2 b. Mickey Mouse	..	10	10
536	3 b. Huey, Dewey and Louie	..	10	10
537	4 b. Goofy (*different*)	..	10	10
538	5 b. Donald Duck	..	10	10
539	10 b. Chip 'n Dale	..	10	10
540	60 b. Pluto	..	35	40
541	90 b. Scrooge McDuck	..	50	60
542	5 d. Morty and Ferdie	..	2·25	2·75
534/42		*Set of 9*	3·00	3·75
MS543	125 × 100 mm. 5 d. Donald Duck (*different*). P 13½ × 14		3·50	3·50

135 Young Crocodiles Hatching   136 Port Banjul

(Des Doreen McGuinness. Litho Format)

1984 (23 May). *Endangered Species. The Nile Crocodile.* T **135** and similar horiz designs. Multicoloured. P 14.
544	4 b. Type **135**	..	55	55
545	6 b. Adult carrying young	..	55	55
546	90 b. Adult	..	4·50	3·00
547	1 d. 50, Crocodile at riverbank	..	5·50	7·00
544/7		*Set of 4*	10·00	10·00
MS548	126 × 94 mm. As Nos. 544/7, but without W.W.F. logo		4·50	7·00

Nos. 544/8 come with a pattern of blue fluorescent security markings, resembling rosettes, printed on the reverse beneath the gum.

(Des C. Collins. Litho Questa)

1984 (1 June). *250th Anniv of "Lloyd's List" (newspaper).* T **136** and similar vert designs. Multicoloured. P 14½ × 14.
549	60 b. Type **136**	..	60	50
550	85 b. Bulk carrier	..	75	80
551	90 b. Sinking of the *Dagomba*	..	75	90
552	1 d. 25, 19th century frigate	..	1·25	1·60
549/52		*Set of 4*	3·00	3·50

Nos. 549/52 come with a pattern of blue fluorescent security markings, resembling rosettes, printed on the reverse beneath the gum.

19th UPU CONGRESS HAMBURG (137)   138 Sprinting

1984 (19 June). *Universal Postal Union Congress, Hamburg. Nos. 507/8 optd with T **137**.*
553	2 d. 50, *Banjul* (car ferry)	..	1·00	1·50
554	5 d. *Bintang Bolong* (ferry)	..	1·75	2·50

(Des G. Vasarhelyi. Litho Walsall)

1984 (27 July). *Olympic Games, Los Angeles* (2nd issue). T **138** and similar horiz designs. Multicoloured. P 14.
555	60 b. Type **138**	..	25	30
556	85 b. Long jumping	..	35	40
557	90 b. Long-distance running	..	35	40
558	1 d. 25, Triple jumping	..	50	55
555/8		*Set of 4*	1·25	1·50

Nos. 555/8 come with a pattern of blue fluorescent security markings, resembling rosettes, printed on the reverse beneath the gum.

139 Airship LZ-127 *Graf Zeppelin*

(Des D. Hartley-Marjoram. Litho Questa)

1984 (1 Nov). *50th Anniv of Gambia–South America Trans-atlantic Flights.* T **139** and similar horiz designs. Multicoloured. P 14.
559	60 b. Type **139**	..	1·10	1·00
560	85 b. Dornier Do-J II 10-t *Wal* on S.S. *Westfalen*		1·60	1·75
561	90 b. Dornier DO-18	..	1·75	2·50
562	1 d. 25, Dornier Do-J II 10-t *Wal*		1·75	2·75
559/62		*Set of 4*	5·50	7·25

Nos. 559/62 come with a pattern of blue fluorescent security markings, resembling rosettes, printed on the reverse beneath the gum.

140 Pink Shrimp

(Des Pam Johnson. Litho Questa)

1984 (27 Nov). *Marine Life.* T **140** and similar horiz designs. Multicoloured. P 14.
563	55 b. Type **140**	..	35	30
564	75 b. Atlantic Loggerhead Turtle	..	55	40
565	1 d. 50, Portuguese Man-of-War	..	90	1·00
566	2 d. 35, Fiddler Crab	..	1·40	1·60
563/6		*Set of 4*	2·75	3·00
MS567	105 × 70 mm. 5 d. Cowrie Snail		2·75	4·00

141 *Antanartia hippomene*

(Des Pam Johnson. Litho Questa)

1984 (27 Nov). *Butterflies.* T **141** and similar horiz designs. Multicoloured. P 14.
568	10 b. Type **141**	..	30	20
569	85 b. *Pseudacraea eurytus*	..	80	90
570	90 b. *Charaxes lactitinctus*	..	80	90
571	3 d. *Graphium pylades*	..	2·00	3·75
568/71		*Set of 4*	3·50	5·25
MS572	105 × 75 mm. 5 d. *Eurema hapale*		10·00	9·50

---

142 Oral Re-hydration Therapy

(Des L. Curtis. Litho Harrison)

1985 (27 Feb). *Campaign for Child Survival.* T **142** and similar horiz designs. P 14.
573	10 b. black, cobalt and deep cinnamon		10	10
574	85 b. multicoloured	..	35	45
575	1 d. 10, multicoloured	..	45	65
576	1 d. 50, multicoloured	..	60	80
573/6		*Set of 4*	1·25	1·75

Designs:—85 b. Growth monitoring; 1 d. 10, Health care worker with women and babies ("Promotion of breast feeding"); 1 d. 50, Universal immunisation.

Nos. 573/6 come with a pattern of blue fluorescent security markings, resembling rosettes, printed on the reverse beneath the gum.

143 Women at Market   144 Turkey Vulture

(Des G. Vasarhelyi. Litho Format)

1985 (11 Mar). *Women and Development.* T **143** and similar horiz design. Multicoloured. P 14.
577	60 b. Type **143**	..	25	35
578	85 b. Type **143**	..	35	50
579	1 d. Woman office worker	..	40	60
580	1 d. 25, As 1 d.	..	50	90
577/80		*Set of 4*	1·40	2·10

Nos. 577/80 come with a pattern of blue fluorescent security markings, resembling rosettes, printed on the reverse beneath the gum.

(Des and litho Questa)

1985 (15 July). *Birth Bicentenary of John J. Audubon (ornithologist).* T **144** and similar multicoloured designs showing original paintings. P 14.
581	60 b. Type **144**	..	1·40	75
582	85 b. American Anhinga	..	1·60	1·50
583	1 d. 50, Green Heron	..	2·00	3·25
584	5 d. Wood Duck	..	3·25	5·50
581/4		*Set of 4*	7·50	10·00
MS585	100 × 70 mm. 10 d. Great Northern Diver (inscr "Common Loon") (*horiz*)		4·75	4·00

145 The Queen Mother   (146)

(Des J.W. Litho Questa)

1985 (29 July). *Life and Times of Queen Elizabeth the Queen Mother.* T **145** and similar vert designs. Multicoloured. P 14.
586	85 b. The Queen Mother and King George VI reviewing Home Guard		35	30
587	3 d. Type **145**	..	1·00	1·00
588	5 d. The Queen Mother with posy	..	1·75	1·75
586/8		*Set of 3*	2·75	2·75
MS589	56 × 85 mm. 10 d. The Queen Mother in Garter robes		3·00	3·25

(Des Walt Disney Studios. Litho Questa)

1985 (30 Oct). *150th Birth Anniv of Mark Twain (author).* Horiz designs as T **118** of Anguilla showing Walt Disney cartoon characters in scenes from "Life on the Mississippi". Multicoloured. P 14 × 13½.
590	1 d. 50, Mickey Mouse steering the *Calamity Jane*	1·25	1·25
591	2 d. Mickey and Minnie Mouse at antebellum mansion	1·50	1·50
592	2 d. 50, Donald Duck and Goofy heaving the lead	1·75	1·75
593	3 d. Poker game aboard the *Gold Dust*	2·00	2·00
590/3	*Set of 4*	6·00	6·00
MS594	126 × 101 mm. 10 d. Mickey Mouse and riverboat	6·00	4·25

(Des Walt Disney Productions. Litho Questa)

1985 (30 Oct). *Birth Bicentenaries of Grimm Brothers (folklorists). Designs as T 119 of Anguilla, but vert, showing Walt Disney cartoon characters in scenes from "Faithful John". Multicoloured. P* 13½ × 14.

595	60 b. The King (Mickey Mouse) and portrait of the Princess (Minnie Mouse)		40	40
596	85 b. The King showing the Princess his treasures		50	50
597	2 d. 35, Faithful John (Goofy) playing trumpet		1·40	1·40
598	5 d. Faithful John turned to stone		2·50	2·50
595/8		*Set of* 4	4·25	4·25
MS599	126 × 101 mm. 10 d. Faithful John after recovery		6·50	5·00

1985 (11 Nov). *Olympic Gold Medal Winners, Los Angeles. Nos.* 527/33 *optd as T* 146.

600	60 b. Type 133 (optd with T 146)		40	40
601	85 b. High jumping (optd "GOLD MEDALLIST ULRIKE MEYFARTH WEST GERMANY")		50	50
602	90 b. Wrestling (optd "GOLD MEDALLIST PASQUALE PASSARELLI WEST GERMANY")		50	50
603	1 d. Gymnastics (optd "GOLD MEDALLIST LI NING CHINA")		55	55
604	1 d. 25, Swimming (optd "GOLD MEDALLIST MICHAEL GROSS WEST GERMANY")		70	70
605	2 d. Diving (optd "GOLD MEDALLIST SYLVIE BERNIER CANADA")		1·00	1·00
600/5		*Set of* 6	3·25	3·25
MS606	100 × 80 mm. 5 d. Yachting (opt "GOLD MEDAL STAR CLASS U.S.A.")		2·00	2·00

147 Inspecting Maize

(Des J. Farleo. Litho Questa)

1985 (15 Nov). *United Nations Anniversaries. T* 147 *and similar horiz designs. Multicoloured. P* 14.

607	60 b. Type 147		40	35
608	85 b. Football match, Independence Stadium, Banjul		50	40
609	1 d. 10, Rice fields		60	60
610	2 d. Central Bank of The Gambia		85	1·00
611	3 d. Cow and calf		1·50	1·75
612	4 d. Banjul harbour		2·00	2·25
613	5 d. Gambian fruits		2·25	2·50
614	6 d. Oyster Creek Bridge		2·50	3·00
607/14		*Set of* 8	9·50	10·50

Nos. 607, 609, 611 and 613 commemorate the 40th anniversary of the Food and Agriculture Organization and Nos. 608, 610, 612 and 614 the 40th anniversary of the United Nations Organization.

148 Fishermen in Fotoba, Guinea   149 "Virgin and Child" (Dieric Bouts)

(Des B. Bundock. Litho Questa)

1985 (24 Dec). *50th Anniv of Diocese of The Gambia and Guinea. T* 148 *and similar horiz designs. Multicoloured. P* 14.

615	60 b. Type 148		40	30
616	85 b. St. Mary's Primary School, Banjul		40	40
617	1 d. 10, St. Mary's Cathedral, Banjul		40	65
618	1 d. 50, Mobile dispensary at Christy Kunda		60	85
615/18		*Set of* 4	1·60	2·00

(Des Mary Walters. Litho Format)

1985 (24 Dec). *Christmas. Religious Paintings. T* 149 *and similar vert designs. Multicoloured. P* 15.

619	60 b. Type 149		20	25
620	85 b. "The Annunciation" (Robert Campin)		25	30
621	1 d. 50, "Adoration of the Shepherds" (Gerard David)		45	50
622	5 d. "The Nativity" (Gerard David)		1·60	1·75
619/22		*Set of* 4	2·25	2·50
MS623	106 × 84 mm. 10 d. "Adoration of the Magi" (Hieronymus Bosch)		3·50	4·00

No. MS623 exists imperforate from stock dispersed by the liquidator of Format International Security Printers Ltd.

150 Enrolment Card

(Des N. Waldman. Litho Questa)

1985 (27 Dec). *75th Anniv of Girl Guide Movement. T* 150 *and similar multicoloured designs. P* 14.

624	60 b. Type 150		40	30
625	85 b. 2nd Bathurst Company centre		50	35
626	1 d. 50, Lady Baden-Powell (*vert*)		70	1·00
627	5 d. Miss Rosamond Fowlis (Gambian Guide Association leader) (*vert*)		2·00	3·75
624/7		*Set of* 4	3·25	4·75
MS628	97 × 67 mm. 10 d. Gambian Girl Guides (*vert*)		4·50	6·00

151 Girl and Village Scene   152 Two Players competing for Ball

(Des B. Bundock. Litho Questa)

1985 (31 Dec). *International Youth Year. T* 151 *and similar horiz designs. Multicoloured. P* 14.

629	60 b. Type 151		30	30
630	85 b. Youth and wrestling bout		35	35
631	1 d. 10, Girl and Griot storyteller		45	1·00
632	1 d. 50, Youth and crocodile pool		70	1·40
629/32		*Set of* 4	1·60	2·75
MS633	106 × 76 mm. 5 d. Herdsman with cattle		2·00	3·00

(Des W. Hanson. Litho Questa)

1986 (18 Apr). *Appearance of Halley's Comet (1st issue). Horiz designs as T* 123 *of Anguilla. Multicoloured. P* 14.

634	10 b. Maria Mitchell (astronomer) and Kitt Peak National Observatory, Arizona		40	20
635	20 b. Neil Armstrong, first man on Moon, 1969		55	25
636	75 b. "Skylab 4" and Comet Kohoutek, 1973		85	65
637	1 d. N.A.S.A.'s infra-red astronomical satellite and Halley's Comet		1·00	80
638	2 d. Comet of 1577 from Turkish painting		1·50	1·50
639	10 d. N.A.S.A.'s International Cometary Explorer		4·00	5·50
634/9		*Set of* 6	7·50	8·00
MS640	102 × 70 mm. 10 d. Halley's Comet		5·00	6·50

See also Nos. 679/84.

(Des and litho Questa)

1986 (21 Apr). *60th Birthday of Queen Elizabeth II. Vert designs as T* 125 *of Anguilla. P* 14.

641	1 d. black and yellow		25	30
642	2 d. 50, multicoloured		65	80
643	10 d. multicoloured		2·50	3·50
641/3		*Set of* 3	3·00	4·25
MS644	120 × 85 mm. 10 d. black and grey-brown		2·50	3·00

Designs:—No. 641, Duke of York and family, Royal Tournament, 1936; 642, Queen attending christening, 1983; 643, In West Germany, 1978; **MS644**, Duchess of York with her daughters, Balmoral, 1935.

(Des J. Birdsong. Litho Questa)

1986 (2 May). *World Cup Football Championship, Mexico. T* 152 *and similar vert designs. Multicoloured. P* 14.

645	75 b. Type 152		75	60
646	1 d. Player kicking ball		1·00	85
647	2 d. 50, Player kicking ball (*different*)		2·00	2·25
648	10 d. Player heading ball		5·00	6·00
645/8		*Set of* 4	8·00	8·75
MS649	100 × 70 mm. 10 d. Goalkeeper saving goal		7·50	7·00

153 Mercedes "500" (1986)

(Des P. Rhymer. Litho Format)

1986 (31 May). *"Ameripex" International Stamp Exhibition, Chicago. Centenary of First Benz Motor Car (1985). T* 153 *and similar horiz designs. Multicoloured. P* 15.

650	25 b. Type 153		20	15
651	75 b. Cord "810" (1935)		40	40
652	1 d. Borgward "Isabella Coupe" (1957)		60	60
653	1 d. 25, Lamborghini "Countach" (1985/6)		70	70
654	2 d. Ford "Thunderbird" (1955)		75	1·25
655	2 d. 25, Citroen "DS19" (1956)		75	1·60
656	5 d. Bugatti "Atlante" (1936)		1·00	3·00
657	10 d. Horch "853" (1936)		1·25	5·00
650/7		*Set of* 8	5·00	11·50
MS658	Two sheets, each 100 × 70 mm. (a) 12 d. Benz "8/20" (1913). (b) 12 d. Steiger "10/50" (1924)	*Set of* 2 *sheets*	6·00	12·00

The 25 b. value is inscribed "MECEDES" and the 10 d. "LARL BENZ".

Nos. 650/2 and 657 exist imperforate from stock dispersed by the liquidator of Format International Security Printers Ltd.

(Des J. Iskowitz. Litho Questa)

1986 (10 June). *Centenary of Statue of Liberty (1st issue). Multicoloured designs as T* 211 *of Dominica showing the Statue of Liberty and immigrants to the U.S.A. P* 14.

659	20 b. John Jacob Astor (financier)		10	10
660	1 d. Jacob Riis (journalist)		40	50
661	1 d. 25, Igor Sikorsky (aeronautics engineer)		60	65
662	5 d. Charles Boyer (actor)		2·50	2·50
659/62		*Set of* 4	3·25	3·25
MS663	114 × 80 mm. 10 d. Statue of Liberty (*vert*)		4·00	4·50

See also Nos. 705/14.

(Litho Questa)

1986 (1 July). *Royal Wedding. Vert designs as T* 213 *of Antigua. Multicoloured. P* 14.

664	1 d. Prince Andrew and Miss Sarah Ferguson		40	45
665	2 d. 50, Prince Andrew		1·00	1·40
666	4 d. Prince Andrew as helicopter pilot		1·60	2·00
664/6		*Set of* 3	2·75	3·50
MS667	88 × 88 mm. 7 d. Prince Andrew and Miss Sarah Ferguson (*different*)		4·25	3·50

1986 (16 Sept). *World Cup Football Championship Winners, Mexico. Nos.* 645/9 *optd with T* 216 *of Antigua in gold.*

668	75 b. Type 152		30	40
669	1 d. Player kicking ball		40	55
670	2 d. 50, Player kicking ball (*different*)		1·00	1·25
671	10 d. Player heading ball		4·25	4·75
668/71		*Set of* 4	5·25	6·25
MS672	100 × 70 mm. 10 d. Goalkeeper saving goal		4·50	4·50

154 Minnie Mouse (Great Britain)

(Des Walt Disney Co. Litho Format)

1986 (4 Nov). *Christmas. T* 154 *and similar vert designs showing Walt Disney cartoon characters posting letters in various countries. Multicoloured. P* 11.

673	1 d. Type 154		75	60
674	1 d. 25, Huey (U.S.A.)		80	80
675	2 d. Huey, Dewey and Louie (France)		1·25	1·40
676	2 d. 35, Kanga and Roo (Australia)		1·40	1·75
677	5 d. Goofy (Germany)		2·25	3·00
673/7		*Set of* 5	5·75	6·75
MS678	127 × 101 mm. 10 d. Goofy (Sweden). P 13½ × 14		4·75	5·50

Nos. 673/8 also show the emblem of "Stockholmia '86" International Stamp Exhibition.

1986 (21 Dec). *Appearance of Halley's Comet (2nd issue). Nos.* 634/40 *optd with T* 218 *of Antigua in silver.*

679	10 b. Maria Mitchell (astronomer) and Kitt Peak National Observatory, Arizona		30	15
680	20 b. Neil Armstrong, first man on Moon, 1969		50	20
681	75 b. "Skylab 4" and Comet Kohoutek, 1973		75	50
682	1 d. N.A.S.A.'s infra-red astronomical satellite and Halley's Comet		85	60
683	2 d. Comet of 1577 from Turkish painting		1·40	1·75
684	10 d. N.A.S.A.'s International Cometary Explorer		5·75	6·00
679/84		*Set of* 6	6·75	8·25
MS685	102 × 70 mm. 10 d. Halley's Comet		3·00	4·25

155 Bugarab and Tabala   156 "Snowing"

(Des B. Bundock. Litho Format)

1987 (21 Jan). *Manding Musical Instruments.* T **155** *and similar multicoloured designs.* P 15.

686	75 b. Type **155**	15	20
687	1 d. Balaphong and fiddle	15	25
688	1 d. 25, Bolongbato and konting (*vert*)	20	35
689	10 d. Antique and modern koras (*vert*)	1·60	3·00
686/9	*Set of 4*	1·90	3·50
MS690	100×70 mm. 12 d. Sabarr	1·90	2·50

(Litho Questa)

1987 (6 Feb). *Birth Centenary of Marc Chagall (artist).* T **156** *and similar multicoloured designs.* P 13½×14.

691	75 b. Type **156**	40	40
692	85 b. "The Boat"	50	50
693	1 d. "Maternity"	65	65
694	1 d. 25, "The Flute Player"	75	75
695	2 d. 35, "Lovers and the Beast"	1·25	1·25
696	4 d. "Fishers at Saint Jean"	1·50	2·00
697	5 d. "Entering the Ring"	1·75	2·50
698	10 d. "Three Acrobats"	2·75	3·75
691/8	*Set of 8*	8·50	10·50
MS699	Two sheets. (a) 110×68 mm. 12 d. "The Cattle Driver" (104×61 *mm*). (b) 109×95 mm. 12 d. "The Sabbath" (104×89 *mm*). Imperf.		
	Set of 2 sheets	7·50	8·50

157 *America*, 1851   **158** Arm of Statue of Liberty

(Des S. Heinmann. Litho Questa)

1987 (3 Apr). *America's Cup Yachting Championship.* T **157** *and similar horiz designs. Multicoloured.* P 14.

700	20 b. Type **157**	20	15
701	1 d. *Courageous*, 1974	35	35
702	2 d. 50, *Volunteer*, 1887	75	1·10
703	10 d. *Intrepid*, 1967	2·25	3·25
700/3	*Set of 4*	3·25	4·25
MS704	114×89 mm. 12 d. *Australia II*, 1983	3·50	3·00

(Des P. Kaplan. Litho Questa)

1987 (9 Apr). *Centenary of Statue of Liberty (1986) (2nd issue).* T **158** *and similar multicoloured designs.* P 14.

705	1 b. Type **158**	10	10
706	2 b. Launch passing Statue (*horiz*)	10	10
707	3 b. Schooner passing Statue (*horiz*)	10	10
708	5 b. U.S.S. *John F. Kennedy* (aircraft carrier) and *Queen Elizabeth* 2 (liner) (*horiz*)	10	10
709	50 b. Checking Statue for damage	40	40
710	75 b. Cleaning in progress	55	55
711	1 d. Working on Statue	70	70
712	1 d. 25, Statue and fireworks	80	80
713	10 d. Statue illuminated	4·25	4·25
714	12 d. Statue and fireworks (*different*)	4·50	4·50
705/14	*Set of 10*	10·50	10·50

159 *Lantana camara*   **160** Front of Mail Bus

(Des Dot Barlowe. Litho Questa)

1987 (25 May). *Flowers of Abuko Nature Reserve.* T **159** *and similar vert designs. Multicoloured.* P 14.

715	75 b. Type **159**	15	15
716	1 d. *Clerodendrum thomsoniae*	15	20
717	1 d. 50, *Haemanthus multiflorus*	25	30
718	1 d. 70, *Gloriosa simplex*	25	35
719	1 d. 75, *Combretum microphyllum*	30	40
720	2 d. 25, *Eulophia quineensis*	35	45
721	5 d. *Erythrina senegalensis*	80	1·25
722	15 d. *Dichrostachys glomerata*	2·40	3·50
715/22	*Set of 8*	4·25	6·00
MS723	Two sheets, each 100×70 mm. (a) 15 d. *Costus spectabilis.* (b) 15 d. *Strophanthus preussii*		
	Set of 2 sheets	4·75	6·50

(Des BG Studio. Litho Questa)

1987 (15 June). *"Capex '87" International Stamp Exhibition, Toronto and 10th Anniv of Gambia Public Transport Corporation. Mail Buses.* T **160** *and similar multicoloured designs.* P 14.

724	20 b. Type **160**	50	20
725	75 b. Bus in Banjul (*horiz*)	80	45
726	1 d. Passengers queuing for bus (*horiz*)	80	45
727	10 d. Two buses on rural road	3·25	5·50
724/7	*Set of 4*	4·75	6·00
MS728	77×70 mm. 12 d. Parked bus fleet (*horiz*)	3·50	4·25

161 Basketball   **162** "A Partridge in a Pear Tree"

(Litho Questa)

1987 (3 July). *Olympic Games, Seoul (1988) (1st issue).* T **161** *and similar vert designs. Multicoloured.* P 14.

729	50 b. Type **161**	35	20
730	1 d. Volleyball	50	35
731	3 d. Hockey (*horiz*)	1·10	85
732	10 d. Handball (*horiz*)	2·50	2·25
724/32	*Set of 4*	4·00	3·25
MS733	101×85 mm. 15 d. Football (*horiz*)	3·00	2·75

See also Nos. 779/83.

(Des Dot Barlowe. Litho Questa)

1987 (2 Nov). *Christmas.* T **162** *and similar multicoloured designs showing a Victorian couple in scenes from carol "The Twelve Days of Christmas".* P 14.

734	20 b. Type **162**	30	40
	a. Sheetlet. Nos. 734/45	7·75	
735	40 b. "Two turtle doves"	35	45
736	60 b. "Three French hens"	40	50
737	75 b. "Four calling birds"	40	55
738	1 d. "Five golden rings"	40	55
739	1 d. 25, "Six geese a-laying"	50	60
740	1 d. 50, "Seven swans a-swimming"	50	60
741	2 d. "Eight maids a-milking"	60	70
742	3 d. "Nine ladies dancing"	70	75
743	5 d. "Ten lords a-leaping"	1·00	1·10
744	10 d. "Eleven pipers piping"	1·60	1·75
745	12 d. "Twelve drummers drumming"	1·90	2·00
734/45	*Set of 12*	7·75	9·00
MS746	100×70 mm. 15 d. Exchanging presents (*horiz*)	2·40	3·25

Nos. 734/45 were printed together, *se-tenant*, in sheetlets of twelve.

163 Campfire Singsong

(Litho Questa)

1987 (9 Nov). *World Scout Jamboree, Australia.* T **163** *and similar horiz designs. Multicoloured.* P 14.

747	75 b. Type **163**	50	30
748	1 d. Scouts examining African Katydid	60	40
749	1 d. 25, Scouts watching Red-tailed Tropic Bird	75	75
750	2 d. Scouts helping bus passenger	2·75	3·75
747/50	*Set of 4*	4·25	4·75
MS751	72×98 mm. 15 d. Scouts on field trip	4·50	5·50

(Des Walt Disney Company. Litho Questa)

1987 (9 Dec). *60th Anniv of Mickey Mouse (Walt Disney cartoon character) (1st issue). Multicoloured designs as* T **220** *of Dominica, but horiz.* P 14×13½.

752	60 b. Morty and Ferdie examining Trevithick's locomotive, 1804	25	25
753	75 b. Clarabelle Cow in "Empire State Express", 1893	30	30
754	1 d. Donald Duck inspecting Stephenson's *Rocket*, 1829	40	40
755	1 d. 25, Piglet and Winnie the Pooh with Santa Fe Railroad locomotive, 1920	45	45
756	2 d. Donald and Daisy Duck with Pennsylvania Railroad Class GG1 electric locomotive, 1933	70	70
757	5 d. Mickey Mouse in *Stourbridge Lion*, 1829	1·60	1·75
758	10 d. Goofy in *Best Friend of Charleston*, 1830	2·75	3·00
759	12 d. Brer Bear and Brer Rabbit with Union Pacific diesel locomotive No. M10001, 1934	3·00	3·25
752/9	*Set of 8*	8·50	9·00
MS760	Two sheets, each 127×101 mm. (a) 15 d. Chip n'Dale in *The General*, 1855. (b) 15 d. Donald Duck and Mickey Mouse in modern French "TGV" train		
	Set of 2 sheets	7·50	8·00

See also Nos. 849/58.

164 Common Duiker and Acacia   **165** Wedding Portrait, 1947

(Des Mary Walters. Litho Format)

1988 (9 Feb). *Flora and Fauna.* T **164** *and similar multicoloured designs.* P 15.

761	50 b. Type **164**	20	10
762	75 b. Red-billed Hornbill and casuarina (*vert*)	50	30
763	90 b. West African Dwarf Crocodile and rice	30	20
764	1 d. Leopard and papyrus (*vert*)	30	20
765	1 d. 25, Crowned Crane and millet	50	45
766	2 d. Waterbuck and baobab tree (*vert*)	40	60
767	3 d. Oribi and Senegal palm	50	1·25
768	5 d. Hippopotamus and papaya (*vert*)	80	1·75
761/8	*Set of 8*	3·25	4·25
MS769	98×69 mm. (a) 12 d. Red-throated Bee Eater and acacia (*vert*). (b) 12 d. Eastern White Pelican		
	Set of 2 sheets	2·75	4·50

No. **MS**769 exists imperforate from stock dispersed by the liquidator of Format International Security Printers Ltd.

(Des and litho Questa)

1988 (15 Mar). *Royal Ruby Wedding.* T **165** *and similar vert designs.* P 14.

770	75 b. deep brown, black and brown-orange	30	15
771	1 d. deep brown, black and bright new blue	40	20
772	3 d. multicoloured	90	1·00
773	10 d. multicoloured	2·25	3·25
770/3	*Set of 4*	3·50	4·25
MS774	100×75 mm. 15 d. multicoloured	2·25	3·25

Designs:— 1 d. Engagement photograph; 3 d. Wedding portrait, 1947 (*different*); 10 d. Queen Elizabeth II and Prince Philip (photo by Karsh), 1986; 15 d. Wedding portrait with page, 1947.

1988 (19 Apr). *Stamp Exhibitions. Nos. 689, 703, 722 and 726 optd as* T **241** *of Antigua with various emblems.*

775	1 d. Passengers queuing for bus (optd "Independence 40", Israel)	25	25
776	10 d. Antique and modern koras (optd "FINLANDIA 88", Helsinki)	2·00	2·50
777	10 d. *Intrepid* (yacht), 1967 (optd "Praga '88", Prague)	2·00	2·50
778	15 d. *Dichrostachys glomerata* (optd "OLYMPHILEX '88", Seoul)	2·75	3·00
775/8	*Set of 4*	6·25	7·50

(Des A. DiLorenzo. Litho Questa)

1988 (3 May). *Olympic Games, Seoul (2nd issue). Multicoloured designs as* T **161**. P 14.

779	1 d. Archery	30	20
780	1 d. 25, Boxing	30	25
781	5 d. Gymnastics	1·00	1·10
782	10 d. Start of 100 metre race (*horiz*)	1·75	2·25
779/82	*Set of 4*	3·00	3·50
MS783	74×102 mm. 15 d. Medal winners on rostrum	2·40	3·25

166 Red Cross Flag (125th anniv)

(Des W. Wright. Litho Questa)

1988 (15 May). *Anniversaries and Events.* T **166** *and similar multicoloured designs.* P 14.

784	50 b. Type **166**	55	55
785	75 b. "Friendship" 7 spacecraft (25th anniv of first American manned Earth orbit)	60	60
786	1 d. British Airways Concorde (10th anniv of Concorde London–New York service)	1·00	1·00
787	1 d. 25, Ryan NYP Special *Spirit of St. Louis* (60th anniv of first solo transatlantic flight)	1·00	1·00
788	2 d. North American X-15 (20th anniv of fastest aircraft flight)	1·40	1·40
789	3 d. Bell XS-1 rocket plane (40th anniv of first supersonic flight)	1·50	1·50
790	10 d. English and Spanish galleons (400th anniv of Spanish Armada)	3·50	3·50
791	12 d. *Titanic* (75th anniv of sinking)	3·75	3·75
784/91	*Set of 8*	12·00	12·00
MS792	Two sheets. (a) 113×85 mm. 15 d. Kaiser Wilhelm Memorial Church, Berlin (*vert*) (750th anniv of Berlin). (b) 121×90 mm. 15 d. Kangaroo (Bicentenary of Australian Settlement)		
	Set of 2 sheets	4·75	7·00

(Litho Questa)

1988 (7 July). *500th Birth Anniv of Titian (artist). Vert designs as* T **238** *of Antigua. Multicoloured.* P 13½×14.

793	25 b. "Emperor Charles V"	20	20
794	50 b. "St. Margaret and the Dragon"	35	35
795	60 b. "Ranuccio Farnese"	40	40
796	75 b. "Tarquin and Lucretia"	55	55
797	1 d. "The Knight of Malta"	70	70
798	5 d. "Spain succouring Faith"	2·25	2·50
799	10 d. "Doge Francesco Venier"	3·50	3·50
800	12 d. "Doge Grimani before the Faith" (detail)	3·75	3·75
793/800	*Set of 8*	10·50	10·50
MS801	110×95 mm. (a) 15 d. "Jealous Husband" (detail). (b) 15 d. "Venus blindfolding Cupid"		
	Set of 2 sheets	4·75	7·00

NEW INFORMATION

The editor is always interested to correspond with people who have new information that will improve or correct the Catalogue.

167 John Kennedy sailing

(Des G. Hinlecky. Litho Questa)

1988 (1 Sept). *25th Death Anniv of President John F. Kennedy. T **167** and similar multicoloured designs. P 14.*

802	75 b. Type **167**		15	15
803	1 d. Kennedy signing Peace Corps legislation, 1962		15	20
804	1 d. 25, Speaking at U.N., New York (*vert*)		20	25
805	12 d. Grave and eternal flame, Arlington National Cemetery (*vert*)		1·90	2·75
802/5		*Set of 4*	2·10	3·00
MS806	99×72 mm. 15 d. John F. Kennedy (*vert*)		2·40	3·50

168 Airship LZ-127 *Graf Zeppelin* (first regular air passenger service), 1910

169 Emmett Kelley

(Des A. Fagbohun. Litho Questa)

1988 (1 Nov). *Milestones of Transportation. T **168** and similar multicoloured designs. P 14.*

807	25 b. Type **168**		60	35
808	50 b. Stephenson's *Locomotion* (first permanent public railway), 1825		90	50
809	75 b. G.M. *Sun Racer* (first world solar challenge), 1987		1·00	65
810	1 d. Sprague's *Premiere* (first operational electric tramway), 1888		1·25	80
811	1 d. 25, *Gold Rush* Bicycle (holder of man-powered land speed record), 1986		1·50	85
812	2 d. 50 Robert Goddard and rocket launcher (first liquid fuel rocket), 1925		1·60	1·25
813	10 d. *Orukter Amphibolos* (first steam traction engine), 1805		3·50	3·25
814	12 d. *Sovereign of the Seas* (largest cruise liner), 1988		3·50	3·50
807/14		*Set of 8*	12·00	10·00
MS815	Two sheets, each 71 × 92 mm. (a) 15 d. U.S.S. *Nautilus* (first nuclear-powered submarine), 1954 (*vert*). (b) 15 d. Fulton's *Nautilus* (first fish-shaped submarine), 1800's (*vert*)	*Set of 2 sheets*	5·50	7·00

No. 807 is incorrectly inscribed "LZ-7".

(Des J. Iskowitz. Litho Questa)

1988 (9 Nov). *Entertainers. T **169** and similar multicoloured designs. P 14.*

816	20 b. Type **169**		10	10
817	1 d. Gambia National Ensemble		25	25
818	1 d. 25, Jackie Gleason		30	30
819	1 d. 50, Laurel and Hardy		40	40
820	2 d. 50, Yul Brynner		75	75
821	3 d. Cary Grant		95	95
822	10 d. Danny Kaye		3·00	3·00
823	20 d. Charlie Chaplin		5·50	5·50
816/23		*Set of 8*	10·00	10·00
MS824	Two sheets. (a) 110 × 77 mm. 15 d. Marx Brothers (*horiz*). (b) 70 × 99 mm. 15 d. Fred Astaire and Rita Hayworth (*horiz*)	*Set of 2 sheets*	9·50	9·50

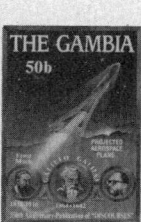

170 Prince Henry the Navigator and Caravel

171 Projected Space Plane and Ernst Mach (physicist)

(Des A. Fagbohun. Litho Questa)

1988 (1 Dec). *Exploration of West Africa. T **170** and similar multicoloured designs. P 14.*

825	50 b. Type **170**		60	60
826	75 b. Jesse Ramsden's sextant, 1785		70	70
827	1 d. 15th-century hourglass		80	80
828	1 d. 25, Prince Henry the Navigator and Vasco da Gama		95	95
829	2 d. 50, Vasco da Gama and ship		1·60	1·60
830	5 d. Mungo Park and map of Gambia River (*horiz*)		2·50	2·50

831	10 d. Map of West Africa, 1563 (*horiz*)		3·75	3·75
832	12 d. Portuguese caravel (*horiz*)		4·00	4·00
825/32		*Set of 8*	13·50	13·50
MS833	Two sheets, each 65 × 100 mm. (a) 15 d. Ship from Columbus's fleet off Gambia. (b) 15 d. 15th-century ship moored off Gambia	*Set of 2 sheets*	5·50	6·00

(Des G. Welker. Litho Questa)

1988 (12 Dec). *350th Anniv of Publication of Galileo's "Discourses". Space Achievements. T **171** and similar multicoloured designs. P 14.*

834	50 b. Type **171**		40	30
835	75 b. OAO III astronomical satellite and Niels Bohr (physicist)		50	40
836	1 d. Space shuttle, projected space station and Robert Goddard (physicist) (*horiz*)		60	45
837	1 d. 25, Jupiter probe, 1979, and Edward Barnard (astronomer) (*horiz*)		80	60
838	2 d. Hubble Space Telescope and George Hale (physicist) (*horiz*)		1·00	75
839	3 d. Earth-to-Moon laser measurement and Albert Michaelson (physicist) (*horiz*)		1·00	85
840	10 d. HEAO-2 *Einstein* orbital satellite and Albert Einstein (physicist)		2·50	2·75
841	20 d. *Voyager* (first non-stop round-the-world flight), 1987, and Wright Brothers (aviation pioneers) (*horiz*)		4·50	5·00
834/41		*Set of 8*	10·00	10·00
MS842	Two sheets. (a) 99 × 75 mm. 15 d. Great Red Spot on Jupiter (*horiz*). (b) 88 × 71 mm. 15 d. Neil Armstrong (first man on Moon), 1969	*Set of 2 sheets*	6·00	8·00

172 Passing Out Parade

(Des J. Genzo. Litho Questa)

1989 (10 Feb). *Army Day. T **172** and similar multicoloured designs. P 14.*

843	75 b. Type **172**		25	25
844	1 d. Standards of The Gambia Regiment		25	25
845	1 d. 25, Side drummer in ceremonial uniform (*vert*)		30	30
846	10 d. Marksman with Atlantic Shooting Cup (*vert*)		2·00	2·00
847	15 d. Soldiers on assault course (*vert*)		2·75	2·75
848	20 d. Gunner with 105 mm field gun		3·00	3·00
843/8		*Set of 6*	7·75	7·75

173 Mickey Mouse, 1928

174 "Le Coup de Lance" (detail)

(Des Walt Disney Company. Litho B.D.T.)

1989 (6 Apr). *60th Birthday of Mickey Mouse (2nd issue). T **173** and similar multicoloured designs. P 13.*

849	2 d. Type **173**		65	70
	a. Sheetlet of 9. Nos. 849/57		5·25	
850	2 d. Mickey Mouse, 1931		65	70
851	2 d. Mickey Mouse, 1936		65	70
852	2 d. Mickey Mouse, 1955		65	70
853	2 d. Mickey Mouse, 1947		65	70
854	2 d. Mickey Mouse as magician, 1940		65	70
855	2 d. Mickey Mouse with palette, 1960		65	70
856	2 d. Mickey Mouse as Uncle Sam, 1976		65	70
857	2 d. Mickey Mouse, 1988		65	70
849/57		*Set of 9*	5·25	5·75
MS858	138×109 mm. 15 d. Mickey Mouse at 60th birthday party (132×103 *mm*). *Imperf*		4·00	4·00

Nos. 849/57 were printed together, *se-tenant* as a composite design, in sheetlets of nine.

(Litho Questa)

1989 (14 Apr). *Easter. Religious Paintings by Rubens. T **174** and similar vert designs showing details. Multicoloured. P 13½×14.*

859	50 b. Type **174**		25	25
860	75 b. "Flagellation of Christ"		35	35
861	1 d. "Lamentation for Christ"		35	35
862	1 d. 25, "Descent from the Cross"		40	40
863	2 d. "Holy Trinity"		60	70
864	5 d. "Doubting Thomas"		1·25	1·50
865	10 d. "Lamentation over Christ"		2·00	2·50
866	12 d. "Lamentation with Virgin and St. John"		2·25	2·75
859/66		*Set of 8*	6·75	8·00
MS867	Two sheets each 96×110 mm. (a) 15 d. "The Last Supper". (b) 15 d. "Raising of the Cross"	*Set of 2 sheets*	4·50	5·50

175 African Emerald Cuckoo

176 *Druryia antimachus*

(Des W. Wright. Litho Questa)

1989 (24 Apr). *West African Birds. T **175** and similar horiz designs. Multicoloured. P 14.*

868	20 b. Type **175**		70	30
869	50 b. Grey-headed Bush Shrike		95	50
870	75 b. South African Crowned Crane		1·00	55
871	1 d. Secretary Bird		1·25	60
872	2 d. Red-billed Hornbill		1·75	1·00
873	5 d. Superb Sunbird		2·25	2·75
874	10 d. Pearl-spotted Owlet ("Little Owl")		3·00	4·00
875	12 d. Bateleur		3·00	4·00
868/75		*Set of 8*	12·50	12·00
MS876	Two sheets, each 115×86 mm. (a) 15 d. Ostrich. (b) 15 d. Red-billed Fire Finch	*Set of 2 sheets*	7·00	8·00

(Des Mary Walters. Litho Questa)

1989 (15 May). *Butterflies of Gambia. T **176** and similar vert designs. Multicoloured. P 14.*

877	50 b. Type **176**		30	30
878	75 b. *Euphaedra neophron*		45	45
879	1 d. *Aterica rabena*		45	45
880	1 d. 25, *Salamis parhassus*		55	55
881	5 d. *Precis rhadama*		1·75	2·00
882	10 d. *Papilio demodocus*		2·25	2·50
883	12 d. *Charaxes etesipe*		2·50	2·75
884	15 d. *Danaus formosa*		2·50	2·75
877/84		*Set of 8*	9·75	10·50
MS885	Two sheets, each 99×68 mm. (a) 15 d. *Euptera pluto*. (b) 15 d. *Euphaedra ceres*	*Set of 2 sheets*	9·00	10·00

177 Class "River" Steam Locomotive No. 021, 1959, Nigeria

(178) PHILEXFRANCE '89

(Des A. Fagbohun. Litho Walsall)

1989 (15 June). *African Steam Locomotives. T **177** and similar multicoloured designs. P 14.*

886	50 b. Type **177**		35	35
887	75 b. Class 14A steam locomotive, Rhodesia		45	45
888	1 d. British-built steam locomotive No. 120, Sudan		55	55
889	1 d. 25, Steam locomotive, 1925, U.S.A.		65	65
890	5 d. North British steam locomotive, 1955		1·75	1·75
891	7 d. Scottish-built steam locomotive No. 120, 1926		2·00	2·00
892	10 d. East African Railways Class 1T steam tank locomotive		2·25	2·25
893	12 d. American-built steam locomotive, Ghana		2·50	2·50
886/93		*Set of 8*	9·50	9·50
MS894	Two sheets, each 82×58 mm. (a) 15 d. East African Railways Class 25 steam locomotive No. 2904 (*vert*). (b) 15 d. East African Railways Class 25 steam locomotive No. 3700A (*vert*)	*Set of 2 sheets*	7·00	8·00

1989 (23 June). *"Philexfrance '89" International Stamp Exhibition, Paris. Nos. 686/90 optd with T **178**.*

895	75 b. Type **155**		10	10
896	1 d. Balaphong and fiddle		15	20
897	1 d. 25, Bolongbato and konting (*vert*)		20	25
898	10 d. Antique and modern koras (*vert*)		1·50	2·25
895/8		*Set of 4*	1·75	2·50
MS899	100×70 mm. 12 d. Sabarr		1·40	2·00

(Litho Questa)

1989 (7 July). *Japanese Art. Multicoloured designs as T **250** of Antigua. P 13½×14.*

900	50 b. "Sparrow and Bamboo" (Hiroshige) (*vert*)		40	30
901	75 b. "Peonies and a Canary" (Hokusai) (*vert*)		50	40
902	1 d. "Crane and Marsh Grasses" (Hiroshige) (*vert*)		60	45
903	1 d. 25, "Crossbill and Thistle" (Hokusai) (*vert*)		70	60
904	2 d. "Cuckoo and Azalea" (Hokusai) (*vert*)		90	90
905	5 d. "Parrot on a Pine Branch" (Hiroshige) (*vert*)		1·50	1·75
906	10 d. "Mandarin Ducks in a Stream" (Hiroshige) (*vert*)		2·25	2·50
907	12 d. "Bullfinch and Drooping Cherry" (Hokusai) (*vert*)		2·25	2·50
900/7		*Set of 8*	8·25	8·50
MS908	Two sheets, each 102×77 mm. (a) 15 d. "Tit and Peony" (Hiroshige). (b) 15 d. "Peony and Butterfly" (Shigenobou). P 14×13½	*Set of 2 sheets*	6·00	7·00

Nos. 900/7 were each printed in sheets of 10 containing two vertical strips of 5 stamps separated by printed labels commemorating Emperor Hirohito.

179 Rialto Bridge, Venice   180 *Vitex doniana*

(Des L. Fried. Litho B.D.T.)

1989 (25 Aug). *World Cup Football Championship, Italy (1990) (1st issue). T* 179 *and similar horiz designs, each showing landmarks and players. Multicoloured. P* 14.

909	75 b. Type 179	45	45
910	1 d. 25, The Baptistery, Pisa	60	60
911	7 d. Casino, San Remo	2·25	2·75
912	12 d. Colosseum, Rome	3·00	3·50
909/12	*Set of 4*	5·50	6·50

MS913 Two sheets, each 104×78 mm. (a) 15 d. St. Mark's Cathedral, Venice. (b) 15 d. Piazza Colonna, Rome   *Set of 2 sheets* 7·00 8·00
See also Nos. 1064/8.

(Des Jennifer Toombs. Litho Questa)

1989 (18 Sept). *Medicinal Plants. T* 180 *and similar vert designs. Multicoloured. P* 14.

914	20 b. Type 180	20	20
915	50 b. *Ricinus communis*	30	30
916	75 b. *Palisota hirsuta*	45	45
917	1 d. *Smilax kraussiana*	55	55
918	1 d. 25, *Aspilia africana*	65	65
919	5 d. *Newbouldia laevis*	1·75	2·00
920	8 d. *Monodora tenuifolia*	1·90	2·50
921	10 d. *Gossypium arboreum*	2·00	2·50
914/21	*Set of 8*	7·00	8·25

MS922 Two sheets, each 87×72 mm. (a) 15 d. *Kigelia africana*. (b) 15 d. *Spathodea campanulata*   *Set of 2 sheets* 8·00 9·00

181 Lookdown

(Des Mary Walters. Litho B.D.T.)

1989 (19 Oct). *Fishes. T* 181 *and similar horiz designs. Multicoloured. P* 14.

923	20 b. Type 181	25	25
924	75 b. Boarfish	55	55
925	1 d. Grey Triggerfish	65	65
926	1 d. 25, Skipjack Tuna	75	75
927	2 d. Striped Rudderfish	95	95
928	4 d. Atlantic Manta	1·60	1·75
929	5 d. Flat-headed Grey Mullet	1·75	1·90
930	10 d. Ladyfish	2·75	3·25
923/30	*Set of 8*	8·25	9·00

MS931 Two sheets, each 104×72 mm. (a) 15 d. Porcupinefish. (b) 15 d. Shortfin Mako
    Set of 2 sheets 9·00 10·00

(Des Walt Disney Co. Litho Questa)

1989 (29 Nov). *"World Stamp Expo '89" International Stamp Exhibition, Washington (1st issue). Horiz designs as T* 256 *of Antigua, each showing Walt Disney cartoon characters and American carousel horses. Multicoloured. P* 14×13½.

932	20 b. Little Hiawatha on Daniel Muller Indian Pony	50	50
933	50 b. Morty on Herschell-Spillman stander	70	50
934	75 b. Goofy on Gustav Dentzel stander	85	65
935	1 d. Mickey Mouse on Daniel Muller armoured stander	90	70
936	1 d. 25, Minnie Mouse on jumper from Smithsonian Collection	1·00	80
937	2 d. Webby on Illion "American Beauty"	1·50	1·25
938	8 d. Donald Duck on Zalar jumper	3·50	4·00
939	10 d. Mickey Mouse on Parker bucking horse	3·50	4·00
932/9	*Set of 8*	11·00	11·00

MS940 Two sheets, each 127×102 mm. (a) 12 d. Donald, Mickey and Goofy in carousel car. (b) 12 d. Donald's nephews on Roman chariot horses
    Set of 2 sheets 9·00 10·00

(Des Design Element. Litho Questa)

1989 (29 Nov). *"World Stamp Expo '89" International Stamp Exhibition, Washington (2nd issue). Landmarks of Washington. Sheet* 78×61 *mm containing horiz design as T* 257 *of Antigua. Multicoloured. P* 14.
MS941 10 d. White House   1·40 2·00

183 Mickey and Minnie Mouse in Pierce-Arrow, 1922

(Des Walt Disney Co. Litho Questa)

1989 (29 Nov). *Christmas. T* 183 *and similar horiz designs showing Walt Disney cartoon characters with cars. Multicoloured. P* 14×13½.

942	20 b. Type 183	50	25
943	50 b. Goofy in Spyker, 1919	70	45
944	75 b. Donald and Grandma Duck with Packard, 1929	80	55
945	1 d. Mickey Mouse driving Daimler, 1920	85	65
946	1 d. 25, Mickey Mouse in Hispano "Suiza", 1924	90	90
947	2 d. Mickey and Minnie Mouse in Opel "Laubfrosch", 1924	1·25	1·25
948	10 d. Donald Duck driving Vauxhall "30/98", 1927	3·25	4·00
949	12 d. Goofy with Peerless, 1923	3·25	4·00
942/9	*Set of 8*	10·50	11·00

MS950 Two sheets, each 127×102 mm. (a) 15 d. Mickey and Minnie Mouse picnicking by Stutz "Blackhawk Speedster", 1928. (b) 15 d. Donald Duck, Mickey and Minnie Mouse in Bentley "Supercharged", 1930   *Set of 2 sheets* 10·00 12·00

184 Charles Nicolle (typhus transmission) and Vaccination   185 *Bulbophyllum lepidum*

(Des J. Iskowitz. Litho Walsall)

1989 (12 Dec). *Great Medical Discoveries. T* 184 *and similar horiz designs. Multicoloured. P* 14.

951	20 b. Type 184	50	20
952	50 b. Paul Ehrlich (immunization pioneer) and medical examination	70	30
953	75 b. Selman Waksman (discoverer of streptomycin) and T.B. clinic	85	40
954	1 d. Edward Jenner (smallpox vaccination), and Jenner conducting experiment, 1796	1·00	50
955	1 d. 25, Robert Koch (developer of tuberculin test) and Gambian using vaccination gun	1·25	75
956	5 d. Sir Alexander Fleming (discoverer of penicillin) and doctor giving injection	2·00	2·50
957	8 d. Max Theiler (developer of yellow fever vaccine) and child clinic	2·50	3·00
958	10 d. Louis Pasteur (bacteriologist) and health survey	2·50	3·00
951/8	*Set of 8*	10·00	9·50

MS959 Two sheets, each 121×86 mm. (a) 15 d. Hughes 369 Viking medical helicopter. (b) 15 d. B.A.C. One Eleven Nightingale C.9 medical relief plane   *Set of 2 sheets* 7·50 8·50
No. MS959a is incorrectly inscribed "Vicking".

(Des Mary Walters. Litho Walsall)

1989 (18 Dec). *Orchids. T* 185 *and similar vert designs. Multicoloured. P* 14.

960	20 b. Type 185	30	30
961	75 b. *Tridactyle tridactylites*	55	55
962	1 d. *Vanilla imperialis*	70	70
963	1 d. 25, *Oeceoclades maculata*	80	90
964	2 d. *Polystachya affinis*	1·10	1·25
965	4 d. *Ancistrochilus rothschildianus*	1·90	2·25
966	5 d. *Angraecum distichum*	2·00	2·25
967	10 d. *Liparis guineensis*	3·25	4·00
960/7	*Set of 8*	9·75	11·00

MS968 Two sheets, each 99×67 mm. (a) 15 d. *Plectrelminthus caudatus*. (b) 15 d. *Eulophia guineensis*   *Set of 2 sheets* 8·50 8·50

186 John Newcombe   187 Lunar Module *Eagle*

(Des D. Miller. Litho Questa)

1990 (2 Jan). *Wimbledon Tennis Champions. T* 186 *and similar vert designs. Multicoloured. P* 14½.

969	20 b. Type 186	10	10
	a. Vert pair. Nos. 969/70	20	20
970	20 b. Mrs. G. W. Hillyard	10	10
971	50 b. Roy Emerson	20	20
	a. Vert pair. Nos. 971/2	40	40
972	50 b. Dorothy Chambers	20	20
973	75 b. Donald Budge	30	30
	a. Vert pair. Nos. 973/4	60	60
974	75 b. Suzanne Lenglen	30	30
975	1 d. Laurence Doherty	35	35
	a. Vert pair. Nos. 975/6	70	70
976	1 d. Helen Wills Moody	35	35
977	1 d. 25, Bjorn Borg	40	40
	a. Vert pair. Nos. 977/8	80	80
978	1 d. 25, Maureen Connolly	40	40
979	4 d. Jean Borotra	1·00	1·00
	a. Vert pair. Nos. 979/80	2·00	2·00
980	4 d. Maria Bueno	1·00	1·00

981	5 d. Anthony Wilding	1·00	1·00
	a. Vert pair. Nos. 981/2	2·00	2·00
982	5 d. Louise Brough	1·00	1·00
983	7 d. Fred Perry	1·40	1·40
	a. Vert pair. Nos. 983/4	2·75	2·75
984	7 d. Margaret Court	1·40	1·40
985	10 d. Bill Tilden	2·00	2·00
	a. Vert pair. Nos. 985/6	4·00	4·00
986	10 d. Billie Jean King	2·00	2·00
987	12 d. Rod Laver	2·25	2·25
	a. Vert pair. Nos. 987/8	4·50	4·50
988	12 d. Martina Navratilova	2·25	2·25
969/88	*Set of 20*	16·00	16·00

MS989 Two sheets, each 101×76 mm. (a) 15 d. Rod Laver (*different*). (b) 15 d. Martina Navratilova (*different*) *Set of 2 sheets* 8·50 9·50
The two designs for each value were printed together, *se-tenant*, in vertical pairs throughout the sheets of 20.

(Des K. Gromell. Litho B.D.T.)

1990 (16 Feb). *20th Anniv of First Manned Landing on Moon (1989). T* 187 *and similar multicoloured designs. P* 14.

990	20 b. Type 187	40	20
991	50 b. Lift-off of "Apollo 11" (*vert*)	50	30
992	75 b. Neil Armstrong stepping on to Moon	65	45
993	1 d. Buzz Aldrin and American flag	70	55
994	1 d. 25, "Apollo 11" emblem (*vert*)	80	60
995	1 d. 75, Crew of "Apollo 11"	1·00	90
996	8 d. Lunar Module *Eagle* on Moon	2·75	3·25
997	12 d. Recovery of "Apollo 11" after splashdown	3·00	3·50
990/7	*Set of 8*	9·00	8·75

MS998 Two sheets, each 110×89 mm. (a) 15 d. Neil Armstrong (*vert*). (b) 15 d. View of Earth from Moon (*vert*)   *Set of 2 sheets* 6·50 7·50

188 Bristol Type 142 Blenheim Mk 1   189 White-faced Scops Owl

(Des J. Batchelor. Litho B.D.T.)

1990 (8 May). *R.A.F. Aircraft of Second World War. T* 188 *and similar horiz designs. Multicoloured. P* 14.

999	10 b. Type 188	45	40
1000	20 b. Fairey Battle	60	40
1001	50 b. Bristol Type 142 Blenheim Mk IV	80	40
1002	60 b. Vickers-Armstrong Wellington Mk 1c	85	40
1003	75 b. Armstrong Whitworth Whitley Mk V	90	40
1004	1 d. Handley Page Hampden Mk 1	90	45
1005	1 d. 25, Supermarine Spitfire Mk 1A and Hawker Hurricane Mk I	1·10	50
1006	2 d. Avro Manchester	1·25	90
1007	3 d. Short Stirling Mk I	1·50	1·40
1008	5 d. Handley Page Halifax Mk I	1·75	2·00
1009	10 d. Avro Type 683 Lancaster Mk III	2·50	3·00
1010	12 d. De Havilland D.H.98 Mosquito Mk IV	2·50	3·00
999/1010	*Set of 12*	13·50	12·00

MS1011 Two sheets, each 107×77 mm. (a) 15 d. Supermarine Spitfire Mk 1A. (b) 15 d. Avro Type 683 Lancaster Mk III (*different*) *Set of 2 sheets* 6·50 8·00

(Des Jennifer Toombs. Litho B.D.T.)

1990 (14 May). *African Birds. T* 189 *and similar horiz designs. Multicoloured. P* 14.

1012	1 d. 25, Type 189	60	60
	a. Sheetlet No. 1012/31	11·00	
1013	1 d. 25, Village Weaver	60	60
1014	1 d. 25, Red-throated Bee Eater	60	60
1015	1 d. 25, Brown Harrier Eagle	60	60
1016	1 d. 25, Red Bishop	60	60
1017	1 d. 25, Scarlet-chested Sunbird	60	60
1018	1 d. 25, Red-billed Hornbill	60	60
1019	1 d. 25, Mosque Swallow	60	60
1020	1 d. 25, White-faced Whistling Duck	60	60
1021	1 d. 25, African Fish Eagle	60	60
1022	1 d. 25, Eastern White Pelican	60	60
1023	1 d. 25, Carmine Bee Eater	60	60
1024	1 d. 25, Hadada Ibis	60	60
1025	1 d. 25, Egyptian Plover	60	60
1026	1 d. 25, Variable Sunbird	60	60
1027	1 d. 25, African Skimmer	60	60
1028	1 d. 25, Woodland Kingfisher	60	60
1029	1 d. 25, African Jacana	60	60
1030	1 d. 25, African Pygmy Goose	60	60
1031	1 d. 25, Hammerkop	60	60
1012/31	*Set of 20*	11·00	11·00

Nos. 1012/31 were printed together, *se-tenant*, in sheetlets of twenty, forming a composite design of birds at a lake.

190 Penny Black   191 Flag and National Assembly Building

(Des S. Pollard. Litho Questa)

1990 (4 June). *150th Anniv of the Penny Black. P* 14.
1032	**190**	1 d. 25, black and bright ultramarine		85	50
1033		12 d. black and scarlet		3·25	4·00
MS1034		79×73 mm. **190** 15 d. black, silver and dull orange		4·00	5·00

The design of No. **MS**1034 is without the additional stamps behind the Penny Black as shown on Type **190**.

(Des and litho Questa)

1990 (5 June). *25th Anniv of Independence. T* **191** *and similar vert designs. Multicoloured. P* 14.
1035		1 d. Type **191**		50	25
1036		3 d. Pres. Sir Dawda Jawara		50	50
1037		12 d. Map of Yundum airport and Boeing 707 airliner		4·00	4·50
1035/7			*Set of 3*	4·50	4·75
MS1038		100×69 mm. 18 d. State arms		3·50	4·50

192 Baobab Tree

(Des W. Hanson Studio. Litho Questa)

1990 (14 June). *Gambian Life. T* **192** *and similar multicoloured designs. P* 14.
1039	5 b.	Type **192**		30	30
1040	10 b.	Woodcarving, Albert Market, Banjul		10	30
1041	20 b.	President Jawara planting seedling (*vert*)		10	10
1042	50 b.	Sailing canoe and map		50	10
1043	75 b.	Batik fabric		20	10
1044	1 d.	Hibiscus and Bakau beach		30	20
1045	1 d. 25,	Bougainvilla and Tendaba Camp		30	20
1046	2 d.	Shrimp fishing and sorting		45	35
1047	5 d.	Groundnut oil mill, Denton Bridge		80	1·25
1048	10 d.	Handicraft pot and kora (musical instrument)		1·50	2·50
1049	15 d.	*Ansellia africana* (orchid) (*vert*)		4·25	5·00
1050	30 d.	*Euriphene gambiae* (butterfly) and ancient stone ring near Georgetown		7·00	8·50
1039/50			*Set of 12*	14·00	17·00

193 Daisy Duck at 10 Downing Street

194 Lady Elizabeth Bowes-Lyon in High Chair

(Des Walt Disney Co. Litho Questa)

1990 (19 June). *"Stamp World London 90" International Stamp Exhibition. T* **193** *and similar multicoloured designs each showing Walt Disney cartoon characters in England. P* 14.
1051	20 b.	Type **193**		40	30
1052	50 b.	Goofy in Trafalgar Square		45	35
1053	75 b.	Mickey Mouse on White Cliffs of Dover (*horiz*)		60	50
1054	1 d.	Mickey Mouse at Tower of London		60	50
1055	5 d.	Mickey Mouse and Goofy at Hampton Court Palace (*horiz*)		2·00	2·25
1056	8 d.	Mickey Mouse by Magdalen Tower, Oxford		2·25	2·75
1057	10 d.	Mickey Mouse on Old London Bridge (*horiz*)		2·50	3·00
1058	12 d.	Scrooge McDuck and Rosetta Stone, British Museum (*horiz*)		2·50	3·00
1051/8			*Set of 8*	11·00	11·50

MS1059 Two sheets, each 125×100 mm. (a) 18 d. Mickey Mouse and Donald Duck at Piccadilly Circus (*horiz*). (b) 18 d. Mickey Mouse steering tug on River Thames (*horiz*) . . *Set of 2 sheets* 10·00 12·00

(Des Young Phillips Studio. Litho Questa)

1990 (19 July). *90th Birthday of Queen Elizabeth the Queen Mother. T* **194** *and similar vert portraits, 1900–09. P* 14.
1060	6 d.	black, dp magenta & greenish yellow		1·25	1·60
	a.	Strip of 3. Nos. 1060/2		3·25	
1061	6 d.	black, dp magenta & greenish yellow		1·25	1·60
1062	6 d.	black, dp magenta & greenish yellow		1·25	1·60
1060/2			*Set of 3*	3·25	4·25
MS1063		90×75 mm. 18 d. multicoloured		3·50	4·50

Designs:—Nos. 1061, MS1063, Lady Elizabeth Bowes-Lyon as a young girl; No. 1062, Lady Elizabeth Bowes-Lyon with wild flowers.
Nos. 1060/2 were printed together, horizontally and vertically *se-tenant*, in sheetlets of 9 (3×3).

---

195 Vialli, Italy   196 Summit Logo

(Des Young Phillips Studio. Litho Questa)

1990 (24 Sept). *World Cup Football Championship, Italy (2nd issue). T* **195** *and similer vert designs. Multicoloured. P* 14.
1064	1 d.	Type **195**		30	30
1065	1 d. 25,	Cannegia, Argentina		35	35
1066	3 d.	Marchena, Costa Rica		80	90
1067	5 d.	Shaiba, United Arab Emirates		1·10	1·40
1064/7			*Set of 4*	2·25	2·75

MS1068 Two sheets, each 75×92 mm. (a) 18 d. Hagi, Rumania. (b) 18 d. Van Basten, Netherlands . . . . *Set of 2 sheets* 9·00 9·50

(Des B. Grout. Litho Questa)

1990 (1 Nov). *Olympic Games, Barcelona (1992) (1st issue). Multicoloured designs as T* **268** *of Antigua. P* 14.
1069	20 b.	Men's discus		45	15
1070	50 b.	Men's 100 metres		55	20
1071	75 b.	Women's 400 metres		65	30
1072	1 d.	Men's 200 metres		70	40
1073	1 d. 25,	Women's rhythmic gymnastics		75	50
1074	3 d.	Football		1·25	1·50
1075	10 d.	Men's marathon		2·50	3·25
1076	12 d.	"Tornado" class yachting		2·50	3·25
1069/76			*Set of 8*	8·50	8·50

MS1077 Two sheets, each 101×71 mm. (a) 15 d. Parade of national flags (*horiz*). (b) 15 d. Opening ceremony (*horiz*) . . *Set of 2 sheets* 8·00 9·00
See also Nos. 1289/97 and 1351/63.

(Litho Questa)

1990 (24 Dec). *Christmas. Paintings by Renaissance Masters. Multicoloured designs as T* **272** *of Antigua, but vert. P* 13½×14.
1078	20 b.	"The Annunciation, with St. Emidius" (detail) (Crivelli)		20	10
1079	50 b.	"The Annunciation" (detail) (Campin)		30	10
1080	75 b.	"The Solly Madonna" (detail) (Raphael)		40	20
1081	1 d. 25,	"The Tempi Madonna" (Raphael)		40	30
1082	2 d.	"Madonna of the Linen Window" (detail) (Raphael)		60	50
1083	7 d.	"The Annunciation, with St. Emidius" (different detail) (Crivelli)		2·00	2·75
1084	10 d.	"The Orleans Madonna" (Raphael)		2·25	2·75
1085	15 d.	"Madonna and Child" (detail) (Crivelli)		2·75	3·75
1078/85			*Set of 8*	8·00	9·50

MS1086 72×101 mm. 15 d. "Niccolini-Cowper Madonna" (Raphael) . . . . 4·50 5·50

(Litho Questa)

1990 (24 Dec). *350th Death Anniv of Rubens. Multicoloured designs as T* **273** *of Antigua. P* 14×13½.
1087	20 b.	"The Lion Hunt" (sketch)		15	15
1088	75 b.	"The Lion Hunt" (detail)		25	25
1089	1 d.	"The Tiger Hunt" (detail)		30	30
1090	1 d. 25,	"The Tiger Hunt" (different detail)		35	35
1091	3 d.	"The Tiger Hunt" (different detail)		75	80
1092	5 d.	"The Boar Hunt" (detail)		1·10	1·25
1093	10 d.	"The Lion Hunt" (different detail)		1·75	2·25
1094	15 d.	"The Tiger Hunt" (different detail)		2·40	3·00
1087/94			*Set of 8*	6·25	7·50

MS1095 Four sheets. (a) 100×71 mm. 15 d. "The Boar Hunt". P 14×13½. (b) 100×71 mm. 15 d. "The Lion Hunt". P 14×13½. (c) 100×71 mm. 15 d. "The Crocodile and Hippopotamus Hunt". P 14×13½. (d) 71×100 mm. 15 d. "St. George slays the Dragon" (*vert*). P 13½×14
. . . . *Set of 4 sheets* 12·00 13·00

(Litho Questa)

1991 (2 Jan). *World Summit for Children, New York. P* 14.
1096	**196**	1 d. multicoloured		40	40

(Des Walt Disney Co. Litho Questa)

1991 (14 Feb). *International Literacy Year (1990). Multicoloured designs as T* **269** *of Antigua showing scenes from Disney cartoon film* The Sword in the Stone. *P* 14×13½.
1097	3 d.	Sir Kay and Wart searching for lost arrow (*horiz*)		1·10	1·25
	a.	Sheetlet. Nos. 1097/105		9·00	
1098	3 d.	Merlin the Magician (*horiz*)		1·10	1·25
1099	3 d.	Merlin teaching Wart (*horiz*)		1·10	1·25
1100	3 d.	Wart writing on blackboard (*horiz*)		1·10	1·25
1101	3 d.	Wart transformed into bird and Madame Mim (*horiz*)		1·10	1·25
1102	3 d.	Merlin and Madame Mim (*horiz*)		1·10	1·25
1103	3 d.	Madame Mim transformed into dragon (*horiz*)		1·10	1·25
1104	3 d.	Wart pulling sword from stone (*horiz*)		1·10	1·25
1105	3 d.	King Arthur on throne (*horiz*)		1·10	1·25
1097/105			*Set of 9*	9·00	10·00

MS1106 Two sheets, each 131×106 mm. (a) 20 d. Sword in stone. (b) 20 d. Merlin. P 13½×14
. . . . *Set of 2 sheets* 13·00 14·00
Nos. 1097/105 were printed together, *se-tenant*, in sheetlets of 9.

---

197 *Bebearia senegalensis*   198 *Papilio dardanus*

(Des Mary Walters. Litho Questa)

1991 (13 May). *Wildlife. T* **197** *and similar multicoloured designs. P* 14.
1107	1 d.	Type **197**		45	50
	a.	Sheetlet. Nos. 1107/22		6·00	
1108	1 d.	*Graphium ridleyanus* (butterfly)		45	50
1109	1 d.	*Precis antilope* (butterfly)		45	50
1110	1 d.	*Charaxes ameliae* (butterfly)		45	50
1111	1 d.	Addax		45	50
1112	1 d.	Sassaby		45	50
1113	1 d.	Civet		45	50
1114	1 d.	Green Monkey		45	50
1115	1 d.	Spur-winged Goose		45	50
1116	1 d.	Red-billed Hornbill		45	50
1117	1 d.	Osprey		45	50
1118	1 d.	Glossy Ibis		45	50
1119	1 d.	Egyptian Plover		45	50
1120	1 d.	Golden-tailed Woodpecker		45	50
1121	1 d.	Green Wood Hoopoe		45	50
1122	1 d.	Gaboon Viper		45	50
1123	1 d. 50,	Red-billed Fire Finch		50	55
	a.	Sheetlet. Nos. 1123/38		7·00	
1124	1 d. 50,	Leaf-Love		50	55
1125	1 d. 50,	Piapiac		50	55
1126	1 d. 50,	African Emerald Cuckoo		50	55
1127	1 d. 50,	Red Colobus Monkey		50	55
1128	1 d. 50,	African Elephant		50	55
1129	1 d. 50,	Duiker		50	55
1130	1 d. 50,	Giant Eland		50	55
1131	1 d. 50,	Oribi		50	55
1132	1 d. 50,	Western African Dwarf Crocodile		50	55
1133	1 d. 50,	Crowned Crane		50	55
1134	1 d. 50,	Jackal		50	55
1135	1 d. 50,	Yellow-throated Longclaw		50	55
1136	1 d. 50,	Abyssinian Ground Hornbill		50	55
1137	1 d. 50,	*Papilio hesperus*		50	55
1138	1 d. 50,	*Papilio antimachus*		50	55
1139	5 d.	Martial Eagle		1·00	1·10
	a.	Sheetlet. Nos. 1139/54		14·00	
1140	5 d.	Red-cheeked Cordon-bleu		1·00	1·10
1141	5 d.	Red Bishop		1·00	1·10
1142	5 d.	Eastern White Pelican		1·00	1·10
1143	5 d.	Patas Monkey		1·00	1·10
1144	5 d.	Vervet Monkey		1·00	1·10
1145	5 d.	Roan Antelope		1·00	1·10
1146	5 d.	Western Hartebeest		1·00	1·10
1147	5 d.	Waterbuck		1·00	1·10
1148	5 d.	Warthog		1·00	1·10
1149	5 d.	Spotted Hyena		1·00	1·10
1150	5 d.	Olive Baboon		1·00	1·10
1151	5 d.	*Palla decius*		1·00	1·10
1152	5 d.	*Acraea pharsalus*		1·00	1·10
1153	5 d.	*Neptidopsis ophione*		1·00	1·10
1154	5 d.	*Acraea caecilia*		1·00	1·10
1107/154			*Set of 48*	26·00	30·00

MS1155 Three sheets, each 101×69 mm. (a) 18 d. African Spoonbill (*vert*). (b) 18 d. White-billed Buffalo Weaver (*vert*). (c) 18 d. Lion (*vert*) . . . . *Set of 3 sheets* 11·00 13·00
Nos. 1107/22, 1123/38 and 1139/54 were printed together, *se-tenant*, in sheetlets of 16, each forming a composite design.

(Des L. Nelson. Litho Questa)

1991 (1 June). *Butterflies. T* **198** *and similar vert designs. Multicoloured. P* 14.
1156	20 b.	Type **198**		60	30
1157	50 b.	*Bematistes poggei*		80	40
1158	1 d.	*Vanessa cardui*		90	55
1159	1 d. 50,	*Amphicallia tigris*		1·00	85
1160	3 d.	*Hypolimnas dexithea*		1·75	1·25
1161	8 d.	*Acraea egina*		2·25	3·00
1162	10 d.	*Salamis temora*		2·25	3·00
1163	15 d.	*Precis octavia*		2·75	4·00
1156/63			*Set of 8*	11·00	12·00

MS1164 Four sheets, each 100×70 mm. (a) 18 d. *Danaus chrysippus*. (b) 18 d. *Charaxes jasius* (male). (c) 18 d. *Papilio demodocus*. (d) 18 d. *Papilio nireus* . . . . *Set of 4 sheets* 15·00 15·00

(Des D. Miller. Litho Walsall)

1991 (12 Aug). *65th Birthday of Queen Elizabeth II. Horiz designs as T* **280** *of Antigua. Multicoloured. P* 14.
1165	50 b.	The Queen and Prince Charles at Windsor polo match		30	20
1166	1 d.	The Queen and Princess Anne at the Derby, 1988		45	35
1167	1 d. 25,	The Queen at the Royal London Hospital, 1970		55	50
1168	12 d.	The Queen and Prince Philip at Balmoral, 1976		3·00	3·50
1165/8			*Set of 4*	3·75	4·25
MS1169		68×90 mm. 18 d. Separate photographs of The Queen and Prince Philip		3·75	4·50

(Des D. Miller. Litho Walsall)

1991 (12 Aug). *10th Wedding Anniv of Prince and Princess of Wales. Horiz designs as T* **280** *of Antigua. Multicoloured.* P 14.
1170	20 b.	Prince and Princess with sons in June, 1989		35	25
1171	75 b.	Separate photographs of Prince, Princess and sons		60	50

1172	1 d. 50, Prince Henry on first day of school, 1987, and Prince William at polo match	80	70
1173	15 d. Separate photographs of Prince and Princess of Wales	4·00	4·50
1170/3		*Set of 4* 5·25	5·50
MS1174	68×90 mm. 18 d. The family in Italy, 1985	4·25	5·00

(Des Walt Disney Co. Litho Questa)

1991 (22 Aug). *"Phila Nippon '91" International Stamp Exhibition, Tokyo. Multicoloured designs as T 279 of Antigua showing Walt Disney cartoon chartacters playing Japanese sports and games.* P 14×13½ (*horiz*) or 13½ × 14 (*vert*).

1175	50 b. Donald Duck and Mickey Mouse playing "go" (*horiz*)	50	30
1176	75 b. Morty, Ferdie and Pete as Sumo wrestlers (*horiz*)	65	40
1177	1 d. Minnie Mouse, Clarabelle Cow and Daisy Duck playing battledore and shuttlecock (*horiz*)	70	45
1178	1 d. 25, Goofy and Mickey at Okinawa bullfight	80	55
1179	5 d. Mickey flying hawk	2·00	2·00
1180	7 d. Mickey, Minnie and Donald playing "jan-ken-pon"	2·25	2·50
1181	10 d. Goofy as archer (*horiz*)	2·50	2·75
1182	15 d. Morty and Ferdie flying kites	3·00	3·25
1175/82		*Set of 8* 11·00	11·00

MS1183 Four sheets, each 127×102 mm. (a) 20 d. Mickey climbing Mt Fuji. (b) 20 d. Mickey fishing. (c) 20 d. Scrooge McDuck and Mickey playing football. (d) 20 d. Goofy playing baseball.

Set of 4 sheets 14·00 15·00

(Des Walt Disney Co. Litho Questa)

1991 (28 Aug). *International Literacy Year (1990). Multicoloured designs as T 269 of Antigua showing Walt Disney cartoon characters in Kipling's "Just So" stories.* P 14×13½.

1184	50 b. "How the Whale got his Throat" (*horiz*)	50	30
1185	75 b. "How the Camel got his Hump" (*horiz*)	65	40
1186	1 d. "How the Leopard got his Spots" (*horiz*)	70	45
1187	1 d. 25, "The Elephant's Child" (*horiz*)	80	55
1188	1 d. 50, "The Singsong of Old Man Kangaroo" (*horiz*)	95	80
1189	7 d. "The Crab that played with the Sea" (*horiz*)	2·25	2·50
1190	10 d. "The Cat that walked by Himself" (*horiz*)	2·50	2·75
1191	15 d. "The Butterfly that Stamped" (*horiz*)	3·00	3·25
1184/91		*Set of 8* 10·00	10·00

MS1192 Four sheets, each 127×102 mm. (a) 20 d. Mickey Mouse reading story to Morte and Ferdie (*horiz*). P 14×13½. (b) 20 d. "How the Rhinoceros got his Skin" (*horiz*). P 14×13½. (c) 20 d. "How the Alphabet was made". P 14×13½. (d) 20 d. "How the first Letter was written". P 13½×14

Set of 4 sheets 14·00 15·00

199 Canadian Pacific Steel Cupola Caboose 200 Tiger Shark

(Litho Cartor)

1991 (12 Sept). *Railway Brake-vans. T 199 and similar multicoloured designs.* P 14×13½.

1193	1 d. Type 19	25	25
	a. Sheetlet. Nos. 1193/1201	2·00	
1194	1 d. Cumberland & Pennsylvania Railroad four-wheeled caboose, U.S.A.	25	25
1195	1 d. Ferrocarril Interoceanico caboose, Mexico	25	25
1196	1 d. Northern Pacific Railroad steel cupola caboose, U.S.A.	25	25
1197	1 d. Morriston & Erie Railroad four-wheeled caboose, U.S.A.	25	25
1198	1 d. Burlington Northern Railroad streamlined cupola caboose, U.S.A.	25	25
1199	1 d. McCloud River Railroad caboose-coach, U.S.A.	25	25
1200	1 d. Santa Fe Railroad wide-vision caboose, U.S.A.	25	25
1201	1 d. Frisco Railroad wide-vision caboose, U.S.A.	25	25
1202	1 d. 50, Colorado & Southern Railroad four-wheeled caboose, U.S.A.	35	40
	a. Sheetlet. Nos. 1202/10	2·75	
1203	1 d. 50, Santa Fe Railroad transfer caboose, U.S.A.	35	40
1204	1 d. 50, Canadian National wooden cupola caboose	35	40
1205	1 d. 50, Union Pacific steel transfer caboose, U.S.A.	35	40
1206	1 d. 50, Virgina & Truckee Railroad caboose-coach, U.S.A.	35	40
1207	1 d. 50, British Railways standard brake van	35	40
1208	1 d. 50, International Railways of Central America caboose	35	40
1209	1 d. 50, Northern Pacific Railroad steel cupola caboose, U.S.A.	35	40
1210	1 d. 50, Burlington Northern Railroad wooden caboose, U.S.A.	35	40
1211	2 d. Oahu Railway caboose, Hawaii	40	50
	a. Sheetlet. Nos. 1211/19	3·25	
1212	2 d. British Railways standard brake van	40	50
1213	2 d. Union Pacific steel wide-view caboose, U.S.A.	40	50

1214	2 d. Belt Railway of Chicago four-wheeled caboose, U.S.A.	40	50
1215	2 d. McCloud River Railroad four-wheeled caboose, U.S.A.	40	50
1216	2 d. Angelina County Lumber Co caboose, U.S.A.	40	50
1217	2 d. Coahuila & Zacatecas caboose, Mexico	40	50
1218	2 d. United Railways of Yucatan caboose, Mexico	40	50
1219	2 d. Rio Grande Railroad steel cupola caboose, U.S.A.	40	50
1193/219		*Set of 27* 8·00	9·25

MS1220 Three sheets, each 79×56 mm. (a) 20 d. Wooden caboose on steam goods train. P 13×12. (b) 20 d. Pennsylvania Railroad steel caboose on electric goods train (*vert*). P 12×13. (c) 20 d. Wooden caboose on passenger train and railwayman with flag (*vert*). P 12×13

Set of 3 sheets 12·00 13·00

Nos. 1193/1201, 1202/10 and 1211/19 were printed together, *se-tenant*, in sheetlets of 9.

(Des R. Sauber. Litho Questa)

1991 (28 Oct). *Fishes. T 200 and similar horiz designs. Multicoloured.* P 14×14½.

1221	20 b. Type 200	15	15
1222	25 b. Common Jewelfish	15	15
1223	50 b. Five-spotted Cichlid	25	25
1224	75 b. Small-toothed Sawfish	25	25
1225	1 d. Spotted Tilapia	30	30
1226	1 d. 25, Dwarf Jewelfish	35	35
1227	1 d. 50, Five-spotted Jewelfish	40	40
1228	3 d. Lion-headed Cichlid	65	65
1229	10 d. Egyptian Mouthbrooder	2·00	2·50
1230	15 d. Burton's Mouthbrooder	2·75	3·50
1221/30		*Set of 10* 6·50	7·50

MS1231 Two sheets, each 118×83 mm. (a) 18 d. Great Barracuda. (b) 18 d. Yellow-tailed Snapper

Set of 2 sheets 8·50 9·50

(Litho Questa)

1991 (9 Nov). *Hummel Figurines. Vert designs as T 302 of Antigua. Multicoloured.* P 14.

1232	20 b. Waving children	10	10
1233	75 b. Children under umbrella	15	15
1234	1 d. Girl kissing friend	20	20
1235	1 d. 50, Children at window	30	30
1236	2 d. 50, Two girls in aprons	45	45
1237	5 d. Two boys in bow ties	85	85
1238	10 d. Two girls sitting on fence with birds	1·75	2·00
1239	15 d. Boy and girl in Swiss costume	2·50	3·00
1232/9		*Set of 8* 5·50	6·50

MS1240 Two sheets, each 98×128 mm. (a) 4 d. × 4 As Nos. 1233/5 and 1239. (b) 5 d. × 4 As Nos. 1232 and 1236/8

Set of 2 sheets 7·00 8·00

(Litho Questa)

1991 (5 Dec). *Death Centenary of Vincent van Gogh (artist). Multicoloured designs as T 278 of Antigua.* P 14×13½ (*horiz*) or 13½×14 (*vert*).

1241	20 b. "The Old Cemetery Tower at Nuenen in the Snow" (*horiz*)	15	15
1242	25 b. "Head of Peasant Woman with White Cap"	15	15
1243	50 b. "The Green Parrot"	20	20
1244	75 b. "Vase with Carnations"	20	20
1245	1 d. "Vase with Red Gladioli"	25	25
1246	1 d. 25, "Beach at Scheveningen in Calm Weather" (*horiz*)	30	30
1247	1 d. 50, "Boy cutting Grass with Sickle" (*horiz*)	35	35
1248	2 d. "Coleus Plant in a Flowerpot" (detail)	40	40
1249	3 d. "Self-portrait, 1887"	60	60
1250	4 d. "Self-portrait" (*different*)	70	70
1251	5 d. "Self-portrait" (*different*)	85	85
1252	6 d. "Self-portrait, 1887" (*different*)	1·25	1·25
1253	8 d. "Still Life with Bottle, Two Glasses, Cheese and Bread" (detail)	1·75	1·75
1254	10 d. "Still Life with Cabbage, Clogs and Potatoes" (*horiz*)	2·25	2·25
1255	12 d. "Montmartre: The Street Lamps"	2·75	2·75
1256	15 d. "Head of a Peasant Woman with Brownish Cap"	3·00	3·00
1241/56		*Set of 16* 13·50	13·50

MS1257 Four sheets, each 127×102 mm. (a) 20 d. "The Potato Eaters" (*horiz*). (b) 20 d. "Montmartre: Quarry and Mills" (*horiz*). (c) 20 d. "Autumn Landscape" (*horiz*). (d) 20 d. "Arles: View from the Wheat Fields" (detail) (*horiz*). Imperf

Set of 4 sheets 16·00 17·00

(Litho Walsall)

1991 (23 Dec). *Christmas. Religious Paintings by Fra Angelico. Vert designs as T 287 of Antigua. Multicoloured.* P 12.

1258	20 b. "The Madonna of Humility"	10	10
1259	50 b. "Madonna and Child with Angels"	20	20
1260	75 b. "Virgin and Child with Angels"	25	25
1261	1 d. "The Annunciation"	30	30
1262	1 d. 25, "Presentation in the Temple"	35	35
1263	5 d. "The Annunciation" (*different*)	1·25	1·50
1264	10 d. "Madonna della Stella"	2·00	2·50
1265	15 d. "Naming of St. John the Baptist"	2·50	3·25
1258/65		*Set of 8* 6·25	7·50

MS1266 Two sheets, each 102×128 mm. (a) 20 d. "Coronation of the Virgin". (b) 20 d. "Annunciation and Adoration of the Magi". P 14

Set of 2 sheets 7·00 8·00

201 Son House 202 Pope John Paul II

(Des R. Sauber. Litho Questa)

1992 (12 Feb). *Famous Blues Singers. T 201 and similar vert designs. Multicoloured.* P 14.

1267	20 b. Type 201	15	15
1268	25 b. W. C. Handy	15	15
1269	50 b. Muddy Waters	30	30
1270	75 b. Lightnin Hopkins	40	40
1271	1 d. Ma Rainey	45	45
1272	1 d. 25, Mance Lipscomb	50	50
1273	1 d. 50, Mahalia Jackson	60	60
1274	2 d. Ella Fitzgerald	70	70
1275	3 d. Howlin Wolf	85	85
1276	5 d. Bessie Smith	1·25	1·25
1277	7 d. Leadbelly	1·50	1·50
1278	10 d. Joe Willie Wilkins	2·00	2·00
1267/78		*Set of 12* 8·00	8·00

MS1279 Three sheets, each 110×78 mm. (a) 20 d. String Drum. (b) 20 d. Elvis Presley. (c) 20 d. Billie Holiday

Set of 3 sheets 11·00 12·00

(Des G. Vasarhelyi. Litho Questa)

1992 (20 Feb). *Papal Visit. T 202 and similar horiz designs. Multicoloured.* P 14.

1280	1 d. Type 202	40	40
1281	1 d. 25, Pope John Paul II and Pres. Sir Dawda Jawara	50	50
1282	20 d. Gambian and Papal flags	4·75	5·50
1280/2		*Set of 3* 5·00	5·75

MS1283 104×70 mm. 25 d. Pope giving blessing 6·00 8·00

A 50 d. value, as Type 202, but embossed on gold foil, exists from a limited printing.

(Des D. Miller. Litho Questa)

1992 (2 Mar). *40th Anniv of Queen Elizabeth II's Accession. Horiz designs as T 288 of Antigua. Multicoloured.* P 14.

1284	20 b. Pottery market	15	10
1285	50 b. Ruins of early fort	25	20
1286	1 d. Fishing boat	40	30
1287	15 d. Canoes on beach	3·25	4·00
1284/7		*Set of 4* 3·50	4·25

MS1288 Two sheets, each 75×97 mm. (a) 20 d. *Lady Chilel Jawara* (river vessel). (b) 20 d. River ferry being loaded

Set of 2 sheets 8·00 9·00

203 N. Comaneci (Rumania) (combined gymnastic events) and Map of Barcelona

(Litho Questa)

1992 (16 Mar). *Olympic Games, Barcelona (2nd issue). Past Medal Winners. T 203 and similar multicoloured designs.* P 14.

1289	20 b. Type 203	10	10
1290	50 b. D. Moorcroft (G.B.) (5000 metres) and map	20	20
1291	75 b. M. Nemeth (Hungary) (javelin) and decorative tiles	25	25
1292	1 d. J. Pedraza (Mexico) (20k walk) and decorative plate	30	30
1293	1 d. 25, "Soling" class yachting (Brazil), state arms and flag	40	40
1294	1 d. 50, Women's hockey (G.D.R.) and Barcelona building	45	45
1295	12 d. M. Jordan (U.S.A.) (basketball) and map	2·50	3·25
1296	15 d. V. Borzov (U.S.S.R.) (100 metres) and galleon	3·00	3·50
1289/96		*Set of 8* 6·50	7·50

MS1297 Two sheets. (a) 82×112 mm. 20 d. Silhouette of flamenco dancer on map (*vert*). (b) 112×82 mm. 20 d. Silhouette of bull on map

Set of 2 sheets 7·25 7·50

204 Mickey Mouse as Christopher Columbus 205 *Hibiscus rosa-sinensis*

(Des Walt Disney Co. Litho Questa)

1992 (8 Apr). *International Stamp Exhibitions. T 204 and similar multicoloured designs showing Walt Disney cartoon characters. P 13½×14.*

(a) "Granada '92", Spain. Voyage of Columbus

1298	20 b. Type 204	30	15
1299	75 b. Mickey's plans derided	45	25
1300	1 d. 50, Mickey lands in America	65	60
1301	15 d. Mickey presents treasure to Minnie	3·25	4·00
1298/1301	*Set of 4*	4·25	4·50
MS1302	127×102 mm. 18 d. Mickey embarks for America	4·00	4·50

(b) World Columbian Stamp "Expo '92". Chicago Landmarks

1303	50 b. Navy Pier	20	10
1304	1 d. Wrigley Building	30	25
1305	1 d. 25, University of Chicago	35	30
1306	12 d. Alder Planetarium	2·25	3·25
1303/6	*Set of 4*	2·75	3·50
MS1307	127×102 mm. 18 d. Goofy hanging over Chicago (*horiz*). P 14×13½	4·00	4·50

(Litho Questa)

1992 (16 Apr). *Easter. Religious Paintings. Multicoloured designs as T 291 of Antigua, but vert. P 13½×14.*

1308	20 b. "Christ presented to the People" (Rembrandt)	10	10
1309	50 b. "Christ carrying the Cross" (Grünewald)	20	20
1310	75 b. "The Crucifixion" (Grünewald)	25	25
1311	1 d. "The Crucifixion" (Rubens)	30	30
1312	1 d. 25, "The Road to Calvary" (detail) (Tintoretto)	35	35
1313	1 d. 50, "The Road to Calvary" (Tintoretto) (*different*)	40	40
1314	15 d. "The Crucifixion" (Masaccio)	2·75	3·25
1315	20 d. "The Descent from the Cross" (detail) (Rembrandt)	3·50	4·00
1308/15	*Set of 8*	7·00	8·00
MS1316	Two sheets, each 72×101 mm. (a) 25 d. "The Crowning with Thorns" (detail) (Van Dyck). (b) 25 d. "The Crowning with Thorns" (detail) (Titian) ... *Set of 2 sheets*	8·50	9·50

(Des Mary Walters. Litho B.D.T.)

1992 (21 July). *Flowers. T 205 and similar vert designs. Multicoloured. P 14.*

1317	20 b. Type 205	10	10
1318	50 b. Monodora myristica	20	20
1319	75 b. Bombax costatum	25	25
1320	1 d. Oncoba spinosa	30	30
1321	1 d. 25, Combretum grandiflorum	35	35
1322	1 d. 50, Rothmannia longiflora	40	40
1323	2 d. Clerodendrum splendens	55	55
1324	5 d. Mussaenda erythrophylla	1·10	1·25
1325	10 d. Nauclea latifolia	1·75	2·00
1326	12 d. Clerodendrum capitatum	1·90	2·25
1327	15 d. Costus spectabilis	2·50	2·75
1328	18 d. Strophanthus preussii	2·75	3·00
1317/28	*Set of 12*	11·00	12·00
MS1329	Four sheets, each 102×71 mm. (a) 20 d. Bougainvillea glabra. (b) 20 d. Nymphaea. (c) 20 d. Adansonia digitata. (d) 20 d. Clitoria ternatea ... *Set of 4 sheets*	12·00	13·00

206 Joven Antonia (River Gambia)

(Des C. Abbott. Litho Questa)

1992 (3 Aug). *River Boats of the World. T 206 and similar horiz designs. Multicoloured. P 14.*

1330	20 b. Type 206	10	10
1331	50 b. Dresden (River Elbe)	20	20
1332	75 b. Medway Queen (River Medway)	25	25
1333	1 d. Lady Wright (River Gambia)	30	30
1334	1 d. 25, Devin (River Vltava)	35	35
1335	1 d. 50, Lady Chilel Jawara (River Gambia)	40	50
1336	5 d. Robert Fulton (River Hudson)	1·10	1·25
1337	10 d. Coonawarra (River Murray)	1·75	2·00
1338	12 d. Nakusp (River Columbia)	2·00	2·25
1339	18 d. Lucy Ashton (Firth of Clyde)	2·50	2·75
1330/9	*Set of 10*	8·00	9·00
MS1340	Two sheets, each 107×69 mm. (a) 20 d. City of Cairo (Mississippi). (b) 20 d. Rüdesheim (Rhine) ... *Set of 2 sheets*	8·00	9·00

(Des W. Wright. Litho Questa)

1992 (8 Aug). *50th Anniv of Japanese Attack on Pearl Harbor. Horiz designs as T 286 of Antigua. Multicoloured. P 14½.*

1341	2 d. U.S.S. Pennsylvania (battleship)	90	90
	a. Sheetlet. Nos. 1341/50	8·00	
1342	2 d. Japanese Mitsubishi AGM Zero-Sen aircraft over Pearl Harbor	90	95
1343	2 d. U.S.S. Ward (destroyer) sinking midget submarine	90	95
1344	2 d. Ford Naval Station under attack	90	95
1345	2 d. Agency report of Japanese attack	90	95
1346	2 d. Newspaper headline	90	95
1347	2 d. Japanese troops on Guam	90	95
1348	2 d. U.S. forces regaining Wake Island	90	95
1349	2 d. North American B-25B Mitchell bomber raid on Japan	90	95
1350	2 d. American Douglas SBD Dauntless dive bomber attacking Japanese carrier, Midway	90	95
1341/50	*Set of 10*	8·00	8·50

Nos. 1341/50 were printed together, *se-tenant*, in sheetlets of 10 with the stamps arranged in two horizontal strips of 5 separated by a gutter showing dogfight over Pearl Harbor.

207 Women's Double Sculls

208 Pres. Jawara playing Golf and Map of Australia

(Litho Questa)

1992 (10 Aug). *Winter Olympic Games, Albertville, and Olympic Games, Barcelona (3rd issue). T 207 and similar multicoloured designs. P 14.*

1351	20 b. Type 207	20	15
1352	50 b. Men's kayak (*vert*)	30	20
1353	75 b. Women's rapid precision pistol shooting	40	30
1354	1 d. Judo (*vert*)	45	30
1355	1 d. 25, Men's javelin (*vert*)	55	35
1356	1 d. 50, Men's vaulting horse (*vert*)	70	40
1357	2 d. Men's downhill skiing (*vert*)	85	55
1358	3 d. Windsurfing (*vert*)	1·00	90
1359	5 d. Men's high jump	1·50	1·50
1360	10 d. Four-man bobsled (*vert*)	2·25	2·50
1361	12 d. 90 metre ski-jump (*vert*)	2·50	3·00
1362	15 d. Men's slalom skiing	2·75	3·50
1351/62	*Set of 12*	12·00	12·00
MS1363	Four sheets, each 100×70 mm. (a) 18 d. Table tennis (*vert*). (b) 18 d. Men's 500 metre speed skating. (c) 18 d. Women's 200 metre backstroke. (d) 18 d. Pairs figure skating (*vert*) ... *Set of 4 sheets*	13·00	14·00

(Litho B.D.T.)

1992 (21 Sept). *"Genova '92" International Thematic Stamp Exhibition. Dinosaurs. Vert designs as T 290 of Antigua. Multicoloured. P 14.*

1364	20 b. Dryosaurus	30	10
1365	25 b. Saurolophus	30	10
1366	50 b. Allosaurus	35	20
1367	75 b. Fabrosaurus	40	25
1368	1 d. Deinonychus	40	30
1369	1 d. 25, Cetiosaurus	50	35
1370	1 d. 50, Camptosaurus	50	35
1371	2 d. Ornithosuchus	55	45
1372	3 d. Spinosaurus	60	60
1373	5 d. Ornithomimus	1·00	1·25
1374	10 d. Kentrosaurus	1·75	2·25
1375	12 d. Schlermochus	1·90	2·50
1364/75	*Set of 12*	7·75	7·75
MS1376	Three sheets, each 104×75 mm. (a) 25 d. As No. 1366. (b) 25 d. As No. 1369. (c) 25 d. As No. 1371 ... *Set of 3 sheets*	14·00	15·00

(Des Kerri Schiff. Litho Questa)

1992 (28 Oct). *Postage Stamp Mega Event, New York. Sheet 100×70 mm containing horiz design as T 299 of Antigua. Multicoloured. P 14.*

MS1377	18 d. Immigration Centre, Ellis Island	3·75	4·00

(Litho Questa)

1992 (3 Nov). *Christmas. Religious Paintings. Vert designs as T 300 of Antigua. Multicoloured. P 13½×14.*

1378	50 b. "The Holy Family" (Raphael)	20	20
1379	75 b. "The Little Holy Family" (Raphael)	25	25
1380	1 d. "The Little Holy Family" (detail) (Raphael)	30	30
1381	1 d. 25, "Escape to Egypt" (Melchior Broederlam)	35	35
1382	1 d. 50, "Flight into Egypt" (Adriaen Isenbrant)	35	35
1383	2 d. "The Holy Family" (El Greco)	45	45
1384	2 d. "Flight into Egypt" (detail) (Cosimo Tura)	45	45
1385	2 d. "Flight into Egypt" (detail) (Master of Hoogstraelen)	45	45
1386	4 d. "The Holy Family" (Bernard van Orley)	80	90
1387	5 d. "Holy Family with Infant Jesus Sleeping" (detail) (Charles Le Brun)	95	1·10
1388	10 d. "Rest on The Flight to Egypt" (Orazio Gentileschi)	1·75	2·25
1389	12 d. "Rest on The Flight to Egypt" (detail) (Orazio Gentileschi)	1·90	2·50
1378/89	*Set of 12*	7·50	8·50
MS1390	Three sheets, each 102×77 mm. (a) 25 d. "The Holy Family" (detail) (Giorgione). (b) 25 d. "Flight into Egypt" (detail) (Vittore Carpaccio). (c) 25 d. "Rest on The Flight to Egypt" (detail) (Simone Cantarino) ... *Set of 3 sheets*	11·00	12·00

(Des Walt Disney Co. Litho Questa)

1992 (16 Nov). *60th Anniv of Goofy (Disney cartoon character). Multicoloured designs as T 258 of Dominica. P 14×13½.*

1391	50 b. Goofy in Orphan's Benefit, 1934	30	20
1392	75 b. Goofy and Donald Duck in Moose Hunters, 1937	40	30
1393	1 d. Goofy in Mickey's Amateurs, 1937	50	40
1394	1 d. 25, Goofy, Donald and Mickey Mouse in Lonesome Ghosts, 1937	55	55
1395	5 d. Goofy, Donald and Mickey in Boat Builders, 1938	1·40	1·40
1396	7 d. Goofy, Donald and Mickey in The Whalers, 1938	1·75	2·00
1397	10 d. Goofy and Wilbur the grasshopper in Goofy and Wilbur, 1939	2·00	2·25
1398	15 d. Goofy in Saludos Amigos, 1941	2·50	2·75
1391/8	*Set of 8*	8·50	9·00
MS1399	Two sheets, each 127×102 mm. (a) 20 d. Goofy in The Band Concert, 1935 (*vert*). (b) 20 d. Goofy today (*vert*). P 13½×14 ... *Set of 2 sheets*	9·00	10·00

(Litho B.D.T.)

1992 (8 Dec). *Open Golf Championships. T 208 and similar multicoloured designs. P 14.*

1400	20 b. Type 208	30	15
1401	1 d. Pres. Jawara and Gambia Open trophy	65	45
1402	1 d. 50, Pres. Jawara (winner of Gambia Open, 1985)	90	55
1403	2 d. Pres. Jawara and map of Japan	1·00	70
1404	3 d. Pres. Jawara and map of U.S.A.	1·25	1·00
1405	5 d. Gambia Open trophy	1·75	1·75
1406	10 d. Pres. Jawara and map of Scotland	2·75	3·25
1407	12 d. Pres. Jawara and map of Italy	2·75	3·25
1400/7	*Set of 8*	10·00	10·00
MS1408	Two sheets. (a) 106×71 mm. 10 d. Pres. Jawara playing shot. (b) 67×99 mm. 18 d. Flag of Gambia (*horiz*) ... *Set of 2 sheets*	9·00	10·00

209 Launch of European "Ariane 4"

210 Peace Corps and Gambian Flags

(Des W. Wright and L. Fried (Nos. 1409, 1419, **MS**1423a), W. Wright and W. Hanson (Nos. 1411, 1422, **MS**1423c), W. Wright (others). Litho B.D.T.)

1993 (7 Jan). *Anniversaries and Events. T 209 and similar multicoloured designs. P 14.*

1409	2 d. Type 209	50	50
1410	2 d. Konrad Adenauer and Berlin Airlift (*horiz*)	50	50
1411	2 d. Airship LZ-129 Hindenburg, 1928 (*horiz*)	50	50
1412	5 d. Santa Maria (*horiz*)	1·25	1·25
1413	6 d. Jentink's Duiker (*horiz*)	1·40	1·40
1414	7 d. World map and emblem (*horiz*)	1·40	1·40
1415	9 d. Wolfgang Amadeus Mozart	1·75	1·75
1416	10 d. Lions Club emblem	1·75	1·75
1417	10 d. Enterprise (yacht), 1930	1·75	1·75
1418	10 d. Imperial Amazon ("Sisserou Parrot")	1·75	1·75
1419	12 d. American space shuttle	2·00	2·00
1420	12 d. Fleet of Columbus (*horiz*)	2·00	2·00
1421	15 d. Adenauer and returning prisoners of war (*horiz*)	2·40	2·40
1422	18 d. Airship LZ-1, 1900 (*horiz*)	3·00	3·00
1409/22	*Set of 14*	20·00	20·00
MS1423	Six sheets. (a) 104×76 mm. 18 d. Nose of projected European space station "Hermes". (b) 113×87 mm. 18 d. Konrad Adenauer. (c) 85×65 mm. 18 d. Count von Zeppelin. (d) 103×75 mm. 18 d. Green-winged Macaw and bow of ship. (e) 85×65 mm. 18 d. Globe. (f) 99×69 mm. 18 d. Dancers from The Marriage of Figaro ... *Set of 6 sheets*	18·00	20·00

Anniversaries and Events:—Nos. 1409, 1419, **MS**1423a, International Space Year; Nos. 1410, 1421, **MS**1423b, 25th death anniv of Konrad Adenauer (German statesman); Nos. 1411, 1422, **MS**1423c, 75th death anniv of Count Ferdinand von Zeppelin; Nos. 1412, 1420, **MS**1423d, 500th anniv of Discovery of America by Columbus; Nos. 1413, 1418, **MS**1423e, Earth Summit '92, Rio; No. 1414, International Conference on Nutrition, Rome; Nos. 1415, **MS**1423f, Death bicent of Mozart; No. 1416, 75th anniv of International Association of Lions Clubs; No. 1417, Americas Cup Yachting Championship.

No. 1409 is inscribed "Arienne 4" and No. 1411 "LZ-127", both in error.

(Des A. Nahigian. Litho Walsall)

1993 (7 Jan). *15th Death Anniv of Elvis Presley (singer) (1992). Vert designs as Nos. 1666/8 of Dominica. Multicoloured. P 14.*

1424	3 d. Elvis Presley	70	70
	a. Strip of 3. Nos. 1424/6	1·90	
1425	3 d. Elvis with guitar	70	70
1426	3 d. Elvis with microphone	70	70
1424/6	*Set of 3*	1·90	1·90

Nos. 1424/6 were printed together, horizontally and vertically *se-tenant*, in sheetlets of 9 (3×3).

(Litho Walsall)

1993 (7 Jan). *Bicentenary of the Louvre, Paris. Vert designs as T 305 of Antigua showing paintings. Multicoloured. P 12.*

1427	3 d. "St. John the Baptist" (Da Vinci)	65	70
	a. Sheetlet. Nos. 1427/34	4·50	
1428	3 d. "Virgin of the Rocks" (Da Vinci)	65	70
1429	3 d. "Bacchus" (Da Vinci)	65	70
1430	3 d. "Lady of the Court, Milan" (Da Vinci)	65	70
1431	3 d. "Virgin of the Rocks" (detail) (Da Vinci)	65	70
1432	3 d. "Mona Lisa" (Da Vinci)	65	70
1433	3 d. "Mona Lisa" (detail) (Da Vinci)	65	70
1434	3 d. Sketches for "Two Horsemen" (Da Vinci)	65	70
1435	3 d. "The Oath of Horatii" (left detail) (David)	65	70
	a. Sheetlet. Nos. 1435/42	4·50	
1436	3 d. "The Oath of Horatii" (right detail) (David)	65	70
1437	3 d. "The Love of Paris and Helen" (detail) (David)	65	70
1438	3 d. "The Sabine Women" (detail) (David)	65	70
1439	3 d. "Leonidas at Thermopylae" (detail) (David)	65	70
1440	3 d. "The Coronation of Napoleon" (left detail) (David)	65	70
1441	3 d. "The Coronation of Napoleon" (centre detail) (David)	65	70
1442	3 d. "The Coronation of Napoleon" (right detail) (David)	65	70

1443	3 d. "Peasant Family at Home" (detail) (L. le Nain)		65	70
	a. Sheetlet. Nos. 1443/50		4·50	
1444	3 d. "Smoking Room" (left detail) (L. le Nain)		65	70
1445	3 d. "Smoking Room" (right detail) (L. le Nain)		65	70
1446	3 d. "The Cart" (detail) (L. le Nain)		65	70
1447	3 d. "Peasants' Repast" (detail) (L. le Nain)		65	70
1448	3 d. "Portrait in an Interior" (detail) (L. le Nain)		65	70
1449	3 d. "Portrait in an Interior" (different detail) (L. le Nain)		65	70
1450	3 d. "The Forge" (L. le Nain)		65	70
1427/50		Set of 24	13·50	15·00

MS1451 Two sheets, each 70×100 mm. (a) 20 d. "Allegory of Victory" (M. le Nain) (52×86 mm). (b) 20 d. "Madame Vigee-Le Brun and Daughter" (Le Brun) (52×86 mm). P 14½ .. Set of 2 sheets 9·00 10·00
Nos. 1427/34, 1435/42 and 1443/50 were each printed together, se-tenant, in sheetlets of 8 stamps and one centre label. Nos. 1432/3 are incorrectly inscribed "Monna Lisa".

(Litho Questa)

1993 (3 Mar). *25th Anniv of United States Peace Corps.* P 14.
1452 210 2 d. multicoloured 60 60

211 Jackie Robinson and Ruby Dee (*The Jackie Robinson Story*)

(Des P. Wolff. Litho Questa)

1993 (25 Mar). *Baseball Films.* T **211** and similar multicoloured designs. P 13.
1453	3 d. Type 211		70	80
	a. Sheetlet. Nos. 1453/60		5·00	
1454	3 d. Robert DeNiro (*Bang the Drum Slowly*)		70	80
1455	3 d. James Earl Jones and Billy Dee Williams (*The Bingo Long Travelling All-Stars and Motor Kings*)		70	80
1456	3 d. Kevin Costner and Susan Sarandon (*Bull Durham*)		70	80
1457	3 d. Cast photograph (*Eight Men Out*)		70	80
1458	3 d. Ray Liotta (*Field of Dreams*)		70	80
1459	3 d. Charlie Sheen (*Major League*)		70	80
1460	3 d. Tom Selleck (*Mr. Baseball*)		70	80
1461	3 d. Wallace Beery, 1927, and Elliott Gould, 1986 (*Casey at the Bat*)		70	80
	a. Sheetlet. Nos. 1461/8		5·00	
1462	3 d. Anna Nilsson and Babe Ruth (*Babe comes Home*)		70	80
1463	3 d. Joe Brown (*Elmer the Great*)		70	80
1464	3 d. Bud Abbott and Lou Costello (*The Naughty Nineties*)		70	80
1465	3 d. Frank Sinatra, Gene Kelly and Esther Williams (*Take Me Out to the Ball Game*)		70	80
1466	3 d. Tab Hunter and Gwen Verdon (*Damn Yankees*)		70	80
1467	3 d. Dan Dailey (*The Pride of St. Louis*)		70	80
1468	3 d. John Candy and Richard Pryor (*Brewster's Millions*)		70	80
1453/68		Set of 16	10·00	11·50

MS1469 Four sheets, each 132×107 mm. (a) 20 d. John Goodman (*The Babe*). (b) 20 d. Ronald Reagan (*The Winning Team*). (c) 20 d. Tom Hanks and Madonna (*A League of Their Own*) (*vert*). (d) 20 d. Robert Redford (*The Natural*) (*vert*) .. .. .. Set of 4 sheets 15·00 17·00
Nos. 1453/60 and 1461/8 were each printed together, se-tenant, in sheetlets of 8.

212 Giraffe   213 Long-tailed Pangolin hanging by Tail

(Des D. Burkhart. Litho Questa)

1993 (5 Apr). *Animals of West Africa.* T **212** and similar vert designs. Multicoloured. P 14.
1470	2 d. Type 212		55	60
	a. Sheetlet. Nos. 1470/81		6·00	
1471	2 d. Baboon		55	60
1472	2 d. Caracal		55	60
1473	2 d. Large-spotted Genet		55	60
1474	2 d. Bushbuck		55	60
1475	2 d. Red-fronted Gazelle		55	60
1476	2 d. Red-flanked Duiker		55	60
1477	2 d. Cape Buffalo		55	60
1478	2 d. African Civet		55	60
1479	2 d. Side-striped Jackal		55	60

1480	2 d. Ratel		55	60
1481	2 d. Striped Polecat		55	60
1482	5 d. Vervet		85	90
	a. Sheetlet. Nos. 1482/93		9·00	
1483	5 d. Blackish-green Guenon		85	90
1484	5 d. Long-tailed Pangolin		85	90
1485	5 d. Leopard		85	90
1486	5 d. Elephant		85	90
1487	5 d. Hunting Dog		85	90
1488	5 d. Spotted Hyena		85	90
1489	5 d. Lion		85	90
1490	5 d. Hippopotamus		85	90
1491	5 d. Nile Crocodile		85	90
1492	5 d. Aardvark		85	90
1493	5 d. Warthog		85	90
1470/93		Set of 24	15·00	16·00

MS1494 101×72 mm. 20 d. As No. 1483 .. 3·75 4·50
Nos. 1470/81 and 1482/93 were each printed together, se-tenant, in sheetlets of 12, with the backgrounds forming composite designs.

(Des D. Burkhart. Litho Questa)

1993 (15 Apr). *Endangered Species. Long-tailed Pangolin.* T **213** and similar vert designs. Multicoloured. P 14.
1495	1 d. 25, Type 213		45	25
1496	1 d. 50, Sitting on branch		55	40
1497	2 d. Climbing up branch		65	60
1498	5 d. Climbing down branch		1·60	2·00
1495/8		Set of 4	3·00	3·00

MS1499 72×100 mm. 20 d. As No. 1496 .. 4·00 4·50

214 Osprey   215 Rose-ringed Parakeet

(Des W. Wright. Litho Questa)

1993 (15 Apr). *Birds of Prey.* T **214** and similar multicoloured designs. P 14.
1500	1 d. 25, Type 214		90	50
1501	1 d. 50, Egyptian Vulture (*horiz*)		1·00	50
1502	2 d. Martial Eagle		1·10	55
1503	3 d. Ruppell's Griffon (*horiz*)		1·40	75
1504	5 d. Augur Buzzard		1·75	1·25
1505	8 d. Greater Kestrel		2·25	2·50
1506	10 d. Secretary Bird		2·25	2·50
1507	15 d. Bateleur (*horiz*)		2·75	3·50
1500/7		Set of 8	12·00	11·00

MS1508 Two sheets, each 108×80 mm. (a) 20 d. Owl ("Tawny Owl") (57×42½ mm). (b) 20 d. Verreaux's Eagle (57×42½ mm) Set of 2 sheets 9·00 10·00

(Des W. Wright. Litho Questa)

1993 (15 Apr). *African Birds.* T **215** and similar vert designs. Multicoloured. P 14.
1509	2 d. Type 215		1·10	1·25
	a. Sheetlet. Nos. 1509/20		12·00	
1510	2 d. Variable Sunbird		1·10	1·25
1511	2 d. Red-billed Hornbill		1·10	1·25
1512	2 d. Red-billed Fire Finch		1·10	1·25
1513	2 d. Go-away Bird		1·10	1·25
1514	2 d. Burchell's Gonolek ("Crimson-breasted Shrike")		1·10	1·25
1515	2 d. Grey-headed Bush Shrike		1·10	1·25
1516	2 d. Western Nicator		1·10	1·25
1517	2 d. Egyptian Plover		1·10	1·25
1518	2 d. Congo Peafowl		1·10	1·25
1519	2 d. Painted Snipe		1·10	1·25
1520	2 d. South African Crowned Crane		1·10	1·25
1509/20		Set of 12	12·00	13·00

Nos. 1509/20 were printed together, se-tenant, in sheetlets of 12.
No. 1509a exists imperforate from a limited printing.

(Des Kerri Schiff. Litho Questa)

1993 (2 June). *40th Anniv of Coronation.* Vert designs as T **307** of Antigua. P 13½×14.
1521	2 d. multicoloured		85	90
	a. Sheetlet. Nos. 1521/4×2		9·75	
1522	5 d. multicoloured		1·40	1·50
1523	8 d. reddish brown and black		1·50	1·60
1524	10 d. multicoloured		1·75	1·90
1521/4		Set of 4	5·00	5·50

MS1525 70×100 mm. 20 d. multicoloured. P 14 5·00 5·50
Designs: (38×47 mm)—2 d. Queen Elizabeth II at Coronation (photograph by Cecil Beaton); 5 d. Orb and Sceptre; 8 d. Sir Winston Churchill; 10 d. Queen Elizabeth II at Trooping the Colour. (28½×42½ mm)—20 d. "Queen Elizabeth II, 1972" (detail) (Joe King).
Nos. 1521/4 were printed together in sheetlets of 8 containing two se-tenant blocks of 4.

216 Hugo Eckener and LZ-127 *Graf Zeppelin*

(Litho Questa)

1993 (7 June). *Aviation Anniversaries.* T **216** and similar multicoloured designs. P 14.
1526	2 d. Type 216		55	50
1527	2 d. Guyot's balloon, 1785 (*vert*)		55	50
1528	5 d. Zeppelin LZ-3 *Luftschiffe 3* and crown		1·00	1·00
1529	5 d. Sopwith Snipe (fighter)		1·00	1·00
1530	8 d. Eckener and LZ-127 *Graf Zeppelin*		1·60	1·75
1531	10 d. *Comte D'Artois* (hot air balloon), 1785 (*vert*)		1·90	2·00
1532	15 d. Royal Aircraft Factory S.E.5 (fighter)		2·40	2·50
1526/32		Set of 7	8·00	8·25

MS1533 Three sheets. (a) 105×84 mm. 20 d. Eckener and LZ-127 *Graf Zeppelin* (airship). (b) 84×105 mm. 20 d. Blanchard's balloon, 1785 (*vert*). (c) 84×105 mm. 20 d. Avro 504k (biplane) .. .. .. Set of 3 sheets 14·00 15·00
Anniversaries:—Nos. 1526, 1528, 1530, MS1533a, 125th birth anniv of Hugo Eckener (airship pioneer); Nos. 1527, 1531, MS1533b, Bicentenary of first airmail flight; Nos. 1529, 1532, MS1533c, 75th anniv of Royal Air Force.
Nos. 1526 and MS1533a are incorrectly inscribed "Zeppelin Luftschiffe 3". All three stamps and the miniature sheet for Eckener's birth anniversary are inscribed with the wrong dates, 1870–1940 instead of 1868–1954.

217 Henry Ford and "Model T", 1910   218 Marilyn Monroe

(Des R. Sauber. Litho Questa)

1993 (7 June). *Centenaries of Henry Ford's First Petrol Engine* (Nos. 1534/45) *and Karl Benz's First Four-wheeled Car* (Nos. 1546/57). T **217** and similar horiz designs. Multicoloured. P 14.
1534	2 d. Type 217		45	50
	a. Sheetlet. Nos. 1534/45		4·75	
1535	2 d. Car of 1896		45	50
1536	2 d. Henry Ford with Barney Oldfield and "999", 1902		45	50
1537	2 d. Henry Ford, 1893, and car of 1896		45	50
1538	2 d. "Model A", 1903		45	50
1539	2 d. "Model T" with roof lowered, 1908		45	50
1540	2 d. "Model T" with roof raised, 1908		45	50
1541	2 d. "Model K", 1906		45	50
1542	2 d. "Model A", 1931		45	50
1543	2 d. "Model A", 1906		45	50
1544	2 d. "Model N", 1906		45	50
1545	2 d. "Model F", 1905		45	50
1546	2 d. Benz "Velo", 1894		45	50
	a. Sheetlet. Nos. 1546/57		4·75	
1547	2 d. Car of 1894		45	50
1548	2 d. Three-wheeled car of 1885 from side		45	50
1549	2 d. "Mannheim", 1905		45	50
1550	2 d. Car of 1892		45	50
1551	2 d. Car of 1900 from front		45	50
1552	2 d. Racing car of 1911 from side		45	50
1553	2 d. "Velo", 1893		45	50
1554	2 d. Black car of 1900 from side		45	50
1555	2 d. Red car of 1900 from side		45	50
1556	2 d. Racing car of 1911 from front		45	50
1557	2 d. Three-wheeled car of 1885 from back		45	50
1534/57		Set of 24	9·50	11·00

MS1558 Two sheets, each 132×115 mm. (a) 20 d. Ford car of 1896. (b) 20 d. Benz car of 1900 .. .. .. Set of 2 sheets 7·50 8·00
Nos. 1534/45 and 1546/57 were each printed together, se-tenant, in sheetlets of 12 with the backgrounds forming composite designs.

(Des Susan Rini. Litho B.D.T.)

1993 (26 July). *Musical Entertainers.* T **218** and similar vert designs. P 14.
1559/93 3 d.×35 multicoloured .. .. 27·00 28·00
Nos. 1559/93 were issued as four sheetlets, three of nine different designs (Nos. 1559/85) and one of eight (Nos. 1586/93), depicting Marilyn Monroe (Nos. 1559/67), Elvis Presley (Nos. 1568/76), Madonna (Nos. 1577/85) and Buddy Holly, Otis Redding, Bill Haley, Dinah Washington, musical instruments, Ritchie Valens, Clyde McPhatter, Elvis Presley (Nos. 1586/93).

219 Siamese   220 "Woman with a Comb" (Picasso)

(Des R. Sauber. Litho Questa)

1993 (13 Sept). *Oriental Cats.* T **219** and similar multicoloured designs. P 14.
1594	2 d. Type 219		80	80
	a. Sheetlet. Nos. 1594/1605		8·50	
1595	2 d. Colourpoint Longhair sitting		80	80

1596	2 d. Burmese		80	80
1597	2 d. Birman		80	80
1598	2 d. Snowshoe		80	80
1599	2 d. Tonkinese		80	80
1600	2 d. Foreign Shorthair stretching		80	80
1601	2 d. Balinese		80	80
1602	2 d. Oriental Shorthair		80	80
1603	2 d. Foreign Shorthair lying		80	80
1604	2 d. Colourpoint Longhair with black face standing		80	80
1605	2 d. Colourpoint Longhair with white face standing		80	80
1594/1605		Set of 12	8·50	8·50

MS1606 Two sheets, each 121×90 mm. (a) 20 d. Colourpoint shorthair (vert). (b) 20 d. Burmese (vert) .. .. Set of 2 sheets 7·75 8·00
Nos. 1594/1605 were printed together, se-tenant, in sheetlets of 12 with the background forming a composite design.
No. MS1606 exists imperforate from a limited printing.

(Des R. Sauber. Litho Questa)

1993 (13 Sept). *Royal Dogs. Horiz designs as T 219. Multicoloured. P 14.*

1607	2 d. Shih Tzu (Emperor of China)		70	75
	a. Sheetlet. Nos. 1607/18		7·50	
1608	2 d. Skye Terrier (Queen Victoria)		70	75
1609	2 d. Berner Laufhund (King Louis XVI, France)		70	75
1610	2 d. Boxer (King Francis I, France)		70	75
1611	2 d. Welsh Corgi (Queen Elizabeth II)		70	75
1612	2 d. Dumfrieshire (Princess Anne)		70	75
1613	2 d. Lurcher (King George VI)		70	75
1614	2 d. Welsh Corgi (Princess Anne)		70	75
1615	2 d. Pekinese (Empress Ts'Eu-Hi, China)		70	75
1616	2 d. Papillon (King Louis XIII, France)		70	75
1617	2 d. Otterhound (King John)		70	75
1618	2 d. Pug (Napoleon I, France)		70	75
1607/18		Set of 12	7·50	8·00

MS1619 Two sheets, each 120×90 mm. (a) 20 d. Cairn Terrier (Mary, Queen of Scots). (b) 20 d. Long-haired Dachshund (Queen Victoria)
.. .. Set of 2 sheets 7·75 8·00
Nos. 1607/18 were printed together, se-tenant, in sheetlets of 12 with the background forming a composite design.
No. MS1619 exists imperforate from a limited printing.

(Des Kerri Schiff. Litho Questa)

1993 (27 Sept). *Asian International Stamp Exhibitions. Multicoloured designs as T 268 of Dominica. P 13½×14.*

(a) "Indopex '93", Surabaya, Indonesia

1620	20 b. National Monument and statue, Jakarta		20	20
1621	20 b. Pura Taman Ayun Temple, Bali		20	20
1622	2 d. Guardian statue, Singosari Palace, Java		60	60
1623	2 d. Candi Jawi, Java		60	60
1624	5 d. Telek Luh mask		1·40	1·40
	a. Sheetlet. Nos. 1624/9		7·50	
1625	5 d. Jero Gde mask		1·40	1·40
1626	5 d. Barong Macan mask		1·40	1·40
1627	5 d. Monkey mask		1·40	1·40
1628	5 d. Mata Gde mask		1·40	1·40
1629	5 d. Jauk Kras mask		1·40	1·40
1630	5 d. "Tree Mask" (Soedibio)		1·40	1·40
	a. Sheetlet. Nos. 1630/5		7·50	
1631	5 d. "Dry Land" (Hendra Gunawan)		1·40	1·40
1632	5 d. "The Corn Eater" (Sudjana Kerton)		1·40	1·40
1633	5 d. "Night Watchman" (Djoko Pekik)		1·40	1·40
1634	5 d. "Hunger" (Kerton)		1·40	1·40
1635	5 d. "Arje Mask" (Soedjojono)		1·40	1·40
1636	5 d. Central Temple, Lara Djonggrang		1·40	1·40
1637	5 d. Irian Jaya Monument, Jakarta		1·40	1·40
1638	15 d. Brahma and Siva Temples, Java		2·75	3·25
1639	15 d. Date of the Year Temple, Java		2·75	3·25
1620/39		Set of 20	20·00	21·00

MS1640 Two sheets, each 135×105 mm. (a) 18 d. Tomb effigies, Torajaland (horiz). (b) 18 d. Relief from Borobudur, Java (horiz). P 14×13½.
.. .. Set of 2 sheets 7·50 8·00

(b) "Taipei '93", Taiwan

1641	20 b. Fawang Si Pagoda, Henan		20	20
1642	20 b. Wanshoubao Pagoda, Shashi		20	20
1643	2 d. Red Pavilion, Shibaozhai		60	60
1644	2 d. Songyue Si Pagoda, Henan		60	60
1645	5 d. Pottery camel (walking)		1·40	1·40
	a. Sheetlet. Nos. 1645/50		7·50	
1646	5 d. Pottery horse and rider		1·40	1·40
1647	5 d. Pottery camel (standing with mouth closed)		1·40	1·40
1648	5 d. Yellow-glazed pottery horse		1·40	1·40
1649	5 d. Pottery camel (standing with mouth open)		1·40	1·40
1650	5 d. Pottery saddled horse		1·40	1·40
1651	5 d. Qianlong vase		1·40	1·40
	a. Sheetlet. Nos. 1651/6		7·50	
1652	5 d. Small wine cup		1·40	1·40
1653	5 d. Mei-ping vase		1·40	1·40
1654	5 d. Urn vase		1·40	1·40
1655	5 d. Tureen		1·40	1·40
1656	5 d. Lidded potiche		1·40	1·40
1657	5 d. Tianning Si Pagoda, Beijing		1·40	1·40
1658	5 d. Bond Centre, Hong Kong		1·40	1·40
1659	15 d. Forbidden City pavilion, Beijing		2·75	3·25
1660	15 d. Xuanzhuang Pagoda, Shenxi		2·75	3·25
1641/60		Set of 20	20·00	21·00

MS1661 Two sheets, each 135×105 mm. (a) 18 d. Seated Buddha, Shanhua Temple, Shanxi. P 13½×14. (b) 18 d. Statues, Upper Huayan Si Temple, Datong (horiz). P 14×13½.
.. .. Set of 2 sheets 7·50 8·00

(c) "Bangkok '93", Thailand

1662	20 b. Sanctuary of Prasat Phanom Wan		20	20
1663	20 b. Lai Kham Vihan, Chiang Mai		20	20
1664	2 d. Upmarket spirit shrine, Bangkok		60	60
1665	2 d. Walking Buddha statue, Wat Phra Si Ratana Mahathat		60	60
1666	5 d. "Early Fruit Stand"		1·40	1·40
	a. Sheetlet. Nos. 1666/71		7·50	
1667	5 d. Scene Rendered in Chinese Style"		1·40	1·40

1668	5 d. "Buddha descends from Tauatimsa"		1·40	1·40
1669	5 d. "Sang Thong Tales" (detail)		1·40	1·40
1670	5 d. "The Damned in Hell"		1·40	1·40
1671	5 d. "King Sanjaya travels on Elephant"		1·40	1·40
1672	5 d. U Thong C Buddha (bronze)		1·40	1·40
	a. Sheetlet. Nos. 1672/7		7·50	
1673	5 d. Seated Buddha (bronze)		1·40	1·40
1674	5 d. Phra Chai Buddha (ivory and gold)		1·40	1·40
1675	5 d. Buddha (bronze)		1·40	1·40
1676	5 d. U Thong A Buddha (bronze)		1·40	1·40
1677	5 d. Crowned Buddha (bronze)		1·40	1·40
1678	5 d. Statue of Buddha, Wat Mahathat		1·40	1·40
1679	5 d. The Gopura of Prasat Phanom Rung		1·40	1·40
1680	15 d. Slender Chedis, Mongkon		2·75	3·25
1681	15 d. The Prang of Prasat Hin Phimai		2·75	3·25
1662/81		Set of 20	20·00	21·00

MS1682 Two sheets, each 135×105 mm. (a) 18 d. Khon (Thai dance drama). P 13½×14. (b) 18 d. Ceramics (horiz). P 14×13½ .. Set of 2 sheets 7·50 8·00
Nos. 1624/9, 1630/5, 1645/50, 1651/6, 1666/71 and 1672/7 were each printed, se-tenant, in sheetlets of 6.

(Litho Cartor (Nos. 1686, 1690, MS1691c) or Questa (others))

1993 (7 Oct). *Anniversaries and Events. T 220 and similar multicoloured designs. P 14 (Nos. 1683/5, 1687/9) or 13½×14 (Nos. 1686, 1690).*

1683	2 d. Type 220		75	75
1684	2 d. Niedzica Castle (horiz)		75	75
1685	5 d. "The Mirror" (Picasso)		1·40	1·40
1686	5 d. Early astronomical instrument		1·40	1·40
1687	7 d. "Woman on a Pillow" (Picasso)		1·60	1·60
1688	10 d. "Honegger's Liturgical Symphony" (Marian Bogusz) (horiz)		2·25	2·50
1689	10 d. "Pont-Neut in Paris" (Hanna Rudzka-Cybisowa) (horiz)		2·25	2·50
1690	10 d. Modern Telescope		2·25	2·50
1683/90		Set of 8	11·00	12·00

MS1691 Three sheets. (a) 75×105 mm. 18 d. "The Three Dancers" (detail) (Picasso). P 14. (b) 105×75 mm. 18 d. "When You enter here, Whisper my Name soundlessly" (detail) (Henryk Waniek) (horiz). P 14. (c) 102×74 mm. 18 d. Copernicus. P 12×13 .. Set of 3 sheets 12·00 13·00
Anniversaries and Events:—Nos. 1683, 1685, 1687, MS1691a, 20th death anniv of Picasso (artist); Nos. 1684, 1688/9, MS1691b, "Polska '93" International Stamp Exhibition, Poznań; Nos. 1686, 1690, MS1691c, 450th death anniv of Copernicus (astronomer).
The captions printed on Nos. 1684 and 1689 are transposed in error.
No. MS1691b is inscribed "WHISPERT" in error.

221 Mudville Player at the Plate

(Des Rosemary DeFiglio. Litho Questa)

1993 (25 Oct). *Casey at the Bat. T 221 and similar multicoloured designs showing scenes from Walt Disney's cartoon film. P 14×13½.*

1692	2 d. Type 221		80	85
	a. Sheetlet. Nos. 1692/1700		6·50	
1693	2 d. Mudville player out		80	85
1694	2 d. Umpire and player arguing		80	85
1695	2 d. Fans applauding		80	85
1696	2 d. Casey reading newspaper at plate		80	85
1697	2 d. Casey letting second pitch go by		80	85
1698	2 d. Over-confident Casey		80	85
1699	2 d. Casey's striking out		80	85
1700	2 d. Casey striking out at night		80	85
1692/1700		Set of 9	6·50	7·00

MS1701 Two sheets, each 129×103 mm. (a) 20 d. Mudville manager. P 14×13½. (b) 20 d. Pitcher (vert). P 13½×14 .. Set of 2 sheets 8·50 10·00
Nos. 1692/1700 were printed together, se-tenant, in sheetlets of 9.

(Des Rosemary DeFiglio, Litho Cartor)

1993 (22 Nov). *World Cup Football Championship 1994, U.S.A. (1st issue). Multicoloured designs as T 310 of Antigua. P 13½×14.*

1702	1 d. 25, Hannich (Hungary) and Stopyra (France)		75	40
1703	1 d. 50, Labd (Morocco) and Gary Lineker (England)		85	50
1704	2 d. Segota (Canada) and Morozov (Russia)		1·10	65
1705	3 d. Roger Milla (Cameroun)		1·40	1·25
1706	5 d. Rodax (Austria) and Weiss (Czechoslovakia)		1·75	1·75
1707	10 d. Claesen (Belgium), Bossis and Amoros (France)		2·25	2·50
1708	12 d. Candida (Brazil) and Ramirez (Costa Rica)		2·50	2·75
1709	15 d. Silva (Brazil) and Michel Platini (France)		2·75	3·25
1702/9		Set of 8	12·00	11·50

MS1710 Two sheets, each 100×70 mm. (a) 25 d. Muller (Brazil) and McDonald (Ireland) (horiz). (b) 25 d. Diego Maradona (Argentina) and Matthaeus (Germany) (horiz). P 13
.. .. Set of 2 sheets 9·75 10·00
See also Nos. 1882/90.

(Litho Questa)

1993 (1 Dec). *Christmas. Religious Paintings. Designs as T 270 of Dominica. Black, pale lemon and red (Nos. 1712/13, 1715/17 and MS1719b) or multicoloured (others). P 13½×14.*

1711	25 b. "The Adoration of the Magi" (detail) (Rubens)		20	20
1712	1 d. "The Holy Family with Joachim and Anna" (Dürer)		45	20
1713	1 d. 50, "The Annunciation" (Dürer)		60	30
1714	2 d. "The Adoration of the Magi" (different detail) (Rubens)		75	60
1715	2 d. "The Virgin Mary worshipped by Albrecht Bonstetten" (Dürer)		75	60
1716	7 d. "The Holy Family with Two Angels in a Portico" (detail) (Dürer)		2·00	2·75
1717	10 d. "Virgin on a Throne, crowned by an Angel" (Dürer)		2·25	2·75
1718	15 d. "The Adoration of the Magi" (different detail) (Rubens)		2·50	3·75
1711/18		Set of 8	8·50	10·00

MS1719 Two sheets, each 102×127 mm. (a) 20 d. "The Adoration of the Magi" (different detail) (Rubens). P 13½×14. (b) 20 d. "The Holy Family with Two Angels in a Portico" (different detail) (Dürer) (horiz). P 14×13½ .. Set of 2 sheets 7·75 8·50

(Des Kerri Schiff. Litho Questa)

1993 (15 Dec). *Famous Paintings by Rembrandt and Matisse. Multicoloured designs as T 316 of Antigua. P 13½×14.*

1720	50 b. "A Man in a Cap" (Rembrandt)		50	20
1721	1 d. 50, "Pierre Matisse" (Matisse)		80	35
1722	2 d. "Man with a Gold Helmet" (Rembrandt)		85	55
1723	2 d. "Auguste Pellerin" (Matisse)		85	55
1724	5 d. "Andre Derain" (Matisse)		1·75	1·75
1725	7 d. "A Franciscan Monk" (Rembrandt)		2·25	2·75
1726	12 d. "The Young Sailor (II)" (Matisse)		2·75	3·50
1727	15 d. "The Apostle Paul" (Rembrandt)		2·75	3·75
1720/7		Set of 8	11·00	12·00

MS1728 Two sheets, each 127×102 mm. (a) 20 d. "Dr. Tulp demonstrating the Anatomy of the Arm" (detail) (Rembrandt) (horiz). (b) 20 d. "Pianist and Draughts Players" (detail) (Matisse) (horiz). P 14×13½ .. Set of 2 sheets 9·00 10·00

222 Mickey Mouse
performing Ski Ballet

(Des Alvin White Studios. Litho Questa)

1993 (20 Dec). *Winter Sports. T 222 and similar vert designs showing Walt Disney cartoon characters. Multicoloured. P 13½×14.*

1729	50 b. Type 222		40	15
1730	75 b. Clarabelle and Horace ice dancing		50	15
1731	1 d. Donald Duck and Dale speed skating		55	20
1732	1 d. 25, Donald in biathlon		60	20
1733	4 d. Donald and nephews in bob-sled		1·60	1·60
1734	5 d. Goofy on luge		1·75	1·75
1735	7 d. Minnie Mouse figure skating		2·25	2·75
1736	10 d. Goofy downhill skiing		2·50	2·75
1737	15 d. Goofy playing ice hockey		2·75	3·25
1729/37		Set of 9	11·50	11·50

MS1738 Two sheets, each 128×102 mm. (a) 20 d. Minnie mogul skiing. (b) 20 d. Goofy cross-country skiing .. .. Set of 2 sheets 8·50 9·50

(Des W. Hanson. Litho Questa)

1994 (18 Feb). *"Hong Kong '94" International Stamp Exhibition (1st issue). Horiz design as T 317 of Antigua. Multicoloured. P 14.*

1739	1 d. 50, Hong Kong 1979 $2 Butterflies stamp and "Spring Garden" (M. Bruce) (left detail)		50	65
	a. Horiz pair. Nos. 1739/40		1·00	1·25
1740	1 d. 50, Gambia 1990 50 d. Gambian Life stamp and "Spring Garden" (M. Bruce) (right detail)		50	65

MS1741 82×117 mm. 20 d. Hong Kong 1970 Chinese New Year 10 c. stamp .. .. 3·25 3·50
Nos. 1739/40 were printed together, se-tenant, in horizontal pairs throughout the sheet with the centre part of each pair forming the complete painting.

(Des Kerri Schiff. Litho Questa)

1994 (18 Feb). *"Hong Kong '94" International Stamp Exhibition (2nd issue). Qin Dynasty Terracotta Figures. Multicoloured designs as T 318 of Antigua, but vert. P 14.*

1742	1 d. 50, Warriors and horses		40	50
	a. Sheetlet. Nos. 1742/7		2·25	
1743	1 d. 50, Head of warrior		40	50
1744	1 d. 50, Kneeling warrior		40	50
1745	1 d. 50, Chariot driver		40	50
1746	1 d. 50, Dog		40	50
1747	1 d. 50, Warriors as excavated		40	50
1742/7		Set of 6	2·25	2·75

Nos. 1742/7 were printed together, se-tenant, in sheetlets of 6.

223 Pluto the Racer, 1934–35

224 Ludwig von Drake and Easter Bunny

(Des Alvin White Studios. Litho Questa)

1994 (11 Apr). *Chinese New Year ("Year of the Dog"). T 223 and similar multicoloured designs showing Walt Disney cartoon dogs. P 13½×14.*

1748	25 b. Type 223					30	20
1749	50 b. Fifi, 1933					45	30
1750	75 b. Pluto Jnr, 1942					60	30
1751	1 d. 25, Goofy and Bowser					80	30
1752	1 d. 50, Butch, 1940					90	45
1753	2 d. Toliver, 1936					1·00	60
1754	3 d. Ronnie, 1946					1·25	1·00
1755	6 d. Primo, 1950					1·50	1·40
1756	8 d. Pluto's kid brother, 1946					2·00	2·25
1757	10 d. The army mascot, 1942					2·25	2·50
1758	12 d. Pluto and Fifi's puppies, 1937					2·25	2·75
1759	18 d. Bent Tail Jnr, 1949					2·75	3·50
1748/59				*Set of 12*		14·50	14·00

MS1760 Three sheets, each 127×102 mm. (a) 20 d. Pluto and Fifi's puppies, 1937 (*different*). P 13½×14. (b) 20 d. Pluto and Dinah, 1950. P 13½×14. (c) 20 d. Pflip (*horiz*). P 14×13½
Set of 3 sheets 11·00 12·00

No. 1748/59 were issued in small sheets of 10 (5×2). No. 1748 also exists as a sheetlet of 6 (3×2).

Nos. 1758 and MS1760a are inscribed "DINAH'S PUPPIES" in error.

(Des Alvin White Studios. Litho Questa)

1994 (11 Apr). *Easter. T 224 and similar vert designs showing Walt Disney cartoon characters. Multicoloured. P 13½×14.*

1761	25 b. Type 224					30	10
1762	50 b. Minnie Mouse and Daisy Duck carrying banner					45	10
1763	3 d. Mickey Mouse wearing top hat					1·10	85
1764	4 d. Von Drake holding hatching egg					1·25	1·25
1765	5 d. Donald Duck pushing trolley full of eggs					1·40	1·40
1766	8 d. Bunny taking photograph of Von Drake					1·75	2·00
1767	10 d. Goofy dressed as Easter Bunny					2·00	2·50
1768	12 d. Von Drake holding dinosaur egg					2·25	2·75
1761/8				*Set of 8*		9·50	9·75

MS1769 Two sheets. (a) 102×123 mm. 20 d. Mickey and Minnie. (b) 123×102 mm. 20 d. Ludwig von Drake
Set of 2 sheets 7·50 8·50

(Litho Questa)

1994 (25 Apr). *Centenary of Sierra Club (environmental protection society) (1992). Endangered Environments. Multicoloured designs as T 320 of Antigua. P 14.*

1770	5 d. Briksdal Fjord					80	90
	a. Sheetlet. Nos. 1770/5					4·25	
1771	5 d. Glacier, Briksdal Fjord					80	90
1772	5 d. Waterfall, Briksdal Fjord					80	90
1773	5 d. Frozen lake, Yosemite					80	90
1774	5 d. Cliffs and river, Yosemite					80	90
1775	5 d. Forest, Yosemite					80	90
1776	5 d. Mother and child, Tibetan Plateau					80	90
	a. Sheetlet. Nos. 1776/83					5·50	
1777	5 d. Yellowstone in winter					80	90
1778	5 d. Ross Island					80	90
1779	5 d. Mount Erebus					80	90
1780	5 d. Tibetan Plateau					80	90
1781	5 d. Waterfall, Yellowstone					80	90
1782	5 d. Sunset on the Serengeti					80	90
1783	5 d. Dead trees, Ansel Adams Wilderness					80	90
1784	5 d. Ansel Adams Wilderness in winter (*horiz*)					80	90
	a. Sheetlet. Nos. 1784/91					5·50	
1785	5 d. Ansel Adams Wilderness in summer (*horiz*)					80	90
1786	5 d. Ridge on Mount Erebus (*horiz*)					80	90
1787	5 d. Mount Erebus from a distance (*horiz*)					80	90
1788	5 d. Prince William Sound (*horiz*)					80	90
1789	5 d. Geysers, Yellowstone (*horiz*)					80	90
1790	5 d. Local dwelling, Tibetan Plateau (*horiz*)					80	90
1791	5 d. Sierra Club Centennial emblem (*horiz*)					80	90
1792	5 d. Frozen lake, Prince William Sound (*horiz*)					80	90
	a. Sheetlet. Nos. 1792/7					4·25	
1793	5 d. Forest, Prince William Sound (*horiz*)					80	90
1794	5 d. Baobab Tree, Serengeti (*horiz*)					80	90
1795	5 d. Plains, Serengeti (*horiz*)					80	90
1796	5 d. Volcano, Ross Island (*horiz*)					80	90
1797	5 d. Mountains, Ross Island (*horiz*)					80	90
1770/97				*Set of 28*		19·00	23·00

Nos. 1770/5, 1776/83, 1784/91 and 1792/7 were each printed together, *se-tenant*, in two sheetlets of 6 (Nos. 1770/5 and 1792/7) or two sheetlets of 8 (Nos. 1776/91).

ALTERED CATALOGUE NUMBERS

Any Catalogue numbers altered from the last edition are shown as a list in the introductory pages.

225 *Oeceoclades maculata*

226 "Girl with a Kitten" (Perronneau)

(Des Wendy Smith-Griswold. Litho Questa)

1994 (1 May). *Orchids. T 225 and similar multicoloured designs. P 14.*

1798	1 d. Type 225					35	20
1799	1 d. 25, Angraecum distichum (*horiz*)					45	30
1800	2 d. Plectrelminthus caudatus					60	35
1801	5 d. Tridactyle tridactylites (*horiz*)					1·25	1·25
1802	8 d. Bulbophyllum lepidum (*horiz*)					1·40	1·50
1803	10 d. Angraecum eburneum					1·60	1·90
1804	12 d. Eulophia guineensis					1·75	2·00
1805	15 d. Angraecum eichleranum (*horiz*)					2·00	2·50
1798/1805				*Set of 8*		8·50	9·00

MS1806 Two sheets, each 100×70 mm. (a) 25 d. *Vanilla imperialis*. (b) 25 d. *Ancistrochilus rothschildianus* (*horiz*) ... *Set of 2 sheets* 9·00 10·00

(Des Kerri Schiff. Litho Questa)

1994 (11 July). *Cats. T 226 and similar multicoloured designs showing paintings of cats. P 14.*

1807	5 d. Type 226					1·40	1·40
	a. Sheetlet. Nos. 1807/18					15·00	
1808	5 d. "Still Life with Cat and Fish" (Chardin)					1·40	1·40
1809	5 d. "Tinkle a Cat"					1·40	1·40
1810	5 d. "Naughty Puss!" (advertisement)					1·40	1·40
1811	5 d. "Cats" (T.-A. Steinlen)					1·40	1·40
1812	5 d. "Girl in Red with Cat and Dog" (Phillips)					1·40	1·40
1813	5 d. "Cat, Butterfly and Begonia" (Harunobu)					1·40	1·40
1814	5 d. "Cat and Kitten" (Pamela Higgins)					1·40	1·40
1815	5 d. "Woman with a Cat" (Renoir)					1·40	1·40
1816	5 d. "Minnie from Outskirts of the Village" (Thrall)					1·40	1·40
1817	5 d. "The Fisher" (Raphael Tuck postcard)					1·40	1·40
1818	5 d. "Artist and His Family" (detail) (Vaenius)					1·40	1·40
1819	5 d. "The Arena" (Harold Weston) (*horiz*)					1·40	1·40
	a. Sheetlet. Nos. 1819/30					15·00	
1820	5 d. "Cat killing a Bird" (Picasso) (*horiz*)					1·40	1·40
1821	5 d. "Cat and Butterfly" (Hokusai) (*horiz*)					1·40	1·40
1822	5 d. "Winter: Cat on a Cushion" (Steinlen) (*horiz*)					1·40	1·40
1823	5 d. "Rattoun Tigers" (Prang) (*horiz*)					1·40	1·40
1824	5 d. "Cat on the Floor" (Steinlen) (*horiz*)					1·40	1·40
1825	5 d. "Cat and Kittens" (*horiz*)					1·40	1·40
1826	5 d. "Cats looking over Fence" (Prang) (*horiz*)					1·40	1·40
1827	5 d. "Little White Kittens into Mischief" (Ives) (*horiz*)					1·40	1·40
1828	5 d. "Cat Bathing" (Hiroshige) (*horiz*)					1·40	1·40
1829	5 d. "Playtime" (Tuck postcard) (*horiz*)					1·40	1·40
1830	5 d. "Summer: Cat on a Balustrade" (Steinlen) (*horiz*)					1·40	1·40
1807/30				*Set of 24*		30·00	30·00

MS1831 Two sheets, each 100×70 mm. (a) 20 d. "The Graham Children" (detail) (William Hogarth). (b) 20 d. "The Morning Rising" (detail) (Michel Lepicie) ... *Set of 2 sheets* 8·00 9·00
Nos. 1807/18 and 1819/30 were printed together, *se-tenant*, in sheetlets of 12.

227 Patas Monkey

228 *Mylothris rhodope*

(Des D. Burkhart. Litho Questa)

1994 (1 Aug). *Monkeys. T 227 and similar vert designs. Multicoloured. P 14.*

1832	1 d. Type 227					45	20
1833	1 d. 50, Collared Mangabey					65	30
1834	2 d. Black and White Colobus					75	35
1835	4 d. Mona Monkey					1·25	1·10
1836	8 d. Kirk's Colobus					1·50	2·00
1837	10 d. Vervet					1·75	2·25
1838	12 d. Red Colobus					2·00	2·50
1839	15 d. Guinea Baboon					2·25	2·75
1832/9				*Set of 8*		9·50	10·50

MS1840 Two sheets, each 106×77 mm. (a) 25 d. Head of Guinea Baboon. (b) 25 d. Head of Collared Mangabey ... *Set of 2 sheets* 10·50 11·00

(Des W. Hanson. Litho B.D.T.)

1994 (16 Aug). *25th Anniv of First Moon Landing. Horiz designs as T 326 of Antigua. Multicoloured. P 14.*

1841	2 d. Yuri Gagarin (first cosmonaut)			60	60
	a. Sheetlet. Nos. 1841/9			4·75	
1842	2 d. Valentina Tereshkova (first woman in Space)			60	60
1843	2 d. Ham (first chimpanzee in Space)			60	60
1844	2 d. Alexei Leonov (first man to walk in Space)			60	60
1845	2 d. Neil Armstrong (first man on Moon)			60	60
1846	2 d. Svetlana Savitskaya (first woman to walk in Space)			60	60
1847	2 d. Marc Garneau (first Canadian in Space)			60	60
1848	2 d. Vladimir Komarov (first Soviet Space casualty)			60	60
1849	2 d. Ulf Merbold (first German in Space)			60	60
1841/9			*Set of 9*	4·75	4·75

MS1850 81×81 mm. 30 d. "Apollo 11" crew at news conference ... 6·50 7·00
Nos. 1841/9 were printed together, *se-tenant*, in sheetlets of 9.

(Des Kerri Schiff. Litho Questa)

1994 (16 Aug). *Centenary of International Olympic Committee. Gold Medal Winners. Multicoloured designs as T 327 of Antigua, but vert. P 14.*

1851	1 d. 50, Daley Thompson (Great Britain) (decathlon), 1980 and 1984			40	30
1852	5 d. Heide Marie Rosendohl (Germany) (long jump), 1972			1·10	1·25

MS1853 106×76 mm. 20 d. Sweden (ice hockey), 1994 ... 4·50 5·00

(Des J. Batchelor. Litho Questa)

1994 (16 Aug). *50th Anniv of D-Day. Horiz designs as T 331 of Antigua. Multicoloured. P 14.*

1854	50 b. Soema (Dutch sloop)			50	50
1855	75 b. H.M.S. Belfast (cruiser)			60	60
1856	1 d. U.S.S. Texas (battleship)			70	70
1857	2 d. Georges Leygues (French cruiser)			1·25	1·25
1854/7			*Set of 4*	2·75	2·75

MS1858 105×76 m. 20 d. H.M.S. Ramillies (battleship) firing broadside ... 4·00 4·50

(Des Kerri Schiff. Litho Questa (Nos. 1859, 1870/2) or B.D.T. (Nos. 1860/9))

1994 (16 Aug). *"Philakorea '94" International Stamp Exhibition, Seoul. Multicoloured designs as T 281 of Dominica. P 14 (50 b., 2 d., 3 d.) or 13½×14 (others).*

1859	50 b. Kungnakchon Hall (38×25 mm)			30	30
1860	1 d. Soldiers on horses			40	40
	a. Sheetlet. Nos. 1860/9			3·50	
1861	1 d. Soldiers defending fort			40	40
1862	1 d. Archers			40	40
1863	1 d. General on horse			40	40
1864	1 d. Three soldiers in battle			40	40
1865	1 d. Army in retreat			40	40
1866	1 d. Archers using fire arrows			40	40
1867	1 d. Horsemen attacking fort			40	40
1868	1 d. Women in summer house			40	40
1869	1 d. Old man, child and house			40	40
1870	2 d. Kettle of Popchusa (38×25 mm)			60	60
1871	3 d. Pomun tourist resort (38×25 mm)			70	70
1859/71			*Set of 13*	5·00	5·00

MS1872 98×68 mm. 20 d. Tomb guardian, Taenung (38×25 mm). P 14 ... 4·50 5·00
Nos. 1860/9 were printed together, *se-tenant*, in sheetlets of 10 showing screen paintings of the "Sanguozhi".

(Des B. Hargreaves. Litho Questa)

1994 (18 Aug). *Butterflies. T 228 and similar horiz designs. Multicoloured. P 14.*

1873	1 d. Type 228			50	25
1874	1 d. 25, Iolaphilus menas			65	35
1875	2 d. Neptis nemetes			75	40
1876	5 d. Antanartia delius			1·25	1·10
1877	8 d. Acraea caecilia			1·50	2·00
1878	10 d. Papilio nireus			1·50	2·00
1879	12 d. Papilio menestheus			1·75	2·50
1880	15 d. Iolaphilus julus			2·00	2·75
1873/80			*Set of 8*	9·00	10·00

MS1881 Two sheets, each 97×68 mm. (a) 25 d. *Bematistes epaea*. (b) 25 d. *Colotis evippe* ... *Set of 2 sheets* 11·00 12·00

229 Bobby Charlton (England)

230 *Suillus luteus*

(Litho Questa)

1994 (1 Sept). *World Cup Football Championships, U.S.A. (2nd issue). T 229 and similar vert designs. Multicoloured. P 14.*

1882	50 b. Type 229			40	20
1883	75 b. Ferenc Puskás (Hungary)			55	25
1884	1 d. Paolo Rossi (Italy)			65	25
1885	2 d. Biri Biri (Spain)			90	40
1886	3 d. Diego Maradona (Argentina)			1·00	80
1887	8 d. Johann Cruyff (Netherlands)			1·75	2·00
1888	10 d. Franz Beckenbauer (Germany)			1·75	2·00

1889	15 d. Thomas Dooley (U.S.A.)	.. ..		2·25	3·00
1882/9		*Set of 8*		8·00	8·00

MS1890 Two sheets, each 70×100 mm. (a) 25 d.
Pelé (Brazil). (b) 25 d. Gordon Banks (England)
Set of 2 sheets 9·50 10·00

(Des Mary Walters. Litho Questa)

1994 (30 Sept). *Fungi.* T **230** *and similar vert designs. Multicoloured.* P 14.

1891	5 d. Type 230		90	90
	a. Sheetlet. Nos. 1891/9		7·00	
1892	5 d. *Bolbitius vitellinus*		90	90
1893	5 d. *Clitocybe nebularis*		90	90
1894	5 d. *Omphalotus olearius*		90	90
1895	5 d. *Auricularia auricula*		90	90
1896	5 d. *Macrolepiota rhacodes*		90	90
1897	5 d. *Volvariella volvacea*		90	90
1898	5 d. *Psilocybe coprophila*		90	90
1899	5 d. *Suillus granulatus*		90	90
1900	5 d. *Agaricus campestris*		90	90
	a. Sheetlet. Nos. 1900/8		7·00	
1901	5 d. *Lepista nuda*		90	90
1902	5 d. *Podaxis pistillaris*		90	90
1903	5 d. *Oudemansiella radicata*		90	90
1904	5 d. *Schizophyllum commune*		90	90
1905	5 d. *Chlorophyllum molybdites*		90	90
1906	5 d. *Hypholoma fasciculare*		90	90
1907	5 d. *Mycena pura*		90	90
1908	5 d. *Ganoderma lucidum*		90	90
1891/1908		*Set of 18*	14·00	14·00

MS1909 Two sheets, each 100×70 mm. (a) 20 d.
Leucoagaricus naucinus. (b) 20 d. *Cyathus striatus.* *Set of 2 sheets* 8·50 9·50
Nos. 1891/9 and 1900/8 were printed together, *se-tenant*, in sheetlets of 9.

(Litho Questa)

1994 (5 Dec). *Christmas. Religious Paintings. Vert designs as* T **336** *of Antigua. Multicoloured.* P 13½×14.

1910	50 b. "Expectant Madonna with St. Joseph" (French 15th-century)	30	10
1911	75 b. "Rest of the Holy Family" (Louis le Nain)	40	20
1912	1 d. "Rest on the Flight into Egypt" (Antoine Watteau)	45	20
1913	2 d. "Rest on the Flight into Egypt" (Jean-Honore Fragonard)	60	60
1914	2 d. "Rest on the Flight into Egypt" (Francois Boucher)	60	60
1915	2 d. "Noon" (Claude Lorrain)	60	60
1916	10 d. "The Holy Family" (Nicolas Poussin)	2·00	2·75
1917	12 d. "Mystical Marriage of St. Catherine" (Pierre-Francois Mignard)	2·00	2·75
1910/17	*Set of 8*	6·25	7·00

MS1918 Two sheets, each 122×87 mm. (a) 25 d.
"Adoration of the Shepherds" (detail) (Mathieu le Nain). (b) 25 d. "The Nativity by Torchlight" (detail) (Louis le Nain) .. *Set of 2 sheets* 9·00 10·00

231 Marilyn Monroe

232 Elvis as a Child

(Des R. Rundo. Litho Questa)

1995 (8 Jan). *Marilyn Monroe (American entertainer) Commemoration.* T **231** *and similar vert designs. Multicoloured.* P 14.

1919	4 d. Type 231		85	90
	a. Sheetlet. Nos. 1919/27		7·00	
1920	4 d. Wearing pendant necklace		85	90
1921	4 d. In blue jacket		85	90
1922	4 d. With sun-glasses on head		85	90
1923	4 d. Looking over right arm		85	90
1924	4 d. Wearing gold beret and jacket		85	90
1925	4 d. Wearing hooped earrings		85	90
1926	4 d. Smiling		85	90
1927	4 d. Laughing		85	90
1919/27		*Set of 9*	7·00	7·50

MS1928 Two sheets, each 70×100 mm. (a) 25 d.
Marilyn Monroe in red dress. (b) 25 d. With pendant earrings .. *Set of 2 sheets* 8·50 9·00
Nos. 1919/27 were printed together, *se-tenant*, in sheetlets of 9.

(Des Isabelle Tanner. Litho Questa)

1995 (8 Jan). *60th Birth Anniv of Elvis Presley (singer).* T **232** *and similar vert designs. Multicoloured.* P 14.

1929	4 d. Type 232		85	90
	a. Sheetlet. Nos. 1929/37		7·00	
1930	4 d. Wearing white shirt		85	90
1931	4 d. With his mother Gladys		85	90
1932	4 d. With his wife Priscilla		85	90
1933	4 d. With large gold medallion		85	90
1934	4 d. In army uniform		85	90
1935	4 d. In purple shirt		85	90
1936	4 d. Wearing stetson		85	90
1937	4 d. With his daughter Lisa-Marie		85	90
1929/37		*Set of 9*	7·00	7·50

Nos. 1929/37 were printed together, *se-tenant*, in sheetlets of 9.

233 Pteranodon

234 Pig (Chinese characters in bright green)

(Des R. Sauber. Litho Questa)

1995 (6 Feb). *Prehistoric Animals.* T **233** *and similar multicoloured designs.* P 14.

1938	2 d. Type 233		50	50
	a. Sheetlet. Nos. 1938/49		5·50	
1939	2 d. Archaeopteryx		50	50
1940	2 d. Rhamphorhynchus		50	50
1941	2 d. Ornithomimus		50	50
1942	2 d. Stegosaurus		50	50
1943	2 d. Heterodontosaurus		50	50
1944	2 d. Lystrosaurus		50	50
1945	2 d. Euoplocephalus		50	50
1946	2 d. Coelophysis		50	50
1947	2 d. Staurikosaurus		50	50
1948	2 d. Giantoperis		50	50
1949	2 d. Diarthrognathus		50	50
1950	3 d. Archaeopteryx		55	55
	a. Sheetlet. Nos. 1950/61		6·00	
1951	3 d. Vangehuanosaurus		55	55
1952	3 d. Celophysis		55	55
1953	3 d. Plateosaurus		55	55
1954	3 d. Baryonyx		55	55
1955	3 d. Ornitholestes		55	55
1956	3 d. Dryosaurus		55	55
1957	3 d. Estemmenosuchus		55	55
1958	3 d. Macroplata		55	55
1959	3 d. Shonisaurus		55	55
1960	3 d. Muraeonosaurus		55	55
1961	3 d. Archelon		55	55
1938/61		*Set of 24*	11·50	11·50

MS1962 Four sheets, each 100×70 mm. (a) 20 d.
Bactrosaurus. (b) 22 d. Tyrannosaurus rex (*vert*).
(c) 25 d. Triceratops (*vert*). (d) 25 d. Spinosaurus
Set of 4 sheets 18·00 19·00
Nos. 1938/49 and 1950/61 were each printed together, *se-tenant*, in sheetlets of 12 stamps forming composite designs.

(Des Y. Lee. Litho Questa)

1995 (4 May). *Chinese New Year ("Year of the Pig").* T **234** *and similar horiz designs showing symbolic pigs.* P 14½.

1963	234	3 d. scarlet-vermilion, black & brt grn	45	55
		a. Sheetlet. Nos. 1963/6	1·60	
1964		3 d. multicoloured (characters in deep ultramarine)	45	55
1965		3 d. reddish orange, orange-vermilion and black (characters in white)	45	55
1966		3 d. dull rose, scarlet-vermilion and black (characters in black)	45	55
1963/6		*Set of 4*	1·60	2·00

MS1967 76×106 mm. 10 d. deep magenta and orange-vermilion (three pigs) .. .. 1·50 2·00
Nos. 1963/6 were printed together, *se-tenant*, in sheetlets of 4.

235 Great White Egret

236 Rural Road

(Litho B.D.T.)

1995 (8 May). *Water Birds.* T **235** *and similar horiz designs. Multicoloured.* P 14.

1968	2 d. Type 235		55	55
1969	3 d. Pintails		60	65
	a. Sheetlet. Nos. 1969/80		6·50	
1970	3 d. Fulvous Whistling Duck		60	65
1971	3 d. Garganey		60	65
1972	3 d. White-faced Whistling Duck		60	65
1973	3 d. White-backed Duck		60	65
1974	3 d. Egyptian Goose		60	65
1975	3 d. African Pygmy Geese		60	65
1976	3 d. Little Bitterns		60	65
1977	3 d. Redshanks		60	65
1978	3 d. Ringed Plovers		60	65
1979	3 d. Black-winged Stilt		60	65
1980	3 d. Squacco Herons		60	65
1981	8 d. Hammerkop		1·75	2·00
1982	10 d. Common Shovelers		2·00	2·25
1983	12 d. Crowned Crane		2·25	2·50
1968/83		*Set of 16*	12·50	13·50

MS1984 Two sheets, each 106×76 mm. (a) 25 d.
Ferruginous Ducks. (b) 25 d. Moorhen
Set of 2 sheets 9·00 9·50
Nos. 1969/80 were printed together, *se-tenant*, in sheetlets of 12, forming a composite design.

(Litho Questa)

1995 (30 May). *20th Anniv of Economic Community of West African States (E.C.O.W.A.S.).* T **236** *and similar vert design. Multicoloured.* P 14.

1985	2 d. Type 236		30	25
1986	5 d. Pres. Yayah Jammeh		95	1·00

237 Leather Back Turtle

238 First Stage of Lariat Knot

(Des J. Barbarus and G. Lott. Litho B.D.T.)

1995 (20 June). *Marine Life.* T **237** *and similar multicoloured designs.* P 14.

1987	3 d. Type 237		60	65
	a. Sheetlet. Nos. 1987/98		6·50	
1988	3 d. Tiger Shark		60	65
1989	3 d. Powder-blue Surgeonfish		60	65
1990	3 d. Emperor Angelfish		60	65
1991	3 d. Blue Parrotfish		60	65
1992	3 d. Clown Triggerfish		60	65
1993	3 d. Seahorse		60	65
1994	3 d. Lionfish		60	65
1995	3 d. Moray Eel		60	65
1996	3 d. Melon Butterflyfish		60	65
1997	3 d. Octopus		60	65
1998	3 d. Common Stingray		60	65
1999	8 d. Stoplight Parrotfish ("Multicolored Parrot Fish") (*vert*)		1·75	2·00
	a. Horiz strip of 4. Nos. 1999/2002		6·00	
2000	8 d. Stoplight Parrotfish ("Sparisoma viride") (*vert*)		1·75	2·00
2001	8 d. Queen Parrotfish (*vert*)		1·75	2·00
2002	8 d. Bicoloured Parrotfish (*vert*)		1·75	2·00
1987/2002		*Set of 16*	12·50	14·00

MS2003 Two sheets, each 98×68 mm. (a) 25 d.
Queen Angelfish (*Angelichthys isabelita*). (b) 25 d.
Rock Beauty (*Holacanthus ciliaris*).
Set of 2 sheets 9·00 9·50
Nos. 1987/98 and 1999/2002 were printed together, *se-tenant*, in sheetlets of 12 (Nos. 1987/98) or horizontal strips of 4 (Nos. 1999/2002) with the backgrounds forming composite designs.
No. 1991 is inscribed "BLUE PARRO FISH" in error.

(Des P. Chinelli. Litho Questa)

1995 (14 July). *18th World Scout Jamboree, Netherlands.* T **238** *and similar vert designs. Multicoloured.* P 14.

MS2004 Two sheets, each 101×65 mm. (a) 2 d.
Type 238; 2 d. Second stage of knot with ropes end at right; 2 d. Completed Lariat knot. (b) 5 d.
Completed Bowline knot; 12 d. Second stage of knot; 12 d. First stage of knot .. *Set of 2 sheets* 5·75 6·00

MS2005 Two sheets, each 72×102 mm. (a) 25 d.
Scout in rope using Hitch knot. (b) 25 d. Injured scout supported by Bowline knot *Set of 2 sheets* 7·00 7·50

(Des L. Fried. Litho B.D.T.)

1995 (1 Aug). *50th Anniv of End of Second World War in Europe. Film Stars. Black and scarlet (Nos. 2008 and 2010) or multicoloured designs (others) as* T **340** *of Antigua.* P 14.

2006	3 d. Peter Lawford		60	60
	a. Sheetlet. Nos. 2006/13		4·25	
2007	3 d. Gene Tierney and Dana Andrews		60	60
2008	3 d. Groucho and Harpo Marx		60	60
2009	3 d. James Stewart		60	60
2010	3 d. Chico and Zeppo Marx		60	60
2011	3 d. Tyrone Power		60	60
2012	3 d. Cary Grant and Ingrid Bergman		60	60
2013	3 d. Veronica Lake		60	60
2006/13		*Set of 8*	4·25	4·25

MS2014 105×75 mm. 25 d. "A Lady Fights Back" film poster (*vert*) .. .. .. 4·50 5·00
Nos. 2006/13 were printed together, *se-tenant*, in sheetlets of 8 with the stamps arranged in two horizontal strips of 4 separated by a gutter showing Laurel and Hardy, Anna Neagle and Orson Wells.
No. 2012 is inscribed "BERMAN" in error.

(Des Bryna Waldman. Litho)

1995 (1 Aug). *50th Anniv of United Nations. Vert designs as* T **341** *of Antigua. Multicoloured.* P 14.

2015	3 d. Children in class		80	80
	a. Horiz strip of 3. Nos. 2015/17		2·25	
2016	3 d. Teacher helping child		80	80
2017	3 d. Child writing on blackboard		80	80
2015/17		*Set of 3*	2·25	2·25

MS2018 104×74 mm. 25 d. Nurse weighing baby 3·75 4·25
Nos. 2015/17 were printed together in sheets of 9 containing three *se-tenant* horizontal strips, each forming a composite design.

(Des Bryna Waldman. Litho)

1995 (1 Aug). *50th Anniv of Food and Agriculture Organization. Vert designs as* T **342** *of Antigua. Multicoloured.* P 14.

2019	3 d. Woman carrying sack on head		80	80
	a. Horiz strip of 3. Nos. 2019/21		2·25	
2020	3 d. Two men carrying sacks		80	80
2021	3 d. Man carrying sack		80	80
2019/21		*Set of 3*	2·25	2·25

MS2022 104×74 mm. 25 d. Fisherman with net 3·75 4·25
Nos. 2019/21 were printed together in sheets of 9 containing three *se-tenant* horizontal strips, each forming a composite design.

239 Paul Harris (founder) and Rotary Emblem   **240** Kenichi Fukui (1981 Chemistry)

1995 (1 Aug). *90th Anniv of Rotary International. T* **239** *and similar horiz design. Multicoloured. Litho. P* 14.

2023	15 d. Type **239**			2·00	2·50
MS2024	75×105 mm. 20 d. National flag and Rotary emblem			2·75	3·00

(Litho Questa)

1995 (1 Aug). *95th Birthday of Queen Elizabeth the Queen Mother. Vert designs as T* **344** *of Antigua. P* 13½×14.

2025	5 d. orange-brown, pale brown and black			1·00	1·10
	a. Sheetlet. Nos. 2025/8×2			7·00	
2026	5 d. multicoloured			1·00	1·10
2027	5 d. multicoloured			1·00	1·10
2028	5 d. multicoloured			1·00	1·10
2025/8			*Set of* 4	3·50	4·00
MS2029	102×126 mm. 25 d. multicoloured			4·50	4·50

Designs:—No. 2025, Queen Elizabeth the Queen Mother (pastel drawing); No. 2026, Wearing blue hat and dress; No. 2027, At desk (oil painting); No. 2028, Wearing green hat and dress; No. **MS**2029, Wearing lavender hat and dress.

Nos. 2025/8 were printed together in sheetlets of 8 containing two *se-tenant* horizontal strips of 4.

(Des J. Batchelor. Litho Questa)

1995 (1 Aug). *50th Anniv of End of Second World War in the Pacific. Horiz designs as T* **340** *of Antigua. Multicoloured. P* 14.

2030	5 d. Fairey Firefly			1·00	1·10
	a. Sheetlet. Nos. 2030/5			5·50	
2031	5 d. Fairey Barracuda Mk III			1·00	1·10
2032	5 d. Supermarine Seafire II			1·00	1·10
2033	5 d. H.M.S. *Repulse* (battle cruiser)			1·00	1·10
2034	5 d. H.M.S. *Illustrious* (aircraft carrier)			1·00	1·10
2035	5 d. H.M.S. *Exeter* (cruiser)			1·00	1·10
2030/5			*Set of* 6	5·50	6·00
MS2036	108×76 mm. 25 d. Kamikaze aircraft heading for British "County" class cruiser			4·50	4·50

Nos. 2030/5 were printed together, *se-tenant*, in sheetlets of 6 with the stamps arranged in two horizontal strips of 3 separated by a gutter showing Lord Louis Mountbatten and the sinking of H.M.S. *Kelly.*

(Des Shayna Magid. Litho Questa)

1995 (1 Aug). *Centenary of Nobel Prize Trust Fund. Past Prize Winners. T* **240** *and similar vert designs. Multicoloured. P* 14.

2037	2 d. Type **240**			40	40
2038	3 d. Gustav Stresemann (1929 Peace)			50	50
2039	5 d. Thomas Mann (1929 Literature)			80	80
2040	5 d. Marie Curie (1911 Chemistry)			80	85
	a. Sheetlet. Nos. 2040/8			6·50	
2041	5 d. Adolf Butenandt (1939 Chemistry)			80	85
2042	5 d. Susumu Tonegwa (1987 Medicine)			80	85
2043	5 d. Nelly Sachs (1966 Literature)			80	85
2044	5 d. Yasunari Kawabata (1968 Literature)			80	85
2045	5 d. Hideki Yukawa (1949 Physics)			80	85
2046	5 d. Paul Ehrlich (1908 Medicine)			80	85
2047	5 d. Bisaku Sato (1974 Peace)			80	85
2048	5 d. Carl von Ossietsky (1935 Peace)			80	85
2049	8 d. Albert Schweitzer (1952 Peace)			1·40	1·50
2050	12 d. Leo Esaki (1973 Physics)			1·75	2·00
2051	15 d. Lech Walęsa (1983 Peace)			2·00	2·50
2037/51			*Set of* 15	12·50	14·00
MS2052	75×105 mm. 25 d. Willy Brandt (1971 Peace)			3·75	4·25

Nos. 2040/8 were printed together, *se-tenant*, in sheetlets of 9, forming a composite design.

No. 2048 is dated "1974" and No. 2051 inscribed "Lech Walsea", both in error.

241 Bruce Jenner (U.S.A.) (decathlon)

(Des A. Di Lorenzo. Litho Questa)

1995 (17 Aug). *Olympic Games, Atlanta* (1996) (1st issue). *T* **241** *and similar multicoloured designs. P* 14.

2053	1 d. Type **241**			20	30
2054	1 d. 25, Greg Louganis (U.S.A.) (diving)			20	30
2055	1 d. 50, Michael Gross (Germany) (50 metre butterfly)			25	30
2056	2 d. Vasily Alexeev (Russia) (weight-lifting)			30	30
2057	3 d. Ewing (U.S.A.) and Corbalan (Spain) (basketball)			50	50
2058	3 d. Stefano Cerioni (Italy) (fencing) (*vert*)			50	55
	a. Sheetlet. Nos. 2058/65			3·50	

2059	3 d. Alberto Cova (Italy) (10000 metres) (*vert*)			50	55
2060	3 d. Mary Lou Retton (U.S.A.) (gymnastics) (*vert*)			50	55
2061	3 d. Vladimir Artemov (Russia) (gymnastics) (*vert*)			50	55
2062	3 d. Florence Griffith-Joyner (U.S.A.) (400 metre relay) (*vert*)			50	55
2063	3 d. Brazil (football) (*vert*)			50	55
2064	3 d. Nelson Vails (U.S.A.) (sprint cycling) (*vert*)			50	55
2065	3 d. Cheryl Miller (U.S.A.) (basketball) (*vert*)			50	55
2066	5 d. U.S.A. v Brazil (men's volleyball)			85	95
2067	10 d. Svenden (West Germany) and Fernandez (U.S.A.) (water polo)			1·50	1·75
2068	15 d. Pertii Karppinen (Finland) (single sculls)			2·25	2·75
2053/68			*Set of* 16	9·00	10·50
MS2069	Two sheets, each 71×101 mm. (a) 25 d. Karen Stives (U.S.A.) (equestrian) (*vert*). (b) 25 d. Edwin Moses (U.S.A.) (400 metre hurdles) (*vert*)		*Set of* 2 sheets	7·50	8·00

Nos. 2058/65 were printed together, *se-tenant*, in sheetlets of 8.

No. 2059 is inscribed "Alberto Covo" and No. 2064 "Nelson Valis", both in error.

See also Nos. 2281/303.

242 Rotary Emblem and Rotarians supporting School for the Deaf   **243** *Zantedeschia rehmannii*

(Litho Questa)

1995 (5 Sept). *Local Rotary and Boy Scout Projects. T* **242** *and similar multicoloured designs. P* 14.

2070	2 d. Type **242**			30	30
2071	5 d. Scout wood badge course, 1980			85	95
2072	5 d. Scout Commissioner M. J. E. Sambou (*vert*)			85	95
2070/2			*Set of* 3	1·75	2·00

(Des Mary Walters. Litho Questa)

1995 (2 Oct). *African Flowers. T* **243** *and similar vert designs. Multicoloured. P* 14.

2073	2 d. Type **243**			45	45
2074	3 d. *Kigelia africana*			50	55
	a. Sheetlet. Nos. 2074/82			4·00	
2075	3 d. *Hibiscus schizopetalus*			50	55
2076	3 d. *Dombeya mastersii*			50	55
2077	3 d. *Agapanthus orientalis*			50	55
2078	3 d. *Strelitzia reginae*			50	55
2079	3 d. *Spathodea companulata*			50	55
2080	3 d. *Rhodolaena bakeriana*			50	55
2081	3 d. *Gazania rigens*			50	55
2082	3 d. *Ixianthes retzioides*			50	55
2083	3 d. *Canarina abyssinica*			50	55
	a. Sheetlet. Nos. 2083/91			4·00	
2084	3 d. *Nerine bowdenii*			50	55
2085	3 d. *Zantedeschia aethiopica*			50	55
2086	3 d. *Aframomum sceptrum*			50	55
2087	3 d. *Schotia brachypetala*			50	55
2088	3 d. *Catharanthus roseus*			50	55
2089	3 d. *Protea grandiceps*			50	55
2090	3 d. *Plumbago capensis*			50	55
2091	3 d. *Uncarina grandidieri*			50	55
2092	5 d. *Euadenia eminens*			85	95
2093	10 d. *Passiflora vitifolia*			1·50	1·75
2094	15 d. *Dietes grandiflora*			2·25	2·75
2073/94			*Set of* 22	13·00	14·00
MS2095	Two sheets, each 106×75 mm. (a) 25 d. *Eulophia quartiniana.* (b) 25 d. *Gloriosa simplex*		*Set of* 2 sheets	8·50	9·00

Nos. 2074/82 and 2083/91 were printed together, *se-tenant*, in sheetlets of 9 forming composite background designs.

244 Children outside Huts

1995 (9 Oct). *Kinderdorf International S.O.S. Children's Villages. T* **244** *and similar multicoloured designs. Litho. P* 14.

2096	2 d. Type **244**			30	35
2097	2 d. Charity worker with children (*vert*)			30	35
2098	5 d. Children at party			80	95
2096/8			*Set of* 3	1·25	1·50

245 Roy Orbison

1995 (1 Dec). *History of Rock n' Roll Music. T* **245** *and similar vert designs. Multicoloured. Litho. P* 13½×14.

2099	3 d. Type **245**			55	55
	a. Sheetlet. Nos. 2099/107			4·50	
2100	3 d. Mick Jagger			55	55
2101	3 d. Bruce Springsteen			55	55
2102	3 d. Jimi Hendrix			55	55
2103	3 d. Bill Hailey			55	55
2104	3 d. Gene Vincent			55	55
2105	3 d. Buddy Holly			55	55
2106	3 d. Jerry Lee Lewis			55	55
2107	3 d. Chuck Berry			55	55
2099/107			*Set of* 9	4·50	4·50
MS2108	116×86 mm. 25 d. Elvis Presley			4·50	4·50

Nos. 2099/2107 were printed together, *se-tenant*, in sheetlets of 9 forming a composite design.

1995 (1 Dec). *Centenary of Cinema. Vert designs as T* **245**, *but depicting James Dean. Multicoloured. Litho. P* 13½×14.

2109	3 d. As a boy			55	55
	a. Sheetlet. Nos. 2109/17			4·50	
2110	3 d. On motorbike			55	55
2111	3 d. With sports car and trophy			55	55
2112	3 d. Close-up portrait			55	55
2113	3 d. Facing left			55	55
2114	3 d. Holding girl			55	55
2115	3 d. *Rebel without a Cause* (film)			55	55
2116	3 d. *Giant* (film)			55	55
2117	3 d. *East of Eden* (film)			55	55
2109/17			*Set of* 9	4·50	4·50
MS2118	116×86 mm. 25 d. James Dean in *Rebel without a Cause*			4·50	4·50

Nos. 2109/17 were printed together, *se-tenant*, in sheetlets of 9 forming a composite design.

(Litho Questa)

1995 (18 Dec). *Christmas. Religious Paintings. Vert designs as T* **357** *of Antigua. Multicoloured. P* 13½×14.

2119	75 b. "Madonna and Child" (Maria della Vallicella)			20	10
2120	1 d. "Madonna" (Giotto)			20	10
2121	2 d. "The Flight into Egypt" (Luca Giordano)			35	25
2122	5 d. "The Epiphany" (Bondone)			80	75
2123	8 d. "Virgin and Child" (Burgkmair)			1·40	1·75
2124	12 d. "Madonna" (Bellini)			1·75	2·25
2119/24			*Set of* 6	4·25	4·50
MS2125	Two sheets, each 101×127 mm. (a) 25 d. "Christ" (Carpaccio). (b) 25 d. "Madonna and Child" (Rubens)		*Set of* 2 sheets	9·00	9·50

246 Terminal Building   **247** U.P.U. Emblem

(Litho Questa)

1995 (21 Dec). *Opening of New Terminal Building, Banjul International Airport. P* 14.

2126	**246** 1 d. multicoloured			20	10
2127	2 d. multicoloured			35	25
2128	3 d. multicoloured			45	45
2129	5 d. multicoloured			75	1·00
2126/9			*Set of* 4	1·60	1·60

(Litho Questa)

1995 (21 Dec). *121st Anniv of Universal Postal Union. P* 14.

2130	**247** 1 d. black and deep bluish violet			20	10
2131	2 d. black and bright greenish blue			35	25
2132	3 d. black and bright scarlet			45	45
2133	7 d. black and bright emerald			1·25	1·50
2130/3			*Set of* 4	2·00	2·00

COVER PRICES

Cover factors are quoted at the beginning of each country for most issues to 1945. An explanation of the system can be found on page x. The factors quoted do not, however, apply to philatelic covers.

248 Commerson's Dolphin

(Litho Questa)

1995 (22 Dec). *Whales and Dolphins.* T **248** *and similar multicoloured designs. P* 14.

2134	2 d. Type **248**			..	20	25
2135	3 d. Bryde's Whale	..	..	..	35	40
	a. Sheetlet. Nos. 2135/43		..	..	3·00	
2136	3 d. Sperm Whale	..	..	..	35	40
2137	3 d. Humpback Whale	..	..	..	35	40
2138	3 d. Sei Whale	..	..	..	35	40
2139	3 d. Blue Whale ..	..	..	..	35	40
2140	3 d. Grey Whale ..	..	..	..	35	40
2141	3 d. Fin Whale	..	..	..	35	40
2142	3 d. Killer Whale	..	..	..	35	40
2143	3 d. Right Whale	..	..	..	35	40
2144	3 d. Northern Right Whale Dolphin				35	40
	a. Sheetlet. Nos. 2144/52		..		3·00	
2145	3 d. Spotted Dolphin	..	..	..	35	40
2146	3 d. Common Dolphin	..	..	..	35	40
2147	3 d. Pacific White-sided Dolphin				35	40
2148	3 d. Atlantic Humpbacked Dolphin				35	40
2149	3 d. Atlantic White-sided Dolphin				35	40
2150	3 d. White-beaked Dolphin		..		35	40
2151	3 d. Striped Dolphin	..	..		35	40
2152	3 d. Risso's Dolphin	..	..		35	40
2153	5 d. Narwhal	..	..	..	60	65
2154	8 d. True's Beaked Whale		..		90	95
2155	10 d. Rough-toothed Dolphin		..		1·10	1·25
2134/55				*Set of* 22	9·00	10·00

MS2156 Two sheets, each 110×80 mm. (a) 25 d. Beluga and Clymene Dolphin. (b) 25 d. Bowhead Whale and Blue Shark (*vert*) .. *Set of 2 sheets* 5·75 6·00

Nos. 2135/43 and 2144/52 were printed together, *se-tenant*, in sheetlets of 9 forming composite designs.

249 Big Pete as Seminole with Alligator

(Des Alvin White Studios. Litho Questa)

1995 (22 Dec). *Disney Cowboys and Indians.* T **249** *and similar multicoloured designs showing Walt Disney cartoon characters. P* 14×13½.

2157	15 b. Type **249**	..	..	..	10	10
2158	20 b. Donald Duck as Chinook fisherman				10	10
2159	25 b. Huey, Dewey and Louie as Blackfoot braves				10	10
2160	30 b. Minnie Mouse shooting bottles				10	10
2161	40 b. Donald riding bull		..		10	10
2162	50 b. Mickey Mouse branding steer				10	10
2163	2 d. Donald in Tlingit mask				30	25
2164	3 d. Mickey bronco-busting		..		45	40
2165	12 d. Grandma Duck with lasso		..		2·00	2·00
2166	15 d. Mickey in Pomo canoe		..		2·50	2·50
2167	15 d. Goofy as ranch hand		..		2·50	2·50
2168	20 d. Goofy and Minnie with Navaho weaving				2·75	2·75
2157/68				*Set of* 12	10·00	10·00

MS2169 Four sheets, each 127×102 mm. (a) 25 d. Minnie as Massachusetts squaw. P 14×13½. (b) 25 d. Minnie as Shoshoni squaw (*vert*). P 13½×14. (c) 25 d. Pluto singing to the Moon (*vert*). P 13½×14. (d) 25 d. Donald and steer (*vert*). P 13½×14 .. *Set of 4 sheets* 16·00 17·00

250 Rat

251 "Don Tiburcio Pérez y Cuervo (detail) (Goya)

(Des Y. Lee. Litho Questa)

1996 (2 Jan). *Chinese New Year ("Year of the Rat"). T* **250** *and similar horiz designs showing different stylised rats. P* 14½.

2170	63 b. multicoloured	..	..		10	10
	a. Horiz strip of 4. Nos. 2170/3				85	
2171	75 b. multicoloured	..	..		10	10

2172	1 d. 50, multicoloured	..	..		20	25
2173	4 d. multicoloured	..	..		45	50
2170/3				*Set of* 4	1·00	

MS2174 84×68 mm. 3 d. × 4 As Nos. 2170/3 .. 1·40 1·50
MS2175 76×106 mm. 10 d. orange-vermilion, deep violet and yellow-brown .. .. 1·10 1·25

Nos. 2170/3 were printed together, *se-tenant*, as horizontal strips of 4 in sheets of 12.

(Litho Questa)

1996 (29 Jan). *125th Anniv of Metropolitan Museum of Art, New York. T* **251** *and similar multicoloured designs. P* 14.

2176/83 4 d. × 8 (Type **251**; "Jean Antoine Moltedo" (Ingres); "The Letter" (Corot); "General Etienne Gerard" (David); "Portrait of the Artist" (Van Gogh); "Joseph Henri Altés" (Degas); "Princess de Broglie" (Ingres); "Lady at the Table" (Cassatt))
     a. Sheetlet. Nos. 2176/83 .. 3·50

2184/91 4 d. × 8 ("Broken Eggs" (Greuze); "Johann Joachim Wincklemann" (Mengs); "Col. George Coussmaker" (Reynolds); "Self Portrait with Pupils" (Labille-Guiard); "Courtesan holding a Fan" (Utamaro); "The Woodgatherers" (Gainsborough); "Mrs. Grace Elliott" (Gainsborough); "The Drummond Children" (Raeburn))
     a. Sheetlet. Nos. 2184/91 .. 3·50

2192/9 4 d. × 8 ("Sunflowers" (Monet); "Still Life with Pansies" (Fantin-Latour); "Parisians enjoying the Parc" (Monet); "La Mére Larchevêque" (Pissarro); "Rue de L'Epicerie, Rouen" (Pissarro); "The Abduction of Rebecca" (Delacroix); "Daughter, Abraham-Ben-Chimol" (Delacroix); "Christ on Lake of Gennesaret" (Delacroix))
     a. Sheetlet. Nos. 2192/9 .. 3·50

2200/7 4 d. × 8 ("Henry, Prince of Wales" (Peake); "Saints Peter, Martha, Mary and Leonard" (Correggio); "Marriage Feast at Cana" (Juan de Flandes); "Portrait of One of Wedigh Family" (Holbein); "Guillaume Budé" (Clouet); "Portrait of a Cardinal" (El Greco); "St. Jerome as a Cardinal" (El Greco); "Portrait of a Man" (Titian))
     a. Sheetlet. Nos. 2200/7 .. 3·50
2176/207 .. .. .. *Set of* 32 14·00 14·50

MS2208 Four sheets, each 95×70 mm containing horiz designs, 81×53 mm. (a) 25 d. "Israelites gathering Manna in the Desert" (Rubens). (b) 25 d. "Henry IV at the Battle of Ivry" (Rubens). (c) 25 d. "The Creation of the World and the Expulsion from Paradise" (Giovanni di Paolo). (d) 25 d. "The Harvesters" (Bruegel). P 14
     Set of 4 sheets 12·00 12·50

Nos. 2176/83, 2184/91, 2192/9 and 2200/7 were each printed together, *se-tenant*, in sheetlets of 8 stamps and one centre label.

252 Fire-eater

253 Bruce Lee

(Litho Questa)

1996 (29 Jan). *Fire-eating in the Gambia. T* **252** *and similar designs. P* 14.

2209	1 d. multicoloured	..	..		10	10
2210	2 d. multicoloured (*horiz*)		..		20	25
2211	3 d. multicoloured	..	..		35	40
2212	7 d. multicoloured (*horiz*)		..		80	85
2209/12				*Set of* 4	1·40	1·60

(Des Y. Lee. Litho)

1996 (1 Apr). *Bruce Lee (film star) Commemoration. T* **253** *and similar vert designs showing different portraits. Multicoloured. P* 14.

2213	3 d. Wearing cap and mask		..		45	50
	a. Sheetlet. Nos. 2213/21			..	3·25	
2214	3 d. Type **253**	..	..		35	40
2215	3 d. Facing left	..	..		35	40
2216	3 d. Wearing blue jumper and with hand to face				35	40
2217	3 d. Wearing buff jacket		..		35	40
2218	3 d. Wearing brown jacket (Chinese characters in chestnut)				35	40
2219	3 d. Wearing black shirt (Chinese characters in lilac)				35	40
2220	3 d. Wearing white shirt		..		35	40
2221	3 d. Bare-chested	..	..		35	40
2213/21				*Set of* 9	3·25	3·50

MS2222 Two sheets. (a) 140×85 mm. 5 d. Deng Xiao Ping (Chinese leader) (78×51 *mm*). P 13. (b) 70×100 mm. 25 d. Bruce Lee. P 14
     Set of 2 sheets 6·25 6·50

Nos. 2213/21 were printed together, *se-tenant*, in numbered sheetlets of 9, which also included "CHINA '96 9th Asian International Philatelic Exhibition" emblem on the sheet margin.

254 Donald Duck and Big Pete giving Blood

(Litho Questa)

1996 (12 Apr). *Voluntary Activities. T* **254** *and similar horiz designs showing Walt Disney cartoon characters. Multicoloured. P* 14×13½.

2223	1 d. Type **254**		15	10
2224	4 d. Daisy Duck and Minnie Mouse adopting pets		65	50
2225	5 d. Goofy as one-man band raising money for the needy		75	65
2226	10 d. Goofy teaching outdoor skills		1·40	1·60
2227	15 d. Minnie teaching reading		2·00	2·50
2228	20 d. Donald, Mickey and Goofy as volunteer fire fighters		2·50	2·75
2223/9		*Set of* 6	6·75	7·25

MS2229 Two sheets, each 127×102 mm. (a) 25 d. Minnie counting whales. (b) 25 d. Mickey planting roadside sapling .. *Set of 2 sheets* 7·50 8·00

255 Roan Antelope

(Litho Questa)

1996 (15 Apr). *Wildlife. T* **255** *and similar multicoloured designs. P* 14.

2230	3 d. Type **255**		35	40
	a. Sheetlet. Nos. 2230/5 each × 2		4·25	
2231	3 d. Lesser Bushbaby	..	35	40
2232	3 d. Black Leopard	..	35	40
2233	3 d. Guinea Forest Red Colobus		35	40
2234	3 d. Kobs		35	40
2235	3 d. Common Eland	..	35	40
2236	4 d. African Buffalo	..	45	50
	a. Sheetlet. Nos. 2236/44		4·00	
2237	4 d. Herd of Topi		45	50
2238	4 d. Vervet		45	50
2239	4 d. Hippopotamuses	..	45	50
2240	4 d. Waterbuck	..	45	50
2241	4 d. Senegal Chameleon	..	45	50
2242	4 d. Western Green Mamba		45	50
2243	4 d. Slender-snouted Crocodile		45	50
2244	4 d. Adanson's Mud Turtle		45	50
2245	15 d. African Civet	..	1·75	1·90
2230/45		*Set of* 16	7·75	8·75

MS2246 Two sheets, each 98×68 mm. (a) 25 d. Lion (*vert*). (b) 25 d. Chimpanzee (*vert*)
     Set of 2 sheets 5·75 6·00

Nos. 2230/5 and 2236/44 were printed together, *se-tenant*, in sheetlets of 12 (Nos. 2230/5 × 2) or 9 (Nos. 2236/44), the latter forming a composite design.

(Litho Questa)

1996 (9 May). *70th Birthday of Queen Elizabeth II. Multicoloured designs as T* **364** *of Antigua showing different photographs. P* 13½×14.

2247	8 d. As Type **364** of Antigua		90	95
	a. Strip of 3. Nos. 2247/9		2·75	
2248	8 d. Wearing tiara facing right		90	95
2249	8 d. Wearing tiara facing left	..	90	95
2247/9		*Set of* 3	2·75	3·00

MS2250 125×104 mm. 25 d. Buckingham Palace (*horiz*). P 14×13½ .. .. 3·00 3·25

Nos. 2247/9 were printed together, *se-tenant*, in horizontal and vertical strips of 3 throughout sheets of 9.

256 Pumper Hose Cart, U.S.A. (1850)

1996 (27 May). *Classic Road Transport. T* **256** *and similar horiz designs showing fire engines (Nos. 2251/6) or cars (Nos. 2257/62). Multicoloured. Litho. P* 14.

2251	4 d. Type **256**		45	50
	a. Sheetlet. Nos. 2251/6		2·75	
2252	4 d. Steam fire engine, U.S.A. (1891)		45	50
2253	4 d. Lausitzer engine, Germany (1864) ..		45	50
2254	4 d. Chemical engine, Great Britain (1902)		45	50

2255	4 d. Motor fire engine, Great Britain (1904)	45	50
2256	4 d. Colonia No. 5 engine, Germany (1860)	45	50
2257	4 d. Fiat Tipo 510, Italy (1912)	45	50
	a. Sheetlet. Nos. 2257/62	2·75	
2258	4 d. Toyota Model 4B Phaeton, Japan (1936)	45	50
2259	4 d. Nag C4B, Germany (1924)	45	50
2260	4 d. Cadillac, U.S.A. (1903)	45	50
2261	4 d. Bentley, Great Britain (1925)	45	50
2262	4 d. Renault Model AX, France (1909)	45	50
2251/62	*Set of 12*	5·50	6·00

MS2263 (a) 76×58 mm. 25 d. Amoskeag Steamer (fire engine), U.S.A. (1865). (b) 81×59 mm. 25 d. Mitsubishi Model A, Japan (1917) *Set of 2 sheets* 5·75 6·00
Nos. 2251/6 and 2257/62 were each printed together, *se-tenant*, in sheetlets of 6.

257 Bulgarian Team   **258** Ray Ewry (U.S.A.) (standing high jump), 1912

1996 (8 June). *European Football Championship, England. T 257 and similar multicoloured designs. Litho. P 14×13½.*

2264	2 d. Type 257	20	25
2265	2 d. Croatian team	20	25
2266	2 d. Czech Republic team	20	25
2267	2 d. Danish team	20	25
2268	2 d. English team	20	25
2269	2 d. French team	20	25
2270	2 d. German team	20	25
2271	2 d. Dutch team	20	25
2272	2 d. Italian team	20	25
2273	2 d. Portuguese team	20	25
2274	2 d. Rumanian team	20	25
2275	2 d. Russian team	20	25
2276	2 d. Scottish team	20	25
2277	2 d. Spanish team	20	25
2278	2 d. Swiss team	20	25
2279	2 d. Turkish team	20	25
2264/79	*Set of 16*	3·25	4·00

MS2280 Sixteen sheets. (a) 115×85 mm. 25 d. Danish team celebrating (43×28 *mm*). (b) 85×115 mm. 25 d. Ruud Gullit (Netherlands) (28×43 *mm*). (c) 85×115 mm. 25 d. Gary McAllister (Scotland) (28×43 *mm*). (d) 115×85 mm. 25 d. Oleg Salenko (Russia) (28×43 *mm*). (e) 85×115 mm. 25 d. Hami Mandirali (Turkey) (28×43 *mm*). (f) 85×115 mm. 25 d. Hristo Stoitchkov (Bulgaria) (28×43 *mm*). (g) 115×85 mm. 25 d. European Championship Trophy (28×43 *mm*). (h) 85×115 mm. 25 d. Davor Suker (Croatia) (28×43 *mm*). (i) 115×85 mm. 25 d. Jurgen Klinsmann (Germany) (43×28 *mm*). (j) 85×115 mm. 25 d. Juan Goikoetxea (Spain) (28×43 *mm*). (k) 85×115 mm. 25 d. Eusebio (Portugal) (28×43 *mm*). (l) 115×85 mm. 25 d. Bryan Robson (England) (43×28 *mm*). (m) 85×115 mm. 25 d. Roberto Baggio (Italy) (28×43 *mm*). (n) 85×115 mm. 25 d. Christophe Ohrel (Switzerland) (28×43 *mm*). (o) 85×115 mm. 25 d. Pavel Hapal (Czech Republic) (28×43 *mm*). (p) 85×115 mm. 25 d. Gheorge Hagi (Rumania) (28×43 *mm*). P 14 ... *Set of 16 sheets* 48·00 50·00
Nos. 2264/79 were each printed in sheetlets of 8 stamps with a central label.

(Des Y. Lee. Litho Questa)

1996 (18 July). *Olympic Games, Atlanta (2nd issue). Previous Gold Medal Winners. T 258 and similar multicoloured designs. P 14.*

2281	1 d. Type 258	10	10
2282	2 d. Fanny Durack (Australia) (100m freestyle swimming), 1912	20	25
2283	3 d. Fu Mingxia (China) (platform diving), 1992	30	35
	a. Sheetlet. Nos. 2283/91	2·50	
2284	3 d. H. Henkel (Germany) (high jump) 1992	30	35
2285	3 d. Spanish team (soccer), 1992	30	35
2286	3 d. Jackie Joyner-Kersee (U.S.A.) (heptathlon), 1988 and 1992	30	35
2287	3 d. T. Gutsu (Russia) (gymnastics), 1992	30	35
2288	3 d. M. Johnson (U.S.A.) (400m running), 1992	30	35
2289	3 d. Lin Li (China) (200m medley swimming), 1992	30	35
2290	3 d. G. Devers (U.S.A.) (100m running), 1992	30	35
2291	3 d. Michael Powell (U.S.A.) (long jump), 1992	30	35
2292	3 d. Japanese volleyball team, 1964	30	35
	a. Sheetlet. Nos. 2292/2300	2·50	
2293	3 d. Li Neng (China) (floor exercises), 1984	30	35
2294	3 d. S. Bubka (U.S.S.R.) (pole vault), 1988	30	35
2295	3 d. Nadia Comaneci (Romania) (gymnastics), 1976	30	35
2296	3 d. Edwin Moses (U.S.A.) (400m hurdles), 1984	30	35
2297	3 d. Victor Scherbo (Russia) (gymnastics), 1992	30	35
2298	3 d. Evelyn Ashford (U.S.A.) (100m running), 1984	30	35
2299	3 d. Mohammed Ali (U.S.A.) (light heavyweight boxing), 1960	30	35

2300	3 d. Carl Lewis and C. Smith (U.S.A.) (400m relay), 1984	30	35
2301	5 d. Stockholm Olympic arena, 1912	60	65
2302	10 d. Jim Thorpe (U.S.A.) (decathalon and pentathlon), 1912	1·10	1·25
2281/2302	*Set of 22*	7·00	8·50

MS2303 Two sheets each 100×70 mm. 25 d. Michael Gross (Germany) (butterfly swimming), 1984 and 1988 (*horiz*). 25 d. Ulrike Meyfarth (Germany) (high jump), 1972 and 1984 ... *Set of 2 sheets* 5·75 6·00
Nos. 2283/91 and 2292/2300 were printed together, *se-tenant*, in sheetlets of 9.

(Litho Questa)

1996 (25 July). *50th Anniv of U.N.I.C.E.F. Multicoloured designs as T 366 of Antigua. P 14.*

2304	63 b. Boy holding shoes	10	10
2305	3 d. Girl being inoculated	35	40
2306	8 d. Boy holding ladle	90	95
2307	10 d. Child with blanket	1·10	1·25
2304/7	*Set of 4*	2·40	2·75

MS2308 105×75 mm. 25 d. Boy being inoculated (*horiz*) ... 3·00 3·25

259 Roman Officer and Pillar of Absalom   **260** Jacqueline Kennedy Onassis in Wedding Dress

(Des J. Genzo. Litho Questa)

1996 (25 July). *3000th Anniv of Jerusalem. T 259 and similar multicoloured designs. P 14.*

2309	1 d. 50, Type 259	20	25
2310	2 d. Turk and Gate of Mercy	20	25
2311	3 d. Ancient Greek and Church of the Holy Sepulchre	35	40
2312	10 d. Modern Hasidic Jew at Wailing Wall	1·10	1·25
2309/12	*Set of 4*	1·75	2·25

MS2313 100×70 mm. 25 d. City coat of arms (*vert*) ... 3·00 3·25

(Des J. Genzo. Litho Questa)

1996 (25 July). *Centenary of Radio. Entertainers. Vert designs as T 368 of Antigua. Multicoloured. P 13½×14.*

2314	1 d. Glenn Miller	10	10
2315	4 d. Louis Armstrong	45	50
2316	5 d. Nat "King" Cole	60	65
2317	10 d. The Andrew Sisters	1·10	1·25
2314/17	*Set of 4*	2·25	2·50

MS2318 105×74 mm. 25 d. President Truman 3·00 3·25
No. 2314 is inscribed "Glen Miller" in error.

(Des Zina Sanders (Nos. 2319/27 and MS2336), R. Sauber (Nos. 2328/35). Litho Questa)

1996 (22 Aug). *Famous People of the 20th Century. T 260 and similar vert designs. Multicoloured. P 14.*

2319	5 d. Type 260	60	65
	a. Sheetlet. Nos. 2319/27	5·50	
2320	5 d. Jaqueline Kennedy and White House	60	65
2321	5 d. Jaqueline Kennedy wearing pink hat	60	65
2322	5 d. Jaqueline Kennedy and motor yacht	60	65
2323	5 d. Jacqueline Kennedy wearing red jumper	60	65
2324	5 d. Jacqueline Kennedy and horse	60	65
2325	5 d. Jacqueline Kennedy on book	60	65
2326	5 d. Jacqueline Kennedy in blue dress and three rows of pearls	60	65
2327	5 d. Jacqueline Kennedy and corner of fountain	60	65
2328	5 d. President John Kennedy	60	65
	a. Sheetlet. Nos. 2328/35	4·75	
2329	5 d. Jacqueline Kennedy (inscr in capitals)	60	65
2330	5 d. Willy Brandt	60	65
2331	5 d. Marilyn Monroe	60	65
2332	5 d. Mao Tse-tung	60	65
2333	5 d. Sung Ching Ling	60	65
2334	5 d. Charles De Gaulle	60	65
2335	5 d. Marlene Dietrich	60	65
2319/35	*Set of 17*	10·00	11·00

MS2336 105×74 mm. 25 d. Jacqueline Kennedy (*different*) ... 3·00 3·25
Nos. 2319/27 and 2328/35 were each printed together, *se-tenant*, in sheetlets of 9 or 8.
No. 2330 is inscr "WILLIE BRANDT", No. 2331 "MARYLYN MONROE" and No. 2332 "MAO TSE TONG", all in error.

PRICES OF SETS

Set prices are given for many issues, generally those containing three stamps or more. Definitive sets include one of each value or major colour change, but do not cover different perforations, die types or minor shades. Where a choice is possible the set prices are based on the cheapest versions of the stamps included in the listings.

---

261 Richard Petty's 1969 Ford   **262** Elvis Presley with Microphone

(Des W. Wright. Litho Questa)

1996 (26 Aug). *Richard Petty (stock car driver) Commemoration. T 261 and similar horiz designs. Multicoloured. P 14.*

2337	5 d. Type 261	60	65
	a. Sheetlet. Nos. 2337/42	3·50	
2338	5 d. Richard Petty	60	65
2339	5 d. Dodge Magnum, 1978	60	65
2340	5 d. Pontiac, 1987	60	65
2341	5 d. Pontiac, 1989	60	65
2342	5 d. Dodge Daytona, 1975	60	65
2337/42	*Set of 6*	3·50	4·00

MS2343 104×74 mm. 25 d. Plymouth, 1972 (84×27 *mm*) ... 3·00 3·25
Nos. 2337/42 were printed together, *se-tenant*, in sheetlets of 6.

1996 (26 Aug). *Results of European Football Championship, England. As Nos. 2265/6, 2268, 2270, 2272, 2275 and MS2280 (d, h, i, l, m, o), but each additionally inscribed with date and match result. Multicoloured. Litho. P 14×13½.*

2344	2 d. Croatian team ("23/6/96 Germany 2, Croatia 1")	20	25
2345	2 d. Czech Republic team ("9/6/96 Germany 2, Czech Rep. 0")	20	25
2346	2 d. English team ("26/6/96 Germany 6, England 5")	20	25
2347	2 d. German team ("30/6/96 Germany 2, Czech Rep. 1")	20	25
2348	2 d. Italian team ("19/6/96 Germany 0, Italy 0")	20	25
2349	2 d. Russian team ("16/6/96 Germany 3, Russia 0")	20	25
2344/9	*Set of 6*	1·25	1·50

MS2350 Six sheets. (a) 114×84 mm. 25 d. Oleg Salenko (Russia) (28×43 *mm*) ("16/6/96 Germany 3, Russia 0"). (b) 84×114 mm. 25 d. Davor Suker (Croatia) (28×43 *mm*) ("23/6/96 Germany 2, Croatia 1"). (c) 114×84 mm. 25 d. Jurgen Klinsmann (Germany) (43×28 *mm*) ("Final 30/6/96 Germany 2, Czech Republic 1"). (d) 114×84 mm. 25 d. Bryan Robson (England) (28×43 *mm*) ("26/6/96 Germany 6 England 5"). (e) 84×114 mm. 25 d. Roberto Baggio (Italy) (28×43 *mm*) ("19/6/96 Germany 0 Italy 0"). (f) 84×114 mm. 25 d. Pavel Hapal (Czech Rep) (43×28 *mm*) ("9/6/96 Germany 2 Czech Republic 0") ... *Set of 6 sheets* 18·00 19·00
On No. MS2350 the dates and match results are shown on the sheet margins.

(Des Y. Lee. Litho Questa)

1996 (8 Sept). *Elvis Presley Commemoration. T 262 and similar vert designs showing different portraits. Multicoloured. P 14.*

2351	5 d. Type 262	60	65
	a. Sheetlet. Nos. 2351/6	3·50	
2352	5 d. In dinner jacket	60	65
2353	5 d. In Mexican outfit	60	65
2354	5 d. Wearing blue jumper	60	65
2355	5 d. In leather jacket	60	65
2356	5 d. Wearing lei	60	65
2351/6	*Set of 6*	3·50	4·00

Nos. 2351/6 were printed together, *se-tenant*, in numbered sheetlets of 6 with an illustrated margin.

263 Bob Dylan   **264** Supermarine Spitfire Prototype K5054

(Des J. Iskowitz. Litho Questa)

1996 (8 Sept). *Rock and Roll Legends. Bob Dylan. P 14.*

2357	**263** 5 d. multicoloured	60	65

No. 2357 was issued in sheet of 16 with an enlarged illustrated right-hand margin.

(Des W. Wright. Litho Questa)

1996 (13 Sept). *65th Anniv of Britain's Victory in Schneider Trophy Air Race. T 264 and similar horiz designs. Multicoloured. P 13½×14.*

2358	4 d. Type 264	45	50
	a. Sheetlet. Nos. 2358/66	4·00	
2359	4 d. First production Spitfire K9787	45	50

2360	4 d. Spitfire Mk 1A in Battle of Britain	45	50
2361	4 d. Spitfire Lfmk IXE with D-Day markings	45	50
2362	4 d. Spitfire Mk XII (first with "Griffon" engine)	45	50
2363	4 d. Spitfire Mk XIVC with jungle markings	45	50
2364	4 d. Spitfire XIX of Royal Swedish Air Force	45	50
2365	4 d. Spitfire Mk XIX	45	50
2366	4 d. Spitfire FMk 22/24 (final variant)	45	50
2367	4 d. Spitfire Mk XIX of Royal Swedish Air Force (from below)	45	50
	a. Sheetlet. Nos. 2367/75	4·00	
2368	4 d. Spitfire Mk VB of United States Army Air Corps	45	50
2369	4 d. Spitfire Mk VC of French Air Force	45	50
2370	4 d. Spitfire Mk VB of Soviet Air Force	45	50
2371	4 d. Spitfire Mk IXE of Netherlands East Indies Air Force	45	50
2372	4 d. Spitfire Mk IXE of Israeli Air Force	45	50
2373	4 d. Spitfire Mk VIII of Royal Australian Air Force	45	50
2374	4 d. Spitfire Mk VB of Turkish Air Force	45	50
2375	4 d. Spitfire Mk XI of Royal Danish Air Force	45	50
2358/75	*Set of 18*	8·00	9·00

MS2376 Two sheets, each 97×67 mm. (a) 25 d. Supermarine S 6B S1595 seaplane taking off (42×29 *mm*). (b) 25 d. Supermarine S 6B S1595 in flight (42×29 *mm*). P 14 .. *Set of 2 sheets* 5·75 6·00
Nos. 2358/66 and 2367/75 were each printed together, *se-tenant*, in sheetlets of 9.

265 Egyptian Plover
266 Sylvester Stallone as Rocky Balboa

(Des D. Burkhart. Litho Questa)

1996 (22 Oct)–97. *Birds.* T **265** *and similar square designs. Multicoloured.* P 14.

2377	50 b. Type **265**	10	10
2378	63 b. Painted Snipe	10	10
2379	75 b. Golden-breasted Bunting	10	10
2380	1 d. Bateleur	10	10
2381	1 d. 50, Didric Cuckoo	20	25
2382	2 d. Turtle Dove	20	25
2383	3 d. Village Weaver	35	40
2384	4 d. Common Roller	45	50
2385	5 d. Cut-Throat	60	65
2386	10 d. Hoopoe	1·10	1·25
2387	15 d. White-faced Scops Owl	1·75	1·90
2388	20 d. Narina Trogon	2·25	2·40
2389	25 d. Lesser Pied Kingfisher	3·00	3·25
2390	30 d. Common Kestrel	3·50	3·75
2391	40 d. Temminck's Courser (25.3.97)	4·75	5·00
2392	50 d. European Bee-eater (25.3.97)	5·75	6·00
2392a	100 d. Green-winged Teal (25.3.97)	11·50	12·50
2377/92a	*Set of 17*	34·00	36·00

No. 2388 is inscribed "TROGAN" in error

(Litho Questa)

1996 (18 Nov). *Christmas. Religious Paintings. Designs as* T **369** *of Antigua, showing different details of "Assumption of the Madonna" (Tiziano Vecellio) (Nos. 2393/8).* P 13½×14.

2393	1 d. multicoloured	10	10
2394	1 d. 50, multicoloured	20	25
2395	2 d. multicoloured	20	25
2396	3 d. multicoloured	35	40
2397	10 d. multicoloured	1·10	1·25
2398	15 d. multicoloured	1·75	1·90
2393/8	*Set of 6*	3·50	4·00

MS2399 Two sheets, each 76×106 mm. (a) 25 d. blackish brown, black and yellow-brown ("Adoration of the Magi" (Filippo Lippi)) (*horiz*). P 14×13½. (b) 25 d. carmine-red, black and pale brown-rose ("Virgin and Child with Infant St. John" (Raphael)). P 13½×14 .. *Set of 2 sheets* 5·75 6·00
No. **MS**2399(a) is inscribed "Flippo Lippi" in error.

(Des Shannon. Litho Questa)

1996 (21 Nov). *20th Anniv of Rocky (film).* Sheet 143×182 *mm.* P 14×13½.
MS2400 **266** 10 d.×3 multicoloured .. .. 3·50 3·75

267 Ox
268 "Arch 22" Monument

(Des Y. Lee. Litho Questa)

1997 (16 Jan). *Chinese New Year ("Year of the Ox").* T **267** *and similar horiz designs showing symbolic oxen.* P 14½.

2401	63 b. multicoloured	10	10
	a. Horiz strip of 4. Nos. 2401/4	1·00	
2402	75 b. multicoloured	10	10
2403	1 d. 50, multicoloured	20	25
2404	4 d. multicoloured	45	50
2401/4	*Set of 4*	85	90

MS2405 84×68 mm. 3 d. × 4. As Nos. 2401/4 1·40 1·50
MS2406 76×106 mm. 10 d. multicoloured (ox and sleeping peasant) (39½×24½ *mm*). P 14 1·10 1·25
Nos. 2401/4 were printed together, *se-tenant*, as horizontal strips of 4 in sheets of 12.

(Litho Questa)

1997 (28 Jan). *Economic Development.* T **268** *and similar multicoloured designs.* P 14.

2407	63 b. Type **268**	10	10
2408	1 d. Tractor (*horiz*)	10	10
2409	1 d. 50, Man planting rice	20	25
2410	2 d. As Type **268**, but with white panel at top	20	25
2411	3 d. Model of Banjul International Airport terminal building (*horiz*)	35	40
2412	5 d. Chamoi Bridge (*horiz*)	60	65
2407/12	*Set of 6*	1·25	1·75

MS2413 Two sheets. (a) 106×76 mm. 20 d. Workers in rice field (*horiz*). (b) 76×106 mm. 25 d. As Type **268** .. *Set of 2 sheets* 5·25 5·50

269 Monkey King extinguishing Fire on Flame Mountain
270 Jackie Chan

1997 (28 Jan). *Mickey Mouse's Journey to the West.* T **269** *and similar multicoloured designs showing Disney cartoon characters. Litho.* P 14×13½.

2414	2 d. Type **269**	40	40
	a. Sheetlet. Nos. 2414/19	2·25	
2415	2 d. Demon Ox and Monkey King fighting	40	40
2416	2 d. Mickey, Donald, Monkey King and Master San Tsang	40	40
2417	2 d. Fighting the Spider Demon	40	40
2418	2 d. Fighting the White Skeleton Demon	40	40
2419	2 d. The real and the fake Monkey King	40	40
2420	3 d. Monkey King trapped in furnace	50	50
	a. Sheetlet. Nos. 2420/5	2·75	
2421	3 d. Monkey King with magic weapon	50	50
2422	3 d. Type **269**	50	50
2423	3 d. At the Gate of South Heaven	50	50
2424	3 d. Tasting the celestial peaches	50	50
2425	3 d. Monkey King rescued from Five-Finger Mountain	50	50
2414/25	*Set of 12*	5·00	5·00

MS2426 Four sheets, each 134×109 mm. (a) 5 d. Mickey and Donald with Master San Tsang (*vert*). P 13½×14. (b) 10 d. Monkey King, Mickey and monkeys. P 14×13½. (c) 10 d. Monkey King, Mickey and tortoise (*vert*). P 13½×14. (d) 5 d. Mickey and Minnie with Buddhist scriptures. P 14×13½ .. .. *Set of 4 sheets* 7·00 8·00
Nos. 2414/19 and 2420/5 were each printed together, *se-tenant*, in sheetlets of 6.
Nos. 2414/25 were re-issued on the 15 September 1998 with the margins of the sheetlets overprinted "70TH ANNIVERSARY OF MICKEY & MINNIE" and the "HAPPY BIRTHDAY" logo. The logo was also added to the margins of No. **MS**2426.

(Des Y. Lee. Litho Questa)

1997 (12 Feb). *"HONG KONG '97" International Stamp Exhibition. Jackie Chan (film star).* T **270** *and similar multicoloured designs.* P 14.

2427	4 d. Type **270**	45	50
	a. Sheetlet. Nos. 2427/34	3·50	
2428	4 d. Wearing red jacket	45	50
2429	4 d. In open-necked shirt	45	50
2430	4 d. Bare-chested	45	50
2431	4 d. Wearing black jacket	45	50
2432	4 d. Wearing black and white spotted shirt	45	50
2433	4 d. Wearing white T-shirt and red anorak	45	50
2434	4 d. Wearing white sleeveless T-shirt	45	50
2427/34	*Set of 8*	3·50	4·00

MS2435 76×106 mm. 25 d. Jackie Chan in action (*horiz*) .. .. .. 3·00 3·25
Nos. 2427/34 were printed together, *se-tenant*, in sheetlets of 8.

271 Clouded Leopard
272 Monkey

1997 (24 Feb). *Endangered Species.* T **271** *and similar horiz designs. Multicoloured. Litho.* P 14.

2436	1 d. 50, Type **271**	20	25
	a. Sheetlet. Nos. 2436/55	4·00	
2437	1 d. 50, Audouin's Gull	20	25
2438	1 d. 50, Leatherback Turtle	20	25
2439	1 d. 50, White Eared-Pheasant	20	25
2440	1 d. 50, Kakapo	20	25
2441	1 d. 50, Right Whale	20	25
2442	1 d. 50, Black-footed Ferret	20	25
2443	1 d. 50, Dwarf Lemur	20	25
2444	1 d. 50, Peacock Pheasant	20	25
2445	1 d. 50, Brown Hyena	20	25
2446	1 d. 50, Cougar	20	25
2447	1 d. 50, Gharial	20	25
2448	1 d. 50, Monk Seal	20	25
2449	1 d. 50, Mountain Gorilla	20	25
2450	1 d. 50, Blyth's Tragopan	20	25
2451	1 d. 50, Malayan Tapir	20	25
2452	1 d. 50, Black Rhinoceros	20	25
2453	1 d. 50, Polar Bear	20	25
2454	1 d. 50, Red Colobus	20	25
2455	1 d. 50, Tiger	20	25
2456	1 d. 50, Arabian Oryx	20	25
	a. Sheetlet. Nos. 2456/75	4·00	
2457	1 d. 50, Baiji	20	25
2458	1 d. 50, Ruffed Lemur	20	25
2459	1 d. 50, California Condor	20	25
2460	1 d. 50, Blue-headed Quail Dove	20	25
2461	1 d. 50, Numbat	20	25
2462	1 d. 50, Congo Peacock	20	25
2463	1 d. 50, White Uakari	20	25
2464	1 d. 50, Eskimo Curlew	20	25
2465	1 d. 50, Gouldian Finch	20	25
2466	1 d. 50, Coelacanth	20	25
2467	1 d. 50, Toucan Barbet	20	25
2468	1 d. 50, Snow Leopard	20	25
2469	1 d. 50, Queen Alexandra's Birdwing	20	25
2470	1 d. 50, Dalmatian Pelican	20	25
2471	1 d. 50, Chaco Tortoise	20	25
2472	1 d. 50, Giant Catfish	20	25
2473	1 d. 50, Helmeted Hornbill	20	25
2474	1 d. 50, White-eyed River Martin	20	25
2475	1 d. 50, Fluminense Swallowtail	20	25
2436/75	*Set of 40*	8·00	10·00

MS2476 Three sheets, each 103×72 mm. (a) 25 d. Giant Panda; (b) 25 d. Humpback Whale; (c) 25 d. Japanese Crane .. *Set of 3 sheets* 8·75 9·00
Nos. 2436/55 and 2456/75 were each printed, *se-tenant*, in sheetlets of 20, with enlarged top margins incorporating the "HONG KONG '97" International Stamp Exhibition.

1997 (24 Feb). *The Jungle Book by Rudyard Kipling.* T **272** *and similar vert designs. Multicoloured.* P 14.

2477	3 d. Type **272**	35	40
	a. Sheetlet. Nos. 2477/88	4·25	
2478	3 d. Baloo (bear)	35	40
2479	3 d. Elephant	35	40
2480	3 d. Monkey and temple	35	40
2481	3 d. Bagheera (panther)	35	40
2482	3 d. Buffalo	35	40
2483	3 d. Mandrill	35	40
2484	3 d. Shere Khan (tiger)	35	40
2485	3 d. Rama (wolf)	35	40
2486	3 d. Kaa (cobra)	35	40
2487	3 d. Mongoose	35	40
2488	3 d. Mowgli	35	40
2477/88	*Set of 12*	4·25	4·75

Nos. 2477/88 were printed together, *se-tenant*, in sheetlets of 12 with the background forming a composite design.

273 *Polyporus squamosus*

(Litho Questa)

1997 (10 Mar). *Fungi.* T **273** *and similar multicoloured designs.* P 14.

2489	1 d. Type **273**	10	15
2490	3 d. *Armillaria tabescens*	35	40
2491	4 d. *Amanita caesarea* (*vert*)	45	50
	a. Sheetlet. Nos. 2491/9	4·00	
2492	4 d. *Lepiota procera* (*vert*)	45	50
2493	4 d. *Hygrophorus psittacinus* (*vert*)	45	50
2494	4 d. *Russula xerampelina* (*vert*)	45	50
2495	4 d. *Laccaria amethystina* (*vert*)	45	50
2496	4 d. *Coprinus micaceus* (*vert*)	45	50
2497	4 d. *Boletus edulis* (*vert*)	45	50
2498	4 d. *Morchella esculenta* (*vert*)	45	50
2499	4 d. *Otidea auricula* (*vert*)	45	50
2500	5 d. *Collybia velutipes*	60	65
2501	10 d. *Sarcoscypha coccinea*	1·10	1·25
2489/501	*Set of 13*	6·25	7·00

MS2502 76×106 mm. 25 d. *Volvariella bombycina* .. .. .. 3·00 3·25
Nos. 2491/9 were printed together, *se-tenant*, in sheetlets of 9.

(Des M. Freedman and Dena Rubin, Litho Questa)

1997 (24 Mar). *50th Anniv of U.N.E.S.C.O. Multicoloured designs as* T **374** *of Antigua.* P 14×13½ (*horiz*) or 13½×14 (*vert*).

2503	1 d. Cloister, Horyu-ji, Japan	10	15
2504	2 d. Great Wall, China	20	25
2505	3 d. Statues, Ayutthaya, Thailand	35	40
2506	4 d. Ascension Convent, Santa Maria, Philippines	45	50
2507	4 d. Mount Nimba Nature Reserve, Guinea (*vert*)	45	50
	a. Sheetlet. Nos. 2507/14 and 1 central label	3·50	

2508	4 d.	Banc d'Argun National Park, Mauritania (*vert*)	45	50
2509	4 d.	Doorway, Marrakesh, Morocco (*vert*)	45	50
2510	4 d.	Ichkeul National Park, Tunisia (*vert*)	45	50
2511	4 d.	Village pottery, Mali (*vert*)	45	50
2512	4 d.	Hippopotamus, Salonga National Park, Zaire (*vert*)	45	50
2513	4 d.	Timgad Roman Ruins, Algeria (*vert*)	45	50
2514	4 d.	Wooden statue, Benin (*vert*)	45	50
2515	4 d.	Temple, Magao Caves, China (*vert*)	45	50
	a.	Sheetlet. Nos. 2515/22 and 1 central label		3·50
2516	4 d.	Statue, Magao Caves (*vert*)	45	50
2517	4 d.	Domes, Magao Caves (*vert*)	45	50
2518	4 d.	Great Wall from the air, China (*vert*)	45	50
2519	4 d.	Statue, Great Wall (*vert*)	45	50
2520	4 d.	Bronze Bird, Imperial Palace, China (*vert*)	45	50
2521	4 d.	Temples, Imperial Palace, China (*vert*)	45	50
2522	4 d.	Dragon statue, Imperial Palace (*vert*)	45	50
2523	4 d.	Kyoto Gardens, Japan (*vert*)	45	50
	a.	Sheetlet. Nos. 2523/30 and 1 central label		3·50
2524	4 d.	Himeji Castle, Japan (*vert*)	45	50
2525	4 d.	Horyu-ji Temple, Japan (*vert*)	45	50
2526	4 d.	Buddha, Horyu-ji, Japan (*vert*)	45	50
2527	4 d.	Yakushima Forest, Japan (*vert*)	45	50
2528	4 d.	Ancient tree, Yakushima Forest, Japan (*vert*)	45	50
2529	4 d.	Temple, Kyoto, Japan (*vert*)	45	50
2530	4 d.	Pavilion, Kyoto, Japan (*vert*)	45	50
2531	5 d.	Riverside houses, Inselstadt, Germany	60	65
	a.	Sheetlet. Nos. 2531/5 and 1 corner label		3·00
2532	5 d.	Rosaleda Gardens, Bamberg, Germany	60	65
2533	5 d.	Bamberg Cathedral, Germany	60	65
2534	5 d.	Timbered house, Maulbronn, Germany	60	65
2535	5 d.	Maulbronn Monastery, Germany	60	65
2536	5 d.	Ruins at Delphi, Greece	60	65
	a.	Sheetlet. Nos. 2536/40 and 1 corner label		3·00
2537	5 d.	Rhodes waterfront, Greece	60	65
2538	5 d.	Knights' Hospital, Rhodes, Greece	60	65
2539	5 d.	Temple, Delphi, Greece	60	65
2540	5 d.	Delphi from air, Greece	60	65
2541	5 d.	Foliage, Shirakami-Sanchi, Japan	60	65
	a.	Sheetlet. Nos. 2541/5 and 1 corner label		3·00
2542	5 d.	Notice board, Shirakami-Sanchi, Japan	60	65
2543	5 d.	Tower, Himeji Castle, Japan	60	65
2544	5 d.	Roof tops, Himeji Castle, Japan	60	65
2545	5 d.	Gateway, Himeji Castle, Japan	60	65
2546	10 d.	Komodo Dragons, Indonesia	1·10	1·40
2547	15 d.	Ancient hut, Timbuktu, Mali	1·75	1·90
2503/47		*Set of 44*	23·00	26·00

MS2548 Four sheets, each 127×102 mm. (a) 25 d. Plitvice Lakes National Park, Croatia; (b) 25 d. Ruins of Kilwa Kisiwani, Tanzania; (c) 25 d. Santa Maria de Alcobaca cloisters, Portugal; (d) 25 d. Watergarden, Kyoto, Japan *Set of 4 sheets* 11·50 12·00
Nos. 2507/14, 2515/22 and 2523/30 were each printed together, *se-tenant*, in sheetlets of 8 stamps with a centre label and Nos. 2531/5, 2536/40 and 2541/5 in sheetlets of 5 stamps with a top left-hand corner label.

274 Minnie Mouse, 1928

1997 (1 May). *Minnie Mouse Through the Years. T* **274** *and similar vert designs showing Disney cartoon character in years stated. Multicoloured. Litho. P* 13½×14.

2549	4 d.	Type 274	70	75
	a.	Sheetlet. Nos. 2549/57		5·50
2550	4 d.	In 1933	70	75
2551	4 d.	In 1934	70	75
2552	4 d.	In 1937	70	75
2553	4 d.	In 1938	70	75
2554	4 d.	In 1941	70	75
2555	4 d.	In 1950	70	75
2556	4 d.	In 1990	70	75
2557	4 d.	In 1997	70	75
2549/57		*Set of 9*	5·50	6·00

MS2558 133×108 mm. 25 d. In 1987 4·50 5·50
Nos. 2549/57 were printed together, *se-tenant*, in sheetlets of 9.

OMNIBUS ISSUES

Details, together with prices for complete sets, of the various Omnibus issues from the 1935 Silver Jubilee series to date are included in a special section following Zimbabwe at the end of Volume 2.

---

275 Dipstick

(Des Alvin White Studios. Litho Questa)

1997 (1 May). *101 Dalmatians. T* **275** *and similar multicoloured designs showing Disney cartoon characters.* P 13½×14 (*vert*) or 14×13½ (*horiz*).

2559	50 b.	Type 275	20	20
	a.	Sheetlet. Nos. 2559/64		1·10
2560	50 b.	Fidget	20	20
2561	50 b.	Jewel	20	20
2562	50 b.	Lucky	20	20
2563	50 b.	Two-Tone	20	20
2564	50 b.	Wizzer	20	20
2565	2 d.	Two puppies playing (*horiz*)	35	35
	a.	Sheetlet. Nos. 2565/73		2·75
2566	2 d.	Puppy and pig (*horiz*)	35	35
2567	2 d.	Two puppies with butterfly (*horiz*)	35	35
2568	2 d.	Puppy lying on back (*horiz*)	35	35
2569	2 d.	Puppy with ball (*horiz*)	35	35
2570	2 d.	Puppy with bone (*horiz*)	35	35
2571	2 d.	One puppy pulling another puppy's tail (*horiz*)	35	35
2572	2 d.	Two puppies pulling third puppy's ears (*horiz*)	35	35
2573	2 d.	Puppy with teddy bear (*horiz*)	35	35
2574	3 d.	Puppy asleep on biscuit box (*horiz*)	45	45
	a.	Sheetlet. Nos. 2574/82		3·50
2575	3 d.	Puppy with hose (*horiz*)	45	45
2576	3 d.	Puppy and bottle (*horiz*)	45	45
2577	3 d.	Puppy and biscuit bowl (*horiz*)	45	45
2578	3 d.	Puppy wearing hat (*horiz*)	45	45
2579	3 d.	Three puppies with lipstick (*horiz*)	45	45
2580	3 d.	Puppy tying another up with string (*horiz*)	45	45
2581	3 d.	Two puppies and lunch box (*horiz*)	45	45
2582	3 d.	Three puppies and computer (*horiz*)	45	45
2559/82		*Set of 24*	6·50	6·50

MS2583 Six sheets, each 127×103 mm. (a) 25 d. Sheep and puppies (*horiz*). (b) 25 d. Cruella de Vil (*horiz*). (c) 25 d. Puppy looking at photograph (*horiz*). (d) 25 d. Puppies in mail sack. (e) 25 d. Two puppies covered in paint (*horiz*). (f) 25 d. Two puppies playing computer game (*horiz*). *Set of 6 sheets* 25·00 27·00
Nos. 2559/64, 2565/73 and 2574/82 were each printed together, *se-tenant*, in sheetlets of 6 (Nos. 2559/64) or 9 (others).

276 Juventus Team, 1897

277 "Morning Glory and Cricket"

1997 (9 May). *Centenary of Juventus Football Team. T* **276** *and similar horiz designs. Multicoloured. Litho.* P 14×13½.

2584	5 d.	Type 276	60	65
	a.	Sheetlet. Nos. 2584/9		3·50
2585	5 d.	Centenary emblem and player	60	65
2586	5 d.	Giampiero Boniperti	60	65
2587	5 d.	Roberto Bettega	60	65
2588	5 d.	Juventus team, 1996	60	65
2589	5 d.	Juventus '97 logo	60	65
2584/89		*Set of 6*	3·50	4·00

Nos. 2584/9 were printed together, *se-tenant*, in sheetlets of 6.

(Des R. Rundo. Litho Questa)

1997 (20 May). *300th Anniv of Mother Goose Nursery Rhymes. Horiz design as T* **309** *of Dominica. Sheet* 72×102 *mm. Multicoloured.* P 14.
MS2590 25 d. Young girl ("I'll Tell You a Story") 3·00 3·25

(Litho Questa)

1997 (20 May). *10th Anniv of Chernobyl Nuclear Disaster. Vert designs as T* **376** *of Antigua. Multicoloured.* P 13½.

2591	15 d.	As Type 376 of Antigua	1·75	1·90
2592	15 d.	As No. 2591 but inscribed "CHABAD'S CHILDREN OF CHERNOBYL"	1·75	1·90

(Des J. Iskowitz. Litho Questa)

1997 (20 May). *50th Death Anniv of Paul Harris (founder of Rotary International). Horiz designs as T* **377** *of Antigua. Multicoloured.* P 14.
2593 10 d. Rotary President Sydney Pascall planting tree of friendship 1·10 1·25
MS2594 78×108 mm. 25 d. Paul Harris and Preserve Planet Earth emblem 3·00 3·25

(Litho Questa)

1997 (20 May). *Golden Wedding of Queen Elizabeth and Prince Philip. Horiz designs as T* **378** *of Antigua. Multicoloured.* P 14.

2595	4 d.	Queen Elizabeth II	45	50
	a.	Sheetlet. Nos. 2595/600		2·75
2596	4 d.	Royal coat of arms	45	50
2597	4 d.	Queen Elizabeth and Prince Philip applauding	45	50
2598	4 d.	Queen Elizabeth and Prince Philip taking the salute	45	50
2599	4 d.	Royal Yacht *Britannia*	45	50
2600	4 d.	Prince Philip	45	50
2595/600		*Set of 6*	2·75	3·00

MS2601 100×70 mm. 20 d. Princess Elizabeth, 1948 2·25 2·40
Nos. 2595/600 were printed together, *se-tenant*, in sheetlets of 6.

(Des J. Iskowitz. Litho Questa)

1997 (20 May). *"Pacific '97" International Stamp Exhibition, San Francisco. Death Centenary of Henrich von Stephan (founder of U.P.U.). Horiz designs as T* **379** *of Antigua.* P 14.

2602	5 d.	deep magenta	60	65
	a.	Sheetlet. Nos. 2602/4		1·75
2603	5 d.	chestnut	60	65
2604	5 d.	turquoise-green and black	60	65
2602/4		*Set of 3*	1·75	1·90

MS2605 82×118 mm. 25 d. turquoise-green and black 3·00 3·25
Designs:—No. 2602, Von Stephan and Otto von Bismarck; No. 2603, Von Stephan and Mercury; No. 2604, Mail wagon, Boston, 1900; No. MS2605, Von Stephan and Hamburg–Lübeck postilion.
Nos. 2602/4 were printed together, *se-tenant*, in sheetlets of 3 with enlarged illustrated right-hand margin.

1997 (20 May). *Birth Bicentenary of Hiroshige (Japanese painter). T* **277** *and similar vert designs. Multicoloured. Litho.* P 13½×14.

2606/11	4 d.	× 6 (Type **277**; "Dragonfly and Begonia"; "Two Ducks swimming among Reeds"; "A Black-naped Oriole perched on a Stem of Rose Mallow"; "A Pheasant on a Snow-covered Pine"; "A Cuckoo flying through the Rain")		
	a.	Sheetlet. Nos. 2606/11		2·75
2612/17	4 d.	× 6 ("An Egret among Rushes"; "Peacock and Peonies"; "Three Wild Geese flying across the Moon"; "A Cock in the Snow"; "A Pheasant and Bracken"; "Peonies")		
	a.	Sheetlet. Nos. 2612/17		2·75
2618/23	4 d.	× 6 ("Sparrow and Bamboo"; "Mandarin Ducks on an Icy Pond with Brown Leaves falling"; "Blossoming Plum Tree"; "Java Sparrow and Magnolia"; "Chinese Bellflowers and Miscanthus"; "A Small Black Bird clinging to a Tendril of Ivy")		
	a.	Sheetlet. Nos. 2618/23		2·75
2624/9	5 d.	× 6 ("Sparrows and Camellia in Snow"; "Parrot on a Branch of Pine"; "A Long-tailed Blue Bird on a Branch of Flowering Plum"; "Sparrow and Bamboo"; "Bird in a Tree"; "A Wild Duck swimming beneath Snow-laden reeds")		
	a.	Sheetlet. Nos. 2624/9		3·50
2630/5	5 d.	× 6 ("Kingfisher above a Yellow-flowered Water Plant"; "Wagtail and Roses"; "A Mandarin Duck on a Snowy Bank"; "A Japanese White-eye on a Persimmon Branch"; "Sparrows and Camellia in Snow"; "Kingfisher and Moon above a Yellow-flowered Water Plant")		
	a.	Sheetlet. Nos. 2630/5		3·50
2636/41	5 d.	× 6 ("Sparrow and Bamboo by Night"; "Birds Flying over Waves"; "Blossoming Plum Tree with Full Moon"; "Kingfisher and Iris"; "A Blue-and-White Flycatcher on a Hibiscus Flower"; "Mandarin Ducks in Snowfall")		
	a.	Sheetlet. Nos. 2636/41		3·50
2606/41		*Set of 35*	15·00	16·00

MS2642 Six sheets each 95×120 mm. (a) 25 d. Hawk on perch. (b) 25 d. Two green birds on branch. (c) 25 d. Kingfisher hovering. (d) 25 d. "Three Wild Geese flying across moon". (e) 25 d. Red parrot on branch. (f) 25 d. White bird on flowering bush *Set of 6 sheets* 17·00 18·00
Nos. 2606/11, 2612/17, 2618/23, 2624/9, 2630/5 and 2636/41 were each printed together, *se-tenant*, in sheetlets of 6.

(Des R. Rundo. Litho Questa)

1997 (20 May). *175th Anniv of Brothers Grimm's Third Collection of Fairy Tales. Little Red Riding Hood. Multicoloured designs as T* **380** *of Antigua.* P 13½×14.

2643	10 d.	Grandma's cottage	1·10	1·25
	a.	Sheetlet. Nos. 2643/5		3·25
2644	10 d.	Little Red Riding Hood	1·10	1·25
2645	10 d.	The Wolf	1·10	1·25
2643/5		*Set of 3*	3·25	3·50

MS2646 124×96 mm. 10 d. Little Red Riding Hood (*horiz*). P 14×13½. 1·10 1·25
Nos. 2643/5 were printed together, *se-tenant*, in sheetlets of 3 with an illustrated margin.

278 Coelophysis chasing Ornitholestes

(Des W. Wright. Litho Questa)

1997 (23 June). *Dinosaurs. T* **278** *and similar horiz designs. Multicoloured. P* 14.

2647	50 b. Type **278**	10	10
2648	63 b. Spinosaurus	10	10
2649	75 b. Kentrosaurus	10	10
2650	1 d. Ceratosaurus	10	10
2651	1 d. 50, Stygimoloch	20	25
2652	2 d. Troodon	20	25
2653	3 d. Velociraptor	35	40
2654	4 d. Triceratops	45	50
2655	4 d. Anurognathus	45	50
	a. Sheetlet. Nos. 2655/63	4·00	
2656	4 d. Pteranodon	45	50
2657	4 d. Pterosaurus	45	50
2658	4 d. Saltasaurus	45	50
2659	4 d. Agathaumus	45	50
2660	4 d. Stegosaurus	45	50
2661	4 d. Albertosaurus libratus	45	50
2662	4 d. Three Lesothosauruses running	45	50
2663	4 d. Five Lesothosauruses running	45	50
2664	4 d. Tarbosaurus bataar	45	50
	a. Sheetlet. Nos. 2664/72	4·00	
2665	4 d. Brachiosaurus	45	50
2666	4 d. Styracosaurus	45	50
2667	4 d. Baryonyx	45	50
2668	4 d. Coelophysis	45	50
2669	4 d. Carnotaurus	45	50
2670	4 d. Compsognathus longipes	45	50
2671	4 d. Compsognathus "Elegant Jaw"	45	50
2672	4 d. Stenonychosaurus	45	50
2673	5 d. Protoceratops	60	65
2674	10 d. Ornithomimus	1·10	1·25
2675	15 d. Stegosaurus	1·75	1·90
2676	20 d. Ankylosaurus saichania	2·25	2·40
2647/76	*Set of 30*	15·00	17·00

MS2677 Two sheets, each 106×81 mm. (a) 25 d. Head of Deinonychus (50×37 *mm*). (b) 25 d. Seismosaurus (88×27 *mm*) . . *Set of 2 sheets* 5·75 6·00

Nos. 2655/63 and 2664/72 were each printed together, *se-tenant*, in sheetlets of 9 with the backgrounds forming composite designs.

279 Margaret Thatcher and Deng Xiaoping toasting Joint Declaration, 1984

1997 (1 July). *Return of Hong Kong to China. T* **279** *and similar horiz designs. Multicoloured. Litho. P* 14.

2678	3 d. Type **279**	35	40
	a. Sheetlet. Nos. 2678/81	1·40	
2679	3 d. Signing Joint Declaration on Hong Kong, 1984	35	40
2680	3 d. Signing Joint Declaration on Macao, 1987	35	40
2681	3 d. Deng Xiaoping toasting Prime Minister Anibal Silva of Portugal	35	40
2682	4 d. Hong Kong in 1843 and Governor Sir Henry Pottinger	45	50
	a. Sheetlet. Nos. 2682/4	1·40	
2683	4 d. Kowloon in 1860 and Governor Sir Hercules Robinson	45	50
2684	4 d. Reception in New Territories, 1898, and Governor Sir Henry Blake	45	50
2685	5 d. Governor Sir Henry Pottinger and British warship	60	65
	a. Sheetlet. Nos. 2685/7	1·75	
2686	5 d. Governor Christopher Patten and Lantau Bridge	60	65
2687	5 d. Chief Executive C.H. Tung and Hong Kong by night	60	65
2688	6 d. Signing the Treaty of Nanking, 1842	70	75
	a. Sheetlet. Nos. 2688/90	2·10	
2689	6 d. Signing the Japanese Surrender of Hong Kong, 1945	70	75
2690	6 d. Signing of the Sino-British Joint Declaration, 1984	70	75
2678/90	*Set of 13*	6·50	7·25

Nos. 2678/81, 2682/4, 2685/7 and 2688/90 were each printed together, *se-tenant*, in sheetlets of 4 (Nos. 2678/81) or 3 (others).

280 Great Mosque, Samarra, Iran

281 Downhill Skiing

(Des W. Wright. Litho Questa)

1997 (15 July). *Natural and Man-made Wonders of the World. T* **280** *and similar multicoloured designs. P* 14 (*Nos.* 2691/6) *or* 13½×14 (*others*).

2691	63 b. Type **280**	10	10
2692	75 b. Moai statues, Easter Island (*horiz*)	10	10
2693	1 d. Golden Gate Bridge, San Francisco (*horiz*)	10	10
2694	1 d. 50, The Statue of Liberty, New York	20	25
2695	2 d. The Parthenon, Athens (*horiz*)	20	25
2696	3 d. Pyramid of the Sun, Mexico (*horiz*)	35	40
2697	5 d. The Rock of Gibraltar (*horiz*)	60	65
	a. Sheetlet. Nos. 2697/702	3·50	
2698	5 d. St. Peter's Basilica, Rome (*horiz*)	60	65
2699	5 d. Santa Sophia, Istanbul (*horiz*)	60	65
2700	5 d. "Gateway to the West" monument, St. Louis (*horiz*)	60	65
2701	5 d. Great Wall of China (*horiz*)	60	65
2702	5 d. City of Carcassonne, France (*horiz*)	60	65
2703	5 d. Stonehenge, England (*horiz*)	60	65
	a. Sheetlet. Nos. 2703/8	3·50	
2704	5 d. Hughes HK-1 *Spruce Goose* flying boat (World's largest aircraft) (*horiz*)	60	65
2705	5 d. Hoverspeed "Seacat" catamaran (fastest Atlantic crossing by a commercial catamaran) (*horiz*)	60	65
2706	5 d. "Thrust 2" car (official land speed record) (*horiz*)	60	65
2707	5 d. Stepped Pyramid, Egypt (*horiz*)	60	65
2708	5 d. L.N.E.R. Class A4 *Mallard* (fastest steam locomotive),1938 (*horiz*)	60	65
2691/708	*Set of 18*	8·00	9·00

MS2709 Three sheets, each 98×68 mm. (a) 25 d. Mount Everest (42×28 *mm*). (b) 25 d. The Grand Canyon, Colorado (42×28 *mm*). (c) 25 d. Washington Monument (33×51 *mm*). P 14.
. . *Set of 3 sheets* 9·00 9·25

Nos. 2697/702 and 2703/8 were each printed together, *se-tenant*, in sheetlets of 6.

No. 2702 is inscribed "CARCASSONNNE" in error.

(Litho B.D.T.)

1997 (21 July). *Winter Olympic Games, Nagano* (1998). *T* **281** *and similar multicoloured designs. P* 14.

2710	5 d. Type **281**	60	65
2711	5 d. Two-man bob-sleigh (*vert*)	60	65
	a. Sheetlet. Nos. 2711/19	5·50	
2712	5 d. Freestyle skiing (*vert*)	60	65
2713	5 d. Speed skating (*vert*)	60	65
2714	5 d. Downhill skiing (No. 8 on bib) (*vert*)	60	65
2715	5 d. Womens figure skating (*vert*)	60	65
2716	5 d. Downhill skiing (No. 4 on bib) (*vert*)	60	65
2717	5 d. Pairs figure skating (*vert*)	60	65
2718	5 d. Cross-country (*vert*)	60	65
2719	5 d. Ski jumping (*vert*)	60	65
2720	5 d. One-man luge	60	65
	a. Sheetlet. Nos. 2720/8	5·50	
2721	5 d. Ice hockey	60	65
2722	5 d. Four-man bob-sleigh	60	65
2723	5 d. Ski-jumping	60	65
2724	5 d. Curling	60	65
2725	5 d. Figure skating	60	65
2726	5 d. Speed skating	60	65
2727	5 d. Biathlon	60	65
2728	5 d. Downhill skiing (*different*)	60	65
2729	10 d. One-man luge	1·10	1·25
2730	15 d. Speed skating	1·75	1·90
2731	20 d. Ice hockey	2·25	2·40
2710/31	*Set of 22*	17·00	18·00

MS2732 Two sheets. (a) 97×67 mm. 25 d. Bob-sleigh. (b) 67×97 mm. 25 d. Pairs figure skating (*vert*) . . . . *Set of 2 sheets* 5·75 6·00

Nos. 2711/19 and 2720/8 were each printed togther, *se-tenant*, in sheetlets of 9.

282 Brown Pelican

(Des J. Ruff. Litho Questa)

1997 (4 Aug). *Sea Birds. T* **282** *and similar multicoloured designs. P* 14.

2733	3 d. Type **282**	35	40
	a. Sheetlet. Nos. 2733/44	4·25	
2734	3 d. Galapagos Penguin	35	40
2735	3 d. Red-billed Tropic Bird	35	40
2736	3 d. Little Tern	35	40
2737	3 d. Dunlin	35	40
2738	3 d. Kittiwake	35	40
2739	3 d. Atlantic Puffin	35	40
2740	3 d. Wandering Albatross	35	40
2741	3 d. Masked Booby	35	40
2742	3 d. Glaucous Winged Gull	35	40
2743	3 d. Arctic Tern	35	40
2744	3 d. Piping Plover	35	40
2745	5 d. Roseate Tern	60	65
2746	10 d. Red-legged Cormorant	1·10	1·25
2747	15 d. Blue-footed Booby	1·75	1·90
2748	20 d. Sanderling	2·25	2·40
2733/48	*Set of 16*	10·00	11·00

MS2749 Two sheets, each 106×76 mm. (a) 23 d. Long-tailed Skua (*vert*). (b) 23 d. Osprey (*vert*) . . . . *Set of 2 sheets* 2·50 2·75

Nos. 2733/44 were printed together, *se-tenant*, in sheetlets of 12.

No. 2743 is inscribed "ARTIC TERN" and the captions on Nos. 2745/6 are transposed, both in error.

283 Scottish Fold Cat   **284** Diana, Princess of Wales

(Des D. Burkhart. Litho Questa)

1997 (12 Aug). *Cats and Dogs. T* **283** *and similar horiz designs. Multicoloured. P* 14.

2750	63 b. Type **283**	10	10
2751	75 b. Dalmatian	10	10
2752	1 d. Rottweiler	10	15
2753	1 d. 50, American Curl cat	20	25
2754	2 d. British Bi-colour cat	20	25
2755	3 d. Newfoundland	35	40
2756	3 d. Devon Rex cat	35	40
2757	4 d. Great Dane	45	50
2758	5 d. Burmilla cat	60	65
	a. Sheetlet. Nos. 2758/63	3·50	
2759	5 d. Blue Burmese cat	60	65
2760	5 d. Korat cat	60	65
2761	5 d. British Tabby cat	60	65
2762	5 d. Foreign White cat	60	65
2763	5 d. Somali cat	60	65
2764	5 d. Akita	60	65
	a. Sheetlet. Nos. 2764/9	3·50	
2765	5 d. Welsh Corgi	60	65
2766	5 d. German Shepherd	60	65
2767	5 d. Saint Bernard	60	65
2768	5 d. Bullmastiff	60	65
2769	5 d. Malamute	60	65
2770	6 d. Silver Tabby cat	70	75
2771	10 d. Old English Sheepdog	1·10	1·25
2772	15 d. Queensland Heeler cat	1·75	1·90
2773	20 d. Abyssinian cat	2·25	2·40
2750/73	*Set of 24*	14·50	16·50

MS2774 Four sheets, each 107×78 mm. (a) 25 d. Cornish Rex cat. (b) 25 d. Siamese cat. (c) 25 d. Boxer. (d) 25 d. Doberman Pinscher
. . . . *Set of 4 sheets* 12·00 12·50

Nos. 2758/63 and 2764/9 were each printed together, *se-tenant*, in sheetlets of 6.

(Litho Questa)

1997 (4 Sept). *World Cup Football Championship, France* (1998). *Designs as T* **383** *of Antigua. P* 14×13½ (*horiz*) or 13½×14 (*vert*).

2775	1 d. black	10	10
2776	1 d. 50, black	20	25
2777	2 d. black	20	25
2778	3 d. black	35	40
2779/86	4 d. × 8 mult or agate (Nos. 2782/3)		
	a. Sheetlet. Nos. 2779/86 and central label	3·50	
2787/94	4 d. × 8 multicoloured or blk (No. 2788)		
	a. Sheetlet. Nos. 2787/94 and central label	3·50	
2795/802	4 d. × 8 blackish brown (Nos. 2795/6, 2800 and 2802) or multicoloured		
	a. Sheetlet. Nos. 2795/802 and central label	3·50	
2803/10	4 d. × 8 multicoloured		
	a. Sheetlet. Nos. 2803/10 and central label	3·50	
2811	5 d. black	60	65
2812	10 d. black	1·10	1·25
2775/812	*Set of 38*	16·50	18·00

MS2813 Four sheets, each 102×127 mm. (a) 25 d. multicoloured. (b) 25 d. multicoloured. (c) 25 d. black. (d) 25 d. blackish brown
. . . . *Set of 4 sheets* 12·00 12·50

Designs: *Horiz*—No. 2775, Uruguay team, 1950; No. 2776, West German team, 1954; No 2777, Brazilian team, 1970; No. 2778, Brazilian team, 1962; No. 2779, Brazilian team, 1994; No. 2780, Argentine team, 1986; No. 2781, Brazilian team, 1970; No. 2782, Italian team, 1934; No. 2783, Uruguay team, 1958; No. 2784, English team, 1966; No. 2785, Brazilian team, 1962; No. 2786, West German team, 1990; No. 2787, Mario Kempes, Argentina (1978); No. 2788, Joseph Gaetjens, U.S.A. (1950) (inscr "ADEMIR BRAZIL" in error); No. 2789, Muller, West Germany (1970); No. 2790, Lineker, England (1986); No. 2791, Eusebio, Portugal (1966); No. 2792, Schillaci, Italy (1990); No. 2793, Lato, Poland (1974); No. 2794, Rossi, Italy (1982); No. 2811, Italian team, 1938; No. 2812, Uruguay team, 1930; No. **MS**2813a, Philippe Albert, Belgium; No. **MS**2813b, Juninho, Brazil; No. **MS**2813c, Eusebio, Portugal; No. **MS**2813d, Pele, Brazil. *Vert*—No. 2795, Moore, England (1996); No. 2796, Fritzwalter, West Germany (1954); No. 2797, Beckenbauer, West Germany (1974); No. 2798, Zoff, Italy (1982); No. 2799, Maradona, Argentina (1986); No. 2800, Passarella, Argentina (1978); No. 2801, Mattahus, West Germany (1990); No. 2802, Dunga, Brazil (1994); No. 2803, Kinkladze, Georgia; No. 2804, Shearer, England; No. 2805, Dani, Portugal; No. 2806, Weah, Portugal; No. 2807, Ravanelli, Italy; No. 2808, Raducioiu, Rumania; No. 2809, Schmeichel, Denmark; No. 2810, Bergkamp, Holland;

Nos. 2779/86, 2787/94, 2795/802 and 2803/10 were each printed together, *se-tenant*, in sheetlets of 8 stamps and 1 central label.

NEW INFORMATION

The editor is always interested to correspond with people who have new information that will improve or correct the Catalogue.

(Des J. Iskowitz. Litho Questa)

1997 (26 Nov). *Diana, Princess of Wales Commemoration.* T **284** *and similar vert designs each red-brown and black* (Nos. 2814/17). P 14.

2814	10 d. Type **284**	1·10	1·25
	a. Sheetlet. Nos. 2814/17	4·50	
2815	10 d. Wearing open-necked shirt	1·10	1·25
2816	10 d. Wearing polo-neck jumper	1·10	1·25
2817	10 d. Wearing diamond-drop earrings	1·10	1·25
2814/17	*Set of 4*	4·50	5·00
MS2818	76×106 mm. 25 d. Diana, Princess of Wales (multicoloured)	3·00	3·25

Nos. 2814/17 were printed together, *se-tenant*, in sheetlets of 4 with enlarged illustrated margins.

Nos. 2814/18 exist imperforate from a limited printing.

(Litho B.D.T.)

1997 (8 Dec). *Christmas. Paintings. Vert designs as* T **386** *of Antigua. Multicoloured.* P 14.

2819	1 d. "Angel" (Rembrandt)	10	15
2820	1 d. 50, "Initiation into the Rites of Dionysus", Villa dei Misteri	20	25
2821	2 d. "Pair of Erotes with Purple Cloaks"	20	25
2822	3 d. "The Ecstasy of Saint Theresa" (Gianlorenzo Bernini)	35	40
2823	5 d. "Virgin and Child with Angels" (Matthias Grunewald)	60	65
2824	10 d. "Angel playing the Organ" (Stefan Lochner)	1·10	1·25
2819/24	*Set of 6*	2·50	3·00
MS2825	Two sheets, each 105×95 mm. (a) 25 d. "The Rest on the Flight into Egypt" (Caravaggio). (b) 25 d. "The Education of Cupid" (Titian) ... *Set of 2 sheets*	5·75	6·00

No. MS2825b is inscribed "TITAN" in error.

285 Tiger

286 Class 91 Electric Train, Great Britain

(Des Y. Lee. Litho Questa)

1998 (5 Jan). *Chinese New Year ("Year of the Tiger").* T **285** *and similar horiz designs. Multicoloured.* P 14½.

2826	3 d. Type **285** ("GAMBIA" in emerald)	35	40
	a. Sheetlet. Nos. 2826/9	1·40	
2827	3 d. Tiger ("GAMBIA" in magenta)	35	40
2828	3 d. Tiger ("GAMBIA" in lilac)	35	40
2829	3 d. Tiger ("GAMBIA" in deep violet-blue)	35	40
2826/9	*Set of 4*	1·40	1·60
MS2830	73×103 mm. 10 d. Tiger (42×28 mm)	1·10	1·25

Nos. 2826/9 were printed together, *se-tenant*, in sheetlets of 4.

(Des R. Sauber. Litho Questa)

1998 (19 May). *Trains of the World.* T **286** *and similar horiz designs. Multicoloured.* P 14.

2831	5 d. Type **286**	60	65
	a. Sheetlet. Nos. 2831/6	3·75	
2832	5 d. Class 26 steam locomotive No. 3450 *Red Devil*, South Africa	60	65
2833	5 d. TGV express train, France	60	65
2834	5 d. People Mover railcar, Great Britain	60	65
2835	5 d. ICE high speed train, Germany	60	65
2836	5 d. Montmartre funicular car, France	60	65
2837	5 d. Burlington Northern SD70 diesel locomotive No. 9716, U.S.A.	60	65
	a. Sheetlet. Nos. 2837/42	3·75	
2838	5 d. L.N.E.R. Class A4 steam locomotive *Mallard*, 1938	60	65
2839	5 d. Baldwin steam locomotive, Peru	60	65
2840	5 d. Amtrak Class ARM-7 electric locomotive, U.S.A.	60	65
2841	5 d. Rack steam locomotive No. B2503, Amberawa, Java	60	65
2842	5 d. Beyer-Peacock steam locomotive No. 3108, Pakistan	60	65
2831/42	*Set of 12*	7·50	7·75
MS2843	Two sheets, each 84×110 mm. (a) 25 d. Futuristic monorail train, Great Britain. (b) 25 d. Southern Pacific GS4 stream-lined steam locomotive, U.S.A. ... *Set of 2 sheets*	5·75	6·00

Nos. 2831/6 and 2837/42 were each printed together, *se-tenant*, in sheetlets of 6.

No. 2832 is inscribed "BEACONSFIELD CHINA", No. 2836 "MOUNTMAETRE FUNICULAR" and No. 2840 "SWEDEN RAIL 125 MPH", all in error.

287 Yellow Orchid

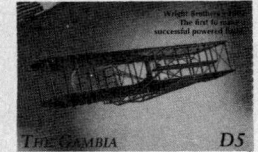
288 Wright *Flyer I*, 1903

(Des R. Martin. Litho Questa)

1998 (2 June). *African Flowers.* T **287** *and similar multi-coloured designs.* P 14.

2844	75 b. Type **287**	10	10
2845	1 d. 50, Transvaal Daisy	20	25
2846	3 d. Torch Lily	35	40
2847	4 d. *Ancistrochilus rothschildianus*	45	50
2848	5 d. *Adenium multiflorum* (horiz)	60	65
	a. Sheetlet. Nos. 2848/53	3·75	
2849	5 d. *Huernia namaquensis* (horiz)	60	65
2850	5 d. *Gloriosa superba* (horiz)	60	65
2851	5 d. *Strelitzia reginae* (horiz)	60	65
2852	5 d. *Passiflora mollissima* (horiz)	60	65
2853	5 d. *Bauhinia variegata* (horiz)	60	65
2854	10 d. *Polystachya vulcanica*	1·10	1·25
2855	15 d. Gladiolus	1·75	1·90
2844/55	*Set of 12*	7·50	8·25
MS2856	Two sheets, each 106×76 mm. (a) 25 d. *Aerangis rhodosticta*. (b) 25 d. *Ansella gigantea* ... *Set of 2 sheets*	5·75	6·00

Nos. 2848/53 were printed together, *se-tenant*, in sheetlets of 6, forming a composite background design.

1998 (16 June). *History of Aviation.* T **288** *and similar horiz designs. Multicoloured. Litho.* P 14.

2857	5 d. Type **288**	60	65
	a. Sheetlet. Nos. 2857/62	3·50	
2858	5 d. Curtiss A-1 seaplane, 1910	60	65
2859	5 d. Farman biplane, 1907	60	65
2860	5 d. Bristol monoplane, 1911	60	65
2861	5 d. Antoinette IV, 1908	60	65
2862	5 d. Sopwith "Bat Boat" amphibian, 1912	60	65
2863	5 d. Short Type 38, 1913	60	65
	a. Sheetlet. Nos. 2863/8	3·50	
2864	5 d. Fokker F.VIIb/3m, 1925	60	65
2865	5 d. Junkers J.13, 1919	60	65
2866	5 d. Pitcairn "Mailwing", 1927	60	65
2867	5 d. Douglas, 1920	60	65
2868	5 d. Curtiss T-32 Condor II airliner, 1934	60	65
2857/68	*Set of 12*	7·00	7·75
MS2869	Two sheets, each 106×76 mm. (a) 25 d. Albatross, 1913 (84×28 mm). (b) 25 d. Boeing 247 airliner, 1932 (84×28 mm) ... *Set of 2 sheets*	6·00	6·25

Nos. 2857/62 and 2863/8 were each printed together, *se-tenant*, in sheetlets of 6, forming composite background designs.

No. 2857 is dated "1902" in error.

289 Mulan

290 Chinese Junk

(Des Walt Disney Co. Litho)

1998 (1 July). *Mulan (film).* T **289** *and similar vert designs showing Disney cartoon characters. Multicoloured.* P 13½×14.

2870	4 d. Type **289**	65	65
	a. Sheetlet. Nos. 2870/7	4·75	
2871	4 d. Mushu	65	65
2872	4 d. Little Brother	65	65
2873	4 d. Cri-kee	65	65
2874	4 d. Grandmother Fa	65	65
2875	4 d. Fa Li	65	65
2876	4 d. Fa Zhou	65	65
2877	4 d. Mulan and Khan	65	65
2878	5 d. Mulan riding Khan	75	75
	a. Sheetlet. Nos. 2878/85	6·00	
2879	5 d. Shang	75	75
2880	5 d. Chi-fu	75	75
2881	5 d. Chien-po	75	75
2882	5 d. Yao	75	75
2883	5 d. Ling	75	75
2884	5 d. Shan-yu	75	75
2885	5 d. Mulan, Shang and Mushu	75	75
2870/85	*Set of 16*	10·50	10·50
MS2886	Four sheets. (a) 102×127 mm. 25 d. Mulan and Khan. (b) 127×102 mm. 25 d. Mulan and firework. (c) 127×102 mm. 25 d. Mulan in front of house. (d) 127×102 mm. 25 d. Mulan performing karate kick ... *Set of 4 sheets*	15·00	16·00

Nos. 2870/7 and 2878/85 were each printed together, *se-tenant*, in sheetlets of 8.

(Des D. Keren, R. Sauber and Zina Saunders. Litho Questa)

1998 (12 Oct). *Millennium Series. Famous People of the Twentieth Century. Multicoloured designs as* T **398** *of Antigua.* P 14.

(a) Famous Jazz Musicians

2887	4 d. Sidney Bechet	45	50
	a. Sheetlet. Nos. 2887/94	3·50	
2888	4 d. Sidney Bechet playing saxophone (53×38 mm)	45	50
2889	4 d. Duke Ellington conducting (53×38 mm)	45	50
2890	4 d. Duke Ellington	45	50
2891	4 d. Louis Armstrong	45	50
2892	4 d. Louis Armstrong playing trumpet (53×38 mm)	45	50
2893	4 d. Charlie "Bird" Parker playing saxophone (53×38 mm)	45	50
2894	4 d. Charlie "Bird" Parker	45	50

(b) Famous Theatrical Composers

2895	4 d. Cole Porter	45	50
	a. Sheetlet. Nos. 2895/902	3·50	
2896	4 d. Born to Dance (Cole Porter) (53×38 mm)	45	50
2897	4 d. Porgy and Bess (George Gershwin) (53×38 mm)	45	50
2898	4 d. George Gershwin	45	50
2899	4 d. Rogers and Hammerstein	45	50
2900	4 d. The King and I (Rogers and Hammerstein) (53×38 mm)	45	50
2901	4 d. West Side Story (Leonard Bernstein) (53×38 mm)	45	50
2902	4 d. Leonard Bernstein	45	50
2887/902	*Set of 16*	7·00	8·00
MS2903	Two sheets, each 76×106 mm. (a) 25 d. Ella Fitzgerald. (b) 25 d. "Oh How I Hate to Get Up in the Morning" (Irving Berlin) ... *Set of 2 sheets*	6·00	6·25

Nos. 2887/94 and 2895/902 were each printed together, *se-tenant*, in sheetlets of 8 with enlarged illustrated margins.

(Des G. Bibby. Litho Questa)

1998 (15 Oct). *Ships.* T **290** *and similar multicoloured designs.* P 14.

2904	2 d. Type **290**	20	25
2905	3 d. H.M.S. *Victory* (ship of the line, 1765)	35	40
2906	5 d. *Santa Maria* (Columbus)	60	65
	a. Sheetlet. Nos. 2906/11	3·50	
2907	5 d. *Mary Rose* (galleon)	60	65
2908	5 d. *Mayflower* (Pilgrim Fathers)	60	65
2909	5 d. *Ark Royal* (galleon, 1587)	60	65
2910	5 d. H.M.S. *Beagle* (Darwin)	60	65
2911	5 d. H.M.S. *Bounty* (Bligh)	60	65
2912	5 d. H.M.S. *Dreadnought* (battleship)	60	65
	a. Sheetlet. Nos. 2912/17	3·50	
2913	5 d. American "Truxton" class cruiser	60	65
2914	5 d. *Queen Mary* (liner)	60	65
2915	5 d. *Canberra* (liner)	60	65
2916	5 d. *Queen Elizabeth* (liner)	60	65
2917	5 d. *Queen Elizabeth II* (liner)	60	65
2918	10 d. British "County" class destroyer	1·10	1·25
2919	15 d. Viking longship	1·75	1·90
2904/19	*Set of 16*	11·50	12·50
MS2920	Two sheets. (a) 70×100 mm. 25 d. *Cutty Sark* (clipper) (41×56 mm). (b) 100×70 mm. 25 d. *Sovereign of the Seas* (liner) (56×41 mm) ... *Set of 2 sheets*	6·00	6·25

Nos. 2906/11 and 2912/17 were each printed together, *se-tenant*, in sheetlets of 6.

291 Captain Edward Smith

292 Mahatma Gandhi

(Des J. Iskowitz (Nos. 2921/6), R. Rundo (No. MS2927). Litho)

1998 (15 Oct). *Titanic Commemoration.* T **291** *and similar designs.* P 14.

2921	5 d. yellow-brown, black and dull violet-blue	60	65
	a. Sheetlet. Nos. 2921/6	3·50	
2922	5 d. yellow-brown, black & deep violet-blue	60	65
2923	5 d. yellow-brown and black	60	65
2924	5 d. dull violet-blue and black	60	65
2925	5 d. dull mauve and black	60	65
2926	5 d. dull mauve and black	60	65
2921/6	*Set of 6*	3·50	3·75
MS2927	Three sheets, each 110×85 mm. (a) 25 d. multicoloured. (b) 25 d. sepia and black. (c) 25 d. multicoloured ... *Set of 3 sheets*	9·00	9·25

Designs: Vert—No. 2921, Type **291**; No. 2922, Mrs. J. J. "Molly" Brown (passenger); No. 2923, Newspaper boy with placard; No. 2924, Benjamin Guggenheim (passenger); No. 2925, Isidor Strauss (passenger); No. 2926, Ida Strauss (passenger). Horiz—No. MS2927a, *Titanic* on postcard; No. MS2927b, *Titanic* sinking; No. MS2927c, Wreckage of *Titanic* on seabed.

Nos. 2921/6 were printed together, *se-tenant*, in sheetlets of 6 with enlarged illustrated margins.

(Des Diana Catherines. Litho Questa)

1998 (29 Oct). *25th Death Anniv of Pablo Picasso (painter). Multicoloured designs as* T **400** *of Antigua.* P 14½.

2928	3 d. "Death of Casagemas"	35	40
2929	5 d. "Seated Woman" (vert)	60	65
2930	10 d. "Mother and Child" (vert)	1·10	1·25
2928/30	*Set of 3*	2·00	2·25
MS2931	102×126 mm. 25 d. "Child playing with Toy Truck" (vert)	3·00	3·25

(Des Zina Saunders. Litho Questa)

1998 (29 Oct). *19th World Scout Jamboree, Chile. Designs as* T **402** *of Antigua, but vert. Multicoloured (except No. MS2935).* P 14.

2932	10 d. Scout handshake	1·10	1·25
	a. Sheetlet. Nos. 2932/4	3·25	
2933	10 d. Dinghy sailing	1·10	1·25
2934	10 d. Scout salute	1·10	1·25
2932/4	*Set of 3*	3·25	3·75
MS2935	47×61 mm. 25 d. Lord Baden-Powell (olive-bistre and black)	3·00	3·25

Nos. 2932/4 were printed together, *se-tenant*, in sheetlets of 3 with illustrated margins.

(Des Zina Saunders. Litho Questa)

1998 (29 Oct). *50th Death Anniv of Mahatma Gandhi.* T **292** *and similar multicoloured designs.* P 14.

2936	10 d. Type **292**	1·10	1·25
	a. Sheetlet. Nos. 2936/9	4·25	
2937	10 d. Gandhi on Salt March with Mrs. Sarojini Naidu (53×38 *mm*)	1·10	1·25
2938	10 d. Gandhi spinning yarn (53×38 *mm*)	1·10	1·25
2939	10 d. Gandhi in 1916	1·10	1·25
2936/9	*Set of 4*	4·25	5·00
MS2940	53×71 mm. 25 d. Gandhi writing	3·00	3·25

Nos. 2936/9 were printed together, *se-tenant*, in sheetlets of 4 with enlarged illustrated margins.

(Des D. Miller. Litho Questa)

1998 (29 Oct). *80th Anniv of Royal Air Force. Horiz designs as* T **404** *of Antigua. Multicoloured.* P 14.

2941	5 d. Sepecat Jaguar GR1A (from above)	60	65
	a. Sheetlet. Nos. 2941/4	2·40	
2942	5 d. Panavia Tornado GR1A	60	65
2943	5 d. Sepecat Jaguar GR1A (side view)	60	65
2944	5 d. BAe Hawk 200	60	65
2945	5 d. Sepecat Jaguar GR1A firing Sparrow missile	60	65
	a. Sheetlet. Nos. 2945/8	2·40	
2946	5 d. BAe Harrier GR 7 firing SNEB rockets	60	65
2947	5 d. Panavia Tornado GR1 firing AIM-9L missile	60	65
2948	5 d. Panavia Tornado GR1 in low level flight	60	65
2949	7 d. Panavia Tornado GR1 (facing left)	80	85
	a. Sheetlet. Nos. 2949/52	3·00	
2950	7 d. BAe Hawk T1A	80	85
2951	7 d. Sepecat Jaguar GR1A	80	85
2952	7 d. Panavia Tornado GR1 (facing right)	80	85
2941/52	*Set of 12*	7·75	8·50
MS2953	Six sheets, each 90×68 mm. (a) 20 d. EF-2000 Eurofighter. (b) 25 d. Bristol F2B Fighter and bird of prey in flight. (c) 25 d. Falcon's head and Bristol F2B Fighter. (d) 25 d. Bristol F2B Fighter and Golden Eagle (bird). (e) 25 d. Lancaster and EF-2000 Eurofighter. (f) 25 d. Lightning and EF-2000 Eurofighter		
	Set of 6 sheets	17·00	18·00

Nos. 2941/4, 2945/8 and 2949/52 were each printed together, *se-tenant*, in sheetlets of 4.

293 "Mule-drivers from Tetuan"

294 Puppy in Stocking

(Litho Questa)

1998 (29 Oct). *Birth Centenary of Eugéne Delacroix (painter).* T **293** *and similar multicoloured designs.* P 14.

2954	4 d. Type **293**	45	50
	a. Sheetlet. Nos. 2954/61	3·50	
2955	4 d. "Encampment of Arab Mule-drivers"	45	50
2956	4 d. "An Orange Seller"	45	50
2957	4 d. "The Banks of the River"	45	50
2958	4 d. "View of Tangier from the Seashore"	45	50
2959	4 d. "Arab Horses fighting in a Stable"	45	50
2960	4 d. "Horses at the Trough"	45	50
2961	4 d. "The Combat of Giaour and Hassan"	45	50
2962	4 d. "Turk on a Sofa, smoking"	45	50
	a. Sheetlet. Nos. 2962/9	3·50	
2963	4 d. "View of Tangier"	45	50
2964	4 d. "The Spanish Coast at Salobrena"	45	50
2965	4 d. "The Aissaouas"	45	50
2966	4 d. "The Sea from the Cliffs of Dieppe"	45	50
2967	4 d. "The Fanatics of Tangier"	45	50
2968	4 d. "Arab Musicians"	45	50
2969	4 d. "An Arab Camp at Night"	45	50
2970	4 d. "Moroccan from Tangier, standing" (vert)	45	50
	a. Sheetlet. Nos. 2970/7	3·50	
2971	4 d. "A Man of Tangier" (vert)	45	50
2972	4 d. "Young Arab standing with a Rifle" (vert)	45	50
2973	4 d. "Moroccan Chieftain" (vert)	45	50
2974	4 d. "Jewish Bride, Tangier" (vert)	45	50
2975	4 d. "Seated Jewess from Morocco" (vert)	45	50
2976	4 d. "Young Arab seated by a Wall" (vert)	45	50
2977	4 d. "Arab Dancer" (vert)	45	50
2954/77	*Set of 24*	10·50	11·50
MS2978	Three sheets. (a) 100×85 mm. 25 d. "Massacre at Chios". (b) 85×85 mm. 25 d. "Women of Algiers in their Apartment". (c) 85×100 mm. 25 d. "Self-portrait" (vert)		
	Set of 3 sheets	9·00	9·25

Nos. 2954/61, 2962/8 and 2970/7 were each printed together, *se-tenant*, in sheetlets of 8, containing two *se-tenant* horizontal strips of 4 separated by a gutter showing the paintings depicted on Nos. 2956 and 2961, 2965 and 2968 or 2973 and 2977.

The captions on the sheet margin for Nos. 2966 and 2967 are transposed in error.

(Litho Questa)

1998 (29 Oct). *First Death Anniv of Diana, Princess of Wales. Vert design as* T **405** *of Antigua.* P 14¹/₂×14.

2979	10 d. multicoloured	1·10	1·25
	a. Sheetlet of 6	6·50	

No. 2979 was printed in sheetlets of 6 with an enlarged illustrated right-hand margin.

(Litho B.D.T.)

1998 (1 Dec). *Christmas.* T **294** *and similar vert designs. Multicoloured.* P 14.

2980	1 d. Type **294**	10	15
2981	2 d. Giraffe in Christmas wreath	20	25
2982	3 d. Rainbow Bee Eater (bird) with bauble	35	40
2983	4 d. Deer	45	50
2984	5 d. Fawn	60	65
2985	10 d. Puppy in gift box	1·10	1·25
2980/5	*Set of 6*	2·75	3·00
MS2986	Two sheets, each 105×76 mm. (a) 25 d. Brown Classic Tabby. (b) 25 d. Basset Hound and Rough Collie		
	Set of 2 sheets	6·00	6·25

295 Rabbit

296 Mowgli and Baloo (bear)

(Des Y. Lee. Litho Questa)

1999 (4 Jan). *Chinese New Year ("Year of the Rabbit").* T **295** *and similar horiz designs. Multicoloured.* P 14¹/₂.

2987	3 d. Type **295**	35	40
	a. Sheetlet. Nos. 2987/90	1·40	
2988	3 d. Rabbit looking over shoulder	35	40
2989	3 d. Rabbit facing left	35	40
2990	3 d. Rabbit running	35	40
2987/90	*Set of 4*	1·40	1·60
MS2991	73×103 mm. 10 d. Rabbit (42×28 *mm*). P 14	1·10	1·25

Nos. 2987/90 were printed together, *se-tenant*, in sheetlets of 4.

1999 (11 Mar). *The Jungle Book (film).* T **296** *and similar multicoloured designs showing Walt Disney cartoon characters.* Litho. P 13¹/₂.

2992	5 d. Type **296**	60	65
	a. Sheetlet. Nos. 2992/9	4·75	
2993	5 d. Kaa (snake) and Mowgli	60	65
2994	5 d. King Louie at ruined temple	60	65
2995	5 d. Monkey playing leaf "guitar"	60	65
2996	5 d. Village girl collecting water	60	65
2997	5 d. King Louie on throne with Mowgli	60	65
2998	5 d. Mowgli and vultures	60	65
2999	5 d. Shere Khan (tiger)	60	65
2992/9	*Set of 8*	4·75	5·25
MS3000	Two sheets, each 127×102 mm. (a) 25 d. Baloo (bear) (50×37 *mm*). (b) 25 d. Baby elephant (50×37 *mm*). P 14×13¹/₂ *Set of 2 sheets*	5·75	6·00

Nos. 2992/9 were printed together, *se-tenant*, in sheetlets of 8.

297 *Danaus chrysippus*

298 Prince Edward and Miss Sophie Rhys-Jones

1999 (12 Apr). *"Australia '99" World Stamp Exhibition, Melbourne. African Butterflies.* T **297** *and similar multicoloured designs.* Litho. P 14.

3001	6 d. Type **297**	70	75
	a. Sheetlet. Nos. 3001/6	4·25	
3002	6 d. Papilio zalmoxis	70	75
3003	6 d. Papilio menestheus	70	75
3004	6 d. Poecilmitis thysbe	70	75
3005	6 d. Euxanthe wakefieldii	70	75
3006	6 d. Pseudacraea boisduvalii	70	75
3007	6 d. Eurytela dryope	70	75
	a. Sheetlet. Nos. 3007/12	4·25	
3008	6 d. Papilio demodocus	70	75
3009	6 d. Hemiolaus coeculus	70	75
3010	6 d. Charaxes jasius	70	75
3011	6 d. Junonia orithya	70	75
3012	6 d. Kallimoides rumia	70	75
3001/12	*Set of 12*	8·50	9·00
MS3013	Two sheets, each 106×76 mm. (a) 25 d. Charaxes jasius (vert). (b) 25 d. Catacroptera cloanthe (vert)		
	Set of 2 sheets	5·75	6·00

Nos. 3001/6 and 3007/12 were each printed together, *se-tenant*, in sheetlets of 6 within enlarged, illustrated top margins.

No. 3003 is inscribed "Papilio mnestheus" in error.

1999 (19 June). *Royal Wedding.* T **298** *and similar multicoloured designs.* Litho. P 13¹/₂.

3014	10 d. Type **298**	1·10	1·25
	a. Sheetlet. Nos. 3014/16	3·25	
3015	10 d. Prince Edward and Miss Sophie Rhys-Jones (with long hair)	1·10	1·25
3016	10 d. Prince Edward and Miss Sophie Rhys-Jones (wearing a red jacket)	1·10	1·25
3014/16	*Set of 3*	3·25	3·75
MS3017	78×78 mm. 25 d. Prince Edward and Miss Sophie Rhys-Jones (39×29 *mm*). P 13×13¹/₂	3·00	3·25

Nos. 3014/16 were printed together, as a *se-tenant* horizontal strip of 3, in sheetlets with illustrated top margin.

(Litho Questa)

1999 (6 July). *"iBRA '99" International Stamp Exhibition, Nuremberg. Horiz designs as* T **416** *of Antigua. Multicoloured.* P 14.

3018	4 d. Railway locomotive Adler, 1835, and Samoa 1914 G.R.I, 2¹/₂d. on 20 pf. variety	45	50
3019	5 d. Railway locomotive Adler, 1835, and Samoa 1900 25 p optd on Germany	60	65
3020	10 d. Friedrech August (full-rigged ship) and Samoa 1900 Yacht type 50 and 80 pf. stamps	1·10	1·25
3021	15 d. Friedrech August (full-rigged ship) and Samoa 1900 Yacht type 2 m. stamp	1·75	1·90
3018/21	*Set of 4*	4·00	4·25
MS3022	162×107 mm. 25 d. Samoa 1900 Yacht type 3 m. stamp postmarked Palauli (60×40 *mm*). P 14×14¹/₂	3·00	3·25

1999 (6 July). *150th Death Anniv of Katsushika Hokusai (Japanese artist). Vert designs as* T **417** *of Antigua. Multicoloured.* Litho. P 13¹/₂×14.

3023	5 d. "Exotic Beauty"	60	65
	a. Sheetlet. Nos. 3023/8	3·50	
3024	5 d. "Wind" (two people)	60	65
3025	5 d. "Dancing Monkey"	60	65
3026	5 d. "Lady and Maiden on an Outing"	60	65
3027	5 d. "Wind" (three people)	60	65
3028	5 d. "Courtesan with Fan"	60	65
3029	5 d. "Bunshosei"	60	65
	a. Sheetlet. Nos 3029/34	3·50	
3030	5 d. "Overthrower of Castles, Overthrower of Nations"	60	65
3031	5 d. "Bee on Wild Rose"	60	65
3032	5 d. "Sei Shonagon"	60	65
3033	5 d. "Kuan-yu"	60	65
3034	5 d. "The Fifth Month"	60	65
3023/34	*Set of 12*	7·00	7·75
MS3035	Two sheets, each 72×103 mm. (a) 25 d. "People on the Balcony of the Sazaido". (b) 25 d. "Caocao before the Battle of Chibi"		
	Set of 2 sheets	5·75	6·00

Nos. 3023/8 and 3029/34 were each printed together, *se-tenant*, in sheetlets of 6.

1999 (6 July). *10th Anniv of United Nations Rights of the Child Convention. Vert designs as* T **419** *of Antigua. Multicoloured.* Litho. P 14.

3036	10 d. Child asleep	1·10	1·25
	a. Sheetlet. Nos. 3036/8	3·25	
3037	10 d. Child drinking	1·10	1·25
3038	10 d. Child drawing	1·10	1·25
3036/8	*Set of 3*	3·25	3·75
MS3039	112×85 mm. 25 d. Child laughing	3·00	3·25

Nos. 3036/8 were printed together, *se-tenant*, in sheetlets of 3, forming a composite design.

1999 (6 July). *"PhilexFrance '99" International Stamp Exhibition, Paris. Railway Transport. Two sheets, each 106×81 mm, containing horiz designs as* T **420** *of Antigua. Multicoloured.* Litho. P 14×13¹/₂.

MS3040	(a) 25 d. Road carriage on wagon. (b) 25 d. Passenger locomotive, 1846 *Set of 2 sheets*	5·75	6·00

1999 (6 July). *250th Birth Anniv of Johann von Goethe (German writer). Horiz designs as* T **421** *of Antigua.* Litho. P 14.

3041	15 d. bluish violet, black and bright purple	1·75	1·90
	a. Sheetlet. Nos. 3041/3	5·25	
3042	15 d. ultramarine and black	1·75	1·90
3043	15 d. sepia, black and dull yellow-green	1·75	1·90
3041/3	*Set of 3*	5·25	5·75
MS3044	76×106 mm. 25 d. deep ultramarine, black and brown	3·00	3·25

Designs: *Horiz*—No. 3041, Faust quaffs the Spirit's nectar: No. 3042, Von Goethe and Von Schiller: No. 3043, Faust contemplates mortality. *Vert*—No. **MS**3044, Johann von Goethe.

Nos. 3041/3 were printed together, *se-tenant*, in sheetlets of 3 with enlarged illustrated margins.

1999 (6 July). *30th Anniv of First Manned Landing on Moon. Multicoloured designs as* T **333** *of Dominica.* Litho. P 14.

3045	6 d. Bell X-14A VTOL aircraft (vert)	70	75
	a. Sheetlet. Nos. 3045/50	4·25	
3046	6 d. Lunar landing practice rig (vert)	70	75
3047	6 d. Early prototype lander (vert)	70	75
3048	6 d. Astronaut during zero gravity training (vert)	70	75
3049	6 d. Jet pack training (vert)	70	75
3050	6 d. Lunar lander pilot training (vert)	70	75
3045/50	*Set of 6*	4·25	4·50
MS3051	Two sheets. (a) 76×105 mm. 25 d. "Apollo 11" splashdown. (b) 85×110 mm. 25 d. Lunar module Eagle		
	Set of 2 sheets	5·75	6·00

Nos. 3045/50 were printed together, *se-tenant*, in sheetlets of 6, forming a composite design.

299 Swallow-tailed Gull

(Litho Questa)

1999 (1 Aug). *Marine Life of the Galapagos Islands. T* **299** *and similar horiz designs. Multicoloured. P* 14.

3052	1 d. 50, Type **299**	..	20	25
	a. Sheetlet. Nos. 3052/91	..	8·00	
3053	1 d. 50, Frigate Birds	..	20	25
3054	1 d. 50, Red-footed Booby	..	20	25
3055	1 d. 50, Galapagos Hawk ..	..	20	25
3056	1 d. 50, Great Blue Heron	..	20	25
3057	1 d. 50, Masked Booby	..	20	25
3058	1 d. 50, Bottlenose Dolphins	..	20	25
3059	1 d. 50, Black Grunts	..	20	25
3060	1 d. 50, Surgeonfish	..	20	25
3061	1 d. 50, Stingray	..	20	25
3062	1 d. 50, Short-finned Pilot Whales	..	20	25
3063	1 d. 50, Pacific Green Sea Turtle ..	..	20	25
3064	1 d. 50, Great White Shark	..	20	25
3065	1 d. 50, Sealion	..	20	25
3066	1 d. 50, Marine Iguana	..	20	25
3067	1 d. 50, Pacific Manta Ray	..	20	25
3068	1 d. 50, Moorish Idol	..	20	25
3069	1 d. 50, Galapagos Penguins	..	20	25
3070	1 d. 50, Silver Grunts	..	20	25
3071	1 d. 50, Sea Urchin	..	20	25
3072	1 d. 50, Wrasse	..	20	25
3073	1 d. 50, Almaco Amber Jack	..	20	25
3074	1 d. 50, Blue Parrotfish	..	20	25
3075	1 d. 50, Yellow Sea Urchin	..	20	25
3076	1 d. 50, Lobster	..	20	25
3077	1 d. 50, Grouper	..	20	25
3078	1 d. 50, Scorpionfish	..	20	25
3079	1 d. 50, Squirrelfish	..	20	25
3080	1 d. 50, Octopus	..	20	25
3081	1 d. 50, King Angelfish	..	20	25
3082	1 d. 50, Horned Shark	..	20	25
3083	1 d. 50, Galapagos Hogfish	..	20	25
3084	1 d. 50, Pufferfish	..	20	25
3085	1 d. 50, Moray Eel	..	20	25
3086	1 d. 50, Orange Tube Coral	..	20	25
3087	1 d. 50, Whitestripe Chromis	..	20	25
3088	1 d. 50, Long-nosed Hawkfish	..	20	25
3089	1 d. 50, Sea Cucumbers	..	20	25
3090	1 d. 50, Spotted Hawkfish	..	20	25
3091	1 d. 50, Zebra Moray Eel	..	20	25
3052/91		*Set of* 40	8·00	10·00

MS3092   106×76 mm. 25 d. Emperor Penguins .. .. 3·00   3·25
Nos. 3051/90 were printed together, *se-tenant*, in sheetlets of 40 with the backgrounds forming a composite design.

300 "Telstar 1" Satellite, 1962

(Litho Questa)

1999 (1 Aug). *History of Space Exploration. T* **300** *and similar multicoloured designs. P* 14.

3093	1 d. Type **300**	..	10	15
3094	1 d. 50, "Skylab", 1973 (*vert*)	..	20	25
3095	2 d. "Mars 3" spacecraft, 1971 (*vert*)	..	20	25
3096	3 d. "Cobe", 1989 (*vert*)	..	35	40
3097	6 d. "Mariner 4", 1964	..	70	75
	a. Sheetlet. Nos. 3097/102	..	4·25	
3098	6 d. "Viking" Mars Orbiter, 1975	..	70	75
3099	6 d. Giotto, 1985	..	70	75
3100	6 d. "Luna 9", 1966	..	70	75
3101	6 d. "Voyager 1", 1977	..	70	75
3102	6 d. Galileo, 1989	..	70	75
3103	6 d. Soviet "Vostok 1", 1961	..	70	75
	a. Sheetlet. Nos. 3103/8	..	4·25	
3104	6 d. "Apollo" command and service module, 1968	..	70	75
3105	6 d. "Mercury" capsule, 1961	..	70	75
3106	6 d. "Apollo 16" lunar module, 1972	..	70	75
3107	6 d. "Gemini 8", 1966	..	70	75
3108	6 d. Soviet "Soyuz", 1975	..	70	75
3109	6 d. German "V 2" rocket, 1942 (*vert*)	..	70	75
	a. Sheetlet. Nos. 3109/14	..	4·25	
3110	6 d. "Delta Straight 8", 1972 (*vert*)	..	70	75
3111	6 d. "Ariane 4", 1988 (*vert*)	..	70	75
3112	6 d. "Mercury MA-A Atlas", 1962 (*vert*)	..	70	75
3113	6 d. "Saturn 1B", 1975 (*vert*)	..	70	75
3114	6 d. "Cassini", 1997 (*vert*)	..	70	75
3115	10 d. Bruce McCandless outside shuttle, 1984 (*vert*)	..	1·10	1·25
3116	15 d. "Apollo 13" after splashdown, 1970 (*vert*)	..	1·75	1·90
3093/116		*Set of* 24	16·00	18·00

MS3117   Two sheets (a) 85×110 mm. 25 d. "Mars Pathfinder", 1997 (56×41 *mm*). (b) 110×85 mm. 25 d. "Apollo" and "Soyuz" joint mission, 1975 (56×41 *mm*) .. .. *Set of 2 sheets* 6·00   6·25
Nos. 3097/102, 3103/8 and 3109/14 were each printed together, *se-tenant*, in sheetlets of 6 with enlarged illustrated margins.

NEW INFORMATION

The editor is always interested to correspond with people who have new information that will improve or correct the Catalogue.

301 Carnotaurus

(Litho Questa)

1999 (1 Aug). *Prehistoric Animals. T* **301** *and similar horiz designs. Multicoloured. P* 14.

3118	3 d. Type **301**	..	35	40
	a. Sheetlet. Nos. 3118/29	..	4·25	
3119	3 d. Quetzalcoatlus	..	35	40
3120	3 d. Peteinosaurus	..	35	40
3121	3 d. Prenocephale	..	35	40
3122	3 d. Hesperornis	..	35	40
3123	3 d. Coelophysis	..	35	40
3124	3 d. Camptosaurus	..	35	40
3125	3 d. Panderichthys	..	35	40
3126	3 d. Garudimimus	..	35	30
3127	3 d. Cacops	..	35	40
3128	3 d. Ichthyostega	..	35	40
3129	3 d. Scutellosaurus	..	35	40
3130	3 d. Diatryma	..	35	40
	a. Sheetlet. Nos. 3130/41	..	4·25	
3131	3 d. Pteranodon	..	35	40
3132	3 d. Stegodon	..	35	40
3133	3 d. Icaronycthris ..	..	35	40
3134	3 d. Archaeopteryx	..	35	40
3135	3 d. Chasmatosaurus	..	35	40
3136	3 d. Tytthostonyx	..	35	40
3137	3 d. Hyaenodon	..	35	40
3138	3 d. Uintatherium	..	35	40
3139	3 d. Hesperocyon ..	..	35	40
3140	3 d. Ambelodon	..	35	40
3141	3 d. Indricotherium	..	35	40
3118/41		*Set of* 24	8·50	9·50

MS3142   Four sheets, each 110×85 mm. (a) 25 d. Deinonychus. (b) 25 d. Sabre-tooth Tiger. (c) 25 d. Lepisosteus. (d) 25 d. Microceratops .. .. *Set of 4 sheets* 12·00 12·50
Nos. 3118/29 and 3130/41 were each printed together, *se-tenant*, in sheetlets of 12 with the backgrounds forming composite designs.

302 Seagull

303 *Sophrocattleya*

(Litho Questa)

1999 (1 Aug). *Marine Life. T* **302** *and similar horiz designs. Multicoloured. P* 14.

3143	1 d. Type **302**	..	10	15
3144	1 d. 50, Portugese Man-o-War	..	20	25
3145	3 d. Whale Shark	..	35	40
	a. Sheetlet. Nos. 3145/56	..	4·25	
3146	3 d. Grey Reef Shark	..	35	40
3147	3 d. New England Octopus	..	35	40
3148	3 d. Pufferfish	..	35	40
3149	3 d. Lionfish	..	35	40
3150	3 d. Squid	..	35	40
3151	3 d. Chambered Nautilus	..	35	40
3152	3 d. Clownfish	..	35	40
3153	3 d. Moray Eel	..	35	40
3154	3 d. Spiny Lobster	..	35	40
3155	3 d. Spotted Ray	..	35	40
3156	3 d. Clown Anemone	..	35	40
3157	3 d. Angelfish	..	35	40
	a. Sheetlet. Nos. 3157/68	..	4·25	
3158	3 d. Leafy Seadragon	..	35	40
3159	3 d. Hawksbill Turtle	..	35	40
3160	3 d. Mandarinfish	..	35	40
3161	3 d. Candy Cane Sea Star	..	35	40
3162	3 d. Plate Coral	..	35	40
3163	3 d. Butterflyfish	..	35	40
3164	3 d. Coral polyp	..	35	40
3165	3 d. Hermit Crab	..	35	40
3166	3 d. Strawberry Shrimp	..	35	40
3167	3 d. Giant Blue Clam	..	35	40
3168	3 d. Sea Cucumber	..	35	40
3169	5 d. Walrus	..	60	65
3170	10 d. Manatee	..	1·10	1·25
3143/70		*Set of* 28	10·50	12·00

MS3171   110×85 mm. 25 d. Common Dolphin   3·00   3·25
Nos. 3145/56 and 3157/68 were each printed together, *se-tenant*, in sheetlets of 12 with the backgrounds forming composite designs.

(Litho Questa)

1999 (1 Aug). *Orchids of the World. T* **303** *and similar vert designs. Multicoloured. P* 14.

3172	2 d. Type **303**	..	20	25
3173	3 d. Cattleya and butterfly	..	35	40
3174	4 d. Brassolaeliocattleya (pink)	..	45	50
3175	5 d. Brassoepidendrum	..	60	65
3176	6 d. Brassolaeliocattleya (yellow)	..	70	75
	a. Sheetlet. Nos. 3176/81	..	4·25	
3177	6 d. Cattleytonia ..	..	70	75
3178	6 d. Lacliocattleya	..	70	75
3179	6 d. Miltonia	..	70	75

3180	6 d. Cattleya forbesii	..	70	75
3181	6 d. Odontoglossum cervantesii	..	70	75
3182	6 d. Lycaste macrobulbon	..	70	75
	a. Sheetlet. Nos. 3182/7	..	4·25	
3183	6 d. Laeliocattleya	..	70	75
3184	6 d. Brassocattleya (pink)	..	70	75
3185	6 d. Cattleya	..	70	75
3186	6 d. Brassocattleya (red spotted)	..	70	75
3187	6 d. Brassolaeliocattleya (yellow and red)	..	70	75
3188	10 d. Sophrolaeliocattleya and butterfly ..		1·10	1·25
3189	15 d. Iwanagaara and butterfly	..	1·75	1·90
3172/89		*Set of* 18	13·00	14·00

MS3190   Two sheets. (a) 81×106 mm. 25 d. Lycaste. (b) 85×110 mm. 25 d. *Brassolaelio-cattleya* (pink and white) .. *Set of 2 sheets* 6·00   6·25
Nos. 3176/81 and 3182/7 were each printed together, *se-tenant*, in sheetlets of 6 with illustrated margins.

304 American Black Oystercatcher

(Litho Questa)

1999 (1 Aug). *Sea Birds. T* **304** *and similar horiz designs. Multicoloured. P* 14.

3191	2 d. Type **304**	..	20	25
3192	3 d. Blue-footed Booby	..	35	40
3193	4 d. Atlantic Puffin	..	45	50
	a. Sheetlet. Nos. 3193/201	..	4·00	
3194	4 d. Red-tailed Tropic Bird	..	45	50
3195	4 d. Reddish Egret	..	45	50
3196	4 d. Laughing Gull	..	45	50
3197	4 d. Great Egret	..	45	50
3198	4 d. Northern Gannet	..	45	50
3199	4 d. Forster's Tern	..	45	50
3200	4 d. Common Cormorant ("Great Cormorant")	..	45	50
3201	4 d. Razorbill (perched on rocks)	..	45	50
3202	4 d. Adélie Penguin	..	45	50
	a. Sheetlet. Nos. 3202/10	..	4·00	
3203	4 d. Black Skimmer	..	45	50
3204	4 d. Big Crested Penguin	..	45	50
3205	4 d. Heermann's Gull	..	45	50
3206	4 d. Glaucous Gull	..	45	50
3207	4 d. Laysan Albatross	..	45	50
3208	4 d. American White Pelican	..	45	50
3209	4 d. Tufted Puffin	..	45	50
3210	4 d. Black Guillemot	..	45	50
3211	5 d. Razorbill (in flight)	..	60	65
	a. Sheetlet. Nos. 3211/16	..	3·50	
3212	5 d. Shelduck	..	60	65
3213	5 d. Sandwich Tern	..	60	65
3214	5 d. Arctic Skua ..	..	60	65
3215	5 d. Gannet	..	60	65
3216	5 d. Common Gull	..	60	65
3217	10 d. Western Gull	..	1·10	1·25
3218	15 d. Brown Pelican	..	1·75	1·90
3191/218		*Set of* 28	15·00	17·00

MS3219   Three sheets. (a) 110×85 mm. 25 d. Pelican. (b) 105×76 mm. 25 d. Gentoo Penguin. (c) 106×76 mm. 25 d. California Gull .. .. *Set of 3 sheets* 9·00   9·25
Nos. 3193/201, 3202/10 and 3211/16 were each printed together, *se-tenant*, in sheetlets of 6 (forming a composite design) or 9 with enlarged illustrated margins.
Nos. 3202 and 3207 are inscribed "ADELIES PENGUIN" or "LAYSON ALBATROSS", both in error.

(Litho Questa)

1999 (4 Aug). *"Queen Elizabeth the Queen Mother's Century". Vert designs as T* **334** *of Dominica. P* 14.

3220	10 d. multicoloured	..	1·10	1·25
	a. Sheetlet. Nos. 3220/3	..	4·50	
3221	10 d. black and gold	..	1·10	1·25
3222	10 d. black and gold	..	1·10	1·25
3223	10 d. multicoloured	..	1·10	1·25
3220/3		*Set of* 4	4·50	5·00

MS3224   153×155 mm. 25 d. multicoloured. P 13½×14 .. .. 3·00   3·25
Designs: (As Type **334** of Dominica)—No. 3220, Duchess of York and Princess Elizabeth, 1928; No. 3221, Lady Elizabeth Bowes-Lyon, 1923; No. 3222, Queen Elizabeth, 1946; No. 3223, Queen Mother and Prince Harry. (37×50 *mm*)—No. **MS**3224, Queen Mother on 89th Birthday, 1989.
Nos. 3220/3 were printed together, *se-tenant*, as a sheetlet of 4 stamps and a central label with inscribed and embossed margins.
No. **MS**3224 also shows the Royal Arms embossed in gold.

305 Temple of A-Ma

(Litho Questa)

1999 (20 Aug). *"China '99" World Philatelic Exhibition, Beijing. Return of Macao to China. T **305** and similar horiz designs. Multicoloured. P 14.*

3225	7 d. Type **305**	..	..	80	85
	a. Sheetlet. Nos. 3225/7	..		2·40	
3226	7 d. Border Gate	..	..	80	85
3227	7 d. Ruins of St. Paul's	..	..	80	85
3225/7	..	..	*Set of* 3	2·40	2·50

Nos. 3225/7 were printed together, *sc-tenant*, in sheetlets of 3 with an enlarged illustrated and inscribed left-hand margin.

306 John F. Kennedy Jr as Baby, 1961

(Litho Questa)

1999 (7 Dec). *John F. Kennedy Jr Commemoration. T **306** and similar vert designs. Each brownish black, slate-blue and black. P 13½×14.*

3228	15 d. Type **306**	..	..	1·75	1·90
	a. Sheetlet. Nos. 3228/30	..		5·25	
3229	15 d. John F. Kennedy Jr as teenager	..	1·75	1·90
3230	15 d. John F. Kennedy Jr in 1997	..	1·75	1·90
3228/30	..	..	*Set of* 3	5·25	5·75

Nos. 3228/30 were printed together, *se-tenant*, in sheetlets of 3 with enlarged illustrated and inscribed margins.

STAMP BOOKLETS

1979 (17 Oct). *Tenth Anniv of Moon Landing. Multicoloured cover, 165×93 mm, showing "Apollo 11" on the front and Abuko Satellite Earth Station on the back. Pane attached by selvedge.*

SB1　4 d. 26, booklet containing *se-tenant* pane of 6 (No. 427a) and pane of 1 (No. 430a) .. .. 2·75

The cover of No. SB1 is folded five times "concertina fashion" and when opened out measures 165×465 mm.

1983 (12 Dec). *Bicentenary of Manned Flight. Bistre-brown and bright scarlet cover, 121×81 mm, showing Bicentenary of Manned Flight logo on front and advertisement on reverse. Stitched.*

SB2　11 d. 20, booklet containing *se-tenant* panes of 4 (Nos. 522a, 524a) and pane of 1 (No. 526a)　5·75

Ghana
(*formerly* Gold Coast)

GOLD COAST

Gold Coast originally consisted of coastal forts, owned by the Royal African Company, trading with the interior. In 1821, due to raids by the Ashanti king, the British Government took over the forts, together with some of the hinterland, and the Gold Coast was placed under the Governor of Sierra Leone.

The administration was handed back to a merchantile company in 1828, but the forts returned to British Government rule in 1843. The colony was reconstituted by Royal Charter on 24 July, 1874, and at that time also included the settlement at Lagos which became a separate colony in January, 1886.

Following the end of the final Ashanti War the whole of the territory was annexed in September 1901.

A postal service was established at Cape Coast Castle in 1853. There is no record of British stamps being officially issued in the Colony before 1875, apart from those used on board the ships of the West African Squadron, but examples do, however, exist cancelled by Gold Coast postmarks.

CROWN COLONY

PRICES FOR STAMPS ON COVER TO 1945	
Nos. 1/3	*from* × 15
Nos. 4/8	*from* × 20
Nos. 9/10	*from* × 10
Nos. 11/20	*from* × 25
Nos. 22/5	—
Nos. 26/34	*from* × 10
Nos. 35/6	*from* × 20
Nos. 38/69	*from* × 6
Nos. 70/98	*from* × 3
Nos. 100/2	—
Nos. 103/12	*from* × 5
Nos. 113/16	*from* × 3
Nos. 117/19	*from* × 4
Nos. 120/32	*from* × 3
Nos. D1/4	*from* × 8

1   (2)

ONE PENNY.

(Typo D.L.R.)

1875 (1 July). *Wmk Crown CC. P* 12½.
1	1	1d. blue		£425	80·00
2		4d. magenta		£400	£120
3		6d. orange		£600	65·00

1876–84. *Wmk Crown CC. P* 14.
4	1	½d. olive-yellow (1879)		50·00	22·00
5		1d. blue		15·00	6·50
		a. Bisected (½d.) (on cover) (1884)		† £3250	
		w. Wmk inverted		£160	80·00
6		2d. green (1879)		65·00	9·00
		a. Bisected (1d.) (on cover) (1884)		† £2750	
		b. Quartered (½d.) (on cover) (1884)		† £4500	
7		4d. magenta		£150	6·00
		a. Bisected (2d.) (on cover) (1884)		† £5000	
		b. Quartered (1d.) (on cover) (1884)		† £6500	
		w. Wmk inverted		£325	
8		6d. orange		95·00	18·00
		a. Bisected (3d.) (on cover) (1884)		† £6000	
		b. Sixth (1d.) (on cover) (1884)		† £7500	

During 1884 some values were in short supply and the use of bisects and other divided stamps is known as follows:
No. 5a. Used as part of 2½d. rate from Accra and Quittah
No. 6a. Used as 1d. rate from Addah, Cape Coast Castle, Quittah, Salt Pond, Secondee and Winnebah
No. 6b. Used as part of 2½d. rate from Cape Coast Castle
No. 7a. Used as 2d. or as part of 2½d. rate from Quittah
No. 7b. Used as 1d. rate from Appam, Axim, Cape Coast Castle and Winnebah
No. 8a. Used as 3d. rate from Secondee
No. 8b. Used as 1d. rate from Cape Coast Castle and Winnebah.

Examples of bisects used on piece are worth about 10% of the price quoted for those on cover.

The 4d., No. 7, is known surcharged "1 d". This was previously listed as No. 8c, but there are now serious doubts as to its authenticity. The three examples reported of this stamp all show *different surcharges!*

1883. *Wmk Crown CA. P* 14.
9	1	½d. olive-yellow (January)		£160	60·00
10		1d. blue (May)		£850	65·00

PENNY

Short "P" and distorted "E" (Pl 1
R. 5/6) ("P" repaired for Pl 2)

1884 (Aug)–**91.** *Wmk Crown CA. P* 14.
11	1	½d. green		2·00	75
		a. Dull green		1·75	70
		w. Wmk inverted		80·00	
12		1d. rose-carmine		2·50	50
		a. Carmine		2·50	50
		b. Bisected (½d.) (on cover)		† £3750	
		c. Short "P" and distorted "E"		75·00	

13	1	2d. grey		8·00	3·75
		aw. Wmk inverted		£130	£130
		b. Slate		1·75	50
		c. Bisected (1d.) (on cover)		† £4250	
		d. Quartered (½d.) (on cover)			
14		2½d. ultramarine and orange (13.3.91)		3·00	60
15		3d. olive-yellow (9.89)		6·00	4·50
		a. Olive		6·00	4·50
16		4d. deep mauve (3.85)		6·00	1·25
		a. Rosy mauve		8·50	3·00
17		6d. orange (1.89)		5·00	5·00
		a. Orange-brown		5·00	5·00
		b. Bisected (3d.) (on cover)			
18		1s. violet (1888)		30·00	12·00
		a. Bright mauve		3·75	1·25
19		2s. yellow-brown (1888)		80·00	35·00
		a. Deep brown		35·00	15·00
11/19a			*Set of 9*	55·00	26·00
14/15, 18/19	Optd "Specimen"		*Set of 4*	£150	

During 1884 to 1886 and in 1889 some values were in short supply and the use of bisects and other divided stamps is known as follows:
No. 12b. Used as part of 2½d. rate from Cape Coast Castle
No. 13c. Used as 1d. or as part of 2d. rate from Cape Coast Castle, Chamah, Dixcove and Elmina
No. 13d. Used as part of 2½d. rate from Cape Coast Castle
No. 17b. Used as 3d. from Appam

1889 (Mar). *No. 17 surch with T* **2**.
20	1	1d. on 6d. orange		£100	48·00
		a. Surch double		† £3000	

In some sheets examples may be found with the bar and "PENNY" spaced 8 mm, the normal spacing being 7 mm.

USED HIGH VALUES. Until the introduction of airmail in 1929 there was no postal use for values over 10s. Post Offices did, however, apply postal cancellations to high value stamps required for telegram fees.

3

4

1889 (Sept)–**94.** *Wmk Crown CA. P* 14.
22	3	5s. dull mauve and blue		65·00	12·00
23		10s. dull mauve and red		75·00	15·00
		a. Dull mauve and carmine		£475	£170
24		20s. green and red		£3250	
25		20s. dull mauve and black/*red* (4.94)		£150	35·00
		w. Wmk inverted		£200	75·00
22/5	Optd "Specimen"		*Set of 4*	£400	

No. 24 was withdrawn from sale in April 1893 when a large part of the stock was stolen. No 20s. stamps were available until the arrival of the replacement printing a year later.

1898 (May)–**1902.** *Wmk Crown CA. P* 14.
26	3	½d. dull mauve and green		2·00	1·00
27		1d. dull mauve and rose		2·00	50
		aw. Wmk inverted		—	80·00
27b		1d. dull mauve and orange-red (1902)		38·00	£100
28	3	2½d. dull mauve and ultramarine		4·50	4·25
29	4	3d. dull mauve and orange		4·75	1·50
30		6d. dull mauve and violet		5·50	1·50
31	3	1s. green and black (1899)		9·00	11·00
32		2s. green and carmine		9·00	17·00
33		5s. green and mauve (1900)		50·00	26·00
34		10s. green and brown (1900)		£140	50·00
26/34			*Set of 10*	£225	£190
26/34	Optd "Specimen"		*Set of 10*	£180	

1901 (6 Oct). *Nos.* 28 *and* 30 *surch with T* **2**.
35		1d. on 2½d. dull mauve and ultramarine		2·00	3·00
		a. "ONE" omitted		£1000	
36		1d. on 6d. dull mauve and violet		2·00	3·00
		a. "ONE" omitted		£275	£550

6

7

8

1902. *Wmk Crown CA. P* 14.
38	6	½d. dull purple and green (Aug)		1·00	40
39		1d. dull purple and carmine (May)		1·25	15
		w. Wmk inverted		—	45·00
40	7	2d. dull purple and orange-red (Apr)		17·00	7·00
		w. Wmk inverted			
41	6	2½d. dull purple and ultramarine (Aug)		4·50	9·00
42	7	3d. dull purple and orange (Aug)		2·75	1·50
43		6d. dull purple and violet (Aug)		3·00	1·50
		w. Wmk inverted		—	60·00
44	6	1s. green and black (Aug)		10·00	3·25
45		2s. green and carmine (Aug)		13·00	16·00
46		5s. green and mauve (Aug)		35·00	80·00
47		10s. green and brown (Aug)		50·00	£130
48		20s. purple and black/*red* (Aug)		£130	£180
38/48			*Set of 11*	£225	£375
38/48	Optd "Specimen"		*Set of 11*	£200	

Examples of Nos. 45/8 are known showing a forged Accra postmark dated "25 MAR 1902".

1904–06. *Wmk Mult Crown CA. Ordinary paper* (½d. to 6d.) *or chalk-surfaced paper* (2s. 6d.).
49	6	½d. dull purple and green (3.06)		2·50	6·00
50		1d. dull purple and carmine (10.04)		5·50	30
		a. Chalk-surfaced paper (5.06)		7·00	2·00
		w. Wmk inverted			

51	7	2d. dull purple and orange-red (11.04)		4·50	50
		a. Chalk-surfaced paper (8.06)		20·00	1·75
52	6	2½d. dull purple and ultramarine (6.06)		48·00	40·00
53	7	3d. dull purple and orange (8.05)		55·00	5·00
		a. Chalk-surfaced paper (4.06)		14·00	60
54		6d. dull purple and violet (3.06)		48·00	2·00
		a. Chalk-surfaced paper (9.06)		40·00	£18
57		2s. 6d. green & yell (3.06) (Optd S. £45)		28·00	£100
49/57			*Set of 7*	£130	£130

1907–13. *Wmk Mult Crown CA. Ordinary paper* (½d. to 2½d. *and* 2s.) *or chalk-surfaced paper* (3d. to 1s., 2s. 6d., 5s.). P 14.
59	6	½d. dull green (5.07)		2·50	30
		a. Blue-green (1909)		5·50	1·50
60		1d. red (2.07)		5·00	40
61	7	2d. greyish slate (4.09)		2·25	40
62	6	2½d. blue (4.07)		4·00	1·75
		w. Wmk inverted			
63	7	3d. purple/*yellow* (16.4.09)		7·00	55
64		6d. dull and deep purple (12.08)		15·00	55
		a. Dull and bright purple (1911)		3·75	3·50
65	6	1s. black/*green* (10.09)		7·50	50
66		2s. purple and blue/*blue* (1910)		6·50	16·00
		a. Chalk-surfaced paper (1912)		16·00	16·00
67	7	2s. 6d. blue and red/*blue* (1911)		26·00	70·00
68	6	5s. green and red/*yellow* (1913)		55·00	£140
59/68			*Set of 10*	£110	£200
59/68	Optd "Specimen"		*Set of 10*	£225	

A 10s. green and red on green, and a 20s. purple and black on red, both Type **6**, were prepared for use but not issued. Both exist overprinted "Specimen" (*Price for* 10s. *in this condition* £300).

(Typo D.L.R.)

1908 (Nov). *Wmk Mult Crown CA. P* 14.
69	8	1d. red (Optd S. £45)		2·75	10

9   10   11

(Typo D.L.R.)

1913–21. *Die I. Wmk Mult Crown CA. Chalk-surfaced paper* (3d. to 20s.). P 14.
70	9	½d. green		1·50	1·00
		a. Yellow-green (1916)		2·25	1·25
72	10	1d. red		70	10
		a. Scarlet (1917)		85	50
74	11	2d. grey		1·50	2·50
		a. Slate-grey (1920)		7·50	7·50
		w. Wmk inverted		†	£120
76	9	2½d. bright blue		4·25	1·00
		a. "A" of "CA" missing from wmk		£350	
		x. Wmk reversed		†	£120
77	11	3d. purple/*yellow* (8.15) (Optd S. £32)		1·50	70
		aw. Wmk inverted		—	60·00
		b. White back (9.13)		40	40
		c. On orange-buff (1919)		3·50	7·00
		cw. Wmk inverted			
		d. On buff (1920)			
		e. Die II. On pale yellow (1921)		27·00	5·00
78		6d. dull and bright purple		2·00	2·25
79	9	1s. black/*green*		1·50	1·25
		a. Wmk sideways			
		bw. Wmk inverted			
		c. On blue-green, olive back (1916) (Optd S. £35)		4·00	75
		cw. Wmk inverted			
		d. On emerald back (1920) (Optd S. £32)		2·00	2·00
		e. Die II. On emerald back (1921) (Optd S. £38)		1·50	50
		ew. Wmk inverted			
80		2s. purple and blue/*blue*		7·00	2·75
		aw. Wmk inverted		—	£130
		b. Die II (1921)		£140	65·00
81	11	2s. 6d. black and red/*blue*		5·00	13·00
		a. Die II (1921)		22·00	38·00
82	9	5s. green & red/*yell* (1916) (Optd S. £42)		7·00	48·00
		a. White back (10.13)		9·00	50·00
		b. On orange-buff (1919)		70·00	75·00
		c. On buff (1920)			
		d. On pale yellow (1921)		£100	£130
		e. Die II. On pale yellow (1921)		30·00	£130
		ew. Wmk inverted		£140	
83		10s. green and red/*green*		48·00	85·00
		a. On blue-green, olive back (1916)		18·00	50·00
		b. On emerald back (1921)		30·00	£100
84		20s. purple and black/*red*		£120	80·00
70/84			*Set of 12*	£150	£190
70/6, 77b, 78/81, 82a/4	Optd "Specimen"		*Set of 12*	£250	

The 10s. and 20s. were withdrawn locally from September 1920 and, in common with other Gold Coast stamps, were not available to stamp dealers from the Crown Agents in London.

WAR TAX

ONE PENNY

(12)

13 King George V and Christiansborg Castle

1918 (17 June). *Surch with T* **12**.
85	10	1d. on 1d. red (Optd S. £50)		40	40

1921–24. *Die I* (15s., £2) *or Die II* (others). *Wmk Mult Script CA. Chalk-surfaced paper* (6d. to £2). P 14.
86	9	½d. green		40	30
87	10	1d. chocolate-brown (1922)		40	10
88	11	1½d. red (1922)		1·25	10
89		2d. grey		1·25	30

90	9	2½d. yellow-orange (1922)		50	8·50
91	11	3d. bright blue (1922)		1·25	60
94		6d. dull and bright purple		1·40	3·00
95	9	1s. black/*emerald* (1924)		2·25	3·00
96		2s. purple and blue/*blue* (1923)		2·50	3·25
97	11	2s. 6d. black and red/*blue* (1924)		6·50	17·00
98	9	5s. green and red/*pale yellow* (1924)		9·50	42·00
100	11	15s. dull purple and green (Die I)		£120	£300
		a. Die II (1924) (Optd S. £100)		£110	£275
102		£2 green and orange (Die I)		£350	£850
86/100a			*Set of 12*	£120	£300
86/102 Optd "Specimen"			*Set of 13*	£350	

The Duty plate for the 1½d., 15s. and £2 has the words "GOLD COAST" in distinctly larger letters.

Examples of Nos. 100/a and 102 are known showing parts of forged Accra postmarks. These are dated "3 MAY 44" and "8 MAY 44", but are invariably positioned so that the year date is not shown.

(Des W. Palmer. Photo Harrison)

1928 (1 Aug). *Wmk Mult Script CA. P* 13½×15.

103	13	½d. blue-green		60	40
104		1d. red-brown		60	10
105		1½d. scarlet		60	1·50
106		2d. slate		60	20
107		2½d. orange-yellow		1·25	3·50
108		3d. bright blue		60	40
109		6d. black and purple		85	40
110		1s. black and red-orange		2·00	75
111		2s. black and bright violet		15·00	14·50
112		5s. carmine and sage-green		48·00	40·00
103/12			*Set of 10*	65·00	45·00
103/12 Optd "Specimen"			*Set of 10*	£180	

1935 (6 May). *Silver Jubilee. As Nos. 91/4 of Antigua, but printed by B.W. P* 11 × 12.

113		1d. ultramarine and grey-black		60	50
		a. Extra flagstaff		£120	
		b. Short extra flagstaff		£130	
		c. Lightning conductor		90·00	
		d. Flagstaff on right-hand turret		£140	
114		3d. brown and deep blue		3·00	6·00
		a. Extra flagstaff		£120	
		c. Lightning conductor		£110	
115		6d. green and indigo		5·00	11·00
		a. Extra flagstaff		£130	
		b. Short extra flagstaff		£200	
		c. Lightning conductor		£120	
		d. Flagstaff on right-hand turret		£250	
116		1s. slate and purple		3·75	11·00
		a. Extra flagstaff		£140	
		b. Short extra flagstaff		£160	
		c. Lightning conductor		£130	
113/16			*Set of 4*	11·00	26·00
113/16 Perf "Specimen"			*Set of 4*	85·00	

For illustrations of plate varieties see Catalogue Introduction.

1937 (12 May). *Coronation. As Nos. 95/7 of Antigua. P* 11×11½.

117		1d. buff		1·00	1·50
118		2d. slate		1·10	3·00
119		3d. blue		1·25	1·25
117/19			*Set of 3*	3·00	5·25
117/19 Perf "Specimen"			*Set of 3*	50·00	

14 **15** King George VI and Christiansborg Castle, Accra

(Recess B.W.)

1938 (1 Apr)–**44**. *Wmk Mult Script CA. P* 11½×12 (1s. 3d., 10s.) *or* 12 (*others*).

120	14	½d. green		2·00	1·25
		a. Perf 12×11½ (1940)		40	50
121		1d. red-brown		2·00	30
		a. Perf 12×11½ (1939)		40	10
122		1½d. scarlet		2·00	1·25
		a. Perf 12×11½ (1940)		40	50
123		2d. slate		2·00	80
		a. Perf 12×11½ (1940)		40	10
124		3d. blue		2·00	60
		a. Perf 12×11½ (1940)		40	35
125		4d. magenta		2·75	2·50
		a. Perf 12×11½ (1942)		70	1·25
126		6d. purple		2·75	45
		a. Perf 12×11½ (1939)		70	20
127		9d. orange		2·75	1·25
		a. Perf 12×11½ (1940)		90	55
128	15	1s. black and olive-green		5·00	2·00
		a. Perf 11½×12 (1940)		1·00	50
129		1s. 3d. brown & turquoise-bl (12.4.41)		2·00	40
130		2s. blue and violet		16·00	9·00
		a. Perf 11½×12 (1940)		4·50	9·00
131		5s. olive-green & carmine		27·00	12·00
		a. Perf 11½×12 (1940)		9·00	12·00
132		10s. black and violet (7.40)		7·00	17·00
120/32			*Set of 13*	25·00	38·00
120/32 Perf "Specimen"			*Set of 13*	£170	

All values except 1s. 3d. and 10s. exist in two perforations: (a) Line-perforated 12, from early printings; (b) Comb-perforated 12×11.8 (vertical design) or 11.8×12 (horiz design) from later printings. The 1s. 3d. and 10s. only exist comb-perforated 11.8×12.

The ½d. and 1d. values exist in coils constructed from normal sheets.

1946 (14 Oct). *Victory. As Nos. 110/11 of Antigua. P* 13½×14.

133		2d. slate-violet		12·00	2·25
		a. Perf 13½		10	10
134		4d. claret		1·50	2·75
		a. Perf 13½		1·00	2·75
133/4 Perf "Specimen"			*Set of 2*	50·00	

16 Northern Territories Mounted Constabulary   **17** Christiansborg Castle

(Des B. A. Johnston (1½d.), M. Ziorkley and B. A. Abban (2d.), P.O. draughtsman (2½d.), C. Gomez (1s.), M. Ziorkley (10s.); others from photographs. Recess B.W.)

1948 (1 July). *T* **16/17** *and similar designs. Wmk Mult Script CA. P* 12 × 11½ (*vert*) *or* 11½ × 12 (*horiz*).

135		½d. emerald-green		20	30
136		1d. blue		15	15
137		1½d. scarlet		1·25	70
138		2d. purple-brown		55	10
139		2½d. yellow-brown and scarlet		2·00	2·75
140		3d. light blue		4·00	45
141		4d. magenta		3·50	1·25
142		6d. black and orange		30	30
143		1s. black and vermilion		60	30
144		2s. sage-green and magenta		3·00	2·00
145		5s. purple and black		20·00	4·50
146		10s. black and sage-green		8·00	4·50
135/46			*Set of 12*	10·00	15·00
135/46 Perf "Specimen"			*Set of 12*	£225	

Designs: *Horiz*—1½d. Emblem of Joint Provincial Council; 2½d. Map showing position of Gold Coast; 3d. Nsuta manganese mine; 4d. Lake Bosumtwi; 1s. Breaking cocoa pods; 2s. Gold Coast Regt Trooping the Colour; 5s. Surfboats. *Vert*—2d. Talking drums; 6d. Cocoa farmer; 10s. Forest.

Nos. 135/6 exist in coils constructed from normal sheets.

1948 (20 Dec). *Royal Silver Wedding. As Nos. 112/13 of Antigua.*

147		1½d. scarlet		30	30
148		10s. grey-olive		13·00	18·00

1949 (10 Oct). *75th Anniv of U.P.U. As Nos. 114/17 of Antigua.*

149		2d. red-brown		30	30
150		2½d. orange		2·00	2·00
151		3d. deep blue		50	70
152		1s. blue-green		50	50
149/52			*Set of 4*	3·00	3·25

28 Northern Territories Mounted Constabulary

(Recess B.W.)

1952 (19 Dec)–**54**. *Designs previously used for King George VI issue, but with portrait of Queen Elizabeth II, as in T* **28**. *Portrait faces left on* ½d., 4d., 6d., 1s. *and* 5s. *Wmk Mult Script CA. P* 12 × 11½ (*vert*) *or* 11½ × 12 (*horiz*).

153		½d. yellow-brown and scarlet (1.4.53)		10	10
		a. Bistre-brown and scarlet (7.4.54)		10	20
154		1d. deep blue (1.3.54)		30	10
155		1½d. emerald-green (1.4.53)		30	1·25
156		2d. chocolate (1.3.54)		30	10
157		2½d. scarlet		35	35
158		3d. magenta (1.4.53)		50	10
159		4d. blue (1.4.53)		30	30
160		6d. black and orange (1.3.54)		30	15
161		1s. black and orange-red (1.3.54)		30	15
162		2s. brown-olive and carmine (1.3.54)		11·00	85
163		5s. purple and black (1.3.54)		17·00	5·00
164		10s. black and olive-green (1.3.54)		15·00	12·00
153/64			*Set of 12*	40·00	18·00

Designs: *Horiz*—½d. Map showing position of Gold Coast; 1d. Christiansborg Castle; 1½d. Emblem of Joint Provincial Council; 3d. Nsuta manganese mine; 4d. Lake Bosumtwi; 1s. Breaking cocoa pods; 2s. Gold Coast Regt Trooping the Colour; 5s. Surfboats. *Vert*—2d. Talking drums; 6d. Cocoa farmer; 10s. Forest.

Nos. 153a/4 exist in coils constructed from normal sheets.

1953 (2 June). *Coronation. As No. 120 of Antigua, but ptd by B.W.*

165		2d. black and sepia		60	10

Gold Coast became the Dominion of Ghana on 6 March 1957.

GHANA

DOMINION

GHANA INDEPENDENCE 6TH MARCH, 1957.

(30)

29 Dr. Kwame Nkrumah, Palm-nut Vulture and Map of Africa

(Photo Harrison)

1957 (6 Mar). *Independence. Wmk Mult Script CA. P* 14 × 14½.

166	29	2d. scarlet		10	10*
167		2½d. green		10	15*
168		4d. brown		10	15*
169		1s. 3d. deep blue		15	15*
166/9			*Set of 4*	40	45*

1957 (6 Mar)–**58**. *Nos. 153a/64 of Gold Coast optd as T* **30**.

170		½d. bistre-brown and scarlet		10	10*
		a. Olive-brown and scarlet		10	10*
171		1d. deep blue (R.)		10	10*
172		1½d. emerald-green		10	10*
173		2d. chocolate (26.5.58)		30	30
174		2½d. scarlet (26.5.58)		1·00	1·25
175		3d. magenta		30	10*
176		4d. blue (26.5.58)		3·75	6·00
177		6d. black and orange (R.)		10	10*
		a. Opt double		† £275	
178		1s. black and orange-red		10	10*
179		2s. brown-olive and carmine		60	10*
180		5s. purple and black		75	10*
181		10s. black and olive-green		75	60*
170/81			*Set of 12*	7·00	7·50*

Nos. 173/4 and 176 were officially issued on 26 May 1958 although, in error, small quantities were sold at certain post offices when the rest of the set appeared.

Nos. 170 and 171 exist in coils constructed from normal sheets.

31 Viking Ship

(Des W. Wind. Recess E. A. Wright Bank Note Co., Philadelphia)

1957 (27 Dec). *Inauguration of Black Star Shipping Line. T* **31** *and similar horiz designs. No wmk. P* 12.

182		2½d. emerald-green		70	20
		a. Imperf between (vert pair)		£350	
		b. Imperf between (horiz pair)		£350	
183		1s. 3d. deep blue		75	1·25
		a. Imperf horiz (vert pair)		£400	
184		5s. bright purple		1·00	3·00
		a. Imperf vert (horiz pair)		£475	
182/4			*Set of 3*	2·25	4·00

Designs:—1s. 3d. Galleon; 5s. M.V. *Volta River.*

PRINTERS. Nos. 185/**MS**568 were printed in photogravure by Harrison & Sons *except where otherwise stated.*

34 Ambassador Hotel, Accra   **35** Ghana Coat of Arms

1958 (6 Mar). *First Anniv of Independence. T* **34/5** *and similar designs. Wmk Mult Script CA. P* 14½ × 14 (2s.) *or* 14 × 14½ (*others*).

185		½d. black, red, yellow, green and carmine		10	10
186		2½d. black, red, green and yellow		10	10
187		1s. 3d. black, red, yellow, green and blue		30	10
188		2s. red, yellow, blue, green, brown and black		45	35
185/8			*Set of 4*	75	45

Designs: *Horiz as T* **34**—2½d. State Opening of Parliament; 1s. 3d. National Monument.

38 Map showing the Independent African States   **39** Map of Africa and Flaming Torch

(Des R. Milton)

1958 (15 Apr). *First Conference of Independent African States, Accra. Wmk Mult Script CA. P* 13½ × 14½ (2½d., 3d) *or* 14½ × 13½ (*others*).

189	38	2½d. black, bistre and bright carmine-red		10	10
190		3d. black, bistre, brown and bright green		10	10
191	39	1s. black, yellow, red and dull blue		20	10
192		2s. 6d. black, yellow, red and dull violet		40	35
189/92			*Set of 4*	60	40

40 Palm-nut Vulture over Globe

41 Bristol 175 Britannia 309 Airliner

(Des M. Goaman (2½d., 2s. 6d.), R. Milton (1s. 3d.), W. Wind (2s.))

1958 (15 July). *Inauguration of Ghana Airways. T 40/1 and similar designs. Wmk Mult Script CA. P 15 × 14 (2s. 6d.) or 14 × 15 (others).*

193	2½d. black, yellow-bistre & rose-carmine		45	10
194	1s. 3d. multicoloured		90	20
195	2s. multicoloured		1·00	55
196	2s. 6d. black and bistre		1·00	95
193/6		Set of 4	3·00	1·60

Designs: Horiz (as T 41)—2s. Boeing 377 Stratocruiser and Yellow-nosed Albatross. (As T 40)—2s. 6d. Palm-nut Vulture and Vickers VC-10 aircraft.

PRIME MINISTER'S VISIT, U.S.A. AND CANADA

(44)   **45**

1958 (18 July). *Prime Minister's Visit to the United States and Canada. Nos. 166/9 optd with T 44.*

197	29	2d. scarlet	10	10
198		2½d. green	10	10
199		4d. brown	10	15
200		1s. 3d. deep blue	15	25
197/200		Set of 4	30	45

(Des W. Wind)

1958 (24 Oct). *United Nations Day. Wmk Mult Script CA. P 14 × 14½.*

201	45	2½d. purple-brown, green and black	10	10
202		1s. 3d. purple-brown, blue and black	20	10
203		2s. 6d. purple-brown, violet and black	25	35
201/3		Set of 3	40	40

46 Dr. Nkrumah and Lincoln Statue, Washington   **47**

(Des M. Goaman)

1959 (12 Feb). *150th Birth Anniv of Abraham Lincoln. W 47. P 14 × 14½.*

204	46	2½d. pink and deep purple	10	10
205		1s. 3d. light blue and blue	15	10
206		2s. 6d. orange-yellow & dp olive-green	20	35
204/6		Set of 3	30	45
MS206a	102 × 77 mm. Nos. 204/6. Imperf		55	2·00

48 Kente Cloth and Traditional Symbols

(Des Mrs. T. Sutherland (½d.), M. Karoly (2½d.), K. Antubam (1s. 3d.), A. M. Medina (2s.))

1959 (6 Mar). *Second Anniv of Independence. T 48 and similar multicoloured designs. W 47. P 14½ × 14 (2s.) or 14 × 14½ (others).*

207	½d. Type 48		10	10
208	2½d. Talking drums and elephant-horn blower		10	10
209	1s. 3d."Symbol of Greeting" (vert)		15	10
210	2s. Map of Africa, Ghana flag and palms		30	1·25
207/10		Set of 4	50	1·40

52 Globe and Flags

(Des Mrs. H. Potter)

1959 (15 Apr). *Africa Freedom Day. W 47 (sideways). P 14½ × 14.*

211	52	2½d. multicoloured	15	10
212		8½d. multicoloured	15	20

53 "God's Omnipotence"   **54** Nkrumah Statue, Accra

55 Ghana Timber   **56** Volta River

65a Red-fronted Gazelle

Two Types of ½d. and 3d:

I. Inscr "GOD'S OMNIPOTENCE"
II. Inscr "GYE NYAME"

(Des Mrs. T. Sutherland (½d., 3d.), Ghana Information Bureau (source of 1d. and 2d.), O. Haulkland (1½d.), A. Medina (2½d., 4d.), M. Goaman (6d., 1s. 3d., 2s. 6d.), W. Wind (11d., 1s., 2s., 5s.), W. H. Brown (10s.), M. Shamir (£1))

1959 (5 Oct)—61. *T 53/6, 65a, and similar multicoloured designs. W 47 (sideways on horiz designs). P 11½ × 12 (½d.), 12 × 11½ (1d.), 14 × 14½ (1½d., 11d., 1s., 2s. and 5s.), 14 × 15 (10s.) or 14½ × 14 (others). (a) Postage.*

213	½d. Type 53 (I)		10	10
	a. Type II (29.4.61)		30	10
214	1d. Type 54		10	10
215	1½d. Type 55		10	10
216	2d. Type 56		10	10
217	2½d. Cocoa bean		10	10
218	3d. "God's Omnipotence" (I)		10	10
	a. Type II (29.4.61)		30	10
219	4d. Diamond and Mine		4·50	65
220	6d. Red-crowned Bishop		50	10
	a. Green (flag) omitted		70·00	
221	11d. Golden Spider Lily		25	10
222	1s. Shell Ginger		25	10
223	2s. 6d. Great Blue Turaco		2·25	15
224	5s. Tiger Orchid		4·00	50
225	10s. Jewel Cichlid		1·00	70
225a	£1 Type 65a (29.4.61)		8·00	4·75

(b) Air

226	1s. 3d. Pennant-winged Nightjar		2·50	10
227	2s. Crowned Cranes		1·75	10
213/27		Set of 16	23·00	6·00

Nos. 217/224 and 226/7 are as Types 55/6, the 11d., 1s., 5s. and 2s. (air) being vertical and the remainder horizontal. No. 225 is as Type 65a.

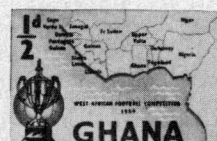

68 Gold Cup and West African Map

(Des K. Lehmann (½d., 3d.), M. & G. Shamir (1d.), W. Wind (8d.), and K. Antubam (2s. 6d.))

1959 (15 Oct). *West African Football Competition, 1959. T 68 and similar multicoloured designs. W 47 (sideways on horiz designs). P 14 × 14½ (1d., 2s. 6d) or 14½ × 14 (others).*

228	½d. Type 68		10	10*
229	1d. Footballers (vert)		10	10*
230	3d. Goalkeeper saving ball		10	10*
231	8d. Forward attacking goal		60	15*
232	2s. 6d. "Kwame Nkrumah" Gold Cup (vert)		70	15*
228/32		Set of 5	1·25	40*

73 The Duke of Edinburgh and Arms of Ghana

(Des A. S. B. New)

1959 (24 Nov). *Visit of the Duke of Edinburgh to Ghana. W 47 (sideways). P 15 × 14.*

233	73	3d. black and magenta	30	10*

74 Ghana Flag and Talking Drums   **75** Ghana Flag and U.N. Emblem

(Des K. Antubam (2s. 6d.), A. Medina (others))

1959 (10 Dec). *United Nations Trusteeship Council. T 74/5 and similar multicoloured designs. W 47 (sideways on 3d.). P 14½ × 14 (3d.) or 14 × 14½ (others).*

234	3d. Type 74		10	10*
235	6d. Type 75		10	10*
236	1s. 3d. Ghana flag and U.N. emblem (vert)		30	15*
237	2s. 6d. "Totem Pole" (vert)		40	15*
234/7		Set of 4	75	45*

78 Eagles in Flight   **79** Fireworks

(Des A. Medina (½d.), M. Goaman (3d.), W. Wind (1s. 3d., 2s.))

1960 (6 Mar). *Third Anniv of Independence. T 78/9 and similar vert designs. Multicoloured. W 47. P 14 × 14½.*

238	½d. Type 78		10	10*
239	3d. Type 79		10	10*
240	1s. 3d. "Third Anniversary"		30	10*
241	2s. "Ship of State"		30	15*
238/41		Set of 4	70	30*

82 "A" of National Flags

(Des W. Wind)

1960 (15 Apr). *Africa Freedom Day. T 82 and similar horiz designs. Multicoloured. W 47 (sideways). P 14½ × 14.*

242	3d. Type 82		10	10*
243	6d. Letter "f"		20	10*
244	1s. 3d. Letter "d"		20	10*
242/4		Set of 3	40	20*

REPUBLIC

85 President Nkrumah

(Des A. Medina (3d., 10s.), W. Wind (1s. 3d., 2s.))

1960 (1 July). *Republic Day. T 85 and similar multicoloured designs. W 47. P 14½ × 14 (10s.) or 14 × 14½ (others).*

245	3d. Type 85		10	10
246	1s. 3d. Ghana flag		25	10
247	2s. Torch of Freedom		30	20
248	10s. Arms of Ghana (horiz)		70	1·25
245/8		Set of 4	1·10	1·50
MS248a	102 × 77 mm. Nos. 245/8. Imperf		40	1·50

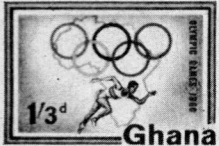

89 Olympic Torch   **90** Athlete

(Des A. Medina (T **89**), W. Wind (T **90**))

1960 (15 Aug). *Olympic Games.* W **47** (*sideways on* T **90**).
P 14 × 14½ (T **89**) *or* 14½ × 14 (T **90**).

249	**89**	3d. multicoloured	..	..	10	10
250		6d. multicoloured	..	..	15	10
251	**90**	1s. 3d. multicoloured	..	..	25	10
252		2s. 6d. multicoloured	..	..	35	60
249/52				*Set of 4*	70	70

91 President Nkrumah   **94** U.N. Emblem and Ghana Flag

(Des M. Goaman (3d., 6d.), W. Wind (1s. 3d.))

1960 (21 Sept). *Founder's Day.* T **91** *and similar multicoloured designs.* W **47** (*sideways on* 3d.). P 14½ × 14 (3d.) *or* 14 × 14½ (*others*).

253		3d. Type **91**	..	..	10	10
254		6d. President Nkrumah (*vert*)	..	..	10	10
255		1s. 3d. Flag-draped column over map of African (*vert*)			20	20
253/5				*Set of 3*	30	30

(Des M. Goaman (3d., 1s. 3d.), W. Wind (6d.))

1960 (10 Dec). *Human Rights Day.* T **94** *and similar vert designs.* W **47**. P 14 × 14½.

256		3d. multicoloured	..	..	10	10
257		6d. yellow, black and blue	..	..	20	10
258		1s. 3d. multicoloured	..	..	40	30
256/8	..			*Set of 3*	60	40

Designs:—6d. U.N. emblem and Torch; 1s. 3d. U.N. emblem.

97 Talking Drums   **100** Eagle on Column

(Des M. Goaman (3d.), A. S. B. New (6d.), W. Wind (2s.))

1961 (15 Apr). *Africa Freedom Day.* T **97** *and similar designs.* W **47** (*sideways on* 2s.). P 14½ × 14 (2s.) *or* 14 × 14½ (*others*).

259		3d. multicoloured	..	..	10	10
260		6d. red, black and green	..	..	20	10
261		2s. multicoloured	..	..	50	45
259/61				*Set of 3*	70	50

Designs: *Vert.*—6d. Map of Africa. *Horiz.*—2s. Flags and map.

(Des A. S. B. New (3d.), M. Shamir (1s. 3d.), W. Wind (2s.))

1961 (1 July). *First Anniv of Republic.* T **100** *and similar vert designs. Multicoloured.* W **47**. P 14 × 14½.

262		3d. Type **100**	..	..	10	10
263		1s. 3d. "Flower"	..	..	10	10
264		2s. Ghana flags	..	..	20	80
262/4				*Set of 3*	30	90

103 Dove with Olive Branch   **106** Pres. Nkrumah and Globe

(Des V. Whiteley)

1961 (1 Sept). *Belgrade Conference.* T **103** *and similar designs.* W **47** (*sideways on* 1s. 3d., 5s.). P 14 × 14½ (3d.) *or* 14½ × 14 (*others*).

265		3d. yellow-green	..	..	10	10
266		1s. 3d. deep blue	..	..	15	10
267		5s. bright reddish purple	..	..	60	70
265/7				*Set of 3*	70	75

Designs: *Horiz.*—1s. 3d. World map, chain and olive branch; 5s. Rostrum, conference room.

(Des A. Medina (3d.), M. Goaman (1s. 3d.), Miriam Karoly (5s.))

1961 (21 Sept). *Founder's Day.* T **106** *and similar multicoloured designs.* W **47** (*sideways on* 3d.). P 14½ × 14 (3d.) *or* 14 × 14½ (*others*).

268		3d. Type **106**	..	..	10	10
269		1s. 3d. President and Kente Cloth (*vert*)			25	10
270		5s. President in national costume (*vert*)			95	2·50
268/70				*Set of 3*	1·10	2·50

MS270a Three sheets 86 × 86 mm (3d.) *or* 86 × 106 mm (*others*) each with Nos. 268/70 in block of four. Imperf ... *Three sheets* 4·50 14·00
The 1s. 3d. Miniature Sheet is known with the brown colour omitted.

109 Queen Elizabeth II and African Map

(Des M. Goaman)

1961 (9 Nov). *Royal Visit.* W **47**. P 14½ × 14.

271	**109**	3d. multicoloured	..	..	15	10
272		1s. 3d. multicoloured	..	..	50	20
273		5s. multicoloured	..	..	1·60	3·00
271/3	..			*Set of 3*	2·00	3·00

MS273a 106 × 84 mm. No. 273 in block of four. Imperf ... 3·50 7·50

110 Ships in Tema Harbour

(Des C. Bottiau. Litho Enschedé & Sons)

1962 (10 Feb). *Opening of Tema Harbour.* T **110** *and similar horiz designs. Multicoloured. No wmk.* P 14 × 13. (a) *Postage.*

274		3d. Type **110**	..	..	15	10

(b) *Air*

275		1s. 3d. Douglas DC-8 aircraft and ships at Tema			80	15
276		2s. 6d. As 1s. 3d.	..	..	1·00	2·00
274/6				*Set of 3*	1·75	2·00

112 Africa and Peace Dove   **113** Compass over Africa

(Des R. Hegeman. Litho Enschedé)

1962 (6 Mar). *First Anniv of Casablanca Conference. No wmk.* P 13 × 14. (a) *Postage.*

277	**112**	3d. multicoloured	..	..	10	10

(b) *Air*

278	**112**	1s. 3d. multicoloured	..	..	30	15
279		2s. 6d. multicoloured	..	..	40	1·40
277/9				*Set of 3*	70	1·50

(Des R. Hegeman)

1962 (24 Apr). *Africa Freedom Day.* W **47**. P 14 × 14½.

280	**113**	3d. sepia, blue-green and reddish purple			10	10
281		6d. sepia, blue-green and orange-brown			10	15
282		1s. 3d. sepia, blue-green and red			15	15
280/2	..			*Set of 3*	30	30

COVER PRICES

Cover factors are quoted at the beginning of each country for most issues to 1945. An explanation of the system can be found on page x. The factors quoted do not, however, apply to philatelic covers.

---

114 Ghana Star and "Five Continents"   **115** Atomic Bomb-burst "Skull"

(Des M. Goaman (3d.), M. Shamir (6d.), W. Wind (1s. 3d.))

1962 (21 June). *Accra Assembly,* T **114/15** *and similar vert design.* W **47**. P 14 × 14½.

283		3d. black and lake-red	..	..	10	10
284		6d. black and scarlet	..	..	25	35
285		1s. 3d. turquoise	..	..	30	50
283/5				*Set of 3*	55	80

Design:—1s. 3d. Dove of Peace.

117 Patrice Lumumba   **118** Star over Two Columns

(Des A. S. B. New)

1962 (30 June). *1st Death Anniv of Lumumba.* W **47**. P 14½ × 14.

286	**117**	3d. black and orange-yellow	..	..	10	10
287		6d. black, green and lake	..	..	10	30
288		1s. 3d. black, pink and black-green			15	35
286/8	..			*Set of 3*	30	60

(Des A. S. B. New (3d.), A. Medina (6d.), M. Goaman (1s. 3d.) Litho Enschedé)

1962 (1 July). *2nd Anniv of Republic.* T **118** *and similar multi-coloured designs.* P 14 × 13½ (1s. 3d.) *or* 13½ × 14 (*others*).

289		3d. Type **118**	..	..	10	10
290		6d. Flaming torch	..	..	20	30
291		1s. 3d. Eagle trailing flag (*horiz*)			40	55
289/91				*Set of 3*	60	80

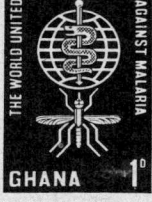

121 President Nkrumah   **125** Campaign Emblem

(Litho Enschedé)

1962 (21 Sept). *Founder's Day.* T **121** *and similar vert designs.* P 13 × 14½.

292		1d. multicoloured	..	..	10	10
293		3d. multicoloured	..	..	10	10
294		1s. 3d. black and bright blue			30	15
295		2s. multicoloured	..	..	30	60
292/5				*Set of 4*	70	80

Designs:—3d. Nkrumah medallion; 1s. 3d. President Nkrumah and Ghana Star; 2s. Laying "Ghana" Brick.

1962 (3 Dec). *Malaria Eradication.* W **47**. P 14 × 14½.

296	**125**	1d. cerise	..	..	15	10
297		4d. yellow-green	..	..	40	1·00
298		6d. bistre	..	..	40	30
299		1s. 3d. bluish violet	..	..	40	90
296/9	..			*Set of 4*	1·25	2·00

MS299a 90 × 115 mm. Nos. 296/9. Imperf ... 75 1·50

126 Campaign Emblem   **129** Map of Africa

1963 (21 Mar). *Freedom from Hunger.* T **126** *and similar designs.* W **47** *(sideways on* 4d., 1s. 3d.). P 14 × 14½ (1d.) or 14½ × 14 *(others).*

300		1d. multicoloured		15	10
301		4d. sepia, yellow and orange		75	45
302		1s. 3d. ochre, black and green		1·60	80
300/2			*Set of 3*	2·25	1·25

Designs: Horiz—4d. Emblem in hands; 1s. 3d. World map and emblem.

1963 (15 Apr). *Africa Freedom Day.* T **129** *and similar designs.* W **47** *(sideways on* 4d.). P 14½ × 14 (4d.) or 14 × 14½ *(others).*

303		1d. gold and red		10	10
304		4d. red, black and yellow		10	10
305		1s. 3d. multicoloured		35	10
306		2s. 6d. multicoloured		50	1·25
303/6			*Set of 4*	85	1·40

Designs: Horiz—4d. Carved stool. *Vert*—1s. 3d. Map and bowl of fire; 2s. 6d. Topi (antelope) and flag.

133 Red Cross   **137** "3rd Anniversary"

(Des R. Hegeman (4d.), M. Shamir (others))

1963 (28 May). *Red Cross Centenary.* T **133** *and similar multicoloured designs.* W **47** *(sideways on* 1½d., 4d.). P 14½ × 14 (1d., 1s. 3d.) or 14 × 14½ *(others).*

307		1d. Type **133**		60	15
308		1½d. Centenary emblem *(horiz)*		90	1·25
309		4d. Nurses and child *(horiz)*		2·25	20
310		1s. 3d. Emblem, globe and laurel		3·50	2·00
307/10			*Set of 4*	6·50	3·25
MS310a		102 × 127 mm. Nos. 307/10. Imperf		2·75	11·00

(Des M. Goaman (1d., 4d.), R. Hegeman (others))

1963 (1 July). *3rd Anniv of Republic.* T **137** *and similar multicoloured designs.* W **47** *(sideways on* 1d., 4d.). P 14½ × 14 *(horiz)* or 14 × 14½ *(vert).*

311		1d. Type **137**		10	10
312		4d. Three Ghanaian flags		10	10
	a. Black (stars on flag) omitted		†	£300
313		1s. 3d. Map, flag and star *(vert)*		35	15
314		2s. 6d. Flag and torch *(vert)*		55	1·50
311/14			*Set of 4*	1·00	1·50

141 President Nkrumah and Ghana Flag   **145** Rameses II, Abu Simbel

(Des R. Hegeman (1d., 4d.), M. Shamir (1s. 3d.), G. Rose (5s.))

1963 (21 Sept). *Founder's Day.* T **141** *and similar designs.* W **47** *(sideways on* 1s. 3d., 5s.). P 14 × 14½ *(vert)* or 14½ × 14 *(horiz).*

315		1d. multicoloured		10	10
316		4d. multicoloured		15	10
317		1s. 3d. multicoloured		30	10
	a. Green omitted			60·00
318		5s. yellow and bright reddish purple		65	75
315/18			*Set of 4*	1·00	85

Designs: Vert—4d. Nkrumah and flag. *Horiz*—1s. 3d. Nkrumah and fireworks; 5s. Symbol of Wisdom.

(Des M. Farrar Bell and R. Hegeman. Litho (1½d., 2d.) or photo (others) Enschedé)

1963 (1 Nov). *Nubian Monuments Preservation.* T **145** *and similar multicoloured designs.* No wmk. P 11½ × 11 *(vert)* or 11 × 11½ *(horiz).*

319		1d. Type **145**		15	10
320		1½d. Rock paintings *(horiz)*		20	65
321		2d. Queen Nefertari *(horiz)*		20	10
322		4d. Sphinx, Sebua		35	15
323		1s. 3d. Rock Temple, Abu Simbel *(horiz)*		80	90
319/23			*Set of 5*	1·60	1·75

150 Class 248 Steam Locomotive and Diesel-electric Locomotive No. 1401   **151** Eleanor Roosevelt and "Flame of Freedom"

(Des H. L. W. Stevens)

1963 (1 Dec). *60th Anniv of Ghana Railway.* W **47** *(sideways).*

324	150	1d. multicoloured		10	10
325		6d. multicoloured		60	10
326		1s. 3d. multicoloured		1·00	60
327		2s. 6d. multicoloured		1·75	2·25
324/7			*Set of 4*	3·00	2·75

(Des R. Hegeman and F. H. Savage. Photo Enschedé)

1963 (10 Dec). *15th Anniv of Declaration of Human Rights.* T **151** *and similar multicoloured designs.* No wmk. P 11 × 11½ (1s. 3d.) or 11½ × 11 *(others).*

328		1d. Type **151**		10	10
329		4d. Type **151**		10	30
330		6d. Eleanor Roosevelt		10	10
331		1s. 3d. Eleanor Roosevelt and emblems *(horiz)*		15	15
328/31			*Set of 4*	30	50

No. 329 differs from No. 328 in the arrangement of the trailing "flame" and of the background within the circular emblem.

154 Sun and Globe Emblem   **155** Harvesting Corn on State Farm

1964 (15 June). *International Quiet Sun Years.* W **47** *(sideways). Each blue, yellow, red and green; background colours given.* P 14½.

332	154	3d. pale brown		15	10
333		6d. pale grey		25	10
334		1s. 3d. mauve		25	15
332/4			*Set of 3*	60	30
MS334a		90 × 90 mm. No. 334 in block of four. Imperf		75	2·50

Nos. 332/4 each exist in a miniature sheet of 12 in different colours (i.e. 3d. in colours of 6d.; 6d. in colours of 1s. 3d.; 1s. 3d. in colours of 3d.) but these were not generally available to the public.

(Des M. Shamir. Photo Govt Printer, Israel)

1964 (1 July). *4th Anniv of Republic.* T **155** *and similar horiz designs.* P 13 × 14.

335		3d. olive, brown and yellow-olive		10	10
336		6d. bluish green, brown and turquoise-green		10	10
337		1s. 3d. brown-red, brown and salmon-red		10	10
338		5s. multicoloured		40	70
335/8			*Set of 4*	55	75
MS338a		126 × 100 mm. Nos. 335/8. Imperf		55	2·00
	ab. Olive (central design and face value of 3d.) omitted			

Designs:—6d. Oil refinery, Tema; 1s. 3d. "Communal Labour"; 5s. Procession headed by flag.

159 Globe and Dove   **163** Pres. Nkrumah and Hibiscus Flowers

(Des M. Shamir. Litho Lewin-Epstein Ltd, Bat Yam, Israel)

1964 (15 July). *1st Anniv of African Unity Charter.* T **159** *and similar designs.* P 14.

339		3d. multicoloured		10	10
340		6d. deep bronze-green and red		10	10
341		1s. 3d. multicoloured		15	10
342		5s. multicoloured		45	70
339/42			*Set of 4*	65	75

Designs: Vert—6d. Map of Africa and quill pen; 5s. Planting flower. *Horiz*—1s. 3d. Hitched rope on map of Africa.

1964 (21 Sept). *Founder's Day.* W **47** *(sideways).* P 14 × 14½.

343	163	3d. sepia, red, deep green and light blue		10	10
344		6d. sepia, red, deep green and yellow		15	10
345		1s. 3d. sepia, red, deep green and grey		25	10
346		2s. 6d. sepia, red, dp grn & light emerald		40	60
343/6			*Set of 4*	75	70
MS346a		90 × 122 mm. No. 346 in block of four. Imperf		70	2·50

IMPERFORATE STAMPS. Many issues, including miniature sheets, from here onwards exist imperforate, but these were not sold at post offices.

164 Hurdling

(Des A. S. B. New (No. 352))

1964 (25 Oct). *Olympic Games, Tokyo.* T **164** *and similar multicoloured designs.* W **47** *(sideways on* 1d., 2½d., 6d., 5s.). P 14½ × 14 *(horiz)* or 14 × 14½ *(vert).*

347	164	1d. Type **164**		10	10
348		2½d. Running		10	1·25
349		3d. Boxing *(vert)*		10	10
350		4d. Long-jumping *(vert)*		10	10
351		6d. Football *(vert)*		15	10
352		1s. 3d. Athlete holding Olympic Torch *(vert)*		20	10
353		5s. Olympic Rings and flags		85	3·25
347/53			*Set of 7*	1·40	4·25
MS353a		128 × 102 mm. Nos. 351/3. Imperf		75	2·50

171 G. Washington Carver (botanist) and Plant   **173** African Elephant

(Des M. Shamir)

1964 (7 Dec). *U.N.E.S.C.O. Week.* W **47**. P 14½.

354	171	6d. deep blue and green		15	10
355	—	1s. 3d. reddish purple & greenish blue		60	10
	w. Wmk inverted			11·00	
356	171	5s. sepia and orange-red		1·25	4·00
354/6			*Set of 3*	1·75	4·00
MS356a		127×77 mm. Nos. 354/6. Imperf		75	2·00

Design:—1s. 3d. Albert Einstein (scientist) and atomic symbol.

(Des A. S. B. New (No. 360). Photo Enschedé)

1964 (14 Dec). *Multicoloured designs as* T **173**. P 11½ × 11 *(vert)* or 11 × 11½ *(horiz).*

357	173	1d. Type **173**		50	50
358		1½d. Secretary Bird *(horiz)*		1·00	2·25
359		2½d. Purple Wreath (flower)		60	2·25
360		3d. Grey Parrot		1·50	50
361		4d. Blue-naped Mousebird *(horiz)*		1·50	70
362		6d. African Tulip Tree *(horiz)*		60	30
363		1s. 3d. Violet Starling *(horiz)*		1·75	1·25
364		2s. 6d. Hippopotamus *(horiz)*		1·75	5·50
357/64			*Set of 8*	8·25	12·00
MS364a		(a) 150×86 mm. Nos. 357/9. (b) 150×110 mm. Nos. 360/4. Imperf *Set of 2 sheets*		5·50	14·00

181 I.C.Y. Emblem   **182** I.T.U. Emblem and Symbols

(Litho Enschedé)

1965 (22 Feb). *International Co-operation Year.* P 14 × 12½.

365	181	1d. multicoloured		35	60
366		4d. multicoloured		1·50	1·40
367		6d. multicoloured		1·50	60
368		1s. 3d. multicoloured		1·75	2·75
365/8			*Set of 4*	4·50	4·75
MS368a		100 × 100 mm. No. 368 in block of four. Imperf		2·75	5·00

(Litho Enschedé)

1965 (12 Apr). *I.T.U. Centenary.* P 13½.

369	182	1d. multicoloured		15	15
370		6d. multicoloured		55	15
371		1s. 3d. multicoloured		1·00	25
372		5s. multicoloured		2·25	2·75
369/72			*Set of 4*	3·50	3·00
MS372a		132 × 115 mm. Nos. 369/72. Imperf		5·50	8·00

183 Lincoln's Home

(Des M. Farrar Bell (6d.), A. S. B. New (1s. 3d., 5s.), R. Hegeman (2s.))

1965 (17 May). *Death Centenary of Abraham Lincoln.* T **183** *and similar square-shaped designs.* W **47** *(sideways).* P 12½.

373		6d. multicoloured		15	10
374		1s. 3d. black, red and blue		25	15
375		2s. black, orange-brown and greenish yellow		30	30
376		5s. black and red		70	1·50
373/6			*Set of 4*	1·25	1·75
MS376a		115 × 115 mm. Nos. 373/6. Imperf		1·25	3·50
	ab. Green (part of flag on 6d.) omitted			

Designs:—1s. 3d. Lincoln's Inaugural Address; 2s. Abraham Lincoln; 5s. Adaptation of U.S. 90 c. Lincoln Stamp of 1869.

(New Currency. 100 pesewas = 1 cedi)

187 Obverse (Pres. Nkrumah) and Reverse of 5 p. Coin

(Photo Enschedé)

1965 (19 July). *Introduction of Decimal Currency. T* **187** *and similar horiz designs. Multicoloured. P* 11 × 13 (5 p., 10 p.), 13 × 12½ (25 p.) or 13½ × 14 (50 p.).

377	5 p. Type **187**		25	10
378	10 p. As Type **187**		30	10
379	25 p. Size 63 × 39 mm.		1·00	1·00
380	50 p. Size 71 × 43½ mm		2·00	2·25
377/80		Set of 4	3·25	3·00

The coins in Nos. 378/80 are all circular and express the same denominations as on the stamps.

₵2·40

Ghana New Currency 19th July. 1965.

(188)

1965 (19 July). *Nos. 214, 216 and 218a/27 surch as T* **188** *diagonally upwards, (D) or horizontally, (H), by Govt Printer, Accra.*

(a) Postage

381	1 p. on 1d. multicoloured (R.) (D)		10	10
	a. Surch inverted		15·00	
	b. Surch double		45·00	
382	2 p. on 2d. multicoloured (Ultram.) (H)		10	10
	a. Surch inverted			
	b. Surch double		11·00	
	c. Surch on back only			
	d. Surch on front and back			
	e. Red surch		27·00	
	f. Orange surch		27·00	
	g. Indigo surch			
	ga. Surch sideways			
383	3 p. on 3d. multicoloured (II) (Br.) (H)		95	4·50
	a. Surch inverted		18·00	
	b. Indigo surch			
384	4 p. on 4d. multicoloured (B.) (H)		4·00	45
	a. Surch inverted		40·00	
	b. Surch double			
	c. Red surch			
385	6 p. on 6d. multicoloured (Blk.) (H)		50	10
	a. Surch inverted		8·50	
	b. Surch double		15·00	
	c. Horiz pair, one without surch		50·00	
	d. Green (flag) omitted		60·00	
386	11 p. on 11d. multicoloured (W.) (D)		25	10
	a. Surch inverted		11·00	
387	12 p. on 1s. multicoloured (B.) (D)		25	10
	a. Surch double			
	b. Surch double, one albino inverted			
	c. Black surch		9·00	
	ca. Surch inverted		9·00	
388	30 p. on 2s. 6d. multicoloured (B.) (H).		3·00	2·75
389	60 p. on 5s. multicoloured (B.) (D)		4·50	70
	a. Surch double (G. + B.)		27·00	
390	1 c. 20 on 10s. multicoloured (B.) (D)		75	2·25
	a. Surch double (G. + B.)		85·00	
391	2 c. 40 on £1 multicoloured (B.) (D)		1·00	6·00

(b) Air

392	15 p. on 1s. 3d. multicoloured (W.) (H)		2·50	70
	a. Surch inverted			
393	24 p. on 2s. multicoloured (G.) (D)		2·50	30
	a. Surch on front and back		25·00	
381/93		Set of 13	17·00	16·00

On the diagonal surcharges the values are horizontal.
The 30 p. was not released in Ghana until 30 July and the 3 p. sometime later.
Numerous minor varieties exist.

189 "OAU" and Flag

190 "OAU", Heads and Flag

191 "OAU" Emblem and Flag

192 African Map and Flag

1965 (21 Oct). *O.A.U. Summit Conference, Accra. T* **189/92** *and similar horiz designs. Multicoloured. W* **47** *(sideways* except on 6p.). P* 14 (T **189/91**) *or* 14½×14 *(others).*

394	1 p. Type **189**		10	10
	a. Red (part of flag) omitted		70·00	
395	2 p. Type **190**		10	10
396	5 p. Type **191**		10	10
397	6 p. Type **192**		10	10
398	15 p. "Sunburst", map and flag		20	30
399	24 p. "O.A.U." on map, and flag		35	60
	w. Wmk top of G to left			
394/9		Set of 6	75	1·10

*The 1 p. also exists with the watermark facing left or right, but positional blocks are required to show the two types. The normal sideways watermark has top of G to right, *as seen from the back of the stamp.*

195 Goalkeeper saving Ball

198 Pres. Kennedy and Grave Memorial

(Photo Enschedé)

1965 (15 Nov). *African Soccer Cup Competition. T* **195** *and similar multicoloured designs. P* 13 × 14 (15 p.) *or* 14 × 13 *(others).*

400	6 p. Type **195**		25	10
401	15 p. Player with ball (*vert*)		40	25
402	24 p. Players, ball and soccer cup		45	50
400/2		Set of 3	1·00	75

(Des A. S. B. New (No. 405))

1965 (15 Dec)**–66**. *2nd Anniv of President Kennedy's Death. T* **198** *and similar square-shaped designs. W* **47** *(sideways). P* 12½.

403	6 p. multicoloured		15	10
404	15 p. violet, red and green		25	35
405	24 p. black and reddish violet		30	60
406	30 p. dull purple and black		40	75
403/6		Set of 4	1·00	1·60
MS407	114½ × 114 mm. Nos. 403/6. Imperf (21.3.66)		3·75	6·50

Designs:—15 p. Pres. Kennedy and Eternal Flame; 24 p. Pres. Kennedy and memorial inscription; 30 p. President Kennedy.

202 Section of Dam and Generators

(206)

Black Stars Retain Africa Cup 21st Nov. 1965

(Des A. S. B. New (No. 411). Photo Enschedé)

1966 (22 Jan). *Volta River Project. T* **202** *and similar horiz designs. P* 11 × 11½.

408	6 p. multicoloured		15	10
409	15 p. multicoloured		20	15
410	24 p. multicoloured		25	20
411	30 p. black and new blue		35	50
408/11		Set of 4	85	85

Designs:—15 p. Dam and Lake Volta; 24 p. Word "GHANA" as dam; 30 p. "Fertility".

1966 (7 Feb). *"Black Stars" Victory in African Soccer Cup Competition. Nos.* 400/2 *optd with T* **206**, *in black.*

412	6 p. Type **195**		25	10
	a. Green opt			
	b. Green opt double, one inverted		20·00	
	c. Stop after "Nov" omitted (R. 5/1)			
413	15 p. Player with ball		40	20

414	24 p. Players, ball and cup		45	35
	a. Opt inverted*		26·00	
	ab. Vert pair, one without opt, the other with opt inverted			
	b. Error. Opt for 15 p. on 24 p. inverted*			
	c. Stop after "Nov" omitted (R. 5/1)			
412/14		Set of 3	1·00	60

*In No. 414a the overprint reads downwards (top right to bottom left), but in No. 414b it reads upwards (bottom right to top left).

DATES OF ISSUE of miniature sheets are approximate as they are generally released some time after the related ordinary stamps, but it is known that the G.P.O. sometimes applied first-day cancellations months after the dates shown on the cancellations.

207 W.H.O. Building and Ghana Flag

1966 (1 July). *Inauguration of W.H.O. Headquarters, Geneva. T* **207** *and similar horiz design. Multicoloured. W* **47**. *P* 14½ × 14.

415	6 p. Type **207**		50	10
416	15 p. Type **207**		1·25	65
417	24 p. W.H.O. Building and emblem		1·40	1·25
418	30 p. As 24 p.		1·60	1·60
415/18		Set of 4	4·25	4·00
MS419	120 × 101 mm. Nos. 415/18. Imperf (11.66)		17·00	18·00

209 Atlantic Herring

214 African "Links" and Ghana Flag

(Des O. Hamann. Photo Enschedé)

1966 (10 Aug). *Freedom from Hunger. T* **209** *and similar horiz designs. Multicoloured. P* 14 × 13.

420	6 p. Type **209**		20	10
421	15 p. Turbot		45	15
422	24 p. Spadefish		75	35
423	30 p. Red Snapper		80	1·10
424	60 p. Blue-finned Tuna		2·00	4·00
420/4		Set of 5	3·75	5·00
MS425	126×109 mm. No. 423 in block of four. Imperf (Nov)		9·00	12·00

(Photo Enschedé)

1966 (11 Oct). *Third Anniv of African Charter. T* **214** *and similar multicoloured designs. P* 13½.

426	6 p. Type **214**		15	10
427	15 p. Flags as "Quill", and diamond (*horiz*)		35	55
428	24 p. Ship's wheel, map and cocoa bean (*horiz*)		40	70
426/8		Set of 3	80	1·25

217 Player heading Ball, and Jules Rimet Cup

1966 (14 Nov). *World Cup Football Championships, England. T* **217** *and similar horiz designs. Multicoloured. W* **47**. *P* 14½ × 14.

429	5 p. Type **217**		30	10
430	15 p. Goalkeeper clearing ball		70	20
	w. Wmk inverted		1·60	
431	24 p. Player and Jules Rimet Cup (replica)		85	35
432	30 p. Players and Jules Rimet Cup (replica)		1·10	1·25
433	60 p. Players with ball		1·75	5·50
	w. Wmk inverted			
429/33		Set of 5	4·25	6·50
MS434	120×102 mm. 60 p. (block of four). Imperf		20·00	20·00

ALTERED CATALOGUE NUMBERS

Any Catalogue numbers altered from the last edition are shown as a list in the introductory pages.

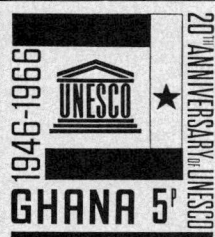

222 U.N.E.S.C.O. Emblem

1966 (23 Dec). 20th Anniv of U.N.E.S.C.O. W **47** (sideways). P 14½.

435	**222**	5 p. multicoloured		25	15
436		15 p. multicoloured		70	40
437		24 p. multicoloured		1·00	85
438		30 p. multicoloured		1·40	2·50
439		60 p. multicoloured		2·25	5·00
435/9			Set of 5	5·00	8·00
MS440		140 × 115 mm. Nos. 435/9. Imperf		19·00	21·00

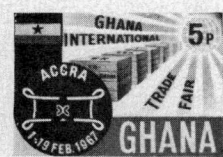

223 Fair Emblem and Crates

1967 (1 Feb). Ghana Trade Fair, Accra. T **223** and similar multicoloured designs. W **47** (sideways on 24 p.) P 14 × 14½ (24 p.) or 14½ × 14 (others).

441	5 p. Type **223**	10 10
442	15 p. Fair emblem and world map	15 20
443	24 p. Shipping and flags (vert).	25 30
444	36 p. Fair emblem and hand-held hoist	40 2·25
441/4	Set of 4	70 2·50

(New Currency. 100 new pesewas = 1 new cedi (1·2 old cedi))

1½Np   N₵2.00

(227)   (228)   229 Ghana Eagle and Flag

1967 (23 Feb). Nos. 216, 219/23, 225/6 and 393 surch as T **227/8**.

(a) Postage

445	1½ n.p. on 2d. multicoloured (Blk.)	3·00	4·00
446	3½ n.p. on 4d. multicoloured (R.)	4·50	1·25
	a. Surch double, one sideways		
447	5 n.p. on 6d. multicoloured (R.)	1·25	70
448	9 n.p. on 11d. multicoloured (W.)	30	20
449	10 n.p. on 1s. multicoloured (W.)	30	30
450	25 n.p. on 2s. 6d. multicoloured (R.)	3·50	5·00
451	1 n.c. on 10s. multicoloured (R.)	3·00	14·00
452	2 n.c. on £1 multicoloured (R.)	6·00	24·00

(b) Air

453	12½ n.p. on 1s. 3d. multicoloured (W.)	4·00	2·25
454	20 n.p. on 24 p. on 2s. multicoloured (R.)	4·75	3·50
445/54	Set of 10	28·00	50·00

Inverted surcharges in a different type face on the 3½, 5 and 25 n.p. are fakes.

(Des M. Shamir)

1967 (24 Feb). First Anniv of February 24 Revolution. W **47** (sideways). P 14 × 14½.

455	**229**	1 n.p. multicoloured	10	30
456		4 n.p. multicoloured	10	10
457		12½ n.p. multicoloured	40	60
458		25 n.p. multicoloured	85	2·75
455/8			Set of 4	1·25 3·25
MS459		89 × 108 mm. Nos. 455/8. Perf or imperf	5·00	12·00

230 Maize   231 Forest Kingfisher

---

235 Rufous-crowned Roller   236 Akosombo Dam

1967 (1 June–4 Sept). T 230/1, 235/6 and similar designs. W 47 (1½, 2, 4, 50 n.p. and 1 n.c.) or sideways (others). P 11½ × 12 (1, 8 n.p.), 12 × 11½ (4 n.p.), 14 × 14½ (1½, 2, 2½, 20 n.p., 2 n.c. 50) or 14½ × 14 (others).

460	1 n.p. multicoloured		10	10
	a. Salmon omitted**			
461	1½ n.p. multicoloured		90	2·00
	a. Blue omitted*		75·00	
	b. Green printed double, once inverted†			
	c. Green omitted†			
462	2 n.p. multicoloured (4.9)		10	10
	a. Green (part of flag omitted			
	b. Gold (frame) omitted			
	w. Wmk inverted		10·00	
463	2½ n.p. multicoloured (4.9)		35	10
	a. Wmk upright		10·00	
	ab. Face value omitted		£180	
464	3 n.p. multicoloured		20	40
	a. Green (part of flag) omitted			
465	4 n.p. multicoloured		1·50	10
	a. Green (part of flag) omitted		38·00	
	b. Red (part of flag) omitted			
	c. Black (star, bird markings and shadow) omitted		65·00	
466	6 n.p. multicoloured		15	75
467	8 n.p. multicoloured		15	10
468	9 n.p. multicoloured (4.9)		75	10
469	10 n.p. multicoloured		15	10
470	20 n.p. deep blue and new blue (4.9)		20	10
471	50 n.p. multicoloured		5·00	1·75
472	1 n.c. multicoloured (4.9.)		2·25	75
473	2 n.c. multicoloured (4.9.)		2·00	3·50
474	2 n.c. 50, multicoloured		3·00	7·50
460/74		Set of 15	15·00	15·00

Designs: Vert (as T **231**)—2 n.p. The Ghana Mace; 2½ n.p. Commelina; 20 n.p. Bush Hare; 2 n.c. Frangipani; 2 n.c. 50, Seat of State. Horiz (as T **236**)—3 n.p. West African Lungfish; 9 n.p. Chameleon; 10 n.p. Tema Harbour; 50 n.p. Black-winged Stilt; 1 n.c. Wooden Stool. (As T **230**)—8 n.p. Adomi Bridge.

*In this stamp the blue not only affects the bird but is printed over the yellow background to give the value in green, so that its omission results in the value also being omitted.

**This affects the maize flowers, corn and foreground.

†This affects the feather-tips and the flag.

The 2 n.p. and 20 n.p. were officially issued on 4 September but small quanties of both were released in error on 1 June. The 2½ n.p. is also known to have been released in error in June.

245 Kumasi Fort   249 "Luna 10"

(Des O. Hamann)

1967 (1 July). Castles and Forts. T **245** and similar designs. Multicoloured. W **47** (diagonal). P 14½.

475	4 n.p. Type **245**	25	10
476	12½ n.p. Christiansborg Castle and British galleon	1·00	1·00
477	20 n.p. Elmina Castle and Portuguese galleon	1·40	2·75
478	25 n.p. Cape Coast Castle and Spanish galleon	1·75	3·50
475/8	Set of 4	4·00	6·50

(Des M. Shamir. Photo Enschedé)

1967 (16 Aug). "Peaceful Use of Outer Space". T **249** and similar square designs. Multicoloured. P 13½ × 14.

479	4 n.p. Type **249**	10	10
480	12½ n.p. "Orbiter 1"	10	45
481	12½ n.p. Man in Space	20	80
479/81	Set of 3	35	1·25
MS482	140 × 90 mm. Nos. 479/81. Imperf	1·50	3·00

252 Scouts and Camp-fire

(Photo Enschedé)

1967 (18 Sept). 50th Anniv of Ghanaian Scout Movement. T **252** and similar horiz designs. Multicoloured. P 14½ × 13.

483	4 n.p. Type **252**	20	20
484	10 n.p. Scout on march	50	50
485	12½ n.p. Lord Baden-Powell	70	1·75
483/5	Set of 3	1·25	2·00
MS486	167 × 95 mm. Nos. 483/5. Imperf	6·00	9·50

---

255 U.N. Headquarters Building   256 General View of U.N. H.Q., Manhattan

(Litho D.L.R.)

1967 (20 Nov). United Nations Day (24 October). P 13½.

487	**255**	4 n.p. multicoloured	10	10
488		10 n.p. multicoloured	10	15
489		50 n.p. multicoloured	30	70
490	**256**	2 n.c. 50, multicoloured	1·00	4·00
487/90		Set of 4	1·25	4·50
MS491		76 × 75 mm. No. 490. Imperf (4.12.67)	2·75	9·50

257 Leopard

1967 (28 Dec). International Tourist Year. T **257** and similar diamond-shaped designs. Multicoloured. W **47** (diagonal). P 12½.

492	4 n.p. Type **257**	1·00	20
493	12½ n.p. Papilio demodocus (butterfly)	2·50	1·50
494	20 n.p. Carmine Bee Eater	3·00	3·50
495	50 n.p. Waterbuck	3·00	7·00
492/5	Set of 4	8·50	11·00
MS496	126 × 126 mm. Nos. 493/5. Imperf	16·00	17·00

261 Revolutionaries entering Accra

(Litho D.L.R.)

1968 (24 Feb). 2nd Anniv of February Revolution. T **261** and similar horiz designs. Multicoloured. P 14.

497	4 n.p. Type **261**	10	10
498	12½ n.p. Marching troops	20	20
499	20 n.p. Cheering people	30	40
500	40 n.p. Victory celebrations	50	1·50
497/500	Set of 4	1·00	2·00

265 Microscope and Cocoa Beans

1968 (18 Mar). Cocoa Research. T **265** and similar horiz design. Multicoloured. W **47** (sideways). P 14½ × 14.

501	2½ n.p. Type **265**	10	60
502	4 n.p. Microscope and cocoa tree, beans and pods	10	10
503	10 n.p. Type **265**	15	20
504	25 n.p. As 4 n.p.	60	1·10
501/4	Set of 4	80	1·75
MS505	102 × 102 mm. Nos. 501/4. Imperf	2·25	4·00

267 Kotoka and Flowers   271 Tobacco

(Des A. S. B. New (No. 508) and F. Mate (others) Litho D.L.R.)

1968 (17 Apr). *1st Death Anniv of Lt.-Gen. E. K. Kotoka. T* **267** *and similar multicoloured designs. P* 14.

506	4 n.p. Type 267	10	10
507	12½ n.p. Kotoka and wreath	20	30
508	20 n.p. Kotoka in civilian clothes	35	75
509	40 n.p. Lt.-Gen. Kotoka (*vert*)	50	1·60
506/9	*Set of 4*	1·00	2·50

(Des A. S. B. New (5 n.p.))

1968 (19 Aug). *Flora and Fauna. T* **271** *and similar vert designs. Multicoloured. W* **47** (*sideways*). *P* 14×14½.

510	4 n.p. Type 271	15	10
511	5 n.p. North African Crested Porcupine	15	60
512	12½ n.p. Rubber	50	50
513	20 n.p. *Cymothoe sangaris* (butterfly)	2·25	2·75
514	40 n.p. *Charaxes ameliae* (butterfly)	2·50	4·75
510/14	*Set of 5*	5·00	8·00
MS515	88×114 mm. Nos. 510, 512/14. Imperf	3·75	9·00

276 Surgeons, Flag and W.H.O. Emblem

277 Hurdling

(Photo Enschedé)

1968 (11 Nov). *20th Anniv of World Health Organization. P* 14 × 13.

516	**276** 4 n.p. multicoloured	25	10
517	12½ n.p. multicoloured	60	40
518	20 n.p. multicoloured	95	1·25
519	40 n.p. multicoloured	1·50	3·25
516/19	*Set of 4*	3·00	4·50
MS520	132 × 110 mm. Nos. 516/19. Imperf	3·75	6·50

1969 (10 Jan). *Olympic Games, Mexico* (1968). *T* **277** *and similar vert designs. Multicoloured. W* **47** (*sideways*). *P* 14 × 14½.

521	4 n.p. Type 277	10	10
522	12½ n.p. Boxing	20	30
523	20 n.p. Torch, Olympic Rings and flags	40	75
524	40 n.p. Football	70	2·75
521/4	*Set of 4*	1·25	3·50
MS525	89 × 114 mm. Nos. 521/4. Imperf (17.1.69)	3·50	6·50

281 U.N. Building

285 Dr. J. B. Danquah

(Litho D.L.R.)

1969 (1 Feb). *United Nations Day* (1968). *T* **281** *and similar square-shaped designs. Multicoloured. P* 13½.

526	4 n.p. Type 281	10	10
527	12½ n.p. Native stool, staff and U.N. emblem	15	25
528	20 n.p. U.N. building and emblem over Ghanaian flag	20	40
529	40 n.p. U.N. emblem encircled by flags	40	1·50
526/9	*Set of 4*	75	2·00
MS530	127 × 117 mm. No. 526/9. Imperf	75	3·25

1969 (7 Mar). *Human Rights Year. T* **285** *and similar horiz design. Multicoloured. W* **47** (*sideways on MS535*). *P* 14½ × 14.

531	4 n.p. Type 285	10	10
532	12½ n.p. Dr. Martin Luther King	20	35
533	20 n.p. As 12½ n.p.	35	75
534	40 n.p. Type 285	50	1·60
531/4	*Set of 4*	1·00	2·50
MS535	116 × 50 mm. Nos. 531/4. Imperf (17.4.69)	80	3·00

287 Constituent Assembly Building

1969 (10 Sept). *Third Anniv of the Revolution. T* **287** *and similar horiz design. W* **47** (*sideways on MS540*). *P* 14½ × 14.

536	4 n.p. Type 287	10	10
537	12½ n.p. Arms of Ghana	10	15
538	20 n.p. Type 287	15	20
539	40 n.p. As 12½ n.p.	20	50
536/9	*Set of 4*	40	80
MS540	114 × 89 mm. Nos. 536/9. Imperf	70	2·25

NEW CONSTITUTION 1969

(289)

290 Map of Africa and Flags

1969 (1 Oct). *New Constitution. Nos. 460/74 optd with T* **289** *in various positions by Government Press, Accra.*

541	1 n.p. multicoloured (Horiz)	10	1·25
542	1½ n.p. multicoloured (Vert down)	85	2·25
	a. Opt vert up	6·00	
	b. Horiz opt	25·00	
	ba. Opt omitted (in vert pair with normal)	£180	
543	2 n.p. multicoloured (Vert up)	10	2·00
	a. Opt vert down	5·00	
	b. Opt double	12·00	
544	2½ n.p. multicoloured (Vert up)	10	1·50
	a. Opt vert down	18·00	
545	3 n.p. multicoloured (Horiz)	60	1·75
	a. Opt inverted	15·00	
546	4 n.p. multicoloured (Y.) (Vert down)	2·25	30
	a. Black opt (vert down)	7·00	1·25
	b. Black opt (vert up)	10·00	
	c. Red opt (vert down)	18·00	
	d. Opt double (White vert down + yellow vert up)	27·00	
547	6 n.p. multicoloured (Horiz)	15	1·75
548	8 n.p. multicoloured (Horiz)	15	1·40
549	9 n.p. multicoloured (Horiz)	15	1·75
550	10 n.p. multicoloured (Horiz)	20	1·25
551	20 n.p. deep blue and new blue (Vert up)	35	1·25
	a. Opt vert down	20·00	
552	50 n.p. multicoloured (Horiz)	45	1·75
	a. Opt double	5·00	6·00
553	1 n.c. multicoloured (Horiz)	1·75	7·00
554	2 n.c. multicoloured (R.) (Vert up)	2·75	8·50
	a. Opt double (vert up and down)		
555	2 n.c. 50, multicoloured (Vert down)	2·75	9·50
541/55	*Set of 15*	14·00	42·00

The 1 n.p. is known with the overprint inverted, "NEW CONSTITUTION" appearing between the stamps across the perforations.

(Litho D.L.R.)

1969 (4 Dec). *Inauguration of Second Republic. T* **290** *and similar vert designs. Multicoloured. P* 14.

556	4 n.p. Type 290	10	10
557	12½ n.p. Figure "2", branch and Ghanaian colours	20	10
558	20 n.p. Hands receiving egg	35	30
559	40 n.p. Type 290	60	70
556/9	*Set of 4*	1·10	1·00

293 I.L.O. Emblem and Cog-wheels

1970 (5 Jan). *50th Anniv of International Labour Organisation. W* **47** (*sideways*). *P* 14½ × 14.

560	**293** 4 n.p. multicoloured	10	10
561	12½ n.p. multicoloured	20	30
562	20 n.p. multicoloured	30	55
560/2	*Set of 3*	55	85
MS563	117 × 89 mm. Nos. 560/2. Imperf	70	2·75

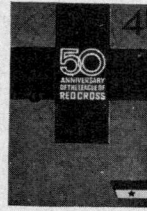

294 Red Cross and Globe

298 General Kotoka, Vickers VC-10 and Airport

1970 (2 Feb). *50th Anniv of League of Red Cross Societies. T* **294** *and similar multicoloured designs. W* **47** (*sideways on* 4 *n.p.*). *P* 14 × 14½ (4 *n.p.*) or 14½ × 14 (*others*).

564	4 n.p. Type 294	30	10
565	12½ n.p. Henri Dunant and Red Cross emblem (*horiz*)	35	20
	w. Wmk inverted		
566	20 n.p. Patient receiving medicine (*horiz*)	40	55
567	40 n.p. Patient having arm bandaged (*horiz*)	60	1·40
564/7	*Set of 4*	1·50	2·00
MS568	114×89 mm. Nos. 564/7. Imperf	2·00	6·00

NEW INFORMATION

The editor is always interested to correspond with people who have new information that will improve or correct the Catalogue.

(Des G. Vasarhelyi. Litho D.L.R.)

1970 (17 Apr). *Inauguration of Kotoka Airport. T* **298** *and similar horiz designs. Multicoloured. P* 13 × 13½.

569	4 n.p. Type 298	15	10
570	12½ n.p. Control tower and tail of Vickers VC-10	25	15
571	20 n.p. Aerial view of airport	40	30
572	40 n.p. Airport and flags	75	80
569/72	*Set of 4*	1·40	1·25

302 Lunar Module landing on Moon

306 Adult Education

(Des A. Medina (4 n.p., 12½ n.p.), G. Vasarhelyi (others). Litho D.L.R.)

1970 (15 June). *Moon Landing. T* **302** *and similar multicoloured designs. P* 12½.

573	4 n.p. Type 302	30	10
574	12½ n.p. Astronaut's first step onto the Moon.	85	60
575	20 n.p. Astronaut with equipment on Moon (*horiz*)	1·25	1·40
576	40 n.p. Astronauts (*horiz*)	1·75	3·00
573/6	*Set of 4*	3·75	4·50
MS577	142 × 142 mm. Nos. 573/6. Imperf (with or without simulated perfs)	3·50	12·00

On 18 September 1970 Nos. 573/6 were issued overprinted "PHILYMPIA LONDON 1970" but it is understood that only 900 sets were made available for sale in Ghana and we do not consider that this is sufficient to constitute normal postal use. The miniature sheet was also overprinted but not issued in Ghana.

(Litho D.L.R.)

1970 (10 Aug). *International Education Year. T* **306** *and similar horiz designs. Multicoloured. P* 13.

578	4 n.p. Type 306	10	10
579	12½ n.p. International education	20	20
580	20 n.p. "Ntesie" and I.E.Y. symbols	35	30
581	40 n.p. Nursery schools	60	85
578/81	*Set of 4*	1·10	1·25

310 Saluting March-Past

314 *Crinum ornatum*

(Litho D.L.R.)

1970 (1 Oct). *First Anniv of the Second Republic. T* **310** *and similar horiz designs. Multicoloured. P* 13 × 13½.

582	4 n.p. Type 310	10	10
583	12½ n.p. Busia declaration	15	15
584	20 n.p. Doves symbol	25	30
585	40 n.p. Opening of Parliament	50	65
582/5	*Set of 4*	90	1·00

(Des G. Vasarhelyi. Photo Harrison)

1970 (2 Nov). *Flora and Fauna. T* **314** *and similar horiz designs. Multicoloured. W* **47** (*sideways*). *P* 14½ × 14.

586	4 n.p. Type 314	1·50	10
	w. Wmk inverted	7·00	
587	12½ n.p. Lioness	1·50	85
588	20 n.p. *Anselia africana* (flower)	1·60	1·25
589	40 n.p. African Elephant	4·75	5·50
586/9	*Set of 4*	8·50	7·00

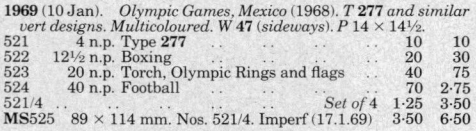

315 Kuduo Brass Casket

(Des G. Vasarhelyi. Photo Harrison)

1970 (7 Dec). *Monuments and Archaeological Sites in Ghana. T* **315** *and similar horiz designs. Multicoloured. W* **47**. *P* 14½ × 14.

590	4 n.p. Type 315	15	10
	w. Wmk inverted		
591	12½ n.p. Akan traditional house	40	10
592	20 n.p. Larabanga Mosque	55	50
593	40 n.p. Funerary clay head	70	1·10
590/3	*Set of 4*	1·60	1·75
MS594	89×71 mm. Nos. 590, 592 and 12½ n.p. Basilica of Pompeii, 40 n.p. Pistrinum of Pompeii (wmk sideways). Imperf (2.71)	5·50	8·00

316 Trade Fair Building

(Des G. Drummond (4 n.p., 50 n.p.), A. Larkins (others).
Photo Harrison)

1971 (5 Feb). *International Trade Fair, Accra. T **316** and similar multicoloured designs. W **47** (sideways, except 50 n.p.). P 14 × 14½ (50 n.p.) or 14½ × 14 (others).*

595	4 n.p. Type **316**	10	10
596	12½ n.p. Cosmetics and Pharmaceutical Goods	60	20
597	20 n.p. Vehicles	65	25
598	40 n.p. Construction Equipment	95	95
599	50 n.p. Transport and Packing Case (*vert*)	1·10	1·10
595/9	*Set of 5*	3·00	2·25

317 Christ on the Cross

318 Corn Cob

(Des from stained-glass windows. Litho D.L.R.)

1971 (19 May). *Easter. T **317** and similar square designs. Multicoloured. P 13.*

600	4 n.p. Type **317**	20	10
601	12½ n.p. Christ and Disciples	45	45
602	20 n.p. Christ blessing Disciples	65	1·10
600/2	*Set of 3*	1·10	1·50

(Photo Harrison)

1971 (15 June). *Freedom from Hunger Campaign. W **47**. P 14 × 14½.*

603	**318** 4 n.p. multicoloured	10	10
604	12½ n.p. multicoloured	35	70
605	20 n.p. multicoloured	65	1·40
603/5	*Set of 3*	1·00	2·00

Remainder stocks of the above were overprinted on the occasion of the death of Lord Boyd Orr and the 4 n.p. surcharged 60 n.p.
It is understood that 8,070 sets from the New York Agency were overprinted locally and returned to the Agency. Limited remainders of these stamps (only 330 of the 60 n.p.) were sold at the G.P.O. We do not list these as they were not freely on sale in Ghana.

319 Guides Emblem and Ghana Flag

320 Child-care Centre

(Des and litho Questa)

1971 (22 July). *Ghana Girl Guides Golden Jubilee. T **319** and similar horiz designs each with Guides Emblem. Multicoloured. P 14.*

606	4 n.p. Type **319**	20	10
607	12½ n.p. Mrs. E. Ofuatey-Kodjoe (founder) and guides with flags	60	50
608	20 n.p. Guides laying stones	90	90
609	40 n.p. Camp-fire and tent	1·50	1·75
610	50 n.p. Signallers	1·75	2·00
606/10	*Set of 5*	4·50	4·75
MS611	133 × 105 mm. Nos. 606/10. Imperf	11·00	13·00

(Des and litho D.L.R.)

1971 (7 Aug). *Y.W.C.A. World Council Meeting, Accra. T **320** and similar horiz designs. Multicoloured. P 13.*

612	4 n.p. Type **320**	10	10
613	12½ n.p. Council meeting	10	15
614	20 n.p. School typing-class	15	30
615	40 n.p. Building Fund Day	30	60
612/15	*Set of 4*	55	1·00
MS616	84 × 83 mm. Nos. 612/15. Imperf	70	1·00

321 Firework Display

322 Weighing Baby

(Photo Harrison)

1971 (22 Nov). *Christmas. T **321** and similar horiz designs. Multicoloured. W **47** (sideways on 3 and 6 n.p.). P 14 × 14½ (1 n.p.) or 14½ × 14 (others).*

617	1 n.p. Type **321**	10	60
618	3 n.p. African Nativity	15	70
619	6 n.p. The flight into Egypt	15	70
617/19	*Set of 3*	30	1·75

(Litho D.L.R.)

1971 (20 Dec). *25th Anniv of U.N.I.C.E.F. T **322** and similar multicoloured designs, each showing the U.N.I.C.E.F. symbol. No wmk (MS624) or W **47** (sideways on 5 and 30 n.p.). P 13.*

620	5 n.p. Type **322**	10	10
621	15 n.p. Mother and child (*horiz*)	20	30
622	30 n.p. Nurse	30	70
623	50 n.p. Young boy (*horiz*)	50	2·25
620/3	*Set of 4*	1·00	3·00
MS624	111 × 120 mm. Nos. 620/3. Imperf	3·00	6·50

323 Unity Symbol and Trade Fair Emblem

(Litho Questa)

1972 (23 Feb). *All-Africa Trade Fair. T **323** and similar horiz designs. Multicoloured. W **47**. P 14.*

625	5 n.p. Type **323**	10	10
626	15 n.p. Horn of Plenty	15	30
627	30 n.p. Fireworks on map of Africa	25	70
628	60 n.p. "Participating Nations"	35	2·00
629	1 n.c. As No. 628	50	2·50
625/9	*Set of 5*	1·10	5·00

All designs include the Trade Fair Emblem as in T **323**.
On 24 June 1972, on the occasion of the Belgian International Philatelic Exhibition, Nos. 625/9 were issued overprinted ' "BELGICA 72" ' in red. Only very limited supplies were sent to Ghana (we understand not more than 900 sets), and for this reason we do not list them.

(New Currency. 100 pesewas = 1 cedi = 0.8 (1967) new cedi)

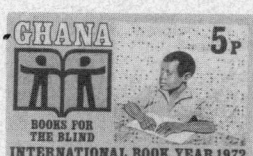

324 Books for the Blind

(Des and litho D.L.R.)

1972 (21 Apr). *International Book Year. T **324** and similar multicoloured designs. P 13.*

630	5 p. Type **324**	20	10
631	15 p. Children's books	55	50
632	30 p. Books for recreation	1·00	1·25
633	50 p. Books for students	1·75	2·75
634	1 c. Book and flame of knowledge (*vert*)	2·50	3·75
630/4	*Set of 5*	5·50	7·50
MS635	99 × 106 mm. Nos. 630/4. Imperf.	8·00	11·00

325 Hypoxis urceolata

(Litho D.L.R.)

1972 (3 July). *Flora and Fauna. T **325** and similar horiz designs. Multicoloured. P 13½.*

636	5 p. Type **325**	30	10
637	15 p. Mona Monkey	65	65
638	30 p. Crinum ornatum	5·50	4·00
639	1 c. De Winton's Tree Squirrel	6·00	8·00
636/9	*Set of 4*	11·00	11·50

326 Football

(Litho D.L.R.)

1972 (5 Sept). *Olympic Games, Munich. T **326** and similar horiz designs. Multicoloured. P 13.*

640	5 p. Type **326**	20	10
641	15 p. Running	35	20
642	30 p. Boxing	60	65
643	50 p. Long-jumping	80	2·25
644	1 c. High-jumping	1·40	3·50
640/4	*Set of 5*	3·00	6·00
MS645	86 × 43 mm. 40 p. as No. 642 *se-tenant* with 60 p. as No. 640	2·50	7·00

327 Senior Scout and Cub

(Litho Questa)

1972 (2 Oct). *65th Anniv of Boy Scouts. T **327** and similar diamond-shaped designs. Multicoloured. P 13½.*

646	5 p. Type **327**	30	10
647	15 p. Scout and tent	65	45
648	30 p. Sea scouts	1·00	1·25
649	50 p. Leader with cubs	1·40	2·00
650	1 c. Training school	2·25	3·50
646/50	*Set of 5*	5·00	6·50
MS651	110 × 110 mm. 40 p. as 30 p.; 60 p. as 1 c.	3·25	5·50

328 "The Holy Night" (Correggio)

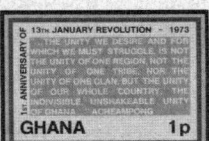

329 Extract from Speech

(Des G. Vasarhelyi and L. Apelt. Litho Questa)

1972 (1 Dec). *Christmas. T **328** and similar vert designs. Multicoloured. P 13½.*

652	1p. Type **328**	10	10
653	3p. "Adoration of the Kings" (Holbein the Elder)	10	10
654	15p. "Madonna of the Passion" (School of Ricco)	40	30
655	30p. "King Melchior"	70	70
656	60p. "King Gaspar, Mary and Jesus"	1·00	2·00
657	1 c. "King Balthasar"	1·50	3·00
652/7	*Set of 6*	3·25	5·50
MS658	139×90 mm. Nos. 655/7. Imperf	8·00	9·00

Nos. 655/7 are from a 16th-cent. Norman stained-glass window.

(Des and litho D.L.R.)

1973 (10 Apr). *First Anniv of January 13 Revolution. T **329** and similar multicoloured designs. P 13 × 14 (5, 15 p.) or 14 × 13 (others).*

659	1 p. Type **329**	10	10
660	3 p. Market scene	10	10
661	5 p. Selling bananas (*vert*)	10	10
662	15 p. Farmer with hoe and produce (*vert*)	20	25
663	30 p. Market traders	30	40
664	1 c. Farmer cutting palm-nuts	70	1·40
659/64	*Set of 6*	1·25	1·90
MS665	90 × 55 mm. 40 p. as 1 c. and 60 p. Miners	70	2·25

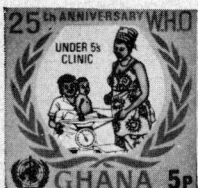

330 Under 5's Clinic

(Litho D.L.R.)

1973 (24 July). *25th Anniv of W.H.O. T **330** and similar square designs. Multicoloured. P 13½.*

666	5 p. Type **330**	10	10
667	15 p. Radiography	25	30
668	30 p. Immunisation	35	50
669	50 p. Starving child	50	1·25
670	1 c. W.H.O. H.Q., Geneva	75	2·00
666/70	*Set of 5*	1·75	4·00

1st WORLD SCOUTING CONFERENCE IN AFRICA
(331)

1973 (14 Aug). *First World Scouting Conference, Nairobi/Addis Ababa. Nos. 646/51 optd with T* **331.**

671	5 p. Type **327**	..	..	..	10	15
672	15 p. Scout and tent		..	..	35	60
673	30 p. Sea scouts	..	..	..	60	1·40
674	50 p. Leader with cubs..		..	..	80	2·00
675	1 c. Training school	..	..	..	1·50	3·00
671/5			..	*Set of 5*	3·00	6·50
MS676	110 × 110 mm. 40 p. as 30 p.; 60 p. as 1 c.				2·00	6·50

332 Poultry Farming

(Litho Questa)

1973 (11 Sept). *Tenth Anniv of World Food Programme. T* **332** *and similar horiz designs. Multicoloured. P* 14.

677	5 p. Type **332**	..	..	..	10	10
678	15 p. Mechanisation	..	..	..	15	15
679	50 p. Cocoa harvest	..	..	..	40	90
680	1 c. F.A.O. H.Q., Rome	..	..	..	60	1·90
677/80				*Set of 4*	1·00	2·75
MS681	92 × 104 mm. 40 p. as 15 p.; 60 p. as 1 c.				60	2·25

333 "Green Alert"

(Litho D.L.R.)

1973 (1 Oct). *50th Anniv of Interpol. T* **333** *and similar horiz designs. Multicoloured. P* 13.

682	5 p. Type **333**	..	..	..	15	10
683	30 p. "Red Alert"	..	..	..	75	80
684	50 p. "Blue Alert"	..	..	..	1·50	1·75
685	1 c. "Black Alert"	..	..	..	3·00	4·00
682/5	..			*Set of 4*	4·75	6·00

334 Handshake

(Litho Format)

1973 (22 Oct). *Tenth Anniv of O.A.U. T* **334** *and similar horiz designs. Multicoloured. P* 14 × 14½.

686	5 p. Type **334**	..	..	..	10	10
687	30 p. Africa Hall, Addis Ababa		..	..	15	30
688	50 p. O.A.U. emblem	..	..	..	20	1·00
689	1 c. "X" in colours of Ghana flag		..	..	35	1·50
686/9	..			*Set of 4*	70	2·50

335 Weather Balloon   336 Epiphany Scene

(Des G. Vasarhelyi. Litho Format)

1973 (16 Nov). *I.M.O./W.M.O. Centenary. T* **335** *and similar horiz designs. Multicoloured. P* 14 × 14½.

690	5 p. Type **335**	..	..	..	10	10
691	15 p. Satellite "Tiros"	..	..	..	15	20
692	30 p. Computer weather map		..	..	30	65
693	1 c. Radar	..	..	..	60	2·25
690/3	..			*Set of 4*	1·00	2·75
MS694	120 × 95 mm. 40 p. as 15 p.; 60 p. as 30 p.				1·25	3·25

(Litho D.L.R.)

1973 (10 Dec). *Christmas. T* **336** *and similar vert designs. Multicoloured. P* 14.

695	1 p. Type **336**	..	..	..	10	10
696	3 p. Madonna and Child	..	..	..	10	10
697	30 p. "Madonna and Child" (Murillo) ..			..	30	75
698	1 c. "Adoration of the Magi" (Tiepolo)			..	45	1·00
695/8	..			*Set of 4*	1·25	2·75
MS699	77 × 103 mm. Nos. 695/8. Imperf.				1·25	3·00

---

337 "Christ carrying the Cross" (Thomas de Kolozsvar)

338 Letters

(Des M. Shamir and A. Larkins. Litho D.L.R.)

1974 (17 Apr). *Easter. T* **337** *and similar vert designs. P* 14.

700	5 p. multicoloured	..	..	..	10	10
701	30 p. bright blue, silver and sepia		..	20	35
702	50 p. light orange-vermilion, silver and sepia			30	60
703	1 c. dull yellow-green, silver and sepia			50	1·25
700/3	..			*Set of 4*	90	2·00
MS704	111 × 106 mm. 15 p. as No. 700, 20 p. as No. 701, 25 p. as No. 702. Imperf				80	1·75

Designs (from 15th-century English carved alabaster):—30 p. "The Betrayal"; 50 p. "The Deposition"; 1 c. "The Risen Christ and Mary Magdalene".

(Des A. Larkins. Litho Questa)

1974 (21 May). *Centenary of Universal Postal Union. T* **338** *and similar horiz designs. Multicoloured. P* 14½.

705	5 p. Type **338**	..	..	..	10	10
706	9 p. U.P.U. Monument and H.Q.		..	10	15
707	50 p. Airmail letter	..	..	..	35	1·00
708	1 c. U.P.U. Monument and Ghana stamp			60	1·75
705/8	..			*Set of 4*	1·00	2·75
MS709	108 × 90 mm. 20 p. as No. 705, 30 p. as No. 706, 40 p. as No. 707, 60 p. as No. 708.				75	1·60

Nos. 705/8 were issued both in sheets of 30 and in sheets of 5 stamps and 1 label.

1974 (7 June). *"Internaba 1974" Stamp Exhibition, Basle. Nos.* 705/9 *additionally inscribed* "INTERNABA 1974".

710	5 p. Type **338**	..	..	..	10	10
711	9 p. U.P.U. Monument and H.Q.		..	10	15
712	50 p. Airmail letter	..	..	..	30	1·00
713	1 c. U.P.U. Monument and Ghana stamp			45	1·75
710/13	..			*Set of 4*	80	2·75
MS714	108 × 90 mm. 20 p. as No. 710; 30 p. as No. 711; 40 p. as No. 712; 60 p. as No. 713			1·50	4·00

339 Footballers

(Des G. Vasarhelyi. Litho Format)

1974 (17 June). *World Cup Football Championships, West Germany. T* **339** *and similar horiz designs showing footballers. P* 14½.

715	339	5 p. multicoloured	..	..	10	10
716	–	30 p. multicoloured	..	..	20	60
717	–	50 p. multicoloured	..	..	25	85
718	–	1 c. multicoloured	..	..	30	1·50
715/18				*Set of 4*	75	2·75
MS719	148 × 94 mm. 25, 40, 55 and 60 p. as Nos. 715/18				1·00	3·25

Nos. 715/18 also exist perf 13 (*price for set of 4 75p mint, £3·25 used*) from additional sheetlets of 5 stamps and 1 label. Stamps perforated 14½ are from normal sheets of 25.

The sheetlets, together with No. MS719, exist imperforate from stock dispersed by the liquidator of Format International Security Printers Ltd.

340 Roundabout   (341)

(Des and litho B.W.)

1974 (16 July). *Change to Driving on the Right. T* **340** *and similar designs. P* 13½ (5 and 15 p.) *or* 14½ × 14 (*others*).

720	5 p. bright yellow-grn, rose-vermilion & blk			10	10
721	15 p. lavender, dull red and black		..	25	35
722	30 p. multicoloured	..	..	..	45	60
723	50 p. multicoloured	..	..	..	70	1·10
724	1 c. multicoloured	..	..	..	1·40	2·00
720/4	..			*Set of 5*	2·75	3·75

Designs: *Horiz*—15 p. Warning triangle sign. *Vert* (29 × 42 mm)—30 p. Highway arrow and slogan; 50 p. Warning hands; 1 c. Car on symbolic hands.

1974 (30 Aug). *West Germany's Victory in World Cup. Nos.* 715/19 *optd with T* **341.** *P* 14½.

725	339	5 p. multicoloured	..	..	10	10
726	–	30 p. multicoloured	..	..	35	40
727	–	50 p. multicoloured	..	..	50	55
728	–	1 c. multicoloured	..	..	90	1·25
725/8				*Set of 4*	1·75	2·10
MS729	148 × 94 mm. 25, 40, 55, 60 p. as Nos. 725/8				1·40	2·50

This overprint also exists on the stamps perforated 13 mentioned below No. MS719 (*Price for set of 4 £2·25 mint or used*).

342 "Planned Family"

(Des and litho D.L.R.)

1974 (12 Sept). *World Population Year. T* **342** *and similar horiz designs. Multicoloured. P* 12½.

730	5 p. Type **342**	..	..	..	10	10
731	30 p. Family planning clinic		..	..	25	35
732	50 p. Immunization	..	..	..	35	60
733	1 c. Population census enumeration..			60	1·40
730/3	..			*Set of 4*	1·10	2·25

343 Angel

APOLLO SOYUZ JULY 15, 1975

(344)

(Des A. Medina (5 and 7 p.), A. Larkins (others). Litho D.L.R.)

1974 (19 Dec). *Christmas. T* **343** *and similar multicoloured designs. P* 13½.

734	5 p. Type **343**	..	..	..	10	10
735	7 p. The Magi (*diamond* 47 × 47 *mm*)			10	10
736	9 p. The Nativity	..	..	..	10	10
737	1 c. The Annunciation	..	..	..	60	1·40
734/7	..			*Set of 4*	80	1·50
MS738	128 × 128 mm. 15 p. Type **343**; 30 p. as 7 p.; 45 p. as 9 p.; 60 p. as 1 c. Imperf			80	2·50

1975 (15 Aug). *"Apollo–Soyuz" Space Link. Nos.* 715/19 *optd with T* **344.** *P* 14½.

739	5 p. multicoloured	..	..	..	10	10
740	30 p. multicoloured	..	..	..	25	25
741	50 p. multicoloured	..	..	..	45	55
742	1 c. multicoloured	..	..	..	70	80
739/42				*Set of 4*	1·25	1·50
MS743	148 × 94 mm. 25, 40, 55, 60 p. as Nos. 739/42				1·25	2·00

This overprint also exists on the stamps perforated 13 mentioned below No. MS719 (*Price for set of 4 £6 mint, £7 used*).

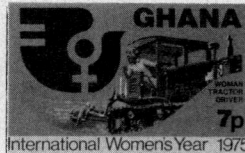

345 Tractor Driver

(Des and litho D.L.R.)

1975 (3 Sept). *International Women's Year. T* **345** *and similar horiz designs each showing I.W.Y. emblem. Multicoloured. P* 14 × 13½.

744	7 p. Type **345**	..	..	..	35	10
745	30 p. Motor mechanic	..	..	..	85	35
746	60 p. Factory workers	..	..	..	1·00	80
747	1 c. Cocoa research	..	..	..	1·25	1·40
744/7	..			*Set of 4*	3·00	2·40
MS748	136 × 110 mm. 15, 40, 65 and 80 p. as Nos. 744/7. Imperf				2·00	6·00

346 Angel

(Litho D.L.R.)

1975 (31 Dec). *Christmas. T 346 and similar horiz designs. P 14 × 13½.*

749	2 p. multicoloured	10	10
750	5 p. greenish yellow and light green..	10	10
751	7 p. greenish yellow and light green..	10	10
752	30 p. greenish yellow and light green..	20	20
753	1 c. greenish yellow and light green..	50	1·00
749/53	*Set of 5*	80	1·25
MS754	98 × 87 mm. 15, 40, 65 and 80 p. as Nos.		
750/3. Imperf		90	3·00

Designs:—5 p. Angel with harp; 7 p. Angel with lute; 30 p. Angel with viol; 1 c. Angel with trumpet.

347 Map Reading

(Litho Format)

1976 (5 Jan). *14th World Scout Jamboree, Norway. T 347 and similar horiz designs. Multicoloured. P 13½ × 14.*

755	7 p. Type 347	20	10
756	30 p. Sailing	60	90
757	60 p. Hiking	90	2·25
758	1 c. Life-saving	1·10	2·50
755/8	*Set of 4*	2·50	5·25
MS759	133 × 99 mm. 15, 40, 65 and 80 p. as Nos.		
755/8		2·25	6·50

Nos. 755/9 exist imperforate from stock dispersed by the liquidator of Format International Security Printers Ltd.

348 Bottles (litre)

(Litho D.L.R.)

1976 (5 Jan). *Metrication Publicity. T 348 and similar horiz designs. Multicoloured. P 14.*

760	7 p. Type 348	15	10
761	30 p. Scales (kilogramme)	40	40
762	60 p. Tape measure and bale of cloth (metre)	80	1·00
763	1 c. Ice, thermometer and kettle (temperature)	1·25	1·75
760/3	*Set of 4*	2·40	2·75

349 Fair Site

(Litho Format)

1976 (6 Apr). *International Trade Fair, Accra. T 349 and similar horiz designs. P 13½.*

764	349	7 p. multicoloured	10	10
765	—	30 p. multicoloured	20	20
766	—	60 p. multicoloured	35	60
767	—	1 c. multicoloured	55	1·00
764/7		*Set of 4*	1·10	1·60

Nos. 765/7 are as T 349 but show different views of the Fair.
Nos. 764/7 exist imperforate from stock dispersed by the liquidator of Format International Security Printers Ltd.

351 Shot-put

1976 (28 May). *Interphil Stamp Exhibition, Philadelphia. Nos. 755/9 optd with T 350 in blue.*

768	7 p. Type 347	15	15
769	30 p. Sailing	35	50
770	60 p. Hiking	55	75
771	1 c. Life-saving	80	1·25
768/71	*Set of 4*	1·75	2·40
MS772	133 × 99 mm. 15, 40, 65 and 80 p. as Nos.		
768/71		1·50	2·50

Nos. 768/71 exist imperforate from stock dispersed by the liquidator of Format International Security Printers Ltd.

352 Supreme Court

(Des PAD Studio. Litho Format)

1976 (9 Aug). *Olympic Games, Montreal. T 351 and similar vert designs. Multicoloured. P 13½.*

773	7 p. Type 351	15	10
774	30 p. Football	30	25
775	60 p. Women's 1500 metres	45	50
776	1 c. Boxing	60	80
773/6	*Set of 4*	1·40	1·50
MS777	103 × 135 mm. 15, 40, 65 and 80 p. as Nos.		
773/6		1·50	1·50

Nos. 773/6 also exist perf 15 (*Price for set of 4 £2·25 mint or used*) from additional sheetlets of 5 stamps and 1 label. Stamps perforated 13½ are from normal sheets of 30. The sheetlets also exist imperforate from stock dispersed by the liquidator of Format International Security Printers Ltd.

(Litho D.L.R.)

1976 (7 Sept). *Centenary of Supreme Court. T 352 and similar horiz designs. P 14.*

778	352	8 p. multicoloured	10	10
779	—	30 p. multicoloured	20	25
780	—	60 p. multicoloured	35	50
781	—	1 c. multicoloured	60	1·00
778/81		*Set of 4*	1·10	1·75

Nos. 779/81 show different views of the Court Building.

353 Examination for River Blindness

(Des and litho D.L.R.)

1976 (28 Oct). *Prevention of Blindness. T 353 and similar horiz designs. Multicoloured. P 14 × 13½.*

782	7 p. Type 353	65	10
783	30 p. Entomologist	1·75	1·40
784	60 p. Normal vision	2·75	2·75
785	1 c. Blackfly eradication	4·25	4·50
782/5	*Set of 4*	8·50	8·00

354 Fireworks Party, Christmas Eve

(Des A. Adom & A. Larkins. Litho D.L.R.)

1976 (15 Dec). *Christmas. T 354 and similar horiz designs. Multicoloured. P 13.*

786	6 p. Type 354	15	10
787	8 p. Children and gifts	15	10
788	30 p. Christmas feast	35	30
789	1 c. As 8 p.	75	1·75
786/9	*Set of 4*	1·25	2·00
MS790	122 × 98 mm. 15, 40, 65 and 80 p. as Nos.		
786/9. Imperf		2·00	4·00

355 "Gallows Frame" Telephone and Alexander Graham Bell

(Des A. Larkins. Litho Format)

1976 (17 Dec). *Telephone Centenary. T 355 and similar horiz designs showing telephones and Alexander Graham Bell. Multicoloured. P 13.*

791	8 p. Type 355	15	10
792	30 p. 1895 telephone	20	30
793	60 p. 1929 telephone	40	70
794	1 c. 1976 telephone	60	1·25
791/4	*Set of 4*	1·25	2·00
MS795	125 × 92 mm. 15, 40, 65 and 80 p. as Nos.		
791/4		1·25	1·40

1977 (22 Feb). *Olympic Winners. Nos. 773/7 optd with the name of the country given, as T 356. P 13½.*

796	7 p. East Germany	15	15
797	30 p. East Germany	35	40
798	60 p. U.S.S.R.	45	85
799	1 c. U.S.A.	65	1·50
796/9	*Set of 4*	1·40	2·50
MS800	103 × 135 mm. 15, 40, 65 and 80 p. as Nos.		
796/9		2·25	2·50

357 Dipo Dancers and Drum Ensemble

(Des A. Larkins. Litho Format)

1977 (24 Mar). *Second World Black and African Festival of Arts and Culture, Nigeria. T 357 and similar horiz designs. Multicoloured. P 13½.*

801	8 p. Type 357	15	15
802	30 p. Arts and Crafts	30	60
803	60 p. Acon music and dancing priests..	50	1·25
804	1 c. African huts	60	2·00
801/4	*Set of 4*	1·40	3·50
MS805	164 × 120 mm. 15, 40, 65 and 80 p. as Nos.		
801/4		1·40	1·50

PRINCE CHARLES VISITS GHANA 17th TO 25th MARCH, 1977
(358)

1977 (2 June). *Prince Charles's Visit to Ghana. Nos. 791/5 optd with T 358.*

806	8 p. Type 355	50	55
807	30 p. 1895 telephone	1·25	1·00
808	60 p. 1929 telephone	1·75	2·00
809	1 c. 1976 telephone	2·25	2·50
806/9	*Set of 4*	5·25	5·50
MS810	125 × 92 mm. 15, 40, 65 and 80 p. as Nos.		
806/9		8·00	8·50

359 Olive Colobus

360 "Le Chapeau de Paille" (Rubens— 400th Birth Anniv)

(Des PAD Studio. Litho Format)

1977 (22 June). *Wildlife. T 359 and similar horiz designs. Multicoloured. P 13½.*

811	8 p. Type 359	45	15
812	20 p. Temminck's Giant Squirrel	1·25	80
813	30 p. Hunting Dog	1·75	1·25
814	60 p. African Manatee	3·00	2·75
811/14	*Set of 4*	5·75	4·50
MS815	140 × 101 mm. 15, 40, 65 and 80 p. as Nos.		
811/14		5·50	5·50

No. MS815 exists imperforate from stock dispersed by the liquidator of Format International Security Printers Ltd.

(Des PAD Studio. Litho Format)

1977 (Sept). *Painters' Anniversaries. T 360 and similar vert designs. Multicoloured. P 14 × 13½.*

816	8 p. Type 360	25	10
817	30 p. "Isabella of Portugal" (Titian—500th Birth Anniv)	40	40
818	60 p. "Duke and Duchess of Cumberland" (Gainsborough—250th Birth Anniv)	55	65
819	1 c. "Rubens and Isabella Brandt"	75	1·25
816/19	*Set of 4*	1·75	2·25
MS820	99 × 149 mm. 15, 40, 65 and 80 p. as Nos.		
816/19		2·50	2·25

No. MS820 exists imperforate from stock dispersed by the liquidator of Format International Security Printers Ltd.

REFERENDUM 1978
VOTE EARLY

361 The Magi, Madonna
and Child

(362)

(Litho De La Rue, Colombia)

1977 (30 Dec). *Christmas. T 361 and similar multicoloured designs.* P 14 (1 p., 8 p.) or 14 × 13½ (others).

821	1 p. Type **361**	..	10	10
822	2 p. Choir from Abossey Okai (45 × 27 mm)	..	10	10
823	6 p. Methodist Church, Wesley, Accra (45 × 27 mm)		10	10
824	8 p. Madonna and Child		10	10
825	30 p. Holy Spirit Cathedral, Accra (45 × 27 mm)		30	50
826	1 c. Ebeneezer Presbyterian Church, Accra (45 × 27 mm)		1·00	1·60
821/6	..	*Set of 6*	1·25	2·25
MS827	122 × 97 mm. 15, 40, 65 and 80 p. as Nos. 822/3 and 825/6. Imperf		1·75	3·75

Nos. 822/3 and 825/6 all have as a background the score to the carol "Hark the Herald Angels Sing".

1978 (Mar). *1978 Referendum. Nos. 821/7 optd with T 362 by De La Rue, Colombia.*

828	1 p. Type **361**	..	10	10
829	2 p. Choir from Abossey Okai	..	10	10
830	6 p. Methodist Church, Wesley, Accra		10	10
831	8 p. Madonna and Child		10	10
832	30 p. Holy Spirit Cathedral, Accra		30	50
833	1 c. Ebeneezer Presbyterian Church, Accra	1·00	1·50
828/33	..	*Set of 6*	1·25	2·10
MS834	122 × 97 mm. 15, 40, 65, 80 p. as Nos. 829/30 and 832/3		27·00	17·00

363 Cutting Bananas

(Litho De La Rue, Colombia)

1978 (15 May). *Operation "Feed Yourself". T 363 and similar horiz designs. Multicoloured.* P 14.

835	2 p. Type **363**	..	10	10
836	8 p. Home produce	..	10	10
837	30 p. Market	..	25	35
838	60 p. Fishing	..	60	60
839	1 c. Mechanisation	..	80	1·25
835/9	..	*Set of 5*	1·60	2·10

"CAPEX 78
JUNE 9-18 1978"

364 Wright Flyer III

(365)

(Des J.W. Litho Format)

1978 (6 June). *75th Anniv of Powered Flight. T 364 and similar vert designs.* P 14 × 13½.

840	8 p. black, deep brown and brown-ochre	20	10
841	30 p. black, deep brown and blue-green	30	30
842	60 p. black, deep brown and rosine	40	60
843	1 c. black, deep brown and ultramarine	1·50	1·10
840/3	..	*Set of 4*	2·25	1·90
MS844	167 × 100 mm. 15, 40, 65, 80 p. as Nos. 840/3		2·00	1·40

Designs:—30 p. Handley Page H.P.42; 60 p. De Havilland D.H.106 Comet 1; 1 c. Concorde.

No. 841 exists imperforate from stock dispersed by the liquidator of Format International Security Printers Ltd.

1978 (9 June). *"CAPEX 1978" International Stamp Exhibition, Toronto. Nos. 840/4 optd with T 365.*

845	8 p. black, deep brown and brown-ochre	15	15
846	30 p. black, deep brown and blue-green	25	25
847	60 p. black, deep brown and rosine	50	50
848	1 c. black, deep brown and ultramarine	1·10	80
845/8	..	*Set of 4*	1·75	1·50
MS849	167 × 100 mm. 15, 40, 65, 80 p. as Nos. 845/8		1·25	1·60

---

366 Players and African Cup Emblem

(Litho Format)

1978 (1 July). *Football Championships. T 366 and similar horiz designs. Multicoloured.* P 13½ × 14.

850	8 p. Type **366**	..	20	15
851	30 p. Players and African Cup emblem (different)		25	30
852	60 p. Players and World Cup emblem		40	60
853	1 c. Goalkeeper and World Cup emblem		55	1·00
850/3	..	*Set of 4*	1·25	1·90
MS854	111 × 105 mm. 15, 40, 65, 80 p. as Nos. 850/3		1·10	1·25

The 8 and 30 p. values commemorate the African Nations Cup; the other values the World Cup Football Championship, Argentina.

Nos. 850/3 exist imperforate from stock dispersed by the liquidator of Format International Security Printers Ltd.

367 "The Betrayal"   **"GHANA WINNERS"**
(368)

(Litho Format)

1978 (15 July). *Easter. Details from drawings by Dürer. T 367 and similar vert designs.* P 14 × 13½.

855	11 p. black and bright reddish violet	..	10	10
856	39 p. black and flesh	..	25	30
857	60 p. black and orange-yellow	..	40	45
858	1 c. black and pale yellow-green	..	60	65
855/8	..	*Set of 4*	1·25	1·40

Designs:—39 p. "The Crucifixion"; 60 p. "The Deposition"; 1 c. "The Resurrection".

1978 (21 Aug). *Ghana—Winners of African Nations Football Cup and Argentina—Winners of World Cup Football Championship. Nos. 850/1 and MS854 optd with T 368 and Nos. 852/3 optd "ARGENTINA WINS".*

859	8 p. Type **366**	..	25	15
860	30 p. Players and African Cup emblem (different)		35	30
861	60 p. Players and World Cup emblem		45	45
862	1 c. Goalkeeper and World Cup emblem		55	75
859/62	..	*Set of 4*	1·40	1·50
MS863	111 × 105 mm. 15, 40, 65, 80 p. as Nos. 859/62 but all opt with T **368**		1·00	1·10

Nos. 859/60 exist imperforate from stock dispersed by the liquidator of Format International Security Printers Ltd.

369 *Bauhinia purpurea*

(Litho Format)

1978 (20 Nov). *Flowers. T 369 and similar vert designs. Multicoloured.* P 14 × 13½.

864	11 p. Type **369**	..	15	10
865	39 p. *Cassia fistula*	..	30	55
866	60 p. *Plumeria acutifolia*	..	40	70
867	1 c. *Jacaranda mimosifolia*	..	45	1·00
864/7	..	*Set of 4*	1·10	2·10

No. 864 exists imperforate from stock dispersed by the liquidator of Format International Security Printers Ltd.

ALTERED CATALOGUE NUMBERS

Any Catalogue numbers altered from the last edition are shown as a list in the introductory pages.

---

370 Mail Van

1978 (4 Dec). *75th Anniv of Ghana Railways. T 370 and similar horiz designs. Multicoloured.* P 13½ × 14.

868	11 p. Type **370**	..	25	10
869	39 p. Pay and bank car	..	35	65
870	60 p. Steam locomotive No. 1 *Amanful,* 1922	40	1·00
871	1 c. Diesel-electric locomotive No. 1651, 1960	40	1·40
868/71	..	*Set of 4*	1·25	2·75

Nos. 868/71 exist imperforate from stock dispersed by the liquidator of Format International Security Printers Ltd.

371 "Orbiter" Spacecraft

(Litho Format)

1979 (5 July). *"Pioneer" Venus Space Project. T 371 and similar horiz designs. Multicoloured.* P 14 × 13½.

872	11 p. Type **371**	..	15	10
873	39 p. "Multiprobe" spacecraft	..	25	30
874	60 p. "Orbiter" and "Multiprobe" spacecraft in Venus orbit		40	45
875	3 c. Radar chart of Venus		60	1·60
872/5	..	*Set of 4*	1·25	2·25
MS876	135 × 94 mm. 15, 40, 65 p., 2 c. as Nos. 872/5. Imperf		1·10	1·25

372 "O Come All Ye Faithful"   **373** Dr. J. B. Danquah
(lawyer and nationalist)

(Litho D.L.R.)

1979 (20 Dec). *Christmas. Opening Lines and Scenes from well known Carols. T 372 and similar horiz designs. Multicoloured.* P 14 × 14½.

877	8 p. Type **372**	..	10	10
878	10 p. "O Little Town of Bethlehem"	..	10	10
879	15 p. "We Three Kings of Orient Are"	..	10	10
880	20 p. "I Saw Three Ships come Sailing By"	..	10	10
881	2 c. "Away in a Manger"	..	30	80
882	4 c. "Ding Dong Merrily on High"	..	50	1·40
877/82	..	*Set of 6*	80	2·40
MS883	110 × 95 mm. 25, 65 p., 1, 2 c. as Nos. 877, 879 and 881/2		75	1·00

(Litho D.L.R.)

1980 (21 Jan). *Great Ghanaians. T 373 and similar vert designs. Multicoloured.* P 14 × 13½.

884	20 p. Type **373**	..	10	10
885	65 p. John Mensah Sarbah (nationalist)	..	15	20
886	80 p. Dr. J. E. K. Aggrey (educationalist)	..	15	30
887	2 c. Dr. Kwame Nkrumah (nationalist)	..	30	40
888	4 c. G. E. (Paa) Grant (lawyer)	..	60	1·10
884/8	..	*Set of 5*	1·10	1·75

374 Tribesman ringing   **375** Children in
Clack Bells   Classroom

(Des G. Vasarhelyi. Litho Format)

1980 (12 Mar). *Death Centenary of Sir Rowland Hill (1979). T 374 and similar horiz designs. Multicoloured.* (a) P 14½.

889	20 p. Type **374**	..	15	15
890	65 p. Chieftain with Golden Elephant staff	..	30	30
891	2 c. Tribesman banging drums	..	50	1·00
892	4 c. Chieftain with ivory and gold staff	..	75	2·00
889/92	..	*Set of 4*	1·50	3·00

893	25 p. Type **374**			15	20
894	50 p. As 65 p.			25	40
895	1 c. As 2 c.			40	85
896	5 c. As 4 c.			1·00	3·00
893/6			*Set of 4*	1·60	4·00
MS897	115 × 86 mm. Nos. 893/6. P 14½.			1·00	1·50

Nos. 893/6 were each printed in small sheets of 6 including one *se-tenant* stamp-size label.

(Des J.W. Litho Questa)

1980 (2 Apr). *International Year of the Child* (1979). *T* **375** *and similar vert designs. Multicoloured. P* 14½.

898	20 p. Type **375**			15	15
899	65 p. Children playing football			25	45
900	2 c. Children playing in boat.			40	1·00
901	4 c. Mother and child.			60	1·75
898/901			*Set of 4*	1·25	3·00
MS902	156 × 94 mm. 25, 50 p., 1, 3 c. as Nos. 898/901			1·25	1·75

"LONDON 1980"
6th - 14th May 1980
(376)

"PAPAL VISIT"
8th - 9th May
1980
(377)

1980 (6 May). *"London 1980" International Stamp Exhibition. Nos.* 889/97 *optd with T* **376**. (*a*) *P* 14½.

903	20 p. Type **374**			15	15
904	65 p. Chieftain with Golden Elephant staff			25	50
905	2 c. Tribesman banging drums			50	1·25
906	4 c. Chieftain with ivory and gold staff			75	2·25
903/6			*Set of 4*	1·50	3·75

(*b*) *P* 13½

907	25 p. Type **374**			80	1·00
908	50 p. As 65 p.			1·10	1·75
909	1 c. As 2 c.			2·00	2·50
910	5 c. As 4 c.			3·75	5·00
907/10			*Set of 4*	7·00	9·25
MS911	115 × 86 mm. Nos. 907/10. P 14½			1·00	2·00

1980 (8 May). *Papal Visit. Nos.* 898/902 *optd with T* **377**.

912	20 p. Type **375**			55	25
913	65 p. Children playing football			1·00	60
914	2 c. Children playing in boat.			1·75	1·40
915	4 c. Mother and child.			2·50	2·50
912/15			*Set of 4*	5·25	4·25
MS916	156 × 94 mm. 25, 50 p., 1, 3 c. as Nos. 912/15			9·00	7·50

378 Parliament House

379 Boeing 737 Airliner and Map of West Africa

(Litho Questa)

1980 (4 Aug). *Third Republic Commemoration. T* **378** *and similar horiz designs. Multicoloured. P* 14.

917	20 p. Type **378**			10	10
918	65 p. Supreme Court			20	25
919	2 c. The Castle			40	70
917/19			*Set of 3*	60	95
MS920	72 × 113 mm. 25 p., 1, 3 c. As Nos. 917/19			60	1·10

(Litho Questa)

1980 (5 Nov). *Fifth Anniv of E.C.O.W.A.S.* (*Economic Community of West African States*). *T* **379** *and similar horiz designs showing symbols named and map of West Africa. Multicoloured. P* 14.

921	20 p. Type **379**			10	10
922	65 p. Radio antenna			15	20
923	80 p. Cog-wheels			20	25
924	2 c. Corn ear			35	50
921/4			*Set of 4*	70	90

380 "O.A.U."

381 "The Adoration of the Magi"

(Litho Questa)

1980 (26 Nov). *Organisation of African Unity First Economic Summit, Nigeria. T* **380** *and similar vert designs. Multicoloured. P* 14½ × 14.

925	20 p. Type **380**			10	10
926	65 p. Banner with maps of Africa and Ghana			15	20
927	80 p. Map of Africa			15	25
928	2 c. Ghana flag, banner and map of Africa			20	65
925/8			*Set of 4*	55	1·00

(Litho Format)

1980 (10 Dec). *Christmas. Paintings by Fra Angelico. T* **381** *and similar vert designs. Multicoloured. P* 14.

929	15 p. Type **381**			10	10
930	20 p. "The Virgin and Child enthroned with four Angels"			10	10
931	2 c. "The Virgin and Child enthroned with eight Angels"			35	80
932	4 c. "The Annunciation"			60	1·60
929/32			*Set of 4*	1·00	2·25
MS933	77 × 112 mm. 25, 50 p., 1, 3 c. As Nos. 929/32			75	1·25

382 "Health"

383 Narina Trogon

(Litho Format)

1980 (18 Dec). *75th Anniv of Rotary International. T* **382** *and similar horiz designs. Multicoloured. P* 14.

934	20 p. Type **382**			10	10
935	65 p. Rotary emblem and motto with maps of World and Ghana			15	30
936	2 c. Rotary emblem, globe and outstretched hands			35	85
937	4 c. "Eradication of Hunger".			60	1·50
934/7			*Set of 4*	1·10	2·50
MS938	121 × 93 mm. 25, 50 p., 1, 3 c. As Nos. 934/7			1·10	2·00

(Des G. Drummond. Litho Harrison)

1981 (12 Jan). *Birds. T* **383** *and similar vert designs. Multicoloured. P* 14.

939	20 p. Type **383**			1·25	15
940	65 p. White-crowned Robin Chat			2·25	50
941	2 c. Swallow-tailed Bee Eater			2·75	1·75
942	4 c. Rose-ringed Parakeet			4·25	3·25
939/42			*Set of 4*	9·50	5·00
MS943	89×121 mm. 25, 50 p., 1, 3 c. As Nos. 939/42. P 14½			5·00	4·00

384 Pope John Paul II and Archbishop of Canterbury with President Limann during Papal Visit

385 Royal Yacht *Britannia*

(Litho Format)

1981 (3 Mar). *First Anniv of Papal Visit. P* 14 × 13½.

944	**384** 20 p. multicoloured			25	15
945	65 p. multicoloured			45	55
946	80 p. multicoloured			60	70
947	2 c. multicoloured			1·10	2·00
944/7			*Set of 4*	2·25	3·00

(Des J.W. Litho Questa)

1981 (8 July–16 Sept). *Royal Wedding. T* **385** *and similar vert designs. Multicoloured.* (i) *Sheet stamps* (8 July). (*a*) *P* 14.

948	20 p. Prince Charles and Lady Diana Spencer			10	10
949	80 p. Prince Charles on visit to Ghana			15	20
950	4 c. Type **385**			50	80
948/50			*Set of 3*	60	1·00
MS951	95 × 85 mm. 7 c. St. Paul's Cathedral			70	1·25

(*b*) *P* 12

952	65 p. As 20 p.			15	25
953	1 c. As 80 p.			25	35
954	3 c. Type **385**			70	1·10
952/4			*Set of 3*	1·00	1·50

(ii) *Booklet stamps. P* 14 (16 Sept)

955	2 c. Type **385**			1·00	1·50
	a. Booklet pane. Nos. 955/6 each × 2			4·00	
956	5 c. As 20 p.			1·00	2·75

The 65 p., 1 and 3 c. values were each printed in small sheets of 6 including one *se-tenant* stamp-size label.

The above exist imperforate from a restricted printing (*price for Nos.* 948/50 *set of 3* £5, **MS**951 £6, *Nos.* 952/4 *set of 3* £7·50 *and booklet pane No.* 955a £12, *all mint*).

STANLEY GIBBONS STAMP COLLECTING SERIES

Introductory booklets on *How to Start, How to Identify Stamps* and *Collecting by Theme*. A series of well illustrated guides at a low price.
Write for details.

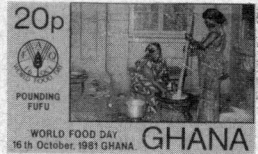

386 Earth Satellite Station

387 Pounding Fufu

(Litho Questa)

1981 (28 Sept). *Commissioning of Earth Satellite Station. T* **386** *and similar vert designs. Multicoloured. P* 14.

957	20 p. Type **386**			10	10
958	65 p. Satellites beaming signals to Earth			15	15
959	80 p. Satellite			15	20
960	4 c. Satellite orbiting Earth			1·00	1·60
957/60			*Set of 4*	1·25	1·75
MS961	112 × 100 mm. 25 p., 50 p., 1 c., 3 c. As Nos. 957/60			70	1·40

(Des BG Studio. Litho Format)

1981 (16 Oct). *World Food Day. T* **387** *and similar horiz designs. Multicoloured. P* 13½ × 14.

962	20 p. Type **387**			10	10
963	65 p. Plucking Cocoa			25	35
964	80 p. Preparing Banku			35	45
965	2 c. Garri processing			75	2·25
962/5			*Set of 4*	1·25	2·75
MS966	131 × 99 mm. 25 p., 50 p., 1 c., 3 c. As Nos. 962/5			1·00	1·50

388 "The Betrothal of St. Catherine of Alexandria" (Lucas Cranach)

389 Blind Person

(Des Clover Mill. Litho Format)

1981 (26 Nov). *Christmas. Details from Paintings. T* **388** *and similar vert designs. Multicoloured. P* 15.

967	15 p. Type **388**			15	10
968	20 p. "Angelic Musicians play for Mary and Child" (Aachener Altares)			15	10
969	65 p. "Child Jesus embracing his Mother" (Gabriel Metsu)			20	15
970	80 p. "Madonna and Child" (Fra Filippo Lippi)			20	20
971	2 c. "The Madonna with Infant Jesus" (Barnaba da Modena)			40	70
972	4 c. "The Immaculate Conception" (Murillo)			45	1·10
967/72			*Set of 6*	1·40	2·00
MS973	82 × 102 mm. 6 c. "Madonna and Child with Angels" (Hans Memling)			1·00	2·25

(Des G. Vasarhelyi. Litho Questa)

1982 (8 Feb). *International Year for Disabled Persons. T* **389** *and similar horiz designs. Multicoloured. P* 14.

974	20 p. Type **389**			10	10
975	65 p. Disabled person with crutches			30	35
976	80 p. Blind child reading braille			40	45
977	4 c. Disabled people helping one another			1·75	2·25
974/7			*Set of 4*	2·25	2·75
MS978	109 × 85 mm. 6 c. Group of disabled people			2·75	3·00

390 African Clawless Otter

391 *Precis westermanni*

(Des G. Drummond. Litho Harrison)

1982 (22 Feb). *Flora and Fauna. T* **390** *and similar vert designs. Multicoloured. P* 14.

979	20 p. Type **390**			25	15
980	65 p. Bushbuck			60	40
981	80 p. Aardvark			70	50
982	1 c. Scarlet Bell Tree			85	60
983	2 c. Glory-Lilies			1·60	1·25
984	4 c. Blue-Pea			2·75	2·25
979/84			*Set of 6*	6·00	4·75
MS985	76 × 100 mm. 5 c. Chimpanzee			2·00	5·00

(Litho Harrison)

1982 (3 May). *Butterflies. T* **391** *and similar vert designs. Multi-coloured. P* 14.

986	20 p. Type **391**		70	15
987	65 p. *Papilio menestheus*		1·50	1·00
988	2 c. *Antanartia delius*		2·50	3·50
989	4 c. *Charaxes castor*		4·00	4·75
986/9		*Set of* 4	8·00	8·50
MS990	98×123 mm. 25 p., 50 p., 1 c., 3 c. As Nos. 986/9. P 14½		9·00	12·00

392 Scouts planting Tree

(Des M. Diamond. Litho Format)

1982 (1 June). *75th Anniv of Boy Scout Movement. T* **392** *and similar multicoloured designs. P* 14½ × 15.

991	20 p. Type **392**		25	15
992	65 p. Scouts cooking on camp-fire		70	65
993	80 p. Sea Scouts sailing		90	85
994	3 c. Scouts observing elephant		2·25	3·25
991/4		*Set of* 4	3·50	4·50
MS995	101 × 71 mm. 5 c. Lord Baden-Powell (*vert*). P 15 × 14½		2·75	6·50

393 Initial Stages of Construction

(Des C. Tetteh. Litho Questa)

1982 (28 June). *Kpong Hydro-Electric Project. T* **393** *and similar horiz designs. Multicoloured. P* 14.

996	20 p. Type **393**		65	10
997	65 p. Truck removing rubble		1·40	45
998	80 p. Hydro-electric turbines		1·60	65
999	2 c. Aerial view of completed plant		3·00	1·60
996/9		*Set of* 4	6·00	2·50

394 Footballers

(Des M. and S. Gerber Studio. Litho Format)

1982 (19 July). *World Cup Football Championship, Spain. T* **394** *and similar horiz designs showing footballers.* (a) P 14½.

1000	**394**	20 p. multicoloured	20	10
1001	—	65 p. multicoloured	45	35
1002	—	80 p. multicoloured	60	45
1003	—	4 c. multicoloured	1·50	2·00
1000/3		*Set of* 4	2·50	2·50
MS1004	110 × 90 mm. 6 c. multicoloured		3·75	2·75

(b) P 14 × 14½

1005	**394**	30 p. multicoloured	20	20
1006	—	80 p. multicoloured (as No. 1001)	35	45
1007	—	1 c. multicoloured (as No. 1002)	40	55
1008	—	3 c. multicoloured (as No. 1003)	1·00	1·60
1005/8		*Set of* 4	1·75	2·50

Nos. 1005/8 were each printed in small sheets including one *se-tenant*, stamp-size, label.

395 The Fight against Tuberculosis 396 The Shepherds worship Jesus

(Des M. Diamond. Litho Harrison)

1982 (9 Aug). *Centenary of Robert Koch's Discovery of Tubercle Bacillus. T* **395** *and similar horiz designs. Multicoloured. P* 14.

1009	20 p. Type **395**		70	20
1010	65 p. Robert Koch		1·60	1·25
1011	80 p. Robert Koch in Africa		2·00	1·75
1012	1 c. Centenary of discovery of Tuberculosis		2·25	2·75
1013	2 c. Robert Koch and Nobel Prize, 1905		3·25	4·00
1009/13		*Set of* 5	9·00	9·00

(Des E. Mensah. Litho Format)

1982 (22 Dec). *Christmas. T* **396** *and similar vert designs. Multicoloured. P* 14½.

1014	15 p. Type **396**		10	10
1015	20 p. Mary, Joseph and baby Jesus		10	10
1016	65 p. The Three Kings sight star		25	30
1017	4 c. Winged Angel		1·00	1·75
1014/17		*Set of* 4	1·25	2·00
MS1018	90 × 110 mm. 6 c. The Three Kings with Jesus		90	1·75

Nos. 1014/18 exist imperforate from stock dispersed by the liquidator of Format International Security Printers Ltd.

WINNER ITALY
3-1
(398)

397 Ghana and
Commonwealth Flags
with Coat of Arms

(Des J.W. Litho Format)

1983 (14 Mar). *Commonwealth Day. T* **397** *and similar vert designs. Multicoloured. P* 14½.

1019	20 p. Type **397**		25	15
1020	55 p. Satellite view of Ghana		45	65
1021	80 p. Minerals of Ghana		1·00	1·60
1022	3 c. African Fish Eagle		1·50	4·25
1019/22		*Set of* 4	2·75	5·75

Nos. 1019/22 exist imperforate from stock dispersed by the liquidator of Format International Security Printers Ltd.

1983 (30 May). *Italy's Victory in World Cup Football Championship* (1982). *Nos.* 1000/8 *optd with T* **398**, *in gold.* (a) P 14½.

1023	**394**	20 p. multicoloured	15	10
1024	—	65 p. multicoloured	25	15
1025	—	80 p. multicoloured	25	20
1026	—	4 c. multicoloured	1·40	1·75
1023/6		*Set of* 4	1·90	2·00
MS1027	110 × 90 mm. 6 c. multicoloured		1·75	1·50

(b) P 14 × 14½

1028	**394**	30 p. multicoloured	20	40
1029	—	80 p. multicoloured	60	1·00
1030	—	1 c. multicoloured	70	1·10
1031	—	3 c. multicoloured	1·50	2·25
1028/31		*Set of* 4	2·75	4·25

No. MS1027 has an additional overprint, "FINAL: ITALY V. W. GERMANY", on the sheet margin.

INFLATION HANDSTAMPS. During 1983 the value of the Ghanaian currency fell drastically and as a result, there was a considerable rise in postal rates.

To cope with this situation supplies of past commemorative issues were made available from the post offices, many being hand-stamped "NOT FOR PHILATELIC USE" in one line within a frame. These handstamps were usually applied in blue, haphazardly across the sheet with examples so far reported on Nos. 656/7, 664, 670, 680, 689, 703, 708, 718, 746/7, 753, 757, 762/3, 766, 775, 780/1, 791, 793, 799, 814, 817, 846/7, 850/1, 853, 856/7, 860, 865, 867, 869, 875 and 882.

(398a) 399 Short-finned Pilot Whale

1983 (Oct). *No.* 470 *surch with T* **398a**.

1031a	1 c. on 20 n.p. deep blue and new blue		40	40
	ab. Surch triple			
	ac. Surch double			
	ad. Surch double, one inverted			

(Des J. Iskowitz. Litho Format)

1983 (15 Nov). *Coastal Marine Mammals. T* **399** *and similar horiz designs. Multicoloured. P* 14½.

1032	1 c. Type **399**		1·00	1·00
1033	1 c. 40, Risso's Dolphin		1·10	1·10
1034	2 c. 30, False Killer Whale		1·25	1·25
1035	3 c. Spinner Dolphin		1·60	1·60
1036	5 c. Atlantic Hump-backed Dolphin		2·00	2·00
1032/6		*Set of* 5	6·25	6·25
MS1037	117 × 76 mm. 6 c. As 5 c.		1·25	1·00

Nos. 1033/7 exist imperforate from stock dispersed by the liquidator of Format International Security Printers Ltd.

400 Banded
Jewelfish

401 Communication
Devices

(Des and litho D.L.R.)

1983 (12 Dec). *T* **400** *and similar designs. P* 14.

1038	5 p. multicoloured		30	20
1039	10 p. multicoloured		30	20
1040	20 p. multicoloured		40	20
1041	50 p. deep grey-green, yellow-orange and black		40	30
1042	1 c. yellow-orange, violet-blue and black		50	20
1043	2 c. multicoloured		50	30
1044	3 c. multicoloured		90	30
1045	4 c. multicoloured		40	40
1046	5 c. multicoloured		50	40
1047	10 c. multicoloured		65	1·00
1038/47		*Set of* 10	4·25	3·25

Designs: *Horiz*—10 p. Banded Jewelfish (*different*); 2 c. Jet airliner. *Vert*—20 p. *Haemanthus rupestris*; 50 p. Mounted warrior; 1 c. Scorpion; 3 c. White-collared Mangabey; 4 c. Demidoff's Galago; 5 c. *Kaempferia nigerica*; 10 c. Grey-backed Camaroptera.

(Des PAD Studio. Litho Questa)

1983 (13 Dec). *World Communications Year. T* **401** *and similar vert designs. Multicoloured. P* 14.

1048	1 c. Type **401**		15	25
1049	1 c. 40, Satellite dish aerial		20	30
1050	2 c. 30, Cable and *Long Lines* (cable ship)		35	55
1051	3 c. Switchboard operators		40	65
1052	5 c. Aircraft cockpit and air traffic controllers		55	85
1048/52		*Set of* 5	1·50	2·40
MS1053	95×70 mm. 6 c. Space satellite		30	50

402 Children receiving Presents 403 Soldiers with Rifles

(Des Designs Images. Litho Questa)

1983 (28 Dec). *Christmas. T* **402** *and similar multicoloured designs. P* 14 × 13½ (70 p. and 3 c.) or 14½ × 14 (*others*).

1054	70 p. Type **402**		15	10
1055	1 c. Nativity and Star of Bethlehem (28 × 36 mm)		15	10
1056	1 c. 40, Children celebrating (28 × 36 mm)		25	55
1057	2 c. 30, Family praying (28 × 36 mm)		35	1·00
1058	3 c. Dancing to bongo drum		45	1·25
1054/8		*Set of* 5	1·25	2·50
MS1059	70 × 90 mm. 6 c. As 2 c. 30		30	1·00

(Des and litho B.D.T.)

1984 (26 Jan). *Namibia Day. T* **403** *and similar vert designs. P* 14.

1060	50 p. blue-green and black		10	10
1061	1 c. multicoloured		10	10
1062	1 c. 40, new blue, bright blue and black		15	15
1063	2 c. 30, multicoloured		20	25
1064	3 c. multicoloured		25	30
1060/4		*Set of* 5	65	75

Designs:—1 c. Soldiers supported by tank; 1 c. 40, Machete cutting chains; 2 c. 30, Peasant woman; 3 c. Soldiers and artillery support.

(404) (405)

1984 (8 Feb)–**85**. (a) *Nos.* 948/52 *and* 954 *surch as T* **404**

1065	1 c. on 20 p. Prince Charles and Lady Diana Spencer		2·50	3·00
1066	9 c. on 65 p. Prince Charles and Lady Diana Spencer (1985)		3·00	4·00
1067	9 c. on 80 p. Prince Charles on visit to Ghana		3·00	4·00
	a. Imperf (pair) with surch inverted		£275	
1068	20 c. on 3 c. Type **385** (1985)		3·50	6·00
1069	20 c. on 4 c. Type **385**		3·50	6·00
MS1070	95×85 mm. 60 c. on 7 c. St. Paul's Cathedral		1·40	3·00

The above exist imperforate from a restricted printing (*Price for Nos.* 1065, 1067, 1069 *set of* 3 £8, *Nos.* 1066 *and* 1068 *set of* 2 £10 *and No.* MS1070 £20, *all mint*).

(b) *Nos.* 991/2 *and* 994/5 *surch as T* **405**

1071	1 c. on 20 p. Type **392**		40	45
1072	19 c. on 65 p. Scouts cooking on camp-fire		80	85
1073	20 c. on 3 c. Scouts observing elephant		1·50	1·50
MS1074	101 × 71 mm. 60 c. on 5 c. Lord Baden-Powell		1·50	3·50

(c) *Nos.* 1000/6 *and* 1008 *surch as T* **405**

1075	**394**	1 c. on 20 p. multicoloured	30	30
1076	—	9 c. on 65 p. multicoloured	70	70
1077	—	9 c. on 3 c. multicoloured	70	70
1078	**394**	10 c. on 30 p. multicoloured	70	70
1079	—	10 c. on 80 p. mult (No. 1002)	70	70
1080	—	20 c. on 4 c. mult (No. 1006)	1·50	1·50
1081	—	20 c. on 4 c. multicoloured	1·50	1·50
MS1082	110×90 mm. 60 c. on 6 c. multicoloured		1·50	2·25

(d) *Nos.* 1019/22 *surch as T* **405**

1083	1 c. on 20 p. Type **397**		10	10
1084	9 c. on 55 p. Satellite view of Ghana		40	45
1085	30 c. on 80 p. Minerals of Ghana		1·50	1·50
1086	50 c. on 3 c. African Fish Eagle		2·50	3·00

(e) Nos. 1023/9 and 1031 surch as T 405

1087	394	1 c. on 20 p. multicoloured ..	..	10	10
1088	–	9 c. on 65 p. multicoloured ..	..	40	45
1089	–	9 c. on 3 c. multicoloured ..	..	40	45
1090	394	10 c. on 30 p. multicoloured ..	..	40	45
1091	–	10 c. on 80 p. mult (No. 1025)	..	40	45
1092	–	20 c. on 80 p. mult (No. 1029)	..	80	85
1093	–	20 c. on 4 c. multicoloured ..	..	80	85
MS1094		110×90 mm. 60 c. on 6 c. multicoloured		1·00	2·00
1065/9, 1071/3, 1075/81, 1083/93			*Set of 26*	30·00	35·00

c10

19ᵀᴴ U.P.U CONGRESS - HAMBURG

(406)

1984 (19 June). *Universal Postal Union Congress, Hamburg. Nos. 1035/7 surch as T 406.*

1095	10 c. on 3 c. Spinner Dolphin		40	45
1096	50 c. on 5 c. Atlantic Hump-backed Dolphin		2·10	2·25
MS1097	117×76 mm. 60 c. on 6 c. As No. 1096	..	2·50	3·50

407 Cross and Crown of Thorns   **408** Women's 400 Metre Race

(Litho Format)

1984 (26 June). *Easter. T 407 and similar vert designs. Multicoloured. P 15.*

1098	1 c. Type 407	..	10	10
1099	1 c. 40, Christ praying	..	10	10
1100	2 c. 30, The Resurrection ..	..	10	10
1101	3 c. Palm Sunday ..	..	10	15
1102	50 c. Christ on the road to Emmaus		1·10	2·25
1098/102	.. .. ..	*Set of 5*	1·25	2·40
MS1103	102×86 mm. 60 c. Type 407	..	1·00	2·50

No. 1098 exists imperforate from stock dispersed by the liquidator of Format International Security Printers Ltd.

(Des P. Cox and J. Iskowitz. Litho Format)

1984 (13 Aug). *Olympic Games, Los Angeles. T 408 and similar vert designs. Multicoloured. P 15.*

1104	1 c. Type 408	..	10	10
1105	1 c. 40, Boxing	..	15	10
1106	2 c. 30, Hockey	..	20	15
1107	3 c. Men's 400 metre hurdles race	..	20	15
1108	50 c. Rhythmic gymnastics..	..	1·75	3·50
1104/8		*Set of 5*	2·10	3·50
MS1109	103×78 mm. 70 c. Football	..	2·50	3·50

No. 1108 is inscribed "RYTHMIC" in error.

Nos. 1104/8 exist imperforate from stock dispersed by the liquidator of Format International Security Printers Ltd.

409 *Amorphophallus johnsonii*   **410** Young Bongo

(Litho Harrison)

1984 (24 Aug). *Flowers. T 409 and similar vert designs. Multicoloured. P 14.*

1110	1 c. Type 409	..	10	10
1111	1 c. 40, *Pancratium trianthum*	..	10	10
1112	2 c. 30, *Eulophia cucullata*	..	15	15
1113	3 c. *Amorphophallus abyssinicus*..	..	15	15
1114	50 c. *Chlorophytum togoense*	..	2·50	5·00
1110/14		*Set of 5*	2·50	5·00
MS1115	70×96 mm. 60 c. Type 409	..	2·00	3·50

(Des Susan David. Litho B.D.T.)

1984 (7 Sept). *Endangered Antelopes. T 410 and similar horiz designs. Multicoloured. P 14.*

1116	1 c. Type 410	..	30	20
1117	2 c. 30, Bongo bucks fighting	..	55	55
1118	3 c. Bongo family	..	70	70
1119	20 c. Bongo herd in high grass	..	2·50	3·50
1116/19		*Set of 4*	3·50	4·50
MS1120	Two sheets, each 100×71 mm. (a) 70 c. Head of Kob; (b) 70 c. Head of Bush buck			
		Set of 2 sheets	9·00	12·00

411 Dipo Girl   **412** The Three Wise Men Bringing Gifts

(Des and litho B.D.T.)

1984 (3 Oct). *Ghanaian Culture. T 411 and similar vert designs. Multicoloured. P 14.*

1121	1 c. Type 411	.. ..	10	10
1122	1 c. 40, Adowa dancer	..	10	10
1123	2 c. 30, Agbadza dancer	..	10	15
1124	3 c. Damba dancer ..	..	10	15
1125	50 c. Dipo dancer	..	1·40	3·00
1121/5		*Set of 5*	1·50	3·25
MS1126	70×84 mm. 70 c. Mandolin player. P 14×15		2·00	3·00

(Litho D.L.R.)

1984 (19 Nov). *Christmas. T 412 and similar vert designs. Multicoloured. P 12×12½.*

1127	70 p. Type 412	..	10	10
1128	1 c. Choir of angels	..	10	10
1129	1 c. 40, Mary and shepherds at manger ..		10	15
1130	2 c. 30, The flight into Egypt	..	10	15
1131	3 c. Simeon blessing Jesus	..	10	15
1132	50 c. Holy Family and angels	..	1·40	3·00
1127/32		*Set of 6*	1·50	3·25
MS1133	70×90 mm. 70 c. Type 412	..	2·00	2·75

VALERIE BRISCO-HOOKS U.S.A.

(413)

414 The Queen Mother attending Church Service

1984 (3 Dec). *Olympic Medal Winners, Los Angeles. Nos. 1104/9 optd as T 413 in gold.*

1134	1 c. Type 408 (optd with T 413)	..	10	10
1135	1 c. 40, Boxing (optd "U.S. WINNERS")	..	10	10
1136	2 c. 30, Field hockey (optd "PAKISTAN FIELD HOCKEY")	..	10	10
1137	3 c. Men's 400 metre hurdles race (optd "EDWIN MOSES U.S.A.")	..	10	10
1138	50 c. Rhythmic gymnastics (optd "LAURI FUNG CANADA")	..	1·50	1·60
1134/8		*Set of 5*	1·60	1·75
MS1139	103×78 mm. 70 c. Football (optd "FRANCE")		1·75	2·50

Nos. 1135 and MS1139 have the overprint in one line and Nos. 1136/8 in two.

(Des J.W. Litho Questa)

1985 (24 July). *Life and Times of Queen Elizabeth the Queen Mother. T 414 and similar vert designs. Multicoloured. P 14.*

1140	5 c. Type 414	..	10	15
1141	12 c. At Ascot Races	..	25	30
1142	100 c. At Clarence House on her 84th birthday		1·75	2·50
1140/2		*Set of 3*	1·75	2·75
MS1143	56×84 mm. 110 c. With Prince Charles at Garter ceremony		1·75	3·00

Stamps as Nos. 1140/2, but with face values of 8 c., 20 c. and 70 c., exist from additional sheetlets of 5 plus a label issued December 1985. These also have changed background colours and are perforated 12×12½ (*Price for set of 3 stamps £2.25 mint*).

Nos. 1140/3 and the stamps from the additional sheetlets also exist surcharged "90th Birthday 4th August 1990", but are reported not to have been available in Ghana.

415 Moslems going to Mosque   **416** Youths clearing Refuse ("Make Ghana Clean")

(Des E. Mensah. Litho B.D.T.)

1985 (1 Aug). *Islamic Festival of Id-el-Fitr. T 415 and similar vert designs. Multicoloured. P 14.*

1144	5 c. Type 415	..	25	20
1145	8 c. Moslems at prayer	..	35	30
1146	12 c. Pilgrims visiting the Dome of the Rock		55	45
1147	18 c. Preaching the Koran ..	..	70	60
1148	50 c. Banda Nkwanta Mosque, Accra, and map of Ghana		1·75	1·60
1144/8		*Set of 5*	3·25	2·75

(Des E. Mensah. Litho Format)

1985 (9 Aug). *International Youth Year. T 416 and similar vert designs. Multicoloured. P 14×13½.*

1149	5 c. Type 416	..	10	10
1150	8 c. Planting sapling ("Make Ghana Green")		15	15
1151	12 c. Youth carrying bananas ("Feed Ghana")		20	25
1152	100 c. Open-air class ("Educate Ghana")		90	2·25
1149/52		*Set of 4*	1·25	2·50
MS1153	103×78 mm. 110 c. As 8 c.	..	1·25	3·00

Nos. 1149/53 exist imperforate from stock dispersed by the liquidator of Format International Security Printers Ltd.

417 Honda "Interceptor", 1984   **418** Fork-tailed Flycatcher

(Litho Questa)

1985 (9 Sept). *Centenary of the Motorcycle. T 417 and similar multicoloured designs. P 14.*

1154	5 c. Type 417	..	55	55
1155	8 c. DKW, 1938	..	65	75
1156	12 c. BMW "R 32", 1923	..	1·00	1·00
1157	100 c. NSU, 1900	..	5·50	7·00
1154/7		*Set of 4*	7·00	8·50
MS1158	78×108 mm. 110 c. Zündapp, 1973 (vert)		4·50	4·75

(Litho Questa)

1985 (16 Oct). *Birth Bicentenary of John J. Audubon (ornithologist). T 418 and similar vert designs showing original paintings. Multicoloured. P 14.*

1159	5 c. Type 418	..	1·25	50
1160	8 c. Barred Owl	..	2·25	2·00
1161	12 c. Black-throated Mango	..	2·25	2·00
1162	100 c. White-crowned Pigeon	..	6·50	9·50
1159/62		*Set of 4*	11·00	12·50
MS1163	85×115 mm. 110 c. Downy Woodpecker		6·50	3·50

No. 1159 is inscribed "York-tailed Fly Catcher" in error.

Nos. 1159/63 also exist imperforate from a limited printing.

419 United Nations Building, New York

(Des Mary Walters. Litho D.L.R.)

1985 (24 Oct). *40th Anniv of United Nations Organization. T 419 and similar horiz designs. Multicoloured. P 14½ (18 c.) or 14½×14 (others).*

1164	5 c. Type 419	..	10	10
1165	8 c. Flags of member nations and U.N. Building		10	15
1166	12 c. Dove with olive branch	..	10	25
1167	18 c. General Assembly	..	15	35
1168	100 c. Flags of Ghana and United Nations		90	1·75
1164/8		*Set of 5*	1·25	2·40
MS1169	90×70 mm. 110 c. United Nations (New York) 1955 4 cent 10th anniv stamp		1·25	1·75

Nos. 1164/9 also exist imperforate from a limited printing.

420 Coffee

(Des J. Iskowitz. Litho B.D.T.)

1985 (4 Nov). *20th Anniv of United Nations Conference on Trade and Development. T 420 and similar horiz designs showing export products. Multicoloured. P 14.*

1170	5 c. Type 420	..	10	10
1171	8 c. Cocoa	..	15	15
1172	12 c. Timber	..	25	25
1173	18 c. Bauxite	..	1·25	90
1174	100 c. Gold	..	6·50	8·50
1170/4		*Set of 5*	7·50	9·00
MS1175	104×74 mm. 110 c. Agricultural produce and plate of food. P 15×14 ..		2·00	2·50

421 Growth Monitoring

(Des E. Mensah. Litho B.D.T.)

1985 (16 Dec). *U.N.I.C.E.F. Child Survival Campaign. T* **421** *and similar horiz designs. Multicoloured. P* 14.

1176	5 c. Type **421**		30	10
1177	8 c. Oral rehydration therapy	..	50	30
1178	12 c. Breast feeding	..	70	40
1179	100 c. Immunization	..	2·50	4·50
1176/9		*Set of* 4	3·50	4·75
MS1180	99×69 mm. 110 c. Campaign logo.			
P 15×14 ..			1·75	2·25

422 Airline Stewardess and Boys with Stamp Album

(Litho Questa)

1986 (27 Oct). *"Ameripex" International Stamp Exhibition, Chicago. T* **422** *and similar multicoloured designs. P* 14.

1181	5 c. Type **422**		15	15
1182	25 c. Globe and Douglas DC-10 aircraft		60	45
1183	100 c. Ghana Airways stewardess (*vert*)		2·25	3·00
1181/3		*Set of* 3	2·75	3·25
MS1184	90×70 mm. 150 c. Stamp collecting class			
..	..		2·25	2·50

Nos. 1181/4 also exist imperforate from a limited printing.

423 Kejetia Roundabout, Kumasi   424 Tackling

(Litho B.D.T.)

1986 (10 Nov). *"Inter-Tourism '86" Conference. T* **423** *and similar horiz designs. Multicoloured. P* 14.

1185	5 c. Type **423**	..		10	10
1186	15 c. Fort St. Jago, Elmina	..		30	30
1187	25 c. Tribal warriors	..		45	45
1188	100 c. Chief holding audience	..		1·75	3·25
1185/8			*Set of* 4	2·40	3·75
MS1189	110×70 mm. 150 c. African Elephants.				
P 15 × 14 ..				3·75	5·50

(Litho D.L.R.)

1987 (16 Jan). *World Cup Football Championship, Mexico* (1986). *T* **424** *and similar vert designs. Multicoloured. P* 14×14½.

1190	5 c. Type **424**		20	10
1191	15 c. Player taking control of ball		30	15
1192	25 c. Player kicking ball	..	50	25
1193	100 c. Player with ball	..	1·50	1·25
1190/3		*Set of* 4	2·25	1·50
MS1194	90×70 mm. 150 c. Player kicking ball			
(*different*) ..			1·50	2·00

Nos. 1190/4 also exist imperforate from a limited printing.

425 Fertility Doll   426 Children of Different Races, Peace Doves and Sun

(Litho D.L.R.)

1987 (22 Jan). *Ghanaian Fertility Dolls. T* **425** *and similar vert designs showing different dolls. P* 14×14½.

1195	**425**	5 c. multicoloured		10	10
1196	—	15 c. multicoloured		20	15
1197	—	25 c. multicoloured		35	25
1198	—	100 c. multicoloured		1·25	1·50
1195/8			*Set of* 4	1·60	1·75
MS1199	90×70 mm. **425** 150 c. multicoloured	..	1·50	2·00

(Litho D.L.R.)

1987 (2 Mar). *International Peace Year* (1986). *T* **426** *and similar multicoloured designs. P* 14 × 14½ (100 c.) *or* 14½ × 14 (*others*).

1200	5 c. Type **426**		15	10
1201	25 c. Plough, peace dove and rising sun		75	25
1202	100 c. Peace dove, olive branch and globe (*vert*)		2·50	3·00
1200/2		*Set of* 3	3·00	3·00
MS1203	90×70 mm. 150 c. Dove perched on plough (*vert*). P 14×14½..		1·75	2·25

427 Lumber and House under Construction   428 Demonstrator and Arms breaking Shackles

(Des and litho B.D.T.)

1987 (10 Mar). *"Gifex '87" International Forestry Exposition, Accra. T* **427** *and similar horiz designs. Multicoloured. P* 14.

1204	5 c. Type **427**		10	10
1205	15 c. Planks and furniture		15	15
1206	25 c. Felled trees		30	25
1207	200 c. Logs and wood carvings		1·90	2·25
1204/7		*Set of* 4	2·25	2·50

(Des W. Hanson. Litho D.L.R.)

1987 (8 Apr). *Appearance of Halley's Comet* (1986). *Horiz designs as T* **123** *of Anguilla. Multicoloured. P* 14½×14.

1208	5 c. Mikhail Lomonosov (scientist) and Chamber of Curiosities, St. Petersburg		20	10
1209	25 c. Lunar probe "Surveyor 3", 1966		70	30
1210	200 c. Wedgwood plaques for Isaac Newton, 1790, and "Apollo 11" Moon landing, 1968		3·25	2·25
1208/10		*Set of* 3	3·75	2·40
MS1211	100×70 mm. 250 c. Halley's Comet ..		3·50	2·75

Nos. 1208/11 also exist imperforate from a limited printing.

(Litho D.L.R.)

1987 (18 May). *Solidarity with the People of Southern Africa. T* **428** *and similar vert designs. Multicoloured. P* 14×14½.

1212	5 c. Type **428**		10	10
1213	15 c. Miner and gold bars ..		40	15
1214	25 c. Xhosa warriors		30	25
1215	100 c. Nelson Mandela and shackles		1·25	2·00
1212/15		*Set of* 4	1·75	2·25
MS1216	70×90 mm. 150 c. Nelson Mandela		1·50	2·00

429 Aerophones

(Litho D.L.R.)

1987 (13 July). *Musical Instruments. T* **429** *and similar horiz designs. Multicoloured. P* 14½×14.

1217	5 c. Type **429**	..	10	10
1218	15 c. Xylophone		15	15
1219	25 c. Chordophones		30	25
1220	100 c. Membranophones		1·00	1·25
1217/20		*Set of* 4	1·40	1·50
MS1221	90×70 mm. 200 c. Idiophones ..		1·90	2·25

430 Woman filling Water Pot at Pump   431 Ga Women preparing Kpokpoi for Homowo Festival

(Litho B.D.T.)

1987 (21 Sept). *International Year of Shelter for the Homeless. T* **430** *and similar horiz designs. Multicoloured. P* 14.

1222	5 c. Type **430**		10	10
1223	15 c. Building house from breeze-blocks		15	15
1224	25 c. Modern village with stream		25	25
1225	100 c. Modern houses with verandahs		1·25	1·25
1222/5		*Set of* 4	1·50	1·50

(Litho Format)

1988 (6 Jan). *Ghana Festivals. T* **431** *and similar vert designs. Multicoloured. P* 15.

1226	5 c. Type **431**		10	10
1227	15 c. Efute hunters with deer, Aboakyir festival		15	15
1228	25 c. Fanti chief dancing at Odwira festival		25	25
1229	100 c. Chief in palanquin, Yam festival		90	1·25
1226/9		*Set of* 4	1·25	1·50

Nos. 1226/9 exist imperforate from stock dispersed by the liquidator of Format International Security Printers Ltd.

432 Port Installation   433 Nurse giving Injection

(Litho National Ptg Wks. Havana)

1988 (26 Jan). *5th Anniversary of 31 December Revolution* (1987). *T* **432** *and similar horiz designs. Multicoloured. P* 14.

1230	5 c. Type **432**		1·25	40
1231	15 c. Repairing railway line		9·00	25
1232	25 c. Planting cocoa		1·75	55
1233	100 c. Miners with ore truck		10·00	10·00
1230/3		*Set of* 4	20·00	12·00

(Litho Format)

1988 (1 Feb). *U.N.I.C.E.F. Global Immunization Campaign. T* **433** *and similar vert designs. Multicoloured. P* 15.

1234	5 c. Type **433**		20	10
1235	15 c. Girl receiving injection		25	20
1236	25 c. Schoolgirl crippled by polio		35	50
1237	100 c. Nurse giving oral vaccine to baby		60	2·25
1234/7		*Set of* 4	1·25	2·75

Nos. 1234/7 exist imperforate from stock dispersed by the liquidator of Format International Security Printers Ltd.

434 Fishing   435 Akwadjan Men

(Des E. Mensah. Litho National Ptg Wks. Havana)

1988 (14 Apr). *10th Anniv of International Fund for Agricultural Development. T* **434** *and similar horiz designs. Multicoloured. P* 13.

1238	5 c. Type **434**		55	20
1239	15 c. Women harvesting crops		85	30
1240	25 c. Cattle		1·10	40
1241	100 c. Village granaries		3·00	5·00
1238/41		*Set of* 4	5·00	5·50

(Litho Questa)

1988 (9 May). *Tribal Costumes. T* **435** *and similar vert designs. Multicoloured. P* 14.

1242	5 c. Type **435**		15	10
1243	25 c. Banaa man		35	20
1244	250 c. Agwasen woman		1·50	2·00
1242/4		*Set of* 3	1·75	2·00

₵20.00   ₵20.00

(436)   (436a)

₵50.00   ₵50

(437)   (437a)

₵50.00 ▮   ₵50·00

(438)   (438a)

1988 (19 July)–90. *Nos. 460, 464/6, 469/70, 1031a, 1038/42, 1044 and 1046 surch as T 436/8a.*

1245	—	20 c. on 50 p. dp grey-green, yell-orge & blk (No. 1041) (surch as T 436)	30	15
		a. Horiz pair, one without surch		
		b. Surch inverted	†	—
1246	—	20 c. on 1 c. yell-orge, vio-blue & black (No. 1042) (surch T 436) (9.88)	30	15
		a. Surch double		
		b. Surch double, one albino		
		c. Surch double, one albino and one inverted		
		d. Surch double, one inverted (T 436 + 436a)		
		e. Pair, one without surch		
		f. Surch sideways		
		g. Surch triple		
		h. "2" omitted (R. 4/3)		
1246m	—	20 c. on 1 c. yellow-orange, violet-bl & blk (No. 1042) (surch T 436a)		
		ma. Surch double		
		mb. Surch double, one inverted		
		mc. Surch double, one sideways		
		md. Surch inverted		
		me. Pair, one without surch		
		mf. Albino surch		
		mg. Small "0"s in surch (R. 2/6)		
		mh. Space between "C 20." and "00" (R. 1/5)		
1247	—	50 c. on 10 n.p. multicoloured (No. 469) (surch T 437)	30	25
		a. Vert pair, one without surch		
		b. Surch inverted		
1248	—	50 c. on 20 n.p. deep blue & new blue (No. 470) (surch T 437a) (1990)	3·00	45
1249	—	50 c. on 20 n.p. deep blue and new blue (No. 470) (surch as T 437, reading down) (1990)	3·00	45
		a. Surch double		
1250	—	50 c. on 10 p. multicoloured (No. 1039) (surch T 438) (9.88)	30	15
		a. Pair, one without surch		
1250d	—	50 c. on 10 p. multicoloured (No. 1039) (surch T 438a)		
		da. Pair, one without surch		
		db. Surch inverted		
		dc. Surch on front and back		
		dd. Surch on front and surch inverted on back		
		de. Surch on front and double surch, one inverted, one sideways, on back		
1251	—	50 c. on 1 c. on 20 n.p. deep blue and new blue (No. 1031a) (surch T 437a) (1990)	3·00	45
		a. Surch inverted		
		b. Pair, one without surch		
		c. Surch omitted, inverted on back		
		d. Albino surch (T 437a)		
1252	—	50 c. on 1 c. on 20 n.p. deep blue and new blue (No. 1031a) (surch as T 437 reading down) (1990)	3·00	45
		a. Surch double		
		b. "5C0.00" (R. 1/2)		
		c. Surch omitted, inverted on back		
		d. Albino surch		
		e. Surch as T 437 reading up		
		ea. Surch double, both reading up		
		eb. Surch double, reading up and down		
		ec. Surch triple, two reading up (one albino) and one reading down		
		ed. "5C0.00" (R. 6/4)		
		ee. Pair, one without surch		
1253	—	50 c. on 1 c. on 20 n.p. deep blue and new blue (No. 1031a) (horiz surch as T 437) (1990)	3·00	45
1254	—	50 c. on 1 c. yellow-orge, violet-blue and black (No. 1042) (surch as T 436) (1990)	3·00	45
		a. Decimal point omitted from surcharge (R. 4/6)		
1255	230	60 c. on 1 n.p. multicoloured (surch as T 437) (1990)	3·00	45
		a. Surch inverted		
		b. Surch double		
		c. Surch double, one inverted		
		d. Surch double, one sideways		
		e. Surch double, one albino		
		f. Surch triple		
		g. Surch triple, one albino		
		h. Surch on front, inverted surch on back		
		i. Pair, one without surch		
1256	235	60 c. on 4 n.p. mult (surch as T 437)	3·00	30
		a. Surch double		
		b. Surch double, one inverted		
		c. Surch double, one albino		
		d. Surch inverted		
1257	—	60 c. on 3 c. multicoloured (No. 1044) (surch as T 438) (1989)	50	30
		a. Decimal point omitted from surch (R. 4/5)		
		b. Vert pair, one without surch		
1258	400	80 c. on 5 p. mult (surch as T 437)		
		a. Pair, one without surch		
		b. Surch double		
1259	—	80 c. on 5 c. multicoloured (No. 1046) (surch as T 438) (1990)	3·75	4·00
1260	—	100 c. on 3 n.p. multicoloured (No. 464) (surch T 437) (1990)	6·50	6·50
		a. Surch inverted		
1261	—	100 c. on 20 n.p. deep blue and new blue (No. 470) (surch as T 437)	50	55
		a. Horiz pair, one without surch		
1262	—	100 c. on 20 p. multicoloured (No. 1040) (surch as T 436) (9.88)	50	55
		a. Surch double, one sideways		
		b. Horiz pair, one without surch		
		c. Surch inverted		

1263	—	100 c. on 3 c. multicoloured (No. 1044) (surch as T 438a) (1990)	50	55
1264	236	200 c. on 6 n.p. mult (surch as T 437)	50	65
		a. Surch double		

Other handstamped and manuscript surcharges can be found used during 1988–89, but it is understood that only those listed above were issued by the postal authorities.

440 Boxing   **441** Nutrition Lecture

(Litho Questa)

1988 (10 Oct). *Olympic Games, Seoul. T 440 and similar horiz designs. Multicoloured. P 14.*

1265	20 c. Type 440		20	15
1266	60 c. Athletics		55	55
1267	80 c. Discus-throwing		60	80
1268	100 c. Javelin-throwing		70	1·10
1269	350 c. Weightlifting		1·75	3·00
1265/9		Set of 5	3·50	5·00
MS1270	75×105 mm. 500 c. As 80 c.		4·00	3·00

Nos. 1265/70 also exist imperforate from a limited printing.

(Litho B.D.T.)

1988 (14 Dec). *125th Anniv of International Red Cross. T 441 and similar vert designs. Multicoloured. P 14.*

1271	20 c. Type 441		40	15
1272	50 c. Red Cross volunteer with blind woman		90	90
1273	60 c. Distributing flood relief supplies		1·00	1·00
1274	200 c. Giving first aid		2·50	3·25
1271/4		Set of 4	4·25	4·75

442 Tropical Forest   **443** "African Solidarity"

(Litho B.D.T.)

1988 (19 Dec). *Christmas. T 442 and similar multicoloured designs. P 14.*

1275	20 c. Type 442		15	10
1276	60 c. Christ Child (*vert*)		35	35
1277	80 c. Virgin and Child with Star (*vert*)		50	60
1278	100 c. Three Wise Men following Star		60	70
1279	350 c. Symbolic Crucifixion (*vert*)		2·00	2·50
1275/9		Set of 5	3·25	3·75
MS1280	100×70 mm. 500 c. Virgin and Child (*vert*)		2·50	2·75

Nos. 1275/80 also exist imperforate from a limited printing.

(Litho B.D.T.)

1989 (3 Jan). *25th Anniv of Organization of African Unity (1988). T 443 and similar multicoloured designs. P 14.*

1281	20 c. Type 443		10	10
1282	50 c. O.A.U. Headquarters, Addis Ababa		15	20
1283	60 c. Emperor Haile Selassie and Ethiopian flag (*horiz*)		20	25
1284	200 c. Kwame Nkrumah (former Ghanaian President) and flag (*horiz*)		60	85
1281/4		Set of 4	90	1·25

444 "Amor"   A. ZUELOW DDR 60 KG (445)

(Litho B.D.T.)

1989 (16 Jan). *500th Birth Anniversary of Titian (artist). T 444 and similar vert designs. Multicoloured. P 14.*

1285	20 c. Type 444		40	15
1286	60 c. "The Appeal"		80	65
1287	80 c. "Bacchus and Ariadne" (detail)		90	85
1288	100 c. "Portrait of Musician"		1·00	1·60
1289	350 c. "Philip II seated"		2·25	4·50
1285/9		Set of 5	4·75	7·00
MS1290	77×115 mm. 500 c. "Portrait of a Gentleman"		2·50	2·75

1989 (23 Jan). *Olympic Medal Winners, Seoul. Nos. 1265/70 optd as T 445.*

1291	20 c. Type 440 (optd with T 445)		15	10
1292	60 c. Athletics (optd "G. BORDIN ITALY MARATHON")		25	25
1293	80 c. Discus-throwing (optd "J. SCHULT DDR")		30	30
1294	100 c. Javelin-throwing (optd "T. KORJUS FINLAND")		35	35
1295	350 c. Weightlifting (optd "B. GUIDIKOV BULGARIA 75 KG")		1·25	1·10
1291/5		Set of 5	2·10	1·90
MS1296	75×105 mm. 500 c. As 80 c. (optd "GOLD J. SCHULT DDR SILVER R. OUBARTAS USSR BRONZE R. DANNEBERG W. GERMANY" on sheet margin)		2·40	2·10

¢100 (446)   **¢100** (447)   C60

1989 (3 July–20 Nov). *Various stamps surch as T 446/7.*

(a) On Nos. 949/50 and 952/4 (20 Nov)

1297	80 c. on 65 p. Prince Charles and Lady Diana Spencer		35	40
1298	100 c. on 80 p. Prince Charles on visit to Ghana		45	50
1299	100 c. on 1 c. Prince Charles on visit to Ghana		45	50
1300	300 c. on 3 c. Type 385		1·25	1·60
1301	500 c. on 4 c. Type 385		2·25	2·75
1297/1301		Set of 5	4·25	5·25

(b) On Nos. 1048/51 and MS1053 (18 Sept)

1302	60 c. on 1 c. Type 401		50	50
1303	80 c. on 1 c. 40, Satellite dish aerial		65	65
1304	200 c. on 2 c. 30, Cable and cable-laying ship		1·75	2·00
1305	300 c. on 3 c. Switchboard operators		2·00	2·25
1302/5		Set of 4	4·50	4·75
MS1306	95×70 mm. 500 c. on 6 c. Space satellite		4·50	5·50

(c) On Nos. 1104/7 and MS1109

1307	60 c. on 1 c. Type 408		30	30
1308	80 c. on 1 c. 40, Boxing		40	40
1309	200 c. on 2 c. 30, Hockey		1·25	1·60
1310	300 c. on 3 c. Men's 400 metre hurdles race		1·40	1·75
1307/10		Set of 4	3·00	3·50
MS1311	103×78 mm. 600 c. on 70 c. Football		3·00	4·00

(d) On Nos. 1134/7 and MS1139

1312	60 c. on 1 c. Type 408 (optd with T 413)		85	90
1313	80 c. on 1 c. 40, Boxing (optd "U.S. WINNERS")		1·10	1·25
1314	200 c. on 2 c. 30, Field hockey (optd "PAKISTAN (FIELD HOCKEY)")		3·25	3·50
1315	300 c. on 3 c. Men's 400 metre hurdles race (optd "EDWIN MOSES U.S.A.")		3·50	3·75
1312/15		Set of 4	8·00	8·50
MS1316	103×78 mm. 600 c. on 70 c. Football (optd "FRANCE")		5·00	5·50

(e) On Nos. 1140/3 (20 Nov)

1317	80 c. on 5 c. Type 414		35	40
1318	250 c. on 12 c. At Ascot Races		1·10	1·75
1319	300 c. on 100 c. At Clarence House on her 84th birthday		1·25	1·75
1317/19		Set of 3	2·50	3·50
MS1320	56×84 mm. 500 c. on 110 c. With Prince Charles at Garter Ceremony		3·25	4·00

(f) On Nos. 1159/61 and MS1163 (20 Nov)

1321	80 c. on 5 c. Type 418		1·00	1·00
1322	100 c. on 8 c. Barred Owl		2·25	2·25
1323	300 c. on 12 c. Black-throated Mango		2·50	3·00
1321/3		Set of 3	5·00	5·50
MS1324	500 c. on 110 c. Downy Woodpecker		6·00	6·50

(g) On Nos. 1190/2 and MS1194

1325	60 c. on 5 c. Type 424		45	45
1326	200 c. on 15 c. Player taking control of ball		1·50	2·00
1327	300 c. on 25 c. Player kicking ball		2·00	2·50
1325/7		Set of 3	3·50	4·50
MS1328	90×70 mm. 600 c. on 150 c. Player kicking ball (*different*)		5·50	6·00

(h) As Nos. 1190/2 and MS1194, but with unissued "WINNERS" opt as T 216 of Antigua (18 Sept)

1329	60 c. on 5 c. Type 424		30	30
1330	200 c. on 15 c. Player taking control of ball		1·00	1·50
1331	300 c. on 25 c. Player kicking ball		1·40	2·00
1329/31		Set of 3	2·40	3·50
MS1332	90×70 mm. 600 c. on 150 c. Player kicking ball (*different*)		3·75	4·50

(i) On Nos. 1208/11

1333	60 c. on 5 c. Mikhail Lomonosov (scientist) and Chamber of Curiosities, St. Petersburg		65	55
1334	80 c. on 25 c. Lunar probe "Surveyor 3", 1966		85	70
1335	500 c. on 200 c. Wedgwood plaques for Isaac Newton, 1790, and "Apollo 11" Moon landing, 1968		3·25	4·50
1333/5		Set of 3	4·25	5·25
MS1336	100×70 mm. 750 c. on 250 c. Halley's Comet		4·00	5·00
	a. Surch double, one inverted			

(j) As Nos. 1208/11, but with unissued logo opt as T 218 of Antigua (18 Sept)

1337	60 c. on 5 c. Mikhail Lomonosov (scientist) and Chamber of Curiosities, St. Petersburg		35	40
1338	80 c. on 25 c. Lunar probe "Surveyor 3", 1966		45	50
1339	500 c. on 200 c. Wedgwood plaques for Isaac Newton, 1790, and "Apollo 11" Moon landing, 1968		2·50	4·00
1337/9		Set of 3	3·00	4·50
MS1340	100×70 mm. 750 c. on 250 c. Halley's Comet		5·50	6·50

The stamps, as Nos. 1140/3, from additional sheetlets also exist surcharged as 80 c. on 20 c., 200 c. on 8 c. and 250 c. on 70 c. On No. MS1336a the inverted surcharge occurs towards the bottom left of the miniature sheet.

448 French Royal Standard and Field Gun

449 Storming the Bastille

(Litho B.D.T.)

1989 (7 July). *"Philexfrance 89" International Stamp Exhibition, Paris. T 448 and similar multicoloured designs. P 14.*
1341	20 c. Type **448**	50	25
1342	60 c. Regimental standard, 1789, and French infantryman	1·00	90
1343	80 c. Revolutionary standard, 1789, and pistol	1·25	1·00
1344	350 c. Tricolour, 1794, and musket	3·25	5·00
1341/4		Set of 4	5·50	6·50
MS1345	77×106 mm. 600 c. Street plan of Paris, 1789 (*horiz*)	3·00	3·50

(Litho Questa)

1989 (21 Aug). *Japanese Art. Portraits. Multicoloured designs as T 250 of Antigua. P 13½×14.*
1346	20 c. "Minamoto-no-Yoritomo" (Fujiwara-no-Takanobu) (*vert*)	25	20
1347	50 c. "Takami Senseki" (Watanabe Kazan) (*vert*)	35	30
1348	60 c. "Ikkyu Sojun" (study) (Bokusai) (*vert*)	40	35
1349	75 c. "Nakamura Kuranosuka" (Ogata Korin) (*vert*)	45	40
1350	125 c. "Portrait of a Lady" (Kyoto branch, Kano School) (*vert*)	75	75
1351	150 c. "Portrait of Zemmui" (anon, 12th-century) (*vert*)	80	80
1352	200 c. "Ono no Komachi the Poetess" (Hokusai) (*vert*)	1·00	1·25
1353	500 c. "Kobo Daisi as a Child" (anon) (*vert*)	2·50	3·50
1346/53		Set of 8	6·00	6·75
MS1354	Two sheets, each 102×77 mm. (a) 500 c. "Kodai-no-Kimi" (attr Fujiwara-no-Nobuzane) (*vert*). P 13½×14. (b) 500 c. "Emperor Hanazono" (Fujiwara-no-Goshin). P 14×13½ Set of 2 sheets	8·50	8·50

Nos. 1346/53 were each printed in sheetlets of 10 containing two vertical strips of 5 stamps separated by printed labels commemorating Emperor Hirohito.

(Litho B.D.T.)

1989 (22 Sept). *Bicentenary of the French Revolution. T 449 and similar multicoloured designs. P 14×13½ (vert) or 13½×14 (horiz).*
1355	20 c. Type **449**	40	20
1356	60 c. Declaration of Human Rights	70	50
1357	80 c. Storming the Bastille (*horiz*)	90	75
1358	200 c. Revolution monument (*horiz*)	2·00	2·25
1359	350 c. Tree of Liberty (*horiz*)	2·75	3·50
1355/9		Set of 5	6·00	6·50

450 Collybia fusipes

451 "The Course of True Love .."

(Des L. Nelson. Litho B.D.T.)

1989 (2 Oct). *Fungi (1st series). T 450 and similar vert designs. Multicoloured. P 14.*
1360	20 c. Type **450**	25	25
1361	50 c. Coprinus comatus	40	40
1362	60 c. Xerocomus subtomentosus	40	45
1363	80 c. Lepista nuda	55	55
1364	150 c. Suillus placidus	95	95
1365	200 c. Lepista nuda (*different*)	1·25	1·25
1366	300 c. Marasmius oreades	1·75	1·75
1367	500 c. Agaricus campestris	3·00	3·00
1360/7		Set of 8	7·75	7·75
MS1368	Two sheets, each 110×80 mm. (a) 600 c. Boletus rhodoxanthus. (b) 600 c. Amanita rubescens	Set of 2 sheets	7·50	8·00

Nos. 1360/8 also exist imperforate from a limited printing.
See also Nos. 1489/97.

(Des N. Waldman. Litho Walsall)

1989 (9 Oct). *425th Birth Anniv of Shakespeare. T 451 and similar vert designs showing lines and scenes from A Midsummer Night's Dream. Multicoloured. P 13½×13.*
1369	40 c. Type **451**	65	65
	a. Sheetlet. Nos. 1369/89		12·00	
1370	40 c. "Love looks not with the eye, but with the mind"	65	65
1371	40 c. "Nature here shows art"	65	65
1372	40 c. "Things growing are not ripe till their season"	65	65
1373	40 c. "He is defiled that draws a sword on thee"	65	65
1374	40 c. "It is not enough to speak, but to speak true"	65	65
1375	40 c. "Thou art as wise as thou art beautiful"	65	65
1376	40 c. Wildcat in wood (face value at left)	65	65
1377	40 c. Man	65	65
1378	40 c. Woman with flower	65	65
1379	40 c. King and queen	65	65
1380	40 c. Bottom	65	65
1381	40 c. Wildcat in wood (face value at right)	65	65
1382	40 c. Woman	65	65
1383	40 c. Leopard	65	65
1384	40 c. Tree trunk and man	65	65
1385	40 c. Meadow flowers	65	65
1386	40 c. Mauve flowers	65	65
1387	40 c. Plants	65	65
1388	40 c. Lion	65	65
1389	40 c. Fern and flowers	65	65
1369/89		Set of 21	12·00	12·00

Nos. 1369/89 were printed together, *se-tenant*, as a sheetlet of 21, forming a composite design.

(Des Mary Walters. Litho B.D.T.)

1989 (16 Oct)–**90**. *Birds. Multicoloured designs as T 244 of Dominica. P 14.*
1390	20 c. Bronze Mannikin (*horiz*)	30	10
1391	50 c. African Pied Wagtail (*horiz*)	45	30
1392	60 c. African Pygmy Kingfisher (inscr "Halcyon malimbicus") (*horiz*)	1·25	1·75
1392a	60 c. African Pygmy Kingfisher (inscr "Ispidina picta") (6.90) (*horiz*)	2·00	2·00
1393	80 c. Blue-breasted Kingfisher (inscr "Ispidina picta") (*horiz*)	1·75	2·25
1393a	80 c. Blue-breasted Kingfisher (inscr "Halcyon malimbicus") (6.90) (*horiz*)	2·00	2·50
1394	150 c. Striped Kingfisher (*horiz*)	1·10	1·25
1395	200 c. Shikra	1·25	1·40
1396	300 c. Grey Parrot	1·50	1·75
1397	500 c. Black Kite	2·50	3·25
1390/7		Set of 10	12·50	15·00
MS1398	Two sheets. (a) 128×83 mm. 600 c. Cinnamon-breasted Rock Bunting and Barn Swallow (*horiz*). (b) 83×128 mm. 600 c. Senegal Puff-back Flycatcher (*horiz*) Set of 2 sheets	13·00	14·00

The original printings of Nos. 1392/3 had the Latin names of the birds transposed. Corrected versions of the two designs were supplied during 1990.

Nos. 1390/8 also exist imperforate from a limited printing.

452 Command Module *Columbia* orbiting Moon

(Des K. Gromell. Litho B.D.T.)

1989 (6 Nov). *20th Anniv of First Manned Landing on Moon. T 452 and similar horiz designs. Multicoloured. P 14.*
1399	20 c. Type **452**	30	15
1400	80 c. Neil Armstrong's footprint on Moon	50	60
1401	200 c. Edwin Aldrin on Moon	1·25	1·75
1402	300 c. "Apollo 11" capsule on parachutes	1·60	2·00
1399/1402		Set of 4	3·25	4·00
MS1403	Two sheets, each 100×72 mm. (a) 500 c. Launch of "Apollo 11". (b) 500 c. Earth seen from Moon	Set of 2 sheets	5·50	7·00

453 Desertification of Pasture

(Litho B.D.T.)

1989 (15 Nov). *World Environment Day. T 453 and similar horiz designs. Multicoloured. P 14.*
1404	20 c. Type **453**	50	15
1405	60 c. Wildlife fleeing bush fire	90	80
1406	400 c. Industrial pollution	2·75	3·50
1407	500 c. Erosion	3·00	3·75
1404/7		Set of 4	6·50	7·50

454 Bebearia arcadius

455 Great Ribbed Cockle (*Cardium costatum*)

(Des Mary Walters. Litho B.D.T.)

1990 (20 Feb). *Butterflies. T 454 and similar horiz designs. Multicoloured. P 14.*
1408	20 c. Type **454**	35	20
1409	60 c. Charaxes laodice	50	40
1410	80 c. Euryphura porphyrion	60	45
1411	100 c. Neptis nicomedes	70	50
1412	150 c. Citrinophila erastus	90	90
1413	200 c. Aethiopana honorius	1·25	1·25
1414	300 c. Precis westermanni	1·50	1·75
1415	500 c. Cymothoe hypatha	2·00	2·50
1408/15		Set of 8	7·00	7·00
MS1416	Two sheets, each 104×72 mm. (a) 600 c. Telipna acraea. (b) 600 c. Pentila abraxas	Set of 2 sheets	9·00	10·00

Nos. 1408/16 also exist imperforate from a limited printing.

(Des E. Mensah. Litho D.L.R.)

1990 (23 Feb). *Seashells. T 455 and similar vert designs. Multicoloured. P 14×14½.*
1417	20 c. Type **455**	60	25
1418	60 c. Elephant's Snout (Cymbium glans)	75	40
1419	80 c. Garter Cone (Conus genuanus)	85	80
1420	200 c. Tankerville's Ancilla (Amalda tankervillii)	2·25	2·50
1421	350 c. Coronate Prickly-winkle (Tectarius coronatus)	3·00	4·00
1417/21		Set of 5	6·75	7·00

Nos. 1417/18 show the shell descriptions transposed in error.

456 Nehru welcoming President Nkrumah of Ghana

(Des E. Mensah. Litho D.L.R.)

1990 (27 Mar). *Birth Centenary of Jawaharlal Nehru (Indian statesman). T 456 and similar multicoloured designs. P 14½×14 (horiz) or 14×14½ (others).*
1422	20 c. Type **456**	60	25
1423	60 c. Nehru addressing Bandung Conference, 1955	75	30
1424	80 c. Nehru with garland and flowers (*vert*)	80	55
1425	200 c. Nehru releasing pigeon (*vert*)	1·25	1·50
1426	350 c. Nehru (*vert*)	1·75	2·75
1422/6		Set of 5	4·75	4·75

457 Wyon Medal, 1838

458 Anniversary Emblem

(Des S. Pollard. Litho B.D.T.)

1990 (23 May). *150th Anniv of Penny Black. T 457 and similar horiz designs. P 13½.*
1427	20 c. black and reddish violet	30	20
1428	60 c. black and deep grey-green	55	30
1429	80 c. black and reddish violet	70	35
1430	200 c. black and deep grey-green	1·50	1·25
1431	350 c. black and deep grey-green	2·00	2·50
1432	400 c. black and rosine	2·00	2·50
1427/32		Set of 6	6·25	6·25
MS1433	Two sheets, each 112×83 mm. (a) 600 c. red-brown and black; (b) 600 c. deep brown, buff and black	Set of 2 sheets	6·00	7·00

Designs:—60, 600 c. (No. MS1433b) Bath mail coach, 1840; 80 c. Leeds mail coach, 1840; 200 c. Proof of Queen's head engraved by Heath, 1840; 350 c. Master die, 1840; 400 c. London mail coach, 1840; 600 c. (No. MS1433a) Printing the Penny Black.

Nos. 1427/33 also exist imperforate from a limited printing.

(Litho D.L.R.)

1990 (5 June). *Tenth Anniv (1989) of 4 June Revolution. T 458 and similar vert designs. Multicoloured. P 14½×14.*
1434	20 c. Type **458**	15	15
1435	60 c. Foodstuffs	20	20
1436	80 c. Cocoa	25	30
1437	200 c. Mining	1·50	1·75
1438	350 c. Scales of Justice and sword	1·75	2·25
1434/8		Set of 5	3·50	4·25

459 Map of Africa and Satellite Network

(Litho D.L.R.)

1990 (12 July). *25th Anniv of Intelsat Satellite System. T* **459** *and similar horiz designs. Multicoloured. P* 14×14½.

1439	20 c. Type **459**	..	20	20
1440	60 c. Map of Americas	..	30	30
1441	80 c. Map of Asia and Pacific	..	35	35
1442	200 c. Map of South America and Africa		90	1·00
1443	350 c. Map of Indian Ocean and Pacific		1·50	2·00
1439/43		*Set of 5*	3·00	3·50

460 Housewife using Telephone

461 Blue Flycatcher

(Litho D.L.R.)

1990 (16 July). *Second Anniversary of Introduction of International Direct Dialling Service. T* **460** *and similar horiz designs. Multicoloured. P* 14×14½.

1444	20 c. Type **460**	..	25	20
1445	60 c. Businessman using telephone	..	35	35
1446	80 c. Man using phonecard telephone	..	40	40
1447	200 c. Public telephones for internal and IDD services	..	90	1·00
1448	350 c. Satellite station	..	1·50	2·00
1444/8		*Set of 5*	3·00	3·50

(Des W. Wright. Litho Questa)

1990 (25 Oct). *African Tropical Rain Forest. T* **461** *and similar multicoloured designs. P* 14×14½.

1449	40 c. Type **461**	..	60	65
	a. Sheetlet. Nos. 1449/68	..	11·00	
1450	40 c. Boomslang (snake)	..	60	65
1451	40 c. Superb Sunbird	..	60	65
1452	40 c. Bateleur	..	60	65
1453	40 c. Yellow-casqued Hornbill	..	60	65
1454	40 c. Salamis temora (butterfly)	..	60	65
1455	40 c. Potto	..	60	65
1456	40 c. Leopard	..	60	65
1457	40 c. Bongo	..	60	65
1458	40 c. Grey Parrot	..	60	65
1459	40 c. Okapi	..	60	65
1460	40 c. Gorilla	..	60	65
1461	40 c. Flap-necked Chameleon	..	60	65
1462	40 c. West African Dwarf Crocodile		60	65
1463	40 c. Python	..	60	65
1464	40 c. Giant Ground Pangolin	..	60	65
1465	40 c. Pseudacraea boisduvali (butterfly)		60	65
1466	40 c. North African Crested Porcupine		60	65
1467	40 c. Rosy-columned Aerangis (orchid)		60	65
1468	40 c. Cymothoe sangaris (butterfly)	..	60	65
1449/68		*Set of 20*	11·00	12·00

MS1469 100×75 mm. 600 c. Head of Leopard (*vert*). P 14½×14 .. 4·50 5·00

Nos. 1449/68 were printed together, *se-tenant*, as a sheetlet of 20, forming a composite design.

462 Jupiter

463 Eulophia guineensis

(Des K. Gromell. Litho Questa)

1990 (13 Dec). *Space Flight of "Voyager 2". T* **462** *and similar multicoloured designs. P* 14.

1470	100 c. Type **462**	..	70	70
	a. Sheetlet. Nos. 1470/8	..	5·75	
1471	100 c. Neptune and Triton	..	70	70
1472	100 c. Ariel, moon of Uranus	..	70	70
1473	100 c. Saturn from Mimas	..	70	70
1474	100 c. Saturn	..	70	70
1475	100 c. Rings of Saturn	..	70	70
1476	100 c. Neptune	..	70	70
1477	100 c. Uranus from Miranda	..	70	70
1478	100 c. Volcano on Io	..	70	70
1470/8		*Set of 9*	5·75	5·75

MS1479 Two sheets. (a) 111×81 mm. 600 c. "Voyager 2" spacecraft (*vert*). (b) 80×111 mm. 600 c. Lift off of "Voyager 2" (*vert*) *Set of 2 sheets* 4·50 5·00

Nos. 1470/8 were printed together, *se-tenant*, as a sheetlet of 9.

(Litho B.D.T.)

1990 (17 Dec). *Orchids. T* **463** *and similar vert designs. Multicoloured. P* 14.

1480	20 c. Type **463**	..	45	45
1481	40 c. Eurychone rothschildiana	..	60	60
1482	60 c. Bulbophyllum barbigerum	..	80	80
1483	80 c. Polystachya galeata	..	1·10	1·10
1484	200 c. Diaphananthe kamerunensis	..	1·75	1·75
1485	300 c. Podangis dactyloceras	..	2·00	2·00
1486	400 c. Ancistrochilus rothschildianus		2·00	2·00

1487	500 c. Rangaeris muscicola	..	2·00	2·00
1480/7		*Set of 8*	9·50	9·50

MS1488 Two sheets, each 101×70 mm. (a) 600 c. *Bolusiella imbricata.* (b) 600 c. *Diaphananthe rutila* .. .. *Set of 2 sheets* 9·50 10·00

464 *Coprinus atramentarius*

(Litho B.D.T.)

1990 (18 Dec). *Fungi (2nd series). T* **464** *and similar horiz designs. Multicoloured. P* 14.

1489	20 c. Type **464**	..	70	45
1490	50 c. Marasmius oreades	..	90	65
1491	60 c. Oudemansiella radicata	..	1·00	70
1492	80 c. Boletus edulis ("Cep")	..	1·25	90
1493	150 c. Hebeloma crustuliniforme	..	1·75	1·50
1494	200 c. Coprinus micaceus	..	2·00	2·00
1495	300 c. Macrolepiota procera ("Lepiota procera")		2·25	2·50
1496	500 c. Amanita phalloides	..	2·50	3·00
1489/96		*Set of 8*	11·00	10·50

MS1497 Two sheets, each 104×82 mm. (a) Nos. 1489, 1491/2 and 1496. (b) Nos. 1490 and 1493/5 *Set of 2 sheets* 8·00 9·00

465 Italian and Swedish Players chasing Ball

466 Manganese Ore

(Des Young Phillips Studio. Litho Questa)

1990 (18 Dec). *World Cup Football Championship, Italy. T* **465** *and similar multicoloured designs. P* 14.

1498	20 c. Type **465**		45	20
1499	50 c. Egyptian player penetrating Irish defence		55	30
1500	60 c. Cameroon players celebrating		60	30
1501	80 c. Rumanian player beating challenge		70	40
1502	100 c. Russian goalkeeper Dassayev		85	65
1503	150 c. Roger Milla of Cameroon (*vert*)		1·40	1·10
1504	400 c. South Korean player challenging opponent		2·25	2·00
1505	600 c. Klinsman of West Germany celebrating		2·75	3·50
1498/505		*Set of 8*	8·75	8·00

MS1506 Two sheets, each 88×98 mm. (a) 800 c. United Arab Emirates player watching ball. (b) 800 c. Colombian player .. *Set of 2 sheets* 5·50 6·50

(Litho Questa)

1990 (24 Dec). *350th Death Anniv of Rubens. Multicoloured designs as T* **273** *of Antigua, but vert. P* 13½×14.

1507	20 c. "Duke of Mantua"	..	30	20
1508	50 c. "Jan Brant"	..	40	30
1509	60 c. "Portrait of a Young Man"	..	40	30
1510	80 c. "Michel Ophovius"	..	55	40
1511	100 c. "Caspar Gevaerts"	..	65	55
1512	200 c. "Head of Warrior" (detail)	..	1·00	1·25
1513	300 c. "Study of a Bearded Man"	..	1·50	1·75
1514	400 c. "Paracelsus"	..	1·90	2·50
1507/14		*Set of 8*	6·00	6·50

MS1515 Two sheets, each 71×100 mm. (a) 600 c. "Warrior with two Pages" (detail). (b) 600 c. "Archduke Ferdinand" (detail) .. *Set of 2 sheets* 8·00 9·00

(Des E. Mensah. Litho D.L.R.)

1991 (2 May). *Minerals. T* **466** *and similar vert designs. Multicoloured. P* 14½×14.

1516	20 c. Type **466**	..	55	30
1517	60 c. Iron ore	..	70	60
1518	80 c. Bauxite ore	..	90	65
1519	200 c. Gold ore	..	2·00	2·00
1520	350 c. Diamond	..	3·00	4·00
1516/20		*Set of 5*	6·50	7·00

MS1521 70×90 mm. 600 c. Uncut and cut diamonds .. .. .. 6·00 7·00

467 Dance Drums

468 *Amorphophallus dracontioides*

(Des E. Mensah. Litho D.L.R.)

1991 (9 May). *Tribal Drums. T* **467** *and similar vert designs. Multicoloured. P* 14½×14.

1522	20 c. Type **467**	..	20	20
1523	60 c. Message drums	..	50	40
1524	80 c. War drums	..	60	50
1525	200 c. Dance drums (different)	..	1·50	1·75
1526	350 c. Ceremonial drums	..	2·00	3·00
1522/6		*Set of 5*	4·25	5·25

MS1527 70×90 mm. 600 c. Drum with carrying strap .. .. .. 4·50 6·00

(Des E. Mensah. Litho D.L.R.)

1991 (15 May). *Flowers (1st series). T* **468** *and similar vert designs. Multicoloured. P* 14½×14.

1528	20 c. Type **468**	..	65	25
1529	60 c. Anchomanes difformis	..	85	50
1530	80 c. Kaemferia nigerica	..	1·00	70
1531	200 c. Aframomum sceptrum	..	2·00	2·50
1532	350 c. Amorphophallus flavovirens		2·50	3·50
1528/32		*Set of 5*	6·25	6·75

MS1533 70×90 mm. 600 c. Amorphophallus flavovirens (different) .. .. 4·50 5·50

(Des E. Mensah. Litho D.L.R.)

1991 (17 May). *Flowers (2nd series). Vert designs as T* **468**, *but inscr "GHANA" in block capitals. Multicoloured. P* 14½×14.

1534	20 c. Urginea indica	..	65	25
1535	60 c. Hymenocallis littoralis	..	85	50
1536	80 c. Crinum jagus	..	1·50	70
1537	200 c. Dipcadi tacazzeanum	..	2·00	2·50
1538	350 c. Haemanthus rupestris	..	2·50	3·50
1534/8		*Set of 5*	6·75	6·75

MS1539 70×90 mm. 600 c. Urginea indica (different) .. .. .. 4·50 5·50

469 Transport and Telecommunication Symbols

470 Drawing of Scout from First Handbook

(Des E. Mensah. Litho Francoise-Charles Oberthur)

1991 (21 June). *40th Anniv of United Nations Development Programme. T* **469** *and similar vert designs. Multicoloured. P* 13½×14.

1540	20 c. Type **469**	..	30	20
1541	60 c. Agricultural research	..	50	40
1542	80 c. Literacy	..	60	55
1543	200 c. Advances in agricultural crop growth	1·40	1·60
1544	350 c. Industrial symbols	..	1·90	2·75
1540/4		*Set of 5*	4·25	5·00

(Des W. Hanson Studio. Litho B.D.T.)

1991 (18 July). *50th Death Anniv of Lord Baden-Powell. T* **470** *and similar designs. P* 14.

1545	20 c. black and pale buff	..	50	20
1546	50 c. grey, pale blue and black	..	70	40
1547	60 c. multicoloured	..	70	45
1548	80 c. black and pale buff	..	80	55
1549	100 c. multicoloured	..	1·10	75
1550	200 c. multicoloured	..	1·75	1·75
1551	500 c. multicoloured	..	2·50	3·25
1552	600 c. multicoloured	..	3·00	4·00
1545/52		*Set of 8*	10·00	10·00

MS1553 Two sheets. (a) 104×75 mm. 800 c. multicoloured; (b) 74×105 mm. 800 c. mult *Set of 2 sheets* 6·50 8·00

Designs: *Vert*—50 c. Lord Baden-Powell; 80 c. Handbook illustration by Norman Rockwell; 500 c. Scout at prayer. *Horiz*—60 c. Hands holding Boy Scout emblem; 100 c. Mafeking Siege 1d. Goodyear stamp and African runner; 200 c. Scouts with blitz victim, London, 1944; 600 c. Mafeking Siege 1d. Goodyear stamp; 800 c. (**MS**1553a) Scout camp; 800 c. (**MS**1553b) Envelope from Mafeking Siege.

PRICES OF SETS

Set prices are given for many issues, generally those containing three stamps or more. Definitive sets include one of each value or major colour change, but do not cover different perforations, die types or minor shades. Where a choice is possible the set prices are based on the cheapest versions of the stamps included in the listings.

471 Women sorting Fish

(Litho D.L.R.)

1991 (22 July). *Chorkor Smoker (fish smoking process). T 471 and similar horiz designs. Multicoloured.* P 14×14½.
1554	20 c. Type 471	..	..	30	20
1555	60 c. Cleaning the ovens	..	..	55	40
1556	80 c. Washing fish	..	..	65	55
1557	200 c. Laying fish on pallets	..		1·25	1·50
1558	350 c. Stacking pallets over ovens	..	1·75	2·75
1554/8		*Set of 5*	4·00	4·75

472 African Hind

(Des E. Mensah. Litho B.D.T.)

1991 (29 July). *Fishes. T 472 and similar horiz designs. Multicoloured.* P 14.
1559	20 c. Type 472	..	..	25	25
1560	50 c. Shrew Squeaker	..	..	40	40
1561	80 c. West African Triggerfish	..	55	55
1562	100 c. Stonehead	..	..	70	70
1563	200 c. Lesser Pipefish	..	..	1·50	1·50
1564	300 c. Aba	..	..	1·60	1·60
1565	400 c. Jewel Cichlid	..	..	1·75	1·75
1566	500 c. Smooth Hammerhead	..	1·90	1·90
1559/66		*Set of 8*	7·75	7·75

MS1567 Two sheets, each 108×81 mm. (a) 800 c. Bayad. (b) 800 c. Eastern Flying Gurnard.
Set of 2 sheets 6·00 7·00

(Litho B.D.T.)

1991 (12 Aug). *Death Centenary of Vincent van Gogh (artist) (1990). Multicoloured designs as T 278 of Antigua.* P 13.
1568	20 c. "Reaper with Sickle"	..	..	35	25
1569	50 c. "The Thresher"	..	..	55	40
1570	60 c. "The Sheaf-Binder"	..	..	60	50
1571	80 c. "The Sheep-Shearers"	..	70	65
1572	100 c. "Peasant Woman cutting Straw"	85	80
1573	200 c. "The Sower"	..	..	1·60	1·75
1574	500 c. "The Plough and the Harrow" (horiz)	2·25	2·50
1575	600 c. "The Woodcutter"	..	2·25	2·50
1568/75		*Set of 8*	8·25	8·50

MS1576 Two sheets, each 117×80 mm. (a) 800 c. "Evening: The Watch" (*horiz*). (b) 800 c. "Evening: The End of the Day" (*horiz*). Imperf
Set of 2 sheets 7·00 8·00

473 Gamal Nasser (Egypt)
and Conference Hall

474 Green-winged
Pytilia

(Litho Cartor)

1991 (2 Sept). *10th Non-Aligned Ministers' Conference, Accra. T 473 and similar horiz designs showing statesmen. Multicoloured.* P 13½.
1577	20 c. Type 473	..	..	50	30
1578	60 c. Josip Tito (Yugoslavia)	..	55	45
1579	80 c. Pandit Nehru (India)	..	1·75	1·25
1580	200 c. Kwame Nkrumah (Ghana)	1·75	2·25
1581	350 c. Achmad Sukarno (Indonesia)	1·90	3·00
1577/81	..	..	*Set of 5*	5·75	6·50

(Des S. Barlowe. Litho Questa)

1991 (14 Oct). *Birds. T 474 and similar vert designs. Multicoloured.* P 14½×14.
1582/1629 80 c. × 16, 100 c. × 32 *Set of 48* 22·00 25·00

MS1630 Three sheets, each 107×86 mm. (a) 800 c. Marabou Stork. (b) 800 c. African Fish Eagle. (c) 800 c. Saddle-bill Stork *Set of 3 sheets* 10·00 11·00
Nos. 1582/1629 were issued together, *se-tenant*, as three sheetlets of 16 forming composite designs. The 80 c. values show Green-winged Pytilia, Orange-cheeked Waxbill, African Paradise Flycatcher, Great Blue Turaco ("Blue Plantain-eater"), Red Bishop, Splendid Glossy Starling, Red-faced Lovebird, African Palm Swift, Narina Trogon, Tawny Eagle, Bateleur, Hoopoe, Secretary Bird, African White-backed Vulture, White-necked Bald Crow ("Bare-headed Rockfowl"), Abyssinian Ground Hornbill, and the 100 c. African Open-bill Stork, African Spoonbill, Pink-backed Pelican, Little Bittern, Purple Swamphen ("King Reed-hen"), Saddle-bill Stork, Glossy Ibis, White-faced Whistling Duck, Black-headed Heron, Hammerkop, African Darter, Woolly-necked Stork, Yellow-billed Stork, Black-winged Stilt, Goliath Heron, African Jacana ("Lily Trotter"), Shikra, Abyssinian Roller, Carmine Bee Eater, Pin-tailed Whydah, Purple Glossy Starling, Yellow-mantled Whydah, Pel's Fishing Owl, Crested Touraco, Red-cheeked Cordon-bleu, Olive-bellied Sunbird, Red-billed Hornbill, Red-billed Quelea, South African Crowned Crane, Blue Quail, Egyptian Vulture and Helmet Guineafowl.

475 Nularda (beetle)

476 Boti Falls

(Litho Cartor)

1991 (25 Oct). *Insects. T 475 and similar horiz designs. Multicoloured.* P 14×13½.
1631	20 c. Type 475	..	..	50	20
1632	50 c. Zonocrus (grasshopper)	..	65	30
1633	60 c. Gryllotalpa africana (mole cricket)	70	30
1634	80 c. Weevil	..	..	80	60
1635	100 c. Coenagrion (dragonfly)	..	90	70
1636	150 c. Sahlbergella (fly)	..	1·25	1·60
1637	200 c. Anthia (ant)	..	..	1·40	1·75
1638	350 c. Megacephala (beetle)	..	2·00	2·75
1631/8		*Set of 8*	7·50	7·50

MS1639 106×79 mm. 600 c. Lacetus (lacewing). P 13×12
6·00 7·00

Two types of 100 c.:

I. Cross bars of "A" in "GHANA" slope to left. Line in currency abbreviation diagonal. "CAPE COAST CASTLE" 10 mm long.
II. Inscriptions redrawn. Cross bars of "A" slope to right. Line in currency abbreviation upright. "CAPE COAST CASTLE" 13 mm long.

(Litho R. Alhelou Marfo Co Ltd, Accra)

1991 (21 Nov)–99. *T 476 and similar multicoloured designs.* P 13½.
1639a	20 c. Oil palm fruit (4.93)	..	10	10
	ab. Imperf (horiz pair) ..		†	—
1640	50 c. Type 476	..	..	20	10
	a. Imperf (pair)				
1641	60 c. Larabanga Mosque (horiz) (12.12.91)	10	10
	a. Black (inscriptions) omitted			
1642	80 c. Fort Sebastian, Shama (horiz) (12.12.91)	10	10
1643	100 c. Cape Coast Castle (horiz) (I) (12.12.91)	20	20
	a. Black (inscriptions) omitted	†	—
	b. Perf 14 (1996)			
	c. Type II (1999)			
1644	200 c. White-toothed Cowrie (Cyraea leucodon) (horiz) (12.12.91)	60	30
	a. Black (inscriptions) omitted			
	b. Perf 14 (1996)			
1645	400 c. True Achatina (Achatina achatina) (horiz) (12.12.91)	1·00	55
	a. Perf 14 (1996)			
1639a/45		*Set of 7*	2·00	1·40

Examples of No. 1643a have been seen used on commercial cover.
Nos. 1643b and 1645a show "GHANA" and the face value in black redrawn.

(Litho Walsall)

1991 (23 Dec). *Christmas. Religious Paintings. Vert designs as T 287 of Antigua. Multicoloured.* P 12.
1646	20 c. "Adoration of the Magi" (Bosch)	..	35	20
1647	50 c. "The Annunciation" (Campin)	..	50	30
1648	60 c. "Virgin and Child" (detail) (Bouts)	55	30
1649	80 c. "Presentation in the Temple" (Memling)	..	65	50
1650	100 c. "Virgin and Child enthroned with Angel and Donor" (Memling)	85	65
1651	200 c. "Virgin and Child with Saints and Donor" (Van Eyck)	1·50	1·75
1652	400 c. "St. Luke painting the Virgin" (Van der Weyden)	2·50	3·00
1653	700 c. "Virgin and Child" (Bouts)	3·50	4·50
1646/53		*Set of 8*	9·50	10·00

MS1654 Two sheets, each 103×128 mm. (a) 800 c. "Virgin and Child standing in a Niche" (Van der Weyden). (b) 800 c. "The Annunciation" (Memling). P 14
Set of 2 sheets 7·00 8·50

477 Women collecting
Water from Bore Hole

478 Mount Fuji and Flying
Fish

(Litho R. Alhelou Marfo Co Ltd, Accra)

1992 (2 Feb). *Decade of Revolutionary Progress. T 477 and similar horiz designs. Multicoloured.* P 14×13½.
1655	20 c. Type 477	..	..	15	10
1656	50 c. Miners	..	..	20	15
1657	60 c. Wood carver	..	..	20	15
1658	80 c. Forestry	..	..	25	20
1659	200 c. Cacao tree	..	..	50	75
1660	350 c. Village electrification	..	75	1·00
1655/60		*Set of 6*	1·90	2·00

(Litho B.D.T.)

1992 (16 Feb). *"Phila Nippon '91" International Stamp Exhibition, Tokyo. T 478 and similar horiz designs. Multicoloured.* P 14.
1661	20 c. Type 478	..	..	35	30
1662	50 c. Itsukushima Jingu Shrine	..	45	40
1663	80 c. Geisha	..	..	60	50
1664	100 c. Samurai house	..	..	80	70
1665	200 c. Bonsai tree	..	..	1·50	1·50
1666	400 c. Olympic Sports Hall	..	2·00	2·25

1667	500 c. Great Buddha (statue)	..	2·25	2·50
1668	600 c. Nagoya Castle	..	..	2·40	2·75
1661/8		*Set of 8*	9·25	9·75

MS1669 Two sheets, each 109×80 mm. (a) 800 c. Takamatsu Castle. (b) 800 c. Heian Shrine
Set of 2 sheets 8·50 9·00

479 East and West Germans
celebrating

480 Steam Side-tank
Locomotive, 1903

(Litho Questa)

1992 (17 Feb). *Reunification of Germany. T 479 and similar multicoloured designs.* P 14.
1670	20 c. Type 479	..	..	30	20
1671	60 c. Signing Reunification Treaty	40	40
1672	80 c. Chariot on Brandenburg Gate and fireworks	..	45	45
1673	1000 c. Germans with unified currency	6·00	8·00
1670/3		*Set of 4*	6·50	8·00

MS1674 Three sheets. (a) 109×78 mm. 400 c. Doves and Brandenburg Gate; 400 c. Chancellor Kohl and Prime Minister De Maizière. (b) 125×87 mm. 800 c. Chancellor Kohl and members of last German Democratic Republic administration. (c) 130×92 mm. 300 c. President Gorbachev (*vert*); 300 c. Chancellor Kohl (*vert*); 300 c. Map of Western Germany (face value in black) (*vert*); 300 c. Map of Eastern Germany (face value in white) (*vert*) *Set of 3 sheets* 8·50 9·50

(Des W. Hanson. Litho B.D.T.)

1992 (2 Mar). *Ghanaian Railways. T 480 and similar horiz designs. Multicoloured.* P 14.
1675	20 c. Type 480	..	..	40	30
1676	50 c. A1A-A1A diesel locomotive	..	60	40
1677	60 c. First class coach, 1931	..	60	45
1678	80 c. Railway inspection coach No. 2212	70	70
1679	100 c. Steam locomotive No. 401 on Kumasi turntable	..	90	90
1680	200 c. Cocoa wagon, 1921	..	1·40	1·50
1681	500 c. Steam locomotive No. 223 Prince of Wales	2·25	2·75
1682	600 c. Cattle wagon	..	2·25	2·75
1675/82		*Set of 8*	8·00	8·75

MS1683 Two sheets. (a) 106×76 mm. 800 c. Beyer-Garratt steam locomotive No. 301, 1943. (b) 76×106 mm. 800 c. German-built steam locomotive .. .. *Set of 2 sheets* 7·50 8·50

(Litho Questa)

1992 (3 Mar). *Olympic Games, Albertville and Barcelona. Past Medal Winners. Multicoloured designs as T 204 of Gambia.* P 14.
1684	20 c. E. Blay (Ghana) (boxing) and windmill	30	20
1685	60 c. M. Ahey (Ghana) (athletics) and Catalan coat of arms	50	35
1686	80 c. T. Wilson (U.S.A.) (70 metres ski jump) and grapes	70	50
1687	100 c. Four-man Bob-sleighing (East Germany) and passport	85	75
1688	200 c. G. Louganis (U.S.A.) (platform diving) and decorative vase	1·50	1·25
1689	300 c. L. Visser (Netherlands) (5000 metres speed skating) and wine bottle cork	1·75	1·75
1690	350 c. J. Passler (Italy) (biathlon) and lily	1·90	2·00
1691	400 c. M. Retton (U.S.A.) (gymnastics) and silhouette of castle	2·00	2·25
1692	500 c. J. Hingsen (West Germany) (decathlon) and gold and silver coins	2·00	2·25
1693	600 c. R. Neubert (West Germany) (heptathlon) and leather work	2·00	2·25
1684/93		*Set of 10*	12·00	12·00

MS1694 Two sheets. (a) 112×82 mm. 800 c. Silhouette of windmill. (b) 82×112 mm. 800 c. Silhouette of folk dancer (*vert*) *Set of 2 sheets* 9·50 11·00

481 Angides lugubris

482 Danaus
chrysippus

(Litho B.D.T.)

1992 (30 Mar). *Reptiles. T 481 and similar horiz designs. Multicoloured.* P 14.
1695	20 c. Type 481	..	..	20	20
1696	50 c. Kinixys erosa (tortoise)	..	30	30
1697	60 c. Agama agama (lizard)	..	30	30
1698	80 c. Chameleo gracilis (chameleon)	40	40
1699	100 c. Naja melanleuca (snake)	..	50	50
1700	200 c. Crocodylus niloticus (crocodile)	90	1·10
1701	400 c. Chelonia mydas (turtle)	..	1·75	2·25
1702	500 c. Varanus exanthematicus (lizard)	1·90	2·50
1695/1702		*Set of 8*	5·50	6·75

MS1703 94×66 mm. 600 c. Tortoise and snake 2·75 3·50

(Litho Questa)

1992 (13 Apr). *Easter. Religious Paintings. Multicoloured designs as T 291 of Antigua.* P 13½×14.

1704	20 c.	"The Four Apostles" (detail) (Dürer) (vert)		25	20
1705	50 c.	"The Last Judgement" (detail) (Rubens) (vert)		35	30
1706	60 c.	"The Four Apostles" (different detail) (Dürer) (vert)		35	30
1707	80 c.	"The Last Judgement" (different detail) (Rubens) (vert)		50	40
1708	100 c.	"Crucifixion" (Rubens) (vert)		60	50
1709	200 c.	"The Last Judgement" (different detail) (Rubens) (vert)		1·10	1·25
1710	500 c.	"Christum Videre" (Rubens) (vert)		2·00	2·50
1711	600 c.	"The Last Judgement" (different detail) (Rubens) (vert)		2·25	2·75
1704/11		*Set of 8*		6·50	7·50

MS1712 Two sheets. (a) 69×100 mm. 800 c. "Last Communion of St. Francis of Assisi" (detail) (Rubens) P 13½×13 (horiz) or 13×13½ (vert). (b) 100×69 mm. 800 c. "Scourging the Money Changers from the Temple" (detail) (El Greco). P 14×13½
Set of 2 sheets 7·50 8·50

(Litho B.D.T.)

1992 (4 May). *"Granada '92" International Stamp Exhibition, Spain. Spanish Paintings. Multicoloured designs as T 292 of Antigua.* P 13½×13 (horiz) or 13×13½ (vert).

1713	20 c.	"Two Men at Table" (Velázquez) (horiz)		20	20
1714	60 c.	"Christ in the House of Mary and Martha" (detail) (Velázquez) (horiz)		30	30
1715	80 c.	"The Supper at Emmaus" (Velázquez) (horiz)		40	40
1716	100 c.	"Three Musicians" (Velázquez) (horiz)		50	50
1717	200 c.	"Old Woman Cooking Eggs" (Velázquez)		90	90
1718	400 c.	"Old Woman Cooking Eggs" (detail) (Velázquez)		1·60	1·75
1719	500 c.	"The Surrender of Breda" (detail) (Velázquez)		1·75	1·90
1720	700 c.	"The Surrender of Breda" (different detail) (Velázquez)		2·00	2·50
1713/20		*Set of 8*		7·00	7·50

MS1721 Two sheets. (a) 95×120 mm. 900 c. "The Waterseller of Seville" (Velázquez) (86×111 mm). (b) 120×95 mm. 900 c. "They still Say that Fish is Expensive" (Joaquín Sorolla y Bastida) (111×86 mm). Imperf . . *Set of 2 sheets* 7·50 8·50

(Des L. Nelson. Litho Walsall)

1992 (25 May). *"Genova '92" International Thematic Stamp Exhibition. Butterflies. T 482 and similar vert designs. Multicoloured.* P 14.

1722	20 c.	Type 482		50	30
1723	60 c.	*Papilio dardanus*		80	45
1724	80 c.	*Cynthia cardui*		90	60
1725	100 c.	*Meneris tulbaghia*		1·00	75
1726	200 c.	*Salamis temora*		1·50	1·60
1727	400 c.	*Charaxes jasius*		2·00	2·50
1728	500 c.	*Precis oenone*		2·25	2·50
1729	700 c.	*Precis sophia*		2·50	2·75
1722/9		*Set of 8*		10·00	10·00

MS1730 Two sheets, each 100×70 mm. (a) 900 c. *Papilio demodocus.* (b) 900 c. *Precis octavia*
Set of 2 sheets 7·50 8·50

Examples of Nos. 1722/30 overprinted "40th Anniversary of the Accession of HM Queen Elizabeth II 1952–1992" in silver are reported as not having been issued in Ghana.

(Litho Walsall)

1992 (1 June). *Prehistoric Animals. Vert designs as T 290 of Antigua. Multicoloured.* P 14.

1731	20 c.	Iguanodon		35	25
1732	50 c.	Anchisaurus		50	35
1733	60 c.	Heterodontosaurus		55	35
1734	80 c.	Ouranosaurus		60	45
1735	100 c.	Anatosaurus		75	55
1736	200 c.	Elaphrosaurus		1·25	1·50
1737	500 c.	Coelophysis		2·25	2·75
1738	600 c.	Rhamphorynchus		2·50	3·00
1731/8		*Set of 8*		8·00	8·25

MS1739 Two sheets, each 100×70 mm. (a) 1500 c. As 200 c. (b) 1500 c. As 500 c.
Set of 2 sheets 9·00 10·00

483 Martin Pinzon and *Pinta*

484 Olive-grey Ancilla (*Agaronia hiatula*)

(Des J.-L. Puvilland. Litho Questa)

1992 (20 July). *World Columbian Stamp "Expo '92", Chicago. 500th Anniv of Discovery of America by Columbus. T 483 and similar vert designs. Multicoloured.* P 14.

1740	200 c.	Type 483		90	1·00
	a.	Sheetlet. Nos. 1740/7		6·50	
1741	200 c.	Vincente Pinzon and *Nina*		90	1·00
1742	200 c.	Columbus and Father Marchena at La Rabida		90	1·00

1743	200 c.	Columbus in his cabin		90	1·00
1744	200 c.	Fleet sights land		90	1·00
1745	200 c.	Columbus on Samana Cay		90	1·00
1746	200 c.	Wreck of *Santa Maria*		90	1·00
1747	200 c.	Amerindians at Spanish Court		90	1·00
1740/7		*Set of 8*		6·50	7·00

MS1748 122×86 mm. 500 c. Columbus and *Santa Maria* . . 2·75 3·50
Nos. 1740/7 were printed together, *se-tenant*, in sheetlets of 8.

(Litho Questa)

1992 (30 Sept–5 Oct). *Shells. T 484 and similar vert designs. Multicoloured.* P 14.

1749	20 c.	Type 484		20	20
1750	20 c.	Radula Cerith (*Tympanotonus fuscatus radula*) (5 Oct)		20	20
1751	60 c.	Rugose Donax (*Donax rugosus*)		30	30
1752	60 c.	Horned Murex (*Murex cornutus*) (5 Oct)		30	30
1753	80 c.	Concave Ear Moon (*Sinum concavum*)		40	40
1754	80 c.	Triple Tivella (*Tivella tripla*) (5 Oct)		40	40
1755	200 c.	*Pila africana*		90	1·00
1756	200 c.	Rat Cowrie (*Cypraea stercoraria*) (5 Oct)		90	1·00
1757	350 c.	*Thais hiatula*		1·60	1·90
1758	350 c.	West African Helmet (*Cassis tessellata*) (5 Oct)		1·60	1·90
1749/58		*Set of 10*		6·00	7·00

MS1759 Two sheets, each 87×117 mm. (a) 600 c. Fanel Moon (*Natica fanel*). (b) 600 c. Giant Hairy Melongena (*Pugilina moria*) . . *Set of 2 sheets* 6·00 7·00

485 "Presentation in the Temple" (Master of the Braunschweiti)

486 *Calappa rubroguttata*

(Litho Questa)

1992 (16 Dec). *Christmas. Religious Paintings. T 485 and similar vert designs. Multicoloured.* P 13½×14.

1760	20 c.	Type 485		25	20
1761	50 c.	"Presentation in the Temple" (detail) (Master of St. Severin)		35	30
1762	60 c.	"The Visitation" (Sebastiano del Piombo)		35	30
1763	80 c.	"The Visitation" (detail) (Giotto)		45	40
1764	100 c.	"The Circumcision" (detail) (Studio of Bellini)		55	50
1765	200 c.	"The Circumcision" (Studio of Garofalo)		1·10	1·10
1766	500 c.	"The Visitation" (Studio of Van der Weyden)		1·90	2·25
1767	800 c.	"The Visitation" (detail) (Studio of Van der Weyden)		2·40	3·00
1760/7		*Set of 8*		6·50	7·25

MS1768 Two sheets, each 77×102 mm. (a) 900 c. "Presentation in the Temple" (Bartolo di Fredi). (b) 900 c. "The Visitation" (larger detail) (Giotto) . . *Set of 2 sheets* 7·00 8·00

(Litho Francoise-Charles, Oberthur)

1993 (15 Feb). *Crabs. T 486 and similar horiz designs. Multicoloured.* P 13½×14.

1769	20 c.	Type 486		40	20
1770	60 c.	*Cardisoma amatum*		70	25
1771	80 c.	*Maia squinado*		80	30
1772	400 c.	*Ocypoda cursor*		1·40	1·75
1773	800 c.	*Grapus grapus*		2·25	3·00
1769/73		*Set of 5*		5·00	5·00

MS1774 127×97 mm. Nos. 1769/72 . . 4·00 4·50

487 *Clerodendrum thomsoniae*

488 Zeppelin LZ-3 entering Floating Hangar, Lake Constance

(Litho Questa)

1993 (1 Mar). *Flowers. T 487 and similar vert designs. Multicoloured.* P 14.

1775	20 c.	Type 487		20	15
1776	20 c.	*Lagerstroemia flos-reginae*		20	15
1777	60 c.	*Cassia fistula*		35	25

1778	60 c.	*Spathodea campanulata*		35	25
1779	80 c.	*Hildegardia barteri*		40	25
1780	80 c.	*Mellitea ferrugenea*		40	25
1781	200 c.	*Petrea volubilis*		60	85
1782	200 c.	*Ipomoea asarifolia*		60	85
1783	350 c.	*Bryphyllum pinnatum*		90	1·25
1784	350 c.	*Ritchiea reflexa*		90	1·25
1775/84		*Set of 10*		4·50	5·00

MS1785 Two sheets, each 86×125 mm. (a) 50 c. As No. 1777; 100 c. As No. 1783; 150 c. As No. 1782; 300 c. As No. 1779. (b) 50 c. As No. 1778; 100 c. As No. 1776; 150 c. As No. 1780; 300 c. As No. 1784 . . *Set of 2 sheets* 4·50 5·00

(Des W. Wright and W. Hanson (Nos. 1786, 1792, **MS**1793a). W. Wright and L. Fried (Nos. 1787, 1791, **MS**1793b). J. Genzo (Nos. 1790, **MS**1793d). W. Wright (others). Litho B.D.T.)

1993 (8 Mar). *Anniversaries and Events. T 488 and similar multicoloured designs.* P 14.

1786	20 c.	Type 488		60	30
1787	100 c.	Launch of European "Ariane 4" rocket (vert)		1·00	75
1788	200 c.	Leopard		1·75	1·75
1789	300 c.	Colosseum and fruit		1·90	2·00
1790	400 c.	Mozart (vert)		2·50	2·50
1791	600 c.	Launch of Japanese "H-1" rocket (vert)		2·75	3·25
1792	800 c	Zeppelin LZ-10 *Schwaben*		3·00	3·50
1786/92		*Set of 7*		12·00	12·50

MS1793 Four sheets. (a) 106×76 mm. 900 c. Count Ferdinand von Zeppelin (vert). (b) 76×106 mm. 900 c. Launch of American space shuttle (vert). (c) 106×76 mm. 900 c. Bongo. (d) 99×69 mm. 900 c. Cherubino from *The Marriage of Figaro* (vert) . . *Set of 4 sheets* 14·00 15·00
Anniversaries and Events:—Nos. 1786, 1792, **MS**1793a, 75th death anniv of Count Ferdinand von Zeppelin; Nos. 1787, 1791, **MS**1793b, International Space Year; Nos. 1788, **MS**1793c, Earth Summit '92, Rio; No. 1789, International Conference on Nutrition, Rome; Nos. 1790, **MS**1793d, Death bicent of Mozart.

(Litho Walsall)

1993 (8 Mar). *Bicentenary of the Louvre, Paris. Multicoloured designs as T 305 of Antigua.* P 12.

1794	200 c.	"Carnival Minuet" (left detail) (Giovanni Domenico Tiepolo)		85	1·00
	a.	Sheetlet. Nos. 1794/1801		6·25	
1795	200 c.	"Carnival Minuet" (centre detail) (Giovanni Domenico Tiepolo)		85	1·00
1796	200 c.	"Carnival Minuet" (right detail) (Giovanni Domenico Tiepolo)		85	1·00
1797	200 c.	"The Tooth Puller" (left detail) (Giovanni Domenico Tiepolo)		85	1·00
1798	200 c.	"The Tooth Puller" (right detail) (Giovanni Domenico Tiepolo)		85	1·00
1799	200 c.	"Rebecca at the Well" (Giovanni Battista Tiepolo)		85	1·00
1800	200 c.	"Presenting Christ to the People" (left detail) (Giovanni Battista Tiepolo)		85	1·00
1801	200 c.	"Presenting Christ to the People" (right detail) (Giovanni Battista Tiepolo)		85	1·00
1794/1801		*Set of 8*		6·25	7·25

MS1802 100×70 mm. 700 c. "Chancellor Seguier" (Charles le Brun) (85×52 mm). P 14½ 2·10 2·40
Nos. 1794/1801 were printed together, *se-tenant*, in sheetlets of 8 stamps and one centre label.

489 Energy Foods

(Litho Questa)

1993 (22 Mar). *International Conference on Nutrition, Rome. T 489 and similar horiz designs. Multicoloured.* P 14.

1803	20 c.	Type 489		20	15
1804	60 c.	Body-building foods		30	20
1805	80 c.	Protective foods		35	25
1806	200 c.	Disease prevention equipment		80	1·00
1807	400 c.	Quality control and preservation of fish products		1·50	2·00
1803/7		*Set of 5*		2·75	3·25

490 Kwame Nkrumah Mausoleum

491 Resurrection Egg

(Litho Questa)

1993 (8 Apr). *Proclamation of Fourth Republic. T **490** and similar multicoloured designs. P 14.*

1808	50 c. Type **490**		20	15
1809	100 c. Kwame Nkrumah Conference Centre		35	25
1810	200 c. Book of Constitution (*vert*)		80	80
1811	350 c. Independence Square (*vert*)		1·60	2·00
1812	400 c. Christiansborg Castle (*vert*)		1·75	2·00
1808/12		Set of 5	4·25	4·75

(Des Kerri Schiff. Litho Questa)

1993 (26 Apr). *Easter. Faberge Eggs. T **491** and similar multicoloured designs. P 14.*

1813	50 c. Type **491**		40	15
1814	80 c. Imperial Red Cross egg with Resurrection triptych		65	25
1815	100 c. Imperial Uspensky Cathedral egg		75	25
1816	150 c. Imperial Red Cross egg with portraits		1·10	65
1817	200 c. Orange Tree egg		1·25	1·25
1818	250 c. Rabbit egg		1·25	1·50
1819	400 c. Imperial Coronation egg		2·00	2·50
1820	900 c. Silver-gilt enamel Easter egg		3·25	5·00
1813/20		Set of 8	9·50	10·50

MS1821 Two sheets, each (a) 73×100 mm. 1000 c. Renaissance egg. (b) 100×73 mm. 1000 c. Egg charms (*horiz*) ... Set of 2 sheets 8·00 9·00

(Des W. Wright. Litho Questa)

1993 (3 May). *Centenary of Henry Ford's First Petrol Engine (Nos. 1823/4, **MS1826b**) and Karl Benz's First Four-wheeled Car (others). Horiz designs as T **264** of Dominica. Multicoloured. P 14.*

1822	150 c. Mercedes Benz "300 SLR", Mille Miglia, 1955		75	50
1823	400 c. Ford "Depot Wagon", 1920		1·75	1·75
1824	600 c. Ford "Mach 1 Mustang", 1970		2·25	2·75
1825	800 c. Mercedes Benz racing car, Monaco Grand Prix, 1937		3·50	4·50
1822/5		Set of 4	7·50	8·50

MS1826 Two sheets, each 110×80 mm. (a) 1000 c. Mercedes Benz "Type 196" racing car, 1955 (85½×28½ mm). (b) 1000 c. Ford "Super T", 1910 (85½×28½ mm) ... Set of 2 sheets 7·75 8·25

(Des W. Wright. Litho Questa)

1993 (3 May). *Aviation Anniversaries. Multicoloured designs as T **266** of Dominica. P 14.*

1827	50 c. LZ-127 *Graf Zeppelin* over Alps (*vert*)		50	30
1828	150 c. Zeppelin LZ-7 *Deutschland*		85	55
1829	400 c. Avro Vulcan jet bomber		1·75	1·75
1830	400 c. U.S. Mail Ford 4-AT Trimotor		1·75	1·75
1831	600 c. Nieuport 27 (*vert*)		2·25	2·25
1832	600 c. Loading mail on LZ-127 *Graf Zeppelin*		2·25	2·25
1833	800 c. Zeppelin LZ-10 *Schwaben*		3·50	4·00
1827/33		Set of 7	11·50	11·50

MS1834 Three sheets, each 111×80 mm. (a) 1000 c. LZ-127 *Graf Zeppelin*. (b) 1000 c. S.E.5A, 1918. (c) 1000 c. Early airmail flight by Walter Edwards between Portland and Vancouver (57×42½ mm) ... Set of 3 sheets 11·50 12·00
Anniversaries:—Nos. 1827/8, 1833, **MS1834a**, 125th birth anniv of Hugo Eckener (airship commander); Nos. 1829, 1831, **MS1834b**, 75th anniv of Royal Air Force; Nos. 1830, 1832, **MS1834c**, Bicentenary of First Airmail Flight.

492 African Buffalo

40TH ANNIVERSARY
OF CORONATION
H.M. ELIZABETH II
(493)

(Des T. Muse. Litho Questa)

1993 (24 May). *Wild Animals. T **492** and similar horiz designs. Multicoloured. P 14.*

1835	20 c. Type **492**		25	15
1836	50 c. Giant Forest Hog		30	20
1837	60 c. Potto		40	25
1838	80 c. Bay Duiker		50	30
1839	100 c. Royal Antelope		60	35
1840	200 c. Serval		90	90
1841	500 c. Golden Cat		1·75	2·00
1842	800 c. *Megaloglossus woermanni* (bat)		3·00	3·50
1835/42		Set of 8	7·00	7·00

MS1843 Two sheets, each 68×98 mm. (a) 900 c. Dormouse. (b) 900 c. White-collared Mangabey ... Set of 2 sheets 7·00 7·50

1993 (18 June). *40th Anniv of Coronation. Nos. 1549/53 optd with T **493**.*

1844	100 c. multicoloured		60	25
1845	200 c. multicoloured		1·00	70
1846	500 c. multicoloured		2·75	3·00
1847	600 c. multicoloured		3·00	3·25
1844/7		Set of 4	6·50	6·50

MS1848 Two sheets. (a) 104×75 mm. 800 c. mult. (b) 74×105 mm. 800 c. mult Set of 2 sheets 7·50 8·00
The sheets of No. **MS1848** also carry a commemorative overprint on the margin.

---

35 YEARS OF
ROTARY INTERNATIONAL
GHANA 1958
(494)

✚ GHANA
RED CROSS SOCIETY
FOUNDED 1932
(495)

1993 (18 June). *35th Anniv of Rotary International and 60th Anniv of Ghana Red Cross Society (1992). Nos. 1562 and 1564/7 optd with T **494** (Nos. 1849, 1852, **MS1853a**) or T **495** (others).*

1849	100 c. Stonehead		60	30
1850	300 c. Aba (R.)		1·75	1·75
1851	400 c. Jewel Cichlid (R.)		2·00	2·00
1852	500 c. Smooth Hammerhead		2·25	2·50
1849/52		Set of 4	6·00	6·00

MS1853 Two sheets, each 108×81 mm. (a) 800 c Bayad. (b) 800 c. Eastern Flying Gurnard (R.) ... Set of 2 sheets 7·50 8·00
The sheets of No. **MS1853** also carry a commemorative overprint on the margin.

496 *Cantharellus cibarius*

497 "The Actor"
(Picasso)

(Des L. Nelson (Nos. 1861/2, 1866/8), E. Mensah (others). Litho Questa)

1993 (30 July). *Mushrooms. T **496** and similar vert designs. Multicoloured. P 14.*

1854	20 c. Type **496**		40	25
1855	50 c. *Russula cyanoxantha*		50	30
1856	60 c. *Clitocybe rivulosa*		55	30
1857	80 c. *Cortinarius elatior*		60	35
1858	80 c. *Mycena galericulata*		60	35
1859	200 c. *Tricholoma gambosum*		1·00	1·00
1860	200 c. *Boletus edulis*		1·00	1·00
1861	200 c. *Lepista saeva*		1·00	1·00
1862	250 c. *Gyroporus castaneus*		1·10	1·10
1863	300 c. *Boletus chrysenteron*		1·25	1·25
1864	350 c. *Nolanea sericea*		1·40	1·40
1865	350 c. *Hygrophorus punicea* ("*Hygrophorus puiceus*")		1·40	1·40
1866	500 c. *Gomphidius glutinosus*		1·60	1·75
1867	600 c. *Russula olivacea*		1·75	2·00
1868	1000 c. *Russula aurata*		2·25	2·75
1854/68		Set of 15	14·50	14·50

MS1869 Two sheets, each 85×130 mm. (a) 50 c. As No. 1856; 100 c. As No. 1858; 150 c. As No. 1860; 1000 c. As No. 1864. (b) 100 c. As Type **496**; 150 c. As No. 1857; 300 c. As No. 1859; 600 c. As No. 1865 ... Set of 2 sheets 9·50 11·00

(Litho Cartor (Nos. 1871, 1873, **MS1877c/d**), Questa (others))

1993 (19 Oct). *Anniversaries and Events. T **497** and similar multicoloured designs. P 13½×14 (Nos. 1871, 1873) or 14 (others).*

1870	20 c. Type **497**		40	20
1871	20 c. Early astronomical equipment		40	20
1872	80 c. "Portrait of Allan Stein" (Picasso)		50	30
1873	200 c. Modern telescope		90	1·00
1874	200 c. "Tattoo" (Lesek Sobocki)		90	1·00
1875	600 c. "Prison" (Sasza Blonder)		2·25	3·00
1876	800 c. "Seated Male Nude" (Picasso)		3·00	3·50
1870/6		Set of 7	7·50	8·25

MS1877 Four sheets. (a) 75×105 mm. 900 c. "Guernica" (Picasso). P 14. (b) 75×105 mm. 1000 c. "Bajika o Czlowieku Szczesliwym" (detail) (Antoni Mickalak) (*horiz*). P 14. (c) 105×75 mm. 1000 c. Copernicus (face value at top left). P 12×13. (d) 105×75 mm. 1000 c. Copernicus (face value at centre top). P 12×13 ... Set of 4 sheets 14·00 15·00
Anniversaries and Events:—Nos. 1870, 1872, 1876, **MS1877a**, 20th death anniv of Picasso (artist); Nos. 1871, 1873, **MS1877c/d**, 450th death anniv of Copernicus (astronomer); Nos. 1874/5, **MS1877b**, "Polska '93" International Stamp Exhibition, Poznań.

498 Abedi Pele
(Ghana)

499 Common Turkey

(Litho Questa)

1993 (1 Dec). *World Cup Football Championship, U.S.A. (1st issue). T **498** and similar vert designs. Multicoloured. P 13×14.*

1878	50 c. Type **498**		60	35
1879	80 c. Pedro Troglio (Argentina)		70	40
1880	100 c. Fernando Alvez (Uruguay)		80	40
1881	200 c. Franco Baresi (Italy)		1·50	1·25
1882	250 c. Gomez (Colombia) and Katanec (Yugoslavia)		1·50	1·50
1883	600 c. Diego Maradona (Argentina)		3·00	3·25
1884	800 c. Hasek (Czechoslovakia) and Wynalda (U.S.A.)		3·50	3·75
1885	1000 c. Lothar Matthaeus (Germany)		3·75	4·50
1878/85		Set of 8	14·00	14·00

MS1886 Two sheets, each 70×100 mm. (a) 1200 c. Rabie Yassein (Egypt) and Ruud Gullit (Netherlands). (b) 1200 c. Giuseppe Giannini (Italy). P 13 ... Set of 2 sheets 12·00 13·00
See also Nos. 2037/43.

(Litho Questa)

1993 (8 Dec). *Domestic Animals. T **499** and similar horiz designs. Multicoloured. P 14.*

1887	50 c. Type **499**		50	25
1888	100 c. Goats		70	40
1889	150 c. Muscovy Ducks		1·00	75
1890	200 c. Donkeys		1·25	1·00
1891	250 c. Red Junglefowl cock		1·25	1·25
1892	300 c. Pigs		1·40	1·40
1893	400 c. Helmet Guineafowl		1·75	1·75
1894	600 c. Dog		2·50	2·75
1895	800 c. Red Junglefowl hen		3·00	3·50
1896	1000 c. Sheep		3·50	4·00
1887/96		Set of 10	15·00	15·00

MS1897 Two sheets, each 133×106 mm. (a) 100 c. As No. 1888; 250 c. No. 1894; 350 c. No. 1892; 500 c. No. 1896. (b) 100 c. No. 1893; 250 c. As No. 1891; 350 c. No. 1895; 500 c. Type **499** ... Set of 2 sheets 11·00 12·00

(Litho Questa)

1993 (20 Dec). *Christmas. Religious Paintings. Designs as T **270** of Dominica. Black, pale lemon and red (Nos. 1898, 1900/1, 1905 and **MS1906a**) or multicoloured (others). P 13½×14.*

1898	50 c. "Adoration of the Magi" (Dürer)		50	20
1899	100 c. "The Virgin and Child with St. John and an Angel" (Botticelli)		70	25
1900	150 c. "Mary as Queen of Heaven" (Dürer)		90	45
1901	200 c. "Saint Anne" (Dürer)		1·00	65
1902	250 c. "The Madonna of the Magnificat" (Botticelli)		1·10	75
1903	400 c. "The Madonna of the Goldfinch" (Botticelli)		1·75	2·00
1904	600 c. "The Virgin and Child with the young St. John the Baptist" (Botticelli)		2·25	3·00
1905	1000 c. "Adoration of the Shepherds" (Dürer)		3·00	5·00
1898/1905		Set of 8	10·00	11·00

MS1906 Two sheets, each 102×128 mm. (a) 1000 c. "Madonna in a Circle" (detail) (Dürer). P 13½×14. (b) 1000 c. "Mystic Nativity" (detail) (Botticelli) (*horiz*). P 14×13½ ... Set of 2 sheets 8·50 10·00

500 Doll

501 Mickey Mouse in *Steamboat Willie*, 1928

(Des E. Mensah. Litho Questa)

1994 (24 Jan). *Traditional Crafts. T **500** and similar vert designs. Multicoloured. P 14.*

1907	50 c. Type **500**		30	20
1908	50 c. Pot with "head" lid		30	20
1909	200 c. Bead necklace		70	70
1910	200 c. Snake charmers (statuette)		70	70
1911	250 c. Hoe		70	70
1912	250 c. Scabbard		70	70
1913	600 c. Pipe		1·75	2·00
1914	600 c. Deer (carving)		1·75	2·00
1915	1000 c. Mask		2·50	3·00
1916	1000 c. Doll (*different*)		2·50	3·00
1907/16		Set of 10	10·50	12·00

MS1917 Two sheets, each 95×128 mm. (a) 100 c. As Type **500**; 250 c. As No. 1909; 350 c. As No. 1911; 500 c. No. 1913. (b) 100 c. As No. 1908; 250 c. As No. 1910; 350 c. As No. 1912; 500 c. As No. 1914 ... Set of 2 sheets 5·00 6·50

(Des W. Hanson. Litho Questa)

1994 (18 Feb). *"Hong Kong '94" International Stamp Exhibition (1st issue). Horiz designs as T **317** of Antigua. Multicoloured. P 14.*

1918	200 c. Hong Kong 1986 50 c. "Expo '86" stamp and tram		90	1·00
	a. Horiz pair. Nos. 1918/19		1·75	2·00
1919	200 c. Ghana 1992 20 c. Railways stamp and tram		90	1·00

Nos. 1918/19 were printed together, *se-tenant*, in horizontal pairs throughout the sheet with the centre part of each pair forming the complete design.

(Des Kerri Schiff. Litho Questa)

1994 (18 Feb). *"Hong Kong '94" International Stamp Exhibition (2nd issue). Imperial Palace Clocks. Designs as T* **318** *of Antigua, but vert. Multicoloured.* P 14.

1920	100 c. Windmill clock	70	80
	a. Sheetlet. Nos. 1920/5	3·75	
1921	100 c. Horse clock	70	80
1922	100 c. Balloon clock	70	80
1923	100 c. Zodiac clock	70	80
1924	100 c. Shar-pei Dog clock	70	80
1925	100 c. Cat clock	70	80
1920/5	*Set of 6*	3·75	4·25

Nos. 1920/5 were printed together, *se-tenant*, in sheetlets of 6.

(Litho Questa)

1994 (1 Mar). *65th Anniv of Mickey Mouse (Walt Disney cartoon character) (1993). T* **501** *and similar vert designs showing scenes from various cartoon films.* P 13½×14.

1926	50 c. Type **501**	30	15
1927	100 c. *The Band Concert*, 1935	40	20
1928	150 c. *Moose Hunters*, 1937	55	35
1929	200 c. *Brave Little Tailor*, 1938	65	50
1930	250 c. *Fantasia*, 1940	70	60
1931	400 c. *The Nifty Nineties*, 1941	1·50	1·75
1932	600 c. *Canine Caddy*, 1941	1·75	2·00
1933	1000 c. *Mickey's Christmas Carol*, 1983	2·50	3·00
1926/33	*Set of 8*	7·50	7·75

MS1934 Two sheets, each 127×102 mm. (a) 1200 c. *Mickey's Elephant*, 1936. (b) 1200 c. *Mickey's Amateurs*, 1937 ... *Set of 2 sheets* 7·00 7·50
No. 1929 is inscribed "TAYLOR" in error. The dates on Nos. 1927 and 1932 are incorrectly shown as "1937" and "1944".

(Litho Questa)

1994 (6 Apr). *Easter. Hummel Figurines. Vert designs as T* **302** *of Antigua. Multicoloured.* P 14.

1935	50 c. Boy hiker	30	15
1936	100 c. Girl with basket behind back	40	20
1937	150 c. Boy with rabbits	55	35
1938	200 c. Boy holding basket	65	60
1939	250 c. Girl with chicks	70	60
1940	400 c. Girl with lamb	1·50	1·75
1941	600 c. Girl waving red handkerchief with lamb	1·75	2·00
1942	1000 c. Girl with basket and posy	2·50	3·00
1935/42	*Set of 8*	7·50	7·75

MS1943 Two sheets, each 93×126 mm. (a) 50 c. As No. 1935; 150 c. As No. 1942; 500 c. As No. 1936; 1200 c. As No. 1938. (b) 200 c. As No. 1940; 300 c. As No. 1939; 500 c. As No. 1941; 1000 c. As No. 1937 ... *Set of 2 sheets* 7·50 8·00

502 Diana Monkey with Young

503 Norwegian Forest Cat

(Des S. Barlowe. Litho Questa)

1994 (16 May). *Wildlife. T* **502** *and similar multicoloured designs.* P 14.

1944	50 c. Type **502**	40	15
	a. Horiz strip of 4. Nos. 1944 and 1947/9	3·75	
1945	100 c. Bushbuck (*horiz*)	40	20
1946	150 c. Spotted Hyena (*horiz*)	55	35
1947	200 c. Diana Monkey on branch facing left	75	50
1948	500 c. Diana Monkey on branch facing right	1·25	1·50
1949	800 c. Head of Diana Monkey	1·75	2·00
1950	1000 c. Aardvark (*horiz*)	2·00	2·50
1944/50	*Set of 7*	6·25	6·50

MS1951 Two sheets, each 106×76 mm. (a) 2000 c. Leopard. (b) 2000 c. Waterbuck ... *Set of 2 sheets* 9·00 10·00
In addition to normal sheets of each value Nos. 1944 and 1947/9 were also available in sheets of 12 with the stamps available both vertically and horizontally *se-tenant*. Designs of Nos. 1944 and 1947/9 include the W.W.F. Panda emblem.

(Des Jennifer Toombs. Litho Questa)

1994 (6 June). *Cats. T* **503** *and similar horiz designs. Multicoloured.* P 14.

1952	200 c. Type **503**	50	50
	a. Sheetlet. Nos. 1952/63	5·50	
1953	200 c. Blue Longhair	50	50
1954	200 c. Red Self Longhair	50	50
1955	200 c. Black Longhair	50	50
1956	200 c. Chinchilla	50	50
1957	200 c. Dilute Calico Longhair	50	50
1958	200 c. Blue Tabby and White Longhair	50	50
1959	200 c. Ruby Somali	50	50
1960	200 c. Blue Smoke Longhair	50	50
1961	200 c. Calico Longhair	50	50

1962	200 c. Brown Tabby Longhair	50	50
1963	200 c. Balinese	50	50
1964	200 c. Sorrel Abyssinian	50	50
	a. Sheetlet. Nos. 1964/75	5·50	
1965	200 c. Silver Classic Tabby	50	50
1966	200 c. Chocolate-point Siamese	50	50
1967	200 c. Brown Tortie Burmese	50	50
1968	200 c. Exotic Shorthair	50	50
1969	200 c. Havana Brown	50	50
1970	200 c. Devon Rex	50	50
1971	200 c. Black Manx	50	50
1972	200 c. British Blue Shorthair	50	50
1973	200 c. Calico American Wirehair	50	50
1974	200 c. Spotted Oriental Siamese	50	50
1975	200 c. Red Classic Tabby	50	50
1952/75	*Set of 24*	11·00	11·00

MS1976 Two sheets, each 102×89 mm. (a) 2000 c. Brown Mackerel Tabby Scottish Fold. (b) 2000 c. Seal-point Colourpoint ... *Set of 2 sheets* 8·50 9·00
Nos. 1952/63 and 1964/75 were printed together, *se-tenant*, in sheetlets of 12.
No. 1957 is inscribed "Dilut" in error.

504 Red-bellied Paradise Flycatcher

(Des Mary Walters. Litho Questa)

1994 (13 June). *Birds. T* **504** *and similar horiz designs. Multicoloured.* P 14.

1977	200 c. Type **504**	55	55
	a. Sheetlet. Nos. 1977/88	6·00	
1978	200 c. Many-coloured Bush Shrike	55	55
1979	200 c. Broad-tailed Paradise Whydah	55	55
1980	200 c. White-crowned Robin Chat	55	55
1981	200 c. Violet Turaco ("Violet Plantain-eater")	55	55
1982	200 c. Village Weaver	55	55
1983	200 c. Red-crowned Bishop	55	55
1984	200 c. Common Shoveler	55	55
1985	200 c. Spur-winged Goose	55	55
1986	200 c. African Crake	55	55
1987	200 c. Purple Swamphen ("King Reed-hen")	55	55
1988	200 c. African Tiger Bittern	55	55
1989	200 c. Oriole Warbler ("Moho")	55	55
	a. Sheetlet. Nos. 1989/2000	6·00	
1990	200 c. Superb Sunbird	55	55
1991	200 c. Blue-breasted Kingfisher	55	55
1992	200 c. African Blue Cuckoo Shrike	55	55
1993	200 c. Great Blue Turaco ("Blue Plantain-eater")	55	55
1994	200 c. Greater Flamingo	55	55
1995	200 c. African Jacana ("Lily-trotter")	55	55
1996	200 c. Black-crowned Night Heron	55	55
1997	200 c. Black-winged Stilt	55	55
1998	200 c. White-spotted Crake	55	55
1999	200 c. African Pygmy Goose	55	55
2000	200 c. African Pitta	55	55
1977/2000	*Set of 24*	12·00	12·00

MS2001 Two sheets, each 113×83 mm. (a) 2000 c. African Spoonbill. (b) 2000 c. Goliath Heron ... *Set of 2 sheets* 8·50 9·50
Nos. 1977/88 and 1989/2000 were printed together, *se-tenant*, in sheetlets of 12.

505 Women at Stand-pipe

(Litho Questa)

1994 (11 July). *First Anniversary of Fourth Republic. T* **505** *and similar horiz designs. Multicoloured.* P 14.

2002	50 c. Type **505**	25	15
2003	100 c. Presenting certificate to farmers	35	20
2004	200 c. Village electricity supply	50	35
2005	600 c. Bridge	1·25	1·75
2006	800 c. National Theatre	1·50	2·00
2007	1000 c. Lighting Perpetual Flame	1·75	2·25
2002/7	*Set of 6*	5·00	6·00

(Des W. Hanson. Litho B.D.T.)

1994 (20 July). *25th Anniv of First Moon Landing. Horiz designs as T* **326** *of Antigua showing scientists. Multicoloured.* P 14.

2008	300 c. Sigmund Jahn	90	1·00
	a. Sheetlet. Nos. 2008/16	7·00	
2009	300 c. Ulf Merbold	90	1·00
2010	300 c. Hans Wilhelm Schegal	90	1·00
2011	300 c. Ulrich Walter	90	1·00
2012	300 c. Reinhard Furrer	90	1·00
2013	300 c. Ernst Messerschmid	90	1·00
2014	300 c. Mamoru Mohri	90	1·00
2015	300 c. Klaus-Dietrich Flade	90	1·00
2016	300 c. Chaiki Naito-Mukai	90	1·00
2008/16	*Set of 9*	7·00	8·00

MS2017 130×118 mm. 2000 c. Poster for *Frau im Mond* (film) by Fritz Lang ... 5·00 5·50
Nos. 2008/16 were printed together, *se-tenant*, in sheetlets of 9.

(Des Kerri Schiff. Litho B.D.T.)

1994 (20 July). *Centenary of International Olympic Committee. Gold Medal Winners. Designs as T* **327** *of Antigua, but vert. Multicoloured.* P 14.

2018	300 c. Dieter Modenburg (Germany) (high jump), 1984	60	65
2019	400 c. Ruth Fuchs (Germany) (javelin), 1972 and 1976	80	85

MS2020 77×106 mm. 1500 c. Jans Weissflog (Germany) (ski jump), 1994 ... 3·75 4·00

(Des J. Batchelor. Litho B.D.T.)

1994 (20 July). *50th Anniv of D-Day. Horiz designs as T* **331** *of Antigua. Multicoloured.* P 14.

2021	60 c. H.M.S. *Roberts* (monitor)	80	60
2022	100 c. H.M.S. *Warspite* (battleship)	1·10	90
2023	200 c. U.S.S. *Augusta* (cruiser)	1·75	2·00
2021/3	*Set of 3*	3·25	3·25

MS2024 107×76 mm. 1500 c. U.S.S. *Nevada* (battleship) firing salvo ... 4·50 4·75

(Des Kerri Schiff. Litho Questa (Nos. 2027/34), B.D.T. (others))

1994 (20 July). *"Philakorea '94" International Stamp Exhibition, Seoul. Multicoloured designs as T* **279** *of Dominica.* P 14 (*Nos.* 2025/6, 2035) *or* 13 (*others*).

2025	20 c. Ch'unghak-dong village elder in traditional costume (24½×38 *mm*)	15	15
2026	150 c. Stone Pagoda, Punhwangsa (24½×38 *mm*)	40	40
2027	250 c. Character with eggs	45	50
	a. Sheetlet. Nos. 2027/34	3·25	
2028	250 c. Character with pair of birds on house	45	50
2029	250 c. Character with cock	45	50
2030	250 c. Character with dragon and pagoda	45	50
2031	250 c. Character with orange flowers	45	50
2032	250 c. Character with parrot and pagoda	45	50
2033	250 c. Character with plant	45	50
2034	250 c. Character with fish	45	50
2035	300 c. Traditional country house, Andong (24½×34 *mm*)	50	55
2025/35	*Set of 11*	4·25	4·50

MS2036 100×70 mm. 1500 c. Temple judges deliberating (42½×28½ *mm*). P 14 ... 3·50 4·00
Nos. 2027/34 were printed together, *se-tenant*, in sheetlets of 8 and show illuminated Korean characters.

506 Dennis Bergkamp (Netherlands)

(Litho Questa)

1994 (22 July). *World Cup Football Championship, U.S.A. (2nd issue). T* **506** *and similar multicoloured designs.* P 14.

2037	200 c. Type **506**	50	60
	a. Sheetlet. Nos. 2037/42	2·75	
2038	200 c. Lothar Matthaus (Germany)	50	60
2039	200 c. Giuseppe Signori (Italy)	50	60
2040	200 c. Carlos Valderama (Colombia)	50	60
2041	200 c. Jorge Campos (Mexico)	50	60
2042	200 c. Tony Meola (U.S.A.)	50	60
2037/42	*Set of 6*	2·75	3·25

MS2043 Two sheets, each 100×70 mm. (a) 1200 c. Giants' Stadium, New Jersey (*vert*). (b) 1200 c. Citrus Bowl, Orlando (*vert*) ... *Set of 2 sheets* 5·00 6·00
Nos. 2037/42 were printed together, *se-tenant*, in sheetlets of 6.

507 Common ("Crowned") Duiker

508 Northern Region Dancer

(Des E. Mensah. Litho Questa)

1994 (1 Sept). *Duikers (Antelopes). T* **507** *and similar horiz designs. Multicoloured.* P 14.

2044	50 c. Type **507**	30	15
2045	100 c. Red-flanked Duiker	40	25
2046	200 c. Yellow-backed Duiker	60	40
2047	400 c. Ogilby's Duiker	1·00	1·25
2048	600 c. Bay Duiker	1·25	1·75
2049	800 c. Jentink's Duiker	1·50	2·00
2044/9	*Set of 6*	4·50	5·25

MS2050 Two sheets, each 106×76 mm. (a) 2000 c. Red Forest Duiker. (b) 2000 c. Black Duiker ... *Set of 2 sheets* 8·00 8·50

(Litho Questa)

1994 (5 Dec). *Christmas. Religious Paintings. Vert designs as T 336 of Antigua. Multicoloured. P 13½×14.*

2051	100 c. "Madonna of the Annunciation" (Simone Martini)		30	15
2052	200 c. "Madonna and Child" (Niccolo di Pietro Gerini)		45	20
2053	250 c. "Virgin and Child on the Throne with Angels and Saints" (Raffaello Botticini)		55	45
2054	300 c. "Madonna and Child with Saints" (Antonio Fiorentino)		75	75
2055	400 c. "Adoration of the Magi" (Bartolo di Fredi)		90	90
2056	500 c. "The Annunciation" (Cima da Congeliano)		1·00	1·00
2057	600 c. "Virgin and Child with the Young St. John the Baptist" (workshop of Botticelli)		1·25	1·50
2058	1000 c. "The Holy Family" (Giorgione)		1·75	2·50
2051/8		*Set of 8*	6·25	6·75

MS2059 Two sheets, each 135×95 mm. (a) 2000 c. "Adoration of the Kings" (detail showing Holy Family) (Giorgione). (b) 2000 c. "Adoration of the Kings" (detail showing King and attendants) (Giorgione) .. *Set of 2 sheets* 8·50 9·00

(Litho B.D.T.)

1994 (9 Dec). *Panafest '94 (2nd Pan-African Historical Theatre Festival). T 508 and similar vert designs. Multicoloured. P 13½×13.*

2060	50 c. Type 508		20	15
2061	100 c. Traditional artefacts		35	25
2062	200 c. Chief with courtiers		65	60
2063	400 c. Woman in ceremonial costume		1·25	1·75
2064	600 c. Cape Coast Castle		1·75	2·25
2065	800 c. Clay figurines		2·25	3·00
2060/5		*Set of 6*	6·00	6·75

509 Red Cross Stretcher-bearers 510 Fertility Doll

(Des E. Mensah. Litho Questa)

1994 (20 Dec). *75th Anniv of Red Cross. T 509 and similar horiz designs. Multicoloured. P 14.*

2066	50 c. Type 509		30	15
2067	200 c. Worker with children		60	35
2068	600 c. Workers erecting tents		1·50	2·00
2066/8		*Set of 3*	2·25	2·25

MS2069 147×99 mm. Nos. 2066/7 and 1000 c. As 600 c. .. .. 3·00 3·25

(Des E. Mensah. Litho Questa)

1994 (20 Dec). *Fertility Dolls. T 510 and similar vert designs showing different dolls. P 14.*

2070	50 c. multicoloured		20	10
2071	100 c. multicoloured		30	15
2072	150 c. multicoloured		45	30
2073	200 c. multicoloured		50	30
2074	400 c. multicoloured		80	70
2075	600 c. multicoloured		1·00	1·10
2076	800 c. multicoloured		1·25	1·50
2077	1000 c. multicoloured		1·60	1·75
2070/7		*Set of 8*	5·50	5·50

MS2078 147×99 mm. Nos. 2071, 2074/5 and 250 c. As 1000 c. .. .. 4·50 5·00

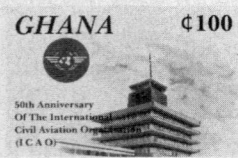

511 Ghanaian Family 512 Control Tower and Emblem

(Des E. Mensah. Litho Questa)

1994 (20 Dec). *International Year of the Family. T 511 and similar vert designs. Multicoloured. P 14.*

2079	50 c. Type 511		20	15
2080	100 c. Teaching carpentry		30	15
2081	200 c. Child care		50	25
2082	400 c. Care for the elderly		80	70
2083	600 c. Learning pottery		1·00	1·25
2084	1000 c. Adult education students		1·50	2·00
2079/84		*Set of 6*	3·75	4·00

(Des E. Mensah. Litho Questa)

1994 (24 Dec)–95. *50th Anniv of International Civil Aviation Organization. T 512 and similar horiz designs. Multicoloured. P 14. (a) Inscr "50th Anniversary Of Ghana Civil Aviation Authority"*

2085	100 c. Type 512		30	
2086	400 c. Communications equipment		80	
2087	1000 c. Airliner taking off		1·60	
2085/7		*Set of 3*	2·40	

(b) *Inscr "50th Anniversary Of The International Civil Aviation Organisation (I.C.A.O.)" (4.95)*

2088	100 c. Type 512		30	20
2089	400 c. Communications equipment		80	80
2090	1000 c. Airliner taking off		1·60	1·75
2088/90		*Set of 3*	2·40	2·50

Nos. 2085/7 were withdrawn from post offices in Ghana soon after issue when it was realised that the wrong organisation had been commemorated. Supplies were, however, distributed by the New York philatelic agent.

513 Pluto, Donald Duck and Chip n'Dale around Table

(Des Alvin White Studio. Litho Questa)

1995 (2 Feb). *60th Anniv of Donald Duck. T 513 and similar multicoloured designs showing Walt Disney cartoon characters at birthday party. P 14×13½.*

2091	40 c. Type 513		25	15
2092	50 c. Mickey Mouse and pup with banner		25	15
2093	60 c. Daisy Duck with balloons		25	20
2094	100 c. Goofy making cake		30	20
2095	150 c. Goofy on roller blades delivering cake		40	30
2096	250 c. Donald pinning donkey tail on Goofy		50	50
2097	400 c. Ludwig von Drake singing to Pluto		70	70
2098	500 c. Grandma Duck giving cake to puppies		80	80
2099	1000 c. Mickey and Minnie Mouse at piano		1·40	1·75
2100	1500 c. Pluto with bone and ball		2·25	2·75
2091/100		*Set of 10*	6·25	6·75

MS2101 Two sheets. (a) 117×95 mm. 2000 c. Donald blowing out birthday candles (*vert*). (b) 95×117 mm. 2000 c. Donald wearing party hat (*vert*). P 13½×14 .. .. *Set of 2 sheets* 7·50 8·00

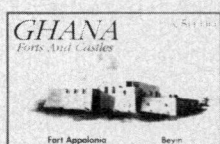

514 Fort Appolonia, Beyin

(Des E. Mensah. Litho B.D.T.)

1995 (3 Apr). *Forts and Castles of Ghana. T 514 and similar multicoloured designs. P 14.*

2102	50 c. Type 514		10	10
2103	200 c. Fort Patience, Apam		20	15
2104	250 c. Fort Amsterdam, Kormantin		25	25
2105	300 c. Fort St. Jago, Elmina		30	30
2106	400 c. Fort William, Anomabo		40	40
2107	600 c. Kumasi Fort		55	65
2102/7		*Set of 6*	1·60	1·60

MS2108 Two sheets, each 102×72 mm. (a) 800 c. Elmina Castle (*vert*). (b) 1000 c. Fort St. Antonio, Axim .. .. .. *Set of 2 sheets* 2·75 2·75

515 Cochem Castle, Germany

(Des R. Sauber. Litho B.D.T.)

1995 (3 Apr). *Castles of the World. T 515 and similar horiz designs. Multicoloured. P 14.*

2109	150 c. Type 515		30	30
2110	500 c. Windsor Castle, England		50	50
	a. Sheetlet. Nos. 2110/18		4·00	
2111	500 c. Osaka Castle, Japan		50	50
2112	500 c. Vaj Dahunyad Castle, Hungary		50	50
2113	500 c. Karlstejn Castle, Czech Republic		50	50
2114	500 c. Kronborg Castle, Denmark		50	50
2115	500 c. Alcázar of Segovia, Spain		50	50
2116	500 c. Chambourd Castle, France		50	50
2117	500 c. Linderhof Castle, Germany		50	50
2118	500 c. Red Fort, Delhi, India		50	50
2119	600 c. Hohenzollern Castle, Germany		60	60

2120	800 c. Uwajima Castle, Japan		80	80
2121	800 c. Hohenschwangau Castle, Germany		90	90
2109/21		*Set of 13*	6·25	6·25

MS2122 Two sheets, each 102×72 mm. (a) 2500 c. Neuschwanstein Castle, Germany (b) 2500 c. Himeji Castle, Japan .. *Set of 2 sheets* 8·00 8·00

Nos. 2110/18 were printed together, *se-tenant*, in sheetlets of 9.

516 European Pochard ("Eurasian Pochard") 517 Cycling

(Litho B.D.T.)

1995 (28 Apr). *Ducks. T 516 and similar horiz designs. Multicoloured. P 14.*

2123	200 c. Type 516		35	35
2124	400 c. African Pygmy Goose		55	55
	a. Sheetlet. Nos. 2124/35		6·00	
2125	400 c. Southern Pochard		55	55
2126	400 c. Cape Teal		55	55
2127	400 c. Ruddy Shelduck		55	55
2128	400 c. Fulvous Whistling Duck		55	55
2129	400 c. White-faced Whistling Duck		55	55
2130	400 c. Ferruginous Duck ("Ferruginous White-eye")		55	55
2131	400 c. Hottentot Teal		55	55
2132	400 c. African Black Duck		55	55
2133	400 c. African Yellow-bill		55	55
2134	400 c. Bahama Pintail ("White-checked Pintail Duck")		55	55
2135	400 c. Hartlaub's Duck		55	55
2136	500 c. Maccoa Duck		60	60
2137	800 c. Cape Shoveler		80	80
2138	1000 c. Red-crested Pochard		90	90
2123/38		*Set of 16*	8·50	8·50

MS2139 Two sheets, each 104×74 mm. (a) 2500 c. Roseate Tern. (b) 2500 c. Common Shoveler ("Northern Shoveler") .. *Set of 2 sheets* 8·50 9·00

Nos. 2124/35 were printed together, *se-tenant*, in sheetlets of 12 with the backgrounds forming a composite design. Nos. 2128 is inscribed "Wistling" in error.

(Des J. Iskowitz. Litho Questa)

1995 (2 May). *Olympic Games, Atlanta (1996) (1st issue). T 517 and similar vert designs. Multicoloured. P 14.*

2140	300 c. Type 517		40	40
	a. Sheetlet. Nos. 2140/51		4·25	
2141	300 c. Archery		40	40
2142	300 c. Diving		40	40
2143	300 c. Swimming		40	40
2144	300 c. Women's Gymnastics		40	40
2145	300 c. Fencing		40	40
2146	300 c. Boxing		40	40
2147	300 c. Men's Gymnastics		40	40
2148	300 c. Javelin		40	40
2149	300 c. Tennis		40	40
2150	300 c. Football		40	40
2151	300 c. Equestrian		40	40
2152	500 c. Carl Lewis (U.S.A.)		50	50
2153	800 c. Eric Liddell (Great Britain)		75	75
2154	900 c. Jesse Owens (U.S.A.)		85	85
2155	1000 c. Jim Thorpe (U.S.A.)		90	90
2140/55		*Set of 16*	7·00	7·00

MS2156 Two sheets, each 70×100 mm. (a) 1200 c. Pierre de Coubertin (founder of International Olympic Committee). (b) 1200 c. John Akii Bua (Uganda) .. *Set of 2 sheets* 3·25 3·75

Nos. 2140/51 were printed together, *se-tenant*, in sheetlets of 12 with the backgrounds forming a composite design. See Nos. 2334/55.

518 Cymothoe beckeri (butterfly) 519 Ghanaian Scouts

(Des E. Mensah. Litho Ikam Security Ptg Ltd, Accra)

1995 (19 June)–97. *T 518 and similar multicoloured designs. P 13½×14 (vert) or 14×13½ (horiz).*

2157	400 c. Type 518		15	20
2158	500 c. Graphium policenes (butterfly)		20	25
2158a	550 c. Atumpan drums (vert) (30.5.97)		20	25
2158b	800 c. Cyrestis camillus (butterfly) (vert) (4.6.97)		30	35
2159	1000 c. African Long-tailed Hawk (vert)		35	40
2159a	1100 c. Kente cloth (7.6.97)		40	45
2160	2000 c. Swordfish		70	75
2161	3000 c. Guinean Fingerfish		1·10	1·25
2162	5000 c. Purple Heron (vert)		1·90	2·00
2157/62		*Set of 9*	5·25	6·00

(Des R. Rundo. Litho Questa)

1995 (6 July). *18th World Scout Jamboree, Netherlands.* T **519** *and similar vert designs showing Ghanaian scouts.* P 14.

2163	400 c. multicoloured	70	80
	a. Horiz strip of 3. Nos. 2163/5	2·40	
2164	800 c. multicoloured	90	1·00
2165	1000 c. multicoloured	1·00	1·25
2163/5	*Set of 3*	2·40	2·75
MS2166	70×100 mm. 1200 c. multicoloured	1·90	2·00

Nos. 2163/5 were printed together in sheets of 9 containing three *se-tenant* horizontal strips of 3.

(Des W. Wright. Litho B.D.T.)

1995 (6 July). *50th Anniv of End of Second World War in Europe. Multicoloured designs as* T **340** *of Antigua.* P 14.

2167	400 c. Winston Churchill	65	65
	a. Sheetlet. Nos. 2167/74	4·75	
2168	400 c. Gen. Dwight D. Eisenhower	65	65
2169	400 c. Air Marshal Sir Arthur Tedder	65	65
2170	400 c. Field-Marshal Sir Bernard Montgomery	65	65
2171	400 c. Gen. Omar Bradley	65	65
2172	400 c. Gen. Charles de Gaulle	65	65
2173	400 c. French resistance fighters	65	65
2174	400 c. Gen. George S. Patton	65	65
2167/74	*Set of 8*	4·75	4·75
MS2175	104×74 mm. 1200 c. "GIVE ME FIVE YEARS & YOU WILL NOT RECOGNISE GERMANY AGAIN" quote by Adolf Hitler in English and German (42×57 *mm*)	1·90	2·00

Nos. 2167/74 were printed together, *se-tenant*, in sheetlets of 8 with the stamps arranged in two horizontal strips of 4 separated by a gutter showing celebrations around the Arc de Triomphe.

520 Trygve Lie (1946–52) and United Nations Building

521 Preserving Fish

(Litho Questa)

1995 (6 July). *50th Anniv of United Nations. Secretary-Generals.* T **520** *and similar multicoloured designs.* P 14.

2176	200 c. Type **520**	30	40
	a. Sheetlet. Nos. 2176/81	3·00	
2177	300 c. Dag Hammarskjold (1953–61)	40	50
2178	400 c. U. Thant (1961–71)	50	60
2179	500 c. Kurt Waldheim (1972–81)	60	70
2180	600 c. Javier Perez de Cuellar (1982–91)	70	80
2181	800 c. Boutrous Boutrous-Ghali (1992)	80	90
2176/81	*Set of 6*	3·00	3·50
MS2182	104×74 mm. 1200 c. U.N. flag (*horiz*)	1·90	2·00

Nos. 2176/81 were printed together, *se-tenant*, in sheetlets of 6.

(Litho Questa)

1995 (6 July). *50th Anniv of Food and Agriculture Organization.* T **521** *and similar horiz designs. Multicoloured.* P 14.

2183	200 c. Type **521**	40	15
2184	300 c. Fishermen with fish traps	50	30
2185	400 c. Ox-drawn plough	60	50
2186	600 c. Harvesting bananas	70	80
2187	800 c. Planting saplings	80	90
2183/7	*Set of 5*	2·75	2·40
MS2188	100×70 mm. 2000 c. Canoe and cattle	3·00	3·25

522 National Flag and Rotary Emblem

523 Seismosaurus

(Litho Questa)

1995 (6 July). *90th Anniv of Rotary International.* T **522** *and similar multicoloured design.* P 14.

2189	600 c. Type **522**	70	80
MS2190	94×65 mm. 1200 c. Ghanaian Rotary banner (*vert*)	1·90	2·00

(Litho Questa)

1995 (6 July). *95th Birthday of Queen Elizabeth the Queen Mother. Vert designs as* T **344** *of Antigua. Multicoloured.* P 13½×14.

2191	600 c. orange-brown, pale brown and black	90	90
	a. Sheetlet. Nos. 2191/4×2	6·50	
2192	600 c. multicoloured	90	90
2193	600 c. multicoloured	90	90
2194	600 c. multicoloured	90	90
2191/4	*Set of 4*	3·25	3·25
MS2195	102×127 mm. 2500 c. multicoloured	4·00	4·00

Designs:—No. 2191, Queen Elizabeth the Queen Mother (pastel drawing); No. 2192, Wearing light blue hat and floral dress; No. 2193, At desk (oil painting); No. 2194, Wearing red hat and dress; No. **MS**2195, Wearing pale blue hat and jacket.

Nos. 2191/4 were printed together in sheetlets of 8, containing two *se-tenant* strips of 4.

(Des J. Batchelor. Litho Questa)

1995 (6 July). *50th Anniv of End of Second World War in the Pacific. Medals. Horiz designs as* T **340** *of Antigua. Multicoloured.* P 14.

2196	500 c. Navy Cross and Purple Heart, U.S.A.	80	80
	a. Sheetlet. Nos. 2196/2201	4·25	
2197	500 c. Air Force Cross and Distinguished Flying Cross, Great Britain	80	80
2198	500 c. Navy and Marine Corps Medal and Distinguished Service Cross, U.S.A.	80	80
2199	500 c. Distinguished Service Medal and Distinguished Conduct Medal, Great Britain	80	80
2200	500 c. Military Medal and Military Cross, Great Britain	80	80
2201	500 c. Distinguished Service Cross and Distinguished Service Order, Great Britain	80	80
2196/2201	*Set of 6*	4·25	4·25
MS2202	108×76 mm. 1200 c. Congressional Medal of Honor, U.S.A.	2·50	2·50

Nos. 2196/2201 were printed together, *se-tenant*, in sheetlets of 6 with the stamps arranged in two horizontal strips of 3 separated by a gutter showing American troops in Japan.

(Litho Questa)

1995 (8 Aug). *"Singapore '95" International Stamp Exhibition. Prehistoric Animals.* T **523** *and similar multicoloured designs.* P 14.

2203	400 c. Type **523**	65	65
	a. Sheetlet. Nos. 2203/11	5·25	
2204	400 c. Supersaurus	65	65
2205	400 c. Ultrasaurus	65	65
2206	400 c. Saurolophus	65	65
2207	400 c. Lambeosaurus	65	65
2208	400 c. Parasaurolophus	65	65
2209	400 c. Triceratops	65	65
2210	400 c. Styracosaurus	65	65
2211	400 c. Pachyrhinosaurus	65	65
2212	400 c. Peteinosaurus	65	65
	a. Sheetlet. Nos. 2212/20	5·25	
2213	400 c. Quetzalcoatlus	65	65
2214	400 c. Eudimorphodon	65	65
2215	400 c. Allosaurus	65	65
2216	400 c. Daspletosaurus	65	65
2217	400 c. Tarbosaurus bataar	65	65
2218	400 c. Velociraptor mongoliensis	65	65
2219	400 c. Herrerasaurus	65	65
2220	400 c. Coelophysis	65	65
2203/20	*Set of 18*	10·50	10·50
MS2221	Two sheets, each 106×76 mm. (a) 2500 c. Tyrannosaurus rex (*horiz*). (b) 2500 c. Albertosaur (*horiz*) *Set of 2 sheets*	8·00	8·50

Nos. 2203/11 and 2212/20 were printed together, *se-tenant*, in sheetlets of 9, each forming a composite design.

524 Arms of Otumfuo Opoku Ware II

525 Nelson Mandela (1993 Peace)

(Litho Ikam Security Ptg Ltd, Accra)

1995 (9 Aug). *Silver Jubilee of Otumfuo Opoku Ware II (King of Ashanti).* T **524** *and similar vert designs. Multicoloured.* P 13½×13.

2222	50 c. Type **524**	10	10
2223	100 c. Silver casket	15	10
2224	200 c. Golden stool	25	20
2225	400 c. Busummuru sword bearer	45	45
2226	600 c. Otumfuo Opoku Ware II	65	75
2227	800 c. Otumfro Opoku Ware II under umbrella	80	90
2228	1000 c. Mponponsuo sword bearer	90	1·00
2222/8	*Set of 7*	3·00	3·00

(Des R. Sauber. Litho Questa)

1995 (2 Oct). *Centenary of Nobel Prize Trust Fund. Past Prize Winners.* T **525** *and similar vert designs. Multicoloured.* P 14.

2229	400 c. Type **525**	60	60
	a. Sheetlet. Nos. 2229/37	4·75	
2230	400 c. Albert Schweitzer (1952 Peace)	60	60
2231	400 c. Wole Soyinka (1986 Literature)	60	60
2232	400 c. Emil Fischer (1902 Chemistry)	60	60
2233	400 c. Rudolf Mossbauer (1961 Physics)	60	60
2234	400 c. Archbishop Desmond Tutu (1984 Peace)	60	60
2235	400 c. Max Born (1954 Physics)	60	60
2236	400 c. Max Planck (1918 Physics)	60	60
2237	400 c. Herman Hesse (1946 Literature)	60	60
2229/37	*Set of 9*	4·75	4·75
MS2238	104×75 mm. 1200 c. Paul Ehrlich (1908 Medicine) and medal	1·75	2·00

Nos. 2229/37 were printed together, *se-tenant*, in sheetlets of 9.

(Litho Questa)

1995 (1 Dec). *Christmas. Religious Paintings. Vert designs as* T **357** *of Antigua. Multicoloured.* P 13½×14.

2239	50 c. "The Child Jesus and the Young St. John" (Murillo)	15	10
2240	80 c. "Rest on the Flight into Egypt" (Memling)	15	10
2241	300 c. "Holy Family" (Van Dyck)	40	35
2242	600 c. "Enthroned Madonna and Child" (Uccello)	70	80
2243	800 c. "Madonna and Child" (Van Eyck)	85	1·00
2244	1000 c. "Head of Christ" (Rembrandt)	1·00	1·25
2239/44	*Set of 6*	3·00	3·00
MS2245	Two sheets, each 101×127 mm. (a) 2500 c. "The Holy Family" (Pulzone). (b) 2500 c. "Madonna and Child with Two Saints" (Montagna) *Set of 2 sheets*	7·75	8·00

526 Ernemann Camera (1903)

527 John Lennon

(Des H. Friedman. Litho Questa)

1995 (8 Dec). *Centenary of Cinema.* T **526** *and similar vert designs. Multicoloured.* P 13½×14.

2246	400 c. Type **526**	65	65
	a. Sheetlet. Nos. 2246/54	5·25	
2247	400 c. Charlie Chaplin	65	65
2248	400 c. Rudolph Valentino	65	65
2249	400 c. Will Rogers	65	65
2250	400 c. Greta Garbo	65	65
2251	400 c. Jackie Cooper	65	65
2252	400 c. Bette Davis	65	65
2253	400 c. John Barrymore	65	65
2254	400 c. Shirley Temple	65	65
2246/54	*Set of 9*	5·25	5·25
MS2255	106×76 mm. 2500 c. Laurel and Hardy	3·75	3·75

Nos. 2246/54 were printed together, *se-tenant*, in sheetlets of 9.

No. 2246 is inscribed "ERNMANN" in error.

(Litho Questa)

1995 (8 Dec). *John Lennon (musician) Commemoration.* T **527** *and similar vert designs. Multicoloured.* P 14 (No. 2265) or 13½×14 (others).

2256	400 c. Type **527**	1·10	1·10
	a. Sheetlet. Nos. 2256/64	10·00	
2257	400 c. Full face portrait (green background)	1·10	1·10
2258	400 c. With guitar	1·10	1·10
2259	400 c. Wearing glasses and caftan	1·10	1·10
2260	400 c. Full face portrait (verm background)	1·10	1·10
2261	400 c. Wearing headphones	1·10	1·10
2262	400 c. Wearing purple T-shirt	1·10	1·10
2263	400 c. Full face portrait (blue background)	1·10	1·10
2264	400 c. Facing right	1·10	1·10
2265	400 c. As No. 2263, but smaller (24×39 mm)	1·10	1·10
2256/65	*Set of 10*	10·00	10·00
MS2266	102×73 mm. 2000 c. John Lennon playing guitar	6·00	6·50

Nos. 2256/64 were printed together, *se-tenant*, in sheetlets of 9.

No. 2265 was printed in sheetlets of 16 with a large illustrated margin at right.

528 Louis Pasteur in Laboratory

529 Rat Musicians

(Des E. Mensah. Litho Questa)

1995 (13 Dec). *Death Centenary of Louis Pasteur (scientist).* T **528** *and similar vert designs. Multicoloured.* P 14.

2267	600 c. Type **528**	1·10	1·10
	a. Sheetlet. Nos. 2267/71	5·00	
2268	600 c. Pasteur injecting rabid dog	1·10	1·10
2269	600 c. Pasteur and microscope slide	1·10	1·10
2270	600 c. Laboratory equipment and birds	1·10	1·10
2271	600 c. Yeast vats	1·10	1·10
2267/71	*Set of 5*	5·00	5·00

Nos. 2267/71 were printed together, *se-tenant*, in sheetlets of 5.

(Des Y. Lee. Litho Questa)

1996 (28 Jan). *Chinese New Year ("Year of the Rat"). T* **529** *and similar designs.* P 14.

2272	250 c. orange-brown, violet and rosine ..	10	15
	a. Horiz strip of 4. Nos. 2272/5 ..	35	
2273	250 c. orange-brown, violet and rosine ..	10	15
2274	250 c. orange-brown, violet and rosine ..	10	15
2275	250 c. orange-brown, violet and rosine ..	10	15
2272/5	*Set of 4*	35	40
MS2276	142×60 mm. As Nos. 2272/5, but face values in rosine instead of white	35	40
MS2277	106×75 mm. 1000 c. scarlet-vermilion and yellow-orange	35	40

Designs: *Vert*—No. 2272, Type **529**; No. 2273, Rats carrying banners; No. 2274, Rats carrying palanquin; No. 2275, Rats with offerings. *Horiz*—No. **MS**2277, Four rats carrying palanquin.

Nos. 2272/5 were printed together, *se-tenant,* in horizontal strips of 4 throughout the sheets.

(Litho Questa)

1996 (12 Feb). *125th Anniv of Metropolitan Museum of Art, New York. Multicoloured designs as T* **251** *of Gambia.* P 13½×14.

2278	400 c. "Portrait of a Man" (Van der Goes)	15	20
	a. Sheetlet. Nos. 2278/85 plus centre label	1·25	
2279	400 c. "Paradise" (detail) (Di Paolo) ..	15	20
2280	400 c. "Portrait of a Young Man" (Messina)	15	20
2281	400 c. "Tommaso Portinari" (detail) (Memling)	15	20
2282	400 c. "Maria Portinari" (detail) (Memling)	15	20
2283	400 c. "Portrait of a Lady" (detail) (Ghirlandaio)	15	20
2284	400 c. "St. Christopher and the Infant Christ" (Ghirlandaio)	15	20
2285	400 c. "Francesco D'Este" (detail) (Weyden)	15	20
2286	400 c. "The Interrupted Sleep" (Boucher)	15	20
	a. Sheetlet. Nos. 2286/93 plus centre label	1·25	
2287	400 c. "Diana and Cupid" (detail) (Batoni)	15	20
2288	400 c. "Boy blowing Bubbles" (Chardin) ..	15	20
2289	400 c. "Ancient Rome" (detail) (Pannini) ..	15	20
2290	400 c. "Modern Rome" (detail) (Pannini) ..	15	20
2291	400 c. "The Calmady Children" (Lawrence)	15	20
2292	400 c. "The Triumph of Marius" (detail) (Tiepolo)	15	20
2293	400 c. "Garden at Vaucression" (detail) (Vuillard)	15	20
2278/93	*Set of 16*	2·50	3·25
MS2294	Two sheets, each 95×70 mm. (a) 2500 c. "The Epiphany" (detail) (Giotto) (80×56 *mm*). (b) 2500 c. "The Calling of Matthew" (detail) (Hemessen) (80×56 *mm*). P 14 . *Set of 2 sheets*	1·90	2·00

Nos. 2278/85 and 2286/93 were each printed together, *se-tenant,* in sheetlets of 8 stamps and one centre label.

530 Toco Toucan

531 Pagoda of Kaiyuan Si Temple, Fujian

(Des Y. Lee. Litho)

1996 (15 Apr). *Wildlife of the Rainforest. T* **530** *and similar vert designs. Multicoloured.* P 14.

2295	400 c. Type **530**	15	20
	a. Sheetlet. Nos. 2295/2306 ..	1·75	
2296	400 c. Two-toed Sloth	15	20
2297	400 c. Orang-utan	15	20
2298	400 c. Crested Hawk Eagle ..	15	20
2299	400 c. Tiger	15	20
2300	400 c. Yellow-billed Stork ..	15	20
2301	400 c. Green-winged Macaw ..	15	20
2302	400 c. Common Squirrel-monkey ..	15	20
2303	400 c. Crab-eating Macaque ..	15	20
2304	400 c. *Cithaerias menander* and *Ithomiidae* (butterflies)	15	20
2305	400 c. *Coryptophanes cristatus* and *Gekkonidae* (lizards)	15	20
2306	400 c. Boa Constrictor	15	20
2307	400 c. Hoatzin	15	20
	a. Sheetlet. Nos. 2307/18 ..	1·75	
2308	400 c. Western Tarsier	15	20
2309	400 c. Golden Lion Tamarin ..	15	20
2310	400 c. *Pteropus gouldii* (bat) ..	15	20
2311	400 c. Guianan Cock of the Rock ..	15	20
2312	400 c. Resplendent Quetzal ..	15	20
2313	400 c. Tree Frog and Poison-arrow Frog ..	15	20
2314	400 c. Ring-tailed Lemur	15	20
2315	400 c. Iguana	15	20
2316	400 c. *Heliconius burneyi* (butterfly) ..	15	20
2317	400 c. Vervain Hummingbird ..	15	20
2318	400 c. Verreaux's Sifaka	15	20
2295/2318	*Set of 24*	3·50	4·75
MS2319	Two sheets, each 74×104 mm. (a) 3000 c. King of Saxony Bird of Paradise. (b) 3000 c. King Vulture .. *Set of 2 sheets*	2·25	2·40

Nos. 2295/2306 and 2307/18 were each printed together, *se-tenant,* in sheetlets of 12.

1996 (13 May). *"CHINA '96" 9th Asian International Stamp Exhibition. Pagodas. T* **531** *and similar vert designs. Multicoloured. Litho.* P 14.

2320	400 c. Type **531**	15	20
	a. Sheetlet. Nos. 2320/3×2	1·25	
2321	400 c. Kaiyuan Si Temple, Hebei	15	20
2322	400 c. Fogong Si Temple, Shanxi	15	20
2323	400 c. Xiangshan, Beijing ..	15	20
2320/3	*Set of 4*	60	80
MS2324	Two sheets. (a) 100×70 mm. 1000 c. Baima Si Temple, Henan. (b) 143×98 mm. 1000 c. Gold statue (38×50 *mm*) *Set of 2 sheets*	70	75

Nos. 2320/3 were printed together, *se-tenant,* in sheetlets of 8 containing two of each design.

(Litho Questa)

1996 (10 June). *70th Birthday of Queen Elizabeth II. Multicoloured designs as T* **364** *of Antigua showing different photographs.* P 13½×14.

2325	1000 c. As Type **364** of Antigua ..	35	40
	a. Strip of 3. Nos. 2325/7 ..	1·00	
2326	1000 c. In blue hat and coat ..	35	40
2327	1000 c. Wearing straw hat and carrying bouquet	35	40
2325/7		1·00	1·25
MS2328	125×103 mm. 2500 c. In open carriage at Trooping the Colour (*horiz*). P 14×13½	90	95

Nos. 2325/7 were printed together, *se-tenant,* in horizontal and vertical strips of 3 throughout the sheet.

532 Serafim Todorow (Bulgaria)

533 Ancient Greek Wrestlers

(Litho B.D.T.)

1996 (27 June). *50th Anniv of International Amateur Boxing Association. T* **532** *and similar vert designs. Multicoloured.* P 14.

2329	300 c. Type **532**	10	15
2330	400 c. Oscar de la Hoya (U.S.A.) ..	15	20
2331	800 c. Ariel Hernandez (Cuba) ..	30	35
2332	1500 c. Arnoldo Mesa (Cuba) ..	55	60
2329/32	*Set of 4*	1·10	1·25
MS2333	80×110 mm. 3000 c. Tadahiro Sasaki (Japan)	1·10	1·25

(Litho B.D.T.)

1996 (27 June). *Olympic Games, Atlanta (2nd issue). Previous Medal Winners. T* **533** *and similar multicoloured designs.* P 14.

2334	300 c. Type **533**	10	15
2335	400 c. Aileen Riggin, 1920 (U.S.A.) ..	15	20
	a. Sheetlet. Nos. 2335/43 ..	1·40	
2336	400 c. Pat McCormick, 1952 (U.S.A.) ..	15	20
2337	400 c. Dawn Fraser, 1956 (Australia) ..	15	20
2338	400 c. Chris von Saltza, 1960 (U.S.A.) ..	15	20
2339	400 c. Anita Lonsbrough, 1960 (Great Britain)	15	20
2340	400 c. Debbie Meyer, 1968 (U.S.A.) ..	15	20
2341	400 c. Shane Gould, 1972 (Australia) ..	15	20
2342	400 c. Petra Thuemer, 1976 (Germany) ..	15	20
2343	400 c. Marjorie Gestring, 1936 (U.S.A.) ..	15	20
2344	400 c. Abedi Pele (Ghana) (*vert*) ..	15	20
	a. Sheetlet. Nos. 2344/52 ..	1·40	
2345	400 c. Quico Navarez (Spain) (*vert*)	15	20
2346	400 c. Heino Hanson (Denmark) (*vert*)	15	20
2347	400 c. Mostafa Ismail (Egypt) (*vert*)	15	20
2348	400 c. Anthony Yeboah (Ghana) (*vert*)	15	20
2349	400 c. Jurgen Klinsmann (Germany) (*vert*)	15	20
2350	400 c. Cobi Jones (U.S.A.) (*vert*) ..	15	20
2351	400 c. Franco Baresi (Italy) (*vert*) ..	15	20
2352	400 c. Igor Dobrovolski (Russia) (*vert*)	15	20
2353	500 c. Wilma Rudolph (U.S.A.) (track and field, 1960)	20	25
2354	600 c. Olympic Stadium, 1960, and Roman landmarks	20	25
2355	800 c. Ladies Kayak pairs, 1960 (Soviet Union)	30	35
2334/55	*Set of 22*	3·50	4·50
MS2356	Two sheets, each 110×80 mm. (a) 2000 c. Tracy Caulkins (U.S.A.) (swimming, 1984). (b) 2000 c. Kornelia Ender (Germany) (200m freestyle, 1976) .. *Set of 2 sheets*	1·40	1·50

Nos. 2335/43 (swimming and diving) and 2344/52 (football) were each printed together, *se-tenant,* in sheetlets of 9, with the backgrounds forming composite designs.

PRICES OF SETS

Set prices are given for many issues, generally those containing three stamps or more. Definitive sets include one of each value or major colour change, but do not cover different perforations, die types or minor shades. Where a choice is possible the set prices are based on the cheapest versions of the stamps included in the listings.

---

534 E. W. Agyare (35 years service with Ghana Broadcasting)

535 Fiddles

(Litho Questa)

1996 (31 July). *Local Broadcasting.* P 14.

2357	**534** 100 c. multicoloured	10	10

(Litho Questa)

1996 (31 July). *50th Anniv of U.N.I.C.E.F. Multicoloured designs as T* **366** *of Antigua.* P 14.

2358	400 c. Ghanaian child	15	20
2359	500 c. Mother and child	20	25
2360	600 c. Mother and child drinking ..	20	25
2358/60	*Set of 3*	55	70
MS2361	74×104 mm. 1000 c. Young child ..	35	40

(Des Jennifer Toombs. Litho Questa)

1996 (31 July). *3000th Anniv of Jerusalem. Multicoloured designs as T* **367** *of Antigua.* P 14½.

2362	400 c. St. Stephen's Gate and *Jasminum mesnyi*	15	20
2363	600 c. The Citadel, Tower of David and *Nerium oleander*	20	25
2364	800 c. Chapel of the Ascension and *Romulea bulbocodium* ..	30	35
2362/4	*Set of 3*	65	80
MS2365	65×80 mm. 2000 c. Russian Orthodox Church of St. Mary Magdalene (48×30 *mm*). P 14	70	75

(Des R. Sauber. Litho Questa)

1996 (31 July). *Centenary of Radio. Entertainers. Multicoloured designs as T* **368** *of Antigua.* P 13½×14.

2366	500 c. Frank Sinatra	20	25
2367	600 c. Judy Garland	20	25
2368	600 c. Bing Crosby	20	25
2369	800 c. Martin and Lewis	30	35
2366/9	*Set of 4*	90	1·10
MS2370	81×110 mm. 2000 c. Edgar Bergen and Charlie McCarthy	70	75

(Des M. Freedman and Dena Rubin. Litho Questa)

1996 (31 July). *50th Anniv of U.N.E.S.C.O. Multicoloured designs as T* **374** *of Antigua.* P 14×13½ (1000 c.) or 13½×14 (*others*).

2371	400 c. The Citadel, Haiti (*vert*) ..	15	20
2372	800 c. Ait-Ben-Hadou (fortified village), Morocco (*vert*)	30	35
2373	1000 c. Spissky Hrad, Slovakia ..	35	40
2371/3	*Set of 3*	80	95
MS2374	106×76 mm. 2000 c. Cape Coast Castle, Ghana. P 14×13½	70	75

1996 (5 Aug). *Musical Instruments. T* **535** *and similar vert designs. Multicoloured. Litho.* P 14.

2375	500 c. Type **535**	20	25
	a. Sheetlet. Nos. 2375/9 ..	1·00	
2376	500 c. Proverbial drum	20	25
2377	500 c. Double clapless bell and castanet ..	20	25
2378	500 c. Gourd rattle	20	25
2379	500 c. Horns	20	25
2375/9	*Set of 5*	1·00	1·25

Nos. 2375/9 were printed together, *se-tenant,* in sheetlets of 5.

536 Ariel, Flounder and Sebastian

(Des Alvin White Studios. Litho Questa)

1996 (25 Aug). *Disney Friends. T* **536** *and similar multicoloured designs showing Disney cartoon characters.* P 14×13½.

2380	60 c. Type **536**	30	30
2381	60 c. Pinocchio and Jiminy Cricket ..	30	30
2382	60 c. Cogsworth and Lumiere ..	30	30
2383	60 c. Copper and Tod	30	30
2384	60 c. Pocahontas, Meeko and Flit ..	30	30
2385	60 c. Bambi, Flower and Thumper ..	30	30
2386	150 c. As No. 2381	50	50
	a. Sheetlet. Nos. 2386/91 ..	5·00	
2387	200 c. Type **536**	50	50
2388	200 c. As No. 2383	50	50
2389	300 c. As No. 2385	60	60
2390	350 c. As No. 2382	60	60
2391	450 c. As No. 2384	65	65
2392	600 c. Aladdin and Abu	70	70
2393	700 c. Penny and Rufus	75	75

2394	800 c. Mowgli and Baloo	.. ..		80	80
2380/94		*Set of 15*		6·50	6·50

MS2395 Two sheets. (a) 98×124 mm. 3000 c. Winnie the Pooh (*vert*). P 13½×14. (b) 133×108 mm. 3000 c. Simba and Timon .. *Set of 2 sheets* 6·00 6·50

Nos. 2386/94 were printed together, *se-tenant*, in sheetlets of 9.

(Des Shannon. Litho Questa)

1996 (21 Nov). *20th Anniv of Rocky (film). Sheet 143×182 mm, containing vert design as T 266 of Gambia. Multicoloured. P 14×13½.*

MS2396 2000 c.×3 Sylvester Stallone in *Rocky II* 2·75 3·00

No. **MS2396** was printed with an enlarged illustrated left hand margin.

537 Herd Boy and Ox

538 The Tomb of Dr. Hideyo Noguchi

(Des Y. Lee. Litho Questa)

1997 (22 Jan). *Chinese New Year ("Year of the Ox"). "The Herd Boy and Weaver". T 537 and similar vert designs. Each lake-brown, silver and black. P 13½×14.*

2397	500 c. Type **537**	..		20	25
	a. Sheetlet. Nos. 2397/405		..	1·75	
2398	500 c. Ox and weaver in lake	..		20	25
2399	500 c. Weaver at work	..		20	25
2400	500 c. Herd boy with dying Ox	..		20	25
2401	500 c. Weaver flying out of window	..		20	25
2402	500 c. Herd boy carrying children	..		20	25
2403	500 c. Family separated by "river"	..		20	25
2404	500 c. Petitioning the emperor	..		20	25
2405	500 c. Family reunited	..		20	25
2397/405	..	*Set of 9*		1·75	2·25

Nos. 2397/405 were printed together, *se-tenant*, in sheetlets of 9 with an enlarged illustrated right-hand margin.

1997 (3 Mar). *120th Birth Anniv of Dr. Hideyo Noguchi (bacteriologist). T 538 and similar vert designs. Multicoloured. Litho. P 14.*

2406	1000 c. Type **538**	..		35	40
	a. Sheetlet. Nos. 2406/10		..	1·75	
2407	1000 c. Dr. Hideyo Noguchi	..		35	40
2408	1000 c. Birthplace of Dr. Noguchi at Sanjogarta			35	40
2409	1000 c. Noguchi Institute, Legon	..		35	40
2410	1000 c. Noguchi Gardens, Accra	..		35	40
2406/10		*Set of 5*		1·75	2·00

MS2411 Two sheets, each 67×97 mm. (a) 3000 c. Dr. Noguchi in his laboratory. (b) 3000 c. Statue of Dr. Noguchi .. .. *Set of 2 sheets* 2·25 2·40

Nos. 2406/10 were printed together, *se-tenant*, in sheetlets of 5.

539 Dipo Hairstyle

540 Independence Anniversary Emblem

1997 (3 Mar). *Ghanaian Women's Hairstyles. T 539 and similar vert designs. Multicoloured. Litho. P 14.*

2412	1000 c. Type **539**	..		35	40
	a. Sheetlet. Nos. 2412/16		..	1·75	
2413	1000 c. Oduku with flowers	..		35	40
2414	1000 c. Dansinkran	..		35	40
2415	1000 c. Mbobom	..		35	40
2416	1000 c. Oduku with hair pins	..		35	40
2417	1000 c. African Corn Row	..		35	40
	a. Sheetlet. Nos. 2417/21		..	1·75	
2418	1000 c. Chinese Raster	..		35	40
2419	1000 c. Chinese Raster with top knot	..		35	40
2420	1000 c. Corn Row	..		35	40
2421	1000 c. Mbakaa	..		35	40
2412/21		*Set of 10*		3·50	4·00

Nos. 2412/16 and 2417/21 were each printed together, *se-tenant*, in sheetlets of 5.

(Des J. Iskowitz (No. **MS**2427b), Dena Rubin (others). Litho B.D.T.)

1997 (6 Mar). *40th Anniv of Independence. T 540 and similar multicoloured designs. P 14.*

2422	200 c. Type **540**	..		10	10
2423	200 c. President J. J. Rawlings (*vert*)	..		1·50	1·50
2424	550 c. Dr. Kwame Nkrumah (first President) (*vert*)			30	35

2425	800 c. Children in class	..		40	45
2426	1100 c. Akosombo Dam	..		55	60
2422/6		*Set of 5*		2·50	2·75

MS2427 Two sheets. (a) 70×100 mm. 2000 c. Dr. Nkrumah proclaiming independence (*vert*). (b) 101×141 mm. 3000 c. United Nations Secretary-General Kofi Annan (37×50 *mm*) *Set of 2 sheets* 2·50 2·75

No. 2423 was withdrawn on 22 March at the request of the Office of the President.

No. 2425 is inscribed "Acheivement" in error

(Litho Questa)

1997 (8 Apr). *10th Anniv of Chernobyl Nuclear Disaster. Vert designs as T 376 of Antigua. Multicoloured. P 13½.*

2428	800 c. As Type **376** of Antigua			30	35
2429	1000 c. As No. 2428, but inscribed "CHABAD'S CHILDREN OF CHERNOBYL" at foot			35	40

541 Deng Xiaoping

542 Jackie Gleason

(Des Y. Lee. Litho Questa)

1997 (25 Apr). *Deng Xiaoping (Chinese statesman) Commemoration. T 541 and similar vert designs showing different portraits. Multicoloured. P 14×13½.*

2430	300 c. Type **541**	..		10	15
	a. Sheetlet. Nos. 2430, 2432, 2434 and 2436			95	
2431	500 c. Looking thoughtful	..		20	25
	a. Sheetlet. Nos. 2431, 2433, 2435 and 2437			1·00	
2432	600 c. Wearing glasses	..		20	25
2433	600 c. Delivering speech	..		20	25
2434	800 c. As No. 2432	..		30	35
2435	800 c. As No. 2433	..		30	35
2436	1000 c. Type **541**	..		35	40
2437	1000 c. As No. 2431	..		35	40
2430/7		*Set of 8*		2·00	2·40

MS2438 Two sheets, each 101×70 mm. (a) 3000 c. Deng Xiaoping making speech (47×34 *mm*). (b) 4000 c. Deng Xiaoping with hand raised (47×34 *mm*) .. .. *Set of 2 sheets* 2·50 2·75

Nos. 2430, 2432, 2434 and 2436, and 2431, 2433, 2435 and 2437 were each printed together, *se-tenant*, in sheetlets of 4 with an enlarged illustrated margin at left or right.

(Des J. Iskowitz. Litho Questa)

1997 (29 May). *50th Death Anniv of Paul Harris (founder of Rotary International). Horiz designs as T 377 of Antigua. Multicoloured. P 14.*

2439	2000 c. Paul Harris and Egyptian patient receiving polio vaccination			70	75

MS2440 78×107 mm. 3000 c. Paul Harris with Rotary and PolioPlus emblems .. .. 1·10 1·25

(Litho Questa)

1997 (29 May). *Golden Wedding of Queen Elizabeth and Prince Philip. Horiz designs as T 378 of Antigua. Multicoloured. P 14.*

2441	800 c. Queen Elizabeth II	..		30	35
	a. Sheetlet. Nos. 2441/6		..	1·75	
2442	800 c. Royal coat of arms	..		30	35
2443	800 c. Queen Elizabeth and Prince Philip waving			30	35
2444	800 c. Queen Elizabeth and Prince Philip on offical visit			30	35
2445	800 c. Queen in Irish State Coach	..		30	35
2446	800 c. Prince Philip in 1947	..		30	35
2441/6		*Set of 6*		1·75	2·10

MS2447 100×71 mm. 3000 c. Princess Elizabeth in 1947 .. .. .. 1·10 1·25

Nos. 2441/6 were printed together, *se-tenant*, in sheetlets of 6.

(Des J. Iskowitz. Litho Questa)

1997 (29 May). *"Pacific '97" International Stamp Exhibition, San Francisco. Death Centenary of Heinrich von Stephan (founder of the U.P.U.). Horiz designs as T 379 of Antigua. P 14.*

2448	1000 c. deep blue	..		35	45
	a. Sheetlet. Nos. 2448/50		..	1·00	
2449	1000 c. orange-brown	..		35	45
2450	1000 c. pale Indian red	..		35	45
2448/50		*Set of 3*		1·00	1·25

MS2451 82×119 mm. 3000 c. turquoise-green 1·10 1·25

Designs:—No. 2448, Early motor car; No. 2449, Von Stephan and Mercury; No. 2450, Blanchard's balloon flight, 1784; No. **MS**2451, African messenger.

Nos. 2448/50 were printed together, *se-tenant*, in sheetlets of 3 with enlarged illustrated right-hand margin.

(Litho Questa)

1997 (29 May). *Birth Bicentenary of Hiroshige (Japanese painter). "One Hundred Famous Views of Edo". Vert designs as T 310 of Dominica. Multicoloured. P 13½×14.*

2452	600 c. "Nihonbashi Bridge and Edobashi Bridge"			20	25
	a. Sheetlet. Nos. 2452/7		..	1·25	

2453	600 c. "View of Nihonbashi Tori 1-chome"			20	25
2454	600 c. "Open Garden at Fukagawa Hachiman Shrine"			20	25
2455	600 c. "Inari Bridge and Minato Shrine, Teppozu"			20	25
2456	600 c. "Bamboo Yards, Kyobashi Bridge"			20	25
2457	600 c. "Hall of Thirty-Three Bays, Fukagawa"			20	25
2452/7		*Set of 6*		1·25	1·50

MS2458 Two sheets, each 102×127 mm. (a) 3000 c. "Sumiyoshi Festival, Tsukudajima". (b) 3000 c. "Teppozu and Tsukjji Honganji Temple" .. .. *Set of 2 sheets* 2·25 2·40

Nos. 2452/7 were printed together, *se-tenant*, in sheetlets of 6.

(Des E. Mensah (No. **MS**2468b), Zina Saunders (others). Litho Questa)

1997 (1 July). *Famous Comedians. T 542 and similar vert designs. Multicoloured. P 13½×14.*

2459	600 c. Type **542**	..		70	70
	a. Sheetlet. Nos. 2459/67		..	5·50	
2460	600 c. Danny Kaye	..		70	70
2461	600 c. John Cleese	..		70	70
2462	600 c. Lucille Ball	..		70	70
2463	600 c. Jerry Lewis	..		70	70
2464	600 c. Sidney James	..		70	70
2465	600 c. Louis Defuenes	..		70	70
2466	600 c. Mae West	..		70	70
2467	600 c. Bob Hope	..		70	70
2459/67		*Set of 9*		5·50	5·50

MS2468 Two sheets. (a) 83×113 mm. 3000 c. Groucho Marx. P 13½×14. (b) 76×106 mm. 2000 c. Professor Ajax Bukana in front of curtain; 2000 c. Professor Ajax Bukana (*different*) (both 28×42 *mm*). P 14 *Set of 2 sheets* 4·25 4·75

Nos. 2459/67 were printed together, *se-tenant*, in sheetlets of 9.

543 *Galerina calyptrata*

544 African Pygmy Angelfish

(Litho Questa)

1997 (9 July). *Fungi of the World. T 543 and similar vert designs. Multicoloured. P 14.*

2469	200 c. Type **543**	..		10	10
2470	300 c. *Lepiota ignivolvata*	..		10	15
2471	400 c. *Omphalotus olearius*	..		15	20
2472	550 c. *Amanita phalloides*	..		20	25
2473	600 c. *Entoloma conferendum*	..		20	25
2474	800 c. *Entoloma nitidum*	..		30	35
2475	800 c. *Coprinus picaceus*	..		30	35
	a. Sheetlet. Nos. 2475/80		..	1·75	
2476	800 c. *Stropharia aurantiaca*	..		30	35
2477	800 c. *Cortinarius splendens*	..		30	35
2478	800 c. *Gomphidius roseus*	..		30	35
2479	800 c. *Russula sardonia*	..		30	35
2480	800 c. *Geastrum schmidelia*	..		30	35
2469/80		*Set of 12*		2·75	3·50

MS2481 Two sheets, each 73×103 mm. (a) 3000 c. *Craterellus cornucopioides*. (b) 3000 c. *Mycena crocata* .. .. *Set of 2 sheets* 1·25 1·40

Nos. 2475/80 were printed together, *se-tenant*, in sheetlets of 6.

(Litho Questa)

1997 (12 July). *World Football Championship, France (1998). Horiz designs as T 383 of Antigua. Multicoloured. P 14×13½.*

2482	200 c. Azteca Stadium, Mexico	..		10	10
2483	300 c. The Rose Bowl, U.S.A.	..		10	15
2484	400 c. Stadio Giuseppe Meazza, Italy	..		15	20
2485	500 c. Olympiastadion, Germany	..		20	25
2486	600 c. Patrick Kluivert, Netherlands	..		20	25
	a. Sheetlet. Nos. 2486/93 and central label			1·60	
2487	600 c. Roy Keane, Republic of Ireland	..		20	25
2488	600 c. Abedi Ayew Pele, Ghana	..		20	25
2489	600 c. Peter Schmeichel, Denmark	..		20	25
2490	600 c. Roberto di Matteo, Italy	..		20	25
2491	600 c. Bebeto, Brazil	..		20	25
2492	600 c. Steve McManaman, England	..		20	25
2493	600 c. George Oppon Weah, Liberia	..		20	25
2494	1000 c. Maracana Stadium, Brazil	..		35	40
2495	2000 c. Bernabeu Stadium, Spain	..		70	75
2482/95		*Set of 14*		3·00	3·75

MS2496 Two sheets. (a) 127×102 mm. 3000 c. David Seaman, England. (b) 102×127 mm. 3000 c. Juninho, Brazil .. *Set of 2 sheets* 2·25 2·40

Nos. 2486/93 were printed together, *se-tenant*, in sheetlets of 8 stamps and 1 central label.

(Des R. Martin. Litho Questa)

1997 (15 July). *Marine Life. T 544 and similar horiz designs. Multicoloured. P 14.*

2497	400 c. Type **544**	..		15	20
2498	500 c. Violet-crested Turaco	..		20	25
	a. Sheetlet. Nos. 2498/509		..	2·40	
2499	500 c. Pied Avocet	..		20	25
2500	500 c. Bottle-nosed Dolphin	..		20	25
2501	500 c. Bottle-nosed Dolphin and Long-toed Lapwing			20	25
2502	500 c. Longfinned Spadefish	..		20	25
2503	500 c. Imperial Angelfish and Manta	..		20	25
2504	500 c. Racoon Butterflyfish and African Pompano			20	25

2505	500 c. Silvertip Shark		20	25
2506	500 c. Longfin Banner Fish		20	25
2507	500 c. Longfin Banner Fish and Manta		20	25
2508	500 c. Rust Parrotfish		20	25
2509	500 c. Coral Trout		20	25
2510	600 c. Angelfish		20	25
2511	800 c. Broomtail Wrasse		30	35
2512	1000 c. Indian Butterflyfish		35	40
2497/512		Set of 16	3·50	4·25

MS2513 Two sheets, each 106×76 mm. (a) 3000 c. King Angelfish. (b) 3000 c. Crown Butterflyfish *Set of 2 sheets* 2·25 2·40
Nos. 2498/509 were printed together, *se-tenant*, in sheetlets of 12 with the backgrounds forming a composite design.

545 Ghanaian Players holding Trophy   **546** *Eurychone rothschildiana*

1997 (25 July). *J.V.C. Under-17 World Soccer Champions (1995).* T **545** *and similar multicoloured designs.* Litho. *P* 13½×13 *(vert) or* 13×13½ *(horiz).*

2514	200 c. + 50 c. Type 545	10	10
2515	550 c. + 50 c. Ghana football team (*horiz*)	20	25
2516	800 c. + 50 c. Abu Iddrisu	30	35
2517	1100 c. + 50 c. Emmanuel Bentil (*captain*)	40	45
2518	1500 c. + 50 c. Basiru Gambo	55	60
2514/18	..	Set of 5	1·50 1·75

(Des Jennifer Toombs. Litho Questa)

1997 (1 Aug). *Flowers of the World.* T **546** *and similar multicoloured designs.* P 14×14½ *(horiz) or* 14½×14 *(vert).*

2519	200 c. Type 546	10	10
2520	550 c. *Bulbophyllum lepidum*	20	25
2521	800 c. *Ansellia africana*	30	35
2522	800 c. *Strophanthus preusii* (*vert*)	30	35
	a. Sheetlet. Nos. 2522/30	2·75	
2523	800 c. *Ancistrochilus rothschildlanus* (*vert*)	30	35
2524	800 c. *Mussaenda arcuata* (*vert*)	30	35
2525	800 c. *Microcoelia guyoniane* (*vert*)	30	35
2526	800 c. *Gloriosa simplex* (*vert*)	30	35
2527	800 c. *Brachycorythis kalbreyeri* (*vert*)	30	35
2528	800 c. *Aframomum sceptrum* (*vert*)	30	35
2529	800 c. *Thunbergia alata* (*vert*)	30	35
2530	800 c. *Clerodendrum thomsoniae* (*vert*)	30	35
2531	1100 c. *Combbretum grandiflorum*	40	45
2519/31		Set of 13	3·75 4·25

MS2532 Two sheets each 82×77 mm. (a) 3000 c. *Kigelia africana* (*vert*). (b) 3000 c. *Spathodea campanulata* (*vert*) .. *Set of 2 sheets* 2·25 2·40
Nos. 2522/30 were printed together, *se-tenant*, in sheetlets of 9 with the backgrounds forming a composite design.

547 Goldfinch   **548** Havana Cat

(Des D. Burkhart. Litho B.D.T.)

1997 (20 Oct). *Birds of Africa.* T **547** *and similar vert designs. Multicoloured.* P 14.

2533	200 c. Type 547	10	10
2534	300 c. Cape Puff-back Flycatcher ("Batis")	10	15
2535	400 c. Red-headed Barbet	15	20
2536	500 c. African White-necked Raven	20	25
2537	600 c. Purple Grenadier	20	25
2538	800 c. Black Bustard	30	35
	a. Sheetlet. Nos. 2538/46	2·75	
2539	800 c. Lapwing	30	35
2540	800 c. Lichtenstein's Sandgrouse	30	35
2541	800 c. Red-crested Turaco	30	35
2542	800 c. White-browed Coucal	30	35
2543	800 c. Lilac-breasted Roller	30	35
2544	800 c. Golden Pipet	30	35
2545	800 c. Burchell's Gonolek	30	35
2546	800 c. Blackcap	30	35
2547	1000 c. Zebra Waxbill	35	40
2533/47		Set of 5	3·75 4·50

MS2548 Two sheets, each 106×75 mm. (a) 3000 c. Shaft-tailed Whydah. (b) 3000 c. Yellow-tufted Malachite Sunbird *Set of 2 sheets* 2·25 2·40
Nos. 2538/46 were printed together, se-tenant, in sheetlets of 9.

(Des D. Burkhart. Litho Questa)

1997 (20 Oct). *Cats and Dogs.* T **548** *and similar horiz designs. Multicoloured.* P 14.

2549	20 c. Type 548	10	10
2550	50 c. Singapura cat	10	10
2551	80 c. Papillon	10	10
2552	100 c. Sphinx cat	10	10
2553	150 c. British White cat	10	10
2554	200 c. Bulldog	10	10
2555	300 c. Snowshoe cat	10	15
2556	400 c. Shetland Sheepdog	15	20
2557	500 c. Schnauzer	20	25
2558	600 c. Persian cat	20	25
2559	800 c. Shih Tzu	30	35
2560	1000 c. Russian Wolfhound	35	40
	a. Sheetlet. Nos. 2560/5	2·10	
2561	1000 c. Birman cat	35	40
2562	1000 c. Basset Hound	35	40
2563	1000 c. Silver Tabby cat	35	40
2564	1000 c. Afghan	35	40
2565	1000 c. Burmilla cat	35	40
2566	1000 c. Abyssinian cat	35	40
	a. Sheetlet. Nos. 2566/71	2·10	
2567	1000 c. Border Terrier	35	40
2568	1000 c. Scottish Fold cat	35	40
2569	1000 c. Boston Terrier	35	40
2570	1000 c. Oriental cat	35	40
2571	1000 c. Keeshond	35	40
2572	2000 c. Chow Chow	70	75
2549/72		Set of 24	6·00 7·00

MS2573 Two sheets, each 73×100 mm. (a) 3000 c. Alaskan Malamute. (b) 3000 c. Ragdoll cat .. *Set of 2 sheets* 2·25 2·40
Nos. 2560/5 and 2566/71 were each printed together, se-tenant, in sheetlets of 6.

549 "Landscape" (Huang Binhong)   **550** Diana, Princess of Wales

(Des Y. Lee. Litho Questa)

1997 (10 Nov). *Return of Hong Kong to China.* T **549** *and similar designs showing landscape paintings by Huang Binhong (Nos.* 2574/81 *and* **MS**2582) *or historical scenes (No.* **MS**2583). P 14.

2574	200 c. multicoloured	10	10
	a. Sheetlet. Nos. 2574/81	2·10	
2575	300 c. multicoloured	10	15
2576	400 c. multicoloured	15	20
2577	500 c. multicoloured	20	25
2578	600 c. multicoloured	20	25
2579	800 c. multicoloured	30	35
2580	1000 c. multicoloured	35	40
2581	2000 c. multicoloured	70	75
2574/81		Set of 8	2·10 2·50

MS2582 138×105 mm. (a) 2000 c. multicoloured (farm). (b) 2000 c. multicoloured (mountains) (*each* 50×37 *mm*). P 14×13½ .. 1·40 1·50
MS2583 150×125 mm. (a) 1000 c. × 2 multicoloured (Lin Tse-Hue). (b) 1000 c. × 2 multicoloured (Gwen Tian-Pei) (*each* 63×31 *mm*) .. 1·40 1·50
Nos. 2574/81 were printed together, se-tenant, in sheetlets of 8.

(Litho B.D.T.)

1997 (8 Dec). *Christmas. Paintings.* Vert designs as T **386** of Antigua. Multicoloured. P 14.

2584	200 c. "Cupid" (Botticelli)	10	10
2585	550 c. "Zephyr and Chloris" (Botticelli)	20	25
2586	800 c. "Triumphant Cupid" (Caravaggio)	30	35
2587	1100 c. "The Seven Works of Mercy" (Caravaggio)	40	45
2588	1500 c. "The Toilet of Venus" (Diego Velazquez)	55	60
2589	2000 c. "Freeing of St. Peter" (Raphael)	70	75
2584/9		Set of 6	2·25 2·50

MS2590 Two sheets. (a) 95×105 mm. 5000 c. "The Cavalcanti Annunciation" (Donatello). (b) 105 x 95 mm. 5000 c. Ancient Egyptian painting of Isis and Nephthys .. *Set of 2 sheets* 3·75 4·00

(Litho Questa)

1997 (22 Dec). *Diana, Princess of Wales Commemoration.* T **550** *and similar vert designs. Multicoloured (except Nos.* 2591, 2596, 2602 *and* **MS**2603b). P 14.

2591	1200 c. Type 550 (brown-red)	45	50
	a. Sheetlet. Nos. 2591/6	2·75	
2592	1200 c. Wearing blue suit and holding flowers	45	50
2593	1200 c. Looking right	45	50
2594	1200 c. Sitting crossed-legged	45	50
2595	1200 c. With Prince William	45	50
2596	1200 c. Wearing spotted scarf (blue & blk)	45	50
2597	1200 c. Wearing pink shirt	45	50
	a. Sheetlet. Nos. 2597/602	2·75	
2598	1200 c. Wearing red dress	45	50
2599	1200 c. Carrying bouquet	45	50
2600	1200 c. Wearing sunglasses	45	50
2601	1200 c. With children	45	50
2602	1200 c. Wearing hat (light brown & black)	45	50
2591/602		Set of 12	5·50 6·00

MS2603 Two sheets. (a) 100×70 mm. 3000 c. Diana, Princess of Wales. (b) 70×100 mm. 3000 c. Diana, Princess of Wales (dull vio & blk) *Set of 2 sheets* 2·25 2·40
Nos. 2591/6 and 2597/602 were each printed together, se-tenant, in sheetlets of 6.

551 Horse   **552** Mortie and Ferdie (January)

(Litho Questa)

1998 (15 Jan). *Animals of the Chinese Lunar Calendar.* T **551** *and similar vert designs. Multicoloured.* P 13½.

2604	400 c. Type 551	15	20
	a. Sheetlet. Nos. 2604/15	1·75	
2605	400 c. Monkey	15	20
2606	400 c. Ram	15	20
2607	400 c. Cock	15	20
2608	400 c. Dog	15	20
2609	400 c. Ox	15	20
2610	400 c. Rabbit	15	20
2611	400 c. Pig	15	20
2612	400 c. Snake	15	20
2613	400 c. Dragon	15	20
2614	400 c. Tiger	15	20
2615	400 c. Rat	15	20
2604/15		Set of 12	1·75 2·40

Nos. 2604/15 were printed together, se-tenant, in sheetlets of 12.

(Des Walt Disney Co. Litho Questa)

1998 (29 Jan). *A Year in the Life of Mickey Mouse and Friends.* T **552** *and similar multicoloured designs showing Walt Disney cartoon characters.* P 13½×14.

2616	1000 c. Type 552	1·00	1·00
	a. Sheetlet. Nos. 2616/21	5·50	
2617	1000 c. Minnie on Valentine's Day (February)	1·00	1·00
2618	1000 c. Goofy with kite (March)	1·00	1·00
2619	1000 c. Mickey, Minnie and Pluto in rain (April)	1·00	1·00
2620	1000 c. Minnie with flowers (May)	1·00	1·00
2621	1000 c. Daisy watering garden (June)	1·00	1·00
2622	1000 c. Donald at Independance Day celebrations (July)	1·00	1·00
	a. Sheetlet. Nos. 2622/7	5·50	
2623	1000 c. Donald and Daisy on the beach (August)	1·00	1·00
2624	1000 c. Morty and Ferdie returning to school (September)	1·00	1·00
2625	1000 c. Hewey, Dewey and Louie at Hallowe'en (October)	1·00	1·00
2626	1000 c. Mickey on Thanksgiving Day (November)	1·00	1·00
2627	1000 c. Mickey and Minnie at Christmas (December)	1·00	1·00
2616/27		Set of 12	11·00 11·00

MS2628 Four sheets, each 132×107 mm. (a) 5000 c. Mickey bottle feeding calf (Spring) (*horiz*). (b) 5000 c. Minnie camping (Summer). (c) 5000 c. Goofy sweeping leaves (Autumn). (d) 5000 c. Daisy and Nephews on ice (Winter) (*horiz*). P 13½×14 (*vert*) or 14×13½ (*horiz*) *Set of 4 sheets* 18·00 18·00
Nos. 2616/21 and 2622/7 were each printed together, se-tenant, in sheetlets of 6.
Nos. 2616/28 were re-issued on 4 August 1998 overprinted on the sheet margins with "70th Anniversary Year" and emblem (Nos. 2616/27) or emblem only (No. **MS**2628).

553 Union Pacific SD60M Diesel Locomotive No. 6331, U.S.A.   **554** Maya Angelou

(Des G. Bibby. Litho Questa)

1998 (26 Feb). *Trains of the World.* T **553** *and similar horiz designs. Multicoloured.* P 14.

2629	300 c.	Type 553	10	15
2630	500 c.	ETR 450 high-speed train, Italy	20	25
2631	800 c.	X200 high-speed train, Sweden	30	35
2632	800 c.	SPS steam locomotive, Pakistan	30	35
		a. Sheetlet. Nos. 2632/40	2·75	
2633	800 c.	Class WP steam locomotive, India	30	35
2634	800 c.	Class QJ steam locomotive, China	30	35
2635	800 c.	Type 12 steam locomotive, Belgium	30	35
2636	800 c.	Class P8 steam locomotive, Germany	30	35
2637	800 c.	Class "Castle" steam locomotive, Great Britain	30	35
2638	800 c.	Tank locomotive, Austria	30	35
2639	800 c.	Class P36 steam locomotive, Russia	30	35
2640	800 c.	Steam locomotive *William Mason*, U.S.A.	30	35
2641	800 c.	AVE high-speed train, Spain	30	35
		a. Sheetlet. Nos. 2641/9	2·75	
2642	800 c.	Diesel locomotive No. 1602, Luxembourg	30	35
2643	800 c.	"Hikari" express train, Japan	30	35
2644	800 c.	Santa Fe Railroad GM F7 "Warbonnet" diesel locomotive, U.S.A.	30	35
2645	800 c.	Class E1500 diesel locomotive, Morocco	30	35
2646	800 c.	Class "Deltic" diesel locomotive, Great Britain	30	35
2647	800 c.	XPT high-speed train, Australia	30	35
2648	800 c.	Channel Tunnel shuttle train, France and Great Britain	30	35
2649	800 c.	Class 201 diesel locomotive, Ireland	30	35
2650	1000 c.	TGV Duplex high-speed train, France	35	40
2651	2000 c.	Class EL diesel locomotive, Australia	70	75
2652	3000 c.	Eurostar high-speed train, Great Britain	1·10	1·25
2626/52		*Set of 24*	8·25	9·50

MS2653 Two sheets, each 106×76 mm. (a) 5500 c. Class "Duchess" steam locomotive heading the "Irish Mail", Great Britain (56×42 *mm*). (b) 5500 c. TGV express train, France (56×42 *mm*) ... *Set of 2 sheets* 4·00 4·25

Nos. 2632/40 and 2641/9 were each printed together, *se-tenant*, in sheetlets of 9.

1998 (25 Mar). *Great Writers of the 20th Century.* T **554** *and similar vert designs. Multicoloured.* P 14.

2654	350 c.	Type 554	15	20
		a. Sheetlet. Nos. 2654/9	90	
2655	350 c.	Alex Haley	15	20
2656	350 c.	Charles Johnson	15	20
2657	350 c.	Richard Wright	15	20
2658	350 c.	Toni Cade Bambara	15	20
2659	350 c.	Henri Louis Gates Jr	15	20
2654/9		*Set of 6*	90	1·25

Nos. 2654/9 were printed together, *se-tenant*, in sheetlets of 6.

555 Breguet Br 14 B2, France

1998 (5 May). *History of Aviation.* T **555** *and similar horiz designs. Multicoloured. Litho.* P 14.

2660	800 c.	Type 555	30	35
		a. Sheetlet. Nos. 2660/8	2·75	
2661	800 c.	Curtiss BF2C-1 Goshawk, U.S.A.	30	35
2662	800 c.	Supermarine Spitfire Mk IX, Great Britain	30	35
2663	800 c.	Fiat G.50, Italy	30	35
2664	800 c.	Douglas B-18A, U.S.A.	30	35
2665	800 c.	Boeing FB-5, U.S.A.	30	35
2666	800 c.	Bristol F2B "Brisfit", Great Britain	30	35
2667	800 c.	Hawker Fury I, Great Britain	30	35
2668	800 c.	Fiat CR-42, Italy	30	35
2669	800 c.	Messerschmitt Bf 109 E-7, Germany	30	35
		a. Sheetlet. Nos. 2669/77	2·75	
2670	800 c.	Lockheed PV-2 Harpoon, U.S.A.	30	35
2671	800 c.	Airspeed Oxford Mk 1, Great Britain	30	35
2672	800 c.	Junkers Ju 87D-1, Germany	30	35
2673	800 c.	Yakovlev Yak-9D, U.S.S.R.	30	35
2674	800 c.	North American P-51D Mustang, U.S.A.	30	35
2675	800 c.	Douglas A-206 Havoc, U.S.A.	30	35
2676	800 c.	Supermarine Attacker F1, Great Britain	30	35
2677	800 c.	Mikoyan Gurevich MiG-15, U.S.S.R.	30	35
2660/77		*Set of 18*	5·50	6·25

MS2678 Two sheets, each 106×76 mm. (a) 3000 c. Supermarine Spitfires Mk 1 and Mk XIV, Great Britain (58×43 *mm*). (b) 3000 c. Mitsubishi AGM8 Reisen, Japan (58×43 *mm*) ... *Set of 2 sheets* 2·25 2·40

Nos. 2660/8 and 2669/77 were printed together, *se-tenant*, in sheetlets of 9.

NEW INFORMATION

The editor is always interested to correspond with people who have new information that will improve or correct the Catalogue.

---

556 *Empress of Ireland* (liner)   **(557)**

(Des S. Thurston. Litho B.D.T.)

1998 (5 May). *Famous Ships.* T **556** *and similar multicoloured designs.* P 14.

2679	800 c.	Type 556	30	35
		a. Sheetlet. Nos. 2679/87	2·75	
2680	800 c.	*Transylvania* (liner)	30	35
2681	800 c.	*Mauretania I* (liner)	30	35
2682	800 c.	*Reliance* (liner)	30	35
2683	800 c.	*Aquitania* (liner)	30	35
2684	800 c.	*Lapland* (liner)	30	35
2685	800 c.	*Cap Polonio* (liner)	30	35
2686	800 c.	*France I, 1910* (liner)	30	35
2687	800 c.	*Imperator* (liner)	30	35
2688	800 c.	H.M.S. *Rodney* (battleship)	30	35
		a. Sheetlet. Nos. 2688/96	2·75	
2689	800 c.	U.S.S. *Alabama* (battleship)	30	35
2690	800 c.	H.M.S. *Nelson* (battleship)	30	35
2691	800 c.	*Ormonde* (camouflaged liner)	30	35
2692	800 c.	U.S.S. *Radford* (destroyer)	30	35
2693	800 c.	*Empress of Russia* (camouflaged liner)	30	35
2694	800 c.	Type XIV U-boat	30	35
2695	800 c.	Japanese Type A midget submarine	30	35
2696	800 c.	*Brin* (Italian submarine)	30	35
2679/96		*Set of 18*	5·50	6·25

MS2697 Two sheets, each 100×75 mm. (a) 5500 c. *Titanic* (liner) (43×57 *mm*). (b) 5500 c. *Amistad* (slave schooner) (43×57 *mm*) ... *Set of 2 sheets* 4·00 4·25

Nos. 2679/87 and 2688/96 were each printed together, *se-tenant*, in sheetlets of 9.

Nos. 2681 is inscribed "MAURITANIA" in error.

1998 (13 May). *"Israel 98" International Stamp Exhibition, Tel-Aviv. Nos. 2362/5 optd with T* **557**.

2698	400 c.	St. Stephen's Gate and *Jasminum mesnyi*	15	20
2699	600 c.	The Citadel, Tower of David and *Nerium oleander*	20	25
2700	800 c.	Chapel of the Ascension and *Romulea bulbocodium*	30	35
		a. Opt inverted		
2698/700		*Set of 3*	65	80

MS2701 65×80 mm. 2000 c. Russian Orthodox Church of St. Mary Magdalene (48×30 *mm*) ... 70 75

No. **MS**2701 is additionally overprinted "ISRAEL 98 – WORLD STAMP EXHIBITION TEL-AVIV 13–21 MAY 1998" on the sheet margin.

558 *Renanthera imschootiana*   **559** Elvis Presley

1998 (2 June). *Orchids of the World.* T **558** *and similar vert designs. Multicoloured. Litho.* P 14.

2702	800 c.	Type 558	30	35
		a. Sheetlet. Nos. 2702/7	1·75	
2703	800 c.	*Arachnis flos-aeris*	30	35
2704	800 c.	*Restrepia lansbergi*	30	35
2705	800 c.	*Paphiopedilum tonsum*	30	35
2706	800 c.	*Phalaenopsis ebauche*	30	35
2707	800 c.	*Pleione limprichti*	30	35
2708	800 c.	*Phragmipedium schroderae*	30	35
		a. Sheetlet. Nos. 2708/13	1·75	
2709	800 c.	*Zygopetalum clayii*	30	35
2710	800 c.	*Vanda coerulea*	30	35
2711	800 c.	*Odontonia boussole*	30	35
2712	800 c.	*Disa uniflora*	30	35
2713	800 c.	*Dendrobium bigibbum*	30	35
2702/13		*Set of 12*	3·50	4·25

MS2714 Two sheets, each 98×68 mm. (a) 5500 c. *Cypripedium calceolus*. (b) 5500 c. *Sobralia candida* ... *Set of 2 sheets* 4·00 4·25

Nos. 2702/7 and 2708/13 were each printed together, *se-tenant*, in sheetlets of 6.

1998 (16 June). *30th Anniv of Elvis Presley's "68 Special" Television Programme.* T **559** *and similar vert designs. Multicoloured.* P 13½.

2715	800 c.	Type 559	30	35
		a. Sheetlet. Nos. 2715/20	1·75	
2716	800 c.	Elvis in white suit	30	35
2717	800 c.	In leather jacket, holding microphone	30	35
2718	800 c.	Wearing light blue jacket	30	35
2719	800 c.	Elvis with silhouetted figures in background	30	35
2720	800 c.	Elvis with guitar and microphone	30	35
2715/20		*Set of 6*	1·75	2·10

Nos. 2715/20 were printed together, *se-tenant*, in sheetlets of 6 with enlarged illustrated margins.

---

560 Crest of Accra Metropolitan Assembly and Surf Boats   **561** Tetteh Quarshie (cocoa industry pioneer)

(Litho Cartor)

1998 (8 July). *Centenary of Accra Metropolitan Assembly.* T **560** *and similar horiz designs. Multicoloured.* P 13×13½.

2721	200 c.	Type 560	10	10
2722	550 c.	King Tackie Tawiah I	20	25
2723	800 c.	Achimota School	30	35
2724	1100 c.	Korle Bu Hospital	40	45
2725	1500 c.	Christianborg Castle	55	60
2721/5		*Set of 5*	1·50	1·75

(Litho Cartor)

1998 (8 July). *50th Anniv of Ghana Cocoa Board.* T **561** *and similar horiz designs. Multicoloured.* P 13×13½.

2726	200 c.	Type 561	10	10
2727	550 c.	Ripe hybrid cocoa pods	20	25
2728	800 c.	Opening cocoa pods	30	35
2729	1100 c.	Fermenting cocoa beans	40	45
2730	1500 c.	Loading freighter with cocoa	55	60
2726/30		*Set of 5*	1·50	1·75

562 Bamboo   **563** Two Dolphins

(Des Kang Cheng Weng. Litho Questa)

1998 (14 July). *Oriental Flowers.* T **562** *and similar multicoloured designs.* P 14.

2731	2000 c.	Type 562	70	75
		a. Sheetlet. Nos. 2731/4	2·75	
2732	2000 c.	Cherry blossom	70	75
2733	2000 c.	Yellow chrysanthemum	70	75
2734	2000 c.	Orchid	70	75
2735	2000 c.	Green peony	70	75
		a. Sheetlet. Nos. 2735/8	2·75	
2736	2000 c.	Red peony	70	75
2737	2000 c.	Pink peony	70	75
2738	2000 c.	White peony	70	75
2731/8		*Set of 8*	5·50	6·00

MS2739 Two sheets, each 109×85 mm. (a) 5500 c. Cherry blossom (*horiz*). (b) 5500 c. Peonies (*horiz*) ... *Set of 2 sheets* 4·00 4·25

Nos. 2731/4 and 2735/8 were each printed together, *se-tenant*, in sheetlets of 4.

(Des S. Stines. Litho Questa)

1998 (18 Aug). *International Year of the Ocean.* T **563** *and similar horiz designs. Multicoloured.* P 14.

2740	500 c.	Type 563	20	25
		a. Sheetlet. Nos. 2740/55	3·25	
2741	500 c.	Dolphin	20	25
2742	500 c.	Seagull	20	25
2743	500 c.	Least Tern	20	25
2744	500 c.	Emperor Angelfish	20	25
2745	500 c.	White Ear (juvenile)	20	25
2746	500 c.	Blue Shark and diver	20	25
2747	500 c.	Parrotfish	20	25
2748	500 c.	Dottyback	20	25
2749	500 c.	Blue-spotted Stingray	20	25
2750	500 c.	Masked Butterflyfish	20	25
2751	500 c.	Jackknife-Fish	20	25
2752	500 c.	Octopus	20	25
2753	500 c.	Lionfish	20	25
2754	500 c.	Seadragon	20	25
2755	500 c.	Rock Cod	20	25
2740/55		*Set of 16*	3·25	4·00

MS2756 Two sheets. (a) 63×98 mm. 3000 c. Great White Shark. (b) 98×63 mm. 3000 c. Devil Ray ... *Set of 2 sheets* 2·25 2·40

Nos. 2740/55 were printed together, *se-tenant*, in sheetlets of 16 with the backgrounds forming a composite design.

No. 2745 is inscribed "Whit Ear" in error.

(Des S. Stirnweiss. Litho B.D.T.)

1998 (1 Sept). *Millennium Series. Famous People of the Twentieth Century. Inventors. Multicoloured designs as T* **398** *of Antigua.* P 14.

2757	1000 c.	Thomas Edison	35	40
		a. Sheetlet. Nos. 2757/64	2·75	
2758	1000 c.	Peephole kinetoscope (Edison) (53×38 *mm*)	35	40
2759	1000 c.	Tesla coil (53×38 *mm*)	35	40
2760	1000 c.	Nikola Tesla	35	40
2761	1000 c.	Gottlieb Daimler	35	40
2762	1000 c.	Motorcycle (Daimler) (53×38 *mm*)	35	40

2763	1000 c.	Early transmitter circuit (Marconi) and dish aerial (53×38 *mm*)	35	40
2764	1000 c.	Guglielmo Marconi	35	40
2765	1000 c.	Orville and Wilbur Wright	35	40
		a. Sheetlet. Nos. 2765/72	2·75	
2766	1000 c.	*Flyer I* (Wright Brothers) (53×38 *mm*)	35	40
2767	1000 c.	Neon lights and signs (Claude) (53×38 *mm*)	35	40
2768	1000 c.	Georges Claude	35	40
2769	1000 c.	Alexander Graham Bell	35	40
2770	1000 c.	Early telephone transmitter (Bell) (53×38 *mm*)	35	40
2771	1000 c.	Uses of lasers (Townes) (53×38 *mm*)	35	40
2772	1000 c.	Charles Townes	35	40
2757/72		*Set of 16*	5·50	6·50

MS2773 Two sheets, each 76×106 mm. (a) 5500 c. Paul Ehrlich. (b) 5500 c. Robert Goddard
Set of 2 sheets 4·00 4·25
Nos. 2757/64 and 2765/72 were each printed together, *se-tenant*, in sheetlets of 8 with enlarged illustrated margins.

564 British Colourpoint with Tree Decoration

565 Farmer working

(Litho B.D.T.)

1998 (1 Dec). *Christmas. Cats and Dogs. T* 564 *and similar vert designs. Multicoloured. P* 14.

2774	500 c.	Type 564	20	25
2775	600 c.	American Shorthair kitten with basket	20	25
2776	800 c.	Peke-faced Persian on piano keys	30	35
2777	1000 c.	German Spitz dog in box	35	40
2778	2000 c.	British Shorthair Blue with antlers	70	75
2779	3000 c.	Persian in sleigh	1·10	1·25
2774/9		*Set of 6*	2·75	3·25

MS2780 Two sheets, each 76×106 mm. (a) 5500 c. English Pointer puppy. (b) 5500 c. Manx cat with decoration .. *Set of 2 sheets* 4·00 4·25

(Des Diana Catherines. Litho Questa)

1999 (4 Jan). *25th Death Anniv of Pablo Picasso (painter). Multicoloured designs as T* 400 *of Antigua. P* 14½.

2781	1000 c.	"Composition with Butterfly"	35	40
2782	1000 c.	"Mandolin and Clarinet" (*vert*)	35	40
2783	2000 c.	"Woman throwing a Stone"	70	75
2781/3		*Set of 3*	1·40	1·50

MS2784 101×127 mm. 5500 c. "Tomato Plant" (*vert*) .. .. 2·00 2·10

(Des F. Rivera. Litho Questa)

1999 (4 Jan). *Birth Centenary of Enzo Ferrari (car manufacturer). Horiz designs as T* 401 *of Antigua. Multicoloured. P* 14.

2785	2000 c.	Lampredi	70	75
		a. Sheetlet. Nos. 2785/7	2·10	
2786	2000 c.	250 GT Cabriolet	70	75
2787	2000 c.	121 LM	70	75
2785/7		*Set of 3*	2·10	2·25

MS2788 100×70 mm. 3000 c. 365 GTS/4 Spyder (91×34 *mm*). P 14×14½ .. 1·10 1·25
Nos. 2785/7 were printed together, *se-tenant*, in sheetlets of 3.
Nos. 2785/8 also exist imperforate from a limited printing.

(Litho Questa)

1999 (4 Jan). *19th World Scout Jamboree, Chile. Designs as T* 402 *of Antigua, but vert. Multicoloured (except No.* MS2792*). P* 14.

2789	2000 c.	Scout salute	70	75
		a. Sheetlet. Nos. 2789/91	2·10	
2790	2000 c.	Scout with backpack	70	75
2791	2000 c.	Bowline knot	70	75
2789/91		*Set of 3*	2·10	2·25

MS2792 55×70 mm. 5000 c. Lord Baden-Powell (olive-bistre and black) .. 1·90 2·00
Nos. 2789/91 were printed together, *se-tenant*, in sheetlets of 3 with illustrated margins.

(Des M. LeBoeuf. Litho Questa)

1999 (4 Jan). *50th Death Anniv of Mahatma Gandhi. Multicoloured designs as T* 403 *of Antigua. P* 14.

2793	2000 c.	Gandhi, 1931	70	75
		a. Sheetlet. Nos. 2793/6	2·75	
2794	2000 c.	On Salt March, 1930 (53×38 *mm*)	70	75
2795	2000 c.	Collecting natural salt, 1930 (53×38 *mm*)	70	75
2796	2000 c.	After graduating from high school, 1887	70	75
2793/6		*Set of 4*	2·75	3·00

MS2797 60×79 mm. 5500 c. Mahatma Gandhi seated, 1931 .. .. .. 2·00 2·10
Nos. 2793/6 were printed together, *se-tenant*, in sheetlets of 4 with enlarged illustrated margins.

(Des D. Miller. Litho Questa)

1999 (4 Jan). *80th Anniv of Royal Air Force. Horiz designs as T* 404 *of Antigua. Multicoloured. P* 14.

2798	2000 c.	C-130 Hercules on tarmac	70	75
		a. Sheetlet. Nos. 2798/801	2·75	
2799	2000 c.	HC2 Chinook helicopter	70	75
2800	2000 c.	C-130 Hercules W2 taking off	70	75
2801	2000 c.	Panavia Tornado F3	70	75
2798/801		*Set of 4*	2·75	3·00

MS2802 Two sheets, each 90×70 mm. (a) 5500 c. Chipmunk and EF-2000 Euro-fighter. (b) 5500 c. Bristol F2B fighter and eagle . *Set of 2 sheets* 4·00 4·25
Nos. 2798/801 were printed together, *se-tenant*, in sheetlets of 4 with enlarged illustrated margins.

(Litho Questa)

1999 (4 Jan). *1st Death Anniv of Diana, Princess of Wales. Vert design as T* 405 *of Antigua. P* 14½×14.

2803	1000 c.	multicoloured	35	40
		a. Sheetlet of 6	2·10	

No. 2803 was printed in sheetlets of 6 with enlarged illustrated left-hand margin.

(Des Y. Lee. Litho Questa)

1999 (4 Jan). *Chinese New Year ("Year of the Rabbit"). "Farmer and the Hare" (Han Fei Tzu). T* 565 *and similar vert designs. Multicoloured. P* 13½×14.

2804	1400 c.	Type 565	50	55
		a. Sheetlet. Nos. 2804/7	2·00	
2805	1400 c.	Farmer watching hare hit tree	50	55
2806	1400 c.	Farmer with dead hare	50	55
2807	1400 c.	Farmer asleep under tree	50	55
2804/7		*Set of 4*	2·00	2·25

Nos. 2804/7 were printed together, *se-tenant*, in sheetlets of 4 with an enlarged illustrated right-hand margin.

566 Shirley Temple praying

(Des Rita Dubas. Litho Questa)

1999 (1 Mar). *70th Birthday of Shirley Temple (actress). T* 566 *and similar multicoloured designs showing film scenes from* Curly Top. *P* 13½×14 (*vert*) *or* 14×13½ (*horiz*).

2808	1000 c.	Type 566	35	40
		a. Sheetlet. Nos. 2808/11	1·40	
2809	1000 c.	Man looking at painting	35	40
2810	1000 c.	With butler	35	40
2811	1000 c.	As old woman in rocking chair	35	40
2812	1000 c.	With mother (*horiz*)	35	40
		a. Sheetlet. Nos. 2812/17	2·10	
2813	1000 c.	Wearing brown coat and bowler hat (*horiz*)	35	40
2814	1000 c.	With cuddly toys (*horiz*)	35	40
2815	1000 c.	Pulling father's tie (*horiz*)	35	40
2816	1000 c.	With family (*horiz*)	35	40
2817	1000 c.	Watching parents (*horiz*)	35	40
2808/17		*Set of 10*	3·50	4·00

MS2818 106×76 mm. 5000 c. Shirley Temple on piano .. .. 1·90 2·00
Nos. 2808/11 and 2812/17 were each printed together, *se-tenant* in sheetlets of 4 (Nos. 2808/11) or 6 (Nos. 2812/17) with enlarged illustrated right-hand margins.

567 Corythosaurus

1999 (1 Mar). *Prehistoric Animals. T* 567 *and similar multicoloured designs. P* 13½.

2819	400 c.	Type 567	15	20
2820	600 c.	Struthiomimus	20	25
2821	800 c.	Pterodactylus	30	35
		a. Sheetlet. Nos. 2821/9	2·75	
2822	800 c.	Scelidosaurus	30	35
2823	800 c.	Pteranodon	30	35
2824	800 c.	Plateosaurus	30	35
2825	800 c.	Ornithosuchus	30	35
2826	800 c.	Kentrosaurus	30	35
2827	800 c.	Hypsognathus	30	35
2828	800 c.	Erythrosuchus	30	35
2829	800 c.	Stegoceras	30	35
2830	800 c.	Ankylosaurus	30	35
		a. Sheetlet. Nos. 2830/8	2·75	
2831	800 c.	Anatosaurus	30	35
2832	800 c.	Diplodocus	30	35
2833	800 c.	Monoclonius	30	35
2834	800 c.	Tyrannosaurus	30	35
2835	800 c.	Camptosaurus	30	35
2836	800 c.	Ornitholestes	30	35
2837	800 c.	Archaeopteryx	30	35
2838	800 c.	Allosaurus	30	35
2839	1000 c.	Lambeosaurus	35	40
2840	2000 c.	Hesperasuchus	70	75
2819/40		*Set of 22*	6·75	8·00

MS2841 Two sheets, each 85×110 mm. (a) 5000 c. Dimorphodon (*vert*). (b) 5000 c. Apatosaurus .. .. *Set of 2 sheets* 3·75 4·00
Nos. 2821/9 and 2830/8 were each printed together, *se-tenant*, in sheetlets of 9, with the backgrounds forming composite designs.

568 Badgers

(Des E. Moreiro. Litho Questa)

1999 (29 Mar). *Endangered Species. T* 568 *and similar multicoloured designs. P* 14.

2842	200 c.	Type 568	10	15
2843	400 c.	Azure-winged Magpie (*Cyanopica cyana*)	15	20
2844	600 c.	White Stork (*Ciconia ciconia*)	20	25
2845	800 c.	Red Fox	30	35
2846	1000 c.	European Bee Eater (*Merops apiaster*)	35	40
		a. Sheetlet. Nos. 2846/51	2·10	
2847	1000 c.	Hoopoe (*Upupa epops*)	35	40
2848	1000 c.	Red Deer	35	40
2849	1000 c.	Short-toed Eagle (*Cycaetus gallicus*)	35	40
2850	1000 c.	*Lacerta oceliata* (lizard)	35	40
2851	1000 c.	Lynx	35	40
2852	1000 c.	Pine Martin	35	40
		a. Sheetlet. Nos. 2852/7	2·10	
2853	1000 c.	Tawny Owl (*Strix aluco*)	35	40
2854	1000 c.	Wild Boar	35	40
2855	1000 c.	Northern Goshawk (*Accipiter gentilis*)	35	40
2856	1000 c.	Garden Dormouse	35	40
2857	1000 c.	Stag Beetles	35	40
2858	2000 c.	European Black Vulture (*Aegypius monachus*) (*vert*)	70	75
2859	3000 c.	Jay (*Garrulus glandarius*) (*vert*)	1·10	1·25
2842/59		*Set of 18*	6·75	7·75

MS2860 Two sheets, each 85×110 mm. (a) 5000 c. Imperial Eagle. (b) 5000 c. Wolf cub (*vert*)
Set of 2 sheets 3·75 4·00
Nos. 2846/51 and 2852/7 were each printed together, *se-tenant*, in sheetlets of 6 with the backgrounds forming composite designs.

569 California Sister Butterfly

570 *Amorphophallus flavovirens*

(Des L. Schwinger. Litho Questa)

1999 (26 Apr). *"Australia '99" International Stamp Exhibition, Melbourne. Butterflies. T* 569 *and similar multicoloured designs. P* 14.

2861	300 c.	Type 569	10	15
2862	500 c.	Red-splashed Sulphur	20	25
2863	600 c.	Checked White	20	25
2864	800 c.	Blue Emperor	30	35
2865	1000 c.	Red Admiral (*vert*)	35	40
		a. Sheetlet. Nos. 2865/72	2·75	
2866	1000 c.	Buckeye (*vert*)	35	40
2867	1000 c.	Desert Chequered Skipper (*vert*)	35	40
2868	1000 c.	Orange Sulphur (*vert*)	35	40
2869	1000 c.	Tiger Swallowtail (*vert*)	35	40
2870	1000 c.	Orange-bordered Blue (*vert*)	35	40
2871	1000 c.	Gulf Fritillary (*Agraulis vanillae*) (*vert*)	35	40
2872	1000 c.	Monarch (*vert*)	35	40
2873	1000 c.	Small Tortoiseshell (*vert*)	35	40
		a. Sheetlet. Nos. 2873/80	2·75	
2874	1000 c.	Brimstone (*vert*)	35	40
2875	1000 c.	Camberwell Beauty (*vert*)	35	40
2876	1000 c.	Marbled White (*vert*)	35	40
2877	1000 c.	Purple Emperor (*vert*)	35	40
2878	1000 c.	Clouded Yellow (*vert*)	35	40
2879	1000 c.	*Ladoga camilla* (*vert*)	35	40
2880	1000 c.	Marsh Fritillary (*vert*)	35	40
2861/80		*Set of 20*	6·50	7·50

MS2881 Two sheets, each 106×76 mm. (a) 5000 c. Homerus Swallowtail (*vert*). (b) 5000 c. Blue Copper .. .. *Set of 2 sheets* 3·75 4·00
Nos. 2865/72 and 2873/80 were each printed together, *se-tenant*, in sheetlets of 8 with the backgrounds forming composite designs.
No. 2862 is inscribed "Red-splashed Sulfer" and No. 2864 "Blue Emperorl", both in error.

(Litho Ikam Security Ptg Ltd, Accra)

1999 (6 May). *P* 13½×14.

2882	**570** 200 c.	multicoloured	10	15

571 ICE 2 (Germany), 1966   **572** Gate of Understanding, Macao

(Litho B.D.T.)

1999 (10 May). *Railways of the World. T **571** and similar horiz designs. Multicoloured. P 14.*

2883	400 c. Type **571**	15	20
2884	500 c. M41 No. 2112 (Hungary), 1982	20	25
2885	600 c. DVR No. 2526 (Finland), 1963	20	25
2886	1000 c. Class AVE 100 (Spain), 1992	35	40
2887	1300 c. Conrail EMD SD80 No. 4110 (U.S.A.), 1993	50	55
	a. Sheetlet. Nos. 2887/92	3·00	
2888	1300 c. Columbus and Greenville EMD SDP35 No. 701 (U.S.A.), 1964–6	50	55
2889	1300 c. Providence and Worcester MLW M420 (U.S.A.), 1973–77	50	55
2890	1300 c. Missouri Pacific C36-7 No. 9044 (U.S.A.), 1978–85	50	55
2891	1300 c. Virginia and Maryland ALCO C-420 No. 203 (U.S.A.), 1963–68	50	55
2892	1300 c. Reading EMD GP30 No. 3615 (U.S.A.), 1961–63	50	55
2893	1300 c. Illinois Terminal EMD GP7 No. 1506 (U.S.A.), 1949–54	50	55
	a. Sheetlet. Nos. 2893/8	3·00	
2894	1300 c. Canadian Pacific EMD SD 38-2 (Canada), 1972–79	50	55
2895	1300 c. EMD SD 60M 500 No. 6058 (U.S.A.), 1989–96	50	55
2896	1300 c. GE U25C No. 2808 (U.S.A.), 1963–65	50	55
2897	1300 c. EMD GP 28 (U.S.A.), 1961–63	50	55
2898	1300 c. EMD SD 9 No. 162 (U.S.A.), 1954–59	50	55
2883/98	*Set of 16*	7·00	7·75

MS2899 Two sheets (a) 85×110 mm. 5000 c. Swiss Federal Class RE 6/6 No. 11630, 1972. (b) 110×85 mm. 5000 c. AGP44 (U.S.A.), 1990–91
      Set of 2 sheets 3·75 4·00

Nos. 2887/92 and 2893/8 were each printed together, *se-tenant*, in sheetlets of 6.

(Litho Questa)

1999 (3 Aug). *"iBRA '99" International Stamp Exhibition, Nuremberg. Multicoloured designs as T **416** of Antigua. P 14×14½.*

2900	500 c. *Schomberg* (sailing ship) and Hanover 1850 1 ggr. stamp	20	25
2901	800 c. Class P8 railway locomotive and Hamburg 1859 ½ s.	30	35
2902	1000 c. *Schomberg* (sailing ship) and Lübeck 1859 ½ s.	35	40
2903	2000 c. Class P8 railway locomotive and Heligoland 1867 ½ s.	70	75
2900/3	*Set of 4*	1·50	1·75

MS2904 134×106 mm. 5000 c. Germany 3 pf. stamp on 1912 Bork-Bruck flown cover (*vert*). P 14½×14   1·90 2·00

1999 (3 Aug). *150th Death Anniv of Katsushika Hokusai (Japanese artist). Multicoloured designs as T **417** of Antigua. Litho. P 13½.*

2905	1300 c. "Girl picking Plum Blossoms"	50	55
	a. Sheetlet. Nos. 2905/10	3·00	
2906	1300 c. "Surveying a Region"	50	55
2907	1300 c. "Sumo Wrestler" (bending down)	50	55
	a. Sheetlet. Nos. 2907 and 2911/15	3·00	
2908	1300 c. "Sumo Wrestler" (dancing)	50	55
2909	1300 c. "Landscape with Seaside Village"	50	55
2910	1300 c. "Courtiers crossing a Bridge"	50	55
2911	1300 c. "Climbing the Mountain"	50	55
2912	1300 c. "Nakahara in Sagami Province"	50	55
2913	1300 c. "Sumo Wrestlers"	50	55
2914	1300 c. "An Oiran and Maid by a Fence"	50	55
2915	1300 c. "Fujiwara Yoshitaka"	50	55
2905/15	*Set of 11*	5·50	6·00

MS2916 Two sheets, each 100×70 mm. (a) 5000 c. "Palanquin Bearers on a Steep Hill" (*vert*). (b) 5000 c. "Three Ladies by a Well" (*vert*)   *Set of 2 sheets* 3·75 4·00

Nos. 2905/10 and 2907 with 2911/15 were each printed together, *se-tenant*, in sheetlets of 6.

1999 (3 Aug). *10th Anniv of United Nations Rights of the Child Convention. Vert designs as T **419** of Antigua. Multicoloured. Litho. P 14.*

2917	3000 c. Boy smiling and U.N. Head-quarters Building	1·10	1·25
	a. Sheetlet. Nos. 2917/19	3·25	
2918	3000 c. Dove and Earth	1·10	1·25
2919	3000 c. Mother and baby	1·10	1·25
2917/19	*Set of 3*	3·25	3·75

MS2920 110×85 mm. 5000 c. Boy and U.N.I.C.E.F. emblem   1·90 2·00

Nos. 2917/19 were printed together, *se-tenant*, in sheetlets of 3 forming a composite design.

1999 (3 Aug). *"PhilexFrance '99" International Stamp Exhibition, France. Railway Locomotives. Two sheets, each 106×76 mm, containing horiz designs as T **420** of Antigua. Multicoloured. P 14×13½.*

MS2921 (a) 5000 c. Western Railway suburban tank locomotive. (b) 5000 c. National Railways Class 232-U1   *Set of 2 sheets* 3·75 4·00

1999 (3 Aug). *250th Birth Anniv of Johann von Goethe (German writer). Horiz designs as T **421** of Antigua. Multicoloured. Litho. P 14.*

2922	2000 c. Wagner entreats Faust in his Study	70	75
	a. Sheetlet. Nos. 2922/4	2·10	
2923	2000 c. Von Goethe and Von Schiller	70	75
2924	2000 c. Mephistopheles disguised as the Fool	70	75
2922/4	*Set of 3*	2·10	2·25

MS2925 106×71 mm. 5000 c. Faust attended by Spirits   1·90 2·00

Nos. 2922/4 were printed together, *se-tenant*, in sheetlets of 3 with illustrated margins.

1999 (3 Aug). *30th Anniv of First Manned Landing on Moon. Multicoloured designs as T **333** of Dominica. Litho. P 14.*

2926	1300 c. Command module (*vert*)	50	55
	a. Sheetlet. Nos. 2926/31	3·00	
2927	1300 c. Lunar module ascending (*vert*)	50	55
2928	1300 c. Giant moon rock (*vert*)	50	55
2929	1300 c. Lunar module's aerials and Earth from Moon (*vert*)	50	55
2930	1300 c. Neil Armstrong (*vert*)	50	55
2931	1300 c. "One small step" (alighting on lunar surface) (*vert*)	50	55
2926/31	*Set of 6*	3·00	3·25

MS2932 71×106 mm. 5000 c. Earth from Moon 1·90 2·00

Nos. 2926/31 were printed together, *se-tenant*, in sheetlets of 6 forming a composite design.

No. 2927 is inscribed "LUNAR MODULE ASCENSION" in error

1999 (3 Aug). *"China '99" World Philatelic Exhibition, Beijing. Return of Macao to China. Litho. P 14×13½.*

2933	**572** 1000 c. multicoloured	35	40
	a. Sheetlet of 4	1·40	

No. 2933 was printed in sheetlets of 4 with enlarged, illustrated right-hand margin.

1999 (4 Aug). *"Queen Elizabeth the Queen Mother's Century". Vert designs as T **334** of Dominica. Litho. P 14.*

2934	2000 c. black and gold	70	75
	a. Sheetlet. Nos. 2934/7	2·75	
2935	2000 c. black and gold	70	75
2936	2000 c. multicoloured	70	75
2937	2000 c. multicoloured	70	75
2934/7	*Set of 4*	2·75	3·00

MS2938 153×157 mm. 5000 c. multicoloured. P 13½×14   1·90 2·00

Designs: (As *Type **334*** of Dominica)—No. 2934, Lady Elizabeth Bowes-Lyon with her brother, David, 1904; No. 2935, Queen Mother in Rhodesia, 1957; No. 2936, Queen Mother seated, 1970; No. 2937 Queen Mother holding bouquet, 1992. (37×50 *mm*)—No. **MS**2938, Queen Mother in garden, 1970.

Nos. 2934/7 were printed together, *se-tenant*, as a sheetlet of 4 stamps and a central label with embossed and inscribed margins. No. **MS**2938 also shows the Royal Arms embossed in gold.

573 Dr. Ephraim Apu   **574** Grandma Alice and Village

(Litho Cartor)

1999 (15 Nov). *Birth Centenary of Dr. Ephraim Apu (traditional musicologist). T **573** and similar vert designs. Multicoloured. P 13½×13.*

2939	200 c. Type **573**	10	15
2940	800 c. Playing Odurugya flute	30	35
2941	1100 c. Indigenious flutes	40	45
2939/41	*Set of 3*	80	85

(Litho Cartor)

1999 (15 Nov). *25th Anniv of S.O.S. in Ghana (200, 1100 c.) and 50th Anniv of S.O.S. Kinderdorf International (children's villages) (others). T **574** and similar horiz designs. Multicoloured. P 13×13½.*

2942	200 c. Type **574**	10	15
2943	550 c. Kindergarten	20	25
2944	800 c. Hermann Gneiner (founder) and Asiakwa S.O.S. building	30	35
2945	1100 c. Preparing food	40	45
2942/5	*Set of 4*	1·00	1·10

575 Fishes inside Cloud   **576** Peace Doves flying from Ghana

(Litho Cartor)

1999 (17 Nov). *Save the Ozone Layer Campaign. T **575** and similar vert designs. Multicoloured. P 13½×13.*

2946	200 c. Type **575**	10	15
2947	550 c. African looking at diagram of ozone layer	20	25
2948	800 c. Earth weeping	30	35
2949	1100 c. Africans shielding Earth	40	45
2950	1500 c. CFC and no-CFC appliances	55	60
2946/50	*Set of 5*	1·50	1·75

1999 (28 Dec). *New Millennium. T **576** and similar multicoloured designs. Litho. P 13½×13 (vert) or 13×13½ (horiz).*

2951	300 c. Type **576**	10	15
2952	700 c. Kwame Nkrumah (first President) speaking (*horiz*)	25	30
2953	1200 c. Clock tower, University of Ghana	45	50
2951/3	*Set of 3*	80	95

577 Liu-Yi meets Daughter of the Dragon King

(Des Y. Lee. Litho Questa)

2000 (5 Feb). *Chinese New Year ("Year of the Dragon"). T **577** and similar vert designs showing scenes from "Daughter of the Dragon King". Each design lake-brown and silver. P 14½.*

2954	1600 c. Type **577**	60	65
	a. Sheetlet. Nos. 2954/9	3·60	
2955	1600 c. Liu-Yi and Fairy Soldier	60	65
2956	1600 c. Liu-Yi and the Dragon King	60	65
2957	1600 c. Liu-Yi, Dragon King and Red Dragon	60	65
2958	1600 c. Red Dragon and Dragon of Jing River fighting	60	65
2959	1600 c. Dragon King with his daughter and brother	60	65
2960	1700 c. Dragon King's brother inviting Liu-Yi to marry his niece	65	70
	a. Sheetlet. Nos. 2960/5	3·75	
2961	1700 c. Liu-Yi bidding farewell to Dragon King	65	70
2962	1700 c. Liu-Yi with gifts from Dragon King	65	70
2963	1700 c. Liu-Yi with third wife	65	70
2964	1700 c. Liu-Yi with third wife and son	65	70
2965	1700 c. Liu-Yi realises that third wife is Daughter of the Dragon King	65	70
2954/65	*Set of 12*	7·25	8·00

Nos. 2954/9 and 2960/5 were each printed together, *se-tenant*, in sheetlets of 6 with enlarged illustrated and inscribed right-hand margins.

COVER PRICES

Cover factors are quoted at the beginning of each country for most issues to 1945. An explanation of the system can be found on page x. The factors quoted do not, however, apply to philatelic covers.

STAMP BOOKLETS

1916 (Dec).
SB1   2s. booklet containing twelve ½d. and eighteen 1d.
       (Nos. 70a, 72) in blocks of 6

1961. *Red (No. SB2), yellow (No. SB3) or green (No. SB4) covers. Stitched.*
SB2   3s. booklet containing twelve 3d. (No. 218a) in
       blocks of 4 .... 6·00
SB3   6s. booklet containing eight 3d. and eight 6d.
       (Nos. 218a, 220) in blocks of 4 .... 7·50
SB4   10s. booklet containing four 3d., eight 6d. and four
       1s. 3d. (Nos. 218a, 220, 226) in blocks of 4 .. 9·50

1963 (Jan). *Black on red (No. SB5), black on yellow (No. SB6) or black on green (No. SB7) covers. Stitched.*
SB5   4s. booklet containing twelve 4d. (No. 219) in
       blocks of 4
SB6   6s. booklet containing twelve 4d. and four 6d.
       (Nos. 219/20) in blocks of 4
SB7   11s. booklet containing twelve 4d., four 6d. and
       four 1s. 3d. (Nos. 219/20, 226) in blocks of 4

1981 (16 Sept). *Royal Wedding. Multicoloured cover, 120×82 mm, showing Prince Charles and Lady Diana Spencer on front and map of Ghana on back. Stapled.*
SB8   14 c. booklet containing *se-tenant* pane of 4 (No.
       955a) .... 4·50

POSTAGE DUE STAMPS

D 1

(Typo D.L.R.)

1923 (6 Mar). *Yellowish toned paper. Wmk Mult Script CA. P 14.*
D1   D 1   ½d. black .. .. 14·00   £110
D2   1d. black 75   1·25
D3   2d. black .. .. 13·00   9·00
D4   3d. black .. .. 22·00   6·00
D1/4   *Set of 4* 45·00   £110
D1/4 Optd "Specimen" .. .. .. *Set of 4* 70·00

A bottom marginal strip of six of No. D2 is known showing the "A" of "CA" omitted from the watermark in the margin below the third vertical column.

3d.   **3**d.

Normal   Lower serif
             at left of
             "3" missing
             (R. 9/1)

1/-   **1/-**

Row 4   Row 5
(No. D8)   (No. D8c)

The degree of inclination of the stroke on the 1s. value varies for each vertical row of the sheet: Rows 1, 2 and 6 104°, Row 3 108°, Row 4 107° and Row 5 (No. D8c) 100°.

1951–52. *Chalk-surfaced paper. Wmk Mult Script CA. P 14.*
D5   D 1   2d. black (13.12.51) .. .. 3·00   18·00
             a. Error. Crown missing, W 9a   £550
             b. Error. St. Edward's Crown, W 9b   £300
             c. Large "d" (R. 9/6, 10/6)   18·00
D6   3d. black (13.12.51) .. .. 1·50   16·00
             a. Error. Crown missing, W 9a   £550
             b. Error. St. Edward's Crown, W 9b   £300
             c. Missing serif   22·00
D7   6d. black (1.10.52) .. .. 1·75   8·00
             a. Error. Crown missing, W 9a   £700
             b. Error. St. Edward's Crown, W 9b   £500
D8   1s. black (1.10.52) .. .. 1·75   60·00
             b. Error. St. Edward's Crown, W 9b   £650
             c. Upright stroke .. .. 12·00
D5/8   *Set of 4* 7·25   90·00
For illustration of No. D5c see Nos. D4/6 of Botswana.

GHANA   GHANA
               1d.
               POSTAGE DUE

(D 2)   D 3

1958 (25 June). *Nos. D5/8 and similar 1d. value optd with Type D 2 in red.*
D 9   D 1   1d. black 10   30
D10   2d. black 10   30
              c. Large "d" .. .. 2·25
D11   3d. black 10   30
              a. Missing serif   4·50
D12   6d. black 15   65
D13   1s. black 20   1·50
              c. Upright stroke   1·50
D9/13   .. .. *Set of 5* 50   2·75

(Typo De La Rue)

1958 (1 Dec). *Chalk-surfaced paper. Wmk Mult Script CA. P 14.*
D14   D 3   1d. carmine 10   30
D15   2d. green 10   30
              c. Large "d" .. .. 2·25
D16   3d. orange 10   30
              a. Missing serif   4·25
D17   6d. bright ultramarine .. 10   50
D18   1s. reddish violet 15   2·00
              c. Upright stroke   1·50
D14/18   *Set of 5* 45   3·00

3p.

Ghana New Currency   **1½Np**
19th July, 1965.

(D 4)   (D 5)

1965 (19 July). *Nos. D14/18 surch as Type D 4 diagonally upwards (D) or horiz (H), by Govt Printer, Accra.*
D19   D 3   1 p. on 1d. (D) 10   60
              a. Surch inverted .. 8·00
              b. Surch double
D20   2 p. on 2d. (B.) (H) .. 10   60
              a. Surch inverted .. 6·00
              c. Large "d" .. .. 2·25
D21   3 p. on 3d. (indigo) (H) .. 10   60
              a. Surch inverted
              b. Surch omitted (in horiz pair with
                 normal) ..
              c. Ultramarine surch
              ca. Surch inverted .. .. 9·00
              cb. Surch on front and back
              d. Black surch
              e. Missing serif .. .. 3·00
D22   6 p. on 6d. (R.) (H) .. 10   1·50
              a. Surch inverted ..
              b. Purple-brown surch
              ba. Surch double .. .. 19·00
              c. Green surch .. .. 13·00
D23   12 p. on 1s. (B.) (D) .. 15   2·00
              c. Upright stroke .. 1·50
D19/23   *Set of 5* 45   4·75
On the diagonal surcharges the figures of value are horizontal.
No. D21b occurs in the first or second vertical row of one sheet which shows the surcharges shifted progressively to the right.

1968 (Feb)–**70.** *Nos. D20/2 additionally surch as Type D 5, in red (1½ n.p., 5 n.p.) or black (2½ n.p.).*
D24   D 3   1½ n.p. on 2 p. on 2d. .. 5·50   4·25
              a. Type D 5 double, one albino
              b. Albino surch (Type D 4)
              c. Large "d" .. .. 20·00
D25   2½ n.p. on 3 p. on 3d. (4.7.70) .. 1·00   5·00
              a. Type D 5 double, one albino   5·50
              b. Missing serif   5·00
D26   5 n.p. on 6 p. on 6d. (1970) .. 1·00
D24/6   *Set of 3* 6·00
The above were three in a series of surcharges, the others being 1 n.p. on 1 p. and 10 n.p. on 12 p., which were prepared, but owing to confusion due to the two surcharges in similar currency it was decided by the authorities not to issue the stamps, however, Nos. D24/6 were issued in error.

(Litho D.L.R.)

1970. *Inscr in new currency. P 14¼×14.*
D27   D 3   1 n.p. carmine-red .. .. 1·00   3·50
D28   1½ n.p. green .. .. .. 1·00   4·00
D29   2½ n.p. yellow-orange .. 1·40   4·50
D30   5 n.p. ultramarine .. .. 2·00   4·75
D31   10 n.p. reddish violet .. 2·75   6·00
D27/31   *Set of 5* 7·25   20·00

(Litho D.L.R.)

1980–81. *Currency described as "p". P 14½ × 14.*
D32   D 3   2 p. reddish orange .. .. 1·00   2·75
D33   3 p. brown .. .. .. 1·00   2·75

Gibraltar

CROWN COLONY

Early details of postal arrangements in Gibraltar are hard to establish, although it is known that postal facilities were provided by the Civil Secretary's Office from the early 1750s. Gibraltar became a packet port in 1806, although the Civil Secretary's Office continued to be responsible for other mail. The two services were amalgamated on 1 January 1857 as a Branch Office of the British G.P.O., the control of the postal services not reverting to Gibraltar until 1 January 1886.

Spanish stamps could be used at Gibraltar from their introduction in 1850 and, indeed, such franking was required on letters weighing over ½ oz. sent to Spain after 1 July 1854. From 1 July 1856 until 1 July 1875 all mail to Spain required postage to be prepaid by Spanish stamps and these issues were supplied by the Gibraltar postal authorities, acting as a Spanish Postal Agent. The mail, forwarded under this system was cancelled at San Roque with a horizontal barred oval, later replaced by a cartwheel type mark showing numeral 63. From 1857 combination covers showing the ship mail fee paid in British stamps and the inland postage by Spanish issues exist.

Stamps of Great Britain were issued for use in Gibraltar from 3 September 1857 (earliest recorded cover is dated 7 September 1857) to the end of 1885.

The initial supply contained 1d., 4d. and 6d. values. No supplies of the 2d. or 1s. were sent until the consignment of October 1857. No other values were supplied until early 1862.

For illustrations of the postmark types see BRITISH POST OFFICES ABROAD notes, following GREAT BRITAIN.

Stamps of GREAT BRITAIN cancelled "G" as Type **1** *(3 Sept 1857 to 19 Feb 1859)*

Z 1	1d. red-brown (1854) Die I, *wmk* Small Crown, *Perf* 16		£350
Z 2	1d. red-brown (1855), Die II, *wmk* Small Crown, *perf* 16		£600
Z 3	1d. red-brown (1855), Die II, *wmk* Small Crown, *perf* 14		£300
Z 4	1d. red-brown (1855), Die II, *wmk* Large Crown, *perf* 14		70·00
Z 5	1d. rose-red (1857), Die II, *wmk* Large Crown, *perf* 14		21·00
Z 6	2d. blue (1855), *wmk* Small Crown, *perf* 14		£375
Z 7	2d. blue (1855–58), *wmk* Large Crown, *perf* 16		£325
Z 8	2d. blue (1855), *wmk* Large Crown, *perf* 14	*From*	55·00
	Plate Nos. 5, 6.		
Z 9	2d. blue (1858) (Plate No. 7)		£225
Z10	4d. rose (1857)		50·00
	a. Thick glazed paper		
Z11	6d. lilac (1856)		40·00
Z12	6d. lilac (1856) (blued *paper*)		£750
Z13	1s. green (1856)		£110
	a. Thick paper		
Z14	1s. green (1856) (blued *paper*)		£1300

Stamps of GREAT BRITAIN cancelled "A 26" as in Types **2, 5, 11** *or* **14** *(20 Feb 1859 to 31 Dec 1885).*

Z15	½d. rose-red (1870–79)	*From*	24·00
	Plate Nos. 4, 5, 6, 8, 10, 11, 12, 13, 14, 15, 19, 20.		
Z16	1d. red-brown (1841), *imperf*		£1200
Z17	1d. red-brown (1855), *wmk* Large Crown, *perf* 14	*From*	£170
Z18	1d. rose-red (1857), *wmk* Large Crown, *perf* 14		12·00
Z19	1d. rose-red (1864–79)	*From*	19·00
	Plate Nos. 71, 72, 73, 74, 76, 78, 79, 80, 81, 82, 83, 84, 85, 86, 87, 88, 89, 90, 91, 92, 93, 94, 95, 96, 97, 98, 99, 100, 101, 102, 103, 104, 105, 106, 107, 108, 109, 110, 111, 112, 113, 114, 115, 116, 117, 118, 119, 120, 121, 122, 123, 124, 125, 127, 129, 130, 131, 132, 133, 134, 135, 136, 137, 138, 139, 140, 141, 142, 143, 144, 145, 146, 147, 148, 149, 150, 151, 152, 153, 154, 155, 156, 157, 158, 159, 160, 161, 162, 163, 164, 165, 166, 167, 168, 169, 170, 171, 172, 173, 174, 175, 176, 177, 178, 179, 180, 181, 182, 183, 184, 185, 186, 187, 188, 189, 190, 191, 192, 193, 194, 195, 196, 197, 198, 199, 200, 201, 202, 203, 204, 205, 206, 207, 208, 209, 210, 211, 212, 213, 214, 215, 216, 217, 218, 219, 220, 221, 222, 223, 224, 225.		
Z20	1½d. lake-red (1870) (Plate No. 3)		£375
Z21	2d. blue (1855), *wmk* Large Crown, *perf* 14		£120
	Plate No. 6.		
Z22	2d. blue (1858–69)	*From*	18·00
	Plate Nos. 7, 8, 9, 12, 13, 14, 15.		
Z23	2½d. rosy mauve (1875) (blued *paper*)	*From*	£100
	Plate Nos. 1, 2, 3.		
Z24	2½d. rosy mauve (1875–76) (Plate Nos. 1, 2, 3)	*From*	27·00
Z25	2½d. rosy mauve (*Error of Lettering*)		£1800
Z26	2½d. rosy mauve (1876–79)	*From*	20·00
	Plate Nos. 3, 4, 5, 6, 7, 8, 9, 10, 11, 12, 13, 14, 15, 16, 17.		
Z27	2½d. blue (1880–81) (Plate Nos. 17, 18, 19, 20)	*From*	12·00
Z28	2½d. blue (1881) (Plate Nos. 21, 22, 23)	*From*	10·00
Z29	3d. carmine-rose (1862)		£170
Z30	3d. rose (1865) (Plate No. 4)		65·00
Z31	3d. rose (1867–73)	*From*	30·00
	Plate Nos. 4, 5, 6, 7, 8, 9, 10.		
Z32	3d. rose (1873–76)	*From*	35·00
	Plate Nos. 11, 12, 14, 15, 16, 17, 18, 19, 20.		
Z33	3d. rose (1881) (Plate Nos. 20, 21)		
Z34	3d. lilac (1883) (3d. *on* 3d)		£110
Z35	4d. rose (1857)		48·00
Z36	4d. red (1862) (Plate Nos. 3, 4)	*From*	48·00
Z37	4d. vermilion (1865–73)	*From*	30·00
	Plate Nos. 7, 8, 9, 10, 11, 12, 13, 14.		
Z38	4d. vermilion (1876) (Plate No. 15)		£250
Z39	4d. sage-green (1877) (Plate Nos. 15, 16)		£110
Z40	4d. grey-brown (1880) *wmk* Large Garter		£200
	Plate No. 17.		
Z41	4d. grey-brown (1880) *wmk* Crown	*From*	40·00
	Plate Nos. 17, 18.		
Z42	6d. lilac (1856)		42·00
Z43	6d. lilac (1862) (Plate Nos. 3, 4)	*From*	38·00
Z44	6d. lilac (1865–67) (Plate Nos. 5, 6).	*From*	32·00
Z45	6d. lilac (1867) (Plate No. 6).		42·00
Z46	6d. violet (1867–70) (Plate Nos. 6, 8, 9)	*From*	32·00
Z47	6d. buff (1872–73) (Plate Nos. 11, 12)	*From*	£180
Z48	6d. chestnut (1872) (Plate No. 11)		30·00

Z49	6d. grey (1873) (Plate No. 12)		95·00
Z50	6d. grey (1874–80)	*From*	30·00
	Plate Nos. 13, 14, 15, 16, 17.		
Z51	6d. grey (1881) (Plate Nos. 17, 18)		£180
Z52	6d. lilac (1883) (6d. *on* 6d.)		90·00
Z53	8d. orange (1876)		£300
Z54	9d. bistre (1862)		£180
Z55	9d. straw (1862)		£600
Z56	9d. straw (1865)		£550
Z57	9d. straw (1867)		£170
Z58	10d. red-brown (1867)		£150
Z59	1s. green (1856)		£100
Z60	1s. green (1862)		70·00
Z61	1s. green (1862) ("K" *variety*)		£2000
Z62	1s. green (1865) (Plate No. 4)		60·00
Z63	1s. green (1867–73) (Plate Nos. 4, 5, 6, 7)	*From*	18·00
	Plate Nos. 8, 9, 10, 11, 12, 13.		
Z64	1s. green (1873–77)	*From*	50·00
Z65	1s. orange-brown (1880) (Plate No. 13)		£275
Z66	1s. orange-brown (1881) (Plate Nos. 13, 14)	*From*	70·00
Z67	2s. blue (1867)		£160
Z68	5s. rose (1867) (Plate No. 1)..		£650

1880.

Z69	½d. deep green		21·00
Z70	½d. pale green		21·00
Z71	1d. Venetian red		22·00
Z72	1½d. Venetian red		£190
Z73	2d. pale rose ..		70·00
Z74	2d. deep rose . .		70·00
Z75	5d. indigo		£120

1881.

Z76	1d. lilac (14 *dots*)		23·00
Z77	1d. lilac (16 *dots*)		9·00

1884.

Z78	½d. slate-blue		20·00
Z79	2d. lilac		80·00
Z80	2½d. lilac		15·00
Z81	3d. lilac		
Z82	4d. dull green		
Z83	6d. dull green		£140

POSTAL FISCAL

Z83a	1d. purple (Die 4) (1878) *wmk* Small Anchor	£600
Z84	1d. purple (1881), *wmk* Orb	£1100

PRICES FOR STAMPS ON COVER TO 1945	
Nos. 1/2	*from* × 25
No. 3	*from* × 10
No. 4	*from* × 25
Nos. 5/6	*from* × 8
Nos. 7/33	*from* × 6
Nos. 39/45	*from* × 5
Nos. 46/109	*from* × 3
Nos. 110/13	*from* × 4
Nos. 114/17	*from* × 3
Nos. 118/20	*from* × 5
Nos. 121/31	*from* × 3

GIBRALTAR
(1)

1886 (1 Jan). *Contemporary types of Bermuda optd with T* **1** *by D.L.R. Wmk Crown CA. P* 14.

1	**9**	½d. dull green	9·50	6·50
2	**1**	1d. rose-red	50·00	4·25
3	**2**	2d. purple-brown	£100	75·00
		w. Wmk inverted		
4	**11**	2½d. ultramarine	£120	3·25
		a. Optd in blue-black	£500	£150
		w. Wmk inverted		
5	**10**	4d. orange-brown	£120	85·00
6	**4**	6d. deep lilac	£200	£180
7	**5**	1s. yellow-brown	£425	£350
1/7			*Set of 7* £900	£650
1/3, 4a/7		Optd "Specimen"	*Set of 7* £2500	

PRINTER. All Gibraltar stamps to No. 109 were typographed by De La Rue & Co, Ltd.

2

3

4

5

1886 (Nov)–**87.** *Wmk Crown CA. P* 14.

8	**2**	½d. dull green (1.87)	8·00	3·50
9	**3**	1d. rose (12.86)	42·00	4·00
10	**4**	2d. brown-purple (12.86)	30·00	17·00
		w. Wmk inverted	£275	
11	**5**	2½d. blue	70·00	2·50
		w. Wmk inverted	£160	60·00
12	**4**	4d. orange-brown (16.4.87)	75·00	75·00
13		6d. lilac (16.4.87)	£100	£100
14		1s. bistre (2.87)	£180	£180
		w. Wmk inverted		
8/14			*Set of 7* £450	£350
8/14		Optd "Specimen"	*Set of 7* £500	
		See also Nos. 39 to 45.		

5 CENTIMOS
(6)

7

1889 (1 Aug). *Surch as T* **6.**

15	**2**	5 c. on ½d. green	6·00	15·00
16	**3**	10 c. on 1d. rose	11·00	6·50
17	**4**	25 c. on 2d. brown-purple	4·50	5·00
		a. Small "I" (R.6/2)	£100	£140
		b. Broken "N" (R.10/5)	£100	£140
18	**5**	25 c. on 2½d. bright blue	25·00	2·25
		a. Small "I" (R.6/2)	£300	£100
		b. Broken "N" (R.10/5)	£300	£100
19	**4**	40 c. on 4d. orange-brown	60·00	80·00
20		50 c. on 6d. bright lilac	60·00	80·00
21		75 c. on 1s. bistre..	65·00	75·00
15/21			*Set of 7* £200	£225
15/21		Optd "Specimen"	*Set of 7* £350	

10 c., 40 c. and 50 c. values from this issue and that of 1889–96 are known bisected and used for half their value from various post offices in Morocco (*price on cover from* £500). These bisects were never authorised by the Gibraltar Post Office.

Two varieties of the figure "5" of the 5 c., 25 c., 50 c. and 75 c. may be found.

Broken "M" (Pl 2 R. 4/5)

Flat top to "C" (Pl 2 R. 4/4)

1889 (8 Oct)*–**96.** *Issue in Spanish currency. Wmk Crown CA. P* 14.

22	**7**	5 c. green	4·00	70
		a. Broken "M"	£100	50·00
		w. Wmk inverted	£180	£150
23		10 c. carmine	4·00	45
		b. Value omitted	£5000	
24		20 c. olive-green and brown (2.1.96)	38·00	18·00
25		20 c. olive-green (8.7.96)	10·00	50·00
		a. Flat top to "C"	£150	
		w. Wmk inverted		
26		25 c. ultramarine	13·00	70
		a. Deep ultramarine	25·00	80
27		40 c. orange-brown	3·50	2·50
28		50 c. bright lilac (1890)	3·00	1·75
29		75 c. olive-green (1890)	32·00	32·00
30		1 p. bistre (11.89)	75·00	20·00
31		1 p. bistre and ultramarine (6.95)	4·50	3·75
32		2 p. black and carmine (2.1.96)	9·50	26·00
33		5 p. slate-grey (12.89)	42·00	£100
22/33			*Set of 12* £200	£225
22/4, 26/33		Optd "Specimen"	*Set of 11* £375	

*Earliest recorded postmark date.

1898 (1 Oct). *Reissue in Sterling currency. Wmk Crown CA. P* 14.

39	**2**	½d. grey-green	4·00	1·25
		w. Wmk inverted		
40	**3**	1d. carmine	5·50	35
		w. Wmk inverted	† £1000	
41	**4**	2d. brown-purple and ultramarine	21·00	1·50
42	**5**	2½d. bright ultramarine	24·00	40
		w. Wmk inverted	£160	60·00
43	**4**	4d. orange-brown and green	18·00	6·50
44		6d. violet and red	40·00	20·00
45		1s. bistre and carmine	35·00	16·00
		w. Wmk inverted		
39/45			*Set of 7* £130	42·00
39/45		Optd "Specimen"	*Set of 7* £250	

No. 39 is greyer than No. 8, No. 40 brighter and deeper than No. 9 and No. 42 much brighter than No. 11.

8

TWO SHILLINGS

9

½ ½

Normal   Large "2"
2½d.

This occurs on R.10/1 in each pane of 60. The diagonal stroke is also longer.

1903 (1 May). *Wmk Crown CA. P* 14.

46	**8**	½d. grey-green and green	10·00	9·50
47		1d. dull purple/*red*	28·00	60
48		2d. grey-green and carmine	17·00	25·00
49		2½d. dull purple and black/*blue*	4·25	60
		a. Large "2" in "½"	£170	90·00
50		6d. dull purple and violet	14·00	20·00

51	**8**	1s. black and carmine	..	..	28·00 32·00
52	**9**	2s. green and blue	..	..	£110 £140
53		4s. dull purple and green	..	..	80·00 £140
54		8s. dull purple and black/*blue*	..		£110 £140
55		£1 dull purple and black/*red*	..	..	£475 £550
46/55				*Set of 10*	£800 £950
46/55 Optd "Specimen"				*Set of 10*	£500

1904–8. *Wmk Mult Crown CA. Ordinary paper* (¹/₂d. *to* 2d. *and* 6d. *to* 2s.) *or chalk-surfaced paper* (*others*). *P* 14.

56	**8**	¹/₂d. dull and bright green (16.4.04*)	..	..	8·00 2·50
		a. Chalk-surfaced paper (10.05)	..	..	11·00 7·00
57		1d. dull purple/*red* (6.9.04*)	..	..	7·00 40
		a. Bisected (¹/₂d.) (on card)	..	..	† £1200
		bw. Wmk inverted			
		c. Chalk-surfaced paper (16.9.05)	..	..	3·25 85
58		2d. grey-green and carmine (9.1.05)	..		10·00 3·50
		a. Chalk-surfaced paper (2.07)	..	..	8·00 3·75
59		2¹/₂d. purple and black/*blue* (4.5.07)	..		35·00 90·00
		a. Large "2" in "¹/₂"	..	..	£450 £750
60		6d. dull purple and violet (19.4.06)	..		25·00 18·00
		a. Chalk-surfaced paper (4.08)	..	..	22·00 8·50
61		1s. black and carmine (13.10.05)	..		42·00 11·00
		a. Chalk-surfaced paper (4.06)	..	..	50·00 11·00
62	**9**	2s. green and blue (2.2.05)	..		65·00 85·00
		a. Chalk-surfaced paper (10.07)	..	..	75·00 80·00
63		4s. deep purple and green (6.08)	..		£190 £225
64		£1 deep purple and black/*red* (15.3.08)			£475 £550
56/64				*Set of 9*	£750 £850

*Earliest known date of use.

1906 (Oct)**–12.** *Colours changed. Wmk Mult Crown CA. Chalk-surfaced paper* (6d. *to* 8s.). *P.* 14.

66	**8**	¹/₂d. blue-green	..	..	2·50 90
67		1d. carmine	..	..	5·00 45
		a. Wmk sideways	..	..	— £3250
		w. Wmk inverted	..	..	† £500
68		2d. greyish slate (5.10)	..	..	7·50 9·00
69		2¹/₂d. ultramarine (6.07)	..	..	5·00 1·40
		a. Large "2" in "¹/₂"	..	..	£190 95·00
70		6d. dull and bright purple (18.3.12)	..		£120 £375
71		1s. black/*green* (1910)	..	..	22·00 20·00
72	**9**	2s. purple and bright blue/*blue* (4.10)	..		48·00 45·00
73		4s. black and carmine (4.10)	..	..	90·00 £130
		x. Wmk reversed	..	..	£1200
74		8s. purple and green (1911)	..	..	£180 £180
66/74				*Set of 9*	£425 £650
67/74 Optd "Specimen"				*Set of 8*	£500

10   11

"HALEPENNY" (Pl 1 R. 7/3.
Occurs on ptgs after 1918)

1912 (17 July)**–24.** *Wmk Mult Crown CA. Ordinary paper* (¹/₂d. *to* 2¹/₂d.) *or chalk-surfaced paper* (*others*). *P* 14.

76	**10**	¹/₂d. blue-green	..	..	3·00 70
		a. *Yellow-green* (4.17)	..	..	4·00 1·75
		b. "HALEPENNY"	..	..	£100
		w. Wmk inverted			
		x. Wmk reversed	..	..	† £1000
77		1d. carmine-red	..	..	3·25 75
		a. *Scarlet* (6.16)	..	..	3·25 1·25
78		2d. greyish slate	..	..	7·00 1·50
79		2¹/₂d. deep bright blue	..	..	4·00 2·00
		a. Large "2" in "¹/₂"	..	..	£130 95·00
		b. *Pale ultramarine* (1917)	..	..	6·50 2·00
		ba. Large "2" in "¹/₂"	..	..	£250 £120
80		6d. dull purple and mauve	..	..	8·00 12·00
81		1s. black/*green*	..	..	8·00 3·25
		a. Ordinary paper (8.18)	..	..	12·00 26·00
		b. *On blue-green, olive back* (1919)			12·00 26·00
		c. *On emerald surface* (12.23)	..		24·00 55·00
		d. *On emerald back* (3.24) (Optd S. £70)			18·00 75·00
82	**11**	2s. dull purple and blue/*blue*	..		26·00 3·50
83		4s. black and carmine	..	..	30·00 55·00
84		8s. dull purple and green	..	..	75·00 90·00
85		£1 dull purple and black/*red*	..		£140 £190
76/85				*Set of 10*	£275 £325
76/85 Optd "Specimen"				*Set of 10*	£450

WAR TAX

(12)

1918 (15 Apr). *Optd with T* **12** *by Beanland, Malin & Co, Gibraltar.*

86	**10**	¹/₂d. green	..	..	70 1·75
		a. Opt double	..	..	£700
		w. Wmk inverted	..	..	£350
		y. Wmk inverted and reversed	..		£350

Two printings of this overprint exist, the second being in slightly heavier type on a deeper shade of green.

---

3 PENCE		**THREE PENCE**
(I)		(II)

1921–27. *Wmk Mult Script CA. Chalk-surfaced paper* (6d. *to* 8s.). *P* 14.

89	**10**	¹/₂d. green (25.4.27)	..	..	1·25 1·25
90		1d. carmine-red (2.21)	..	..	1·50 80
91		1¹/₂d. chestnut (1.12.22)	..	..	1·50 40
		a. *Pale chestnut* (7.24)	..	..	1·50 30
		w. Wmk inverted	..	..	† £500
93		2d. grey (17.2.21)	..	..	1·25 1·00
94		2¹/₂d. bright blue (2.21)	..	..	19·00 26·00
		a. Large "2" in "¹/₂"	..	..	£325 £350
95		3d. bright blue (I) (1.1.22)	..	..	2·75 4·25
		a. *Ultramarine*	..	..	2·00 1·50
97		6d. dull purple and mauve (1.23)	..		6·00 3·75
		a. *Bright purple & magenta* (22.7.26)		1·60 3·50
98		1s. black/*emerald* (20.6.24)	..		8·50 13·00
99	**11**	2s. grey-purple and blue/*blue* (20.6.24)		19·00 65·00
		a. *Reddish purple and blue/blue* (1925)		6·50 38·00
100		4s. black and carmine (20.6.24)	..		60·00 £100
101		8s. dull purple and green (20.6.24)	..		£190 £350
89/101				*Set of 11*	£250 £475
89/101 Optd "Specimen"				*Set of 11*	£500

The ¹/₂d. exists in coils constructed from normal sheets.

1925 (15 Oct). *New values and colours changed. Wmk Mult Script CA. Chalk-surfaced paper. P* 14.

102	**10**	1s. sage-green and black (8.1.29)	..	14·00 21·00
		a. *Olive and black* (1932)	..	..	14·00 12·00
103	**11**	2s. red-brown and black (8.1.29)	..	9·50 29·00
104		2s. 6d. green and black	..	..	9·50 17·00
105		5s. carmine and black	..	..	14·00 50·00
106		10s. deep ultramarine and black	..	32·00 70·00
107		£1 red-orange and black (16.11.27)		£140 £180
108		£5 violet and black (Optd S. £700)		£1400 £3500
102/7				*Set of 6*	£200 £325
102/7 Optd/Perf "Specimen"			*Set of 6*	£400

Examples of Nos. 83/5, 99/101 and 102/8 are known showing forged oval registered postmarks dated "24 JA 25" or "6 MY 35".

1930 (12 Apr). *T* **10** *inscribed* "THREE PENCE". *Wmk Mult Script CA. P* 14.

109		3d. ultramarine (II) (Perf S. £70)	..		7·50 2·00

13 The Rock of Gibraltar

(Des Capt. H. St. C. Garrood. Recess D.L.R.)

1931–33. *Wmk Mult Script CA. P* 14.

110	**13**	1d. scarlet (1.7.31)	..	..	2·25 2·50
		a. Perf 13¹/₂×14	..	..	14·00 5·50
111		1¹/₂d. red-brown (1.7.31)	..	..	1·75 2·25
		a. Perf 13¹/₂×14	..	..	11·00 4·00
112		2d. pale grey (1.11.32)	..	..	5·00 1·25
		a. Perf 13¹/₂×14	..	..	12·00 2·25
113		3d. blue (1.6.33)	..	..	5·00 2·75
		a. Perf 13¹/₂×14	..	..	21·00 26·00
110/13				*Set of 4*	12·50 8·00
110a/13a				*Set of 4*	50·00 35·00
110/13 Perf "Specimen"				*Set of 4*	£160

Figures of value take the place of both corner ornaments at the base of the 2d. and 3d.

1935 (6 May). *Silver Jubilee. As Nos.* 91/4 *of Antigua but ptd by B.W.P* 11 × 12.

114		2d. ultramarine and grey-black	..	1·60 2·50
		a. Extra flagstaff	..	..	60·00 70·00
		b. Short extra flagstaff	..	..	90·00 £100
		c. Lightning conductor	..	..	60·00 70·00
		d. Flagstaff on right-hand turret	..	£130 £140
		e. Double flagstaff	..	..	£130 £140
115		3d. brown and deep blue	..	..	3·25 3·50
		a. Extra flagstaff	..	..	£300 £300
		b. Short extra flagstaff	..	..	£250 £250
		c. Lightning conductor	..	..	£275 £275
116		6d. green and indigo	..	..	9·50 12·00
		a. Extra flagstaff	..	..	£225 £250
		b. Short extra flagstaff	..	..	£300 £325
		c. Lightning conductor	..	..	£225 £250
117		1s. slate and purple	..	..	9·50 9·50
		a. Extra flagstaff	..	..	£200 £200
		b. Short extra flagstaff	..	..	£275 £275
		c. Lightning conductor	..	..	£200 £200
114/17				*Set of 4*	21·00 25·00
114/17 Perf "Specimen"				*Set of 4*	£160

For illustrations of plate varieties see Catalogue Introduction.

1937 (12 May). *Coronation. As Nos.* 95/7 *of Antigua. P* 11×11¹/₂.

118		¹/₂d. green	..	..	25 15
119		2d. grey-black	..	..	80 2·25
120		3d. blue	..	..	2·00 2·25
118/20				*Set of 3*	2·75 4·00
118/20 Perf "Specimen"				*Set of 3*	75·00

4 King George VI   **15** Rock of Gibraltar

---

16 The Rock (North Side)

Broken second "R" in "GIBRALTAR"
(Frame Pl.2 R.9/4)

(Des Captain H. St. C. Garrood. Recess D.L.R.)

1938 (25 Feb)**–51.** *Designs as T* **14/16.** *Wmk Mult Script CA.*

121		¹/₂d. deep green (p 13¹/₂×14)	..	10 40
122		1d. yellow-brown (p 14)	..	24·00 2·25
		a. Perf 13¹/₂	..	..	26·00 2·25
		ab. Perf 13. Wmk sideways (1940)		6·50 7·00
		b. Perf 13. Wmk sideways. *Red-brown* (1942)		50 55
		c. Perf 13. Wmk sideways. *Deep brown* (1944)		30 3·50
		d. Perf 13. *Red-brown* (1949)		1·50 1·50
123		1¹/₂d. carmine (p 14)	..	..	35·00 75
		a. Perf 13¹/₂	..	..	£250 35·00
123b		1¹/₂d. slate-violet (p 13) (1.1.43)	..	30 1·25
124		2d. grey (p 14)	..	..	26·00 40
		a. Perf 13¹/₂	..	..	55 35
		ab. Perf 13¹/₂. Wmk sideways (1939)	£600 42·00
		b. Perf 13. Wmk sideways (1943)		30 1·25
		ba. "A" of "CA" missing from wmk	£1200
124c		2d. carm (p 13) (*wmk sideways*) (15.7.44)	40 60
125		3d. light blue (p 13¹/₂)	..	16·00 1·00
		a. Perf 14	..	..	£130 5·00
		b. Perf 13 (1942)	..	..	30 30
		ba. *Greenish blue* (2.51)	..	3·50 2·50
125c		5d. red-orange (p 13) (1.10.47)	..	70 1·25
126		6d. carm & grey-violet (p 13¹/₂) (16.3.38)	48·00 3·00
		a. Perf 14	..	..	£120 1·25
		b. Perf 13 (1942)	..	..	2·25 1·75
		c. Perf 13. *Scarlet and grey-violet* (1945)	4·25 3·50
127		1s. black and green (p 14) (16.3.38)	38·00 23·00
		a. Perf 13¹/₂	..	..	60·00 7·00
		b. Perf 13 (1942)	..	..	3·00 4·00
		ba. Broken "R" ..	..	..	£150
128		2s. black and brown (p 14) (16.3.38)	65·00 25·00
		a. Perf 13¹/₂	..	..	£120 32·00
		b. Perf 13 (1942)	..	..	4·00 6·50
		ba. Broken "R" ..	..	..	£170
129		5s. black and carmine (p 14) (16.3.38)	95·00 £150
		a. Perf 13¹/₂	..	..	38·00 17·00
		b. Perf 13 (1944)	..	..	12·00 17·00
		ba. Broken "R" ..	..	..	£225
130		10s. black and blue (p 14) (16.3.38)	65·00 £120
		a. Perf 13 (1943)	..	..	35·00 25·00
		ab. Broken "R" ..	..	..	£325
131		£1 orange (p 13¹/₂×14) (16.3.38)	38·00 45·00
121/31				*Set of 14*	£120 85·00
121/31 Perf "Specimen"				*Set of 14*	£500

Designs:—¹/₂d., £1, Type **14.** Horiz as T **15/16**—1d., 1¹/₂d. (*both*), Type **15**; 2d. (*both*), Type **16**; 3d., 5d. Europa Point; 6d. Moorish Castle; 1s. Southport Gate; 2s. Eliott Memorial; 5s. Government House; 10s. Catalan Bay.

The ¹/₂d., 1d. and both colours of the 2d. exist in coils constructed from normal sheets. These were originally joined vertically, but, because of technical problems, the 1d. and 2d. grey were subsequently issued in horizontal coils. The 2d. carmine only exists in the horizontal version.

1946 (12 Oct). *Victory. As Nos.* 110/11 *of Antigua.*

132		¹/₂d. green	..	..	10 40
133		3d. ultramarine	..	..	30 40
132/3 Perf "Specimen"			*Set of 2*	60·00

1948 (1 Dec). *Royal Silver Wedding. As Nos.* 112/13 *of Antigua.*

134		¹/₂d. green	..	..	70 1·00
135		£1 brown-orange	..	..	50·00 65·00

1949 (10 Oct). *75th Anniv of Universal Postal Union. As Nos.* 114/17 *of Antigua.*

136		2d. carmine	..	..	1·00 1·25
137		3d. deep blue	..	..	2·50 1·25
138		6d. purple	..	..	2·00 1·25
139		1s. blue-green	..	..	1·60 2·75
136/9				*Set of 4*	6·50 6·00

NEW CONSTITUTION
1950
(23)

1950 (1 Aug). *Inauguration of Legislative Council. Nos.* 124c, 125b, 126b *and* 127b *optd as T* **23**.

140	**16**	2d. carmine	..	..	30 1·00
141	—	3d. light blue	..	..	55 1·00
142	—	6d. carmine and grey-violet	..	65 1·60
		a. Opt double	..	..	£650 £750
143	—	1s. black and green (R.)	..	65 1·60
		a. Broken "R"	..	..	50·00
140/3				*Set of 4*	1·90 4·75

On stamps from the lower part of the sheet of No. 142a the two impressions are almost coincident.

1953 (2 June). *Coronation. As No.* 120 *of Antigua.*

144		¹/₂d. black and bronze-green	..	..	30 1·00

24 Cargo and Passenger Wharves

25 Tower of Homage, Moorish Castle

26 Arms of Gibraltar

Major re-entry causing doubling of "ALTA" in "GIBRALTAR" (R. 4/6)

(Des N. Cummings. Recess (except £1, centre litho) De La Rue)

1953 (19 Oct)–59. *T 24/26 and similar designs. Wmk Mult Script CA. P 13.*

145	½d.	indigo and grey-green	..	15	30
146	1d.	bluish green	..	1·50	30
	a.	*Deep bluish green* (31.12.57)	..	2·50	60
147	1½d.	black	..	90	90
148	2d.	deep olive-brown	..	1·50	50
	a.	*Sepia* (18.6.58)	..	2·50	1·00
149	2½d.	carmine	..	4·00	85
	a.	*Deep carmine* (11.9.56)	..	2·75	80
	aw.	*Wmk inverted*	..	£300	
150	3d.	light blue	..	3·75	10
	a.	*Deep greenish blue* (8.6.55)	..	6·00	10
	b.	*Greenish blue* (18.6.58)	..	8·50	30
151	4d.	ultramarine	..	2·50	2·00
	a.	*Blue* (17.6.59)	..	9·50	5·50
152	5d.	maroon	..	70	70
	a.	Major re-entry	..	22·00	
	b.	*Deep maroon* (31.12.57)	..	1·50	1·50
	ba.	Major re-entry	..	26·00	
153	6d.	black and pale blue	..	65	60
	a.	*Black and blue* (24.4.57)	..	3·50	1·25
	b.	*Black and grey-blue* (17.6.59)	..	4·50	3·00
154	1s.	pale blue and red-brown	..	40	60
	a.	*Pale blue and deep red-brown* (27.3.56)	..	30	60
155	2s.	orange and reddish violet	..	28·00	6·00
	a.	*Orange and violet* (17.6.59)	..	19·00	3·75
156	5s.	deep brown	..	26·00	12·00
157	10s.	reddish brown and ultramarine	..	50·00	35·00
158	£1	scarlet and orange-yellow	..	50·00	38·00
145/58			Set of 14	£140	85·00

Designs: *Horiz as T 24*—1d. South View from Straits; 1½d. Tuna Fishing Industry; 2d. Southport Gate; 2½d. Sailing in the Bay; 3d. *Saturnia* (liner); 4d. Coaling wharf; 5d. Airport; 6d. Europa Point; 1s. Straits from Buena Vista; 2s. Rosia Bay and Straits; 5s. Main Entrance, Government House.

Nos. 145/6, 148 and 150 exist in coils, constructed from normal sheets.

1954 (10 May). *Royal Visit. As No. 150 but inscr "ROYAL VISIT 1954" at top.*

159	3d.	greenish blue	..	15	20

38 Gibraltar Candytuft

40 Rock and Badge of Gibraltar Regiment

39 Moorish Castle

(Des J. Celecia (½d., 2d., 2½d., 2s., 10s.), N. A. Langdon (1d., 3d., 6d., 7d., 9d., 1s.), M. Bonilla (4d.), L. V. Gomez (5s.), Sgt. T. A. Griffiths (£1). Recess (£1) or photo (others) D.L.R.)

1960 (29 Oct)–62. *Designs as T 38/9, and T 40. W w 12 (upright). P 14 (£1) or 13 (others).*

160	½d.	bright purple and emerald-green		15	30
161	1d.	black and yellow-green	..	20	10
162	2d.	indigo and orange-brown		30	20
163	2½d.	black and blue		55	65
	a.	*Black and grey-blue* (16.10.62)		40	30
164	3d.	deep blue and red-orange		30	10
165	4d.	deep red-brown and turquoise		2·75	70
166	6d.	sepia and emerald		70	60
167	7d.	indigo and carmine-red		90	90
168	9d.	grey-blue and greenish blue		50	60
169	1s.	sepia and bluish green		1·00	50
170	2s.	chocolate and ultramarine		14·00	2·50
171	5s.	turquoise-blue and olive-brown		8·00	6·00
172	10s.	yellow and blue		16·00	11·00
173	£1	black and brown-orange		17·00	12·00
160/73			Set of 14	50·00	32·00

Designs: *Horiz*—2d. St. George's Hall; 3d. The Rock by moonlight; 4d. Catalan Bay; 1s. Barbary Ape; 2s. Barbary Partridge; 5s. Blue Rock Thrush. *Vert*—2½d. The Keys; 6d. Map of Gibraltar; 7d. Air terminal; 9d. American War Memorial; 10s. Rock Lily (*Narcissus niveus*).

The 1d. imperforate comes from stolen printer's waste.

Vignette cylinders 2A and 2B, used for printings of the 9d. from 13 March 1962 onwards, have a finer screen (250 dots per inch instead of the 200 of the original printing).

Nos. 160/2, 164 and 166 exist in coils, constructed from normal sheets.

See also No. 199.

1963 (4 June). *Freedom from Hunger. As No. 146 of Antigua.*

174	9d.	sepia	..	9·00	1·50

1963 (2 Sept). *Red Cross Centenary. As Nos. 147/8 of Antigua.*

175	1d.	red and black		1·50	1·75
176	9d.	red and blue		14·00	3·50

1964 (23 Apr). *400th Birth Anniv of William Shakespeare. As No. 164 of Antigua.*

177	7d.	bistre-brown		50	20

NEW CONSTITUTION 1964.

(52)

53 Red Seabream

1964 (16 Oct). *New Constitution. Nos. 164 and 166 optd with T 52.*

178	3d.	deep blue and red-orange		20	10
179	6d.	sepia and emerald		20	40
	a.	No stop after "1964" (R.2/5)		16·00	26·00

1965 (17 May). *I.T.U. Centenary. As Nos. 166/7 of Antigua.*

180	4d.	light emerald and yellow		4·00	50
	w.	*Wmk inverted*		26·00	
181	2s.	apple-green and deep blue		11·00	3·25

1965 (25 Oct). *International Co-operation Year. As Nos. 168/9 of Antigua.*

182	½d.	deep bluish green and lavender		20	1·50
183	4d.	reddish purple and turquoise-green		1·25	80

The value of the ½d. stamp is shown as "1/2".

1966 (24 Jan). *Churchill Commemoration. As Nos. 170/3 of Antigua.*

184	½d.	new blue		20	1·50
	w.	*Wmk inverted*		32·00	
185	1d.	deep green		30	10
186	4d.	brown		1·25	10
187	9d.	bluish violet		1·25	2·25
184/7			Set of 4	2·75	3·50

1966 (1 July). *World Cup Football Championships. As Nos. 176/7 of Antigua.*

188	2½d.	violet, yellow-green, lake & yellow-brn		75	50
189	6d.	chocolate, blue-green, lake & yellow-brn		1·00	50

PRINTERS. All stamps from here to No. 239 were printed in photogravure by Harrison and Sons Ltd, London.

(Des A. Ryman)

1966 (27 Aug). *European Sea Angling Championships, Gibraltar. T 53 and similar designs. W w 12 (sideways on 1s.). P 13½ × 14 (1s.) or 14 × 13½ (others).*

190	4d.	rosine, bright blue and black	..	30	10
191	7d.	rosine, deep olive-green and black		30	50
	a.	Black (value and inscr) omitted		£950	
	w.	*Wmk inverted*		2·75	
192	1s.	lake-brown, emerald and black		40	30
190/2			Set of 3	90	80

Designs: *Horiz*—7d. Red Scorpionfish. *Vert*—1s. Stone Bass.

1966 (20 Sept). *Inauguration of W.H.O. Headquarters, Geneva. As Nos. 178/9 of Antigua.*

193	6d.	black, yellow-green and light blue		2·75	1·75
194	9d.	black, light purple and yellow-brown		3·25	1·75

56 "Our Lady of Europa"

57 H.M.S. *Victory*

(Des A. Ryman)

1966 (15 Nov). *Centenary of Re-enthronement of "Our Lady of Europa". W w 12. P 14 × 14½.*

195	**56**	2s. bright blue and black	..	30	80

1966 (1 Dec). *20th Anniv of U.N.E.S.C.O. As Nos. 196/8 of Antigua.*

196	2d.	slate-violet, red, yellow and orange	..	25	10
197	7d.	orange-yellow, violet and deep olive		80	10
198	5s.	black, bright purple and orange..		3·25	3·00
196/8	..		Set of 3	3·75	3·00

1966 (23 Dec). *As No. 165 but wmk w 12 sideways.*

199	4d.	deep red-brown and turquoise	..	30	70

(Des A. Ryman)

1967 (3 Apr)–69. *Horiz designs as T 57. Multicoloured. W w 12. P 14 × 14½.*

200	½d.	Type 57		10	15
	a.	Grey (sails, etc) omitted	..	£425	
201	1d.	*Arab* (early steamer)		10	10
	w.	Wmk inverted		3·00	2·50
202	2d.	H.M.S. *Carmania* (merchant cruiser)		15	10
	a.	Grey-blue (hull) omitted	..	£2500	
203	2½d.	*Mons Calpe* (ferry)		30	30
204	3d.	*Canberra* (liner)	..	20	10
	w.	Wmk inverted		21·00	6·50
205	4d.	H.M.S. *Hood* (battle cruiser)		30	10
205a	5d.	*Mirror* (cable ship) (7.7.69)		3·25	55
	aw.	Wmk inverted			
206	6d.	*Xebec* (sailing vessel)		30	50
207	7d.	*Amerigo Vespucci* (Italian cadet ship)		30	45
	w.	Wmk inverted		14·00	
208	9d.	*Raffaello* (liner)	..	30	60
209	1s.	*Royal Katherine* (galleon)	..	30	35
210	2s.	H.M.S. *Ark Royal* (aircraft carrier), 1937		3·50	2·50
211	5s.	H.M.S. *Dreadnought* (nuclear submarine)	..	3·50	6·50
212	10s.	*Neuralia* (liner)	..	14·00	22·00
213	£1	*Mary Celeste* (sailing vessel)		14·00	22·00
200/13			Set of 15	35·00	50·00

No. 202a results from the misaligning of the grey-blue cylinder. The bottom horizontal row of the sheet involved has this colour completely omitted except for the example above the cylinder numbers which shows the grey-blue "1A" towards the top of the stamp.

The ½d., 1d., 2d., 3d., 6d., 2s., 5s. and £1 exist with PVA gum as well as gum arabic, but the 5d. exists with PVA gum only.

Nos. 201/2, 204/5 and 206 exist in coils constructed from normal sheets.

58 Aerial Ropeway

(Des A. Ryman)

1967 (15 June). *International Tourist Year. T 58 and similar designs but horiz. Multicoloured. W w 12 (sideways on 7d.). P 14½ × 14 (7d.) or 14 × 14½ (others).*

214	7d.	Type 58	..	15	10
215	9d.	Shark fishing	..	15	10
216	1s.	Skin-diving	..	20	15
214/16	..		Set of 3	45	30

59 Mary, Joseph and Child Jesus

60 Church Window

1967 (1 Nov). *Christmas. W w 12 (sideways* on 6d.). P 14.*

217	**59**	2d. multicoloured		15	10
		w. Wmk inverted	..	1·25	
218	**60**	6d. multicoloured		15	10
		w. Wmk Crown to right of CA	..	£130	

*The normal sideways watermark shows Crown to left of CA, as seen from the back of the stamp.

61 Gen. Eliott and Route Map

62 Eliott directing Rescue Operations

(Des A. Ryman)

1967 (11 Dec). *250th Birth Anniv of General Eliott. Multicoloured designs as T* **61** *(4d. to 1s.) or T* **62**. W w **12** *(sideways on horiz designs). P* 14 × 15 (1s.) *or* 15 × 14 *(others)*.

219	4d.	Type 61	15	10
220	9d.	Heathfield Tower and Monument, Sussex (38×22 *mm*)	20	10
221	1s.	General Eliott (22×38 *mm*)	20	10
222	2s.	Type 62	40	50
219/22		*Set of 4*	85	70

65 Lord Baden-Powell

(Des A. Ryman)

1968 (27 Mar). *60th Anniv of Gibraltar Scout Association. T* **65** *and similar horiz designs.* W w **12**. *P* 14 × 14½.

223	4d.	buff and bluish violet	20	10
224	7d.	ochre and blue-green	20	20
225	9d.	bright blue, yellow-orange and black	25	30
226	1s.	greenish yellow and emerald	25	30
223/6		*Set of 4*	80	75

Designs:—7d. Scout Flag over the Rock; 9d. Tent, scouts and salute; 1s. Scout badges.

66 Nurse and W.H.O. Emblem   **68** King John signing Magna Carta

(Des A. Ryman)

1968 (1 July). *20th Anniv of World Health Organization. T* **66** *and similar horiz design.* W w **12**. *P* 14 × 14½.

227	2d.	ultramarine, black and yellow	10	15
228	4d.	slate, black and pink	10	15

Design:—4d. Doctor and W.H.O. emblem.

(Des A. Ryman)

1968 (26 Aug). *Human Rights Year. T* **68** *and similar vert design.* W w **12** *(sideways). P* 13½ × 14.

229	1s.	yellow-orange, brown and gold	15	10
230	2s.	myrtle and gold	15	20

Design:—2s. "Freedom" and Rock of Gibraltar.

70 Shepherd, Lamb and Star   **72** Parliament Houses

(Des A. Ryman)

1968 (1 Nov). *Christmas. T* **70** *and similar vert design. Multicoloured.* W w **12**. *P* 14½ × 13½.

231	4d.	Type 70	20	15
		a. Gold (star) omitted	£250	
232	9d.	Mary holding Holy Child	20	15

(Des A. Ryman)

1969 (26 May). *Commonwealth Parliamentary Association Conference. T* **72** *and similar designs.* W w **12** *(sideways on 2s.). P* 14 × 14½ (2s.) *or* 14½ × 14 *(others)*.

233	4d.	green and gold	10	10
234	9d.	bluish violet and gold	10	10
235	2s.	multicoloured	15	20
233/5		*Set of 3*	30	30

Designs: *Horiz*—9d. Parliamentary emblem and outline of "The Rock". *Vert*—2s. Clock Tower, Westminster (Big Ben) and arms of Gibraltar.

75 Silhouette of Rock, and Queen Elizabeth II   **77** Soldier and Cap Badge, Royal Anglian Regiment, 1969

(Des A. Ryman)

1969 (30 July). *New Constitution.* W w **12**. *P* 14 × 13½ (*in addition, the outline of the Rock is perforated*).

236	75	½d. gold and orange	10	10
237		5d. silver and bright green	25	10
		a. Portrait and inscr in gold and silver*		
238		7d. silver and bright purple	25	10
239		5s. gold and ultramarine	1·00	1·10
236/9		*Set of 4*	1·40	1·25

*No. 237a was first printed with the head and inscription in gold and then in silver but displaced slightly to lower left.

(Des A. Ryman. Photo D.L.R.)

1969 (6 Nov). *Military Uniforms* (1st series). *T* **77** *and similar vert designs. Multicoloured.* W w **12**. *P* 14.

240	1d.	Royal Artillery officer, 1758 and modern cap badge	20	10
241	6d.	Type 77	45	20
242	9d.	Royal Engineers' Artificer, 1786 and modern cap badge	55	30
243	2s.	Private, Fox's Marines, 1704 and modern Royal Marines cap badge	2·00	1·25
240/3		*Set of 4*	2·75	1·60

Nos. 240/3 have a short history of the Regiment printed on the reverse side over the gum, therefore, once the gum is moistened the history disappears.

See also Nos. 248/51, 290/3, 300/3, 313/16, 331/4, 340/3 and 363/6.

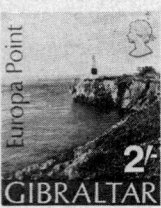

80 "Madonna of the Chair" (detail, Raphael)   **83** Europa Point

(Des A. Ryman. Photo Enschedé)

1969 (1 Dec). *Christmas. T* **80** *and similar vert designs. Multicoloured.* W w **12** *(sideways). P* 14 × Roulette 9.

244	5d.	Type 80	10	20
		a. Strip of 3. Nos. 244/6	45	
245	7d.	"Virgin and Child" (detail, Morales)	20	20
246	1s.	"The Virgin of the Rocks" (detail, Leonardo da Vinci)	20	20
244/6		*Set of 3*	45	55

Nos. 244/6 were issued together in *se-tenant* strips of three throughout the sheet.

(Des A. Ryman. Photo Enschedé)

1970 (8 June). *Europa Point.* W w **12**. *P* 13½.

247	83	2s. multicoloured	45	30
		w. Wmk inverted	2·00	1·90

(Des A. Ryman. Photo D.L.R.)

1970 (28 Aug). *Military Uniforms* (2nd series). *Vert designs as T* **77**. *Multicoloured.* W w **12**. *P* 14.

248	2d.	Royal Scots officer, 1839 and cap badge	35	10
249	5d.	South Wales Borderers private, 1763 and cap badge	70	10
250	7d.	Queen's Royal Regiment private, 1742 and cap badge	70	15
251	2s.	Royal Irish Rangers piper, 1969 and cap badge	2·75	1·25
248/51		*Set of 4*	4·00	1·40

Nos. 248/51 have a short history of the Regiment printed on the reverse side under the gum.

90 "The Virgin Mary" (stained-glass window by Gabriel Loire)

(Photo Enschedé)

1970 (1 Dec). *Christmas.* W w **12**. *P* 13 × 14.

254	90	2s. multicoloured	30	30

(New Currency: 100 pence = £1)

91 Saluting Battery, Rosia

92 Saluting Battery, Rosia, Modern View

(Des A. Ryman. Litho Questa)

1971 (15 Feb). *Decimal Currency. Designs as T* **91/2**. W w **12** *(sideways* on horiz designs). P* 14.

255	½p.	multicoloured	20	30
		a. Pair. Nos. 255/6	40	60
256	½p.	multicoloured	20	30
257	1p.	multicoloured	80	30
		a. Pair. Nos. 257/8	1·60	60
258	1p.	multicoloured	80	30
259	1½p.	multicoloured	20	50
		a. Pair. Nos. 259/60	40	1·00
260	1½p.	multicoloured	20	50
261	2p.	multicoloured	1·50	2·00
		a. Pair. Nos. 261/2	3·00	4·00
262	2p.	multicoloured	1·50	2·00
263	2½p.	multicoloured	20	50
		a. Pair. Nos. 263/4	40	1·00
264	2½p.	multicoloured	20	50
265	3p.	multicoloured	20	20
		a. Pair. Nos. 265/6	40	40
266	3p.	multicoloured	20	20
267	4p.	multicoloured	2·00	2·25
		a. Pair. Nos. 267/8	4·00	4·50
268	4p.	multicoloured	2·00	2·25
269	5p.	multicoloured	35	35
		a. Pair. Nos. 269/70	70	70
270	5p.	multicoloured	35	35
271	7p.	multicoloured	65	65
		aw. Wmk Crown to right of CA	48·00	
		b. Pair. Nos. 271/2	1·25	1·25
		bw. Pair. Nos. 271aw/2aw	95·00	
272	7p.	multicoloured	65	65
		aw. Wmk Crown to right of CA	48·00	
273	8p.	multicoloured	70	80
		a. Pair. Nos. 273/4	1·40	1·60
274	8p.	multicoloured	70	80
275	9p.	multicoloured	70	80
		a. Pair. Nos. 275/6	1·40	1·60
276	9p.	multicoloured	70	80
277	10p.	multicoloured	80	80
		aw. Wmk Crown to right of CA	80·00	
		b. Pair. Nos. 277/8	1·60	1·60
		bw. Pair. Nos. 277aw/8aw	£160	
278	10p.	multicoloured	80	80
		aw. Wmk Crown to right of CA	80·00	
279	12½p.	multicoloured	1·00	1·75
		a. Pair. Nos. 279/80	2·00	3·50
280	12½p.	multicoloured	1·00	1·75
281	25p.	multicoloured	1·10	1·75
		a. Pair. Nos. 281/2	2·10	3·50
282	25p.	multicoloured	1·10	1·75
283	50p.	multicoloured	1·25	2·50
		a. Pair. Nos. 283/4	2·50	5·00
284	50p.	multicoloured	1·25	2·50
285	£1	multicoloured	2·00	4·00
		a. Pair. Nos. 285/6	4·00	8·00
286	£1	multicoloured	2·00	4·00
255/86		*Set of 32*	24·00	35·00

Designs (the two versions of each value show the same Gibraltar view taken from an early 19th-century print (first design) or modern photograph (second design): *Horiz*—1p. Prince George of Cambridge Quarters and Trinity Church; 1½p. The Wellington Bust, Alameda Gardens; 2p. Gibraltar from the North Bastion; 2½p. Catalan Bay; 3p. Convent Garden; 4p. The Exchange and Spanish Chapel; 5p. Commercial Square and Library; 7p. South Barracks and Rosia Magazine; 8p. Moorish Mosque and Castle; 9p. Europa Pass Road; 10p. South Barracks from Rosia Bay; 12½p. Southport Gates; 25p. Trooping the Colour, The Alameda. *Vert*—50p. Europa Pass Gorge; £1 Prince Edward's Gate.

The two designs of each value were printed together, *se-tenant*, in horizontal and vertical pairs throughout.

*The normal sideways watermark shows Crown to left of CA, *as seen from the back of the stamp.*

See also Nos. 317/20 and 344/5.

88 No. 191a and Rock of Gibraltar

(Des A. Ryman. Litho D.L.R.)

1970 (18 Sept). *"Philympia 1970" Stamp Exhibition, London. T* **88** *and similar horiz design.* W w **12** *(sideways). P* 13.

252	1s.	vermilion and bronze-green	15	10
253	2s.	bright blue and magenta	25	65

Design:—2s. Victorian stamp (No. 23b) and Moorish Castle.
The stamps shown in the designs are well-known varieties with values omitted.

93   94 Regimental Arms

(Des A. Ryman. Photo Harrison)

1971 (15 Feb). *Coil Stamps.* W w **12.** P 14½ × 14.
287	93	½p. red-orange		15	30
		a. Coil strip (287 × 2, 288 × 2 and 289 se-tenant)		1·00	
288		1p. blue		15	30
289		2p. bright green		50	1·10
287/9		*Set of 3*		70	1·50

(Des A. Ryman. Litho Questa)

1971 (6 Sept). *Military Uniforms (3rd series). Multicoloured designs as T* **77**, *showing uniform and cap-badge.* W w **12.** P 14.
290	1p. The Black Watch (1845)		35	30
291	2p. Royal Regt of Fusiliers (1971)		65	30
	w. Wmk inverted			
292	4p. King's Own Royal Border Regt (1704)		1·25	50
293	10p. Devonshire and Dorset Regt (1801)		3·75	3·00
	w. Wmk inverted		4·50	6·00
290/3	*Set of 4*		5·50	3·50

Nos. 290/3 have a short history of the regiment printed on the reverse side under the gum.

(Des A. Ryman. Litho Harrison)

1971 (25 Sept). *Presentation of Colours to the Gibraltar Regiment.* W w **12** (sideways). P 12½ × 12.
294	94	3p. black, gold and red	45	30

95 Nativity Scene   96 Soldier Artificer, 1773

(Des A. Ryman. Photo Enschedé)

1971 (1 Dec). *Christmas. T* **95** *and similar horiz design. Multicoloured.* W w **12.** P 13 × 13½.
295	3p. Type 95		60	60
296	5p. Mary and Joseph going to Bethlehem		65	65

(Des A. Ryman. Litho Questa)

1972 (6 Mar). *Bicentenary of Royal Engineers in Gibraltar. T* **96** *and similar multicoloured designs.* W w **12** (sideways on 1 and 3p). P 13½ × 14 (5p.) or 14 × 13½ (others).
297	1p. Type 96		65	60
298	3p. Modern tunneller		80	80
299	5p. Old and new uniforms and badge (horiz)		1·00	90
297/9	*Set of 3*		2·25	2·10

(Des A. Ryman. Litho Questa)

1972 (19 July). *Military Uniforms (4th series). Multicoloured designs as T* **77**. W w **12** (sideways). P 14.
300	1p. Duke of Cornwall's Light Infantry, 1704		60	20
301	3p. King's Royal Rifle Corps, 1830		1·75	40
302	7p. Officer, 37th North Hampshire, 1825		2·75	70
303	10p. Royal Navy, 1972		3·25	1·50
300/3	*Set of 4*		7·50	2·50

Nos. 300/303 have a short history of the Regiment printed on the reverse side under the gum.

97 "Our Lady of Europa"   98 Keys of Gibraltar and *Narcissus niveus*

(Des A. Ryman. Litho Harrison)

1972 (4 Oct). *Christmas.* W w **12** (sideways*). P 14½×14.
304	97	3p. multicoloured	10	20
		w. Wmk Crown to right of CA	9·00	
305		5p. multicoloured	10	35
		w. Wmk Crown to right of CA	1·00	

*The normal sideways watermark shows Crown to left of CA, as seen from the back of the stamp.
These stamps have an inscription printed on the reverse side.

(Des (from photograph by D. Groves) and photo Harrison)

1972 (20 Nov). *Royal Silver Wedding. Multicoloured; background colour given.* W w **12.** P 14 × 14½.
306	98	5p. carmine-red		25	20
		w. Wmk inverted		40·00	
307		7p. deep grey-green		25	20
		w. Wmk inverted			

99 Flags of Member Nations and E.E.C. Symbol   100 Skull

(Des A. Ryman. Litho Questa)

1973 (22 Feb). *Britain's Entry into E.E.C.* W w **12** (sideways). P 14½ × 14.
308	99	5p. multicoloured	70	50
309		10p. multicoloured	80	1·00

(Des A. Ryman. Litho B.W.)

1973 (22 May). *125th Anniv of Gibraltar Skull Discovery. T* **100** *and similar horiz designs. Multicoloured.* W w **12.** P 13 (10p.) or 13½ (others).
310	4p. Type 100		1·25	50
	a. Gold ("GIBRALTAR") omitted		£1700	
311	6p. Prehistoric man		1·25	70
312	10p. Prehistoric family (40×26 mm)		1·75	1·25
310/12	*Set of 3*		3·75	2·25

Four mint examples of No. 310a have been found in presentation packs.

(Des A. Ryman. Litho Questa)

1973 (22 Aug). *Military Uniforms (5th series). Multicoloured designs as T* **77**. W w **12** (sideways). P 14.
313	1p. King's Own Scottish Borderers, 1770		50	50
314	4p. Royal Welch Fusiliers, 1800		1·50	1·10
315	6p. Royal Northumberland Fusiliers, 1736		2·25	2·25
316	10p. Grenadier Guards, 1898		3·00	4·50
313/16	*Set of 4*		6·50	7·50

Nos. 313/16 have a short history of the Regiment printed on the reverse side under the gum.

1973 (12 Sept). *As Nos. 261/2 and 267/8 but W w* **12** *upright.*
317	2p. multicoloured		1·25	2·00
	a. Pair. Nos. 317/18		2·50	4·00
318	2p. multicoloured		1·25	2·00
319	4p. multicoloured		1·40	2·25
	a. Pair. Nos. 319/20		2·75	4·50
320	4p. multicoloured		1·40	2·25
317/20	*Set of 4*		4·75	7·50

101 "Nativity" (Danckerts)   102 Victorian Pillar-box

(Des and litho Enschedé)

1973 (17 Oct). *Christmas.* W w **12.** P 12½ × 12.
321	101	4p. violet and Venetian red	40	15
322		6p. magenta and turquoise-blue	60	1·10

1973 (14 Nov). *Royal Wedding. As Nos. 165/6 of Anguilla. Centre multicoloured.* W w **12** (sideways). P 13½.
323	6p. turquoise		10	10
324	14p. yellow-green		20	20

(Des A. Ryman. Litho Walsall)

1974 (2 May). *Centenary of Universal Postal Union. T* **102** *and similar vert designs. Multicoloured.* (a) W w **12** (sideways). P 14½.
325	2p. Type 102		15	30
326	6p. Pillar-box of George VI		30	35
327	14p. Pillar-box of Elizabeth II		50	80
325/7	*Set of 3*		85	1·25

(b) *No wmk. Imperf × roul 5*. Self-adhesive (from booklets)*
328	2p. Type 102		25	1·00
	a. Booklet pane Nos. 328/30 se-tenant		7·00	
	b. Booklet pane Nos. 328 × 3 and 329 × 3		1·40	
329	6p. As No. 326		25	1·00
330	14p. As No. 327		7·00	8·50
328/30	*Set of 3*		7·00	9·50

*Nos. 328/30 were separated by various combinations of rotary-knife (giving a straight edge) and roulette.

(Des A. Ryman. Litho Questa)

1974 (21 Aug). *Military Uniforms (6th series). Multicoloured designs as T* **77**. W w **12** (sideways*). P 14.
331	4p. East Lancashire Regt, 1742		50	50
332	6p. Somerset Light Infantry, 1833		70	70
333	10p. Royal Sussex Regt, 1790		1·00	1·40
334	16p. R.A.F. officer, 1974		2·25	4·00
	w. Wmk Crown to right of CA		£120	
331/4	*Set of 4*		4·00	6·00

*The normal sideways watermark shows Crown to left of CA, as seen from the back of the stamp.
Nos. 331/4 have a short history of the regiment printed on the reverse side under the gum.

103 "Madonna with the Green Cushion" (Solario)   104 Churchill and Houses of Parliament

(Des A. Ryman and M. Infante. Litho Questa)

1974 (5 Nov). *Christmas. T* **103** *and similar vert design. Multicoloured.* W w **12.** P 14.
335	4p. Type 103		40	30
336	6p. "Madonna of the Meadow" (Bellini)		60	95

(Des L. Curtis. Litho Harrison)

1974 (30 Nov). *Birth Centenary of Sir Winston Churchill. T* **104** *and similar horiz design.* W w **12.** P 14 × 14½.
337	6p. black, reddish purple and light lavender		25	15
338	20p. brownish black, lake-brown and light orange-red		50	85
MS339	114×93 mm. Nos. 337/8. W w **12** (sideways*). P 14		4·50	6·50
	w. Wmk Crown to right of CA		£325	

Design:—20p. Churchill and *King George V* (battleship).
*The normal sideways watermark shows Crown to left of CA, as seen from the back of the stamp.

(Des A. Ryman. Litho Questa)

1975 (14 Mar). *Military Uniforms (7th series). Multicoloured designs as T* **77**. W w **14.** P 14.
340	4p. East Surrey Regt, 1846		40	30
341	6p. Highland Light Infantry, 1777		60	50
342	10p. Coldstream Guards, 1704		80	90
343	20p. Gibraltar Regt, 1974		1·50	2·75
340/3	*Set of 4*		3·00	4·00

Nos. 340/3 have a short history of each regiment printed on the reverse side under the gum.

1975 (9 July). *As Nos. 257/8 but W w* **14** (sideways).
344	1p. multicoloured		1·25	2·00
	a. Pair. Nos. 344/5		2·50	4·00
345	1p. multicoloured		1·25	2·00

105 Girl Guides' Badge   106 Child at Prayer

(Des A. Ryman. Litho Harrison)

1975 (10 Oct). *50th Anniv of Gibraltar Girl Guides.* W w **12.** P 13 × 13½.
346	105	5p. gold, light blue and dull violet	35	55
		a. Tête-bêche (pair)	85	1·25
		w. Wmk inverted	50	70
347		7p. gold, sepia and light lake-brown	45	60
		a. Tête-bêche (pair)	1·10	1·40
		w. Wmk inverted	65	80
348		15p. silver, brownish black & yellow-brn	75	1·25
		a. Tête-bêche (pair)	1·75	2·75
		b. Silver omitted		
		w. Wmk inverted	1·00	1·50
346/8		*Set of 3*	1·40	2·25

No. 348 is as T **105** but shows a different badge.
Nos. 346/8 were each issued in sheets of 25 (5×5) with each horizontal row containing three upright stamps and two inverted.

(Des A. Ryman. Litho Walsall)

1975 (26 Nov). *Christmas.* T **106** *and similar vert designs. Multicoloured.* W w 14 *(sideways*).* P 14.

349	6p. Type 106				40	60
	aw. Wmk Crown to right of CA				6·00	
	b. Sheetlet. Nos. 349/54				2·10	
	bw. Sheetlet. Nos. 349aw/54aw				32·00	
350	6p. Angel with lute				40	60
	aw. Wmk Crown to right of CA				6·00	
351	6p. Child singing carols				40	60
	aw. Wmk Crown to right of CA				6·00	
352	6p. Three children				40	60
	aw. Wmk Crown to right of CA				6·00	
353	6p. Girl at prayer				40	60
	aw. Wmk Crown to right of CA				6·00	
354	6p. Boy and lamb				40	60
	aw. Wmk Crown to right of CA				6·00	
349/54				Set of 6	2·10	3·25

*The normal sideways watermark shows Crown to left of CA, as seen from the back of the stamp.

Nos. 349/54 were issued together *se-tenant* in sheetlets of 6 (3×2).

107 Bruges Madonna

108 Bicentennial Emblem and Arms of Gibraltar

(Des Jennifer Toombs. Litho Walsall)

1975 (17 Dec). *500th Birth Anniv of Michelangelo.* T **107** *and similar vert designs. Multicoloured.*

(a) W w 14 *(sideways*).* P 14

355	6p. Type 107				25	25
356	9p. Taddei Madonna				30	40
357	15p. Pietà				40	1·10
	w. Wmk Crown to right of CA				95·00	
355/7				Set of 3	85	1·60

(b) *No wmk. Imperf×roul 5†. Self-adhesive (from booklets)*

358	6p. Type 107				35	45
	a. Booklet pane. Nos. 358/60 se-tenant				1·50	
	b. Booklet pane. Nos. 358×2, 359×2 and 360×2				3·00	
359	9p. As No. 356				55	75
360	15p. As No. 357				80	1·25
358/60				Set of 3	1·50	2·25

*The normal sideways watermark shows Crown to left of CA, as seen from the back of the stamp.
†Nos. 358/60 were separated by various combinations of rotary knife (giving a straight edge) and roulette.

(Des A. Ryman. Litho Walsall)

1976 (28 May). *Bicentenary of American Revolution.* W w 14 *(inverted).* P 14.

361	108	25p. multicoloured			50	50
MS362		85 × 133 mm. No. 361 × 4			4·50	7·00

The edges of MS362 are rouletted.

(Des A. Ryman. Litho Walsall)

1976 (21 July). *Military Uniforms (8th series). Multicoloured designs as* T **77**. W w 14 *(inverted).* P 14.

363	1p. Suffolk Regt, 1795				25	15
364	6p. Northamptonshire Regt, 1779				60	30
365	12p. Lancashire Fusiliers, 1793				85	55
366	25p. Ordnance Corps, 1896				1·25	1·10
363/6				Set of 4	2·75	1·90

Nos. 363/6 have a short history of each regiment printed on the reverse side under the gum.

109 The Holy Family

110 Queen Elizabeth II, Royal Arms and Gibraltar Arms

(Des A. Ryman. Litho Questa)

1976 (3 Nov). *Christmas.* T **109** *and similar vert designs showing stained-glass windows in St. Joseph's Church, Gibraltar. Multicoloured.* W w 14. P 14.

367	6p. Type 109				25	15
368	9p. Madonna and Child				35	25
369	12p. St. Bernard				50	60
370	20p. Archangel Michael				85	1·25
367/70				Set of 4	1·75	2·00

(Des A. Ryman. Litho J.W.)

1977 (7 Feb). *Silver Jubilee.* W w 14. P 13½.

371	110	6p. multicoloured			25	20
372		£1 multicoloured			1·40	2·25
MS373		124 × 115 mm. Nos. 371/2. P 13			1·60	2·25

The outer edges of the miniature sheet are either guillotined or rouletted.

111 Toothed Orchid (*Orchis tridentata*)

(Des A. Ryman. Litho Questa)

1977 (1 Apr)–**82**. *Multicoloured designs as* T **111**. W w 14 *(sideways* on horiz designs; inverted on £5). Chalk-surfaced paper* (15p., £5). *Imprint date at foot.* P 14.

374	½p. Type 111			60	1·75
	a. Chalk-surfaced paper (22.2.82)			3·75	3·25
375	1p. Red Mullet (*Mullus surmuletus*) (horiz)			15	30
	w. Wmk Crown to right of CA			6·00	6·50
376	2p. Maculinea arion (butterfly) (horiz)			30	70
377	2½p. Sardinian Warbler (*Sylvia melanocephala*)			40	1·50
378	3p. Giant Squill (*Scilla peruviana*)			20	10
379	4p. Grey Wrasse (*Crenilabrus cinereus*) (horiz)			30	30
	b. Chalk-surfaced paper (21.4.81)			55	70
380	5p. Vanessa atalanta (butterfly) (horiz)			50	90
381	6p. Black Kite (*Milvus migrans*)			1·75	45
	w. Wmk inverted			85·00	
382	9p. Shrubby Scorpion-vetch (*Coronilla valentina*)			70	70
383	10p. John Dory (fish) (*Zeus faber*) (horiz)			40	20
	a. Chalk-surfaced paper (21.4.81)			70	1·25
384	12p. Colias crocea (butterfly) (horiz)			1·00	35
	a. Chalk-surfaced paper (21.4.81)			4·00	4·25
384b	15p. Winged Asparagus Pea (*Tetragonolobus purpureus*) (12.11.80)			1·50	55
	bw. Wmk inverted			85·00	
385	20p. Audouin's Gull (*Larus audouinii*)			1·50	2·25
386	25p. Barbary Nut (iris) (*Iris sisyrinchium*)			1·25	2·00
	a. Chalk-surfaced paper (21.4.81)			4·25	4·75
387	50p. Swordfish (*Xiphias gladius*) (horiz)			2·00	95
	a. Chalk-surfaced paper (21.4.81)			5·50	6·50
388	£1 Papilio machaon (butterfly) (horiz)			4·25	4·50
389	£2 Hoopoe (*Upupa epops*)			8·50	10·00
389a	£5 Arms of Gibraltar (16.5.79)			10·00	11·00
374/89a			Set of 18	30·00	35·00

The ½p. to £2 values have a descriptive text printed on the reverse, beneath the gum.

*The normal sideways watermark shows Crown to left of CA, as seen from the back of the stamp.

Imprint dates: "1977", Nos. 374/84, 385/9; "1978", No. 382; "1979", No. 389a; "1980", No. 384b; "1981", Nos. 379b, 383a, 384a, 386a, 387a; "1982", No. 374a.

112 "Our Lady of Europa" Stamp

(Des J. Cooter. Litho Questa)

1977 (27 May). *"Amphilex 77" Stamp Exhibition. Amsterdam.* T **112** *and similar vert designs. Multicoloured.* W w 14 *(sideways on 6p.; inverted on 12p.).* P 13½.

390	6p. Type 112				10	20
391	12p. "Europa Point" stamp				15	30
	w. Wmk upright				21·00	
392	25p. "E.E.C. Entry" stamp				20	50
	w. Wmk inverted				2·25	
390/2				Set of 3	40	90

113 "The Annunciation" (Rubens)

114 Aerial View of Gibraltar

(Des A. Ryman. Litho Enschedé)

1977 (2 Nov). *Christmas and Rubens' 400th Birth Anniv.* T **113** *and similar multicoloured designs.* W w 14 *(sideways on 12p.).* P 13½.

393	3p. Type 113				10	10
394	9p. "The Adoration of the Magi"				25	20

395	12p. "The Adoration of the Magi" (horiz)			30	30
396	15p. "The Holy Family under the Apple Tree"			30	40
393/6			Set of 4	85	85
MS397	110 × 200 mm. Nos. 393/6 (wmk upright).			2·75	4·00

(Des A. Ryman. Litho Enschedé)

1978 (3 May). *Gibraltar from Space.* P 13½.

398	114	12p. multicoloured			25	50
		a. Horiz pair imperf 3 sides			£3000	
MS399		148×108 mm. 25p. multicoloured			80	80

Design:—25p. Aerial view of Straits of Gibraltar.
No. 398a occurs on the bottom pair from two sheets of 10 (2×5) and shows the stamps perforated at top only.

115 Holyroodhouse

(Des and litho Walsall)

1978 (12 June). *25th Anniv of Coronation.* T **115** *and similar horiz designs. Multicoloured.* (a) *From sheets.* P 13½ × 14.

400	6p. Type 115				20	15
401	9p. St. James's Palace				25	15
402	12p. Sandringham				30	30
403	18p. Balmoral				40	75
400/3				Set of 4	1·00	1·25

(b) *From booklets. Imperf × roul 5*. Self-adhesive.*

404	12p. As No. 402				35	75
	a. Booklet pane. Nos. 404/5, each × 3				2·00	
405	18p. As No. 403				40	90
406	25p. Windsor Castle				90	1·75
	a. Booklet pane of 1				90	
404/6				Set of 3	1·50	3·00

*Nos. 404/5 were separated by various combinations of rotary-knife (giving a straight edge) and roulette. No. 406 exists only with straight edges.

116 Short S.25 Sunderland, 1938–58   117 "Madonna with Animals"

(Des A. Theobald. Litho Harrison)

1978 (6 Sept). *60th Anniv of Royal Air Force.* T **116** *and similar horiz designs. Multicoloured.* W w 14 *(sideways).* P 14.

407	3p. Type 116				15	10
408	9p. Caudron G-3, 1918				35	40
409	16p. Avro Shackleton M.R.2, 1953–66				40	55
410	16p. Hawker Hunter F.6, 1954–77				45	80
411	18p. Hawker Siddeley H.S.801 Nimrod M.R.1, 1969–78				50	90
407/11				Set of 5	1·75	2·50

(Des A. Ryman. Litho Questa)

1978 (1 Nov). *Christmas. Paintings by Dürer.* T **117** *and similar vert designs. Multicoloured.* W w 14. P 14.

412	5p. Type 117				20	10
413	9p. "The Nativity"				25	15
414	12p. "Madonna of the Goldfinch"				30	40
415	15p. "Adoration of the Magi"				35	75
412/15				Set of 4	1·00	1·25

118 Sir Rowland Hill and 1d. Stamp of 1886

(Des A. Ryman. Litho Format)

1979 (7 Feb). *Death Centenary of Sir Rowland Hill.* T **118** *and similar horiz designs.* W w 14 *(sideways*).* P 13½×14.

416	3p. multicoloured				10	10
417	9p. multicoloured				20	15
418	12p. multicoloured				25	20
	w. Wmk Crown to right of CA				70·00	
419	25p. black, dull claret and yellow				35	50
416/19				Set of 4	80	80

Designs:—9p. Sir Rowland Hill and 1p. coil stamp of 1971; 12p. Sir Rowland Hill and Post Office Regulations document, 1840; 25p. Sir Rowland Hill and "G" cancellation.
*The normal sideways watermark shows Crown to left of CA, as seen from the back of the stamp.

NEW INFORMATION

The editor is always interested to correspond with people who have new information that will improve or correct the Catalogue.

119 Posthorn, Dish Antenna and Early Telephone   **120** African Child

(Des A. Ryman. Litho Format)

1979 (16 May). *Europa. Communications.* W w 14 (*sideways*). P 13½.

420	119	3p. green and pale green		15	10
421		9p. lake-brown and ochre		30	90
422		12p. ultramarine and dull violet-blue		35	1·25
420/2			Set of 3	70	2·00

(Des G. Hutchins. Litho Walsall)

1979 (14 Nov). *Christmas. International Year of the Child.* T **120** and similar vert designs. Multicoloured. W w 14 (*sideways*). P 14.

423		12p. Type **120**		25	30
		a. Block of 6. Nos. 423/8		1·40	
424		12p. Asian child		25	30
425		12p. Polynesian child		25	30
426		12p. American Indian child		25	30
427		12p. Children of different races and Nativity scene		25	30
428		12p. European child		25	30
423/8			Set of 6	1·40	1·60

Nos. 423/8 were printed together, *se-tenant*, in blocks of 6, with margin separating the two blocks in each sheet.

121 Early Policemen   **122** Peter Amigo (Archbishop)

(Des C. Abbott. Litho Questa)

1980 (5 Feb). *150th Anniv of Gibraltar Police Force.* T **121** and similar horiz designs. Multicoloured. W w 14 (*sideways*). P 14.

429		3p. Type **121**		20	10
430		6p. Policemen of 1895, early 1900s and 1980		20	15
431		12p. Policeman and police ambulance		25	20
432		37p. Policewoman and police motor-cyclist		55	1·25
429/32			Set of 4	1·10	1·50

(Des A. Ryman. Litho Questa)

1980 (6 May). *Europa. Personalities.* T **122** and similar vert designs. Multicoloured. W w 14 (*inverted on No. 434*). P 14½ × 14.

433		12p. Type **122**		20	30
434		12p. Gustavo Bacarisas (artist)		20	30
435		12p. John Mackintosh (philanthropist)		20	30
433/5			Set of 3	55	80

123 Queen Elizabeth the Queen Mother   **124** "Horatio Nelson" (J. F. Rigaud)

(Des Harrison. Litho Questa)

1980 (4 Aug). *80th Birthday of Queen Elizabeth the Queen Mother.* W w 14 (*sideways*). P 14.

436	123	15p. multicoloured		30	30

(Des BG Studio. Litho Questa)

1980 (20 Aug). *175th Death Anniv of Nelson. Paintings.* T **124** and similar multicoloured designs. W w 14 (*sideways on 9 and 40p.*). P 14.

437		3p. Type **124**		15	10
438		9p. "H.M.S. *Victory*" (*horiz*)		25	25
439		15p. "Horatio Nelson" (Sir William Beechey)		35	35
440		40p. "H.M.S. *Victory* being towed into Gibraltar" (Clarkson Stanfield) (*horiz*)		80	1·00
437/40			Set of 4	1·40	1·50
MS441		159 × 99 mm. No. 439		75	1·75

Examples of the 3p. value showing Nelson facing left in error were prepared, but not issued by the Gibraltar Post Office.

125 Three Kings   **126** Hercules creating Mediterranean Sea

(Des A. Ryman. Litho Questa)

1980 (12 Nov). *Christmas.* T **125** and similar horiz design, each in deep brown and orange-yellow. W w 14 (*sideways*). P 14½.

442		15p. Type **125**		25	35
		a. Horiz pair. Nos. 442/3		50	70
443		15p. Nativity scene		25	35

Nos. 442/3 were printed together, *se-tenant*, in horizontal pairs throughout the sheet.

(Des G. Vasarhelyi. Litho Enschedé)

1981 (24 Feb). *Europa. Folklore.* T **126** and similar vert design. Multicoloured. W w 14. P 13½ × 13.

444		9p. Type **126**		20	15
445		15p. Hercules and Pillars of Hercules (Straits of Gibraltar)		25	35

127 Dining-room   **128** Prince Charles and Lady Diana Spencer

(Des A. Ryman. Litho Harrison)

1981 (22 May). *450th Anniv of The Convent (Governor's Residence).* T **127** and similar square designs. Multicoloured. W w 14 (*sideways*). P 14½ × 14.

446		4p. Type **127**		10	10
447		14p. King's Chapel		15	15
448		15p. The Convent		15	15
449		55p. Cloister		60	80
446/9			Set of 4	85	1·00

(Des A. Ryman. Litho Questa)

1981 (27 July). *Royal Wedding.* W w 14 (*sideways*). P 14½.

450	128	£1 multicoloured		1·50	1·50

129   **130** Paper Aeroplane

(Des A. Ryman. Litho Questa)

1981 (2 Sept). W w 14. P 13½×14.

451	129	1p. black		30	30
		a. Booklet pane. Nos. 451/2 and 453×3 plus printed label		1·40	
		b. Booklet pane. Nos. 451/2×2 and 453×6 plus two printed labels		2·00	
452		4p. Prussian blue		30	30
453		15p. light green		30	30
451/3			Set of 3	80	80

Nos. 451/3 were only issued in 50p. and £1 stamp booklets.

(Des A. Ryman. Litho Walsall)

1981 (29 Sept*). *50th Anniv of Gibraltar Airmail Service.* T **130** and similar horiz designs. Multicoloured. W w 14 (*sideways*). P 14½ × 14.

454		14p. Type **130**		15	15
455		15p. Airmail letters, post box and aircraft tail fin		15	15
456		55p. Jet airliner circling globe		60	70
454/6			Set of 3	80	90

*This is the local release date. The Crown Agents released the stamps on 21 September.

131 Carol Singers   **132** I.Y.D.P. Emblem and Stylised Faces

(Des Clive Torres (15p.); Peter Parody (55p.); adapted G. Vasarhelyi. Litho Questa)

1981 (19 Nov). *Christmas. Children's Drawings.* T **131** and similar multicoloured design. W w 14 (*sideways on 15p.*). P 14.

457		15p. Type **131**		30	15
458		55p. Postbox (*vert*)		1·00	85

(Des A. Ryman. Litho Questa)

1981 (19 Nov). *International Year For Disabled Persons.* W w 14 (*sideways*). P 14 × 14½.

459	132	14p. multicoloured		30	30

133 Douglas DC-3   **134** Crest, H.M.S. *Opossum*

(Des A. Theobald. Litho J.W.)

1982 (10 Feb). *Aircraft. Horiz designs as* T **133**. Multicoloured. W w 14. *Imprint date at foot.* P 14.

460		1p. Type **133**		25	1·00
461		2p. Vickers Viking 1B		30	1·00
462		3p. Airspeed A.S.57 Ambassador		30	90
463		4p. Vickers Viscount 800		40	20
464		5p. Boeing 727-100		90	60
465		10p. Vickers 953 Vanguard		1·75	50
466		14p. Short S.45A Solent 2		1·25	2·50
467		15p. Fokker F.27 Friendship		2·50	2·25
468		17p. Boeing 737		1·00	55
469		20p. B.A.C. One Eleven		1·00	50
470		25p. Lockheed Constellation		4·00	3·00
471		50p. Hawker Siddeley Comet 4B		4·00	2·25
472		£1 Saro A.21 Windhover		5·50	2·25
473		£2 Hawker Siddeley Trident 2E		6·50	5·00
474		£5 De Havilland D.H.89A Dragon Rapide		9·00	14·00
460/74			Set of 15	32·00	32·00

Imprint dates: "1982", Nos. 460/74; "1985", No. 469.
For 2p. and 5p. values watermarked w **16** see Nos. 549 and 552.

(Des A. Ryman. Litho Questa)

1982 (14 Apr). *Naval Crests (1st series).* T **134** and similar vert designs. Multicoloured. W w 14. P 14.

475		½p. Type **134**		10	10
476		15½p. H.M.S. *Norfolk*		55	65
477		17p. H.M.S. *Fearless*		60	70
478		60p. H.M.S. *Rooke*		1·40	2·75
		w. Wmk inverted		35·00	
475/8			Set of 4	2·25	3·75

See also Nos. 493/6, 510/13, 522/5, 541/4, 565/8, 592/5, 616/19, 638/41 and 651/4.

135 Hawker Hurricane Mk 1 and Supermarine Spitfires at Gibraltar   **136** Gibraltar Chamber of Commerce Centenary

(Des A. Ryman. Litho Questa)

1982 (11 June). *Europa. Operation Torch.* T **135** and similar horiz design. Multicoloured. W w 14 (*sideways*). P 14.

479		14p. Type **135**		25	70
480		17p. General Giraud, General Eisenhower and Gibraltar		35	80

(Des A. Ryman. Litho Questa)

1982 (22 Sept). *Anniversaries.* T **136** and similar vert designs. Multicoloured. W w 14 (*sideways*). P 14½.

481		14p. Type **136**		10	10
482		15½p. British Forces Postal Service centenary		30	25
483		60p. 75th anniv of Gibraltar Scout Association		1·10	1·25
481/3			Set of 3	1·25	1·40

137 Printed Circuit forming Map of World

(Des A. Ryman. Litho Harrison)

1982 (1 Oct). *International Direct Dialling.* W w 14 (*sideways*). P 14½.

484	137	17p. black, pale blue and bright orange		35	35

138 Gibraltar illuminated at Night and Holly

(Des A. Ryman. Litho Questa)

1982 (18 Nov). *Christmas. T* **138** *and similar horiz design. Multi-coloured. W* w **14** *(sideways). P* 14 × 14½.
485	14p. Type **138**	..	..	..	45	30
486	17p. Gibraltar illuminated at night and Mistletoe	..	..	..	50	35

139 Yacht Marina

(Des Olympia Reyes. Litho Questa)

1983 (14 Mar). *Commonwealth Day. T* **139** *and similar multi-coloured designs. W* w **14** *(sideways on 4, 14p.). P* 14.
487	4p. Type **139**	..	..	..	10	10
488	14p. Scouts and Guides Commonwealth Day Parade	..	..	..	20	15
489	17p. Flag of Gibraltar (*vert*)	..	..	..	25	20
490	60p. Queen Elizabeth II (from photo by Tim Graham) (*vert*)	..	..	..	70	1·00
487/90		..	..	*Set of 4*	1·00	1·25

140 St George's Hall Gallery

(Des A. Ryman. Litho Harrison)

1983 (21 May). *Europa. T* **140** *and similar horiz design. W* w **14** *(sideways). P* 13½ × 14.
491	16p. black and brown-ochre	..	..	..	30	35
492	19p. black and pale blue	..	..	..	40	40

Design:—19p. Water catchment slope.

(Des A. Ryman. Litho Questa)

1983 (1 July). *Naval Crests (2nd series). Vert designs as T* **134**. *Multicoloured. W* w **14**. *P* 14.
493	4p. H.M.S. *Faulknor*	..	..	..	30	10
494	14p. H.M.S. *Renown*	..	..	..	70	35
495	17p. H.M.S. *Ark Royal*	..	..	..	75	40
496	60p. H.M.S. *Sheffield*	..	..	..	1·75	1·50
	w. Wmk inverted	..	..	..	28·00	
493/6		..	..	*Set of 4*	3·25	2·10

141 Landport Gate, 1729

(Des Olympia Reyes. Litho Enschedé)

1983 (13 Sept). *Fortress Gibraltar in the 18th Century. T* **141** *and similar horiz designs. Multicoloured. W* w **14** *(sideways*). P* 13 × 13½.
497	4p. Type **141**	..	..	..	15	10
498	17p. Koehler Gun, 1782	..	..	..	35	30
499	77p. King's Bastion, 1779	..	..	..	1·00	1·25
497/9		..	..	*Set of 3*	1·40	1·50
MS500	97 × 145 mm. Nos. 497/9	..	..	..	2·25	1·50

*The normal sideways watermark shows Crown to right of CA on Nos. 497/9 and Crown to left on No. MS500, both as seen from the back of the stamp.

142 "Adoration of the Magi" (Raphael)   **143** 1932 2d. Stamp and Globe

(Des A. Ryman. Litho Questa)

1983 (17 Nov). *Christmas. 500th Birth Anniv of Raphael. T* **142** *and similar multicoloured designs. W* w **14** *(sideways on 4p.). P* 14.
501	4p. Type **142**	..	..	..	25	10
502	17p. "Madonna of Foligno" (*vert*)	..	..	70	35
503	60p. "Sistine Madonna" (*vert*)	..	..	1·75	1·40
501/3		..	..	*Set of 3*	2·40	1·60

(Des E. Field. Litho Walsall)

1984 (6 Mar). *Europa. Posts and Telecommunications. T* **143** *and similar vert design. Multicoloured. W* w **14**. *P* 14½ × 14.
504	17p. Type **143**	..	..	..	35	50
505	23p. Circuit board and globe	..	..	45	1·00
	w. Wmk inverted	..	..	..	95·00	

144 Hockey   **145** Mississippi River Boat Float

(Des A. Ryman. Litho Walsall)

1984 (25 May). *Sports. T* **144** *and similar horiz designs. Multicoloured. W* w **14** *(sideways). P* 14 × 14½.
506	20p. Type **144**	..	..	..	55	65
507	21p. Basketball	..	..	..	55	65
508	26p. Rowing	..	..	..	65	1·00
509	29p. Football	..	..	..	70	1·10
506/9		..	..	*Set of 4*	2·25	3·00

(Des A. Ryman. Litho Walsall)

1984 (21 Sept). *Naval Crests (3rd series). Vert designs as T* **134**. *Multicoloured. W* w **14**. *P* 13½ × 13.
510	20p. H.M.S. *Active*	..	..	..	1·60	1·75
511	21p. H.M.S. *Foxhound*	..	..	1·60	2·00
512	26p. H.M.S. *Valiant*	..	..	1·75	2·00
513	29p. H.M.S. *Hood*	..	..	..	1·90	2·25
	w. Wmk inverted	..	..	..	12·00	
510/13		..	..	*Set of 4*	6·25	7·25

(Des A. Ryman. Litho Questa)

1984 (7 Nov). *Christmas. Epiphany Floats. T* **145** *and similar horiz design. Multicoloured. W* w **14** *(sideways). P* 14 × 14½.
514	20p. Type **145**	..	..	..	30	30
515	80p. Roman Temple float	..	..	1·40	2·25

146 Musical Symbols, and Score from Beethoven's 9th (Choral) Symphony   **147** Globe and Stop Polio Campaign Logo

(Des Olympia Reyes. Photo Courvoisier)

1985 (26 Feb). *Europa. European Music Year. T* **146** *and similar horiz design. Multicoloured. Granite paper. P* 12½.
516	146 20p. multicoloured	..	..	..	35	30
517	29p. multicoloured	..	..	..	55	1·50

The 29p. is as T **146** but shows different symbols.

(Des E. Field. Litho J.W.)

1985 (3 May). *Stop Polio Campaign. Vert designs as T* **147**. *Multicoloured. W* w **14** *(inverted). P* 13 × 13½.
518	26p. multicoloured (Type **147**)	..	..	90	1·25
	a. Horiz strip of 4. Nos. 518/21	..	3·25	
519	26p. multicoloured ("ST" visible)	..	90	1·25
520	26p. multicoloured ("STO" visible)	..	90	1·25
521	26p. multicoloured ("STOP" visible)	..	90	1·25
518/21		..	..	*Set of 4*	3·25	4·50

Nos 518/21 were printed in horizontal *se-tenant* strips of four within the sheet. Each design differs in the position of the logo across the centre of the globe. On the left hand stamp in the strip only the letter "S" is visible, on the next "ST", on the next "STO" and on the last "STOP".
Other features of the design also differ, so that the word "Year" moves towards the top of the stamp and on No. 521 the upper logo is omitted.

(Des A. Ryman. Litho Questa)

1985 (3 July). *Naval Crests (4th series). Vert designs as T* **134**. *Multicoloured. W* w **16**. *P* 14.
522	4p. H.M.S. *Duncan*	..	..	..	60	10
523	9p. H.M.S. *Fury*	..	..	..	90	50
524	21p. H.M.S. *Firedrake*	..	..	2·00	2·00
525	80p. H.M.S. *Malaya*	..	..	4·00	6·00
522/5		..	..	*Set of 4*	6·75	7·75

148 I.Y.Y. Logo   **149** St. Joseph

(Des Olympia Reyes. Litho Walsall)

1985 (6 Sept). *International Youth Year. T* **148** *and similar horiz designs. Multicoloured. W* w **14** *(sideways). P* 14 × 14½.
526	4p. Type **148**	..	..	..	25	10
527	20p. Hands passing diamond	..	..	95	1·10
528	80p. 75th anniv logo of Girl Guide Movement	..	2·50	3·25
526/8		..	..	*Set of 3*	3·25	4·00

(Des A. Ryman (4p.), Olympia Reyes (80p.). Litho Cartor)

1985 (25 Oct). *Christmas. Centenary of St. Joseph's Parish Church. T* **149** *and similar vert designs. Multicoloured. W* w **16**. *P* 13½*.
529	4p. Type **149**	..	..	..	65	90
	a. Vert pair. Nos. 529/30	..	..	1·25	1·75
530	4p. St. Joseph's Parish Church	..	65	90
531	80p. Nativity crib	..	..	3·50	4·00
529/31		..	..	*Set of 3*	4·25	5·25

*Nos. 529/30 were printed together in panes of 25; No. 529 on rows 1, 3 and 5, and No. 530 on rows 2 and 4. *Se-tenant* vertical pairs from rows 1/2 and 3/4, forming composite designs, have the stamps separated by a line of roulettes instead of perforations. Examples of No. 529 from row 5 have perforations on all four sides.

150 *Papilio machaon* (butterfly) and The Convent.   **151** 1887 Queen Victoria 6d. Stamp

(Des E. Field. Litho Walsall)

1986 (10 Feb). *Europa. Nature and the Environment. T* **150** *and similar horiz design. Multicoloured. W* w **16** *(sideways). P* 13 × 13½.
532	22p. Type **150**	..	..	..	1·25	50
533	29p. Herring Gull and Europa Point	..	1·75	4·25

(Des A. Ryman. Litho Walsall)

1986 (26 Mar). *Centenary of First Gibraltar Postage Stamps. T* **151** *and similar vert designs showing stamps. Multicoloured. W* w **16**. *P* 14 × 13½ (44p.) or 13½ × 13 (others).
534	4p. Type **151**	..	..	..	30	10
535	22p. 1903 Edward VII 2½d.	..	..	1·00	1·00
536	32p. 1912 George V 1d.	..	..	1·50	2·00
537	36p. 1938 George VI £1	..	..	1·60	2·50
538	44p. 1953 Coronation ½d. (29 × 46 *mm*)	2·00	3·00
534/8		..	..	*Set of 5*	5·75	7·75
MS539	102×73 mm. 29p. 1886 "GIBRALTAR" overprint on Bermuda 1d.	..	2·50	2·75
	w. Wmk inverted	..	..	..		

152 Queen Elizabeth II in Robes of Order of the Bath   **153** Prince Andrew and Miss Sarah Ferguson

(Des A. Ryman. Litho Walsall)

1986 (22 May). *60th Birthday of Queen Elizabeth II. W* w **16.**
P 14×13½.
540 **152** £1 multicoloured .. .. .. 1·60 3·00

(Des A. Ryman. Litho Questa)

1986 (28 Aug). *Naval Crests (5th series). Vert designs as T* **134.**
Multicoloured. W w **16.** *P* 14.
541 22p. H.M.S. *Lightning* .. .. .. 1·75 1·00
542 29p. H.M.S. *Hermione* .. .. .. 2·00 1·75
543 32p. H.M.S. *Laforey* .. .. .. 2·25 3·25
544 44p. H.M.S. *Nelson* .. .. .. 2·75 4·00
541/4 .. .. *Set of 4* 8·00 9·00

(Des A. Ryman. Litho Questa)

1986 (28 Aug). *Royal Wedding. Sheet* 115×85 *mm. W* w **16.**
P 14½.
MS545 **153** 44p. multicoloured .. .. 1·10 2·00

154 Three Kings and   **155** Neptune House
Cathedral of St. Mary
the Crowned

(Des M. Infante. Litho Walsall)

1986 (14 Oct). *Christmas. International Peace Year. T* **154** *and
similar vert design. Multicoloured. W* w **16.** *P* 14.
546 18p. Type **154** .. .. .. 1·00 50
547 32p. St. Andrew's Church .. .. 1·50 2·75

(Litho Questa)

1986 (12 Dec)–87. *As Nos.* 461 *and* 464, *but W* w **16** (*sideways*).
With "1986" *imprint date. P* 14.
549 2p. Vickers Viking 1B .. .. 2·00 2·75
552 5p. Boeing 727-100 (2.1.87) .. .. 2·00 2·75

(Des M. Infante. Litho Questa)

1987 (17 Feb). *Europa. Architecture. T* **155** *and similar horiz
design. Multicoloured. W* w **16.** *P* 14½.
563 22p. Type **155** .. .. .. 1·50 50
564 29p. Ocean Heights .. .. .. 2·00 4·00

(Des A. Ryman. Litho Walsall)

1987 (15 Apr). *Naval Crests (6th series). Vert designs as T* **134.**
Multicoloured. W w **16.** *P* 13½×13.
565 18p. H.M.S. *Wishart* (destroyer) .. 1·25 75
566 22p. H.M.S. *Charybdis* (cruiser) .. 1·40 1·10
567 32p. H.M.S. *Antelope* (destroyer) .. 1·90 3·00
568 44p. H.M.S. *Eagle* (aircraft carrier).. 2·50 4·00
565/8 .. .. *Set of 4* 6·50 8·00

156 13-inch Mortar, 1783   **157** Victoria Stadium

(Des A. Ryman. Litho Format)

1987 (1 June). *Guns. T* **156** *and similar horiz designs. Multicoloured. W* w **14.** *P* 12½.
569 1p. Type **156** 20 60
570 2p. 6-inch coastal gun, 1909 .. 30 60
571 3p. 8-inch howitzer, 1783 .. 30 60
572 4p. Bofors "L40/70" AA gun, 1951 .. 40 10
573 5p. 100 ton rifled muzzle-loader, 1882 40 50
    w. Wmk inverted .. .. .. †
574 10p. 5.25-inch heavy AA gun, 1953 .. 40 55
575 18p. 25-pounder gun-how, 1943 .. 65 90
576 19p. 64-pounder rifled muzzle-loader, 1873 70 1·00
577 22p. 12-pounder gun, 1758 .. 70 50
578 50p. 10-inch rifled muzzle-loader, 1870 .. 1·40 3·00
579 £1 Russian 24-pounder gun, 1854 .. 2·50 2·50
580 £3 9.2-inch "MK. 10" coastal gun, 1935 5·00 14·00
581 £5 24-pounder gun, 1779 .. 8·00 16·00
569/81 .. .. .. *Set of 13* 19·00 38·00

(Des A. Ryman. Litho Walsall)

1987 (16 Sept). *Bicentenary of Royal Engineers' Royal Warrant.
T* **157** *and similar vert designs. Multicoloured. W* w **16.** *P* 14½.
582 18p. Type **157** .. .. .. 1·25 65
583 22p. Freedom of Gibraltar scroll and casket 1·75 3·00
584 44p. Royal Engineers' badge.. .. 2·50 4·00
582/4 .. .. *Set of 3* 5·00 7·00

158 The Three Kings

(Des Olympia Reyes. Litho Walsall)

1987 (12 Nov). *Christmas. T* **158** *and similar horiz designs.
Multicoloured. W* w **16** (*sideways*). *P* 14½.
585 4p. Type **158** 15 10
586 22p. The Holy Family .. .. 90 1·00
587 44p. The Shepherds .. .. .. 1·75 3·25
585/7 .. .. *Set of 3* 2·50 3·75

159 *Canberra* (liner) passing   **160** European Bee Eater
Gibraltar

(Des Olympia Reyes. Litho Format)

1988 (16 Feb). *Europa. Transport and Communications. T* **159**
and similar horiz designs. Multicoloured. W w **14.**
P 14½ × 14 × *roul between se-tenant pairs.*
588 22p. Type **159** .. .. .. 1·50 2·25
    a. Horiz pair. Nos. 588/9 .. .. 3·00 4·50
589 22p. *Gibline I* (ferry), dish aerial and Boeing
    737 .. .. 1·50 2·25
590 32p. Horse-drawn carriage and modern
    coach .. .. .. 2·00 2·75
    a. Horiz pair. Nos. 590/1 .. .. 4·00 5·50
591 32p. Car, telephone and Rock of Gibraltar 2·00 2·75
588/91 .. .. *Set of 4* 6·25 9·00
The two designs for each value were printed in sheets of ten,
each containing five horizontal *se-tenant* pairs in which the
stamps were rouletted between vertically.

(Des A. Ryman. Litho Walsall)

1988 (7 Apr). *Naval Crests (7th series). Vert designs as T* **134.**
W w **16.** *P* 13½×13.
592 18p. multicoloured .. .. .. 1·50 65
593 22p. black, brownish black and gold .. 2·00 1·25
594 32p. multicoloured .. .. .. 2·25 3·25
595 44p. multicoloured .. .. .. 3·00 4·50
592/5 .. .. *Set of 4* 8·00 8·75
Designs:—18p. H.M.S. *Clyde*; 22p. H.M.S. *Foresight*; 32p.
H.M.S. *Severn*; 44p. H.M.S. *Rodney*.

(Des Olympia Reyes. Litho B.D.T.)

1988 (15 June). *Birds. T* **160** *and similar horiz designs.
Multicoloured. W* w **14** (*sideways*). *P* 13½.
596 4p. Type **160** 65 20
597 22p. Atlantic Puffin .. .. .. 1·50 90
598 32p. Honey Buzzard .. .. .. 2·00 3·00
599 44p. Blue Rock Thrush .. .. 2·50 4·25
596/9 .. .. *Set of 4* 6·00 7·50

161 *Zebu* (brigantine)   **162** "Snowman"
(Rebecca Falero)

(Des A. Ryman. Litho B.D.T.)

1988 (14 Sept). *Operation Raleigh. T* **161** *and similar horiz
designs. Multicoloured. W* w **14.** *P* 13.
600 19p. Type **161** 65 60
601 22p. Miniature of Sir Walter Raleigh and
    logo 75 70
602 32p. *Sir Walter Raleigh* (expedition ship)
    and world map .. .. .. 1·10 1·75
600/2 .. .. *Set of 3* 2·25 2·75
MS603 135×86 mm. 22p. As No. 601; 44p. *Sir
Walter Raleigh* (expedition ship) passing
Gibraltar .. .. .. 3·75 4·50

(Des A. Ryman. Litho Questa)

1988 (2 Nov). *Christmas. Children's Paintings. T* **162** *and
similar multicoloured designs. W* w **16** (*sideways*). *P* 14½
(44p.) *or* 14 (*others*).
604 4p. Type **162** 15 10
605 22p. "The Nativity" (Dennis Penalver) .. 55 60
606 44p. "Father Christmas" (Gavin Key)
    (23×31 mm) .. .. .. 1·00 1·50
604/6 .. .. *Set of 3* 1·50 2·00

NEW INFORMATION

The editor is always interested to correspond with
people who have new information that will
improve or correct the Catalogue.

163 Soft Toys and Toy Train   **164** Port Sergeant
with Keys

(Des Olympia Reyes. Litho Walsall)

1989 (15 Feb). *Europa. Children's Toys. T* **163** *and similar
horiz design. Multicoloured. W* w **16** (*sideways*). *P* 13 × 13½.
607 25p. Type **163** .. .. .. 1·25 75
608 32p. Soft toys, toy boat and doll's house .. 1·75 2·75

(Des A. Ryman. Litho Walsall)

1989 (28 Apr). *50th Anniv of Gibraltar Regiment. T* **164** *and
similar vert designs. Multicoloured. W* w **14.** *P* 13½×13.
609 4p. Type **164** 40 10
610 22p. Regimental badge and colours .. 1·25 1·10
611 32p. Drum major .. .. .. 1·75 2·75
609/11 .. .. *Set of 3* 3·00 3·50
MS612 124×83 mm. 22p. As No. 610; 44p.
Former Gibraltar Defence Force badge .. 3·50 4·00

165 Nurse and Baby   **166** One Penny
Coin

(Des E. Field. Litho Questa)

1989 (7 July). *125th Anniv of International Red Cross. T* **165**
and similar vert designs. W w **16.** *P* 15×14½.
613 25p. black, bright scarlet and grey-brown .. 75 60
614 32p. black, bright scarlet and grey-brown .. 95 1·60
615 44p. black, bright scarlet and grey-brown .. 1·25 2·75
613/15 .. .. *Set of 3* 2·75 4·50
Designs:—32p. Famine victims; 44p. Accident victims.

(Des A. Ryman. Litho B.D.T.)

1989 (7 Sept). *Naval Crests (8th series). Vert designs as T* **134.**
W w **16.** *P* 14×13½.
616 22p. multicoloured .. .. .. 1·50 75
617 25p. black and gold .. .. .. 1·50 1·50
618 32p. gold, black and bright scarlet .. 2·00 2·50
619 44p. multicoloured .. .. .. 3·00 4·00
616/19 .. .. *Set of 4* 7·25 8·00
Designs:—22p. H.M.S. *Blankney*; 25p. H.M.S. *Deptford*; 32p.
H.M.S. *Exmoor*; 44p. H.M.S. *Stork*.

(Des A. Ryman. Litho Questa)

1989 (11 Oct). *New Coinage. T* **166** *and similar vert designs in
two miniature sheets. W* w **16** (*sideways*). *P* 14½.
MS620 72×94 mm. 4p. bronze, black & dull verm
(Type **166**); 4p. bronze, blk & dp brn (two pence);
4p. silver, blk & greenish yellow (ten pence); 4p.
silver, black and emerald (five pence) .. 1·25 1·75
MS621 100×95 mm. 22p. silver, black & reddish
orge (fifty pence); 22p. gold, black & ultram (five
pounds); 22p. gold, blk & orge-brn (two pounds);
22p. gold, blk & brt emer (one pound); 22p. gold,
blk & brt reddish vio (obverse of coin series); 22p.
silver, black and pale violet-blue (twenty pence) 4·75 6·00

167 Father Christmas in   **168** General Post
Sleigh   Office Entrance

(Des M. Infante. Litho Questa)

1989 (11 Oct). *Christmas. T* **167** *and similar horiz designs. Multicoloured. W w* 16 *(sideways). P* 14½.

622	4p. Type **167**	15	10
623	22p. Shepherds and sheep	70	70
624	32p. The Nativity	1·10	1·75
625	44p. The Three Wise Men	1·75	3·00
622/5	*Set of* 4	3·25	5·00

(Des Olympia Reyes. Litho Questa)

1990 (6 Mar). *Europa. Post Office Buildings. T* **168** *and similar vert designs. Multicoloured. P* 14½×*roul between se-tenant pairs.*

626	22p. Type **168**	1·00	1·50
	a. Horiz pair. Nos. 626/7	2·00	3·00
627	22p. Interior of General Post Office	1·00	1·50
628	32p. Interior of South District Post Office	1·50	2·25
	a. Horiz pair. Nos. 628/9	3·00	4·50
629	32p. South District Post Office	1·50	2·25
626/9	*Set of* 4	4·50	6·50

Nos. 626/7 and 628/9 were printed in *se-tenant* horizontal pairs within separate sheets of eight, the stamps in each pair being divided by a line of roulettes.

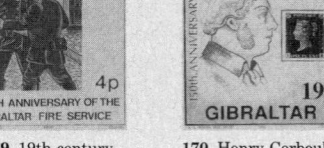

169 19th-century Firemen	170 Henry Corbould (artist) and Penny Black

(Des D. Gonzalez. Litho Questa)

1990 (2 Apr). *125th Anniv of Gibraltar Fire Service. T* **169** *and similar multicoloured designs. P* 14½×14 *(vert) or* 14×14½ *(horiz).*

630	4p. Type **169**	60	15
631	20p. Early fire engine (*horiz*)	1·50	1·10
632	42p. Modern fire engine (*horiz*)	1·75	3·00
633	44p. Fireman in breathing apparatus	2·00	3·00
630/3	*Set of* 4	5·25	6·50

(Des A. Ryman. Litho Questa)

1990 (3 May). *150th Anniv of the Penny Black. T* **170** *and similar vert designs. P* 13½×14.

634	19p. Type **170**	95	80
635	22p. Bath Royal Mail coach	1·10	90
636	32p. Sir Rowland Hill and Penny Black	2·25	3·50
634/6	*Set of* 3	3·75	4·75
MS637	145×95 mm. 44p. Penny Black with Maltese Cross cancellation. P 14½×14	4·00	4·50

(Des A. Ryman. Litho Questa)

1990 (10 July). *Naval Crests (9th series). Vert designs as T* **134**. *Multicoloured. P* 14.

638	22p. H.M.S. *Calpe*	1·50	70
639	25p. H.M.S. *Gallant*	1·60	1·75
640	32p. H.M.S. *Wrestler*	2·00	2·75
641	44p. H.M.S. *Greyhound*	2·50	4·25
638/41	*Set of* 4	7·00	8·50

171 Model of Europort Development	172 Candle and Holly

(Des A. Ryman. Litho Questa)

1990 (10 Oct). *Development Projects. T* **171** *and similar horiz designs. Multicoloured. P* 14½.

642	22p. Type **171**	75	80
643	23p. Construction of building material factory	75	1·40
644	25p. Land reclamation	95	1·40
642/4	*Set of* 3	2·25	3·25

(Des D. Gonzalez. Litho B.D.T.)

1990 (10 Oct). *Christmas. T* **172** *and similar vert designs. Multicoloured. P* 13½.

645	4p. Type **172**	15	10
646	22p. Father Christmas	75	65
647	42p. Christmas Tree	1·50	2·25
648	44p. Nativity crib	1·50	2·25
645/8	*Set of* 4	3·50	4·75

MINIMUM PRICE

The minimum price quote is 10p which represents a handling charge rather than a basis for valuing common stamps. For further notes about prices see introductory pages.

173 Space Laboratory and Spaceplane (Colombus Development Programme)	174 Shag

(Des D. Gonzalez. Litho B.D.T.)

1991 (26 Feb). *Europa. Europe in Space. T* **173** *and similar horiz design. Multicoloured. P* 13½×13.

649	25p. Type **173**	75	75
650	32p. "ERS-1" earth resources remote sensing satellite	1·00	2·00

(Des A. Ryman. Litho Walsall)

1991 (9 Apr). *Naval Crests (10th series). Vert designs as T* **134**. *P* 13½×13.

651	4p. black, new blue and gold	35	10
652	21p. multicoloured	1·25	1·25
653	22p. multicoloured	1·25	1·25
654	62p. multicoloured	3·25	6·00
651/4	*Set of* 4	5·50	7·75

Designs:—4p. H.M.S. *Hesperus*; 21p. H.M.S. *Forester*; 22p. H.M.S. *Furious*; 62p. H.M.S. *Scylla*.

(Des Olympia Reyes. Litho B.D.T.)

1991 (30 May). *Endangered Species. Birds. T* **174** *and similar horiz designs. Multicoloured. P* 13½.

655	13p. Type **174**	85	1·10
	a. Block of 4. Nos. 655/8	3·00	
656	13p. Barbary Partridge	85	1·10
657	13p. Egyptian Vulture	85	1·10
658	13p. Black Stork	85	1·10
655/8	*Set of* 4	3·00	4·00

Nos. 655/8 were printed together, *se-tenant*, in differently arranged blocks of 4 throughout the sheet of 16.

≡ £1.05 (175)	176 "North View of Gibraltar" (Gustavo Bacarisas)

1991 (30 May). *No.* 580 *surch with T* **175**.

659	£1.05 on £3 9.2-inch "Mk.10" coastal gun, 1935	3·50	1·60

(Des A. Ryman. Litho B.D.T.)

1991 (10 Sept). *Local Paintings. T* **176** *and similar multicoloured designs. P* 14×15 *(42p.) or* 15×14 *(others).*

660	22p. Type **176**	85	50
661	26p. "Parson's Lodge" (Elena Mifsud)	1·00	1·00
662	32p. "Governor's Parade" (Jacobo Azagury)	1·50	2·25
663	42p. "Waterport Wharf" (Rudesindo Mannia) (*vert*)	2·25	3·50
660/3	*Set of* 4	5·00	6·50

177 "Once in Royal David's City"	178 Danaus chrysippus

(Des D. Gonzalez. Litho Questa)

1991 (15 Oct). *Christmas. Carols. T* **177** *and similar horiz designs. Multicoloured. P* 14×14½.

664	4p. Type **177**	25	10
665	24p. "Silent Night"	1·25	70
666	25p. "Angels We have Heard on High"	1·25	1·25
667	49p. "O Come All Ye Faithful"	2·00	3·50
664/7	*Set of* 4	4·25	5·00

(Des A. Ryman. Litho Questa)

1991 (15 Nov). *"Phila Nippon '91" International Stamp Exhibition, Tokyo. Sheet* 116×91 *mm. P* 14½.

MS668	178 £1.05, multicoloured	3·50	4·25

179 Columbus and Santa Maria	180 Compass Rose, Sail and Atlantic Map

(Des Olympia Reyes. Litho Walsall)

1992 (6 Feb). *Europa. 500th Anniv of Discovery of America by Columbus. T* **179** *and similar horiz designs. Multicoloured. P* 14½.

669	24p. Type **179**	1·25	1·75
	a. Horiz pair. Nos. 669/70	2·50	3·50
670	24p. Map of Old World and *Nina*	1·25	1·75
671	34p. Map of New World and *Pinta*	1·50	2·00
	a. Horiz pair. Nos. 671/2	3·00	4·00
672	34p. Map of Old World and look-out	1·50	2·00
669/72	*Set of* 4	5·00	6·75

The two designs of each value were printed together, *se-tenant*, in sheets of eight, the background to each horizontal pair forming a composite design.

(Des D. Miller. Litho Questa (54p), B.D.T. (others))

1992 (6 Feb). *40th Anniv of Queen Elizabeth II's Accession. Horiz designs as T* **143** *of Ascension. Multicoloured. W w* 14 *(sideways). P* 14.

673	4p. Gibraltar from North	15	10
674	20p. H.M.S. *Arrow* (frigate) and Gibraltar from South	60	60
675	24p. Southport Gates	75	80
676	44p. Three portraits of Queen Elizabeth	1·25	1·60
677	54p. Queen Elizabeth II	1·60	1·90
673/7	*Set of* 5	4·00	4·50

(Des E. Field. Litho B.D.T.)

1992 (15 Apr). *Round the World Yacht Rally. T* **180** *and similar multicoloured designs, each incorporating compass rose and sail. P* 13½.

678	21p. Type **180**	75	80
679	24p. Map of Indonesian Archipelago (*horiz*)	95	1·40
680	25p. Map of Indian Ocean (*horiz*)	95	1·75
678/80	*Set of* 3	2·40	3·50
MS681	108×72 mm. 21p. Type **180**; 49p. Map of Mediterranean and Red Sea	2·50	3·50

181 Holy Trinity Cathedral	182 Sacred Heart of Jesus Church

(Des M. Infante. Litho Questa)

1992 (21 Aug). *150th Anniv of Anglican Diocese of Gibraltar-in-Europe. T* **181** *and similar multicoloured designs. P* 14.

682	4p. Type **181**	20	10
683	24p. Diocesan crest and map (*horiz*)	1·00	65
684	44p. Construction of Cathedral and Sir George Don (*horiz*)	1·75	2·75
685	54p. Bishop Tomlinson	2·00	3·00
682/5	*Set of* 4	4·50	6·00

(Des W. Stagnetto. Litho B.D.T.)

1992 (10 Nov). *Christmas. Churches. T* **182** *and similar vert designs. Multicoloured. P* 14×13½.

686	4p. Type **182**	25	10
687	24p. Cathedral of St. Mary the Crowned	1·25	55
688	34p. St. Andrew's Church of Scotland	1·75	2·50
689	49p. St. Joseph's Church	2·50	4·25
686/9	*Set of* 4	5·25	6·50

183 "Drama and Music"	184 H.M.S. *Hood* (battle cruiser)

(Des E. Field. Litho Questa)

1993 (2 Mar). *Europa. Contemporary Art. T* **183** *and similar vert designs. Multicoloured. P* 14½×14.

690	24p. Type **183**	1·50	1·75
	a. Horiz pair. Nos. 690/1	3·00	3·50
691	24p. "Sculpture, Art and Pottery"	1·50	1·75
692	34p. "Architecture"	2·00	2·50
	a. Horiz pair. Nos. 692/3	4·00	5·00
693	34p. "Printing and Photography"	2·00	2·50
690/3	*Set of* 4	6·25	7·75

Nos. 690/1 and 692/3 were printed together, *se-tenant*, as horizontal pairs in sheetlets of 8 with decorative margins.

(Des D. Miller. Litho B.D.T.)

1993 (27 Apr). *Second World War Warships (1st series). Sheet* 120×79 *mm containing T* **184** *and similar horiz designs. Multicoloured. P* 14.

MS694	24p. Type **184**; 24p. H.M.S. *Ark Royal* (aircraft carrier, 1937); 24p. H.M.A.S. *Waterhen* (destroyer); 24p. U.S.S. *Gleaves* (destroyer)	7·00	7·00

See also Nos. MS724, MS748, MS779 and MS809.

185 Landport Gate

186 £sd and Decimal British Coins (25th anniv of Decimal Currency)

(Des Olympia Reyes. Litho and thermography Cartor (£5), litho Cartor (6, 7, 8, 9, 20, 30, 40p. and £2) or B.D.T. (others))

1993 (28 June)–**95.** *Architectural Heritage. T 185 and similar multicoloured designs. P 13.*

695	1p.	Type **185**		10	20
696	2p.	St. Mary the Crowned Church (*horiz*)		20	20
697	3p.	Parsons Lodge Battery (*horiz*)		20	20
698	4p.	Moorish Castle (*horiz*)		20	20
699	5p.	General Post Office		20	10
699a	6p.	House of Assembly (1.9.95)		30	30
699b	7p.	Bleak House (*horiz*) (1.9.95)		30	30
699c	8p.	General Eliott Memorial (1.9.95)		30	30
699d	9p.	Supreme Court Building (*horiz*) (1.9.95)		30	30
700	10p.	South Barracks (*horiz*)		30	30
700a	20p.	The Convent (*horiz*) (1.9.95)		60	55
701	21p.	American War Memorial		60	55
702	24p.	Garrison Library (*horiz*)		70	55
703	25p.	Southport Gates		70	55
704	26p.	Casemates Gate (*horiz*)		70	55
704a	30p.	St. Bernard's Hospital (1.9.95)		75	65
704b	40p.	City Hall (*horiz*) (1.9.95)		1·00	1·00
705	50p.	Central Police Station (*horiz*)		1·50	1·25
706	£1	Prince Edward's Gate		2·00	2·50
706a	£2	Church of the Sacred Heart of Jesus (1.9.95)		4·00	4·50
707	£3	Lighthouse, Europa Point		6·50	6·75
708	£5	Coat of arms and Fortress keys (6.6.94)		10·00	10·50
695/708		*Set of 22*		28·00	29·00

(Des W. Stagnetto. Litho Cartor)

1993 (21 Sept). *Anniversaries. T 186 and similar horiz designs. Multicoloured. P 13.*

709	21p.	Type **186**		75	65
710	24p.	R.A.F. crest with Handley Page 0/400 biplane and Panavia Tornado F Mk 3 fighter (75th anniv)		1·25	75
711	34p.	Garrison Library badge and building (Bicent)		1·40	2·00
712	49p.	Sir Winston Churchill and air raid (50th anniv of visit)		2·25	3·50
709/12		*Set of 4*		5·00	6·25

187 Mice decorating Christmas Tree

(Des Josie Evans. Litho Cartor)

1993 (16 Nov). *Christmas. T 187 and similar horiz designs. Multicoloured. P 13½.*

713	5p.	Type **187**		20	10
714	24p.	Mice pulling cracker		90	70
715	44p.	Mice singing carols		1·75	2·50
716	49p.	Mice building snowman		1·90	2·75
713/16		*Set of 4*		4·25	5·50

188 Exploding Atom (Lord Penney)

(Des M. Braunewell. Litho Cartor)

1994 (1 Mar). *Europa. Scientific Discoveries. T 188 and similar horiz designs. Multicoloured. P 13½.*

717	24p.	Type **188**		1·00	1·25
	a.	Horiz pair. Nos. 717/18		2·00	2·50
718	24p.	Polonium and radium experiment (Marie Curie)		1·00	1·25
719	34p.	First oil engine (Rudolph Diesel)		1·25	1·75
	a.	Horiz pair. Nos. 719/20		2·50	3·50
720	34p.	Early telescope (Galileo)		1·25	1·75
717/20		*Set of 4*		4·00	5·50

Nos. 717/18 and 719/20 were each printed together, *se-tenant*, in horizontal pairs in sheetlets of 8 with decorative margins.

189 World Cup and Map of U.S.A

(Des M. Braunewell. Litho Cartor)

1994 (19 Apr). *World Cup Football Championship, U.S.A. T 189 and similar multicoloured designs. P 13½.*

721	26p.	Type **189**		80	55
722	39p.	Players and pitch in shape of U.S.A.		1·25	1·75
723	49p.	Player's legs (*vert*)		1·60	2·50
721/3		*Set of 3*		3·25	4·25

(Des D. Miller. Litho Cartor)

1994 (6 June). *Second World War Warships (2nd series). Sheet 112×72 mm containing horiz designs as T 184. Multicoloured. P 13.*

MS724	5p.	H.M.S. *Penelope* (cruiser); 25p. H.M.S. *Warspite* (battleship); 44p. U.S.S. *McLanahan* (destroyer); 49p. *Isaac Sweers* (Dutch destroyer)		5·00	6·50

190 Pekingese

191 Golden Star Coral

(Des M. Braunewell. Litho B.D.T.)

1994 (16 Aug). *"Philakorea '94" International Stamp Exhibiton, Seoul. Sheet 102×76 mm. P 13.*

MS725	190	£1.05, multicoloured		3·00	4·00

(Des M. Whyte. Litho Walsall)

1994 (27 Sept). *Marine Life. T 191 and similar square designs. Multicoloured. P 14½×14.*

726	21p.	Type **191**		75	45
727	24p.	Star Fish		90	55
728	34p.	Gorgonian Sea-fan		1·50	2·25
729	49p.	Peacock Wrasse ("Turkish Wrasse")		2·00	3·25
726/9		*Set of 4*		4·75	6·00

192 Throwing the Discus and Centenary Emblem

193 Great Tit

(Des S. Perera. Litho Walsall)

1994 (22 Nov). *Centenary of International Olympic Committee. T 192 and similar horiz design. Multicoloured. P 14.*

730	49p.	Type **192**		1·75	2·25
731	54p.	Javelin throwing and emblem		1·75	2·50

(Des W. Stagnetto. Litho B.D.T.)

1994 (22 Nov). *Christmas. Songbirds. T 193 and similar multicoloured designs. P 14×13½ (vert) or 13½×14 (horiz).*

732	5p.	Type **193**		40	10
733	24p.	European Robin (*horiz*)		1·25	70
734	34p.	Blue Tit (*horiz*)		1·50	1·50
735	54p.	Goldfinch		2·25	3·25
732/5		*Set of 4*		4·75	5·00

194 Austrian Flag, Hand and Star

(Des R. Ollington. Litho Questa)

1995 (3 Jan). *Expansion of European Union. T 194 and similar horiz designs. Multicoloured. P 14.*

736	24p.	Type **194**		60	55
737	26p.	Finnish flag, hand and star		60	60
738	34p.	Swedish flag, hand and star		90	1·50
739	49p.	Flags of new members and European Union emblem		1·60	3·00
736/9		*Set of 4*		3·25	5·00

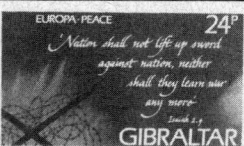

195 Barbed Wire and Quote from Isaiah Ch 2.4

(Des Jennifer Toombs. Litho B.D.T.)

1995 (28 Feb). *Europa. Peace and Freedom. T 195 and similar horiz designs. Multicoloured. P 13½.*

740	24p.	Type **195**		90	1·25
	a.	Horiz pair. Nos. 740/1		1·75	2·50
741	24p.	Rainbow and hands releasing peace dove		90	1·25
742	34p.	Shackles on wall and quote from Isaiah ch 61.1		1·25	1·75
	a.	Horiz pair. Nos. 742/3		2·50	3·50
743	34p.	Hands and sea-birds		1·25	1·75
740/3		*Set of 4*		3·75	5·50

Nos. 740/1 and 742/3 were each printed together, *se-tenant*, as horizontal pairs in sheetlets of 8 with decorative margins.

196 Fairey Swordfish, I Class Destroyer and Rock of Gibraltar

(Des A. Theobald. Litho B.D.T.)

1995 (8 May). *50th Anniv of End of Second World War. Sheet 101×66 mm. P 13½.*

MS744	196	£1.05, multicoloured		3·00	3·75

197 Yachting

198 Bee Orchid

(Des S. Perera. Litho B.D.T.)

1995 (8 May). *Island Games '95. T 197 and similar vert designs. Multicoloured. P 14×13½.*

745	24p.	Type **197**		70	60
	a.	Booklet pane. No. 745×3, with margins all round		1·90	
	b.	Booklet pane. Nos. 745/7, with margins all round		3·50	
746	44p.	Athlete on starting blocks		1·60	2·50
	a.	Booklet pane. No. 746×3, with margins all round		4·25	
747	49p.	Swimmer at start of race		1·60	2·50
	a.	Booklet pane. No. 747×3, with margins all round		4·25	
745/7		*Set of 3*		3·50	5·00

(Des D. Miller. Litho Questa)

1995 (6 June). *Second World War Warships (3rd series). Sheet 133×85 mm containing horiz designs as T 184. Multicoloured. P 13½×14.*

MS748	5p.	H.M.S. *Calpe* (destroyer); 24p. H.M.S. *Victorious* (aircraft carrier); 44p. U.S.S. *Weehawken* (attack transport); 49p. *Savorgan de Brazza* (French destroyer)		6·50	6·50

(Des R. Gorringe. Litho B.D.T.)

1995 (1 Sept). *"Singapore '95" International Stamp Exhibition. Orchids. T 198 and similar vert designs. Multicoloured. P 14×14½.*

749	22p.	Type **198**		1·00	1·10
	a.	Horiz strip of 5. Nos. 749/53		4·50	
750	23p.	Brown Bee Orchid		1·00	1·10
751	24p.	Pyramidal Orchid		1·00	1·10
752	25p.	Mirror Orchid		1·00	1·10
753	26p.	Sawfly Orchid		1·00	1·10
749/53		*Set of 5*		4·50	5·00

Nos. 749/53 were printed together, *se-tenant*, in horizontal strips of 5.

NEW INFORMATION

The editor is always interested to correspond with people who have new information that will improve or correct the Catalogue.

199 Handshake and United
Nations Emblem

(Des S. Perera. Litho B.D.T.)

1995 (24 Oct). *50th Anniv of United Nations. T* **199** *and similar horiz design. Multicoloured. P* 13½.
754	34p. Type **199**	..		..	..	1·25	1·10
755	49p. Peace dove and U.N. emblem					1·50	2·25

200 Marilyn Monroe   **201** Father Christmas

(Des M. Whyte. Litho Questa)

1995 (13 Nov). *Centenary of Cinema. T* **200** *and similar horiz designs showing film stars. Multicoloured. P* 14½×14.
MS756 Two sheets, each 116×80 mm. (a) 5p. Type **200**; 25p. Romy Schneider; 28p. Yves Montand; 38p. Audrey Hepburn. (b) 24p. Ingrid Bergman; 24p. Vittorio de Sica; 24p. Marlene Dietrich; 24p. Laurence Olivier *Set of 2 sheets* 4·50 5·50

(Des M. Whyte. Litho B.D.T.)

1995 (27 Nov). *Christmas. T* **201** *and similar square designs. Multicoloured. P* 14.
757	5p. Type **201**	..		..	..	20	10
758	24p. Toys in sack	..		..	..	75	55
759	34p. Reindeer			..	..	1·00	1·25
760	54p. Sleigh over houses	..		..	..	1·60	2·50
757/60					*Set of 4*	3·25	4·00

202 Shih Tzu

(Des Doreen McGuinness. Litho B.D.T.)

1996 (24 Jan). *Puppies. T* **202** *and similar horiz designs. Multicoloured. P* 14.
761	5p. Type **202**	..		..	..	40	60
	a. Sheetlet. Nos. 761/6	..		..	4·00		
762	21p. Dalmatians	..		..	..	75	85
763	24p. Cocker Spaniels	..		..	..	80	90
764	25p. West Highland White Terriers			..	..	80	90
765	34p. Labrador	..		..	..	90	95
766	35p. Boxer	..		..	..	90	95
761/6				..	*Set of 6*	4·00	4·75

Nos. 761/6 were printed together, *se-tenant*, in sheetlets of 6. No. 762 is inscr "Dalmation" in error.

203 Princess Anne   **204** West German Player, 1980

(Des R. Ollington. Litho B.D.T.)

1996 (9 Feb). *Europa. Famous Women. T* **203** *and similar horiz designs. P* 13½.
767	**203** 24p. black and yellow	..		..		85	85
768	– 24p. black and deep turquoise-green				..	85	85
769	– 34p. black and vermilion	..		..		1·25	1·75
770	– 34p. black and purple	..		..		1·25	1·75
767/70					*Set of 4*	3·75	4·75

Details:—No. 768, Princess Diana; No. 769, Queen Elizabeth II; No. 770, Queen Elizabeth the Queen Mother.
Nos. 767/70 were each printed in sheets of 10 with inscribed margins all round.

(Des S. Noon. Litho Walsall)

1996 (2 Apr). *European Football Championship, England. T* **204** *and similar vert designs showing players from previous winning teams. Multicoloured. P* 13.
771	21p. Type **204**			..	..	55	45
772	24p. French player, 1984	..		..	..	65	55
773	34p. Dutch player, 1988	..		..		95	1·10
774	£1.20, Danish player, 1992	..				3·00	4·25
771/4					*Set of 4*	4·75	5·75
MS775	135×91 mm. As Nos. 771/4. P 13×13½					6·50	7·00

205 Ancient Greek   **206** Asian Children
Athletes

(Des K. Bassford. Litho Walsall)

1996 (2 May). *Centenary of Modern Olympic Games. T* **205** *and similar horiz designs. P* 13½.
776	34p. black, deep reddish purple & brt orange					95	90
777	49p. black and grey-brown	..		..		1·40	1·75
778	£1.05, multicoloured	..		..		2·75	3·50
776/8					*Set of 3*	4·50	5·50

Designs:—49p. Start of early race; £1.05, Start of modern race.

(Des D. Miller. Litho Walsall)

1996 (8 June). *Second World War Warships (4th series). Sheet,* 118×84 *mm, containing horiz designs as T* **184**. *Multicoloured. P* 14.
MS779 5p. H.M.S. *Starling* (sloop); 25p. H.M.S. *Royalist* (cruiser); 49p. U.S.S. *Philadelphia* (cruiser); 54p. H.M.C.S. *Prescott* (corvette) .. 4·25 5·00

(Des S. Noon. Litho Walsall)

1996 (8 June). *50th Anniv of U.N.I.C.E.F. T* **206** *and similar horiz designs showing children from different continents. P* 13½×13.
780	21p. multicoloured	..		..		60	80
	a. Horiz strip of 4. Nos. 780/3	..		3·50			
781	24p. multicoloured	..		..		70	90
782	49p. multicoloured	..		..		1·25	1·40
783	54p. multicoloured	..		..		1·40	1·60
780/3					*Set of 4*	3·50	4·25

Nos. 780/3 were printed together, *se-tenant*, in horizontal strips of 4 throughout the sheet.

207 Red Kites in Flight

(Des R. Gorringe. Litho Walsall)

1996 (30 Sept). *Endangered Species. Red Kite. T* **207** *and similar horiz designs. Multicoloured. P* 14½.
784	34p. Type **207**	..		..		1·00	1·25
	a. Block of 4. Nos. 784/7	..		3·50			
785	34p. Red Kite on ground	..		..		1·00	1·25
786	34p. On rock	..		..		1·00	1·25
787	34p. Pair at nest	..		..		1·00	1·25
784/7					*Set of 4*	3·50	4·50

Nos. 784/7 were printed together, *se-tenant*, in blocks of four throughout the sheet.

208 Christmas Pudding   **209** *Mary Celeste* passing Gibraltar

(Des K. Bassford. Litho Questa)

1996 (27 Nov). *Christmas. T* **208** *and similar horiz designs created from "Lego" blocks. Multicoloured. P* 14×14½.
788	5p. Type **208**	..		..		15	15
789	21p. Snowman face	..		..		70	45
790	24p. Present	..		..		80	55
791	34p. Father Christmas face	..		..		1·10	1·45
792	54p. Candle	..		..		1·50	2·50
788/92					*Set of 5*	3·75	4·50

(Des S. Tarabay. Litho Questa)

1997 (12 Feb). *Europa. Tales and Legends. The Mary Celeste. T* **209** *and similar square designs. Multicoloured. P* 14.
793	28p. Type **209**	..		..		80	90
794	28p. Boarding the *Mary Celeste*	..				80	90
795	30p. Crew leaving *Mary Celeste*			..		90	1·10
796	30p. *Mary Celeste* found by *Dei Gratia*					90	1·10
793/6					*Set of 4*	3·00	3·50

210 American Shorthair   **211** *Anthocharis*
Silver Tabby   *belia euphenoides*

(Des Colleen Corlett. Litho B.D.T.)

1997 (12 Feb). *Kittens. T* **210** *and similar horiz designs. Multicoloured. P* 13½×14.
797	5p. Type **210**	..		..	40	60
	a. Booklet pane. Nos. 797, 799 and 801 with margins all round	..		1·75		
	b. Booklet pane. Nos. 797/8 and 801/2 with margins all round			2·50		
798	24p. Rumpy Manx Red Tabby	..		..	75	85
	a. Booklet pane. Nos. 798/800 with margins all round	..		2·00		
799	26p. Blue Point Birmans	..			75	85
	a. Booklet pane. Nos. 799/802 with margins all round			3·00		
800	28p. Red Self Longhair	..			80	95
801	30p. British Shorthair Tortoiseshell and White	..			80	95
802	35p. British Bicolour Shorthairs			..	90	1·10
797/802				*Set of 6*	4·00	4·75
MS803	132×80 mm. Nos. 797/802 with "HONG KONG '97" International Stamp Exhibition logo at bottom left	..			5·50	6·00
	a. Booklet pane. As No. MS803, but without "HONG KONG '97" logo and with additional line of roulettes at left ..					5·00

Nos. 797/802 were only issued in £5 stamp booklets or miniature sheet No. **MS803**.

(Des R. Gorringe. Litho Enschedé)

1997 (7 Apr). *Butterflies. T* **211** *and similar vert designs. Multicoloured. P* 14×13½.
804	23p. Type **211**	..		..		70	50
805	26p. *Charaxes jasius*	..		..		85	60
806	30p. *Vanessa cardui*	..		..		95	90
807	£1.20, *Iphiclides podalirius*			..		3·25	4·50
804/7					*Set of 4*	5·25	6·00
MS808	135×90 mm. Nos. 804/7	..				5·25	6·50

(Des D. Miller. Litho Cartor)

1997 (9 June). *Second World War Warships (5th series). Sheet,* 117×82 *mm, containing horiz designs as T* **184**. *Multicoloured. P* 13½.
MS809 24p. H.M.S. *Enterprise* (cruiser); 26p. H.M.S. *Cleopatra* (cruiser); 38p. U.S.S. *Iowa* (battleship); 50p. *Orkan* (Polish destroyer) .. 3·50 4·00

212 Queen Elizabeth and Prince Philip
at Carriage-driving Trials

(Des C. Abbott. Litho Questa)

1997 (10 July). *Golden Wedding of Queen Elizabeth and Prince Philip. T* **212** *and similar horiz design. Multicoloured. P* 13½.
810	£1.20, Type **212**	..		..		3·25	3·75
	a. Horiz pair. Nos. 810/11	..				6·50	7·50
811	£1.40 Queen Elizabeth in Trooping the Colour uniform	..		..		3·25	3·75

Nos. 810/11 were printed together, *se-tenant*, in horizontal pairs throughout the sheet.

PRICES OF SETS

Set prices are given for many issues, generally those containing three stamps or more. Definitive sets include one of each value or major colour change, but do not cover different perforations, die types or minor shades. Where a choice is possible the set prices are based on the cheapest versions of the stamps included in the listings.

213 Christian Dior Evening Dress

214 "Our Lady and St. Bernard" (St. Joseph's Parish Church)

(Des M. Whyte. Litho B.D.T.)

1997 (24 Oct). *Christian Dior Spring/Summer '97 Collection designed by John Galliano. T 213 and similar vert designs. Multicoloured. P 13½.*

812	30p. Type **213**	80	1·10
	a. Horiz pair. Nos. 812 and 814	2·00	2·50
813	35p. Tunic top and skirt	1·10	1·50
	a. Horiz pair. Nos. 813 and 815	2·50	3·25
814	50p. Ballgown	1·25	1·40
815	62p. Two-piece suit	1·60	1·90
812/15	*Set of 4*	4·25	5·50
MS816	110×90 mm. £1.20, Ballgown (*different*)	2·75	3·50

Nos. 812 with 814 and 813 with 815 were each printed together, *se-tenant*, in sheets of 8 with enlarged illustrated right-hand margin.

(Des S. Perera. Litho Cartor)

1997 (18 Nov). *Christmas. Stained Glass Windows. T 214 and similar vert designs. Multicoloured. P 13½.*

817	5p. Type **214**	20	10
818	26p. "The Epiphany" (Our Lady of Sorrows Church)	75	60
819	38p. "St. Joseph" (Our Lady of Sorrows Church)	1·00	95
820	50p. "The Holy Family" (St. Joseph's Parish Church)	1·50	1·60
821	62p. "The Miraculous Medal" (St. Joseph's Parish Church)	1·75	2·50
817/21	*Set of 5*	4·75	5·25

215 Sir Joshua Hassan

216 Wales v Brazil (1958)

(Des S. Perera. Litho Cartor)

1997 (15 Dec). *Sir Joshua Hassan (former Chief Minister) Commemoration. P 13.*

822	**215** 26p. black	55	60

(Des L. Montgomery. Litho Cartor)

1998 (23 Jan). *World Football Championship, France (1998). T 216 and similar vert designs. Multicoloured. P 13.*

823	5p. Type **216**	20	10
824	26p. Northern Ireland v France (1958)	75	60
825	38p. Scotland v Holland (1978)	1·00	90
826	$1.20, England v West Germany (1966)	4·25	4·00
823/6	*Set of 4*	4·25	5·00
MS827	153×96 mm. Nos. 823/6	4·25	5·00

(Des D. Miller. Litho Questa)

1998 (31 Mar). *Diana, Princess of Wales Commemoration. Sheet, 145×70 mm, containing vert designs as T 177 of Ascension. Multicoloured. P 14½×14.*

MS828 26p. Wearing jacket with white fur collar, 1988; 26p. Wearing pink checked suit and hat; 38p. Wearing black jacket, 1995; 38p. Wearing blue jacket with gold embroidery, 1987 (*sold at £1.28 + 20p. charity premium*) .. .. 3·25 3·50

(Des A. Theobald. Litho B.D.T.)

1998 (1 Apr). *80th Anniv of Royal Air Force. Horiz designs as T 178 of Ascension. Multicoloured. P 14.*

829	24p. Saro London (flying boat)	70	55
830	26p. Fairey Fox	75	60
831	38p. Handley Page Halifax GR.VI	95	95
832	50p. Hawker Siddeley Buccaneer S.2B	1·25	1·75
829/32	*Set of 4*	3·25	3·50
MS833	110×77 mm. 24p. Sopwith 1½ Strutter; 26p. Bristol M.IB; 38p. Supermarine Spitfire XII; 50p. Avro York	3·25	3·75

217 Miss Gibraltar saluting

218 Striped Dolphin

(Des S. Perera. Litho Cartor)

1998 (22 May). *Europa. Festivals. National Day. T 217 and similar vert designs showing Miss Gibraltar in various costumes. Multicoloured. P 13½×13.*

834	26p. Type **217**	70	80
835	26p. In black bodice and long red skirt	70	80
836	38p. In black bodice and short red skirt, with Gibraltar flag	95	1·10
837	38p. In Genoese-style costume	95	1·10
834/7	*Set of 4*	3·00	3·50

Nos. 834/7 were each printed in sheets of 10 with enlarged illustrated right-hand margins.

(Des L. Montgomery. Litho Questa)

1998 (22 May). *International Year of the Ocean. Sheet, 155×64 mm, containing T 218 and similar multicoloured designs. P 14.*

MS838 5p. Type **218**; 5p. Common Dolphin (*vert*); 26p. Killer Whale (*vert*); £1.20, Blue Whale .. 3·75 4·50

219 Nileus (dog) with Hat and Telescope

220 "Love comforts like Sunshine after Rain" (William Shakespeare)

(Des M. Hargreaves. Litho Cartor)

1998 (1 Aug). *Bicentenary of Battle of the Nile. T 219 and similar multicoloured designs. P 13½.*

839	12p. Type **219**	35	30
	a. Booklet pane. Nos. 839/41 with margins all round	2·00	
	b. Booklet pane. Nos. 839/43 with margins all round	3·75	
840	26p. Rear-Admiral Sir Horatio Nelson	65	55
	a. Booklet pane. No. 840 with margins all round	1·00	
	b. Booklet pane. Nos. 840×2 and 842/3 with margins all round	3·50	
	c. Booklet pane. Nos. 840 and 842/3 with margins all round	3·00	
841	28p. Frances Nisbet, Lady Nelson	75	75
842	35p. H.M.S. *Vanguard* (ship of the line)	95	1·10
843	50p. Battle of the Nile (47×29 *mm*)	1·25	1·75
839/43	*Set of 5*	3·50	4·00

(Des M. Whyte. Litho Questa)

1998 (6 Oct). *Famous Quotations. T 220 and similar horiz designs. Multicoloured. P 14½.*

844	26p. Type **220**	70	80
845	26p. "The price of greatness is responsibility" (Sir Winston Churchill)	70	80
846	38p. "Hate the sin, love the sinner" (Mahatma Gandhi)	90	1·00
847	38p. "Imagination is more important than knowledge" (Albert Einstein)	90	1·00
844/7	*Set of 4*	3·00	3·25

Nos. 844/7 were each issued in sheets of 6 stamps and 6 half stamp-size labels showing the quotations in different languages.

221 The Nativity

222 Barbary Macaque

(Des Petula Stone. Litho Walsall)

1998 (10 Nov). *Christmas. T 221 and similar vert designs. Multicoloured. P 13½.*

848	5p. Type **221**	15	10
849	26p. Star and stable	75	70
850	30p. King with gold	90	75
851	35p. King with myrrh	1·00	85
852	50p. King with frankincense	1·40	1·75
848/52	*Set of 5*	3·75	3·75

(Des R. Gorringe. Litho Cartor)

1999 (4 Mar). *Europa. Parks and Gardens. Upper Rock Nature Reserve. T 222 and similar vert designs. Multicoloured. P 13½×13.*

853	30p. Type **222**	80	90
854	30p. Dartford Warbler	80	90
855	42p. Dusky Grouper	1·10	1·25
856	42p. Common Kingfisher	1·10	1·25
853/6	*Set of 4*	3·50	3·75

223 Queen Elizabeth II

224 Roman Marine and Galley

(Des S. Perera. Litho B.D.T.)

1999 (4 Mar). *(a) P 14 (50p., £1, £3) or 13½×13 (others).*

857	**223** 1p. reddish purple	10	10
858	2p. olive-sepia	10	10
859	4p. light greenish blue	10	10
860	5p. emerald	10	10
861	10p. orange	20	25
862	12p. rosine	25	30
863	20p. turquoise-green	40	45
864	28p. magenta	55	60
865	30p. reddish orange	60	65
866	40p. deep olive-grey	80	85
867	42p. deep grey-green	85	90
868	50p. bistre	1·00	1·10
869	£1 brownish black	2·00	2·10
870	£3 bright blue	6·00	6·25

(b) Self-adhesive. P 9½

871	**223** (1st) reddish orange	55	60
857/71	*Set of 15*	13·00	13·50

Nos. 868/71 are larger, 25×30 mm.
No. 871 was printed in rolls of 100, on which the surplus self-adhesive paper around each stamp was retained, and was initially sold at 26p.

(Des S. Williams. Litho Cartor)

1999 (4 Mar). *Maritime Heritage. T 224 and similar square designs. Multicoloured. P 12½.*

872	5p. Type **224**	15	10
873	30p. Arab sailor, medieval galley house and dhow	75	65
874	42p. Marine officer and British ship of the line (1779–83)	1·10	1·10
875	$1.20, Naval rating, Queen Alexandra Dry Dock and H.M.S. *Berwick* (cruiser) (1904)	2·75	3·00
872/5	*Set of 4*	4·25	4·25
MS876	116×76 mm. Nos. 872/5	4·50	5·00

No. **MS**876 includes the "Australia '99" International Stamp Exhibition, Melbourne, emblem on the sheet margin.

225 John Lennon (musician)

226 Postal Van at Dockside, 1930s

(Des S. Perera. Litho Cartor)

1999 (20 Mar). *30th Wedding Anniv of John Lennon and Yoko Ono. T 225 and similar vert designs showing John Lennon. P 13½×13.*

877	20p. multicoloured	50	45
878	30p. black and pale turquoise-blue	75	65
879	40p. multicoloured	95	95
877/9	*Set of 3*	2·00	1·90
MS880	Two sheets, each 62×100 mm. (a) £1 black and deep slate-blue. (b) £1 multicoloured		
	Set of 2 sheets	4·75	5·00

Designs:—20p. With flower over left eye; 40p. Wearing orange glasses; £1 (No. **MS**880a), Holding marriage certificate; £1 (No. **MS**880b), Standing on aircraft steps

Nos. 877/9 were each printed in small sheets of 10 with enlarged illustrated right margins.

(Des N. Watton. Litho Cartor)

1999 (20 Mar). *125th Anniv of Universal Postal Union. T 226 and similar square design. Multicoloured. P 12½.*

881	5p. Type **226**	15	10
882	30p. Space shuttle and station	75	80

NEW INFORMATION

The editor is always interested to correspond with people who have new information that will improve or correct the Catalogue.

| 227 EF-2000 Eurofighter | 228 Prince Edward and Sophie Rhys-Jones |

(Des M. Atkinson. Litho Cartor)

1999 (17 June). *"Wings of Prey". Birds of Prey and R.A.F. Fighter Aircraft. T* **227** *and similar horiz designs. Multicoloured. P* 13×13½.

883	30p. Type 227					80	90
	a. Horiz pair. Nos. 883 and 886					1·60	1·90
884	30p. Panavia Tornado F3					80	90
	a. Horiz pair. Nos. 884 and 887					1·60	1·90
885	30p. BAe Harrier II GR7					80	90
	a. Horiz pair. Nos. 885 and 888					1·60	1·90
886	42p. Lesser Kestrel					90	1·00
887	42p. Peregrine Falcon					90	1·00
888	42p. Common Kestrel					90	1·00
883/8					*Set of* 6	4·50	5·00
MS889	Two sheets, each 105×86 mm. (a) Nos.						
	883/5. (b) Nos. 886/8			*Set of* 2 sheets	4·75	5·50	

Nos. 883 with 886, 884 with 887 and 885 with 888 were each printed together, *se-tenant*, as horizontal pairs in sheets of 10 with enlarged illustrated margins at right and foot.

(Des S. Perera. Litho Cartor)

1999 (19 June–11 Oct). *Royal Wedding. T* **228** *and similar multicoloured designs. P* 13×13½ (*horiz*) *or* 13½×13 (*vert*).

890	30p. Type 228					70	65
891	42p. Prince Edward and Sophie Rhys-Jones						
	holding hands (*vert*)					1·00	90
892	54p. In carriage on wedding day (11 Oct)				1·40	1·50	
893	66p. On Chapel steps after wedding (*vert*)						
	(11 Oct)					1·50	1·60
890/3					*Set of* 4	4·25	4·25

Nos. 890/3 were printed in sheets with illustrated gutter margins.

| 229 Football | 230 "Seasons Greetings" |

(Des J. Sayer. Litho Cartor)

1999 (2 July). *Local Sporting Centenaries. T* **229** *and similar vert designs. Multicoloured. P* 13½×13.

894	30p. Type 229					75	65
895	42p. Rowing					1·00	90
896	£1.20, Cricket					2·75	3·00
894/6					*Set of* 3	4·00	4·00

(Des S. Williams. Litho B.D.T.)

1999 (11 Nov). *Christmas. T* **230** *and similar square designs. Multicoloured. P* 14.

897	5p. Type 230					10	10
898	5p. "Happy Christmas"					10	10
899	30p. "Happy Millennium"					60	65
900	30p. "Happy Christmas" and Santa with						
	reindeer					60	65
901	42p. Santa Claus in chimney					85	90
902	54p. Santa Claus leaving presents				1·10	1·25	
897/902					*Set of* 6	3·25	3·75

231 "People travelling with Environmentally-friendly Jet-packs" (Colin Grech)

(Litho Questa)

2000 (28 Jan). *"Stampin' the Future" (children's stamp design competition). T* **231** *and similar horiz designs. Multicoloured. P* 14½×14.

903	30p. Type 231					60	65
	a. Strip of 4. Nos. 903/6					3·75	
904	42p. "Robotic Postman" (Kim Barea)				85	90	
905	54p. "Living on the Moon" (Stephan						
	Williamson-Fa)					1·10	1·25
906	66p. "Jet-powered Cars" (Michael Podesta)				1·25	1·40	
903/6					*Set of* 4	3·75	4·00

Nos. 903/6 were printed together, *se-tenant*, as vertical or horizontal strips of 4 in sheets of 16.

STAMP BOOKLETS

1909. *Black on red cover. Stapled.*
SB1 2s. ½d. booklet containing twenty-four ½d. and twelve 1d. (Nos. 66/7) in blocks of 6 .. ..

1912 (15 May). *Black on red cover with Edwardian cypher. Stapled.*
SB2 2s. ½d. booklet containing twenty-four ½d. and twelve 1d. (Nos. 76/7) in blocks of 6 .. ..

1921. *Black on red cover. Stapled.*
SB2a 2s. booklet containing twenty-four ½d. and twelve 1d. (Nos. 89/90) in blocks of 6 .. ..

B 1
(Illustration reduced. Actual size 152×79 mm)

1974 (2 May). *Centenary of Universal Postal Union. Multicoloured cover as Type B 1. Stitched.*
SB3 46p. booklet containing *se-tenant* panes of 3 (No. 328a) and 6 (No. 328b) .. .. .. 7·50

1975 (17 Dec). *500th Birth Anniv of Michelangelo. Multicoloured cover as Type B 1, but 165×91 mm showing Michelangelo. Stitched.*
SB4 90p. booklet containing *se-tenant* panes of 3 (No. 358a) and 6 (No. 358b) .. .. .. 4·50

1978 (12 June). *25th Anniv of Coronation. Multicoloured cover as Type B 1, but 165×92 mm showing Buckingham Palace. Stitched.*
SB5 £1.15, booklet containing *se-tenant* pane of 6 (No. 404a) and pane of 1 (No. 406a) .. .. 2·75

B 2

1981 (2 Sept). *Black and vermilion (No. SB6) and black and ultramarine (No. SB7) covers as Type B 2. Stamps attached by selvedge.*
SB6 50p. booklet containing *se-tenant* pane of 5 and 1 label (No. 451a) .. .. .. 1·40
SB7 £1 booklet containing *se-tenant* pane of 10 and 2 labels (No. 451b) .. .. .. 2·00

B 3 Moorish Castle

1993 (21 Sept). *Multicoloured covers as Type B 3. Stamps affixed by selvedge.*
SB8 20p. booklet containing 5p. (No. 699) in strip of 4 .. 80
SB9 £1.20 booklet containing 24p. (No. 702) in strip of 5 .. .. 3·50

B 4 Rock of Gibraltar and Games Events
(Illustration reduced. Actual size 175×97 mm)

1995 (8 May). *Island Games '95. Multicoloured cover as Type B 4. Stitched.*
SB10 £4.68, booklet containing four panes of 3 (Nos. 745a/b, 746a and 747a) .. .. .. 13·00

B 5
(Illustration reduced. Actual size 150×80 mm)

1997 (12 Feb). *Kittens. Multicoloured cover as Type B 5. Stitched.*
SB11 £5 booklet containing five *se-tenant* panes (Nos. 797a/b, 798a, 799a and MS803a) .. .. 14·00

B 6 Battle of the Nile
(Illustration reduced. Actual size 145×102 mm)

1998 (1 Aug). *Bicent of Battle of the Nile. Multicoloured cover as Type B 6. Stitched.*
SB12 £5 booklet containing five panes (Nos. 839a/b and 840a/c) .. .. 13·00

POSTAGE DUE STAMPS

D 1   **D 2**   **D 3** Gibraltar Coat of Arms

(Typo D.L.R.)

1956 (1 Dec). *Chalk-surfaced paper. Wmk Mult Script CA. P 14.*
D1	D 1	1d. green	..	2·50	4·00
D2		2d. sepia	..	2·50	3·75
		a. Large "d" (R. 9/6, 10/6) ..		24·00	
D3		4d. blue	..	3·25	6·75
D1/3		*Set of 3*		7·50	13·00

For illustrations of No. D2a. see above No. D4 of Botswana.

1971 (15 Feb). *As Nos. D1/3 but inscr in decimal currency. W 12. P 17½ × 18.*
D4	D 1	½p. green	..	30	80
D5		1p. sepia	..	30	70
D6		2p. blue ..	..	30	80
D4/6		*Set of 3*		80	2·10

(Des A. Ryman. Litho Questa)

1976 (13 Oct). *W w 14. P 14 × 13½.*
D 7	D 2	1p. light red-orange	..	15	60
D 8		3p. bright blue	..	15	75
D 9		5p. orange-vermilion	..	20	75
D10		7p. reddish violet	..	25	75
D11		10p. greenish slate	..	35	75
D12		20p. green	..	70	1·00
D7/12		*Set of 6*		1·60	4·25

(Des A. Ryman. Litho B.D.T.)

1984 (2 July). *W w 14 (sideways). P 15×14.*
D13	D 3	1p. black	..	25	50
D14		3p. vermilion	..	35	50
D15		5p. ultramarine	..	40	50
D16		10p. new blue	..	50	50
D17		25p. deep mauve ..	..	90	1·00
D18		50p. reddish orange	..	1·40	1·50
D19		£1 blue-green	..	2·25	2·75
D13/19		*Set of 7*		5·50	6·50

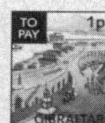

D 4 Water Port Gates

(Des Olympia Reyes. Litho B.D.T.)

1996 (30 Sept). *Gibraltar Landmarks. Type D 4 and similar vert designs. P 14½×14.*
D20	1p. black, emerald & bright yellow-green		10	10
D21	10p. black and bluish grey	..	20	25
D22	25p. black, red-brown and chestnut		50	55
D23	50p. black and reddish lilac	..	1·00	1·10
D24	£1 black, olive-brown and chestnut	..	2·00	2·10
D25	£2 black and light blue ..	..	4·00	4·25
D20/5	*Set of 6*		7·50	8·25

Designs:—10p. Naval Dockyard; 25p. Military Hospital; 50p. Governor's Cottage; £1 Swans on the Laguna; £2 Catalan Bay.

Gilbert and Ellice Islands

No organised postal service existed in the Gilbert and Ellice Islands before the introduction of stamp issues in January 1911. A New Zealand Postal Agency was, however, provided on Fanning Island, one of the Line Islands, primarily for the use of the staff of the Cable & Wireless Ltd cable station which was established in 1902. The agency opened on 29 November 1902 and continued to operate until replaced by a Protectorate post office on 14 February 1939. The cable station closed on 16 January 1964. Fanning Island is now known as Tabuaeran.

Z 1

The following NEW ZEALAND *stamps are know postmarked on Fanning Island with Type Z* 1 (*in use from November* 1902 *until November* 1936. *The earliest known cover is postmarked* 20 *December* 1902.

1882–1900 Q.V. (*p* 11) ½d., 1d., 2d. (*Nos.* 236/8)
1898 Pictorials (*no wmk*) 1d., 2d. (*Nos.* 247/8)
1900 Pictorials (*W* 38) ½d., 1½d., 2d. (*Nos.* 273, 275b, 276)
1901 1d. "Universal" (*W* 38) (*No.* 278)
1902 1d. "Universal" (*no wmk*) (*No.* 295)
1902–09 Pictorials (*W* 43) 2½d., 6d., 8d., 9d., 1s., 2s. (*Nos.* 312/13, 315, 320, 326, 328)
1907–08 Pictorials (*W* 43) 4d. (*No.* 379)
1908 1d. "Universal" (*De La Rue paper*) 1d. (*No.* 386)
1909–12 King Edward VII (*typo*) ½d. (*No.* 387)
1909–16 King Edward VII (*recess*) 2d., 3d., 4d., 5d., 6d., 8d., 1s. (*Nos.* 388/91, 393/6, 398)
1909–26 1d. "Universal" (*W* 43) 1d. (*Nos.* 405, 410)
1915–30 King George V (*recess*) 1½d., 2d. bright violet, 2½d., 3d., 4d. bright violet, 6d., 7½d., 9d., 1s. (*Nos.* 416/17, 419/20, 422, 425/6, 429/30)
1915–34 King George V (*typo*) ½d., 1½d. (*all* 3), 2d., 3d. (*Nos.* 435/40, 446, 448, 449)
1915 "WAR STAMP" opt ½d. (*No.* 452)
1920 Victory 1d., 1½d. (*Nos.* 454/5)
1922 2d. on ½d. (*No.* 459)
1923–25 Penny Postage 1d. (*No.* 460)
1926–34 Admiral design 1d. (*No.* 468)
1935–36 Pictorials ½d., 2d., 4d., 8d., 1s. (*Nos.* 556, 559, 562 565, 567)
1935 Silver Jubilee ½d., 1d., 6d. (*Nos.* 573/5)
1936 Anzac 1d.+1d. (*No.* 592)

Z 2

The following NEW ZEALAND *stamps are known postmarked on Fanning Island with Type Z* 2 (*in use from* 7 *December* 1936 *to* 13 *February* 1939):

1935–36 Pictorials (*W* 43) 1d (*No.* 557)
1936–39 Pictorials (*W* 98) ½d., 1d., 1½d. (*Nos.* 577/9)
1936 Chambers of Commerce Congress ½d. (*No.* 593)
1936 Health 1d. + 1d. (*No.* 598)
1937 Coronation 1d., 2½d., 6d. (*Nos.* 599/601)
1938–39 King George VI ½d., 1d., 1½d. (*Nos.* 603, 605, 607)

The schooner which carried the mail from Fanning Island also called at Washington Island, another of the Line group. Problems arose, however, as the authorities insisted that mail from Washington must first pass through the Fanning Island Postal Agency before being forwarded which resulted in considerable delays. Matters were resolved by the opening of a New Zealand Postal Agency on Washington Island which operated from 1 February 1921 until the copra plantations were closed in early 1923. The postal agency was re-established on 15 May 1924, but finally closed on 30 March 1934. Covers from this second period occur with incorrectly dated postmarks. Manuscript markings on New Zealand Nos. 578, 599/600 and 692 were unofficial and were applied during the resettlement of the island between 1937 and 1948. Washington Island is now known as Teraina.

NEW INFORMATION

The editor is always interested to correspond with people who have new information that will improve or correct the Catalogue.

Z 3

The following NEW ZEALAND *stamps are known postmarked on Washington Island with Type Z* 3:

1909–16 King Edward VII 5d., 8d. (*Nos.* 402, 404b)
1915–30 King George V (*recess*) 6d., 7½d., 8d., 9d., 1s. (*Nos.* 425/7, 429/30)
1915–34 King George V (*typo*) ½d., 1½d., 2d., 3d. (*Nos.* 435, 438/9, 449)
1915 "WAR STAMP" opt ½d (*No.* 452)
1920 Victory 1d., 1½d., 6d. (*Nos.* 454/5, 457)
1922 2d. on ½d. (*No.* 459)
1926–34 Admiral design 1d. (*No.* 468)

The above information is based on a special survey undertaken by members of the Kiribati & Tuvalu Philatelic Society and the Pacific Islands Study Circle, co-ordinated by Mr. Michael Shaw.

PRICES FOR STAMPS ON COVER TO 1945

Nos. 1/7	*from* × 5
Nos. 8/11	*from* × 10
Nos. 12/23	*from* × 6
No. 24	—
No. 26	*from* × 15
Nos. 27/30	*from* × 6
No. 35	—
Nos. 36/9	*from* × 4
Nos. 40/2	*from* × 12
Nos. 43/54	*from* × 4
Nos. D1/8	*from* × 5

BRITISH PROTECTORATE

GILBERT & ELLICE

PROTECTORATE

(1)   2 Pandanus Pine

1911 (1 Jan). *Stamps of Fiji optd with T* **1**. *Wmk Mult Crown CA. Chalk-surfaced paper* (5d. *to* 1s.).

1	**23**	½d. green		4·50	40·00
2		1d. red		45·00	27·00
3	**24**	2d. grey		8·50	14·00
4	**23**	2½d. ultramarine		12·00	25·00
5		5d. purple and olive-green		38·00	65·00
6	**24**	6d. dull and bright purple		20·00	40·00
7	**23**	1s. black/green (R.)		20·00	50·00
1/7			*Set of* 7	£130	£225

1/7 Optd "Specimen" . . *Set of* 7 £275

The 2d. to 6d. are on special printings which were not issued without overprint.
Examples of Nos. 1/7 are known showing a forged Ocean Island postmark dated "JY 15 11".

(Recess D.L.R.)

1911 (Mar). *Wmk Mult Crown CA. P* 14.

8	**2**	½d. green		4·25	12·00
9		1d. carmine		2·00	6·50
10		2d. grey		1·50	6·50
11		2½d. blue		4·00	9·50
8/11			*Set of* 4	10·50	30·00

8/11 Optd "Specimen" . . *Set of* 4 £140

3   (5)

WAR TAX

(Typo D.L.R.)

1912 (May)–**24**. *Die I* (½d. *to* 5s.) *or Die II* (£1). *Wmk Mult Crown CA. Chalk-surfaced paper* (3d. *to* £1). *P* 14.

12	**3**	½d. green (7.12)		30	4·25
		a. Yellow-green (1914)		4·50	9·50
13		1d. carmine (12.12)		2·00	4·25
		a. Scarlet (1915)		3·75	10·00
14		2d. greyish slate (1.16)		14·00	23·00
15		2½d. bright blue (1.16)		1·75	11·00
16		3d. purple/yellow (1918)		2·50	8·50
17		4d. black and red/yellow (10.12)		60	6·00
18		5d. dull purple and sage-green		1·50	7·00
19		6d. dull and bright purple		1·25	7·50
20		1s. black/green		1·25	5·50
21		2s. purple and blue/blue (10.12)		14·00	30·00
22		2s. 6d. black and red/blue (10.12)		15·00	25·00
23		5s. green and red/yellow (10.12)		32·00	55·00
24		£1 purple and black/red (Die II) (3.24)		£600	£1400
12/24			*Set of* 13	£600	£1400

12/24 Optd "Specimen" . . *Set of* 13 £550

CROWN COLONY

1918 (June). *Optd with T* **5**.

26	**3**	1d. red (Optd S. £60)		30	6·50

1922–27. *Die II. Wmk Mult Script CA. Chalk-surfaced paper* (10s.). *P* 14.

27	**3**	½d. green (1923)		2·50	2·50
28		1d. violet (1927)		3·75	4·25
29		1½d. scarlet (1924)		3·75	1·75
30		2d. slate-grey		6·00	22·00
35		10s. green and red/emerald (3.24)		£160	£350
27/35		Optd "Specimen"	*Set of* 5	£250	

Examples of most values between Nos. 12 and 35 are known showing part strikes of the forged postmark mentioned below Nos. 1/7. Collectors should exercise particular caution when buying used examples of Nos. 24 and 35.

1935 (6 May). *Silver Jubilee. As Nos.* 91/4 *of Antigua, but ptd by B.W. P* 11 × 12.

36		1d. ultramarine and grey-black		2·25	9·00
		d. Flagstaff on right-hand turret		£160	
		e. Double flagstaff		£225	
37		1½d. deep blue and scarlet		1·75	3·75
		d. Flagstaff on right-hand turret		£160	
		e. Double flagstaff		£225	
38		3d. brown and deep blue		5·50	12·00
		d. Flagstaff on right-hand turret		£250	
		e. Double flagstaff		£275	
39		1s. slate and purple		35·00	24·00
		d. Flagstaff on right-hand turret		£375	
		e. Double flagstaff		£400	
36/9			*Set of* 4	40·00	45·00

36/9 Perf "Specimen" . . *Set of* 4 £110
For illustrations of plate varieties see Catalogue Introduction.

1937 (12 May). *Coronation. As Nos.* 95/7 *of Antigua, but ptd by D.L.R. P* 14.

40		1d. violet		35	65
41		1½d. scarlet		35	65
42		3d. bright blue		40	70
40/2			*Set of* 3	1·00	1·75

40/2 Perf "Specimen" *Set of* 3 65·00

6 Great Frigate Bird   7 Pandanus Pine

8 Canoe crossing Reef

(Recess B.W. (½d., 2d., 2s. 6d.), Waterlow (1d., 5d., 6d., 2s., 5s.), D.L.R. (1½d., 2½d., 3d., 1s.))

1939 (14 Jan)–**55**. *T* **6/8** *and similar horiz designs. Wmk Mult Script CA* (*sideways on* ½d., 2d. *and* 2s. 6d.). *P* 11½×11 (½d., 2d., 2s. 6d.), 12½ (1d., 5d., 6d., 2s., 5s.) *or* 13½ (1½d., 2½d., 3d., 1s.).

43		½d. indigo and deep bluish green		30	85
		a. "A" of "CA" missing from wmk			
44		1d. emerald and plum		30	1·50
45		1½d. brownish black and bright carmine		30	90
46		2d. red-brown and grey-black		60	1·00
47		2½d. brownish black and deep olive		40	70
		a. Brownish black & olive-green (12.5.43)		3·00	3·25
48		3d. brownish black and ultramarine		45	1·00
		a. Perf 12. Black and bright blue (24.8.55)		50	2·25
49		5d. deep ultramarine and sepia		4·25	1·25
		a. Ultramarine and sepia (12.5.43)		4·75	5·00
		b. Ultramarine & blackish brn (20.10.44)		4·25	4·25
50		6d. olive-green and deep violet		40	50
51		1s. brownish black and turquoise-green		8·50	2·00
		a. Brownish black & turquoise-bl (12.5.43)		4·50	2·25
		ab. Perf 12 (8.5.51)		3·75	13·00
52		2s. deep ultramarine and orange-red		16·00	12·00
53		2s. 6d. deep blue and emerald		17·00	14·00
54		5s. deep rose-red and royal blue		18·00	16·00
43/54			*Set of* 12	55·00	42·00

43/54 Perf "Specimen" *Set of* 12 £250

Designs: As *T* **6**—2d. Canoe and boat-house; 2s. 6d. Gilbert Islands canoe. As *T* **7**—5d. Ellice Islands canoe; 6d. Coconut palms; 2s. H.M.C.S. *Nimanoa*; 5s. Coat of arms. As *T* **8**—2½d. Native house; 3d. Seascape; 1s. Cantilever jetty, Ocean Island.

1946 (16 Dec). *Victory. As Nos.* 110/11 *of Antigua.*

55		1d. purple		15	40
56		3d. blue		15	40
55/6		Perf "Specimen"	*Set of* 2	55·00	

1949 (29 Aug). *Royal Silver Wedding. As Nos.* 112/13 *of Antigua.*

57		1d. violet		40	50
58		£1 scarlet		15·00	18·00

1949 (10 Oct). *75th Anniv of U.P.U. As Nos.* 114/17 *of Antigua.*

59		1d. purple		55	90
60		2d. grey-black		2·25	2·25
61		3d. deep blue		1·00	2·00
62		1s. blue		1·25	2·00
59/62			*Set of* 4	4·50	6·50

1953 (2 June). *Coronation. As No.* 120 *of Antigua.*

63		2d. black and grey-black		55	2·25

18 Great Frigate Bird

19 Loading Phosphate from Cantilever

(Recess B.W. (½d., 2d., 2s. 6d.), Waterlow (1d., 5d., 6d., 2s., 5s.), D.L.R. (2½d., 3d., 1s., 10s. and after 1962, 1d., 5d.))

1956 (1 Aug)–62. *Designs previously used for King George VI issue; but with portrait of Queen Elizabeth II as in T* **18**. *Wmk Mult Script CA. P* 11½×11 (½d., 2d., 2s. 6d.), 12½ (1d., 5d., 6d., 2s., 5s.) *or* 12 (2½d., 3d., 1s., 10s.).

64	½d. black and deep bright blue		45	1·25
65	1d. brown-olive and deep violet		60	70
66	2d. bluish green and deep purple		90	2·50
	a. *Bluish green and purple* (30.7.62)		19·00	19·00
67	2½d. black and myrtle-green		50	60
68	3d. black and carmine-red		50	60
69	5d. ultramarine and red-orange		8·50	2·75
	a. *Ultramarine & brn-orge* (DLR) (30.7.62)	15·00	23·00
70	6d. chestnut and black-brown		55	2·00
71	1s. black and bronze-green		1·75	60
72	2s. deep bright blue and sepia		8·50	5·50
73	2s. 6d. scarlet and deep blue		10·00	5·50
74	5s. greenish blue and bluish green		12·00	9·00
75	10s. black and turquoise		28·00	15·00
64/75		Set of 12	65·00	42·00

Designs: *Horiz* (30 × 22½ *mm*)—1d. Pandanus pine; 5d. Ellice Islands canoe; 6d. Coconut palms; 2s. H.M.C.S. *Nimanoa*; 5s. Coat of arms. (35½ × 22½ *mm*)—Canoe and boat-house; 2½d. Native house; 3d. Seascape; 1s. Cantilever jetty, Ocean Island; 2s. 6d. Gilbert Islands canoe; 10s. Canoe crossing reef.

See also Nos. 85/6.

(Des R. Turrell (2d.), M. Thoma (2½d.), M. A. W. Hook and A. Larkins (1s.). Photo D.L.R.)

1960 (1 May). *Diamond Jubilee of Phosphate Discovery at Ocean Island. T* **19** *and similar horiz designs. W w* **12**. *P* 12.

76	2d. green and carmine-rose		70	85
77	2½d. black and olive-green		70	85
78	1s. black and deep turquoise		70	85
76/8		Set of 3	1·90	2·40

Designs:—2½d. Phosphate rock; 1s. Phosphate mining.

1963 (1 Aug). *Freedom from Hunger. As No.* 146 *of Antigua.*

79	10d. ultramarine		1·25	30

1963 (5 Oct). *Red Cross Centenary. As Nos.* 147/8 *of Antigua.*

80	2d. red and black		1·00	50
81	10d. red and blue		2·00	2·75

22 De Havilland D.H.114 Heron 2 and Route Map

24 De Havilland D.H.114 Heron 2 over Tarawa Lagoon

23 Eastern Reef Heron in Flight

(Des Margaret Barwick. Litho Enschedé)

1964 (20 July). *First Air Service. W w* **12** (*sideways* on* 3d., 3s. 7d.). *P* 11×11½ (1s.) *or* 11½×11 (*others*).

82	**22** 3d. blue, black and light blue		70	30
	w. Wmk Crown to right of CA		70	30
83	**23** 1s. light blue, black and deep blue		90	30
84	**24** 3s. 7d. deep green, black & light emerald	1·40	1·50
82/4		Set of 3	2·75	1·90

*The normal sideways watermark shows Crown to left of CA, as seen from the back of the stamp.

(Recess B.W. (2d.), D.L.R. (6d.))

1964 (30 Oct)–**65**. *As Nos.* 66a *and* 70 *but wmk w* **12**.

85	2d. bluish green and purple		75	2·00
86	6d. chestnut and black-brown (26.4.65)*	1·25	2·25

*Earliest known postmark date.

1965 (4 June). *I.T.U. Centenary. As Nos.* 166/7 *of Antigua.*

87	3d. red-orange and deep bluish green		20	10
88	2s. 6d. turquoise-blue and light purple		80	20

25 Maneaba and Gilbertese Man blowing Bu Shell

26 Gilbertese Women's Dance

(Des V. Whiteley from drawings by Margaret Barwick. Litho B.W.)

1965 (16 Aug). *Vert designs as T* **25** (½d. *to* 2s.) *or horiz designs as T* **26** (3s. 7d. *to* £1). *Centres multicoloured. W w* **12**. *P* 12 × 11 (½d. *to* 2s.) *or* 11 × 12 (3s. 7d. *to* £1).

89	½d. turquoise-green		10	10
90	1d. deep violet-blue		10	10
91	2d. bistre		10	10
92	3d. rose-red		10	10
93	4d. purple		15	10
94	6d. cerise		20	10
95	6d. turquoise-blue		20	10
96	7d. bistre-brown		25	10
97	1s. bluish violet		50	10
98	1s. 6d. lemon		1·00	65
99	2s. yellow-olive		1·00	1·40
100	3s. 7d. new blue		2·25	65
101	5s. light yellow-olive		2·25	20
102	10s. dull green		4·00	1·25
103	£1 light turquoise-blue		4·50	2·50
89/103		Set of 15	15·00	6·50

Designs:—1d. Ellice Islanders reef fishing by flare; 2d. Gilbertese girl weaving head garland; 3d. Gilbertese woman performing Ruoia; 4d. Gilbertese man performing Kamei; 5d. Gilbertese girl drawing water; 6d. Ellice islander performing a Fatele; 7d. Ellice youths performing spear dance; 1s. Gilbertese girl tending Ikaroa Babai plant; 1s. 6d. Ellice islanders dancing a Fatele; 2s. Ellice islanders pounding Pulaka; 5s. Gilbertese boys playing stick game; 10s. Ellice youths beating the box for the Fatele; £1 Coat of arms.

1965 (25 Oct). *International Co-operation Year. As Nos.* 168/9 *of Antigua.*

104	½d. reddish purple and turquoise-green		10	10
105	3s. 7d. deep bluish green and lavender		75	20

1966 (24 Jan). *Churchill Commemoration. As Nos.* 170/3 *of Antigua.*

106	½d. new blue		10	10
107	3d. deep green		20	10
108	3s. brown		35	35
109	3s. 7d. bluish violet		40	35
106/9		Set of 4	90	75

(New Currency, 100 cents = 1 Australian dollar)

(40)

41 H.M.S. *Royalist*

1966 (14 Feb). *Decimal currency. Nos.* 89/103 *surch as T* **40**.

110	1 c. on 1d. deep violet-blue		10	10
111	2 c. on 2d. bistre		10	10
112	3 c. on 3d. rose-red		10	10
113	4 c. on ½d. turquoise-green		10	10
114	5 c. on 6d. turquoise-blue		15	10
115	6 c. on 4d. purple		15	10
116	8 c. on 6d. cerise		15	10
117	10 c. on 1s. bluish violet		15	10
118	15 c. on 7d. bistre-brown		80	40
119	20 c. on 1s. 6d. lemon		45	25
120	25 c. on 2s. yellow-olive		45	20
121	35 c. on 3s. 7d. new blue		1·25	20
122	50 c. on 5s. light yellow-olive		75	35
123	$1 on 10s. dull green		75	40
124	$2 on £1 light turquoise-blue		1·50	2·50
110/24		Set of 15	6·00	4·25

1966 (1 July). *World Cup Football Championships. As Nos.* 176/7 *of Antigua.*

125	3 c. violet, yellow-green, lake & yellow-brn	20	10
126	35 c. chocolate, blue-green, lake & yell-brn	55	20

1966 (20 Sept). *Inauguration of W.H.O. Headquarters, Geneva. As Nos.* 178/9 *of Antigua.*

127	3 c. black, yellow-green and light blue	20	10
128	12 c. black, light purple and yellow-brown	45	40

1966 (1 Dec). *20th Anniv of U.N.E.S.C.O. As Nos.* 196/8 *of Antigua.*

129	5 c. slate-violet, red, yellow and orange	25	25
130	10 c. orange-yellow, violet and deep olive	35	10
131	20 c. black, bright purple and orange	60	45
129/31		Set of 3	1·10	70

(Des V. Whiteley. Photo Harrison)

1967 (1 Sept). *75th Anniv of the Protectorate. T* **41** *and similar horiz designs. W w* **12**. *P* 14½.

132	3 c. red, blue and myrtle-green		30	50
133	10 c. multicoloured		15	15
134	35 c. sepia, orange-yellow & dp bluish green	30	50
132/4		Set of 3	65	1·00

Designs:—10 c. Trading Post; 35 c. Island family.

44 Gilbertese Women's Dance

1968 (1 Jan). *Decimal Currency. Designs as Nos.* 89/103 *but with values inscr in decimal currency as T* **44**. *W w* **12** (*sideways on horiz designs*). *P* 12 × 11 (*vert*) *or* 11 × 12 (*horiz*).

135	1 c. deep violet-blue (as 1d.)		10	10
136	2 c. bistre (as 2d.)		15	10
137	3 c. rose-red (as 3d.)		15	10
138	4 c. turquoise-green (as ½d.)		15	10
139	5 c. turquoise-blue (as 6d.)		15	10
140	6 c. purple (as 4d.)		20	10
141	8 c. cerise (as 5d.)		20	10
142	10 c. bluish violet (as 1s.)		20	10
143	15 c. bistre-brown (as 7d.)		50	20
144	20 c. lemon (as 1s. 6d.)		65	15
	w. Wmk inverted		14·00	14·00
145	25 c. yellow-olive (as 2s.)		1·25	20
146	35 c. new blue		1·50	20
147	50 c. light yellow-olive (as 5s.)		1·50	2·50
148	$1 dull green (as 10s.)		1·50	3·75
149	$2 light turquoise-blue (as £1)		4·00	3·75
135/49		Set of 15	11·00	10·00

45 Map of Tarawa Atoll

(Des V. Whiteley. Photo D.L.R.)

1968 (21 Nov). *25th Anniv of the Battle of Tarawa. T* **45** *and similar designs. Multicoloured. W w* **12** (*sideways*). *P* 14.

150	3 c. Type **45**		20	30
151	10 c. Marines landing		20	20
152	15 c. Beach-head assault		30	35
153	35 c. Raising U.S. and British flags		40	50
150/3		Set of 4	1·00	1·25

46 Young Pupil against outline of Abemama Island

47 "Virgin and Child" in Pacific Setting

(Des J.W. (from original designs by Mrs V. J. Anderson and Miss A. Loveridge). Litho D.L.R.)

1969 (2 June). *End of Inaugural Year of South Pacific University. T* **46** *and similar horiz designs. W w* **12** (*sideways*). *P* 12½.

154	3 c. multicoloured		10	25
155	10 c. multicoloured		10	10
156	35 c. black, brown and grey-green		15	30
154/6		Set of 3	30	55

Designs:—10 c. Boy and girl students and Tarawa atoll; 35 c. University graduate and South Pacific islands.

(Des Jennifer Toombs. Litho B.W.)

1969 (20 Oct). *Christmas. W w* **12** (*sideways*). *P* 11½.

157	2 c. olive-grn & multicoloured (*shades*)	15	20
158	**47** 10 c. olive-grn & multicoloured (*shades*)	15	10

Design:—2 c. As T **47** but foreground has grass instead of sand.

48 "The Kiss of Life"

(Des Manate Tenang Manate. Litho J.W.)

1970 (9 Mar*). *Centenary of British Red Cross.* W w **12** (*sideways*).
P 14.

159	48	10 c. multicoloured		20	10
160	–	15 c. multicoloured		30	45
161	–	35 c. multicoloured		60	90
159/61			Set of 3	1·00	1·25

Nos. 160/1 are as T **48**, but arranged differently.
*The above were released by the Crown Agents on 2 March, but not sold locally until the 9 March.

49 Foetus and Patients

(Des Jennifer Toombs. Litho Enschedé)

1970 (26 June). *25th Anniv of United Nations.* T **49** and similar horiz designs. W w **12** (*sideways*). P 12½ × 13.

162	5 c. multicoloured		15	30
163	10 c. black, grey and red		15	15
164	15 c. multicoloured		20	30
165	35 c. new blue, black and turquoise-green		30	45
162/5		Set of 4	70	1·10

Designs:—10 c. Nurse and surgical instruments; 15 c. X-ray plate and technician; 35 c. U.N. emblem and map.

53 Map of Gilbert Islands   **57** "Child with Halo" (T. Collis)

(Des G. Vasarhelyi. Litho Harrison)

1970 (1 Sept). *Centenary of Landing in Gilbert Islands by London Missionary Society.* T **53** and similar designs. W w **12** (*sideways on vert designs*). P 14½ × 14 (2 c., 35 c.) or 14 × 14½ (*others*).

166	2 c. multicoloured		15	90
167	10 c. black and pale green		25	15
168	25 c. chestnut and cobalt		20	20
169	35 c. turquoise-blue, black and red		50	70
166/9		Set of 4	1·00	1·75

Designs: *Vert*—10 c. Sailing-ship *John Williams III*; 25 c. Rev. S. J. Whitmee. *Horiz*—35 c. M.V. *John Williams VII*.

(Des L. Curtis. Litho Format)

1970 (3 Oct). *Christmas. Sketches.* T **57** and similar vert designs. Multicoloured. W w **12**. P 14½.

170	2 c. Type **57**		10	30
171	10 c. "Sanctuary, Tarawa Cathedral" (Mrs. A. Burroughs)		10	10
172	35 c. "Three ships inside star" (Mrs. C. Barnett)		20	20
170/2		Set of 3	35	50

60 Casting Nets

(Des G. Drummond. Litho Walsall)

1971 (31 May). *Multicoloured designs as T **60**.* W w **12** (*sideways* on 2, 3, 4, 5, 20, 25 and 35 c.). P 14.

173	1 c. Cutting toddy (*vert*)		10	10
174	2 c. Lagoon fishing		15	30
	w. Wmk Crown to right of CA		10·00	
175	3 c. Cleaning pandanus leaves		15	15
	w. Wmk Crown to right of CA			
176	4 c. Type **60**		20	25
	w. Wmk Crown to right of CA			
177	5 c. Gilbertese canoe		45	15
	w. Wmk Crown to right of CA			
178	6 c. De-husking coconuts (*vert*)		30	45
179	8 c. Weaving pandanus fronds (*vert*)		35	15
180	10 c. Weaving a basket (*vert*)		40	15
	w. Wmk inverted		1·50	1·50
181	15 c. Tiger Shark and fishermen (*vert*)		2·50	1·50
182	20 c. Beating a rolled pandanus leaf		1·50	90
	w. Wmk Crown to right of CA		3·75	
183	25 c. Loading copra		2·00	1·00
184	35 c. Fishing at night		2·25	50
	w. Wmk Crown to left of CA		3·50	
185	50 c. Local handicrafts (*vert*)		1·25	1·50
186	$1 Weaving coconut screens (*vert*)		1·75	2·25
187	$2 Coat of Arms (*vert*)		5·00	11·00
173/87		Set of 15	16·00	18·00

*The normal sideways watermark shows Crown to right of CA on 35 c., and Crown to left of CA on the others, *as seen from the back of the stamp.*
See also Nos. 203/7.

61 House of Representatives   **62** Pacific Nativity Scene

(Des V. Whiteley. Litho J.W.)

1971 (1 Aug). *New Constitution.* T **61** and similar horiz design. Multicoloured. W w **12** (*sideways*). P 14.

188	3 c. Type **61**		10	20
189	10 c. Maneaba Betio (Assembly hut)		20	10

(Des L. Curtis and T. Collis. Litho Questa)

1971 (1 Oct). *Christmas.* T **62** and similar vert designs. W w **12**. P 14 × 14½.

190	3 c. black, yellow and ultramarine		10	20
191	10 c. black, gold and turquoise-blue		10	10
192	35 c. black, gold and magenta		25	35
190/2		Set of 3	40	60

Designs:—10 c. Star and palm leaves; 35 c. Outrigger canoe and star.

63 Emblem and Young Boys

(Des G. Vasarhelyi. Litho Questa)

1971 (11 Dec). *25th Anniv of UNICEF.* T **63** and similar horiz designs, showing UNICEF emblem and young boys. W w **12** (*sideways*). P 14.

193	3 c. multicoloured		10	60
194	10 c. multicoloured		15	15
195	35 c. multicoloured		45	60
193/5		Set of 3	60	1·25

64 Flag and Map of South Pacific

(Des A. New. Litho Questa)

1972 (21 Feb). *25th Anniv of South Pacific Commission.* T **64** and similar horiz designs. Multicoloured. W w **12**. P 13½.

196	3 c. Type **64**		10	65
197	10 c. Flag and native boats		15	20
198	35 c. Flags of member nations		15	95
196/8		Set of 3	30	1·60

65 Alveopora   **66** Star of Peace

(Des Sylvia Goaman after original designs by H. Wickison. Litho Questa)

1972 (26 May). *Coral.* T **65** and similar horiz designs. Multicoloured. W w **12** (*sideways**). P 14.

199	3 c. Type **65**		25	45
200	10 c. Euphyllia		30	15
201	15 c. Melithea		40	35
	w. Wmk Crown to left of CA		1·75	
202	35 c. Spongodes		80	60
199/202		Set of 4	1·60	1·40

*The normal sideways watermark shows Crown to right of CA, *as seen from the back of the stamp.*

1972 (7 Sept)–73. *As Nos. 174, 177/8 and 181/2 but* W w **12** upright on 2, 5 and 20 c.; sideways on 6 and 15 c.

203	2 c. Lagoon fishing (13.6.73)		11·00	14·00
204	5 c. Gilbertese canoe		4·00	4·50
205	6 c. De-husking coconuts (13.6.73)		11·00	15·00
206	15 c. Tiger Shark and fishermen		4·50	4·50
207	20 c. Beating a rolled pandanus leaf		4·50	4·50
203/7		Set of 5	32·00	38·00

(Des T. Matarena (35 c.), Father Bermond (others); adapted by Jennifer Toombs. Litho Questa)

1972 (15 Sept). *Christmas.* T **66** and similar multicoloured designs. W w **12** (*sideways* on 3 and 10 c.). P 13½.

208	3 c. Type **66**		10	10
209	10 c. "The Nativity"		10	10
210	35 c. Baby in "manger" (*horiz*)		30	30
208/10		Set of 3	40	40

67 Floral Head-dresses

(Des (from photograph by D. Groves) and photo Harrison)

1972 (20 Nov). *Royal Silver Wedding.* Multicoloured; background colour given. W w **12**. P 14 × 14½.

211	**67** 3 c. brown-olive		10	15
	w. Wmk inverted		6·00	
212	35 c. lake-brown		25	15
	w. Wmk inverted		38·00	

68 Funafuti ("The Land of Bananas")   **69** Dancer

(Des H. Wickison; adapted J. Cooter. Litho Walsall)

1973 (5 Mar). *Legends of Island Names* (1st series). T **68** and similar horiz designs. Multicoloured. W w **12**. P 14½ × 14.

213	3 c. Type **68**		15	50
214	10 c. Butaritari ("The Smell of the Sea")		25	20
215	25 c. Tarawa ("The Centre of the World")		40	50
216	35 c. Abemama ("The Land of the Moon")		45	60
	w. Wmk inverted			
213/16		Set of 4	1·10	1·60

See also Nos. 252/5.

(Des Sister Juliette (3 c.), R. P. Turner (10 and 35 c.), C. Potts (50 c.); adapted Jennifer Toombs. Litho Questa)

1973 (24 Sept). *Christmas.* T **69** and similar vert designs. Multicoloured. W w **12** (*sideways**). P 14.

217	3 c. Type **69**		10	15
218	10 c. Canoe and lagoon		10	10
	w. Wmk Crown to right of CA		8·50	
219	35 c. Lagoon at evening		30	15
220	50 c. Map of Christmas Island		40	1·25
	w. Wmk Crown to right of CA		6·50	
217/20		Set of 4	80	1·50

*The normal sideways watermark shows Crown to left of CA, *as seen from the back of the stamp.*

1973 (14 Nov). *Royal Wedding. As Nos. 165/6 of Anguilla. Centre multicoloured.* W w **12** (*sideways*). P 13½.

221	3 c. pale green		10	15
222	35 c. Prussian blue		20	15

70 Meteorological Observation

(Des E. S. Cheek; adapted PAD Studio. Litho Questa)

1973 (26 Nov). *I.M.O./W.M.O. Centenary.* T **70** and similar horiz designs. Multicoloured. W w **12**. P 14.

223	3 c. Type **70**		50	30
224	10 c. Island observing-station		50	20
225	35 c. Wind-finding radar		70	25
226	50 c. World weather watch stations		1·10	1·25
223/6		Set of 4	2·50	1·75

71 Te Mataaua Crest

(Des J. Cooter. Litho Questa)

1974 (4 Mar). *Canoe Crests.* T **71** and similar horiz designs showing sailing craft and the canoe crests given. Multicoloured. W w **12**. P 13½.

227	3 c. Type **71**		10	10
228	10 c. Te Nimta-wawa		15	10
229	35 c. Tara-tara-venei-na,		25	10
230	50 c. Te Bou-uoua		35	60
227/30		Set of 4	75	75
MS231	154 × 130 mm. Nos. 227/30		2·00	5·00

72 £1 Stamp of 1924 and Te Koroba (canoe)

(Des E. S. Cheek; adapted J. Cooter. Litho Questa)

1974 (10 June). *Centenary of Universal Postal Union. T* **72** *and similar horiz designs. W w* **12**. *P* 14.

232	4 c. multicoloured	..	..	20	20
233	10 c. multicoloured	..	..	20	10
234	25 c. multicoloured	..	..	25	30
	w. Wmk inverted			50·00	
235	35 c. light vermilion and black	..	30	30
232/5			*Set of 4*	85	80

Designs:—10 c. 5s. stamp of 1939 and sailing vessel *Kiakia*; 25 c. $2 stamp of 1971 and B.A.C. One Eleven airplane; 35 c. U.P.U. emblem.

73 Toy Canoe   **74** North Front Entrance, Blenheim Palace

(Des H. Wickison and G. J. Hayward; adapted J. Cooter. Litho Questa)

1974 (5 Sept). *Christmas. T* **73** *and similar horiz designs. Multicoloured. W w* **12** (*sideways**). *P* 14.

236	4 c. Type **73**	..	..	10	20
237	10 c. Toy windmill	..	..	15	10
	w. Wmk Crown to right of CA	..	1·25	
238	25 c. Coconut "ball"	..	..	20	35
239	35 c. Canoes and constellation Pleiades	25	45
236/9			*Set of 4*	65	1·00

*The normal sideways watermark shows Crown to left of CA, as seen from the back of the stamp.

(Des J. Cooter. Litho Questa)

1974 (30 Nov). *Birth Centenary of Sir Winston Churchill. T* **74** *and similar vert designs. Multicoloured. W w* **14**. *P* 14.

240	4 c. Type **74**	..	..	10	35
241	10 c. Churchill painting	..	..	10	10
242	35 c. Churchill's statue, London	..	25	40
240/2			*Set of 3*	40	75

75 Barometer Crab

(Des J. Cooter. Litho Questa)

1975 (27 Jan). *Crabs. T* **75** *and similar horiz designs. Multicoloured. W w* **12** (*sideways**). *P* 14.

243	4 c. Type **75**	..	..	40	70
	w. Wmk Crown to right of CA	..	6·00	
244	10 c. *Ranina ranina*	..	..	50	20
245	25 c. Pelagic Swimming Crab	..	90	70
246	35 c. Ghost Crab	..	..	1·00	1·25
243/6			*Set of 4*	2·50	2·50

*The normal sideways watermark shows Crown to left of CA, as seen from the back of the stamp.

76 Eyed Cowrie   **77** "Christ is Born" (*Cypraea argus*)

(Des E. S. Cheek; adapted J. Cooter. Litho Questa)

1975 (26 May). *Cowrie Shells. T* **76** *and similar vert designs. Multicoloured. W w* **14**. *P* 14.

247	4 c. Type **76**	..	..	55	60
248	10 c. Sieve Cowrie (*Cypraea cribraria*)	80	20
249	25 c. Mole Cowrie (*Cypraea talpa*)	..	1·75	1·10
250	35 c. All-red Map Cowrie (*Cypraea mappa panerythra*)		2·00	2·00
247/50			*Set of 4*	4·50	3·50
MS251	146×137 mm. Nos. 247/50	..	13·00	16·00

(Des J. Cooter. Litho Questa)

1975 (1 Aug). *Legends of Island Names (2nd series). Horiz designs as T* **68**. *Multicoloured. W w* **12** (*sideways**). *P* 14.

252	4 c. Beru ("The Bud")	..	..	10	30
253	10 c. Onotoa ("Six Giants")	..	10	15
254	25 c. Abaiang ("Land to the North")	20	35
	w. Wmk Crown to right of CA	..	8·50	
255	35 c. Marakei ("Fish-trap floating on eaves")	30	50
252/4			*Set of 4*	60	1·10

*The normal sideways watermark shows Crown to left of CA, as seen from the back of the stamp.

(Des C. J. Barnett (4 and 25 c.), Philatelic Advisory Committee (10 c.), P. T. Burangke (35 c.); adapted J. Cooter. Litho Questa)

1975 (22 Sept). *Christmas. T* **77** *and similar vert designs. Multicoloured. W w* **14**. *P* 14.

256	4 c. Type **77**	..	..	20	50
257	10 c. Protestant Chapel, Tarawa	..	20	30
258	25 c. Catholic Church, Ocean Island	35	90
259	35 c. Fishermen and star	..	40	1·50
256/9			*Set of 4*	1·00	2·75

POSTAGE DUE STAMPS

D 1

(Typo B.W.)

1940 (Aug). *Wmk Mult Script CA. P* 12.

D1	D 1	1d. emerald-green	..	..	8·50	22·00
D2		2d. scarlet	..	..	9·50	22·00
D3		3d. brown	..	..	14·00	23·00
D4		4d. blue	..	..	16·00	29·00
D5		5d. grey-green	..	..	21·00	29·00
D6		6d. purple	..	..	21·00	29·00
D7		1s. violet	..	..	23·00	40·00
D8		1s. 6d. turquoise-green	..	45·00	85·00
D1/8				*Set of 8*	£140	£250
D1/8	Perf "Specimen"			*Set of 8*	£160	

Examples of all values are known showing a forged Post Office Ocean Island postmark dated "16 DE 46".

Stamps for the Gilbert and Ellice Islands were withdrawn on 31 December 1975 when the separate colonies of KIRIBATI (GILBERT ISLANDS) and TUVALU were created.

Gilbert Islands
see Kiribati

Gold Coast
see Ghana

Grenada

The earliest recorded postmark of the British administration of Grenada dates from 1784, and, although details of the early period are somewhat sparse, it would appear that the island's postal service was operated at a branch of the British G.P.O. In addition to a Packet Agency at St. George's, the capital, there was a philatelic agency at Carriacou, in the Grenadines, which operated for a few years from 15 September 1847.

Stamps of Great Britain were supplied to the St. George's office from April 1858 until the colony assumed responsibility for the postal service on 1 May 1860. Following the take-over the crowned-circle handstamp, No. CC2, was again used until the Grenada adhesives were issued in 1861.

There was no internal postal service before 1861.

For illustrations of the handstamp and postmark types see BRITISH POST OFFICE ABROAD notes, following GREAT BRITAIN.

CARRIACOU

CROWNED-CIRCLE HANDSTAMPS

CC1   CC **1**   CARRIACOU (13.11.1846)   ..   ..   .. †

Although recorded in the G.P.O. proof book no example of No. CC1 has been reported used from Grenada.

ST. GEORGE'S

CROWNED-CIRCLE HANDSTAMPS

CC2   CC **1**   GRENADA (R.) (24.10.1850)   *Price on cover* £1100

Stamps of GREAT BRITAIN *cancelled* "A 15" *as Type* **2**

1858 to **1860**.

Z1	1d. rose-red (1857), *perf* 14	..	£350
Z2	2d. blue (1858) (Plate No. 7)	..	£650
Z3	4d. rose (1857)	..	£225
Z4	6d. lilac (1856)	..	£120
Z5	1s. green (1856)	..	£650

CROWN COLONY

PRINTERS. Types 1 and 5 recess-printed by Perkins, Bacon and Co.

PERKINS BACON "CANCELLED". For notes on these handstamps, showing "CANCELLED" between horizontal bars forming an oval, see Catalogue Introduction.

1   **2** Small Star

(Eng C. Jeens)

1861 (3 June)–**62**. *No wmk. Wove paper.*

    (a) *Rough perf* 14 *to* 16.

1	**1**	1d. bluish green	..	£4500	£300
2		1d. green (5.62)	..	50·00	40·00
		a. Imperf between (horiz pair)	..	—	
3		6d. rose (*shades*) (H/S "CANCELLED" in oval £6000)	..	£800	90·00

    (b) *Perf* 11 *to* 12½

3a	**1**	6d. lake-red (6.62)	..	£750

The 1d. green also exists handstamped "CANCELLED" in oval, but the only known example is in the Royal Collection.

No. 3a is only known unused, and may be the result of perforating machine trials undertaken by Perkins, Bacon. It has also been seen on horizontally laid paper (*Price* £1100).

SIDEWAYS WATERMARK. W **2/3** when sideways show two points of star downwards.

1863–71. W **2** (*Small Star*). *Rough perf* 14 *to* 16.

4	**1**	1d. green (3.64)	..	60·00	12·00
		a. Wmk sideways	..	—	20·00
5		1d. yellowish green	..	£100	26·00
6		6d. rose (*shades*) (5.63)	..	£600	12·00
		a. Wmk sideways	..	—	60·00
7		6d. orange-red (*shades*) (5.66)	..	£650	12·00
8		6d. dull rose-red (*wmk sideways*)	£3000	£225
9		6d. vermilion (5.71)	..	£750	12·00
		a. Double impression	..	—	£1800

1873 (Jan). W **2** (*Small Star, sideways*). *Clean-cut perf* 15.

10	**1**	1d. deep green	..	75·00	30·00
		a. Bisected diag (on cover)	..	† £6000	
		b. Imperf between (pair)	..	—	£4000

No. 10a, and later bisected 1d. values, were authorised until 1881 to pay the island newspaper rate (½d.) or the newspaper rate to Great Britain (1½d.). Examples also exist on covers to France.

3 Large Star   **4** Broad-pointed Star

1873 (Sept)–**74**. W **3** (*Large Star*). *Intermediate perf* 15.

11	**1**	1d. blue-green (*wmk sideways*) (2.74)	..	65·00	19·00
		a. Double impression		
		b. Bisected diag (on cover)	..	†
12		6d. orange-vermilion	..	£600	26·00

POSTAGE

ONE SHILLING

5   (**6**)

NOTE. The early ½d., 2½d., 4d. and 1s. postage stamps were made by surcharging the undenominated Type **5** design.

The surcharges were from two founts of type—one about 1½ mm high, the other 2 mm high—so there are short and tall letters on the same stamp; also the spacing varies considerably, so that the length of the words varies.

Examples of Type **5** with surcharges, but without the "POSTAGE" inscription, are revenue stamps.

1875 (July). *Surch with T* **6**. *W* **3**. *P* 14.
13	5	1s. deep mauve (B.)			£650	9·50
		a. "SHLLIING"			†	£700
		b. "NE SHILLING"			†	£2500
		c. Inverted "S" in "POSTAGE"		£3500	£500
		d. "OSTAGE"			†	£2000

1875 (Dec). *W* **3** (*Large Star, upright*).
14	1	1d. green *to yellow-green* (*p* 14)		60·00	6·50
		a. Bisected diag (on cover)			£6500
15		1d. green (*p* 15)			£7000	£2000

No. 14 was perforated at Somerset House. 40 sheets of No. 15 were perforated by Perkins, Bacon to replace spoilages to complete the order.

1878 (Aug). *W* **2** (*Small Star, sideways*). *Intermediate perf* 15.
16	1	1d. green			£225	28·00
		b. Bisected diag (on cover)			†	—
17		6d. deep vermilion			£750	28·00
		a. Double impression			—	£1500

1879 (Dec). *W* **2** (*Small Star, upright*). *Rough perf* 15.
18	1	1d. pale green (*thin paper*)		£300	22·00
		a. Double impression			
		b. Bisected diag (on cover)			†	—

1881 (Apr). *W* **2** (*Small Star, sideways*). *Rough perf* 14½.
| 19 | 1 | 1d. green | | | £110 | 7·00 |
| | | a. Bisected diag (on cover) | | | † | £6500 |

POSTAGE **POSTAGE** **POSTAGE**

HALF-PENNY **TWO PENCE HALF-PENNY.** **FOUR PENCE**

(7) (8) (9)

1881 (Apr). *Surch with T* **7/9**. *P* 14½. (a) *W* **3** (*Large Star, sideways on ½d.*)
20	5	½d. pale mauve			30·00	10·00
21		½d. deep mauve			11·00	5·50
		a. Imperf (pair)			£300	
		ab. Ditto. "OSTAGE" (R.9/4)		£3250	
		b. Surch double			£275	
		c. "OSTAGE" (R.9/4)			£180	£130
		d. No hyphen			£180	£130
		e. "ALF-PENNY"			£3000	
		f. Wmk upright			£300	£140
		g. Ditto. "OSTAGE" (R.9/4)		£1700	£1100
22		2½d. rose-lake			50·00	5·50
		a. Imperf (pair)			£425	
		b. Imperf between (horiz pair)	£3250	
		c. No stop			£250	75·00
		d. "PENCF" (R.8/12)			£450	£180
23		4d. blue			95·00	8·00
		a. Wmk sideways				
		b. Inverted "S" in "POSTAGE"			

(b) *W* **4** (*Broad-pointed Star*)
24	5	2½d. rose-lake			£130	48·00
		a. No stop			£550	£200
		b. "PENCF" (R.8/12)			£750	£275
25		2½d. claret			£400	£120
		a. No stop			£1000	£475
		b. "PENCF" (R.8/12)		£1500	£600
25c		2½d. deep claret			£600	£225
		d. No stop			£2250	£900
		e. "PENCF" (R.8/12)		£2750	£1100
26		4d. blue			£250	£180

Examples of the "F" for "E" error on the 2½d. value should not be confused with a somewhat similar broken "E" variety. The latter is always without the stop and shows other damage to the "E". The authentic error always occurs with the full stop shown.
The "no stop" variety occurs on R.3/4, R.6/2, R.8/3 and R.9/7.

POSTAGE **POSTAGE** **POSTAGE**
ONE PENNY POSTAGE.

(10) (11) (12)

1883 (Jan). *Revenue stamps* (*T* **5** *with green surcharge as in T* **10**) *optd for postage. W* **2** (*Small Star*). *P* 14½.

(a) *Optd horizontally with T* **11**.
27	5	1d. orange			£275	48·00
		a. "POSTAGE" inverted		£1700	£1200
		b. "POSTAGE" double		£1200	£1100
		c. Inverted "S" in "POSTAGE"	£800	£600
		d. Bisected diag (on cover)		†	£3000

(b) *Optd diagonally with T* **11** *twice on each stamp, the stamp being cut and each half used as ½d.*
28	5	Half of 1d. orange		£650	£225
		a. Unsevered pair		£3750	£1200
		b. "POSTAGE" inverted		—	£1100

(c) *Optd with T* **12**, *the stamps divided diagonally and each half used as ½d.*
| 29 | 5 | Half of 1d. orange | | £225 | £110 |
| | | a. Unsevered pair | | £1200 | £450 |

Nos. 27/9 exist with wmk either upright or sideways.
1d. Revenue stamps with "POSTAGE" added in black manuscript were used at Gouyave during February and March 1883 (*Price* £2250, *used*). Similar manuscript overprints in black or red, were also used at Sauteurs in September 1886 (*Price* £3250, *used*).

GRENADA POSTAGE (13) **d.** **1** **POSTAGE.** (14) GRENADA POSTAGE & REVENUE ONE PENNY (15)
ONE PENNY

(T*ypo D.L.R.*)

1883. *Wmk Crown CA. P* 14.
30	13	½d. dull green (February)		1·00	1·00
		a. *Tête-bêche* (vert pair)		4·00	14·00
31		1d. carmine (February)		65·00	3·25
		a. *Tête-bêche* (vert pair)		£225	£225
32		2½d. ultramarine (May)		6·50	1·00
		a. *Tête-bêche* (vert pair)		24·00	50·00
33		4d. greyish slate (May)		4·50	1·75
		a. *Tête-bêche* (vert pair)		17·00	55·00
34		6d. mauve (May)		3·00	4·00
		a. *Tête-bêche* (vert pair)		18·00	55·00
35		8d. grey-brown (February)		8·50	12·00
		a. *Tête-bêche* (vert pair)		32·00	75·00
36		1s. pale violet (April)		£110	55·00
		a. *Tête-bêche* (vert pair)		32·00	75·00
30/36			Set of 7	£180	65·00

Types **13** and **15** were printed in rows *tête-bêche* in the sheets, so that 50% of the stamps have inverted watermarks.

1886. *Revenue stamps* (*T* **5** *with green surch as T* **10**), *surch with T* **14**. *P* 14. (a) *Wmk Large Star, T* **3**.
37	5	1d. on 1½d. orange (October)	38·00	29·00
		a. Surch inverted		£300	£300
		b. Surch double		£475	£300
		c. "THRFE"		£250	£225
		d. "PFNCE"		£250	£225
		e. "HALH"		£250	£225
		f. Bisected diag (on cover)		†	£1900
38		1d. on 1s. orange (December)	32·00	30·00
		a. "POSTAGE" (no stop)		£375	
		b. "SHILLNG"		£425	£375
		c. Wide space (3½ mm) between "ONE" and "SHILLING"	£300	£250
		d. Bisected diag (on cover)		†	£1900

(b) *Wmk Small Star, T* **2**.
| 39 | 5 | 1d. on 4d. orange (November) | £140 | 90·00 |

1887 (Jan). *Wmk Crown CA. P* 14.
| 40 | 15 | 1d. carmine (Optd S. £50) | | 60 | 60 |
| | | a. *Tête-bêche* (vert pair) | | 1·75 | 17·00 |

4d. **HALF PENNY** **POSTAGE** **POSTAGE**

(16) (17)

1888 (31 Mar)–**91**. *Revenue stamps* (*T* **5** *with green surch as T* **10**) *further surcharged. W* **2**. *P* 14½, *and No.* 35.

I. *Surch with T* **16**.
(a) 4 *mm between value and* "POSTAGE"
41	5	4d. on 2s. orange		38·00	17·00
		a. Upright "d" (R. 5/6)		£750	£400
		b. Wide space (2¼ mm) between "TWO" and "SHILLINGS"	£250	£150
		c. First "S" in "SHILLINGS" inverted	£450	£325
		d. Imperf between (horiz pair)			

(b) 5 *mm between value and* "POSTAGE"
42	5	4d. on 2s. orange		60·00	28·00
		a. Wide space		£300	£225
		b. "S" inverted		£650	£550

II. *Surch as T* **17** (December 1889)
43	5	½d. on 2s. orange		12·00	17·00
		a. Surch double		£300	£325
		b. Wide space		£110	£130
		c. "S" inverted		£275	£300

POSTAGE **POSTAGE** **d.** **AND** **1** **AND** **REVENUE** **REVENUE** **1d.** **2½d.**

(18) (19) (20)

III. *Surch with T* **18** (December 1890)
44	5	1d. on 2s. orange		70·00	70·00
		a. Surch inverted		£600	
		b. Wide space		£325	£325
		c. "S" inverted		£650	£650

IV. *Surch with T* **19** (January 1891)
45	5	1d. on 2s. orange		50·00	50·00
		a. No stop after "1d" (R.3/8)	£325	
		b. Wide space		£250	£250
		c. "S" inverted		£500	£500
46	13	1d. on 8d. grey-brown		9·00	11·00
		a. *Tête-bêche* (vert pair)		40·00	60·00
		b. Surch inverted		£300	£275
		c. No stop after "1d" (R.6/5)	£250	£250

V. *Surch with T* **20** (December 1891)
47	13	2½d. on 8d. grey-brown (Optd S. £65)	8·00	11·00
		a. *Tête-bêche* (vert pair)		40·00	60·00
		b. Inverted surcharge			
		c. Double surcharge		£750	£800
		d. Double surcharge, one inverted	£550	£500
		e. Treble surcharge		—	£900
		f. Treble surcharge, two inverted	—	£850

The wide space between "TWO" and "SHILLINGS" occurs on R. 1/4 and 10/3 of the original 2s. Revenue stamp which was printed in sheets of 120 (12×10).

The surcharges, Types **16/19**, were applied to half sheets as a setting of 60 (12×5).
There are two varieties of fraction in Type **20**, which each occur 30 times in the setting; in one the "1" has horizontal serif and the "2" commences in a ball; in the other the "1" has sloping serif and the "2" is without ball.
See also D4/7.

GRENADA 1d GRENADA 8d GRENADA 2d

21 22 23 Flagship of Columbus. (Columbus named Grenada "La Concepcion")

(T*ypo D.L.R.*)

1895 (6 Sept)–**99**. *Wmk Crown CA. P* 14.
48	22	½d. mauve and green (9.99)		2·50	1·50
49	21	1d. mauve and carmine (5.96)		4·50	70
50		2d. mauve and brown (9.99)		40·00	32·00
		x. Wmk reversed			
51		2½d. mauve and ultramarine		5·00	1·50
52	22	3d. mauve and orange		6·50	16·00
53	21	6d. mauve and green		10·00	21·00
54	22	8d. mauve and black		12·00	38·00
55		1s. green and orange		17·00	32·00
48/55			Set of 8	85·00	£130
48/55		Optd "Specimen"	Set of 8	£150	

(*Recess D.L.R.*)

1898 (15 Aug). 400*th Anniv of Discovery of Grenada by Columbus. Wmk Crown CC. P* 14
| 56 | 23 | 2½d. ultramarine (Optd S. £85) | 13·00 | 6·00 |
| | | a. Bluish paper | | 32·00 | 40·00 |

GRENADA ½d GRENADA 1d

24 25

(T*ypo D.L.R.*)

1902. *Wmk Crown CA. P* 14.
57	24	½d. dull purple and green		3·00	65
58	25	1d. dull purple and carmine		4·00	20
59		2d. dull purple and brown		3·00	9·00
60		2½d. dull purple and ultramarine		3·50	2·50
61	24	3d. dull purple and orange		3·50	8·00
62	25	6d. dull purple and green		2·50	17·00
63	24	1s. green and orange		3·25	23·00
64		2s. green and ultramarine		20·00	55·00
65	25	5s. green and carmine		38·00	55·00
66	24	10s. green and purple		£110	£200
57/66			Set of 10	£170	£325
57/66		Optd "Specimen"	Set of 10	£180	

1904–6. *Wmk Mult Crown CA. Ordinary paper. P* 14.
67	24	½d. purple and green (1905)		17·00	23·00
68	25	1d. purple and carmine		9·00	2·50
69		2d. purple and brown (1905)		48·00	95·00
70	24	2½d. purple and ultramarine (1905)	48·00	65·00
71	24	3d. purple and orange (1905)		2·50	6·50
		a. Chalk-surfaced paper		2·50	8·50
72	25	6d. purple and green (1906)		4·50	9·00
		a. Chalk-surfaced paper		7·50	16·00
73	24	1s. green and orange (1905)		6·00	24·00
74		2s. green and ultramarine (1906)	38·00	70·00
		a. Chalk-surfaced paper		25·00	75·00
75	25	5s. green and carmine (1906)		60·00	95·00
76	24	10s. green and purple (1906)		£140	£225
67/76			Set of 10	£300	£500

Examples of most values between Nos. 57 and 76 are known showing a forged G.P.O. Grenada B.W.I. postmark dated "OC 6 09".

GRENADA HALF PENNY GRENADA THREE PENCE

26 Badge of the Colony 27

(*Recess D.L.R.*)

1906. *Wmk Mult Crown CA. P* 14.
77	26	½d. green		3·00	30
78		1d. carmine		4·00	10
		y. Wmk inverted and reversed			
79		2d. orange		2·00	3·00
80		2½d. blue		4·50	1·50
		a. Ultramarine		7·50	3·50

(T*ypo D.L.R.*)

1908. *Wmk Crown CA. Chalk-surfaced paper. P* 14.
| 82 | 27 | 1s. black/green | | 22·00 | 45·00 |
| 83 | | 10s. green and red/green | | 80·00 | £160 |

1908–11. *Wmk Mult Crown CA. Chalk-surfaced paper.* P 14.

84	27	3d. dull purple/*yellow*	..	..	3·75	1·75
85		6d. dull purple and purple		..	18·00	23·00
86		1s. black/*green* (1911)	..	..	5·50	4·25
87		2s. blue and purple/*blue*		..	18·00	12·00
88		5s. green and red/*yellow*		..	50·00	65·00
77/88				*Set of 11*	£180	£250
77/80, 82/5, 87/8 Optd "Specimen"				*Set of 10*	£200	

Examples of Nos. 82/8 are known showing a forged G.P.O. Grenada B.W.I. postmark dated "OC 6 09".

WAR TAX   WAR TAX

28	(29)	(30

(Typo D.L.R.)

1913 (3 Jan)–**22.** *Wmk Mult Crown CA. Chalk-surfaced paper* (3d. to 10s.). P 14.

89	28	½d. yellow-green	..	..	90	1·60
90		½d. green	..	..	90	1·00
91		1d. red	..	..	2·25	30
92		1d. scarlet (1916)	..	..	2·75	70
		w. Wmk inverted				
93		2d. orange	..	..	1·50	30
94		2½d. bright blue	..	..	1·60	3·25
95		2½d. dull blue (1920)	..		4·50	4·50
96		3d. purple/*yellow*	..		65	85
		a. White back (3.14) (Optd S. £32)		65	1·50
		b. On lemon (1917)	..		4·00	8·50
		c. On pale yellow (1921)			6·00	26·00
97		6d. dull and bright purple			1·25	8·50
98		1s. black/*green*	..		1·00	9·00
		a. White back (3.14) (Optd S. £32)		1·00	6·00
		b. On blue-green, olive back (1917)		48·00	80·00
		c. On emerald surface			1·50	10·00
		d. On emerald back (6.22) (Optd S. £32)		1·00	9·50
		dw. Wmk inverted			75·00	
99		2s. purple and blue/*blue*			5·50	12·00
100		5s. green and red/*green*			16·00	60·00
		a. On pale yellow (1921) (Optd S. £45)		24·00	75·00
101		10s. green and red/*green*			48·00	£100
		a. On emerald back (6.22) (Optd S. £55)		50·00	£140
89/101				*Set of 10*	70·00	£160
89/101 Optd "Specimen"				*Set of 10*	£160	
98 Optd in black instead of red			..	32·00	

1916 (1 June). *Optd by Govt Press, St. George's. With T* **29.**

109	28	1d. red (*shades*) (H/S S. £50)	..	2·25	1·75
		a. Opt inverted	..		£275	
		b. "T△X"	..		55·00	70·00

A small "A" in "WAR", 2 mm high is found on Nos. 29, 38 and 48 of the setting of 60 and a very small "A" in "TAX", 1½ mm high, on No. 11. Value about twice normal. The normal "A" is 2¼ mm high. No. 109b is on No. 56 of the setting.

1916 (1 Sept)–**18.** *Optd with T* **30** *in London.*

111	28	1d. scarlet	..	..	30	20
		a. Carmine-red/*bluish* (5.18)	..	3·25	1·50
		w. Wmk inverted				
111 Optd "Specimen"			..	40·00	

1921–32. *Wmk Mult Script CA. Chalk-surfaced paper* (3d. (No. 122) to 10s.) P 14.

112	28	½d. green	..	..	1·25	15
113		1d. carmine-red	..	..	80	50
114		1d. brown (1923)	..	..	1·50	20
115		1½d. rose-red (6.22)	..	..	1·50	1·50
116		2d. orange	..	..	1·25	15
117		2d. grey (1926)	..	..	2·50	2·25
117a		2½d. dull blue	..	..	4·00	3·00
118		2½d. grey (6.22)	..	..	75	8·50
119		2½d. bright blue (1926)	..	4·00	3·50
120		2½d. ultramarine (1931)	..	4·50	8·50
120a		2½d. chalky blue and blue (1932)	50·00	48·00
121		3d. bright blue (6.22)	..	1·25	10·00
122		3d. purple/*yellow* (1926)	..	3·00	5·00
123		4d. black and red/*yellow* (1926)	..	1·00	3·75
124		5d. dull purple & sage-green (27.12.22)	1·50	4·00
125		6d. dull and bright purple	..	1·25	18·00
126		6d. black and carmine (1926)	..	2·25	2·50
127		9d. dull purple and black (27.12.22)	2·25	8·50
128		1s. black/*emerald* (1923)	..	2·50	35·00
129		1s. chestnut (1926)	..	3·00	10·00
130		2s. purple and blue/*black* (1922)	6·00	17·00
131		2s. 6d. black and carmine/*blue* (1929)	6·50	17·00
132		3s. green and violet (27.12.22)	..	16·00	40·00
133		5s. green and red/*pale yellow* (1923)	12·00	35·00
134		10s. green and red/*emerald* (1923)	50·00	£130
112/19, 121/34			*Set of 22*	£100	£300
112/34 Optd/Perf "Specimen"		*Set of 23*	£325	

31 Grand Anse Beach

32 Badge of the Colony

---

33 Grand Etang

34 St. George's

(Recess Waterlow)

1934 (23 Oct)–**36.** *Wmk Mult Script CA* (sideways on T **32**). P 12½.

135	31	½d. green	..		15	1·00
		a. Perf 12½ × 13½ (1936)	..	4·00	38·00
136	32	1d. black and sepia	..		80	2·50
		a. Perf 13½ × 12½ (1936)	..	60	35
137	33	1½d. black and scarlet	..	4·75	2·50
		a. Perf 12½ × 13½ (1936)	..	1·00	55
138	32	2d. black and orange	..		90	40
139	34	2½d. blue	..	..	50	30
140	32	3d. black and olive-green	..	70	2·25
141		6d. black and purple	..	1·60	1·25
142		1s. black and brown	..	1·25	3·00
143		2s. 6d. black and ultramarine	..	7·00	27·00
144		5s. black and violet	..	32·00	50·00
135/144			*Set of 10*	40·00	75·00
135/44 Perf "Specimen"		*Set of 10*	£160	

1935 (6 May). *Silver Jubilee. As Nos. 91/4 of Antigua but ptd by Waterlow.* P 11×12.

145		½d. black and green	..		60	1·00
		k. Kite and vertical log		38·00	
		l. Kite and horizontal log		45·00	
146		1d. ultramarine and grey	..	60	1·50
		l. Kite and horizontal log		45·00	
147		1½d. deep blue and scarlet	..	60	1·50
		l. Kite and horizontal log		60·00	
148		1s. slate and purple	..	6·00	16·00
		l. Kite and horizontal log		£150	
145/8			*Set of 4*	7·00	18·00
145/8 Perf "Specimen"		*Set of 4*	70·00	

For illustrations of plate varieties see Catalogue Introduction.

1937 (12 May). *Coronation. As Nos. 95/7 of Antigua.* P 11x11½.

149		1d. violet	..	..	40	20
150		1½d. carmine	..		40	40
151		2½d. blue	..	..	80	30
149/51			*Set of 3*	1·40	65
149/51 Perf "Specimen"		*Set of 3*	50·00	

35 King George VI

(Photo Harrison)

1937 (12 July)–**50.** *Wmk Mult Script CA. Chalk-surfaced paper.* P 15×14.

152	35	¼d. brown	..		1·40	10
		a. Ordinary paper (11.42)	..	30	60
		b. Ordinary paper. *Chocolate* (1.45)	20	60
		c. Chalk-surfaced paper. *Chocolate* (8.50)	50	3·00

The ordinary paper is thick, smooth and opaque.

36 Grand Anse Beach

40 Badge of the Colony

Colon flaw
(R. 5/8. Corrected on ptg of Nov 1950)

(Recess D.L.R. (10s.), Waterlow (others))

1938 (16 Mar)–**50.** *As T* **31/4** (but portrait of King George VI as in T **36**) and *T* **40.** *Wmk Mult Script CA* (sideways on T **32**). P 12½ or 12 × 13 (10s.).

153	36	½d. yellow-green	..		4·50	1·00
		a. Perf 12½ × 13½ (1938)	..	6·00	80
		b. Perf 12½. *Blue-green*	..	60	1·25
		ba. Perf 12½ × 13½. *Blue-green*	6·00	5·00
154	32	1d. black and sepia	..	1·00	20
		a. Perf 13½ × 12½ (1938)	..	50	50
155	33	1½d. black and scarlet	..	50	70
		a. Perf 13½ × 12½ (1938)	..	2·25	30
156	32	2d. black and orange	..	30	50
		a. Perf 13½ × 12½ (1938)	..	2·50	70

157	34	2½d. bright blue	..	..	30	30
		a. Perf 12½ × 13½ (?March 1950)	£4250	£225
158	32	3d. black and olive-green	..	9·50	1·40
		a. Perf 13½ × 12½ (16.3.38)	..	6·00	80
		ab. Perf 13½ × 12½. *Black and brown-olive* (1942)	30	80
		b. Perf 12½. *Black and brown-olive* (16.8.50)	30	1·60
		ba. Colon flaw	..	50·00	
159		6d. black and purple	..	1·25	40
		a. Perf 13½ × 12½ (1942)	..	2·25	50
160		1s. black and brown	..	2·25	30
		a. Perf 13½ × 12½ (1941)	..	3·50	1·25
161		2s. black and ultramarine	..	16·00	1·50
		a. Perf 13½ × 12½ (1941)	..	20·00	1·50
162		5s. black and violet	..	3·50	1·50
		a. Perf 13½ × 12½ (1947)	..	2·75	5·50
163	40	10s. steel blue and carmine (*narrow*) (p 12 × 13)	55·00	9·00
		a. Perf 14. *Steel blue and bright carmine* (*narrow*)	£180	45·00
		b. Perf 14. *Slate-blue and bright carmine* (*narrow*) (1943)	£190	£110
		c. Perf 12. *Slate-blue and bright carmine* (*narrow*) (1943)	£450	£800
		d. Perf 14. *Slate-blue and carmine-lake* (*wide*) (1944)	90·00	8·00
		e. Perf 14. *Blue-black and carmine* (*narrow*) (1943)	27·00	8·50
		f. Perf 14. *Blue-black and bright carmine* (*wide*) (1947)	25·00	25·00
152/63e			*Set of 12*	45·00	13·00
152/63 Perf "Specimen"		*Set of 12*	£225	

In the earlier printings of the 10s. the paper was dampened before printing and the subsequent shrinkage produced narrow frames 23½ to 23¾ mm wide. Later printings were made on dry paper producing wide frames 24¼ mm wide.

No. 163a is one of the earlier printings line perf 13.8×14.1. Later printings of the 10s. are line perf 14.1.

Nos. 163b/c show a blurred centre caused by the use of a worn plate.

Nos. 163a and 163b may be found with gum more or less yellow due to local climatic conditions.

Examples of No. 163c are known showing forged St. George's postmarks dated "21 AU 42", "21 AU 43" or "2 OC 43".

1946 (25 Sept). *Victory. As Nos. 110/11 of Antigua.*

164		1½d. carmine	..	..	10	10
165		3½d. blue	..	..	10	20
164/5 Perf "Specimen"		*Set of 2*	50·00	

1948 (27 Oct). *Royal Silver Wedding. As Nos. 112/13 of Antigua.*

166		1½d. scarlet	..	..	15	10
167		10s. slate-green	..	..	8·00	16·00

(New Currency. 100 cents = 1 West Indian, later Eastern Caribbean, dollar)

1949 (10 Oct). *75th Anniv of Universal Postal Union. As Nos. 114/17 of Antigua.*

168		5 c. ultramarine	..	..	20	10
169		6 c. olive	..	..	90	1·25
170		12 c. magenta	..	..	35	30
171		24 c. red-brown	..	..	35	30
168/71			*Set of 4*	1·60	1·60

41 King George VI

42 Badge of the Colony

43 Badge of the Colony

(Recess B.W. (T **41**), D.L.R. (others))

1951 (8 Jan). *Wmk Mult Script CA.* P 11½ (T **41**), 11½ × 12½ (T **42**), and 11½ × 13 (T **43**).

172	41	½ c. black and red-brown	..	15	1·00
173		1 c. black and emerald-green	..	15	25
174		2 c. black and brown	..	15	30
175		3 c. black and rose-carmine	..	15	10
176		4 c. black and orange	..	35	40
177		5 c. black and violet	..	20	10
178		6 c. black and olive	..	30	60
179		7 c. black and light blue	..	1·75	10
180		12 c. black and purple	..	2·25	30
181	42	24 c. black and sepia	..	2·25	50
182		50 c. black and blue	..	6·50	40
183		$1.50, black and yellow-orange	..	7·50	6·50
184	43	$2.50, slate-blue and carmine	..	5·50	5·50
172/184			*Set of 13*	24·00	14·00

1951 (16 Feb). *Inauguration of B.W.I. University College. As Nos. 118/19 of Antigua.*

185		3 c. black and carmine	..	..	45	20
186		6 c. black and olive	..	..	45	20

NEW CONSTITUTION

1951
(44)

1951 (21 Sept). *New Constitution. Nos. 175/7 and 180 optd with T 44 by B.W.*

187	41	3 c. black and rose-carmine	10	10
188		4 c. black and orange	10	10
189		5 c. black and violet (R.)	10	10
190		12 c. black and purple	10	15
187/90		*Set of 4*	30	40

1953 (3 June). *Coronation. As No. 120 of Antigua.*

191	3 c. black and carmine-red	20	10

45 Queen Elizabeth II   46 Badge of the Colony   47 Badge of the Colony

(Recess B.W. (T 45), D.L.R. (T 46/7))

1953 (15 June)–59. *Wmk Mult Script CA. P 11½ (T 45), 11½ × 12½ (T 46), or 11½ × 13 (T 47).*

192	45	½ c. black and brown (28.12.53)	10	10
193		1 c. black and deep emerald	10	10
194		2 c. black and sepia (15.9.53)	30	10
195		3 c. black and carmine-red (22.2.54)	10	10
196		4 c. black and brown-orange (22.2.54)	10	10
197		5 c. black and deep violet (22.2.54)	10	10
198		6 c. black and olive-green (28.12.53)	45	1·25
199		7 c. black and blue (6.6.55)	1·25	10
200		12 c. black and reddish purple	30	10
201	46	25 c. black and sepia (10.1.55)	1·25	20
202		50 c. black and deep blue (2.12.55)	5·50	40
203		$1.50, black & brown-orange (2.12.55)	11·00	13·00
204	47	$2.50, slate-blue & carmine (16.11.59)	18·00	10·00
192/204		*Set of 13*	35·00	23·00

On 23 December 1965, No. 203 was issued surcharged "2" but this was intended for fiscal and revenue purposes and it was not authorised to be used postally, although some are known to have passed through the mail.

For stamps in Types 45/6 watermarked w 12 see Nos. 214/20.

1958 (22 Apr). *Inauguration of British Caribbean Federation. As Nos. 135/7 of Antigua.*

205	3 c. deep green	35	10
206	6 c. blue	45	60
207	12 c. scarlet	55	10
205/7	*Set of 3*	1·25	70

48 Queen Victoria, Queen Elizabeth II, Mail Van and Post Office, St. George's

(Photo Harrison)

1961 (1 June). *Grenada Stamp Centenary. T 48 and similar horiz designs. W w 12. P 14½ × 14.*

208	3 c. crimson and black	25	10
209	8 c. bright blue and orange	55	25
210	25 c. lake and blue	55	25
208/10	*Set of 3*	1·25	55

Designs:—8 c. Queen Victoria, Queen Elizabeth II and flagship of Columbus; 25 c. Queen Victoria, Queen Elizabeth II, *Solent I* (paddle-steamer) and Douglas DC-3 aircraft.

1963 (4 June). *Freedom from Hunger. As No. 146 of Antigua.*

211	8 c. bluish green	30	15

1963 (2 Sept). *Red Cross Centenary. As Nos. 147/8 of Antigua.*

212	3 c. red and black	20	15
213	25 c. red and blue	40	15

1964 (12 May)–66. *As Nos. 194/8, 201/1, but wmk w 12.*

214	45	2 c. black and sepia	10	10
215		3 c. black and carmine-red	15	10
216		4 c. black and brown-orange	15	50
217		5 c. black and deep violet	15	10
218		6 c. black and olive-green (4.1.66)	£190	65·00
219		12 c. black and reddish purple	20	10
220	46	25 c. black and sepia	2·50	50
214/20		*Set of 7*	£190	65·00

1965 (17 May). *I.T.U. Centenary. As Nos. 166/7 of Antigua.*

221	2 c. red-orange and yellow-olive	10	10
222	50 c. lemon and light red	25	20

1965 (25 Oct). *International Co-operation Year. As Nos. 168/9 of Antigua.*

223	1 c. reddish purple and turquoise-green	10	15
224	25 c. deep bluish green and lavender	20	15

1966 (24 Jan). *Churchill Commemoration. As Nos. 170/3 of Antigua.*

225	1 c. new blue	10	15
226	3 c. deep green	10	15
227	25 c. brown	15	10
228	35 c. bluish violet	25	15
225/8	*Set of 4*	45	40

1966 (4 Feb). *Royal Visit. As Nos. 174/5 of Antigua.*

229	3 c. black and ultramarine	25	15
230	35 c. black and magenta	65	15

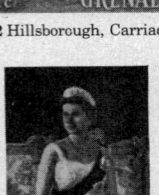

52 Hillsborough, Carriacou   53 Badge of the Colony

54 Queen Elizabeth II   55 Map of Grenada

(Des V. Whiteley. Photo Harrison)

1966 (1 Apr). *Horiz designs as T 52, and T 53/5. Multicoloured. W w 12. P 14½ ($1, $2, $3) or 14½×13½ (others).*

231	1 c. Type 52	20	55
232	2 c. Bougainvillea	20	10
233	3 c. Flamboyant plant	30	30
234	5 c. Levera beach	60	10
235	6 c. Carenage, St. George's	60	10
236	8 c. Annandale Falls	60	10
	w. Wmk inverted		
237	10 c. Cocoa pods	30	10
238	12 c. Inner Harbour	30	60
239	15 c. Nutmeg	30	60
240	25 c. St. George's	30	10
241	35 c. Grand Anse beach	30	10
242	50 c. Bananas	1·50	1·50
243	$1 Type 53	7·00	3·00
244	$2 Type 54	5·00	6·00
245	$3 Type 55	4·50	12·00
231/45	*Set of 15*	19·00	23·00

1966 (1 July). *World Cup Football Championships. As Nos. 176/7 of Antigua.*

246	5 c. violet, yellow-green, lake & yellow-brn	10	10
247	50 c. chocolate, blue-green, lake & yelllow-brn	40	75

1966 (20 Sept). *Inauguration of W.H.O. Headquarters, Geneva. As Nos. 178/9 of Antigua.*

248	8 c. black, yellow-green and light blue	15	10
249	25 c. black, light purple and yellow-brown	30	20

1966 (1 Dec). *20th Anniv of U.N.E.S.C.O. As Nos. 196/8 of Antigua.*

250	2 c. slate-violet, red, yellow and orange	10	10
251	15 c. orange-yellow, violet and deep olive	15	10
252	50 c. black, bright purple and orange	30	80
250/2	*Set of 3*	45	90

ASSOCIATED STATEHOOD

ASSOCIATED STATEHOOD 1967	EXPO 67 MONTREAL CANADA	1c
(67)	(68)	

1967 (3 Mar). *Statehood. Nos. 232/3, 236 and 240 optd with T 67, in silver*

253	2 c. Bougainvillea	10	15
254	3 c. Flamboyant plant	10	10
255	8 c. Annandale Falls	15	10
256	25 c. St. George's	15	15
253/6	*Set of 4*	30	30

1967 (June). *World Fair, Montreal. Nos. 232, 237, 239 and 243/4 surch as T 68 or optd with "Expo" emblem only.*

257	1 c. on 15 c. Nutmeg	10	20
	a. Surch and opt albino	14·00	
258	2 c. Bougainvillea	10	20
259	3 c. on 10 c. Cocoa pods	10	20
	w. Wmk inverted	7·00	
260	$1 Type 53	30	25
261	$2 Type 54	45	30
257/61	*Set of 5*	70	1·00

COVER PRICES

Cover factors are quoted at the beginning of each country for most issues to 1945. An explanation of the system can be found on page x. The factors quoted do not, however, apply to philatelic covers.

ASSOCIATED STATEHOOD

(69)   70 Kennedy and Local Flower

1967 (Oct). *Statehood. Nos. 231/45 optd with T 69.*

262	1 c. Type 52	10	10
263	2 c. Bougainvillea	10	10
264	3 c. Flamboyant plant	10	10
265	5 c. Levera beach	10	10
266	6 c. Carenage, St. George's	10	10
267	8 c. Annandale Falls	10	10
268	10 c. Cocoa pods	10	10
269	12 c. Inner Harbour	15	10
270	15 c. Nutmeg	10	10
271	25 c. St. George's	20	10
272	35 c. Grand Anse beach	55	10
273	50 c. Bananas	70	20
274	$1 Type 53	80	60
275	$2 Type 54	1·25	3·50
276	$3 Type 55	2·25	3·50
262/76	*Set of 15*	5·50	8·00

See also No. 295.

(Des M. Shamir. Photo Harrison)

1968 (13 Jan). *50th Birth Anniv of President Kennedy. T 70 and similar horiz designs. Multicoloured. P 14½ × 14.*

277	1 c. Type 70	10	15
278	15 c. Type 70	10	10
279	25 c. Kennedy and strelitzia	10	10
280	35 c. Kennedy and roses	10	10
281	50 c. As 25 c.	15	20
282	$1 As 35 c.	25	60
277/82	*Set of 6*	55	90

73 Scout Bugler   76 "Near Antibes"

(Des K. Plowitz. Photo Govt Printer, Israel)

1968 (17 Feb). *World Scout Jamboree, Idaho. T 73 and similar vert designs. Multicoloured. P 13 × 13½.*

283	1 c. Type 73	10	10
284	2 c. Scouts camping	10	10
285	3 c. Lord Baden-Powell	10	10
286	35 c. Type 73	25	10
287	50 c. As 2 c.	35	20
288	$1 As 3 c.	50	55
283/8	*Set of 6*	1·10	80

(Des G. Vasarhelyi. Photo Harrison)

1968 (23 Mar). *Paintings by Sir Winston Churchill. T 76 and similar horiz designs. Multicoloured. P 14 × 14½.*

289	10 c. Type 76	10	10
290	12 c. "The Mediterranean"	15	10
291	15 c. "St. Jean Cap Ferratt"	15	10
292	25 c. Type 76	20	10
293	35 c. As 15 c.	25	10
294	50 c. Sir Winston painting	35	25
289/94	*Set of 6*	1·10	45

CHILDREN NEED MILK		CHILDREN NEED MILK
$5		
	2cts. + 3cts.	
		1c. + 3cts.
(80)	(81)	(82)

1968 (18 May). *No. 275 surch with T 80*

295	54	$5 on $2 multicoloured	1·25	2·25

1968 (22 July–19 Aug). *"Children Need Milk".*

(a) Nos. 244/5 surch locally as T 81 (22 July)

296	54	2 c. + 3 c. on $2 multicoloured	10	10
297	55	3 c. + 3 c. on $3 multicoloured	10	10
		a. Surch inverted	50·00	15·00
		b. Surch double	22·00	
		c. Surch double, one albino		

(b) Nos. 243/4 surch locally as T 82 (19 Aug)

298	53	1 c. + 3 c. on $1 multicoloured	10	40
		a. Surch on No. 274	70·00	70·00
		b. Surch double	35·00	
299	54	2 c. + 3 c. on $2 multicoloured	13·00	45·00
		a. Surch on No. 275	80·00	
296/9		*Set of 4*	13·00	45·00

83 Edith McGuire (U.S.A.)   86 Hibiscus

(Des M. Shamir. Photo Harrison)

1968 (24 Sept). *Olympic Games, Mexico. T 83 and similar square designs. P 12½.*

300	1 c. brown, black and blue	10	20
301	2 c. orange, brown, blue and lilac	10	20
	a. Orange (badge, etc.) omitted		
302	3 c. scarlet, brown and dull green	10	20
	a. Scarlet (rings, "MEXICO" etc.) omitted £650		
303	10 c. brown, black, blue and vermilion	15	20
304	50 c. brown, brown, blue and turquoise	55	75
305	60 c. scarlet, brown and red-orange	60	80
300/5	*Set of 6*	1·25	2·00

Designs:—2, 50 c. Arthur Wint (Jamaica); 3, 60 c. Ferreira da Silva (Brazil); 10 c. Type 83.

Nos. 300/2 and 303/5 were issued in separate composite sheets containing three strips of three, with three *se-tenant* labels showing Greek athlete (Nos. 300/2) or Discobolos (Nos. 303/5). (*Price for two sheets £6 mint, £8 used.*)

(Des G. Vasarhelyi (No. 314a), V. Whiteley (75 c.), M. Shamir (others). Litho Format (Nos. 314a and 317a). Photo Harrison (others))

1968 (Oct)–**71.** *Multicoloured designs as T 86. P 13½ (Nos. 314a and 317a), 13½ × 14½ (vert except No. 314a) or 14½ × 13½ (horiz except No. 317a).*

306	1 c. Type 86	10	10
307	2 c. Strelitzia	10	10
308	3 c. Bougainvillea (1.7.69)	10	10
309	5 c. Rock Hind (*horiz*) (4.2.69)	10	10
310	6 c. Sailfish	10	10
311	8 c. Red Snapper (*horiz*) (1.7.69)	10	30
312	10 c. Marine Toad (*horiz*) (4.2.69)	10	10
313	12 c. Turtle	15	10
314	15 c. Tree Boa (*horiz*)	90	60
314a	15 c. Thunbergia (1970)	4·00	2·50
315	25 c. Greater Trinidadian Murine Opossum (4.2.69)	30	10
316	35 c. Nine-banded Armadillo (*horiz*) (1.7.69)	35	10
317	50 c. Mona Monkey	45	25
317a	75 c. Yacht in St. George's Harbour (*horiz*) (9.10.71)	12·00	8·50
318	$1 Bananaquit	3·00	1·50
319	$2 Brown Pelican (4.2.69)	6·00	9·00
320	$3 Magnificent Frigate Bird	4·50	5·00
321	$5 Bare-eyed Thrush (1.7.69)	8·00	16·00
306/21	*Set of 18*	35·00	40·00

Nos. 314a, 317a and the dollar values are larger—29×45½, 44×28½ and 25½×48 mm respectively.

No. 317a exists imperforate from stock dispersed by the liquidator of Format International Security Printers Ltd.

102 Kidney   106 "The Adoration of the
Transplant   Kings" (Veronese)

(Des M. Shamir. Litho B.W.)

1968 (25 Nov). *20th Anniv of World Health Organization. T 102 and similar vert designs. Multicoloured. P 13 × 13½.*

322	5 c. Type 102	20	10
323	25 c. Heart transplant	30	10
324	35 c. Lung transplant	30	10
325	50 c. Eye transplant	35	50
322/5	*Set of 4*	1·10	60

(Photo Harrison)

1968 (3 Dec). *Christmas. T 106 and similar square designs. P 12½.*

326	5 c. multicoloured	10	10
327	15 c. multicoloured	10	10
328	35 c. multicoloured	10	10
329	$1 multicoloured	30	40
326/9	*Set of 4*	40	45

Designs:—15 c. "Madonna and Child with Sts. John and Catherine" (Titian); 35 c. "Adoration of the Kings" (Botticelli); $1 "A Warrior Adoring" (Catena).

VISIT CARIFTA EXPO '69
April 5-30

(110)

1969 (Feb). *Caribbean Free Trade Area Exhibition. Nos. 300/5 surch in red as T 110.*

330	5 c. on 1 c. brown, black and blue	10	10
	a. Surch double		
331	8 c. on 2 c. orange, brown, blue and lilac	10	10
	a. Surch double		
332	25 c. on 3 c. scarlet, brown and dull green	10	10
	a. Surch double		
333	35 c. on 10 c. brown, black, blue and vermilion	10	10
334	$1 on 50 c. orange, brown, blue & turquoise	20	30
335	$2 on 60 c. scarlet, brown and red-orange	35	60
	a. Scarlet (rings, "MEXICO" etc) omitted	†	—
330/5		65	95

The centre of the composite sheets is also overprinted with a commemorative inscription publicising CARIFTA EXPO 1969 (*Price for two sheets £11 mint or used*).

111 Dame Hylda Bynoe (Governor)
and Island Scene

(Des and litho D.L.R.)

1969 (1 May). *Carifta Expo 1969. T 111 and similar horiz designs. Multicoloured. P 13 × 13½.*

336	5 c. Type 111	10	10
337	15 c. Premier E. M. Gairy and Island scene	10	10
338	50 c. Type 111	10	25
339	60 c. Emblems of 1958 and 1967 World's Fairs	10	40
336/9	*Set of 4*	30	70

114 Dame Hylda Bynoe   115 "Balshazzar's Feast"
(Rembrandt)

(Photo Enschedé)

1969 (8 June). *Human Rights Year. T 114/15 and similar multi-coloured design. P 12½ × 13 ($1) or 13 × 12½ (others).*

340	5 c. Type 114	10	10
341	25 c. Dr. Martin Luther King (*vert*)	15	10
342	35 c. Type 114	15	10
343	$1 Type 115	30	45
340/3	*Set of 4*	55	55

117 Batsman and Wicket-keeper

(Des M. Shamir and L. W. Denyer. Photo Harrison)

1969 (1 Aug). *Cricket. T 117 and similar horiz designs. P 14 × 14½.*

344	3 c. yellow, brown and ultramarine	25	1·00
	a. Yellow (caps and wicket) omitted	£400	
345	10 c. multicoloured	30	40
346	25 c. brown, ochre and myrtle-green	60	85
347	35 c. multicoloured	80	90
344/7	*Set of 4*	1·75	2·75

Designs:—10 c. Batsman playing defensive stroke; 25 c. Batsman sweeping ball; 35 c. Batsman playing on-drive.

Nos. 344/7 were each issued in small sheets of 9 (3 × 3) with decorative borders.

129 Astronaut handling Moon Rock

(Des G. Vasarhelyi. Photo)

1969 (24 Sept). *First Man on the Moon. T 129 and similar multi-coloured designs. P 13½ (½ c.) or 12½ (others).*

348	½ c. As Type 129 but larger (56 × 35 *mm*)	10	10
349	1 c. Moon rocket and moon	10	10
350	2 c. Module landing	10	10
351	3 c. Declaration left on moon	10	10
352	8 c. Module leaving rocket	10	10
353	25 c. Rocket lifting-off (*vert*)	20	10
354	35 c. Spacecraft in orbit (*vert*)	20	10
355	50 c. Capsule with parachutes (*vert*)	30	30
356	$1 Type 129	45	1·00
348/56	*Set of 9*	1·25	1·60
MS357	115 × 90 mm. Nos. 351 and 356. Imperf	1·00	2·50

---

130 Gandhi

(Des A. Robledo. Litho B.W.)

1969 (8 Oct). *Birth Centenary of Mahatma Gandhi. T 130 and similar designs. P 11½.*

358	130	6 c. multicoloured	15	10
359	—	15 c. multicoloured	20	10
360	—	25 c. multicoloured	25	10
361	—	$1 multicoloured	50	60
358/61		*Set of 4*	1·00	75
MS362	155 × 122 mm. Nos. 358/61. Imperf		2·25	3·50

Designs: *Vert*—15 c. Gandhi standing; 25 c. Gandhi walking. *Horiz*—$1 Head of Gandhi.

═══1969

(134)   135 "Blackbeard"
(Edward Teach)

1969 (23 Dec). *Christmas. Nos. 326/9 surch with T 134 in black (2 c.) or optd with new date only in silver (others).*

363	2 c. on 15 c. multicoloured	10	30
	a. Surch inverted	40·00	
364	5 c. multicoloured	10	10
	a. Opt double	40·00	
365	35 c. multicoloured	20	10
	a. Opt inverted	40·00	
	b. Horiz pair, one with opt omitted	£200	
	c. Opt double, one vertical	45·00	
366	$1 multicoloured	80	1·75
	a. Opt inverted	40·00	
363/6	*Set of 4*	1·00	2·00

(Des K. Plowitz. Recess B.W.)

1970 (2 Feb). *Pirates. T 135 and similar vert designs. P 13½.*

367	15 c. black	35	10
368	25 c. dull green	50	10
369	50 c. lilac	90	20
370	$1 carmine	1·50	75
367/70	*Set of 4*	3·00	1·00

Designs:—25 c. Anne Bonney; 50 c. Jean Lafitte; $1 Mary Read.

5c **5c**

(139)   (140)

1970 (18 Mar). *No. 348 surch with T 139.*

371	5 c. on ½ c. multicoloured	10	10
	a. Surch double	25·00	
	b. Surch with T 140	70	70
	ba. Surch double, one inverted	40·00	

141 "The Last Supper" (detail, 142
Del Sarto)

(Des and litho B.W.)

1970 (13 Apr). *Easter. Paintings. T 141/2 and similar vert designs. Multicoloured. P 11½.*

372	5 c. ⎱ Type 141/2	10	15
373	5 c. ⎰	10	15
374	15 c. ⎱ "Christ crowned with Thorns" (detail,	15	25
375	15 c. ⎰ Van Dyck)	15	25
376	25 c. ⎱ "The Passion of Christ" (detail,	20	30
377	25 c. ⎰ Memling)	20	30
378	60 c. ⎱ "Christ in the Tomb" (detail, Rubens)	30	55
379	60 c. ⎰	30	55
372/9	*Set of 8*	1·25	2·25
MS380	120 × 140 mm. Nos. 376/9	75	1·25

Nos. 372/9 were issued with each design spread over two se-tenant stamps of the same denomination.

149 Girl with Kittens in Pram

(Des A. Robledo. Litho Questa)

1970 (27 May). *Birth Bicentenary of William Wordsworth (poet).
"Children and Pets". T* **149** *and similar horiz designs. Multicoloured.* P 11.

381	5 c. Type 149	15	15
382	15 c. Girl with puppy and kitten	20	15
383	30 c. Boy with fishing rod and cat	25	30
384	60 c. Boys and girls with cats and dogs	40	1·25
381/4	*Set of 4*	90	1·60
MS385	Two sheets each 114 × 126 mm. Nos. 381, 383 and Nos. 382, 384. Imperf	1·25	2·00

153 Parliament of India

(Des G. Vasarhelyi. Litho Questa)

1970 (15 June). *Seventh Regional Conference of Commonwealth
Parliamentary Association. T* **153** *and similar horiz designs.
Multicoloured.* P 14.

386	5 c. Type 153	10	10
387	25 c. Parliament of Great Britain, Westminster	10	10
388	50 c. Parliament of Canada	20	15
389	60 c. Parliament of Grenada	20	15
386/9	*Set of 4*	50	35
MS390	126 × 90 mm. Nos. 386/9	50	90

157 Tower of the Sun

(Litho Kyodo Printing Co, Tokyo)

1970 (8 Aug). *World Fair, Osaka. T* **157** *and similar multicoloured designs.* P 13.

391	1 c. Type 157	10	10
392	2 c. Livelihood and Industry Pavilion (*horiz*)	10	10
393	3 c. Flower painting, 1634	10	10
394	10 c. "Adam and Eve" (Tintoretto) (*horiz*)	15	10
395	25 c. O.E.C.D. (Organisation for Economic Co-operation and Development) Pavilion (*horiz*)	20	10
396	50 c. San Francisco Pavilion	45	1·25
391/6	*Set of 6*	90	1·50
MS397	121 × 91 mm. $1 Japanese Pavilion (56 × 34 mm)	55	1·50

164 Roosevelt and "Raising U.S. Flag on Iwo Jima"

(Litho Questa)

1970 (3 Sept). *25th Anniv of Ending of World War II. T* **164** *and
similar horiz designs. Multicoloured.* P 11.

398	½ c. Type 164	10	40
399	5 c. Zhukov and "Fall of Berlin"	70	30
400	15 c. Churchill and "Evacuation at Dunkirk"	1·50	45
401	25 c. De Gaulle and "Liberation of Paris"	1·50	45
402	50 c. Eisenhower and "D-Day Landing"	2·00	1·50
403	60 c. Montgomery and "Battle of Alamein"	2·00	3·00
398/403	*Set of 6*	7·00	5·50
MS404	163 × 113 mm. Nos. 398, 400, 402/3	3·25	7·00
	a. Brown (panel) on 60 c. value omitted	£700	

*PHILYMPIA
LONDON 1970*
(169)

170 U.P.U. Emblem, Building and
Transport

1970 (18 Sept). *"Philympia 1970" Stamp Exhibition, London.*
Nos. 353/6 *optd with T* **169**

405	25 c. Rocket lifting-off	10	10
	a. Albino opt	4·50	
	b. Opt inverted	15·00	
406	35 c. Spacecraft in orbit	10	10
	a. Opt inverted	40·00	
	b. Opt double, one albino, one inverted		
407	50 c. Capsule with parachutes	15	15
	a. Albino opt	3·50	
408	$1 Type 129 (Sil.) (optd vert upwards)	20	30
	a. Albino opt	6·50	
405/8	*Set of 4*	40	50

The miniature sheet was also overprinted but we understand
that only 300 of these were put on sale in Grenada.

(Litho Questa)

1970 (17 Oct). *New U.P.U. Headquarters Building. T* **170** *and
similar multicoloured designs.* P 14.

409	15 c. Type 170	35	10
410	25 c. As Type 170, but modern transport	35	10
411	50 c. Sir Rowland Hill and U.P.U. Building	35	30
412	$1 Abraham Lincoln and U.P.U. Building	40	1·50
409/12	*Set of 4*	1·25	1·75
MS413	79 × 85 mm. Nos. 411/12	90	3·00

The 50 c. and $1 are both vertical designs.

171 "The Madonna of the   172 19th-Century Nursing
Goldfinch" (Tiepolo)

(Des G. Vasarhelyi. Litho Questa)

1970 (5 Dec). *Christmas. T* **171** *and similar vert designs. Multicoloured.* P 13½.

414	½ c. Type 171	10	10
415	½ c. "The Virgin and Child with St. Peter and St. Paul" (Bouts)	10	10
416	½ c. "The Virgin and Child" (Bellini)	10	10
417	2 c. "The Madonna of the Basket" (Correggio)	10	10
418	3 c. Type 171	10	10
419	35 c. As No. 415	20	10
420	50 c. As 2 c.	30	35
421	$1 As No. 416	50	1·50
414/21	*Set of 8*	1·10	2·00
MS422	102 × 87 mm. Nos. 420/1	1·25	3·00

(Des G. Vasarhelyi. Litho Questa)

1970 (12 Dec). *Centenary of British Red Cross. T* **172** *and similar
horiz designs. Multicoloured.* P 14½ × 14.

423	5 c. Type 172	20	10
424	15 c. Military Ambulance, 1918	25	10
425	25 c. First-Aid Post, 1941	35	10
426	60 c. Red Cross Transport, 1970	90	80
423/6	*Set of 4*	1·50	95
MS427	113 × 82 mm. Nos. 423/6	2·00	1·60
	a. Error. Imperf	25·00	

173 John Dewey and Art Lesson

(Des G. Vasarhelyi. Litho Questa)

1971 (1 May). *International Education Year (1970). T* **173** *and
similar horiz designs. Multicoloured.* P 13½.

428	5 c. Type 173	10	10
429	10 c. Jean-Jacques Rousseau and "Alpha-betisation"	15	10
430	50 c. Maimonides and laboratory	50	15
431	$1 Bertrand Russell and mathematics class	95	40
428/31	*Set of 4*	1·50	55
MS432	90 × 98 mm. Nos. 430/1	1·00	2·00

NEW INFORMATION

The editor is always interested to correspond with
people who have new information that will
improve or correct the Catalogue.

174 Jennifer Hosten and   176 "Napolean reviewing
outline of Grenada   the Guard" (E. Detaille)

175 French and Canadian Scouts

(Des local artist; adapted G. Drummond. Litho Format)

1971 (1 June). *Winner of "Miss World" Competition (1970).*
P 13½.

433	174	5 c. multicoloured	10	10
434		10 c. multicoloured	10	10
435		15 c. multicoloured	15	10
436		25 c. multicoloured	15	10
437		35 c. multicoloured	15	10
438		50 c. multicoloured	35	55
433/8		*Set of 6*	80	75
MS439	92 × 89 mm. 174 50 c. multicoloured. Printed on silk. Imperf		75	1·75

(Litho Format)

1971 (11 Sept). *13th World Scout Jamboree, Asagiri, Japan.
T* **175** *and similar horiz designs. Multicoloured.* P 11.

440	5 c. Type 175	10	10
441	35 c. German and American scouts	30	25
442	50 c. Australian and Japanese scouts	40	50
443	75 c. Grenada and British scouts	50	75
440/3	*Set of 4*	1·10	1·40
MS444	101 × 114 mm. Nos. 442/3	1·25	2·50

(Des G. Vasarhelyi. Litho Questa)

1971 (9 Oct). *150th Death Anniversary of Napolean Bonaparte.
T* **176** *and similar vert designs showing paintings. Multicoloured.* P 13½.

445	5 c. Type 176	15	15
446	15 c. "Napoleon before Madrid" (Vernet)	25	15
447	35 c. "Napoleon crossing Mt St. Bernard" (David)	30	15
448	$2 "Napoleon in his Study" (David)	75	1·50
445/8	*Set of 4*	1·25	1·75
MS449	101 × 76 mm. No. 447. Imperf	1·25	1·60

177 1d. Stamp of 1861 and Badge of Grenada

(Des R. Granger Barrett. Litho Questa)

1971 (6 Nov). *110th Anniv of the Postal Service. T* **177** *and similar
horiz designs. Multicoloured.* W w 12 (*sideways**). P 11.

450	5 c. Type 177	20	20
451	15 c. 6d. stamp of 1861 and Queen Elizabeth II	25	15
452	35 c. 1d. and 6d. stamps of 1861 and badge of Grenada	50	20
453	50 c. Scroll and 1d. stamp of 1861	65	1·75
450/3	*Set of 4*	1·40	2·10
MS454	96 × 114 mm. Nos. 452/3	90	1·00

* This issue is printed on thick paper and consequently the
watermark is very faint.

178 Apollo Splashdown

(Des R. Granger Barrett. Litho Questa)

1971 (13 Nov). *Apollo Moon Exploration Series.* T **178** *and similar multicoloured designs.* P 11.

455	1 c.	Type **178**		10	10
456	2 c.	Recovery of Apollo 13		10	10
457	3 c.	Separation of Lunar Module from Apollo 14		10	10
458	10 c.	Shepard and Mitchell taking samples of moon rock		25	10
459	25 c.	Moon Buggy		75	20
460	$1	Apollo 15 blast-off (*vert*)		2·00	3·25
455/60			Set of 6	2·75	3·25
MS461	77 × 108 mm. 50 c. as $1			1·40	1·50

179 67th Regiment of Foot, 1787   **180** "The Adoration of the Kings" (Memling)

(Des G. Vasarhelyi. Litho Format)

1971 (11 Dec). *Military Uniforms.* T **179** *and similar vert designs. Multicoloured.* P 13½.

462	½ c.	Type **179**		10	10
463	1 c.	45th Regiment of Foot, 1792		10	10
464	2 c.	29th Regiment of Foot, 1794		10	10
465	10 c.	9th Regiment of Foot, 1801		45	10
466	25 c.	2nd Regiment of Foot, 1815		85	20
467	$1	70th Regiment of Foot, 1764		2·50	2·00
462/7			Set of 6	3·50	2·25
MS468	108 × 99 mm. Nos. 466/7. P 15			2·75	3·25

(Des G. Vasarhelyi. Litho Questa)

1972 (15 Jan). *Christmas* (1971). T **180** *and similar vert designs. Multicoloured.* P 14 × 13½.

469	15 c.	Type **180**		15	10
470	25 c.	"Madonna and Child" (Michelangelo)		20	10
471	35 c.	"Madonna and Child" (Murillo)		25	10
472	50 c.	"The Virgin with the Apple" (Memling)		30	15
469/72			Set of 4	80	1·40
MS473	105 × 80 mm. $1 "The Adoration of the Kings" (Mostaert)			75	1·25

183 King Arthur

(Litho Questa)

1972 (4 Mar). *U.N.I.C.E.F.* T **183** *and similar multicoloured designs.* P 14.

482	½ c.	Type **183**		10	10
483	1 c.	Robin Hood		10	10
484	2 c.	Robinson Crusoe (*vert*)		10	10
485	25 c.	Type **183**		10	10
486	50 c.	As No. 483		25	40

WINTER OLYMPICS FEB. 3-13, 1972 SAPPORO, JAPAN   VOTE FEB. 28 1972

(181)   (182)

1972 (3 Feb). *Winter Olympic Games, Sapporo, Japan. Nos. 462/4 and* MS**468** *surch or optd only* (MS**475**).

(a) Postage. As T **181**

474	$2 on 2 c. multicoloured			50	90
MS475	108 × 99 mm. Nos. 466/7 (R.)			1·00	1·25

(b) Air. As T **181**, *but additionally surch* "AIR MAIL"

476	35 c. on ½ c. multicoloured			15	25
477	50 c. on 1 c. multicoloured			15	35

1972 (25 Feb). *General Election. Nos. 307/8, 310 and 315 optd with T* **182**.

478	2 c. multicoloured			10	10
	b. Stop after "1972" (R.1/2, 1/10)			6·00	
479	3 c. multicoloured			10	10
	a. Opt inverted			95·00	
	b. Stop after "1972" (R.1/2, 1/10)			6·00	
480	6 c. multicoloured			10	15
	b. Stop after "1972" (R.1/2, 1/10)			6·00	
481	25 c. multicoloured			15	30
	b. Stop after "1972" (R.1/2, 1/10)			7·50	
478/81			Set of 4	40	60

487	75 c. As No. 484			30	1·00
488	$1 Mary and her little lamb (*vert*)			45	1·25
482/8			Set of 7	1·10	2·50
MS489	65 × 98 mm. No. 488			55	80

INTERPEX 1972   12¢   AIR MAIL

(184)   (185)   (186)

1972 (17 Mar). *"Interpex" Stamp Exhibition, New York. Nos. 433/9 optd with T* **184**.

490	**174**	5 c. multicoloured		10	10
491		10 c. multicoloured		10	10
492		15 c. multicoloured		10	10
493		25 c. multicoloured		10	10
494		35 c. multicoloured		15	15
		a. Opt double			
495		50 c. multicoloured		25	30
		a. Vert pair, top stamp with opt omitted		£100	
490/5			Set of 6	60	65
MS496	92×89 mm. **174** 50 c. multicoloured. Printed on silk. Imperf			6·00	11·00

1972 (20 Apr). *Nos. 306/8 surch with T* **185**, *and No. 433 surch similarly, but with obliterating bars under* "12c".

497	12 c. on 1 c. Type **88**			40	55
498	12 c. on 2 c. Strelitzia			40	55
499	12 c. on 3 c. Bougainvillea			40	55
	a. Horiz pair, left stamp with surch omitted				
500	12 c. on 5 c. Type **174**			40	55
497/500			Set of 4	1·40	2·00

1972. *Air.* (a) *Nos. 306/12, 314a/17 and 318/21 optd as T* **186** *or surch in addition* (2 May)

501	5 c. Rock Hind			10	10
	a. Opt double			28·00	
502	8 c. Snapper			15	10
	a. Opt double			60·00	
503	10 c. Marine Toad			15	10
	a. Opt double			40·00	
504	15 c. Thunbergia			30	10
505	25 c. Greater Trinidadian Murine Opossum			35	20
	a. Horiz pair, one without opt			£130	
506	30 c. on 1 c. Type **86**			40	25
507	35 c. Nine-banded Armadillo			40	25
508	40 c. on 2 c. Strelitzia			50	25
509	45 c. on 3 c. Bougainvillea			55	35
510	50 c. Mona Monkey			55	35
	a. Horiz pair, one without opt			90·00	
	b. Opt double			£180	
511	60 c. on 5 c. Rock Hind			60	40
512	70 c. on 6 c. Sailfish			70	50
513	$1 Bananaquit			4·50	60
514	$1·35 on 8 c. Snapper			3·25	1·75
515	$2 Brown Pelican			6·50	5·00
516	$3 Magnificent Frigate Bird			7·00	5·00
517	$5 Bare-eyed Thrush			8·50	11·00

(b) Nos. 440/3 optd as T **186** (5 June)

518	**175**	5 c. multicoloured		75	10
519	—	35 c. multicoloured		2·00	30
520	—	50 c. multicoloured		2·25	45
521	—	75 c. multicoloured		3·00	1·00
501/21			Set of 21	38·00	25·00

187 Yachting

(Litho Format)

1972 (8 Sept) *Olympic Games, Munich.* T **187** *and similar multicoloured designs.* P 14. (a) *Postage.*

522	½ c.	Type **187**		10	10
523	1 c.	Show-jumping		10	10
524	2 c.	Running (*vert*)		10	10
525	35 c.	As 2 c.		30	10
526	50 c.	As 1 c.		40	40

(b) Air

527	25 c. Boxing			25	10
528	$1 As 25 c.			65	85
522/8			Set of 7	1·50	1·40
MS529	82 × 85 mm. 60 c. as 25 c. and 70 c. as 1 c.			1·00	1·40

188 Badge of Grenada and Nutmegs

(Des (from photographs by D. Groves) and photo Harrison)

1972 (20 Nov). *Royal Silver Wedding. Multicoloured; background colour given.* W w 12. P 14 × 14½.

530	**188**	8 c. olive-brown		10	10
531		$1 ultramarine		45	55

---

189 Boy Scout Saluting   **190** Madonna and Child

(Des R. Granger Barrett. Litho Questa)

1972 (2 Dec). *65th Anniv of Boy Scouts.* T **189** *and similar horiz designs. Multicoloured.* P 14. (a) *Postage.*

532	½ c.	Type **189**		10	10
533	1 c.	Scouts knotting ropes		10	10
534	2 c.	Scouts shaking hands		10	10
535	3 c.	Lord Baden-Powell		10	10
536	75 c.	As 2 c.		85	2·75
537	$1	As 3 c.		90	2·75

(b) Air

538	25 c.	Type **189**		50	20
539	35 c.	As 1 c.		70	20
532/9			Set of 8	2·75	5·50
MS540	87 × 88 mm. 60 c. as 3 c., and 70 c. as 2 c.			1·50	1·50

(Des V. Whiteley. Litho Format)

1972 (9 Dec). *Christmas.* T **190** *and similar vert designs. Multicoloured.* P 13½.

541	1 c.	Type **190**		10	10
542	3 c.	The Three Kings		10	10
543	5 c.	The Nativity		10	10
544	25 c.	Type **190**		15	10
545	35 c.	As 3 c.		15	10
546	$1	As 5 c.		40	75
541/6			Set of 6	75	1·00
MS547	102 × 76 mm. 60 c. Type **190** and 70 c. as 3 c. P 15			60	80

191 Greater Flamingoes

(Des M. and G. Shamir. Litho Questa)

1973 (26 Jan). *National Zoo.* T **191** *and similar horiz designs. Multicoloured.* P 14½.

548	25 c.	Type **191**		80	35
549	35 c.	Brazilian Tapir		80	35
550	60 c.	Blue and Yellow Macaw, and Scarlet Macaw		1·50	1·50
551	70 c.	Ocelot		1·50	1·75
548/51			Set of 4	4·25	3·50

192 Class II Racing Yacht

(Des V. Whiteley. Litho Format)

1973 (26 Feb). *Yachting.* T **192** *and similar horiz designs. Multicoloured.* P 13½.

552	25 c.	Type **192**		25	10
553	35 c.	Harbour, St George's		30	10
554	60 c.	Yacht *Bloodhound*		45	65
555	70 c.	St. George's		50	75
552/5			Set of 4	1·40	1·40

193 Helios (Greek god) and Earth orbiting the Sun

(Des G. Vasarhelyi. Litho Format)

1973 (6 July). *I.M.O./W.M.O. Centenary.* T **193** *and similar horiz designs showing Greek Gods. Multicoloured.* P 13½.

556	½ c.	Type **193**		10	10
557	1 c.	Poseidon and "Normad" storm detector		10	10
558	2 c.	Zeus and radarscope		10	10
559	3 c.	Iris and weather balloon		10	10
560	35 c.	Hermes and "ATS-3" satellite		30	10
561	50 c.	Zephyrus and diagram of pressure zones		40	30
562	75 c.	Demeter and space photo		50	60
563	$1	Selene and rainfall diagram		50	1·00
556/63			Set of 8	1·50	2·00
MS564	123 × 92 mm. $2 Computer weather map (42 × 31 mm). P 13½.			90	1·25

½ c GRENADA

194 Racing Class Yachts

195 Ignatius Semmelweis (obstetrician)

(Des G. Drummond. Litho Format)

1973 (3 Aug). *Carriacou Regatta. T* **194** *and similar horiz designs. Multicoloured. P* 13½.

565	½ c. Type **194**		10	10
566	1 c. Cruising Class Yacht		10	10
567	2 c. Open-decked sloops		10	10
568	35 c. *Mermaid* (sloop)		30	10
569	50 c. St. George's Harbour		35	25
570	75 c. Map of Carriacou		40	55
571	$1 Boat-building		55	70
565/71		*Set of* 7	1·40	1·40
MS572	109 × 88 mm. $2 End of Race		90	1·75

(Des G. Vasarhelyi. Litho Format)

1973 (17 Sept). *25th Anniv of W.H.O. T* **195** *and similar vert designs. Multicoloured. P* 14½.

573	½ c. Type **195**		10	10
574	1 c. Louis Pasteur		10	10
575	2 c. Edward Jenner		10	10
576	3 c. Sigmund Freud		10	10
577	25 c. Emil Von Behring (bacteriologist)		65	10
578	35 c. Carl Jung		75	20
579	50 c. Charles Calmette (bacteriologist)		1·10	80
580	$1 William Harvey		1·40	2·25
573/80		*Set of* 8	3·50	4·00
MS581	105 × 80 mm. $2 Marie Curie		1·60	1·60

25 c GRENADA CHRISTMAS 1973 ½ c

196 Princess Anne and Capt. Mark Phillips

197 "Virgin and Child" (Maratti)

(Des G. Drummond. Litho Format)

1973 (14 Nov). *Royal Wedding. P* 13½.

582	**196** 25 c. multicoloured		10	10
583	$2 multicoloured		30	45
MS584	79 × 100 mm. 75 c. and $1 as Nos. 582/3		40	30

Nos. 582/3 were each issued in small sheets of five stamps and one stamp-size label.

(Litho Format)

1973 (10 Dec). *Christmas. T* **197** *and similar vert designs. Multicoloured. P* 14½.

585	½ c. Type **197**		10	10
586	1 c. "Madonna and Child" (Crivelli)		10	10
587	2 c. "Virgin and Child with Two Angels" (Verrocchio)		10	10
588	3 c. "Adoration of the Shepherds" (Roberti)		10	10
589	25 c. "The Holy Family with the Infant Baptist" (Barocci)		15	10
590	35 c. "The Holy Family" (Bronzino)		15	10
591	75 c. "Mystic Nativity" (Botticelli)		20	20
592	$1 "Adoration of the Kings" (Geertgen)		25	30
585/92		*Set of* 8	75	60
MS593	89 × 89 mm. $2 "Adoration of the Kings" (Mostaert) (30 × 45 *mm*). P 13½		85	1·10

INDEPENDENT

10 CENTS GRENADA
INDEPENDENCE 7TH FEB. 1974

(198)

199 Creative Arts Theatre, Jamaica Campus

1974 (7 Feb). *Independence. Nos.* 306/9, 311/13, 315/16 *and* 317a/21 *optd as T* **198**.

594	1 c. Hibiscus		10	10
595	2 c. Strelitzia		10	10
596	3 c. Bougainvillea		10	10
597	5 c. Rock Hind		10	10
598	8 c. Snapper		10	10
599	10 c. Marine Toad		20	15
600	12 c. Turtle		20	15
601	25 c. Greater Trinidadian Murine Opossum		45	35
602	35 c. Nine-banded Armadillo		75	50
603	75 c. Yacht in St. George's Harbour		2·00	1·25
604	$1 Bananaquit		3·75	1·50
605	$2 Brown Pelican		6·00	6·00
606	$3 Magnificent Frigate Bird		8·00	7·50
607	$5 Bare-eyed Thrush		12·00	15·00
594/607		*Set of* 14	30·00	29·00

1974 (10 Apr). *25th Anniv of University of West Indies. T* **199** *and similar multicoloured designs. P* 13½ × 14.

608	10 c. Type **199**		10	10
609	25 c. Marryshow House		10	10
610	50 c. Chapel, Jamaica Campus (*vert*)		20	10
611	$1 University arms (*vert*)		30	30
608/11		*Set of* 4	55	50
MS612	69 × 86 mm. $2 as No. 611		50	90

INDEPENDENCE 1974 3 c

½ c WEST GERMANY · CHILE Grenada

200 Nutmeg Pods and Scarlet Mace

201 Footballers (West Germany v Chile)

(Des G. Drummond. Litho Format)

1974 (19 Aug). *Independence. T* **200** *and similar vert designs. Multicoloured. P* 13½.

613	3 c. Type **200**		10	10
614	8 c. Map of Grenada		10	10
615	25 c. Prime Minister Eric Gairy		15	10
616	35 c. Grand Anse Beach and flag		15	10
617	$1 Coat of arms		35	40
613/17		*Set of* 5	70	60
MS618	91 × 125 mm. $2 as $1		55	90

(Des G. Vasarhelyi. Litho Format)

1974 (3 Sept). *World Cup Football Championships, West Germany. T* **201** *and similar multicoloured designs showing footballers of the countries given. P* 14½.

619	½ c. Type **201**		10	10
620	1 c. East Germany v Australia		10	10
621	2 c. Yugoslavia v Brazil		10	10
622	10 c. Scotland v Zaire		10	10
623	25 c. Netherlands v Uruguay		15	10
624	50 c. Sweden v Bulgaria		20	10
625	75 c. Italy v Haiti		35	15
626	$1 Poland v Argentina		50	25
619/26		*Set of* 8	1·25	60
MS627	114 × 76 mm. $2 Country flags. P 13		90	1·75

GRENADA
202 Early U.S. Mail-trains and Concorde

(Des G. Vasarhelyi. Litho Format)

1974 (8 Oct). *Centenary of Universal Postal Union. T* **202** *and similar horiz designs. Multicoloured. P* 14½.

628	½ c. Type **202**		10	10
629	1 c. *Caesar* (snow) (1839) and Westland Wessex HU Mk 5 helicopter		10	10
630	2 c. Airmail transport		10	10
631	8 c. Pigeon post (1480) and telephone dial		15	10
632	15 c. 18th-century bellman and tracking antenna		30	10
633	25 c. Messenger (1450) and satellite		35	10
634	35 c. French pillar-box (1850) and mail-boat		50	10
635	$1 18th-century German postman and British Advanced Passenger Train		1·50	85
628/35		*Set of* 8	2·50	1·00
MS636	105 × 66 mm. $2 St. Gotthard mail-coach (1735). P 13		1·00	1·75

35 CENTS GRENADA 35
CENTENARY OF THE BIRTH OF SIR WINSTON CHURCHILL 1874 1974

CHRISTMAS 1974
GRENADA ½ c

203 Sir Winston Churchill

204 "Madonna and Child of the Eucharist" (Botticelli)

(Des G. Vasarhelyi. Litho Format)

1974 (28 Oct). *Birth Centenary of Sir Winston Churchill. T* **203** *and similar portrait design. P* 13½.

637	**203** 35 c. multicoloured		15	10
638	$2 multicoloured		45	50
MS639	129 × 96 mm. 75 c. as 35 c. and $1 as $2		75	75

(Des. M. Shamir. Litho Format)

1974 (18 Nov). *Christmas. T* **204** *and similar vert designs, showing "The Madonna and Child" by the artists given. Multicoloured. P* 14½.

640	½ c. Type **204**		10	10
641	1 c. Niccolo di Pietro		10	10
642	2 c. Van der Weyden		10	10

643	3 c. Bastiani		10	10
644	10 c. Giovanni		10	10
645	25 c. Van der Weyden		20	10
646	50 c. Botticelli		25	20
647	$1 Mantegna		35	50
640/7		*Set of* 8	85	80
MS648	117 × 96 mm. $2 as 1 c. P 13		75	90

GRENADA ½

205 Yachts, Point Saline

(Des G. Drummond. Litho Format)

1975 (13 Jan)–*78. Multicoloured designs as T* **205**. *P* 14½ (½ *to* 50 *c.*) *or* 13½ (75 *c. to* $10).

649	½ c. Type **205** (inscr "POINT SALINE")		10	55
	a. Inscr "POINT SALINES"		50·00	
650	1 c. Yacht club race		10	10
	a. Perf 13 (1978)		10	50
651	2 c. Carenage taxi		10	10
	a. Perf 13 (1978)		10	50
652	3 c. Large working boats		10	10
	a. Perf 13 (1978)		10	30
653	5 c. Deep-water dock		20	10
	a. Perf 13 (1978)		10	15
654	6 c. Cocoa beans in drying trays		10	10
	a. Perf 13 (1978)		10	30
655	8 c. Nutmegs		75	10
656	10 c. Rum distillery, River Antoine Estate, c 1785		10	10
	a. Perf 13 (1978)		15	40
657	12 c. Cocoa tree		30	10
658	15 c. Fisherman at Fontenoy		10	10
	a. Perf 13 (1978)		15	45
659	20 c. Parliament Building, St. George's		15	15
	a. Perf 13 (1978)		20	55
660	25 c. Fort George cannons		20	15
	a. Perf 13 (1978)		25	55
661	35 c. Pearls Airport		20	15
	a. Perf 13 (1978)			
662	50 c. General Post Office		25	30
	a. Perf 13 (1978)		45	90
663	75 c. Carib's Leap, Sauteurs Bay (45 × 28 *mm*) (22.1.75)		45	50
664	$1 Carenage, St. George's (45 × 28 *mm*) (22.1.75)		50	70
665	$2 St. George's Harbour by night (45 × 28 *mm*) (22.1.75)		65	1·50
666	$3 Grand Anse Beach (45 × 28 *mm*) (22.1.75)		75	2·00
667	$5 Canoe Bay and Black Bay from Point Saline Lighthouse (45 × 28 *mm*) (22.1.75)		90	3·00
668	$10 Sugar-loaf Island from Levera Beach (45 × 28 *mm*) (26.3.75)		2·50	6·50
649/68		*Set of* 20	7·00	13·00

No. 649a occurs on R. 6/1 and 7/1 from plate 1A and R. 10/5 from plate 1C. It is believed that the plate was originally produced showing the incorrect inscription ("POINT SALINES") on every stamp. Each position was then individually corrected, but those noted were missed.

Nos. 649/59, 661/4 and 666/8 exist imperforate from stock dispersed by the liquidator of Format International Security Printers Ltd.

BIG GAME FISHING
GRENADA

206 Sailfish

(Des V. Whiteley. Litho Format)

1975 (3 Feb). *Big Game Fishing. T* **206** *and similar horiz designs. Multicoloured. P* 14½.

669	½ c. Type **206**		10	10
670	1 c. Blue Marlin		10	10
671	2 c. White Marlin		10	10
672	10 c. Yellow-finned Tuna		10	10
673	25 c. Wahoo		25	10
674	50 c. Dolphin (fish)		40	15
675	70 c. Giant Grouper		60	20
676	$1 Great Barracuda		80	35
669/76		*Set of* 8	2·00	70
MS677	107 × 80 mm. $2 Short-finned Mako. P 13		1·25	1·25

GRENADA ADMITTED TO U.N. September 17th 1974

½ c GRENADA

GRENADA ½ c

207 Granadilla Barbadine

208 Dove, Grenada Flag and U.N. Emblem

(Des G. Vasarhelyi. Litho Format)

1975 (26 Feb). *Flowers. T 207 and similar horiz designs. Multicoloured. P 14½.*
678	½ c.	Type 207	..	10	10
679	1 c.	Bleeding Heart (Easter Lily)	..	10	10
680	2 c.	Poinsettia	..	10	10
681	3 c.	Cocoa flower	..	10	10
682	10 c.	Gladioli	..	10	10
683	25 c.	Redhead/Yellowhead	..	25	10
684	50 c.	Plumbago	..	45	15
685	$1	Orange flower	..	70	25
678/85			*Set of 8*	1·40	55
MS686	102 × 82 mm. $2 Barbados Gooseberry.				
	P 13	.. ..	..	1·10	1·25

(Des G. Drummond. Litho Format)

1975 (19 Mar). *Grenada's Admission to the U.N. (1974). T 208 and similar designs. Multicoloured. P 14½.*
687	½ c.	Type 208	..	10	10
688	1 c.	Grenada and U.N. flags	..	10	10
689	2 c.	Grenada coat of arms	..	10	10
690	35 c.	U.N. emblem over map of Grenada		15	10
691	50 c.	U.N. buildings and flags	..	20	15
692	$2	U.N. emblem and scroll	..	45	45
687/92			*Set of 6*	80	70
MS693	122 × 91 mm. 75 c. Type 208 and $1 as 2 c.				
	P 13	.. ..	..	65	90

CANCELLED REMAINDERS*. Some of the following issues have been remaindered, cancelled-to-order, at a fraction of their face-value. For all practical purposes these are indistinguishable from genuine postally used copies. Our used quotations which are indicated by an asterisk are the same for cancelled-to-order or postally used copies.

209 Paul Revere's Midnight Ride   **210** "Blood of the Redeemer" (G. Bellini)

(Des J. Cornel (½ to 10 c.), PAD Studio (40 c. to $1), J.W. (**MS704**). Litho Format)

1975 (6 May). *Bicentenary of American Revolution (1st issue). T 209 and similar multicoloured designs. P 14½.*

(a) Postage. Horiz designs
694	½ c.	Type 209	..	10	10*
695	1 c.	Crispus Attucks	..	10	10*
696	2 c.	Patrick Henry	..	10	10*
697	3 c.	Franklin visits Washington	..	10	10*
698	5 c.	Rebel troops	..	10	10*
699	10 c.	John Paul Jones	..	10	10*

(b) Air. Vert designs
700	40 c.	"John Hancock" (Copley)	..	25	10*
701	50 c.	"Benjamin Franklin" (Roslin)	..	40	15*
702	75 c.	"John Adams" (Copley)	..	55	15*
703	$1	"Lafayette" (Casanova)	..	60	20*
694/703			*Set of 10*	1·75	60*
MS704	Two sheets 131 × 102 mm: $2 Grenada arms and U.S. seal; $2 Grenada and U.S. flags.				
	P 13½	.. ..	..	90	60*

Stamps from **MS704** are horiz and larger: 47½ × 35mm.
Nos. 694/703 also exist perf 13 (*Price for set of 10 £1·75 mint or used*) from additional sheetlets of 5 stamps and 1 label. Stamps perforated 14½ are from normal sheets of 40.
See also Nos. 785/92.

(Des M. Shamir. Litho Format)

1975 (21 May). *Easter. T 210 and similar vert designs. Multicoloured. P 14½.*
705	½ c.	Type 210	..	10	10*
706	1 c.	"Pietà" (Bellini)	..	10	10*
707	2 c.	"The Entombment" (Van der Weyden)	..	10	10*
708	3 c.	"Pietà" (Bellini)	..	10	10*
709	35 c.	"Pietà" (Bellini)	..	20	10*
710	75 c.	"The Dead Christ" (Bellini)	..	25	10*
711	$1	"The Dead Christ supported by Angels" (Procaccini)	..	30	10*
705/11			*Set of 7*	75	30*
MS712	117 × 100 mm. $2 "Pietà" (Botticelli). P 13			75	30*

211 Wildlife Study   **212** Leafy Jewel Box (*Chama macerophylla*)

(Des J.W. Litho Format)

1975 (2 July). *14th World Scout Jamboree, Norway. T 211 and similar horiz designs. Multicoloured. P 14.*
713	½ c.	Type 211	..	10	10*
714	1 c.	Sailing	..	10	10*
715	2 c.	Map-reading	..	10	10*
716	35 c.	First-aid	..	40	10*
717	40 c.	Physical training	..	45	10*
718	75 c.	Mountaineering	..	60	10*
719	$2	Sing-song	..	1·25	20*
713/19			*Set of 7*	2·50	40*
MS720	106 × 80 mm. $1 Boat-building			90	30*

(Des J.W. Litho Questa)

1975 (1 Aug). *Seashells. T 212 and similar vert designs. Multicoloured. P 14.*
721	½ c.	Type 212	..	10	10*
722	1 c.	Emerald Nerite (*Smaragdia viridis viridemaris*)	..	10	10*
723	2 c.	Yellow American Cockle (*Trachycardium muricatum*)	..	10	10*
724	25 c.	Common Purple Janthina (*Janthina janthina*)	..	85	10*
725	50 c.	Atlantic Turkey Wing (*Arca zebra*)	..	1·75	15*
726	75 c.	West Indian Fighting Conch (*Strombus pugilis*)	..	2·25	20*
727	$1	Noble Wentletrap (*Sthenorytis pernobilis*)	..	2·25	20*
721/7			*Set of 7*	6·50	75*
MS728	102×76 mm. $2 Music Volute (*Voluta musica*)			2·00	80*

213 *Lycorea ceres*   **214** Rowing

(Des J.W. Litho Format)

1975 (22 Sept). *Butterflies. T 213 and similar vert designs. Multicoloured. P 14.*
729	½ c.	Type 213	..	10	10*
730	1 c.	Adelpha cytherea	..	10	10*
731	2 c.	Atlides polybe	..	10	10*
732	35 c.	Anteos maerula	..	80	10*
733	45 c.	Parides neophilus	..	85	10*
734	75 c.	Nymula orestes	..	1·25	15*
735	$2	Euptychia cephus	..	1·75	20*
729/35			*Set of 7*	4·25	50*
MS736	108×83 mm. $1 *Papilio astyalus* (sub-species *lycophron*)			1·25	40*

(Des J.W. Litho Questa)

1975 (13 Oct). *Pan-American Games, Mexico City. T 214 and similar vert designs. Multicoloured. P 14.*
737	½ c.	Type 214	..	10	10*
738	1 c.	Swimming	..	10	10*
739	2 c.	Show-jumping	..	10	10*
740	35 c.	Gymnastics	..	15	10*
741	45 c.	Football	..	15	10*
742	75 c.	Boxing	..	25	15*
743	$2	Cycling	..	65	20*
737/43			*Set of 7*	1·10	40*
MS744	106 × 81 mm. $1 Yachting			1·00	40*

215 "The Boy David" (Michelangelo)   **216** "Madonna and Child" (Filippino Lippi)

(Des M. and G. Shamir. Litho J.W.)

1975 (3 Nov). *500th Birth Anniv of Michelangelo. T 215 and similar vert designs. Multicoloured. P 14.*
745	½ c.	Type 215	..	10	10*
746	1 c.	"Young Man" (detail)	..	10	10*
747	2 c.	"Moses"	..	10	10*
748	40 c.	"Prophet Zachariah"	..	40	10*
749	50 c.	"St John the Baptist"	..	40	15*
750	75 c.	"Judith and Holofernes"	..	55	20*
751	$2	"Doni Madonna" (detail from "Holy Family")	..	90	25*
745/51			*Set of 7*	2·00	65*
MS752	104 × 89 mm. $1 "Madonna" (head from Pietà)			1·00	30*

The sculpture on No. 749 though ascribed to Michelangelo, shows a work by Francesco Sangallo.

(Des M. Shamir. Litho Questa)

1975 (8 Dec). *Christmas. T 216 and similar vert designs showing "Virgin and Child". Multicoloured. P 14.*
753	½ c.	Type 216	..	10	10*
754	1 c.	Mantegna	..	10	10*
755	2 c.	Luis de Morales	..	10	10*
756	35 c.	G. M. Morandi	..	15	10*
757	50 c.	Antonello da Messina	..	15	10*
758	75 c.	Dürer	..	20	10*
759	$1	Velasquez	..	25	10*
753/9			*Set of 7*	75	35*
MS760	125 × 98 mm. $2 Bellini	..		90	30*

217 Bananaquit   **218** Carnival Time

(Des G. Drummond. Litho Questa)

1976 (20 Jan). *Flora and Fauna. T 217 and similar multicoloured designs. P 14.*
761	½ c.	Type 217	..	10	10*
762	1 c.	Brazilian Agouti	..	10	10*
763	2 c.	Hawksbill Turtle (*horiz*)	..	10	10*
764	5 c.	Dwarf Poinciana	..	10	10*
765	35 c.	Black-finned Tuna ("Albacore") (*horiz*)		90	10*
766	40 c.	Cardinal's Guard	..	95	10*
767	$2	Nine-banded Armadillo (*horiz*)	..	2·50	30*
761/7			*Set of 7*	4·00	60*
MS768	82×89 mm. $1 Belted Kingfisher	..		7·50	90*

(Des G. Drummond. Litho Questa)

1976 (25 Feb). *Tourism. T 218 and similar horiz designs. Multicoloured. P 14.*
769	½ c.	Type 218	..	10	10*
770	1 c.	Scuba diving	..	10	10*
771	2 c.	Liner Southward at St. George's		10	10*
772	35 c.	Game fishing	..	65	10*
773	50 c.	St George's Golf Course	..	2·25	20*
774	75 c.	Tennis	..	2·50	25*
775	$1	Ancient rock carvings at Mount Rich		2·75	25*
769/75			*Set of 7*	7·50	80*
MS776	100×73 mm. $2 Small boat sailing	..		1·75	60*

219 "Pietà" (Master of Okolicsno)   **220** Sharpshooters

(Des M. and G. Shamir. Litho Questa)

1976 (29 Mar). *Easter. T 219 and similar vert designs by the artists listed. Multicoloured. P 14.*
777	½ c.	Type 219	..	10	10*
778	1 c.	Correggio	..	10	10*
779	2 c.	Van der Weyden	..	10	10*
780	3 c.	Dürer	..	10	10*
781	35 c.	Master of the Holy Spirit	..	15	10*
782	75 c.	Raphael	..	30	15*
783	$1	Raphael	..	35	20*
777/83			*Set of 7*	80	50*
MS784	108 × 86 mm. $2 Crespi	..		85	60*

(Des J.W. Litho Questa)

1976 (15 Apr). *Bicentenary of American Revolution (2nd issue). T 220 and similar vert designs. Multicoloured. P 14.*
785	½ c.	Type 220	..	10	10*
786	1 c.	Defending the Liberty Pole	..	10	10*
787	2 c.	Loading muskets	..	10	10*
788	35 c.	The fight for Liberty	..	30	10*
789	50 c.	Peace Treaty, 1783	..	35	10*
790	$1	Drummers	..	50	20*
791	$3	Gunboat	..	90	30*
785/91			*Set of 7*	2·00	60*
MS792	93 × 79 mm. 75 c. as 35 c. and $2 as 50 c.			75	60*

PRICES OF SETS

Set prices are given for many issues, generally those containing three stamps or more. Definitive sets include one of each value or major colour change, but do not cover different perforations, die types or minor shades. Where a choice is possible the set prices are based on the cheapest versions of the stamps included in the listings.

221 Nature Study

222 Volleyball

(Des G. Vasarhelyi. Litho Questa)

1976 (1 June). *50th Anniv of Girl Guides in Grenada. T* **221** *and similar vert designs. Multicoloured. P* 14.

793	½ c. Type **221**	..	..	10	10*
794	1 c. Campfire cooking	..	..	10	10*
795	2 c. First Aid	..	..	10	10*
796	50 c. Camping	..	..	65	10*
797	75 c. Home economics	..	..	90	15*
798	$2 First Aid	..	..	1·25	25*
793/8			*Set of* 6	2·50	55*
MS799	111 × 85 mm. $1 Painting			85	70*

(Des J.W. Litho Questa)

1976 (21 June). *Olympic Games, Montreal. T* **222** *and similar vert designs. Multicoloured. P* 14.

800	½ c. Type **222**	..	..	10	10*
801	1 c. Cycling	..	..	10	10*
802	2 c. Rowing	..	..	10	10*
803	35 c. Judo	..	..	30	10*
804	45 c. Hockey	..	..	60	10*
805	75 c. Gymnastics	..	..	60	20*
806	$1 High jump	..	..	60	20*
800/6			*Set of* 7	2·00	60*
MS807	106 × 81 mm. $3 Equestrian event			1·25	80*

223 "Cha-U-Kao at the Moulin Rouge"

224 Piper PA-23 Apache 235

(Des M. Shamir. Litho Questa)

1976 (20 July). *75th Death Anniv of Toulouse Lautrec. T* **223** *and similar vert designs. Multicoloured. P* 14.

808	½ c. Type **223**	..	..	10	10*
809	1 c. "Quadrille at the Moulin Rouge"	..	10	10*
810	2 c. "Profile of a Woman"	..	10	10*
811	3 c. "Salon in the Rue des Moulins"	..	10	10*
812	40 c. "The Laundryman"	..	55	10*
813	50 c. "Marcelle Lender dancing the Bolero"	65	10*
814	$2 "Signor Boileau at the Cafe"	..	1·75	25*
808/14			*Set of* 7	2·75	55*
MS815	152 × 125 mm. $1 "Woman with Boa"		2·25	70*

1976 (26 July). *West Indian Victory in World Cricket Cup. As Nos.* 559/60 *of Barbados.*

816	35 c. Map of the Caribbean	..	..	1·25	35
817	$1 The Prudential Cup	..	..	2·25	5·00

(Des J.W. Litho Questa)

1976 (18 Aug). *Airplanes. T* **224** *and similar horiz designs. Multicoloured. P* 14.

818	½ c. Type **224**	..	..	10	10*
819	1 c. Beech 50 Twin Bonanza	..	10	10*
820	2 c. De Havilland D.H.C.6 Twin Otter 100	10	10*
821	40 c. Britten Norman Islander	..	70	10*
822	50 c. De Havilland D.H.114 Heron 2	..	75	10*
823	$2 Hawker Siddeley H.S.748	..	2·50	50*
818/23			*Set of* 6	3·50	70*
MS824	75×83 mm. $3 B.A.C. One Eleven 500	2·00	80*

225 Satellite Assembly

226 S.S. Geestland

(Des PAD Studio. Litho Questa)

1976 (1 Sept). *Viking and Helios Space Missions. T* **225** *and similar multicoloured designs. P* 14.

825	½ c. Type **225**	..	..	10	10*
826	1 c. Helios satellite	..	..	10	10*
827	2 c. Helios encapsulation	..	..	10	10*
828	15 c. Systems test	..	..	10	10*
829	45 c. Viking lander (*horiz*)	..	20	10*
830	75 c. Lander on Mars	..	..	30	15*
831	$2 Viking encapsulation	..	..	60	25*
825/31			*Set of* 7	1·10	55*
MS832	110 × 85 mm. $3 Orbiter and lander		1·00	75*

(Des J.W. Litho Format)

1976 (3 Nov). *Ships. T* **226** *and similar horiz designs. Multicoloured. P* 14½.

833	½ c. Type **226**	..	..	10	10*
834	1 c. M. V. *Federal Palm*	..	..	10	10*
835	2 c. H.M.S. *Blake*	..	..	10	10*
836	25 c. M. V. *Vistafjord*	..	..	45	10*
837	75 c. S.S. *Canberra*	..	..	90	15*
838	$1 S.S. *Regina*	..	..	1·10	20*
839	$5 S.S. *Arandora Star*	..	..	2·25	40*
833/39			*Set of* 7	4·25	85*
MS840	91 × 78 mm. $2 *Santa Maria*		1·60	4·00

227 "Altarpiece of San Barnaba" (Botticelli)

(Des PAD Studio. Litho Questa)

1976 (8 Dec). *Christmas. T* **227** *and similar horiz designs. Multicoloured. P* 14.

841	½ c. Type **227**	..	..	10	10*
842	1 c. "Annunciation" (Botticelli)	..	10	10*
843	2 c. "Madonna of Chancellor Rolin" (Jan van Eyck)	..	10	10*
844	35 c. "Annunciation" (Fra Filippo Lippi)	15	10*
845	50 c. "Madonna of the Magnificat" (Botticelli)	20	10*
846	75 c. "Madonna of the Pomegranate" (Botticelli)	30	15*
847	$3 "Madonna with St. Cosmas and Other Saints" (Botticelli)	70	25*
841/7			*Set of* 7	1·25	50*
MS848	71 × 57 mm. $2 "Gypsy Madonna" (Titian)	1·00	60*

228 Alexander Graham Bell and Telephones

229 Coronation Scene

(Des G. Vasarhelyi. Litho Questa)

1976 (17 Dec). *Telephone Centenary. T* **228** *and similar horiz designs. Multicoloured. P* 14.

849	½ c. Type **228**	..	..	10	10*
850	1 c. Telephone-users within globe	..	10	10*
851	2 c. Telephone satellite	..	10	10*
852	18 c. Telephone viewer and console	..	20	10*
853	40 c. Satellite and tracking stations	..	25	10*
854	$1 Satellite transmitting to ships	..	35	15*
855	$2 Dish aerial and modern telephone	..	55	25*
849/55			*Set of* 7	1·25	55*
MS856	107 × 80 mm. $5 Globe encircled by flags	1·50	75*

(Des J.W. Litho Questa (Nos. 857/62), Walsall (863/6))

1977 (8 Feb). *Silver Jubilee. T* **229** *and similar vert designs. Multicoloured.* (*a*) *Sheet stamps. P* 13½ × 14.

857	½ c. Type **229**	..	..	10	10*
858	1 c. Sceptre and orb	..	..	10	10*
859	35 c. Queen on horseback	..	..	10	10*
860	$2 Spoon and ampulla	..	..	25	15*
861	$2.50 Queen and Prince Philip	..	25	15*
857/61			*Set of* 5	60	45*
MS862	103 × 79 mm. $5 Royal Visit to Grenada	75	60*

Nos. 857/61 also exist perf 11½×12 (*price for set of* 5 60p. *mint or used*) from additional sheetlets of 5 stamps and 1 label. They also have different frame colours to those perforated 13½×14 which come from normal sheets of 40.

(*b*) *Booklet stamps. Roul* 5 × *imperf**. *Self-adhesive*

863	35 c. As No. 861	..	..	15	25
	a. Booklet pane of 6	..	..	70	
864	50 c. As No. 860	..	..	25	1·00
	a. Booklet pane. Nos. 864/6.	..	1·90	
865	$1 As No. 858	..	..	50	1·40
866	$3 As No. 859	..	..	1·25	2·75
863/6			*Set of* 4	2·00	4·75

*No. 863/6 are separated by various combinations of rotary knife (giving a straight edge) and roulette.

230 Water Skiing

(Des G. Drummond. Litho Questa)

1977 (Apr). *Easter Water Parade. T* **230** *and similar horiz designs. Multicoloured. P* 14.

867	½ c. Type **230**	..	..	10	10*
868	1 c. Speedboat race	..	..	10	10*
869	2 c. Row boat race	..	..	10	10*
870	22 c. Swimming	..	..	20	10*
871	35 c. Work boat race	..	..	30	10*
872	75 c. Water polo	..	..	50	15*
873	$2 Game fishing	..	..	1·00	20*
867/73			*Set of* 7	1·90	55*
MS874	115 × 85 mm. $3 Yacht race		1·25	75*

231 Meeting Place, Grand Anse Beach

(Litho Questa)

1977 (14 June). *Seventh Meeting of Organization of American States. P* 14.

875	**231** 35 c. multicoloured	..	..	10	10
876	$1 multicoloured	..	..	25	60
877	$2 multicoloured	..	..	40	1·75
875/7			*Set of* 3	65	2·25

232 Rafting

(Des G. Drummond. Litho Questa)

1977 (6 Sept). *Caribbean Scout Jamboree, Jamaica. T* **232** *and similar horiz designs. Multicoloured. P* 14.

878	½ c. Type **232**	..	..	10	10*
879	1 c. Tug-of-war	..	..	10	10*
880	2 c. Sea Scouts regatta	..	..	10	10*
881	18 c. Camp fire	..	..	25	10*
882	40 c. Field kitchen	..	..	35	10*
883	$1 Scouts and sea scouts	..	..	75	15*
884	$2 Hiking and map reading	..	1·00	25*
878/84			*Set of* 7	2·25	60*
MS885	107 × 85 mm. $3 Semaphore	..	2·00	80*

233 Angel and Shepherd · · · Royal Visit W. I. 1977 (234)

(Des G. Vasarhelyi. Litho Questa)

1977 (3 Nov). *Christmas. T* **233** *and similar horiz designs showing ceiling panels from the church of St. Martin in Zillis. Multicoloured. P* 14.

886	½ c. Type **233**	..	..	10	10*
887	1 c. St. Joseph	..	..	10	10*
888	2 c. Virgin and Child Fleeing to Egypt	10	10*
889	22 c. Angel	..	..	10	10*
890	35 c. A Magus on horseback	..	15	10*
891	75 c. Three horses	..	..	20	15*
892	$2 Virgin and Child	..	..	50	25*
886/92			*Set of* 7	85	50*
MS893	85 × 112 mm. $3 Magus offering gifts	1·00	70*

1977 (10 Nov). *Royal Visit. Nos.* 857/62 *optd with T* **234**. *P* 13½×14 (35 c., $2, $2.50) *or* 11½×12 (*others*).

894	½ c. Type **229**	..	..	10	10
895	1 c. Sceptre and orb	..	..	10	10
896	35 c. Queen on horseback	..	..	10	10
897	$2 Spoon and ampulla	..	..	30	40
898	$2.50, Queen and Prince Philip	..	35	45
894/8			*Set of* 5	75	85
MS899	103 × 79 mm. $5 Royal Visit to Grenada	75	1·25

Nos. 894/5 only exist perforated 11½×12, but the remaining three values come perforated 13½×14 or 11½×12 (Nos. 896/8 perf 11½×12. *Price for set of* 3 75p *mint or used*).

235 Christjaan Eijkman (Medicine) · · · 236 Count von Zeppelin and First Zeppelin Airship LZ-1

(Des J.W. Litho Questa)

1978 (25 Jan). *Nobel Prize Winners. T* **235** *and similar vert designs. Multicoloured. P* 14.

900	½ c. Type 235		10	10*
901	1 c. Sir Winston Churchill (Literature)		30	10*
902	2 c. Woodrow Wilson (Peace)		10	10*
903	35 c. Frederic Passy (Peace)		15	10*
904	$1 Albert Einstein (Physics)		1·00	15*
905	$3 Carl Bosch (Chemistry)		1·75	25*
900/5		*Set of 6*	3·00	55*
MS906	114 × 99 mm. $2 Alfred Nobel		70	60*

(Des G. Vasarhelyi. Litho Questa)

1978 (13 Feb). *75th Anniv of First Zeppelin Flight and 50th Anniv of Lindbergh's Transatlantic Flight. T* **236** *and similar horiz designs. Multicoloured. P* 14.

907	½ c. Type 236		10	10*
908	1 c. Lindbergh with Ryan NYP Special *Spirit of St. Louis*		10	10*
909	2 c. Airship LZ-7 *Deutschland*		10	10*
910	22 c. Lindbergh's arrival in France		30	10*
911	75 c. Lindbergh and Ryan NYP Special *Spirit of St. Louis* in flight		60	10*
912	$1 LZ-127 *Graf Zeppelin* over Alps		65	15*
913	$3 LZ-127 *Graf Zeppelin* over White House		1·40	25*
907/13		*Set of 7*	2·75	55*
MS914	103×85 mm. Lindbergh in cockpit; $2 Count von Zeppelin and airship LZ-5		1·40	60*

237 Rocket Launching   238 Black-headed Gull

(Des J.W. Litho Questa)

1978 (28 Feb). *Space Shuttle. T* **237** *and similar vert designs. Multicoloured. P* 14.

915	½ c. Type 237		10	10*
916	1 c. Booster jettison		10	10*
917	2 c. External tank jettison		10	10*
918	18 c. Space shuttle in orbit		30	10*
919	75 c. Satellite placement		65	10*
920	$2 Landing approach		1·40	20*
915/20		*Set of 6*	2·25	50*
MS921	103 × 85 mm. $3 Shuttle after landing		1·40	60*

(Des G. Drummond. Litho Questa)

1978 (9 Mar). *Wild Birds of Grenada. T* **238** *and similar vert designs. Multicoloured. P* 14.

922	½ c. Type 238		10	10*
923	1 c. Wilson's Petrel		10	10*
924	2 c. Killdeer		10	10*
925	50 c. White-necked Jacobin		1·75	10*
926	75 c. Blue-faced Booby		2·00	15*
927	$1 Broad-winged Hawk		3·25	20*
928	$2 Red-necked Pigeon		4·00	30*
922/8		*Set of 7*	10·00	80*
MS929	103×94 mm. $3 Scarlet Ibis		6·00	1·00*

239 "The Landing of   240 Ludwig van Beethoven
Marie de Medici
at Marseilles"

(Des PAD Studio. Litho Questa)

1978 (30 Mar). *400th Birth Anniv of Rubens. T* **239** *and similar vert designs showing paintings. Multicoloured. P* 13½ × 14.

930	5 c. Type 239		10	10*
931	15 c. "Rubens and Isabella Brandt"		10	10*
932	18 c. "Marchesa Brigida Spindola-Doria"		10	10*
933	25 c. "Ludovicus Nonninus"		10	10*
934	45 c. "Helene Fourment and her Children"		15	10*
935	75 c. "Clara Serena Rubens"		25	10*
936	$3 "Le Chapeau de Paille"		60	20*
930/6		*Set of 7*	1·10	50*
MS937	65 × 100 mm. $5 "Self Portrait"		1·50	60*

(Des PAD Studio. Litho Questa)

1978 (24 Apr). *150th Death Anniv of Beethoven. T* **240** *and similar multicoloured designs. P* 14.

938	5 c. Type 240		10	10*
939	15 c. Woman violinist (*horiz*)		15	10*
940	18 c. Musical instruments (*horiz*)		20	10*
941	22 c. Piano (*horiz*)		20	10*
942	50 c. Violins		40	10*
943	75 c. Piano and sonata score		60	15*
944	$3 Beethoven's portrait and home (*horiz*)		1·75	25*
938/44		*Set of 7*	3·00	60*
MS945	83 × 62 mm. $2 Beethoven and score		1·10	60*

241 King Edward's   242 Queen Elizabeth II taking
Chair   Salute at Trooping the Colour

(Des J.W. Litho Questa. (Nos. 946/9). Manufactured by Walsall. (Nos. 950/2))

1978 (2 May–14 June). *25th Anniv of Coronation. Multicoloured.*

(*a*) *Sheet stamps. Vert designs as T* **241**. *P* 14 (14 June)

946	35 c. Type 241		10	10
947	$2 Queen with regalia		30	35
948	$2.50, St. Edward's Crown		30	40
946/8		*Set of 3*	60	75
MS949	102 × 76 mm. $5 Queen and Prince Philip		80	80

(*b*) *Booklet stamps. Vert designs as T* **242**. *Roul* 5 × *imperf*. Self-adhesive* (2 May)

950	25 c. Type 242		15	15
	a. Booklet pane. Nos. 950/1, each × 3		80	
951	35 c. Queen taking part in Maundy Thursday ceremony		15	25
952	$5 Queen and Prince Philip at Opening of Parliament		1·50	2·50
	a. Booklet pane of 1		1·50	
950/2		*Set of 3*	1·60	2·50

Nos. 946/8 also exist perf 12 (*Price for set of 3 75p. mint or used*) from additional sheetlets of 3 stamps and 1 label, issued 2 June. These have different frame colours from the stamps perforated 14, which come from normal sheets of 50.

*Nos. 950/1 are separated by various combinations of rotary-knife (giving a straight edge) and roulette. No. 952 exists only with straight edges.

243 Goalkeeper   244 Aerial Phenomena, Germany,
reaching for Ball   1561 and U.S.A., 1952

(Des M. Rubin. Litho Format)

1978 (1 Aug). *World Cup Football Championship, Argentina. T* **243** *and similar vert designs showing goalkeeper reaching for ball. P* 14½.

953	40 c. multicoloured		10	10
954	60 c. multicoloured		15	20
955	90 c. multicoloured		25	30
956	$2 multicoloured		60	60
953/6		*Set of 4*	1·00	1·00
MS957	130×97 mm. $2.50, multicoloured		1·10	1·10

(Des G. Vasarhelyi. Litho Format)

1978 (17 Aug). *U.F.O. Research. T* **244** *and similar horiz designs. Multicoloured. P* 14½.

958	5 c. Type 244		15	10
959	35 c. Various aerial phenomena, 1950		35	25
960	$3 U.F.O.'s, 1965		2·00	1·75
958/60		*Set of 3*	2·25	1·90
MS961	112 × 89 mm. $2 Sir Eric Gairy and U.F.O. research laboratory		1·25	1·25

245 Wright Flyer III

(Des G. Vasarhelyi. Litho Questa)

1978 (28 Aug). *75th Anniv of Powered Flight. T* **245** *and similar horiz designs. Multicoloured. P* 14.

962	5 c. Type 245		10	10
963	15 c. Flyer I, 1903		10	10
964	18 c. Wright Type A		10	10
965	22 c. Flyer I from above		15	10
966	50 c. Orville Wright and Wright Type A		20	20
967	75 c. Wright Type A in Pau, France, 1908		25	25
968	$3 Wilbur Wright and Wright glider No. IV		80	70
962/8		*Set of 7*	1·40	1·25
MS969	114×85 mm. $2 Wright glider No. III		1·00	75

246 Cook and Hawaiian Feast   247 "Paumgartner Altarpiece" (detail)

(Des G. Vasarhelyi. Litho Questa)

1978 (5 Dec). *Bicentenary of Discovery of Hawaii and 250th Birth Anniv of Captain Cook. T* **246** *and similar horiz designs. Multicoloured. P* 14.

970	18 c. Type 246		60	20
971	35 c. Cook and Hawaiian warriors		75	25
972	75 c. Cook and Honolulu Harbour		1·50	1·00
973	$3 Cook (statue) and H.M.S. *Resolution*		2·50	5·50
970/3		*Set of 4*	4·75	6·25
MS974	116×88 mm. $4 Cook and death scene		3·75	2·00

(Des M. Rubin. Litho Questa)

1978 (20 Dec). *Christmas. Paintings by Dürer. T* **247** *and similar vert designs. Multicoloured. P* 14.

975	40 c. Type 247		20	15
976	60 c. "The Adoration of the Magi"		25	20
977	90 c. "The Virgin and Child"		30	20
978	$2 "Virgin and Child with St. Anne" (detail)		55	55
975/8		*Set of 4*	1·10	1·10
MS979	113 × 83 mm. $4 "Madonna and Child"		1·10	1·50

248 National Convention and   249 *Acalypha hispida*
Cultural Centre (interior)

(Des BG Studio. Litho Questa)

1979 (8 Feb). *5th Anniv of Independence. T* **248** *and similar vert designs. Multicoloured. P* 14.

980	5 c. Type 248		10	10
981	18 c. National Convention and Cultural Centre (exterior)		10	10
982	22 c. Easter Water Parade, 1978		10	10
983	35 c. Sir Eric M. Gairy (Prime Minister)		15	10
984	$3 The Cross, Fort Frederick		60	80
980/4		*Set of 5*	80	90

(Des J.W. Litho Questa)

1979 (26 Feb). *Flowers. T* **249** *and similar vert designs. Multicoloured. P* 14.

985	18 c. Type 249		10	10
986	50 c. *Hibiscus rosa sinensis*		20	15
987	$1 *Thunbergia grandiflora*		30	25
988	$3 *Nerium oleander*		80	1·10
985/8		*Set of 4*	1·25	1·40
MS989	115 × 90 mm. $2 *Lagerstroemia speciosa*		75	1·00

250 Birds in Flight   251 Children playing Cricket

(Des M. Rubin. Litho Questa)

1979 (15 Mar). *30th Anniv of Declaration of Human Rights. T* **250** *and similar vert design. Multicoloured. P* 14.

990	15 c. Type 250		10	10
991	$2 Bird in flight		55	65

(Des J.W. Litho Questa)

1979 (23 Apr). *International Year of the Child* (1st issue). *T* **251** *and similar vert designs. Multicoloured. P* 14.

992	18 c. Type 251		40	30
993	22 c. Children playing baseball		40	30
994	$5 Children playing in tree		3·25	6·00
992/4		*Set of 3*	3·50	6·00
MS995	114×92 mm. $4 Children with model spaceship		1·75	2·25

See also Nos. 1006/7 and 1025/34.

252 "Around the World in 80 Days"

(Des G. Vasarhelyi. Litho Questa)

1979 (4 May). *150th Birth Anniv of Jules Verne (author). T* **252** *and similar horiz designs showing scenes from his books and modern technological developments. Multicoloured. P* 14.

996	18 c. Type **252**	..	..	25	10
997	35 c. "20,000 Leagues under the Sea"..	..	35	15
998	75 c. "From the Earth to the Moon"..	..	50	50
999	$3 "Master of the World"	..	1·40	1·60
996/9			*Set of 4*	2·25	2·00
MS1000	110×85 mm. $4 "Clipper of the Clouds"	1·25	1·25

253 Mail Runner, Africa (early 19th-century)

254 "The Pistol of Peace" (vaccination gun), Map of Grenada and Children

(Des J.W. Litho Questa)

1979 (23 July). *Death Centenary of Sir Rowland Hill. T* **253** *and similar horiz designs. Multicoloured. P* 14.

1001	20 c. Type **253**	..	..	10	10
1002	40 c. Pony Express, America (mid 19th-century)	..	10	10
1003	$1 Pigeon post	..	..	20	25
1004	$3 Mail coach, Europe (18th-19th-century)	50	80
1001/4			*Set of 4*	80	1·10
MS1005	127 × 100 mm. $5 Sir Rowland Hill and 1891 1d. on 8d. *tête-bêche* block of 4		75	1·10

Nos. 1001/4 also exist perf 12 (*Price for set of 4 80p. mint or used*) from additional sheetlets of 5 stamps and 1 label, issued 8 August. These have different background colours from the stamps perforated 14, which come from normal sheets of 40.

(Des G. Vasarhelyi. Litho Questa)

1979 (20 Aug). *International Year of the Child (2nd Issue).* "Grenada—First Nation 100% Immunized". P 14.

1006	**254**	5 c. multicoloured	..	25	30
1007		$1 multicoloured	..	75	2·00

255 Reef Shark

(Des G. Drummond. Litho Questa)

1979 (22 Aug). *Marine Wildlife. T* **225** *and similar horiz designs. Mutlicoloured. P* 14.

1008	40 c. Type **255**	..	..	40	30
1009	45 c. Spotted Eagle Ray	..	40	30
1010	50 c. Many-toothed Conger	..	45	40
1011	60 c. Golden Olive (shell) ..	..	70	75
1012	70 c. West Indian Murex (shell)	..	85	90
1013	75 c. Giant Tun (shell)	..	90	1·00
1014	90 c. Brown Booby	..	..	2·25	2·00
1015	$1 Magnificent Frigate Bird	..	2·25	2·00
1008/15			*Set of 8*	7·50	7·00
MS1016	109×78 mm. $2.50, Sooty Tern	2·50	2·00

256 The Flight into Egypt

(Des W. Grout. Litho Questa)

1979 (19 Oct). *Christmas. Religious Tapestries. T* **256** *and similar multicoloured designs. P* 14.

1017	6 c. Type **256**	..	..	10	10
1018	25 c. The Flight into Egypt (detail) ..	..	10	10
1019	30 c. Angel (*vert*)	..	..	10	10
1020	40 c. Doge Marino Grimani (detail) (*vert*)	10	10
1021	90 c. The Annunciation to the Shepherds (*vert*)	20	15
1022	$1 The Flight into Egypt (Rome) (*vert*)	20	15
1023	$2 The Virgin in Glory (*vert*)	35	40
1017/23			*Set of 7*	90	80
MS1024	111 × 148 mm. $4 Doge Marino Grimani (*vert*)		70	1·00

257 Mickey Mouse playing Baseball

258 Paul Harris (founder)

(Litho Format)

1979 (2 Nov). *International Year of the Child (3rd issue). Walt Disney Cartoon Characters. T* **257** *and similar vert designs showing characters playing sport. Multicoloured. P* 11.

1025	½ c. Type **257**	..	..	10	10
1026	1 c. Donald Duck high-jumping	..	10	10
1027	2 c. Goofy playing basketball	..	10	10
1028	3 c. Goofy hurdling	..	..	10	10
1029	4 c. Donald Duck playing golf	..	10	10
1030	5 c. Mickey Mouse playing cricket	..	10	10
1031	10 c. Mickey Mouse playing football..	10	10
1032	$2 Mickey Mouse playing tennis ..	2·75	3·25
1033	$2.50, Minnie Mouse riding horse..	2·75	3·25
1025/33			*Set of 9*	5·50	6·50
MS1034	125 × 100 mm. $3 Goofy in riding gear. P 13½.		1·50	1·50

(Des J.W. Litho Questa)

1980 (25 Feb). *75th Anniv of Rotary International. T* **258** *and similar vert designs. Multicoloured. P* 14.

1035	6 c. Type **258**	..	..	10	10
1036	30 c. "Health"..	..	..	10	15
1037	90 c. "Hunger"	..	..	25	30
1038	$2 "Humanity"	..	..	55	80
1035/8			*Set of 4*	90	1·10
MS1039	104 × 89 mm. $4 Rotary International emblem		1·00	1·60

PEOPLE'S REVOLUTION 13 MARCH 1979

(259)

1980 (28 Feb–8 Apr). *1st Anniv of Revolution (1st issue).* Nos. 651A/2A, 654A/7A, 659A, 660B and 662A/8A *optd with T* **259**.

1040	2 c. Carenage taxi	..	..	10	10
	a. Optd on No. 651B	..	7·00	
1041	3 c. Large working boats	..	10	10
	a. Optd on No. 652B	..	7·00	
1042	6 c. Cocoa beans in drying trays	..	10	10
1043	8 c. Nutmegs	..	..	10	10
1044	10 c. River Antoine Estate Rum Distillery, *c.* 1785		10	10
1045	12 c. Cocoa Tree	..	..	10	10
1046	20 c. Parliament Building, St. George's	10	15
1047	25 c. Fort George cannons (8.4.80)	..	30	30
1048	50 c. General Post Office	..	30	30
1049	75 c. Caribs Leap, Sauteurs Bay	..	50	40
1050	$1 Carenage, St. George's	..	60	60
1051	$2 St. George's Harbour by night	..	1·25	2·00
1052	$3 Grand Anse Beach	..	1·50	3·25
1053	$5 Canoe Bay and Black Bay from Point Saline Lighthouse	..	2·00	5·00
1054	$10 Sugar Loaf Island from Levera Beach	3·25	7·50
1040/54			*Set of 15*	9·00	18·00

See also Nos. 1069/73.

260 Boxing

261 Tropical Kingbird

(Des Design Images Inc. Litho Questa)

1980 (24 Mar). *Olympic Games, Moscow. T* **260** *and similar horiz designs. Multicoloured. P* 14.

1055	25 c. Type **260**	..	..	10	10
1056	40 c. Cycling	..	..	15	15
1057	90 c. Show-jumping	..	..	20	30
1058	$2 Running	..	..	40	1·00
1055/8			*Set of 4*	75	1·40
MS1059	128 × 95 mm. $4 Sailing. ..	80	1·40

(Des G. Drummond. Litho Questa)

1980 (8 Apr). *Wild Birds. T* **261** *and similar vert designs. Multicoloured. P* 14.

1060	20 c. Type **261**	..	..	85	15
1061	40 c. Rufous-breasted Hermit	..	1·25	25
1062	$1 Troupial	..	..	1·75	1·75
1063	$2 Ruddy Quail Dove	..	2·25	3·50
1060/3			*Set of 4*	5·50	5·00
MS1064	85×114 mm. $3 Prairie Warbler..	3·75	1·75

LONDON 1980

(262)

263 Free Hot Lunch at Schools

1980 (6 May). *"London 1980" International Stamp Exhibition.* Nos. 1001/4 optd with T **262**. P 12.

1065	20 c. Type **253**	..	..	15	15
1066	40 c. Pony Express, America (mid 19th-century)	..	20	20
1067	$1 Pigeon Post	..	..	40	40
1068	$3 Mail coach, Europe (18th-19th-century)	1·25	1·25
1065/8			*Set of 4*	1·75	1·75

(Des M. Diamond. Litho Questa)

1980 (19 May). *1st Anniv of Revolution (2nd issue). T* **263** *and similar horiz designs. Multicoloured. P* 14.

1069	10 c. Type **263**	..	..	10	10
1070	40 c. "From tree to can" (agro-industry)	..	15	15
1071	$1 National Health care	..	30	30
1072	$2 New housing projects	..	50	70
1069/72			*Set of 4*	85	1·10
MS1073	110 × 85 mm. $5 Prime Minister Maurice Bishop (*vert*)		75	85

264 Jamb Statues, West Portal, Chartres Cathedral

(Des J.W. Litho Questa)

1980 (15 July). *Famous Works of Art. T* **264** *and similar horiz designs. Multicoloured. P* 13½.

1074	8 c. Type **264**	..	..	10	10
1075	10 c. "Les Demoiselles D'Avignon" (painting by Picasso)	..	10	10
1076	40 c. Winged Victory of Samothrace (statue)	15	15
1077	50 c. "The Night Watch" (painting by Rembrandt)	..	15	15
1078	$1 "Portrait of Edward VI as a Child" (painting by Holbein the Younger)	25	25
1079	$3 Portrait head of Queen Nefertiti (carving)..	..	70	70
1074/9			*Set of 6*	1·25	1·25
MS1080	101 × 101 mm. $4 "Weier Haws" (detail of painting by Dürer) (*vert*)		75	75

265 Carib Canoes

(Des G. Drummond. Litho Questa)

1980 (9 Sept–84. *Shipping. Horiz designs as T* **265**. *Multicoloured. A. Without imprint date. P* 14.

1081A	½ c. Type **265**	..	..	10	10
1082A	1 c. Boat building	..	..	10	10
1083A	2 c. Small working boat	..	15	10
1084A	4 c. Columbus' *Santa Maria*	..	40	10
1085A	5 c. West Indiaman barque, *circa* 1840	40	10
1086A	6 c. *Orinoco* (paddle-steamer), *circa* 1851	40	10
1087A	10 c. Working schooner	..	50	10
1088A	12 c. Trimaran at Grand Anse anchorage	50	10
1089A	15 c. Spice Island cruising yacht *Petite Amie*		50	10
1090A	20 c. Fishing pirogue	..	1·00	10
1091A	25 c. Harbour police launch	..	1·75	20
1092A	30 c. Grand Anse speed-boat	..	1·50	20
1093A	40 c. *Seimstrand* (freighter)	..	1·50	25
1094A	50 c. *Ariadne* (cadet schooner)	..	1·50	35
1095A	90 c. *Geestide* (freighter)	..	1·75	50
1096A	$1 *Cunard Countess* (liner)	..	2·00	70
1097A	$3 Rum-runner	..	..	2·50	4·00
1098A	$5 *Statendam* (liner) off St. George's	3·50	7·00
1099A	$10 Coastguard patrol boat	..	6·00	13·00
1081A/99A			*Set of 19*	23·00	24·00

B. With imprint date at foot of design. P 14 ($1) or 12 (others).

1081B	½ c. Type **265** (1982)	..	75	1·50
1085B	5 c. West Indiaman barque, *circa* 1840 (1982)	..	1·25	1·25
1087B	10 c. Working schooner (1982)	..	1·50	60
	a. Perf 14	..	..	†	
1090B	20 c. Fishing pirogue (1982)	..	2·00	95
1091B	25 c. Harbour police launch (1982)	..	2·25	90
	a. Perf 14	..	..	2·50	3·00
1092B	30 c. Grand Anse speed-boat (1982)	..	2·00	1·25
	a. Perf 14	..	..	2·50	3·00
1093B	40 c. *Seimstrand* (freighter) (1982)	..	2·75	1·60
1094B	50 c. *Ariadne* (cadet schooner) (1.84)	..	50	50
	a. Perf 14	..	..	55	50
1096B	$1 *Cunard Countess* (liner) (1982)	..	28·00	14·00
1097B	$3 Rum-runner (1982)	..	2·75	6·50

1098B	$5 *Statendam* (liner) off St. George's (1982)	3·50	9·00
1099B	$10 *Coastguard patrol boat* (1.84)	6·00	8·50
1081B/99B	*Set of 12*	48·00	42·00

Imprint dates: "1982", Nos. 1081B, 1085B, 1087B/aB, 1090B, 1091B/aB, 1092B/aB, 1093B, 1096B/8B; "1984", Nos. 1094B/aB, 1099B.

(Litho Walsall)

1980 (25 Sept). *Christmas. Walt Disney Cartoon Scenes from "Snow White and the Seven Dwarfs". Horiz designs as T 257. Multicoloured. P 11.*

1100	½ c. Snow White at well	10	10
1101	1 c. The Wicked Queen	10	10
1102	2 c. Snow White singing to animals	10	10
1103	3 c. Snow White doing housework for Dwarfs	10	10
1104	4 c. The Seven Dwarfs	10	10
1105	5 c. Snow White with Dwarfs	10	10
1106	10 c. Witch offering Snow White apple	10	10
1107	$2.50, Snow White with Prince, and Dwarfs	3·00	1·75
1108	$3 Snow White and Prince	3·50	2·00
1100/8	*Set of 9*	6·50	3·75
MS1109	127 × 102 mm. $4 Snow White sleeping (*vert*)	4·25	1·50

(Litho Format)

1981 (19 Jan). *50th Anniv of Walt Disney's Cartoon Character, Pluto. Vert designs as T 257. Multicoloured. P 13½.*

1110	$2 Pluto with birthday cake	1·25	1·00
MS1111	127 × 102 mm. $4 Pluto in scene from film *Pueblo Pluto*	2·25	1·25

No. 1110 was printed in small sheets of 8 stamps.

266 Revolution and Grenada Flags

1981 (13 Mar). *Festival of the Revolution. T 266 and similar triangular designs. Multicoloured. Litho. P 12½.*

1112	5 c. Type 266	10	10
1113	10 c. Teacher, pupil, book and pencil ("education")	10	10
1114	15 c. Food processing plant ("industry")	10	10
1115	25 c. Selection of fruits and farm scene ("agriculture")	15	10
1116	40 c. Crawfish and boat ("fishing")	20	15
1117	90 c. *Cunard Countess* arriving at St. George's Harbour ("shipping")	50	30
1118	$1 Straw-work ("native handicrafts")	60	40
1119	$3 Map of Caribbean with expanded view of Grenada	1·75	1·75
1112/19	*Set of 8*	3·00	2·50

(Litho Format)

1981 (7 Apr). *Easter. Walt Disney Cartoon Characters. Vert designs as T 257. Multicoloured. P 11.*

1120	35 c. Mickey Mouse and Goofy	40	15
1121	40 c. Donald Duck, Chip and Daisy Duck	40	15
1122	$2 Minnie Mouse	1·40	1·25
1123	$2.50 Pluto and Mickey Mouse	1·60	1·40
1120/3	*Set of 4*	3·50	2·75
MS1124	127×101 mm. $4 Goofy. P 13½	3·00	2·75

267 "Woman-Flower"   268 Prince Charles playing Polo

(Des J.W. Litho Questa)

1981 (28 Apr). *Birth Centenary of Picasso. T 267 and similar vert designs. Multicoloured. P 13½ × 14.*

1125	25 c. Type 267	15	10
1126	30 c. "Portrait of Madame"	20	10
1127	90 c. "Cavalier with Pipe"	30	30
1128	$4 "Large Heads"	1·00	1·25
1125/8	*Set of 4*	1·50	1·50
MS1129	128 × 103 mm. $5 "Woman on the Banks of the Seine" (after Courbet). Imperf	3·00	1·40

(Des J.W. Litho Format)

1981 (16 June). *Royal Wedding (1st issue). T 268 and similar vert designs. Multicoloured. (a) P 15.*

1130	50 c. Prince Charles and Lady Diana Spencer	10	10
1131	$2 Holyrood House	35	50
1132	$4 Type 268	50	75
	a. Imperf (pair)	£400	
1130/2	*Set of 3*	85	1·25
MS1133	98 × 84 mm. $5 Glass Coach	75	75

(b) P 15 × 14½

1134	30 c. As 50 c.	20	20
1135	40 c. As $2	30	30

The 30 and 40 c. values were each printed in small sheets of 6 including one *se-tenant* stamp-size label.

The $4 value, with changed background colour, also exists perforated 15×14½ (*price 90p. mint or used*) from similar sheetlets in addition to the original version issued in sheets of 40.

269 Lady Diana Spencer   270 "The Bath" (Mary Cassatt)

(Manufactured by Walsall)

1981 (16 June). *Royal Wedding (2nd issue). T 269 and similar vert designs. Multicoloured. Roul 5 × imperf*. Self-adhesive.*

1136	$1 Type 269	30	65
	a. Booklet pane. Nos. 1136/7 each × 3	1·60	
1137	$2 Prince Charles	30	65
1138	$5 Prince Charles and Lady Diana Spencer	1·00	1·75
	a. Booklet pane of 1	1·00	
1136/8	*Set of 3*	1·40	2·75

*The $1 and $2 values were each separated by various combinations of rotary knife (giving a straight edge) and roulette. The $5 value exists only with straight edges.
Nos. 1136/8 were only issued in $14 stamp booklets.

(Des BG Studio. Litho Questa)

1981 (Oct). *"Decade for Women". Paintings. T 270 and similar multicoloured designs. P 14.*

1139	15 c. Type 270	10	10
1140	40 c. "Mademoiselle Charlotte du Val d'Ognes" (Constance Marie Charpentier)	20	10
1141	60 c. "Self-portrait (Mary Beale)	30	20
1142	$3 "Woman in White Stockings" (Suzanne Valadon)	1·25	1·00
1139/42	*Set of 4*	1·60	1·25
MS1143	101×77 mm. $5 "The Artist hesitating between the Arts of Music and Painting" (Angelica Kauffman) (*horiz*)	1·75	2·00

(Litho Questa)

1981 (Nov). *Christmas. Horiz designs as T 257 showing scenes from Walt Disney's cartoon film "Cinderella". P 13½.*

1144	½ c. multicoloured	10	10
1145	1 c. multicoloured	10	10
1146	2 c. multicoloured	10	10
1147	3 c. multicoloured	10	10
1148	4 c. multicoloured	10	10
1149	5 c. multicoloured	10	10
1150	10 c. multicoloured	15	10
1151	$2.50, multicoloured	3·50	2·25
1152	$3 multicoloured	3·50	2·50
1144/52	*Set of 9*	7·00	4·75
MS1153	127 × 103 mm. $5 multicoloured	5·50	3·25

271 Landing   272 West German Footballer and Flag

(Des M. Brodie. Litho Format)

1981 (12 Nov). *Space Shuttle Project. T 271 and similar vert designs. Multicoloured. P 14½.*

1154	30 c. Type 271	20	15
1155	40 c. Working in space	40	30
1156	70 c. Lift off	45	35
1157	$3 Separation	1·10	1·25
1154/7	*Set of 4*	1·90	1·75
MS1158	117 × 89 mm. $5 In orbit	1·75	1·25

(Des Clover Mill. Litho Format)

1981 (30 Nov.) *World Cup Football Championship, Spain (1982). T 272 and similar multicoloured designs. P 14.*

1159	25 c. + 10 c. Type 272	55	30
1160	40 c. + 20 c. Argentinian footballer and flag	70	40
1161	50 c. + 25 c. Brazilian footballer and flag	80	50
1162	$1 + 50 c. English footballer and flag	1·25	95
1159/62	*Set of 4*	3·00	1·90
MS1163	141 × 128 mm. $5 + 50 c. Spanish orange mascot and Jules Rimet Trophy (*vert*)	3·50	2·00

Nos. 1159/62 were each printed in sheetlets of 12 on an overall background design showing a football.

273 General Post Office,   274 Artist without St. George's   Hands

(Des J.W. Litho Format)

1981 (10 Dec). *Centenary of U.P.U. Membership. T 273 and similar horiz designs. Multicoloured. P 15.*

1164	25 c. Type 273	20	15
1165	30 c. 1861 1d. stamp	25	20
1166	90 c. 1970 New U.P.U. Headquarters Building 25 c. commemorative	55	50
1167	$4 1961 Stamp Centenary 25 c. commemorative	1·25	2·00
1164/7	*Set of 4*	2·00	2·50
MS1168	113×87 mm. $5 1974 Centenary of U.P.U. ½ c. commemorative	3·00	3·25

(Litho Questa)

1982 (4 Feb). *International Year for the Disabled (1981). T 274 and similar vert designs. Multicoloured. P 14.*

1169	30 c. Type 274	30	10
1170	40 c. Computer operator without hands	30	10
1171	70 c. Blind schoolteacher teaching braille	60	15
1172	$3 Midget playing drums	1·25	80
1169/72	*Set of 4*	2·25	1·10
MS1173	101 × 72 mm. $4 Auto mechanic confined to wheelchair	3·00	2·25

275 Tending Vegetable Patch   276 *Dryas julia*

(Des Design Images. Litho Format)

1982 (19 Feb). *75th Anniv of Boy Scout Movement and 125th Birth Anniv of Lord Baden-Powell. T 275 and similar horiz designs. Multicoloured. P 14½.*

1174	70 c. Type 275	50	45
1175	90 c. Map-reading	55	55
1176	$1 Bee-keeping	65	65
1177	$4 Hospital reading	2·25	2·75
1174/7	*Set of 4*	3·50	4·00
MS1178	100 × 71 mm. $5 Presentation of trophies	2·00	1·50

(Des G. Drummond. Litho Questa)

1982 (24 Mar). *Butterflies. T 276 and similar vert designs. Multicoloured. P 14.*

1179	10 c. Type 276	75	30
1180	60 c. *Phoebis agarithe*	2·50	1·50
1181	$1 *Anartia amathea*	3·00	2·00
1182	$3 *Battus polydamas*	4·25	7·00
1179/82	*Set of 4*	9·50	9·75
MS1183	111×85 mm. $5 *Junonia evarete*	7·50	3·00

277 "Saying Grace"   278 Kensington Palace

(Des M.B.I. Studio. Litho Questa)

1982 (14 Apr). *Norman Rockwell (painter) Commemoration. T 277 and similar vert designs. Multicoloured. P 14 × 13½.*

1184	15 c. Type 277	40	10
1185	30 c. "Nothing Up His Sleeve" (inscr "Card Tricks")	65	15
1186	60 c. "Pharmacist"	85	15
1187	70 c. "Hobo" (inscr "Pals")	90	35
1184/7	*Set of 4*	2·50	75

(Des PAD Studio. Litho Questa)

1982 (1 July). *21st Birthday of Princess of Wales. T 278 and similar vert designs. Multicoloured. P 14½ × 14.*

1188	50 c. Type 278	40	45
1189	60 c. Type 278	80	45
1190	$1 Prince and Princess of Wales	90	1·00
1191	$2 As $1	1·75	1·25
1192	$3 Princess of Wales	2·00	2·25

1193	$4 As $3	2·25 2·25
1188/93		Set of 6 7·25 7·00
MS1194	103 × 75 mm. $5 Princess Diana	
(different)		2·50 1·50

Nos. 1188, 1190 and 1192 come from sheetlets of 5 stamps and 1 label.

279 Mary McLeod Bethune appointed Director of Negro Affairs, 1942

(Des Design Images. Litho Questa)

1982 (27 July). *Birth Centenary of Franklin D. Roosevelt. T 279 and similar horiz designs. Multicoloured.* P 14.

1195	10 c. Type 279	10 10
1196	60 c. Huddie Ledbetter ("Leadbelly") in concert (Works Progress administration)	35 20
1197	$1.10, Signing bill No. 8802, 1941 (Fair Employment committee)	50 40
1198	$3 Farm Security administration	75 80
1195/8		Set of 4 1·50 1·25
MS1199	100×70 mm. $5 William Hastie, first Negro judicial appointee	1·25 1·25

1982 (30 Aug). *Birth of Prince William of Wales. Nos. 1188/94 optd with T 171 of Antigua.*

1200	50 c. Type 278	30 60
1201	60 c. Type 278	35 35
1202	$1 Prince and Princess of Wales	55 85
1203	$2 As $1	1·00 1·00
1204	$3 Princess of Wales	1·75 1·90
1205	$4 As $3	1·90 1·90
1200/5		Set of 6 5·50 6·00
MS1206	103 × 75 mm. $5 Princess Diana	
(different)		2·00 1·25

Nos. 1200, 1202 and 1204 come from sheetlets of 5 stamps and 1 label.

280 Apostle and Tormentor

(Des Clover Mill. Litho Format)

1982 (2 Sept). *Easter. Details from Painting "The Way to Calvary" by Raphael. T 280 and similar multicoloured designs.* P 14 × 14½ (40 c.) or 14½ × 14 (others).

1207	40 c. Type 280	30 10
1208	70 c. Captain of the guards (vert)	40 15
1209	$1.10, Christ and apostle (vert)	50 25
1210	$4 Mourners (vert)	1·00 1·25
1207/10		Set of 4 2·00 1·60
MS1211	102 × 126 mm. $5 Christ falls beneath the cross (vert)	2·00 2·00

281 "Orient Express"

(Des Artists International. Litho Format)

1982 (4 Oct). *Famous Trains of the World. T 281 and similar horiz designs. Multicoloured.* P 15 × 14½.

1212	30 c. Type 281	50 35
1213	60 c. "Trans-Siberian Express"	60 70
1214	70 c. "Fleche d'Or"	70 80
1215	90 c. "Flying Scotsman"	85 1·00
1216	$1 German Federal Railways steam locomotive	1·00 1·25
1217	$3 German National Railways Class 05 steam locomotive	2·25 4·00
1212/17		Set of 6 5·50 7·25
MS1218	109×81 mm. $5 "20th Century Limited"	2·50 2·50

No. 1217 exists imperforate from stock dispersed by the liquidator of Format International Security Printers Ltd.

282 Footballers   **283** Killer Whale

(Des D. Miller. Litho Questa)

1982 (2 Dec). *World Cup Football Championship Winners. T 282 and similar horiz designs.* P 14 × 13½.

1219	60 c. multicoloured	35 35
1220	$4 multicoloured	2·00 2·00
MS1221	93 × 119 mm. $5 multicoloured	2·50 2·25

(Litho Questa)

1982 (14 Dec). *Christmas. Horiz designs as T 257 depicting scenes from Walt Disney's cartoon film "Robin Hood".* P 13½.

1222	½ c. multicoloured	10 10
1223	1 c. multicoloured	10 10
1224	2 c. multicoloured	10 10
1225	3 c. multicoloured	10 10
1226	4 c. multicoloured	10 10
1227	5 c. multicoloured	10 10
1228	10 c. multicoloured	10 10
1229	$2.50, multicoloured	2·75 2·75
1230	$3 multicoloured	2·75 2·75
1222/30		Set of 9 5·25 5·25
MS1231	121 × 96 mm. $5 multicoloured	6·50 4·00

(Des Artists International. Litho Questa)

1983 (10 Jan). *Save the Whales. T 283 and similar vert designs. Multicoloured.* P 14.

1232	15 c. Type 283	1·00 30
1233	40 c. Sperm Whale	2·25 90
1234	70 c. Blue Whale	2·75 2·75
1235	$3 Common Dolphin	3·50 6·50
1232/5		Set of 4 8·50 9·50
MS1236	84 × 74 mm. $5 Humpback Whale	6·50 4·00

284 "Construction of Ark"

(Des Design Images. Litho Format)

1983 (15 Feb). *500th Birth Anniv of Raphael. T 284 and similar horiz designs showing painting details. Multicoloured.* P 13½.

1237	25 c. Type 284	20 10
1238	30 c. "Jacob's Vision"	20 10
1239	90 c. "Joseph interprets the Dreams to his Brothers"	30 30
1240	$4 "Joseph interprets Pharaoh's Dreams"	1·10 1·40
1237/40		Set of 4 1·60 1·75
MS1241	128 × 100 mm. $5 "Creation of the Animals"	1·25 1·75

Nos. 1237/41 exist imperforate from stock dispersed by the liquidator of Format International Security Printers Ltd.

285 Dentistry at Health Centre

(Des J.W. Litho Questa)

1983 (14 Mar). *Commonwealth Day. T 285 and similar horiz designs. Multicoloured.* P 14.

1242	10 c. Type 285	10 10
1243	70 c. Airport runway construction	35 35
1244	$1.10, Tourism	40 55
1245	$3 Boat-building	80 1·40
1242/5		Set of 4 1·50 2·10

286 Maritime Communications via Satellite

(Des G. Vasarhelyi. Litho Questa)

1983 (29 Mar). *World Communications Year. T 286 and similar horiz designs. Multicoloured.* P 14.

1246	30 c. Type 286	15 15
1247	40 c. Rural telephone installation	20 15
1248	$2.50, Satellite weather map	1·00 1·00
1249	$3 Airport control room	1·10 1·10
1246/9		Set of 4 2·25 2·25
MS1250	111 × 85 mm. $5 Communications satellite	1·50 1·50

NEW INFORMATION

The editor is always interested to correspond with people who have new information that will improve or correct the Catalogue.

---

287 Franklin Sport Sedan, 1928

(Des J. Mendola. Litho Format)

1983 (4 May). *75th Anniv of Model "T" Ford Car. T 287 and similar horiz designs showing cars of the 20th century. Multicoloured.* P 14½.

1251	6 c. Type 287	15 10
1252	10 c. Delage "D8", 1933	20 10
1253	40 c. Alvis, 1938	35 25
1254	60 c. Invicta "S-type" tourer, 1931	45 45
1255	70 c. Alfa-Romeo "1750 Gran Sport", 1930	55 55
1256	90 c. Isotta Fraschini, 1930	60 65
1257	$1 Bugatti "Royale Type 41"	70 65
1258	$2 BMW "328", 1938	1·40 1·50
1259	$3 Marmon "V16", 1931	1·60 2·25
1260	$4 Lincoln "K8" saloon, 1932	1·90 2·75
1251/60		Set of 10 7·00 8·50
MS1261	114 × 90 mm. $5 Cougar "XR 7", 1972	1·50 2·00

Nos. 1251/60 were each issued in sheets of eight stamps with a stamp-size label in the centre position.

288 N.1 *Norge* (airship)

(Des W. Wright. Litho Questa)

1983 (18 July). *Bicentenary of Manned Flight. T 288 and similar multicoloured designs.* P 14.

1262	30 c. Type 288	60 30
1263	60 c. Gloster VI seaplane	1·00 1·00
1264	$1.10, Curtiss NC-4 flying boat	3·50 4·50
1265	$4 Dornier Do-18 flying boat *Aeolus*	3·50 4·50
1262/5		Set of 4 6·00 6·75
MS1266	114×85 mm. $5 Modern hot-air balloon (vert)	1·75 1·75

289 Morty

(Litho Format)

1983 (7 Nov). *Christmas. T 289 and similar vert designs showing Disney cartoon characters in scenes from "It's beginning to look a lot like Christmas" (song). Multicoloured.* P 11.

1267	½ c. Type 289	10 10
1268	1 c. Ludwig von Drake	10 10
1269	2 c. Gyro Gearloose	10 10
1270	3 c. Pluto and Figaro	10 10
1271	4 c. Morty and Ferdie	10 10
1272	5 c. Mickey Mouse and Goofy	10 10
1273	10 c. Chip'n Dale	10 10
1274	$2.50, Mickey and Minnie Mouse	2·75 3·50
1275	$3 Donald and Grandma Duck	3·00 3·50
1267/75		Set of 9 5·75 7·00
MS1276	127 × 102 mm. $5 Goofy with Christmas tree. P 13½	4·50 4·50

290 Daisy Duck on Pommel Horse   **291** William I

(Litho Questa)

1984 (17 Jan–May). *Olympic Games, Los Angeles. T 290 and similar horiz designs showing Disney cartoon characters in Olympic events. Multicoloured.*

A. *Inscr* "1984 LOS ANGELES". P 14×13½

1277A	½ c. Type 290	10 10
1278A	1 c. Mickey Mouse boxing	10 10
1279A	2 c. Daisy Duck in archery event	10 10

1280A	3 c. Clarabelle Cow on uneven bars	..	10	10
1281A	4 c. Mickey and Minnie Mouse in hurdles race	..	10	10
1282A	5 c. Donald Duck with Chip and Dale weightlifting	..	10	10
1283A	$1 Little Hiawatha in single kayak	..	2·00	2·00
1284A	$2 The Tortoise and the Hare in marathon	..	2·50	3·00
1285A	$3 Mickey Mouse pole-vaulting	..	3·00	3·25
1277A/85A		Set of 9	7·25	8·00
MS1286A	127×101 mm. $5 Donald Duck in medley relay (*vert*). P 13½×14	..	5·50	3·50

B. *Inscr* "1984 OLYMPICS LOS ANGELES *and Olympic emblem. P* 12 (May)

1277B	½ c. Type 290	..	10	10
1278B	1 c. Mickey Mouse boxing	..	10	10
1279B	2 c. Daisy Duck in archery event	..	10	10
1280B	3 c. Clarabelle Cow on uneven bars	..	10	10
1281B	4 c. Mickey and Minnie Mouse in hurdles race	..	10	10
1282B	5 c. Donald Duck with Chip and Dale weightlifting	..	10	10
1283B	$1 Little Hiawatha in single kayak	..	2·00	2·00
1284B	$2 The Tortoise and the Hare in marathon	..	2·50	3·00
1285B	$3 Mickey Mouse pole-vaulting	..	3·00	3·25
1277B/85B		Set of 9	7·25	8·00
MS1286B	127×101 mm. $5 Donald Duck in medley relay (*vert*). P 13½×14	..	6·50	5·50

1984 (25 Jan). *British Monarchs. T* **291** *and similar vert designs. Multicoloured. Litho. P* 14.

1287	$4 Type 291	..	2·50	3·25
	a. Sheetlet. Nos. 1287/93	..	16·00	
1288	$4 William II	..	2·50	3·25
1289	$4 Henry I	..	2·50	3·25
1290	$4 Stephen	..	2·50	3·25
1291	$4 Henry II	..	2·50	3·25
1292	$4 Richard I	..	2·50	3·25
1293	$4 John	..	2·50	3·25
1294	$4 "Henry III"	..	2·50	3·25
	a. Sheetlet. Nos. 1294/1300	..	16·00	
1295	$4 Edward I	..	2·50	3·25
1296	$4 Edward II	..	2·50	3·25
1297	$4 Edward III	..	2·50	3·25
1298	$4 Richard II	..	2·50	3·25
1299	$4 Henry IV	..	2·50	3·25
1300	$4 Henry V	..	2·50	3·25
1301	$4 Henry VI	..	2·50	3·25
	a. Sheetlet. Nos. 1301/7	..	16·00	
1302	$4 Edward IV	..	2·50	3·25
1303	$4 Edward V	..	2·50	3·25
1304	$4 Richard III	..	2·50	3·25
1305	$4 Henry VII	..	2·50	3·25
1306	$4 Henry VIII	..	2·50	3·25
1307	$4 Edward VI	..	2·50	3·25
1308	$4 Lady Jane Grey	..	2·50	3·25
	a. Sheetlet. Nos. 1308/14	..	16·00	
1309	$4 Mary I	..	2·50	3·25
1310	$4 Elizabeth I	..	2·50	3·25
1311	$4 James I	..	2·50	3·25
1312	$4 Charles I	..	2·50	3·25
1313	$4 Charles II	..	2·50	3·25
1314	$4 James II	..	2·50	3·25
1315	$4 William III	..	2·50	3·25
	a. Sheetlet. Nos. 1315/21	..	16·00	
1316	$4 Mary II	..	2·50	3·25
1317	$4 Anne	..	2·50	3·25
1318	$4 George I	..	2·50	3·25
1319	$4 George II	..	2·50	3·25
1320	$4 George III	..	2·50	3·25
1321	$4 George IV	..	2·50	3·25
1322	$4 William IV	..	2·50	3·25
	a. Sheetlet. Nos. 1322/8	..	16·00	
1323	$4 Victoria	..	2·50	3·25
1324	$4 Edward VII	..	2·50	3·25
1325	$4 George V	..	2·50	3·25
1326	$4 Edward VIII	..	2·50	3·25
1327	$4 George VI	..	2·50	3·25
1328	$4 Elizabeth II	..	2·50	3·25
1287/1328		Set of 42	95·00	£120

Nos. 1287/93, 1294/1300, 1301/7, 1308/14, 1315/21 and 1322/8 were printed together, in small sheets of 8 including one *se-tenant* stamp-size label.

Although inscribed "Henry III" the portrait on No. 1294 is actually of Edward II.

Although announced as all being issued on 25 January 1984 the different sheetlets were distributed at monthly intervals.

292 Lantana

(Des P.U.B. Graphics. Litho *Format*)

1984 (9 Apr). *Flowers. T* **292** *and similar horiz designs. Multicoloured. P* 15.

1329	25 c. Type 292	..	20	15
1330	30 c. Plumbago	..	25	20
1331	90 c. Spider Lily	..	70	60
1332	$4 Giant Alocasia	..	2·00	3·00
1329/32		Set of 4	2·75	3·50
MS1333	108 × 90 mm. $5 Orange Trumpet Vine		1·25	1·50

Nos. 1329/32 exist imperforate from stock dispersed by the liquidator of Format International Security Printers Ltd.

COVER PRICES

Cover factors are quoted at the beginning of each country for most issues to 1945. An explanation of the system can be found on page x. The factors quoted do not, however, apply to philatelic covers.

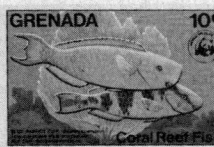

293 Blue Parrotfish   (**294**)

(Litho Questa)

1984 (21 May). *Coral Reef Fishes. T* **293** *and similar horiz designs. Multicoloured. P* 14.

1334	10 c. Type 293	..	1·40	45
1335	30 c. Flame-backed Angelfish	..	2·75	1·10
1336	70 c. Painted Wrasse	..	4·00	3·25
1337	90 c. Rosy Razorfish	..	4·75	3·50
1334/7		Set of 4	11·50	7·50
MS1338	81×85 mm. $5 Spanish Hogfish	..	6·00	4·75

1984 (19 June). *Universal Postal Union Congress, Hamburg. Nos.* 1331/3 *optd with T* **294**.

1339	90 c. Spider Lily	..	60	65
1340	$4 Giant Alocasia	..	2·00	2·50
MS1341	108 × 90 mm. $5 Orange Trumpet Vine		1·50	2·50

295 Freighter   **296** "The Night" (detail)
(Coreggio)

(Des Artists International. Litho *Format*)

1984 (16 July). *Ships. T* **295** *and similar horiz designs. Multicoloured. P* 15.

1342	40 c. Type 295	..	1·25	55
1343	70 c. *Queen Elizabeth 2*	..	1·50	1·50
1344	90 c. Sailing boats	..	1·60	2·00
1345	$4 *Amerikanis*	..	3·50	8·00
1342/5		Set of 4	7·00	11·00
MS1346	107×80 mm. $5 Spanish galleon	..	5·00	7·00

Nos. 1342/6 exist imperforate from stock dispersed by the liquidator of Format International Security Printers Ltd.

(Litho Questa)

1984 (22 Aug). *450th Death Anniv of Correggio (painter). T* **296** *and similar vert designs showing paintings. Multicoloured. P* 14.

1347	10 c. Type 296	..	45	15
1348	30 c. "The Virgin adoring the Child".	..	80	50
1349	90 c. "The Mystical Marriage of St. Catherine with St. Sebastian"	..	2·00	1·75
1350	$4 "The Madonna and the Fruit Basket"	..	4·50	5·50
1347/50		Set of 4	7·00	7·00
MS1351	54 × 73 mm. $5 "The Madonna at the Spring"	..	4·25	3·00

297 "L'Absinthe" (Degas)   **298** Train on Puffing
Billy Line, Victoria

(Litho Questa)

1984 (22 Aug). *150th Birth Anniv of Edgar Degas (painter). T* **297** *and similar multicoloured designs showing paintings. P* 14.

1352	25 c. Type 297	..	80	30
1353	70 c. "Pouting" (*horiz*)	..	1·50	1·25
1354	$1.10, "The Millinery Shop"	..	2·00	2·00
1355	$3 "The Bellelli Family" (*horiz*)	..	3·75	4·25
1352/5		Set of 4	7·25	7·00
MS1356	84 × 54 mm. $5 "The Cotton Market"	..	4·25	3·00

(Des Bonny Redecker. Litho Questa)

1984 (21 Sept). *"Ausipex" International Stamp Exhibition, Melbourne. T* **298** *and similar vert designs. Multicoloured. P* 14.

1357	$1.10, Type 298	..	2·25	1·75
1358	$4 Yacht *Australia II* (winner of America's Cup)	..	4·75	5·25
MS1359	107 × 76 mm. $5 Melbourne tram	..	4·75	4·50

299 George Stephenson's   (**300**)
Locomotion (1825)

(Des J.W. Litho *Format*)

1984 (3 Oct). *Railway Locomotives. T* **299** *and similar horiz designs. Multicoloured. P* 15.

1360	30 c. Type 299	..	80	35
1361	40 c. Braithwaite and Ericsson's *Novelty* (1829)	..	95	40
1362	60 c. William Norris's *Washington Farmer* (1836)	..	1·00	75
1363	70 c. French Crampton type (1859)	..	1·00	1·00
1364	90 c. Dutch State Railways (1873)	..	1·10	1·50
1365	$1.10, *Champion*, U.S.A. (1882)	..	1·25	2·00
1366	$2 Webb Compound type (1893)	..	1·75	3·25
1367	$4 Berlin "No. 74" (1900)	..	2·75	5·50
1360/7		Set of 8	9·50	13·00
MS1368	Two sheets, each 100×70 mm. (a) $5 Crampton *Phoenix* (1863); (b) $5 Mikado type, Japan (1897)	*Set of 2 sheets*	6·00	6·50

1984 (28 Oct). *Opening of Point Saline International Airport (1st issue). Nos.* 1247 *and* 1249/50 *optd as T* **300**.

1369	40 c. Rural telephone installation	..	30	30
1370	$3 Airport control room	..	2·00	2·00
MS1371	111×85 mm. $5 Communications satellite	..	3·50	3·25

On No. **MS**1371 the overprint, 54 × 8 mm., appears in two lines on the sheet margin only.

See also Nos. 1393/6.

301 Donald Duck as Father Christmas looking into Mirror

(Litho Questa)

1984 (26 Nov). *Christmas. Walt Disney Cartoon Characters. T* **301** *and similar vert designs. Multicoloured. P* 12 ($2) *or* 13½ × 14 *(others).*

1372	45 c. Type 301	..	1·25	40
1373	70 c. Donald Duck filling stocking with presents	..	1·50	55
1374	90 c. As Father Christmas pulling a sleigh	..	2·00	1·10
1375	$2 As Father Christmas decorating Christmas tree	..	3·50	3·50
1376	$4 Donald Duck and nephews singing carols	..	5·00	5·50
1372/6		Set of 5	12·00	10·00
MS1377	127 × 102 mm. $5 As Father Christmas in sleigh	..	7·00	8·00

No. 1375 was printed in sheetlets of 8 stamps.

(Litho Questa)

1985 (11 Feb). *Birth Bicentenary of John J. Audubon (ornithologist) (1st issue). Multicoloured designs as T* **198** *of Antigua showing original paintings. P* 14.

1378	50 c. Clapper Rail (*vert*)	..	2·00	75
1379	70 c. Hooded Warbler (*vert*)	..	2·25	1·50
1380	90 c. Common Flicker (*vert*)	..	2·75	1·75
1381	$4 Bohemian Waxwing (*vert*)	..	5·50	8·00
1378/81		Set of 4	11·00	11·00
MS1382	82×112 mm. $5 Merlin ("Pigeon Hawk")	..	9·00	4·50

See also Nos. 1480/4.

302 Honda "XL500R"

(Des R. Sentnor. Litho Questa)

1985 (11 Mar). *Centenary of the Motor Cycle. T* **302** *and similar horiz designs. Multicoloured. P* 14.

1383	25 c. Type 302	..	90	50
1384	50 c. Suzuki "GS1100ES"	..	1·40	1·00
1385	90 c. Kawasaki "KZ700"	..	2·00	2·00
1386	$4 BMW "K100"	..	5·50	6·50
1383/6		Set of 4	8·75	9·00
MS1387	109 × 81 mm. $5 Yamaha "500CC V Four"	..	6·50	5·00

303 "Explorer"

(Des Susan David. Litho Questa)

1985 (15 Apr). *75th Anniv of Girl Guide Movement. T* **303** *and similar horiz designs, showing work for Guide badges. Multicoloured. P* 14.

1388	25 c. Type **303**				55	30
1389	60 c. "Cook"				90	65
1390	90 c. "Musician"				1·50	1·10
1391	$3 "Home nurse"				3·00	4·50
				Set of 4	5·50	6·00
MS1392	97×70 mm. $5 Flags of Girl Guides and Grenada				2·50	2·50

304 Hawker Siddeley H.S.748 on Inaugural Flight from Barbados

(Des Susan David. Litho Questa)

1985 (30 Apr). *Opening of Point Saline International Airport (1984) (2nd issue). T* **304** *and similar horiz designs. Multicoloured. P* 14.

1393	70 c. Type **304**			2·50	1·00
1394	$1 Lockheed L-1011 TriStar 500 on inaugural flight from New York			3·25	1·50
1395	$4 Lockheed L-1011 TriStar 500 on inaugural flight to Miami			6·50	8·00
1393/5			*Set of 3*	11·00	9·50
MS1396	101×72 mm. $5 Point Saline Airport terminal and Hawker Siddeley H.S.748 on tarmac			5·50	3·75

305 Douglas DC-8-61

(Des BG Studio. Litho Questa)

1985 (15 May). *40th Anniv of International Civil Aviation Organization. T* **305** *and similar horiz designs. Multicoloured. P* 14.

1397	10 c. Type **305**			40	20
1398	50 c. Lockheed L.1649A Starliner			1·00	75
1399	60 c. Vickers 952 Cargoliner			1·25	85
1400	$4 De Havilland D.H.C.6 Twin Otter 200/300			4·50	6·00
1397/400			*Set of 4*	6·50	7·00
MS1401	102×64 mm. $5 Hawker Siddeley H.S.748 turboprop			3·00	3·00

306 Model Boat Racing   **307** Bird of Paradise (flower)

(Litho Format)

1985 (15 June). *Water Sports. T* **306** *and similar horiz designs. Multicoloured. P* 15.

1402	10 c. Type **306**			20	10
1403	50 c. Scuba diving, Carriacou			45	35
1404	$1.10, Windsurfers on Grand Anse Beach			75	1·00
1405	$4 Windsurfing			2·00	4·00
1402/5			*Set of 4*	3·00	5·00
MS1406	107×77 mm. $5 Beach scene			2·25	2·75

Nos. 1402/5 exist imperforate from stock dispersed by the liquidator of Format International Security Printers Ltd.

(Des Mary Walters. Litho Questa)

1985 (1 July)–88. *Native Flowers. T* **307** *and similar vert designs. Multicoloured. Chalk-surfaced paper.*

A. Without imprint date. P 14

1407	½ c. Type **307**			40	60
	a. Perf 12 (3.86)			50	60
1408	1 c. Passion Flower			50	60
	a. Perf 12 (3.86)			50	60
1409	2 c. Oleander			50	60
	a. Perf 12 (3.86)			50	60
1410	4 c. Bromeliad			85	60
	a. Perf 12 (3.86)			70	60
1411	5 c. Anthurium			85	40
	a. Perf 12 (3.86)			70	40
1412	6 c. Bougainvillea			85	50
	a. Perf 12 (3.86)			70	50
1413	10 c. Hibiscus			1·00	40
	a. Perf 12 (7.86)			70	30
1414	15 c. Ginger			1·75	40
	a. Perf 12 (3.86)			1·00	30
1415	25 c. Poinsettia			1·75	40
	a. Perf 12 (3.86)			1·00	30

1416	30 c. Mexican Creeper				1·75	70
	a. Perf 12 (3.86)				1·00	30
1417	40 c. Angel's Trumpet				2·00	70
	a. Perf 12 (3.86)				1·00	50
1418	50 c. Amaryllis				2·00	1·00
	a. Perf 12 (3.86)				1·00	75
1419	60 c. Prickly Pear				2·00	1·75
	a. Perf 12 (3.86)				1·00	90
1420	70 c. Chenille Plant				2·00	1·75
	a. Perf 12 (7.86)				1·00	1·00
1420b	75 c. Cordia (1.12.88)				1·25	1·75
1421	$1 Periwinkle				3·25	2·00
	a. Perf 12 (3.86)				2·00	1·75
1422	$1.10, Ixora				3·50	2·75
	a. Perf 12 (3.86)				2·25	2·50
1423	$3 Shrimp Plant				4·75	6·00
	a. Perf 12 (3.86)				2·75	6·00
1424	$5 Plumbago				4·75	7·00
	a. Perf 12 (7.86)				2·50	7·00
1425	$10 *Lantana camara* (11.11.85)				4·75	9·50
	a. Perf 12 (12.86)				4·00	10·00
1425b	$20 Peregrina (1.8.86)				8·50	16·00
	ba. Ordinary paper (5.8.87)				9·00	16·00
1407/25b				*Set of 21*	32·00	45·00

B. With imprint date. P 14

1425c	10 c. Hibiscus (7.88)			3·00	3·25
1425d	30 c. Mexican Creeper (1987)			20	60
1425e	50 c. Amaryllis (1987)			30	75
1425f	60 c. Prickly Pear (1987)			30	1·00
1425g	$1 Periwinkle (1987)			35	1·25
1425c/g			*Set of 5*	3·75	6·00

Imprint dates: "1987", Nos. 1425d/g; "1988", No. 1425c.

308 The Queen Mother at Royal Opera House, London   **309** Youth Gardening (Horticulture)

(Des J.W. Litho Questa)

1985 (3 July). *Life and Times of Queen Elizabeth the Queen Mother. T* **308** *and similar multicoloured designs. P* 14.

1426	$1 Type **308**			40	60
1427	$1.50, The Queen Mother playing snooker at London Press Club (*horiz*)			55	85
1428	$2.50, At Epsom Races, 1960			95	1·50
1426/8			*Set of 3*	1·75	2·75
MS1429	56×85 mm. $5 With Prince of Wales on 80th Birthday			1·75	3·00

Stamps as Nos. 1426/8, but with face values of 90 c., $1 and $3, exist from additional sheetlets of 5 plus a label issued December 1985. These also have changed background colours and are perforated 12½×12 ($1) or 12×12½ (others) (*Price for set of 3 stamps £1.50 mint*).

(Des Liane Fried. Litho Format)

1985 (21 Aug). *International Youth Year. T* **309** *and similar vert designs. Multicoloured. P* 15.

1430	25 c. Type **309**			25	20
1431	50 c. Young people on beach (Leisure)			35	40
1432	$1.10, Girls in classroom (Education)			60	1·10
1433	$3 Nurse and young patient (Health Care)			1·50	2·50
1430/3			*Set of 4*	2·40	3·75
MS1434	111×80 mm. $5 Children of different races			1·50	3·00

(Des Susan David. Litho Questa)

1985 (3 Sept). *300th Birth Anniv of Johann Sebastian Bach (composer). Vert designs as T* **206** *of Antigua. P* 14.

1435	25 c. multicoloured			80	20
1436	70 c. multicoloured			1·50	85
1437	$1 multicoloured			2·00	1·25
1438	$3 multicoloured			3·00	5·00
1435/8			*Set of 4*	6·50	6·50
MS1439	104×74 mm. $5 black, lavender-grey and cinnamon			3·50	3·75

Designs:—25 c. Crumhorn; 70 c. Oboe d'amore; $1 Violin; $3 Harpsichord; $5 Johann Sebastian Bach.

310 Cub Scouts Camping

(Des A. DiLorenzo. Litho Questa)

1985 (5 Sept). *4th Caribbean Cuboree. T* **310** *and similar multicoloured designs. P* 14.

1440	10 c. Type **310**			30	15
1441	50 c. Cub scouts swimming ("Physical Fitness")			65	40
1442	$1 Stamp collecting			1·50	80
1443	$4 Birdwatching			3·50	3·00
1440/3			*Set of 4*	5·50	4·00
MS1444	103×75 mm. $5 Cub scouts saluting leader (*vert*)			3·25	3·50

(Des Mary Walters. Litho Format)

1985 (4 Nov). *Royal Visit. Multicoloured designs as T* **207** *of Antigua. P* 14½.

1445	50 c. Flags of Great Britain and Grenada			75	40
1446	$1 Queen Elizabeth II (*vert*)			1·00	1·25
1447	$4 Royal Yacht *Britannia*			2·50	5·00
1445/7			*Set of 3*	3·75	6·00
MS1448	111×83 mm. $5 Map of Grenada			1·75	3·25

(Des Walt Disney Productions. Litho Questa)

1985 (4 Nov). *150th Birth Anniv of Mark Twain (author). Horiz designs as T* **118** *of Anguilla showing Walt Disney cartoon characters in scenes from "The Prince and the Pauper". Multicoloured. P* 14×13½.

1449	25 c. Mortie as Tom meeting the Prince (Ferdie)			60	20
1450	50 c. Tom and the Prince exchanging clothes			80	50
1451	$1.10, The Prince with John Cantry			1·75	1·75
1452	$1.50, The Prince knights Mike Hendon (Goofy)			2·25	2·75
1453	$2 Tom and the Whipping Boy			2·50	3·00
1449/53			*Set of 5*	7·00	7·50
MS1454	124×100 mm. $5 The Prince, Tom and Mike Hendon			6·00	6·00

(Des Walt Disney Productions. Litho Questa)

1985 (4 Nov). *Birth Bicentenaries of Grimm Brothers (folklorists). Horiz designs as T* **119** *of Anguilla, showing Walt Disney cartoon characters in scenes from "The Fisherman and his Wife". Multicoloured. P* 14×13½.

1455	30 c. The Fisherman (Goofy) catching enchanted fish			65	30
1456	60 c. The Fisherman scolded by his Wife (Clarabelle)			90	80
1457	70 c. The Fisherman's Wife with dream cottage			1·10	95
1458	$1 The Fisherman's Wife as King			1·75	1·50
1459	$3 The Fisherman and Wife in their original shack			3·25	4·50
1455/9			*Set of 5*	7·00	7·25
MS1460	126×100 mm. $5 The Fisherman in boat			6·00	6·00

311 Red-spotted Hawkfish

(Des R. Sauber. Litho Questa)

1985 (15 Nov). *Marine Life. T* **311** *and similar horiz designs. Multicoloured. P* 14.

1461	25 c. Type **311**			1·25	55
1462	50 c. Spot-finned Butterflyfish			2·00	1·10
1463	$1.10, Fire Coral and Orange Sponges			3·25	3·25
1464	$3 Pillar Coral			6·00	7·50
1461/4			*Set of 4*	11·00	11·00
MS1465	127×100 mm. $5 Bigeye			3·75	4·50

(Litho Format)

1985 (22 Nov). *40th Anniv of United Nations Organization. Multicoloured designs as T* **208** *of Antigua showing United Nations (New York) stamps. P* 14½.

1466	50 c. Mary McLeod Bethune (educationist) and 1975 International Women's Year 10 c.			30	30
1467	$2 Maimonides (physician) and 1966 W.H.O. 5 c.			2·50	3·50
1468	$2.50, Alexander Graham Bell (telephone inventor) and 1956 I.T.U. 3 c.			2·00	4·00
1466/8			*Set of 3*	4·25	7·00
MS1469	110×85 mm. $5 Dag Hammarskjold (Secretary-General) (*vert*)			1·50	2·00

VISIT OF

PRES REAGAN

20 FEB. 1986

312 "The Adoration of the Shepherds" (Mantegna)   (**313**)

(Des Mary Walters. Litho Format)

1985 (23 Dec). *Christmas. Religious Paintings. T* **312** *and similar horiz designs. Multicoloured. P* 15.

1470	25 c. Type **312**			20	15
1471	60 c. "Journey of the Magi" (Sassetta)			30	40
1472	90 c. "Madonna and Child enthroned with Saints" (Raphael)			35	70
1473	$4 "Nativity" (Monaco)			1·00	3·50
1470/3			*Set of 4*	1·75	4·25
MS1474	107×81 mm. $5 "Madonna and Child enthroned with Saints" (Gaddi)			1·50	2·50

(Des J. Iskowitz. Litho Questa)

1986 (6 Jan). *Centenary of Statue of Liberty (1st issue). Multicoloured designs as T* **211** *of Dominica. P* 15.

1475	5 c. Columbus Monument, 1893 (*vert*)			15	20
1476	25 c. Columbus Monument, 1986 (*vert*)			30	20
1477	40 c. Mounted police, Central Park, 1895			1·75	1·10
1478	$4 Mounted police, 1986			5·00	8·00
1475/8			*Set of 4*	6·50	8·50
MS1479	104×76 mm. $5 Statue of Liberty (*vert*)			2·25	2·50

See also Nos. 1644/52.

(Litho Questa)

1986 (20 Jan). *Birth Bicentenary of John J. Audubon (ornithologist) (2nd issue). Multicoloured designs as T 198 of Antigua.*
P 12 × 12½.
1480 50 c. Snowy Egret .. .. .. 2·00 80
1481 90 c. Greater Flamingo .. .. 2·75 2·00
1482 $1.10, Canada Goose .. .. 2·75 2·50
1483 $3 Smew .. .. 4·50 6·00
1480/3 *Set of 4* 11·00 10·00
MS1484 103 × 72 mm. $5 Brent Goose (*horiz*).
P 14 13·00 13·00
Nos. 1480/3 were each issued in sheetlets of five stamps and
one stamp-size label, which appears in the centre of the bottom
row.

1986 (20 Feb). *Visit of President Reagan. Nos. 1418A and
1424A optd with T 313.*
1485 50 c. Amaryllis 50 50
1486 $5 Plumbago .. .. .. 3·00 5·00

314 Methodist Church,
St. Georges
315 Player with
Ball

(Litho Format)

1986 (24 Feb). *Bicentenary of Methodist Church in Grenada.
T 314 and similar horiz design. Multicoloured.* P 15.
1487 60 c. Type 314 .. .. 70 1·00
MS1488 102 × 73 mm. $5 St. Georges .. 1·00 3·00

(Des N. Waldman. Litho Questa)

1986 (6 Mar). *World Cup Football Championship, Mexico.
T 315 and similar vert designs. Multicoloured.* P 14.
1489 50 c. Type 315 .. .. .. 80 55
1490 70 c. Player heading ball .. .. 1·00 1·00
1491 90 c. Player controlling ball .. 1·50 1·50
1492 $4 Player controlling ball with right foot 5·50 7·00
1489/92 *Set of 4* 8·00 9·00
MS1493 101 × 71 mm. $5 Player tackling .. 4·25 5·00

(Des W. Hanson. Litho Questa)

1986 (20 Mar). *Appearance of Halley's Comet (1st issue). Horiz
designs as T 123 of Anguilla. Multicoloured.* P 14.
1494 5 c. Clyde Tombaugh (astronomer) and
Dudley Observatory, New York .. 40 40
1495 20 c. N.A.S.A. – U.S.A.F. "X-24B" Space
Shuttle prototype, 1973 .. 50 30
1496 40 c. German comet medal, 1618 .. 70 45
1497 $4 Destruction of Sodom and Gomorrah,
1949 B.C. .. .. .. 3·50 4·50
1494/7 *Set of 4* 4·50 5·00
MS1498 102 × 70 mm. $5 Halley's Comet over
Grenada .. .. 6·50 7·00
See also Nos. 1533/7 and 1980/4.

(Litho Questa)

1986 (21 Apr). *60th Birthday of Queen Elizabeth II. Vert
designs as T 125 of Anguilla.* P 14.
1499 2 c. black and yellow 10 15
1500 $1.50, multicoloured 60 80
1501 $4 multicoloured .. .. 1·50 2·50
1499/1501 *Set of 3* 2·00 3·00
MS1502 120 × 85 mm. $5 black and grey-brown .. 1·75 3·25
Designs:—2 c. Princess Elizabeth in 1951; $1.50, Queen
presenting trophy at polo match, Windsor, 1965; $4 At Epsom,
Derby Day, 1977; $5 King George VI and family, 1939.

(Des Walt Disney Productions. Litho Format)

1986 (22 May). *"Ameripex" International Stamp Exhibition,
Chicago. Horiz designs as T 212 of Dominica, showing Walt
Disney cartoon characters playing baseball. Multicoloured.*
P 11.
1503 1 c. Goofy as pitcher 10 10
1504 2 c. Goofy as catcher 10 10
1505 3 c. Mickey Mouse striking ball and Donald
Duck as catcher 10 10
1506 4 c. Huey forcing out Dewey .. 10 10
1507 5 c. Chip n'Dale chasing flyball .. 10 10
1508 6 c. Mickey Mouse, Donald Duck and Clara-
belle in argument 10 10
1509 $2 Minnie Mouse and Donald Duck read-
ing baseball rules .. .. 1·75 2·75
1510 $3 Ludwig von Drake as umpire with
Goofy and Pete colliding .. 2·25 3·25
1503/10 *Set of 8* 4·00 6·00
MS1511 Two sheets, each 126 × 101 mm. (a) $5
Donald Duck striking ball. (b) $5 Minnie and
Mickey Mouse running between bases.
P 14 × 13½ *Set of 2 sheets* 11·00 13·00

(Litho Questa)

1986 (1 July). *Royal Wedding. Vert designs as T 213 of
Antigua. Multicoloured.* P 14.
1512 2 c. Prince Andrew and Miss Sarah Ferguson 10 20
1513 $1.10, Prince Andrew 70 80
1514 $4 Prince Andrew with H.M.S. *Brazen's*
Westland WG-13 Lynx helicopter .. 2·75 3·25
1512/14 *Set of 3* 3·25 3·75
MS1515 88 × 88 mm. $5 Prince Andrew and Miss
Sarah Ferguson (*different*) .. .. 4·00 5·00

316 Brown-lined Latirus
317 *Lepiota roseolamellata*

(Des L. Birmingham. Litho Format)

1986 (15 July). *Sea Shells. T 316 and similar horiz designs.
Multicoloured.* P 15.
1516 25 c. Type 316 .. .. .. 45 25
1517 60 c. Lamellose Wentletrap 75 90
1518 70 c. Atlantic Turkey Wing .. .. 85 1·00
1519 $4 Rooster-tail Conch .. .. 2·75 5·00
1516/19 .. .. .. *Set of 4* 4·25 6·50
MS1520 110 × 75 mm. $5 Angular Triton .. 2·75 5·50

(Des R. Sauber. Litho Format)

1986 (1 Aug). *Mushrooms. T 317 and similar vert designs.
Multicoloured.* P 15.
1521 10 c. Type 317 .. .. .. 60 40
1522 60 c. *Lentinus bertieri* .. .. 1·75 1·75
1523 $1 *Lentinus retinervis* .. .. 2·50 2·50
1524 $4 *Eccilia cystiophorus* .. .. 5·75 7·50
1521/4 .. .. .. *Set of 4* 9·50 11·00
MS1525 127 × 100 mm. $5 *Cystolepiota eriophora* 10·00 13·00
No. MS1525 exists imperforate from stock dispersed by the
liquidator of Format International Security Printers Ltd.

1986 (15 Sept). *World Cup Football Championship Winners,
Mexico. Nos. 1489/93 optd with T 216 of Antigua in gold.*
1526 50 c. Type 315 .. .. .. 85 85
1527 70 c. Player heading ball .. .. 1·00 1·00
1528 90 c. Player controlling ball .. 1·40 1·60
1529 $4 Player controlling ball with right foot 4·50 5·00
1526/9 .. .. .. *Set of 4* 7·00 7·75
MS1530 101 × 71 mm. $5 Player tackling .. 3·50 4·50

318 Dove on Rifles
and Mahatma Gandhi
(Disarmament Week)
319 Cockerel and Hen

(Des Mary Walters. Litho Format)

1986 (15 Sept). *International Events. T 318 and similar
multicoloured design.* P 15.
1531 60 c. Type 318 .. .. .. 50 50
1532 $4 Hands passing olive branch and Mar-
tin Luther King (International Peace
Year) (*horiz*) .. .. 1·50 3·00
Nos. 1531/2 exist imperforate from stock dispersed by the
liquidator of Format International Security Printers Ltd.

1986 (15 Oct). *Appearance of Halley's Comet (2nd issue). Nos.
1494/8 optd with T 218 of Antigua (in silver on $5).*
1533 5 c. Clyde Tombaugh (astronomer) and
Dudley Observatory, New York .. 60 60
1534 20 c. N.A.S.A.—U.S.A.F. "X-24B" Space
Shuttle prototype, 1973 .. 85 60
1535 40 c. German comet medal, 1618 .. 1·25 70
1536 $4 Destruction of Sodom and Gomorrah,
1949 B.C. .. .. .. 5·00 7·00
1533/6 .. .. .. *Set of 4* 7·00 8·00
MS1537 102 × 70 mm. $5 Halley's Comet over
Grenada .. .. 3·50 4·25

(Des Walt Disney Co. Litho Format)

1986 (3 Nov). *Christmas. Multicoloured designs as T 220 of
Antigua showing Walt Disney cartoon characters.* P 11.
1538 30 c. Mickey Mouse asleep in armchair
(*vert*) 35 25
1539 45 c. Young Mickey Mouse with Father
Christmas (*vert*) 45 30
1540 60 c. Donald Duck with toy telephone .. 60 50
1541 70 c. Pluto with pushcart 70 70
1542 $1.10, Daisy Duck with doll .. 1·00 1·25
1543 $2 Goofy as Father Christmas (*vert*) .. 1·75 2·00
1544 $2.50, Goofy singing carols at piano (*vert*) 2·00 2·50
1545 $3 Mickey Mouse, Donald Duck and
nephew riding toy train .. 2·25 3·00
1538/45 .. .. .. *Set of 8* 8·00 9·50
MS1546 Two sheets, each 127 × 101 mm. (a) $5
Donald Duck, Goofy and Mickey Mouse delivering presents (*vert*). P 13½ × 14. (b) $5 Father
Christmas playing toy piano. P 14 × 13½
Set of 2 sheets 7·00 10·00

(Litho Questa)

1986 (17 Nov). *Fauna and Flora. T 319 and similar horiz
designs. Multicoloured.* P 14.
1547 10 c. Type 319 .. .. .. 20 10
1548 30 c. Fish-eating Bat 35 20
1549 60 c. Goat 55 45

1550 70 c. Cow 60 50
1551 $1 Anthurium .. .. .. 1·50 1·25
1552 $1.10, Royal Poinciana .. .. 1·50 1·25
1553 $2 Frangipani .. .. .. 2·50 3·25
1554 $4 Orchid .. .. .. 8·50 9·50
1547/54 .. .. .. *Set of 8* 14·00 15·00
MS1555 Two sheets, each 104 × 73 mm. (a) $5
Grenada landscape. (b) $5 Horse *Set of 2 sheets* 12·00 13·00

320 Maserati "Biturbo" (1984)
321 Pole Vaulting

(Des J. Martin. Litho Format)

1986 (20 Nov). *Centenary of Motoring. T 320 and similar horiz
designs. Multicoloured.* P 15.
1556 10 c. Type 320 .. .. .. 25 25
1557 30 c. AC "Cobra" (1960) 40 40
1558 60 c. Corvette (1963) 60 60
1559 70 c. Dusenberg "SJ7" (1932) .. 70 70
1560 90 c. Porsche (1957).. .. .. 85 1·00
1561 $1.10, Stoewer (1930) .. .. 1·00 1·25
1562 $2 Volkswagen "Beetle" (1957) .. 1·60 2·00
1563 $3 Mercedes "600 Limo" (1963) .. 1·90 2·50
1556/63 .. .. .. *Set of 8* 6·50 8·00
MS1564 Two sheets, each 106 × 77 mm. (a) $5
Stutz (1914). (b) $5 Packard (1941)
Set of 2 sheets 5·50 7·00

(Des BG Studio. Litho Format)

1986 (1 Dec). *Olympic Games, Seoul, South Korea (1988). T 321
and similar vert designs. Multicoloured.* P 15.
1565 10 c. + 5 c. Type 321 .. .. 10 30
1566 50 c. + 20 c. Gymnastics 35 60
1567 70 c. + 30 c. Putting the shot .. 50 85
1568 $2 + $1 high jumping .. .. 1·00 2·25
1565/8 .. .. .. *Set of 4* 1·75 3·50
MS1569 80 × 100 mm. $3 + $1 Swimming .. 1·50 3·25
The premiums on Nos. 1565/9 were to support the participation of the Grenada team.
Nos. 1565/9 exist imperforate from stock dispersed by the
liquidator of Format International Security Printers Ltd.

(Litho Questa)

1986 (19 Dec). *Birth Centenary of Marc Chagall (artist).
Designs as T 225 of Antigua, showing various paintings.*
P 13½ × 14 (*vert*) or 14 × 13½ (*horiz*).
1570/1609 $1 × 40 multicoloured .. *Set of 40* 24·00 26·00
MS1610 Ten sheets, each 110 × 95 mm. $5 × 10
multicoloured (*each 104 × 89 mm*). Imperf
Set of 10 sheets 24·00 26·00
Although announced as all being released on 19 December
1986 the issue was distributed in ten parts, each of four stamps
and one miniature sheet, at monthly intervals.

(Des J. Iskowitz. Litho Format)

1987 (5 Feb). *America's Cup Yachting Championship. Vert
designs as T 222 of Antigua. Multicoloured.* P 15.
1611 10 c. *Columbia*, 1958 .. .. 25 20
1612 60 c. *Resolute*, 1920 .. .. 55 60
1613 $1.10, *Endeavor*, 1934 .. .. 85 1·25
1614 $4 *Rainbow*, 1934.. .. .. 1·75 3·50
1611/14 .. .. .. *Set of 4* 3·00 5·00
MS1615 113 × 84 mm. $5 *Weatherly*, 1962 .. 2·25 4·00

322 Virgin Mary and Outline
Map of Grenada
323 Black Grouper

(Des G. Hamilton (10, 30, 50 c.), Mary Walters (others). Litho
Format)

1987 (27 Apr). *500th Anniv of Discovery of America by
Columbus (1992) (1st issue). T 322 and similar multicoloured
designs.* P 15.
1616 10 c. Type 322 .. .. .. 20 20
1617 30 c. *Santa Maria, Pinta and Nina* (*horiz*) .. 60 35
1618 50 c. Columbus and outline map of Grenada 70 45
1619 60 c. Christopher Columbus .. 70 55
1620 90 c. King Ferdinand and Queen Isabella of
Spain (*horiz*) 70 80
1621 $1.10, Map of Antilles by Columbus .. 90 1·00
1622 $2 Caribs with sailing raft (*horiz*) .. 1·10 2·25
1623 $3 Columbus in the New World, 1493
(contemporary drawing) .. 1·25 2·25
1616/23 .. .. .. *Set of 8* 5·50 7·00
MS1624 Two sheets, each 104 × 72 mm. (a) $5
Route map and Columbus' signature. (b) $5
Columbus carrying Christ Child (*vert*) .. 5·00 7·50
Nos. 1616/23 exist imperforate from stock dispersed by the
liquidator of Format International Security Printers Ltd.
See also Nos. 2051/5, 2091/9, 2222/30, 2389/95 and 2423/4.

(Des W. Wright. Litho Questa)

1987 (18 May). *Milestones of Transportation. Horiz designs as T* **226** *of Antigua. Multicoloured. P* 14.

1625	10 c. Cornu's first helicopter, 1907	70	55
1626	16 c. *Monitor* and *Merrimack* (first battle between ironclad warships), 1862	70	60
1627	30 c. LZ1 (first Zeppelin), 1900	90	80
1628	50 c. *Sirius* (first transatlantic paddle-steamer crossing), 1838	1·00	85
1629	60 c. Steam locomotive on Trans-Siberian Railway (longest line)	1·25	1·00
1630	70 c. U.S.S. *Enterprise* (largest aircraft carrier), 1960	1·25	1·25
1631	90 c. Blanchard and Jeffries' balloon (first balloon across English Channel), 1785	1·40	1·40
1632	$1.50, U.S.S. *Holland 1* (first steam-powered submarine), 1900	2·00	2·25
1633	$2 *Oceanic I* (first luxury liner), 1871	2·50	2·75
1634	$3 Lamborghini "Countach" (fastest commercial car), 1984	2·75	3·25
1625/34	*Set of* 10	13·00	13·00

(Des J. Martin. Litho Format)

1987 (15 June). *"Capex '87" International Stamp Exhibition, Toronto. Game Fishes. T* **323** *and similar multicoloured designs. P* 15.

1635	10 c. Type **323**	30	15
1636	30 c. Blue Marlin (*horiz*)	40	15
1637	60 c. White Marlin	60	55
1638	70 c. Bigeye Threshershark (*horiz*)	70	70
1639	$1 Bonefish (*horiz*)	90	1·00
1640	$1.10, Wahoo (*horiz*)	1·00	1·25
1641	$2 Sailfish (*horiz*)	1·75	2·25
1642	$4 Albacore (*horiz*)	2·75	3·50
1635/42	*Set of* 8	7·50	8·50
MS1643	Two sheets, each 100×70 mm. (a) $5 Yellow-finned Tuna. (b) $5 Great Barracuda (*horiz*) *Set of* 2 *sheets*	7·00	9·00

(Litho Questa)

1987 (5 Aug). *Centenary of Statue of Liberty* (1986) (*2nd issue*). *Multicoloured designs as T* **227** *of Antigua. P* 14.

1644	10 c. Computer projections of Statue and base (*horiz*)	15	15
1645	25 c. Statue and fireworks (*horiz*)	20	15
1646	50 c. Statue and fireworks (*different*) (*horiz*)	35	35
1647	60 c. Statue and boats	45	45
1648	70 c. Computer projections of top of Statue (*horiz*)	50	50
1649	$1 Rear view of Statue and fireworks	80	80
1650	$1.10, Aerial view of Statue	95	1·25
1651	$2 Statue and flotilla	2·00	2·25
1652	$4 *Queen Elizabeth 2* in New York Harbour	3·50	4·00
1644/52	*Set of* 9	8·00	9·00

324 Alice and the Rabbit Hole

(Des Walt Disney Co. Litho Questa)

1987 (9 Sept). *50th Anniv of First Full-Length Disney Cartoon Film. T* **324** *and similar designs. P* 14×13½.

1653/1706	30 c. × 54 multicoloured	*Set of* 54	16·00	17·00
MS1707	Six sheets, each 127×102 mm. $5×6 multicoloured. P 13½×14 (*vert*) or 14×13½ (*horiz*)	*Set of* 6 *sheets*	30·00	30·00

Nos. 1653/1706 (issued as six sheetlets each of nine different designs) and No. **MS**1707 depict scenes from *Alice in Wonderland, Cinderella, Peter Pan, Pinocchio, Sleeping Beauty* and *Snow White and the Seven Dwarfs.*

325 Isaac Newton holding Apple (Law of Gravity)

(Litho Questa)

1987 (9 Sept). *Great Scientific Discoveries. T* **325** *and similar horiz designs. Multicoloured. P* 14.

1708	50 c. Type **325**	85	85
1709	$1.10, John Jacob Berzelius and symbols of chemical elements	1·75	1·75
1710	$2 Robert Boyle (law of Pressure and Volume)	2·50	3·25
1711	$3 James Watt and drawing of steam engine	4·25	4·50
1708/11	*Set of* 4	8·50	9·50
MS1712	105×75 mm. $5 *Voyager* (experimental aircraft) and Wright glider No. IV	3·00	4·00

No. 1711 is inscribed "RUDOLF DIESEL" and No. **MS**1712 "Flyer I", both in error.

326 Wade Boggs (Boston Red Sox)　　(327)

(Des W. Storozuk. Litho Questa)

1987 (2 Nov). *All-Star Baseball Game, Oakland, California. Sheet* 114 × 82 *mm, containing T* **326** *and similar horiz design. Multicoloured. P* 14×13½.

MS1713	$1 Type **326**; $1 Eric Davis (Cincinnati Reds)	75	1·50

1987 (2 Nov). *60th Anniv of International Social Security Association. Nos.* 1413A, 1418A *and* 1423A *optd with T* **327**.

1714	10 c. Hibiscus	10	15
1715	50 c. Amaryllis	25	35
1716	$3 Shrimp Plant	1·40	2·25
1714/16	*Set of* 3	1·50	2·50

(Litho Questa)

1987 (2 Nov). *Bicentenary of U.S. Constitution. Multicoloured designs as T* **232** *of Antigua. P* 14.

1717	15 c. Independence Hall, Philadelphia (*vert*)	10	10
1718	50 c. Benjamin Franklin (Pennsylvania delegate) (*vert*)	25	35
1719	60 c. State Seal, Massachusetts	25	35
1720	$4 Robert Morris (Pennsylvania delegate) (*vert*)	1·75	2·75
1717/20	*Set of* 4	2·10	3·25
MS1721	105×75 mm. $5 James Madison (Virginia delegate) (*vert*)	2·00	3·50

Nos. 1717/20 were each issued in sheetlets of five stamps and one stamp-size label, which appears in the centre of the bottom row.

328 Goofy in "The Shadow"　　329 "The Annunciation" (Fra Angelico)

(Des Walt Disney Co. Litho Questa)

1987 (16 Nov). *"Hafnia '87" International Stamp Exhibition, Copenhagen. T* **328** *and similar vert designs showing Walt Disney cartoon characters in scenes from Hans Christian Andersen's fairy tales. Multicoloured. P* 13½×14.

1722	25 c. Type **328**	50	30
1723	30 c. Mother Stork and brood in "The Storks"	50	30
1724	50 c. King Richard, Robin Hood and Little John (from *Robin Hood*) in "The Emperor's New Clothes"	75	55
1725	60 c. Goofy and Pluto in "The Tinderbox"	75	55
1726	70 c. Daisy and Donald Duck in "The Shepherdess and the Chimney Sweep"	80	70
1727	$1.50, Mickey and Minnie Mouse in "The Little Mermaid"	1·60	1·75
1728	$3 Clarabelle and Goofy in "The Princess and the Pea"	2·50	3·50
1729	$4 Minnie Mouse and Pegleg Pete in "The Marsh King's Daughter"	2·50	3·50
1722/9	*Set of* 8	9·00	10·00
MS1730	Two sheets, each 127×102 mm. (a) $5 Goofy in "The Flying Trunk". (b) $5 Goofy as "The Sandman" *Set of* 2 *sheets*	12·00	14·00

(Litho Questa)

1987 (15 Dec). *Christmas. T* **329** *and similar vert designs showing religious paintings. Multicoloured. P* 14.

1731	15 c. Type **329**	55	10
1732	30 c. "The Annunciation" (attr. Hubert van Eyck)	90	30
1733	60 c. "The Adoration of the Magi" (Januarius Zick)	1·75	1·40
1734	$4 "The Flight into Egypt" (Gerard David)	5·50	7·00
1731/4	*Set of* 4	8·00	8·00
MS1735	99×75 mm. $5 "The Circumcision" (Giovanni Bellini studio)	7·00	8·00

330 T. Albert Marryshow

(Litho Questa)

1988 (22 Jan). *Birth Centenary of T. Albert Marryshow* (*nationalist*). *P* 14.

1736	**330** 25 c. reddish brown, chestnut & brt crim	30	30

(Des and litho Questa)

1988 (15 Feb). *Royal Ruby Wedding. Vert designs as T* **234** *of Antigua. P* 14.

1737	15 c. deep brown, black and bright new blue	35	10
1738	50 c. multicoloured	70	50
1739	$1 deep brown and black	1·25	2·00
1740	$4 multicoloured	3·00	4·00
1737/40	*Set of* 4	4·75	6·00
MS1741	76×100 mm. $5 multicoloured	2·25	3·25

Designs:—15 c. Wedding photograph, 1947; 50 c. Queen Elizabeth II with Prince Charles and Princess Anne, *c.* 1955; $1 Queen with Princess Anne, *c.* 1957; $4 Queen Elizabeth (from photo by Tim Graham), 1980; $5 Princess Elizabeth in wedding dress, 1947.

331 Goofy and Daisy Duck lighting Olympic Torch, Olympia　　332 Scout fishing from Boat

(Des Walt Disney Company. Litho Questa)

1988 (13 Apr). *Olympic Games, Seoul. T* **331** *and similar vert designs showing Walt Disney cartoon characters. Multicoloured. P* 13½×14.

1742	1 c. Type **331**	10	10
1743	2 c. Donald and Daisy Duck carrying Olympic torch	10	10
1744	3 c. Donald Duck, Goofy and Mickey Mouse carrying flags of U.S., Korea and Spain	10	10
1745	4 c. Donald Duck releasing doves	10	10
1746	5 c. Mickey Mouse flying with rocket belt	10	10
1747	10 c. Morty and Ferdie carrying banner with Olympic motto	10	10
1748	$6 Donald Duck, Minnie Mouse and Hodori the Tiger (mascot of Seoul Games)	5·50	5·50
1749	$7 Pluto, Hodori and old post office, Seoul	5·50	5·50
1742/9	*Set of* 8	10·00	10·00
MS1750	Two sheets, each 127×101 mm. (a) $5 Mickey Mouse taking athlete's oath. (b) $5 Donald and Daisy Duck as athletes at Closing Ceremony *Set of* 2 *sheets*	8·50	10·00

1988 (19 Apr). *Stamp Exhibitions. Nos.* 1631/4 *optd as T* **241** *of Antigua with various emblems.*

1751	90 c. Blanchard and Jeffries' balloon, 1785 (optd "OLYMPHILEX '88", Seoul)	85	85
1752	$1.50, U.S.S. *Holland 1*, 1900 (optd "INDEPENDENCE 40", Israel)	1·10	1·25
1753	$2 *Oceanic I*, 1871 (optd "FINLANDIA 88", Helsinki)	1·60	2·00
1754	$3 Lamborghini "Countach", 1984 (optd "Praga 99", Prague)	2·00	2·50
1751/4	*Set of* 4	5·00	6·00

(Des J. Martin. Litho Questa)

1988 (3 May). *World Scout Jamboree, Australia. T* **332** *and similar multicoloured designs. P* 14.

1755	20 c. Type **332**	40	15
1756	70 c. Scouts hiking through forest (*horiz*)	1·00	1·00
1757	90 c. Practicing first aid (*horiz*)	1·40	1·40
1758	$3 Shooting rapids in inflatable canoe	3·00	3·75
1755/8	*Set of* 4	5·25	5·75
MS1759	114×80 mm. $5 Scout with Koala	2·10	3·00

333 Santa Maria de Guia (Columbus), 1498, and Map of Rotary District　　334 Roseate Tern

(Des W. Hanson. Litho Questa)

1988 (5 May). *Rotary District 405 Conference, St. George's.*
T 333 and similar multicoloured design. P 13½×14.

1760	$2 Type 333		1·00	1·25
MS1761	133×90 mm. $10 Rotary emblem (*horiz*). P 14×13½		4·25	6·00

(Des Mary Walters. Litho Questa)

1988 (31 May). *Birds. T 334 and similar vert designs.*
Multicoloured. P 14.

1762	10 c. Type 334		60	30
1763	25 c. Laughing Gull		80	30
1764	50 c. Osprey		1·25	70
1765	60 c. Rose-breasted Grosbeak		1·25	70
1766	90 c. Purple Gallinule		1·25	90
1767	$1.10, White-tailed Tropic Bird		1·25	1·00
1768	$3 Blue-faced Booby		1·75	2·75
1769	$4 Common Shoveler		1·90	3·00
1762/9		*Set of 8*	9·00	8·75
MS1770	Two sheets, each 100×71 mm. (a) $5 Belted Kingfisher. (b) $5 Grenada Flycatcher ("Rusty-tailed Flycatcher")	*Set of 2 sheets*	7·00	9·00

335 Vauxhall Type "OE 30/98", 1925

336 LZ-127 *Graf Zeppelin* over Chicago World's Fair, 1933

(Des W. Wright. Litho B.D.T.)

1988 (1 June). *Cars. T 335 and similar vert designs.*
Multicoloured. P 13.

1771	$2 Type 335		1·10	1·25
	a. Sheetlet. Nos. 1771/80		10·00	
1772	$2 Wills "Sainte Claire", 1926		1·10	1·25
1773	$2 Bucciali, 1928		1·10	1·25
1774	$2 Irving Napier "Golden Arrow", 1929		1·10	1·25
1775	$2 Studebaker "President", 1930		1·10	1·25
1776	$2 Thomas "Flyer", 1907		1·10	1·25
1777	$2 Isotta-Fraschini "Tipo J", 1908		1·10	1·25
1778	$2 Fiat 10/14HP, 1910		1·10	1·25
1779	$2 Mercer "Type 35 Raceabout", 1911		1·10	1·25
1780	$2 Marmon "Model 34 Cloverleaf", 1917		1·10	1·25
1781	$2 Tatra "Type 77", 1934		1·10	1·25
	a. Sheetlet. Nos. 1781/90		10·00	
1782	$2 Rolls-Royce "Phantom III", 1938		1·10	1·25
1783	$2 Studebaker "Champion Starlight", 1947		1·10	1·25
1784	$2 Porsche "Gmund", 1948		1·10	1·25
1785	$2 Tucker, 1948		1·10	1·25
1786	$2 Peerless "V-16", 1931		1·10	1·25
1787	$2 Minerva "AL", 1931		1·10	1·25
1788	$2 Reo "Royale", 1933		1·10	1·25
1789	$2 Pierce Arrow "Silver Arrow", 1933		1·10	1·25
1790	$2 Hupmobile "Aerodynamic", 1934		1·10	1·25
1791	$2 Peugeot "404", 1965		1·10	1·25
	a. Sheetlet. Nos. 1791/1800		10·00	
1792	$2 Ford "Capri", 1969		1·10	1·25
1793	$2 Ferrari "312T", 1975		1·10	1·25
1794	$2 Lotus "T-79", 1978		1·10	1·25
1795	$2 Williams-Cosworth "FW07", 1979		1·10	1·25
1796	$2 H.R.G. "1500 Sports", 1948		1·10	1·25
1797	$2 Crosley "Hotshot", 1949		1·10	1·25
1798	$2 Volvo "PV444", 1955		1·10	1·25
1799	$2 Maserati "Tipo 61", 1960		1·10	1·25
1800	$2 Saab "96", 1963		1·10	1·25
1771/1800		*Set of 30*	29·00	30·00

Nos. 1771/80, 1781/90 and 1791/1800 were each printed together, *se-tenant,* in sheetlets of 10.

(Litho Questa)

1988 (15 June). *500th Birth Anniv of Titian (artist).*
Multicoloured designs as T 238 of Antigua. P 13½×14.

1801	10 c. "Lavinia Vecellio"		10	10
1802	20 c. "Portrait of a Man"		10	10
1803	25 c. "Andrea de Franceschi"		10	15
1804	90 c. "Head of a Soldier"		40	45
1805	$1 "Man with a Flute"		45	50
1806	$2 "Lucrezia and Tarquinius"		80	1·00
1807	$3 "Duke of Mantua with Dog"		1·25	1·60
1808	$4 "La Bella di Tiziano"		1·60	2·00
1801/8		*Set of 8*	4·25	5·25
MS1809	Two sheets, each 110×95 mm. (a) $5 "Allegory of Alfonso D'Avalos" (detail). P 13½×14. (b) $5 "Fall of Man" (detail) (*horiz*). P 14×13½	*Set of 2 sheets*	4·25	5·50

(Des W. Hanson. Litho Questa)

1988 (1 July). *Airships. T 336 and similar multicoloured designs.* P 14.

1810	10 c. Type 336		20	20
1811	15 c. LZ-1 over Lake Constance, 1901 (*horiz*)		25	25
1812	25 c. Washington (balloon) and *George Washington Curtis* (balloon barge), 1862		30	30
1813	45 c. LZ-129 *Hindenburg* and Maybach "Zeppelin" car (*horiz*)		40	40
1814	50 c. Goodyear Aerospace airship in Statue of Liberty Centenary Race, 1986		40	40
1815	60 c. LZ-129 *Hindenburg* over Statue of Liberty, 1937 (*horiz*)		50	50
1816	90 c. Heinkel biplane docking experiment with LZ-129 *Hindenburg*, 1936 (*horiz*)		80	80
1817	$2 LZ-129 *Hindenburg* over Olympic Stadium, Berlin, 1936		1·60	1·60
1818	$3 LZ-129 *Hindenburg* over Christ of the Andes Monument, 1937		2·00	2·00
1819	$4 LZ-129 *Hindenburg* and *Bremen* (liner), 1936 (*horiz*)		2·25	2·25
1810/19		*Set of 10*	8·00	8·00
MS1820	(a) 75×95 mm. $5 LZ-127 *Graf Zeppelin*, 1930 (*horiz*). (b) 95×75 mm. $5 LZ-129 *Hindenburg*, 1935 (*horiz*)	*Set of 2 sheets*	4·75	5·50

337 Tasmanian Wolf, Mickey Mouse and Pluto

338 Pineapple

(Des Walt Disney Co. Litho Questa)

1988 (1 Aug). *"Sydpex '88" National Stamp Exhibition, Sydney and 60th Birthday of Mickey Mouse. T 337 and similar horiz designs. Multicoloured.* P 14×13½.

1821	1 c. Type 337		10	10
1822	2 c. Mickey Mouse feeding wallabies		10	10
1823	3 c. Mickey Mouse and Goofy with kangaroo		10	10
1824	4 c. Mickey and Minnie Mouse riding emus		10	10
1825	5 c. Mickey and Minnie Mouse with wombat		10	10
1826	10 c. Mickey Mouse and Donald Duck watching platypus		10	10
1827	$5 Mickey Mouse and Goofy photographing Blue-winged Kookaburra		4·50	5·00
1828	$6 Mickey Mouse and Koala on map of Australia		4·50	5·00
1821/8		*Set of 8*	8·50	9·50
MS1829	Two sheets, each 127×102 mm. (a) $5 Mickey Mouse with birthday cake. (b) $5 Mickey and Minnie Mouse with Rainbow Lories	*Set of 2 sheets*	9·00	12·00

(Des J. Martin. Litho Questa)

1988 (11 Aug). *10th Anniv of International Fund for Agricultural Development. T 338 and similar multicoloured designs.* P 14.

1830	25 c. Type 338		25	15
1831	75 c. Bananas		60	60
1832	$3 Mace and nutmeg (*horiz*)		2·00	2·75
1830/2		*Set of 3*	2·50	3·25

339 Lignum Vitae

(Des W. Wright. Litho Questa)

1988 (30 Sept). *Flowering Trees and Shrubs. T 339 and similar horiz designs. Multicoloured.* P 14.

1833	15 c. Type 339		15	15
1834	25 c. Saman		20	15
1835	35 c. Red Frangipani		25	20
1836	45 c. Flowering Maple		30	25
1837	60 c. Yellow Poui		40	40
1838	$1 Wild Chestnut		60	70
1839	$3 Mountain Immortelle		1·50	2·25
1840	$4 Queen of Flowers		1·75	2·50
1833/40		*Set of 8*	4·50	6·00
MS1841	Two sheets, each 117 × 88 mm. (a) $5 Flamboyant. (b) $5 Orchid Tree	*Set of 2 sheets*	4·25	5·50

340 Mickey Mantle (New York Yankees)

(Des Rosemary De Figlio. Litho Questa)

1988 (28 Nov). *Major League Baseball Players (1st series). T 340 and similar horiz designs showing portraits or league emblems.* P 14 × 13½.

1842/1922	30 c. × 81 multicoloured	*Set of 81*	9·50	11·00

Nos. 1842/1922 were issued as nine sheetlets, each of nine different designs.

One sheetlet was subsequently reissued with the Pete Rose stamp replaced by a label inscribed "U.S. BASEBALL SERIES I".

(Des Walt Disney Co. Litho Questa)

1988 (1 Dec). *Christmas. "Mickey's Christmas Eve". Vert designs as T 246 of Antigua showing Walt Disney cartoon characters. Multicoloured.* P 13½ × 14.

1923	$1 Donald Duck's nephew on mantelpiece		65	65
	a. Sheetlet. Nos. 1923/30		4·75	
1924	$1 Goofy with string of popcorn		65	65
1925	$1 Chip n' Dale decorating Christmas tree		65	65
1926	$1 Father Christmas in sleigh		65	65
1927	$1 Donald's nephew with stocking		65	65
1928	$1 Donald's nephew unpacking Xmas decorations		65	65
1929	$1 Donald Duck with present		65	65
1930	$1 Mickey Mouse with present		65	65
1923/90		*Set of 8*	4·75	4·75
MS1931	Two sheets, each 127×102 mm. (a) $5 Ferdie leaving drink for Father Christmas. (b) $5 Mordie and Ferdie asleep	*Set of 2 sheets*	7·00	8·50

Nos. 1923/30 were printed together, *se-tenant,* in a sheetlet of eight forming a composite design.

341 Tina Turner

342 Atlantic Railway No. 2, 1889, Canada

(Litho Questa)

1988 (5 Dec). *Entertainers. T 341 and similar vert designs. Multicoloured.* P 14.

1932	10 c. Type 341		25	20
1933	25 c. Lionel Ritchie		25	20
1934	45 c. Whitney Houston		35	30
1935	60 c. Joan Armatrading		50	45
1936	75 c. Madonna		70	60
1937	$1 Elton John		1·00	80
1938	$3 Bruce Springsteen		2·00	2·75
1939	$4 Bob Marley		3·00	3·50
1932/9		*Set of 8*	7·25	8·00
MS1940	115×155 mm. 55 c.×2 Yoko Minamino; $1×2 Yoko Minamino (*different*)		1·90	2·75

No. 1935 is incorrectly inscribed "JOAN AMMERTRADING".

(Des T. Hadley and W. Wright. Litho B.D.T.)

1989 (23 Jan). *North American Railway Locomotives. T 342 and similar vert designs. Multicoloured.* P 13.

1941	$2 Type 342		1·25	1·25
	a. Sheetlet. Nos. 1941/50		11·00	
1942	$2 Virginia & Truckee Railroad "J. W. Bowker" type, 1875, U.S.A.		1·25	1·25
1943	$2 Philadelphia & Reading Railway *Ariel*, 1872, U.S.A.		1·25	1·25
1944	$2 Chicago & Rock Island Railroad "America" type, 1867, U.S.A.		1·25	1·25
1945	$2 Lehigh Valley Railroad Consolidation No. 63, 1866, U.S.A.		1·25	1·25
1946	$2 Great Western Railway *Scotia*, 1860, Canada		1·25	1·25
1947	$2 Grand Trunk Railway Class "Birkenhead", 1854, Canada		1·25	1·25
1948	$2 Camden & Amboy Railroad *Monster*, 1837, U.S.A.		1·25	1·25
1949	$2 Baltimore & Ohio Railroad Class "Grasshopper", 1834, U.S.A.		1·25	1·25
1950	$2 Peter Cooper's *Tom Thumb*, 1829, Baltimore & Ohio Railroad, U.S.A.		1·25	1·25
1951	$2 United Railways of Yucatan *Yucatan*, 1925, Mexico		1·25	1·25
	a. Sheetlet. Nos. 1951/60		11·00	
1952	$2 Canadian National Railways Class T2, 1924		1·25	1·25
1953	$2 St. Louis–San Francisco Railroad Class "Light Mikado", 1919, U.S.A.		1·25	1·25
1954	$2 Atlantic Coast Line Railroad Class "Light Pacific", 1919, U.S.A.		1·25	1·25
1955	$2 Edaville Railroad No. 7, 1913, U.S.A.		1·25	1·25
1956	$2 Denver & Rio Grande Western Railroad Class K 27, 1903, U.S.A.		1·25	1·25
1957	$2 Pennsylvania Railroad Class E-2 No. 7002, 1902, U.S.A.		1·25	1·25
1958	$2 Pennsylvania Railroad Class H6, 1899, U.S.A.		1·25	1·25
1959	$2 John Jarvis's *De Witt Clinton*, 1831, Mohawk & Hudson Railroad, U.S.A.		1·25	1·25
1960	$2 St. Clair Tunnel Company locomotive No. 598, 1891, Canada		1·25	1·25
1961	$2 Chesapeake & Ohio Railroad Class M-1 steam turbine electric locomotive No. 500, 1947, U.S.A.		1·25	1·25
	a. Sheetlet. Nos. 1961/70		11·00	
1962	$2 Rutland Railroad steam locomotive No. 93, 1946, U.S.A.		1·25	1·25

1963	$2 Pennsylvania Railroad Class T 1, 1942, U.S.A.	1·25	1·25
1964	$2 Chesapeake & Ohio Railroad Class H-8, 1942, U.S.A.	1·25	1·25
1965	$2 Atchison, Topeka & Santa Fe Railway Model FT diesel, 1941, U.S.A.	1·25	1·25
1966	$2 Gulf, Mobile & Ohio Railroad Models S-1 and S-2 diesels, 1940, U.S.A.	1·25	1·25
1967	$2 New York, New Haven & Hartford Railroad Class 15, 1937, U.S.A.	1·25	1·25
1968	$2 Seaboard Air Line Railroad Class R, 1936, U.S.A.	1·25	1·25
1969	$2 Newfoundland Railway Class R-2, 1930	1·25	1·25
1970	$2 Canadian National Railway diesel No. 9000, 1928	1·25	1·25
1941/70	*Set of 30*	32·00	32·00

Nos. 1941/50, 1951/60 and 1961/70 were each printed together, *se-tenant*, in sheetlets of 10.

343 Women's Long Jump (Jackie Joyner-Kersee, U.S.A.)

344 Nebulae

(Des L. Fried. Litho B.D.T.)

1989 (6 Apr). *Olympic Gold Medal Winners, Seoul* (1988). T *343 and similar vert designs. Multicoloured.* P 14.

1971	10 c. Type 343	20	20
1972	25 c. Women's Singles Tennis (Steffi Graf, West Germany)	50	35
1973	45 c. Men's 1500 metres (Peter Rono, Kenya)	60	40
1974	75 c. Men's 1000 metres single kayak (Greg Barton, U.S.A.)	70	60
1975	$1 Women's team foil (Italy)	85	75
1976	$2 Women's 100 metres freestyle swimming (Kristin Otto, East Germany)	1·75	2·00
1977	$3 Men's still rings gymnastics (Holger Behrendt, East Germany)	2·10	2·25
1978	$4 Synchronized swimming pair (Japan)	2·40	2·50
1971/8	*Set of 8*	8·25	8·25
MS1979	Two sheets, each 76×100 mm. (a) $6 Olympic flame. (b) $6 Runner with Olympic torch *Set of 2 sheets*	8·50	9·50

(Litho Questa)

1989 (25 Apr). *Appearance of Halley's Comet* (1986) (*3rd issue*). T *344 and similar horiz designs.* P 14.

1980	25 c. + 5 c. multicoloured	40	50
1981	75 c. + 5 c. black and turquoise-green	75	95
1982	90 c. + 5 c. multicoloured	85	1·10
1983	$2 + 5 c. multicoloured	1·25	1·75
1980/3	*Set of 4*	2·75	3·75
MS1984	111×78 mm. $5 + 5 c. multicoloured. Imperf	3·00	4·00

Designs: (*As T 344*)—75 c. + 5 c. Marine astronomical experiments; 90 c. + 5 c. Moon's surface; $2 + 5 c. Edmond Halley, Sir Isaac Newton and his book *Principia*. (102×69 *mm*)—$5 + 5 c. 17th-century warships and astrological signs.

(Litho Questa)

1989 (15 May). *Japanese Art. Paintings by Hiroshige. Horiz designs as* T *250 of Antigua. Multicoloured.* P 14×13¹⁄₂.

1985	10 c. "Shinagawa on Edo Bay"	30	20
1986	25 c. "Pine Trees on the Road to Totsuka"	40	30
1987	60 c. "Kanagawa on Edo Bay"	60	50
1988	75 c. "Crossing Banyu River to Hiratsuka"	65	55
1989	$1 "Windy Shore at Odawara"	80	70
1990	$2 "Snow-Covered Post Station of Mishima"	1·40	1·75
1991	$3 "Full Moon at Fuchu"	1·60	2·00
1992	$4 "Crossing the Stream at Okitsu"	2·25	2·50
1985/92	*Set of 8*	7·25	7·75
MS1993	Two sheets, each 102×76 mm. (a) $5 "Mountain Pass at Nissaka". (b) $5 "Mt Uzu at Okabe" *Set of 2 sheets*	4·25	5·50

Nos. 1985/92 were each printed in sheetlets of 10 containing two horizontal strips of 5 stamps separated by printed labels commemorating Emperor Hirohito.

345 Great Blue Heron

(Des D. Bruckner. Litho Questa)

1989 (6 June)-**94**. *Birds.* T *345 and similar multicoloured designs.* P 14.

1994	5 c. Type 345	40	50
	a. Perf 11¹⁄₂×12¹⁄₂ (1993)	40	50
1995	10 c. Green Heron	50	40
	a. Perf 11¹⁄₂×12¹⁄₂ (1993)	40	40
1996	15 c. Turnstone	60	40
	a. Perf 11¹⁄₂×12¹⁄₂ (1993)	45	40

1997	25 c. Blue-winged Teal	65	20
	a. Perf 11¹⁄₂×12¹⁄₂ (1993)	50	20
1998	35 c. Little Ringed Plover (*vert*)	70	20
	a. Perf 12¹⁄₂×11¹⁄₂ (1993)	55	20
1999	45 c. Green-throated Carib ("Emerald-throated Hummingbird") (*vert*)	85	30
	a. Perf 12¹⁄₂×11¹⁄₂ (1993)	60	30
2000	50 c. Rufous-breasted Hermit (*vert*)	90	45
	a. Perf 12¹⁄₂×11¹⁄₂ (1993)	65	35
2001	60 c. Lesser Antillean Bull-finch (*vert*)	1·00	50
	a. Perf 12¹⁄₂×11¹⁄₂ (1993)	70	50
2002	75 c. Brown Pelican (*vert*)	1·25	65
	a. Perf 12¹⁄₂×11¹⁄₂ (1993)	80	60
2003	$1 Black-crowned Night Heron (*vert*)	1·50	90
	a. Perf 12¹⁄₂×11¹⁄₂ (1993)	1·00	80
2004	$3 American Kestrel ("Sparrow Hawk") (*vert*)	2·75	3·00
	a. Perf 12¹⁄₂×11¹⁄₂ (1993)	1·75	2·50
2005	$5 Barn Swallow (*vert*)	3·50	4·00
	a. Perf 12¹⁄₂×11¹⁄₂ (1993)	2·50	3·50
2006	$10 Red-billed Tropic Bird (*vert*) (13.11.89)	6·00	8·00
	a. Perf 12¹⁄₂×11¹⁄₂ (1993)	7·00	9·00
2007	$20 Barn Owl (*vert*) (22.1.90)	12·00	14·00
	a. Perf 12¹⁄₂×11¹⁄₂ (1994)	16·00	18·00
1994/2007	*Set of 14*	29·00	30·00
1994a/2007a	*Set of 14*	29·00	32·00

Nos. 1994a/2007a show a larger perforation hole on every sixth perforation, both vertically and horizontally.

(Des D. Bruckner. Litho B.D.T.)

1989 (12 June). *World Cup Football Championship, Italy* (1990) (*1st issue*). *Vert designs as* T *252 of Antigua. Multicoloured.* P 14.

2008	10 c. Scotland player	40	20
2009	25 c. England and Brazil players	50	30
2010	60 c. Paolo Rossi (Italy)	75	55
2011	75 c. Jairzinho (Brazil)	90	70
2012	$1 Sweden striker	1·10	90
2013	$2 Péle (Brazil)	2·25	2·00
2014	$3 Mario Kempes (Argentina)	3·00	2·75
2015	$4 Pat Jennings (Northern Ireland)	3·25	3·00
2008/15	*Set of 8*	11·00	9·50
MS2016	Two sheets. (a) 70×93 mm. $6 Players jumping for ball. (b) 82×71 mm. $6 Goalkeeper *Set of 2 sheets*	8·50	10·00

See also Nos. 2174/8 and MS2179.

346 Xebec and Sugar Cane

(Des T. Agans. Litho B.D.T.)

1989 (7 July). *"Philexfrance 89" International Stamp Exhibition, Paris.* T *346 and similar horiz designs showing French sailing vessels and plantation crops. Multicoloured.* P 14.

2017	25 c. Type 346	80	30
2018	75 c. Lugger and cotton	1·40	85
2019	$1 Full-rigged ship and cocoa	1·60	1·10
2020	$4 Ketch and coffee	3·50	5·50
2017/20	*Set of 4*	6·50	7·00
MS2021	114×70 mm. $6 "View of Fort and Town of St. George, 1779" (105×63 *mm*). Imperf	4·25	5·50

347 Alan Shepard and "Freedom 7" Spacecraft, 1961 (first American in Space)

348 *Hygrocybe occidentalis*

(Des L. Birmingham. Litho Questa)

1989 (20 July). *20th Anniv of First Manned Landing on Moon.* T *347 and similar horiz designs. Multicoloured.* P 14.

2022	15 c. Type 347	50	40
2023	35 c. "Friendship 7" spacecraft, 1962 (first manned earth orbit)	65	55
2024	45 c. "Apollo 8" orbiting Moon, 1968 (first manned lunar orbit)	75	65
2025	70 c. "Apollo 15" lunar rover, 1972	1·00	85
2026	$1 "Apollo 11" emblem and lunar module *Eagle* on Moon, 1969	1·25	1·10
2027	$2 "Gemini 8" and "Agena" rocket, 1966 (first space docking)	2·25	2·00
2028	$3 Edward White in space, 1965 (first U.S. space walk)	3·00	2·75
2029	$4 "Apollo 7" emblem	3·50	3·25
2022/9	*Set of 8*	11·50	10·50
MS2030	Two sheets, each 101×71 mm. (a) $5 Moon and track of "Apollo 11", 1969. (b) $5 Armstrong and Aldrin raising U.S. flag on Moon, 1969 *Set of 2 sheets*	8·50	8·50

(Des J. Cooter. Litho B.D.T.)

1989 (17 Aug). *Fungi.* T *348 and similar vert designs. Multicoloured.* P 14.

2031	15 c. Type 348	50	40
2032	40 c. *Marasmius haematocephalus*	65	55
2033	50 c. *Hygrocybe hyphohaemacta*	75	65
2034	70 c. *Lepiota pseudoignicolor*	1·00	90
2035	90 c. *Cookeina tricholoma*	1·25	1·25
2036	$1.10, *Leucopaxillus gracillimus*	1·50	1·50
2037	$2.25, *Hygrocybe nigrescens*	2·75	3·00
2038	$4 *Clathrus crispus*	3·75	4·00
2031/8	*Set of 8*	11·00	11·00
MS2039	Two sheets, each 57×70 mm. (a) $6 *Mycena holoporphyra*. (b) $6 *Xeromphalina tenuipes* *Set of 2 sheets*	12·00	13·00

349 Y.W.C.A. Logo and Grenada Scenery

350 *Historis odius*

(Litho Questa)

1989 (11 Sept). *Centenary of Young Women's Christian Association.* T *349 and similar multicoloured design.* P 14.

2040	50 c. Type 349	45	45
2041	75 c. Y.W.C.A. logo and town (*horiz*)	80	80

(Des Deborah Dudley Max. Litho B.D.T.)

1989 (2 Oct). *Butterflies.* T *350 and similar horiz designs. Multicoloured.* P 14.

2042	6 c. Type 350	30	30
2043	30 c. *Marpesia petreus*	55	55
2044	40 c. *Danaus gilippus*	60	60
2045	60 c. *Dione juno*	80	80
2046	$1.10, *Agraulis vanillae*	1·25	1·25
2047	$1.25, *Danaus plexippus*	1·50	1·50
2048	$4 *Papilio androgeus* (inscr "*Battus polydamas*")	3·25	3·25
2049	$5 *Dryas julia*	3·25	3·25
2042/9	*Set of 8*	10·50	10·50
MS2050	Two sheets, each 87×115 mm. (a) $6 *Anartia jatrophae*. (b) $6 *Strymon simaethis* *Set of 2 sheets*	9·50	11·00

351 Amerindian Hieroglyph

352 Amos leaving Home

(Litho Questa)

1989 (16 Oct). *500th Anniv of Discovery of America by Columbus* (1992) (*2nd issue*). T *351 and similar vert designs showing different hieroglyphs.* P 14.

2051	45 c. brownish black, black and new blue	70	50
2052	60 c. brownish black, black & bright green	80	60
2053	$1 brownish black, black & dp reddish vio	1·25	1·00
2054	$4 brownish black, black & orange-brn	3·75	4·50
2051/4	*Set of 4*	6·00	6·00
MS2055	74×86 mm. $6 brownish black, black and vermilion	4·00	5·50

(Des Walt Disney Co. Litho Questa)

1989 (20 Nov). *"World Stamp Expo '89" International Stamp Exhibition, Washington.* T *352 and similar multicoloured designs showing Walt Disney cartoon characters in scenes from* Ben and Me. P 14×13¹⁄₂.

2056	1 c. Type 352	10	10
2057	2 c. Meeting of Benjamin Franklin and Amos	10	10
2058	3 c. The Franklin stove	10	10
2059	4 c. Ben and Amos with bi-focals	10	10
2060	5 c. Amos on page of *Pennsylvania Gazette*	10	10
2061	6 c. Ben working printing press	10	10
2062	10 c. Conducting experiment with electricity	10	10
2063	$5 Ben disembarking in England	5·00	5·50
2064	$6 Ben with Document of Agreement	5·50	6·00
2056/64	*Set of 9*	10·00	11·00
MS2065	Two sheets, each 127×101 mm. (a) $6 Benjamin Franklin teaching (*vert*). P 13¹⁄₂×14. (b) $6 Signatories of Declaration of Independence. P 14×13¹⁄₂ *Set of 2 sheets*	8·00	10·00

(Litho Questa)

1990 (4 Jan). *Christmas. Paintings by Rubens. Vert designs as T 259 of Antigua. Multicoloured. P 14.*

2066	20 c.	"Christ in the House of Mary and Martha"	30	25
2067	35 c.	"The Circumcision"	45	40
2068	60 c.	"Trinity adored by Duke of Mantua and Family"	75	65
2069	$2	"Holy Family with St. Francis"	2·25	2·50
2070	$3	"The Ildefonso Altarpiece"	2·75	3·00
2071	$4	"Madonna and Child with Garland and Putti"	3·25	3·50
2066/71		*Set of 6*	8·75	9·25

MS2072 Two sheets, each 70×95 mm. (a) $5 "Adoration of the Magi". (b) $5 "Virgin and Child adored by Angels" .. *Set of 2 sheets* 7·50 9·00

353 Alexander Graham Bell and Early Telephone System (150th anniv of invention)

354 *Odontoglossum triumphans*

(Des J. Genzo. Litho B.D.T.)

1990 (12 Feb). *Anniversaries. T 353 and similar horiz designs. Multicoloured. P 14.*

2073	10 c.	Type 353	30	20
2074	25 c.	George Washington and Capitol (bicent of presidential inauguration)	30	20
2075	35 c.	Shakespeare and birthplace, Stratford (425th birth anniv)	75	30
2076	75 c.	Nehru and Gandhi (birth cent of Nehru)	2·00	1·25
2077	$1	Dr. Hugo Eckener, Ferdinand von Zeppelin and LZ-127 *Graf Zeppelin* (80th anniv of first passenger Zeppelin)	1·50	1·25
2078	$2	Charlie Chaplin (birth cent)	3·00	2·75
2079	$3	Container ship in Hamburg Harbour (800th anniv)	2·50	3·25
2080	$4	Friedrich Ebert (first President) and Heidelberg gate (70th anniv of German Republic)	2·50	3·25
2073/80		*Set of 8*	11·50	11·00

MS2081 Two sheets, each 100×72 mm. (a) $6 13th-century ships in Hamburg Harbour (*vert*) (800th anniv). (b) $6 Concorde (20th anniv of first test flight) .. *Set of 2 sheets* 8·50 10·00
No. 2080 is inscribed "40th Anniversary of German Republic" in error.

(Des L. Nelson. Litho Questa)

1990 (6 Mar). *"EXPO 90" International Garden and Greenery Exhibition, Osaka. Caribbean Orchids. T 354 and similar vert designs. Multicoloured. P 14.*

2082	1 c.	Type 354	10	10
2083	25 c.	*Oncidium splendidum*	30	20
2084	60 c.	*Laelia anceps*	60	60
2085	75 c.	*Cattleya trianaei*	75	75
2086	$1	*Odontoglossum rossii*	1·00	1·00
2087	$2	*Brassia gireoudiana*	1·75	1·75
2088	$3	*Cattleya dowiana*	2·25	2·25
2089	$4	*Sobralia macrantha*	2·50	2·50
2082/9		*Set of 8*	8·25	8·25

MS2090 Two sheets, each 97×68 mm. (a) $6 *Oncidium lanceanum*. (b) $6 *Laelia rubescens* .. *Set of 2 sheets* 8·50 9·50

(Des Mary Walters. Litho Questa)

1990 (16 Mar). *500th Anniv of Discovery of America by Columbus (1992) (3rd issue). New World Natural History – Butterflies. Vert designs as T 260 of Antigua. Multicoloured. P 14.*

2091	15 c.	*Marpesia petreus*	45	20
2092	25 c.	*Junonia evarete*	60	25
2093	75 c.	*Siproeta stelenes*	1·10	70
2094	90 c.	*Historis odius*	1·25	85
2095	$1	*Mestra cana*	1·25	90
2096	$2	*Biblis hyperia*	2·00	2·25
2097	$3	*Dryas julia*	2·50	3·00
2098	$4	*Anartia amathea*	2·50	3·00
2091/8		*Set of 8*	10·50	10·00

MS2099 Two sheets, each 101×69 mm. (a) $6 *Pseudolycaena marsyas*. (b) $6 *Phoebis philea* .. *Set of 2 sheets* 9·00 10·00

(Des J. Barbaris. Litho B.D.T.)

1990 (3 Apr). *Local Fauna. Multicoloured designs as T 254 of Antigua. P 14.*

2100	10 c.	Caribbean Monk Seal	20	20
2101	15 c.	Little Brown Bat	25	25
2102	45 c.	Brown Rat	50	50
2103	60 c.	Common Rabbit	60	60
2104	$1	Water Opossum	95	90
2105	$2	White-nosed Ichneumon	1·75	1·75
2106	$3	Little Big-eared Bat (*vert*)	2·25	2·25
2107	$4	Mouse Opossum	2·25	2·25
2100/7		*Set of 8*	8·00	8·00

MS2108 Two sheets, each 107×80 mm. (a) $6 Common Rabbit (*different*). (b) $6 Water Opossum (*different*) .. *Set of 2 sheets* 8·50 10·00

(Des W. Wright. Litho Questa)

1990 (30 Apr). *50th Anniv of Second World War. Horiz designs as T 274 of Antigua. Multicoloured. P 14.*

2109	25 c.	British tanks during Operation Battleaxe, 1941	30	30
2110	35 c.	Allied tank in southern France, 1944	40	40
2111	45 c.	U.S. forces landing on Guadalcanal, 1942	45	45
2112	50 c.	U.S. attack in New Guinea, 1943	50	50
2113	60 c.	Hoisting U.S. flag on Leyte, Phillippines, 1944	60	60
2114	75 c.	U.S. tanks entering Cologne, 1945	75	75
2115	$1	Anzio offensive, 1944	95	95
2116	$2	Battle of the Bismarck Sea, 1943	1·75	1·75
2117	$3	U.S.S. *Langley* and U.S.S. *Ticonderoga* (aircraft carriers)	2·25	2·25
2118	$4	Focke Wulf Fw190A German fighter attacking Salerno landing, 1943	2·50	2·50
2109/18		*Set of 10*	9·50	9·50

MS2119 111×83 mm. $6 German *U-30* submarine, 1939 .. .. 3·50 4·00

(Des Walt Disney Co. Litho Questa)

1990 (21 June). *"Stamp World London 90" International Stamp Exhibition (1st issue). Multicoloured designs as T 193 of Gambia showing Walt Disney cartoon characters and British trains. P 14×13½.*

2120	5 c.	Mickey Mouse driving S.R. "King Arthur" Class locomotive, 1925 (*horiz*)	30	10
2121	10 c.	Mickey and Minnie Mouse with *Puffing Billy*, 1813 (*horiz*)	30	10
2122	20 c.	Mickey Mouse with Pluto pulling Durham colliery waggon, 1765 (*horiz*)	50	15
2123	45 c.	Mickey Mouse timing L.N.E.R. locomotive No. 2509, *Silver Link*, 1935 (*horiz*)	80	25
2124	$1	Mickey Mouse and Donald Duck with locomotive No. 60149, *Amadis*, 1948 (*horiz*)	1·75	1·00
2125	$2	Goofy and Mickey Mouse with Liverpool & Manchester Railway locomotive, 1830 (*horiz*)	2·50	2·75
2126	$4	Goofy and Donald Duck with Great Northern locomotive No. 1, 1870 (*horiz*)	3·25	4·00
2127	$5	Mickey Mouse and Gyro the Mechanic with Advanced Passenger Train, 1972 (*horiz*)	3·25	4·00
2120/7		*Set of 8*	11·50	11·00

MS2128 Two sheets, each 127×101 mm. (a) $6 Minnie Mouse, Donald and Daisy Duck in Trevithick's *Catch-Me-Who-Can*, 1808 (*horiz*). P 14×13½. (b) $6 Donald Duck and *Locomotion*, 1825. P 13½×14 .. *Set of 2 sheets* 11·00 12·00
No. 2126 is inscribed "Flying Scotsman" in error.
See also No. MS2146.

355 U.S. Paratroop Drop over Grenada

(Litho B.D.T.)

1990 (3 July). *50th Anniv of United States' Airborne Forces. T 355 and similar horiz designs. Multicoloured. P 14.*

2129 75 c. Type 355 .. .. 1·00 1·00
MS2130 Two sheets, each 115×87 mm. (a) $2.50, Paratrooper landing. (b) $6 Paratroop uniforms of 1940 and 1990 .. *Set of 2 sheets* 5·50 6·50

(Des Young Phillips Studio. Litho Questa)

1990 (5 July). *90th Birthday of Queen Elizabeth the Queen Mother. Vert designs as T 194 of Gambia showing photographs, 1960–69. Multicoloured. P 14.*

2131	$2	Queen Mother in coat and hat	1·75	1·75
		a. Strip of 3. Nos. 2131/3	4·75	
2132	$2	Queen Mother in evening dress	1·75	1·75
2133	$2	Queen Mother in Garter robes	1·75	1·75
2131/3		*Set of 3*	4·75	4·75

MS2134 90×75 mm. $6 Queen Mother (as No. 2131) .. .. 3·50 4·00
Nos. 2131/3 were printed together, horizontally and vertically *se-tenant*, in sheetlets of 9 (3×3).

(Des B. Grout. Litho Questa)

1990 (9 July). *Olympic Games, Barcelona (1992) (1st issue). Vert designs as T 268 of Antigua. Multicoloured. P 14.*

2135	10 c.	Men's steeplechase	20	20
2136	15 c.	Dressage	30	30
2137	45 c.	Men's 200 m butterfly swimming	45	45
2138	50 c.	Men's hockey	80	60
2139	65 c.	Women's beam gymnastics	60	60
2140	75 c.	"Flying Dutchman" class sailing	80	80
2141	$2	Freestyle wrestling	1·75	1·75
2142	$3	Men's springboard diving	2·25	2·50
2143	$4	Women's 1000 m sprint cycling	3·00	3·00
2144	$5	Men's basketball	3·75	3·75
2135/44		*Set of 10*	12·50	12·50

MS2145 Two sheets, each 101×70 mm. (a) $8 Equestrian three-day event. (b) $8 Men's 10000 metres .. *Set of 2 sheets* 9·50 11·00
See also Nos. 2414/22

COVER PRICES

Cover factors are quoted at the beginning of each country for most issues to 1945. An explanation of the system can be found on page x. The factors quoted do not, however, apply to philatelic covers.

---

356 Map of North America and Logo

(Des M. Pollard. Litho Questa)

1990 (12 July). *"Stamp World London 90" International Stamp Exhibition (2nd issue). Sheet 97×75 mm. P 14.*
MS2146 **356** $6 deep mauve .. .. 4·25 5·50

357 Yellow Goatfish

(Des Mary Walters. Litho B.D.T.)

1990 (8 Aug). *Coral Reef Fishes. T 357 and similar horiz designs. Multicoloured. P 14.*

2147	10 c.	Type 357	30	30
2148	25 c.	Black Margate	45	35
2149	65 c.	Blue-headed Wrasse	85	75
2150	75 c.	Puddingwife	95	85
2151	$1	Four-eyed Butterflyfish	1·10	95
2152	$2	Honey Damselfish	2·00	2·00
2153	$3	Queen Angelfish	2·50	2·50
2154	$5	Cherub Angelfish	3·00	3·50
2147/54		*Set of 8*	10·00	10·00

MS2155 Two sheets, each 103×72 mm. (a) $6 Smooth Trunkfish. (b) $6 Sergeant Major .. *Set of 2 sheets* 8·00 9·00

358 Tropical Mockingbird

(Des J. Anderton. Litho B.D.T.)

1990 (10 Sept). *Birds. T 358 and similar horiz designs. Multicoloured. P 14.*

2156	15 c.	Type 358	30	30
2157	25 c.	Grey Kingbird	35	35
2158	65 c.	Bare-eyed Thrush	75	75
2159	75 c.	Antillean Crested Hummingbird	85	85
2160	$1	House Wren	1·00	1·00
2161	$2	Purple Martin	1·75	1·75
2162	$4	Hooded Tanager	2·50	2·50
2163	$5	Scaly-breasted Ground Dove	3·00	3·00
2156/63		*Set of 8*	9·50	9·50

MS2164 Two sheets, each 101×72 mm. (a) $6 Fork-tailed Flycatcher. (b) $6 Smooth-billed Ani .. *Set of 2 sheets* 12·00 13·00

359 Coral Crab

360 Cameroun Player

(Des Deborah Dudley Max. Litho Questa)

1990 (17 Sept). *Crustaceans. T 359 and similar horiz designs. Multicoloured. P 14.*

2165	5 c.	Type 359	10	10
2166	10 c.	Smoothtail Spiny Lobster	15	15
2167	15 c.	Flamestreaked Box Crab	15	15
2168	25 c.	Spotted Swimming Crab	25	25
2169	75 c.	Sally Lightfoot Rock Crab	60	60
2170	$1	Spotted Spiny Lobster	80	80
2171	$3	Longarm Spiny Lobster	2·00	2·50
2172	$20	Caribbean Spiny Lobster	13·00	18·00
2165/72		*Set of 8*	15·00	20·00

MS2173 Two sheets, 106×75 mm. (a) $6 Copper Lobster. (b) $6 Spanish Lobster .. *Set of 2 sheets* 8·00 9·00

(Des Young Phillips Studio. Litho Questa)

1990 (24 Sept). *World Cup Football Championship, Italy (2nd issue). T 360 and similar vert designs. Multicoloured. P 14.*

2174	10 c.	Type 360	20	15
2175	25 c.	Michel (Spain)	25	15
2176	$1	Brehme (West Germany)	85	85
2177	$5	Nevin (Scotland)	3·00	4·00
2174/7		*Set of 4*	3·75	4·50

MS2178 Two sheets, each 95×90 mm. (a) $6 Giannini (Italy). (b) $6 Perdomo (Uruguay) .. *Set of 2 sheets* 8·50 10·00

1990 W GERMANY 1 ARGENTINA 0
(361)

1990 (30 Nov). *World Cup Football Championship, Italy (1990) (3rd issue).* No. MS2016a optd with T **361**.
MS2179 70×93 mm. $6 Players jumping for ball 6·00 7·00
No. **MS2179** shows the overprint, Type **361**, added to the list of match results in the sheet margin.

(Litho Questa)

1990 (31 Dec). *Christmas. Paintings by Raphael. Multicoloured designs as T 272 of Antigua, but vert.* P 13½×14.
2180 10 c. "The Ansidei Madonna" 20 10
2181 15 c. "The Sistine Madonna" 20 10
2182 $1 "The Madonna of the Baldacchino" 1·50 70
2183 $2 "The Large Holy Family" (detail) 2·25 2·50
2184 $5 "Madonna in the Meadow" 3·75 5·50
2180/4 *Set of 5* 7·00 8·00
MS2185 Two sheets, each 71×101 mm. (a) $6 "Madonna of the Diadem" (detail). (b) $6 "The Madonna of the Veil" (detail) ... *Set of 2 sheets* 11·00 13·00

A 50 c. value in a similar design, showing "The Canigiani Holy Family" by Raphael, was prepared, but not issued.

(Litho Questa)

1991 (31 Jan). *350th Death Anniv of Rubens. Horiz designs as T 273 of Antigua. Multicoloured.* P 14×13½.
2186 5 c. "The Brazen Serpent" (detail) 15 10
2187 10 c. "The Garden of Love" 15 10
2188 25 c. "Head of Cyrus" (detail) 30 20
2189 75 c. "Tournament in Front of a Castle" 70 60
2190 $1 "The Brazen Serpent" (different detail) 85 75
2191 $2 "Judgement of Paris" (detail) 1·75 2·00
2192 $4 "The Brazen Serpent" 2·50 3·50
2193 $5 "The Karmesse" 3·00 3·50
2186/93 *Set of 8* 8·50 9·50
MS2194 Two sheets, each 101×70 mm. (a) $6 "Anger of Neptune" (detail). (b) $6 "The Prodigal Son" (detail) ... *Set of 2 sheets* 9·00 11·00

362 "The Sorcerer's Apprentice"

(Des Walt Disney Co. Litho Questa)

1991 (4 Feb). *50th Anniv of Fantasia (cartoon film). T 362 and similar horiz designs. Multicoloured.* P 14×13½.
2195 5 c. Type **362** 30 15
2196 10 c. Dancing mushrooms ("The Nutcracker Suite") 30 15
2197 20 c. Pterodactyls ("The Rite of Spring") 55 15
2198 45 c. Centaurs ("The Pastoral Symphony") 1·00 40
2199 $1 Bacchus and Jacchus ("The Pastoral Symphony") 1·75 1·00
2200 $2 Dancing ostrich ("Dance of the Hours") 2·50 3·00
2201 $4 Elephant ballet ("Dance of the Hours") 3·50 4·25
2202 $5 Diana ("The Pastoral Symphony") 3·50 4·25
2195/202 *Set of 8* 12·00 12·00
MS2203 Two sheets, each 122×102 mm. (a) $6 Mickey Mouse as the Sorcerer's Apprentice; (b) $6 Mickey Mouse with Leopold Stokowski (conductor) *Set of 2 sheets* 11·00 12·00
MS2204 176×213 mm. $12 Mickey Mouse as the Sorcerer's Apprentice (vert). P 13½×14 11·00 12·00

363 *Adelpha iphicla* **364** *Psilocybe cubensis*

(Des W. Wright. Litho Questa)

1991 (8 Apr). *Butterflies. T 363 and similar horiz designs. Multicoloured.* P 14.
2205 5 c. Type **363** 30 15
2206 10 c. *Nymphalidae claudina* 30 20
2207 15 c. *Brassolidae polyxena* 35 20
2208 20 c. Zebra Longwing 40 20
2209 25 c. *Marpesia corinna* 40 25
2210 30 c. *Morpho hecuba* 40 30
2211 45 c. *Morpho rhetenor* 55 45
2212 50 c. *Dismorphia spio* 65 55
2213 60 c. *Prepona omphale* 75 65
2214 70 c. *Morpho anaxibia* 85 75
2215 75 c. *Marpesia iole* 90 80
2216 $1 *Amarynthis meneria* 1·00 90

2217 $2 *Morpho cisseis* 1·75 2·25
2218 $3 *Danaidae plexippus* 2·25 2·75
2219 $4 *Morpho achilleana* 2·75 3·50
2220 $5 *Calliona argenissa* 3·25 4·00
2205/20 *Set of 16* 15·00 16·00
MS2221 Four sheets, each 118×80 mm. (a) $6 *Anteos clorinde.* (b) $6 *Haetera piera.* (c) $6 *Papilio cresphontes.* (d) $6 *Prepona pheridames.*
Set of 4 sheets 17·00 19·00

(Des T. Agans. Litho Questa)

1991 (29 Apr). *500th Anniv of Discovery of America by Columbus (1992) (4th issue). History of Exploration. Multicoloured designs as T 277 of Antigua.* P 14.
2222 5 c. Vitus Bering in Bering Sea, 1728–29 30 30
2223 10 c. De Bougainville off Pacific island, 1766–69 30 30
2224 25 c. Polynesian canoe 30 30
2225 50 c. De Mendana off Solomon Islands, 1567–69 75 40
2226 $1 Darwin's H.M.S. *Beagle*, 1831–35 1·50 1·00
2227 $2 Cook's H.M.S. *Endeavour*, 1768–71 3·00 3·00
2228 $4 Willem Schouten in LeMaire Strait, 1615–17 3·25 3·50
2229 $5 Tasman off New Zealand, 1642–44 3·25 3·50
2222/9 *Set of 8* 11·50 11·00
MS2230 Two sheets, each 116×77 mm. (a) $6 *Santa Maria* sinking. (b) $6 Bow of *Santa Maria* (vert) ... *Set of 2 sheets* 8·50 9·50

(Des Walt Disney Co. Litho Questa)

1991 (6 May). *"Phila Nippon '91" International Stamp Exhibition, Tokyo. Multicoloured designs as T 279 of Antigua showing Walt Disney cartoon characters at Japanese festivals.* P 14×13½.
2231 5 c. Minnie Mouse and Daisy Duck at Dolls festival (horiz) 20 20
2232 10 c. Morty and Ferdie with Boys' Day display (horiz) 25 20
2233 20 c. Mickey and Minnie Mouse at Star festival (horiz) 45 20
2234 45 c. Minnie and Daisy folk-dancing (horiz) 80 35
2235 $1 Huey, Dewey and Louie wearing Eboshi headdresses (horiz) 1·40 85
2236 $2 Mickey and Goofy pulling decorated cart at Gion festival (horiz) 2·75 3·00
2237 $4 Minnie and Daisy preparing rice broth, Seven Plants festival (horiz) 3·50 4·00
2238 $5 Huey and Dewey with straw boat at Lanterns festival (horiz) 3·50 4·00
2231/8 *Set of 8* 11·50 11·50
MS2239 Three sheets, each 127×101 mm. (a) $6 Minnie Mouse in kimono. P 13½×14. (b) $6 Mickey taking photo (horiz). P 14×13½. (c) $6 Goofy behind fair stall (horiz). P 14×13½
Set of 3 sheets 14·00 15·00

(Litho Walsall)

1991 (13 May). *Death Centenary of Vincent van Gogh (artist) (1990). Multicoloured designs as T 278 of Antigua.* P 13½.
2240 20 c. "Blossoming Almond Branch in Glass" 15 15
2241 25 c. "La Mousmé sitting" 15 15
2242 30 c. "Still Life with Red Cabbages and Onions" (horiz) 20 20
2243 40 c. "Japonaiserie: Flowering Plum Tree" 30 30
2244 45 c. "Japonaiserie: Bridge in Rain" 30 30
2245 60 c. "Still Life with Basket of Apples" (horiz) 50 50
2246 75 c. "Italian Woman" 60 60
2247 $1 "The Painter on his Way to Work" 80 80
2248 $2 "Portrait of Pére Tanguy" 1·50 1·50
2249 $3 "Still Life with Plaster Statuette, a Rose and Two Novels" 2·25 2·25
2250 $4 "Still Life: Bottle, Lemons and Oranges" (horiz) 2·50 2·50
2251 $5 "Orchard with Blossoming Apricot Trees" (horiz) 2·75 2·75
2240/51 *Set of 12* 11·00 11·00
MS2252 Five sheets. (a) 76×102 mm. $6 "Roubine du Roi Canal with Washerwoman" (73×99 mm). (b) 102×76 mm. $6 "Farmhouse in a Wheatfield" (99×73 mm). (c) 102×76 mm. $6 "The Gleize Bridge over the Vigueirat Canal" (99×73 mm). (d) 102×76 mm. $6 "Rocks with Oak Tree" (99×73 mm). (e) 76×102 mm. $6 "Japonaiserie: Oiran" (73×99 mm). Imperf.
Set of 5 sheets 18·00 21·00

(Des Mary Walters. Litho Questa)

1991 (1 June). *Fungi. T 364 and similar vert designs. Multicoloured.* P 14.
2253 15 c. Type **364** 50 30
2254 25 c. *Leptonia caeruleocapitata* 60 30
2255 65 c. *Cystolepiota eriophora* 1·10 75
2256 75 c. *Chlorophyllum molybdites* 1·25 85
2257 $1 *Xerocomus hypoxanthus* 1·40 1·10
2258 $2 *Xulvariella cubensis* 2·25 2·50
2259 $4 *Xerocomus coccolobae* 3·25 3·75
2260 $5 *Pluteus chrysophlebius* 3·25 3·75
2253/60 *Set of 8* 12·00 12·00
MS2261 Two sheets, each 100×70 mm. (a) $6 *Psathyrella tuberculata.* (b) $6 *Hygrocybe miniata* ... *Set of 2 sheets* 13·00 14·00

365 Johannes Kepler (astronomer)

(Des G. Vasarhelyi. Litho Questa)

1991 (21 June). *Exploration of Mars. T 365 and similar horiz designs showing astronomers, spacecraft and Martian landscapes. Multicoloured.* P 14×13½.
2262/97 75 c. × 9, $1.25 × 9, $2 × 9, $7 × 9
Set of 36 48·00 48·00
MS2298 Three sheets, each 112×92 mm. (a) $6 Projected spacecraft. (b) $6 Mars and part of spacecraft. (c) $6 Phobos satellite over Mars. P 13×12 ... *Set of 3 sheets* 11·00 12·00
Nos. 2262/97 were issued as four sheetlets, each containing nine different designs of the same face values.

(Des D. Miller. Litho Walsall)

1991 (5 July). *65th Birthday of Queen Elizabeth II. Horiz designs as T 280 of Antigua. Multicoloured.* P 14.
2299 15 c. Royal Family on balcony after Trooping the Colour, 1985 15 15
2300 40 c. Queen and Prince Philip at Peterborough, 1988 35 35
2301 $2 Queen and Queen Mother at Windsor, 1986 1·75 1·75
2302 $4 Queen and Prince Philip on visit to United Arab Emirates 2·50 3·00
2299/302 *Set of 4* 4·25 4·75
MS2303 68×90 mm. $5 Separate photographs of the Queen and Prince Philip ... 3·50 4·25

(Des D. Miller. Litho Walsall)

1991 (5 July). *10th Wedding Anniv of the Prince and Princess of Wales. Horiz designs as T 280 of Antigua. Multicoloured.* P 14.
2304 10 c. Prince and Princess in July 1985 30 10
2305 50 c. Separate photographs of Prince, Princess and sons 75 45
2306 $1 Prince Henry at Trooping the Colour and Prince William in Majorca 1·00 1·00
2307 $5 Separate photographs of Prince Charles and Princess Diana 3·75 4·50
2304/7 *Set of 4* 5·25 5·50
MS2308 68×90 mm. $5 Prince, Princess and sons on holiday in Majorca ... 4·50 4·75

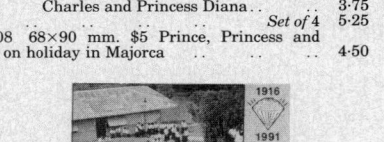

366 Anglican High School Pupils

(Litho Questa)

1991 (29 July). *75th Anniv of Anglican High School (10, 25 c.) and 40th Anniv of University of the West Indies (45, 50 c.). T 366 and similar horiz designs. Multicoloured.* P 14.
2309 10 c. Type **366** 20 20
2310 25 c. Artist's impression of new Anglican High School 30 20
2311 45 c. Marryshow House, Grenada 55 55
2312 50 c. University Administrative Building, Barbados 65 75
2309/12 *Set of 4* 1·50 1·50

367 George Stephenson's First Locomotive, 1814 (Great Britain)

(Des G. Vasarhelyi. Litho Walsall)

1991 (2 Dec). *Great Railways of the World. T 367 and similar horiz designs. Multicoloured.* P 14.
2313 75 c. Type **367** 60 60
a. Sheetlet. Nos. 2313/21 4·75
2314 75 c. George Stephenson 60 60
2315 75 c. Killingworth locomotive, 1816 (Great Britain) 60 60
2316 75 c. George Stephenson's *Locomotion*, 1825 (Great Britain) 60 60
2317 75 c. *Locomotion* in Darlington, 1825 (Great Britain) 60 60
2318 75 c. Opening of Stockton & Darlington Railway, 1825 60 60
2319 75 c. Timothy Hackworth's *Royal George*, 1827 (Great Britain) 60 60
2320 75 c. *Northumbrian*, 1831 (Great Britain) 60 60
2321 75 c. *Planet*, 1830 (Great Britain) 60 60
2322 $1 *Old Ironsides*, 1830 (U.S.A.) 80 80
a. Sheetlet. Nos. 2322/30 6·50
2323 $1 *Wilberforce*, 1832 (Great Britain) 80 80
2324 $1 *Adler*, 1835 (Germany) 80 80
2325 $1 *North Star*, 1837 (Great Britain) 80 80
2326 $1 London & Birmingham Railway No. 1, 1838 (Great Britain) 80 80
2327 $1 Stephenson's *Austria*, 1838 (Austria) 80 80
2328 $1 Baltimore & Ohio Railroad No. 378 *Muddigger*, 1840 (U.S.A.) 80 80
2329 $1 Baltimore & Ohio Railroad *Norris*, 1840 (U.S.A.) 80 80
2330 $1 *Centaur*, 1840 (Great Britain) 80 80
2331 $2 *Lion*, 1841 (Great Britain) 1·50 1·50
a. Sheetlet. Nos. 2331/9 12·50
2332 $2 *Beuth*, 1843 (Germany) 1·50 1·50
2333 $2 *Derwent*, 1845 (Great Britain) 1·50 1·50
2334 $2 *Bets*, 1846 (Hungary) 1·50 1·50

2335	$2 Opening of Budapest to Vac railway, 1846 (Hungary)	1·50	1·50
2336	$2 Carriages, Stockton & Darlington Railway, 1846 (Great Britain)	1·50	1·50
2337	$2 "Long Boiler" type, 1847 (France)	1·50	1·50
2338	$2 Baldwin locomotive, 1850 (U.S.A.)	1·50	1·50
2339	$2 Steam locomotive, 1850 (Germany)	1·50	1·50
2313/39	*Set of 27*	23·00	23·00

MS2340 Two sheets, each 116×86 mm. (a) $6 Part of Stephenson's *Locomotion*, 1825 (Great Britain). (b) $6 Train on Liverpool & Manchester Railway, 1833 (Great Britain) .. *Set of 2 sheets* 11·00 12·00
Nos. 2313/21, 2322/30 and 2331/9 were printed together, se-tenant, in sheetlets of 9.

368 Barbu

(Des I. MacLaury. Litho Questa)

1991 (5 Dec). *Marine Life of the Sandflats. T* 368 *and similar horiz designs. Multicoloured. P* 14.

2341	50 c. Type 368	65	65
	a. Sheetlet. Nos. 2341/55	8·50	
2342	50 c. Beau Gregory	65	65
2343	50 c. Porcupinefish	65	65
2344	50 c. Queen or Pink Conch and Conchfish	65	65
2345	50 c. Hermit Crab	65	65
2346	50 c. Bluestripe Lizardfish	65	65
2347	50 c. Spot-finned Mojarra	65	65
2348	50 c. Southern Stingray	65	65
2349	50 c. Long-spined Sea Urchin and Slippery Dick	65	65
2350	50 c. Peacock Flounder	65	65
2351	50 c. West Indian Sea Star	65	65
2352	50 c. Spotted Goatfish	65	65
2353	50 c. Netted Olive and West Indian Sea Egg	65	65
2354	50 c. Pearly Razorfish	65	65
2355	50 c. Spotted Jawfish and Yellow-headed Jawfish	65	65
2341/55	*Set of 15*	8·50	8·50

MS2356 105×76 mm. $6 Short-nosed Batfish 8·50 9·50
Nos. 2341/55 were printed together, se-tenant, in sheetlets of fifteen, forming a composite design.

(Litho Walsall)

1991 (9 Dec). *Christmas. Religious Paintings by Albrecht Dürer. Vert designs as T* 287 *of Antigua. Multicoloured. P* 12.

2357	10 c. "Adoration of the Magi" (detail)	30	10
2358	35 c. "Madonna with the Siskin" (detail) ..	60	25
2359	50 c. "Feast of the Rose Garlands" (detail)	80	45
2360	75 c. "Virgin with the Pear" (detail)	1·25	70
2361	$1 "Virgin in Half-length" (detail)	1·50	90
2362	$2 "Madonna and Child" (detail)	2·50	2·75
2363	$4 "Virgin and Child with St. Anne" (detail)	3·00	4·00
2364	$5 "Virgin and Child" (detail)	3·00	4·00
2357/64	*Set of 8*	11·50	12·00

MS2365 Two sheets, each 102×127 mm. (a) $6 "Virgin with a Multitude of Animals" (detail). (b) $6 "The Nativity" (detail). P 14½×14
Set of 2 sheets 9·50 11·00

369 Goofy windsurfing

(Des Walt Disney Co. Litho Questa)

1992 (11 Feb). *Thrill Sports. T* 369 *and similar multicoloured designs showing Walt Disney cartoon characters. P* 14×13½.

2366	5 c. Type 369	25	20
2367	10 c. Mickey Mouse skateboarding	30	20
2368	20 c. Daisy Duck gliding	50	20
2369	45 c. Mickey's nephews stunt kite flying	85	25
2370	$1 Donald Duck mountain biking	1·50	85
2371	$2 Donald and Chipmunk parachuting	2·25	2·50
2372	$4 Mickey go-karting	3·50	4·25
2373	$5 Minnie water skiing	3·50	4·25
2366/73	*Set of 8*	11·50	11·50

MS2374 Four sheets, each 128×102 mm. (a) $6 Mickey bungee jumping (*vert*). P 13½×14. (b) $6 Mickey and Minnie river rafting. P 14×13½. (c) $6 Donald's nephews playing roller hockey. P 14×13½. (d) $6 Mickey hang-gliding. P 14×13½ .. .. .. *Set of 4 sheets* 16·00 17·00

(Des D. Miller. Litho Questa)

1992 (2 Mar). *40th Anniv of Queen Elizabeth II's Accession. Horiz designs as T* 288 *of Antigua. Multicoloured. P* 14.

2375	10 c. Waterfall	35	20
2376	50 c. Street in St. George's	55	40
2377	$1 Colonial-style houses, St. George's ..	90	80

2378	$5 St. George's from the sea	3·50	4·00
2375/8	*Set of 4*	4·75	4·75

MS2379 Two sheets, each 75×96 mm. (a) $6 Village on hillside. (b) $6 Yacht at anchor off village .. .. .. *Set of 2 sheets* 9·00 10·00

(Litho B.D.T.)

1992 (30 Apr). *"Granada '92" International Stamp Exhibition, Spain. Spanish Paintings. Multicoloured designs as T* 292 *of Antigua.* P 13×13½ (*vert*) or 13½×13 (*horiz*).

2380	10 c. "The Corpus Christi Procession in Seville" (Manuel Cabral y Aguado) (*horiz*)	20	20
2381	35 c. "The Mancorbo Channel" (Carlos de Haes)	35	20
2382	50 c. "Amalia de Llano y Dotres, Countess of Vilches" (Federico de Madrazo y Kuntz)	50	40
2383	75 c. "Conchita Serrano y Domínguez, Countess of Santovenia" (Eduardo Rosales Gallina)	70	60
2384	$1 "Queen María Isabel de Braganza" (Bernardo López Piquer)	85	75
2385	$2 "The Presentation of Don John of Austria to Charles V" (detail) (Gallina)	1·60	1·90
2386	$4 "The Presentation of Don John of Austria to Charles V" (different detail) (Gallina)	3·00	3·75
2387	$5 "The Testament of Isabella the Catholic" (Gallina) (*horiz*)	3·00	3·75
2380/7	*Set of 8*	9·00	10·50

MS2388 Two sheets, each 120×95 mm. (a) $6 "The Horse Corral in the Old Madrid Bullring" (Manuel Castellano) (111×85 *mm*). (b) $6 "Meeting of Poets in Antonio María Esquivel's Studio" (Antonia María Esquivel y Suárez de Urbina) (111×85 *mm*). Imperf .. *Set of 2 sheets* 8·00 9·00

370 Green-winged Macaw

371 Gracie Fields

(Des L. Fried. Litho Questa)

1992 (7 May). *500th Anniv of Discovery of America by Columbus (5th issue). World Columbian Stamp "Expo '92", Chicago. T* 370 *and similar vert designs. Multicoloured. P* 14.

2389	10 c. Type 370	40	30
2390	25 c. *Santa Maria*	45	30
2391	35 c. Christopher Columbus	55	30
2392	50 c. 15th-century sandglass	60	55
2393	75 c. Queen Isabella	70	80
2394	$4 Cantino map of 1502 (detail)	4·00	5·50
2389/94	*Set of 6*	6·00	7·00

MS2395 Two sheets, each 80×108 mm. (a) $6 Map of Genoa (detail). (b) $6 Detail of 15th-century map by Thomas Bly .. *Set of 2 sheets* 9·00 10·00

(Des R. Brickman. Litho Questa)

1992 (28 May). *"Genova '92" International Thematic Stamp Exhibition. Hummingbirds. Multicoloured designs as T* 295 *of Antigua, but vertical. P* 14.

2396	10 c. Ruby-throated Hummingbird	20	15
2397	25 c. Vervain Hummingbird	30	20
2398	35 c. Blue-headed Hummingbird	35	25
2399	50 c. Cuban Emerald	55	55
2400	75 c. Antillean Mango	75	75
2401	$2 Purple-throated Carib	1·50	1·75
2402	$4 Puerto Rican Emerald	2·75	3·25
2403	$5 Green-throated Carib	2·75	3·25
2396/403	*Set of 8*	8·25	9·25

MS2404 Two sheets, each 109×80 mm. (a) $6 Young Antillean Crested Hummingbird. (b) $6 Rufous-breasted Hermit .. *Set of 2 sheets* 12·00 13·00

(Des R. Jung. Litho B.D.T.)

1992 (1 June). *50th Anniv of United Service Organization (forces' entertainment programme). T* 371 *and similar vert designs. Multicoloured. P* 14.

2405	15 c. Type 371	30	20
2406	25 c. Jack Benny	30	20
2407	35 c. Jinx Falkenburg	30	25
2408	50 c. Francis Langford	45	40
2409	75 c. Joe E. Brown	80	70
2410	$1 Phil Silvers	90	80
2411	$2 Danny Kaye	1·75	2·00
2412	$5 Frank Sinatra	4·00	4·25
2405/12	*Set of 8*	8·00	8·00

MS2413 Two sheets, each 107×80 mm. (a) $6 Bob Hope. (b) $6 Anna May Wong *Set of 2 sheets* 8·00 9·00

STANLEY GIBBONS
STAMP COLLECTING SERIES

Introductory booklets on *How to Start, How to Identify Stamps* and *Collecting by Theme.* A series of well illustrated guides at a low price.
Write for details.

372 Badminton

373 *Matador* (yacht), Newport News Regatta

(Litho Questa)

1992 (17 June). *Olympic Games, Barcelona (2nd issue). T* 372 *and similar multicoloured designs. P* 14.

2414	10 c. Type 372	15	15
2415	25 c. Women's long jump	20	20
2416	35 c. Women's 100 metres	30	30
2417	50 c. 1000 metres cycling sprint	50	50
2418	75 c. Decathlon (*horiz*)	70	70
2419	$2 Judo (*horiz*)	1·60	1·75
2420	$4 Women's gymnastics – asymmetrical bars	2·75	3·25
2421	$5 Men's javelin	2·75	3·25
2414/21	*Set of 8*	8·00	9·00

MS2422 Two sheets, each 100×70 mm. (a) $6 Men's gymnastics – vault. (b) $6 Men's gymnastics – floor exercise .. *Set of 2 sheets* 8·00 9·00

(Des F. Paul ($1), J. Esquino ($2). Litho Questa)

1992 (24 Aug). *500th Anniv of Discovery of America by Columbus (6th issue). Organization of East Caribbean States. As Nos.* 1670/1 *of Antigua. Multicoloured. P* 14½.

2423	$1 Columbus meeting Amerindians	70	70
2424	$2 Ships approaching island	1·40	1·60

(Des W. Hanson. Litho B.D.T.)

1992 (22 Oct). *Toy Trains from American Manufacturers. Multicoloured designs as T* 257 *of Dominica. P* 14.

2425	10 c. *The Blue Comet* locomotive, Boucher (1933)	15	15
2426	35 c. No. 2220 switching locomotive, Voltamp (1906)	25	25
2427	40 c. No. 221 tunnel locomotive, Knapp (1905)	30	30
2428	75 c. "Grand Canyon" locomotive, American Flyer (1931)	55	55
2429	$2 "Streamliner" tin locomotive, Hafner (1930s)	70	70
2430	$2 No. 237 switching locomotive, Elektoy (1911)	1·40	1·75
2431	$4 Parlour car, Ives (1928)	2·75	3·25
2432	$5 "Improved President's Special" locomotive, American Flyer (1927)	2·75	3·25
2425/32	*Set of 8*	8·00	9·00

MS2433 Two sheets, each 133×103 mm. (a) $6 No. 1122 locomotive, Ives (1921) (38½×50 *mm*). (b) $6 No. 3239 locomotive, Ives (1912) (50×38½ *mm*). P 13 .. .. .. *Set of 2 sheets* 8·00 9·00

(Des Kerri Schiff. Litho Questa)

1992 (28 Oct). *Postage Stamp Mega Event, New York. Sheet* 100×70mm *containing multicoloured design as T* 299 *of Antigua. P* 14.

MS2434 $6 Guggenheim Museum .. .. 3·50 4·25

(Litho Questa)

1992 (12 Nov). *World Regattas. T* 373 *and similar multicoloured designs. P* 14.

2435	15 c. Type 373	20	20
2436	25 c. *Awesome,* Antigua	25	25
2437	35 c. *Mistress Quickly,* Bermuda	30	30
2438	50 c. *Emeraude,* St. Tropez	50	50
2439	$1 *Diva G,* German Admirals Cup	80	80
2440	$2 *Lady Be,* French Admirals Cup	1·50	1·75
2441	$4 *Midnight Sun,* Admirals Cup	2·75	3·25
2442	$5 *Carat,* Sardinia Cup	2·75	3·25
2435/42	*Set of 8*	8·00	9·00

MS2443 Two sheets, each 113×85 mm. (a) $6 Yachts, Grenada Regatta (*horiz*). (b) $6 Fastnet Race, 1979 (*horiz*) .. *Set of 2 sheets* 8·50 10·00

(Litho Questa)

1992 (16 Nov). *Christmas. Religious Paintings. Vert designs as T* 300 *of Antigua. Multicoloured. P* 13½×14.

2444	10 c. "Adoration of the Magi" (detail) (Fra Filippo Lippi)	25	15
2445	15 c. "Madonna adoring Child in a Wood" (Lippi)	30	20
2446	25 c. "Adoration of the Magi" (detail) (Botticelli)	40	20
2447	35 c. "The Epiphany - Adoration of the Magi" (detail) (Hieronymus Bosch) ..	45	20
2448	50 c. "Adoration of the Magi" (detail) (Giovanni de Paolo)	70	45
2449	75 c. "Adoration of the Magi" (Gentile da Fabriano)	90	60
2450	90 c. "Adoration of the Magi" (detail) (Juan Batista Maino)	1·10	70

2451	$1 "Adoration of the Child" (Master of Liesborn)		1·25	80
2452	$2 "Adoration of the Kings" (Master of Liesborn)		2·00	2·25
2453	$3 "Adoration of the Three Wise Men" (Pedro Berruguete)		2·25	3·00
2454	$4 "Adoration of the Child" (Lippi)		3·00	3·50
2455	$5 "Adoration of the Child" (Correggio)		3·00	3·50
2444/55		*Set of 12*	14·00	14·00

MS2456 Three sheets, each 72×97 mm. (a) $6 "Adoration of the Magi" (detail) (Andrea Mantegna). (b) $6 "Adoration of the Magi" (detail) (Hans Memling). (c) $6 "Adoration of the Shepherds" (La Tour) .. *Set of 3 sheets* 14·00 16·00
No. 2447 is inscribed "Hieronymous" in error.

374 Cher   **375** Grenada Dove

(Des J. Genzo. Litho Questa)

1992 (19 Nov). *Gold Record Award Winners. T* **374** *and similar vert designs. Multicoloured. P* 14.

2457	90 c. Type 374		1·25	1·25
	a. Sheetlet. Nos. 2457/64		8·50	
2458	90 c. Michael Jackson		1·25	1·25
2459	90 c. Elvis Presley		1·25	1·25
2460	90 c. Dolly Parton		1·25	1·25
2461	90 c. Johnny Mathis		1·25	1·25
2462	90 c. Madonna		1·25	1·25
2463	90 c. Nat King Cole		1·25	1·25
2464	90 c. Janice Joplin		1·25	1·25
2457/64		*Set of 8*	8·50	8·50

MS2465 Two sheets, each 100×70 mm. (a) $3 Chuck Berry; $3 James Brown. (b) $3 Frank Sinatra; $3 Perry Como .. *Set of 2 sheets* 12·00 12·00
Nos. 2457/64 were printed together, *se-tenant*, in sheetlets of 8 with a composite background design.

(Des W. Wright and W. Hanson (Nos. 2467, 2476, MS2478a), W. Wright and L. Fried (Nos. 2468, 2474, MS2478b), J. Genzo (Nos. 2473, MS2478e), W. Wright (others). Litho B.D.T.)

1992 (15 Dec). *Anniversaries and Events. T* **375** *and similar multicoloured designs. P* 14.

2466	10 c. Type 375		50	40
2467	25 c. Airship LZ-1 on maiden flight, 1900 (*horiz*)		70	30
2468	50 c. ENDOSAT (robot plane) project (*horiz*)		75	55
2469	75 c. Konrad Adenauer (German statesman) and industrial skyline (*horiz*)		80	70
2470	$1.50, Golden Lion Tamarin (*horiz*)		2·00	2·00
2471	$2 Mountain Gorilla (*horiz*)		2·50	2·50
2472	$2 Outline of man and heart (*horiz*)		2·50	2·50
2473	$3 Wolfgang Amadeus Mozart		3·25	3·25
2474	$4 "Voyager 2" and Neptune (*horiz*)		3·50	3·50
2475	$4 Adenauer with flag and map of West Germany (*horiz*)		3·50	3·50
2476	$5 Count von Zeppelin and LZ-127 *Graf Zeppelin* (*horiz*)		3·50	3·50
2477	$5 Admiral Richard Byrd (polar explorer) (*horiz*)		3·50	3·50
2466/77		*Set of 12*	24·00	24·00

MS2478 Five sheets. (a) 110×80 mm. $6 Count von Zeppelin (*horiz*). (b) 110×80 mm. $6 Space shuttle recovering "Intelsat 6" satellite. (c) 110×80 mm. $6 Konrad Adenauer (*horiz*). (d) 95×70 mm. $6 Spotted Little Owl (*horiz*). (e) 100×70 mm. $6 Papageno costume from *The Magic Flute* .. *Set of 5 sheets* 18·00 20·00
Anniversaries and Events:—No. 2466, National bird; Nos. 2467, 2476, MS2478a, 75th death anniv of Count Ferdinand von Zeppelin; Nos. 2468, 2475, MS2478b, International Space Year; Nos. 2469, 2475, MS2478c, 25th death anniv of Konrad Adenauer; Nos. 2470/1, MS2478d, Earth Summit '92, Rio; No. 2472, United Nations World Health Organization Projects; No. 2473, MS2478e, Death bicent of Mozart; No. 2477, 75th anniv of International Association of Lions Clubs.

376 Care Bear on Beach

(Des T.C.F.C. Inc. Litho Questa)

1992 (15 Dec). *Ecology. T* **376** *and similar multicoloured design showing Care Bear cartoon characters. P* 14.

2479	75 c. Type 376		45	45

MS2480 71×101 mm. $2 Care Bear and butterfly (*vert*) .. .. 1·75 1·90

---

377 Samoyed and St. Basil's Cathedral, Moscow   **378** Baha'i Shrine, Haifa

(Des Joan Popeio. Litho Questa)

1993 (20 Jan). *Dogs of the World. T* **377** *and similar horiz designs. Multicoloured. P* 14.

2481	10 c. Type 377		40	30
2482	15 c. Chow and Ling Yin Monastery, China		50	30
2483	25 c. Boxer and Tower of London		55	30
2484	90 c. Basenji and Yamma Mosque, Niger		1·00	75
2485	$1 Golden Labrador and Parliament Building, Ottawa		1·00	80
2486	$3 St. Bernard and Parsenn, Switzerland		2·25	2·75
2487	$4 Rhodesian Ridgeback and Melrose House, South Africa		2·50	3·00
2488	$5 Afghan Hound and Mazar-i-Sharif, Afghanistan		2·50	3·00
2481/8		*Set of 8*	9·50	10·00

MS2489 Two sheets, each 100×70 mm. (a) $6 Australian Cattle Dog. (b) $6 Alaskan Malamute .. .. *Set of 2 sheets* 9·00 9·50
No. MS2489(a) is inscribed "Australian" in error.

(Litho Walsall)

1993 (8 Mar). *Bicentenary of the Louvre, Paris. Paintings by Jean-Antoine Watteau. Multicoloured designs as T* **305** *of Antigua. P* 12.

2490	$1 "The Faux-pas"		70	80
	a. Sheetlet. Nos. 2490/7		5·00	
2491	$1 "Portrait of a Gentleman"		70	80
2492	$1 "Young Lady with Archlute"		70	80
2493	$1 "Young Man Dancing"		70	80
2494	$1 "Autumn, Pamona and a Cherub"		70	80
2495	$1 "Judgement of Paris"		70	80
2496	$1 "Pierrot" (detail)		70	80
2497	$1 "Pierrot" (different detail)		70	80
2490/7		*Set of 8*	5·00	5·75

MS2498 100×70 mm. $6 "The Embarkation for Cythére" (85×52 *mm*). P 14½ .. .. 4·00 4·75
Nos. 2490/7 were printed together, *se-tenant*, in sheetlets of 8 stamps and one centre label.

(Litho Cartor)

1993 (7 Apr). *Centenary of Baha'i Faith. P* 13½×14

2499	378 75 c. multicoloured		75	75

379 *Citheronia magnifica*   **380** Heliconia

(Litho Questa)

1993 (13 Apr). *Moths. T* **379** *and similar multicoloured designs. P* 14.

2500	10 c. Type 379		25	25
2501	35 c. *Automeris metali*		40	25
2502	45 c. *Thysania zenobia*		50	30
2503	75 c. *Agrius cingulatus*		70	55
2504	$1 *Composia fidelissima*		80	65
2505	$2 *Synchlora xysteraria*		1·50	1·75
2506	$4 *Eumorpha labruscae*		2·50	2·75
2507	$5 *Ascalapha odorata*		2·50	2·75
2500/7		*Set of 8*	8·25	8·25

MS2508 Two sheets, each 100×70 mm. (a) $6 *Epimecis detexta* (*vert*). (b) $6 *Xylophanes titana* (*vert*) .. .. *Set of 2 sheets* 7·50 8·50

(Des D. Delouise. Litho Questa)

1993 (17 May). *Flowers. T* **380** *and similar multicoloured designs. P* 14.

2509	10 c. Type 380		25	25
2510	35 c. Pansy		40	25
2511	45 c. Water Lily		50	30
2512	75 c. Bougainvillea		70	55
2513	$1 Calla Lily		80	65
2514	$2 California Poppy		1·50	1·75
2515	$4 Red Ginger		2·50	3·00
2516	$5 Anthurium		2·50	3·00
2509/16		*Set of 8*	8·25	8·75

MS2517 Two sheets, each 70×100 mm. (a) $6 Christmas Rose (*horiz*). (b) $6 Moth Orchid (*horiz*) .. .. *Set of 2 sheets* 7·50 8·50

(Des Kerri Schiff. Litho Questa)

1993 (2 June). *40th Anniv of Coronation. Vert designs as T* **307** *of Antigua. P* 13½×14.

2518	35 c. multicoloured		70	75
	a. Sheetlet. Nos. 2518/21×2		8·00	
2519	70 c. multicoloured		80	85
2520	$1 reddish brown and black		85	90
2521	$5 multicoloured		2·25	2·50
2518/21		*Set of 4*	4·25	4·50

MS2522 70×100 mm. $6 multicoloured. P 14 4·00 4·50
Designs: (38×47 *mm*)—35 c. Queen Elizabeth II at Coronation (photograph by Cecil Beaton); 70 c. Sceptres; $1 Queen Elizabeth receiving sceptre from Archbishop of Canterbury; $5 Queen and Prince Philip with their children, 1960s. (28½×42½ *mm*)—$6 "Queen Elizabeth II, 1965" (detail) (Peter Greenham).
Nos. 2518/21 were printed together in sheetlets of 8 containing two *se-tenant* blocks of 4.

381 "Woman with Loaves" (Picasso)   **382** Red-eyed Vireo

(Litho Questa)

1993 (1 July). *Anniversaries and Events. T* **381** *and similar designs. Each reddish brown, deep brown and black (Nos. 2527, 2535, MS2536d) or multicoloured (others). P* 14.

2523	25 c. Type 381		30	20
2524	35 c. 16th-century telescope		35	20
2525	35 c. Public Library building		35	20
2526	35 c. Gaetan Boucher (speed skating, 1984)		35	20
2527	50 c. Willy Brandt with Senator Edward Kennedy (*horiz*)		40	30
2528	75 c. Carnival float (*horiz*)		50	40
2529	90 c. "Weeping Woman" (Picasso)		65	45
2530	$1 "Marii Prohaska" (Tyrus Czyzewski)		70	50
2531	$3 "Marysia et Burek a Geylan" (S. Wirkiewicz)		2·25	2·25
2532	$4 "Woman seated in Airchair" (Picasso)		2·75	2·75
2533	$4 Astronaut on Moon		2·75	2·75
2534	$5 Norbert Schramm (figure skating, 1984)		2·75	2·75
2535	$5 Willy Brandt and Kurt Waldheim (*horiz*)		2·75	2·75
2523/35		*Set of 13*	15·00	14·00

MS2536 Five sheets. (a) 76×107 mm. $5 Copernicus. (b) 75×105 mm. $6 "Three Women at the Spring" (detail) (Picasso). (c) 76×105 mm. $6 Women's Super G skiing medal winners, 1988 (*horiz*). (d) 105×75 mm. $6 Newspaper headline, 1974. (e) 105×76 mm. $6 "Parting" (detail) (Witold Wojtkiewicz) .. .. *Set of 5 sheets* 17·00 18·00
Anniversaries and Events:—Nos. 2523, 2529, 2532, MS2536b, 20th death anniv of Picasso (artist); Nos. 2524, 2533, MS2536a, 450th death anniv of Copernicus (astronomer); No. 2525, Centenary of Grenada Public Library (1992); Nos. 2526, 2534, MS2536c, Winter Olympic Games '94, Lillehammer; Nos. 2527, 2535, MS2536d, 80th birth anniv of Willy Brandt (German politician) (1992); No. 2528, Grenada Carnival; Nos. 2530/1, MS2536e, "Polska '93" International Stamp Exhibition, Poznań.

(Des R. Sauber. Litho B.D.T.)

1993 (13 July). *Songbirds. T* **382** *and similar horiz designs. Multicoloured. P* 14.

2537	15 c. Type 382		50	50
	a. Sheetlet. Nos. 2537/48		9·00	
2538	25 c. Fork-tailed Flycatcher ("Scissor-tailed Flycatcher")..		55	55
2539	35 c. Palm Chat		60	60
2540	35 c. Chaffinch		60	60
2541	45 c. Yellow Wagtail		70	70
2542	45 c. Painted Bunting		70	70
2543	50 c. Short-tailed Pygmy Tyrant ("Short-tailed Pygmy Flycatcher")		70	70
2544	65 c. Orange-breasted Bunting ("Rainbow Bunting")		80	80
2545	75 c. Red Crossbill		80	80
2546	75 c. Akialoa		80	80
2547	$1 Yellow-throated Longclaw ("Yellow-throated Wagtail")		90	90
2548	$4 Barn Swallow		2·50	2·50
2537/48		*Set of 12*	9·00	9·00

MS2549 Two sheets, each 105×86 mm. (a) $6 Song Thrush. (b) $6 White-crested Laughing Thrush .. .. .. *Set of 2 sheets* 7·00 8·00
Nos. 2537/48 were printed together, *se-tenant*, in sheetlets of 12 with the backgrounds forming a composite design.

PRICES OF SETS

Set prices are given for many issues, generally those containing three stamps or more. Definitive sets include one of each value or major colour change, but do not cover different perforations, die types or minor shades. Where a choice is possible the set prices are based on the cheapest versions of the stamps included in the listings.

383 Atlantic Grey Cowrie
(*Cypraea cinerea*) and Atlantic
Yellow Cowrie (*Cypraea spurca
acicularis*)

384 James K.
Spensley

(Des I. MacLaury. Litho B.D.T.)

1993 (19 July). *Sea Shells.* T **383** *and similar horiz designs.
Multicoloured.* P 14.
2550	15 c. Type 383	..	45	45
	a. Sheetlet. Nos. 2550/61	..	8·00	
2551	15 c. Candy-stick Tellin (*Tellina similis*) and Sunrise Tellin (*Tellina radiata*)		45	45
2552	25 c. Caribbean Vase (*Vasum muricatum*)		50	50
2553	35 c. Lightning Venus (*Pitar fulminatus*) and Royal Comb Venus (*Pitar dione*)		55	55
2554	35 c. Crown Cone (*Conus regius*)		55	55
2555	45 c. Reticulated Cowrie-helmet (*Cypraecassis testiculus*)		65	65
2556	50 c. Barbados Mitre (*Mitra barbadensis*) and Variegated Turret Shell (*Turritella variegata*)		65	65
2557	50 c. Common Egg Cockle (*Laevicardium laevigatum*) and Atlantic Strawberry Cockle (*Americardia media*)		65	65
2558	75 c. Measled Cowrie (*Cypraea zebra*)	..	75	75
2559	75 c. Rooster-tail Conch (*Strombus gallus*)		75	75
2560	$1 Lion's-paw Scallop (*Lyropecten nodosa*) and Antillean Scallop (*Lyropecten antillarum*)		85	85
2561	$4 Dog-head Triton (*Cymatium moritinctum caribbaeum*)		2·25	2·25
2550/61		*Set of 12*	8·00	8·00

MS2562 Two sheets, each 76×106 mm. (a) $6 Dyson's Keyhole Limpet (*Diodora dysoni*). (b) $6 Virgin Nerite (*Neritina virginea*) and Emerald Nerite (*Smaragdia viridis viridemaris*)
.. .. .. *Set of 2 sheets* 9·50 10·00

Nos. 2550/61 were printed together, *se-tenant*, in sheetlets of 12 with the backgrounds forming a composite design.

(Litho Questa)

1993 (13 Aug). *Asian International Stamp Exhibitions.
Multicoloured designs as T **268** of Dominica.* P 13½×14.

(a) *"Indopex '93", Surabaya, Indonesia*
2563	35 c. Megalithic Carving, Sumba Island	..	35	25
2564	45 c. Entrance to Gao Gajah, Bali	..	45	30
2565	$1.50, Statue of kris holder	..	1·00	1·00
	a. Sheetlet. Nos. 2565/70		5·50	
2566	$1.50, Hanuman protecting Sita		1·00	1·00
2567	$1.50, Sendi of Visu mounted on Garuda		1·00	1·00
2568	$1.50, Wahana (votif figure)		1·00	1·00
2569	$1.50, Hanuman (*different*)		1·00	1·00
2570	$1.50, Singa (symbolic lion)		1·00	1·00
2571	$2 Loving-mother Bridge, Taroko Gorge National Park		1·40	1·50
2572	$4 Head of Kala over temple gateway, Northern Bali		2·50	2·75
2563/72		*Set of 10*	9·50	9·25

MS2573 104×134 mm. $6 Slow Loris .. 3·75 4·25

(b) *"Taipei '93", Taiwan*
2574	35 c. Fire-breathing Dragon, New Year's Fair, Chongqing		35	25
2575	45 c. Stone pavilion, Ming Tomb, Nanjing		45	30
2576	$1.50, "Ornamental Cock" (Han Meilin)		1·00	1·00
	a. Sheetlet. Nos. 2576/81		5·50	
2577	$1.50, "He's even afraid of Cows" (Meilin)		1·00	1·00
2578	$1.50, "On a Moonlit Night" (Meilin)		1·00	1·00
2579	$1.50, "Eyes that see in the Dark" (Meilin)		1·00	1·00
2580	$1.50, "He's well behaved" (Meilin)		1·00	1·00
2581	$1.50, "He doesn't Bite" (Meilin)		1·00	1·00
2582	$2 Marble peifang, Ming 13 Tombs, Beijing		1·40	1·50
2583	$4 Stone pillar, Nanjing		2·50	2·75
2574/83		*Set of 10*	9·50	9·75

MS2584 104×134 mm. $6 Orang-utan, Mt Leuser National Park .. .. 3·75 4·25

(c) *"Bangkok 1993", Thailand*
2585	35 c. Nora Nair, Prasad Phra Thepidon, Wat Phra Kaew		35	25
2586	45 c. Stucco deities at Library of Wat Phra Singh		45	30
2587	$1.50, Wooden carved horses	..	1·00	1·00
	a. Sheetlet. Nos. 2587/92		5·50	
2588	$1.50, Wheel of the law	..	1·00	1·00
2589	$1.50, Lanna bronze elephant		1·00	1·00
2590	$1.50, Kendi in the form of elephant		1·00	1·00
2591	$1.50, Bronze duck	..	1·00	1·00
2592	$1.50, Horseman	..	1·00	1·00
2593	$2 Naga snake, Chiang Mai's Temple		1·40	1·50
2594	$4 Stucco figures, Wat Chang Lom		2·50	2·75
2585/94		*Set of 10*	9·50	9·75

MS2595 134×104 mm. $6 Elephant calf (*horiz*). P 14×13½. .. .. .. 3·75 4·25

Nos. 2565/70, 2576/81 and 2571/92 were each printed together, *se-tenant*, in sheetlets of 6.
No. 2590 is incorrectly inscribed "Kendi in the form of an Elphant".

(Des Rosemary DeFiglio. Litho Questa)

1993 (7 Sept). *World Cup Football Championship, U.S.A.
(1994) (1st issue). Vert designs as T **310** of Antigua.
Multicoloured.* P 14.
2596	10 c. Nikolai Larionov (Russia)	..	20	20
2597	25 c. Andrea Carnevale (Italy)	..	40	25

2598	35 c. Enzo Schifo (Belgium) and Soon-Ho Choi (South Korea)	..	50	25
2599	45 c. Gary Lineker (England)	..	70	30
2600	$1 Diego Maradona (Argentina)	..	1·25	80
2601	$2 Lothar Matteaus (Germany)	..	1·60	2·00
2602	$4 Jan Karas (Poland) and Julio César Silva (Brazil)		2·25	3·25
2603	$5 Claudio Caniggia (Argentina)		2·50	3·25
2596/603		*Set of 8*	8·50	9·50

MS2604 Two sheets, each 75×104 mm. (a) $6 Wlodzimierz (Poland). (b) $6 José Basualdo (Argentina) .. .. *Set of 2 sheets* 7·00 8·00
See also Nos. 2721/7.

(Litho Questa)

1993 (7 Sept). *Centenary of Italian Football.* T **384** *and similar designs showing past and present Genoa players. Each blue-black, bright vermilion and black (Nos. 2605/16) or multicoloured (No. MS2617).* P 14.
2605	$3 Type 384	..	2·25	2·25
	a. Sheetlet. Nos. 2605/10		12·00	
2606	$3 Renzo de Vecchi		2·25	2·25
2607	$3 Giovanni de Pra'		2·25	2·25
2608	$3 Luigi Burlando		2·25	2·25
2609	$3 Felice Levratto		2·25	2·25
2610	$3 Guglielmo Stabile		2·25	2·25
2611	$3 Vittorio Sardelli		2·25	2·25
	a. Sheetlet. Nos. 2611/16		12·00	
2612	$3 Juan Carlos Verdeal		2·25	2·25
2613	$3 Fosco Becattini		2·25	2·25
2614	$3 Julio Cesar Abadie		2·25	2·25
2615	$3 Luigi Meroni		2·25	2·25
2616	$3 Roberto Pruzzo		2·25	2·25
2605/16		*Set of 12*	24·00	24·00

MS2617 Two sheets. (a) 100×75 mm. $15 Genoa Football Club badge (29×45 mm). P 14. (b) 129×106 mm. $15 Genoa team of 1991–92 (48×35 mm). P 14×13½ .. *Set of 2 sheets* 21·00 22·00
Nos. 2605/10 and 2611/16 were printed together, *se-tenant*, in sheetlets of 6.

385 *The Band Concert*, 1935

(Des Rosemary DeFiglio. Litho Questa)

1993 (11 Nov). *65th Anniv of Mickey Mouse.* T **385** *and similar multicoloured designs showing Mickey Mouse in scenes from Walt Disney cartoon films.* P 14×13½.
2618	25 c. Type 385	..	55	20
2619	35 c. *Mickey's Circus*, 1936		60	20
2620	50 c. *Magician Mickey*, 1937		75	35
2621	75 c. *Moose Hunters*, 1937		1·00	60
2622	$1 *Mickey's Amateurs*, 1937		1·25	80
2623	$2 *Tugboat Mickey*, 1940		1·75	1·75
2624	$4 *Orphan's Benefit*, 1941		2·75	3·25
2625	$5 *Mickey's Christmas Carol*, 1983		2·75	3·25
2618/25		*Set of 8*	10·00	9·50

MS2626 Two sheets, each 127×102 mm. (a) $6 *Mickey's Birthday Party*, 1942. P 14×13½. (b) $6 *Mickey's Trailer*, 1938 (*vert*). P 13½×14 .. .. .. *Set of 2 sheets* 9·50 10·00
No. 2624 is inscribed "Oprhan's Benefit" in error.

(Litho Questa)

1993 (22 Nov). *Christmas. Religious Paintings. Vert designs as T **270** of Dominica. Black, pale lemon and red (Nos. 2627/8, 2632, 2634, MS2635a) or multicoloured (others).* P 13½×14.
2627	10 c. "The Nativity" (Dürer)		25	15
2628	25 c. "The Annunciation" (Dürer)		35	15
2629	35 c. "The Litta Madonna" (Da Vinci)		40	20
2630	60 c. "The Virgin and Child with St. John the Baptist and St. Anne" (Da Vinci)		50	40
2631	90 c. "The Madonna with the Carnation" (Da Vinci)		65	65
2632	$1 "Adoration of the Magi" (Dürer)		75	75
2633	$4 "The Benois Madonna" (Da Vinci)		2·50	3·25
2634	$5 "The Virgin Mary in the Sun" (Dürer)		2·50	3·25
2627/34		*Set of 8*	7·25	8·00

MS2635 Two sheets, each 102×128 mm. (a) $6 "The Holy Family with Three Hares" (detail) (Dürer). (b) $6 "Adoration of the Magi" (Da Vinci) .. .. *Set of 2 sheets* 7·00 8·00
Nos. 2629/31, 2633 and MS2635b are inscribed "LEONARDO DI VINCI".

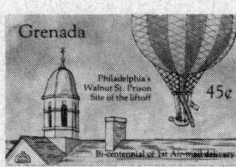

386 Blanchard's Balloon over
Walnut St. Prison

(Litho Questa)

1993 (21 Dec). *Aviation Anniversaries.* T **386** *and similar multicoloured designs.* P 14.
2636	35 c. Airship LZ-127 *Graf Zeppelin* over Vienna at night		35	20
2637	45 c. Type 386	..	20	25
2638	50 c. Lysander	..	50	35
2639	75 c. *Graf Zeppelin* over Pyramids		75	55
2640	$2 Blanchard waving hat from balloon (*vert*)		90	95
2641	$3 Hawker Typhoon		2·00	2·50
2642	$5 *Graf Zeppelin* over Rio de Janeiro		3·25	3·75
2636/42		*Set of 7*	7·25	7·75

MS2643 Three sheets, each 106×77 mm. (a) $6 *Graf Zeppelin*. (b) $6 Blanchard's balloon (*vert*). (c) $6 Hawker Hurricane .. *Set of 3 sheets* 10·50 11·00
Anniversaries:—Nos. 2636, 2639, 2642, MS2643a, 125th birth anniv of Hugo Eckener (airship commander); Nos. 2637, 2640, MS2643b, Bicentenary of First Airmail Flight; Nos. 2638, 2641, MS2643c, 75th anniv of Royal Air Force

387 Mercedes Benz "370 S"
Cabriolet, 1932

388 Fishermen
with Blue Marlin

(Des K. Gromell. Litho Questa)

1993 (21 Dec). *Centenaries of Henry Ford's First Petrol Engine (Nos. 2645/6, MS2648b) and Karl Benz's First Four-wheeled Car (others).* T **387** *and similar horiz designs. Multicoloured.* P 14.
2644	35 c. Type 387	..	40	20
2645	45 c. Ford "Mustang", 1966		50	30
2646	$3 Ford "Model A" Phaeton, 1930		3·00	3·50
2647	$4 Mercedes Benz "300 Sl" Gullwing		3·50	4·00
2644/7		*Set of 4*	6·75	7·25

MS2648 Two sheets, each 76×106 mm. (a) $6 Mercedes Benz "290", 1934. (b) $6 Ford "Model A", 1903 .. .. .. *Set of 2 sheets* 8·00 9·00

(Des Kerri Schiff. Litho Questa)

1993 (31 Dec). *Famous Paintings by Rembrandt and Matisse. Multicoloured designs as T **316** of Antigua.* P 13½×14.
2649	15 c. "Self-portrait", 1900 (Matisse)		30	20
2650	35 c. "Self-portrait", 1629 (Rembrandt)		35	20
2651	45 c. "Self-portrait", 1918 (Matisse)		40	25
2652	50 c. "Self-portrait", 1640 (Rembrandt)		50	35
2653	75 c. "Self-portrait", 1652 (Rembrandt)		65	55
2654	$2 "Self-portrait", 1906 (Matisse)		1·40	1·75
2655	$4 "Self-portrait", 1900 (*different*) (Matisse)		2·50	3·25
2656	$5 "Self-portrait", 1625–31 (Rembrandt)		2·75	3·25
2649/56		*Set of 8*	8·00	8·75

MS2657 Two sheets. (a) 100×125 mm. $6 "The Painter in his Studio" (detail) (Matisse). P 13½×14. (b) 125×100 mm. $6 "The Sampling Officials of the Drapers' Guild" (detail) (Rembrandt) (*horiz*). P 14×13½ *Set of 2 sheets* 7·00 8·00

(Litho Questa)

1994 (21 Jan). *25th Anniv of Spice Island Billfish Tournament.* T **388** *and similar vert designs. Multicoloured.* P 14.
2658	15 c. Type 388	..	40	30
2659	25 c. Sailfish and angler		45	30
2660	35 c. Yellow-finned Tuna with angler		55	30
2661	50 c. White Marlin with angler		65	50
2662	75 c. Catching a Sailfish		75	80
2658/62		*Set of 5*	2·50	2·00

389 National Flag
and Ketch in Bay

390 *Hygrocybe
acutoconica*

(Litho Questa)

1994 (8 Feb). *25th Anniv of Independence.* T **389** *and similar vert design. Multicoloured.* P 14.
2663	35 c. Type 389	..	30	30

MS2664 76×106 mm. $6 Map of Grenada .. 3·75 4·50

(Des W. Hanson. Litho Questa)

1994 (18 Feb). *"Hong Kong '94" International Stamp Exhibition (1st issue). Horiz designs as T **317** of Antigua. Multicoloured.* P 14.
2665	40 c. Hong Kong 1971 Scouting 50 c. stamp and "Hong Kong Post Office, 1846" (left detail) (M. Bruce)		35	50
	a. Horiz pair. Nos. 2665/6		70	1·00

2666 40 c. Grenada 1988 Rotary $2 and "Hong Kong Post Office, 1846" (right detail) (M. Bruce) 35 50
Nos. 2665/6 were printed together, *se-tenant*, in horizontal pairs throughout the sheet with the centre part of each pair forming the complete painting.

(Des Kerri Schiff. Litho Questa)

1994 (18 Feb). *"Hong Kong '94" International Stamp Exhibition (2nd issue). Qing Dynasty Porcelain. Multicoloured designs as T 318 of Antigua, but vert. P 14.*
2667 45 c. Vase with dragon decoration .. 35 40
    a. Sheetlet. Nos. 2667/72 .. 1·90
2668 45 c. Hat stand with brown base .. 35 40
2669 45 c. Gourd-shaped vase 35 40
2670 45 c. Rotating vase with openwork .. 35 40
2671 45 c. Candlestick with dogs .. 35 40
2672 45 c. Hat stand with orange base .. 35 40
2667/72 .. .. .. Set of 6 1·90 2·25
Nos. 2667/72 were printed together, *se-tenant*, in sheetlets of 6.

(Des Susan Carlson. Litho Questa)

1994 (6 Apr). *Fungi. T 390 and similar vert designs. Multicoloured. P 14.*
2673 35 c. Type **390** 50 30
2674 45 c. *Leucopaxillus gracillimus* .. 55 30
2675 50 c. *Leptonia caeruleocapitata* .. 55 30
2676 75 c. *Leucocoprinus birnbaumii* .. 70 50
2677 $1 *Marasmius atrorubens* .. 85 75
2678 $2 *Boletellus cubensis* .. .. 1·40 1·50
2679 $4 *Chlorophyllum molybdites* .. 2·25 2·75
2680 $5 *Psilocybe cubensis* .. .. 2·25 2·75
2673/80 .. .. .. Set of 8 8·00 8·00
MS2681 Two sheets, each 100×70 mm. (a) $6 *Mycena pura.* (b) $6 *Pyrrhoglossum lilaceipes*
    .. .. .. Set of 2 sheets 9·00 9·00

391 Quetzalcoatlus

392 *Brassavola cuculatta*

(Des V. DiFate. Litho Questa)

1994 (13 Apr). *Prehistoric Animals. T 391 and similar multicoloured designs. P 14.*
2682 75 c. Type **391** 55 55
    a. Sheetlet. Nos. 2682/93 .. 6·00
2683 75 c. Pteranodon ingens 55 55
2684 75 c. Tropeognathus 55 55
2685 75 c. Phobetor 55 55
2686 75 c. Alamosaurus 55 55
2687 75 c. Triceratops 55 55
2688 75 c. Tyrannosaurus rex 55 55
2689 75 c. Head of Tyrannosaurus rex .. 55 55
2690 75 c. Lambeosaurus 55 55
2691 75 c. Spinosaurus 55 55
2692 75 c. Parasaurolophus 55 55
2693 75 c. Hadrosaurus 55 55
2694 75 c. Germanodactylus 55 55
    a. Sheetlet. Nos. 2694/705 .. 6·00
2695 75 c. Dimorphodon 55 55
2696 75 c. Ramphorynchus 55 55
2697 75 c. Apatosaurus 55 55
2698 75 c. Pterodactylus 55 55
2699 75 c. Stegosaurus 55 55
2700 75 c. Brachiosaurus 55 55
2701 75 c. Allosaurus 55 55
2702 75 c. Plesiosaurus 55 55
2703 75 c. Ceratosaurus 55 55
2704 75 c. Compsognathus 55 55
2705 75 c. Elaphosaurus 55 55
2682/705 .. .. .. Set of 24 12·00 12·00
MS2706 Two sheets. (a) 100×70 mm. $6 Pteranodon ingens (*different*). (b) 70×100 mm. $6 Head of Plateosaurus (*vert*) .. Set of 2 sheets 7·50 8·00
Nos. 2682/93 and 2694/705 were printed together, *se-tenant*, in sheetlets of 12 forming composite designs.

(Des W. Hanson. Litho B.D.T.)

1994 (4 Aug). *25th Anniv of First Moon Landing. Space Shuttle* Challenger. *Horiz designs as T 326 of Antigua. Multicoloured. P 14.*
2707 $2 Space Shuttle *Challenger* .. 1·10 1·40
    a. Sheetlet. Nos. 2707/12 .. 6·00
2708 $2 Judith Resnick (astronaut) .. 1·10 1·40
2709 $2 Aircraft in memorial fly past .. 1·10 1·40
2710 $2 Dick Scobee (astronaut) .. 1·10 1·40
2711 $2 Mission logo .. .. 1·10 1·40
2712 $2 Michael Smith (astronaut) .. 1·10 1·40
2707/12 .. .. .. Set of 6 6·00 7·50
MS2713 107×76 mm. $6 *Challenger* crew 3·75 4·50
Nos. 2707/12 were printed together, *se-tenant*, in sheetlets of 6.

(Litho Questa)

1994 (4 Aug). *Centenary of International Olympic Committee. Gold Medal Winners. Multicoloured designs as T 327 of Antigua, but vert. P 14.*
2714 50 c. Heike Dreschler (Germany) (long jump), 1992 .. .. 40 30
2715 $1.50, Nadia Comaneci (Rumania) (gymnastics), 1976 and 1980 .. 1·40 1·40
MS2716 107×76 mm. $6 Dan Jansen (U.S.A.) (1000 metre speed skating), 1994 .. 3·50 4·00

(Litho Questa)

1994 (4 Aug). *International Year of the Family. Horiz design as T 328 of Antigua. Multicoloured. P 14.*
2717 $1 Grenadian family 70 70

(Des J. Batchelor. Litho Questa)

1994 (4 Aug). *50th Anniv of D-Day. Horiz designs as T 331 of Antigua. Multicoloured. P 14.*
2718 40 c. Sherman amphibious tank leaving landing craft 50 30
2719 $2 Tank on Churchill "Ark" bridging vehicle .. .. .. 1·75 1·75
2720 $3 Churchill "Bobbin" tank laying roadway .. .. .. 2·00 2·25
2718/20 .. .. .. Set of 3 3·75 3·75
MS2721 107×76 mm. $6 Churchill AVRE with fascine .. .. .. 3·50 4·00

(Des Kerri Schiff. Litho Questa (Nos. 2724/31, **MS2733**), B.D.T. (others))

1994 (4 Aug). *"Philakorea '94" International Stamp Exhibition, Seoul. Multicoloured designs as T 279 of Dominica. P 13½×14 (Nos. 2724/31) or 14 (others).*
2722 40 c. Wonson Park (*horiz*) .. 20 25
2723 $1 Pusan (*horiz*) 45 50
2724 $1 "Lady in a Hooded Cloak" (left detail) (Sin Yunbok) .. 45 50
    a. Sheetlet. Nos. 2724/31 .. 3·50
2725 $1 "Lady in a Hooded Cloak" (right detail) 45 50
2726 $1 "Kiaseng House" (left detail) (Sin Yunbok) 45 50
2727 $1 "Kiaseng House" (right detail) .. 45 50
2728 $1 "Amorous Youth on a Picnic" (left detail) (Sin Yunbok) .. 45 50
2729 $1 "Amorous Youth on a Picnic" (right detail) 45 50
2730 $1 "Chasing a Cat" (left detail) (Sin Yunbok) 45 50
2731 $1 "Chasing a Cat" (right detail) .. 45 50
2732 $4 Korean orchestra, National Theatre, Seoul (*horiz*) .. .. 1·90 2·00
2722/32 .. .. .. Set of 11 6·00 6·75
MS2733 70×102 mm. $6 "Roof Tiling" (detail) (Kim Hongdo). P 14 .. .. 3·25 3·50
Nos. 2724/31, each 26×49 mm, were printed together, *se-tenant*, in sheetlets of 8. Paintings are shown across horizontal pairs without white vertical margins in the centre.

(Des Claudia Sergeant. Litho Questa)

1994 (7 Aug). *Orchids. T 392 and similar vert designs. Multicoloured. P 14.*
2734 15 c. Type **392** 30 20
2735 25 c. *Comparettia falcata* .. 40 20
2736 45 c. *Epidendrum ciliare* .. 50 30
2737 75 c. *Epidendrum cochleatum* .. 70 50
2738 $1 *Ionopsis utricularioides* .. 80 70
2739 $2 *Onicidium ceboletta* .. 1·25 1·40
2740 $4 *Onicidium luridium* .. 2·25 2·50
2741 $5 *Rodriquezia secunda* .. 2·25 2·50
2734/41 .. .. .. Set of 8 7·50 7·50
MS2742 Two sheets, each 100×70 mm. (a) $6 *Ionopsis utricularioides* (*different*). (b) $6 *Onicidium luridium* (*different*) .. Set of 2 sheets 7·50 8·00
No. **MS2742**(b) is inscribed "Onicium luridum" in error.

393 Tony Meola (U.S.A.)

394 Yellow-tailed Snapper

(Litho Questa)

1994 (11 Aug). *World Cup Football Championship, U.S.A. (2nd issue). T 393 and similar vert designs. Multicoloured. P 14.*
2743 75 c. Type **393** 50 55
    a. Sheetlet. Nos. 2743/8 .. 2·75
2744 75 c. Steve Mark (Grenada) .. 50 55
2745 75 c. Gianluigi Lentini (Italy) .. 50 55
2746 75 c. Belloumi (Algeria) .. 50 55
2747 75 c. Nunoz (Spain) 50 55
2748 75 c. Lothar Matthaus (Germany) .. 50 55
2743/8 .. .. .. Set of 6 2·75 3·00
MS2749 Two sheets. (a) 99×70 mm. $6 World Cup Championship poster, 1930. (b) 70×114 mm. $6 Steve Mark (Grenada) (*different*)
    .. .. .. Set of 2 sheets 7·50 8·00
Nos. 2743/8 were printed together, *se-tenant*, in sheetlets of 6.

(Litho Questa)

1994 (1 Sept). *First Recipients of Order of the Caribbean Community. Horiz designs as Nos. 2046/8 of Antigua. Multicoloured. P 14.*
2750 15 c. Sir Shridath Ramphal .. 10 10
2751 65 c. William Demas 40 40
2752 $2 Derek Walcott .. .. 1·40 1·60
2750/2 .. .. .. Set of 3 1·60 1·75

(Des P. Gonzalez. Litho Questa)

1994 (1 Sept). *Fishes. T 394 and similar multicoloured designs. P 14.*
2753 15 c. Type **394** 30 20
2754 20 c. Blue Tang 30 20
2755 25 c. Porkfish (*vert*) 30 20
2756 75 c. Four-eyed Butterflyfish .. 65 50
2757 $1 Reid's Seahorse (*vert*) .. 75 70
2758 $2 Spotted Moray (*vert*) .. 1·25 1·50
2759 $4 Royal Gramma ("Fairy Basslet") 2·25 2·50
2760 $5 Queen Triggerfish (*vert*) .. 2·25 2·50
2753/60 .. .. .. Set of 8 7·25 7·50
MS2761 Two sheets, each 106×76 mm. (a) $6 Queen Angelfish. (b) $6 Long-spined Squirrelfish
    .. .. .. Set of 2 sheets 7·50 8·00

395 Mickey Mouse bathing Pluto

396 *Anartia amathea*

(Des Alvin White Studios. Litho Questa)

1994 (22 Sept). *Chinese New Year ("Year of the Dog"). T 395 and similar horiz designs showing Walt Disney cartoon characters. Multicoloured. P 14×13½.*
2762 2 c. Type **395** 10 10
2763 3 c. Dog taking mouthwash .. 10 10
2764 4 c. Dog with curlers in tail .. 10 10
2765 5 c. Brushing dog's eyelashes .. 10 10
2766 10 c. Giving dog manicure .. 20 10
2767 15 c. Mickey spraying Pluto with flea powder 30 15
2768 20 c. Dogs on display 30 20
2769 $4 Judge checking Pluto's teeth .. 3·00 3·50
2770 $5 Pluto wearing "1st Prize" rosette 3·00 3·50
2762/70 .. .. .. Set of 9 6·50 7·00
MS2771 Three sheets, each 127×102 mm. (a) $6 King Charles Spaniel rubbing against judge's leg. (b) $6 Pluto holding rosette. (c) $6 Pluto with No. 13 on coat .. .. Set of 3 sheets 11·00 12·00

(Des I. MacLaury. Litho Questa)

1994 (28 Sept)–**96**. *Butterflies. T 396 and similar vert designs. Multicoloured. A. Without imprint date. P 14*
2772A 10 c. Type **396** 10 10
2773A 15 c. Marpesia petreus 10 10
2774A 25 c. Hylephila phylaeus .. 30 20
2775A 35 c. Junonia evarete 30 20
2776A 45 c. Pseudolycaena marsyas .. 20 25
2777A 50 c. Heliconius charitonius .. 20 25
2778A 75 c. Hypolimnas misippus .. 35 40
2779A $1 Cepheuptychia cephus .. 45 50
2780A $2 Historis odius 85 90
2781A $3 Phoebis philea .. .. 1·25 1·40
2782A $4 Urbanus proteus .. .. 1·75 1·90
2783A $5 Battus polydamas .. .. 2·10 2·25
2784A $10 Philaethia dido .. .. 4·25 4·50
2785A $20 Hamadryas arethusa .. 8·75 9·00
2772A/85A .. .. Set of 14 20·00 22·00

B. *With imprint date ("1996"). P 12 (7.11.96)*
2774B 25 c. Hylephila phylaeus .. 10 10
2775B 35 c. Junonia evarete 15 20
2778cB 90 c. Pyrgus oileus 40 45
2779cB $1.50, Allosmaitia piplea .. 70 75
2774B/9cB .. .. Set of 4 1·25 1·40

(Litho Questa)

1994 (5 Dec). *Christmas. Religious Paintings by Francisco de Zurbaran. Multicoloured designs as T 336 of Antigua. P 13½×14.*
2786 10 c. "The Virgin and Child with St. John" (1658) 20 15
2787 15 c. "The Circumcision" .. 30 20
2788 25 c. "Adoration of St. Joseph" .. 30 20
2789 35 c. "Adoration of the Magi" .. 30 20
2790 75 c. "The Portiuncula" 60 45
2791 $1 "The Virgin and Child with St. John" (1662) 75 60
2792 $2 "The Virgin and Child with St. John" (1658/64) .. .. 1·25 1·50
2793 $4 "The Flight into Egypt" .. 2·25 3·00
2786/93 .. .. .. Set of 8 5·00 5·50
MS2794 Two sheets. (a) 74×86 mm. $6 "Our Lady of Ransom and Two Mercedarians" (detail). P 13½×14. (b) 114×100 mm. $6 "Adoration of the Shepherds" (detail) (*horiz*). P 14×13½
    .. .. .. Set of 2 sheets 7·50 8·00

397 Grenada Dove on Nest

(Litho Questa)

1995 (10 Jan). *Birds. T 397 and similar multicoloured designs.* P 14.
2795	25 c. Type 397		55	30
2796	35 c. Pair of Grenada Doves at nest		60	30
2797	45 c. Cuban Tody (*vert*)		65	30
2798	75 c. Grenada Dove on branch (*vert*)		80	80
2799	75 c. Painted Bunting		80	80
2800	$1 Grenada Dove in flight (*vert*)		90	90
2801	$1 Red-legged Honeycreeper		90	90
2802	$5 Green Jay		2·75	3·50
2795/802		*Set of 8*	7·25	7·00

MS2803 Two sheets, each 101×71 mm. (a) $6 Chaffinch. (b) $6 Chestnut-sided Shrike Vireo
	Set of 2 sheets	7·50	8·00

Nos. 2795/6, 2798 and 2800 also show the W.W.F. Panda emblem.

(Des A. Melville-Brown. Litho Questa)

1995 (12 Jan). *Centenary of First English Cricket Tour to the West Indies. Multicoloured designs as T 329 of Antigua.* P 14.
2804	25 c. Junior Murray (West Indies) (*vert*)		30	20
2805	35 c. Richie Richardson (West Indies) (*vert*)		35	25
2806	$2 Alex Stewart (England) and Wisden Trophy		1·40	1·60
2804/6		*Set of 3*	1·90	1·90

MS2807 75×95 mm. $3 West Indian team, 1994 1·75 2·00

398 Hooded Merganser

(Litho Questa)

1995 (27 Mar). *Water Birds of the World. T 398 and similar horiz designs. Multicoloured.* P 14.
2808	25 c. Type 398		30	30
2809	35 c. Green-winged Teal		35	30
2810	75 c. King Eider		70	75
	a. Sheetlet. Nos. 2810/21		7·50	
2811	75 c. Common Shoveler		70	75
2812	75 c. Long-tailed Duck		70	75
2813	75 c. Chiloe Wigeon		70	75
2814	75 c. Red-breasted Merganser		70	75
2815	75 c. Falcated Teal		70	75
2816	75 c. Versicolor Teal		70	75
2817	75 c. Smew		70	75
2818	75 c. Red-crested Pochard		70	75
2819	75 c. Pintail		70	75
2820	75 c. Barrow's Goldeneye		70	75
2821	75 c. Stellar's Eider		70	75
2822	$1 Harlequin Duck		75	75
2823	$3 European Wigeon		1·75	2·00
2808/23		*Set of 16*	10·50	10·50

MS2824 Two sheets, each 74×104 mm. (a) $5 Common Shelduck ("European Wigeon"). (b) $6 Egyptian Goose
	Set of 2 sheets	5·50	7·00

Nos. 2810/21 were printed together, *se-tenant*, in sheetlets of 12 with the background forming a composite design. No. 2811 is inscribed "Shobeler" in error.

399 Pig Priest, China *400 Yellow-tailed Damselfish*

(Des R. Sauber. Litho Questa)

1995 (21 Apr). *Chinese New Year ("Year of the Pig"). T 399 and similar vert designs showing ornaments. Multicoloured.* P 14.
2825	50 c. Type 399		35	45
	a. Horiz strip of 3. Nos. 2825/7		1·10	
2826	75 c. Porcelain pig, Scotland		45	55
2827	$1 Seated porcelain pig, Italy		50	60
2825/7		*Set of 3*	1·10	1·40

MS2828 107×77 mm. $2 Jade pig, China 85 90

Nos. 2825/7 were printed together, *se-tenant*, in horizontal strips of 3 throughout the sheet.

(Des D. Burkhart. Litho Questa)

1995 (24 Apr). *Marine Life. T 400 and similar horiz designs. Multicoloured.* P 14.
2829	$1 Type 400		65	65
	a. Sheetlet. Nos. 2829/34		3·50	
2830	$1 Blue-headed Wrasse		65	65
2831	$1 Balloonfish		65	65
2832	$1 Shy Hamlet		65	65
2833	$1 Orange Tube Coral		65	65
2834	$1 Rock Beauty		65	65
2835	$1 Creole Wrasse		65	65
	a. Sheetlet. Nos. 2835/43		5·25	
2836	$1 Queen Angelfish		65	65
2837	$1 Trumpetfish		65	65
2838	$1 Barred Hamlet		65	65
2839	$1 Tube Sponge		65	65
2840	$1 Porcupine Fish		65	65
2841	$1 Firecoral		65	65

2842	$1 Royal Gramma ("Fairy Basslet")		65	65
2843	$1 Sea Anemone		65	65
2829/43		*Set of 15*	8·75	8·75

MS2844 Two sheets, each 106×76 mm. (a) $5 Seahorse. (b) $6 Elkhorn Coral .. *Set of 2 sheets* 4·75 5·00

Nos. 2829/34 and 2835/43 were printed together, *se-tenant*, in sheetlets of 6 (with narrow horizontal gutter) (Nos. 2829/34) or 9 (Nos. 2835/43) forming composite designs.

401 National Flags *402 Cocker Spaniel*

(Litho Questa)

1995 (27 Apr). *Grenada–Taiwan (Republic of China) Friendship. T 401 and similar horiz design. Multicoloured.* P 14.
2845	75 c. Type 401		35	45
2846	$1 Prime Minister Brathwaite and President Lee Teng-hui		45	55

MS2847 76×106 mm. Nos. 2845/6 1·10 1·25

(Des D. Burkhart. Litho Questa)

1995 (3 May). *Domestic Animals. T 402 and similar vert designs. Multicoloured.* P 14.
2848	10 c. Type 402		20	20
2849	15 c. Pinto (horse)		30	20
2850	25 c. Rottweiler		30	20
2851	35 c. German Shepherd		40	20
2852	45 c. Persian (cat)		50	25
2853	50 c. Snowshoe (cat)		50	25
2854	75 c. Percheron (horse)		70	50
2855	$1 Scottish Fold (cat)		75	60
2856	$2 Arabian (horse)		1·40	1·40
2857	$3 Andalusian (horse)		1·75	2·00
2858	$4 C.P. Shorthair (cat)		2·00	2·50
2859	$5 Chihuahua		2·40	2·75
2848/59		*Set of 12*	10·00	10·00

MS2860 Three sheets, each 100×71 mm. (a) $5 Manx (cat). (b) $5 Donkey. (c) $6 Shar Pei
	Set of 3 sheets	6·50	6·75

(Litho Questa)

1995 (5 May). *Centenary of Sierra Club (environmental protection society) (1992). Endangered Species. Multicoloured designs as T 320 of Antigua.* P 14.
2861	$1 Head of Margay at night		70	70
	a. Sheetlet. Nos. 2861/9		5·50	
2862	$1 Margay sitting		70	70
2863	$1 Head of Margay in daylight		70	70
2864	$1 Head of Andean Condor		70	70
2865	$1 Andean Condor facing right		70	70
2866	$1 Andean Condor facing left		70	70
2867	$1 White-faced Saki on branch		70	70
2868	$1 White-faced Saki showing mane		70	70
2869	$1 Patagonia landscape		70	70
2870	$1 Lesser Rheas feeding (*horiz*)		70	70
	a. Sheetlet. Nos. 2870/8		5·50	
2871	$1 Pair of Lesser Rheas (*horiz*)		70	70
2872	$1 Lesser Rhea (*horiz*)		70	70
2873	$1 Sunset over snow-covered mountains, Patagonia (*horiz*)		70	70
2874	$1 Volcanic eruption, Patagonia (*horiz*)		70	70
2875	$1 White-faced Saki (*horiz*)		70	70
2876	$1 Common Caracara on branch (*horiz*)		70	70
2877	$1 Pair of Common Caracaras at nest (*horiz*)		70	70
2878	$1 Common Caracara facing left (*horiz*)		70	70
2861/78		*Set of 18*	11·00	11·00

Nos. 2861/9 and 2870/8 were printed together, *se-tenant*, in sheetlets of 9.

403 Grenadian Scout *404 "Swords into Ploughshares"*

(Litho Questa)

1995 (8 May). *18th World Scout Jamboree, Netherlands. T 403 and similar horiz designs. Multicoloured.* P 14.
2879	75 c. Type 403		45	50
	a. Horiz strip of 3. Nos. 2879/81		1·75	
2880	$1 Scout abseiling		55	60
2881	$2 Scout saluting and national flag		85	1·00
2879/81		*Set of 3*	1·75	1·90

MS2882 107×77 mm. $6 Scouts in canoe 2·75 3·25

Nos. 2879/81 were printed together in sheets of 9 containing three *se-tenant* horizontal strips of 3.

(Des W. Wright. Litho Questa)

1995 (8 May). *50th Anniv of End of Second World War in Europe. Fighter Aircraft. Horiz designs as T 340 of Antigua. Multicoloured.* P 14.
2883	$2 Lavochkin La-7 (fighter)		1·25	1·25
	a. Sheetlet. Nos. 2883/90		9·50	
2884	$2 Hawker Hurricane		1·25	1·25
2885	$2 North American P-51D Mustang		1·25	1·25
2886	$2 Messerschmitt Bf 109		1·25	1·25
2887	$2 Bristol Type 152 Beaufighter		1·25	1·25
2888	$2 Messerschmitt Me 262		1·25	1·25
2889	$2 Republic P-47 Thunderbolt		1·25	1·25
2890	$2 Hawker Tempest		1·25	1·25
2883/90		*Set of 8*	9·50	9·50

MS2891 106×76 mm. $6 Nose of Republic P-47 Thunderbolt 2·50 2·75

Nos. 2883/90 were printed together, *se-tenant*, in sheetlets of 8 with the stamps arranged in two horizontal strips of 4 separated by a gutter showing a dogfight.

(Des J. Iskowitz. Litho Questa)

1995 (8 May). *50th Anniv of United Nations. T 404 and similar multicoloured designs.* P 14.
2892	75 c. Type 404		40	50
	a. Horiz strip of 3. Nos. 2892/4		1·60	
2893	$1 Globe and dove		50	60
2894	$2 U.N. Building, New York		85	90
2892/4		*Set of 3*	1·60	1·75

MS2895 101×71 mm. $6 Anniversary logo (*horiz*) 2·50 2·75

Nos. 2892/4 were printed together in sheets of 9 containing three *se-tenant* horizontal strips of 3.

405 Woman with Baskets *406 National Flag and Rotary Logo*

(Des J. Iskowitz. Litho Questa)

1995 (8 May). *50th Anniv of Food and Agriculture Organization. T 405 and similar vert designs. Multicoloured.* P 14.
2896	75 c. Type 405		40	50
	a. Horiz strip of 3. Nos. 2896/8		1·60	
2897	$1 Boy with basket on head		50	60
2898	$2 Men harvesting bananas		85	90
2896/8		*Set of 3*	1·60	1·75

MS2899 72×102 mm. $6 F.A.O. logo 2·50 2·75

Nos. 2896/8 were printed together in sheets of 9 containing three *se-tenant* horizontal strips of 3.

(Litho Questa)

1995 (8 May). *90th Anniv of Rotary International. T 406 and similar vert design. Multicoloured.* P 14.
2900	$5 Type 406		2·10	2·25

MS2901 76×106 mm. $6 Paul Harris (founder) and logo 2·75 3·25

(Litho Questa)

1995 (8 May). *95th Birthday of Queen Elizabeth the Queen Mother. Vert designs as T 344 of Antigua.* P 13½×14.
2902	$1.50, orange-brown, pale brown and black		1·10	1·10
	a. Sheetlet. Nos. 2902/5×2		8·00	
2903	$1.50, multicoloured		1·10	1·10
2904	$1.50, multicoloured		1·10	1·10
2905	$1.50, multicoloured		1·10	1·10
2902/5		*Set of 4*	4·00	4·00

MS2906 127×102 mm. $6 multicoloured 3·00 3·25

Designs:—No. 2902, Queen Elizabeth the Queen Mother (pastel drawing); No. 2903, Holding rose; No. 2904, At desk (oil painting); No. 2905, In blue hat and white coat; No. MS2906, Wearing floral hat.

Nos. 2902/5 were printed together in sheetlets of 8, containing two *se-tenant* horizontal strips of 4.

(Des J. Batchelor. Litho Questa)

1995 (8 May). *50th Anniv of End of Second World War in the Pacific. Horiz designs as T 340 of Antigua. Multicoloured.* P 14.
2907	$2 Dogfight over the Marianas		1·25	1·25
	a. Sheetlet. Nos. 2907/12		6·50	
2908	$2 U.S. dive-bomber and burning aircraft carrier, Battle of Midway		1·25	1·25
2909	$2 U.S. aircraft attacking Japanese transport, Battle of the Bismarck Sea		1·25	1·25
2910	$2 *Mushashi* (Japanese battleship) on fire in Leyte Gulf		1·25	1·25
2911	$2 U.S. aircraft taking off from Henderson Field		1·25	1·25
2912	$2 Battleships at Guadalcanal		1·25	1·25
2907/12		*Set of 6*	6·50	6·50

MS2913 108×77 mm. $6 U.S. bomber 2·75 3·25

No. 2907/12 were printed together, *se-tenant*, in sheetlets of 6 with the stamp arranged in two horizontal strips of 3 separated by a gutter showing Doolittle's B-25 *Ruptured Duck* leaving U.S.S. *Hornet*.

407 Tian Bingyi
(China) (badminton)

408 Junior Murray
(West Indies)

(Litho B.D.T.)

1995 (23 June). *Olympic Games, Atlanta (1996) (1st issue).
T 407 and similar vert designs. Multicoloured. P 14.*
2914	75 c. Type 407			70	70
	a. Horiz strip of 4. Nos. 2914/17		2·50		
2915	75 c. Waldemar Leigien (Poland) and Frank Wieneke (West Germany) (judo)			70	70
2916	75 c. Nelli Kim (U.S.S.R) (gymnastics)			70	70
2917	75 c. Alessandro Andri (Italy) (shot put)			70	70
2918	$2 Jackie Joyner (U.S.A.) (heptathlon)			1·25	1·25
	a. Horiz strip of 4. Nos. 2918/21		4·50		
2919	$2 Mitsuo Tsukahara (Japan) (gymnastics)			1·25	1·25
2920	$2 Flo Hyman (U.S.A.) and Zhang Rung Fang (China) (volleyball)			1·25	1·25
2921	$2 Steffi Graf (West Germany) (tennis)			1·25	1·25
2914/21			*Set of 8*	7·00	7·00

MS2922 Two sheets, each 72×102 mm. (a) $6
Wilma Rudolph (U.S.A.) (athletics). (b) $6 Soling
class yacht . . . . *Set of 2 sheets* 5·25 5·50
Nos. 2914/17 and 2918/21 were printed together in sheets of
12 containing three *se-tenant* strips of 4.
No. MS2922(b) is inscribed "Sailing" in error.
See also Nos. 3102/24.

(Litho Questa)

1995 (18 Aug). *Anniversaries and Events. T 408 and similar
vert designs. Multicoloured. P 14.*
2923	25 c. Type 408 (Centenary of first English cricket tour to the West Indies)			30	20
2924	75 c. Nutmeg (Opening of Grenada Spice Factory)			50	50
2925	$1 Sendall Tunnel (Centenary (1994)			60	65
2926	$1 Caribbean Development Bank building (25th anniv)			60	65
2923/6			*Set of 4*	1·75	1·75

409 Ajamu

410 Elvis Presley
and Signature

(Litho Questa)

1995 (5 Sept). *Local Entertainers. T 409 and similar vert
designs. Multicoloured. P 14.*
2927	35 c. Type 409			30	30
2928	35 c. Mighty Sparrow			30	30
2929	50 c. Mighty Sparrow in evening dress			40	40
2930	75 c. Ajamu (different)			55	65
2927/30			*Set of 4*	1·40	1·50

(Des Y. Lee. Litho Questa)

1995 (5 Sept). *Entertainment Legends. T 410 and similar vert
design. Multicoloured. P 14.*
2931	75 c. Type 410			50	50
2932	75 c. Marilyn Monroe			50	50

Nos. 2931/2 were each issued in numbered sheets of 16
including an enlarged illustrated right-hand margin.

411 Elvis Presley

(Des Isabelle Tanner. Litho Questa)

1995 (5 Sept). *60th Birth Anniv of Elvis Presley (singer). T 411
and similar vert designs. Multicoloured. P 14.*
2933	$1 Type 411			65	65
	a. Sheetlet. Nos. 2933/41		5·25		
2934	$1 With beard			65	65
2935	$1 With long hair and microphone			65	65
2936	$1 Wearing white shirt			65	65
2937	$1 Wearing pink shirt and purple jacket			65	65
2938	$1 With short hair and microphone			65	65
2939	$1 Wearing magenta shirt			65	65
2940	$1 Wearing orange shirt			65	65
2941	$1 Wearing purple shirt			65	65
2933/41			*Set of 9*	5·25	5·25

Nos. 2933/41 were printed together, *se-tenant*, in sheetlets of
9.

412 Film Reel and Oscar
Statuette

(Des J. Rosata. Litho Questa)

1995 (5 Sept). *Centenary of Cinema. T 412 and similar
multicoloured designs. P 13¹/₂×14.*
2942	$1 Type 412			65	65
	a. Sheetlet. Nos. 2942/50		5·25		
2943	$1 "HOLLYWOOD" sign			65	65
2944	$1 Charlie Chaplin			65	65
2945	$1 Shirley Temple			65	65
2946	$1 Spencer Tracy and Katherine Hepburn			65	65
2947	$1 Marilyn Monroe			65	65
2948	$1 John Wayne			65	65
2949	$1 Marlon Brando			65	65
2950	$1 Tom Cruise			65	65
2942/50			*Set of 9*	5·25	5·25

MS2951 107×77 mm. $5 Orson Welles (horiz).
P 14×13¹/₂ . . . . 4·00 4·00
Nos. 2942/50 were printed together, *se-tenant*, in sheetlets of
9 forming a composite design.

413 "B1 Level Vista Dome"
Electric Locomotive, Japan

414 Teresa Teng

(Des D. Miller. Litho Questa)

1995 (5 Sept). *Trains of the World (1st series). T 413 and
similar horiz designs. Multicoloured. P 14.*
2952	$1 Type 413			70	70
	a. Sheetlet. Nos. 2952/60		5·50		
2953	$1 Rolios Rail Class 25NC steam locomotive, South Africa			70	70
2954	$1 Class 460 electric locomotive, Switzerland			70	70
2955	$1 Central Railway diesel locomotive No. 605, Peru			70	70
2956	$1 X2000 tilt body train, Sweden			70	70
2957	$1 Via Rail Toronto to Vancouver observation car, Canada			70	70
2958	$1 Intercity 125 diesel locomotive, Great Britain			70	70
2959	$1 The Flying Scotsman steam locomotive, Great Britain			70	70
2960	$1 "Indian Pacific" diesel locomotive, Australia			70	70
2961	$1 ETR 450 electric train, Italy			70	70
	a. Sheetlet. Nos. 2961/9		5·50		
2962	$1 Isparta to Bozanonu Line steam locomotive, Turkey			70	70
2963	$1 TGV train, France			70	70
2964	$1 ICE train, Germany			70	70
2965	$1 Nishi Line electric locomotive, Japan			70	70
2966	$1 "Hikari" train, Japan			70	70
2967	$1 Central Pacific Jupiter steam locomotive, U.S.A.			70	70
2968	$1 Amtrak Type 9000 electric locomotive, U.S.A.			70	70
2969	$1 Sir Nigel Gresley steam locomotive, Great Britain			70	70
2952/69			*Set of 18*	11·00	11·00

MS2970 Two sheets, each 106×76 mm. (a) $5
Diesel hydraulic train, Korea. (b) $6 Peking–
Ulan Bator express, Mongolia . . *Set of 2 sheets* 6·50 7·00
Nos. 2952/60 and 2961/9 (which include the "Singapore '95"
International Stamp Exhibition logo) were printed together,
se-tenant, in sheetlets of 9.
See also Nos. 3167/83.

(Litho Questa)

1995 (29 Sept). *Teresa Teng (Chinese actress) Commemoration. T 414 and similar vert designs showing different
portraits. Multicoloured unless otherwise indicated. P 14 (Nos.
2971/86) or 13¹/₂×14 (others).*
2971	35 c. Type 414			30	30
	a. Sheetlet. Nos. 2971/86		4·25		
2972	35 c. As a child (agate, ochre & orge-yellow)			30	30
2973	35 c. Wearing feather boa (black, pale grey and orange-yellow)			30	30
2974	35 c. With motor scooter			30	30
2975	35 c. Holding microphone			30	30
2976	35 c. In white sweater			30	30
2977	35 c. Playing flute			30	30
2978	35 c. With hand to hair (black, pale grey and orange-yellow)			30	30
2979	35 c. Wearing gold decorated dress			30	30
2980	35 c. With fan			30	30
2981	35 c. As South-sea islander			30	30
2982	35 c. With hands clasped			30	30
2983	35 c. In kimono			30	30
2984	35 c. Holding bow tie			30	30
2985	35 c. Wearing black blouse			30	30
2986	35 c. Resting on chair arm			30	30
2987	75 c. In army uniform			55	55
	a. Sheetlet. Nos. 2987/95		4·50		
2988	75 c. In navy uniform			55	55
2989	75 c. In air force uniform			55	55
2990	75 c. Singing with hand outstretched (black, pale grey and orange-yellow)			55	55
2991	75 c. Singing with flower in hair			55	55
2992	75 c. Singing in blue floral dress			55	55
2993	75 c. With pink scarf			55	55
2994	75 c. In fringed dress			55	55
2995	75 c. In pale green sweater			55	55
2996	75 c. With hands to face			55	55
2971/96			*Set of 26*	8·75	8·75

Nos. 2987/96 are larger, 34×46 mm.
Nos. 2971/86 and 2987/95 were each printed together,
se-tenant, in sheetlets of 16 with a large illustrated margin at
right (Nos. 2971/86), or 9 (Nos. 2987/95).

415 Mickey Mouse
fighting Big Pete

416 Albert Michelson
(1907 Physics)

(Des Walt Disney Company and Rosemary DeFiglio. Litho
Questa)

1995 (2 Oct). *Mickey's Pirate Adventure. T 415 and similar
vert designs showing Walt Disney cartoon characters. Multicoloured. P 13¹/₂×14.*
2997	15 c. Type 415			30	20
2998	25 c. Mickey with treasure chest			30	20
2999	35 c. Minnie Mouse trying on plunder			30	20
3000	75 c. Goofy with telescope and Mickey swimming with barrel			55	40
3001	$3 Big Pete			2·00	2·25
3002	$5 Mickey and monkey, seagull and handkerchief			2·50	3·00
2997/3002			*Set of 6*	5·50	5·50

MS3003 Two sheets, each 108×130 mm. (a) $6
Sea rat pirate. (b) $6 Minnie being thrown
overboard by pirates . . . *Set of 2 sheets* 8·00 8·50

(Des B. DuRand. Litho Questa)

1995 (18 Oct). *Centenary of Nobel Trust Fund. T 416 and
similar vert designs. Multicoloured. P 14.*
3004	$1 Type 416			70	70
	a. Sheetlet. Nos. 3004/12		5·50		
3005	$1 Ralph Bunche (1950 Peace)			70	70
3006	$1 Edwin Neher (1991 Medicine)			70	70
3007	$1 Klaus Vonklitzing (1985 Physics)			70	70
3008	$1 Johann Deisenhofer (1988 Chemistry)			70	70
3009	$1 Max Delbruck (1969 Medicine)			70	70
3010	$1 J. Georg Bednorz (1987 Physics)			70	70
3011	$1 Feodor Lynen (1964 Medicine)			70	70
3012	$1 Walther Bothe (1954 Physics)			70	70
3013	$1 James Franck (1925 Physics)			70	70
	a. Sheetlet. Nos. 3013/21		5·50		
3014	$1 Gustav Hertz (1925 Physics)			70	70
3015	$1 Friedrich Bergius (1931 Chemistry)			70	70
3016	$1 Otto Loewi (1936 Medicine)			70	70
3017	$1 Fritz Lipmann (1953 Medicine)			70	70
3018	$1 Otto Meyerhof (1922 Medicine)			70	70
3019	$1 Paul Heyse (1910 Literature)			70	70
3020	$1 Jane Addams (1931 Peace)			70	70
3021	$1 Carl Braun (1909 Physics)			70	70
3022	$1 Hans Dehmelt (1989 Physics)			70	70
	a. Sheetlet. Nos. 3022/30		5·50		
3023	$1 Heinrich Böll (1972 Literature)			70	70
3024	$1 Georges Köhler (1984 Medicine)			70	70
3025	$1 Wolfgang Pauli (1945 Physics)			70	70
3026	$1 Sir Bernard Katz (1970 Medicine)			70	70
3027	$1 Ernest Ruska (1986 Physics)			70	70
3028	$1 William Golding (1983 Literature)			70	70
3029	$1 Hartmut Michel (1988 Chemistry)			70	70
3030	$1 Hans Bethe (1967 Physics)			70	70
3004/30			*Set of 27*	16·00	16·00

MS3031 Three sheets, each 105×76 mm. (a) $6
Theodore Roosevelt (1906 Peace). (b) $6
Woodrow Wilson (1919 Peace). (c) $6 Sir Winston
Churchill (1953 Literature) . . *Set of 3 sheets* 8·50 9·50
Nos. 3004/12, 3013/21 and 3022/30 were each printed
together, *se-tenant*, in sheetlets of 9 forming composite designs.
No. 3015 is inscribed "Freidrich" in error.

(Litho Questa)

1995 (28 Nov). *Christmas. Religious Paintings. Vert designs as T 357 of Antigua. Multicoloured. P 13½×14.*

3032	15 c. "The Madonna" (Bartolommeo Montagna)	20	10
3033	25 c. "Sacred Conversation Piece" (Bonifacio dei Pitati)	20	10
3034	35 c. "Nativity" (Van Loo)	25	10
3035	75 c. "Madonna of the Fountain" (Van Eyck)	45	40
3036	$2 "The Apparition of the Virgin to St. Philip Neri" (Giovanni Tiepolo)	1·25	1·40
3037	$5 "The Holy Family" (Ribera)	2·50	3·00
3032/7	*Set of 6*	4·25	4·50

MS3038 Two sheets. (a) 127×101 mm. $6 "Madonna and Child" (detail) (Van Dyck). (b) 101×127 mm. $6 "The Vision of St. Anthony" (detail) (Van Dyck) .. .. *Set of 2 sheets* 7·00 7·50

417 Pres. Ronald Reagan at Fort George

418 Pres. Ronald Reagan

(Des J. Iskowitz. Litho Questa)

1995 (8 Dec). *12th Anniv of Liberation of Grenada (1st issue). T 417 and similar horiz designs. Multicoloured. P 14.*

3039	75 c. Type 417	50	55
	a. Horiz strip of 3. Nos. 3039/41	1·40	
3040	75 c. Pres. Reagan with U.S. and Grenadian flags	50	55
3041	75 c. St. George's	50	55
3039/41	*Set of 3*	1·40	1·50

MS3042 Two sheets, each 70×100 m. (a) $5 Pres. Reagan and beach. (b) $6 Pres Reagan and waterfall .. .. *Set of 2 sheets* 4·75 5·50

Nos. 3039/41 were printed in sheets of 9 containing three se-tenant horizontal strips, each strip forming a composite design.

(Litho Questa)

1995 (8 Dec). *12th Anniv of Liberation of Grenada (2nd issue). T 418 and similar vert designs each showing Ronald Reagan. Multicoloured. P 13½×14.*

3043	$1 With wife	55	60
	a. Sheetlet. Nos. 3043/51	4·50	
3044	$1 Type 418	55	60
3045	$1 With microphones	55	60
3046	$1 Wearing stetson	55	60
3047	$1 In front of U.S. flag	55	60
3048	$1 In front of Brandenburg Gate, Berlin	55	60
3049	$1 Saluting by helicopter	55	60
3050	$1 On horseback	55	60
3051	$1 Addressing troops	55	60
3043/51	*Set of 9*	4·50	4·75

Nos. 3043/51 were printed together, *se-tenant*, in sheetlets of 9 with an enlarged illustrated right margin.

419 Pope John Paul II and Statue of Liberty

420 Rat asleep

(Des R. Rundo. Litho Questa)

1995 (13 Dec). *Papal Visit to New York. T 419 and similar vert designs. Multicoloured. P 14.*

3052	$1 Type 419	65	65
3053	$1 Pope John Paul II and cathedral	65	65
MS3054	105×76mm. $6 Pope John Paul II	3·00	3·00

Nos. 3052/3 were printed separately in sheets of 9 with enlarged illustrated margin at right.

A $30 value embossed on gold foil exists from a limited printing.

(Des Y. Lee. Litho Questa)

1996 (2 Jan). *Chinese New Year ("Year of the Rat"). T 420 and similar designs. P 14.*

3055	420 75 c. buff, brown-olive and deep brown	35	40
	a. Horiz strip of 3. Nos. 3055/7	1·10	
3056	– 75 c. salmon, deep rose-red & dp violet	35	40
3057	– 75 c. buff, dull verm & blackish green	35	40
3055/7	*Set of 3*	1·10	1·25
MS3058	95×58 mm. Nos. 3055/7	1·10	1·25
MS3059	76×106 mm. $1 multicoloured	45	50

Designs: *Vert*—No. 3056, Rat eating; No. 3057, Rat asleep (T 420 reversed). *Horiz*—No. MS3059, Two rats.

Nos. 3055/7 were printed together, *se-tenant*, in horizontal strips of 3 throughout the sheet.

Grenada 15c

421 "Young Woman" (Dürer)

(Litho Questa)

1996 (29 Jan). *Famous Drawings and Paintings by Dürer and Rubens. T 421 and similar vert designs. P 13½×14.*

3060	15 c. Type 421	20	10
3061	25 c. "Four Horsemen of the Apocalypse" (Dürer)	20	15
3062	35 c. "Assumption and Coronation of the Virgin" (Dürer)	20	20
3063	75 c. "Mulay Ahmed" (Rubens)	45	40
3064	$1 "Anthony van Dyck aged 15" (Rubens)	60	50
3065	$2 "Head of a Young Monk" (Rubens)	1·25	1·40
3066	$3 "A Scholar inspired by Nature" (Rubens)	1·60	1·75
3067	$5 "Hanns Dürer" (Dürer)	2·40	2·75
3060/7	*Set of 8*	6·25	6·50

MS3068 Two sheets, each 102×127 mm. (a) $5 "Martyrdom of St. Ursula" (detail) (Rubens). (b) $6 "The Death of the Virgin" (detail) (Dürer) .. *Set of 2 sheets* 5·50 6·50

Grenada 35c

The Tap Dancer

422 Goofy tap-dancing

(Litho Questa)

1996 (26 Feb). *Famous Dances. T 422 and similar multicoloured designs showing Walt Disney cartoon characters dancing. P 13½×14 (vert) or 14×13½ (horiz).*

3069	35 c. Type 422	25	20
3070	45 c. Donald Duck doing Mexican hat dance (horiz)	30	25
3071	75 c. Daisy Duck as hula dancer	55	50
3072	90 c. Mickey and Minnie Mouse doing the tango (horiz)	60	55
3073	$1 Donald and Daisy doing the jitterbug	70	60
3074	$2 Mickey and Minnie performing Ukrainian folk dance (horiz)	1·40	1·50
3075	$3 Goofy and Pluto as ballet dancers (horiz)	1·75	2·00
3076	$4 Mickey and Minnie line-dancing	1·90	2·25
3069/76	*Set of 8*	6·75	7·00

MS3077 Two sheets, each 133×109 mm. (a) $5 Minnie doing the can-can (horiz). (b) $6 Scrooge McDuck doing Scottish sword dance .. *Set of 2 sheets* 6·50 7·00

(Litho Questa)

1996 (8 May). *70th Birthday of Queen Elizabeth II. Vert designs as T 364 of Antigua showing different photographs. Multicoloured. P 13½×14.*

3078	35 c. As Type 364 of Antigua	15	20
	a. Strip of 3. Nos. 3078/80	2·25	
3079	75 c. Wearing white hat	35	40
3080	$4 With bouquet	1·75	1·90
3078/80	*Set of 3*	2·25	2·40
MS3081	103×125 mm. $6 Queen and Prince Philip	2·50	2·75

Nos. 3078/80 were printed together, *se-tenant*, in horizontal and vertical strips of 3 throughout the sheet.

423 Ferrari "125 F1"

424 Lions' Gate, Jerusalem

(Des W. Wright. Litho)

1996 (8 May). *Ferrari Racing Cars. T 423 and similar horiz designs. Multicoloured. P 14.*

3082	$1.50, Type 423	65	70
	a. Sheetlet. Nos. 3082/7	3·75	
3083	$1.50, "Tipo 625"	65	70
3084	$1.50, "P4"	65	70
3085	$1.50, "312P"	65	70
3086	$1.50, "312" Formula 1	65	70
3087	$1.50, "312B"	65	70
3082/7	*Set of 6*	3·75	4·25
MS3088	100×71 mm. $6 "F333 SP" (84×28 mm)	2·50	2·75

Nos. 3082/7 were printed together, *se-tenant* in sheetlets of 6, which include the "CHINA '96" International Stamp Exhibition logo on the margin.

(Litho Questa)

1996 (26 June). *50th Anniv of U.N.I.C.E.F. Multicoloured designs as T 366 of Antigua. P 14.*

3089	35 c. Child writing in book (horiz)	15	20
3090	$2 Child planting seedling (horiz)	85	90
3091	$3 Children and U.N.I.C.E.F. emblem (horiz)	1·25	1·40
3089/91	*Set of 3*	2·25	2·40
MS3092	75×106 mm. $5 Young boy	2·10	2·25

(Des Rachel Deitch. Litho Questa)

1996 (26 June). *3,000th Anniv of Jerusalem. T 424 and similar multicoloured designs. P 14.*

3093	75 c. Type 424	35	40
3094	$2 New Gate	85	90
3095	$3 Dung Gate	1·25	1·40
3093/5	*Set of 3*	2·40	2·50
MS3096	114×74 mm. $5 The Old City (horiz)	2·10	2·25

(Des J. Iskowitz. Litho Questa)

1996 (26 June). *Centenary of Radio. Entertainers. Multicoloured designs as T 368 of Antigua. P 13½.*

3097	35 c. Jack Benny	15	20
3098	75 c. Gertrude Berg	35	40
3099	$1 Eddie Cantor	45	50
3100	$2 Groucho Marx	85	90
3097/100	*Set of 4*	1·60	1·90
MS3101	70×100 mm. $6 George Burns and Gracie Allen (horiz)	2·50	2·75

425 Olympic Stadium, Athens, 1896

(Litho B.D.T.)

1996 (8 July). *Olympic Games, Atlanta (2nd issue). Previous Medal Winners. T 425 and similar multicoloured designs. P 14.*

3102	35 c. Gold medal of 1896 (vert)	15	20
3103	75 c. Type 425	35	40
3104	$1 Boughera el Quafi (France) (Gold, 1928)	45	50
	a. Sheetlet. Nos. 3104/12	4·00	
3105	$1 Gustav Jansson (Sweden) (Bronze, 1952)	45	50
3106	$1 Spiridon Louis (Greece) (Gold, 1896)	45	50
3107	$1 Basil Heatley (Great Britain) (Silver, 1964)	45	50
3108	$1 Emil Zatopek (Czechoslovakia) (Gold, 1952)	45	50
3109	$1 Frank Shorter (U.S.A.) (Gold, 1972)	45	50
3110	$1 Alain Minoun O'Kacha (France) (Gold, 1956)	45	50
3111	$1 Kokichi Tsu Uraya (Japan) (Bronze, 1964)	45	50
3112	$1 Delfo Cabrera (Argentina) (Gold, 1948)	45	50
3113	$1 Harald Sakata (U.S.A.) (Silver – light heavyweight, 1948)	45	50
	a. Sheetlet. Nos. 3113/21	4·00	
3114	$1 Tom Kono (U.S.A.) (Gold – middleweight, 1952 and 1956)	45	50
3115	$1 Naim Suleymanoglu (Turkey) (Gold – featherweight, 1988)	45	50
3116	$1 Lee Hyung Kun (South Korea) (Gold – light heavyweight, 1988)	45	50
3117	$1 Vassily Alexeyev (U.S.S.R.) (Gold – super heavyweight, 1972 and 1976)	45	50
3118	$1 Chen Weiqiang (China) (Gold – featherweight, 1984)	45	50
3119	$1 Ye Huanming (China) (Gold – featherweight, 1988)	45	50
3120	$1 Manfred Nerlinger (Germany) (Silver – super heavyweight, 1988)	45	50
3121	$1 Joseph Depietro (U.S.A.) (Gold – bantamweight, 1948)	45	50
3122	$2 Ancient Greek runners	85	90
3123	$3 Spiridon Louis (Greece) (Gold – marathon, 1896)	1·25	1·40
3102/23	*Set of 22*	10·00	11·50

MS3124 Two sheets, each 75×105 mm. (a) $5 Manfred Nerlinger (Germany) (Silver – super heavyweight weightlifting, 1988) (vert). (b) $6 Thomas Hicks (U.S.A.) (Gold – marathon, 1904) (vert) .. .. *Set of 2 sheets* 4·75 5·00

Nos. 3104/12 (marathon runners) and 3113/21 (weightlifters) were each printed together, *se-tenant*, in sheetlets of 9, with the backgrounds forming composite designs.

426 Mercedes-Benz, 1929

1996 (25 July). *Classic Cars. T* **426** *and similar horiz designs. Multicoloured. Litho.* P 14.

3125	35 c. Type **426**			15	20
	a. Sheetlet. Nos. 3125/8 and 3135/6			3·50	
3126	50 c. Bugatti Type 35, 1927			25	30
3127	75 c. J. Dusenberg, 1935			35	40
3128	$1 Mercer, 1914			45	50
3129	$1 Type 57C Atalante, 1939			45	50
	a. Sheetlet. Nos. 3129/34			2·50	
3130	$1 Cannstatt-Daimler, 1900			45	50
3131	$1 Delage, 1925			45	50
3132	$1 Coventry Daimler, 1899			45	50
3133	$1 Vauxhall, 1900			45	50
3134	$1 T-15 Hispano-Suza, 1912			45	50
3135	$2 Alfa Romeo, 1929			85	90
3136	$3 Rolls Royce, 1910			1·25	1·40
3125/36			*Set of 12*	6·00	6·75

MS3137 Two sheets, each 66×96 mm. (a) $6 L-Head Mercer, 1915 (56×42 *mm*). (b) $6 Mercedes, 1937 (56×42 *mm*) . . *Set of 2 sheets* 5·25 5·50
Nos. 3125/8 with 3135/6 and 3129/34 were each printed together, *se-tenant*, in sheetlets of 6.

427 *Gorch Fock* (cadet barque), Germany, 1916

428 Jacqueline Kennedy

(Des R. Sauber. Litho Questa)

1996 (14 Aug). *Ships. T* **427** *and similar horiz designs. Multicoloured.* P 14.

3138	$1 Type **427**			45	50
	a. Sheetlet. Nos. 3138/46			4·00	
3139	$1 Henry B. Hyde, U.S.A., 1886			45	50
3140	$1 *Resolution* (galleon), Great Britain, 1652			45	50
3141	$1 U.S.S. *Constitution* (frigate), U.S.A., 1797			45	50
3142	$1 *Nippon Maru* (cadet ship), Japan, 1930			45	50
3143	$1 *Preussen* (full-rigged sailing ship), Germany, 1902			45	50
3144	$1 *Taeping* (clipper), Great Britain, 1852			45	50
3145	$1 *Chariot of Fame* (clipper), U.S.A., 1853			45	50
3146	$1 *Star of India* (clipper), U.S.A., 1861			45	50
3147	$1 H.M.S. *Bounty*			45	50
	a. Sheetlet. Nos. 3147/55			4·00	
3148	$1 *Bismarck* (German battleship)			45	50
3149	$1 *Chuii Apoo* and two junks			45	50
3150	$1 *Lubeck* (German frigate)			45	50
3151	$1 Dutch galleon			45	50
3152	$1 *Augsburg* (German frigate)			45	50
3153	$1 *Henri Grace a Dieu* (British galleon)			45	50
3154	$1 H.M.S. *Prince of Wales* (battleship)			45	50
3155	$1 *Santa Anna* (Spanish carrack)			45	50
3138/55			*Set of 18*	8·00	9·00

MS3156 Two sheets, each 104×74 mm. (a) $5 H.M.S. *Victory* (ship of the line), Great Britain, 1805. (b) $6 *Cutty Sark* (clipper), Great Britain, 1869 . . . . *Set of 2 sheets* 4·75 5·00
Nos. 3138/46 and 3147/55 were each printed together, *se-tenant*, in sheetlets of 9.
No. 3151 is inscribed "BARBARY CORSAIR" and No. 3153 is stated to be French, both in error.

1996 (26 Aug). *Jacqueline Kennedy Onassis Commemoration. T* **428** *and similar vert designs. Multicoloured. Litho.* P 14.

3157	$1 Type **428**			45	50
	a. Sheetlet. Nos. 3157/65			4·00	
3158	$1 Wearing mauve blouse			45	50
3159	$1 In evening dress (inscr at right)			45	50
3160	$1 In evening dress (inscr at left)			45	50
3161	$1 Wearing pink dress			45	50
3162	$1 Wearing blue dress with collar embroidered			45	50
3163	$1 Wearing white jacket and brooch			45	50
3164	$1 In yellow jacket and green shirt			45	50
3165	$1 Wearing black jacket			45	50
3157/65			*Set of 9*	4·00	4·50

MS3166 76×106 mm. $6 Jacqueline Kennedy Onassis (*different*) . . . . . . 2·50 2·75
Nos. 3157/65 were printed together, *se-tenant*, in sheetlets of 9 with an enlarged illustrated left-hand margin

MINIMUM PRICE

The minimum price quote is 10p which represents a handling charge rather than a basis for valuing common stamps. For further notes about prices see introductory pages.

429 Class C51 Locomotive of Imperial Train, Japan

(Litho Questa)

1996 (28 Aug). *Trains of the World* (2nd series). *T* **429** *and similar horiz designs. Multicoloured.* P 14.

3167	35 c. Type **429**			15	10
3168	75 c. "*Rheingold*" express, Germany			35	40
3169	$1 Atlantic Coast Line locomotive No. 153, 1894, U.S.A.			45	50
	a. Sheetlet. Nos. 3169/74			2·50	
3170	$1 Smith Compound No. 1619, Great Britain			45	50
3171	$1 Trans-Siberian Soviet Railways			45	50
3172	$1 Palatinate Railway Krauss locomotive, 1898, Germany			45	50
3173	$1 Paris, Lyons and Mediterranean line, France			45	50
3174	$1 Diesel-electric 0341 locomotive, Italy			45	50
3175	$1 Class C62 locomotive, Japan			45	50
	a. Sheetlet. Nos. 3175/80			2·50	
3176	$1 Shantung Railways locomotive, China			45	50
3177	$1 Class C57 locomotive, Japan			45	50
3178	$1 Diesel express train, Japan			45	50
3179	$1 Shanghai–Nanking Railway locomotive, China			45	50
3180	$1 Class D51 locomotive, Japan			45	50
3181	$2 *Pioneer*, 1851, U.S.A.			85	90
3182	$3 *France*, France			1·25	1·40
3167/82			*Set of 16*	7·50	8·75

MS3183 Two sheets, each 105×73 mm. (a) $5 Baden State Railways locomotive, Germany, (b) $6 Class C11 locomotive, Japan. . *Set of 2 sheets* 5·00 5·25
Nos. 3169/74 and 3175/80 were each printed together, *se-tenant*, in sheetlets of 6.
No. 3180 is inscribed "051" in error.

430 Winter Jasmine

(Des H. Friedman. Litho Questa)

1996 (9 Sept). *Flowers. T* **430** *and similar multicoloured designs.* P 14.

3184	$1 Type **430**			45	50
	a. Sheetlet. Nos. 3184/92			4·00	
3185	$1 Chrysanthemum			45	50
3186	$1 Lilac			45	50
3187	$1 Japanese Iris			45	50
3188	$1 Hibiscus			45	50
3189	$1 Sacred Lotus			45	50
3190	$1 Apple blossom			45	50
3191	$1 Gladiolus			45	50
3192	$1 Japanese Quince			45	50
3193	$1 Canterbury Bell (*vert*)			45	50
	a. Sheetlet. Nos. 3193/201			4·00	
3194	$1 Rose (*vert*)			45	50
3195	$1 Nasturtium (*vert*)			45	50
3196	$1 Daffodil (*vert*)			45	50
3197	$1 Tulip (*vert*)			45	50
3198	$1 Snapdragon (*vert*)			45	50
3199	$1 Zinnia (*vert*)			45	50
3200	$1 Sweetpea (*vert*)			45	50
3201	$1 Pansy (*vert*)			45	50
3184/201			*Set of 18*	8·00	9·00

MS3202 Two sheets. (a) 104×74 mm. $5 Aster. (b) 74×104 mm. $6 Peony (*vert*) . . *Set of 2 sheets* 4·75 6·00
Nos. 3184/92 and 3193/201 were each printed together, *se-tenant*, in sheetlets of 9 with the backgrounds forming composite designs.

431 Zeppelin L-31 (Germany)

(Des R. Rundo. Litho Questa)

1996 (9 Sept). *Airships. T* **431** *and similar horiz designs. Multicoloured.* P 14.

3203	30 c. Type **431**			15	20
	a. Sheetlet. Nos. 3203/6 and 3213/14			3·50	
3204	30 c. Zeppelin L-35 (Germany)			15	20
3205	50 c. Zeppelin L-30 (Germany)			25	30
3206	75 c. Zeppelin L-2 10 (Germany)			35	40
3207	$1.50, Zeppelin L-21 (Germany)			65	70
	a. Sheetlet. Nos. 3207/12			3·75	
3208	$1.50, Zodiac Type 13 Spiess (France)			65	70
3209	$1.50, N1 *Norge* (Roald Amundsen)			65	70
3210	$1.50, LZ-127 *Graf Zeppelin* (Germany)			65	70
3211	$1.50, LZ-129 *Hindenburg* (Germany)			65	70

3212	$1.50, Zeppelin NT (Germany)			65	70
3213	$3 Zeppelin L-3 (Germany)			1·25	1·40
3214	$3 Beardmore No. 24 (Great Britain)			1·25	1·40
3203/14			*Set of 12*	7·00	8·00

MS3215 Two sheets, each 104×74 mm. (a) $6 Zeppelin ZT (Germany). (b) $6 Zeppelin L-13 (Germany) . . . . *Set of 2 sheets* 5·25 5·50
Nos. 3203/6 with 3213/14 and 3207/12 were each printed together, *se-tenant*, in sheetlets of 9.

432 Horned Guan

1996 (18 Sept). *West Indian Birds. T* **432** *and similar horiz designs. Multicoloured. Litho.* P 14.

3216	$1.50, Type **432**			65	70
	a. Sheetlet. Nos. 3216/21			3·75	
3217	$1.50, St. Lucia Parrot			65	70
3218	$1.50, Black Penelopina			65	70
3219	$1.50, Grenada Dove			65	70
3220	$1.50, St. Vincent Parrot			65	70
3221	$1.50, White-breasted Trembler			65	70
3216/21			*Set of 6*	3·75	4·00

MS3222 Two sheets, each 100×70 mm. (a) $5 Semper's Warbler. (b) $6 Barbados Yellow Warbler. . . . . *Set of 2 sheets* 4·75 5·00
Nos. 3216/21 were printed together, *se-tenant*, in sheetlets of 6 with the backgrounds forming a composite design.
The inscriptions on Nos. **MS3222a** and **MS3222b** are transposed in error.

433 Blue Whale

434 Killer Whale

1996 (18 Sept). *Whales and Turtles. T* **433** *and similar horiz designs. Multicoloured. Litho.* P 14.

3223	$1.50, Type **433**			65	70
	a. Sheetlet. Nos. 3223/8			3·75	
3224	$1.50, Humpback Whale			65	70
3225	$1.50, Right Whale			65	70
3226	$1.50, Hawksbill Turtle			65	70
3227	$1.50, Leatherback Turtle			65	70
3228	$1.50, Green Turtle			65	70
3223/8			*Set of 6*	3·75	4·00

Nos. 3223/8 were printed together, *se-tenant*, in sheetlets of 6.

(Des T. Wood. Litho Questa)

1996 (7 Nov). *Marine Life. T* **434** *and similar multicoloured designs.* P 14.

3229	$1 Type **434**			45	50
	a. Sheetlet. Nos. 3229/37			4·00	
3230	$1 Dolphin			45	50
3231	$1 Two dolphins			45	50
3232	$1 Sea Lion and Regal Angelfish			45	50
3233	$1 Dolphins and Hawksbill Turtle			45	50
3234	$1 Three Hawksbill Turtles			45	50
3235	$1 Regal Angelfish and Pennant Coralfish			45	50
3236	$1 Pennant Coralfish			45	50
3237	$1 Sea Lion and Squirrelfish			45	50
3238	$1 Brown Pelican			45	50
	a. Sheetlet. Nos. 3238/46			4·00	
3239	$1 Killer Whale (*different*)			45	50
3240	$1 Whale			45	50
3241	$1 Dolphins and Sea Lion			45	50
3242	$1 Shortfin Pilot Whale, Blue-ringed Octopus and Sea Lion			45	50
3243	$1 Hammerhead Sharks and Sea Lion			45	50
3244	$1 Blue-striped Grunts			45	50
3245	$1 Stingray and Van Gogh Fusilier			45	50
3246	$1 Van Gogh Fusilier, Ribbon Moray and percoid fish			45	50
3229/46			*Set of 18*	8·00	9·00

MS3247 Two sheets, each 106×76 mm. (a) $6 Pair of Sea Lions (*horiz*). (b) $6 Pair of Dolphins (*horiz*) . . . . *Set of 2 sheets* 5·25 5·50
Nos. 3229/37 and 3238/46 were each printed together, *se-tenant*, in sheetlets of 9 with the backgrounds forming composite designs.

(Litho Questa)

1996 (18 Nov). *Christmas. Religious Paintings. Vert designs as T* **369** *of Antigua. Multicoloured.* P 13½×14.

3248	25 c. "The Visitation" (Tintoretto)			10	15
3249	35 c. "Virgin with the Child" (Palma Vecchio)			15	20
3250	50 c. "The Adoration of the Magi" (Botticelli)			25	30
3251	75 c. "The Annunciation" (Titian)			35	40
3252	$1 "The Flight into Egypt" (Tintoretto)			45	50
3253	$3 "The Holy Family with the Infant Saint John" (Andrea del Sarto)			1·25	1·40
3248/53			*Set of 6*	2·25	2·75

MS3254 Two sheets, each 106×76 mm. (a) $6 "Adoration of the Magi" (Paolo Schiavo). (b) $6 "Madonna and Child with Saints" (Vincenzo Poppa) .. .. *Set of 2 sheets* 5·25 5·50
No. 3250 in inscr "Botticelli" in error.

(Des Shannon. Litho Questa)

1996 (21 Nov). *20th Anniv of Rocky (film). Sheet 143×182 mm, containing vert design as T 266 of Gambia. Multicoloured. P 14×13¹/₂.*
MS3255 $2×3, Sylvester Stallone in *Rocky V* .. 2·50 2·75

435 Ox

(Des Y. Lee. Litho Walsall)

1997 (2 Jan). *Chinese New Year ("Year of the Ox"). Sheet, 150×75 mm, containing T 435 and similar triangular designs. Multicoloured. Self-adhesive on silver foil. P 9¹/₂.*
MS3256 $2 Type 435 ("GRENADA" in black); $2 Ox ("GRENADA" in pink); $2 Ox ("GRENADA" in blue).. .. .. 2·50 2·75
No. MS3256 also exists on gold foil from a limited printing.

436 Mickey at Tram Stop   437 Devon Rex

(Des Speedy Studio. Litho Questa)

1997 (12 Feb). *"HONG KONG '97" International Stamp Exhibition. Mickey in Hong Kong. T 436 and similar multicoloured designs showing Disney cartoon characters. P 14×13¹/₂.*

3257	35 c. Type 436	..	40	50
	a. Sheetlet. Nos. 3257/60 and 3267/8		3·75	
3258	50 c. Mickey and Donald fishing at Victoria Harbour	..	40	50
3259	75 c. Donald and Mickey parachuting		50	60
3260	90 c. Mickey and Minnie visiting Bank of China	..	50	60
3261	$1 Mickey with pet parrot	..	70	75
	a. Sheetlet. Nos. 3261/6		3·75	
3262	$1 Mickey drinking Kung-fu Tea	..	70	75
3263	$1 Mickey, Minnie and Goofy shopping at Chinese Wet Market		70	75
3264	$1 Mickey, Minnie and Goofy with grasshoppers		70	75
3265	$1 Mickey and Goofy with lanterns	..	70	75
3266	$1 Mickey and Minnie practising Tai-chi	70	75
3267	$2 Goofy delivering bottled gas	..	1·10	1·25
3268	$3 Mickey, Minnie and Donald at *Jumbo* floating restaurant		1·40	1·50
3257/68		*Set of 12*	7·50	8·50

MS3269 Four sheets, each 132×108 mm. (a) $3 Mickey and skyscrapers (*vert*). (b) $4 Mickey and Minnie dancing (*vert*). (c) $5 Mickey pulling rickshaw (*vert*). (d) $6 Mickey with noodles (*vert*). P 13¹/₂×14 .. .. *Set of 4 sheets* 9·50 11·00
Nos. 3257/60 with 3267/8 and 3261/6 were each printed together, *se-tenant*, in sheetlets of 6.
Nos. MS3269a and MS3269c show the "HONG KONG '97" International Stamp Exhibition logo on the margins.

(Des M. Freedman and Dena Rubin. Litho Questa)

1997 (3 Apr). *50th Anniv of U.N.E.S.C.O. Multicoloured designs as T 374 of Antigua. P 14×13¹/₂ (horiz) or 13¹/₂×14 (vert).*

3270	35 c. Temple, Kyoto, Japan	..	15	20
3271	75 c. Timbered houses, Quedlinburg, Germany	..	35	40
3272	90 c. View from walls, Dubrovnik, Croatia	40	45
3273	$1 Ruins at Delphi, Greece	..	45	50
3274	$1 Bryggen Wharf, Bergen, Norway (*vert*)		45	50
	a. Sheetlet. Nos. 3274/81 and central label		3·50	
3275	$1 Old city, Berne, Switzerland (*vert*) ..	45	50
3276	$1 Warsaw, Poland (*vert*)	..	45	50
3277	$1 Fortress walls, Luxembourg (*vert*) ..	45	50
3278	$1 Interior of Drottningholm Palace, Sweden (*vert*)	..	45	50
3279	$1 Petajavesi Church, Finland (*vert*) ..	45	50
3280	$1 Vilnius, Lithuania (*vert*)	..	45	50
3281	$1 Jelling Church, Denmark (*vert*) ..	45	50
3282	$1 Entrance to caves, Desert of Taklamakan, China (*vert*)		45	50
	a. Sheetlet. Nos. 3282/9 and central label		3·50	
3283	$1 House, Desert of Taklamakan, China (*vert*)	..	45	50

3284	$1 Monument, Desert of Taklamakan, China (*vert*)	..	45	50
3285	$1 Palace of Cielos Purpuras, Wudang, China (*vert*)	..	45	50
3286	$1 House, Wudang, China (*vert*)	..	45	50
3287	$1 Stone Guardian, The Great Wall, China (*vert*)	..	45	50
3288	$1 Ming Dynasty statue, Wudang, China (*vert*)		45	50
3289	$1 The Great Wall, China (*vert*)	..	45	50
3290	$1.50, Segovia Cathedral, Spain	..	65	70
	a. Sheetlet. Nos. 3290/4 and label		3·25	
3291	$1.50, Wurtzburg, Germany	..	65	70
3292	$1.50, Plitvice Lakes, Croatia	..	65	70
3293	$1.50, Batalha Monastery, Portugal	..	65	70
3294	$1.50, River Seine, Paris, France	..	65	70
3295	$2 Tomar, Portugal	..	85	90
3296	$3 Palace of Chaillot, Paris, France ..	1·25	1·40
3270/96		*Set of 27*	13·00	14·50

MS3297 Three sheets, each 127×102 mm. (a) $6 Popocatepetl Monastery, Mexico. (b) $6 Woodland path, Shirakami-Sanchi, Japan. (c) $6 Interior of the Hieronymites' Monastery, Portugal .. .. .. *Set of 3 sheets* 7·50 7·75
Nos. 3274/81 and 3282/9 were each printed together, *se-tenant*, in sheetlets of 8 stamps with a centre label and Nos. 3290/4 in a sheetlet of 5 with a top left-hand corner label.

(Des D. Miller. Litho Questa)

1997 (10 Apr). *Cats and Dogs. T 437 and similar vert designs. Multicoloured. P 14.*

3298	35 c. Type 437	..	15	20
3299	75 c. King Charles Spaniel	..	35	40
3300	90 c. Japanese Bobtail	..	40	45
3301	$1 Afghan Hound	..	45	50
3302	$1 Turkish Van	..	45	50
	a. Sheetlet. Nos. 3302/10		4·00	
3303	$1 Ragdoll	..	45	50
3304	$1 Siberian	..	45	50
3305	$1 Egyptian Mau	..	45	50
3306	$1 American Shorthair	..	45	50
3307	$1 Bengal	..	45	50
3308	$1 Asian Longhair	..	45	50
3309	$1 Somali	..	45	50
3310	$1 Turkish Angora	..	45	50
3311	$1 Lhasa Apso ..	..	45	50
	a. Sheetlet. Nos. 3311/19		4·00	
3312	$1 Rough Collie	..	45	50
3313	$1 Norwich Terrier	..	45	50
3314	$1 American Cocker Spaniel	..	45	50
3315	$1 Chinese Crested Dog	..	45	50
3316	$1 Old English Sheepdog	..	45	50
3317	$1 Standard Poodle	..	45	50
3318	$1 German Shepherd	..	45	50
3319	$1 German Shorthair Pointer	..	45	50
3320	$2 Cornish Rex	..	85	90
3321	$3 Pekingese	..	1·25	1·40
3298/321		*Set of 24*	11·00	12·00

MS3322 Two sheets, each 106×76 mm. (a) $6 Singapura. (b) $6 Bernese Mountain Dog
.. .. *Set of 2 sheets* 5·25 5·50
Nos. 3302/10 (cats) and 3311/19 (dogs) were each printed together, *se-tenant*, in sheetlets of 9.

438 Dunkleosteus

(Litho Questa)

1997 (15 Apr). *Dinosaurs. T 438 and similar multicoloured designs. P 14.*

3323	35 c. Type 438	..	15	20
3324	75 c. Tyrannosaurus rex	..	35	40
3325	$1.50, Sordes	..	65	70
	a. Sheetlet. Nos. 3325/30		3·75	
3326	$1.50, Dimorphodon	..	65	70
3327	$1.50, Diplodocus	..	65	70
3328	$1.50, Allosaurus	..	65	70
3329	$1.50, Pentaceratops	..	65	70
3330	$1.50, Protoceratops	..	65	70
3331	$2 Askeptosaurus (*vert*)	..	85	90
3332	$3 Triceratops (*vert*)	..	1·25	1·40
3323/32		*Set of 10*	6·00	6·50

MS3333 Two sheets, each 103×74 mm. (a) $6 Tristychius (*vert*). (b) $6 Maiasaura (*vert*)
.. .. *Set of 2 sheets* 5·25 5·50
Nos. 3325/30 were printed together, *se-tenant*, in sheetlets of 6 with the backgrounds forming a composite design.

439 Porcelain Crab

(Des R. Rundo. Litho Questa)

1997 (2 May). *Marine Life. T 439 and similar multicoloured designs. P 14.*

3334	45 c. Type 439	..	20	25
3335	75 c. Humpback Whale	..	35	40
3336	90 c. Hermit Crab	..	40	45
3337	$1 Great White Shark	..	45	50

3338	$1.50, Octopus (*vert*)	..	65	70
	a. Sheetlet. Nos. 3338/43		3·75	
3339	$1.50, Lei Triggerfish (*vert*)	..	65	70
3340	$1.50, Lionfish (*vert*)	..	65	70
3341	$1.50, Harlequin Wrasse (*vert*)	..	65	70
3342	$1.50, Clown Fish (*vert*)	..	65	70
3343	$1.50, Moray Eel (*vert*)	..	65	70
3344	$3 Green Sea Turtle	..	1·25	1·40
3345	$4 Whale Shark	..	1·75	1·90
3334/45		*Set of 12*	8·00	8·50

MS3346 Two sheets, each 106×76 mm. (a) $6 Pacific Barracudas. (b) $6 Scalloped Hammerhead Shark .. .. *Set of 2 sheets* 5·25 5·50
Nos. 3338/43 were printed together, *se-tenant*, in sheetlets of 6 with the backgrounds forming a composite design.

(Des R. Rundo. Litho Questa)

1997 (28 May). *300th Anniv of Mother Goose Nursery Rhymes. Sheet 72×102 mm containing multicoloured design as T 309 of Dominica. P 14.*
MS3347 $5 Boy holding umbrella ("Rain") (*vert*) 2·10 2·25

(Litho Questa)

1997 (28 May). *10th Anniv of Chernobyl Nuclear Disaster. Vert designs as T 376 of Antigua. P 13¹/₂×14.*
3348 $2 As Type 376 of Antigua .. 85 90
3349 $2 As No. 3348, but inscribed "CHABAD'S CHILDREN OF CHERNOBYL" at foot 85 90

(Des J. Iskowitz. Litho Questa)

1997 (28 May). *50th Death Anniv of Paul Harris (founder of Rotary International). Horiz designs as T 377 of Antigua. Multicoloured. P 14.*
3350 $3 Paul Harris and vocational training programme, Philippines .. 1·25 1·40
MS3351 78×107 mm. $6 Hands holding globe and doves .. .. .. 2·00 2·75

(Litho Questa)

1997 (28 May). *Golden Wedding of Queen Elizabeth and Prince Philip. Horiz designs as T 378 of Antigua. Multicoloured. P 14.*
3352 $1 Queen Elizabeth and Prince Philip waving 45 50
   a. Sheetlet. Nos. 3352/7 .. 2·75
3353 $1 Royal coat of arms 45 50
3354 $1 Queen Elizabeth with Prince Philip in naval uniform 45 50
3355 $1 Queen Elizabeth and Prince Philip at Buckingham Palace 45 50
3356 $1 Windsor Castle 45 50
3357 $1 Prince Philip 45 50
3352/7 .. .. *Set of 6* 2·50 2·75
MS3358 100×70 mm. $6 Queen Elizabeth with Prince Philip in naval uniform (*different*) 2·75 3·00
Nos. 3352/7 were printed together, *se-tenant*, in sheetlets of 6.

(Des J. Iskowitz. Litho Questa)

1997 (28 May). *"Pacific '97" International Stamp Exhibition, San Francisco (1st issue). Death Centenary of Heinrich von Stephan (founder of the U.P.U.). Horiz designs as T 379 of Antigua. P 14.*
3359 $2 turquoise-green and black .. 85 90
   a. Sheetlet. Nos. 3359/61 .. 2·50
3360 $2 chestnut 85 90
3361 $2 dull blue 85 90
3359/61 .. .. *Set of 3* 2·50 2·75
MS3362 82×119 mm. $6 violet and black 2·50 2·75
Designs:—No. 3359, Postman on motorcycle; No. 3360, Von Stephan and Mercury; No. 3361, Postman on skis, Rocky Mountains, 1900s; No. MS3362, Von Stephan and Chinese letter carrier.
Nos. 3359/61 were printed together, *se-tenant*, in sheets of 3 with enlarged right-hand margin.
See also Nos. 3392/409.

(Litho Questa)

1997 (28 May). *Birth Bicentenary of Hiroshige (Japanese painter). "One Hundred Famous Views of Edo". Vert designs as T 310 of Dominica. Multicoloured. P 13¹/₂×14.*
3363 $1.50, "Nihon Embankment, Yoshiwara" 65 70
   a. Sheetlet. Nos. 3363/8 .. 3·75
3364 $1.50, "Asakusa Ricefields and Torinomachi Festival" 65 70
3365 $1.50, "Senju Great Bridge" .. 65 70
3366 $1.50, "Dawn inside the Yoshiwara" .. 65 70
3367 $1.50, "Tile Kilns and Hasiba Ferry, Sumida River" 65 70
3368 $1.50, "View from Massaki of Suijin Shrine, Uchigawa Inlet and Sekiya" .. 65 70
3363/8 .. .. *Set of 6* 3·75 4·00
MS3369 Two sheets, each 102×127 mm. (a) $6 "Kinryuzan Temple, Asakusa"; (b) "Night view of Saruwaka-machi" .. *Set of 2 sheets* 5·25 5·50
Nos. 3363/8 were printed together, *se-tenant*, in sheetlets of 6.

(Des R. Sauber. Litho Questa)

1997 (28 May). *175th Anniv of Brothers Grimm's Third Collection of Fairy Tales. Snow White. Vert designs as T 380 of Antigua. Multicoloured. P 14.*
3370 $2 Queen looking in mirror .. 85 90
   a. Sheetlet. Nos. 3370/2 .. 2·50
3371 $2 Snow White and the Seven Dwarfs .. 85 90
3372 $2 Snow White and Prince .. 85 90
3370/2 .. .. *Set of 3* 2·50 2·75
MS3373 124×96 mm. $6 Witch with apple 2·50 2·75
Nos. 3370/2 were printed together, *se-tenant*, in sheetlets of 3 with illustrated margins.

440 One-man Luge   441 Bank of China

(Litho B.D.T.)

1997 (26 June). *Winter Olympic Games, Nagano, Japan. T 440 and similar multicoloured designs. P 14.*

3374	45 c. Type 440			20	25
3375	75 c. Men's speed-skating			35	40
3376	$1 One-man luge (*different*)			45	50
	a. Sheetlet. Nos. 3376/84			4·00	
3377	$1 Ski-jumping (blue ski suit)			45	50
3378	$1 Downhill skiing			45	50
3379	$1 Speed-skating			45	50
3380	$1 Two-man bobsleigh			45	50
3381	$1 Women's figure-skating			45	50
3382	$1 Alpine combined			45	50
3383	$1 Ice hockey			45	50
3384	$1 Ski-jumping (yellow ski suit)			45	50
3385	$2 Men's figure-skating			90	95
3386	$3 Slalom			1·40	1·50
3374/86			*Set of 13*	6·75	7·50

MS3387 Two sheets, each 96×69 mm. (a) $6 Four-man bobsleigh; (b) $6 Downhill skiing (*vert*)
Set of 2 sheets 5·50 5·75
Nos. 3376/84 were printed together, *se-tenant*, in sheetlets of 9.

(Des Y. Lee. Litho Questa)

1997 (1 July). *Return of Hong Kong to China. T 441 and similar multicoloured designs. P 14×13½ (90 c., $1) or 14 (others).*

3388	90 c. Type 441			40	45
	a. Sheetlet of 4			1·60	
3389	$1 Skyscrapers			45	50
	a. Sheetlet of 4			1·75	
3390	$1.75, "Hong Kong '97" on modern buildings (63×32 mm)			70	75
	a. Sheetlet of 3			2·10	
3391	$2 Deng Xiaoping and Hong Kong (63×32 mm)			85	90
	a. Sheetlet of 3			2·50	
3388/91			*Set of 4*	2·40	2·50

Nos. 3388/91 were printed in sheetlets of 3 or 4, each with enlarged illustrated margins.

442 Minnie Mouse dancing the Hula

(Des Alvin White Studios. Litho Questa)

1997 (7 Aug). *"Pacific '97" International Stamp Exhibition, San Francisco (2nd issue). Centenary of the Cinema. Minnie Mouse in Hawaiian Holiday. T 442 and similar horiz designs showing a series of cartoon frames. Multicoloured. P 14×13½.*

3392	50 c. Type 442 (Frame 1)			40	40
	a. Sheetlet. Nos. 3392/9 and 1 label			2·75	
3393	50 c. Frame 2			40	40
3394	50 c. Frame 3			40	40
3395	50 c. Frame 4			40	40
3396	50 c. Frame 5			40	40
3397	50 c. Frame 6			40	40
3398	50 c. Frame 7			40	40
3399	50 c. Frame 8			40	40
3400	50 c. Frame 9			40	40
	a. Sheetlet. Nos. 3400/8			3·25	
3401	50 c. Frame 10			40	40
3402	50 c. Frame 11			40	40
3403	50 c. Frame 12			40	40
3404	50 c. Frame 13			40	40
3405	50 c. Frame 14			40	40
3406	50 c. Frame 15			40	40
3407	50 c. Frame 16			40	40
3408	50 c. Frame 17			40	40
3392/408			*Set of 17*	6·00	6·00

MS3409 110×130 mm. $6 Frame 18 .. 4·00 4·50
Nos. 3392/9 and 3400/8 were printed together, *se-tenant*, in sheetlets of 8 or 9. It is intended that the stamps should be separated and used as a flip book to produce a moving image.

OMNIBUS ISSUES

Details, together with prices for complete sets, of the various Omnibus issues from the 1935 Silver Jubilee series to date are included in a special section following Zimbabwe at the end of Volume 2.

443 Hercules lifting Rock

(Des Alvin White Studios. Litho Questa)

1997 (7 Aug). *Hercules (cartoon film) (1st series). T 443 and similar vert designs showing Disney cartoon characters. Multicoloured. P 13½×14.*

3410	$1 Type 443			70	70
	a. Sheetlet. Nos. 3410/17			5·00	
3411	$1 Pegasus			70	70
3412	$1 Megara			70	70
3413	$1 Philoktetes			70	70
3414	$1 Nessus			70	70
3415	$1 Hydra			70	70
3416	$1 Pain and Panic			70	70
3417	$1 Hades			70	70
3410/17			*Set of 8*	5·00	5·00

MS3418 Two sheets (a) 131×104 mm. $6 Hercules as a boy. (b) 104×131 mm. $6 The Muses .. *Set of 2 sheets* 7·50 8·00
Nos. 3410/17 were printed together, *se-tenant*, in sheetlets of 8.
See also Nos. 3561/85.

(Litho Questa)

1997 (11 Aug). *World Cup Football Championship, France (1998). Designs as T 383 of Antigua. Multicoloured (except Nos. 3422/3 and 3428). P 13½×14 (vert) or 14×13½ (horiz).*

3419	15 c. West German and Italian players, 1982 (*vert*)			10	10
3420	75 c. Italian player holding World Cup, 1982 (*vert*)			35	40
3421	90 c. West German and Italian players wearing "20" shirts, 1982 (*vert*)			40	45
3422	$1 Uruguay team, 1950 (agate)			45	50
	a. Sheetlet. Nos. 3422/9 and central label			3·50	
3423	$1 Brazilian team, 1958 (agate)			45	50
3424	$1 West German team, 1974			45	50
3425	$1 Argentine team, 1986			45	50
3426	$1 Italian team, 1982			45	50
3427	$1 West German team, 1990			45	50
3428	$1 Italian team, 1934 (agate)			45	50
3429	$1 Brazilian team, 1970			45	50
3430	$1 Seaman, England			45	50
	a. Sheetlet. Nos. 3430/7 and central label			3·50	
3431	$1 Klinsmann, Germany			45	50
3432	$1 Berger, Czech Republic			45	50
3433	$1 McCoist, Scotland			45	50
3434	$1 Gascoigne, England			45	50
3435	$1 Djorkaeff, France			45	50
3436	$1 Sammer, Germany			45	50
3437	$1 Futre, Portugal			45	50
3438	$2 Italian player beating goal keeper, 1982 (*vert*)			85	90
3439	$3 Goal-mouth melee, 1982 (*vert*)			1·25	1·40
3440	$4 Two West German players tackling Italian player (*vert*)			1·75	1·90
3419/40			*Set of 22*	10·00	11·00

MS3441 Two sheets. (a) 102×127 mm. $6 Beckenbaur holding World Cup, Germany (*vert*). (b) 127×102 mm. $6 Moore, England
Set of 2 sheets 5·25 5·50
Nos. 3422/9 and 3430/7 were each printed together, *se-tenant*, in sheetlets of 8 with central label.

444 Peacock

(Des Joni Popes. Litho Questa)

1997 (12 Aug). *Butterflies and Moths. T 444 and similar horiz designs. Multicoloured. P 14.*

3442	45 c. Type 444			20	25
3443	75 c. Orange Flambeau			35	40
3444	90 c. Eastern Tailed Blue			45	50
3445	$1 Brimstone			45	50
	a. Sheetlet. Nos. 3445/52			3·50	
3446	$1 Mocker Swallowtail			45	50
3447	$1 American Painted Lady			45	50
3448	$1 Tiger Swallowtail			45	50
3449	$1 Long Wing			45	50
3450	$1 Sunset Moth			45	50
3451	$1 Australian Blue Mountain Swallowtail			45	50
3452	$1 Bird Wing			45	50
3453	$2 Black and Red			85	90
3454	$3 Large White			1·25	1·40
3455	$4 Oriental Swallowtail			1·75	1·90
3442/55			*Set of 14*	8·25	9·00

MS3456 Two sheets, each 76×106 mm. (a) $5 Monarch. (b) $5 Blue Morpho .. *Set of 2 sheets* 4·25 4·50
Nos. 3445/52 were printed together, *se-tenant*, in sheetlets of 8.

445 *Paphiopedilum urbanianum*

(Des R. Rundo. Litho B.D.T.)

1997 (4 Sept). *Orchids of the World. T 445 and similar multicoloured designs. P 14.*

3457	20 c. Type 445			10	10
3458	35 c. Trichoceros parviflorus			15	20
3459	45 c. Euanthe sanderiana (vert)			20	25
3460	75 c. Oncidium macranthum (vert)			35	40
3461	90 c. Psychopsis kramerianum (vert)			40	45
3462	$1 Oncidium hastatum (vert)			45	50
3463	$2 Broughtonia sanguinea (vert)			90	95
	a. Sheetlet. Nos. 3463/8			5·50	
3464	$2 Anguloa virginalis (vert)			90	95
3465	$2 Dendrobium bigibbum (vert)			90	95
3466	$2 Lucasiana (vert)			90	95
3467	$2 Cymbidium (vert)			90	95
3468	$2 Cymbidium and vase (vert)			90	95
3469	$2 Odontoglossum crispum (vert)			90	95
	a. Sheetlet. Nos. 3469/74			5·50	
3470	$2 Cattleya brabantiae (vert)			90	95
3471	$2 Cattleya bicolor (vert)			90	95
3472	$2 Trichopilia suavia (vert)			90	95
3473	$2 Encyclia mariae (vert)			90	95
3474	$2 Angraecum leonis (vert)			90	95
3475	$3 Masdevallia saltatix (vert)			1·40	1·50
3476	$4 Cattleya luteola			1·90	2·00
3457/76			*Set of 20*	16·00	17·00

MS3477 Two sheets. (a) 76×106 mm. $6 Laelia milleri. (b) 106×76 mm. $6 Oncidium onustum
Set of 2 sheets 5·50 5·75
Nos. 3463/8 and 3469/74 were each printed together, *se-tenant*, in sheetlets of 6 with the backgrounds forming composite designs.

446 *Boletus erythropus*

(Litho B.D.T.)

1997 (4 Sept). *Fungi of the World. T 446 and similar horiz designs. Multicoloured. P 14.*

3478	35 c. Type 446			15	20
3479	75 c. Armillariella mellea			35	40
3480	90 c. Amanita flavorubens			40	45
3481	$1 Indigo Milky			45	50
3482	$1.50, Agaricus solidipes			65	70
	a. Sheetlet. Nos. 3482/7			3·75	
3483	$1.50, Salmon Waxy Cap			65	70
3484	$1.50, Fused Maramius			65	70
3485	$1.50, Shellfish-scented Russula			65	70
3486	$1.50, Red-capped Scaber Stalk			65	70
3487	$1.50, Calocybe gambosum			65	70
3488	$1.50, Boletus parasiticus			65	70
	a. Sheetlet. Nos. 3488/93			3·75	
3489	$1.50, Frostis bolete			65	70
3490	$1.50, Amanita myscara flavilolvata			65	70
3491	$1.50, Volvariella volvacea			65	70
3492	$1.50, Stuntz's Blue Legs			65	70
3493	$1.50, Orange-latex Milky			65	70
3494	$2 Tylopilus balloui			85	90
3495	$4 Boletus parasiticus			1·75	1·90
3478/95			*Set of 18*	11·00	12·00

MS3496 Two sheets, each 97×67 mm. (a) $6 Agaricus argenteus. (b) $6 Omphalotus illudens
Set of 2 sheets 5·25 5·50
Nos. 3482/7 and 3488/93 were each printed together, *se-tenant*, in sheetlets of 6.

447 Princess Diana with Landmine Victims   448 "Angel" (Matthias Grünewald)

(Des R. Sauber. Litho Questa)

1997 (15 Oct). *Diana, Princess of Wales Commemoration. T 447 and similar horiz designs. Multicoloured. P 14½.*

3497	$1.50, Type 447			60	65
	a. Sheetlet. Nos. 3497/502			3·75	
3498	$1.50, With sick child			60	65
3499	$1.50, With young boy on crutches			60	65
3500	$1.50, With leper			60	65
3501	$1.50, Holding baby			60	65
3502	$1.50, Walking through minefield			60	65
3497/502			*Set of 6*	3·75	4·25

MS3503 76×106 mm. $5 With Mother Theresa 2·10 2·25
Nos. 3497/502 were printed together, *se-tenant*, in sheetlets of 6 with enlarged illustrated right-hand margin.
Two different $20 values embossed on gold foil and a $6 on silver foil showing a hologram exist from limited printings.

(Litho Questa)

1997 (5 Dec). *Christmas. Religious Paintings.* T **448** and similar multicoloured designs. P 14.

3504	35 c. Type 448	15	20
3505	50 c. "St. Demetrius" (icon)	20	25
3506	75 c. Three-panelled reliquary	35	40
3507	$1 "Angel of the Annunciation" (Jan van Eyck)	45	50
3508	$3 "The Annunciation" (Simone Martini)	1·25	1·40
3509	$4 "St. Michael" (icon)	1·75	1·90
3504/9	Set of 6	4·00	4·50

MS3510 Two sheets. (a) 104×114 mm. $6 "The Coronation of the Virgin" (Fra Angelico). (b) 114×104 mm. $6 "The Annunciation" (Titian) (horiz) .. Set of 2 sheets 5·25 5·50

(Des Y. Lee. Litho Walsall)

1998 (5 Jan). *Chinese New Year ("Year of the Tiger").* Sheet 150×75 mm containing triangular designs as T **435** showing tigers. Multicoloured. Self-adhesive on silver foil. P 9½.

MS3511 $1.50, "GRENADA" in pink; $1.50, "GRENADA" in gold; $1.50, "GRENADA" in bronze .. .. 2·00 2·10
No. MS3511 also exists on gold foil

449 Black-tailed Damselfish

(Litho B.D.T.)

1998 (10 Feb). *Fishes.* T **449** and similar horiz designs. Multicoloured. P 14.

3512	65 c. Type 449	30	35
3513	90 c. Yellow Sweetlips	40	45
3514	$1 Common Squirrelfish	45	50
3515	$1.50, Blue Tang	65	70
	a. Sheetlet. Nos. 3515/20	3·75	
3516	$1.50, Porkfish	65	70
3517	$1.50, Banded Butterflyfish	65	70
3518	$1.50, Thread-finned Butterflyfish	65	70
3519	$1.50, Hooded Butterflyfish ("Red-headed")	65	70
3520	$1.50, Emperor Angelfish	65	70
3521	$1.50, Duboulay's Angelfish ("Scribbled Angelfish")	65	70
	a. Sheetlet. Nos. 3521/6	3·75	
3522	$1.50, Lemon-peel Angelfish	65	70
3523	$1.50, Bandit Angelfish	65	70
3524	$1.50, Bicoloured Angelfish ("Biclor Cherub")	65	70
3525	$1.50, Palette Surgeonfish ("Regal Tang")	65	70
3526	$1.50, Yellow Tang	65	70
3527	$2 Powder-blue Surgeonfish	85	90
3512/27	Set of 16	9·50	10·50

MS3528 Two sheets, each 110×80 mm. (a) $6 Two-banded Anemonefish. (b) $6 Forceps Butterflyfish ("Long-nosed Butterflyfish")
Set of 2 sheets 5·25 5·50

Nos. 3515/20 and 3521/6 were each printed together, se-tenant, in sheetlets of 6 with the backgrounds forming composite designs.

450 Sophronitis grandiflora

1998 (21 Apr). *Flowers of the World.* T **450** and similar horiz designs. Multicoloured. Litho. P 14.

3529	$1.50, Type 450	65	70
	a. Sheetlet. Nos. 3529/34	3·75	
3530	$1.50, Phalaenopsis amboinensis	65	70
3531	$1.50, Zygopetalum intermedium	65	70
3532	$1.50, Paphiopedilum purpuratum	65	70
3533	$1.50, Miltonia regnellii	65	70
3534	$1.50, Dendrobium parishii	65	70
3535	$1.50, Arachnis clarkei	65	70
	a. Sheetlet. Nos. 3535/40	3·75	
3536	$1.50, Cymbidium eburneum	65	70
3537	$1.50, Dendrobium chrysotoxum	65	70
3538	$1.50, Paphiopedilum insigne	65	70
3539	$1.50, Paphiopedilum venustum	65	70
3540	$1.50, Renanthera imschootiana	65	70
3529/40	Set of 12	7·50	8·25

MS3541 Two sheets, each 104×72 mm. (a) $6 Pleione maculata. (b) $6 Lycaste aromatica
Set of 2 sheets 5·25 5·50

Nos. 3529/34 and 3535/40 were each printed together, se-tenant, in sheetlets of 6.

COVER PRICES

Cover factors are quoted at the beginning of each country for most issues to 1945. An explanation of the system can be found on page x. The factors quoted do not, however, apply to philatelic covers.

451 Dhow

452 Arctic Skua

(Des S. Thurston. Litho Questa)

1998 (26 Apr). *Famous Ships.* T **451** and similar horiz designs. Multicoloured. P 14.

3542	$1 Type 451	45	50
	a. Sheetlet. Nos. 3542/50	4·00	
3543	$1 Galleon	45	50
3544	$1 Felucca	45	50
3545	$1 Schooner	45	50
3546	$1 Aircraft carrier	45	50
3547	$1 Knau	45	50
3548	$1 Destroyer	45	50
3549	$1 Viking longship	45	50
3550	$1 Queen Elizabeth 2 (liner)	45	50
3551	$1 Brig	45	50
	a. Sheetlet. Nos. 3551/9	4·00	
3552	$1 Clipper	45	50
3553	$1 Caique	45	50
3554	$1 Mississippi riverboat	45	50
3555	$1 Luxury liner	45	50
3556	$1 Mayflower (Pilgrim Fathers)	45	50
3557	$1 Frigate	45	50
3558	$1 Janggolan	45	50
3559	$1 Junk	45	50
3542/59	Set of 18	8·00	9·00

MS3560 Two sheets, each 100×75 mm. (a) $6 Nuclear submarine (58×43 mm). (b) $6 Lusitania (liner) (86×29 mm) .. Set of 2 sheets 5·25 5·50

Nos. 3542/50 and 3551/9 were each printed together, se-tenant, in sheetlets of 9, forming composite background designs.

1998 (16 June). *Hercules (cartoon film) (2nd series).* Multicoloured designs as T **443** showing Disney cartoon characters. Litho. P 13½×14.

3561/8 10 c. × 8 Hercules and giant statue; Hercules, Pegasus and Philoktetes; Hercules and Philoktetes with shield and arrows; Hercules swinging from blades; Nessus carrying off Megara; Hercules fighting Nessus; Hercules fighting giant lion; Hercules and Pegasus leaving prints on pavement
a. Sheetlet. Nos. 3561/8 .. 2·00

3569/76 $1 × 8 Baby Hercules with Zeus and Alcmene; Baby Hercules with Hades; Hades in the Underworld; Baby Hercules and young Pegasus; Baby Hercules with Pain and Panic; Baby Hercules with mortal parents; Hercules towing hay waggon; Hercules receiving gold medallion
a. Sheetlet. Nos. 3569/76 .. 4·50

3577/84 $1 × 8 Hercules and Megara; Megara and Hades; Hercules training with Philoktetes; Hercules confronting Hades; Giant destroying city; Zeus; Hercules saving Megara by lifting pillar; Hercules diving into sea
a. Sheetlet. Nos. 3577/84 .. 4·50

3561/84 Set of 24 10·00 11·00

MS3585 Six sheets, each 127×102 mm. (a) $6 Hades. (b) $6 Baby Pegasus. (c) $6 Hercules with sword. (d) $6 Hades on fire. (e) $6 Zeus and Hercules (horiz). (f) $6 Hercules and Megara riding Pegasus (horiz). P 13½×14 (vert) or 14×13½ (horiz) .. .. Set of 6 sheets 20·00 21·00

Nos. 3561/8, 3569/76 and 3577/84 were each printed together, se-tenant, in sheetlets of 8.

(Des D. Brown. Litho Questa)

1998 (30 June). *Seabirds.* T **452** and similar multicoloured designs. P 14.

3586	90 c. Type 452	40	45
3587	$1 Northern Fulmar (horiz)	45	50
	a. Sheetlet. Nos. 3587/95	4·00	
3588	$1 Black-legged Kittiwake (horiz)	45	50
3589	$1 Cape Petrel (horiz)	45	50
3590	$1 Mediterranean Gull (horiz)	45	50
3591	$1 Brandt's Cormorant (horiz)	45	50
3592	$1 Greater Shearwater (horiz)	45	50
3593	$1 Black-footed Albatross (horiz)	45	50
3594	$1 Red-necked Phalarope (horiz)	45	50
3595	$1 Black Skimmer (horiz)	45	50
3596	$1.10, Humboldt Penguin	50	55
3597	$2 Herring Gull	85	90
3598	$3 Red Knot	1·25	1·40
3586/98	Set of 13	7·00	7·75

MS3599 Two sheets, each 100×70 mm. (a) $5 Black-browed Albatross. (b) $5 King Penguin
Set of 2 sheets 4·25 4·50

Nos. 3587/95 were printed together, se-tenant, in sheetlets of 9, with the backgrounds forming a composite design.

453 Supermarine Spitfire Mk I

(Des M. Servino. Litho Questa)

1998 (20 July). *History of the Supermarine Spitfire (aircraft).* T **453** and similar horiz designs showing different versions. Multicoloured. P 14.

3600	$1.50, Type 453	65	70
	a. Sheetlet. Nos. 3600/5	3·75	
3601	$1.50, Mark VIII	65	70
3602	$1.50, Mark III	65	70
3603	$1.50, Mark XVI	65	70
3604	$1.50, Mark V	65	70
3605	$1.50, Mark XIX	65	70
3606	$1.50, Mark IX	65	70
	a. Sheetlet. Nos. 3606/11	3·75	
3607	$1.50, Mark XIV	65	70
3608	$1.50, Mark XII	65	70
3609	$1.50, Mark XI	65	70
3610	$1.50, H.F. Mark VIII	65	70
3611	$1.50, Mark VB	65	70
3600/11	Set of 12	7·50	8·25

MS3612 Two sheets, each 80×106 mm. (a) $6 Mark IA. (b) $6 Mark IX (different) (both 56×41 mm) .. Set of 2 sheets 5·25 5·50

Nos. 3600/5 and 3606/11 were each printed together, se-tenant, in sheetlets of 6 with enlarged illustrated top margins.

454 Walrus

1998 (19 Aug). *International Year of the Ocean.* T **454** and similar horiz designs. Multicoloured. Litho. P 14.

3613	75 c. Type 454	35	40
	a. Sheetlet. Nos. 3613/28	5·50	
3614	75 c. African Black-footed Penguins	35	40
3615	75 c. African Black-footed Penguin	35	40
3616	75 c. California Sealion	35	40
3617	75 c. Green Turtle	35	40
3618	75 c. Redfin Anthias	35	40
3619	75 c. Sperm Whale	35	40
3620	75 c. French Angelfish and Australian Sealion	35	40
3621	75 c. Jellyfish	35	40
3622	75 c. Sawfish	35	40
3623	75 c. Cuckoo Wrasse	35	40
3624	75 c. Garibaldi	35	40
3625	75 c. Spinecheek Anemonefish	35	40
3626	75 c. Leafy Seadragon	35	40
3627	75 c. Blue-spotted Goatfish	35	40
3628	75 c. Two-spot Gobies	35	40
3613/28	Set of 16	5·50	6·25

MS3629 Two sheets, each 98×68 mm. (a) $5 Atlantic Spotted Dolphins. (b) $6 Octopus
Set of 2 sheets 4·75 5·00

Nos. 3613/28 were printed together, se-tenant, in sheetlets of 16 with the backgrounds forming a composite design.

(Des R. Sauber. Litho Questa)

1998 (15 Sept). *25th Anniv of Caribbean Community.* Horiz design as T **395** of Antigua. Multicoloured. P 13½.
3630 $1 Flags of Grenada and CARICOM .. 45 50

(Litho Questa)

1998 (15 Sept). *50th Anniv of Organization of American States.* Vert design as T **399** of Antigua. P 13½×14.
3631 $1 multicoloured 45 50

(Des Diana Catherines. Litho Questa)

1998 (15 Sept). *25th Death Anniv of Pablo Picasso (painter).* Multicoloured designs as T **400** of Antigua. P 14½.

3632	45 c. "The Bathers" (vert)	20	25
3633	$2 "Luncheon on the Grass"	85	90
3634	$3 "The Swimmer"	1·25	1·40
3632/4	Set of 3	2·25	2·50

MS3635 102×127 mm. $5 "Tomato Plant" (vert) 2·10 2·25

(Des F. Rivera. Litho Questa)

1998 (15 Sept). *Birth Centenary of Enzo Ferrari (car manufacturer).* Multicoloured designs as T **401** of Antigua. P 14.

3636	$2 250 GT Berlinetta Lusso	85	90
	a. Sheetlet. Nos. 3636/8	2·50	
3637	$2 250 GTO	85	90
3638	$2 250 GT Boano/Ellena cabriolet	85	90
3636/8	Set of 3	2·50	2·75

MS3639 104×70 mm. $5 246 GTS Dino (91×34 mm). P 14×14½ 2·10 2·25

Nos. 3636/8 were printed together, se-tenant, in sheetlets of 3.

(Des G. Bibby. Litho Questa)

1998 (15 Sept). *19th World Scout Jamboree, Chile.* Multicoloured designs as T **402** of Antigua. P 14.

3640	$2 Scout saluting (vert)	85	90
3641	$3 International Scout flag (vert)	1·25	1·40
3642	$4 Applying First Aid (vert)	1·75	1·90
3640/2	Set of 3	3·75	4·00

MS3643 106×76 mm. $6 International Scout flag 2·50 2·75

(Des J. Iskowitz. Litho Questa)

1998 (15 Sept). *50th Death Anniv of Mahatma Gandhi.* Vert designs as T **403** of Antigua. P 14.

3644	$1 black, grey and dull mauve	45	50
	a. Sheetlet of 4	1·75	

MS3645 70×100 mm. $6 multicoloured .. 2·50 2·75

Designs:—$1 Mahatma Gandhi; $6 Gandhi and spinning wheel.

No. 3644 was issued in sheetlets of 4 with enlarged illustrated margins at top and right.

(Des D. Miller. Litho Questa)

1998 (15 Sept). *80th Anniv of Royal Air Force. Horiz designs as T **404** of Antigua. Multicoloured. P 14.*

3646	$2 Supermarine Spitfire Mk IIa		85	90
	a. Sheetlet. Nos. 3646/9		3·25	
3647	$2 Supermarine Spitfire Mk IXb from above		85	90
3648	$2 Supermarine Spitfire Mk IXb from side		85	90
3649	$2 Hawker Hurricane Mk IIC of Battle of Britain Memorial Flight		85	90
3650	$2 EF-2000 Eurofighter above clouds		85	90
	a. Sheetlet. Nos. 3650/3		3·25	
3651	$2 Nimrod MR2P (maritime reconnaissance)		85	90
3652	$2 EF-2000 Eurofighter at low level		85	90
3653	$2 C-47 Dakota (transport)		85	90
3646/53		*Set of 8*	6·50	7·00

MS3654 Four sheets, each 93×70 mm. (a) $6 Bristol F2B fighter and head of Golden Eagle. (b) $6 Bristol F2B fighter and Falcon (bird). (c) $6 Jet Provost (trainer) and EF-2000 Eurofighter. (d) $6 VC10 (transport) and EF-2000 Eurofighter .. .. .. *Set of 4 sheets* 10·00 10·50

Nos. 3646/9 and 3650/3 were each printed together, se-tenant, in sheetlets of 4 with enlarged illustrated margins.

455 "Knights in Combat"

(Litho Questa)

1998 (15 Sept). *Birth Bicentenary of Eugène Delacroix (painter). T **455** and similar horiz designs. Multicoloured. P 14.*

3655	$1 Type **455**		45	50
	a. Sheetlet. Nos. 3655/62		3·50	
3656	$1 "Murder of Bishop of Liége"		45	50
3657	$1 "Still Life"		45	50
3658	$1 "Battle of Nancy"		45	50
3659	$1 "Shipwreck of Don Juan"		45	50
3660	$1 "The Death of Ophelia"		45	50
3661	$1 "Attila the Hun"		45	50
3662	$1 "Arab Entertainers"		45	50
3655/62		*Set of 8*	3·50	4·00

MS3663 100×92 mm. $5 "The Capture of Constantinople" .. .. 2·10 2·25

Nos. 3655/62 were printed together in sheetlets of 8, containing two se-tenant horizontal strips of 4 separated by a gutter showing the paintings depicted on Nos. 3658 and 3661.

(Litho Questa)

1998 (15 Sept). *1st Death Anniv of Diana, Princess of Wales. Multicoloured design as T **405** of Antigua. P 14½×14.*

3664	$1 Diana, Princess of Wales		45	50
	a. Sheetlet of 6		2·75	

No. 3664 was printed in sheetlets of 6 with an enlarged illustrated left margin.

456 Arthur Ashe

457 Dove of Peace with Stars and Streamers

(Litho Questa)

1998 (28 Oct). *Famous Tennis Players. T **456** and similar horiz designs. Multicoloured. P 14.*

3665	45 c. Type **456**		20	25
3666	75 c. Martina Hingis		35	40
3667	90 c. Chris Evert		40	45
3668	$1 Steffi Graf		45	50
3669	$1.50, A. Sanchez Vicario		65	70
3670	$2 Monica Seles		85	90
3671	$3 Martina Navratilova		1·25	1·40
3665/71		*Set of 7*	4·25	4·50

MS3672 81×108 mm. $6 Martina Hingis (different) .. .. 2·50 2·75

(Litho Walsall)

1998 (30 Nov). *Grenada's Participation in U.N. Peacekeeping Operations, Beirut, 1982–4. P 14.*

3673 **457** $1 multicoloured 45 50

MINIMUM PRICE

The minimum price quote is 10p which represents a handling charge rather than a basis for valuing common stamps. For further notes about prices see introductory pages.

---

458 "The Angel's parting from Tobias" (Jean Bilevelt)

459 Blue-hooded Euphonia

1998 (1 Dec). *Christmas. Religious Paintings. T **458** and similar vert designs. Multicoloured. Litho. P 14.*

3674	35 c. Type **458**		15	20
3675	45 c. "Allegory of Faith" (Moretto Da Brescia)		20	25
3676	90 c. "Crucifixion" (Ugolino Di Tedice)		40	45
3677	$1 "The Triumphal Entry into Jerusalem" (Master of the Thuison Altarpiece		45	50
3674/7		*Set of 4*	1·10	1·40

(Litho B.D.T.)

1998 (1 Dec). *Christmas. Birds. T **459** and similar multicoloured designs. P 13½×14.*

3678	45 c. Type **459**		20	25
3679	75 c. Red-billed Whistling Duck ("Black-bellied Whistling Duck")		35	40
3680	90 c. Purple Martin		40	45
3681	$1 Imperial Amazon ("Imperial Parrot")		45	50
3682	$2 Adelaide's Warbler		85	90
3683	$3 Greater Flamingo ("Roseate Flamingo")		1·25	1·40
3678/83		*Set of 6*	3·50	3·75

MS3684 Two sheets, each 97×84 mm. (a) $5 Green-throated Carib. (b) $6 Purple-throated Carib and Canada 1898 Imperial Penny Postage 2 c. stamp (37×60 mm) .. *Set of 2 sheets* 4·75 5·00

(Litho Questa)

1999 (4 Jan). *Chinese New Year ("Year of the Rabbit"). Sheet 150×75 mm containing triangular designs as T **453** showing rabbits. Multicoloured. Self-adhesive on silver foil. P 9½.*

MS3685 $1 "GRENADA" in green; $1 "GRENADA" in orange; $1 "GRENADA" in pink 1·25 1·40

(Litho Questa)

1999 (1 Mar). *Millennium Series. Great Thinkers of the Past and Present. Multicoloured designs as T **398** of Antigua. P 14.*

3686	$1 Martin Luther King, Jr (civil rights leader)		45	50
	a. Sheetlet. Nos. 3686/93		3·50	
3687	$1 Socrates (Greek philosopher) (56×41 mm)		45	50
3688	$1 Sir Thomas More (English scholar) (56×41 mm)		45	50
3689	$1 Chaim Weizmann (first President of Israel)		45	50
3690	$1 Alexander Solzhenitsyn (Russian writer)		45	50
3691	$1 Galileo Galilei (Italian astronomer) (56×41 mm)		45	50
3692	$1 Michael Servetus (Spanish theologian) (56×41 mm)		45	50
3693	$1 Salman Rushdie (British novelist)		45	50
3686/93		*Set of 8*	3·50	4·00

MS3694 106×76 mm. $6 Mother Teresa (founder of Missionaries of Charity) .. .. 2·50 2·75

Nos. 3686/93 were printed together, se-tenant, in sheetlets of 8 with enlarged illustrated margins.

No. 3692 is inscribed "MICHAEL SERVENTUS" in error.

460 Robert H. Goddard (rocket scientist)

461 Goofy as Best Man

1999 (5 Mar). *Space Exploration. T **460** and similar vert designs. Multicoloured. Litho. P 14.*

3695	$1.50, Type **460**		65	70
	a. Sheetlet. Nos. 3695/700		3·75	
3696	$1.50, Wernher von Braun (rocket scientist)		65	70
3697	$1.50, Yuri A. Gagarin (first cosmonaut to orbit Earth, 1961)		65	70
3698	$1.50, "Freedom 7" (first American manned Space flight, 1961)		65	70
3699	$1.50, Aleksei Leonov (first Russian to walk in Space, 1965)		65	70
3700	$1.50, Neil Armstrong and Edwin Aldrin (first astronauts on Moon, 1969)		65	70

3701	$1.50, "Mariner 9" (first spacecraft to orbit Mars, 1971)		65	70
	a. Sheetlet. Nos. 3701/6		3·75	
3702	$1.50, "Voyager 1" (Jupiter probe, 1979)		65	70
3703	$1.50, Bruce McCandless (first astronaut to work in Space unattached, 1984)		65	70
3704	$1.50, Giotto probe (study of Halley's Comet, 1986)		65	70
3705	$1.50, Space Shuttle *Atlantis* (launch of *Galileo* probe, 1989)		65	70
3706	$1.50, *Magellan* (Venus probe, 1990)		65	70
3695/706		*Set of 12*	7·75	8·25

MS3707 Two sheets, each 60×76 mm. (a) $6 John Glenn (first American to orbit Earth, 1962). (b) $6 Neil Armstrong (first astronaut to walk on Moon, 1969) .. *Set of 2 sheets* 5·25 5·50

Nos. 3695/700 and 3701/6 were each printed together, se-tenant, in sheetlets of 6 with the backgrounds forming composite designs.

1999 (12 Mar). *70th Birthday of Mickey Mouse. Mickey's Dream Wedding. T **461** and similar multicoloured designs showing Walt Disney cartoon characters. Litho. P 13½×14.*

3708	$1 Type **461**		45	50
	a. Sheetlet. Nos. 3708/15		3·50	
3709	$1 Mickey as groom		45	50
3710	$1 Minnie as bride		45	50
3711	$1 Daisy Duck as bridesmaid		45	50
3712	$1 Donald Duck		45	50
3713	$1 Pluto in love		45	50
3714	$1 Huey, Duey and Louie		45	50
3715	$1 Lady (Pekingese)		45	50
3708/15		*Set of 8*	3·50	4·00

MS3716 Two sheets. (a) 102×127 mm. $6 Mickey's nephew eating cake. P 13½×14. (b) 127×102 mm. $6 Mickey and Minnie in carriage (horiz). P 14×13½ .. *Set of 2 sheets* 5·25 5·50

Nos. 3708/15 were printed together, se-tenant, in sheetlets of 8 with the backgrounds forming a composite design.

462 Grand Trunk Western, U.S.A.

(Des L. Schinger. Litho Questa)

1999 (15 Mar). *Trains of the World. T **462** and similar horiz designs. Multicoloured. P 14.*

3717	25 c. Type **462**		10	15
3718	35 c. Louisville & Nashville, U.S.A.		15	20
3719	45 c. Gulf, Mobile and Ohio, U.S.A.		20	25
3720	75 c. Missouri Pacific, U.S.A.		35	40
3721	90 c. "RTG" National Railway, France		40	45
3722	$1 Florida East Coast, U.S.A.		45	50
3723	$1.50, Rio Grande, U.S.A.		65	70
	a. Sheetlet. Nos. 3723/8		3·75	
3724	$1.50, Erie Lackawanna, U.S.A.		65	70
3725	$1.50, New York Central, U.S.A.		65	70
3726	$1.50, Pennsylvania, U.S.A.		65	70
3727	$1.50, Milwaukee Road, U.S.A.		65	70
3728	$1.50, Illinois Central, U.S.A.		65	70
3729	$1.50, Burlington Route, U.S.A.		65	70
	a. Sheetlet. Nos. 3729/34		3·75	
3730	$1.50, "Texas Special", Missouri, Kansas and Texas, U.S.A.		65	70
3731	$1.50, City of Los Angeles, U.S.A.		65	70
3732	$1.50, Northwestern, U.S.A.		65	70
3733	$1.50, Canadian National		65	70
3734	$1.50, Rock Island, U.S.A.		65	70
3735	$1.50, TGV, French National Railways		65	70
	a. Sheetlet. Nos. 3735/40		3·75	
3736	$1.50, HST, British Railways		65	70
3737	$1.50, TEE, Trans Europe Express		65	70
3738	$1.50, Ancona Express, Italy		65	70
3739	$1.50, XPT, Australia		65	70
3740	$1.50, APT-P, British Railways		65	70
3741	$1.50, Western Pacific, U.S.A.		65	70
	a. Sheetlet. Nos. 3741/6		3·75	
3742	$1.50, Union Pacific, U.S.A.		65	70
3743	$1.50, Chesapeake and Ohio, U.S.A.		65	70
3744	$1.50, Southern Pacific, U.S.A.		65	70
3745	$1.50, Baltimore and Ohio, U.S.A.		65	70
3746	$1.50, Wabash, U.S.A.		65	70
3747	$3 Kansas City Southern, U.S.A.		1·25	1·40
3748	$4 New Haven, U.S.A.		1·75	1·90
3717/48		*Set of 32*	19·00	22·00

MS3749 Four sheets, each 98×68 mm. (a) $6 Eld 4, Netherlands. (b) $6 "Hikari" express train, Japan. (c) $6 Santa Fe, U.S.A. (d) $6 Inter City express, Germany .. *Set of 4 sheets* 10·00 10·50

Nos. 3723/8, 3729/34, 3735/40 and 3741/6 were each printed together, se-tenant, in sheetlets of 6 with the backgrounds forming composite designs.

463 *Papilio blumei* (butterfly)

(Des R. Rundo. Litho B.D.T.)

1999 (12 Apr). *"Australia '99" International Stamp Exhibition, Melbourne. Wildlife. T 463 and similar multicoloured designs. P 14.*

3750	75 c. Type **463**	..	35	40
	a. Sheetlet. Nos. 3750/61	..	4·00	
3751	75 c. Egret	..	35	40
3752	75 c. Kumarahou (flower)	..	35	40
3753	75 c. Javan Rhinoceros	..	35	40
3754	75 c. Silver-eye (bird)	..	35	40
3755	75 c. Kiore (rodent)	..	35	40
3756	75 c. *Cyclorana novaehollandiae* (frog)		35	40
3757	75 c. Caterpillar	..	35	40
3758	75 c. Grey Duck	..	35	40
3759	75 c. Honey Blue-eye (fish)	..	35	40
3760	75 c. Krefft's Turtle	..	35	40
3761	75 c. Archer Fish	..	35	40
3762	75 c. Binturong (*vert*)	..	35	40
	a. Sheetlet. Nos. 3762/73	..	4·00	
3763	75 c. Two Indian Elephants (*vert*)		35	40
3764	75 c. Indian Elephant (*vert*)	..	35	40
3765	75 c. Chestnut-capped Laughing Thrush ("*Garkulax mitratus*") (*vert*)		35	40
3766	75 c. *Vanda hookeriana* (orchid) (*vert*)		35	40
3767	75 c. Heron (*vert*)	..	35	40
3768	75 c. Fur Seal (*vert*)	..	35	40
3769	75 c. Shag (bird) (*vert*)	..	35	40
3770	75 c. Round Batfish (*vert*)	..	35	40
3771	75 c. Loggerhead Turtle (*vert*)		35	40
3772	75 c. Three Harlequin Sweetlips (*vert*)		35	40
3773	75 c. Two Harlequin Sweetlips (*vert*)		35	40
3774	$1 Orang-utan	..	45	50
3775	$2 Douroucouli (monkey)	..	85	90
3776	$3 Black Caiman (alligator)	..	1·25	1·40
3777	$4 Panther ("Black Leopard") (*vert*)		1·75	1·90
3750/77		*Set of 16*	13·00	14·00

MS3778 Two sheets. (a) 110×85 mm. $6 Impala. (b) 85×110 mm. $6 Ring-tailed Lemur

	Set of 2 sheets	5·25	5·50

Nos. 3750/61 and 3762/73 were each printed together, *se-tenant*, in sheetlets of 12, with the backgrounds forming composite designs. Nos. 3774/7 were issued in separate sheets of 6.

No. 3753 is inscribed "JAUAN RHINOCEROS" and No. 3775 "DOUROCOULI", both in error.

(Litho Questa)

1999 (24 May). *"iBRA '99" International Stamp Exhibition, Nuremberg. Horiz designs as T 416 of Antigua. Multicoloured. P 14.*

3779	75 c. Railway locomotive, 1893, and Prussia 1860 ½ sgr. stamp		35	40
3780	90 c. *Humboldt* (sailing ship) and Mecklenburg-Schwerin 1856 4 × ¼ s.		40	45
3781	$1 Railway locomotive, 1893, and Saxony 1850 3 pf.		45	50
3782	$2 *Humboldt* (sailing ship) and Mecklenburg-Strelitz 1864 ¼ sgr.		85	90
3779/82		*Set of 4*	2·00	2·25

MS3783 121×104 mm. $6 Saxony 1850 3 pf. with Leipzig postmark. P 14×14½ .. .. 2·50 2·75

1999 (24 May). *150th Death Anniv of Katsushika Hokusai (Japanese artist). Multicoloured designs as T 417 of Antigua but vert. Litho. P 13½×14.*

3784	$1.50, "The Actor Ichikawa Danjuro Danjūrō as Tomoe Gozen"		65	70
	a. Sheetlet. Nos. 3784/9 ..		3·75	
3785	$1.50, "Washing Clothes" (drawing)		65	70
3786	$1.50, "The Prostitute of Eguchi"		65	70
3787	$1.50, "Sudden Shower from a Fine Sky"		65	70
3788	$1.50, "Hanging Clothes out to dry" (drawing)		65	70
3789	$1.50, "Shimada"		65	70
3790	$1.50, "Head of Old Man"		65	70
	a. Sheetlet. Nos. 3790/5 ..		3·75	
3791	$1.50, "Piebald Horse" (drawing)		65	70
3792	$1.50, "Girl making Cord for binding Hats"		65	70
3793	$1.50, "Li Po admiring Waterfall of Lo-shan"		65	70
3794	$1.50, "Bay Horse" (drawing)		65	70
3795	$1.50, "Potted Dwarf Pine with Basin"		65	70
3784/95		*Set of 12*	7·75	8·25

MS3796 Two sheets, each 72×102 mm. (a) $6 "The Guardian God Fudo Myoo and his Attendants". (b) $6 "Women on the Beach at Enoshima" .. .. *Set of 2 sheets* 5·25 5·50

Nos. 3784/9 and 3790/5 were each printed together, *se-tenant*, in sheetlets of 6.

No. 3788 is inscribed "DRAWINFS" in error.

1999 (24 May). *10th Anniv of United Nations Rights of the Child Convention. Vert designs as T 419 of Antigua. Multicoloured. Litho. P 14.*

3797	$3 Eskimo girl and Russian boy	..	1·25	1·40
	a. Sheetlet. Nos. 3797/9 ..		3·75	
3798	$3 American girl	..	1·25	1·40
3799	$3 African boy and Indian girl	..	1·25	1·40
3797/9		*Set of 3*	3·75	4·00

MS3800 110×85 mm. $6 Young boy .. 2·50 2·75

Nos. 3797/9 were printed together, *se-tenant*, in sheetlets of 3 forming a composite design.

1999 (24 May). *"PhilexFrance '99" International Stamp Exhibition, Paris. Railway Locomotives. Two sheets containing horiz designs as T 420 of Antigua. Multicoloured. Litho. P 14×13½.*

MS3801 (a) 106×76 mm. $6 Paris, Lyons and Mediterranean Railway Compound Pacific. (b) 106×81 mm. $6 French heavy freight locomotive

	Set of 2 sheets	5·25	5·50

1999 (24 May). *250th Birth Anniv of Johann von Goethe (German poet and dramatist). Designs as T 421 of Antigua. Litho. P 14.*

3802	$3 cerise, deep claret and black ..		1·25	1·40
	a. Sheetlet. Nos. 3802/4 ..		3·75	
3803	$3 chalky blue, slate-lilac and black	..	1·25	1·40

3804	$3 brt reddish violet, bluish violet & black		1·25	1·40
3802/4		*Set of 3*	3·75	4·00
MS3805	76×106 mm. $6 orange-brn, brn & blk		2·50	2·75

Designs: *Horiz*—No. 3802, Faust contemplating Moon; No. 3803, Goethe and Friedrich von Schiller (dramatist); No. 3804, Faust talking with Wagner. *Vert*—No. **MS**3805, Margaret (from *Faust*).

Nos. 3802/4 were printed together, *se-tenant*, in sheetlets of 3 with enlarged illustrated margins.

1999 (24 May). *30th Anniv of First Manned Landing on Moon. Multicoloured designs as T 333 of Dominica. Litho. P 14.*

3806	$1.50, The Moon	..	65	70
	a. Sheetlet. Nos. 3806/11	..	3·75	
3807	$1.50, Edward White on first space walk		65	70
3808	$1.50, Edwin "Buzz" Aldrin	..	65	70
3809	$1.50, The Earth	..	65	70
3810	$1.50, Michael Collins	..	65	70
3811	$1.50, Neil Armstrong	..	65	70
3812	$1.50, Footprint on the Moon	..	65	70
	a. Sheetlet. Nos. 3812/17	..	3·75	
3813	$1.50, V2 rocket	..	65	70
3814	$1.50, Command module *Columbia*		65	70
3815	$1.50, Lunar Rover	..	65	70
3816	$1.50, Lunar module *Eagle*	..	65	70
3817	$1.50, Command module re-entering Earth's atmosphere		65	70
3806/17		*Set of 12*	7·75	8·25

MS3818 Two sheets (a) 110×85 mm. $6 Neil Armstrong with American flag. (b) 85×111 mm. $6 Launch of "Apollo 11" (*vert*) .. *Set of 2 sheets* 5·25 5·50

Nos. 3806/11 and 3812/17 were each printed together, *se-tenant*, in sheetlets of 6 with enlarged illustrated margins.

464 *Astronaut with Letter*   465 *Carry On Doctor*

1999 (24 May). *125th Anniv of Universal Postal Union. Space Mail. T 464 and similar horiz designs. Multicoloured. Litho. P 14.*

3819	$2 Type **464**	..	85	90
	a. Sheetlet. Nos. 3819/22	..	3·25	
3820	$2 Supply spaceship *Progress*	..	85	90
3821	$2 Postmark of space station *MIR*		85	90
3822	$2 *Buran* shuttle and *MIR*	..	85	90
3819/22		*Set of 4*	3·25	3·50

MS3823 104×75 mm. $6 Space station *MIR* .. 2·50 2·75

Nos. 3819/22 were printed together, *se-tenant*, in sheetlets of 4.

1999 (24 May). *50th Anniv of the Variety Club of Great Britain. Scenes from "Carry On" Films. T 465 and similar multicoloured designs. Litho. P 13½×14.*

3824	$1 *Carry On Dick*	..	45	50
	a. Sheetlet. Nos. 3824/31	..	3·50	
3825	$1 Type **465**	..	45	50
3826	$1 *Carry On England*	..	45	50
3827	$1 *Carry On Matron*	..	45	50
3828	$1 *Carry On Round The Bend*	..	45	50
3829	$1 *Carry On Up The Jungle*	..	45	50
3830	$1 *Carry On Loving*	..	45	50
3831	$1 *Carry On Up The Khyber*	..	45	50
3824/31		*Set of 8*	3·50	4·00

MS3832 110×86 mm. $6 Actors from "Carry On" films .. .. 2·50 2·75

Nos. 3824/31 were printed, *se-tenant*, in sheetlets of 8 with illustrated margins.

1999 (18 June). *Royal Wedding. Multicoloured designs as T 418 of Antigua. Litho. P 13½.*

3833	$3 Prince Edward	..	1·25	1·40
	a. Sheetlet. Nos. 3833/5 ..		3·75	
3834	$3 Sophie and Prince Edward	..	1·25	1·40
3835	$3 Sophie Rhys-Jones	..	1·25	1·40
3833/5		*Set of 3*	3·75	4·00

MS3836 78×108 mm. $6 Prince Edward and Sophie Rhys-Jones (*horiz*) .. 2·50 2·75

Nos. 3833/5 were printed together, *se-tenant*, in sheetlets of 3 with enlarged illustrated margins.

466 *U.S.S. Enterprise NCC 1701 (from original series)*

1999 (20 July). *Spacecraft of Star Trek. T 466 and similar vert designs. Multicoloured. Litho. P 13½.*

3837	$1.50, Type **466**	..	65	70
	a. Sheetlet. Nos. 3837/45	..	5·75	
3838	$1.50, Kazon warship (blue and orange planets in background) (Voyager series)		65	70
3839	$1.50, U.S.S. *Enterprise 1701* (green planet in background) (Next Generation series)		65	70
3840	$1.50, *Voyager* (below blue planet)		65	70
3941	$1.50, Romulan (in front of orange planet) (original series)		65	70
3942	$1.50, U.S.S. *Enterprise 1701* (pink planet in background) (original series)		65	70
3943	$1.50, Borg Cube (Next Generation series)		65	70
3944	$1.50, U.S.S. *Enterprise NCC 1701* (in front of multicoloured flames)		65	70
3945	$1.50, Klingon Bird of Prey (original series)		65	70
3837/45		*Set of 9*	5·75	6·25

Nos. 3837/45 were printed together, *se-tenant*, in sheetlets of 9.

(Litho Questa)

1999 (16 Aug). *"Queen Elizabeth the Queen Mother's Century". Vert designs as T 334 of Dominica. P 14.*

3846	$2 black and gold	..	85	90
	a. Sheetlet. Nos. 3846/9	..	3·50	
3847	$2 multicoloured ..		85	90
3848	$2 black and gold	..	85	90
3849	$2 multicoloured ..		85	90
3846/9		*Set of 4*	3·50	3·75

MS3850 154×157 mm. $6 multicoloured .. 2·50 2·75

Designs: (*As Type* 334 *of Dominica*)—No. 3846, Queen with Prince Charles, 1948 ; No. 3847, Queen Mother in pink outfit, 1970; No. 3848, Queen Mother in Australia, 1958; No. 3849, Queen Mother waving. (37×50 *mm*)—No. **MS**3850, Queen Mother in Coronation dress, 1953.

Nos. 3846/9 were printed together, *se-tenant*, as a sheetlet of 4 stamps and a central label with inscribed and embossed margins. No. **MS**3850 also shows the Royal Arms embossed in gold.

A $20 value embossed on gold foil also exists from a limited printing.

467 *George Gershwin*

1999 (18 Aug). *American Entertainers. T 467 and similar horiz designs. Multicoloured. Litho. P 14.*

3851	$1 Type **467**	..	45	50
	a. Sheetlet. Nos. 3851/8 ..		3·50	
3852	$1 Florence Mills	..	45	50
3853	$1 Sam Beckett	..	45	50
3854	$1 Bessie Smith	..	45	50
3855	$1 Billie Holiday	..	45	50
3856	$1 Bert Williams	..	45	50
3857	$1 Cole Porter	..	45	50
3858	$1 Sofie Tucker	..	45	50
3859	$1 Lon Chaney	..	45	50
	a. Sheetlet. Nos. 3859/66	..	3·50	
3860	$1 Buster Keaton	..	45	50
3861	$1 Norma Shearer	..	45	50
3862	$1 James Cagney	..	45	50
3863	$1 Hedda Hopper	..	45	50
3864	$1 Jean Harlow	..	45	50
3865	$1 Marlene Dietrich	..	45	50
3866	$1 Ramon Novarro	..	45	50
3851/66		*Set of 16*	7·00	8·00

MS3867 Two sheets, each 76×86 mm. (a) $6 Clark Gable. (b) $6 Louis Armstrong

	Set of 2 sheets	5·25	5·50

Nos. 3851/8 and 3859/66 were each printed together, *se-tenant*, in sheetlets of 8 with the backgrounds forming composite designs and enlarged, illustrated right margins

468 *Ouranosaurus*

(Litho B.D.T.)

1999 (1 Sept). *Prehistoric Animals. T 468 and similar multicoloured designs. P 14.*

3868	35 c. Type **468**	..	15	20
3869	45 c. Struthiomimus (*vert*)	..	20	25
3870	75 c. Parasaurolophus (*vert*)	..	35	40
3871	$1 Archaeopteryx	..	45	50
	a. Sheetlet. Nos. 3871/9 ..		4·00	
3872	$1 Brachiosaurus	..	45	50
3873	$1 Dilophosaurus	..	45	50
3874	$1 Dimetrodon	..	45	50
3875	$1 Psittacosaurus	..	45	50
3876	$1 Acrocanthosaurus	..	45	50
3877	$1 Stenonychosaurus	..	45	50
3878	$1 Dryosaurus	..	45	50
3879	$1 Campsognathus	..	45	50
3880	$1 Agathaumas	..	45	50
	a. Sheetlet. Nos. 3880/8 ..		4·00	

3881	$1 Camarosaurus	..	..	..	45	50
3882	$1 Quetzalcoatlus	..	..	..	45	50
3883	$1 Alioramus	..	..	..	45	50
3884	$1 Camptosaurus	..	..	..	45	50
3885	$1 Albertosaurus	..	..	..	45	50
3886	$1 Anatosaurus	..	..	..	45	50
3887	$1 Spinosaurus	..	..	..	45	50
3888	$1 Centrosaurus	..	..	..	45	50
3889	$2 Triceratops	..	..	..	85	90
3890	$3 Stegoceras	..	..	..	1·25	1·40
3891	$4 Stegosaurus ..	..	..	..	1·75	1·90
3868/91			Set of 24		12·50	14·00

MS3892 Two sheets, each 85×110 mm. (a) $6
Velociraptor (vert). (b) $6 Tyrannosaurus (vert)
Set of 2 sheets 5·00 5·25

Nos. 3871/9 and 3880/8 were each printed together, se-tenant, in sheetlets of 9 with the backgrounds forming composite designs.

No. 3871 is inscribed "ARCHEOPTERYX" in error.

STAMP BOOKLETS

1977 (8 Feb). *Silver Jubilee. Multicoloured cover,* 165×92 mm, *showing Queen in Coronation Coach. Stitched.*
SB1 $6.60, booklet containing 35 c. in pane of 6 (No.
863a) and se-tenant pane of 3 (No. 864a) .. 2·50

1978 (2 May). *25th Anniv of Coronation. Multicoloured cover,* 165×92 mm, *showing photograph of Queen Elizabeth II. Stitched.*
SB2 $6.80, booklet containing se-tenant pane of 6 (No.
950a) and pane of 1 (No. 952a) .. 2·00

1981 (16 June). *Royal Wedding. Multicoloured cover,* 95×166 mm, *showing commemorative inscription on front and Queen, Prince Charles, Lady Diana Spencer and group of Privy Councillors on back. Stitched.*
SB3 $14 booklet containing se-tenant pane of 6 (No.
1136a) and pane of 1 (No. 1138a) .. 2·50

POSTAGE DUE STAMPS

1d.

SURCHARGE
POSTAGE

D 1 (D 2)

(Typo D.L.R.)

1892 (18 Apr–Oct). (a) *Type* D 1. *Wmk Crown CA.* P 14.

D1	D 1	1d. blue-black	..	..	24·00	1·50
D2		2d. blue-black	..	..	£140	1·50
D3		3d. blue-black	..	..	£140	2·50
D1/3	..		Set of 3		£275	5·00

(b) *Nos. 34 and 35 surch locally as Type* D 2

D4	13	1d. on 6d. mauve (10.92)	..	75·00	1·25
		a. Tête-bêche (vert pair)	..	£1000	£750
		b. Surch double	..	—	£150
D5		1d. on 8d. grey-brown (8.92)	..	£600	3·25
		a. Tête-bêche (vert pair)	..	£3000	£1300
D6		2d. on 6d. mauve (10.92)	..	£140	2·50
		a. Tête-bêche (vert pair)	..	£1500	£1000
D7		2d. on 8d. grey-brown (8.92)	..	£1100	9·50
		a. Tête-bêche (vert pair)	..	£4500	£2750

Nos. D4/7 were in use from August to November 1892. As supplies of Nos. D1/3 were available from April or May of that year it would not appear that they were intended for postage due purposes. There was a shortage of 1d. postage stamps in July and August, but this was alleviated by Nos. 44/5 which were still available. The provisionals *may* have been intended for postal purposes, but the vast majority appear to have been used philatelically.

1906 (July)–**11**. *Wmk Mult Crown CA.* P 14.

D 8	D 1	1d. blue-black (1911)	..	..	3·00	7·00
D 9		2d. blue-black	..	..	10·00	1·75
D10		3d. blue-black (9.06)	..	..	12·00	6·00
D8/10 ..	..	..	Set of 3		23·00	13·00

1921 (Dec)–**22**. *As Type* D 1, *but inscr* "POSTAGE DUE". *Wmk Mult Script CA.* P 14.

D11	1d. black	..	..	90	1·00
D12	1½d. black (15.12.22)	..	..	8·50	17·00
D13	2d. black	..	..	2·00	1·75
D14	3d. black	..	..	2·00	4·25
D11/14		Set of 4		12·00	22·00
D11/14 Optd "Specimen" ..		Set of 4		80·00	

1952 (1 Mar). *As Type* D 1, *but inscr* "POSTAGE DUE". *Value in cents. Chalk-surfaced paper. Wmk Mult Script CA.* P 14.

D15	2 c. black	..	..	30	5·50
	a. Error. Crown missing. W 9a	..		90·00	
	b. Error. St. Edward Crown. W 9b ..			45·00	
D16	4 c. black	..	..	30	11·00
	a. Error. Crown missing. W 9a	..		90·00	
	b. Error. St. Edward Crown. W 9b ..			45·00	
D17	6 c. black	..	..	45	11·00
	a. Error. Crown missing. W 9a	..		£130	
	b. Error. St. Edward Crown. W 9b ..			85·00	
D18	8 c. black	..	..	75	11·00
	a. Error. Crown missing. W 9a	..		£225	
	b. Error. St. Edward Crown. W 9b ..			£140	
D15/18	..	..	Set of 4		1·60	35·00

OFFICIAL STAMPS

P.R.G.

(O 1)
(= People's Revolutionary Government)

1982 (June). *Various stamps optd with Type* O 1.

(a) *Nos.* 1085A/97A *and* 1099A

O 1	5 c. West Indiaman barque, circa 1840			30	20
O 2	6 c. R.M.S.P. Orinoco, circa 1851	..		30	20
O 3	10 c. Working Schooner			30	20
O 4	12 c. Trimaran at Grand Anse anchorage			30	20
O 5	15 c. Spice Island cruising yacht Petite Amie			30	20
O 6	20 c. Fishing pirogue			35	20
O 7	25 c. Harbour police launch			40	30
O 8	30 c. Grand Anse speedboat			40	30
O 9	40 c. M.V. Seimstrand			50	30
O10	50 c. Three-masted schooner Ariadne	..		60	40
O11	90 c. M.V. Geestide			90	80
O12	$1 M.V. Cunard Countess	..		90	80
O13	$3 Rum-runner			2·25	3·75
O14	$10 Coast-guard patrol boat..			6·00	12·00

(b) *Nos.* 1130/2 *and* 1134/5

O15	30 c. Prince Charles and Lady Diana Spencer		1·50	2·25
O16	40 c. Holyrood House	..	2·25	2·75
O17	50 c. Prince Charles and Lady Diana Spencer		1·25	2·00
O18	$2 Holyrood House	..	2·25	3·50
O19	$4 Type **268**	..	5·00	8·00
O1/19		Set of 19	23·00	35·00

The $4 from sheetlets, perforated 14½×14 and with changed background colour, also exists with the overprint (*Price* £4 *mint,* £7 *used*).

GRENADINES OF GRENADA (CARRIACOU AND PETITE MARTINIQUE)

Part of a group of islands north of Grenada, the most important of which is Carriacou. The Grenadine islands further north are administered by St. Vincent, and their stamps are listed after that country.

GRENADINES

	GRENADINES	
(1)		(2)

1973 (29 Dec). *Royal Wedding. Nos. 582/4 of Grenada optd with T 1.*

1	**196**	25 c. multicoloured	20	10
2		$2 multicoloured	70	50
		a. Albino opt		
MS3		79 × 100 mm. 75 c. and $1 as Nos. 1/2	1·00	50

1974 (29 May). *Nos. 306 etc of Grenada optd with T 2.*

4	1 c. multicoloured	10	10
5	2 c. multicoloured	10	10
6	3 c. multicoloured	10	10
7	5 c. multicoloured	15	10
8	8 c. multicoloured	15	10
9	10 c. multicoloured	15	10
10	12 c. multicoloured	20	10
11	25 c. multicoloured	45	10
12	$1 multicoloured	2·50	45
13	$2 multicoloured	3·00	1·25
14	$3 multicoloured	3·00	1·75
15	$5 multicoloured	3·75	2·25
4/15	Set of 12	12·00	5·50

1974 (17 Sept). *World Cup Football Championships. As Nos. 619/27 of Grenada but additionally inscr "GRENADINES".*

16	½ c. Type **201**	10	10
17	1 c. East Germany v Australia	10	10
18	2 c. Yugoslavia v Brazil	10	10
19	10 c. Scotland v Zaire	20	10
20	25 c. Netherlands v Uruguay	25	10
21	50 c. Sweden v Bulgaria	30	15
22	75 c. Italy v Haiti	30	20
23	$1 Poland v Argentina	35	25
16/23	Set of 8	1·25	70
MS24	114 × 76 mm. $2 Country flags	75	80

1974 (8 Oct). *Centenary of Universal Postal Union. Designs as Nos. 628 etc of Grenada, but additionally inscr "GRENADINES".*

25	8 c. Mailboat Caesar (1839) and helicopter	10	10
26	25 c. Messenger (1450) and satellite	15	10
27	35 c. Airmail transport	15	10
28	$1 Type **202**	70	40
25/8	Set of 4	1·00	60
MS29	172×109 mm. $1 Bellman and antenna; $2 18th-century postman and British Advanced Passenger Train. P 13	1·00	1·00

1974 (11 Nov). *Birth Centenary of Sir Winston Churchill. As Nos. 637/9 of Grenada but additionally inscr "GRENADINES".*

30	**203**	35 c. multicoloured	15	10
31		$1 multicoloured	40	45
MS32		129 × 96 mm. 75 c. as 35 c. and $1 as $2	35	80

1974 (27 Nov). *Christmas. As Nos. 640/8 of Grenada but additionally inscr "GRENADINES".*

33	½ c. Type **204**	10	10
34	1 c. Niccolo di Pietro	10	10
35	2 c. Van der Weyden	10	10
36	3 c. Bastiani	10	10
37	10 c. Giovanni	10	10
38	25 c. Van der Weyden	10	10
39	50 c. Botticelli	15	15
40	$1 Mantegna	30	25
33/40	Set of 8	65	60
MS41	117 × 96 mm. $2 as 1 c.	45	60

CANCELLED REMAINDERS*. Some of the following issues have been remaindered, cancelled-to-order, at a fraction of their face value. For all practical purposes these are indistinguishable from genuine postally used copies. Our quoted quotations, which are indicated by an asterisk, are the same for cancelled-to-order or postally used copies.

1975 (17 Feb). *Big Game Fishing. As Nos. 669 etc of Grenada, but additionally inscr "GRENADINES" and background colours changed.*

42	½ c. Type **206**	10	10
43	1 c. Blue Marlin	10	10
44	2 c. White Marlin	10	10
45	10 c. Yellow-finned Tuna	10	10
46	25 c. Wahoo	15	10
47	50 c. Dolphin (fish)	20	15
48	70 c. Giant Grouper	25	20
49	$1 Great Barracuda	35	35
42/9	Set of 8	90	85
MS50	107×80 mm. $2 Short-finned Mako	60	90

1975 (11 Mar). *Flowers. As Nos. 678 etc of Grenada, but additionally inscr. "GRENADINES".*

51	½ c. Type **207**	10	10
52	1 c. Bleeding Heart (Easter Lily)	10	10
53	2 c. Poinsettia	10	10
54	3 c. Cocoa flower	10	10
55	10 c. Gladioli	10	10
56	25 c. Redhead/Yellowhead	20	15
57	50 c. Plumbago	30	20
58	$1 Orange flower	30	20
51/8	Set of 8	65	50
MS59	102 × 82 mm. $2 Barbados Gooseberry	60	70

3 "Christ Crowned with Thorns" (Titian)

4 "Dawn" (detail from Medici Tomb)

(Des M. Shamir. Litho Format)

1975 (24 June). *Easter. T 3 and similar vert designs showing Crucifixion and Deposition scenes by the artists listed. Multicoloured. P 14½.*

60	½ c. Type **3**	10	10*
61	1 c. Giotto	10	10*
62	2 c. Tintoretto	10	10*
63	3 c. Cranach	10	10*
64	35 c. Caravaggio	15	10*
65	75 c. Tiepolo	20	15*
66	$2 Velasquez	40	15*
60/6	Set of 7	70	30*
MS67	105 × 90 mm. $1 Titian. P 13	60	30

(Des M. Shamir. Litho Format)

1975 (16 July). *500th Birth Anniv of Michelangelo. T 4 and similar vert designs. Multicoloured. P 14½.*

68	½ c. Type **4**	10	10*
69	1 c. "Delphic Sibyl"	10	10*
70	2 c. "Giuliano de Medici"	10	10*
71	40 c. "The Creation" (detail)	15	10*
72	50 c. "Lorenzo de Medici"	15	10*
73	75 c. "Persian Sibyl"	20	10*
74	$2 "Head of Christ"	30	15*
68/74	Set of 7	75	35*
MS75	118 × 96 mm. $1 "The Prophet Jeremiah". P 13	75	50

1975 (12 Aug). *Butterflies. Designs as Nos. 729 etc of Grenada, but additionally inscr "GRENADINES". P 14½.*

76	½ c. Morpho peleides	10	10*
77	1 c. Danaus eresimus ("Danaus gilippus")	10	10*
78	2 c. Dismorphia amphione	10	10*
79	35 c. Hamadryas feronia	35	10*
80	45 c. Philaethria dido	45	10*
81	75 c. Phoebis argante	70	15*
82	$2 Prepona laertes	1·40	30*
76/82	Set of 7	2·75	60*
MS83	104×77 mm. $1 Siproeta stelenes. P 13	2·75	2·25

5 Progress "Standard" Badge

(Des J.W. Litho Format)

1975 (22 Aug). *14th World Scout Jamboree, Norway. T 5 and similar horiz designs. Multicoloured. P 14½.*

84	½ c. Type **5**	10	10*
85	1 c. Boatman's badge	10	10*
86	2 c. Coxswain's badge	10	10*
87	35 c. Interpreter's badge	15	10*
88	45 c. Ambulance badge	20	10*
89	75 c. Chief Scout's award	25	10*
90	$2 Queen's Scout award	35	15*
84/90	Set of 7	85	35*
MS91	106 × 80 mm. $1 Venture award. P 13	55	30*

6 The Surrender of Lord Cornwallis

(Des J.W. Litho Questa)

1975 (30 Sept)–76. *Bicentenary of American Revolution (1st issue). Multicoloured.* (a) *Horiz designs as T 6. P 14.*

92	½ c. Type **6**	10	10*
93	1 c. Minute-men	10	10*
94	2 c. Paul Revere's ride	10	10*
95	3 c. Battle of Bunker Hill	10	10*
96	5 c. Fifer and drummers	10	10*
97	45 c. Backwoodsman	20	10*
98	75 c. Boston Tea Party	30	10*
99	$2 Naval engagement	60	10*

(b) *Larger designs. P 11 (16.1.76)*

100	$2 George Washington (35 × 60 mm)	60	35
101	$2 White House and flags (60 × 35 mm)	60	35
92/101	Set of 10	2·25	85
MS102	Two sheets 113 × 128 mm containing No. 100, and 128 × 113 mm containing No. 101. Imperf	1·40	1·40

See also Nos. 176/MS183.

7 Fencing

8 "Madonna and Child" (Dürer)

(Des J.W. Ltd. Litho Format)

1975 (27 Oct). *Pan-American Games. Mexico City. T 7 and similar horiz designs. Multicoloured. P 14½.*

103	½ c. Type **7**	10	10*
104	1 c. Hurdling	10	10*
105	2 c. Pole-vaulting	10	10*
106	35 c. Weightlifting	15	10*
107	45 c. Throwing the javelin	15	10*
108	75 c. Throwing the discus	15	10*
109	$2 Diving	35	15*
103/109	Set of 7	75	35*
MS110	78 × 104 mm. $1 Sprinter. P 13	40	20*

1975 (5 Nov)–76. *As Nos. 649A/68A of Grenada but additionally inscribed "GRENADINES". Multicoloured.*

111	½ c. Yachts, Port Saline	10	30
112	1 c. Yacht Club race, St. George's	10	15
113	2 c. Carenage taxi	10	15
114	3 c. Large working boats	10	15
115	5 c. Deep-water dock, St. George's	10	15
116	6 c. Cocoa beans in drying trays	10	15
117	8 c. Nutmegs	10	15
118	10 c. Rum distillery, River Antoine Estate, circa 1785	10	15
119	12 c. Cocoa tree	10	15
120	15 c. Fishermen landing catch at Fontenoy	10	15
121	20 c. Parliament Building, St. George's	10	40
122	25 c. Fort George cannons	10	15
123	35 c. Pearls Airport	50	15
124	50 c. General Post Office	20	75
125	75 c. Caribs Leap, Sauteurs Bay	40	60
126	$1 Carenage, St. George's	60	85
127	$2 St. George's Harbour by night	90	2·00
128	$3 Grand Anse beach	1·10	2·50
129	$5 Canoe Bay and Black Bay from Point Saline Lighthouse	1·50	5·50
130	$10 Sugar-loaf Island from Levera Beach (1.76)	2·25	5·50
111/30	Set of 20	7·00	17·00

(Des M. Shamir. Litho Questa)

1975 (17 Dec). *Christmas. T 8 and similar vert designs showing "Virgin and Child". Multicoloured. P 14.*

131	½ c. Type **8**	10	10*
132	1 c. Dürer	10	10*
133	2 c. Correggio	10	10*
134	40 c. Botticelli	15	10*
135	50 c. Niccolo da Cremona	15	10*
136	75 c. Correggio	15	10*
137	$2 Correggio	30	15*
131/7	Set of 7	70	35*
MS138	114 × 102 mm. $1 Bellini. P 14	60	50*

9 Bleeding Tooth (Nerita peloronta)

(Des J.W. Litho Questa)

1976 (13 Jan). *Shells. T 9 and similar horiz designs. Multicoloured. P 14.*

139	½ c. Type **9**	10	10*
140	1 c. Toothed Donax (Donax denticulatus)	10	10*
141	2 c. Hawk-wing Conch (Strombus raninus)	10	10*
142	3 c. Atlantic Distorsio (Distorsio clathrata)	10	10*
143	25 c. Scotch Bonnet (Phalium ganulatum)	40	10*
144	50 c. King Helmet (Cassis tuberosa)	70	10*
145	75 c. Queen or Pink Conch (Strombus gigas)	1·00	15*
139/45	Set of 7	2·00	30*
MS146	79×105 mm. $2 Atlantic Trumpet Triton (Charonia variegata)	1·00	70*

10 Cocoa Thrush

(Des J.W. Litho Questa)

1976 (4 Feb). *Flora and Fauna. T 10 and similar horiz designs. Multicoloured. P 14.*

147	½ c. Lignum vitae	10	10*
148	1 c. Type **10**	10	10*
149	2 c. Eurypelma sp (spider)	10	10*
150	35 c. Hooded Tanager	1·25	10*
151	50 c. Nyctaginaceae	1·00	15*
152	75 c. Grenada Dove	2·50	25*
153	$1 Marine Toad	2·50	25*
147/53	Set of 7	6·50	70*
MS154	108 × 84 mm. $2 Blue-hooded Euphonia	3·75	1·00*

11 Hooked Sailfish

(Des G. Drummond. Litho Questa)

1976 (17 Feb). *Tourism.* T **11** *and similar horiz designs. Multi-coloured.* P 14.

155	½ c. Type 11		10	10*
156	1 c. Careened schooner, Carriacou		10	10*
157	2 c. Carriacou Annual Regatta		10	10*
158	18 c. Boat building on Carriacou		20	10*
159	22 c. Workboat race, Carriacou Regatta		20	10*
160	75 c. Cruising off Petit Martinique		30	20*
161	$1 Water skiing		40	20*
155/61		*Set of 7*	1·00	60*
MS162	105 × 87 mm. $2 Yacht racing at Carriacou		70	75*

12 Making a Camp Fire

13 "Christ Mocked" (Bosch)

(Des G. Vasarhelyi. Litho Questa)

1976 (17 Mar). *50th Anniv of Girl Guides in Grenada.* T **12** *and similar horiz designs. Multicoloured.* P 14.

163	½ c. Type 12		10	10*
164	1 c. First aid		10	10*
165	2 c. Nature study		10	10*
166	50 c. Cookery		65	15*
167	$1 Sketching		1·00	25*
163/7		*Set of 5*	1·60	50*
MS168	85 × 110 mm. $2 Guide playing guitar		1·00	75*

(Des PAD Studio. Litho Questa)

1976 (28 Apr). *Easter.* T **13** *and similar vert designs. Multi-coloured.* P 14.

169	½ c. Type 13		10	10*
170	1 c. "Christ Crucified" (Antonello da Messina)		10	10*
171	2 c. "Adoration of the Trinity" (Dürer)		10	10*
172	3 c. "Lamentation of Christ" (Dürer)		10	10*
173	35 c. "The Entombment" (Van der Weyden)		20	15*
174	$3 "The Entombment" (Raphael)		75	30*
169/74		*Set of 6*	95	50*
MS175	57 × 72 mm. $2 "Blood of the Redeemer" (G. Bellini)		65	70*

14 *South Carolina (frigate)*

(Des J.W. Litho Questa)

1976 (18 May). *Bicentenary of American Revolution (2nd issue).* T **14** *and similar horiz designs. Multicoloured.* P 14.

176	½ c. Type 14		10	10*
177	1 c. *Lee* (schooner)		10	10*
178	2 c. H.M.S. *Roebuck* (frigate)		10	10*
179	35 c. *Andrew Doria* (brig)		50	10*
180	50 c. *Providence* (sloop)		60	15*
181	$1 *Alfred* (frigate)		1·00	20*
182	$2 *Confederacy* (frigate)		1·50	30*
176/82		*Set of 7*	3·25	75*
MS183	72×85 mm. $3 *Revenge* (cutter)		1·25	1·00*

15 *Piper PA-23 Apache*

(Des J.W. Litho Format)

1976 (10 June). *Aircraft.* T **15** *and similar horiz designs. Multicoloured.* P 14.

184	½ c. Type 15		10	10*
185	1 c. Beech 50 Twin Bonanza		10	10*
186	2 c. De Havilland D.H.C.6 Twin Otter 100		10	10*
187	40 c. Britten Norman Islander		30	10*
188	50 c. De Havilland D.H.114 Heron 2		40	10*
189	$2 Hawker Siddeley H.S.748		1·25	20*
184/9		*Set of 6*	1·75	55*
MS190	71×85 mm. $3 B.A.C. One Eleven 500		1·00	1·00*

16 Cycling

**17 "Virgin and Child"
(Cima)**

(Des J.W. Litho Format)

1976 (1 July). *Olympic Games, Montreal.* T **16** *and similar horiz designs. Multicoloured.* P 14.

191	½ c. Type 16		10	10*
192	1 c. Pommel horse		10	10*
193	2 c. Hurdling		10	10*
194	35 c. Shot putting		10	10*
195	45 c. Diving		15	10*
196	75 c. Sprinting		15	10*
197	$2 Rowing		35	20*
191/7		*Set of 7*	70	60*
MS198	101 × 76 mm. $3 Sailing		80	75*

(Litho Format)

1976 (19 Oct). *Christmas.* T **17** *and similar multicoloured designs.* P 13½.

199	½ c. Type 17		10	10*
200	1 c. "The Nativity" (Romanino)		10	10*
201	2 c. "The Nativity" (Romanino) (*different*)		10	10*
202	35 c. "Adoration of the Kings" (Bruegel)		15	10*
203	50 c. "Madonna and Child" (Girolamo)		20	10*
204	75 c. "Adoration of the Magi" (Giorgione) (*horiz*)		20	15*
205	$2 "Adoration of the Kings" (School of Fra Angelico) (*horiz*)		40	25*
199/205		*Set of 7*	1·00	60*
MS206	120 × 100 mm. $3 "The Holy Family" (Garofalo)		60	2·25

**18 Alexander Graham Bell and
First Telephone**

(Des G. Vasarhelyi. Litho Questa)

1977 (28 Jan). *Telephone Centenary (1976).* T **18** *and similar horiz designs showing Alexander Graham Bell and telephone. Multicoloured.* P 14.

207	½ c. Type 18		10	10*
208	1 c. Telephone, 1895		10	10*
209	2 c. Telephone, 1900		10	10*
210	35 c. Telephone, 1915		15	10*
211	75 c. Telephone, 1920		20	10*
212	$1 Telephone, 1929		25	15*
213	$2 Telephone, 1963		35	25*
207/13		*Set of 7*	85	60*
MS214	107 × 78 mm. $3 Telephone, 1976		1·10	75*

19 Coronation Coach

20 Royal Visit

(Des Jennifer Toombs. Litho and embossed Walsall. (Nos. 215/18). Des and litho Walsall (Nos. 219/22))

1977 (7 Feb). *Silver Jubilee. Multicoloured.*

(a) *Sheet stamps. Horiz designs as* T **19.** P 13½

215	35 c. Type 19		10	10*
216	$2 Queen entering Abbey		20	10*
217	$4 Queen crowned		35	25*
215/17		*Set of 3*	55	35*
MS218	100 × 70 mm. $5 The Mall on Coronation Night		60	1·25

Nos. 215/17 also exist perf 11 (*Price for set of 3 60p. mint or used*) from additional sheetlets of 3 stamps and 1 label. These have different background colours from the stamps perforated 13½, which come from normal sheets of 25.

(b) *Booklet stamps. Vert designs as* T **20.** Roul 5 × imperf.* *Self-adhesive*

219	35 c. Type 20		15	20
	a. Booklet pane of 6.		70	
220	50 c. Crown of St. Edward		30	80
	a. Booklet pane. Nos. 220/2.		1·25	

221	$2 The Queen and Prince Charles		50	1·60
222	$5 Royal Standard		60	1·75
219/22		*Set of 4*	1·40	4·00

*Nos. 219/22 are separated by various combinations of rotary knife (giving a straight edge) and roulette.

**21 "Disrobing of Christ"
(Fra Angelico)**

**22 "The Virgin adoring
the Child" (Correggio)**

(Des J.W. Litho Questa)

1977 (5 July). *Easter.* Vert designs as T **21** *showing paintings by the artists given. Multicoloured.* P 14.

223	½ c. Type 21		10	10*
224	1 c. Fra Angelico		10	10*
225	2 c. El Greco		10	10*
226	18 c. El Greco		10	10*
227	35 c. Fra Angelico		15	10*
228	50 c. Giottino		20	10*
229	$2 Antonello da Messina		50	25*
223/9		*Set of 7*	85	50*
MS230	121 × 94 mm. $3 Fra Angelico		85	75*

(Des J.W. Litho Questa)

1977 (17 Nov). *Christmas.* T **22** *and similar vert designs. Multicoloured.* P 14.

231	½ c. Type 22		10	10*
232	1 c. "Virgin and Child" (Giorgione)		10	10*
233	2 c. "Virgin and Child" (Morales)		10	10*
234	18 c. "Madonna della Tenda" (Raphael)		10	10*
235	35 c. "Rest on the Flight into Egypt" (Van Dyck)		15	10*
236	50 c. "Madonna and Child" (Lippi)		20	10*
237	$2 "Virgin and Child" (Lippi) (*different*)		60	25*
231/7		*Set of 7*	95	50*
MS238	114 × 99 mm. $3 "Virgin and Child with Angels and Saints" (Ghirlandaio)		85	75*

ROYAL VISIT   W.I. 1977

(23)

1977 (23 Nov). *Royal Visit. Nos. 215/18 optd with* T **23.** P 13½.

239	35 c. Type 19		10	10
240	$2 Queen entering Abbey		25	20
241	$4 Queen crowned		40	30
239/41		*Set of 3*	60	50
MS242	100 × 70 mm. $5 The Mall on Coronation Night		70	90

This overprint also exists on the stamps perforated 11, mentioned below No. MS218 (*price for set of 3 90p. mint or used*).

24 Life-saving

(Des G. Drummond. Litho Questa)

1977 (7 Dec). *Caribbean Scout Jamboree, Jamaica.* T **24** *and similar horiz designs. Multicoloured.* P 14.

243	½ c. Type 24		10	10*
244	1 c. Overnight hike		10	10*
245	2 c. Cubs tying knots		10	10*
246	22 c. Erecting a tent		15	10*
247	35 c. Gang show limbo dance		25	10*
248	75 c. Campfire cooking		40	15*
249	$3 Sea Scouts in "Mirror" dinghies		80	30*
243/9		*Set of 7*	1·40	65*
MS250	109×85 mm. $2 Pioneering project— Spring bridge		1·10	90*

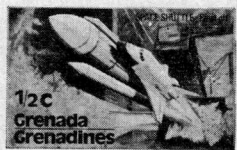

25 Blast-off

(Des J.W. Litho Questa)

1978 (3 Feb). *Space Shuttle.* T **25** *and similar horiz designs. Multicoloured.* P 14.

251	½ c. Type 25		10	10*
252	1 c. Booster jettison		10	10*
253	2 c. External tank jettison		10	10*
254	22 c. Working in orbit		15	10*
255	50 c. Shuttle re-entry		25	10*
256	$3 Shuttle landing		85	30*
251/6		*Set of 6*	1·10	50*
MS257	85 × 103 mm. $2 Shuttle being towed		60	70*

26 Alfred Nobel and Physiology/Medicine Medal

(Des J.W. Litho Questa)

1978 (22 Feb). *Nobel Prize Awards. T **26** and similar horiz designs. Multicoloured. P* 14.
258	½ c. Type 26		10	10*
259	1 c. Physics and Chemistry medal		10	10*
260	2 c. Peace medal		10	10*
261	22 c. Nobel Institute, Oslo		25	10*
262	75 c. Peace Prize committee		50	15*
263	$3 Literature medal		1·50	30*
258/63		*Set of* 6	2·00	60*
MS264	127 × 103 mm. $2 Peace medal and Nobel's will		50	60*

27 German Zeppelin Stamp of 1930

(Des J.W. Litho Questa)

1978 (15 Mar). *75th Anniv of First Zeppelin Flight and 50th Anniv of Lindbergh's Trans-atlantic Flight. T **27** and similar horiz designs. Multicoloured. P* 14 × 13½.
265	5 c. Type 27		20	10*
266	15 c. French Concorde stamp, 1970		60	10*
267	25 c. Liechtenstein Zeppelin stamp, 1931		20	10*
268	35 c. Panama Lindbergh stamp, 1928		20	10*
269	50 c. Russian airship stamp, 1931		25	10*
270	$3 Spanish Lindbergh stamp, 1930		75	30*
265/70		*Set of* 6	2·00	50*
MS271	140×79 mm. 75 c. U.S.A. Lindbergh stamp, 1927; $2 German LZ-129 Hindenburg stamp, 1936		1·10	90*

28 Coronation Ring   **29** Drummer, Royal Regiment of Fusiliers.

(Des J.W. Litho Questa (Nos. 272/5). Manufactured by Walsall (Nos. 276/8))

1978 (12 Apr). *25th Anniv of Coronation. Multicoloured.*

*(a) Sheet stamps. Horiz designs as T **28**. P* 14
272	50 c. Type 28		10	10
273	$2 Queen's Orb		25	30
274	$2.50, Imperial State Crown		30	35
272/4		*Set of* 3	60	65
MS275	97 × 67 mm. $5 Queen Elizabeth II		60	60

Nos. 272/4 also exist perf 12 (*Price for set of 3 90p. mint or used*) from additional sheetlets of 3 stamps and 1 label, issued 2 June. These have different background colours to the stamps perforated 14, which come from normal sheets of 50.

*(b) Booklet stamps. Vert designs as T **29**. Roul 5 × imperf.**
Self-adhesive
276	18 c. Type 29		15	35
	a. Booklet pane. Nos. 276/7 × 3		70	
277	50 c. Drummer, Royal Anglian Regiment		15	45
278	$5 Drum Major, Queen's Regiment		1·00	3·00
	a. Booklet pane of 1		1·00	
276/8		*Set of* 3	1·10	3·50

*Nos. 276/7 are separated by various combinations of rotary-knife (giving a straight edge) and roulette. No. 278 exists only with straight edges.

30 "Le Chapeau de Paille"   **31** Wright Flyer I

(Litho Questa)

1978 (18 May). *400th Birth Anniv of Rubens. T **30** and similar vert designs. Multicoloured. P* 14.
279	5 c. Type 30		10	10
280	15 c. "Achilles slaying Hector"		15	10

281	18 c. "Helene Fourment and her Children"		15	10
282	22 c. "Rubens and Isabella Brandt"		20	10
283	35 c. "The Ildefonso Altarpiece"		20	10
284	$3 "Heads of Negroes" (detail)		1·10	1·00
279/84		*Set of* 6	1·60	1·25
MS285	85 × 127 mm. $2 "Self-portrait"		70	1·00

(Des BG Studio. Litho Questa)

1978 (10 Aug). *75th Anniv of Powered Flight. T **31** and similar designs. P* 14.
286	5 c. black, chestnut and pale blue		10	10
287	15 c. black, vermilion and yellow-ochre		10	10
288	18 c. black, vermilion and yellow-ochre		10	10
289	25 c. multicoloured		10	10
290	35 c. black, purple and magenta		15	10
291	75 c. multicoloured		25	25
292	$3 black, magenta and new blue		75	75
286/92		*Set of* 7	1·10	1·10
MS293	126 × 83 mm. $2 black, blue and bright blue-green		75	1·00

Designs: *Vert*—15 c. Orville Wright; 18 c. Wilbur Wright. *Horiz*—25 c. Wright Flyer III; 35 c. Wright glider No. 1; 75 c. Wright Flyer I; $2 Various Wright aircraft; $3 Wright Type A .

32 Audubon's Shearwater   **33** Players with Ball

(Des Jennifer Toombs. Litho Questa)

1978 (28 Sept). *Birds. T **32** and similar multicoloured designs. P* 14.
294	5 c. Type 32		50	10
295	10 c. Semipalmated Plover		70	10
296	18 c. Purple-throated Carib (*horiz*)		1·00	15
297	22 c. Red-billed Whistling Duck (*horiz*)		1·00	20
298	40 c. Caribbean Martin (*horiz*)		1·50	35
299	$1 White-tailed Tropic Bird.		2·25	75
300	$2 Long-billed Curlew		3·25	1·25
294/300		*Set of* 7	9·00	2·50
MS301	78 × 78 mm. $5 Snowy Egret		5·00	2·75

(Des G. Vasarhelyi. Litho Questa)

1978 (2 Nov). *World Cup Football Championship, Argentina. T **33** and similar vert designs showing football scenes. P* 14.
302	15 c. multicoloured		10	10
303	35 c. multicoloured		20	10
304	50-c. multicoloured		25	20
305	$3 multicoloured		80	90
302/5		*Set of* 4	1·10	90
MS306	114 × 85 mm. $2 multicoloured		80	1·25

34 Captain Cook and Kalaniopu (king of Hawaii), 1778   **35** "Virgin at Prayer"

(Des BG Studio. Litho Questa)

1978 (13 Dec). *250th Birth Anniv of Captain Cook and Bicentenary of Discovery of Hawaii. T **34** and similar horiz designs. Multicoloured. P* 14.
307	18 c. Type 34		45	10
308	22 c. Captain Cook and native of Hawaii		60	15
309	50 c. Captain Cook and death scene, 14 February 1779		1·00	30
310	$3 Captain Cook and offering ceremony		2·25	1·75
307/10		*Set of* 4	3·75	2·00
MS311	171 × 113 mm. $4 H.M.S. Resolution (*vert*)		2·00	1·50

(Des M. Rubin. Litho Questa)

1978 (20 Dec). *Christmas. Paintings by Dürer. T **35** and similar vert designs. Multicoloured. P* 14.
312	40 c. Type 35		20	10
313	60 c. "The Dresden Altarpiece"		25	15
314	90 c. "Madonna and Child with St. Anne"		30	15
315	$2 "Madonna and Child with Pear"		60	50
312/15		*Set of* 4	1·25	80
MS316	114 × 84 mm. $4 "Salvator Mundi"		1·00	1·40

36 *Strelitzia reginae*   **37** Children with Pig

(Des J.W. Litho Questa)

1979 (15 Feb). *Flowers. T **36** and similar vert designs. Multicoloured. P* 14.
317	22 c. Type 36		15	10
318	40 c. *Euphorbia pulcherrima*		25	15
319	$1 *Heliconia humilis*		45	30
320	$3 *Thunbergia alata*		80	80
317/20		*Set of* 4	1·50	1·10
MS321	114 × 90 mm. $2 *Bougainvillea glabra*		75	1·00

(Des G. Drummond. Litho Questa)

1979 (22 Mar). *International Year of the Child. T **37** and similar horiz designs. Multicoloured. P* 14.
322	18 c. Type 37		10	10
323	50 c. Children with donkey		20	25
324	$1 Children with goats		25	30
325	$3 Children fishing		65	80
322/5		*Set of* 4	1·00	1·25
MS326	104 × 86 mm. $4 Child with coconuts		1·00	1·90

38 20,000 *Leagues Under the Sea*

(Des G. Vasarhelyi. Litho Questa)

1979 (20 Apr). *150th Birth Anniv of Jules Verne (author). T **38** and similar horiz designs showing scenes from his books and modern technological developments. Multicoloured. P* 14.
327	18 c. Type 38		30	10
328	38 c. *From the Earth to the Moon*		35	20
329	75 c. *From the Earth to the Moon* (*different*)		45	35
330	$3 *Five Weeks in a Balloon*		85	1·00
327/30		*Set of* 4	1·75	1·50
MS331	111 × 86 mm. $4 *Around the World in 80 days*		1·00	1·60

39 Sir Rowland Hill and Mail Van

(Des BG Studio. Litho Questa)

1979 (30 July). *Death Centenary of Sir Rowland Hill. T **39** and similar horiz designs showing Sir Rowland Hill and mail transport. Multicoloured. P* 14.
332	15 c. Type 39		10	10
333	$1 *Britanis* (cargo liner)		20	20
334	$2 Diesel mail train		30	30
335	$3 Concorde		90	70
332/5		*Set of* 4	1·25	1·10
MS336	85×67 mm. $4 Sir Rowland Hill		75	1·00

Nos. 332/5 also exist perf 12 (*Price for set of 4 £1.25 mint or used*) from additional sheetlets of 5 stamps and 1 label issued 6 September. These have different background colours to the stamps perforated 14, which come from normal sheets of 40.

40 "Virgin and Child Enthroned" (11th-century Byzantine)   **41** Great Hammerhead

(Des G. Vasarhelyi. Litho Questa)

1979 (23 Oct). *Christmas. Sculptures. T **40** and similar vert designs. Multicoloured. P* 14.
337	6 c. Type 40		10	10
338	25 c. "Presentation in the Temple" (Andre Beauneveu)		10	10
339	30 c. "Flight to Egypt", Utrecht, *circa* 1510		10	10
340	40 c. "Madonna and Child" (Jacopo della Quercia)		10	10
341	90 c. "Madonna della Mela" (Luca della Robbia)		15	15
342	$1 "Madonna and Child" (Antonio Rossellino)		20	20
343	$2 "Madonna", Antwerp, 1700		35	35
337/43		*Set of* 7	80	80
MS344	125 × 95 mm. $4 "Virgin", Krumau		65	1·10

(Des J.W. Litho Questa)

1979 (9 Nov). *Marine Life. T **41** and similar horiz designs. Multicoloured. P* 14 × 13½.
345	40 c. Type 41		40	30
346	45 c. Spot-finned Butterflyfish		45	30
347	50 c. Permit (fish)		45	40
348	60 c. Threaded Turban (shell)		65	55
349	70 c. Milk Conch (shell)		75	75
350	75 c. Great Blue Heron		1·25	90
351	90 c. Colourful Atlantic Moon (shell)		95	1·00

352	$1 Red-footed Booby	1·75	1·75
345/52	*Set of 8*	6·00	5·50
MS353	99 × 86 mm. $2.50 Collared Plover	2·00	1·10

42 Goofy as Doctor   **43** Classroom

(Litho Format)

1979 (12 Dec). *International Year of the Child. Walt Disney Cartoon Characters. T 42 and similar multicoloured designs showing characters at various occupations.* P 11.

354	½ c. Type 42	10	10
355	1 c. Mickey Mouse as admiral	10	10
356	2 c. Goofy as fireman	10	10
357	3 c. Minnie Mouse as nurse	10	10
358	4 c. Mickey Mouse as drum major	10	10
359	5 c. Donald Duck as policeman	10	10
360	10 c. Donald Duck as pilot	10	10
361	$2 Goofy as postman (*horiz*)	2·25	2·25
362	$2.50, Donald Duck as train driver (*horiz*)	2·25	2·25
354/62	*Set of 9*	4·50	4·50
MS363	128 × 102 mm. $3 Mickey Mouse as fireman. P 13½	1·75	2·00

1980 (10 Mar). *1st Anniv of Revolution. Nos. 116 and 119/30 optd with T 259 of Grenada.*

364	6 c. Cocoa beans in drying trays	10	10
365	12 c. Cocoa Tree	10	10
366	15 c. Fishermen landing catch at Fontenoy	10	10
367	20 c. Parliament Building, St. George's	10	10
368	25 c. Fort George cannons	15	10
369	35 c. Pearls Airport	20	10
370	50 c. General Post Office	35	15
371	75 c. Caribs Leap, Sauteurs Bay	40	20
372	$1 Carenage, St. George's	55	30
373	$2 St. George's Harbour by night	85	70
374	$3 Grand Anse Beach	1·60	1·60
375	$5 Canoe Bay and Black Bay from Point Saline Lighthouse	2·25	2·50
376	$10 Sugar Loaf Island from Levera Beach	3·75	4·25
364/76	*Set of 13*	9·50	9·00

(Des BG Studio. Litho Questa)

1980 (12 Mar). *75th Anniv of Rotary International. T 43 and similar horiz designs. Multicoloured.* P 14.

377	6 c. Type 43	10	10
378	30 c. Rotary International emblem encircled by people of different races	20	10
379	60 c. Rotary International executive presenting doctor with cheque	35	20
380	$3 Nurses with young patients	1·60	75
377/80	*Set of 4*	2·00	1·00
MS381	85 × 72 mm. $4 Paul P. Harris (founder)	1·00	1·60

44 Yellow-bellied Seedeater   **45** Running

(Des G. Drummond. Litho Questa)

1980 (14 Apr). *Wild Birds. T 44 and similar vert designs. Multicoloured.* P 14.

382	25 c. Type 44	50	15
383	40 c. Blue-hooded Euphonia	55	20
384	90 c. Yellow Warbler	1·25	65
385	$2 Tropical Mockingbird	1·75	1·25
382/5	*Set of 4*	3·50	2·00
MS386	83 × 110 mm. $3 Barn Owl	4·00	2·00

(Des G. Vasarhelyi. Litho Questa)

1980 (21 Apr). *Olympic Games, Moscow. T 45 and similar horiz designs. Multicoloured.* P 14.

387	30 c. Type 45	20	15
388	40 c. Football	15	10
389	90 c. Boxing	35	35
390	$2 Wrestling	70	75
387/90	*Set of 4*	1·25	1·25
MS391	104 × 75 mm. $4 Athletes in silhouette	75	1·10

LONDON 1980

(46)   **47** Long-jawed Squirrelfish

1980 (6 May). *"London 1980" International Stamp Exhibition. Nos. 332/5 optd with T 46.* P 12.

392	15 c. Type 39	15	15
393	$1 *Britanis* (cargo liner)	75	35
394	$2 Diesel mail train	1·50	1·00
395	$3 Concorde	2·25	2·00
392/5	*Set of 4*	4·25	3·25

(Des G. Drummond. Litho Questa)

1980 (6 Aug)–87. *Fishes. Horiz designs as T 47. Multicoloured.* P 14. A. *Without imprint date.*

396A	½ c. Type 47	10	10
397A	1 c. Blue Chromis	10	10
398A	2 c. Four-eyed Butterflyfish	10	10
399A	4 c. Sergeant Major	10	10
400A	5 c. Yellow-tailed Snapper	10	10
401A	6 c. Mutton Snapper	10	10
402A	10 c. Cocoa Damselfish	10	10
403A	12 c. Royal Gramma	10	10
404A	15 c. Cherub Angelfish	15	10
405A	20 c. Black-barred Soldierfish	15	10
406A	25 c. Mottled Grouper	15	15
407A	30 c. Caribbean Long-nosed Butterflyfish	15	20
408A	40 c. Puddingwife	20	25
409A	50 c. Midnight Parrotfish	25	35
410A	90 c. Red-spotted Hawkfish	40	55
411A	$1 Hogfish	45	60
412A	$3 Beau Gregory	1·25	1·50
413A	$5 Rock Beauty	2·00	2·50
414A	$10 Barred Hamlet	3·50	5·00
396A/414A	*Set of 19*	8·00	10·00

B. *With imprint date at foot of design.*

396B	½ c. Type 47 (*p 12*) (1982)	5·00	8·00
402B	10 c. Cocoa Damselfish (1984)	30	30
405B	20 c. Black-barred Soldierfish (1987)	1·00	1·00
346B/405B	*Set of 3*	7·50	8·50

Imprint dates: "1982", No. 396B; "1984", No. 402B; "1987", No. 405B.

(Litho Walsall)

1980 (7 Oct). *Christmas. Walt Disney Cartoon Scenes from "Bambi". Horiz designs as T 42. Multicoloured.* P 11.

415	½ c. Bambi with Mother	10	10
416	1 c. Bambi with quails	10	10
417	2 c. Bambi meets Thumper the rabbit	10	10
418	3 c. Bambi meets Flower the skunk	10	10
419	4 c. Bambi and Faline	10	10
420	5 c. Bambi with his father	10	10
421	10 c. Bambi on ice	10	10
422	$2.50, Faline with foals	1·75	1·25
423	$3 Bambi and Faline	1·75	1·25
415/23	*Set of 9*	3·50	2·50
MS424	127 × 102 mm. $4 Bambi as Prince of the Forest (*vert*)	2·00	2·00

48 "The Unicorn in Captivity" (15th-century unknown artist)   **49** "Bust of a Woman"

(Litho Format)

1981 (25 Jan). *Paintings. T 48 and similar multicoloured designs.* P 13½.

425	6 c. Type 48	10	10
426	10 c. "The Fighting *Temeraire*" (Turner) (*horiz*)	10	10
427	25 c. "Sunday Afternoon on the Ile de la Grande-Jatte" (Georges-Pierre Seurat) (*horiz*)	15	15
428	90 c. "Max Schmitt in a Single Scull" (Thomas Eakins) (*horiz*)	45	45
429	$2 "The Burial of the Count of Orgaz" (El Greco)	85	85
430	$3 "George Washington" (Gilbert Stuart)	1·10	1·10
425/30	*Set of 6*	2·40	2·40
MS431	66 × 101 mm. $5 "Kaiser Karl de Grosse" (detail, Dürer)	1·75	2·00

Nos. 425/31 exist imperforate from stock dispersed by the liquidator of Format International Security Printers Ltd.

(Litho Format)

1981 (26 Jan). *50th Anniv of Walt Disney's Cartoon Character, Pluto. Vert designs as T 42. Multicoloured.* P 13½.

432	$2 Mickey Mouse serving birthday cake to Pluto	90	80
MS433	127 × 101 mm. $4 Pluto in scene from film *Pluto's Dream House*	1·50	1·50

No. 432 was printed in small sheets of 8 stamps.

(Litho Format)

1981 (14 Apr). *Easter. Walt Disney Cartoon Characters. Vert designs as T 42. Multicoloured.* P 11.

434	35 c. Chip	20	20
435	40 c. Dewey	20	20
436	$2 Huey	60	60
437	$2.50, Mickey Mouse	75	75
434/7	*Set of 4*	1·60	1·60
MS438	126 × 102 mm. $4 Jiminy Cricket. P 13½	2·00	1·50

(Des J.W. Litho Questa)

1981 (5 May). *Birth Centenary of Picasso. T 49 and similar vert designs. Multicoloured.* P 14.

439	6 c. Type 49	10	10
440	40 c. Woman (study for "Les Demoiselles d'Avignon")	25	15

441	90 c. "Nude with raised Arms (The Dancer of Avignon)"	40	30
442	$4 "The Dryad"	1·25	1·25
439/42	*Set of 4*	1·75	1·50
MS443	103 × 128 mm. $5 "Les Demoiselles d'Avignon". Imperf	1·40	1·25

50 Balmoral Castle   **51** Lady Diana Spencer

(Des J.W. Litho Format)

1981 (16 June). *Royal Wedding (1st issue). T 50 and similar vert designs. Multicoloured.* (a) P 15.

444	40 c. Prince Charles and Lady Diana Spencer	15	15
445	$2 Type 50	35	35
446	$4 Prince Charles as parachutist	50	50
MS447	97 × 84 mm. $5 Royal Coach	90	90

(b) *P 15 × 14½*

448	30 c. As No. 444	20	20
449	40 c. Type 50	20	20
444/9	*Set of 5*	1·25	1·25

The 30 and 40 c. values were each printed in small sheets of 6 including one *se-tenant* stamp-size label.

The $4 value, with changed background colour, also exists perforated 15×14½ (price £1.10 *mint or used*) from similar sheetlets in addition to the original version from sheets of 40.

(Manufactured by Walsall)

1981 (16 June). *Royal Wedding (2nd issue). T 51 and similar multicoloured designs. Roul 5 × imperf*. Self-adhesive.*

450	$1 Type 51	20	35
	a. Booklet pane. Nos. 450/1 each × 3	1·25	
451	$2 Prince Charles	25	50
452	$5 Prince Charles and Lady Diana Spencer (*horiz*)	1·25	2·00
	a. Booklet pane of 1.	1·25	
450/2	*Set of 3*	1·50	2·50

*The $1 and $2 values were each separated by various combinations of rotary knife (giving a straight edge) and roulette. The $5 value exists only with straight edges.

Nos. 450/2 were only issued in $14 stamp booklets.

52 Amy Johnson (1st solo flight, Britain to Australia by Woman, May 1930)   **53** Boeing 747 SCA

(Des BG Studio. Litho Questa)

1981 (13 Oct). *"Decade for Women". Famous Female Aviators. T 52 and similar vert designs. Multicoloured.* P 14.

453	30 c. Type 52	45	20
454	70 c. Mme la Baronne de Laroche (1st qualified woman pilot, March 1910)	70	30
455	$1.10, Ruth Nichols (solo Atlantic flight attempt, June 1931)	80	40
456	$3 Amelia Earhart (1st North Atlantic solo flight by woman, May 1932)	1·75	1·10
453/6	*Set of 4*	3·25	1·75
MS457	90 × 85 mm. $5 Valentina Nikolayeva-Tereshkova (1st woman in space, June 1963)	1·25	1·40

(Litho Questa)

1981 (2 Nov). *Christmas. Horiz designs as T 42 showing scenes from Walt Disney's cartoon film "Lady and the Tramp".* P 13½.

458	½ c. multicoloured	10	10
459	1 c. multicoloured	10	10
460	2 c. multicoloured	10	10
461	3 c. multicoloured	10	10
462	4 c. multicoloured	10	10
463	5 c. multicoloured	10	10
464	10 c. multicoloured	10	10
465	$2.50, multicoloured	3·00	1·25
466	$3 multicoloured	1·75	1·25
458/66	*Set of 9*	5·75	2·50
MS467	128 × 103 mm. $5 multicoloured	4·50	3·00

(Des M. Brodie. Litho Format)

1981 (2 Nov). *Space Shuttle Project. T 53 and similar horiz designs. Multicoloured.* P 14½.

468	10 c. Type 53	30	10
469	No. Re-entry	65	15
470	$1.10, External tank separation	1·25	45
471	$3 Touchdown"	1·75	1·00
468/71	*Set of 4*	3·50	1·50
MS472	117 × 89 mm. $5 Launch	2·50	1·60

54 Footballer   **55** Mail Van and Stage-Coach

(Des Clover Mill. Litho Questa)

1981 (30 Nov). *World Cup Football Championship, Spain* (1982).
T **54** *and similar vert designs showing footballers. P* 14.

473	20 c. multicoloured			15	10
474	40 c. multicoloured			20	15
475	$1 multicoloured			35	30
476	$2 multicoloured			65	55
473/6			*Set of 4*	1·25	1·00
MS477	106 × 128 mm. $4 multicoloured			1·40	1·60

Nos. 473/6 were each printed in small sheets of 6 including one
se-tenant stamp-size label.

(Des G. Vasarhelyi. Litho Format)

1982 (13 Jan). *Centenary of U.P.U. Membership. T* **55** *and similar
horiz designs. Multicoloured. P* 14½.

478	30 c. Type **55**			30	15
479	40 c. U.P.U. emblem			30	15
480	$2.50, *Queen Elizabeth 2* (liner) and sailing ship			1·50	70
481	$4 Concorde and De Havilland D.H.9 biplane			2·25	1·25
478/81			*Set of 4*	4·00	2·00
MS482	117×78 mm. $5 British Advanced Passenger Train and steam mail trains			3·50	2·25

56 National Sports Meeting

(Des M. Diamond. Litho Format)

1982 (19 Feb). *75th Anniv of Boy Scout Movement and 125th Birth
Anniv of Lord Baden-Powell. T* **56** *and similar horiz designs.
Multicoloured. P* 14½.

483	6 c. Type **56**			15	10
484	90 c. Sea scouts sailing			50	30
485	$1.10, Handicraft			65	60
486	$3 Animal tending			1·40	1·40
483/6			*Set of 4*	2·40	2·10
MS487	100 × 71 mm. $5 Music around campfire			1·40	1·75

57 *Anartia jatrophae*   **58** Prince and Princess
of Wales

(Des J.W. Litho Questa)

1982 (24 Mar). *Butterflies. T* **57** *and similar horiz designs. Multicoloured. P* 14.

488	30 c. Type **57**			75	30
489	40 c. *Chioides vintra*			80	35
490	$1.10, *Cynthia cardui*			1·75	75
491	$3 *Historis odius*			2·75	1·60
488/91			*Set of 4*	5·50	2·75
MS492	103×77 mm. $5 *Dione juno*			3·25	2·50

(Des PAD Studio. Litho Questa)

1982 (1 July). *21st Birthday of Princess of Wales. T* **58** *and similar
vert designs. Multicoloured. P* 14½ × 14.

493	50 c. Blenheim Palace			50	90
494	60 c. As 50 c.			60	75
495	$1 Type **58**			70	1·60
496	$2 Type **58**			1·50	1·75
497	$3 Princess of Wales			2·25	2·25
498	$4 As $3			2·50	2·50
493/8			*Set of 6*	7·25	8·75
MS499	103 × 75 mm. $5 Princess Diana (*different*)			3·50	2·50

Nos. 493, 495 and 497 come from sheetlets of 5 stamps and 1
label.

59 "New Deal"—Soil   **60** "Presentation of Christ
Conservation   in the Temple"

(Des M. Diamond. Litho Questa)

1982 (27 July). *Birth Centenary of Franklin D. Roosevelt. T* **59**
and similar horiz designs. Multicoloured. P 14.

500	30 c. Type **59**			25	15
501	40 c. Roosevelt and George Washington Carver (scientist)			25	15
502	70 c. Civilian conservation corps and reafforestation			40	30
503	$3 Roosevelt with Pres. Barclay of Liberia, Casablanca Conference, 1943			1·00	90
500/3			*Set of 4*	1·75	1·40
MS504	100 × 72 mm. $5 Roosevelt delivering address at Howard University			1·75	1·75

1982 (30 Aug). *Birth of Prince William of Wales. Nos. 493/9 optd
with T* **171** *of Antigua.*

505	50 c. Blenheim Palace			50	50
506	60 c. As 50 c.			55	60
507	$1 Type **58**			70	75
508	$2 Type **58**			1·00	1·25
509	$3 Princess of Wales			1·25	1·75
510	$4 As $3			1·50	1·75
505/10			*Set of 6*	5·00	6·00
MS511	103 × 75 mm. $5 Princess Diana (*different*)			2·10	2·25

Nos. 505, 507 and 509 come from sheetlets of 5 stamps and 1
label.

(Des Clover Mill. Litho Format)

1982 (2 Sept). *Easter. T* **60** *and similar vert designs depicting
Easter paintings by Rembrandt. Multicoloured. P* 14½.

512	30 c. Type **60**			35	15
513	60 c. "Descent from the Cross"			45	20
514	$2 "Raising of the Cross"			85	75
515	$4 "Resurrection of Christ"			1·40	1·50
512/15			*Set of 4*	2·75	2·40
MS516	101 × 126 mm. $5 "The Risen Christ"			2·40	2·00

61 "Santa Fe", U.S.A.

(Des Artists International. Litho Format)

1982 (4 Oct). *Famous Trains of the World. T* **61** *and similar
vert designs. Multicoloured. P* 15.

517	10 c. Type **61**			50	15
518	40 c. "Mistral", France			70	20
519	70 c. "Rheingold", Germany			80	45
520	$1 "ET 403", France			1·00	50
521	$1.10, Steam locomotive *Mallard*, Great Britain			1·25	60
522	$2 Tokaido Shinkansen "Hikari", Japan			1·40	90
517/22			*Set of 6*	5·00	2·50
MS523	121×95 mm. $5 "Settebello", Italy			1·75	2·00

62 Footballers

(Des D. Miller. Litho Questa)

1982 (2 Dec). *World Cup Football Championship Winners. T* **62**
and similar horiz designs. P 14 × 13½.

524	60 c. multicoloured			75	35
525	$4 multicoloured			2·00	1·25
MS526	92 × 134 mm. $5 multicoloured			1·50	1·50

(Litho Questa)

1982 (14 Dec). *Christmas. Horiz designs as T* **42** *showing scenes
from Walt Disney's cartoon film "The Rescuers". P* 13½.

527	½ c. multicoloured			10	10
528	1 c. multicoloured			10	10
529	2 c. multicoloured			10	10
530	3 c. multicoloured			10	10
531	4 c. multicoloured			10	10
532	5 c. multicoloured			10	10
533	10 c. multicoloured			10	10
534	$2.50, multicoloured			2·75	1·75
535	$3 multicoloured			2·75	1·75
527/35			*Set of 9*	5·50	3·50
MS536	120 × 96 mm. $5 multicoloured			5·00	2·75

63 Short-finned Pilot Whale

(Des Artists International. Litho Questa)

1983 (10 Jan). *Save the Whales. T* **63** *and similar horiz designs.
Multicoloured. P* 14.

537	10 c. Type **63**			85	55
538	60 c. Dall's Porpoise			2·00	1·75
539	$1.10, Humpback Whale			3·50	2·75
540	$3 Bowhead Whale			6·00	7·00
537/40			*Set of 4*	11·00	11·00
MS541	113 × 84 mm. $5 Spotted Dolphin			4·50	4·00

64 "David and Goliath"

(Des Design Images. Litho Format)

1983 (15 Feb). *500th Birth Anniv of Raphael. T* **64** *and similar
horiz designs showing painting details. Multicoloured. P* 13½.

542	25 c. Type **64**			15	15
543	30 c. "David sees Bathsheba"			15	15
544	70 c. "Triumph of David"			30	35
545	$4 "Anointing of Solomon"			70	90
542/5			*Set of 4*	1·10	1·40
MS546	126 × 101 mm. $5 "Anointing of David"			80	1·10

Nos. 542/6 exist imperforate from stock dispersed by the
liquidator of Format International Security Printers Ltd.

65 Voice and Visual Communication

(Des Artists International. Litho Questa)

1983 (7 Apr). *World Communications Year. T* **65** *and similar
horiz designs. Multicoloured. P* 14.

547	30 c. Type **65**			10	10
548	60 c. Ambulance			25	20
549	$1.10, Westland Whirlwind helicopters			45	45
550	$3 Satellite			1·00	1·00
547/50			*Set of 4*	1·60	1·60
MS551	127×85 mm. $5 Diver and Bottle-nosed Dolphin			2·00	2·00

66 Chrysler "Imperial Roadster", 1931

(Des R. Sauber. Litho Format)

1983 (4 May). *75th Anniv of Model "T" Ford Car. T* **66** *and similar
horiz designs showing cars of the 20th century. Multicoloured.
P* 14½.

552	10 c. Type **66**			15	15
553	30 c. Doble steam car, 1925			25	25
554	40 c. Ford "Mustang", 1965			25	30
555	60 c. Packard tourer, 1930			35	40
556	70 c. Mercer "Raceabout" 1913			35	40
557	90 c. Corvette "Stingray", 1963			35	40
558	$1.10, Auburn "851 Supercharger Speedster", 1935			40	45
559	$2.50, Pierce-Arrow "Silver Arrow", 1933			65	95
560	$3 Duesenberg dual cowl phaeton, 1929			75	1·25
561	$4 Mercedes-Benz "SSK", 1928			75	1·50
552/61			*Set of 10*	3·75	5·50
MS562	119 × 90 mm. $5 McFarlan "Knickerbocker" cabriolet, 1923			1·50	2·50

Nos. 552/61 were each issued in sheets of eight stamps with a
stamp-size label in the centre position.

67 Short S.45A Solent 2
Flying Boat

(Des W. Wright. Litho Questa)

1983 (18 July). *Bicentenary of Manned Flight. T **67** and similar horiz designs. Multicoloured. P 14.*

563	40 c. Type 67	75	20
564	70 c. Curtiss R3C-2 seaplane	90	35
565	90 c. Hawker Nimrod biplane	1·10	40
566	$4 Montgolfier balloon	3·25	2·75
563/6	*Set of 4*	5·50	3·25
MS567	112×85 mm. $5 LZ-11 *Viktoria Luise* (airship)	1·75	2·00

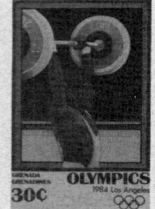

68 Goofy   **69** Weightlifting

(Litho Walsall)

1983 (7 Nov). *Christmas. T **68** and similar vert designs showing Disney cartoon characters in scenes from "Jingle Bells" (Christmas carol). Multicoloured. P 11.*

568	½ c. Type 68	10	10
569	1 c. Clarabelle Cow	10	10
570	2 c. Donald Duck	10	10
571	3 c. Pluto	10	10
572	4 c. Morty and Ferdie	10	10
573	5 c. Huey, Dewey and Louie	10	10
574	10 c. Daisy and Chip 'n Dale	10	10
575	$2.50, Big Bad Wolf	4·75	5·00
576	$3 Mickey Mouse	5·00	5·50
568/76	*Set of 9*	9·00	10·00
MS577	102 × 124 mm. $5 Donald Duck in sleigh. P 13½	8·00	8·50

(Des N. Waldman. Litho Questa)

1984 (9 Jan). *Olympic Games, Los Angeles. T **69** and similar vert designs. Multicoloured. P 14.*

578	30 c. Type 69	20	15
579	60 c. Gymnastics	45	35
580	70 c. Archery	50	40
581	$4 Sailing	1·90	1·90
578/81	*Set of 4*	2·50	2·50
MS582	70 × 102 mm. $5 Basketball	2·00	2·25

70 Frangipani   **71** Goofy

(Des J. Cooter. Litho Format)

1984 (9 Apr). *Flowers. T **70** and similar vert designs. Multicoloured. P 15.*

583	15 c. Type 70	15	10
584	40 c. Dwarf Poinciana	30	25
585	70 c. Walking Iris	55	45
586	$4 Lady's Slipper	1·75	2·50
583/6	*Set of 4*	2·50	3·00
MS587	66 × 57 mm. $5 Brazilian Glory Vine	1·50	2·50

Nos. 583/6 exist imperforate from stock dispersed by the liquidator of Format International Security Printers Ltd.

(Litho Format)

1984 (1 May). *Easter. T **71** and similar vert designs showing Disney cartoon characters with Easter hats. Multicoloured. P 11.*

588	½ c. Type 71	10	10
589	1 c. Chip and Dale	10	10
590	2 c. Daisy Duck and Huey	10	10
591	3 c. Daisy Duck	10	10
592	4 c. Donald Duck	10	10
593	5 c. Merlin and Madam Mim	10	10
594	10 c. Flower	10	10
595	$2 Minnie and Mickey Mouse	1·50	2·00
596	$4 Minnie Mouse	2·25	2·75
588/96	*Set of 9*	3·75	4·75
MS597	126 × 100 mm. $5 Minnie Mouse (different). P 13½ × 14	3·00	3·75

72 Bobolink   (**73**)

19TH U.P.U. CONGRESS HAMBURG

(Litho Questa)

1984 (21 May). *Songbirds. T **72** and similar horiz designs. Multicoloured. P 14.*

598	40 c. Type 72	1·75	1·50
599	50 c. Eastern Kingbird	2·00	1·60
600	60 c. Barn Swallow	2·25	2·00
601	70 c. Yellow Warbler	2·25	2·00
602	$1 Rose-breasted Grosbeak	2·50	2·50
603	$1.10, Yellowthroat	2·75	2·75
604	$2 Catbird	3·50	4·50
598/604	*Set of 7*	15·00	15·00
MS605	71 × 65 mm. $5 Fork-tailed Flycatcher	6·50	5·00

1984 (19 June). *Universal Postal Union Congress, Hamburg. Nos. 585/7 optd with T **73**.*

606	70 c. Walking Iris	1·00	1·00
607	$4 Lady's Slipper	4·50	5·00
MS608	66 × 57 mm. $5 Brazilian Glory Vine	2·25	3·00

74 Geeststar (freighter)   **75** Col. Steven's Model (1825)

(Litho Format)

1984 (16 July). *Ships. T **74** and similar horiz designs. Multicoloured. P 15.*

609	30 c. Type 74	75	75
610	60 c. *Daphne* (liner)	1·00	1·25
611	$1.10 *Southwind* (schooner)	1·25	2·00
612	$4 *Oceanic* (liner)	2·00	5·50
609/12	*Set of 4*	4·50	8·50
MS613	108×80 mm. $5 Pirate ship	3·00	4·00

Nos. 609/13 exist imperforate from stock dispersed by the liquidator of Format International Security Printers Ltd.

(Litho Questa)

1984 (22 Aug). *450th Death Anniv of Correggio (painter). Multicoloured designs as T **296** of Grenada showing paintings. P 14.*

614	10 c. "The Hunt—Blowing the Horn"	10	10
615	30 c. "St. John the Evangelist" (horiz)	15	15
616	90 c. "The Hunt—The Deer's Head"	50	50
617	$4 "The Virgin crowned by Christ" (horiz)	2·00	2·00
614/17	*Set of 4*	2·50	2·50
MS618	73 × 63 mm. $5 "Martyrdom of the Four Saints"	2·40	3·00

(Litho Questa)

1984 (22 Aug). *150th Birth Anniv of Edgar Degas (painter). Vert designs as T **297** of Grenada showing paintings. Multicoloured. P 14.*

619	25 c. "The Song of the Dog"	40	15
620	70 c. "Cafe-concert"	70	50
621	$1.10, "The Orchestra of the Opera"	1·50	1·25
622	$3 "The Dance Lesson"	2·75	2·75
619/22	*Set of 4*	4·75	4·25
MS623	53 × 73 mm. $5 "Madame Camus at the Piano"	2·40	3·00

(Des Bonny Redecker. Litho Questa)

1984 (21 Sept). *"Ausipex" International Stamp Exhibition, Melbourne. Horiz designs as T **298** of Grenada. Multicoloured. P 14.*

624	$1.10, Queen Victoria Gardens, Melbourne	50	50
625	$4 Ayers Rock	2·00	2·00
MS626	107 × 76 mm. $5 River Yarra, Melbourne	2·00	3·00

(Des Bonny Redecker. Litho Format)

1984 (3 Oct). *Railway Locomotives. T **75** and similar horiz designs. Multicoloured. P 15.*

627	20 c. Type 75	55	25
628	50 c. *Royal George* (1827)	70	50
629	60 c. *Stourbridge Lion* (1829)	75	65
630	70 c. *Liverpool* (1830)	80	85
631	90 c. *South Carolina* (1832)	90	1·25
632	$1.10, *Monster* (1836)	90	1·50
633	$2 *Lafayette* (1837)	1·10	2·25
634	$4 *Lion* (1838)	1·40	3·75
627/34	*Set of 8*	6·25	10·00
MS635	Two sheets, each 100×70 mm. (a) $5 Sequin's locomotive (1829); (b) $5 *Adler* (1835)		
	Set of 2 sheets	6·00	8·00

1984 (28 Oct). *Opening of Point Saline International Airport. Nos. 547, 549 and **MS551** optd as T **300** of Grenada.*

636	30 c. Type 65	30	25
637	$1.10, Westland Whirlwind helicopters	95	75
MS638	127×85 mm. Diver and Bottle-nosed Dolphin	3·75	3·50

The overprint on No. **MS638** appears on the sheet margin as for No. **MS1371** of Grenada.

(Litho Questa)

1984 (26 Nov). *Christmas. Walt Disney Cartoon Characters. Vert designs as T **301** of Grenada. Multicoloured. P 12 ($2) or 13½×14 (others).*

639	45 c. Donald Duck, and nephews knitting Christmas stockings	70	40
640	60 c. Donald Duck and nephews sitting on sofa	80	65
641	90 c. Donald Duck getting out of bed	1·25	1·00

642	$2 Donald Duck putting presents in wardrobe	2·00	2·50
643	$4 Nephews singing carols outside Donald Duck's window	3·25	4·25
639/43	*Set of 5*	7·25	8·00
MS644	126×102 mm. $5 Donald Duck filming nephews	4·25	4·00

No. 642 was printed in sheetlets of 8 stamps.

(Litho Questa)

1985 (11 Feb). *Birth Bicentenary of John J. Audubon (ornithologist) (1st issue). Multicoloured designs as T **198** of Antigua showing original paintings. P 14.*

645	50 c. Blue-winged Teal	2·00	60
646	90 c. White Ibis	2·50	1·25
647	$1.10, Swallow-tailed Kite	3·50	2·00
648	$3 Moorhen ("Common Gallinule")	4·50	4·75
645/8	*Set of 4*	11·00	7·75
MS649	82×111 mm. $5 Mangrove Cuckoo (vert)	3·25	3·75

See also Nos. 736/40.

76 Kawasaki "750" (1972)   **77** Nursing Cadets folding Bandages (Health)

(Des BG Studio. Litho Questa)

1985 (11 Mar). *Centenary of the Motor Cycle. T **76** and similar multicoloured designs. P 14.*

650	30 c. Type 76	65	45
651	60 c. Honda "Goldwing GL1000" (1974) (horiz)	90	1·00
652	70 c. Kawasaki "Z650" (1976) (horiz)	1·00	1·10
653	$4 Honda "CBX" (1977)	4·00	6·50
650/3	*Set of 4*	6·00	8·00
MS654	113×76 mm. $5 BMW "R100RS" (1978).	3·50	4·25

(Des Susan David. Litho Questa)

1985 (15 Apr). *International Youth Year. T **77** and similar horiz designs. Multicoloured. P 14.*

655	50 c. Type 77	70	45
656	70 c. Scuba diver and turtle (Environment)	1·00	80
657	$1.10, Yachting (Leisure)	1·60	1·50
658	$3 Boys playing chess (Education)	6·00	7·00
655/8	*Set of 4*	8·50	8·75
MS659	98×70 mm. $5 Hands touching globe	2·75	3·00

(Des BG Studio. Litho Questa)

1985 (30 Apr). *40th Anniv of International Civil Aviation Organization. Horiz designs as T **305** of Grenada. Multicoloured. P 14.*

660	5 c. Lockheed L.18 Lodestar	40	20
661	70 c. Hawker Siddeley H.S.748	1·75	55
662	$1.10, Boeing 727-200	2·25	90
663	$3 Boeing 707	3·50	2·50
660/3	*Set of 4*	7·00	3·75
MS664	87×68 mm. $4 Pilatus Britten Norman Islander	3·50	3·00

78 Lady Baden-Powell (founder) and Grenadian Guide Leaders

(Des D. Francis. Litho Questa)

1985 (30 May). *75th Anniv of Girl Guide Movement. T **78** and similar multicoloured designs. P 14.*

665	30 c. Type 78	50	20
666	50 c. Guide leader and guides on botany field trip	80	30
667	70 c. Guide leader and guides camping (vert)	1·10	45
668	$4 Guides sailing (vert)	3·50	2·25
665/8	*Set of 4*	5·50	3·00
MS669	100×73 mm. $5 Lord and Lady Baden-Powell (vert)	3·75	4·25

79 Chiomara asychis   **80** The Queen Mother before Prince William's Christening

(Des I. MacLaury. Litho Questa)

1985 (17 June)–**89.** *Butterflies. T* **79** *and similar horis designs. Multicoloured. P* 14.

670	½ c. Type **79**		10	20
	a. Perf 12 (1986)		10	20
671	1 c. *Anartia amathea*		10	20
	a. Perf 12 (1986)		10	20
672	2 c. *Pseudolycaena marsyas*		10	20
	a. Perf 12 (1986)		10	20
673	4 c. *Urbanus proteus*		10	20
	a. Perf 12 (1986)		10	20
674	5 c. *Polygonus manueli*		15	20
	a. Perf 12 (1986)		15	20
675	6 c. *Battus polydamas*		20	20
	a. Perf 12 (1986)		20	15
676	10 c. *Eurema daira*		30	15
	a. Perf 12 (1986)		30	20
677	12 c. *Phoebis agarithe*		45	20
	a. Perf 12 (1986)		45	30
678	15 c. *Aphrissa statira*		45	30
	a. Perf 12 (1986)		45	30
679	20 c. *Strymon simaethis*		60	20
	a. Perf 12 (1986)		60	30
680	25 c. *Mestra cana*		60	25
	a. Perf 12 (1986)		60	30
681	30 c. *Agraulis vanillae*		60	30
	a. Perf 12 (1986)		60	30
682	40 c. *Junonia evarete*		75	45
	a. Perf 12 (1986)		75	45
683	60 c. *Dryas julia*		1·00	65
	a. Perf 12 (1986)		1·00	65
684	70 c. *Philaethria dido*		1·10	75
	a. Perf 12 (1986)		1·10	75
685	$1.10, *Hamadryas feronia*		1·75	1·25
	a. Perf 12 (1986)		1·75	1·25
686	$2.50, *Strymon rufofusca*		3·25	3·00
	a. Perf 12 (9.86)		3·25	4·00
687	$5 *Appias drusilla*		5·00	4·75
	a. Perf 12 (1986)		5·00	6·00
688	$10 *Polites dictynna* (11.11.85)		8·00	9·00
	a. Perf 12 (1986)		8·00	12·00
688*b*	$20 *Euptychia cephus* (1.8.86)		12·00	16·00
	b*a.* Perf 12 (5.89)		12·00	17·00
670/88*b*		Set of 20	32·00	35·00
670a/88ba		Set of 20	32·00	40·00

(Des J.W. Litho Questa)

1985 (3 July). *Life and Times of Queen Elizabeth the Queen Mother. T* **80** *and similar multicoloured designs. P* 14.

689	$1 Type **80**		45	60
690	$1.50, In winner's enclosure at Ascot (*horiz*)		60	75
691	$2.50, With Prince Charles at Garter ceremony, Windsor Castle		85	1·10
689/91		Set of 3	1·75	2·10
MS692	56 × 85 mm. $5 At opening of Royal York Hospice, London		1·75	3·00

Stamps as Nos. 689/91, but with face values of 70 c., $1.10 and $3, exist from additional sheetlets of 5 plus a label issued 28 January 1986. These also have changed background colours and are perforated 12½ × 12 ($1.10) or 12 × 12½ (others) (*Price for set of 3 stamps £1.75 mint*).

81 Scuba Diving

82 Queen or Pink Conch

(Des Marlise Nakaja. Litho Format)

1985 (15 July). *Water Sports. T* **81** *and similar vert designs. Multicoloured. P* 15.

693	15 c. Type **81**		30	10
694	70 c. Boys playing in waterfall		60	45
695	90 c. Water skiing		70	55
696	$4 Swimming		1·50	2·25
693/6		Set of 4	2·75	3·00
MS697	103 × 78 mm. $5 Scuba diver		2·75	3·25

Nos. 693/6 exist imperforate from stock dispersed by the liquidator of Format International Security Printers Ltd.

(Des Mary Walters. Litho Questa)

1985 (1 Aug). *Marine Life. T* **82** *and similar horiz designs. Multicoloured. P* 14.

698	60 c. Type **82**		65	40
699	90 c. Porcupinefish and Fire Coral		85	55
700	$1.10, Ghost Crab		1·00	80
701	$4 West Indies Spiny Lobster		2·50	3·00
698/701		Set of 4	4·50	4·25
MS702	299 × 70 mm. $5 Long-spined Urchin		4·50	4·00

(Des Susan David. Litho Questa)

1985 (3 Sept). *300th Birth Anniv of Johann Sebastian Bach (composer). Vert designs as T* **206** *of Antigua. Multicoloured. P* 14.

703	15 c. Natural trumpet		50	10
704	60 c. Bass viol		85	40
705	$1.10, Flute		1·50	70
706	$3 Double flageolet		2·25	1·75
703/6		Set of 4	4·50	2·75
MS707	110 × 75 mm. $5 Johann Sebastian Bach		3·25	3·50

(Litho Format)

1985 (4 Nov). *Royal Visit. Multicoloured designs as T* **207** *of Antigua. P* 14½.

708	10 c. Arms of Great Britain and Grenada		20	20
709	$1 Queen Elizabeth II (*vert*)		1·00	1·75
710	$4 Royal Yacht *Britannia*		3·50	4·75
708/10		Set of 3	4·25	6·00
MS711	111 × 83 mm. $5 Map of Grenada Grenadines		3·00	3·75

(Litho Format)

1985 (22 Nov). *40th Anniv of United Nations Organization. Multicoloured designs as T* **208** *of Antigua showing United Nations (New York) stamps. P* 14½.

712	$1 Neil Armstrong (first man on Moon) and 1982 Peaceful Uses of Outer Space 20 c.		1·10	1·10
713	$2 Gandhi and 1971 Racial Equality Year 13 c.		3·25	3·75
714	$2.50, Maimonides (physician) and 1956 World Health Organization 3 c.		4·50	5·50
712/14		Set of 3	8·00	9·25
MS715	110 × 85 mm. $5 U.N. Under-Secretary Ralph Bunche (*vert*)		2·75	3·00

(Des Walt Disney Productions. Litho Questa)

1985 (27 Nov). *150th Birth Anniv of Mark Twain (author). Horiz designs as T* **118** *of Anguilla showing Walt Disney cartoon characters illustrating scenes from "Letters from Hawaii". Multicoloured. P* 14 × 13½.

716	25 c. Minnie Mouse dancing the hula		60	30
717	50 c. Donald Duck surfing		90	65
718	$1.50, Donald Duck roasting marshmallow in volcano		2·25	2·25
719	$3 Mickey Mouse and Chip'n'Dale canoeing		3·75	4·00
716/19		Set of 4	6·75	6·50
MS720	127 × 102 mm. $5 Mickey Mouse with cat		4·75	3·75

(Des Walt Disney Productions. Litho Questa)

1985 (27 Nov). *Birth Bicentenaries of Grimm Brothers (folklorists). Designs as T* **119** *of Anguilla, but vert, showing Walt Disney cartoon characters in scenes from "The Elves and the Shoemaker". Multicoloured. P* 13½ × 14.

721	30 c. Mickey Mouse as the unsuccessful Shoemaker		70	40
722	60 c. Two elves making shoes		1·10	85
723	70 c. The Shoemaker discovering the new shoes		1·40	1·00
724	$4 The Shoemaker's wife (Minnie Mouse) making clothes for the elves		4·25	5·00
721/4		Set of 4	6·75	6·50
MS725	126 × 101 mm. $5 The Shoemaker and his wife waving		5·50	5·00

83 "Madonna and Child" (Titian)

VISIT OF PRES. REAGAN

20 FEBRUARY 1986

(84)

(Des Mary Walters. Litho Format)

1985 (23 Dec). *Christmas. Religious Paintings. T* **83** *and similar vert designs. Multicoloured. P* 15.

726	50 c. Type **83**		45	35
727	70 c. "Madonna and Child with St. Mary and John the Baptist" (Bugiardini)		55	50
728	$1.10, "Adoration of the Magi" (Di Fredi)		80	1·40
729	$3 "Madonna and Child with Young St. John the Baptist" (Bartolomeo)		1·25	3·75
726/9		Set of 4	2·75	5·50
MS730	112 × 81 mm. $5 "The Annunciation" (Botticelli)		2·75	6·00

Nos. 726/30 exist imperforate from stock dispersed by the liquidator of Format International Security Printers Ltd.

(Des J. Iskowitz. Litho Questa)

1986 (6 Jan). *Centenary of the Statue of Liberty (1st issue). Multicoloured designs as T* **211** *of Dominica. P* 15.

731	5 c. Croton Reservoir, New York (1875)		10	10
732	10 c. New York Public Library (1986)		10	10
733	70 c. Old Boathouse, Central Park (1894)		25	40
734	$4 Boating in Central Park (1986)		1·40	2·25
731/4		Set of 4	1·50	2·50
MS735	103 × 76 mm. $5 Statue of Liberty (*vert*)		2·50	3·50

See also Nos. 892/903.

(Litho Questa)

1986 (28 Jan). *Birth Bicentenary of John J. Audubon (ornithologist) (2nd issue). Horiz designs as T* **198** *of Antigua. Multicoloured. P* 12½ × 12.

736	50 c. Louisiana Heron		2·00	1·00
737	70 c. Black-crowned Night Heron		2·50	1·50
738	90 c. American Bittern		2·75	2·00
739	$4 Glossy Ibis		5·00	6·50
736/9		Set of 4	11·00	10·00
MS740	103 × 74 mm. $5 King Eider. P 14		6·50	8·50

Nos. 736/9 were each issued in sheetlets of five stamps and one stamp-size label, which appears in the centre of the bottom row.

1986 (20 Feb). *Visit of President Reagan of U.S.A. Nos.* 684A *and* 687A *optd with T* **84**.

741	70 c. *Philaethria dido*		1·50	1·25
742	$5 *Appias drusilla*		6·50	8·00

85 Two Footballers

86 *Hygrocybe firma*

(Des BG Studio. Litho Questa)

1986 (18 Mar). *World Cup Football Championship, Mexico. Vert designs as T* **85** *showing footballers. P* 14.

743	10 c. multicoloured		60	40
744	70 c. multicoloured		1·75	1·25
745	$1 multicoloured		2·00	1·75
746	$4 multicoloured		6·50	6·50
743/6		Set of 4	8·50	9·00
MS747	86 × 104 mm. $5 multicoloured		4·25	5·00

(Des W. Hanson. Litho Questa)

1986 (26 Mar). *Appearance of Halley's Comet (1st issue). Horiz designs as T* **123** *of Anguilla. Multicoloured. P* 14.

748	5 c. Nicholas Copernicus (astronomer) and Earl of Rosse's six foot reflector telescope		40	40
749	20 c. "Sputnik I" (first satellite) orbiting Earth, 1957		60	40
750	40 c. Tycho Brahe's notes and sketch of 1577 Comet		80	60
751	$4 Edmond Halley and 1682 Comet		3·75	4·50
748/51		Set of 4	5·00	5·50
MS752	101 × 70 mm. $5 Halley's Comet		3·00	3·50

The captions of Nos. 750/1 are transposed.
See also Nos. 790/4.

(Litho Questa)

1986 (21 Apr). *60th Birthday of Queen Elizabeth II. Vert designs as T* **125** *of Anguilla. P* 14.

753	2 c. black and yellow		10	15
754	$1.50, multicoloured		80	1·00
755	$4 multicoloured		2·00	2·75
753/5		Set of 3	2·50	3·50
MS756	120 × 85 mm. $5 black and grey-brown		2·00	3·50

Designs:—2 c. Princesses Elizabeth and Margaret, Windsor Park, 1933; $1.50, Queen Elizabeth; $4 In Sydney, Australia, 1970; $5 The Royal Family, Coronation Day, 1937.

(Des Walt Disney Productions. Litho Format)

1986 (22 May). *"Ameripex '86" International Stamp Exhibition, Chicago. Horiz designs as T* **212** *of Dominica showing Walt Disney cartoon characters. Multicoloured. P* 11.

757	30 c. Donald Duck riding mule in Grand Canyon		60	45
758	60 c. Daisy Duck, Timothy Mouse and Dumbo on Golden Gate Bridge, San Francisco		85	1·00
759	$1 Mickey Mouse and Goofy in fire engine and Chicago Watertower		1·50	1·75
760	$3 Mickey Mouse as airmail pilot and White House		3·00	4·00
757/60		Set of 4	5·50	6·50
MS761	126 × 101 mm. $5 Donald Duck and Mickey Mouse watching Halley's Comet over Statue of Liberty. P 14 × 13½		3·75	7·50

No. 757 exists imperforate from stock dispersed by the liquidator of Format International Security Printers Ltd.

(Litho Questa)

1986 (1 July). *Royal Wedding. Vert designs as T* **213** *of Antigua. Multicoloured. P* 14.

762	60 c. Prince Andrew and Miss Sarah Ferguson		55	45
763	70 c. Prince Andrew in car		65	55
764	$4 Prince Andrew with Westland WG-13 Lynx naval helicopter		2·75	3·50
762/4		Set of 3	3·50	4·00
MS765	88 × 88 mm. $5 Prince Andrew and Miss Sarah Ferguson (*different*)		4·00	5·50

(Des BG Studio. Litho Format)

1986 (15 July). *Mushrooms of the Lesser Antilles. T* **86** *and similar vert designs. Multicoloured. P* 15.

766	15 c. Type **86**		80	40
767	50 c. *Xerocomus coccolobae*		1·75	1·25
768	$2 *Volvariella cubensis*		3·50	4·00
769	$3 *Lactarius putidus*		4·50	5·00
766/9		Set of 4	9·50	9·50
MS770	76 × 80 mm. $5 *Leptonia caeruleocapitata*		9·00	12·00

No. MS770 exists imperforate from stock dispersed by the liquidator of Format International Security Printers Ltd.

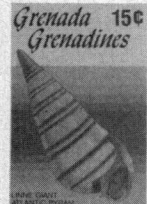

87 Giant Atlantic or Doldorate Pyram (*Pyramidella dolabrata*)

88 Common Opossum

(Des L. Birmingham. Litho Format)

1986 (1 Aug). *Sea Shells.* T **87** and similar multicoloured designs. P 15.

771	15 c. Type **87**		90	90
772	50 c. Beau's Murex (*Murex beauii*)		2·00	1·25
773	$1.10, West Indian Fighting Conch (*Strombus pugilis*)		2·50	2·75
774	$4 Alphabet Cone (*Conus spurius*)		4·75	7·00
771/4		*Set of 4*	9·00	10·50
MS775	109×75 mm. $5 Brown-lined Paper Bubble (*Hydatina vesicaria*)		6·00	8·00

1986 (15 Sept). *World Cup Football Championship Winners, Mexico.* Nos. 743/7 optd with T **216** of Antigua in gold.

776	85	10 c. multicoloured	55	40
777	–	70 c. multicoloured	1·25	1·10
778	–	$1 multicoloured	1·50	1·40
779	–	$4 multicoloured	4·00	5·50
776/9		*Set of 4*	6·50	7·50
MS780	86×104 mm. $5 multicoloured		8·00	10·00

(Des Dot and S. Barlowe. Litho Format)

1986 (15 Sept). *Wildlife.* T **88** and similar multicoloured designs. P 15.

781	10 c. Type **88**	20	20
782	30 c. Giant Toad	40	40
783	60 c. Land Tortoise (*Testudo denticulata*)	80	80
784	70 c. Murine Opossum (*vert*)	85	85
785	90 c. Burmese Mongoose (*vert*)	90	1·00
786	$1.10, Nine-banded Armadillo	1·00	1·25
787	$2 Agouti	1·75	2·25
788	$3 Humpback Whale	4·00	4·25
781/8	*Set of 8*	9·00	10·00
MS789	Two sheets, each 103×72 mm. (a) $5 Mona Monkey (*vert*) (b) $5 Iguana		
	Set of 2 sheets	11·00	14·00

Nos. 781/8 exist imperforate from stock dispersed by the liquidator of Format International Security Printers Ltd.

1986 (15 Oct). *Appearance of Halley's Comet* (2nd issue). Nos. 748/52 optd with T **218** of Antigua (in silver on 20 c., $4 and $5).

790	5 c. Nicholas Copernicus (astronomer) and Earl of Rosse's six foot reflector telescope		60	60
791	20 c. "Sputnik I" (first satellite) orbiting Earth, 1957		80	50
792	40 c. Tycho Brahe's notes and sketch of 1577 Comet		1·00	60
793	$4 Edmond Halley and 1682 Comet		5·00	6·00
790/3		*Set of 4*	6·50	7·00
MS794	102×70 mm. $5 Halley's Comet		4·00	5·50

(Des Walt Disney Co. Litho Format)

1986 (3 Nov). *Christmas.* Multicoloured designs as T **220** of Antigua showing Walt Disney cartoon characters. P 11.

795	25 c. Chip n'Dale with hummingbird		25	15
796	30 c. Robin delivering card to Mickey Mouse (*vert*)		25	20
797	50 c. Piglet, Pooh and Jose Carioca on beach		40	30
798	60 c. Grandma Duck feeding birds (*vert*)		50	40
799	70 c. Cinderella and birds with mistletoe (*vert*)		55	50
800	$1.50, Huey, Dewey and Louie windsurfing		1·25	2·00
801	$3 Mickey Mouse and Morty on beach with turtle		1·50	3·00
802	$4 Kittens playing on piano (*vert*)		2·00	3·50
795/802		*Set of 8*	6·00	9·00
MS803	Two sheets, each 127×102 mm. (a) $5 Mickey Mouse and Willie the Whale. P 14×13½. (b) $5 Bambi, Thumper and Blossom in snow (*vert*). P 13½×14	*Set of 2 sheets*	8·00	11·50

89 Cycling   90 Aston-Martin "Volanté" (1984)

(Des BG Studio. Litho Format)

1986 (18 Nov). *Olympic Games, Seoul, South Korea* (1988). T **89** and similar vert designs. Multicoloured. P 15.

804	10 c. + 5 c. Type **89**		50	40
805	50 c. + 20 c. Sailing		60	90
806	70 c. + 30 c. Gymnastics		75	1·00
807	$2 + $1 Horse trials		2·00	3·00
804/7		*Set of 4*	3·50	4·75
MS808	80×100 mm. $3 + $1 Marathon		2·50	4·50

The premiums on Nos. 804/8 were to support the participation of the Grenada team.

Nos. 804/8 exist imperforate from stock dispersed by the liquidator of Format International Security Printers Ltd.

(Des W. Wright. Litho Format)

1986 (20 Nov). *Centenary of Motoring.* T **90** and similar horiz designs. Multicoloured. P 15.

809	10 c. Type **90**		25	25
810	30 c. Jaguar "Mk V" (1948)		45	45
811	60 c. Nash "Ambassador" (1956)		60	65
812	70 c. Toyota "Supra" (1984)		60	70
813	90 c. Ferrari "Testarossa" (1985)		70	70
814	$1 BMW "501B" (1955)		70	95

815	$2 Mercedes-Benz "280 SL" (1968)		1·00	2·00
816	$3 Austro-Daimler "ADR8" (1932)		1·25	2·50
809/16		*Set of 8*	5·00	7·50
MS817	Two sheets, each 116 × 85 mm. (a) $5 Morgan "+8" (1977). (b) $5 Checker taxi			
		Set of 2 sheets	5·50	11·00

Nos. 809/16 exist imperforate from stock dispersed by the liquidator of Format International Security Printers Ltd.

(Litho Questa)

1986 (19 Dec). *Birth Centenary of Marc Chagall* (artist). Designs as T **225** of Antigua, showing various paintings. P 13½×14 (*vert*) or 14×13½ (*horiz*).

818/57	$1.10×40 multicoloured	*Set of 40*	28·00	28·00
MS858	Ten sheets, each 110×95 mm. $5×10 multicoloured (*each 104×89 mm*). Imperf			
		Set of 10 sheets	28·00	28·00

Although announced as all being released on 19 December 1986 the issue was distributed in ten parts, each of four stamps and one miniature sheet, at monthly intervals.

(Des J. Iskowitz. Litho Format)

1987 (5 Feb). *America's Cup Yachting Championship.* Multicoloured designs as T **222** of Antigua. P 15.

859	25 c. *Defender*, 1895		60	40
860	45 c. *Galatea*, 1886		80	60
861	70 c. *Azzurra*, 1981		1·00	1·00
862	$4 *Australia II*, 1983		2·00	3·50
859/62		*Set of 4*	4·00	5·00
MS863	113×83 mm. $5 *Columbia* defeating *Shamrock*, 1899 (*horiz*)		5·00	7·00

(Des Mary Walters. Litho Format)

1987 (27 Apr). *500th Anniv of Discovery of America by Columbus* (1992) (1st issue). Vert designs as T **322** of Grenada. Multicoloured. P 15.

864	15 c. Christopher Columbus		25	25
865	30 c. Queen Isabella of Castile		30	30
866	50 c. *Santa Maria*		45	50
867	60 c. Claiming the New World for Spain		50	60
868	90 c. Early Spanish map of Lesser Antilles		65	75
869	$1 King Ferdinand of Aragon		70	80
870	$2 Fort La Navidad (drawing by Columbus)		1·40	2·00
871	$3 Galley and Caribs, Hispaniola (drawing by Columbus)		1·90	2·50
864/71		*Set of 8*	5·50	7·00
MS872	Two sheets, 104×72 mm. (a) $5 Caribs pearl fishing. (b) $5 *Santa Maria* at anchor			
		Set of 2 sheets	7·00	11·00

See also Nos. 1191/5, 1224/32, 1366/74, 1494/1500 and 1519/20.

(Des W. Wright. Litho Questa)

1987 (18 May). *Milestones of Transportation.* Horiz designs as T **226** of Antigua. Multicoloured. P 15.

873	10 c. Saunders Roe "SR-N1" (first hovercraft), 1959		40	30
874	15 c. Bugatti "Royale" (largest car), 1931		50	35
875	30 c. Aleksei Leonov and "Voskhod II" (first spacewalk), 1965		65	55
876	50 c. C.S.S. *Hunley* (first submarine to sink enemy ship), 1864		85	75
877	60 c. Rolls Royce "Flying Bedstead" (first VTOL aircraft), 1954		95	85
878	70 c. *Jenny Lind* (first mass produced locomotive class), 1847		1·10	1·00
879	70 c. Duryea "Buggyaut" (first U.S. petrol-driven car), 1893		1·25	1·25
880	$1.50, Steam locomotive, Metropolitan Railway, London (first underground line), 1863		2·00	2·25
881	$2 S.S. *Great Britain* (first transatlantic crossing by screw-steamship), 1843		2·50	2·75
882	$3 "Budweiser Rocket" (fastest car), 1979		3·00	3·25
873/82		*Set of 10*	12·00	12·00

(Des Susan Barrasi. Litho Format)

1987 (15 June). "*Capex '87*" *International Stamp Exhibition, Toronto. Game Fishes.* Multicoloured designs as T **323** of Grenada, but horiz. P 15.

883	6 c. Yellow Chub		15	15
884	30 c. King Mackerel		40	30
885	50 c. Short-finned Mako		55	55
886	60 c. Dolphin (fish)		60	60
887	90 c. Skipjack Tuna ("Bonito")		75	75
888	$1.10, Cobia		1·00	1·25
889	$3 Tarpon		2·25	2·75
890	$4 Swordfish		2·50	3·25
883/90		*Set of 8*	7·50	8·75
MS891	Two sheets, each 100×70 mm. (a) $5 Spotted Jewfish. (b) $5 Amberjack	*Set of 2 sheets*	8·00	11·00

(Litho Questa)

1987 (5 Aug). *Centenary of Statue of Liberty* (1986) (2nd issue). Multicoloured designs as T **227** of Antigua. P 14.

892	10 c. Cleaning face of Statue		20	20
893	15 c. Commemorative lapel badges		30	30
894	25 c. Band playing and Statue		40	40
895	30 c. Band on parade and Statue		45	45
896	45 c. Face of Statue		50	50
897	50 c. Cleaning head of Statue (*horiz*)		55	55
898	60 c. Models of Statue (*horiz*)		65	60
899	70 c. Small boat flotilla (*horiz*)		75	85
900	$1 Unveiling ceremony		85	90
901	$1.10, Statue and Manhattan skyline		90	1·00
902	$2 Parade of warships		1·75	2·00
903	$3 Making commemorative flags		1·90	2·25
892/903		*Set of 12*	8·25	9·00

(Litho Questa)

1987 (9 Sept). *Great Scientific Discoveries.* Horiz designs as T **325** of Grenada. Multicoloured. P 14.

904	60 c. Newton medal		85	80
905	$1 Louis Daguerre (inventor of daguerreotype)		1·25	1·00

906	$2 Antoine Lavoisier and apparatus		2·25	2·75
907	$3 Rudolf Diesel and first oil engine		4·50	4·50
904/7		*Set of 4*	8·00	8·50
MS908	105×75 mm. $5 Halley's Comet		6·00	7·50

No. 907 is inscribed "JAMES WATT" in error.

(Litho Questa)

1987 (1 Nov). *Bicentenary of U.S. Constitution.* Multicoloured designs as T **232** of Antigua. P 14.

909	10 c. Washington addressing delegates, Constitutional Convention		25	20
910	50 c. Flag and State Seal, Georgia		85	75
911	60 c. Capitol, Washington (*vert*)		85	80
912	$4 Thomas Jefferson (statesman) (*vert*)		3·75	5·50
909/12		*Set of 4*	5·25	6·50
MS913	105×75 mm. $5 Alexander Hamilton (New York delegate) (*vert*)		3·00	4·00

Nos. 909/12 were each issued in sheetlets of five stamps and one stamp-size label, which appears in the centre of the bottom row.

(Des Walt Disney Co. Litho Questa)

1987 (16 Nov). "*Hafnia '87*" *International Stamp Exhibition, Copenhagen.* Designs as T **328** of Grenada, but horiz, illustrating Hans Christian Andersen's fairy tales. Multicoloured. P 14×13½.

914	25 c. Donald and Daisy Duck in "The Swineherd"		50	30
915	30 c. Mickey Mouse, Donald and Daisy Duck in "What the Good Man Does is Always Right"		55	35
916	50 c. Mickey and Minnie Mouse in "Little Tuk"		75	75
917	60 c. Minnie Mouse and Ferdie in "The World's Fairest Rose"		75	75
918	70 c. Mickey Mouse in "The Garden of Paradise"		80	80
919	$1.50, Goofy and Mickey Mouse in "The Naughty Boy"		2·00	2·25
920	$3 Goofy in "What the Moon Saw"		2·75	3·00
921	$4 Alice as "Thumbelina"		3·25	3·50
914/21		*Set of 8*	10·00	10·50
MS922	Two sheets, each 127×101 mm. (a) $5 Daisy Duck in "Hans Clodhopper". (b) $5 Aunt Matilda and Mickey Mouse in "Elder-Tree Mother"	*Set of 2 sheets*	11·00	12·00

91 "The Virgin and Child with Saints Martin and Agnes"   92 Scout signalling with Semaphore Flags

(Litho Questa)

1987 (15 Dec). *Christmas. Religious Paintings by El Greco.* T **91** and similar vert designs. Multicoloured. P 14.

923	10 c. Type **91**		40	15
924	50 c. "St. Agnes" (detail from "The Virgin and Child with Saints Martin and Agnes")		1·25	75
925	60 c. "The Annunciation"		1·25	75
926	$4 "The Holy Family with St. Anne"		4·75	7·25
923/6		*Set of 4*	7·00	8·00
MS927	75×101 mm. $5 "The Adoration of the Shepherds"		7·50	8·50

(Des and litho Questa)

1988 (15 Feb). *Royal Ruby Wedding.* Vert designs as T **234** of Antigua. Multicoloured. P 14.

928	20 c. deep brown, black and light green		35	15
929	30 c. deep brown and black		40	20
930	$2 multicoloured		2·00	2·50
931	$3 multicoloured		2·50	3·25
928/31		*Set of 4*	4·75	5·50
MS932	76×100 mm. $5 multicoloured		3·50	4·50

Designs:—20 c. Queen Elizabeth II with Princess Anne, c. 1957; 30 c. Wedding photograph, 1947; $2 Queen with Prince Charles and Princess Anne, c. 1955; $3 Queen Elizabeth (from photo by Tim Graham), 1980; $5 Princess Elizabeth in wedding dress, 1947.

(Des Walt Disney Company. Litho Questa)

1988 (13 Apr). *Olympic Games, Seoul.* Multicoloured designs as T **331** of Grenada, showing Walt Disney cartoon characters as Olympic competitors. P 14×13½.

933	1 c. Minnie Mouse as rhythmic gymnast (*horiz*)		10	10
934	2 c. Pete and Goofy as pankration wrestlers (*horiz*)		10	10
935	3 c. Huey and Dewey as synchronized swimmers (*horiz*)		10	10
936	4 c. Huey, Dewey and Louey in hoplite race (*horiz*)		10	10
937	5 c. Clarabelle and Daisy Duck playing baseball (*horiz*)		10	10
938	10 c. Goofy and Donald Duck in horse race (*horiz*)		10	10
939	$6 Donald Duck and Uncle Scrooge McDuck windsurfing (*horiz*)		4·50	5·50
940	$7 Mickey Mouse in chariot race (*horiz*)		4·75	5·50
933/40		*Set of 8*	9·00	10·00
MS941	Two sheets, each 127×101 mm. (a) $5 Mickey Mouse throwing discus in pentathlon. (b) $5 Donald Duck playing tennis. P 13½×14	*Set of 2 sheets*	7·50	9·00

(Des J. Martin. Litho Questa)

1988 (3 May). *World Scout Jamboree, Australia.* T **92** *and similar multicoloured designs.* P 14.

942	15 c. Type **92**	50	35
943	70 c. Canoeing	60	50
944	$1 Cooking over campfire (*horiz*)	70	65
945	$3 Scouts around campfire (*horiz*)	2·00	3·00
942/5	*Set of* 4	3·50	4·00
MS946	110×77 mm. $5 Erecting tent (*horiz*)	3·50	4·50

(Des Mary Walters. Litho Questa)

1988 (31 May). *Birds. Designs as* T **334** *of Grenada, but horiz. Multicoloured.* P 14.

947	20 c. Yellow-crowned Night Heron	30	25
948	25 c. Brown Pelican	30	25
949	45 c. Audubon's Shearwater	40	35
950	60 c. Red-footed Booby	50	45
951	70 c. Bridled Tern	55	50
952	90 c. Red-billed Tropic Bird	70	70
953	$3 Blue-winged Teal	1·75	2·25
954	$4 Sora	2·00	2·75
947/54	*Set of* 8	6·00	6·75
MS955	Two sheets, each 105×75 mm. (a) $5 Purple-throated Carib. (b) $5 Little Blue Heron		
	Set of 2 *sheets*	4·75	6·50

(Litho Questa)

1988 (15 June). *500th Birth Anniv of Titian (artist). Vert designs as* T **238** *of Antigua. Multicoloured.* P 13½×14.

956	15 c. "Man with Blue Eyes"	15	15
957	30 c. "The Three Ages of Man" (detail)	20	20
958	60 c. "Don Diego Mendoza"	35	35
959	75 c. "Emperor Charles V seated"	50	50
960	$1 "A Young Man in a Fur"	60	60
961	$2 "Tobias and the Angel"	1·10	1·40
962	$3 "Pietro Bembo"	1·60	1·90
963	$4 "Pier Luigi Farnese"	1·75	2·25
956/63	*Set of* 8	5·50	6·50
MS964	110×95 mm. (a) $5 "Sacred and Profane Love" (detail). (b) $5 "Venus and Adonis" (detail)		
	Set of 2 *sheets*	7·00	8·00

(Des W. Hanson. Litho Questa)

1988 (1 July). *Airships. Multicoloured designs as* T **336** *of Grenada.* P 14.

965	10 c. LZ-129 *Hindenburg* over Sugarloaf Mountain, Rio de Janeiro, 1937 (*horiz*)	35	20
966	20 c. LZ-129 *Hindenburg* over New York, 1937 (*horiz*)	45	30
967	30 c. U.S. Navy "K" Class airships on Atlantic escort duty, 1944 (*horiz*)	50	35
968	40 c. LZ-129 *Hindenburg* approaching Lakehurst, 1937	60	45
969	60 c. LZ-127 *Graf Zeppelin* and LZ-129 *Hindenburg* over Germany, 1936	75	60
970	70 c. LZ-129 *Hindenburg* and ZR-3 *Los Angeles* moored at Lakehurst, 1936 (*horiz*)	75	70
971	$1 LZ-130 *Graf Zeppelin II* over Dover, 1939	80	85
972	$2 LZ-8 *Ersatz Deutschland* on scheduled passenger flight, 1912 (*horiz*)	1·40	1·60
973	$3 LZ-127 *Graf Zeppelin* over Dome of the Rock, Jerusalem, 1931 (*horiz*)	1·90	2·25
974	$4 LZ-129 *Hindenburg* over Olympic stadium, Berlin, 1936 (*horiz*)	2·00	2·25
965/74	*Set of* 10	8·50	8·50
MS975	Two sheets (a) 76×95 mm. $5 LZ-127 *Graf Zeppelin*, 1933. (b) 95×76 mm. $5 LZ-127 *Graf Zeppelin*, 1931 (*horiz*) . *Set of* 2 *sheets*	8·00	10·00

93 Bambi and his Mother

(Des Walt Disney Co. Litho Questa)

1988 (25 July). *Disney Animal Cartoon Films.* T **93** *and similar designs.* P 14×13½.

976/1029	30 c.×54 multicoloured *Set of* 54	15·00	15·00
MS1030	Six sheets, each 127×102 mm. $5×6 multicoloured. P 14×13½ (*horiz*) or 13½×14 (*vert*) *Set of* 6 *sheets*	28·00	30·00

Nos. 976/1029 (issued as six sheetlets each of nine different designs) and No. **MS**1030 depict scenes from *Bambi, Dumbo* ($5 vert), *Lady and The Tramp* ($5 vert), *The Aristocats, The Fox and the Hound* and *101 Dalmatians*.

(Des Walt Disney Co. Litho Questa)

1988 (1 Aug). *"Sydpex '88" National Stamp Exhibition, Sydney and 60th Birthday of Mickey Mouse. Horiz designs as* T **337** *of Grenada. Multicoloured.* P 14×13½.

1031	1 c. Mickey Mouse conducting at Sydney Opera House	10	10
1032	2 c. Mickey Mouse and Donald Duck at Ayers Rock	10	10
1033	3 c. Goofy and Mickey Mouse on sheep station	10	10
1034	4 c. Goofy and Mickey Mouse at Lone Pine Koala Sanctuary	10	10
1035	5 c. Mickey Mouse, Donald Duck and Goofy playing Australian football	10	10
1036	10 c. Mickey Mouse and Goofy camel racing	10	10
1037	$5 Donald Duck and his nephews bowling	4·50	5·00

1038	$6 Mickey Mouse with America's Cup trophy and *Australia II* (yacht)	5·50	6·00
1031/8	*Set of* 8	9·50	10·50
MS1039	Two sheets, each 127×102 mm. (a) $5 Goofy diving on Great Barrier Reef. (b) $5 Donald Duck, Mickey and Minnie Mouse at beach barbecue . *Set of* 2 *sheets*	7·50	9·50

(Des W. Wright. Litho Questa)

1988 (30 Sept). *Flowering Trees and Shrubs. Multicoloured designs as* T **339** *of Grenada.* P 14.

1040	10 c. Potato Tree (*vert*)	15	15
1041	20 c. Wild Cotton	15	15
1042	30 c. Shower of Gold (*vert*)	20	20
1043	60 c. Napoleon's Button (*vert*)	35	30
1044	90 c. Geiger Tree (*vert*)	60	70
1045	$1 Fern Tree	70	80
1046	$2 French Cashew	1·25	2·00
1047	$4 Amherstia (*vert*)	2·00	3·00
1040/7	*Set of* 8	5·00	6·50
MS1048	Two sheets, each 117×88 mm. (a) $5 African Tulip Tree (*vert*). (b) $5 Swamp Immortelle . *Set of* 2 *sheets*	4·25	5·50

(Des W. Wright. Litho B.D.T.)

1988 (7 Oct). *Cars. Vert designs as* T **335** *of Grenada. Multicoloured.* P 13.

1049	$2 Doble "Series E", 1925	1·25	1·25
	a. Sheetlet. Nos. 1049/58	11·00	
1050	$2 Alvis "12/50", 1926	1·25	1·25
1051	$2 Sunbeam 3-litre, 1927	1·25	1·25
1052	$2 Franklin "Airman", 1928	1·25	1·25
1053	$2 Delage "D8S", 1929	1·25	1·25
1054	$2 Mors, 1897	1·25	1·25
1055	$2 Peerless "Green Dragon", 1904	1·25	1·25
1056	$2 Pope-Hartford, 1909	1·25	1·25
1057	$2 Daniels "Submarine Speedster", 1920	1·25	1·25
1058	$2 McFarlan 9.3 litre, 1922	1·25	1·25
1059	$2 Frazer Nash "Lemans" replica, 1949	1·25	1·25
	a. Sheetlet. Nos. 1059/68	11·00	
1060	$2 Pegaso "Z102", 1953	1·25	1·25
1061	$2 Siata "Spyder V-8", 1953	1·25	1·25
1062	$2 Kurtis-Offenhauser, 1953	1·25	1·25
1063	$2 Kaiser-Darrin, 1954	1·25	1·25
1064	$2 Tracta, 1930	1·25	1·25
1065	$2 Maybach "Zeppelin", 1932	1·25	1·25
1066	$2 Railton "Light Sports", 1934	1·25	1·25
1067	$2 Hotchkiss, 1936	1·25	1·25
1068	$2 Mercedes-Benz "W163", 1939	1·25	1·25
1069	$2 Aston Martin "Vantage V8", 1982	1·25	1·25
	a. Sheetlet. Nos. 1069/78	11·00	
1070	$2 Porsche "956", 1982	1·25	1·25
1071	$2 Lotus "Esprit Turbo", 1983	1·25	1·25
1072	$2 McLaren "MP4/2", 1984	1·25	1·25
1073	$2 Mercedes-Benz "190E 2.3-16", 1985	1·25	1·25
1074	$2 Ferrari "250 GT Lusso", 1963	1·25	1·25
1075	$2 Porsche "904", 1964	1·25	1·25
1076	$2 Volvo "P1800", 1967	1·25	1·25
1077	$2 McLaren-Chevrolet "M8D", 1970	1·25	1·25
1078	$2 Jaguar "XJ6", 1981	1·25	1·25
1049/78	*Set of* 30	32·00	32·00

Nos. 1049/58, 1059/68 and 1069/78 were each printed together, *se-tenant*, in sheetlets of 10.

(Des Walt Disney Co. Litho Questa)

1988 (1 Dec). *"Mickey's Christmas Parade". Multicoloured designs as* T **246** *of Antigua showing Walt Disney cartoon characters.* P 13½×14.

1079	$1 Dumbo	65	65
	a. Sheetlet. Nos. 1079/86	4·75	
1080	$1 Goofy as Father Christmas	65	65
1081	$1 Minnie Mouse waving from window	65	65
1082	$1 Clarabelle, Mordie and Ferdie watching parade	65	65
1083	$1 Donald Duck's nephews	65	65
1084	$1 Donald Duck as drummer	65	65
1085	$1 Toy soldiers	65	65
1086	$1 Mickey Mouse on wooden horse	65	65
1079/86	*Set of* 8	4·75	4·75
MS1087	Two sheets, each 127 × 102 mm. (a) $7 Peter Pan and Captain Hook on float (*horiz*). (b) $7 Mickey Mouse as Father Christmas and Donald Duck in carnival train (*horiz*). P 14 × 13½ . *Set of* 2 *sheets*	10·00	11·00

94 Middleweight Boxing (Gold, Henry Maske, East Germany)

95 Launch of "Apollo 11"

(Des L. Fried. Litho B.D.T.)

1989 (13 Apr). *Olympic Medal Winners, Seoul (1988).* T **94** *and similar horiz designs. Multicoloured.* P 14.

1088	15 c. Type **94**	30	20
1089	50 c. Freestyle wrestling (130 kg) (Bronze, Andreas Schroeder, East Germany)	50	40
1090	60 c. Women's team gymnastics (Bronze, East Germany)	60	50
1091	75 c. Platform diving (Gold, Greg Louganis, U.S.A.)	70	60
1092	$1 Freestyle wrestling (52 kg) (Gold, Mitsuru Sato, Japan)	80	80
1093	$2 Men's freestyle 4×200 metres relay swimming (Bronze, West Germany)	1·25	1·75
1094	$3 Men's 5000 metres (Silver, Dieter Baumann, West Germany)	1·60	2·00

1095	$4 Women's heptathlon (Gold, Jackie Joyner-Kersee, U.S.A.)	2·00	2·50
1088/95	*Set of* 8	7·00	8·00
MS1096	Two sheets, each 70×100 mm. (a) $6 Weightlifting (67.5 kg) (Gold, Joachim Kunz, East Germany). (b) $6 Team Three-Day Event (Gold, West Germany) . *Set of* 2 *sheets*	6·50	8·50

(Litho Questa)

1989 (15 May). *Japanese Art. Paintings by Hiroshige. Horiz designs as* T **250** *of Antigua. Multicoloured.* P 14×13½.

1097	15 c. "Crossing the Oi at Shimada by Ferry"	25	25
1098	20 c. "Daimyo and Entourage at Arai"	30	30
1099	45 c. "Cargo Portage through Goyu"	50	50
1100	75 c. "Snowfall at Fujigawa"	75	75
1101	$1 "Horses for the Emperor at Chirifu"	85	85
1102	$2 "Rainfall at Tsuchiyama"	1·60	1·60
1103	$3 "An Inn at Ishibe"	2·25	2·25
1104	$4 "On the Shore of Lake Biwa at Otsu"	2·75	2·75
1097/104	*Set of* 8	8·25	8·25
MS1105	Two sheets, each 102×78 mm. (a) $5 "Fishing Village of Yokkaichi on the Mie". (b) $5 "Pilgrimage to Atsuta Shrine at Miya" . *Set of* 2 *sheets*	4·75	7·00

Nos. 1097/104 were each printed in sheetlets of 10 containing two horizontal strips of 5 stamps separated by printed labels commemorating Emperor Hirohito.

(Des D. Bruckner. Litho B.D.T.)

1989 (12 June). *World Cup Football Championship, Italy (1990) (1st issue). Multicoloured designs as* T **252** *of Antigua.* P 14.

1106	15 c. World Cup trophy	50	20
1107	20 c. Flags of Argentina (winners 1986) and International Federation of Football Associations (F.I.F.A.) (*horiz*)	50	20
1108	45 c. Franz Beckenbauer (West Germany) with World Cup, 1974	70	35
1109	75 c. Flags of Italy (winners 1982) and F.I.F.A. (*horiz*)	85	55
1110	$1 Péle (Brazil) with Jules Rimet trophy	1·00	85
1111	$2 Flags of West Germany (winners 1974) and F.I.F.A. (*horiz*)	1·60	2·00
1112	$3 Flags of Brazil (winners 1970) and F.I.F.A. (*horiz*)	1·90	2·75
1113	$4 Jules Rimet trophy and Brazil players	2·00	2·75
1106/13	*Set of* 8	8·00	8·75
MS1114	(a) 100×81 mm. $6 Goalkeeper (*horiz*). (b) 66×95 mm. $6 Péle with Jules Rimet trophy . *Set of* 2 *sheets*	8·00	9·00

See also Nos. 1285/9.

(Des W. Wright. Litho B.D.T.)

1989 (28 June). *North American Railway Locomotives. Vert designs as* T **342** *of Grenada. Multicoloured.* P 13.

1115	$2 Morris & Essex Railroad *Dover*, 1841, U.S.A.	1·50	1·50
	a. Sheetlet. Nos. 1115/24	13·00	
1116	$2 Baltimore & Ohio Railroad No. 57 *Memnon*, 1848, U.S.A.	1·50	1·50
1117	$2 Camden & Amboy Railroad *John Stevens*, 1849, U.S.A.	1·50	1·50
1118	$2 Lawrence Machine Shop *Lawrence*, 1853, U.S.A.	1·50	1·50
1119	$2 South Carolina Railroad *James S. Corry*, 1859, U.S.A.	1·50	1·50
1120	$2 Mine Hill & Schuylkill Haven Railroad flexible beam No. 3, 1860, U.S.A.	1·50	1·50
1121	$2 Delaware, Lackawanna & Western Railroad *Montrose*, 1861, U.S.A.	1·50	1·50
1122	$2 Central Pacific Railroad No. 68 *Pequop*, 1868, U.S.A.	1·50	1·50
1123	$2 Boston & Providence Railroad *Daniel Nason*, 1863, U.S.A.	1·50	1·50
1124	$2 Morris & Essex Railroad *Joe Scranton*, 1870, U.S.A.	1·50	1·50
1125	$2 Central Railroad of New Jersey No. 124, 1871, U.S.A.	1·50	1·50
	a. Sheetlet. Nos. 1125/34	13·00	
1126	$2 Baldwin tramway steam locomotive, 1876, U.S.A.	1·50	1·50
1127	$2 Lackawanna & Bloomsburg Railroad *Luzerne*, 1878, U.S.A.	1·50	1·50
1128	$2 Central Mexican Railroad No. 150, 1892	1·50	1·50
1129	$2 Denver, South Park & Pacific Railroad No. 15 *Breckenridge*, 1879, U.S.A.	1·50	1·50
1130	$2 Miles Planting & Manufacturing Company plantation locomotive *Daisy*, 1894, U.S.A.	1·50	1·50
1131	$2 Central of Georgia Railroad Baldwin 854 No. 1136, 1895, U.S.A.	1·50	1·50
1132	$2 Savannah, Florida & Western Railroad No. 111, 1900, U.S.A.	1·50	1·50
1133	$2 Douglas, Gilmore & Company contractors locomotive No. 3, 1902, U.S.A.	1·50	1·50
1134	$2 Lehigh Valley Coal Company compressed-air locomotive No. 900, 1903, U.S.A.	1·50	1·50
1135	$2 Louisiana & Texas Railroad McKeen motor locomotive, 1908, U.S.A.	1·50	1·50
	a. Sheetlet. Nos. 1135/44	13·00	
1136	$2 Clear Lake Lumber Company Type B Climax locomotive No. 6, 1910, U.S.A.	1·50	1·50
1137	$2 Blue Jay Lumber Company Heisler locomotive No. 10, 1912, U.S.A.	1·50	1·50
1138	$2 Stewartstown Railroad petrol locomotive No. 6, 1920s, U.S.A.	1·50	1·50
1139	$2 Bangor & Aroostock Railroad Class G No. 186, 1921, U.S.A.	1·50	1·50
1140	$2 Hammond Lumber Company Mallet locomotive No. 6, 1923, U.S.A.	1·50	1·50
1141	$2 Central Railway of New Jersey diesel locomotive No. 1000, 1925, U.S.A.	1·50	1·50
1142	$2 Atchison Topeka & Santa Fe Railroad "Super Chief" diesel express, 1935, U.S.A.	1·50	1·50
1143	$2 Norfolk & Western Railroad Class Y-6, 1948, U.S.A.	1·50	1·50

1144 $2 Boston & Maine Railroad Budd diesel
 railcar, 1949, U.S.A. .. .. 1·50 1·50
1115/44 .. .. .. *Set of 30* 38·00 38·00
Nos. 1115/24, 1125/34 and 1135/44 were each printed
together, *se-tenant*, in sheetlets of 10.

(Des Walt Disney Co. Litho Questa)

1989 (7 July). *"Philexfrance 89" International Stamp
Exhibition, Paris. Multicoloured designs as T **251** of Antigua
showing Walt Disney cartoon characters in Paris. P 14×13½
(horiz) or 13½×14 (vert).*
1145 1 c. Mickey Mouse and Donald Duck at
 Ecole Militaire inflating balloon .. 10 10
1146 2 c. Mickey and Minnie Mouse on river
 boat passing Conciergerie .. 10 10
1147 3 c. Mickey Mouse at Hotel de Ville (*vert*) 10 10
1148 4 c. Mickey Mouse at Genie of the Bastille
 monument (*vert*) 10 10
1149 5 c. Mickey and Minnie Mouse arriving at
 Opera House 10 10
1150 10 c. Mickey and Minnie Mouse on tandem
 in Luxembourg Gardens 10 10
1151 $5 Mickey Mouse in aeroplane over
 L'Arch de la Defense (*vert*) .. 5·50 6·50
1152 $6 Mickey Mouse at Place Vendome
 (*vert*) .. .. 5·50 6·50
1145/52 .. .. .. *Set of 8* 10·00 12·00
MS1153 Two sheets, each 127×102 mm. (a) $6
Mickey and Minnie Mouse on scooter in Place de
la Concorde. (b) $6 Donald Duck, Mickey and
Minnie Mouse in balloon over Versailles.
P 14×13½ .. .. .. *Set of 2 sheets* 11·00 13·00

(Des L. Birmingham. Litho Questa)

1989 (20 July). *20th Anniv of First Manned Landing on Moon.
T **95** and similar multicoloured designs. P 14.*
1154 25 c. Type **95** 30 30
1155 50 c. Splashdown (*horiz*) 50 50
1156 60 c. Modules in space 60 60
1157 75 c. Aldrin setting up experiment (*horiz*) 70 70
1158 $1 "Apollo 11" leaving Earth orbit (*horiz*) 80 80
1159 $2 Moving "Apollo 11" to launch site .. 1·60 1·90
1160 $3 Lunar module *Eagle* leaving Moon
 (*horiz*) .. .. 2·00 2·50
1161 $4 *Eagle* landing on Moon .. .. 2·25 2·75
1154/61 .. .. .. *Set of 8* 8·00 9·00
MS1162 (a) 71×100 mm. $5 Armstrong stepping
onto Moon. (b) 101×72 mm. $5 Armstrong's
footprint on Moon .. .. *Set of 2 sheets* 6·50 8·00

(Des J. Cooter. Litho B.D.T.)

1989 (17 Aug). *Fungi. Vert designs as T **348** of Grenada.
Multicoloured. P 14.*
1163 6 c. *Agaricus purpurellus* (incorrectly
 inscr *Collybia aurea*) 35 25
1164 10 c. *Podaxis pistillaris* 35 25
1165 20 c. *Hygrocybe firma* 55 45
1166 30 c. *Agaricus rufoaurantiacus* .. 65 55
1167 75 c. *Leptonia howellii* .. .. 1·40 1·40
1168 $2 *Marasmiellus purpureus* .. .. 2·50 2·75
1169 $3 *Marasmius trinitatis* .. .. 3·00 3·25
1170 $4 *Collybia aurea* (incorrectly inscr
 Hygrocybe martinicensis) .. .. 3·25 3·50
1163/70 .. .. .. *Set of 8* 11·00 11·00
MS1171 Two sheets, each 56×71 mm. (a) $6
Lentinus crinitus (incorrectly inscr *Agaricus
purpurellus*). (b) $6 *Hygrocybe martinicensis*
(incorrectly inscr *Lentinus crinitus*)
 .. .. .. *Set of 2 sheets* 12·00 13·00

(Des Deborah Dudley Max. Litho B.D.T.)

1989 (2 Oct). *Butterflies. Horiz designs as T **350** of Grenada.
Multicoloured. P 14.*
1172 25 c. *Battus polydamas* (inscr "*Papilio
 androgeus*") 40 40
1173 35 c. *Phoebis sennae* 45 45
1174 45 c. *Hamadryas feronia* 55 55
1175 50 c. *Cynthia cardui* 55 55
1176 75 c. *Ascia monuste* 80 80
1177 90 c. *Eurema lisa* 90 90
1178 $2 *Aphrissa statira* .. .. 2·00 2·00
1179 $3 *Hypolimnas misippus* .. .. 2·50 2·50
1172/9 .. .. .. *Set of 8* 7·50 7·50
MS1180 Two sheets, each 87×115 mm. (a) $6
Anartia amathea. (b) $6 *Pseudolycaena marsyas*
 .. .. .. *Set of 2 sheets* 9·00 11·00

96 Ethel Barrymore 97 Buddy Holly

(Des J. Genzo. Litho B.D.T.)

1989 (9 Oct). *425th Birth Anniv of Shakespeare.
Shakespearean Actors. T **96** and similar horiz designs.
Multicoloured. P 14.*
1181 15 c. Type **96** 35 25
1182 $1.10, Richard Burton .. .. 1·50 1·25
1183 $2 John Barrymore .. .. 2·25 2·25
1184 $3 Paul Robeson .. .. .. 2·50 2·75
1181/4 .. .. .. *Set of 4* 6·00 6·00
MS1185 103×77 mm. $6 Bando Tamasaburo and
Nakamura Kanzaburo .. .. .. 4·50 5·50

(Des J. Genzo. Litho B.D.T.)

1989 (9 Oct). *Musicians. T **97** and similar vert designs.
Multicoloured. P 14.*
1186 10 c. Type **97** 35 25
1187 25 c. Jimmy Hendrix 55 40
1188 75 c. Mighty Sparrow 70 70
1189 $4 Katsutoji Kineya .. .. 3·00 4·00
1186/9 .. .. .. *Set of 4* 4·25 4·75
MS1190 103×77 mm. $6 Kurt Weill .. 4·25 4·75

(Des D. Miller. Litho Questa)

1989 (16 Oct). *500th Anniv of Discovery of America by
Columbus (1992) (2nd issue). Pre-Columbian Arawak Society.
Vert designs as T **247** of Antigua. Multicoloured. P 14.*
1191 15 c. Arawaks canoeing 25 25
1192 75 c. Family and campfire 75 75
1193 90 c. Using stone tools 95 95
1194 $3 Eating and drinking .. .. 2·50 3·00
1191/4 .. .. .. *Set of 4* 4·00 4·50
MS1195 84×87 mm. $6 Making fire .. 3·50 4·25

(Des Walt Disney Co. Litho Questa)

1989 (17 Nov). *"World Stamp Expo '89" International Stamp
Exhibition, Washington. Multicoloured designs as T **352** of
Grenada showing Walt Disney cartoon characters illustrating
proverbs from Poor Richard's Almanack. P 14×13½.*
1196 1 c. Scrooge McDuck with gold coins in
 sinking boat 10 10
1197 2 c. Robin Hood shooting apple off Friar
 Tuck 10 10
1198 3 c. Winnie the Pooh with honey .. 10 10
1199 4 c. Goofy, Minnie Mouse and Donald
 Duck exercising 10 10
1200 5 c. Pinnochio holding Jimminy Cricket .. 10 10
1201 6 c. Huey and Dewey putting up
 wallpaper 10 10
1202 8 c. Mickey Mouse asleep in storm .. 15 10
1203 10 c. Mickey Mouse as Benjamin Franklin
 selling *Pennsylvania Gazette* .. 15 10
1204 $5 Mickey Mouse with chicken, recipe
 book and egg .. .. .. 4·00 5·00
1205 $6 Mickey Mouse missing carriage .. 4·50 5·00
1196/1205 .. .. .. *Set of 10* 8·50 9·50
MS1206 Two sheets, each 127×102 mm. (a) $6
Mickey Mouse bowing. P 14×13½. (b) $6 Mickey
Mouse delivering basket of food (*vert*).
P 13½×14 .. .. .. *Set of 2 sheets* 10·50 11·00

(Litho Questa)

1990 (4 Jan). *Christmas. Paintings by Rubens. Vert designs as
T **259** of Antigua. Multicoloured. P 14.*
1207 10 c. "The Annunciation" 35 15
1208 15 c. "The Flight of the Holy Family into
 Egypt" 40 15
1209 25 c. "The Presentation in the Temple" .. 55 15
1210 45 c. "The Holy Family under the Apple
 Tree" 70 25
1211 $2 "Madonna and Child with Saints" .. 2·00 2·50
1212 $4 "The Virgin and Child enthroned with
 Saints" .. .. 3·00 4·00
1213 $5 "The Holy Family" .. .. 3·00 4·00
1207/13 .. .. .. *Set of 7* 9·00 10·00
MS1214 Two sheets, each 70×95 mm. (a) $5
"The Adoration of the Magi" (sketch). (b) $5 "The
Adoration of the Magi" .. .. *Set of 2 sheets* 11·00 13·00

(Des L. Nelson. Litho Questa)

1990 (6 Mar). *"EXPO 90" International Garden and Greenery
Exhibition, Osaka. Caribbean Orchids. Vert designs as T **354**
of Grenada. Multicoloured. P 14.*
1215 15 c. *Brassocattleya* Thalie 30 30
1216 20 c. *Odontocidium* Tigersun .. 35 35
1217 50 c. *Odontioda* Hambuhren .. 55 55
1218 75 c. *Paphiopedilum* Delrosi .. 75 75
1219 $1 *Vuylstekeara* Yokara 95 95
1220 $2 *Paphiopedilum* Geelong .. 1·75 2·00
1221 $3 *Wilsonara* Tigerwood .. .. 2·00 2·25
1222 $4 *Cymbidium* Ormoulu .. .. 2·50 2·75
1215/22 .. .. .. *Set of 8* 8·25 9·00
MS1223 Two sheets, each 98×68 mm. (a) $6
Odontonia Sappho. (b) $6 *Cymbidium* Vieux
Rose .. .. .. *Set of 2 sheets* 11·00 11·50

(Des Mary Walters. Litho Questa)

1990 (16 Mar). *500th Anniv of Discovery of America by
Columbus (1992) (3rd issue). New World Natural History –
Insects. Designs as T **260** of Antigua, but horiz. Multicoloured.
P 14.*
1224 35 c. *Dynastes hercules* (beetle) .. 35 35
1225 40 c. *Chalcolepidius porcatus* (beetle) .. 35 35
1226 50 c. *Acrocinus longimanus* (beetle) .. 40 40
1227 60 c. *Battus polydamas* (butterfly) .. 75 75
1228 $1 *Orthemis ferruginea* (skimmer) .. 95 95
1229 $2 *Psiloptera variolosa* (beetle) .. 1·60 1·75
1230 $3 *Hypolimnas misippus* (butterfly) .. 2·50 2·75
1231 $4 Scarab Beetle .. .. .. 2·50 2·75
1224/31 .. .. .. *Set of 8* 8·50 9·00
MS1232 Two sheets, each 102×70 mm. (a) $6
Calpodes ethlius (butterfly). (b) $6 *Danaus
plexippus* (butterfly) .. .. *Set of 2 sheets* 8·50 9·50

(Des J. Barbaris. Litho B.D.T.)

1990 (3 Apr). *Wildlife. Horiz designs as T **254** of Antigua.
Multicoloured. P 14.*
1233 5 c. West Indies Giant Rice Rat .. 20 20
1234 25 c. Agouti 35 35
1235 30 c. Humpback Whale 70 65
1236 40 c. Pilot Whale 70 65
1237 $1 Spotted Dolphin 95 95
1238 $2 Egyptian Mongoose .. .. 1·75 2·00
1239 $3 Brazilian Tree Porcupine .. .. 2·25 2·75
1240 $4 American Manatee .. .. 2·50 3·00
1233/40 .. .. .. *Set of 8* 8·50 9·50
MS1241 Two sheets, each 107×80 mm. (a) $6
Caribbean Monk Seal. (b) $6 Egyptian Mongoose
(*different*) .. .. .. *Set of 2 sheets* 8·00 9·00

(Des W. Wright. Litho Questa)

1990 (30 Apr). *50th Anniv of Second World War. Horiz designs
as T **274** of Antigua. Multicoloured. P 14.*
1242 6 c. British Tanks in France, 1939 .. 30 30
1243 10 c. Operation "Crusader", North Africa,
 1941 .. .. 30 30
1244 20 c. Retreat of the Afrika Corps, 1942 .. 40 40
1245 45 c. American landing on Aleutian
 Islands, 1943 .. .. .. 50 50
1246 50 c. U.S. marines landing on Tarawa, 1943 55 55
1247 60 c. U.S. army entering Rome, 1944 .. 60 60
1248 75 c. U.S. tanks crossing River Seine, 1944 70 70
1249 $1 Battle of the Bulge, 1944 .. 95 95
1250 $5 American infantry in Italy, 1945 .. 3·00 3·50
1251 $6 Boeing B-29 Superfortress *Enola Gay*
 dropping atomic bomb on Hiroshima,
 1945 .. .. 3·50 3·50
1242/51 .. .. .. *Set of 10* 9·75 10·00
MS1252 112×84 mm. $6 St. Paul's Cathedral in
London Blitz, 1940 .. .. .. 3·75 4·50

(Des Walt Disney Company. Litho Questa)

1990 (3 May). *"Stamp World London 90" International Stamp
Exhibition (1st issue). Multicoloured designs as T **193** of
Gambia showing Walt Disney cartoon characters at
Shakespeare sites. P 14×13½ (15, 60 c., $1, $5) or 13½×14
(others).*
1253 15 c. Daisy Duck at Ann Hathaway's
 Cottage (*horiz*) 40 20
1254 30 c. Minnie and Bill Mouse at
 Shakespeare's birthplace, Stratford 55 35
1255 50 c. Minnie Mouse in front of Mary
 Arden's house, Wilmcote .. 75 70
1256 60 c. Mickey Mouse leaning on hedge in
 New Place gardens, Stratford (*horiz*) 90 90
1257 $1 Mickey Mouse walking in New Place
 gardens, Stratford (*horiz*) .. 1·25 1·25
1258 $2 Mickey Mouse carrying books in
 Scholars Lane, Stratford .. 2·25 2·50
1259 $4 Mickey Mouse and Royal Shakespeare
 Theatre, Stratford .. .. 3·25 4·00
1260 $5 Ludwig von Drake teaching Mickey
 Mouse at the Stratford Grammar
 School (*horiz*) .. .. .. 3·25 4·00
1253/60 .. .. .. *Set of 8* 11·50 12·50
MS1261 Two sheets, each 126×101 mm. (a) $6
Mickey Mouse as Shakespeare. P 13½×14. (b)
$6 Mickey and Minnie Mouse in rowing boat on
River Avon, Stratford (*horiz*). P 14×13½
 .. .. .. *Set of 2 sheets* 11·00 12·00

(Des Young Phillips Studio. Litho Questa)

1990 (5 July). *90th Birthday of Queen Elizabeth the Queen
Mother. Vert designs as T **194** of Gambia, showing
photographs, 1970–79. Multicoloured. P 14.*
1262 $2 Queen Mother in pink hat and coat. 1·10 1·40
 a. Strip of 3. Nos. 1262/4 .. 3·00
1263 $2 Prince Charles and Queen Mother at
 Garter ceremony .. .. 1·10 1·40
1264 $2 Queen Mother in blue floral outfit .. 1·10 1·40
1262/4 .. .. .. *Set of 3* 3·00 3·75
MS1265 90×75 mm. $6 Queen Mother in Garter
robes .. .. 4·25 5·00
Nos. 1262/4 were printed together, horizontally and vertically
se-tenant, in sheetlets of 9 (3×3).

(Des M. Pollard. Litho Questa)

1990 (12 July). *"Stamp World London 90" International Stamp
Exhibition (2nd issue). Sheet 97×75 mm containing horiz
design as T **356** of Grenada. P 14.*
MS1266 $6 blue-green .. .. .. 5·50 6·50
Design:—$6 Map of South America and logo.

(Des J. Anderton. Litho B.D.T.)

1990 (10 Sept). *Birds. Multicoloured designs as T **358** of
Grenada, but vert. P 14.*
1267 25 c. Yellow-bellied Seedeater .. 30 30
1268 45 c. Carib Grackle 50 50
1269 50 c. Black-whiskered Vireo .. 55 55
1270 75 c. Bananaquit 70 70
1271 $1 White-collared Swift 95 95
1272 $2 Yellow-billed Elaenia .. .. 1·50 1·50
1273 $3 Blue-hooded Euphonia .. .. 2·00 2·00
1274 $5 Eared Dove .. .. .. 3·25 3·25
1267/74 .. .. .. *Set of 8* 8·75 8·75
MS1275 Two sheets, each 101×72 mm. (a) $6
Mangrove Cuckoo. (b) $6 Scaly-breasted
Thrasher .. .. .. *Set of 2 sheets* 8·50 10·00

(Des Deborah Dudley Max. Litho Questa)

1990 (17 Sept). *Crustaceans. Horiz designs as T **359** of
Grenada. Multicoloured. P 14.*
1276 10 c. Slipper Lobster 20 20
1277 25 c. Green Reef Crab 30 30
1278 65 c. Caribbean Lobsterette .. 60 60
1279 75 c. Blind Deep Sea Lobster .. 70 70
1280 $1 Flattened Crab 95 95
1281 $2 Ridged Slipper Lobster .. .. 1·75 2·00
1282 $3 Land Crab .. .. .. 2·25 2·75
1283 $4 Mountain Crab .. .. 2·50 2·75
1276/83 .. .. .. *Set of 8* 8·25 9·25
MS1284 Two sheets, each 108×76 mm. (a) $6
Caribbean King Crab. (b) $6 Purse Crab
 .. .. .. *Set of 2 sheets* 8·00 10·00

98 Lineker, England

99 Angel with Star and Lantern

(Des Young Phillips Studio. Litho Questa)

1990 (24 Sept). *World Cup Football Championship, Italy (2nd issue).* T **98** *and similar vert designs. Multicoloured.* P 14.

1285	15 c. Type **98**	25	25
1286	45 c. Burruchaga, Argentina	45	45
1287	$2 Hysen, Sweden	1·75	2·25
1288	$4 Sang Ho, South Korea	2·75	3·75
1285/8	*Set of 4*	4·75	6·00

MS1289 Two sheets, each 76×90 mm. (a) $6 Ramos, U.S.A. (b) $6 Stojkovic, Yugoslavia
Set of 2 sheets 8·50 9·50

(Des B. Grout. Litho Questa)

1990 (1 Nov). *Olympic Games, Barcelona (1992). Vert designs as* T **268** *of Antigua. Multicoloured.* P 14.

1290	10 c. Boxing	10	10
1291	25 c. Olympic flame	20	20
1292	50 c. Football	40	40
1293	75 c. Discus throwing	60	60
1294	$1 Pole vaulting	85	85
1295	$2 Show jumping	1·75	2·00
1296	$4 Women's basketball	3·50	3·75
1297	$5 Men's gymnastics	3·00	3·75
1290/7	*Set of 8*	9·50	10·50

MS1298 Two sheets, each 101×70 mm. $6 Sailboards. (b) 70×101 mm. $6 Decathlon
Set of 2 sheets 8·50 9·50

(Litho Questa)

1991 (31 Jan). *350th Death Anniv of Rubens. Multicoloured designs as* T **273** *of Antigua.* P 13½×14 *(vert) or* 14×13½ *(horiz).*

1299	5 c. "Adam and Eve" (Eve detail) (*vert*)	20	20
1300	15 c. "Esther before Ahasuerus" (detail)	30	20
1301	25 c. "Adam and Eve" (Adam detail) (*vert*)	40	25
1302	50 c. "Expulsion from Eden"	70	60
1303	$1 "Cain slaying Abel" (detail) (*vert*)	1·10	1·10
1304	$2 "Lot's Flight"	1·75	2·25
1305	$4 "Samson and Delilah" (detail)	2·75	3·75
1306	$5 "Abraham and Melchizedek"	3·25	3·75
1299/306	*Set of 8*	9·50	11·00

MS1307 Two sheets, each 101×71 mm. (a) $6 "The Meeting of David and Abigail" (detail). (b) $6 "Daniel in the Lions' Den" (detail)
Set of 2 sheets 7·00 8·50

(Des Mary Walters. Litho B.D.T.)

1991 (5 Feb). *Coral Reef Fishes. Horiz designs as* T **357** *of Grenada. Multicoloured.* P 14.

1308	15 c. Barred Hamlet	50	25
1309	35 c. Long-spined Squirrelfish	80	50
1310	45 c. Red-spotted Hawkfish	85	60
1311	75 c. Bigeye	1·25	1·00
1312	$1 Balloonfish ("Spiny Puffer")	1·50	1·25
1313	$2 Small-mouthed Grunt	2·25	2·50
1314	$3 Harlequin Bass	2·75	3·25
1315	$4 Creole Fish	3·00	3·50
1308/15	*Set of 8*	11·50	11·50

MS1316 Two sheets, each 103×72 mm. (a) $6 Copper Sweeper. (b) $6 Royal Gramma ("Fairy Basslet") ..
Set of 2 sheets 8·50 10·00

(Litho Questa)

1991 (1 Mar). *Christmas (1990). Hummel Figurines.* T **99** *and similar vert designs. Multicoloured.* P 14.

1317	10 c. Type **99**	15	10
1318	15 c. Christ Child and Angel playing mandolin	25	15
1319	25 c. Shepherd	35	25
1320	50 c. Angel with trumpet and lantern	65	50
1321	$1 Nativity scene	1·10	95
1322	$2 Christ Child and Angel holding candle	1·75	2·50
1323	$4 Angel with baskets	2·75	4·00
1324	$5 Angels singing	3·25	4·00
1317/24	*Set of 8*	9·25	11·00

MS1325 Two sheets, each 99×122 mm. (a) 5 c. As No. 1318; 40 c. As No. 1320; 60 c. As No. 1321; $3 As No. 1324. (b) 20 c. As Type **99**; 30 c. As No. 1319; 75 c. As No. 1322; $6 As No. 1323
Set of 2 sheets 10·00 11·00

100 *Brassia maculata*

101 Donald and Daisy Duck with Solar-powered Car

(Des S. Barlowe. Litho Walsall)

1991 (1 Apr)–92. *Orchids.* T **100** *and similar vert designs. Multicoloured.* P 14.

1326	5 c. Type **100**	30	30
1327	10 c. *Oncidium lanceanum*	30	30
1328	15 c. *Broughtonia sanguinea*	35	20
1329	25 c. *Diacrium bicornutum*	40	20
1330	35 c. *Cattleya labiata*	40	20
1331	45 c. *Epidendrum fragrans*	50	25
1332	50 c. *Oncidium papilio*	55	30
1333	75 c. *Neocogniauxia monophylla*	70	50
1334	$1 *Epidendrum polybulbon*	80	70
1335	$2 *Spiranthes speciosa*	1·40	1·40
1336	$4 *Epidendrum ciliare*	2·25	2·75
1337	$5 *Phais tankervilliae*	2·50	3·00
1338	$10 *Brassia caudata* (27.11.91)	4·50	5·50
1339	$20 *Brassavola cordata* (29.6.92)	9·25	11·00
1326/39	*Set of 14*	22·00	24·00

(Des W. Wright. Litho Questa)

1991 (8 Apr). *Butterflies. Horiz designs as* T **363** *of Grenada. Multicoloured.* P 14.

1340	5 c. Crimson-patched Longwing	40	30
1341	10 c. *Morpho helena*	40	30
1342	15 c. *Morpho sulkowskyi*	55	35
1343	20 c. *Dynastor napoleon*	60	40
1344	25 c. *Pieridae callinira*	60	45
1345	30 c. *Anartia amathea*	65	50
1346	35 c. *Heliconiidae dido*	65	50
1347	45 c. *Papilionidae columbus*	75	65
1348	50 c. *Nymphalidae praeneste*	85	70
1349	60 c. *Panacea prola*	1·00	80
1350	75 c. *Dryas julia*	1·00	90
1351	$1 *Papilionidae orthosilaus*	1·25	1·10
1352	$2 *Pyrrhopyge cometes*	1·75	2·00
1353	$3 *Papilionidae paeon*	2·00	2·50
1354	$4 *Morpho cypris*	2·50	3·00
1355	$5 *Choringa*	3·00	3·25
1340/55	*Set of 16*	16·00	16·00

MS1356 Four sheets, each 118×80 mm. (a) $6 *Danaus plexippus*. (b) $6 *Caligo idomenides*. (c) $6 *Nymphalidae amydon*. (d) $6 *Papilio childrenae*
Set of 4 sheets 15·00 15·00

(Des Walt Disney Co. Litho Questa)

1991 (22 Apr). *Ecology Conservation.* T **101** *and similar multicoloured designs showing Walt Disney cartoon characters.* P 14×13½.

1357	10 c. Type **101**	30	20
1358	15 c. Goofy saving water	40	20
1359	25 c. Donald and Daisy on nature hike	55	35
1360	45 c. Donald Duck returning chick to nest	75	55
1361	$1 Donald Duck and balloons	1·40	1·25
1362	$2 Minnie Mouse and Daisy Duck on hot day	2·25	2·50
1363	$4 Mickey's nephews cleaning beach	3·25	3·75
1364	$5 Donald Duck on pedal generator	3·25	3·75
1357/64	*Set of 8*	11·00	11·50

MS1365 Three sheets, each 127×102 mm. (a) $6 Hiawatha and felled forest. P 14×13½. (b) $6 Donald Duck recycling (*vert*). P 13½×14. (c) $6 Mickey Mouse with Arbor Day notice. P 14×13½
Set of 3 sheets 14·00 15·00
d. Error. Imperf (sheet) (a))

(Des T. Agans. Litho Questa)

1991 (29 Apr). *500th Anniv of Discovery of America by Columbus (1992) (4th issue). History of Exploration. Multicoloured designs as* T **277** *of Antigua.* P 14.

1366	15 c. Magellan's *Vitoria* rounding Cape Horn, 1519–21	50	40
1367	20 c. Drake's *Golden Hind*, 1577–80	60	45
1368	50 c. Cook's H.M.S. *Resolution*, 1768–71	90	80
1369	60 c. Douglas World Cruiser seaplane, 1924	90	80
1370	$1 Sputnik I satellite, 1957	1·00	1·00
1371	$2 Gagarin's space flight, 1961	1·75	2·00
1372	$4 Glenn's space flight, 1962	2·50	3·25
1373	$5 Space shuttle, 1981	3·00	3·50
1366/73	*Set of 8*	10·00	11·00

MS1374 Two sheets. (a) 105×78 mm. $6 Bow of *Pinta* (*vert*). (b) 78×105 mm. $6 Fleet of Columbus
Set of 2 sheets 8·00 10·00

(Des Walt Disney Co. Litho Questa)

1991 (6 May). *"Phila Nippon '91" International Stamp Exhibition, Tokyo. Multicoloured designs as* T **279** *of Antigua showing Walt Disney cartoon characters in Japanese scenes.* P 14×13½.

1375	15 c. Minnie Mouse with silkworms (*horiz*)	30	20
1376	30 c. Mickey, Minnie, Morty and Ferdie at Torii Gate (*horiz*)	45	35
1377	50 c. Donald Duck and Mickey Mouse trying origami (*horiz*)	70	60
1378	60 c. Mickey and Minnie diving for pearls (*horiz*)	80	70
1379	$1 Minnie Mouse in kimono (*horiz*)	1·25	1·10
1380	$2 Mickey making masks (*horiz*)	2·25	2·50
1381	$4 Donald and Mickey making paper (*horiz*)	3·00	3·25
1382	$5 Minnie and Pluto making pottery (*horiz*)	3·25	3·50
1375/82	*Set of 8*	11·00	11·00

MS1383 Four sheets, each 122×102 mm. (a) $6 Mickey flower-arranging. (b) $6 Mickey carving a netsuke. (c) $6 Mickey at tea ceremony. (d) $6 Mickey making printing plate. P 13½×14
Set of 4 sheets 16·00 16·00

(Des Mary Walters. Litho Questa)

1991 (1 June). *Fungi. Vert designs as* T **364** *of Grenada. Multicoloured.* P 14.

1384	5 c. *Pyrrhoglossum pyrrhum*	35	25
1385	45 c. *Agaricus purpurellus*	85	50
1386	50 c. *Amanita craseoderma*	85	55
1387	90 c. *Hygrocybe acutoconica*	1·50	95
1388	$1 *Limacella guttata*	1·50	1·25

1389	$2 *Lactarius hygrophoroides*	2·00	2·00
1390	$4 *Boletellus cubensis*	3·25	3·50
1391	$5 *Psilocybe caerulescens*	3·25	3·50
1384/91	*Set of 8*	12·00	11·50

MS1392 Two sheets, each 100×70 mm. (a) $6 *Marasmius haematocephalus*. (b) $6 *Lepiota spiculata*
Set of 2 sheets 12·00 13·00

(Des D. Miller. Litho Walsall)

1991 (5 July). *65th Birthday of Queen Elizabeth II. Horiz designs as* T **280** *of Antigua. Multicoloured.* P 14.

1393	20 c. Queen, Prince Philip, Prince Charles and Prince William at Trooping the Colour, 1990	30	20
1394	25 c. Queen and Prince Charles at polo match, 1985	30	20
1395	$2 Queen and Prince Philip at Maundy service, 1989	2·00	2·50
1396	$4 Queen with Queen Mother on her 87th birthday, 1987	3·25	3·75
1393/6	*Set of 4*	5·25	6·00

MS1397 68×90 mm. $5 The Queen at Caen Hill, 1990, and Prince Philip at R.A.F. Benson, 1989 3·75 4·50

(Des D. Miller. Litho Walsall)

1991 (5 July). *10th Wedding Anniv of Prince and Princess of Wales. Horiz designs as* T **280** *of Antigua. Multicoloured.* P 14.

1398	5 c. Prince and Princess of Wales kissing, 1987	30	15
1399	60 c. Portraits of Prince, Princess and sons	80	70
1400	$1 Prince Henry in 1988 and Prince William in 1987	1·10	1·10
1401	$5 Princess Diana in 1990 and Prince Charles in 1988	4·25	4·75
1398/1401	*Set of 4*	5·75	6·00

MS1402 68×90 mm. $5 Princess with Prince Henry in Majorca, and Prince and Princess with Prince Henry at polo match 4·25 4·50

(Litho Questa)

1991 (18 Nov). *Death Centenary of Vincent van Gogh (artist) (1990). Multicoloured designs as* T **278** *of Antigua.* P 13½×14 *(vert) or* 14×13½ *(horiz).*

1403	5 c. "Two Thistles"	20	20
1404	10 c. "Baby Marcelle Roulin"	25	20
1405	15 c. "Still Life: Basket with Six Oranges" (*horiz*)	30	15
1406	25 c. "Orchard in Blossom"	35	20
1407	45 c. "Armand Roulin"	50	35
1408	50 c. "Wood Gatherers in Snow" (detail) (*horiz*)	60	40
1409	60 c. "Almond Tree in Blossom"	70	50
1410	$1 "An Old Man"	1·00	1·00
1411	$2 "The Seine Bridge at Asnières" (*horiz*)	1·75	2·00
1412	$3 "Vase with Lilacs, Daises and Anemones"	2·25	2·50
1413	$4 "Self Portrait"	2·40	2·75
1414	$5 "Patience Escalier"	2·50	2·75
1403/14	*Set of 12*	11·50	11·50

MS1415 Three sheets. (a) 127×102 mm. $6 "Quay with Men unloading Sand Barges" (*horiz*). (b) 127×102 mm. $6 "Sunset: Wheat Fields near Arles" (*horiz*). (c) 102×127 mm. "Les Alyscamps". Imperf
Set of 3 sheets 12·00 13·00

102 Sargassum Triggerfish

(Litho Questa)

1991 (5 Dec). *Reef Fishes.* T **102** *and similar horiz designs. Multicoloured.* P 14.

1416	50 c. Type **102**	75	75
	a. Sheetlet. Nos. 1416/30	10·00	
1417	50 c. Tobaccofish	75	75
1418	50 c. Caribbean Long-nosed Butterflyfish	75	75
1419	50 c. Cherub Angelfish	75	75
1420	50 c. Black Jack	75	75
1421	50 c. Masked Goby and Black Jack	75	75
1422	50 c. Spot-finned Hogfish	75	75
1423	50 c. Royal Gramma ("Fairy Basslet")	75	75
1424	50 c. Orange-backed Bass	75	75
1425	50 c. Candy Basslet	75	75
1426	50 c. Black-capped Basslet	75	75
1427	50 c. Long-jawed Squirrelfish	75	75
1428	50 c. Jackknife-fish	75	75
1429	50 c. Bigeye	75	75
1430	50 c. Short Bigeye	75	75
1416/30	*Set of 15*	10·00	10·00

MS1431 106×66 mm. $6 Caribbean Flashlight Fish 8·00 10·00
Nos. 1416/30 were printed together, *se-tenant*, as a sheetlet of 15, forming a composite design.

(Litho Walsall)

1991 (9 Dec). *Christmas. Religious Paintings by Martin Schongauer. Vert designs as* T **287** *of Antigua.* P 12.

1432	10 c. black and cinnamon	30	15
1433	35 c. multicoloured	55	30
1434	50 c. multicoloured	75	50
1435	75 c. multicoloured	1·00	80
1436	$1 multicoloured	1·40	1·25
1437	$2 multicoloured	2·25	2·50
1438	$4 black and cinnamon	3·25	3·75

1439	$5 black, grey and vermilion	3·50	4·00
1432/9		*Set of 8* 11·50	12·00

MS1440 Two sheets, each 102×127 mm. (a) $6
multicoloured. (b) $6 multicoloured. P 14½.
Set of 2 sheets 9·50 11·00

Designs:—10 c. "Angel of the Annunciation"; 35 c. "Madonna
of the Rose Hedge" (detail); 50 c. "Madonna of the Rose Hedge"
(different detail); 75 c. "Nativity" (detail); $1 "Adoration of the
Shepherds" (detail); $2 "The Nativity"; $4 "Nativity" (*different*);
$5 "Symbol of St. Matthew"; $6 (No. MS1442a) "Adoration of
the Shepherds" (different detail); $6 (No. MS1442b) "Nativity"

(Des G. Vasarhelyi. Litho Walsall)

1992 (13 Feb). *Great Railways of the World. Horiz designs as
T 367 of Grenada. Multicoloured.* P 14.

1441	75 c. Medoc locomotive No. J-S 58, 1857 (Switzerland)		80	80
	a. Sheetlet. Nos. 1441/9		6·50	
1442	75 c. Stirling single locomotive No. 1, 1870 (Great Britain)		80	80
1443	75 c. Paris Lyon-Mediterranee locomotive No. 90, 1877 (France)		80	80
1444	75 c. Standard type, 1880 (U.S.A.)		80	80
1445	75 c. Class 650 *Vittorio Emanuel II*, 1884 (Italy)		80	80
1446	75 c. Johnson single, 1887 (Great Britain)		80	80
1447	75 c. Locomotive No. 999, 1893 (U.S.A.)		80	80
1448	75 c. Class Q1, 1896 (Great Britain)		80	80
1449	75 c. *Claud Hamilton*, 1900 (Great Britain)		80	80
1450	$1 Class P8, 1906 (Germany)		80	80
	a. Sheetlet. Nos. 1450/8		6·50	
1451	$1 Class P, 1910 (Denmark)		80	80
1452	$1 Southern Railway Class Ps4, 1926 (U.S.A.)		80	80
1453	$1 *Kestrel*, 1932 (Ireland)		80	80
1454	$1 Southern Pacific Class GS-2, 1937 (U.S.A.)		80	80
1455	$1 Class 12, 1938 (Belgium)		80	80
1456	$1 Norfolk and Western Railroad Class J No. 600, 1941 (U.S.A.)		80	80
1457	$1 Alco PA series diesel, 1946 (U.S.A.)		80	80
1458	$1 Class 4E electric, 1954 (South Africa)		80	80
1459	$2 Trans Europe Express train, 1957 (France)		1·40	1·40
	a. Sheetlet. Nos. 1459/67		12·00	
1460	$2 New Haven Railroad Type FL9 diesel, 1960 (U.S.A.)		1·40	1·40
1461	$2 "Hikari" train, 1964 (Japan)		1·40	1·40
1462	$2 Class 103.1 electric, 1970 (Germany)		1·40	1·40
1463	$2 RTG diesel, 1972 (France)		1·40	1·40
1464	$2 ETR 401 Pendolino train, 1976 (Italy)		1·40	1·40
1465	$2 Advanced Passenger Train Class 370, 1981 (Great Britain)		1·40	1·40
1466	$2 Via Rail LRC diesel, 1982 (Canada)		1·40	1·40
1467	$2 MAV BZMOT 601, 1983 (Hungary)		1·40	1·40
1441/67			*Set of 27* 22·00	22·00

MS1468 Two sheets, each 120×80 mm. (a) $6
Werner von Siemens's electric locomotive, 1879
(Germany). (b) ETR 401 Pendolino train, 1976
(Italy) .. .. *Set of 2 sheets* 8·50 9·00
Nos. 1441/9, 1450/8 and 1459/67 were each printed together,
se-tenant, in sheetlets of 9.

(Des D. Miller. Litho Questa)

1992 (2 Mar). *40th Anniv of Queen Elizabeth II's Accession.
Horiz designs as T 288 of Antigua. Multicoloured.* P 14.

1469	60 c. Swimming Jetty on beach		50	40
1470	75 c. View of Grenadines		55	45
1471	$2 Surf on beach		1·60	1·60
1472	$4 Secluded bay		2·75	3·00
1469/72		*Set of 4* 4·75	5·00	

MS1473 Two sheets, each 74×92 mm. (a) $6
Plantation house. (b) $6 St. George's
Set of 2 sheets 8·00 9·00

(Litho Questa)

1992 (23 Mar). *Olympic Games, Barcelona. Vert designs as
T 268 of Antigua. Multicoloured.* P 14.

1474	10 c. Women's backstroke swimming		40	30
1475	15 c. Women's handball		45	30
1476	25 c. Men's 4 × 100 m relay		55	30
1477	35 c. Men's hammer throw		60	35
1478	50 c. Men's 110 m hurdles		70	50
1479	75 c. Men's pole vault		90	80
1480	$1 Men's volleyball		1·10	1·00
1481	$2 Men's weightlifting		2·00	2·25
1482	$5 Men's gymnastics		3·00	3·75
1483	$6 Football		3·25	3·75
1474/83			*Set of 10* 11·50	12·00

MS1484 Two sheets, each 100×70 mm. (a) $15
Finn class single-handed dinghy sailing. (b) $15
Baseball .. .. *Set of 2 sheets* 16·00 17·00

(Litho B.D.T.)

1992 (30 Apr). *"Granada '92" International Stamp Exhibition,
Spain. Spanish Paintings. Multicoloured designs as T 292 of
Antigua.* P 13½×13 (50 c.) or 13×13½ (*others*).

1485	10 c. "The Surrender of Seville" (Zurbarán)		20	20
1486	35 c. "The Liberation of St. Peter by an Angel" (Antonio de Pereda)		35	35
1487	50 c. "Joseph explains the Dreams of the Pharaoh" (Antonio del Castillo Saavedra) (*horiz*)		55	55
1488	75 c. "The Flower Vase" (Juan de Arellano)		70	70
1489	$1 "The Duke of Pastrana" (Juan Carreño de Miranda)		80	80
1490	$2 "The Annunciation" (detail) (Francisco Rizi)		1·60	1·75
1491	$4 "The Annunciation" (different detail) (Francisco Rizi)		2·50	2·75
1492	$5 "Old Women Seated" (attr Antonio Puga)		2·50	2·75
1485/92			*Set of 8* 8·25	8·75

MS1493 Two sheets. (a) 95×120 mm. $6 "The
Triumph of St Hermenegildo" (Francisco de
Herrera the younger) (86×111 *mm*). (b) 120×95
mm. $6 "Relief of Genoa" (De Pereda) (110×84
mm). Imperf .. .. .. *Set of 2 sheets* 7·00 8·00

---

103 Don Isaac Abarbanel,
Minister of Finance

104 *Atalanta* and
Mischief (yachts),
1881

(Des L. Fried. Litho Questa)

1992 (7 May). *500th Anniv of Discovery of America by
Columbus (5th issue). World Columbian Stamp "Expo '92",
Chicago. T 103 and similar horiz designs.* P 14.

1494	10 c. Type 103		15	15
1495	25 c. Columbus on voyage		25	25
1496	35 c. Look-out sighting land		30	30
1497	50 c. King Ferdinand and Queen Isabella of Spain		50	50
1498	60 c. Columbus showing map to Queen Isabella		55	55
1499	$5 *Santa Maria* and bird		4·00	5·50
1494/9			*Set of 6* 5·25	6·50

MS1500 Two sheets, each 100×71 mm. (a) $6
Christopher Columbus. (b) $6 Columbus with
hand to face .. .. .. *Set of 2 sheets* 7·00 8·00

(Des Wendy Griswold-Smith. Litho Questa)

1992 (28 May). *"Genova '92" International Thematic Stamp
Exhibition. Hummingbirds. Multicoloured designs as T 295 of
Antigua, but vertical.* P 14.

1501	5 c. Male Blue-headed Hummingbird		10	10
1502	10 c. Female Rufous-breasted Hermit		10	10
1503	20 c. Female Blue-headed Hummingbird		15	15
1504	45 c. Male Green-throated Carib		30	30
1505	90 c. Male Antillean Crested Hummingbird		60	70
1506	$1·40 Male Purple-throated Carib		1·40	1·60
1507	$4 Female Purple-throated Carib		2·40	2·75
1508	$5 Female Antillean Crested Hummingbird		2·50	2·75
1501/8			*Set of 8* 6·50	7·50

MS1509 Two sheets, each 104×75 mm. (a) $6
Male Rufous-breasted Hermit. (b) $6 Female
Green-throated Carib .. .. *Set of 2 sheets* 9·50 11·00

(Des R. Jung. Litho B.D.T.)

1992 (1 June). *50th Anniv of United Service Organization
(forces' entertainment programme). Vert designs as T 371 of
Grenada. Multicoloured.* P 14.

1510	10 c. James Cagney		15	15
1511	15 c. Anne Sheridan		15	15
1512	35 c. Jerry Colonna		25	25
1513	50 c. Spike Jones		40	40
1514	75 c. Edgar Bergen		55	55
1515	$1 The Andrews Sisters		70	70
1516	$2 Dinah Shore		1·40	1·75
1517	$5 Bing Crosby		3·25	3·75
1510/17			*Set of 8* 6·25	7·00

MS1518 Two sheets, each 107×80 mm. (a) $6
Fred Astaire. (b) $6 Marlene Dietrich
Set of 2 sheets 7·00 7·50
No. 1515 is incorrectly inscribed "THE ANDREW SISTERS".

(Des F. Paul ($1), J. Esquino ($2). Litho Questa)

1992 (24 Aug). *500th Anniv of Discovery of America by
Columbus (6th issue). Organization of East Caribbean States.
As Nos. 1670/1 of Antigua.* P 14½.

1519	$1 Columbus meeting Amerindians		65	65
1520	$2 Ships approaching island		1·25	1·50

(Des W. Hanson. Litho B.D.T.)

1992 (22 Oct). *Toy Trains from American Manufacturers.
Horiz designs as T 257 of Dominica. Multicoloured.* P 14.

1521	15 c. No. 2220 switcher locomotive, Voltamp (1910)		25	15
1522	25 c. Clockwork locomotive of Bridge Port Line, American Miniature Railroad (1907)		35	20
1523	50 c. First electric toy locomotive, Ives (1910)		60	40
1524	75 c. J.C. Penney Special locomotive, American Flyer (1920s)		80	60
1525	$1 Clockwork cast-metal locomotive, Hafner (1916)		95	80
1526	$2 Pull toy copper-plated locomotive, probably Hubley (1900)		1·75	2·00
1527	$4 "Mayflower" locomotive, American Flyer (1928)		3·00	3·25
1528	$5 "Olympian" locomotive, Ives (1929)		3·00	3·25
1521/8			*Set of 8* 9·50	9·50

MS1529 Two sheets. (a) 128×93 mm. $6 Clock-
work locomotive, Ives (1910) (50×38½ *mm*). (b)
142×95 mm. $6 "Statesman" locomotive, Amer-
ican Flyer (50×38½ *mm*). P 13
Set of 2 sheets 7·50 8·50

(Des Kerri Schiff. Litho Questa)

1992 (28 Oct). *Postage Stamp Mega Event, New York. Sheet
100×70 mm containing multicoloured design as T 299 of
Antigua.* P 14.
MS1530 $6 Brooklyn Bridge .. .. 3·50 4·25

(Litho Questa)

1992 (19 Nov). *Christmas. Religious Paintings. Multicoloured
designs as T 300 of Antigua, showing "The Annunciation" by
various artists.* P 14×13½ ($5) or 13½×14 (*others*).

1531	5 c. Robert Campin		10	10
1532	15 c. Melchior Broederlam		15	10
1533	25 c. Fra Filippo Lippi (two-panel diptych)		20	15
1534	35 c. Simone Martini		30	20
1535	50 c. Lippi (detail from left panel)		45	45
1536	75 c. Lippi (detail from right panel)		60	60
1537	90 c. Albert Bouts		70	80
1538	$1 D. di Michelino		80	90
1539	$2 Rogier van der Weyden		1·50	1·75
1540	$3 Sandro Botticelli (detail of angel)		1·90	2·25
1541	$4 Botticelli (detail of Virgin Mary)		2·75	3·00
1542	$5 Bernardo Daddi (*horiz*)		2·75	3·00
1531/42			*Set of 12* 11·00	12·00

MS1543 Three sheets, each 72×97 mm. (a) $6
Van der Weyden (*different*). (b) $6 Botticelli (as
$3). (c) $6 Hubert van Eyck .. *Set of 3 sheets* 10·50 11·00

(Des J. Genzo. Litho Questa)

1992 (19 Nov). *Gold Record Award Winners. Vert designs as
T 374 of Grenada. Multicoloured.* P 14.

1544	90 c. Leonard Bernstein		1·10	1·10
	a. Sheetlet. Nos. 1544/51		8·00	
1545	90 c. Ray Charles		1·10	1·10
1546	90 c. Bob Dylan		1·10	1·10
1547	90 c. Barbara Streisand		1·10	1·10
1548	90 c. Frank Sinatra		1·10	1·10
1549	90 c. Harry Belafonte		1·10	1·10
1550	90 c. Aretha Franklin		1·10	1·10
1551	90 c. Garth Brooks		1·10	1·10
1544/51			*Set of 8* 8·00	8·00

MS1552 Two sheets, each 100×70 mm. (a) $3
Charlie Parker; $3 Miles Davis. (b) $3 Johnny
Cash; $3 Willie Nelson .. *Set of 2 sheets* 7·00 8·00
Nos. 1544/51 were printed together, se-tenant, in sheetlets of
8 with a composite background design.

(Des Walt Disney Co. Litho Questa)

1992 (24 Nov). *60th Anniv of Goofy (Disney cartoon character).
Multicoloured designs as T 258 of Dominica showing Goofy in
various cartoon films.* P 14×13½.

1553	5 c. *Father's Day Off*, 1953		20	20
1554	10 c. *Cold War*, 1951		25	20
1555	15 c. *Home Made Home*, 1951		30	20
1556	25 c. *Get Rich Quick*, 1951		35	25
1557	50 c. *Man's Best Friend*, 1952		55	40
1558	75 c. *Aquamania*, 1961		75	55
1559	90 c. *Tomorrow We Diet*, 1951		85	65
1560	$1 *Teachers Are People*, 1952		90	75
1561	$2 *The Goofy Success Story*, 1955		1·60	1·60
1562	$3 *Double Dribble*, 1946		2·00	2·25
1563	$4 *Hello Aloha*, 1952		2·25	2·50
1564	$5 *Father's Lion*, 1952		2·40	2·75
1553/64			*Set of 12* 11·00	11·00

MS1565 Three sheets, each 128×102 mm. (a) $6
Motor Mania, 1956. P 14×13½. (b) $6 *Hold that
Pose*, 1950 (*vert*). P 13½×14. (c) $6 *Father's
Weekend*, 1953 (*vert*). P 13½×14 *Set of 3 sheets* 12·00 13·00

(Des W. Wright and W. Hanson (Nos. 1566, 1575, MS1577a), W. Wright and L. Fried (Nos. 1567, 1574, MS1577b), J. Genzo (Nos. 1572, MS1577e), W. Wright (others). Litho B.D.T)

1992 (15 Dec). *Anniversaries and Events. Designs as T 375 of
Grenada. Multicoloured, except No. 1571.* P 14.

1566	25 c. Zeppelin LZ-11 *Viktoria Luise* over Kiel Harbour (*horiz*)		55	30
1567	50 c. Space shuttle *Columbia* landing (*horiz*)		65	35
1568	75 c. German Federal Republic flag and arms (*horiz*)		65	50
1569	$1.50, Giant Anteater (*horiz*)		1·00	1·00
1570	$2 Scarlet Macaw		2·00	1·75
1571	$2 W.H.O. emblem (black and new blue) (*horiz*)		1·25	1·25
1572	$3 Wolfgang Amadeus Mozart		3·00	2·50
1573	$4 The Berlin Airlift (*horiz*)		2·75	2·50
1574	$4 Repairing "Intelsat VI" satellite in space (*horiz*)		2·75	2·50
1575	$5 Zeppelin LZ-129 *Hindenburg* on fire (*horiz*)		2·75	2·75
1576	$5 Admiral Richard Byrd's Ford 4-AT-B Trimotor *Floyd Bennett* aircraft (*horiz*)		2·75	2·75
1566/76			*Set of 11* 18·00	17·00

MS1577 Five sheets. (a) 110×80 mm. $6
Zeppelin LZ-4, 1913 (51½×39½ *mm*). P 13. (b)
110×80 mm. $6 First flight of space shuttle
Endeavour (51½×39½ *mm*). P 13. (c)
110×80 mm. $6 Map of West Germany
(39½×51½ *mm*). P 13. (d) 110×80 mm. $6
Jaguar (51½×39½ *mm*). P 13. (e) 98×67 mm. $6
Figaro costume from *The Marriage of Figaro*.
P 14 .. .. *Set of 5 sheets* 18·00 19·00
Anniversaries and Events:—Nos. 1566, 1575, MS1577a, 75th
death anniv of Count Ferdinand von Zeppelin; Nos. 1567, 1574,
MS1577b, International Space Year; Nos. 1568, 1573,
MS1577c, 25th death anniv of Konrad Adenauer (German
statesman); Nos. 1569/70, MS1577d, Earth Summit '92, Rio;
No. 1571, United Nations World Health Organization Projects;
Nos. 1572, MS1577e, Death bicent of Mozart; No. 1576, 75th
anniv of International Association of Lions Clubs.

(Litho Questa)

1992 (15 Dec). *History of the Americas Cup Challenge Trophy.
T 104 and similar multicoloured designs.* P 14.

1578	15 c. Type 104		20	20
1579	25 c. *Valkyrie III* and *Defender*, 1895		30	30
1580	35 c. *Shamrock IV* and *Resolute*, 1920		45	45
1581	75 c. *Endeavour II* and *Ranger*, 1937		70	70
1582	$1 *Sceptre* and *Columbia*, 1958		85	85
1583	$2 *Australia II* and *Liberty*, 1983		1·50	1·75
1584	$4 *Stars & Stripes* and *Kookaburra III*, 1987		2·40	3·00

1585	$5 *New Zealand* and *Stars & Stripes,* 1988	2·50	3·00
1578/85	*Set of 8*	8·00	9·00

MS1586 Two sheets, each 114×85 mm. (a) $6 *America* (schooner), 1851 (57×43 *mm*). (b) $6 *Americas Cup emblems* (57×43 *mm*)
Set of 2 sheets 8·50 9·00

(Des Joan Popeio. Litho Questa)

1993 (20 Jan). *Dogs of the World. Multicoloured designs as T 377 of Grenada, but vertical. P 14.*

1587	35 c. Irish Setter and Glendalough, Ireland	50	35
1588	50 c. Boston Terrier and Boston State House, U.S.A.	70	50
1589	75 c. Beagle and Temple to Athena, Greece	1·00	60
1590	$1 Weimaraner and Nesselwang, Germany	1·25	85
1591	$3 Norwegian Elkhound and Urnes Stave Church, Norway	2·50	3·00
1592	$4 Mastiff and Sphinx, Egypt	2·75	3·00
1593	$5 Akita and Torii Temple, Kyoto, Japan	2·75	3·00
1594	$5 Saluki and Rub'al Khali, Saudi Arabia	2·75	3·00
1587/94	*Set of 8*	13·00	13·00

MS1595 Two sheets, each 99×71 mm. (a) $6 Bull Dog, Great Britain. (b) $6 Shar Pei, China
Set of 2 sheets 7·50 8·50

(Litho Walsall)

1993 (8 Mar). *Bicentenary of the Louvre, Paris. Vert designs as T 305 of Antigua. Multicoloured (except No. 1599). P 12.*

1596	$1 "Madonna and Child with the young John the Baptist" (Botticelli)	90	90
	a. Sheetlet. Nos. 1596/1603	6·50	
1597	$1 "The Buffet" (Chardin)	90	90
1598	$1 "Return from Market" (Chardin)	90	90
1599	$1 "Erasmus" (Dürer) (black & bluish grey)	90	90
1600	$1 "Self-portrait with Eryngium" (Dürer)	90	90
1601	$1 "Jeanne of Aragon" (Raphael)	90	90
1602	$1 "La Belle Jardinière" (detail) (Raphael)	90	90
1603	$1 "La Belle Jardinière" (different detail) (Raphael)	90	90
1596/1603	*Set of 8*	6·50	6·50

MS1604 70×100 mm. $6 "King Charles I Hunting" (Van Dyck) (52×85 *mm*). P 14½ 3·75 4·50
Nos. 1596/1603 were printed together, *se-tenant*, in sheetlets of 8 stamps and one centre label.

105 Battus polydamus

(Litho Questa)

1993 (13 Apr). *Butterflies. T 105 and similar vert designs. Multicoloured. P 14.*

1605	15 c. Type 105	40	20
1606	35 c. *Astraptes talus*	55	20
1607	45 c. *Pseudolycaena marsyas*	55	25
1608	75 c. *Siproeta stelenes*	70	50
1609	$1 *Phoebis sennae*	80	40
1610	$2 *Dione juno*	1·40	1·40
1611	$4 *Chlorostrymon simaethis*	2·25	2·75
1612	$5 *Urbanus proteus*	2·50	2·75
1605/12	*Set of 8*	8·25	7·75

MS1613 Two sheets, each 100×70 mm. (a) $6 *Historis odius* ("Orion"). (b) $6 *Heliconius charithonia* ("Zebra") *Set of 2 sheets* 7·00 8·00

(Des D. Delouise. Litho Questa)

1993 (17 May). *Flowers. Multicoloured designs as T 380 of Grenada. P 14.*

1614	35 c. Hibiscus	50	20
1615	35 c. Columbine	50	20
1616	45 c. Red Ginger	50	25
1617	75 c. Bougainvillea	70	50
1618	$1 Crown Imperial	80	40
1619	$2 Fairy Orchid	1·40	1·40
1620	$4 Heliconia	2·25	2·75
1621	$5 Tulip	2·50	2·75
1614/21	*Set of 8*	8·25	7·75

MS1622 Two sheet, each 70×100 mm. (a) $6 Blackberry Lily (*horiz*). (b) $6 Balloonflower (*horiz*) *Set of 2 sheets* 7·00 8·00

(Des Kerri Schiff. Litho Questa)

1993 (2 June). *40th Anniv of Coronation. Vert designs as T 307 of Antigua. P 13½×14.*

1623	35 c. multicoloured	15	40
	a. Sheetlet. Nos. 1623/6×2	6·25	
1624	50 c. multicoloured	25	50
1625	$2 bronze-green and black	90	1·10
1626	$4 multicoloured	1·90	2·00
1623/6	*Set of 4*	3·00	3·50

MS1627 70×100 mm. $6 multicoloured. P 14 4·75 5·50
Designs: (38×47 *mm*)—35 c. Queen Elizabeth II at Coronation (photograph by Cecil Beaton); 50 c. Ampulla and spoon; $2 Queen Elizabeth II leaving for Coronation; $4 Prince Henry's christening. (28½×42½ *mm*)—$6 "Queen Elizabeth II, 1954" (detail) (Pietro Annigoni).
Nos. 1623/6 were printed together in sheetlets of 8 containing two *se-tenant* blocks of 4.

(Litho Questa)

1993 (1 July). *Anniversaries and Events. Multicoloured designs as T 381 of Grenada. P 14.*

1628	15 c. "Painter and Model" (Picasso) (*horiz*)	55	30
1629	35 c. Keith Tkachuk and Dmitri Mironov (ice hockey, 1992) (*horiz*)	80	40
1630	50 c. Early telescope	85	50
1631	75 c. "Gra w Gudziki" (Ludomir Slerdinski) (*horiz*)	90	70
1632	75 c. Willy Brandt and Lyndon Johnson, 1961 (*horiz*)	90	70
1633	$1 "Artist and Model" (Picasso) (*horiz*)	1·00	80
1634	$2 "Pocalnak Mongolskiego Ksiecia" (S. Wirkiewicz) (*horiz*)	1·40	1·40
1635	$4 "The Drawing Lesson" (Picasso) (*horiz*)	2·25	2·25
1636	$4 Radio telescope	2·25	2·25
1637	$5 Alberto Tomba (Giant Slalom, 1984) (*horiz*)	2·25	2·40
1638	$5 Willy Brandt and Eleanor Hulles, 1957 (*horiz*)	2·25	2·40
1628/38	*Set of 11*	14·00	13·00

MS1639 Five sheets. (a) 105×75 mm. $5 Copernicus. (b) 105×75 mm. $6 Picasso. (c) 75×105 mm. $6 Emil Zogragski (70 metre ski jump, 1984). (d) 75×105 mm. $6 "Allegory" (detail) (Jan Wydra). (e) 105×75 mm. $6 Willy and Rut Brandt (brownish grey and black) (*horiz*) *Set of 5 sheets* 17·00 18·00
Anniversaries and Events:—Nos. 1628, 1633, 1635, **MS1639b**, 20th death anniv of Picasso (artist); Nos. 1629, 1637, **MS1639c**, Winter Olympic Games '94, Lillehammer; Nos. 1630, 1636, **MS1639a**, 450th death anniv of Copernicus (astronomer); Nos. 1631, 1634, **MS1639d**, "Polska '93" International Stamp Exhibition, Poznan; Nos. 1632, 1638, **MS1639e**, 80th birth anniv of Willy Brandt (German politician).

(Des R. Sauber. Litho B.D.T.)

1993 (13 July). *Songbirds. Multicoloured designs as T 382 of Grenada. P 14.*

1640	15 c. Painted Bunting	50	50
	a. Sheetlet. Nos. 1640/51	8·75	
1641	15 c. White-throated Sparrow	50	50
1642	25 c. Common Grackle	60	60
1643	25 c. Amazonian Royal Flycatcher	60	60
1644	35 c. Swallow Tanager	65	65
1645	35 c. Vermilion Flycatcher	65	65
1646	45 c. Black-headed Bunting	70	70
1647	50 c. Rose-breasted Grosbeak	70	70
1648	75 c. Corn Bunting	80	80
1649	75 c. Rose-breasted Thrush Tanager	80	80
1650	$1 Buff-throated Saltator	90	90
1651	$4 Plush-capped Finch	2·25	2·25
1640/51	*Set of 12*	8·75	8·75

MS1652 Two sheets, each 115×86 mm. (a) $6 Pine Grosbeak. (b) $6 Bohemian Waxwing *Set of 2 sheets* 10·00 11·00
Nos. 1640/51 were printed together, *se-tenant*, in sheetlets of 12 with the backgrounds forming a composite design.
Nos. 1645/6 show the scientific inscriptions transposed between the designs.

(Des I. MacLaury. Litho B.D.T.)

1993 (19 July). *Shells. Multicoloured designs as T 383 of Grenada. P 14.*

1653	15 c. Hawk-wing Conch (*Strombus raninus*)	25	25
	a. Sheetlet. Nos. 1653/64	5·75	
1654	15 c. Music Volute (*Volute musica*)	25	25
1655	25 c. Globe Vase (*Vasum globulus nuttingi*) and Deltoid Rock Shell (*Thais deltoidea*)	30	30
1656	35 c. Spiny Caribbean Vase (*Vasum capitellum*)	30	30
1657	35 c. American Common Sundial (*Architectonica nobilis*) and Common Purple Janthina (*Janthina janthina*)	30	30
1658	45 c. Toothed Donax (*Donax denticulatus*) and Gaudy Asaphis (*Asaphis deflorata*)	35	35
1659	45 c. Mouse Cone (*Conus mus*)	35	35
1660	50 c. Gold-mouthed Triton (*Cymatium nicobaricum*)	40	40
1661	75 c. Tulip Mussel (*Modiolus americanus*) and Trigonal Tivela (*Tivella mactroides*)	50	50
1662	75 c. Common Dove Shell (*Columbella mercatoria*) and Chestnut Latirus (*Leucozonia nassa*)	50	50
1663	$1 Wide-mouthed Purpura (*Purpura patula*)	60	60
1664	$4 American Thorny Oyster (*Spondylus americanus*) and Atlantic Wing Oyster (*Pteria columbus*)	1·90	2·00
1653/64	*Set of 12*	5·75	5·75

MS1665 Two sheets, each 76×106 mm. (a) $6 Atlantic Turkey Wing (*Arca zebra*). (b) $6 Zebra or Zigzag Periwinkle (*Littornia ziczac*) *Set of 2 sheets* 8·00 9·00
Nos. 1653/64 were printed together, *se-tenant*, in sheetlets of 12 with the backgrounds forming a composite design.

(Litho Questa)

1993 (13 Aug). *Asian International Stamp Exhibitions. Multicoloured designs as T 268 of Dominica. P 14×13½.*

(a) "Indopex '93", Surabaya, Indonesia

1666	35 c. National Museum, Central Jakarta (*horiz*)	40	20
1667	45 c. Sacred wheel and deer (*horiz*)	45	25
1668	$1 Ramayana relief, Panataran Temple (*horiz*)	70	60
1669	$1.50, "Bullock Carts" (Batara Lubis) (*horiz*)	1·25	1·25
	a. Sheetlet. Nos. 1669/74	6·50	
1670	$1.50, "Surat Irsa II" (A.D. Pirous) (*horiz*)	1·25	1·25
1671	$1.50, "Self-portrait with Goat" (Kartika) (*horiz*)	1·25	1·25
1672	$1.50, "The Cow-est Cow" (Ivan Sagito) (*horiz*)	1·25	1·25
1673	$1.50, "Rain Storm" (Sudjana Kerton) (*horiz*)	1·25	1·25
1674	$1.50, "Story of Pucuk Flower" (Effendi) (*horiz*)	1·25	1·25
1675	$5 Candi Tikus, Trawulan, East Java (*horiz*)	2·50	3·00
1666/75	*Set of 10*	10·00	10·00

MS1676 134×105 mm. $6 Banteng Cattle (*horiz*) 3·50 4·00

(b) "Taipei '93", Taiwan

1677	35 c. Macau Palace Casino, Hong Kong (*horiz*)	40	20
1678	45 c. Stone lion, Ming Tomb, Nanjing (*horiz*)	45	25
1679	$1 Stone camels, Ming Tomb, Nanjing (*horiz*)	70	60
1680	$1.50, Nesting quail incense burner (*horiz*)	1·25	1·25
	a. Sheetlet. Nos. 1680/5	6·50	
1681	$1.50, Standing quail incense burner (*horiz*)	1·25	1·25
1682	$1.50, Seated qilin incense burner (*horiz*)	1·25	1·25
1683	$1.50, Pottery horse, Han period (*horiz*)	1·25	1·25
1684	$1.50, Seated caparisoned elephant (*horiz*)	1·25	1·25
1685	$1.50, Cow in imitation of Delft faience (*horiz*)	1·25	1·25
1686	$5 Stone lion and elephant, Ming Tomb, Nanjing (*horiz*)	2·50	3·00
1677/86	*Set of 10*	10·00	10·00

MS1687 134×105 mm. $6 Sumatran Tiger, Mt Leuser National Park. P 13½×14 3·50 4·00

(c) "Bangkok 1993", Thailand

1688	35 c. Three Naga snakes, Chiang Mai's Temple (*horiz*)	40	20
1689	45 c. Sri Mariamman Temple, Singapore (*horiz*)	45	25
1690	$1 Topiary, Hua Hin Resort (*horiz*)	70	60
1691	$1.50, "Buddha's Victory over Mara" (*horiz*)	1·25	1·25
	a. Sheetlet. Nos. 1691/6	6·50	
1692	$1.50, "Mythological Elephant" (*horiz*)	1·25	1·25
1693	$1.50, "Battle with Mara" (Thon Buri) (*horiz*)	1·25	1·25
1694	$1.50, "Untitled" (Panya Wijinthanasarn) (*horiz*)	1·25	1·25
1695	$1.50, "Temple Mural" (*horiz*)	1·25	1·25
1696	$1.50, "Elephants in Pahcekha Buddha's Heaven" (*horiz*)	1·25	1·25
1697	$5 Pak Tai Temple, Cheung Chau Island (*horiz*)	2·50	3·00
1688/97	*Set of 10*	10·00	10·00

MS1698 134×105 mm. $6 Monkey from Chiang Kong. P 13½×14 3·50 4·00
Nos. 1669/74, 1680/5 and 1691/6 were each printed together, *se-tenant*, in sheetlets of 6.

(Des Rosemary DeFiglio. Litho Questa)

1993 (7 Sept). *World Cup Football Championship, U.S.A. (1994) (1st issue). Multicoloured designs as T 310 of Antigua. P 14.*

1699	15 c. McCall (Scotland) and Verri (Brazil) (*horiz*)	40	20
1700	25 c. Verri (Brazil) and Maradona (Argentina) (*horiz*)	50	20
1701	35 c. Schillaci (Italy) and Saldana (Uruguay) (*horiz*)	55	25
1702	45 c. Gullit (Holland) and Wright (England) (*horiz*)	60	35
1703	$1 Verri (Brazil) and Maradona (Argentina) (different) (*horiz*)	80	70
1704	$2 Zubizarreta and Fernandez (Spain) with Albert (Belgium) (*horiz*)	1·50	1·50
1705	$4 Hagi (Rumania) and McGrath (Ireland) (*horiz*)	2·50	3·00
1706	$5 Gorriz (Spain) and Scifo (Belgium) (*horiz*)	2·50	3·00
1699/1706	*Set of 8*	8·50	8·25

MS1707 Two sheets, each 104×75 mm. (a) $6 Foxboro Stadium, Massachusetts (*horiz*). (b) $6 Rudi Voeller (Germany) *Set of 2 sheets* 8·00 9·00
See also Nos. 1810/16.

(Des Rosemary DeFiglio. Litho Questa)

1993 (11 Nov). *65th Anniv of Mickey Mouse. Multicoloured designs as T 385 of Grenada showing Mickey Mouse in scenes from Walt Disney cartoon films. P 14×13½.*

1708	15 c. Mickey's Rival, 1936	40	25
1709	35 c. The Worm Turns, 1937	55	25
1710	50 c. The Pointer, 1939	70	55
1711	75 c. Society Dog Show, 1939	90	90
1712	$1 A Gentleman's Gentleman, 1941	1·00	1·00
1713	$2 The Little Whirlwind, 1941	1·75	2·00
1714	$4 Mickey Down Under, 1948	2·75	3·00
1715	$5 R'coon Dawg, 1951	2·75	3·00
1708/15	*Set of 8*	9·75	10·00

MS1716 Two sheets, each 127×102 mm. (a) $6 Lonesome Ghosts, 1937. P 14×13½. (b) $6 Mickey's Garden, 1935 (vert). P 13½×14 *Set of 2 sheets* 8·00 8·50

(Litho Questa)

1993 (22 Nov). *Christmas. Religious Paintings. Designs as T 270 of Dominica. Black, pale lemon and red (Nos. 1717, 1721/3 and MS1725a) or multicoloured (others). P 13½×14.*

1717	10 c. "Adoration of the Shepherds" (detail) (Dürer)	30	20
1718	25 c. "Adoration of the Magi" (detail) (Raphael)	40	20
1719	35 c. "Presentation at the Temple" (detail) (Raphael)	45	20
1720	50 c. "Adoration of the Magi" (different detail) (Raphael)	55	35
1721	75 c. "Adoration of the Shepherds" (different detail) (Dürer)	90	60
1722	$1 "Adoration of the Shepherds" (different detail) (Dürer)	1·00	75
1723	$4 "Adoration of the Shepherds" (different detail) (Dürer)	2·50	3·00

619

1724	$5 "Presentation at the Temple" (different detail) (Raphael)	2·50	3·00
1717/24	*Set of 8*	7·75	7·50

MS1725 Two sheets. (a) 102×128 mm. $6 "Adoration of the Shepherds" (different detail) (Dürer) (*horiz*). P 14×13½. (b) 128×102 mm. $6 "Annunciation" (detail) (Raphael). P 13½×14 *Set of 2 sheets* 7·00 8·00

(Litho Questa)

1993 (21 Dec). *Aviation Anniversaries. Multicoloured designs as T 386 of Grenada. P 14.*

1726	15 c. Avro Lancaster	30	20
1727	35 c. Blanchard's balloon crossing the River Delaware	15	20
1728	50 c. Airship LZ-127 *Graf Zeppelin* over Rio de Janeiro	50	35
1729	75 c. Hugo Eckener	65	50
1730	$3 Pres. Washington handing passport to Blanchard	1·40	1·50
1731	$5 Short Sunderland flying boat	2·50	2·75
1732	$5 Eckener in *Graf Zeppelin*	2·50	2·75
1726/32	*Set of 7*	7·25	7·50

MS1733 Three sheets. (a) 76×107 mm. $6 Supermarine Spitfire. (b) 107×76 mm. $6 Blanchard's balloon (*vert*). (c) 107×76 mm. $6 Eckener with Pres. Hoover *Set of 3 sheets* 10·50 11·50 Anniversaries:—Nos. 1726, 1731, **MS**1733a, 75th anniv of Royal Air Force; Nos. 1727, 1730, **MS**1733b, Bicentenary of First Airmail Flight; Nos. 1728/9, 1732, **MS**1733c, 125th birth anniv of Hugo Eckener (airship commander).

(Des K. Gromell. Litho Questa)

1993 (21 Dec). *Centenaries of Henry Ford's First Petrol Engine (Nos. 1735/6, MS1738b) and Karl Benz's First Four-wheeled Car (others). Horiz designs as T 387 of Grenada. Multicoloured. P 14.*

1734	25 c. Mercedes Benz "300 SLR", 1955	40	20
1735	45 c. Ford "Thunderbird", 1957	60	35
1736	$4 Ford "150-A" station wagon, 1929	2·75	3·25
1737	$5 Mercedes Benz "540 K"	2·75	3·25
1734/7	*Set of 4*	6·00	6·25

MS1738 Two sheets, 76×107 mm. (a) $6 Mercedes Benz "SSK", 1929. (b) $6 Ford "Model T", 1924. *Set of 2 sheets* 8·00 9·00

(Des Kerri Schiff. Litho Questa)

1993 (31 Dec). *Famous Paintings by Rembrandt and Matisse. Multicoloured designs as T 316 of Antigua. P 13½×14.*

1739	15 c. "Hendrickje Stoffels as Flora" (Rembrandt)	40	25
1740	35 c. "Lady and Gentleman in Black" (Rembrandt)	50	25
1741	50 c. "Aristotle with the Bust of Homer" (Rembrandt)	60	40
1742	75 c. "Interior: Flowers and Parakeets" (Matisse)	85	60
1743	$1 "Goldfish" (Matisse)	1·00	85
1744	$2 "The Girl with Green Eyes" (Matisse)	1·75	2·00
1745	$3 "Still Life with a Plaster Figure" (Matisse)	2·00	2·50
1746	$5 "Christ and the Woman of Samaria" (Rembrandt)	2·50	2·75
1739/46	*Set of 8*	8·75	8·75

MS1747 Two sheets. (a) 100×125 mm. $6 "Anna accused of stealing the Kid" (Rembrandt). P 13½×14. (b) 125×100 mm. $6 "Tea in the Garden" (detail) (Matisse) (*horiz*). P 14×13½ *Set of 2 sheets* 7·00 8·00

(Des W. Hanson. Litho Questa)

1994 (18 Feb). *"Hong Kong '94" International Stamp Exhibition (1st issue). Horiz designs as T 317 of Antigua. Multicoloured. P 14.*

1748	40 c. Hong Kong 1984 $5 aviation stamp and airliner at Kai Tak Airport	50	65
	a. Horiz pair. Nos. 1748/9	1·00	1·25
1749	40 c. Grenada Grenadines 1988 20 c. airships stamp and junk in Kowloon Bay	50	65

Nos. 1748/9 were printed together, *se-tenant*, in horizontal pairs throughout the sheet with the centre part of each pair forming a composite design.

(Des Kerri Schiff. Litho Questa)

1994 (18 Feb). *"Hong Kong '94" International Stamp Exhibition (2nd issue). Jade Sculptures. Horiz designs as T 318 of Antigua. Multicoloured. P 14.*

1750	45 c. White jade brush washer	35	40
	a. Sheetlet. Nos. 1750/5	1·90	
1751	45 c. Archaic jade brush washer	35	40
1752	45 c. Dark green jade brush washer	35	40
1753	45 c. Green jade almsbowl	35	40
1754	45 c. Archaic jade dog	35	40
1755	45 c. Yellow jade brush washer	35	40
1750/5	*Set of 6*	1·90	2·25

Nos. 1750/5 were printed together, *se-tenant*, in sheetlets of 6.

(Des Susan Carlson. Litho Questa)

1994 (6 Apr). *Fungi. Vert designs as T 390 of Grenada, but with white backgrounds. Multicoloured. P 14.*

1756	35 c. Hygrocybe hyphohaemacta	45	30
1757	45 c. Cantharellus cinnabarinus	55	35
1758	50 c. Marasmius haematocephalus	60	40
1759	75 c. Mycena pura	80	60
1760	$1 Gymnopilus russipes	90	80
1761	$2 Calocybe cyanocephala	1·40	1·50
1762	$4 Pluteus chrysophlebius	2·50	2·75
1763	$5 Chlorophyllum molybdites	2·50	2·75
1756/63	*Set of 8*	8·75	8·50

MS1764 Two sheets, each 100×70 mm. (a) $6 *Xeromphalina tenuipes*. (b) $6 *Collybia fibrosipes*. *Set of 2 sheets* 7·50 8·00 No. 1757 is inscribed "Cantherellus cinnabarinus" and No. 1762 "Pleuteus chrysophlebius", both in error.

(Des V. DiFate. Litho Questa)

1994 (13 Apr). *Prehistoric Animals. Multicoloured designs as T 391 of Grenada. P 14.*

1765	15 c. Spinosaurus	30	25
1766	35 c. Apatosaurus (Brontosaurus)	45	30
1767	45 c. Tyrannosaurus rex	50	35
1768	55 c. Triceratops	50	40
1769	$1 Pachycephalosaurus	85	75
1770	$2 Pteranodon	1·40	1·50
1771	$4 Parasaurolophus	2·50	2·75
1772	$5 Brachiosaurus	2·50	2·75
1765/72	*Set of 8*	8·00	8·25

MS1773 Two sheets, each 100×70 mm. (a) $6 Head of Brachiosaurus (*vert*). (b) $6 Spinosaurus and Tyrannosaurus rex fighting (*vert*) *Set of 2 sheets* 7·50 8·00

(Des W. Hanson. Litho B.D.T.)

1994 (4 Aug). *25th Anniv of First Moon Landing. Space Shuttle Challenger. Multicoloured designs as T 326 of Antigua. P 14.*

1774	$1.10, *Challenger* crew in training	1·00	1·10
	a. Sheetlet. Nos. 1774/9	5·50	
1775	$1.10, Christa McAuliffe (astronaut)	1·00	1·10
1776	$1.10, *Challenger* on launch pad	1·00	1·10
1777	$1.10, Gregory Jarvis (astronaut)	1·00	1·10
1778	$1.10, Ellison Onizuka (astronaut)	1·00	1·10
1779	$1.10, Ronald McNair (astronaut)	1·00	1·10
1774/9	*Set of 6*	5·50	6·00

MS1780 107×76 mm. $6 Judith Resnick (astronaut) (*vert*) 3·75 4·25 Nos. 1774/9 were printed together, *se-tenant*, in sheetlets of 6.

(Litho Questa)

1994 (4 Aug). *Centenary of International Olympic Committee. Gold Medal Winners. Horiz designs as T 327 of Antigua. Multicoloured. P 14.*

1781	50 c. Silke Renk (Germany) (javelin), 1992	35	30
1782	$1.50, Mark Spitz (U.S.A.) (swimming), 1972	90	1·10

MS1783 106×77 mm. $6 Japanese team (Nordic skiing), 1994 3·25 3·75

(Litho Questa)

1994 (4 Aug). *International Year of the Family. Horiz design as T 328 of Antigua. P 14.*

1784	$1 Grenadines family	60	60

(Des J. Batchelor. Litho Questa)

1994 (4 Aug). *50th Anniv of D-Day. Horiz designs as T 331 of Antigua. Multicoloured. P 14.*

1785	40 c. Churchill bridge-laying tank	35	30
1786	$2 Sherman "Firefly" tank leaving landing craft	1·00	1·25
1787	$3 Churchill "Crocodile" flame-thrower	1·60	1·75
1785/7	*Set of 3*	2·75	3·00

MS1788 107×76 mm. $6 Sherman "Crab" flail tank 3·25 3·75

(Des Kerri Schiff. Litho Questa (Nos. 1791/8, **MS**1800), B.D.T. (others))

1994 (4 Aug). *"Philakorea '94" International Stamp Exhibition, Seoul (1st issue). Multicoloured designs as T 281 of Dominica. P 13½×14 (Nos. 1791/8) or 14 (others).*

1789	40 c. Onung Tomb (*horiz*)	30	30
1790	$1 Stone pagoda, Mt Namsam (*horiz*)	55	55
1791	$1 "Admiring Spring in the Country" (left detail) (Sin Yunbok)	55	55
	a. Sheetlet. Nos. 1791/8	4·50	
1792	$1 "Admiring Spring in the Country" (right detail)	55	55
1793	$1 "Woman on Dano Day" (left detail) (Sin Yunbok)	55	55
1794	$1 "Woman on Dano Day" (right detail) (Sin Yunbok)	55	55
1795	$1 "Enjoying Lotuses while Listening to Music" (left detail) (Sin Yunbok)	55	55
1796	$1 "Enjoying Lotuses while Listening to Music" (right detail)	55	55
1797	$1 "Women by a Crystal Stream" (left detail) (Sin Yunbok)	55	55
1798	$1 "Women by a Crystal Stream" (right detail)	55	55
1799	$4 Pusan (*horiz*)	2·25	2·25
1789/99	*Set of 11*	6·75	6·75

MS1800 70×102 mm. $6 "Blacksmith's Shop" (detail) (Kim Duksin). P 14 3·25 3·75 Nos. 1791/8, each 26×49 mm, were printed together, *se-tenant*, in sheetlets of 8. Paintings are shown across horizontal pairs without white vertical margins in the centre.

(Des Claudia Sergeant. Litho Questa)

1994 (7 Aug). *Orchids. Multicoloured designs as T 392 of Grenada. P 14.*

1801	15 c. Cattleya aurantiaca	35	25
1802	25 c. Blettia patula	40	25
1803	45 c. Sobralia macrantha	50	30
1804	75 c. Encyclia belizensis	70	55
1805	$1 Sophrolaeliocattleya	85	75
1806	$2 Encyclia fragrans	1·40	1·50
1807	$4 Schombocattleya	2·50	2·75
1808	$5 Brassolaeliocattleya	2·50	2·75
1801/8	*Set of 8*	8·25	8·25

MS1809 Two sheets, each 100×70 mm. (a) $6 *Ornithidium coccineum* (*horiz*). (b) $6 *Brassavola nodosa* (*horiz*) *Set of 2 sheets* 7·50 8·00

(Litho Questa)

1994 (11 Aug). *World Cup Football Championship, U.S.A. (2nd issue). Vert designs as T 393 of Grenada. Multicoloured. P 14.*

1810	75 c. Steve Mark (Grenada)	50	50
	a. Sheetlet. Nos. 1810/15	2·75	

1811	75 c. Jurgen Kohler (Germany)	50	50
1812	75 c. Almir (Brazil)	50	50
1813	75 c. Michael Windiscmann (U.S.A.)	50	50
1814	75 c. Guiseppe Giannini (Italy)	50	50
1815	75 c. Rashidi Yekini (Nigeria)	50	50
1810/15	*Set of 6*	2·75	2·75

MS1816 Two sheets, each 99×70 mm. (a) $6 Kemari (ancient Japanese game). (b) $6 Hand holding trophy. *Set of 2 sheets* 7·50 8·50 Nos. 1810/15 were printed together, *se-tenant*, in sheetlets of 6.

106 Mickey Mouse and Unjin Mirŭk Window from Kwanch Ok Temple

(Litho Questa)

1994 (16 Aug). *"Philakorea '94" International Stamp Exhibition, Seoul (2nd issue). T 106 and similar multicoloured designs showing Walt Disney cartoon characters. P 14×13½.*

1817	3 c. Type 106	15	15
1818	4 c. Goofy imitating statue of Admiral Yi, Chŏnju	15	15
1819	5 c. Cousin Gus and Donald Duck eating dinner	15	15
1820	10 c. Mickey playing flute	20	15
1821	15 c. Goofy with Tolharubang (statue)	30	20
1822	15 c. Type 106	30	20
1823	20 c. Mickey and Minnie at Hyang-Wonjŏng	30	20
1824	35 c. As 4 c.	40	25
1825	50 c. As 5 c.	50	35
1826	75 c. As 10 c.	70	55
1827	$1 As 15 c.	85	75
1828	$2 As 20 c.	1·40	1·50
1829	$4 Mickey as Somori-Kut shaman	2·50	2·75
1830	$5 Minnie holding ceremonial fan	2·50	2·75
1817/30	*Set of 14*	9·50	9·00

MS1831 Two sheets, each 130×103 mm. (a) $6 Minnie beating Buk drum (*vert*). (b) $6 Mickey in swimming pool at Pugok Hawaii (*vert*). P 13½×14 *Set of 2 sheets* 7·50 8·50

(Litho Questa)

1994 (1 Sept). *First Recipients of Order of the Caribbean Community. Horiz designs as Nos. 2046/8 of Antigua. Multicoloured. P 14.*

1832	25 c. Sir Shridath Ramphal	10	10
1833	50 c. William Demas	25	30
1834	$2 Derek Walcott	1·40	1·60
1832/34	*Set of 3*	1·60	1·75

(Des P. Gonzalez. Litho Questa)

1994 (1 Sept). *Fishes. Horiz designs as T 394 of Grenada. Multicoloured. P 14.*

1835	75 c. Porkfish	55	55
	a. Sheetlet. Nos. 1835/46	6·00	
1836	75 c. Blue Chromis	55	55
1837	75 c. Caribbean Reef Shark (facing left)	55	55
1838	75 c. Long-spined Squirrelfish	55	55
1839	75 c. Four-eyed Butterflyfish	55	55
1840	75 c. Blue Head	55	55
1841	75 c. Royal Gramma	55	55
1842	75 c. Sharp-nosed Puffer	55	55
1843	75 c. Reid's Seahorse	55	55
1844	75 c. Black-barred Soldierfish	55	55
1845	75 c. Red-lipped Blenny	55	55
1846	75 c. Painted Wrasse	55	55
1847	75 c. Yellow-tailed Snapper	55	55
	a. Sheetlet. Nos. 1847/58	6·00	
1848	75 c. Caribbean Reef Shark (facing right)	55	55
1849	75 c. Great Barracuda	55	55
1850	75 c. Red-tailed Parrotfish	55	55
1851	75 c. Blue Tang	55	55
1852	75 c. Queen Angelfish	55	55
1853	75 c. Red Hind	55	55
1854	75 c. Rock Beauty	55	55
1855	75 c. Queen Parrotfish	55	55
1856	75 c. Spanish Hogfish	55	55
1857	75 c. Spotted Moray	55	55
1858	75 c. Queen Triggerfish	55	55
1835/58	*Set of 24*	12·00	12·00

MS1859 Two sheets, each 102×72 mm. (a) $6 Head of Queen Angelfish. (b) $6 Head of Painted Wrasse. *Set of 2 sheets* 7·50 8·00 Nos. 1835/46 and 1847/58 were printed together, *se-tenant*, in sheetlets of 12 each forming composite designs.

(Litho Questa)

1994 (5 Dec). *Christmas. Religious Paintings by Bartolome Murillo. Vert designs as T 336 of Antigua. Multicoloured. P 13½×14.*

1860	15 c. "The Annunciation"	30	20
1861	35 c. "The Adoration of the Shepherds"	40	20
1862	50 c. "Virgin and Child with St. Rose"	50	30
1863	50 c. "Flight into Egypt"	50	30
1864	75 c. "Virgin and Child"	70	45
1865	$1 "Virgin of the Rosary"	85	70
1866	$4 "The Holy Family"	2·50	2·75
1860/6	*Set of 7*	5·25	4·75

MS1867 Two sheets, each 85×95 mm. (a) $6 "Adoration of the Shepherds" (*different*) (detail). (b) 95×125 mm. $6 "The Holy Family with a Little Bird" (detail) *Set of 2 sheets* 7·50 8·00

(Litho Questa)

1995 (10 Jan). *Birds. Multicoloured designs as T 397 of Grenada. Multicoloured. P 14.*

1868	25 c. Scaly-breasted Ground Dove (*vert*)		45	35
1869	50 c. White-winged Dove ..		75	55
1870	$2 Inca Dove (*vert*)	.. ..	1·75	1·75
1871	$4 Mourning Dove ..	.. ..	3·00	3·75
1868/71	.. ..	*Set of 4*	5·50	5·75

(Des A. Melville-Brown. Litho Questa)

1995 (12 Jan). *Centenary of First English Cricket Tour to the West Indies. Multicoloured designs as T 329 of Antigua. P 14.*

1872	50 c. Mike Atherton (England) and Wisden Trophy		55	45
1873	75 c. Curtly Ambrose (West Indies) (*vert*)		75	75
1874	$1 Brian Lara (West Indies) (*vert*)		90	1·10
1872/4		*Set of 3*	2·00	2·10
MS1875	75×95 mm. $3 West Indian team, 1994		2·25	2·50

107 Aspects of London, National Flag and Map

108 Pig

(Des S. and Dot Barlowe. Litho Questa)

1995 (10 Mar). *Capitals of the World. T 107 and similar vert designs showing aspects of various cities, national flags and maps. Multicoloured. P 14.*

1876	$1 Type 107		65	70
	a. Sheetlet. Nos. 1876/85		6·00	
1877	$1 Cairo		65	70
1878	$1 Vienna ..		65	70
1879	$1 Paris		65	70
1880	$1 Rome		65	70
1881	$1 Budapest ..		65	70
1882	$1 Moscow ..		65	70
1883	$1 Peking ("Beijing") ..		65	70
1884	$1 Tokyo ..		65	70
1885	$1 Washington ..		65	70
1876/85		*Set of 10*	6·00	6·25

Nos. 1876/85 were spotted together, *se-tenant*, in sheetlets of 10.

(Des Y. Lee. Litho Questa)

1995 (21 Apr). *Chinese New Year ("Year of the Pig"). T 108 and similar multicoloured designs showing "GRENADA GRENADINES" in colours indicated. P 14¹/₂.*

1886	75 c. Type 108 (deep reddish violet) ..		45	50
	a. Block of 4. Nos. 1886/9		1·60	
1887	75 c. Pig (deep carmine) ..		45	50
1888	75 c. Pig (lake-brown) ..		45	50
1889	75 c. Pig (scarlet-vermilion) ..		45	50
1886/9		*Set of 4*	1·60	1·75
MS1890	Two sheets. (a) 106×77 mm. $2 Two pigs (*horiz*). (b) 67×83 mm. Nos. 1886/9			
		Set of 2 sheets	3·25	3·50

Nos. 1886/9 were printed together, *se-tenant*, as blocks of 4 in sheetlets of 16.

109 Bull Shark and Diver

(Des Y. Lee. Litho Questa)

1995 (3 May). *Marine Life of the Caribbean. T 109 and similar horiz designs. Multicoloured. P 14.*

1891	$1 Type 109		65	70
	a. Sheetlet. Nos. 1891/9		5·25	
1892	$1 Great White Shark ..		65	70
1893	$1 Octopus and shoal of fish ..		65	70
1894	$1 Great Barracuda ..		65	70
1895	$1 Green Moray ..		65	70
1896	$1 Spotted Eagle Ray ..		65	70
1897	$1 Sea Snake ..		65	70
1898	$1 Stingray ..		65	70
1899	$1 Grouper		65	70
1900	$1 Dolphins ..		65	70
	a. Sheetlet. Nos. 1900/8 ..		5·25	
1901	$1 Lionfish ..		65	70
1902	$1 Sea Turtle and Rock Beauty (fish) ..		65	70
1903	$1 Blue-cheeked Butterflyfish and Nurse Shark		65	70
1904	$1 Queen Angelfish ..		65	70
1905	$1 Grouper and Coney ..		65	70
1906	$1 Rainbow Eel and Spotted Moray ..		65	70
1907	$1 Sun Flower-star and Coral Crab ..		65	70
1908	$1 Octopus on sea bed ..		65	70
1891/1908		*Set of 18*	10·50	11·00
MS1909	Two sheets, each 107×77 mm. (a) $5 French Angelfish. (b) $6 Smooth Hammerhead			
		Set of 2 sheets	4·75	5·50

Nos. 1891/9 and 1900/8 were printed together, *se-tenant*, in sheetlets of 9.

110 Suffolk Punch

(Des Jennifer Toombs. Litho Questa)

1995 (3 May). *Domestic Animals. T 110 and similar horiz designs. Multicoloured. P 14.*

1910	15 c. Type 110	.. ..	40	30
1911	25 c. Shetland pony ..		50	30
1912	75 c. Blue Persian (cat) ..		50	55
	a. Sheetlet. Nos. 1912/23		5·50	
1913	75 c. Sorrel Abyssinian (cat) ..		50	55
1914	75 c. White Angora (cat) ..		50	55
1915	75 c. Brown Burmese (cat) ..		50	55
1916	75 c. Red Tabby Exotic Shorthair (cat) ..		50	55
1917	75 c. Seal-point Birman (cat) ..		50	55
1918	75 c. Korat (cat) ..		50	55
1919	75 c. Norwegian Forest Cat		70	55
1920	75 c. Lilac-point Balinese (cat) ..		50	55
1921	75 c. British Shorthair (cat) ..		50	55
1922	75 c. Red Self Longhair (cat) ..		50	55
1923	75 c. Calico Manx (cat) ..		50	55
1924	75 c. Shetland Sheepdog ..		50	55
	a. Sheetlet. Nos. 1924/35		5·50	
1925	75 c. Bull Terrier ..		50	55
1926	75 c. Afghan Hound ..		50	55
1927	75 c. Scottish Terrier ..		50	55
1928	75 c. Labrador Retriever ..		50	55
1929	75 c. English Springer Spaniel ..		50	55
1930	75 c. Samoyed (dog) ..		50	55
1931	75 c. Irish Setter ..		50	55
1932	75 c. Border Collie ..		50	55
1933	75 c. Pekingese ..		50	55
1934	75 c. Dachshund ..		50	55
1935	75 c. Weimaraner (dog) ..		50	55
1936	$1 Arab ..		70	70
1937	$3 Shire horse ..		1·75	2·00
1910/37		*Set of 28*	13·00	14·00
MS1938	Two sheets, each 105×75 mm. (a) $6 Seal-point Colourpoint (cat). (b) $6 English Setter .. .. *Set of 2 sheets*		7·00	7·50

Nos. 1912/23 and 1924/35 were printed together, *se-tenant*, in sheetlets of 12.

(Litho Questa)

1995 (5 May). *Centenary of Sierra Club (environmental protection society) (1992). Endangered Species. Multicoloured designs as T 320 of Antigua. P 14.*

1939	$1 Spotted Owl ..	.. ..	65	70
	a. Sheetlet. Nos. 1939/47	..	5·25	
1940	$1 Brown Pelican on perch ..		65	70
1941	$1 Head of Brown Pelican ..		65	70
1942	$1 Head of Jaguarundi ..		65	70
1943	$1 Jaguarundi looking over shoulder ..		65	70
1944	$1 Maned Wolf in undergrowth ..		65	70
1945	$1 American Wood Stork standing on two legs ..		65	70
1946	$1 American Wood Stork standing on one leg ..		65	70
1947	$1 Close-up of Maned Wolf ..		65	70
1948	$1 Brown Pelican (*horiz*) ..		65	70
	a. Sheetlet. Nos. 1948/56		5·25	
1949	$1 Close-up of Spotted Owl (*horiz*) ..		65	70
1950	$1 Spotted Owl chick (*horiz*) ..		65	70
1951	$1 Jaguarundi (*horiz*) ..		65	70
1952	$1 Central American Spider Monkey sitting with young (*horiz*)		65	70
1953	$1 Central American Spider Monkey carrying young (*horiz*)		65	70
1954	$1 Central American Spider Monkey swinging from branch (*horiz*)		65	70
1955	$1 American Wood Stork (*horiz*) ..		65	70
1956	$1 Pair of Maned Wolves (*horiz*) ..		65	70
1939/56		*Set of 18*	10·50	11·00

Nos. 1939/47 and 1948/56 were printed together, *se-tenant*, in sheetlets of 9.

(Litho Questa)

1995 (8 May). *18th World Scout Jamboree, Netherlands. Horiz designs as T 403 of Grenada. Multicoloured. P 14.*

1957	75 c. Grenadian scout on beach ..		60	70
	a. Horiz strip of 3. Nos. 1957/9		2·25	
1958	$1 Scout with staff on hill ..		80	90
1959	$2 Scout saluting and national flag		1·10	1·25
1957/9		*Set of 3*	2·25	2·50
MS1960	107×77 mm. $6 Scout snorkelling		3·00	3·50

Nos. 1957/9 were printed together in sheets of 9 containing three *se-tenant* horizontal strips of 3.

(Des W. Wright. Litho Questa)

1995 (8 May). *50th Anniv of End of Second World War in Europe. Bombers. Horiz designs as T 340 of Antigua. Multicoloured. P 14.*

1961	$2 Avro Type 683 Lancaster ..		1·25	1·25
	a. Sheetlet. Nos. 1961/8 ..		9·00	
1962	$2 Junkers Ju 88 ..		1·25	1·25
1963	$2 North American B-25 Mitchell ..		1·25	1·25
1964	$2 Boeing B-17 Flying Fortress ..		1·25	1·25
1965	$2 Petlyakov Pe-2 ..		1·25	1·25
1966	$2 Martin B-26 Marauder ..		1·25	1·25
1967	$2 Heinkel He 111H ..		1·25	1·25
1968	$2 Consolidated B-24 Liberator ..		1·25	1·25
1961/8		*Set of 8*	9·00	9·00
MS1969	105×75 mm. $6 Pres. Truman and newspaper headline (57×43 mm) ..		3·00	3·50

Nos. 1961/8 were printed together, *se-tenant*, in sheetlets of 8 with the stamps arranged in two horizontal strips of 4 separated by a gutter showing a De Havilland D.H.98 Mosquito.

(Des R. Martin. Litho Questa)

1995 (8 May). *50th Anniv of United Nations. Vert designs as T 404 of Grenada. Multicoloured. P 14.*

1970	75 c. U. N. Headquarters, New York, and flag		60	70
	a. Horiz strip of 3. Nos. 1970/2		2·25	
1971	$1 Trygve Lie (first Secretary-General) ..		80	90
1972	$2 U.N. soldier		1·10	1·25
1970/2		*Set of 3*	2·25	2·50
MS1973	101×76 mm. $6 Peace dove over emblem		2·50	3·00

Nos. 1970/2 were printed together in sheets of 9 containing three *se-tenant* horizontal strips of 3, each forming a composite design.

(Des R. Martin. Litho Questa)

1995 (8 May). *50th Anniv of Food and Agriculture Organization. Vert designs as T 405 of Grenada. Multicoloured. P 14.*

1974	75 c. Man hoeing		60	70
	a. Horiz strip of 3. Nos. 1974/6		2·25	
1975	$1 Woman hoeing ..		80	90
1976	$1 Man and woman hoeing ..		1·10	1·25
1974/6		*Set of 3*	2·25	2·50
MS1977	106×76 mm. $6 Child eating with chopsticks		2·50	3·00

Nos. 1974/6 were printed together in sheets of 9 containing three *se-tenant* horizontal strips of 3, each forming a composite design.

(Litho Questa)

1995 (8 May). *90th Anniv of Rotary International. Multicoloured designs as T 406 of Grenada. P 14.*

1978	$5 Paul Harris (founder) and logo (*horiz*)		2·50	3·00
MS1979	106×76 mm. $6 Rotary Club and International logos (*horiz*)		2·75	3·25

(Litho Questa)

1995 (8 May). *95th Birthday of Queen Elizabeth the Queen Mother. Vert designs as T 344 of Antigua. P 13¹/₂×14.*

1980	$1.50, orange-brown, pale brown and black		1·10	1·10
	a. Sheetlet. Nos. 1980/3×2		8·00	
1981	$1.50, multicoloured ..		1·10	1·10
1982	$1.50, multicoloured ..		1·10	1·10
1983	$1.50, multicoloured ..		1·10	1·10
1980/3		*Set of 4*	4·00	4·00
MS1984	102×127 mm. $6 multicoloured		3·75	4·00

Designs:—No. 1980, Queen Elizabeth the Queen Mother (pastel drawing); No. 1981, At Remembrance Day service; No. 1982, At desk (oil painting); No. 1983, Wearing green hat; No. MS1984, Unveiling memorial to Blitz victims.

Nos. 1980/3 were printed together in sheetlets of 8, containing two *se-tenant* horizontal strips of 4.

(Des J. Batchelor. Litho Questa)

1995 (8 May). *50th Anniv of End of Second World War in the Pacific. Horiz designs as T 340 of Antigua. Multicoloured. P 14.*

1985	$2 Mitsubishi G4M1 "Betty" (bomber) ..		1·40	1·50
	a. Sheetlet. Nos. 1985/90		7·25	
1986	$2 Japanese submarine "I 14" with seaplane on catapult		1·40	1·50
1987	$2 Mitsubishi GM31 "Nell" (bomber) ..		1·40	1·50
1988	$2 Akizuki (Japanese destroyer) ..		1·40	1·50
1989	$2 Kirishima (Japanese battleship) ..		1·40	1·50
1990	$2 Asigari (Japanese cruiser) ..		1·40	1·50
1985/90		*Set of 6*	7·25	8·00
MS1991	108×76 mm. $6 Japanese Aichi D3A1 "Val" dive bomber ..		2·75	3·25

Nos. 1985/90 were printed together, *se-tenant*, in sheetlets of 6 with the stamps arranged in two horizontal strips of 3 separated by a gutter showing Yokosuka MXY-7 "Okha" (Kamikaze airplane) attacking ships.

(Litho B.D.T.)

1995 (23 June). *Olympic Games, Atlanta (1996). Designs as T 407 of Grenada. Multicoloured. P 14.*

1992	15 c. Rosemary Ackerman (East Germany) (high jump) (*horiz*) ..		30	30
	a. Horiz strip of 3. Nos. 1992/4		80	
1993	15 c. Li Ning (China) (gymnastics) (*horiz*)		30	30
1994	15 c. Denise Parker (U.S.A.) (archery) (*horiz*)		30	30
1995	$3 Terry Carlisle (U.S.A.) (skeet shooting) (*horiz*)		1·75	2·00
	a. Horiz strip of 3. Nos. 1995/7		4·75	
1996	$3 Kathleen Nord (East Germany) (swimming) (*horiz*)		1·75	2·00
1997	$3 Brigit Schmidt (East Germany) (canoeing) (*horiz*)		1·75	2·00
1992/7		*Set of 6*	5·50	6·25
MS1998	Two sheets, each 102×72 mm. (a) $6 Dan Gable (U.S.A.) and Kikuo Wada (Japan) (wrestling). (b) $6 George Foreman (U.S.A.) (boxing) .. .. *Set of 2 sheets*		6·50	7·00

Nos. 1992/4 and 1995/7 were printed in sheets of 12 containing four *se-tenant* horizontal strips of 3.

111 Brown Pelican

(Des T. Wood. Litho Questa)

1995 (5 Sept). *Birds of the Caribbean. T* **111** *and similar horiz designs. Multicoloured. P* 14.

1999	10 c. Type 111		30	40
2000	15 c. Black-necked Stilt		30	40
2001	25 c. Cuban Trogon		30	30
2002	35 c. Greater Flamingo		40	30
2003	75 c. Imperial Amazon		65	45
2004	$1 Pintail		80	85
2005	$1 Great Blue Heron		80	85
	a. Sheetlet. Nos. 2005/12		5·50	
2006	$1 Jamaican Tody		80	85
2007	$1 Laughing Gull		80	85
2008	$1 Purple-throated Carib		80	85
2009	$1 Red-legged Thrush		80	85
2010	$1 Ruddy Duck		80	85
2011	$1 Common Shoveler		80	85
2012	$1 West Indian Red-bellied Woodpecker		80	85
2013	$2 Ringed Kingfisher		1·40	1·60
2014	$3 Stripe-headed Tanager		1·75	2·00
1999/2014		*Set of 16*	11·00	12·00

MS2015 Two sheets, each 104×73 mm. (a) $5 Village Weaver. (b) $5 Blue-hooded Euphonia
Set of 2 sheets 7·00 7·50

Nos. 2005/12 were printed together, *se-tenant*, in sheetlets of 8, and, together with No. **MS**2015, carry the "Singapore '95" exhibition logo.

No. 2001 is inscr "Cuban Trogon", No. 2008 "Purple-throated Carb" and No. 2013 "Ringed King Fisher", all in error.

(Des Walt Disney Company and Rosemary DeFiglio. Litho Questa)

1995 (2 Oct). *Mickey's Pirate Adventure. Multicoloured designs as T* **415** *of Grenada showing Walt Disney cartoon characters. P* 14×13½.

2016	10 c. Goofy and Donald Duck with treasure chests (*horiz*)		20	20
2017	35 c. Mickey and Minnie Mouse at ship's wheel (*horiz*)		30	20
2018	75 c. Mickey, Donald and Goofy opening chest (*horiz*)		55	40
2019	$1 Big Pete and rats confronting Mickey (*horiz*)		70	60
2020	$2 Mickey, Goofy and Donald in boat (*horiz*)		1·40	1·75
2021	$5 Goofy fighting rat pirate with mop (*horiz*)		3·25	3·75
2016/21		*Set of 6*	5·50	6·25

MS2022 Two sheets, each 108×130 mm. (a) $6 Goofy and cannon-balls. (b) $6 Monkey pinching Mickey's nose. P 13½×14 . . *Set of 2 sheets* 7·50 8·00

(Des R. Martin. Litho Questa)

1995 (18 Oct). *Centenary of Nobel Trust Fund. Vert designs as T* **416** *of Grenada. Multicoloured. P* 14.

2023/51	75 c. × 2, $1×27		15·00	17·00

MS2052 Three sheets, each 105×76 mm. (a) $6 Sir Winston Churchill (1953 Literature). (b) $6 Willy Brandt (1971 Peace). (c) $6 Albert Schweitzer (1952 Peace) . . *Set of 3 sheets* 9·00 10·00

Designs:—75 c. W. Arthur Lewis (1979 Economics); Derek Walcott (1992 Literature); $1 Jules Border (1919 Medicine); René Cassin (1968 Peace); Verner von Heidenstam (1916 Literature); José Echegaray (1904 Literature); Otto Wallach (1910 Chemistry); Corneille Heymans (1938 Medicine); Ivar Giaever (1973 Physics); Sir William Cremer (1903 Peace); John Strutt (1904 Physics); James Franck (1925 Physics); Tobias Asser (1911 Peace); Carl Spitteler (1919 Literature); Christiaan Eijkman (1929 Medicine); Ragnar Granit (1967 Medicine); Frederic Passy (1901 Peace); Louis Neel (1970 Physics); Sir William Ramsay (1904 Chemistry); Philip Noel-Baker (1959 Peace); Heike Önnes (1913 Physics); Fridtjof Nansen (1922 Peace); Sir Ronald Ross (1902 Peace); Paul Müller (1948 Medicine); Allvar Gullstrand (1911 Medicine); Gerhart Hauptmann (1912 Literature); Hans Spemann (1935 Medicine); Cecil Powell (1950 Physics); Walther Bothe (1954 Physics).

Nos. 2025/33, 2034/42 and 2043/51 were each printed together, *se-tenant*, in sheetlets of 9 forming composite designs.

No. 2027 (Von Heidenstam) is inscribed "1906" and No. 2044 is inscribed "Fridtjof Nanser", both in error.

112 Nita Naldi and Rudolph Valentino

(Des J. Iskowitz. Litho Questa)

1995 (3 Nov). *Centenary of Cinema. T* **112** *and similar multicoloured designs. P* 13½.

2053	$1 Type 112		65	70
	a. Sheetlet. Nos. 2053/61		5·25	
2054	$1 Ramon Novaro and Alice Terry		65	70
2055	$1 Frederic March and Joan Crawford		65	70
2056	$1 Clark Gable and Vivien Leigh		65	70
2057	$1 Barbara Stanwyck and Burt Lancaster		65	70
2058	$1 Warren Beatty and Natalie Wood		65	70
2059	$1 Spencer Tracy and Katharine Hepburn		65	70
2060	$1 Humphrey Bogart and Lauren Bacall		65	70
2061	$1 Omar Sharif and Julie Christie		65	70
2062	$1 Marion Davis		65	70
	a. Sheetlet. Nos. 2062/70		5·25	

2063	$1 Marlene Dietrich		65	70
2064	$1 Lillian Gish		65	70
2065	$1 Bette Davis		65	70
2066	$1 Elizabeth Taylor		65	70
2067	$1 Veronica Lake		65	70
2068	$1 Ava Gardner		65	70
2069	$1 Grace Kelly		65	70
2070	$1 Kim Novak		65	70
2053/70		*Set of 18*	10·50	11·00

MS2071 Two sheets. (a) 72×102 mm. $6 Sophia Loren. (b) 102×72 mm. $6 Greta Garbo and John Gilbert (*horiz*) . . *Set of 2 sheets* 6·50 7·00

Nos. 2053/61 and 2062/70 were each printed together, *se-tenant*, in sheetlets of 9 forming composite designs.

(Litho Questa)

1995 (7 Nov). *Racing Cars. Multicoloured designs as T* **423** *of Grenada. P* 14.

2072	10 c. Williams-Renault Formula 1, 1990s		20	20
2073	25 c. Porsche "956", Le Mans, 1980s		30	20
2074	35 c. Lotus "John Player Special", 1970s		40	20
2075	75 c. Ford "GT-40", 1960s		65	45
2076	$2 Mercedes-Benz "W196", 1950s		1·50	1·75
2077	$3 Mercedes "SSK", 1920s		2·00	2·25
2072/7		*Set of 6*	4·50	4·50

MS2078 103×73 mm. $6 Jackie Stewart in Tyrrell-Ford, 1971 (*vert*) . . 3·25 3·50

113 Man on Donkey   **114** Symbolic Rat and Candle

(Litho Questa)

1995 (7 Nov). *Local Transport. T* **113** *and similar horiz design. Multicoloured. P* 14.

2079	35 c. Type 113		25	20
2080	75 c. Local bus		40	50

(Des W. Wright. Litho Questa)

1995 (7 Nov). *Evolution of Sailing Ships. Horiz designs as T* **427** *of Grenada. Multicoloured. P* 14.

2081	$1 *Preussen* (full-rigged ship)		65	70
	a. Sheetlet. Nos. 2081/6		3·50	
2082	$1 Japanese junk		65	70
2083	$1 Caribbean pirate ship		65	70
2084	$1 *Mayflower* (Pilgrim Fathers)		65	70
2085	$1 Chinese junk		65	70
2086	$1 *Santa Maria* (Columbus)		65	70
2081/6		*Set of 6*	3·50	3·75

MS2087 103×73 mm. $5 Spanish galleon (56×41 mm) . . 2·50 3·00

Nos. 2081/6 were printed together, *se-tenant*, in sheetlets of 6.

(Litho Questa)

1995 (28 Nov). *Christmas. Religious Paintings. Vert designs as T* **357** *of Antigua. Multicoloured. P* 13½×14.

2088	10 c. "Immaculate Conception" (Piero di Cosimo)		15	10
2089	15 c. "St. Michael dedicating Arms to the Madonna" (Le Nain)		20	10
2090	35 c. "Annunciation" (Lorenzo di Credi)		25	20
2091	50 c. "The Holy Family" (Jacob Jordaens)		40	30
2092	$3 "Madonna and Child" (Lippi)		1·75	2·00
2093	$5 "Madonna and Child with Ten Saints" (Fiorentino)		3·00	3·50
2088/93		*Set of 6*	5·25	5·50

MS2094 102×127 mm. (a) $6 "Adoration of the Shepherds" (detail) (Van Oost). (b) $6 "Holy Family" (detail) (Del Start) . . *Set of 2 sheets* 7·00 7·50

(Des Y. Lee. Litho Questa)

1996 (2 Jan). *Chinese New Year ("Year of the Rat"). T* **114** *and similar multicoloured designs. P* 14½.

2095	75 c. Type 114 (dull blue background)		35	40
	a. Block of 4. Nos. 2095/8		1·40	
2096	75 c. Type 114 (lilac background)		35	40
2097	75 c. Type 114 (orange-brown background)		35	40
2098	75 c. Type 114 (yellow-green background)		35	40
2095/8		*Set of 4*	1·40	1·60

MS2099 69×84 mm. Nos. 2095/8 1·40 1·60
MS2100 76×106 mm. $2 Two rats (*horiz*) 85 90

Nos. 2095/8 were printed together, *se-tenant*, as blocks of 4 in sheets of 16, with the four designs showing different Chinese characters.

(Litho Questa)

1996 (29 Jan). *Works of Art by Dürer and Rubens. Vert designs as T* **421** *of Grenada. Multicoloured. P* 13½×14.

2101	15 c. "The Centaur Family" (Dürer)		15	10
2102	35 c. "Oriental Ruler Seated" (Dürer)		25	20
2103	50 c. "The Entombment" (Dürer)		40	30
2104	75 c. "Man in Armour" (Rubens)		55	40
2105	$1 "Peace embracing Plenty" (Rubens)		65	60
2106	$2 "Departure of Lot" (Rubens)		1·25	1·50
2107	$3 "The Four Evangelists" (Rubens)		1·75	2·00
2108	$5 "Knight, Death and Devil" (Dürer)		3·00	3·50
2101/8		*Set of 8*	7·25	7·75

MS2109 Two sheets, each 101×127 mm. (a) $5 "The Fathers of the Church" (detail) (Rubens). (b) $6 "St. Jerome" (detail) (Dürer)
Set of 2 sheets 6·00 7·00

115 Mickey and Minnie at New Year's Day "Hopping John" Tradition

(Des Alvin White Studios. Litho Questa)

1996 (17 Apr). *Traditional Holidays. T* **115** *and similar multicoloured designs showing Walt Disney cartoon characters. P* 14×13½.

2110	25 c. Type 115		20	15
2111	50 c. Disney characters dancing around maypole		35	30
2112	75 c. Mickey, Minnie and Pluto watching Independence Day fireworks		55	40
2113	90 c. Gyro Gearloose and Donald's nephews in Halloween costumes		65	55
2114	$3 Donald Duck as Puritan and nephews as Indians on Thanksgiving Day		2·00	2·25
2115	$4 Huey and Dewey with Hanukkah dreidle		2·25	2·50
2110/15		*Set of 6*	5·50	5·50

MS2116 Two sheets, each 124×98 mm. (a) $6 Mickey, Minnie and Donald taking part in Caribbean carnival. P 14×13½. (b) $6 Traditional pot of gold in St. Patrick's Day parade (*vert*). P 13½×14 . . *Set of 2 sheets* 7·50 8·00

116 Gateway in Imperial Palace, Peking

1996 (8 May). *"CHINA '96" 9th Asian International Stamp Exhibition, Peking. T* **116** *and similar multicoloured designs. Litho. P* 13.

2117	$1 Type 116		45	50
	a. Sheetlet. Nos. 2117/20		1·75	
2118	$1 Eastern end of Great Wall at Shanhaiguan		45	50
2119	$1 Great Wall fortress, Shanhaiguan		45	50
2120	$1 Gate of Heavenly Peace, Peking		45	50
2121	$1 Sun Yat-sen's Mausoleum, Nanjing		45	50
	a. Sheetlet. Nos. 2121/4		1·75	
2122	$1 Summer Palace, Peking		45	50
2123	$1 Temple of Heaven, Peking		45	50
2124	$1 Hall of Supreme Harmony, Forbidden City, Peking		45	50
2117/24		*Set of 8*	3·50	4·00

MS2125 Three sheets. (a) 150×100 mm. $2 Traditional Chinese painting (39×50 *mm*). (b) 90×68 mm. $6 Great Wall of China from the air (39×50 *mm*). (c) 90×68 mm. $6 Marble Boat, Summer Palace, Peking (50×39 *mm*)
Set of 3 sheets 6·00 6·25

Nos. 2117/20 and 2121/4 were each printed together, *se-tenant*, in sheetlets of 4.

(Litho Questa)

1996 (8 May). *70th Birthday of Queen Elizabeth II. Vert designs as T* **364** *of Antigua. Multicoloured. P* 13½×14.

2126	35 c. As Type 364 of Antigua		15	20
	a. Strip of 3. Nos. 2126/8		2·75	
2127	$2 Queen wearing tiara and green dress		85	90
2128	$4 Windsor Castle		1·75	1·90
2126/8		*Set of 3*	2·75	3·00

MS2129 103×125 mm. $6 Queen Elizabeth at Windsor . . 2·50 2·75

Nos. 2126/8 were printed together, *se-tenant*, in horizontal and vertical strips of 3 throughout the sheet.

(Litho B.D.T.)

1996 (12 June). *Flowers. Multicoloured designs as T* **430** *of Grenada, but vert. P* 14.

2130	35 c. Camellia "Apple Blossom"		15	20
2131	75 c. Odontoglossum		35	40
	a. Sheetlet. Nos. 2131/4×3		4·25	
2132	75 c. Cattleya		35	40
2133	75 c. Paphiopedilum "Venus's Slipper"		35	40
2134	75 c. Laeliocattleya "Marysville"		35	40
2135	75 c. Fuchsia "Citation"		35	40
	a. Sheetlet. Nos. 2135/46		4·25	
2136	75 c. Fuchsia "Amy Lye"		35	40
2137	75 c. Clysonimus (butterfly) and temple		35	40
2138	75 c. Digitalis purpurea (foxglove)		35	40
2139	75 c. Lilium martagon "Martagon Lily"		35	40
2140	75 c. Tulipa "Coleur Cardinal"		35	40
2141	75 c. Galanthus nivalis (snowdrop)		35	40

2142	75 c. *Rosa* "Superstar"	35	40
2143	75 c. Crocus "Dutch Yellow Mammoth"	35	40
2144	75 c. *Lilium speciosum* (Japanese lily)	35	40
2145	75 c. *Lilium* "Joan Evans"	35	40
2146	75 c. *Rosa* "Rosemary Harkness"	35	40
2147	90 c. *Camellia japonica* "Extravaganza"	40	45
2148	$1 Chrysanthemum "Primrose Dorothy Else"	45	50
2149	$2 Dahlia "Brandaris"	85	90
2130/49	*Set of 20*	10·00	11·00
MS2150	Two sheets, each 68×98 mm. (a) $5 Narcissus "Rembrandt". (b) $6 Gladiolus "Flowersong" *Set of 2 sheets*	4·75	5·00

Nos. 2131/4 and 2135/46 were each printed together, se-tenant, in sheetlets of 12 containing three of each design (Nos. 2131/4) or with the backgrounds forming a composite design (Nos. 2135/46).

No. 2135 is inscribed "Fuschcia", No. 2143 "Mammouth" and No. MS2150b "Gladiollus", all in error.

(Litho Questa)

1996 (26 June). *50th Anniv of U.N.I.C.E.F. Horiz designs as T 366 of Antigua. Multicoloured. P 14.*

2151	75 c. Child's face	35	40
2152	$2 Child with spoon	85	90
2153	$3 Girl sewing	1·25	1·40
2151/3	*Set of 3*	2·40	2·50
MS2154	105×75 mm. $6 Mother carrying child	2·75	3·00

(Des Jennifer Toombs. Litho Questa)

1996 (26 June). *3000th Anniv of Jerusalem. Multicoloured designs as T 367 of Antigua, but horiz. P 14.*

MS2155	137×47 mm. $1 Pool of Bethesda and *Papaver rhoeas*; $2 Damascus Gate and *Chrysanthemum coronarium*; $3 Church of All Nations and *Myrtus communis*	2·75	3·00
MS2156	82×62 mm. $6 Church of the Holy Sepulchre	2·50	2·75

(Des J. Iskowitz. Litho Questa)

1996 (26 June). *Centenary of Radio. Entertainers. Multicoloured designs as T 368 of Antigua. P 13½×14.*

2157	35 c. Ed Wynn	15	20
2158	75 c. Red Skelton	35	40
2159	$1 Joe Penner	45	50
2160	$3 Jerry Colonna	1·25	1·40
2157/60	*Set of 4*	2·10	2·50
MS2161	70×99 mm. $6 Bob Elliot and Ray Goulding (*horiz*). P 14×13½	2·75	3·00

(Litho Questa)

1996 (15 July). *Olympic Games, Atlanta. Previous Medal Winners. Multicoloured designs as T 425 of Grenada. P 14.*

2162	35 c. Los Angeles Memorial Coliseum	15	20
2163	75 c. Connie Carpenter-Phinney (U.S.A.) (Cycling)	35	40
2164	$1 Josef Neckermann (Germany) (*vert*)	45	50
	a. Sheetlet. Nos. 2164/72	4·00	
2165	$1 Harry Boldt (Germany) (*vert*)	45	50
2166	$1 Elena Petouchkova (Russia) (*vert*)	45	50
2167	$1 Alwin Schockemoehle (Germany) (*vert*)	45	50
2168	$1 Hans Winkler (Germany) (*vert*)	45	50
2169	$1 Joe Fargis (U.S.A.) (*vert*)	45	50
2170	$1 David Broome (Great Britain) (*vert*)	45	50
2171	$1 Reiner Klimke (Germany) (*vert*)	45	50
2172	$1 Richard Meade (Great Britain) (*vert*)	45	50
2173	$1 Julianne McNamara (U.S.A.) (*vert*)	45	50
	a. Sheetlet. Nos. 2173/81	4·00	
2174	$1 Takuti Hayata (Japan) (*vert*)	45	50
2175	$1 Nikolai Adriana (Russia) (*vert*)	45	50
2176	$1 Mitch Gaylord (U.S.A.) (*vert*)	45	50
2177	$1 Ludmilla Tourischeva (Russia) (*vert*)	45	50
2178	$1 Karin Janz (Germany) (*vert*)	45	50
2179	$1 Peter Kormann (U.S.A.) (*vert*)	45	50
2180	$1 Sawoo Kato (Japan) (*vert*)	45	50
2181	$1 Nadia Comaneci (Rumania) (*vert*)	45	50
2182	$2 Mohamed Bouchighe (Algeria) (Boxing) (*vert*)	85	90
2183	$3 Jackie Joyner Kersee (U.S.A.) (Javelin)	1·25	1·40
2162/83	*Set of 22*	10·00	11·00
MS2184	Two sheets, each 103×74 mm. (a) $5 Child waving flag (*vert*). (b) $6 William Steinkraus (U.S.A.) (Show jumping) *Set of 2 sheets*	4·75	5·00

Nos. 2164/72 (equestrians) and 2173/81 (gymnasts) were each printed together, se-tenant, in sheetlets of 9 with the backgrounds forming composite designs.

(Des J. Puvilland. Litho B.D.T.)

1996 (25 July). *Classic Cars. Multicoloured designs as T 426 of Grenada. P 14.*

2185	35 c. Chevrolet Belair convertible	15	20
	a. Sheetlet. Nos. 2185/8 and 2195/6	3·50	
2186	50 c. V.I.P. car	25	30
2187	75 c. Rolls-Royce Torpedo	35	40
2188	$1 Nissan "Cepric"	45	50
2189	$1 Delaunay-Belleville HB6	45	50
	a. Sheetlet. Nos. 2189/94	2·75	
2190	$1 Bugatti Type-15	45	50
2191	$1 Mazda Type 800	45	50
2192	$1 Mercedes 24/100/140 Sport	45	50
2193	$1 MG K3 Rover	45	50
2194	$1 Plymouth Fury	45	50
2195	$2 Mercedes-Benz 500K	85	90
2196	$3 Bugatti Type-13	1·25	1·40
2185/96	*Set of 12*	6·00	6·50
MS2197	Two sheets, each 106×76 mm. (a) $5 Bugatti "Roadster" Type-55. (b) $6 Lincoln Type-L *Set of 2 sheets*	4·75	5·00

Nos. 2185/8 with 2195/6 and 2189/94 were each printed together, se-tenant, in sheetlets of 6.

(Litho Questa)

1996 (14 Aug). *Ships. Multicoloured designs as T 427 of Grenada. P 14.*

2198	35 c. Grenada schooner	15	20
2199	75 c. Grenada schooner (*different*)	35	40
2200	$1 Athenian triremes, 1000 B.C.	45	50
	a. Sheetlet. Nos. 2200/5	2·75	
2201	$1 Egyptian Nile galley, 30 B.C.	45	50
2202	$1 Bangladesh dinghi, 310 B.C.	45	50
2203	$1 Warship of Queen Hatshepsut, 476 B.C.	45	50
2204	$1 Chinese junk, 200 B.C.	45	50
2205	$1 Polynesian ocean-going canoe, 600 B.C.	45	50
2206	$1 *Europa* (liner), 1957	45	50
	a. Sheetlet. Nos. 2206/11	2·75	
2207	$1 *Lusitania* (liner), 1906	45	50
2208	$1 *Queen Mary* (liner), 1936	45	50
2209	$1 *Bianca C* (liner)	45	50
2210	$1 *France* (liner), 1952	45	50
2211	$1 *Orion* (liner), 1915	45	50
2198/211	*Set of 14*	6·00	6·50
MS2212	Two sheets, each 104×74 mm. (a) $5 *Queen Elizabeth 2* (liner), 1969 (56×42 mm). (b) $6 Viking longship, 610 (42×56 mm) *Set of 2 sheets*	4·75	5·00

Nos. 2200/5 and 2206/11 were each printed together, se-tenant, in sheetlets of 6.

117 Felix Mendelssohn

118 Man Ho Temple, 1841

1996 (26 Aug). *Composers. T 117 and similar vert designs. Multicoloured. Litho. P 14.*

2213	$1 Type 117	45	50
	a. Sheetlet. Nos. 2213/21	4·00	
2214	$1 Franz Schubert	45	50
2215	$1 Franz Joseph Haydn	45	50
2216	$1 Robert Schumann	45	50
2217	$1 Ludwig van Beethoven	45	50
2218	$1 Gioacchino Rossini	45	50
2219	$1 George Frederick Handel	45	50
2220	$1 Pyotr Tchaikovsky	45	50
2221	$1 Frédéric Chopin	45	50
2222	$1 Bela Bartok	45	50
	a. Sheetlet. Nos. 2222/30	4·00	
2223	$1 Giacomo Puccini	45	50
2224	$1 George Gershwin	45	50
2225	$1 Leonard Bernstein	45	50
2226	$1 Kurt Weill	45	50
2227	$1 John Cage	45	50
2228	$1 Aaron Copland	45	50
2229	$1 Sergei Prokofiev	45	50
2230	$1 Igor Stravinsky	45	50
2213/30	*Set of 18*	8·00	9·00
MS2231	Two sheets, each 74×104 mm. (a) $5 Richard Strauss. (b) $6 Wolfgang Amadeus Mozart *Set of 2 sheets*	4·75	5·00

Nos. 2213/21 and 2222/30 were each printed together, se-tenant, in sheetlets of 9 with the backgrounds forming a composite designs.

1996 (28 Aug). *Railway Steam Locomotives. Horiz designs as T 429 of Grenada. Multicoloured. Litho. P 14.*

2232	$1.50, Class 38 No. 382, Germany	65	70
	a. Sheetlet. Nos. 2232/7	3·75	
2233	$1.50, *Duchess of Hamilton*, Great Britain	65	70
2234	$1.50, Class WP, India	65	70
2235	$1.50, Class 141R *Americaine*, France	65	70
2236	$1.50, Class A4 *Mallard*, Great Britain	65	70
2237	$1.50, Class 18 No. 201, Germany	65	70
2238	$1.50, Class A2 *Blue Peter*, Great Britain	65	70
	a. Sheetlet. Nos. 2238/43	3·75	
2239	$1.50, Class P36, Russia	65	70
2240	$1.50, Class QJ, China	65	70
2241	$1.50, Class 12, Belgium	65	70
2242	$1.50, Class "Challenger", U.S.A.	65	70
2243	$1.50, Class 25, South Africa	65	70
2232/43	*Set of 12*	7·75	8·25
MS2244	Two sheets, each 100×70 mm. (a) $5 Class "King", Great Britain. (b) $6 Class "Royal Scot", Great Britain *Set of 2 sheets*	4·75	5·00

Nos. 2232/7 and 2238/43 were each printed together, se-tenant, in sheetlets of 6.

(Litho Questa)

1996 (18 Nov). *Christmas. Religious Paintings. Vert designs as T 369 of Antigua showing different details from "Suffer Little Children to Come Unto Me" by Van Dyck. P 13½×14.*

2245	15 c. multicoloured	10	10
2246	25 c. multicoloured	10	15
2247	$1 multicoloured	45	50
2248	$1.50, multicoloured	65	70
2249	$2 multicoloured	85	90
2250	$4 multicoloured	1·75	1·90
2245/50	*Set of 6*	3·75	4·00
MS2251	Two sheets, each 106×76 mm. (a) $5 "Suffer Little Children to Come Unto Me" (detail) (Van Dyck) (*horiz*). (b) $6 "Adoration of the Magi" (Rembrandt) (*horiz*). P 14×13½ *Set of 2 sheets*	5·25	5·50

(Des Dena Rubin. Litho B.D.T.)

1997 (12 Feb). *"HONG KONG '97" International Stamp Exhibition. Hong Kong Past and Present. T 118 and similar horiz designs. Multicoloured. P 14.*

MS2252	Five sheets, each 120×96 mm. (a) $3 Type 118; $3 Man Ho Temple, 1983. (b) $3 St. John's Cathedral, Victoria 1886; $3 St. John's Cathedral, Victoria 1983. (c) $3 Victoria Harbour, 1858; $3 Victoria Harbour, 1983. (d) $3 Water front skyscraper; $3 Aerial view of central Victoria. (e) $3 Signing of Treaty of Nanking, 1852. $3 Margaret Thatcher signing The Joint Declaration, 1984 *Set of 5 sheets*	12·50	13·00

(Des M. Freedman and Dena Rubin. Litho Questa)

1997 (3 Apr). *50th Anniv of U.N.E.S.C.O. Multicoloured designs as T 374 of Antigua. P 14×13½ (horiz) or 13½×14 (vert).*

2253	15 c. Temple, Kyoto, Japan	10	10
2254	25 c. Roman ruins, Trier, Germany	10	15
2255	$1 Gateway, Mount Taishan, China	45	50
2256	$1 Temple guardian, Kyoto, Japan (*vert*)	45	50
	a. Sheetlet. Nos. 2256/63 and central label	3·50	
2257	$1 Temple deity, Kyoto, Japan (*vert*)	45	50
2258	$1 Temple lamp, Kyoto, Japan (*vert*)	45	50
2259	$1 Ayutthaya, Thailand (*vert*)	45	50
2260	$1 Statue, Borobudur Temple, Indonesia (*vert*)	45	50
2261	$1 Monuments at Pattadakal, India (*vert*)	45	50
2262	$1 Sleeping buddha, Polonnaruwa, Sri Lanka (*vert*)	45	50
2263	$1 Sagarmatha National Park, Nepal (*vert*)	45	50
2264	$1 Congonhas Sanctuary, Brazil (*vert*)	45	50
	a. Sheetlet. No. 2264/71 and central label	3·50	
2265	$1 Cartagena, Colombia (*vert*)	45	50
2266	$1 Pueblo, Guatemala (*vert*)	45	50
2267	$1 Maya statue, Honduras (*vert*)	45	50
2268	$1 Popocatepetl Monastery, Mexico (*vert*)	45	50
2269	$1 Galapagos Islands, Ecuador (*vert*)	45	50
2270	$1 Waterfall, Costa Rica (*vert*)	45	50
2271	$1 Glaciares National Park, Argentina (*vert*)	45	50
2272	$1.50, Notre Dame Cathedral, Paris, France	65	70
	a. Sheetlet. Nos. 2272/6	2·50	
2273	$1.50, Timbered house, Maulbronn, Germany	65	70
2274	$1.50, Gateway, Himeji-jo, Japan	65	70
2275	$1.50, Lion statues, Delphi, Greece	65	70
2276	$1.50, Palace of Fontainebleau, France	65	70
2277	$1.50, Scandola Nature Reserve, France	65	70
2278	$2 Citadel, Dubrovnik, Croatia	85	90
2279	$4 Angra do Heroismo, Portugal	1·75	1·90
2253/79	*Set of 7*	14·00	15·00
MS2280	Three sheets, each 127×102 mm. (a) $6 Mont St. Michel, France; (b) $6 Ruins of Teotihuacan, Mexico; (c) $6 Temple, Chengde, China *Set of 3 sheets*	7·50	7·75

Nos. 2256/63 and 2264/71 were each printed together, se-tenant, in sheetlets of 8 stamps with a centre label and Nos. 2272/6 in sheetlet of 5 stamps with a top left-hand corner label.

119 Springer Spaniel **120** Hong Kong

(Des R. Rundo. Litho Questa)

1997 (10 Apr). *Cats and Dogs. T 119 and similar multicoloured designs. P 14.*

2281	35 c. Type 119	15	20
2282	45 c. Abyssinian Blue	20	25
2283	50 c. Burmese Cream (*vert*)	25	30
2284	75 c. Doberman Pinscher	35	40
2285	90 c. Persian Tortoiseshell and White	40	45
2286	$1 Italian Spinone (*vert*)	45	50
2287	$1.50, Siamese Chocolate Point	70	75
	a. Sheetlet. Nos. 2287/92	3·75	
2288	$1.50, Oriental Shorthair White	65	70
2289	$1.50, Burmese Sable	65	70
2290	$1.50, Abyssinian Tabby	65	70
2291	$1.50, Persian Shaded Silver	65	70
2292	$1.50, Tonkinese Natural Mink	65	70
2293	$1.50, Leonberger	65	70
	a. Sheetlet. Nos. 2293/8	3·75	
2294	$1.50, Newfoundland	65	70
2295	$1.50, Boxer	65	70
2296	$1.50, St. Bernard	65	70
2297	$1.50, Silky Terrier	65	70
2298	$1.50, Miniature Schnauzer	65	70
2299	$2 Cocker Spaniel (*vert*)	85	90
2300	$3 Oriental Shorthair Agouti (*vert*)	1·25	1·40
2281/300	*Set of 20*	10·00	10·50
MS2301	Two sheets. (a) 75×105 mm. $6 Sphynx (*vert*). (b) 105×75 mm. $6 Golden Retriever puppy *Set of 2 sheets*	5·25	5·50

Nos. 2287/92 (cats) and 2293/8 (dogs) were each printed together, se-tenant, in sheetlets of 6 with the backgrounds forming composite designs.

(Litho Questa)

1997 (15 Apr). *Dinosaurs. Multicoloured designs as T 438 of Grenada. P 14.*

2302	45 c. Stegosaurus	..	..	20	25
2303	90 c. Diplodocus	..	..	40	45
2304	$1 Pteranodon (vert)	..	..	45	50
2305	$1.50, Rhamphorhynchus and head of Brachiosaurus		..	65	70
	a. Sheetlet. Nos. 2305/10		..	3·75	
2306	$1.50, Archaeopteryx	..	..	65	70
2307	$1.50, Anurognathus and body of Brachiosaurus		..	65	70
2308	$1.50, Head of Albertosaurus		..	65	70
2309	$1.50, Herrerasaurus and legs of Brachiosaurus		..	65	70
2310	$1.50, Platyhystrix and body of Albertosaurus		..	65	70
2311	$2 Deinonychus and Ankylasaurus (vert)			85	90
2302/11			Set of 10	5·50	5·75

MS2312 Two sheets, each 103×74 mm. (a) $6 Allosaurus (vert). (b) $6 Hydacrosaurus

		Set of 2 sheets	5·25	5·50

Nos. 2305/10 were printed together, *se-tenant*, in sheetlets of 6 with the backgrounds forming a composite design.

(Des R. Rundo. Litho Questa)

1997 (28 May). *300th Anniv of Mother Goose Nursery Rhymes. Sheet 72×102 mm containing vert design as T 309 of Dominica. Multicoloured. P 14.*

MS2313 $6 Girl and sheep ("Baa, Baa, Black Sheep") .. .. 2·50 2·75

(Des J. Iskowitz. Litho Questa)

1997 (28 May). *50th Death Anniv of Paul Harris (founder of Rotary International). Horiz design as T 377 of Antigua. Multicoloured. P 14.*

2314	$3 Paul Harris and village women with water pump, Burkina Faso	..	1·25	1·40

MS2315 78×108 mm. $6 Early Rotary parade float .. .. 2·50 2·75

(Litho Questa)

1997 (28 May). *Golden Wedding of Queen Elizabeth and Prince Philip. Horiz designs as T 378 of Antigua. Multicoloured (except Nos. 2318/19). P 14.*

2316	$1 Engagement photograph, 1947	..	45	50
	a. Sheetlet. Nos. 2316/21		2·75	
2317	$1 Royal coat of arms	..	45	50
2318	$1 Queen Elizabeth and Duke of Edinburgh, 1953 (blackish brown)		45	50
2319	$1 Formal portrait of Queen Elizabeth with Prince Philip in uniform (blackish brown)		45	50
2320	$1 Sandringham House	..	45	50
2321	$1 Queen Elizabeth and Prince Philip in carriage		45	50
2316/21		Set of 6	2·75	3·00

MS2322 100×70 mm. $6 Wedding photograph, 1947 .. .. 2·50 2·75

Nos. 2316/21 were printed together, *se-tenant*, in sheetlets of 6.

A $20 value embossed on gold foil exists from a limited printing.

(Des J. Iskowitz. Litho Questa)

1997 (28 May). *"Pacific '97" International Stamp Exhibition, San Francisco. Death Centenary of Heinrich von Stephan (founder of the U.P.U.). Horiz design as T 379 of Antigua. P 14.*

2323	$1.50, olive-green	..	..	..	65	70
	a. Sheetlet. Nos. 2323/5			1·90		
2324	$1.50, chestnut	..	..	..	65	70
2325	$1.50, violet	..	..	..	65	70
2323/5			Set of 3	1·90	2·10

MS2326 82×118 mm. $6 deep blue and black 2·50 2·75

Designs:—No. 2323, Pony Express, 1860; No. 2324, Von Stephan and Mercury; No. 2325, American steam locomotive; No. **MS**2326 Von Stephan and camel courier, Baghdad.

Nos. 2323/5 were printed together, *se-tenant*, in sheets of 3 with enlarged right-hand margin.

(Litho Questa)

1997 (28 May). *Birth Bicentenary of Hiroshige (Japanese painter). "One Hundred Famous Views of Edo". Horiz designs as T 310 of Dominica. Multicoloured. P 13½×14.*

2327	$1, "Koume Embankment"	..	65	70
	a. Sheetlet. Nos. 2327/32		3·75	
2328	$1.50, "Azuma Shrine and the Entwined Camphor"		65	70
2329	$1.50, "Yanagishima"	..	65	70
2330	$1.50, "Inside Akiba Shrine, Ukeji"		65	70
2331	$1.50, "Distant View of Kinryuzan Temple and Azuma Bridge"		65	70
2332	$1.50, "Night View of Matsuchiyama and the San'ya Canal"		65	70
2327/32		Set of 6	3·75	4·00

MS2333 Two sheets, each 102×127 mm. (a) $6 "Five Pines, Onagi Canal". (b) $6 "Spiral Hall, Five Hundred Rakan Temple" .. Set of 2 sheets 5·25 5·50

Nos. 2327/32 were printed together, *se-tenant*, in sheetlets of 6.

(Des R. Rundo. Litho Questa)

1997 (28 May). *175th Anniv of Brothers Grimm's Third Collection of Fairy Tales. The Fox and the Geese. Multicoloured designs as T 380 of Antigua. P 13½×14.*

2334	$2 Fox and geese	..	85	90
	a. Sheetlet. Nos. 2334/6		2·50	
2335	$2 Fox with knife and fork and geese		85	90
2336	$2 Fox asleep and singing geese		85	90
2334/6		Set of 3	2·50	2·75

MS2337 124×96 mm. $6 Fox (horiz). P 14×13½ 2·50 2·75

Nos. 2334/6 were printed together, *se-tenant*, in sheetlets of 3 with an illustrated margin.

(Litho B.D.T.)

1997 (26 June). *Winter Olympic Games, Nagano, Japan. Multicoloured designs as T 440 of Grenada. P 14.*

2338	90 c. Slalom	..	..	40	45
2339	$1 Downhill skiing	..	..	45	50
	a. Sheetlet. Nos. 2339/47		4·00		
2340	$1 Freestyle ski-jumping (blue and green ski suit)		..	45	50
2341	$1 Curling	..	..	45	50
2342	$1 Ski-jumping (pink ski suit)	..	45	50
2343	$1 Four-man bobsleigh	..	45	50
2344	$1 Nordic combined	..	..	45	50
2345	$1 Speed skating	..	..	45	50
2346	$1 Ice hockey	..	..	45	50
2347	$1 Cross-country skiing	..	45	50
2348	$2 One-man luge	..	..	85	90
2349	$3 Men's figure-skating	..	1·25	1·40
2350	$5 Speed skating (different)	..	2·10	2·25
2338/50			Set of 13	9·00	10·00

MS2351 Two sheets, each 97×67 mm. (a) $6 Figure skating. (b) $6 One-man luge (vert)

		Set of 2 sheets	5·25	5·50

Nos. 2339/47 were printed together, *se-tenant*, in sheetlets of 9.

(Des Y. Lee. Litho Questa)

1997 (1 July). *Return of Hong Kong to China. T 120 and similar multicoloured designs showing modern Hong Kong through inscription. P 14×13½ (Nos. 2352/3) or 14 (others).*

2352	$1 multicoloured	..	..	45	50
	a. Sheetlet of 4			1·75	
2353	$1.25, multicoloured	..		50	55
	a. Sheetlet of 4			2·00	
2354	$1.50, multicoloured (63×32 mm)		65	70
	a. Sheetlet of 3			1·90	
2355	$2 multicoloured (63×32 mm)		85	90
	a. Sheetlet of 3			2·50	
2352/5			Set of 4	2·40	2·50

Nos. 2352/5 were printed in sheetlets of 3 or 4, each with enlarged illustrated margins.

(Litho Questa)

1997 (22 July). *Marine Life. Horiz designs as T 439 of Grenada. Multicoloured. P 14.*

2356	10 c. Wimplefish	..	..	10	10
2357	15 c. Clown Triggerfish	..	10	10
2358	25 c. Ringed Emperor Angelfish		10	15
2359	35 c. Hooded Butterflyfish	..	15	20
2360	45 c. Semicircle Angelfish	..	20	25
2361	75 c. Scribbled Angelfish	..	35	40
2362	90 c. Threadfin Butterflyfish	..	40	45
2363	$1.10, Clown Surgeonfish	..	50	55
2364	$2 Bottle-nosed Dolphin	..	85	90
2365	$5 Triggerfish	..	..	2·10	2·25
2366	$10 Lionfish	..	..	4·25	4·50
2367	$20 Jackknife Fish	..	..	8·75	9·00
2356/67			Set of 12	16·00	17·00

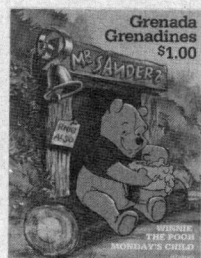

121 Winnie the Pooh as Monday's Child

(Des Alvin White Studios. Litho Questa)

1997 (7 Aug). *"Monday's Child" (poem). T 121 and similar vert designs showing Disney cartoon characters from Winnie the Pooh illustrating the various verses. Multicoloured. P 13½×14.*

2368	$1 Type 121	..	..	65	70
	a. Sheetlet. Nos. 2368/73		3·50		
2369	$1 Kanga as Tuesday's child	..	65	70
2370	$1 Eeyore as Wednesday's child	..	65	70
2371	$1 Tigger as Thursday's child	..	65	70
2372	$1 Piglet as Friday's child	..	65	70
2373	$1 Rabbit as Saturday's child	..	65	70
2368/73			Set of 6	3·50	3·75

MS2374 128×107 mm. $6 Christopher Robin as Sunday's child .. .. .. 3·75 4·00

Nos. 2368/73 were printed together, *se-tenant*, in sheetlets of 6.

122 Snow White kissing Grumpy

(Des Alvin White Studios. Litho Questa)

1997 (7 Aug). *Disney Sweethearts. T 122 and similar multicoloured designs showing Disney cartoon characters kissing. P 14×13½.*

2375	$1 Type 122	..	65	70
	a. Sheetlet. Nos. 2375/83		5·25	
2376	$1 Figaro the Cat and Cleo the Fish		65	70
2377	$1 Peter Pan and Wendy	..	65	70
2378	$1 Cinderella and the Prince	..	65	70
2379	$1 Ariel and Eric	..	65	70
2380	$1 Beauty and the Prince	..	65	70
2381	$1 Aladdin and Jasmine	..	65	70
2382	$1 Pocahontas and Captain John Smith		65	70
2383	$1 Phoebus and Esmeralda	..	65	70
2375/83		Set of 9	5·25	5·75

MS2384 127×102 mm. $5 Georges Hautecourt kissing cat's tail (vert). P 13½×14 3·25 3·50

Nos. 2375/83 were printed together, *se-tenant*, in sheetlets of 9.

(Litho Questa)

1997 (11 Aug). *World Football Championship, France (1998). Designs as T 383 of Antigua. P 14×13½ (horiz) or 13½×14 (vert).*

2385	10 c. steel-blue	..	..	10	10
2386	20 c. multicoloured	..	..	10	10
2387	45 c. sepia	..	..	20	25
2388	$1 black	..	..	45	50
2389	$1 sepia	..	..	45	50
	a. Sheetlet. Nos. 2389/96 and central label			3·50	
2390	$1 black	..	..	45	50
2391	$1 sepia	..	..	45	50
2392	$1 multicoloured	..	..	45	50
2393	$1 multicoloured	..	..	45	50
2394	$1 black	..	..	45	50
2395	$1 sepia	..	..	45	50
2396	$1 multicoloured	..	..	45	50
2397	$1 black	..	..	45	50
	a. Sheetlet. Nos. 2397/404 and central label			3·50	
2398	$1 black	..	..	45	50
2399	$1 black	..	..	45	50
2400	$1 black	..	..	45	50
2401	$1 black	..	..	45	50
2402	$1 black	..	..	45	50
2403	$1 black	..	..	45	50
2404	$1 black	..	..	45	50
2405	$1.50, multicoloured	..	..	65	70
2406	$5 multicoloured	..	..	2·10	2·25
2385/406			Set of 22	10·00	11·00

MS2407 Two sheets. (a) 127×102 mm. $6 black. (b) 102×127 mm. $6 black .. Set of 2 sheets 5·25 5·50

Designs: *Horiz*—No. 2385, Italian team, 1934; No. 2386, Angolan team; No. 2387, Brazilian team, 1958; No. 2388, Uruguay team, 1950; No. 2389, Winning England team, 1966; No. 2390, West German team, 1954; No. 2391, Uruguay officials with Jules Rimet trophy, 1930; No. 2392, West German players celebrating, 1990; No. 2393, Maradonna (Argentine player), 1986; No. 2394, Brazilian players, 1994; No. 2395, Argentine players, 1978; No. 2396, West German player holding World Cup, 1974; No. 2405, West German team, 1974; No. 2406, Italian team, 1938; No. **MS**2407b, Paulao, Angola. *Vert*—No. 2397, Ademir, Brazil; No. 2398, Kocsis, Hungary; No. 2399, Leonidas, Brazil; No. 2400, Nejedly, Czechoslovakia; No. 2401, Schiavio, Italy; No. 2402, Stabile, Uruguay; No. 2403, Pele, Brazil; No. 2404, Fritzwalter, West Germany, No. **MS**2407a, Shearer, England.

Nos. 2389/96 and 2397/404 were each printed together, *se-tenant*, in sheetlets of 8 stamps and a central label.

1997 (12 Aug). *Butterflies. Multicoloured designs as T 444 of Grenada. Litho. P 14.*

2408	75 c. Polyura dehaani	..	..	35	40
2409	90 c. Polyura dolon	..	..	40	45
2410	$1 Charaxes candiope	..	..	45	50
2411	$1.50, Pantaporia punctata	..	65	70
2412	$1.50, Euthalia confucius	..	65	70
	a. Sheetlet. Nos. 2412/17		3·75		
2413	$1.50, Euthalia kardama	..	65	70
2414	$1.50, Limenitis albomaculata		65	70
2415	$1.50, Hestina assimilis	..	65	70
2416	$1.50, Kallima inachus	..	65	70
2417	$1.50, Euthalia teutoides	..	65	70
2418	$1.50, Euphaedra francina	..	65	70
	a. Sheetlet. Nos. 2418/23		3·75		
2419	$1.50, Euphaedra eleus	..	65	70
2420	$1.50, Euphaedra harpalyce	..	65	70
2421	$1.50, Euphaedra cyparissa	..	65	70
2422	$1.50, Euphaedra gausape	..	65	70
2423	$1.50, Euphaedra imperialis	..	65	70
2424	$2 Charaxes etesippe	..	..	85	90
2425	$3 Charaxes castor	..	..	1·25	1·40
2408/25			Set of 18	11·00	11·50

MS2426 Two sheets, each 106×76 mm. (a) $5 Charaxes nobilis (vert). (b) $6 Charaxes numenes (vert) .. .. Set of 2 sheets 4·75 5·00

Nos. 2412/17 and 2418/23 were each printed together, *se-tenant*, in sheetlets of 6 with the backgrounds forming composite designs.

123 James Dean

124 Symphyglossum sanguineum

(Des Shannon. Litho Questa)

1997 (22 Aug). *James Dean (actor) Commemoration.* T **123** *and similar vert designs showing different portraits. Multicoloured.* P 13½×14.

2427	$1 Type **123**	45	50
	a. Sheetlet. Nos. 2427/35	4·00	
2428	$1 Wearing purple jumper	45	50
2429	$1 Wearing stetson and smoking	45	50
2430	$1 Wearing dinner jacket and tie	45	50
2431	$1 Full-face portrait	45	50
2432	$1 Grimacing	45	50
2433	$1 Wearing stetson	45	50
2434	$1 Leaning on arms	45	50
2435	$1 Smoking	45	50
2427/35	*Set of 9*	4·00	4·50

Nos. 2427/35 were printed together, *se-tenant*, in sheetlets of 9 with enlarged illustrated right-hand margin.

(Des T. Wood. Litho B.D.T.)

1997 (4 Sept). *Orchids of the World.* T **124** *and similar vert designs. Multicoloured.* P 14.

2436	35 c. Type **124**	15	20
2437	45 c. *Doritaenopsis* "Mythic Beauty"	20	25
2438	75 c. *Odontoglossum cervantesii*	35	40
2439	90 c. *Cattleya* "Pumpernickel"	40	45
2440	$1 *Vanda* "Patricia Low"	45	50
2441/9	$1 × 9 (*Lycaste* "Aquila"; *Brassolaeliocattleya* "Dorothy Bertsch"; *Phalaenopsis* "Zuma Urchin"; *Promenaea xanthina*; *Amesiella philippinensis*; *Brassocattleya* "Angel Lace"; *Brassoepidendrum* "Peggy Ann"; *Miltoniaseine*; *Sophralaeliocattleya* "Precious Stones")		
	a. Sheetlet. Nos. 2441/9	4·25	
2450/8	$1 × 9 (*Cymbidium* "Showgirl"; *Disa blackii*; *Phalaenopsis aphrodite*; *Iwanagaara* "Apple Blossom"; *Masdevallia* "Copper Angel"; *Paphiopedilum micranthum*; *Paphiopedilum* "Clare de Lune"; *Cattleya forbesii*; *Dendrobium* "Dawn Maree")		
	a. Sheetlet. Nos 2450/8	4·25	
2459	$1.50, *Odontonia* "Debutante"	65	70
2460/5	$1.50 × 6 (*Miltoniopsis* "Jean Sabourin"; *Cymbididium* "Red Beauty"; *Brassocattleya* "Green Dragon"; *Phalaenopsis* hybrid; *Laeliocattleya* "Mary Ellen Carter"; *Disa* hybrid)		
	a. Sheetlet. Nos 2460/5	3·75	
2466/71	$1.50 × 6 (*Lycaste macrobulbon*; *Cochleanthes discolor*; *Cymbidium* "Nang Carpenter"; *Paphiopedilum* "Clare de Lune"; *Masdevallia caudata*; *Cymbidium* "Showgirl")		
	a. Sheetlet. Nos 2466/71	3·75	
2472	$2 *Laeliocattleya* "Mini Purple"	85	90
2473	$3 *Phragmipedium dominiarum*	1·25	1·40
2436/73	*Set of 38*	20·00	21·00

MS2474 Two sheets, each 76×106mm. (a) $5 *Phalenopsis* "Medford Star"; (b) $6 *Brassolaeliocattleya* "Dorothy Bertsch" ... *Set of 2 sheets* 4·75 5·00

Nos. 2441/9, 2450/8, 2460/5 and 2466/71 were each printed together, *se-tenant*, in sheetlets of 9 (Nos. 2441/9, 2450/8) or 6 some with the backgrounds forming a composite design (Nos. 2460/5, 2466/71).

125 *Clitocybe metachroa*

126 Ludwig van Beethoven

(Litho Questa)

1997 (4 Sept). *Fungi.* T **125** *and similar horiz designs. Multicoloured.* P 14.

2475	75 c. Type **125**	35	40
2476	90 c. *Clavulinopsis helvola*	40	45
2477	$1 *Lycoperdon pyriforme*	45	50
2478	$1.50, *Auricularia auricula-judae*	65	70
2479	$1.50, *Entoloma incanum*	65	70
	a. Sheetlet. Nos. 2479/84	3·75	
2480	$1.50, *Coprinus atramentarius*	65	70
2481	$1.50, *Mycena polygramma*	65	70
2482	$1.50, *Lepista nuda*	65	70
2483	$1.50, *Pleurotis cornucopiae*	65	70
2484	$1.50, *Laccaria amethystina*	65	70
2485	$2 *Clathrus archeri*	85	90
2486	$3 *Lactarius trivialis*	1·25	1·40
2475/86	*Set of 12*	7·50	8·00

MS2487 Two sheets, each 106×76mm. (a) $6 *Morchella esculenta*. (b) $6 *Amanita muscaria* ... *Set of 2 sheets* 5·25 5·50

Nos. 2479/84 were printed together, *se-tenant*, in sheetlets of 6.

(Des Christina de Musée. Litho Questa)

1997 (10 Oct). *Classical Composers.* T **126** *and similar vert designs. Multicoloured.* P 14½.

2488	$1 Type **126**	45	50
	a. Sheetlet. Nos. 2488/95 and label	3·50	
2489	$1 Pyotr Tchaikovsky	45	50
2490	$1 Johann Christian Bach	45	50
2491	$1 Frédéric Chopin	45	50
2492	$1 Igor Stravinsky	45	50
2493	$1 Franz Joseph Haydn	45	50

2494	$1 Gustav Mahler	45	50
2495	$1 Gioacchino Antonio Rossini	45	50
2488/95	*Set of 8*	3·50	4·00

MS2496 Two sheets, each 106×76mm. (a) $6 Wolfgang Amadeus Mozart. (b) $6 Franz Schubert ... *Set of 2 sheets* 5·25 5·50

Nos. 2488/95 were printed together, *se-tenant*, in sheetlets of 8 stamps and one central label.

127 Diana, Princess of Wales and Buckingham Palace

128 Tiger (hologram)

(Des Y. Lee. Litho Questa)

1997 (10 Nov). *Diana, Princess of Wales Commemoration.* T **127** *and similar horiz designs. Multicoloured.* P 14.

2497	$1.50, Type **127**	65	70
	a. Sheetlet. Nos. 2497/502	3·75	
2498	$1.50, Princess Diana and lake at Althorp	65	70
2499	$1.50, Princess Diana and Westminster Abbey	65	70
2500	$1.50, Princess Diana and gates to Althorp	65	70
2501	$1.50, Princess Diana in pink hat and gates to Kensington Palace	65	70
2502	$1.50, Princess Diana and Althorp House	65	70
2497/502	*Set of 6*	3·75	4·00

MS2503 115×80mm, $6 Holding bouquet (60×40 mm). P 14×14½ ... 2·50 2·75

Nos. 2497/502 were printed together, *se-tenant*, in sheetlets of 6 with enlarged illustrated right-hand margin.

Two different $20 values embossed on gold foil and an $8 on silver foil showing a hologram exist from limited printings.

(Litho Questa)

1997 (5 Dec). *Christmas. Religious Paintings. Multicoloured designs as* T **448** *of Grenada.* P 14.

2504	20 c. "Choir of Angels" (Simon Marmion)	10	15
2505	75 c. "The Annunciation" (Giotto)	35	40
2506	90 c. "Festival of the Rose Garlands" (Albrecht Dürer)	40	45
2507	$1.50, "Madonna with Two Angels" (Hans Memling)	65	70
2508	$2 "The Ognissanti Madonna" (Giotto)	85	90
2509	$3 "Angel with Candlestick" (Michelangelo)	1·25	1·40
2504/9	*Set of 6*	3·50	4·00

MS2510 Two sheets, each 114×104 mm. (a) $6 "The Rising of the Sun" (detail) (*horiz*) (Francois Boucher). (b) $6 "Cupid" (detail) (*horiz*) (Jean-Baptiste Huet) ... *Set of 2 sheets* 4·75 5·00

No. 2506 is inscribed "DUER" in error.

1997 (12 Dec). *Fishes. Multicoloured designs as* T **449** *of Grenada.* Litho. P 14.

2511	$1 Queen Angelfish	45	50
	a. Sheetlet. Nos. 2511/19	4·00	
2512	$1 Clown Triggerfish	45	50
2513	$1 Four-spot Butterflyfish	45	50
2514	$1 Yellow-tailed Damselfish	45	50
2515	$1 Yellow-headed Wrasse	45	50
2516	$1 Royal Gramma	45	50
2517	$1 Candy Basslet	45	50
2518	$1 Smooth Trunkfish	45	50
2519	$1 Coral Hind	45	50
2511/19	*Set of 9*	4·00	4·50

MS2520 Two sheets. (a) 102×72 mm. $6 Black-finned Reef Shark. (b) 72×102 mm. $6 Yellow-headed Jawfish (*vert*) ... *Set of 2 sheets* 5·25 5·50

Nos. 2511/19 were printed together, *se-tenant*, in sheetlets of 9 with the backgrounds forming a composite design.

1998 (10 Feb). *Chinese New Year ("Year of the Tiger").* Litho. Die-cut perf 11.

2521	**128** $1.50, black on silver foil	65	70
	a. Sheetlet of 4	2·75	

MS2522 64×76 mm. **128** $3 black on silver foil (52×65 mm) ... 1·25 1·40

No. 2521 was printed in sheetlets of 4 with an overall pattern of Chinese characters which varies from stamp to stamp.

129 Alabama (Confederate warship)

(Des R. Sauber. Litho Questa)

1998 (7 May). *Famous Ships.* T **129** *and similar multicoloured designs.* P 14.

(a) Ships of the 1860s

2523	75 c. Type **129**	35	40
	a. Sheetlet. Nos. 2523/34	4·00	
2524	75 c. *Persia* (paddle-steamer)	35	40
2525	75 c. *Ariel* (clipper)	35	40
2526	75 c. *Florida* (Confederate warship)	35	40
2527	75 c. *Great Eastern* (paddle-steamer)	35	40

2528	75 c. *Jacob Bell* on fire	35	40
2529	75 c. *Star of India* (clipper)	35	40
2530	75 c. *Robert E. Lee* (Mississippi paddle-steamer)	35	40
2531	75 c. U.S.S. *Passaic* (monitor)	35	40
2532	75 c. *Madagascar* (clipper)	35	40
2533	75 c. H.M.S. *Devastation* (battleship)	35	40
2534	75 c. *General Grant* (clipper)	35	40

(b) Ships of the American Civil War

2535	$1 Clark Gable as Rhett Butler in *Gone with the Wind* (*vert*)	45	50
	a. Sheetlet. Nos. 2535/42	3·50	
2536	$1 Crew abandoning blockade runner wrecked on Sullivan's Island (*vert*)	45	50
2537	$1 Margaret Mitchell (author of *Gone with the Wind*) (*vert*)	45	50
2538	$1 George Alfred Trenholm (ship owner) (*vert*)	45	50
2539	$1 Dock Street Theatre, Charleston (*vert*)	45	50
2540	$1 *Howlett* (paddle-steamer) sinking (*vert*)	45	50
2541	$1 U.S.S. *Tecumseh* on fire (*vert*)	45	50
2542	$1 City Jail, Charleston (*vert*)	45	50
2523/42	*Set of 20*	7·50	8·75

MS2543 Two sheets, each 106×76 mm. (a) $6 *Nashville* sinking Union clipper *Harvey Birch* (57×42 mm). (b) $6 *Hatteras* (paddle-steamer) on fire (42×57 mm) ... *Set of 2 sheets* 5·00 5·25

Nos. 2523/34 were printed together, *se-tenant*, in sheetlets of 12, and Nos. 2535/42 were printed together, *se-tenant*, in sheetlets of 8 showing the stamps arranged in two horizontal strips of 4 separated by stamp-size labels.

130 Concept Strike Fighter

131 *Lycaste deppei*

(Litho Questa)

1998 (13 May). *Aircraft Designs of the Future.* T **130** *and similar horiz designs. Multicoloured.* P 14.

2544	70 c. Type **130**	30	35
2545	90 c. Concept space shuttle	40	45
2546	$1 Velocity 173 RG Elite	45	50
	a. Sheetlet. Nos. 2546/53	3·50	
2547	$1 Davis DA-9	45	50
2548	$1 Concorde	45	50
2549	$1 Voyager	45	50
2550	$1 Factimobile	45	50
2551	$1 RAF 2000	45	50
2552	$1 Boomerang	45	50
2553	$1 N1M Flying Wing	45	50
2554	$2 Concept air and space jet	85	90
2555	$3 V Jet II	1·25	1·40
2544/55	*Set of 12*	6·25	7·50

MS2556 Two sheets, each 100×70 mm. (a) $6 Concept aeropod. (b) $6 Delmar ... *Set of 2 sheets* 5·25 5·50

Nos. 2546/53 were printed together, *se-tenant*, in sheetlets of 8.

(Litho Questa)

1998 (19 May). *Orchids of the World.* T **131** *and similar vert designs. Multicoloured.* P 14.

2557	$1 Type **131**	45	50
	a. Sheetlet. Nos. 2557/65	4·00	
2558	$1 *Dendrobium victoriae*	45	50
2559	$1 *Dendrobium nobile*	45	50
2560	$1 *Cymbidium dayanum*	45	50
2561	$1 *Cymbidium* Starbright	45	50
2562	$1 *Cymbidium giganteum*	45	50
2563	$1 *Chysis aurea*	45	50
2564	$1 *Broughtonia sanguinea*	45	50
2565	$1 *Cattleya guttata*	45	50
2566	$1 *Calanthe vestita*	45	50
	a. Sheetlet. Nos. 2566/74	4·00	
2567	$1 *Cattleya bicolor*	45	50
2568	$1 *Laelia anceps*	45	50
2569	$1 *Epidendrum prismatocarpum*	45	50
2570	$1 *Coelogyne ochracea*	45	50
2571	$1 *Doritaenopsis eclantant*	45	50
2572	$1 *Laelia gouldiana*	45	50
2573	$1 *Encyclia vitellina*	45	50
2574	$1 *Maxillaria praestans*	45	50
2575	$1 *Laelia tenebrosa*	45	50
2576	$1.50, *Phragmipedium besseae*	65	70
2577	$2 *Pschopsis papilio*	85	90
2578	$3 *Masdevallia coccinea*	1·25	1·40
2557/78	*Set of 22*	10·50	12·00

MS2579 Two sheets, each 29×43 mm. (a) $6 *Masdevallia ignea*. (b) $6 *Encyclia brassavolae* ... *Set of 2 sheets* 5·25 5·50

Nos. 2557/65 and 2566/74 were each printed together, *se-tenant*, in sheetlets of 9.

1998 (30 June). *Seabirds. Multicoloured designs as* T **452** *of Grenada.* Litho. P 14.

2580	75 c. Bonaparte's Gull (*horiz*)	35	40
2581	90 c. Western Sandpiper (*horiz*)	40	45
2582	$1.50, Common Tern (*horiz*)	65	70
	a. Sheetlet. Nos. 2582/7	3·75	
2583	$1.50, Brown Pelican (*horiz*)	65	70
2584	$1.50, Black-legged Kittiwake and White Tern (*horiz*)	65	70
2585	$1.50, Herring Gull (*horiz*)	65	70
2586	$1.50, Lesser Noddy (*horiz*)	65	70

2587	$1.50, Black-legged Kittiwake (*horiz*) ..	65	70
2588	$1.50, Whimbrel (*horiz*) ..	65	70
	a. Sheetlet. Nos. 2588/93 ..	3·75	
2589	$1.50, Golden White-tailed Tropic Bird		
	(*horiz*)	65	70
2590	$1.50, Arctic Tern (*horiz*) ..	65	70
2591	$1.50, Ruddy Turnstone (*horiz*) ..	65	70
2592	$1.50, Imperial Shag (*horiz*) ..	65	70
2593	$1.50, Magellan Gull (*horiz*) ..	65	70
2594	$2 Great Black-backed Gull (*horiz*) ..	85	90
2595	$3 Dotterell (*horiz*)	1·25	1·40
2580/95	*Set of 16*	10·00	11·50

MS2596 Two sheets, each 100×70 mm. (a) $5
Broad-billed Prion (*horiz*). (b) $5 Yellow-nosed
Albatross .. .. .. *Set of 2 sheets* 4·25 4·50
Nos. 2582/7 and 2588/93 were each printed together,
se-tenant, in sheetlets of 6, with the backgrounds forming
composite designs.

1998 (19 Aug). *International Year of the Ocean. Horiz designs
as T **454** of Grenada. Multicoloured. Litho. P 14.*

2597	75 c. Great Black-backed Gull ..	35	40
	a. Sheetlet. Nos. 2597/608 ..	4·00	
2598	75 c. Common Dolphin	35	40
2599	75 c. Seal	35	40
2600	75 c. Amazonian Catfish ..	35	40
2601	75 c. Shark	35	40
2602	75 c. Goldfish	35	40
2603	75 c. Cyathopharynx ..	35	40
2604	75 c. Killer Whale	35	40
2605	75 c. Telmatochromis ..	35	40
2606	75 c. Crab	35	40
2607	75 c. Octopus	35	40
2608	75 c. Turtle	35	40
2609	90 c. Two Dolphins ..	40	45
	a. Sheetlet. Nos. 2609/20 ..	4·75	
2610	90 c. Seal	40	45
2611	90 c. Turtle on rock ..	40	45
2612	90 c. Leopard Shark ..	40	45
2613	90 c. Flame Angelfish ..	40	45
2614	90 c. Syndontis	40	45
2615	90 c. Lamprologus ..	40	45
2616	90 c. *Krptopterus bicirrhus* ..	40	45
2617	90 c. *Pterophyllum scalare* ..	40	45
2618	90 c. Swimming Pancake ..	40	45
2619	90 c. Cowfish	40	45
2620	90 c. Seahorse	40	45
2597/620	*Set of 24*	8·75	10·00

MS2621 Two sheets, each 98×68 mm. (a) $6
Tetraodon mbu. (b) $6 Goldfish .. *Set of 2 sheets* 5·25 5·50
No. 2597/608 and 2609/20 were each printed together,
se-tenant, in sheetlets of 12 with the backgrounds forming
composite designs.

(Des M. Friedman. Litho Questa)

1998 (15 Sept). *50th Anniv of Organization of American
States. As T **399** of Antigua, but showing a stylised "50".
P 13½×14.*

2622	$1 bluish violet, dull orange and black ..	45	50

(Des Diana Catherines. Litho Questa)

1998 (15 Sept). *25th Death Anniv of Pablo Picasso (painter).
Multicoloured designs as T **400** of Antigua. P 14½.*

2623	45 c. "Bust of a Woman" (*vert*) ..	20	25
2624	$2 "Three Musicians"	85	90
2625	$3 "Studio at La Californie" ..	1·25	1·40
2623/5	*Set of 3*	2·25	2·50

MS2626 102×127 mm. $5 "Woman with a Blue
Hat" .. .. 2·10 2·25

(Des F. Rivera. Litho Questa)

1998 (15 Sept). *Birth Centenary of Enzo Ferrari (car manufacturer). Horiz designs as T **401** of Antigua. Multicoloured. P 14.*

2627	$2 275 GTB	85	95
	a. Sheetlet. Nos. 2627/9 ..	2·50	
2628	$2 340 MM	85	95
2629	$2 250 GT SWB Berlinetta "Hot Rod" ..	85	95
2627/9	*Set of 3*	2·50	2·75

MS2630 104×72 mm. $5 First Ferrari cabriolet
(91×34 mm) P 14×14½ .. .. 2·10 2·25
Nos. 2627/9 were printed together, *se-tenant*, in sheetlets of 3.

(Des G. Bibby. Litho Questa)

1998 (15 Sept). *19th World Scout Jamboree, Chile. Multicoloured designs as T **402** of Antigua. P 14.*

2631	90 c. Scout greeting ..	40	45
2632	$1.50, Lord Baden-Powell ..	65	70
2633	$5 Scout salute	2·10	2·25
2631/3	*Set of 3*	3·00	3·25

MS2634 76×106 mm. $6 Lord Baden-Powell
(*vert*) .. .. 2·50 2·75

(Des J. Iskowitz. Litho Questa)

1998 (15 Sept). *50th Death Anniv of Mahatma Gandhi. Vert
portraits as T **403** of Antigua. P 14.*

2635	$1 bluish grey, brownish black and black ..	45	50
	a. Sheetlet of 4	1·75	

MS2636 100×70 mm. $6 bluish grey, orange-
brown and black .. .. 2·50 2·75
No. 2635 was issued in sheetlets of 4 with enlarged illustrated
margins at top and left.

(Des D. Miller. Litho Questa)

1998 (15 Sept). *80th Anniv of Royal Air Force. Horiz designs
as T **404** of Antigua. Multicoloured. P 14.*

2637	$2 Tornado GR1	90	95
	a. Sheetlet. Nos. 2637/40 ..	3·50	
2638	$2 BAe Hawk T1A ..	90	95
2639	$2 Sepecat Jaguar GR1 ..	90	95
2640	$2 Harrier GR7	90	95
2641	$2 Chinook helicopter carrying three loads	90	95
	a. Sheetlet. Nos. 2641/4 ..	3·50	
2642	$2 Silhouette of BAe Harrier GR5 ..	90	95

2643	$2 Panavia Tornado F3 ADV at sunset ..	90	95
2644	$2 Chinook HC2 carrying 105 mm light		
	gun	90	95
2637/44	*Set of 8*	7·00	7·50

MS2645 Four sheets, each 93×70 mm. (a) $6
Bristol F2B fighter and head of eagle (bird). (b)
$6 Bristol F2B fighter and bird in flight. (c) $6
Hawker Hunter and EF-2000 Eurofighter. (d) $6
Tornado and EF-2000 Eurofighter *Set of 4 sheets* 10·00 10·50
Nos. 2637/40 and 2641/4 were each printed together,
se-tenant, in sheetlets of 4 with enlarged illustrated margins.

(Litho Questa)

1998 (15 Sept). *Birth Bicentenary of Eugéne Delacroix
(painter). Multicoloured designs as T **455** of Grenada. P 14.*

2646	$1 "The Natchez"	45	50
	a. Sheetlet. Nos. 2646/53 ..	3·50	
2647	$1 Christ and His Disciples crossing the		
	Sea of Galilee"	45	50
2648	$1 "Sunset"	45	50
2649	$1 "Moroccans outside the Walls of		
	Tangier"	45	50
2650	$1 "The Fireplace"	45	50
2651	$1 "Forest View with an Oak Tree" ..	45	50
2652	$1 "View of the Harbour at Dieppe" ..	45	50
2653	$1 "Arab Tax Collectors" ..	45	50
2646/53	*Set of 8*	3·50	4·00

MS2654 85×105 mm. $5 "Young Orphan" .. 2·10 2·25
Nos. 2646/53 were printed together in sheetlets of 8,
containing two *se-tenant* horizontal strips of 4 separated by a
gutter showing paintings depicted on Nos. 2647 and 2650.

(Litho Questa)

1998 (15 Sept). *1st Death Anniv of Diana, Princess of Wales.
Vert design as T **405** of Antigua. P 14½×14.*

2655	$1.50, multicoloured ..	65	70
	a. Sheetlet of 6	4·00	

No. 2655 was printed in sheetlets of 6 with an enlarged
illustrated left margin.

132 Father Christmas and Hare

1998 (15 Oct). *Disney's Christmas Trains. T **132** and similar
horiz designs showing cartoon characters in train carriages.
Multicoloured. Litho. P 14×13½.*

2656	$1 Type **132**	45	50
	a. Sheetlet. Nos. 2656/60 ..	2·25	
2657	$1 Giraffe, elephant and tiger ..	45	50
2658	$1 Three Pigs and Wolf ..	45	50
2659	$1 Pied Piper, Jiminy Cricket, penguins		
	and children	45	50
2660	$1 Swans, Little Hiawatha and tortoise ..	45	50
2661	$1 Mickey Mouse as train driver ..	45	50
	a. Sheetlet. Nos. 2661/5 ..	2·25	
2662	$1 Pluto, Chip and Dale ..	45	50
2663	$1 Donald and Daisy Duck ..	45	50
2664	$1 Goofy, Huey, Dewey and Louie ..	45	50
2665	$1 Minnie Mouse and presents ..	45	50
2666	$1 Piglet as train driver ..	45	50
	a. Sheetlet. Nos. 2666/70 ..	2·25	
2667	$1 Winnie the Pooh and honey ..	45	50
2668	$1 Rabbit and Owl	45	50
2669	$1 Kanga, Roo and Christopher Robin ..	45	50
2670	$1 Eeyore and Tigger ..	45	50
2656/70	*Set of 15*	6·75	7·50

MS2671 Three sheets, each 133×109 mm. (a) $6
Father Christmas and toy train. (b) $6 Mickey
Mouse as train driver. (c) $6 Rabbit, Winnie the
Pooh, Piglet and Eeyore .. *Set of 3 sheets* 7·50 7·75
Nos. 2656/60, 2661/5 and 2666/70 were each printed together,
se-tenant, in sheetlets containing horizontal strips of 5.

1999 (4 Jan). *Chinese New Year ("Year of the Rabbit"). Sheet
150×76 mm, containing triangular designs as T **435** of
Grenada each showing rabbits. Multicoloured. Self-adhesive
on gold foil. P 9½.*

MS2672 $1.50, "GRENADA GRENADINES" in
emerald; $1.50, "GRENADA GRENADINES" in
orange; $1.50, "GRENADA GRENADINES" in
red .. .. 1·90 2·00

GRENADA
GRENADINES

Grenada
Grenadines 15¢

133 Troodon

134 Great Indian Peninsula
Passenger and Mail Locomotive

1999 (1 Mar). *"Australia '99" International Stamp Exhibition,
Melbourne. Prehistoric Animals. T **133** and similar multicoloured designs. Litho. P 14.*

2673	$1 Type **133**	45	50
	a. Sheetlet. Nos. 2673/8 ..	2·50	
2674	$1 Camptosaurus	45	50
2675	$1 Parasaurolophus ..	45	50
2676	$1 Dryosaurus	45	50
2677	$1 Gallimimus	45	50
2678	$1 Camarasaurus	45	50
2679	$1.50, Duckbill (*horiz*) ..	65	70
	a. Sheetlet. Nos. 2679/86 ..	5·00	
2680	$1.50, Lambeosaurus (*horiz*) ..	65	70
2681	$1.50, Iguanodon (*horiz*) ..	65	70
2682	$1.50, Euoplocephalus (*horiz*) ..	65	70
2683	$1.50, Triceratops (*horiz*) ..	65	70
2684	$1.50, Brachiosaurus (*horiz*) ..	65	70
2685	$1.50, Ponoptosaurus (*horiz*) ..	65	70
2686	$1.50, Stegosaurus (*horiz*) ..	65	70
2673/86	*Set of 14*	7·50	8·50

MS2687 Three sheets. (a) $6 106×76 mm. $6
Edmontosaurus (*horiz*). (b) 76×106 mm. $6
Tyrannosaurus Rex. (c) 76×106 mm. $6 Haltico-
saurus .. .. .. *Set of 3 sheets* 7·50 7·75
Nos. 2673/8 and 2679/86 were each printed together,
se-tenant, in sheetlets of 6 or 8.

(Des F. Rivera. Litho Questa)

1999 (12 Apr). *Steam Trains of the World. T **134** and similar
horiz designs. Multicoloured. P 14.*

2688	15 c. Type **134**	10	10
2689	75 c. Midland Great Western passenger		
	locomotive (Ireland) ..	35	40
2690	90 c. Canada Pacific express locomotive ..	40	45
2691	$1.50, East Indian Railway express		
	locomotive	65	70
2692	$2 Victorian Railways suburban tank		
	locomotive (Australia) ..	85	90
2693	$2 Eastern Railways compound		
	locomotive (France) ..	85	90
	a. Sheetlet. Nos. 2693/6 ..	3·25	
2694	$2 Govt Railways Class WF tank		
	locomotive (New Zealand) ..	85	90
2695	$2 Burma Railways oil-burning tank		
	locomotive, 1899 ..	85	90
2696	$2 Federated Malay States Railway		
	Class G steam locomotive, 1899 ..	85	90
2697	$2 Belfast and Northern Counties		
	Railway narrow-gauge tank		
	locomotive	85	90
	a. Sheetlet. Nos. 2697/700 ..	3·25	
2698	$2 Shunting tank locomotive (Russia) ..	85	90
2699	$2 G.N.R. Ivatt large-boilered "Atlantic"		
	type	85	90
2700	$2 Palatine Railway "Atlantic" type		
	express locomotive (Germany) ..	85	90
2701	$2 Belgian State Railways "Dunalastair"		
	type locomotive ..	85	90
	a. Sheetlet. Nos. 2701/4 ..	3·25	
2702	$2 Swedish State Railways Class Cc		
	locomotive	85	90
2703	$2 Antofagasta and Bolivian Railway		
	tank locomotive (Chile) ..	85	90
2704	$2 Bolivian State Fairlie type locomotive	85	90
2705	$2 Belgian State Railways express		
	locomotive	85	90
	a. Sheetlet. Nos. 2705/8 ..	3·25	
2706	$2 London and South Western Railway		
	Drummond's mixed traffic locomotive	85	90
2707	$2 Belfast and Northern Counties		
	Railway Compound locomotive ..	85	90
2708	$2 Dutch State Railway express		
	passenger locomotive ..	95	90
2709	$2 Gothard Railway heavy freight		
	locomotive (Switzerland) ..	85	90
	a. Sheetlet. Nos. 2709/12 ..	3·25	
2710	$2 Waterford, Limerick and Western		
	Railway goods locomotive (Ireland) ..	85	90
2711	$2 Atchison, Topeka and Santa Fe		
	Railroad tandem compound express		
	locomotive (U.S.A) ..	85	90
2712	$2 Midland Railway Class "Princess of		
	Wales" locomotive (Great Britain) ..	85	90
2713	$3 Glasgow and South Western Railway		
	Stirling type locomotive ..	1·25	1·40
2688/713	*Set of 26*	21·00	22·00

MS2714 Two sheets, each 100×70 mm. (a) $6
Paris, Lyons and Mediterranean compound
locomotive (France). (b) $6 Italian Southern
Railway compound locomotive .. *Set of 2 sheets* 5·25 5·50
Nos. 2693/6, 2697/700, 2701/4, 2705/8 and 2709/12 were each
printed together, *se-tenant*, in sheetlets of 4, with illustrated top
or bottom margins.
No. 2701 is inscribed "Dunalastiar" in error.

75¢

GRENADA
GRENADINES

135 Porkfish

(Des T. Wood. Litho Questa)

1999 (26 Apr). *Fauna and Flora. T **135** and similar multicoloured designs. P 14.*

2715	75 c. Type **135**	35	40
2716	90 c. Leatherback Turtle ..	40	45
2717	$1 White-tailed Tropic Bird (*vert*) ..	45	50
	a. Sheetlet. Nos. 2717/25 ..	4·00	
2718	$1 Laughing Gull (*vert*) ..	45	50
2719	$1 Palm Tree (*vert*) ..	45	50
2720	$1 Humpback Whale (*vert*) ..	45	50
2721	$1 Painted Bunting (*vert*) ..	45	50
2722	$1 Common Grackle (*vert*) ..	45	50

2723	$1 Green Anole (lizard) (*vert*)	..	45	50
2724	$1 *Morpho peleides* (butterfly) (*vert*)	..	45	50
2725	$1 *Prepona meander* (butterfly) (*vert*)	..	45	50
2726	$1 Common Dolphin (*vert*)	..	45	50
	a. Sheetlet. Nos. 2726/34	..	4·00	
2727	$1 *Catonephele numilia* (butterfly) (*vert*)	..	45	50
2728	$1 Sooty Tern (*vert*)	..	45	50
2729	$1 Vermilion Flycatcher (*vert*)	..	45	50
2730	$1 Blue Grosbeak (*vert*)	..	45	50
2731	$1 Great Egret (*vert*)	..	45	50
2732	$1 *Actinate pellenea* (butterfly) (*vert*)	..	45	50
2733	$1 *Anteos clorinde* (butterfly) (*vert*)	..	45	50
2734	$1 Common Iguana (*vert*)	..	45	50
2735	$1.50, Ruby-throated Hummingbird	..	65	70
2736	$2 *Theope eudocia* (butterfly)	..	85	90
2715/36		*Set of 22*	11·00	11·50

MS2737 Two sheets, each 85×110 mm. (a) $6 Bananaquit. (b) $6 Beaugregory (fish)

Set of 2 sheets 5·25 5·50

Nos. 2717/25 and 2726/34 were each printed together, *se-tenant*, in sheetlets of 9 with the backgrounds forming composite designs.

Nos. 2727 and **MS**2737 (b) are inscribed "numili" or "BEAY GREGORY", both in error.

136 John H. Glenn
(astronaut), 1998

137 Sophie
Rhys-Jones

1999 (24 May). *John Glenn's (first American to orbit Earth) Return to Space. T **136** and similar designs. Multicoloured (except Nos. 2739, 2741 and 2743/4). Litho. P 14½.*

2738	$1 Type **136**		45	50
	a. Sheetlet. Nos. 2738/43		2·60	
2739	$1 Glenn and Pres. John F. Kennedy (chocolate and deep rose-red)	..	45	50
2740	$1 Inside *Discovery*, 1998	..	45	50
2741	$1 Climbing from *Friendship 7* capsule, 1962 (red-brown and deep rose-red)	..	45	50
2742	$1 Medical checkup	..	45	50
2743	$1 Climbing into space capsule, 1962 (red-brown and deep rose-red)	..	45	50
2744	$1 As Democratic Senator for Ohio, 1974 (*vert*) (chocolate and deep rose-red)	..	45	50
	a. Sheetlet. Nos. 2744/51	..	3·50	
2745	$1 In space suit, 1962 (*vert*)	..	45	50
2746	$1 Smiling during suit up test, 1998 (*vert*)	..	45	50
2747	$1 Preparing for *Discovery* flight (*vert*)	..	45	50
2748	$1 At press conference (with microphone) (*vert*)	..	45	50
2749	$1 Smiling at camera (wearing glasses) (*vert*)	..	45	50
2750	$1 Participating in medical research (*vert*)	..	45	50
2751	$1 Posing in space suit, 1998 (*vert*)	..	45	50
2738/51		*Set of 14*	6·25	7·00

Nos. 2738/43 and 2744/51 were each printed together, *se-tenant*, in sheetlets of 6 or 8 with enlarged, illustrated top margins.

No. 2744 is inscribed "Junior Senator form Ohio (1974)" in error.

(Litho Questa)

1999 (24 May). *"iBRA '99" International Stamp Exhibition, Nuremberg. Horiz designs as T **416** of Antigua. Multicoloured. P 14.*

2752	35 c. *Luckenbach* (full-rigged ship) and Thurn and Taxis Northern District 1852 1/4 sgr. stamp		15	20
2753	45 c. Leipzig–Dresden Railway carriage and Schleswig-Holstein 1850 1 s.	..	20	25
2754	$1.50, Leipzig–Dresden Railway carriage and Oldenburg 1852 1/3 sgr.		65	70
2755	$3 *Luckenbach* (full-rigged ship) and North German Confederation 1868 1/4 g.	..	1·25	1·40
2752/5		*Set of 4*	2·25	2·50

MS2756 154×86 mm. $6 Thurn and Taxis Northern District 1865 1/4 sgr. rouletted pair used on cover. P 14×14½

2·50 2·75

1999 (24 May). *150th Death Anniv of Katsushika Hokusai (Japanese artist). Multicoloured designs as T **417** of Antigua. Litho. P 13½.*

2757	$1.50, "Fuchu"	..	65	70
	a. Sheetlet. Nos. 2757/62		3·75	
2758	$1.50, "Doll Fair at Fikkendana"	..	65	70
2759	$1.50, "Sumo Wrestlers" (in arm hold)	..	65	70
2760	$1.50, "Sumo Wrestlers" (in head lock)	..	65	70
2761	$1.50, "Sojo Henjo"	..	65	70
2762	$1.50, "Twin Gardens Gateway of Asakusa Kannon Temple"	..	65	70
2763	$1.50, "A Breeze on a Fine Day"	..	65	70
	a. Sheetlet. Nos. 2763/8	..	3·75	
2764	$1.50, "Ejiri"	..	65	70
2765	$1.50, "Horse Drawings" (galloping)	..	65	70
2766	$1.50, "Horse Drawings" (stationary)	..	65	70
2767	$1.50, "View along Bank of Sumida River"	..	65	70
2768	$1.50, "Thunderstorm below the Mountain"	..	65	70
2757/68		*Set of 12*	7·50	8·00

MS2769 Two sheets, each 102×72 mm. (a) $6 "Stretching Cloth" (*vert*). (b) $6 "Kobo Daishi exorcising Demon that causes Sickness" (*vert*)

Set of 2 sheets 5·25 5·50

Nos. 2757/62 and 2763/8 were each printed together, *se-tenant*, in sheetlets of 6.

No. 2762 is inscribed "TWIN GARDAINS GATEWAY" in error.

1999 (24 May). *10th Anniv of United Nations Rights of the Child Convention. Vert designs as T **419** of Antigua. Multicoloured. Litho P 14.*

2770	$3 African boy	..	1·25	1·40
	a. Sheetlet. Nos. 2770/2	..	3·75	
2771	$3 Liv Ullman (.U.N.I.C.E.F.'s first female ambassador)	..	1·25	1·40
2772	$3 African woman in head scarf	..	1·25	1·40
2770/2		*Set of 3*	3·75	4·00

MS2773 110×84 mm. $6 Maurice Pate (Founding Director of U.N.I.C.E.F.)

2·50 2·75

Nos. 2770/2 were printed together, *se-tenant*, in a sheetlet of 3 forming a composite design.

1999 (24 May). *"PhilexFrance '99" International Stamp Exhibition, Paris. Railway Locomotives. Two sheets containing horiz designs as T **420** of Antigua. Multicoloured. Litho. P 14×13½.*

MS2774 (a) 106×81 mm. $6 Paris, Orleans and Mediterranean Railway Cha Pelon type steam locomotive. (b) 106×76 mm. $6 French National Railways Class 7000 high speed electric locomotive

Set of 2 sheets 5·25 5·50

1999 (24 May). *250th Birth Anniv of Johann von Goethe (German writer). Designs as T **421** of Antigua. Litho. P 14.*

2775	$3 multicoloured	..	1·25	1·40
	a. Sheetlet. Nos. 2775/7		3·75	
2776	$3 ultramarine and black	..	1·25	1·40
2777	$3 ultramarine, bluish violet and black	..	1·25	1·40
2775/7		*Set of 3*	3·75	4·00

MS2778 71×106 mm. $6 red-brn, chestnut & blk 2·50 2·75

Designs: *Horiz*—No. 2775, Peasants dancing under lindentree; No. 2776, Von Goethe and Von Schiller; No. 2777, Faust dreaming of soaring above the mortal. *Vert*—No. **MS**2778, Johann von Goethe.

Nos. 2775/7 were printed together, *se-tenant*, in sheetlets of 3 with enlarged illustrated margins.

NOTE. From No. 2779 stamps for the Grenada Grenadines were inscribed "Grenada Carriacou & Petite Martinique".

1999 (18 June). *Royal Wedding. T **137** and similar vert designs. Multicoloured. Litho. P 13½.*

2779	$3 Type **137**	..	1·25	1·40
	a. Sheetlet. Nos. 2779/81	..	3·25	
2780	$3 Sophie and Prince Edward	..	1·25	1·40
2781	$3 Prince Edward	..	1·25	1·40
2779/81		*Set of 3*	3·75	4·00

MS2782 78×108 mm. $6 Sophie and Prince Edward on wedding day

2·50 2·75

Nos. 2779/81 were printed together, *se-tenant*, in sheetlets of 3 with enlarged illustrated margins.

(Litho Questa)

1999 (16 Aug). *"Queen Elizabeth the Queen Mother's Century". Vert designs as T **334** of Dominica. Multicoloured. P 14.*

2783	$2 black and gold	..	85	90
	a. Sheetlet. Nos. 2783/6		3·50	
2784	$2 multicoloured	..	85	90
2785	$2 black and gold		85	90
2786	$2 multicoloured		85	90
2783/6		*Set of 4*	3·50	3·75

MS2787 153×157 mm. $6 mult. P 13½×14 2·50 2·75

Designs: (*As Type **334** of Dominica*)—No. 2783, Lady Elizabeth Bowes-Lyon as a child; No. 2784, Queen Mother in Rhodesia, 1957; No. 2785, Queen Mother with Princesses Elizabeth and Anne, 1950; No. 2786, Queen Mother, 1988. (37×50 *mm*)—No. **MS**2787, Queen Mother reviewing Black Watch, Berlin.

Nos. 2783/6 were printed together, *se-tenant*, as a sheetlet of 4 stamps and a central label with inscribed and embossed margins. No. **MS**2787 also shows the Royal Arms embossed in gold.

A $20 value embossed on gold foil also exists from a limited printing.

STAMP BOOKLETS

1977 (7 Feb). *Silver Jubilee. Multicoloured cover, 165×92 mm, showing the Queen enthroned. Stitched.*

SB1 $9.60, booklet containing 35 c. in pane of 6 (No. 219a) and *se-tenant* pane of 3 (No. 220a) .. 1·75

1978 (12 Apr). *25th Anniv of Coronation. Multicoloured cover, 165×92 mm, showing the Queen's Division on parade. Stitched.*

SB2 $7.04, booklet containing *se-tenant* pane of 6 (No. 276a) and pane of 1 (No. 278a) .. 1·60

1981 (16 June). *Royal Wedding. Multicoloured cover, 90×165 mm, showing Prince Charles on front and back. Panes attached by selvedge.*

SB3 $14 booklet containing *se-tenant* pane of 6 (No. 450a) and pane of 1 (No. 452a) .. .. 2·50

The cover of No. SB3 is folded five times "concertina fashion" and when opened up measures 550×165 mm.

OFFICIAL STAMPS

1982 (June). *Various stamps optd with Type O **1** of Grenada.*

(a) *Nos. 400/12 and 414*

O 1	5 c.	Yellow-tailed Snapper		..	10	15
O 2	6 c.	Mutton Snapper		..	10	15
O 3	10 c.	Cocoa Damselfish		..	10	15
O 4	12 c.	Royal Gramma		..	10	15
O 5	15 c.	Cherub Angelfish		..	10	15
O 6	20 c.	Black-barred Soldierfish		..	10	20
O 7	25 c.	Mottled Grouper		..	10	20
O 8	30 c.	Long-snouted Butterflyfish		..	15	20
O 9	40 c.	Puddingwife		..	15	25
O10	50 c.	Midnight Parrotfish		..	20	30
O11	90 c.	Red-spotted Hawkfish		..	40	55
O12	$1	Hogfish		..	40	60
O13	$3	Beau Gregory		..	1·25	2·25
O14	$10	Barred Hamlet		..	4·25	6·00

(b) *Nos. 444/6 and 448/9*

O15	30 c.	Prince Charles and Lady Diana Spencer			2·00	2·00
O16	40 c.	Prince Charles and Lady Diana Spencer			1·60	1·60
O17	40 c.	Type 50		..	2·00	2·75
O18	$2	Type 50		..	2·50	3·50
O19	$4	Prince Charles as parachutist		..	6·50	8·50

The Royal Wedding $4 from sheetlets, perforated 14½×14 and with changed background colour, also exists with this overprint (*Price £6 mint, £8 used*).

(c) *Nos. 473/6*

O20	54	20 c. multicoloured		..	10	20
O21	—	40 c. multicoloured		..	15	25
O22	—	$1 multicoloured		..	35	70
O23	—	$2 multicoloured		..	70	1·40
O1/23	..			*Set of 23*	20·00	29·00

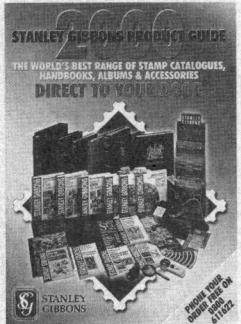

Griqualand West
see South Africa

Guyana
(*formerly* British Guiana)

BRITISH GUIANA

The postal service from what was to become British Guiana dates from the last years of the 18th-century, being placed on a more regular basis after the final British occupation.

An inland postal system was organised in 1850, using the adhesive stamps of British Guiana, but, until 1 May 1860, overseas mails continued to be the province of the British G.P.O. The stamps of Great Britain were supplied for use on such letters from 11 May 1858 and examples of their use in combination with British Guiana issues have been recorded.

For illustration of the handstamp and postmark type see BRITISH POST OFFICES ABROAD notes, following GREAT BRITAIN.

CROWNED-CIRCLED HANDSTAMPS

The provision of a handstamp, probably as Type CC 1, inscribed "DEMERARA", is recorded in the G.P.O. proof book under 1 March 1856. No examples have been reported. A further handstamp, as Type CC 6, recorded in the proof book on 17 February 1866, is known used as a cancellation in at least two instances, *circa* 1868.

GEORGETOWN (DEMERARA)

Stamps of GREAT BRITAIN *cancelled* "A 03" *as Type* **2**.
1858 to 1860.
Z1	1d. rose-red (1857), *perf* 14	..	..	..	£225
Z2	4d. rose (1857)	..	..	..	£130
Z3	6d. lilac (1856)	..	..	..	£100
	a. Azure paper	..	..	..	
Z4	1s. green (1856)	..	..	..	£1100

NEW AMSTERDAM (BERBICE)

Stamps of GREAT BRITAIN *cancelled* "A 04" *as Type* **2**.
1858 to 1860.
Z5	1d. rose-red (1857), *perf* 14	..	..	..	£650
Z6	2d. blue (1858) (Plate Nos. 7, 8)	..	..	£650
Z7	4d. rose (1857)	..	..	..	£300
Z8	6d. lilac (1856)	..	..	..	£200
Z9	1s. green (1856)	..	..	..	£1300

PRICES FOR STAMPS ON COVER TO 1945		
Nos. 1/21	*from* × 3	
No. 23		†
Nos. 24/7	*from* × 3	
Nos. 29/115	*from* × 4	
Nos. 116/24	*from* × 6	
Nos. 126/36	*from* × 5	
Nos. 137/59	*from* × 6	
Nos. 162/5	*from* × 8	
Nos. 170/4	*from* × 5	
Nos. 175/89	*from* × 6	
No. 192	*from* × 20	
Nos. 193/210	*from* × 4	
Nos. 213/15	*from* × 5	
Nos. 216/21	*from* × 3	
Nos. 222/4	*from* × 8	
Nos. 233/50	*from* × 3	
No. 251	—	
formerly Nos. 252/7	*from* × 3	
Nos. 259/82	*from* × 4	
Nos. 283/7	*from* × 5	
Nos. 288/300	*from* × 4	
Nos. 301/4	*from* × 5	
Nos. 305/7	*from* × 6	
Nos. 308/19	*from* × 5	
Nos. D1/4	*from* × 12	
Nos. O1/12	*from* × 12	

CROWN COLONY

(Currency. 100 cents = 1 dollar)

1

2

(Set up and printed at the office of the *Royal Gazette*, Georgetown, British Guiana)

1850 (1 July)–**51.** *Type-set. Black impression. (a) Medium wove paper. Prices are for*—I. Cut square. II. Cut round.
					I Used	II Used
1	1	2 c. rose (1.3.51)	..	..	—	£70000
2		4 c. orange	..	..	£25000	£4000
3		4 c. lemon-yellow (1851)	..	£38000	£4750
4		8 c. green	..	..	£15000	£3250
5		12 c. blue	..	..	£5500	£2000
6		12 c. indigo	..	..	£9500	£2750
7		12 c. pale blue (1851)	..	£8500	£3000
		a. "2" of "12" with straight foot	—	£5000
		b. "1" of "12" omitted		† £35000

(b) *Pelure paper* (1851)
8	1	4 c. pale yellow	..	..	£48000	£5000

These stamps were initialled by the postmaster, or the Post Office clerks, before they were issued. The initials are—E. T. E. D(alton), E. D. W(ight), J. B. S(mith), H. A. K(illikelley), and W. H. L(ortimer). There are several types of each value and it has been suggested that the setting contained one horizontal row of four slightly different impressions.

Ten examples of No. 1 have been recorded, including three pairs on separate covers.

(Litho Waterlow)
1852 (1 Jan). *Surface-coloured paper. Imperf.*
					Un	Used
9	2	1 c. black/*magenta*	..	..	£8500	£4250
10		4 c. black/*deep blue*	..	£11000	£5500

There are two types of each value.

Reprints on thicker paper and perf 12½, were made in 1865 (*Price £17 either value*).

Such reprints with the perforations removed are sometimes offered as genuine originals.

CONDITION. Prices for Nos. 9 to 21 are for fine copies. Poor to medium specimens can be supplied when in stock at much lower rates.

3

4

5

(Dies eng and stamps litho Waterlow)
1853–59. *Imperf. (a) Original printing.*
11	3	1 c. vermilion	..	..	£3000	£1000

This 1 c. in *reddish brown* is probably a proof (*Price £650*).

A. "O" large and 1 mm from left corner.
B. "O" small and ¾ mm from left corner.
C. "O" small and ¾ mm from left corner. "NT" widely spaced.
D. "ONE" close together, "O" 1¼ mm from left corner.

(b) *Fresh lithographic transfers from the 4 c. with varying labels of value. White line above value* (1857–59).
12	3	1 c. dull red (A)	..	£2750	£950
13		1 c. brownish red (A)	..	£6000	£1300
14		1 c. dull red (B)	..	£3250	£1000
15		1 c. brownish red (B)	..	£6000	£1400
16		1 c. dull red (C)	..	£4000	£1300
16a		1 c. brownish red (C)	..	—	£1600
17		1 c. dull red (D)	..	£9500	£4250

1853–55. *Imperf.*
18	4	4 c. deep blue	..	£1800	£650
		a. Retouched	..	£2750	£900
19		4 c. blue (1854)	..	£1100	£425
		a. Retouched	..	£1700	£600
20		4 c. pale blue (1855)	..	£850	£325
		a. Retouched	..	£1500	£550

The 4 c. value was produced from transfers from the original 1 c., with the bottom inscription removed, teamed with a new face value. The join often shows as a white line or traces of it above the label of value and lower corner figures. In some stamps on the sheet this line is missing, owing to having been retouched, and in these cases a line of colour usually appears in its place.

The 1 c. and 4 c. stamps were printed in 1865 from fresh transfers of five varieties. These are on thin paper and perf 12½ (*Price £14 each unused*).

1860 (May). *Figures in corners framed. Imperf.*
21	5	4 c. blue	..	..	£2500	£450

6

(Type-set and printed at the *Official Gazette* by Baum and Dallas, Georgetown.)

1856. (a) *Surface-coloured paper.*
23	6	1 c. black/*magenta*	..	..	—
24		4 c. black/*magenta* (Feb)	†	£6000
25		4 c. black/*rose-carmine* (Sept)	£20000	£8500
26		4 c. black/*blue* (Oct)	† £40000

(b) *Paper coloured through*
27	6	4 c. black/*deep blue* (Aug)	..	† £55000

Since only one example of No. 23 is known, no market price can be given. This celebrated stamp frequently termed "the world's rarest", was last on the market in 1980.

These stamps, like those of the first issue, were initialled before being issued; the initials are—E.T.E.D (alton), E.D.W (ight), C.A. W(atson), and W.H.L (ortimer). The unique 1 c. is initialled by E.D. Wight.

The 4 c. is known in four types, differing in the position of the inscriptions.

PAPERMAKERS' WATERMARKS. Seven different papermakers' watermarks were used in the period 1860 to 1875 and stamps bearing portions of these are worth a premium.

7

A	B
C	D
E	F

(Dies eng and litho Waterlow)
1860 (July)–**63.** *Tablets of value as illustrated. Thick paper.* P 12.
29	7	1 c. pale rose	..	£1200	£200
30		2 c. deep orange (8.60)	..	£170	40·00
31		2 c. pale orange	..	£170	40·00
32		4 c. deep blue (8.60)	..	£400	70·00
33		4 c. blue	..	£250	50·00
34		8 c. brownish rose	..	£425	80·00
35		8 c. pink	..	£350	65·00
36		12 c. lilac (12.60)	..	£425	35·00
37		12 c. grey-lilac	..	£350	32·00
38		24 c. deep green (6.63)	..	£1000	95·00
39		24 c. green	..	£850	65·00

The 1 c. was reprinted in 1865 on *thin* paper, P 12½–13, and in a different shade. *Price £14.*

The 12 c. in both shades is frequently found surcharged with a large "5d" in *red*; this is to denote the proportion of postage repayable by the colony to Great Britain for overseas letters.

1861 (3 Aug*). *Colour changed. Thick paper.* P 12.
40	7	1 c. reddish brown	..	..	£300	90·00

*Earliest known postmark date.

1862–65. (a) *Thin paper.* P 12.
41	7	1 c. brown	..	£400	£170
42		1 c. black (1863)	..	90·00	48·00
43		2 c. orange	..	85·00	35·00
44		4 c. blue	..	£100	35·00
45		4 c. pale blue	..	85·00	24·00
46		8 c. pink (1863)	..	£110	50·00
47		12 c. dull purple (1863)	..	£120	22·00
48		12 c. purple	..	£140	25·00
49		12 c. lilac	..	£150	35·00
50		24 c. green	..	£750	85·00

(b) *Thin paper.* P 12½–13 (1863)
51	7	1 c. black	..	55·00	17·00
52		2 c. orange	..	70·00	17·00
53		4 c. blue	..	75·00	17·00
54		8 c. pink	..	£200	75·00
55		12 c. brownish lilac	..	£450	£100
56		24 c. green	..	£550	65·00

Copies are found on *pelure* paper.

(c) *Medium paper.* P 12½–13
57	7	1 c. black (1864)	..	45·00	30·00
58		2 c. deep orange (1864)	..	60·00	19·00
59		2 c. orange	..	65·00	17·00
60		4 c. greyish blue (1864)	..	75·00	14·00
61		4 c. blue	..	90·00	21·00
62		8 c. pink (1864)	..	£130	50·00
63		12 c. brownish lilac (1865)	..	£400	90·00
64		24 c. green (1864)	..	£170	50·00
65		24 c. deep green	..	£300	70·00

(d) *Medium paper.* P 10 (Nov 1865)
65a	7	12 c. grey-lilac	..	..	£400	70·00

8   9

G   H

I   K

New transfers for the 1 c., 2 c., 8 c., and 12 c. with the spaces between values and the word "CENTS" about 1 mm.

1863–76. *Medium paper (a) P 12½–13 (1863–68).*
66	8	1 c. black (1866)	35·00	22·00
67		2 c. orange-red (1865)	42·00	4·75
68		2 c. orange	38·00	4·75
69	9	6 c. blue (1865)	95·00	45·00
70		6 c. greenish blue	£100	50·00
71		6 c. deep blue	£150	55·00
72		6 c. milky blue	95·00	48·00
73	8	8 c. pink (1868)	£170	17·00
74		8 c. carmine	£190	18·00
75		12 c. grey-lilac (1867)	£400	25·00
76		12 c. brownish purple	£475	32·00
77	9	24 c. green (*perf* 12)	£200	19·00
78		24 c. yellow-green (*perf* 12)	£130	9·50
79		24 c. yellow-green (*perf* 12½–13)	£130	8·00
80		24 c. green (*perf* 12½–13) (1864)	£130	9·50
81		24 c. blue-green (*perf* 12½–13)	£170	19·00
82		48 c. pale red	£200	45·00
83		48 c. deep red	£225	48·00
84		48 c. carmine-rose	£250	48·00

The 4 c. corresponding to this issue can only be distinguished from that of the previous issue by minor plating flaws.

There is a variety of the 6 c. with stop before "VICISSIM".

Varieties of most of the values of issues of 1863–64 and 1866 are to be found on both very thin and thick papers.

(b) P 10 (1866–71)
85	8	1 c. black (1869)	9·00	3·50
86		1 c. grey-black	10·00	7·00
87		2 c. orange (1868)	22·00	3·00
88		2 c. reddish orange	30·00	4·00
89		4 c. slate-blue	70·00	13·00
90		4 c. blue	75·00	9·50
		a. Bisected (on cover)	†	£4500
		b. Ditto Imperf (on cover)	†	
91		4 c. pale blue	70·00	9·50
92	9	6 c. milky blue (1867)	£100	27·00
93		6 c. ultramarine	£110	42·00
94		6 c. dull blue	£100	32·00
95	8	8 c. pink (5.71)	£100	20·00
96		8 c. brownish pink	£120	22·00
96a		8 c. carmine	£180	27·00
97		12 c. pale lilac (1867)	£190	13·00
98		12 c. grey-lilac	£150	13·00
99		12 c. brownish grey	£140	16·00
100		12 c. lilac	£140	16·00
101	9	24 c. deep green	£200	9·00
102		24 c. bluish green	£190	8·00
103		24 c. yellow-green	£150	7·50
104		48 c. crimson (1867)	£275	28·00
105		48 c. red	£275	24·00
104		Handstamped "Specimen"	£200	
104		Perf "Specimen"	£160	

(c) P 15 (1875–76)
106	8	1 c. black	40·00	7·50
107		2 c. orange-red	£120	8·50
108		2 c. orange	£120	8·50
109		4 c. bright blue	£200	85·00
111	9	6 c. ultramarine	£450	70·00
112	8	8 c. deep rose (1876)	£200	75·00
113		12 c. lilac	£500	50·00
114	9	24 c. yellow-green	£500	35·00
115		24 c. deep green	£700	55·00

There is a variety of the 48 c. with stop after "P" in "PETIMUSQUE".

Imperforate stamps of this and of the previous issue are considered to be proofs, although examples of the 24 c. imperforate from the 1869–73 period are known commercially used.

PRICES for stamps of the 1862 issue are for good average copies. Copies with roulettes on all sides very seldom occur and do not exist in marginal positions.

10	11	12
13	**14**	**15**

(Type-set and printed at the Office of the *Royal Gazette*, Georgetown)

1862 (Sept). *Black on coloured paper. Roul 6.*
116	10	1 c. *rose*	£2250	£450
		a. Unsigned		£250
		b. Wrong ornament (as T 13) at left (R. 1/1)	—	£750
		c. "1" for "I" in "BRITISH" (R. 1/5)	—	£750
117	11	1 c. *rose*	£3000	£600
		a. Unsigned		£300
		b. Narrow "T" in "CENTS" (R. 3/1)	—	£750
		c. Wrong ornament (as T 15) at top (R. 3/3)	—	£750
		d. "1" for "I" in "BRITISH" and italic "S" in "POSTAGE" (R. 3/5)	—	£750
118	12	1 c. *rose*	£4500	£800
		a. Unsigned		£500
		b. "1" for "I" in "GUIANA" (R. 4/4)	—	£800
		c. Wrong ornament (as T 15) at left (R. 4/5)	—	£800
		d. "C" for "O" in "POSTAGE" (R. 4/6)	—	£800
119	10	2 c. *yellow*	£2250	£300
		a. Unsigned		£800
		b. Wrong ornament (as T 13) at left (R. 1/1)	—	£500
		c. "1" for "I" in "BRITISH" (R. 1/5)	—	£500

120	11	2 c. *yellow*	£3000	£375
		a. Unsigned		£850
		b. "C" for "O" in "TWO" and narrow "T" in "CENTS" (R. 3/1)	—	£500
		c. Wrong ornament (as T 15) at top (R. 3/3)	—	£500
		d. Italic "S" in "CENTS" (R. 3/4)	—	£500
		e. "1" for "I" in "BRITISH" and italic "S" in "POSTAGE" (R. 3/5)	—	£500
		f. Italic "T" in "TWO" (R. 3/6)	—	£500
121	12	2 c. *yellow*	£4500	£600
		a. Unsigned		£1000
		b. "1" for "I" in "GUIANA" (R. 4/4)	—	£600
		c. Wrong ornament (as T 15) at left (R. 4/5)	—	£600
		d. "C" for "O" in "POSTAGE" (R. 4/6)	—	£600
122	13	4 c. *blue*	£2500	£475
		a. Unsigned		£475
		b. Wrong ornament (as T 15) at left (R. 1/6)	—	£800
		c. Wrong ornament (as T 15) at top and italic "S" in "CENTS" (R. 2/2)	—	£800
		d. Ornament omitted at right (R. 2/4)	—	£800
123	14	4 c. *blue*	£3250	£650
		a. Unsigned		£500
		b. With inner frame lines (as in T 10/13) (R. 2/5–6)	£4250	£1300
		ba. "1" for "I" in "BRITISH" (R. 2/5)	£4250	£1300
		c. "1" for "I" in "BRITISH" and "GUIANA" (R. 4/1)	—	£800
124	15	4 c. *blue*	£3250	£650
		a. Unsigned		£550
		b. Wrong ornament (as T 12) at foot (R. 3/1)	—	£800
		c. Italic "S" in "CENTS" (R. 3/2)	—	£800
		d. Italic "S" in "BRITISH" (R. 3/3)	—	£800

Stamps were initialled across the centre before use by the Acting Receiver-General, Robert Mather. Black was used on the 1 c., red for the 2 c. and an ink which appears white for the 4 c.

The three values of this provisional were each printed in sheets of 24 (6 × 4). The 1 c. and 2 c. were produced from the same setting of the border ornaments which contained 12 examples as Type 10 (Rows 1 and 2), 8 as Type 11 (R. 3/1 to R. 4/2) and 4 as Type 12 (R. 4/3–6).

The setting of the 4 c. contained 10 examples as Type 13 (R. 1/1 to R. 2/4), 8 as Type 14 (R. 2/5–6 and Row 4) and 6 as Type 15 (Row 3).

16	(17)

(Typo D.L.R.)

1876 (1 July)–**79.** *Wmk Crown CC. (a) P 14.*
126	16	1 c. slate	2·75	1·40
127		2 c. orange	42·00	1·75
		w. Wmk inverted		
128		4 c. blue	£120	9·00
129		6 c. brown	75·00	7·00
130		8 c. rose	£100	75
		w. Wmk inverted		
131		12 c. pale violet	50·00	1·25
		w. Wmk inverted		
132		24 c. emerald-green	60·00	3·00
		w. Wmk inverted		
133		48 c. red-brown	£110	26·00
134		96 c. olive-bistre	£475	£250
126/34			*Set of 9*	£900	£250
126/32, 134		Handstamped/Perf "Specimen"	*Set of 8*	£600	

(b) P 12½ (1877)
135	16	4 c. blue	£1200	£200

(c) Perf compound of 14×12½ (1879)
136	16	1 c. slate	—	£200

1878. *Provisionals. Various stamps with old values ruled through with thick bars, in black ink, the bars varying in depth of colour.*

(a) With two horiz bars (17 Apr)
137	16	(1 c.) on 6 c. brown	38·00	£100

(b) Official stamps with horiz bars across "OFFICIAL" (end Aug)
138	8	1 c. black	£180	70·00
139	16	1 c. slate	£130	55·00
140		2 c. orange	£250	65·00

(c) With horiz and vert bars as T 17 (6 Nov)
141	9	(1 c.) on 6 c. ultramarine (93)	£130	75·00
142	16	(1 c.) on 6 c. brown	£250	95·00

(d) Official stamps with bars across "OFFICIAL" (23 Nov)

(i) With two horiz bars and one vert
144	16	(1 c.) on 4 c. blue	£200	90·00
145		(1 c.) on 6 c. brown	£275	90·00
146	8	(2 c.) on 8 c. rose	£1100	£250

(ii) With one horiz bar and one vert
147	16	(1 c.) on 4 c. blue	†	£2000
148		(2 c.) on 8 c. rose	£250	95·00

1	**2**	**2**
(18)	(19)	(20)

1881 (21 Dec). *No. 134 with old value ruled through with bar in black ink and surch.*
149	18	1 on 96 c. olive-bistre	3·50	6·00
		a. Bar in red		
		b. Bar omitted		
150	19	2 on 96 c. olive-bistre	4·00	11·00
		a. Bar in red		
		b. Bar omitted		
151	20	2 on 96 c. olive-bistre	45·00	80·00

In the setting of 60 Type **19** occurs on the first five vertical rows and Type **20** on the sixth.

1	**2**	**2**
(21)	(23)	(24)

1881 (28 Dec). *Various stamps with old value ruled with bar and surch. (a) On No. 105.*
152	21	1 on 48 c. red	40·00	5·00
		a. Bar omitted	—	£500

(b) On Official stamps (including unissued 48 c. optd with Type O 2)
153	21	1 on 12 c. brownish purple (O4)	£110	70·00
154		1 on 48 c. red-brown	£120	90·00
155	23	2 on 12 c. pale violet (O11)	60·00	24·00
		a. Pair. Nos. 155/6	£750	£800
		b. Surch double	£850	£400
		c. Surch double (T 23 + 24)	£2250	
		d. Extra bar through "OFFICIAL"		
156	24	2 on 12 c. pale violet (O11)	£400	£275
157	23	2 on 24 c. emerald-green (O12)	70·00	38·00
		a. Pair. Nos. 157/8	£900	£1000
		b. Surch double	£900	
158	24	2 on 24 c. emerald-green (O12)	£550	£550
159	19	2 on 24 c. green (O5)	£225	£120

On Nos. 149/59 the bar is found in various thicknesses ranging from 1 to 4 mm.

It is believed that the same composite surcharge setting of 60 (6×10) was used for Nos. 155/6 and 157/8. Type **24** occurs on R. 7/2, 4–6 and R. 8/1.

26	27

(Type-set, Baldwin & Co. Georgetown)

1882 (9 Jan). *Black impression. P 12. Perforated with the word "SPECIMEN" diagonally.*
162	26	1 c. *magenta*	38·00	28·00
		a. Imperf between (horiz pair)	†	
		b. Without "SPECIMEN"	£450	£325
		c. "1" with foot	80·00	60·00
163		2 c. *yellow*	65·00	48·00
		a. Without "SPECIMEN"	£400	£375
		b. Small "2"	65·00	48·00
164	27	1 c. *magenta*	38·00	28·00
		a. Without "SPECIMEN"	£450	£325
		b. "1" with foot	80·00	60·00
		c. Imperf between (horiz pair)	†	£4000
165		2 c. *yellow*	60·00	42·00
		a. Bisected diagonally (1 c.) (on cover)		
		b. Without "SPECIMEN"	£400	£375
		c. Small "2"	95·00	80·00

These stamps were perforated "SPECIMEN" as a precaution against fraud. Stamps are known with "SPECIMEN" double.

The 1 c. and 2 c. stamps were printed in separate sheets, but utilising the same clichés, these being altered according to the face value required. Two settings were used, common to both values:—

1st setting. Four rows of three, T **26** being Nos. 5, 6, 7, 8, 11 and 12, and T **27** the remainder.

From this setting there were two printings of the 2 c., but only one of the 1 c.

2nd setting. Six rows of two, T **26** being Nos. 3, 7, 8, 9, 11 and 12, and T **27** the remainder.

There were two printings of each value from this setting.

Se-tenant pairs are worth about 20% more.

The "1" with foot occurs on T **27** on No. 9 in the first setting and on T **26** on No. 7 in the first printing only of the second setting.

The small "2" appears on T **26** in the first setting on Nos. 6, 7, 8 and 12 in the first printing and on Nos. 7, 8 and 12 only in the second printing: in the second setting it comes on Nos. 3, 9 and 12 in the first printing and on Nos. 9, 11 and 12 in the second printing. On T **27** the variety occurs in the first setting on No. 9 of the second printing only and in the second setting on No. 10 in both printings.

(Typo D.L.R.)

1882. *Wmk Crown C.A. P 14.*
170	16	1 c. slate (27 Jan)	8·50	30
171		2 c. orange (27 Jan)	21·00	15
		a. Value doubly printed	†	
		x. Wmk reversed		
172		4 c. blue	80·00	5·00
173		6 c. brown	5·00	6·50
		w. Wmk inverted		
174		8 c. rose	85·00	40
		x. Wmk reversed		
170/4			*Set of 5*	£180	11·00
170/4		Perf "Specimen"	*Set of 5*	£250	

INLAND   **4 CENTS**   **4 CENTS**

	(a)	(b)
	Two types of "4"	

2 CENTS
REVENUE
(28)

6   **6**
(c)	(d)
Two types of "6"	

1888–89. *T* **16** (*without value in lower label*) *optd.* "INLAND REVENUE", *and surch with value as T* **28**, *by D.L.R. Wmk Crown CA. P* 14.

175	1 c. dull purple (8.89)		1·25	20
176	2 c. dull purple (25.5.89)		1·25	30
177	3 c. dull purple		75	20
178	4 c. dull purple (a)		5·50	30
	a. Larger figure "4" (b)		20·00	6·00
179	6 c. dull purple (c)		6·00	3·50
	a. Figure 6 with straight top (d)		19·00	4·00
180	8 c. dull purple (8.89)		1·50	30
181	10 c. dull purple		6·00	2·50
182	20 c. dull purple		19·00	10·00
183	40 c. dull purple		20·00	17·00
184	72 c. dull purple (1.10.88)		35·00	45·00
185	$1 green (1.10.88)		£400	£400
186	$2 green (1.10.88)		£180	£180
187	$3 green (1.10.88)		£120	£120
188	$4 green (a) (1.10.88)		£375	£400
	a. Larger figure "4" (b)		£1000	£1100
189	$5 green (1.10.88)		£225	£200
175/189		*Set of* 15	£1200	£1200

Nos. 175/89 were surcharged in settings of 60 (6×10). No. 178a occurs on all stamps in the third vertical row, No. 179a in the fourth and sixth vertical rows and No. 188a in the second vertical row.

	2			
(29)		30	(31)	

1889 (6 June). *No.* 176 *surch with T* **29** *in red by Official Gazette.*

192	"2" on 2 c. dull purple		1·25	15

The varieties with figure "2" *inverted* or *double* were made privately by a postal employee in Demerara.

1889 (Sept). *Wmk Crown CA. P* 14.

193	30	1 c. dull purple and slate-grey	2·75	1·75
194		2 c. dull purple and orange	1·50	10
		w. Wmk inverted		
195		4 c. dull purple and ultramarine	4·50	1·75
196		4 c. dull purple and cobalt	21·00	2·25
197		6 c. dull purple and brown	35·00	12·00
198		6 c. dull purple and maroon	7·00	11·00
199		8 c. dull purple and rose	12·00	75
		w. Wmk inverted	—	50·00
200		12 c. dull purple and bright purple	18·00	1·75
200a		12 c. dull purple and mauve	8·50	2·00
201		24 c. dull purple and green	6·00	2·50
202		48 c. dull purple and orange-red	15·00	9·00
		x. Wmk reversed		
203		72 c. dull purple and red-brown	28·00	38·00
204		72 c. dull purple and yellow-brown	65·00	75·00
205		96 c. dull purple and carmine	65·00	70·00
		x. Wmk reversed		
206		96 c. dull purple and rosine	75·00	80·00
193/205			*Set of* 10	£130 £120
193/205	Optd "Specimen"		*Set of* 10	£140

1890 (15 July). *Stamps of* 1888–89 *surch locally* "One Cent", *in red, as in T* **31**.

207	1 c. on $1 (No. 185)		1·25	35
	a. Surch double			80·00
208	1 c. on $2 (No. 186)		1·00	60
	a. Surch double			75·00
209	1 c. on $3 (No. 187)		1·40	1·25
	a. Surch double			85·00
210	1 c. on $4 (No. 188)		2·00	6·50
	a. Surch double			75·00
	b. Larger figure "4" (b)		10·00	25·00
207/10			*Set of* 4	5·00 8·00

1890–91. *Colours changed. Wmk Crown CA. P* 14.

213	30	1 c. sea-green (12.90)	40	10
214		5 c. ultramarine (1.91)	2·75	10
215		8 c. dull purple and greenish black (10.90)	2·75	1·10
213/15			*Set of* 3	5·50 1·10
213/215	Optd "Specimen"		*Set of* 3	60·00

32 Mount Roraima	33 Kaieteur Falls

(Recess D.L.R.)

1898 (18 July). *Queen Victoria's Jubilee. Wmk Crown CC* (*sideways* on T* **32**). *P* 14.

216	32	1 c. blue-black and carmine-red	3·75	75
		w. Wmk Crown to left of CC		
		x. Wmk sideways reversed		
		y. Wmk sideways inverted and reversed		
217	33	2 c. brown and indigo	14·00	1·75
		a. Imperf between (horiz pair)	£4500	
218		2 c. brown and blue	18·00	2·25
219	32	5 c. deep green and sepia	38·00	3·25
		a. Imperf between (horiz pair)		
		w. Wmk Crown to left of CC		
220	33	10 c. blue-black and brown-red	18·00	20·00
221	32	15 c. red-brown and blue	27·00	16·00
216/21			*Set of* 5	90·00 38·00
216/21	Optd "Specimen"		*Set of* 5	£110

*The normal sideways watermark on Type **32** shows Crown to right of CC, *as seen from the back of the stamp.*

A second plate was later used for the 1 c. on which the lines of shading on the mountains in the background are strengthened, and those along the ridge show distinct from each other, whereas, in the original, they are more or less blurred. In the second plate the shading of the sky is less pronounced.

TWO CENTS.	**CE**	POSTAGE AND REVENUE $2.40
(34)	Shaved "E"	35

(*Surch at Printing Office of the* Daily Chronicle, *Georgetown*)

1899 (24 Feb–15 June). *Surch with T* **34**.

222	32	2 c. on 5 c. (No. 219) (15 June)	2·50	2·00
		a. No stop after "CENTS"	80·00	65·00
		b. Comma after "CENTS" (R. 7/2)		
		c. "CINTS" (R. 4/1)	90·00	
		d. Shaved "E" (R. 6/2)	24·00	
		w. Wmk Crown to left of CC		
223	33	2 c. on 10 c. (No. 220)	2·00	2·00
		a. No stop after "CENTS" (R. 5/5 or 2/9)	20·00	50·00
		b. "GENTS" for "CENTS" (R. 5/7)	50·00	70·00
		c. Surch inverted	£375	£425
		ca. Surch inverted and stop omitted	£2500	
		d. Shaved "E" (R. 4/2 or 3/8)	17·00	
224	32	2 c. on 15 c. (No. 221)	1·50	1·25
		a. No stop after "CENTS" (R. 9/2)	65·00	65·00
		b. Surch double	£550	£700
		ba. Surch double, one without stop		
		d. Surch inverted	£400	£475
		da. Surch inverted and stop omitted		
		f. Shaved "E" (R. 6/2)	19·00	
222/4			*Set of* 3	5·50 4·75

No. 222c was caused by damage to the first "E" of "CENTS" which developed during surcharging. The listing is for an example with only the upright stroke of the letter visible.

There were two settings of No. 223 with the no stop and shaved "E" varieties occurring on R.5/5 and R.4/2 of the first and on R.2/9 and R.3/8 of the second.

No. 224b occurred on the first five vertical columns of one sheet, the surcharges on the right hand vertical column being normal.

Only two examples of No. 224ba are known.

There is only one known example of No. 224da.

1900–7. *T* **30**. *Wmk Crown CA. P* 14.

233	1 c. grey-green (1907)		1·75	3·25
234	2 c. dull purple and carmine		3·25	30
235	2 c. dull purple and black/red (1901)		1·00	10
236	6 c. grey-black and ultramarine (1902)		6·50	11·00
237	48 c. grey and purple-brown (1901)		50·00	35·00
	a. Brownish grey and brown (1907)		29·00	28·00
238	60 c. green and rosine (1903)		60·00	£170
233/8			*Set of* 6	90·00 £190
233/8	Optd "Specimen"		*Set of* 6	95·00

No. 233 is a reissue of No. 213 in non-fugitive ink.

1905–7. *Wmk Multiple Crown CA. Ordinary paper* (1 c. to 60 c.) *or chalk-surfaced paper* (72, 96 c.).

240	30	1 c. grey-green	3·50	30
		aw. Wmk inverted		
		b. Chalk-surfaced paper	4·00	30
241		2 c. purple and black/red	9·00	10
		a. Chalk-surfaced paper	3·50	10
242		4 c. dull purple and ultramarine	8·00	12·00
		a. Chalk-surfaced paper	6·00	12·00
243		5 c. dull pur & bl/bl (1.5.05) (Optd S. £20)	11·00	7·00
		a. Chalk-surfaced paper	3·50	6·50
244		6 c. grey-black and ultramarine	16·00	42·00
		a. Chalk-surfaced paper	15·00	42·00
		aw. Wmk inverted		
245		12 c. dull and bright purple	22·00	32·00
		a. Chalk-surfaced paper	22·00	32·00
246		24 c. dull purple and green (1906)	11·00	10·00
		a. Chalk-surfaced paper	3·75	4·50
247		48 c. grey and purple-brown	24·00	28·00
		a. Chalk-surfaced paper	14·00	20·00
248		60 c. green and rosine	25·00	85·00
		a. Chalk-surfaced paper	14·00	85·00
249		72 c. purple and orange-brown (1907)	32·00	65·00
250		96 c. black & vermilion/yellow (20.11.05) (Optd S. £30)	35·00	45·00
240/50			*Set of* 11	£130 £275

1905. *Optd* "POSTAGE AND REVENUE". *Wmk Multiple Crown CA. Chalk-surfaced paper. P* 14.

251	35	$2.40 green and violet (S. £75)	£160	£275

1907–10. *Colours changed. Wmk Mult Crown CA. P* 14

252	30	1 c. blue-green	15·00	2·75
253		2 c. rose-red	14·00	10
		a. Redrawn (1910)	8·50	10
254		4 c. brown and purple	2·25	60
255		5 c. ultramarine	10·00	1·25
256		6 c. grey and black	13·00	7·00
257		12 c. orange and mauve	4·00	4·00
252/7			*Set of* 6	48·00 14·00
253/7	Optd "Specimen"		*Set of* 5	75·00

In No. 253a the flag at the main truck is close to the mast, whereas in the original type it appears to be flying loose from halyards. There are two background lines above the value "2 CENTS" instead of three and the "S" is further away from the end of the tablet.

BRITISH GUIANA 2c POSTAGE AND REVENUE	War Tax
37	(38)

(Typo D.L.R.)

1913–21. *Wmk Mult Crown CA. Chalk-surfaced paper* (4 c. and 48 c. to 96 c.). *P* 14.

259	37	1 c. yellow-green	1·50	80
		a. Blue-green (1917)	1·50	25
260		2 c. carmine	70	10
		a. Scarlet (1916)	2·50	10
		b. Wmk sideways	†	£1500
261		4 c. brown and bright purple (1914)	4·25	25
		aw. Wmk inverted		
		b. Deep brown and purple	3·50	25
262		5 c. bright blue	1·75	40
263		6 c. grey and black	1·75	85
264		12 c. orange and violet	1·00	90
265		24 c. dull purple and green (1915)	3·25	4·00
266		48 c. grey and purple-brown (1914)	18·00	17·00
267		60 c. green and rosine (1915)	15·00	50·00
268		72 c. purple and orange-brown (1915)	40·00	70·00
269		96 c. black and vermilion/yellow (1915)	30·00	60·00
		a. White back (1913)	17·00	42·00
		b. On lemon (1916) (Optd S. £30)	18·00	42·00
		c. On pale yellow (1921) (Optd S. £30)	19·00	60·00
259/69a			*Set of* 11	90·00 £170
259/69a	Optd "Specimen"		*Set of* 11	£130

1918 (4 Jan). *As No.* 260a *optd with T* **38**, *by D.L.R.*

271	37	2 c. scarlet	50	15

The relative position of the words "WAR" and "TAX" vary considerably in the sheet.

1921–27. *Wmk Mult Script CA. Chalk-surfaced paper* (24 c. to 96 c.). *P* 14.

272	37	1 c. green (1922)	4·50	30
273		2 c. rose-carmine	3·50	20
		w. Wmk inverted	†	£100
274		2 c. bright violet (1923)	2·50	10
275		4 c. brown and bright purple (1922)	4·75	10
276		6 c. bright blue (1922)	2·75	30
277		12 c. orange and violet (1922)	2·75	1·50
278		24 c. dull purple and green	2·00	4·50
279		48 c. black and purple (1926)	9·50	3·50
280		60 c. green and rosine (1926)	10·00	48·00
281		72 c. dull purple & orange-brown (1923)	19·00	50·00
282		96 c. black and red/yellow (1927)	18·00	45·00
272/82			*Set of* 11	70·00 £140
272/82	Optd "Specimen"		*Set of* 11	£160

39 Ploughing a Rice Field	40 Indian shooting Fish

(Recess Waterlow)

1931 (21 July). *Centenary of County Union T* **39/40** *and similar designs. Wmk Mult Script CA. P* 12½.

283		1 c. emerald-green	2·50	75
284		2 c. brown	2·00	10
285		4 c. carmine	1·75	45
286		6 c. blue	2·25	2·75
287		$1 violet	21·00	42·00
283/7			*Set of* 5	27·00 42·00
283/7	Perf "Specimen"		*Set of* 5	75·00

Designs: *Vert*—4 c., $1 Kaieteur Falls. *Horiz*—6 c. Public buildings, Georgetown.

43 Ploughing a Rice Field	44 Gold Mining

(Recess Waterlow)

1934 (1 Oct)–**51**. *T* **40** (*without dates at top of frame*), **43/4** *and similar designs. Wmk Mult Script CA* (*sideways on horiz designs*). *P* 12½.

288	43	1 c. green	60	50
289	40	2 c. red-brown	1·50	50
290	44	3 c. scarlet	30	10
		aa. Wmk error. Crown missing	—	£1500
		a. Perf 12½ × 13½ (30.12.43)	40	75
		b. Perf 13 × 14 (28.4.49)	40	10
291		4 c. slate-violet	2·00	95
		a. Imperf between (vert pair)	†	£13000
		b. Imperf horiz (vert pair)	£6500	£7000
292		6 c. deep ultramarine	2·50	3·00
293		12 c. red-orange	10	30
		a. Perf 14 × 13 (16.4.51)	20	85
294		24 c. purple	3·00	4·25
295		48 c. black	7·00	8·50
296		50 c. green	10·00	17·00
297		60 c. red-brown	26·00	27·00
298		72 c. purple	1·25	2·25
299		96 c. black	20·00	30·00
300		$1 bright violet	32·00	30·00
288/300			*Set of* 13	95·00 £110
288/300	Perf "Specimen"		*Set of* 13	£140

Designs: *Vert*—4 c., 50 c. Kaieteur Falls (as No. 285, but with dates omitted); 96 c. Sir Walter Raleigh and his son. *Horiz*—6 c. Shooting logs over falls; 12 c. Stabroek Market 24 c. Sugar cane in punts; 48 c. Forest road; 60 c. Victoria Regia Lilies; 72 c. Mount Roraima; $1 Botanical Gardens.

1935 (6 May). *Silver Jubilee. As Nos.* 91/4 *of Antigua.*

301		2 c. ultramarine and grey	20	10
		f. Diagonal line by turret	25·00	
		h. Dot by flagstaff	48·00	

302	6 c. brown and deep blue	..	..	1·00	1·00
	f. Diagonal line by turret	..	..	55·00	
	g. Dot to left of chapel	..	..	85·00	
	h. Dot by flagstaff	..	..	85·00	
303	12 c. green and indigo	..	..	3·00	7·50
	f. Diagonal line by turret	..	..	75·00	
	h. Dot by flagstaff	..	..	£120	
	i. Dash by turret	..	..	£120	
304	24 c. slate and purple	..	..	4·75	7·50
	h. Dot by flagstaff	..	..	£160	
	i. Dash by turret	..	..	£160	
301/4			Set of 4	8·00	14·50
301/4 Perf "Specimen"			Set of 4	70·00	

For illustrations of plate varieties see Catalogue Introduction.

1937 (12 May). *Coronation. As Nos. 95/7 of Antigua, but ptd by D.L.R. P 14.*

305	2 c. yellow-brown	..	..	15	10
306	4 c. grey-black	..	..	50	30
307	6 c. bright blue	..	..	60	1·00
305/7			Set of 3	1·10	1·25
305/7 Perf "Specimen"			Set of 3	50·00	

53 South America   **54** Victoria Regia Lilies

(Recess Waterlow)

1938 (1 Feb)–**1952**. *As earlier types but with portrait of King George VI as in T* **53/4**. *Wmk Mult Script CA. P* 12½

308	**43**	1 c. yellow-green	..	14·00	55
		aa. Green (1944)	..	30	10
		a. Perf 14 × 13 (1949)	..	30	80
309	—	2 c. slate-violet	..	60	10
		a. Perf 13 × 14 (28.4.49)	..	30	10
310	**53**	4 c. scarlet and black	..	70	30
		a. Imperf horiz (vert pair)	..	£12000	£9000
		b. Perf 13 × 14 (1952)	..	45	15
311	**40**	6 c. deep ultramarine	..	40	10
		a. Perf 13 × 14 (24.10.49)	..	30	30
312	—	24 c. blue-green	..	26·00	10·00
		a. Wmk sideways	..	1·25	10
313	—	36 c. bright violet (7.3.38)	..	2·00	20
		a. Perf 13 × 14 (13.12.51)	..	3·00	30
314	—	48 c. orange	..	60	40
		a. Perf 14 × 13 (8.5.51*)	..	1·50	1·25
315	—	60 c. red-brown	..	11·00	3·75
316	—	96 c. purple	..	2·50	2·75
		a. Perf 12½ × 13½ (1944)	..	6·00	8·00
		b. Perf 13 × 14 (8.2.51)	..	2·75	6·00
317	—	$1 bright violet	..	11·00	35
		a. Perf 14 × 13 (1951)	..	£300	£400
318	—	$2 purple (11.6.45)	..	4·50	14·00
		a. Perf 14 × 13 (9.8.50)	..	10·00	15·00
319	**54**	$3 red-brown (2.7.45)	..	27·00	25·00
		a. Bright red-brown (12.46)	..	28·00	28·00
		b. Perf 14 × 13. Red-brown (29.10.52)	..	25·00	45·00
308a/19			Set of 12	55·00	40·00
308/19 Perf "Specimen"			Set of 12	£200	

Designs: *Vert*—2 c., 36 c. Kaieteur Falls; 96 c. Sir Walter Raleigh and his son. *Horiz*—24 c. Sugar cane in punts; 48 c. Forest road; 60 c. Shooting logs over falls; $1 Botanical Gardens; $2 Mount Roraima.

* *Earliest known postmark date.*

1946 (1 Oct). *Victory. As Nos. 110/11 of Antigua.*

320	3 c. carmine	..	..	10	20
321	6 c. blue	..	..	30	50
320/1 Perf "Specimen"			Set of 2	48·00	

1948 (20 Dec). *Royal Silver Wedding. As Nos. 112/13 of Antigua, but $3 in recess.*

322	3 c. scarlet	..	..	10	40
323	$3 red-brown	..	..	12·00	23·00

1949 (10 Oct). *75th Anniv of Universal Postal Union. As Nos. 114/17 of Antigua.*

324	4 c. carmine	..	..	30	20
325	6 c. deep blue	..	..	90	65
326	12 c. orange	..	..	30	45
327	24 c. blue-green	..	..	30	60
324/7			Set of 4	1·60	1·75

1951 (16 Feb). *University College of B.W.I. As Nos. 118/19 of Antigua.*

328	3 c. black and carmine	..	..	30	30
329	6 c. black and blue	..	..	30	60

1953 (2 June). *Coronation. As No. 120 of Antigua.*

330	4 c. black and scarlet	..	..	20	10

55 G.P.O., Georgetown   **62** Felling Greenheart.

(Centre litho, frame recess ($1); recess (others). Waterlow (until 1961), then D.L.R.)

1954 (1 Dec)–**63**. *T* **55**, **62** *and similar designs. Wmk Mult Script CA. P* 12½ × 13* (*horiz*) *or* 13 (*vert*).

331	1 c. black	..	..	10	10
332	2 c. myrtle-green	..	..	10	10
333	3 c. brown-olive and red-brown	..	3·50	20
	w. Wmk inverted				

334	4 c. violet	..	..	20	10
	a. D.L.R. ptg (5.12.61)	..	7·50	2·75
	ab. Deep violet (3.1.63)	..	9·50	1·75
335	5 c. scarlet and black	..	30	10
	w. Wmk inverted				
336	6 c. yellow-green	..	..	30	10
	a. D.L.R. ptg. Green (22.5.62)	..	40	1·75
337	8 c. ultramarine	..	..	15	20
	a. D.L.R. ptg. Blue (19.9.61)	..	8·50	65
338	12 c. black and reddish brown	..	60	40
	a. Black and light brown (13.6.56)	..	15	10
	b. D.L.R. ptg. Black and brown (11.7.61)	20·00	3·25
239	24 c. black and brownish orange	..	4·50	10
	a. Black and orange (13.6.56)	..	5·50	10
340	36 c. rose-carmine and black	..	3·50	1·25
	w. Wmk inverted				
341	48 c. ultramarine and brown-lake	..	60	70
	a. Brt ultram & pale brown-lake (13.6.56)	50	60
	ab. D.L.R. ptg (19.9.61)	..	26·00	20·00
342	72 c. carmine and emerald	..	12·00	2·75
	a. D.L.R. ptg (17.7.62)	..	12·00	20·00
343	$1 pink, yellow, green and black	..	18·00	2·75
344	$2 deep mauve	..	..	18·00	6·00
	a. D.L.R. ptg. Reddish mauve (11.7.61)	42·00	7·50
345	$5 ultramarine and black	..	12·00	20·00
	a. D.L.R. ptg (19.9.61)	..	45·00	35·00
331/45			Set of 15	60·00	30·00

Designs: *Horiz*—2 c. Botanical Gardens; 3 c. *Victoria regia* water-lilies; 5 c. Map of Caribbean; 6 c. Rice combine-harvester; 8 c. Sugar cane entering factory; 24 c. Mining for bauxite; 36 c. Mount Roraima; $1 Channel-billed Toucan; $2 Dredging gold. *Vert*—4 c. Amerindian shooting fish; 48 c. Kaieteur Falls; 72 c. Arapaima (fish); $5 Arms of British Guiana.

On the Waterlow printings there is *always* a single wide-tooth perforation on each side at the top of the stamps. For the De La Rue stamps these teeth can occur *either* at the top or the bottom. Those listed De La Rue printings, which do not differ in shade, are for examples with the wide-tooth perforation at the bottom.

*All the Waterlow printing and early De La Rue printings of the horizontal designs measure 12.3×12.8, but De La Rue printings from 22 May 1962 (including those on the Block CA watermark) measure 12.3×12.6.

The 1 c. and 2 c., printed by Waterlow, exist in coils constructed from normal sheets.

See also Nos. 354/65.

SELF-GOVERNMENT

70

(Photo Harrison)

1961 (23 Oct). *History and Culture Week. W w* **12** *P* 14½ × 14.

346	**70**	5 c. sepia and orange-red	..	20	10
347		6 c. sepia and blue-green	..	20	15
348		30 c. sepia and yellow-orange	..	45	45
346/8			Set of 3	75	60

1963 (14 July). *Freedom from Hunger. As No. 146 of Antigua.*

349	20 c. reddish violet	..	..	30	10

1963 (2 Sept). *Red Cross Centenary. As Nos. 147/8 of Antigua.*

350	5 c. red and black	..	..	20	20
351	20 c. red and blue	..	..	55	35

1963–65. *As Nos. 333/44, but wmk w* **12**.

354	3 c. brown-olive and red-brown (12.65)	..	5·00	5·50
356	5 c. scarlet and black (28.5.64)	..	30	10
	w. Wmk inverted				
359	12 c. black and yellowish brown (6.10.64)	20	10
360	24 c. black and bright orange (10.12.63)	3·75	10
361	36 c. rose-carmine and black (10.12.63)	60	60
362	48 c. brt ultram & Venetian red (25.11.63)	1·25	2·25
	w. Wmk inverted				
363	72 c. carmine and emerald (25.11.63)	4·25	20·00
364	$1 pink, yellow, green & black (10.12.63)	7·00	90
365	$2 reddish mauve (10.12.63)	..	9·00	14·00
354/65			Set of 9	28·00	38·00

There was no London release of No. 354.
The 5 c. exists in coils constructed from normal sheets.
For 1 c. value, see No. 429a.

71 Weightlifting

(Photo D.L.R.)

1964 (1 Oct). *Olympic Games, Tokyo. W w* **12**. *P* 13 × 13½.

367	**71**	5 c. orange	..	15	10
368		8 c. blue	..	15	25
369		25 c. magenta	..	25	40
367/9			Set of 3	50	65

1965 (17 May). *I.T.U. Centenary. As Nos. 166/7 of Antigua.*

370	5 c. emerald and yellow-olive	..	10	15
371	25 c. light blue and magenta	..	20	15

1965 (25 Oct). *International Co-operation Year. As Nos. 168/9 of Antigua.*

372	5 c. reddish purple and turquoise-green	..	15	10
373	25 c. deep bluish green and lavender	..	30	20

72 St. George's Cathedral, Georgetown

(Des Jennifer Toombs, Photo Harrison)

1966 (24 Jan). *Churchill Commemoration. W w* **12**. *P* 14 × 14½.

374	**72**	5 c. black, crimson and gold	..	50	10
375		25 c. black, blue and gold	..	1·40	50

1966 (3 Feb). *Royal Visit. As Nos. 174/5 of Antigua.*

376	3 c. black and ultramarine	..	50	15
377	25 c. black and magenta	..	1·50	60

GUYANA

British Guiana became independent as Guyana on 25 May 1966.

GUYANA INDEPENDENCE 1966

1966 (26 May)–**67**. *Various stamps as Nos. 331/45 optd with T* **73** *by De La Rue*. (a) *Wmk Mult Script CA.*

378	2 c. myrtle-green	..	..	30	30
379	3 c. brown-olive and red-brown	..	2·50	5·50
380	4 c. violet	..	..	75	30
381	6 c. yellow-green	..	..	30	10
382	8 c. ultramarine	..	..	80	60
383	12 c. black and reddish brown	..	90	60
384	$5 ultramarine and black	..	24·00	40·00
378/84			Set of 7	26·00	42·00

(b) *Wmk w* **12** (*upright*)

385	1 c. black	..	..	10	30
386	3 c. brown-olive and red-brown	..	1·25	10
387	4 c. violet (28.2.67)	..	10	60
388	5 c. scarlet and black	..	20	10
389	6 c. green (28.2.67)	..	10	20
390	8 c. ultramarine (14.3.67)	..	40	1·50
391	12 c. black and yellowish brown	..	10	10
392	24 c. black and bright orange	..	3·75	20
393	36 c. rose-carmine and black	..	30	30
394	48 c. bright ultramarine and Venetian red	2·50	8·00
395	72 c. carmine and emerald	..	50	50
396	$1 pink, yellow, green and black	..	1·75	35
397	$2 reddish mauve	..	..	1·50	75
398	$5 ultramarine and black	..	1·00	1·75
385/98			Set of 14	12·00	13·00

(c) *Wmk w* **12** (*sideways*)

399	1 c. black	..	..	10	10
400	4 c. violet	..	..	10	10
401	8 c. ultramarine	..	..	10	10
402	12 c. black and yellowish brown (28.2.67)	10	10
403	24 c. black and bright orange	..	2·00	40
404	36 c. rose-carmine and black (28.2.67)	30	90
405	48 c. bright ultramarine and Venetian red	30	30
406	72 c. carmine and emerald (28.2.67)	..	1·75	3·25
407	$1 pink, yellow, green and black (14.3.67)	2·50	3·25
407a	$2 reddish mauve (28.2.67)	..	2·50	3·25
407b	$5 ultramarine and black (28.2.67)	..	1·50	3·25
399/407b			Set of 11	10·00	13·50

See also Nos. 420/40.

74 Flag and Map   **75** Arms of Guyana

(Des V. Whiteley. Photo Harrison)

1966 (26 May). *Independence. P* 14½.

408	**74**	5 c. multicoloured	..	15	10
409		15 c. multicoloured	..	20	10
410	**75**	25 c. multicoloured	..	20	10
411		$1 multicoloured	..	65	1·25
408/11			Set of 4	1·10	1·25

76 Bank Building

(Des R. Granger Barrett. Photo Enschedé)

1966 (11 Oct). *Opening of Bank of Guyana. P* 13½ × 14.

412	**76**	5 c. multicoloured	..	10	10
413		25 c. multicoloured	..	10	10

CANCELLED REMAINDERS.* In 1969 remainders of some issues were put on the market cancelled-to-order in such a way as to be indistinguishable from genuine postally used copies for all practical purposes. Our used quotations which are indicated by an asterisk are the same for cancelled-to-order or postally used copies.

77 British Guiana One Cent Stamp of 1856

(Des V. Whiteley. Litho D.L.R.)

1967 (23 Feb). *World's Rarest Stamp Commemoration.* P 12½.
414	77	5 c. black, magenta, silver & light ochre	10 10*
415		25 c. black, magenta, gold and light green	10 10*

78 Château Margot   (82)

GUYANA
INDEPENDENCE
1966

(Des R. Granger Barrett. Photo Harrison)

1967 (26 May). *First Anniv of Independence.* T **78** and similar multicoloured designs. P 14 (6 c.), 14½ × 14 (15 c.) or 14 × 14½ (others).
416	6 c. Type **78**		10 10*
417	15 c. Independence Arch		10 10*
418	25 c. Fort Island (horiz)		10 10*
419	$1 National Assembly (horiz)		20 15
416/19		Set of 4	20 15

1967–68. Stamps as Nos. 331/45 optd with T **82** locally.

(i) Wmk Mult Script CA
420	1 c. black (3.10.67)		10 10
	a. Opt inverted		35·00
	b. Date misplaced 5 mm		9·50
	c. Date misplaced 2 mm		9·50
421	2 c. myrtle-green (3.10.67)		10 10
	a. "1966" for "GUYANA"		18·00
	b. Date misplaced 5 mm		9·50
	c. Date misplaced 2 mm		9·50
422	3 c. brown-olive and red-brown (3.10.67)		30 10
	a. "1966" for "GUYANA"		15·00
	b. Vert pair, one without opt		£375
	c. Date misplaced 2 mm		9·00
423	4 c. violet (10.67)		10 10
	a. Deep violet		65 65
	b. Opt inverted		48·00
424	6 c. yellow-green (11.67)		10 10
	a. "1966" for "GUYANA"		24·00
	b. Opt inverted		42·00
	c. Opt double		55·00
425	8 c. ultramarine (12.67)		10 10
426	12 c. black and brown (12.67)		10 10
426a	24 c. black and orange (date?)		£275 90·00
427	$2 reddish mauve (12.67)		1·25 1·75
428	$5 ultramarine and black (12.67)		1·50 2·25

(ii) Wmk w **12** (upright)
429	1 c. black (2.68)		10 30
	a. Opt omitted		£130
430	2 c. myrtle-green (2.68)		40 1·25
431	3 c. brown-olive and red-brown (3.10.67)		30 10
	a. "1966" for "GUYANA"		75·00
	b. Opt inverted		30·00
432	4 c. violet (2.68)		10 80
433	5 c. scarlet and black (3.10.67)		2·00 1·50
	a. Deep scarlet and black		80 1·50
	aw. Wmk inverted		
	c. Date misplaced 2 mm		9·50
434	6 c. yellow-green (2.68)		30 65
	a. Opt double, one diagonal		70·00
435	24 c. black and bright orange (11.12.67)		3·00 10
	a. Opt double, one diagonal (horiz pair)		£180
436	36 c. rose-carmine and black (12.67)		90 10
437	48 c. bright ultram & Venetian red (12.67)		90 50
	a. Opt inverted		60·00
438	72 c. carmine and emerald (12.67)		1·75 50
439	$1 pink, yellow, green and black (12.67)		3·00 50
440	$2 reddish mauve (12.67)		3·00 4·00
420/40 (excl. 426a)		Set of 21	16·00 13·00

The "1966" errors occurred on R. 7/10 and were later corrected. Nos. 425/8 and 436/40 were issued in mid-December, but some were cancelled-to-order with a November date in error.

On Nos. 420b and 421b the "1" of "1966" is below the second "D" of "INDEPENDENCE" (R. 6/3). On Nos. 420c, 421c, 422c and 433c it is below the second "E" (R. 6/1).

No. 433a is from a printing made specially for this overprint.

NEW INFORMATION

The editor is always interested to correspond with people who have new information that will improve or correct the Catalogue.

---

83 "Millie"
(Blue and Yellow Macaw)

84 Wicket-keeping

(Des V. Whiteley. Photo Harrison)

1967–68. *Christmas.* P 14½ × 14. (a) First issue (6 Nov 1967).
441	83	5 c. yellow, new blue, blk & bronze-grn	10 10*
442		25 c. yellow, new blue, black and violet	15 10*

(b) Second issue. Colours changed (22 Jan 1968)
443	83	5 c. yellow, new blue, black and red	10 10*
444		25 c. yellow, new blue, blk & apple-grn	15 10*

(Des V. Whiteley. Photo Harrison)

1968 (8 Jan). *M.C.C.'s West Indies Tour.* T **84** and similar vert designs. P 14.
445	5 c. Type **84**		10 10*
	a. Strip of 3. Nos. 445/7		70
446	6 c. Batting		10 10*
447	25 c. Bowling		30 10*
445/7		Set of 3	70 15*

Nos. 445/7 were issued in small sheets of 9 containing three se-tenant strips.

87 Pike Cichlid

102 "Christ of St John of the Cross" (Salvador Dali)

(Des R. Granger Barrett. Photo Harrison)

1968 (4 Mar). *Multicoloured designs as T* **87**, *showing fish* (1 to 6 c.), birds (10 to 40 c.) or animals (others). No wmk. P 14 × 14½.
448	1 c. Type **87**		10 10
449	2 c. Red Piranha ("Pirai")		10 10
450	3 c. Peacock Cichlid ("Lukunani")		10 10
451	5 c. Armoured Catfish ("Hassar")		10 10
452	6 c. Black Acara ("Patua")		55 10
453	10 c. Spix's Guan (vert)		55 10
454	15 c. Harpy Eagle (vert)		1·60 10
455	20 c. Hoatzin (vert)		60 10
456	25 c. Guianan Cock of the Rock (vert)		60 10
457	40 c. Great Kiskadee (vert)		1·00 50
458	50 c. Brazilian Agouti ("Accouri")		80 50
459	60 c. White-lipped Peccary		80 10
460	$1 Paca ("Labba")		80 10
461	$2 Nine-banded Armadillo		1·25 2·00
462	$5 Ocelot		1·25 3·00
448/62		Set of 15	8·50 5·50

For Nos. 448/62 with W **106** see Nos. 485/99.

(Des and photo Harrison)

1968 (25 Mar). *Easter.* P 14.
463	102	5 c. multicoloured	10 10*
464		25 c. multicoloured	20 10*

103 "Efficiency Year"

104 "Savings Bonds"

(Des W. Starzmann. Litho B.W.)

1968 (22 July). *"Savings Bonds and Efficiency".* P 14.
465	103	6 c. multicoloured	10 10*
466		25 c. multicoloured	10 10*
467	104	30 c. multicoloured	10 10*
468		40 c. multicoloured	10 10*
465/8		Set of 4	30 15*

---

105 Open Book, Star and Crescent

(Des R. Gates. Photo D.L.R.)

1968 (9 Oct). *1400th Anniv of the Holy Quran.* P 14.
469	105	6 c. black, gold and flesh	10 10*
470		25 c. black, gold and lilac	10 10*
471		30 c. black, gold and light apple-green	10 10*
472		40 c. black, gold and cobalt	10 10*
469/72		Set of 4	30 15*

106 Lotus Blossoms

107 Broadcasting Greetings

(Des L. Pritchard; adapted G. Vasarhelyi. Litho D.L.R.)

1968 (11 Nov). *Christmas.* T **107** and similar vert design. W **106**. P 14.
473	6 c. brown, blue and green		10 10*
474	25 c. brown, reddish violet and green		10 10*
475	30 c. blue-green and turquoise-green		10 10*
476	40 c. red and turquoise-green		10 10*
473/6		Set of 4	30 15*

Designs:—25 c. Type **107**; 30, 40 c. Map showing radio link, Guyana–Trinidad.

109 Festival Ceremony

(Des J. Cooter. Litho P.B.)

1969 (26 Feb). *Hindu Festival of Phagwah.* T **109** and similar horiz design. Multicoloured. W **106** (sideways). P 13½.
477	6 c. Type **109**		10 10
478	25 c. Ladies spraying scent		10 10
479	30 c. Type **109**		10 10
480	40 c. As 25 c.		10 10
477/80		Set of 4	30 20

111 "Sacrament of the Last Supper" (Dali)

112 Map showing "CARIFTA" Countries

(Photo D.L.R.)

1969 (10 Mar). *Easter.* W **106** (sideways). P 13½ × 13.
481	111	6 c. multicoloured	10 10
482		25 c. multicoloured	10 10
483		30 c. multicoloured	10 10
484		40 c. multicoloured	10 10
481/4		Set of 4	30 15

1969–71. As Nos. 448/62, but Wmk **106** (sideways* on 1 to 6 c. and 50 c. to $5). Chalk-surfaced paper.
485	1 c. Type **87**		10 10
486	2 c. Red Piranha ("Pirai")		10 30
487	3 c. Peacock Cichlid ("Lukunani")		10 40
488	5 c. Armoured Catfish ("Hassar")		10 10
489	6 c. Black Acara ("Patua")		10 50
490	10 c. Spix's Guan		30 40
	a. Glazed paper (wmk inverted) (21.12.71)		1·00 3·25
491	15 c. Harpy Eagle		30 10
	aw. Wmk inverted		
	b. Glazed paper (wmk inverted) (21.12.71)		1·25 3·75
492	20 c. Hoatzin		30 60
493	25 c. Guianan Cock of the Rock		30 10
	a. Glazed paper (wmk inverted) (21.12.71)		1·50 4·50
494	40 c. Great Kiskadee		60 70
495	50 c. Brazilian Agouti ("Accouri")		35 15
496	60 c. White-lipped Peccary		35 1·00
497	$1 Paca ("Labba")		70 1·10
	a. Glazed paper (wmk top of blossom to right) (21.12.71)		1·75 11·00

498	$2 Nine-banded Armadillo	1·00	3·25
499	$5 Ocelot	1·50	5·50
485/99	*Set of 15*	5·00	12·00

*The normal sideways watermark shows the top of the blossom to the left, *as seen from the back of the stamp.*

These were put on sale by the Crown Agents on 25 March 1969 but although supplies were sent to Guyana in time they were not released there until needed as ample supplies remained of the stamps without watermark. It is understood that the 3 c. and 5 c. were put on sale in early May 1969 followed by the 25 c. but there are no records of when the remainder were released.

(Des J. Cooter. Litho P.B.)

1969 (30 Apr). *First Anniv of CARIFTA (Caribbean Free Trade Area). T 112 and similar design. W 106 (sideways on 25 c.). P 13½.*

500	6 c. rose-red, ultramarine and turquoise-blue	15	15
501	25 c. lemon, brown and rose-red	15	15

Design: *Horiz*—25 c. "Strength in Unity".

114 Building *Independence* (first aluminium ship)   **116** Scouts raising Flag

(Des R. Gates. Litho B.W.)

1969 (30 Apr). *50th Anniv of International Labour Organization. T 114 and similar design. W 106 (sideways on 40 c.). P 12 × 11 (30 c.) or 11 × 12 (40 c.).*

502	30 c. turquoise-blue, black and silver	40	25
503	40 c. multicoloured	50	25

Design: *Horiz*—40 c. Bauxite processing plant.

(Des Jennifer Toombs. Litho B.W.)

1969 (13 Aug). *Third Caribbean Scout Jamboree and Diamond Jubilee of Scouting in Guyana. T 116 and similar horiz design. Multicoloured. W 106 (sideways). P 13.*

504	6 c. Type **116**	10	10
505	8 c. Camp-fire cooking	10	10
506	25 c. Type **116**	10	10
507	30 c. As 8 c.	10	10
508	50 c. Type **116**	15	15
504/8	*Set of 5*	30	30

118 Gandhi and Spinning-wheel   **119** "Mother Sally Dance Troupe"

(Des G. Drummond. Litho Format)

1969 (1 Oct). *Birth Centenary of Mahatma Gandhi. W 106 (sideways). P 14½.*

509	**118** 6 c. black, brown and yellowish olive	20	50
510	15 c. black, brown and lilac	25	50

(Des V. Whiteley (5, 25 c.), J.W. (others). Litho B.W. (5, 25 c.), D.L.R. (others))

1969 (17 Nov). *Christmas. T 119 and similar vert designs. Multicoloured. No wmk (5, 25 c.) or W 106 (others). P 13½ (5, 25 c.) or 13½×13½ (others).*

511	5 c. Type **119**	10	10
	a. Opt omitted	28·00	
	b. Opt double	25·00	
512	6 c. City Hall, Georgetown	10	10
	a. Opt omitted	28·00	
	b. Opt inverted	30·00	
513	25 c. Type **119**	10	10
	a. Opt omitted	28·00	
514	60 c. As 6 c.	20	25
511/14	*Set of 4*	30	30

Nos. 511/14 are previously unissued stamps optd as in T **119** by Guyana Lithographic Co, Ltd.

REPUBLIC

121 Forbes Burnham and Map   **125** "The Descent from the Cross"

(Des L. Curtis. Litho D.L.R.)

1970 (23 Feb). *Republic Day. T 121 and similar designs. W 106 (sideways on 15 and 25 c.). P 14.*

515	5 c. sepia, ochre and pale blue	10	10
516	6 c. multicoloured	10	10
517	15 c. multicoloured	15	10
518	25 c. multicoloured	20	15
515/18	*Set of 4*	40	30

Designs: *Vert*—6 c. "Rural Self-help". *Horiz*—15 c. University of Guyana; 25 c. Guyana House.

(Des J. Cooter. Litho Questa)

1970 (24 Mar). *Easter. Paintings by Rubens. T 125 and similar vert design. Multicoloured. W 106 (inverted). P 14 × 14½.*

519	5 c. Type **125**	10	10
520	6 c. "Christ on the Cross"	10	10
521	15 c. Type **125**	20	10
522	25 c. As 6 c.	20	15
519/22	*Set of 4*	45	40

127 "Peace" and U.N. Emblem   **128** "Mother and Child" (Philip Moore)

(Des and litho Harrison)

1970 (26 Oct). *25th Anniv of United Nations. T 127 and similar horiz design. Multicoloured. W 106 (inverted). P 14.*

523	5 c. Type **127**	10	10
524	6 c. U.N. Emblem, Gold-panning and Drilling	10	10
525	15 c. Type **127**	10	10
526	25 c. As 6 c.	15	15
523/6		30	30

(Des Harrison. Litho J.W.)

1970 (8 Dec). *Christmas. W 106. P 13½.*

527	**128** 5 c. multicoloured	10	10
528	6 c. multicoloured	10	10
529	15 c. multicoloured	15	15
530	25 c. multicoloured	15	15
527/30	*Set of 4*	30	30

129 National Co-operative Bank   **130** Racial Equality Symbol

(Des E. Samuels. Litho J.W.)

1971 (23 Feb). *Republic Day. W 106 (sideways). P 14.*

531	**129** 6 c. multicoloured	10	10
532	15 c. multicoloured	15	15
533	25 c. multicoloured	15	15
531/3	*Set of 3*	30	30

(Des E. Samuels. Litho Harrison)

1971 (22 Mar). *Racial Equality Year. W 106 (sideways). P 14.*

534	**130** 5 c. multicoloured	10	10
535	6 c. multicoloured	10	10
536	15 c. multicoloured	15	15
537	25 c. multicoloured	15	15
534/7	*Set of 4*	30	30

131 Young Volunteer felling Tree (from painting by J. Criswick).   **132** Yellow Allamanda

(Des and litho Harrison)

1971 (19 July). *First Anniv of Self-help Road Project. W 106. P 14.*

538	**131** 5 c. multicoloured	10	10
539	20 c. multicoloured	20	10
540	25 c. multicoloured	20	10
541	50 c. multicoloured	30	1·75
538/41	*Set of 4*	70	1·75

Two types of 25 c.:

I Flowers facing up. Value in centre.

II Flowers facing down. Value to right. Colours changed.

(Des V. Whiteley (1 to 40 c.), PAD Studio (others). Litho D.L.R. (1 to 6 c.), J.W. (10 c. to 40 c.), Format (50 c. to $5))

1971 (17 Sept)–**76**. *Flowering Plants. Vert designs as T **132**. Multicoloured. W 106 (sideways on 1 c. to 40 c.). P 13 × 13½ (1 to 6 c.) or 13½ (10 c. to $5).*

542	1 c. Pitcher Plant of Mt Roraima (15.1.72)	10	10
543	2 c. Type **132**	10	10
544	3 c. Hanging Heliconia	10	10
545	5 c. Annatto tree	10	10
546	6 c. Cannon-ball tree	10	10
547	10 c. Cattleya (18.9.72)	3·25	10
	a. Perf 13 (28.1.76)	3·50	10
548	15 c. Christmas Orchid (18.9.72)	80	10
	a. Perf 13 (3.9.76)	65	10
549	20 c. *Paphinia cristata* (18.9.72)	3·00	20
	a. Perf 13 (28.1.76)	4·00	20
550	25 c. Marabunta (I) (18.9.72)	5·00	6·50
550a	25 c. Marabunta (II) (wmk inverted) (20.8.73)	30	85
	ab. Perf 13 (wmk sideways) (3.9.76)	45	10
551	40 c. Tiger Beard (18.9.72)	3·50	10
552	50 c. *Guzmania lingulata* (3.9.73)	40	85
553	60 c. Soldier's Cap (3.9.73)	30	65
554	$1 *Chelonanthus uliginoides* (3.9.73)	30	55
555	$2 *Norantea guianensis* (3.9.73)	35	55
556	$5 *Odontadenia grandiflora* (3.9.73)	55	55
542/56	*Set of 16*	16·00	9·50

The watermark is often indistinct, particularly on the early printings.

133 Child praying at Bedside   **134** Obverse and Reverse of Guyana $1 Coin

(Des V. Bassoo (T **133**), M. Austin (25, 50 c.). Litho J.W.)

1971 (29 Nov). *Christmas. T 133 and similar vert design. Multicoloured. W 106 (sideways on 5 c. and 20 c.). P 13½.*

557	5 c. Type **133**	10	10
558	20 c. Type **133**	10	10
559	25 c. Carnival Masquerader	10	10
560	50 c. As 25 c.	20	60
557/60	*Set of 4*	35	75

(Des G. Drummond. Litho Questa)

1972 (23 Feb). *Republic Day. T 134 and similar vert design. W 106 (sideways). P 14½ × 14.*

561	**134** 5 c. silver, black and orange-red	10	10
562	20 c. silver, black and magenta	15	10
563	**134** 25 c. silver, black and ultramarine	15	15
564	50 c. silver, black and yellow-green	25	45
561/4	*Set of 4*	55	70

Design:—20, 50 c. Reverse and obverse of Guyana $1 coin.

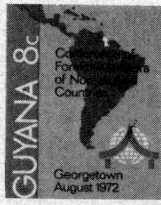

135 Hands and Irrigation Canal   **136** Map and Emblem

(Des J. Criswick. Litho J.W.)

1972 (3 Apr). *Youman Nabi (Mohammed's Birthday). W 106. P 14.*

565	**135** 5 c. multicoloured	10	10
566	25 c. multicoloured	10	10
567	30 c. multicoloured	10	10
568	60 c. multicoloured	20	20
565/8	*Set of 4*	35	35

(Des J. Criswick. Litho J.W.)

1972 (20 July). *Conference of Foreign Ministers of Non-aligned Countries. W 106. P 13½.*

569	**136** 8 c. multicoloured	10	10
570	25 c. multicoloured	10	10
571	40 c. multicoloured	15	15
572	50 c. multicoloured	20	20
569/72	*Set of 4*	40	40

OMNIBUS ISSUES

Details, together with prices for complete sets, of the various Omnibus issues from the 1935 Silver Jubilee series to date are included in a special section following Zimbabwe at the end of Volume 2.

137 Hand reaching for Sun

138 Joseph, Mary, and the Infant Jesus

(Des G. Bowen. Litho J.W.)

1972 (25 Aug). *First Caribbean Festival of Arts.* W **106** (inverted on 40, 50 c.). P 13½.

573	137	8 c. multicoloured	..	10	10
574		25 c. multicoloured	..	10	10
575		40 c. multicoloured	..	15	20
576		50 c. multicoloured	..	20	25
573/6	..		Set of 4	45	55

(Des Megan Anderson. Litho B.W.)

1972 (18 Oct). *Christmas.* W **106**. P 13 × 13½.

577	138	8 c. multicoloured	..	10	10
578		25 c. multicoloured	..	10	10
579		40 c. multicoloured	..	15	25
580		50 c. multicoloured	..	15	25
577/80	..		Set of 4	40	60

139 Umana Yana (Meeting-house)

140 Pomegranate

(Des J. Cooter. Litho Questa)

1973 (23 Feb). *Republic Day.* T **139** and similar vert design. Multicoloured. W **106** (inverted on 8 c.). P 14.

581		8 c. Type 139	..	10	10
582		25 c. Bethel Chapel	..	10	10
583		40 c. As 25 c.	..	20	20
584		50 c. Type 139	..	25	20
581/4	..		Set of 4	55	50

(Des E. Samuels. Litho Format)

1973 (19 Apr). *Easter.* T **140** and similar multicoloured design. W **106** (sideways on 25 and 40 c.). P 14½ (8, 50 c.) or 13½ (others).

585		8 c. Type 140	..	10	10
586		25 c. Cross and map (34 × 47 mm)	..	10	10
587		40 c. As 25 c.	..	10	10
588		50 c. Type 140	..	15	15
585/8	..		Set of 4	35	35

141 Stylized Blood Cell

142 Steel-Band Players

(Des S. Greaves. Litho Harrison)

1973 (1 Oct). *25th Anniv of Guyana Red Cross.* W **106**. P 14.

589	141	8 c. vermilion and black	..	10	10
590		25 c. vermilion and bright purple	..	25	15
591		40 c. vermilion and ultramarine	..	35	50
592		50 c. vermilion and blackish olive	..	50	1·00
589/92	..		Set of 4	1·00	1·50

(Des E. Samuels; adapted J. Cooter. Litho Questa)

1973 (20 Nov). *Christmas.* T **142** and similar vert design. Multicoloured. W **106**. P 14 (8, 25 c.) or 13½ (others).

593		8 c. Type 142	..	10	10
594		25 c. Type 142	..	20	10
595		40 c. "Virgin and Child" (stained-glass window) (34 × 47 mm)	..	50	75
596		50 c. As 40 c.	..	55	75
593/6	..		Set of 4	1·25	1·50

143 Symbol of Progress (144)

(Des PAD Studio. Litho Questa)

1974 (23 Feb). *Republic Day.* T **143** and similar vert design. Multicoloured. W **106**. P 13½.

597		8 c. Type 143	..	10	10
598		25 c. Wai-Wai Indian	..	10	10
599		40 c. Type 143	..	15	30
600		50 c. As 25 c.	..	15	40
597/600	..		Set of 4	40	75

1974 (18 Mar). *No. 546 surch with T 144.*

601		8 c. on 6 c. Cannon-ball tree	10	10

See also No. 620.

145 Kite with Crucifixion Motif

146 British Guiana 24 c. Stamp of 1874

(Des R. Savory; adapted J. Cooter. Litho Questa)

1974 (8 Apr). *Easter.* T **145** and similar vert design. W **106**. P 13½.

602	145	8 c. multicoloured	..	10	10
603	—	25 c. black and dull green	..	10	10
604	—	40 c. black and magenta	..	10	15
605	145	50 c. multicoloured	..	15	25
602/5	..		Set of 4	35	50

Design:—Nos. 603/4, "Crucifixion" in pre-Columbian style.

(Des R. Savory. Litho Harrison)

1974 (18 June). *Centenary of Universal Postal Union.* T **146** and similar horiz design. W **106** (sideways on 8 and 40 c.). P 13½ × 14 (8, 40 c.) or 14 (others).

606	146	8 c. multicoloured	..	25	10
607	—	25 c. bright yellow-green, deep slate-violet and black	..	35	10
608	146	40 c. multicoloured	..	35	20
609	—	50 c. bright yellow-green, reddish chest-nut and black	..	45	45
606/9	..		Set of 4	1·25	75

Design (42 × 25 mm):—25 c., 50 c. U.P.U. emblem and Guyana postman.

147 Guides with Banner

148 Buck Toyeau

(Des M. Broodhagen; adapted J. Cooter. Litho Questa)

1974 (1 Aug). *Girl Guides' Golden Jubilee.* T **147** and similar horiz design. Multicoloured. W **106** (sideways). P 14½.

610		8 c. Type 147	..	20	10
611		25 c. Guides in camp	..	30	15
612		40 c. As 25 c.	..	45	40
613		50 c. Type 147	..	45	45
610/13	..		Set of 4	1·25	1·00
MS614		170 × 137 mm. Nos. 610/13		1·25	2·75

(Des S. Greaves and R. Granger Barrett. Litho Enschedé)

1974 (18 Nov). *Christmas.* T **148** and similar vert designs. Multicoloured. W **106**. P 13½ × 13.

615		8 c. Type 148	..	10	10
616		25 c. Five-fingers and awaras	..	10	10
617		50 c. Pawpaw and tangerine	..	15	10
618		$1 Pineapple and sapodilla	..	30	60
615/18	..		Set of 4	55	70
MS619		127 × 94 mm. Nos. 615/18		90	2·50

1975 (20 Jan). *No. 544 surch as T 144.*

620		8 c. on 3 c. Hanging Heliconia	10	10

149 Golden Arrow of Courage

150 Old Sluice Gate

(Des L. Curtis. Litho D.L.R.)

1975 (23 Feb). *Republic Day. Guyana Orders and Decorations.* T **149** and similar vert designs. W **106**. P 13½.

621		10 c. Type 149	..	10	10
622		35 c. Cacique's Crown of Honour	..	10	15
623		50 c. Cacique's Crown of Valour	..	15	20
624		$1 Order of Excellence	..	35	60
621/4	..		Set of 4	60	90

(Des E. Samuels; adapted PAD Studio. Litho Questa)

1975 (2 May). *Silver Jubilee of International Commission on Irrigation and Drainage.* T **150** and similar horiz design. Multicoloured. W **106** (sideways on 35 c. and $1). P 14.

625		10 c. Type 150	..	10	10
626		35 c. Modern sluice gate	..	10	15
627		50 c. Type 150	..	15	30
628		$1 As 35 c.	..	35	60
625/8	..		Set of 4	60	1·00
MS629		162 × 121 mm. Nos. 625/8. Wmk sideways	75	2·50

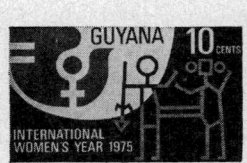
151 I.W.Y. Emblem and Rock Drawing

152 Freedom Monument

(Des C. Henriques; adapted PAD Studio. Litho Questa)

1975 (1 July). *International Women's Year.* T **151** and similar horiz designs showing different rock drawings. W **106** (sideways). P 14.

630	151	10 c. grey-green and yellow	..	10	10
631	—	35 c. reddish violet and greenish blue	..	15	10
632	—	50 c. royal blue and orange	..	20	15
633	—	$1 brown and bright blue	..	30	45
630/3	..		Set of 4	65	65
MS634		178 × 89 mm. Nos. 630/3		75	3·00

(Des PAD Studio. Litho Questa)

1975 (26 Aug). *Namibia Day.* T **152** and similar vert design. Multicoloured. W **106**. P 14.

635		10 c. Type 152	..	10	10
636		35 c. Unveiling of Monument	..	15	10
637		50 c. Type 152	..	25	15
638		$1 As 35 c.	..	35	35
635/8	..		Set of 4	70	60

153 G.N.S. Emblem

154 Court Building, 1875 and Forester's Badge

(Des C. Henriques; adapted PAD Studio. Litho Questa)

1975 (1 Oct*). *First Anniv of National Service.* W **106**. P 14.

639	153	10 c. greenish yellow, light green and light reddish violet		10	10
640	—	35 c. orange, lt green & reddish violet	..	10	10
641	—	50 c. light violet-blue, light green and light yellow-brown	..	15	15
642	—	$1 light mauve, dull green & lt emerald	..	40	40
639/42			Set of 4	60	60
MS643		196 × 133 mm. Nos. 639/42. W **106** (inverted)	75	2·00

*This is the local date of issue; the Crown Agents released the stamps a day later.

Nos. 640/2 are as T **153** but have different symbols within the circle.

(Des R. Savory; adapted PAD Studio. Litho Questa)

1975 (14 Nov). *Centenary of Guyanese Ancient Order of Foresters. T 154 and similar horiz designs. Multicoloured. W 106 (sideways). P 14.*

644	10 c. Type **154**			10	10
645	35 c. Rock drawing of hunter and quarry			10	10
646	50 c. Crossed axes and bugle-horn			15	10
647	$1 Bow and arrow			40	40
644/7			Set of 4	60	50
MS648	129 × 97 mm. Nos. 644/7			75	2·25

(155)

156 Shoulder Flash

35c

1976 (10 Feb). *No. 553 surch with T 155.*

649	35 c. on 60 c. Soldier's Cap		20	15

(Des C. Henriques; adapted J.W. Litho Questa)

1976 (29 Mar). *50th Anniv of the St. John Ambulance in Guyana. T 156 and similar vert designs. W 106. P 14.*

650	**156**	8 c. silver, black and magenta		10	10
651	—	15 c. silver, black and orange		10	10
652	—	35 c. silver, black and green		20	20
653	—	40 c. silver, black and new blue		25	25
650/3			Set of 4	55	50

Nos. 651/3 are as T **156** but show different shoulder flashes.

157 Triumphal Arch   158 Flame in Archway

(Des C. Henriques. Litho J.W.)

1976 (25 May). *Tenth Anniv of Independence. T 157 and similar vert designs. Multicoloured. W 106. P 13½.*

654	8 c. Type **157**		10	10
655	15 c. Stylised Victoria Regia lily		10	10
656	35 c. "Onward to Socialism"		15	15
657	40 c. Worker pointing the way		15	15
654/7		Set of 4	35	35
MS658	120×100 mm. Nos. 654/7. Wmk inverted. P 14½		50	1·50

1976 (3 Aug). *West Indian Victory in World Cricket Cup. As Nos. 559/60 of Barbados.*

659	15 c. Map of the Caribbean	1·25	1·75
660	15 c. Prudential Cup	1·25	1·75

(Des G. Vasarhelyi. Litho J.W.)

1976 (21 Oct). *Deepavali Festival. T 158 and similar vert designs. Multicoloured. W 106. P 14.*

661	8 c. Type **158**		10	10
662	15 c. Flame in hand		10	10
663	35 c. Flame in bowl		15	20
664	40 c. Goddess Latchmi		15	25
661/4		Set of 4	35	50
MS665	94 × 109 mm. Nos. 661/4		50	1·50

159 Festival Emblem and "Musical Instrument"   160 1 c. and 5 c. Coins

(Des C. Henriques. Litho Questa)

1977 (1 Feb). *Second World Black and African Festival of Arts and Culture, Nigeria. W 106. P 14.*

666	**159**	10 c. dull red, black and gold		10	10
667		35 c. deep violet, black and gold		15	10
668		50 c. ultramarine, black and gold		20	25
669		$1 blue-green, black and gold		35	75
666/9			Set of 4	65	1·00
MS670	90 × 157 mm. Nos. 666/9			75	3·00

The above were scheduled for release in 1975, and when finally issued had the original inscription obliterated and a new one applied by overprinting. Examples of Nos. 666/70 are known without overprint.

(Des J.W. Litho Questa)

1977 (26 May). *New Coinage. T 160 and similar horiz designs. W 106. P 14.*

671	8 c. multicoloured			20	10
672	15 c. yellow-brown, grey and black			25	10
673	35 c. bright yellow-green, grey and black			45	30
674	40 c. carmine-red, grey and black			50	35
675	$1 multicoloured			1·00	1·25
676	$2 multicoloured			1·50	2·75
671/6			Set of 6	3·50	4·25

Designs:—15 c. 10 and 25 c. coins; 35 c. 50 c. and $1 coins; 40 c. $5 and $10 coins; $1 $50 and $100 coins; $2 Reverse of $1 coin.

161 Hand Pump, *circa* 1850   162 Cuffy Monument

(Des J. Porteous Wood. Litho Harrison)

1977 (15 Nov). *National Fire Prevention Week. T 161 and similar horiz designs. Multicoloured. W 106. P 14 × 14½.*

677	8 c. Type **161**		50	10
678	15 c. Steam engine, *circa* 1860		85	10
679	35 c. Fire engine, *circa* 1930		1·00	60
680	40 c. Fire engine, 1977		1·10	85
677/80		Set of 4	3·00	1·50

(Des BG Studio. Litho Questa)

1977 (7 Dec). *Cuffy Monument (commemorating 1763 Slave Revolt). W 106. P 14.*

681	**162**	8 c. multicoloured		10	10
682	—	15 c. multicoloured		10	10
683	**162**	35 c. multicoloured		15	20
684	—	40 c. multicoloured		15	30
681/4			Set of 4	35	55

Nos. 682 and 684 show a different view of the monument.

163 American Manatee

(Des BG Studio. Litho Questa)

1978 (15 Feb). *Wildlife Conservation. T 163 and similar multicoloured designs. W 106 (sideways on 8 and 15 c.). P 14.*

685	8 c. Type **163**		65	10
686	15 c. Giant sea turtle		85	20
687	35 c. Harpy Eagle (*vert*)		3·25	1·50
688	40 c. Iguana (*vert*)		3·25	1·50
685/8		Set of 4	7·25	3·00

164 L. F. S. Burnham (Prime Minister) and Parliament Buildings, Georgetown   165 Dr. George Giglioli (scientist and physician)

(Des Walsall. Litho Questa)

1978 (27 Apr). *25th Anniv of Prime Minister's Entry into Parliament. T 164 and similar horiz designs. W 106 (sideways). P 13½ × 14.*

689	8 c. black, violet and bluish grey		10	10
690	15 c. black, light violet-blue and bluish grey		10	10
691	35 c. black, red and bluish grey		15	20
692	40 c. black, red-orange and bluish grey		15	20
689/92		Set of 4	40	45
MS693	176 × 118 mm. Nos. 689/92		55	1·50

Designs:—15 c. Burnham, graduate and children ("Free Education"); 35 c. Burnham and industrial works (Nationalization of Bauxite industry); 40 c. Burnham and village scene ("The Co-operative Village").

(Des J.W. Litho Harrison)

1978 (4 Sept). *National Science Research Council. T 165 and similar multicoloured designs. W 106 (sideways on 10 and 50 c.). P 13½ × 14 (10, 50 c.) or 14 × 13½ (others).*

694	10 c. Type **165**		15	10
695	30 c. Institute of Applied Science and Technology (*horiz*)		20	15
696	50 c. Emblem of National Science Research Council		25	25
697	60 c. Emblem of Commonwealth Science Council (commemorating the 10th Meeting) (*horiz*)		25	25
694/7		Set of 4	75	60

166 Prepona pheridamas   167 Agrias claudina

(Des J. Cooter. Litho J.W.)

1978 (1 Oct)–**80.** *Butterflies. Horiz designs as T 166 (5 to 60 c.) or vert as T 167 ($1 to $10). Multicoloured. W 106. P 14 × 13½ (5 to 60 c.) or 13 ($1 to $10).*

698	5 c. Type **166**		1·50	10
699	10 c. Archonias bellona		1·50	10
700	15 c. Eryphanis polyxena		1·50	10
701	20 c. Helicopis cupido		1·50	10
702	25 c. Nessaea batesii		1·50	10
702a	30 c. Nymphidium mantus (25.1.80)		1·25	1·75
703	35 c. Anaea galanthis		1·50	10
704	40 c. Morpho rhetenor (male)		1·50	10
705	50 c. Hamadryas amphinome		1·50	20
705a	60 c. Papilio androgeus (25.1.80)		1·25	1·00
706	$1 Type **167**		3·75	20
707	$2 Morpho rhetenor (female)		5·50	35
708	$5 Morpho deidamia		6·50	90
708a	$10 Elbella patrobas (25.1.80)		6·50	4·25
698/708a		Set of 14	32·00	8·00

168 Amerindian Stone-chip Grater in Preparation   169 Dish Aerial by Night

(Des L. Curtis. Litho Questa)

1978 (18 Dec). *National/International Heritage Year. T 168 and similar vert designs. Multicoloured. W 106. P 14.*

709	10 c. Type **168**		10	10
710	30 c. Cassiri and decorated Amerindian jars		15	10
711	50 c. Fort Kyk-over-al		20	15
712	60 c. Fort Island		20	20
709/12		Set of 4	55	45

(Des L. Curtis. Litho Questa)

1979 (7 Feb). *Satellite Earth Station. T 169 and similar horiz designs. Multicoloured. W 106 (sideways). P 14 × 14½.*

713	10 c. Type **169**		10	10
714	30 c. Dish aerial by day		20	15
715	50 c. Satellite with solar veins		30	15
716	$3 Cylinder satellite		1·00	90
713/16		Set of 4	1·40	1·10

170 Sir Rowland Hill and British Guiana 1850 12 c. "Cottonreel" Stamp   171 "Me and my Sister"

(Des and litho J.W.)

1979 (11 June). *Death Centenary of Sir Rowland Hill. T 170 and similar multicoloured designs. W 106 (sideways on 10 and 50 c.). P 14.*

717	10 c. Type **170**		15	10
718	30 c. British Guiana 1856 1 c. black on magenta stamp (*vert*)		25	15
719	50 c. British Guiana 1898 1 c. stamp		35	25
720	$3 Printing press used for early British Guiana stamps (*vert*)		70	1·10
717/20		Set of 4	1·25	1·40

(Des J.W. Litho Questa)

1979 (20 Aug). *International Year of the Child. Paintings by local children. T 171 and similar multicoloured designs. W 106 (sideways on 30, 50 c. and $3). P 13½.*

721	10 c. Type **171**		10	10
722	30 c. "Fun with the Fowls" (*horiz*)		15	15
723	50 c. "Two Boys catching Ducks" (*horiz*)		20	20
724	$3 "Mango Season" (*horiz*)		65	1·25
721/4		Set of 4	90	1·50

172 "An 8 Hour Day"

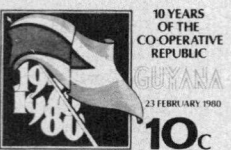
173 Guyana Flag

(Des C. Rodriguez. Litho Walsall)

1979 (27 Sept). 60th Anniv of Guyana Labour Union. T 172 and similar multicoloured designs. W 106 (sideways on 30 c.). P 14 × 14½ (30 c.) or 14½ × 14 (others).

725	10 c. Type 172	10	10
726	30 c. "Abolition of Night Baking" (horiz)	10	10
727	50 c. "Introduction of the Workmen's Compensation Ordinance"	15	15
728	$3 H. N. Critchlow (founder)	55	90
725/8	Set of 4	75	1·10

(Des BG Studio. Litho Questa)

1980 (23 Feb). 10th Anniv of Republic. T 173 and similar horiz designs. W 106 (sideways). P 14.

729	10 c. multicoloured	10	10
730	35 c. black and red-orange	30	10
731	60 c. multicoloured	50	20
732	$3 multicoloured	80	90
729/32	Set of 4	1·50	1·10

Designs:—35 c. View of Demerara River Bridge; 60 c. Kaieteur Falls; $3 "Makanaima the Great Ancestral Spirit of the Amerindians".

174 Common Snook

175 Children's Convalescent Home (Community Service)

(Des J.W. Litho Questa)

1980 (6 May). "London 1980" International Stamp Exhibition. Fishes. T 174 and similar horiz designs. Multicoloured. W 106 (sideways). P 14½.

733	35 c. Type 174	25	20
	a. Block of 12. Nos. 733/44	2·75	
734	35 c. Trahira ("Haimara")	25	20
735	35 c. Electric Eel	25	20
736	35 c. Golden Rivulus	25	20
737	35 c. Golden Pencilfish	25	20
738	35 c. Four-eyed Fish	25	20
739	35 c. Red Piranha ("Pirai")	25	20
740	35 c. Smoking Hassar	25	20
741	35 c. Manta	25	20
742	35 c. Festive Cichlid ("Flying Patwa")	25	20
743	35 c. Arapaima	25	20
744	35 c. Peacock Cichlid ("Lukanani")	25	20
733/44	Set of 12	2·75	2·25

Nos. 733/44 were printed together, se-tenant, in a block of 12 within the sheetlet containing one of each design.

(Des local artist; adapted J.W. Litho Walsall)

1980 (23 June). 75th Anniv of Rotary International. T 175 and similar multicoloured designs. P 14.

745	10 c. Type 175	10	10
746	30 c. Rotary Club of Georgetown and Rotary emblems	10	10
747	50 c. District 404 emblem (vert)	20	20
748	$3 Rotary anniversary emblem (vert)	80	80
745/8	Set of 4	1·00	1·10

176 "C" encircling Globe, Caduceus Emblem and Sea

177 Virola surinamensis

(Des L. Curtis. Litho Enschedé)

1980 (23 Sept). 25th Anniv of Commonwealth Caribbean Medical Research Council. T 176 and similar horiz designs. Multicoloured. W 106 (sideways). P 13.

749	10 c. Type 176	10	10
750	60 c. Researcher with microscope, Caduceus emblem, stethoscope and beach scene	40	20
751	$3 Caduceus emblem, "C" encircling researcher and island silhouettes	1·10	1·00
749/51	Set of 3	1·40	1·10

(Des L. Curtis. Litho Format)

1980 (1 Dec). Christmas. Trees and Foliage. T 177 and similar horiz designs. Multicoloured. W 106 (sideways). P 13½.

752	10 c. Type 177	10	10
753	30 c. Hymenaea courbaril	20	10
754	50 c. Mora excelsa	30	15
755	$3 Peltogyne venosa	1·25	1·10
752/5	Set of 4	1·75	1·25

178 Brazilian Tree Porcupine

$1·05 X
(179)

(Des G. Drummond. Litho Questa)

1981 (2 Mar–1 Sept). Wildlife. T 178 and similar horiz designs. Multicoloured. W 106 (sideways). P 14.

756	30 c. Type 178	40	45
	a. Sheetlet of 12. Nos. 756/67	4·00	
757	30 c. Red Howler	40	45
758	30 c. Common Squirrel-Monkey	40	45
759	30 c. Two-toed Sloth	40	45
760	30 c. Brazilian Tapir	40	45
761	30 c. Collared Peccary	40	45
762	30 c. Six-banded Armadillo	40	45
	a. Perf 12 (1 Sept)	40	15
763	30 c. Tamandua ("Ant Eater")	40	45
764	30 c. Giant Anteater	40	45
765	30 c. Murine Opossum	40	45
766	30 c. Brown Four-eyed Opossum	40	45
767	30 c. Brazilian Agouti	40	45
756/67	Set of 12	4·00	4·50

Nos. 756/67 were printed together, se-tenant, within the sheet of 12.

No. 762a was printed in sheets of 50.

1981 (4 May). Liberation of Southern Africa Conference. No. 635 surch with T 179 by Govt Printer.

768	$1.05 on 10 c. Type 152	40	30

ROYAL WEDDING 1981
$3·60
X
(180)

X
(181) Map of Guyana

7·20
(182)

1981 (6 May). Royal Wedding (1st issue). Nos. 554 and 556 surch as T 180 by Govt Printer in blue.

769	$3.60 on $5 Odontadenia grandiflora	75	75
	a. Surch inverted	£100	
	b. Surch double	13·00	11·00
	c. Black surch	60	65
770	$7.20 on $1 Chelonanthus uliginoides	60	60
	b. Surch double	18·00	15·00
	c. Surch triple		
	d. Black surch	75	75
	da. Surch on No. 556	18·00	

See also Nos. 841/3 and 930/6.

(Surch by Govt Printer)

1981 (11 May). W 106 (sideways). P 13.

771	181 10 c. on 3 c. black, ind & Venetian red	30	10
772	30 c. on 2 c. black, ind & greenish grey	35	15
773	50 c. on 2 c. black, ind & greenish grey	40	15
774	60 c. on 2 c. black, ind & greenish grey	45	15
775	75 c. on 3 c. black, ind & Venetian red	45	20
	a. Surch double	40·00	
	b. Surch triple	60·00	
771/5	Set of 5	1·75	60

Nos. 771/5 are fiscal stamps surcharged for postal use.
See also Nos. 940/76, 988/9 and 1029.

1981 (11 May). No. 544 surch with T 182 by Govt Printer.

775c	720 c. on 3 c. Hanging Heliconia	70·00	15·00
	ca. Surch quadruple	75·00	

1981
(183)

1981 (8 June). Optd with T 183 by Bovell's Printery.

776	105 25 c. black, gold and lilac (R.)	10	10
777	30 c. black, gold & lt apple-green (R.)	15	10
778	— 35 c. multicoloured (No. 645) (R.)	15	10
779	— $1 multicoloured (No. 554)	70	40
776/9	Set of 4	1·00	55

210
(184)

7
X
(185)

ESSEQUIBO IS OURS
15
(186)

ESSEQUIBO IS OURS
15
(186a)

1981 (8 June–1 July) Nos. 545 and 556 surch with T 184 (No. 780) or as T 185, all by Bovell's Printery.

780	75 c. on 5 c. Annatto tree	50	50
781	210 c. on $5 Odontadenia grandiflora	80	1·00
	a. Surch inverted	60·00	
781b	220 c. on 5 c. Annatto tree (1 July)	85·00	8·50

1981 (8 June). Nos. D8/11 surch in black (15 c.) or red (others) by Bovell's Printery. A. As T 186.

782A	D 2 10 c. on 2 c. black	15	10
	c. Surch omitted (in vert pair with normal)		
	w. Wmk inverted		
783A	15 c. on 12 c. bright scarlet	15	15
784A	20 c. on 1 c. olive	15	15
	w. Wmk inverted		
785A	45 c. on 2 c. black	60	20
786A	55 c. on 4 c. dull ultramarine	20	20
	c. Surch inverted		
	d. Surch double, one inverted (T 186 + T 186)		
	da. Ditto, but T 186 + T 186a		
	e. Surch double (55 c. + 60 c.)		
	f. Vert pair, one surch inverted, one surch albino		
	w. Wmk inverted		
788A	65 c. on 2 c. black	30	20
789A	70 c. on 4 c. dull ultramarine	80	55
	w. Wmk inverted		
790A	80 c. on 4c. dull ultramarine	30	20
	c. Surch omitted		
	d. Surch omitted (in vert pair with inverted)		
782/90A	Set of 8	2·40	1·60

B. As T 186a.

782B	D 2 10 c. on 2 c. black	30	10
	w. Wmk inverted		
783B	15 c. on 12 c. bright scarlet	30	10
784B	20 c. on 1 c. olive	20	10
	a. "ESSEQUIBO"	25·00	
	c. Surch omitted (in vert pair with normal)		
	w. Wmk inverted		
785B	45 c. on 2 c. black	30	15
786B	55 c. on 4 c. dull ultramarine	4·50	2·50
	c. Surch inverted		
	db. Surch double, one inverted (T 186a + T 186)		
	w. Wmk inverted		
787B	60 c. on 4 c. dull ultramarine	30	10
	a. "ESSEQUIBO"	10·00	
	c. Surch omitted (in vert pair with normal)		
788B	65 c. on 2 c. black	30	15
789B	70 c. on 4 c. dull ultramarine	30	30
	w. Wmk inverted		
790B	80 c. on 4 c. dull ultramarine	30	20
782B/90B	Set of 9	6·00	3·25

With the exception of No. 787 these stamps were surcharged with a setting of eighteen (three horizontal rows) as Type 186 and twelve as Type 186a. The two types of surcharge can, therefore, be found as vertical se-tenant pairs.

No. 787 was produced from a setting of 12 containing Type 186a only. The same setting was also used for the bottom two rows of the 20 c. on 1 c. value. The "ESSEQUIBO" error occurs on the first stamp in the second horizontal row of this setting.

Examples of all surcharges, except the 80 c., are also known on stamps with watermark w 12.

1981
(187)

1981
(188)

1981
(189)

1981 (8 June–1 July). Nos. 491, 494 and 555 optd with T 187, 188 or 189, all by Bovell's Printery.

791	15 c. Harpy Eagle (R.)	9·00	10
	a. Opt omitted (in vert pair with normal)		†
	b. Opt double		
	c. Opt inverted	40·00	
	d. Opt in black	42·00	5·00
	da. Opt double, one inverted	40·00	
792	40 c. Great Kiskadee (1.7.81)	9·00	40
	a. Opt double	30·00	
793	$2 Norantea guianensis (1.7.81)	1·50	40
791/3	Set of 3	18·00	75

X 120
50c ■
(190)

■
(191)

150
X
(192)

(Surch by Bovell's Printery)

1981 (1 July). (a) Postage. (i) No. 545 surch with T 190.

794	50 c. on 5 c. Annatto tree	30	20
	a. Surch inverted	6·00	2·00

(ii) No. 554 surch as T 191

795	120 c. on $1 Chelonanthus uliginoides	75	40
796	140 c. on $1 Chelonanthus uliginoides	70	40

(iii) Nos. F7 and F9 surch as T 192

797	150 c. on $2 Norantea guianensis	75	40
798	360 c. on $2 Norantea guianensis	3·00	60
799	720 c. on 60 c. Soldier's Cap	3·00	1·00

(iv) *Nos. 556 and 716 surch as T 185*

800	220 c. on $3 Cylinder satellite (surch vert – reading downwards)	1·75	45
	a. Surch reading upwards ..	30·00	
801	250 c. on $5 *Odontadenia grandiflora* ..	1·25	45
802	280 c. on $5 *Odontadenia grandiflora* ..	1·50	50
803	375 c. on $5 *Odontadenia grandiflora* ..	1·75	55
	a. Surch inverted		
	b. "7" of "375" omitted		

(b) Air. No. 843 with commemorative opt cancelled by three bars

804	$1.10 on $2 *Norantea guianensis* ..	1·50	1·25

No. 803b was subsequently corrected by the insertion of a very uneven "7".

100 (193)

15 (193)   **AIR** (194)

(Surch by Bovell's Printery)

1981 (1 July). *No. 485 surch. (a) Postage. With T 193.*

805	15 c. on 1 c. Type 87	70	20
	a. Horiz strip of 3. Nos. 805/7 ..	2·00	
	b. Surch inverted	48·00	
	c. Surch double	40·00	

(b) Air. As T 194

806	100 c. on 1 c. Type 87	70	40
807	110 c. on 1 c. Type 87	70	40

Nos. 805/7 were printed together, *se-tenant*, within the same sheet providing 36 examples of No. 805 and 32 each of the others. No. 805 appears in the six vertical columns of Rows 3 to 8 with horizontal pairs of Nos. 806/7 in vertical columns 1, 2, 9, 10 and vertical pairs in the central six vertical columns of Rows 1, 2, 9, 10.

ESSEQUIBO IS OURS (195)   **ESSEQUIBO IS OURS** (195a)   **1981** (196)

1981 (1 July). *No. 700 optd with T 195 by Bovell's Printery.*

808	15 c. *Eryphanis polyxena*	2·25	10
	a. Opt T 195a	2·25	15
	ab. "I" of "IS" omitted		

No. 808ab is believed to occur on either R. 5/1 or R. 5/5.

1981 (7 July–15 Sept). *Various stamps optd with T 196 by Bovell's Printery.*

809	–	15 c. multicoloured (No. 548) ..	6·00	10
		a. Opt inverted		
810	–	15 c. multicoloured (No. 659) (opt vert —reading downwards) ..	6·00	20
		a. Opt reading upwards ..	26·00	
		b. Opt albino	26·00	
811	–	15 c. multicoloured (No. 660) ..	4·50	20
		a. Opt inverted		
		b. Vert pair, one with opt omitted		
811c	–	40 c. multicoloured (No. F5)	—	£200
812	–	50 c. multicoloured (No. 623) ..	60	20
		a. Opt inverted	28·00	
		b. Opt double, one albino inverted	50·00	
813	150	50 c. multicoloured	1·00	20
814	–	50 c. royal blue and orange (No. 632) ..	23·00	2·00
		a. Opt inverted	30·00	
815	–	50 c. multicoloured (No. 646) ..	2·75	20
		a. Opt inverted	30·00	
816	159	50 c. ultramarine, black and gold ..	13·00	2·00
817	–	50 c. multicoloured (No. F6) ..	4·00	20
818	–	60 c. multicoloured (No. 731) (15.9.81)	60	20
819	–	60 c. multicoloured (No. 750) (15.9.81)	60	20
820	–	$1 multicoloured (No. 624) ..	6·00	55
		a. Opt inverted	20·00	
821	159	$1 blue-green, black and gold ..	6·00	30
		a. Opt inverted	30·00	
822	–	$2 multicoloured (No. 555) ..	9·00	75
823	–	$3 multicoloured (No. 732) ..	2·50	65
		a. Opt inverted	16·00	
824	–	$5 multicoloured (No. 556) ..	3·25	1·25

Overprints on Nos. 814/15 and 823 are vertical, reading upwards.

55 (197)   **55** (198)

110 (199)

440 (200)   **440** (201)

---

550 (202)   **5·50** (203)

240 (204)

(Surch by Bovell's Printery)

1981 (7 July–15 Sept). *(a) Various stamps surch as T 197/203.*

825	116	55 c. on 6 c. multicoloured (surch T 197) (15.9.81)	3·50	80
		a. Surch with T 198	6·00	3·50
		b. Vert pair. Nos. 825/a ..	9·50	4·50
826	111	70 c. on 6 c. multicoloured (15.9.81) ..	1·00	20
827		100 c. on 6 c. multicoloured ..	1·25	20
		a. Surch inverted	2·75	75
		b. Surch albino inverted ..	9·00	
828	–	100 c. on 8 c. multicoloured (No. 505) ..	3·00	20
829	152	100 c. on $1.05 on 10 c. mult (No. 768) (surch vert—reading upwards) ..	32·00	4·00
		a. Surch reading downwards ..	35·00	
830	116	110 c. on 6 c. multicoloured ..	2·00	30
831	149	110 c. on 10 c. multicoloured (surch vert—reading downwards) ..	2·50	30
832	151	110 c. on 10 c. grey-green and yellow ..	6·00	45
833	154	110 c. on 10 c. multicoloured ..	5·00	45
834	–	125 c. on $2 multicoloured (No. 555) ..	12·00	80
835	116	180 c. on 6 c. multicoloured (15.9.81) ..	2·25	45
836		400 c. on 6 c. multicoloured ..	2·25	80
837		440 c. on 6 c. multicoloured (surch T 200)	7·50	3·50
		a. Surch with T 201	1·50	55
		b. Vert pair. Nos. 837/a ..	9·00	6·00
838	–	550 c. on $10 multicoloured (No. O21) (surch T 202) (15.9.81) ..	5·50	1·00
		a. Surch with T 203	13·00	5·50
		b. Vert pair. Nos. 838/a ..	17·00	8·00
839	–	625 c. on 40 c. multicoloured (No. F5) ..	14·00	1·75

(b) No. 728 surch with T 204

840	–	240 c. on $3 multicoloured (15.9.81) ..	8·00	75

Nos. 825/a, 837/a and 838/a were each printed together, *se-tenant*, in vertical pairs throughout sheets containing five of these pairs plus an additional fifteen examples of Nos. 825, 837a and 838.

75

Royal Wedding 1981 (205)   **Royal Wedding 1981** (206)

X 60

Air Mail 1.10 Royal Wedding 1981 (207)

(Surch by Bovell's Printery)

1981 (22 July). *Royal Wedding (2nd issue). (a) Postage. Nos. 544 and 556 surch with T 205/6.*

841	60 c. on 3 c. Hanging Heliconia ..	30	35
	a. Surch inverted	55·00	
	b. "Royal Wedding" diagonal (as T 206) ..	55·00	
	c. Surch double (T 205 + T 206) ..	20·00	
	d. Surch T 205 double	70·00	
842	75 c. on $5 *Odontadenia grandiflora* ..	30	35

(b) Air. No. 555 surch with T 207

843	$1.10 on $2 *Norantea guianensis* ..	30	35
	a. Surch double	38·00	
	b. Surch inverted	80·00	
841/3	.. .. Set of 3	80	95

It is believed No. 841b comes from trial sheets which were accidentally included in supplies of the normal No. 841.

1831-1981

Espana 82 (208)   **Von Stephan 330** (209)

1981 (22 July). *World Cup Football Championship, Spain (1982) (1st issue). No. 781b optd with T 208 by Bovell's Printery.*

844	220 c. on 5 c. Annatto tree ..	1·25	40
	a. Opt double	30·00	
	b. Opt double, one albino ..	30·00	

See also Nos. 937/9 and 1218.

1981 (22 July). *150th Birth Anniv of Heinrich von Stephan (founder of U.P.U.). No. 720 surch with T 209.*

845	330 c. on $3 Printing press used for early British Guiana stamps ..	1·10	55
	a. Surch inverted	30·00	

12 (211)

(211)

1981 (24 Aug). *No. 452 surch as T 211 by Bovell's Printery.*

847	12 c. on 12 c. on 6 c. Black Acara ("Patua")		20	25
	a. Large surch omitted ..	15·00		
	b. Strip of 3. Nos. 847/9 ..		50	
	c. Strip of 3. Nos. 847, 850/1 ..		50	
848	15 c. on 10 c. on 6 c. Black Acara ("Patua")		15	10
849	15 c. on 30 c. on 6 c. Black Acara ("Patua")		15	10
	a. Small surch omitted	25·00		
850	15 c. on 50 c. on 6 c. Black Acara ("Patua")		15	10
851	15 c. on 60 c. on 6 c. Black Acara ("Patua")		15	10

Nos. 847/51 are further surcharges on previously unissued stamps.

No. 847 exists with the smaller of the two 12 c. surcharges printed by either lithography or typography.

Nos. 847/9 and 847, 850/1 were each printed together, *se-tenant*, within the sheets providing 36 examples of No. 847 and 30 each of Nos. 848/9 or 850/1. Each sheet also contained four stamps cancelled with a black diagonal cross. In each instance No. 847 appeared in the six central vertical columns of Rows 3 to 8 with horizontal pairs of Nos. 848/9 or 850/1 in vertical columns 1, 2, 9, 10 and vertical pairs in R. 1/4–8, R. 2/4–8, R. 9/3–7 and R. 10/3–7.

214 Coromantyn Free Negro Armed Ranger, *circa* 1772 and Cuffy Monument   215 Louis Braille

(Des G. Drummond. Litho Rosenbaum Bros, Vienna)

1981 (1 Oct). *16th Anniv of Guyana Defence Force. T 214 and similar vert designs. Multicoloured. W 106 (inverted on $1). P 13½.*

853	15 c. on 10 c. Type 214	30	10
854	50 c. Private, 27th Foot Regiment, *circa* 1825	45	30
855	$1 on 30 c. Private, Col. Fourgeoud's Marines, *circa* 1775 ..	55	45
856	$1.10 on $3 W.O. and N.C.O., Guyana Defence Force, 1966 ..	60	70
853/6	.. .. Set of 4	1·75	1·40

The 15 c., $1 and $1.10 values are surcharged on previously unissued stamps.

(Des G. Vasarhelyi. Litho Questa)

1981 (2 Nov). *International Year for Disabled Persons. Famous Disabled People. T 215 and similar horiz designs. Multicoloured. W 106 (sideways). P 13½ × 14.*

857	15 c. on 10 c. Type 215	25	10
858	50 c. Helen Keller and Rajkumari Singh ..	50	40
859	$1 on 60 c. Beethoven and Sonny Thomas	55	50
	a. Surch double	55·00	
860	$1.10 on $3 Renoir	55	55
	a. Surch double	30·00	
857/60	.. .. Set of 4	1·60	1·40

The 15 c., $1 and $1.10 values are surcharged, by Bovell's Printery, on previously unissued stamps. Examples of Nos. 857, 859 and 860 are known without surcharge.

12 (216)   **X 50** (217)   **AIR**

(Surch by Bovell's Printery)

1981 (10 Nov). *Nos. 452 and 489 surch. (a) Postage. With T 216.*

861	12 c. on 6 c. Black Acara ("Patua") (No. 452)	15	10
	a. Strip of 3. Nos. 861/3 ..	1·25	
861b	12 c. on 6 c. Black Acara ("Patua") (No. 489)	15	10
	ba. Strip of 3. Nos. 861b/3b ..	1·10	

(b) Air. As T 217

862	50 c. on 6 c. Black Acara ("Patua") (No. 452)	25	15
862b	50 c. on 6 c. Black Acara ("Patua") (No. 489)	20	15
863	$1 on 6 c. Black Acara ("Patua") (No. 452)	50	30
863b	$1 on 6 c. Black Acara ("Patua") (No. 489)	50	30

Nos. 861/3 were printed together, *se-tenant*, throughout the sheet. All sheets of Nos. 861b/3b and about half of Nos. 861/3 contained 36 examples of the 12 c., 35 of the 50 c. and 29 of the $1. On the remainder of the unwatermarked sheets there were the same number of the 12 c., but 34 of the 50 c. and 30 of the $1. No. 861 appeared in the six central vertical columns of Rows 3 to 8 with horizontal pairs of Nos. 862/3 in vertical columns 1, 2, 9, 10 and vertical pairs in the six central vertical columns of Rows 1, 2, 9, 10. The additional $1 value on the second stage of the setting occurred on R. 9/1

1981
(218)

1981 (14 Nov). Nos. 548 and 554/5 optd with T 218 in red by Bovell's Printery.
864	15 c. Christmas Orchid		4·00	10
	a. Optd on No. 548a		5·00	
	b. Opt inverted			
865	$1 Chelonanthus uliginoides		40	20
866	$2 Norantea guianensis		90	35

110

Nov 81

110 ⊙ 50c ⊙

(219)   (220)   (221)

1981 (14 Nov). (a) Nos. 601, 620, 644, and O13 surch with T 219/20 in blue by Bovell's Printery.
867	110 c. on 10 c. Type 154 (surch T 219)		3·00	30
868	110 c. on 110 c. on 8 c. on 3 c. Hanging Heliconia (surch T 219 + 220)		3·00	40
	a. Type 220 albino		25·00	
869	110 c. on 110 c. on 8 c. on 6 c. Cannon-ball tree (surch T 219 + 220)		3·00	40
	a. Type 219 albino		26·00	
869b	110 c. on 10 c. on 25 c. Marabunta (surch T 219 vert)		2·25	

(b) Nos. 717, 720, 728, 749, 751 and 755 surch with T 220 by Bovell's Printery.
870	110 c. on 10 c. Type 170 (R.)		2·00	30
	a. Surch albino		15·00	
871	110 c. on 10 c. Type 176 (B.)		8·00	50
872	110 c. on $3 Printing press used for early British Guiana stamps. (R.) (surch vert)		1·75	30
	a. Surch albino		15·00	
873	110 c. on $3 H.N. Critchlow (B.) (surch vert)		6·50	45
874	110 c. on $3 Caduceus emblem, "C" encircling researcher, and island silhouettes (B.)		2·00	30
	a. Surch inverted		15·00	
	b. Surch in red		2·75	70
	ba. Surch inverted		15·00	
	bb. Surch double		30·00	
875	110 c. on $3 Peltogyne venosa (B.)		4·00	50
	a. Surch inverted		20·00	
	b. Surch double		65·00	
	c. Surch in red		48·00	6·50

(c) No. 698 surch with T 221 by Herald Printing-Kitty.
876	50 c. on 5 c. Type 166		5·50	20

X   X

Human Rights Day 1981

110   AIR

222 Yellow Allamanda
(Allamanda cathartica)   (223)

1981 (14 Nov)–82. Flowers. Coil stamps. Vert designs as T 222. W 106. P 15 × 14.
877	15 c. on 2 c. grey-lilac, blue & turquoise-green		15	15
	a. Vert pair. Nos. 877/8		50	45
	b. New blue surch (12.82)		20	10
	ba. Vert pair. Nos. 877b/8b		65	50
878	15 c. on 8 c. grey-lilac, blue and mauve		15	15
	b. New blue surch (12.82)		20	10

Design:—15 c. on 8 c. Mazaruni Pride (Sipanea prolensis).
Nos. 877/8 are surcharges on previously unissued stamps and were printed together, se-tenant, in vertical pairs throughout the coil.

1981 (14 Nov). Air. Human Rights Day. No. 748 surch with T 223 in blue by Bovell's Printery.
879	110 c. on $3 Rotary anniversary emblem		1·25	60

U.N.I.C.E.F. 1946 - 1981

125   XX

(224)

1981 (14 Nov). 35th Anniv of U.N.I.C.E.F. No. 724 surch with T 224 by Bovell's Printery.
880	125 c. on $3 "Mango Season"		1·00	40
	a. Surch inverted		30·00	
	b. Surch double, one inverted		30·00	

Cancun 81

⊙ 50c ⊙

(224a)

1981 (14 Nov). "Cancun 81" International Conference. No. 698 surch with T 224a by Herald Printing-Kitty.
880a	50 c. on 5 c. Type 166		4·00	55

---

225 Tape Measure and Guyana Metrication Board Van

1982
(226)

(Des local artist; adapted A. Theobald. Litho Questa)

1982 (18 Jan). Metrication. T 225 and similar vert designs. Multicoloured. W 106. P 14½ × 14.
881	15 c. Type 225		25	25
	a. Sheetlet of 6. Nos. 881/6		1·40	
882	15 c. "Metric man"		25	25
883	15 c. "Postal service goes metric"		25	25
884	15 c. Weighing child on metric scales		25	25
885	15 c. Canje Bridge		25	25
886	15 c. Tap filling litre bucket		25	25
881/6		Set of 6	1·40	1·40

Nos. 881/6 were printed together, se-tenant, in a sheetlet of 6.

1982 (8 Feb). Various stamps optd with T 226 in blue by Autoprint.
887	– 20 c. multicoloured (No. 549)		1·50	20
	a. Optd on No. 549a		3·75	1·75
888	105 25 c. black, gold and lilac		60	15
889	– 25 c. multicoloured (No. 550a)		2·00	20
	a. Optd on No. 550		3·50	3·00
	b. Optd on No. 550ab		3·00	2·50

See also Nos. 914/17, 919/21, 923/4, 977, 992/8, 1001, 1004, 1006/8, 1015, 1017, 1059, 1117 and OP3/4.

20c
(227)

≡ 20 ≡
(228)

POSTAGE
(229)

1982 (8 Feb). Nos. 506, 546 and 601 surch or optd as T 227/9 by Bovell's Printery (No. 890) or Autoprint (others).
890	20 c. on 6 c. Cannon-ball tree (surch T 227) (G.)		35	10
891	20 c. on 6 c. Cannon-ball tree (surch T 228) (B.)		35	10
892	25 c. Type 116 (optd T 229) (B.)		1·00	10
893	125 c. on 8 c. on 6 c. Cannon-ball tree (surch T 228) (B.)		35	20

230 Guyana Soldier and Flag

1982 (8 Feb). Savings Campaign. W 106 (sideways). P 14 × 14½.
894	230 $1 multicoloured		30	30
	a. Opt inverted		42·00	

No. 894 is a fiscal stamp overprinted, by Bovell's Printery, for postal use.

110   X

BADEN POWELL

1857 - 1982
(231)

1982 (15–22 Feb). 125th Birth Anniv of Lord Baden-Powell and 75th Anniv of Boy Scout Movement. Nos. 543, 545 and 601 surch as T 231 by Bovell's Printery.
895	15 c. on 2 c. Type 132 (surch T 231) (22 Feb)		10	30
	a. Sheetlet of 25. Nos. 895/6, each × 8, Nos. 897/8, each × 4 and No. 899		8·00	
	ab. Surch inverted (sheetlet of 25)			

896	15 c. on 2 c. Type 132 (surch "Scout Movement 1907–1982") (22 Feb)		10	30
897	15 c. on 2 c. Type 132 (surch "1907–1982") (22 Feb)		15	40
898	15 c. on 2 c. Type 132 (surch "1857–1982") (22 Feb)		15	15
899	15 c. on 2 c. Type 132 (surch "1982") (22 Feb)		10	10
900	110 c. on 5 c. Annatto tree (surch T 231)		1·00	60
	a. Sheetlet of 25. Nos. 900/1, each × 8, Nos. 902/3, each × 4, and No. 904 (22 Feb)		18·00	
901	110 c. on 5 c. Annatto tree (surch "Scout Movement 1907–1982")		60	20
902	110 c. on 5 c. Annatto tree (surch "1907–1982") (22 Feb)		1·50	1·00
903	110 c. on 5 c. Annatto tree (surch "1857–1982") (22 Feb)		1·50	1·00
904	110 c. on 5 c. Annatto tree (surch "1982") (22 Feb)		60	20
	a. "110" larger		95·00	
905	125 c. on 8 c. on 6 c. Cannon-ball tree (surch T 231) (G.)		1·00	20
	a. Sheetlet of 25. Nos. 905/6, each × 8, Nos. 907/8, each × 4, and No. 909 (22 Feb)		20·00	
906	125 c. on 8 c. on 6 c. Cannon-ball tree (surch "Scout Movement 1907–1982") (G.)		1·00	20
907	125 c. on 8 c. on 6 c. Cannon-ball tree (surch "1907–1982") (G.) (22 Feb)		1·50	1·00
908	125 c. on 8 c. on 6 c. Cannon-ball tree (surch "1857–1982") (G.) (22 Feb)		1·50	1·00
909	125 c. on 8 c. on 6 c. Cannon-ball tree (surch "1982") (G.) (22 Feb)		75	20
895/909		Set of 15	10·00	5·00

In addition to the sheetlets of 25, Nos. 895a, 900a and 905a, Nos. 899/901, 904/6 and 909 also come from sheets containing one type of surcharge only.
No. 904a occurs in the printing of sheets containing this surcharge only. The "110" is in the same size as the surcharge on Type 241.

(232)   (233)

1982 (15 Feb). 250th Birth Anniv of George Washington. Nos. 708, 718 and 720 surch as T 232 by Herald Printing-Kitty or optd only with T 233 by Autoprint.
910	100 c. on $3 Printing press used for early British Guiana stamps.		45	30
911	400 c. on 30 c. British Guiana 1856 1 c. black on magenta stamp		1·60	1·25
	a. Surch inverted		20·00	
912	$5 Morpho deidamia (B.)		7·50	5·50
910/12		Set of 3	8·50	6·25

1982 (3 Mar). Savings Campaign. Horiz design as T 230. Multicoloured. W 106. P 14 × 14½.
913	110 c. on $5 Guyana male and female soldiers with flag		50	20

No. 913 is a fiscal stamp surcharged, by Bovell's Printery, for postal use.
See also No. 990.

45   20   210

(234)   (235)   (236)

1982 (15 Mar). Easter. Nos. 481/4 optd with T 226, in blue, or surch as T 234, all by Autoprint.
914	111 25 c. multicoloured		20	15
915	30 c. multicoloured		20	15
916	45 c. on 6 c. multicoloured (B.)		20	25
917	75 c. on 40 c. multicoloured (R.)		35	25
914/17		Set of 4	85	70

No. 917 exists with the surcharge either at the right or in the centre of the design.

1982 (15 Mar). No. 703 surch with T 235 by Herald Printing-Kitty.
918	20 c. on 35 c. Anaea galanthis		3·50	10

1982 (8 Apr). No. F5 optd with T 226 and surch as T 228 in blue, both by Autoprint.
919	180 c. on 40 c. Tiger Beard		3·50	40

1982 (23 Apr). Nos. 555/6 optd with T 226 in blue by Autoprint.
920	$2 Norantea guianensis		80	30
921	$5 Odontadenia grandiflora		1·40	70

1982 (23 Apr). No. 542 surch as T 228 in blue by Autoprint.
922	220 c. on 1 c. Pitcher Plant of Mt Roraima		1·25	40

1982 (27 Apr). Nos. 472 and 684 optd with T 226 in blue by Autoprint.
923	105 40 c. black, gold and cobalt		35	15
924	– 40 c. multicoloured		50	25

1982 (27 Apr). Nos. 469, 751, 842 and 843 surch as T 228, vertically (Nos. 925/7), or as T 236 (others), all in blue by Autoprint.
925	105 80 c. on 6 c. black, gold and flesh		30	20
926	85 c. on 6 c. black, gold and flesh		50	20
927	– 160 c. on $1.10 on $2 multicoloured (No 843)		60	30

928 — 210 c. on $3 multicoloured (No. 751)
(surch reading up) .. .. 2·50 40
  a. Surch reading down .. 12·00
929 — 235 c. on 75 c. on $5 multicoloured (No. 842) .. 2·50 60
The surcharge on No. 929 is as Type 236, but horizontal.

(237) (238)

(239)

(Surch by Herald Printing-Kitty)

1982 (27 Apr–May). *Royal Wedding (3rd issue). Coil stamps. Nos. 841/3 surch as T 237 (No. 930), 238 (Nos. 931/2, 934/5) or 239 (others).*
930 85 c. on 60 c. on 3 c. Hanging Heliconia .. 2·50 50
931 130 c. on 60 c. on 3 c. Hanging Heliconia .. 1·75 45
  a. Surch (as T 238) inverted .. £100
932 160 c. on $1.10 on $2 *Norantea guianensis* (vert surch) .. 2·25 1·00
  a. Surch (as T 238) double .. 32·00
933 170 c. on $1.10 on $2 *Norantea guianensis* 6·00 4·50
  a. Surch inverted .. 45·00
934 210 c. on 75 c. on $5 *Odontadenia grandiflora* (B.) .. 1·25 40
  a. Surch as T 238) inverted .. 18·00
935 235 c. on 75 c. on $5 *Odontadenia grandiflora* .. 2·00 1·40
  a. Surch (T 206) omitted .. 75·00
  b. Surch (as T 238) double ..
936 330 c. on $1.10 on $2 *Norantea guianensis* 1·75 40
930/6 *Set of 7* 16·00 7·75

220 AIR

Princess of Wales

ESPANA 1982 (240) **1961 - 1982** (241)

1982 (15 May). *World Cup Football Championship, Spain (2nd issue). Nos. 544, 546 and 554 optd with T 240 or surch also as T 228, both by Autoprint.*
937 $1 *Chelonanthus uliginoides* .. 75 40
  a. Opt inverted .. 15·00
938 110 c. on 3 c. Hanging Heliconia (B.) 75 25
939 250 c. on 6 c. Cannon-ball tree (B.) .. 1·00 90
937/9 *Set of 3* 2·25 1·10
See also No. 1218

(Optd Govt Printer and surch by Autoprint)

1982 (17 May). *W 106 (sideways). P 13.*
940 **181** 15 c. on 2 c. black, ind & greenish grey 50 15
  a. Opt ("ESSEQUIBO etc") omitted 18·00
941 20 c. on 2 c. black, ind & greenish grey 3·50 30
942 25 c. on 2 c. black, ind & greenish grey 5·00 20
943 30 c. on 2 c. black, ind & greenish grey 50 15
944 40 c. on 2 c. black, ind & greenish grey 9·00 30
  a. Surch inverted .. 9·50
945 45 c. on 2 c. black, ind & greenish grey 1·75 45
946 50 c. on 2 c. black, ind & greenish grey 8·50 30
  a. Opt ("ESSEQUIBO etc") omitted 18·00
947 60 c. on 2 c. black, ind & greenish grey 7·00 20
948 75 c. on 2 c. black, ind & greenish grey 6·00 25
949 80 c. on 2 c. black, ind & greenish grey 5·00 20
950 85 c. on 2 c. black, ind & greenish grey 75 25
951 100 c. on 3 c. black, ind and Venetian red 1·00 35
952 110 c. on 3 c. black, ind and Venetian red 80 30
953 120 c. on 3 c. black, ind and Venetian red 8·00 35
954 125 c. on 3 c. black, ind and Venetian red 2·25 35
955 130 c. on 3 c. black, ind and Venetian red 1·00 35
  a. Surch inverted .. 17·00
  b. Error. Nos. 952 and 955 se-tenant
  c. Error. Nos. 955 and 956 se-tenant
956 150 c. on 3 c. black, ind and Venetian red 8·50 40
957 160 c. on 3 c. black, ind and Venetian red 2·00 40
958 170 c. on 3 c. black, ind and Venetian red 1·40 45
959 175 c. on 3 c. black, ind and Venetian red 6·00 45
960 180 c. on 3 c. black, ind and Venetian red 2·00 60
961 200 c. on 3 c. black, ind and Venetian red 2·25 45
962 210 c. on 3 c. black, ind and Venetian red 7·00 50
963 220 c. on 3 c. black, ind and Venetian red 8·50 50
964 235 c. on 3 c. black, ind and Venetian red 8·00 50
965 240 c. on 3 c. black, ind and Venetian red 9·00 50
966 250 c. on 3 c. black, ind and Venetian red 2·25 50
967 300 c. on 3 c. black, ind and Venetian red 12·00 55
968 330 c. on 3 c. black, ind and Venetian red 2·75 65
969 375 c. on 3 c. black, ind and Venetian red 7·00 75
970 400 c. on 3 c. black, ind and Venetian red 10·00 75
971 440 c. on 3 c. black, ind and Venetian red 4·00 75
972 500 c. on 3 c. black, ind and Venetian red 3·50 1·10
973 550 c. on 3 c. black, ind and Venetian red 4·00 1·25

974 **181** 625 c. on 3 c. black, ind and Venetian red 2·75 1·75
975 1500 c. on 2 c. black, ind & greenish grey 11·00 3·00
976 2000 c. on 2 c. black, ind & greenish grey 11·00 3·75
940/76 *Set of 37* £160 21·00
Nos. 940/76 are fiscal stamps, surcharged for postal use, as Type 181, but with the overprinted inscription and face value redrawn. On the 15 to 85 c., the surcharged face value is in blue, on the 100 to 625 c. in black, and on the 1500 and 2000 c. in red.
Nos. 955b/c come from the first printing of the 130 c. which had one cliché of the 110 c. surcharge (R. 4/1) and three of the 150 c. (R. 2/8–10) included in error.
For 25 c. and 40 c. surcharges in black see Nos. 988/9 and for the 25 c. in red, No. 1029.

1982 (7 June). *No. 548 optd with T 226 in blue by Autoprint.*
977 15 c. Christmas Orchid .. 7·00 10
  a. Optd on No. 548a. .. 48·00 12·00

1982 (15 June). *No. O26 optd with T 229 in blue by Autoprint.*
978 110 c. on 6 c. Type 116 .. 3·50 35

1982 (25 June). *Air. 21st Birthday of Princess of Wales. Nos. 542, 545 and 555 surch as T 241 by Bovell's Printery.*
979 110 c. on 5 c. Annatto tree (R.) .. 50 30
  a. Surch in black .. 20·00
980 220 c. on 1 c. Pitcher Plant of Mt Roraima .. 80 60
  a. Surch double .. 65·00
981 330 c. on $2 *Norantea guianensis* (B.) .. 90 90
  a. Surch in greenish blue ..
  ab. Surch double .. 48·00
979/81 *Set of 3* 2·00 1·60

GUYANA

H.R.H.
Prince William
21st June 1982

ooo
oooooooooo $1.10
(242)

H.R.H.
Prince William
21st June 1982

$2.20
(243)

1982 (12 July). *Birth of Prince William of Wales. Surch as T 242 (50 c. and $1.10) or with T 243 (others), all in blue by Autoprint.*

(a) On stamps of British Guiana
982 50 c. on 2 c. myrtle-green (No. 332) .. 40 30
  a. Surch as T 243 (lines at foot) 32·00
983 $1.10 on 3 c. brown-olive and red-brown (No. 354) .. 80 50
  a. Surch inverted .. 18·00
  b. Surch double ..
  c. Surch on No. 333 .. 80 50
  ca. Surch inverted .. 55·00
  cb. Surch double .. 75·00
  cc. Surch as T 243 (lines at foot) 45·00

(b) On stamps of Guyana previously optd "GUYANA INDEPENDENCE 1966"
984 50 c. on 2 c. myrtle-green (No. 430) .. 10·00 3·25
985 $1.10 on 3 c. brn-olive & red-brn (No. 431) 17·00 3·25
  a. Surch on No. 422 .. 18·00 10·00
986 $1.25 on 6 c. yellow-green (No. 389) .. 60 40
  a. Surch inverted .. 20·00
  b. Surch double .. 75·00
  c. Surch on No. 434 .. 4·00 2·00
987 $2.20 on 24 c. black and brownish orange (No. 403) .. 1·50 1·50
  a. Surch inverted .. 75·00
  b. Surch on No. 392 .. 8·00 8·00
  c. Surch on No. 435 .. 20·00 17·00
982/7 *Set of 6* 27·00 8·50
Nos. 982, 983c and 985a have Mult Script CA watermark and the remainder watermark w 12 (sideways on No. 987).

1982 (13 July). *As Nos. 942 and 944 but with surcharged face values in black by Autoprint.*
988 **181** 25 c. on 2 c. black, ind & greenish grey 2·25 20
989 40 c. on 2 c. black, ind & greenish grey 1·00 15

1982 (13 July). *Savings Campaign. Coil stamp. As No. 913 but showing inverted comma before "OURS" in overprint.*
990 110 c. on $5 Guyana male and female soldiers with flag .. 5·50 75

ITALY **50**

C.A. & CARIB GAMES
$2.35 **1982**
(244) (245)

1982 (15 July). *Italy's Victory in World Cup Football Championship. No. F7 optd as T 240 and surch with T 244, both in blue by Autoprint.*
991 $2.35 on 180 c. on 60 c. Soldier's Cap .. 3·50 55

1982 (16 Aug). *Wildlife Protection. Nos. 687 and 733/8 optd with T 226 (vert on Nos. 993/8) in blue by Autoprint.*
992 35 c. Harpy Eagle .. .. 2·00 40
  a. Opt inverted .. 32·00
993 35 c. Type 174 .. 2·00 40
  a. Block of 6. Nos. 993/8 .. 12·50
994 35 c. Trahira ("Haimara") .. 2·00 40
995 35 c. Electric Eel .. 2·00 40
996 35 c. Golden Rivulus .. 2·00 40
997 35 c. Golden Pencilfish .. 2·00 40
998 35 c. Four-eyed Fish .. 2·00 40
992/8 *Set of 7* 12·50 2·50

1982 (16 Aug). *Central American and Caribbean Games, Havana. Nos. 542/3 surch as T 245 by Autoprint.*
999 50 c. on 2 c. Type 132 .. 1·00 25
  a. Surch inverted .. †
1000 60 c. on 1 c. Pitcher Plant of Mt Roraima .. 1·25 15

1982 (15 Sept). *No. 730 optd with T 226 vertically in blue by Autoprint.*
1001 35 c. black and red-orange .. 30 20

1982 (15 Sept). *Nos. 841 and 979 further surch as T 228 (No. 1003 has solid bar) in blue by Autoprint.*
1002 130 c. on 60 c. on 3 c. Hanging Heliconia 40 30
  a. Surch as T 228 inverted .. £150
1003 170 c. on 110 c. on 5 c. Annatto tree .. 70 45
  a. With six lines as in T 228 .. 90·00

1982 (15 Sept). *No. 841 optd with T 226 and surch as T 228, both in blue by Autoprint.*
1004 440 c. on 60 c. on 3 c. Hanging Heliconia 75 45
  a. T 226 and T 228 both inverted .. 20·00
  b. Surch and optd on No. 841b .. 1·75 2·25
  c. Without opt T 226 .. 2·25 55
No. 1004c also differs from No. 1004 by showing a "c" after the surcharge "60" on Type 205.

Commonwealth GAMES AUSTRALIA 1982 1.25 (246) **INT. FOOD DAY 1982** (247)

1982 (27 Sept). *Commonwealth Games, Brisbane, Australia. No. 546 surch with T 246 in blue by Autoprint.*
1005 $1.25 on 6 c. Cannon-ball tree .. 1·00 30

1982 (1 Oct). *Nos. 552, 641 and 719 optd with T 226 (vertically reading upwards on Nos. 1007/8) in blue by Autoprint.*
1006 50 c. multicoloured (No. 552) .. 2·00 25
1007 50 c. lt vio-bl, lt grn & lt yell-brn (No. 641) 1·50 25
1008 50 c. multicoloured (No. 719) .. 60 25
  a. Opt reading downwards

1982 (1 Oct). *Various Official stamps additionally optd for postal purposes as T 229, but smaller (29 mm in length), all in blue by Autoprint.*
1009 15 c. Christmas Orchid (No. O23) (vert opt) .. 8·00 30
1010 50 c. Guzmania lingulata (No. O14) (vert opt) .. 90 15
1011 100 c. on $3 Cylinder satellite (No. O19) 1·25 35
  a. Opt double .. 20·00

1982 (15 Oct). *International Food Day. No. 617 optd with T 247 in blue by Autoprint.*
1012 50 c. Pawpaw and tangerine .. 11·00 65

INT. YEAR OF THE ELDERLY (248) **Dr. R. KOCH CENTENARY TBC BACILLUS DISCOVERY** (249) **F. D. ROOSEVELT 1882-1982** (250)

1982 (15 Oct). *International Year of the Elderly. No. 747 optd with T 248 in blue by Autoprint.*
1013 50 c. District 404 emblem .. 7·00 50

1982 (15 Oct). *Centenary of Robert Koch's Discovery of Tubercle Bacillus. No. 750 optd with T 249 in blue by Autoprint.*
1014 60 c. Researcher with microscope, Caduceus emblem, stethoscope and beach scene .. 2·00 30

1982 (15 Oct). *International Decade for Women. No. 633 optd with T 226 in blue by Autoprint.*
1015 $1 brown and bright blue .. 2·50 60
  a. Opt inverted .. 18·00

1982 (15 Oct). *Birth Centenary of F. D. Roosevelt (American statesman). No. 706 optd with T 250 in blue by Autoprint.*
1016 $1 Type 167 .. .. 3·25 50

(251) GAC Inaug. Flight Georgetown— Boa Vista, Brasil

200

50

(252) CARICOM Heads of Gov't Conference July 1982

1982 (15 Oct). *1st Anniv of G.A.C. Inaugural Flight Georgetown to Boa Vista, Brazil. No. 842 optd with T 226 and surch with T 251, both in blue by Autoprint.*
1017 200 c. on 75 c. on $5 *Odontadenia grandiflora* 8·00 1·40

1982 (18 Nov). *CARICOM Heads of Government Conference, Kingston, Jamaica. Nos. 881/6 surch with T 252 by Herald Printing-Kitty.*
1018 50 c. on 15 c. Type 225 . .. .. 1·25 30
a. Sheetlet of 6. Nos. 1018/23 .. .. 6·75
1019 50 c. on 15 c. "Metric man" .. .. 1·25 30
1020 50 c. on 15 c. "Postal service goes metric" 1·25 30
1021 50 c. on 15 c. Weighing child on metric scales 1·25 30
1022 50 c. on 15 c. Canje Bridge .. .. 1·25 30
1023 50 c. on 15 c. Tap filling litre bucket .. 1·25 30
1018/23 .. .. .. *Set of 6* 6·75 1·75

(253) CHRISTMAS 1982

15 **(254)**

50 **(255)**

1982 (1 Dec). *Christmas. Nos. 895/9 optd with T 253 in red by Autoprint.*
1024 15 c. on 2 c. Type 132 (surch T 231) 25 15
a. Sheetlet of 25. Nos. 1024/5, each × 8, Nos. 1026/7, each × 4 and No. 1028 .. 14·00
1025 15 c. on 2 c. Type 132 (surch "Scout Movement 1907–1982") 25 15
1026 15 c. on 2 c. Type 132 (surch "1907–1982") .. 65 50
1027 15 c. on 2 c. Type 132 (surch "1857–1982") .. 65 60
1028 15 c. on 2 c. Type 132 (surch "1982") .. 6·50 70
1024/8 .. .. .. *Set of 5* 7·50 7·50
Nos. 1024/8 were only issued in the *se-tenant* sheetlets of 25.

1982 (15 Dec). *As No. 942 but with surcharged face value in red by Autoprint.*
1029 181 25 c. on 2 c. black, indigo and greenish grey 50 10

1982 (15 Dec). *Nos. 543 and 546 surch as T 254 by Autoprint.*
1030 15 c. on 2 c. Type 132 (B.) 15 10
1031 20 c. on 6 c. Cannon-ball tree (Blk.) .. 25 10
For similar surcharges in different colours see Nos. 1034/5 and 1063; and for surcharges incorporating "c" Nos. 1085/7 and 1098/9.

1982 (15 Dec). *No. 489 surch as T 255 by Autoprint.*
1032 50 c. on 6 c. Black Acara ("Patua") .. 20 15
1033 100 c. on 6 c. Black Acara ("Patua") .. 40 30

1983 (5 Jan). *As Nos. 1030/1, but with colours of surcharge changed.*
1034 15 c. on 2 c. Type 132 (Blk.) .. 10 10
1035 20 c. on 6 c. Cannon-ball tree (G.) .. 10 10

1983 POSTAGE

(256) **(257)** 258 Guyana Flag (inscr "60th BIRTHDAY ANNIVERSARY")

1983 (1 Feb). *Optd with T 256 by Autoprint.*
1036 – 15 c. multicoloured (No. 655) (opt vert) 3·50 1·00
1037 – 15 c. yellow-brown, grey and black (No. 672) 60 10
1038 – 15 c. multicoloured (No. 682) (opt vert) .. 40 10
1039 214 15 c. on 10 c. multicoloured (opt vert) .. 35 10
1040 215 15 c. on 10 c. multicoloured .. 15 10
1041 – 50 c. multicoloured (No. 646) .. 4·00 25
1042 – 50 c. multicoloured (No. 696) (opt vert) .. 4·00 25
1043 – 50 c. multicoloured (No. 719) .. 6·50 25
1036/43 .. .. .. *Set of 8* 13·00 1·75
See also Nos. 1060/1, 1069/70, 1072/9c, 1096, 1101 and 1110/16.

1983 (1 Feb). *No. O17 optd for postal purposes with T 257 in red by Autoprint.*
1044 15 c. Harpy Eagle .. .. .. 13·00 10

1983 (8 Feb). *National Heritage. Nos. 710/12 and No. 778 surch as T 234 in black (No. 1045) or blue (others) by Autoprint.*
1045 90 c. on 30 c. Cassiri and decorated Amerindian jars .. .. .. 1·25 50
1046 90 c. on 35 c. Rock drawing of hunter and quarry 35 20
1047 90 c. on 50 c. Fork Kyk-over-al .. 1·25 50
1048 90 c. on 60 c. Fort Island .. .. 1·75 20
1045/8 .. .. .. *Set of 4* 4·25 1·25

(Des K. Everett (25 c.). Litho Format)

1983 (19 Feb). *President Burnham's 60th Birthday and 30 Years in Parliament. T 258 and similar multicoloured designs. W 106 (sideways) (25 c., $1.30). P 13½ ($1.30) or 14 (others).*
1049 25 c. Type 258 .. .. .. 15 20
a. Horiz pair. Nos. 1049/50 .. .. 25 40
1050 25 c. As T 258, but position of flag reversed and inscr "30th ANNIVERSARY IN PARLIAMENT" 15 20
1051 $1.30, Youth display (41 × 25 mm) .. 40 65
1052 $6 Presidential standard (43½ × 25 mm) 1·00 2·75
1049/52 .. .. .. *Set of 4* 1·50 3·50
Nos. 1049/50 were printed together, *se-tenant*, in horizontal pairs throughout the sheet.
Nos. 1049/50 and 1052 exist imperforate from stock dispersed by the liquidator of Format International Security Printers Ltd.
For stamps as Nos. 1049/50, but without commemorative inscriptions, see Nos. 1108/9.

PRINTERS. Nos. 1053/1126 were surcharged or overprinted by Autoprint, Georgetown.

FIFTY CENTS **(259)**

20 X **(260)**

1983 (7 Mar). *Surch as T 259.*
1053 170 50 c. on 10 c. mult (No. 717) (R.) 2·00 30
1054 – 50 c. on 400 c. on 30 c. multicoloured (No. 911) (surch vert) .. 2·50 30
1055 152 $1 on 10 c. multicoloured (No. 635) (surch vert) .. 7·50 45
1056 $1 on $1.05 on 10 c. multicoloured (No. 768) (surch vert) .. 6·50 45
1056a $1 on $1.10 on $2 multicoloured (No. 843) .. .. 1·00 2·50
1057 – $1 on 220 c. on 5 c. mult (No. 844) (B.) 7·50 75
1058 – $1 on 330 c. on $2 mult (No. 981) (B.) 60 45
1059 – $1 on $12 on $1.10 on $2 mult (similar to No. P3) (B.) .. 2·50 2·00
1053/9 .. .. .. *Set of 8* 27·00 6·50
Nos. 1057/9 have thin bars cancelling previous surcharges and, in addition, No. 1059 is optd with T 226 in blue.
See also Nos. 1062 and 1080/4.

1983 (7 Mar). *No. 859 optd with T 256.*
1060 $1 on 60 c. Beethoven and Sonny Thomas .. 6·00 45

1983 (11 Mar). *Conference of Foreign Ministers of Non-aligned Countries, New Delhi. No. 569 surch with T 259 and No. 570 optd with T 256.*
1061 136 25 c. multicoloured (opt vert) .. 75 25
1062 50 c. on 8 c. mult (surch vert) (R.) .. 1·50 25

1983 (14 Mar). *As No. 1030, but colour of surcharge changed.*
1063 15 c. on 2 c. Type 132 (R.) .. .. 1·50 10

1983 (14 Mar). *No. 771 further surch with T 260 in blue.*
1064 181 20 c. on 10 c. on 3 c. black, indigo and Venetian red 55 10

Commonwealth Day 14 March 1983

(261) $1.30

(262) $4.80

1983 (14 Mar). *Commonwealth Day. Nos. 389 and 403 surch as T 261 in black (25 c., $1.30) or blue (others).*
1065 25 c. on 6 c. yellow-green .. .. 1·00 20
1066 $1.20 on 6 c. yellow-green 50 50
1067 $1.30 on 24 c. black and bright orange .. 1·75 55
1068 $2.40 on 24 c. black and bright orange .. 2·25 1·25
1065/8 .. .. .. *Set of 4* 5·00 2·25

1983 (17 Mar). *Easter. Nos. 482/3 optd with T 256.*
1069 111 25 c. multicoloured 15 10
1070 30 c. multicoloured 30 15

1983 (17 Mar). *25th Anniv of International Maritime Organization. British Guiana fiscal stamp optd in red as T 262. Wmk Mult Crown CA. P 14.*
1071 $4.80, bright blue and deep dull green .. 2·00 4·00

1983 (1 Apr). *Optd with T 256.*
1072 152 50 c. mult (No. 637) (opt vert) .. 1·50 25
1073 159 50 c. ultramarine, black and gold (No. 668) (opt vert) .. 2·00 25
1073a – 50 c. multicoloured (No. 723) .. 25·00 2·00
1074 – 50 c. mult (No. 854) (opt vert) .. 60 25
1075 – 50 c. multicoloured (No. 858) .. 1·75 25
1076 – $1 mult (No. 628) .. .. 4·00 45
1077 – $1 mult (No. 638) (opt vert) .. 4·75 45
1078 – $1 multicoloured (No. 675) .. 4·00 45
1079 – $1 on 30 c. mult (No. 855) (opt vert) 1·25 45
1079a – $3 multicoloured (No. 720) .. 17·00 90
1079b – $3 multicoloured (No. 724) .. 22·00 1·50
1079c – $3 multicoloured (No. 748) .. 65·00 7·00

1983 (1 Apr). *Surch with T 259, vertically, in black (No. 1082) or blue (others).*
1080 148 50 c. on 8 c. multicoloured (No. 615) .. 1·75 25
1081 162 50 c. on 8 c. multicoloured (No. 681) .. 6·00 25
1082 171 50 c. on 10 c. multicoloured (No. 721) .. 3·00 25
1083 – 50 c. on 10 c. on 25 c. mult (No. O13) .. 5·00 25
1084 – 50 c. on 330 c. on $3 mult (No. 845) .. 4·00 25

1983 (2 May). *Surch with T 254 in black "after new face value.*
1085 105 15 c. on 6 c. black, gold and flesh (No. 469) (B.) 30 10
1086 – 20 c. on 6 c. multicoloured (No. 546) .. 30 10
1087 111 50 c. on 6 c. multicoloured (No. 481) .. 40 30
For No. 1085 with black overprint, see No. 1098.

(263) 110

(264) $1

ITU 1983

25 **(265)**

1983 (2 May). *No. 489 surch with T 263.*
1088 $1 on 6 c. Black Acara ("Patua") .. 1·25 30

1983 (2 May). *No. 639 surch with T 264 in blue.*
1089 153 110 c. on 10 c. greenish yellow, light green and light reddish violet.. 1·75 50
a. Error. Surch on 35 c (No. 640) £100

1983 (2 May). *Nos. 551 and 556 surch as T 228 in blue.*
1090 250 c. on 40 c. Tiger Beard .. .. 7·50 55
1091 400 c. on $5 *Odontadenia grandiflora* .. 5·50 70

1983 (17 May). *World Telecommunications and Health Day. Nos. 842 and 980 further surch as T 265.*
1092 25 c. on 220 c. on 1 c. Pitcher Plant of Mt Roraima (surch T 265) (R.) .. 30 30
a. Sheetlet of 25. Nos. 1092/3 each × 8 and No. 1094 × 9 .. .. 6·50
b. Six bars only at top
1093 25 c. on 220 c. on 1 c. Pitcher Plant of Mt Roraima (surch "WHO 1983 25") (R.) .. 30 30
b. Six bars only at top
1094 25 c. on 220 c. on 1 c. Pitcher Plant of Mt Roraima (surch "17 MAY '83 ITU/WHO 25") (R.) 30 30
b. Six bars only at top
1095 $4.50 on 75 c. on $5 *Odontadenia grandiflora* (surch "ITU/WHO 17 MAY 1983") (B.) .. .. 13·00 1·50
a. Surch on 235 c. on 75 c. on $5 (No. 929).. 1·50 1·25
1092/5 .. .. .. *Set of 4* 13·00 2·25

1983 (18 May). *30th Anniv of President's Entry into Parliament. Nos. 690 and 692 surch as T 259, the former additionally optd with T 256.*
1096 $1 on 15 c. black, light violet-blue and bluish grey .. .. .. 6·00 50
1097 $1 on 40 c. black, red-orange and bluish grey 9·00 50
No. MS693 was also reissued with examples of Nos. 1096/7 affixed over the 8 c. and 35 c. values, and an example of No. 1050 added to the righthand sheet margin. These miniature sheets, revalued to $6, numbered on the reverse and cancelled with First Day of Issue postmarks, were for presentation purposes and were not available for postage.

1983 (23 May). *Surch as T 254, but with "c" after new face value.*
1098 105 15 c. on 6 c. black, gold and flesh (No. 469) (Blk.) 10 10
1099 – 50 c. on 6 c. multicoloured (No. 489) (Blk.) 30 30

1983 (23 May). *No. 546 surch as T 228, but with "c" after new face value.*
1100 20 c. on 6 c. Cannon-ball tree 15 10

1983 (23 May). *No. 611 optd with T 256.*
1101 25 c. Guides in camp .. .. .. 48·00 4·00

(266) $1

CANADA 1983 **(267)**

120 **$1.30**

XXX **(268)**

1983 (23 May). *No. 489 surch with T 266 in red.*
1102 $1 on 6 c. Black Acara ("Patua") .. 1·25 35

1983 (15 June). *15th World Scout Jamboree, Alberta. Nos. 835/6 and O25 additionally surch or optd as T 267.*
1103 – $1.30 on 100 c. on 8 c. multicoloured .. 2·50 1·25
1104 116 180 c. on 6 c. multicoloured .. 2·50 2·00
1105 $3.90 on 400 c. on 6 c. multicoloured .. 2·75 4·00
1103/5 .. .. .. *Set of 3* 7·00 6·50

1983 (22 June). *Nos. 659/60 surch as T 254.*
1106	60 c. on 15 c. Map of the Caribbean			9·00	40
1107	$1.50 on 15 c. Prudential Cup			10·00	1·25

1983 (1 July). *As Nos. 1049/50, but without commemorative inscr above flag. W 106 (sideways). P 14.*
1108	25 c. As Type 258			15	15
	a. Horiz pair. Nos. 1108/9			30	30
1109	25 c. As No. 1050			15	15

Nos. 1108/9 were printed together, *se-tenant* in horizontal pairs throughout the sheet.

1983 (1 July). *Optd with T 256.*
1110	105	30 c. black, gold and light apple-green (No. 471)		75	20
1111	–	30 c. multicoloured (No. 695)		9·50	30
1112	–	30 c. multicoloured (No. 718) (opt vert)		4·50	20
1113	–	30 c. multicoloured (No. 722)		8·00	20
1114	–	30 c. multicoloured (No. 746)		14·00	20
1115	–	60 c. multicoloured (No. 697)		4·50	20
1116	–	60 c. multicoloured (No. 731)		5·50	20
1110/16			*Set of 7*	42·00	1·25

1983 (1 July). *No. 553 optd with T 226 in blue.*
1117	60 c. Soldier's Cap			4·00	35

1983 (1 July). *Surch as T 264 in blue.*
1118	157	120 c. on 8 c. multicoloured (No. 654)		2·75	40
1119	159	120 c. on 10 c. dull red, black and gold (No. 666)		3·00	40
1120	–	120 c. on 35 c. multicoloured (No. 622)		3·00	40
		a. Surch reading upwards			
1121	–	120 c. on 35 c. orange, light green and reddish violet (No. 640)		3·00	40

1983 (1 July). *Nos. 716 and 729 surch as T 268.*
1122	120 c. on 10 c. Type 173 (R.)			2·75	40
1123	120 c. on 375 c. on $3 Cylinder satellite			5·50	40

No. 1123 also carries an otherwise unissued surcharge in red, reading "INTERNATIONAL SCIENCE YEAR 1982 375". As issued much of this is obliterated by two heavy bars.

CARICOM DAY 1983

(269)   (270)

1983 (1 July). *British Guiana No. D1a and Guyana No. D8 surch with T 269 in blue.*
1124	D 1	120 c. on 1 c. deep green		2·00	45
1125	D 2	120 c. on 1 c. olive		2·00	45

1983 (1 July). *CARICOM Day. No. 823 additionally surch with T 270 in red.*
1126	60 c. on $3 "Makanaima the Great Ancestral Spirit of the Amerindians"			1·25	35

271 *Kurupukari*

(Litho Format)

1983 (11 July*). *Riverboats. T 271 and similar horiz designs. W 106. P 14.*
1127	30 c. black and vermilion			20	20
	a. *Tête-bêche* (vert pair)			75	
	w. Wmk inverted			55	35
1128	60 c. black and bright reddish violet			25	35
	a. *Tête-bêche* (vert pair)			1·00	
	w. Wmk inverted			65	60
1129	120 c. black and bright lemon			30	60
	a. *Tête-bêche* (vert pair)			1·40	
	w. Wmk inverted			90	95
1130	130 c. black			30	65
	a. *Tête-bêche* (vert pair)			1·40	
	w. Wmk inverted			90	95
1131	150 c. black and bright emerald			30	80
	a. *Tête-bêche* (vert pair)			1·40	
	w. Wmk inverted			95	1·00
1127/31			*Set of 5*	1·25	2·40

Designs:—60 c. Makouria; 120 c. Powis; 130 c. Pomeroon; 150 c. Lukanani.

*Although not finally issued until 11 July First Day Covers of Nos. 1127/31 are postmarked with the intended release date of 1 July.

Nos. 1127/31 were each issued in sheets of 80 (10 × 8) with the bottom three rows inverted forming *tête-bêche* vertical pairs from Rows 5 and 6.

2.30

(272)

1983 (22 July). *Unissued Royal Wedding surcharge, similar to No. 843, surch as T 272 in blue by Autoprint.*
1132	$2.30 on $1.10 on $2 *Norantea guianensis*			60	40
1133	$3.20 on $1.10 on $2 *Norantea guianensis*			60	40

BW   Mont Golfier
(273)   1783-1983
             (274)

1983 (5 Sept). *Bicentenary of Manned Flight and 20th Anniv of Guyana Airways. Nos. 701/2a optd as T 273/4, in red (Nos. 1134/47) or blue (Nos. 1148/68) by Autoprint.*
1134	20 c. multicoloured (optd T 273)			40	35
	a. Sheetlet of 25. Nos. 1134/8 each × 4 and 1139 × 5			9·00	
1135	20 c. multicoloured (optd "LM")			40	35
1136	20 c. multicoloured (optd "GY 1963 1983")			40	35
1137	20 c. multicoloured (optd "JW")			40	35
1138	20 c. multicoloured (optd "CU")			40	35
1139	20 c. multicoloured (optd T 274)			40	35
1140	70 c. multicoloured (optd "BGI")			70	25
	a. Sheetlet of 25. Nos. 1140 × 2, 1141 × 8, 1142/44 each × 2, 1145 × 5 and 1146/7 each × 2			9·50	
1141	25 c. multicoloured (optd "GEO")			25	10
1142	25 c. multicoloured (optd "MIA")			70	25
1143	25 c. multicoloured (optd "BVB")			70	25
1144	25 c. multicoloured (optd "PBM")			70	25
1145	25 c. multicoloured (optd T 274)			30	15
1146	25 c. multicoloured (optd "POS")			70	25
1147	25 c. multicoloured (optd "JFK")			70	25
1148	50 c. multicoloured (optd "AHL")			50	30
	a. Sheetlet of 25. Nos. 1148/54, 1155 × 5 and 1156/68			10·00	
1149	30 c. multicoloured (optd "BCG")			50	30
1150	30 c. multicoloured (optd "BMJ")			50	30
1151	30 c. multicoloured (optd "EKE")			50	30
1152	30 c. multicoloured (optd "GEO")			50	30
1153	30 c. multicoloured (optd "GFO")			50	30
1154	30 c. multicoloured (optd "IBM")			50	30
1155	30 c. multicoloured (optd T 274)			25	15
1156	30 c. multicoloured (optd "KAI")			50	30
1157	30 c. multicoloured (optd "KAR")			50	30
1158	30 c. multicoloured (optd "KPG")			50	30
1159	30 c. multicoloured (optd "KRG")			50	30
1160	30 c. multicoloured (optd "KTO")			50	30
1161	30 c. multicoloured (optd "LTM")			50	30
1162	30 c. multicoloured (optd "MHA")			50	30
1163	30 c. multicoloured (optd "MWJ")			50	30
1164	30 c. multicoloured (optd "MYM")			50	30
1165	30 c. multicoloured (optd "NAI")			50	30
1166	30 c. multicoloured (optd "ORJ")			50	30
1167	30 c. multicoloured (optd "USI")			50	30
1168	30 c. multicoloured (optd "VEG")			50	30
1134/68			*Set of 35*	15·00	8·00

The overprints on the 20 c. value represent airlines, on the 25 c. international airports and on the 30 c. internal airports. Those on Nos. 1150 and 1154 were incorrect and examples of the former exist with the manuscript correction "PMT".

240   240
(275)   (275a)

1983 (14 Sept). *No. 649 surch with T 275 in blue by Autoprint.*
1169	240 c. on 35 c. on 60 c. Soldier's Cap			1·25	1·00
	a. Surch with T 275a			1·25	1·00
	b. Pair. Nos. 1169/a			2·50	

Types 275 and 275a occur *se-tenant* within the sheet.

FAO 1983

30

(276)

277 G.B. 1857 1d. with
Georgetown "AO3" Postmark

1983 (15 Sept). *F.A.O. Fisheries Project. Nos. 485 and 487 surch as T 276 in red by Autoprint.*
1170	30 c. on 1 c. Type 87			15	15
1171	$2.60 on 3 c. Peacock Cichlid ("Lukunani")			1·50	2·25

(Des K. Everett. Litho Format)

1983 (1 Oct). *125th Anniv of Use of Great Britain Stamps in Guyana. T 277 and similar square designs. P 14½.*

(a) Inscriptions in black. W 106
1172	277	25 c. lake-brown and black		15	10
		a. *Tête-bêche* (pair)		75	
		w. Wmk inverted		60	
1173	–	30 c. rose-red and black		15	15
		a. *Tête-bêche* (pair)		75	
		w. Wmk inverted		60	
1174	–	60 c. bright violet and black		25	30
		a. *Tête-bêche* (pair)		1·50	
		w. Wmk inverted		1·10	
1175	–	120 c. dull green and black		50	55
		a. *Tête-bêche* (pair)		2·75	
		w. Wmk inverted		2·25	

(b) Inscriptions in bright blue. W 106 (inverted)
1176	277	25 c. lake-brown and black		15	10
		a. Block of 4. Nos. 1176/9		55	
1177	–	25 c. rose-red and black		15	10
1178	–	25 c. bright violet and black		15	10
1179	–	25 c. dull green and black		15	10
1180	277	30 c. lake-brown and black		15	15
		a. Block of 4. Nos. 1180/3		55	
1181	–	30 c. rose-red and black		15	15
1182	–	30 c. bright violet and black		15	15
1183	–	30 c. dull green and black		15	15
1184	277	45 c. lake-brown and black		30	25
		a. Block of 4. Nos. 1184/7		1·10	
1185	–	45 c. rose-red and black		30	25

1186	–	45 c. bright violet and black		30	25
1187	–	45 c. dull green and black		30	25
1188	277	120 c. lake-brown and black		30	55
		a. Block of 4. Nos. 1188/91		1·10	
1189	–	130 c. rose-red and black		30	60
1190	–	150 c. bright violet and black		30	70
1191	–	200 c. dull green and black		30	95
1172/91			*Set of 20*	3·75	5·00

Designs:—Nos. 1173, 1177, 1181, 1185, 1189, G.B. 1857 4d. rose; Nos. 1174, 1178, 1182, 1186, 1190, G.B. 1856 6d. lilac; Nos. 1175, 1179, 1183, 1187, 1191, G.B. 1856 1s. green.

Each design incorporates the "AO3" postmark except Nos. 1189/91 which show mythical postmarks of the Crowned-circle type inscribed "DEMERARA", "BERBICE" or "ESSEQUIBO".

Nos. 1172/5 were each printed in sheets with the bottom row inverted, forming vertical *tête-bêche* pairs. Nos. 1176/87 were issued in sheets of 60, one for each value, with the four designs *se-tenant*. Nos. 1188/91 were issued in sheets of 20, containing five *se-tenant* blocks.

75

INT.
COMMUNICATIONS
YEAR   50

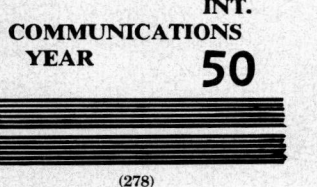

(278)   (279)

1983 (15 Oct). *International Communications Year. No. 716 surch with T 278 by Autoprint.*
1192	50 c. on 375 c. on $3 Cylinder satellite			4·50	30

No. 1192 also carries an otherwise unissued "375" surcharge. As issued much of this surcharge is obliterated by two groups of six thin horizontal lines.

1983 (15 Oct). *St. John Ambulance Commemoration. Nos. 650 and 653 surch as T 279, vertically on No. 1194 by Autoprint.*
1193	156	75 c. on 8 c. silver, black and magenta		4·50	50
1194	–	$1.20 on 40 c. silver, black and new blue		6·50	75

$1.20

Int. Food Day   1918-1983
1983

I.L.O.
(280)   (281)

1983 (15 Oct). *International Food Day. No. 616 surch with T 280 by Autoprint.*
1195	$1.20 on 35 c. Five-fingers and awaras			1·00	50

1983 (15 Oct). *65th Anniv of I.L.O. and 25th Death Anniv. of H. N. Critchlow (founder of Guyana Labour Union). No. 840 further optd with T 281 by Autoprint.*
1196	240 c. on $3 H. N. Critchlow			1·50	1·50

25c.   Human Rights Day
(282)   (283)

1983 (1 Nov). *Deepavali Festival. Nos. 661 and 663/4 surch as T 282 by Autoprint.*
1197	25 c. on 8 c. Type 158			20	10
1198	$1.50 on 35 c. Flame in bowl			1·25	60
1199	$1.50 on 40 c. Goddess Latchmi			80	60
1197/9			*Set of 3*	2·00	1·25

On Nos. 1198/9 the original face values are obliterated by "XX" and the surcharges are horizontal.

1983 (3 Nov). *No. 732 optd with T 226 and No. 798 further optd with T 256, both vertically reading upwards by Autoprint.*
1200	$3 "Makanaima the Great Ancestral Spirit of the Amerindians" (B.)			1·25	70
	a. Opt reading downwards			15·00	
1201	360 c. on $2 *Norantea guianensis*			1·25	80

1983 (15 Nov). *Wildlife Protection. Nos. 686 and 688 surch as T 234, and No. 852 optd with T 256 by Autoprint.*
1202	30 c. Six-banded Armadillo			50	15
1203	60 c. on 15 c. Giant sea turtle			75	30
1204	$1.20 on 40 c. Iguana			1·25	50
1202/4			*Set of 3*	2·25	85

1983 (1 Dec). *Human Rights Day. No. 1079c optd with T 283 by Autoprint.*
1205	$3 Rotary anniversary emblem			2·00	1·25

LOS ANGELES
1984

125 ●●●
(284)

●●● 55
(284a)

1983 (6 Dec). *Olympic Games, Los Angeles (1984) (1st issue). Nos. 733/44 surch with T 284 by Herald Printing-Kitty or further surch with T 284a by Autoprint.*

1206	55 c. on 125 c. on 35 c. Type 174		25	25
	a. Block of 12. Nos. 1206/17		3·50	
1207	55 c. on 125 c. on 35 c. Trahira ("Haimara")		25	25
1208	55 c. on 125 c. on 35 c. Electric Eel		25	25
1209	55 c. on 125 c. on 35 c. Golden Rivulus		25	25
1210	55 c. on 125 c. on 35 c. Golden Pencilfish		25	25
1211	55 c. on 125 c. on 35 c. Four-eyed Fish		25	25
1212	55 c. on 125 c. on 35 c. Red Piranha ("Pirai")		25	25
1213	55 c. on 125 c. on 35 c. Smoking Hassar		25	25
1214	55 c. on 125 c. on 35 c. Manta		25	25
1215	55 c. on 125 c. on 35 c. Festive Cichlid ("Flying Patwa")		25	25
1216	55 c. on 125 c. on 35 c. Arapaima		25	25
1217	55 c. on 125 c. on 35 c. Peacock Cichlid ("Lukanani")		25	25
1217a	125 c. on 35 c. Type 174		6·00	
	ab. Block of 12. Nos. 1217a/l		65·00	
1217b	125 c. on 35 c. Trahira ("Haimara")		6·00	
1217c	125 c. on 35 c. Electric Eel		6·00	
1217d	125 c. on 35 c. Golden Rivulus		6·00	
1217e	125 c. on 35 c. Golden Pencilfish		6·00	
1217f	125 c. on 35 c. Four-eyed Fish		6·00	
1217g	125 c. on 35 c. Red Piranha ("Pirai")		6·00	
1217h	125 c. on 35 c. Smoking Hassar		6·00	
1217i	125 c. on 35 c. Manta		6·00	
1217j	125 c. on 35 c. Festive Cichlid ("Flying Patwa")		6·00	
1217k	125 c. on 35 c. Arapaima		6·00	
1217l	125 c. on 35 c. Peacock Cichlid ("Lukanani")		6·00	

See also Nos. 1308/17 and 1420.

1983 (14 Dec). *No. F7 with unissued "ESPANA 1982" surch, as Nos. 938/9 in blue, further optd with T 256 vertically by Autoprint.*

|1218|180 c. on 60 c. Soldier's Cap| |3·00|65|
| |a. Opt (T 256) omitted| |15·00| |

COMMONWEALTH HEADS OF GOV'T MEETING—INDIA 1983

150
(285)

CHRISTMAS
1983
20c
(286)

1983 (14 Dec). *Commonwealth Heads of Government Meeting, New Delhi. No. 542 surch with T 285 by Autoprint.*

|1219|150 c. on 1 c. Pitcher Plant of Mt Roraima| |3·00|60|

1983 (14 Dec). *Christmas. No. 861 further surch with T 286 by Autoprint.*

|1220|20 c. on 12 c. on 6 c. Black Acara ("Patua")|2·00|10|
| |a. On No. 861b (Wmk 106)|2·00|10|

1984 (8 Jan). *Nos. 838 and F9 optd as T 229, but smaller 24×6 mm, vertically in blue by Autoprint.*

1221	$2 Norantea guianensis		3·50	70
	a. Opt inverted		6·50	
1221b	550 c. on $10 Elbella patrobas		13·00	7·50

17¢
(287)

1984 (Jan). *Flowers. Unissued coil stamps as T 222 handstamped with T 287 in blue.*

1222	17 c. on 2 c. grey-lilac, blue & turquoise-green	1·50	1·25
	a. Vert pair. Nos. 1222/3	3·00	2·50
1223	17 c. on 8 c. grey-lilac, blue and mauve	1·50	1·25

Nos. 1222/3 were intended for use on 8 c. postal stationery envelopes to uprate them to the new price of 25 c.

STANLEY GIBBONS
STAMP COLLECTING SERIES

Introductory booklets on *How to Start, How to Identify Stamps* and *Collecting by Theme.* A series of well illustrated guides at a low price.
Write for details.

ALL
OUR HERITAGE

1984

● 25   ● 25
(288)   (289)

1984

● 25   ● 25
(290)   (291)

1984 (24 Feb). *Republic Day. No. 703 surch as T 288/91 in black and No. 705a optd as T 288/9 in blue by Autoprint.*

1224	25 c. on 35 c. multicoloured (surch T 288)	35	20
	a. Sheetlet of 25. No. 1224 × 6, Nos. 1225/7 each × 4, Nos. 1228/30 each × 2 and No. 1231	25·00	
1225	25 c. on 35 c. multicoloured (surch T 289)	50	30
1226	25 c. on 35 c. multi (surch "REPUBLIC DAY")	50	30
1227	25 c. on 35 c. multicoloured (surch T 290)	50	30
1228	25 c. on 35 c. multi (surch "BERBICE")	2·00	2·00
1229	25 c. on 35 c. multi (surch "DEMERARA")	2·00	2·00
1230	25 c. on 35 c. multi (surch "ESSEQUIBO")	2·00	2·00
1231	25 c. on 35 c. multicoloured (surch T 291)	8·00	8·50
1232	60 c. multicoloured (opt T 288)	70	40
	a. Sheetlet of 25. Nos. 1232/3 each × 8 and No. 1234 × 9	16·00	
1233	60 c. multicoloured (opt "REPUBLIC DAY")	70	40
1234	60 c. multicoloured (opt T 289)	70	40
1224/34		Set of 11	16·00	15·00

25¢ POSTAGE (+ 2.25) (SURTAX)
OLYMPIC GAMES 84
○ ○ ○ ○ ○
(292)

1984 (1 Mar). *Guyana Olympic Committee Appeal. Nos. 841/3 handstamped with T 292 in blue.*

1235	25 c. + $2.25 on 60 c. on 3 c. Hanging Heliconia	2·00	4·50
1236	25 c. + $2.25 on 75 c. on $5 Odontadenia grandiflora	2·00	4·50
1237	25 c. + $2.25 on £1.10 on $2 Norantea guianensis	2·00	4·50
1235/7		Set of 3	5·50	12·00

Nos. 1235/7 come from stamp booklets, the $2.25 charity premium on each stamp being donated to the local Olympic Committee Appeal Fund. All examples of these handstamps are inverted.

PRINTERS. Nos. 1238/97 and 1302/27 were overprinted or surcharged by Autoprint, Georgetown.

(XXXX)
90
Protecting Our Heritage
(293)   (294)

1984 (5 Mar). *Nature Protection. Various stamps optd with T 293 in black (except for No. 1239 in blue) with some additionally surch as T 272 (Nos. 1238/40, 1250/1 and 1254/5) or as T 294 (Nos. 1242, 1247 and 1252/3) all in blue.*

1238	20 c. on 15 c. multicoloured (No. 491) (opt + surch vert)	8·50	10
	a. Opt T 293 in blue	17·00	50
1239	20 c. on 15 c. multicoloured (No. 791) (opt + surch vert)	8·50	10
	a. Surch on No. 791a (pair)		
1240	20 c. on 15 c. multicoloured (No. 1044) (opt + surch vert)	42·00	1·75
	a. Opt T 293 in blue	17·00	1·25
1241	25 c. multicoloured (No. 550a)	13·00	10
	a. On No. 550ab	45·00	3·50
1242	30 c. on 15 c. multicoloured (No. 548)	20·00	30
1243	40 c. multicoloured (No. 494) (opt vert)	12·00	20
1244	50 c. multicoloured (No. 552)	1·50	25
1245	50 c. multicoloured (No. F6)	1·50	25
	a. Opt Type F 1 double	26·00	
1246	60 c. multicoloured (No. 459)	9·50	30
	a. On No. 496	55·00	4·00
1247	90 c. on 40 c. multicoloured (No. 551)	16·00	50
	a. On No. F5	£110	7·50
1248	180 c. on 40 c. multicoloured (No. 919)	16·00	90
1249	$2 multicoloured (No. 461)	50·00	1·50
1250	225 c. on 10 c. multicoloured (No. 490a) (opt + surch vert)	23·00	1·00
1251	260 c. on $1 multicoloured (No. 497a)	11·00	1·00
1252	320 c. on 40 c. multicoloured (No. 551)	12·00	2·25
1253	350 c. on 40 c. multicoloured (No. 551)	20·00	2·50
1254	390 c. on 50 c. multicoloured (No. 495)	6·00	2·50
	a. On No. 458	80·00	20·00
1255	450 c. on $5 multicoloured (No. 499)	7·00	2·50
1238/55		Set of 18	£225	15·00

ITU DAY 1984
25
(296)

1984
(295)

1984 (17 Mar). *Easter. Nos. 483 and 916/17 optd with T 295, and No. 481 surch as T 272, but without decimal point, all in blue.*

|1256|111|30 c. multicoloured| |20|20|
|1257| |45 c. on 6 c. multicoloured| |25|25|
|1258| |75 c. on 40 c. multicoloured| |35|35|
|1259| |130 c. on 6 c. multicoloured| |65|60|
|1256/9| | |Set of 4|1·40|1·25|

No. 1258 exists with the previous surcharge either at the right or in the centre of the design.

1984 (2 Apr). *Nos. 937/9 and 991 surch as T 294.*

1260	75 c. on $1 Chelonanthus uliginoides	9·50	35
1261	75 c. on 110 c. on 3 c. Hanging Heliconia	9·50	35
1262	225 c. on 250 c. on 6 c. Cannon-ball tree	3·00	1·25
1263	230 c. on $2.35 on 180 c. on 60 c. Soldier's Cap	3·00	1·00

1984 (2 May). *Nos. 899/901, 904/6 and 909 surch as T 294.*

1264	20 c. on 15 c. on 2 c. Type 132 (No. 899)	1·50	30
1265	75 c. on 110 c. on 5 c. Annatto tree (No. 904)	9·00	70
1266	90 c. on 110 c. on 5 c. Annatto tree (No. 900) (B.)	5·50	85
1267	90 c. on 110 c. on 5 c. Annatto tree (No. 901) (B.)	7·00	85
1268	120 c. on 125 c. on 8 c. on 6 c. Cannon-ball tree (No. 905)	7·00	1·00
1269	120 c. on 125 c. on 8 c. on 6 c. Cannon-ball tree (No. 906)	7·00	1·00
1270	120 c. on 125 c. on 8 c. on 6 c. Cannon-ball tree (No. 909)	2·75	1·00
1264/70		Set of 7	35·00	5·25

Nos. 1264/70 were surcharged on the sheets which contained one type of the previous surcharge only.

1984 (17 May). *World Telecommunications and Health Day. Nos. 802 and 980 surch as T 296 in blue.*

1271	25 c. on 220 c. on 1 c. Pitcher Plant of Mt Roraima (surch T 296)	20	20
	a. Sheetlet of 25. Nos. 1271/2 each × 8 and No. 1273 × 9	4·50	
1272	25 c. on 220 c. on 1 c. Pitcher Plant of Mt Roraima (surch "WHO DAY 1984")	20	20
1273	25 c. on 220 c. on 1 c. Pitcher Plant of Mt Roraima (surch "ITU/WHO DAY 1984")	20	20
1274	$4.50 on 280 c. on $5 Odontadenia grandiflora (surch "ITU/WHO DAY 1984")	1·75	1·25
1271/4		Set of 4	2·10	1·75

The surcharge is horizontal on No. 1274 and vartical on the others.

1984 (11 June). *No. 1005 surch vertically as T 272, but without decimal point.*

|1275|120 c. on $1.25 on 6 c. Cannon-ball tree| |7·00|55|

1984 (15 June). *World Forestry Conference. Nos. 752/5 surch as T 272, but without decimal point, or optd with T 295 ($3), and No. 875 surch as T 294.*

1276	55 c. on 30 c. Hymenaea courbaril	2·75	30
1277	75 c. on 110 c. on $3 Peltogyne venosa (B.)	40	35
1278	160 c. on 50 c. Mora excelsa (B.)	75	70
1279	260 c. on 10 c. Type 177 (B.)	1·25	1·25
1280	$3 Peltogyne venosa (B.)	1·40	1·40
1276/80		Set of 5	6·00	3·00

1984 (18 June). *No. 625 surch vertically as T 294.*

|1281|55 c. on 110 c. on 10 c. Type 150 (B.)|1·00|30|
|1282|90 c. on 110 c. on 10 c. Type 150 (B.)|1·25|45|

Nos. 1281/2 also carry an otherwise unissued 110 c. surcharge in blue as Type 264.

UPU Congress 1984 Hamburg
60
(297)   (298)

1984 (19 June). *U.P.U. Congress, Hamburg. Nos. 1188/91 optd with T 297.*

1283	120 c. lake-brown and black	50	60
	a. Block of 4. Nos. 1283/6	2·25	
1284	130 c. rose-red and black	55	70
1285	150 c. bright violet and black	60	75
1286	200 c. dull green and black	80	90
1283/6		Set of 4	2·25	2·75

1984 (21 June). *Nos. 982/3 and 986/7 surch with T 298 (60 c.) or as T 272, but without the decimal point (others).*

1287	45 c. on 50 c. on 2 c. myrtle-green	60	25
1288	60 c. on $1.10 on 3 c. brown-olive and red-brown (B.)	2·25	40
	a. Surch on No. 983c	2·50	40
1289	120 c. on $1.25 on 6 c. yellow-green	75	55
1290	200 c. on $2.20 on 24 c. black and brownish orange (B.)	6·00	1·10

1984 (30 June). *Nos. 979/80 and 1003 surch as T 294, and No. 981 optd vertically with T 295.*

1291	75 c. on 110 c. on 5 c. Annatto tree	60	35
1292	120 c. on 170 c. on 110 c. on 5 c. Annatto tree	80	55
1293	200 c. on 220 c. on 1 c. Pitcher Plant of Mt Roraima (B.)	12·00	85
1294	330 c. on $2 Norantea guianensis (B.)	1·75	1·75

CARICOM DAY 1984

60 **XX**

(299)

1984 (30 June). *CARICOM Day. No. 1200 additionally surch with T* **299**.
1295   60 c. on $3 "Makanaima the Great Ancestral
          Spirit of the Amerindians" 40   30

1984 (30 June). *No. 544 surch as T* **275** *in blue.*
1296   150 c. on 3 c. Hanging Heliconia .. .. 1·25   65

60

**CARICOM
HEADS OF GOV'T
CONFERENCE
JULY 1984**

X

(300)

301 Children and Thatched School

1984 (2 July). *CARICOM Heads of Government Conference.
No.* 544 *surch with T* **300** *in blue.*
1297   60 c. on 3 c. Hanging Heliconia 40   30

(Litho Format)

1984 (16 July). *Centenary of Guyana Teachers' Association. T* **301**
and similar horiz designs. Multicoloured. W **106** *(sideways).
P* 14.
1298   25 c. Type **301** 10   15
       a. Block of 4. Nos. 1298/301 .. 35
1299   25 c. Torch and graduates 10   15
1300   25 c. Torch and target emblem .. 10   15
1301   25 c. Teachers of 1884 and 1984 in front of
          school 10   15
1298/301 .. .. .. *Set of* 4 35   55
Nos. 1298/301 were printed together, *se-tenant*, in blocks of 4
throughout the sheet.

**INT.
CHESS
FED.
1924-1984**

25

**TRACK
AND
FIELD**

25 XX

(302)   (303)

1984 (20 July). *60th Anniv of International Chess Federation.
No.* 1048 *optd or surch as T* **302** *or optd with T* **295**, *all in blue.*
1302   25 c. on 90 c. on 60 c. Fort Island (surch T **302**) 1·25   25
       a. Sheetlet of 25. No. 1302 × 16 and No.
          1303 × 9 .. .. 35·00
1303   25 c. on 90 c. on 60 c. Fort Island (opt T **295**)   2·25   45
1304   75 c. on 90 c. on 60 c. Fort Island (surch T **302**) 1·25   40
       a. Sheetlet of 25. No. 1304 × 16 and No.
          1305 × 9 .. .. 35·00
1305   75 c. on 90 c. on 60 c. Fort Island (opt T **295**) .. 2·25   70
1306   90 c. on 60 c. Fort Island (opt T **302**) .. 1·25   50
       a. Sheetlet of 25. No. 1306 × 16 and No.
          1307 × 9 .. .. 35·00
1307   90 c. on 60 c. Fort Island (opt T **295**) .. 2·25   90
1302/7 .. .. .. *Set of* 6 9·50 2·75
Overprints as Type **295** occur in the central horizontal and
vertical rows of each sheet.

1984 (28 July). *Olympic Games, Los Angeles* (2nd issue). *No.*
1051 *surch as T* **303** *in blue.*
1308   25 c. on $1.30, multicoloured (surch T **303**) .. 20   25
       a. Booklet pane of 10. No. 1308 × 4 and Nos.
          1309/10, each × 3 .. 2·50
       b. Coil strip of 5. Nos. 1308 × 2, 1311 × 2
          and 1312 .. 4·25
1309   25 c. on $1.30, mult (surch "BOXING") .. 20   30
1310   25 c. on $1.30, mult (surch "OLYMPIC
          GAMES 1984 LOS ANGELES") .. 20   30
1311   25 c. on $1.30, mult (surch "CYCLING") .. 1·00   50
1312   25 c. on $1.30, mult (surch "OLYMPIC
          GAMES 1984") .. .. 3·00 1·25
1313 $1.20 on $1.30, multicoloured (surch T **303**) 1·00 1·10
       a. Booklet pane of 10. No. 1313 × 4 and Nos.
          1314/15 each × 3 .. 10·00
       b. Coil strip of 5. Nos. 1313 × 2, 1316 × 2
          and 1317 .. 7·00
1314 $1.20 on $1.30, mult (surch "BOXING") .. 1·00 1·10
1315 $1.20 on $1.30, mult (surch "OLYMPIC
          GAMES 1984 LOS ANGELES") .. 1·00 1·25
1316 $1.20 on $1.30, mult (surch "CYCLING") .. 1·75 1·50
1317 $1.20 on $1.30, multicoloured (surch
          "OLYMPIC GAMES 1984") .. 3·50 3·00
1308/17 .. .. .. *Set of* 10 11·50 9·50
Nos. 1308 and 1313 come from booklets and coils, Nos. 1309/10
and 1314/15 from booklets only, and Nos. 1311/12 and 1316/17 from
coils only.
The coils were constructed from normal sheets with coil joins on
every fifth stamp.

**GIRL
GUIDES
1924-1984**

(304)

1984 (15 Aug). *60th Anniv of Girl Guide Movement in Guyana.
Nos.* 900/9 *surch with T* **304** *in blue.*
1318   25 c. on 110 c. on 5 c. Annatto tree (No. 900) 20   20
       a. Sheetlet of 25. Nos. 1318/19, each × 8,
          Nos. 1320/1, each × 4 and No. 1322 10·50
1319   25 c. on 110 c. on 5 c. Annatto tree (No. 901) .. 20   20
1320   25 c. on 110 c. on 5 c. Annatto tree (No. 902) .. 70   60
1321   25 c. on 110 c. on 5 c. Annatto tree (No. 903) .. 70   60
1322   25 c. on 110 c. on 5 c. Annatto tree (No. 904) .. 5·50 6·00
1323   25 c. on 125 c. on 8 c. on 6 c. Cannon-ball tree
          (No. 905) 20   20
       a. Sheetlet of 25. Nos. 1323/4, each × 8, Nos.
          1325/6, each × 4 and No. 1327 .. 10·50
1324   25 c. on 125 c. on 8 c. on 6 c. Cannon-ball tree
          (No. 906) 20   20
1325   25 c. on 125 c. on 8 c. on 6 c. Cannon-ball tree
          (No. 907) 70   60
1326   25 c. on 125 c. on 8 c. on 6 c. Cannon-ball tree
          (No. 908) 70   60
1327   25 c. on 125 c. on 8 c. on 6 c. Cannon-ball tree
          (No. 909) .. .. 5·50 6·00
1318/27 .. .. .. *Set of* 10 13·00 13·50

— 25 130 1984

(305)   (306)   (307)

1984

(308)

1984

(309)

1984 (Sept–Nov). *Various stamps surch or optd.*

(a) As T **294** *or as T* **298** (60 c.)
1328   20 c. on 15 c. on 2 c. Type **132** (No. 1030) .. 30   10
1329   20 c. on 15 c. on 2 c. Type **132** (No. 1034) .. 65   10
1330   20 c. on 15 c. on 2 c. Type **132** (No. 1063) .. 2·00   10
1331   60 c. on 110 c. on 8 c. on 3 c. Hanging Heli-
          conia (as No. 868, but without T **219**)
          (two vert obliterating panels) .. 29·00 4·50
       a. One vert obliterating panel* .. 90·00
1332   120 c. on 125 c. on 8 c. on 6 c. Cannon-ball tree
          (No. 893) .. .. 5·00   50
1333   120 c. on 125 c. on $2 *Norantea guianensis*
          (No. 834) .. .. 40·00 5·50
1334   120 c. on 125 c. on $2 *Norantea guianensis*
          (No. O20) .. .. 2·75   50
1335   120 c. on 140 c. on $1 *Chelonanthus uligino-
          ides* (No. 796) .. .. 5·50   50
1336   200 c. on 220 c. on 1 c. Pitcher Plant of Mt
          Roraima (No. 922) (B.) .. 10·00   75
1337   320 c. on $1.10 on $2 *Norantea guianensis*
          (No. 804) (B.) .. .. 1·25   75
1338   350 c. on 375 c. on $5 *Odontadenia grandiflora*
          (No. 803) (B.) .. .. 3·25   80
1339   300 c. on 400 c. on $5 *Odontadenia grandiflora*
          (No. 1091) (B.) .. .. 4·00   90
1340   450 c. on $5! *Odontadenia grandiflora* (No.
          O16) (B.) .. .. 7·00 2·75
*The small original printing of the 60 c. surcharge has the "8 c"
and "110" values obliterated by a single vertical block of six lines.
On the vast majority of the supply these features were covered by
two vertical blocks of six lines each.

(b) As T **305** *(figures surch, bar in ballpoint pen)*
1341   25 c. on 10 c. Cattleya (No. 547) .. 35·00 2·00
       a. Surch on No. 547a .. .. 55·00 3·25
1342   25 c. on 15 c. Christmas Orchid (No. 864a) .. 14·00   15
1342a 25 c. on 35 c. on 60 c. Soldier's Cap (No. 649) 90·00 4·50

(c) As T **306** *(on Nos.* 1343/8 *the original face value is obliterated
by a fleur-de-lys)*
1343   25 c. on 15 c. Christmas Orchid (No. 548) £120 5·00
1344   25 c. on 15 c. Christmas Orchid (No. 809) 60·00 3·00
1345   25 c. on 15 c. Christmas Orchid (No. 864) 26·00 2·25
1346   25 c. on 15 c. Christmas Orchid (No. 977) 13·00   10
       a. Surch on No. 977a .. .. £120 6·00
1347   25 c. on 15 c. Christmas Orchid (No. 1009) 13·00   10
1348   25 c. on 15 c. Christmas Orchid (No. O23) 13·00   10
1349   130 c. on 110 c. on $2 *Norantea guianensis*
          (No. 804) .. .. 70·00 4·00
1350   130 c. on 110 c. on $2 *Norantea guianensis*
          (No. O22) .. .. 1·75 1·25
1351   600 c. on $7.20 on $1 *Chelonanthus uligino-
          ides* (No. 770) .. .. 1·75   75
       a. With two fleur-de-lys over original
          opt .. .. 1·75   75
       b. Surch on No. 770d .. .. 1·75 1·50
       ba. With two fleur-de-lys over original
          opt 75   75

(d) With T **307** (Nov)
1352   20 c. *Paphinia cristata* (No. 549) .. 22·00   10
       a. Optd on No. 549a .. .. £120 5·00
1353 $3.60 on $5 *Odontadenia grandiflora*
          (No. 769) .. .. 1·10 1·10
       a. Optd on No. 769c .. .. 2·00 1·00

(e) With T **308** *vertically in blue* (Nov)
1354   50 c. on 8 c. Type **136** (No. 1062) .. 10·00   25
1355   60 c. on 1 c. Pitcher Plant of Mt Roraima (No.
          1000) 65   25
1356 $2 *Norantea guianensis* (No. O33) .. 1·50   60

(f) With T **309**
1357   20 c. *Paphinia cristata* (No. 549) .. 55·00 3·25
       a. Optd on No. 549a .. .. £120 6·00
1357b 20 c. *Paphinia cristata* (No. 887a) ("1984"
          omitted) .. .. 55·00 3·25
1358   25 c. Marabunta (No. 550) .. .. 85·00 4·50
1358a 25 c. Marabunta (No. 889) ("1984"
          omitted) .. .. 85·00 4·50
1358b 25 c. Marabunta (No. 889b) ("1984"
          omitted) .. .. 35·00 2·50
1359   25 c. Marabunta (No. F4) .. .. 4·25   50
       a. Optd on No. F4a .. .. 2·00   30
1360 $3.60 on $5 *Odontadenia grandiflora*
          (No. 769) .. .. 85 1·10
       a. Optd on No. 769c .. .. 85 1·40

ICAO

ICAO

(310)   (311)

1984 (6 Sept). *40th Anniv of International Civil Aviation
Organization. Nos.* 981 *(with previously unissued surcharge),*
1017 *and* 1148/68 *optd as T* **310** (30 c.) *or T* **311** (200 c.), *all in
blue by Autoprint.*
1361   30 c. multicoloured (No. 1148) .. 60   60
       a. Sheetlet of 25. Nos. 1361/71, 1372 × 2
          and 1373/84 .. 13·00
1362   30 c. multicoloured (No. 1149) .. 60   60
1363   30 c. multicoloured (No. 1150) .. 60   60
1364   30 c. multicoloured (No. 1151) .. 60   60
1365   30 c. multicoloured (No. 1152) .. 60   60
1366   30 c. multicoloured (No. 1153) .. 60   60
1367   30 c. mult (No. 1154) (optd "IMB/ICAO") .. 60   60
1368   30 c. mult (No. 1155) (optd "KCV/ICAO") .. 60   60
1369   30 c. mult (No. 1156) (optd "KAI/ICAO") .. 60   60
1370   30 c. multicoloured (No. 1157) .. 60   60
1371   30 c. multicoloured (No. 1158) .. 60   60
1372   30 c. mult (No. 1155) (optd "1984") .. 60   60
1373   30 c. mult (No. 1155) (optd "KPM/ICAO") .. 60   60
1374   30 c. multicoloured (No. 1159) .. 60   60
1375   30 c. multicoloured (No. 1160) .. 60   60
1376   30 c. multicoloured (No. 1161) .. 60   60
1377   30 c. mult (No. 1155) (optd "PMT/ICAO") .. 60   60
1378   30 c. multicoloured (No. 1162) .. 60   60
1379   30 c. multicoloured (No. 1163) .. 60   60
1380   30 c. multicoloured (No. 1164) .. 60   60
1381   30 c. multicoloured (No. 1165) .. 60   60
1382   30 c. multicoloured (No. 1166) .. 60   60
1383   30 c. multicoloured (No. 1167) .. 60   60
1384   30 c. multicoloured (No. 1168) .. 60   60
1385   200 c. on 330 c. on $2 mult (No. 981) .. 65   70
       a. Opt T **311** omitted .. 35·00
1386   200 c. on 75 c. on $5 mult (No. 1017) .. 2·25 1·75
1361/86 .. .. .. *Set of* 26 16·00 16·00
No. 1385 also carries an otherwise unissued surcharge
"G.A.C. Inaug. Flight Georgetown—Toronto 200" in black.

1984

$1.50

X

(312)   (313)   (314)

1984 (15 Sept). *Wildlife Protection. Nos.* 756/67 *optd with
T* **312** *by Autoprint.*
1387   30 c. Type **178** 30   25
       a. Sheetlet of 12. Nos. 1387/98 .. 3·25
1388   30 c. Red Howler 30   25
1389   30 c. Common Squirrel-Monkey .. 30   25
1390   30 c. Two-toed Sloth. 30   25
1391   30 c. Brazilian Tapir 30   25
1392   30 c. Collared Peccary 30   25
1393   30 c. Six-banded Armadillo. .. 30   25
1394   30 c. Tamandua ("Ant Eater") .. 30   25
1395   30 c. Giant Anteater 30   25
1396   30 c. Murine Opossum 30   25
1397   30 c. Brown Four-eyed Opossum .. 30   25
1398   30 c. Brazilian Agouti 30   25
1387/98 .. .. .. *Set of* 12 3·25 2·75

1984 (1 Oct). *Nos.* D6/7 *and* D10/11 *surch with T* **269** *in blue by
Autoprint.*
1399   D 2   120 c. on 4 c. dp ultramarine (No. D6) 3·25   45
1400   120 c. on 4 c. dull ultram (No. D10) 21·00 1·50
1401   120 c. on 12 c. reddish scarlet (No. D7) 3·25   45
1402   120 c. on 12 c. bright scarlet (No. D11) 3·25   45
1399/402 .. .. .. *Set of* 4 28·00 2·40

1984 (15 Oct). *175th Birth Anniv of Louis Braille (inventor of
alphabet for the blind). No.* 1040 *surch with T* **313** *in blue by
Autoprint.*
1403 $1.50 on 15 c. on 10 c. Type **215** .. 6·50   55

1984 (15 Oct). *International Food Day. No. 1012 surch with T* **314** *by Tip Torres.*
1404 150 c. on 50 c. Pawpaw and tangerine .. 1·75 55
Type **314** places a "1" alongside the original face value and obliterates the "1982" date on the previous overprint.

1984 (15 Oct). *Birth Centenary of H. N. Critchlow (founder of Guyana Labour Union). No. 873, surch horizontally as T* **236**, *and No. 1196, both optd with T* **312** *by Autoprint.*
1405 240 c. on 110 c. on $3 H. N. Critchlow (No.
 873) .. .. .. 1·00 65
1406 240 c. on $3 H. N. Critchlow (No. 1196) .. 6·50 70

1984 (22 Oct). *Nos. 910/12 surch as T* **272**, *but vertically and without the decimal point, and Nos. 1184/7 surch as T* **234** *by Autoprint.*
1407 **277** 25 c. on 45 c. lake-brown and black .. 15 15
 a. Block of 4. Nos. 1407/10 .. 55
1408 — 25 c. on 45 c. rose-red and black (No.
 1185) .. 15 15
1409 — 25 c. on 45 c. bright violet and black
 (No. 1186) .. 15 15
1410 — 25 c. on 45 c. dull green and black
 (No. 1187) .. 15 15
1411 — 120 c. on 100 c. on $3 multicoloured
 (No. 910) .. 9·50 45
1412 — 120 c. on 400 c. on 30 c. multicoloured
 (No. 911) .. 90 45
1413 — 320 c. on $5 mult (No. 912) (B.) .. 17·00 1·75
1407/13 .. .. .. *Set of* 7 25·00 3·00

25 X

MAHA SABHA
1934-1984

Philatelic Exhibition
New York 1984

(315) (316)

1984 (1 Nov). *Deepavali Festival. Nos. 544/5 surch as T* **315** *in blue by Autoprint.*
1414 25 c. on 5 c. Annatto tree .. 30 10
1415 $1.50 on 3 c. Hanging Heliconia.. .. 1·75 55

1984 (15 Nov). *A.S.D.A. Philatelic Exhibition, New York. Nos. 1188/91 optd with T* **316** *in red by Autoprint.*
1416 **277** 120 c. lake-brown and black.. .. 40 45
 a. Block of 4. Nos. 1416/19 .. 1·90
1417 — 130 c. rose-red and black .. 45 50
1418 — 150 c. bright violet and black .. 50 55
1419 — 200 c. dull green and black .. 70 75
1416/19 .. .. .. *Set of* 4 1·90 2·00

(Litho Format)

1984 (16 Nov). *Olympic Games, Los Angeles (3rd issue). Design as No. 1051, but with Olympic rings and inscr "OLYMPIC GAMES 1984 LOS ANGELES". P* 13½.
1420 $1.20, Youth display (41 × 25 mm).. .. 1·50 45
No. 1420 also exists from coils of 500 or 1,000 with numbers on the reverse of each stamp.
No. 1420 exists imperforate from stock dispersed by the liquidator of Format International Security Printers Ltd.

X 20

(317)

318 Pair of Swallow-tailed
Kites on Tree

1984 (24 Nov). *Nos. 847, 861b, 1099 and 1102 surch as T* **317**.
1421 20 c. on 12 c. on 12 c. on 6 c. mult (No. 847) 60 10
1422 20 c. on 12 c. on 6 c. mult (No. 861b) 65·00 4·50
1423 25 c. on 50 c. on 6 c. mult (No. 1099) .. 30 10
1424 60 c. on $1 on 6 c. multicoloured (No. 1102) 45 25
No. 1423 shows the previous surcharge obliterated by horizontal parallel lines.

(Litho Questa)

1984 (3 Dec). *Christmas. Swallow-tailed Kites. T* **318** *and similar horiz designs. Multicoloured. W* **106** (*sideways*).
P 14 × 14½.
1425 60 c. Type **318** .. .. 3·00 1·75
 a. Horiz strip of 5. Nos. 1425/9 .. 13·50
1426 60 c. Swallow-tailed Kite on branch .. 3·00 1·75
1427 60 c. Kite in flight with wings raised .. 3·00 1·75
1428 60 c. Kite in flight with wings lowered .. 3·00 1·75
1429 60 c. Kite gliding .. .. 3·00 1·75
1425/9 .. .. .. *Set of* 5 13·50 8·00
Nos. 1425/9 were printed together, *se-tenant*, in horizontal strips of 5 throughout the sheet with the backgrounds forming a composite design. Each stamp is inscribed "CHRISTMAS 1982".

319 St. George's Cathedral,
Georgetown

(Litho Format)

1985 (8 Feb–Oct). *Georgetown Buildings. T* **319** *and similar horiz designs, each black and stone. W* **106** (*sideways*). *P* 14.
1430 25 c. Type **319** .. 10 10
1431 60 c. Demerara Mutual Life Assurance
 Building 15 25
1432 120 c. As No. 1431 .. .. 20 45
 a. Horiz strip of 3. Nos. 1432/4 .. 55
 b. No wmk (10.85) .. 40 45
 ba. Horiz strip of 3. Nos. 1432b/4b .. 1·10
1433 120 c. Town Hall 20 45
 b. No wmk (10.85) .. 40 45
1434 120 c. Victoria Law Courts.. .. 20 45
 b. No wmk (10.85) .. 40 45
1435 200 c. As No. 1433 .. .. 20 75
1436 300 c. As No. 1434 .. .. 20 1·10
1430/6 .. .. .. *Set of* 7 1·10 3·25
Nos. 1432/4 were printed together, *se-tenant*, in horizontal strips of 3 within the sheet, forming a composite design.

International Youth Year 1985	Republic Day 1970-1985
(320)	(321)

1985 (15 Feb). *International Youth Year. As No. 1420, but W* **106** (*sideways*), *optd with T* **320** *by Tip Torres.*
1437 $1.20, Youth display .. .. .. 2·00 45
Examples used for this overprint all show the second line of the original inscription as "LOS ANGELLES".

1985 (22 Feb). *Republic Day. Nos 1049/50 and 1052 optd or surch as T* **321** *in red by Autoprint.*
1438 25 c. Type **238** 30 30
 a. Horiz pair. Nos. 1438/9 .. 60 60
1439 25 c. Flag (inscr "30th ANNIVERSARY
 IN PARLIAMENT") 30 30
1440 120 c. on $6 Presidential standard.. .. 80 80
1441 130 c. on $6 Presidential standard.. .. 90 90
1438/41 .. .. .. *Set of* 4 2·10 2·10
Examples of Nos. 1438/9 overprinted "1980–1985" in error come from stock dispersed by the liquidator of Format International Security Printers Ltd.

322 Young Ocelot on Branch

International Youth Year 1985

(323)

(Des K. Everett. Litho Format)

1985 (11 Mar)–**87**. *Wildlife Protection. T* **322** *and similar multicoloured designs. W* **106** (*inverted*). *A. P* 14½ (320 c., 330 c.) *or* 12½ (*others*). *Without imprint*
1442A 25 c. Type **322** (grey-olive background) 1·50 10
1443A 60 c. Young Ocelot (*different*) (yellow-
 -brown background) .. 30 25
1444A 120 c. As No. 1443A .. 50 55
 c. Vert strip of 3. Nos. 1444A/6A 1·50
1445A 120 c. Type **322** .. 50 55
1446A 120 c. Young Ocelot (*different*) (red-
 brown background) .. 50 55
1447A 130 c. As No. 1446A .. 45 60
1448A 320 c. Scarlet Macaw (28 × 46 mm) .. 3·00 1·50
1449A 330 c. Young Ocelot reaching for branch
 (28 × 46 mm) .. 90 1·50
1442A/9A .. .. *Set of* 8 7·00 5·00

B. *P* 14. *With imprint date at foot* (18.2.87).
1444B 120 c. As No. 1443A .. 15 20
 c. Vert strip of 3. Nos. 1444B/6B 40
1445B 120 c. Type **322** .. 15 20
1446B 120 c. Young Ocelot (*different*) (red-brown
 background) .. 15 20
Nos. 1444/6 were printed together, *se-tenant*, in vertical strips of 3 throughout the sheet.
Examples of the 25 c. with imprint date and perforated 14 come from stock dispersed by the liquidator of Format International Security Printers Ltd.

1985 (11 Mar–11 Apr). *No. 940 and Revenue stamp, as T* **181**, *surch as T* **305** *with fleur-de-lys over existing value, by Tip Torres, and Nos. 912, 1016 and O 24 surch as T* **272**, *but without the decimal point, by Autoprint.*
1450 30 c. on 50 c. multicoloured (No. O24) (B.) 50 10
1451 55 c. on 2 c. black, indigo & greenish grey 65 20
 a. Opt "ESSEQUIBO etc" omitted .. 10·00
1452 55 c. on 15 c. on 2 c. black, indigo and
 greenish grey (No. 940) .. 65 20

1453 90 c. on $1 multicoloured (No. 1016) (B.) .. 5·00 30
1454 225 c. on $5 multicoloured (No. 912) (11.4) 8·50 90
1455 230 c. on $5 multicoloured (No. 912) (B.) .. 8·50 95
1456 260 c. on $5 multicoloured (No. 912) (B.) .. 8·50 1·00
1450/6 .. .. .. *Set of* 7 29·00 3·25
On Nos. 1454/6 the surcharges are sideways.

1985 (15 Apr). *International Youth Year Save the Children Fund Campaign. Nos. 880, 1073a, 1079b and 1082 optd or surch as T* **323** *in blue by Autoprint.*
1457 50 c. "Two Boys catching Ducks" (No.
 1073a).. .. .. 2·25 20
1458 50 c. on 10 c. Type **171** (No. 1082) .. 7·00 20
1459 120 c. on 125 c. on $3 "Mango Season" (No.
 880) .. .. 2·25 45
1460 $3 "Mango Season" (No.1079b) .. 2·25 1·10
 a. Opt Type **256** ("1983") omitted .. 12·00
1457/60 .. .. .. *Set of* 4 12·00 1·75
On Nos. 1457 and 1459/60 the overprints and surcharge as Type **323** are sideways.

Airy Hall

25	1985
(324)	(325)

1985 (2 May). *125th Anniv of British Guiana Post Office (1st issue). No. 699 surch as T* **324** *in blue by Autoprint.*
1461 25 c. on 10 c. multicoloured (surch T **324**) 65 65
 a. Sheetlet of 25. Nos. 1461/85 .. 14·00
1462 25 c. on 10 c. multicoloured (surch "Belfield
 Arab. Coast") .. 65 65
1463 25 c. on 10 c. multicoloured (surch "Belfield
 E. C. Dem.") .. 65 65
1464 25 c. on 10 c. mult (surch "Belladrum") .. 65 65
1465 25 c. on 10 c. multicoloured (surch
 "Beterver-wagting") .. 65 65
1466 25 c. on 10 c. multicoloured (surch "Blair-
 mont Ferry") .. 65 65
1467 25 c. on 10 c. mult (surch "Boeraserie") .. 65 65
1468 25 c. on 10 c. mult (surch "Brahm") .. 65 65
1469 25 c. on 10 c. mult (surch "Bushlot") .. 65 65
1470 25 c. on 10 c. mult (surch "De Kinderen") .. 65 65
1471 25 c. on 10 c. multicoloured (surch "Fort
 Wellington") .. 65 65
1472 25 c. on 10 c. mult (surch "Georgetown") .. 65 65
1473 25 c. on 10 c. mult (surch "Hague").. .. 65 65
1474 25 c. on 10 c. mult (surch "Leguan") .. 65 65
1475 25 c. on 10 c. mult (surch "Mahaica") .. 65 65
1476 25 c. on 10 c. mult (surch "Mahaicony") .. 65 65
1477 25 c. on 10 c. multicoloured (surch "New
 Amsterdam") .. 65 65
1478 25 c. on 10 c. mult (surch "Plaisance") .. 65 65
1479 25 c. on 10 c. multicoloured (surch "No. 6
 Police Station") .. 65 65
1480 25 c. on 10 c. mult (surch "Queenstown") .. 65 65
1481 25 c. on 10 c. mult (surch "Vergenoegen") .. 65 65
1482 25 c. on 10 c. mult (surch "Vigilance") .. 65 65
1483 25 c. on 10 c. mult (surch "Vreed-en-Hoop") .. 65 65
1484 25 c. on 10 c. mult (surch "Wakenaam") .. 65 65
1485 25 c. on 10 c. mult (surch "Windsor Castle") .. 65 65
1461/85 .. .. *Set of* 25 14·00 14·00
The surcharged names are those of the post offices and postal agencies open in 1860.
See also Nos. 1694/1717, 2140/64 and 2278/301.

1985 (17 May). *I.T.U./W.H.O. Day. Nos. 1148/68 optd with T* **325**, *or with single capital letter, in red by Autoprint.*
1486 30 c. multicoloured (No. 1148) .. 65 65
 a. Sheetlet of 25. Nos. 1486/510.. .. 14·00
1487 30 c. multicoloured (No. 1149) .. 65 65
1488 30 c. multicoloured (No. 1150) .. 65 65
1489 30 c. multicoloured (No. 1151) .. 65 65
1490 30 c. multicoloured (No. 1152) .. 65 65
1491 30 c. multicoloured (No. 1153) .. 65 65
1492 30 c. multicoloured (No. 1154) (optd "T") .. 65 65
1493 30 c. multicoloured (No. 1155) (optd "T") .. 65 65
1494 30 c. multicoloured (No. 1156) (optd "U") .. 65 65
1495 30 c. multicoloured (No. 1157) .. 65 65
1496 30 c. multicoloured (No. 1158) .. 65 65
1497 30 c. multicoloured (No. 1155) (optd "W") .. 65 65
1498 30 c. multicoloured (No. 1155) (optd "H") .. 65 65
1499 30 c. multicoloured (No. 1155) (optd "O") .. 65 65
1500 30 c. multicoloured (No. 1159) .. 65 65
1501 30 c. multicoloured (No. 1160) .. 65 65
1502 30 c. multicoloured (No. 1161) (optd "D") .. 65 65
1503 30 c. multicoloured (No. 1155) (optd "A") .. 65 65
1504 30 c. multicoloured (No. 1162) (optd "Y") .. 65 65
1505 30 c. multicoloured (No. 1163) .. 65 65
1506 30 c. multicoloured (No. 1164) .. 65 65
1507 30 c. multicoloured (No. 1165) .. 65 65
1508 30 c. multicoloured (No. 1166) .. 65 65
1509 30 c. multicoloured (No. 1167) .. 65 65
1510 30 c. multicoloured (No. 1168) .. 65 65
1486/1510 .. .. *Set of* 25 14·00 14·00

60

20

CARDI
1975-1985

(326) (327)

1985 (21 May). *No. 861b surch with T* **326** *by Autoprint.*
1511 20 c. on 12 c. on 6 c. Black Acara ("Patua") 3·00 10
 a. Surch on No. 861 (no wmk) .. 6·00 1·50
For a similar surcharge, but with new face value at right see Nos. 1655/6.

1985 (29 May). *10th Anniv of Caribbean Agricultural Research Development Institute. No. 544 surch with T 327 in blue by Autoprint.*
1512   60 c. on 3 c. Hanging Heliconia   ..   .. 1·75   25

1985 (3 June). *No. 839 surch as Type O 10 by Autoprint, but with two blocks of obliterating bars over the previous surch.*
1513   600 c. on 625 c. on 40 c. Tiger Beard   .. 20·00 2·75

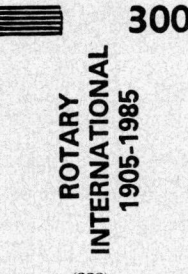

(328)

1985 (21 June). *80th Anniv of Rotary International. Nos. 707 and 879 surch as T 328 in red by Autoprint.*
1514   120 c. on 110 c. on $3 Rotary anniversary
emblem   ..   .. 11·00   45
1515   300 c. on $2 *Morpho rhetenor*   ..   7·00 2·50
No. 1205 exists with a similar 120 c. horizontal surcharge. A limited quantity was available mint, but examples are mainly found on First Day Covers (*Price £8 on First Day Cover*).

CARICOM DAY 1985

(329)

1985 (28 June). *CARICOM Day. No. 1200 surch with T 329 in red.*
1516   60 c. on $3 "Makanaima the Great Ancestral Spirit of the Amerindians"   .. 60   30

**135th Anniversary
Cotton Reel
1850-1985**

120

(330)

1985 (28 June). *135th Anniv of First British Guiana Stamps. No. 870 surch with T 330 in red.*
1517   120 c. on 110 c. on 10 c. Type **170** 65   55

"REICHENBACHIA" ISSUES. Due to the proliferation of these designs the catalogue uses the book plate numbers as description for each design. The following index gives the species on each plate and the stamp numbers on which they occur.

Series 1
Plate No. 1 – *Odontoglossum crispum* – 1578, 2112
Plate No. 2 – *Cattleya percivaliana* – 1519, 2026, 2394, 3293, 4321
Plate No. 3 – *Cypripedium sanderianum* – 1525, 2084
Plate No. 4 – *Odontoglossum rossi* – 1533, **MS**1539, 2095, **MS**2105
Plate No. 5 – *Cattleya dowiana aurea* – 1667, 1779, 1942/3, 2030, 2464
Plate No. 6 – *Coelogyne cristata maxima* – 1526, **MS**1685, 1759, 2085, 2093, 2119, **MS**2234, 2519, 2751
Plate No. 7 – *Odontoglossum insleayi splendens* – 1520, 1967
Plate No. 8 – *Laelia euspatha* – 1571, 1933, 1950
Plate No. 9 – *Dendrobium wardianum* – 1552, 1763, 1979/80, 1981a, 1996, 2002, 2005, 2017, 2022, 2138/9, 2387, 2748
Plate No. 10 – *Laelia autumnalis xanthotropis* – 1521, 1968, 2027, 3290, 4319
Plate No. 11 – *Phalaenopsis grandiflora aurea* – 1579, 2113
Plate No. 12 – *Cattleya lawrenceana* – 1518, 1935
Plate No. 13 – *Masdevallia shuttleworthii* and *M. xanthocorys* – 1527, 1684, 1760, 2092, 2107, 2110, 2120, 2233, 2448, 2520, 3839
Plate No. 14 – *Aeranthus sesquipedalis* – 1584, 2096, 2472
Plate No. 15 – *Cattleya mendelii* Duke of Marlborough – 1752, 1804, 2009, 2050, 2259, 2532
Plate No. 16 – *Zygopetalum intermedium* – 1559, 2090
Plate No. 17 – *Phaius humblotii* – 1732, 1792, 1885, 1965, 1977a, 2062, 2393
Plate No. 18 – *Chysis bractescens* – 1528, 1536, 2087, 2133

Plate No. 19 – *Masdevallia backhousiana* – 1522, 1969, 2028, 3292, 4320
Plate No. 20 – *Cattleya citrina* – 1529, **MS**1570, 1761, 2086, 2094, **MS**2106, 2121, 2449, 2521
Plate No. 21 – *Oncidium jonesianum* and *Oncidium jonesianum phaeanthum* – 1585, 2097, 2129
Plate No. 22 – *Saccolabium giganteum* – 1553, **MS**1619, 1764, 1940/1, 1989, 1997, 2006, 2018, 2023, **MS**2232, 2388, **MS**2531
Plate No. 23 – *Cypripedium io* – 1572, 1936
Plate No. 24 – *Odontoglossum blandum* – 1635, 1774, 1864/5, 1931, 1961, 2019, 2047, 2344, 2527, 2529
Plate No. 25 – *Maxillaria sanderiana* – 1530, 1762, 2108, 2111, 2122, 2522, 2752/3
Plate No. 26 – *Odontoglossum* Edward II – 1633, 2137, 2258, 2450
Plate No. 27 – *Vanda teres* – 1524, 2438
Plate No. 28 – *Odontoglossum hallii xanthoglossum* – 1580, 2114
Plate No. 29 – *Odontoglossum crispum hrubyanum* – 1531, 1537, 2088, 2134
Plate No. 30 – *Oncidium concolor* – 1532, 1538, 2089, 2135
Plate No. 31 – *Trichopilia suavis alba* – 1523, 1970, 2029, 3291, 4322
Plate No. 32 – *Cattleya superba splendens* – 1561, 2512
Plate No. 33 – *Odontoglossum luteo-purpureum* – 1634, 2098, 2342, 2479, 3827
Plate No. 34 – *Cypripedium niveum* – 1562
Plate No. 35 – *Stanhopea shuttleworthii* – 1563
Plate No. 36 – *Laelia anceps percivaliana* – 1558, 2439
Plate No. 37 – *Odontoglossum hebraicum* – 1627, 2115, 2440
Plate No. 38 – *Cypripedium oenanthum superbum* – 1560, 2445
Plate No. 39 – *Dendrobium superbiens* – 1737, 1797, 1985, 2063, 2104, 2414, 2515
Plate No. 40 – *Laelia harpophylla* – 1581, 1767, 2123, 2126, 2523, 3350
Plate No. 41 – *Lycaste skinneri* and *alba* – 1564
Plate No. 42 – *Phalaenopsis stuartiana* – 1582, 1657, 1768, 1993, 2125, 2127, 2524, 3349
Plate No. 43 – *Cattleya trianaei ernesti* – 1586, 1658, 1770, 2099, 2130/1, 2525, 3351/2
Plate No. 44 – *Sobralia xantholeuca* – 1556, 1971
Plate No. 45 – *Odontoglossum crispum kinlesideanum* – 1583, 1769, 2124, 2128, 2526, 3348
Plate No. 46 – *Cattleya trianaei schroederiana* – 1628, 2116, 2476
Plate No. 47 – *Epidendrum vitellinum* – 1557, 1972
Plate No. 48 – *Laelia anceps stella* and *barkeriana* – 1565
Plate No. 49 – *Odontoglossum harryanum* – 1554, 1765, 1912, 1964, 1966, 1994, 2003, 2007, 2015, 2024, 2749
Plate No. 50 – *Dendrobium leechianum* – 1672, 1784, 2031, 2403, 2496, 2558
Plate No. 51 – *Phalaenopsis speciosa* – 1573, 1934
Plate No. 52 – *Laelia elegans schilleriana* – 1551, 1949
Plate No. 53 – *Zygopetalum wendlandi* – 1621, 1771, 1930, 1954, 1962, 1983, 1986, 2020, 2048, 2361, 2364, E4
Plate No. 54 – *Cypripedium selligerum majus* – 1664, 1776, 2032, 2381, 2404
Plate No. 55 – *Angraecum articulatum* – 1597, 1625, 1772, 1927, 1990, 2046, 2265, 2463, 2465
Plate No. 56 – *Laelia anceps sanderiana* – 1629, 2117, 2441, 3841
Plate No. 57 – *Vanda coerulea* – 1622, 1973, 2395/6, 3828
Plate No. 58 – *Dendrobium nobile sanderianum* – 1630, 2118, 2442, 3840
Plate No. 59 – *Laelia gouldiana* – 1620, 2243, 2359
Plate No. 60 – *Odontoglossum grande* – 1682, 1789, 1944, 2038, 2514, 2528
Plate No. 61 – *Cypripedium rothschildianum* – 1574, 2356
Plate No. 62 – *Vanda sanderiana* – 1566, 2513
Plate No. 63 – *Dendrobium aureum* – 1575, 2357
Plate No. 64 – *Oncidium macranthum* – 1555, 1766, 1913, 1981/2, 1995, 2004, 2008, 2016, 2025, 2750
Plate No. 65 – *Cypripedium tautzianum* – 1598, 1626, 1773, 1963, 2021, 2049, 2221, 2434, 2437, 2530, E1
Plate No. 66 – *Cymbidium mastersi* – 1632, 2091, 2136, 2257, 2446
Plate No. 67 – *Angraecum caudatum* – 1631, 2132, 2256, 2443
Plate No. 68 – *Laelia albida* – 1734, 1794, 1884, 1937, 2056, 2378/9, 2435
Plate No. 69 – *Odontoglossum roezlii* – 1680, 1787, 2033, 2405, 2444
Plate No. 70 – *Oncidium ampliatum majus* – 1576, 2358
Plate No. 71 – *Renanthera lowii* – 1679, 1786, 1952, 1976, 2034, 2360
Plate No. 72 – *Cattleya warscewiczii* – 1577, 1951, 2429
Plate No. 73 – *Oncidium lanceanum* – 1623, 1974, 2397, 3826
Plate No. 74 – *Vanda hookeriana* – 1736, 1796, 1984, 2064, 2103, 2415, 2454
Plate No. 75 – *Cattleya labiata gaskelliana* – 1624, 1975, 2398/9, 3829
Plate No. 76 – *Epidendrum prismatocarpum* – 1751, 1803, 2058, 2453
Plate No. 77 – *Cattleya guttata leopoldi* – 1663, 1775, 1955, 1958, 2042, 2372/3
Plate No. 78 – *Oncidium splendidum* – 1669, 1781, 1959, 2043, 2451
Plate No. 79 – *Odontoglossum hebraicum aspersum* – 1670, 1782, 2035, 2100, 2343, 2406, 2473
Plate No. 80 – *Cattleya dowiana var chrysotoxa* – 1754, 1806, 2059, 2517
Plate No. 81 – *Cattleya trianae alba* – 1748, 1800, 1957, 2010, 2051, 2382
Plate No. 82 – *Odontoglossum humeanum* – 1753, 1805, 2011, 2052, 2260, 2516
Plate No. 83 – *Cypripedium argus* – 1671, 1783, 2039, 2466, 2480
Plate No. 84 – *Odontoglossum luteo-purpureum prionopetalum* – 1668, 1780, 2044, 2421
Plate No. 85 – *Cattleya rochellensis* – 1673, 1785, 1960, 2045, 2497, 2518
Plate No. 86 – *Odontoglossum triumphans* – 1731, 1791, 1847, 1868, 1953, 1956, 1956a, 2055, 2055a, 2377, E2, E2a, E11. (Nos. 1847, 1956a, 2055a, 2264, E2 and E11 are inscr "ONTOGLOSSUM" in error)
Plate No. 87 – *Phalaenopsis casta* – 1681, 1788, 1977, 2036, 2452, 2474, 2478
Plate No. 88 – *Oncidium tigrinum* – 1750, 1802, 2060, 2436
Plate No. 89 – *Cypripedium lemoinierianum* – 1749, 1801, 1978, 2012, 2053, 2422

Plate No. 90 – *Catasetum bungerothii* – 1738, 1798, 1938, 1947/8, 1988, 2014, 2057, 2380, 2433
Plate No. 91 – *Cattleya ballantiniana* – 1735, 1795, 1987, 2013, 2054, 2109, 2375/6, 2447
Plate No. 92 – *Dendrobium brymerianum* – 1665, 1777, 1945, 1988a, 2040, 2384
Plate No. 93 – *Cattleya eldorado crocata* – 1733, 1793, 1991/2, 2065, 2401, 2416
Plate No. 94 – *Odontoglossum sanderianum* – 1683, 1790, 2037, 2345, 2407, 2484
Plate No. 95 – *Cattleya labiata warneri* – 1666, 1778, 1990a, 2041, 2400, 2467
Plate No. 96 – *Odontoglossum schroderianum* – 1747, 1799, 2061, 2374

Series 2
Plate No. 1 – *Cypripedium morganiae burfordiense* – 2178, 2556
Plate No. 2 – *Cattleya bowringiana* – 1886, 1929, 2102, 2426
Plate No. 3 – *Dendrobium formosum* – 1919, 1998, 2389
Plate No. 4 – *Phaius tuberculosus* – 1813, 2428, 2500
Plate No. 5 – *Odontoglossum crispum mundyanum* – 1815, 2475
Plate No. 6 – *Laelia praestans* – 1881, 1999, 2390, 2624/6
Plate No. 7 – *Dendrobium phalaenopsis var statterianum* – 1917, 2365
Plate No. 8 – *Cypripedium boxalli atratum* – 1811, 2408
Plate No. 9 – *Odontoglossum wattianum* – 1816, 2101, 2409/10
Plate No. 10 – *Cypripedium lathamianum inversum* – 1869, 1880, 2423, 2482
Plate No. 11 – *Paphinia rugosa* and *Zygopetalum xanthinum* – 2503, E6
Plate No. 12 – *Dendrobium melanodiscus* – 1817, 2411/12, **MS**2590
Plate No. 13 – *Laelia anceps schroderiana* – 1877, 1907, 2385, 2424
Plate No. 14 – *Phaius hybridus cooksonii* – 1920, 2366/7
Plate No. 15 – *Disa grandiflora* – 1918, 1926, 2386, 2419
Plate No. 16 – *Selenipedium hybridum grande* – 2314, 2331
Plate No. 17 – *Cattleya schroederae alba* – 1872, 2413, 2610/11
Plate No. 18 – *Lycaste skinnerii armeniaca* – 1923, 1928, 1946, 2420, 2557
Plate No. 19 – *Odontoglossum excellens* – 2175
Plate No. 20 – *Laelio-cattleya elegans var blenheimensis* – 1916, 2000, 2391
Plate No. 21 – *Odontoglossum coradinei* – 1810, 2383, 4711
Plate No. 22 – *Odontoglossum wilckeanum var rothschildianum* – 1922, 2368
Plate No. 23 – *Cypripedium lawrenceanum hyeanum* – 2504, 2601, O65
Plate No. 24 – *Cattleya intermedia punctatissima* – 1887, 1914, 2418
Plate No. 25 – *Laelia purpurata* – 2067, 2576
Plate No. 26 – *Masdevallia harryana splendens* – 2505, 2596, O59
Plate No. 27 – *Selenipedium hybridum nitidissimum* – 1874, 1915, 2402, 2425
Plate No. 28 – *Cattleya mendelii var measuresiana* – 1924, 2369/70
Plate No. 29 – *Odontoglossum vexillarium (miltonia vexillaria)* – 1818, 2485
Plate No. 30 – *Saccolabium coeleste* – 1809, 2363, 2430
Plate No. 31 – *Cypripedium hybridum youngianum* – 2324, 2594, O57
Plate No. 32 – *Miltonia (hybrida) bleuana* – 1921, 2001, 2392
Plate No. 33 – *Laelia grandis* – 1873, 2616/19, 4712
Plate No. 34 – *Cattleya labiata var lueddemanniana* – 1819, 2341, 2481
Plate No. 35 – *Odontoglossum coronarium* – 2511, E9
Plate No. 36 – *Cattleya granulosa var schofieldiana* – 2316, 2592, O55
Plate No. 37 – *Odontoglossum (hybridum) leroyanum* – 2174
Plate No. 38 – *Cypripedium (hybridum) laucheanum* and *eyermanianum* – 1814, 2477, 2580
Plate No. 39 – *Cychnoches chlorochilon* – 2172
Plate No. 40 – *Cattleya O'Brieniana* – 2276
Plate No. 41 – *Odontoglossum ramosissimum* – 2066, 2581
Plate No. 42 – *Dendrobium phalaenopsis var* – 1812, 2427, 2499
Plate No. 43 – *Cypripedium (hybridum) pollettianum* and *maynardii* – 2216, 2593, O56
Plate No. 44 – *Odontoglossum naevium* – 1878, 2498, 2656
Plate No. 45 – *Cypripedium (hybridum) castleanum* – 1876, 1925, 2371, 2417
Plate No. 46 – *Odontoglossum cervantesii decorum* – **MS**2275, **MS**2332
Plate No. 47 – *Cattleya amethystoglossa* – 2171
Plate No. 48 – *Cattleya (hybrida) arnoldiana* – 2217, O53
Plate No. 49 – *Cattleya labiata* – 2239, 2605, 2614/15, 2646/7
Plate No. 50 – *Dendrobium (hybridum) venus* and *cassiope* – 1879, 2501, 2620/1
Plate No. 51 – *Selenipedium (hybridum) weidlichianum* – 2177, 2502
Plate No. 52 – *Cattleya mossiae var. reineckiana* – 2072, 2577
Plate No. 53 – *Cymbidium lowianum* – 2236, 2585, 2606
Plate No. 54 – *Oncidium loxense* – 2176, 2579
Plate No. 55 – *Cattleya (hybrida) hardyana* – **MS**2275, **MS**2332
Plate No. 56 – *Coelogyne sanderae* – 1875, 2612/13, 2627
Plate No. 57 – *Cypripedium leeanum var giganteum* – **MS**2275, **MS**2332
Plate No. 58 – *Coelogyne pandurata* – 2173, 2582
Plate No. 59 – *Schomburgkia sanderiana* – 2323, 2595, O61
Plate No. 60 – *Oncidium superbiens* – 2227, 2607
Plate No. 61 – *Dendrobium johnsoniae* – 2235, O58
Plate No. 62 – *Laelia hybrida behrensiana* – 2322, 2509, 2622/3
Plate No. 63 – Hybrid *Calanthes* Victoria Regina, Bella and *Burfordiense* – 2510, E8
Plate No. 64 – *Cattleya mendelii* Quorndon House var – 2238, 2608
Plate No. 65 – *Arachnanthe clarkei* – 2073, 2578
Plate No. 66 – *Zygopetalum burtii* – 2240, 2583
Plate No. 67 – *Cattleya (hybrida) parthenia* – 2318, 2584
Plate No. 68 – *Phalaenopsis sanderiana* and *intermedia portei* – 2225, 2597, O60
Plate No. 69 – *Phaius blumei var assamicus* – 2317, 2598, O62

Plate No. 70 – *Angraecum humblotii* – 2470, 2602, O67
Plate No. 71 – *Odontoglossum pescatorei* – 2471, 2603, O68
Plate No. 72 – *Cattleya rex* – 2193
Plate No. 73 – *Zygopetalum crinitum* – 2315, 2329,
Plate No. 74 – *Cattleya lueddemanniana alba* – 2219/20, 2222/3, 2328
Plate No. 75 – *Cymbidium (hybridum) winnianum* – 2506, O64
Plate No. 76 – Hybrid *Masdevallias courtauldiana, geleniana* and *measuresiana* – 2242
Plate No. 77 – *Cypripedium (hybridum) calypso* – 2191
Plate No. 78 – *Masdevallia chimaera* var *mooreana* – 2325
Plate No. 79 – *Miltonia phalaenopsis* – 2241, 2508
Plate No. 80 – *Lissochilus giganteus* – 2190
Plate No. 81 – *Aerides savageanum* – **MS2275, MS2332**
Plate No. 82 – *Thunia brymeriana* – 2069, 2483
Plate No. 83 – *Miltonia moreliana* – 2182
Plate No. 84 – *Oncidium kramerianum* – 2469, 2604, O69
Plate No. 85 – *Cattleya Victoria Regina* – 2068
Plate No. 86 – *Zygopetalum klabochorum* – 2180
Plate No. 87 – *Laelia autumnalis alba* – 2070, 2432
Plate No. 88 – *Spathoglottis kimballiana* – 2071
Plate No. 89 – *Laelia-cattleya* ("The Hon. Mrs. Astor") – 2181
Plate No. 90 – *Phaius hybridus amabilis* and *marthiae* – 2468, 2599, O63
Plate No. 91 – *Zygopetalum rostratum* – 2277
Plate No. 92 – *Coelogyne swaniana* – 2218, 2591, O54
Plate No. 93 – *Laelio-cattleya (hybrida) phoebe* – 2507, E7
Plate No. 94 – *Epidendrum atro-purpureum* var *randianum* – 2192
Plate No. 95 – *Dendrobium imperatrix* – 2226, 2600, O66
Plate No. 96 – *Vanda parishii* var *marriottiana* – 2237, 2330

331 *Cattleya lawrenceana*
(Plate No. 12 (Series 1))

332 Arms of Guyana

(Litho Format)

1985 (9 July). *Centenary of Publication of Sanders' Reichenbachia* (1st issue). T **331** *and similar vert designs showing orchids. Multicoloured. No wmk. P* 13½ × 14.

1518	25 c. Type **331**	..	50	30
1519	60 c. Plate No. 2 (Series 1)	..	60	35
1520	60 c. Plate No. 7 (Series 1)	..	60	35
1521	60 c. Plate No. 10 (Series 1)	..	60	35
1522	60 c. Plate No. 19 (Series 1)	..	60	35
1523	60 c. Plate No. 31 (Series 1)	..	60	35
1524	120 c. Plate No. 27 (Series 1)	..	75	55
1525	130 c. Plate No. 3 (Series 1)	..	75	55
1526	130 c. Plate No. 6 (Series 1)	..	1·40	55
1527	130 c. Plate No. 13 (Series 1)	..	75	55
1528	130 c. Plate No. 18 (Series 1)	..	2·50	55
1529	130 c. Plate No. 20 (Series 1)	..	1·25	55
1530	130 c. Plate No. 25 (Series 1)	..	75	55
1531	130 c. Plate No. 29 (Series 1)	..	1·75	55
1532	130 c. Plate No. 30 (Series 1)	..	1·75	55
1533	200 c. Plate No. 4 (Series 1)	..	1·75	85
1518/33	.. .. ..	*Set of* 16	15·00	7·00

Nos. 1518/33 were printed in four sheets each of 16 orchid stamps, arranged as blocks of four of each design, and 9 examples of Type **332** which appear on the vertical and horizontal gutters between the blocks.

For 130 c. stamps as Nos. 1526/7 and 1529/30, but with watermark **106** see Nos. 1759/62.

(Litho Format)

1985 (9 July–16 Sept). *No wmk.*

1534	**332**	25 c. multicoloured (*imperf* × *p* 14)	20	25
1534a		25 c. multicoloured (*imperf* × *p* 13½) (16 Sept)	20	25
1534b		25 c. multicoloured (*p* 13½×14)	20	25
1535		25 c. multicoloured (*p* 13½×*imperf*)	20	25
1535a		25 c. mult (*p* 14×*imperf*) (16 Sept)	20	25
1535b		25 c. mult (*p* 14×13½) (16 Sept)	15	20
1534/5b		*Set of* 6	1·00	1·25

See note below No. 1533. Examples of Nos. 1534/5b, which were issued in booklets or coils, were cut from the gutters of the orchid sheets and the white area surrounding the design varies considerably in size. Nos. 1534, 1534b and 1535 occur from sheets with vertical orchid designs and Nos. 1534a and 1535a/b from those with horizontal designs.

See also Nos. 1807/8b (watermarked **106**), 1820/1a (additionally inscribed "1996–1986" and 2183/4c (within frame).

(333)   (334)

1985 (9 July). *85th Birthday of Queen Elizabeth the Queen Mother* (1st issue). *Nos.* 1528 *and* 1531/3 *optd with T* **333** (*in two lines on No.* 1538) *or with similar opts (No.* **MS**1539), *all in blue by Format.*

1536	130 c. Plate No. 18 (Series 1)	..	75	80
1537	130 c. Plate No. 29 (Series 1)	..	75	80
1538	130 c. Plate No. 30 (Series 1)	..	75	80
1536/8		*Set of* 3	2·00	2·25
MS1539	100 × 126 mm. 200 c. × 4 Plate No. 4 (Series 1)		4·50	5·00

The four stamps in No. **MS**1539 are overprinted "LADY BOWES-LYON 1900–1923", "DUCHESS OF YORK 1923–1937", "QUEEN ELIZABETH 1937–1952" or "QUEEN MOTHER 1952–1985", all reading upwards.

See also No. **MS**1570.

1985 (18 July). *International Youth Year. Nos.* 900/4 *surch with T* **334** *in red by Autoprint.*

1540	25 c. on 110 c. on 5 c. mult (No. 900)		15	15
	a. Sheetlet of 25. Nos. 1540/1, each × 8, Nos. 1542/3, each × 4 and No. 1544 ..		9·00	
1541	25 c. on 110 c. on 5 c. mult (No. 901)		15	15
1542	25 c. on 110 c. on 5 c. mult (No. 902)		50	50
1543	25 c. on 110 c. on 5 c. mult (No. 903)		50	50
1544	25 c. on 110 c. on 5 c. mult (No. 904)		3·50	3·50
1540/4	.. .. ..	*Set of* 5	4·25	4·25

In addition to the sheetlet containing the five different original surcharges, Type **334** can also be found on the sheets of No. 900.

J. J. Audubon
1785-1985

240

225

1910 - 1985

(335)   (336)

1985 (26 July). *75th Anniv of Girl Guide Movement. No.* 612 *surch with T* **335** *by Tip Torres.*

1545	225 c. on 350 c. on 225 c. on 40 c. Guides in camp		28·00	2·00
	a. Inverted "L"s for 1's in surcharged dates			

No. 1545a occurs on all stamps in the bottom row.

In addition to Type **335** No. 1545 also carries two otherwise unissued surcharges at top right.

Nos. 610 and 613 also exist surcharged with Type **335**. A limited quantity was available mint, but examples were mainly found on First Day Covers (Price £25 per pair on First Day Cover).

1985 (26 July). *Birth Bicentenary of John J. Audubon (ornithologist). No.* 992 *surch with T* **336** *by Tip Torres.*

1546	240 c. on 35 c. Harpy Eagle	..	21·00	2·25

Guyana/Libya
Friendship 1985

150

337 Leaders of the 1763 Rebellion   (338)

(Des K. Everett (150 c.). Litho Format)

1985 (29 July). *150th Anniv of Abolition of Slavery* (1984) (1st issue). T **337** *and similar horiz designs.* P 14.

1547	25 c. black and bluish grey	..	25	10
1548	60 c. black and mauve	..	20	25
1549	130 c. black and light greenish blue		25	50
1550	150 c. black and rose-lilac ..		60	55
1547/50		*Set of* 4	1·10	1·25

Designs:—60 c. Damon and Parliament Buildings, Georgetown; 130 c. Quamina and Demerara, 1823; 150 c. *Den Arendt* (slave ship), 1627.

Nos. 1549/50 exist imperforate from stock dispersed by the liquidator of Format International Security Printers Ltd.

For these designs in changed colours see Nos. 2552/5.

(Litho Format)

1985 (1 Aug). *Centenary of Publication of Sanders' Reichenbachia* (2nd issue). *Vert designs as* T **331** *showing orchids. Multicoloured. No wmk.* P 13½ × 14.

1551	25 c. Plate No. 52 (Series 1)	..	80	25
1552	55 c. Plate No. 9 (Series 1)	..	70	35
1553	55 c. Plate No. 22 (Series 1)	..	70	35
1554	55 c. Plate No. 49 (Series 1)	..	70	25
1555	55 c. Plate No. 64 (Series 1)	..	70	35
1556	60 c. Plate No. 44 (Series 1)	..	70	35
1557	60 c. Plate No. 47 (Series 1)	..	70	35
1558	120 c. Plate No. 36 (Series 1)	..	1·25	55
1559	130 c. Plate No. 16 (Series 1)	..	1·25	55
1560	130 c. Plate No. 38 (Series 1)	..	1·25	55
1561	150 c. Plate No. 32 (Series 1)	..	1·25	55
1562	150 c. Plate No. 34 (Series 1)	..	1·25	55
1563	150 c. Plate No. 35 (Series 1)	..	1·25	55
1564	150 c. Plate No. 41 (Series 1)	..	1·25	55
1565	150 c. Plate No. 48 (Series 1)	..	1·25	55
1566	150 c. Plate No. 62 (Series 1)	..	1·25	55
1551/66		*Set of* 16	14·00	6·50

Nos. 1551/66 were printed in a similar sheet format to Nos. 1518/33.

For 55 c. stamps as Nos. 1552/5, but with watermark **106** see Nos. 1763/6.

For 50 c. stamps in designs of Nos. 1554/5 see Nos. 1912/13.

1985 (16 Aug). *Signing of Guyana—Libya Friendship Treaty. No.* 621 *surch with T* **338** *by Autoprint.*

1567	150 c. on 10 c. Type 149	..	9·00	2·75

ALTERED CATALOGUE NUMBERS

Any Catalogue numbers altered from the last edition are shown as a list in the introductory pages.

200

(339) (340) (341)

1985 (16 Aug). *Namibia Day. No. 636 surch with T **339** in deep carmine by Tip Torres.*
1568 150 c. on 35 c. Unveiling of Monument .. 2·75 55

1985 (16 Aug). *World Cup Football Championship. Mexico (1986) (1st issue). No. F2 surch with T **340** by Autoprint.*
1569 275 c. on 3 c. Hanging Heliconia .. .. 6·50 1·10
See also No. 1727.

1985 (12 Sept). *85th Birthday of Queen Elizabeth the Queen Mother (2nd issue). Sheet 120 × 129 mm containing No. 1529 × 4 optd as No.* **MS**1539, *each stamp surch with T **341** by Tip Torres.*
MS1570 200 c. on 130 c. × 4 Plate No. 20 (Series 1) 14·00 6·00

(Litho Format)

1985 (16 Sept). *Centenary of Publication of Sanders' Reichenbachia (3rd issue). Multicoloured designs as T **331**. No wmk. P 13½ × 14 (Nos. 1571/7 and 1584) or 14 × 13½ (others).*
1571 25 c. Plate No. 8 (Series 1) .. .. 1·00 20
1572 25 c. Plate No. 23 (Series 1) .. .. 1·00 20
1573 25 c. Plate No. 51 (Series 1) .. .. 1·00 20
1574 25 c. Plate No. 61 (Series 1) .. .. 1·00 20
1575 25 c. Plate No. 63 (Series 1) .. .. 1·00 20
1576 25 c. Plate No. 70 (Series 1) .. .. 1·00 20
1577 25 c. Plate No. 72 (Series 1) .. .. 1·00 20
1578 120 c. Plate No. 1 (Series 1) (horiz) .. 1·25 55
1579 120 c. Plate No. 11 (Series 1) (horiz) .. 1·25 55
1580 120 c. Plate No. 28 (Series 1) (horiz) .. 1·25 55
1581 150 c. Plate No. 40 (Series 1) (horiz) .. 75 65
1582 150 c. Plate No. 42 (Series 1) (horiz) .. 75 65
1583 150 c. Plate No. 45 (Series 1) (horiz) .. 75 65
1584 200 c. Plate No. 14 (Series 1) .. .. 1·50 80
1585 200 c. Plate No. 21 (Series 1) (horiz) .. 1·50 80
1586 200 c. Plate No. 43 (Series 1) (horiz) .. 1·50 80
1571/86 .. .. Set of 16 15·00 6·75
Nos. 1571/86 were printed in a similar sheet format to Nos. 1518/33.
For 150 c. and 200 c. stamps as Nos. 1581/3 and 1586, but with watermark **106** see Nos. 1767/70.

120

1955-1985

(342)

1965-1985

25

(343)

1985 (23 Sept). *30th Anniv of Commonwealth Caribbean Medical Research Council. Nos. 819, 871, 874/a, 928a and 1014 surch or optd (vertically reading upwards on Nos. 1587/8) as T **342** by Autoprint.*
1587 – 60 c. multicoloured (No. 819) 20 25
1588 – 60 c. multicoloured (No. 1014) 20 25
1589 176 120 c. on 110 c. on 10 c. multicoloured
  (No. 871) 40 45
1590 – 120 c. on 110 c. on $3 mult (No. 874) .. 40 45
1591 – 120 c. on 110 c. on $3 mult (No. 874a).. 40 45
1592 – 120 c. on 210 c. on $3 mult (No. 928a).. 40 45
1587/92 .. .. Set of 6 1·75 2·10

1985 (30 Sept). *20th Anniv of Guyana Defence Force. No. 856 surch as T **343** by Autoprint.*
1593 25 c. on $1·10 on $3 W.O. and N.C.O.,
  Guyana Defence Force, 1966 .. 1·00 10
1594 225 c. on $1·10 on $3 W.O. and N.C.O.,
  Guyana Defence Force, 1966 .. 2·50 1·25

1985 (5 Oct). *Fire Prevention. Nos. 678 and 680 optd with T **325** and surch as T **255** by Autoprint.*
1595 25 c. on 40 c. Fire engine, 1977 .. 8·00 20
1596 320 c. on 15 c. Steam engine, circa 1860 15·00 3·75
  a. Surch double, one albino .. .. 55·00

(Litho Format)

1985 (7 Oct). *Centenary of Publication of Sanders' Reichenbachia (4th issue). Vert design as T **331**. Multicoloured. No wmk. P 13½ × 14.*
1597 60 c. Plate No. 55 (Series 1) .. .. 1·00 30

CRISTOBAL COLON 1492-1992

SIR WINSTON CHURCHILL 1965-1985

350

(344) (345)

1985 (12 Oct). *Columbus Day. Unissued value as T **331** surch with T **344** in red. Multicoloured. P 13½ × 14.*
1598 350 c. on 120 c. Plate No. 65 (Series 1) .. 4·50 2·50

1985 (15 Oct). *20th Death Anniv of Sir Winston Churchill. No. 707 optd with T **345** by Autoprint.*
1599 $2 Morpho rhetenor (female) .. .. 8·00 1·60

XX **1950-1985 200** **United Nations 1945-1985** **POSTAGE**

(346) (347) (348)

1985 (15 Oct). *35th Anniv of International Commission on Irrigation and Drainage. No. 625 with unissued surcharge as T **264** in blue further surch as T **346** by Autoprint.*
1600 **150** 25 c. on 110 c. on 10 c. multicoloured 30 10
1601 200 c. on 110 c. on 10 c. multicoloured .. 1·25 85

1985 (24 Oct). *40th Anniv of United Nations Organization. Nos. 714/16, 800 and O19 optd with T **347** by Autoprint.*
1602 30 c. multicoloured (No. 714) .. 1·75 10
1603 50 c. multicoloured (No. 715) .. 1·75 20
1604 100 c. on $3 multicoloured (No. O19) .. 1·50 40
1605 225 c. on 220 c. on $3 multicoloured (No. 800) 8·00 75
1606 $3 multicoloured (No. 716) .. 3·50 1·75
1602/6 .. .. .. Set of 5 15·00 2·75

1985 (29 Oct). *Nos. 551/3, O14/15, O18, O21, OP1/2 and F7 optd as T **348** (horizontally 22 × 4 on Nos. 1607 and 1615/16) by Autoprint.*
1607 30 c. on $2 Norantea guianensis (No. O18).. 40 10
1608 40 c. Tiger Beard (No. 551) .. .. 32·00 40
1609 50 c. Guzmania lingulata (No. 552) .. 40 20
1610 50 c. Guzmania lingulata (No. O14) .. 40 20
1611 60 c. Soldier's Cap (No. 553) .. 3·00 25
1612 60 c. Soldier's Cap (No. O15) .. 2·75 25
1613 60 c. Soldier's Cap (No. F7).. .. 1·50 25
1614 $10 Elbella patrobas (No. O21) .. 17·00 5·50
1615 $15 on $1 Chelonanthus uliginoides (No. OP1) .. 8·00 9·00
1616 $20 on $1 Chelonanthus uliginoides (No. OP2) .. 9·00 11·00
1607/16 .. .. .. Set of 10 65·00 24·00

150 **X**

Deepavali 1985 **Christmas 1985**

(349) (350)

1985 (1 Nov). *Deepavali Festival. Nos. 542/3 surch as T **349** by Autoprint.*
1617 25 c. on 2 c. Type **132** 20 10
1618 150 c. on 1 c. Pitcher Plant of Mt Roraima .. 1·40 55

1985 (3 Nov). *Christmas. Sheet 120 × 129 mm containing No. 1553 × 4 optd as T **350** in red by Format.*
MS1619 55 c. × 4 Plate No. 22 (Series 1), each with a different overprint (Type 350, "Happy New Year", "Merry Christmas" or "Happy Holidays") .. .. 7·00 4·00

(Litho Format)

1985 (4 Nov). *Centenary of Publication of Sanders' Reichenbachia (5th issue). Multicoloured designs as T **331** showing orchids. No wmk. P 14 × 13½ (60, 200 c.) or 13½ × 14 (others).*
1620 25 c. Plate No. 59 (Series 1) 75 20
1621 30 c. Plate No. 53 (Series 1) 80 20
1622 60 c. Plate No. 57 (Series 1) (horiz) .. 90 35
1623 60 c. Plate No. 73 (Series 1) (horiz) .. 90 35
1624 60 c. Plate No. 75 (Series 1) (horiz) .. 90 35
1625 75 c. Plate No. 55 (Series 1) .. 1·25 40
1626 100 c. Plate No. 65 (Series 1) .. 1·50 50

1627 120 c. Plate No. 37 (Series 1) .. 1·50 55
1628 120 c. Plate No. 46 (Series 1) .. 1·50 55
1629 120 c. Plate No. 56 (Series 1) .. 1·50 55
1630 120 c. Plate No. 58 (Series 1) .. 1·50 55
1631 120 c. Plate No. 67 (Series 1) .. 1·50 55
1632 130 c. Plate No. 66 (Series 1) .. 1·60 65
1633 150 c. Plate No. 26 (Series 1) .. 1·75 75
1634 200 c. Plate No. 33 (Series 1) (horiz) .. 2·00 85
1635 225 c. Plate No. 24 (Series 1) .. 2·00 95
1620/35 .. .. Set of 16 20·00 7·50
Nos. 1620/35 were printed in a similar sheet format to Nos. 1518/33.
The 30, 75, 100 and 225 c. values show face values and "Guyana" in blue. Examples of these four stamps with face values and "Guyana" in black were prepared, but not issued.
For stamps as Nos. 1621, 1625/6 and 1635, but with watermark **106** see Nos. 1771/4.
For 50 c. in design of No. 1625 see No. 1927.

REICHENBACHIA 1886-1986

351 Clive Lloyd (352)
(cricketer)

(Litho Format)

1985 (7 Nov). *Clive Lloyd's Testimonial Year. T **351** and similar vert designs. Multicoloured. W **106** (sideways on $3.50). P 14½ × 14 (25 c.), 12½ ($3.50) or 14 (others).*
1636 25 c. Type **351** 40 60
  a. Horiz strip of 3. Nos. 1636/8 .. 1·10
1637 25 c. Clive Lloyd, bat and wicket .. 40 60
1638 25 c. Cricket equipment 40 60
1639 60 c. As No. 1638 (25 × 33 mm) .. 45 40
1640 $1.30, As No. 1637 (25 × 33 mm) .. 50 85
1641 $2.25, Type **351** (25 × 33 mm) .. 60 1·25
1642 $3.50, Clive Lloyd with the Prudential Cup (36 × 56 mm) .. 65 1·75
1636/42 .. .. .. Set of 7 3·00 5·50
Nos. 1636/8 were printed together, se-tenant, in horizontal strips of 3 throughout the sheet.

1985 (15 Nov). *Wildlife Protection. Nos. 756/67 optd with T **325** vertically in red by Autoprint.*
1643 30 c. Type **178** 75 75
  a. Sheetlet of 12. Nos. 1643/54 .. 8·00
1644 30 c. Red Howler 75 75
1645 30 c. Common Squirrel Monkey .. 75 75
1646 30 c. Two-toed Sloth. 75 75
1647 30 c. Brazilian Tapir 75 75
1648 30 c. Collared Peccary 75 75
1649 30 c. Six-banded Armadillo. .. 75 75
1650 30 c. Tamandua ("Ant Eater") .. 75 75
1651 30 c. Giant Anteater 75 75
1652 30 c. Murine Opossum 75 75
1653 30 c. Brown Four-eyed Opossum .. 75 75
1654 30 c. Brazilian Agouti 75 75
1643/54 .. .. .. Set of 12 8·00 8·00

1985 (23 Dec). *Nos. 847 and 861b surch as T **326**, but with face value of surch at right.*
1655 20 c. on 12 c. on 12 c. on 6 c. Black Acara ("Patua") .. .. .. 1·75 15
1656 20 c. on 12 c. on 6 c. Black Acara ("Patua") (No. 861b) .. .. .. 1·75 15

1986 (13 Jan). *Centenary of the Appearance of Reichenbachia Volume I. Nos. 1582 and 1586 optd with T **352** in reddish violet.*
1657 150 c. Plate No. 42 (Series 1) .. 2·50 60
1658 200 c. Plate No. 43 (Series 1) .. 2·50 75

Republic Day

1986 **1986**

(353) (354)

1986 (22 Feb). *Republic Day. Nos. 1108/9 and 1052 optd or surch as T **353** by Autoprint.*
1659 25 c. As Type **258** 10 10
  a. Horiz pair. Nos. 1659/60 .. 15 20
1660 25 c. As No. 1050 .. .. 10 10
1661 120 c. on $6 Presidential standard (surch vert) 40 45
1662 225 c. on $6 Presidential standard (surch vert) 70 75
1659/62 .. .. .. Set of 4 1·10 1·25

(Litho Format)

1986 (26 Feb). *Centenary of Publication of Sanders' Reichenbachia (6th issue). Vert designs as T **331**. Multicoloured. No wmk. P 13½ × 14.*
1663 40 c. Plate No. 77 (Series 1) .. 55 20
1664 45 c. Plate No. 54 (Series 1) .. 55 25
1665 50 c. Plate No. 92 (Series 1) .. 55 25
1666 60 c. Plate No. 95 (Series 1) .. 60 30
1667 75 c. Plate No. 5 (Series 1) .. 65 35
1668 90 c. Plate No. 84 (Series 1) .. 75 40
1669 150 c. Plate No. 78 (Series 1) .. 95 60
1670 200 c. Plate No. 79 (Series 1) .. 1·25 80
1671 300 c. Plate No. 83 (Series 1) .. 1·75 1·25
1672 320 c. Plate No. 50 (Series 1) .. 1·75 1·40
1673 360 c. Plate No. 85 (Series 1) .. 1·90 1·50
1663/73 .. .. .. Set of 11 10·00 6·50
Nos. 1663/73 were printed in a similar sheet format to Nos. 1518/33.
For stamps as Nos. 1663/73, but with watermark **106** see Nos. 1775/85.

1986 (24 Mar). *Easter. No. 481 optd with T 354 and surch as T 317, but without the "X", both by Autoprint.*

1674	111	25 c. on 6 c. multicoloured	..	35	10
1675		50 c. on 6 c. multicoloured	..	50	20
1676		100 c. on 6 c. multicoloured	..	75	40
1677		200 c. on 6 c. multicoloured	..	1·50	70
1674/7		.. ..	Set of 4	2·75	1·25

(355) (356)

QUEEN ELIZABETH
1926 1986 1926 150 X 1986

1986 (27 Mar). *60th Anniv of St. John's Ambulance in Guyana. No. 652 surch with T 355 by Autoprint.*

1678	150 c. on 35 c. silver, black and green	..	3·00	55

(Litho Format)

1986 (4 Apr). *Centenary of Publication of Sanders' Reichenbachia (7th issue). Multicoloured designs as T 331. No wmk. P 13½×14 (225 c.) or 14×13½ (others).*

1679	25 c. Plate No. 71 (Series 1) (horiz)	..	60	20
1680	120 c. Plate No. 69 (Series 1) (horiz)	..	1·50	55
1681	150 c. Plate No. 87 (Series 1) (horiz)	..	1·75	65
1682	225 c. Plate No. 60 (Series 1)	..	1·75	60
1683	350 c. Plate No. 94 (Series 1) (horiz)	..	2·25	1·50
1679/83	.. ..	Set of 5	7·00	3·50

Nos. 1679/83 were printed in a similar sheet format to Nos. 1518/33.

For stamps as Nos. 1679/83, but with watermark **106** see Nos. 1786/90.

1986 (21 Apr). *60th Birthday of Queen Elizabeth II. Nos. 1526/7 optd or surch as T 356 by Tip Torres.*

1684	130 c. Plate No. 13 (Series 1)	..	1·50	50
MS1685	100×126 mm. 130 c. on 130 c., 200 c. on 130 c., 260 c. on 130 c., 330 c. on 130 c., Plate No. 6 (Series 1)		4·75	5·00

The original face values on No. **MS** 1685 are obliterated by a floral pattern.

Protect the

GUYANA
INDEPENDENCE
1966-1986
60 25

(357) (358)

1986 (3 May). *Wildlife Protection. Nos. 685, 739/44 and 993/8 surch as T 357 by Tip Torres.*

1686	60 c. on 35 c. Type 174	..	35	35
	a. Block of 6. Nos. 1686/91	..	1·90	
1687	60 c. on 35 c. Trahira ("Haimara")	..	35	35
1688	60 c. on 35 c. Electric Eel	..	35	35
1689	60 c. on 35 c. Golden Rivulus	..	35	35
1690	60 c. on 35 c. Golden Pencilfish	..	35	35
1691	60 c. on 35 c. Four-eyed Fish	..	35	35
1691a	60 c. on 35 c. Red Piranha ("Pirai")	..	5·50	2·00
	ab. Block of 6. Nos. 1691a/f	..	30·00	
1691b	60 c. on 35 c. Smoking Hassar	..	5·50	2·00
1691c	60 c. on 35 c. Manta	..	5·50	2·00
1691d	60 c. on 35 c. Festive Cichlid ("Flying Patwa")	..	5·50	2·00
1691e	60 c. on 35 c. Arapaima ..	..	5·50	2·00
1691f	60 c. on 35 c. Peacock Cichlid ("Lukanani")	..	5·50	2·00
1692	$6 on 8 c. Type 163 ..	..	3·00	2·50
1686/92	.. ..	Set of 13	32·00	15·00

Nos. 1686/91 were previously overprinted with Type **226**.
On No. 1692 the previous value is covered by a fleur-de-lys.

1986 (5 May). *No. 799 surch as T 326 by Autoprint*

1693	600 c. on 720 c. on 60 c. Soldier's Cap	..	10·00	75

1986 (15 May). *125th Anniv of British Guiana Post Office (2nd issue). No. 702a surch as T 324 by Autoprint.*

1694	25 c. on 30 c. multicoloured (surch "Abary")	60	60
	a. Sheetlet of 25. Nos. 1694/1704, 1705×2, 1706/17	13·00	
1695	25 c. on 30 c. mult (surch "Anna Regina")	60	60
1696	25 c. on 30 c. mult (surch "Aurora")	60	60
1697	25 c. on 30 c. mult (surch "Bartica Grove")	60	60
1698	25 c. on 30 c. mult (surch "Bel Air")	60	60
1699	25 c. on 30 c. mult (surch "Belle Plaine") ..	60	60
1700	25 c. on 30 c. multicoloured (surch "Clonbrook")	60	60
1701	25 c. on 30 c. multicoloured (surch "T.P.O. Dem. Railway")	60	60
1702	25 c. on 30 c. mult (surch "Enmore")	60	60
1703	25 c. on 30 c. multicoloured (surch "Fredericksburg")	60	60
1704	25 c. on 30 c. mult (surch "Good Success")	60	60
1705	25 c. on 30 c. multicoloured (surch "1986")	60	60
1706	25 c. on 30 c. mult (surch "Mariabba")	60	60
1707	25 c. on 30 c. multicoloured (surch "Massaruni")	60	60
1708	25 c. on 30 c. multicoloured (surch "Nigg")	60	60
1709	25 c. on 30 c. mult (surch "No. 50")	60	60

1710	25 c. on 30 c. mult (surch "No. 63 Benab")	60	60
1711	25 c. on 30 c. multicoloured (surch "Philadelphia")	60	60
1712	25 c. on 30 c. mult (surch "Sisters")	60	60
1713	25 c. on 30 c. mult (surch "Skeldon")	60	60
1714	25 c. on 30 c. mult (surch "Suddie")	60	60
1715	25 c. on 30 c. multicoloured (surch "Taymouth Manor")	60	60
1716	25 c. on 30 c. multicoloured (surch "Wales")	60	60
1717	25 c. on 30 c. multicoloured (surch "Whim")	60	60
1694/717		Set of 24	13·00	13·00

The surcharged names are those of postal agencies opened between 1860 and 1880.

1986 (26 May). *20th Anniv of Independence. (a) No. 332 surch as T 358 by Autoprint, Nos. 389, 403 surch with "1986", bars and new value by Autoprint and No. 656 surch as T 339 by Tip Torres.*

1718	25 c. on 2 c. myrtle-green (No. 332)	15	10
1719	25 c. on 35 c. multicoloured (No. 656)	15	10
1720	60 c. on 2 c. myrtle-green (No. 332)	25	10
1721	120 c. on 6 c. yellow-green (No. 389)	40	20
1722	130 c. on 24 c. black & brt orange (No. 403)	4·75	30

(b) *Nos. 1188/91 surch as T 358, but without "GUYANA", by Autoprint.*

1723	277	25 c. on 120 c. lake-brown, black and bright blue (No. 1188)	..	25	20
		a. Block of 4. Nos. 1723/6	..	1·25	
1724	—	25 c. on 130 c. rose-red, black and bright blue (No. 1189)	..	25	20
1725	—	25 c. on 150 c. bright violet, black and bright blue (No. 1190)	..	25	20
1726	—	225 c. on 200 c. dull green, black and bright blue (No. 1191)	..	65	60
1718/26			Set of 9	6·50	1·75

On Nos. 1721/2 "1986" has been added below the existing overprint.

Nos. 1718 and 1720 have Mult Script CA watermark, No. 1721 watermark w **12** upright and No. 1722 watermark w **12** sideways.

MEXICO
1986

225 CARICOM
DAY 1986

(359) (360)

1986 (31 May). *World Cup Football Championship, Mexico (2nd issue). No. 544 surch with T 359 in blue by Autoprint.*

1727	225 c. on 3 c. Hanging Heliconia	..	8·50	70

1986 (28 June). *CARICOM Day. No. 705a optd with T 360 in blue by Autoprint.*

1728	60 c. Papilio androgeus	..	..	6·00	30

CARICOM HEADS OF GOVT CONFERENCE JULY 1986 60

INT. YEAR OF PEACE 25

(361) (362)

1986 (1 July). *CARICOM Heads of Government Conference, Georgetown. Nos. 544 and 601 surch as T 361 in blue by Autoprint.*

1729	25 c. on 8 c. on 6 c. Cannon-ball Tree	..	1·25	10
1730	60 c. on 3 c. Hanging Heliconia	..	1·75	25

(Litho Format)

1986 (10 July). *Centenary of Publication of Sanders' Reichenbachia (8th issue). Vert designs as T 331. Multicoloured. No wmk. P 13½×14.*

1731	30 c. Plate No. 86 (Series 1)	..	50	15
1732	55 c. Plate No. 17 (Series 1)	..	50	20
1733	60 c. Plate No. 93 (Series 1)	..	50	20
1734	100 c. Plate No. 68 (Series 1)	..	1·00	20
1735	130 c. Plate No. 91 (Series 1)	..	1·10	30
1736	250 c. Plate No. 74 (Series 1)	..	75	60
1737	260 c. Plate No. 39 (Series 1)	..	75	60
1738	375 c. Plate No. 90 (Series 1)	..	2·25	85
1731/8		Set of 8	6·50	2·75

Nos. 1731/8 were printed in a similar sheet format to Nos. 1518/33.

For stamps as Nos. 1731/8, but with watermark **106** see Nos. 1791/8.

For these designs with different face values see Nos. 1822, 1868 and 1884/5.

1986 (14 July). *International Peace Year. Nos. 542 and 546 surch as T 362 in blue (No. 1739) or black (others).*

1739	25 c. on 1 c. Pitcher Plant of Mt Roraima ..	20	20
	a. Sheetlet of 25. No. 1739×24 and one label	4·00	
1740	60 c. on 6 c. Cannon-ball Tree	50	50
	a. Sheetlet of 25. Nos. 1740/3, each×4, and nine labels	7·00	
1741	120 c. on 6 c. Cannon-ball Tree	50	50
1742	130 c. on 6 c. Cannon-ball Tree	50	50
1743	150 c. on 6 c. Cannon-ball Tree	50	50
1739/43		Set of 5	2·00	2·00

As surcharged the sheet of No. 1739 contained a stamp

without face value, overprinted "1986", in the centre position. Nos. 1740/3 were each surcharged in blocks of four from the corner positions of the same sheet. Stamps in the central horizontal and vertical rows were without value and were overprinted with one letter of "PEACE".

HALLEY'S COMET 1910
320 c
GUYANA
POSTAGE & REVENUE
2 CENTS
STAMP IN USE IN 1910

363 Halley's Comet and British Guiana 1907 2 c. Stamp

(Litho Format)

1986 (19 July). *Appearance of Halley's Comet. T 363 and similar vert design. P 13½×14.*

1744	363	320 c. rosine, black & deep reddish lilac	30	50
		a. Horiz pair. Nos. 1744/5 ..	60	1·00
		ab. Imperf between (horiz pair)		
1745	—	320 c. multicoloured	30	50
MS1746	76×50 mm. Nos. 1744/5. Imperf	1·50	1·50

Design:—No. 1745, Guyana 1985 320 c. Scarlet Macaw stamp.

(Litho Format)

1986 (24 July). *Centenary of Publication of Sanders' Reichenbachia (9th issue). Vert designs as T 331. Multicoloured. No wmk. P 13½×14.*

1747	40 c. Plate No. 96 (Series 1)	..	90	15
1748	45 c. Plate No. 81 (Series 1)	..	30	15
1749	90 c. Plate No. 89 (Series 1)	..	50	20
1750	100 c. Plate No. 88 (Series 1)	..	1·50	20
1751	150 c. Plate No. 76 (Series 1)	..	1·75	35
1752	180 c. Plate No. 15 (Series 1)	..	50	40
1753	320 c. Plate No. 82 (Series 1)	..	60	70
1754	330 c. Plate No. 80 (Series 1)	..	1·75	90
1747/54		Set of 8	7·00	2·75

Nos. 1747/54 were printed in a similar sheet format to Nos. 1518/33.

For stamps as Nos. 1747/54, but with watermark **106** see Nos. 1799/1806.

1986 (28 July). *No. 489 surch as T 317, but without the "X".*

1755	20 c. on 6 c. Patua ..	..	..	3·75	15

GUSIA 1936-1986

REGIONAL
PHARMACY
CONFERENCE
1986
130

(364) (365)

1986 (15 Aug). *50th Anniv of Guyana United Sadr Islamic Association. Nos. 469/70 optd or surch as T 364 by Autoprint.*

1756	105	25 c. black, gold and lilac	..	1·50	10
1757		$1.50 on 6 c. black, gold and flesh	..	3·00	80

1986 (19 Aug). *Regional Pharmacy Conference. No. 545 surch with T 365 in blue.*

1758	130 c. on 5 c. Annatto Tree..		4·50	30

1986 (21 Aug)–87. *As previous Reichenbachia issues, but W 106 (sideways on horiz designs). P 13½×14 (vert) or 14×13½ (horiz).*

(a) *As Nos. 1526/7 and 1529/30*

1759	130 c. Plate No. 6 (Series 1)	..	..	75	20
1760	130 c. Plate No. 13 (Series 1)	..	..	75	20
1761	130 c. Plate No. 20 (Series 1)	..	..	75	20
1762	130 c. Plate No. 25 (Series 1)	..	..	75	20
1759/62	.. ..		Set of 4	2·75	70

(b) *As Nos. 1552/5*

1763	55 c. Plate No. 9 (Series 1)	..	..	30	10
1764	55 c. Plate No. 22 (Series 1)	..	..	30	10
1765	55 c. Plate No. 49 (Series 1)	..	..	30	10
1766	55 c. Plate No. 64 (Series 1)	..	..	30	10
1763/6	..		Set of 4	1·10	30

(c) *As Nos. 1581/3 and 1586*

1767	150 c. Plate No. 40 (Series 1) (horiz)	..	45	20
1768	150 c. Plate No. 42 (Series 1) (horiz)	..	45	20
1769	150 c. Plate No. 45 (Series 1) (horiz)	..	45	20
1770	200 c. Plate No. 43 (Series 1) (horiz)	..	55	30
1767/70	..	Set of 4	1·75	80

(d) *As Nos. 1621, 1625/6 and 1635*

1771	30 c. Plate No. 53 (Series 1) (10.86)	..	30	10
1772	75 c. Plate No. 55 (Series 1) (1.87)	..	35	15
1773	100 c. Plate No. 65 (Series 1) (1.87)	..	35	15
1774	225 c. Plate No. 24 (Series 1) (10.86)	..	45	35
1771/4		Set of 4	1·25	60

(e) *As Nos. 1663/73 (1987)*

1775	40 c. Plate No. 77 (Series 1)	..	1·50	1·50
1776	45 c. Plate No. 54 (Series 1)	..	1·50	1·50
1777	50 c. Plate No. 92 (Series 1)	..	1·50	1·50
1778	60 c. Plate No. 95 (Series 1)	..	2·00	2·00
1779	75 c. Plate No. 5 (Series 1)	..	2·50	2·50

1780	90 c. Plate No. 84 (Series 1)	..	..	3·00	3·00
1781	150 c. Plate No. 78 (Series 1)	..	..	5·00	5·00
1782	200 c. Plate No. 79 (Series 1)	..	..	6·50	6·50
1783	300 c. Plate No. 83 (Series 1)	..	..	10·00	10·00
1784	320 c. Plate No. 50 (Series 1)	..	..	11·00	11·00
1785	360 c. Plate No. 85 (Series 1)	..	..	12·50	12·50
1775/85			*Set of 11*	50·00	50·00

(f) As Nos. 1679/83 (1987)

1786	25 c. Plate No. 71 (Series 1)	..	..	1·50	1·50
1787	120 c. Plate No. 69 (Series 1)	..	..	6·00	6·00
1788	150 c. Plate No. 87 (Series 1)	..	..	7·00	7·00
1789	225 c. Plate No. 60 (Series 1)	..	..	8·50	8·50
1790	350 c. Plate No. 94 (Series 1)	..	..	15·00	15·00
1786/90			*Set of 5*	32·00	32·00

(g) As Nos. 1731/8 (1987)

1791	30 c. Plate No. 86 (Series 1)	..	..	1·00	1·00
1792	55 c. Plate No. 17 (Series 1)	..	..	1·50	1·50
1793	60 c. Plate No. 93 (Series 1)	..	..	1·50	1·50
1794	100 c. Plate No. 68 (Series 1)	..	..	2·00	2·00
1795	130 c. Plate No. 91 (Series 1)	..	..	2·50	2·50
1796	250 c. Plate No. 74 (Series 1)	..	..	5·00	5·00
1797	260 c. Plate No. 39 (Series 1)	..	..	5·00	5·00
1798	375 c. Plate No. 90 (Series 1)	..	..	7·00	7·00
1791/8			*Set of 8*	20·00	20·00

(h) As Nos. 1747/54 (1987)

1799	40 c. Plate No. 96 (Series 1)	..	..	1·00	1·00
1800	45 c. Plate No. 81 (Series 1)	..	..	1·00	1·00
1801	90 c. Plate No. 89 (Series 1)	..	..	2·00	2·00
1802	100 c. Plate No. 88 (Series 1)	..	..	2·00	2·00
1803	150 c. Plate No. 76 (Series 1)	..	..	3·00	3·00
1804	180 c. Plate No. 15 (Series 1)	..	..	4·00	4·00
1805	320 c. Plate No. 82 (Series 1)	..	..	5·50	5·50
1806	330 c. Plate No. 80 (Series 1)	..	..	6·50	6·50
1799/1806			*Set of 8*	22·00	22·00

Nos. 1759/1806 were printed in a similar sheet format to Nos. 1518/33.

These stamps, together with other unwatermarked values from the 1st to the 9th issues, also exist made up into two small books which reproduce the order of the plates in the original volumes.

Some designs in these booklets show changed face values, as detailed below, but there is no evidence that such printings were available for postal purposes without surcharge.

Plate No. 5	=	60 c.	Plate No. 76	= 65 c.
Plate No. 6	=	100 c.	Plate No. 77	= 45 c.
Plate No. 9	=	50 c.	Plate No. 78	= 45 c.
Plate No. 13	=	100 c.	Plate No. 79	= 60 c.
Plate No. 15	=	55 c.	Plate No. 80	= 65 c.
Plate No. 22	=	50 c.	Plate No. 81	= 55 c.
Plate No. 24	=	50 c.	Plate No. 82	= 55 c.
Plate No. 25	=	100 c.	Plate No. 83	= 75 c.
Plate No. 39	=	80 c.	Plate No. 84	= 45 c.
Plate No. 40	=	100 c.	Plate No. 85	= 45 c.
Plate No. 43	=	100 c.	Plate No. 87	= 60 c.
Plate No. 45	=	100 c.	Plate No. 88	= 65 c.
Plate No. 50	=	60 c.	Plate No. 89	= 55 c.
Plate No. 53	=	50 c.	Plate No. 90	= 40 c.
Plate No. 54	=	60 c.	Plate No. 92	= 75 c.
Plate No. 60	=	75 c.	Plate No. 93	= 80 c.
Plate No. 65	=	50 c.	Plate No. 94	= 60 c.
Plate No. 69	=	60 c.	Plate No. 95	= 75 c.
Plate No. 71	=	60 c.	Plate No. 96	= 65 c.
Plate No. 74	=	80 c.		

See also after No. 2471.

1986 (21 Aug). *Booklet and Coil Stamps. As Nos. 1534/5b, but W 14 × 13½ (sideways on Nos. 1807a, 1808a/b).*

1807	*332* 25 c. multicoloured (*imperf × p 14*)		20	25
1807a	25 c. multicoloured (*imperf × p 13½*)		20	25
1807b	25 c. multicoloured (*p 13½×14*)		20	25
1808	25 c. multicoloured (*p 13½×imperf*)		20	25
1808a	25 c. multicoloured (*p 14×imperf*)		20	25
1808b	25 c. multicoloured (*p 14×13½*)		20	25
1807/8b		*Set of 6*	1·10	1·40

The note below Nos. 1534/5b also applies to Nos. 1807/8b.

(Litho Format)

1986 (23 Sept). *Centenary of Publication of Sanders' Reichenbachia (10th issue). Multicoloured designs as T 331. No wmk. P 14 × 13½ (Nos. 1810, 1812, 1815, 1818) or 13½ × 14 (others).*

1809	30 c. Plate No. 30 (Series 2)	..	50	15
1810	45 c. Plate No. 21 (Series 2) (*horiz*)		50	15
1811	75 c. Plate No. 8 (Series 2)	..	50	15
1812	80 c. Plate No. 42 (Series 2) (*horiz*)		50	15
1813	90 c. Plate No. 4 (Series 2)	..	55	25
1814	130 c. Plate No. 38 (Series 2)	..	1·50	35
1815	160 c. Plate No. 5 (Series 2) (*horiz*)		1·75	40
1816	200 c. Plate No. 9 (Series 2)	..	75	50
1817	320 c. Plate No. 12 (Series 2)	..	1·50	70
1818	350 c. Plate No. 29 (Series 2) (*horiz*)		1·75	70
1819	360 c. Plate No. 34 (Series 2)	..	3·00	70
1809/19		*Set of 11*	11·50	3·75

Nos. 1809/19, together with Nos. 1820/1a, were printed in a similar sheet format to Nos. 1518/33.

(Litho Format)

1986 (23 Sept). *20th Anniv of Independence (2nd issue). T 332 additionally inscr "1966–1986" at foot. No wmk.*

1820	25 c. multicoloured (*imperf×p 14*)		20	25
1821	25 c. multicoloured (*p 13½×imperf*)		20	25
1821a	25 c. multicoloured (*p 13½×14*)		20	25
1820/1a		*Set of 3*	55	65

Nos. 1820/1a together with Nos. 1809/19, were printed in the sheet format described beneath No. 1533. They were only issued in booklets or coils.

(Litho Format)

1986 (26 Sept). *Centenary of Publication of Sanders' Reichenbachia (11th issue). Design as No. 1735, but with different face value. Multicoloured. No wmk. P 13½×14.*

1822	40 c. Plate No. 91 (Series 1)	..	75	15

650 🌿

(366) 120

(367) 12th World Orchid Conference TOKYO JAPAN MARCH 1987

1986 (3 Oct). *Nos. 1361/84 surch with T 366 by Autoprint.*

1823	120 c. on 30 c. multicoloured (No. 1361)	..	90	90
	a. Sheetlet of 25. Nos. 1823/33, 1834×2 and 1835/46		19·00	
1824	120 c. on 30 c. multicoloured (No. 1362)	..	90	90
1825	120 c. on 30 c. multicoloured (No. 1363)	..	90	90
1826	120 c. on 30 c. multicoloured (No. 1364)	..	90	90
1827	120 c. on 30 c. multicoloured (No. 1365)	..	90	90
1828	120 c. on 30 c. multicoloured (No. 1366)	..	90	90
1829	120 c. on 30 c. multicoloured (No. 1367)	..	90	90
1830	120 c. on 30 c. multicoloured (No. 1368)	..	90	90
1831	120 c. on 30 c. multicoloured (No. 1369)	..	90	90
1832	120 c. on 30 c. multicoloured (No. 1370)	..	90	90
1833	120 c. on 30 c. multicoloured (No. 1371)	..	90	90
1834	120 c. on 30 c. multicoloured (No. 1372)	..	90	90
1835	120 c. on 30 c. multicoloured (No. 1373)	..	90	90
1836	120 c. on 30 c. multicoloured (No. 1374)	..	90	90
1837	120 c. on 30 c. multicoloured (No. 1375)	..	90	90
1838	120 c. on 30 c. multicoloured (No. 1376)	..	90	90
1839	120 c. on 30 c. multicoloured (No. 1377)	..	90	90
1840	120 c. on 30 c. multicoloured (No. 1378)	..	90	90
1841	120 c. on 30 c. multicoloured (No. 1379)	..	90	90
1842	120 c. on 30 c. multicoloured (No. 1380)	..	90	90
1843	120 c. on 30 c. multicoloured (No. 1381)	..	90	90
1844	120 c. on 30 c. multicoloured (No. 1382)	..	90	90
1845	120 c. on 30 c. multicoloured (No. 1383)	..	90	90
1846	120 c. on 30 c. multicoloured (No. 1384)	..	90	90
1823/46	.. ..	*Set of 24*	19·00	19·00

1986 (6 Oct). *12th World Orchid Conference, Tokyo (1st issue). Unissued design as No. 1731, but with different face value, surch with T 367 by Tip Torres.*

1847	650 c. on 40 c. Plate No. 86 (Series 1)	..	8·50	3·75

No. 1847 is inscribed "ONTOGLOSSUM TRIUMPHANS" in error.

See also Nos. 2138/9.

⚜️

1492-1992 CHRISTOPHER COLUMBUS

320

(368)

1986 (10–30 Oct). *Columbus Day. Unissued design as No. 1635, but with different face value, surch with T 368 by Tip Torres.*

1864	320 c. on 150 c. Plate No. 24 (Series 1) (surch in black (figures and obliterating device) and red) ..	..	2·50	90
1865	320 c. on 150 c. Plate No. 24 (Series 1) (entire surch in red) (30 Oct)	..	2·50	90

AIR UNICEF 1946-1986

1986 50

120

(369)

(370)

1986 (15 Oct). *International Food Day. Nos. 1170/1 further surch as T 369 by Autoprint.*

1866	50 c. on 30 c. on 1 c. Type 87	..	1·50	15
1867	225 c. on $2.60 on 3 c. Peacock Cichlid ("Lukunani")	..	4·50	75

(Litho Format)

1986 (23 Oct). *Centenary of Publication of Sanders' Reichenbachia (12th issue). Vert designs as T 331, one as No. 1731 with different face value. Multicoloured. No wmk. P 13½ × 14.*

1868	40 c. Plate No. 86 (Series 1)	..	50	15
1869	90 c. Plate No. 10 (Series 2)	..	75	30

1986 (24 Oct). *Air. 40th Anniv of U.N.I.C.E.F. and U.N.E.S.C.O. No. 706 surch as T 370 by Autoprint.*

1870	120 c. on $1 Type 167 (surch T 370)		3·75	3·75
	a. Pair. Nos. 1870/1		7·50	7·50
1871	120 c. on $1 Type 167 (surch "UNESCO 1946–1986")		3·75	3·75

Nos. 1870/1 were surcharged together, *se-tenant*, in horizontal and vertical pairs throughout the sheet.

(Litho Format)

1986 (30 Oct). *Centenary of Publication of Sanders' Reichenbachia (13th issue). Vert designs as T 331. Multicoloured. No wmk. P 13½ × 14.*

1872	45 c. Plate No. 17 (Series 2)	..	30	15
1873	50 c. Plate No. 33 (Series 2)	..	30	15
1874	60 c. Plate No. 27 (Series 2)	..	45	15
1875	75 c. Plate No. 56 (Series 2)	..	55	20
1876	85 c. Plate No. 45 (Series 2)	..	2·00	20
1877	90 c. Plate No. 13 (Series 2)	..	70	20
1878	200 c. Plate No. 44 (Series 2)	..	1·00	45
1879	300 c. Plate No. 50 (Series 2)	..	1·50	60
1880	320 c. Plate No. 10 (Series 2)	..	1·50	70
1881	390 c. Plate No. 6 (Series 2)	..	1·50	95
1872/81		*Set of 10*	9·00	3·25

Nos. 1872/81 were printed in a similar sheet format to Nos. 1518/33.

For these designs with different face values see Nos. 1907, 1915 and 1925.

25 **X** CHRISTMAS 1986

Deepavali 1986

20

(371)

(372)

1986 (3 Nov). *Deepavali Festival. Nos. 543 and 601 surch as T 371 by Autoprint.*

1882	25 c. on 2 c. Type 132	..	75	10
1883	200 c. on 8 c. on 6 c. Cannon-ball Tree	..	2·25	40

(Litho Format)

1986 (25 Nov). *Centenary of Publication of Sanders' Reichenbachia (14th issue). Vert designs as T 331, two as Nos. 1732 and 1734 with different face values. Multicoloured. No wmk. P 13½×14.*

1884	40 c. Plate No. 68 (Series 1)	..	1·25	15
1885	80 c. Plate No. 17 (Series 1)	..	2·00	25
1886	200 c. Plate No. 2 (Series 2)	..	1·40	60
1887	225 c. Plate No. 24 (Series 2)	..	1·40	70
1884/7		*Set of 4*	5·50	1·50

Nos. 1884/7 were printed in a similar sheet format to Nos. 1518/33.

For these designs with different face values see Nos. 1914 and 1929.

1986 (26 Nov). *Christmas. No. 452 surch with T 372 and previously unissued miniature sheet containing Nos. 1425/9, each surch as T 342, but without dates, all in red by Autoprint.*

1888	20 c. on 6 c. Black Acara ("Patua")	..	1·25	10
MS1889	215×75 mm. 120 c. on 60 c. × 5 Nos. 1425/9	..	7·00	7·00

1986

$15 ▬▬▬

(373)

(374)

1986 (26 Nov). *Wildlife Protection. Nos. 756/67 optd with T 373 in blue by Autoprint.*

1894	30 c. Type 178	..	90	90
	a. Sheetlet of 12. Nos. 1894/905..	9·50		
1895	30 c. Red Howler	..	90	90
1896	30 c. Common Squirrel-Monkey	..	90	90
1897	30 c. Two-toed Sloth..	..	90	90
1898	30 c. Brazilian Tapir	..	90	90
1899	30 c. Collared Peccary	..	90	90
1900	30 c. Six-banded Armadillo..	..	90	90
1901	30 c. Tamandua ("Ant Eater")	..	90	90
1902	30 c. Giant Anteater	..	90	90
1903	30 c. Murine Opossum	..	90	90
1904	30 c. Brown Four-eyed Opossum	..	90	90
1905	30 c. Brazilian Agouti	..	90	90
1894/905		*Set of 12*	9·50	9·50

1986 (1 Dec). *No. 1642 surch with T 374 in red by Autoprint.*

1906	$15 on $3.50, Clive Lloyd with the Prudential Cup ..	..	22·00	13·00

(Litho Format)

1986 (3 Dec). *Centenary of Publication of Sanders' Reichenbachia (15th issue). Design as No. 1877, but with different face value. Multicoloured. No wmk. P 13½×14.*
1907   50 c. Plate No. 13 (Series 2)   65   15

G P O C

$10

375 Memorial   1977   1987   (376)

(Litho Format)

1986 (13 Dec). *President Burnham Commemoration. T 375 and similar multicoloured designs. P 12½.*
1908   25 c. Type 375   10   10
1909   120 c. Map of Guyana and flags   20   20
1910   130 c. Parliament Buildings and mace   ..   20   20
1911 $6 L. F. Burnham and Georgetown mayoral chain (vert)   60   1·25
1908/11   ..   ..   ..   Set of 4   90   1·60

(Litho Format)

1986 (15–22 Dec). *Centenary of Publication of Sanders' Reichenbachia (16th issue). Multicoloured designs as Nos. 1554/5, 1874 and 1887 with different face values. W 106 (Nos. 1912/13) or no wmk (others). P 13½×14.*
1912   50 c. Plate No. 49 (Series 1) (22.12)   ..   75   20
1913   50 c. Plate No. 64 (Series 1)   75   20
1914   85 c. Plate No. 24 (Series 2)   75   35
1915   90 c. Plate No. 27 (Series 2)   75   35
1912/15   ..   ..   ..   Set of 4   2·75   1·00

(Litho Format)

1986 (27 Dec). *Centenary of Publication of Sanders' Reichenbachia (17th issue). Vert designs as T 331. Multicoloured. No wmk. P 13½×14.*
1916   25 c. Plate No. 20 (Series 2)   ..   35   15
1917   40 c. Plate No. 7 (Series 2)   ..   35   15
1918   85 c. Plate No. 15 (Series 2)   ..   50   20
1919   90 c. Plate No. 3 (Series 2)   ..   50   20
1920   120 c. Plate No. 14 (Series 2)   ..   50   30
1921   130 c. Plate No. 32 (Series 2)   ..   50   30
1922   150 c. Plate No. 22 (Series 2)   ..   60   35
1923   320 c. Plate No. 18 (Series 2)   ..   80   55
1924   330 c. Plate No. 28 (Series 2)   ..   80   70
1916/24   ..   ..   ..   Set of 9   4·50   2·75

Nos. 1916/24 were printed in a similar sheet format to Nos. 1518/33.
For these designs with different face values see Nos. 1926 and 1928.

(Litho Format)

1987 (5–16 Jan). *Centenary of Publication of Sanders' Reichenbachia (18th issue). Multicoloured designs as Nos. 1625, 1876, 1886, 1918 and 1923 with different face values. W 106 (No. 1927) or no wmk (others). P 13½×14.*
1925   35 c. Plate No. 45 (Series 2)   ..   40   15
1926   50 c. Plate No. 15 (Series 2)   ..   40   15
1927   50 c. Plate No. 55 (Series 1) (16.1)   ..   40   15
1928   85 c. Plate No. 18 (Series 2)   ..   1·25   25
1929   90 c. Plate No. 2 (Series 2)   ..   50   25
1925/9   ..   ..   ..   Set of 5   2·75   85

Nos. 1925/9 were printed in a similar sheet format to Nos. 1518/33.

1987 (19 Jan). *10th Anniv of Guyana Post Office Corporation (1st issue). Unissued designs as Nos. 1621 and 1635, but with different face values, surch or optd as T 376 by Tip Torres.*
1930 $2.25, Plate No. 53 (Series 1)   ..   1·50   35
1931 $10 on 150 c. Plate No. 24 (Series 1)   ..   4·00   4·50
See also Nos. 2074/80.

200

(377)   (378)

200

TWO DOLLARS

(379)   (380)

1987

15.00

(381)

225   120

(382)   (383)

120

(384)

1987 (9 Feb–Sept). *Various Reichenbachia issues surch as T 377/84.*

(a) As T 377 in red by Tip Torres (9 Feb)
1932   200 c. on 40 c. Plate No. 90 (Series 1)   60   50

(b) As T 378 by Tip Torres (6 Mar)
1933   200 c. on 25 c. Plate No. 8 (Series 1) (No. 1571)   60   50
1934   200 c. on 25 c. Plate No. 51 (Series 1) (No. 1573)   60   50

(c) As T 379 by Tip Torres (No. 1935 without ornament) (6 Mar)
1935 $2 on 25 c. Plate No. 12 (Series 1) (No. 1518)   60   50
1936 $2 on 25 c. Plate No. 23 (Series 1) (No. 1572)   60   50

(d) As T 380 by Tip Torres (17 Mar)
1937   200 c. on 40 c. Plate No. 68 (Series 1) (No. 1884) (ornament inverted)   60   50
   a. Ornament upright   60   50
1938   200 c. on 40 c. Plate No. 90 (Series 1)   60   50
1939   200 c. on 50 c. Plate No. 92 (Series 1) (No. 1665)   60   50
1940   200 c. on 50 c. Plate No. 22 (Series 1) (wmkd)   60   50
1941   200 c. on 55 c. Plate No. 22 (Series 1) (No. 1764) (wmkd)   60   50
1942   200 c. on 60 c. Plate No. 5 (Series 1) (ornament inverted)   60   50
1943   200 c. on 75 c. Plate No. 5 (Series 1) (No. 1667) (ornament inverted)   60   50
1944   200 c. on 75 c. Plate No. 60 (Series 1)   60   50
1945   200 c. on 75 c. Plate No. 92 (Series 1)   60   50
1946   200 c. on 85 c. Plate No. 18 (Series 2) (No. 1928)   60   50
1947   200 c. on 375 c. Plate No. 90 (Series 1) (No. 1738)   60   50
1948   200 c. on 375 c. Plate No. 90 (Series 1) (No. 1798) (wmkd)   60   50
1937/48   ..   ..   Set of 12   6·50   5·50

(e) As T 377 by Tip Torres (March)
1949   200 c. on 25 c. Plate No. 52 (Series 1) (No. 1551)   60   50
1950   200 c. on 25 c. Plate No 8 (Series 1) (No. 1571)   60   50
1951   200 c. on 25 c. Plate No. 72 (Series 1) (No. 1577)   60   50
1952   200 c. on 25 c. Plate No. 71 (Series 1) (No. 1679) (surch vert—reading downwards)   60   50
1953   200 c. on 30 c. Plate No. 86 (Series 1) (No. 1731)   60   50

1954   200 c. on 30 c. Plate No. 53 (Series 1) (No. 1771) (wmkd)   60   50
1955   200 c. on 40 c. Plate No. 77 (Series 1) (No. 1663)   60   50
1956   200 c. on 40 c. Plate No. 86 (Series 1) (No. 1868)   60   50
   a. Inscr "ONTOGLOSSUM TRIUMPHANS" in error
1957   220 c. on 45 c. Plate No. 81 (Series 1) (No. 1748)   60   50
1958   200 c. on 45 c. Plate No. 77 (Series 1)   60   50
1959   200 c. on 45 c. Plate No. 78 (Series 1)   60   50
1960   200 c. on 45 c. Plate No. 85 (Series 1)   60   50
1961   200 c. on 50 c. Plate No. 24 (Series 1) (wmkd)   60   50
1962   200 c. on 50 c. Plate No. 53 (Series 1) (wmkd)   60   50
1963   200 c. on 50 c. Plate No. 65 (Series 1) (wmkd)   60   50
1964   200 c. on 55 c. Plate No. 49 (Series 1) (No. 1554)   60   50
1965   200 c. on 55 c. Plate No. 17 (Series 1) (No. 1732)   60   50
1966   200 c. on 55 c. Plate No. 49 (Series 1) (No. 1765) (wmkd)   60   50
1967   200 c. on 60 c. Plate No. 7 (Series 1) (No. 1520)   60   50
1968   200 c. on 60 c. Plate No. 10 (Series 1) (No. 1521)   60   50
1969   200 c. on 60 c. Plate No. 19 (Series 1) (No. 1522)   60   50
1970   200 c. on 60 c. Plate No. 31 (Series 1) (No. 1523)   60   50
1971   200 c. on 60 c. Plate No. 44 (Series 1) (No. 1556)   60   50
1972   200 c. on 60 c. Plate No. 47 (Series 1) (No. 1557)   60   50
1973   200 c. on 60 c. Plate No. 57 (Series 1) (No. 1622) (surch vert – reading down)   60   50
1974   200 c. on 60 c. Plate No. 73 (Series 1) (No. 1623) (surch vert – reading up)   60   50
1975   200 c. on 60 c. Plate No. 75 (Series 1) (No. 1624) (surch vert – reading down)   60   50
1976   200 c. on 60 c. Plate No. 71 (Series 1) (surch vert – reading down)   60   50
1977   200 c. on 60 c. Plate No. 87 (Series 1) (surch vert–reading down)   60   50
1977a   200 c. on 80 c. Plate No. 17 (Series 1) (No. 1885)   1·50   1·25
1978   225 c. on 90 c. Plate No. 89 (Series 1) (No. 1749)   65   55
1949/78   ..   ..   Set of 31   17·00   14·00

(f) As T 381 by Gardy Ptg (March)
1979   120 c. on 50 c. Plate No. 9 (Series 1) (wmkd)   50   30
1980   120 c. on 55 c. Plate No. 9 (Series 1) (No. 1552)   50   30
1981   120 c. on 55 c. Plate No. 64 (Series 1) (No. 1555)   50   30
1981a   120 c. on 55 c. Plate No. 9 (Series 1) (No. 1763) (wmkd)   1·50   1·00
1982   120 c. on 55 c. Plate No. 64 (Series 1) (No. 1766) (wmkd)   50   30
1983 $10 on 25 c. Plate No. 53 (Series 1)   2·00   2·25
1984 $12 on 80 c. Plate No. 74 (Series 1)   2·25   2·50
1985 $15 on 80 c. Plate No. 39 (Series 1)   2·75   3·00
1986 $25 on 25 c. Plate No. 53 (Series 1)   4·50   5·00
1979/86   ..   ..   Set of 9   13·50   13·50

Nos. 1979/82 do not show a date as part of the surcharge. On No. 1986 the surcharge is achieved by a dollar sign in front of the original face value.

(g) With T 382 by Gardy Ptg (June)
1987   225 c. on 40 c. Plate No. 91 (Series 1) (No. 1822)   70   60
1988   225 c. on 40 c. Plate No. 90 (Series 1)   70   60
1988a   225 c. on 50 c. Plate No. 92 (Series 1) No. 1665)   10·00   3·00
1989   225 c. on 50 c. Plate No. 22 (Series 1) (wmkd)   70   60
1990   225 c. on 60 c. Plate No. 55 (Series 1) (No. 1597)   70   60
1990a   225 c. on 60 c. Plate No. 95 (Series 1) (No. 1666)   10·00   3·00
1991   225 c. on 60 c. Plate No. 93 (Series 1) (No. 1733)   70   60
1992   225 c. on 80 c. Plate No. 93 (Series 1)   70   60
1993   225 c. on 150 c. Plate No. 42 (Series 1) (No. 1657) (surch vert–reading down)   70   60
1987/93   ..   ..   Set of 9   22·00   9·00

(h) As T 383 (July)
1994   120 c. on 50 c. Plate No. 49 (Series 1) (No. 1912) (wmkd)   50   40
1995   120 c. on 50 c. Plate No. 64 (Series 1) (No. 1913) (wmkd)   50   40
1996   120 c. on 50 c. Plate No. 9 (Series 1) (wmkd)   50   40
1997   120 c. on 50 c. Plate No. 22 (Series 1) (wmkd)   50   40
1998   120 c. on 50 c. Plate No. 3 (Series 2)   50   40
1999   120 c. on 50 c. Plate No. 6 (Series 2)   50   40
2000   120 c. on 50 c. Plate No. 20 (Series 2)   50   40
2001   120 c. on 50 c. Plate No. 32 (Series 2)   50   40
2002   120 c. on 55 c. Plate No. 9 (Series 1) (No. 1552)   50   40
2003   120 c. on 55 c. Plate No. 49 (Series 1) (No. 1554)   50   40
2004   120 c. on 55 c. Plate No. 64 (Series 1) (No. 1555)   50   40
2005   120 c. on 55 c. Plate No. 9 (Series 1) (No. 1763) (wmkd)   50   40
2006   120 c. on 55 c. Plate No. 22 (Series 1) (No. 1764) (wmkd)   50   40
2007   120 c. on 55 c. Plate No. 49 (Series 1) (No. 1765) (wmkd)   50   40
2008   120 c. on 55 c. Plate No. 64 (Series 1) (No. 1766) (wmkd)   50   40
2009   120 c. on 55 c. Plate No. 15 (Series 1)   50   40
2010   120 c. on 55 c. Plate No. 81 (Series 1)   50   40
2011   120 c. on 55 c. Plate No. 82 (Series 1)   50   40
2012   120 c. on 55 c. Plate No. 89 (Series 1)   50   40
1994/2012   ..   ..   Set of 19   8·50   7·00

	(i) As T 384 by Gardy Ptg (Sept)		
2013	120 c. on 40 c. Plate No. 91 (Series 1) (No. 1822)	50	40
2014	120 c. on 40 c. Plate No. 90 (Series 1)	50	40
2015	120 c. on 50 c. Plate No. 49 (Series 1) (No. 1912) (wmkd)	50	40
2016	120 c. on 50 c. Plate No. 64 (Series 1) (No. 1913) (wmkd)	50	40
2017	120 c. on 50 c. Plate No. 9 (Series 1) (wmkd)	50	40
2018	120 c. on 50 c. Plate No. 22 (Series 1) (wmkd)	50	40
2019	120 c. on 50 c. Plate No. 24 (Series 1) (wmkd)	50	40
2020	120 c. on 50 c. Plate No. 53 (Series 1) (wmkd)	50	40
2021	120 c. on 50 c. Plate No. 65 (Series 1) (wmkd)	50	40
2022	120 c. on 55 c. Plate No. 9 (Series 1) (No. 1763) (wmkd)	50	40
2023	120 c. on 55 c. Plate No. 22 (Series 1) (No. 1764) (wmkd)	50	40
2024	120 c. on 55 c. Plate No. 49 (Series 1) (No. 1765) (wmkd)	50	40
2025	120 c. on 55 c. Plate No. 64 (Series 1) (No. 1766) (wmkd)	50	40
2026	120 c. on 60 c. Plate No. 2 (Series 1) (No. 1519)	50	40
2027	120 c. on 60 c. Plate No. 10 (Series 1) (No. 1521)	50	40
2028	120 c. on 60 c. Plate No. 19 (Series 1) (No. 1522)	50	40
2029	120 c. on 60 c. Plate No. 31 (Series 1) (No. 1523)	50	40
2030	120 c. on 60 c. Plate No. 5 (Series 1)	50	40
2031	120 c. on 60 c. Plate No. 50 (Series 1)	50	40
2032	120 c. on 60 c. Plate No. 54 (Series 1)	50	40
2033	120 c. on 60 c. Plate No. 69 (Series 1) (surch vert – reading down)	50	40
2034	120 c. on 60 c. Plate No. 71 (Series 1) (surch vert – reading up)	50	40
	a. Surch reading down	50	40
2035	120 c. on 60 c. Plate No. 79 (Series 1)	50	40
2036	120 c. on 60 c. Plate No. 87 (Series 1) (surch vert – reading up)	50	40
	a. Surch reading down	50	40
2037	120 c. on 60 c. Plate No. 94 (Series 1) (surch vert – reading down)	50	40
2038	120 c. on 75 c. Plate No. 60 (Series 1)	50	40
2039	120 c. on 75 c. Plate No. 83 (Series 1)	50	40
2040	120 c. on 75 c. Plate No. 92 (Series 1)	50	40
2041	120 c. on 75 c. Plate No. 95 (Series 1)	50	40
2042	200 c. on 45 c. Plate No. 77 (Series 1)	50	40
2043	200 c. on 45 c. Plate No. 78 (Series 1)	50	40
2044	200 c. on 45 c. Plate No. 84 (Series 1)	50	40
2045	200 c. on 45 c. Plate No. 85 (Series 1)	50	40
2046	200 c. on 50 c. Plate No. 55 (Series 1) (No. 1927) (wmkd)	90	50
2047	200 c. on 50 c. Plate No. 24 (Series 1) (wmkd)	90	50
2048	200 c. on 50 c. Plate No. 53 (Series 1) (wmkd)	90	50
2049	200 c. on 50 c. Plate No. 65 (Series 1) (wmkd)	90	50
2050	200 c. on 55 c. Plate No. 15 (Series 1)	2·00	50
2051	200 c. on 55 c. Plate No. 81 (Series 1)	2·00	50
2052	200 c. on 55 c. Plate No. 82 (Series 1)	5·00	50
2053	200 c. on 55 c. Plate No. 89 (Series 1)	2·00	50
2054	225 c. on 40 c. Plate No. 91 (Series 1) (No. 1822)	1·25	60
2055	225 c. on 40 c. Plate No. 86 (Series 1) (No. 1868)	1·25	60
	a. Inscr "ONTOGLOSSUM TRIUM-PHANS" in error	1·00	60
2056	225 c. on 40 c. Plate No. 68 (Series 1) (No. 1884)	90	60
2057	225 c. on 40 c. Plate No. 90 (Series 1)	90	60
2058	225 c. on 65 c. Plate No. 76 (Series 1)	90	60
2059	225 c. on 65 c. Plate No. 80 (Series 1)	90	60
2060	225 c. on 65 c. Plate No. 88 (Series 1)	90	60
2061	225 c. on 65 c. Plate No. 96 (Series 1)	90	60
2062	600 c. on 80 c. Plate No. 17 (Series 1) (No. 1885)	1·50	1·50
2063	600 c. on 80 c. Plate No. 39 (Series 1)	1·50	1·50
2064	600 c. on 80 c. Plate No. 74 (Series 1)	1·50	1·50
2065	600 c. on 80 c. Plate No. 93 (Series 1)	1·50	1·50
2013/65	Set of 53	40·00	24·00

Initially some values were surcharged in sheets of sixteen orchid stamps together with nine examples of No. 2081. Subsequently, however, the surcharges appeared in the individual blocks of 4 with the arms design issued separately as Nos. 2082/3.

For 600 c. on 900 c. with surcharge as T 384 see No. 2219.

(Litho Format)

1987 (16 Feb). *Centenary of Publication of Sanders' Reichenbachia (19th issue). Vert designs as T 331. Multicoloured. No wmk. P 13½×14.*

2066	180 c. Plate 41 (Series 2)	75	40
2067	230 c. Plate 25 (Series 2)	80	50
2068	300 c. Plate 85 (Series 2)	3·00	65
2069	330 c. Plate 82 (Series 2)	3·25	70
2070	425 c. Plate 87 (Series 2)	3·25	85
2071	440 c. Plate 88 (Series 2)	3·25	85
2072	590 c. Plate 52 (Series 2)	1·50	1·25
2073	650 c. Plate 65 (Series 2)	1·75	1·50
2066/73	Set of 8	16·00	6·00

Nos. 2066/73 were printed in a similar sheet format to Nos. 1518/33.

PRICES OF SETS

Set prices are given for many issues, generally those containing three stamps or more. Definitive sets include one of each value or major colour change, but do not cover different perforations, die types or minor shades. Where a choice is possible the set prices are based on the cheapest versions of the stamps included in the listings.

1987

▤

Post Office Corp. 1977-1987

25c

(385)

⚙

200

(386)

1987 (17 Feb). *10th Anniv of Guyana Post Office Corporation (2nd issue). Nos. 543, 545, 548a and 601 surch as T 385 in blue by Autoprint.*

2074	25 c. on 2 c. Type 132	15	10
2075	25 c. on 5 c. Annatto tree	15	10
2076	25 c. on 8 c. on 6 c. Cannon-ball tree	15	10
2077	25 c. on 15 c. Christmas Orchid	1·75	10
2078	60 c. on 15 c. Christmas Orchid	3·25	15
2079	$1.20 on 2 c. Type 132	75	75
2080	$1.30 on 15 c. Christmas Orchid	3·50	1·25
2074/80	Set of 7	8·75	2·25

1987 (6 Mar). *Nos. 1534/5 surch with T 386 by Tip Torres.*

2081	332	200 c. on 25 c. mult (p 13½×14)	1·00	1·00
2082		200 c. on 25 c. mult (imperf × p 14)	1·00	1·00
2083		200 c. on 25 c. mult (p 13½ × imperf)	1·00	1·00
2081/3		Set of 3	2·75	2·75

See note below No. 2065.

1987 *1987* **1987** 1987

(387)   (388)   (389)   (390)

1987 (6 Mar–Dec). *Various Reichenbachia issues optd as T 387/90.*

(a) With T 387 by Tip Torres (March)

2084	130 c. Plate No. 3 (Series 1) (No. 1525)	50	40
2085	130 c. Plate No. 6 (Series 1) (No. 1526)	50	40
2086	130 c. Plate No. 20 (Series 1) (No. 1529)	50	40
2087	130 c. Plate No. 18 (Series 1) (No. 1536)	50	40
2088	130 c. Plate No. 29 (Series 1) (No. 1537)	50	40
2089	130 c. Plate No. 30 (Series 1) (No. 1538)	50	40
2090	130 c. Plate No. 16 (Series 1) (No. 1559)	50	40
2091	130 c. Plate No. 66 (Series 1) (No. 1632)	50	40
2092	130 c. Plate No. 13 (Series 1) (No. 1684)	50	40
2093	130 c. Plate No. 6 (Series 1) (No. 1759) (wmkd)	50	40
2094	130 c. Plate No. 20 (Series 1) (No. 1761) (wmkd)	50	40
2095	200 c. Plate No. 4 (Series 1) (No. 1533)	60	50
2096	200 c. Plate No. 14 (Series 1) (No. 1584)	60	50
2097	200 c. Plate No. 21 (Series 1) (No. 1585) (opt vert – reading down)	60	50
2098	200 c. Plate No. 33 (Series 1) (No. 1634) (opt vert – reading down)	60	50
2099	200 c. Plate No. 43 (Series 1) (No. 1658) (opt vert – reading down)	60	50
2100	200 c. Plate No. 79 (Series 1) (No. 1670)	60	50
2101	200 c. Plate No. 9 (Series 2) (No. 1816)	60	50
2102	200 c. Plate No. 2 (Series 2) (No. 1886)	60	50
2103	250 c. Plate No. 74 (Series 1) (No. 1736)	70	60
2104	260 c. Plate No. 39 (Series 1) (No. 1737)	70	60
2084/2104	Set of 21	10·50	8·50
MS2105	100×129 mm. 200 c.×4 Plate 4 (Series 1) (No. MS1539)	2·00	1·75
MS2106	100×129 mm. 200 c. on 130 c.×4 Plate 20 (Series 1) (No. MS1570)	2·00	1·75

(b) With T 388 by Gardy Ptg (March)

2107	130 c. Plate No. 13 (Series 1) (No. 1527)	50	40
2108	130 c. Plate No. 25 (Series 1) (No. 1530)	50	40
2109	130 c. Plate No. 91 (Series 1) (No. 1735)	50	40
2110	130 c. Plate No. 13 (No. 1760) (wmkd)	50	40
2111	130 c. Plate No. 25 (No. 1762) (wmkd)	50	40
2107/11	Set of 5	2·25	1·75

(c) With T 389 by Gardy Ptg (July)

2112	120 c. Plate No. 1 (Series 1) (No. 1578) (opt vert – reading down)	2·00	60
2113	120 c. Plate No. 11 (Series 1) (No. 1579) (opt vert – reading down)	1·50	60
2114	120 c. Plate No. 28 (Series 1) (No. 1580) (opt vert – reading down)	2·00	60
2115	120 c. Plate No. 37 (Series 1) (No. 1627)	1·00	60
2116	120 c. Plate No. 46 (Series 1) (No. 1628)	4·50	60
2117	120 c. Plate No. 56 (Series 1) (No. 1629)	1·50	60
2118	120 c. Plate No. 58 (Series 1) (No. 1630)	1·50	60
2119	130 c. Plate No. 6 (Series 1) (No. 1759) (wmkd)	1·50	60
2120	130 c. Plate No. 13 (Series 1) (No. 1760) (wmkd)	1·50	60
2121	130 c. Plate No. 20 (Series 1) (No. 1761) (wmkd)	1·00	60
2122	130 c. Plate No. 25 (Series 1) (No. 1762) (wmkd)	1·25	60
2123	150 c. Plate No. 40 (Series 1) (No. 1581) vert–reading down	1·25	70
2124	150 c. Plate No. 45 (Series 1) (No. 1583) vert–reading down	1·00	70
2125	150 c. Plate No. 42 (Series 1) (No. 1657) vert–reading down	3·00	70
2126	150 c. Plate No. 40 (Series 1) (No. 1767) (wmkd) (opt vert–reading up)	1·00	70
2127	150 c. Plate No. 42 (Series 1) (No. 1768) (wmkd) (opt vert–reading up)	1·50	70
2128	150 c. Plate No. 45 (Series 1) (No. 1769) (wmkd) (opt vert–reading up)	1·25	70
2129	200 c. Plate No. 21 (Series 1) (No. 1585) (opt vert–reading down)	1·00	70
2130	200 c. Plate No. 43 (Series 1) (No. 1658) (opt vert–reading down)	3·00	75

2131	200 c. Plate No. 43 (Series 1) (No. 1770) (wmkd) (opt vert–reading up)	3·00	75
2112/31	Set of 20	32·00	11·50

(d) With T 390 by Gardy Ptg (Dec)

2132	120 c. Plate No. 67 (Series 1) (No. 1631)	50	40
2133	130 c. Plate No. 18 (Series 1) (No. 1536)	50	40
2134	130 c. Plate No. 29 (Series 1) (No. 1537)	50	40
2135	130 c. Plate No. 30 (Series 1) (No. 1538)	50	40
2136	130 c. Plate No. 66 (Series 1) (No. 1632)	50	40
2137	150 c. Plate No. 26 (Series 1) (No. 1633)	50	50
2132/7	Set of 6	2·75	2·25

🕊 650

12th World Orchid Conference   TOKYO JAPAN

28 MARCH 1927 PAA GEO-POS

(391)   (392)

1987 (12 Mar). *12th World Orchid Conference, Tokyo (2nd issue). Nos. 1552 and 1763 surch with T 391 by Tip Torres.*

2138	650 c. on 55 c. Plate No. 9 (Series 1) (No. 1552)	4·25	2·75
2139	650 c. on 55 c. Plate No. 9 (Series 1) (No. 1763)	4·25	2·75

1987 (17 Mar). *125th Anniv of British Guiana Post Office (3rd issue). No. 699 surch as T 324 by Autoprint.*

2140	25 c. on 10 c. mult (surch "AGRICOLA")	70	40
	a. Sheetlet of 25. Nos. 2140/64	15·00	
2141	25 c. on 10 c. mult (surch "BAGOTVILLE")	70	40
2142	25 c. on 10 c. mult (surch "BOURDA")	70	40
2143	25 c. on 10 c. mult (surch "BUXTON")	70	40
2144	25 c. on 10 c. mult (surch "CABACABURI")	70	40
2145	25 c. on 10 c. multicoloured (surch "CARMICHAEL STREET")	70	40
2146	25 c. on 10 c. mult (surch "COTTON TREE")	70	40
2147	25 c. on 10 c. mult (surch "DUNOON")	70	40
2148	25 c. on 10 c. mult (surch "FELLOWSHIP")	70	40
2149	25 c. on 10 c. mult (surch "GROVE")	70	40
2150	25 c. on 10 c. mult (surch "HACKNEY")	70	40
2151	25 c. on 10 c. mult (surch "LEONORA")	70	40
2152	25 c. on 10 c. mult (surch "1987")	70	40
2153	25 c. on 10 c. mult (surch "MALLALI")	70	40
2154	25 c. on 10 c. mult (surch "PROVIDENCE")	70	40
2155	25 c. on 10 c. mult (surch "RELIANCE")	70	40
2156	25 c. on 10 c. mult (surch "SPARTA")	70	40
2157	25 c. on 10 c. multicoloured (surch "STEWARTVILLE")	70	40
2158	25 c. on 10 c. mult (surch "TARLOGY")	70	40
2159	25 c. on 10 c. multicoloured (surch "T.P.O. BERBICE RIV.")	70	40
2160	25 c. on 10 c. multicoloured (surch "T.P.O. DEM. RIV.")	70	40
2161	25 c. on 10 c. multicoloured (surch "T.P.O. ESSEO. RIV.")	70	40
2162	25 c. on 10 c. multicoloured (surch "T.P.O. MASSARUNI RIV.")	70	40
2163	25 c. on 10 c. multicoloured (surch "TUSCHEN (De VRIENDEN)")	70	40
2164	25 c. on 10 c. multicoloured (surch "ZORG")	70	40
2140/64	Set of 25	15·00	9·00

The surcharged names are those of postal agencies opened by 1885.

1987 (28 Mar). *50th Anniv of First Georgetown to Port-of-Spain Flight by P.A.A. No. 708a optd with T 392 by Autoprint.*

2165	$10 Elbella patrobas	10·00	5·00

1987 (6 Apr). *No. 704 surch with figures only as T 324 by Autoprint.*

2166	25 c. on 40 c. Morpho rhetenor (male)	5·00	10

1987

120   1987   CAPEX '87

(393)   (394)   (395)

1987 (21 Apr). *Easter. Nos. 481/2 and 484 optd or surch as T 393 by Autoprint.*

2167	111	25 c. multicoloured	40	10
2168		120 c. on 6 c. multicoloured	60	20
2169		320 c. on 6 c. multicoloured	90	55
2170		500 c. on 40 c. multicoloured	1·50	90
2167/70		Set of 4	3·00	1·50

(Litho Format)

1987 (24 Apr). *Centenary of Publication of Sanders' Reichenbachia (20th issue). Multicoloured designs as T 331. No wmk. P 13½×14 (240, 260, 500, 560 c.) or 13½×14 (others).*

2171	240 c. Plate No. 47 (Series 2)	80	45
2172	260 c. Plate No. 39 (Series 2)	90	55

2173	275 c.	Plate No. 58 (Series 2) (horiz) ..	90	55
2174	390 c.	Plate No. 37 (Series 2) (horiz) ..	1·10	70
2175	450 c.	Plate No. 19 (Series 2) (horiz) ..	1·50	90
2176	460 c.	Plate No. 54 (Series 2) (horiz) ..	1·50	90
2177	500 c.	Plate No. 51 (Series 2)	1·75	1·10
2178	560 c.	Plate No. 1 (Series 2)	2·00	1·50
2171/8		Set of 8	9·50	6·00

Nos. 2171/8 were printed in a similar sheet format to Nos. 1518/33.

1987 (Apr). No. 706 optd with T **394** by Autoprint.

2179	167	$1 multicoloured ..	4·00	15

(Litho Format)

1987 (2 June). Centenary of Publication of Sanders' Reichenbachia (21st issue). Vert designs as T **331**. Multicoloured. No wmk. P 13½×14.

2180	500 c.	Plate No. 86 (Series 2)	1·50	1·10
2181	520 c.	Plate No. 89 (Series 2)	1·50	1·25
2182	$20	Plate No. 83 (Series 2)	4·50	7·00
2180/2		Set of 3	6·75	8·50

Nos. 2180/2 were printed in a similar sheet format to Nos. 1518/33, but included Nos. 2183/4 instead of Nos. 1534/5.

Two types of bird in coat of arms:

A. Bird with short tail   B. Bird with long tail

(Litho Format)

1987 (2 June–29 Sept). As T **332**, but within frame. No wmk.

2183	25 c.	mult (Type A) (imperf × p 14) ..	30	30
	a. Perf 13½×14		30	30
	b. Perf 13½×imperf		30	30
2184	25 c.	multicoloured (Type B) (imperf × p 14) (29 Sept)	30	30
	a. Perf 13½×14		30	30
	b. Perf 13½×imperf		30	30
	c. Perf 14×13½		30	30

Nos. 2183/4 were cut from the gutters of the orchid stamps as detailed in the note below No. 1533. They were only issued in booklets or coils.

1987 (10 June). "Capex '87" International Stamp Exhibition, Toronto. Nos. 1744/5 optd with T **395**.

2185	363	320 c. rosine, black and dp reddish lilac	1·00	1·25
	a. Horiz pair. Nos. 2185/6		2·00	2·50
	ab. Imperf between (horiz pair)			
2186	–	320 c. multicoloured	1·00	1·25

1987 (15 July). Commonwealth Heads of Government Meeting, Vancouver. Nos. 1066/8 further optd with T **394**.

2187	$1.20 on 6 c. yellow-green		45	20
2188	$1.30 on 24 c. black and bright orange	..	3·75	30
2189	$2.40 on 24 c. black and bright orange	..	4·75	1·25
2187/9		Set of 3	8·00	1·60

(Litho Format)

1987 (22 July). Centenary of Publication of Sanders' Reichenbachia (22nd issue). Vert designs as T **331**. Multicoloured. No wmk. P 13½×14.

2190	400 c.	Plate No. 80 (Series 2)	1·25	80
2191	480 c.	Plate No. 77 (Series 2)	1·50	1·00
2192	600 c.	Plate No. 94 (Series 2)	1·50	1·50
2193	$25	Plate No. 72 (Series 2)	4·50	8·00
2190/3		Set of 4	8·00	10·00

Nos. 2190/3 were printed in a similar sheet format to Nos. 1518/33.

396 Steam Locomotive No. 4 Alexandra

FAIREY NICHOLL
8 AUG 1927
GEO-MAZ

(397)

(Litho Format)

1987 (3 Aug–4 Dec). Guyana Railways. T **396** and similar horiz designs. No wmk. P 12½ ($10, $12) or 15 (others).

2194	396	$1.20, bronze-green	..	25	30
		a. Block of 4. Nos. 2194/7 ..		90	
2195	–	$1.20, bronze-green		25	30
2196	–	$1.20, bronze-green		25	30
2197	–	$1.20, bronze-green		25	30
2198	396	$1.20, maroon (4 Dec)		25	30
		a. Block of 4. Nos. 2198/201		90	
2199	–	$1.20, maroon (4 Dec)		25	30
2200	–	$1.20, maroon (4 Dec)		25	30
2201	–	$1.20, maroon (4 Dec)		25	30
2202	396	$3.20, deep dull blue		80	90
		a. Block of 5. Nos. 2202/6 ..		3·50	
2203	–	$3.20, deep dull blue		80	90
2204	–	$3.20, deep dull blue		80	90
2205	–	$3.20, deep dull blue		80	90
2206	–	$3.20, deep dull blue		80	90
2207	396	$3.30, brownish black (4 Dec)		80	90
		a. Block of 5. Nos. 2207/11 ..		3·50	

2208	396	$3.30, brownish black (4 Dec)	..	80	90
2209	–	$3.30, brownish black (4 Dec)		80	90
2210	–	$3.30, brownish black (4 Dec)		80	90
2211	–	$3.30, brownish black (4 Dec)		80	90
2212	–	$10 multicoloured (4 Dec)		60	1·50
2213	–	$12 multicoloured ..		60	1·75
2194/213		Set of 20	10·00	13·00

Designs: (As T **396**)—Nos. 2195, 2199, 2203, 2207, Front view of diesel locomotive; Nos. 2196, 2200, 2204, 2210, Steam locomotive with searchlight; Nos. 2197, 2201, 2205, 2209, Side view of diesel locomotive No. 21. (82×55 mm)—No. 2206, Molasses warehouses and early locomotive; No. 2211, Diesel locomotive and passenger train. (88×39 mm)—No. 2212, Cattle train and Parika–Rosignol Railway route map; No. 2213, Molasses train and Parika–Rosignol Railway route map.

Nos. 2194/7 and 2198/201 were each printed together, se-tenant, in blocks of 4, within the sheets of 40.

Nos. 2202/6 and 2207/11 were each printed together, se-tenant, in blocks of 5 within the sheets of 25. The order of the stamps as Type **396** differs in the $3.30 block.

1987 (7 Aug). 50th Anniv of First Flights from Georgetown to Massaruni and Mabaruna. No. 706 optd as T **397** by Autoprint.

2214	167	$1 multicoloured (optd T **397**)	5·00	5·00
		a. Pair. Nos. 2214/15	10·00	10·00
2215		$1 mult (optd "FAIREY NICHOLL 15 AUG 1927 GEO-MAB")	5·00	5·00

Nos. 2214/15 were overprinted together, se-tenant, in vertical or horizontal pairs within the sheet.

(Litho Format)

1987 (29 Sept). Centenary of Publication of Sanders' Reichenbachia (23rd issue). Vert designs as T **331**. Multicoloured. No wmk. P 13½×14.

2216	200 c.	Plate No. 43 (Series 2)	2·50	80
2217	200 c.	Plate No. 48 (Series 2)	2·50	80
2218	200 c.	Plate No. 92 (Series 2)	2·50	80
2216/18		Set of 3	6·75	2·25

Nos. 2216/18 were printed in a similar sheet format to Nos. 1518/33.

(Litho Format)

1987 (9 Oct). Centenary of Publication of Sanders' Reichenbachia (24th issue). Vert design as T **331**, optd as T **384** by Gardy Ptg (600 c.). Multicoloured. No wmk. P 13½ × 14.

2219	600 c. on 900 c. Plate No. 74 (Series 2)		2·25	2·50
	a. Pair. Nos. 2219/20		7·00	7·00
2220	900 c. Plate No. 74 (Series 2)		2·25	2·50

Nos. 2219/20 were printed in a similar sheet format to Nos. 1518/33 with the surcharge on the first and last stamp of each block of four.

950

CRISTOVAO COLOMBO
1492 — 1992

(398)

THE PASSING OF HALLEY'S COMET: PROPHESY OF THE ARRIVAL OF HERNAN CORTES 1519.

V CENTENARY OF THE LANDING OF CHRISTOPHER COLUMBUS

$20.oo IN THE AMERICAS

(399)

1987 (9 Oct). Columbus Day. No. 1598 further surch with T **382**, No. 2220 surch as T **398** and No. MS1746 surch with T **399**.

2221	225 c. on 350 c. on 120 c. Plate No. 65 (Series 1)		75	40
2222	950 c. on 900 c. Plate No. 74 (Series 2) (surch with T **398**)		1·75	2·25
	a. Horiz pair. Nos. 2222/3		3·50	4·50
2223	950 c. on 900 c. Plate No. 74 (Series 2) (surch "950 CHRISTOPHE COLOMB 1492 — 1992")		1·75	2·25
2221/3		Set of 3	3·75	4·50
MS2224	76 × 50 mm. $20 on 320 c. × 2 Nos. 1744/5		6·00	7·00

Nos. 2222/3 were surcharged together, se-tenant, in horizontal pairs in the sheetlet of 4.

(Litho Format)

1987 (26 Oct). Centenary of Publication of Sanders' Reichenbachia (25th issue). Multicoloured designs as T **331**. No wmk. P 13½ × 14 (575 c.) or 14 × 13½ (others).

2225	325 c.	Plate No. 68 (Series 2) (horiz)	1·50	90
2226	420 c.	Plate No. 95 (Series 2) (horiz)	1·75	1·25
2227	575 c.	Plate No. 60 (Series 2)	4·50	2·25
2225/7		Set of 3	7·00	4·00

Nos. 2225/7, together with No. E7, were printed in a similar sheet format to Nos. 1518/33.

DEEPAVALI
1987
25

(400)

1987 (2 Nov). Deepavali Festival. Nos. 544/5 surch as T **400**.

2228	25 c. on 3 c. Hanging Heliconia	..	50	10
2229	$3 on 5 c. Annatto tree	..	2·00	85

120

CHRISTMAS
1987
20   1987

(401)   (402)

1987 (9 Nov). Christmas. No. 452 surch with T **401** in red, previously unissued miniature sheet containing Nos. 1425/9 each surch with T **402** in blue and No. MS1619 with each stamp surch with T **382**.

2230	20 c. on 6 c. Black Acara ("Patua")		1·00	10
MS2231	215×75 mm. 120 c. on 60 c. × 5 Nos. 1425/9		7·00	3·50
MS2232	120×129 mm. 225 c. on 55 c. × 4 Plate No. 22 (Series 1), each with a different overprint (Type **350**, "Happy New Year", "Merry Christmas" or "Happy Holidays")		1·40	1·50

1987 (20 Nov). Royal Ruby Wedding. Nos. 1684/5 optd with T **390** (130 c.) or surch as T **384** by Gardy Ptg.

2233	130 c. Plate No. 13 (Series 1)		1·75	30
MS2234	600 c. on 130 c. on 130 c., 600 c. on 200 c. on 130 c., 600 c. on 260 c. on 130 c., 600 c. on 330 c. on 130 c., Plate No. 6 (Series 1) ..		8·00	9·00

(Litho Format)

1987 (23 Nov). Centenary of Publication of Sanders' Reichenbachia (26th issue). Vert designs as T **331**. Multicoloured. No wmk. P 13½ × 14.

2235	255 c.	Plate No. 61 (Series 2)	2·75	1·25
2236	290 c.	Plate No. 53 (Series 2)	2·75	1·50
2237	375 c.	Plate No. 96 (Series 2)	2·00	1·60
2238	680 c.	Plate No. 64 (Series 2)	6·00	2·50
2239	720 c.	Plate No. 49 (Series 2)	7·00	4·00
2240	750 c.	Plate No. 66 (Series 2)	3·00	4·00
2241	800 c.	Plate No. 79 (Series 2)	3·00	4·50
	a. Face value omitted			
2242	850 c.	Plate No. 76 (Series 2)	3·00	4·50
	a. Face value omitted			
2235/42		Set of 8	27·00	21·00

Nos. 2235/42 were printed in a similar sheet format to Nos. 1518/33.

Nos. 2241a and 2242a occurred in the same sheet as Nos. 2276a and 2277a.

AIR

75

(403)

1987 (Nov). Air. No. 1620 surch with T **403** by Gardy Ptg.

2243	75 c. on 25 c. Plate No. 59 (Series 1)	..	3·75	50

ALTERED CATALOGUE NUMBERS

Any Catalogue numbers altered from the last edition are shown as a list in the introductory pages.

Protect our Heritage '87

320

PROTECT OUR
HERITAGE '87

(404)   (405)

1987 (9 Dec). *Wildlife Protection. Nos. 756/67 optd vertically with T 394, Nos. 1432b/4b surch with T 404 in red and Nos. 1631/3, 1752/3 and 1847 optd with T 405.*

2244	30 c. Type 178	20	15
	a. Sheetlet of 12. Nos. 2244/55	2·25	
2245	30 c. Red Howler	20	15
2246	30 c. Common Squirrel-Monkey	20	15
2247	30 c. Two-toed Sloth	20	15
2248	30 c. Brazilian Tapir	20	15
2249	30 c. Collared Peccary	20	15
2250	30 c. Six-banded Armadillo	20	15
2251	30 c. Tamandua ("Ant Eater")	20	15
2252	30 c. Giant Anteater	20	15
2253	30 c. Murine Opossum	20	15
2254	30 c. Brown Four-eyed Opossum	20	15
2255	30 c. Brazilian Agouti	20	15
2256	120 c. Plate No. 67 (Series 1)	50	30
2257	130 c. Plate No. 66 (Series 1)	50	30
2258	150 c. Plate No. 26 (Series 1)	55	35
2259	180 c. Plate No. 15 (Series 1)	60	40
2260	320 c. Plate No. 82 (Series 1)	80	60
2261	320 c. on 120 c. Demerara Mutual Life Assurance Building	80	80
	a. Horiz strip of 3. Nos. 2261/3	2·25	
	b. Surch on No. 1432		
	ba. Horiz strip of 3. Nos. 2261b/3b		
2262	320 c. on 120 c. Town Hall	80	80
	b. Surch on No. 1433		
2263	320 c. on 120 c. Victoria Law Courts	80	80
	b. Surch on No. 1434		
2264	650 c. on 40 c. Plate No. 86 (Series 1)	2·00	2·00
2244/64	*Set of 21*	8·75	7·00

AIR

(406)

1987 (Dec). *Air. No. 1597 optd with T 406.*

2265	60 c. Plate No. 55 (Series 1)	3·50	4·00

No. 2265 was only issued in $15 stamp booklets.

★ AUSTRALIA ★
1987 JAMBOREE 1988
(407)

★ AUSTRALIA ★
1987 Jamboree 1988
(408)

1988 (7 Jan). *World Scout Jamboree, Australia. Nos. 830, 837/a and 1104 handstamped with T 407 (No. 2266) or surch with T 408 by Tip Torres (others), all in red.*

2266	116 440 c. on 6 c. multicoloured (No. 837a) (surch T 201)	3·75	30
	a. On No. 837 (surch T 200)	8·50	
2267	$10 on 110 c. on 6 c. mult (No. 830)	75	70
2268	$10 on 180 c. on 6 c. mult (No. 1104)	75	70
2269	$10 on 440 c. on 6 c. mult (No. 837)	2·50	2·00
	a. On No. 837a	75	70
2266/9a	*Set of 4*	5·50	2·25

IFAD
For a World
Without Hunger
25
(409)

Republic Day 1988
25
(410)

1988 (26 Jan). *10th Anniv of International Fund for Agricultural Development. Nos. 485 and 487 surch as T 409 by Autoprint.*

2270	25 c. on 1 c. Type 87	50	10
2271	$5 on 3 c. Lukunani	2·25	1·00

1988 (23 Feb). *Republic Day. Nos. 545, 548a and 555 surch as T 410 in blue.*

2272	25 c. on 5 c. Annatto tree	10	10
2273	120 c. on 15 c. Christmas Orchid	2·25	50
2274	$10 on $2 Noranthea guianensis	2·50	2·50
2272/4	*Set of 3*	4·25	2·75

(Litho Format)

1988 (26 Feb). *Centenary of Publication of Sanders' Reichenbachia (27th issue). Four sheets, each 102×127 mm, containing vert designs as T 331. Multicoloured. No wmk. P 13½×14.*

MS2275 (a) 320 c. Plate No. 46 (Series 2); 330 c. Plate No. 55 (Series 2); 350 c. Plate No. 57 (Series 2); 500 c. Plate No. 81 (Series 2). (b) 320 c. Plate No. 55 (Series 2); 330 c. Plate No. 46 (Series 2); 350 c. Plate No. 81 (Series 2); 500 c. Plate No. 57 (Series 2). (c) 320 c. Plate No. 57 (Series 2); 330 c. Plate No. 81 (Series 2); 350 c. Plate No. 46 (Series 2); 500 c. Plate No. 55 (Series 2). (d) 320 c. Plate No. 81 (Series 2); 330 c. Plate No. 57 (Series 2); 350 c. Plate No. 55 (Series 2); 500 c. Plate No. 46 (Series 2)

    Set of 4 sheets 15·00 12·00

(Litho Format)

1988 (24 Mar). *Centenary of Publication of Sanders' Reichenbachia (28th issue). Vert designs as T 331. Multicoloured. No wmk. P 13½×14.*

2276	$10 Plate No. 40 (Series 2)	1·50	2·00
	a. Face value omitted		
2277	$12 Plate No. 91 (Series 2)	1·50	2·00
	a. Face value omitted		

Nos. 2276/7 were printed in a similar sheet format to Nos. 1518/33.
Nos. 2276a/7a occurred in the same sheet as Nos. 2241a and 2242a.

1988 (5 Apr). *125th Anniv of British Guiana Post Office (4th issue). No. 702a surch as T 324 by Autoprint.*

2278	25 c. on 30 c. mult (surch "Albouystown")	70	50
	a. Sheetlet of 25. Nos. 2278/88, 2289×2, 2290/301	15·00	
2279	25 c. on 30 c. mult (surch "Anns Grove")	70	50
2280	25 c. on 30 c. mult (surch "Amacura")	70	50
2281	25 c. on 30 c. mult (surch "Arakaka")	70	50
2282	25 c. on 30 c. mult (surch "Baramanni")	70	50
2283	25 c. on 30 c. mult (surch "Cuyuni")	70	50
2284	25 c. on 30 c. mult (surch "Hope Placer")	70	50
2285	25 c. on 30 c. mult (surch "H M P S")	70	50
2286	25 c. on 30 c. multicoloured (surch "Kitty")	70	50
2287	25 c. on 30 c. mult (surch "M'M'Zorg")	70	50
2288	25 c. on 30 c. mult (surch "Maccaseema")	70	50
2289	25 c. on 30 c. multicoloured (surch "1988")	70	50
2290	25 c. on 30 c. mult (surch "Morawhanna")	70	50
2291	25 c. on 30 c. mult (surch "Naamryck")	70	50
2292	25 c. on 30 c. multicoloured (surch "Purini")	70	50
2293	25 c. on 30 c. mult (surch "Potaro Landing")	70	50
2294	25 c. on 30 c. mult (surch "Rockstone")	70	50
2295	25 c. on 30 c. mult (surch "Rosignol")	70	50
2296	25 c. on 30 c. mult (surch "Stanleytown")	70	50
2297	25 c. on 30 c. mult (surch "Santa Rosa")	70	50
2298	25 c. on 30 c. mult (surch "Tumatumari")	70	50
2299	25 c. on 30 c. mult (surch "Weldaad")	70	50
2300	25 c. on 30 c. mult (surch "Wismar")	70	50
2301	25 c. on 30 c. multicoloured (surch "TPO Berbice Railway")	70	50
2278/301	*Set of 24*	15·00	11·00

The surcharged names are those of postal agencies opened between 1886 and 1900.

120

Olympic Games 1988
(411)

Caricom Day 1988
25
(412)

1988 (3 May). *Olympic Games, Seoul (1st issue). Nos. 1206/17 further surch with T 411.*

2302	120 c. on 55 c. on 125 c. on 35 c. Type 174	1·00	1·00
	a. Block of 12. Nos. 2302/13	11·00	
2303	120 c. on 55 c. on 125 c. on 35 c. Trahira ("Haimara")	1·00	1·00
2304	120 c. on 55 c. on 125 c. on 35 c. Electric Eel	1·00	1·00
2305	120 c. on 55 c. on 125 c. on 35 c. Golden Rivulus	1·00	1·00
2306	120 c. on 55 c. on 125 c. on 35 c. Golden Pencilfish	1·00	1·00
2307	120 c. on 55 c. on 125 c. on 35 c. Four-eyed Fish	1·00	1·00
2308	120 c. on 55 c. on 125 c. on 35 c. Red Piranha ("Pirai")	1·00	1·00
2309	120 c. on 55 c. on 125 c. on 35 c. Smoking Hassar	1·00	1·00
2310	120 c. on 55 c. on 125 c. on 35 c. Manta	1·00	1·00
2311	120 c. on 55 c. on 125 c. on 35 c. Festive Cichlid ("Flying Patwa")	1·00	1·00
2312	120 c. on 55 c. on 125 c. on 35 c. Arapaima	1·00	1·00
2313	120 c. on 55 c. on 125 c. on 35 c. Peacock Cichlid ("Lukanani")	1·00	1·00
2302/13	*Set of 12*	11·00	11·00

See also Nos. 2476/95.

(Litho Format)

1988 (1 June). *Centenary of Publication of Sanders' Reichenbachia (29th issue). Vert designs as T 331. Multicoloured. No wmk. P 13½×14.*

2314	320 c. Plate No. 2 (Series 2)	1·25	40
2315	475 c. Plate No. 73 (Series 2)	1·50	70
2316	525 c. Plate No. 36 (Series 2)	2·00	90
2317	530 c. Plate No. 69 (Series 2)	1·00	90
2318	$15 Plate No. 67 (Series 2)	2·00	90
2314/18	*Set of 5*	7·00	6·25

Nos. 2314/18 were printed in a similar sheet format to Nos. 1518/33.

1988 (15 June). *CARICOM Day. Nos. 545/6 and 555 surch as T 412.*

2319	25 c. on 5 c. Annatto tree	15	10
2320	$1.20 on 6 c. Cannon-ball tree	40	10
2321	$10 on $2 Norantea guianensis	2·25	2·50
2319/21	*Set of 3*	2·50	2·50

(Litho Format)

1988 (15 June). *Centenary of Publication of Sanders' Reichenbachia (30th issue). Vert designs as T 331. Multicoloured. No wmk. P 13½×14.*

2322	700 c. Plate No. 62 (Series 2)	1·00	1·25
2323	775 c. Plate No. 59 (Series 2)	1·25	1·40
2324	875 c. Plate No. 31 (Series 2)	3·50	1·50
2325	950 c. Plate No. 78 (Series 2)	1·75	1·75
2322/5	*Set of 4*	6·75	5·50

Nos. 2322/5 were printed in a similar sheet format to Nos. 1518/33.

WHO
1948-1988
(413)

1988
(414)

1988 (17 June). *40th Anniv of World Health Day. No. 705a optd with T 413 or T 414 by Autoprint.*

2326	60 c. Papilio androgeus (T 413)	8·50	9·50
	a. Sheetlet of 25. Nos. 2326 and 2327×24	10·50	
2327	60 c. Papilio androgeus (T 414)	15	10

Nos. 2326 and 2327 were overprinted together, se-tenant, in a sheetlet of 25 showing a single example of No. 2326 in the central position.

(Litho Format)

1988 (22 June). *Centenary of Publication of Sanders' Reichenbachia (31st issue). Vert design as T 331. No wmk. P 13½×14.*

2328	350 c. Plate No. 74 (Series 2)	90	40

No. 2328 was printed in a similar sheet format to Nos. 1518/33.

(Litho Format)

1988 (9 July). *Centenary of Publication of Sanders Reichenbachia (32nd issue). Vert designs as T 331, with Nos. 2329/31 additional inscr "1985 – 1988". No wmk. P 13½×14.*

2329	130 c. Plate No. 73 (Series 2)	85	25
2330	200 c. Plate No. 96 (Series 2)	50	30
2331	260 c. Plate No. 16 (Series 2)	1·50	45
2329/31	*Set of 3*	2·50	90

MS2332 Four sheets, each 102×127 mm. (a) 120 c. Plate No. 81 (Series 2); 120 c. Plate No. 57 (Series 2); 120 c. Plate No. 55 (Series 2); 120 c. Plate No. 46 (Series 2). (b) 150 c. Plate No. 57 (Series 2); 150 c. Plate No. 81 (Series 2); 150 c. Plate No. 46 (Series 2); 150 c. Plate No. 55 (Series 2). (c) 225 c. Plate No. 46 (Series 2); 225 c. Plate No. 55 (Series 2); 225 c. Plate No. 57 (Series 2); 225 c. Plate No. 81 (Series 2). (d) 305 c. Plate No. 55 (Series 2); 305 c. Plate No. 46 (Series 2); 305 c. Plate No. 81 (Series 2); 305 c. Plate No. 57 (Series 2)   *Set of 4 sheets* 7·50 5·00

CONSERVE TREES
(415)

CONSERVE WATER
(416)

1988 (15 July). *Conservation of Resources.*

(a) Nos. 1444B/6B optd as T 415 by Gardy Ptg

2333	120 c. Young Ocelot (No. 1444B) (opt T 415)	50	40
	a. Block of 9. Nos. 2333/41	4·00	
2334	120 c. Young Ocelot (No. 1444B) (opt "CONSERVE ELECTRICITY")	50	40
2335	120 c. Young Ocelot (No. 1444B) (opt "CONSERVE WATER")	50	40
2336	120 c. Type 322 (opt "CONSERVE ELECTRICITY")	50	40
2337	120 c. Type 322 (opt "CONSERVE WATER")	50	40
2338	120 c. Type 322 (opt T 415)	50	40
2339	120 c. Young Ocelot (No. 1446B) (opt "CONSERVE WATER")	50	40
2340	120 c. Young Ocelot (No. 1446B) (opt T 415)	50	40
2341	120 c. Young Ocelot (No. 1446B) (optd "CONSERVE ELECTRICITY")	50	40

(b) Nos. 1634, 1670, 1683 and 1774 optd with T 416 (opt vert–reading upwards on Nos. 2342, 2345) by Tip Torres.

2342	200 c. Plate No. 33 (Series 1)	50	40
2343	200 c. Plate No. 79 (Series 1)	50	40
2344	225 c. Plate No. 24 (Series 1)	50	40
2345	350 c. Plate No. 94 (Series 1)	60	60
2333/45	*Set of 13*	6·00	4·75

The three different overprints as T 415 were applied, se-tenant, in strips of three, both horizontally and vertically, on blocks of nine.

BEWARE OF ANIMALS
(417)

120
(418)

1988 (15 July). *Road Safety Campaign. Nos. 2194/2201 optd as T 417 by Gardy Ptg.*

2346	396 $1.20, bronze-green (opt T 417)	1·10	1·10
	a. Block of four. Nos. 2346/9	4·00	
2347	— $1.20, bronze-green (No. 2195) (opt "BEWARE OF CHILDREN")	1·10	1·10
2348	— $1.20, bronze-green (No. 2196) (opt "DRIVE SAFELY")	1·10	1·10
2349	— $1.20, bronze-green (No. 2197) (opt "DO NOT DRINK AND DRIVE")	1·10	1·10

2350	396	$1.20, maroon (opt T 417) ..		1·10	1·10
		a. Block of four. Nos. 2350/3		4·00	
2351	–	$1.20, maroon (No. 2199) (opt "BEWARE OF CHILDREN") ..		1·10	1·10
2352	–	$1.20, maroon (No. 2200) (opt "DRIVE SAFELY") ..		1·10	1·10
2353	–	$1.20, maroon (No. 2201) (opt "DO NOT DRINK AND DRIVE") ..		1·10	1·10
2346/53		.. .. .. Set of 8		8·00	8·00

1988 (July). *No. 706 optd with T 414 or surch with T 418, both by Autoprint.*

2354		$1 Type 167		3·00	70
2355		120 c. on $1 Type 167 ..		3·00	70

120

(419)

120 **240**
(420) (421)

1988 (July–Oct). *Various Reichenbachia issues surch by Gardy Ptg.*

(a) As T 419

2356	120 c. on 25 c. Plate No. 61 (Series 1) (No. 1574)		60	40
2357	120 c. on 25 c. Plate No. 63 (Series 1) (No. 1575)		60	40
2358	120 c. on 25 c. Plate No. 70 (Series 1) (No. 1576)		60	40
2359	120 c. on 25 c. Plate No. 59 (Series 1) (No. 1620)		60	40
2360	120 c. on 30 c. Plate No. 71 (Series 1) (No. 1679) (surch vert - reading down)		60	40
2361	120 c. on 30 c. Plate No. 53 (Series 1) (No. 1621)		60	40
2362	120 c. on 30 c. Plate No. 86 (Series 1) (No. 1731)		60	40
2363	120 c. on 30 c. Plate No. 30 (Series 2) (No. 1809)		60	40
	a. Horiz pair, one without surch		2·50	
2364	120 c. on 30 c. Plate No. 53 (Series 1) (No. 1771) (wmkd)		60	40
2365	120 c. on 30 c. Plate No. 7 (Series 2)		60	40
2366	120 c. on 30 c. Plate No. 14 (Series 2) ("120" at foot)		60	40
2367	120 c. on 30 c. Plate No. 14 (Series 2) ("120" at top below bars)		60	40
2368	120 c. on 30 c. Plate No. 22 (Series 2)		60	40
2369	120 c. on 30 c. Plate No. 28 (Series 2) ("120" at bottom right)		60	40
2370	120 c. on 30 c. Plate No. 28 (Series 2) ("120" at top left)		60	40
2371	120 c. on 35 c. Plate No. 45 (Series 2) (No. 1925)		60	40
	a. Horiz pair, one without surch		2·50	
2372	120 c. on 40 c. Plate No. 77 (Series 1) (No. 1663) ("120" at bottom right)		60	40
2373	120 c. on 40 c. Plate No. 77 (Series 1) (No. 1663) ("120" at top left)		60	40
2374	120 c. on 40 c. Plate No. 96 (Series 1) (No. 1747)		60	40
2375	120 c. on 40 c. Plate No. 91 (Series 1) (No. 1822) ("120" at bottom right)		60	40
2376	120 c. on 40 c. Plate No. 91 (Series 1) (No. 1822) ("120" at top left)		60	40
2377	120 c. on 40 c. Plate No. 86 (Series 1) (No. 1868)		60	40
2378	120 c. on 40 c. Plate No. 68 (Series 1) (No. 1884) ("120" at top left)		60	40
2379	120 c. on 40 c. Plate No. 68 (Series 1) (No. 1884) ("120" at bottom left)		60	40
2380	120 c. on 40 c. Plate No. 90 (Series 1)		60	40
2381	120 c. on 45 c. Plate No. 54 (Series 1) (No. 1664)		60	40
2382	120 c. on 45 c. Plate No. 81 (Series 1) (No. 1748)		60	40
2383	120 c. on 45 c. Plate No. 21 (Series 2) (No. 1810)		60	40
	a. Vert pair, one without surch		2·50	
2384	120 c. on 50 c. Plate No. 92 (Series 1) (No. 1665)		60	40
2385	120 c. on 50 c. Plate No. 13 (Series 2) (No. 1907)		60	40
	a. Horiz pair, one without surch		2·50	

2386	120 c. on 50 c. Plate No. 15 (Series 2) (No. 1926)		60	40
	a. Horiz pair, one without surch		2·50	
2387	120 c. on 50 c. Plate No. 9 (Series 1) (wmkd)		60	40
2388	120 c. on 50 c. Plate No. 22 (Series 1) (wmkd)		60	40
2389	120 c. on 50 c. Plate No. 3 (Series 2)		60	40
2390	120 c. on 50 c. Plate No. 6 (Series 2)		60	40
2391	120 c. on 50 c. Plate No. 20 (Series 2)		60	40
2392	120 c. on 50 c. Plate No. 32 (Series 2)		60	40
2393	120 c. on 55 c. Plate No. 17 (Series 1) (No. 1732)		60	40
2394	120 c. on 60 c. Plate No. 2 (Series 1) (No. 1519)		60	40
2395	120 c. on 60 c. Plate No. 57 (Series 1) (No. 1622) (surch vert at top - reading down)		60	40
2396	120 c. on 60 c. Plate No. 57 (Series 1) (No. 1622) (surch vert at foot - reading down)		60	40
2397	120 c. on 60 c. Plate No. 73 (Series 1) (No. 1623) (surch vert - reading up)		60	40
2398	120 c. on 60 c. Plate No. 75 (Series 1) (No. 1624) (surch vert at top - reading down)		60	40
2399	120 c. on 60 c. Plate No. 75 (Series 1) (No. 1624) (surch vert at foot - reading down)		60	40
2400	120 c. on 60 c. Plate No. 95 (Series 1) (No. 1666)		60	40
2401	120 c. on 60 c. Plate No. 93 (Series 1) (No. 1733)		60	40
2402	120 c. on 60 c. Plate No. 27 (Series 2) (No. 1874)		60	40
	a. Horiz pair, one without surch		2·50	
2403	120 c. on 60 c. Plate No. 50 (Series 1)		60	40
2404	120 c. on 60 c. Plate No. 54 (Series 1)		60	40
2405	120 c. on 60 c. Plate No. 69 (Series 1) (surch vert—reading up)		60	40
2406	120 c. on 60 c. Plate No. 79 (Series 1)		60	40
2407	120 c. on 60 c. Plate No. 94 (Series 1) (surch vert - reading down)		60	40
2408	120 c. on 70 c. Plate No. 8 (Series 2)		60	40
2409	120 c. on 70 c. Plate No. 9 (Series 2) ("120" at foot above bars)		60	40
2410	120 c. on 70 c. Plate No. 9 (Series 2) ("120" at top right)		60	40
2411	120 c. on 70 c. Plate No. 12 (Series 2) ("120" at foot above bars)		60	40
2412	120 c. on 70 c. Plate No. 12 (Series 2) "120" at top left)		60	40
2413	120 c. on 70 c. Plate No. 17 (Series 2)		60	40
2414	120 c. on 80 c. Plate No. 39 (Series 1)		60	40
2415	120 c. on 80 c. Plate No. 74 (Series 1)		60	40
2416	120 c. on 80 c. Plate No. 93 (Series 1)		60	40
2417	120 c. on 85 c. Plate No. 45 (Series 2) (No. 1876)		60	40
2418	120 c. on 85 c. Plate No. 24 (Series 2) (No. 1914)		60	40
	a. Horiz pair, one without surch		2·50	
2419	120 c. on 85 c. Plate No. 15 (Series 2) (No. 1918)		60	40
2420	120 c. on 85 c. Plate No. 18 (Series 2) (No. 1928)		60	40
	a. Horiz pair, one without surch		2·50	
2421	120 c. on 90 c. Plate No. 84 (Series 1) (No. 1668)		60	40
2422	120 c. on 90 c. Plate No. 89 (Series 1) (No. 1749)		60	40
2423	120 c. on 90 c. Plate No. 10 (Series 1) (No. 1869)		60	40
	a. Horiz pair, one without surch		2·50	
2424	120 c. on 90 c. Plate No. 13 (Series 1) (No. 1877)		60	40
2425	120 c. on 90 c. Plate No. 27 (Series 2) (No. 1915)		60	40
2426	120 c. on 90 c. Plate No. 2 (Series 2) (No. 1929)		60	40
	a. Horiz pair, one without surch		2·50	
2427	200 c. on 80 c. Plate No. 42 (Series 2) (No. 1812) (surch vert—reading down)		60	40
2428	200 c. on 90 c. Plate No. 4 (Series 2) (No. 1813)		60	40

(b) As T 420 (Sept)

2429	120 c. on 25 c. Plate No. 72 (Series 1) (No. 1577)		60	40

(c) As T 421 (Oct)

2430	240 c. on 140 c. Plate No. 30 (Series 2)		60	40
2431	240 c. on 140 c. Plate No. 34 (Series 2)		60	40
2432	240 c. on 425 c. Plate No. 87 (Series 2) (No. 2070)		60	40
2433	260 c. on 375 c. Plate No. 90 (Series 1) (No. 1738)		60	40
2356/433	.. .. Set of 78		40·00	27·00

Nos. 2363, 2371, 2383, 2385/6, 2402, 2418, 2420, 2423 and 2426 come from sheetlets of four on which the surcharge was applied to two of the stamps only.

On No. 2433 there are no bars and the surcharge is placed over the original face value.

CONSERVE OUR RESOURCES **+** **AIR**
(422) (423) (424)

1988 (July). *Conservation of Resources. Various Reichenbachia issues optd with T 422 by Gardy Ptg.*

2434	100 c. Plate No. 65 (Series 1) (No. 1626)		60	40
2435	100 c. Plate No. 68 (Series 1) (No. 1734)		60	40
2436	100 c. Plate No. 88 (Series 1) (No. 1750)		60	40
2437	100 c. Plate No. 65 (Series 1) (No. 1773) (wmkd)		60	40
2438	120 c. Plate No. 27 (Series 1) (No. 1524)		60	40
2439	120 c. Plate No. 36 (Series 1) (No. 1558)		60	40
2440	120 c. Plate No. 37 (Series 1) (No. 1627)		60	40
2441	120 c. Plate No. 56 (Series 1) (No. 1629)		60	40
2442	120 c. Plate No. 58 (Series 1) (No. 1630)		60	40
2443	120 c. Plate No. 67 (Series 1) (No. 1631)		60	40
2444	120 c. Plate No. 69 (Series 1) (No. 1680) (opt vert - reading down)		60	40
2445	130 c. Plate No. 38 (Series 1) (No. 1560)		60	40

2446	130 c. Plate No. 66 (Series 1) (No. 1632)		60	40
2447	130 c. Plate No. 91 (Series 1) (No. 1735)		60	40
2448	130 c. Plate No. 13 (Series 1) (No. 1760)		60	40
	a. Opt inverted		60	40
2449	130 c. Plate No. 20 (Series 1) (No. 1761) (wmkd)		60	40
2450	150 c. Plate No. 26 (Series 1) (No. 1633)		60	40
2451	150 c. Plate No. 78 (Series 1) (No. 1669)		60	40
2452	150 c. Plate No. 87 (Series 1) (No. 1681) (opt vert - reading down)		60	40
2453	150 c. Plate No. 76 (Series 1) (No. 1751)		60	40
2454	250 c. Plate No. 74 (Series 1) (No. 1736)		70	60
2434/54	.. .. Set of 21		11·50	7·50

The 130 c., No. 2448, exists in equal quantities with the overprint either upright or inverted.

1988 (3 Aug). *125th Anniv of International Red Cross. Nos. 2202/5 and 2207/10 optd with T 423 in red by Gardy Ptg.*

2455	396	$3.20, deep dull blue	90	90
		a. Vert pair. Nos. 2455 and 2457	1·75	1·75
2456	–	$3.20, deep dull blue (No. 2203)	90	90
		a. Vert pair. Nos. 2456 and 2458	1·75	1·75
2457	–	$3.20, deep dull blue (No. 2204)	90	90
2458	–	$3.20, deep dull blue (No. 2205)	90	90
2459	–	$3.30, brownish black (No. 2207)	90	90
		a. Vert pair. Nos. 2459 and 2461	1·75	1·75
2460	396	$3.30, brownish black	90	90
		a. Vert pair. Nos. 2460 and 2462	1·75	1·75
2461	–	$3.30, brownish black (No. 2209)	90	90
2462	–	$3.30, brownish black (No. 2210)	90	90
2455/62		Set of 8	6·50	6·50

Nos. 2455/62 were issued in vertical strips of ten, each strip containing two designs se-tenant.

1988 (Aug). *Air. Various Reichenbachia issues optd with T 424 by Gardy Ptg.*

2463	75 c. Plate No. 55 (Series 1) (No. 1625)		1·25	70
2464	75 c. Plate No. 5 (Series 1) (No. 1667)		1·25	70
2465	75 c. Plate No. 55 (Series 1) (No. 1772) (wmkd)		1·25	70
2466	75 c. Plate No. 83 (Series 1)		1·25	70
2467	75 c. Plate No. 95 (Series 1)		1·25	70
2463/7	.. Set of 5		5·50	3·25

(Litho Format)

1988 (15 Aug). *Centenary of Publication of Sanders' Reichenbachia (33rd issue). Multicoloured designs as T 331. P 13½×14 (270 c., 360 c.) or 14×13½ (others).*

2468	270 c. Plate No. 90 (Series 2)		1·10	60
2469	360 c. Plate No. 84 (Series 2)		75	75
2470	550 c. Plate No. 70 (Series 2) (horiz)		1·25	1·40
2471	670 c. Plate No. 71 (Series 2) (horiz)		1·50	1·75
2468/71	.. Set of 4		4·25	4·00

Nos. 2468/71 were printed in a similar sheet format to Nos. 1518/33.

A further small book similar to those described under Nos. 1767/1806, containing stamps showing plate numbers 1 to 48 of the second series, was issued on 23 August 1988.

Some designs in this booklet show changed face values, as detailed below, but there is no evidence that such printings were available for postal purposes without surcharge:

Plate No.	1	= 175 c.	Plate No. 25	= 140 c.
Plate No.	3	= 50 c.	Plate No. 28	= 30 c.
Plate No.	5	= 130 c.	Plate No. 29	= 130 c.
Plate No.	6	= 50 c.	Plate No. 32	= 50 c.
Plate No.	7	= 30 c.	Plate No. 33	= 100 c.
Plate No.	8	= 70 c.	Plate No. 34	= 140 c.
Plate No.	9	= 70 c.	Plate No. 37	= 175 c.
Plate No.	12	= 70 c.	Plate No. 38	= 140 c.
Plate No.	14	= 30 c.	Plate No. 39	= 175 c.
Plate No.	17	= 70 c.	Plate No. 40	= 250 c.
Plate No.	19	= 175 c.	Plate No. 41	= 140 c.
Plate No.	20	= 50 c.	Plate No. 46	= 150 c.
Plate No.	22	= 30 c.	Plate No. 47	= 175 c.

1928 – 1988

CRICKET

JUBILEE

(425)

1988 (5 Sept). *60th Anniv of Cricket in Guyana. Nos. 1584, 1670, 1681 and 1815 optd as T 425 or surch also by Gardy Ptg.*

2472	200 c. Plate No. 14 (Series 1)		12·00	14·00
2473	200 c. Plate No. 79 (Series 1)		1·00	40
2474	800 c. on 150 c. Plate No. 87 (Series 1)		6·50	8·00
2475	800 c. on 160 c. Plate No. 5 (Series 2)		3·25	3·25
2472/5	.. Set of 4		20·00	23·00

Nos. 2472 and 2474 were only issued in $20 stamp booklets.

OLYMPIC GAMES
1988
(426)

KOREA 1988

150

(427)

1988 (16 Sept). *Olympic Games, Seoul (2nd issue).* (a) *Nos. 1628, 1634, 1671, 1681, 1683, 1814, 1818/19, 1880 and 2069 optd as T **426** or surch also by Gardy Ptg.*

2476	120 c. Plate No. 46 (Series 1)	.. ..	20	20
2477	130 c. Plate No. 38 (Series 2)		20	20
2478	150 c. Plate No. 87 (Series 1)		20	20
2479	200 c. Plate No. 33 (Series 1)		20	20
2480	300 c. Plate No. 83 (Series 1)		30	30
2481	300 c. on 360 c. Plate No. 34 (Series 2)		30	30
2482	320 c. Plate No. 10 (Series 2)		30	30
2483	330 c. Plate No. 82 (Series 2)		30	30
2484	350 c. Plate No. 94 (Series 1) (opt vert - reading up)		30	30
2485	350 c. Plate No. 29 (Series 2)		30	30

(b) *Design as No. 1420, but incorrectly inscr "LOS ANGELLES", optd or surch as T **427**, inscr "OLYMPICS 1988" (A) or "KOREA 1988" (B), by Gardy Ptg.*

2486	$1.20, multicoloured (A)		20	20
	a. Horiz strip of 5. Nos. 2486, 2488, 2490, 2492 and 2494		1·10	
	b. Booklet pane of 10. Nos. 2486/95		14·00	
2487	$1.20, multicoloured (B)		20	20
2488	130 c. on $1.20, multicoloured (A)		20	20
2489	130 c. on $1.20, multicoloured (B)		20	20
2490	150 c. on $1.20, multicoloured (A)		20	20
2491	150 c. on $1.20, multicoloured (B)		20	20
2492	200 c. on $1.20, multicoloured (A)		25	25
2493	200 c. on $1.20, multicoloured (B)		25	25
2494	350 c. on $1.20, multicoloured (A)		35	35
2495	350 c. on $1.20, multicoloured (B)		35	35
2476/95		Set of 20	4·50	4·50

Nos. 2486/95 were issued in $20 stamp booklets which included pane No. 2486b. Nos. 2486, 2488, 2490, 2492 and 2494 were also available from sheets containing horizontal *se-tenant* strips of 5. All values later appeared in coils of 500 or 1,000.

V CENTENARY OF THE LANDING OF CHRISTOPHER COLUMBUS IN THE AMERICAS
(428)

1988 (12 Oct). *Columbus Day. Nos. 1672/3 optd or surch as T **428** by Gardy Ptg.*

2496	320 c. Plate No. 50 (Series 1)		1·25	30
2497	$15 on 360 c. Plate No. 85 (Series 1)		2·75	3·50

(Litho Format)

1988 (3 Nov). *Centenary of Publication of Sanders' Reichenbachia (34th issue). Multicoloured designs as T **331**. P 14×13½ (130 c.) or 13¼×14 (others).*

2498	100 c. Plate No. 44 (Series 2)	..	60	55
2499	130 c. Plate No. 42 (Series 2) (horiz)	..	60	55
2500	140 c. Plate No. 4 (Series 2)	..	75	65
2501	160 c. Plate No. 50 (Series 1)	..	75	65
2502	175 c. Plate No. 51 (Series 1)	..	90	75
2503	200 c. Plate No. 11 (Series 1)	..	2·00	75
2504	200 c. Plate No. 23 (Series 1)	..	2·00	75
2505	200 c. Plate No. 26 (Series 1)	..	2·00	75
2506	200 c. Plate No. 75 (Series 2)	..	2·00	75
2507	200 c. Plate No. 93 (Series 1)	..	2·00	75
2508	250 c. Plate No. 79 (Series 2)	..	1·00	90
2509	280 c. Plate No. 62 (Series 1)	..	1·25	1·00
2510	285 c. Plate No. 63 (Series 1)	..	2·50	1·00
2511	380 c. Plate No. 35 (Series 1)	..	2·75	1·25
2498/511		Set of 14	19·00	12·50

Nos. 2498/511 were printed in a similar sheet format to Nos. 1518/33.

SEASON'S

GREETINGS

120

SEASON'S
GREETINGS
(429)   (430)

SEASON'S
GREETINGS

SEASON'S
GREETINGS
1988
(431)

240

(432)

1988 (10 Nov). *Christmas (1st issue). Various Reichenbachia issues optd or surch by Gardy Ptg*

(a) With T **429**

2512	150 c. Plate No. 32 (Series 1) (No. 1561)	50	50
2513	150 c. Plate No. 62 (Series 1) (No. 1566)	50	50
2514	225 c. Plate No. 60 (Series 1) (No. 1682)	50	50
2515	260 c. Plate No. 39 (Series 1) (No. 1737)	50	50
2516	320 c. Plate No. 82 (Series 1) (No. 1753)	50	50
2517	330 c. Plate No. 80 (Series 1) (No. 1754)	50	50
2518	360 c. Plate No. 85 (Series 1) (No. 1673)	50	50

(b) As T **430** in blue

2519	120 c. on 100 c. Plate No. 6 (Series 1) (wmkd)	50	50
2520	120 c. on 100 c. Plate No. 13 (Series 1) (wmkd)	50	50
2521	120 c. on 100 c. Plate No. 20 (Series 1) (wmkd)	50	50
2522	120 c. on 100 c. Plate No. 25 (Series 1) (wmkd)	50	50
2523	120 c. on 100 c. Plate No. 40 (Series 1) (horiz) (wmkd)	50	50
2524	120 c. on 100 c. Plate No. 42 (Series 1) (horiz) (wmkd)	50	50
2525	120 c. on 100 c. Plate No. 43 (Series 1) (horiz) (wmkd)	50	50
2526	120 c. on 100 c. Plate No. 45 (Series 1) (horiz) (wmkd)	50	50

(c) With T **431** in blue

2527	225 c. Plate No. 24 (Series 1) (No. 1635)	75	75
2528	225 c. Plate No. 60 (Series 1) (No. 1682)	75	75
2529	225 c. Plate No. 24 (Series 1) (No. 1774) (wmkd)	75	75
2530	225 c. on 350 c. on 120 c. Plate No. 65 (Series 1) (No. 2221)	75	75
MS2531	120×129 mm. 225 c. on 55 c.×4 Plate No. 22 (Series 1) each with a different overprint (Type **350**, "Happy New Year", "Merry Christmas" or "Happy Holidays") (No. MS2232)	2·50	2·50

(d) With T **432**

2532	240 c. on 180 c. Plate No. 15 (Series 1) (No. 1752)	60	60
2512/30 and 2532		Set of 20	10·00	10·00

CHRISTMAS
1988
20

Protect yourself
from AIDS.
Better safe
than sorry.

(433)   (434)

1988 (16 Nov). *Christmas (2nd issue). Nos. 489, 1188/91 and 1449 surch or optd as T **433** by Autoprint.*

2533	—	20 c. on 6 c. mult (No. 489) (R.)	..	15	10
2534	**277**	120 c. on lake-brown, black & bright blue	25	35
		a. Block of 4. Nos. 2534/7		90	
2535	—	120 c. on 130 c. rose-red, black and bright blue (No. 1189)	25	35
2536	—	120 c. on 150 c. bright violet, black and bright blue (No. 1190)	25	35
2537	—	120 c. on 200 c. dull green, black and bright blue (No. 1191)	25	35
2538	—	500 c. on 330 c. mult (No. 1449) (R.)	1·50	1·75
2533/8		Set of 6	2·40	2·75

No. 2538 shows "CHRISTMAS 1988" vertical, reading up.

1988 (1 Dec). *AIDS Information Campaign. Nos. 707/8a optd as T **434** or surch also.*

2539	120 c. on $5 *Morpho deidamia* (A)	..	2·00	2·00
	a. Strip of 5. Nos. 2539/43		9·00	
2540	120 c. on $5 *Morpho deidamia* (B)	..	2·00	2·00
2541	120 c. on $5 *Morpho deidamia* (C)	..	2·00	2·00
2542	120 c. on $5 *Morpho deidamia* (D)	..	2·00	2·00
2543	120 c. on $5 *Morpho deidamia* (Type **434**)	2·00	2·00
2544	120 c. on $10 *Elbella patrobas* (A)	..	2·00	2·00
	a. Strip of 5. Nos. 2544/8		9·00	
2545	120 c. on $10 *Elbella patrobas* (B)	..	2·00	2·00
2546	120 c. on $10 *Elbella patrobas* (C)	..	2·00	2·00
2547	120 c. on $10 *Elbella patrobas* (D)	..	2·00	2·00
2548	120 c. on $10 *Elbella patrobas* (Type **434**)	2·00	2·00
2549	$2 *Morpho rhetenor* (female) (Type **434**)	5·50	2·00
2550	$5 *Morpho deidamia* (Type **434**)	..	8·00	4·50
2551	$10 *Elbella patrobas* (Type **434**)	..	9·50	7·00
2539/51		Set of 13	38·00	30·00

Nos. 2539/43 and 2544/8 were surcharged horizontally and vertically *se-tenant* with Type **434** and four other slogans: (A) "Be compassionate towards AIDS victims."; (B) "Get information on AIDS. it may save your life."; (C) "Get the facts. Education helps to prevent AIDS."; (D) "Say no to Drugs and limit the spread of AIDS.".

(Des K. Everett (150 c.). Litho Format)

1988 (16 Dec). *150th Anniv of Abolition of Slavery (1984) (2nd issue). Designs as Nos. 1547/50, but colours changed. P 14.*

2552	**337**	25 c. black and bistre-brown	..	15	10
2553	—	60 c. black and brown-lilac	..	20	15
2554	—	130 c. black and blue-green	..	25	40
2555	—	150 c. black and dull blue	..	30	45
2552/5		Set of 4	80	1·00

Nos. 2552/5 exist imperforate from stock dispersed by the liquidator of Format International Security Printers Ltd.

The new-issue supplement to this Catalogue appears each month in

GIBBONS
STAMP MONTHLY

—from your newsagent or by postal subscription—
sample copy and details on request.

1050

SALUTING WINNERS
OLYMPIC GAMES
1988

(435)

1989 (3 Jan). *Olympic Medal Winners, Seoul. Nos. 1672, 1923 and 2178 surch as T **435** by Gardy Ptg.*

2556	550 c. on 560 c. Plate No. 1 (Series 2)	..	1·25	1·00
2557	900 c. on 320 c. Plate No. 18 (Series 2)		1·75	2·00
2558	1050 c. on 320 c. Plate No. 50 (Series 1)		2·25	2·75
2556/8		Set of 3	4·75	5·25

A further small book, similar to these described under Nos. 1767/1806, containing stamps showing plate numbers 49 to 96 of the second series, was issued on 3 January 1989.

REPUBLIC DAY 1989   **$5.00**
(436)   (437)

1989 (22 Feb). *Republic Day. Nos. 2194/201 and 2212 optd with T **436** in red by Gardy Ptg.*

2559	**396**	$1.20, bronze-green		30	40
		a. Block of 4. Nos. 2559/62		1·10	
2560	—	$1.20, bronze-green (No. 2196)		30	40
2561	—	$1.20, bronze-green (No. 2196)		30	40
2562	—	$1.20, bronze-green (No. 2197)		30	40
2563	**396**	$1.20, maroon		30	40
		a. Block of 4. Nos. 2563/6		1·10	
2564	—	$1.20, maroon (No. 2199)		30	40
2565	—	$1.20, maroon (No. 2200)		30	40
2566	—	$1.20, maroon (No. 2201)		30	40
2567	—	$10 multicoloured		2·00	2·50
2559/67		Set of 9	4·00	5·00

1989 (22 Feb). *Nos. 2202/5 and 2207/10 surch with T **437** in red.*

2568	**396**	$5 on $3.20, deep dull blue	..	1·25	1·50
		a. Vert pair. Nos. 2568 and 2570		2·50	3·00
2569	—	$5 on $3.20, deep dull blue (No. 2203)	1·25	1·50
		a. Vert pair. Nos. 2569 and 2571		2·50	3·00
2570	—	$5 on $3.20, deep dull blue (No. 2204)	1·25	1·50
2571	—	$5 on $3.20, deep dull blue (No. 2205)	1·25	1·50
2572	—	$5 on $3.30, brownish blk (No. 2207)	1·25	1·50
		a. Vert pair. Nos. 2572 and 2574		2·50	3·00
2573	**396**	$5 on $3.30, brownish black	1·25	1·50
		a. Vert pair. Nos. 2573 and 2575		2·50	3·00
2574	—	$5 on $3.30, brownish blk (No. 2209)	1·25	1·50
2575	—	$5 on $3.30, brownish blk (No. 2210)	1·25	1·50
2568/75		Set of 8	9·00	11·00

Nos. 2568/75 were issued in vertical strips of ten, each strip containing two designs *se-tenant*.

1989 (22 Feb–Mar). *Various Reichenbachia issues surch by Gardy Ptg.*

(a) As T **420** in red

2576	120 c. on 140 c. Plate No. 25 (Series 2)	..	1·00	1·00
2577	120 c. on 140 c. Plate No. 52 (Series 2)	..	1·00	1·00
2578	120 c. on 140 c. Plate No. 65 (Series 2)	..	1·00	1·00
2579	120 c. on 175 c. Plate No. 54 (Series 1) (surch vert–reading down)	1·00	1·00

(b) As T **421**, but with two bars only

2580	120 c. on 140 c. Plate No. 38 (Series 2)	..	1·00	1·00
2581	120 c. on 140 c. Plate No. 41 (Series 2)	..	1·00	1·00
2582	170 c. on 175 c. Plate No. 58 (Series 2) (Mar)	1·25	1·25
2583	250 c. on 280 c. Plate No. 66 (Series 2) (Mar)	1·50	1·50
2584	250 c. on 280 c. Plate No. 67 (Series 2) (Mar)	1·50	1·50
2585	300 c. on 290 c. Plate No. 53 (Series 2) (No. 2236) (Mar)	1·60	1·60
2576/85		Set of 10	10·50	10·50

TEN DOLLARS

$10.00   **TEN DOLLARS**
(438)   (439)

1989 (22 Feb). *Nos. 1744/5 and 2185/6 surch with T 438 (Nos. 2586, 2588) or T 439 (Nos. 2587, 2589), both in red.*
2586	363	$10 on 320 c. rosine, black and deep reddish violet (No. 1744) ..	1·75	2·25
		a. Horiz pair. Nos. 2586/7	3·50	4·50
2587	–	$10 on 320 c. multicoloured (No. 1745)	1·75	2·25
2588	363	$10 on 320 c. rosine, black and deep reddish violet (No. 2185) ..	1·75	2·25
		a. Horiz pair. Nos. 2588/9	3·50	4·50
2589	–	$10 on 320 c. multicoloured (No. 2186)	1·75	2·25
2586/9		.. .. Set of 4	7·00	9·00

EASTER

≡ **125**

POSTAGE

(440)   (441)

1989 (22 Mar). *Easter. No. 1817 in block of four surch as T 440.*
MS2590 97×124 mm. 125 c. on 320 c., 250 c. on 320 c., 300 c. on 320 c., 350 c. on 320 c., Plate No. 12 (Series 2) .. .. .. 2·25 2·50

1989 (Mar). *Nos. O54/7, O59/63 and O65/9 optd with T 441 or surch additionally as T 421 with two bars only by Gardy Ptg.*
2591	125 c. on 130 c. Plate No. 92 (Series 2) ..		80	80
2592	125 c. on 140 c. Plate No. 36 (Series 2) ..		80	80
2593	150 c. Plate No. 43 (Series 2)		80	80
2594	150 c. on 175 c. Plate No. 31 (Series 2) ..		80	80
2595	250 c. Plate No. 59 (Series 2)		1·00	1·00
2596	250 c. on 225 c. Plate No. 26 (Series 2) (surch at top) ..		1·00	1·00
	a. Surch at foot		1·00	1·00
2597	250 c. on 230 c. Plate No. 68 (Series 2)		1·00	1·00
2598	250 c. on 260 c. Plate No. 69 (Series 2) (surch at top) ..		1·00	1·00
	a. Surch in centre		1·00	1·00
2599	300 c. on 275 c. Plate No. 90 (Series 2)		1·00	1·00
2600	350 c. Plate No. 95 (Series 2) (opt vert – reading up)..		1·00	1·00
	a. Opt vert – reading down		1·00	1·00
2601	350 c. on 330 c. Plate No. 23 (Series 2)		1·00	1·00
2602	600 c. Plate No. 70 (Series 2) (opt vert – reading up)..		1·25	1·25
2603	$12 Plate No. 71 (Series 2) (opt vert – reading up)..		2·25	2·75
2604	$15 Plate No. 84 (Series 2)		2·50	3·00
2591/604	.. .. .. Set of 14		14·50	15·00

1989 (Mar). *Centenary of Publication of Sanders' Reichenbachia (35th issue). Vert designs as T 331. Multicoloured. P 13½×14.*
2605	200 c. Plate No. 49 (Series 2) ..	..	75	75
2606	200 c. Plate No. 53 (Series 2) ..	..	75	75
2607	200 c. Plate No. 60 (Series 2) ..	..	75	75
2608	200 c. Plate No. 64 (Series 2) ..	..	75	75
2605/8		Set of 4	2·75	2·75
Nos. 2605/8 were printed in a similar sheet format to Nos. 1518/33.

≡ **250**

(442)

1989 (Mar). *As No. 1442, but with imprint date, surch with T 442. P 14.*
2609	322	250 c. on 25 c. multicoloured ..	..	1·60	15

≡ **375**

RED CROSS

1948

1988

(443)

1989 (Apr). *40th Anniv of Guyana Red Cross. No. 1872 surch as T 443.*
2610	375 c. on 45 c. Plate No. 17 (Series 2)	1·50	80
2611	425 c. on 45 c. Plate No. 17 (Series 2)	1·50	80

≡

HEALTH
FOR ALL

250

(444)

1989 (3 Apr). *World Health Day. Nos. 1875 and 2239 surch as T 444.*
2612	250 c. on 75 c. Plate No. 56 (Series 2) (surch T 444) ..	90	90
	a. Pair. Nos. 2612/13 ..	1·75	1·75
2613	250 c. on 75 c. Plate No. 56 (Series 2) (surch "ALL FOR HEALTH")	90	90
2614	675 c. on 720 c. Plate No. 49 (Series 2) (surch "ALL FOR HEALTH")	1·75	1·75
	a. Pair. Nos. 2614/15 ..	3·50	3·50
2615	675 c. on 720 c. Plate No. 49 (Series 2) (surch as T 444) ..	1·75	1·75
2612/15	Set of 4	4·75	4·75
Nos. 2612/13 and 2614/15 were each issued, *se-tenant*, in horizontal and vertical pairs, within the sheets of four.

PHOTOGRAPHY
1839 - 1989

BOY SCOUTS **550**
1909   1989 ≡
(445)   (446)

1989 (11 Apr). *Scouting Anniversaries. Nos. 1873, 1879, 2322, 2509 and unissued value as No. 1873 optd or surch as T 445.*
2616	250 c. on 50 c. Plate No. 33 (Series 2) (surch T 445) ..	75	75
	a. Pair. Nos. 2616/17 ..	1·50	1·50
2617	250 c. on 50 c. Plate No. 33 (Series 2) (surch "GIRL GUIDES 1924 1989")	75	75
2618	250 c. on 100 c. Plate No. 33 (Series 2) (surch as T 445) ..	75	75
	a. Pair. Nos. 2618/19 ..	1·50	1·50
2619	250 c. on 100 c. Plate No. 33 (Series 2) (surch "GIRL GUIDES 1924 1989")	75	75
2620	300 c. Plate No. 50 (Series 2) (optd as T 445)	90	90
	a. Pair. Nos. 2620/1 ..	1·75	1·75
2621	300 c. Plate No. 50 (Series 2) (optd "GIRL GUIDES 1924 1989")	90	90
2622	$25 on 280 c. Plate No. 62 (Series 2) (surch "LADY BADEN POWELL 1889 – 1989")	4·50	5·50
2623	$25 on 700 c. Plate No. 62 (Series 2) (surch "LADY BADEN POWELL 1889 – 1989")	4·50	5·50
2616/23	Set of 8	12·50	14·00
The events commemorated are the 80th anniversary of Boy Scout Movement in Guyana, 65th anniversary of Girl Guide Movement in Guyana and birth centenary of Lady Baden-Powell.
On Nos. 2616/17 the surcharge is a "2" applied in front of the original face value to form "250".
Nos. 2616/17, 2618/19 and 2620/1 were each issued, *se-tenant*, in horizontal and vertical pairs within the sheets of four.

1989 (15 Apr). *150 Years of Photography. No. 1881 surch as T 446.*
2624	550 c. on 390 c. Plate No. 6 (Series 2) ..	1·00	1·00
	a. Pair. Nos. 2624/5	2·00	2·00
2625	650 c. on 390 c. Plate No. 6 (Series 2) (original value cancelled by two bars)	1·00	1·00
2626	650 c. on 390 c. Plate No. 6 (Series 2) (original value cancelled by six bars)	1·00	1·00
2624/6	Set of 3	2·75	2·75
No. 2624 exists either as complete sheets of four or horizontally and vertically *se-tenant* with No. 2625. No. 2626 only comes as sheets of four all showing the same surcharge.

PRICES OF SETS

Set prices are given for many issues, generally those containing three stamps or more. Definitive sets include one of each value or major colour change, but do not cover different perforations, die types or minor shades. Where a choice is possible the set prices are based on the cheapest versions of the stamps included in the listings.

≡

I.L.O.
1919-1989

300

(447)

1989 (2 May). *70th Anniv of International Labour Organization. No. 1875 surch with T 447.*
2627	300 c. on 75 c. Plate No. 56 (Series 2)	3·50	40

80c

(448)

≡ **$6.40**

(449)

$5

$2·55   X   ≡ $6.40
(450)   (451)   (452)

1989 (8 May)–**92?**. *Various stamps surch*
(a) As T 448 with short obliterating bars over original value
2628		80 c. on 6 c. Patua (No. 452) ..	40	20
2629		$1 on 2 c. Type 132 (15.6.89) ..	40	20
2630		$2.05 on 3 c. Hanging Heliconia (No. 544) (15.6.89) ..	40	25
2631		$2.55 on 5 c. Annatto tree (No. 545) (15.6.89) ..	40	30
2632		$3.25 on 6 c. Cannon-ball tree (No. 546) (15.6.89) ..	40	30
2633		$5 on 6 c. Type 111 (16.8.89) ..	40	30
2634		$6.40 on 10 c. Archonias bellona (No. 699) (18.5.89) ..	3·25	75
2635		$8.90 on 60 c. Papilio androgeus (No. 705a) (26.5.89) ..	4·25	85
(b) As T 449 (larger figures on 80 c.) without any obliterating bars
2636		80 c. on 6 c. Patua (No. 452) ..	40	20
2637		$6.40 on 10 c. Archonias bellona (No. 699) (18.5.89) ..	3·25	75
2637a		$7.65 on 35 c. Anaea galanthus (No. 703) (1992?) ..	3·75	80
2638		$7.65 on 40 c. Morpho rhetenor (male) (No. 704) (18.5.89) ..	3·75	80
2639		$8.90 on 60 c. Papilio androgeus (No. 705a) (26.5.89) ..	4·25	85
(c) As T 450 (larger figures on $1) with "X" over original value
2640		$1 on 2 c. Type 132 (15.6.89) ..	40	20
2641		$2.55 on 5 c. Annatto tree (No. 545) (15.6.89) ..	40	25
2642		$3.25 on 6 c. Cannon-ball tree (No. 546)	40	25
2643		$50 on $2 Morpho rhetenor (female) (No. 707) (5.6.89) ..	12·00	4·50
2644		$100 on $2 Morpho rhetenor (female) (No. 707) (5.6.89) ..	17·00	11·00
(d) As T 451
2645		$5 on 6 c. Type 111 (with T 451) (16.8.89)	40	20
2645a		$5 on 6 c. Type 111 (as T 451, but with "X" instead of bars at foot) (1992) ..	40	20
(e) As T 421, but two obliterating bars only
2646		640 c. on 675 on 720 c. Plate No. 49 (Series 2) (surch "ALL FOR HEALTH") (No. 2614) ..	1·25	1·25
		a. Pair. Nos. 2646/7 ..	2·50	2·50
2647		640 c. on 675 c. on 720 c. Plate No. 49 (Series 2) (surch "HEALTH FOR ALL") (No. 2615)	1·25	1·25
(f) As T 452
2648	–	$6.40 on $3.30, brownish black (No. 2207) ..	3·00	2·00
		a. Vert pair. Nos. 2648 and 2650	6·00	4·00
2649	396	$6.40 on $3.30, brownish black	3·00	2·00
		a. Vert pair. Nos. 2649 and 2651	6·00	4·00
2650	–	$6.40 on $3.30, brownish black (No. 2209) ..	3·00	2·00
2651	–	$6.40 on $3.30, brownish black (No. 2210) ..	3·00	2·00
2652	396	$7.65 on $3.20, deep dull blue ..	3·00	2·00
		a. Vert pair. Nos. 2652 and 2654	6·00	4·00
2653	–	$7.65 on $3.20, dp dull blue (No. 2203)	3·00	2·00
		a. Vert pair. Nos. 2653 and 2655	6·00	4·00
2654	–	$7.65 on $3.20, dp dull blue (No. 2204)	3·00	2·00
2655	–	$7.65 on $3.20, dp dull blue (No. 2205)	3·00	2·00
2628/55		Set of 30	70·00	35·00

CARICOM DAY

125
═══

(453)

454 *Stalachtis calliope*

1989 (26 June). *CARICOM Day. No.* 1878 *surch with T* **453**.
2656 125 c. on 200 c. Plate No. 44 (Series 2) .. 1·75 30
    a. Original face value cancelled by 6
    thin lines .. .. 2·00 50

(Des Mary Walters. Litho Questa)

1989 (7 Sept). *Butterflies* (1st series). T **454** and similar vert
designs. Multicoloured. P 14.
2657 80 c. Type **454** 50 10
2658 $2.25, Morpho rhetenor 60 15
2659 $5 Agrias claudia 70 15
2660 $6.40, Marpesia marcella 75 20
2661 $7.65, Papilio zagreus 80 30
2662 $8.90, Chorinea faunus 90 30
2663 $25 Euptychia cephus .. .. .. 2·50 2·50
2664 $100 Nessaea regina .. .. .. 6·50 7·50
2657/64 .. .. *Set of* 8 12·00 10·00
For miniature sheets accompanying this issue see Nos.
EMS18/19.
See also Nos. 2789/861.

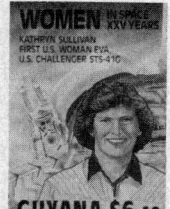

═══
AHMADIYYA CENTENARY 1889-1989
$8.90

455 Kathryn Sullivan
(first U.S woman to walk
in space)

(456)

(Des M. Dorfman. Litho Questa)

1989 (8 Nov). *25 Years of Women in Space*. T **455** and similar
vert designs. Multicoloured. P 14.
2665 $6.40, Type **455** 50 20
2666 $12.80, Svetlana Savitskaya (first Soviet
    woman to walk in space) .. 80 45
2667 $15.30, Judy Resnik and Christa
    McAuliffe with *Challenger* logo .. 80 45
2668 $100 Sally Ride (first U.S. woman
    astronaut) .. .. 5·00 6·00
2665/8 .. .. *Set of* 4 6·50 6·50
For miniature sheet accompanying this issue see No. EMS20.

1989 (22 Nov). *Centenary of Ahmadiyya* (*Moslem
organization*). Nos. 543/5 surch as T **456**.
2669 80 c. on 2 c. Type **132** .. .. 1·75 40
2670 $6.40 on 3 c. Hanging Heliconia .. 6·00 3·25
2671 $8.90 on 5 c. Annatto tree .. .. 6·50 4·00
2669/71 .. .. *Set of* 3 13·00 7·00

Guyana $2.25 $15 Guyana

457 Head of   458 Channel-billed
Harpy Eagle   Toucan

(Des J. Barbaris. Litho Questa)

1990 (23 Jan). *Endangered Species. Harpy Eagle.* T **457** and
similar vert designs. Multicoloured. P 14.
2672 $2.25, Type **457** 75 25
2673 $5 Harpy Eagle with monkey prey .. 1·00 30
2674 $8.90, Eagle on branch (facing right) .. 1·25 50
2675 $30 Eagle on branch (facing left) .. 3·00 3·50
2672/5 .. .. *Set of* 4 5·50 4·00

(Des J. Barbaris. Litho Questa)

1990 (23 Jan). *Birds of Guyana.* T **458** and similar
multicoloured designs. P 14.
2676 $15 Type **458** 90 40
2677 $25 Blue and Yellow Macaw .. .. 1·40 70
2678 $50 Wattled Jacana (horiz) .. .. 2·75 2·25
2679 $60 Hoatzin (horiz) .. .. .. 3·00 2·50
2676/9 .. .. *Set of* 4 7·25 5·25
MS2680 Two sheets, each 110×80 mm. (a) $100
Great Kiskadee. (b) $100 Amazon Kingfisher
.. .. *Set of* 2 sheets 9·50 9·00

Rotary International 1905-1990

(459)

460 Indian Post Runner, 1837

1990 (15 Mar). *85th Anniv of Rotary International.* Optd as
T **459** in silver. (a) On Nos. 2657/64
2681 80 c. Type **454** 60 20
2682 $2.25, Morpho rhetenor 90 30
2683 $5 Agrias claudia .. .. .. 1·25 30
2684 $6.40, Marpesia marcella .. .. 1·40 35
2685 $7.65, Papilio zagreus .. .. 1·50 50
2686 $8.90, Chorinea faunus .. .. 1·60 55
2687 $25 Euptychia cephus .. .. 2·75 3·25
2688 $100 Nessaea regina .. .. .. 8·00 9·00
2681/8 .. .. *Set of* 8 16·00 13·00

(b) On Nos. 2665/8
2689 $6.40, Type **455** 85 40
2690 $12.80, Svetlana Savitskaya (first Soviet
    woman to walk in space) .. 1·50 80
2691 $15.30, Judy Resnik and Christa
    McAuliffe with *Challenger* logo .. 1·60 90
2692 $100 Sally Ride (first U.S. woman astro-
    naut) .. .. 6·00 7·00
2689/92 .. .. *Set of* 4 9·00 8·25

(Des G. Vasarhelyi. Litho Questa)

1990 (3 May). *150th Anniv of Penny Black and 500th Anniv of
Thurn and Taxis Postal Service.* T **460** and similar horiz
designs. Multicoloured. P 14.
2693/2746 $15.30×27, $17.80×9, $20×18
.. .. *Set of* 54 28·00 29·00
MS2747 Three sheets, each 116×86 mm. (a)
$150 Post boy; (b) $150 Thurn and Taxis
(Northern District) 3 sgr. of 1852; (c) $150 Thurn
and Taxis (Southern District) 6 k. of 1852
.. .. *Set of* 3 sheets 11·00 12·00
Nos. 2693/746 (issued as six sheetlets each of nine different
designs) depict various forms of mail transport.

80

ROTARY DISTRICT 405 9th CONFERENCE MAY 1990 GEORGETOWN

(461)

90th Birthday
H.M. The Queen Mother

(462)

1990 (8 May). *9th Conference of Rotary District 405,
Georgetown.* Nos. 1526, 1530, 1552 and 1554/5 surch as T **461**.
2748 80 c. on 55 c. Plate No. 9 (Series 1) ..
2749 80 c. on 55 c. Plate No. 49 (Series 1) ..
2750 80 c. on 55 c. Plate No. 64 (Series 1) ..
2751 $6.40, on 130 c. Plate No. 6 (Series 1) ..
2752 $6.40, on 130 c. Plate No. 25 (Series 1)
2753 $7.65 on 130 c. Plate No. 25 (Series 1)

1990 (8 June). *90th Birthday of Queen Elizabeth the Queen
Mother.* Nos. 2657/64 surch with T **462**.
2754 80 c. Type **454** 50 20
2755 $2.25, Morpho rhetenor 75 30
2756 $5 Agrias claudia 90 30
2757 $6.40, Marpesia marcella .. .. 1·00 40
2758 $7.65, Papilio zagreus .. .. 1·25 50
2759 $8.90, Chorinea faunus .. .. 1·50 55
2760 $25 Euptychia cephus .. .. 3·00 3·25
2761 $100 Nessaea regina .. .. .. 8·00 9·00
2754/61 .. .. *Set of* 8 15·00 13·00
For miniature sheets accompanying this issue see Nos.
EMS31/3.

GUYANA

$2·55

463 Collared Trogon

Guyana 80¢

464 Melinaea idae

(Litho Format)

1990 (12 Sept). *Birds.* T **463** and similar multicoloured
designs. P 13½×14 (80 c.) or 14×13½ (others).
2762 80 c. Guiana Partridge (horiz) 30 10
2763 $2.55, Type **463** 40 15
2764 $3.25, Derby Aracari 40 15
2765 $5 Black-necked Aracari 50 20

2766 $5.10, Green Aracari 50 30
2767 $5.80, Ivory-billed Aracari 50 30
2768 $6.40, Guiana Toucanet 50 30
2769 $6.50, Sulphur-breasted Toucan .. 50 30
2770 $7.55, Red-billed Toucan 65 30
2771 $7.65, Toco Toucan 65 30
2772 $8.25, Natterers Toucanet 65 30
2773 $8.90, Welcome Trogon 65 30
2774 $9.75, Doubtful Trogon 65 30
2775 $11.40, Banded Aracari 75 40
2776 $12.65, Golden-headed Train Bearer .. 75 40
2777 $12.80, Rufous-breasted Hermit .. 75 40
2778 $13.90, Band Tail Barbthroat .. 75 40
2779 $15.30, White-tipped Sickle Bill .. 80 50
2780 $17.80, Black Jacobin 90 60
2781 $19.20, Fiery Topaz 90 60
2782 $22.95, Tufted Coquette .. .. 1·00 70
2783 $26.70, Ecuadorian Pied-tail .. 1·00 70
2784 $30 Quetzal .. .. 1·00 70
2785 $50 Green-crowned Brilliant .. 1·75 1·25
2786 $100 Emerald-chinned Hummingbird .. 2·75 2·75
2787 $190 Lazuline Sabre-wing .. .. 4·50 5·00
2788 $225 Beryline Hummingbird .. 4·50 5·50
2762/88 .. .. .. *Set of* 27 26·00 20·00
Nos. 2762/88 exist imperforate from stock dispersed by the
liquidator of Format International Security Printers Ltd.

(Litho Questa)

1990 (26 Sept). *Butterflies* (2nd series). T **464** and similar
multicoloured designs. P 14.
2789/2860 80 c., $2.55, $5, $6.40, $7.65, $8.90,
$10×64, $50 and $100 .. *Set of* 72 12·00 13·00
MS2861 Four sheets, each 102×71 mm. (a) $150
Heliconius aoede. (b) $150 Phyciodes clio (horiz).
(c) $190 Thecla hemon. (d) $190 Nymphidium
caricae .. .. .. *Set of* 4 sheets 17·00 18·00
Designs: Vert—$2.55, Rhetus dysonii; $5 Actinote anteas;
$6.40, Heliconius tales; $7.65, Thecla telemus; $8.90, Theope
eudocia; $10 (No. 2795), Heleconius vetustus; No. 2796,
Mesosemia eumene; No. 2797, Parides phosphorus; No. 2798,
Polystichtis emylius; No. 2799, Xanthocleis aedesia; No. 2800,
Doxocopa agathina; No. 2801, Adelpha plesaure; No. 2802,
Heliconius wallacei; No. 2803, Notheme eumeus; No. 2804,
Melinaea mediatrix; No. 2805, Theritas coronata; No. 2806,
Dismorphia orise; No. 2807, Phyciodes ianthe; No. 2808, Morpho
aega; No. 2809, Zaretis isidora; No. 2810, Pierella lena; No.
2811, Heliconius silvana; No. 2812, Eunica alcmena; No. 2813,
Mechanitis polymnia; No. 2814, Mesosemia ephyne; No. 2815,
Thecla erema; No. 2816, Callizona acesta; No. 2817, Stalachtis
phaedusa; No. 2818, Battus belus; No. 2819, Nymula phliasus;
No. 2820, Parides childrenae; No. 2821, Stalachtis euterpe; No.
2822, Dysmathia portia; No. 2823, Tithorea hermias; No. 2824,
Prepona pheridamas; No. 2825, Dismorphia fortunata; No.
2826, Hamadryas amphinome; $50 Heliconius vicini; $100
Amarynthis meneria. Horiz—$10 (No. 2827), Thecla falerina;
No. 2828, Pheles heliconides; No. 2829, Echenias leucocyana;
No. 2830, Heliconius xanthocles; No. 2831, Mesopthalma idotea;
No. 2832, Parides aeneas; No. 2833, Heliconius numata; No.
2834, Thecla critola; No. 2835, Themone pais; No. 2836, Nymula
agle; No. 2837, Adelpha cocala; No. 2838, Anaea eribotes; No.
2839, Prepona demophon; No. 2840, Selenophanes cassiope; No.
2841, Consul hippona; No. 2842, Antirrhaea avernus; No. 2843,
Thecla telemus; No. 2844, Thyridia confusa; No. 2845,
Heliconius burneyi; No. 2846, Parides lysander; No. 2847,
Eunica orphise; No. 2848, Adelpha melona; No. 2849, Morpho
menelaus; No. 2850, Nymula phylleus; No. 2851, Stalachtis
phlegia; No. 2852, Theope barea; No. 2853, Morpho perseus; No.
2854, Lycorea ceres; No. 2855, Archonias bellona; No. 2856;
Caeronis chorinaeus; No. 2857, Vila azeca; No. 2858, Nessaea
batesii.
Nos. 2795/2810, 2811/26, 2827/42 and 2843/58 were printed
together, *se-tenant*, in sheetlets of 16 with the backgrounds
forming composite designs.

GUYANA   GUYANA

$7·65
Vanilla inodora

465 Vanilla   466 Ivory-billed
inodora   Woodpecker

(Litho B.D.T.)

1990 (16 Oct). *Flowers.* T **465** and similar multicoloured
designs. P 14.
2862/2965 $7.65, $8.90, $10×32, $12.80×65,
$15.30, $17.80, $20, $25 and $100 *Set of* 104 14·00 15·00
MS2966 Five sheets. (a) 95×95 mm. $150
Delonix regia (horiz). (b) 86×65 mm. $150
Hexisea bidentata (horiz). (c) 70×105 mm. $150
Galeandra devoniana (horiz). (d) 68×110 mm.
$150 Lecythis ollaria. (e) 74×104 mm. $190
Ionopsis utricularioides .. .. *Set of* 5 sheets 11·00 12·00
Designs: Vert—$8.90, Epidendrum ibaguense; $10 (No. 2864),
Dichea muricata; No. 2865, Octomeria erosilabia; No. 2866,
Spiranthes orchioides; No. 2867, Brassavola nodosa; No. 2868,
Epidendrum rigidum; No. 2869, Brassia caudata; No. 2870,
Pleurothallis diffusa; No. 2871, Aspasia variegata; No. 2872,
Stenia pallida; No. 2873, Cyrtopodium punctatum; No. 2874,
Cattleya deckeri; No. 2875, Cryptarrhena lunata; No. 2876,
Cattleya violacea; No. 2877, Caularthron bicornutum; No. 2878,
Oncidium carthagenense; No. 2879, Galeandra devoniana; No.
2880, Bifrenaria aurantiaca; No. 2881, Epidendrum ciliare; No.
2882, Dichaea picta; No. 2883, Scaphyglottis violacea; No. 2884,
Cattleya percivaliana; No. 2885, Map and national flag; No.
2886, Epidendrum difforme; No. 2887, Eulophia maculata; No.
2888, Spiranthes tenuis; No. 2889, Peristoria guttata; No. 2890,
Pleurothallis pruinosa; No. 2891, Cleistes rosea; No. 2892,
Maxillaria variabilis; No. 2893, Brassavola cuculata; No. 2894,
Epidendrum moyobambae; No. 2895, Oncidium orthostate;
$12.80, Maxillaria parkeri; $12.80 (No. 2897), Brassavola
martiana; No. 2898, Paphinia cristata; No. 2899, Aganisia
pulchella; No. 2900, Oncidium lanceanum; No. 2901, Lockhartia

imbricata; No. 2902, *Caularthron bilamellatum*; No. 2903, *Oncidium nanum*; No. 2904, *Pleurothallis ovalifolia*; No. 2905, *Galeandra dives*; No. 2906, *Cycnoches loddigesii*; No. 2907, *Ada aurantiaca*; No. 2908, *Catasetum barbatum*; No. 2909, *Palmorchis pubescens*; No. 2910, *Epidendrum anceps*; No. 2911, *Huntleya meleagris*; No. 2912, *Sobralia sessilis*; $15.30, *Epidendrum nocturnum*; $17.80, *Catasetum discolor*; $20 *Scuticaria hadwenii*; $25 *Epidendrum fragrans*; $100 *Epistephium parviflorum*. *Horiz*—$12.80 (No. 2913), *Cochlospermum vitifolium*; No. 2914, *Eugenia malaccensis*; No. 2915, *Plumiera rubra*; No. 2916, *Erythrina glauca*; No. 2917, *Spathodea campanulata*; No. 2918, *Jacaranda filicifolia*; No. 2919, *Samanea saman*; No. 2920, *Cassia fistula*; No. 2921, *Abutilon integerrimum*; No. 2922, *Lagerstroemia speciosa*; No. 2923, *Tabebuia serratifolia*; No. 2924, *Guaiacum officinale*; No. 2925, *Solanum macranthum*; No. 2926, *Peltophorum roxburghii*; No. 2927, *Bauhinia variegata*; No. 2928, *Plumiera alba*; No. 2929, *Maxillaria camaridii*; No. 2930, *Vanilla pompona*; No. 2931, *Stanhopea grandiflora*; No. 2932, *Oncidium pusillum*; No. 2933, *Polycycnis vittata*; No. 2934, *Cattleya lawrenceana*; No. 2935, *Menadenium labiosum*; No. 2936, *Rodriguezia secunda*; No. 2937, *Mormodes buccinator*; No. 2938, *Otostylis brachystalix*; No. 2939, *Maxillaria discolor*; No. 2940, *Liparis elata*; No. 2941, *Gongora maculata*; No. 2942, *Koellensteinia graminea*; No. 2943, *Rudolfiella aurantiaca*; No. 2944, *Scuticaria steelei*; No. 2945, *Gloriosa rothschildiana*; No. 2946, *Pseudocalymma alliaceum*; No. 2947, *Callichlamys latifolia*; No. 2948, *Distictis riversii*; No. 2949, *Maurandya barclaiana*; No. 2950, *Beaumontia fragrans*; No. 2951, *Phaseolus caracalla*; No. 2952, *Mandevilla splendens*; No. 2953, *Solandra longiflora*; No. 2954, *Passiflora coccinea*; No. 2955, *Allamanda cathartica*; No. 2956, *Bauhinia galpini*; No. 2957, *Verbena maritima*; No. 2958, *Mandevilla sauveolens*; No. 2959, *Phryganocydia corymbosa*; No. 2960, *Jasminum sambac*.

Nos. 2864/79, 2880/95, 2897/2912, 2913/28, 2929/44 and 2945/60 were each printed together, *se-tenant*, in sheetlets of 16 with the backgrounds forming composite designs.

Nos. **MS**2966b/c and **MS**2966e show the "EXPO '90" logo on the sheet margin.

1990 (16 Nov). *Fauna*. T **466** *and similar multicoloured designs. Litho*. P 14×13½ (*vert*) or 13½×14 (*horiz*).

2967/86	$12.80×20	(*vert* designs showing endangered birds)	
2987/3006	$12.80×20	(*vert* designs showing tropical birds)	
3007/26	$12.80×20	(*vert* designs showing prehistoric animals)	
3027/46	$12.80×20	(*horiz* designs showing endangered wildlife)	
2967/3046		*Set of 80* 32·00 32·00	

Designs: *Vert*—No. 2968, Cauca Guan; No. 2969, Sun Conure; No. 2970, Quetzal; No. 2971, Long-wattled Umbrellabird; No. 2972, Banded Cotinga; No. 2973, Blue-chested Parakeet; No. 2974, Rufous-bellied Chachalaca; No. 2975, Yellow-faced Amazon; No. 2976, Toucan Barbet; No. 2977, Red Siskin; No. 2978, Cock-of-the-Rock; No. 2979; Hyacinth Macaw; No. 2980, Yellow Cardinal; No. 2981, Bare-necked Umbrellabird; No. 2982, Saffron Toucanet; No. 2983, Red-billed Curassow; No. 2984, Spectacled Parrotlet; No. 2985, Lovely Cotinga; No. 2986, Black-breasted Gnateater; No. 2987, Swallow-tailed Kite; No. 2988, Hoatzin; No. 2989, Ruby-Topaz Hummingbird; No. 2990, American Black Vulture; No. 2991, Rufous-tailed Jacamar; No. 2992, Scarlet Macaw; No. 2993, Rose-breasted Thrush Tanager; No. 2994, Toco Toucan; No. 2995, Bearded Bellbird; No. 2996, Blue-crowned Motmot; No. 2997, Green Oropendola; No. 2998, Pompadour Cotinga; No. 2999; Vermilion Flycatcher; No. 3000, Blue and Yellow Macaw; No. 3001, White-barred Piculet; No. 3002, Great Razor-billed Curassow; No. 3003, Ruddy Quail Dove; No. 3004, Paradise Tanager; No. 3005, American Darter ("Anhinga"); No. 3006, Greater Flamingo; No. 3007, Palaelotus; No. 3008, Archaeotrogon; No. 3009, Vulture; No. 3010, Bradypus tridactylus; No. 3011, Natalus stramineus bat; No. 3012, Cebidae; No. 3013, Cuvieronius; No. 3014, Phororhacos; 3015, Smilodectes; No. 3016, Megatherium; No. 3017, Titanotylopus; No. 3018, Teleoceras; No. 3019, Macrauchenia; No. 3020, Mylodon; No. 3021, Smilodon; No. 3022, Glyptodon; No. 3023, Protohydrocherus; No. 3024, Archaeohyrax; No. 3025, Pyrotherium; No. 3026, Platypittamys. *Horiz*—$12.80 (No. 3027), Harpy Eagle and Hyacinth Macaw; No. 3028, Andean Condor; No. 3029, Amazonian Umbrellabird; No. 3030, Spider Monkeys; No. 3031, Hyacinth Macaws; No. 3032, Red Siskin; No. 3033, Toucan Barbet; No. 3034, Three-toed Sloth; No. 3035, Guanacos; No. 3036, Spectacled Bear; No. 3037, White-lipped Peccary; No. 3038, Maned Wolf; No. 3039, Jaguar; No. 3040, Spectacled Cayman; No. 3041, Giant Armadillo; No. 3042, Giant Anteater; No. 3043, South American River Otter; No. 3044, Yapok; No. 3045, Central American River Turtle; No. 3046, Cauca Guan.

Nos. 2967/86, 2987/3006, 3007/26 and 3027/46 were printed together, *se-tenant*, in sheetlets of 20 forming composite designs.

No. 2982 is inscribed "Toucanette" and No. 2995 inscribed "Bellbird" both in error.

For miniature sheets accompanying this issue see Nos. EMS34/5.

467 National Flag

1991 (26 May). *25th Anniv of Independence. Sheet* 100×70 mm. *Litho. Imperf.*
MS3047 **467** $225 multicoloured .. .. 5·50 6·00

NEW INFORMATION

The editor is always interested to correspond with people who have new information that will improve or correct the Catalogue.

---

468 Ramon Folist (Cuba)   (469)
(fencing, 1900)

(Litho Cartor)

1991 (12 Aug). *Winter Olympic Games, Albertville (1st issue) and Olympic Games, Barcelona, Previous Gold Medal Winners*. T **468** *and similar multicoloured designs.* P 14×13½.

3048/3119 $15.30×9, $17.80×9, $20×18, $25 ×18 and $30×18 .. .. *Set of 72* 30·00 32·00
MS3120 Three sheets, each 98×70 mm. (a) $150 Johannes Kolehmainen (Finland) (10,000 metres, 1912) (*vert*). (b) $150 Paavo Nurmi (Finland) (5000 metres, 1924) (*vert*). (c) $190 Nedo Nadi (Italy) (fencing, 1920) (*vert*). P 13×13½ .. .. .. *Set of 3 sheets* 11·00 12·00

Designs:—$15.30 (No. 3049), Lucien Gaudin (France) (fencing, 1924); No. 3050, Ole Lilloe-Olsen (Norway) (shooting, 1924); No. 3051, Morris Fisher (U.S.A.) (rifle shooting, 1924); No. 3052, Ray Ewry (U.S.A.) (long jump, 1900); No. 3053, Hubert van Innes (Belgium) (archery, 1900); No. 3054, Alvin Kraenzlein (U.S.A.) (hurdles, 1900); No. 3055, Johnny Weissmuller (U.S.A.) (swimming, 1924); No. 3056, Hans Winkler (West Germany) (show jumping, 1956); $17.80 (No. 3057), Viktor Chukarin (Russia) (gymnastics, 1952); No. 3058, Agnes Keleti (Hungary) (gymnastics, 1952); No. 3059, Barbel Wochel (East Germany) (200 metres, 1980); No. 3060, Eric Heiden (U.S.A.) (speed skating, 1980); No. 3061, Alvodár Gerevich (Hungary) (fencing, 1932); No. 3062, Giuseppe Delfino (Italy) (fencing, 1952); No. 3063, Alexander Tikhonov (Russia) (skiing, 1980); No. 3064, Pahud de Mortanges (Netherlands) (equestrian, 1932); No. 3065 Patricia McCormick (U.S.A.) (diving, 1952); $20 (No. 3066), Olga Korbut (Russia) (gymnastics, 1972); No. 3067, Lyudmila Turischeva (Russia) (gymnastics, 1972); No. 3068, Lasse Viren (Finland) (10,000 metres, 1972); No. 3069, George Miez (Switzerland) (gymnastics, 1936); No. 3070, Roland Matthes (East Germany) (swimming, 1972); No. 3071 Pal Kovaks (Hungary) (fencing, 1936); No. 3072, Jesse Owens (U.S.A.) (200 metres, 1936); No. 3073, Mark Spitz (U.S.A.) (swimming, 1972); No. 3074, Eduardo Mangiarotti (Italy) (fencing, 1936); No. 3075, Nelli Kim (Russia) (gymnastics, 1976); No. 3076, Viktor Krovopuskov (Russia) (fencing, 1976); No. 3077, Viktor Sidiak (Russia) (fencing, 1976); No. 3078, Nikolai Andrianov (Russia) (gymnastics, 1976); No. 3079, Nadia Comaneci (Rumania) (gymnastics, 1976); No. 3080, Mitsuo Tsukahara (Japan) (gymnastics, 1976); No. 3081, Yelena Novikova-Belova (Russia) (fencing, 1976); No. 3082, John Naber (U.S.A.) (swimming, 1976); No. 3083, Kornella Ender (Rumania) (swimming, 1976); $25 (No. 3084), Lydia Skoblikova (Russia) (speed skating, 1964); No. 3085, Ivar Ballangrud (Norway) (speed skating, 1936); No. 3086, Clas Thunberg (Finland) (speed skating, 1928); No. 3087, Anton Heida (U.S.A.) (gymnastics, 1904); No. 3088, Akinori Nakayama (Japan) (gymnastics, 1968); No. 3089, Sixten Jernberg (Sweden) (skiing, 1964); No. 3090, Yevgeniy Grischin (Russia) (speed skating, 1956); No. 3091, Paul Radmilovic (East Germany) (waterpolo, 1920); No. 3092, Charles Daniels (U.S.A.) (swimming, 1904); No. 3093, Sawao Kato (Japan) (gymnastics, 1968); No. 3094, Rudolf Karpáti (Hungary) (fencing, 1948); No. 3095, Jenö Fuchs (Hungary) (fencing, 1908); No. 3096, Emil Zátopek (Czechoslovakia) (10,000 metres, 1948); No. 3097, Fanny Blankers-Koen (Netherlands) (hurdles, 1948); No. 3098, Melvin Sheppard (U.S.A.) (4 x 400 metres relay, 1908); No. 3099, Gert Fredriksson (Sweden) (kayak, 1948); No. 3100, Paul Elvstrom (Denmark) (sailing, 1948); No. 3101, Harrison Dillard (U.S.A.) (100 metres, 1948); $30 (No. 3102), Al Oerter (U.S.A.) (discus, 1956); No. 3103, Polina Atsakhova (Russia) (gymnastics, 1956); No. 3104, Takashi Ono (Japan) (gymnastics, 1956); No. 3105, Valentin Muratov (Russia) (gymnastics, 1956); No. 3106, Henri St. Cyr (Sweden) (equestrian, 1956); No. 3107, Iain Murray Rose (Australia) (swimming, 1956); No. 3108, Larisa Latynina (Russia) (gymnastics, 1956); No. 3109, Carlo Pavesi (Italy) (fencing, 1956); No. 3110, Dawn Fraser (Australia) (swimming, 1956); No. 3111, Betty Cuthbert (Australia) (400 metres, 1964); No. 3112, Vera Cáslavská (Czechoslovakia) (gymnastics, 1964); No. 3113, Galin Kulakova (Russia) (skiing, 1972); No. 3114, Yukio Endo (Japan) (gymnastics, 1972); No. 3115, Vladimir Morozov (Russia) (kayak, 1972); No. 3116, Boris Shaklin (Russia) (gymnastics, 1964); No. 3117, Don Schollander (U.S.A.) (swimming, 1964); No. 3118, Gyözö Kulscár (Hungary) (fencing, 1964); No. 3119, Christian D'Oriloa (France) (fencing, 1956).

Nos. 3048/56, 3057/65, 3066/74, 3075/83, 3084/92, 3093/3101, 3102/10 and 3111/19 were each printed together, *se-tenant*, in sheetlets of 9 forming composite designs.

Sheetlets containing Nos. 3057/65, 3084/92 and 3111/19 were subsequently re-issued with Nos. 3063, 3086 and 3113 overprinted "ALBERTVILLE '92". No. **MS**3120 also exists with the 1992 venues printed on the sheet margins.

See also Nos. 3186/94 and 3246/54.

1991 (29 Oct). *85th Anniv of Rotary International (1990).*

(*a*) Nos. 2789/94 and 2859/60 optd or surch as T **469** (A) or with Rotary emblem and "1905–1990" (B)

3121	80 c. Type **464** (B)	..	10	10
3122	$2.55, *Rhetus dysonii* (B)	..	10	10
3123	$5 *Actinote anteas* (A)	..	10	10
3124	$6.40, *Heliconius tales* (A)	..	10	10
3125	$7.65, *Thecla telemus* (A)	..	10	10
3126	$100 on $8.90, *Theope eudocia* (A)	..	1·25	1·40
3127	$190 on $50 *Heliconius vicini* (B)	..	2·25	2·50
3128	$225 on $100 *Amarynthis meneria* (B)	..	2·50	2·75

(*b*) Nos. 2795/2810 and **MS**2861a/b optd or surch as Nos. 3121/8, but some with emblems and inscriptions of other international organizations.

3129	$10 *Heliconius vetustus* (B)	15	15
	a. Sheetlet. Nos. 3129/44	6·00	
3130	$10 *Mesosemia eumene* (optd Boy Scout emblem and "1907–1992")	15	15
3131	$10 *Parides phosphorus* (optd Lions Club emblem and "1917–1992")	15	15
3132	$10 *Polystichtis emylius* (A)	15	15
3133	$10 *Xanthocleis aedesia* (optd "125 Years Red Cross" and cross)	15	15
3134	$10 *Doxocopa agathina* (optd with part Rotary emblem)	15	15
3135	$10 *Adelpha plesaure* (optd with part Rotary emblem)	15	15
3136	$10 *Heliconius wallacei* (optd "125 Years Red Cross" and cross)	15	15
3137	$10 *Notheme eumeus* (optd Lions Club emblem and "1917–1992")	15	15
3138	$10 *Melinaea mediatrix* (optd with part Rotary emblem)	15	15
3139	$10 *Theritas coronata* (optd with part Rotary emblem)	15	15
3140	$10 *Dismorphia orise* (optd Boy Scout emblem and "1907–1992")	15	15
3141	$50 on $10 *Phyciodes ianthe* (A)	65	65
3142	$75 on $10 *Morpho aega* (surch Boy Scout emblem and "1907–1992")	1·00	1·10
3143	$100 on $10 *Zaretis isidora* (surch Lions Club emblem and "1917–1992")	1·25	1·40
3144	$190 on $10 *Pierella lena* (B)	2·25	2·50
3121/44		*Set of 24* 12·00	13·00
MS3145	Two sheets, each 102×71 mm. (a) $400 on $150 *Heliconius aoede*. (b) $500 on $150 *Phyciodes clio* .. .. *Set of 2 sheets*	9·00	9·25

Nos. 3134/5 and 3138/9 show the Rotary International emblem overprinted at the centre of the block of four.

Nos. **MS**3145a/b only show the new face values on the stamps and have international organization emblems overprinted on the sheet margins.

(Des D. Miller. Litho B.D.T.)

1991 (25 Nov). *65th Birthday of Queen Elizabeth II and 70th Birthday of Prince Philip. Horiz designs as* T **280** *of Antigua. Multicoloured.* P 14.

3146	$12.80, Queen and Prince Philip in evening dress	15	20
3147	$15.30, Queen Elizabeth II	15	20
3148	$100 Queen and Prince Philip	1·00	1·10
3149	$130 Prince Philip	1·25	1·40
3150	$150 Prince Philip in R.A.F. uniform	1·50	1·60
3151	$200 The Queen with Queen Elizabeth the Queen Mother	2·25	2·40
3146/51		*Set of 6* 5·75	6·25
MS3152	68×90 mm. $225 Queen Elizabeth II	3·00	3·25

(Des D. Miller. Litho B.D.T.)

1991 (25 Nov). *10th Wedding Anniv of Prince and Princess of Wales. Horiz designs as* T **280** *of Antigua. Multicoloured.* P 14.

3153	$8.90, Prince and Princess of Wales	20	20
3154	$50 Separate portraits of Princess and sons	80	80
3155	$75 Prince Charles with Prince William	1·25	1·25
3156	$190 Princess Diana with Prince Henry	2·75	3·00
3153/6		*Set of 4* 4·50	4·75
MS3157	68×90 mm. $225 Separate portraits of Prince Charles, Prince William and Princess Diana with Prince Henry	3·25	3·50

$100

Melvin Jones
Founder   1880-1961

(470)

1991 (26 Nov). *75th Anniv of Lions International (1992).* (*a*) Nos. 2789/94 and 2859/60 optd or surch as T **470** (A) or with Lions Club emblem and "Lions International 1917–1992" (B)

3158	80 c. Type **464** (B)	..	15	10
3159	$2.55, *Rhetus dysonii* (B)	..	20	15
3160	$5 *Actinote anteas* (A)	..	30	20
3161	$6.40, *Heliconius tales* (A)	..	30	25
3162	$7.65, *Thecla telemus* (A)	..	35	25
3163	$100 on $8.90, *Theope eudocia* (A)	..	1·50	1·50
3164	$190 on $50 *Heliconius vicini* (B)	..	2·50	2·75
3165	$225 on $100 *Amarynthis meneria* (B)	..	2·75	3·00

(*b*) Nos. 2843/58 and **MS**2861c/d optd or surch in black or red as Nos. 3158/65, but some with emblems and inscriptions of other international organizations.

3166	$10 *Thecla telemus* (optd Lions Club emblem and "1917–1992")	15	15
	a. Sheetlet. Nos. 3166/81	6·00	
3167	$10 *Thyridia confusa* (optd Rotary emblem and "1905–1990")	15	15
3168	$10 *Heliconius burneyi* (optd Boy Scout emblem and "1907–1992")	15	15
3169	$10 *Parides lysander* (A)	15	15
3170	$10 *Eunica orphise* (optd "125 Years Red Cross" and cross)	15	15
3171	$10 *Adelpha melona* (optd with part Lions Club emblem)	15	15
3172	$10 *Morpho menelaus* (optd with part Lions Club emblem)	15	15
3173	$10 *Nymula phylleus* (optd "125 Years Red Cross" and cross)	15	15
3174	$10 *Stalachtis phlegia* (optd Rotary emblem and "1905–1990")	15	15
3175	$10 *Theope barea* (optd with part Lions Club emblem)	15	15

3176	$10 *Morpho perseus* (optd with part Lions Club emblem)		15	15
3177	$10 *Lycorea ceres* (optd Boy Scout emblem and "1907–1992")		15	15
3178	$50 on $10 *Archonias bellona* (A)		65	65
3179	$75 on $10 *Caerois chorinaeus* (surch Boy Scout emblem and "1907–1992")		1·00	1·10
3180	$100 on $10 *Vila azeca* (surch Rotary emblem and "1905–1990")		1·25	1·40
3181	$190 on $10 *Nessaea batesii* (surch Lions Club emblem and "1917–1992")		2·25	2·50
3158/81		*Set of 24*	12·00	13·00

MS3182 Two sheets, each 102×71 mm. (a) $400 on $190 *Nymphidium caricae*. (b) $500 on $190 *Thecla hemon* .. .. .. *Set of 2 sheets* 9·00 9·25

Nos. 3171/2 and 3175/6 show the Lions Club International emblem overprinted at the centre of the block of four.

Nos. MS3182a/b only show new face values on the stamps and have international organization emblems overprinted on the sheet margins.

$50
(471)

1991 (29 Nov). *"Phila Nippon '91" International Stamp Exhibition, Tokyo.* Sheetlets containing Nos. 2880/95 and 2897/2912, now sold as miniature sheets, and **MS2966d** with some stamps such as T **471** and inscriptions and exhibition logo on the sheet margins, all in red.

MS3183	135×203 mm. $10×12; $25 on $10; $50 on $10; $75 on $10; $130 on $10	6·00	6·50
MS3184	135×203 mm. $12.80×12; $25 on $12.80; $50 on $12.80; $75 on $12.80; $100 on $12.80	6·00	6·50
MS3185	68×110 mm. $250 on $150 *Lecythis ollaria*	3·75	4·00

ALBERTVILLE 92

$100 **$600**
(472) (473)

1991 (3 Dec). *Winter Olympic Games, Albertville* (1992) (2nd issue). Nos. 2738/46 optd or surch with T **472** or "XVIth Olympic Winter Games in Albertville" (No. 3190), in black or red.

3186/94	$20×6, $70 on $20, £100 on $20, $190 on $20 .. .. *Set of 9*	8·50	9·00

1991 (19 Dec). *John F. Kennedy and Sir Winston Churchill Commemorations.* Nos. **MS2966c** and **MS2966e** surch with T **473** in black or red.

MS3195 70×105 mm. $600 on $150 *Galeandra devoniana* (horiz)
MS3196 74×104 mm. $600 on $190 *Ionopsis utricularioides*

No. **MS3195** is additionally overprinted with "IN MEMORIAM John F. Kennedy 1917–1963", "First Man on Moon July 20, 1969" and "Apollo 11" emblem, and No. **MS3196** "IN MEMORIAM Sir Winston S. Churchill 1874–1965" and "50th Anniversary World War II" on sheet margins.

GUYANA $50

474 *Akagi* (Japanese aircraft carrier)

(Des J. Batchelor. Litho Questa)

1991 (23 Dec). *50th Anniv of Japanese Attack on Pearl Harbor.* T **474** and similar horiz designs, each deep ultramarine, bright scarlet and black. P 14½.

3197	$50 Type **474**	85	85
	a. Sheetlet. No. 3197/206	7·50	
3198	$50 Beached Japanese midget submarine	85	85
3199	$50 Mitsubishi A6M Zero-Sen fighter	85	85
3200	$50 U.S.S. *Arizona* (battleship) under attack	85	85
3201	$50 Aichi D3A1 "Val" dive bomber	85	85
3202	$50 U.S.S. *California* (battleship) sinking	85	85
3203	$50 Curtiss P-40 fighters taking off	85	85
3204	$50 U.S.S. *Cassin* and U.S.S. *Downes* damaged in dry dock	85	85
3205	$50 Boeing B-17 Flying Fortress crash landing at Bellows Field	85	85
3206	$50 U.S.S. *Nevada* (battleship) on fire	85	85
3197/206		*Set of 10*	7·50	7·50

Nos. 3197/206 were printed together, *se-tenant*, in sheetlets of 10 with the stamps arranged in two horizontal rows of 5 separated by an illustrated gutter showing American battleships after the attack.

475 Brandenburg Gate and Location Plan

(Des L. Fried (Nos. 3207/8, 3220, **MS3225c**), W. Hanson (Nos. 3209/11, 3221, **MS3225d**), J. Iskowitz (Nos. 3212/14, 3217/18, 3222/3, **MS3225a/b**, **MS3225e**), W. Wright (Nos. 3215/16, 3219, 3224, **MS3225f**). Litho Questa)

1991 (23 Dec). *Anniversaries and Events.* T **475** and similar multicoloured designs. P 14.

3207	$10 Type **475**	20	20
3208	$25 President Bush, President Lech Walesa of Poland and Brandenburg Gate	50	50
3209	$25 Scout handshake	50	50
3210	$30 Scouts hiking at Philmont Scout Ranch	60	60
3211	$40 Jamboree and Scout Movement emblems	70	70
3212	$60 General de Gaulle at Venice, 1944	90	90
3213	$75 De Gaulle with Khrushchev, 1960	1·25	1·25
3214	$75 Mozart and Castle of Laxenburg	1·25	1·25
3215	$75 Caroline Herschel (astronomer) and Old Town Hall, Hanover	1·25	1·25
3216	$75 Map of Switzerland and woman in Valais costume	1·25	1·25
3217	$80 De Gaulle at Algiers, 1958	1·40	1·40
3218	$80 Mozart and death of Leopold II	1·40	1·40
3219	$80 Otto Lilienthal and *Flugzeug Nr. 3*	1·40	1·40
3220	$100 Chancellor Kohl, Foreign Minister Genscher and Brandenburg Gate	1·50	1·50
3221	$100 Lord Baden-Powell (vert)	1·50	1·50
3222	$100 De Gaulle with Pope Paul VI, 1967	1·50	1·50
3223	$100 Mozart and birthplace, Salzburg	1·50	1·50
3224	$100 Class P 36 steam locomotive	1·50	1·50
3207/24		*Set of 18*	18·00	18·00

MS3225 Six sheets. (a) 67×99 mm. $150 General De Gaulle (vert). (b) 75×104 mm. $190 General De Gaulle (different) (vert). (c) 101×71 mm. $190 Ceremonial helmet and statues from Brandenburg Gate. (d) 114×83 mm. $190 Rocket-flown commemorative cover, 1960. (e) 73×104 mm. $190 Mozart cameo (vert). (f) 103×74 mm. $190 Arms of Berne and Solothurn .. *Set of 6 sheets* 15·00 16·00

Anniversaries and Events:—Nos. 3207/8, 3220, **MS3225c**, Bicentenary of Brandenburg Gate, Berlin; Nos. 3209/11, 3221, **MS3225d**, 17th World Scout Jamboree, Korea; Nos. 3212/13, 3217, 3222, **MS3225a/b**, Birth centenary of Charles de Gaulle (French statesman) (1990); Nos. 3214, 3218, 3223, **MS3225e**, Death bicentenary of Mozart; No. 3215, 750th anniv of Hanover; No. 3216, 400th anniv of Swiss Confederation; No. 3219, Centenary of Otto Lilienthal's first gliding experiments; No. 3224, Centenary of Trans-Siberian Railway.

No. 3222 is inscribed "Pope John VI" in error.

476 Disney Characters Carol Singing, 1989

(Des Walt Disney Co. Litho Questa)

1991 (30 Dec). *Christmas. Walt Disney Christmas Cards.* T **476** and similar multicoloured designs. P 14×13½ (horiz) or 13½×14 (vert).

3226	80 c. Type **476**	10	10
3227	$2.55, Disney characters and carol singers in tram, 1962	15	15
3228	$5 Donald Duck and Pluto with parcel, 1971	20	20
3229	$6.40, "SEASON'S GREETINGS" and Mickey Mouse with candle, 1948	20	20
3230	$7.65, Mickey Mouse as Father Christmas, 1947	20	20
3231	$8.90, Shadow of Pinocchio with candle, 1939	20	20
3232	$50 Three Little Pigs dancing on wolf rug, 1933	90	90
3233	$50 Conductor and Donald Duck, 1940 (vert)	90	90
	a. Horiz strip of 5. Nos. 3233/7	4·00	
3234	$50 Elephant and ostrich carol singing, 1940 (vert)	90	90
3235	$50 Hippo, centaurs, Pinocchio and Goofy, 1940 (vert)	90	90
3236	$50 Snow White, Dopey, Mickey and Minnie, 1940 (vert)	90	90
3237	$50 Dino, Pluto and Walt Disney, 1940 (vert)	90	90
3238	$50 Mickey Mouse in sleigh, 1974 (vert)	90	90
	a. Horizontal strip of 6. Nos. 3238/43	4·75	
3239	$50 Three Little Pigs, Winnie the Pooh, Bambi and Thumper, 1974 (vert)	90	90
3240	$50 Baloo, King Louis, Lady and the Tramp, 1974 (vert)	90	90
3241	$50 Alice, Robin Hood, the Cheshire Cat and Goofy, 1974 (vert)	90	90
3242	$50 Dumbo, Pinocchio, Peter Pan, Tinkerbelle, Seven Dwarfs and Donald Duck, 1974 (vert)	90	90
3243	$50 Pluto pulling sleigh, 1974 (vert)	90	90
3244	$200 Mickey and mice carol singing, 1949	3·50	4·00
3226/44		*Set of 19*	13·00	13·50

MS3245 Eight sheets. (a) 127×101 mm. $260 Mickey, Minnie, Clarabelle and Pluto in mail coach, 1932 (vert). (b) 127×101 mm. $260 Mickey's House, 1935 (vert). (c) 101×127 mm. $260 Jose Carioca, Rooster and Donald Duck on flying carpet, 1944 (vert). (d) 101×127 mm. $260 Casey at the Bat and dancers, 1945. (e) 127×101 mm. $260 Mickey, Donald and Goofy on musical score, 1946. (f) 127×101 mm. $260 Picture of Winnie the Pooh, 1969. (g) 127×101 mm. $260

Father Christmas in chimney, 1969 (vert). (h) 101×127 mm. $260 Letters of film titles forming Mickey Mouse, 1978 (vert) .. *Set of 8 sheets* 25·00 26·00
Nos. 3233/7 and 3238/43 were each printed together, *se-tenant*, in horizontal strips of 5 or 6 throughout the sheets, each strip showing the design of the complete card.

477 Gus Gander playing Ice Hockey

(Des Walt Disney Co. Litho B.D.T.)

1991 (30 Dec). *Winter Olympic Games, Albertville* (1992) (3rd issue). T **477** and similar horiz designs showing Walt Disney cartoon characters. Multicoloured. P 13.

3246	$6.40, Type **477**	20	10
3247	$7.65, Mickey and Minnie Mouse in bobsleigh	20	10
3248	$8.90, Donald's Nephews on luge and skis	25	10
3249	$12.80, Goofy freestyle skiing	40	20
3250	$50 Goofy ski jumping	1·00	1·00
3251	$100 Donald and Daisy Duck speed skating	1·75	1·75
3252	$130 Pluto cross-country skiing	2·00	2·25
3253	$190 Mickey and Minnie Mouse ice dancing	3·00	3·50
3246/53		*Set of 8*	8·00	8·00

MS3254 Two sheets, each 125×100 mm. (a) $225 Donald's nephew curling; (b) $225 Donald Duck slalom skiing .. .. *Set of 2 sheets* 8·00 8·50

478 Columbus landing on Trinidad

479 Tom Mix in *The Great K&A Train Robbery*, 1926

(Des J. Genzo. Litho Questa)

1992 (2 Jan). *500th Anniv of Discovery of America by Columbus.* T **478** and similar multicoloured designs. P 14.

3255	$6.40, Type **478**	40	40
3256	$7.65, Columbus the map-maker	45	45
3257	$8.90, Fleet blown off course	45	45
3258	$12.80, Map of Third Voyage and Columbus in chains	55	55
3259	$15.30, Sighting land	55	55
3260	$50 *Nina* and *Pinta*	90	90
3261	$75 *Santa Maria*	1·25	1·25
3262	$100 Columbus trading with Amerindians	1·75	1·75
3263	$125 Crew and sea monster	2·00	2·00
3264	$130 Columbus landing on San Salvador and map of First Voyage	2·00	2·00
3265	$140 Priest and Amerindians	2·00	2·00
3266	$150 Columbus before King Ferdinand and Queen Isabella of Spain	2·00	2·00
3255/66		*Set of 12*	13·00	13·00

MS3267 Three sheets, each 126×91 mm. (a) $280 *Nina* (vert). (b) $280 Columbus (vert). (c) $280 Early map of Caribbean .. *Set of 3 sheets* 13·00 14·00

(Litho B.D.T.)

1992 (11 Mar). *Classic Movie Posters.* T **479** and similar multicoloured designs. P 14.

3268	$8.90, Type **479**	40	40
3269	$12.80, Richard Dix and Irene Dunne in *Cimarron*, 1931	50	50
3270	$15.30, Fatty Arbuckle in *Buzzin' Around*, 1934	50	50
3271	$25 Tom Tyler in *The Adventures of Captain Marvel*, 1941	70	70
3272	$30 Boris Karloff in *The Mummy*, 1932	85	85
3273	$50 Rudolph Valentino in *A Sainted Devil*, 1924	1·10	1·10
3274	$75 Seven posters for *A Tale of Two Cities*, 1935	1·40	1·40
3275	$100 Chester Conklin in *A Tugboat Romeo*, 1916	1·90	1·90
3276	$130 Douglas Fairbanks in *The Thief of Bagdad*, 1924	2·25	2·25
3277	$150 Laurel and Hardy in *Bacon Grabbers*, 1929	2·75	2·75
3278	$190 Marx Brothers in *A Night at the Opera*, 1935	3·50	3·50
3279	$200 Orson Welles in *Citizen Kane*, 1941	3·50	3·50
3268/79		*Set of 12*	17·00	17·00

MS3280 Four sheets (a) 70×99 mm. $225 Babe Ruth in *Babe Comes Home*, 1927. (b) 70×99 mm. $225 Mae West in *She Done Him Wrong*, 1933. (c) 70×99 mm. $225 Charlie Chaplin in *The Circus*, 1928. (d) 99×70 mm. $225 Poster for never-made film *Zeppelin*, 1933. Imperf .. .. *Set of 4 sheets* 15·00 16·00

(Litho Questa)

1992 (11 May). *Easter. Paintings by Dürer. Multicoloured designs as T 291 of Antigua, but vert.* P 13½×14.

3281	$6.40, "The Martyrdom of Ten Thousand" (detail)		25	10
3282	$7.65, "Adoration of the Trinity" (detail of Virgin Mary)		25	10
3283	$12.80, "The Martyrdom of Ten Thousand" (execution detail)		40	20
3284	$15.30, "Adoration of the Trinity" (different detail)		45	25
3285	$50 "The Martyrdom of Ten Thousand" (detail of bishop)		1·00	75
3286	$100 "Adoration of the Trinity" (different detail)		1·50	1·50
3287	$130 "The Martyrdom of Ten Thousand" (different detail)		1·75	2·00
3288	$190 "Adoration of the Trinity" (different detail)		3·25	4·00
3281/8		*Set of 8*	8·00	8·00

MS3289 Two sheets, each 71×101 mm. (a) $225 "The Martyrdom of Ten Thousand". (b) $225 "Adoration of the Trinity" (detail of Christ on cross) .. .. .. *Set of 2 sheets* 8·00 8·50

$6.40 **X**

BAHA'I HOLY YEAR 1992

(480)

1992 (29 May). *Baha'i Holy Year. Nos. 1519 and 1521/3 surch as T 480.*

3290	$6.40 on 60 c. Plate No. 10 (Series 1) (No. 1521)		
3291	$7.65 on 60 c. Plate No. 31 (Series 1) (No. 1523)		
3292	$8.90 on 60 c. Plate No. 19 (Series 1) (No. 1522)		
3293	$50 on 60 c. Plate No. 2 (Series 1) (No. 1519)		

481 Queen Elizabeth II and Duke of Edinburgh

(Litho Questa)

1992 (1 June). *40th Anniv of Queen Elizabeth II's Accession. T 481 and similar horiz designs. Multicoloured.* P 14.

3294	$8.90, Type 481		35	25
3295	$12.80, Queen at Trooping the Colour		40	30
3296	$100 Queen at Coronation		2·25	2·25
3297	$130 Queen in Garter robes		2·50	2·50
3294/7		*Set of 4*	5·00	4·75

MS3298 Two sheets, each 119×79 mm. (a) $225 Queen in Coronation robes. (b) $225 Queen in blue dress .. .. .. *Set of 2 sheets* 8·00 8·50

482 Holy Cross Church, Annai Rupununi   483 Burmese

(Litho B.D.T.)

1992 (10 Aug). *150th Anniv of Diocese of Guyana. T 482 and similar multicoloured designs.* P 14.

3299	$6.40, Type 482		15	10
3300	$50 St. Peter's Church		80	65
3301	$100 Interior of St. George's Cathedral (vert)		1·50	1·60
3302	$190 Map of Guyana (vert)		2·75	3·25
3299/302		*Set of 4*	4·75	5·00

MS3303 104×70 mm. $225 Religious symbols 3·75 4·25

(Des S. Barlowe. Litho Questa)

1992 (10 Aug). *Cats. T 483 and similar multicoloured designs. P 14 (Nos. 3309/16) or 14½×13½ (others).*

3304	$5 Type 483		10	10
3305	$6.40, Turkish Van		10	10
3306	$12.80, American Shorthair		15	20
3307	$15.30, Sphynx		15	20
3308	$50 Egyptian Mau		50	55
3309	$50 Russian Blue		50	55
	a. Sheetlet. Nos. 3309/16		4·00	
3310	$50 Havana Brown		50	55
3311	$50 Himalayan		50	55
3312	$50 Manx		50	55
3313	$50 Cornish Rex		50	55
3314	$50 Black Persian		50	55
3315	$50 Scottish Fold		50	55
3316	$50 Siamese		50	55
3317	$100 Japanese Bobtail		1·00	1·10
3318	$130 Abyssinian		1·25	1·40
3319	$225 Oriental Shorthair		2·25	2·40
3304/19		*Set of 16*	9·25	10·25

MS3320 Four sheets, each 99×69 mm. (a) $250 Chartreuse (vert). (b) $250 Turkish Angora (vert). (c) $250 Maine Coon (vert). (d) $250 Chinchilla (vert). P 13½×14½ .. *Set of 4 sheets* 10·00 10·50
Nos. 3309/16 were printed together, *se-tenant*, in sheetlets of 8.

484 Red Howler

(Des L. Nelson. Litho Questa)

1992 (10 Aug). *Animals of Guyana. T 484 and similar multicoloured designs.* P 14.

3321	$8.90, Type 484		20	10
3322	$12.80, Ring-tailed Coati		25	20
3323	$15.30, Jaguar		30	20
3324	$25 Two-toed Sloth		50	30
3325	$50 Giant Armadillo		1·00	80
3326	$75 Giant Anteater		1·50	1·75
3327	$100 Capybara		1·75	1·90
3328	$130 Ocelot		2·00	2·25
3321/8		*Set of 8*	6·75	6·75

MS3329 Two sheets, each 70×100 mm. (a) $225 Woolly Opossum (vert). (b) $225 Night Monkey (vert) .. .. .. *Set of 2 sheets* 8·00 8·50
No. MS3329a is inscribed "WOLLY OPOSSUM" in error.

485 Oligocene Mammoth   486 Palomino

(Des J.-L. Puvilland. Litho Questa)

1992 (10 Aug). *Elephants. T 485 and similar horiz designs. Multicoloured.* P 14.

3330	$50 Type 485		1·25	1·25
	a. Sheetlet. Nos. 3330/7		9·00	
3331	$50 Mid-Miocene Stegodon		1·25	1·25
3332	$50 Pliocene Mammoth		1·25	1·25
3333	$50 Carthaginian elephant crossing Alps, 219 B.C.		1·25	1·25
3334	$50 Ceremonial elephant of Maharaja of Mysore, India		1·25	1·25
3335	$50 Elephant pulling teak trunks, Burma		1·25	1·25
3336	$50 Tiger-hunting by elephant, India		1·25	1·25
3337	$50 Elephant towing raft on River Kwai, Thailand		1·25	1·25
3330/7		*Set of 8*	9·00	9·00

MS3338 110×80 mm. $225 African Elephants 4·50 4·50
Nos. 3330/7 were printed together, *se-tenant*, in sheetlets of 8.

(Des S. Barlowe. Litho Questa)

1992 (10 Aug). *Horses. T 486 and similar horiz designs. Multicoloured.* P 14.

3339	$190 Type 486		3·00	3·00
	a. Sheetlet. Nos. 3339/46		22·00	
3340	$190 Appaloosa		3·00	3·00
3341	$190 Clydesdale		3·00	3·00
3342	$190 Arab		3·00	3·00
3343	$190 Morgan		3·00	3·00
3344	$190 Friesian		3·00	3·00
3345	$190 Pinto		3·00	3·00
3346	$190 Thoroughbred		3·00	3·00
3339/40		*Set of 8*	22·00	22·00

MS3347 109×80 mm. $190 Lipizzaner (47×29 mm) .. .. 4·00 4·25
Nos. 3339/46 were printed together, *se-tenant*, in sheetlets of 8.
No. 3340 is inscribed "APALOOSA" in error.

X

INT. CONFERENCE ON NUTRITION 1992

$6.40

(487)

1992 (2 Nov). *International Conference on Nutrition, Rome. Nos. 1658 and 1767/9 surch as T 487.*

3348	$6.40 on 150 c. Plate No. 45 (Series 1) (No. 1769)	
3349	$7.65 on 150 c. Plate No. 42 (Series 1) (No. 1768)	
3350	$8.90 on 150 c. Plate No. 40 (Series 1) (No. 1767)	
3351	$10 on 200 c. Plate No. 43 (Series 1) (No. 1658)	
3352	$50 on 200 c. Plate No. 43 (Series 1) (No. 1658)	

488 Marklin Swiss "Crocodile" Locomotive, 1933

(Des W. Hanson. Litho B.D.T.)

1992 (25 Nov). *"Genova '92" International Thematic Stamp Exhibition. Toy Trains from German Manufacturers. T 488 and similar horiz designs. Multicoloured.* P 14.

3353/61	$45 × 9 (Made by Marklin: Type 488; French tramcar, 1902; British "Flatiron" tank engine, 1913; German switching engine, 1970; Third class carriage, 1909; American style locomotive, 1904; Zurich tramcar, 1928; Central London Railway locomotive in Paris–Orleans livery, 1904; British GWR *Great Bear* locomotive, 1909)		
	a. Sheetlet. Nos. 3353/61		5·50
3362/70	$45 × 9 (Made by Marklin: LMS "Precursor" tank engine, 1923; American "Congressional Limited" passenger carriage, 1908; Swiss Type "Ae 3/6" locomotive, 1934; German Class 80, 1975; British Southern Railways third class carriage, 1926; LNWR Bowen-Cooke tank engine, 1913; London Underground "Two Penny Tube", 1901; Fench Paris–Orsay steeple-cab, 1920; Passenger locomotive, 1895)		
	a. Sheetlet. Nos. 3362/70		5·50
3371/9	$45 x 9 (Made by Marklin: American style locomotive, 1907; German passenger carriage, 1908; British Great Eastern Railway locomotive, 1908; London Underground steeplecab, 1904; Santa Fe Railroad diesel locomotive, 1962; British GNR locomotive, 1903; Caledonian Railway *Cardean*, 1906; British LNWR passenger carriage, 1903; Swiss St. Gotthard Railway locomotive, 1920)		
	a. Sheetlet. Nos. 3371/9		5·50
3380/8	$45 × 9 (Made by Marklin; British LB & SCR tank engine No. 22, 1920; Central London Railway steeplecab locomotive, 1904; German "Borsig" streamlined, 1935; French Paris–Lyon–Mediterranee first class carriage, 1929; American style locomotive No. 1021, 1904; French Paris–Orsay long-nose steeplecab, 1920; British LNER *Cock o' the North*, 1936; Prussian State Railways Class P8, 1975; German diesel railcar set, 1937)		
	a. Sheetlet. Nos. 3380/8		5·50
3389/97	$45 × 9 (Marklin North British Railway "Atlantic", 1913; Bing British LNWR "Precursor", 1916; Marklin British GWR *King George V*, 1937; Marklin "Kaiser Train" passenger carriage, 1901; Bing side tank locomotive No. 88, 1904; Marklin steeplecab, 1912; Marklin *Adler*, 1935; Bing British GWR *County of Northampton*, 1909; Bing British Midland Railway *Black Prince*, 1908)		
	a. Sheetlet. Nos. 3389/97		5·50
3398/406	$45 × 9 (Made by Bing: Midland Railway "Deeley Type" No. 483, 1909; British Midland Railway No. 2631, 1903; German Pacific, 1927; British GWR third class carriage, 1926; British LSWR "M7" No. 109, 1909; Side tank engine *Pilot*, 1901; British LNWR Webb *Cauliflower*, 1912; Side tank locomotive No. 112 1910; British GNR "Stirling Single", 1904)		
	a. Sheetlet. Nos. 3398/406		5·50
3407/15	$45 × 9 (Carette tin "Penny Bazaar" train, 1904; Winteringham locomotive, 1917; Carette British Northeastern Railway Smith Compound, 1905; Carette S.E. & C.R. steam railcar, 1908; Carette British Great Northern Railway Stirling Single No. 776, 1903; Carette British Midland Railways locomotive No. 1132M, 1911; Carette London Metropolitan Railway Co. Westinghouse locomotive No. 5,		

1908; Carette Clestory carriage, 1907; Carette steam railcar No. 1, 1906)

a. Sheetlet. Nos. 3407/15. .. 5·50

3416/24 $45 × 9 (Made by Bing: Engine and tender, 1895; British Midland Railway Single No. 650, 1913; No. 524/510 reversible locomotive, 1916; "Kaiser Train" passenger carriage, 1902; British rural station, 1915; British LSWR M7 tank locomotive, 1909; "Windcutter", 1912; British Great Central Railway *Sir Sam Fay*, 1914; Scottish Caledonian Railway *Dunalastair* locomotive, 1910)

a. Sheetlet. Nos. 3416/24 .. 5·50

3353/424 .. .. *Set of 72* 40·00 45·00

MS3425 Eight sheets, each 116×83 mm. (a) $350 Bing contractor's locomotive No. 18, 1904 (51×39 *mm*); (b) $350 Marklin rack railway steeplecab locomotive, 1908 (51×39 *mm*); (c) $350 Bing British GWR *County of Northampton* locomotive, 1909 (51×39 *mm*); (d) $350 Marklin French Paris–Lyon–Mediterranean Pacific locomotive, 1912 (51×39 *mm*); (e) $350 Bing Pabst Blue Ribbon beer refrigerator wagon, 1925 (51×39 *mm*); (f) $350 Marklin French "Mountain Etat" locomotive, 1933 (51×39 *mm*); (g) $350 Marklin German National Railroad Class 0-1 Pacific locomotive, 1937 (51×39 *mm*); (g) $350 Marklin American *Commodore Vanderbilt* locomotive, 1937 (51×39 *mm*). P 13

Set of 8 sheets 30·00 32·00

Nos. 3353/61, 3362/70, 3371/9, 3380/8, 3389/97, 3398/406, 3407/15 and 3416/24 were each printed together, *se-tenant*, in sheetlets of nine.

(Des Kerri Schiff. Litho Questa)

1992 (29 Dec). *Postage Stamp Mega Event, New York. Sheet 100×70 mm containing multicoloured design as T 299 of Antigua, but vert.* P 14.

MS3426 $325 Statue of Liberty .. .. 6·00 7·00

489 Aquarius

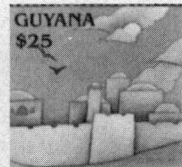
490 City Walls and Two Birds

1992 (29 Dec). *Signs of the Zodiac. T 489 and similar horiz designs. Multicoloured. Litho.* P 14×13½.

3427	$30	Type 489	80	80
	a. Sheetlet. Nos. 3427/38		8·50	
3428	$30	Pisces	80	80
3429	$30	Aries	80	80
3430	$30	Taurus	80	80
3431	$30	Gemini	80	80
3432	$30	Cancer	80	80
3433	$30	Leo	80	80
3434	$30	Virgo	80	80
3435	$30	Libra	80	80
3436	$30	Scorpio	80	80
3437	$30	Sagittarius	80	80
3438	$30	Capricorn	80	80
3427/38		*Set of 12*	8·50	8·50

Nos. 3427/38 were printed together, *se-tenant*, in sheetlets of 12.

(Des N. Waldman. Litho B.D.T.)

1992 (29 Dec). *Bible Stories (1st series). David and Goliath. T 490 and similar square designs. Multicoloured.* P 14.

3439	$25	Type 490	50	50
	a. Sheetlet. Nos. 3439/63		11·00	
3440	$25	City walls and one bird at right	50	50
3441	$25	Sun over city gateway	50	50
3442	$25	City walls and one bird at left	50	50
3443	$25	City walls and no birds	50	50
3444	$25	Philistine army and edge of shield	50	50
3445	$25	Goliath's head and torso	50	50
3446	$25	Goliath's arm and spear	50	50
3447	$25	Philistine army and spearhead	50	50
3448	$25	Philistine infantry	50	50
3449	$25	Philistine cavalry and infantry	50	50
3450	$25	Goliath's shield	50	50
3451	$25	Goliath's waist and thigh	50	50
3452	$25	David with sling	50	50
3453	$25	Israelite soldier with spear	50	50
3454	$25	Two Israelite soldiers with spears and shields	50	50
3455	$25	Goliath's right leg	50	50
3456	$25	Goliath's left leg (face value at foot)	50	50
3457	$25	David's leg and Israelite standard	50	50
3458	$25	Three Israelite soldiers	50	50
3459	$25	Israelite soldier and parts of two shields	50	50
3460	$25	Israelite soldier with sword	50	50
3461	$25	Back of Israelite soldier	50	50
3462	$25	Israelite soldier leaning on rock	50	50
3463	$25	Israelite soldier looking left	50	50
3439/63		*Set of 25*	11·00	11·00

Nos. 3439/63 were printed together, *se-tenant*, forming a composite design.

See also Nos. 4020/4116.

COVER PRICES

Cover factors are quoted at the beginning of each country for most issues to 1945. An explanation of the system can be found on page x. The factors quoted do not, however, apply to philatelic covers.

491 Count Ferdinand von Zeppelin and Airship over Lake Constance, 1909

(Des W. Hanson and W. Wright (Nos. 3464, 3474, **MS**3475a), W. Wright and L. Fried (Nos. 3465, 3472, **MS**3475b), W. Wright (others). Litho B.D.T.)

1992 (29 Dec). *Anniversaries and Events. T 491 and similar multicoloured designs.* P 14.

3464	$12.80, Type 491		50	35
3465	$50 *Voyager I and Jupiter*		1·50	1·00
3466	$50 Chancellor Adenauer with President Kennedy, 1961		1·00	1·00
3467	$100 Aeromedical airlift		2·00	2·00
3468	$100 Boutu ("Amazon Dolphin")		2·00	2·00
3469	$130 Baby gorilla		2·50	2·50
3470	$130 Mobile eye screening unit and doctor with child		2·50	2·50
3471	$130 *Stars and Stripes* (winning yacht, 1987)		2·50	2·50
3472	$130 Lift-off of *Voyager I*, 1977		2·50	2·50
3473	$190 Adenauer with President De Gaulle of France, 1962		3·25	3·25
3474	$225 Von Zeppelin and airship preparing for take-off, 1905		3·50	3·50
3464/74		*Set of 11*	21·00	21·00

MS3475 Four sheets. (a) 76×105 mm. $225 Ferdinand von Zeppelin (*vert*). (b) 116×80 mm. $225 Earth from Space (*vert*). (c) 84×111 mm. $225 Konrad Adenauer (*vert*). (d) 87×111 mm. $225 *Hyperohus marmoratus* (tree frog) (*vert*)

Set of 4 sheets 15·00 16·00

Anniversaries and Events:—Nos. 3464, 3474, **MS**3475a, 75th death anniv of Count Ferdinand von Zeppelin; Nos. 3465, 3472, **MS**3475b, International Space Year; Nos. 3466, 3473, **MS**3475c, 75th death anniv of Konrad Adenauer (German statesman); No. 3467, United Nations World Health Organization projects; Nos. 3468/9, **MS**3475d, Earth Summit '92, Rio; No. 3470, 75th anniv of International Association of Lions Clubs; No. 3471, Americas Cup Yachting Championship.

492 Hyacinth Macaw

493 Crimson Topaz

(Des R. Duburke. Litho B.D.T.)

1993 (10 Mar). *South American Parrots. T 492 and similar multicoloured designs.* P 14.

3476	80 c. Type 492		30	15
3477	$6.40, Scarlet Macaw (preening)		50	25
3478	$7.65, Buffon's Macaw ("Green Macaw") (*vert*)		50	25
3479	$15.30, Orange-chinned Parakeet ("Tovi Parakeet")		70	50
3480	$50 Blue and Yellow Macaw		1·00	80
3481	$100 Military Macaw (*vert*)		1·50	1·25
3482	$130 Green-winged Macaw ("Red and Green Macaw") (*vert*)		1·75	1·75
3483	$190 Chestnut-fronted Macaw ("Severa Macaw")		2·50	3·00
3476/83		*Set of 8*	8·00	7·00

MS3484 Two sheets, each 108×74 mm. (a) $225 Scarlet Macaw. (b) $225 Green Conure ("Green Parakeet") (*vert*) .. *Set of 2 sheets* 7·00 7·50

(Des P. Chenelli. Litho Questa)

1993 (10 Mar). *Birds of Guyana. T 493 and similar multi-coloured designs.* P 14.

3485	$50 Type 493		75	75
	a. Sheetlet. Nos. 3485/96		8·00	
3486	$50 Bearded Bellbird		75	75
3487	$50 Amazonian Umbrellabird		75	75
3488	$50 Paradise Jacamar		75	75
3489	$50 Paradise Tanager		75	75
3490	$50 White-tailed Trogon		75	75
3491	$50 Scarlet Macaw		75	75
3492	$50 Hawk-headed Parrot ("Red-fan Parrot")		75	75
3493	$50 Cuvier's Toucan ("Red-billed Toucan")		75	75
3494	$50 White-faced Antcatcher ("White-plumed Antbird")		75	75
3495	$50 Crimson-hooded Manakin		75	75
3496	$50 Guianan Cock of the Rock		75	75
3485/96		*Set of 12*	8·00	8·00

MS3497 70×100 mm. $325 Tufted Coquette (*horiz*) .. .. .. 5·00 5·00

Nos. 3485/96 were printed together, *se-tenant*, in sheetlets of 12, with the backgrounds forming a composite design.

494 Manatee surfacing

495 Tamandua

(Des P. Chenelli. Litho Questa)

1993 (10 Mar). *Endangered Species. American Manatee ("Caribbean Manatee"). T 494 and similar horiz designs. Multicoloured.* P 14½.

3498	$6.40, Type 494		50	30
3499	$7.65, Cow and calf feeding		50	30
3500	$8.90, Manatee underwater		50	30
3501	$50 Two Manatees		2·00	2·00
3498/501		*Set of 4*	3·25	2·50

(Des P. Chenelli. Litho Questa)

1993 (10 Mar). *Animals of Guyana. T 495 and similar vert designs. Multicoloured.* P 14.

3502	$50 Type 495		75	75
	a. Sheetlet. Nos. 3502/13		8·00	
3503	$50 Pale-throated Sloth ("Three-toed Sloth")		75	75
3504	$50 Red Howler		75	75
3505	$50 Four-eyed Opossum		75	75
3506	$50 Black Spider Monkey		75	75
3507	$50 Giant Otter		75	75
3508	$50 Red Brocket		75	75
3509	$50 Brazilian Tree Porcupine		75	75
3510	$50 Tayra		75	75
3511	$50 Brazilian Tapir		75	75
3512	$50 Ocelot		75	75
3513	$50 Giant Armadillo		75	75
3502/13		*Set of 12*	8·00	8·00

MS3514 100×70 mm. $325 Paca .. 4·50 5·00

Nos. 3502/13 were printed together, *se-tenant*, in sheetlets of 12, the backgrounds forming a composite design.

496 Pteranodon

(Des R. Sauber. Litho B.D.T.)

1993 (10 Mar). *Prehistoric Animals. T 496 and similar horiz designs. Multicoloured.* P 14.

3515/26 $30 × 12 (Type 496; Cearadactylus; Eudimorphodon; Pterodactylus; Stauirkosaurus; Euoplocephalus; Tuojiangosaurus; Oviraptor; Protoceratops; Panaoplosaurus; Psittacosaurus; Corythosaurus)

a. Sheetlet. Nos. 3515/26 .. 5·00

3527/38 $30 × 12 (Sordes; Quetzalcoatlus; Archaeopteryx in flight; Rhamphorynchus; Spinosaurus; Anchisaurus; Stegosaurus; Leaellynosaurs; Minmi; Heterdontosaurus; Lesothosaurus; Deninonychus)

a. Sheetlet. Nos. 3527/38 .. 5·00

3539/50 $30 × 12 (Archaeopteryx on branch; Pteranodon (*different*); Quetzalcoatlus (three); Protoavis; Dicraeosaurus; Moschops; Lystrosaurus; Dimetrondon; Stauirkosaurus; Cacops; Diarthrognathus; Estemmenosuchus)

a. Sheetlet. Nos. 3539/50 .. 5·00

3515/50 .. .. *Set of 36* 13·50 15·00

Nos. 3515/26, 3527/38 and 3539/50 were each printed together, *se-tenant*, in sheetlets of 12, with the backgrounds forming composite designs.

(Des Kerri Schiff. Litho Questa)

1993 (2 June). *40th Anniv of Coronation. Vert designs as T 307 of Antigua. Multicoloured.* P 13½×14.

3551	$25	Queen Elizabeth II in Coronation robes (photograph by Cecil Beaton)	85	85
	a. Sheetlet. Nos. 3551/4×2		9·50	
3552	$50	Royal gems	1·25	1·25
3553	$75	Queen Elizabeth and Prince Philip	1·40	1·50
3554	$130	Queen opening Parliament	1·75	2·00
3551/4		*Set of 4*	4·75	5·00

MS3555 69×100 mm. $325 "Queen in Coronation Robes" (Sir James Gunn) (28½×42½ *mm*). P 14 .. .. .. 5·00 5·50

Nos. 3551/4 were printed together, *se-tenant*, in sheetlets of 8, containing two *se-tenant* blocks of 4.

497 Gabriel Marquez (author)   **498** "Bather, Paris" (Picasso)

(Des J. Genzo. Litho Questa)

1993 (26 July). *Famous People of the Twentieth Century. T* **497** *and similar horiz designs. Multicoloured. P* 14.

(a) Arts and Literature

3556	$50	Type **497**	75	75
		a. Sheetlet. Nos. 3556/64	6·00	
3557	$50	Pablo Picasso (artist)	75	75
3558	$50	Cecil De Mille (film director)	75	75
3559	$50	Martha Graham (dancer)	75	75
3560	$50	Peace dove (inscr "20th Century Arts and Literature")	75	75
3561	$50	Charlie Chaplin (actor)	75	75
3562	$50	Paul Robeson (actor)	75	75
3563	$50	Rudolph Dunbar (musician)	75	75
3564	$50	Louis Armstrong (musician)	75	75
3556/64		*Set of 9*	6·00	6·00
MS3565		100×70 mm. $250 Elvis Presley (singer) (*vert*)	3·50	3·50

(b) Science and Medicine

3566	$50	Louis Leakey (archaeologist and anthropologist)	75	75
		a. Sheetlet. Nos. 3566/74	6·00	
3567	$50	Jonas Salk (discoverer of polio vaccine)	75	75
3568	$50	Hideyo Noguchi (bacteriologist)	75	75
3569	$50	Karl Landsteiner (pathologist)	75	75
3570	$50	As No. 3550, but inscr "20th Century Science and Medicine"	75	75
3571	$50	Sigmund Freud (founder of psychoanalysis)	75	75
3572	$50	Louis Pasteur (chemist)	75	75
3573	$50	Madame Curie (physicist)	75	75
3574	$50	Jean Baptiste Perrin (physicist)	75	75
3566/74		*Set of 9*	6·00	6·00
MS3575		100×70 mm. $250 Einstein's Theory of Relativity equation (*vert*)	3·50	3·50

(c) Sports Personalities

3576	$50	O. J. Simpson (American football)	75	75
		a. Sheetlet. Nos. 3576/84	6·00	
3577	$50	Rohan Kanhai (cricket)	75	75
3578	$50	Gabriela Sabatini (tennis)	75	75
3579	$50	Severiano Ballesteros (golf)	75	75
3580	$50	As No. 3550, but inscr "20th Century Sports"	75	75
3581	$50	Franz Beckenbauer (football)	75	75
3582	$50	Pele (football)	75	75
3583	$50	Wilt Chamberlain (basketball)	75	75
3584	$50	Nadia Comaneci (gymnastics)	75	75
3576/84		*Set of 9*	6·00	6·00
MS3585		100×70 mm. $250 Jackie Robinson (baseball) (*vert*)	3·50	3·50

(d) Peace and Humanity

3586	$100	Mahatma Gandhi (India)	1·10	1·10
		a. Sheetlet. Nos. 3586/94	9·00	
3587	$100	Dalai Lama (Tibet)	1·10	1·10
3588	$100	Michael Manley (Jamaica)	1·10	1·10
3589	$100	Pérez de Cuéllar (U.N. Secretary-General)	1·10	1·10
3590	$100	Peace dove and globe	1·10	1·10
3591	$100	Mother Teresa (India)	1·10	1·10
3592	$100	Martin Luther King (U.S.A.)	1·10	1·10
3593	$100	Pres. Nelson Mandela (South Africa)	1·10	1·10
3594	$100	Raoul Wallenberg (Sweden)	1·10	1·10
3586/94		*Set of 9*	9·00	9·00
MS3595		100×70 mm. $250 Nobel Peace Prize scroll (*vert*)	3·50	3·50

(e) Politics

3596	$100	Nehru (India)	1·10	1·10
		a. Sheetlet. Nos. 3596/604	9·00	
3597	$100	Dr. Eric Williams (Trinidad and Tobago)	1·10	1·10
3598	$100	Pres. John F. Kennedy (U.S.A.)	1·10	1·10
3599	$100	Pres. Hugh Desmond Hoyte (Guyana)	1·10	1·10
3600	$100	Peace dove and map of the Americas	1·10	1·10
3601	$100	Friedrich Ebert (Germany)	1·10	1·10
3602	$100	Pres. F. D. Roosevelt (U.S.A.)	1·10	1·10
3603	$100	Mikhail Gorbachev (Russia)	1·10	1·10
3604	$100	Sir Winston Churchill (Great Britain)	1·10	1·10
3596/604		*Set of 9*	9·00	9·00
MS3605		100×70 mm. $250 Flags of United Nations and member countries (*vert*)	3·50	3·50

(f) Transportation and Technology

3606	$100	Douglas DC-3 cargo plane	1·10	1·10
		a. Sheetlet. Nos. 3606/14	9·00	
3607	$100	Space Shuttle	1·10	1·10
3608	$100	Concord	1·10	1·10
3609	$100	Count Ferdinand von Zeppelin and Graf Zeppelin	1·10	1·10
3610	$100	Peace dove and rocket trails	1·10	1·10
3611	$100	Marconi and aerial tower	1·10	1·10
3612	$100	Adrian Thompson (mountaineer) and Mt Roraima	1·10	1·10
3613	$100	"Hikari" express train, Japan	1·10	1·10
3614	$100	Johann von Neumann and computer	1·10	1·10
3606/14		*Set of 9*	9·00	9·00
MS3615		100×70 mm. $250 Lunar module *Eagle* on Moon	3·50	3·50

Nos. 3556/64, 3566/74, 3576/84, 3586/94, 3596/604 and 3606/14 were each printed together, *se-tenant*, in sheetlets of 9 with composite background designs on Nos. 3586/94, 3596/604 and 3606/14.

No. 3562 is inscribed "Paul Roebeson" in error.

(Des Kerri Schiff (Nos. 3619, 3624, **MS**3628e). Litho Questa)

1993 (16 Aug). *Anniversaries and Events. T* **498** *and similar multicoloured designs (except No. **MS**3628c). P* 14.

3616	$15.30, Type **498**		15	20
3617	$25 Willy Brandt with Prime Minister of Israel Golda Meir, 1969 (*horiz*)		40	40
3618	$50 "Pantaloons" (left half) (Tadeusz Brzozowski)		50	55
	a. Horiz pair. Nos. 3618 and 3623		1·75	
3619	$50 Georg Hackl (men's single luge, 1992)		70	70
3620	$50 Astrolabe		70	70
3621	$75 Miedzyrecz Castle		75	80
3622	$100 "Two Nudes" (Picasso)		1·00	1·10
3623	$130 "Pantaloons" (right half) (Tadeusz Brzozowski)		1·25	1·40
3624	$130 Karen Magnussen (women's figure skating, 1972)		1·50	1·50
3625	$190 "Nude seated on a Rock" (Picasso)		1·90	2·00
3626	$190 Willy Brandt at Georgsmarienhutten Steel Mill, 1969 (*horiz*)		2·25	2·25
3627	$190 Dish aerial		2·25	2·25
3616/27		*Set of 12*	12·00	13·00

MS3628 Five sheets. (a) 104×75 mm. $300 Copernicus. (b) 75×104 mm. $325 "The Rescue" (detail) (Picasso). (c) 104×75 mm. $325 Willy Brandt giving interview, 1969 (lake-brown and black). (d) 99×70 mm. $325 "Children in the Garden" (Wladyslaw Podkowinski) (*horiz*). (e) 75×104 mm. $325 German four-man bobsleigh team, 1992 ... *Set of 5 sheets* 20·00 22·00

Anniversaries and Events:—Nos. 3616, 3622, 3625, **MS**3628b, 20th death anniv of Picasso (artist); Nos. 3617, 3626, **MS**3628c, 80th birth anniv of Willy Brandt (German politician) (1992); Nos. 3618, 3621, 3623, **MS**3628d, "Polska '93" International Stamp Exhibition, Poznań; Nos. 3619, 3624, **MS**3628e, Winter Olympic Games '94, Lillehammer; Nos. 3620, 3627, **MS**3628a, 450th death anniv of Copernicus (astronomer).

Nos. 3618 and 3623 were printed together, *se-tenant*, in horizontal pairs throughout the sheet, each pair forming a composite design showing the complete painting.

499 Audie Murphy (most decorated U.S. serviceman)

(Des K. Gromoll. Litho Questa)

1993 (27 Sept). *50th Anniv of Second World War* (1st issue). *T* **499** *and similar horiz designs. Multicoloured. P* 14.

3629	$6.40, Type **499**		40	20
3630	$7.65, Allied troops in Normandy (8 June 1944)		40	25
3631	$8.90, American howitzer crew, Battle of Monte Cassino (18 May 1944)		45	30
3632	$12.80, American aircraft attacking *Yamato* (Japanese battleship), Battle of East China Sea (7 April 1945)		60	50
3633	$15.30, St. Basil's Cathedral, Moscow (Foreign Ministers' Conference, 19 October 1943)		60	50
3634	$50 American troops crossing Rhine at Remagen (7 March 1945)		1·00	75
3635	$100 Boeing B-29 Superfortresses raiding Japan from China (15 June 1944)		1·75	1·60
3636	$130 General Patton and map of Sicily (17 August 1943)		1·90	2·00
3637	$190 Destruction of *Tirpitz* (German battleship) (12 November 1944)		2·75	3·00
3638	$200 American forces in Brittany (1 August 1944)		2·75	3·00
3639	$225 American half-track (ceasefire in Italy, 2 May 1945)		3·00	3·50
3629/39		*Set of 11*	14·00	14·00

MS3640 100×69 mm. $325 Meeting of American and Russian troops on the Elbe (25 April 1945) ... 5·00 5·50

No. 3631 is inscribed "Monte Cassino" in error.

See also Nos. 3641/60 and 3942/61.

500 R.A.A.F. Bristol Type 156 Beaufighter, Battle of the Bismarck Sea (2–4 March 1943)

501 Stuart Pearce (England)

1993 (27 Sept). *50th Anniv of Second World War* (2nd issue). *T* **500** *and similar horiz designs. Multicoloured. P* 14½.

3641	$50 Type **500**		80	80
	a. Sheetlet. Nos. 3641/50		7·00	
3642	$50 Lockheed P-38 Lightning attacking Admiral Yamamoto's plane, Bougainville (7 April 1943)		80	80
3643	$50 Consolidated B-24 Liberator bombers, Tarawa (17–19 September 1943)		80	80
3644	$50 North American B-25 Mitchell bomber, Rabaul (12 October 1943)		80	80
3645	$50 U.S. Navy aircraft attacking Makin (19 November 1943)		80	80
3646	$50 U.S.A.A.F. bombers on first daylight raid over Germany (27 January 1943)		80	80
3647	$50 R.A.F. De Havilland D.H.98 Mosquito bombers on first daylight raid over Berlin (30 January 1943)		80	80
3648	$50 Allied aircraft over Hamburg (24–30 July 1943)		80	80
3649	$50 Consolidated B-24 Liberators bombing Ploesti oil refineries, Rumania (1 August 1943)		80	80
3650	$50 German nightfighter attacking Allied bombers over Berlin (18 November 1943)		80	80
3651	$50 Japanese aircraft carriers during Operation 1 (7 April 1943)		80	80
	a. Sheetlet. Nos. 3651/60		7·00	
3652	$50 Lt. John F. Kennedy's motor torpedo boat U.S.S. *PT109* in Blackett Strait (1 August 1943)		80	80
3653	$50 U.S.S. *Enterprise* (aircraft carrier)		80	80
3654	$50 American battleships bombarding Rabaul (12 October 1943)		80	80
3655	$50 American landing craft at Cape Gloucester (26 December 1943)		80	80
3656	$50 Commissioning of U.S.S. *Bogue* (first anti-submarine escort carrier) (February 1943)		80	80
3657	$50 Grumman FM-2 Wildcat fighters from U.S.S. *Bogue* sinking *U-118*		80	80
3658	$50 U-boat launching torpedo during peak of Battle of the Atlantic (March 1943)		80	80
3659	$50 Surrender of Italian fleet at Malta (10 September 1943)		80	80
3660	$50 H.M.S. *Duke of York* (battleship) sinking *Scharnhorst* (26 December 1943)		80	80
3641/60		*Set of 20*	14·00	14·00

Nos. 3641/50 and 3651/60 were each printed together, *se-tenant*, in sheetlets of 10 with the stamps arranged in two horizontal strips of 5 separated by gutters showing the Dambusters Raid (Nos. 3641/50) or the sinking of *Chuyo* (Japanese aircraft carrier) by U.S.S. *Sailfish* (Nos. 3651/60).

(Des Rosemary DeFiglio. Litho Questa)

1993 (27 Sept). *World Cup Football Championship, U.S.A.* (1994) (1st issue). *T* **501** *and similar multicoloured designs. P* 14.

3661	$5 Type **501**		15	10
3662	$6.40, Ronald Koeman (Netherlands)		15	10
3663	$7.65, Gianluca Vialli (Italy)		20	10
3664	$12.80, McStay (Scotland) and Alemao (Brazil)		30	20
3665	$15.30, Ceulemans (Belgium) and Butcher (England)		30	20
3666	$50 Dragan Stojkovic (Yugoslavia)		75	65
3667	$100 Ruud Gullit (Netherlands)		1·25	1·25
3668	$130 Miloslav Kadlec (Czechoslovakia)		1·40	1·50
3669	$150 Ramos (Uruguay) and Berthold (Germany)		1·75	2·00
3670	$190 Baggio (Italy) and Wright (England)		2·25	2·50
3671	$200 Yarentchuck (Russia) and Renquin (Belgium)		2·40	2·75
3672	$225 Timofte (Rumania) and Aleinikov (Russia)		2·50	3·00
3661/72		*Set of 12*	12·00	12·50

MS3673 Two sheets. (a) 101×73 mm. $325 Salvatore Schillaci (Italy) and José Pintos (Uruguay) (*horiz*). (b) 73×101 mm. $325 Rene Higuita (Colombia) ... *Set of 2 sheets* 8·00 8·50

See also Nos. 4142/58.

502 Sir Shridath Ramphal   **503** Donald's Better Self, 1938

(Litho Questa)

1993 (29 Nov). *First Recipients of Order of the Caribbean Community. T* **502** *and similar vert designs. Multicoloured. P* 14.

3674	$7.65, Type **502**		60	50
3675	$7.65, William Demas		60	50
3676	$7.65, Derek Walcott		1·00	65
3674/6		*Set of 3*	2·00	1·50

(Adapted Pauline Cianciolo. Litho Questa)

1993 (1 Dec). *Christmas. Paintings by Rubens and Dürer. Vert designs as T* **270** *of Dominica. Black, pale lemon and red* (Nos. 3678, 3680/1, 3684, **MS**3685b) *or multicoloured* (*others*). *P* 13½×14.

3677	$6.40, "The Holy Family under the Apple Tree" (detail) (Rubens)		10	10
3678	$7.65, "The Virgin in Glory" (detail) (Dürer)		10	10
3679	$12.80, "The Holy Family under the Apple Tree" (different detail) (Rubens)		10	15
3680	$15.30, "The Virgin in Glory" (different detail) (Dürer)		15	20
3681	$50 "The Virgin in Glory" (different detail) (Dürer)		50	50
3682	$130 "The Holy Family under the Apple Tree" (different detail) (Rubens)		1·25	1·40

3683 $190 "The Holy Family under the Apple Tree" (different detail) (Rubens) .. 1·90 2·00
3684 $250 "The Virgin in Glory" (different detail) (Dürer) .. .. 2·50 2·75
3677/84 .. .. Set of 8 6·50 7·25
MS3685. Two sheets. (a) 126×101 mm. $325 "The Holy Family under the Apple Tree" (Rubens). (b) 101×126 mm. $325 "The Virgin in Glory" (woodcut by Dürer from *The Life of the Virgin*) Set of 2 sheets 6·50 7·75

(Litho Questa)

1993 (6 Dec). *Bicentenary of the Louvre, Paris. Vert designs as T 305 of Antigua. Multicoloured. P 13½×14.*
3686 $50 "Mona Lisa" (Leonardo da Vinci) 50 55
 a. Sheetlet. No. 3686×8 .. 4·00
3687/94 $50 × 8 "Self-portrait with Spectacles" (Chardin); "Infanta Maria Theresa" (Velázquez); "Spring" (Arcimboldo); "The Virgin of Sorrows" (Bouts); "The Student" (Fragonard); "François I" (Clouet); "Le Condottière" (Antonello da Messina); "La Bohémienne" (Hals)
 a. Sheetlet. Nos. 3687/94 .. 4·00
3695/702 $50 × 8 "The Village Bride" (left detail) (Greuze); "The Village Bride" (centre detail); "The Village Bride" (right detail); "Self-portrait" (Melendez); "The Knight, the Girl and the Mountain" (Baldung-Grien); "The Young Beggar" (Murillo); "The Pilgrims of Emmaus" (left detail) (Le Nain); "The Pilgrims of Emmaus" (right detail)
 a. Sheetlet. Nos. 3695/3702 .. 4·00
3703/10 $50 × 8 "Woman with a Flea" (detail) (Crespi); "The Woman with Dropsy" (detail) (Dou); "Portrait of a Couple" (Ittenbach); "Cleopatra" (Moreau); "Riches" (Vouet); "Old Man and Young Boy" (Ghirlandaio); "Louis XIV" (Rigaud); "The Drinker" (Pieter de Hooch)
 a. Sheetlet. Nos. 3703/10 .. 4·00
3711/18 $50 × 8 "Woman with a Flea" (Crespi); "Self-portrait at Easel" (Rembrandt); "Algerian Women" (detail) (Delacroix); "Head of a Young Man" (Raphael); "Venus and The Graces" (detail) (Botticelli); "Still Life with Chessboard" (detail) (Lubin Baugin); "Lady Macbeth" (Füssli); "The Smoke-filled Room" (detail) (Chardin)
 a. Sheetlet. Nos. 3711/18 .. 4·00
3719/26 $50 × 8 "The Virgin with the Rabbit" (Titian); "The Virgin with the Rabbit" (detail of head) (Titian); "The Beautiful Gardener" (detail) (Raphael); "The Lace-maker" (Vermeer); "Jeanne d'Aragon" (detail) (Raphael); "The Astronomer" (Vermeer); "The Rialto Bridge" (detail) (Canaletto); "Sigismond Malatesta" (Piero della Francesca)
 a. Sheetlet. Nos. 3719/26 .. 4·00
3686/726 .. .. Set of 41 18·00 19·00
MS3727 Six sheets, each 95×70 mm. (a) $325 "Mona Lisa" and details (Leonardi da Vinci) (84×56 mm); (b) $325 "The Coronation of Napoleon I" (David) (84×56 mm); (c) $325 "Farmyard" (Jan Brueghel the Younger) (84×56 mm); (d) $325 "The Marriage Feast at Cana" (Veronese) (84×56 mm); (e) $325 "The Fortune-teller" (Caravaggio) (84×56 mm); (f) $325 "The Rialto Bridge" (Canaletto) (84×56 mm). P 12 Set of 6 sheets 23·00 24·00
Nos. 3686×8, 3687/94, 3695/702, 3703/10, 3711/18 and 3719/26 were each printed together, *se-tenant*, in sheetlets of 8 stamps and one centre label.

(Litho Questa)

1993 (6 Dec). *Donald Duck Film Posters. T 503 and similar multicoloured designs. P 13½×14 (vert) or 14×13½ (horiz).*
3728/35 $60 × 8 Type 503; Donald's Golf Game, 1938; Sea Scouts, 1939; Donald's Penguin, 1939; A Good Time for a Dime, 1941; Truant Officer Donald; Orphan's Benefit, 1941; Chef Donald, 1941
 a. Sheetlet. Nos. 3728/35 .. 5·50
3736/43 $60 × 8 The Village Smithy; Donald's Snow Fight; Donald's Garden; Donald's Gold Mine; The Vanishing Private; Sky Trooper; Bellboy Donald; The New Spirit, all 1942
 a. Sheetlet. Nos. 3736/43 .. 5·50
3744/51 $60 × 8 Saludos Amigos, 1943; The Eyes Have It, 1945; Donald's Crime, 1945; Straight Shooters, 1947; Donald's Dilemma, 1947; Bootle Beetle, 1947; Daddy Duck, 1948; Soup's On, 1948
 a. Sheetlet. Nos. 3744/51 .. 5·50
3752/9 $80 × 8 Donald's Happy Birthday, 1949; Sea Salts, 1949; Honey Harvester, 1949; All in a Nutshell, 1949; The Greener Yard, 1949; Slide, Donald, Slide, 1949; Lion Around, 1950; Trailer Horn, 1950
 a. Sheetlet. Nos. 3752/9 .. 7·00
3760/7 $80 × 8 Bee at the Beach, 1950; Out on a Limb, 1950; Corn Chips, 1951; Test Pilot Donald, 1951; Lucky Number, 1951; Out of Scale, 1951; Bee on Guard, 1951; Let's Stick Together, 1952
 a. Sheetlet. Nos. 3760/7 .. 7·00

3768/75 $80 × 8 Trick or Treat, 1952; Don's Fountain of Youth, 1953; Rugged Bear, 1953; Canvas Back Duck, 1953; Dragon Around, 1954; Grin and Bear It, 1954; The Flying Squirrel, 1954; Up a Tree, 1955
 a. Sheetlet. Nos. 3768/75 .. 7·00
3776/81 $80 × 6 Scenes from Pirate Gold: In the crow's nest; Aracuan Bird carrying treasure chest; Donald with treasure map; Donald with treasure stall; Aracuan Bird with Donald; Donald on jetty (all horiz)
 a. Sheetlet. Nos. 3776/81 .. 5·50
3728/81 .. .. Set of 56 40·00 45·00
MS3782 Five sheets, each 129×103 mm. (a) $500 Book cover of The Wise Little Hen, 1934 (horiz). P 14×13½; (b) $500 Sketch for Timber, 1941. P 13½×14; (c) $500 Fan-card for The Three Caballeros, 1945 (horiz). P 14×13½; (d) $500 Fan-card for Melody Time, 1948. Imperf; (e) $500 Donald Duck. P 14×13½ .. Set of 5 sheets 25·00 26·00
Nos. 3728/35, 3736/43, 3744/51, 3752/9, 3760/7, 3768/75 and 3776/81 were each printed together, *se-tenant*, in sheetlets of 8 or 6 (Nos. 3776/81).

504 Aladdin

505 President Dr. Cheddi Jagan

(Des Walt Disney Co. Litho Questa)

1993 (6 Dec). *Aladdin (film). T 504 and similar multicoloured designs showing Disney cartoon characters. P 13½×14 (vert) or 14×13½ (horiz).*
3783/90 $7.65 × 8 Type 504; Abu the monkey; Jasmine; Rajah the tiger; Jafar; Iago the parrot; The Sultan; The Genie
 a. Sheetlet. Nos. 3783/90 .. 60
3791/9 $50 × 9 Jafar and magic scarab; Tiger Head entrance, Cave of Wonders; Jafar; Aladdin and Abu at breakfast; Aladdin rescuing Jasmine; Aladdin, Jasmine and Abu; Rajah comforts Jasmine; Jafar disguised as an old man; Aladdin and Abu in treasure chamber (all horiz)
 a. Sheetlet. Nos. 3791/9 .. 4·50
3800/8 $65 × 9 Aladdin with lamp and magic carpet; The Genie measuring Aladdin; Abu turned into an elephant; Aladdin in disguise at palace; Aladdin and Jasmine on magic carpet; Aladdin in disguise, Jasmine and Sultan; Aladdin fighting Jafar; Aladdin and Jasmine; The Genie with suitcase and golf clubs (all horiz)
 a. Sheetlet. Nos. 3800/8 .. 5·50
3783/808 .. .. Set of 26 10·50 11·00
MS3809 Four sheets, each 127×102 mm. (a) $325 Aladdin, The Genie, Abu and magic carpet in Cave of Wonders (horiz); (b) $325 Aladdin in disguise on elephant; (c) $325 Aladdin and Jasmine on magic carpet (horiz); (d) $325 The Genie, The Sultan, Jasmine, Aladdin and Abu (horiz) .. .. Set of 4 sheets 16·00 17·00
Nos. 3783/90, 3791/9 and 3800/8 were printed together, *se-tenant*, in sheetlets of 8 (Nos. 3783/90) or 9 (others).

1993 (17 Dec). *1st Anniv of Election of President Jagan. T 505 and similar multicoloured design. Litho. P 13½×14.*
3810 $6.40, Type 505 .. .. 30 30
MS3811 97×69 mm. $325 "REBIRTH OF DEMOCRACY" emblem. P 13 .. .. 3·50 4·00

(Des W. Hanson. Litho Questa)

1994 (18 Feb). *"Hong Kong '94" International Stamp Exhibition (1st issue). Horiz designs as T 317 of Antigua. Multicoloured. P 14.*
3812 $50 Hong Kong 1984 Royal Hong Kong Jockey Club $1.30 stamp and Happy Valley Racecourse 70 80
 a. Horiz pair. Nos. 3812/13 .. 1·40 1·60
3813 $50 Guyana 1992 Movie Posters $190 stamp and Happy Valley Racecourse 70 80
Nos. 3812/13 were printed together, *se-tenant*, in horizontal pairs throughout the sheet with the centre part of each pair forming a composite design.

(Des Kerri Schiff. Litho Questa)

1994 (18 Feb). *"Hong Kong '94" International Stamp Exhibition (2nd issue). Ch'ing Dynasty Snuff Boxes (Nos. 3814/19) or Porcelain (Nos. 3820/5). Multicoloured designs as T 318 of Antigua, but vert. P 14.*
3814 $20 Painted enamel in shape of bamboo 30 30
 a. Sheetlet. No. 3814/19 .. 1·60
3815 $20 Painted enamel showing woman 30 30
3816 $20 Amber with lions playing ball 30 30
3817 $20 Agate in shape of two gourds 30 30
3818 $20 Glass overlay with dog design 30 30

3819 $20 Glass with foliage design .. 30 30
3820 $20 Covered jar with dragon design 30 30
 a. Sheetlet. Nos. 3820/5 .. 1·60
3821 $20 Rotating brush-holder 30 30
3822 $20 Covered jar with horses design 30 30
3823 $20 Amphora vase with bats and peaches 30 30
3824 $20 Tea caddy with Fo dogs 30 30
3825 $20 Vase with camellias and peaches design 30 30
3814/25 .. .. Set of 12 3·25 3·25
Nos. 3814/19 and 3820/5 were each printed together, *se-tenant*, in sheetlets of 6.

$20.00   XX

CENTENARY Sign For The MAHDI 1894-1994

(506)

1994 (21 Mar). *Centenary of the Sign for the Mahdi. Nos. 1622/4 and 1634 surch as T 506 in blue.*
3826 $6 on 60 c. Plate No. 73 (Series 1) (horiz)
3827 $20 on 200 c. Plate No. 33 (Series 1) (horiz)
3828 $30 on 60 c. Plate No. 57 (Series 1) (horiz)
3829 $35 on 60 c. Plate No. 75 (Series 1) (horiz)
The surcharges on Nos. 3826 and 3828 show the third line as "MADHI".

(Litho Questa)

1994 (5 May). *Hummel Figurines. Vert designs as T 302 of Antigua. Multicoloured. P 14.*
3830 $20 Girl holding inscribed heart 20 25
3831 $25 Boy with heart under arm .. 25 30
3832 $35 Baker 35 40
3833 $50 Girl with pot of flowers 50 55
3834 $60 Girl with trumpet, pot plant and bird 60 65
3835 $130 Four girls .. .. 1·25 1·40
3836 $190 Boy and two girls with dog .. 1·90 2·00
3837 $250 Boy with cake and dog .. 2·50 2·75
3830/7 .. .. Set of 8 7·50 8·50
MS3838 Two sheets, each 92×124 mm. (a) $6 As No. 3835; $25 No. 3831; $30 As No. 3830; $190 No. 3836. (b) $20 As No. 3832; $35 As No. 3837; $60 No. 3834; $130 As No. 3833 Set of 2 sheets 5·00 5·25

I L O 75th Anniversary 1919-1994

$6.00   XX

(507)

1994 (16 May). *75th Anniv of International Labour Organization. Nos. 1527 and 1629/30 surch as T 507.*
3839 $6 on 130 c. Plate No. 13 (Series 1) ..
3840 $30 on 120 c. Plate No. 58 (Series 1) ..
3841 $35 on 120 c. Plate No. 56 (Series 1) ..

1994 (20 May). *Centenary of Sierra Club (environmental protection society) (1992). Endangered Species. Multicoloured designs as T 320 of Antigua. P 14.*
3842 $70 Red Kangaroo with young .. 90 90
 a. Sheetlet. No. 3842/9 .. 6·50
3843 $70 Head of American Alligator .. 90 90
3844 $70 Head of Bald Eagle 90 90
3845 $70 Giant Panda eating bamboo .. 90 90
3846 $70 Head of Red Kangaroo .. 90 90
3847 $70 Alaskan Brown Bear sitting .. 90 90
3848 $70 Bald Eagle 90 90
3849 $70 Head of Giant Panda .. 90 90
3850 $70 Red Kangaroo (horiz) .. 90 90
 a. Sheetlet. Nos. 3850/7 .. 6·50
3851 $70 Whooping Crane facing left (horiz) .. 90 90
3852 $70 Male Whooping Crane in courtship display (horiz) 90 90
3853 $70 Whooping Crane looking right (horiz) 90 90
3854 $70 Alaskan Brown Bear and cub (horiz) 90 90
3855 $70 Alaskan Brown Bear fishing (horiz) 90 90
3856 $70 Bald Eagle on branch (horiz) .. 90 90
3857 $70 Giant Panda (horiz) .. 90 90
3858 $70 American Alligator (logo at left) (horiz) 90 90
 a. Sheetlet. Nos. 3858/63 .. 4·75
3859 $70 American Alligator (logo at right) (horiz) 90 90
3860 $70 Italian Alps at sunrise (horiz) .. 90 90
3861 $70 Italian Alps and meadow (horiz) .. 90 90
3862 $70 Mono Lake at sunset (horiz) .. 90 90
3863 $70 Rock pinnacles, Mono Lake (horiz) 90 90
3864 $70 Sea Lion 90 90
 a. Sheetlet. Nos. 3864/72 .. 7·00
3865 $70 Head of Sea Lion .. 90 90
3866 $70 Sea Lions on rocks .. 90 90
3867 $70 Rock pinnacles, Mono Lake .. 90 90
3868 $70 Sierra Club Centennial emblem (black, buff and deep blue-green) .. 90 90

3869	$70 Lake, Italian Alps	90	90
3870	$70 Summit of Matterhorn	90	90
3871	$70 Matterhorn and village	90	90
3872	$70 Clouds over Matterhorn	90	90
3842/72	*Set of 31*	24·00	24·00

Nos. 3842/9, 3850/7, 3858/63 and 3864/72 were printed together, *se-tenant* in sheetlets of 8 (Nos. 3842/9 and 3850/7), 6 (Nos. 3858/63) or 9 (Nos. 3864/72).

ROYAL VISIT FEB 19-22, 1994
(508)

1994 (26 May). *Royal Visit. Nos. 3551/5 optd as T 508 (in three lines on $75 or two lines on $130).*
3873 $25 Queen Elizabeth II in Coronation robes (photograph by Cecil Beaton) 55 60
  a. Sheetlet. Nos. 3873/6×2 7·50
3874 $50 Royal gems .. .. 90 1·00
3875 $75 Queen Elizabeth and Prince Philip .. 1·25 1·40
3876 $130 Queen opening Parliament .. 1·50 1·75
3873/6 *Set of 4* 3·75 4·25
MS3877 69×100 mm. $325 "Queen in Coronation Robes" (Sir James Gunn) (28½×42½ mm) 4·25 4·50
No. MS3877 shows the overprint in three lines on the sheet margin.

509 Cestrum parqui

1994 (20 June). *Flowers. T 509 and similar horiz designs. Multicoloured. Litho. P 14×13½.*
3878 $6.40, Type 509 .. .. 10 10
3879 $7.65, *Brunfelsia calycina* 10 10
3880 $12.80, *Datura rosei* 10 15
3881 $15.30, *Ruellia macrantha* 15 20
3882 $50 *Portlandia albiflora* 50 55
3883 $50 *Clusia grandiflora* 50 55
  a. Sheetlet. Nos. 3883/94 6·00
3884 $50 *Begonia haageana* 50 55
3885 $50 *Fuchsia simplicicaulis* 50 55
3886 $50 *Guaiacum officinale* 50 55
3887 $50 *Pithecoctenium cynanchoides* .. 50 55
3888 $50 *Sphaeralcea umbellata* .. 50 55
3889 $50 *Erythrina poeppigiana* .. 50 55
3890 $50 *Steriphoma paradoxa* .. 50 55
3891 $50 *Allemanda violacea* .. 50 55
3892 $50 *Centropogon cornutus* .. 50 55
3893 $50 *Passiflora quadrangularis* .. 50 55
3894 $50 *Victoria amazonica* .. 50 55
3895 $50 *Cobaea scandens* .. 50 55
  a. Sheetlet. Nos. 3895/906 6·00
3896 $50 *Pyrostegia venusta* .. 50 55
3897 $50 *Petrea kohautiana* .. 50 55
3898 $50 *Hippobroma longiflora* .. 50 55
3899 $50 *Cleome hassleriana* .. 50 55
3900 $50 *Verbena peruviana* .. 50 55
3901 $50 *Tropaeolum peregrinum* .. 50 55
3902 $50 *Plumeria rubra* .. 50 55
3903 $50 *Selenicereus grandiflorus* .. 50 55
3904 $50 *Mandevilla splendens* .. 50 55
3905 $50 *Pereskia aculeata* .. 50 55
3906 $50 *Ipomoea learii* .. 50 55
3907 $130 *Pachystachys coccinea* .. 1·25 1·40
3908 $190 *Beloperone guttata* .. 1·90 2·00
3909 $250 *Ferdinandusa speciosa* .. 2·50 2·75
3878/909 *Set of 32* 19·00 20·00
MS3910 Two sheets, each 99×70 mm. (a) $325 *Lophospermum erubescens.* (b) $325 *Columnea fendleri.* P 13 *Set of 2 sheets* 6·50 6·75
Nos. 3883/94 and 3895/906 were printed together, *se-tenant*, in sheetlets of 12, forming composite background designs.

(Des W. Hanson. Litho)
1994 (20 June). *25th Anniv of First Moon Landing (1st issue). Horiz designs as T 326 of Antigua. Multicoloured. P 14.*
3911 $60 Walter Dornberger and launch of first A-4 rocket .. 90 90
  a. Sheetlet. Nos. 3911/16 .. 4·75
3912 $60 Rudolph Nebel and "Surveyor 1" 90 90
3913 $60 Robert H. Goddard and "Apollo 7" 90 90
3914 $60 Kurt Debus and view of Earth from Moon ("Apollo 8") 90 90
3915 $60 James T. Webb and "Apollo 9" 90 90
3916 $60 George E. Mueller and "Apollo 10" lunar module 90 90
3917 $60 Wernher von Braun and launch of "Apollo 11" 90 90
  a. Sheetlet. Nos. 3917/22 4·75
3918 $60 Rocco A. Petrone and "Apollo 11" astronaut on Moon .. 90 90
3919 $60 Eberhard Rees and "Apollo 12" astronaut on Moon .. 90 90
3920 $60 Charles A. Berry and damaged "Apollo 13" 90 90
3921 $60 Thomas O. Paine and "Apollo 14" before splashdown 90 90
3922 $60 A. F. Staats and "Apollo 15" on Moon 90 90
3923 $60 Robert R. Gilruth and "Apollo 16" astronaut on Moon .. 90 90
  a. Sheetlet. Nos. 3923/8 4·75
3924 $60 Ernst Stuhlinger and "Apollo 17" crew on Moon 90 90
3925 $60 Christopher C. Kraft and X-30 National Aero-Space Plane 90 90
3926 $60 Rudolf Opitz and Messerschmitt Me 163B Komet (rocket engine), 1941 90 90
3927 $60 Clyde W. Tombaugh and "face" on Mars 90 90

3928 $60 Hermann Oberth and scene from *The Girl in the Moon* 90 90
3911/28 *Set of 18* 13·00 13·00
MS3929 125×112 mm. $325 Frank J. Everest Jr and "Apollo 11" anniversary logo 4·50 5·00
Nos. 3911/16, 3917/22 and 3923/8 were each printed together, *se-tenant*, in sheetlets of 6.
See also Nos. 4169/87.

(Des Kerri Schiff. Litho B.D.T.)
1994 (20 June). *Centenary of International Olympic Committee. Medal Winners. Multicoloured designs as T 327 of Antigua, but vert. P 14.*
3930 $20 Nancy Kerrigan (U.S.A.) (1994 figure skating silver) 30 30
3931 $35 Sawao Kato (Japan) (1976 gymnastics gold) 50 50
3932 $130 Florence Griffith Joyner (U.S.A.) (1988 100 and 200 metres gold) 1·75 2·00
3930/2 *Set of 3* 2·25 2·50
MS3933 110×80 mm. $325 Mark Wasmeier (Germany) (1994 super giant slalom and giant slalom gold) 4·00 4·50

(Des A. Melville-Brown. Litho B.D.T.)
1994 (20 June). *Centenary of First English Cricket Tour to the West Indies (1995). Multicoloured designs as T 329 of Antigua. P 14.*
3934 $20 Clive Lloyd (Guyana and West Indies) (vert) 40 30
3935 $35 Carl Hooper (Guyana and West Indies) and Wisden Trophy .. 55 50
3936 $60 Graham Hick (England) and Wisden Trophy 90 1·00
3934/6 *Set of 3* 1·60 1·60
MS3937 79×100 mm. $200 English team of 1895 (black and grey-brown) 2·50 2·75

(Des J. Batchelor. Litho B.D.T.)
1994 (20 June). *50th Anniv of D-Day. Aircraft. Horiz designs as T 331 of Antigua. Multicoloured. P 14.*
3938 $6 Supermarine Spitfire Mk XI fighter on photo reconnaissance 20 15
3939 $35 North American B-25 Mitchell bomber 60 50
3940 $190 Republic P-47 Thunderbolt fighters 2·50 3·00
3938/40 *Set of 3* 3·00 3·25
MS3941 109×79 mm. $325 Avro Type 683 Lancaster bomber of 419 Squadron 4·25 4·50

(Des J. Batchelor (Nos. 3942/51), W. Wright (Nos. 3952/60). Litho B.D.T.)
1994 (20 June). *50th Anniv of Second World War (3rd issue). Horiz designs as T 500. Multicoloured. P 13.*
3942 $60 Paratroops drop, D-Day 80 80
  a. Sheetlet. Nos. 3942/51 7·00
3943 $60 Glider assault, D-Day 80 80
3944 $60 U.S.S. *Arkansas* (battleship) bombarding Omaha Beach, D-Day 80 80
3945 $60 U.S. fighters attacking train 80 80
3946 $60 Allied landing craft approaching beaches 80 80
3947 $60 Troops in beach obstacles 80 80
3948 $60 Commandos leaving landing craft 80 80
3949 $60 U.S. flail tank destroying mines 80 80
3950 $60 U.S. tank breaking through sea wall 80 80
3951 $60 Tanks and infantry advancing 80 80
3952 $60 Landings at Anzio (22 January 1944) 80 80
  a. Sheetlet. Nos. 3952/61 7·00
3953 $60 R.A.F. attacking Amiens Prison (18 February 1944) 80 80
3954 $60 Soviet Army tank in Sevastopol (9 May 1944) 80 80
3955 $60 British bren-gun carriers at the Gustav Line (19 May 1944) 80 80
3956 $60 D-Day landings (6 June 1944) 80 80
3957 $60 "V-1" over London (13 June 1944) 80 80
3958 $60 Allies entering Paris (19 August 1944) 80 80
3959 $60 German "V-2" rocket ready for launch (8 September 1944) 80 80
3960 $60 Sinking of *Tirpitz* (German battleship) (12 November 1944) 80 80
3961 $60 U.S. tanks at Bastogne (29 December 1944) 80 80
3942/61 *Set of 20* 14·00 14·00
Nos. 3942/51 and 3952/61 were each printed together, *se-tenant*, in sheetlets of 10 with the stamps arranged in two horizontal strips of 5 separated by gutters showing a D-Day Mulberry Harbour (Nos. 3942/51) or map of Europe and North Africa (Nos. 3952/61).

(Des Kerri Schiff. Litho Questa (Nos. 3964/83) or B.D.T. (others))
1994 (20 June). *"Philakorea '94" International Stamp Exhibition, Seoul (1st issue). Multicoloured designs as T 330 of Antigua. P 13 (Nos. 3964/83) or 14 (others).*
3962 $6 Socialist ideals statue, Pyongyang (vert) 10 10
3963 $25 Statue of Admiral Yi Sun-sin (vert) 25 30
3964 $60 Fruits and mountain peaks 60 65
  a. Sheetlet. Nos. 3964/73 6·00
3965 $60 Manchurian crane, bamboo and peaks 60 65
3966 $60 Rising sun and two cranes on pine 60 65
3967 $60 Five cranes on pine and peak 60 65
3968 $60 Three cranes in flight 60 65
3969 $60 Sea, rocky shore and fungi 60 65
3970 $60 Sea, rocky shore and fruit 60 65
3971 $60 Hind at seashore and fruit 60 65
3972 $60 Stag in pine forest 60 65
3973 $60 Deer and fungi by waterfall 60 65
3974 $60 Tops of pines and mountain peaks 60 65
  a. Sheetlet. Nos. 3974/83 6·00
3975 $60 Manchurian crane in flight 60 65
3976 $60 Three cranes on pine tree 60 65
3977 $60 Crane on pine tree 60 65
3978 $60 Top of fruit tree 60 65

3979 $60 Stag and two hinds on mountainside 60 65
3980 $60 Deer and fungi 60 65
3981 $60 Stag by waterfall and hind drinking 60 65
3982 $60 Pine tree, fruit and fungi 60 65
3983 $60 Fungi on mountainside 60 65
3984 $120 Sŏkkat'ap Pagoda, Pulguksa 1·25 1·40
3985 $130 Village Guardian (statue), Chejudo Island 1·25 1·40
3962/85 *Set of 24* 15·00 16·00
MS3986 Two sheets. (a) 104×73 mm. $325 Europeans at the Korean Court (early lithograph). (b) 73×104 mm. $325 Pagoda by Ch'urae-am Rock. P 14 *Set of 2 sheets* 6·50 6·75
Nos. 3964/73 and 3974/83, all 23×49 mm, were printed together, *se-tenant*, in sheetlets of 10, each sheetlet forming a composite design showing panels from a screen painting of longevity symbols from the late Chosun dynasty.
See also Nos. 4117/41.

510 Miki Maya

1994 (20 June). *80th Anniv of Takarazuka Revue of Japan. T 510 and similar multicoloured designs. Litho. P 14½×15.*
3987 $20 Type 510 55 60
  a. Sheetlet. Nos. 3987/94 4·75
3988 $20 Fubuki Takane 55 60
3989 $20 Seika Kuze 55 60
3990 $20 Saki Asaji 55 60
3991 $60 Mira Anju (34×47 mm) 75 80
3992 $60 Yuki Amami (34×47 mm) 75 80
3993 $60 Maki Ichiro (34×47 mm) 75 80
3994 $60 Yu Shion (34×47 mm) 75 80
3987/94 *Set of 8* 4·75 5·00
Nos. 3987/94 were printed together, *se-tenant*, in sheetlets of 8 stamps and 4 34×21½ mm labels.

511 Heliconius melpomene   512 Jacob

(Litho Questa)
1994 (5 July). *Butterflies. T 511 and similar horiz designs. Multicoloured. P 14½ (Nos. 4000/15) or 14 (others).*
3995 $6 Type 511 20 20
3996 $20 *Helicopis cupido* 45 45
3997 $25 *Agrias claudina* 50 50
3998 $30 *Parides coelus* 60 60
3999 $50 *Heliconius hecale* 75 75
4000 $50 *Anaea marthesia* 75 75
  a. Sheetlet. Nos. 4000/15 11·00
4001 $50 *Brassolis astyra* 75 75
4002 $50 *Heliconius melpomene* 75 75
4003 $50 *Haetera piera* 75 75
4004 $50 *Morpho diana* 75 75
4005 $50 *Parides coelus* 75 75
4006 $50 *Catagramma pitheas* 75 75
4007 $50 *Nessaea obrinus* 75 75
4008 $50 *Automeris janus* 75 75
4009 $50 *Papilio torquatus* 75 75
4010 $50 *Eunica sophonisba* 75 75
4011 $50 *Ceratinia nise* 75 75
4012 $50 *Panacea procilla* 75 75
4013 $50 *Pyrrhogyra neaerea* 75 75
4014 $50 *Morpho deidamia* 75 75
4015 $50 *Dismorphia orise* 75 75
4016 $50 *Morpho diana* 85 85
4017 $190 *Dismorphia orise* 2·50 3·00
4018 $250 *Morpho deidamia* 3·00 3·50
3995/4018 *Set of 24* 18·00 19·00
MS4019 Four sheets. (a) 104×76 mm. $325 *Anaea eribotes.* P 14. (b) 104×76 mm. $325 *Eunica sophonisba.* P 14. (c) 110×80 mm. $325 *Hamadryas velutina* (39×30 mm). P 14½. (d) 110×80 mm. $325 *Agrias claudina* (39×30 mm). P 14½ *Set of 4 sheets* 13·00 13·50
Nos. 4000/15, which measure 39×30 mm, were printed together, *se-tenant*, in sheetlets of 16.

(Des Bryna Waldman (Nos. 4020/43), K. Tanner (Nos. 4044/91), Marilyn Abramowitz (Nos. 4092/116). Litho Questa)
1994 (4 Aug). *Bible Stories (2nd series). T 512 and similar square designs. Multicoloured. P 14.*
(a) Joseph
4020/43 $20 × 24 arranged as blocks of 4 depicting Jacob giving Joseph a coat of many colours (Type 512 at top left): Joseph thrown into a pit; Joseph sold as a slave; Joseph accused by Potiphar's wife; Joseph interprets Pharoah's dreams; Joseph reunited with his brothers
  a. Sheetlet. Nos. 4020/43 .. 6·00

(b) The Parting of the Red Sea

4044/67 $20 × 24 Palm trees on shore; Pyramids; Palm trees on shore and black cloud; Three palm trees; Blue and white dove; Red and white bird; Egyptian army engulfed by sea; Yellow and white dove; Red and green fishes; Egyptian chariot with wall of water at left; Chariots between walls of water; Dolphins; Two doves; Israelites and water to left; Israelites and water to right; Turquoise and purple fishes; Israelites with tree at left; Iraelites with goats; Moses; Israelites with tree at right; Israelites with woman on horse; Israelites with old man and woman carrying pack; Israelites with woman carrying young child; Israelites with cart

a. Sheetlet. Nos. 4044/67 .. .. 6·00

(c) Ruth

4068/91 $20 × 24 arranged as blocks of 6 depicting Ruth and Naomi; Ruth gleaning in cornfield; Boaz establishing kinsman's rights; Naomi with Ruth, Boaz and Obed

a. Sheetlet. Nos. 4068/91 .. .. 6·00

(d) Daniel in the Lions' Den

4092/116 $20 × 25 Palm fronds and hibiscus flower; Frigate bird and palm fronds; Frigate birds and tops of stone pillars; Frigate bird, pillars and sail at bottom right; Hibiscus, sails of ship and top of pillar; Yellow arum lilies and palm trees; Heads of adult and immature frigate birds and palm trees; Palm trees, butterfly and stone pillars; Two butterflies and stone pillars; Stone pillar and sailing ship; Standing heron; Purple irises and palm trees; Daniel; Angel; Donkey foal; Orchids; Lioness and two cubs; Daniel's legs and lions; Lion; Three crowns; Goat and kid; Kid; Cub and head of lion; Lioness; Heron in flight

a. Sheetlet. Nos. 4020/116 .. 6·00

4020/116 .. .. *Set of 97* 22·00 24·00·

Nos. 4020/43, 4044/67, 4068/91 and 4092/116 were each printed together, *se-tenant*, in sheetlets of 25 (Nos. 4092/116) or 24 (others), forming composite designs.

GUYANA

513 Peregrine Falcon

514 Paulo Futre (Portugal)

(Des G. Bibby. Litho Questa)

1994 (16 Aug). *"Philakorea '94" International Stamp Exhibition, Seoul (2nd issue). Birds of the World.* T **513** *and similar vert designs. Multicoloured. P 14.*

4117	$35 Type **513**	45	50
	a. Sheetlet. Nos. 4117/28	4·75	
4118	$35 Great Spotted Woodpecker	45	50
4119	$35 White-throated Kingfisher	45	50
4120	$35 Peruvian Cock of the Rock	45	50
4121	$35 Yellow-headed Amazon	45	50
4122	$35 Victoria Crowned Pigeon	45	50
4123	$35 Little Owl	45	50
4124	$35 Ring-necked Pheasant	45	50
4125	$35 Goldfinch	45	50
4126	$35 Jay	45	50
4127	$35 Sulphur-breasted Toucan	45	50
4128	$35 Japanese Blue Flycatcher	45	50
4129	$35 Northern Goshawk	45	50
	a. Sheetlet. Nos. 4129/40	4·75	
4130	$35 Lapwing	45	50
4131	$35 Ornate Umbrellabird	45	50
4132	$35 Slaty-headed Parakeet	45	50
4133	$35 Regent Bowerbird	45	50
4134	$35 Egyptian Goose	45	50
4135	$35 White-winged Crossbill	45	50
4136	$35 Waxwing	45	50
4137	$35 Ruff	45	50
4138	$35 Hoopoe	45	50
4139	$35 Superb Starling	45	50
4140	$35 Great Jacamar	45	50
4117/40	.. .. *Set of 24*	9·50	11·00

MS4141 Two sheets, each 70×100 mm. (a) $325 American Bald Eagle; (b) $325 Gould's Violet-ear .. .. .. *Set of 2 sheets* 8·00 8·50

Nos. 4117/28 and 4129/40 were each printed together, *se-tenant*, in sheetlets of 12.

(Litho B.D.T.)

1994 (1 Sept). *World Cup Football Championship, U.S.A. (2nd issue).* T **514** *and similar vert designs. Multicoloured. P 14.*

4142	$6 Type **514**	10	10
4143	$35 Lyndon Hooper (Canada)	35	40
4144	$60 Enzo Francescoli (Uruguay)	60	65
4145	$60 Paolo Maldini (Italy)	60	65
	a. Sheetlet. Nos. 4145/50	3·50	
4146	$60 Guyana player	60	65
4147	$60 Bwalya Kalusha (Zambia)	60	65

4148	$60 Diego Maradona (Argentina)	60	65
4149	$60 Andreas Brehme (Germany)	60	65
4150	$60 Eric Wynalda (U.S.A.) (pursuing ball)	60	65
4151	$60 John Doyle (U.S.A.)	60	65
	a. Sheetlet. Nos. 4151/6	3·50	
4152	$60 Eric Wynalda (U.S.A.) (kicking ball)	60	65
4153	$60 Thomas Dooley (U.S.A.)	60	65
4154	$60 Ernie Stewart (U.S.A.)	60	65
4155	$60 Marcelo Balboa (U.S.A.)	60	65
4156	$60 Bora Milutinovic (U.S.A. coach)	60	65
4157	$190 Freddy Rincón (Colombia)	1·90	2·00
4142/57	.. .. *Set of 16*	10·00	11·00

MS4158 Two sheets. (a) 105×75 mm. $325 "94" symbol and player. (b) 75×105 mm. $325 Oiler Watson (U.S.A.) .. .. *Set of 2 sheets* 6·50 6·75

Nos. 4145/50 and 4151/6 were each printed together, *se-tenant*, in sheetlets of 6, forming composite background designs.

515 Anja Fichtel (individual foil, 1988)

(Des Kerri Schiff. Litho Questa)

1994 (28 Sept). *Olympic Games, Atlanta (1996) (1st issue). Previous German Gold Medal Winners.* T **515** *and similar multicoloured designs. P 14.*

4159	$6 Type **515**	10	10
4160	$25 Annegret Richter (100 metres, 1976) *(vert)*	25	30
4161	$30 Heike Henkel (high jump, 1992) *(vert)*	30	35
4162	$35 Armin Hary (100 metres, 1960) *(vert)*	35	40
4163	$50 Heide Rosendahl (long jump, 1972) *(vert)*	50	55
4164	$60 Josef Neckermann (dressage, 1968) *(vert)*	60	65
4165	$130 Heike Drechsler (long jump, 1988) *(vert)*	1·25	1·40
4166	$190 Ulrike Mayfarth (high jump, 1984) *(vert)*	1·90	2·00
4167	$250 Michael Gross (200 metres freestyle and 100 metres butterfly, 1984)	2·50	2·75
4159/67	.. .. *Set of 9*	7·75	8·50

MS4168 Three sheets. (a) 105×75 mm. $135 Markus Wasmeier (skiing, 1994) *(vert)*; $190 Katja Seizinger (skiing, 1994) *(vert)*. (b) 105×75 mm. $325 Franziska van Almsick (swimming, 1992) *(vert)*. (c) 75×105 mm. $325 Steffi Graf (tennis, 1988, 1992) *(vert)* .. *Set of 3 sheets* 6·50 7·00

See also Nos. 4492/4508 and 4739/88.

516 Dog Laika and Rocket, 1957

(Des J.-L. Puviland. Litho Questa)

1994 (10 Nov). *25th Anniv of First Moon Landing (2nd issue).* T **516** *and similar vert designs. Multicoloured. P 13½×14.*

4169	$60 Type **516**	80	80
	a. Sheetlet. Nos. 4169/77	6·50	
4170	$60 Yuri Gagarin (first man in space), 1961	80	80
4171	$60 John Glenn (first American to orbit Earth), 1962	80	80
4172	$60 Edward White walking in space, 1965	80	80
4173	$60 Neil Armstrong, walking on Moon and "Apollo 11" logo	80	80
4174	$60 "Luna 16" leaving Moon, 1970	80	80
4175	$60 Lunar Module 1 on Moon, 1970	80	80
4176	$60 Skylab 1, 1973	80	80
4177	$60 Astronauts and Apollo–Soyuz link-up, 1975	80	80
4178	$60 "Mars 3"	80	80
	a. Sheetlet. Nos. 4178/86	6·50	
4179	$60 "Mariner 10"	80	80
4180	$60 "Voyager"	80	80
4181	$60 "Pioneer"	80	80
4182	$60 "Giotto"	80	80
4183	$60 "Magellan"	80	80
4184	$60 "Galileo"	80	80
4185	$60 "Ulysses"	80	80
4186	$60 "Cassini"	80	80
4169/86	.. .. *Set of 18*	13·00	13·00

MS4187 Two sheets, each 142×104 mm. (a) $325 "Apollo 11" astronauts. (b) $325 "Galileo" .. .. *Set of 2 sheets* 8·50 9·00

Nos. 4169/77 and 4178/86 were each printed together, *se-tenant*, in sheetlets of 9, with the backgrounds of Nos. 4178/86 forming a composite design of Space.

517 South Carolina Railroad *Best Friend of Charleston*, 1830, U.S.A.

(Des R. Sauber. Litho Questa)

1994 (15 Nov). *History of Trains. Steam Locomotives.* T **517** *and similar horiz designs. Multicoloured. P 14.*

4188	$25 Type **517**	40	40
4189	$25 South Eastern Railway No. 285, 1891	40	40
4190	$30 Camden & Amboy Railroad No. 1 *John Bull*, 1831, U.S.A.	45	45
	a. Sheetlet. Nos. 4190/7	3·25	
4191	$30 Stephenson "Patentee" type locomotive, 1837	45	45
4192	$30 *Atlantic*, 1832	45	45
4193	$30 *Stourbridge Lion*, 1829, U.S.A.	45	45
4194	$30 Polonceau locomotive, 1854	45	45
4195	$30 *Thomas Rogers*, 1855, U.S.A.	45	45
4196	$30 *Vulcan*, 1858	45	45
4197	$30 *Namur*, 1846	45	45
4198	$30 John Jarvis's *De Witt Clinton*, 1831, U.S.A.	45	45
	a. Sheetlet. Nos. 4198/205	3·25	
4199	$30 Seguin locomotive, 1829	45	45
4200	$30 Stephenson's *Planet*, 1830	45	45
4201	$30 Norris locomotive, 1840	45	45
4202	$30 *Sampson*, 1867, U.S.A.	45	45
4203	$30 *Andrew Jackson*, 1832	45	45
4204	$30 *Herald*, 1831	45	45
4205	$30 *Cumberland*, 1845, U.S.A.	45	45
4206	$30 Pennsylvania Railroad Class K, 1880	45	45
	a. Sheetlet. Nos. 4206/13	3·25	
4207	$30 Cooke locomotive No. 11, 1885	45	45
4208	$30 *John B. Turner*, 1867, U.S.A.	45	45
4209	$30 Baldwin locomotive, 1871	45	45
4210	$30 Richard Trevithick's locomotive, 1803	45	45
4211	$30 John Stephens's locomotive, 1825	45	45
4212	$30 John Blenkinsop's locomotive , 1814	45	45
4213	$30 *Pennsylvania*, 1803	45	45
4214	$300 Mount Washington Cog Railway locomotive No. 6, 1886	3·00	3·00
4215	$300 Stroudley locomotive *Brighton*, 1872	3·00	3·00
4188/215	.. .. *Set of 28*	15·00	15·00

MS4216 Two sheets, 100×70 mm. (a) $250 Est Railway locomotive, 1878; (b) $300 *Claud Hamilton*, 1900 .. .. *Set of 2 sheets* 7·50 8·00

Nos. 4190/7, 4198/205 and 4206/13 were each printed together, *se-tenant*, in sheetlets of 8, with the stamps arranged in two horizontal strips of 4 separated by a large illustrated gutter.

No. 4198 is inscribed "West Point Foundry 1832 Locomotive" and No. 4202 "Union Iron Works os San Francisco", both in error.

(Litho Questa)

1994 (1 Dec). *Christmas. Religious Paintings. Vert designs as* T **336** *of Antigua. Multicoloured. P 13½×14.*

4217	$6 "Joseph with the Christ Child" (Guido Reni)	15	10
4218	$20 "Adoration of the Christ Child" (Girolamo Romanino)	25	25
4219	$25 "Adoration of the Christ Child with St. Barbara and St. Martin" (Raffaello Botticini)	30	30
4220	$30 "Holy Family" (Pompeo Batoni)	35	35
4221	$35 "Flight into Egypt" (Bartolommeo Carducci)	40	40
4222	$60 "Holy Family and the Baptist" (Andrea del Sarto)	70	70
4223	$120 "Sacred Conversation" (Cesare de Sesto)	1·75	2·00
4224	$190 "Madonna and Child with Saints Joseph and John the Baptist" (Pontormo)	2·75	3·25
4217/24	.. .. *Set of 8*	6·00	6·50

MS4225 (a) 112×93 mm. $325 "Presentation of Christ in the Temple" (Fra Bartolommeo). (b) 85×95 mm. $325 "Holy Family and St. Elizabeth and St. John the Baptist" (Francisco Primaticcio) .. .. *Set of 2 sheets* 7·50 8·00

518 Riker and Dr. Crusher

519 Cross and Map of Guyana

(Des J. Gordon. Litho Questa)

1994 (7 Dec). *Star Trek Generations (film).* T **518** *and similar multicoloured designs showing Enterprise crew in 19th-century naval uniforms (Nos. 4226/34) or in 23rd-century (Nos. 4235/43). P 13½×14.*

4226	$100 Type **518**	1·50	1·50
	a. Sheetlet. Nos. 4226/34	12·00	
4227	$100 Geordi, Dr. Crusher with Lt. Worf in chains	1·50	1·50
4228	$100 Captain Picard	1·50	1·50
4229	$100 Data and Geordi	1·50	1·50

4230	$100	"U.S.S. *Enterprise*" (sailing ship)	1·50	1·50
4231	$100	Captain Picard and Riker on quarterdeck	1·50	1·50
4232	$100	Data	1·50	1·50
4233	$100	Lt. Worf	1·50	1·50
4234	$100	Dr. Crusher	1·50	1·50
4235	$100	Captain Picard	1·50	1·50
		a. Sheetlet. Nos. 4235/43	12·00	
4236	$100	Riker	1·50	1·50
4237	$100	Captain Kirk	1·50	1·50
4238	$100	Soron with phaser	1·50	1·50
4239	$100	Captains Kirk and Picard on horseback	1·50	1·50
4240	$100	Klingon women	1·50	1·50
4241	$100	Captains Kirk and Picard	1·50	1·50
4242	$100	Troi	1·50	1·50
4243	$100	Captain Picard and Data	1·50	1·50
4244	$100	"BOLDLY GO" film poster	1·50	1·50
4226/44		Set of 18	24·00	24·00

MS4245 86×103 mm. $500 U.S.S. *Enterprise* from film poster (*horiz*). P 14×13½ .. 5·50 6·00

Nos. 4226/34 and 4235/43 were each printed together, *se-tenant*, in sheetlets of 9. No. 4244 was printed in sheets of 9 of the one design.

Two $1000 values with designs as Nos. 4235 with 4237 and 4239 embossed on gold foil also exist from limited printings.

(Litho Questa)

1994 (12 Dec). *Centenary of Sisters of Mercy in Guyana.* P 14.
4246 **519** $60 multicoloured 80 80

(Litho Questa)

1994 (12 Dec). *First Recipients of Order of the Caribbean Community. Horiz designs as Nos. 2046/8 of Antigua. Multicoloured.* P 14.

4247	$60	Sir Shridath Ramphal	65	75
4248	$60	William Demas	65	75
4249	$60	Derek Walcott	65	75
4247/9		Set of 3	1·75	2·00

520 Garfield Sobers congratulating Brian Lara

521 Babe Ruth

(Litho Questa)

1995 (3 Feb). *Brian Lara's Achievements in Cricket.* T **520** and similar multicoloured designs. P 14.

4250	$20	Type **520**	35	25
4251	$30	Brian Lara setting world record for highest Test Match score (*vert*)	45	35
4252	$375	Lara and Chanderpaul	4·25	4·75
4250/2		Set of 3	4·50	4·75

MS4253 70×100 mm. $300 Brian Lara (*vert*) .. 3·00 3·25

(Des J. Gordon. Litho Questa)

1995 (6 Feb). *Birth Centenary of Babe Ruth (baseball player).* T **521** and similar designs, all reddish brown and black. P 13½×14.

4254	$65	Type **521**	70	80
		a. Sheetlet. Nos. 4254/65	7·75	
4255	$65	Preparing to bat (full-length photo)	70	80
4256	$65	Head and shoulders portrait (cap with limp brim)	70	80
4257	$65	In retirement (bare-headed)	70	80
4258	$65	Running (in plain shirt)	70	80
4259	$65	Head and shoulders portrait (cap with emblem and stiff brim)	70	80
4260	$65	Wearing "NEW YORK" shirt	70	80
4261	$65	Preparing to hit (in "NEW YORK" shirt)	70	80
4262	$65	Wearing "YANKEES" shirt	70	80
4263	$65	At base with bat on shoulder (in striped shirt)	70	80
4264	$65	Watching the ball (in striped shirt)	70	80
4265	$65	In cap and coat at Old Timer's Day, Yankee Stadium, 1948	70	80
4254/65		Set of 12	7·75	8·50

MS4266 89×118 mm. $500 Babe Ruth (*horiz*). P 14×13½ .. .. .. 5·00 5·25

Nos. 4254/65 were printed together, *se-tenant*, in sheetlets of 12.

A $1000 value, showing a similar portrait, embossed on gold foil exists from a limited printing.

522 Mickey Mouse as Family Doctor

(Des Alvin White Studio. Litho Questa)

1995 (24 Feb). *Disney Characters at Work.* T **522** and similar multicoloured designs. P 14×13½ (*horiz*) or 13½×14 (*vert*).

4267/75 $30 × 9 Type **522**; Goofy and optometrist; Daisy Duck as nurse; Scrooge McDuck as psychiatrist; Goofy as physiotherapist; Horace Horsecollar and dentist; Goofy and radiologist; Goofy as pharmacist; Big Pete as chiropractor
 a. Sheetlet. Nos. 4267/75 .. 3·25

4276/84 $30 × 9 Mickey Mouse as vet; Donald Duck training seals; Ludwig von Duck as animal psychiatrist; Goofy as ornithologist; Daisy Duck grooming Old English Sheepdog; Minnie Mouse as herpetologist; Mickey Mouse as pet shop keeper with Pluto; J. Audubon Woodlore as park ranger; Donald Duck as aquarist
 a. Sheetlet. Nos. 4276/84 .. 3·25

4285/93 $30 × 9 Mickey Mouse as animator with Pluto; Goofy the tailor with Mickey Mouse; Pete the glassblower with Morty; Minnie Mouse painting Clarabelle; Daisy Duck sculpting Donald; Donald Duck as potter; Chip and Dale the watchmakers; Donald Duck the locksmith; Grandma Duck making quilt;
 a. Sheetlet. Nos. 4285/93 .. 3·25

4294/301 $35 × 8 Mickey Mouse as policeman; Donald Duck as fireman; Uncle Scrooge as ambulance driver; Grandma Duck as crossing patrol; Daisy Duck as museum attendant and Donald as visitor; Goofy as census taker and family of rabbits; Horace Horsecollar and Big Pete as street maintenance workers; Donald Duck as sanitation worker at recyling bin (*all vert*)
 a. Sheetlet. Nos. 4294/301 .. 3·25

4302/9 $35 × 8 Mickey Mouse with Pluto driving lorry; Mickey Mouse as carpenter sawing; Goofy riding road drill; Minnie Mouse with electric drill; Donald Duck driving forklift; Minnie Mouse and Goofy as construction contractors; Mickey Mouse with Pluto as carpenter making table; Pluto driving bulldozer (*all vert*)
 a. Sheetlet. Nos. 4302/9 .. 3·25

4310/17 $35 × 8 Mickey Mouse as plumber; Mickey Mouse the paperboy; Huey, Dewey and Louie moving furniture; Big Pete as handyman; Donald Duck and nephews house painting; Goofy as washing machine repairman; Minnie Mouse as babysitter; Daisy Duck as carer (*all vert*)
 a. Sheetlet. Nos. 4310/17 .. 3·25

4267/317 .. .. Set of 51 18·00 20·00

MS4318 Six sheets. (a) 132×107 mm. $200 Goofy as surgeon. (b) 107×129 mm. $200 Goofy the zookeeper. (c) 132×107 mm. $200 Ferdie riding Pluto for photographer (*vert*). (d) 107×129 mm. $200 Horace Horsecollar campaigning for mayor. (e) 132×107 mm. $200 Minnie Mouse as carpenter and puppies. (f) 107×129 mm. $200 Minnie Mouse as maid .. Set of 6 sheets 18·00 19·00

Nos. 4267/75, 4276/84, 4285/93, 4294/301, 4302/9 and 4310/17 were printed together, *se-tenant*, in sheetlets of 9 (Nos. 4267/75, 4276/84 and 4285/93) or 8 (others).

No. 4271 is inscribed "PHYSICAL THEREPIST" in error.

$20.00

**SALVATION
ARMY
1895 — 1995**

(523)

524 Pig

1995 (24 Apr). *Centenary of Salvation Army. Nos. 1519 and 1521/3 surch as T* **523** *in red.*

4319	$6 on 60 c. Plate No. 10 (Series 1)			
4320	$20 on 60 c. Plate No. 19 (Series 1)			
4321	$30 on 60 c. Plate No. 2 (Series 1)			
4322	$35 on 60 c. Plate No. 31 (Series 1)			

1995 (4 May). *Chinese New Year ("Year of the Pig").* T **524** and similar vert designs showing symbolic pigs. Multicoloured. P 14½.

4323	$20	Type **524**	30	40
		a. Block of 4. Nos. 4323/6	2·00	
4324	$30	Pig facing left	40	50
4325	$50	Pig facing front (face value bottom right)	50	55
4326	$100	Pig facing front (face value bottom left)	1·00	1·10
4323/6		Set of 4	2·00	2·25

MS4327 67×89 mm. $50×4 As Nos. 4323/6 .. 2·50 2·75
MS4328 104×76 mm. $150 Pig's head .. 1·75 2·00

Nos. 4323/6 were printed together, *se-tenant*, in blocks of 4 throughout the sheet.

GUYANA

$5

525 Goshawk

Guyana $35

526 Norwegian Forest Cat

(Litho Questa)

1995 (8 May). *Birds.* T **525** and similar vert designs. Multicoloured. P 14½×14.

4329	$5	Type **525**	10	10
4330	$6	Lapwing	10	10
4331	$8	Ornate Umbrellabird	10	10
4332	$15	Slaty-headed Parakeet	10	10
4333	$19	Regent Bowerbird	20	25
4334	$20	Egyptian Goose	20	25
4335	$25	White-winged Crossbill	25	30
4336	$30	Waxwing	30	35
4337	$35	Ruff	35	40
4338	$60	Hoopoe	60	65
4339	$100	Superb Starling	1·00	1·10
4340	$500	Great Jacamar	5·00	5·25
4329/40		Set of 12	8·25	9·00

(Des T. Wood. Litho Questa)

1995 (11 June). *"Singapore '95" International Stamp Exhibition.* T **526** and similar vert designs. Multicoloured. P 14.

4341/52 $35 × 12 Cats (Type **526**; Scottish Fold; Red Burmese; British Blue-hair; Abyssinian; Siamese; Exotic Shorthair; Turkish Van Cat; Black Persian; Black-tipped Burmilla; Singapura; Calico Shorthair)
 a. Sheetlet. Nos. 4341/52 .. 4·25

4353/64 $35 × 12 Dogs (Gordon Setter; Long-haired Chihuahua; Dalmatian; Afghan Hound; Old English Bulldog; Miniature Schnauzer; Clumber Spaniel; Pekingese; St. Bernard; English Cocker Spaniel; Alaskan Malamute; Rottweiler)
 a. Sheetlet. Nos. 4353/64 .. 4·25

4365/76 $35 × 12 Horses (chestnut Thoroughbred colt; liver chestnut Quarter horse; black Friesian; chestnut Belgian; Appaloosa; Lippizaner; chestnut hunter; British Shire; Palomino; Pinto ("Seal Brown Point"); Arab; Afghanistan Kabardin)
 a. Sheetlet. Nos. 4365/76 .. 4·25

4341/76 .. .. Set of 36 13·00 15·00

MS4377 Three sheets, each 87×71 mm. (a) $300 Maine Coon. (b) $300 Golden Retriever. (c) $300 American Anglo-Arab .. Set of 3 sheets 9·00 9·25

Nos. 4341/52, 4353/64 and 4365/76 were printed together, *se-tenant*, in sheetlets of 12.

No. 4355 is inscribed "Dalmation", No. 4367 "Freisian" and No. 4370 "Lipizzanas", all in error.

527 Captain John Smith leaving for New World, 1607

(Des Walt Disney Co. Litho Questa)

1995 (28 June–9 Oct). *Pocahontas.* T **527** and similar multicoloured designs showing characters and scenes from Disney cartoon film.

(*a*) *Vert designs showing characters.* P 13½×14

4378/85 $50 × 8 Pocahontas and Meeko; John Smith; Chief Powhatan; Kocoum; Ratcliffe; Wiggins; Nakoma; Thomas
 a. Sheetlet. Nos. 4378/85 .. 10·00

(*b*) *Horiz designs showing film scenes.* P 14×13½ (9 Oct)

4386/94 $8 × 9 Type **527**; Ratcliffe; Chief Powhatan greeted by his people; Pocahontas standing on cliff; Pocahontas, Nakoma and Meeko in canoe; Powhatan asking Pocahontas to marry Kocoum; Pocahontas receiving her mother's necklace; Pocahontas seeking guidance from Grandmother Willow; Pocahontas watching arrival of *Susan Constant*
 a. Sheetlet. Nos. 4386/94 .. 3·50

4395/403 $30 × 9 Ratcliffe claiming land for English Crown; Kekata having vision; Meeting of John Smith and Pocahontas; Namantack watching settlers; Powhatan and wounded Namantack; Pocahontas showing John Smith the colours of the wind; Nakoma finds Pocahontas with John Smith; Pocahontas offering John "Indian gold" (corn); Pocahontas, John Smith and Grandmother Willow
a. Sheetlet. Nos. 4395/403 .. 7·00
4404/12 $35 × 9 Kocoum telling Pocahontas about the war council; Nakoma telling Kocoum to find Pocahontas; John Smith and Kocoum wrestling over knife; Powhatan sentencing John to death; Pocahontas and Grandmother Willow; Pocahontas saving John Smith; Ratcliffe under arrest; Powhatan draping his cloak over wounded John Smith; Pocahontas and John Smith saying goodbye
a. Sheetlet. Nos. 4404/12 .. 8·50
4378/412 .. .. .. Set of 35 26·00 27·00
MS4413 Four sheets. (a) 98×120 mm. $300 Meeko (9 Oct). P 14×13¹/₂⅓. (b) 132×107 mm. $325 Pocahontas hiding. P 14×13¹/₂. (c) 132×107 mm. $325 Powhatan and Pocahontas. P 14×13¹/₂. (d) 132×107 mm. $325 Pocahontas kneeling (vert). P 13¹/₂×14 Set of 4 sheets 21·00 22·00
Nos. 4378/85, 4386/94, 4395/403 and 4404/12 were printed together, se-tenant, in sheetlets of 8 (Nos. 4378/85) or 9 (others).

(Litho Questa)

1995 (6 July). 95th Birthday of Queen Elizabeth the Queen Mother. Vert designs as T 344 of Antigua. P 13¹/₂×14.
4414 $100 orange-brown, pale brown and black 1·25 1·25
a. Sheetlet. Nos. 4414/17×2 .. 9·00
4415 $100 multicoloured .. .. 1·25 1·25
4416 $100 multicoloured .. .. 1·25 1·25
4417 $100 multicoloured .. .. 1·25 1·25
4414/17 .. .. .. Set of 4 4·50 4·50
MS4418 121×126 mm. $325 multicoloured .. 3·50 4·00
Designs:—No. 4414, Queen Elizabeth the Queen Mother (pastel drawing); No. 4415, Wearing purple hat; No. 4416, Wearing turquoise hat; No. 4417, At desk (oil painting); No. MS4418, Wearing blue dress and mink stole
Nos. 4414/17 were printed together in sheetlets of 8, containing two se-tenant horizontal strips of 4.

528 Paul Harris (founder) and Rotary Emblem   529 Girl carrying Sack on Head

(Litho Questa)

1995 (6 July). 90th Anniv of Rotary International. T 528 and similar horiz design. Multicoloured. P 14.
4419 $200 Type 528 .. .. 2·00 2·10
MS4420 104×74 mm. $300 Rotary emblems 3·00 3·25

(Des R. Martin. Litho)

1995 (6 July). 50th Anniv of Food and Agriculture Organization. T 529 and similar vert designs. Multicoloured. P 14.
4421 $35 Type 529 .. .. 50 55
a. Horiz strip of 3. Nos. 4421/3 .. 3·00
4422 $60 Man and woman carrying sacks of food aid 80 85
4423 $200 Woman holding sack .. 2·00 2·10
4421/3 .. .. .. Set of 3 3·00 3·25
MS4424 104×74 mm. $300 Bowl of food and F.A.O. emblem .. .. 3·00 3·25
Nos. 4421/3 were printed together in sheets of 9 (3×3) containing three se-tenant horizontal strips, each forming a composite design.

530 Scouts around Campfire

(Litho Questa)

1995 (6 July). 18th World Scout Jamboree, Netherlands. T 530 and similar horiz designs. Multicoloured. P 14.
4425 $20 Type 530 .. .. 30 25
4426 $25 Scout on beach 35 30
4427 $30 Scouts hiking 40 35
4428 $35 Scout snorkelling 45 40
4429 $60 Scout saluting and flag of Guyana .. 70 65
4430 $200 Scout fishing from boat .. 2·00 2·50
4425/30 .. .. .. Set of 6 3·75 4·00
MS4431 Two sheets, each 100×70 mm. (a) $300 Scouts putting up tent. (b) $300 Scouts canoeing Set of 2 sheets 6·00 6·25

(Des W. Wright. Litho Questa)

1995 (6 July). 50th Anniv of End of World War II in Europe. Horiz designs as T 340 of Antigua. Multicoloured. P 14.
4432 $60 American tank during Battle of the Bulge 65 75
a. Sheetlet. Nos. 4432/9 .. 4·75
4433 $60 Allied tanks crossing Siegfried Line 65 75
4434 $60 Liberated concentration camp prisoners 65 75
4435 $60 Allied plane dropping food to Dutch 65 75
4436 $60 U.S. infantry patrol, North Italy 65 75
4437 $60 Daily Mail headline announcing Hitler's death 65 75
4438 $60 Soviet tanks entering Berlin 65 75
4439 $60 Surrender of U858 in U.S. waters 65 75
4432/9 .. .. .. Set of 8 4·75 5·50
MS4440 105×74 mm. $300 Soviet troops raising flag on Brandenburg Gate (56×42 mm) .. 3·00 3·25
Nos. 4432/9 were printed together, se-tenant, in sheetlets of 8 with the stamps arranged in two horizontal strips of 4 separated by a gutter showing sounding of ceasefire on the Western Front. No. 4433 was incorrectly inscribed "SIGFRIED LINE".

(Des J. Batchelor. Litho Questa)

1995 (6 July). 50th Anniv of End of Second World War in the Pacific. U.S. Ships and Aircraft. Horiz designs as T 340 of Antigua. Multicoloured. P 14.
4441 $60 P61 Black Widow 65 75
a. Sheetlet. Nos. 4441/6 .. 3·50
4442 $60 PT boat 65 75
4443 $60 Martin B-26 Marauder bomber 65 75
4444 $60 U.S.S. San Juan (cruiser) .. 65 75
4445 $60 "Gato" class submarine .. 65 75
4446 $60 Destroyer 65 75
4441/6 .. .. .. Set of 6 3·50 4·00
MS4447 107×77 mm. $300 Cruiser and aircraft carrier .. .. 3·00 3·25
Nos. 4441/6 were printed together, se-tenant, in sheetlets of 6 with the stamps arranged in two horizontal strips of 3 separated by a gutter showing Curtiss P-40B Tomahawk II Flying Tiger aircraft.

531 Thanksgiving (U.S.A.)   532 Map of the Americas and U.N. Soldier

(Des R. Sauber. Litho Questa)

1995 (8 Aug). Holidays of the World. T 531 and similar horiz designs. Multicoloured. P 14.
4448 $60 Type 531 .. .. 65 75
a. Sheetlet. Nos. 4448/55 .. 4·75
4449 $60 Christmas (Germany) .. 65 75
4450 $60 Hanukkah (Israel) .. 65 75
4451 $60 Easter (Spain) 65 75
4452 $60 Carnivale (Brazil) .. 65 75
4453 $60 Bastille Day (France) .. 65 75
4454 $60 Independence Day (India) .. 65 75
4455 $60 St. Patrick's Day (Ireland) .. 65 75
4448/55 .. .. .. Set of 8 4·75 5·50
MS4456 105×76 mm. $300 Chinese New Year (China) .. .. 3·00 3·25
Nos. 4448/55 were printed together, se-tenant, in sheetlets of 8, with the designs extending onto the sheetlet margin.

(Des R. Martin. Litho)

1995 (1 Sept). 50th Anniv of United Nations. T 532 and similar vert designs. Multicoloured. P 14.
4457 $35 Type 532 .. .. 50 55
a. Horiz strip of 3. Nos. 4457/9 .. 3·00
4458 $60 Map of Africa and Western Asia 80 85
4459 $200 Map of Eastern Asia and Australasia with refugees .. .. 2·00 2·10
4457/9 .. .. .. Set of 3 3·00 3·25
MS4460 74×104 mm. $300 Secretary-General Boutros Boutros Ghali .. 3·00 3·25
Nos. 4457/9 were printed together in sheets of 9 (3×3) containing three se-tenant horizontal strips, each forming a composite design.

533 Four-eyed Butterflyfish   534 Pole Vaulting

(Des D. Burkhart. Litho Questa)

1995 (5 Sept). Marine Life. T 533 and similar multicoloured designs. P 14.
4461 $30 Type 533 .. .. 30 35
a. Sheetlet. Nos. 4461, 4463, 4465 and 4489 .. .. 3·25
4462 $30 Lemon Shark 30 35
a. Sheetlet. Nos. 4462, 4464, 4466 and 4490 .. .. 3·25
4463 $35 Blue-headed Wrasse .. 35 40
4464 $35 Green Turtle 35 40
4465 $60 Three-spotted Damselfish 60 65
4466 $60 Sawfish 60 65
4467 $60 Sei Whales 60 65
a. Sheetlet. Nos. 4467/75 .. 5·50
4468 $60 Great Barracuda .. 60 65
4469 $60 Mutton Snapper .. 60 65
4470 $60 Hawksbill Turtle .. 60 65
4471 $60 Spanish Hogfish .. 60 65
4472 $60 Queen Angelfish .. 60 65
4473 $60 Porkfish 60 65
4474 $60 Trumpetfish 60 65
4475 $60 Lesser Electric Ray .. 60 65
4476 $60 Tiger Shark 60 65
a. Sheetlet. Nos. 4476/84 .. 5·50
4477 $60 Needlefish 60 65
4478 $60 Horse-eyed Jack .. 60 65
4479 $60 Princess Parrotfish .. 60 65
4480 $60 Yellow-tailed Snapper .. 60 65
4481 $60 Spotted Snake Eel .. 60 65
4482 $60 Buffalo Trunkfish .. 60 65
4483 $60 Cherubfish Angelfish .. 60 65
4484 $60 French Angelfish .. 60 65
4485 $80 Cocoa Damselfish (vert) .. 80 85
a. Horiz strip of 4. Nos. 4485/8 .. 3·25
4486 $80 Sergeant Major (vert) .. 80 85
4487 $80 Beaugregory (vert) .. 80 85
4488 $80 Yellow-tailed Damselfish (vert) 80 85
4489 $200 Fin-spot Wrasse .. 2·00 2·10
4490 $200 Stingray .. .. 2·00 2·10
4461/90 .. .. .. Set of 30 21·00 22·00
MS4491 Two sheets, each 100×70 mm. (a) $300 Great White Shark. (b) $300 Leatherback Turtle Set of 2 sheets 8·00 8·50
Nos. 4461, 4463, 4465 and 4489, Nos. 4462, 4464, 4466 and 4490, Nos. 4467/75 and Nos. 4476/84 were each printed together, se-tenant, in sheetlets of 4 or 9, the backgrounds forming composite designs.
Nos. 4485/8 were printed together, se-tenant, in horizontal strips of 4, each strip forming a composite background design.

(Litho B.D.T.)

1995 (9 Oct). Olympic Games, Atlanta (1996) (2nd issue). T 534 and similar vert designs. Multicoloured. P 14.
4492 $60 Type 534 .. .. 60 65
a. Sheetlet. Nos. 4492/9 .. 4·75
4493 $60 Long jumping 60 65
4494 $60 Woman with relay baton .. 60 65
4495 $60 Wrestling 60 65
4496 $60 Discus (side view) .. 60 65
4497 $60 Basketball 60 65
4498 $60 Boxing 60 65
4499 $60 Weightlifting 60 65
4500 $60 Shot put 60 65
a. Sheetlet. Nos. 4500/7 .. 4·75
4501 $60 Man in relay race .. 60 65
4502 $60 Female gymnast on beam .. 60 65
4503 $60 Cycling 60 65
4504 $60 Synchronized swimming .. 60 65
4505 $60 Hurdling 60 65
4506 $60 Male gymnast on pommel horse 60 65
4507 $60 Discus (front view) .. 60 65
4492/507 .. .. .. Set of 18 9·50 10·50
MS4508 Two sheets (a) 105×75 mm. $300 Athletes at start of race. (b) 75×105 mm. $300 Long jumping .. Set of 2 sheets 6·00 6·25
Nos. 4492/9 and 4500/7 were each printed together, se-tenant, in sheetlets of 8, the backgrounds forming composite designs.

535 Sand Martin   536 Queenstown Jama Masjid

(Des Mary Walters. Litho Questa)

1995 (18 Oct). Wildlife. T 535 and similar vert designs. Multicoloured. P 14.
4509 $20 Type 535 .. .. 20 25
a. Block of 4. Nos. 4509/11 and 4521 .. 3·25
4510 $35 House Martin 35 40
4511 $60 Hobby 60 65
4512 $60 Olive Colobus 60 65
a. Sheetlet. Nos. 4512/20 .. 5·50
4513 $60 Violet-backed Starling .. 60 65
4514 $60 Diana Monkey 60 65
4515 $60 African Palm Civet .. 60 65
4516 $60 Giraffe and zebras .. 60 65
4517 $60 African Linsang .. 60 65
4518 $60 Royal Antelope .. 60 65
4519 $60 Duikers 60 65
4520 $60 Palm Squirrel 60 65
4521 $200 Long-tailed Skua .. 2·00 2·10
4509/21 .. .. .. Set of 13 8·75 9·25
MS4522 Two sheets, each 110×80 mm. (a) $300 Brush Pig and Giant Forest Hog. (b) $300 Chimpanzee .. Set of 2 sheets 6·00 6·25
Nos. 4509/11 and 4521 were printed together, se-tenant, in blocks of 4, each block forming a composite background design.
Nos. 4512/20 were printed together, se-tenant, in sheetlets of 9, forming a composite background design.

(Des R. Sauber. Litho Questa)

1995 (1 Dec). *Centenary of Queenstown Jama Masjid (mosque), Georgetown.* P 14.
4523 **536** $60 multicoloured 40 45

537 Woman Soldier with Sub-machine Gun

538 Bank Logo and Headquarters

(Des Rina Lamphe. Litho Questa)

1995 (1 Dec). *30th Anniv of Guyana Defence Force. T 537 and similar vert design. Multicoloured.* P 14.
4524 $6 Type **537** 10 10
4525 $60 Soldier with rifle 40 45

(Des M. Friedman. Litho Questa)

1995 (1 Dec). *25th Anniv of Caribbean Development Bank.* P 14.
4526 **538** $60 multicoloured 40 45

(Litho Questa)

1995 (4 Dec). *Christmas. Religious Paintings. Vert designs as T 357 of Antigua. Multicoloured.* P 13½×14.
4527 $25 "Angel of the Annunciation" (Carracci) 30 30
4528 $30 "Virgin of the Annunciation" (Carracci) 35 35
4529 $35 "Assumption of the Madonna" (Carracci) 40 40
4530 $60 "Baptism of Christ" (Carracci) 70 70
4531 $100 "Madonna and Child with Saints" (detail) (Carracci) .. 1·25 1·50
4532 $300 "Birth of the Virgin" (Carracci) 3·00 3·50
4527/32 .. .. .. *Set of 6* 5·50 6·00
MS4533 Two sheets, each 101×127 mm. (a) $325 "Madonna and Child enthroned with Ten Saints" (Rosso Fiorentino). (b) $325 "Mystic Marriage of St. Catherine" (Carracci) .. *Set of 2 sheets* 6·50 7·00

539 John Lennon

540 Albrecht Kossel (1910 Medicine)

(Litho Questa)

1995 (8 Dec). *15th Death Anniv of John Lennon (musician).* P 14.
4534 **539** $35 multicoloured 65 65
No. 4534 was printed in numbered sheets of 16 with enlarged illustrated left-hand margin.

(Des R. Cassilla (Nos. 4580/8) or R. Martin (others). Litho Questa)

1995 (20 Dec). *Centenary of Nobel Trust Fund. T 540 and similar vert designs. Multicoloured.* P 14.
4535/43 $35 × 9 Type **540**; Arthur H. Compton (1927 Physics); N. M. Butler (1931 Peace); Charles Laveran (1907 Medicine); George R. Minot (1934 Medicine); Henry H. Dale (1936 Medicine); Jacques Monod (1965 Medicine); Alfred Hershey (1969 Medicine); Pär Lagerkvist (1951 Literature)
a. Sheetlet. Nos. 4535/43 .. 2·25
4544/52 $35 × 9 Norman F. Ramsey (1989 Physics); Chen Ning Yang (1957 Physics); Earl W. Sutherland Jr. (1971 Medicine); Paul Karrer (1937 Chemistry); Harmut Michel (1988 Chemistry); Richard Kuhn (1938 Chemistry); P. A. M. Dirac (1933 Physics); Victor Grignard (1912 Chemistry); Richard Willstätter (1915 Chemistry)
a. Sheetlet. Nos. 4544/52 .. 2·25
4553/61 $35 × 9 Adolf von Baeyer (1905 Chemistry); Hideki Yukawa (1949 Physics); George W. Beadle (1958 Medicine); Edwin M. McMillan (1951 Chemistry); Samuel C. C. Ting (1976 Physics); Saint-John Perse (1960 Literature); John F. Enders (1954 Medicine); Felix Bloch (1952 Physics); P. B. Medawar (1960 Medicine)
a. Sheetlet. Nos. 4553/61 .. 2·25

4562/70 $35 × 9 Nikolai Basov (1964 Physics); Klas Arnoldson (1908 Peace); René Sully-Prudhomme (1901 Literature); Robert W. Wilson (1978 Physics); Hugo Theorell (1955 Medicine); Nelly Sachs (1966 Literature); Hans von Euler-Chelpin (1929 Chemistry); Mairead Corrigan (1976 Peace); Willis E. Lamb Jr (1955 Physics)
a. Sheetlet. Nos. 4562/70 .. 2·25
4571/9 $35 × 9 Francis Crick (1962 Medicine); Manne Siegbahn 1924 Physics); Eisaku Sato (1974 Peace); Robert Koch (1905 Medicine); Edgar D. Adrian (1932 Medicine); Erwin Neher (1991 Medicine); Henry Taube (1983 Chemistry); Norman Angell (1933 Peace); Robert Robinson (1947 Chemistry)
a. Sheetlet. Nos. 4571/9 .. 2·25
4580/8 $35 × 9 Henri Becquerel (1903 Physics); Igor Tamm (1958 Physics); Georges Köhler (1984 Medicine); Gerhard Domagk (1939 Medicine); Yasunari Kawabata (1968 Literature); Maurice Allais (1988 Economic Sciences); Aristide Briand (1926 Peace); Pavel Cherenkov (1958 Physics); Feodor Lynen (1964 Medicine)
a. Sheetlet. Nos. 4580/8 .. 2·25
4535/88 .. .. *Set of 54* 13·50 14·50
MS4589 Six sheets, each 106×76 mm. (a) $300 Lech Walesa (1983 Peace). (b) $300 Heinrich Böll (1972 Literature). (c) $300 Henry A. Kissinger (1973 Peace). (d) $300 Kenichi Fukui (1981 Chemistry). (e) $300 Yasunari Kawabata (1968 Literature). (f) $300 Le Duc Tho (1973 Peace) .. .. *Set of 6 sheets* 12·00 13·00
Nos. 4535/43, 4544/52, 4553/61, 4562/70, 4571/9 and 4580/8 were each printed together, *se-tenant*, in sheetlets of 9, with the backgrounds forming composite designs.

541 David Copperfield

(Des R. Sauber. Litho Questa)

1995 (29 Dec). *David Copperfield (magician). T 541 and similar vert designs. Multicoloured.* P 13½×14.
4590 $60 Type **541** 40 45
a. Sheetlet. Nos. 4590/8 .. 3·50
4591 $60 David Copperfield in cloak and top hat 40 45
4592 $60 With flaming torch .. 40 45
4593 $60 David Copperfield in close up .. 40 45
4594 $60 Head of Statue of Liberty .. 40 45
4595 $60 David Copperfield climbing rope 40 45
4596 $60 With handcuffs .. 40 45
4597 $60 With woman dancer .. 40 45
4598 $60 David Copperfield wearing white shirt 40 45
4590/8 .. .. .. *Set of 9* 3·50 4·00
MS4599 76×106 mm. $300 David Copperfield with rose .. .. 2·00 2·10
Nos. 4590/8 were printed together, *se-tenant*, in sheetlets of 9, with the backgrounds forming a composite design.

542 Marilyn Monroe

543 Rat

(Des M. Staples. Litho Questa)

1995 (29 Dec). *70th Birth Anniv of Marilyn Monroe (entertainer). T 542 and similar multicoloured designs.* P 13½×14.
4600 $60 Type **542** 40 45
a. Sheetlet. Nos. 4600/8 .. 3·50
4601 $60 Marilyn Monroe with circular earrings 40 45
4602 $60 Marilyn Monroe (deep red top right corner) 40 45
4603 $60 Marilyn Monroe (signature at bottom right) 40 45
4604 $60 With hair over left eye .. 40 45
4605 $60 With pink satin at left .. 40 45
4606 $60 With arm raised .. 40 45

4607 $60 With pink satin at bottom right .. 40 45
4608 $60 With square earring .. 40 45
4600/8 .. .. .. *Set of 9* 3·50 4·25
MS4609 76×105 mm. $300 Marilyn Monroe in pink satin dress (*horiz*) .. 2·00 2·10
Nos. 4600/8 were printed together, *se-tenant*, in sheetlets of 9, with the background forming a composite design.

(Des Y. Lee. Litho Questa)

1995 (29 Dec). *Chinese New Year ("Year of the Rat"). T 543 and similar vert designs showing symbolic rats.* P 14½.
4610 $20 multicoloured 15 20
a. Block of 4. Nos. 4610/13 .. 1·40
4611 $30 multicoloured (face value bottom left) 20 25
4612 $50 multicoloured (face value top right) 35 40
4613 $100 multicoloured (face value top left) 70 75
4610/13 .. .. .. *Set of 4* 1·40 1·50
MS4614 68×92 mm. $50×4 As Nos. 4610/13 1·40 1·50
MS4615 106 x 76 mm. $150 multicoloured 1·00 1·10
Nos. 4610/13 were printed together, *se-tenant*, in blocks of 4 throughout sheets of 16.

544 City Children

(Des M. Friedman. Litho Questa)

1996 (2 Jan). *50th Anniv of U.N.I.C.E.F. Sheet, 110×87 mm, containing T 544 and similar horiz designs. Multicoloured.* P 14.
MS4616 $1100 Type **544**; $1100 Youth worker and children (face value at top right); $1100 City children (face value at bottom right; $1100 Youth worker and children (face value at bottom right) .. .. .. 30·00

(Litho Questa)

1996 (29 Jan). *Paintings by Rubens. Multicoloured designs as T 421 of Grenada.* P 13½×14.
4617 $6 "The Garden of Love" (detail) 10 10
4618 $10 "Two Sleeping Children" .. 10 10
4619 $20 "All Saints Day" .. 15 20
4620 $25 "Sacrifice of Abraham" .. 20 25
4621 $30 "The Last Supper" .. 20 25
4622 $35 "The Birth of Henry of Navarre" 25 30
4623 $40 Study of standing female saint 30 35
4624 $50 "The Garden of Love" (different detail) 35 40
4625 $60 "The Garden of Love" (different detail) 40 45
4626 $200 "The Martyrdom of St. Livinus" 1·40 1·50
4627 $200 "St. Francis of Paola" .. 1·40 1·50
4628 $300 "The Union of Maria de Medici and Henry IV" .. .. 2·00 2·10
4617/28 .. .. .. *Set of 12* 6·75 7·50
MS4629 Three sheets. (a) 70×100 mm. $325 "The Three Crosses" (56×84 *mm*). (b) 100×70 mm. $325 "Decius Mus addressing the Legions" (84×56 *mm*). (c) 100×70 mm. $325 "Triumph of Henry IV" (84×56 *mm*). P 14 .. *Set of 3 sheets* 6·75 7·00

545 Apatosaurus

546 Giant Panda

1996 (29 Jan). *Prehistoric Animals. T 545 and similar multicoloured designs. Litho.* P 14.
4630/41 $35 × 12 Type **545**; Archaeopteryx; Dimorphodon; Deinonychus; Coelophysis; Tyrannosaurus; Triceratops; Anatosaurus; Saltasaurus; Allosaurus; Oviraptor; Stegosaurus
a. Sheetlet. Nos. 4630/41 .. 3·00
4642/53 $35 × 12 Ornithomimus; Pteranodon; Rhamphorynchus; Ornitholestes; Brachiosaurus; Parasaurolophus; Ceratosaurus; Camarasaurus; Euoplocephalus; Scutellosaurus; Compsognathus; Stegoceras
a. Sheetlet. Nos. 4642/53 .. 3·00
4654/65 $35 × 12 Eudimorphodon; Criorhynchus; Elasmosaurus; Rhomaleosaurus; Ceresiosaurus; Mesosaurus; Grendelius; Nothosaurus; Mixosaurus; Placodus; Coelacanth; Mosasaurus
a. Sheetlet. Nos. 4654/65 .. 3·00
4666/77 $35 × 12 Tarbosaurus; Hadrosaurus; Polacanthus; Psittacosaurus; Ornitholestes; Yangchuanosaurus; Scelidosaurus; Kentrosaurus; Coelophysis; Lesothosaurus; Plateosaurus; Staurikosaurus (*all vert*)
a. Sheetlet. Nos. 4666/77 .. 3·00
4630/77 .. .. *Set of 48* 12·00 13·00
MS4678 Two sheets, each 101×58 mm. (a) $60 Saurolophus; $60 Muttaburrasaurus; $60 Dicraeosaurus; $60 Heterodontosaurus; (b) $60 Compsognathus; $60 Ornithomimosaure (*all vert*) .. .. *Set of 2 sheets* 2·40 2·50

MS4679 Five sheets. (a) 106×76 mm. $300 Struthiomimus. (b) 76×106 mm. $300 Tyrannosaurus rex (*vert*). (c) 76×106 mm. $300 Apatosaurus and Allosaurus. (d) 106×76 mm. $300 Quetzalcoatlus. (e) 106×76 mm. $300 Lagosuchus. .. .. .. *Set of 5 sheets* 10·00 11·00
Nos. 4630/41, 4642/53, 4654/65 and 4666/77 were each printed together, *se-tenant*, in sheetlets of 12, with the backgrouds forming composite designs.

1996 (1 Apr). *"CHINA 96" International Stamp Exhibition, Beijing. T 546 and similar vert designs. Multicoloured. Litho. P 13 (No. MS4680) or 14 (Nos. MS4681).*
MS4680 130×95 mm. $60 Summer Palace, Beijing (39×51 *mm*) 40 45
MS4681 Two sheets, each 146×116 mm. (a) $60 Type 546; $60 Panda holding bamboo stem; $60 Eating bamboo stalk; $60 On all fours. (b) $60 Panda lying on tree branch (logo at left); $60 Lying on branch (logo at right); $60 Exploring hollow in tree (logo at left); $60 Sitting on trunk (logo at right) .. .. *Set of 2 sheets* 3·25 3·50
The stamps in No. MS4681 form composite designs showing rocks and stream (a) or dead tree (b).

546a Deng Xiaoping writing Inscription

1996 (12 Apr). *Deng Xiaoping (Chinese leader) Commemoration. T 546a and similar multicoloured designs. Litho. P 13.*
4681c $30 Type 546a 20 25
  ca. Horiz strip of 4. Nos. 4681c/f .. 80
  cb. Horiz strip of 4. Nos. 4681c and 4681g/h 80
4681d $30 Deng Xiaoping addressing meeting (value in red) 20 25
4681e $30 Signing first day cover for army officer (value in yellow) 20 25
4681f $30 Waving 20 25
4681g $30 As No. 4681d (value in yellow) .. 20 25
4681h $30 As No. 4681e (value in red) .. 20 25
4681c/h .. .. .. *Set of 6* 1·10 1·50
MS4681i 73×101 mm. $300 Deng Xiaoping applauding (*vert*) .. .. .. 2·00 2·10
Nos. 4681c/h were printed together, *se-tenant* both horizontally and vertically, in sheets of 16 which contain one horizontal strip as No. 4681ca and three as No. 4681cb.

COMMONWEALTH PHARMACY WEEK JUNE 16th 22nd 1996

$60.000

547 *Morchella esculenta* and *Doryphorella princeps* (leaf beetle)   (548)

(Des Rinah Lyamphe. Litho Questa)
1996 (15 May). *Fungi of Guyana. T 547 and similar multicoloured designs. P 14.*
4682 $20 Type 547 .. .. .. 15 20
4683 $25 Green-spored Mushroom .. 20 25
4684 $30 Common Mushroom and leaf beetle .. 20 25
4685 $35 Pine Cone Mushroom and *Danaus plexippus* caterpillar .. 25 30
4686 $60 *Armillaria mellea* 40 45
  a. Sheetlet. Nos. 4686/93 .. 3·25
4687 $60 *Gomphus floccosus* 40 45
4688 $60 *Pholiota astragalina* 40 45
4689 $60 *Helvella crispa* 40 45
4690 $60 *Hygrophorus miniatus* 40 45
4691 $60 *Omphalotus olearius* 40 45
4692 $60 *Hygrocybe acutoconica* 40 45
4693 $60 *Mycena viscosa* 40 45
4694 $60 Cockle-shell Lentinus 40 45
  a. Sheetlet. Nos. 4694/7, each × 2 3·25
4695 $60 *Volvariella surrecta* 40 45
4696 $60 *Lepiota josserandii* 40 45
4697 $60 *Boletellus betula* 40 45
4698 $60 *Amanita muscaria* 40 45
  a. Sheetlet. Nos. 4698/701, each × 2 3·25
4699 $60 *Russula claroflava* and *Semiotus angulatus* (click beetle) .. 40 45
4700 $60 *Dictyophora duplicata* and *Musca domestica* (house fly) .. 40 45
4701 $60 *Stropharia* and *Editha magnifica* (butterfly hunter) 40 45

4702 $60 *Leotia viscosa* 40 45
  a. Sheetlet. Nos. 4702/5, each × 2 3·25
4703 $60 *Calostoma cinnabarina* .. 40 45
4704 $60 Stalkless Paxillus 40 45
4705 $60 *Amanita spissa* 40 45
4682/705 .. .. .. *Set of 36* 14·00 15·00
MS4706 Two sheets, each 114×84 mm. (a) $300 *Mycena leaiana* and Yellow Crosbeak (bird). (b) $300 *Tubifera ferryginosa*, *Clavulina amethystina* and *Ramaria formosa* (*horiz*) *Set of 2 sheets* 4·00 4·25
Nos. 4686/93, 4694/7, 4698/701 and 4702/5 were each printed together, *se-tenant*, in sheetlets of 8, containing 8 different designs (Nos. 4686/93) or two of each design (others).
Nos. 4686 and 4692 are inscribed "Armillauella mellea" and "Hygzocybe acutoconica", both in error.

(Litho Questa)
1996 (1 June). *70th Birthday of Queen Elizabeth II. Vert designs as T 364 of Antigua. Multicoloured. P 13½×14.*
4707 $100 As Type 364 of Antigua 70 75
  a. Strip of 3. Nos. 4707/9 .. 2·10
4708 $100 Queen wearing green and blue jacket and hat 70 75
4709 $100 Queen at State Opening of Parliament 70 75
4707/9 .. .. .. *Set of 3* 2·10 2·25
MS4710 103×125 mm. $325 Queen in Garter robes .. .. .. 2·25 2·40
Nos. 4707/9 were printed together, *se-tenant*, in horizontal and vertical strips of 3 throughout the sheet.

1996 (17 June). *Commonwealth Pharmacy Week. Unissued values in designs of Nos. 1810 and 1873 surch as T 548.*
4711 $6 on 130 c. Plate No. 21 (Series 2)
4712 $60 on 100 c. Plate No. 33 (Series 2)

(Litho Questa)
1996 (8 July). *Centenary of Radio. Entertainers. Vert designs as T 368 of Antigua. Multicoloured. P 13½×14.*
4713 $20 Frank Sinatra 15 20
4714 $35 Gene Autry 25 30
4715 $60 Groucho Marx 40 45
4716 $200 Red Skelton .. .. .. 1·40 1·50
4713/16 .. .. .. *Set of 4* 2·25 2·40
MS4717 104×74 mm. $300 Burl Ives .. 2·00 2·10

549 Hulda Gates   550 Long-billed Starthroat

(Des R. Sauber. Litho Questa)
1996 (8 July). *3000th Anniv of Jerusalem. T 549 and similar vert designs. Multicoloured. P 14.*
4718 $30 Type 549 .. .. .. 20 25
  a. Sheetlet. Nos. 4718/20 .. 1·90
4719 $35 Church of St. Mary Magdalene .. 25 30
4720 $200 Absalom's Tomb, Kidron Valley .. 1·40 1·50
4718/20 .. .. .. *Set of 3* 1·90 2·00
MS4721 105×76 mm. $300 Children's Holocaust Memorial, Yad Vashem .. .. 2·00 2·10
Nos. 4718/20 were printed together, *se-tenant*, in sheetlets of 3 with enlarged illustrated margin at foot.

1996 (10 July). *Birds of the World. T 550 and similar multicoloured designs. Litho. P 14.*
4722 $60 Type 550 .. .. .. 40 45
  a. Sheetlet. Nos. 4722/9 .. 3·25
4723 $60 Velvet-purple Coronet 40 45
4724 $60 Racquet-tailed Coquette 40 45
4725 $60 Violet-tailed Sylph 40 45
4726 $60 Broad-tailed Hummingbird 40 45
4727 $60 Blue-tufted Starthroat 40 45
4728 $60 White-necked Jacobin 40 45
4729 $60 Ruby-throated Hummingbird .. 40 45
4730 $60 Blue and Yellow Macaw .. 40 45
  a. Sheetlet. Nos. 4730/7 .. 3·25
4731 $60 Andean Condor 40 45
4732 $60 Guiana Crested Eagle 40 45
4733 $60 White-tailed Trogon 40 45
4734 $60 Toco Toucan 40 45
4735 $60 Great Horned Owl 40 45
4736 $60 Andean Cock-of-the-Rock .. 40 45
4737 $60 Great Curassow 40 45
4722/37 .. .. .. *Set of 16* 6·50 7·00
MS4738 Two sheets, each 101×70 mm. (a) $300 Gould's Sparkling Violet-ear. (b) $300 Ornate Hawk Eagle (*horiz*) .. *Set of 2 sheets* 4·00 4·25
Nos. 4722/9 and 4730/7 were each printed together, *se-tenant*, in sheetlets of 8, the backgrounds forming composite designs.

551 Pancratium (ancient Olympic event)

(Litho Questa)
1996 (19 July). *Olympic Games, Atlanta (3rd issue). T 551 and similar multicoloured designs. P 14.*
4739 $20 Type 551 .. .. .. 15 20
4740 $30 Olympic Stadium, Melbourne, 1956 20 25
4741/9 $50 × 9 Volleyball; Basketball; Tennis; Table tennis; Baseball; Handball; Hockey; Water polo; Football
  a. Sheetlet. Nos. 4741/9 .. .. 3·25
4750/8 $50 × 9 Cycling; Hurdling; High jumping; Diving; Weightlifting; Canoeing; Wrestling; Gymnastics; Running (*all vert*)
  a. Sheetlet. Nos. 4750/8 .. 3·25
4759/67 $50 × 9 Florence Griffith-Joyner (track and field) (U.S.A.); Ines Geissler (swimming) (Germany); Nadia Comaneci (gymnastics) (Rumania); Tatiana Gutsu (gymnastics) (Unified team); Ogla Korbut (gymnastics) (Russia); Barbara Krause (swimming) (Germany); Olga Bryzgina (track and field) (Russia); Fanny Blankers-Koen (track and field) (Holland); Irena Szewinska (track and field) (Poland) (*all vert*)
  a. Sheetlet. Nos. 4759/67 .. 3·25
4768/76 $50 × 9 Gerd Wessig (Germany); Jim Thorpe (U.S.A.); Norman Read (New Zealand); Lasse Viren (Finland); Milt Campbell (U.S.A.); Abebe Bikila (Ethiopia); Jesse Owens (U.S.A.); Viktor Saneev (Russia); Waldemer Cierpinski (Germany) (all track and field) (*all vert*)
  a. Sheetlet. Nos. 4768/76 .. 3·25
4777/85 $50 × 9 Ditmar Schmidt (handball) (Germany); Pam Shriver (tennis doubles) (U.S.A.); Zina Garrison (tennis doubles) (U.S.A); Hyun Jung-Hua (table tennis doubles) (Korea); Steffi Graf (tennis) (Germany); Michael Jordan (basketball) (U.S.A.); Karch Kiraly (volleyball) (U.S.A.); "Magic" Johnson (basketball) (U.S.A.); Ingolf Weigert (handball) (Germany) (*all vert*)
  a. Sheetlet. Nos. 4777/85 .. 3·25
4786 $60 Leonid Spirin winning 20 kilometre walk, 1956 (*vert*) 40 45
4787 $200 Lars Hall, Gold medal winner, Modern Pentathlon, 1952 and 1956 (Sweden) (*vert*) .. .. 1·40 1·50
4739/87 .. .. .. *Set of 49* 18·00 19·00
MS4788 Two sheets. (a) 104×74 mm. $300 Carl Lewis, Gold medal winner, track and field, 1984, 1988 and 1992 (U.S.A.). (b) 74×104 mm. $300 U.S.A. defeating Korea at baseball, 1988 .. .. .. *Set of 2 sheets* 4·00 4·25
Nos. 4741/9, 4750/8, 4759/67, 4768/76 and 4777/85 (the last three showing Gold medal winners) were each printed together, *se-tenant*, in sheetlets of 9, forming composite background designs.
No. MS4788 (a) is inscribed "1985" in error.

552 Mickey's Bait Shop

(Des Walt Disney Co. Litho Questa)
1996 (26 July). *Mickey Mouse and Friends Outdoors. T 552 and similar multicoloured designs. P 14×13½ (horiz) or 13½×14 (vert).*
4789 $60 Type 552 .. .. .. 85 85
  a. Horiz strip of 3. Nos. 4789/91 2·25
4790 $60 Mickey and Pluto as lumberjacks .. 85 85
4791 $60 Mickey fishing 85 85
4792 $80 Donald Duck in BMX Bike Championships (*vert*) .. .. 1·00 1·00
  a. Horiz strip of 3. Nos. 4792/4 2·75
4793 $80 Goofy as ice hockey superstar (*vert*) 1·00 1·00
4794 $80 Donald Duck at Malibu Surf City (*vert*) .. .. 1·00 1·00
4795 $100 Mickey as naval captain (*vert*) 1·25 1·25
  a. Horiz strip of 3. Nos. 4795/7 3·25
4796 $100 Captain Mickey's Seamanship School (*vert*) .. .. 1·25 1·25
4797 $100 Mickey as sailor with ship's wheel and full-rigged sailing ship (*vert*) 1·25 1·25
4789/97 .. .. .. *Set of 9* 8·25 8·25
MS4798 Five sheets. (a) 124×101 mm. $250 Mickey as Pinkerton detective (*vert*). (b) 104×126 mm. $250 Mickey as U.S. Marshal (*vert*). (c) 125×104 mm. $250 Mickey as train conductor and Transcontinental Railroad locomotive. (d) 101×124 mm. $300 Donald Duck as mountaineer. (e) 104×124 mm. $325 Mickey as trapper (*vert*) .. *Set of 5 sheets* 16·00 17·00
Nos. 4789/91, 4792/4 and 4795/7 were each printed together, *se-tenant*, in horizontal strips of 3 throughout sheets of 9.

NEW INFORMATION

The editor is always interested to correspond with people who have new information that will improve or correct the Catalogue.

553 Two Gun Mickey   554 Elvis Presley

1996 (26 July). *Disney Antique Toys. T* **553** *and similar vert designs. Multicoloured. Litho.* P 13¹/₂×14.

4799	$6 Type 553		20	20
	a. Sheetlet. Nos. 4799/806		1·40	
4800	$6 Wood-jointed Mickey figure		20	20
4801	$6 Donald jack-in-the-box		20	20
4802	$6 Rocking Minnie		20	20
4803	$6 Fireman Donald Duck		20	20
4804	$6 Long-billed Donald Duck		20	20
4805	$6 Painted-wood Mickey figure		20	20
4806	$6 Wind-up Jiminy Cricket		20	20
4799/806		*Set of 8*	1·40	1·40

MS4807 Two sheets, each 131×105 mm. (a) $300 Mickey doll. (b) $300 Carousel .. *Set of 2 sheets* 7·00 7·50
Nos. 4799/806 were printed together, *se-tenant*, in sheetlets of 8

1996 (8 Sept). *60th Birth Anniv of Elvis Presley* (1995). *T* **554** *and similar vert portraits. Multicoloured: background colours given. Litho.* P 13¹/₂×14.

4808	$100 carmine-red (Type 554)		70	75
	a. Sheetlet. Nos. 4808/13		4·25	
4809	$100 cerise		70	75
4810	$100 lake-brown		70	75
4811	$100 dull ultramarine		70	75
4812	$100 purple		70	75
4813	$100 turquoise-blue		70	75
4808/13		*Set of 6*	4·25	4·50

Nos. 4808/13 were printed together, *se-tenant*, in sheetlets of 6 with enlarged illustrated margins.

555 Piece of Meteorite showing Fossil   556 Birman

(Des L. Birmingham. Litho Questa)

1996 (7 Oct). *Mars Meteorite. Sheet* 104×76 *mm.* P 14¹/₂×14.
MS4814 555 $50 multicoloured .. .. 1·00 90

1996 (7 Oct). *Cats of the World. T* **556** *and similar multicoloured designs. Litho.* P 14.

4815	$60 Type 556		40	45
	a. Sheetlet. Nos. 4815/23		3·50	
4816	$60 American Curl		40	45
4817	$60 Turkish Angora		40	45
4818	$60 European Shorthair (Italy)		40	45
4819	$60 Persian (Great Britain)		40	45
4820	$60 Scottish Fold		40	45
4821	$60 Sphynx (Canada)		40	45
4822	$60 Malayan (Thailand)		40	45
4823	$60 Cornish Rex (Great Britain)		40	45
4824	$60 Norwegian Forest (*vert*)		40	45
	a. Sheetlet. Nos. 4824/32		3·50	
4825	$60 Russian Shorthair (*vert*)		40	45
4826	$60 European Shorthair (Italy) (*vert*)		40	45
4827	$60 Birman (*vert*)		40	45
4828	$60 Ragdoll (U.S.A.) (*vert*)		40	45
4829	$60 Egyptian Mau (*vert*)		40	45
4830	$60 Persian (Great Britain) (*vert*)		40	45
4831	$60 Turkish Angora (*vert*)		40	45
4832	$60 Siamese (*vert*)		40	45
4815/32		*Set of 18*	7·00	8·00

MS4833 Two sheets, each 107×72 mm. (a) $300 Himalayan (U.S.A.). (b) $300 Maine Coon (U.S.A.) (*vert*) .. *Set of 2 sheets* 4·00 4·25
Nos. 4815/23 and 4824/32 were each printed together, *se-tenant*, in sheetlets of 9 with the backgrounds forming composite designs.

PRICES OF SETS

Set prices are given for many issues, generally those containing three stamps or more. Definitive sets include one of each value or major colour change, but do not cover different perforations, die types or minor shades. Where a choice is possible the set prices are based on the cheapest versions of the stamps included in the listings.

---

557 Hyed Snapper   558 Snow White and Reindeer

(Des I. MacLaury (Nos. 4838/52), Rina Lyamphe (others). Litho Questa)

1996 (2 Dec). *Marine Life. T* **557** *and similar horiz designs. Multicoloured.* P 14.

4834	$6 Type 557		10	10
4835	$6 Angelfish		10	10
4836	$20 Boxfish		15	20
4837	$25 Golden Damselfish		20	25
4838	$30 Goblin Shark and Coelacanth		20	25
	a. Sheetlet. Nos. 4838/52		3·00	
4839	$30 *Jason* (American remote-controlled submersible)		20	25
4840	$30 Deep-water invertebrates		20	25
4841	$30 Submarine *NR-1*		20	25
4842	$30 Giant Squid		20	25
4843	$30 Sperm Whale		20	25
4844	$30 Volcanic vents and *Alvin* (submersible)		20	25
4845	$30 Air-recycling pressure suits and shipwreck		20	25
4846	$30 *Shinkai 6500* (submersible)		20	25
4847	$30 Giant Tube Worms		20	25
4848	$30 Anglerfish		20	25
4849	$30 Six-gill Shark		20	25
4850	$30 Autonomous Underwater Vehicle ABE		20	25
4851	$30 Octopus and Viperfish		20	25
4852	$30 Swallower and Hatchetfish		20	25
4853	$35 Clown Triggerfish		25	30
4854	$60 Red Gorgonians		40	45
	a. Sheetlet. Nos. 4854/62		3·50	
4855	$60 Soft Coral and Butterflyfish		40	45
4856	$60 Soft Coral and Slender Snapper		40	45
4857	$60 Common Clownfish, Anemone and Mushroom Coral		40	45
4858	$60 Anemone and Horse-eyed Jack		40	45
4859	$60 Splendid Coral Trout		40	45
4860	$60 Anemones		40	45
4861	$60 Brain Coral		40	45
4862	$60 Cup Coral		40	45
4863	$200 Harlequin Tuskfish		1·40	1·50
4834/63		*Set of 30*	8·25	9·75

MS4864 Two sheets, each 98×68 mm. (a) $300 Caribbean Flower Coral. (b) $300 Sea Anemone .. *Set of 2 sheets* 2·00 4·00
Nos. 4838/52 and 4854/62 were each printed together, *se-tenant*, in sheetlets of 15 or 9, with the backgrounds forming composite designs.
No. 4853 is inscribed "CLOWN TUGGERFISH" in error.

(Des Walt Disney Co. Litho Questa)

1996 (2 Dec). *Christmas. Disney's Snow White and the Seven Dwarfs. T* **558** *and similar vert designs. Multicoloured.* P 13¹/₂×14.

4865	$6 Type 558		15	10
4866	$20 Doc with presents		35	25
4867	$25 Dopey and Sneezy		35	30
4868	$30 Sleepy, Happy and Bashful		40	35
4869	$35 Dopey and Santa Claus		40	40
4870	$60 Dopey with socks at fireplace		75	65
4871	$100 Dopey and Grumpy		1·40	1·50
4872	$200 Dopey dressed as Santa Claus		2·75	3·00
4865/72		*Set of 8*	6·00	6·00

MS4873 Two sheets, each 122×102 mm. (a) $300 Snow White, Doc and squirrel. (b) $300 Dopey and Christmas tree .. *Set of 2 sheets* 8·00 8·50

559 Hotel Tower   561 Ox

(Litho B.D.T.)

1996 (30 Dec). *50th Anniv of Hotel Tower, Georgetown.* P 14×14¹/₂.
4874 559 $30 multicoloured 20 25

(Des Y. Lee. Litho Questa)

1997 (10 Feb). *Chinese New Year. "Year of the Ox". T* **561** *and similar vert designs showing symbolic oxen.* P 14¹/₂.

4882	$20 multicoloured		15	20
	a. Block of 4. Nos. 4882/5		95	
4883	$30 multicoloured		20	25

4884	$35 multicoloured		25	30
4885	$50 multicoloured		35	40
4882/5		*Set of 4*	95	1·10

MS4886 101×72 mm. $150 multicoloured 1·00 1·10
MS4887 68×90 mm. $50 As No. 4882 (value bottom right); $50 As No. 4883 (value bottom left); $50 As No. 4884 (value top right); $50 As No. 4885 (value top left) .. 1·40 1·50
Nos. 4882/5 were printed together, *se-tenant*, in blocks of 4 throughout sheets of 16.

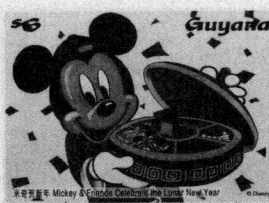

562 Mickey with Traditional Box of Sweets

(Des Walt Disney Co. Litho Questa)

1997 (10 Feb). *Mickey Mouse and Friends celebrate Chinese New Year. T* **562** *and similar multicoloured designs showing Disney cartoon characters.* P 14×13¹/₂.

4888	$6 Type 562		10	10
	a. Sheetlet. Nos. 4888/91 and 4898/9		1·25	
4889	$20 Mickey and Minnie at home with friends		15	20
4890	$25 Mickey and Minnie hanging fortune lantern		20	25
4891	$30 Minnie and Daisy with paper silhouette		20	25
4892	$30 Mickey and friends receiving traditional red money		20	25
	a. Sheetlet. Nos. 4892/7		1·25	
4893	$30 Mickey in lion dance		20	25
4894	$30 Mickey preparing Chinese calligraphy wall hangings		20	25
4895	$30 Mickey with symbols of surplus		20	25
4896	$30 Donald Duck playing with fireworks		20	25
4897	$30 Donald, Mickey and Minnie on ox		20	25
4898	$35 Donald Duck and friends at New Year flower market		25	30
4899	$60 Mickey and Minnie as "harmonious man and woman"		40	45
4888/99		*Set of 12*	2·50	3·00

MS4900 Two sheets, each 133×109 mm. (a) $150 Mickey Mouse marching (*vert*). P 13¹/₂×14. (b) $200 Mickey and ox. P 14×13¹/₂ *Set of 2 sheets* 2·40 2·50
Nos. 4888/91 with 4898/9 and 4892/7 were printed together, *se-tenant*, in sheetlets of 6.

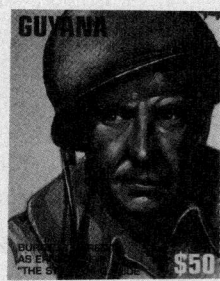

563 Burgess Meredith as Ernie Pyle in *The Story of G.I. Joe*

1997 (21 Feb). *Centenary of Cinema. Second World War Films. T* **563** *and similar multicoloured designs. Litho.* P 13¹/₂×14.

4901	$50 Type 563		35	40
	a. Sheetlet. Nos. 4901/9		3·00	
4902	$50 M. E. Clifton-James as General Montgomery in *I was Monty's Double*		35	40
4903	$50 Audie Murphy as himself in *To Hell and Back*		35	40
4904	$50 Gary Cooper as Dr. Wassell in *The Story of Dr. Wassell*		35	40
4905	$50 James Mason as Erwin Rommel in *The Desert Fox*		35	40
4906	$50 Manart Kippen as Stalin in *Mission to Moscow*		35	40
4907	$50 Robert Taylor as Col. Paul Tibbets in *Above and Beyond*		35	40
4908	$50 James Cagney as Admiral Bill Halsey in *The Gallant Hours*		35	40
4909	$50 John Garfield as Al Schmid in *Pride of the Marines*		35	40
4901/9		*Set of 9*	3·00	3·50

MS4910 105×75 mm. $300 George C. Scott as Gen. George S. Patton in *Patton* (*horiz*). P 14×13¹/₂ .. 2·00 2·10
Nos. 4901/9 were printed together, *se-tenant*, in sheetlets of 9.

STAMP BOOKLETS

1909 (14 June). *Black on pink cover without face value. Stapled.*
SB1　49 c. booklet containing twelve 1 c. and eighteen
　　　2 c. (Nos. 252/3) in blocks of 6 　.. 　..

1923. *Black on pink cover without face value. Stapled.*
SB2　30 c. booklet containing six 1 c. and twelve 2 c.
　　　(Nos. 272, 274) in blocks of 6 　.. 　..

1923. *Black on pink without face value. Stapled.*
SB3　48 c. booklet containing twelve 1 c. and eighteen
　　　2 c. (Nos. 272, 274) in blocks of 6 　.. 　　£950
　　　a. With face value on front cover

1923. *Black on red cover without face value. Stapled.*
SB4　72 c. booklet containing twelve 1 c., six 2 c. and
　　　twelve 4 c. (Nos. 272, 274/5) in blocks of 6 　£1300

1934. *Black on orange cover. Stitched.*
SB5　24 c. booklet containing eight 1 c. and eight 2 c.
　　　(Nos. 288/9) in blocks of 4 　..

1934. *Black on orange cover. Stitched.*
SB6　36 c. booklet containing four 1 c., eight 2 c. and
　　　four 4 c. (Nos. 288/9, 291) in blocks of 4 　..

1938. *Black on orange cover. Stitched.*
SB7　36 c. booklet containing four 1 c., eight 2 c. and
　　　four 4 c. (Nos. 308/10) in blocks of 4 　..　£190

1944. *Black on orange cover. Stitched.*
SB8　24 c. booklet containing eight 1 c. and eight 2 c.
　　　(Nos. 308/9) in blocks of 4 　.. 　.. 　..　£150

1945–49. *Black on red cover. Stitched.*
SB9　24 c. booklet containing 1 c., 2 c. and 3 c. (Nos. 290,
　　　308, 309), each in block of 4 　.. 　..　65·00
　　　a. Containing Nos. 290, 308aa, 309 　..　65·00
　　　b. Containing Nos. 290, 308aa, 309a 　..　65·00
　　　c. Containing Nos. 290a, 308aa, 309 　..　65·00
　　　d. Containing Nos. 290b, 308aa, 309 　..　65·00
　　　e. Containing Nos. 290b, 308aa, 309a 　..　65·00
　　　f. Containing Nos. 290b, 308a, 309a 　..　65·00

B 1

1981 (1 July). *Blue cover as Type B 1, printed in black. Stapled.*
SB10　$6 booklet containing two 15 c. (Nos. 808/9),
　　　three 50 c. on 5 c. (No. 794), two 100 c. on 1 c.
　　　(No. 806) and two 110 c. on 1 c. (No. 807) 　..　4·25

B 2

1981 (22 July). *Royal Wedding. Red, yellow and blue cover as Type B 2. Stitched.*
SB11　$5 booklet containing two 60 c. on 3 c., two 75 c.
　　　on $5 and two $1.10 on $2 (Nos. 841/3) in pairs
　　　and pane of four air mail labels 　.. 　..　2·50

1981 (1 Aug). *Green cover as Type B 1, printed in black. Stapled.*
SB12　$3 booklet containing ten 15 c. on 10 c. on 6 c. and
　　　ten 15 c. on 30 c. on 6 c. (Nos. 848/9) 　..　5·00
SB13　$3 booklet containing ten 15 c. on 50 c. on 6 c. and
　　　ten 15 c. on 60 c. on 6 c. (Nos. 850/1) 　..　5·00

1981 (10 Nov). *Cover as Nos. SB12/13 surcharged "$5". Stapled.*
SB14　$5 on $3 booklet containing six 50 c. on 6 c. (No.
　　　862 or 862b) and two $1 on 6 c. (No. 863 or
　　　863b) 　.. 　.. 　.. 　.. 　..　4·50

1981 (10 Nov). *Blue cover as Type B 1, printed in black, Stapled.*
SB15　$6 booklet containing four 50 c. on 6 c. (No. 862
　　　or 862b) and four $1 on 6 c. (No. 863 or 863b) 　4·50

1982 (Apr). *Cover as Nos. SB12/13 surcharged "$5". Stapled.*
SB16　$5 on $3 booklet containing ten 20 c. on 35 c. (No.
　　　918), two 50 c. on 6 c. (No. 862 or 862b) and
　　　two $1 on 6 c. (No. 863 or 863b) 　.. 　..　11·00

1982 (15 June). *75th Anniv of Boy Scout Movement. Cover as No. SB16 further overprinted "SCOUT MOVEMENT 1907–1982". Stapled.*
SB17　$5 on $3 booklet containing two 125 c. on 8 c. on
　　　6 c. and two 125 c. on 8 c. on 6 c. (Nos. 905/6) 　5·50

1982 (15 June). *75th Anniv of Boy Scout Movement. Cover as No. SB15 overprinted "SCOUT MOVEMENT 1907–1982" in red. Stapled.*
SB18　$6 booklet containing two 25 c. and five 110 c. on
　　　6 c. (Nos. 892, 978) 　.. 　.. 　..　22·00

1982 (15 July). *75th Anniv of Boy Scout Movement. Cover as No. SB16 further overprinted "SCOUT MOVEMENT 1907–1982". Stapled.*
SB19　$5 on $3 booklet containing two 15 c. on 2 c., two
　　　15 c. on 2 c. and four 110 c. on 6 c. (Nos. 895/6,
　　　978) 　.. 　.. 　.. 　.. 　..　14·00
SB20　$5 on $3 booklet containing 15 c. on 2 c., 15 c. on
　　　2 c., 110 c. on 5 c., 110 c. on 5 c., 125 c. on 8 c.
　　　on 6 c. and 125 c. on 8 c. on 6 c. (Nos. 895/6,
　　　900/1, 905/6) 　.. 　.. 　.. 　..　4·00

1982 (15 July). *75th Anniv of Boy Scout Movement. Covers as No. SB15 overprinted "SCOUT MOVEMENT 1907–1982" in red. Stapled.*
SB21　$6 booklet containing four 15 c. on 2 c., four 15 c.
　　　on 2 c., four 15 c. on 2 c., three 25 c., 110 c. on
　　　5 c., 110 c. on 5 c. and 125 c. on 8 c. on 6 c. (Nos.
　　　895/7, 892, 900/1, 905) 　.. 　.. 　..　9·50
SB22　$6 booklet containing four 15 c. on 2 c., four 15 c.
　　　on 2 c., four 15 c. on 2 c., three 25 c., 110 c. on
　　　5 c., 110 c. on 5 c. and 125 c. on 8 c. on 6 c. (No.
　　　895/6, 898, 892, 900/1, 906) 　.. 　..　9·50

1983 (July). *Covers as Type B 1, printed in black on green ($3), surcharged as No. SB16 ($5) or on blue ($6). Stapled.*
SB23　$3 booklet containing ten 30 c. (No. 1127) 　..　3·50
SB24　$5 on $3 booklet containing twenty 25 c. (No.
　　　1108a) 　.. 　.. 　.. 　.. 　..　4·50
SB25　$6 booklet containing ten 60 c. (No. 1128) 　..　6·50
SB26　$6 booklet containing five 120 c. (No. 1129) 　..　6·50
SB27　$6 booklet containing four 150 c. (No. 1131) 　..　6·50

1983 (Oct). *Covers as Type B 1, printed in black on green ($3), surcharged as No. SB16 ($5) or on blue ($6). Stamps attached by selvedge.*
SB28　$3 booklet containing ten 30 c. (No. 1173) 　..　2·50
SB29　$5 on $3 booklet containing twenty 25 c. (No.
　　　1172) 　.. 　.. 　.. 　.. 　..　3·50
SB30　$6 booklet containing ten 30 c. and five 60 c. (Nos.
　　　1173/4) 　.. 　.. 　.. 　.. 　..　2·75
SB31　$6 booklet containing ten 60 c. (No. 1174) 　..　2·75
SB32　$6 booklet containing five 120 c. (No. 1175) 　..　2·75

1984 (1 Mar). *Guyana Olympic Committee Appeal. Booklet No. SB11 with cover surcharged "HELP SEND OUR ATHLETES TO THE 1984 OLYMPICS BOOKLET $15.00" in blue.*
SB33　$15 on $5 booklet containing two 25 c.+2.25 c. on
　　　60 c. on 3 c., two 25 c.+2.25 c. on 75 c. on $5
　　　and two 25 c.+2.25 c. on $1.10 on $2 (Nos.
　　　1235/7) and pane of four air mail labels 　..　10·00

1984 (28 July). *Olympic Games, Los Angeles. Covers as Nos. SB10 and SB12 surcharged "OLYMPIC GAMES 1984" and "$5.00" on $3 black on green or "$12.00" on $6 black on blue.*
SB34　$5 on $3 booklet containing two panes of 10 (No.
　　　1308a) 　.. 　.. 　.. 　.. 　..　6·00
SB35　$12 on $6 booklet containing two panes of 10 (No.
　　　1313a) 　.. 　.. 　.. 　.. 　..　18·00

1985 (9 July). *Green cover as Type B 1, printed in black. Stapled.*
SB36　$3 booklet containing twelve 25 c. (No. 1534) in
　　　pairs 　.. 　.. 　.. 　.. 　..　2·50

1986 (26 May). *20th Anniv of Independence (1st issue). Green cover as Type B 1, printed in black. Stamps attached by selvedge.*
SB37　$3 booklet containing 25 c. on 120 c., 25 c. on
　　　130 c., 25 c. on 150 c. and 225 c. on 200 c. (No.
　　　1723a) 　.. 　.. 　.. 　.. 　..　4·25

1986 (14 July). *International Peace Year. Blue cover as Type B 1, printed in black. Stamps attached by selvedge.*
SB38　$6 booklet containing twenty-four 25 c. on 1 c.
　　　(No. 1739) and label as block of 25 　.. 　..　4·25

1986 (21 Aug). *Green cover as Type B 1, printed in black. Stapled.*
SB39　$3 booklet containing twelve 25 c. (No. 1807) in
　　　pairs 　.. 　.. 　.. 　.. 　..　4·75

1986 (23 Sept). *20th Anniv of Independence (2nd issue). Green cover as Type B 1, printed in black. Stapled.*
SB40　$3 booklet containing twelve 25 c. (No. 1820) in
　　　pairs 　.. 　.. 　.. 　.. 　..　4·75

B 3

1987 (17 Feb). *10th Anniv of Guyana Post Office Corporation. Covers as Type B 3, printed in black with face value handstamped in blue. Stapled.*
SB41　$5 booklet containing twenty 25 c. (Nos. 2074/7)
　　　in strips of 5 　.. 　.. 　.. 　..　8·00
SB42　$20 booklet containing five 60 c., five $1.20 and
　　　five $1.30 (Nos. 2078/80), each in strips of 5,
　　　and two $2.25 (No. 1930) in pair 　.. 　..　18·00

1987 (2 June). *Green cover as Type B 1, printed in black. Stamps attached by selvedge.*
SB43　$3 booklet containing twelve 25 c. (No. 2183) in
　　　pairs 　.. 　.. 　.. 　.. 　..　2·50

1987 (29 Sept). *Green cover as Type B 1, printed in black. Stamps attached by selvedge.*
SB44　$3 booklet containing twelve 25 c. (No. 2184) in
　　　pairs 　.. 　.. 　.. 　.. 　..　3·00

1987 (Dec). *Covers as Nos. SB10 and SB12 handstamped with new face value in blue. Stamps attached by selvedge.*
SB45　$15 on $3 booklet containing twelve $1.20 (No.
　　　2194a) in blocks of 4 and one 60 c. (No. 2265) 　9·00
SB46　$15 on $3 booklet containing twelve $1.20 (No.
　　　2198a) in blocks of 4 and one 60 c. (No. 2265) 　9·00
SB47　$24 on $6 booklet containing twenty $1.20 (No.
　　　2194a) in blocks of 4 or 8 　.. 　..　10·00
SB48　$24 on $6 booklet containing twenty $1.20 (No.
　　　2198a) in blocks of 4 or 8 　.. 　..　10·00
Blocks of Nos. 2194a and 2198a in booklet Nos. SB45/8 have
the perforations at top and bottom removed by guillotine.

1988 (3 Sept). *60th Anniv of Cricket in Guyana. Cream covers with black inscr. Stamps attached by selvedge.*
SB49　$20 booklet containing two 200 c. and two 800 c.
　　　on 150 c. (Nos. 2472, 2474), each in pair 　..　32·00
SB50　$20 booklet containing two 200 c. and two 800 c.
　　　on 150 c. (Nos. 2473/4), each in pair 　..　15·00

1988 (16 Sept). *Olympic Games, Seoul. Greenish yellow covers with black inscr. Stamps attached by selvedge.*
SB51　$20 booklet containing four 25 c. (No. 1534) in
　　　pairs and se-tenant pane of 10 (No. 2486b) 　15·00
SB52　$20 booklet containing four 25 c. (No. 1535a) in
　　　pairs and se-tenant pane of 10 (No. 2486b) 　15·00

EXPRESS LETTER STAMPS

$12.00

EXPRESS

(E 1)

1986 (10 Nov). *Various stamps surch as Type* E 1 *by Tip Torres.*
E1	$12 on 350 c. on 120 c. mult (No. 1598)			6·50	6·50
E2	$15 on 40 c. multicoloured (as No. 1868, but inscr "ONTOGLOSSUM")			8·50	8·50
	a. Surch on No. 1868 (inscr "ODONTO-GLOSSUM")			8·50	8·50
E3	$20 on $6.40, multicoloured (No. **MS**1746)			6·50	6·50
E4	$25 on 25 c. multicoloured (as No. 1621, but value changed)			12·00	12·00
E1/4			*Set of 4*	30·00	30·00

The surcharges on Nos. E2/3 include a pattern of leaves over the original value. On No. E4 a dollar sign has been added in front of the original value and a small maltese cross overprinted above "EXPRESS" at bottom right.

1987 (3 Mar). *No.* E3 *additionally optd with small Maltese cross above surch.*
E5	$20 on $6.40, multicoloured			7·00	7·00
	a. With additional "2" optd at bottom left			7·00	7·00

(Litho Format)

1987 (1 Sept)–88. *Centenary of Publication of Sanders' Reichenbachia. Vert designs as* T **331** *additionally inscr "EXPRESS". Multicoloured. No wmk. P* 13½×14.
E6	$15 Plate No. 11 (Series 2) (29.9.87)			4·00	4·00
E7	$20 Plate No. 93 (Series 2) (17.5.88)			3·50	4·00
E8	$25 Plate No. 63 (Series 2) (26.10.87)			3·75	4·25
E9	$45 Plate No. 35 (Series 2)			7·00	8·00
E6/9			*Set of 4*	16·00	18·00

Nos. E6/9, in conjunction with postage issues, were printed in a similar sheet format to Nos. 1518/33.

EXPRESS

★

FORTY DOLLARS

(E 2) (*Illustration reduced. Actual size of surcharge* 64 × 36 *mm*)

1987 (Nov). *No.* 1744ab *surch with Type* E 2 *by Gardy Ptg.*
E10	$40 on $6.40, multicoloured			11·00	11·00

1987 (Dec). *No.* E 2 *additionally optd with* T **390** *by Gardy Ptg.*
E11	$15 on 40 c. multicoloured (inscr "ONTO-GLOSSUM")			9·50	5·00

SPECIAL DELIVERY

$40·00

(E 3)
(*Illustration reduced. Actual size of surcharge* 80×45 *mm*)

1988 (10 Aug). *Nos.* 2206 *and* 2211 *surch as Type* E 3 *in red by Gardy Ptg.*
E12	$40 on $3.20, deep dull blue			10·00	10·00
E13	$45 on $3.30, brownish black			10·00	10·00

Nos. E12/13 were only issued in vertical strips of five, being the remainders of the sheets utilised to produce Nos. 2455/62.

EXPRESS

FORTY DOLLARS

(E 4)

1989 (Mar). *Nos.* 1744ab *and* 2185ab *surch with Type* E 4 *in red.*
E14	$40 on $6.40, multicoloured (No. 1744ab)	5·50	5·50
E15	$40 on $6.40, multicoloured (No. 2185ab)	5·50	5·50

1989 (May). *Nos.* 2206 *and* 2211 *surch as Type* E 3.
E16	$190 on $3.30, brownish black		14·00	16·00
E17	$225 on $3.20, deep dull blue		15·00	17·00

Nos. E16/17 were surcharged on the remains of the sheets utilized for Nos. 2648/55.

EXPRESS

(E 5)

(E 6)

(Des Mary Walters. Litho Questa)

1989 (7 Sept). *Butterflies. Two sheets, each* 97×67 *mm, containing vert designs as* T **454** *optd with Type* E **5**. *Multicoloured. P* 14.
EMS18	$130 *Phareas coeleste*			5·00	5·00
EMS19	$190 *Papilio torquatus*			6·00	6·00

(Des M. Dorfman. Litho Questa)

1989 (8 Nov). *Women in Space. Sheet,* 92×67 *mm, containing vert design as* T **455** *optd with Type* E **5**. *Multicoloured. P* 14.
EMS20	$190 Valentina Tereshkova (first woman cosmonaut)			4·25	4·50

1989 (17 Nov). *"World Stamp Expo '89" International Stamp Exhibition, Washington. Nos.* EMS18/19 *optd with Type* E **6**.
EMS21	$130 *Phareas coeleste*			4·00	4·00
EMS22	$190 *Papilio torquatus*			4·50	4·50

Nos. EMS21/22 show additional overprints on sheet margins.

1990 (15 Mar). *85th Anniv of Rotary International. Nos.* EMS18/20 *optd* "ROTARY INTERNATIONAL 1905–1990" *and emblem on sheet margins only.*
EMS23	$130 *Phareas coeleste*			3·75	3·75
EMS24	$190 *Papilio torquatus*			5·50	5·50
EMS25	$190 Valentina Tereshkova (first woman cosmonaut)			4·00	5·50
EMS23/5			*Set of 3*	12·00	13·00

1990 (3 May). *"Stamp World London '90" International Stamp Exhibition. Nos.* EMS18/20 *optd* "Stamp World London '90" *and emblem on sheet margins only.*
EMS26	$130 *Phareas coeleste* (R.)			3·75	3·75
	a. Opt in black				
EMS27	$190 *Papilio torquatus*			5·50	5·50
EMS28	$190 Valentina Tereshkova (first woman cosmonaut)			4·00	5·50
EMS26/8			*Set of 3*	12·00	13·00

1990 (2 June). *"Belgica '90" International Stamp Exhibition, Brussels. Nos.* EMS18 *and* EMS20 *additionally optd* "BELGICA PHILATELIC EXPOSITION 1990" *and emblem on sheet margins only.*
EMS29	$130 *Phareas coeleste*			4·00	4·00
EMS30	$190 Valentina Tereshkova (first woman cosmonaut)			4·50	5·00

1990 (8 June). *90th Birthday of Queen Elizabeth the Queen Mother. Nos.* EMS18/20 *optd* "90TH BIRTHDAY H.M. THE QUEEN MOTHER" *on sheet margins only.*
EMS31	$130 *Phareas coeleste*			3·50	3·50
EMS32	$190 *Papilio torquatus*			4·00	4·00
EMS33	$190 Valentina Tereshkova (first woman cosmonaut)			4·00	4·00
EMS31/3			*Set of 3*	10·50	10·50

(Des W. Wright. Litho)

1990 (16 Nov). *Fauna. Two sheets, each* 110×80 *mm, containing vert designs as* T **466**, *but larger* (40×55 *mm*) *inscr* "EXPRESS". *Multicoloured. P* 14.
EMS34	$130 Harpy Eagle			3·50	3·50
EMS35	$150 Ocelot			3·50	3·50

STANLEY GIBBONS
STAMP COLLECTING SERIES

Introductory booklets on *How to Start, How to Identify Stamps* and *Collecting by Theme*. A series of well illustrated guides at a low price.
Write for details.

PARCEL POST STAMPS

PARCEL POST

X	X	PARCEL POST
$15.00	$15.00	$12.00
(P 1)		(P 2)

1981 (8 June). *No.* 554 *surch as Type* P 1 *by Bovell's Printery.*
P1	$15 on $1 *Chelonanthus uliginoides*		10·00	3·00
P2	$20 on $1 *Chelonanthus uliginoides*		10·00	6·00

1983 (15 Jan). *No.* 843 *surch with Type* P 2 *in blue by Autoprint.*
P3	$12 on $1.10 on $2 *Norantea guianensis*		3·25	2·00

Parcel Post
$12.00

(P 3)

1983 (14 Sept). *Unissued Royal Wedding surch, similar to No.* 843, *further surch with Type* P 3 *in blue by Autoprint.*
P4	$12 on $1.10 on $2 *Norantea guianensis*		1·00	1·75

TWENTY FIVE DOLLARS
PARCEL POST 25·00

(P 4)

1985 (25 Apr). *No.* 673 *surch with Type* P 4 *in red by Tip Torres.*
P5	$25 on 35 c. bright yellow-green, grey & black	22·00	18·00

POSTAGE DUE STAMPS

D 1

D 2

(Typo D.L.R.)

1940 (Mar)–**55**. *Wmk Mult Script CA. Chalk-surfaced paper* (4 c.). *P* 14.
D1	D 1	1 c. green			3·75	6·50
		a. Chalk-surfaced paper. *Deep green*, (30.4.52)			1·50	8·50
		ab. W9*a* (Crown missing)				£190
		ac. W9*b* (St. Edward's Crown)				85·00
D2		2 c. black			14·00	2·00
		a. Chalk-surfaced paper (30.4.52)			1·50	3·50
		ab. W9*a* (Crown missing)				£160
		ac. W9*b* (St. Edward's Crown)				75·00
D3		4 c. bright blue (1.5.52)			30	8·50
		a. W9*a* (Crown missing)				£140
		b. W9*b* (St. Edward's Crown)				75·00
D4		12 c. scarlet			25·00	6·00
		a. Chalk-surfaced paper (19.7.55)			11·00	22·00
D1a/4a				*Set of 4*	13·00	35·00
D1, D2 and D4 Perf "Specimen"				*Set of 3*	50·00	

(Typo D.L.R.)

1967–8. *Chalk-surfaced paper. W w* 12. *P* 14.
D5	D 2	2 c. black (11.12.68)			70	15·00
D6		4 c. deep ultramarine			30	4·25
D7		12 c. reddish scarlet			30	4·75
D5/7				*Set of 3*	1·10	22·00

1973 (24 May). *Glazed, ordinary paper. W* 106. *P* 14.
D 8	D 2	1 c. olive			20	3·00
D 9		2 c. black			20	3·00
D10		4 c. dull ultramarine			20	3·00
D11		12 c. bright scarlet			30	3·00
D8/11				*Set of 4*	80	11·00

OFFICIAL STAMPS

OFFICIAL	OFFICIAL	OFFICIAL
(O 1)	(O 1a)	(O 2)

1875. *Optd with Type* O 1 (1 c.) *or* O 1a (*others*) *by litho. P* 10.
O1	8	1 c. black (R.)			42·00	15·00
		a. Imperf between (horiz pair)			—	£4750
O2		2 c. orange			£150	14·00
O3		8 c. rose			£300	£120
O4	7	12 c. brownish purple			£1500	£475
O5	9	24 c. green			£850	£225

Two types of the word "OFFICIAL" are found on each value. On the 1 c. the word is either 16 or 17 mm long. On the other values the chief difference is in the shape and position of the letter "o" in "OFFICIAL". In one case the "o" is upright, in the other it slants to the left.

1877. *Optd with Type O 2 by typo. Wmk Crown CC. P 14.*

O 6	**16**	1 c. slate	£200	55·00
		a. Imperf between (vert pair)	—	£7000
O 7		2 c. orange	90·00	15·00
O 8		4 c. blue	80·00	20·00
O 9		6 c. brown	£2500	£600
O10		8 c. rose	£1700	£450

Prepared for use, but not issued

O11	**16**	12 c. pale violet		£1000
O12		24 c. green		£1100

The "OFFICIAL" overprints have been extensively forged.

The use of Official stamps was discontinued in June 1878, but was resumed in June 1981.

10   **OPS**
(O 3)

OPS
(O 4)

OPS
(O 5)

1981 (8 June). *Nos. 556, F4a and F6/7 surch or optd with Types O 3/5 by Bovell's Printery.*

O13	10 c. on 25 c. Marabunta (Blk. + R.)	1·50	2·00
O14	50 c. *Guzmania lingulata* (R.)	1·25	30
O15	60 c. Soldier's Cap (R.)	1·25	20
O16	$5 *Odontadenia grandiflora* (opt Type O 5) (R.)	2·25	1·75
O13/16	Set of 4	5·50	3·75

OPS   **OPS**
100

OPS
(O 6)   (O 7)

1981 (1 July). *(a) Postage. Nos. 491, 708a, 716, 834 and F9 optd or surch as Types O 5/7 or additionally surch as T 227.*

O17	15 c. Harpy Eagle (opt Type O 6)	9·00	65
O18	30 c. on $2 *Norantea guianensis* (No. F9) (opt Type O 5) (Blk. + R.)	45	30
O19	100 c. on $3 Cylinder satellite (surch Type O 7) (Blk. + R.)	3·00	40
O20	125 c. on $2 *Norantea guianensis* (opt Type O 5) (R.)	1·25	60
O21	$10 *Elbella patrobas* (opt Type O 5)	7·50	8·50

(b) Air. No. 804 optd with Type O 5 in red

O22	$1.10 on $2 *Norantea guianensis*	75	2·00
	a. Opt Type O 5 double		£110
O17/22	Set of 6	20·00	11·00

1981 (7 July). *Nos. 548, 719, 828 and 830 optd with Type O 5.*

O23	15 c. Christmas Orchid	8·00	1·50
O24	50 c. British Guiana 1898 1 c. stamp	1·25	35
O25	100 c. on 8 c. Camp-fire cooking	1·25	50
O26	110 c. on 6 c. Type 116	2·50	1·25

OPS

OPS   **250**
(O 8)   (O 9)

(Surch or optd by Autoprint)

1982 (17 May). *(a) Postage. (i) Various stamps optd with Type O 8 in blue.*

O27	–	20 c. multicoloured (No. 701)	4·25	60
O28	**136**	40 c. multicoloured	75	15
O29	–	40 c. carmine-red, grey & blk (No. 674)	1·00	15
O30	–	$2 multicoloured (No. 676)	7·00	75
O27/30		Set of 4	12·00	1·50

(ii) No. 911 additionally surch with Type O 9 in blue

O31	–	250 c. on 400 c. on 30 c. multicoloured	80	60

(b) Air. No. 980 additionally optd with Type O 8 in blue

O32	–	220 c. on 1 c. multicoloured	1·00	60

1982 (12 July). *No. F9 optd with Type O 5 in red by Bovell's Printery.*

O33	$2 *Norantea guianensis*	8·00	2·00

1982 (15 Sept). *Air. No. 979 optd with Type O 8 by Autoprint.*

O34	110 c. on 5 c. Annatto tree	1·25	40

1984 (2 Apr). *No. 912 surch as Type O 9 vertically, in blue (except for No. O37 which has "OPS" in blue and "225" in black) by Autoprint.*

O35	150 c. on $5 multicoloured	5·50	2·75
O36	200 c. on $5 multicoloured	6·00	3·00
O37	225 c. on $5 multicoloured	6·00	3·25
O38	230 c. on $5 multicoloured	6·00	3·25
O39	260 c. on $5 multicoloured	6·00	3·50
O40	320 c. on $5 multicoloured	7·50	4·00
O41	350 c. on $5 multicoloured	8·00	4·50
O42	600 c. on $5 multicoloured	9·50	5·50
O35/42	Set of 8	48·00	27·00

25
(O 10)

(Surch or optd by Autoprint)

1984 (25 June). *Nos. O32 and O34 surch as Type O 10 (25 c., 60 c.) or as T 294 (others), and No. 981 optd vertically with Type O 8.*

O43	25 c. on 110 c. on 5 c. Annatto tree	90	30
O44	30 c. on 110 c. on 5 c. Annatto tree (B.)	1·00	35
O45	45 c. on 220 c. on 1 c. Pitcher Plant of Mt Roraima	1·10	40
O46	55 c. on 110 c. on 5 c. Annatto tree (B.)	1·40	50
O47	60 c. on 220 c. on 1 c. Pitcher Plant of Mt Roraima	1·40	50
O48	75 c. on 220 c. on 1 c. Pitcher Plant of Mt Roraima	1·50	60
O49	90 c. on 220 c. on 1 c. Pitcher Plant of Mt Roraima (B.)	1·50	70
O50	120 c. on 220 c. on 1 c. Pitcher Plant of Mt Roraima	1·75	85
O51	130 c. on 220 c. on 1 c. Pitcher Plant of Mt Roraima (B.)	2·00	90
O52	330 c. on $2 *Norantea guianensis* (B.)	3·50	2·75
O43/52	Set of 10	14·50	7·00

(Litho Format)

1987 (5 Oct)–**88**. *Centenary of Publication of Sanders' Reichenbachia. Multicoloured designs as T 331 additionally inscr "OFFICIAL". No wmk. P 14×13½ (230, 350, 600 c., $12) or 13½×14 (others).*

O53	120 c. Plate No. 48 (Series 2)	90	25
O54	130 c. Plate No. 92 (Series 2)	90	25
O55	140 c. Plate No. 36 (Series 2) (5.10.88)	60	25
O56	150 c. Plate No. 43 (Series 2)	90	25
O57	175 c. Plate No. 31 (Series 2) (5.10.88)	70	30
O58	200 c. Plate No. 61 (Series 2)	1·00	35
O59	225 c. Plate No. 26 (Series 2)	1·00	35
O60	230 c. Plate No. 68 (Series 2) (horiz)	50	35
O61	250 c. Plate No. 59 (Series 2) (5.10.88)	50	40
O62	260 c. Plate No. 69 (Series 2) (5.10.88)	50	40
O63	275 c. Plate No. 90 (Series 2)	1·00	40
O64	320 c. Plate No. 75 (Series 2)	1·00	50
O65	330 c. Plate No. 23 (Series 2)	1·75	60
O66	350 c. Plate No. 95 (Series 2) (horiz)	50	60
O67	600 c. Plate No. 70 (Series 2) (horiz)	75	1·25
O68	$12 Plate No. 71 (Series 2) (horiz)	1·40	2·00
O69	$15 Plate No. 84 (Series 2)	1·50	2·25
O53/69	Set of 17	14·00	9·50

Nos. O53/69 were printed in a similar sheet format to Nos. 1518/33.

OFFICIAL PARCEL POST STAMPS

1981 (8 June). *Nos. P1/2 optd with Type O 5 in red by Bovell's Printery.*

OP1	$15 on $1 *Chelonanthus uliginoides*	7·50	2·25
	a. Opt in black	65·00	8·00
OP2	$20 on $1 *Chelonanthus uliginoides*	10·00	2·75

OPS

Parcel Post
$12.00
(OP 1)

1983 (15 Jan). *No. 843 surch with Type OP 1, and optd with T 226, both in blue by Autoprint.*

OP3	$12 on $1.10 on $2 *Norantea guianensis*	65·00	17·00
	a. Surch Type OP 1 omitted	90·00	

1983 (22 Aug). *As No. OP3, but additionally optd with Type O 8 by Autoprint.*

OP4	$12 on $1.10 on $2 *Norantea guianensis*	20·00	4·00

1983 (3 Nov). *No. P4 additionally optd with Type O 8 in blue by Autoprint.*

OP5	$12 on $1.10 on $2 *Norantea guianensis*	6·00	4·00

POSTAL FISCAL STAMPS

REVENUE ONLY

✱
(F 1)

1975 (1 Nov). *Nos. 543/5 and 550a/56 optd with Type F 1.*

F 1	2 c. Type **132**		40	40
F 2	3 c. Hanging Heliconia		40	40
F 3	5 c. Annatto tree		65	30
F 4	25 c. Marabunta (Type II)		2·50	30
	a. Optd on No. 550 (Type I)		15·00	13·00
F 5	40 c. Tiger Beard		5·00	30
F 6	50 c. *Guzmania lingulata*		60	40
F 7	60 c. Soldier's Cap		75	50
F 8	$1 *Chelonanthus uliginoides*		75	1·25
F 9	$2 *Norantea guianensis*		1·00	2·75
F10	$5 *Odontadenia grandiflora*		1·75	9·00
F1/F10	Set of 10		12·00	14·00

Although intended for fiscal use Nos. F1/10 were allowed, by the postal authorities, as "an act of grace" to do duty as postage stamps until 30 June 1976.

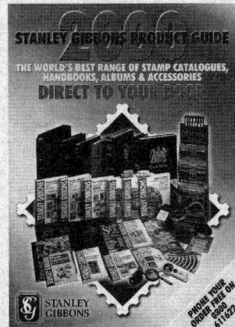

Heligoland

PRICES FOR STAMPS ON COVER

Nos. 1/19   from × 3

PRINTERS. All the stamps of Heligoland were typographed at the Imperial Printing Works, Berlin.

REPRINTS. Many of the stamps of Heligoland were subsequently reprinted at Berlin (between 1875 and 1885), Leipzig (1888) and Hamburg (1892 and 1895). Of these only the Berlin productions are difficult to distinguish from the originals so separate notes are provided for the individual values. Leipzig reprints can be identified by their highly surfaced paper and those from Hamburg by their 14 perforation. All of these reprints are worth much less than the original stamps priced below.

There was, in addition, a small reprinting of Nos. 13/19, made by the German government in 1890 for exchange purposes, but examples of this printing are far scarcer than the original stamps.

Forgeries, printed by lithography instead of typography, also exist for Nos. 1/4, 6 and 8 perforated 12½ or 13. Forged cancellations can also be found on originals and, on occasion, genuine postmarks on reprints.

1

(Currency. 16 schillings = 1 mark)

Three Dies of Embossed Head for Types **1** and **2**:

Die I   Die II

Die III

Die I.   Blob instead of curl beneath the chignon. Outline of two jewels at top of diadem.
Die II.   Curl under chignon. One jewel at top of diadem.
Die III.   Shorter curl under chignon. Two jewels at top of diadem.

(Des Wedding. Die eng E. Schilling)

1867 (Mar)–**68**. *Head Die I embossed in colourless relief. Roul.*

1	1	½ sch. blue-green and rose		£300	£800
		a. Head Die II (7.68)		£700	£1100
2		1 sch. rose and blue-green (21.3.67)		£160	£180
3		2 sch. rose and grass-green (21.3.67)		10·00	55·00
4		6 sch. green and rose		12·00	£250

For Nos. 1/4 the second colour given is that of the spandrels on the ½ and 1 sch., and of the spandrels and central background for the 2 and 6 sch.

All four values exist from the Berlin, Leipzig and Hamburg reprintings. The following points are helpful in identifying originals from Berlin reprints; for Leipzig and Hamburg reprints see general note above:

½ sch. — Reprints are all in yellowish green and show Head Die II
1 sch. — All reprints are Head Die III
2 sch. — Berlin reprints are in dull rose with a deeper blue-green
6 sch. — Originals show white specks in green. Berlin reprints have a more solid bluish green

---

1869 (Apr)–**73**. *Head embossed in colourless relief. P 13½×14½.*

5	1	¼ sch. rose and green (background) (I) (*quadrillé paper*) (8.73)		26·00	£1500
		a. Error. Green and rose (background) (9.73)		£110	£3000
		b. *Deep rose and pale green* (background) (11.73)		85·00	£1500
6		½ sch. blue-green and rose (II)		£190	£200
		a. *Yellow-green and rose* (7.71)		£140	£190
		b. Quadrillé paper (6.73)		95·00	£150
7		¾ sch. green and rose (I) (*quadrillé paper*) (12.73)		29·00	£1100
8		1 sch. rose and yellow-green (III) (7.71)		£140	£180
		a. Quadrillé paper. *Rose and pale blue-green* (6.73)		£120	£180
9		1½ sch. grn & rose (I) (*quadrillé paper*) (9.73)		65·00	£250

For Nos. 5/9 the second colour given is that of the spandrels on the ½ and 1 sch., of the central background on the ¼ and 1½ sch., and of the central background, side labels and side marginal lines of the ¾ sch.

No. 5a was a printing of the ¼ sch. made in the colour combination of the 1½ sch. by mistake.

A further printing of the ¼ sch. (head die I) in deep rose-red and yellowish green (background), on non-*quadrillé* paper, was made in December 1874, but not issued (*Price £15, unused*).

All five values exist from the Berlin, Leipzig and Hamburg reprintings. The following points are helpful in identifying originals from Berlin reprints; for Leipzig and Hamburg reprints see general note above:

¼ sch. — All Berlin and some Hamburg reprints are Head Die II
½ sch. — Berlin reprints on thinner paper with solid colour in the spandrels
¾ sch. — Berlin reprints on thinner, non-quadrillé paper
1 sch. — Berlin reprints are on thinner paper or show many breaks in the rose line beneath "SCHILLING" at the top of the design or in the line above it at the foot.
1½ sch. — All Berlin and some Hamburg reprints are Head Die II

Berlin, Leipzig and Hamburg reprints also exist of the 2 and 6 sch., but these values do not come as perforated originals.

(New Currency. 100 pfennig = 1 mark)

2   3   4

5

(Des H. Gätke. Die eng E. Schilling (T **2**), A. Schiffner (others)

1875 (Feb)–**90**. *Head Die II on T **2** embossed in colourless relief. P 13½×14½.*

10	2	1 pf. (¼d.) deep green and rose		10·00	£500
11		2 pf. (½d.) deep rose and deep green		10·00	£600
12	3	3 pf. (⁵⁄₈d.) pale green, red and yellow (6.76)		£225	£1100
		a. *Green, red and orange* (4.80)		£160	£850
13	2	5 pf. (¾d.) deep yellow-green and rose		10·00	18·00
		a. *Deep green and rose* (6.90)		12·00	40·00
14		10 pf. (1½d.) deep rose and deep green		30·00	20·00
		a. *Scarlet and pale blue-green* (5.87)		10·00	20·00
15	3	20 pf. (2½d.) rose, green and yellow (6.76)		£200	£120
		a. *Rose-carmine, dp green & orge* (4.80)		£150	50·00
		b. *Dull red, pale green and lemon* (7.88)		12·00	28·00
		c. *Aniline verm, brt grn & lemon* (6.90)		12·00	50·00
16	2	25 pf. (3d.) deep green and rose		12·00	26·00
17		50 pf. (6d.) rose and green		18·00	32·00
18	4	1 m. (1s.) deep green, scarlet & black (8.79)		£140	£200
		a. Perf 11½		£1000	
		b. *Deep green, aniline rose & black* (5.89)		£140	£200
19	5	5 m. (5s.) deep green, aniline rose, black and yellow (8.79)		£150	£950
		a. Perf 11½		£1000	
		ab. Imperf between (horiz pair)		£3500	

For stamps as Type **2** the first colour is that of the central background and the second that of the frame. On the 3 pf. the first colour is of the frame and the top band of the shield, the second is the centre band and the third the shield border. The 20 pf. is similar, but has the centre band in the same colour as the frame and the upper band on the shield in the second colour.

The 1, 2 and 3 pf. exist from the Berlin, Leipzig and Hamburg reprintings. There were no such reprints for the other values. The following points are helpful in identifying originals from Berlin reprints; for Leipzig and Hamburg reprints see general note above:

1 pf. — Berlin printings show a peculiar shade of pink
2 pf. — All reprints are much lighter in shade than the deep rose and deep green of the originals
3 pf. — Berlin reprints either show the band around the shield in brownish orange, or have this feature in deep yellow with the other two colours lighter.

Heligoland was ceded to Germany on 9 August 1890.

MINIMUM PRICE

The minimum price quote is 10p which represents a handling charge rather than a basis for valuing common stamps. For further notes about prices see introductory pages.

Hong Kong

CROWN COLONY

Hong Kong island was formally ceded to Great Britain on 26 January 1841. The Hong Kong Post Office was established in October 1841, when much of the business previously transacted through the Macao postal agency was transferred to the island. The first cancellation is known from April 1842, but local control of the posts was shortlived as the Hong Kong Office became a branch of the British G.P.O. on 15 April 1843.

The colonial authorities resumed control of the postal service on 1 May 1860 although the previously established postal agencies in the Chinese Treaty Ports remained part of the British G.P.O. system until 1 May 1868.

For illustrations of the handstamp types see BRITISH POST OFFICES ABROAD notes, following GREAT BRITAIN.

CROWNED-CIRCLE HANDSTAMPS

CC1 CC1b   HONG KONG (R.) (17.10.1843)   *Price on cover £500*
CC2 CC1   HONG KONG (R.) (21.8.1844)   *Price on cover £750*
CC3 CC3   HONG KONG (R.) (16.6.1852)   *Price on cover £325*

We no longer list the Great Britain stamps with obliteration "B 62" within oval. The Government notification dated 29 November 1862 stated that only the Hong Kong stamps to be issued on 8 December would be available for postage and the stamps formerly listed were all issued in Great Britain later than the date of the notice.

(Currency. 100 cents = 1 Hong Kong dollar)

PRICES FOR STAMPS ON COVER TO 1945

Nos. 1/27	*from* × 6
Nos. 28/36	*from* × 4
Nos. 37/9	*from* × 5
Nos. 40/4	*from* × 4
Nos. 45/8	*from* × 10
Nos. 49/50	*from* × 4
No. 51	*from* × 15
Nos. 52/61	*from* × 5
Nos. 62/99	*from* × 4
Nos. 100/32	*from* × 3
Nos. 133/6	*from* × 2
Nos. 137/9	*from* × 4
Nos. 140/68	*from* × 2
Nos. D1/12	*from* × 8
Nos. F1/11	*from* × 4
No. F12	*from* × 3
Nos. P1/3	*from* × 2

PRINTERS. All definitive issues up to 1962 were typographed by De La Rue and Co., *except for some printings between 1941 and 1945.*

1   2   3

1862 (8 Dec)–**63**. *No wmk. P 14.*

1	1	2 c. brown		£375	85·00
		a. *Deep brown* (1863)		£500	£100
2		8 c. yellow-buff		£600	60·00
3		12 c. pale greenish blue		£475	48·00
4	3	18 c. lilac		£500	45·00
5		24 c. green		£900	90·00
6		48 c. rose		£2500	£325
7		96 c. brownish grey		£3500	£425

1863 (Aug)–**71**. *Wmk Crown CC. P 14.*

8	1	2 c. deep brown (11.64)		£250	27·00
		a. *Brown*		£110	7·00
		b. *Pale yellowish brown*		£130	11·00
		w. Wmk inverted		£375	45·00
		x. Wmk reversed		—	65·00
9	4	4 c. grey		£120	13·00
		a. *Slate*		95·00	5·50
		aw. Wmk inverted		£275	45·00
		b. *Deep slate*		£140	10·00
		c. *Greenish grey*		£275	45·00
		cw. Wmk inverted		†	£225
		d. *Bluish slate*		£450	21·00
		dw. Wmk inverted		£800	£110
		e. Perf 12½. *Slate* (12.70)		£8000	£275
		ew. Wmk inverted		—	£450
10		6 c. lilac		£350	9·50
		a. *Mauve*		£450	10·00
		w. Wmk inverted		£700	40·00
		x. Wmk reversed		—	50·00
11	1	8 c. dull orange (10.64)		£450	9·50
		a. *Brownish orange*		£400	11·00
		b. *Bright orange*		£350	11·00
		w. Wmk inverted		£700	50·00
		x. Wmk reversed		£700	50·00
12		12 c. pale greenish blue (4.65)		£950	29·00
		a. *Pale blue*		25·00	5·50
		b. *Deep blue*		£190	12·00
		w. Wmk inverted		—	50·00
		x. Wmk reversed		—	45·00

13	3	18 c. lilac (1866)	..	..	£5500	£300
		w. Wmk inverted	..	..	†	£650
		x. Wmk reversed	..	..	†	£750
14		24 c. green (10.64)	..	..	£500	8·50
		a. Pale green	..	..	£600	15·00
		b. Deep green	..	..	£800	28·00
		w. Wmk inverted	..	..	—	55·00
		x. Wmk reversed	..	..	£1100	55·00
15	2	30 c. vermilion	..	..	£750	14·00
		a. Orange-vermilion	..		£650	15·00
		w. Wmk inverted	..	..	£1800	55·00
		x. Wmk reversed	..	..	—	55·00
16		30 c. mauve (14.8.71)	..	..	£180	5·50
		w. Wmk inverted	..	..	£500	50·00
		x. Wmk reversed	..	..	—	55·00
17		48 c. pale rose (1.65)	..	..	£950	40·00
		a. Rose-carmine	..	..	£800	23·00
		w. Wmk inverted	..	..	£1500	70·00
		x. Wmk reversed	..	..	—	90·00
18		96 c. olive-bistre (1.65)	..	..	£25000	£550
		w. Wmk inverted	..	..		†£1200
19		96 c. brownish grey (1865)	..	..	£1000	42·00
		a. Brownish black	..	..	£1100	35·00
		w. Wmk inverted	..	..	£1400	90·00

There is a wide range of shades in this issue, of which we can only indicate the main groups.

No. 12 is the same shade as No. 3 without wmk, the impression having a waxy appearance.

A single used example of the 48 c. in a bright claret shade is known. No other stamps in this shade, either mint or used, have been discovered.

See also Nos. 22 and 28/31.

16 cents. (4)   28 cents. (5)   5 cents. (6)   10 cents. (7)

ts.

No. 20b

1876 (Aug)–77. *Nos. 13 and 16 surch with T 4 or 5 by Noronha and Sons, Hong Kong.*

20	3	16 c. on 18 c. lilac (1.4.77)	..	£1900	£150
		a. Space between "n" and "t"	..	£6000	£800
		b. Space between "s" and stop	..	£6000	£800
		w. Wmk inverted	..	£4000	£500
21	2	28 c. on 30 c. mauve	..	£1100	48·00

1877 (Aug). *New value. Wmk Crown CC. P 14.*

22	3	16 c. yellow	..	£1200	65·00
		w. Wmk inverted	..	£2250	£200

1880 (1 Mar–Sept). *Surch with T 6 or 7 by Noronha and Sons.*

23	1	5 c. on 8 c. brt orange (No. 11b) (Sept)	..	£700	90·00
		a. Surch inverted	..		†£10000
		b. Surch double	..		†£15000
24	3	5 c. on 18 c. lilac (No. 13)	..	£700	60·00
		x. Wmk reversed	..		£1000
25	1	10 c. on 12 c. pale blue (No. 12a)	..	£800	55·00
		a. Blue	..	£1000	75·00
26	3	10 c. on 16 c. yellow (No. 22) (May)	..	£3750	£150
		a. Surch inverted	..		†£40000
		b. Surch double	..		†£50000
		w. Wmk inverted	..	†	£800
27		10 c. on 24 c. green (No. 14) (June)	..	£1200	90·00
		w. Wmk inverted	..	†	£190

Two examples of No. 26b are known, both used in Shanghai.

1880 (Mar–Dec). *Colours changed and new values. Wmk Crown CC. P 14.*

28	1	2 c. dull rose	..	..	£120	18·00
		a. Rose	..	..	£130	19·00
29	2	5 c. blue (Dec)	..	..	£300	30·00
		w. Wmk inverted	..	..	—	80·00
30		10 c. mauve (Nov)	..	..	£450	13·00
		w. Wmk inverted	..	..	—	55·00
31	3	48 c. brown	..	..	£1000	90·00

1882 (May)–96. *Wmk Crown CA. P 14.*

32	1	2 c. rose-lake (7.82)	..	..	£130	26·00
		a. Rose-pink	..	..	£180	32·00
		ab. Perf 12	..	..	£70000	£70000
		w. Wmk inverted	..	..	—	80·00
33		2 c. carmine (1884)	..	..	26·00	85
		a. Aniline carmine	..	..	28·00	85
		w. Wmk inverted	..	..	—	55·00
34	2	4 c. slate-grey (1.4.96)	..	..	9·00	85
		w. Wmk inverted	..	..	—	55·00
35		5 c. pale blue	..	..	21·00	85
		a. Blue	..	..	22·00	85
		aw. Wmk inverted	..	..	£160	55·00
		x. Wmk reversed	..	..	—	£110
36		10 c. dull mauve (8.82)	..	..	£550	9·00
		w. Wmk inverted	..	..	—	80·00
37		10 c. deep blue-green (1884)	..	..	£1700	38·00
		a. Green (2.84)	..	..	£110	1·00
38		10 c. purple/red (1.1.91)	..	..	19·00	1·00
		w. Wmk inverted	..	..	£250	55·00
		x. Wmk reversed	..	..	£275	65·00
		y. Wmk inverted and reversed				
39		30 c. yellowish green (1.1.91)	..	..	£120	38·00
		a. Grey-green	..	..	60·00	16·00
38, 39a		Optd "Specimen"	..	Set of 2	£400	

Examples of No. 39 should not be confused with washed or faded stamps from the grey-green shade which tend to turn to a very yellow-green when dampened.

For other stamps with this watermark, but in colours changed to the U.P.U. scheme see Nos. 56/61.

20 CENTS (8)   50 CENTS (9)   1 DOLLAR (10)

1885 (Sept). *As Nos. 15, 19 and 31, but wmkd Crown CA, surch with T 8 to 10 by De La Rue.*

40	2	20 c. on 30 c. orange-red	..	..	90·00	5·00
		a. Surch double				
		w. Wmk inverted	..	..	£550	£110
41	3	50 c. on 48 c. yellowish brown	..	..	£325	26·00
		w. Wmk inverted	..	..	—	90·00
42		$1 on 96 c. grey-olive	..	..	£600	50·00
40/2		Optd "Specimen"	..	Set of 3	£900	

7 cents. (11)   14 cents. (12)

(13) (20 c.)   (14) (50 c.)   (15) ($1)

1891 (1 Jan–Mar). *(a) Nos. 16 and 37 surch with T 11 or 12 by Noronha and Sons, Hong Kong*

43	2	7 c. on 10 c. green	..	60·00	7·50
		a. Antique "t" in "cents" (R.1/1)	..	£550	£150
		b. Surch double	..	£6000	£1300
44		14 c. on 30 c. mauve (Feb)	..	£120	50·00
		a. Antique "t" in "cents" (R.1/1)	..	£2250	£900

(b) As Nos. 40/2 (surch with T 8 to 10 by De La Rue), but colours changed

45	2	20 c. on 30 c. yellowish green (No. 39)	..	£160	£150
		a. Grey-green (No. 39a)	..	£100	£130
46	3	50 c. on 48 c. dull purple	..	£225	£250
47		$1 on 96 c. purple/red	..	£650	£350
45a/7		Optd "Specimen"	..	Set of 3	£650

(c) Nos. 45/7 with further surch, T 13/15, in Chinese characters, handstamped locally (Mar)

48	2	20 c. on 30 c. yellowish green	..	55·00	6·50
		a. Grey-green	..	26·00	5·00
49	3	50 c. on 48 c. dull purple	..	70·00	5·50
50		$1 on 96 c. purple/red	..	£400	22·00
		w. Wmk inverted	..		

The true antique "t" variety (Nos. 43a and 44a) should not be confused with a small "t" showing a short foot. In the antique "t" the crossbar is accurately bisected by the vertical stroke, which is thicker at the top. The lower curve bends towards the right and does not turn upwards to the same extent as on the normal.

The handstamped surcharges on Nos. 48/50 were applied over the original Chinese face values. The single character for "2"

was intended to convert "30 c." to "20 c.". There were six slightly different versions of the "2" handstamp and three for the "50 c.".

A used example of No. 48 in the Royal Philatelic Collection shows surcharge Type **8** double.

The errors of the Chinese surcharges previously listed on the above issue and also on Nos. 52 and 55 are now omitted as being outside the scope of the catalogue. While some without doubt possess philatelic merit, it is impossible to distinguish between the genuine errors and the clandestine copies made to order with the original chops. No. 55c is retained as this represents a distinctly different chop which was used for the last part of the printing.

1841
Hong Kong
JUBILEE   10
1891   CENTS   拾   拾

(16)   (17)   (18)   (19)

1891 (22 Jan). *50th Anniversary of Colony. Optd with T* **16** *by Noronha and Sons, Hong Kong.*

51	**1**	2 c. carmine (No. 33)	£375	95·00
		a. Short "J" in "JUBILEE" (R. 1/6)	£550	£140
		b. Short "U" in "JUBILEE" (R. 1/1)	£550	£140
		c. Broken "1" in "1891" (R. 2/1)	£700	£200
		d. Tall narrow "K" in "Kong" (R. 1/3)	£1100	£425
		e. Opt double	£16000	£12000
		f. Space between "O" and "N" of "Hong" (R. 1/5)	£1500	£650

Most of the supply of No. 51, which was only on sale for three days, was overprinted from a setting of 12 (6×2) applied five times to complete each sheet. There were six printings from this setting, but a second setting, possibly of 30 or 60, was used for the seventh. Positions quoted are from the setting of twelve. Most varieties only occur in some printings and many less marked overprint flaws also exist.

The prices quoted for No. 51e are for examples on which the two impressions are distinctly separated. Examples on which the two impressions are almost coincidental are worth considerably less.

1898 (1 Apr). *Wmk Crown CA. P* 14. (a) *Surch with T* **10** *by D.L.R. and handstamped Chinese characters as T* **15**

52	**3**	$1 on 96 c. black	£130	27·00
		a. Grey-black	£130	26·00

(b) *Surch with T* **10** *only*

53	**3**	$1 on 96 c. black	£3000	£3750
		a. Grey-black (Optd S. £600)	£2750	£3500

1898 (1 Apr). (a) *Surch with T* **17** *by Noronha and Sons, Hong Kong*

54	**2**	10 c. on 30 c. grey-green (No. 39a)	£450	£750
		a. Figures "10" widely spaced (1½ mm)	£3500	
		b. Surch double		

Type **17** was applied in a horizontal setting of 12, No. 54a appearing on position 12 for the early printings only.

(b) *As No.* 54, *but with handstamped Chinese characters, T* **18**, *in addition*

55	**2**	10 c. on 30 c. grey-green (No. 39a) (H/S S. £130)	38·00	70·00
		a. Yellowish green (Optd S. £150)	80·00	£110
		b. Figures "10" widely spaced (1½ mm)	£700	£800
		c. Chinese character large (Type 19)	£850	£950
		ca. Ditto. Figures "10" widely spaced	£6500	
		d. Surch Type 17 double		

1900 (Aug)–**01**. *Wmk Crown CA. P* 14.

56	**1**	2 c. dull green	25·00	85
		w. Wmk inverted	£110	55·00
57	**2**	4 c. carmine (1901)	14·00	85
58		5 c. yellow	17·00	6·50
59		10 c. ultramarine	45·00	1·75
		w. Wmk inverted	—	70·00
60	**1**	12 c. blue (1901)	32·00	42·00
61	**2**	30 c. brown (1901)	30·00	20·00
56/61			Set of 6	£140	60·00
56/9, 61 Optd "Specimen"			Set of 5	£450	

20

21

22

23

1903 (Jan–July). *Wmk Crown CA. P* 14.

62	**20**	1 c. dull purple and brown	2·00	50
63		2 c. dull green (July)	6·50	1·50
		w. Wmk inverted		
64	**21**	4 c. purple/red (July)	8·00	40
65		5 c. dull green and brown-orange (July)	9·00	9·00
66		8 c. slate and violet (12 Feb)	7·50	1·25
67	**20**	10 c. purple and blue/blue (July)	28·00	4·25
68	**23**	12 c. green and purple/yellow (18 Feb)	7·00	4·25
69		20 c. slate and chestnut (June)	35·00	3·00
70	**22**	30 c. dull green and black (21 May)	35·00	18·00
71	**23**	50 c. dull green and magenta (June)	28·00	28·00
72	**20**	$1 purple and sage-green (June)	65·00	20·00

73	**23**	$2 slate and scarlet (July)	£180	£225
74	**22**	$3 slate and dull blue (July)	£190	£325
75	**23**	$5 purple and blue-green (June)	£350	£425
76	**22**	$10 slate and orange/blue (July)	£850	£400
62/76			Set of 15	£1600	£1300
62/76 Optd "Specimen"			Set of 15	£1200	

1904 (4 Oct)–**06**. *Wmk Mult Crown CA. Chalk-surfaced paper* (8, 12 c., $3, $5) *or ordinary paper (others). P* 14.

77	**20**	2 c. dull green	4·25	1·25
		a. Chalk-surfaced paper (1906)	7·00	2·50
78	**21**	4 c. purple/red	9·50	40
		a. Chalk-surfaced paper (1906)	5·50	60
79		5 c. dull green and brown-orange	18·00	6·00
		a. Chalk-surfaced paper (1906)	10·00	5·00
		aw. Wmk inverted		
80		8 c. slate and violet (1906)	8·00	2·00
81	**20**	10 c. purple and blue/blue (3.05)	14·00	90
82	**23**	12 c. green and purple/yellow (1906)	10·00	5·50
83		20 c. slate and chestnut	26·00	2·25
		a. Chalk-surfaced paper (1906)	22·00	2·25
		w. Wmk inverted	†	£275
84	**22**	30 c. dull green and black (1906)	27·00	14·00
		a. Chalk-surfaced paper (1906)	32·00	16·00
85	**23**	50 c. green and magenta (1906)	48·00	7·00
		a. Chalk-surfaced paper (1906)	48·00	10·00
86	**20**	$1 purple and sage-green (1906)	90·00	18·00
		a. Chalk-surfaced paper (1906)	85·00	18·00
87	**23**	$2 slate and scarlet (1906)	£160	90·00
		a. Chalk-surfaced paper (1905)	£150	80·00
88	**22**	$3 slate and dull blue (1905)	£160	£180
89	**23**	$5 purple and blue-green (1905)	£350	£300
90	**22**	$10 slate and orange/blue (5.05)	£1400	£950
		a. Chalk-surfaced paper (1906)	£1300	£750
77/90			Set of 14	£2000	£1200

1907–**11**. *Colours changed and new value. Wmk Mult Crown CA. Chalk-surfaced paper* (6 c. *and* 20 c. *to* $2). *P* 14.

91	**20**	1 c. brown (9.10)	3·00	90
92		2 c. deep green	17·00	1·75
		a. Green	17·00	1·50
93	**21**	4 c. carmine-red	4·75	40
94	**22**	6 c. orange-vermilion and purple (10.07)	16·00	3·50
95	**20**	10 c. bright ultramarine	17·00	40
96	**23**	20 c. purple and sage-green (3.11)	35·00	38·00
97	**22**	30 c. purple and orange-yellow (3.11)	48·00	19·00
98	**23**	50 c. black/green (3.11)	38·00	14·00
99		$2 carmine-red and black (1910)	£250	£225
91/9			Set of 9	£375	£275
91, 93/9 Optd "Specimen"			Set of 8	£750	

24

25

26

27

28

(A)

(B)

In Type A of the 25 c. the upper Chinese character in the left-hand label has a short vertical stroke crossing it at the foot. In Type B this stroke is absent.

1912 (9 Nov)–**21**. *Wmk Mult Crown CA. Chalk-surfaced paper* (12 c. *to* $10). *P* 14.

100	**24**	1 c. brown	2·00	55
		a. Black-brown	3·50	2·00
		b. Crown broken at right (R. 9/2)	£190	£140
101		2 c. deep green	5·00	30
		a. Green	5·00	30
102	**25**	4 c. carmine-red	4·00	30
		a. Scarlet (1914)	15·00	1·75
103	**26**	6 c. yellow-orange	3·75	85
		a. Brown-orange	4·25	1·25
		w. Wmk inverted		
104	**25**	8 c. grey	23·00	4·50
		a. Slate (1914)	30·00	4·50
105	**24**	10 c. ultramarine	29·00	30
		a. Deep bright ultramarine	24·00	30
106	**27**	12 c. purple/yellow	3·75	5·50
		a. White back (Optd S. £85) (1914)	7·00	11·00
107		20 c. purple and sage-green	5·00	90
108		25 c. purple & magenta (Type A) (1.14)	16·00	18·00
109		25 c. purple & magenta (Type B) (8.19)	£130	50·00
110		30 c. purple and orange-yellow	25·00	5·00
		a. Purple and orange	12·00	4·50
		w. Wmk inverted		
111	**27**	50 c. black/blue-green	11·00	1·50
		a. White back (Optd S. £130) (5.14)	10·00	4·25
		b. On blue-green, olive back (1917)	£950	28·00
		c. On emerald surface (9.19)	19·00	8·00
		d. On emerald back (Optd S. £130) (7.12.21)	20·00	6·50
112	**24**	$1 purple and blue/blue	32·00	2·25
		w. Wmk inverted	£100	75·00
113	**27**	$2 carmine-red and grey-black	£100	38·00
114	**26**	$3 green and purple	£170	65·00
115	**27**	$5 green and red/green	£475	£300
		a. White back (Optd S. £250) (5.14)	£475	£250
		b. On blue-green, olive back (Optd S. £275) (1917)	£850	£225
		bw. Wmk inverted		
116	**26**	$10 purple and black/red	£500	80·00
100/16			Set of 17	£1300	£375
100/16 Optd "Specimen"			Set of 17	£1500	

No. 100b occurred on R. 9/2 of the lower right pane of the first MCA printing before being retouched.

Broken flower at top right
(Upper left pane R. 1/3)

1921 (Jan)–**37**. *Wmk Mult Script CA. Chalk-surfaced paper* (12 c. *to* $5). *P* 14.

117	**24**	1 c. brown	1·00	40
118		2 c. blue-green	2·25	30
		a. Yellow-green (1932)	6·50	30
		bw. Wmk inverted	55·00	
118c		2 c. grey (14.4.37)	14·00	5·00
119	**25**	3 c. grey (8.10.31)	4·00	1·00
120		4 c. carmine-rose	3·25	70
		a. Carmine-red (1932)	2·25	30
		b. Top of lower Chinese characters at right broken off (R. 9/4)	75·00	60·00
121		5 c. violet (16.10.31)	4·75	30
122		8 c. grey	9·00	32·00
123		8 c. orange (7.12.21)	3·50	1·00
124	**24**	10 c. bright ultramarine	2·75	30
		aw. Wmk inverted		
124b	**27**	12 c. purple/yellow (3.4.33)	11·00	95
125		20 c. purple and sage-green (7.12.21)	3·50	30
126	**28**	25 c. purple and magenta (B) (7.12.21)	3·25	40
		a. Broken flower	30·00	35·00
		w. Wmk inverted	†	£120
127	**26**	30 c. purple & chrome-yellow (7.12.21)	10·00	1·50
		a. Purple and orange-yellow	22·00	7·00
		w. Wmk inverted		£110
128	**27**	50 c. black/emerald (1924)	8·50	30
129	**24**	$1 purple and blue/blue (7.12.21)	22·00	50
130	**27**	$2 carmine-red & grey-black (7.12.21)	85·00	6·00
131		$3 green and dull purple (1926)	£150	48·00
132	**27**	$5 green and red/emerald (1925)	£400	65·00
117/32			Set of 18	£650	£140
117/32 Optd/Perf "Specimen"			Set of 18	£1400	

No. 120b occurs on R. 9/4 of the lower left pane.

1935 (6 May). *Silver Jubilee. As Nos.* 91/4 *of Antigua, but ptd by B.W. P* 11×12.

133		3 c. ultramarine and grey-black	4·00	3·25
		c. Lightning conductor	£300	£180
134		5 c. green and indigo	8·00	3·25
		a. Extra flagstaff	£275	£250
		b. Short extra flagstaff	£325	
		c. Lightning conductor	£275	
		d. Flagstaff on right-hand turret	£325	
135		10 c. brown and deep blue	20·00	1·60
136		20 c. slate and purple	38·00	7·50
		b. Short extra flagstaff	£600	£225
		d. Flagstaff on right-hand turret	£550	£225
		e. Double flagstaff	£550	£225
133/6			Set of 4	60·00	14·00
133/6 Perf "Specimen"			Set of 4	£300	

For illustrations of plate varieties see Catalogue Introduction.

1937 (12 May). *Coronation. As Nos.* 95/7 *of Antigua. P* 11×11½.

137		4 c. green	4·50	2·50
138		15 c. carmine	10·00	3·25
139		25 c. blue	13·00	2·50
137/9			Set of 3	25·00	7·50
137/9 Perf "Specimen"			Set of 3	£180	

29 King George VI

Short right leg to "R" (Right pane R. 7/3, left pane R. 3/1)

1938–**52**. *Wmk Mult Script CA. Chalk-surfaced paper* (80 c., $1 (No. 155), $2 (No. 157), $5 (No. 159), $10 (No. 161)). *P* 14.

140	**29**	1 c. brown (24.5.38)	1·75	80
		a. Pale brown (4.2.52)	2·00	4·75
141		2 c. grey (5.4.38)	2·00	30
		a. Perf 14½×14 (28.9.45)	1·75	4·50
142		4 c. orange (5.4.38)	3·25	1·25
		a. Perf 14½×14 (28.9.45)	4·50	3·25
143		5 c. green (24.5.38)	1·25	20
		a. Perf 14½×14 (28.9.45)	2·50	5·00
144		8 c. red-brown (1.11.41)	1·75	2·25
		a. Imperf (pair)	£23000	
145		10 c. bright violet (13.4.38)	50·00	75
		a. Perf 14½×14. Dull violet (28.9.45)	8·50	20
		b. Dull reddish violet (9.4.46)	6·00	70
		c. Reddish lilac (9.4.47)	15·00	20
146		15 c. scarlet (13.4.38)	1·75	30
147		20 c. black (1.2.46)	1·25	30
148		20 c. scarlet-vermilion (1.4.48)	7·00	40
		a. Rose-red (25.4.51)	15·00	5·50
149		25 c. bright blue (5.4.38)	26·00	80
150		25 c. pale yellow-olive (9.4.46)	4·75	1·25
151		30 c. yellow-olive (13.4.48)	£150	1·40
		a. Perf 14½×14. Yellowish olive (28.9.45)	22·00	8·00
152		30 c. blue (9.4.46)	7·00	20
153		50 c. reddish purple (13.4.38)	45·00	70
		a. Perf 14½×14. Deep magenta (28.9.45)	29·00	1·10
		ab. Printed both sides, inverted on reverse	£7500	
		b. Chalk-surfaced paper. Brt purple (9.4.47)	9·00	20
154		80 c. carmine (2.2.48)	5·00	95

155	29	$1 dull lilac and blue (*chalk-surfaced paper*) (27.4.38)	.. ..	8·00	2·50
		a. Short right leg to "R"		£110	
		b. *Ordinary paper. Pale reddish lilac and blue* (28.9.45)		11·00	6·50
156		$1 red-orange and green (9.4.46)	..	17·00	30
		a. Short right leg to "R"		£160	
		b. Chalk-surfaced paper (21.6.48)	..	45·00	3·50
		ba. Short right leg to "R"		£275	
		c. Chalk-surfaced paper. *Yellow-orange and green* (6.11.52)		70·00	15·00
157		$2 red-orange and green (24.5.38)	..	70·00	14·00
158		$2 reddish violet and scarlet (9.4.46)		26·00	2·00
		a. Chalk-surfaced paper (9.4.47)		32·00	95
159		$5 dull lilac and scarlet (2.6.38)	..	55·00	48·00
160		$5 green and violet (9.4.46)	..	80·00	15·00
		a. *Yellowish green and violet* (9.4.46)		£150	16·00
		ab. Chalk-surfaced paper (9.4.47)		95·00	2·75
161		$10 green and violet (2.6.38)	..	£400	85·00
162		$10 bright lilac and blue (9.4.46)	..	£140	23·00
		a. Chalk-surfaced paper. *Reddish violet and blue* (9.4.47)		£180	18·00
140/62			Set of 23	£750	£150
140/62 Perf "Specimen"			Set of 23	£2000	

Following bomb damage to the De La Rue works on the night of 29 December 1940 various emergency arrangements were made to complete current requisitions for Hong Kong stamps:

Nos. 141a, 143a, 145a, 151a and 153a (all printings perforated 14½×14 except the 4 c.) were printed and perforated by Bradbury, Wilkinson & Co. Ltd. using De La Rue plates. These stamps are on rough-surfaced paper.

Nos. 142a and 144 were printed by Harrison & Sons in sheets of 120 (12×10) instead of the normal 120 two panes (6×10).

Printings of the $1 and $2 values were made by Williams, Lea & Co. using De La Rue plates.

With the exception of the 8 c. it is believed that none of these printings were issued in Hong Kong before its occupation by the Japanese on 25 December 1941, although examples could be obtained in London from late 1941. The issue dates quoted are those on which the stamps were eventually released in Hong Kong following liberation in 1945.

Nos. 160/a were separate printings released in Hong Kong on the same day.

No. 144a. One imperforate sheet was found and most of the stamps were sold singly to the public at a branch P.O. and used for postage.

30 Street Scene   **31** *Empress of Japan (liner) and Junk*

(Des W. E. Jones. Recess B.W.)

1941 (26 Feb). *Centenary of British Occupation.* T **30**/1 *and similar designs. Wmk Mult Script CA* (*sideways on horiz designs*). P 13½ × 13 (2 c. *and* 25 c.) *or* 13 × 13½ (*others*).

163		2 c. orange and chocolate	.. ..	4·50	1·75
164		4 c. bright purple and carmine	..	4·50	1·75
165		5 c. black and green ..		2·50	50
166		15 c. black and scarlet..		5·50	1·00
167		25 c. chocolate and blue	..	12·00	3·50
168		$1 blue and orange	..	45·00	7·00
163/168			Set of 6	65·00	14·00
163/8 Perf "Specimen"			Set of 6	£325	

Designs: *Horiz*—5 c. The University; 15 c. The Harbour; $1 *Falcon* (clipper) and Short S.23 Empire "C" Class flying boat. *Vert*—25 c. The Hong Kong Bank.

Hong Kong was under Japanese occupation from 25 December 1941 until 30 August 1945. The Japanese post offices in the colony were closed from 31 August and mail was carried free, marked with cachets reading "HONG KONG/1945/POSTAGE PAID". Military administration lasted until 1 May 1946. Hong Kong stamps were re-introduced on 28 September 1945.

36 King George VI and Phoenix   **37** Queen Elizabeth II

Extra stroke (R. 1/2)

(Des W. E. Jones. Recess D.L.R.)

1946 (29 Aug). *Victory. Wmk Mult Script CA. P* 13.

169	36	30 c. blue and red (*shades*)	..	2·00	1·25
		a. Extra stroke	..	45·00	
170		$1 brown and red	..	3·50	75
		a. Extra stroke	..	80·00	
169/70 Perf "Specimen"			Set of 2	£160	

Spur on "N" of "KONG" (R. 2/9)

1948 (22 Dec). *Royal Silver Wedding. As Nos.* 112/13 *of Antigua.*

171		10 c. violet	.. ..	2·75	80
		a. Spur on "N"	..	55·00	
172		$10 carmine	..	£250	75·00

1949 (10 Oct). *75th Anniv of Universal Postal Union. As Nos.* 114/17 *of Antigua.*

173		10 c. violet	..	3·75	50
174		20 c. carmine-red	..	15·00	3·00
175		30 c. deep blue	..	12·00	1·75
176		80 c. bright reddish purple	..	35·00	9·50
173/6			Set of 4	60·00	13·00

1953 (2 June). *Coronation. As No.* 120 *of Antigua.*

177		10 c. black and slate-lilac	..	5·00	30

1954 (5 Jan)–**62**. *Chalk-surfaced paper* (20 c. *to* $10). *Wmk Mult Script CA.* P 14.

178	37	5 c. orange	..	1·50	20
		a. Imperf (pair)	..	£1100	
179		10 c. lilac	..	2·50	10
		aw. Wmk inverted	..	£140	
		b. *Reddish violet* (18.7.61)		7·00	10
180		15 c. green	..	4·25	45
		a. *Pale green* (6.12.55)		4·00	45
181		20 c. brown	..	5·00	30
182		25 c. scarlet	..	3·50	1·00
		a. *Rose-red* (26.5.58)		3·00	70
183		30 c. grey	..	4·50	20
		a. *Pale grey* (26.2.58)		7·00	20
184		40 c. bright blue	..	4·50	40
		a. *Dull blue* (10.1.61)		10·00	70
185		50 c. reddish purple	..	4·75	20
186		65 c. grey (20.6.60)	..	19·00	7·50
187		$1 orange and green	..	7·50	20
188		$1.30, blue and red (20.6.60)	..	23·00	1·00
		a. *Bright blue and red* (23.1.62)		42·00	2·75
189		$2 reddish violet and scarlet	..	12·00	40
		a. *Lt reddish violet & scarlet* (26.2.58)		13·00	60
190		$5 green and purple	..	75·00	1·50
		a. *Yellowish green and purple* (7.3.61)		90·00	2·25
191		$10 reddish violet and bright blue	..	60·00	8·50
		a. *Lt reddish violet & brt blue* (26.2.58)		65·00	8·50
178/91			Set of 14	£200	19·00

No. 178a exists from two sheets, each of which had 90 stamps imperforate and 10 perforated on three sides only.
The 10 c. exists in coils constructed from normal sheets.

38 University Arms   **39** Statue of Queen Victoria

(Des and photo Harrison)

1961 (11 Sept). *Golden Jubilee of Hong Kong University.* W w **12**. P 11½ × 12.

192	38	$1 multicoloured	..	7·00	2·00
		a. Gold ptg omitted	..	£1300	

(Des Cheung Yat-man. Photo Harrison)

1962 (4 May). *Stamp Centenary.* W w **12**. P 14½.

193	39	10 c. black and magenta	..	60	10
194		20 c. black and light blue	..	1·75	2·00
195		50 c. black and bistre	..	4·00	40
193/5			Set of 3	5·75	2·25

40 Queen Elizabeth II (after Annigoni)   **41**

(Photo Harrison)

1962 (4 Oct)–**73**. W w **12** (*upright*). *Chalk-surfaced paper.* P 15 × 14 (5 c. *to* $1) *or* 14 × 14½ (*others*).

196	40	5 c. red-orange	..	60	60
197		10 c. bright reddish violet	..	1·50	10
		a. *Reddish violet* (19.11.71)		4·00	10
		ab. Glazed paper (14.4.72)		8·50	1·75
198		15 c. emerald	..	2·50	85
199		20 c. red-brown	..	1·75	85
		a. *Brown* (13.12.71)		7·00	2·00
		ab. Glazed paper (27.9.72)		13·00	8·50

200	40	25 c. cerise	..	2·50	1·75
201		30 c. deep grey-blue	..	2·50	10
		a. *Chalky blue* (19.11.71)		6·50	2·00
		ab. Glazed paper (27.9.72)		14·00	4·50
202		40 c. deep bluish green	..	2·00	40
203		50 c. scarlet	..	1·75	30
		a. *Vermilion* (13.12.71)		12·00	2·00
		ab. Glazed paper (27.9.72)		10·00	2·50
204		65 c. ultramarine	..	17·00	2·00
205		$1 sepia	..	17·00	40
206	41	$1.30, multicoloured	..	5·00	20
		a. Pale yellow omitted	..	38·00	
		b. Pale yellow inverted (horiz pair)		£3000	
		c. Ochre (sash) omitted	..	27·00	
		d. Glazed paper (3.2.71)	..	13·00	2·25
		da. Ochre (sash) omitted	..	32·00	
		dw. Wmk inverted	..	16·00	
207		$2 multicoloured	..	7·00	50
		a. Pale yellow omitted†	..	38·00	
		b. Ochre (sash) omitted	..	35·00	
		c. Pale yellow† and ochre (sash) omitted	..	£160	
		dw. Wmk inverted	..	10·00	
		e. Glazed paper (1973)*		£150	6·50
208		$5 multicoloured	..	17·00	1·25
		a. Ochre (sash) omitted	..	38·00	
		bw. Wmk inverted	..	25·00	
		c. Glazed paper (3.2.71)		25·00	9·50
		cw. Wmk inverted	..	40·00	
209		$10 multicoloured	..	30·00	2·50
		a. Ochre (sash) omitted	..	£110	
		b. Pale yellow† and ochre (sash) omitted	..	£160	
		cw. Wmk inverted	..	70·00	
		d. Glazed paper (1973)*		£1900	£120
210		$20 multicoloured	..	£140	23·00
		w. Wmk inverted	..	£600	
196/210			Set of 15	£225	30·00

*These are from printings which were sent to Hong Kong in March 1973 but not released in London.
†This results in the Queen's face appearing pinkish.

It is believed that No. 206b comes from the last two vertical rows of a sheet, the remainder of which had the pale yellow omitted.

The $1.30 to $20 exist with PVA gum as well as gum arabic. The glazed paper printings are with PVA gum only.

See also Nos. 222, etc.

1963 (4 June). *Freedom from Hunger. As No.* 146 *of Antigua, but additionally inscr in Chinese characters.*

211		$1.30, bluish green	..	55·00	8·00

1963 (2 Sept). *Red Cross Centenary. As Nos.* 147/8 *of Antigua, but additionally inscr in Chinese characters at right.*

212		10 c. red and black	..	5·00	30
213		$1.30, red and blue ..	..	35·00	8·00

1965 (17 May). *I.T.U. Centenary. As Nos.* 166/7 *of Antigua.*

214		10 c. light purple and orange-yellow	..	4·00	25
		w. Wmk inverted		42·00	
215		$1.30, olive-yellow and deep bluish green		25·00	5·50

1965 (25 Oct). *International Co-operation Year. As Nos.* 168/9 *of Antigua.*

216		10 c. reddish purple and turquoise-green	..	3·00	25
		w. Wmk inverted		4·25	
217		$1.30, dp bluish green & lavender (*shades*)	20·00	5·50

1966 (24 Jan). *Churchill Commemoration. As Nos.* 170/3 *of Antigua but additionally inscr in Chinese characters.*

218		10 c. new blue	..	3·00	15
		w. Wmk inverted	..	13·00	
219		50 c. deep green	..	3·50	30
		w. Wmk inverted	..	3·50	
220		$1.30, brown	..	24·00	3·00
221		$2 bluish violet	..	38·00	10·00
		w. Wmk inverted	..	£150	
218/21			Set of 4	60·00	12·00

1966 (Aug)–**72**. *As Nos.* 196/208 *and* 210 *but wmk* W w **12** (*sideways**). *Chalk-surfaced paper* (5 c. *to* $1) *or glazed, ordinary paper* ($1.30 *to* $20).

222	40	5 c. red-orange (5.12.66)	..	65	1·00
223		10 c. reddish violet (31.3.67)†	..	70	40
		a. Imperf (horiz pair)	..	£500	
		w. Wmk Crown to right of CA	£140	
224		15 c. emerald (31.3.67)†	..	2·00	1·75
225		20 c. red-brown	..	1·75	1·75
		a. Glazed, ordinary paper (14.4.72)	..	8·00	8·00
226		25 c. cerise (31.3.67)†	..	3·00	3·50
		aw. Wmk Crown to right of CA		9·00	
		b. Glazed, ordinary paper (14.4.72)	..	14·00	14·00
227		30 c. deep grey-blue (31.3.70)	..	10·00	2·00
		a. Glazed, ordinary paper (14.4.72)	..	13·00	8·00
228		40 c. deep bluish green (1967)	..	3·25	1·50
		a. Glazed, ordinary paper (14.4.72)	..	13·00	12·00
229		50 c. scarlet (31.3.67)†	..	2·50	80
		w. Wmk Crown to right of CA (13.5.69)	3·50	1·25
230		65 c. ultramarine (29.3.67)†	..	6·00	6·50
		a. *Bright blue* (16.7.68)		6·00	6·50
231		$1 sepia (29.3.67)†	..	12·00	1·50
		w. Wmk Crown to right of CA		40·00	
232	41	$1.30, multicoloured (14.4.72)	..	10·00	2·00
		w. Wmk Crown to right of CA (17.11.72)	..	12·00	2·25
233		$2 multicoloured (13.12.71)	..	11·00	2·50
		a. Ochre (sash) omitted	..	38·00	
		w. Wmk Crown to right of CA (17.11.72)	..	12·00	3·25
234		$5 multicoloured (13.12.71)	..	65·00	12·00
236		$20 multicoloured (14.4.72)	..	£150	60·00
222/36			Set of 14	£250	85·00

*The normal sideways watermark shows Crown to left of CA, as seen from the back of the stamp.
†Earliest known postmark dates.

The 5 c. to 25 c., 40 c. and 50 c. exist with PVA gum as well as gum arabic, but the 30 c., and all stamps on glazed paper exist with PVA gum only.

1966 (20 Sept). *Inauguration of W.H.O. Headquarters, Geneva. As Nos. 178/9 of Antigua, but additionally inscr in Chinese characters.*
237   10 c. black, yellow-green and light blue   3·00   30
238   50 c. black, light purple and yellow-brown   10·00   1·75

1966 (1 Dec). *20th Anniv of U.N.E.S.C.O. As Nos. 196/8 of Antigua, but additionally inscr in Chinese characters.*
239   10 c. slate-violet, red, yellow and orange   3·50   20
240   50 c. orange-yellow, violet and deep olive   13·00   90
241   $2 black, light purple and orange   55·00   20·00
239/41   Set of 3   65·00   20·00

42 Rams' Heads on Chinese Lanterns

(Des V. Whiteley. Photo Harrison)

1967 (17 Jan). *Chinese New Year ("Year of the Ram"). T 42 and similar horiz design. W w 12 (sideways). P 14½.*
242   10 c. rosine, olive-green and light yellow-olive   4·00   50
243   $1.30, emerald, rosine and light yellow-olive   32·00   11·00
Design:—$1.30, Three rams.

44 Cable Route Map

(Des V. Whiteley. Photo Harrison)

1967 (30 Mar). *Completion of Malaysia–Hong Kong Link of SEACOM Telephone Cable. W w 12. P 12½.*
244   44 $1.30, new blue and red   17·00   4·50

45 Rhesus Macaques in Tree ("Year of the Monkey")

(Des R. Granger Barrett. Photo Harrison)

1968 (23 Jan). *Chinese New Year ("Year of the Monkey"). T 45 and similar horiz design. W w 12 (sideways). P 14½.*
245   10 c. gold, black and scarlet   4·50   50
246   $1.30, gold, black and scarlet   30·00   10·00
Design:—$1.30, Family of Rhesus Macaques.

47 *Iberia* (liner) at Ocean Terminal

(Des and litho D.L.R.)

1968 (24 Apr). *Sea Craft. T 47 and similar horiz designs. P 13.*
247   10 c. multicoloured   2·00   15
   a. Dull orange and new blue omitted   £950
248   20 c. cobalt-blue, black and brown   3·25   1·00
249   40 c. orange, black and mauve   11·00   9·00
250   50 c. orange-red, black and green   7·50   75
   a. Green omitted   £800
251   $1 greenish yellow, black and red   16·00   4·50
252   $1.30, Prussian blue, black and pink   45·00   4·25
247/52   Set of 6   75·00   18·00
Designs:—20 c. Pleasure launch; 40 c. Car ferry; 50 c. Passenger ferry; $1, Sampan; $1.30, Junk.

53 *Bauhinia blakeana*   **54** Arms of Hong Kong

(Des V. Whiteley. Photo Harrison)

1968 (25 Sept)–**73**. *W w 12. P 14 × 14½.*
(a) *Upright wmk. Chalk-surfaced paper*
253   53   65 c. multicoloured   9·00   50
   aw. Wmk inverted   17·00
   b. Glazed, ordinary paper (3.73)   55·00   14·00
254   54 $1 multicoloured   9·00   40
(b) *Sideways wmk. Glazed, ordinary paper*
254a   53   65 c. multicoloured (27.9.72)   38·00   16·00
254b   54 $1 multicoloured (13.12.71)   7·50   2·25
Nos. 253/4 exist with PVA gum as well as gum arabic; Nos. 254a/b with PVA gum only.

55 "Aladdin's Lamp" and Human Rights Emblem

(Des R. Granger Barrett. Litho B.W.)

1968 (20 Nov). *Human Rights Year. W w 12 (sideways). P 13½.*
255   55   10 c. orange, black and myrtle-green   1·50   75
256   50 c. yellow, black & dp reddish purple   4·50   2·25

56 Cockerel

(Des R. Granger Barrett. Photo Enschedé)

1969 (11 Feb). *Chinese New Year ("Year of the Cock"). T 56 and similar multicoloured design. P 13½.*
257   10 c. Type 56   5·00   1·00
   a. Red omitted   £170
258   $1.30, Cockerel (*vert*)   65·00   14·00

58 Arms of Chinese University   **59** Earth Station and Satellite

(Des V. Whiteley. Photo Govt Ptg Bureau, Tokyo)

1969 (26 Aug). *Establishment of Chinese University of Hong Kong. P 13½.*
259   58   40 c. violet, gold and pale turquoise-blue   7·00   3·50

(Des V. Whiteley. Photo Harrison)

1969 (24 Sept). *Opening of Communications Satellite Tracking Station. W w 12. P 14½.*
260   59 $1 multicoloured   24·00   4·50

60 Chow's Head   **62** "Expo 70" Emblem

(Des R. Granger Barrett. Photo D.L.R.)

1970 (28 Jan). *Chinese New Year ("Year of the Dog"). T 60 and similar design. W w 12 (sideways on $1.30). P 14½×14 (10 c.) or 14×14½ ($1.30).*
261   10 c. lemon-yellow, orange-brown and black   5·50   1·25
262   $1.30, multicoloured   65·00   14·00
Design:—*Horiz*—$1.30, Chow standing.

(Des and litho B.W.)

1970 (14 Mar). *World Fair, Osaka. T 62 and similar multi-coloured design. W w 12 (sideways on 25 c.). P 13½ × 13 (15 c.) or 13 × 13½ (25 c.).*
263   15 c. Type 62   65   85
264   25 c. "Expo '70" emblem and junks (*horiz*)   1·40   1·50

64 Plaque in Tung Wah Hospital   **65** Symbol

(Des M. F. Griffith. Photo Harrison)

1970 (9 Apr). *Centenary of Tung Wah Hospital. W w 12 (sideways*). P 14½.*
265   64   10 c. multicoloured   75   25
266   50 c. multicoloured   3·25   1·50
   w. Wmk Crown to right of CA   4·00
*The normal sideways watermark shows Crown to left of CA, as seen from the back of the stamp.

(Des J. Cooter. Litho B.W.)

1970 (5 Aug). *Asian Productivity Year. W w 12. P 14 × 13½.*
267   65   10 c. multicoloured   1·00   60

66 Pig

(Des Kan Tai-keung. Photo Govt Ptg Bureau, Tokyo)

1971 (20 Jan). *Chinese New Year ("Year of the Pig"). P 13½.*
268   66   10 c. multicoloured   5·00   90
269   $1.30, multicoloured   30·00   11·00

67 "60" and Scout Badge   **68** Festival Emblem

(Des Kan Tai-keung. Litho Harrison)

1971 (23 July). *Diamond Jubilee of Scouting in Hong Kong. W w 12 (sideways). P 14×15.*
270   67   10 c. black, scarlet and yellow   75   10
271   50 c. black, green and blue   3·50   1·00
272   $2 black, magenta and bluish violet   20·00   11·00
270/2   Set of 3   22·00   11·00

(Des Kan Tai-keung. Litho J.W.)

1971 (2 Nov). *Hong Kong Festival. T 68 and similar designs. W w 12 (sideways on 10 c. and 50 c.). P 14 (10 c.) or 14½ (others).*
273   68   10 c. orange and purple   1·25   20
274   –   50 c. multicoloured   2·75   90
275   – $1 multicoloured   8·50   6·50
273/5   Set of 3   11·00   7·00
Designs: *Horiz* (39 × 23 mm)—50 c. Coloured streamers. *Vert* (23 × 39 mm)—$1 "Orchid".

69 Stylised Rats

(Des Kan Tai-keung. Photo D.L.R.)

1972 (8 Feb). *Chinese New Year ("Year of the Rat"). W w 12. P 13½.*
276   69   10 c. red, gold and black   3·50   50
277   $1.30, gold, red and black   32·00   11·00
   w. Wmk inverted   45·00

70 Tunnel Entrance

(Des G. Drummond from painting by G. Baxter. Litho Harrison)

1972 (20 Oct). *Opening of Cross-Harbour Tunnel. W w 12. P 14×15.*
278   70 $1 multicoloured   5·00   2·25
   w. Wmk inverted   60·00

71 Phoenix and Dragon   **72** Ox

(Des (from photograph by D. Groves) and photo Harrison)

1972 (20 Nov). *Royal Silver Wedding. W w 12. P 14×15.*
279   71   10 c. multicoloured   30   15
   a. Gold omitted   £750
280   50 c. multicoloured   1·10   1·40
   a. Dull purple ("50 c", "HONG KONG" and background) double   £600
   w. Wmk inverted   38·00

(Des R. Granger Barrett. Photo Harrison)

1973 (25 Jan). *Chinese New Year ("Year of the Ox"). W w 12 (sideways on 10 c.). P 14½.*
281 72 10 c. reddish orange, brown and black .. 2·00 50
282 – $1.30, lt yellow, yellow-orange & black .. 6·50 7·00
    w. Wmk inverted .. .. .. 8·00
Design:—$1.30, similar to 10 c., but horiz.

73   Queen Elizabeth II   **74**

(Des from coinage. Photo ($10 and $20 also embossed) Harrison)

1973 (12 June)–**74.** *W w 12 (sideways* on 15, 30, 40 c. $1.30, 2, 5, 10, $20). P 14½×14 (Nos. 283/91) or 14×14½ (292/6).*
283 73 10 c. bright orange .. .. .. 1·00 60
    a. Wmk sideways (from coils) .. 1·75 2·25
284   15 c. yellow-green .. .. .. 7·00 6·00
    w. Wmk Crown to left of CA (21.1.74) 9·00 6·50
285   20 c. reddish violet 75 30
    w. Wmk inverted .. .. 3·00
286   25 c. lake-brown .. .. .. 11·00 6·50
287   30 c. ultramarine .. .. .. 1·00 60
    w. Wmk Crown to left of CA (21.1.74) 4·50 1·10
288   40 c. turquoise-blue .. .. .. 2·50 2·50
    a. Printed on the gummed side .. £500
289   50 c. light orange-vermilion .. 1·25 60
290   65 c. greenish bistre .. .. 12·00 11·00
291    $1 bottle-green .. .. .. 2·25 80
292 74 $1.30, pale yellow and reddish violet 7·00 90
293    $2 pale green and reddish brown .. 8·00 1·25
294    $5 pink and royal blue .. .. 11·00 3·50
    a. Imperf (horiz pair) £550
    b. Pink omitted £1000
295    $10 pink and deep blackish olive .. 15·00 8·50
296    $20 pink and brownish black .. 25·00 28·00
    w. Wmk Crown to right of CA
283/96 .. .. *Set of 4* 90·00 65·00
*The normal sideways watermark shows Crown to right of CA on the 15 and 30 c., and to left of CA on 40 c. and T 74, as seen from the back of the stamp.
Nos. 295/6 are known with embossing omitted, but it has been reported that such errors can be faked.
See also Nos. 311/24c and 340/53.

1973 (14 Nov). *Royal Wedding. As Nos. 165/6 of Anguilla, but additionally inscr in Chinese characters.*
297   50 c. ochre 50 15
    w. Wmk Crown to right of CA .. 26·00
298    $2 bright mauve .. .. .. 2·25 1·50
The normal sideways watermark shows Crown to left of CA, as seen from the back of the stamp.

75 Festival Symbols forming Chinese Character

(Des Kan Tai-keung. Litho B.W.)

1973 (23 Nov). *Hong Kong Festival. T 75 and similar horiz designs. W w 12. P 14½.*
299 75 10 c. brownish red and bright green .. 40 10
    w. Wmk inverted .. .. 3·50
300   50 c. deep magenta and reddish orange 2·00 95
    w. Wmk inverted .. .. 6·50
301    $1 bright green and deep mauve .. 4·75 4·75
299/301 .. .. *Set of 3* 6·50 5·25
Each value has the festival symbols arranged to form a Chinese character. "Hong" on the 10 c.; "Kong" on the 50 c.; "Festival" on the $1.

76 Tiger   **77** Chinese Mask

(Des R. Granger Barrett. Litho Harrison)

1974 (8 Jan). *Chinese New Year ("Year of the Tiger"). W w 12 (sideways* on $1.30). P 14½.*
302 76 10 c. multicoloured .. .. .. 3·50 50
    w. Wmk inverted .. .. 10·00
303    $1.30, multicoloured .. .. 11·00 12·00
    w. Wmk Crown to left of CA .. 15·00
Design:—$1.30, Similar to T 76, but vert.
*The normal sideways watermark shows Crown to right of CA, as seen from the back of the stamp.

(Des R. Hookham. Litho Enschedé)

1974 (1 Feb). *Arts Festival. Vert designs as T 77 showing Chinese opera masks. W w 12 (sideways). P 12 × 12½.*
304 77 10 c. multicoloured 75 10
305    $1 multicoloured .. .. .. 6·00 4·25
306    $2 multicoloured .. .. .. 9·00 8·50
304/6 .. .. *Set of 3* 14·00 11·50
MS307 159×94 mm. Nos. 304/6. Wmk upright.
    P 14×13 .. .. .. 60·00 48·00

78 Pigeons with Letters

(Des Kan Tai-keung. Litho Harrison)

1974 (9 Oct). *Centenary of Universal Postal Union. T 78 and similar horiz designs. W w 12 (sideways* on 10 and 50 c.). P 14½.*
308   10 c. lt greenish blue, lt yell-grn & slate-blk 40 10
    aw. Wmk Crown to right of CA .. 3·00
    b. No wmk .. .. .. 35·00
309   50 c. deep mauve, orange and slate-black 1·00 40
    w. Wmk Crown to right of CA .. 32·00
310    $2 multicoloured .. .. .. 5·25 4·25
    w. Wmk inverted .. ..
308/10 .. .. *Set of 3* 6·00 4·25
Designs:—50 c. Globe within letter; $2 Hands holding letters.
*The normal sideways watermark shows Crown to left of CA, as seen from the back of the stamp.

1975 (21 Jan). *New values (60, 70, 80 and 90 c.) or as Nos. 283/96 but w w 14 (sideways* on 10, 20, 25, 50, 65 c. and $1).*
311 73 10 c. bright orange (21.2.75) .. 55 30
    a. Wmk upright (from coils) (10.78) 4·50 4·75
312   15 c. yellow-green (21.1.75) .. 16·00 9·50
313   20 c. reddish violet (19.3.75) .. 50 10
    a. *Deep reddish mauve* (21.6.77) 1·25 10
    b. *Deep reddish purple* (22.6.79) 1·25 10
    bw. Wmk Crown to right of CA .. 1·25 20
314   25 c. lake-brown (19.3.75) .. 15·00 12·00
315   30 c. ultramarine (9.4.75) .. 70 30
    a. *Deep ultramarine* (20.4.78) 1·50 55
    w. Wmk inverted .. .. 4·50
316   40 c. turquoise-blue (19.3.75) .. 1·25 1·50
    w. Wmk inverted .. .. 4·00
317   50 c. light orange-vermilion (19.3.75) 2·25 50
318   60 c. lavender (4.5.77) .. .. 1·75 2·00
    w. Wmk inverted .. .. 6·50
319   65 c. greenish bistre (19.3.75) .. 18·00 13·00
320   70 c. yellow (4.5.77) .. .. 1·75 30
    a. *Chrome-yellow* (24.1.80) .. 2·75 90
    w. Wmk inverted .. .. 5·00
321   80 c. bright magenta (4.5.77) .. 2·25 2·75
    a. *Magenta* (24.1.80) .. .. 2·75 3·00
    bw. Wmk inverted .. .. 6·00
321c 73 90 c. sepia (1.10.81) .. .. 7·50 1·40
322    $1 bottle-green (19.3.75) .. 3·00 60
    a. *Blackish olive* (24.1.80) .. 3·00 70
    w. Wmk Crown to right of CA .. 3·75
323 74 $1.30, pale yell & reddish vio (19.3.75) 2·50 30
    w. Wmk inverted .. .. 4·00
324    $2 pale green & reddish brn (19.3.75) 3·00 1·25
    a. *Pale green and brown* (10.5.82) 8·50 3·00
    bw. Wmk inverted .. .. 5·50
324c $5 pink and royal blue (20.4.78) 4·75 1·75
    ca. *Pink & deep ultramarine* (10.5.82) 13·00 4·50
    cw. Wmk inverted (10.5.82) .. 9·00 4·50
324d $10 pink & deep blackish olive (20.4.78) 8·00 5·50
    dw. Wmk inverted .. .. 9·00
324e $20 pink and brownish black (20.4.78) 13·00 11·00
    ea. Imperf (horiz pair) £600
    ew. Wmk inverted .. .. 17·00
311/24e .. .. *Set of 18* 90·00 55·00
*The normal sideways watermark shows Crown to left of CA, as seen from the back of the stamp.
Nos. 324d/e are known with the embossing omitted. See note after No. 296.

79 Stylized Hare

(Des Kan Tai-keung. Litho Harrison)

1975 (5 Feb). *Chinese New Year ("Year of the Hare"). T 79 and similar horiz design. P 14½. (a) No wmk.*
325 79 10 c. silver and light red .. .. 1·00 75
326    $1.30, gold and light green .. 8·50 11·00
       (b) W w 12
327 79 10 c. silver and light red .. .. 1·00 60
    w. Wmk inverted .. .. 38·00
328    $1.30, gold and light green .. 8·00 8·00
    w. Wmk inverted .. .. 48·00
Design:—$1.30, Pair of hares.

COVER PRICES

Cover factors are quoted at the beginning of each country for most issues to 1945. An explanation of the system can be found on page x. The factors quoted do not, however, apply to philatelic covers.

---

80 Queen Elizabeth II, the Duke of   **81** Mid-Autumn
Edinburgh and Hong Kong Arms   Festival

(Des PAD Studio. Litho Questa)

1975 (30 Apr). *Royal Visit. W w 14 (sideways). P 13½×14.*
329 80 $1.30, multicoloured .. .. 2·75 2·00
330    $2 multicoloured .. .. .. 3·75 4·25

(Des Tao Ho. Litho De La Rue, Bogotá)

1975 (31 July). *Hong Kong Festivals of 1975. T 81 and similar vert designs. Multicoloured. No wmk. P 14.*
331   50 c. Type 81 .. .. .. 2·00 50
332    $1 Dragon-boat Festival .. .. 8·00 2·50
    a. Black (oars, etc) omitted .. £550
    b. Printed on the gummed side
333    $2 Tin Hau Festival .. .. 28·00 8·50
331/3 .. .. *Set of 3* 35·00 10·50
MS334 102×83 mm. Nos. 331/3 .. £110 45·00

82 Hwamei   **83** Dragon

(Des C. Kuan. Litho Harrison)

1975 (29 Oct). *Birds. T 82 and similar vert designs. Multicoloured. W w 14. P 14½.*
335   50 c. Type 82 .. .. .. 2·50 50
    w. Wmk inverted .. .. 5·00
336    $1.30, Chinese Bulbul .. .. 8·50 5·00
337    $2 Black-capped Kingfisher .. 16·00 12·00
    w. Wmk inverted .. .. 17·00
335/7 .. .. *Set of 3* 24·00 16·00

(Des Kan Tai-keung. Litho Questa)

1976 (21 Jan). *Chinese New Year ("Year of the Dragon"). T 83 and similar horiz design. W w 14 (sideways*). P 14½.*
338 83 20 c. mauve, dull lake and gold .. 75 10
    w. Wmk Crown to right of CA .. 55·00
339    $1.30, light yellow-green, lt red & gold 6·50 3·25
No. 339 is as T 83 but has the design reversed.
*The normal sideways watermark shows Crown to left of CA, as seen from the back of the stamp.

1976 (20 Feb–19 Mar). *As Nos. 283, 285, 287 and 293/6 but without wmk.*
340 73 10 c. bright orange (coil stamp) (19.3.76) 24·00 8·50
342   20 c. reddish violet .. .. .. 3·50 1·25
    a. Imperf (pair) £550
344   30 c. ultramarine .. .. .. 7·00 2·25
    a. Imperf (pair) £650
350 74 $2 pale green and reddish brown .. 9·00 3·75
351    $5 pink and royal blue .. .. 9·00 7·00
352    $10 pink & dp blackish olive (19.3.76) 75·00 42·00
353    $20 pink and brownish black (19.3.76) £160 60·00
340/53 .. .. *Set of 7* £250 £110
No. 353 is known with the embossing omitted. See note after No. 296.

84 "60" and Girl Guides Badge   **85** "Postal Services" in
                                         Chinese Characters

(Des P. Ma. Photo Harrison)

1976 (23 Apr). *Girl Guides Diamond Jubilee. T 84 and similar horiz design. Multicoloured. W w 12. P 14½.*
354   20 c. Type 84 .. .. .. 50 10
    w. Wmk inverted .. .. 3·00
355    $1.30, Badge, stylised diamond and "60" 5·50 4·00
    w. Wmk inverted .. .. 10·00

(Des Tao Ho. Litho Harrison)

1976 (11 Aug). *Opening of new G.P.O. T 85 and similar vert designs.* W w 14. P 14½.
356	20 c. yellow-green, lt greenish grey & black		75	10
	w. Wmk inverted			
357	$1.30, reddish orge, lt greenish grey & blk		3·75	2·00
358	$2 yellow, light greenish grey and black		6·50	4·50
356/8		*Set of 3*	10·00	6·00

Designs:—$1.30, Old G.P.O.; $2 New G.P.O.

86 Tree Snake on Branch

(Des Jennifer Wong. Litho J.W.)

1977 (6 Jan). *Chinese New Year ("Year of the Snake"). T 86 and similar horiz design.* W w 14 (*sideways*). P 13½.
359	86	20 c. multicoloured	50	15
360	—	$1.30, multicoloured	4·25	4·75
		w. Wmk Crown to left of CA	8·50	

The $1.30 shows a snake facing left.
*The normal sideways watermark shows Crown to right of CA, as seen from the back of the stamp.

87 Presentation of the Orb

88 Tram Cars

(Des Hong Kong Govt Services Dept; adapted J.W. Litho Harrison)

1977 (7 Feb). *Silver Jubilee. T 87 and similar multicoloured designs.* W w 14 (*sideways on $2*). P 14½ × 14 ($2) or 14 × 14½ (*others*).
361	20 c. Type 87		40	10
	w. Wmk inverted		30·00	
362	$1.30, Queen's visit, 1975		1·25	1·25
363	$2 The Orb (*vert*)		1·50	1·50
361/3		*Set of 3*	2·75	2·50

(Des Tao Ho. Litho J.W.)

1977 (30 June). *Tourism. T 88 and similar vert designs. Multicoloured.* W w 14. P 13½.
364	20 c. Type 88		55	10
	w. Wmk inverted		£500	£200
365	60 c. Star Ferryboat		1·50	2·25
	w. Wmk inverted		2·75	
366	$1.30, The Peak Railway		2·75	2·25
	w. Wmk inverted		12·00	
367	$2 Junk and sampan		3·50	3·75
	w. Wmk inverted		6·00	
364/7		*Set of 4*	7·50	7·50

89 Buttercup Orchid   **90 Horse**

(Des Beryl Walden. Litho Questa)

1977 (12 Oct). *Orchids. T 89 and similar vert designs. Multicoloured.* W w 14. P 14½.
368	20 c. Type 89		1·25	20
369	$1.30, Lady's Slipper Orchid		4·00	2·25
370	$2 Susan Orchid		6·00	4·75
368/70		*Set of 3*	10·00	6·50

(Des Graphic Atelier Ltd, Hong Kong. Litho Harrison)

1978 (26 Jan). *Chinese New Year ("Year of the Horse").* W w 14 (*sideways*). P 14½.
371	90	20 c. magenta, yellow-olive & brn-olive	50	10
		w. Wmk Crown to left of CA	2·75	
372	—	$1.30, orange, yell-brn & reddish brn	3·75	4·25

*The normal sideways watermark shows Crown to right of CA, as seen from the back of the stamp.

NEW INFORMATION

The editor is always interested to correspond with people who have new information that will improve or correct the Catalogue.

91 Queen Elizabeth II

92 Girl and Boy holding Hands

(Des G. Vasarhelyi. Litho Harrison)

1978 (2 June). *25th Anniv of Coronation.* W w 14. P 14×14½.
373	91	20 c. magenta and ultramarine	40	10
374		$1.30, ultramarine and magenta	1·50	2·25
		w. Wmk inverted	27·00	

(Des Annette Walker. Litho Harrison)

1978 (8 Nov). *Centenary of Po Leung Kuk (child care organisation). T 92 and similar horiz design. Multicoloured.* W w 14 (*sideways**). P 14½.
375	20 c. Type 92		30	15
	w. Wmk Crown to left of CA		30	15
376	$1.30, Ring of children		1·75	2·25
	w. Wmk Crown to left of CA		1·75	2·25

*The normal sideways watermark shows the Crown to the right of CA *as seen from the back of the stamp.*

93 Electronics Industry

94 *Precis orithya*

(Litho Harrison)

1979 (9 Jan). *Industries. T 93 and similar horiz designs.* W w 14 (*sideways*). P 14½.
377	20 c. orange-yellow, olive-yellow & yell-olive		30	10
378	$1.30, multicoloured		1·10	1·75
379	$2 multicoloured		1·10	2·25
377/9		*Set of 3*	2·25	3·75

Designs:—$1.30, Toy industry; $2, Garment industry.

(Des Jane Thatcher. Photo Harrison)

1979 (20 June). *Butterflies. T 94 and similar vert designs. Multicoloured. No wmk.* P 14½×14.
380	20 c. Type 94		1·00	1·00
381	$1 *Graphium sarpedon*		1·75	80
382	$1.30, *Heliophorus epicles*		2·50	1·60
383	$2 *Danus genutia*		2·75	3·50
380/3		*Set of 4*	7·00	5·50

95 Diagrammatic view of Railway Station

96 Tsui Shing Lau Pagoda

(Des Tao Ho. Litho J.W.)

1979 (1 Oct). *Mass Transit Railway. T 95 and similar horiz designs. Multicoloured.* W w 14 (*sideways**). P 13½.
384	20 c. Type 95		80	10
	w. Wmk Crown to left of CA		3·50	
385	$1.30, Diagrammatic view of car		2·25	80
	w. Wmk Crown to left of CA		13·00	
386	$2 Plan showing route of railway		2·50	2·25
	w. Wmk Crown to left of CA		55·00	
384/6		*Set of 3*	5·00	2·75

*The normal sideways watermark shows Crown to right of CA, *as seen from the back of the stamp.*

(Des D. Leonard. Litho J.W.)

1980 (14 May). *Rural Architecture. T 96 and similar designs.* W w 14 (*sideways on $1.30 and $2*). P 13 × 13½ (20 c.) or 13½ × 13 (*others*).
387	20 c. black, magenta and yellow		40	20
	w. Wmk inverted		26·00	
388	$1.30, multicoloured		1·10	1·25
389	$2 multicoloured		1·60	2·50
387/9		*Set of 3*	2·75	3·50

Designs: *Horiz*—$1.30, Village House, Sai O; $2, Ching Chung Koon Temple.

97 Queen Elizabeth the Queen Mother

98 Botanical Gardens

(Des Harrison. Litho Questa)

1980 (4 Aug). *80th Birthday of Queen Elizabeth the Queen Mother.* W w 14 (*sideways*). P 14.
390	97	$1.30, multicoloured	1·25	1·50

(Des D. Chan. Litho J.W.)

1980 (12 Nov). *Parks. T 98 and similar vert designs. Multicoloured.* W w 14. P 13½.
391	20 c. Type 98		50	15
392	$1 Ocean Park		85	60
393	$1.30, Kowloon Park		90	95
394	$2 Country Parks		2·00	2·75
391/4		*Set of 4*	3·75	4·00

99 Red-spotted Grouper   *Epinephelus akaara*

100 Wedding Bouquet from Hong Kong

(Des Jane Thatcher. Litho J.W.)

1981 (28 Jan). *Fishes. T 99 and similar horiz designs. Multicoloured.* W w 14 (*sideways**). P 13½.
395	20 c. Type 99		40	15
	w. Wmk Crown to left of CA		4·00	
396	$1 Golden Thread-finned Bream		1·10	70
397	$1.30, Scar-breasted Tuskfish		1·25	95
398	$2 Blue-barred Orange Parrotfish		2·00	3·25
395/8		*Set of 4*	4·25	4·50

*The normal sideways watermark shows Crown to right of CA, *as seen from the back of the stamp.*

(Des J.W. Photo Harrison)

1981 (29 July). *Royal Wedding. T 100 and similar vert designs. Multicoloured.* W w 14 (*sideways*). P 14.
399	20 c. Type 100		30	10
400	$1.30, Prince Charles in Hong Kong		70	50
401	$5 Prince Charles and Lady Diana Spencer		2·25	3·00
399/401		*Set of 3*	3·00	3·25

101 Suburban Development

102 "Victoria from the Harbour, c 1855"

(Des Tao Ho. Litho J.W.)

1981 (14 Oct). *Public Housing. T 101 and similar vert designs showing suburban development.* W w 14. P 13½.
402	20 c. multicoloured		25	10
	a. Red (jacket and trousers) omitted		£130	
	w. Wmk inverted (pair)		£500	
403	$1 multicoloured		90	70
404	$1.30, multicoloured		1·25	1·25
405	$2 multicoloured		1·40	2·25
402/5		*Set of 4*	3·50	3·75
MS406	148×105 mm. Nos. 402/5. Wmk inverted		4·25	6·00
	w. Wmk upright		25·00	25·00

(Des R. Solley. Litho Questa)

1982 (5 Jan). *Port of Hong Kong, Past and Present. T 102 and similar horiz designs. Multicoloured.* W w 14. P 14½.
407	20 c. Type 102		60	15
408	$1 "West Point, Hong Kong, 1847"		1·75	90
409	$1.30, Fleet of Junks		2·25	1·10
410	$2 Liner *Queen Elizabeth 2* at Hong Kong		3·00	3·00
407/10		*Set of 4*	7·00	4·50

103 Large Indian Civet

(Des Karen Phillipps. Litho Harrison)

1982 (4 May). *Wild Animals.* T **103** *and similar horiz designs.*
W w 14 (*sideways**). P 14½.
411	20 c. black, salmon-pink and olive-bistre	..		60	15
	w. Wmk Crown to right of CA	..	..	13·00	
412	$1 multicoloured	..	..	1·25	90
413	$1.30, black, emerald and yellow-orange			1·50	1·10
	w. Wmk Crown to right of CA	..	..	20·00	
414	$5 black, orange-brown & greenish yellow		3·00	4·50
411/14			*Set of 4*	5·50	6·50

Designs:—$1 Chinese Pangolin; $1.30, Chinese Porcupine; $5 Indian Muntjac ("Barking Deer").

The normal sideways watermark shows Crown to left of CA, as seen from the back of the stamp.

104   Queen Elizabeth II   **105**

(Des and photo ($5 to $50 also embossed) Harrison)

1982 (30 Aug). W w 14 (*sideways** on Nos. 427/30). P 14½×14
(*Nos.* 415/26) *or* 14×14½ (*others*).
415	**104**	10 c. bright carmine, carmine and lemon	80	60
416		20 c. bluish violet, violet and lavender	..	90	70
417		30 c. bluish violet, violet and salmon	..	1·50	30
418		40 c. vermilion and pale blue	..	1·50	30
419		50 c. chestnut, orange-brn & sage-green	..	1·50	30
420		60 c. bright purple and brownish grey	..	3·00	1·40
421		70 c. dp grey-grn, myrtle-grn & orge-yell	3·00	40
		a. Imperf (pair)	£500	
422		80 c. bistre-brown, lt brown & sage-grn	3·00	1·50
423		90 c. bottle-green, deep grey-green and pale turquoise-green	5·50	40
424		$1 reddish orge, red-orge & pale rose	2·75	30
425		$1.30, turquoise-blue and mauve	4·00	30
426		$2 ultramarine and flesh	..	7·00	1·00
427	**105**	$5 dp magenta, brt purple & olive-yell	7·00	2·50
		w. Wmk Crown to right of CA	8·00	
428		$10 sepia and grey-brown	..	8·50	5·00
		w. Wmk Crown to right of CA	9·00	
429		$20 deep claret and pale blue	14·00	16·00
		w. Wmk Crown to right of CA	15·00	
430		$50 deep claret and brownish grey	35·00	32·00
		w. Wmk Crown to right of CA	42·00	
415/30		*Set of 16*	85·00	55·00

The normal sideways watermark shows Crown to left of CA, as seen from the back of the stamp.

Nos. 415/30 come with a fluorescent security marking, "Hong Kong" in Chinese characters encircled by the same in English, printed over the central oval of the design.

Nos. 415 and 424 also exist from coils.

No. 428 is known with the embossing omitted. See note after No. 296.

For similar stamps without watermark see Nos. 471/87.

106 Table Tennis   **107** Dancing

(Des A. Wong. Litho J.W.)

1982 (20 Oct). *Sport for the Disabled.* T **106** *and similar horiz designs. Multicoloured.* W w 14. P 14 × 14½.
431	30 c. Type **106**	..	..	50	10
432	$1 Racing	..	..	75	80
433	$1.30, Basketball	..	..	2·75	1·50
434	$5 Archery	..	..	5·00	6·50
431/4	..	..	*Set of 4*	8·00	8·00

(Des Tao Ho. Litho J.W.)

1983 (26 Jan). *Performing Arts.* T **107** *and similar vert designs.* W w 14 (*sideways*). P 14½×14.
435	30 c. cobalt and deep grey-blue	..	50	10
436	$1.30, rose and brown-purple	..	2·00	1·25
437	$5 bright green and deep green	..	6·50	5·50
435/7	..	..	*Set of 3*	8·00	6·00

Designs:—$1.30, "Theatre"; $5 "Music".

---

108 Aerial View of Hong Kong

(Des local artist. Litho Enschedé)

1983 (14 Mar). *Commonwealth Day.* T **108** *and similar horiz designs. Multicoloured.* W w 14 (*sideways**). P 14½×13.
438	30 c. Type **108**	..	..	70	10
	w. Wmk Crown to right of CA	..	2·50	
439	$1 *Liverpool Bay* (container ship)	1·75	1·25
	w. Wmk Crown to right of CA	..	5·50	
440	$1.30, Hong Kong flag	..	1·75	1·25
	w. Wmk Crown to right of CA	..	5·00	
441	$5 Queen Elizabeth II and Hong Kong	3·50	5·00
438/41		*Set of 4*	7·00	6·75

The normal sideways watermark shows Crown to left of CA, as seen from the back of the stamp.

109 Victoria Harbour

(Des Tao Ho. Litho Harrison)

1983 (17 Aug). *Hong Kong by Night.* T **109** *and similar horiz designs. Multicoloured.* W w 14 (*sideways**). P 14½.
442	30 c. Type **109**	..	..	1·25	15
	w. Wmk Crown to right of CA	..	4·75	
443	$1 Space Museum, Tsim Sha Tsui Cultural Centre	..	3·75	1·50
444	$1.30, Fireworks display	..	4·75	2·00
	a. Silver (value and inscr) omitted	£950	
445	$5 *Jumbo*, floating restaurant	..	15·00	8·50
	a. Silver (value and inscr) omitted	£1000	
442/5		*Set of 4*	22·00	11·00

The normal sideways watermark shows Crown to left of CA, as seen from the back of the stamp.

110 Old and New Observatory Buildings

(Des C. Shun Wah. Litho Harrison)

1983 (23 Nov). *Centenary of Hong Kong Observatory.* T **110** *and similar horiz designs.* W w 14 (*sideways*). P 14½.
446	40 c. yellow-orange, bistre-brown and black	75	10
447	$1 reddish mauve, deep mauve and black	2·00	1·75
448	$1.30, new blue, steel-blue and black	2·75	1·75
449	$5 olive-yellow, brown-olive and black	8·00	9·00
446/9		*Set of 4*	12·00	11·00

Designs:—$1 Wind-measuring equipment; $1.30, Thermometer; $5 Ancient and modern seismometers.

111 De Havilland D.H.86 Dragon Express *Dorado* (Hong Kong–Penang Service, 1936)

(Des M. Harris. Litho J.W.)

1984 (7 Mar). *Aviation in Hong Kong.* T **111** *and similar multicoloured designs.* W w 14 (*sideways** on 40 c. to $1.30, inverted on $5). P 13½.
450	40 c. Type **111**	..	..	1·00	15
	w. Wmk Crown to left of CA	..	4·75	
451	$1 Sikorsky S-42B flying boat (San Francisco–Hong Kong Service, 1937)	2·25	1·75
452	$1.30, Cathay-Pacific Boeing 747 jet leaving Kai Tak Airport	..	3·25	1·75
453	$5 Baldwin brothers' balloon, 1891 (*vert*)	9·00	10·00
450/3		*Set of 4*	14·00	12·00

The normal sideways watermark shows Crown to right of CA, as seen from the back of the stamp.

112 Map by Capt E. Belcher, 1836

(Des R. Solley. Litho B.D.T.)

1984 (21 June). *Maps of Hong Kong.* T **112** *and similar horiz designs. Multicoloured.* W w 14 (*sideways*). P 14.
454	40 c. Type **112**	..	..	1·00	20
455	$1 Bartholomew map of 1929	..	1·75	1·25
456	$1.30, Early map of Hong Kong waters	3·00	1·75
457	$5 Chinese-style map of 1819	..	11·00	10·00
454/7		*Set of 4*	15·00	12·00

113 Cockerel

(Des J. Yim. Litho Cartor)

1984 (6 Sept). *Chinese Lanterns.* T **113** *and similar horiz designs showing stylised animals as lanterns. Multicoloured.* W w 14 (*sideways**). P 13½×13.
458	40 c. Type **113**	..	..	80	15
	w. Wmk Crown to right of CA	..	9·00	
459	$1 Dog	..	..	1·75	1·25
460	$1.30, Butterfly	..	..	3·00	1·75
461	$5 Fish	..	..	9·00	8·50
458/61		*Set of 4*	13·00	10·50

The normal sideways watermark shows Crown to left of CA, as seen from the back of the stamp.

114 Jockey on Horse and Nurse with Baby ("Health Care")

(Des M. Harris. Litho Walsall)

1984 (21 Nov). *Centenary of Royal Hong Kong Jockey Club.* T **114** *and similar horiz designs showing aspects of Club's charity work. Multicoloured.* W w 14 (*sideways**). P 14½.
462	40 c. Type **114**	..	..	1·25	20
463	$1 Disabled man playing handball ("Support for Disabled")	2·00	1·75
464	$1.30, Ballerina ("The Arts")	..	3·00	2·00
	w. Wmk Crown to right of CA	..	3·00	
465	$5 Humboldt Penguins ("Ocean Park")	9·00	11·00
462/5		*Set of 4*	14·00	13·50
MS466	178×98 mm. Nos. 462/5	..	22·00	24·00

The normal sideways watermark shows Crown to left of CA, as seen from the back of the stamp.

115 Hung Sing Temple

(Des M. Harris. Litho J.W.)

1985 (14 Mar). *Historic Buildings.* T **115** *and similar horiz designs. Multicoloured.* P 13½.
467	40 c. Type **115**	..	..	60	20
468	$1 St. John's Cathedral	..	1·75	1·60
469	$1.30, The Old Supreme Court Building	2·25	1·75
470	$5 Wan Chai Post Office	..	9·50	8·50
467/70		*Set of 4*	12·50	11·00

1985 (13 June)–87. *As Nos.* 415/16, 418/30 *and new value* ($1.70). *No wmk.* P 14½×14 (10 c. to $2) or 14×14½ (*others*).
471	**104**	10 c. brt carm, carm & lemon (23.10.85)	70	70
472		20 c. bluish violet, vio & lavender (6.87)	17·00	15·00
474		40 c. vermilion and pale blue (23.10.85)	90	1·25
475		50 c. chestnut, orange-brown and sage-green (23.10.85)	90	40
476		60 c. brt purple & brnish grey (23.10.85)	1·50	1·10
477		70 c. deep grey-green, myrtle-green and orange-yellow (23.10.85)	2·25	40
478		80 c. bistre-brown, light brown and sage-green (23.10.85)	2·50	1·75
479		90 c. bottle-green, deep grey-green and pale turquoise-green (23.10.85)	2·50	50
480		$1 reddish orange, red-orange and pale rose (23.10.85)	1·75	40
		a. Imperf (horiz pair)		
481		$1.30, turquoise-blue and mauve	2·50	45
482		$1.70, dull ultramarine, bright blue and bright green (2.9.85)	4·00	1·50
483		$2 ultramarine and flesh (23.10.85)	3·75	1·50
484	**105**	$5 deep magenta, bright purple and olive-yellow (23.10.85)	7·00	3·25
485		$10 sepia and grey-brown (23.10.85)	8·00	4·00
486		$20 deep claret and pale blue (23.10.85)	10·00	7·50
487		$50 dp claret & brownish grey (23.10.85)	30·00	25·00
471/87		*Set of 16*	85·00	55·00

116 Prow of Dragon Boat

117 The Queen Mother with Prince Charles and Prince William, 1984

(Des R. Hookham. Litho Cartor)

1985 (19 June). *10th International Dragon Boat Festival. T* **116** *and similar horiz designs showing different parts of dragon boat. Multicoloured. P* 13½×13.

488	40 c. Type 116 ..	..	50	15
489	$1 Drummer and rowers	..	1·75	1·25
490	$1.30, Rowers	..	3·00	1·60
491	$5 Stern of boat	..	9·25	8·00
488/91	.. ..	*Set of* 4	13·00	10·00
MS492	190×100 mm. Nos. 488/91. P 13×12		22·00	22·00

(Des C. Abbott. Litho Questa)

1985 (7 Aug). *Life and Times of Queen Elizabeth the Queen Mother. T* **117** *and similar vert designs. Multicoloured. P* 14½×14.

493	40 c. At Glamis Castle, aged 7	..	60	10
494	$1 Type 117	..	1·75	1·25
495	$1.30, The Queen Mother, 1970 (from photo by Cecil Beaton) ..		2·00	1·40
496	$5 With Prince Henry at his christening (from photo by Lord Snowdon) ..		3·25	4·00
493/6 ..	.. ..	*Set of* 4	7·00	6·00

118 Melastoma

(Des N. Jesse. Litho B.D.T.)

1985 (25 Sept). *Native Flowers. T* **118** *and similar horiz designs. Multicoloured. P* 13½.

497	40 c. Type 118 ..	..	1·50	20
498	50 c. Chinese Lily	..	1·75	40
499	60 c. Grantham's Camellia	..	2·00	90
500	$1.30, Narcissus	..	3·25	1·25
501	$1.70, Bauhinia	..	3·75	1·50
502	$5 Chinese New Year Flower	..	7·00	9·00
497/502		*Set of* 6	17·00	12·00

119 Hong Kong Academy for Performing Arts

(Des N. Jesse. Litho Format)

1985 (27 Nov). *New Buildings. T* **119** *and similar multi-coloured designs. P* 15.

503	50 c. Type 119 ..	..	80	15
504	$1.30, Exchange Square (vert)	..	1·75	1·50
505	$1.70, Hong Kong Bank Headquarters (vert)	..	2·50	1·75
506	$5 Hong Kong Coliseum	..	8·00	11·00
503/6 ..		*Set of* 4	11·50	13·00

120 Halley's Comet in the Solar System

(Des A. Chan. Litho Cartor)

1986 (26 Feb). *Appearance of Halley's Comet. T* **120** *and similar horiz designs. Multicoloured. P* 13½×13.

507	50 c. Type 120 ..	..	1·25	20
508	$1.30, Edmond Halley and Comet	..	2·00	1·40
509	$1.70, Comet over Hong Kong	..	2·75	1·50
510	$5 Comet passing the Earth	..	11·00	8·00
507/10		*Set of* 4	15·00	10·00
MS511	135×80 mm. Nos. 507/10		22·00	18·00

(Des A. Theobald. Litho Harrison)

1986 (21 Apr). *60th Birthday of Queen Elizabeth II. Vert designs as T* **110** *of Ascension. Multicoloured. P* 14½×14.

512	50 c. At wedding of Miss Celia Bowes-Lyon, 1931		50	10
513	$1 Queen in Garter procession, Windsor Castle, 1977		85	60
514	$1.30, In Hong Kong, 1975	..	1·10	70
515	$1.70, At Royal Lodge, Windsor, 1980 (from photo by Norman Parkinson) ..		1·25	75
516	$5 At Crown Agents Head Office, London, 1983		4·00	5·00
512/16	.. ..	*Set of* 5	7·00	6·25

121 Mass Transit Train, Boeing 747 Airliner and Map of World

(Des Agay Ng Kee Chuen. Litho B.D.T.)

1986 (18 July). *"Expo '86" World Fair, Vancouver. T* **121** *and similar horiz designs. Multicoloured. P* 13½.

517	50 c. Type 121 ..	..	80	30
518	$1.30, Hong Kong Bank Headquarters and map of world		1·50	1·00
519	$1.70, Container ship and map of world	..	2·25	1·40
520	$5 Dish aerial and map of world	..	6·50	7·00
517/20	.. ..	*Set of* 4	10·00	8·75

122 Hand-liner Sampan   123 "The Second Puan Khequa" (attr Spoilum)

(Des Graphic Communications Ltd. Litho B.D.T.)

1986 (24 Sept). *Fishing Vessels. T* **122** *and similar horiz designs, each showing fishing boat and outline of fish. Multicoloured. P* 13½.

521	50 c. Type 122 ..	..	80	15
522	$1.30, Stern trawler	..	1·50	1·10
523	$1.70, Long liner junk	..	2·25	1·40
524	$5 Junk trawler	..	7·00	7·50
521/4 ..		*Set of* 4	10·50	9·00

(Des R. Solley. Litho B.D.T.)

1986 (9 Dec). *19th-century Hong Kong Portraits. T* **123** *and similar vert designs. Multicoloured. P* 14×13½.

525	50 c. Type 123 ..	..	55	15
526	$1.30, "Chinese Lady" (19th-century copy)		1·50	1·10
527	$1.70, "Lamqua" (self-portrait)	..	1·75	1·40
528	$5 "Wife of Wo Hing Qua" (attr G. Chinnery)		5·50	5·50
525/8 ..	.. ..	*Set of* 4	8·50	7·50

MACHINE LABELS. A single machine operated at the G.P.O. from 30 December 1986 issuing 10 c., 50 c., $1.30 and $1.70 labels showing a carp. These are inscribed "O1". A second machine was installed at Tsim Sha Tsui post office from 18 August 1987 which issued labels coded "O2".

From 1987 a new design was introduced each year to reflect the Chinese calendar. Details of the various issues are as follows:

Year of the Rabbit	18 August 1987	10 c., 50 c., $1.30, $1.70
Year of the Dragon	23 March 1988	10 c., 50 c., $1.30, $1.70
	1 September 1988	10 c., 60 c., $1.40, $1.80
Year of the Snake	24 February 1989	10 c., 60 c., $1.40, $1.80
Year of the Horse	21 February 1990	10 c., 60 c., $1.40, $1.80
Year of the Ram	21 February 1991	10 c., 60 c., $1.40, $1.80
	2 April 1991	10 c., 80 c., $1.80, $2.30
Year of the Monkey	12 March 1992	10 c., 80 c., 90 c., $1.70, $1.80, $2.30, $5
Year of the Cock	10 February 1993	10 c., 80 c., 90 c., $1.70, $1.80, $2.30, $5
	1 November 1993	10 c., $1, $1.90, $2.40
Year of the Dog	1 March 1994	10 c., 80 c., $1, $1.20, $1.30, $1.90, $2, $2.40, $5

Year of the Pig	15 February 1995	10 c., 80 c., $1, $1.20, $1.30, $1.90, $2, $2.40, $5
Year of the Rat	28 February 1996	10 c., $1.20, $1.50, $2.10, $2.30, $2.60, $5
Year of the Ox	12 March 1997	10 c., $1.30, $1.60, $2.50, $2.60, $3.10, $5

From 8 November 1991 the "O1" machine, in addition to the fixed face values, could be used to produce labels of any value in 10 c. steps between 10 c. and $5.

124 Rabbit

(Des Kan Tai-keung. Litho B.D.T.)

1987 (21 Jan). *Chinese New Year ("Year of the Rabbit"). T* **124** *and similar horiz designs showing stylized rabbits. P* 13½.

529	50 c. multicoloured ..	..	65	15
530	$1.30, multicoloured	..	1·50	1·25
531	$1.70, multicoloured	..	1·75	1·40
532	$5 multicoloured	..	6·50	6·00
529/32		*Set of* 4	9·50	8·00
MS533	133×84 mm. Nos. 529/32		32·00	25·00

Nos. 530/1 have the "0" omitted from their face values.

125 "Village Square, Hong Kong Island, 1838" (Auguste Borget)   126 Queen Elizabeth II and Central Victoria

(Des J. Yim. Litho B.D.T.)

1987 (23 Apr). *19th-century Hong Kong Scenes. T* **125** *and similar horiz designs. Multicoloured. P* 14.

534	50 c. Type 125 ..	..	60	15
535	$1.30, "Boat Dwellers, Kowloon Bay, 1838" (Auguste Borget)		1·75	1·10
536	$1.70, "Flagstaff House, 1846" (Murdoch Bruce) ..		2·25	1·40
537	$5 "Wellington Street, late 19th-century" (C. Andrasi) ..		7·00	7·50
534/7 ..	.. ..	*Set of* 4	10·50	9·00

Two types of Nos. 538/52.

I. Heavy shading under mouth and cheek   II. Lighter shading

(Des R. Hookham. Litho Leigh-Mardon Ltd, Melbourne)

1987 (13 July)–**88**. *T* **126** *and similar vert designs, each showing Queen Elizabeth II and Hong Kong skyline. P* 14½×14 (10 c. to $2) or 14 ($5 to $50). A. *Shading as Type* I.

538A	**126** 10 c. multicoloured ..	..	80	90
539A	40 c. multicoloured ..	..	1·50	1·40
540A	50 c. multicoloured ..	..	1·50	40
541A	60 c. multicoloured ..	..	1·75	75
542A	70 c. multicoloured ..	..	2·00	80
543A	80 c. multicoloured ..	..	2·00	1·50
544A	90 c. multicoloured ..	..	2·25	70
545A	$1 multicoloured ..	..	2·25	70
546A	$1.30, multicoloured	..	3·00	80
547A	$1.70, multicoloured	..	3·00	80
548A	$2 multicoloured	..	3·00	1·50
549A	– $5 multicoloured	..	7·50	2·50
550A	– $10 multicoloured	..	8·50	4·75
551A	– $20 multicoloured	..	13·00	13·00
552A	– $50 multicoloured	..	25·00	27·00
538A/52A		*Set of* 15	70·00	50·00

B. *Shading as Type* II (1.9.88)

538B	**126** 10 c. multicoloured ..	..	75	65
539B	40 c. multicoloured ..	..	1·50	1·40
540B	50 c. multicoloured ..	..	1·50	30
541B	60 c. multicoloured ..	..	1·75	60
542B	70 c. multicoloured ..	..	2·00	80
543B	80 c. multicoloured ..	..	2·00	1·50
544B	90 c. multicoloured ..	..	2·25	70
545B	$1 multicoloured ..	..	8·00	1·25
546B	$1.30, multicoloured	..	3·00	90
546cB	$1.40, multicoloured	..	3·00	2·00
547B	$1.70, multicoloured	..	8·00	1·40
547cB	$1.80, multicoloured	..	3·00	1·75
548B	$2 multicoloured	..	3·25	90
549B	– $5 multicoloured	..	4·75	2·25
550B	– $10 multicoloured	..	8·50	4·25
551B	– $20 multicoloured	..	15·00	9·50
552B	– $50 multicoloured	..	35·00	16·00
538B/52B		*Set of* 17	90·00	40·00

Designs (25×31 mm): $5 Kowloon; $10 Victoria Harbour; $20 Legislative Council Building; $50 Government House.
Nos. 538/52 carry the fluorescent security markings as described beneath Nos. 415/30 with the $5 to $50 values showing an additional vertical fluorescent bar at right.
For these stamps as Type II, but with imprint dates, see Nos. 600/15.

127 Hong Kong Flag   **128** Alice Ho Miu Ling Nethersole Hospital, 1887

(Des R. Hookham. Photo Enschedé)

1987 (13 July)–**92**. *Coil Stamps. T* **127** *and similar vert designs. P* 14½×14. (*a*) *Without imprint date*
553	10 c. multicoloured	1·00	1·50
554	50 c. bistre, lake and black	2·00	3·00

(*b*) *With imprint date*
554*a*	10 c. multicoloured (1.8.89)	50	50
554*b*	50 c. bistre, lake and black (1.8.89)	1·25	1·50
554*c*	80 c. brt mauve, dp bl-grn & blk (26.3.92)	70	1·50
554*d*	90 c. brt blue, reddish brn & blk (26.3.92)	70	90
554*e*	$1.80, brt emer, royal bl & blk (26.3.92)	1·40	1·75
554*f*	$2.30, orge-brn, dp vio & blk (26.3.92)	1·60	2·25
554*a/f*	*Set of 6*	5·50	7·50

Design:—50 c. to $2.30, Map of Hong Kong.
Nos. 553/4*f* carry the fluorescent security marking as described beneath Nos. 415/30.
The printings with imprint date have every fifth stamp in the rolls of 1,000 numbered on the reverse.
Imprint dates: "1989", Nos. 554*a/b*; "1990", No. 554*a*, "1991", Nos. 554*a/f*.

(Des A. Fung. Litho Walsall)

1987 (8 Sept). *Hong Kong Medical Centenaries. T* **128** *and similar horiz designs. Multicoloured. P* 14½.
555	50 c. Type **128**	1·00	20
556	$1.30, Matron and nurses, Nethersole Hospital, 1891	2·25	1·40
557	$1.70, Scanning equipment, Faculty of Medicine	2·75	1·40
558	$5 Nurse and patient, Faculty of Medicine	8·50	8·00
555/8	*Set of 4*	13·00	10·00

129 Casual Dress with Fringed Hem, 220–589

(Des Sumiko Davies. Litho CPE Australia Ltd, Melbourne)

1987 (18 Nov). *Historical Chinese Costumes. T* **129** *and similar horiz designs. Multicoloured. P* 13½.
559	50 c. Type **129**	55	10
560	$1.30, Two-piece dress and wrap, 581–960	1·40	1·25
561	$1.70, Formal dress, Song Dynasty, 960–1279	1·75	1·50
562	$5 Manchu empress costume, 1644–1911	5·75	6·50
559/62	*Set of 4*	8·50	8·50

130 Dragon   **131** White-breasted Kingfisher

(Des Kan Tai-keung. Litho CPE Australia Ltd, Melbourne)

1988 (27 Jan). *Chinese New Year ("Year of the Dragon"). T* **130** *and similar horiz designs showing dragons. P* 13½.
563	50 c. multicoloured	75	15
564	$1.30, multicoloured	1·75	1·25
565	$1.70, multicoloured	2·00	1·40
566	$5 multicoloured	4·00	5·00
563/6	*Set of 4*	7·50	7·00
MS567	134×88 mm. Nos. 563/6	11·00	12·00

(Des Karen Phillipps. Litho CPE Australia Ltd, Melbourne)

1988 (20 Apr). *Hong Kong Birds. T* **131** *and similar vert designs. Multicoloured. P* 13½.
568	50 c. Type **131**	1·25	30
569	$1.30, Fukien Niltava	2·50	1·40
570	$1.70, Black Kite	3·00	1·50
571	$5 Lesser Pied Kingfisher	5·50	6·00
568/71	*Set of 4*	11·00	8·50

132 Chinese Banyan   **133** Lower Terminal, Peak Tramway

(Des A. Chan. Litho B.D.T.)

1988 (16 June). *Trees of Hong Kong. T* **132** *and similar vert designs. Multicoloured. P* 13½.
572	50 c. Type **132**	40	10
573	$1.30, Hong Kong Orchid Tree	85	65
574	$1.70, Cotton Tree	1·25	85
575	$5 Schima	3·50	4·50
572/5	*Set of 4*	5·50	5·50
MS576	135×85 mm. Nos. 572/5	11·00	7·50

(Des Lilian Tang. Litho Leigh-Mardon Ltd, Melbourne)

1988 (4 Aug). *Centenary of The Peak Tramway. T* **133** *and similar vert designs. Multicoloured. P* 14½×15.
577	50 c. Type **133**	60	10
578	$1.30, Tram on incline	1·00	1·00
579	$1.70, Peak Tower Upper Terminal	1·10	1·00
580	$5 Tram	3·50	4·50
577/80	*Set of 4*	5·50	6·00
MS581	160×90 mm. Nos. 577/80	8·00	8·00

134 Hong Kong Catholic Cathedral   **135** Deaf Girl

(Des C. Buendia. Litho CPE Australia Ltd, Melbourne)

1988 (30 Sept). *Centenary of Hong Kong Catholic Cathedral. P* 14.
582	**134** 60 c. multicoloured	1·25	75

(Des M. Tucker. Litho Harrison)

1988 (30 Nov). *Community Chest Charity. T* **135** *and similar vert designs. P* 14½.
583	60 c. + 10 c. brownish black, vermilion and greenish blue	60	75
584	$1.40 + 20 c. brownish black, vermilion and bright green	80	1·00
585	$1.80 + 30 c. brownish black, vermilion and bright orange	1·50	1·60
586	$5 + $1 brownish blk, verm and yell-brn	4·25	5·50
583/6	*Set of 4*	6·50	8·00

Designs:—$1.40, Elderly woman; $1.80, Blind boy using braille typewriter; $5 Mother and baby.

136 Snake   **137** Girl and Doll

(Des Kan Tai-keung. Litho Enschedé)

1989 (18 Jan). *Chinese New Year. ("Year of the Snake"). T* **136** *and similar horiz designs. Multicoloured. P* 13½×14.
587	60 c. Type **136**	30	15
	a. Booklet pane. Nos. 587 and 589, each ×5	6·50	
588	$1.40, Snake and fish	1·25	70
589	$1.80, Snake on branch	1·75	85
590	$5 Coiled snake	5·50	5·50
587/90	*Set of 4*	8·00	6·50
MS591	135×85 mm. Nos. 587/90	12·00	7·50

(Des M. Tucker. Litho B.D.T.)

1989 (4 May). *Cheung Chau Bun Festival. T* **137** *and similar vert designs. Multicoloured. P* 13½.
592	60 c. Type **137**	55	15
593	$1.40, Girl in festival costume	1·25	70
594	$1.80, Paper effigy of god Taai Si Wong	1·40	80
595	$5 Floral gateway	3·50	4·25
592/5	*Set of 4*	6·00	5·50

138 "Twins" (wood carving, Cheung Yee)   **139** Lunar New Year Festivities

(Des Kan Tai-keung. Litho Enschedé)

1989 (19 July). *Modern Art. T* **138** *and similar vert designs. Multicoloured. P* 12×12½.
596	60 c. Type **138**	50	15
597	$1.40, "Figures" (acrylic on paper, Chan Luis)	1·25	70
598	$1.80, "Lotus" (copper sculpture, Van Lau)	1·40	80
599	$5 "Zen Painting" (ink and colour on paper, Lui Shou-kwan)	3·00	4·25
596/9	*Set of 4*	5·50	5·50

1989 (1 Aug)–**91**. *As Nos.* 538B/52B, *and new values, with imprint date added to designs. P* 14½×14 (10 c. to $2.30) *or* 14 ($5 to $50).
600	**126**	10 c. multicoloured	60	75
601		40 c. multicoloured	1·50	1·75
602		50 c. multicoloured	90	30
603		60 c. multicoloured	90	30
604		70 c. multicoloured	90	60
605		80 c. multicoloured	90	40
606		90 c. multicoloured	90	40
607		$1 multicoloured	90	30
607*a*		$1.20, multicoloured (2.4.91)	2·75	2·50
608		$1.30, multicoloured	1·75	50
609		$1.40, multicoloured	1·75	70
609*a*		$1.70, multicoloured (2.4.91)	2·75	2·50
610		$1.80, multicoloured	1·25	60
611		$2 multicoloured	1·25	50
611*a*		$2.30, multicoloured (2.4.91)	2·75	2·75
612	—	$5 multicoloured	4·50	1·50
613	—	$10 multicoloured	6·00	3·25
614	—	$20 multicoloured	8·00	8·00
615	—	$50 multicoloured	19·00	17·00
600/15		*Set of 19*	50·00	40·00

Imprint dates: "1989", Nos. 600/7, 608/9, 610/11, 612/15; "1990", Nos. 600/7, 608/9, 610/11, 612/15; "1991", Nos. 600, 602/7*a*, 609*a*/15.
For miniature sheets containing No. 613 see Nos. **MS**646, **MS**684/5 and **MS**701.

(Des Sumiko Davies. Litho Enschedé)

1989 (6 Sept). *Hong Kong People. T* **139** *and similar vert designs. Multicoloured. P* 13×14½.
616	60 c. Type **139**	50	10
617	$1.40, Shadow boxing and horse racing	1·25	80
618	$1.80, Foreign-exchange dealer and traditional builder	1·60	90
619	$5 Multi-racial society	4·00	5·50
616/19	*Set of 4*	6·50	6·50

For miniature sheet containing design as $5, but smaller (75×35 mm), see No. **MS**847.

140 University of Science and Technology

(Des I. Leung. Litho CPE Australia Ltd, Melbourne)

1989 (5 Oct). *Building for the Future. T* **140** *and similar square designs. P* 13.
620	60 c. blue-black, orange-yellow & yellow-brn	35	15
621	70 c. black, pale rose and rose	40	30
622	$1.30, black, brt yellow-green & blue-grn	90	70
623	$1.40, black, azure and bright blue	90	70
624	$1.80, brownish black, pale turquoise-green and turquoise-blue	1·10	1·00
625	$5 agate, pale red-orange and orange-red	3·75	4·00
620/5	*Set of 6*	6·50	6·25

Designs:—70 c. Cultural Centre; $1.30, Eastern Harbour motorway interchange; $1.40, New Bank of China Building; $1.80, Convention and Exhibition Centre; $5 Mass Transit electric train.

141 Prince and Princess of Wales and Hong Kong Skyline

142

(Des Ng Kee-chuen. Litho Leigh-Mardon Ltd, Melbourne)

1989 (8 Nov). *Royal Visit.* T **141** *and similar vert designs, each showing portrait and different view. Multicoloured.* W **142** (*sideways*). P 14½.

626	60 c. Type **141**	75	15
627	$1.40, Princess of Wales	1·25	80
628	$1.80, Prince of Wales	1·40	1·10
629	$5 Prince and Princess of Wales in evening dress	5·50	6·00
626/9	Set of 4	8·00	7·25
MS630	128×75 mm. No. 629	10·00	8·00

143 Horse

144 Chinese Lobster Dish

(Des Kan Tai-keung. Litho Enschedé)

1990 (23 Jan). *Chinese New Year.* ("*Year of the Horse*"). T **143** *and similar horiz designs.* P 13½×12½.

631	60 c. multicoloured	60	20
	a. Booklet pane. Nos. 631 and 633, each×3	4·50	
632	$1.40, multicoloured	1·40	1·00
633	$1.80, multicoloured	1·50	1·25
634	$5 multicoloured	4·75	5·50
631/4	Set of 4	7·50	7·00
MS635	135×85 mm. Nos. 631/4	13·00	12·00

(Des N. Yung and Sumiko Davies. Litho Enschedé)

1990 (26 Apr). *International Cuisine.* T **144** *and similar vert designs showing various dishes. Multicoloured.* P 12½×13.

636	60 c. Type **144**	50	15
637	70 c. Indian	50	30
638	$1.30, Chinese vegetables	90	65
639	$1.40, Thai	90	65
640	$1.80, Japanese	1·25	80
641	$5 French	4·25	5·50
636/41	Set of 6	7·50	7·25

145 Air Pollution and Clean Air

146 Street Lamp and Des Voeux Road, 1890

(Litho Leigh-Mardon Ltd, Melbourne)

1990 (5 June). *United Nations World Environment Day.* T **145** *and similar vert designs. Multicoloured.* P 14½.

642	60 c. Type **145**	40	15
643	$1.40, Noise pollution and music	85	70
644	$1.80, Polluted and clean water	1·00	80
645	$5 Litter on ground and in bin	2·75	3·50
642/5	Set of 4	4·50	4·75

(Des R. Hookham and I. Leung. Litho Leigh-Mardon Ltd, Melbourne)

1990 (24 Aug). "*New Zealand 1990*" *International Stamp Exhibition, Auckland. Sheet* 130×75 *mm containing No. 613.* P 14.

MS646	$10 multicoloured	95·00	95·00

The stamp in No. **MS646** shows the imprint date as "1990".

(Des M. Tucker. Litho Leigh-Mardon Ltd, Melbourne)

1990 (2 Oct). *Centenary of Electricity Supply.* T **146** *and similar horiz designs.* P 14½.

647	60 c. black, olive-bistre & pale orange-brown	50	10
648	$1.40, multicoloured	1·10	90
649	$1.80, black, olive-bistre and deep cobalt	1·25	1·00
650	$5 multicoloured	2·50	4·00
647/50	Set of 4	4·75	5·50
MS651	155×85 mm. Nos. 648 and 650	6·00	8·00

Designs:—$1.40, Street lamp and *Jumbo* (floating restaurant), 1940; $1.80, Street lamp and pylon, 1960; $5 Street lamp and Hong Kong from harbour, 1980.

147 Christmas Tree and Skyscrapers

(Litho Leigh-Mardon Ltd, Melbourne)

1990 (8 Nov). *Christmas.* T **147** *and similar horiz designs. Multicoloured.* P 14½.

652	50 c. Type **147**	25	10
653	60 c. Dove with holly	25	15
654	$1.40, Firework display	80	40
655	$1.80, Father Christmas hat on skyscraper	1·00	50
656	$2 Children with Father Christmas	1·40	1·25
657	$5 Candy stick with bow and Hong Kong skyline	3·00	4·50
652/7	Set of 6	6·00	6·25

148 Ram

149 Letter "A", Clock, Teddy Bear and Building Bricks (Kindergarten)

(Des Kan Tai-keung. Litho Enschedé)

1991 (24 Jan). *Chinese New Year.* ("*Year of the Ram*"). T **148** *and similar horiz designs.* P 13½×12½.

658	60 c. multicoloured	25	15
	a. Booklet pane. Nos. 658 and 660, each × 3, with margins all round	4·25	
659	$1.40, multicoloured	65	45
660	$1.80, multicoloured	80	60
661	$5 multicoloured	2·75	3·75
658/61	Set of 4	4·00	4·50
MS662	135×85 mm. Nos. 658/61	6·50	7·50

(Litho Enschedé)

1991 (18 Apr). *Education.* T **149** *and similar vert designs. Multicoloured.* P 13½×13.

663	80 c. Type **149**	50	20
664	$1.80, Globe, laboratory flask and mathematical symbols (Primary and Secondary)	1·25	70
665	$2.30, Machinery (Vocational)	1·40	1·25
666	$5 Mortar board, computer and books (Tertiary)	3·00	4·50
663/6	Set of 4	5·50	6·00

150 Rickshaw

151 Victorian Pillar Box and Cover of 1888

(Des C. Tillyer. Litho B.D.T.)

1991 (6 June). *100 Years of Public Transport.* T **150** *and similar square designs. Multicoloured.* P 14.

667	80 c. Type **150**	30	15
668	90 c. Double-decker bus	70	40
669	$1.70, Harbour ferry	1·10	75
670	$1.80, Double-deck tram	1·40	75
671	$2.30, Mass Transit electric train	2·00	1·75
672	$5 Jetfoil	3·50	5·00
667/72	Set of 6	8·00	8·00

(Des H. Choi. Litho B.D.T.)

1991 (25 Aug). *150th Anniv of Hong Kong Post Office* (*1st issue*). T **151** *and similar vert designs. Multicoloured.* P 14.

673	80 c. Type **151**	40	15
674	$1.70, Edwardian pillar box and cover of 1935	90	75
675	$1.80, King George V pillar box and cover of 1935	1·00	75
676	$2.30, King George VI pillar box and cover of 1938	1·40	1·75
677	$5 Queen Elizabeth II pillar box and cover of 1989	3·75	5·50
673/7	Set of 5	6·75	8·00
MS678	130×75 mm. $10 As No. 677	12·00	14·00

See also Nos. **MS745** and **MS899**.

152 Bronze Buddha, Lantau Island

153 Monkey

(Litho Questa)

1991 (24 Oct). *Landmarks.* T **152** *and similar vert designs.* P 14.

679	80 c. rosine and black	50	15
680	$1.70, bright emerald and black	1·00	80
681	$1.80, reddish violet and black	1·25	80
682	$2.30, new blue and black	1·25	1·75
683	$5 bright yellow-orange and black	3·50	5·00
679/83	Set of 5	6·75	7·75

Designs:—$1.70, Peak Pavilion; $1.80, Clocktower of Kowloon–Canton Railway Station; $2.30, Catholic Cathedral; $5 Wong Tai Sin Temple.

(Des Kan Tai-keung. Litho Leigh-Mardon Ltd, Melbourne)

1991 (16 Nov). "*Phila Nippon '91*" *International Stamp Exhibition, Tokyo. Sheet* 130×75 *mm containing No. 613.* P 14.

MS684	$10 multicoloured	35·00	27·00

The stamp in No. **MS684** shows the imprint date as "1991".

(Des Li Shik-kwong. Litho Leigh-Mardon Ltd, Melbourne)

1991 (4 Dec). *Olympic Games, Barcelona* (1992) (*1st issue*). *Sheet* 130×75 *mm. containing No. 613.* P 14.

MS685	$10 multicoloured	15·00	15·00

The stamp in No. **MS685** shows the imprint date as "1991".
See also Nos. **696/700** and **MS722**.

(Des Kan Tai-keung. Litho Leigh-Mardon Ltd, Melbourne)

1992 (22 Jan). *Chinese New Year.* ("*Year of the Monkey*"). T **153** *and similar horiz designs.* P 14½.

686	80 c. multicoloured	40	15
	a. Booklet pane. Nos. 686 and 688, each × 3, with margins all round	4·50	
687	$1.80, multicoloured	70	55
688	$2.30, multicoloured	1·25	1·40
689	$5 multicoloured	2·75	4·50
686/9	Set of 4	4·50	6·00
MS690	135×85 mm. Nos. 686/9	8·50	11·00

(Des D. Miller. Litho Leigh-Mardon Ltd, Melbourne)

1992 (11 Feb). *40th Anniv of Queen Elizabeth II's Accession. Horiz designs as* T **143** *of Ascension. Multicoloured.* P 14½.

691	80 c. Royal barge in Hong Kong harbour	30	15
692	$1.70, Queen watching dancing display	60	35
693	$1.80, Fireworks display	60	35
694	$2.30, Three portraits of Queen Elizabeth	90	85
695	$5 Queen Elizabeth II	2·00	2·75
691/5	Set of 5	4·00	4·00

154 Running

155 Queen Elizabeth II

(Des Li Shik-kwong. Litho Leigh-Mardon Ltd, Melbourne)

1992 (2 Apr). *Olympic Games, Barcelona* (2nd issue). T **154** *and similar horiz designs.* P 14½.

696	80 c. Type **154**	40	20
697	$1.80, Swimming and javelin	80	80
698	$2.30, Cycling	1·60	1·75
699	$5 High jump	2·25	3·75
696/9	Set of 4	4·50	6·00
MS700	130×75 mm. As Nos. 696/9*	5·50	7·00

* The stamps from No. **MS700** show the inscriptions in different colours, instead of the black on Nos. 696/9. The designs of the $1.80 and $5 values from the miniature sheet have also been rearranged so that "HONG KONG" and the Royal Cypher occur at the right of the inscription.
For No. **MS700** additionally inscribed for the opening of the Games see No. **MS722**.

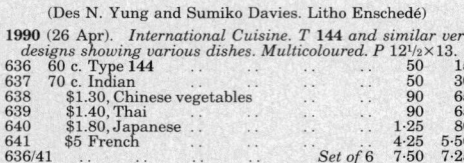

(Des Kan Tai-keung. Litho Leigh-Mardon Ltd, Melbourne)

1992 (22 May). *"World Columbian Stamp Expo '92" Exhibition, Chicago. Sheet 130×75 mm containing No. 613, but colours changed. P 14.*

MS701 $10 multicoloured .. .. 4·00 7·00
The stamp in No. MS701 shows the imprint date as "1992".

(Des I. Leung. Photo Enschedé)

1992 (16 June)–**96**. *P* 14½×14 (10 c. to $5) or 14 ($10, $20, $50).

702	155	10 c. magenta, black and pale cerise ..	30	40
		ap. Two phosphor bands (24.4.96) ..	70	80
702b		20 c. black, blue-blk & pale bl (1.11.93)	80	90
		bp. Two phosphor bands (24.4.96) ..	70	80
703		50 c. orange-red, black and yellow ..	30	30
		p. Two phosphor bands (24.4.96) ..	70	70
704		60 c. greenish blue, black and light blue	65	45
705		70 c. bright mauve, black and rose-lilac	65	65
706		80 c. cerise, black and rose ..	30	20
707		90 c. bronze-green, blk & greenish grey	30	20
708		$1 red-brown, black & orange-yellow	35	20
		ap. Two phosphor bands (24.4.96) ..	80	40
708b		$1.10, deep carmine, black and pale salmon (1.6.95) ..	55	50
		bp. Two phosphor bands (24.4.96) ..	80	1·00
709		$1.20, bright violet, black and lilac	35	25
		ap. Two phosphor bands (24.4.96) ..	90	1·00
709b		$1.30, blue, brownish black and salmon (1.11.93) ..	1·50	45
		bp. Two phosphor bands (24.4.96) ..	90	1·00
709c		$1.40, brt yellow-grn, blk & greenish yell (two phosphor bands) (2.9.96)	35	30
709d		$1.50 reddish brn, blk & lt bl (1.6.95)	80	60
		dp. Two phosphor bands (24.4.96) ..	90	1·10
709e		$1.60, light green, black and rose-lilac (two phosphor bands) (2.9.96)	45	50
710		$1.70, ultramarine, blk & pale bl	80	75
711		$1.80, deep magenta, black and grey	1·25	55
711a		$1.90, deep blue-green, brownish black and yellow-ochre (1.11.93)	80	75
		ap. Two phosphor bands (24.4.96) ..	1·25	1·40
712		$2 turq-blue, black & brt turq-green	1·50	60
		ap. Two phosphor bands (24.4.96) ..	1·25	1·00
712b		$2.10, bright crimson, black & pale turquoise-green (1.6.95) ..	1·25	75
		bp. One centre phosphor band (24.4.96) ..	1·25	1·40
		bq. Two phosphor bands (2.9.96)	3·00	3·50
713		$2.30, blackish brn, blk & rose-pink	1·25	75
713a		$2.40, dull ultramarine, black and brownish grey (1.11.93) ..	2·00	1·00
713b		$2.50, brown-olive, black and lemon (one centre phosphor band) (2.9.96)	55	70
713c		$2.60, choc, blk & yellow-brn (1.6.95)	1·25	1·25
		cp. One centre phosphor band (24.4.96) ..	1·50	1·75
713d		$3.10, orange-brown, black & pale bl (one centre phosphor band) (2.9.96)	65	80
714		$5 bright blue-green, black & lt green	2·50	1·75
		p. One centre phosphor band (24.4.96) ..	2·50	2·25
715	–	$10 red-brown, black and cinnamon	3·25	2·75
716	–	$20 rosine, black and bright salmon	4·25	4·50
717	–	$50 grey-black, black and grey ..	8·50	11·00
702/17		.. .. Set of 28	32·00	30·00

Nos. 715/17 are as Type 155, but larger, 26×30 mm, and show a large perforation hole at each corner of the stamp.

Nos. 702/17 show "HONG KONG" printed in yellow fluorescence as a security marking. Nos. 715/17 additionally show a horizontal line at foot in green fluorescence.

Nos. 702, 703, 706/7, 709bp, 709e, 711, 713, 713b and 713d also exist from coils with every fifth stamp numbered on the reverse.

For stamps in this design from stamp booklets, printed in lithography without watermark or with watermark w 14, see Nos. 757/65.

For miniature sheets containing designs as Nos. 714 and 715 see Nos. MS723, MS745/6, MS751, MS771, MS782, MS810/11, MS821, MS827 and MS841/2.

156 Stamps and Perforation Gauge

157 Principal Male Character

(Des Kan Tai-keung. Litho Leigh-Mardon Ltd, Melbourne)

1992 (15 July). *Stamp Collecting. T 156 and similar horiz designs. Multicoloured. P 14½.*

718	80 c. Type 156 ..	30	20
719	$1.80, Handstamp of 1841, 1891 Jubilee overprint and tweezers ..	60	65
720	$2.30, Stamps of 1946 and 1949 under magnifying glass ..	85	1·00
721	$5 2 c. of 1862 and watermark detector	2·00	3·25
718/21	.. .. Set of 4	3·25	4·50

(Des Li Shik-kwong. Litho Leigh-Mardon Ltd, Melbourne)

1992 (25 July). *Olympic Games, Barcelona (3rd issue). As No. MS700, but additionally inscribed "To Commemorate the Opening of the 1992 Summer Olympic Games 25 July 1992", in English and Chinese, at foot of sheet.*

MS722 130×75 mm. As Nos. 696/9 .. 3·50 4·75

(Des C. Tillyer. Litho Enschedé)

1992 (1 Sept). *"Kuala Lumpur '92" International Stamp Exhibition. Sheet 130×75 mm containing design as No. 715, but litho and colours changed. P 14.*

MS723 $10 dull ultramarine, black and pale blue 4·75 6·50
No. MS723 shows "HONG KONG" printed in yellow fluorescence with a horizontal green fluorescent line beneath as a security marking. There is a larger perforation hole at each corner of the stamp.

(Des I. Leung. Litho Enschedé)

1992 (24 Sept). *Chinese Opera. T 157 and similar vert designs. Multicoloured. P 13½.*

724	80 c. Type 157 ..	50	25
725	$1.80, Martial character ..	1·00	1·00
	a. Grey (face value and inscr) omitted ..	£750	
726	$2.30, Principal female character	1·40	1·50
	a. Grey (face value and inscr) omitted ..	£750	
727	$5 Comic character ..	2·50	4·50
724/7	.. .. Set of 4	4·75	6·50

Nos. 725a and 726a each occur on the bottom row of a sheet and were caused by the upward displacement of the grey colour. One example of each also exists showing the plate number from the bottom margin printed in the design.

158 Hearts

(Des C. Tillyer. Litho Leigh-Mardon Ltd, Melbourne)

1992 (19 Nov). *Greetings Stamps. T 158 and similar horiz designs. Multicoloured. P 14½.*

728	80 c. Type 158 ..	30	20
	a. Booklet pane. Nos. 728×3 and 729/31 with margins all round ..	4·50	
729	$1.80, Stars ..	55	60
730	$2.30, Presents ..	75	95
731	$5 Balloons ..	1·60	2·50
728/31	.. .. Set of 4	2·75	3·75

159 Cockerel

160 Pipa

(Des Kan Tai-keung. Litho Enschedé)

1993 (7 Jan). *Chinese New Year. ("Year of the Cock"). T 159 and similar horiz designs. P 13½.*

732	80 c. multicoloured ..	30	20
	a. Booklet pane. Nos. 732 and 734, each × 3, with margins all round ..	3·75	
733	$1.80, multicoloured ..	70	80
734	$2.30, multicoloured ..	95	1·10
735	$5 multicoloured ..	2·25	3·50
732/5	.. .. Set of 4	3·75	5·00
MS736	133×84 mm. Nos. 732/5	4·75	6·50

(Des Sumiko Davies. Litho Leigh-Mardon Ltd, Melbourne)

1993 (14 Apr). *Chinese String Musical Instruments. T 160 and similar vert designs. Multicoloured. Fluorescent paper. P 14½.*

737	80 c. Type 160 ..	40	20
738	$1.80, Erhu ..	70	70
739	$2.30, Ruan ..	90	1·00
740	$5 Gehu ..	2·00	3·25
737/40	.. .. Set of 4	3·50	4·75

161 Central Waterfront, Hong Kong in 1954

(Des C. Tillyer. Litho Leigh-Mardon Ltd, Melbourne)

1993 (2 June). *40th Anniv of Coronation. T 161 and similar horiz designs. Multicoloured. Fluorescent paper. P 14.*

741	80 c. Type 161 ..	40	20
742	$1.80, Hong Kong in 1963 ..	70	65
743	$2.30, Hong Kong in 1975 ..	90	1·10
744	$5 Hong Kong in 1992 ..	2·25	3·00
741/4	.. .. Set of 4	3·75	4·50

(Des Julia Brown and G. Smith. Litho Enschedé)

1993 (6 July). *150th Anniv of Hong Kong Post Office (2nd issue). Sheet 130×75 mm containing design as No. 715, but litho. P 14.*

MS745 $10 red-brown, black and cinnamon 4·50 5·50
No. MS745 shows "HONG KONG" printed in yellow fluorescence with a horizontal green fluorescent line beneath as a security marking. There is a larger perforation hole at each corner of the stamp.

(Des Lam Bing-pui. Litho Enschedé)

1993 (12 Aug). *"Hong Kong '94" International Stamp Exhibition. Sheet 115×78 mm containing design as No. 715, but litho and colours changed. P 14.*

MS746 $10 deep purple, black, bistre-yellow and greenish blue .. 4·50 5·00
No. MS746 shows "HONG KONG" printed in yellow fluorescence with a horizontal green fluorescent line beneath as a security marking. There is a larger perforation hole at each corner of the stamp.

162 University of Science and Technology Building and Student

(Des Lam Bing-pui. Litho Leigh-Mardon Ltd, Melbourne)

1993 (8 Sept). *Hong Kong's Contribution to Science and Technology. T 162 and similar horiz designs. Multicoloured. P 14½.*

747	80 c. Type 162 ..	30	20
748	$1.80, Science Museum building and energy machine exhibit ..	50	40
749	$2.30, Governor's Award and circuit board	60	90
750	$5 Dish aerials and world map ..	1·40	3·00
747/50	.. .. Set of 4	2·50	4·00

(Des Lam Bing-pui. Litho Enschedé)

1993 (5 Oct). *"Bangkok '93" International Stamp Exhibition. Sheet 131×75 mm containing design as No. 715, but litho and colours changed. P 14.*

MS751 $10 bright emerald, blackish green and bright blue-green .. 2·75 3·50
No. MS751 shows "HONG KONG" printed in yellow fluorescence with a horizontal green fluorescent line beneath as a security marking. There is a larger perforation hole at each corner of the stamp.

163 Red Calico Egg-fish

(Des N. Young. Litho Leigh-Mardon Ltd, Melbourne)

1993 (17 Nov). *Goldfish. T 163 and similar horiz designs. Multicoloured. P 14½.*

752	$1 Type 163 ..	35	20
753	$1.90, Red Cap Oranda ..	60	50
754	$2.40, Red and White Fringetail ..	90	1·00
755	$5 Black and Gold Dragon-eye ..	2·25	3·50
752/5	.. .. Set of 4	3·75	4·75
MS756	130×75 mm. Nos. 752/5 ..	6·50	7·50

1993 (14 Dec)–**97**. *As Nos. 702, 708, 709, 709bp, 709e, 710/12, 712b, 713a and 714, but printed in lithography by Leigh-Mardon Ltd (Nos. 757, 758, 759 and 760/5) or Enschedé (others). P* 14½×14.

(a) No wmk

757	155	$1 red-brown, black & orange-yellow	75	75
		a. Booklet pane. No. 757×10 with margins all round	7·50	
757b		$1.20, brt violet, black & lilac (1.6.95)	70	75
		ba. Booklet pane. No. 757b×10 with margins all round	7·00	
757c		$1.30, blue, deep brown and salmon (two phosphor bands) (2.9.96)	50	65
		ca. Booklet pane. No. 757c×10 with margins all round	5·00	
		cb. Sheetlet. Nos. 757c×4 and 759e×2 with margins all round (14.2.97)	4·00	
		cc. Booklet pane. As No. 757cb, but with enlarged margins at left and foot (14.2.97)	7·00	
757d		$1.60, light green, black and rose-lilac (two phosphor bands) (14.2.97)	85	1·40
		da. Sheetlet Nos. 757d×2 and 759d×4 with margins all round (14.2.97)	4·00	
		db. Booklet pane. As No. 759da, but with enlarged margins at left and foot	7·00	
758		$1.90, dp blue-green, brownish black and yellow-ochre (28.12.93)	90	1·25
		a. Booklet pane. No. 758×10 with margins all round	9·00	
758b		$2.10, deep claret, black & turquoise-green (1.6.95)	90	1·25
		ba. Booklet pane. No. 758b×10 with margins all round	9·00	
		bb. Two phosphor bands (14.2.97)	1·00	1·60
		bc. Sheetlet Nos. 758bb×2 and 759b×4 with margins all round	4·25	
		bd. Booklet pane. As No. 758bc, but with enlarged margins at left and foot	7·00	
759		$2.40, dull ultramarine, black and brownish grey (28.12.93)	95	1·40
		a. Booklet pane. No. 759×10 with margins all round	9·50	

759b	155	$2.50, bistre, black and lemon (one centre phosphor band) (2.9.96)	70	1·00
	ba.	Booklet pane. No. 759b×10 with margins all round	7·00	
759c		$2.60, dp choc, black & brown (1.6.95)	95	1·40
	ca.	Booklet pane. No. 759c×10 with margins all round	9·50	
759d		$3.10, orge-brown, blk & pale bl (one centre phosphor band) (2.9.96)	75	1·40
	da.	Booklet pane. No. 759d×10 with margins all round	7·50	
759e		$5 bright blue-green, black and light green (one centre phosphor band) (14.2.97)	1·00	1·75
757/9e		Set of 11	8·00	12·00

(b) W w 14 (12.1.94)

760	155	10 c. magenta, black and pale cerise	2·50	3·50
	a.	Booklet pane. Nos. 760 and 764×5 with margins all round	5·50	
761		$1 red-brown, black & orange-yellow	60	75
	a.	Booklet pane. Nos. 761×5 and 765 with margins all round	5·50	
762		$1.70 dull ultram, black & pale blue	2·50	3·50
	a.	Booklet pane. Nos. 762 and 763×5 with margins all round	5·50	
763		$1.80, deep magenta, black and grey	60	75
764		$2 turquoise-blue, blk & brt turq-grn	60	75
765		$5 brt blue-green, black & lt green	2·50	3·50
760/5		Set of 6	8·50	11·50

Nos. 757/65 show "HONG KONG" printed in yellow fluorescence as a security marking.

Nos. 757/9d come from definitive booklets and Nos. 760/5 from the Prestige booklet issued to commemorate the 130th anniversary of Hong Kong stamps.

164 Dog

(Des Kan Tai-keung. Litho Leigh-Mardon Ltd, Melbourne)

1994 (27 Jan). *Chinese New Year. ("Year of the Dog"). T 164 and similar horiz designs. P 14½.*

766		$1 multicoloured	30	20
	a.	Booklet pane. Nos. 766 and 768, each × 3, with margins all round	4·50	
767		$1.90, multicoloured	50	55
768		$2.40, multicoloured	70	90
769		$5 multicoloured	1·75	3·00
766/9		Set of 4	3·00	4·25
MS770		133×84 mm. Nos. 766/9	8·00	7·50

(Des Lam Bing-pui. Litho Leigh-Mardon Ltd, Melbourne)

1994 (18 Feb). *"Hong Kong '94" International Stamp Exhibition. Sheet 130×75 mm containing design as No. 714, but litho. P 14½×14.*

MS771	155	$5 bright blue-green, black & lt green	4·00	6·00

No. MS771 shows "HONG KONG" printed in yellow fluorescence as a security marking.

165 Modern Police Constables on Traffic Duty

166 Dragon Boat Festival

(Des Li Shik-kwong. Litho Enschedé)

1994 (4 May). *150th Anniv of Royal Hong Kong Police Force. T 165 and similar horiz designs. Multicoloured. P 13½.*

772		$1 Type 165	30	20
773		$1.20, Marine policeman with binoculars	40	35
774		$1.90, Police uniforms of 1950	55	45
775		$2 Tactical firearms unit officer with sub-machine gun	75	65
776		$2.40, Early 20th-century police uniforms	90	1·00
777		$5 Sikh and Chinese constables of 1900	2·75	3·75
772/7		Set of 6	5·00	5·75

(Des Li Shik-kwong. Litho Questa)

1994 (8 June). *Traditional Chinese Festivals. T 166 and similar vert designs. Multicoloured. P 14½.*

778		$1 Type 166	35	20
779		$1.90, Lunar New Year	60	60
780		$2.40, Seven Sisters Festival	85	1·10
781		$5 Mid-Autumn Festival	1·75	3·00
778/81		Set of 4	3·25	4·50

(Des C. Tillyer. Litho Enschedé)

1994 (16 Aug). *Conference of Commonwealth Postal Administrations, Hong Kong. Sheet 134×83 mm, containing design as No. 715, but litho. P 14.*

MS782		$10 red-brown, black and cinnamon	5·00	6·00

No. MS782 shows "HONG KONG" printed in yellow fluorescence with a horizontal green fluorescent line beneath as a security marking. There is a larger perforation hole at each corner of the stamp.

167 Swimming

(Des C. Tillyer. Litho Walsall)

1994 (25 Aug). *15th Commonwealth Games, Victoria, Canada. T 167 and similar horiz designs. Multicoloured. P 14½.*

783		$1 Type 167	25	20
784		$1.90, Bowls	40	50
785		$2.40, Gymnastics	60	85
786		$5 Weightlifting	1·25	2·50
783/6		Set of 4	2·50	3·50

168 Dr. James Legge and Students

169 Alcyonium Coral

(Des Lai Wai-kwan. Litho Leigh-Mardon Ltd, Melbourne)

1994 (5 Oct). *Dr. James Legge (Chinese scholar) Commemoration. P 14½.*

787	168	$1 multicoloured	55	60

(Des Brushstroke Design. Litho Questa)

1994 (17 Nov). *Corals. T 169 and similar square designs. Multicoloured. P 14.*

788		$1 Type 169	35	20
789		$1.90, Zoanthus	45	55
790		$2.40, Tubastrea	65	1·00
791		$5 Platygyra	1·25	2·50
788/91		Set of 4	2·40	3·75
MS792		130×75 mm. Nos. 788/91	4·50	5·50

170 Pig

(Des Kan Tai-keung. Litho Leigh-Mardon Ltd, Melbourne)

1995 (17 Jan). *Chinese New Year ("Year of the Pig"). T 170 and similar horiz designs. P 14½.*

793		$1 multicoloured	30	30
	a.	Booklet pane. Nos. 793 and 795, each × 3, with margins all round	3·25	
794		$1.90, multicoloured	50	70
795		$2.40, multicoloured	60	95
796		$5 multicoloured	1·00	2·00
793/6		Set of 4	2·25	3·50
MS797		130×84 mm. Nos. 793/6	4·25	5·00

171 Hong Kong Rugby Sevens

(Des Kan Tai-keung and Roxy Lou Sze-wan. Litho Leigh-Mardon Ltd, Melbourne)

1995 (22 Mar). *International Sporting Events in Hong Kong. T 171 and similar horiz designs. Multicoloured. P 14½.*

798		$1 Type 171	45	20
799		$1.90, The China Sea Yacht Race	60	65
800		$2.40, International Dragon Boat Races	85	1·00
801		$5 Hong Kong International Horse Races	1·75	2·75
798/801		Set of 4	3·25	4·25

172 Tsui Shing Lau Pagoda

173 Regimental Badge

(Des I. Leung. Recess and litho Enschedé)

1995 (24 May). *Hong Kong Traditional Rural Buildings. T 172 and similar horiz designs. Multicoloured. P 13½.*

802		$1 Type 172	30	20
803		$1.90, Sam Tung Uk Village	45	55
804		$2.40, Lo Wai Village	60	1·00
805		$5 Man Shek Tong house	1·10	2·50
802/5		Set of 4	2·25	3·75

(Des Lam Bing-pui. Litho Leigh-Mardon Ltd, Melbourne)

1995 (16 Aug). *Disbandment of the Royal Hong Kong Regiment. T 173 and similar multicoloured designs. P 14½.*

806		$1.20, Type 173	40	25
807		$2.10, Regimental guidon (horiz)	50	55
808		$2.60, Colour of Hong Kong Volunteer Defence Corps, 1928 (horiz)	60	85
809		$5 Cap badge of Royal Hong Kong Defence Force, 1951	1·00	2·00
806/9		Set of 4	2·25	3·25

(Des C. Tillyer and Valerie Carter. Litho Enschedé)

1995 (1 Sept). *"Singapore '95" International Stamp Exhibition. Sheet 130×75 mm, containing design as No. 715, but litho and colours changed. P 14.*

MS810		$10 dp mag, yellow-olive, yell & brn-lilac	4·00	5·50

No. MS810 shows "HONG KONG" printed in yellow fluorescence with a horizontal green fluorescent line beneath as a security marking. There is a larger perforation hole at each corner of the stamp.

(Des D. Lai. Litho Enschedé)

1995 (9 Oct). *50th Anniv of End of Second World War. Sheet 130×75 mm, containing design as No. 715, but litho. P 14.*

MS811		$10 red-brown, black and cinnamon	4·00	5·50

No. MS811 shows "HONG KONG" printed in yellow fluorescence with a horizontal green fluorescent line beneath as a security marking. There is a larger perforation hole at each corner of the stamp.

174 Bruce Lee

(Des Lau Siu-hong and Wong Kum. Litho Enschedé)

1995 (15 Nov). *Hong Kong Film Stars. T 174 and similar horiz designs. Multicoloured. P 13½.*

812		$1.20, Type 174	1·50	55
813		$2.10, Leung Sing-por	1·75	1·40
814		$2.60, Yam Kim-fai	2·75	1·60
815		$5 Lin Dai	2·75	3·25
812/15		Set of 4	8·00	6·00

175 Rat

176 Rhythmic Gymnastics

(Des Kan Tai-keung. Litho Enschedé)

1996 (31 Jan). *Chinese New Year ("Year of the Rat"). T 175 and similar horiz designs. P 13½.*

816		$1.20, multicoloured	25	30
	a.	Booklet pane. Nos. 816 and 818, each × 3, with margins all round	2·50	
817		$2.10, multicoloured	45	55
818		$2.60, multicoloured	50	65
819		$5 multicoloured	1·25	1·75
816/19		Set of 4	2·25	3·00
MS820		133×83 mm. Nos. 816/19	2·50	3·50

(Des Lam Bing-pui. Litho Enschedé)

1996 (23 Feb). *Visit "HONG KONG '97" Stamp Exhibition (1st issue). Sheet 130×80 mm, containing designs as No. 715, but litho and colours changed. P 14.*

MS821		$10 yellow-orange, black & bright green	4·50	6·50

No. MS821 shows "HONG KONG" printed in yellow fluorescence with a horizontal green fluorescent line beneath as a security marking. There is a large perforation hole at each corner of the stamp.

See also Nos. MS827, MS841 and MS872/3.

(Des B. Kwan. Litho Ashton-Potter America Inc, New York)

1996 (20 Mar). *Olympic Games, Atlanta. T 176 and similar vert designs. Multicoloured with Royal Cypher and face values in black and Olympic Rings multicoloured (Nos. 822/5). Two phosphor bands ($1.20) or one side phosphor band (others). P 13½.*

822		$1.20, Type 176	25	25
823		$2.10, Diving	45	55

824	$2.60, Athletics	..	..	55	75
825	$5 Basketball	..	..	1·50	2·50
822/5			*Set of 4*	2·50	3·50

MS826 130×75 mm. As Nos. 822/5, but Royal Cypher and Olympic Rings in gold and face values in black (medal in bottom sheet margin) 2·50 3·50
For these designs with Royal Cypher and Olympic Rings in gold see Nos. 832/6.

(Des A. Lam. Litho Enschedé)

1996 (18 May). *Visit "HONG KONG '97" Stamp Exhibition (2nd issue). Sheet 130×80 mm, containing design as No. 715, but litho and colours changed. P 14.*
MS827 $10 brt emer, greenish blk & bluish vio 2·50 3·00
No. **MS**827 shows "HONG KONG" printed in yellow fluorescence with a horizontal green fluorescent line beneath as a security marking. There is a large perforation hole at each corner of the stamp.

177 Painted Pottery Basin, c. 4500–3700 B.C.

(Des I. Leung. Litho Enschedé)

1996 (26 June). *Archaeological Discoveries. T **177** and similar horiz designs. Multicoloured. Two phosphor bands ($1.20) or one side band (others). P 13½.*

828	$1.20, Type **177**			35	25
829	$2.10, Stone "yue" (ceremonial axe), c. 2900–2200 B.C.			40	65
830	$2.60, Stone "ge" (halberd), c. 2200–1500 B.C.			45	1·00
831	$5 Pottery tripod, c. 25–220 A.D.			1·00	2·50
828/31	..	..	*Set of 4*	2·00	4·00

(Des B. Kwan, Litho Ashton-Potter America Inc, New York)

1996 (19 July). *Opening of Centennial Olympic Games, Atlanta. Designs as Nos. 822/5, but with Royal Cypher and Olympic Rings in gold and face values in colours quoted. Two phosphor bands ($1.20) or one side band (others). P 14½.*

832	$1.20, Type **176** (bright magenta)			35	25
833	$2.10, As No. 823 (deep ultramarine)			40	60
834	$2.60, As No. 824 (light green)	..		45	90
835	$5 As No. 825 (orange-vermilion)			1·00	2·75
832/5			*Set of 4*	2·00	4·00

MS836 130×75 mm. As No. **MS**826, but with medal in top margin. P 13½ 2·50 4·00
The stamps in Nos. **MS**826 and **MS**836 are similar. The miniature sheets differ in the marginal inscriptions and illustrations. No. **MS**826 is inscribed "1996 OLYMPIC GAMES" and has a Gold Medal in the bottom margin. No. **MS**836 is inscribed "TO COMMEMORATE THE OPENING OF THE CENTENNIAL OLYMPIC GAMES 19 JULY 1996" and has the medal in the top margin.

178 Pat Sin Leng Mountain

(Des Lam Bing-pui. Litho Harrison)

1996 (24 Sept). *Mountains. T **178** and similar multicoloured designs. Two phosphor bands ($1.30) or one side phosphor band (others). P 13½×14½ ($1.30), 14×14½ ($2.50), 14½×14 ($3.10) or 14½×13½ ($5).*

837	$1.30, Type **178**			40	35
838	$2.50, Ma On Shan (40×35 mm)	..		60	1·00
839	$3.10, Lion Rock (35×40 mm)	..		80	1·40
840	$5 Lantau Peak (25×46½ mm)			1·00	2·25
837/40			*Set of 4*	2·50	4·50

(Des A. Lam. Litho Enschedé)

1996 (16 Oct). *Visit "HONG KONG '97" Stamp Exhibition (3rd issue). Sheet 130×80 mm, containing design as No. 715, but litho and colours changed. P 14½×14.*
MS841 $10 apple-green, black and rose-carmine 2·50 3·50
No. **MS**841 shows "HONG KONG" printed in yellow fluorescence with a horizontal green fluorescent line beneath as a security marking. There is a larger perforation hole at each corner of the stamp.

(Des B. Kwan. Litho Enschedé)

1996 (29 Oct). *Hong Kong Team's Achievements at Atlanta Olympic Games. Sheet 130×75 mm, containing design as No. 715 but litho. P 14½×14.*
MS842 $10 red-brown, black and cinnamon 2·50 3·25
No. **MS**842 shows "HONG KONG" printed in yellow fluorescence with a horizontal green fluorescent line beneath as a security marking. There is a larger perforation hole at each corner of the stamp.

---

179 Main Building, University of Hong Kong, 1912

180 Part of Hong Kong Skyline

(Des T. Li. Recess and litho Ashton-Potter America Inc, New York)

1996 (20 Nov). *Urban Heritage. T **179** and similar horiz designs. Multicoloured. Two phosphor bands ($1.30) or one phosphor band (others). P 13½.*

843	$1.30, Type **179**	..	..	40	30
844	$2.50, Western Market, 1906	..		60	85
845	$3.10, Old Pathological Institute, 1905		65	1·00
846	$5 Flagstaff House, 1846	..		80	2·25
843/6			*Set of 4*	2·25	4·00

(Des A. Lam. Litho Walsall)

1996 (4 Dec). *Serving the Community. Sheet 130×75 mm, containing design as No. 619, but smaller, 25×35 mm. Multicoloured. One phosphor band. P 13×13½.*
MS847 $5 Multi-racial society .. 1·00 1·25

(Des Kan Tai-keung)

1997 (26 Jan). *T **180** and similar vert designs showing different sections of Hong Kong skyline. Two phosphor bands (10 c. to $2.10), one centre phosphor band ($2.50 to $5) or phosphorised paper ($10).*

(a) Sheet stamps. Litho Ashton-Potter America Inc, New York. P 13½×13 (10 c. to $5) or 14×13½ ($10, $20, $50)

848	10 c. purple and rose-pink	..		15	20
849	20 c. purple-brown and orange-red	..		30	30
850	50 c. deep green and bright orange	..		20	20
851	$1 greenish blue and orange-yellow	..		30	20
852	$1.20, deep dull green and olive-yellow	..		30	25
853	$1.30, deep violet and apple green	..		30	25
	a. Booklet pane. No. 853×10 with margins all round			2·50	
854	$1.40, maroon and bright green	..		30	25
855	$1.60, deep purple and bright blue-green		30	30
856	$2 deep olive and greenish blue	..		40	35
857	$2.10, deep turquoise-blue and bright blue		40	35
858	$2.50, violet and bright mauve	..		50	55
	a. Booklet pane. No. 858×10 with margins all round			4·00	
859	$3.10, purple and cerise	..		60	70
	a. Booklet pane. No. 859×10 with margins all round			5·00	
860	$5 deep magenta and bright orange	..		1·25	1·00
861	$10 multicoloured (28×32 mm)	..		2·00	2·00
862	$20 multicoloured (28×32 mm)	..		3·50	4·00
863	$50 multicoloured (28×32 mm)	..		8·00	9·00
848/63			*Set of 16*	17·00	18·00

MS864 273×53 mm. Nos. 848/57, and as Nos. 858/60 each with one side phosphor band 5·00 6·00
MS865 95×72 mm. Nos. 861/3 15·00 17·00

(b) Coil stamps. Designs as Nos. 849, 851, 853, 856 and 859/60, but photo Enschedé. P 14½×14.

866	10 c. purple and rose-pink	..		15	30
867	50 c. deep green and bright orange	..		20	30
868	$1.30, deep violet and apple-green	..		35	40
869	$1.60, deep purple and bright blue-green		35	45
870	$2.50, violet and bright mauve	..		55	75
871	$3.10, purple and cerise	..		60	80
866/71			*Set of 6*	2·00	2·75

Nos. 848/71 show "HONG KONG" printed in yellow fluorescence. The perforations on Nos. 848/65 showing alternate small and large holes.
Nos. 866/71 were printed in coils with every fifth stamp numbered on the reverse.
For miniature sheets containing No. 861 see Nos. **MS**872/3 and **MS**892.

(Des Kan Tai-keung. Litho Ashton-Potter America Inc, New York)

1997 (12 Feb). *Visit "HONG KONG '97" Stamp Exhibition (4th issue). Sheet 130×80 mm containing design as No. 861, but ordinary paper, and with marginal illustration in bluish violet. P 14×13.*
MS872 $10 multicoloured 2·25 3·50
No. **MS**872 shows "HONG KONG" in yellow fluorescence. The perforations show alternate small and large holes.

(Des Kan Tai-keung. Litho Ashton-Potter America Inc, New York)

1997 (16 Feb). *Visit "HONG KONG '97" Stamp Exhibition (5th issue). Sheet 130×80 mm, containing design as No. 861, but ordinary paper, and with marginal illustration in chestnut. P 14×13.*
MS873 $10 multicoloured 2·25 3·50
No. **MS**873 shows "HONG KONG" in yellow fluorescence. The perforations show alternate small and large holes.

181 Ox

(Des Kan Tai-keung)

1997 (27 Feb). *Chinese New Year ("Year of the Ox"). T **181** and similar horiz designs. Two phosphor bands ($1.30) or one phosphor band (others).*

(a) Litho Ashton-Potter America Inc, New York. P 14½

874	$1.30, multicoloured	..	..	25	25
875	$2.50, multicoloured	..	..	50	55
876	$3.10, multicoloured	..	..	75	90
877	$5 multicoloured	..	..	1·25	2·00
874/7			*Set of 4*	2·50	3·25

MS878 133×84 mm. Nos. 874/7 2·50 3·50

(b) Litho Enschedé. P 13½

879	$1.30, multicoloured	..		25	25
	a. Booklet pane. Nos. 879 and 881 each × 3			6·00	
880	$2.50, multicoloured	..		50	55
881	$3.10, multicoloured	..		75	90
882	$5 multicoloured	..		1·25	2·00
879/82			*Set of 4*	2·50	3·25

MS883 133×84 mm. Nos. 879/82 2·50 3·50

182 Yellow-breasted Bunting

(Des Shek Tak-sheun. Litho Enschedé)

1997 (27 Apr). *Migratory Birds. T **182** and similar horiz designs. Multicoloured. Two phosphor bands ($1.30) or one phosphor band (others). P 13½.*

884	$1.30, Type **182**	..	..	30	35
885	$2.50, Great Knot	..	..	50	55
886	$3.10, Falcated Teal	..	..	75	90
887	$5 Black-faced Spoonbill	..		1·25	2·00
884/7			*Set of 4*	2·50	3·25

183 Hong Kong Stadium

(Des M. Chan)

1997 (18 May). *Modern Landmarks. T **183** and similar horiz designs. Multicoloured. Two phosphor bands ($1.30) or one phosphor band (others). (a) Litho Enschedé. P 13½*

888	$1.30, Type **183**	..	..	25	25
889	$2.50, Peak Tower	..	..	50	55
890	$3.10, Hong Kong Convention and Exhibition Centre			75	1·00
891	$5 Lantau Bridge	..		1·10	2·00
888/91			*Set of 4*	2·40	3·50

MS892 130×76 mm. No. 891 1·25 1·75

(b) Photo Walsall. P 14×14½

893	$1.30, Type **183**	..	..	25	25
894	$2.50, Peak Tower	..	..	50	55
895	$3.10, Hong Kong Convention and Exhibition Centre			75	1·00
896	$5 Lantau Bridge	..		1·10	2·00
893/6			*Set of 4*	2·40	3·50

MS897 130×76 mm. No. 896 1·25 1·75

(Des G. Lai and Leung Ka-shun. Litho Ashton-Potter America Inc, New York)

1997 (1 June). *Paralympic Games, Atlanta (1996). Sheet 130×75 mm containing design as No. 861 but on ordinary paper. P 14×13.*
MS898 $10 multicoloured 2·00 2·75
No. **MS**898 shows "HONG KONG" printed in yellow fluorescence. The perforations show alternate small and large holes.

(Des A. Lam. Litho Courvoisier)

1997 (30 June). *History of the Hong Kong Post Office. Sheet 130×75 mm containing design as No. 677, but redrawn smaller, 22×38 mm. One phosphor band. P 11½.*
MS899 $5 multicoloured 1·10 1·75
Details of the Post Office buildings depicted on the miniature sheet are printed on the reverse.

Hong Kong became a Special Administrative Region of the People's Republic of China on 1 July 1997 when all previous stamp issues, with exception of Nos. 848/71, were withdrawn and invalidated. Later issues are included in the *Part 17* (China) catalogue.

PRICES OF SETS

Set prices are given for many issues, generally those containing three stamps or more. Definitive sets include one of each value or major colour change, but do not cover different perforations, die types or minor shades. Where a choice is possible the set prices are based on the cheapest versions of the stamps included in the listings.

STAMP BOOKLETS

1903 (Mar). *Black on white cover. Postage rates on front. Stapled.*
SB1 $1 booklet containing twelve 1 c. (No. 62), twelve 2 c. (No. 56), each in blocks of 6, and sixteen 4 c. (No. 57) in blocks of 8   ..   ..   ..

1904 (1 Jan). *Black on white cover. Postage rates on front. Stapled.*
SB2 $1 booklet containing twelve 1 c. (No. 62), twelve 2 c. (No. 56), each in blocks of 6, and sixteen 4 c. (No. 64) in blocks of 8   ..   ..   £4250

1904. *Black on white cover. Postage rates on front. Stapled.*
SB3 $1 booklet containing twelve 1 c., twelve 2 c. (Nos. 62/3), each in blocks of 6, and sixteen 4 c. (No. 64) in blocks of 8   ..   ..   £3250

1907–08. *Black on white cover. Stapled.*
SB4 $1 booklet containing twelve 1 c., twelve 2 c. (Nos. 62, 92), each in blocks of 6, and sixteen 4 c. (No. 93) in blocks of 8   ..   ..   £2750
    a. 4 c. in two blocks of 6 and block of 4 (1908) ..   £2750

1910. *Black on white cover. Contents on front. Stapled.*
SB5 $1 booklet containing twelve 1 c., twelve 2 c. (Nos. 91/2), each in blocks of 6, and sixteen 4 c. (No. 93) in two blocks of 6 and block of 4   ..   £2750

1912. *Black on white cover. Stapled.*
SB6 $1 booklet containing twelve 1 c., twelve 2 c. (Nos 100/1), each in block of 12, and sixteen 4 c. (No. 102) in block of 12 and block of 4   ..   £2500

1929. *Black on white cover. Stapled.*
SB7 $1 booklet containing twelve 1 c., twelve 2 c. (Nos. 117/18), each in block of 12, and sixteen 4 c. (No. 120) in blocks of 8   ..   ..   £2250

1965 (10 May). *Orange-brown (No. SB8) or yellow-green (No. SB9) covers. Stitched.*
SB8 $2 booklet containing eight 5 c. and sixteen 10 c. (Nos. 196/7) in blocks of 4   ..   ..   35·00
SB9 $5 booklet containing twelve 5 c., eight 10 c., eight 20 c. and four 50 c. (Nos. 196/7, 199, 203) in blocks of 4   ..   ..   £120

1973 (12 June). *Buff (No. SB10) or green (No. SB11) covers. Stitched.*
SB10 $2 booklet containing twenty 10 c. (No. 283) in blocks of 4   ..   ..   32·00
SB11 $5 booklet containing eight 10 c., four 15 c., eight 20 c. and four 50 c. (Nos. 283, 284/5, 289) each in blocks of 4   ..   ..   70·00

1975 (27 Jan). *Covers as Nos. SB10/11. Stitched.*
SB12 $2 booklet containing twenty 10 c. (No. 311) in blocks of 4   ..   ..   32·00
SB13 $5 booklet containing eight 10 c., four 15 c., eight 20 c. and four 50 c. (Nos. 311/13, 317) in blocks of 4   ..   ..   65·00

1976 (1 July). *Orange (No. SB14) or green (No. SB15) covers. Stitched.*
SB14 $2 booklet containing four 10 c. and eight 20 c. (Nos. 311, 313) in blocks of 4   ..   27·00
SB15 $5 booklet containing eight 10 c., four 15 c., eight 20 c. and four 50 c. (Nos. 311, 284, 313, 289) in blocks of 4   ..   ..   55·00

B 1   *World Map*

1985 (1 Apr–Nov). *Multicoloured cover as Type B 1. Stamps attached by selvedge.*
SB16 $13 booklet containing $1.30 (No. 464) in block of 10   ..   ..   27·00
    a. Containing No. 469 in block of 10 ..   22·00
    b. Containing No. 490 in block of 10 (June) ..   28·00
    c. Containing No. 500 in block of 10 (Sept) ..   29·00
    d. Containing No. 504 in block of 10 (Nov) ..   25·00
   Supplies of a similar $13 booklet, but containing ten examples of No. 495, were produced for sale by the Crown Agents Stamp Bureau. Such booklets are reported not to have been available from post offices in Hong Kong.

1985 (2 Sept)–87. *Multicoloured cover as Type B 1. Stamps attached by selvedge.*
SB18 $17 booklet containing $1.70 (No. 482) in block of 10   ..   ..   35·00
    a. Containing No. 547 in block of 10 (1987)   28·00

1985 (28 Oct)–87. *Multicoloured cover as Type B 1, showing map of Hong Kong. Stamps attached by selvedge.*
SB19 $5 booklet containing 50 c. (No. 475) in block of 10   ..   ..   7·00
    a. Containing No. 540 in block of 10 (1987) ..   5·50

B 2   Hong Kong Bank Headquarters and Lion's Head
(Illustration further reduced. Actual size 159×86 mm)

1986 (7 Apr). *New Hong Kong Bank Headquarters. Multicoloured cover as Type B 2. Booklet contains text and illustrations on interleaving pages. Stitched.*
SB20 $29 booklet containing 50 c. in block of 24 and $1.70 in block of 10 (Nos. 475, 505)   ..   40·00

B 3   Early and Modern Views of the Peak Tramway
(Illustration further reduced. Actual size 161×91 mm)

1988 (26 Aug). *Centenary of The Peak Tramway. Multicoloured cover as Type B 3. Booklet contains text and illustrations on interleaving pages. Stitched.*
SB21 $26 booklet containing No. MS581×3 ..   ..   22·00

B 4   *(Illustration further reduced. Actual size 145×55 mm)*

1989 (18 Jan). *Year of the Snake. Multicoloured cover as Type B 4. Pane attached by selvedge.*
SB22 $12 booklet containing se-tenant pane of 10 (No. 587a)   ..   ..   6·50

B 5   *(Illustration further reduced. Actual size 140×65 mm)*

1990 (23 Jan). *Year of the Horse. Multicoloured cover as Type B 5. Pane attached by selvedge.*
SB23 $14.50, booklet containing two se-tenant panes of 6 (No. 631a)   ..   ..   9·00

1990 (3 May). *"Stamp World London 90" International Stamp Exhibition. As No. SB23, but "Stamp World London 90" emblem printed on cover and top selvedge of each pane.*
SB24 $14.50, booklet. Contents as No. SB23 ..   15·00
   No. SB24 additionally includes an imperforate black print on gummed paper of the 60 c. and $1.80 values of the New Year issue.

B 6   Hong Kong Skyline at Night
(Illustration further reduced. Actual size 168×86 mm)

1990 (29 Nov). *Centenary of Electricity Supply. Multicoloured cover as Type B 6. Booklet contains text and illustrations on interleaving pages. Stitched.*
SB25 $26 booklet containing No. MS651×4 ..   25·00

1991 (24 Jan). *Year of the Ram. Multicoloured cover as Type B 5. Pane attached by selvedge.*
SB26 $14.40, booklet containing two se-tenant panes of 6 (No. 658a)   ..   ..   8·50

1992 (22 Jan). *Year of the Monkey. Multicoloured cover as Type B 5. Panes attached by selvedge.*
SB27 $18.60, booklet containing two se-tenant panes of 6 (No. 686a)   ..   ..   9·00

B 7   "Greetings"
(Illustration further reduced. Actual size 153×67 mm)

1992 (19 Nov). *Greetings Stamps. Multicoloured cover as Type B 7. Panes attached by selvedge.*
SB28 $24 booklet containing two se-tenant panes of 6 (No. 728a) and 24 half stamp-size labels ..   9·00

1993 (7 Jan). *Year of the Cock. Multicoloured cover as Type B 5. Panes attached by selvedge.*
SB29 $18.60, booklet containing two se-tenant panes of 6 (No. 732a)   ..   ..   7·50

B 8   Skyscrapers

1993 (14–28 Dec). *Multicoloured cover as Type B 8. Panes attached by selvedge.*
SB30 $10 booklet containing pane of ten $1 (No. 757a)   7·50
SB31 $19 booklet containing pane of ten $1.90 (No. 758a) (cover showing Exhibition Centre) (28 Dec)   ..   ..   9·00
SB32 $24 booklet containing pane of ten $2.40 (No. 759a) (cover showing historical buildings) (28 Dec)   ..   ..   9·50

B 9   *(Illustration further reduced. Actual size 160×85 mm)*

1994 (12 Jan). *"A History of Hong Kong Definitive Stamps 1862–1992". Multicoloured cover Type B 9. Booklet contains text and illustrations on panes and on interleaving pages. Stapled.*
SB33 $38 booklet containing three different se-tenant panes of 6 (Nos. 760a/2a)   ..   16·00

1994 (27 Jan). *Year of the Dog. Multicoloured cover as Type B 5. Panes attached by selvedge.*
SB34 $20.40, booklet containing two se-tenant panes of 6 (No. 766a)   ..   ..   9·00

1995 (17 Jan). *Year of the Pig. Multicoloured cover as Type B 5. Panes attached by selvedge.*
SB35 $20.40, booklet containing two se-tenant panes of 6 (No. 793a)   ..   ..   6·50

1995 (1 June). *Multicoloured covers as Nos. SB30/2. Panes attached by selvedge.*
SB36 $12 booklet containing pane of ten $1.20 (No. 757ba) (Type B 8 cover)   ..   7·00
SB37 $21 booklet containing pane of ten $2.10 (No. 758ba) (cover as No. SB31)   ..   9·00
SB38 $26 booklet containing pane of ten $2.60 (No. 759ca) (cover as No. SB32)   ..   9·50
   On the initial supply of No. SB36 the inside of the card covers were matt. A printing later in 1995 showed both sides of the cover card glossy.

1996 (31 Jan). *Year of the Rat. Multicoloured cover as Type B 5. Panes attached by selvedge.*
SB39 $22.80, booklet containing two se-tenant panes of 6 (No. 816a)   ..   ..   5·00

1996 (2 Sept). *Multicoloured covers as Nos. SB30/2. Panes attached by selvedge.*
SB40 $13 booklet containing pane of ten $1.30 (No. 757ca) (Type B 8 cover)   ..   5·00
SB41 $25 booklet containing pane of ten $2.50 (No. 759ba) (cover as No. SB31)   ..   7·00
SB42 $31 booklet containing pane of ten $3.10 (No. 759da) (cover as No. SB32)   ..   7·50

B 10 Water Front

1997 (26 Jan). *Multicoloured covers as Type* **B 10**, *each incorporating the design from the stamps included. Panes attached by selvedge.*
SB43 $13 booklet containing pane of ten $1.30 (No. 853a)   ..   ..   ..   2·50
SB44 $25 booklet containing pane of ten $2.50 (No. 858a)   ..   ..   ..   4·00
SB45 $31 booklet containing pane of ten $3.10 (No. 859a)   ..   ..   ..   5·00

B 11   Hong Kong Waterfront
(Illustration further reduced. Actual size 183×130 mm)

1997 (14 Feb). *Hong Kong Past and Present. Multicoloured cover as Type* **B 11**. *Booklet containing text and illustrations on interleaving pages. Stitched.*
SB46 $55 booklet containing three different *se-tenant* panes of 6 (Nos. 757cc, 757db and 758bd)   ..   20·00

1997 (27 Feb). *Year of the Ox. Multicoloured cover as Type* **B 5**. *Panes attached by selvedge.*
SB47 $26.40, booklet containing two panes of 6 (No. 879a)   ..   ..   ..   12·00

POSTAGE DUE STAMPS

PRINTERS. Nos. D1/23 were typographed by De La Rue & Co.

D 1   Post-office Scales   D 2

1923 (Dec)–56. *Wmk Mult Script CA. Ordinary paper. P* 14.
D1   D 1   1 c. brown   ..   ..   2·50   65
    a. Wmk sideways (1931)   ..   1·50   3·25
    ab. Chalk-surfaced paper (21.3.56)   30   1·00
D2   2 c. green   ..   ..   17·00   5·00
    a. Wmk sideways (1928)   ..   10·00   5·00
D3   4 c. scarlet   ..   ..   32·00   6·00
    a. Wmk sideways (1928)   ..   27·00   7·00
D4   6 c. yellow   ..   ..   26·00   13·00
    a. Wmk sideways (1931)   ..   50·00   30·00
D5   10 c. bright ultramarine   ..   23·00   8·00
    a. Wmk sideways (1934)   ..   80·00   16·00
D1/5   ..   ..   Set of 5   90·00   30·00
D1a/5a   ..   ..   Set of 5   £150   55·00
D1/5 Optd "Specimen"   ..   Set of 5   £225

1938 (Feb)–63. *Wmk Mult Script CA (sideways). Ordinary paper. P* 14.
D6   D 1   2 c. grey   ..   ..   13·00   9·00
    a. Chalk-surfaced paper (21.3.56)   9·00   9·00
D 7   4 c. orange   ..   ..   17·00   6·50
    a. Chalk-surfaced paper. *Orange-yellow* (23.5.61)   ..   2·50   9·50
D 8   6 c. scarlet   ..   ..   9·50   5·50
D 9   8 c. chestnut (26.2.46)   ..   5·50   32·00
D10   10 c. violet   ..   ..   30·00   45
    a. Chalk-surfaced paper (17.9.63)   16·00   8·50
D11   20 c. black (26.2.46)   ..   11·00   3·00
D12   50 c. blue (7.47)   ..   ..   40·00   15·00
D6a/12   ..   ..   Set of 7   75·00   65·00
D6/12 Perf "Specimen"   ..   Set of 7   £300

1965 (15 Apr)–72. *Chalk-surfaced paper. P* 14.
(a) Wmk w **12** *(sideways)*
D13   D 1   4 c. yellow-orange   ..   8·00   27·00
D14   5 c. red (13.5.69)   ..   3·25   5·00
    a. Glazed paper (17.11.72)   ..   11·00   30·00
D15   10 c. violet (27.6.67)   ..   3·50   4·25
D16   20 c. black (1965)   ..   4·25   4·25
D17   50 c. deep blue (1965)   ..   26·00   9·00
    a. Blue (13.5.69)   ..   ..   25·00   9·00
D13/17   ..   ..   Set of 5   40·00   45·00

(b) Wmk w **12** *(upright)*
D18   D 1   5 c. red (20.7.67)   ..   2·25   5·00
D19   50 c. deep blue (26.8.70)   ..   38·00   10·00
The 5 c. is smaller, 21 × 18 mm.

1972 (17 Nov)–74. *Glazed, ordinary paper. W w* **12** *(sideways).*
(a) P 14 × 14½
D20   D 1   10 c. bright reddish violet   ..   6·50   4·50
D21   20 c. grey-black   ..   ..   7·50   6·50
D22   50 c. deep dull blue   ..   4·50   10·00
(b) P 13½ × 14
D23   D 1   5 c. brown-red (1.5.74)   ..   2·50   5·50
D20/3   ..   ..   Set of 4   19·00   24·00

(Typo Walsall)
1976 (19 Mar*)–78. *Smaller design (21 × 17 mm) with redrawn value-tablet. Glazed, ordinary paper. W w* **14**. *P* 14.
D25   D 1   10 c. bright reddish violet   ..   80   4·00
    a. Chalk-surfaced paper (15.12.78)   80   2·00
D26   20 c. grey-black   ..   ..   1·25   4·50
    a. Chalk-surfaced paper (15.12.78)   90   2·25
D27   50 c. deep dull blue   ..   1·25   5·00
    a. Chalk-surfaced paper (15.12.78)   90   2·75
D28 $1 yellow (1.4.76)   ..   ..   11·00   12·00
    a. Chalk-surfaced paper (15.12.78)   1·40   4·00
D25/8   ..   ..   Set of 4   13·00   23·00
D25a/8a   ..   ..   Set of 4   3·50   10·00
This is the London release date. It is believed that the stamps were not released locally until 14 April.

(Typo Walsall)
1986 (11 Jan). *As Nos. D27a/8a, but without watermark. P* 14.
D29   D 1   50 c. slate-blue   ..   ..   2·00   4·25
D30 $1 lemon   ..   ..   ..   2·50   5·50

(Des A. Chan. Litho B.D.T.)
1987 (25 Mar). *P* 14 × 15.
D31   D 2   10 c. light green   10   10
D32   20 c. red-brown   10   10
D33   50 c. bright violet   10   10
D34 $1 yellow-orange   15   20
D35 $5 dull ultramarine   80   1·10
D36 $10 bright rose-red   ..   ..   1·60   2·25
D31/6   ..   ..   Set of 6   2·75   3·50

POSTCARD STAMPS

Stamps specially surcharged for use on Postcards.

PRICES. Those in the left-hand column are for unused examples on complete postcards; those on the right for used examples off card. Examples used on postcards are worth more.

3   **THREE**
CENTS   CENTS
(P 1)   (P 2)

1879 (1 Apr). *Nos. 22 and 13 surch as Type* P **1** *by D.L.R.*
P1   3   3 c. on 16 c. yellow (No. 22)   ..   £300   £325
P2   5 c. on 18 c. lilac (No. 13)   ..   £275   £325

1879 (Nov). *No. P2 handstamped with Type* P **2**.
P3   3   3 c. on 5 c. on 18 c. lilac   ..   £5500   £7000

POSTAL FISCAL STAMPS

I. Stamps inscribed "STAMP DUTY"

NOTE. The dated circular "HONG KONG" cancellation with "PAID ALL" in lower segment was used for fiscal purposes, in black, from 1877. Previously it appears in red on mail to the U.S.A., but is usually not used as a cancellation.

F 1   F 2

F 3

1874–1902. *Wmk Crown CC. (a) P* 15½×15
F1   F 1 $2 olive-green   ..   ..   £300   45·00
F2   F 2 $3 dull violet   ..   ..   £275   32·00
    b. Bluish paper
F3   F 3 $10 rose-carmine £7000   £650

(b) P 14
F4   F 1 $2 dull bluish green (10.97)   ..   £350   £225
F5   F 2 $3 dull mauve (3.02)   ..   £425   £350
    a. Bluish paper £1500
F6   F 3 $10 grey-green (1892)   ..   £10000   £10000
F4/5 Optd "Specimen"   ..   Set of 2   £450
Nos. F1/3 and F7 exist on various papers, ranging from thin to thick.
All three of the values perforated 15½×15 were authorised for postal use in 1874. The $10 was withdrawn from such use in 1880, the $2 in September 1897 and the $3 in 1902. The $2 and $3 perforated 14 were available for postal purposes until July 1903. The $10 in grey-green was issued for fiscal purposes in 1892 and is known with postal cancellations.

12 CENTS. (F 4)   F 5

1880. *No. F3 surch with Type* F **4** *by Noronha and Sons, Hong Kong.*
F7   F 3   12 c. on $10 rose-carmine   ..   £700   £250

1890 (24 Dec). *Wmk Crown CA. P* 14.
F8   F 5   2 c. dull purple   ..   ..   65·00   14·00
    w. Wmk inverted
No. F8 was authorised for postal use between 24 and 31 December 1890.

5 DOLLARS (F 6)   **ONE DOLLAR** (F 7)   F 8

1891 (1 Jan). *Surch with Type* F **6** *by D.L.R. Wmk Crown CA. P* 14.
F9   F 3 $5 on $10 purple/red (Optd S. £160)   ..   £275   95·00
No. F9 was in use for postal purposes until June 1903.

1897 (Sept). *Surch with Type* F **7** *by Noronha and Sons, Hong Kong, and with the value in Chinese characters subsequently applied twice by handstamp as T* **15**.
F10   F 1 $1 on $2 olive-green (No. F1)   ..   £180   95·00
    a. Both Chinese handstamps omitted   £2750   £1800
F11 $1 on $2 dull bluish green (No. F4) (H/S S, £140) £200   £120
    a. Both Chinese handstamps omitted   £1500   £1100
    b. Diagonal Chinese handstamp omitted £9500
    c. Vertical Chinese handstamp omitted   ..   ..

1938 (11 Jan). *Wmk Mult Script CA. P* 14.
F12   F 8   5 c. green   ..   ..   ..   50·00   9·50
No. F12 was authorised for postal use between 11 and 20 January 1938 due to a shortage of the 5 c., No. 121.
Forged cancellations are known on this stamp inscribed "VICTORIA 9.AM 11 JA 38 HONG KONG" without side bars between the rings.

II. Stamps overprinted "S.O." (Stamp Office), or "S.D." (Stamp Duty)

S. O.   **S. D.**

邱 厘   邱 厘
(S 1)   (S 2)

1891 (1 Jan). *Optd with Types* S **1** *or* S **2**.
S1   S 1   2 c. carmine (No. 33)   ..   £750   £275
S2   S 2   2 c. carmine (No. 33)   ..   £350   £150
    a. Opt inverted   ..   ..   † £3750
S3   S 1   10 c. purple/red (No. 38)   ..   £1200   £350
Examples of No. S1 exist with the "O" amended to "D" in manuscript.

Other fiscal stamps are found apparently postally used, but there is no evidence that this use was authorised.

JAPANESE OCCUPATION OF HONG KONG

Hong Kong surrendered to the Japanese on 25 December 1941. The postal service was not resumed until 22 January 1942 when the G.P.O. and Kowloon Central Office re-opened.

Japanese postmarks used in Hong Kong can be identified by the unique combination of horizontal lines in the central circle and three stars in the lower segment of the outer circle. Dates shown on such postmarks are in the sequence Year/Month/Day with the first shown as a Japanese regnal year number so that Showa 17 = 1942 and so on.

Initially six current Japanese definitives, 1, 2, 3, 4, 10 and 30 s. (Nos. 297, 315/17, 322 and 327), were on sale, but the range gradually expanded to cover all values between ½ s. and 10 y. with Nos. 313/14, 318, 325, 328/31, 391, 395/6, 398/9 and 405 of Japan also available from Hong Kong post offices during the occupation. Philatelic covers exist showing other Japanese stamps, but these were not available from the local post offices. Supply of these Japanese stamps was often interrupted and, during the period between 28 July 1942 and 21 April 1943, circular "Postage Paid" handstamps were sometimes used. A substantial increase in postage rates on 16 April 1945 led to the issue of the local surcharges, Nos. J1/3.

PRICES FOR STAMPS ON COVER
Nos. J1/3 *from* × 7

(1)   (2)

1945 (16 Apr). *Stamps of Japan surch with T* **1** *(No.* J1) *or as T* **2**.

J1	1.50 yen on 1 s. brown	..	..	26·00 21·00
J2	3 yen on 2 s. scarlet	..	..	12·00 18·00
J3	5 yen on 5 s. claret..	..	..	£850 £130

Designs (18½ × 22 *mm*):—1 s. Girl Worker; 2 s. Gen. Nogi; 5 s. Admiral Togo.

No. J3 has four characters of value similarly arranged but differing from T **2**.

BRITISH POST OFFICES IN CHINA

Under the terms of the 1842 Treaty of Nanking China granted Great Britain and its citizens commercial privileges in five Treaty Ports, Amoy, Canton, Foochow, Ningpo and Shanghai. British Consuls were appointed to each Port and their offices, as was usual during this period, collected and distributed mail for the British community. This system was formally recognised by a Hong Kong Government notice published on 16 April 1844. Mail from the consular offices was postmarked when it passed through Hong Kong.

The number of Chinese Treaty Ports was increased to sixteen by the ratification of the Treaty of Peking in 1860 with British postal facilities being eventually extended to the Ports of Chefoo, Hankow, Kiungchow (Hoihow), Swatow, Tainan (Anping) and Tientsin.

As postal business expanded the consular agencies were converted into packet agencies or post offices which passed under the direct control of the Hong Kong postal authorities on 1 May 1868.

In May 1898 the British Government leased the territory of Wei Hai Wei from China for use as a naval station to counter the Russian presence at Port Arthur.

The opening of the Trans-Siberia Railway and the extension of Imperial Penny Postage to the Treaty Port agencies resulted in them becoming a financial burden on the colonial post office. Control of the agencies reverted to the G.P.O., London, on 1 January 1911.

The pre-adhesive postal markings of the various agencies are a fascinating, but complex, subject. Full details can be found in *Hong Kong & the Treaty Ports of China & Japan* by F.W. Webb (reprinted edition J. Bendon, Limassol, 1992) and in various publications of the Hong Kong Study Circle.

From 15 October 1864 the use of Hong Kong stamps on mail from the Treaty Ports became compulsory, although such stamps were, initially, not cancelled (with the exception of Amoy) until they reached Hong Kong where the "B62" killer was applied. Cancellation of mail at the actual Ports commenced during 1866 at Shanghai and Ningpo, spreading to all the agencies during the next ten years. Shanghai had previously used a c.d.s. on adhesives during 1863 and again in 1865–66.

The main types of cancellation used between 1866 and 1930 are illustrated below. The illustrations show the style of each postmark and no attempt has been made to cover differences in type letters or figures, arrangement, diameter or colour.

Until 1885 the vertical and horizontal killers were used to obliterate the actual stamps with an impression of one of the circular date stamps shown elsewhere on the cover. Many of the early postmarks were also used as backstamps or transit marks and, in the notes which follow, references to use are for the first appearance of the mark, not necessarily its first use as an obliterator.

Illustrations in this section are taken from *Hong Kong & the Treaty Ports of China & Japan* by F. W. Webb and are reproduced with the permission of the Royal Philatelic Society, London.

Details of the stamps known used from each post office are taken, with permission, from *British Post Offices in the Far East* by Edward B. Proud, published by Proud-Bailey Co. Ltd.

Postmark Types

Type A Vertical killer	**Type B** Horizontal killer
Type C Name horizontal	**Type D** Name curved
Type E Double circle Name at top	**Type F** Double circle Name at foot

Type G Single circle Name at top

PRICES. The prices quoted in this section are for fine used stamps which show a clear impression of a substantial part of the cancellation.

AMOY

One of the five original Treaty Ports, opened to British trade by the Treaty of Nanking in 1842. A consular postal agency was established in 1844 which expanded in 1876 into two separate offices, one on the off-shore island of Ku Lang Seu and the other in Amoy itself.

Amoy "PAID" *(supplied* 1858*) used* 1859–67
Type **A** ("A1") *(supplied* 1866*) used at Ku Lang Seu* 1869–82
Type **D** *(supplied* 1866*) used* 1867–1922
Type **B** ("D27") *(supplied* 1876*) used at Amoy* 1876–84
Type **C** *used* 1876–94
Type **F** *(supplied* 1913*) used* 1916–22

Stamps of HONG KONG *cancelled at Amoy between* 1864 *and* 1916 *with postmarks detailed above.*

1862. *No wmk* (*Nos.* 1/7).

Z1	2 c. brown	..	..	..	£130
Z2	8 c. yellow-buff	..	..	..	£120
Z3	12 c. pale greenish blue	..	..	..	£100
Z4	18 c. lilac	..	..	..	65·00
Z5	24 c. green	..	..	..	£130
Z6	48 c. rose				
Z7	96 c. brownish grey	..	..	..	£500

1863–71. *Wmk Crown CC* (*Nos.* 8/19).

Z 8	2 c. brown	..	..	..	30·00
Z 9	4 c. grey	..	..	..	28·00
	a. Perf 12½				
Z10	6 c. lilac	..	..	..	42·00
Z11	8 c. orange	..	..	..	35·00
Z12	12 c. blue	..	..	..	16·00
Z13	18 c. lilac	..	..	..	£475
Z14	24 c. green	..	..	..	42·00
Z15	30 c. vermilion	..	..	..	60·00
Z16	30 c. mauve	..	..	..	11·00

Z17	48 c. rose	..	..	..	38·00
Z18	96 c. olive-bistre	..	..	..	£1000
Z19	96 c. brownish grey	..	..	..	£150

1876–77. (*Nos.* 20/1).

Z20	16 c. on 18 c. lilac	..	..	..	£275
Z21	28 c. on 30 c. mauve	..	..	..	£120

1877. *Wmk Crown CC* (*No.* 22).

Z22	16 c. yellow	..	..	..	90·00

1880. (*Nos.* 23/7).

Z23	5 c. on 8 c. orange				£110
Z24	5 c. on 18 c. lilac				95·00
Z25	10 c. on 12 c. blue				95·00
Z26	10 c. on 16 c. yellow				£180
Z27	10 c. on 24 c. green				£110

1880. *Wmk Crown CC* (*Nos.* 28/31).

Z28	2 c. rose	..	..	..	38·00
Z29	5 c. blue	..	..	..	50·00
Z30	10 c. mauve	..	..	..	42·00
Z31	48 c. brown	..	..	..	£120

1882–96. *Wmk Crown CA* (*Nos.* 32/9).

Z31a	2 c. rose-lake				
Z32	2 c. carmine	..	..	..	3·00
Z33	4 c. slate-grey	..	..	..	6·00
Z34	5 c. blue	..	..	..	3·00
Z35	10 c. dull mauve	..	..	..	22·00
Z36	10 c. green	..	..	..	3·50
Z37	10 c. purple/red	..	..	..	3·50
Z38	30 c. green	..	..	..	23·00

1885. (*Nos.* 40/2).

Z39	20 c. on 30 c. orange-red	..	..	9·00
Z40	50 c. on 48 c. yellowish brown	..	40·00
Z41	$1 on 96 c. grey-olive	..	..	70·00

1891. (*Nos.* 43/4, 48/50).

Z42	7 c. on 10 c. green	..	..	18·00
Z43	14 c. on 30 c. mauve	..	..	75·00
Z44	20 c. on 30 c. green	..	..	10·00
Z45	50 c. on 48 c. dull purple	..	..	13·00
Z46	$1 on 96 c. purple/red	..	..	32·00

1891. *50th Anniv of Colony* (*No.* 51).

Z47	2 c. carmine	..	..	..	£800

1898. (*No.* 52).

Z48	$1 on 96 c. black	..	..	..	40·00

1898. (*No.* 55).

Z49	10 c. on 30 c. green	..	..	£170

1900–01. *Wmk Crown CA* (*Nos.* 56/61).

Z50	2 c. dull green	..	..	..	3·00
Z51	4 c. carmine	..	..	..	2·10
Z52	5 c. yellow	..	..	..	13·00
Z53	10 c. ultramarine	..	..	..	3·50
Z54	12 c. blue	..	..	..	90·00
Z55	30 c. brown	..	..	..	48·00

1903. *Wmk Crown CA* (*Nos.* 62/76).

Z56	1 c. dull purple and brown	..	..	3·50
Z57	2 c. dull green	..	..	2·75
Z58	4 c. purple/red	..	..	1·75
Z59	5 c. dull green and brown-orange		13·00
Z60	8 c. slate and violet	..	..	5·00
Z61	10 c. purple and blue/blue	..	..	2·75
Z62	12 c. green and purple/yellow	..	9·00
Z63	20 c. slate and chestnut	..	..	7·50
Z64	30 c. dull green and black	..	..	32·00
Z65	50 c. dull green and magenta	..	48·00
Z67	$2 slate and scarlet	..	..	£275
Z68	$3 slate and dull blue	..	..	£400

1904–06. *Wmk Mult Crown CA* (*Nos.* 77/90).

Z71	2 c. dull green	..	..	..	2·75
Z72	4 c. purple/red	..	..	..	1·75
Z73	5 c. dull green and brown-orange		10·00
Z74	8 c. slate and violet	..	..	7·50
Z75	10 c. purple and blue/blue	..	..	2·50
Z76	12 c. green and purple/yellow	..	12·00
Z77	20 c. slate and chestnut	..	..	6·50
Z78	30 c. dull green and black..	..	21·00
Z79	50 c. green and magenta	..	..	18·00
Z83	$5 purple and blue-green	..	..	£375

1907–11. *Wmk Mult Crown CA* (*Nos.* 91/9).

Z85	1 c. brown	..	..	..	3·25
Z86	2 c. green	..	..	..	2·75
Z87	4 c. carmine-red	..	..	..	1·75
Z88	6 c. orange-vermilion and purple		10·00
Z89	10 c. bright ultramarine	..	..	2·50
Z90	20 c. purple and sage-green	..	45·00
Z91	30 c. purple and orange-yellow	..	40·00

1912–15. *Wmk Mult Crown CA* (*Nos.* 100/16).

Z 93	1 c. brown	..	..	..	4·00
Z 94	2 c. green	..	..	..	3·75
Z 95	4 c. red	..	..	..	1·75
Z 96	6 c. orange	..	..	..	3·00
Z 97	8 c. grey	..	..	..	16·00
Z 98	10 c. ultramarine	..	..	..	3·00
Z 99	12 c. purple/yellow	..	..	..	14·00
Z100	20 c. purple and sage-green	..	5·00
Z102	30 c. purple and orange-yellow		11·00
Z103	50 c. black/green	..	..	..	7·50
Z104	$1 purple and blue/blue	..	..	16·00
Z105	$3 green and purple	..	..	95·00

POSTCARD STAMPS

1879. (*Nos. P1/2*).
ZP106	3 c. on 16 c. yellow	.. .. ..	£425
ZP107	5 c. on 18 c. lilac	.. .. ..	£475

POSTAL FISCAL STAMPS

1874–1902. *Wmk Crown CC.* (a) P 15½×15 (*Nos. F1/3*)
ZF109	$2 olive-green	.. .. ..	95·00
ZF110	$3 dull violet ..	.. .. ..	85·00

1891. (*No. F9*).
ZF116	$5 on $10 purple/*red*	.. ..	£180

1897. (*No. F10*).
ZF118	$1 on $2 olive-green	.. ..	

ANPING

Anping is the port for Tainan, on the island of Formosa, opened to British trade in 1860. A British Vice-consulate operated in the port and mail is known postmarked there between 1889 and 1895. Formosa passed under Japanese control in 1895 and British Treaty Port rights then lapsed.

Type D *used 1889–95*

Stamps of HONG KONG *cancelled at Anping between 1889 and 1895 with postmark detailed above.*

1882–91. *Wmk Crown CA* (*Nos. 32/9*).
Z120	2 c. carmine	.. .. ..	£600
Z121	5 c. blue ..	.. .. ..	£425
Z123	10 c. green	.. .. ..	£600
Z124	10 c. purple/*red* ..	.. ..	£750

1885. (*Nos. 40/2*).
Z126	20 c. on 30 c. orange-red	.. ..	£600
Z127	50 c. on 48 c. yellowish brown	..	£800

CANTON

A British postal service was organised in Cantom from 1834, but was closed when the foreign communities were evacuated in August 1839. The city was one of the original Treaty Ports and a consular agency was opened there in 1844. The consulate closed during the riots of 1857, being replaced by a temporary postal agency at Whampoa, further down the river. When British forces reached Canton a further temporary agency was set up in 1859, but both closed in July 1863 when the consulate was re-established.

Type A ("C1") (*supplied 1866*) *used 1875–84*
Type C (*supplied 1866*) *used 1870–1901*
Type D *used 1890–1922*

Stamps of HONG KONG *cancelled at Canton between 1870 and 1916 with postmarks detailed above.*

1862. *No wmk* (*Nos. 1/7*).
Z135	18 c. lilac	.. .. ..	85·00

1863–71. *Wmk Crown CC* (*Nos. 8/19*).
Z136	2 c. brown	.. ..	29·00
Z137	4 c. grey	.. ..	32·00
Z138	6 c. lilac	.. ..	38·00
Z139	8 c. orange	.. ..	32·00
Z140	12 c. blue	.. ..	16·00
Z142	24 c. green	.. ..	42·00
Z143	30 c. vermilion ..		
Z144	30 c. mauve	.. ..	14·00
Z145	48 c. rose	.. ..	55·00
Z147	96 c. brownish grey	.. ..	65·00

1876–77. (*Nos. 20/1*).
Z148	16 c. on 18 c. lilac	..	£225
Z149	28 c. on 30 c. mauve	.. ..	90·00

1877. *Wmk Crown CC* (*No. 22*).
Z150	16 c. yellow	..	£110

1880. (*Nos. 23/7*).
Z151	5 c. on 8 c. orange	..	£120
Z152	5 c. on 18 c. lilac	..	£100
Z153	10 c. on 12 c. blue	..	95·00
Z154	10 c. on 16 c. yellow	..	£190
Z155	10 c. on 24 c. green	..	£120

1880. *Wmk Crown CC* (*Nos. 28/31*).
Z156	2 c. rose	.. ..	32·00
Z157	5 c. blue	.. ..	42·00
Z158	10 c. mauve	.. ..	38·00

1882–96. *Wmk Crown CA* (*Nos. 32/9*).
Z159	2 c. rose-lake	.. ..	1·60
Z160	2 c. carmine	.. ..	7·00
Z161	4 c. slate-grey	.. ..	3·50
Z162	5 c. blue	.. ..	18·00
Z163	10 c. dull mauve	.. ..	6·00
Z164	10 c. green	.. ..	3·25
Z165	10 c. purple/*red* ..	.. ..	24·00
Z166	30 c. green	.. ..	

1885. (*Nos. 40/2*).
Z167	20 c. on 30 c. orange-red	..	8·50
Z168	50 c. on 48 c. yellowish brown	..	40·00
Z169	$1 on 96 c. grey-olive	..	70·00

1891. (*Nos. 43/5, 48/50*).
Z170	7 c. on 10 c. green	.. ..	16·00
Z171	14 c. on 30 c. mauve	.. ..	80·00
Z171a	20 c. on 30 c. green (No. 45)	..	£160
Z172	20 c. on 30 c. green (No. 48)	..	12·00
Z173	50 c. on 48 c. dull purple	..	14·00
Z174	$1 on 96 c. purple/*red*	..	38·00

1891. *50th Anniv of Colony* (*No. 51*).
Z175	2 c. carmine	.. ..	£750

1898. (*No. 52*).
Z176	$1 on 96 c. black	.. ..	40·00

1898. (*No. 55*)
Z177	10 c. on 30 c. grey-green		

1900–01. *Wmk Crown CA* (*Nos. 56/61*).
Z178	2 c. dull green ..	..	3·00
Z179	4 c. carmine	..	2·75
Z180	5 c. yellow	..	22·00
Z181	10 c. ultramarine	..	2·75
Z182	12 c. blue	..	60·00
Z183	30 c. brown	..	42·00

1903. *Wmk Crown CA* (*Nos. 62/76*).
Z184	1 c. dull purple and brown	..	3·00
Z185	2 c. dull green	..	2·75
Z186	4 c. purple/*red* ..	..	1·75
Z187	5 c. dull green and brown-orange	..	13·00
Z188	8 c. slate and violet	..	6·00
Z189	10 c. purple and blue/*blue*	..	2·75
Z190	12 c. green and purple/*yellow*	..	9·50
Z191	20 c. slate and chestnut	..	5·00
Z192	30 c. dull green and black	..	28·00

1904–06. *Wmk Mult Crown CA* (*Nos. 77/90*).
Z199	2 c. dull green ..	..	2·75
Z200	4 c. purple/*red* ..	..	1·75
Z201	5 c. dull green and brown-orange	..	12·00
Z202	8 c. slate and violet	..	9·50
Z203	10 c. purple and blue/*blue*	..	2·50
Z204	12 c. green and purple/*yellow*	..	14·00
Z205	20 c. slate and chestnut	..	8·00
Z206	30 c. dull green and black	..	19·00
Z207	50 c. green and magenta	..	21·00
Z208	$1 purple and sage-green	..	35·00
Z212	$10 slate and orange/*blue*	..	£1100

1907–11. *Wmk Mult Crown CA* (*Nos. 91/9*).
Z213	1 c. brown	.. ..	3·00
Z214	2 c. green	.. ..	3·00
Z215	4 c. carmine-red	.. ..	1·75
Z216	6 c. orange-vermilion and purple	..	11·00
Z217	10 c. bright ultramarine	..	2·50
Z218	20 c. purple and sage-green	..	48·00
Z219	30 c. purple and orange-yellow ..	..	35·00
Z220	50 c. black/*green*	.. ..	29·00

1912–15. *Wmk Mult Crown CA* (*Nos. 100/16*).
Z222	1 c. brown	.. ..	3·25
Z223	2 c. green	.. ..	2·50
Z224	4 c. red	.. ..	1·50
Z225	6 c. orange	.. ..	2·75
Z226	8 c. grey	.. ..	14·00
Z227	10 c. ultramarine	.. ..	2·75
Z228	12 c. purple/*yellow*	.. ..	11·00
Z229	20 c. purple and sage-green	..	4·00
Z231	30 c. purple and orange-yellow ..	..	11·00
Z232	50 c. black/*green*	.. ..	3·50
Z235	$3 green and purple	.. ..	£100

POSTCARD STAMPS

1879. (*Nos. P1/2*).
ZP236	3 c. on 16 c. yellow	.. .. ..	£400
ZP237	5 c. on 18 c. lilac	.. .. ..	£450

POSTAL FISCAL STAMPS

1874–1902. *Wmk Crown CC.* (a) P 15½×15 (*Nos. F1/3*)
ZF238	$2 olive-green ..	.. ..	£120

1891. (*No. F9*).
ZF246	$5 on $10 purple/*red*	..	£250

1897. (*No. F10*).
ZF247	$1 on $2 olive-green		

CHEFOO

Chefoo was opened to British trade in 1860. Although a consulate was established in 1863 no organised postal agency was provided until 1 January 1903 when one was opened at the premises of Curtis Brothers, a commercial firm.

Type E (*supplied 1902*) *used 1903–20*
Type D (*supplied 1907*) *used 1907–13*
Type F *used 1916–22*

Stamps of HONG KONG *cancelled at Chefoo between 1903 and 1916 with postmarks detailed above.*

1882–96. *Wmk Crown CA* (*Nos. 32/9*).
Z249	5 c. blue ..	.. ..	21·00

1891. (*Nos. 43/50*)
Z250	20 c. on 30 c. grey-green (No. 48a)	..	30·00

1898. (*No. 52*).
Z251	$1 on 96 c. black	..	65·00

1900–01. *Wmk Crown CA* (*Nos. 56/61*).
Z252	2 c. dull green ..	..	20·00
Z253	4 c. carmine	..	19·00
Z254	5 c. yellow	..	38·00
Z255	10 c. ultramarine	..	20·00
Z257	30 c. brown	..	80·00

1903. *Wmk Crown CA* (*Nos. 62/76*).
Z258	1 c. dull purple and brown	..	7·50
Z259	2 c. dull green	..	7·00
Z260	4 c. purple/*red* ..	..	6·50
Z261	5 c. dull green and brown-orange	..	15·00
Z262	8 c. slate and violet	..	13·00
Z263	10 c. purple and blue/*blue*	..	8·00
Z264	12 c. green and purple/*yellow*	..	18·00

1904–06. *Wmk Mult Crown CA* (*Nos. 77/90*)
Z273	2 c. dull green	..	6·00
Z274	4 c. purple/*red* ..	..	5·50
Z275	5 c. dull green and brown-orange	..	12·00
Z276	8 c. slate and violet	..	12·00
Z277	10 c. purple and blue/*blue*	..	6·00
Z278	12 c. green and purple/*yellow*	..	17·00
Z279	20 c. slate and chestnut	..	15·00
Z280	30 c. dull green and black	..	30·00
Z281	50 c. green and magenta	..	35·00
Z283	$2 slate and scarlet	..	£160
Z284	$3 slate and dull blue	..	£300
Z285	$5 purple and blue-green	..	

1907–11. *Wmk Mult Crown CA* (*Nos. 91/9*).
Z287	1 c. brown	.. ..	7·50
Z288	2 c. green	.. ..	7·00
Z289	4 c. carmine-red	.. ..	6·00
Z290	6 c. orange-vermilion and purple	..	18·00
Z291	10 c. bright ultramarine	..	6·50
Z292	20 c. purple and sage-green	..	50·00
Z293	30 c. purple and orange-yellow ..	..	35·00
Z295	$2 carmine-red and black	..	

1912–15. *Wmk Mult Crown CA* (*Nos. 100/16*).
Z296	1 c. brown	.. ..	5·00
Z297	2 c. green	.. ..	5·50
Z298	4 c. red	.. ..	4·50
Z299	6 c. orange	.. ..	9·00
Z301	10 c. ultramarine	.. ..	5·00
Z302	12 c. purple/*yellow*	.. ..	18·00
Z303	20 c. purple and sage-green	..	8·00
Z305	30 c. purple and orange-yellow ..	..	11·00
Z306	50 c. black/*green*	.. ..	6·50
Z307	$1 purple and blue/*blue*	..	8·50
Z308	$2 carmine-red and grey-black	..	55·00
Z309	$3 green and purple	..	85·00
Z310	$5 green and red/*green*	..	£350
Z311	$10 purple and black/*red*	..	£200

FOOCHOW

Foochow, originally known as Foochowfoo, was one of the original Treaty Ports opened to British trade in 1842. A British consulate and postal agency was established in June 1844.

Type A ("F1") (*supplied 1866*) *used 1873–84*
Type D (inscr "FOOCHOWFOO") (*supplied 1866*) *used 1867–1905*
Type D (inscr "FOOCHOW") (*supplied 1894*) *used 1894–1917*
Type E (inscr "B.P.O.") *used 1906–10*
Type F *used 1915–22*

Stamps of HONG KONG *cancelled at Foochow between 1867 and 1916 with postmarks detailed above.*

1862. *No wmk* (*Nos. 1/7*).
Z312	18 c. lilac	.. ..	95·00

1863–71. *Wmk Crown CC* (*Nos. 8/19*).
Z313	2 c. brown	.. ..	32·00
Z314	4 c. grey	.. ..	32·00
Z315	6 c. lilac	.. ..	42·00
Z316	8 c. orange	.. ..	35·00
Z317	12 c. blue	.. ..	15·00
Z318	18 c. lilac	.. ..	£500
Z319	24 c. green	.. ..	55·00
Z320	30 c. vermilion ..		
Z321	30 c. mauve	.. ..	12·00
Z322	48 c. rose	.. ..	60·00
Z324	96 c. brownish grey	.. ..	70·00

1876–77. (*Nos. 20/1*).
Z325	16 c. on 18 c. lilac	..	£325
Z326	28 c. on 30 c. mauve	.. ..	£150

1877. *Wmk Crown CC* (*No. 22*).
Z327	16 c. yellow	..	£110

1880. (*Nos. 23/7*).
Z328	5 c. on 8 c. orange	..	£350
Z329	5 c. on 18 c. lilac	..	£130
Z330	10 c. on 12 c. blue	..	£130
Z331	10 c. on 16 c. yellow	..	£170
Z332	10 c. on 24 c. green	..	£170

1880. *Wmk Crown CC (Nos. 28/31).*

Z333	2 c. rose	30·00
Z334	5 c. blue	50·00
Z335	10 c. mauve	38·00
Z336	48 c. brown	£140

1882–96. *Wmk Crown CA (Nos. 32/9).*

Z336a	2 c. rose-lake	
Z337	2 c. carmine	1·60
Z338	4 c. slate-grey	4·75
Z339	5 c. blue	2·75
Z340	10 c. dull mauve	23·00
Z341	10 c. green	9·50
Z342	10 c. purple/*red*	3·25
Z343	30 c. green	29·00

1885. *(Nos. 40/2).*

Z344	20 c. on 30 c. orange-red	10·00
Z345	50 c. on 48 c. yellowish brown	40·00
Z346	$1 on 96 c. grey-olive	70·00

1891. *(Nos. 43/4, 48/50).*

Z348	14 c. on 30 c. mauve	80·00
Z349	20 c. on 30 c. green	16·00
Z350	50 c. on 48 c. dull purple	18·00
Z351	$1 on 96 c. purple/*red*	40·00

1898. *(No. 52).*

Z353	$1 on 96 c. black	50·00

1898. *(No. 55).*

Z354	10 c. on 30 c. green	£160

1900–01. *Wmk Crown CA (Nos. 56/61).*

Z355	2 c. dull green	2·75
Z356	4 c. carmine	3·25
Z357	5 c. yellow	12·00
Z358	10 c. ultramarine	2·75

1903. *Wmk Crown CA (Nos. 62/76).*

Z361	1 c. dull purple and brown	3·50
Z362	2 c. dull green	2·75
Z363	4 c. purple/*red*	1·75
Z364	5 c. dull green and brown-orange	13·00
Z365	8 c. slate and violet	7·50
Z366	10 c. purple and blue/*blue*	3·00
Z367	12 c. green and purple/*yellow*	9·50
Z368	20 c. slate and chestnut	7·00
Z369	30 c. dull green and black	26·00
Z370	50 c. dull green and magenta	38·00

1904–06. *Wmk Mult Crown CA (Nos. 77/90).*

Z376	2 c. dull green	2·75
Z377	4 c. purple/*red*	1·75
Z378	5 c. dull green and brown-orange	8·50
Z379	8 c. slate and violet	7·00
Z380	10 c. purple and blue/*blue*	3·00
Z381	12 c. green and purple/*yellow*	13·00
Z382	20 c. slate and chestnut	6·50
Z383	30 c. dull green and black	19·00
Z384	50 c. green and magenta	19·00
Z385	$1 purple and sage-green	35·00

1907–11. *Wmk Mult Crown CA (Nos. 91/9).*

Z390	1 c. brown	2·75
Z391	2 c. green	2·75
Z392	4 c. carmine-red	1·75
Z393	6 c. orange-vermilion and purple	11·00
Z394	10 c. bright ultramarine	2·50
Z395	20 c. purple and sage-green	48·00
Z396	30 c. purple and orange-yellow	35·00
Z397	50 c. black/*green*	28·00

1912–15. *Wmk Mult Crown CA (Nos. 100/16).*

Z399	1 c. brown	3·00
Z400	2 c. green	2·75
Z401	4 c. red	1·75
Z402	6 c. orange	7·00
Z403	8 c. grey	15·00
Z404	10 c. ultramarine	2·75
Z406	20 c. purple and sage-green	4·25
Z407	25 c. purple and magenta (Type A)	
Z408	30 c. purple and orange-yellow	6·50

POSTCARD STAMPS

1879. *(Nos. P1/2).*

ZP413	3 c. on 16 c. yellow	£475

POSTAL FISCAL STAMPS

1874–1902. *Wmk Crown CC. (a) P 15½×15 (Nos. F1/3)*

ZF415	$2 olive-green	95·00
ZF416	$3 dull violet	85·00

HANKOW

Hankow, on the Yangtse River 600 miles from the sea, became a Treaty Port in 1860. A British consulate opened the following year, but no organised British postal agency was established until 1872.

Type **D** *(supplied 1874) used* 1874–1916
Type **B** ("D29") *(supplied 1876) used* 1878–83
Type **F** *used* 1916–22

Stamps of HONG KONG *cancelled at Hankow between* 1874 *and* 1916 *with postmarks detailed above.*

1862. *No wmk (Nos. 1/7).*

Z426	18 c. lilac	£130

1863–71. *Wmk Crown CC (Nos. 8/19).*

Z427	2 c. brown	65·00
Z428	4 c. grey	65·00
Z429	6 c. lilac	80·00
Z430	8 c. orange	65·00
Z431	12 c. blue	24·00
Z432	18 c. lilac	£550
Z433	24 c. green	80·00
Z435	30 c. mauve	90·00
Z436	48 c. rose	£100
Z438	96 c. brownish grey	

1876–77. *(Nos. 20/1).*

Z439	16 c. on 18 c. lilac	£275
Z440	28 c. on 30 c. mauve	£150

1877. *Wmk Crown CC (No. 22).*

Z441	16 c. yellow	£130

1880. *(Nos. 23/7).*

Z442	5 c. on 8 c. orange	£140
Z443	5 c. on 18 c. lilac	£120
Z444	10 c. on 12 c. blue	£130
Z445	10 c. on 16 c. yellow	£225
Z446	10 c. on 24 c. green	£150

1880. *Wmk Crown CC (Nos. 28/31).*

Z447	2 c. rose	50·00
Z448	5 c. blue	60·00
Z449	10 c. mauve	60·00
Z450	48 c. brown	£170

1882–96. *Wmk Crown CA (Nos. 32/9).*

Z451	2 c. carmine	5·00
Z452	4 c. slate-grey	10·00
Z453	5 c. blue	5·50
Z454	10 c. dull mauve	40·00
Z455	10 c. green	7·00
Z456	10 c. purple/*red*	6·00
Z457	30 c. green	32·00

1885. *(Nos. 40/2).*

Z458	20 c. on 30 c. orange-red	18·00
Z459	50 c. on 48 c. yellowish brown	45·00
Z460	$1 on 96 c. grey-olive	85·00

1891. *(Nos. 43/4, 48/50).*

Z461	7 c. on 10 c. green	20·00
Z462	14 c. on 30 c. mauve	85·00
Z463	20 c. on 30 c. green	14·00
Z464	50 c. on 48 c. dull purple	14·00
Z465	$1 on 96 c. purple/*red*	40·00

1898. *(No. 52).*

Z467	$1 on 96 c. black	50·00

1898. *(No. 55).*

Z468	10 c. on 30 c. green	£170

1900–01. *Wmk Crown CA (Nos. 56/61).*

Z469	2 c. dull green	3·50
Z470	4 c. carmine	3·50
Z471	5 c. yellow	15·00
Z472	10 c. ultramarine	4·50
Z473	12 c. blue	80·00
Z474	30 c. brown	45·00

1903. *Wmk Crown CA (Nos. 62/76).*

Z475	1 c. dull purple and brown	3·50
Z476	2 c. dull green	3·25
Z477	4 c. purple/*red*	2·75
Z478	5 c. dull green and brown-orange	12·00
Z479	8 c. slate and violet	9·50
Z480	10 c. purple and blue/*blue*	3·25
Z481	12 c. green and purple/*yellow*	11·00
Z482	20 c. slate and chestnut	7·50
Z483	30 c. dull green and black	23·00
Z484	50 c. dull green and magenta	42·00
Z485	$1 purple and sage-green	32·00

1904–06. *Wmk Mult Crown CA (Nos. 77/90).*

Z490	2 c. dull green	3·25
Z491	4 c. purple/*red*	2·75
Z492	5 c. dull green and brown-orange	12·00
Z493	8 c. slate and violet	7·00
Z494	10 c. purple and blue/*blue*	3·25
Z495	12 c. green and purple/*yellow*	14·00
Z496	20 c. slate and chestnut	12·00
Z497	30 c. dull green and black	19·00
Z498	50 c. green and magenta	16·00
Z499	$1 purple and sage-green	35·00

1907–11. *Wmk Mult Crown CA (Nos. 91/9).*

Z504	1 c. brown	3·25
Z505	2 c. green	3·25
Z506	4 c. carmine-red	1·90
Z507	6 c. orange-vermilion and purple	14·00
Z508	10 c. bright ultramarine	3·25
Z509	20 c. purple and sage-green	55·00
Z510	30 c. purple and orange-yellow	40·00

1912–15. *Wmk Mult Crown CA (Nos. 100/16).*

Z513	1 c. brown	3·75
Z514	2 c. green	3·75
Z515	4 c. red	2·75
Z516	6 c. orange	7·00
Z518	10 c. ultramarine	3·25
Z520	20 c. purple and sage-green	8·50
Z522	30 c. purple and orange-yellow	12·00
Z523	50 c. black/*green*	7·50
Z527	$5 green and red/*green*	£325

POSTCARD STAMPS

1879. *(Nos. P1/2).*

ZP528	3 c. on 16 c. yellow	£700

POSTAL FISCAL STAMPS

1874–1902. *Wmk Crown CC. (a) P 15½×15 (Nos. F1/3)*

ZF529	$2 olive-green	£130

(b) P 14 (Nos. F4/6)

ZF532	$2 dull bluish green	

KIUNGCHOW (HOIHOW)

Kiungchow, a city on the island of Hainan, and its port of Hoihow was added to the Treaty Port system in 1860. A consular postal agency was opened at Kiungchow in 1876, being transferred to Hoihow in 1878. A second agency was opened at Kiungchow in 1879.

Type **B** ("D28") *(supplied 1876) used* 1879–83
Type **D** (inscr "KIUNG-CHOW") *(supplied 1876) used* 1879–81

"REGISTERED KIUNG-CHOW" with "REGISTERED" removed *(originally supplied 1876) used* 1883–85
Type **D** (inscr "HOIHOW") *used* 1885–1922

Stamps of HONG KONG *cancelled at Kiungchow (Hoihow) between* 1879 *and* 1916 *with postmarks detailed above.*

1863–71. *Wmk Crown CC (Nos. 8/19).*

Z540	2 c. brown	£650
Z541	4 c. grey	£425
Z542	6 c. lilac	£750
Z543	8 c. orange	£475
Z544	12 c. blue	£450
Z546	24 c. green	£650
Z547	30 c. vermilion	
Z548	30 c. mauve	£600
Z549	48 c. rose	£650
Z551	96 c. brownish grey	£750

1876–77. *(Nos. 20/1).*

Z552	16 c. on 18 c. lilac	£650
Z553	28 c. on 30 c. mauve	£500

1877. *(No. 22)*

Z554	16 c. yellow	£850

1880. *(Nos. 23/7).*

Z555	5 c. on 8 c. orange	£475
Z556	5 c. on 18 c. lilac	£475
Z557	10 c. on 12 c. blue	£475
Z558	10 c. on 16 c. yellow	£900
Z559	10 c. on 24 c. green	

1880. *Wmk Crown CC (Nos. 28/31).*

Z561	5 c. blue	£425
Z562	10 c. mauve	£550

1882–96. *Wmk Crown CA (Nos. 32/9).*

Z564	2 c. carmine	32·00
Z565	4 c. slate-grey	42·00
Z566	5 c. blue	32·00
Z567	10 c. dull mauve	£325
Z568	10 c. green	40·00
Z569	10 c. purple/*red*	32·00
Z570	30 c. green	65·00

1885. *(Nos. 40/2).*

Z571	20 c. on 30 c. orange-red	70·00
Z572	50 c. on 48 c. yellowish brown	75·00
Z573	$1 on 96 c. grey-olive	£120

1891. *(Nos. 43/4, 48/50).*

Z574	7 c. on 10 c. green	£130
Z576	20 c. on 30 c. green	32·00
Z577	50 c. on 48 c. dull purple	40·00
Z578	$1 on 96 c. purple/*red*	85·00

1891. *50th Anniv of Colony (No. 51).*
Z579 2 c. carmine .. ..

1898. *(No. 52).*
Z580 $1 on 96 c. black £160

1898. *(No. 55).*
Z581 10 c. on 30 c. green £350

1900–01. *Wmk Crown CA (Nos. 56/61).*
Z583 4 c. carmine .. .. 23·00
Z584 5 c. yellow .. .. 50·00
Z585 10 c. ultramarine .. .. .. 25·00
Z587 30 c. brown £110

1903. *Wmk Crown CA (Nos. 62/76).*
Z588 1 c. dull purple and brown .. 17·00
Z589 2 c. dull green .. .. .. 17·00
Z590 4 c. purple/*red* .. .. .. 12·00
Z591 5 c. dull green and brown-orange .. 28·00
Z592 8 c. slate and violet .. .. 26·00
Z593 10 c. purple and blue/*blue* .. 14·00
Z594 12 c. green and purple/*yellow* .. 32·00
Z598 $1 purple and sage-green .. 75·00

1904–06. *Wmk Mult Crown CA (Nos. 77/90).*
Z603 2 c. dull green .. .. .. 15·00
Z604 4 c. purple/*red* .. .. .. 12·00
Z605 5 c. dull green and brown-orange .. 28·00
Z606 8 c. slate and violet .. .. 19·00
Z607 10 c. purple and blue/*blue* .. 13·00
Z608 12 c. green and purple/*yellow* .. 32·00
Z609 20 c. slate and chestnut .. 38·00
Z610 30 c. dull green and black .. 48·00

1907–11. *Wmk Mult Crown CA (Nos. 91/9).*
Z617 1 c. brown .. .. 15·00
Z618 2 c. green .. .. 14·00
Z619 4 c. carmine-red .. .. .. 12·00
Z620 6 c. orange-vermilion and purple .. 32·00
Z621 10 c. bright ultramarine .. 13·00
Z622 20 c. purple and sage-green .. 60·00

1912–15. *Wmk Mult Crown CA (Nos. 100/16).*
Z625 1 c. brown .. .. 14·00
Z626 2 c. green .. .. 13·00
Z627 4 c. red .. .. 12·00
Z628 6 c. orange .. .. 18·00
Z629 8 c. grey .. ..
Z630 10 c. ultramarine .. .. .. 12·00
Z631 12 c. purple/*yellow* .. .. 32·00
Z632 20 c. purple and sage-green .. 26·00
Z633 25 c. purple and magenta (Type A) .. 55·00
Z635 50 c. black/*green* .. .. 38·00
Z636 $1 purple and blue/*blue* .. 42·00

POSTAL FISCAL STAMPS

1874–1902. *Wmk Crown CC. (a) P 15½×15 (Nos. F1/3)*
ZF641 $2 olive-green £140

   (b) P 14 (Nos. F4/6)
ZF644 $2 dull bluish green £275

1897. *(Nos. F10/11)*
ZF650 $1 on $2 olive-green £250

NINGPO

Ningpo was one of the 1842 Treaty Ports and a consular postal agency was established there in 1844.

   Type **A** ("N1") (*supplied* 1866) *used* 1870–82
   Type **C** (*supplied* 1866) *used* 1870–99
   Type **D** *used* 1899–1922

Stamps of HONG KONG *cancelled at Ningpo between* 1866 *and* 1916 *with postmarks detailed above.*

1862. *No wmk (Nos. 1/7).*
Z652 18 c. lilac £225

1863–71. *Wmk Crown CC (Nos. 8/19).*
Z653 2 c. brown £120
Z654 4 c. grey £120
   a. Perf 12½ £140
Z655 6 c. lilac £140
Z656 8 c. orange £110
Z657 12 c. blue .. .. 85·00
Z658 18 c. lilac .. ..
Z659 24 c. green £140
Z660 30 c. vermilion £150
Z661 30 c. mauve .. .. 75·00
Z662 48 c. rose £160
Z663 96 c. olive-bistre .. .. ..
Z664 96 c. brownish grey £200

1876–77. *(Nos. 20/1).*
Z665 16 c. on 18 c. lilac £325
Z666 28 c. on 30 c. mauve £160

1877. *Wmk Crown CC (No. 22).*
Z667 16 c. yellow £160

1880. *(Nos. 23/7).*
Z668 5 c. on 8 c. orange £180
Z669 5 c. on 18 c. lilac £170
Z670 10 c. on 12 c. blue £180
Z672 10 c. on 24 c. green £180

1880. *Wmk Crown CC (Nos. 28/31).*
Z674 5 c. blue .. .. 95·00
Z675 10 c. mauve .. .. 95·00
Z676 48 c. brown £325

1882–96. *Wmk Crown CA (Nos. 32/9).*
Z677 2 c. carmine .. .. 24·00
Z678 4 c. slate-grey .. .. .. 35·00
Z679 5 c. blue .. .. 24·00
Z680 10 c. dull mauve .. .. .. 90·00
Z681 10 c. green .. .. 26·00
Z682 10 c. purple/*red* .. .. .. 26·00
Z683 30 c. green .. .. 50·00

1885. *(Nos. 40/2).*
Z685 50 c. on 48 c. yellowish brown .. 60·00

1891. *(Nos. 43/4, 48/50).*
Z686 7 c. on 10 c. green .. .. 29·00
Z687 14 c. on 30 c. mauve .. ..
Z688 20 c. on 30 c. green .. .. 20·00
Z689 50 c. on 48 c. dull purple .. 35·00
Z690 $1 on 96 c. purple/*red* .. 60·00

1898. *(No. 52).*
Z692 $1 on 96 c. black .. .. .. 70·00

1898. *(No. 55).*
Z693 10 c. on 30 c. green £170

1900–01. *Wmk Crown CA (Nos. 56/61).*
Z694 2 c. dull green .. .. .. 14·00
Z695 4 c. carmine .. .. 13·00
Z697 10 c. ultramarine .. .. .. 14·00

1903. *Wmk Crown CA (Nos. 62/76).*
Z700 1 c. dull purple and brown .. 13·00
Z701 2 c. dull green .. .. .. 13·00
Z702 4 c. purple/*red* .. .. .. 9·50
Z703 5 c. dull green and brown-orange .. 24·00
Z704 8 c. slate and violet .. .. 15·00
Z705 10 c. purple and blue/*blue* .. 11·00
Z706 12 c. green and purple/*yellow* .. 30·00
Z709 50 c. dull green and magenta .. 45·00

1904–06. *Wmk Mult Crown CA (Nos. 77/90).*
Z715 2 c. dull green .. .. .. 13·00
Z716 4 c. purple/*red* .. .. .. 11·00
Z718 8 c. slate and violet .. .. 22·00
Z720 12 c. green and purple/*yellow* .. 32·00
Z721 20 c. slate and chestnut .. 32·00
Z722 30 c. dull green and black .. 40·00
Z724 $1 purple and sage-green .. 48·00

1907–11. *Wmk Mult Crown CA (Nos. 91/9).*
Z729 1 c. brown .. .. 10·00
Z730 2 c. green .. .. 10·00
Z731 4 c. carmine-red .. .. .. 8·50
Z733 10 c. bright ultramarine .. 9·50
Z734 20 c. purple and sage-green .. 60·00
Z735 30 c. purple and orange-yellow .. 45·00

1912–15. *Wmk Mult Crown CA (Nos. 100/16).*
Z738 1 c. brown .. .. 11·00
Z739 2 c. green .. .. 10·00
Z740 4 c. red .. .. 9·00
Z742 8 c. grey .. .. 30·00
Z743 10 c. ultramarine .. .. .. 10·00
Z745 20 c. purple and sage-green .. 60·00
Z749 $1 purple and blue/*blue* .. 32·00

POSTCARD STAMPS

1879. *(Nos. P1/2).*
ZP751 3 c. on 16 c. yellow £600

POSTAL FISCAL STAMPS

1874–1902. *Wmk Crown CC. (a) P 15½×15 (Nos. F1/3)*
ZF754 $2 olive-green £150

1881. *(No. F7).*
ZF760 12 c. on $10 rose-carmine .. ..

1897. *(No. F10).*
ZF763 $1 on $2 olive-green .. .. ..

SHANGHAI

Shanghai was one of the original Treaty Ports of 1842 and a packet agency was opened at the British consulate in April 1844. It moved to a separate premises in 1861 and was upgraded to a Post Office in September 1867.
   British military post offices operated in Shanghai from 1927 until 1940.

Type **D** (inscr "SHANGHAE" (*supplied* 1861) *used* 1861–99

Sunburst *used* 1864–65
Type **A** ("S1") (*supplied* 1866) *used* 1866–85
Type **D** (inscr "SHANGHAI") (*supplied* 1885) *used* 1886–1906
Type **G** (inscr "B.P.O." at foot) (*supplied* 1904) *used* 1904–21
Type **G** (inscr "Br.P.O." at foot) (*supplied* 1907) *used* 1907–22
Type **E** (figures "I" to "VIII" at foot) *used* 1912–22

Stamps of HONG KONG *cancelled at Shanghai between* 1863 *and* 1916 *with postmarks detailed above.*

1862. *No wmk (Nos. 1/7).*
Z765 2 c. brown .. .. 90·00
Z766 8 c. yellow-buff .. .. .. 75·00
Z767 12 c. pale greenish blue .. 60·00
Z768 18 c. lilac .. .. 48·00
Z769 24 c. green £100
Z770 48 c. rose £350
Z771 96 c. brownish grey £450

1863–71. *Wmk Crown CC (Nos. 8/19).*
Z772 2 c. brown .. .. 7·50
Z773 4 c. grey .. .. 6·00
   a. Perf 12½ £275
Z774 6 c. lilac .. .. 10·00
Z775 8 c. orange .. .. 10·00
Z776 12 c. blue .. .. 6·00
Z777 18 c. lilac £325
Z778 24 c. green .. .. 9·00
Z779 30 c. vermilion .. .. .. 15·00
Z780 30 c. mauve .. .. 5·50
Z781 48 c. rose .. .. 24·00
Z782 96 c. olive-bistre £650
Z783 96 c. brownish grey .. .. 38·00

1876–77. *(Nos. 20/1).*
Z784 16 c. on 18 c. lilac £160
Z785 28 c. on 30 c. mauve .. .. 50·00

1877. *Wmk Crown CC (No. 22).*
Z786 16 c. yellow .. .. 65·00

1880. *(Nos. 23/7).*
Z787 5 c. on 8 c. orange .. .. 90·00
Z788 5 c. on 18 c. lilac .. .. 60·00
Z789 10 c. on 12 c. blue .. .. 55·00
Z790 10 c. on 16 c. yellow £160
Z791 10 c. on 24 c. green .. .. 85·00

1880. *Wmk Crown CC (Nos. 28/31).*
Z792 2 c. rose .. .. 19·00
Z793 5 c. blue .. .. 32·00
Z794 10 c. mauve .. .. 14·00
Z795 48 c. brown .. .. 95·00

1882–96. *Wmk Crown CA (Nos. 32/9).*
Z795a 2 c. rose-lake 90
Z796 2 c. carmine 90
Z797 4 c. slate-grey .. .. .. 1·00
Z798 5 c. blue .. .. 9·50
Z799 10 c. dull mauve .. .. .. 1·40
Z800 10 c. green .. .. 1·25
Z801 10 c. purple/*red* .. .. .. 17·00
Z802 30 c. green .. ..

1885. *(Nos. 40/2).*
Z803 20 c. on 30 c. orange-red .. 5·50
Z804 50 c. on 48 c. yellowish brown .. 27·00
Z805 $1 on 96 c. grey-olive .. 55·00

1891. *(Nos. 43/44, 46/50).*
Z806 7 c. on 10 c. green .. .. 10·00
Z807 14 c. on 30 c. mauve .. .. 55·00
Z807a 50 c. on 48 c. dull purple (No. 46) .. £275
Z807b $1 on 96 c. purple/*red* (No. 47) .. £375
Z808 20 c. on 30 c. green .. .. 5·50
Z809 50 c. on 48 c. dull purple (No. 49) .. 6·00
Z810 $1 on 96 c. purple/*red* (No. 50) .. 23·00

1898. *(No. 52).*
Z812 $1 on 96 c. black .. .. .. 27·00

1898. *(No. 55).*
Z813 10 c. on 30 c. green .. .. 75·00

1900–01. *Wmk Crown CA (Nos. 56/61).*
Z814 2 c. dull green 90
Z815 4 c. carmine 90
Z816 5 c. yellow .. .. 7·00
Z817 10 c. ultramarine .. .. .. 2·00
Z818 12 c. blue .. .. 50·00
Z819 30 c. brown .. .. 22·00

1903. *Wmk Crown CA (Nos. 62/76).*

Z820	1 c. dull purple and brown		60
Z821	2 c. dull green		1·60
Z822	4 c. purple/*red*		45
Z823	5 c. dull green and brown-orange		9·50
Z824	8 c. slate and violet		1·50
Z825	10 c. purple and blue/*blue*		1·50
Z826	12 c. green and purple/*yellow*		4·75
Z827	20 c. slate and chestnut		2·75
Z828	30 c. dull green and black		19·00
Z829	50 c. dull green and magenta		30·00
Z830	$1 purple and sage-green		21·00
Z832	$3 slate and dull blue		£350
Z833	$5 purple and blue-green		£450
Z834	$10 slate and orange/*blue*		£475

1904–06. *Wmk Mult Crown CA (Nos. 77/90).*

Z835	2 c. dull green		1·50
Z836	4 c. purple/*red*		50
Z837	5 c. dull green and brown-orange		6·00
Z838	8 c. slate and violet		2·25
Z839	10 c. purple and blue/*blue*		1·00
Z840	12 c. green and purple/*yellow*		6·50
Z841	20 c. slate and chestnut		2·50
Z842	30 c. dull green and black		15·00
Z843	50 c. green and magenta		7·50
Z844	$1 purple and sage-green		19·00
Z845	$2 slate and scarlet		90·00
Z846	$3 slate and dull blue		£200
Z847	$5 purple and blue-green		£300
Z848	$10 slate and orange/*blue*		£750

1907–11. *Wmk Mult Crown CA (Nos. 91/9).*

Z849	1 c. brown		1·00
Z850	2 c. green		1·75
Z851	4 c. carmine-red		50
Z852	6 c. orange-vermilion and purple		3·25
Z853	10 c. bright ultramarine		50
Z854	20 c. purple and sage-green		40·00
Z855	30 c. purple and orange-yellow		20·00
Z856	50 c. black/*green*		15·00
Z857	$2 carmine-red and black		£250

1912–15. *Wmk Mult Crown CA (Nos. 100/16).*

Z858	1 c. brown		65
Z859	2 c. green		40
Z860	4 c. red		40
Z861	6 c. orange		1·00
Z862	8 c. grey		7·00
Z863	10 c. ultramarine		40
Z864	12 c. purple/*yellow*		6·00
Z865	20 c. purple and sage-green		1·00
Z867	30 c. purple and orange-yellow		5·00
Z868	50 c. black/*green*		2·00
Z869	$1 purple and blue/*blue*		2·75

POSTCARD STAMPS

1879. (*Nos. P1/2*).

ZP871	3 c. on 16 c. yellow		£325
ZP872	5 c. on 18 c. lilac		£325

POSTAL FISCAL STAMPS

1874–1902. *Wmk Crown CC.* (a) P 15½×15 (*Nos. F1/5*)

ZF874	$2 olive-green		50·00
ZF875	$3 dull violet		35·00
ZF876	$10 rose-carmine		£600

(b) P 14

ZF877	$2 dull bluish green		£200
ZF878	$3 dull mauve		£350

1881. (*No. F7*).

ZF880	12 c. on $10 rose-carmine		£250

1891. (*No. F9*).

ZF882	$5 on $10 purple/*red*		£100

1897. (*No. F10/11*).

ZF883	$1 on $2 olive-green		£150
ZF884	$1 on $2 dull bluish green		£200

SWATOW

Swatow became a Treaty Port in 1860 and a consular packet agency was opened in the area made available for foreign firms during the following year. In 1867 the original agency was transferred to the Chinese city on the other side of the Han river, but a second agency was subsequently opened in the foreign concession during 1883.

Type A ("S2") (*supplied* 1866) *used* 1875–85
Type C (*supplied* 1866) *used* 1866–90
Type D (*supplied* 1883) *used* 1884–1922
Type F *used* 1916–22

Stamps of HONG KONG *cancelled at Swatow between 1866 and 1916 with postmarks detailed above.*

1862. *No wmk (Nos. 1/7).*

Z885	18 c. lilac		£150

1863–71. *Wmk Crown CC (Nos. 8/19).*

Z886	2 c. brown		75·00
Z887	4 c. grey		75·00
	a. Perf 12½		
Z888	6 c. lilac		£325
Z889	8 c. orange		80·00
Z890	12 c. blue		80·00
Z891	18 c. lilac		£550
Z892	24 c. green		80·00
Z893	30 c. vermilion		
Z894	30 c. mauve		35·00
Z895	48 c. rose		90·00
Z896	96 c. brownish grey		£475

1876–77. (*Nos. 20/1*).

Z898	16 c. on 18 c. lilac		£325
Z899	28 c. on 30 c. mauve		£140

1877. *Wmk Crown CC (No. 22).*

Z900	16 c. yellow		£300

1880. (*Nos. 23/7*).

Z901	5 c. on 8 c. orange		£140
Z902	5 c. on 18 c. lilac		£130
Z903	10 c. on 12 c. blue		£140
Z904	10 c. on 16 c. yellow		£250
Z905	10 c. on 24 c. green		£180

1880. *Wmk Crown CC (Nos. 28/31).*

Z906	2 c. rose		65·00
Z907	5 c. blue		65·00
Z908	10 c. mauve		80·00

1882–96. *Wmk Crown CA (Nos. 32/9).*

Z910	2 c. carmine		4·00
Z911	4 c. slate-grey		12·00
Z912	5 c. blue		4·50
Z913	10 c. dull mauve		50·00
Z914	10 c. green		6·00
Z915	10 c. purple/*red*		4·00
Z916	30 c. green		30·00

1885. (*Nos. 40/2*).

Z917	20 c. on 30 c. orange-red		8·50

1891. (*No. 43/4, 48/50*).

Z920	7 c. on 10 c. green		16·00
Z921	14 c. on 30 c. mauve		75·00
Z922	20 c. on 30 c. green		14·00
Z923	50 c. on 48 c. dull purple		15·00
Z924	$1 on 96 c. purple/*red*		32·00

1891. *50th Anniv of Colony (No. 51).*

Z925	2 c. carmine		£800

1898. (*No. 52*).

Z926	$1 on 96 c. black		45·00

1898. (*No. 55*).

Z927	10 c. on 30 c. green		£140

1900–01. *Wmk Crown CA (Nos. 56/61).*

Z928	2 c. dull green		4·50
Z929	4 c. carmine		3·75
Z930	5 c. yellow		14·00
Z931	10 c. ultramarine		4·25
Z933	30 c. brown		35·00

1903. *Wmk Crown CA (Nos. 62/76).*

Z934	1 c. dull purple and brown		4·00
Z935	2 c. dull green		4·00
Z936	4 c. purple/*red*		3·00
Z937	5 c. dull green and brown-orange		11·00
Z938	8 c. slate and violet		7·00
Z939	10 c. purple and blue/*blue*		4·00
Z940	12 c. green and purple/*yellow*		9·00
Z941	20 c. slate and chestnut		5·50
Z942	30 c. dull green and black		25·00

1904–06. *Wmk Mult Crown CA (Nos. 77/90).*

Z949	2 c. dull green		4·00
Z950	4 c. purple/*red*		3·00
Z951	5 c. dull green and brown-orange		11·00
Z952	8 c. slate and violet		7·00
Z953	10 c. purple and blue/*blue*		3·75
Z954	12 c. green and purple/*yellow*		9·50
Z955	20 c. slate and chestnut		7·00
Z956	30 c. dull green and black		22·00
Z957	50 c. green and magenta		16·00
Z958	$1 purple and sage-green		38·00
Z959	$2 slate and scarlet		£140
Z962	$10 slate and orange/*blue*		£900

1907–11. *Wmk Mult Crown CA (Nos. 91/9).*

Z963	1 c. brown		4·50
Z964	2 c. green		4·50
Z965	4 c. carmine-red		3·25
Z966	6 c. orange-vermilion and purple		8·50
Z967	10 c. bright ultramarine		3·75
Z969	30 c. purple and orange-yellow		35·00
Z970	50 c. black/*green*		24·00

1912–15. *Wmk Mult Crown CA (Nos. 100/16).*

Z972	1 c. brown		3·25
Z973	2 c. green		3·25
Z974	4 c. red		2·75
Z975	6 c. orange		4·50
Z976	8 c. grey		14·00
Z977	10 c. ultramarine		2·50
Z978	12 c. purple/*yellow*		8·50
Z979	20 c. purple and sage-green		4·00
Z980	25 c. purple and magenta (Type A)		29·00
Z981	30 c. purple and orange-yellow		12·00
Z982	50 c. black/*green*		6·00
Z983	$1 purple and blue/*blue*		11·00

POSTCARD STAMPS

1879. (*Nos. P1/2*).

ZP986	3 c. on 16 c. yellow		£650

POSTAL FISCAL STAMPS

1874–1902. *Wmk Crown CC.* (a) P 15½×15 (*Nos. F1/3*)

ZF988	$2 olive-green		80·00
ZF989	$3 dull violet		70·00

(b) P 14

ZF991	$2 dull bluish green		£250

TIENTSIN

Tientsin became a Treaty Port in 1860. A British consulate was established in 1861, but no formal postal agency was organised there until 1882. It was not, however, very successful and was closed during 1890. The British Post Office reopened on 1 October 1906 under the management of the Chinese Engineering and Mining Company.

British military post offices operated in Tientsin from 1927 until 1940.

Type E *used* 1906–13
Type G (*supplied* 1907) *used* 1907–22

Stamps of HONG KONG *cancelled at Tientsin between 1906 and 1916 with postmarks detailed above.*

1903. *Wmk Crown CA (Nos. 62/76).*

Z 998	1 c. dull purple and brown		7·00
Z 999	5 c. dull green and brown-orange		17·00
Z1000	8 c. slate and violet		6·00

1904–06. *Wmk Mult Crown CA (Nos. 77/90).*

Z1001	2 c. dull green		3·50
Z1002	4 c. purple/*red*		2·50
Z1003	5 c. dull green and brown-orange		9·00
Z1004	8 c. slate and violet		7·00
Z1005	10 c. purple and blue/*blue*		3·00
Z1006	12 c. green and purple/*yellow*		10·00
Z1007	20 c. slate and chestnut		7·00
Z1008	30 c. dull green and black		20·00
Z1009	50 c. green and magenta		15·00
Z1010	$1 purple and sage-green		29·00
Z1011	$2 slate and scarlet		£130
Z1013	$5 purple and blue-green		£400
Z1014	$10 slate and orange/*blue*		£900

1907–11. *Wmk Mult Crown CA (Nos. 91/9).*

Z1015	1 c. brown		3·50
Z1016	2 c. green		2·75
Z1017	4 c. carmine-red		2·10
Z1018	6 c. orange-vermilion and purple		10·00
Z1019	10 c. bright ultramarine		2·50
Z1020	20 c. purple and sage-green		48·00
Z1021	30 c. purple and orange-yellow		35·00
Z1022	50 c. black/*green*		28·00

1912–15. *Wmk Mult Crown CA (Nos. 100/16).*

Z1024	1 c. brown		2·75
Z1025	2 c. green		2·75
Z1026	4 c. red		1·75
Z1027	6 c. orange		4·00
Z1028	8 c. grey		17·00
Z1029	10 c. ultramarine		3·25
Z1031	20 c. purple and sage-green		5·50
Z1033	30 c. purple and orange-yellow		8·00
Z1034	50 c. black/*green*		4·75
Z1035	$1 purple and blue/*blue*		6·50
Z1037	$3 green and purple		95·00

WEI HAI WEI

The territory of Wei Hai Wei was leased from the Chinese by the British Government from 24 May 1898 having been previously occupied by the Japanese. At that time there were no organised postal services from the area, although a private local post did operate between the port and Chefoo from 8 December 1898 until 15 March 1899. A Chinese Imperial post office opened in March 1899 to be followed by a British postal agency on the offshore island of Liu Kung Tau on 1 September 1899. A second British agency opened at Port Edward on 1 April 1904.

Liu Kung Tau oval *used* 1899–1901
Type D (inscr "LIU KUNG TAU") (*supplied* 1899) *used* 1901–30

Stamps of HONG KONG *cancelled at Liu Kung Tau between 1899 and 1916 with postmarks detailed above.*

1882–96. *Wmk Crown CA (Nos. 32/9).*

Z1040	2 c. carmine		29·00
Z1041	4 c. slate-grey		40·00
Z1042	5 c. blue		29·00
Z1043	10 c. purple/*red*		18·00
Z1044	30 c. green		35·00

1891. (*Nos. 48/50*).

Z1045	20 c. on 30 c. green		24·00
Z1046	50 c. on 48 c. dull purple		24·00

1898. *(No. 52).*

Z1047	$1 on 96 c. black	.. .. ..	48·00

1900–01. *Wmk Crown CA (Nos. 56/61).*

Z1049	2 c. dull green	.. ..	4·00
Z1050	4 c. carmine	.. ..	4·00
Z1051	5 c. yellow	.. ..	14·00
Z1052	10 c. ultramarine	.. ..	4·00
Z1053	12 c. blue	.. ..	70·00
Z1054	30 c. brown	.. ..	40·00

1903. *Wmk Crown CA (Nos. 62/76).*

Z1055	1 c. dull purple and brown	..	4·00
Z1056	2 c. dull green	..	3·25
Z1057	4 c. purple/red	..	3·25
Z1058	5 c. dull green and brown-orange		11·00
Z1059	8 c. slate and violet	..	7·00
Z1060	10 c. purple and blue/blue	..	5·00
Z1061	12 c. green and purple/yellow	..	15·00
Z1062	20 c. slate and chestnut	..	7·00
Z1063	30 c. dull green and black	..	24·00
Z1064	50 c. dull green and magenta	..	42·00
Z1065	$1 purple and sage-green	..	35·00

1904–06. *Wmk Mult Crown CA (Nos. 77/90).*

Z1070	2 c. dull green	.. ..	3·75
Z1071	4 c. purple/red	.. ..	3·25
Z1073	8 c. slate and violet	..	6·00
Z1076	20 c. slate and chestnut	..	
Z1078	50 c. green and magenta	..	30·00

1907–11. *Wmk Mult Crown CA (Nos. 91/9).*

Z1084	1 c. brown	.. ..	3·75
Z1085	2 c. green	.. ..	3·75
Z1086	4 c. carmine-red	.. ..	3·00
Z1088	10 c. bright ultramarine	..	3·25
Z1089	20 c. purple and sage-green	..	50·00
Z1090	30 c. purple and orange-yellow	..	38·00
Z1091	50 c. black/green	.. ..	32·00

1912–15. *Wmk Mult Crown CA (Nos. 100/16).*

Z1093	1 c. brown	.. ..	4·00
Z1094	2 c. green	.. ..	3·00
Z1095	4 c. red	.. ..	2·75
Z1096	6 c. orange	.. ..	6·00
Z1097	8 c. grey	.. ..	17·00
Z1098	10 c. ultramarine	.. ..	3·25
Z1104	$1 purple and blue/blue	..	15·00

POSTAL FISCAL STAMPS

1874–1902. *Wmk Crown CC. (b) P 14 (Nos. F4/6).*

Z1106	$2 dull bluish green	.. .. ..	£550

Port Edward rectangle used 1904–08
Type **D** (inscr "WEI-HAI-WEI" at top and "PORT EDWARD" at foot) *(supplied* 1907) *used* 1907–30

Stamps of HONG KONG *cancelled at Port Edward between* 1904 *and* 1916 *with postmarks detailed above.*

1900–01. *Wmk Crown CA (Nos. 56/61).*

Z1109	2 c. dull green	.. ..	40·00
Z1110	10 c. ultramarine	.. ..	42·00

1903. *Wmk Crown CA (Nos. 62/76).*

Z1111	1 c. dull purple and brown	..	14·00
Z1112	2 c. dull green	..	14·00
Z1113	4 c. purple/red	..	12·00
Z1114	5 c. dull green and brown-orange		17·00
Z1115	8 c. slate and violet	..	18·00
Z1116	10 c. purple and blue/blue	..	15·00
Z1117	12 c. green and purple/yellow	..	24·00
Z1118	20 c. slate and chestnut	..	38·00
Z1119	30 c. dull green and black	..	32·00
Z1120	50 c. dull green and magenta	..	38·00
Z1121	$1 purple and sage-green	..	40·00

1904–06. *Wmk Mult Crown CA (Nos. 77/90).*

Z1126	2 c. dull green	.. ..	8·00
Z1127	4 c. purple/red	.. ..	7·50
Z1128	5 c. dull green and brown-orange		12·00
Z1129	8 c. slate and violet	..	8·50
Z1132	20 c. slate and chestnut	..	40·00
Z1133	30 c. dull green and black	..	28·00
Z1134	50 c. green and magenta	..	35·00

1907–11. *Wmk Mult Crown CA (Nos. 91/9).*

Z1140	1 c. brown	.. ..	8·00
Z1141	2 c. green	.. ..	8·00
Z1142	4 c. carmine-red	.. ..	5·50
Z1143	6 c. orange-vermilion and purple		
Z1144	10 c. bright ultramarine	..	6·50

1912–15. *Wmk Mult Crown CA (Nos. 100/16).*

Z1151	1 c. brown	.. ..	7·00
Z1152	2 c. green	.. ..	5·50
Z1153	4 c. red	.. ..	3·50
Z1155	8 c. grey	.. ..	15·00
Z1156	10 c. ultramarine	.. ..	3·50
Z1158	20 c. purple and sage-green	..	9·50
Z1161	50 c. black/green	.. ..	9·00
Z1162	$1 purple and blue/blue	..	9·50

PRICES FOR STAMPS ON COVER	
Nos. 1/14	*from* × 50
Nos. 15/17	—
Nos. 18/28	*from* × 30

The overprinted stamps Nos. 1/17 were introduced on 1 January 1917 to prevent currency speculation in the Treaty Ports. They were used in the then-existing agencies of Amoy, Canton, Chefoo, Foochow, Hankow, Hoihow, Ningpo, Shanghai, Swatow, Tientsin and were also supplied to the British naval base of Wei Hai Wei.

CHINA

(1)

1917 (1 Jan)**–21.** *Stamps of Hong Kong, 1912–21 (wmk Mult Crown CA), optd with T 1, at Somerset House.*

1	1 c. brown	.. ..	2·50	1·50
	a. Black-brown	.. ..	2·00	2·50
	b. Crown broken at right	..	£275	£325
	c. Wmk sideways	..	†	£2500
2	2 c. green	.. ..	3·00	30
3	4 c. carmine-red	..	3·25	30
4	6 c. orange	..	3·50	60
5	8 c. slate	.. ..	9·00	1·25
6	10 c. ultramarine	..	8·50	30
	y. Wmk inverted and reversed		†	£300
7	12 c. purple/yellow	..	5·50	2·50
8	20 c. purple and sage-green	..	11·00	60
9	25 c. purple and magenta (A)	..	7·50	15·00
11	30 c. purple and orange-yellow	..	24·00	5·00
12	50 c. black/blue-green (olive back)		45·00	50·00
	a. Emerald surface (1917?)	..	30·00	8·50
	b. On emerald back (1919)	..	23·00	5·00
	c. On white back (1920)	..	£200	50·00
13	$1 reddish purple and bright blue/blue		60·00	2·50
	a. Grey-purple and blue/blue (1921)		60·00	7·00
14	$2 carmine-red and grey-black	..	£180	48·00
15	$3 green and purple	..	£325	£160
16	$5 green and red/blue-green (olive back)		£325	£200
17	$10 purple and black/red	..	£325	£200
1/17		Set of 16	£1600	£750
12/17 H/S	"Specimen"	..	Set of 6	£1600

1922 (Mar)**–27.** *As last, but wmk Mult Script CA.*

18	1 c. brown	.. ..	1·75	3·50
19	2 c. green	.. ..	2·75	2·25
	w. Wmk inverted		£100	
20	4 c. carmine-rose	..	3·75	2·00
	a. Lower Chinese character at right broken at top	..	£140	£120
21	6 c. orange-yellow	..	3·50	4·25
22	8 c. grey	.. ..	4·50	13·00
23	10 c. bright ultramarine	..	6·00	2·50
	w. Wmk inverted		£100	
24	20 c. purple and sage-green	..	9·00	5·00
25	25 c. purple and magenta (B)	..	15·00	60·00
	a. Broken flower	..	£325	
26	50 c. black/emerald (1927) (H/S S. £225)		48·00	£150
27	$1 purple and blue/blue	..	60·00	40·00
28	$2 carmine-red and grey-black	..	£190	£250
18/28		Set of 11	£300	£475

STAMP BOOKLETS

1917. *Black on red cover inscribed "BRITISH POST OFFICE AGENCIES IN CHINA". Stapled.*

SB1	$1 booklet containing eight 2 c., six 4 c. and six 10 c. (Nos. 2/3, 6)	..

1922. *Cover as No. SB1. Stapled.*

SB2	$1 booklet containing eight 2 c., six 4 c., and six 10 c. (Nos. 19/20, 23)	£3750

The British P.O.'s in the Treaty Ports closed by agreement with the Chinese on 30 November 1922, but the above overprinted issues continued in use at the Wei Hai Wei offices until they in turn closed on 30 September 1930. Under the terms of the Convention signed with China the Royal Navy continued to use the base at Wei Hai Wei until the mid-1930s.

BRITISH POST OFFICES IN JAPAN

Under the terms of the Anglo-Japanese Treaty of Yedo, signed on 26 August 1858, five Japanese ports were opened to British trade. British consulates were established at Decima (Nagasaki), Kanagawa (Yokohama), Hiogo (Kobe) and Hakodadi (Hakodate). The postage stamps of Hong Kong became available at the Yokohama and Nagasaki consulates during October 1864 and at Hiogo in 1869, although cancellation of mail did not commence until 1866 at Yokohama and Nagasaki or 1876 at Hiogo. Japan became a member of the U.P.U. on 1 June 1877 and all of the British Postal Agencies were closed by the end of 1879.

For illustrations of postmark types see BRITISH POST OFFICES IN CHINA.

HAKODATE

A British consular office existed at Hakodate, but it was never issued with a c.d.s., obliterator or Hong Kong stamps. No British covers are recorded from this consulate prior to opening of the Japanese Post Office.

HIOGO

The Port of Hiogo (Kobe) was first opened to foreigners on 1 January 1868. The British Consular mail service at Hiogo commenced during 1869 to serve the foreigners at Hiogo, Kobe and Osaka. The cities of Hiogo and Kobe later merged to become the single city of Kobe. The consular office at Hiogo closed on 30 November 1879.

Type **B** ("D30") *(supplied* 1876) *used* 1876–79
Type **D** *(supplied* 1876) *used* 1876–79

Stamps of HONG KONG *cancelled at Hiogo between* 1876 *and* 1879 *with postmarks detailed above.*

1863–71. *Wmk Crown CC (Nos. 8/19).*

Z 1	2 c. brown	.. ..	£3500
Z 2	4 c. grey	.. ..	£2500
Z 3	6 c. lilac	..	£3000
Z 4	8 c. orange	..	£2750
Z 5	12 c. blue	..	£3500
Z 6	18 c. lilac	..	
Z 7	24 c. green	..	£2500
Z 8	30 c. vermilion	..	
Z 9	30 c. mauve	..	£3500
Z10	48 c. rose	..	£4000
Z12	96 c. brownish grey	..	£4000

1877. *(Nos. 20/1).*

Z13	16 c. on 18 c. lilac	..	

1877. *Wmk Crown CC (No. 22).*

Z15	16 c. yellow	.. ..	£3250

NAGASAKI

The British Consulate opened in Nagasaki on 14 June 1859, but, with few British residents at the port, the consular staff found it inconvenient to carry out postal duties so that few Nagasaki c.d.s. or "N2" cancellations exist. The postal service was terminated on 30 September 1879.

Type **A** ("N2") *(supplied* 1866) *used* 1876–79
Type **D** *(supplied* 1866) *used* 1876–79

Stamps of HONG KONG *cancelled at Nagasaki between* 1876 *and* 1879 *with postmarks detailed above.*

1862. *No wmk (Nos. 1/8).*

Z15a	18 c. lilac	.. ..	£1000

1863–71. *Wmk Crown CC (Nos. 8/19).*

Z16	2 c. brown	.. ..	£900
Z17	4 c. grey	.. ..	£700
Z18	6 c. lilac	..	£800
Z19	8 c. orange	..	£700
Z20	12 c. blue	..	£800
Z21	18 c. lilac	..	£1400
Z22	24 c. green	..	£1100
Z24	30 c. mauve	..	£1000
Z25	48 c. rose	..	£1500
Z27	96 c. brownish grey	..	

1876–77. *(Nos. 20/1).*

Z28	16 c. on 18 c. lilac	..	£1100
Z29	28 c. on 30 c. mauve	..	£800

1877. *Wmk Crown CC (No. 22).*

Z30	16 c. yellow	.. ..	£850

YOKOHAMA

The British Consulate opened in Kanagawa on 21 July 1859, but was relocated to Yokohama where it provided postal services from 1 July 1860 until a separate Post Office was established in July 1867. The British Post Office in Yokohama closed on 31 December 1879.

Type **A** ("Y1") *(supplied* 1866) *used* 1867–79
Type **D** *(supplied* 1866) *used* 1866–79

Stamps of HONG KONG *cancelled at Yokohama between* 1866 *and* 1879 *with postmarks detailed above.*

1862. *No wmk (Nos. 1/8).*

Z30a	8 c. yellow-buff	.. ..	£140
Z31	18 c. lilac	.. ..	70·00

1863–71. *Wmk Crown CC (Nos. 8/19).*

Z32	2 c. brown	.. ..	16·00
Z33	4 c. grey	.. ..	16·00
	a. Perf 12½	..	£450
Z34	6 c. lilac	..	22·00
Z35	8 c. orange	..	22·00
Z36	12 c. blue	..	16·00
Z37	18 c. lilac	..	£450
Z38	24 c. green	..	18·00
Z39	30 c. vermilion	..	29·00
Z40	30 c. mauve	..	16·00
Z41	48 c. rose	..	35·00
Z43	96 c. brownish grey	..	45·00

1876–77. *(Nos. 20/1).*

Z44	16 c. on 18 c. lilac	..	£225
Z45	28 c. on 30 c. mauve	..	70·00

1877. *Wmk Crown CC (No. 22).*

Z46	16 c. yellow	.. ..	90·00

POSTAL FISCAL STAMPS

1874. *Wmk Crown CC. P 15½×15 (Nos. F1/3).*

ZF47	$2 olive-green	.. ..	70·00
ZF48	$3 dull violet	.. ..	65·00
ZF49	$10 rose-carmine	..	£1100

India

(Currency. 12 pies = 1 anna; 16 annas = 1 rupee)

ISSUE FOR SIND PROVINCE

1

1852 (1 July). "Scinde Dawk." *Embossed.*
S1	**1**	½ a. white	.. .. ..	£4500 £800
S2		½ a. blue	.. .. ..	£12000 £3500
S3		½ a. scarlet	.. .. ..	£65000 £8000

These stamps were issued under the authority of Sir Bartle Frere, Commissioner in Sind. They were suppressed in October 1854.

No. S3 is on sealing wax (usually cracked). Perfect copies are very rare.

EAST INDIA COMPANY ADMINISTRATION

2 (*Much reduced*)

3

The ½ a., 1 a. and 4 a. were lithographed in Calcutta at the office of the Surveyor-General. The die was engraved by Mr Maniruddin (spelling uncertain). *Ungummed* paper watermarked as T **2** (the "No. 4" paper) with the Arms of the East India Co in the sheet. The watermark is sideways on the ½ a. and 1 a., and upright on the 4 a. where the paper was trimmed so that only the central portion showing the oval and the arms was used. Imperforate.

1854 (April).
1	**3**	½ a. vermilion	.. .. ..	£800
		a. Deep vermilion	..	£1200

This stamp, with 9½ arches in the side border, was prepared for use and a supply was sent to Bombay, but was not officially issued.

The vermilion shade is normally found on toned paper and the deep vermilion on white.

The new-issue supplement to this Catalogue appears each month in

GIBBONS
STAMP MONTHLY

—from your newsagent or by postal subscription— sample copy and details on request.

ILLUSTRATIONS. Types 4/8 are shown twice actual size.

4

1854 (1 Oct). *Die I.*
2	4	½ a. blue	.. .. ..	55·00 14·00
		a. Printed on both sides	.. ..	† £8000
		b. Printed double	.. ..	† £6000
3		½ a. pale blue	.. ..	85·00 19·00
4		½ a. deep blue	.. ..	70·00 19·00
5		½ a. indigo	.. ..	£250 65·00

We give the official date of validity. Stamps were on sale to the public from mid September. Actual usage at Toungoo, Burma, is known from mid August.

These stamps were printed between 5 May and 29 July 1854 (Printing 30 millions).

4a

Die II
6	4a	½ a. blue ..	.. ..	50·00 75·00
7		½ a. indigo	.. ..	60·00 85·00

The bulk were printed between 1 and 12 August 1854, with some extra sheets on or before 2 November (Printing about 2 millions).

5

Die III
8	5	½ a. pale blue	.. .. ..	£750 38·00
8a		½ a. blue	.. ..	£700 35·00
9		½ a. greenish blue	.. ..	£1500 £160
10		½ a. deep blue	.. ..	£950 70·00

These stamps were printed between 3 July and 25 August 1855 (Printing about 4¾ millions).

THE THREE DIES OF THE ½ ANNA

DIE I. *Chignon shading* mostly solid blobs of colour. *Corner ornaments,* solid blue stars with long points, always conspicuous. *Band below diadem* always heavily shaded. *Diadem and jewels.* The middle and right-hand jewels usually show a clearly defined cross. *Outer frame lines.* Stamps with white or faintly shaded chignons and weak frame lines are usually Die I (worn state).

DIE II. *Chignon* normally shows much less shading. A strong line of colour separates hair and chignon. *Corner ornaments.* The right blue star is characteristic (see illustration) but tends to disappear. It never obliterates the white cross. *Band below diadem.* As Die I but heavier, sometimes solid. *Diadem and jewels.* As Die I but usually fainter. *Outer frame lines.* Always strong and conspicuous.

DIE III. *Chignon shading* shows numerous fine lines, often blurred. *Corner ornaments* have a small hollow blue star with short points, which tends to disappear as in Die II. *Band below diadem,* shows light shading or hardly any shading. *Diadem and jewels.* Jewels usually marked with a solid squat star. The ornaments between the stars appear in the shape of a characteristic white "w". *Frame lines* variable.

The above notes give the general characteristics of the three Dies, but there are a few exceptions due to retouching, etc.

---

6 (*See note below No. 14*)

Die I
11	6	1 a. deep red	.. ..	£375 45·00
12		1 a. red	.. ..	£225 32·00

Printing of these stamps commenced on 26 July 1854, and continued into August (Printing, see note below No. 14).

7

Die II: With more lines in the chignon than in Die I, and with white curved line where chignon joins head*
13	7	1 a. deep red	.. ..	£150 48·00
14		1 a. dull red	.. ..	42·00 35·00

**Very worn printings of Die II may be found with chignon nearly as white as in Die I.

In stamps of Die I, however, the small blob of red projecting from the hair into the chignon is always visible.

These stamps were printed in August and September 1854 (Total printing, Dies I and II together, about 7¾ millions).

8

Die III. With pointed bust
15	8	1 a. red	.. .. ..	£900 £130
16		1 a. dull red	.. ..	£1400 £180

These stamps were printed between 7 July and 25 August 1855 (Printing, about 1½ millions).

9

NOTE. Our catalogue prices for Four Annas stamps are for cut-square specimens, with clear margins and in good condition. Cut-to-shape copies are worth from 3% to 20% of these prices according to condition.

Four Dies of the Head:—

I   II

DIE I. Band of diadem and chignon strongly shaded.

DIE II. Lines in band of diadem worn. Few lines in the upper part of the chignon, which, however, shows a strong drawn comma-like mark.

IIIA   III

DIE IIIA. Upper part of chignon partly redrawn, showing two short, curved vertical lines in the NE corner. "Comma" has disappeared.

DIE III. Upper part of chignon completely redrawn, but band of diadem shows only a few short lines.

Two Dies of the Frame:—

Die I. Outer frame lines weak. Very small dots of colour, or none at all, in the "R" and "A's". The white lines to the right of "INDIA" are separated, by a line of colour, from the inner white circle.

Die II. Outer frame lines strengthened. Dots in the "R" and "A's" strong. White lines to right of "INDIA" break into inner white circle.

(Des Capt. H. Thuillier)

1854 (15 Oct). *W 2 upright, central portion only. Imperf.*
1st Printing. Head Die I. Frame Die I. Stamps widely spaced and separated by blue wavy line.

			Un	Used	Us pr
17	**9**	4 a. indigo and red	£4250	£500	£1800
18		4 a. blue and pale red..	£4250	£425	£1600
		a. Head inverted	† £25000/		†
			£80000		

This printing was made between 13 and 28 Oct 1854 (Printing, 206,040).

Twenty-seven confirmed examples of No. 18a are now known, only three of which are cut-square. The range of prices quoted reflects the difference in value between a sound cut-to-shape stamp and the finest example known.

2nd Printing. Head Die II. Frame Die I. Stamps widely spaced and separated by blue wavy line.

19	**9**	4 a. blue and red	£4000	£275	£1000
		a. Blue (head) printed double		† £6000	†
20		4 a. indigo and deep red	£4000	£325	£1200

This printing was made between 1 and 13 Dec 1854 (Printing, 393,960).
No. 19a is only known used cut-to-shape.

3rd Printing. Head Dies II, IIIA and III. Frame Dies I and II. Stamps, often in bright shades, widely spaced and separated by wavy line.

21	**9**	4 a. blue and red (shades) (Head III, Frame I)	£9000	£1100	£3500
		a. Head II, Frame I	—	£1600	£5000
		b. Head IIIA, Frame I	—	£1600	£4750
		c. Head III, Frame II..	—		£9500

This printing was made between 10 March and 2 April 1855 (Printing, 138,960).

4th Printing. Head Die III. Frame Die II. Stamps closely spaced 2 to 2½ mm without separating line.

22	**9**	4 a. deep blue and red	£2750	£275	£850
23		4 a. blue and red	£2500	£225	£750
		a. Blue (head) printed double	† £4500		†
24		4 a. pale blue and pale red	£2750	£300	£900

This printing was made between 3 April and 9 May 1855 (Printing, 540,960).
No. 23a is only known used cut-to-shape.

5th Printing. Head Die III. Frame Die II. Stamps spaced 4 to 6 mm without separating line.

25	**9**	4 a. blue and rose-red	£4500	£400	£1600
26		4 a. deep blue and red	£4500	£400	£1600

This printing was made between 4 Oct and 3 Nov 1855 (Printing, 380,064).

Serrated perf about 18, or pin-perf

27	½ a. blue (Die I)	† £4000	—
28	1 a. red (Die I)	† £2250	—
29	1 a. red (Die II)	† £2000	—
30	4 a. blue and red (Die II)	† £9000	—

This is believed to be an unofficial perforation. Most of the known specimens bear Madras circle postmarks (C122 to C126), but some are known with Bombay postmarks. Beware of fakes.

BISECTS. The bisected stamps for issues between 1854 and 1860 were used exclusively in the Straits Settlements during shortages of certain values. Prices quoted are for those with Singapore "B 172" cancellations. Penang marks are considerably rarer.

10   11

(Plate made at Mint, Calcutta. Typo Stamp Office)

1854 (4 Oct). *Sheet wmk sideways, as W 2 but with "No. 3" at top left. Imperf.*

31	**10**	2 a. green (shades)	85·00	23·00
		a. Bisected (1 a.) (1857) (on cover)	† £95000	
34		2 a. emerald-green	.. £1000	

The 2 a. was also printed on paper with sheet watermark incorporating the words "STAMP OFFICE. One Anna", etc. (Price £475 unused, £375 used).

Apart from the rare emerald-green shade, there is a range of shades of No. 31 varying from bluish to yellowish green.

Many stamps show traces of lines external to the design shown in our illustration. Stamps with this frame on all four sides are scarce.

Many reprints of the ½, 1, 2, and 4 a. exist.

PRINTERS. All Indian stamps from No. 35 to 200 were typographed by De La Rue & Co.

1855 (Oct). *Blue glazed paper. No wmk. P 14.*

35	**11**	4 a. black	£400	13·00
		a. Imperf (pair)	£2750	£2750
		b. Bisected (2 a.) (1859) (on cover)	† £7500	
36		8 a. carmine (Die I)	£375	11·00
		a. Imperf (pair)	£1800	
		b. Bisected (4 a.) (1859) (on cover)	† £35000	

The first supply of the 4 a. was on white paper, but it is difficult to distinguish it from No. 45.

In the 8 a. the paper varies from deep blue to almost white.

For difference between Die I and Die II in the 8 a., see illustrations above No. 73.

1856–64. *No wmk. Paper yellowish to white. P 14.*

37	**11**	½ a. blue (Die I)	50·00	2·75
		a. Imperf (pair)	£325	£950
38		½ a. pale blue (Die I)	42·00	1·25
39		1 a. brown	40·00	1·75
		a. Imperf between (vert pair)		
		b. Imperf (pair)	£750	£1300
		c. Bisected (½ a.) (1859) (on cover)	† £50000	
40		1 a. deep brown	55·00	3·00
41		2 a. dull pink (1861)	£375	23·00
		a. Imperf (pair)	£1700	
42		2 a. yellow-buff (1859)	£170	23·00
		a. Imperf (pair)	£1000	£1800
43		2 a. yellow (1863)	£250	25·00
44		2 a. orange (1858)	£275	25·00
		a. Imperf (pair)		
45		4 a. black	£180	8·00
		a. Bisected diagonally (2 a.) (1859) (on cover)	† £16000	
		b. Imperf (pair)	£1800	£1800
46		4 a. grey-black	£160	4·75
47		4 a. green (1864)	£800	32·00
48		8 a. carmine (Die I)	£180	15·00
49		8 a. pale carmine (Die I)	£225	15·00
		a. Bisected (4 a.) (1859) (on cover)	† £38000	

Prepared for use, but not officially issued

50	**11**	2 a. yellow-green	£700	£800
		a. Imperf (pair)	£1700	

This stamp is known with trial obliterations, and a few are known postally used. It also exists *imperf*, but is not known used thus.

For difference between Die I and Die II in the ½ a., see illustrations above No. 73.

CROWN COLONY

On the 1 November 1858, Her Majesty Queen Victoria assumed the government of the territories in India "heretofore administered in trust by the Honourable East India Company".

 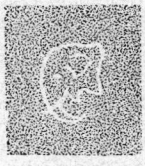

12   13

1860 (9 May). *No wmk. P 14.*

51	**12**	8 p. purple/*bluish*	£200	85·00
52		8 p. purple/*white*	35·00	4·50
		a. Bisected diagonally (4 p.) (1862) (on cover)	† £50000	
		b. Imperf (pair)	£2000	£3000
53		8 p. mauve	45·00	6·00

1865. *Paper yellowish to white. W 13. P 14.*

54	**11**	½ a. blue (Die I)	8·00	50
		a. Imperf	† £800	
		w. Wmk inverted	—	15·00
55		½ a. pale blue (Die I)	8·00	50
56	**12**	8 p. purple	8·50	8·00
		w. Wmk inverted	30·00	
57		8 p. mauve	9·50	8·00
58	**11**	1 a. pale brown	4·00	50
59		1 a. deep brown	3·50	40
		w. Wmk inverted	40·00	20·00
60		1 a. chocolate	8·50	60
61		2 a. yellow	65·00	3·50
62		2 a. orange	42·00	1·25
		a. Imperf (pair)	† £3000	
63		2 a. brown-orange	21·00	2·00
		w. Wmk inverted	50·00	25·00
64		4 a. green	£325	18·00
		w. Wmk inverted	† 75·00	
65		8 a. carmine (Die I)	£1000	75·00
		w. Wmk inverted	£1500	£150

The 8 p. mauve, No. 57, is found variously surcharged "NINE" or "NINE PIE" by local postmasters, to indicate that it was being sold for 9 pies, as was the case during 1874. Such surcharges were made without Government sanction.

The stamps of India, wmk Elephant's Head, surcharged with a crown and value in "cents", were used in the Straits Settlements.

14   (15)   (16)

1866 (28 June). *Fiscal stamps as T 14 optd. Wmk Crown over "INDIA". P 14 (at sides only). (a) As T 15.*

66		6 a. purple (G.)	£600	£110
		a. Overprint inverted	† £9000	

There are 20 different types of this overprint.

(b) With T 16

68		6 a. purple (G.)	£1100	£140

Die I   Die II

17   18

Two Dies of 4 a:—

Die I.—Mouth closed, line from corner of mouth downwards only. Pointed chin.

Die II.—Mouth slightly open; lips, chin, and throat defined by line of colour. Rounded chin.

1866 (Aug)–**1878.** *W 13. P 14.*

69	**17**	4 a. green (Die I)	50·00	2·25
70		4 a. deep green (Die I)	55·00	2·25
71		4 a. blue-green (Die II) (1878)	17·00	1·60
72	**18**	6 a. 8 p. slate (5.67)	32·00	18·00
		a. Imperf (pair)	£1700	

Die I (8 a.) (Die I (½ a.)

Die II (8 a.) Die II (½ a.)

1868 (1 Jan). *Die II. Profile redrawn and different diadem.*
W 13. P 14.

73	11	8 a. rose (Die II)	..	.. 25·00	4·75
		w. Wmk inverted	..	.. —	42·00
74		8 a. pale rose (Die II)	..	.. 25·00	4·75

1873. *Die II. Features, especially the mouth, more firmly drawn. W 13. P 14.*

75	11	½ a. deep blue (Die II)	..	.. 3·50	50
76		½ a. blue (Die II)	..	.. 3·50	50
		y. Wmk inverted and reversed	..	†	55·00

19 20

1874 (18 July–1 Sept). *W 13. P 14.*

77	19	9 p. bright mauve (18.7.74)	..	11·00	11·00
78		9 p. pale mauve	..	11·00	11·00
79	20	1 r. slate (1.9.74)	..	32·00	22·00

21 22

1876 (19 Aug). *W 13. P 14.*

80	21	6 a. olive-bistre	..	.. 5·50	2·25
		w. Wmk inverted	..	.. 50·00	
81		6 a. pale brown	..	.. 5·00	1·50
82	22	12 a. Venetian red	..	.. 7·00	18·00

EMPIRE

Queen Victoria assumed the title of Empress of India in 1877, and the inscription on the stamps was altered from "EAST INDIA" to "INDIA".

23 24 25

26 27 28

29 30 31

32 33 34

1882 (1 Jan)–90. *W 34. P 14.*

84	23	½ a. deep blue-green (1883)	..	3·50	10
85		½ a. blue-green	..	3·50	10
		a. Double impression	..	£400	£500
		w. Wmk inverted	..	—	50·00
86	24	9 p. rose (1883)	..	70	1·50
87		9 p. aniline carmine	..	1·00	1·75
88	25	1 a. brown-purple (1883)	..	3·50	30
89		1 a. plum	..	3·50	30
		w. Wmk inverted	..	—	50·00
90	26	1 a. 6 p. sepia	..	70	90
91	27	2 a. pale blue (1883)	..	3·50	30
92		2 a. blue	..	3·50	30
		a. Double impression	..	£750	£1000
93	28	3 a. orange	..	13·00	5·50
94		3 a. brown-orange (1890)	..	6·00	60
95	29	4 a. olive-green (6.85)	..	12·00	60
96		4 a. slate-green	..	12·00	60
		w. Wmk inverted	..	—	40·00
97	30	4 a. 6 p. yellow-green (1.5.86)	..	15·00	4·00
98	31	8 a. dull mauve (1883)	..	19·00	2·00
99		8 a. magenta	..	19·00	2·00
100	32	12 a. purple/red (1.4.88)	..	6·50	2·75
		w. Wmk inverted	..	—	60·00
101	33	1 r. slate (1883)	..	12·00	5·00
		w. Wmk inverted	..	—	50·00
84/101			Set of 11	75·00	16·00
97, 100	Handstamped "Specimen"		Set of 2	75·00	

No. 92a is from a sheet of 2 a. stamps with a very marked double impression issued in Karachi in early 1898.

2½ As.

(35) 36 37

1891 (1 Jan). *No. 97 surch with T 35 by Govt Press, Calcutta.*

102	30	2½ a. on 4½ a. yellow-green	..	2·25	60

There are several varieties in this surcharge due to variations in the relative positions of the letters and figures.

1892 (Jan)–97. *W 34. P 14.*

103	36	2 a. 6 p. yellow-green	..	1·50	40
104		2 a. 6 p. pale blue-green (1897)	..	2·50	80
105	37	1 r. green and rose	..	20·00	5·50
106		1 r. green and aniline carmine	..	8·00	2·00

¼

38 (39) 40

USED HIGH VALUES. It is necessary to emphasise that used prices quoted for the following and all later high value stamps are for postally used copies.

(Head of Queen from portrait by von Angeli)

1895 (1 Sept). *W 34. P 14.*

107	38	2 r. carmine and yellow-brown	..	35·00	11·00
107a		2 r. carmine and brown	..	40·00	13·00
108		3 r. brown and green	..	25·00	10·00
109		5 r. ultramarine and violet	..	35·00	23·00
107/9	..	..	Set of 3	85·00	40·00

1898 (1 Oct). *No. 85 surch with T 39 by Govt Press, Calcutta.*

110	23	¼ on ½ a. blue-green	..	10	50
		a. Surch double	..	£160	
		b. Double impression of stamp		£225	

1899. *W 34. P 14.*

111	40	3 p. aniline carmine	..	15	10

1900 (1 Oct)–02. *W 34. P 14.*

112	40	3 p. grey	..	50	70
113	23	½ a. pale yellow-green	..	1·40	45
114		½ a. yellow-green	..	1·40	45
115	25	1 a. carmine	..	1·25	15
116	27	2 a. pale violet	..	3·25	10
117		2 a. mauve (1902)	..	7·00	2·25
118	36	2 a. 6 p. ultramarine	..	3·25	3·75
112/18	..	..	Set of 5	8·50	5·25

41 42 43

44 45 46

    (49)

47 48 49

50 51 52

1902 (9 Aug)–11. *W 34. P 14.*

119	41	3 p. grey	..	1·00	10
120		3 p. slate-grey (1904)	..	1·00	10
121	42	½ a. yellow-green	..	1·00	20
122		½ a. green	..	1·00	20
123	43	1 a. carmine	..	1·10	10
124	44	2 a. violet (13.5.03)	..	3·50	40
125		2 a. mauve	..	2·75	10
126	45	2 a. 6 p. ultramarine (1902)	..	4·25	35
		w. Wmk inverted	..	†	£120
127	46	3 a. orange-brown (1902)	..	4·25	40
128	47	4 a. olive (20.4.03)	..	3·00	40
129		4 a. pale olive	..	3·50	40
130		4 a. olive-brown	..	9·00	3·00
131	48	6 a. olive-bistre (6.8.03)	..	12·00	4·75
132		6 a. maize	..	10·00	4·50
133	49	8 a. purple (shades) (8.5.03)	..	8·50	1·00
134		8 a. claret (1910)	..	11·00	1·00
135	50	12 a. purple/red (1903)	..	8·00	2·00
136	51	1 r. green and carmine (1903)	..	6·50	70
137		1 r. green and scarlet (1911)	..	30·00	2·25
138	52	2 r. rose-red and yellow-brown (1903)	..	38·00	4·00
139		2 r. carmine and yellow-brown	..	38·00	4·00
140		3 r. brown and green (1904)	..	25·00	19·00
141		3 r. red-brown and green (1911)	..	35·00	22·00
142		5 r. ultramarine and violet (1904)	..	50·00	35·00
143		5 r. ultramarine and deep lilac (1911)	..	95·00	45·00
144		10 r. green and carmine (1909)	..	£100	26·00
146		15 r. blue and olive-brown (1909)	..	£130	42·00
147		25 r. brownish orange and blue (1909)	..	£750	£800
119/47			Set of 17	£1000	£850

No. 147 can often be found with telegraph cancellation; these can be supplied at one third of the price given above.

1905 (2 Feb). *No. 122 surch with T 39.*

148	42	¼ on ½ a. green	..	.. 55	10
		a. Surch inverted	..	—	£800

It is doubtful if No. 148a exists unused with genuine surcharge.

53 54

1906 (6 Dec)–07. *W 34. P 14.*

149	53	½ a. green	..	2·50	10
150	54	1 a. carmine (7.1.07)	..	1·40	10

55 56 57

58* 59 60

61 62 63

64 65 66

67   "Rs" flaw in right value tablet (R.1/4)

*T **58**. Two types of the 1½ a.; (A) As illustrated. (B) Inscribed "1½ As". "ONE AND A HALF ANNAS".

1911 (Dec)–22. *W* **34**. *P* 14.

151	55	3 p. pale grey (1912)	..	75	20
152		3 p. grey	..	75	20
153		3 p. slate-grey	..	75	20
		a. "Rs" flaw	..	12·00	
154		3 p. blue-slate (1922)	..	2·00	50
		w. Wmk inverted	..	10·00	
155	56	½ a. yellow-green (1912)	..	90	15
156		½ a. pale blue-green	..	90	15
159	57	1 a. rose-carmine	..	2·25	20
160		1 a. carmine	..	2·25	20
161		1 a. aniline carmine	..	2·00	15
162		1 a. pale rose-carmine (*chalk-surfaced paper*) (1918)	..	2·75	40
163	58	1½ a. chocolate (Type A) (1919)	..	2·50	30
164		1½ a. grey-brown (Type A)	..	7·50	2·50
165		1½ a. chocolate (Type B) (1921)	..	2·75	3·50
		w. Wmk inverted	..	8·00	
166	59	2 a. dull purple	..	3·00	30
167		2 a. mauve	..	3·00	30
		w. Wmk inverted	..	15·00	
168		2 a. violet	..	4·50	40
169		2 a. bright purple (1.19)	..	4·75	65
170	60	2 a. 6 p. ultramarine (1912)	..	2·00	3·00
171	61	2 a. 6 p. ultramarine (1913)	..	2·00	20
172	62	3 a. dull orange	..	5·50	45
173		3 a. orange-brown	..	3·50	20
174	63	4 a. deep olive (1912)	..	5·50	50
175		4 a. olive-green	..	5·50	50
		w. Wmk inverted	..	15·00	
176	64	6 a. bistre (1912)	..	4·00	1·00
177		6 a. yellow-bistre	..	4·00	1·10
178		6 a. deep bistre-brown	..	16·00	3·50
179	65	8 a. purple (1912)	..	6·00	1·00
180		8 a. mauve	..	11·00	1·10
181		8 a. deep lilac	..	14·00	1·25
182		8 a. bright aniline mauve	..	27·00	5·00
183	66	12 a. dull claret (1912)	..	10·00	2·50
184		12 a. claret	..	7·00	2·25
185	67	1 r. brown and green (1913)	..	17·00	2·00
186		1 r. red-brown and blue-green	..	13·00	1·50
		w. Wmk inverted	..	32·00	
187		2 r. carmine and brown (1913)	..	18·00	1·50
		w. Wmk inverted	..	45·00	
188		5 r. ultramarine and violet (1913)	..	48·00	6·50
189		10 r. green and scarlet (1913)	..	70·00	12·00
190		15 r. blue and olive (1913)	..	90·00	24·00
191		25 r. orange and blue (1913)	..	£160	32·00
151/91			*Set of* 19	£350	75·00

Examples of the ½ a. printed double are now believed to be forgeries.

FORGERIES.—Collectors are warned against forgeries of all the later surcharges of India, and particularly the errors.

NINE

PIES

(68)

1921. *T* **57** *surch with T* **68**.

192		9 p. on 1 a. rose-carmine	..	60	30
		a. Error. "NINE NINE"	..	70·00	£120
		b. Error. "PIES PIES"	..	70·00	£120
		c. Surch double	..	£140	£170
		w. Wmk inverted		†	40·00
193		9 p. on 1 a. carmine-pink	..	1·75	60
194		9 p. on 1 a. aniline carmine	..	7·50	2·75

In the initial setting of the surcharge No. 192a occurred on R. 2/13–16 of the fourth pane and No. 192b on R. 4/13–16 of the third. For the second setting No. 192a was corrected. Examples of No. 192b still occur but on R. 2/13–16 of the third pane. Later printings showed this corrected also.

1922. *T* **56** *surch with T* **39**.

195	¼ a. on ½ a. yellow-green	..	30	35
	a. Surch inverted	..	9·00	
	b. Surch omitted (in horiz pair with normal)		£200	
196	¼ a. on ½ a. blue-green	..	1·75	65

1922–26. *W* **34**. *P* 14.

197	57	1 a. chocolate	..	60	10
198	58	1½ a. rose-carmine (Type B) (1926)	..	2·50	30
199	61	2 a. 6 p. orange (1926)	..	5·00	3·50
200	62	3 a. ultramarine (1923)	..	12·00	60
197/200			*Set of* 4	18·00	4·00

NEW INFORMATION

The editor is always interested to correspond with people who have new information that will improve or correct the Catalogue.

69   **70**   **71**

PRINTERS. The following issues of postage and contemporary official stamps were all printed by the Security Printing Press, Nasik, *unless otherwise stated.*

1926–33. *Typo. W* **69**. *P* 14.

201	55	3 p. slate	..	30	10
		w. Wmk inverted	..	1·10	30
202	56	½ a. green	..	75	10
		w. Wmk inverted		—	30
203	57	1 a. chocolate	..	50	10
		a. *Tête-bêche* (pair) (1932)	..	1·25	10·00
		w. Wmk inverted	..	50	10
204	58	1½ a. rose-carmine (Type B) (1929)	..	1·25	10
		w. Wmk inverted	..	1·50	30
205	59	2 a. bright purple	..	5·00	5·50
		a. Stop under "s" in right value tablet (R. 4/16)	..	70·00	
206	70	2 a. purple	..	1·00	10
		a. *Tête-bêche* (pair) (1933)	..	8·50	38·00
		w. Wmk inverted	..	1·25	30
207	61	2 a. 6 p. orange (1929)	..	1·25	10
		w. Wmk inverted	..	1·50	40
208	62	3 a. ultramarine	..	7·00	1·00
209		3 a. blue (1928)	..	6·50	10
		w. Wmk inverted	..	7·50	75
210	63	4 a. pale sage-green	..	1·50	10
		w. Wmk inverted		—	5·00
211	71	4 a. sage-green	..	6·00	10
		w. Wmk inverted	..		40
212	65	8 a. reddish purple	..	4·00	10
		w. Wmk inverted	..	6·00	40
213	66	12 a. claret	..	5·00	30
		w. Wmk inverted	..	7·00	80
214	67	1 r. chocolate and green	..	5·00	45
		a. Chocolate (head) omitted	..	£3000	
		w. Wmk inverted	..	8·50	75
215		2 r. carmine and orange	..	10·00	80
		w. Wmk inverted	..	12·00	1·50
216		5 r. ultramarine and purple	..	22·00	1·25
		w. Wmk inverted	..		2·00
217		10 r. green and scarlet (1927)	..	42·00	3·00
		w. Wmk inverted	..	70·00	4·00
218		15 r. blue and olive (1928)	..	38·00	30·00
		w. Wmk inverted	..	24·00	28·00
219		25 r. orange and blue (1928)	..	90·00	30·00
		w. Wmk inverted	..	£100	35·00
201/19			*Set of* 18	£200	60·00

Examples of the ½ a. printed double are believed to be forgeries.

72 De Havilland D.H.66 Hercules

Missing tree-top   Reversed serif on second
(R. 11/6 of 8 a.)   "I" of "INDIA"

(Des R. Grant. Litho)

1929 (22 Oct). *Air. W* **69** (*sideways**). *P* 14.

220	72	2 a. deep blue-green	..	2·00	50
		w. Wmk stars pointing left	..	1·50	60
221		3 a. blue	..	1·00	1·60
		w. Wmk stars pointing left	..	1·50	1·50
222		4 a. olive-green	..	2·25	1·00
		w. Wmk stars pointing left	..	2·75	1·10
223		6 a. bistre	..	2·25	90
		w. Wmk stars pointing left	..	2·50	1·00
224		8 a. purple	..	2·50	1·00
		a. Missing tree-top	..	85·00	55·00
		b. Reversed serif	..	£160	80·00
		w. Wmk stars pointing left	..	3·25	1·00
225		12 a. rose-red	..	9·50	5·00
		w. Wmk stars pointing left	..	12·00	5·00
220/5			*Set of* 6	17·00	9·00

*The normal sideways watermark shows the stars pointing right, *as seen from the back of the stamp.*

73 Purana Qila

(Des H. W. Barr. Litho)

1931 (9 Feb). *Inauguration of New Delhi. T* **73** *and similar horiz designs. W* **69** (*sideways**). *P* 13½×14.

226		¼ a. olive-green and orange-brown	..	1·50	2·50
		a. "F" for "P" in "PURANA"	..	80·00	85·00
		w. Wmk stars pointing left	..	1·50	2·50
227		½ a. violet and green	..	1·25	40
		w. Wmk stars pointing left	..	2·00	40
228		1 a. mauve and chocolate	..	1·25	20
		w. Wmk stars pointing left	..	2·25	25
229		2 a. green and blue	..	1·50	1·75
		w. Wmk stars pointing left	..	2·00	1·25
230		3 a. chocolate and carmine	..	2·50	2·50
		w. Wmk stars pointing left	..	2·50	2·50
231		1 r. violet and green	..	8·00	22·00
		w. Wmk stars pointing left	..	8·00	22·00
226/31			*Set of* 6	14·50	26·00

Designs:—½ a. War Memorial Arch; 1 a. Council House; 2 a. The Viceroy's House; 3 a. Government of India Secretariat; 1 r. Dominion Columns and the Secretariat.

*The normal sideways watermark shows the stars pointing to the right, *as seen from the back of the stamp.*

79   **80**   **81**

82   **83**

(T **82/3** des T. I. Archer. 9 p. litho and typo; 1¼ a., 3½ a. litho; others typo)

1932–36. *W* **69**. *P* 14.

232	79	½ a. green (1934)	..	1·50	10
		w. Wmk inverted	..		50
233	80	9 p. deep green (22.4.32)	..	45	10
		w. Wmk inverted	..	75	50
234	81	1 a. chocolate (1934)	..	3·50	10
		w. Wmk inverted	..		50
235	82	1 a. 3 p. mauve (22.4.32)	..	30	10
		w. Wmk inverted	..	30	30
236	70	2 a. vermilion	..	9·00	4·00
		aw. Wmk inverted	..	9·00	5·50
236b	59	2 a. vermilion (1934)	..	3·75	50
236c		2 a. vermilion (*small die*) (1936)	..	4·50	
		cw. Wmk inverted	..		5·00
237	62	3 a. carmine	..	3·50	10
		w. Wmk inverted	..		1·25
238	83	3 a. 6 p. ultramarine (22.4.32)	..	3·00	20
		w. Wmk inverted	..	3·00	30
239	64	6 a. bistre (1935)	..	7·00	1·50
		w. Wmk inverted	..		10·00
232/9			*Set of* 9	29·00	5·50

No. 236b measures 19×22.6 mm and No. 236c 18.4×21.8 mm.

84 Gateway of India, Bombay   "Bird" flaw (R.9/3)

1935 (6 May). *Silver Jubilee. T* **84** *and similar horiz designs. Litho. W* **69** (*sideways**). *P* 13½×14.

240		½ a. black and yellow-green	..	75	20
		w. Wmk stars pointing left	..	60	15
241		9 p. black and grey-green	..	45	20
		w. Wmk stars pointing left	..	45	30
242		1 a. black and brown	..	55	20
		w. Wmk stars pointing left	..	45	10
243		1¼ a. black and bright violet	..	45	10
		w. Wmk stars pointing left	..	90	15
244		2½ a. black and orange	..	2·50	1·60
		w. Wmk stars pointing left	..	1·75	95
245		3½ a. black and dull ultramarine	..	3·75	3·25
		a. "Bird" flaw	..	90·00	65·00
		w. Wmk stars pointing left	..	4·25	3·25
246		8 a. black and purple	..	3·50	3·25
		w. Wmk stars pointing left	..	5·50	3·75
240/6			*Set of* 7	10·00	7·00

Designs:—9 p. Victoria Memorial Calcutta; 1 a. Rameswaram Temple, Madras; 1¼ a. Jain Temple, Calcutta; 2½ a. Taj Mahal, Agra; 3½ a. Golden Temple, Amritsar; 8 a. Pagoda in Mandalay.

*The normal sideways watermark shows the stars pointing to the right, *as seen from the back of the stamp.*

91 King George VI **92** Dak Runner

93 King George VI

1937 (23 Aug)–40. *Typo. W* **69**. *P* 13½×14 *or* 14×13½ (*T* **93**).
247	**91**	3 p. slate (15.12.37)	..	50	10
248		½ a. red-brown (15.12.37)	..	1·75	10
249		9 p. green	..	5·00	20
250		1 a. carmine	..	70	10
		a. *Tête-bêche* (vert pair) (1940)		1·40	1·75
		w. Wmk inverted (from booklets)		70	70
251	**92**	2 a. vermilion (15.12.37)	..	3·25	30
252	–	2 a. 6 p. bright violet (15.12.37)		75	20
253	–	3 a. yellow-green (15.12.37)	..	4·75	30
254	–	3 a. 6 p. bright blue (15.12.37)		3·25	50
255	–	4 a. brown (15.12.37)	..	13·00	20
256	–	6 a. turquoise-green (15.12.37)		14·00	80
257	–	8 a. slate-violet (15.12.37)	..	7·50	50
258	–	12 a. lake (15.12.37)	..	18·00	1·10
259	**93**	1 r. grey and red-brown (15.12.37)		1·00	15
260		2 r. purple and brown (15.12.37)		3·75	30
		w. Wmk inverted		20·00	
261		5 r. green and blue (15.12.37)		17·00	50
		w. Wmk inverted		35·00	
262		10 r. purple and claret (15.12.37)		15·00	70
263		15 r. brown and green (15.12.37)		70·00	60·00
		w. Wmk inverted		80·00	65·00
264		25 r. slate-violet and purple (15.12.37)		95·00	17·00
247/64			*Set of* 18	£250	75·00

Designs: *Horiz as T* **92**—2 a. 6 p. Dak bullock cart; 3 a. Dak tonga; 3 a. 6 p. Dak camel; 4 a. Mail train; 6 a. *Strathnaver* (liner); 8 a. Mail lorry; 12 a. Armstrong Whitworth A.W.27 Ensign I mail plane (small head).

No. 250a comes from surplus booklet sheets issued as normal stock following the rise in postal rates.

100a King **101** King George VI **102**
George VI

103 Armstrong Whitworth A.W.27 Ensign I Mail Plane (large head)

(T 100a/102 des T. I. Archer. Typo.)

1940–43. *W* **69**. *P* 13½×14.
265	**100a**	3 p. slate	..	30	10
266		½ a. purple (1.10.42)	..	60	10
		w. Wmk inverted	..		
267		9 p. green	..	60	10
268		1 a. carmine (1.4.43)	..	60	10
269	**101**	1 a. 3 p. yellow-brown	..	90	10
		aw. Wmk inverted	..		
269b		1½ a. dull violet (9.42)	..	75	10
270		2 a. vermilion	..	1·50	10
271		3 a. bright violet (1942)	..	2·50	10
		w. Wmk inverted	..	—	10·00
272		3½ a. bright blue	..	70	10
273	**102**	4 a. brown	..	45	10
274		6 a. turquoise-green	..	3·50	10
275		8 a. slate-violet	..	1·50	30
276		12 a. lake	..	3·00	50
277	**103**	14 a. purple (15.10.40)	..	18·00	1·25
265/77			*Set of* 14	32·00	2·25

The 1½ a. and 3 a. were at first printed by lithography and were of finer execution and without Jubilee lines in the sheet margins.

≡ ≡

105 "Victory" and King **3 PIES**
George VI **(106)**

1946 (2 Jan). *Victory. Litho. W* **69**. *P* 13.
278	**105**	9 p. yellow-green (8.2.46)	..	30	40
279		1½ a. dull violet	..	30	30
280		3½ a. bright blue	..	75	60
281		12 a. claret (8.2.46)	..	1·50	65
278/81			*Set of* 4	2·50	1·75

1946 (8 Aug). *Surch with T* **106**.
282	**101**	3 p. on 1 a. 3 p. yellow-brown	..	10	15

DOMINION

301 Asokan Capital **302** Indian National Flag
(Inscr reads
"Long Live India")

303 Douglas DC-4

(Des T. I. Archer. Litho.)

1947 (21 Nov–15 Dec). *Independence. W* **69**. *P* 14 × 13½ (1½ a.) *or* 13½ × 14 (*others*).
301	**301**	1½ a. grey-green (15 Dec)	..	15	10
302	**302**	3½ a. orange-red, blue and green		30	1·10
		w. Wmk inverted		5·50	5·50
303	**303**	12 a. ultramarine (15 Dec)	..	1·50	2·00
301/3			*Set of* 3	1·75	2·75

304 Lockheed Constellation

(Des T. I. Archer. Litho.)

1948 (29 May). *Air. Inauguration of India-U.K. Air Service. W* **69**. *P* 13½ × 14.
304	**304**	12 a. black and ultramarine	..	1·00	2·00

305 Mahatma Gandhi **306**

(Photo Courvoisier)

1948 (15 Aug). *First Anniv of Independence. P* 11½.
305	**305**	1½ a. brown	..	1·75	30
306		3½ a. violet	..	4·25	1·50
307		12 a. grey-green	..	6·00	60
308	**306**	10 r. purple-brown and lake		55·00	40·00
305/8	..		*Set of* 4	60·00	40·00

307 Ajanta **308** Konarak Horse **309** Trimurti
Panel

310 Bodhisattva **311** Nataraja **312** Sanchi Stupa,
East Gate

---

313 Bodh Gaya **314** Bhuvanesvara **315** Gol Gumbad,
Temple Bijapur

316 Kandarya Mahadeva **317** Golden Temple,
Temple Amritsar

318 Victory Tower, **319** Red Fort, Delhi
Chittorgarh

320 Taj Mahal, Agra **321** Qutb Minar,
Delhi

322 Satrunjaya Temple, Palitana

(Des T. I. Archer and I. M. Das. Typo. (low values), litho. (rupee values))

1949 (15 Aug). *W* **69** (*sideways* * *on* 6 p., 1 r. *and* 10 r.). *P* 14 (3 p. to 2 a.), 13½ (3 a. to 12 a.), 14×13½ (1 r. and 10 r.), 13½×14 (2 r. and 5 r.), 13 (15 r.).
309	**307**	3 p. slate-violet	..	15	10
		w. Wmk inverted			
310	**308**	6 p. purple-brown	..	25	10
		w. Wmk star pointing right		3·25	90
311	**309**	9 p. yellow-green	..	40	10
312	**310**	1 a. turquoise	..	60	10
313	**311**	2 a. carmine	..	80	10
		w. Wmk inverted		9·00	90
314	**312**	3 a. brown-orange	..	1·50	10
315	**313**	3½ a. bright blue	..	1·50	2·75
316	**314**	4 a. lake	..	4·00	20
		w. Wmk inverted		13·00	1·00
317	**315**	6 a. violet	..	1·50	10
		w. Wmk inverted		3·00	45
318	**316**	8 a. turquoise-green	..	1·50	10
319	**317**	12 a. dull blue	..	1·50	20
		w. Wmk inverted		5·00	80
320	**318**	1 r. dull violet and green		9·00	10
		w. Wmk star pointing left		20·00	80
321	**319**	2 r. claret and violet	..	10·00	20
		w. Wmk inverted		24·00	1·00
322	**320**	5 r. blue-green and red-brown		28·00	90
		w. Wmk inverted		50·00	1·75
323	**321**	10 r. purple-brown and deep blue		45·00	5·00
		a. *Purple-brown and blue*		90·00	3·75
		aw. Wmk star pointing left			
324	**322**	15 r. brown and claret		14·00	17·00
309/24			*Set of* 16	£110	22·00

*The normal sideways watermark has the star pointing to the left on the 6 p. value and to the right on the 1 r. and 10 r. (323a) *when seen from the back of the stamp.*

For T **310** with statue reversed see No. 333.

323 Globe and Asokan Capital

1949 (10 Oct). *75th Anniv of U.P.U. Litho.* W **69**. *P* 13.

325	323	9 p. green		..	1·00	2·00
326		2 a. rose		..	1·00	2·00
327		3½ a. bright blue	..	..	1·75	2·25
328		12 a. brown-purple	..	..	3·00	2·50
325/8	..	..	..	*Set of 4*	6·00	8·00

REPUBLIC

324 Rejoicing Crowds   **328** As T **310**, but statue reversed

(Des D. J. Keymer & Co. Litho)

1950 (26 Jan). *Inauguration of Republic.* T **324** *and similar designs.* W **69** (*sideways on 3½ a.*). *P* 13.

329		2 a. scarlet	..	..	1·00	40
		w. Wmk inverted	..	..	12·00	1·75
330		3½ a. ultramarine	..	..	1·50	2·75
331		4 a. violet	..	..	1·50	65
332		12 a. maroon	..	..	3·25	2·25
		w. Wmk inverted	..	..	14·00	4·50
329/32	..	..	..	*Set of 4*	6·50	5·50

Designs: *Vert*—3½ a. Quill, ink-well and verse. *Horiz*—4 a. Ear of corn and plough; 12 a. Spinning-wheel and cloth.

1950 (15 July)–51. *Typo.* W **69**. *P* 14 (1 a.), 13½ (*others*).

333	328	1 a. turquoise	..	..	2·50	10
		aw. Wmk inverted	..	..		
333b	313	2½ a. lake (30.4.51)	..	..	2·50	2·50
333c	314	4 a. bright blue (30.4.51)	..	6·00	10
333/c	..	..	..	*Set of 3*	10·00	2·50

329 Stegodon ganesa   **330** Torch

1951 (13 Jan). *Centenary of Geological Survey of India. Litho.* W **69**. *P* 13.

334	329	2 a. black and claret	..	2·00	50

1951 (4 Mar). *First Asian Games, New Delhi. Litho.* W **69** (*sideways*). *P* 14.

335	330	2 a. reddish purple and brown-orange	..	1·00	30
336		12 a. chocolate and light blue	..	4·00	90

PROCESS. All the following issues were printed in photogravure, *except where otherwise stated.*

331 Kabir   **332** Locomotives of 1853 and 1953

1952 (1 Oct). *Indian Saints and Poets.* T **331** *and similar vert designs.* W **69**. *P* 14.

337		9 p. bright emerald-green	..		30	40
338		1 a. carmine	..	..	30	15
339		2 a. orange-red	..	..	1·00	20
340		4 a. bright blue	..	..	1·25	40
341		4½ a. bright mauve	..	..	30	80
342		12 a. brown	..	..	2·25	80
337/42	..	..	..	*Set of 6*	4·75	2·50

Designs:—1 a. Tulsidas; 2 a. Meera; 4 a. Surdas; 4½ a. Ghalib; 12 a. Tagore.

1953 (16 Apr). *Railway Centenary.* W **69**. *P* 14½ × 14.

343	332	2 a. black	..	75	10

333 Mount Everest

1953 (2 Oct). *Conquest of Mount Everest.* W **69**. *P* 14½ × 14.

344	333	2 a. bright violet	..	75	10
345		14 a. brown	..	3·00	25

334 Telegraph Poles of 1851 and 1951

1953 (1 Nov). *Centenary of Indian Telegraphs.* W **69**. *P* 14½ × 14.

346	334	2 a. blue-green	..	30	10
347		12 a. blue	..	2·50	40

335 Postal Transport, 1854

1954 (1 Oct). *Stamp Centenary.* T **335** *and similar horiz designs.* W **69**. *P* 14½ × 14.

348		1 a. reddish purple		30	20
349		2 a. cerise		30	10
350		4 a. orange-brown		2·75	75
351		14 a. blue		1·50	40
348/51	..	*Set of 4*		4·25	1·25

Designs:—2, 14 a. "Airmail"; 4 a. Postal transport, 1954.

338 U.N. Emblem and Lotus

1954 (24 Oct). *United Nations Day.* W **69** (*sideways*). *P* 13.

352	338	2 a. turquoise-green	..	40	30

339 Forest Research Institute

1954 (11 Dec). *Fourth World Forestry Congress, Dehra Dun.* W **69**. *P* 14½ × 14.

353	339	2 a. ultramarine	..	20	10

340 Tractor   **344** Woman Spinning

347 "Malaria Control" (Mosquito and Staff of Aesculapius)

1955 (26 Jan). *Five Year Plan.* T **340**, **344**, **347** *and similar designs.* W **69** (*sideways on small horiz designs*). *P* 14×14½ (*small horiz*) or 14½×14 (*others*).

354		3 p. bright purple	..	30	10
355		6 p. violet	..	30	10
356		9 p. orange-brown	..	40	10
357		1 a. blue-green	..	45	10
358		2 a. light blue	..	30	10
359		3 a. pale blue-green	..	50	10
360		4 a. rose-carmine	..	50	10
361		6 a. yellow-brown	..	1·50	10
362		8 a. blue	..	6·00	10
363		10 a. turquoise-green	..	2·50	1·75
364		12 a. bright blue	..	2·00	10
365		14 a. bright green	..	3·75	20
366		1 r. deep dull green	..	4·00	10
367		1 r. 2 a. grey	..	2·00	2·75
368		1 r. 8 a. reddish purple	..	7·00	4·00
369		2 r. cerise	..	4·25	10
370		5 r. brown	..	14·00	30
371		10 r. orange	..	14·00	4·25
354/71	..	*Set of 18*		50·00	12·00

Designs: *Horiz (as T 340)*—6 p. Power loom; 9 p. Bullock-driven well; 1 a. Damodar Valley Dam; 4 a. Bullocks; 8 a. Chittaranjan Locomotive Works; 12 a. Hindustan Aircraft Factory, Bangalore; 1 r. Telephone engineer; 2 r. Rare Earth Factory, Alwaye; 5 r. Sindri Fertiliser Factory; 10 r. Steel plant. (*As T 347*)—10 a. Marine Drive, Bombay; 14 a. Kashmir landscape; 1 r. 2 a. Cape Comorin; 1 r. 8 a. Mt Kangchenjunga. *Vert (as T 344)*—3 a. Woman weaving with hand loom.

For stamps as Nos. 366, 369/71 but W **374** see Nos. 413/16.

358 Bodhi Tree   **359** Round Parasol and Bodhi Tree

(Des C. Pakrashi (2 a.), R. D'Silva (14 a.))

1956 (24 May). *Buddha Jayanti.* W **69** (*sideways on 14 a.*). *P* 13 × 13½ (2 a.) or 13½ × 13 (14 a.).

372	358	2 a. sepia	..	75	10
373	359	14 a. vermilion	..	4·00	3·50

360 Lokmanya Bal Gangadhar Tilak   **361** Map of India

1956 (23 July). *Birth Centenary of Tilak (journalist).* W **69**. *P* 13 × 13½.

374	360	2 a. chestnut	..	10	10

(New Currency. 100 naye paise = 1 rupee)

1957 (1 Apr)–58. W **69** (*sideways*). *P* 14 × 14½.

375	361	1 n.p. blue-green		10	10
376		2 n.p. light brown		10	10
377		3 n.p. deep brown		10	10
378		5 n.p. bright green		4·25	10
379		6 n.p. grey		10	10
379a		8 n.p. light blue-green (7.5.58)		5·50	1·25
380		10 n.p. deep dull green		4·25	10
381		13 n.p. bright carmine-red		30	10
381a		15 n.p. violet (16.1.58)		3·50	10
382		20 n.p. blue		30	10
383		25 n.p. ultramarine		30	10
384		50 n.p. orange		2·25	10
385		75 n.p. reddish purple		1·25	10
385a		90 n.p. bright purple (16.1.58)		3·50	1·50
375/85a		*Set of 14*		23·00	2·75

The 8, 15 and 90 n.p. have their value expressed as "nP". For similar stamps but W **374** see Nos. 399/412.

362 The Rani of Jhansi   **363** Shrine

1957 (15 Aug). *Indian Mutiny Centenary.* W **69**. *P* 14½ × 14 (15 n.p.) or 13 × 13½ (90 n.p.).

386	362	15 n.p. brown	..	15	10
387	363	90 n.p. reddish purple	..	1·50	70

364 Henri Dunant and Conference Emblem   **365** "Nutrition"

1957 (28 Oct). *19th International Red Cross Conference, New Delhi.* W **69** (*sideways*). *P* 13½ × 13.

388	364	15 n.p. deep grey and carmine	..	10	10

1957 (14 Nov). *Children's Day.* T **365** *and similar designs.* W **69** (*sideways on 90 n.p.*). *P* 14×13½ (90 n.p.) or 13½×14 (*others*).

389		8 n.p. reddish purple	..	10	15
390		15 n.p. turquoise-green	..	10	10
391		90 n.p. orange-brown	..	25	15
389/91		*Set of 3*		30	30

Designs: *Horiz*—15 n.p. "Education". *Vert*—90 n.p. "Recreation".

OMNIBUS ISSUES

Details, together with prices for complete sets, of the various Omnibus issues from the 1935 Silver Jubilee series to date are included in a special section following Zimbabwe at the end of Volume 2.

368 Bombay University   **369** Calcutta University

1957 (31 Dec). *Centenary of Indian Universities. T* **368/9** *and similar design. W* **69** *(sideways on T* **368**)*. P* 14 × 14½ (No. 392) *or* 13½ × 14 (*others*).

392	10 n.p. violet				15	30
393	10 n.p. grey				15	30
394	10 n.p. light brown				30	30
392/4				*Set of 3*	55	80

Design: *Horiz as T* **369**—No. 394, Madras University.

371 J. N. Tata (founder) and Steel Plant   **372** Dr. D. K. Karve

1958 (1 Mar). *50th Anniv of Steel Industry. W* **69**. *P* 14½ × 14.
395	**371**	15 n.p. orange-red			10	10

1958 (18 Apr). *Birth Centenary of Karve (educationalist). W* **69** (*sideways*)*. P* 14.
396	**372**	15 n.p. orange-brown		10	10

373 Westland Wapiti Biplane and Hawker Hunter   **374** Asokan Capital

1958 (30 Apr). *Silver Jubilee of Indian Air Force. W* **69**. *P* 14½ × 14.
397	**373**	15 n.p. blue			1·00	10
398		90 n.p. ultramarine			1·25	1·25

ASOKAN CAPITAL WATERMARK. When the watermark was originally introduced in 1958 the base of each individual capital was 10 mm wide. During 1985 a modified version, with the capital base measurement reduced to 8 mm, was introduced. Examples have been seen on Nos. 921a, 922a, 923a and 928a.

1958–63. *As Nos.* 366, 369/71 *and* 375/85a *but W* **374**.
399	**361**	1 n.p. blue-green (1960)			90	10
		a. Imperf (pair)			£170	
400		2 n.p. light brown (27.10.58)		10	10
401		3 n.p. deep brown (1958)			10	10
402		5 n.p. bright green (27.10.58)		10	10
403		6 n.p. grey (1963)			15	3·25
404		8 n.p. light blue-green (1958)		90	10
405		10 n.p. deep dull green (27.10.58)		15	10
		a. Imperf (pair)			†	—
406		13 n.p. bright carmine-red (1963)		1·00	3·50
407		15 n.p. violet (10.60)			60	10
408		20 n.p. blue (27.10.58)			30	10
409		25 n.p. ultramarine (27.10.58)		30	10
410		50 n.p. orange (1959)			30	10
411		75 n.p. reddish purple (1959)		40	10
412		90 n.p. bright purple (1960)		5·50	10
413	—	1 r. deep dull green (1959)		3·75	10
414	—	2 r. cerise (1959)			5·50	
415	—	5 r. brown (1959)			9·00	10
416	—	10 r. orange (1959)			20·00	4·25
399/416				*Set of 18*	42·00	10·50

The 5, 10, 15, 20, 25 and 50 n.p. with serial numbers on the back are from coils of 810 stamps prepared from sheets for experimenting with vending machines. In the event the machines were not purchased and the stamps were sold over the counter.

375 Bipin Chandra Pal   **376** Nurse with Child Patient

1958 (7 Nov). *Birth Centenary of Pal (patriot). W* **374**. *P* 14 × 13½.
418	**375**	15 n.p. deep dull green		10	10

1958 (14 Nov). *Children's Day. W* **374**. *P* 14 × 13½.
419	**376**	15 n.p. violet			10	10

377 Jagadish Chandra Bose   **378** Exhibition Gate

1958 (30 Nov). *Birth Centenary of Bose (botanist). W* **374**. *P* 14 × 13½.
420	**377**	15 n.p. deep turquoise-green		20	10

1958 (30 Dec). *India 1958 Exhibition, New Delhi. W* **374** (*sideways*)*. P* 14½ × 14.
421	**378**	15 n.p. reddish purple		10	10

379 Sir Jamsetjee Jejeebhoy   **380** "The Triumph of Labour" (after Chowdhury)

1959 (15 Apr). *Death Centenary of Jejeebhoy (philanthropist). W* **374**. *P* 14 × 13½.
422	**379**	15 n.p. brown			10	10

1959 (15 June). *40th Anniv of International Labour Organization. W* **374** (*sideways*)*. P* 14½ × 14.
423	**380**	15 n.p. dull green			10	10

381 Boys awaiting admission to Children's Home   **382** "Agriculture"

1959 (14 Nov). *Children's Day. W* **374**. *P* 14 × 14½.
424	**381**	15 n.p. deep dull green			10	10
		a. Imperf (pair)			£700	

1959 (30 Dec). *First World Agricultural Fair, New Delhi. W* **374**. *P* 13½ × 13.
425	**382**	15 n.p. grey			20	10

383 Thiruvalluvar (philosopher)

1960 (15 Feb). *Thiruvalluvar Commemoration. W* **374**. *P* 14 × 13½.
426	**383**	15 n.p. reddish purple		10	10

384 Yaksha pleading with the Cloud (from the "Meghaduta")   **385** Shakuntala writing a letter to Dushyanta (from the "Shakuntala")

1960 (22 June). *Kalidasa (poet) Commemoration. W* **374**. *P* 13.
427	**384**	15 n.p. grey			30	10
428	**385**	1 r. 3 n.p. pale yellow and brown		1·40	1·00

NEW INFORMATION

The editor is always interested to correspond with people who have new information that will improve or correct the Catalogue.

386 S. Bharati (poet)   **387** Dr. M. Visvesvaraya

1960 (11 Sept). *Subramania Bharati Commemoration. W* **374**. *P* 14 × 13½.
429	**386**	15 n.p. blue			10	10

1960 (15 Sept). *Birth Centenary of Dr. M. Visvesvaraya (engineer). W* **374**. *P* 13 × 13½.
430	**387**	15 n.p. brown and bright carmine		10	10

388 "Children's Health"

1960 (14 Nov). *Children's Day. W* **374**. *P* 13½ × 13.
431	**388**	15 n.p. deep dull green		10	10

389 Children greeting U.N. Emblem   **390** Tyagaraja

1960 (11 Dec). *U.N.I.C.E.F. Day. W* **374**. *P* 13½ × 13.
432	**389**	15 n.p. orange-brown and olive-brown		10	10

1961 (6 Jan). *114th Death Anniv of Tyagaraja (musician). W* **374**. *P* 14 × 13½.
433	**390**	15 n.p. greenish blue			10	10

391 "First Aerial Post" cancellation

392 Air India Boeing 707 Airliner and Humber Sommer Biplane

1961 (18 Feb). *50th Anniv of First Official Airmail Flight, Allahabad-Naini. T* **391/2** *and similar design. W* **374**. *P* 14 (5 *n.p.*) *or* 13 × 13½ (*others*).
434		5 n.p. olive-drab			1·10	30
435		15 n.p. deep green and grey		1·10	30
436		1 r. purple and grey			3·75	1·90
434/6				*Set of 3*	5·50	2·25

Design: *Horiz as T* **392**—1 r. H. Pecquet flying Humber Sommer plane and "Aerial Post" cancellation.

394 Shivaji on horseback   **395** Motilal Nehru (politician)

1961 (17 Apr). *Chatrapati Shivaji (Maratha ruler) Commemoration. W* **374**. *P* 13 × 13½.
437	**394**	15 n.p. brown and green		70	30

1961 (6 May). *Birth Centenary of Pandit Motilal Nehru. W* **374**. *P* 14.
438 **395** 15 n.p. olive-brown and brown-orange .. 20 10

396 Tagore (poet)

397 All India Radio Emblem and Transmitting Aerials

1961 (7 May). *Birth Centenary of Rabindranath Tagore. W* **374**. *P* 13 × 13½.
439 **396** 15 n.p. yellow-orange and blue-green .. 70 30

1961 (8 June). *Silver Jubilee of All India Radio. W* **374**. *P* 13½ × 13.
440 **397** 15 n.p. ultramarine 10 10

398 Prafulla Chandra Ray

399 V. N. Bhatkande

1961 (2 Aug). *Birth Centenary of Ray (social reformer). W* **374**. *P* 14×13½.
441 **398** 15 n.p. grey 10 20

1961 (1 Sept). *Birth Centenary of Bhatkande (composer)* (1960). *W* **374**. *P* 13×13½.
442 **399** 15 n.p. olive-brown 10 10

400 Child at Lathe

401 Fair Emblem and Main Gate

1961 (14 Nov). *Children's Day. W* **374**. *P* 14 × 13½.
443 **400** 15 n.p. brown 10 20

1961 (14 Nov). *Indian Industries Fair, New Delhi. W* **374**. *P* 14 × 14½.
444 **401** 15 n.p. blue and carmine 10 10

402 Indian Forest

1961 (21 Nov). *Centenary of Scientific Forestry. W* **374**. *P* 13 × 13½.
445 **402** 15 n.p. green and brown.. .. .. 30 20

403 Pitalkhora: Yaksha

404 Kalibangan Seal

1961 (14 Dec). *Centenary of Indian Archaeological Survey. W* **374**. *P* 14 × 13½ (15 *n.p.*) *or* 13½ × 14 (90 *n.p.*).
446 **403** 15 n.p. orange-brown 20 10
447 **404** 90 n.p. yellow-olive and light brown .. 40 20

405 M. M. Malaviya

406 Gauhati Refinery

1961 (24 Dec). *Birth Centenary of Malaviya (educationist). W* **374**. *P* 14×13½.
448 **405** 15 n.p. deep slate 10 20

1962 (1 Jan). *Inauguration of Gauhati Oil Refinery. W* **374**. *P* 13×13½.
449 **406** 15 n.p. blue 30 20

407 Bhikaiji Cama

408 Village Panchayati and Parliament Building

1962 (26 Jan). *Birth Centenary of Bhikaiji Cama (patriot). W* **374**. *P* 14.
450 **407** 15 n.p. reddish purple 10 10

1962 (26 Jan). *Inauguration of Panchayati System of Local Government. W* **374**. *P* 13×13½.
451 **408** 15 n.p. bright purple 10 10

409 D. Saraswati (religious reformer)

410 G. S. Vidhyarthi (journalist)

1962 (4 Mar). *Dayanard Saraswati Commemoration. W* **374**. *P* 14.
452 **409** 15 n.p. orange-brown 10 10

1962 (25 Mar). *Ganesh Shankar Vidhyarthi Commemoration. W* **374**. *P* 14×13½.
453 **410** 15 n.p. red-brown 10 10

411 Malaria Eradication Emblem

412 Dr. R. Prasad

1962 (7 Apr). *Malaria Eradication. W* **374**. *P* 13 × 13½.
454 **411** 15 n.p. yellow and claret 10 10

1962 (13 May). *Retirement of President Dr. Rajendra Prasad. W* **374**. *P* 13.
455 **412** 15 n.p. bright purple (*shades*) 30 20

413 Calcutta High Court

416 Ramabai Ranade

1962. *Centenary of Indian High Courts. T* **413** *and similar horiz designs. W* **374**. *P* 14.
456 15 n.p. dull green (1 July) 50 20
457 15 n.p. red-brown (6 August) 50 20
458 15 n.p. slate (14 August) 50 20
456/8 .. .. *Set of* 3 1·40 55
Designs:—No. 457, Madras High Court; No. 458, Bombay High Court.

1962 (15 Aug). *Birth Centenary of Ramabai Ranade (social reformer). W* **374**. *P* 14 × 13½
459 **416** 15 n.p. orange-brown 10 20

417 Indian Rhinoceros

418 "Passing the Flag to Youth"

1962 (1 Oct). *Wild Life Week. W* **374**. *P* 13½ × 14.
460 **417** 15 n.p. red-brown and deep turquoise .. 40 15

INSCRIPTIONS. From No. 461 onwards all designs are inscribed "BHARAT" in Devanagari in addition to "INDIA" in English.

1962 (14 Nov). *Children's Day. W* **374**. *P* 13½ × 13.
461 **418** 15 n.p. orange-red and turquoise-green 15 20

419 Human Eye within Lotus Blossom

420 S. Ramanujan

1962 (3 Dec). *19th International Ophthalmology Congress, New Delhi. W* **374**. *P* 13½ × 13.
462 **419** 15 n.p. deep olive-brown 20 10

1962 (22 Dec). *75th Birth Anniv of Srinivasa Ramanujan (mathematician). W* **374**. *P* 13½×14.
463 **420** 15 n.p. deep olive-brown 60 40

421 S. Vivekananda

Re.1

═

(**422**)

1963 (17 Jan). *Birth Centenary of Vivekananda (philosopher). W* **374**. *P* 14 × 14½.
464 **421** 15 n.p. orange-brown and yellow-olive .. 15 20

1963 (2 Feb). *No.* 428 *surch with T* **422**.
465 **385** 1 r. on 1 r. 3 n.p. pale yellow & brn .. 30 10

423 Hands reaching for F.A.O. Emblem

424 Henri Dunant (founder) and Centenary Emblem

1963 (21 Mar). *Freedom from Hunger. W* **374**. *P* 13.
466 **423** 15 n.p. grey-blue .. .. .. 1·00 30

1963 (8 May). *Red Cross Centenary.* W **374**. *P* 13.
467 **424** 15 n.p. red and grey .. .. .. 2·50 30
       a. Red (cross) omitted £2500

425 Artillery and Helicopter

1963 (15 Aug). *Defence Campaign.* T **425** *and similar horiz design.* W **374**. *P* 14.
468 **15** n.p. grey-green 40 10
469   1 r. red-brown 70 65
Design:—1 r. Sentry and parachutists.

427 D. Naoroji   **428** Annie Besant
(parliamentarian)   (patriot and
                      theosophist)

1963 (4 Sept). *Dadabhai Naoroji Commemoration.* W **374**. *P* 13.
470 **427** 15 n.p. grey 10 10

1963 (1 Oct). *Annie Besant Commemoration.* W **374**. *P* 13½×14.
471 **428** 15 n.p. turquoise-green 15 10
No 471 is incorrectly dated "1837". Mrs. Besant was born in 1847.

429 Gaur   **430** Lesser Panda

1963 (7 Oct). *Wild Life Preservation.* T **429**/30 *and similar designs.* W **374**. *P* 13½ × 14 (10 n.p.) *or* 13 (*others*).
472 10 n.p. black and yellow-orange .. .. 75 1·50
473 15 n.p. orange-brown and green .. 1·50 60
474 30 n.p. slate and yellow-ochre .. .. 3·75 1·50
475 50 n.p. orange and deep grey-green .. 3·50 80
476   1 r. light brown and blue .. .. 2·50 50
472/6 .. .. *Set of* 5 11·00 4·50
Designs: *Vert*—30 n.p. Indian elephant. *Horiz* (*as* T **430**)—50 n.p. Tiger; 1 r. Lion.

434 "School Meals"   **435** Eleanor Roosevelt at
                             Spinning-wheel

1963 (14 Nov). *Children's Day.* W **374**. *P* 14 × 13½.
477 **434** 15 n.p. bistre-brown 10 10

1963 (10 Dec). *15th Anniv of Declaration of Human Rights.* W **374**. *P* 13½ × 13.
478 **435** 15 n.p. reddish purple 10 15

436 Dipalakshmi   **437** Gopabandhu Das
(bronze)   (social reformer)

1964 (4 Jan). *26th International Orientalists Congress, New Delhi.* W **374**. *P* 13 × 13½.
479 **436** 15 n.p. deep ultramarine 20 15

1964 (4 Jan). *Gopabandhu Das Commemoration.* W **374**. *P* 13 × 13½.
480 **437** 15 n.p. deep dull purple 10 10

438 Purandaradasa

1964 (14 Jan). *400th Death Anniv of Purandaradasa* (*composer*). W **374**. *P* 13×13½.
481 **438** 15 n.p. light brown 15 10

439 S. C. Bose and I. N. A.   **440** Bose and Indian National
      Badge   Army

1964 (23 Jan). *67th Birth Anniv of Subhas Chandra Bose* (*nationalist*). W **374**. *P* 13.
482 **439** 15 n.p. yellow-bistre 40 20
483 **440** 55 n.p. black, orange and orange-red .. 40 45

441 Sarojini Naidu   **442** Kasturba Gandhi

1964 (13 Feb). *85th Birth Anniv of Sarojini Naidu* (*poetess*). W **374**. *P* 14.
484 **441** 15 n.p. deep grey-green and purple .. 10 10

1964 (22 Feb). *20th Death Anniv of Kasturba Gandhi.* W **374**. *P* 14 × 13½.
485 **442** 15 n.p. orange-brown 10 10

443 Dr. W. M. Haffkine   **444** Jawaharlal Nehru
(immunologist)   (statesman)

1964 (16 Mar). *Haffkine Commemoration.* W **374**. *P* 13.
486 **443** 15 n.p. deep purple-brown/*buff* .. 10 10

(Value expressed as paisa instead of naye paise.)

1964 (12 June). *Nehru Mourning Issue. No wmk. P* 13½ × 13.
487 **444** 15 p. deep slate 10 10

445 Sir Asutosh Mookerjee   **446** Sri Aurobindo

1964 (29 June). *Birth Centenary of Sir Asutosh Mookerjee* (*education reformer*). W **374**. *P* 13½ × 13.
488 **445** 15 p. bistre-brown and yellow-olive .. 10 10

1964 (15 Aug). *92nd Birth Anniv of Sri Aurobindo* (*religious teacher*). W **374**. *P* 13×13½.
489 **446** 15 p. dull purple 15 10

447 Raja R. Roy (social reformer)   **448** I.S.O. Emblem
                                       and Globe

1964 (27 Sept). *Raja Rammohun Roy Commemoration.* W **374**. *P* 13 × 13½.
490 **447** 15 n.p. brown 10 10

1964 (9 Nov). *Sixth International Organization for Standardization General Assembly, Bombay. No wmk. P* 13 × 13½.
491 **448** 15 p. carmine 15 20

449 Jawaharlal   **450** St. Thomas (after
Nehru (from 1 r.   statue, Ortona
commemorative   Cathedral, Italy)
coin)

1964 (14 Nov). *Children's Day. No wmk. P* 14 × 13½.
492 **449** 15 p. slate 10 10

1964 (2 Dec). *St. Thomas Commemoration. No wmk. P* 14 × 13½.
493 **450** 15 p. reddish purple 10 30
No. 493 was issued on the occasion of Pope Paul's visit to India.

451 Globe   **452** J. Tata (industrialist)

1964 (14 Dec). *22nd International Geological Congress.* W **374**. *P* 14 × 13½.
494 **451** 15 p. blue-green 30 30

1965 (7 Jan). *Jamsetji Tata Commemoration. No wmk. P* 13½ × 13.
495 **452** 15 p. dull-purple and orange .. 30 20

453 Lala Lajpat Rai   **454** Globe and Congress
                                 Emblem

1965 (28 Jan). *Birth Centenary of Lala Lajpat Rai* (*social reformer*). *No wmk. P* 13×13½.
496 **453** 15 p. light brown 20 10

1965 (8 Feb). *20th International Chamber of Commerce Congress, New Delhi. No wmk. P* 13½ × 13.
497 **454** 15 p. grey-green and carmine 15 15

---

455 Freighter *Jalausha* and Visakhapatnam

456 Abraham Lincoln

1965 (5 Apr). *National Maritime Day.* W 374 (*sideways*).
P 14½ × 14.
498 455 15 p. blue ..   30   30

1965 (15 Apr). *Death Centenary of Abraham Lincoln.* W 374. P 13.
499 456 15 p. brown and yellow-ochre   15   10

457 I.T.U. Emblem and Symbols

458 "Everlasting Flame"

1965 (17 May). *I.T.U. Centenary.* W 374 (*sideways*). P 14½ × 14.
500 457 15 p. reddish purple   90   30

1965 (27 May). *First Anniv of Nehru's Death.* W 374. P 13.
501 458 15 p. carmine and blue ..   15   10

459 I.C.Y. Emblem

460 Climbers on Summit

1965 (26 June). *International Co-operation Year.* P 13½ × 13.
502 459 15 p. deep olive and yellow-brown ..   90   60

1965 (15 Aug). *Indian Mount Everest Expedition.* P 13.
503 460 15 p. deep reddish purple ..   20   10

461 Bidri Vase
462 Brass Lamp
466 Electric Locomotive

474 Woman writing a Letter (medieval sculpture)

475 Dal Lake, Kashmir

1965–75. T 461/2, 466, 474/5 *and similar designs.*

(a) W 374 (*sideways on* 2, 3, 5, 6, 8, 30, 50, 60 p., 2, 5, 10 r.).
P 14 × 14½ (4, 10, 15, 20, 40, 70 p., 1 r.) *or* 14½ × 14 (*others*).
504   2 p. red-brown (16.10.67)   ..   10   50
505   3 p. brown-olive (16.10.67)   ..   10   2·25
505a 4 p. lake-brown (15.5.68)   ..   10   2·25
506   5 p. cerise (16.10.67)   ..   10   10
     a. Imperf (pair) £180
507   6 p. grey-black (1.7.66)   ..   10   2·50
508   8 p. red-brown (15.3.67)   ..   30   3·75
509 10 p. new blue (1.7.66)   ..   40   10
510 15 p. bronze-green (15.8.65)   ..   1·75
511 20 p. purple (16.10.67)   ..   5·00
512 30 p. sepia (15.3.67)   ..   15   10
513 40 p. maroon (2.10.68)   ..   15   10
514 50 p. blue-green (15.3.67) ..   20   10
515 60 p. deep grey (16.10.67)   ..   35   10
516 70 p. chalky blue (15.3.67)   ..   60   10

---

517   1 r. red-brown and plum (1.7.66)   60   10
518   2 r. new blue & deep slate-violet (15.3.67)   2·00   10
519   5 r. deep slate-violet and brown (15.3.67)   2·50   75
520 10 r. black and bronze-green (14.11.65)   14·00   80
504/20   *Set of 18* 25·00 11·00

     (b) *No wmk.* P 14½ × 14
520a 5 p. cerise (12.5.74)   ..   30   10

  (c) *Wmk Large Star and "INDIA GOVT"† in sheet.* P 14½ × 14
521   2 p. red-brown (1.3.75)   ..   50   1·50
     aw. Wmk reversed   ..   4·00
521b 5 p. cerise (1.3.75)   ..   85   10

Designs: *Horiz* (*as T 466*)—4 p. Coffee berries; 15 p. Plucking tea; 20 p. Hindustan Aircraft Industries Ajeet jet fighter; 40 p. Calcutta G.P.O.; 70 p. Hampi Chariot (sculpture). (*As T 475*)—5 r. Bhakra Dam, Punjab; 10 r. Atomic reactor, Trombay. *Vert* (*as T 461/2*)—5 p. "Family Planning"; 6 p. Konarak Elephant; 8 p. Spotted Deer ("Chital"); 30 p. Indian dolls; 50 p. Mangoes; 60 p. Somnath Temple.

†The arrangement of this watermark in the sheet results in the words and the star appearing upright, inverted or sideways.

Two different postal forgeries exist of No. 511, both printed in lithography and without watermark. The cruder version is roughly perforated 15, but the more sophisticated is perforated 14 × 14½.

See also Nos. 721/38.

479 G. B. Pant (statesman)

480 V. Patel

1965 (10 Sept). *Govind Ballabh Pant Commemoration.* P 13.
522 479 15 p. brown and deep green   10   20

1965 (31 Oct). *90th Birth Anniv of Vallabhbhai Patel (statesman).* P 14 × 13½.
523 480 15 p. blackish brown   10   10

481 C. Das

482 Vidyapati (poet)

1965 (5 Nov). *95th Birth Anniv of Chittaranjan Das (lawyer and patriot).* P 13.
524 481 15 p. yellow-brown   10   10

1965 (17 Nov). *Vidyapati Commemoration.* P 14 × 14½.
525 482 15 p. yellow-brown   10   10

483 Sikandra, Agra

484 Soldier, Hindustan Aircraft Industries Ajeet jet fighters and Cruiser *Mysore*

1966 (24 Jan). *Pacific Area Travel Association Conference.* New Delhi. P 13½ × 14.
526 483 15 p. slate   10   10

1966 (26 Jan). *Indian Armed Forces.* P 14
527 484 15 p. violet   80   30

485 Lal Bahadur Shastri (statesman)

486 Kambar (poet)

1966 (26 Jan). *Shastri Mourning Issue.* P 13 × 13½.
528 485 15 p. black   40   10

1966 (5 Apr). *Kambar Commemoration.* P 14 × 14½.
529 486 15 p. grey-green   10   10

---

487 B. R. Ambedkar

488 Kunwar Singh (patriot)

1966 (14 Apr). *75th Birth Anniv of Dr. Bhim Rao Ambedkar (lawyer).* P 14 × 13½.
530 487 15 p. purple-brown   10   10

1966 (23 Apr). *Kunwar Singh Commemoration.* P 14 × 13½.
531 488 15 p. chestnut ..   10   10

489 G. K. Gokhale

490 Acharya Dvivedi (poet)

1966 (9 May). *Birth Centenary of Gopal Krishna Gokhale (patriot).* P 13½ × 13.
532 489 15 p. brown-purple and pale yellow ..   10   10

1966 (15 May). *Dvivedi Commemoration.* P 13½ × 14.
533 490 15 p. drab ..   10   10

491 Maharaja Ranjit Singh (warrior)

492 Homi Bhabha (scientist) and Nuclear Reactor

1966 (28 June). *Maharaja Ranjit Singh Commemoration.* P 14 × 13½.
534 491 15 p. purple   30   15

1966 (4 Aug). *Dr. Homi Bhabha Commemoration.* P 14½ × 14.
535 492 15 p. dull purple   15   30

493 A. K. Azad (scholar)

494 Swami Tirtha

1966 (11 Nov). *Abul Kalam Azad Commemoration.* P 13½ × 14.
536 493 15 p. chalky blue ..   15   15

1966 (11 Nov). *60th Death Anniv of Swami Rama Tirtha (social reformer).* P 13 × 13½.
537 494 15 p. turquoise-blue   20   30

495 Infant and Dove Emblem

496 Allahabad High Court

(Des C. Pakrashi)

1966 (14 Nov). *Children's Day.* P 13 × 13½.
538 495 15 p. bright purple   30   20

1966 (25 Nov). *Centenary of Allahabad High Court.* P 14½ × 14.
539 496 15 p. dull purple   30   30

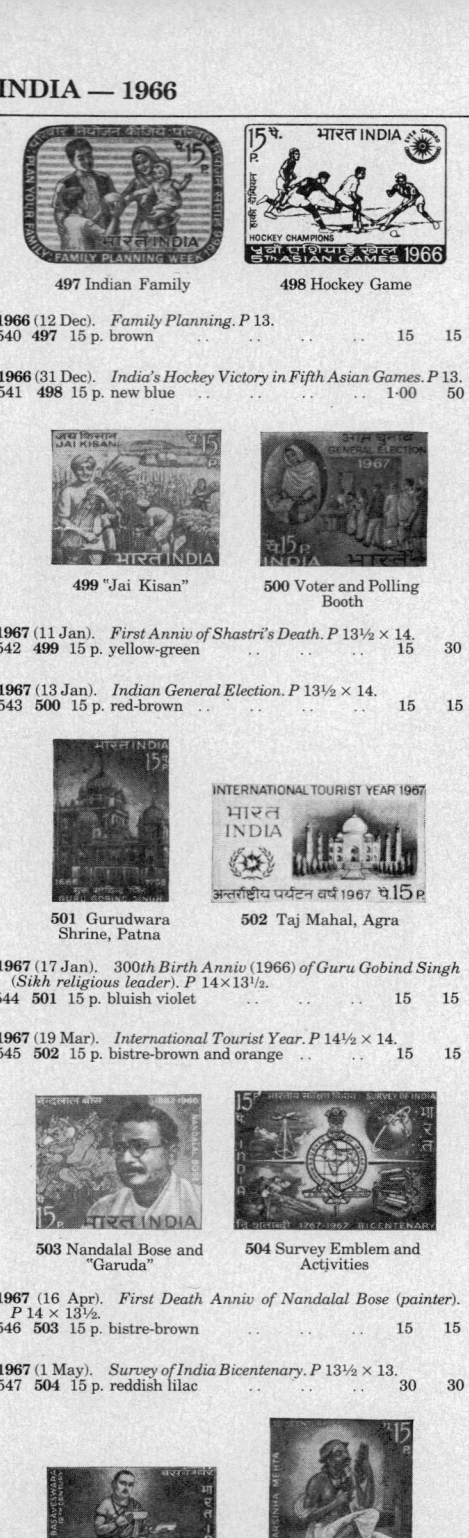

497 Indian Family   498 Hockey Game

1966 (12 Dec). *Family Planning.* P 13.
540 497 15 p. brown   15   15

1966 (31 Dec). *India's Hockey Victory in Fifth Asian Games.* P 13.
541 498 15 p. new blue   ..   ..   1·00   50

499 "Jai Kisan"   500 Voter and Polling Booth

1967 (11 Jan). *First Anniv of Shastri's Death.* P 13½ × 14.
542 499 15 p. yellow-green   15   30

1967 (13 Jan). *Indian General Election.* P 13½ × 14.
543 500 15 p. red-brown   15   15

501 Gurudwara Shrine, Patna   502 Taj Mahal, Agra

1967 (17 Jan). *300th Birth Anniv (1966) of Guru Gobind Singh (Sikh religious leader).* P 14×13½.
544 501 15 p. bluish violet   15   15

1967 (19 Mar). *International Tourist Year.* P 14½ × 14.
545 502 15 p. bistre-brown and orange   ..   15   15

503 Nandalal Bose and "Garuda"   504 Survey Emblem and Activities

1967 (16 Apr). *First Death Anniv of Nandalal Bose (painter).* P 14 × 13½.
546 503 15 p. bistre-brown   15   15

1967 (1 May). *Survey of India Bicentenary.* P 13½ × 13.
547 504 15 p. reddish lilac   30   30

505 Basaveswara   506 Narsinha Mehta (poet)

1967 (11 May). *800th Death Anniv of Basaveswara (reformer and statesman).* P 13½ × 14.
548 505 15 p. orange-red   15   15

1967 (30 May). *Narsinha Mehta Commemoration.* P 14 × 13½.
549 506 15 p. blackish brown   15   15

507 Maharana Pratap   508 Narayana Guru

1967 (11 June). *Maharana Pratap (Rajput leader) Commemoration.* P 14×14½.
550 507 15 p. red-brown   ..   15   15

1967 (21 Aug). *Narayana Guru (philosopher) Commemoration.* P 14.
551 508 15 p. brown   ..   15   20

509 President Radhakrishnan   510 Martyrs' Memorial, Patna

1967 (5 Sept). *75th Birth Anniv of Sarvepalli Radhakrishnan (former President).* P 13.
552 509 15 p. claret   40   15

1967 (1 Oct). *25th Anniv of "Quit India" Movement.* P 14½ × 14.
553 510 15 p. lake   15   15

511 Route Map   512 Wrestling

1967 (9 Nov). *Centenary of Indo-European Telegraph Service.* P 13½ × 14.
554 511 15 p. black and light blue   ..   30   20

1967 (12 Nov). *World Wrestling Championships, New Delhi.* P 13½×14.
555 512 15 p. purple and light orange-brown   30   20

513 Nehru leading Naga Tribesmen   514 Rashbehari Basu (nationalist)

1967 (1 Dec). *4th Anniv of Nagaland as a State of India.* P 13×13½.
556 513 15 p. ultramarine   ..   15   15

1967 (26 Dec). *Rashbehari Basu Commemoration.* P 14.
557 514 15 p. maroon   15   20

515 Bugle, Badge and Scout Salute

1967 (27 Dec). *60th Anniv of Scout Movement in India.* P 14½×14.
558 515 15 p. chestnut   60   30

516 Men embracing Universe   517 Globe and Book of Tamil

1968 (1 Jan). *Human Rights Year.* P 13.
559 516 15 p. bronze-green   ..   30   30

1968 (3 Jan). *International Conference-Seminar of Tamil Studies, Madras.* P 13.
560 517 15 p. reddish lilac   ..   30   15

518 U.N. Emblem and Transport   519 Quill and Bow Symbol

1968 (1 Feb). *United Nations Conference on Trade and Development, New Delhi.* P 14½×14.
561 518 15 p. turquoise-blue   ..   40   15

1968 (20 Feb). *Centenary of Amrita Bazar Patrika (newspaper).* P 13½×14.
562 519 15 p. sepia and orange-yellow   ..   15   15

520 Maxim Gorky   521 Emblem and Medal

1968 (28 Mar). *Birth Centenary of Maxim Gorky.* P 13½.
563 520 15 p. plum   15   20

1968 (31 Mar). *First Triennale Art Exhibition, New Delhi.* P 13.
564 521 15 p. orange, royal blue and light blue   30   20
      a. Orange omitted   ..   £650

522 Letter-box and "100,000"   523 Stalks of Wheat, Agricultural Institute and Production Graph

(Des C. Pakrashi)

1968 (1 July). *Opening of 100,000th Indian Post Office.* P 13.
565 522 20 p. red, blue and black   ..   30   15

1968 (17 July). *Wheat Revolution.* P 13.
566 523 20 p. bluish green and orange-brown   30   15

524 "Self-portrait"   525 Lakshminath Bezbaruah

(Des from self-portrait)

1968 (17 Sept). *30th Death Anniv of Gaganendranath Tagore (painter).* P 13.
567 524 20 p. brown-purple and ochre   ..   30   15

1968 (5 Oct). *Birth Centenary of Lakshminath Bezbaruah (writer).* P 13½ × 14.
568 525 20 p. blackish brown   ..   20   15

526 Athlete's Legs and Olympic Rings

1968 (12 Oct). *Olympic Games, Mexico.* P 14½ × 14.
569 526 20 p. brown and grey   ..   15   15
570   1 r. sepia and brown-olive   ..   40   15

527 Bhagat Singh and Followers

528 Azad Hind Flag, Swords and Chandra Bose (founder)

1968 (19 Oct). *61st Birth Anniv of Bhagat Singh (patriot).* P 13.
571 527 20 p. yellow-brown .. 20 20

1968 (21 Oct). *25th Anniv of Azad Hind Government.* P 14 × 14½.
572 528 20 p. deep blue 20 15

529 Sister Nivedita

530 Marie Curie and Radium Treatment

1968 (27 Oct). *Birth Centenary of Sister Nivedita (social reformer).* P 14×14½.
573 529 20p. deep bluish green 30 30

1968 (6 Nov). *Birth Centenary of Marie Curie.* P 14½ × 14.
574 530 20 p. slate-lilac .. .. 1·40 50

531 Map of the World

532 Cochin Synagogue

1968 (1 Dec). *21st International Geographical Congress, New Delhi.* P 13.
575 531 20 p. new blue .. 15 15

1968 (15 Dec). *400th Anniv of Cochin Synagogue.* P 13.
576 532 20 p. blue and carmine 55 40

533 I.N.S. *Nilgiri* (frigate)

534 Red-billed Blue Magpie

1968 (15 Dec). *Navy Day.* P 13.
577 533 20 p. grey-blue .. .. .. 1·50 40

1968 (31 Dec). *Birds.* T **534** *and similar designs.* P 14 × 14½ (1 r.) or 14½ × 14 (others).
578 20 p. multicoloured .. 55 40
579 50 p. scarlet, black and turquoise-green .. 1·10 1·50
580 1 r. deep blue, yellow-brown and pale blue .. 1·75 1·00
581 2 r. multicoloured .. .. 1·75 1·50
578/81 .. .. *Set of 4* 4·50 4·00
Designs: Horiz—50 p. Brown-fronted Pied Woodpecker; 2 r. Yellow-backed Sunbird. Vert—1 r. Slaty-headed Scimitar Babbler.

538 Bankim Chandra Chatterjee

539 Dr. Bhagavan Das

1969 (1 Jan). *130th Birth Anniv of Bankim Chandra Chatterjee (writer).* P 13½.
582 538 20 p. ultramarine .. 15 20

1969 (12 Jan). *Birth Centenary of Dr. Bhagavan Das (philosopher).* P 13½.
583 539 20 p. pale chocolate .. 15 15

540 Dr. Martin Luther King

541 Mirza Ghalib and Letter Seal

1969 (25 Jan). *Martin Luther King Commemoration.* P 13½.
584 540 20 p. deep olive-brown .. 40 20

1969 (17 Feb). *Death Centenary of Mirza Ghalib (poet).* P 14½ × 14.
585 541 20 p. sepia, brown-red and flesh .. 15 15

542 Osmania University

1969 (15 Mar). *50th Anniv of Osmania University.* P 14½ × 14.
586 542 20 p. olive-green .. 15 20

543 Rafi Ahmed Kidwai and Lockheed Constellation Mail Plane

1969 (1 Apr). *20th Anniv of "ALL-UP" Air Mail Scheme.* P 13.
587 543 20 p. deep blue .. 60 30

544 I.L.O. Badge and Emblem

545 Memorial, and Hands dropping Flowers

1969 (11 Apr). *50th Anniv of International Labour Organisation.* P 14½ × 14.
588 544 20 p. chestnut .. 15 20

1969 (13 Apr). *50th Anniv of Jallianwala Bagh Massacre, Amritsar.* P 14×13½.
589 545 20 p. rose-carmine .. 15 20

546 K. Nageswara Rao Pantulu (journalist)

547 Ardaseer Cursetjee Wadia, and Ships

1969 (1 May). *Kasinadhuni Nageswara Rao Pantulu Commemoration.* P 13½ × 14.
590 546 20 p. brown .. 15 20

1969 (27 May). *Ardaseer Cursetjee Wadia (ship-builder) Commemoration.* P 14½×14.
591 547 20 p. turquoise-green .. 40 30

ALTERED CATALOGUE NUMBERS

Any Catalogue numbers altered from the last edition are shown as a list in the introductory pages.

548 Serampore College

549 Dr. Zakir Husain

1969 (7 June). *150th Anniv of Serampore College.* P 13½.
592 548 20 p. plum .. 15 20

1969 (11 June). *President Dr. Zakir Husain Commemoration.* P 13.
593 549 20 p. sepia .. 15 20

550 Laxmanrao Kirloskar

1969 (20 June). *Birth Centenary of Laxmanrao Kirloskar (agriculturalist).* P 13.
594 550 20 p. grey-black .. 15 15

551 Gandhi and his Wife

552 Gandhi's Head and Shoulders

553 Gandhi walking (woodcut)

554 Gandhi with Charkha

(Des Suraj Sadan (20 p.), P. Chitnis (75 p.), Indian Security Press (1 r.) and C. Pakrashi (5 r.))

1969 (2 Oct). *Birth Centenary of Mahatma Gandhi.* P 13½ × 14 (20 p.), 14 × 14½ (1 r.) or 13 (others).
595 551 20 p. blackish brown 60 30
596 552 75 p. cinnamon and drab.. .. 1·25 90
597 553 1 r. blue .. 1·25 65
598 554 5 r. greyish brown and red-orange .. 4·50 6·50
595/8 .. .. *Set of 4* 7·00 7·50

555 *Ajanta* (bulk carrier) and I.M.C.O. Emblem

1969 (14 Oct). *10th Anniv of Inter-Governmental Maritime Consultative Organization.* P 13.
599 555 20 p. violet-blue .. .. 1·50 40

556 Outline of Parliament Building and Globe

557 Astronaut walking beside Space Module on Moon

1969 (30 Oct). *57th Inter-Parliamentary Conference, New Delhi.*
P 14½ × 14.
600 556 20 p. new blue 15 20

1969 (19 Nov). *First Man on the Moon.* P 14 × 14½.
601 557 20 p. olive-brown 40 30

558 Gurudwara Nankana Sahib (birthplace)

559 Tiger's Head and Hands holding Globe

1969 (23 Nov). *500th Birth Anniv of Guru Nanak Dev (Sikh religious leader).* P 13½.
602 558 20 p. slate-violet 15 20

1969 (24 Nov). *International Union for the Conservation of Nature and Natural Resources Conference, New Delhi.* P 14½ × 14.
603 559 20 p. orange-brown and bronze-green 30 30

560 Sadhu Vaswani

561 Thakkar Bapa

1969 (25 Nov). *90th Birth Anniv of Sadhu Vaswani (educationist).*
P 14 × 14½.
604 560 20 p. grey 15 15

1969 (29 Nov). *Birth Centenary of Thakkar Bapa (humanitarian).*
P 13½.
605 561 20 p. chocolate 15 20

562 Satellite, Television, Telephone and Globe

563 C. N. Annadurai

1970 (21 Jan). *12th Plenary Assembly of International Radio Consultative Committee.* P 13.
606 562 20 p. Prussian blue 40 20

1970 (3 Feb). *First Death Anniv of Conjeevaram Natrajan Annadurai (statesman).* P 13.
607 563 20 p. reddish purple and royal blue 15 15

564 M. N. Kishore and Printing Press

565 Nalanda College

1970 (19 Feb). *75th Death Anniv of Munshi Newal Kishore (publisher).* P 13.
608 564 20 p. lake 15 20

1970 (27 Mar). *Centenary of Nalanda College.* P 14½ × 14.
609 565 20 p. brown 60 40

566 Swami Shraddhanand (social reformer)

567 Lenin

1970 (30 Mar). *Swami Shraddhanand Commemoration.*
P 14 × 13½.
610 566 20 p. yellow-brown 60 40

1970 (22 Apr). *Birth Centenary of Lenin.* P 13.
611 567 20 p. orange-brown and sepia .. 30 20

568 New U.P.U. H.Q. Building

569 Sher Shah Suri (15th-century ruler)

1970 (20 May). *New U.P.U. Headquarters Building, Berne.*
P 13.
612 568 20 p. emerald, grey and black .. 15 20

1970 (22 May). *Sher Shah Suri Commemoration.* P 13.
613 569 20 p. deep bluish green 15 20

570 V. D. Savarkar (patriot) and Cellular Jail, Andaman Islands

571 "UN" and Globe

1970 (28 May). *Vinayak Damodar Savarkar Commemoration.*
P 13.
614 570 20 p. orange-brown 15 20

1970 (26 June). *25th Anniv of United Nations.* P 13.
615 571 20 p. light new blue 30 20

572 Symbol and Workers

1970 (18 Aug). *Asian Productivity Year.* P 14½ × 14.
616 572 20 p. violet 20 20

573 Dr. Montessori and I.E.Y. Emblem

1970 (31 Aug). *Birth Centenary of Dr. Maria Montessori (educationist).* P 13.
617 573 20 p. dull purple 30 30

574 J. N. Mukherjee (revolutionary) and Horse

575 V. S. Srinivasa Sastri

1970 (9 Sept). *Jatindra Nath Mukherjee Commemoration.*
P 14½ × 14.
618 574 20 p. chocolate 75 30

1970 (22 Sept). *Srinivasa Sastri (educationist) Commemoration.* P 13 × 13½.
619 575 20 p. yellow and brown-purple .. 30 30

NEW INFORMATION

The editor is always interested to correspond with people who have new information that will improve or correct the Catalogue.

576 I. C. Vidyasagar

577 Maharishi Valmiki

1970 (26 Sept). *150th Birth Anniv of Iswar Chandra Vidyasagar (educationist).* P 13.
620 576 20 p. brown and purple 30 30

1970 (14 Oct). *Maharishi Valmiki (ancient author) Commemoration.* P 13.
621 577 20 p. purple 30 30

578 Calcutta Port

1970 (17 Oct). *Centenary of Calcutta Port Trust.* P 13½ × 13.
622 578 20 p. greenish blue .. .. 1·00 50

579 University Building

1970 (29 Oct). *50th Anniv of Jamia Millia Islamia University.*
P 14½ × 14.
623 579 20 p. yellow-green 40 40

580 Jamnalal Bajaj

581 Nurse and Patient

1970 (4 Nov). *Jamnalal Bajaj (industrialist) Commemoration.*
W 374. P 13½ × 13.
624 580 20 p. olive-grey 15 30

1970 (5 Nov). *50th Anniv of Indian Red Cross.* W 374 (sideways).
P 13 × 13½.
625 581 20 p. red and greenish blue .. 60 30

582 Sant Namdeo

583 Beethoven

1970 (9 Nov). *700th Birth Anniv of Sant Namdeo (mystic).*
W 374. P 13.
626 582 20 p. orange 15 30

1970 (16 Dec). *Birth Bicentenary of Beethoven.* P 13.
627 583 20 p. orange and greyish black .. 1·50 60

584 Children examining Stamps

585 Girl Guide

1970 (23 Dec). *Indian National Philatelic Exhibition, New Dehli. T 584 and similar horiz design.* P 13.
628 584 20 p. orange and myrtle-green .. 30 10
629 1 r. orange-brown and pale yellow-brown .. 2·25 80
Design:— 1 r. Gandhi commemorative through magnifier.

1970 (27 Dec). *Diamond Jubilee of Girl Guide Movement in India.* P 13.
630 585 20 p. maroon 60 30

586 Hands and Lamp (Emblem)   587 Vidyapith Building

1971 (11 Jan). *Centenary of Indian Life Insurance.* P 13.
631 586 20 p. sepia and crimson 20 30

1971 (10 Feb). *50th Anniv of Kashi Vidyapith University.* P 14½×14.
632 587 20 p. blackish brown 20 30

588 Sant Ravidas   589 C. F. Andrews

1971 (10 Feb). *Sant Ravidas (15th-cent mystic) Commemoration.* P 13.
633 588 20 p. lake 30 30

1971 (12 Feb). *Birth Centenary of Charles Freer Andrews (missionary).* P 13×13½.
634 589 20 p. chestnut 35 30

590 Acharya Narendra Deo (scholar)   591 Crowd and "100"

1971 (19 Feb). *15th Death Anniv of Acharya Narendra Deo.* P 13.
635 590 20 p. dull green 15 30

1971 (10 Mar). *Centenary of Decennial Census.* P 13.
636 591 20 p. brown and blue 30 30

592 Sri Ramana Maharishi (mystic)   593 Raja Ravi Varma and "Damayanti and the Swan"

1971 (14 Apr). *21st Death Anniv of Ramana Maharishi.* P 13½.
637 592 20 p. orange and sepia 20 30

1971 (29 Apr). *65th Death Anniv of Ravi Varma (artist).* P 13.
638 593 20 p. green 40 40

594 Dadasaheb Phalke and Camera   595 "Abhisarika" (Tagore)

1971 (30 Apr). *Birth Centenary of Dadasaheb Phalke (cinematographer).* P 13½×13.
639 594 20 p. deep maroon 70 40

1971 (7 Aug). *Birth Centenary of Abanindranath Tagore (painter).* P 14×14½.
640 595 20 p. grey, buff-yellow & blackish brown 30 30

596 Swami Virjanand (Vedic scholar)   597 Cyrus the Great and Procession

1971 (14 Sept). *Swami Virjanand Commemoration.* P 13½.
641 596 20 p. chestnut 30 40

1971 (12 Oct). *2500th Anniv of Charter of Cyrus the Great.* P 13.
642 597 20 p. blackish brown 75 55

598 Globe and Money Box

1971 (31 Oct). *World Thrift Day.* P 14½ × 14.
643 598 20 p. blue-grey 20 30

599 Ajanta Caves Painting   600 "Women at Work" (Geeta Gupta)

1971 (4 Nov). *25th Anniv of U.N.E.S.C.O.* P 13.
644 599 20 p. red-brown .. .. 1·25 50

(Des from painting by Geeta Gupta)

1971 (14 Nov). *Children's Day.* P 14 × 14½.
645 600 20 p. scarlet 20 40

शरणार्थी REFUGEE RELIEF Refugee Relief शरणार्थी सहायता REFUGEE RELIEF
सहायता
(601) (602) (603)

REFUGEE RELIEF REFUGEE RELIEF Refugee Relief
(604) (605) (606)

Refugee relief शरणार्थी सहायता Refugee Relief
(606a) (606b) 607 Refugees

 ...etc

1971. *Obligatory Tax. Refugee Relief.*

(a) *Provisional issues. No. 506 variously optd*

(i) *For all India, optd at Nasik*
646 601 5 p. cerise (15 Nov) .. 60 10
  a. Opt double .. 2·50

(ii) *For various areas*
647 602 5 p. Bangalore .. .. 2·50 1·00
  a. Opt double, one inverted ..
648 603 5 p. Jaipur .. .. 6·00 1·50
649 604 5 p. Rajasthan .. .. 3·25 1·50
  a. Error. "RELIEF REFUGEE" .. 12·00
  b. Opt inverted ..
650 605 5 p. New Delhi .. .. 14·00 3·25
  a. Opt inverted .. 14·00
650b 606 5 p. Goa .. .. 14·00 3·75
650c 606a 5 p. Jabalpur .. .. 11·00 3·25
650d 606b 5 p. Alwar .. ..

(b) *Definitive issue.* W 374. P 14 × 14½
651 607 5 p. carmine (1 Dec) .. 30 10

From 15 November 1971 until 31 March 1973, the Indian Government levied a 5 p. surcharge on all mail, except postcards and newspapers, for the relief of refugees from the former East Pakistan.

As supplies of the provisional overprint could not be sent to all Indian post offices in time, local postmasters were authorised to make their own overprints. Most of these were applied by rubber stamps and so we do not list them. Those listed have typographed overprints and No. 649 also has a rubber handstamp in native language. Some of the above overprints were also used in areas other than those where they were produced.

608 C. V. Raman (scientist) and Light Graph

1971 (12 Nov). *First Death Anniv of Chandrasekhara Venkata Raman.* P 13.
652 608 20 p. orange and deep brown .. 50 30

609 Visva Bharati Building and Rabindranath Tagore (founder)

1971 (24 Dec). *50th Anniv of Visva Bharati University.* P 14½×14.
653 609 20 p. sepia and yellow-brown .. 20 30

610 Cricketers   611 Map and Satellite

1971 (30 Dec). *Indian Cricket Victories.* P 14½ × 14.
654 610 20 p. green, myrtle-green and sage-green 2·00 65

1972 (26 Feb). *First Anniv of Arvi Satellite Earth Station.* P 13½.
655 611 20 p. plum .. 15 30

612 Elemental Symbols and Plumb-line   613 Signal Box Panel

1972 (29 May). *25th Anniv of Indian Standards Institution.* P 13.
656 612 20 p. turquoise-grey and black .. 15 40

1972 (30 June). *50th Anniv of International Railways Union.* P 13.
657 613 20 p. multicoloured 60 40
  a. Blue omitted .. .. 65·00

614 Hockey-player   615 Symbol of Sri Aurobindo

1972 (10 Aug). *Olympic Games, Munich.* T 614 *and similar horiz design.* P 13.
658 20 p. deep bluish violet .. 1·50 25
659 1 r. 45, light turquoise-green & brown-lake 2·25 2·00
Design:—1 r. 45, Various sports.

1972 (15 Aug). *Birth Centenary of Sri Aurobindo (religious teacher).* P 13½.
660 615 20 p. yellow and new blue .. 20 30

616 Celebrating Independence Day in front of Parliament   617 Inter-Services Crest

1972 (15 Aug). *25th Anniversary of Independence (1st issue).* P 13.
661 **616** 20 p. multicoloured 30 30
See also Nos. 673/4.

1972 (15 Aug). *Defence Services Commemoration.* P 13.
662 **617** 20 p. multicoloured 30 40

618 V. O. Chidambaram Pillai (trade union leader) and Ship   619 Bhai Vir Singh

1972 (5 Sept). *Birth Centenary of V. O. Chidambaram Pillai.* P 13.
663 **618** 20 p. new blue and purple-brown .. 75 40

1972 (16 Oct). *Birth Centenary of Bhai Vir Singh (poet).* P 13.
664 **619** 20 p. plum 30 40

620 T. Prakasam   621 Vemana

1972 (16 Oct). *Birth Centenary of Tanguturi Prakasam (lawyer).* P 13.
665 **620** 20 p. brown 20 40

1972 (16 Oct). *300th Birth Anniv of Vemana (poet).* W 374. P 13½ × 14.
666 **621** 20 p. black 20 40

622 Bertrand Russell   623 Symbol of "Asia 72"

1972 (16 Oct). *Birth Centenary of Bertrand Russell (philosopher).* P 13½ × 14.
667 **622** 1 r. 45, black .. .. 3·25 2·75

1972 (3 Nov). *"Asia '72" (Third Asian International Trade Fair), New Delhi.* T 623 and similar vert design. W 374. P 13.
668 **623** 20 p. black and orange 10 20
669 1 r. 45, orange and slate-black .. .. 60 1·75
Design:—1 r. 45, Hand of Buddha.

624 V. A. Sarabhai and Rocket   625 Flag of U.S.S.R. and Kremlin Tower

1972 (30 Dec). *First Death Anniv of Vikram A. Sarabhai (scientist).* P 13.
670 **624** 20 p. brown and myrtle-green .. 20 40

1972 (30 Dec). *50th Anniv of U.S.S.R.* P 13.
671 **625** 20 p. light yellow and red 20 40

626 Exhibition Symbol   627 "Democracy"

1973 (8 Jan). *"Indipex '73" Stamp Exhibition (1st issue).* P 13.
672 **626** 1 r. 45, light mauve, gold and black .. 45 1·25
See also Nos. 701/MS704.

1973 (26 Jan). *25th Anniv of Independence (2nd issue).* T 627 and similar multicoloured design. P 13 (20 p.) or 14½ × 14 (1 r. 45).
673 20 p. Type 627 .. .. 15 15
674 1 r. 45, Hindustan Aircraft Industries Gnat jet fighters over India Gate (38×20 mm) .. .. 1·40 1·60

628 Sri Ramakrishna Paramahamsa (religious leader)   629 Postal Corps Emblem

1973 (18 Feb). *Sri Ramakrishna Paramahamsa Commemoration.* P 13.
675 **628** 20 p. light brown 20 40

1973 (1 Mar). *First Anniv of Army Postal Service Corps.* P 13.
676 **629** 20 p. deep ultramarine and vermilion .. 40 50

630 Flag and Map of Bangladesh   631 Kumaran Asan

(Des C. Pakrashi)

1973 (10 Apr). *"Jai Bangla" (Inauguration of First Bangladesh Parliament).* P 13.
677 **630** 20 p. multicoloured 15 40

1973 (12 Apr). *Birth Centenary of Kumaran Asan (writer and poet).* P 13.
678 **631** 20 p. sepia 20 45

632 Flag and Flames   633 Dr. B. R. Ambedkar (lawyer)

(Des C. Pakrashi)

1973 (13 Apr). *Homage to Martyrs for Independence.* P 13.
679 **632** 20 p. multicoloured 15 40

(Des Charanjit Lal)

1973 (14 Apr). *Bhim Rao Ambedkar Commemoration.* P 13.
680 **633** 20 p. bronze-green and deep purple .. 20 75

634 "Radha-Kishangarh" (Nihal Chand)   635 Mount Everest

1973 (5 May). *Indian Miniature Paintings.* T 634 and similar vert designs. Multicoloured. P 13.
681 20 p. Type 634 .. .. 30 35
682 50 p. "Dance Duet" (Aurangzeb's period) .. 60 1·50
683 1 r. "Lovers on a Camel" (Nasir-ud-din) .. 1·50 2·75
684 2 r. "Chained Elephant" (Zain-al-Abidin) .. 2·00 3·25
681/4 .. .. *Set of 4* 4·00 7·00

1973 (15 May). *15th Anniv of Indian Mountaineering Foundation.* P 13.
685 **635** 20 p. blue 50 50

---

636 Tail of Boeing 747   637 Cross, Church of St. Thomas' Mount, Madras

(Des Air-India Art Studies from photograph by Jehangir Gazdar)

1973 (8 June). *25th Anniv of Air-India's International Services.* P 13.
686 **636** 1 r. 45, indigo and carmine-red .. 4·00 4·00

1973 (3 July). *19th Death Centenary of St. Thomas.* P 13.
687 **637** 20 p. blue-grey and agate .. 20 50

638 Michael Madhusudan Dutt (poet—Death Centenary)   639 A. O. Hume

1973 (21 July). *Centenaries.* T 638 and similar horiz designs. P 13.
688 20 p. sage-green and orange-brown .. .. 1·00 65
  a. Orange-brown omitted £500
689 30 p. red-brown .. .. 1·25 2·50
690 50 p. deep brown .. .. 1·50 2·50
691 1 r. dull violet and orange-vermilion .. 1·50 1·50
688/91 .. .. .. *Set of 4* 4·75 6·50
Designs:—30 p. Vishnu Digambar Paluskar (musician—birth centenary); 50 p. Dr G. A. Hansen (centenary of discovery of leprosy bacillus); 1 r. Nicolaus Copernicus (astronomer—5th birth centenary).

1973 (31 July). *Allan Octavian Hume (founder of Indian National Congress) Commemoration.* P 13.
692 **639** 20 p. grey 20 40

640 Gandhi and Nehru   641 R. C. Dutt

(Des C. Pakrashi from photograph)

1973 (15 Aug). *Gandhi and Nehru Commemoration.* P 13.
693 **640** 20 p. multicoloured 20 40

1973 (27 Sept). *Romesh Chandra Dutt (writer) Commemoration.* P 13.
694 **641** 20 p. brown 20 40

642 K. S. Ranjitsinhji   643 Vithalbhai Patel

1973 (27 Sept). *K. S. Ranjitsinhji (cricketer) Commemoration.* P 13.
695 **642** 30p. myrtle-green .. .. 3·50 3·25

1973 (27 Sept). *Vithalbhai Patel (lawyer) Commemoration.* P 13.
696 **643** 50 p. light red-brown 20 65

ALTERED CATALOGUE NUMBERS

Any Catalogue numbers altered from the last edition are shown as a list in the introductory pages.

644 Sowar of President's Bodyguard

645 Interpol Emblem

1973 (30 Sept). *Bicentenary of President's Bodyguard.* P 13.
697 **644** 20 p. multicoloured 35 40

1973 (9 Oct). *50th Anniv of Interpol.* P 13.
698 **645** 20 p. brown 30 40

646 Syed Ahmad Khan (social reformer)

647 "Children at Play" (Bela Raval)

1973 (17 Oct). *Syed Ahmad Khan Commemoration.* P 13.
699 **646** 20 p. sepia 20 60

1973 (14 Nov). *Children's Day.* P 13.
700 **647** 20 p. multicoloured 20 30

648 Indipex Emblem

1973 (14 Nov). *"Indipex '73" Philatelic Exhibition, New Delhi (2nd issue).* T **648** *and similar multicoloured designs.* P 13½ × 13 (2 r.) or 13 × 13½ (others).
701 20 p. Type **648** 20 30
702 1 r. Ceremonial elephant and 1½ a. stamp of 1947 (vert) .. .. .. 1·25 2·00
703 2 r. Common Peafowl (vert) .. .. 1·50 3·00
701/3 .. .. .. Set of 3 2·75 4·75
MS704 127 × 127 mm. Nos. 672 and 701/3. Imperf 5·00 8·00

649 Emblem of National Cadet Corps

650 C. Rajagopalachari (statesman)

1973 (25 Nov). *25th Anniv of National Cadet Corps.* P 13.
705 **649** 20 p. multicoloured 20 30

1973 (25 Dec). *Chakravarti Rajagopalachari Commemoration.* P 13.
706 **650** 20 p. olive-brown 20 50

651 "Sun" Mask

652 Chhatrapati

1974 (15 Apr). *Indian Masks.* T **651** *and similar multicoloured designs.* P 13.
707 20 p. Type **651** 15 15
708 50 p. "Moon" mask 30 55
709 1 r. "Narasimha" .. .. .. 70 1·25
710 2 r. "Ravana" (horiz) .. .. 1·00 2·00
707/10 .. .. .. Set of 4 1·90 3·50
MS711 109 × 135 mm. Nos. 707/10 .. 2·75 6·50

1974 (2 June). *300th Anniv of Coronation of Chhatrapati Shri Shivaji Maharaj.* P 13.
712 **652** 25 p. multicoloured .. 40 30

653 Maithili Sharan Gupta (poet)

654 Kandukuri Veeresalingam (social reformer)

1974 (3 July). *Indian Personalities (1st series).* T **653** *and similar vert designs.* P 13.
713 25 p. chestnut 15 45
714 25 p. deep brown 15 45
715 25 p. sepia 15 45
713/15 .. .. .. Set of 3 40 1·25
Portraits:—No. 714, Jainarain Vyas (politician and journalist); No. 715, Utkal Gourab Madhusudan Das (social reformer).

1974 (15 July). *Indian Personalities (2nd series).* T **654** *and similar vert designs.* P 13.
716 25 p. lake-brown 25 50
717 50 p. dull purple .. .. 55 1·75
718 1 r. chestnut-brown .. .. 70 1·75
716/18 .. .. .. Set of 3 1·40 3·50
Portraits:—50 p. Tipu Sultan; 1 r. Max Mueller (Sanskrit scholar).

655 Kamala Nehru

(Des Charanjit Lal)

1974 (1 Aug). *Kamala Nehru Commemoration.* P 14½ × 14.
719 **655** 25 p. multicoloured 50 50

656 W. P. Y. Emblem

1974 (14 Aug). *World Population Year.* P 13½.
720 **656** 25 p. maroon and buff .. 20 30

LARGE STAR AND INDIA GOVT WATERMARK. Two types exist of this sheet watermark. The initial arrangement resulted in the stars appearing upright, inverted and sideways, in either direction, within the same sheet.
Printings issued from the beginning of 1980 shows a second type on which the stars in each sheet all point in the same direction. All commemoratives with this watermark used the second type.

657 Spotted Deer

657b Bidri Vase

657a Vina

Two types of No. 732:

I II

Type I. Left shoulder cut square. Top of Hindi inscription aligns with edge of shoulder.

Type II. Shoulder ends in point. Top of English inscription aligns with edge of shoulder. Portrait redrawn slightly smaller.

Two types of No. 736:

I II

Type I. "INDIA" inscription falls below foot of main design. Distance between foot of "2" in face value and top of Hindi inscription 11 mm.

Type II. "INDIA" above foot of design. Distance between "2" and inscription 10½ mm. Inscription redrawn slightly smaller.

1974 (20 Aug)-**83**. P 14 × 14½ (10, 20, 50 p.) or 14½ × 14 (others).

(*a*) *Various designs with values expressed with "p" or "Re" as T* **657**/a. W **374** (sideways)
721 – 15 p. blackish brown (deep background) (1.10.74) .. .. 3·25 70
722 **657** 25 p. sepia (20.8.74) .. .. 75 1·25
   a. Imperf (pair) £170
723 **657a** 1 r. red-brown and black (1.10.74) 2·50 30
   a. Black (face value and inscr) omitted £100

(*b*) *Various designs with values expressed in numerals only as in T* **657b**

(i) *Wmk Large Star and "INDIA GOVT" in sheet**
724 **657b** 2 p. red-brown (photo) (1.11.76) 70 2·25
724a   2 p. pale reddish brn (litho) (15.3.79) 70 2·25
725   5 p. cerise (as No. 506) (1.11.76) 30 10
   w. Wmk reversed
727 **466** 10 p. new blue (5.7.79) .. 3·25 50

(ii) *W* **374** (sideways† on 15, 25, 30, 60 p., 1, 2, 5, 10 r.)
729 **466** 10 p. new blue (1.11.76) .. 30 15
   a. Imperf (pair) £100
   w. Wmk inverted
730 – 15 p. blackish brn (light background) (15.7.75) .. .. 1·50 10
731 – 20 p. deep dull green (15.7.75) 15 10
   a. Imperf (horiz pair) .. £250
732 – 25 p. reddish brown (I) (25.10.78) 5·50 2·00
   a. Type II (31.5.79) .. 5·50 2·00
732b – 30 p. sepia (as No. 512) (1.5.79) 3·00 55
733 – 50 p. deep violet (15.7.75) .. 4·50 10
734 – 60 p. deep grey (as No. 515) (1.11.76) 1·00 80
735 **657** 1 r. red-brown & grey-blk (15.7.75) 3·25 10
736 – 2 r. violet & blackish brn (I) (15.7.75) 12·00 40
   a. Type II (1977) .. 12·00 40
737 – 5 r. deep slate-violet and brown (as No. 519) (1.11.76) .. 1·50 1·00
738 – 10 r. slate and bronze-green (as No. 520) (1.11.76) .. .. 1·25 1·25
   aw. Wmk capital heads to right .. 2·00 1·25
   b. Printed on the gummed side .. 35·00
   c. Wmk upright .. .. 1·25 1·25
   cw. Wmk inverted .. .. 4·25 1·25
   d. Perf 13 (22.10.83) .. 1·10 1·10
   da. Wmk upright .. .. 1·10 1·10
   dw. Wmk inverted .. .. 20·00
721/38 .. .. .. Set of 18 38·00 11·50
Designs: *Vert as T* **657**, **657b**:—15 p. Tiger; 25 p. Gandhi. *Horiz* (20×17 mm)—20 p. Handicrafts toy; 50 p. Great Egret in flight. *Horiz as T* **657a**:—2 r. Himalayas.
*See note below No. 720. Nos. 724a and 727 exist on both types of watermark, Nos. 724 and 725 on the first type only.
†The normal sideways watermark shows the capital heads to left, *as seen from the back of the stamp.*
No. 724a can be easily identified by the background of horizontal lines.
From early in 1976 Nos. 730, 731 and 735 were printed from new cylinders, which produced stamps with a slightly smaller design area than that of the original issue.
The 2 r. value with the blackish brown omitted is a chemically produced fake.
For stamps as No. 732, but with face value changed to 30 p., 35 p., 50 p., 60 p. or 1 r. see Nos. 968, 979, 1073, 1320 and 1436.

658 President V. Giri

659 U.P.U. Emblem

(Des Charanjit Lal)

1974 (24 Aug). *Retirement of Pres. Giri.* P 13.
739 658 25 p. multicoloured 15 30

(Des C. Pakrashi (25 p.), A. Ramachandran (1 r.), Jyoti Bhatt (2 r.))

1974 (3 Oct). *Centenary of Universal Postal Union.* T **659** and similar designs. P 13.
740 25 p. violet-blue, royal blue and black .. 40 10
741 1 r. multicoloured .. .. .. 75 1·00
742 2 r. multicoloured .. .. .. 1·00 2·00
   a. Red (inscr etc) omitted £325
740/2 .. .. *Set of 3* 1·90 2·75
MS743 108 × 108 mm. Nos. 740/2 .. 2·75 8·00
Designs: *Horiz*—1 r. Birds and nest, "Madhubani" style. *Vert*—2 r. Arrows around globe.

660 Woman Flute-player (sculpture)   661 Nicholas Roerich (medallion by H. Dropsy)

(Des Benoy Sarkar)

1974 (9 Oct). *Centenary of Mathura Museum.* T **660** and similar vert design. P 13½.
744 25 p. chestnut and blackish brown .. 50 45
   a. Horiz pair. Nos. 744/5 .. 1·00 1·60
745 25 p. chestnut and blackish brown .. 50 45
Design:—No. 745, Vidyadhara with garland.
Nos. 744/5 were printed together within the sheet, horizontally *se-tenant.*

1974 (9 Oct). *Birth Centenary of Professor Roerich* (humanitarian). P 13.
746 661 1 r. deep blue-green and greenish yellow 50 55

662 Pavapuri Temple   663 "Cat" (Rajesh Bhatia)

(Des Benoy Sarkar)

1974 (13 Nov). *2,500th Anniv of Bhagwan Mahavira's attainment of Nirvana.* P 13.
747 662 25 p. indigo 40 20

1974 (14 Nov). *Children's Day.* P 13.
748 663 25 p. multicoloured 70 40

664 "Indian Dancers" (Amita Shah)

665 Territorial Army Badge

1974 (14 Nov). *25th Anniv of UNICEF in India.* P 14½ × 14.
749 664 25 p. multicoloured 55 45
   a. Black (name and value) omitted £325
On No. 749a the background is in greenish black instead of the intense black of the normal.

(Des Benoy Sarkar)

1974 (16 Nov). *25th Anniv of Indian Territorial Army.* P 13.
750 665 25 p. black, bright yellow and emerald .. 60 40

666 Krishna as Gopal Bal with Cows (Rajasthan painting on cloth)   667 Symbols and Child's Face

1974 (2 Dec). *19th International Dairy Congress, New Delhi.* P 13½.
751 666 25 p. brown-purple and brown-ochre .. 40 30

(Des Benoy Sarkar)

1974 (8 Dec). *Help for Retarded Children.* P 13.
752 667 25 p. red-orange and black 50 50

668 Marconi   669 St. Francis Xavier's Shrine, Goa

1974 (12 Dec). *Birth Centenary of Guglielmo Marconi* (radio pioneer). P 13.
753 668 2 r. deep slate .. .. .. 2·00 1·25

1974 (24 Dec). *St Francis Xavier Celebration.* P 13.
754 669 25 p. multicoloured 15 30

670 Saraswati (Deity of Language and Learning)   671 Parliament House, New Delhi

1975 (10 Jan). *World Hindi Convention, Nagpur.* P 14 × 14½.
755 670 25 p. slate and carmine-red 30 30
For similar stamp see No. 761.

1975 (26 Jan). *25th Anniv of Republic.* P 13.
756 671 25 p. grey-black, silver and azure .. 30 30

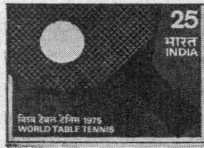

672 Table-tennis Bat

1975 (6 Feb). *World Table-tennis Championships, Calcutta.* P 13.
757 672 25 p. black, vermilion and yellow-olive 55 30

673 "Equality, Development and Peace"   674 Stylised Cannon

(Des Shyama Sarabhai)

1975 (16 Feb). *International Women's Year.* P 13.
758 673 25 p. multicoloured 85 45

(Des Benoy Sarkar)

1975 (8 Apr). *Bicentenary of Indian Army Ordnance Corps.* P 13.
759 674 25 p. multicoloured 65 45

675 Arya Samaj Emblem   676 Saraswati

1975 (11 Apr). *Centenary of Arya Samaj Movement.* P 13.
760 675 25 p. light red-orange & brownish black 30 30

1975 (12 Apr). *World Telugu Language Conference, Hyderabad.* P 14 × 14½.
761 676 25 p. black and deep bluish green .. 45 30

677 Satellite "Aryabhata"

1975 (20 Apr). *Launch of First Indian Satellite.* P 13.
762 677 25 p. lt blue, deep indigo & dull purple .. 50 40

678 Blue-winged Pitta   679 Page from "Ramcharitmanas" Manuscript

(Des J. P. Irani)

1975 (28 Apr). *Indian Birds.* T **678** and similar multicoloured designs. P 13.
763 25 p. Type **678** 65 25
764 50 p. Asian Black-headed Oriole .. 1·50 2·00
765 1 r. Western Tragopan (*vert*) .. 2·25 2·75
766 2 r. Himalayan Monal Pheasant (*vert*) 3·00 5·00
763/6 .. .. *Set of 4* 6·50 9·00

(Des R. K. Joshi)

1975 (24 May). *4th Centenary of Ramcharitmanas* (epic poem by Goswami Tulsidas). P 13.
767 679 25 p. black, orange-yellow and vermilion 40 20

680 Young Women within Y.W.C.A. Badge   681 "The Creation"

(Des Benoy Sarkar)

1975 (20 June). *Centenary of Indian Y.W.C.A.* P 13.
768 680 25 p. multicoloured 30 30

1975 (28 June). *500th Birth Anniv of Michelangelo.* T **681** and similar designs showing "Creation" frescoes from Sistine Chapel. P 14 × 13½.
769 50 p. multicoloured 80 90
   a. Block of 4. Nos 769/72 .. 2·75
   ab. Black (inscr & face value) omitted .. £475
770 50 p. multicoloured 80 90
771 50 p. multicoloured 80 90
772 50 p. multicoloured 80 90
769/72 .. .. *Set of 4* 2·75 3·25
T **681** illustrates No. 769. Nos. 770 and 772 are norizontal designs, size 49 × 34 mm.
Nos. 769/72 were printed in *se-tenant* blocks of four within the sheet, forming two composite designs in horizontal pairs.

682 Commission Emblem   683 Stylised Ground Antenna

1975 (28 July). *25th Anniv of International Commission on Irrigation and Drainage.* P 13½.
773 **682** 25 p. multicoloured 40 20

(Des Benoy Sarkar)

1975 (1 Aug). *Inauguration of Satellite Instructional Television Experiment.* P 13.
774 **683** 25 p. multicoloured 40 20

684 St. Arunagirinathar   685 Commemorative Text

1975 (14 Aug). *600th Birth Anniv of St. Arunagirinathar.* P 13½.
775 **684** 50 p. dull purple and slate-black .. 1·00 1·00

1975 (26 Aug). *Namibia Day.* P 13½.
776 **685** 25 p. grey-black and rose-red 40 40

686 Mir Anees (poet)   687 Memorial Temple to Ahilyabai Holkar (ruler)

1975 (4 Sept). *Indian Celebrities.* P 13½ (No. 777) or 13 (No. 778).
777 **686** 25 p. blackish green 25 65
778 **687** 25 p. chestnut 25 65

688 Bharata Natyam   689 Ameer Khusrau

1975 (20 Oct). *Indian Dances.* T **688** and similar vert designs. Multicoloured. P 13.
779 25 p. Type **668** 65 20
780 50 p. Orissi .. .. .. 1·00 1·50
  a. Turquoise-green (dress) omitted .. 65·00
781 75 p. Kathak .. .. .. 1·25 1·75
782 1 r. Kathakali .. .. .. 1·50 1·25
783 1 r. 50, Kuchipudi .. .. 2·25 3·25
784 2 r. Manipuri .. .. .. 2·25 3·75
779/84 .. .. Set of 6 8·00 10·50

1975 (24 Oct). *650th Death Anniv of Ameer Khusrau (poet).* P 13.
785 **689** 50 p. reddish brown and buff .. 80 1·50

690 V. K. Krishna Menon   691 Text of Poem

1975 (24 Oct). *First Death Anniv of V. K. Krishna Menon (statesman).* P 13 × 13½.
786 **690** 25 p. olive 50 60

(Des R. K. Joshi)

1975 (24 Oct). *Birth Bicentenary of Emperor Bahadur Shah Zafar.* P 13½ × 13.
787 **691** 1 r. black, stone and yellow-brown .. 65 90

692 Sansadiya Soudha, New Delhi   693 V. Patel

1975 (28 Oct). *21st Commonwealth Parliamentary Conference, New Delhi.* P 14½ × 14.
788 **692** 2 r. olive .. .. 2·00 2·50

1975 (31 Oct). *Birth Centenary of Vallabhbhai Patel (statesman).* P 13 × 13½.
789 **693** 25 p. slate-green 15 40

694 N. C. Bardoloi   695 "Cow" (Sanjay Nathubhai Patel)

1975 (3 Nov). *Birth Centenary of Nabin Chandra Bardoloi (politician).* P 13 × 13½.
790 **694** 25 p. reddish brown 30 50

1975 (14 Nov). *Children's Day.* P 13½ × 13.
791 **695** 25 p. multicoloured 60 60

696 Original Printing Works, Nasik Road   697 Gurdwara Sisganj (site of martyrdom)

1975 (13 Dec). *50th Anniv of India Security Press.* P 13.
792 **696** 25 p. multicoloured 40 40

1975 (16 Dec). *Tercentenary of the Martyrdom of Guru Tegh Bahadur (Sikh leader).* P 13.
793 **697** 25 p. multicoloured 40 40

698 Theosophical Society Emblem   699 Weather Cock

1975 (20 Dec). *Centenary of the Theosophical Society.* P 13.
794 **698** 25 p. multicoloured 40 40

(Des Benoy Sarkar)

1975 (24 Dec). *Centenary of the Indian Meteorological Department.* P 13 × 13½.
795 **699** 25 p. multicoloured 50 50

700 Early Mail Cart   701 L. N. Mishra (politician)

(Des Benoy Sarkar)

1975 (25 Dec). *"Inpex 75" National Philatelic Exhibition, Calcutta.* T **700** and similar vert design. P 13.
796 **700** 25 p. black and lake-brown 50 30
797 — 2 r. grey-brown, brown-purple & black 2·25 3·25
Design:—2 r. Indian Bishop Mark, 1775.

1976 (3 Jan). *First Death Anniv of Lalit Narayan Mishra.* P 13.
798 **701** 25 p. olive-sepia 40 40

702 Tiger   703 Painted Storks

1976 (24 Jan). *Birth Centenary of Jim Corbett (naturalist).* P 13.
799 **702** 25 p. multicoloured .. .. 1·00 70

(Des Charanjit Lal)

1976 (10 Feb). *Keoladeo Ghana Bird Sanctuary, Bharatpur.* P 13.
800 **703** 25 p. multicoloured 80 50

704 Vijayanta Tank   705 Alexander Graham Bell

1976 (4 Mar). *Bicentenary of 16th Light Cavalry Regt.* P 13.
801 **704** 25 p. multicoloured .. .. 1·60 30

1976 (10 Mar). *Alexander Graham Bell Commemoration.* P 13.
802 **705** 25 p. grey-black and yellow-ochre .. 70 40

706 Muthuswami Dikshitar   707 Eye and Red Cross

1976 (18 Mar). *Birth Bicentenary of Dikshitar (composer).* P 13½.
803 **706** 25 p. purple 70 40

(Des Benoy Sarkar)

1976 (7 Apr). *World Health Day. Prevention of Blindness.* P 13.
804 **707** 25 p. reddish brown and dull vermilion .. 80 50

708 "Industries"   709 Type WDM Diesel Locomotive, 1963

(Des Benoy Sarkar)

1976 (30 Apr). *Industrial Development.* P 13.
805 **708** 25 p. multicoloured 30 30

1976 (15 May). *Locomotives.* T **709** and similar horiz designs. Multicoloured. P 14½ × 14.
806 25 p. Type **709** 55 10
807 50 p. Radjustan Malvan Railway Class F/1 steam locomotive, 1895 .. 1·50 55
808 1 r. Southern Railway Class WP/1 steam locomotive, 1963 .. 2·75 1·25
809 2 r. Great Peninsular Railway Class GIP steam locomotive, 1853 .. 3·50 2·50
806/9 .. Set of 4 7·50 4·00

710 Nehru   711

712

Three types of Nehru portrait (*illustrated actual size*)
Type 710. Portrait measures 24 mm at base. First character above "NEHRU" has two prongs.
Type 711. Whole portrait is larger, measuring 25½ mm at base. Character above "NEHRU" has three prongs.
Type 712. Small portrait, 23 mm at base, with smaller inscription. Character above "NEHRU" has three prongs.

1976. T **710/12** *and similar vert design.* W **374**. P 13½.
810 **710** 25 p. dull violet (27.5.76) ..   ..   ..   7·50   80
810*a* **711** 25 p. dull violet (9.76) ..   ..   5·00   80
810*b* **712** 25 p. dull violet (14.11.76) ..   4·00   80
811   — 25 p. red-brown (2.10.76) ..   ..   1·00   30
     a. Imperf (pair)   ..   ..   ..
    Design:—No. 811, Gandhi.
    For these designs in a smaller size see Nos. 732, 968/9, 979/80 and 1073/4 and 1320.

713 "Spirit of 76"   **714** K. Kamaraj
(Willard)   (politician)

1976 (29 May). *Bicentenary of American Revolution.* P 13.
812 **713** 2 r. 80, multicoloured ..   1·25   1·25

1976 (15 July). *Kumaraswamy Kamaraj Commemoration.* P 13.
813 **714** 25 p. sepia   15   15

715 "Shooting"   **716** Subhadra Kumari
           Chauhan (poetess)

(Des Gopi Gajwani (25 p., 1 r.), Sukumar Shankar (1 r. 50), India Security Press (2 r. 80))

1976 (17 July). *Olympic Games, Montreal.* T **715** *and similar vert designs.* P 13.
814 25 p. deep violet and vermilion   ..   30   10
815 1 r. multicoloured   ..   ..   1·00   90
816 1 r. 50, deep mauve and grey-black ..   1·75   2·75
817 2 r. 80, multicoloured   ..   1·75   4·00
814/17   Set of 4   4·25   7·00
    Designs:—1 r. Shot-put; 1 r. 50, Hockey; 2 r. 80, Sprinting.

1976 (6 Aug). *S. K. Chauhan Commemoration.* P 13.
818 **716** 25 p. grey-blue   ..   15   40

717 Param Vir Chakra   **718** University Building,
       Medal   Bombay

(Des Benoy Sarkar)

1976 (15 Aug). *Param Vir Chakra Commemoration.* P 13.
819 **717** 25 p. multicoloured   ..   15   50
    Examples of No. 819 are found pre-released at Jodhpur on 28 July 1976.

1976 (3 Sept). *60th Anniv of Shreemati Nathibai Damodar Thackersey Women's University.* P 13½.
820 **718** 25 p. bluish violet   ..   30   30

719 Bharatendu   **720** S. C. Chatterji
Harischandra (writer)

1976 (9 Sept). *Harischandra Commemoration.* P 13.
821 **719** 25 p. agate   15   30

1976 (15 Sept). *Birth Centenary of Sarat Chandra Chatterji (writer).* P 13.
822 **720** 25 p. grey-black   ..   15   30

721 Planned Family   **722** Maharaja Agrasen and
                             Coins

(Des A. K. Nagar)

1976 (22 Sept). *Family Planning.* P 14 × 14½.
823 **721** 25 p. multicoloured   ..   15   30

1976 (24 Sept). *Maharaja Agrasen Commemoration.* P 13.
824 **722** 25 p. red-brown   ..   15   30

723 Swamp Deer   **724** Hands holding Hearts

(Des from photos by Rajesh Bedi)

1976 (1 Oct). *Wildlife.* T **723** *and similar multicoloured designs.* P 14 × 14½ (25, 50 p.) or 14½ × 14 (others).
825 25 p. Type **723**   45   40
     a. Black (name and year date) omitted .. £425
826 50 p. Lion   ..   ..   1·25   2·25
827 1 r. Leopard (*horiz*) ..   ..   1·75   2·25
828 2 r. Caracal (*horiz*) ..   ..   2·00   3·50
825/8   Set of 4   5·00   7·50

(Des B. G. Varma)

1976 (1 Oct). *Voluntary Blood Donation.* P 13.
829 **724** 25 p. yellow-ochre, scarlet and black   60   40

725 Suryakant Tripathi   **726** "Loyal Mongoose"
("Nirala")   (H. D. Bhatia)

1976 (15 Oct). *80th Birth Anniv of "Nirala" (poet).* P 13.
830 **725** 25 p. deep blue   ..   15   30

1976 (14 Nov). *Children's Day.* P 13½ × 14.
831 **726** 25 p. multicoloured   ..   40   40

727 Hiralal Shastri   **728** Dr. Hari Singh Gour
(social reformer)   (lawyer)

1976 (24 Nov). *Shastri Commemoration.* P 13.
832 **727** 25 p. sepia   20   30

1976 (26 Nov). *Dr. Gour Commemoration.* P 13.
833 **728** 25 p. deep reddish purple   ..   20   30

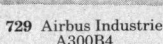

729 Airbus Industrie   **730** Hybrid Coconut Palm
A300B4

1976 (1 Dec). *Inauguration of Indian Airlines' Airbus Service.* P 14½×14.
834 **729** 2 r. multicoloured   ..   2·25   2·25

1976 (27 Dec). *Diamond Jubilee of Coconut Research.* P 13.
835 **730** 25 p. multicoloured   ..   20   30

731 First Stanza of *Vande Mataram*

1976 (30 Dec). *Centenary of "Vande Mataram" (patriotic song by B. C. Chatterjee).* P 13.
836 **731** 25 p. multicoloured   ..   20   30

732 Globe and Film Strip   **733** Seismograph and Crack
                             in Earth's Crust

1977 (3 Jan). *Sixth International Film Festival of India, New Delhi.* P 13.
837 **732** 2 r. multicoloured   ..   1·10   2·00

1977 (10 Jan). *Sixth World Conference on Earthquake Engineering, New Delhi.* P 13.
838 **733** 2 r. deep plum   ..   1·00   2·00

734 Tarun Ram Phookun   **735** Paramahansa Yogananda
                           (religious leader)

1977 (22 Jan). *Birth Centenary of Tarun Ram Phookun (politician).* P 13.
839 **734** 25 p. blackish brown   ..   15   30

1977 (7 Mar). *Yogananda Commemoration.* P 13.
840 **735** 25 p. reddish orange   ..   40   30

736 Asian Regional Red   **737** Fakhruddin Ali
Cross Emblem   Ahmed

1977 (9 Mar). *First Asian Regional Red Cross Conference, New Delhi.* P 13.
841 **736** 2 r. pink, deep blue and scarlet. ..   2·00   2·50

1977 (22 Mar). *Death of President Ahmed.* P 13.
842 **737** 25 p. multicoloured   ..   35   35

738 Emblem of Asian-Oceanic
Postal Union

1977 (1 Apr). *15th Anniv of Asian-Oceanic Postal Union.* P 13.
843 **738** 2 r. multicoloured   ..   1·10   1·75

739 Narottam Morarjee and *Loyalty* (liner) **740** Makhanlal Chaturvedi (writer and poet)

1977 (2 Apr). *Birth Centenary of Morarjee (ship owner).* P 13.
844 **739** 25 p. greenish blue 75 70

1977 (4 Apr). *Chaturvedi Commemoration.* P 13.
845 **740** 25 p. lake-brown 15 30

741 Mahaprabhu Vallabhacharya (philosopher) **742** Federation Emblem

1977 (14 Apr). *Vallabhacharya Commemoration.* P 13.
846 **741** 1 r. sepia 30 40

1977 (23 Apr). *50th Anniv of Federation of Indian Chambers of Commerce and Industry.* P 13.
847 **742** 25 p. dull purple, brown-ochre and buff .. 15 40

744 "Environment Protection" **745** Rajya Sabha Chamber

1977 (5 June). *World Environment Day.* P 13.
848 **744** 2 r. multicoloured .. .. 60 1·25

1977 (21 June). *25th Anniv of Rajya Sabha (Upper House of Parliament).* P 13.
849 **745** 25 p. multicoloured 15 30

746 Lotus

(Des from paintings by J. P. Irani)

1977 (1 July). *Indian Flowers. T **746** and similar multicoloured designs.* P 14½ × 14 (25 p., 2 r.) or 14 × 14½ (others).
850 25 p. Type **746** 25 15
   a. Black (inscription) omitted .. £325
851 50 p. Rhododendron (*vert*) .. 45 90
852 1 r. Kadamba (*vert*) .. 60 1·00
853 2 r. Gloriosa Lily .. .. 90 2·25
850/3 .. .. .. *Set of 4* 2·00 3·75

747 Berliner Gramophone **748** Coomaraswamy and Siva

(Des Benoy Sarkar)

1977 (20 July). *Centenary of Sound Recording.* P 13.
854 **747** 2 r. yellow-brown and black .. 1·00 2·00

1977 (22 Aug). *Birth Centenary of Ananda Kentish Coomaraswamy (art historian).* P 13.
855 **748** 25 p. multicoloured 40 40

749 Ganga Ram and Hospital **750** Dr. Samuel Hahnemann (founder of homeopathy)

1977 (4 Sept). *50th Death Anniv of Sir Ganga Ram (social reformer).* P 14½×14.
856 **749** 25 p. maroon 30 30

1977 (6 Oct). *32nd International Homeopathic Congress, New Delhi.* P 13.
857 **750** 2 r. black and green .. .. 3·50 2·75

751 Ram Manohar Lohia (politician) **752** Early Punjabi Postman

1977 (12 Oct). *R. M. Lohia Commemoration.* P 13.
858 **751** 25 p. red-brown 30 30

1977 (12 Oct). *"Inpex-77" Philatelic Exhibition. Bangalore. T **752** and similar horiz design.* P 13 (25 p.) or 13½ × 14 (2 r.).
859 25 p. multicoloured 50 30
860 2 r. olive-grey/*flesh* .. .. 2·00 2·75
  Design:—2 r. "Lion and Palm" essay, 1853.

753 Scarlet "Scinde Dawks" of 1852 **754** "Mother and Child" (Khajuraho sculpture)

1977 (19 Oct). *"Asiana 77" Philatelic Exhibition, Bangalore. T **753** and similar horiz design.* P 13.
861 1 r. orange, black and yellow .. 1·50 1·00
862 3 r. orange, black and light blue .. 2·50 3·25
  Design:—3 r. Foreign mail arriving at Ballard Pier, Bombay, 1927.

1977 (23 Oct). *15th International Congress of Pediatrics, New Delhi.* P 13.
863 **754** 2 r. reddish brown and grey .. .. 2·25 2·75

755 Statue of Kittur Rani Channamma, Belgaum **756** Symbolic Sun

1977 (23 Oct). *Kittur Rani Channamma (ruler) Commemoration.* P 13.
864 **755** 25 p. grey-green 80 40

1977 (8 Nov). *Union Public Service Commission Commemoration.* P 13.
865 **756** 25 p. multicoloured 35 30

757 Ear of Corn **758** "Cats" (Nikur Dilipbhai Mody)

(Des Benoy Sarkar)

1977 (13 Nov). *"Agriexpo 77" Agricultural Exhibition, New Delhi. W 374 (sideways).* P 13.
866 **757** 25 p. blue-green 40 40

1977 (14 Nov). *Children's Day. T **758** and similar horiz design. Multicoloured.* P 13.
867 25 p. Type **758** 50 30
868 1 r. "Friends" (Bhavsar Ashish Ramanlal) .. 2·25 3·00

759 Jotirao Phooley (social reformer) **760** Diagram of Population Growth

1977 (28 Nov). *Indian Personalities. T **759** and similar vert design. W 374 (sideways).* P 13.
869 25 p. brown-olive 30 45
870 25 p. chestnut 30 45
  Portrait:—No. 870, Senapti Bapat (patriot).

1977 (13 Dec). *41st Session of International Statistical Institute, New Delhi.* P 13.
871 **760** 2 r. blue-green and red .. .. 60 1·00

761 Kamta Prasad Guru and Vyakarna (Hindi Grammar) **762** Kremlin Tower and Soviet Flag

1977 (25 Dec). *Kamta Prasad Guru (writer) Commemoration. W 374 (sideways).* P 13½×14.
872 **761** 25 p. deep brown 20 30

1977 (30 Dec). *60th Anniv of October Revolution.* P 13.
873 **762** 1 r. multicoloured 45 75

763 Climber crossing a Crevice **764** "Shikara" on Lake Dal, Kashmir

1978 (15 Jan). *Conquest of Kanchenjunga (1977). T **763** and similar horiz design. Multicoloured.* P 13
874 25 p. Type **763** 10 10
875 1 r. Indian flag near summit.. .. 45 80

1978 (23 Jan). *27th Pacific Area Travel Association Conference, New Delhi.* P 13.
876 **764** 1 r. multicoloured .. .. 2·00 1·50

765 Children in Library **766** Mother-Pondicherry

1978 (11 Feb). *Third World Book Fair, New Delhi.* P 13.
877 **765** 1 r. chestnut and slate .. 45 80

1978 (21 Feb). *Birth Centenary of Mother-Pondicherry (philosopher).* P 13.
878 **766** 25 p. brown and light grey .. 20 30

767 Wheat and Globe   **768** Nanalal Dalpatram Kavi (poet)

1978 (23 Feb). *Fifth International Wheat Genetics Symposium, New Delhi.* P 13.
879 **767** 25 p. yellow and blue-green 20 30

1978 (16 Mar). *Nanalal Kavi Commemoration.* W 374 (sideways). P 13.
880 **768** 25 p. red-brown 20 30

769 Surjya Sen (revolutionary)   **770** "Two Vaishnavas" (Jamini Roy)

1978 (22 Mar). *Surjya Sen Commemoration.* W 374 (sideways). P 13.
881 **769** 25 p. sepia and orange-red 20 30

1978 (23 Mar). *Modern Indian Paintings.* T 770 and similar vert designs. Multicoloured. P 14.
882 25 p. Type 770 .. .. 20 30
    a. Black (face value and inscr) omitted .. £275
883 50 p. "The Mosque" (Sailoz Mookherjea) .. 40 1·25
884 1 r. "Head" (Rabindranath Tagore) .. 70 1·50
885 2 r. "Hill Women" (Amrita Sher Gil) .. 90 2·00
882/5 .. .. Set of 4 2·00 4·50

771 "Self-portrait" (Rubens)   **772** Charlie Chaplin

1978 (4 Apr). *400th Birth Anniv of Rubens.* P 13.
886 **771** 2 r. multicoloured .. .. .. 2·00 3·00

1978 (16 Apr). *Charlie Chaplin Commemoration.* P 13.
887 **772** 25 p. Prussian blue and gold 90 45

773 Deendayal Upadhyaya (politician)   **774** Syama Prasad Mookerjee

1978 (5 May). *Deendayal Upadhyaya Commemoration.* P 13.
888 **773** 25 p. olive-brown and pale orange .. 20 40

1978 (6 July). *Syama Prasad Mookerjee (politician) Commemoration.* P 13×13½.
889 **774** 25 p. brown-olive 30 50

STANLEY GIBBONS STAMP COLLECTING SERIES

Introductory booklets on *How to Start, How to Identify Stamps* and *Collecting by Theme.* A series of well illustrated guides at a low price. Write for details.

---

775 Airavat (mythological) elephant), Jain Temple, Gujerat (Kachchh Museum)   **776** Krishna and Arjuna in Battle Chariot

1978 (27 July). *Treasures from Indian Museums.* T 775 and similar multicoloured designs. P 13 × 13½ (25, 50 p.) or 13½ × 13 (others).
890 25 p. Type 775 .. .. 30 30
891 50 p. Kalpadruma (magical tree), Besnagar (Indian Museum) .. .. .. 50 1·25
892 1 r. Obverse and reverse of Kushan gold coin (National Museum) (horiz) .. .. 70 1·50
893 2 r. Dagger and knife of Emperor Jehangir, Mughal (Salar Jung Museum) (horiz) .. 1·00 2·00
890/3 .. .. Set of 4 2·25 4·50

1978 (25 Aug). *Bhagawadgeeta (Divine Song of India) Commemoration.* P 13.
894 **776** 25 p. gold and vermilion 20 30

777 Bethune College   **778** E. V. Ramasami

1978 (4 Sept). *Centenary of Bethune College, Calcutta.* P 13.
895 **777** 25 p. deep brown and deep green .. 20 30

1978 (17 Sept). *E. V. Ramasami (social reformer) Commemoration.* P 13.
896 **778** 25 p. black 20 20

779 Uday Shankar   **780** Leo Tolstoy

1978 (26 Sept). *Uday Shankar (dancer) Commemoration.* P 13.
897 **779** 25 p. reddish brown and stone .. 20 30

1978 (2 Oct). *150th Birth Anniv of Leo Tolstoy (writer).* P 13.
898 **780** 1 r. multicoloured 30 30

781 Vallathol Narayana Menon   **782** "Two Friends" (Dinesh Sharma)

1978 (15 Oct). *Birth Centenary of Vallathol Narayana Menon (poet).* P 13.
899 **781** 25 p. bright purple and brown .. 15 40

1978 (14 Nov). *Children's Day.* P 13.
900 **782** 25 p. multicoloured 20 40

783 Machine Operator   **784** Sowars of Skinner's Horse

1978 (17 Nov). *National Small Industries Fair, New Delhi.* P 13½.
901 **783** 25 p. bronze-green 20 30

1978 (25 Nov). *175th Anniv of Skinner's Horse (cavalry regiment).* P 13.
902 **784** 25 p. multicoloured 60 60

785 Mohammad Ali Jauhar   **786** Chakravarti Rajagopalachari

1978 (10 Dec). *Birth Centenary of Mohammad Ali Jauhar (patriot).* P 13.
903 **785** 25 p. olive-green 20 30

1978 (10 Dec). *Birth Centenary of Chakravarti Rajagopalachari (first post-independence Governor-General).* P 13.
904 **786** 25 p. lake-brown 20 30

787 Wright Brothers and Flyer 1   **788** Ravenshaw College

1978 (23 Dec). *75th Anniv of Powered Flight.* W 374 (sideways). P 13 × 13½.
905 **787** 1 r. purple and yellow-ochre .. 65 30

1978 (24 Dec). *Centenary of Ravenshaw College, Cuttack.* P 14.
906 **788** 25 p. lake and deep green 20 30

789 Schubert   **790** Uniforms of 1799, 1901 and 1979 with Badge

1978 (25 Dec). *150th Death Anniv of Franz Schubert (composer).* P 13.
907 **789** 1 r. multicoloured 80 55
    a. Black (face value) omitted £650
Two black cylinders were used for the design of No. 907. No. 907a shows the black still present on the portrait.

(Des Charanjit Lal)

1979 (20 Feb). *Fourth Reunion of Punjab Regiment.* P 13.
908 **790** 25 p. multicoloured 90 70

791 Bhai Parmanand   **792** Gandhi with Young Boy

1979 (24 Feb). *Bhai Parmanand (scholar) Commemoration.* P 13.
909 **791** 25 p. deep violet-blue 20 30

1979 (5 Mar). *International Year of the Child.* T 792 and similar vert design. P 13.
910 25 p. reddish brown and scarlet-vermilion .. 40 30
911 1 r. reddish brown and yellow-orange .. 60 1·50
Design:—1 r. Indian I.Y.C. emblem.

During October 1979 two stamps inscribed "HAPPY CHILD NATION'S PRIDE" with face values of 50 p. and 1 r. were issued to post offices. These were intended for sale as charity labels, without postal validity, the proceeds going to a Child Welfare fund. It would seem that the instructions issued were unclear, however, as some post offices sold these labels as postage stamps and accepted mail franked with them.

793 Albert Einstein

794 Rajarshi Shahu Chhatrapati

1979 (14 Mar). *Birth Centenary of Albert Einstein (physicist).* P 13.
912 **793** 1 r. blue-black 40 50
1979 (1 May). *Rajarshi Shahu Chhatrapati (ruler of Kolhapur State, 1874–1922, and precursor of social reform in India) Commemoration.* P 13.
913 **794** 25 p. deep dull purple 20 30

795 Exhibition Logo

796 Postcards under Magnifying Glass

1979 (2 July). *"India 80" International Stamp Exhibition (1st issue).* P 13.
914 **795** 30 p. deep green and orange 20 30
See also Nos. 942/5 and 955/8.
1979 (2 July). *Centenary of Indian Postcards.* P 13.
915 **796** 50 p. multicoloured 20 40

797 Raja Mahendra Pratap

798 Hilsa, Pomfret and Prawn

799 Rubber Tapping

1979 (15 Aug). *Raja Mahendra Pratap (patriot) Commemoration.* P 13.
916 **797** 30 p. brown-olive 20 40

1979 (3 Sept)–**88**. *Designs as T 798/9.*

(a) Photo. Wmk Large Star and "INDIA GOVT" in sheet*. P 14½×14 (15 p.) or 14×14½ (others)
917 2 p. slate-violet (31.3.80) .. .. 75 2·00
918 5 p. new blue (26.11.79) .. .. 1·50 30
919 15 p. deep bluish green (10.3.80) .. 2·25 30

(b) Photo. W 374† (sideways** on 15, 20, 35 p., 1, 2, 2 r. 25, 2 r. 80, 3 r. 25 and 10 r.). P 14½×14 (15, 20, 35 p., 1, 2 r.), 13 (25 p. (No. 925b), 3 r. 25, 10 r.) or 14×14½ (others).
920 2 p. slate-violet (25.3.81) 10 10
921 5 p. new blue (5.3.81) 30 10
   a. Perf 13 (5.7.82) 10 10
   ab. Wmk sideways (1988) 20 10
   aw. Wmk inverted 60 10
922 10 p. deep green (25.1.82) 70 10
   a. Perf 13 (5.7.82) 20 10
   ab. Printed double .. .. ..
   ac. Wmk sideways (1988) 20 10
923 15 p. deep bluish green (25.3.81) .. 20 10
   a. Perf 13 (5.7.82) 20 10
   ab. Wmk upright 50 10
924 20 p. Indian red (25.3.81) 30 10
   a. Perf 13 (5.7.82) 70 10
   ab. Wmk upright (1988) 30 10
   aw. Wmk capital heads to right .. 70 10
925 25 p. red-brown (26.11.79) 70 10
   a. Perf 13 (5.7.82) 30 10
925b 25 p. deep blue-green (5.9.85) .. 1·00 10
   ba. Printed double .. .. ..
   bb. Wmk sideways (1988) 30 10
926 30 p. yellowish green 90 10
   a. Perf 13 (6.9.82) 60 10
   ab. Wmk sideways (1987) 30 10
   aba. Printed double .. .. ..
   aw. Wmk inverted 70 10
927 35 p. cerise (15.9.80) 50 10
   a. Perf 13 (5.7.82) 60 20
   ab. Wmk upright 80 20
   aw. Wmk capital heads to right .. 70 20
928 50 p. deep violet (25.1.82) .. .. 2·00 10
   a. Imperf (pair) .. .. 30·00
   b. Perf 13 (5.7.82) 50 10
   bb. Imperf between (vert pair) .. .. † —
   bw. Wmk inverted .. .. 5·00
   c. Wmk sideways (p 13) (1988) .. 30 10
929 1 r. bistre-brown (17.6.80) 40 10
   a. Imperf (pair) .. .. 75·00
   b. Perf 13 (10.11.83) 10 10
   ba. Wmk upright (1987) 30 10
   bb. Printed double .. .. ..
932 2 r. deep rose-lilac (7.12.80) .. .. 1·00 10
   a. Perf 13 (10.11.83) 20 10
   ab. Wmk upright (1987) 10 10

933 2 r. 25, red and blue-green (25.3.81) .. 1·25 40
   aw. Wmk capital heads to right .. 2·00 55
   b. Wmk upright .. .. 1·25 40
   bw. Wmk inverted .. .. ..
   c. Perf 13 (*wmk upright*) (1983) .. 10 10
   ca. Wmk sideways* (1987) 75 30
   cw. Wmk capital heads to right .. ..
934 2 r. 80, red and blue-green (25.3.81) .. 70 40
   aw. Wmk capital heads to right .. ..
   b. Wmk upright 75 40
934c 3 r. 25, reddish orange & bl-grn (23.12.82) 70 40
   ca. Wmk upright 10 10
   cw. Wmk inverted .. .. ..
935 5 r. red and emerald (23.11.80) .. 4·50 30
   aw. Wmk inverted .. .. 16·00 60
   b. Wmk sideways* .. .. 4·50 30
   bw. Wmk capital heads to right .. ..
   c. Perf 13×12½ (*wmk upright*) (11.8.83) 60 40
   ca. Wmk sideways 90 40
   cw. Wmk inverted .. .. 5·50 50
936 10 r. maroon and bright green (24.2.84) .. 50 45
   a. Imperf (pair) .. .. ..
   b. Wmk upright (1988) 30 35
920/36 .. .. .. Set of 17 3·75 2·25
(c) Litho. Wmk Large Star and "INDIA GOVT" in sheet* (2 p.) or W 374 (5 p.). P 14×14½ (2 p.) or 13 (5 p.).
937 2 p. slate-violet (2.2.81) 10 60
938 5 p. new blue (29.11.82) 10 10
Designs: *Horiz as T 798*—2 p. Adult education class; 10 p. Irrigation canal; 25 p. (No. 925) Chick hatching from egg; 25 p. (No. 925b) Village, wheat and tractor; 30 p. Harvesting maize; 50 p. Woman dairy farmer, cows and milk bottles. *(36×19 mm)*—10 r. Forest and hillside. *Vert as T 798*—15 p. Farmer and agriculture symbols; 20 p. Mother feeding child; 35 p. "Family". *(17×28 mm)*—1 r. Cotton plant; 2 r. Weaving. *Vert as T 799*—2 r. 25, Cashew; 2 r. 80, Apples; 3 r. 25, Oranges.
*See note concerning this watermark below No. 720. The 2 p. and 5 p. exist on both types of this watermark, the others on the second type only.
†For notes on the amended version of W 374 see above No. 399. The changes in watermark position from 1987 onwards show the reduced size base.
**The normal sideways watermark shows the capital heads to left, *as seen from the back of the stamp.*
Nos. 920/1 and 923/4 were originally intended for issue on 9 March 1981 and First Day Covers showing this date are known from at least one post office.
At least one sheet of No. 924a exists without an impression from the ink cylinder on the first horizontal row.
No. 937 can be easily identified by the background of horizontal lines.
For 75 p. in same design as No. 927 see No. 1214.

800 Jatindra Nath Das

801 De Havilland D.H.80A Puss Moth

1979 (13 Sept). *50th Death Anniv of Jatindra Nath Das (revolutionary).* P 13.
941 **800** 30 p. blackish brown 20 30

1979 (15 Oct). *Air. "India 80" International Stamp Exhibition (2nd issue). Mail-carrying Aircraft. T 801 and similar horiz designs. Multicoloured.* P 14½×14.
942 30 p. Type 801 .. .. 30 25
943 50 p. Indian Air Force Hindustan Aircraft Industries Chetak helicopter .. 50 45
944 1 r. Indian Airlines Boeing 737 airliner .. 65 75
945 2 r. Air India Boeing 747 airliner .. 75 95
942/5 .. .. Set of 4 2·00 2·25

802 Early and Modern Lightbulbs

803 Gilgit Record

1979 (21 Oct). *Centenary of Electric Lightbulb.* P 13.
946 **802** 1 r. brown-purple 20 30

1979 (23 Oct). *International Archives Week.* P 14½×14.
947 **803** 30 p. yellow-ochre and sepia .. 20 50

804 Hirakud Dam, Orissa

805 Fair Emblem

1979 (29 Oct). *50th Anniv, and 13th Congress, of International Commission on Large Dams.* P 13.
948 **804** 30 p. lake-brown and deep blue-green .. 20 30

806 Child learning to Read

1979 (10 Nov). *India International Trade Fair, New Delhi.* P 13.
949 **805** 1 r. grey-black and salmon .. 20 30

1979 (10 Nov). *International Children's Book Fair, New Delhi.* P 14½×14.
950 **806** 30 p. multicoloured 20 30

807 Dove with Olive Branch and I.A.E.A. Emblem

1979 (4 Dec). *23rd I.A.E.A. (International Atomic Energy Agency) Conference, New Delhi.* P 13.
951 **807** 1 r. multicoloured 20 45

808 Hindustan Aircraft Industries HAL-26 Pushpak Light Plane and Rohini-1 Glider

809 Gurdwara Baoli Sahib Temple, Goindwal, Amritsar District

(Des R. N. Pasricha)
1979 (10 Dec). *Flying and Gliding.* P 13.
952 **808** 30 p. black, orange-brown and blue .. 1·00 80

1979 (21 Dec). *500th Birth Anniv of Guru Amar Das (Sikh leader).* P 13.
953 **809** 30 p. multicoloured 20 30

810 Ring of People encircling U.N. Emblem and Cogwheel

811 Army Post Office and Postmarks

1980 (21 Jan). *3rd U.N.I.D.O. (United Nations Industrial Development Organisation) General Conference, New Delhi.* P 13.
954 **810** 1 r. multicoloured 20 30

(Des Benoy Sarkar (30, 50 p.), India Security Press (others))
1980 (25 Jan). *"India 80" International Stamp Exhibition (3rd issue). T 811 and similar vert designs. No wmk (1 r.) or Large Star and "INDIA GOVT" in sheet* (others).* P 13.
955 30 p. grey-olive 40 30
956 50 p. bistre-brown and dull olive-bistre .. 70 1·00
957 1 r. Venetian red .. .. 80 1·00
958 2 r. olive-brown .. .. 80 2·00
955/8 .. .. Set of 4 2·40 3·75
Designs:—50 p. Money order transfer document, 1879; 1 r. Copper prepayment ticket, 1774; 2 r. Sir Rowland Hill and birthplace at Kidderminster.
*See note below No. 720.

812 Energy Symbols

813 Uniforms of 1780 and 1980, Crest and Ribbon

(Des C. Pakrashi)

1980 (17 Feb). *Institution of Engineers (India) Commemoration. Wmk Large Star and "INDIA GOVT" in sheet.* P 13.
959 812 30 p. gold and blue 20 30

1980 (26 Feb). *Bicentenary of Madras Sappers.* P 13.
960 813 30 p. multicoloured 60 50

814 Books

815 Bees and Honey-comb

(Des J. Gupta)

1980 (29 Feb). *4th World Book Fair, New Delhi. Wmk Large Star and "INDIA GOVT" in sheet.* P 13.
961 814 30 p. new blue 30 30

(Des M. Bardhan)

1980 (29 Feb). *2nd International Apiculture Conference, New Delhi.* P 13.
962 815 1 r. deep brown and olive-bistre .. 50 45

816 Welthy Fisher and Saksharta Nicketan (Literacy) House), Lucknow

817 Darul-Uloom, Deoband

(Des M. Choudhury)

1980 (18 Mar). *Welthy Fisher (teacher) Commemoration. Wmk Large Star and "INDIA GOVT" in sheet.* P 13.
963 816 30 p. chalky blue 30 30

(Des Charanjit Lal)

1980 (21 Mar). *Darul-Uloom (college), Deoband Commemoration. Wmk Large Star and "INDIA GOVT" in sheet.* P 13.
964 817 30 p. deep grey-green 20 30

818 Keshub Chunder Sen

819 Chhatrapati Shivaji Maharaj

1980 (15 Apr). *Keshub Chunder Sen (religious and social reformer) Commemoration. Wmk. Large Star and "INDIA GOVT" in sheet.* P 13.
965 818 30 p. bistre-brown 20 30

1980 (21 Apr). *300th Death Anniv of Chhatrapati Shivaji Maharaj (warrior).* P 13.
966 819 30 p. multicoloured 20 30

820 Table Tennis

821 N. M. Joshi

1980 (9 May). *5th Asian Table Tennis Championships, Calcutta. Wmk Large Star and "INDIA GOVT" in sheet.* P 13.
967 820 30 p. deep reddish purple 30 30

1980 (27 May). *Designs as Nos. 732 and 810b. Size 17 × 20 mm.* W 374 (*sideways*). P 14½ × 14.
968 30 p. red-brown (Gandhi) .. .. 3·75 80
969 30 p. dull violet (Nehru) .. .. 1·00 40

1980 (5 June). *Narayan Malhar Joshi (trade-unionist) Commemoration. Wmk Large Star and "INDIA GOVT" in sheet.* P 13.
970 821 30 p. magenta 60 40

822 Ulloor S. Parameswara Iyer

823 S. M. Zamin Ali

1980 (6 June). *Ulloor S. Parameswara Iyer (poet) Commemoration. Wmk Large Star and "INDIA GOVT" in sheet.* P 13.
971 822 30 p. maroon 60 40

1980 (25 June). *Syed Mohammed Zamin Ali (educationist and poet) Commemoration. Wmk Large Star and "INDIA GOVT" in sheet.* P 13.
972 823 30 p. bronze-green 20 40

824 Helen Keller

825 High-jumping

1980 (27 June). *Birth Centenary of Helen Keller (campaigner for the handicapped).* P 13.
973 824 30 p. black and dull orange 50 40

1980 (19 July). *Olympic Games, Moscow. T* **825** *and similar vert design. Multicoloured.* P 13½ × 14.
974 1 r. Type **825** 40 40
975 2 r. 80, Horse-riding .. .. .. 1·40 2·50

826 Prem Chand

827 Mother Teresa and Nobel Peace Prize Medallion

1980 (31 July). *Birth Centenary of Prem Chand (novelist). Wmk Large Star and "INDIA GOVT" in sheet.* P 13.
976 826 30 p. red-brown 20 40

1980 (27 Aug). *Award of 1979 Nobel Peace Prize to Mother Teresa. Wmk Large Star and "INDIA GOVT" in sheet.* P 13.
977 827 30 p. bluish violet 50 30

828 Lord Mountbatten

829 Scottish Church College, Calcutta

1980 (28 Aug). *Lord Mountbatten Commemoration.* P 13.
978 828 2 r. 80, multicoloured .. .. 2·00 2·50

1980 (1 Sept)—82. *As Nos. 968/9, but new face value.* W 374 (*sideways*). P 14½ × 14.
979 35 p. red-brown (Gandhi) (16.9.80) .. 1·00 30
  a. Perf 13 (5.7.82) .. .. 1·00 30
980 35 p. dull violet (Nehru) 30 20
  a. Perf 13 (5.7.82) 30 20

(Des C. Pakrashi)

1980 (27 Sept). *150th Anniv of Scottish Church College, Calcutta. Wmk Large Star and "INDIA GOVT" in sheet.* P 13.
981 829 35 p. deep rose-lilac 20 30

830 Rajah Annamalai Chettiar

831 Gandhi marching to Dandi

1980 (30 Sept). *Rajah Annamalai Chettiar (banker and educationist) Commemoration.* P 14 × 14½.
982 830 35 p. deep lilac 20 30

(Des S. Ramachandran)

1980 (2 Oct). *50th Anniv of "Dandi March" (Gandhi's defiance of Salt Tax Law). T* **831** *and similar vert design.* P 14½ × 14.
983 35 p. black, turquoise-blue and gold .. 25 70
  a. Horiz pair. Nos. 983/4 .. 50 1·40
984 35 p. black, deep mauve and gold .. 25 70
Design:—No. 983, Type **831**; No. 984, Gandhi picking up handful of salt at Dandi.
No. 984 with the deep mauve omitted is a chemically produced fake.
Nos. 983/4 were printed together, *se-tenant*, in horizontal pairs throughout the sheet.

832 Jayaprakash Narayan

833 Great Indian Bustard

(Des Directorate of Advertising and Visual Publicity, New Delhi)

1980 (8 Oct). *Jayaprakash Narayan (socialist) Commemoration. Wmk Large Star and "INDIA GOVT" in sheet.* P 14 × 14½.
985 832 35 p. chocolate 40 40

(Des J. Irani)

1980 (1 Nov). *International Symposium on Bustards, Jaipur.* P 13.
986 833 2 r. 30, multicoloured .. .. 1·00 2·00

834 Arabic Commemorative Inscription

(Des B. Makhmoor)

1980 (3 Nov). *Moslem Year 1400 A.H. Commemoration.* P 13.
987 834 35 p. multicoloured 15 30

835 "Girls Dancing" (Pampa Paul)

836 Dhyan Chand

1980 (14 Nov). *Children's Day.* P 13½ × 13.
988 835 35 p. multicoloured 40 40

1980 (3 Dec). *Dhyan Chand (hockey player) Commemoration.* P 14 × 14½.
989 836 35 p. red-brown 80 75

MINIMUM PRICE

The minimum price quote is 10p which represents a handling charge rather than a basis for valuing common stamps. For further notes about prices see introductory pages.

837 Gold Mining   838 M. A. Ansari

1980 (20 Dec). *Centenary of Kolar Gold Fields, Karnataka. P* 13.
990 837   1 r. multicoloured   1·10   30

1980 (25 Dec). *Mukhtayar Ahmad Ansari (medical practitioner and politician) Commemoration. Wmk Large Star and "INDIA GOVT" in sheet. P* 14×14¹/₂.
991 838   35 p. dull olive   40   40

839 India Government Mint, Bombay   840 Bride from Tamil Nadu

1980 (27 Dec). *150th Anniv of India Government Mint. Bombay. P* 13.
992 839   35 p. black, silver and dull blue   20   30

1980 (30 Dec). *Brides in Traditional Costume. T* 840 *and similar vert designs. Multicoloured. P* 13.
993   1 r. Type 840   40   75
994   1 r. Bride from Rajasthan   40   75
995   1 r. Bride from Kashmir   40   75
996   1 r. Bride from Bengal   40   75
993/6   *Set of* 4   1·40   2·75

841 Mazharul Haque   842 St. Stephen's College

1981 (2 Jan). *Mazharul Haque (journalist) Commemoration. Wmk Large Star and "INDIA GOVT" in sheet. P* 14×14¹/₂.
997 841   35 p. chalky blue   20   40

1981 (1 Feb). *Centenary of St. Stephen's College, Delhi. Wmk Large Star and "INDIA GOVT" in sheet. P* 14 × 14¹/₂.
998 842   35 p. dull scarlet   20   40

843 Gommateshwara   844 G. V. Mavalankar

1981 (9 Feb). *Millenium of Gommateshwara (statue at Shravanabelgola). P* 14×14¹/₂.
999 843   1 r. multicoloured   20   30

1981 (27 Feb). *25th Death Anniv of Ganesh Vasudeo Mavalankar (parliamentarian). P* 14×14¹/₂.
1000 844   35 p. Venetian red   20   30

845 Flame of Martyrdom   846 Heinrich von Stephan and U.P.U. Emblem

---

(Des D. Dey)

1981 (23 Mar). *"Homage to Martyrs". P* 14 × 14¹/₂.
1001 845   35 p. multicoloured   20   30

1981 (8 Apr). *150th Birth Anniv of Heinrich von Stephan (founder of U.P.U.). P* 14¹/₂ × 14.
1002 846   1 r. red-brown and new blue   20   50

847 Disabled Child being helped by Able-bodied Child   848 Bhil

(Des K. Raha)

1981 (20 Apr). *International Year for Disabled Persons. P* 14¹/₂ × 14.
1003 847   1 r. black and blue   20   30

(Des from photographs by A. Pareek (No. 1004), S. Dutta (No. 1005). S. Theodore Baskaran (No. 1006), Kikrumielie Angami (No. 1007))

1981 (30 May). *Tribes of India. T* 848 *and similar vert designs. Multicoloured. P* 14.
1004   1 r. Type 848   40   35
1005   1 r. Dandami Maria   40   35
1006   1 r. Toda   40   35
1007   1 r. Khlamngam Naga   40   35
1004/7   *Set of* 4   1·40   1·25

849 Stylised Trees   850 Nilmoni Phukan

(Des M. Bardhan)

1981 (15 June). *Conservation of Forests. P* 14 × 14¹/₂.
1008 849   1 r. multicoloured   20   30

1981 (22 June). *Nilmoni Phukan (poet) Commemoration. P* 14 × 14¹/₂.
1009 850   35 p. red-brown   20   40

851 Sanjay Gandhi   852 Launch of "SLV 3" and Diagram of "Rohini"

(Des C. Pakrashi)

1981 (23 June). *First Death Anniv of Sanjay Gandhi (politician). P* 13.
1010 851   35 p. multicoloured   40   55

1981 (18 July). *Launch of "SLV 3" Rocket with "Rohini" Satellite. P* 14 × 14¹/₂.
1011 852   1 r. black, pink and pale blue   30   30

853 Games Logo   854 Flame of the Forest

(Des M. Chaudhury (No. 1013))

1981 (28 July). *Asian Games, New Delhi (1st issue). T* 853 *and similar horiz design. Multicoloured. P* 13¹/₂ × 13.
1012   1 r. Type 853   1·00   65
1013   1 r. Games emblem and stylised hockey players   1·00   65
   See also Nos. 1026, 1033, 1057, 1059 and 1061/6.

(Des from photographs by K. Vaid (35 p., 2 r.), R. Bedi (others))

1981 (1 Sept). *Flowering Trees. T* 854 *and similar vert designs. Multicoloured. P* 13 × 13¹/₂.
1014   35 p. Type 854   40   15
1015   50 p. Crateva   75   75
1016   1 r. Golden Shower   1·00   50
1017   2 r. Bauhinia   1·40   2·25
1014/17   *Set of* 4   3·25   3·25

855 W.F.D. Emblem and Wheat   856 Stichophthalma camadeva

(Des M. Bardhan)

1981 (16 Oct). *World Food Day. P* 14 × 14¹/₂.
1018 855   1 r. greenish yellow and Prussian blue   20   20

(Des from paintings by M. Mandal)

1981 (20 Oct). *Butterflies. T* 856 *and similar multicoloured designs. P* 13.
1019   35 p. Type 856   90   15
1020   50 p. Cethosia biblis   1·75   1·40
1021   1 r. Cyrestis achates (vert)   2·25   70
1022   2 r. Teinopalpus imperialis (vert)   2·75   5·00
1019/22   *Set of* 4   7·00   6·50

857 Bellary Raghava   858 Regimental Colour

1981 (31 Oct). *Bellary Raghava (actor) Commemoration. P* 14¹/₂ × 14.
1023 857   35 p. brown-olive   70   30

1981 (9 Nov). *40th Anniv of Mahar Regiment. P* 13 × 13¹/₂.
1024 858   35 p. multicoloured   90   30

859 "Toyseller" (Kumari Ruchita Sharma)   860 Rajghat Stadium

1981 (14 Nov). *Children's Day. P* 14×14¹/₂.
1025 859   35 p. multicoloured   75   30

1981 (19 Nov). *Asian Games, New Delhi (2nd issue). P* 13¹/₂ × 13.
1026 860   1 r. multicoloured   1·50   30

861 Kashi Prasad Jayasawal and Yaudheya Coin   862 India and P.L.O. Flags, and People

1981 (27 Nov). *Birth Centenary of Kashi Prasad Jayasawal (lawyer and historian). P* 14 × 14¹/₂.
1027 861   35 p. chalky blue   50   30

(Des B. Makhmoor)

1981 (29 Nov). *Palestinian Solidarity. P* 14¹/₂ × 14.
1028 862   1 r. multicoloured   2·00   40

863 I.N.S. *Taragiri* (frigate)

864 Henry Heras and Indus Valley Seal

1981 (4 Dec). *Indian Navy Day. P* 14½ × 14.
1029 863 35 p. multicoloured .. .. 2·25 1·25

1981 (14 Dec). *Henry Heras (historian) Commemoration. P* 14½ × 14.
1030 864 35 p. deep rose-lilac 45 30

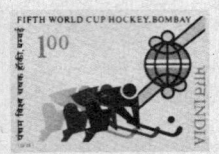

865 Map of South-East Asia showing Cable Route

866 Stylised Hockey-players and Championship Emblem

1981 (24 Dec). *Inauguration of I.O.C.O.M. (Indian Ocean Commonwealth Cable) Submarine Telephone Cable. P* 13½×13.
1031 865 1 r. multicoloured .. .. 2·00 35

(Des C. Lal)

1981 (29 Dec). *World Cup Hockey Championship, Bombay. P* 13½ × 14.
1032 866 1 r. multicoloured 95 30

867 Jawaharlal Nehru Stadium

868 Early and Modern Telephones

1981 (30 Dec). *Asian Games, New Delhi (3rd issue). P* 13½ × 13.
1033 867 1 r. multicoloured 30 20

(Des C. Pakrashi)

1982 (28 Jan). *Centenary of Telephone Services. P* 13.
1034 868 2 r. black, new blue and olive-grey .. 30 30

869 Map of World

870 Sir J. J. School of Art

1982 (8 Feb). *International Soil Science Congress, New Delhi. P* 13.
1035 869 1 r. multicoloured 30 20

(Des M. Patel)

1982 (2 Mar). *125th Anniv of Sir J. J. School of Art, Bombay. P* 14 × 14½.
1036 870 35 p. multicoloured 20 20

871 "Three Musicians"

872 Deer (stone carving), 5th-century A.D.

1982 (15 Mar). *Birth Centenary of Picasso* (1981). *P* 14.
1037 871 2 r. 85, multicoloured .. .. 1·10 50

1982 (23 Mar). *Festival of India. Ancient Sculpture. T* 872 and similar vert design. Multicoloured. P 14 × 14½.
1038 2 r. Type 872 .. .. 20 40
1039 3 r. 05, Kaliya Mardana (bronze statue), 9th-century A.D. 35 60

873 Radio Telescope, Ooty

874 Robert Koch and Symbol of Disease

1982 (23 Mar). *Festival of India. Science and Technology. P* 13½ × 13.
1040 873 3 r. 05, multicoloured 35 40

(Des A. Ramachandran)

1982 (24 Mar). *Centenary of Robert Koch's Discovery of Tubercle Bacillus. P* 13½ × 13.
1041 874 35 p. deep rose-lilac .. 1·40 75

875 Durgabai Deshmukh

876 Blue Poppy

1982 (9 May). *First Death Anniv of Durgabai Deshmukh (social reformer). P* 14½ × 14.
1042 875 35 p. blue 60 70

1982 (29 May). *Himalayan Flowers. T* 876 and similar vert designs. Multicoloured. P 14.
1043 35 p. Type 876 .. .. 65 20
1044 1 r. Showy Inula .. .. 1·50 30
1045 2 r. Cobra Lily .. .. 2·00 3·00
1046 2 r. 85, Brahma Kamal .. .. 2·50 3·75
1043/6 Set of 4 6·00 6·50

877 "Apple" Satellite

878 Bidhan Chandra Roy

1982 (19 June). *1st Anniv of "Apple" Satellite Launch. P* 13½ × 13.
1047 877 2 r. multicoloured 50 80

1982 (1 July). *Birth Centenary of Bidhan Chandra Roy (doctor and politician). P* 15 × 14.
1048 878 50 p. chestnut .. .. 80 1·25

879 Oil Rig *Sagar Samrat*

880 "Bindu" (S. H. Raza)

1982 (14 Aug). *25th Anniv of Oil and Natural Gas Commission. P* 13½ × 13.
1049 879 1 r. multicoloured .. .. 1·00 60

1982 (17 Sept). *Festival of India. Contemporary Paintings. T* 880 and similar vert design. Multicoloured. P 14×14½.
1050 2 r. Type 880 .. .. 40 50
1051 3 r. 05, "Between the Spider and the Lamp" (M. F. Hussain) .. .. 60 1·25

881 Red Deer Stag, Kashmir

882 Westland Wapiti Biplane and Mikoyan Gurevich MiG-25

1982 (1 Oct). *Wildlife Conservation. P* 13 × 13½.
1052 881 2 r. 85, multicoloured .. .. 1·50 1·25

1982 (8 Oct). *50th Anniv of Indian Air Force. P* 13½ × 13.
1053 882 1 r. multicoloured .. .. 4·00 1·25

883 J. Tata with De Havilland D.H.80A Puss Moth

884 Police Patrol

1982 (15 Oct). *50th Anniv of Civil Aviation in India. P* 13½ × 13.
1054 883 3 r. 25, multicoloured .. .. 3·50 1·60

(Des B. Prakash)

1982 (21 Oct). *Police Commemoration Day. P* 13.
1055 884 50 p. bronze-green 50 30

885 Coins and Economic Symbols

886 Wrestling Bout

(Des S. Jha)

1982 (23 Oct). *Centenary of Post Office Savings Bank. P* 13.
1056 885 50 p. brown and cinnamon .. 20 20

(Des A. Ramachandran)

1982 (30 Oct). *Asian Games, New Delhi (4th issue). P* 13½ × 14.
1057 886 1 r. multicoloured 30 30

887 Troposcatter Communication Link

888 Arjuna shooting Arrow at Fish

1982 (2 Nov). *1st Anniv of Troposcatter Communication Link between India and U.S.S.R. P* 13.
1058 887 3 r. 05, multicoloured 30 40

(Des A. Ramachandran)

1982 (6 Nov). *Asian Games, New Delhi (5th issue). P* 13½ × 14.
1059 888 1 r. multicoloured .. .. 1·75 30

PRICES OF SETS

Set prices are given for many issues, generally those containing three stamps or more. Definitive sets include one of each value or major colour change, but do not cover different perforations, die types or minor shades. Where a choice is possible the set prices are based on the cheapest versions of the stamps included in the listings.

889 "Mother and Child" (Deepak Sharma)   890 Stylised Cyclists

1982 (14 Nov). *Children's Day. P* 14 × 14½.
1060 889 50 p. multicoloured   30   30

(Des C. Pakrashi (50 p.), B. Prakash (3 r. 25))

1982 (19 Nov). *Asian Games, New Delhi (6th issue). T* **890** *and similar horiz designs. Multicoloured. P* 13.
1061   50 p. Type **890**   10   10
1062   2 r. Javelin-throwing   25   30
1063   2 r. 85, Discus-throwing   30   45
1064   3 r. 25, Football   40   55
1061/4   ..   ..   ..   *Set of* 4   90   1·25

891 "Enterprise" Dinghies Race   892 Chetwode Building

(Des C. Pakrashi)

1982 (25 Nov). *Asian Games, New Delhi (7th issue). T* **891** *and similar horiz design. Multicoloured. P* 13.
1065   2 r. Type **891**   90   30
1066   2 r. 85, Rowing   ..   ..   1·10   55

1982 (10 Dec). *50th Anniv of Indian Military Academy, Dehradun. P* 13.
1067 892 50 p. multicoloured   30   50

893 Purushottamdas Tandon   894 Darjeeling Himalayan Railway

1982 (15 Dec). *Birth Centenary of Purushottamdas Tandon (politician). P* 12½×13.
1068 893 50 p. yellow-brown   30   70

1982 (18 Dec). *Centenary of Darjeeling Himalayan Railway. P* 13
1069 894 2 r. 85, multicoloured   ..   ..   4·25   4·25

895 Vintage Rail Coach and Silhouette of Steam Locomotive   896 Antarctic Camp

(Des C. Pakrashi)

1982 (30 Dec). *"Inpex 82" Stamp Exhibition. T* **895** *and similar multicoloured design. P* 13 (50 p.) or 13½ × 14 (2 r.).
1070   50 p. Type **895**   75   85
1071   2 r. 1854 ½ a. stamp and 1947 3½ a. Independence commemorative (33 × 44 *mm*)   2·00   2·25

1983 (9 Jan). *First Indian Antarctic Expedition. P* 13.
1072 896 1 r. multicoloured   ..   ..   3·50   2·25

1983 (25 Jan). *As Nos. 968/9, but new face value. W* **374** (*sideways**). *P* 12½×13.
1073   50 p. red-brown (Gandhi)   ..   3·00   1·50
       a. Wmk upright   ..   ..   3·00   1·50
1074   50 p. deep ultramarine (Nehru)   ..   3·00   1·50
       a. Wmk upright   ..   ..   1·50   55
       w. Wmk capital heads to right   ..   4·00   55
*The normal sideways watermark shows the capital heads to left, *as seen from the back of the stamp.*

897 Roosevelt with Stamp Collection   898 "Siberian (Great White) Cranes at Bharatpur" (Diane Pierce)

1983 (30 Jan). *Birth Centenary of Franklin D. Roosevelt (American statesman) (1982). P* 12½ × 13.
1075 897 3 r. 25, bistre-brown   ..   55   1·25

1983 (7 Feb). *International Crane Workshop, Bharatpur. P* 13.
1076 898 2 r. 85, multicoloured   ..   2·00   2·50

899 Jat Regiment Uniforms Past and Present   900 Non-aligned Summit Logo

(Des C. Lal)

1983 (16 Feb). *Presentation of Colours to Battalions of the Jat Regiment. P* 13.
1077 899 50 p. multicoloured   ..   1·50   1·25

(Des N. Srivastava)

1983 (7 Mar). *7th Non-aligned Summit Conference, New Delhi. T* **900** *and similar horiz design. P* 13.
1078   1 r. bistre, orange-brown and black   20   30
1079   2 r. multicoloured   30   95
Design:—2 r. Nehru.

901 Shore Temple, Mahabalipuram   902 Acropolis and Olympic Emblems

(Des R. Pasricha)

1983 (14 Mar). *Commonwealth Day. T* **901** *and similar horiz design. Multicoloured. P* 13.
1080   1 r. Type **901**   15   30
1081   2 r. Gomukh, Gangotri Glacier   ..   30   1·25

(Des B. Makhmoor)

1983 (25 Mar). *International Olympic Committee Session, New Delhi. P* 13.
1082 902 1 r. multicoloured   30   50

903 "St. Francis and Brother Falcon" (statue by Giovanni Collina)   904 Karl Marx and *Das Kapital*

1983 (4 Apr). *800th Birth Anniv of St. Francis of Assisi. P* 13.
1083 903 1 r. bistre-brown   30   30

1983 (5 May). *Death Centenary of Karl Marx. P* 13.
1084 904 1 r. brown   20   30

905 Darwin and Map of Voyage

(Des M. Mandal)

1983 (18 May). *Death Centenary (1982) of Charles Darwin (naturalist). P* 13.
1085 905 2 r. multicoloured   ..   2·25   2·75

ALTERED CATALOGUE NUMBERS

Any Catalogue numbers altered from the last edition are shown as a list in the introductory pages.

906 Swamp Deer   907 Globe and Satellite

1983 (30 May). *50th Anniv of Kanha National Park. P* 13.
1086 906 1 r. multicoloured   ..   ..   1·50   75

(Des M. Mandal)

1983 (18 July). *World Communications Year. P* 13 × 12½.
1087 907 1 r. multicoloured   40   40

908 Simon Bolivar

1983 (24 July). *Birth Bicentenary of Simon Bolivar (South American statesman). P* 12½ × 13.
1088 908 2 r. multicoloured   ..   ..   1·75   2·00

909 Meera Behn   910 Ram Nath Chopra

(Des C. Pakrashi (No. 1091))

1983 (9 Aug–28 Dec). *India's Struggle for Freedom (1st series). T* **909** *and similar designs. P* 14×13½ (*No.* 1091) *or* 13 (*others*).
1089   50 p. dull vermilion and dull green   ..   90   2·00
       a. Horiz pair. Nos. 1089/90   1·75   4·00
1090   50 p. lt brown, dull green & dull vermilion   90   2·00
1091   50 p. multicoloured   90   1·50
1092   50 p. reddish brn, yell-grn & red-orge (18.10) 15 30
1093   50 p. olive-sepia, green and orange (18.10).. 15 30
1094   50 p. olive-green, yellow-grn & orge (28.12) 15 30
1089/94   ..   ..   *Set of* 6   2·75   5·75
Designs: *Vert*—No. 1089, Type **909**; No. 1090, Mahadev Desai; No. 1092, Hemu Kalani (revolutionary); No. 1093, Acharya Vinoba Bhave (social reformer); No. 1094, Surendranath Banerjee (political reformer). *Horiz* (43×31 *mm*)—No. 1091, Quit India Resolution.
Nos. 1089/90 were printed together, *se-tenant*, in horizontal pairs throughout the sheet.
See also Nos. 1119/24, 1144/9, 1191/4, 1230/5, 1287/96 and 1345/9.

1983 (17 Aug). *Ram Nath Chopra (pharmacologist) Commemoration. P* 12½ × 13.
1095 910 50 p. Venetian red   ..   40   80

911 Nanda Devi Mountain   912 Great Indian Hornbill

1983 (27 Aug). *25th Anniv of Indian Mountaineering Federation. P* 13.
1096 911 2 r. multicoloured   ..   ..   1·10   90

(Des J. Irani)

1983 (15 Sept). *Centenary of Natural History Society, Bombay. P* 13.
1097 912 1 r. multicoloured   ..   ..   2·75   90

913 View of Garden   914 Golden Langur

1983 (23 Sept). *Rock Garden, Chandigarh.* P 13.
1098 **913** 1 r. multicoloured .. .. .. 1·25 85

1983 (1 Oct). *Indian Wildlife. Monkeys. T* **914** *and similar horiz design. Multicoloured.* P 13.
1099 1 r. Type **914**. .. .. .. 1·25 50
1100 2 r. Liontail Macaque .. .. .. 2·50 3·25

915 Ghats of Varanasi

916 Krishna Kanta Handique

1983 (3 Oct). *Fifth General Assembly of World Tourism Organization.* P 14 × 13½.
1101 **915** 2 r. multicoloured 50 40

1983 (7 Oct). *Krishna Kanta Handique (scholar) Commemoration.* P 13 × 12½.
1102 **916** 50 p. deep blue 30 70

918 Woman and Child (from "Festival" by Kashyap Premsawala)

920 *Udan Khatola,* First Indian Hot Air Balloon

1983 (14 Nov). *Children's Day.* P 13 × 13½.
1103 **918** 50 p. multicoloured 30 50

1983 (21 Nov). *Bicentenary of Manned Flight. T* **920** *and similar vert design. Multicoloured.* P 13.
1104 1 r. Type **920**. 75 20
1105 2 r. Montgolfier balloon .. .. 1·00 80

921 Tiger

922 Commonwealth Logo

1983 (22 Nov). *Ten Years of "Project Tiger".* P 13 × 13½.
1106 **921** 2 r. multicoloured .. .. 2·50 3·00

(Des K. Raha (1 r.))

1983 (23 Nov). *Commonwealth Heads of Government Meeting, New Delhi. T* **922** *and similar vert design. Multicoloured.* P 13 × 12½.
1107 1 r. Type **922**. 10 15
1108 2 r. Early 19th-century Goanese couple .. 25 30

923 "Pratiksha"

925 Lancer in Ceremonial Uniform

1983 (5 Dec). *Birth Cent of Nanda Lal Bose (artist).* P 13 × 12½.
1109 **923** 1 r. multicoloured 30 30

1984 (7 Jan). *Bicentenary of 7th Light Cavalry Regiment.* P 13 × 12½.
1110 **925** 1 r. multicoloured .. .. 3·25 1·40

---

926 Troopers in Ceremonial Uniform, and Tank

927 Society Building and William Jones (founder)

1984 (9 Jan). *Presentation of Regimental Guidon to the Deccan Horse.* P 13 × 13½.
1111 **926** 1 r. multicoloured .. .. 3·25 1·40

1984 (15 Jan). *Bicentenary of Asiatic Society.* P 13.
1112 **927** 1 r. emerald and bright purple .. 30 50

928 Insurance Logo

929 Hawker Siddeley Sea Harrier

(Des S. Jha)

1984 (1 Feb). *Centenary of Postal Life Insurance.* P 13 × 13½.
1113 **928** 1 r. multicoloured 30 30

(Des Capt. A. Dhir and S. Dheer)

1984 (12 Feb). *President's Review of the Fleet. T* **929** *and similar horiz designs. Multicoloured.* P 13½ × 13.
1114 1 r. Type **929** .. .. 1·50 1·75
 a. Block of 4. Nos. 1114/17 .. 5·50
1115 1 r. *Vikrant* (aircraft carrier) .. 1·50 1·75
1116 1 r. *Vela* (submarine) .. .. 1·50 1·75
1117 1 r. *Kashin* (destroyer) .. .. 1·50 1·75
1114/17 *Set of 4* 5·50 6·25
Nos. 1114/17 were printed in *se-tenant* blocks of four within the sheet, forming a composite design.

930 I.L.A. Logo and Hemispheres

(Des J. Irani)

1984 (20 Feb). *12th International Leprosy Congress.* P 13.
1118 **930** 1 r. multicoloured 30 30

(Des C. Pakrashi (Nos. 1119, 1121/4))

1984 (21 Feb–10 May). *India's Struggle for Freedom (2nd series). Vert portraits as T* **909**. P 13.
1119 50 p. dp brownish olive, yell-grn & brt orge 30 40
1120 50 p. bistre-brown, emerald & brt orge (23.4) 30 40
1121 50 p. multicoloured (10.5) .. 50 60
1122 50 p. multicoloured (10.5) .. 50 60
1123 50 p. multicoloured (10.5) .. 50 60
1124 50 p. multicoloured (10.5) .. 50 60
1119/24 *Set of 6* 2·40 2·75
Designs:—No. 1119, Vasudeo Balvant Phadke (revolutionary); No. 1120, Baba Kanshi Ram (revolutionary); No. 1121, Tatya Tope; No. 1122, Nana Sahib; No. 1123, Begum Hazrat Mahal; No. 1124, Mangal Pandey.

932 "Salyut 7"

(Des R. Pasricha)

1984 (3 Apr). *Indo-Soviet Manned Space Flight.* P 14.
1125 **932** 3 r. multicoloured 55 55

---

935 G. D. Birla

936 Basketball

1984 (11 June). *90th Birth Anniv of G. D. Birla (industrialist).* P 13.
1126 **935** 50 p. chocolate 30 70

(Des K. Reha and S. Jha)

1984 (28 July). *Olympic Games, Los Angeles. T* **936** *and similar multicoloured designs.* P 13.
1127 50 p. Type **936** 90 65
1128 1 r. High jumping 75 30
1129 2 r. Gymnastics (*horiz*) .. 1·00 1·50
1130 2 r. 50, Weightlifting (*horiz*) .. 1·25 2·50
1127/30 *Set of 4* 3·50 4·50

937 Gwalior

938 B.V. Paradkar and Newspaper

1984 (3 Aug). *Forts. T* **937** *and similar multicoloured designs.* P 13½ × 13 (50 p., 2 r.) or 13 × 13½ (*others*).
1131 50 p. Type **937** 70 55
1132 1 r. Vellore (*vert*) 95 30
1133 1 r. 50, Simhagad (*vert*) .. 1·75 2·75
1134 2 r. Jodhpur .. .. 2·00 3·00
1131/4 *Set of 4* 4·75 6·00

1984 (14 Sept). *B. V. Paradkar (journalist) Commemoration.* P 13 × 13½.
1135 **938** 50 p. reddish brown 30 60

939 Dr. D. N. Wadia and Institute of Himalayan Geology, Dehradun

940 "Herdsman and Cattle in Forest" (H. Kassam)

1984 (23 Oct). *Birth Centenary (1983) of Dr. D. N. Wadia (geologist).* P 13.
1136 **939** 1 r. multicoloured .. .. 1·25 30

1984 (14 Nov). *Children's Day.* P 13 × 13½.
1137 **940** 50 p. multicoloured 75 95

941 Indira Gandhi

(Des C. Lal)

1984 (19 Nov). *Prime Minister Indira Gandhi Commemoration (1st issue).* P 15 × 14.
1138 **941** 50 p. black, lavender and bright orange 2·25 2·25
See also Nos. 1151, 1167 and 1170.

942 Congress Emblem   943 Dr. Rajendra Prasad at Desk

1984 (20 Nov). *12th World Mining Congress, New Delhi.* P 13×13½.
1139 **942** 1 r. black and orange-yellow .. 1·25 30

1984 (3 Dec). *Birth Centenary of Dr. Rajendra Prasad (former President).* P 13.
1140 **943** 50 p. multicoloured .. .. .. 1·00 85

944 Mrinalini (rose)   945 "Fergusson College" (Gopal Deuskar)

1984 (23 Dec). *Roses. T 944 and similar vert design. Multicoloured.* P 13.
1141 1 r. 50, Type 944 .. .. 2·00 2·00
1142 2 r. Sugandha .. .. 2·25 2·25

1985 (2 Jan). *Centenary of Fergusson College, Pune.* P 13.
1143 **945** 1 r. multicoloured 55 55

1985 (10 Jan–24 Dec). *India's Struggle for Freedom (3rd series). Portraits as T 909.* P 13.
1144 50 p. chestnut, deep green & bright orange 50 70
1145 50 p. chocolate, emerald & brt orange (21.7) 50 70
1146 50 p. reddish brown, emer & red-orge (22.7) 50 70
1147 50 p. olive-sepia, emer & reddish orge (2.12) 50 70
1148 50 p. royal blue, emerald & brt orge (23.12) 50 70
1149 50 p. grey-black, emerald & brt orge (24.12) 50 70
1144/9 *Set of 6* 2·75 3·75
Designs: *Vert*—No. 1144, Narhar Vishnu Gadgil (politician); No. 1145, Jairamdas Doulatram (journalist); No. 1147, Kaka-saheb Kalelkar (author); No. 1148, Master Tara Singh (politician); No. 1149, Ravishankar Maharaj (politician). *Horiz*—No. 1146, Jatindra and Nellie Sengupta (politicians).

947 Gunner and Howitzer from Mountain Battery

1985 (15 Jan). *50th Anniv of Regiment of Artillery.* P 13½×13.
1150 **947** 1 r. multicoloured .. .. 3·50 1·50

948 Indira Gandhi making speech
(Des R. Chopra)

1985 (31 Jan). *Indira Gandhi Commemoration (2nd issue).* P 14.
1151 **948** 2 r. multicoloured .. 2·75 3·25

949 Minicoy Lighthouse   950 Medical College Hospital

1985 (2 Feb). *Centenary of Minicoy Lighthouse.* P 13.
1152 **949** 1 r. multicoloured .. .. 3·75 85

1985 (20 Feb). *150th Anniv of Medical College, Calcutta.* P 13½×13.
1153 **950** 1 r. yellow, reddish brown and deep reddish purple .. .. .. 2·50 70

951 Medical College, Madras   952 Riflemen of 1835 and 1985, and Map of North-East India

1985 (6 Mar). *150th Anniv of Medical College, Madras.* P 13½×13.
1154 **951** 1 r. yellow-brown and reddish brown .. 2·50 70

(Des A. Sharma)

1985 (29 Mar). *150th Anniv of Assam Rifles.* P 13½×13.
1155 **952** 1 r. multicoloured .. .. 3·25 1·50

953 Potato Plant   954 Baba Jassa Singh Ahluwalia

(Des Indian Council of Agricultural Research)

1985 (1 Apr). *50th Anniv of Potato Research in India.* P 13.
1156 **953** 50 p. deep brown and grey-brown .. 1·50 1·60

1985 (4 Apr). *Death Bicentenary (1983) of Baba Jassa Singh Ahluwalia (Sikh leader).* P 13.
1157 **954** 50 p. deep reddish purple .. 1·50 1·60

955 St. Xavier's College   956 White-winged Wood Duck

1985 (12 Apr). *125th Anniv of St. Xavier's College, Calcutta.* P 13.
1158 **955** 1 r. multicoloured .. .. 1·00 50

1985 (18 May). *Wildlife Conservation. White-winged Wood Duck.* P 14.
1159 **956** 2 r. multicoloured .. .. 4·50 4·50

957 "Mahara"   958 Yaudheya Copper Coin, c 200 B.C.

1985 (5 June). *Bougainvillea. T 957 and similar vert design. Multicoloured.* P 13.
1160 50 p. Type 957 .. .. .. 1·25 2·00
1161 1 r. "H. B. Singh" .. .. .. 1·50 1·50

1985 (7 June). *Festival of India (1st issue).* P 13.
1162 **958** 2 r. multicoloured .. .. 2·25 2·25

MINIMUM PRICE

The minimum price quote is 10p which represents a handling charge rather than a basis for valuing common stamps. For further notes about prices see introductory pages.

959 Statue of Didarganj Yakshi (deity)   962 Swami Haridas

1985 (13 June). *Festival of India (2nd issue).* P 13.
1163 **959** 1 r. multicoloured .. .. 1·25 40

1985 (19 Sept). *Swami Haridas (philosopher) Commemoration.* P 13.
1164 **962** 1 r. multicoloured .. .. 1·75 1·50
Although not officially issued until 19 September 1985 examples of No. 1164 are known to have circulated from 27 November 1984, the date on which it was originally scheduled for release.

963 Stylised Mountain Road

1985 (10 Oct). *25th Anniv of Border Roads Organization.* P 13.
1165 **963** 2 r. brt carmine, bluish violet & black 2·00 2·50

964 Nehru addressing General Assembly

1985 (24 Oct). *40th Anniv of United Nations Organization.* P 13.
1166 **964** 2 r. multicoloured .. .. 1·10 90

965 Indira Gandhi with Crowd

1985 (31 Oct). *Indira Gandhi Commemoration (3rd issue).* P 14.
1167 **965** 2 r. brownish black and black .. 2·50 3·00

966 Girl using Home Computer   967 Halley's Comet

1985 (14 Nov). *Children's Day.* P 13½×13.
1168 **966** 50 p. multicoloured 90 90

1985 (19 Nov). *19th General Assembly of International Astronomical Union, New Delhi.* P 13×13½.
1169 **967** 1 r. multicoloured .. .. 2·00 1·50

968 Indira Gandhi   969 St. Stephen's Hospital

1985 (19 Nov). *Indira Gandhi Commemoration (4th issue).* P 14.
1170 **968** 3 r. multicoloured .. .. 2·50 3·00

1985 (25 Nov). *Centenary of St. Stephen's Hospital, Delhi.* P 13.
1171 **969** 1 r. black and buff 80 40

971 Map showing Member States   **972** Shyama Shastri

1985 (8 Dec). *1st Summit Meeting of South Asian Association for Regional Co-operation, Dhaka, Bangladesh.* T **971** and similar multicoloured design. P 13½×13 (1 r.) or 14 (3 r.).
1172 1 r. Type **971**.. .. .. 1·50 40
1173 3 r. Flags of member nations (44×32 mm).. 2·50 4·00

1985 (21 Dec). *Shyama Shastri (composer) Commemoration.* P 13.
1174 **972** 1 r. multicoloured .. .. 2·25 1·50

975 Young Runners and Emblem

(Des J. Irani)

1985 (24 Dec). *International Youth Year.* P 13½×13.
1175 **975** 2 r. multicoloured .. .. 1·50 75

976 Handel and Bach

1985 (27 Dec). *300th Birth Anniv of George Frederick Handel and Johann Sebastian Bach (composers).* P 13×13½.
1176 **976** 5 r. multicoloured .. .. 3·50 4·00

977 A. O. Hume (founder) and Early Congress Presidents   **978** Bombay and Duncan Dry Docks, Bombay

(Des C. Pakrashi)

1985 (28 Dec). *Centenary of Indian National Congress.* T **977** and similar vert designs showing miniature portraits of Congress Presidents. P 14.
1177 **977** 1 r. black, bright orange, lt green & grey 1·50 1·75
    a. Block of 4. Nos. 1177/80.. .. 5·50
1178 – 1 r. black, bright orange and light green 1·50 1·75
1179 – 1 r. black, bright orange and light green 1·50 1·75
1180 – 1 r. black, bright orange, lt green & grey 1·50 1·75
1177/80   *Set of 4* 5·50 6·25
Nos. 1178/80 each show sixteen miniature portraits. The individual stamps can be distinguished by the position of the face value and inscription which are at the top on Nos. 1177/8 and at the foot on Nos. 1179/80. No. 1180 shows a portrait of Prime Minister Rajiv Gandhi in a grey frame at bottom right.

(Des Capt. A. Dhir)

1986 (11 Jan). *250th Anniv of Naval Dockyard, Bombay.* P 13½×13.
1181 **978** 2 r. 50, multicoloured .. .. 3·25 4·00
                                      3·75

979 Hawa Mahal and Jaipur 1904 2 a. Stamp   **980** I.N.S. Vikrant (aircraft carrier)

(Des C. Pakrashi (2 r.))

1986 (14 Feb). *"INPEX '86" Philatelic Exhibition, Jaipur.* T **979** and similar horiz design. Multicoloured. P 13½×13.
1182 50 p. Type **979** .. .. 1·00 1·00
1183 2 r. Mobile camel post office, Thar Desert 2·25 3·00

(Des A. Sharma)

1986 (16 Feb). *Completion of 25 Years Service by I.N.S. Vikrant.* P 13×13½.
1184 **980** 2 r. multicoloured .. .. 4·50 4·50

981 Humber Sommer Biplane and Later Mail Planes   **982** Triennale Emblem

(Des R. Pasricha)

1986 (18 Feb). *75th Anniversary of First Official Airmail Flight, Allahabad – Naini.* T **981** and similar horiz design. Multicoloured. P 13½×13 (50 p.) or 13 (3 r.).
1185 50 p. Type **981** .. .. 2·25 1·75
1186 3 r. Modern Air India Airbus Industrie A300 mail plane and Humber Sommer biplane (37×24 mm) .. .. 4·75 6·50

1986 (22 Feb). *6th Triennale Art Exhibition, New Delhi.* P 13×13½.
1187 **982** 1 r. black, brt purple & orange-yellow 1·50 95

983 Chaitanya Mahaprabhu   **984** Main Building, Mayo College

1986 (13 Mar). *500th Birth Anniv of Chaitanya Mahaprabhu (religious leader).* P 13.
1188 **983** 2 r. multicoloured .. .. 2·75 3·50

1986 (12 Apr). *Mayo College (public school), Ajmer, Commem.* P 13½×13.
1189 **984** 1 r. multicoloured .. .. 1·50 1·00

985 Two Footballers   **987** Swami Sivananda

(Des Vandana Joshi)

1986 (31 May). *World Cup Football Championship, Mexico.* P 13.
1190 **985** 5 r. multicoloured .. .. 4·25 4·25

1986 (14 Aug–30 Dec). *India's Struggle for Freedom (4th series).* Vert portraits as T **909**. P 13.
1191 50 p. sepia, emerald and orange-red 1·25 1·75
1192 50 p. olive-sepia, emerald & orge-red (26.12) 1·25 1·75
1193 50 p. slate-blk, emer & reddish orge (29.12) 1·25 1·75
1194 50 p. red-brown, emerald & orge-red (30.12) 1·25 1·75
1191/4   *Set of 4* 4·50 6·25
Designs:—No. 1191, Bhim Sen Sachar; No. 1192, Alluri Seeta Rama Raju; No. 1193, Sagarmal Gopa; No. 1194, Veer Surendra Sai.

1986 (8 Sept). *Birth Centenary of Swami Sivananda (spiritual leader).* P 13.
1195 **987** 2 r. multicoloured .. .. 3·00 3·50

988 Volleyball   **989** Madras G.P.O.

(Des Mohinder Dhadwal)

1986 (16 Sept). *Asian Games, Seoul, South Korea.* T **988** and similar vert design. Multicoloured. P 13×13½.
1196 1 r. 50, Type **988** .. .. 2·50 2·75
1197 3 r. Hurdling .. .. 3·00 3·75

1986 (9 Oct). *Bicentenary of Madras G.P.O.* P 13.
1198 **989** 5 r. black and Indian red .. 4·50 5·00

990 Parachutist   **991** Early and Modern Policemen

(Des Nenu Bagga)

1986 (17 Oct). *225th Anniv of 8th Battalion of Coast Sepoys (now 1st Battalion Parachute Regiment).* P 13×13½.
1199 **990** 3 r. multicoloured .. .. 5·00 5·00

(Des A. Ali)

1986 (21 Oct). *125th Anniv of Indian Police.* T **991** and similar vert design showing early and modern police. P 13×13½.
1200 1 r. 50, multicoloured .. .. 3·50 4·00
    a. Horiz pair. Nos. 1200/1.. .. 7·00 8·00
1201 2 r. multicoloured .. .. 3·50 4·00
Nos. 1200/1 were printed together, *se-tenant,* in horizontal pairs with the 2 r. at left, each pair forming a composite design.

992 Hand holding Flower and World Map   **993** "Girl Rock Climber" (Sujasha Dasgupta)

(Des B. Raj)

1986 (24 Oct). *International Peace Year.* P 13½×13.
1202 **992** 5 r. multicoloured .. .. 2·50 1·25

1986 (14 Nov). *Children's Day.* P 13×13½.
1203 **993** 50 p. multicoloured .. .. 2·25 2·25

994 Windmill

1986 (15 Nov)–95. *Science and Technology.* T **994** and similar designs. W **374** (sideways on 75 p., 5, 50 r.). P 13. (a) Photo.
1211 35 p. vermilion (27.2.87) 10 10
    a. Wmk sideways 10 10
1212 40 p. rose-red (15.5.89) 10 10
    a. Wmk sideways 10 10
    w. Wmk inverted 90 10
1213 60 p. emerald and scarlet (27.2.87) .. 10 10
    a. Wmk sideways 10 10
1214 75 p. orange-vermilion (20.11.90) 75 40
    a. Wmk upright 30 20
1215 1 r. black and Indian red (18.2.95) 15 10
1217 5 r. deep brown & reddish orange (1.1.88) 15 20
    a. Wmk upright 50 25
1218 20 r. bistre-brown and blue (30.11.88) 55 60
    a. Wmk sideways 15 10
1219 50 r. black, turquoise-blue and cerise 1·40 1·50
    a. Wmk upright .. .. 1·40 1·50
    w. Wmk inverted .. ..

(b) Litho

1220	40 p. rose-red (15.10.88)	..	10	10
	w. Wmk inverted			
1211/20		*Set of 9*	2·25	2·25

Designs: *Horiz* (20×17 *mm*)—35 p. Family planning. (37×20 *mm*)—60 p. Indian family; 20 r. Bio gas production. *Vert* (17×20 *mm*)—40 p. Television set, dish aerial and transmitter; 75 p. "Family" (as No. 927). (20×37 *mm*)—1 r. Petrol pump nozzle (Oil conservation); 5 r. Solar energy.

Numbers have been left for further values in this new definitive series.

Postal forgeries of the 5 r., No. 1217, were discovered in the village of Nehru Nagar (Hyderabad) in February 1992. A number of these forgeries, which are on unwatermarked paper and perforated 10½ line, have been found commercially used. Similar forgeries of the 20 r. and 50 r. (Nos. 1218/19) also exist.

995 Growth Monitoring   **996** Tansen

1986 (11 Dec). *40th Anniv of United Nations Children's Fund.* T **995** *and similar horiz design. Multicoloured.* P 13½×13.

1221	50 p. Type **995**		2·00	2·00
1222	5 r. Immunization	..	4·25	6·00

1986 (12 Dec). *Tansen (musician and composer) Commem.* P 13.

1223	**996** 1 r. multicoloured		2·00	60

997 Indian Elephant   **998** St. Martha's Hospital

(Des Pratibha Pandey)

1986 (15 Dec). *50th Anniv of Corbett National Park.* T **997** *and similar horiz design. Multicoloured.* P 13½×13.

1224	1 r. Type **997**..	..	3·50	1·00
1225	2 r. Gharial	..	4·00	6·00

1986 (30 Dec). *Centenary of St. Martha's Hospital, Bangalore.* P 13½×13.

1226	**998** 1 r. Prussian blue, vermilion and black	2·00	1·40

999 Yacht *Trishna* and   **1000** Map of Southern
Route Map   Africa and Logo

1987 (10 Jan). *Indian Army Round the World Yacht Voyage, 1985–7.* P 13½×13.

1227	**999** 6 r. 50, multicoloured	..	4·50	4·00

1987 (25 Jan). *Inauguration of AFRICA Fund.* P 14.

1228	**1000** 6 r. 50, black	..	4·50	4·75

1001 Emblem   **1002** Blast Furnace
and Railway Emblem

1987 (11 Feb). *29th Congress of International Chamber of Commerce, New Delhi.* P 13×13½.

1229	**1001** 5 r. bluish violet, new blue and rosine	3·00	1·75

1987 (13 Feb–12 Dec). *India's Struggle for Freedom (5th series). Vert portraits as* T **909**. P 13.

1230	60 p. bistre-brown, emerald & reddish orge	2·00	30
1231	60 p. deep violet, emerald & orge-red (18.3)	30	30
1232	60 p. red-brown, dp green & orge-red (21.3)	30	30
1233	60 p. bl, yellowish grn & reddish orge (25.4)	30	30
1234	60 p. yellowish brn, emer & orge-red (17.6)	30	30
1235	60 p. brown, emerald and orange-red (22.8)	30	30
1236	60 p. brown-red, emerald and reddish orange (31.12)	30	30
1230/6		*Set of 7*	3·50	1·90

Designs:—No. 1230, Hakim Ajmal Khan; No. 1231, Lala Har Dayal; No. 1232, M. N. Roy; No. 1233, Tripuraneni Ramaswamy Chowdary; No. 1234, Dr. Kailas Nath Katju; No. 1235, S. Satyamurti; No. 1236, Pandit Hriday Nath Kunzru.

(Des P. Biswas)

1987 (28 Mar). *Centenary of South Eastern Railway.* T **1002** *and similar multicoloured designs.* P 13×13½ *(vert) or* 13½×13 *(horiz).*

1237	1 r. Type **1002**		40	15
1238	1 r. 50, Tank locomotive No. 691, 1887 (*horiz*)	45	35
1239	2 r. Electric train on viaduct, 1987	..	55	60
1240	4 r. Steam locomotive, *c* 1900 (*horiz*)	80	1·25
1237/40		*Set of 4*	2·00	2·10

1003 Kalia Bhomora Bridge, **1004** Madras Christian College
Tezpur, Assam

1987 (14 Apr). *Inauguration of Brahmaputra Bridge.* P 13½×13.

1241	**1003** 2 r. multicoloured	..	30	30

1987 (16 Apr). *150th Anniv of Madras Christian College.* P 13.

1242	**1004** 1 r. 50, black and brown-lake..	..	20	20

1005 Shree Shree   **1006** "Rabindranath Tagore"
Ma Anandamayee   (self-portrait)

1987 (1 May). *Shree Shree Ma Anandamayee (Hindu spiritual leader) Commem.* P 13×13½.

1243	**1005** 1 r. bistre-brown	..	..	30	20

1987 (8 May). *Rabindranath Tagore (poet) Commem.* P 14.

1244	**1006** 2 r. multicoloured	..	40	30

1007 Garwhal Rifles   **1008** J. Krishnamurti
Uniforms of 1887

1987 (10 May). *Centenary of Garwhal Rifles Regiment.* P 13×13½.

1245	**1007** 1 r. multicoloured	..	50	20

1987 (11 May). *J. Krishnamurti (philosopher) Commem.* P 13×13½.

1246	**1008** 60 p. sepia	..	60	90

1009 Regimental Uniforms   **1010** Hall of Nations, Pragati
of 1887   Maidan, New Delhi

1987 (3 June). *Centenary of 37th Dogra Regt (now 7th Battalion (1 Dogra)), Mechanised Infantry Regt.* P 13½×13.

1247	**1009** 1 r. multicoloured	..	40	20

*(Des P. Biswas (Nos. 1248/9), Nenu Bagga (No. **MS**1250)*

1987 (15 June)–**89**. *"India–89" International Stamp Exhibition, New Delhi (1st issue).* T **1010** *and similar horiz design. Multicoloured.* P 13½×13.

1248	50 p. Exhibition logo		10	15
	a. Booklet pane. No. 1248×4 (20.1.89)		15	
1249	5 r. Type **1010**		45	50
	a. Booklet pane. No. 1249×4 (20.1.89)		1·50	
MS1250	156×58 mm. Nos. 1248/9 (*sold at 8 r.*)	70	1·00

Booklet panes Nos. 1248a and 1249a have margins all round.
See also Nos. 1264/8, 1333/4, 1341/2 and 1358/61.

1011 "Sadyah-Snata"   **1012** Flag and Stylized Birds with
Sculpture, Sanghol   "40" in English and Hindi

1987 (3 July). *Festival of India, U.S.S.R.* P 13.

1251	**1011** 6 r. 50, multicoloured	..	1·00	75

1987 (15 Aug). *40th Anniv of Independence.* P 13×13½.

1252	**1012** 60 p. reddish orange, dp green & new bl	20	20

1013 Sant Harchand   **1014** Guru Ghasidas
Singh Longowal

1987 (20 Aug). *Sant Harchand Singh Longowal (Sikh leader) Commemoration.* P 13×13½.

1253	**1013** 1 r. multicoloured	..	40	20

1987 (1 Sept). *Guru Ghasidas (Hindu leader) Commemoration.* P 13.

1254	**1014** 60 p. deep Indian red	..	20	20

1015 Thakur Anukul   **1016** University of Allahabad
Chandra

1987 (2 Sept). *Thakur Anukul Chandra (spiritual leader) Commemoration.* P 13×13½.

1255	**1015** 1 r. multicoloured	..	40	20

1987 (23 Sept). *Centenary of Allahabad University.* P 13.

1256	**1016** 2 r. multicoloured	..	30	40

1017 Pankha Offering   **1018** Chhatrasal on Horseback

1987 (1 Oct). *Phoolwalon Ki Sair Festival, Delhi.* P 13×13½.

1257	**1017** 2 r. multicoloured	..	30	40

1987 (2 Oct). *Chhatrasal (Bundela ruler) Commemoration.* P 14.

1258	**1018** 60 p. chestnut	..	..	30	20

1019 Family and Stylized Houses   1020 Map of Asia and Logo

1987 (5 Oct). *International Year of Shelter for the Homeless.* P 13½×13.
1259 **1019** 5 r. multicoloured 45 60

1987 (14 Oct). *Asia Regional Conference of Rotary International.* T **1020** *and similar horiz design.* P 13½×13.
1260   60 p. chestnut and emerald .. 15 15
1261   6 r. 50, multicoloured .. 60 80
Design:—6 r. 50, Oral Polio vaccination.

1021 Blind Boy, Braille Books and Computer   1022 Iron Pillar, Delhi

1987 (15 Oct). *Centenary of Service to Blind.* T **1021** *and similar horiz design.* P 13½×13.
1262   1 r. multicoloured 15 15
1263   2 r. deep blue and new blue .. 35 30
Design:—2 r. Eye donation.

1987 (17 Oct)–89. *"India–89" International Stamp Exhibition, New Delhi (2nd issue). Delhi Landmarks.* T **1022** *and similar horiz designs. Multicoloured.* P 13½×13.
1264   60 p. Type **1022** 10 15
    a. Booklet pane. No. 1264×4 (20.1.89) 20
1265   1 r. 50, India Gate 15 20
    a. Booklet pane. No. 1265×4 (20.1.89) 45
1266   5 r. Dewan-e-Khas, Red Fort .. 45 50
    a. Booklet pane. No. 1266×4 (20.1.89) 1·50
1267   6 r. 50, Old Fort 60 65
    a. Booklet pane. No. 1267×4 (20.1.89) 2·00
1264/7   Set of 4 1·10 1·40
MS1268 100×86 mm. Nos. 1264/7 (*sold at 15 r.*) 1·40 2·00
Booklet panes Nos. 1264a, 1265a, 1266a and 1267a have margins all round.

1023 Tyagmurti Goswami Ganeshdutt   1024 "My Home" (Siddharth Deshprabha)

1987 (2 Nov). *Tyagmurti Goswami Ganeshdutt (spiritual leader and social reformer) Commemoration.* P 13×13½.
1269 **1023** 60 p. brown-red 20 20

1987 (14 Nov). *Children's Day.* P 13½×13.
1270 **1024** 60 p. multicoloured 30 20

1025 Chinar   1026 Logo (from sculpture "Worker and Woman Peasant" by V. Mukhina)

(Des O. Ravindran, A. Mehta, T. D. Singh, Sudha Chowdhary)
1987 (19 Nov). *Indian Trees.* T **1025** *and similar multicoloured designs.* P 13×13½ (*vert*) *or* 13½×13 (*horiz*).
1271   60 p. multicoloured 15 15
1272   1 r. 50, multicoloured 20 20
1273   5 r. black, dull yellow-green and chestnut 55 65
1274   6 r. 50, brown, carmine-red & yellow-green 80 80
1271/4   Set of 4 1·40 1·60
Designs: Horiz—1 r. 50, Pipal; 6 r. 50, Banyan. Vert—5 r. Sal.

1987 (21 Nov). *Festival of U.S.S.R., India.* P 14.
1275 **1026** 5 r. multicoloured 50 50

1027 White Tiger   1028 Execution of Veer Narayan Singh

1987 (29 Nov). *Wildlife.* T **1027** *and similar multicoloured design.* P 13×13½ (1 r.) *or* 13½×13 (5 r.).
1276   1 r. Type **1027** 50 15
1277   5 r. Snow Leopard (*horiz*) .. .. 1·25 85

(Des S. Samanta)
1987 (10 Dec). *Veer Narayan Singh (patriot) Commemoration.* P 13½×13.
1278 **1028** 60 p. deep brown 20 20

1029 Rameshwari Nehru   1030 Father Kuriakose Elias Chavara

1987 (10 Dec). *Rameshwari Nehru (women's rights campaigner) Commemoration.* P 13×13½.
1279 **1029** 60 p. red-brown 20 20

1987 (20 Dec). *Father Kuriakose Elias Chavara (founder of Carmelites of Mary Immaculate) Commemoration.* P 13×13½.
1280 **1030** 60 p. bistre-brown 20 20

1031 Dr. Rajah Sir Muthiah Chettiar   1032 Golden Temple, Amritsar

1987 (21 Dec). *Dr. Rajah Sir Muthiah Chettiar (politician) Commemoration.* P 13.
1281 **1031** 60 p. slate 20 20

1987 (26 Dec). *400th Anniv of Golden Temple, Amritsar.* P 13×13½.
1282 **1032** 60 p. multicoloured 30 20

1033 Rukmini Devi and Dancer   1034 Dr. Hiralal

1987 (27 Dec). *Rukmini Devi (Bharatanatyam dance pioneer) Commemoration.* P 13½×13.
1283 **1033** 60 p. deep rose-red 30 20

1987 (31 Dec). *Dr. Hiralal (historian) Commemoration.* P 13×13½.
1284 **1034** 60 p. deep violet-blue 20 20

1035 Light Frequency Experiment and Bodhi Tree   1036 Rural Patient

1988 (7 Jan). *75th Session of Indian Science Congress Association.* P 13.
1285 **1035** 4 r. multicoloured 50 60

(Des M. Sharma)
1988 (28 Jan). *13th Asian Pacific Dental Congress.* P 13×13½.
1286 **1036** 4 r. multicoloured 50 50

1988 (2 Feb–6 Oct). *India's Struggle for Freedom (6th series). Vert portraits as* T **909**. P 13.
1287   60 p. black, emerald and reddish orange .. 20 40
1288   60 p. chestnut, emerald & brt orange (4.2) 20 40
1289   60 p. brt carmine, emer & orge-red (27.2) .. 20 40
1290   60 p. blackish purple, emer & brt orge (7.3) 20 40
1291   60 p. plum, dp green & reddish orge (18.6) 20 40
1292   60 p. slate-blk, dp grn & reddish orge (19.6) 20 40
1293   60 p. deep lilac, dp green & orge-red (28.6) 20 40
1294   60 p. dp bluish green, grn & orge-red (6.9) 20 30
1295   60 p. red-brown, emerald & orge-red (6.10) 20 30
1296   60 p. magenta, dp green & brt orange (5.12) 20 30
1287/96   Set of 10 1·75 3·25
Designs:—No. 1287, Mohan Lal Sukhadia; No. 1288, Dr. S. K. Sinha; No. 1289, Chandra Shekhar Azad; No. 1290, G. B. Pant; No. 1291, Dr. Anugrah Narain Singh; No. 1292, Kuladhor Chaliha; No. 1293, Shivprasad Gupta; No. 1294, Sarat Chandra Bose; No. 1295, Baba Kharak Singh; No. 1296, Sheikh Mohammad Abdullah.

1037 U Tirot Singh   1038 Early and Modern Regimental Uniforms

1988 (3 Feb). *U Tirot Singh (Khasis leader) Commemoration.* P 13×13½.
1297 **1037** 60 p. bistre-brown 20 20

1988 (19 Feb). *Bicentenary of 4th Battalion of the Kumaon Regiment.* P 14.
1298 **1038** 1 r. multicoloured 30 20

1039 Balgandharva   1040 Soldiers and Infantry Combat Vehicle

1988 (22 Feb). *Birth Centenary of Balgandharva (actor).* P 13×13½.
1299 **1039** 60 p. bistre-brown 20 20

1988 (24 Feb). *Presentation of Colours to Mechanised Infantry Regiment.* P 13½×13.
1300 **1040** 1 r. multicoloured 35 20

1041 B. N. Rau   1042 Mohindra Government College

1988 (26 Feb). *B. N. Rau (constitutional lawyer) Commemoration.* P 13.
1301 **1041** 60 p. grey-black 20 20

1988 (14 Mar). *Mohindra Government College, Patiala.* P 13×13½.
1302 **1042** 1 r. cerise 20 20

1043 Dr. D. V. Gundappa   1044 Rani Avantibai

1988 (17 Mar). *Dr. D. V. Gundappa (scholar) Commemoration.*
P 13¹/₂×13.
1303 **1043** 60 p. slate 20 20

1988 (20 Mar). *Rani Avantibai of Ramgarh Commemoration.*
P 13×13¹/₂.
1304 **1044** 60 p. cerise 20 20

1045 Malayala Manorama
Office, Kottayam

1046 Maharshi
Dadhichi

1988 (23 Mar). *Centenary of Malayala Manorama (newspaper).* P 13.
1305 **1045** 1 r. black and new blue 20 20

1988 (26 Mar). *Maharshi Dadhichi (Hindu saint) Commemoration.* P 13×13¹/₂.
1306 **1046** 60 p. Indian red 20 20

1047 Mohammad Iqbal

1048 Samarth
Ramdas

(Des Alka Sharma)
1988 (21 Apr). *50th Death Anniv of Mohammad Iqbal (poet).*
P 13.
1307 **1047** 60 p. gold and rosine 20 20

1988 (1 May). *Samarth Ramdas (Hindu spiritual leader)
Commem.* P 13.
1308 **1048** 60 p. deep yellow-green 20 20

1049 Swati Tirunal
Rama Varma

1050 Bhaurao Patil and
Class

1988 (2 May). *175th Birth Anniv of Swati Tirunal Rama
Varma (composer).* P 13×13¹/₂.
1309 **1049** 60 p. deep mauve 20 20

1988 (9 May). *Bhaurao Patil (educationist) Commemoration.*
P 13¹/₂×13.
1310 **1050** 60 p. reddish brown 20 20

1051 "Rani Lakshmi Bai" (M. F. Husain)

1988 (9 May). *Martyrs from First War of Independence.*
P 13×13¹/₂.
1311 **1051** 60 p. multicoloured 20 20
    a. Myrtle-green (lowest stripe of
    flag, date, etc) omitted ..

NEW INFORMATION

The editor is always interested to correspond with
people who have new information that will
improve or correct the Catalogue.

1052 Broad Peak

1053 Child with
Grandparents

(Des R. Pasricha (1 r. 50, 4 r.), N. Roerich (5 r.))
1988 (19 May). *Himalayan Peaks.* T **1052** *and similar horiz
designs.* P 13¹/₂×13.
1312 1 r. 50, reddish lilac, deep violet and blue 35 30
1313 4 r. multicoloured 70 60
1314 5 r. multicoloured 80 70
1315 6 r. 50, multicoloured 95 85
1312/15   *Set of* 4 2·50 2·25
Designs:—4 r. K 2 (Godwin Austen); 5 r. Kanchenjunga;
6 r.50, Nanda Devi.

(Des Neeta Verma)
1988 (24 May). *"Love and Care for Elders".* P 13×13¹/₂.
1316 **1053** 60 p. multicoloured 20 20

1054 Victoria Terminus,
Bombay

1055 Lawrence School,
Lovedale

1988 (30 May). *Centenary of Victoria Terminus Station,
Bombay.* P 13¹/₂×13.
1317 **1054** 1 r. multicoloured 40 20

1988 (31 May). *130th Anniv of Lawrence School, Lovedale.*
P 13.
1318 **1055** 1 r. red-brown and deep green .. 30 20

1056 Khejri Tree

1988 (5 June). *World Environment Day.* P 14.
1319 **1056** 60 p. multicoloured 20 15

1988 (15 June). *As No. 732, but new face value.* W **374**.
P 12¹/₂ × 13.
1320 60 p. grey-black (Gandhi) 55 15
    a. Wmk sideways 55 15

1057 Rani
Durgawati

1058 Acharya
Shanti Dev

1988 (24 June). *Rani Durgawati (Gondwana ruler) Commemoration.* P 13.
1322 **1057** 60 p. deep rose-red 20 20

1988 (28 July). *Acharya Shanti Dev (Buddhist scholar)
Commemoration.* P 13×13¹/₂.
1323 **1058** 60 p. red-brown 20 20

1059 Y. S. Parmar

1988 (4 Aug). *Dr. Yashwant Singh Parmar (former Chief
Minister of Himachal Pradesh) Commemoration.* P 13×13¹/₂.
1324 **1059** 60 p. slate-violet 20 20

1060 Arm pointing at Proclamation in
Marathi

(Des Contract Advertising (India) Ltd)
1988 (16 Aug). *40th Anniv of Independence. Bal Gangadhar
Tilak (patriot) Commemoration.* T **1060** *and similar horiz
design. Multicoloured.* P 13×13¹/₂.
1325 60 p. Type **1060** 20 20
    a. Vert pair. Nos. 1325/6 .. 40 40
1326 60 p. Battle scene 20 20
Nos. 1325/6 were printed together, *se-tenant*, in vertical pairs
throughout the sheet, each pair forming a composite design
showing a painting by M. F. Husain.

1061 Durgadas
Rathore

1062 Gopinath
Kaviraj

1988 (26 Aug). *150th Birth Anniv of Durgadas Rathore
(Regent of Marwar). Litho.* P 13×13¹/₂.
1327 **1061** 60 p. reddish brown 20 20

1988 (7 Sept). *Gopinath Kaviraj (scholar) Commemoration.*
P 13×13¹/₂.
1328 **1062** 60 p. bistre-brown 20 20

1063 Lotus and
Outline Map of
India

1064 Indian
Olympic
Association
Logo

1988 (14 Sept). *Hindi Day.* P 13×13¹/₂.
1329 **1063** 60 p. orange-verm, grn & reddish brn 20 20

(Des C. Parameswaran (5 p.))
1988 (17 Sept). *"Sports–1988" and Olympic Games, Seoul.*
T **1064** *and similar design.* P 13.
1330 60 p. brown-purple 35 15
1331 5 r. multicoloured .. .. .. 2·25 75
Design: *Horiz*—5 r. Various sports.

1065 Jerdon's
Courser

1066 *Times of India* Front Page

1988 (7 Oct). *Wildlife Conservation. Jerdon's Courser.*
P 13×13¹/₂.
1332 **1065** 1 r. multicoloured .. .. 1·00 30

(Des C. Meena (4 r.), C. Pakrashi (5 r.))
1988 (9 Oct)–89. *"India–89" International Stamp Exhibition,
New Delhi (3rd issue). General Post Offices. Horiz designs as*
T **1022**. *Multicoloured.* P 13¹/₂×13.
1333 4 r. Bangalore G.P.O. 40 35
    a. Booklet pane. No. 1333×6 (20.1.89) 2·25
1334 5 r. Bombay G.P.O. 50 45
    a. Booklet pane. No. 1334×6 (20.1.89) 2·75
Booklet panes Nos. 1333a and 1334a have margins all round.

(Des A. Nath)

1988 (3 Nov). *150th Anniv of* The Times of India. *P* 14.
1335 **1066** 1 r. 50, black, gold and lemon .. 20 20

1067 "Maulana Abul
Kalam Azad"
(K. Hebbar)

1988 (11 Nov). *Birth Centenary of Maulana Abul Kalam Azad (politician). P* 13¹/₂×13.
1336 **1067** 60 p. multicoloured 20 20

1068 Nehru

1988 (14 Nov). *Birth Centenary of Jawaharlal Nehru* (1989) (1st issue). T **1068** *and similar design. P* 13×13¹/₂ (60 p.) or 13¹/₂×13 (1 r.).
1337 **1068** 60 p. grey-black, red-orange & deep green 30 15
1338 1 r. multicoloured 35 15
Design: *Vert*—1 r. "Jawaharlal Nehru" (Svetoslav Roerich).
See also No. 1393

1069 Birsa Munda

(Des S. Samantha)

1988 (15 Nov). *Birsa Munda (Munda leader) Commemoration. P* 13¹/₂ × 13.
1339 **1069** 60 p. reddish brown 20 20

1070 Bhakra Dam

1988 (15 Dec). *25th Anniv of Dedication of Bhakra Dam. P* 14.
1340 **1070** 60 p. bright carmine 35 60

1071 Dead Letter Office
Cancellations of 1886
1072 K. M. Munshi

1988 (20 Dec)–89. *"India–89" International Stamp Exhibition, New Delhi* (4th issue). Postal Cancellations. *T* **1071** *and similar horiz design. P* 13¹/₂×13.
1341 60 p. dp cinnamon, black & carm-vermilion 25 15
a. Booklet pane. No. 1341×6 (20.1.89) 1·40
1342 6 r. 50, orange-brown and black .. 1·00 1·00
a. Booklet pane. No. 1342×6 (20.1.89) 5·50
Design:—6 r. 50, Allahabad–Cawnpore travelling post office handstamp of 1864.
Booklet panes Nos. 1341a and 1342a have margins all round.

1988 (30 Dec). *Birth Centenary of K. M. Munshi (author and politician)* (1987). *P* 13¹/₂ × 13.
1343 **1072** 60 p. deep olive 20 20

1073 Mannathu
Padmanabhan
1074 Lok Sabha Secretariat

1989 (2 Jan). *Mannathu Padmanabhan (social reformer) Commemoration. P* 13 × 13¹/₂.
1344 **1073** 60 p. olive-brown 20 20

1989 (2 Jan–11 May). *India's Struggle for Freedom* (7th series). *Vert portraits as T* **909**. *P* 13.
1345 60 p. blk, dull yellowish grn & reddish orge 20 30
1346 60 p. red-orange, dp grn & dp lilac (8.3.89) 20 50
1347 60 p. grey-black, bottle-green and bright orange (13.4.89) 20 50
1348 60 p. bistre-brown, emerald and reddish orange (13.4.89) 20 50
1349 60 p. brown, dp green & orge-red (11.5.89) 20 30
1345/9 *Set of 5* 90 1·90
Designs:—No. 1345, Hare Krishna Mahtab; No. 1346, Balasaheb Gangadhar Kher; No. 1347, Raj Kumari Amrit Kaur; No. 1348, Saifuddin Kitchlew; No. 1349, Asaf Ali.

1989 (10 Jan). *60th Anniv of Lok Sabha Secretariat (formerly Legislative Assembly Department). P* 13¹/₂ × 13.
1355 **1074** 60 p. brown-olive 20 20

1075 Goddess Durga
seated on Lion (5th-cent
terracotta plaque)
1076 Baldev Ramji
Mirdha

1989 (11 Jan). *125th Anniv of Lucknow Museum. P* 14.
1356 **1075** 60 p. deep blue and new blue .. 20 20

1989 (17 Jan). *Birth Centenary of Baldev Ramji Mirdha (nationalist). P* 13 × 13¹/₂.
1357 **1076** 60 p. slate-green 20 20

1077 Girl with Stamp
Collection
1078 St. John
Bosco and Boy

(Des K. Radhakrishnan (60 p.), M. Jain (1 r. 50))

1989 (20 Jan). *"India–89" International Stamp Exhibition, New Delhi* (5th issue). Philately. *T* **1077** *and similar horiz designs. P* 13¹/₂×13.
1358 60 p. orge-yellow, rose-red & dp violet-blue 15 10
a. Booklet pane. No. 1358×6 .. 80
1359 1 r. 50, brownish grey, orge-yellow & blk 20 15
a. Booklet pane. No. 1359×6 .. 1·10
1360 5 r. dull vermilion and blue .. 60 50
a. Booklet pane. No. 1360×6 .. 3·25
1361 6 r. 50, black, red-brown & turquoise-blue 70 60
a. Booklet pane. No. 1361×6 .. 3·75
1358/61 .. .. .. *Set of 4* 1·50 1·25
Designs:—1 r. 50, Dawk gharry, c. 1842; 5 r. Travancore 1888 2 ch. conch shell stamp; 6 r. 50, Early Indian philatelic magazines.
Booklet panes Nos. 1358a, 1359a, 1360a and 1361a have margins all round.

1989 (31 Jan). *St. John Bosco (founder of Salesian Brothers) Commemoration. P* 13.
1362 **1078** 60 p. carmine 20 20

1079 Modern Tank and
19th-century Sowar
1080 Dargah Sharif, Ajmer

(Des P. Biswas)

1989 (8 Feb). *Third Cavalry Regiment. P* 13¹/₂ × 13.
1363 **1079** 60 p. multicoloured .. 30 20

1989 (13 Feb). *Dargah Sharif (Sufi shrine), Ajmer. P* 13¹/₂ × 13.
1364 **1080** 1 r. multicoloured .. 20 20

1081 Task Force and Indian
Naval Ensign

1989 (15 Feb). *President's Review of the Fleet. P* 14.
1365 **1081** 6 r. 50, multicoloured .. 1·25 1·00

1082 Shaheed Laxman
Nayak and Barbed Wire
Fence
1083 Rao Gopal
Singh

1989 (29 Mar). *Shaheed Laxman Nayak Commemoration. P* 13¹/₂×13.
1366 **1082** 60 p. dp brown, dp green & red-orange 20 20

1989 (30 Mar). *Rao Gopal Singh Commemoration. P* 13×13¹/₂.
1367 **1083** 60 p. olive-brown 20 20

1084 Sydenham College
1085 Bishnu Ram
Medhi

1989 (19 Apr). *75th Anniv of Sydenham College, Bombay* (1988). *P* 13¹/₂×13.
1368 **1084** 60 p. grey-black 30 20

1989 (24 Apr). *Birth Centenary of Bishnu Ram Medhi (politician)* (1988). *P* 13.
1369 **1085** 60 p. yellowish green, deep blue-green and orange-red 30 20

1086 Dr. N. S.
Hardikar
1087 "Advaita" in
Devanagari Script

1989 (13 May). *Birth Centenary of Dr. Narayana Subbarao Hardikar (nationalist). P* 13×13¹/₂.
1370 **1086** 60 p. orange-brown 20 20

1989 (17 May). *Sankaracharya (philosopher) Commemoration. P* 14.
1371 **1087** 60 p. multicoloured 20 20

1088 Gandhi Bhavan,
Punjab University
1089 Scene from
Film *Raja
Harischandra*

1989 (19 May). *Punjab University, Chandigarh.* P 13½×13.
1372 **1088** 1 r. light brown and turquoise-blue .. 20 20

1989 (30 May). *75 Years of Indian Cinema.* P 14.
1373 **1089** 60 p. black and yellow 20 20

1090 Cactus and Cogwheels

1091 Early Class and Modern University Students

1989 (20 June). *Centenary of Kirloskar Brothers Ltd (engineering group).* P 13½×13.
1374 **1090** 1 r. multicoloured 20 20

1989 (27 June). *Centenary of First D.A.V. College.* P 13½×13.
1375 **1091** 1 r. multicoloured 20 20

1092 Post Office, Dakshin Gangotri Base, Antarctica

1093 First Allahabad Bank Building

(Des S. Samantha)

1989 (11 July). *Opening of Post Office, Dakshin Gangotri Research Station, Antarctica.* P 14.
1376 **1092** 1 r. multicoloured 80 20

1989 (19 July). *125th Anniv of Allahabad Bank* (1990). P 14.
1377 **1093** 60 p. maroon and new blue 20 20

1094 Nehru inspecting Central Reserve Police, Neemuch, 1954

1095 Dairy Cow

1989 (27 July). *50th Anniv of Central Reserve Police Force (formerly Crown Representative's Police).* P 13½×13.
1378 **1094** 60 p. brown 60 20

1989 (18 Aug). *Centenary of Military Farms.* P 13½×13.
1379 **1095** 1 r. multicoloured 50 20

1096 Mustafa Kemal Atatürk

1097 Dr. S. Radhakrishnan

1989 (30 Aug). *50th Death Anniv of Mustafa Kemal Atatürk (Turkish statesman)* (1988). P 13×13½.
1380 **1096** 5 r. multicoloured .. .. 1·25 45

1989 (11 Sept). *Birth Centenary of Dr. Sarvepalli Radhakrishnan (former President)* (1988). P 13½×13.
1381 **1097** 60 p. grey-black 20 20

1098 Football Match

1099 Dr. P. Subbarayan

1989 (23 Sept). *Centenary of Mohun Bagan Athletic Club.* P 13½×13.
1382 **1098** 1 r. multicoloured 50 20

1989 (30 Sept). *Birth Centenary of Dr. P. Subbarayan (politician).* P 13×13½.
1383 **1099** 60 p. orange-brown 20 20

1100 Shyamji Krishna Varma

1101 Sayajirao Gaekwad III

1989 (4 Oct). *Shyamji Krishna Varma (nationalist) Commemoration.* P 13.
1384 **1100** 60 p. purple-brown, dp grn & orge-red 20 20

1989 (6 Oct). *50th Death Anniv of Maharaja Sayajirao Gaekwad III of Baroda.* P 13×13½.
1385 **1101** 60 p. brownish grey 20 20

1102 Symbolic Bird with Letter

1103 Namakkal Kavignar

1989 (14 Oct). *"Use Pincode" Campaign.* P 14.
1386 **1102** 60 p. multicoloured 30 20

1989 (19 Oct). *Namakkal Kavignar (writer) Commemoration.* P 13½×13.
1387 **1103** 60 p. brownish black 20 20

1104 Diagram of Human Brain

1105 Pandita Ramabai and Original Sharada Sadan Building

1989 (21 Oct). *18th International Epilepsy Congress and 14th World Congress on Neurology, New Delhi.* P 13½×13.
1388 **1104** 6 r. 50, multicoloured .. .. 2·25 75

1989 (26 Oct). *Pandita Ramabai (women's education pioneer) Commemoration.* P 13½×13.
1389 **1105** 60 p. light brown 30 20

1106 Releasing Homing Pigeons

1107 Acharya Narendra Deo

1989 (3 Nov). *Orissa Police Pigeon Post.* P 13½×13.
1390 **1106** 1 r. Indian red 50 20

1989 (6 Nov). *Birth Centenary of Acharya Narendra Deo (scholar).* P 13.
1391 **1107** 60 p. brown, emerald and red-orange 20 20

1108 Acharya Kripalani

1989 (11 Nov). *Acharya Kripalani (politician) Commemoration.* P 13½×13.
1392 **1108** 60 p. grey-blk, myrtle-grn & orge-red 20 20

1109 Nehru

(Des S. Debnath)

1989 (14 Nov). *Birth Centenary of Jawaharlal Nehru (2nd issue).* P 14×15.
1393 **1109** 1 r. dull brown, purple-brown and buff. 65 20

1110 Meeting Logo

1111 Sir Gurunath Bewoor

1989 (19 Nov). *8th Asian Track and Field Meeting, New Delhi.* P 14.
1394 **1110** 1 r. black, reddish orge & yellowish grn 30 20

1989 (20 Nov). *Sir Gurunath Bewoor (former Director-General, Posts and Telegraphs) Commemoration.* P 13×13½.
1395 **1111** 60 p. light brown 20 20

1112 Balkrishna Sharma Navin

1113 Abstract Painting of Houses

1989 (8 Dec). *Balkrishna Sharma Navin (politician and poet) Commemoration.* P 13×13½.
1396 **1112** 60 p. black 20 20

1989 (15 Dec). *Centenary of Bombay Art Society* (1988). P 13½×13.
1397 **1113** 1 r. multicoloured 20 20

1114 Lesser Florican

1115 Centenary Logo

1989 (20 Dec). *Wildlife Conservation. Lesser Florican.* P 13×13½.
1398 **1114** 2 r. multicoloured .. .. 1·50 55

1989 (29 Dec). *Centenary of Indian Oil Production.* P 14.
1399 **1115** 60 p. red-brown 30 20

1116 Dr. M. G.
Ramachandran

1117 Volunteers working
at Sukhna Lake,
Chandigarh

1990 (17 Jan). *Dr. M. G. Ramachandran (former Chief Minister of Tamil Nadu) Commemoration.* P 13×13½.
1400 1116 60 p. reddish brown 40 20

(Des T. Bedi and S. Singh)

1990 (29 Jan). *Save Sukhna Lake Campaign.* P 13½×13.
1401 1117 1 r. multicoloured 20 20

1118 Gallantry Medals

1990 (21 Feb). *Presentation of New Colours to Bombay Sappers.* P 15×14*.
1402 1118 60 p. multicoloured .. .. .. 80 1·00
*On No. 1402 the left hand side of the triangle is perforated 15 and the remaining two sides 14.

1119 Indian Chank
Shell and Logo

1120 Penny Black
and Envelope

1990 (2 May). *23rd Annual General Meeting of Asian Development Bank, New Delhi.* P 14.
1403 1119 2 r. black, brt orange & greenish yell 75 30

(Des M. Deogawanka)

1990 (6 May). *150th Anniv of the Penny Black.* P 13×13½.
1404 1120 6 r. multicoloured .. .. .. 1·25 40

1121 Ho Chi-Minh and
Vietnamese House

1122 Chaudhary
Charan Singh

1990 (17 May). *Birth Centenary of Ho Chi-Minh (Vietnamese leader).* P 13½×13.
1405 1121 2 r. reddish brown and yellowish green 30 30

1990 (29 May). *3rd Death Anniv of Chaudhary Charan Singh (former Prime Minister).* P 13.
1406 1122 1 r. orange-brown 20 20

1123 Armed Forces'
Badge and Map of Sri
Lanka

1124 Wheat

1990 (30 July). *Indian Peace-keeping Operations in Sri Lanka.* P 13.
1407 1123 2 r. multicoloured 30 30

1990 (31 July). *60th Anniv of Indian Council of Agricultural Research (1989).* P 14.
1408 1124 2 r. blk, brt yellow-grn & dp bluish grn 30 30

1125 Khudiram
Bose

1126 "Life in India" (Tanya
Vorontsova)

1990 (11 Aug). *Khudiram Bose (patriot) Commemoration.* P 13×13½.
1409 1125 1 r. dull vermilion, dull grn & brn-red 20 20

1990 (16 Aug). *Indo-Soviet Friendship. Children's Paintings.* T 1126 *and similar horiz design. Multicoloured.* P 14.
1410 1 r. Type 1126 .. .. 1·50 2·00
    a. Horiz pair. Nos. 1410/11 .. 3·00 4·00
1411 6 r. 50, "St. Basil's Cathedral and Kremlin, Moscow" (Sanjay Adhikari) 1·50 2·00
Nos. 1410/11 were printed together, *se-tenant*, in horizontal pairs throughout the sheet.
Stamps in similar designs were also issued by U.S.S.R.

1127 K. Kelappan

1128 Girl in
Garden

1990 (24 Aug). *K. Kelappan (social reformer) Commemoration.* P 13×13½
1412 1127 1 r. reddish brown 20 20

1990 (5 Sept). *Year of the Girl Child.* P 13×13½.
1413 1128 1 r. multicoloured 50 30

1129 Hand guiding Child's
Writing

1130 Woman
using Water Pump

1990 (8 Sept). *International Literacy Year.* P 13½×13.
1414 1129 1 r. multicoloured 50 30

1990 (10 Sept). *Safe Drinking Water Campaign.* P 13×13½.
1415 1130 4 r. black, scarlet-verm & dp bluish grn 1·25 1·75

1131 Sunder Lal
Sharma

1132 Kabbadi

1990 (28 Sept). *50th Death Anniv of Sunder Lal Sharma (patriot).* P 13×13½.
1416 1131 60 p. lake 50 50

(Des C. Pakrashi (Nos. 1418/19), R. Pasricha (No. 1420))

1990 (29 Sept). *11th Asian Games, Peking.* T 1132 *and similar vert designs. Multicoloured.* P 13×13½.
1417 1 r. Type 1132 .. .. .. 40 20
1418 4 r. Athletics .. .. .. 1·50 2·00
1419 4 r. Cycling .. .. .. 1·50 2·00
1420 6 r. 50, Archery .. .. 1·75 2·50
1417/20 .. .. .. *Set of 4* 4·75 6·00

1133 A. K.
Gopalan

1134 Gurkha
Soldier

1990 (1 Oct). *Ayillyath Kuttiari Gopalan (social reformer) Commemoration.* P 13×13½.
1421 1133 1 r. red-brown 50 30

(Des R. Pasricha)

1990 (1 Oct). *50th Anniv of 3rd and 5th Battalions, 5th Gurkha Rifles.* P 13.
1422 1134 2 r. black and ochre .. .. 1·40 1·60

1135 Suryamall
Mishran

1136 "Doll and Cat"
(Subhash Kumar
Nagarajan)

1990 (19 Oct). *75th Birth Anniv of Suryamall Mishran (poet).* P 13 × 13½.
1423 1135 2 r. brown and pale orange .. 50 65

1990 (14 Nov). *Children's Day.* P 13½×13.
1424 1136 1 r. multicoloured 60 30

1137 Security Post and
Border Guard on Camel

1138 Hearts and
Flowers

1990 (30 Nov). *25th Anniv of Border Security Force.* P 13½×13.
1425 1137 5 r. greenish blue, yellow-brown & blk 1·50 1·75

(Des R. Pasricha (1 r.))

1990 (17 Dec). *Greetings Stamps.* T 1138 *and similar multicoloured design.* P 13×13½ (1 r.) or 13½×13 (4 r.).
1426 1 r. Type 1138 .. .. .. 20 15
1427 4 r. Ceremonial elephants (*horiz*) .. 50 65

1139 Bikaner

1140 Bhakta
Kanakadas and
Udipi Temple

(Des R. Pasricha (4, 5 r.), P. Biswas (6 r. 50))

1990 (24 Dec). *Cities of India.* T 1139 *and similar horiz designs. Multicoloured.* P 13½×13.
1428 4 r. Type 1139 .. .. .. 55 60
1429 5 r. Hyderabad 65 75
1430 6 r. 50, Cuttack .. .. .. 90 1·25
1428/30 .. .. .. *Set of 3* 1·90 2·40

1990 (26 Dec). *Bhakta Kanakadas (mystic and poet) Commemoration.* P 14.
1431 1140 1 r. orange-red 55 30

1141 Shaheed Minar Monument

1142 Dnyaneshwari (poet) and Manuscript

1990 (28 Dec). *300th Anniv of Calcutta.* T **1141** *and similar design.* P 14.
1432 1 r. multicoloured 30 20
1433 6 r. black, ochre and rosine .. .. 1·25 1·50
Design: *Horiz* (44×36 *mm*)—6 r. Eighteenth-century shipping on the Ganges.

1990 (31 Dec). *700th Anniv of Dnyaneshwari (spiritual epic).* P 13×13½.
1434 **1142** 2 r. multicoloured 30 50

1143 Madan Mohan Malaviya (founder) and University

1144 Road Users

1991 (20 Jan). *75th Anniv of Banaras Hindu University.* P 13½×13.
1435 **1143** 1 r. brown-lake 30 20

1991 (30 Jan). *As No. 732, but new face value.* W **374.** P 13.
1436 1 r. orange-brown (Gandhi) 10 10
a. Wmk sideways 75
ab. Imperf (pair) .. .. .. 30·00

(Des J. Das)

1991 (30 Jan). *International Traffic Safety Conference, New Delhi.* P 13½×13.
1437 **1144** 6 r. 50, black, dp blue & orge-vermilion 75 1·00

1145 Exhibition Emblem

1146 Jagannath Sunkersett and Central Railways Headquarters

1991 (12 Feb). *7th Triennale Art Exhibition, New Delhi.* P 13×13½.
1438 **1145** 6 r. 50, multicoloured 60 75

1991 (15 Feb). *125th Death Anniv of Jagannath Sunkersett (educationist and railway pioneer)* (1990). P 13×13½.
1439 **1146** 2 r. royal blue and Indian red .. 50 60

1147 Tata Memorial Centre

1148 River Dolphin

1991 (28 Feb). *50th Anniv of Tata Memorial Medical Centre.* P 13½×13.
1440 **1147** 2 r. light brown and stone .. 30 40

1991 (4 Mar). *Endangered Marine Mammals.* T **1148** *and similar horiz design.* P 13½×13.
1441 4 r. red-brown, turquoise-blue & brt green 1·50 1·50
1442 6 r. 50, multicoloured .. .. 2·00 2·00
Design:—6 r. 50, Sea Cow.

1149 Drugs

1150 Hand, Bomb Explosion and Dove

(Des J. Irani)

1991 (5 Mar). *International Conference on Drug Abuse, Calcutta.* P 13×13½.
1443 **1149** 5 r. bluish violet and bright scarlet .. 1·60 1·60

(Des J. Das)

1991 (7 Mar). *World Peace.* P 13×13½.
1444 **1150** 6 r. 50, black, cinnamon & orge-brown 75 1·00

1151 Remote Sensing Satellite "1A"

1152 Babu Jagjivan Ram

1991 (18 Mar). *Launch of Indian Remote Sensing Satellite "1A".* P 14.
1445 **1151** 6 r. 50, chestnut and deep violet-blue 60 85

1991 (5 Apr). *Babu Jagjivan Ram (politician) Commemoration.* P 13×13½.
1446 **1152** 1 r. yellow-brown 20 20

1153 Dr. B. R. Ambedkar and Demonstration

1154 Valar Dance

1991 (14 Apr). *Birth Centenary of Dr. Bhimrao Ramji Ambedkar (social reformer).* P 13½×13.
1447 **1153** 1 r. reddish brown and deep dull blue 30 20

1991 (30 Apr). *Tribal Dances.* T **1154** *and similar horiz designs.* Multicoloured. P 13½×13.
1448 2 r. 50, Type **1154** 50 40
1449 4 r. Kayang 70 80
1450 5 r. Hozagiri 80 90
1451 6 r. 50, Velakali .. .. .. 1·00 1·40
1448/51 *Set of 4* 2·75 3·25

1155 Ariyakudi Ramanuja Iyengar and Temples

1156 Karpoori Thakur

(Des J. Sharma)

1991 (18 May). *Ariyakudi Ramanuja Iyengar (singer and composer) Commemoration.* P 13½×13.
1452 **1155** 2 r. red-brown and deep bluish green 50 65

(Des L. Sahu)

1991 (30 May). *Jan Nayak Karpoori Thakur (politician and social reformer) Commemoration.* P 13×13½.
1453 **1156** 1 r. reddish brown 20 20

MINIMUM PRICE

The minimum price quote is 10p which represents a handling charge rather than a basis for valuing common stamps. For further notes about prices see introductory pages.

1157 Emperor Penguins

1158 Rashtrapati Bhavan Building, New Delhi

1991 (23 June). *30th Anniv of Antarctic Treaty.* T **1157** *and similar horiz design.* Multicoloured. P 13½×13.
1454 5 r. Type **1157** .. .. .. 1·75 2·00
a. Horiz pair. Nos. 1454/5 .. 3·50 4·00
1455 6 r. 50, Antarctic map and pair of Adelie Penguins .. .. .. 1·75 2·00
Nos. 1454/5 were printed together, *se-tenant,* in horizontal pairs throughout the sheet, each pair forming a composite design.

(Des P. Biswas)

1991 (25 June). *60th Anniv of New Delhi.* T **1158** *and similar horiz designs.* Multicoloured. P 13½×13.
1456 5 r. Type **1158** .. .. .. 1·00 1·40
a. Horiz pair. Nos. 1456/7 .. 2·00 2·75
1457 6 r. 50, New Delhi monuments .. 1·00 1·40
Nos. 1456/7 were printed together, *se-tenant,* in horizontal pairs throughout the sheet, each pair forming a composite design.

1159 Sri Ram Sharma Acharya

1160 "Shankar awarded Padma Vibhushan" (cartoon)

1991 (27 June). *Sri Ram Sharma Acharya (social reformer) Commemoration.* P 13½×13.
1458 **1159** 1 r. turquoise-green and rosine .. 20 20

1991 (31 July). *Keshav Shankar Pillai (cartoonist) Commemoration.* T **1160** *and similar design.* P 13½×13 (4 r.) or 13×13½ (6 r. 50).
1459 4 r. light brown .. .. .. 1·00 1·40
1460 6 r. 50, deep rose-lilac .. .. 1·40 1·75
Design: *Vert*—6 r. 50, "The Big Show".

1161 Sriprakash and Kashi Vidyapith University

1162 Gopinath Bardoloi

1991 (3 Aug). *20th Death Anniv of Sriprakash (politician).* P 13½×13.
1461 **1161** 2 r. red-brown and light brown .. 30 30

1991 (5 Aug). *Birth Centenary of Gopinath Bardoloi (Assamese politician)* (1990). P 13×13½.
1462 **1162** 1 r. deep reddish lilac 20 20

1163 Rajiv Gandhi

(Des R. Chopra)

1991 (20 Aug). *Rajiv Gandhi (Congress Party leader) Commemoration.* P 13.
1463 **1163** 1 r. multicoloured 40 40

1164 Muni Mishrimalji and Memorial

1165 Mahadevi Verma (poetess) and "Varsha"

1991 (24 Aug). *Birth Centenary of Muni Mishrimalji (Jain religious leader).* P 13½×13.
1464 1164 1 r. yellow-brown 30 20

(Des S. Samant)

1991 (16 Sept). *Hindu Writers.* T **1165** *and similar horiz design.* P 13½×13.
1465 1165 2 r. black and light blue .. 15 25
　　a. Horiz pair. Nos. 1465/6 .. 30 50
1466 — 2 r. black and light blue .. 15 25
Design:—No. 1466, Jayshankar Prasad (poet and dramatist) and scene from "Kamayani".
Nos. 1465/6 were printed together, *se-tenant,* in horizontal pairs throughout the sheet.

1166 Parliament House and C.P.A. Emblem　　　**1167** Frog

(Des P. Biswas)

1991 (27 Sept). *37th Commonwealth Parliamentary Association Conference, New Delhi.* P 13½×13.
1467 1166 6 r. 50, blue and reddish brown .. 40 60

1991 (30 Sept). *Greetings Stamps.* T **1167** *and similar vert design.* P 13×13½.
1468 1 r. emerald and deep rose-red .. 20 40
　　a. Horiz pair. Nos. 1468/9 .. 55 95
1469 6 r. 50, deep rose-red and emerald .. 35 55
Design:—6 r. 50, Symbolic bird carrying flower.
Nos. 1468/9 were printed together, *se-tenant,* in horizontal pairs throughout the sheet.

1168 *Cymbidium aloifolium*

1169 Gurkha Soldier in Battle Dress

(Des O. Ravindran)

1991 (12 Oct). *Orchids.* T **1168** *and similar vert designs. Multicoloured.* P 13×13½.
1470 1 r. Type 1168 .. .. 30 15
1471 2 r. 50, *Paphiopedilum venustum* .. 35 35
1472 3 r. *Aerides crispum* 40 50
1473 4 r. *Cymbidium bicolour* 50 65
1474 5 r. *Vanda spathulata* 55 70
1475 6 r. 50, *Cymbidium devonianum* .. 70 1·00
1470/5 .. .. .. Set of 6 2·50 3·00

(Des R. Pasricha)

1991 (18 Oct). *90th Anniv of 2nd Battalion, Third Gurkha Rifles.* P 13½×13.
1476 1169 4 r. multicoloured .. .. 1·50 1·50

1170 Couple on Horse (embroidery)

1171 Chithira Tirunal and Temple Sculpture

1991 (29 Oct). *3rd Death Anniv of Kamaladevi Chattopadhyaya, (founder of All India Handicrafts Board).* T **1170** *and similar vert design.* P 13×13½.
1477 1 r. carmine-lake, crimson and yellow .. 40 20
1478 6 r. 50, multicoloured .. .. 1·50 1·75
Design:—6 r. 50, Traditional puppet.

1991 (7 Nov). *Chithira Tirunal Bala Rama Varma (former Maharaja of Travancore) Commemoration.* P 13½×13.
1479 1171 2 r. slate-violet 65 75

1172 "Children in Traditional Costume" (Arpi Snehalbhai Shah)

1173 Mounted Sowar and Tanks

1991 (14 Nov). *Children's Day.* P 13×13½.
1480 1172 1 r. multicoloured 70 30

(Des R. Pasricha)

1991 (14 Nov). *70th Anniv of the 18th Cavalry Regiment* (1992). P 13½×13.
1481 1173 6 r. 50, multicoloured .. .. 2·00 2·50

1174 Kites

1175 Sports on Bricks

1991 (15 Nov). *India Tourism Year.* P 13½×13.
1482 1174 6 r. 50, multicoloured .. .. 60 1·00
　　It was originally intended to release No. 1482 on 28 January 1991, but the issue was postponed until 15 November. Examples are known used from Jaipur on the original date.

1991 (18 Nov). *International Conference on Youth Tourism, New Delhi.* P 13×13½.
1483 1175 6 r. 50, multicoloured .. .. 1·10 1·50

1176 "Mozart at Piano" (unfinished painting, J. Lange)

1177 Homeless Family

1991 (5 Dec). *Death Bicentenary of Mozart.* P 13×13½.
1484 1176 6 r. 50, multicoloured .. .. 1·50 2·00

(Des N. Srivastav)

1991 (7 Dec). *South Asian Association for Regional Co-operation Year of Shelter.* P 13½×13.
1485 1177 4 r. lake-brown and ochre 55 70

1178 People running on Heart

1179 "Sidhartha with an Injured Bird" (Asit Kumar Haldar)

1991 (11 Dec). *"Run for Your Heart" Marathon, New Delhi.* P 13½×13.
1486 1178 1 r. black, slate and bright scarlet .. 20 20

1991 (28 Dec). *Birth Centenary of Asit Kumar Haldar (artist)* (1990). P 13×13½.
1487 1179 2 r. yellow, Indian red and black .. 30 50

1180 Bhujangasana　　　**1181** Y.M.C.A. Logo

1991 (30 Dec). *Yoga Exercises.* T **1180** *and similar horiz designs. Multicoloured.* P 13½×13.
1488 2 r. Type 1180 .. .. .. 20 25
1489 5 r. Dhanurasana 40 55
1490 6 r. 50, Ustrasana 50 70
1491 10 r. Utthita trikonasana .. .. 85 1·25
1488/91 .. .. .. Set of 4 1·75 2·50

1992 (21 Feb). *Centenary of National Council of Y.M.C.As.* (1991). P 13½×13.
1492 1181 1 r. vermilion and deep dull blue .. 20 20

1182 Madurai Temple Tower and Hooghly River Bridge

1183 Goat Seal from Harappa Culture, 2500 to 1500 B.C.

1992 (1 Mar). *14th Congress of International Association for Bridge and Structural Engineering, New Delhi.* T **1182** *and similar horiz design.* P 13½×13.
1493 1182 2 r. bistre-brown, dull vermilion & bl 45 65
　　a. Horiz pair. Nos. 1493/4 .. 90 1·25
1494 — 2 r. bistre-brown, dull vermilion & bl 45 65
Design:—No. 1494, Gate, Sanchi Stupa and Hall of Nations, New Delhi.
Nos. 1493/4 were printed together, *se-tenant,* in horizontal pairs throughout the sheet.

1992 (2 Mar). *5th International Goat Conference, New Delhi.* P 13×13½.
1495 1183 6 r. royal blue and bistre-brown .. 1·75 2·25

1184 Early 19th-century Letter with Mail Pouch and National Archives Building, New Delhi

1185 Krushna Chandra Gajapathi

(Des C. Pakrashi)

1992 (20 Apr). *Centenary of National Archives* (1991). P 13½×13.
1496 1184 6 r. multicoloured 50 65

1992 (25 Apr). *Krushna Chandra Gajapathi (former Chief Minister of Orissa) Commemoration.* P 13×13½.
1497 1185 1 r. deep lilac.. .. .. .. 15 15

1186 Vijay Singh Pathik　　　**1187** Hang-gliding

1992 (29 Apr). *Vijay Singh Pathik (writer) Commemoration.* P 13×13½.
1498 1186 1 r. reddish brown 15 15

(Des R. Pasricha)

1992 (29 Apr). *Adventure Sports.* T **1187** *and similar horiz designs. Multicoloured.* P 13½×13.

1499	2 r. Type **1187**	..	..	25	20
1500	4 r. Windsurfing	..	..	50	60
1501	5 r. River rafting	..	..	60	70
1502	11 r. Skiing	..	..	1·25	2·00
1499/1502			*Set of 4*	2·40	3·25

1188 Henry Gidney and Anglo-Indians   **1189** Telecommunications Training Centre, Jabalpur

(Des S. Kitson and A. Ali)

1992 (9 May). *50th Death Anniv of Sir Henry Gidney (ophthalmologist).* P 13½×13.

1503 **1188** 1 r. black and light blue	..	30	15

1992 (30 May). *50th Anniv of Telecommunications Training Centre, Jabalpur.* P 13½×13.

1504 **1189** 1 r. bistre	..	20	15

1190 Sardar Udham Singh   **1191** Men's Discus

(Des S. Samanta)

1992 (31 July). *Sardar Udham Singh (patriot) Commemoration.* P 13×13½.

1505 **1190** 1 r. black and light brown	..	20	15

(Des P. Biswas)

1992 (8 Aug). *Olympic Games, Barcelona.* T **1191** *and similar vert designs. Multicoloured.* P 13×13½.

1506	1 r. Type **1191**	..	..	30	10
1507	6 r. Women's gymnastics	..	..	90	1·00
1508	8 r. Men's hockey	..	..	2·00	2·25
1509	11 r. Boxing	..	..	2·00	2·50
1506/9			*Set of 4*	4·75	5·25

1192 Spinning Wheel Emblem   **1193** Treating Casualty

(Des C. Pakrashi)

1992 (9 Aug). *50th Anniv of "Quit India" Movement.* T **1192** *and similar horiz design.* P 13½×13.

1510	1 r. black and brown-rose	..	75	30
1511	2 r. black, lake-brown and grey	..	1·50	1·75
Design:—2 r. Mahatma Gandhi and mantra				

1992 (10 Aug). *50th Anniv of 60th Parachute Field Ambulance.* P 13½×13.

1512 **1193** 1 r. multicoloured	..	1·25	40

1194 Dr. S. R. Ranganathan and Madras University   **1195** "Dev Narayan"

1992 (30 Aug). *Birth Centenary of Shiyali Ramamrita Ranganathan (librarian).* P 13½×13.

1513 **1194** 1 r. deep turquoise-blue	..	65	30

1992 (2 Sept). *Phad Scroll Paintings from Rajasthan.* P 14.

1514 **1195** 5 r. multicoloured	..	55	70

1196 Hanuman Prasad Poddar   **1197** Mikoyan Gurevich MiG-29 Fighter and Ilyushin Il-76 Transport

1992 (19 Sept). *Hanuman Prasad Poddar (editor) Commemoration.* P 13×13½.

1515 **1196** 1 r. deep green	..	15	15

(Des S. Surve)

1992 (8 Oct). *60th Anniv of Indian Air Force.* T **1197** *and similar horiz design. Multicoloured.* P 13½×13.

1516	1 r. Type **1197**		60	75
	a. Horiz pair. Nos. 1516/17		1·60	2·00
1517	10 r. MiG-27 fighter and Westland Wapiti biplane		1·00	1·25

Nos. 1516/17 were printed together, *se-tenant*, in horizontal pairs throughout the sheet.

1198 Lighting Candle   **1199** "Sun" (Harshit Prashant Patel)

(Des S. Samanta)

1992 (13 Nov). *150th Anniv of Sisters of Jesus and Mary's Arrival in India.* P 13×13½.

1518 **1198** 1 r. royal blue and light grey	..	15	15

1992 (14 Nov). *Childrens Day.* P 13½×13.

1519 **1199** 1 r. multicoloured	..	20	15

1200 Yogiji Maharaj   **1201** Army Service Corps Transport

1992 (2 Dec). *Birth Centenary of Yogiji Maharaj (Hindu reformer).* P 13×13½.

1520 **1200** 1 r. deep ultramarine	..	40	15

1992 (8 Dec). *Army Service Corps Commemoration.* P 13½×13.

1521 **1201** 1 r. multicoloured	..	1·25	40

1202 Stephen Smith and Early Rocket Post Covers   **1203** Electricity Pylons, Farmers and Crops

1992 (19 Dec). *Birth Centenary of Stephen Smith (rocket mail pioneer) (1991).* P 13½×13.

1522 **1202** 11 r. multicoloured	..	90	1·25

1992 (20 Dec). *25th Anniv of Haryana State.* P 13½×13.

1523 **1203** 2 r. orange-verm, dp grn & yellow-grn	15	15

MINIMUM PRICE

The minimum price quote is 10p which represents a handling charge rather than a basis for valuing common stamps. For further notes about prices see introductory pages.

1204 Madanlal Dhingra   **1205** Osprey

1992 (28 Dec). *Madanlal Dhingra (revolutionary) Commemoration.* P 13×13½.

1524 **1204** 1 r. deep brown, orange-red & dp green	30	15

1992 (30 Dec). *Birds of Prey.* T **1205** *and similar vert designs. Multicoloured.* P 13½×13.

1525	2 r. Type **1205**		90	60
	a. Error. 1 r. instead of 2 r.	..	£2500	
1526	6 r. Peregrine Falcon	..	1·25	1·10
1527	8 r. Lammergeier	..	1·40	1·75
1528	11 r. Golden Eagle	..	1·60	2·00
1525/8		*Set of 4*	4·75	4·75

No. 1525a was the original printing of this design, incorporating an incorrect Hindi inscription. The stamp was withdrawn before issue and replaced by a 2 r. value with the correct inscription. Three examples of the 1 r. have, however, been found in 1992 Year Packs.

1206 Pandit Ravishankar Shukla   **1207** William Carey

1992 (31 Dec). *Pandit Ravishankar Shukla (social reformer) Commemoration.* P 13×13½.

1529 **1206** 1 r. deep purple	..	15	15

1993 (9 Jan). *Bicentenary of William Carey's Appointment as Baptist Missionary to India.* P 13½×13.

1530 **1207** 6 r. multicoloured	..	1·00	1·00

1208 Fakirmohan Senapati   **1209** Workers and C.S.I.R. Emblem

1993 (14 Jan). *Fakirmohan Senapati Commemoration.* P 13×13½.

1531 **1208** 1 r. Indian red	..	40	15

1993 (28 Feb). *50th Anniv of Council of Scientific and Industrial Research.* P 13½×13.

1532 **1209** 1 r. maroon	..	40	15

1210 Parachute Drop and Field Gun   **1211** Westland Wapiti Biplane

1993 (1 Apr). *50th Anniv of 9th Parachute Field Artillery Regiment.* P 13½.

1533 **1210** 1 r. multicoloured	..	1·25	30

1993 (1 Apr). *60th Anniv of No. 1 Squadron, Indian Air Force.* P 13½.

1534 **1211** 1 r. multicoloured	..	1·25	30

1212 Rahul Sankrityayan

1213 Parliament Building and Emblem

1993 (9 Apr). *Birth Centenary of Rahul Sankrityayan (politician). P* 13½×13.
1535 1212 1 r. blue-black, cinnamon & yellow-brn   20   15

1993 (11 Apr). *89th Inter-Parliamentary Union Conference, New Delhi. P* 13×13½.
1536 1213 1 r. blue-black   20   15

1214 Neral Matheran Railway Tank Locomotive, 1905

1215 Students and College Building

1993 (16 Apr). *Mountain Locomotives. T* 1214 *and similar horiz designs. Multicoloured. P* 13½×13.
1537   1 r. Type 1214   ..   60   20
1538   6 r. Darjeeling and Himalayan Railway, 1889   ..   1·25   1·25
1539   8 r. Nilgiri Mountain Railway, 1914   ..   1·40   1·60
1540   11 r. Kalka–Simla Railway, 1934   ..   1·90   2·25
1537/40   ..   ..   *Set of 4*   4·75   4·75

1993 (25 Apr). *Centenary of Meerut College. P* 14.
1541 1215 1 r. blue-black and orange-brown   ..   20   15

1216 Mahalanobis and Office Block

1217 Bombay Town Hall

1993 (29 June). *Prasanta Chandra Mahalanobis Commemoration. P* 13.
1542 1216 1 r. yellow-brown   20   15

1993 (31 July). *Centenary of Bombay Municipal Corporation. P* 13×13½.
1543 1217 2 r. multicoloured   20   30

1218 Abdul Ghaffar Khan and Mountainside

1219 National Integration Emblem

1993 (9 Aug). *Abdul Ghaffar Khan Commemoration. P* 13½×13.
1544 1218 1 r. multicoloured   15   15

(Des C. Pakrashi)

1993 (19 Aug). *National Integration Campaign. P* 13½×13.
1545 1219 1 r. bright orange and deep green   15   15

1220 Dadabhai Naoroji and Houses of Parliament, London

1221 Swami Vivekananda and Art Institute, Chicago

1993 (26 Aug). *Centenary of Dadabhai Naoroji's Election to the House of Commons. P* 14.
1546 1220 6 r. multicoloured   45   60

(Des C. Pakrashi)

1993 (11 Sept). *Centenary of Swami Vivekananda's Chicago Address. P* 13×13½.
1547 1221 2 r. reddish orange and grey   ..   40   40

1222 *Lagerstroemia speciosa*

1223 College Building and Emblem

(Des O. Ravindran)

1993 (9 Oct). *Flowering Trees. T* 1222 *and similar vert designs. P* 13×13½.
1548   1 r. rose-carmine, yellow-grn & chocolate   20   15
1549   6 r. multicoloured   ..   40   55
1550   8 r. multicoloured   ..   55   70
1551   11 r. multicoloured   ..   75   1·00
1548/51   ..   ..   *Set of 4*   1·75   2·25
Designs:—6 r. *Cochlospermum religiosum*; 8 r. *Erythrina variegata*; 11 r. *Thespesia populnea.*

1993 (8 Nov). *50th Anniv of College of Military Engineering, Pune. P* 13×13½.
1552 1223 2 r. multicoloured   ..   20   30

1224 Dr. Dwaram Venkataswamy Naidu playing Violin

1225 Children on Elephant

(Des Alka Sharma)

1993 (8 Nov). *Birth Centenary of Dwaram Venkataswamy Naidu (violinist). P* 13×13½.
1553 1224 1 r. Indian red   ..   20   20

1993 (14 Nov). *Children's Day. P* 14.
1554 1225 1 r. multicoloured   ..   20   20

1226 People with Stress

1227 Dr. Kotnis performing Operation

1993 (9 Dec). *Heart Care Festival. P* 13½×13.
1555 1226 6 r. 50, multicoloured   ..   60   70

1993 (9 Dec). *Dr. Dwarkananth Kotnis (surgeon) Commemoration. P* 13½×13.
1556 1227 1 r. blue-black   ..   20   20
     a. Printed on the gummed side   ..

1228 Tea Symbol   1229 Papal Seminary Arms and Building

1993 (11 Dec). *Indian Tea Production. P* 13.
1557 1228 6 r. deep dull green and bright carmine   50   65

1993 (16 Dec). *Centenary of Papal Seminary, Pune. P* 13½×13.
1558 1229 6 r. multicoloured   50   65

1230 Meghnad Saha and Eclipse of the Sun

1231 Speedpost Letter and Arrows circling Globe

1993 (23 Dec). *Meghnad Saha (astronomer) Commemoration. P* 13×13½.
1559 1230 1 r. deep violet-blue   30   20

(Des C. Pakrashi (1 r.))

1993 (25–27 Dec). *"Inpex '93" National Philatelic Exhibition, Calcutta. T* 1231 *and similar horiz design. Multicoloured. P* 13½×13.
1560   1 r. Type 1231   ..   20   15
1561   2 r. "Custom-house Wharf, Calcutta" (Sir Charles D'Oyly) (27 Dec)   ..   35   45

1232 Dinanath Mangeshkar   1233 Nargis Dutt

(Des C. Pakrashi)

1993 (29 Dec). *Dinanath Mangeshkar Commemoration. P* 13½×13.
1562 1232 1 r. orange-red   15   15

1993 (30 Dec). *Nargis Dutt Commemoration. P* 13.
1563 1233 1 r. Indian red   15   15

1234 S.C. Bose inspecting Troops

1235 Satyendra Nath Bose and Equation

1993 (31 Dec). *50th Anniv of Indian National Army. P* 13½×13.
1564 1234 1 r. slate-green, dp green & orange-red   30   20

1994 (1 Jan). *Birth Centenary of Satyendra Nath Bose (scientist). P* 13½×13.
1565 1235 1 r. purple-brown   ..   30   15

1236 Dr. Sampurnanand

1994 (10 Jan). *Dr. Sampurnanand (politician) Commemoration. P* 13½×13.
1566 1236 1 r. reddish brn, slate-grn & orge-red   15   10

The new-issue supplement to this Catalogue appears each month in

GIBBONS STAMP MONTHLY

—from your newsagent or by postal subscription— sample copy and details on request.

1237 Scene from *Pather Panchali*

1994 (11 Jan). *Satyajit Ray (film director) Commemoration.* T **1237** *and similar multicoloured design.* P 13.
1567   6 r. Type **1237** .. .. 1·25 1·50
     a. Horiz pair. Nos. 1567/8 2·50 3·00
1568   11 r. Satyajit Ray and Oscar (35×35 *mm*) 1·40 1·60
Nos. 1567/8 were printed together, *se-tenant*, in horizontal pairs throughout the sheet.

1238 Dr. Bhatnagar and University Building

1239 Prajapita Brahma and Memorial

1994 (21 Feb). *Dr. Shanti Swarup Bhatnagar (scientist) Commemoration.* P 13½×13.
1569   **1238**   1 r. deep violet-blue 15 10

1994 (7 Mar). *25th Death Anniv of Prajapita Brahma (social reformer).* P 13½×13.
1570   **1239**   1 r. deep rose-lilac & deep ultramarine 15 10

1240 "Window" (K. Subramanyan)

1241 Agricultural Products and Tea Garden

1994 (14 Mar). *8th Triennale Art Exhibition, New Delhi.* P 13½×13.
1571   **1240**   6 r. salmon, carmine-verm & ultram 40 60

(Des S. Samanta)

1994 (26 Mar). *Centenary of United Planters' Association of Southern India.* P 13×13½.
1572   **1241**   2 r. multicoloured 20 20

1242 Indian Family

1242a Sanchi Stupa

1994 (4 Apr)–98. W 374 (*sideways on 5 r.*). P 13.
1573   **1242**   75 p. brown and vermilion (11.7.94) 10 10
     a. Wmk sideways (1998)
1574   —   1 r. cerise & dp bluish grn (11.7.94) 10 10
     a. Wmk sideways (1997) 10 10
1575   —   3 r. deep claret (21.9.98) .. 15 20
1576   **1242a**   5 r. reddish brown & turquoise-grn 15 20
     a. Wmk upright
Designs: *Horiz* (as T **1242**)—1 r. Family outside home. *Vert* (as T **1242**)—3 r. Baby and drop of polio vaccine.

1243 Rani Rashmoni on River Bank

1244 Indians releasing Peace Doves

1994 (9 Apr). *Birth Bicentenary of Rani Rashmoni.* P 13½×13.
1589   **1243**   1 r. reddish brown 15 10

(Des S. Kumar)

1994 (13 Apr). *75th Anniv of Jallianwala Bagh Massacre, Amritsar.* P 13½×13.
1590   **1244**   1 r. black and rosine .. 15 10

1245 Chandra Singh Garhwali

1246 Emblems and National Flag

1994 (23 Apr). *15th Death Anniv of Chandra Singh Garhwali (nationalist).* P 13½×13.
1591   **1245**   1 r. deep olive-green and red-orange 15 10

1994 (1 May). *75th Anniv of International Labour Organization.* P 13½×13.
1592   **1246**   6 r. multicoloured 40 60

1247 Silhouette of Drummer and Logo

1248 Statue of Sepoy

(Des A. Sharma)

1994 (25 May). *50th Anniv of Indian People's Theatre Association.* P 13.
1593   **1247**   2 r. black, yellowish green and gold 15 15

1994 (12 Aug). *Bicentenary of 4th Battalion, The Madras Regiment.* P 13.
1594   **1248**   6 r. 50, multicoloured 55 65

1249 Institute Building and Emblem

1250 Mahatma Gandhi and Indian Flag

(Des C. Pakrashi)

1994 (23 Sept). *Bicentenary of Institute of Mental Health, Madras.* P 13½×13.
1595   **1249**   2 r. deep rose-red and deep blue .. 15 15

(Des S. Samanta and S. Kumar)

1994 (2 Oct). *125th Birth Anniv of Mahatma Gandhi.* T **1250** *and similar multicoloured design.* P 13.
1596   6 r. Type **1250** .. 1·00 1·25
     a. Horiz pair. Nos. 1596/7 .. 2·25 2·75
1597   11 r. Aspects of Gandhi's life on flag (69×34 *mm*) .. .. 1·25 1·50
Nos. 1596/7 were printed together, *se-tenant*, in horizontal pairs throughout the sheet, with the backgrounds forming a composite design.

1251 Symbols of Cancer

1252 Human Resources Emblem

(Des A. Sharma)

1994 (30 Oct). *16th International Cancer Congress, New Delhi.* P 13×13½.
1598   **1251**   6 r. multicoloured 55 65

1994 (8 Nov). *Human Resource Development World Conference, New Delhi.* P 13½×13.
1599   **1252**   6 r. blue, vermilion and azure .. 55 65

COVER PRICES

Cover factors are quoted at the beginning of each country for most issues to 1945. An explanation of the system can be found on page x. The factors quoted do not, however, apply to philatelic covers.

1253 "Me and My Pals" (Namarata Amit Shah)

1254 Family and Emblem

1994 (14 Nov). *Children's Day.* P 13½×13.
1600   **1253**   1 r. multicoloured 10 10

(Des S. Kumar)

1994 (20 Nov). *International Year of the Family.* P 13.
1601   **1254**   2 r. multicoloured 20 15

1255 "Taj Mahal" (illustration from Badsha Nama)

1256 Andaman Teal

1994 (21 Nov). *Khuda Bakhsh Oriental Public Library, Patna, Commemoration.* P 14.
1602   **1255**   6 r. multicoloured .. .. 4·00 1·00

(Des J. Irani. Litho Madras Security Printers)

1994 (23 Nov). *Endangered Water Birds.* T **1256** *and similar horiz designs. Multicoloured.* P 13½×13.
1603   1 r. Type **1256** .. .. 5·00 2·00
     a. Block of 4. Nos. 1603/6 .. 30·00
1604   6 r. Eastern White Stork .. 8·00 4·00
1605   8 r. Black-necked Crane .. 9·00 4·50
1606   11 r. Pink-headed Duck .. 11·00 6·00
1603/6   Set of 4 30·00 15·00
Nos. 1603/6 were printed together, *se-tenant*, in blocks of 4 throughout the sheet.
It is reported that Nos. 1603/6 were withdrawn shortly after issue due to technical difficulties.

1257 J. R. D. Tata and Aspects of Industrial Symbols

(Des C. Pakrashi)

1994 (29 Nov). *J. R. D. Tata (industrialist) Commemoration.* P 14.
1607   **1257**   2 r. multicoloured 30 30

1258 School Building and Computer Class

1259 Begum Akhtar

1994 (30 Nov). *Centenary of Calcutta Blind School.* P 13½×13.
1608   **1258**   2 r. rosine, chocolate and cinnamon 20 15

(Litho Madras Security Printers)

1994 (2 Dec). *80th Birth Anniv of Begum Akhtar (singer).* P 13½×13.
1609   **1259**   2 r. multicoloured .. .. 4·25 4·25
It is reported that No. 1609 was withdrawn shortly after issue due to technical difficulties

1260 College Building

1261 Cavalryman, Infantryman and Dog Handler

1994 (4 Dec). *125th Anniv of St. Xavier's College, Bombay.* P 13½×13.
1610 **1260** 2 r. purple-brown and azure .. 15 15

1994 (14 Dec). *215th Anniv of Remount Veterinary Corps.* P 13×13½.
1611 **1261** 6 r. multicoloured 75 60

1262 College Building

1263 Righthand Ornament of Bronze Stand

1994 (19 Dec). *Bicentenary of College of Engineering, Guindy, Madras.* P 14.
1612 **1262** 2 r. dull vermilion, red-brown & black 15 10

1994 (20 Dec). *Centenary of Baroda Museum.* T **1263** and similar vert design. P 14.
1613 6 r. bistre-yellow and agate .. .. 2·50 75
　　 a. Horiz pair. Nos. 1613/14 .. .. 5·00 1·50
1614 11 r. bistre-yellow and agate .. .. 2·50 75
Design:—11 r. Bronze Rishabhanatha statue of Buddha on stand.
Nos. 1613/14 were printed together, *se-tenant*, in horizontal pairs throughout the sheet.

1264 "200" and Aspects of Postal Service

(Des M. Rajadhyaksha. Litho Calcutta Security Printers, Kanpur)

1994 (28 Dec). *Bicentenary of Bombay General Post Office.* P 13½×13.
1615 **1264** 6 r. multicoloured .. .. 5·00 1·50

1265 Statue of King Rajaraja Chola

1266 Globe and Emblem

(Litho Madras Security Printers)

1995 (5 Jan). *8th International Conference-Seminar of Tamil Studies, Thanjavur.* P 13×13½.
1616 **1265** 2 r. light blue, ultramarine and black 3·50 75

(Des C. Pakrashi)

1995 (7 Jan). *60th Anniv of National Science Academy.* P 13×13½.
1617 **1266** 6 r. multicoloured 50 60

1267 Chhotu Ram

1268 Film Reel and Globe

1995 (9 Jan). *Chhotu Ram (social reformer) Commemoration.* P 13×13½.
1618 **1267** 1 r. yellow-brown .. .. .. 1·00 25

(Des S. Kumar. Litho Calcutta Security Printers, Kanpur)

1995 (11 Jan). *Centenary of Cinema.* T **1268** and similar horiz design. Multicoloured. P 13½×13.
1619 6 r. Type **1268** 60 70
　　 a. Horiz pair. Nos. 1619/20 .. 1·40 1·60
1620 11 r. Film reel and early equipment .. 80 90
Nos. 1619/20 were printed together, *se-tenant*, in horizontal pairs throughout the sheet.

1269 Symbolic Hands and Children

1270 Prithviraj Kapoor and Mask

1995 (12 Jan). *South Asian Association for Regional Cooperation Youth Year.* P 13×13½.
1621 **1269** 2 r. multicoloured .. 20 20

(Des S. Pawar)

1995 (15 Jan). *50th Anniv of Prithvi Theatre.* P 13×13½.
1622 **1270** 2 r. multicoloured .. .. 3·75 75

1271 Field-Marshal Cariappa

1272 Textile Pattern

1995 (15 Jan). *Field-Marshal K. Cariappa Commemoration.* P 13×13½.
1623 **1271** 2 r. multicoloured 30 20

1995 (18 Jan). *"TEX-STYLES INDIA '95" Fair, Bombay.* P 13×13½.
1624 **1272** 2 r. chestnut, pale buff & brt scarlet 20 20

1273 Rafi Ahmed Kidwai

1274 K. L. Saigal, Film Reel and Gramophone

1995 (18 Feb). *Birth Centenary of Rafi Ahmed Kidwai (politician) (1994).* P 13×13½.
1625 **1273** 1 r. chestnut 15 10

1995 (4 Apr). *90th Birth Anniv of K. L. Saigal (singer).* P 13½×13.
1626 **1274** 5 r. chestnut, grey and black .. 75 80

1275 R. S. Ruikar

1276 Radio Tower, Globe and Dish Aerial

1995 (1 May). *Birth Centenary of R. S. Ruikar (trade unionist).* P 13×13½.
1627 **1275** 1 r. purple-brown 15 10

(Des S. Kumar. Litho Calcutta Security Printers Ltd, Kanpur)

1995 (17 May). *Centenary of Telecommunications.* P 13½×13.
1628 **1276** 5 r. multicoloured 60 70

1277 Leaves and Symbolic Houses

1278 Handshake

(Des D. Banduni. Litho Calcutta Security Printers Ltd, Kanpur)

1995 (23 May). *Delhi Development Authority.* P 13½×13.
1629 **1277** 2 r. multicoloured 20 20

(Des C. Pakrashi. Litho Calcutta Security Printers Ltd, Kanpur)

1995 (26 June). *50th Anniv of United Nations.* T **1278** and similar vert design. Multicoloured. P 13½×13.
1630 1 r. Type **1278** 10 10
1631 6 r. Work of U.N. Agencies .. 45 55

1279 Colonnade on Book Cover

1280 Globe showing South-east Asia

(Des D. Banduni)

1995 (30 Aug). *Centenary of Bharti Bhawan Library, Allahabad.* P 14.
1632 **1279** 6 r. black, chestnut & bright rose-red 55 65

(Des S. Kumar. Litho Calcutta Security Printers Ltd, Kanpur)

1995 (4 Sept). *25th Anniv of Asian-Pacific Postal Training Centre, Bangkok.* P 13½×13.
1633 **1280** 10 r. multicoloured 80 90

1281 "75" and Taurus Formation Sign

1282 Louis Pasteur in Laboratory (from painting by Edelfelt)

1995 (26 Sept). *75th Anniv of Area Army Headquarters, Delhi.* P 13×13½.
1634 **1281** 2 r. multicoloured 30 20

(Des S. Samantha)

1995 (28 Sept). *Death Centenary of Louis Pasteur (chemist).* P 13×13½.
1635 **1282** 5 r. black and stone 70 80

1283 La Martiniere
College, Lucknow

1284 Gandhi in
South Africa

1995 (1 Oct). *150th Anniv of La Martiniere College, Lucknow.*
P 13½×13.
1636 **1283** 2 r. multicoloured 20 20

(Des A. Ainslie)

1995 (2 Oct). *India–South Africa Co-operation. 125th Birth*
Anniv of Mahatma Gandhi (1994). T **1284** *and similar vert*
design. P 13.
1637 1 r. scarlet 25 25
    a. Horiz pair. Nos. 1637/8 .. .. 55 55
1638 2 r. scarlet 30 30
    a. Printed double
MS1639 68×80 mm. Nos. 1637/8 (*sold at 8 r.*) 70 90
Design:—2 r. Gandhi wearing dhoti.
Nos. 1637/8 were issued together, *se-tenant*, in horizontal
pairs throughout the sheet.
Stamps in similar designs were issued by South Africa.

1285 Ears of Grain, "50"
and Emblem on Globe

1286 P. M. Thevar

(Des and litho Calcutta Security Printers Ltd, Kanpur)
1995 (16 Oct). *50th Anniv of Food and Agriculture Organi-*
zation. P 13½×13.
1640 **1285** 5 r. multicoloured 60 70

1995 (30 Oct). *Pasumpon Muthuramalingam Thevar (social*
reformer) Commemoration. P 13.
1641 **1286** 1 r. deep rose-red 15 10

1287 W. C. Rontgen

1288 Children in
Circle

1995 (8 Nov). *150th Birth Anniv of W. C. Rontgen (discoverer*
of X-rays). P 13×13½.
1642 **1287** 6 r. multicoloured 65 75

1995 (14 Nov). *Children's Day. P* 13×13½.
1643 **1288** 1 r. multicoloured 20 10

1289 Sitar

1290 Jat War Memorial,
Bareilly

1995 (19 Nov). *Communal Harmony Campaign. P* 13.
1644 **1289** 2 r. multicoloured 50 30

1995 (20 Nov). *Bicentenary of Jat Regiments. P* 13.
1645 **1290** 5 r. multicoloured 80 80

1291 Men of Rajputana
Rifles

1292 Sant Tukdoji
Maharaj and Rural
Meeting

1995 (28 Nov). *175th Anniv of 5th (Napier's) Battalion,*
Rajputana Rifles. P 13½×13.
1646 **1291** 5 r. multicoloured 80 80

1995 (10 Dec). *Sant Tukdoji Maharaj Commemoration.*
P 13½×13.
1647 **1292** 1 r. yellow-brown 15 10
Although dated "1993" No. 1647 was not issued until the date
quoted above.

1293 Dr. Yellapragada
Subbarow

1294 Pres. Giani
Zail Singh

1995 (19 Dec). *Dr. Yellapragada Subbarow (pharmaceutical*
scientist) Commemoration. P 13.
1648 **1293** 1 r. orange-brown 30 10

1995 (25 Dec). *First Death Anniv of Pres. Giani Zail Singh.*
P 13.
1649 **1294** 1 r. multicoloured 15 10

1295 Dargah of
Ala Hazrat Barelvi

1296 Tata Institute Building

(Litho Calcutta Security Printers Ltd, Kanpur)
1995 (31 Dec). *75th Death Anniv of Ala Hazrat Barelvi*
(Moslem scholar). P 13×13½.
1650 **1295** 1 r. multicoloured 15 10
    a. "1995" omitted from bottom right
    (R. 2/2)

1996 (9 Feb). *50th Anniv of Tata Institute of Fundamental*
Research (1995). P 13½×13.
1651 **1296** 2 r. multicoloured 20 20

1297 Kasturba
Gandhi

1298 Sectioned
Heart

(Des S. Samantha)
1996 (22 Feb). *50th Anniv of the Kasturba Trust. P* 13.
1652 **1297** 1 r. slate, brt green & bright scarlet 15 10

(Litho Calcutta Security Printers Ltd, Kanpur)
1996 (25 Feb). *100 Years of Cardiac Surgery. P* 13×13½.
1653 **1298** 5 r. multicoloured 60 70

NEW INFORMATION

The editor is always interested to correspond with
people who have new information that will
improve or correct the Catalogue.

1299 C. K. Nayudu

1300 "Vasant" (Spring)
(Ragini Basanti)

1996 (13 Mar). *Cricketers. T* **1299** *and similar vert designs.*
Multicoloured. P 14.
1654 2 r. Type **1299** 25 25
1655 2 r. Vinoo Mankad 25 25
1656 2 r. Deodhar 25 25
1657 2 r. Vijay Merchant 25 25
1654/7 .. .. .. *Set of 4* 90 90

(Litho Calcutta Security Printers Ltd, Kanpur)
1996 (13 Mar). *Miniature Paintings of the Seasons. T* **1300** *and*
similar vert designs. Multicoloured. P 13½.
1658 5 r. Type **1300** 60 70
1659 5 r. "Greeshma" (Summer) (Jyestha) .. 60 70
1660 5 r. "Varsha" (Monsoon) (Rag Megh
    Malbar) 60 70
1661 5 r. "Hemant" (Winter) (Pausha) .. 60 70
1658/61 .. .. .. *Set of 4* 2·25 2·50

1301 Kunjilal
Dubey

1302 Morarji Desai

1996 (18 Mar). *Kunjilal Dubey Commemoration. P* 13.
1662 **1301** 1 r. olive-sepia and chocolate .. 15 10

1996 (10 Apr). *Birth Centenary of Morarji Desai (former Prime*
Minister) (1st issue). P 13×13½.
1663 **1302** 1 r. deep rose-red 20 10
See also Nos. 1702

1303 Blood Pheasant

1304 S.K.C.G. College
Building

(Des R. Sukumar (Nos. 1663/4), V. Kumar (Nos. 1665/6). Litho
Calcutta Security Printers Ltd, Kanpur)
1996 (10 May). *Himalayan Ecology. T* **1303** *and similar horiz*
designs. Multicoloured. P 13½×13.
1664 5 r. Type **1303** 60 70
1665 5 r. Markhor (goat) 60 70
1666 5 r. *Meconopis horridula* (Tsher Gnoin)
    (plant) 60 70
1667 5 r. *Saussurea simpsoniana* (Sunflower) 60 70
1664/7 .. .. .. *Set of 4* 2·25 2·50
MS1668 175×105 mm. Nos. 1664/7 (*sold at 30 r.*) 2·10 2·50
No. **MS**1668 exists with either blue or white gum.

(Litho Calcutta Security Printers, Kanpur)
1996 (25 May). *Centenary of S.K.C.G. College, Gajapati.*
P 13½×13.
1669 **1304** 1 r. brown and cream 15 10

1305 Muhammad
Ismail Sahib

1306 Modern
Stadium and
Ancient Athens

1996 (5 June). *Birth Centenary of Muhammad Ismail Sahib (Moslem politician).* P 13×13½.
1670 **1305** 1 r. deep reddish purple 15 10

(Des S. Kumar. Litho Calcutta Security Printers Ltd, Kanpur)

1996 (25 June). *Olympic Games, Atlanta.* T **1306** *and similar vert designs. Multicoloured.* P 13×13½.
1671 5 r. Type **1306** 35 40
1672 5 r. Hand holding Olympic torch 35 40

1307 Sister Alphonsa

1308 "Communications"

(Des S. Samanta)

1996 (19 July). *50th Death Anniv of Sister Alphonsa.* P 13×13½.
1673 **1307** 1 r. black and dull blue 15 10

(Des S. Gujral)

1996 (2 Aug). *125th Anniv of Videsh Sanchar Nigam Limited (telecommunications company).* P 14.
1674 **1308** 5 r. multicoloured 35 40

1309 Sir Pherozeshah Mehta

1310 Ahilyabai

1996 (4 Aug). *150th Birth Anniv of Sir Pherozeshah Mehta (politician).* P 13.
1675 **1309** 1 r. deep slate-blue 15 10

(Des S. Samanta)

1996 (25 Aug). *Death Bicentenary (1995) of Ahilyabai (ruler of Holkar).* P 13×13½.
1676 **1310** 2 r. yellow-brown and purple-brown 20 20

1311 Chembai Vaidyanatha Bhagavathar

1312 Red Junglefowl Cockerel

(Des S. Samanta)

1996 (28 Aug). *Birth Centenary of Chembai Vaidanatha Bhagavathar (musician).* P 13½×13½.
1677 **1311** 1 r. chestnut and deep turquoise-green 15 10

(Des R. Sukumar. Litho Calcutta Security Printers Ltd, Kanpur)

1996 (2 Sept). *20th World Poultry Congress, New Delhi.* P 13½×13.
1678 **1312** 5 r. multicoloured 70 70

1313 Rani Gaidinliu

1314 Nath Pai

1996 (12 Sept). *Rani Gaidinliu (Naga leader) Commemoration.* P 13.
1679 **1313** 1 r. deep turquoise-blue 15 10

1996 (25 Sept). *25th Death Anniv of Nath Pai (politician).* P 13×13½.
1680 **1314** 1 r. dull blue 15 10

1315 Exhibition Logo

1316 Historic Steam Locomotives

(Des S. Samanta. Litho Calcutta Security Printers Ltd, Kanpur)

1996 (5 Oct). *"INDEPEX '97" International Stamp Exhibition, New Delhi (1st issue).* P 13×13½.
1681 **1315** 2 r. gold and brown-purple 20 20
See also Nos. 1713/16, 1722/5, 1741/4, **MS**1756 and 1758/61.

(Des S. Samanta. Litho Calcutta Security Printers Ltd, Kanpur)

1996 (7 Oct). *25th Anniv of National Rail Museum.* P 13½.
1682 **1316** 5 r. multicoloured 70 70

1317 Jananayak Debeswar Sarmah

1318 Monument and Sikh Sentry

(Des S. Samanta. Litho Calcutta Security Printers Ltd, Kanpur)

1996 (10 Oct). *Birth Centenary of Jananayak Debeswar Sarmah (politician).* P 13½×13½.
1683 **1317** 2 r. orange-brown and red-brown 20 20

1996 (19 Oct). *150th Anniv of Sikh Regiment.* P 13.
1684 **1318** 5 r. multicoloured 50 55

1319 Dr. Salim Ali

1320 "Indian Village" (child's painting)

1996 (12 Nov). *Birth Centenary of Salim Ali (ornithologist).* T **1319** *and similar square design. Multicoloured.* P 13.
1685 8 r. Type **1319** .. .. 90 1·00
a. Horiz pair. Nos. 1685/6 .. .. 1·90 2·25
1686 11 r. Storks at nest .. .. 1·00 1·25
Nos. 1685/6 were printed together, *se-tenant*, in horizontal pairs with the backgrounds forming a composite design.

1996 (14 Nov). *Children's Day.* P 13½×13.
1687 **1320** 8 r. multicoloured 50 55

1321 Seeds in a Test-tube

1322 Regimental Shrine

1996 (17 Nov). *2nd International Crop Science Congress, New Delhi.* P 13×13½.
1688 **1321** 2 r. multicoloured 20 20

1996 (4 Dec). *Bicentenary of 2nd Battalion, Grenadiers.* P 14.
1689 **1322** 5 r. multicoloured 50 55

1323 Woman writing

1324 Abai Konunbaev

(Des V. Mehra)

1996 (8 Dec). *10th Anniv of South Asian Association for Regional Co-operation (S.A.A.R.C.).* P 13.
1690 **1323** 11 r. multicoloured 65 70

1996 (9 Dec). *150th Birth Anniv of Abai Konunbaev (Kazakh poet) (1995).* P 13×13½.
1691 **1324** 5 r. chestnut, purple-brn & slate-lilac 35 40

1325 Buglers in front of Memorial

1996 (16 Dec). *25th Anniv of the Liberation of Bangladesh.* P 14.
1692 **1325** 2 r. multicoloured 20 20

1326 Vivekananda Rock Memorial

(Des S. Samanta. Litho Calcutta Security Printers Ltd, Kanpur)

1996 (26 Dec). *25th Anniv of Vivekananda Rock Memorial, Kanyakumari.* P 13½×13.
1693 **1326** 5 r. multicoloured 65 70
It was originally intended to release No. 1693 on 12 January 1996, but the issue was postponed until 26 December. Examples are known used from Bangalore or Jodhpur on the original date

1327 Victorian Doctors performing Operation

1328 Roorkee University Buildings

(Des S. Samanta)

1996 (27 Dec). *150th Anniv of Anaesthetics.* P 13×13½.
1694 **1327** 5 r. multicoloured 50 55

(Des H. Sinvhal)

1997 (1 Jan). *150th Anniv of Roorkee University.* P 13.
1695 **1328** 8 r. multicoloured 60 70

1329 Dr. Vrindavanlal Verma   **1330** Field Post Office

(Des S. Samiti)

1997 (9 Jan). *Dr. Vrindavanlal Verma (writer) Commemoration.* P 13.
1696 1329 2 r. dull scarlet 20 20

(Des S. Samanta)

1997 (22 Jan). *25th Anniv of Army Postal Service Corps.* P 13½×13.
1697 1330 5 r. multicoloured 35 40

1331 Subhas Chandra Bose   **1332** José Martí

1997 (23 Jan). *Birth Centenary of Subhas Chandra Bose (nationalist).* P 13.
1698 1331 1 r. reddish brown 20 10

1997 (28 Jan). *José Martí (Cuban writer) Commemoration.* P 13×13½.
1699 1332 11 r. black and flesh 65 70

1333 Conference Logo   **1334** St. Andrew's Church

1996 (15 Feb). *"Towards Partnership between Men and Women in Politics" Inter-Parliamentary Conference, New Delhi.* P 13.
1700 1333 5 r. multicoloured 35 40

1997 (25 Feb). *St. Andrew's Church, Egmore, Madras Commemoration.* P 13×13½.
1701 1334 8 r. multicoloured 50 55

1335 Morarji Desai   **1336** Shyam Lal Gupt

(Litho Calcutta Security Printers Ltd. Kanpur)

1997 (28 Feb). *Birth Centenary of Morarji Desai (former Prime Minister) (2nd issue).* P 13×13½.
1702 1335 1 r. brown and reddish brown .. 10 10

(Des P. Sansthan. Litho Calcutta Security Printers Ltd, Kanpur)

1997 (4 Mar). *Birth Centenary (1996) of Shyam Lal Gupt (social reformer).* P 13×13½.
1703 1336 1 r. cinnamon and lake-brown .. 10 10

1337 Saint Dnyaneshwar   **1338** Parijati Tree

1997 (5 Mar). *700th Death Anniv of Saint Dnyaneshwar (1996).* P 13×13½.
1704 1337 5 r. multicoloured 30 35

(Des R. Pasricha. Litho Calcutta Security Printers Ltd, Kanpur)

1997 (8 Mar). *Parijati Tree.* T **1338** and similar vert design. Multicoloured. P 13×13½.
1705 5 r. Type 1338 .. .. 30 40
     a. Horiz pair. Nos. 1705/6 .. 60 80
1706 6 r. Parijati flower 30 40
Nos. 1705/6 were printed together, *se-tenant*, in horizontal pairs throughout the sheet.

1339 Monument, Rashtriya Military College   **1340** Ram Manohar Lohia

(Litho Calcutta Security Printers Ltd, Kanpur)

1997 (13 Mar). *75th Anniv of Rashtriya Military College, Dehra Dun.* P 13½.
1707 1339 2 r. multicoloured 40 30

(Litho Calcutta Security Printers Ltd, Kanpur)

1997 (23 Mar). *Ram Manohar Lohia Commemoration.* P 13×13½.
1708 1340 1 r. multicoloured 10 10

1341 Society Centenary Emblem   **1342** Gyandith Award Winners

(Des J. Irani. Litho Calcutta Security Printers Ltd, Kanpur)

1997 (27 Mar). *Centenary of the Philatelic Society of India.* T **1341** and similar vert design. Multicoloured. P 13×13½.
1709 2 r. Type 1341 .. .. 30 35
     a. Horiz pair. Nos. 1709/10 .. 60 70
1710 2 r. Cover of first *Philatelic Journal of India, 1897* 30 35
Nos. 1709/10 were printed together, *se-tenant*, in horizontal pairs throughout the sheet.

1997 (28 Mar). *Gyandith Award Scheme.* P 13.
1711 1342 2 r. multicoloured 15 15

1343 Madhu Limaye   **1344** Nalanda Monastic University

1997 (1 May). *Madhu Limaye Commemoration.* P 13×13½.
1712 1343 2 r. deep dull green 15 15

(Litho Calcutta Security Printers Ltd, Kanpur)

1997 (6 June). *"INDEPEX '97" International Stamp Exhibition, New Delhi (2nd issue). Buddhist Cultural Sites.* T **1344** and similar horiz designs. Multicoloured. P 13½×13.
1713 2 r. Type 1344 .. .. 10 10
     a. Block of 4. Nos. 1713/16 .. 1·10
1714 6 r. The Bodhi Tree, Bodhgaya .. 25 30
1715 10 r. Stupa and Pillar, Vaishali .. 40 45
1716 11 r. Stupa, Kushinagar 40 45
1713/16 .. .. Set of 4 1·10 1·25
Nos. 1713/16 were printed together, *se-tenant*, in blocks of 4 throughout the sheet.

1345 Pandit Omkarnath Thakur   **1346** Ram Sewak Yadav

(Des S. Samanta)

1997 (24 June). *Birth Centenary of Pandit Omkarnath Thakur (musician).* P 13×13½.
1717 1345 2 r. black and deep dull blue .. 20 20

(Litho Calcutta Security Printers Ltd, Kanpur)

1997 (2 July). *Ram Sewak Yadav (politician) Commemoration.* P 13×13½.
1718 1346 2 r. brown 20 20

1347 Sibnath Banerjee   **1348** Rukmini Lakshmipathi

(Litho Calcutta Security Printers Ltd, Kanpur)

1997 (11 July). *Birth Centenary of Sibnath Banerjee (trade unionist).* P 13×13½.
1719 1347 2 r. brown-lake and purple .. 20 20

1997 (6 Aug). *Rukmini Lakshmipathi (social reformer) Commemoration.* P 13×13½.
1720 1348 2 r. reddish brown 30 30

1349 Sri Basaveswara   **1350** Gopalpur-on-Sea Beach

1997 (8 Aug). *Sri Basaveswara (reformer and statesman) Commemoration.* P 13×13½.
1721 1349 2 r. claret 20 20

1997 (11 Aug). *"INDEPEX '97" International Stamp Exhibition, New Delhi (3rd issue). Beaches.* T **1350** and similar horiz designs. Multicoloured. P 13½.
1722 2 r. Type 1350 .. .. 10 10
1723 6 r. Kovalam 25 30
1724 10 r. Anjuna 40 45
1725 11 r. Bogmalo 40 45
1722/5 .. .. Set of 4 1·10 1·25

1351 Newspaper Masthead   **1352** Shah Nawaz Khan, P. K. Sahgal and G. S. Dhillon

1997 (15 Aug). *50th Anniv of Swatantra Bharat (Hindi daily newspaper).* P 13½×13.
1726 **1351** 2 r. multicoloured 20 20

1997 (15 Aug). *I.N.A. Trials Commemoration.* P 13½×13.
1727 **1352** 2 r. multicoloured 30 30
No. 1727 is known pre-released at Jaipur on 11 May 1997.

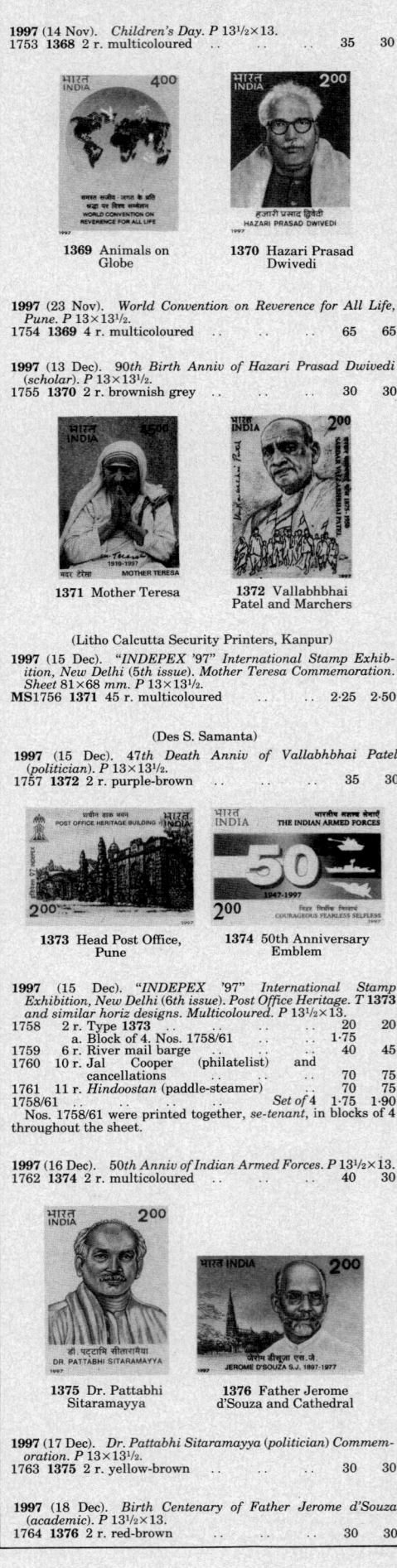

1353 Sir Ronald Ross (bacteriologist)　　**1354** Firaq Gorakhpuri

1997 (20 Aug). *Centenary of the Discovery of the Malaria Parasite by Sir Ronald Ross.* P 13×13½.
1728 **1353** 2 r. slate 40 30

1997 (28 Aug). *Birth Centenary (1996) of Firaq Gorakhpuri (poet).* P 13×13½.
1729 **1354** 2 r. light brown 20 20

1355 Bhaktivedanta Swami　　**1356** Parachute Regiment Emblem

1997 (6 Sept). *Birth Centenary (1996) of Bhaktivedanta Swami (philosopher).* P 13×13½.
1730 **1355** 5 r. chestnut 50 55

1997 (7 Sept). *Bicentenary of 2nd (Maratha) Battalion, Parachute Regiment.* P 13½×13.
1731 **1356** 2 r. multicoloured 30 30

1357 Fossil of *Birbalsahnia divyadarshanii*　　**1358** Swami Brahmanand

1997 (11 Sept). *50th Anniv of Birbal Sahni Institute of Paleobotany, Lucknow. Plant Fossils.* T **1357** *and similar vert designs. Multicoloured.* P 13½×13.
1732 2 r. Type **1357** 20 20
1733 2 r. *Glossopteris* 20 20
1734 6 r. Pentoxylon (reconstruction) .. 50 55
1735 10 r. *Williamsonia sewardiana* (model) 75 85
1732/5 *Set of 4* 1·50 1·60

(Litho Calcutta Security Printers, Kanpur)

1997 (14 Sept). *Swami Brahmanand (social reformer) Commemoration.* P 13½×13.
1736 **1358** 2 r. brownish grey and greenish stone 20 20

1359 "Sir William Jones"　　**1360** Lawrence School Building and Crest

1997 (28 Sept). *250th Birth Anniv (1996) of Sir William Jones (Sanskrit scholar).* P 13×13½.
1737 **1359** 4 r. multicoloured 30 30

1997 (4 Oct). *150th Anniv of Lawrence School, Sanawar.* P 13½×13.
1738 **1360** 2 r. multicoloured 30 30

1361 V. K. Krishna Menon　　**1362** Policemen and Globe

1997 (6 Oct). *Birth Centenary (1996) of V. K. Krishna Menon (politician).* P 13×13½.
1739 **1361** 2 r. brown-red 30 30

1997 (15 Oct). *66th General Assembly Session of ICPO Interpol.* P 13½×13.
1740 **1362** 4 r. multicoloured 65 65

1363 Woman from Arunachal Pradesh　　**1364** Students in Meditation, Astachai

1997 (15 Oct). *"INDEPEX '97" International Stamp Exhibition, New Delhi (4th issue). Women's Costumes.* T **1363** *and similar vert designs. Multicoloured.* P 13½×13.
1741 2 r. Type **1363** 10 10
　　a. Block of 4. Nos. 1741/4 .. 1·25
1742 6 r. Gujarat costume .. 25 30
1743 10 r. Ladakh costume .. 40 45
1744 11 r. Kerala costume .. 45 50
1741/4 *Set of 4* 1·25 1·40
Nos. 1741/4 were printed together, *se-tenant*, in blocks of 4 throughout the sheet.

1997 (20 Oct). *Centenary of Scindia School, Gwalior.* T **1364** *and similar horiz design. Multicoloured.* P 14.
1745 5 r. Type **1364** 30 35
　　a. Horiz pair. Nos. 1745/6 60 70
1746 5 r. Gwalior Fort 30 35
Nos. 1745/6 were printed together, *se-tenant*, in horizontal pairs throughout the sheet.

1365 *Ocimum sanctum*　　**1366** Sant Kavi Sunderdas

1997 (28 Oct). *Medicinal Plants.* T **1365** *and similar vert designs. Multicoloured.* P 14.
1747 2 r. Type **1365** 10 10
　　a. Block of 4. Nos. 1747/50 1·25
1748 5 r. *Curcuma longa* 20 25
1749 10 r. *Rauvolfia serpentina* .. 40 45
1750 11 r. *Aloe barbadensis* .. 45 50
1747/50 *Set of 4* 1·25 1·40
Nos. 1747/50 were printed together, *se-tenant*, in blocks of 4 throughout the sheet.

1997 (8 Nov). *400th Birth Anniv (1996) of Sant Kavi Sunderdas (Hindu theologian).* P 13×13½.
1751 **1366** 2 r. chestnut 30 30

1367 K. Rama Rao　　**1368** Jawaharlal Nehru and Child

1997 (9 Nov). *Birth Cent of K. Rama Rao (parliamentarian and journalist).* P 13×13½.
1752 **1367** 2 r. olive-bistre and bistre-brown 30 30

1997 (14 Nov). *Children's Day.* P 13½×13.
1753 **1368** 2 r. multicoloured 35 30

1369 Animals on Globe　　**1370** Hazari Prasad Dwivedi

1997 (23 Nov). *World Convention on Reverence for All Life, Pune.* P 13×13½.
1754 **1369** 4 r. multicoloured 65 65

1997 (13 Dec). *90th Birth Anniv of Hazari Prasad Dwivedi (scholar).* P 13×13½.
1755 **1370** 2 r. brownish grey 30 30

1371 Mother Teresa　　**1372** Vallabhbhai Patel and Marchers

(Litho Calcutta Security Printers, Kanpur)

1997 (15 Dec). *"INDEPEX '97" International Stamp Exhibition, New Delhi (5th issue). Mother Teresa Commemoration. Sheet 81×68 mm.* P 13×13½.
MS1756 **1371** 45 r. multicoloured .. 2·25 2·50

(Des S. Samanta)

1997 (15 Dec). *47th Death Anniv of Vallabhbhai Patel (politician).* P 13×13½.
1757 **1372** 2 r. purple-brown 35 30

1373 Head Post Office, Pune　　**1374** 50th Anniversary Emblem

1997 (15 Dec). *"INDEPEX '97" International Stamp Exhibition, New Delhi (6th issue). Post Office Heritage.* T **1373** *and similar horiz designs. Multicoloured.* P 13½×13.
1758 2 r. Type **1373** 20 20
　　a. Block of 4. Nos. 1758/61 1·75
1759 6 r. River mail barge .. 40 45
1760 10 r. Jal Cooper (philatelist) and cancellations 70 75
1761 11 r. Hindoostan (paddle-steamer) 70 75
1758/61 *Set of 4* 1·75 1·90
Nos. 1758/61 were printed together, *se-tenant*, in blocks of 4 throughout the sheet.

1997 (16 Dec). *50th Anniv of Indian Armed Forces.* P 13½×13.
1762 **1374** 2 r. multicoloured 40 30

1375 Dr. Pattabhi Sitaramayya　　**1376** Father Jerome d'Souza and Cathedral

1997 (17 Dec). *Dr. Pattabhi Sitaramayya (politician) Commemoration.* P 13×13½.
1763 **1375** 2 r. yellow-brown 30 30

1997 (18 Dec). *Birth Centenary of Father Jerome d'Souza (academic).* P 13½×13.
1764 **1376** 2 r. red-brown 30 30

1377 Ram Prasad
Bismil and
Ashfaqullah Khan

1378 Jail Buildings

(Des Alka Sharma)

1997 (19 Dec). *70th Death Anniv of Ram Prasad Bismil and Ashfaqullah Khan (revolutionaries).* P 13.
1765 **1377** 2 r. red-brown 30 30

1997 (30 Dec). *Cellular Jail, Port Blair.* P 13.
1766 **1378** 2 r. multicoloured 30 30

1379 Sword and
Kukri

1380 Nahar Singh

1998 (2 Jan). *50th Anniv of 11th Gorkha Rifles.* P 13.
1767 **1379** 4 r. multicoloured 65 65

1998 (9 Jan). *140th Death Anniv of Nahar Singh (Sikh leader)* P 13.
1768 **1380** 2 r. reddish purple 30 30

1381 Nanak Singh

1382 Rotary International
Emblem

1998 (10 Jan). *Birth Cent of Nanak Singh (writer) (1997).* P 13.
1769 **1381** 2 r. Indian red 30 30

1998 (12 Jan). *Meeting of Rotary International Council on Legislation, Delhi.* P 13½×13.
1770 **1382** 8 r. lemon and blue 50 55

1383 Maharana
Pratap

1384 V. S. Khandekar

1998 (19 Jan). *400th Death Anniv of Maharana Pratap (Rajput leader).* P 13½×13.
1771 **1383** 2 r. dull purple 30 30

1998 (19 Jan). *Birth Centenary of V. S. Khandekar (writer).* P 13½×13.
1772 **1384** 2 r. scarlet 30 30

1385 Elephant
and Dancers

1386 Jagdish Chandra Jain

1998 (25 Jan). *India Tourism Day.* P 13×13½.
1773 **1385** 10 r. multicoloured .. .. 1·00 1·00

1998 (28 Jan). *Jagdish Chandra Jain (educationist) Commemoration.* P 13.
1774 **1386** 2 r. chestnut 30 30

1387 Gandhi as a
Young Man and
Peasants in Fields

1388 A. Vedaratnam

(Des S. Samanta)

1998 (30 Jan). *50th Death Anniv of Mahatma Gandhi.* T **1387** *and similar vert designs.* P 14.
1775   2 r. Type **1387** 10 10
         a. Block of 4. Nos. 1775/8 .. 1·25
1776   6 r. Woman weaving and Gandhi distributing food 25 30
1777   10 r. Gandhi collecting salt .. 40 45
1778   11 r. Gandhi carrying flag .. 45 50
1775/8   *Set of* 4 1·25 1·40
Nos. 1775/8 were printed together, *se-tenant*, in blocks of 4 throughout the sheet with the backgrounds forming a composite design.

1998 (25 Feb). *Birth Centenary (1997) of A. Vedaratnam (social reformer).* P 13×13½.
1779 **1388** 2 r. slate-purple 30 30

1389 Anniversary
Emblem

1390 Savitribai Phule

1998 (8 Mar). *50th Anniv of Universal Declaration of Human Rights.* P 13×13½.
1780 **1389** 6 r. multicoloured 50 50

1998 (10 Mar). *Death Centenary of Savitribai Phule (educational reformer) (1997).* P 13½×13.
1781 **1390** 2 r. deep brown 30 30

1391 Sir Syed
Ahmad Khan

1392 Barren Landscape and
Living Forest

1998 (27 Mar). *Death Centenary of Sir Syed Ahmed Khan (social reformer).* P 13×13½.
1782 **1391** 2 r. olive-brown 30 30

(Des R. Pasricha)

1998 (1 Apr). *First Assembly Meeting of Global Environment Facility, Delhi.* P 13.
1783 **1392** 11 r. multicoloured 75 80

1393 Ramana Maharshi

1394 College Arms

1998 (14 Apr). *Ramana Maharshi (religious leader) Commemoration.* P 13½×13.
1784 **1393** 2 r. blackish lilac 30 30

1998 (16 Apr). *50th Anniv of Defence Services Staff College, Wellington.* P 14.
1785 **1394** 6 r. deep carmine 50 50

1395 Diesel Train on Viaduct

1998 (1 May). *Completion of Konkan Railway.* P 13.
1786 **1395** 8 r. multicoloured 60 70

1396 Narayan
Ganesh Goray

1397 Dr. Zakir
Husain

1998 (1 May). *Narayan Ganesh Goray (social reformer) Commemoration.* P 13×13½.
1787 **1396** 2 r. red-brown 20 20

1998 (3 May). *Birth Centenary (1997) of Dr. Zakir Husain (former President of India).* P 13×13½.
1788 **1397** 2 r. grey-brown 20 20

1398 Mohammed
Abdurahiman Shahib

1399 Lokanayak
Omeo Kumar Das

1998 (15 May). *Mohammed Abdurahiman Shahib (nationalist) Commemoration.* P 13×13½.
1789 **1398** 2 r. chestnut 20 20

1998 (21 May). *Lokanayak Omeo Kumar Das (writer) Commemoration.* P 14.
1790 **1399** 2 r. bistre-brown 20 20

1400 Vakkom Abdul
Khader, Satyendra
Chandra Bardhan and
Fouja Singh

1401 Bishnu Dey,
Tarashankar
Bandopadhyay and
Ashapurna Devi

1998 (25 May). *Nationalist Martyrs Commemoration.* P 13.
1791 **1400** 2 r. reddish brown and cinnamon .. 20 20

(Des S. Samanta)

1998 (5 June). *Bangla Jnanpith Literary Award Winners Commemoration.* P 13.
1792 **1401** 2 r. bistre-brown 20 20

1402 Big Ben, London

1403 Dr. C. Vijiaraghavachariar

1998 (8 June). *50th Anniv of First Air India International Flight.* T **1402** *and similar multicoloured design.* P 13×13½.
1793 5 r. Type **1402** 30 35
  a. Horiz pair. Nos. 1793/4 .. .. 60 70
1794 6 r. Lockheed Super Constellation airliner, globe and Gateway of India, Bombay (55×35 mm) 30 35
Nos. 1793/4 were printed together, *se-tenant*, in horizontal pairs throughout the sheet, forming a composite design.

1998 (18 June). *Dr. C. Vijiaraghavachariar (lawyer and social reformer) Commemoration.* P 13×13½.
1795 **1403** 2 r. lake-brown 15 15

1404 Anniversary Logo and Savings Stream

1405 Bhagawan Gopinathji

1998 (30 June). *50th Anniv of National Savings Organization.* T **1404** *and similar horiz design. Multicoloured.* P 13½×13.
1796 5 r. Type **1404** 15 20
  a. Vert pair. Nos. 1796/7 .. .. 35 45
1797 6 r. Hand dropping coin into jar .. 20 25
Nos. 1796/7 were printed together, *se-tenant*, in vertical pairs throughout the sheet, each pair forming a composite design.

1998 (3 July). *Birth Centenary of Bhagawan Gopinathji (spiritual leader).* P 13.
1798 **1405** 3 r. yellow-brown 15 20

1406 Ardeshir and Pirojsha Godrej

1407 Aruna Asaf Ali

1998 (11 July). *Centenary of Godrej (industrial conglomerate).* P 13.
1799 **1406** 3 r. emerald 15 20

1998 (16 July). *Aruna Asaf Ali (nationalist) Commemoration.* P 13.
1800 **1407** 3 r. chestnut 15 20

1408 Iswar Chandra Vidyasagar (educationist) and College

1409 Shivpujan Sahai

1998 (29 July). *125th Anniv of Vidyasagar College, Calcutta.* P 13½×13.
1801 **1408** 2 r. slate-black 15 15

1998 (9 Aug). *Shivpujan Sahai (writer) Commemoration.* P 13½×13.
1802 **1409** 2 r. light brown 15 15

1410 Red Fort, Delhi, and Spinning Wheel

1411 Gostha Behari Paul

(Des C. Pakrashi)

1998 (15 Aug). *Homage to Martyrs for Independence.* T **1410** *and similar horiz design. Multicoloured.* P 14.
1803 3 r. Type **1410** 15 20
  a. Horiz pair. Nos. 1803/4 .. 40 50
1804 8 r. Industrial and scientific development in modern India 25 30
Nos. 1803/4 were printed together, *se-tenant*, in horizontal pairs throughout the sheet.

(Des B. Mirchandani)

1998 (20 Aug). *Gostha Paul (footballer) Commemoration.* P 13.
1805 **1411** 3 r. maroon 20 20

1412 Youth Hostel and Logo

1413 Uniforms, Badge and Tank

(Des S. Samant)

1998 (23 Aug). *50th Anniv of Youth Hostels Association of India.* P 14.
1806 **1412** 5 r. multicoloured 30 30

1998 (15 Sept). *Bicentenary of 4th Battalion, Guards' Brigade (1 Rajput).* P 13½×13.
1807 **1413** 6 r. multicoloured 30 35

1414 Bhai Kanhaiyaji

1415 Emblem and Diagram of Head

1998 (18 Sept). *Bhai Kanhaiyaji (Sikh social reformer) Commemoration.* P 13.
1808 **1414** 2 r. red 15 15

1998 (18 Sept). *20th International Congress of Radiology.* P 13½×13.
1809 **1415** 8 r. multicoloured 30 35

1416 Dove of Peace and Boy reading Book

1417 Dr. Tristao Braganza Cunha

1998 (20 Sept). *26th International Books for Young People Congress.* P 13×13½.
1810 **1416** 11 r. multicoloured 30 35

1998 (26 Sept). *Dr. Tristao Braganza Cunha (nationalist) Commemoration.* P 13×13½.
1811 **1417** 3 r. chocolate 15 20

1418 Jananeta Hijam Irawat Singh

1419 Women Aviators and Bi-plane

1998 (30 Sept). *Jananeta Hijam Irawat Singh (social reformer) Commemoration.* P 13×13½.
1812 **1418** 3 r. yellow-brown 15 20

1998 (5 Oct). *Indian Women's Participation in Aviation.* P 13.
1813 **1419** 8 r. chalky blue 30 40

1420 Acharya Tulsi

1998 (20 Oct). *First Death Anniv of Acharya Tulsi (Jain religious leader).* P 13½×13.
1814 **1420** 3 r. red-brown and bright orange .. 15 20

1421 Girl and Bird reading Book

1998 (14 Nov). *Children's Day.* P 13½×13.
1815 **1421** 3 r. multicoloured 15 20

1422 I.N.S. *Delhi* (destroyer)

1423 Mounted Trumpeter

1998 (15 Nov). *Navy Day.* P 13½×13.
1816 **1422** 3 r. multicoloured 15 20

(Litho Calcutta Security Printers Ltd, Kanpur)

1998 (16 Nov). *225th Anniv of President's Bodyguard.* P 13×13½.
1817 **1423** 3 r. multicoloured 15 20

1424 Sir David Sassoon and Library, Bombay

1425 Regimental Arms and Soldier

(Des J. Irani)

1998 (30 Nov). *David Sassoon Library and Reading Room Commemoration.* P 13.
1818 **1424** 3 r. deep ultramarine and pale blue 15 20

(Des S. Chowdhry)

1998 (30 Nov). *Bicent of 2nd Battalion, Rajput Regiment.* P 13.
1819 **1425** 3 r. multicoloured 15 20

1426 Army Postal Service
Centre, Kamptee

1998 (2 Dec). *50th Anniv of Army Postal Service Training Centre.* P 13.
1820 **1426** 3 r. multicoloured 15 20

1427 Connemara Public
Library, Madras

1428 Neem Tree
and Leaves

1998 (5 Dec). *Centenary (1996) of Connemara Public Library.* P 13½×13.
1821 **1427** 3 r. yellow-brown and ochre .. 15 20

(Des R. Sukumar. Litho Calcutta Security Printers Ltd, Kanpur)

1998 (10 Dec). *50th Anniv of The Indian Pharmaceutical Congress Association.* P 13×13½.
1822 **1428** 3 r. multicoloured 15 20

1429 Baba Raghav Das

1430 Lt. Indra Lal
Roy D.F.C.

1998 (12 Dec). *40th Death Anniv of Baba Raghav Das (social reformer).* P 13×13½.
1823 **1429** 2 r. slate-violet 10 15

1998 (19 Dec). *Birth Centenary of Indra Lal Roy (First World War pilot).* P 13×13½.
1824 **1430** 3 r. multicoloured 15 20

1431 Sant Gadge Baba

1432 Rudra Veena
(stringed instrument)

(Des B. Mirchandani)

1998 (20 Dec). *Sant Gadge Baba (social reformer) Commemoration.* P 13×13½.
1825 **1431** 3 r. slate-lilac, new blue and black .. 15 20

(Des S. Samanta)

1998 (29 Dec). *Musical Instruments.* T **1432** *and similar horiz designs. Multicoloured.* P 13½×13.
1826 2 r. Type **1432** 10 15
1827 6 r. Flute 20 25
1828 8 r. Pakhawaj (wooden barrel drum) .. 25 30
1829 10 r. Sarod (stringed instrument) .. 30 35
1826/9 .. .. *Set of* 4 85 1·00

1433 *Chicoreus brunneus*
(Murex shell)

1434 Stylised Police
Officers

1998 (30 Dec). *Shells.* T **1433** *and similar horiz designs. Multicoloured.* P 13½×13.
1830 3 r. Type **1433** 20 25
1831 3 r. *Cassis cornuta* (Horned Helmet) .. 20 25
1832 3 r. *Cypraea staphylaea* (Cowrie) .. 20 25
1833 11 r. *Lambis lambis* (Common Spider
Conch) 50 60
1830/3 .. .. .. *Set of* 4 1·00 1·25

(Des Kamleshawar. Litho Calcutta Security Printers, Kanpur)

1999 (13 Jan). *50th Anniv of Indian Police Service.* P 13½×13.
1834 **1434** 3 r. multicoloured 20 20

1435 Modern Weapon
Systems

1436 Issue of *Orunodoi*
(Assamese newspaper)
for January, 1846

1999 (26 Jan). *40th Anniv of Defence Research and Development Organization.* P 13.
1835 **1435** 10 r. multicoloured 30 35

1999 (29 Jan). *150th Anniv of Newspapers in Assam.* P 13×13½.
1836 **1436** 3 r. black, orange-yellow & red-orange 15 20

1437 College Building

1438 National Defence
Academy and Military
Equipment

1999 (17 Feb). *Centenary of Hindu College, Delhi.* P 13½×13.
1837 **1437** 3 r. slate-blue 15 15

1999 (19 Feb). *50th Anniv of National Defence Academy.* P 13½×13.
1838 **1438** 3 r. multicoloured 15 15

1439 College Building

1440 Patnaik and Tugs

1999 (25 Feb). *175th Anniv of Sanskrit College, Calcutta.* P 13½×13.
1839 **1439** 3 r. chestnut and yellow-ochre .. 15 15

1999 (5 Mar). *Biju Patnaik Commemoration.* P 13½×13.
1840 **1440** 3 r. orange-brown and turquoise-green 15 15

1441 Globe and
Satellite Dish

1442 "Apsara
removing a Thorn
from her Foot"
(temple statue)

(Des A. Cowasjee)

1999 (5 Mar). *50th Anniv of Press Trust of India.* P 13.
1841 **1441** 15 r. multicoloured 50 55

1999 (6 Mar). *Millenary of the Khajuraho Temples.* P 13.
1842 **1442** 15 r. reddish brown, orange-brn & blk 50 55

1443 Dr. K. B.
Hedgewar

1444 Terracotta Model
Boat from Lothal,
2200 B.C., and Seal

(Des B. Prakash)

1999 (18 Mar). *Dr. Keshavrao Hedgewar (founder of Rashtriya Swayamsevak Sangha) Commemoration.* P 13.
1843 **1443** 3 r. multicoloured 15 15

(Litho Calcutta Security Printers Ltd, Kanpur)

1999 (5 Apr). *Maritime Heritage.* T **1444** *and similar horiz design. Multicoloured.* P 13½×13.
1844 3 r. Type **1444** 15 15
1845 3 r. Ghurab (sailing ship) of Kanhoji
Angre, 1700 .. .. .. 15 15

1445 Golden Temple,
Amritsar

1446 Bethune College

1999 (9 Apr). *300th Anniv of the Khalsa (Sikh movement).* P 13½×13.
1846 **1445** 3 r. multicoloured 15 15

1999 (7 May). *150th Anniv of Bethune Collegiate School, Calcutta.* P 13½×13.
1847 **1446** 3 r. bronze-green 15 15

1447 Plane, Satellite and
Rocket orbiting Globe

1448 Mumbai Port

(Des A. Cowasjee. Litho Calcutta Security Ptg Press, Kanpur)

1999 (11 May). *Technology Day.* P 13½.
1848 **1447** 3 r. multicoloured 15 15

1999 (26 June). *125th Anniv of Mumbai (Bombay) Port Trust.* P 13.
1849 **1448** 3 r. slate-blue 15 15

1449 Handshake
and Airliner

1450 Gulzarilal
Nanda

(Des R. Ralte)

1999 (30 June). *Mizoram Accord (peace agreement) Commemoration.* P 13.
1850 **1449** 3 r. multicoloured 15 15

1999 (4 July). *Birth Centenary of Gulzarilal Nanda (former Prime Minister).* P 13×13½.
1851 **1450** 3 r. multicoloured 15 15

MINIMUM PRICE

The minimum price quote is 10p which represents a handling charge rather than a basis for valuing common stamps. For further notes about prices see introductory pages.

1451 Jijabai and Chatrapati Shivaji

1452 P. S. Kumaraswamy Raja

1999 (7 July). *Jijabai (mother of Chatrapati Shivaji (Maratha leader)) Commemoration.* P 14.
1852 **1451** 3 r. dull claret 15 15

(Des P. Rajoria)

1999 (8 July). *P. S. Kumaraswamy Raja (politician) Commemoration.* P 13½×13.
1853 **1452** 3 r. orange-brown and new blue .. 15 15

1453 Balai Chand Mukhopadhyay

1454 River Sindhu, Ladakh

1999 (19 July). *Birth Centenary of Balai Chand Mukhopadhyay, ("Banaphool") (Bengali writer).* P 13×13½.
1854 **1453** 3 r. deep turquoise-blue 15 15

(Des R. Pasricha)

1999 (28 July). *Sindhu Darshan Festival.* P 13½×13.
1855 **1454** 3 r. multicoloured 15 15

1455 Soldier and Young Girl

1456 Sardar Ajit Singh

1999 (12 Aug). *50th Anniv of Geneva Conventions.* P 14.
1856 **1455** 15 r. black and red 40 45

1999 (15 Aug). *Heroes of Struggle for Freedom.* T **1456** and similar horiz designs, each showing the same background. P 13½×13.
1857   3 r. brown and orange-red .. 15 15
1858   3 r. orange-brown and ultramarine 15 15
1859   3 r. blue-black and dull vermilion .. 15 15
1860   3 r. deep claret and drab 15 15
1857/60 .. .. *Set of* 4 40 60
    Designs:—No. 1857, Type **1456**; No.1858, Swami Ramanand Teerth; No. 1859, Vishwambhar Dayalu Tripathi; No. 1860, Swami Keshawanand.

Index to Indian Stamp Designs from 1947

The following index is intended to facilitate the identification of all Indian stamps from 1947 onwards. Portrait stamps are usually listed under surnames only, views under the name of the town or city and other issues under the main subject or a prominent word and date chosen from the inscription. Simple abbreviations have occasionally been resorted to and when the same design or subject appears on more than one stamp, only the first of each series is indicated.

STAMP BOOKLETS

1904. *Black on green (No. SB1) or black on pink (No. SB2) covers. Stapled.*

SB1	12¼ a. booklet containing twenty-four ½ a. (No. 121) in blocks of 6	£800
SB2	12¼ a. booklet containing twelve 1 a. (No. 123) in blocks of 6	£800

1906–11. *Black on green (No. SB3), black on pink (No. SB4) or black on green and pink (No. SB5) match book type covers inscr "Post Office of India" and royal cypher of King Edward VII. Stapled.*

SB3	1 r. booklet containing thirty-two ½ a. (No. 149) in blocks of 4	£450
	a. Without "Post Office of India" inscr	£400
	b. Ditto and showing royal cypher of King George V (1911)	£375
SB4	1 r. booklet containing sixteen 1 a. (No. 150) in blocks of 4 (1907)	£400
	a. Without "Post Office of India" inscr	£350
	b. Ditto and showing royal cypher of King George V (1911)	£375
SB5	1 r. booklet containing sixteen ½ a. and eight 1 a. (Nos. 149/50) in blocks of 4 (1907)	£900
	a. Without "Post Office of India" inscr	£800
	b. Ditto and showing royal cypher of King George V (1911)	£750

1912–22. *Black on green (Nos. SB6/7, SB12), black on pink (No. SB8), black on green and pink (No. SB9), black on purple (Nos. SB10) or black on blue (No. SB11) match book type covers with foreign postage rates on back. Stapled.*

SB 6	1 r. booklet containing sixty-four 3 p. (No. 152) in blocks of 4 (blank back cover)	£475
SB 7	1 r. booklet containing thirty-two ½ a. (No. 155) in blocks of 4	£180
	a. Blank back cover	£180
	b. Advertisement contractor's notice on back cover	£275
	c. Advertisement on back (1922)	£275
SB 8	1 r. booklet containing sixteen 1 a. (No. 159) in blocks of 4	£140
	a. Blank back cover	£140
	b. Advertisements on front flap and back cover (1922)	£180
SB 9	1 r. booklet containing sixteen ½ a. and eight 1 a. (Nos. 155, 159) in blocks of 4 (blank back cover)	£130
SB10	1 r. 8 a. booklet containing sixteen 1½ a. (No. 163) in blocks of 4 (1919)	£325
	a. Blank back cover (1921)	£325
SB11	2 r. booklet containing sixteen 2 a. (No. 169) in blocks of 4 (blank back cover) (1921)	£400
	a. Black on purple cover with postage rates on back (1922)	£400
SB12	2 r. booklet containing sixteen 2 a. (No. 166) in blocks of 4 (1922)	£400
	a. Black on purple cover	£400

1921. *Black on buff match book type cover. Stapled.*

SB13	1 r. 2 a. booklet containing twenty-four 9 p. on 1 a. (No. 192) in blocks of 4	£100

1922. *Black on brown (No. SB14) or black on green and pink (No. SB15) match book type covers with foreign postage rates on back. Stapled.*

SB14	1 r. booklet containing sixteen 1 a. (No. 197) in blocks of 4	£200
	a. Advertisement on back	£200
	b. Advertisements on front flap and back cover	
	c. Black on lilac cover with blank back	£200
	ca. Advertisements on front flap and back cover	£275
	d. Black on pink cover with blank back	£250
SB15	1 r. booklet containing sixteen ½ a. and eight 1 a. (Nos. 155, 197) in blocks of 4 (blank back cover)	£425

1926–28. *Black on brown (No. SB16) or black on purple (No. SB17) match book type covers with foreign postage rates on back. Stapled.*

SB16	1 r. booklet containing sixteen 1 a. (No. 203) in blocks of 4	85·00
SB17	2 r. booklet containing sixteen 2 a. (No. 205) in blocks of 4	£275
	a. Containing No. 206 (1928)	£325

1929. *Black on brown (No. SB18) or black on purple (No. SB19) separate leaf covers. Stitched.*

SB18	1 r. booklet containing sixteen 1 a. (No. 203) in blocks of 4 (blank back cover)	85·00
	a. Advertisement contractor's notice on back cover	85·00
	b. Advertisements on front flap and back cover	£100
	c. Advertisement on back cover	£100
SB19	2 r. booklet containing sixteen 2 a. (No. 205) in blocks of 4 (foreign postage rates on back cover)	£300
	a. Advertisement contractor's notice on back cover	£300
	b. Containing No. 206 (foreign postage rates on back cover)	£350
	ba. Advertisement contractor's notice on back cover	£350

1932. *Black on brown cover. Stitched.*

SB20	1 r. 4 a. booklet containing sixteen 1¼ a. (No. 235) in blocks of 4	£275

1934. *Black on buff cover. Stitched.*

SB21	1 r. booklet containing sixteen 1 a. (No. 234) in blocks of 4	£150

1937. *Black on red cover. Stamps with wmk upright or inverted. Stitched.*

SB22	1 r. booklet containing sixteen 1 a. (No. 250) in blocks of 4	£200

1980 (Jan) *"India 80" International Stamp Exhibition. Green, orange and blue cover, 80×100 mm. showing stamps. Stapled.*

SB23	33 r. 60, booklet containing twelve 30 p., twelve 50 p., eight 1 r. and eight 2 r. (Nos. 914/15, 942/5, 955/8) in blocks of four	6·50

1989 (20 Jan). *"India-89" International Stamp Exhibition, New Delhi. Multicoloured cover, showing stamp No. 1248, boatman and Taj Mahal. Stapled.*

SB24	270 r. booklet containing four 50 p., sixteen 60 p., ten 1 r. 50, six 4 r., twenty 5 r. and sixteen 6 r. 50 in panes of four or six each with margins all round (Nos. 1248a, 1249a, 1264a, 1265a, 1266a, 1267a, 1333a, 1334a, 1341a, 1342a, 1358a, 1359a, 1360a, 1361a)	26·00

1994 (7 Nov). *Bicentenary of Bombay General Post Office. Crimson and brown cover showing G.P.O. Stamps affixed by selvedge.*

SB25	20 r. booklet containing twenty 1 r. (No. 1436a) in block of 20	8·00

OFFICIAL STAMPS

Stamps overprinted "POSTAL SERVICE" or "I.P.N." were not used as postage stamps, and are therefore omitted.

Service.

(O 1)

(Optd by the Military Orphanage Press, Calcutta)

1866 (1 Aug)–72. *Optd with Type O 1. P 14. (a) No wmk.*

O 1	11	½ a. blue		—	£225
O 2		½ a. pale blue		£950	£110
		a. Opt inverted			
O 3		1 a. brown		—	£160
O 4		1 a. deep brown		—	£120
O 5		8 a. carmine		17·00	40·00

(b) Wmk Elephant's Head, T 13

O 6	11	½ a. blue		£200	22·00
		w. Wmk inverted		†	£110
O 7		½ a. pale blue		£200	12·00
		a. Opt inverted			
		b. No dot on "i" (No. 50 on pane)		—	£250
		c. No stop (No. 77 on pane)		—	£200
O 8	12	8 p. purple (1.72)		18·00	45·00
		a. No dot on "i"		£225	£300
		b. No stop		£225	
O 9	11	1 a. brown		£190	15·00
O10		1 a. deep brown		£190	38·00
		a. No dot on "i"		—	£425
		b. No stop		—	£350
O11		2 a. orange		£170	75·00
O12		2 a. yellow		£170	75·00
		a. Opt inverted			
		b. Imperf			
		w. Wmk inverted		£250	
O13		4 a. green		£170	70·00
		a. Opt inverted			
O14	17	4 a. green (Die I)		£950	£250

A variety with wide and more open capital "S" occurs six times in sheets of all values except No. O8. Price four times the normal.
Reprints exist of Nos. O6, O9 and O14; the latter is Die II instead of Die I.
Reprints of the overprint have also been made, in different setting, on the 8 pies, purple, no watermark.

O 2

O 6

O 3

O 4

(No. O15 surch at Calcutta, others optd at Madras)

1866 (Oct). *Fiscal stamps, Nos. O15/18 with top and bottom inscrs removed, surch or optd. Wmk Crown over "INDIA".*

(a) Surch as in Type O 2. Thick blue glazed paper. Imperf × perf 14

O15	O 2	2 a. purple		£275	£225

(b) Optd "SERVICE POSTAGE" in two lines as in Types O 3/4 and similar type. Imperf × perf 14

O16	O 3	2 a. purple (G.)		£800	£400
O17	O 4	4 a. purple (G.)		£3250	£1100
O18	—	8 a. purple (G.)		£3750	£3500
		a. Optd on complete stamp (inscr "FOREIGN BILL")		†	£9500

(c) Optd "SERVICE POSTAGE" in semi-circle. Wmk Large Crown. P 15½ × 15

O19	O 6	½ a. mauve/lilac (G.)		£400	85·00
		a. Opt double		£2750	

So-called reprints of Nos. O15 to O18 are known, but in these the surcharge differs entirely in the spacing, etc., of the words; they are more properly described as Government imitations. The imitations of No. O15 have surcharge in *black* or in *green*. No. O19 exists with reprinted overprint which has a full stop after "POSTAGE".

PRINTERS. The following stamps up to No. O108 were overprinted by De La Rue and thereafter Official stamps were printed or overprinted by the Security Printing Press at Nasik.

Service.	H. M. S.	H. M. S.
(O 7)	(O 8)	(O 9)

1867–73. *Optd with Type O 7. Wmk Elephant's Head. T 13.*
P 14.

O20	11	½ a. blue (Die I)	..	26·00	40
		w. Wmk inverted	..	† 65·00	
O21		½ a. pale blue (Die I) ..	..	32·00	2·00
O22		½ a. blue (Die II) (1873)	..	£150	65·00
O23		1 a. brown	..	32·00	45
		w. Wmk inverted	..	† 80·00	
O24		1 a. deep brown	..	35·00	2·00
O25		1 a. chocolate	..	40·00	2·00
O26		2 a. yellow	..	16·00	2·50
O27		2 a. orange	..	4·75	2·25
O28	17	4 a. pale green (Die I)	..	14·00	2·00
O29		4 a. green (Die I)	..	3·00	1·50
O30	11	8 a. rose (Die II) (1868)	..	3·25	1·50
O30a		8 a. pale rose (Die II)	..	3·25	1·50
		aw. Wmk inverted	..	30·00	20·00

Prepared for use, but not issued

O30b	18	6 a. 8 p. slate	..	£250	

1874–82. *Optd with Type O 8. (a) In black.*

O31	11	½ a. blue (Die II)..	..	7·00	20
O32		1 a. brown	..	11·00	20
O33		2 a. yellow	..	50·00	23·00
O33a		2 a. orange	..	35·00	13·00
O34	17	4 a. green (Die I)	..	12·00	3·00
O35	11	8 a. rose (Die II)	..	5·00	3·75

(b) Optd in blue-black

O36	11	½ a. blue (Die II) (1877)	..	£300	40·00
O37		1 a. brown (1882)	..	£500	£110

1883–99. *Wmk Star, T 34. P 14. Optd with Type O 9.*

O37a	40	3 p. aniline carmine (1899)	..	20	10
O38	23	½ a. deep blue-green	..	90	10
		a. Opt double	..	†£1100	
O39		½ a. blue-green	..	70	10
O40	25	1 a. brown-purple	..	1·75	30
		a. Opt inverted	..	†£350	£450
		aw. Wmk inverted	..	†	£550
		b. Opt double	..	†£1200	
		c. Opt omitted (in horiz pair with normal)	..	£1500	
O41		1 a. plum	..	30	10
O42	27	2 a. pale blue	..	4·00	60
O43		2 a. blue	..	5·00	60
O44	29	4 a. olive-green	..	12·00	45
O44a		4 a. slate-green	..	12·00	35
O45	31	8 a. dull mauve	..	15·00	1·25
O46		8 a. magenta	..	8·00	50
O47	37	1 r. green and rose (1892)	..	38·00	3·75
O48		1 r. green and carmine (1892)	..	9·50	40
O37a/48			Set of 7	32·00	1·75

1900. *Colours changed. Optd with Type O 9.*

O49	23	½ a. pale yellow-green	..	1·75	70
O49a		½ a. yellow-green	..	2·75	50
		ab. Opt double	..	£900	
O50	25	1 a. carmine	..	2·50	10
		a. Opt inverted	..	†£1200	
		b. Opt double	..	†£1300	
O51	27	2 a. pale violet	..	28·00	1·00
O52		2 a. mauve	..	30·00	50
O49/52			Set of 3	29·00	1·00

1902–9. *Stamps of King Edward VII optd with Type O 9.*

O54	41	3 p. grey (1903)	..	2·00	30
O55		3 p. slate-grey (1905)	..	2·00	40
		a. No stop after "M" (R. 6/10)	..	£140	95·00
O56	42	½ a. green	..	1·25	30
O57	43	1 a. carmine ..	..	1·00	10
O58	44	2 a. violet	..	4·50	20
O59		2 a. mauve	..	3·25	10
O60	47	4 a. olive	..	8·00	30
O61		4 a. pale olive	..	8·00	30
O62	48	6 a. olive-bistre (1909)	..	1·50	15
O63	49	8 a. purple (*shades*)	..	6·00	85
O64		8 a. claret	..	8·00	75
O65	51	1 r. green and carmine (1905)	..	4·00	70
O54/65			Set of 8	24·00	2·50

1906. *New types. Optd with Type O 9.*

O66	53	½ a. green	..	90	10
		a. No stop after "M" (R. 6/10)	..	85·00	45·00
O67	54	1 a. carmine	..	1·75	10
		a. No stop after "M" (R. 6/10)	..	£140	75·00

On

H. S.

M.

(O 9a)

1909. *Optd with Type O 9a.*

O68	52	2 r. carmine and yellow-brown..	..	8·00	1·10
O68a		2 r. rose-red and yellow-brown..	..	8·00	1·25
O69		5 r. ultramarine and violet ..	..	14·00	1·50
O70		10 r. green and carmine ..	..	26·00	11·00
O70a		10 r. green and scarlet ..	..	60·00	7·00
O71		15 r. blue and olive-brown ..	..	60·00	35·00
O72		25 r. brownish orange and blue ..	..	£140	60·00
O68/72			Set of 5	£225	90·00

NINE

SERVICE	SERVICE	PIES
(O 10)(14 mm)	(O 11) (21½ mm)	(O 12)

1912–13. *Stamps of King George V (wmk Single Star, T 34) optd with Type O 10 or O 11 (rupee values).*

O73	55	3 p. grey	..	30	10
O74		3 p. slate-grey	..	30	10
O75		3 p. blue-slate	..	2·75	10
		a. Opt omitted (in pair with normal)			
O76	56	½ a. yellow-green	..	30	10
		a. Overprint double	..	£100	
O77		½ a. pale blue-green	..	45	10
O80	57	1 a. rose-carmine	..	1·00	10
O81		1 a. carmine	..	1·40	10
O82		1 a. aniline carmine	..	1·40	10
		a. Overprint double	..	† £900	
O83	59	2 a. mauve	..	55	10
O84		2 a. purple	..	1·00	10
O85	63	4 a. deep olive	..	1·00	10
O86		4 a. olive-green	..	1·00	10
O87	64	6 a. yellow-bistre	..	1·50	2·00
O88		6 a. deep bistre-brown	..	3·50	3·75
O89	65	8 a. purple	..	2·25	80
O89a		8 a. mauve	..	2·25	80
O90		8 a. bright aniline mauve	..	26·00	2·50
O91	67	1 r. red-brown and blue-green (1913).	.	2·50	1·10
O92		2 r. rose-carmine and brown (1913)	..	3·25	4·00
O93		5 r. ultramarine and violet (1913)	..	13·00	17·00
O94		10 r. green and scarlet (1913)	..	42·00	42·00
O95		15 r. blue and olive (1913)	..	90·00	£100
O96		25 r. orange and blue (1913)	..	£200	£160
O73/96			Set of 13	£300	£275

1921. *No. O80 surch with Type O 12.*

O97	57	9 p. on 1 a. rose-carmine		85	75

1922. *No. 197 optd with Type O 10.*

O98	57	1 a. chocolate	.. ..	95	10

ONE
RUPEE

(O 13)	(O 14)

1925. *Official stamps surcharged.*

(a) Issue of 1909, as Type O 13

O 99	52	1 r. on 15 r. blue and olive	..	4·25	3·50
O100		1 r. on 25 r chestnut and blue ..		20·00	65·00
O101		2 r. on 10 r green and scarlet ..		3·75	3·75
O101a		2 r. on 10 r. green and carmine.	.	£200	48·00

(b) Issue of 1912, with Type O 14

O102	67	1 r. on 15 r. blue and olive	..	19·00	70·00
O103		1 r. on 25 r. orange and blue	..	5·50	9·50
		a. Surch inverted	..	£550	

(c) Issue of 1912, as Type O 13

O104	67	2 r. on 10 r. green and scarlet	..	£750	

Examples of the above showing other surcharge errors are believed to be of clandestine origin.

ONE ANNA	SERVICE ONE ANNA
(O 15)	(O 16)

1926. *No. O62 surch with Type O 15.*

O105	48	1 a. on 6 a. olive-bistre ..		30	30

1926. *Postage stamps of 1911–22 (wmk Single Star), surch as Type O 16.*

O106	58	1 a. on 1½ a. chocolate (A)	..	20	10
O107		1 a. on 1½ a. chocolate (B)	..	1·40	3·75
		a. Error. On 1 a. chocolate (197)	..	£160	
O108	61	1 a. on 2 a. 6 p. ultramarine	..	60	80

The surcharge on No. O108 has no bars at top.
Examples of Nos. O106/7 with inverted or double surcharges are believed to be of clandestine origin.

SERVICE	SERVICE
(O 17)(13½ mm)	(O 18) (19½ mm)

1926–31. *Stamps of King George V (wmk Multiple Star, T 69) optd with Types O 17 or O 18 (rupee values).*

O109	55	3 p. slate (1.10.29)	..	15	10
		w. Wmk inverted	..	75	40
O110	56	½ a. green (1931)	..	5·00	30
		w. Wmk inverted	..	—	1·10
O111	57	1 a. chocolate	..	15	10
		w. Wmk inverted	..	1·00	40
O112	70	2 a. purple	..	20	10
		w. Wmk inverted	..	50	30
O113	71	4 a. sage-green	..	40	20
		w. Wmk inverted	..	1·50	50
O115	65	8 a. reddish purple	..	60	10
		w. Wmk inverted	..	60	30
O116	66	12 a. claret (1927)	..	60	1·60
		w. Wmk inverted	..	—	3·00
O117	67	1 r. chocolate and green (1930)	..	2·25	1·00
		w. Wmk inverted	..	1·90	1·25
O118		2 r. carmine and orange (1930)	..	6·50	6·50
O120		10 r. green and scarlet (1931)	..	70·00	48·00
O109/20			Set of 10	75·00	50·00

1930. *As No. O111, but optd as Type O 10 (14 mm).*

O125	57	1 a. chocolate	..	—	4·00
		w. Wmk inverted	..	85·00	5·00

1932–36. *Stamps of King George V (wmk Mult Star, T 69) optd with Type O 17.*

O126	79	½ a. green (1935)	..	60	10
O127	80	9 p. deep green	..	30	10
O127a	81	1 a. chocolate (1936)	..	2·25	10
		aw. Wmk inverted	..	2·75	40
O128	82	1 a. 3 p. mauve	..	30	10
		w. Wmk inverted	..	40	40
O129	70	2 a. vermilion	..	1·00	2·25
O130	59	2 a. vermilion (1935)	..	1·25	1·25
O130a		2 a. vermilion (*small die*) (1936)	..	1·00	10
O131	61	2 a. 6 p. orange (22.4.32)	..	30	10
		w. Wmk inverted	..	1·25	50
O132	63	4 a. sage-green (1935)	..	1·00	10
O133	64	6 a. bistre (1936)	..	20·00	9·50
O126/33			Set of 9	24·00	10·00

1937–39. *Stamps of King George VI optd as Types O 17 or O 18 (rupee values).*

O135	91	½ a. red-brown (1938)	..	16·00	20
O136		9 p. green (1937)	..	17·00	30
O137		1 a. carmine (1937)	..	3·00	10
O138	93	1 r. grey and red-brown (5.38)	..	60	10
O139		2 r. purple and brown (5.38)	..	1·50	2·50
		w. Wmk inverted	..	—	21·00
O140		5 r. green and blue (10.38)	..	2·50	5·50
O141		10 r. purple and claret (1939)	..	14·00	4·75
O135/41			Set of 7	48·00	12·50

1939 (May). *Stamp of King George V, surch with Type O 19.*

O142	82	1 a. on 1¼ a. mauve	..	11·00	20

(Des T. I. Archer)

1939 (1 June)–42. *Typo. W 69. P 14.*

O143	O 20	3 p. slate	..	40	10
O144		½ a. red-brown	..	4·00	10
O144a		½ a. purple (1942)	..	30	10
O145		9 p. green ..	..	30	10
O146		1 a. carmine	..	30	10
O146a		1 a. 3 p. yellow-brown (1941)	..	3·00	70
		aw. Wmk inverted			
O146b		1½ a. dull violet (1942)	..	65	10
O147		2 a. vermilion	..	60	10
O148		2½ a. bright violet	..	60	50
O149		4 a. brown	..	60	10
O150		8 a. slate-violet	..	90	30
O143/50			Set of 11	10·50	1·60

1948 (15 Aug). *First Anniv of Independence. Nos. 305/8 optd as Type O 17.*

O150a	305	1½ a. brown	..	42·00	30·00
O150b		3½ a. violet	..	£750	£450
O150c		12 a. grey-green	..	£2000	£1600
O150d	306	10 r. purple-brown and lake	..	£11000	

Nos. O150a/d were only issued to the Governor-General's Secretariat.

O 21	Asokan Capital	O 22

(Des T. I. Archer)

1950 (2 Jan)–51. *Typo (O 21) or litho (O 22). W 69. P 14.*

O151	O 21	3 p. slate-violet (1.7.50)	..	10	10
O152		6 p. purple-brown (1.7.50)	..	10	10
O153		9 p. green (1.7.50)	..	30	10
O154		1 a. turquoise (1.7.50)	..	70	10
O155		2 a. carmine (1.7.50)	..	1·00	10
		w. Wmk inverted			
O156		3 a. red-orange (1.7.50)	..	3·00	1·75
O157		4 a. lake (1.7.50)	..	5·00	20
O158		4 a. ultramarine (1.10.51)	..	5·00	10
O159		6 a. bright violet (1.7.50)	..	3·00	40
O160		8 a. red-brown (1.7.50)	..	1·50	10
		w. Wmk inverted	..	8·00	
O161	O 22	1 r. violet (1.7.50)	..	2·75	10
		w. Wmk inverted			
O162		2 r. rose-carmine ..	..	1·00	70
O163		5 r. bluish green	..	2·00	1·75
O164		10 r. reddish brown	..	3·00	16·00
O151/64			Set of 14	21·00	19·00

1957 (1 Apr)–58. *Values in naye paise. Typo (t) or litho (l). W 69. P 14.*

O165	O 21	1 n.p. slate (l)	..	30	10
		a. Slate-black (l)	..	30	10
		b. Greenish slate (t)	..	10	10
		w. Wmk inverted	..	3·50	1·25
O166		2 n.p. blackish violet (t)	..	10	10
		w. Wmk inverted			
O167		3 n.p. chocolate (t)	..	10	10
O168		5 n.p. green (l)	..	10	10
		a. Deep emerald (t)	..	55	10

O169	O 21	6 n.p. turquoise-blue (t)	..	10	10
O170		13 n.p. scarlet (t)	..	10	10
O171		15 n.p. reddish violet (l) (6.58)	..	1·50	2·00
		a. Reddish violet (t)	..	1·50	2·00
O172		20 n.p. red (l)	..	15	50
		a. Vermilion (t)	..	80	10
		aw. Wmk inverted			
O173		25 n.p. violet-blue (l)	..	20	10
		a. Ultramarine (l)	..	2·25	10
O174		50 n.p. red-brown (l)	..	40	10
		a. Reddish brown (t)	..	2·25	90
O165/74			Set of 10	2·25	2·25

1958–71. *As Nos. O165/74a and O161/4 but W 374 (upright). Litho (l) or typo (t). P 14.*

O175	O 21	1 n.p. slate-black (t) (1.59)	..	10	10
O176		2 n.p. blackish violet (t) (1.59)	..	10	10
O177		3 n.p. chocolate (t) (11.58)	..	10	10
		w. Wmk inverted		3·50	
O178		5 n.p. deep emerald (t) (11.58)	..	10	10
O179		6 n.p. turquoise-blue (t) (5.59)	..	10	10
O180		10 n.p. deep grey-green (l) (1963)	..	1·75	1·50
		a. Deep grey-green (t) (1966?)	..	3·25	3·25
O181		13 n.p. scarlet (t) (1963)	..	65	2·50
O182		15 n.p. deep violet (t) (11.58)	..	10	10
		a. Light reddish violet (t) (1961)	..	2·25	10
O183		20 n.p. vermilion (t) (5.59)	..	30	10
		a. Red (t) (1966?)	..	4·25	80
O184		25 n.p. ultramarine (t) (7.59)	..	10	10
O185		50 n.p. reddish brown (t) (6.59)	..	15	10
		a. Chestnut (l) (1966?)	..	4·50	1·25
O186	O 22	1 r. reddish violet (l) (2.59)	..	15	10
O187		2 r. rose-carmine (l) (1960)	..	25	10
		a. Wmk sideways.* Pale rose-carmine (l) (1969?)	..	45	75
O188		5 r. slate-green (l) (7.59)	..	40	60
		a. Wmk sideways*. Deep grey-green (l) (1969?)	..	80	90
O189		10 r. brown-lake (l) (7.59)	..	90	80
		a. Wmk sideways* (l) (1971)	..	2·75	3·00
		ab. Printed on the gummed side		38·00	
		aw. Wmk capitals to right		2·75	
O175/89			Set of 15	4·50	5·00

*The normal sideways watermark shows the head of the capitals pointing left, *as seen from the back of the stamp.*

O 23 (see also Type O 26)　　(O 24)　　O 25

1967 (20 Mar)–**73?** *Photo. W 374 (sideways). P 15×14.*

O190	O 23	2 p. violet (1973?)	..	70	90
O191		5 p. green (1973?)	..	70	10
O192		10 p. myrtle-green (2.7.73)	..	1·25	15
O193		15 p. plum (2.7.73)	..	1·75	40
O194		20 p. red (2.7.73)	..	6·00	5·50
O195		30 p. ultramarine (1973)	..	4·00	1·00
O196		50 p. chestnut (2.7.73)	..	3·25	2·75
O197		1 r. dull purple (20.3.67)	..	50	10
		a. Deep slate-purple (1969)	..	90	10
O190/7			Set of 8	16·00	9·75

1967 (15 Nov)–**74(?).** *Wmk Large Star and "INDIA GOVT" in sheet*. Photo. P 15 × 14. No gum.*

O200	O 23	2 p. violet	..	10	90
O201		3 p. chocolate	..	10	1·00
O202		5 p. green	..	10	10
		a. Yellowish green (1969)	..	10	10
		w. Wmk reversed		4·00	
O203		6 p. turquoise-blue	..	65	1·00
O204		10 p. myrtle-green	..	10	30
		a. Bronze-green (1969)	..	90	90
		w. Wmk reversed		4·00	
O205		15 p. plum	..	10	30
		w. Wmk reversed			
O206		20 p. red	..	10	30
		w. Wmk reversed		4·00	
O207		25 p. carmine-red (1974?)	..	8·00	3·75
		w. Wmk reversed		8·50	
O208		30 p. ultramarine	..	10	60
O209		50 p. chestnut	..	10	60
		w. Wmk reversed		4·50	
O200/9			Set of 10	8·50	8·00

*The arrangement of this watermark in the sheet results in the words and the star appearing upright, inverted or sideways.

1971. *Obligatory Tax. Refugee Relief.*

(a) Provisional issue. No. O202 optd with Type O 24.

O210	O 23	5 p. yellowish green (15.11)	..	30	30
		a. Green	..	30	30
		w. Wmk reversed		6·00	

(b) Issue for Bangalore. No. O202 optd with T 602

O211	O 23	5 p. yellowish green	..	1·25	40
		a. Opt inverted	..	3·25	
		w. Wmk reversed		8·00	

(c) Issue for Goa. No. O202 optd with T 606

O212	O 23	5 p. yellowish green	..	3·25	1·00
		w. Wmk reversed		15·00	

(d) Definitive issue. Wmk Large Star and "INDIA GOVT" in sheet. Litho. P 15×14. No gum.*

O213	O 25	5 p. yellowish green (1.12)	..	15	15
		a. Yellow-green	..	15	15
		w. Wmk reversed		6·00	

*See note below No. O209.
The surcharge on mail for the relief of refugees from the former East Pakistan referred to in the note after No. 651 also applied to official mail. The cost of the stamps used by each Government Department was charged against its budget and the additional charge for refugee stamps meant that each Department had to spend less to keep within its budget.

O 26　　　O 27　　　O 28

1976 (1 Apr)–**80.** *Redrawn, showing face-value in figures only and smaller Capital with Hindi motto beneath. P 14 (2, 5, 10 r.) or 15×14 (others). (a) Wmk Large Star and "INDIA GOVT" in sheet.* No gum.

O214	O 26	2 p. deep violet-blue	..	20	1·00
O215		5 p. yellowish green	..	10	30
O216		10 p. myrtle-green	..	15	70
		a. Imperf (pair)			
		b. Deep dull green (1978)	..	10	70
O217		15 p. deep purple	..	10	30
O218		20 p. Indian red	..	15	80
O219		25 p. rose-carmine	..	70	1·25
		a. Bright crimson (1978)	..	90	1·25
O220		30 p. chalky blue (1.5.79)	..	2·25	2·25
O221		35 p. violet (6.12.80)	..	55	10
O222		50 p. chestnut	..	2·75	1·25
O223		1 r. deep brownish purple (13.8.80)	..	4·00	75

(b) W 374 (sideways)†

O224	O 26	1 r. deep brownish purple	..	85	95
O225	–	2 r. rose-red (date?)	..	3·00	3·00
		aw. Wmk capitals to right		3·25	
		b. Wmk upright	..	40	1·50
		bw. Wmk inverted		2·00	
O226	–	5 r. deep green (date?)	..	3·50	4·00
		aw. Wmk capitals to right		3·75	
		b. Wmk upright (1978)	..	60	2·25
		bw. Wmk inverted			
O227	–	10 r. brown-lake (date?)	..	1·25	3·50
		a. Wmk upright	..	3·50	5·00
		aw. Wmk inverted		3·75	
O214/27			Set of 14	12·50	15·00

The 2, 5 and 10 r. are larger, size as Type O 22.
*See note below No. 720. The 2 p. value is only known on the first type of watermark, the 35, 50 p. and 1 r. values on the second and the remaining values on both.
†The normal sideways watermark shows the top of the capitals pointing left, *as seen from the back of the stamp.*

1981 (14 Feb). *Redrawn showing revised border design and inscriptions, with face value figures now in bottom corners. Litho. Wmk Large Star and "INDIA GOVT" in sheet. P 15×14.*

O228	O 27	2 r. vermilion	..	1·50	50
		a. Rose-red (photo)	..	—	50
O229		5 r. deep green	..	1·50	75
		a. Deep dull green (photo)	..	—	75
O230		10 r. purple-brown	..	2·00	1·50
		a. Brown-lake (photo)	..		1·50
O228/30			Set of 3	4·50	2·50

1981 (10 Dec). *As Nos. O215/19, O221/3 and O228/30 but printed on cream paper with simulated perforations as Type O 28. Unwatermarked. Imperf.*

O231	O 28	5 p. dull yellowish green	..	55	75
O232		10 p. deep green	..	70	80
O233		15 p. deep reddish violet	..	70	80
O234		20 p. dull vermilion	..	75	85
O235		25 p. bright rose	..	1·50	1·75
O236		35 p. violet	..	85	50
O237		50 p. orange-brown	..	1·50	1·25
O238		1 r. deep dull purple	..	1·75	1·25
O239		2 r. orange-vermilion	..	1·75	3·75
O240		5 r. deep dull green	..	2·00	4·50
O241		10 r. lake-brown	..	2·50	6·50
O231/41			Set of 11	13·00	20·00

Some values have been unofficially pin-perforated.

1982 (22 Nov). *As Nos. 215/23 and 228/30. Photo. Wmk Large Star and "INDIA GOVT" in sheet. P 12½×13.*

O242	O 26	5 p. light green	..	40	60
O243		10 p. deep dull green	..	50	70
O244		15 p. blackish purple	..	55	70
O245		20 p. Indian red	..	65	70
O246		25 p. cerise	..	75	1·25
O247		30 p. deep ultramarine	..	75	1·25
O248		35 p. bluish violet	..	75	40
O249		50 p. reddish brown	..	1·00	1·25
O250		1 r. deep purple-brown	..	1·10	1·25
O251	O 27	2 r. rose-red	..	1·40	2·25
		a. Vermilion (litho)	..	1·25	2·25
O252		5 r. grey-green	..	1·50	3·75
O253		10 r. chocolate	..	2·25	5·50
O242/53			Set of 12	10·00	17·00

1984 (16 Apr)–**99.** *As Nos. O215/23, O228/30 and new values. Photo. W 374 (sideways*). P 13.*

O254	O 26	5 p. yellowish green	..	10	10
		aw. Wmk capitals to right		10	10
		b. Wmk upright		10	10
O255		10 p. deep dull green	..	10	10
		a. Wmk upright		10	10
O256		15 p. blackish purple	..	10	10
		a. Wmk upright		10	10
O257		20 p. Indian red	..	10	10
		a. Wmk upright		10	10
O258		25 p. rose-carmine (1986)	..	15	10
		a. Wmk upright		15	10
O259		30 p. deep ultramarine	..	15	10
		a. Wmk upright		15	10
O260		35 p. bluish violet	..	20	10
		aw. Wmk capitals to left		10	10
O261		40 p. bright violet (1999)	..	10	10
		a. Wmk upright		10	10
O262		50 p. reddish brown	..	40	10
		aw. Wmk capitals to right		40	10
		b. Wmk upright		40	10
O263		60 p. deep brown (15.4.88)	..	20	10
		a. Wmk upright		20	10
O264		1 r. deep purple-brown	..	45	10
		aw. Wmk capitals to right		45	10
		a. Wmk upright		45	10

O265	O 27	2 r. rose-red	..	55	55
		a. Wmk upright		55	55
O266		5 r. grey-green	..	60	60
		a. Wmk upright		60	60
O267		10 r. chocolate	..	75	75
		w. Wmk capitals to right			
O254/67			Set of 13	3·25	2·50

*The normal sideways watermark shows the top of the capitals pointing right on the 35 p. and to the left on the other values, *all as seen from the back of the stamp.*

1998 (15 Oct)–**99.** *Litho. W 374 (sideways). P 13.*

O268	O 26	40 p. bright violet	..	10	10
		a. Wmk upright		10	10
		w. Wmk inverted		10	10
O269		50 p. yellow-brown (20.6.98)	..	10	10
O270		1 r. deep dull purple (20.6.98)	..	10	10
O271	O 27	2 r. vermilion (20.6.98)	..	10	10
		a. Wmk upright (1999)		10	10
O272		3 r. orange (22.3.99)	..	10	15
		a. Wmk upright		10	15
O273		5 r. deep grey-green (20.6.98)	..	15	20
O274		10 r. red-brown (20.6.98)	..	30	35
O268/74			Set of 7	1·10	1·25

INDIA USED ABROAD

In the years following 1858 the influence of the Indian Empire, political, military and economic, extended beyond its borders into neighbouring states, the Arabian Gulf, East Africa and the Far East. Such influence often led to the establishment of Indian civil post offices in the countries concerned where unoverprinted stamps of India were used.

Such offices operated in the following countries. An * indicates that details will be found under that heading elsewhere in the catalogue.

ADEN (SOUTH ARABIAN FEDERATION)*

Unoverprinted stamps of India used from 1854 until 1937.

BAHRAIN*

Unoverprinted stamps of India used from 1884 until 1933.

BRITISH EAST AFRICA (KENYA, UGANDA AND TANGANYIKA)*

Unoverprinted stamps of India used during August and September 1890.

FRENCH INDIAN SETTLEMENTS

The first Indian post office, at Chandernagore, was open by 1784 to be followed by offices in the other four Settlements. By an agreement with the French, dating from 1814, these offices handled mail destined for British India, Great Britain, the British Empire and most other foreign destinations except France and the French colonies. In later years the system was expanded by a number of sub-offices and it continued to operate until the French territories were absorbed into India on 2 May 1950 (Chandernagore) or 1 November 1954.

Chandernagore. Open by 1784. Used numeral cancellations "B86" or "86".
　Sub-offices:
　　Gondalpara (opened 1906)
　　Lakhiganj (opened 1909)
　　Temata (opened 1891)
Karikal. Open by 1794. Used numeral cancellations "C147", "147" or "6/M–21".
　Sub-offices:
　　Ambagarattur (opened 1904)
　　Kottuchari (opened 1901)
　　Nedungaon (opened 1903)
　　Puraiyar Road (opened 1901)
　　Settur (opened 1905)
　　Tirumalrayapatnam (opened 1875 – used numeral cancellation "6/M–21/1")
　　Tiramilur (opened 1898)
Mahe. Open by 1795. Used numeral cancellations "C192" or "9/M–14".
Pondicherry. Opened 1787. Used numeral cancellations "C111", "111" (also used elsewhere), "6/M–19" (also used elsewhere) or "6/M–20".
　Sub-offices:
　　Ariyankuppam (opened 1904)
　　Bahoor (opened 1885)
　　Mudaliarpet (opened 1897)
　　Muthialpet (opened 1885)
　　Pondicherry Bazaar (opened 1902)
　　Pondicherry Railway Station (opened 1895)
　　Olugarai (opened 1907)
　　Vallinur (opened 1875) – used numeral cancellation "M-19/1"
Yanam. Opened 1876. Used numeral cancellation "5/M-4".

IRAN

The British East India Company was active in the Arabian Gulf from the early years of the 17th century with their first factory (trading centre) being established at Jask in 1619. After 1853 this commercial presence was converted into a political arm of the Indian Government culminating in the appointment of a Political Resident to Bushire in 1862.

The first Indian post office in Iran (Persia) opened at Bushire on 1 May 1864 with monthly mail services operating to the Resident there and to the British Legation at Tehran. Further offices in the other Gulf ports followed, but, unless otherwise stated below, all were closed on 1 April 1923.

Abadan. Opened during First World War.
Ahwaz. Opened March 1915.
Bandar Abbas. Opened 1 April 1867. Used numeral cancellations "22" or "1/K-5".
Bushire. Opened 1 May 1864. Used numeral cancellations "308", "26" (also used elsewhere) or "K-5".
Chabbar. Opened 20 August 1913.
Duzdab. Opened 1922. Closed 1927?

Henjam. Opened 21 June 1913
Jask. Opened 1 September 1880
Kuh-Malik-Siah-Ziarat. Opened January 1906. Closed 1924
Linga. Opened 1 April 1867. Used numeral cancellations
"21" or "2/K-5".
Maidan-i-Naphtun. Opened during First World War. Closed
1920.
Mirjawa. Opened January 1921. Closed 1930.
Mohammera. Opened 19 July 1892.

IRAQ*

Unoverprinted stamps of India used from 1868 until 1918.

KUWAIT*

Unoverprinted stamps of India used from 1904 until 1923.

MALAYSIA (STRAITS SETTLEMENTS)*

Unoverprinted stamps of India used from 1854 until 1867.

MUSCAT*

Unoverprinted stamps of India used from 1864 until 1947.

NEPAL

A post office was opened in the British Residency at Kathmandu in 1816 following the end of the Gurkha War. Stamps of India were used from 1854, initially with "B137", "137" or "C-37" numeral cancellations. The Residency Post Office continued to provide the overseas mail service after Nepal introduced its own issues in 1881.

In 1920 the Residency Post Office became the British Legation Post Office. On the independence of India in 1947 the service was transferred to the Indian Embassy and continued to function until 1965.

PORTUGUESE INDIA

A British post office was open in Damaun by 1823 and Indian stamps were used there until November 1883, some with "13" and "3/B-19" numeral cancellations.

No other British post offices were opened in the Portuguese territories, but from 1854 Indian stamps were sold by the local post offices. Between 1871 and 1877 mail intended for, or passing through, British India required combined franking of India and Portuguese India issues. After 1877 the two postal administrations accepted the validity of each other's stamps.

SOMALILAND PROTECTORATE*

Unoverprinted stamps of India used from 1887 until 1903.

TIBET

The first Indian post office in Tibet accompanied the Tibetan Frontier Commission in 1903. The Younghusband Military Expedition to Lhasa in the following year operated a number of Field Post Offices which were replaced by civil post offices at Gartok (opened 23 September 1906), Gyantse (opened March 1905), Pharijong (opened 1905) and Yatung (opened 1905). All Indian post offices in Tibet closed on 1 April 1955 except Gartok which, it is believed, did not operate after 1943.

TRUCIAL STATES (DUBAI)*

Unoverprinted stamps of India used from 1909 until 1947.

ZANZIBAR (TANZANIA)*

Unoverprinted stamps of India used from 1875 until 1895.

CHINA EXPEDITIONARY FORCE

Following the outbreak of the Boxer Rising in North China the Peking Legations were besieged by the rebels in June 1900. An international force, including an Indian Army division, was assembled for their relief. The Legations were relieved on 14 August 1900, but operations against the Boxers continued in North China with Allied garrisons at key cities and along the Peking–Tientsin–Shanhaikwan railway. The last Indian Army battalion, and accompanying Field Post Offices, did not leave North China until 1 November 1923.

Field Post Offices accompanied the Indian troops and commenced operations on 23 July 1900 using unoverprinted Indian postage and official stamps. The unoverprinted postage issues were replaced in mid-August by stamps overprinted "C.E.F." to prevent currency speculation. The use of unoverprinted official stamps continued as they were not valid for public postage.

PRICES FOR STAMPS ON COVER	
Nos. C1/10	*from* × 15
No. C10*a*	†
Nos. C11/22	*from* × 8
Nos. C23/34	*from* × 20

C. E. F.
(C 1)

Stamps of India overprinted with Type C 1, in black

1900 (16 Aug). *Stamps of Queen Victoria.*

C 1	40	3 p. carmine	..	40	1·25
		a. No stop after "C" (R. 1/2)	..	£130	
		b. No stop after "F" ..	..	£130	
C 2	23	½ a. green	..	75	30
		a. Opt double	..	£130	
		b. No stop after "F" ..	..	£130	
C 3	25	1 a. plum	..	4·00	1·50
		a. No stop after "F" ..	..	£180	
C 4	27	2 a. ultramarine	..	3·00	9·00
		a. No stop after "F" ..	..	£180	
C 5	36	2 a. 6 p. green	..	2·75	13·00
		a. No stop after "F" ..	..	£250	
C 6	28	3 a. orange	..	2·75	16·00
		a. Opt double, one albino	..	£120	
		b. No stop after "F" ..	..	£250	

C 7	29	4 a. olive-green	..	2·75	7·50
		a. Opt double, one albino	..	£120	
		b. No stop after "F" ..	..	£250	
C 8	31	8 a. magenta	..	2·75	17·00
		a. No stop after "F" ..	..	£300	
		b. Opt double, one albino	..	£120	
C 9	32	12 a. purple/*red*	..	16·00	16·00
		a. No stop after "F" ..	..	£160	
		b. No stop after "F" ..	..	£375	
C10	37	1 r. green and carmine	..	18·00	18·00
		a. No stop after "F" ..	..	£375	
		b. Opt double, one albino	..		
C1/10			*Set of 10*	48·00	90·00

Prepared, but not issued

C10*b*	26	1 a. 6 p. sepia	..	£200

The missing stop after "F" variety occurs in the ninth row of the upper pane.

1904 (27 Feb).

C11	25	1 a. carmine	..	28·00	8·00

1905 (16 Sept)–**11**. *Stamps of King Edward VII.*

C12	41	3 p. grey (4.11)	..	4·50	6·50
		a. Opt double, one albino	..	£120	
		b. Opt triple, one albino	..	£375	
		c. Slate-grey	..	3·75	6·50
C13	43	1 a. carmine	..	6·50	70
		a. Opt double, one albino	..	£100	
C14	44	2 a. mauve (11.3.11)	..	14·00	2·00
		a. Opt double, one albino	..	£130	
C15	45	2 a. 6 p. ultramarine (11.3.11)	..	3·25	5·00
C16	46	3 a. orange-brown (11.3.11)	..	3·75	4·00
C17	47	4 a. olive-green (11.3.11)	..	8·50	11·00
C18	49	8 a. claret (11.3.11)	..	8·00	7·50
		a. *Purple*	..	55·00	55·00
C19	50	12 a. purple/*red* (1909)	..	11·00	19·00
		a. No stop after "E"	..	£450	
C20	51	1 r. green and carmine (11.3.11)	..	13·00	28·00
C12/20			*Set of 9*	65·00	75·00

1908 (Dec)–**09**. "POSTAGE & REVENUE".

C21	53	½ a. green (No. 149) (29.9.09)	..	1·50	1·25
		a. Opt double, one albino	..	£110	
C22	54	1 a. carmine (No. 150)	..	1·50	30
		a. Opt double, one albino	..	£150	

1914 (5 May)–**22**. *Stamps of King George V. Wmk Star.*

C23	55	3 p. slate-grey (7.10.14)	..	4·00	23·00
		a. Opt double, one albino	..	£200	
C24	56	½ a. green	..	3·00	5·00
C25	57	1 a. aniline carmine ..	..	3·50	3·50
C26	58	1½ a. chocolate (Type A) (9.3.21)	..	21·00	65·00
		a. Opt double, one albino	..	£140	
C27	59	2 a. mauve (11.19)	..	12·00	50·00
		a. Opt triple	..	£425	
		b. *Dull purple*	..	13·00	50·00
C28	61	2 a. 6 p. bright blue (2.19)	..	9·50	23·00
C29	62	3 a. orange-brown (5.22)	..	23·00	£180
C30	63	4 a. olive-green (5.22)	..	19·00	£150
C32	65	8 a. mauve (12.21)	..	22·00	£325
C33	66	12 a. claret (8.20)	..	19·00	£110
C34	67	1 r. red-brown and blue-green (10.21)	..	55·00	£250
C23/34			*Set of 11*	£160	£1000

Most dates quoted for Nos. C23/34 are those of the earliest recorded postmarks.

On No. C27*a* two of the overprints are only lightly inked.

BRITISH RAILWAY ADMINISTRATION

As a vital communications link the North China Railway (Peking – Tientsin – Shanhaikwan) was captured by Russian forces during operations against the Boxers. Control of the line was subsequently, in February 1901, assigned to the China Expeditionary Force and a British Railway Administration was set up to run it. By international agreement the line was to provide postal services for the other national contingents and also, to a lesser extent, for the civilian population. Travelling post offices were introduced and, on 20 April 1901, a late letter service for which an additional fee of 5 c. was charged.

	B.R.A.
	5
	Five Cents
Type 32 of China	(BR 35)

1901 (20 Apr). *No. 108 of China surch with Type BR 35.*

BR133	32	5 c. on ½ c. brown (Bk.)	..	£325	£100
		a. Surch inverted	..	£8000	£2500
		b. Surch in green	..	£275	£140
		ba. Imperf between (horiz pair)	..	†	£16000

No. BR133 was used for the collection of the 5 c. late letter fee and was affixed to correspondence by a postal official at the railway station. It was cancelled with a violet circular postmark showing "RAILWAY POST OFFICE" at top and the name of the station (PEKING, TIENTSIN, TONGKU, TONGSHAN or SHANHAIKWAN) at foot. With the exception of official mail it could only be used in combination with Indian stamps overprinted "C.E.F.", stamps from the other allied contingents or of the Chinese Imperial Post (*Price used on cover: No. BR133 from* £250. *No. BR133b from* £300).

It is suggested that stamps overprinted in black were used at Tientsin and Tongku while those in green being available at Peking, Tongshan and Shanhaikwan.

The late fee charge was abolished on 20 May 1901 and No. BR133 was then withdrawn. The British Railway Administration continued to run the line, and its travelling post offices, until it was returned to its private owners in September 1902.

INDIAN EXPEDITIONARY FORCES 1914–21

Nos. E1/13 were for use of Indian forces sent overseas during the First World War and its aftermath. Examples were first used in France during September 1914. Other areas where the stamps were used included East Africa, Mesopotamia and Turkey. "I.E.F." overprints ceased to be valid for postage on 15 October 1921.

PRICES FOR STAMPS ON COVER	
Nos. E1/13	*from* × 10

I. E. F.
(E 1)

1914 (Sept). *Stamps of India (King George V) optd with Type E 1.*

E 1	55	3 p. slate-grey	..	15	30
		a. No stop after "F" ..	..	23·00	26·00
		b. No stop after "E" ..	..	£100	£100
		c. Opt double	..	42·00	30·00
E 2	56	½ a. yellow-green	..	30	30
		a. No stop after "F" ..	..	70·00	70·00
		b. Opt double	..	£140	£250
E 3	57	1 a. aniline carmine	..	75	30
		a. No stop after "F" ..	..	32·00	35·00
E 4		1 a. carmine	..	3·50	3·50
E 5	59	2 a. mauve	..	80	30
		a. No stop after "F" ..	..	50·00	65·00
		b. No stop after "E" ..	..	£225	£250
E 6	61	2 a. 6 p. ultramarine ..	..	1·50	3·00
		a. No stop after "F" ..	..	£160	£170
E 7	62	3 a. orange-brown	..	80	90
		a. No stop after "F" ..	..	£150	£160
E 8	63	4 a. olive-green	..	70	90
		a. No stop after "F" ..	..	£225	£250
E 9	65	8 a. purple	..	1·00	2·00
		a. No stop after "F" ..	..	£225	£250
E10		8 a. mauve	..	8·50	12·00
E11	66	12 a. dull claret	..	9·00	13·00
		a. No stop after "F" ..	..	£275	£275
		b. Opt double, one albino	..	55·00	
E12		12 a. claret	..	2·25	5·50
E13	67	1 r. red-brown and blue-green	..	2·50	4·00
		a. Opt double, one albino	..	£160	
E1/13			*Set of 10*	9·50	16·00

The "no stop after F" variety occurred on R. 4/12 of the upper pane, in one printing.

INDIAN CUSTODIAN FORCES IN KOREA

भारतीय
संरक्षा कटक
कोरिया

(K 1)

1953 (17 Oct). *Stamps of India optd with Type K 1.*

K 1	307	3 p. slate-violet	..	1·75	4·50
K 2	308	6 p. purple-brown	..	1·50	4·50
K 3	309	9 p. yellow-green	..	1·75	4·50
K 4	328	1 a. turquoise ..	..	1·50	4·50
K 5	311	2 a. carmine	..	1·50	4·50
K 6	313	2½ a. lake	..	1·50	4·75
K 7	312	3 a. brown-orange	..	1·50	4·75
K 8	314	4 a. bright blue	..	2·00	4·75
K 9	315	6 a. violet	..	8·50	9·00
K10	316	8 a. turquoise-green	..	3·25	9·00
K11	317	12 a. dull blue	..	4·50	17·00
K12	318	1 r. dull violet and green	..	6·00	17·00
K1/12			*Set of 12*	30·00	75·00

INDIAN U.N. FORCE IN CONGO

U.N. FORCE
(INDIA)
CONGO

(U 1)

1962 (15 Jan). *Stamps of India optd with Type U 1. W 69 (sideways) (13 n.p.) or W 374 (others).*

U1	361	1 n.p. blue-green ..	..	90	2·50
U2		2 n.p. light brown	..	90	80
U3		5 n.p. bright green	..	90	55
U4		8 n.p. light blue-green	..	90	30
U5		13 n.p. bright carmine-red	..	90	40
U6		50 n.p. orange	..	90	70
U1/6			*Set of 6*	4·75	4·75

INDIAN U.N. FORCE IN GAZA (PALESTINE) UNEF

UNEF

(G 1)

1965 (15 Jan). *No. 492 of India optd with Type G 1.*

G1	449	15 p. slate (C.)	..	1·50	6·00

INTERNATIONAL COMMISSION IN INDO-CHINA

The International Control Commissions for Indo-China were established in August 1954 as part of the Geneva Declaration which partitioned Vietnam and sought to achieve stable settlements in Cambodia and Laos. The three supervisory commissions were chaired by India with Canada and Poland as the other members. Joint inspection teams of servicemen from the three countries were also provided.

The Indian contingent included a postal unit which handled mail for the three commissions and the inspection teams. The unit arrived in Indo-China on 3 September 1954 and opened field post offices at Saigon (F.P.O. 742), Hanoi (F.P.O. 743), Vientiane (F.P.O. 744) and Phnom Penh (F.P.O. 745).

अन्तर्राष्ट्रीय आयोग अन्तर्राष्ट्रीय आयोग अन्तर्राष्ट्रीय आयोग
कम्बोज   लाओस   वियत नाम
(N 1)   (N 2)   (N 3)

1954 (1 Dec). *Stamps of India.* W 69.

(a) Optd as Type N 1, for use in Cambodia

N 1	307	3 p. slate-violet	1·25	8·00
N 2	328	1 a. turquoise	90	75
N 3	311	2 a. carmine	90	80
N 4	316	8 a. turquoise-green	2·00	3·50
N 5	317	12 a. dull blue	2·00	4·00

(b) Optd as Type N 2, for use in Laos

N 6	307	3 p. slate-violet	1·25	8·00
N 7	328	1 a. turquoise	90	75
N 8	311	2 a. carmine	90	80
N 9	316	8 a. turquoise-green	2·00	3·50
N10	317	12 a. dull blue	2·00	4·00

(c) Optd as Type N 3, for use in Vietnam

N11	307	3 p. slate-violet	1·25	8·00
N12	328	1 a. turquoise	90	75
N13	311	2 a. carmine	90	80
N14	316	8 a. turquoise-green	2·00	3·50
N15	317	12 a. dull blue	2·00	4·00
N1/15		Set of 15	17·00	45·00

1957 (1 Apr). *Stamps of India.* W 69 (sideways).

(a) Optd as Type N 1, for use in Cambodia

N16	361	2 n.p. light brown	75	30
N17		6 n.p. grey	50	30
N18		13 n.p. bright carmine-red	70	40
N19		50 n.p. orange	2·25	1·25
N20		75 n.p. reddish purple	2·25	1·25

(b) Optd as Type N 2, for use in Laos

N21	361	2 n.p. light brown	75	30
N22		6 n.p. grey	50	30
N23		13 n.p. bright carmine-red	70	40
N24		50 n.p. orange	2·25	1·25
N25		75 n.p. reddish purple	2·25	1·25

(c) Optd as Type N 3, for use in Vietnam

N26	361	2 n.p. light brown	75	30
N27		6 n.p. grey	50	30
N28		13 n.p. bright carmine-red	70	40
N29		50 n.p. orange	2·25	1·25
N30		75 n.p. reddish purple	2·25	1·25
N16/30		Set of 15	17·00	9·50

F.P.O. 744 (Vientiane) was closed on 25 July 1958 and F.P.O. 745 (Phnom Penh) on 26 June 1958.

1960 (Sept)–**65**. *Stamps of India.* W 374.

(a) Optd as Type N 2 for use in Laos

N38	361	2 n.p. light brown (15.1.62)	15	2·50
N39		3 n.p. deep brown (1.8.63)	10	20
N40		5 n.p. bright green (1.8.63)	10	15
N41		50 n.p. orange (1965)	3·75	4·00
N42		75 n.p. reddish purple (1965)	3·75	4·25

(b) Optd as Type N 3, for use in Vietnam

N43	361	1 n.p. blue-green	10	20
N44		2 n.p. light brown (15.1.62)	15	2·50
N45		3 n.p. deep brown (1.8.63)	10	20
N46		5 n.p. bright green (1.8.63)	10	15
N47		50 n.p. orange (1965)	3·75	4·00
N48		75 n.p. reddish purple (1965)	3·75	4·25
N38/48		Set of 11	14·00	20·00

F.P.O. 744 (Vientiane) re-opened on 22 May 1961.
Examples of the 2 n.p. value overprinted as Type N 1 for use in Cambodia exist, but were never placed on sale there as the Phnom Penh F.P.O. 745 was closed on 26 June 1958. Used examples appear to originate from unauthorised use of the F.P.O. 745 postmark which was in store at Saigon (*Price* 15p, *unused*).

आई सी सी

ICC   ICC
(N 4)   (N 5)

1965 (15 Jan). *No. 492 of India optd with Type N 4, for use in Laos and Vietnam.*

N49	449	15 p. slate (C.)	60	3·25

F.P.O. 743 (Hanoi) was closed on 13 July 1966.

1968 (2 Oct). *Nos. 504/5, 506, 509/10, 515 and 517/18 etc of India optd as Type N 5, in red, for use in Laos and Vietnam.*

N50	2 p. red-brown	10	2·50
N51	3 p. brown-olive	10	2·50
N52	5 p. cerise	10	75
N53	10 p. new blue	1·75	1·75
N54	15 p. bronze-green	60	1·75
N55	60 p. deep grey	35	1·25
N56	1 r. red-brown and plum	50	1·75
N57	2 r. new blue and deep slate-violet	1·25	8·00
N50/7	Set of 8	4·00	18·00

INDIAN NATIONAL ARMY

The following are stated to have been used in the Japanese occupied areas of India during the drive on Imphal. Issued by the Indian National Army.
Genuine examples are inscribed "PROVISIONAL GOVERNMENT OF FREE INDIA". Forgeries also exist inscribed "PROVISIONAL GOVT. OF FREE INDIA".

Typo in Rangoon. No gum. Perf 11½ or imperf. 1 p. violet, 1 p. maroon, 1 a. green
Price from £50 each unused

JAPANESE OCCUPATION OF THE ANDAMAN AND NICOBAR ISLANDS

The Andaman Islands in the Bay of Bengal were occupied on the 23 March 1942 and the Nicobar Islands in July 1942. Civil administration was resumed in October 1945.
The following Indian stamps were surcharged with large figures preceded by a decimal point:—
Postage stamps—.3 on ½ a. (No. 248), .5 on 1 a. (No. 250), .10 on 2 a. (No. 236b), .30 on 6 a. (No. 274).
Official stamps—.10 on 1 a. 3 p. (No. O146a), .20 on 3 p. (No. O143), .20 in red on 3 p. (No. O143).
Prices from £400 each unused

INDIAN CONVENTION STATES

The following issues resulted from a series of postal conventions agreed between the Imperial Government and the state administrations of Patiala (1 October 1884), Gwalior, Jind and Nabha (1 July 1885), and Chamba and Faridkot (1 January 1887).

Under the terms of these conventions the British Indian Post Office supplied overprinted British India issues to the state administrations which, in turn, had to conform to a number of conditions covering the issue of stamps, rates of postage and the exchange of mail.

Such overprinted issues were valid for postage within the state of issue, to other "Convention States" and to destinations in British India.

Stamps of Chamba, Gwalior, Jind, Nabha and Patiala ceased to be valid for postage on 1 January 1951, when they were replaced by those of the Republic of India, valid from 1 April 1950.

RULERS OF INDIAN CONVENTION AND FEUDATORY STATES. Details of the rulers of the various states during the period when stamps were issued are now provided in a somewhat simplified form which omits reference to minor titles. Dates quoted are of the various reigns, extended to 1971 when the titles of the surviving rulers of the former princely states were abolished by the Indian Government.

During the absorption of the Convention and Feudatory States there was often an interim period during which the administration was handed over. In some instances it is only possible to quote the end of this interim period as the point of transfer.

Stamps of India overprinted

In the Queen Victoria issues we omit varieties due to broken type, including the numerous small "A" varieties which may have come about through damaged type. We do, however, list the small "G", small "R" and tall "R" in "GWALIOR" as these were definitely the result of the use of type of the wrong size.

Variations in the length of the words due to unequal spacing when setting are also omitted.

CHAMBA

PRICES FOR STAMPS ON COVER

Nos. 1/27	from × 20
Nos. 28/120	from × 12
Nos. O1/86	from × 25

Raja Sham Singh, 1873–1904

CHAMBA STATE (1)   **CHAMBA** (2)

1887 (1 Jan)–95. Queen Victoria. Optd with T 1.

No.	Type	Description	Un	Used
1	23	½ a. blue-green	10	40
		a. "CHMABA"	£300	£375
		b. "8TATE"	£600	
		c. Opt double	£600	
2	25	1 a. brown-purple	70	1·00
		a. "CHMABA"	£450	£500
		b. "8TATE"	£950	
3		1 a. plum	1·40	1·00
4	26	1 a. 6 p. sepia (1895)	80	8·50
5	27	2 a. dull blue	1·10	1·25
		b. "CHMABA"	£1800	£1900
		c. "8TATE"	£1800	
6		2 a. ultramarine	1·00	1·25
7	36	2 a. 6 p. green (1895)	26·00	65·00
8	28	3 a. orange (1887)	5·00	15·00
9		3 a. brown-orange (1891)	75	3·25
		a. "CHMABA"	£4250	£4250
		b. Opt inverted		
10	29	4 a. olive-green	3·00	5·50
		a. "CHMABA"	£1300	£1500
		b. "8TATE"	£2500	
11		4 a. slate-green	3·25	4·50
		a. Opt double, one albino	50·00	
12	21	6 a. olive-bistre (1890)	2·25	11·00
		a. Opt treble, two albino	75·00	
13		6 a. bistre-brown	8·50	11·00
14	31	8 a. dull mauve (1887)	5·00	7·00
		a. "CHMABA"	£3750	£3750
15		8 a. magenta (1895)	4·25	11·00
16	32	12 a. purple/red (1890)	4·00	8·50
		a. "CHMABA"	£5500	
		b. First "T" in "STATE" inverted	£5500	
		c. Opt double, one albino	30·00	
17	33	1 r. slate (1887)	28·00	90·00
		a. "CHMABA"	£8000	
18	37	1 r. green and carmine (1895)	4·75	9·50
		a. Opt double, one albino	42·00	
19	38	2 r. carmine and yellow-brown (1895)	70·00	£200
20		3 r. brown and green (1895)	70·00	£180
21		5 r. ultramarine and violet (1895)	80·00	£325
		a. Opt double, one albino	£150	
1/21		*Set of 15*	£250	£800

1900–4. Colours changed.

No.	Type	Description	Un	Used
22	40	3 p. carmine	10	35
		a. Opt double, one albino	30·00	
23		3 p. grey (1904)	15	1·60
		a. Opt inverted	75·00	
24	23	½ a. pale yellow-green (1902)	90	1·75
25		½ a. yellow-green (1903)	15	60
26	25	1 a. carmine (1902)	10	30
27	27	2 a. pale violet (1903)	5·50	20·00
22/7		*Set of 5*	5·50	20·00

Raja Bhuri Singh, 1904–1919

1903–5. King Edward VII. Optd with T 1.

No.	Type	Description	Un	Used
28	41	3 p. pale grey	10	85
29		3 p. slate-grey (1905)	10	85
30	42	½ a. green	10	20
31	43	1 a. carmine	55	25
32	44	2 a. pale violet (1904)	75	1·90
33		2 a. mauve	70	1·75
34	46	3 a. orange-brown (1905)	2·10	3·25
		a. Opt double, one albino	30·00	
35	47	4 a. olive (1904)	2·75	11·00
36	48	6 a. olive-bistre (1905)	2·50	14·00
		a. Opt double, one albino	30·00	
37	49	8 a. purple (shades) (1904)	3·00	13·00
38		8 a. claret	6·00	18·00
39	50	12 a. purple/red (1905)	3·75	17·00
		a. Opt double, one albino	30·00	
40	51	1 r. green and carmine (1904)	4·50	16·00
		a. Opt double, one albino	40·00	
28/40		*Set of 10*	18·00	70·00

1907. Nos. 149/50 of India optd with T 1.

No.	Type	Description	Un	Used
41	53	½ a. green	30	2·50
		a. Opt double, one albino	30·00	
42	54	1 a. carmine	45	2·50

1913. King George V optd with T 1.

No.	Type	Description	Un	Used
43	55	3 p. slate-grey	10	45
44	56	½ a. green	25	50
		w. Wmk inverted		
45	57	1 a. rose-carmine	3·50	5·00
46		1 a. aniline carmine	40	1·75
		a. Opt double, one albino	30·00	
47	59	2 a. mauve	1·50	6·00
48	62	3 a. orange-brown	1·75	4·50
49	63	4 a. olive	1·25	3·00
50	64	6 a. olive-bistre	1·25	3·00
51	65	8 a. purple	2·25	7·50
52	66	12 a. dull claret	1·90	10·00
53	67	1 r. brown and green	10·00	18·00
		a. Opt double, one albino	30·00	
43/53		*Set of 10*	18·00	50·00

Raja Ram Singh, 1919–1935

1921. No. 192 of India optd with T 2.

No.	Type	Description	Un	Used
54	57	9 p. on 1 a. rose-carmine	90	15·00

1923–27. Optd with T 1. New values, etc.

No.	Type	Description	Un	Used
55	57	1 a. chocolate	1·00	2·75
56	58	1½ a. chocolate (Type A)	18·00	80·00
57		1½ a. chocolate (Type B) (1924)	70	3·75
58		1½ a. rose-carmine (Type B) (1927)	60	13·00
59	61	2 a. 6 p. ultramarine	50	3·00
60		2 a. 6 p. orange (1927)	1·00	11·00
61	62	3 a. ultramarine (1924)	1·90	14·00
55/61		*Set of 7*	21·00	£110

Nos. 58 and 60 with inverted overprint are of clandestine origin.

CHAMBA STATE (3)   **CHAMBA STATE** (4)

1927–37. King George V (Nasik printing, wmk Mult Star). Optd at Nasik with T 3 or 4 (1 r.).

No.	Type	Description	Un	Used
62	55	3 p. slate (1928)	10	75
		w. Wmk inverted	2·50	
63	56	½ a. green (1928)	20	1·10
		w. Wmk inverted	70	
64	80	9 p. deep green (1932)	1·50	8·50
65	57	1 a. chocolate	1·40	30
		w. Wmk inverted	2·50	40
66	82	1 a. 3 p. mauve (1932)	85	3·75
		w. Wmk inverted	2·50	3·75
67	58	1½ a. rose-carmine (B) (1932)	3·50	3·50
		w. Wmk inverted	3·50	3·50
68	70	2 a. purple (1928)	90	1·25
69	61	2 a. 6 p. orange (1932)	1·00	12·00
		w. Wmk inverted	1·10	12·00
70	62	3 a. bright blue (1928)	80	12·00
71	71	4 a. sage-green (1928)	60	3·00
72	64	6 a. bistre (wmk inverted) (1937)	25·00	£120
73	65	8 a. reddish purple (1928)	1·00	7·00
		w. Wmk inverted	1·25	7·00
74	66	12 a. claret (1928)	1·10	8·00
75	67	1 r. chocolate and green (1928)	3·75	17·00
		w. Wmk inverted	7·00	17·00
62/75		*Set of 14*	38·00	£180

The 9 p. exists printed by lithography or typography.

Raja Lakshman Singh, 1935–1971

1935–36. New types and colours. Optd with T 3.

No.	Type	Description	Un	Used
76	79	½ a. green	70	6·00
77	81	1 a. chocolate	80	50
78	59	2 a. vermilion (No. 236b)	50	17·00
79		2 a. vermilion (small die, No. 236c)	90·00	£100
80	62	3 a. carmine	1·50	7·00
81	63	4 a. sage-green (1936)	1·50	9·50
76/81		*Set of 6*	90·00	£130

CHAMBA STATE (5)   **CHAMBA** (6)   **CHAMBA** (7)

1938. King George VI. Nos. 247/64 optd with T 3 (3 p. to 1 a.), T 5 (2 a. to 12 a.) or T 4 (rupee values).

No.	Type	Description	Un	Used
82	91	3 p. slate	3·50	8·00
83		1 a. red-brown	90	4·50
84		9 p. green	4·50	21·00
85		1 a. carmine	90	1·40
86	92	2 a. vermilion	3·00	7·00
87	—	2 a. 6 p. bright violet	3·50	15·00
88	—	3 a. yellow-green	4·50	16·00
89	—	3 a. 6 p. bright blue	4·50	8·00
90	—	4 a. brown	14·00	12·00
91	—	6 a. turquoise-green	13·00	38·00
92	—	8 a. slate-violet	14·00	32·00
93	—	12 a. lake	9·00	38·00
94	93	1 r. grey and red-brown	29·00	45·00
95		2 r. purple and brown	42·00	£190
96		5 r. green and blue	70·00	£300
97		10 r. purple and claret	£120	£450
98		15 r. brown and green	£200	£650
99		25 r. slate-violet and purple	£225	£700
82/99		*Set of 18*	£650	£2250

1942–47. Optd with T 6 (to 12 a.), "CHAMBA" only, as in T 5 (14 a.) or T 7 (rupee values). (a) Stamps of 1937. W 69 (inverted on 15 r.).

No.	Type	Description	Un	Used
100	91	½ a. red-brown	25·00	16·00
101		1 a. carmine	28·00	17·00
102	93	1 r. grey and red-brown	21·00	45·00
103		2 r. purple and brown	28·00	£170
104		5 r. green and blue	60·00	£180
105		10 r. purple and claret	85·00	£350
106		15 r. brown and green	£180	£550
107		25 r. slate-violet and purple	£200	£550
100/107		*Set of 8*	£550	£1700

(b) Stamps of 1940–43.

No.	Type	Description	Un	Used
108	100a	3 p. slate	60	3·50
109		½ a. purple (1943)	70	2·50
110		9 p. green	80	9·00
111		1 a. carmine (1943)	90	2·25
112	101	1½ a. dull violet (1943)	90	6·00
113		2 a. vermilion (1943)	2·50	6·50
114		3 a. bright violet	7·50	18·00
115		3½ a. bright blue	4·00	24·00
116	102	4 a. brown	5·50	7·50
117		6 a. turquoise-green	15·00	35·00
118		8 a. slate-violet	14·00	40·00
119		12 a. lake	27·00	50·00
120	103	14 a. purple (1947)	7·00	3·00
108/120		*Set of 13*	75·00	£190

The 3 a. exists printed by lithography or typography.

OFFICIAL STAMPS

SERVICE

CHAMBA STATE (O 1)

1887 (1 Jan)–98. Queen Victoria. Optd with Type O 1.

No.	Type	Description	Un	Used
O 1	23	½ a. blue-green	10	10
		a. "CHMABA"	£180	£180
		b. "SERV CE"		
		c. "8TATE"	£600	
		d. Thin seriffed "I" in "SERVICE"	£100	
O 2	25	1 a. brown-purple	85	60
		a. "CHMABA"	£350	£350
		b. "SERV CE"	£1900	
		c. "8TATE"	£1200	
		d. "SERVICE" double	£1000	£1000
		e. "SERVICE" double, one albino	40·00	
O 3		1 a. plum	70	10
		a. Thin seriffed "I" in "SERVICE"	£120	
O 4	27	2 a. dull blue	1·10	90
		a. "CHMABA"	£950	£1200
O 5		2 a. ultramarine (1887)	90	1·25
		a. Thin seriffed "I" in "SERVICE"	£180	
O 6	28	3 a. orange (1890)		
O 7		3 a. brown-orange (1891)	1·75	8·50
		a. "CHMABA"	£2250	£2500
		b. Thin seriffed "I" in "SERVICE"		
		c. Opt double, one albino		
O 8	29	4 a. olive-green	1·50	3·25
		a. "CHMABA"	£950	£1200
		b. "SERV CE"	£2500	
		c. "8TATE"	£2500	
O 9		4 a. slate-green	1·25	5·00
		a. Thin seriffed "I" in "SERVICE"		
O10	21	6 a. olive-bistre (1890)	3·75	8·00
		a. "SERVICE" double, one albino	40·00	
O11		6 a. bistre-brown		
O12	31	8 a. dull mauve (1887)	2·75	4·25
		a. "CHMABA"	£4250	£4250
O13		8 a. magenta (1895)	1·00	1·75
		a. Thin seriffed "I" in "SERVICE"	£400	
O14	32	12 a. purple/red (1890)	7·50	29·00
		a. "CHMABA"	£4750	
		b. First "T" in "STATE" inverted	£5000	
		c. Thin seriffed "I" in "SERVICE"		
		d. "SERVICE" double, one albino	40·00	
		e. "CHAMBA STATE" double, one albino		
O15	33	1 r. slate (1890)	13·00	85·00
		a. "CHMABA"	£4250	
O16	37	1 r. green and carmine (1898)	6·00	24·00
		a. Thin seriffed "I" in "SERVICE"		
O1/16		*Set of 10*	32·00	£140

Printings up to and including that of December 1895 had the "SERVICE" overprint applied to sheets of stamps already overprinted with Type 1. From the printing of September 1898 onwards both "SERVICE" and "CHAMBA STATE" were overprinted at the same time. Nos. O6, O8 and O12 only exist using the first method, and No. O16 was only printed using the second.

The thin seriffed "I" in "SERVICE" variety occured on R. 19/12 of the September 1898 printing only.

1902–4. Colours changed. Optd as Type O 1.

No.	Type	Description	Un	Used
O17	40	3 p. grey (1904)	15	45
O18	23	½ a. pale yellow-green	20	2·75
O19		½ a. yellow-green	2·25	1·50
O20	25	1 a. carmine	40	40
O21	27	2 a. pale violet (1903)	8·50	22·00
O17/21		*Set of 4*	8·50	22·00

1903–5. King Edward VII. Stamps of India optd as Type O 1.

No.	Type	Description	Un	Used
O22	41	3 p. pale grey	15	15
		a. Opt double, one albino	25·00	
O23		3 p. slate-grey (1905)	10	65
O24	42	½ a. yellow-green	15	10
O25	43	1 a. carmine	45	25

O26	44	2 a. pale violet (1904)	..	..	2·25	75
O27		2 a. mauve		..	70	50
O28	47	4 a. olive (1905)	..	..	3·00	12·00
O29	49	8 a. purple (1905)	..	..	3·50	12·00
O30		8 a. claret	..	..	6·00	17·00
		a. Opt double, one albino	..	..	30·00	
O31	51	1 r. green and carmine (1905)	..	..	1·50	7·00
O22/31				Set of 7	8·50	29·00

The 2 a. mauve King Edward VII, overprinted "On H.M.S.", was discovered in Calcutta, but was not sent to Chamba, and is an unissued variety (Price un. £35).

1907. *Nos. 149/50 of India, optd with Type O 1.*

O32	53	½ a. green	..	..	25	75
		a. Opt inverted	..	..	£4000	£4000
		b. Opt double, one albino	..	..	25·00	
O33	54	1 a. carmine	..	..	1·60	1·10

The inverted overprint, No. O32a, was due to an inverted cliché on R. 20/1 which was corrected after a few sheets had been printed.

1913–14. *King George V Official stamps (wmk Single Star) optd with T 1.*

O34	55	3 p. slate-grey	..	..	25	65
O35		3 p. grey	..	..	20	40
O36	56	½ a. yellow-green	..	..	10	10
O37		½ a. pale blue-green	..	..	1·00	30
O38	57	1 a. aniline carmine	..	..	10	10
O39		1 a. rose-carmine	..	..	3·75	40
O40	59	2 a. mauve (1914)	..	..	1·10	9·50
O41	63	4 a. olive	..	..	1·10	11·00
O42	65	8 a. purple	..	..	1·75	12·00
O43	67	1 r. brown and green (1914)	..	..	3·75	20·00
		a. Opt double, one albino	..	..	27·00	
O34/43				Set of 7	7·25	48·00

No. O36 with inverted overprint and No. O39 with double or inverted overprint (on gummed side) are of clandestine origin.

1914. *King George V. Optd with Type O 1.*

O44	59	2 a. mauve	..	..	11·00	
O45	63	4 a. olive	..	..	10·00	

1921. *No. O97 of India optd with T 2 at top.*

O46	57	9 p. on 1 a. rose-carmine	..	..	15	4·75

1925. *As 1913–14. New colour.*

O47	57	1 a. chocolate	..	..	1·75	50

CHAMBA STATE SERVICE (O 2)

CHAMBA STATE SERVICE (O 3)

1927–39. *King George V (Nasik printing, wmk Mult Star), optd at Nasik with Type O 2 or O 3 (rupee values).*

O48	55	3 p. slate (1928)	..	..	45	30
		w. Wmk inverted		..		60
O49	56	½ a. green (1928)	..	..	35	15
O50	80	9 p. deep green (1932)	..	..	1·50	6·50
O51	57	1 a. chocolate	..	..	20	10
		w. Wmk inverted		..	—	30
O52	82	1 a. 3 p. mauve (1932)	..	..	4·75	50
		w. Wmk inverted		..		
O53	70	2 a. purple (1928)	..	..	90	55
O54	71	4 a. sage-green (1928)	..	..	90	1·00
O55	65	8 a. reddish purple (1930)	..	..	3·25	6·50
		w. Wmk inverted		..	4·50	
O56	66	12 a. claret (1928)	..	..	1·75	16·00
		w. Wmk inverted		..	7·00	
O57	67	1 r. chocolate and green (1930)	..	..	10·00	28·00
O58		2 r. carmine and orange (1939)	..	..	19·00	£170
O59		5 r. ultramarine and purple (1939)	..	..	40·00	£225
O60		10 r. green and scarlet (1939)	..	..	55·00	£225
O48/60				Set of 13	£120	£600

1935–39. *New types and colours. Optd with Type O 2.*

O61	79	½ a. green	..	..	1·50	40
O62	81	1 a. chocolate	..	..	2·00	45
O63	59	2 a. vermilion	..	..	3·00	90
O64		2 a. vermilion (*small die*) (1939)	..	..	2·00	11·00
O65	63	4 a. sage-green (1936)	..	..	3·50	3·00
O61/5..				Set of 5	10·50	14·00

1938–40. *King George VI. Optd with Type O 2 or O 3 (rupee values).*

O66	91	9 p. green	..	..	8·00	35·00
O67		1 a. carmine	..	..	6·50	1·50
O68	93	1 r. grey and red-brown (1940?)	..	..	£500	£750
O69		2 r. purple and brown (1939)	..	..	50·00	£250
O70		5 r. green and blue (1939)	..	..	80·00	£325
O71		10 r. purple and claret (1939)	..	..	£120	£550
O66/71				Set of 6	£700	£1700

CHAMBA SERVICE (O 4)

1940–43. *(a) Official stamps optd with T 6.*

O72	O 20	3 p. slate	..	..	60	60
O73		½ a. red-brown	..	..	12·00	1·40
O74		½ a. purple (1943)	..	..	60	1·60
O75		9 p. green	..	..	3·50	5·50
		w. Wmk inverted		..	12·00	9·00
O76		1 a. carmine (1941)	..	..	60	1·25
O77		1 a. 3 p. yellow-brown (1941)	..	..	40·00	14·00
O78		1½ a. dull violet (1943)	..	..	3·75	4·75
O79		2 a. vermilion	..	..	3·50	4·00
O80		2½ a. bright violet (1941)	..	..	1·75	16·00
O81		4 a. brown	..	..	3·50	7·00
O82		8 a. slate-violet	..	..	10·00	40·00
		w. Wmk inverted		..	9·50	40·00

(b) Postage stamps optd with Type O 4.

O83	93	1 r. grey and red-brown (1942)	..	..	32·00	£140
O84		2 r. purple and brown (1942)	..	..	50·00	£200
O85		5 r. green and blue (1942)	..	..	80·00	£300
O86		10 r. purple and claret (1942)	..	..	£120	£500
O72/86				Set of 15	£325	£1100

Chamba became part of Himachal Pradesh on 15 April 1948.

FARIDKOT

For earlier issues, see under INDIAN FEUDATORY STATES

PRICES FOR STAMPS ON COVER

Nos. 1/17	*from* × 30
Nos. O1/15	*from* × 40

Raja Bikram Singh, 1874–1898

FARIDKOT STATE (1)

1887 (1 Jan)–1900. *Queen Victoria. Optd with T 1.*

1	23	½ a. deep green	..	..	90	90
		a. "ARIDKOT"				
		b. "FAR DKOT"			—	£1100
		c. Opt double, one albino	..		35·00	
2	25	1 a. brown-purple	..	..	1·00	2·00
3		1 a. plum	..	..	1·10	1·25
4	27	2 a. blue	..	..	2·75	3·50
5		2 a. deep blue	..	..	2·75	4·50
6	28	3 a. orange	..	..	4·50	7·50
7		3 a. brown-orange (1893)	..	..	1·50	2·75
8	29	4 a. olive-green	..	..	5·00	13·00
		a. "ARIDKOT"			£1100	
9		4 a. slate-green	..	..	5·00	15·00
10	21	6 a. olive-bistre	..	..	20·00	38·00
		a. "ARIDKOT"			£1600	
		b. Opt double, one albino	..		35·00	
11		6 a. bistre-brown	..	..	1·75	10·00
12	31	8 a. dull mauve	..	..	8·50	27·00
		a. "ARIDKOT"			£2250	
13		8 a. magenta	..	..	12·00	80·00
		a. Opt double, one albino	..		30·00	
14	32	12 a. purple/*red* (1900)	..	..	30·00	£325
15	33	1 r. slate	..	..	30·00	£300
		a. "ARIDKOT"			£2250	
16	37	1 r. green and carmine (1893)	..	..	30·00	70·00
		a. Opt double, one albino	..		50·00	
1/16				Set of 10	£100	£650

The ½ a., 1 a., 2 a., 3 a., 4 a., 8 a. and 1 r. (No. 16) are known with broken "O" (looking like a "C") in "FARIDKOT".

Raja Balbir Singh, 1898–1906

1900. *Optd with T 1.*

17	40	3 p. carmine	..	..	75	32·00

OFFICIAL STAMPS

SERVICE

FARIDKOT STATE (O 1)

1887 (1 Jan)–98. *Queen Victoria. Optd with Type O 1.*

O 1	23	½ a. deep green	..	..	15	60
		a. "SERV CE"			£1500	
		b. "FAR DKOT"				
		c. Thin seriffed "I" in "SERVICE"	£140			
		d. "FARIDKOT STATE" double, one albino	..		30·00	
O 2	25	1 a. brown-purple	..	..	55	1·10
		a. Thin seriffed "I" in "SERVICE"	£150			
		b. Opt double, one albino	..		40·00	
O 3		1 a. plum	..	..	75	1·00
		a. "SERV CE"			£1900	
O 4	27	2 a. dull blue	..	..	1·50	6·50
		a. "SERV CE"			£1900	
O 5		2 a. deep blue	..	..	90	9·00
O 6	28	3 a. orange	..	..	4·25	6·00
		a. "SERVICE" double, one albino	..			
O 7		3 a. brown-orange (12.98)	..	..	1·10	25·00
		a. Thin seriffed "I" in "SERVICE"	£375			
O 8	29	4 a. olive-green	..	..	3·00	15·00
		a. "SERV CE"			£1900	
		b. "ARIDKOT"				
		c. "SERVICE" treble, two albino	..		60·00	
O 9		4 a. slate-green	..	..	8·00	28·00
		a. "SERVICE" double, one albino	..		30·00	
O10	21	6 a. olive-bistre	..	..	25·00	65·00
		a. "ARIDKOT"			£1200	
		b. "SERVIC"			£1800	
		c. "SERVICE" double, one albino	..		40·00	
		d. "FARIDKOT STATE" double, one albino	..		40·00	
O11		6 a. bistre-brown	..	..	15·00	18·00
O12	31	8 a. dull mauve	..	..	4·75	18·00
		a. "SERV CE"			£2000	
O13		8 a. magenta	..	..	11·00	80·00
O14	33	1 r. slate	..	..	40·00	£140
		a. "SERVICE" double, one albino	..		60·00	
O15	37	1 r. green and carmine (12.98)	..	..	75·00	£400
		a. Thin seriffed "I" in "SERVICE"				
O1/15				Set of 9	£130	£550

The ½ a., 1 a., 2 a., 3 a., 4 a., 8 a. and 1 r. (No. O15) are known with the broken "O".

Printings up to and including that of November 1895 had the "SERVICE" overprint applied to sheets already overprinted with Type 1. From December 1898 onwards "SERVICE" and "FARIDKOT STATE" were overprinted at one operation to provide fresh supplies of Nos. O1/3, O7 and O15.

The thin seriffed "I" variety occurs on the December 1898 overprinting only.

This State ceased to use overprinted stamps after 31 March 1901.

GWALIOR

PRICES FOR STAMPS ON COVER

Nos. 1/3	*from* × 10
Nos. 4/11	—
Nos. 12/66	*from* × 5
Nos. 67/128	*from* × 4
Nos. 129/37	*from* × 5
Nos. O1/94	*from* × 12

OVERPRINTS. From 1885 to 1926 these were applied by the Government of India Central Printing Press, Calcutta, and from 1927 at the Security Press, Nasik, *unless otherwise stated*.

Maharaja Jayaji Rao Sindhia, 1843–1886

गवालियर

GWALIOR (1)

GWALIOR गवालियर (2)

GWALIOR
Small "G"

GWALIOR
Small "R"

GWALIOR
Tall "R"
(original state)

GWALIOR
Tall "R"
(damaged state)

OVERPRINT VARIETIES OF TYPE 2.

Small "G"—Occurs on R.7/11 from June 1900 printing of ½, 1, 2, 3, 4 a. and 3 p. (No. 38), and on an unknown position from May 1901 printing of 2, 3 and 5 r.

Small "R"—Occurs on R. 9/3 from June 1900 printing of 3 p. to 4 a. and on R.2/3 from May 1901 printing of 2, 3 and 5 r.

Tall "R" —Occurs on R.20/2 from printings between June 1900 and May 1907. The top of the letter is damaged on printings from February 1903 onwards.

1885 (1 July)–97. *Queen Victoria. I. Optd with T 1.*

(a) Space between two lines of overprint 13 mm. Hindi inscription 13 to 14 mm long (May 1885)

1	23	½ a. blue-green	..	..	90·00	18·00
2	25	1 a. brown-purple	..	..	65·00	24·00
3	27	2 a. dull blue	..	..	55·00	12·00
1/3				Set of 3	£190	48·00

A variety exists of the ½ a. in which the space between the two lines of overprint is only 9½ mm but this is probably from a proof sheet.

(b) Space between two lines of overprint 15 mm on 4 a. and 6 a. and 16 to 17 mm on other values (June 1885). Hindi inscription 13 to 14 mm long

4	23	½ a. blue-green	..	..	40·00	
		a. Opt double, one albino	..		55·00	
		b. Hindi inscr 15 to 15½ mm long	..		90·00	
		ba. Opt double, one albino	..		£130	
		c. Pair. Nos. 4/4b	..	..	£450	
5	25	1 a. brown-purple	..	..	45·00	
		a. Opt double, one albino	..		50·00	
		b. Hindi inscr 15 to 15½ mm long	..		90·00	
		ba. Opt double, one albino	..		£100	
		c. Pair. Nos. 5/5b	..	..	£450	
6	26	1 a. 6 p. sepia	..	..	55·00	
		b. Hindi inscr 15 to 15½ mm long	..		£150	
		c. Pair. Nos. 6/6b	..	..	£500	
7	27	2 a. dull blue	..	..	45·00	
		b. Hindi inscr 15 to 15½ mm long	..		£100	
		c. Pair. Nos. 7/7b	..	..	£325	
8	17	4 a. green	..	..	65·00	
		b. Hindi inscr 15 to 15½ mm long	..		£140	
		c. Pair. Nos. 8/8b	..	..	£550	
9	21	6 a. olive-bistre	..	..	65·00	
		a. Opt double, one albino	..		75·00	
		b. Hindi inscr 15 to 15½ mm long	..		£150	
		ba. Opt double, one albino	..		£170	
		c. Pair. Nos. 9/9b	..	..	£550	
10	31	8 a. dull mauve	..	..	55·00	
		b. Hindi inscr 15 to 15½ mm long	..		£140	
		c. Pair. Nos. 10/10b	..	..	£550	
11	33	1 r. slate	..	..	55·00	
		b. Hindi inscr 15 to 15½ mm long	..		£150	
		c. Pair. Nos. 11/11b	..	..	£550	
4/11				Set of 8	£375	
4b/11b				Set of 8	£900	

The two types of overprint on these stamps occur in the same settings, with about a quarter of the stamps in each sheet showing the long inscription. Nos. 4/7 and 10/11 were overprinted in sheets of 240 and Nos. 8/9 in half-sheets of 160.

II. *Optd with T 2. Hindi inscription 13 to 14 mm long*

(a) In red (Sept 1885)

12	23	½ a. blue-green	..	..	30	20
		b. Hindi inscr 15 to 15½ mm long	..		55	55
		c. Pair. Nos. 12/12b	..	..	8·50	11·00
13	27	2 a. dull blue	..	..	9·50	10·00
		b. Hindi inscr 15 to 15½ mm long	..		24·00	26·00
		c. Pair. Nos. 13/13b	..	..	£275	£300
14	17	4 a. green	..	..	17·00	9·00
		b. Hindi inscr 15 to 15½ mm long	..		£150	80·00
		c. Pair. Nos. 14/14b	..	..	£450	

15	33	1 r. slate		7·50	17·00
		aw. Wmk inverted		15·00	26·00
		b. Hindi inscr 15 to 15½ mm long		26·00	60·00
		bw. Wmk inverted		40·00	80·00
		c. Pair. Nos. 15/15b		50·00	90·00
		cw. Wmk inverted		70·00	
12/15			Set of 4	30·00	32·00
12b/15b			Set of 4	£180	£150

No. 14 was overprinted in half-sheets of 160, about 40 stamps having the Hindi inscription 15 to 15½ mm long. The remaining three values were from a setting of 240 containing 166 13 to 14 mm long and 74 15 to 15½ mm long.

Reprints have been made of Nos. 12 to 15, but the majority of the specimens have the word "REPRINT" overprinted upon them.

(b) In black (1885–97)

16	23	½ a. blue-green (1889)		90	1·25
		a. Opt double			
		b. Opt double, one albino		20·00	
		c. Hindi inscr 15 to 15½ mm long		20	10
		ca. Opt double			
		cb. Opt double, one albino		60·00	
		cc. "GWALICR"		85·00	£100
		cd. Small "G"		60·00	48·00
		ce. Small "R"		65·00	
		cf. Tall "R"		65·00	65·00
		d. Pair. Nos. 16/16c		48·00	50·00
17	24	9 p. carmine (1891)		28·00	50·00
		a. Opt double, one albino		50·00	
		c. Hindi inscr 15 to 15½ mm long		48·00	65·00
		ca. Opt double, one albino		80·00	
		d. Pair. Nos. 17/17c		£190	
18	25	1 a. brown-purple		40	15
		c. Hindi inscr 15 to 15½ mm long		1·50	35
		d. Pair. Nos. 18/18c		11·00	12·00
19		1 a. plum (Hindi inscr 15 to 15½ mm long)		1·50	90
		a. Small "G"		70·00	50·00
		b. Small "R"		80·00	
		c. Tall "R"		85·00	
20	26	1 a. 6 p. sepia		35	90
		c. Hindi inscr 15 to 15½ mm long		70	40
		d. Pair. Nos. 20/20c		11·00	14·00
21	27	2 a. dull blue		4·00	80
		c. Hindi inscr 15 to 15½ mm long		50	10
		ca. "R" omitted		£450	£450
		d. Pair. Nos. 21/21c		£100	
22		2 a. deep blue		4·75	1·60
		c. Hindi inscr 15 to 15½ mm long		1·50	30
		ca. Small "G"		£120	£120
		cb. Small "R"		£170	
		cc. Tall "R"		£180	£180
		d. Pair. Nos. 22/22c		£120	
23	36	2 a. 6 p. yellow-green (Hindi inscr 15 to 15½ mm long) (1896)		5·00	14·00
		a. "GWALICR"		£500	
24	28	3 a. orange		4·25	8·00
		a. Opt double, one albino		40·00	
		c. Hindi inscr 15 to 15½ mm long		42·00	28·00
		d. Pair. Nos. 24/24c		£180	
25		3 a. brown-orange		18·00	3·25
		c. Hindi inscr 15 to 15½ mm long		65	15
		ca. Opt double, one albino		30·00	
		cb. Small "G"		£200	£200
		cc. Small "R"		£375	
		cd. Tall "R"		£170	£170
		d. Pair. Nos. 25/25c		£160	
26	29	4 a. olive-green (1889)		3·50	80
		c. Hindi inscr 15 to 15½ mm long		7·50	2·50
		d. Pair. Nos. 26/26c		£110	
27		4 a. slate-green		4·50	1·40
		c. Hindi inscr 15 to 15½ mm long		1·75	45
		ca. Opt double, one albino		50·00	
		cb. Small "G"		£400	£250
		cc. Small "R"		£400	
		cd. Tall "R"		£275	£275
		d. Pair. Nos. 27/27c		35·00	
28	21	6 a. olive-bistre		4·75	9·00
		c. Hindi inscr 15 to 15½ mm long		2·25	9·00
		d. Pair. Nos. 28/28c		42·00	
29		6 a. bistre-brown		1·40	5·00
		c. Hindi inscr 15 to 15½ mm long		3·25	7·00
		d. Pair. Nos. 29/29c		19·00	
30	31	8 a. dull mauve		7·50	30·00
		c. Hindi inscr 15 to 15½ mm long		2·00	60
		d. Pair. Nos. 30/30c		£200	
31		8 a. magenta (Hindi inscr 15 to 15½ mm long) (1897)		5·50	6·50
32	32	12 a. purple/red (1891)		3·00	8·00
		c. Hindi inscr 15 to 15½ mm long		3·00	65
		ca. Pair, one without opt			
		cb. Tall "R"		£650	£500
		d. Pair. Nos. 32/32c		60·00	
33	33	1 r. slate (1889)		£100	£325
		c. Hindi inscr 15 to 15½ mm long		2·00	85
		d. Pair. Nos. 33/33c		£375	
34	37	1 r. green and carmine (Hindi inscr 15 to 15½ mm long) (1896)		2·50	2·75
		a. Opt double, one albino		60·00	
		b. "GWALICR"		£750	£900
35	38	2 r. carmine and yellow-brown (Hindi inscr 15 to 15½ mm long) (1896)		5·50	3·00
		a. Small "G"		£250	£180
		b. Small "R"		£250	£190
36		3 r. brown and green (Hindi inscr 15 to 15½ mm long) (1896)		7·50	3·50
		a. Small "G"		£275	£190
		b. Small "R"		£300	£200
37		5 r. ultramarine and violet (Hindi inscr 15 to 15½ mm long) (1896)		13·00	6·50
		a. Small "G"		£325	£225
		b. Small "R"		£350	£250
16/37			Set of 16	65·00	80·00

Printings to 1891 continued to use the setting showing both types, but subsequently a new setting containing the larger overprint only was used.

The ½ a., 1 a., 2 a. and 3 a. exist with space between "I" and "O" of "GWALIOR".

The "GWALICR" error occurs on R. 1/5 in the May 1896 printing only.

Maharaja Madhav Rao Sindhia, 1886–1925

1899–1911. *(a) Optd with T 2 (B).*

38	40	3 p. carmine		10	20
		a. Opt inverted		£700	£450
		b. Small "G"		50·00	55·00
		d. Small "R"		60·00	
		e. Tall "R"		42·00	
		f. Opt double, one albino		30·00	
39		3 p. grey (1904)		6·00	60·00
		e. Tall "R"		£200	
		f. Opt double, one albino		50·00	
40	23	½ a. pale yellow-green (1901)		20	1·00
		e. Tall "R"		75·00	
		f. Opt double, one albino		20·00	
40g		½ a. yellow-green (1903)		2·25	1·50
		ge. Tall "R"		£120	
41	25	1 a. carmine (1901)		50	35
		e. Tall "R"		85·00	
		f. Opt double, one albino		35·00	
42	27	2 a. pale violet (1903)		75	3·50
		e. Tall "R"		£130	
43	36	2 a. 6 p. ultramarine (1903)		90	4·00
		e. Tall "R"		£170	
38/43			Set of 6	7·50	65·00

(b) Optd as T 2, but "GWALIOR" 13 mm long. Opt spaced 2¾ mm

44	38	3 r. brown and green (1911)		£150	£160
45		5 r. ultramarine and violet (1910)		55·00	55·00
		a. Opt double, one albino		80·00	

1903–11. *King Edward VII. Optd as T 2.*

A. "GWALIOR" 14 mm long. Overprint spaced 1¾ mm (1903–06).

46A	41	3 p. pale grey		50	20
		e. Tall "R"		28·00	30·00
		f. Slate-grey (1905)		70	30
		fe. Tall "R"		35·00	38·00
48A	42	½ a. green		10	10
		e. Tall "R"		26·00	30·00
49A	43	1 a. carmine		10	10
		e. Tall "R"		30·00	35·00
		f. Opt double, one albino		30·00	
50A	44	2 a. pale violet (1904)		60	60
		e. Tall "R"		75·00	
		f. Mauve		1·25	20
		fe. Tall "R"		85·00	85·00
52A	45	2 a. 6 p. ultramarine (1904)		15·00	60·00
		e. Tall "R"		£700	
53A	46	3 a. orange-brown (1904)		1·10	30
		e. Tall "R"		£120	
54A	47	4 a. olive		1·10	40
		e. Tall "R"		£160	£130
		f. Pale olive		6·00	1·75
		fe. Tall "R"		£225	
56A	48	6 a. olive-bistre (1904)		2·50	2·75
		e. Tall "R"		£750	
57A	49	8 a. purple (shades) (1905)		2·75	1·25
		e. Tall "R"		£325	£200
59A	50	12 a. purple/red (1905)		2·50	13·00
		e. Tall "R"		£800	
60A	51	1 r. green and carmine (1905)		1·75	1·75
		e. Tall "R"		£700	£700
61A	52	2 r. carmine and yellow-brown (1906)		30·00	42·00
		a. Opt double, one albino		£120	
46A/61A			Set of 12	50·00	£110

B. "GWALIOR" 13 mm long. Overprint spaced 2¾ mm (1908–11)

46B	41	3 p. pale grey		1·25	10
		f. Slate-grey		1·60	40
49B	43	1 a. carmine		1·75	80
50/B		2 a. mauve		1·60	15
52B	45	2 a. 6 p. ultramarine		75	6·00
53B	46	3 a. orange-brown		1·90	20
54/B		4 a. pale olive		3·50	50
56B	48	6 a. olive-bistre		3·75	1·00
57B	49	8 a. purple (shades)		5·00	1·50
		f. Claret		12·00	2·25
		fa. Opt double, one albino		40·00	
59B	50	12 a. purple/red		3·50	3·25
		a. Opt double, one albino		50·00	
60B	51	1 r. green and carmine		3·00	1·00
61B	52	2 r. carmine and yellow-brown		8·50	11·00
		a. Opt double, one albino		40·00	
62B		3 r. brown and green (1910)		25·00	40·00
		a. Red-brown and green		60·00	70·00
63B		5 r. ultramarine and violet (1911)		18·00	26·00
46B/63B			Set of 13	70·00	80·00

1907–08. *Nos. 149 and 150 of India optd as T 2.*

(a) "GWALIOR" 14 mm long. Overprint spaced 1¾ mm

64	53	½ a. green		10	70
		e. Tall "R"		42·00	

(b) "GWALIOR" 13 mm long. Overprint spaced 2¾ mm (1908)

65	53	½ a. green		45	15
66	54	1 a. carmine		90	10

1912–14. *King George V. Optd as T 2.*

67	55	3 p. slate-grey		10	10
		a. Opt double		†	£750
		b. "Rs" flaw		24·00	28·00
68	56	½ a. green		20	10
		a. Opt inverted		†	£375
69	57	1 a. aniline carmine		25	10
		a. Opt double		25·00	
70	59	2 a. mauve		40	10
		w. Wmk inverted		†	60·00
71	62	3 a. orange-brown		50	15
72	63	4 a. olive (1913)		50	60
73	64	6 a. olive-bistre		80	80
74	65	8 a. purple (1913)		90	30
75	66	12 a. dull claret (1914)		1·00	2·25
76	67	1 r. brown and green (1913)		3·00	40
		a. Opt double, one albino		£600	
		b. Opt double		£600	
77		2 r. carmine-rose and brown (1913)		4·50	4·25
		a. Opt double, one albino		50·00	
78		5 r. ultramarine and violet (1913)		20·00	6·50
		a. Opt double, one albino		70·00	
67/78			Set of 12	29·00	14·00

GWALIOR
(3)

1921. *No. 192 of India optd with T 3.*

79	57	9 p. on 1 a. rose-carmine		10	40

No. 79 with inverted overprint is of clandestine origin.

1923–7. *Optd as T 2. New colours and values.*

80	57	1 a. chocolate		30	10
		a. Opt double, one albino		30·00	
81	58	1½ a. chocolate (B) (1925)		1·00	50
82		1½ a. rose-carmine (B) (1927)		15	20
83	61	2 a. 6 p. ultramarine (1925)		1·25	1·75
84		2 a. 6 p. orange (1927)		25	50
85	62	3 a. ultramarine (1924)		75	60
80/5			Set of 6	3·25	3·25

No. 82 with inverted overprint is of clandestine origin.

Maharaja George Jivaji Rao Sindhia, 1925–1961

GWALIOR	**GWALIOR**
गवालियर	**गवालियर**
(4)	(5)

1928–36. *King George V (Nasik printing, wmk Mult Star), optd at Nasik with T 4 or 5 (rupee values).*

86	55	3 p. slate (1932)		60	10
		w. Wmk inverted		1·00	1·00
87	56	½ a. green (1930)		1·25	10
		w. Wmk inverted			
88	80	9 p. deep green (1932)		1·50	20
		w. Wmk inverted		2·25	70
89	57	1 a. chocolate		50	10
		w. Wmk inverted		—	60
90	82	1 a. 3 p. mauve (1936)		30	10
91	70	2 a. purple		50	20
		w. Wmk inverted		50	20
92	62	3 a. bright blue		75	40
93	71	4 a. sage-green		85	90
		w. Wmk inverted		1·50	1·75
94	65	8 a. reddish purple (wmk inverted)		1·10	1·10
95	66	12 a. claret		1·25	2·25
96	67	1 r. chocolate and green		1·60	2·75
		w. Wmk inverted		3·00	2·75
97		2 r. carmine and orange		4·00	3·50
		w. Wmk inverted		5·00	3·50
98		5 r. ultramarine and purple (wmk inverted) (1929)		15·00	20·00
99		10 r. green and scarlet (1930)		42·00	30·00
100		15 r. blue & olive (wmk inverted) (1930)		65·00	48·00
101		25 r. orange and blue (1930)		£140	£110
86/101			Set of 16	£250	£200

The 9 p. exists printed by lithography or typography.

1935–36. *New types and colours. Optd with T 4.*

102	79	½ a. green (1936)		40	10
		w. Wmk inverted		2·50	1·75
103	81	1 a. chocolate		10	10
104	59	2 a. vermilion (1936)		60	1·60
102/4			Set of 3	1·00	1·60

1938–48. *King George VI. Nos. 247/50, 253, 255/6, and 259/64 optd with T 4 or 5 (rupee values).*

105	91	3 p. slate		4·00	10
106		½ a. red-brown		4·00	10
107		9 p. green (1939)		32·00	2·75
108		1 a. carmine		4·00	15
109		3 a. yellow-green (1939)		10·00	2·75
110	—	4 a. brown		38·00	1·75
111		6 a. turquoise-green (1939)		2·50	6·00
112	93	1 r. grey and red-brown (1942)		6·00	1·50
113		2 r. purple and brown (1948)		28·00	7·00
114		5 r. green and blue (1948)		38·00	32·00
115		10 r. purple and claret (1948)		38·00	40·00
116		15 r. brown and green (1948)		£120	£160
117		25 r. slate-violet and purple (1948)		£110	£120
105/117			Set of 13	£400	£325

1942–5. *King George VI. Optd with T 4.*

118	100a	3 p. slate		45	10
		w. Wmk inverted		—	13·00
119		½ a. purple (1943)		45	10
120		9 p. green		45	10
121		1 a. carmine (1943)		40	10
		a. Opt double		—	£120
122	101	1½ a. dull violet		3·50	20
123		2 a. vermilion		55	20
124		3 a. bright violet		6·50	30
		a. Opt double		—	£120
125	102	4 a. brown		1·25	20
126		6 a. turquoise-green (1945)		20·00	18·00
127		8 a. slate-violet (1944)		2·75	2·75
128		12 a. lake (1943)		4·50	16·00
118/28			Set of 11	35·00	32·00

The 1½ a. and 3 a. exist printed by lithography or typography.

GWALIOR
गवालियर
(6)

1949 (Apr). *King George VI. Optd with T 6 at the Alizah Printing Press, Gwalior.*

129	100a	3 p. slate		60	50
130		½ a. purple		60	50
131		1 a. carmine		75	60
132	101	2 a. vermilion		15·00	1·75
133		3 a. bright violet		38·00	21·00
134	102	4 a. brown		2·75	2·75
135		6 a. turquoise-green		35·00	45·00
136		8 a. slate-violet		80·00	45·00
137		12 a. lake		£300	£130
129/137			Set of 9	£425	£225

OFFICIAL STAMPS

गवालियर

गवालियर

सरविस	सरविस
(O 1)	(O 2)

1895–96. *Queen Victoria. Optd with Type O 1.*

O 1	23	½ a. blue-green		10	10
		a. Hindi characters transposed		24·00	28·00
		b. 4th Hindi character omitted		£375	40·00
		c. Opt double		†	£850
O 2	25	1 a. brown-purple		6·50	75
O 3		1 a. plum		65	10
		a. Hindi characters transposed		38·00	42·00
		b. 4th Hindi character omitted		—	65·00
O 4	27	2 a. dull blue		1·25	35
O 5		2 a. deep blue		1·00	35
		a. Hindi characters transposed		60·00	80·00
		b. 4th Hindi character omitted		80·00	£100
O 6	29	4 a. olive-green		1·75	75
		a. Hindi characters transposed		£450	£450
		b. 4th Hindi character omitted		£1800	£1300
O 7		4 a. slate-green		1·25	1·00
		a. Hindi characters transposed		£300	
O 8	31	8 a. dull mauve		1·75	1·50
		a. Opt double, one albino		30·00	
O 9		8 a. magenta		1·25	90
		a. Hindi characters transposed		£1200	£1200
		b. 4th Hindi character omitted			
O10	37	1 r. green and carmine (1896)		3·75	3·00
		a. Hindi characters transposed		£2500	
O1/10			Set of 6	7·25	4·50

In the errors listed above it is the last two Hindi characters that are transposed, so that the word reads "Sersiv". The error occurs on R.19/1 in the sheet from the early printings up to May 1896.

1901–04. *Colours changed.*

O23	40	3 p. carmine (1902)		30	20
O24		3 p. grey (1904)		1·00	1·75
O25	23	½ a. pale yellow-green		3·00	15
O26		½ a. yellow-green		20	10
O27	25	1 a. carmine		3·25	10
O28	27	2 a. pale violet (1903)		55	1·50
O23/8			Set of 5	4·75	3·25

1903–08. *King Edward VII. Optd as Type O 1.*

(a) Overprint spaced 10 mm (1903–5)

O29	41	3 p. pale grey		30	10
		a. Slate-grey (1905)		30	10
O31	42	½ a. green		1·75	10
O32	43	1 a. carmine		40	10
O33	44	2 a. pale violet (1905)		1·75	50
		a. Mauve		1·00	20
O35	47	4 a. olive (1905)		10·00	1·00
		a. Opt double, one albino		40·00	
O36	49	8 a. purple (1905)		3·25	70
		a. Claret		10·00	3·75
		ab. Opt double, one albino		30·00	
O38	51	1 r. green and carmine (1905)		2·75	1·40
O29/38			Set of 7	18·00	3·25

(b) Overprint spaced 8 mm (1907–8)

O39	41	3 p. pale grey		3·00	15
		a. Slate-grey		4·50	80
O41	42	½ a. green		1·60	15
O42	43	1 a. carmine		50	10
O43	44	2 a. mauve		9·50	65
O44	47	4 a. olive		2·50	85
O45	49	8 a. purple		3·25	3·75
O46	51	1 r. green and carmine (1908)		25·00	9·50
O39/46			Set of 7	42·00	13·50

1907–08. *Nos. 149 and 150 of India optd as Type O 1.*

(a) Overprint spaced 10 mm (1908)

O47	53	½ a. green		4·75	10
O48	54	1 a. carmine		4·00	15
		a. Opt double, one albino		30·00	

(b) Overprint spaced 8 mm (1907)

O49	53	½ a. green		70	15
O50	54	1 a. carmine		42·00	3·00

1913–23. *King George V. Optd with Type O 1.*

O51	55	3 p. slate-grey		20	10
		a. "Rs" flaw		48·00	
O52	56	½ a. green		20	10
		a. Opt double		95·00	£140
O53	57	1 a. rose-carmine		7·00	50
		a. Aniline carmine		20	10
		ab. Opt double		65·00	
O54		1 a. chocolate (1923)		2·50	15
O55	59	2 a. mauve		45	20
O56	63	4 a. olive		55	80
O57	65	8 a. purple		75	80
O58	67	1 r. brown and green		15·00	14·00
		a. Opt double, one albino		50·00	
O51/8			Set of 8	18·00	15·00

1921. *No. O97 of India optd with T 3.*

O59	57	9 p. on 1 a. rose-carmine		10	30

1927–35. *King George V (Nasik printing, wmk Mult Star), optd at Nasik as Type O 1 (but top line measures 13 mm instead of 14 mm) or with Type O 2 (rupee values).*

O61	55	3 p. slate		30	10
		w. Wmk inverted		10	50
O62	56	½ a. green		10	15
		w. Wmk inverted		1·75	

O63	80	9 p. deep green (1932)		10	15
O64	57	1 a. chocolate		10	10
		w. Wmk inverted		60	35
O65	82	1 a. 3 p. mauve (1933)		50	15
		w. Wmk inverted		2·50	
O66	70	2 a. purple		20	15
		w. Wmk inverted		1·75	
O67	71	4 a. sage-green		50	30
		w. Wmk inverted		—	90
O68	65	8 a. reddish purple (1928)		50	70
		w. Wmk inverted		1·75	1·75
O69	67	1 r. chocolate and green		80	1·75
		w. Wmk inverted		1·75	2·50
O70		2 r. carmine and orange (1935)		7·00	8·50
O71		5 r. ultramarine and purple (1932)		12·00	£130
		w. Wmk inverted		13·00	
O72		10 r. green and scarlet (1932)		90·00	£275
O61/72			Set of 12	£100	£375

1936–37. *New types. Optd as Type O 1 (13 mm).*

O73	79	½ a. green		15	15
		w. Wmk inverted		—	2·50
O74	81	1 a. chocolate		15	15
O75	59	2 a. vermilion		20	40
O76		2 a. vermilion (small die)		2·00	1·10
O77	63	4 a. sage-green (1937)		50	75
O73/7			Set of 5	2·50	2·25

1938. *King George VI. Optd as Type O 1 (13 mm).*

O78	91	½ a. red-brown		6·50	30
O79		1 a. carmine		1·10	20

गवालियर

(O 3)	1A———1A (O 4)

1940–42. *Official stamps optd with Type O 3.*

O80	O 20	3 p. slate		50	10
O81		½ a. red-brown		3·00	25
O82		½ a. purple (1942)		50	10
O83		9 p. green (1942)		70	50
O84		1 a. carmine		2·25	10
O85		1 a. 3 p. yellow-brown (1942)		30·00	1·60
		w. Wmk inverted		—	12·00
O86		1½ a. dull violet (1942)		1·00	30
O87		2 a. vermilion		1·00	30
O88		4 a. brown (1942)		1·25	1·60
O89		8 a. slate-violet (1942)		2·50	6·00
O80/9			Set of 10	38·00	9·75

1941. *Stamp of 1932 (King George V) optd with Type O 1 and surch with Type O 4.*

O90	82	1 a. on 1 a. 3 p. mauve		18·00	2·75
		w. Wmk inverted		21·00	4·75

1942–47. *King George VI. Optd with Type O 2.*

O91	93	1 r. grey and red-brown		8·00	13·00
O92		2 r. purple and brown		21·00	70·00
O93		5 r. green and blue (1943)		38·00	£375
O94		10 r. purple and claret (1947)		£110	£750
O91/4			Set of 4	£160	£1100

Gwalior became part of Madhya Bharat by 1 July 1948.

JIND

For earlier issues, see under INDIAN FEUDATORY STATES

PRICES FOR STAMPS ON COVER	
Nos. 1/4	from × 20
Nos. 5/16	—
Nos. 17/40	from × 15
Nos. 41/149	from × 8
Nos. O1/86	from × 15

Raja Raghubir Singh, 1864–1887

JHIND STATE	JEEND STATE	JHIND STATE
(1)	(2)	(3)

1885 (1 July). *Queen Victoria. Optd with T 1.*

1	23	½ a. blue-green		1·75	2·75
		a. Opt inverted		85·00	95·00
2	25	1 a. brown-purple		22·00	30·00
		a. Opt inverted		£650	£700
3	27	2 a. dull blue		7·50	12·00
		a. Opt inverted		£500	£550
4	31	4 a. green		45·00	60·00
		a. Opt inverted		£400	
5		8 a. dull mauve		£400	
		a. Opt inverted		£8000	
6	33	1 r. slate		£400	
		a. Opt inverted		£9000	
1/6			Set of 6	£800	

The overprint inverted errors occurred on R.10/8 in the setting of 120, although it is believed that one pane of the ½ a. had the overprint inverted on the entire pane. Examples of inverted overprints on the ½ a., 1 a. and 2 a. with the lines much less curved are thought to come from a trial printing.

All six values exist with reprinted overprint. This has the words "JHIND" and "STATE" 8 and 9 mm in length respectively, whereas in the originals the words are 9 and 9½ mm.

1885. *Optd with T 2.*

7	23	½ a. blue-green (R.)		80·00	
8	25	1 a. brown-purple		85·00	
9	27	2 a. dull blue (R.)		85·00	
10	17	4 a. green (R.)		£110	
		a. Opt double, one albino		£150	
11	31	8 a. dull mauve		£120	
12	33	1 r. slate (R.)		£130	
7/12			Set of 6	£550	

1886. *Optd with T 3, in red.*

13	23	½ a. blue-green		21·00	
		a. "JEIND" for "JHIND"		£950	
14	27	2 a. dull blue		21·00	
		a. "JEIND" for "JHIND"		£1200	
		b. Opt double, one albino		50·00	
15	17	4 a. green		38·00	
		a. Opt double, one albino		42·00	
		b. Opt treble, two albino		65·00	
16	33	1 r. slate		40·00	
		a. "JEIND" for "JHIND"		£1700	
13/16			Set of 4	£110	

1886–99. *Optd with T 3.*

17	23	½ a. blue-green		25	10
		a. Opt inverted		£200	
18	25	1 a. brown-purple		75	20
		a. "JEIND" for "JHIND"		£425	
		b. Opt double, one albino		30·00	
19		1 a. plum (1899)		2·00	1·00
20	26	1 a. 6 p. sepia (1896)		1·10	2·50
		a. Opt double, one albino		35·00	
21	27	2 a. dull blue		1·25	40
22		2 a. ultramarine		1·25	50
		a. Opt double, one albino		35·00	
23	28	3 a. brown-orange (1891)		1·25	50
24	29	4 a. olive-green		2·50	1·75
25		4 a. slate-green		2·75	2·75
26	21	6 a. olive-bistre (1891)		5·50	13·00
		a. Opt double, one albino		30·00	
27		6 a. bistre-brown		90	7·00
28	31	8 a. dull mauve		3·75	11·00
		a. "JEIND" for "JHIND"		£1500	
29		8 a. magenta (1897)		5·50	17·00
		a. Opt double, one albino		30·00	
30	32	12 a. purple/red (1896)		3·75	16·00
		a. Opt double, one albino		30·00	
31	33	1 r. slate		7·00	32·00
32	37	1 r. green and carmine (1897)		7·50	38·00
33	38	2 r. carmine and yellow-brown (1896)		£225	£650
34		3 r. brown and green (1896)		£375	£650
35		5 r. ultramarine and violet (1896)		£425	£650
17/35			Set of 14	£950	£1800

Varieties exist in which the word "JHIND" measures 10½ mm and 9¾ mm instead of 10 mm. Such varieties are to be found on Nos. 17, 18, 21, 24, 28 and 31.

Raja (Maharaja from 1911) Ranbir Singh, 1887–1959

1900–4. *Colours changed.*

36	40	3 p. carmine		80	1·00
37		3 p. grey (1904)		15	2·50
38	23	½ a. pale yellow-green (1902)		2·50	4·00
39		½ a. yellow-green (1903)		5·50	9·00
40	25	1 a. carmine (1902)		20	4·00
		a. Opt double, one albino		25·00	
36/40			Set of 4	3·25	10·50

1903–9. *King Edward VII. Optd with T 3.*

41	41	3 p. pale grey		10	10
		a. Opt double, one albino		15·00	
42		3 p. slate-grey (1905)		20	50
43	42	½ a. green		50	1·40
44	43	1 a. carmine		2·00	1·25
45	44	2 a. pale violet		2·00	2·00
46		2 a. mauve (1906)		1·50	60
		a. Opt double, one albino		25·00	
47	45	2 a. 6 p. ultramarine (1909)		30	4·75
		a. Opt double, one albino		20·00	
48	46	3 a. orange-brown		35	40
		a. Opt double		£110	£200
49	47	4 a. olive		5·50	8·00
		a. Opt double, one albino		40·00	
50		4 a. pale olive		5·00	7·00
51	48	6 a. bistre (1905)		5·00	14·00
		a. Opt double, one albino		30·00	
52	49	8 a. purple (shades)		2·25	17·00
53		8 a. claret		9·00	21·00
54	50	12 a. purple/red (1905)		1·90	11·00
55	51	1 r. green and carmine (1905)		2·50	12·00
		a. Opt double, one albino		40·00	
41/55			Set of 11	19·00	60·00

1907–9. *Nos. 149/50 of India optd with T 3.*

56	53	½ a. green		10	20
57	54	1 a. carmine (1909)		10	60

1913. *King George V. Optd with T 3.*

58	55	3 p. slate-grey		10	1·60
59	56	½ a. green		10	60
60	57	1 a. aniline carmine		10	35
61	59	2 a. mauve		15	3·75
62	63	3 a. orange-brown		1·50	8·50
63	64	6 a. olive-bistre		4·50	21·00
58/63			Set of 6	6·00	32·00

JIND STATE	JIND STATE	JIND STATE
(4)	(5)	(6)

1914–27. *King George V. Optd with T 4.*

64	55	3 p. slate-grey		40	20
65	56	½ a. green		1·50	15
66	57	1 a. aniline carmine		70	15
67	58	1½ a. chocolate (Type A) (1922)		70	3·25
68		1½ a. chocolate (Type B) (1924)		35	1·50
69	59	2 a. mauve		1·25	45
70	61	2 a. 6 p. ultramarine (1922)		35	3·75
71	62	3 a. orange-brown		50	2·25
72	63	4 a. olive		1·25	5·00
73	64	6 a. olive-bistre		1·25	9·50
74	65	8 a. purple		3·50	5·50
75	66	12 a. dull claret		1·50	9·50
76	67	1 r. brown and green		6·50	12·00
		a. Opt double, one albino		25·00	
77		2 r. carmine and yellow-brown (1927)		5·00	85·00
78		5 r. ultramarine and violet (1927)		30·00	£170
64/78			Set of 15	50·00	£275

No. 71 with inverted overprint is of clandestine origin.

1922. *No. 192 of India optd "JIND" in block capitals.*
79   57   9 p. on 1 a. rose-carmine   ..   ..   1·25   13·00

1924–27. *Optd with T 4. New colours.*
80   57   1 a. chocolate ..   ..   ..   3·00   1·25
81   58   1½ a. rose-carmine (Type B) (1927)   20   1·50
82   61   2 a. 6 p. orange (1927)   ..   40   5·00
83   62   3 a. bright blue (1925)   ..   1·40   3·25
80/3   *Set of 4*   4·50   10·00
Nos. 81/2 with inverted overprint are of clandestine origin.

1927–37. *King George V (Nasik printing, wmk Mult Star), optd at Nasik with T 5 or 6 (rupee values).*
84   55   3 p. slate   10   10
    w. Wmk inverted   ..   1·75
85   56   ½ a. green (1929)   ..   10   35
86   80   9 p. deep green (1932)   ..   50   40
87   57   1 a. chocolate (1928)   ..   15   10
    w. Wmk inverted   ..   —   1·25
88   82   1 a. 3 p. mauve (1932)   ..   20   30
89   58   1½ a. rose-carmine (Type B) (1930)   40   1·60
    w. Wmk inverted   ..   1·00   1·75
90   70   2 a. purple (1928)   ..   1·10   35
    w. Wmk inverted   ..   1·25   35
91   61   2 a. 6 p. orange (1930)   ..   70
    w. Wmk inverted   ..   80   7·00
92   62   3 a. bright blue (1930)   ..   2·00   8·00
    w. Wmk inverted   ..   7·00
93   83   3 a. 6 p. ultramarine (1937)   2·00
    w. Wmk inverted   ..   50   12·00
94   71   4 a. sage-green (1928)   ..   3·25   1·75
    w. Wmk inverted   ..   1·00   1·75
95   64   6 a. bistre (1937)   ..   55   13·00
    w. Wmk inverted   ..   3·50
96   65   8 a. reddish purple (1930)   ..   2·00   2·00
    w. Wmk inverted   ..   2·00
97   66   12 a. claret (1930)   ..   3·25   14·00
    w. Wmk inverted   ..   3·25   3·50
98   67   1 r. chocolate and green (1930)   3·25   3·50
    w. Wmk inverted
99   2 r. carmine and orange (1930)   25·00   95·00
    w. Wmk inverted   ..   13·00
100   5 r. ultramarine and purple (1928)   10·00   30·00
    w. Wmk inverted   ..   35·00
101   10 r. green and carmine (1928)   12·00   18·00
102   15 r. blue & olive (*wmk inverted*) (1929)   60·00   £400
103   25 r. orange and blue (1929)   ..   90·00   £475
84/103   *Set of 20*   £180   £950

1934. *New types and colours. Optd with T 5.*
104   79   ½ a. green   ..   30   15
105   81   1 a. chocolate ..   ..   1·00   25
    w. Wmk inverted   ..   —   2·50
106   59   2 a. vermilion   90   60
107   62   3 a. carmine   ..   1·40   40
108   63   4 a. sage-green   ..   2·00   90
104/8   *Set of 5*   5·00   2·00

1937–38. *King George VI. Nos. 247/64 optd with T 5 or T 6 (rupee values).*
109   91   3 p. slate   ..   ..   6·00   1·50
110   ½ a. red-brown   ..   60   2·50
111   9 p. green (1937)   ..   60   2·25
112   1 a. carmine (1937)   ..   60   45
113   92   2 a. vermilion   ..   1·50   11·00
114   —   2 a. 6 p. bright violet   ..   1·00   12·00
115   —   3 a. yellow-green   ..   5·00   11·00
116   —   3 a. 6 p. bright blue   ..   2·00   12·00
117   —   4 a. brown   ..   6·00   12·00
118   —   6 a. turquoise-green   ..   3·50   15·00
119   —   8 a. slate-violet   ..   2·50   15·00
120   —   12 a. lake   ..   1·75   17·00
121   93   1 r. grey and red-brown   ..   15·00   28·00
122   2 r. purple and brown   ..   17·00   80·00
123   5 r. green and blue   ..   30·00   60·00
124   10 r. purple and claret   ..   55·00   60·00
125   15 r. brown and green   ..   £150   £600
126   25 r. slate-violet and purple   £325   £600
109/26   *Set of 18*   £550   £1400

JIND
(7)

1941–43. *King George VI. Optd with T 7. (a) Stamps of 1937. W 69 (inverted on 15 r.).*
127   91   3 p. slate   ..   ..   10·00   14·00
128   ½ a. red-brown ..   ..   1·00   50
129   9 p. green   ..   ..   9·00   11·00
130   1 a. carmine   ..   ..   1·00   3·25
131   93   1 r. grey and red-brown   ..   8·00   20·00
132   2 r. purple and brown..   ..   16·00   26·00
133   5 r. green and blue   ..   38·00   70·00
134   10 r. purple and claret ..   ..   55·00   70·00
135   15 r. brown and green   ..   £120   £130
136   25 r. slate-violet and purple   £100   £325
127/136   *Set of 10*   £325   £550

(b) Stamps of 1940–43
137   100a   3 p. slate (1942)   ..   50   60
138   ½ a. purple (1943)   ..   50   85
139   9 p. green (1942)   ..   60   2·25
140   1 a. carmine (1942)   ..   65   85
141   101   1 a. 3 p. yellow-brown   ..   1·00   2·75
142   1½ a. dull violet (1942) ..   ..   5·00   3·50
143   2 a. vermilion   ..   1·75   2·50
144   3 a. bright violet (1942)   ..   12·00   2·75
145   3½ a. bright blue   ..   6·00   6·00
146   102   4 a. brown   ..   3·50   2·75
147   6 a. turquoise-green   ..   3·75   9·50
148   8 a. slate-violet   ..   2·50   9·00
149   12 a. lake   ..   11·00   9·00
137/149   *Set of 13*   42·00   48·00
The 1½ a. and 3 a. exist printed by lithography or typography.

OFFICIAL STAMPS
SERVICE

SERVICE	SERVICE	JHIND STATE
(O 14)	(O 15)	(O 16)

1885 (1 July). *Queen Victoria. Nos. 1/3 of Jind optd with Type O 14.*
O1   23   ½ a. blue-green (R.)   ..   40   30
    a. Opt Type 1 inverted   ..   95·00   60·00
O2   25   1 a. brown-purple   ..   30   10
    a. Opt Type 1 inverted   ..   10·00   7·50
O3   27   2 a. dull blue   ..   28·00   38·00
    a. Opt Type 1 inverted   ..   £850
The three values have had the overprint reprinted in the same way as the ordinary stamps of 1885. See note after No. 6.

1885. *Nos. 7/9 of Jind optd with Type O 15.*
O7   23   ½ a. blue-green (R.)   ..   75·00
    a. "JEEND STATE" double, one albino   £100
O8   25   1 a. brown-purple   ..   70·00
O9   27   2 a. dull blue (R.)   ..   70·00
O7/9   *Set of 3*   £200

1886. *Optd with Type O 16, in red.*
O10   23   ½ a. blue-green   ..   12·00
    a. "ERVICE"   ..   £3000
    b. "JEIND"   ..   £550
    c. "JHIND STATE" double, one albino   50·00
O11   27   2 a. dull blue   ..   18·00
    a. "ERVICE"   ..   £1800
    b. "JEIND"   ..   £850
    c. "SERVICE" double, one albino   32·00
    d. "JHIND STATE" double, one albino   32·00

1886–1902. *Optd with Type O 16.*
O12   23   ½ a. blue-green   ..   50   10
    a. "JHIND STATE" double, one albino   30·00
O13   25   1 a. brown-purple   ..   17·00
    a. "ERVICE"
    b. "JEIND"   ..   £425
    c. "SERVICE" double, one albino   21·00
O14   1 a. plum (1902)   ..   7·50   30
O15   27   2 a. dull blue   ..   1·75   50
    a. "SERVICE" double, one albino   30·00
    b. "SERVICE" treble, two albino   35·00
O16   2 a. ultramarine   ..   50   30
    a. "JHIND STATE" double, one albino   35·00
O17   29   4 a. olive-green (1892)   ..   1·00   50
    a. "JHIND STATE" double, one albino   30·00
O18   4 a. slate-green   ..   1·40   1·10
O19   31   4 a. dull mauve (1892)   ..   3·00   2·00
O20   8 a. magenta (1897)   ..   2·50   4·75
    a. "JHIND STATE" double, one albino   30·00
O21   37   1 r. green and carmine (1896)   6·00   28·00
    a. "SERVICE" double, one albino   40·00
    b. "JHIND STATE" treble, two albino   50·00
O12/21   *Set of 6*   16·00   29·00
Varieties mentioned in note after No. 35 exist on Nos. O12, O15, O17 and O20.
Printings up to and including that of October 1897 had the "SERVICE" overprint. Type O 15, applied to sheets already overprinted with Type 3. From the printing of December 1899 onwards "SERVICE" and "JHIND STATE" were overprinted at one operation, as Type O 16, to provide fresh supplies of Nos. O12, O14 and O21.

1902. *Colour changed. Optd with Type O 16.*
O22   23   ½ a. yellow-green   ..   1·25   20
    a. "V" of "SERVICE" omitted   75·00   40·00
No. O22a normally shows a tiny trace of the "V" remaining. Examples showing the letter completely missing are worth much more.

1903–6. *King Edward VII stamps of India optd with Type O 16.*
O23   41   3 p. pale grey   ..   10   10
O24   3 p. slate-grey (1906)   ..   15   10
O25   42   ½ a. green   ..   2·00   10
    a. "HIND"   ..   £2250   £250
    b. Opt double, one albino   25·00
O26   43   1 a. carmine   ..   90   10
    a. "HIND"   ..   †   £225
    b. Opt double, one albino   25·00
O27   44   2 a. pale violet   ..   1·50   60
O28   2 a. mauve   ..   40   10
O29   47   4 a. olive   ..   40   45
    a. Opt double, one albino   35·00
O30   49   8 a. purple (*shades*)   ..   7·00   5·00
O31   8 a. claret   ..   3·00   1·50
O32   51   1 r. green and carmine (1906)   2·50   2·25
O23/32   *Set of 7*   8·25   4·00

1907. *Nos. 149/50 of India optd with Type O 16.*
O33   53   ½ a. green   ..   15   10
O34   54   1 a. carmine   ..   30   10

1914–27. *King George V. Official stamps of India optd with T 4.*
O35   55   3 p. slate-grey   ..   10   10
    a. "JIND STATE" double, one albino   30·00
O36   56   ½ a. green   ..   10   10
O37   57   1 a. aniline carmine   ..   25   10
O38   1 a. pale rose-carmine   ..   55   10
O39   59   2 a. mauve   ..   15   15
O40   63   4 a. olive   ..   45   15
O41   64   6 a. yellow-bistre (1927)   ..   50   2·25
O42   65   8 a. purple   ..   30   1·00

O43   67   1 r. brown and green   ..   1·00   1·60
    a. "JIND STATE" double, one albino   30·00
O44   2 r. carmine and yellow-brown (1927)   12·00   55·00
O45   5 r. ultramarine and violet (1927)   18·00   £150
O35/45   *Set of 10*   30·00   £190
No. O40 with double overprint is of clandestine origin.

1924. *As 1914-27. New colour.*
O46   57   1 a. chocolate   50   10

JIND STATE SERVICE	JIND STATE SERVICE	JIND SERVICE
(O 17)	(O.18)	(O 19)

1927–37. *King George V (Nasik printing, wmk Mult Star), optd with Types O 17 or O 18 (rupee values).*
O47   55   3 p. slate (1928)   ..   10   20
O48   56   ½ a. green (1929)   ..   10   90
O49   80   9 p. deep green (1932)   ..   40   15
O50   57   1 a. chocolate   ..   10   10
    w. Wmk inverted   ..   60
O51   82   1 a. 3 p. mauve (1932)   ..   40   15
    w. Wmk inverted   ..   60   35
O52   70   2 a. purple (1929)   ..   25   15
O53   61   2 a. 6 p. orange (1937)   ..   50   15·00
O54   71   4 a. sage-green (1929)   ..   35   25
    w. Wmk inverted   ..   1·10   60
O55   64   6 a. bistre (1937)   ..   80
    w. Wmk inverted   ..   2·00   13·00
O56   65   8 a. reddish purple (1929)   ..   —   1·50
    w. Wmk inverted   ..   45   1·50
O57   66   12 a. claret (1928)   ..   1·00   10·00
O58   67   1 r. chocolate and green (1928)   2·25   2·50
O59   2 r. carmine and orange (1930)   30·00   24·00
    w. Wmk inverted   ..   24·00
O60   5 r. ultramarine and purple (1929)   13·00   £160
O61   10 r. green and carmine (1928)   26·00   90·00
    w. Wmk inverted
O47/61   *Set of 15*   60·00   £275
The 9 p. exists printed by lithography or typography.

1934. *Optd with Type O 17.*
O62   79   ½ a. green   ..   20   15
O63   81   1 a. chocolate   20   15
O64   59   2 a. vermilion   30   15
    w. Wmk inverted   ..   40   1·00
O65   63   4 a. sage-green   ..   3·75   30
O62/5   *Set of 4*   4·00   65

1937–40. *King George VI. Optd with Types O 17 or O 18 (rupee values).*
O66   91   ½ a. red-brown (1938)   ..   48·00   30
O67   9 p. green   ..   85   7·50
O68   1 a. carmine   ..   55   30
O69   93   1 r. grey and red-brown (1940) ..   26·00   42·00
O70   2 r. purple and brown (1940)   ..   45·00   £180
O71   5 r. green and blue (1940)   ..   85·00   £325
O72   10 r. purple and claret (1940)   ..   £180   £750
O66/72   *Set of 7*   £350   £1200

1939–43. *(a) Official stamps optd with T 7.*
O73   O 20   3 p. slate   50   70
O74   ½ a. red-brown   ..   1·50   50
O75   ½ a. purple (1943)   ..   60   30
O76   9 p. green   ..   1·50   7·50
O77   1 a. carmine   ..   1·60   15
O78   1½ a. dull violet (1942)   ..   6·00   1·00
O79   2 a. vermilion   ..   3·00   30
    w. Wmk inverted   ..   —   2·50
O80   2½ a. bright violet   ..   2·00   6·00
O81   4 a. brown   ..   3·75   1·40
O82   8 a. slate-violet   ..   3·50   3·00

(b) Postage stamps optd with Type O 19.
O83   93   1 r. grey and red-brown (1942) ..   18·00   42·00
O84   2 r. purple and brown (1942)   ..   42·00   £120
O85   5 r. green and blue (1942)   ..   90·00   £300
O86   10 r. purple and claret (1942)   ..   £160   £375
O73/86   *Set of 14*   £300   £750

Jind was absorbed into the Patiala and East Punjab States Union by 20 August 1948.

NABHA

PRICES FOR STAMPS ON COVER	
Nos. 1/3	*from* × 15
Nos. 4/6	—
Nos. 10/36	*from* × 12
Nos. 37/117	*from* × 7
Nos. O1/68	*from* × 15

Raja Hira Singh, 1871–1911.

NABHA STATE	NABHA STATE
(1)	(2)

1885 (1 July). *Queen Victoria. Optd with T 1.*

1	23	½ a. blue-green	..	1·75	3·25
2	25	1 a. brown-purple	..	30·00	£110
3	27	2 a. dull blue	..	10·00	35·00
4	17	4 a. green	..	60·00	£150
5	31	8 a. dull mauve	..		£300
6	33	1 r. slate	..		£275
1/6			*Set of 6*		£600

All six values have had the overprint reprinted. On the reprints the words "NABHA" and "STATE" both measure 9¼ mm in length, whereas on the originals these words measure 11 and 10 mm respectively. The varieties with overprint double come from the reprints.

1885 (Nov)–**1900**. *Optd with T 2. (a) In red.*

10	23	½ a. blue-green	..	20	45
11	27	2 a. dull blue	..	1·75	1·40
		a. Opt double, one albino	..	40·00	
12	17	4 a. green	..	25·00	£130
13	33	1 r. slate	..	90·00	£170
		a. Opt double, one albino	..	£120	
10/13			*Set of 4*	£110	£275

(b) In black (Nov 1885–97)

14	23	½ a. blue-green (1888)	..	10	10
15	24	9 p. carmine (1892)	..	60	2·50
16	25	1 a. brown-purple	..	1·10	60
17		1 a. plum	..	90	50
18	26	1 a. 6 p. sepia (1891)	..	75	2·00
		a. "ABHA" for "NABHA"	..	£300	
19	27	2 a. dull blue (1888)	..	1·50	90
20		2 a. ultramarine	..	1·25	80
21	28	3 a. orange (1889)	..	5·00	13·00
		a. Opt double, one albino	..	25·00	
22		3 a. brown-orange	..	2·00	1·25
23	29	4 a. olive-green (1888)	..	3·50	1·60
24		4 a. slate-green	..	3·50	1·60
25	21	6 a. olive-bistre (1889)	..	4·00	9·00
26		6 a. bistre-brown	..	1·40	2·00
27	31	8 a. dull mauve	..	1·50	1·60
		a. Opt double, one albino	..	30·00	
28	32	12 a. purple/red (1889)	..	2·50	3·00
		a. Opt double, one albino	..	27·00	
29	33	1 r. slate (1888)	..	7·00	35·00
30	37	1 r. green and carmine (1893)	..	7·00	3·75
		a. "N BHA" for "NABHA"	..		
		b. Opt double, one albino	..	40·00	
31	38	2 r. carmine and yellow-brown (1897)	..	90·00	£180
		a. Opt double, one albino	..	£160	
32		3 r. brown and green (1897)	..	90·00	£225
33		5 r. ultramarine and violet (1897)	..	90·00	£325
14/33			*Set of 15*	£275	£700

(c) New value. In black (Nov 1900)

36	40	3 p. carmine	..	10	15

1903–09. *King Edward VII. Optd with T 2.*

37	41	3 p. pale grey	..	30	15
		a. "NAB STA" for "NABHA STATE"		£800	
		b. Opt double, one albino	..	20·00	
37c		3 p. slate-grey (1906)	..	30	15
38	42	½ a. green	..	40	30
		a. "NABH" for "NABHA"	..	£950	
39	43	1 a. carmine	..	80	60
40	44	2 a. pale violet	..	60	1·75
40a		2 a. mauve	..	1·60	30
40b	45	2 a. 6 p. ultramarine (1909)	..	17·00	80·00
		ba. Opt double, one albino	..	30·00	
41	46	3 a. orange-brown	..	50	30
		a. Opt double, one albino	..	35·00	
42	47	4 a. olive	..	1·40	1·75
43	48	6 a. olive-bistre	..	90	11·00
		a. Opt double, one albino	..	20·00	
44	49	8 a. purple	..	6·00	15·00
44a		8 a. claret	..	8·00	17·00
45	50	12 a. purple/red	..	2·75	17·00
46	51	1 r. green and carmine	..	6·00	9·00
37/46			*Set of 11*	32·00	£120

1907. *Nos. 149/50 of India optd with T 2.*

47	53	½ a. green	..	65	1·10
48	54	1 a. carmine	..	40	70

Maharaja Ripudaman (Gurcharan) Singh, 1911–1928.

1913. *King George V. Optd with T 2.*

49	55	3 p. slate-grey	..	20	20
50	56	½ a. green	..	20	10
51	57	1 a. aniline carmine	..	60	10
52	59	2 a. mauve	..	50	35
53	62	3 a. orange-brown	..	50	35
54	63	4 a. olive	..	55	95
55	64	6 a. olive-bistre	..	55	4·25
56	65	8 a. purple	..	1·50	3·00
57	66	12 a. dull claret	..	1·40	17·00
58	67	1 r. brown and green	..	6·50	3·25
		a. Opt double, one albino	..	32·00	
49/58			*Set of 10*	11·00	27·00

1924. *As 1913. New colour.*

59	57	1 a. chocolate	..	2·75	1·50

No. 59 with inverted or double overprint is of clandestine origin.

NABHA STATE	**NABHA STATE**
(3)	(4)

1927–36. *King George V (Nasik printing, wmk Mult Star), optd as T 3 or 4 (rupee values).*

60	55	3 p. slate (1932)	..	75	15
		w. Wmk inverted	..	2·00	1·00
61	56	½ a. green (1928)	..	30	20
61a	80	9 p. deep green (1934)	..	1·50	1·10
62	57	1 a. chocolate	..	60	15
		w. Wmk inverted	..		
63	82	1 a. 3 p. mauve (1936)	..	80	4·00
		w. Wmk inverted	..	70	

64	70	2 a. purple (1932)	..	1·75	35
65	61	2 a. 6 p. orange (1932)	..	45	6·00
66	62	3 a. bright blue (1930)	..	1·40	1·00
67	71	4 a. sage-green (1932)	..	1·60	1·40
71	67	1 r. carmine and orange (1932)	..	22·00	75·00
72		5 r. ultramarine and purple (*wmk inverted*) (1932)		70·00	£200
60/72			*Set of 11*	90·00	£250

The 9 p. exists printed by lithography or typography.

Maharaja Partab Singh, 1928–1971

1936–37. *New types and colours. Optd as T 3.*

73	79	½ a. green	..	40	30
74	81	1 a. chocolate	..	30	30
75	62	3 a. carmine (1937)	..	3·75	9·00
76	63	4 a. slate-green (1937)	..	2·75	2·25
73/6			*Set of 4*	6·50	10·75

NABHA STATE	NABHA
(5)	(6)

1938. *King George VI. Nos. 247/64 optd as T 3 (3 p. to 1 a.), T 5 (2 a. to 12 a.) or T 4 (rupee values). W 69 (inverted on 15 r.).*

77	91	3 p. slate	..	5·50	30
78		½ a. red-brown	..	3·25	50
79		9 p. green	..	17·00	3·25
80		1 a. carmine	..	1·50	35
81	92	2 a. vermilion	..	1·00	4·25
82	–	2 a. 6 p. bright violet	..	1·00	7·00
83	–	3 a. yellow-green	..	1·10	3·75
84	–	3 a. 6 p. bright blue	..	1·10	14·00
85	–	4 a. brown	..	5·00	5·00
86	–	6 a. turquoise-green	..	2·50	14·00
87	–	8 a. slate-violet	..	1·90	14·00
88	–	12 a. lake	..	2·25	15·00
89	93	1 r. grey and red-brown	..	10·00	21·00
90		2 r. purple and brown	..	19·00	75·00
91		5 r. green and blue	..	45·00	£150
92		10 r. purple and claret	..	70·00	£300
93		15 r. brown and green	..	£180	£550
94		25 r. slate-violet and purple	..	£180	£550
		w. Wmk inverted	..	£300	£650
77/94			*Set of 18*	£500	£1500

1941–45. *King George VI. Optd with T 6. (a) Stamps of 1937.*

95	91	3 p. slate (1942)	..	28·00	2·75
96		½ a. red-brown (1942)	..	65·00	3·75
97		9 p. green (1942)	..	10·00	10·00
98		1 a. carmine (1942)	..	10·00	2·25
95/8			*Set of 4*	£100	17·00

(b) Stamps of 1940–43

105	100a	3 p. slate (1942)	..	80	55
106		½ a. purple (1943)	..	4·00	65
107		9 p. green (1942)	..	3·25	60
108		1 a. carmine (1945)	..	80	2·25
109	101	1 a. 3 p. yellow-brown	..	80	1·75
110		1½ a. dull violet (1942)	..	1·00	1·10
111		2 a. vermilion (1943)	..	80	3·00
112		3 a. bright violet (1943)	..	2·50	2·75
113		3½ a. bright blue (1944)	..	10·00	38·00
114	102	4 a. brown	..	1·60	75
115		6 a. turquoise-green (1943)	..	8·00	38·00
116		8 a. slate-violet (1943)	..	6·00	26·00
117		12 a. lake (1943)	..	4·50	38·00
105/117			*Set of 13*	40·00	£140

The 1½ a. exists printed by lithography or typography.

OFFICIAL STAMPS

SERVICE	
SERVICE	**NABHA STATE**
(O 8)	(O 9)

1885 (1 July). *Nos. 1/3 of Nabha optd with Type O 8.*

O1	23	½ a. blue-green	..	1·75	60
O2	25	1 a. brown-purple	..	30	15
		a. Opt Type O 8 double	..	† £1100	
O3	27	2 a. dull blue	..	50·00	£100
O1/3			*Set of 3*	50·00	£100

The three values have had the overprint reprinted in the same way as the ordinary stamps of 1885.

1885 (Nov)–**97.** *Optd with Type O 9. (a) In red.*

O 4	23	½ a. blue-green	..	4·75	3·75
O 5	27	2 a. deep blue	..	65	55

(b) In black (Nov 1885–97)

O 6	23	½ a. blue-green (1888)	..	10	10
		a. "SERVICE." with stop	..	£110	2·25
		b. "S ATE" for "STATE"			
		c. "SERVICE" double, one albino	..	25·00	
O 7	25	1 a. brown-purple	..	85	45
O 8		1 a. plum	..	75	25
		a. "SERVICE." with stop	..	5·50	75
		ab. "SERVICE." with stop, and "NABHA STATE" double	..	†	£250
O 9	27	2 a. dull blue (1888)	..	1·60	65
O10		2 a. ultramarine	..	2·00	1·00
O11	28	3 a. orange (1889)	..	16·00	55·00
O12		3 a. brown-orange	..	16·00	55·00
		a. "NABHA STATE" double, one albino	..	40·00	
O13	29	4 a. olive-green (1888)	..	2·00	65
O14		4 a. slate-green	..	2·00	65
O15	21	6 a. olive-bistre (1889)	..	12·00	20·00
		a. "SERVICE" double, one albino	..	30·00	
O16		6 a. bistre-brown	..	£600	
O17	31	8 a. dull mauve (1889)	..	1·25	70

O18	32	12 a. purple/red (1889)	..	5·00	14·00
		a. "SERVICE" double, one albino	..	30·00	
		b. "NABHA STATE" double, one albino	..	30·00	
O19	33	1 r. slate (1889)	..	28·00	£180
O20	37	1 r. green and carmine (1.97)	..	25·00	55·00
O6/20			*Set of 10*	80·00	£300

Printings up to and including that of August 1895 had the "SERVICE" overprint applied to sheets of stamps already overprinted with Type 2. From the printing of January 1897 onwards the two parts of the overprint were applied at one operation. This method was only used for printings of the ½ a., 1 a. and 1 r. (O20).

1903–06. *King Edward VII stamps of India optd with Type O 9.*

O24	41	3 p. pale grey (1906)	..	3·75	16·00
O25		3 p. slate-grey (1906)	..	70	9·50
		a. Opt double, one albino	..	25·00	
O26	42	½ a. green	..	40	10
O27	43	1 a. carmine	..	15	10
O28	44	2 a. pale violet	..	1·50	75
O29		2 a. mauve	..	1·25	40
O30	47	4 a. olive	..	1·40	50
O32	49	8 a. purple (*shades*)	..	1·10	1·25
		a. Opt double, one albino	..	25·00	
O33		8 a. claret	..	7·00	3·50
O34	51	1 r. green and carmine	..	1·50	2·25
O24/34			*Set of 7*	6·00	12·50

1907. *Nos. 149/50 of India optd with Type O 9.*

O35	53	½ a. green	..	20	40
		a. Opt double, one albino	..	15·00	
O36	54	1 a. carmine	..	25	25
		a. Opt double, one albino	..	25·00	

1913. *King George V. Optd with Type O 9.*

O37	63	4 a. olive	..	10·00	45·00
O38	67	1 r. brown and green	..	55·00	£300
		a. Opt double, one albino	..	95·00	

1913. *Official stamps of India optd with T 2.*

O39	53	3 p. slate-grey	..	30	5·50
O39a		3 p. bluish slate	..	30	5·50
O40	56	½ a. green	..	15	10
O41	57	1 a. aniline carmine	..	15	10
O42	59	2 a. mauve	..	30	15
O43	63	4 a. olive	..	40	40
O44	65	8 a. dull mauve	..	65	90
O46	67	1 r. brown and green	..	3·25	2·25
O39/46			*Set of 7*	4·75	8·50

NABHA STATE SERVICE	NABHA SERVICE
(O 10)	(O 11)

1932–42?. *King George V (Nasik printing, wmk Mult Star), optd at Nasik with Type O 10.*

O47	55	3 p. slate	..	10	15
O48	81	1 a. chocolate (1935)	..	15	15
O49	63	4 a. sage-green (1942?)	..	19·00	2·25
O50	65	8 a. reddish purple (1937)	..	1·00	1·90
O47/50			*Set of 4*	19·00	4·00

1938. *King George VI. Optd as Type O 10.*

O53	91	9 p. green	..	1·75	2·50
O54		1 a. carmine	..	9·00	15

1940–43. *(a) Official stamps optd with T 6.*

O55	O 20	3 p. slate (1942)	..	60	70
O56		½ a. red-brown (1942)	..	70	30
O57		½ a. purple (1943)	..	2·75	50
O58		9 p. green	..	1·25	20
O59		1 a. carmine (1942)	..	50	20
O61		1½ a. dull violet (1942)	..	60	40
O62		2 a. vermilion (1942)	..	1·40	75
		w. Wmk inverted	..	2·50	1·25
O64		4 a. brown (1942)	..	3·50	2·00
O65		8 a. slate-violet (1942)	..	5·50	13·00

(b) Postage stamps optd with Type O 11.

O66	93	1 r. grey and red-brown (1942)	..	8·50	28·00
O67		2 r. purple and brown (1942)	..	24·00	£150
O68		5 r. green and blue (1942)	..	£200	£475
O55/68			*Set of 12*	£225	£600

Nabha was absorbed into the Patiala and East Punjab States Union by 20 August 1948.

PATIALA

PRICES FOR STAMPS ON COVER	
Nos. 1/6	*from* × 10
Nos. 7/34	*from* × 6
Nos. 35/45	*from* × 8
Nos. 46/115	*from* × 4
Nos. O1/84	*from* × 15

Maharaja Rajindra Singh, 1876–1900

PUTTIALA STATE	STATE	PUTTIALA STATE	PATIALA STATE
(1)		(2)	(3)

1884 (1 Oct). *Queen Victoria. Optd with T **1**, in red.*

1	23	½ a. blue-green				2·25	2·25
		a. Opt double, one sideways				£1800	£600
		b. Opt double, one albino				50·00	
2	25	1 a. brown-purple				38·00	40·00
		a. Opt double					
		b. Optd in red and in black				£600	
3	27	2 a. dull blue				9·00	9·00
4	17	4 a. green				50·00	50·00
5	31	8 a. dull mauve				£275	£650
		a. Opt inverted				£5500	
		b. Optd in red and in black				75·00	£250
		ba. Ditto. Opts inverted				£3750	
		c. Opt double, one albino				£325	
6	33	1 r. slate				£120	£375
1/6					Set of 6	£450	£1000

Nos. 5a and 5ba each occur once in the setting of 120. The 8 a. value also exists with a trial overprint (showing the words more curved) reading downwards (*Price £400 unused*), which should not be confused with No. 5a.

1885. *Optd with T **2**. (a) In red.*

7	23	½ a. blue-green				1·50	20
		a. "AUTTIALLA"				12·00	17·00
		b. "STATE" only					
		c. Wide spacing between lines				4·00	4·25
8	27	2 a. dull blue				3·00	1·25
		a. "AUTTIALLA"				26·00	
		b. Wide spacing between lines				13·00	13·00
		ba. Ditto "AUTTIALLA"				£325	
9	17	4 a. green				2·25	2·00
		a. Optd in red and in black				£190	
		b. Wide spacing between lines				£250	
		c. Opt double, one albino				32·00	
10	33	1 r. slate				6·50	50·00
		a. "AUTTIALLA"				£375	
		b. Wide spacing between lines				£250	

(b) In black

11	25	1 a. brown-purple				20	15
		a. Optd in red and in black				5·00	48·00
		b. "AUTTIALLA"				55·00	
		ba. Ditto. Optd in red and in black				£1300	
		c. Opt double				£225	£250
		d. Wide spacing between lines				£140	
12	31	8 a. dull mauve				12·00	26·00
		a. "AUTTIALLA"				£325	
		b. Opt double, one albino				50·00	
		c. Wide spacing between lines				£250	
7/12					Set of 6	23·00	70·00

The ½, 2 and 4 a. (T **29**), and 1 r. (all overprinted in black), are proofs.

All six values exist with reprinted overprints, and the error "AUTTIALLA STATE" has been reprinted in complete sheets on all values and in addition in black on the ½, 2, 4 a. and 1 r. Nearly all these however, are found with the word "REPRINT" overprinted upon them. On these genuine "AUTTIALLA" errors, which occur on R. 9/12 in the setting of 120, the word "STATE" is 8½ mm long; on the reprints only 7¾ mm.

Nos. 7c, 8b, 9b, 10b, 11d and 12c show 1¼ mm spacing between the two lines of overprint. The normal spacing is ¾ mm.

Nos. 7/8 and 10/12 exist with error "PUTTILLA", but their status is uncertain.

1891–96. *Optd with T **3**.*

13	23	½ a. blue-green (1892)				10	10
14	24	9 p. carmine				45	90
15	25	1 a. brown-purple				80	25
16		1 a. plum				1·25	70
		a. "PATIALA" omitted				£180	£350
		b. "PA" omitted					
		c. "PATIA" omitted					
		d. "PATIAL" omitted					
17	26	1 a. 6 p. sepia				60	50
18	27	2 a. dull blue (1896)				85	25
19		2 a. ultramarine				1·25	60
20	28	3 a. brown-orange				1·25	40
21	29	4 a. olive-green (1896)				1·75	50
		a. "PATIALA" omitted				£400	£200
22		4 a. slate-green				1·75	50
23	21	6 a. bistre-brown				1·50	8·00
24		6 a. olive-bistre				1·60	13·00
		a. Opt double, one albino				40·00	
25	31	8 a. dull mauve					
26		8 a. magenta (1896)				1·25	8·00
27	32	12 a. purple/red				1·25	9·00
28	37	1 r. green and carmine (1896)				3·75	32·00
29	38	2 r. carmine and yellow-brown (1895)				90·00	£500
30		3 r. brown and green (1895)				£130	£550
		a. Opt double, one albino					
		b. Opt treble, two albino				£150	
31		5 r. ultramarine and violet (1895)				£160	£600
13/31					Set of 14	£350	£1500

The errors on the 1 a. plum and 4 a. olive-green occur on R.19/1 in the December 1898 printing. Nos. 16b/d are early stages of the error before the entire word was omitted.

1899–1902. *Colours changed and new value. Optd with T **3**.*

32	40	3 p. carmine (1899)				10	10
		a. Pair, one without opt				£2750	
		b. Opt double, one albino				30·00	
33	23	½ a. pale yellow-green				60	30
34	25	1 a. carmine				2·00	60
32/4					Set of 3	2·50	90

Maharaja Bhupindra Singh, 1900–1938

1903–06. *King Edward VII. Optd with T **3**.*

35	41	3 p. pale grey				10	15
		a. Additional albino opt of Jind Type 3				£200	
		b. "S" in "STATE" sideways (R.20/1)				£900	£900
36		3 p. slate-grey (1906)				10	10
37	42	½ a. green				85	10
38	43	1 a. carmine				10	10
		a. Horiz pair, one without opt				£900	
39	44	2 a. pale violet				80	65
		a. Mauve				6·00	80

40	46	3 a. orange-brown				50	30
41	47	4 a. olive (1905)				2·50	65
42	48	6 a. olive-bistre (1905)				2·50	5·50
43	49	8 a. purple (1906)				2·25	1·10
44	50	12 a. purple/red (1906)				4·50	17·00
45	51	1 r. green and carmine (1905)				1·90	3·00
35/45					Set of 10	14·50	26·00

1912. *Nos. 149/50 of India optd with T **3**.*

46	53	½ a. green				10	15
47	54	1 a. carmine				80	50

1912–26. *King George V. Optd with T **3**.*

48	55	3 p. slate-grey				15	10
		a. "Rs" flaw				21·00	
49	56	½ a. green				50	15
50	57	1 a. aniline carmine				80	15
51	58	1½ a. chocolate (Type A) (1922)				30	55
52	59	2 a. mauve				55	40
53	62	3 a. orange-brown				1·00	60
54	63	4 a. olive				1·90	1·50
55	64	6 a. yellow-brown				2·75	3·50
		a. Yellow-bistre				90	2·75
56	65	8 a. purple				1·75	1·00
57	66	12 a. dull claret				2·00	5·50
58	67	1 r. brown and green				3·50	10·00
		a. Opt double, one albino				30·00	
59		2 r. carmine and yellow-brown (1926)				9·50	£110
60		5 r. ultramarine and violet (1926)				23·00	£110

1923–6. *As 1912–26. New colours.*

61	57	1 a. chocolate				2·00	35
62	62	3 a. ultramarine (1926)				1·75	5·00
48/62					Set of 15	45·00	£225

PATIALA STATE **PATIALA STATE**

(4) (5)

1928–34. *King George V (Nasik printing, wmk Mult Star) optd at Nasik with T **4** or **5** (rupee values).*

63	55	3 p. slate (1932)				1·25	10
		w. Wmk inverted				2·25	1·00
64	56	½ a. green				25	10
		w. Wmk inverted				1·50	1·00
65	80	9 p. deep green (1934)				75	20
66	57	1 a. chocolate				75	20
		w. Wmk inverted				2·25	75
67	82	1 a. 3 p. mauve (1932)				2·50	15
		w. Wmk inverted				2·50	1·00
68	70	2 a. purple				85	30
		w. Wmk inverted				2·25	
69	61	2 a. 6 p. orange (1934)				3·00	1·25
		w. Wmk inverted				2·50	
70	62	3 a. bright blue (1929)				2·00	85
71	71	4 a. sage-green				2·50	70
		w. Wmk inverted				4·50	
72	65	8 a. reddish purple (1933)				3·75	1·60
73	67	1 r. chocolate and green (1929)				5·50	5·50
		w. Wmk inverted				—	8·50
74		2 r. carmine and orange				17·00	
		w. Wmk inverted				8·50	40·00
63/74					Set of 12	28·00	45·00

The 9 p. exists printed by lithography or typography.

1935–37. *Optd with T **4**.*

75	79	½ a. blue-green (1937)				45	20
76	81	1 a. chocolate (1936)				45	15
77	59	2 a. vermilion (No. 236b) (1936)				30	70
78	62	3 a. carmine				4·00	4·00
		w. Wmk inverted				5·00	5·00
79	63	4 a. sage-green				1·25	1·40
75/9					Set of 5	5·75	5·75

PATIALA STATE **PATIALA** **PATIALA**

(6) (7) (8)

1937–8. *King George VI. Nos. 247/64 optd with T **4** (3 p. to 1 a.), T **6** (2 a. to 12 a.), or T **5** (rupee values).*

80	91	3 p. slate				26·00	30
81		½ a. red-brown				7·00	20
82		9 p. green (1937)				2·50	60
83		1 a. carmine (1937)				1·60	20
84	92	2 a. vermilion				1·50	5·50
85	—	2 a. 6 p. bright violet				3·00	12·00
86	—	3 a. yellow-green				2·25	5·00
87	—	3 a. 6 p. bright blue				3·25	16·00
88	—	4 a. brown				17·00	9·50
89	—	6 a. turquoise-green				18·00	32·00
90	—	8 a. slate-violet				18·00	24·00
91	—	12 a. lake				19·00	38·00
92	93	1 r. grey and red-brown				19·00	35·00
93		2 r. purple and brown				27·00	75·00
94		5 r. green and blue				38·00	£160
95		10 r. purple and claret				55·00	£250
96		15 r. brown and green				£100	£400
97		25 r. slate-violet and purple				£130	£475
80/97					Set of 18	£425	£1400

Maharaja Yadavindra Singh, 1938–1971

1941–6. *King George VI. Optd with T **7** or **8** (rupee value).*

(a) Stamps of 1937

98	91	3 p. slate				8·50	75
99		½ a. red-brown				6·50	40
100		9 p. green				£140	2·75
		w. Wmk inverted					
101		1 a. carmine				19·00	75
102	93	1 r. grey and red-brown (1946)				9·00	60·00
98/102					Set of 5	£160	60·00

(b) Stamps of 1940–43

103	100a	3 p. slate (1942)				1·75	15
104		½ a. purple (1943)				1·90	40
		a. Pair, one without opt				£4250	

105	100a	9 p. green (1942)				1·00	15
		a. Vert pair, one without opt				£2750	
106		1 a. carmine (1944)				80	10
107	101	1 a. 3 p. yellow-brown				1·60	1·90
108		1½ a. violet (1942)				7·50	1·75
109		2 a. vermilion (1944)				6·50	25
110		3 a. bright violet (1944)				4·50	1·00
111		3½ a. bright blue (1944)				15·00	22·00
112	102	4 a. brown (1944)				5·00	1·50
113		6 a. turquoise-green (1944)				2·50	15·00
114		8 a. slate-violet (1944)				3·00	8·00
115		12 a. lake (1945)				10·00	48·00
103/15					Set of 13	55·00	90·00

The 1½ a. exists printed by lithography or typography.

OFFICIAL STAMPS

SERVICE **SERVICE**

(O 2) (O 3)

1884 (1 Oct). *Nos. 1/3 of Patiala optd with Type O **2**, in black.*

O1	23	½ a. blue-green				9·00	20
O2	25	1 a. brown-purple				40	10
		a. Opt Type 1 inverted				£1300	£250
		b. Opt Type 1 double				†	£100
		c. "SERVICE" double				£1300	£450
		d. "SERVICE" inverted				†	£1300
		w. Wmk inverted				†	£225
O3	27	2 a. dull blue				£4250	£100

Essays of No. O3 exist on which "STATE" measures 10 mm long (normal 9 mm) and the words of the Type 1 overprint are more curved. These are rare (*Price £850 unused*).

1885–90. *(a) No. 7 of Patiala optd with Type O **2**, in black.*

O4	23	½ a. blue-green				40	10
		a. "SERVICE" double				†	£600
		b. "AUTTIALLA"				60·00	16·00
		ba. "AUTTIALLA", and "SERVICE" double				†	£2500

*(b) No. 11 of Patiala optd with Type O **2**, in black*

O5	25	1 a. brown-purple				30	10
		a. "SERVICE" double				£1300	
		b. "SERVICE" double, one inverted				†	£475
		c. "AUTTIALLA"				£550	45·00
		d. "PUTTIALLA STATE" double				†	£900

*(c) As No. 7 of Patiala, but optd in black, and No. 8, optd with Type O **3***

O6	23	½ a. blue-green (Bk.) (1890)				1·10	10
O7	27	2 a. dull blue (R.)				30	15
		a. "SERVICE" double, one inverted				£170	

Stamps as Nos. O4/5, but with Type O **3** (in red on the ½ a.), were prepared for use but not issued, although some were erroneously overprinted "REPRINT". No. O7 with overprint in *black* is a proof. The ½ a "AUTTIALLA" has been reprinted in complete sheets, and can be found with "AUTTIALLA" double.

No. O7 exists with error "PUTTILLA", but its status is uncertain.

SERVICE

PATIALA STATE **PATIALA STATE SERVICE** **PATIALA STATE SERVICE**

(O 4) (O 5) (O 6)

1891 (Nov)–**1900.** *Optd with Type O **4**, in black.*

O8	23	½ a. blue-green (9.95)				10	10
		a. "SERVICE" inverted				55·00	
		b. "T" of "SERVICE" omitted				£850	
		c. Second "T" of "STATE" omitted				£400	£375
O9	25	1 a. plum (10.1900)				3·75	10
		a. "SERVICE" inverted				60·00	
O10	27	2 a. dull blue (12.98)				4·00	1·25
		a. Deep blue				3·25	1·60
		b. "SERVICE" inverted				60·00	£160
		c. Thin seriffed "I" in "SERVICE"				£140	
O12	28	3 a. brown-orange				50	1·60
		a. "I" of "SERVICE" omitted					
O13	29	4 a. olive-green				40	70
		a. Slate-green (9.95)				50	20
		b. "I" of "SERVICE" omitted					
O15	21	6 a. bistre-brown				1·00	35
		a. Olive-bistre				£1000	
O16	31	8 a. dull mauve				1·60	80
		a. Magenta (12.98)				1·00	80
		b. "I" of "SERVICE" omitted				£2500	
		c. Thin seriffed "I" in "SERVICE"				£275	
O18	32	12 a. purple/red				50	50
		a. "I" of "SERVICE" omitted				£4250	
O19	33	1 r. slate				80	55
		a. "I" of "SERVICE" omitted					
O8/19					Set of 9	10·00	4·75

Stamps from the first printing of November 1891 (Nos. O12/13, O15/16, O18/19) had the "SERVICE" overprint, as Type O **3**, applied to sheets already overprinted with Type 3. Subsequent printings of Nos. O8/10a, O13a and O16a had both overprints applied at one operation as shown on Type O 4.

The errors with "SERVICE" inverted occur from a trial printing, in two operations, during 1894, which was probably not issued. Some of the "I" omitted varieties may also come from the same trial printing.

1902 (Jan)–**03.** *Optd with Type O **4**.*

O20	25	1 a. carmine				15	10
O21	37	1 r. green and carmine (5.03)				5·00	9·00

1903–10. *King Edward VII stamps of India optd with Type O **4**.*

O22	41	3 p. pale grey				10	10
		a. Slate-grey (1909)				15	15
O24	42	½ a. green				10	10
O25	43	1 a. carmine				10	10
O26	44	2 a. pale violet (1905)				30	25
		a. Mauve				20	10

O28	46	3 a. orange-brown	..	..	1·90	1·75
O29	47	4 a. olive (1905)	..	..	70	20
		a. Opt double, one albino	..	40·00		
O30	49	8 a. purple (*shades*)	..	..	60	55
		a. Claret (1910)	..	..	2·75	1·25
O32	51	1 r. green and carmine (1906)	..	..	70	70
O22/32		..	..	*Set of 8*	4·00	3·25

1907. *Nos. 149/50 of India optd with Type O 4.*

O33	53	½ a. green	..	..	10	10
O34	54	1 a. carmine	..	..	10	10

1913–26. *King George V. Official stamps of India optd with T 3.*

O35	55	3 p. slate-grey		..	10	10
		a. Bluish slate (1926)	..	..	30	30
O36	56	½ a. green	..	..	10	10
O37	57	1 a. carmine	..	..	10	10
O38		1 a. brown (1925)	..	..	5·00	1·00
O39	59	2 a. mauve	..	..	50	20
O40	63	4 a. olive	..	..	40	30
O41	64	6 a. yellow-bistre (1926)	..	..	85	1·75
O42	65	8 a. purple	..	..	55	50
O43	67	1 r. brown and green	..	..	1·25	1·40
O44		2 r. carmine and yellow-brown (1926)	..	12·00	35·00	
O45		5 r. ultramarine and violet (1926)	..	9·00	19·00	
O35/45		..	..	*Set of 11*	27·00	55·00

1927–36. *King George V (Nasik printing, wmk Mult Star), optd at Nasik with Type O 5 or Type O 6 (rupee values).*

O47	55	3 p. slate	..	..	10	10
		a. Blue opt	..	..	1·00	1·00
		w. Wmk inverted	..	..	1·75	1·00
O48	56	½ a. green (1932)	..	..	45	55
		w. Wmk inverted	..	..	—	2·25
O49	57	1 a. chocolate	..	..	15	10
		w. Wmk inverted	..	..	1·10	50
O50	82	1 a. 3 p. mauve (1932)	..	..	30	10
		w. Wmk inverted	..	..	2·50	20
O51	70	2 a. purple	..	..	20	30
O52		2 a. vermilion (1933)	..	..	30	35
O53	61	2 a. 6 p. orange (1933)	..	..	1·60	35
		w. Wmk inverted	..	..	60	80
O54	71	4 a. sage-green (1935)	..	..	40	30
		w. Wmk inverted	..	..	1·75	1·10
O55	65	8 a. reddish purple (1929)	..	..	85	65
		w. Wmk inverted	..	..	85	80
O56	67	1 r. chocolate and green (1929)	..	3·25	1·60	
		w. Wmk inverted	..	..	2·50	1·90
O57		2 r. carmine and orange (1936)	..	7·50	27·00	
O47/57		..	..	*Set of 11*	12·00	28·00

1935–9. *New types. Optd with Type O 5.*

O58	79	½ a. green (1936)	..	..	10	10
O59	81	1 a. chocolate (1936)	..	..	10	30
O60	59	2 a. vermilion	..	..	15	15
O61		2 a. vermilion (*small die*) (1939)	..	11·00	2·25	
O62	63	4 a. sage-green (1936)	..	..	1·10	50
O58/62		..	..	*Set of 5*	11·50	3·00

1937–39. *King George VI. Optd with Types O 5 or O 6 (rupee values).*

O63	91	½ a. red-brown (1938)	..	..	75	20
O64		9 p. green (1938)	..	..	13·00	55·00
O65		1 a. carmine	..	..	75	20
O66	93	1 r. grey and red-brown (1939)	..	1·00	4·00	
O67		2 r. purple and brown (1939)	..	6·00	5·00	
O68		5 r. green and blue (1939)	..	15·00	50·00	
O63/8		..	..	*Set of 6*	32·00	£100

1ᴬ——1ᴬ	1ᴬ SERVICE 1ᴬ	**PATIALA SERVICE**
(O 7)	(O 8)	(O 9)

1939–40. *Stamp of 1932 (King George V).*

(a) Optd with Types O 5 and O 7

O69	82	1 a. on 1 a. 3 p. mauve	..	..	7·00	1·60
		w. Wmk inverted	..	..	7·00	2·25

(b) Optd with T 4 and O 8

O70	82	1 a. on 1 a. 3 p. mauve (1940)	..	5·00	1·75	
		w. Wmk inverted	..	..	5·50	2·25

"SERVICE" measures 9¼ mm on No. O69 but only 8¾ mm on O70.

1939–44. *(a) Official stamps optd with T 7.*

O71	O 20	3 p. slate (1940)	..	..	45	10
O72		½ a. red-brown	..	..	3·50	10
O73		½ a. purple (1942)	..	..	45	10
O74		9 p. green	..	..	45	20
		w. Wmk inverted	..	..		
O75		1 a. carmine	..	..	1·25	10
O76		1 a. 3 p. yellow-brown (1941)	..	..	85	25
O77		1½ a. dull violet (1944)	..	..	3·50	50
O78		2 a. vermilion (1940)	..	..	5·00	15
		w. Wmk inverted	..	..		
O79		2½ a. bright violet (1940)	..	..	1·25	65
O80		4 a. brown (1943)	..	..	85	1·25
O81		8 a. slate-violet (1944)	..	..	1·75	4·00

(b) Postage stamps optd with Type O 9.

O82	93	1 r. grey and red-brown (1943)	..	6·00	7·00	
O83		2 r. purple and brown (1944)	..	15·00	45·00	
O84		5 r. green and blue (1944)	..	22·00	65·00	
O71/84		..	..	*Set of 14*	55·00	£110

Patiala became part of the Patiala and East Punjab States Union by 20 August 1948.

 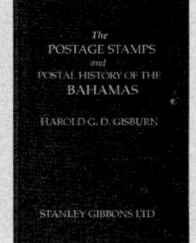

INDIAN FEUDATORY STATES

These stamps were only valid for use within their respective states, *unless otherwise indicated.*

Postage stamps of the Indian States, current at that date, were replaced by those of the Republic of India on 1 April 1950.

Unless otherwise stated, all became obsolete on 1 May 1950 (with the exception of the "Anchal" stamps of Travancore-Cochin, which remained current until 1 July 1951 or Sept 1951 for the Official issues).

ALWAR

Maharao Raja (Maharaja from 1889) Mangal Singh, 1874–1892.

1 (1 a.).

1877. *Litho. Rouletted.*

1	1	¼ a. steel blue	..	..	13·00	7·00
		a. Bright greenish blue	..	..	7·00	7·00
		b. Ultramarine	..	..	3·50	90
		c. Grey-blue *(shades)*	..	..	3·00	80
2		1 a. pale yellowish brown	..	..	7·00	4·50
		a. Brown *(shades)*	..	..	2·75	1·25
		b. Chocolate	..	..	9·00	8·00
		c. Pale reddish brown	..	..	2·00	90

Maharaja Jai Singh, 1892–1937.

1899–1901. *Redrawn. P 12. (a) Wide margins between stamps.*

3	1	¼ a. slate-blue	..	..	6·00	2·50
		a. Imperf between (horiz pair)		..	£300	£350
		b. Imperf between (vert pair)	..		£500	£550
4		¼ a. emerald-green	..		£550	

(b) Narrower margins (1901)

5	1	¼ a. emerald-green	..	..	3·00	2·00
		a. Imperf between (horiz pair)		..	£190	£225
		b. Imperf between (vert pair)	..		£200	£225
		c. Imperf horiz (vert pair)	..		£200	
		d. Imperf (pair)	..		£275	
		e. Pale yellow-green	..	..	5·00	2·00
		ea. Imperf (pair)	..		£450	
		eb. Imperf between (horiz pair)	..		†	£450

In the redrawn type only the bottom outer frameline is thick, whereas in the original 1877 issue the left-hand frameline is also thick, as shown in Type 1.

The stamps of Alwar became obsolete on 1 July 1902.

BAHAWALPUR

See after PAKISTAN

BAMRA

Raja Sudhal Deo, 1869–1903

GUM. The stamps of Bamra were issued without gum.

BAMRA postage ଶ୍ରୀ ... | BAMRA postage ... | BAMRA postage ...

1 (¼ a.)   1a   2 (½ a.)

BAMRA postage ... | BAMRA postage ... | BAMRA postage ...

3 (1 a.)   4 (2 a.)   5 (4 a.)

BAMRA postage ...

6 (8 a.)

(illustrations actual size)

(Typo Jagannata Ballabh Press, Deogarh)

1888. *Imperf.*

1	1	¼ a. black/*yellow*	..	..	£225
		a. "g" inverted (R.5/1)	..	..	£3000
		b. Last native character inverted	..	£3250
		c. Last native character as Type 1*a*	£3250
2	2	½ a. black/*rose*	..	..	70·00
		a. "g" inverted (R.5/1)	..	..	£1500
3	3	1 a. black/*blue*	..	..	45·00
		a. "g" inverted (R.5/1)	..	..	£1300
		b. Scroll inverted (R.8/4)	..	£1100

4	4	2 a. black/*green*	..	..	65·00	£225
		a. "a" omitted (R.8/3)	..		£1500
		b. Scroll inverted (R.8/4)	..		£1300
5	5	4 a. black/*yellow*	..	..	50·00	£200
		a. "a" omitted (R.8/3)	..		£1400
		b. Scroll inverted (R.8/4)	..		£1200
6	6	8 a. black/*rose*	..	..	38·00
		a. "a" omitted (R.8/3)	..		£1200
		b. Horiz pair, one printed on back		£550
		c. Scroll inverted (R.8/4)	..		£1000

These stamps were all printed from the same plate of 96 stamps, 12 × 8, but for some values only part of the plate was used. There are 96 varieties of the ½, 4 and 8 a., 72 of the 1 a., 80 of the 2 a. and not less than 88 of the ¼ a.

The scroll ornament can be found pointing to either the right or the left.

There are two forms of the third native character. In the first five horizontal rows it is as in T 1 and in the last three rows as in T 4.

These stamps have been reprinted: the ¼ a. and ½ a. in blocks of 8 varieties (all showing scroll pointing to right), and all the values in blocks of 20 varieties (all showing scroll pointing to left). On the reprints the fourth character is of a quite different shape.

8

1890 (July)–**93.** *Black on coloured paper. Nos. 24/5 and 39/40 show face value as "One Rupee". (a) "Postage" with capital "P".*

8	8	¼ a. on *rose-lilac*	..	..	3·00	4·00
		a. "Eeudatory" (R. 2/4)	..	13·00	21·00
		b. "Quatrer" (R. 1/3)	..	13·00	21·00
		c. Inverted "e" in "Postage" (R. 2/3)	13·00	21·00
9		¼ a. on *bright rose*	..	1·25	1·90
10		¼ a. on *reddish purple*	..	1·40	1·75
		a. First "a" in "anna" inverted (R. 3/3)	32·00	38·00
		b. "AMRA" inverted (R. 4/4)	48·00	48·00
		c. "M" and second "A" in "BAMRA" inverted (R. 4/4)	60·00	60·00
11		½ a. on *dull green*	..	1·75	2·00
		a. "Eeudatory" (R. 2/4)	..	38·00	45·00
12		½ a. on *blue-green*	..	3·25	3·00
13		1 a. on *bistre-yellow*	..	3·25	1·90
		a. "Eeudatory" (R. 2/4)	..	80·00	85·00
14		1 a. on *orange-yellow*	..	32·00	32·00
		a. "annas" for "anna"	..	£110	£110
15		2 a. on *rose-lilac*	..	12·00	21·00
		a. "Eeudatory" (R. 2/4)	..	£120	£160
16		2 a. on *bright rose*	..	3·00	3·50
17		2 a. on *dull rose*	..	8·00	5·00
18		4 a. on *rose-lilac*	..	£600	£750
		a. "Eeudatory" (R. 2/4)	..	£3750	
19		4 a. on *dull rose*	..	6·50	4·00
		a. "Eeudatory" (R. 2/4)	..	£750	£750
		b. "BAMBA" (R. 2/1)	..	£750	£750
20		4 a. on *bright rose*	..	4·50	6·00
20a		4 a. on *deep pink*	..	12·00	10·00
21		8 a. on *rose-lilac*	..	16·00	40·00
		a. "Foudatory" and "Postagc" (R. 1/2)	£150	£200
		b. "BAMBA" (R. 2/1)	..	£150	£200
22		8 a. on *bright rose*	..	10·00	13·00
23		8 a. on *dull rose*	..	18·00	12·00
24		1 r. on *rose-lilac*	..	38·00	65·00
		a. "Eeudatory" (R. 2/4)	..	£350	£425
		b. "BAMBA" (R. 2/1)	..	£275	£325
		c. "Postagc" (R. 1/2)	..	£275	£325
25		1 r. on *bright rose*	..	15·00	18·00
		a. Small "r" in "rupee"	..	£180	£180

(b) "postage" with small "p" (1891–93)

26	8	¼ a. on *bright rose*	..	1·25	1·90
27		¼ a. on *reddish purple*	..	1·40	1·75
28		½ a. on *dull green*	..	2·25	2·50
		a. First "a" in "anna" inverted (R. 3/3)	25·00	25·00
29		½ a. on *blue-green*	..	3·25	3·00
		a. First "a" in "anna" inverted (R. 3/3)	27·00	27·00
30		1 a. on *bistre-yellow*	..	2·75	2·00
31		1 a. on *orange-yellow*	..	32·00	32·00
32		2 a. on *bright rose*	..	3·00	3·50
33		2 a. on *dull rose* ..	..	8·00	5·00
34		4 a. on *dull rose* ..	..	8·00	3·75
35		4 a. on *bright rose*	..	4·75	6·50
35a		4 a. on *deep pink*	..	15·00	12·00
36		8 a. on *rose-lilac*	..	35·00	65·00
37		8 a. on *bright rose*	..	12·00	14·00
38		8 a. on *dull rose*	..	18·00	12·00
39		1 r. on *rose-lilac*	..	55·00	95·00
40		1 r. on *bright rose*	..	21·00	22·00
		a. Small "r" in "rupee"	..	£225	£225
		b. Small "r" in "rupee" and native characters in the order 2, 3, 1, 4, 5 (R. 4/4)	£1400	£1400

There are 10 settings of Type 8. The first setting (of 20 (4×5)) has capital "P" throughout. The remaining settings (of 16 (4×4)) have capital "P" and small "p" mixed.

For the first setting the 8 a. and 1 r. values were printed within the same block, the ten lefthand stamps being 8 a. values and the ten righthand stamps 1 r.

The various stamps were distributed between the settings as follows:

Setting I—Nos. 8/c, 11/a, 13/a, 15/a, 18/19a, 21, 24/a.
Setting II—Nos. 19, 19b, 21/b, 24, 24b/c, 34, 36, 39
Setting III—Nos. 9, 11, 13, 16, 26, 28, 30, 32
Setting IV—Nos. 20, 22, 25, 35, 37, 40
Setting V—Nos. 10, 10b/c, 20a, 27, 35a
Setting VI—Nos. 11, 12, 28, 28a, 29/a
Setting VII—Nos. 10/a, 12, 17, 19, 23, 25a, 27, 29, 33/4, 38, 40a/b
Setting VIII—Nos. 17, 33
Setting IX—Nos. 10/a, 12, 14/a, 17, 19, 23, 27, 29, 31, 33/4, 38
Setting X—Nos. 19, 34

There are 4 sizes of the central ornament, which represents an elephant's trunk holding a stick: (*a*) 4 mm long; (*b*) 5 mm; (*c*) 6½ mm; (*d*) 11 mm. These ornaments are found pointing to right or left, either upright or inverted.

Ornaments (*a*) are found in all settings; (*b*) in all settings from Settings III to X; (*c*) in Settings I and II; and (*d*) only in Setting I.

The stamps of Bamra have been obsolete since 1 January 1895.

BARWANI

PROCESS. All Barwani stamps are typographed from clichés, and are in sheets of 4, *unless otherwise indicated.*

Issues to about 1930 were printed by the Barwani State Printing Press, and subsequently by the *Times of India* Press, Bombay.

GUM. Nos. 1/31 were issued without gum.

BOOKLET PANES. Those stamps which were printed in sheets of 4 were issued in stamp booklets, binding holes appearing in the side margin.

Rana Ranjit Singh, 1894–1930

1   2   3

1921 (Mar?). *Clear impression. Medium wove paper. P 7 all round.*

1	1	¼ a. blue-green (dull *to* deep)	..	85·00	£250
2		½ a. dull blue	..	..	£200	£400
		a. Imperf (pair)	..		—£1110

No. 1 also exists perforated on two sides only.

1921 (June?). *Blurred impression. Soft wove paper. P 7 on two or three sides.*

3	1	¼ a. green *(shades)*	..	17·00	80·00
4		½ a. ultramarine (dull *to* pale)	..	17·00	£110

NOTE. As the small sheets of Barwani stamps were often not perforated all round, many of the earlier stamps are perforated on two or three sides only. Owing to the elementary method of printing, the colours vary greatly in depth, even within a single sheet.

1921. *Clear impression. Vertically laid bâtonné paper. Imperf.*

5	1	¼ a. green *(shades)*	..	16·00	48·00
6		½ a. green *(shades)*	..	3·75	
		a. Perf 11 at top or bottom only	3·00	

It is suggested that No. 5 may be an error due to printing from the wrong plate.

1922 (?). *Clear impression. Thickish glazed wove paper. P 7 on two or three sides.*

7	1	¼ a. dull blue	..	..	70·00	

1922. *Smooth, soft medium wove paper. P 7 on two or three sides.*

(a) Clear impression

8	1	¼ a. deep grey-blue	..	28·00	70·00

(b) Poor impression

9	1	¼ a. steel blue	..	..	16·00	

Examples of No. 9 exist with perforations on all four sides.

1922. *P 11 on two or three sides.*

(a) Thick, glazed white wove paper

10	2	1 a. vermilion *(shades)*	..	1·90	17·00
		a. Imperf between (vert pair)	..	£200	
		b. Doubly printed	..		£700	
11		2 a. purple (*to* violet)	..	2·00	19·00
		a. Doubly printed	..		£250	
		b. Imperf between (horiz pair)	£160	£225
		c. Imperf between (vert pair)	..	£160	

(b) Thick, toned wove paper

12	2	2 a. purple	..		12·00	40·00

1922. *Poor impression. Thin, poor wove paper. Pin-perf 8½ on two or three sides.*

13	1	¼ a. grey (*to* grey-blue)	..	1·50	35·00
		a. Imperf (pair)	..		£225	
		b. Imperf between (vert pair)	..	£120	

1923. *Thin, smooth, unglazed wove paper. P 11 on two or three sides.*

14	1	½ a. green (pale *to* deep)	..	1·25	16·00
		a. Imperf between (vert pair)	..	£375	
15	2	1 a. brown-red	..		£2250	£2500

1923. *Poor impression. Thick, soft wove paper. P 7.*

16	1	½ a. green (pale *to* deep)	..	24·00	

No. 16 also exists perforated on two or three sides.

1923 (Mar?). *Poor quality wove paper. P 7 on two or three sides.*

17	1	¼ a. black	..	..	55·00	£190
		a. Imperf between (horiz pair)	..	£1500	

1923 (May?). *Horizontally laid bâtonné paper. P 12.*

18	1	¼ a. rose *(shades)*	..	..	1·00	9·50
		a. Imperf between (vert pair)	..	£350	
		ab. Imperf between (horiz pair)	..	£500	
		b. Pin perf 6	..		£100	50·00
		c. Perf compound of 12 and 6	42·00	55·00
		d. Perf 7	..		£400	
		da. On wove paper	..		£1400	

No. 18 was issued in sheets of 12 (3 panes of 4) and was printed on paper showing a sheet watermark of Britannia and a double-lined inscription. No. 18d was only issued in booklet panes of 4.

1925. *Vertically laid bâtonné paper. P 11.*

19	1	¼ a. blue (pale *to* deep)	..	90	9·50
		a. Tête-bêche (horiz pair)			

No. 19 was issued in sheets of 8 and was printed on paper with a sheet watermark of a shell and an inscription "SHELL" in double-lined capitals.

1927. *Very poor impression. Thin, brittle wove paper.* P 7.
20	1	¼ a. milky blue (shades)	..	9·00	28·00
21		½ a. yellow-green (shades)	..	10·00	48·00
		a. Imperf between (horiz pair)		£700	
22	3	4 a. orange-brown	..	60·00	£275
		a. Imperf between (horiz pair)		£1000	
20/2			Set of 3	70·00	£325

On Nos. 20/1 the portrait is nearly invisible.

1927. *Thick wove paper. Sewing machine perf* 6–10.
23	3	4 a. yellow-brown	..	75·00	
		a. Imperf between (horiz pair)		£1500	
		b. Perf 7		20·00	£180
		c. Orange-brown		95·00	£300

1928–32 (?). *Thick glazed paper.* (a) P 7.
24	1	¼ a. deep bright blue	..	11·00	
25		½ a. bright yellow-green	..	21·00	

(b) P 10½ (*rough*) (Nov 1928)
26	1	¼ a. ultramarine	..	4·00	
		a. Tête-bêche (horiz pair)		9·00	
		b. Horiz pair, one stamp printed on reverse			
27		½ a. apple-green	..	4·75	
		a. Tête-bêche (vert pair)		9·00	

(c) P 11 (*clean-cut*) (1929-32?)
28	1	¼ a. bright blue	..	2·25	9·50
		a. Indigo	..	1·75	9·50
		ab. Imperf between (horiz pair)		60·00	
		b. Deep dull blue	..	1·50	9·50
		ba. Imperf between (vert pair)	..	£180	
		c. Ultramarine	..	2·00	10·00
29		½ a. myrtle-green	..	2·75	10·00
		a. Imperf between (horiz pair)		£160	
		b. Turquoise-green	..	3·50	12·00
		ba. Imperf between (vert pair)	..	£350	
30	2	1 a. rose-carmine (1931)	..	11·00	28·00
		a. Imperf between (vert pair)	..	†	£950
31	3	4 a. salmon (to orange) (1931)	..	50·00	£130
		a. Imperf between (horiz pair)		£1400	
28/31			Set of 4	60·00	£160

No. 26 was printed in sheets of 8 (4 × 2) with the two centre pairs *tête-bêche* while No. 27 in similar sheets, had the two horizontal rows *tête-bêche*. Both sheets are always found with one long side imperforate.

Nos. 28/31 were printed in sheets of 8 the two lower values existing either 4 × 2 or 2 × 4 and the two higher values 4 × 2 only. No *tête-bêche* pairs were included in these printings. It is believed that a small printing of No. 31 was produced in sheets of 4, but details are uncertain.

Rana Devi Singh, 1930–1971

4   Rana Devi Singh   5

1932 (Oct)–47. *Medium to thick wove paper.*

A. *Close setting* (2½–4½ mm). P 11, 12 or compound (1932–41)
32A	4	¼ a. slate	..	1·40	15·00
33A		½ a. blue-green	..	1·90	15·00
34A		1 a. brown	..	1·90	14·00
		a. Imperf between (horiz pair)		£1300	
35A		2 a. purple (shades)	..	3·25	24·00
36A		4 a. olive-green	..	6·00	27·00
32A/6A			Set of 5	13·00	85·00

B. *Wide setting* (6–7 mm). P 11 (1945–47)
32B	4	¼ a. slate	..	3·75	20·00
33B		½ a. blue-green	..	3·25	15·00
34B		1 a. brown	..	8·50	15·00
		b. Chocolate. Perf 8½ (1947)		12·50	35·00
35aB		2 a. rose-carmine	..	£170	£350
36B		4 a. olive-green	..	20·00	32·00

The measurements given in the heading indicate the vertical spacing between impressions. There are eight settings of this interesting issue: four "Close" where the overall stamp dimensions from centre to centre of perfs vary in width from 21½ to 23 mm and in height from 25 to 27½ mm; three "Wide", width 23–23½ mm and height 29–30 mm and one "Medium" (26½×31 mm) (No. 34Bb only).

1933–47. P 11.

A. *Close setting* (3–4½ mm). *Thick, cream-surfaced wove paper* (1933 *and* 1941 (*No.* 38Aa)
37A	1	¼ a. black	..	3·00	42·00
38A		½ a. blue-green	..	10·00	23·00
		a. Yellowish green (1941)	..	7·50	20·00
39A	2	1 a. brown (shades)	..	15·00	21·00
42A	3	4 a. sage-green	..	25·00	60·00

B. *Wide setting* (7–10 mm). *Medium to thick wove paper* (1939–47)
37B	1	¼ a. black (1945)	..	2·75	24·00
38aB		½ a. yellowish green (1945)	..	4·25	26·00
39B	2	1 a. brown (shades)	..	11·00	20·00
		a. Perf 8½ (5 mm) (1947)	..	11·00	32·00
40B		2 a. bright purple	..	70·00	£170
41B		2 a. rose-carmine (1945)	..	22·00	85·00
42B	3	4 a. sage-green (1941)	..	24·00	45·00
		a. Pale sage-green (1939)	..	10·00	32·00

There were two "Close" settings (over-all stamp size 25×29 mm) and five "Wide" settings with over-all sizes 26½–31½ × 31–36½ mm. There was also one "Medium" setting (26½×31 mm) but this was confined to the 1 a. perf 8½, No. 39a.

1938. P 11.
43	5	1 a. brown	..	26·00	50·00

Stamps printed in red with designs similar to Types 3 and 5 were intended for fiscal use.

STAMP BOOKLETS

Nos. 1/17, 18d/da and 20/5 are believed to have been issued in sewn or stapled booklets, usually containing thirty-two examples of one value in blocks of 4. All these early booklets had plain covers, often in shades of brown. Few complete booklets have survived from this period.

Nos. 32/47, produced by the *Times of India* Press in a series of nine printings between 1932 and 1947, were only issued in booklet form. Booklets from the 1932, 1933, 1937 and 1939 printings had plain card or paper covers in various colours, usually containing eight blocks of 4, except for the 1933 printing, which contained twenty blocks of 4. Booklets from the 1945 printing had plain white tissue covers from the same stock as the interleaving. All these booklets were stapled at left.

The following booklets, from a printing in 1941 and a series of three printings in 1947, had printed covers, produced by a handstamp in the case of Nos. SB14/15.

1941. *Buff, green (No.* SB3) *or blue (No.* SB7) *card covers inscribed* "BARWANI STATE POSTAGE STAMPS", *booklet value in brackets and number and value of stamps thus* "(Rs 4) 32 2 Annas". *Panes of 4 with margin at left only. Stapled.*

(a) *Booklets* 59×55 mm
SB1	8 a. booklet containing thirty-two ¼ a. (No. 32A)		£250
SB2	1 r. booklet containing thirty-two ½ a. (No. 33A)		£425
SB3	8 r. booklet containing thirty-two 1 a. (No. 34A)		£475
SB4	4 r. booklet containing thirty-two 2 a. (No. 35A)		£275
SB5	8 r. booklet containing thirty-two 4 a. (No. 36A)		£400

(b) *Booklets* 63×60 mm (*No.* SB6) *or* 73×72 mm (*No.* SB7)
SB6	1 r. booklet containing thirty-two ½ a. (No. 38Aa)		£550
SB7	8 r. booklet containing thirty-two 4 a. (No. 42B)		£800

1947. *Grey tissue covers inscribed* "32 STAMPS VALUE....' *Panes of 4 with margins all round. Stapled at left.*

(a) *Booklets* 70×95 mm.
SB 8	1 r. booklet containing thirty-two ½ a. (No. 33B)		£500
SB 9	2 r. booklet containing thirty-two 1 a. (No. 34B)		£750
SB10	8 r. booklet containing thirty-two 4 a. (No. 36B)		£850

(b) *Booklets* 76×95 mm
SB11	8 a. booklet containing thirty-two ¼ a. (No. 37B)		£650
SB12	4 r. booklet containing thirty-two 2 a. (No. 41B)		£700
SB13	8 r. booklet containing thirty-two 4 a. (No. 42Ba)		£400

1947. *Buff paper covers with violet handstamp inscribed* "32 STAMPS VALUE Rs 2/-". *Panes of 4 with margins all round, Sewn with twine at left.*
SB14	2 r. booklets (71×69 mm) containing thirty-two 1 a. (No. 34Bb)		£450
SB15	2 r. booklet (71×73 mm) containing thirty-two 1 a. (No. 39Ba)		£375

1947. *Grey tissue covers inscribed* "32 STAMPS VALUE As 8". *Panes of 4 with margins all round. Stapled at left.*
SB16	8 a. booklet (70×75 mm) containing thirty-two ¼ a. (No. 32B)		£150
SB17	8 a. booklet (85×75 mm) containing thirty-two ¼ a. (No. 37B)		£170

Barwani became part of Madhya Bharat by 1 July 1948

BHOPAL

PRICES FOR STAMPS ON COVER	
Nos. 1/100	*from* × 10
Nos. O301/57	*from* × 15

The correct English inscription on these stamps is "H.H. NAWAB SHAH JAHAN BEGAM". In the case of Nos. 22 and 23 the normal stamps are spelt "BEGAN" and specimens with "BEGAM" are "errors".

As the stamps were printed from lithographic stones on which each unit was drawn separately by hand, numerous errors of spelling occurred. These are constant on all sheets and are listed. Some of our illustrations inadvertently include errors of spelling.

ILLUSTRATIONS. Types 1/3a and 6/12a are shown actual size.

EMBOSSING. Nos. 1/99 were only valid for postage when embossed with the device, in Urdu, of the ruling Begam. On T 1/3 and 6 to 12a. this was intended to fill the central part of the design. Almost all varieties can be found with the embossing inverted or sideways, as well as upright.

Shah Jahan   Sultan Jahan

(*actual size*)

The various basic types were often in concurrent use but for greater convenience the following list is arranged according to types instead of being in strict chronological order.

GUM. Nos. 1/99 were issued without gum.

Nawab Shah Jahan Begam, 16 November 1868–15 June 1901

1 (¼ a.)

1872. *Litho.* (a) *Double frame. Sheets of* 20 (5 × 4)
1	1	¼ a. black	..		£325	£275
		a. "BFGAM" (R.3/1)		£1000	£1000
		b. "BEGAN" (R.2/2, R.4/4)		£600	£600
		c. "EGAM" (R.4/5)		£1000	£1000
2		½ a. red	..		14·00	28·00
		a. "BFGAM" (R.3/1)		60·00	95·00
		b. "BEGAN" (R.2/2, R.4/4)		40·00	70·00
		c. "EGAM" (R.4/5)		60·00	95·00

2 (½ a.)

(b) *Single frame. Sheets of* 20 (4 × 5)
3	2	¼ a. black	..		†	£4500
4		½ a. red	..		21·00	38·00
		a. "NWAB" (R.2/2)	..		95·00	£150

3 (¼ a.)   3a (¼ a.)

1878 (Jan). *All lettered* "EEGAM" *for* "BEGAM". *Sheets of* 20 (4 × 5).

(a) *Plate* 1. *Frame lines extend horiz and vert between stamps throughout sheet*
5	3	¼ a. black	..	4·75	8·50

(b) *Plate* 2. *Frame lines normal*
5a	3a	¼ a. black	..	4·75	10·00

Apart from the frame line difference between Types 3 and 3a the stamps can also be distinguished by the differences in the value tablets, notably the thin vertical line in the centre in Type 3a compared with the slightly diagonal and heavier line in Type 3.

4 (¼ a.)   5 (½ a.)

1878 (June?)–79. *Value in parenthesis (Nos.* 6/7). *Sheets of* 32 (4 × 8). *Imperf.*
6	4	¼ a. green (1879)	..	9·50	16·00
7		¼ a. green (perf) (1879)	..	7·50	11·00
8	5	½ a. red	..	4·75	9·50
		a. "JAHN" (R.5/2)		26·00	
		b. "NWAB" (R.3/2, R.4/2)		16·00	
		c. "EEGAM" (R.1/3)		26·00	
9		½ a. brown	..	21·00	30·00
		a. "JAHN" (R.5/2)		£130	
		b. "NWAB" (R.3/2, R.4/2)		80·00	
		c. "EEGAM" (R.1/3)		£130	

The ¼ a. shows the "N" of "NAWAB" reversed on R.6/4 and the "N" of "JAHAN" reversed on R.1/2–4 and R.2/2–4.

1880. T 5 *redrawn; value not in parenthesis. Sheets of* 32 (4 × 8).

(a) *Imperf*
10		¼ a. blue-green	..	5·50	
		a. "NAWA" (R.2/2–4)		22·00	
		b. "CHAH" (R.8/3)		60·00	
11		½ a. brown-red	..	12·00	15·00

(b) *Perf*
12		¼ a. blue-green	..	7·50	
		a. "NAWA" (R.2/2–4)		32·00	
		b. "CHAH" (R.8/3)		85·00	
13		½ a. brown-red	..	10·00	

The ¼ a. shows the "N" of "NAWAB" reversed on R.8/4. Nos. 12/13 sometimes come with gum.

1884. *T* **5** *again redrawn. Sheets of 32 (4 × 8), some with value in parenthesis, others not. Perf.*
14   ¼ a. greenish blue   ..   ..   3·25   9·00
    a. "ANAWAB" (R.8/1–4)   ..   9·00
   In this plate there is a slanting dash under and to left of the letters "JA" of "JAHAN," instead of a character like a large comma, as on all previous varieties of this design. With the exception of R.1/1 all stamps in the sheet show "N" of "JAHAN" reversed.

1895. *T* **5** *again redrawn. Sheets of 8 (2 × 4). Laid paper.*
15   ¼ a. red (*imperf*)   ..   ..   3·75   1·25
16   ¼ a. red (*perf*) ..   ..   ..   —   £500
   In these cases where the same design has been redrawn several times, and each time in a number of varieties of type, it is not easy to distinguish the various issues. Nos. 6 and 7 may be distinguished from Nos. 10 and 12 by the presence or absence of the parenthesis marks (); 8, 9 and 11 differ principally in colour; 8 and 15 are much alike, but differ in the value as well as in paper.

6 (1 a.)

1881. *Sheets of 24 (4 × 6). Imperf.*
17   6   ¼ a. black   ..   ..   4·00   12·00
    a. "NWAB" (R.6/2–4) ..   9·50
18   ½ a. red   ..   ..   3·25   8·50
    a. "NWAB" (R.6/2–4) ..   8·00
19   1 a. brown   ..   ..   3·00   9·50
    a. "NWAB" (R.6/2–4) ..   7·00
20   2 a. blue   ..   ..   1·40   9·50
    a. "NWAB" (R.6/2–4) ..   4·50
21   4 a. buff   ..   ..   11·00   35·00
    a. "NWAB" (R.6/2–4) ..   29·00
17/21   ..   ..   ..   *Set of 5* 20·00 65·00
   In this issue all values were produced from the same drawing, and therefore show exactly the same varieties of type. The value at foot in this and all the following issues is given in only one form.

7 (½ a.)

1886. *Similar to T* **6** *but normally lettered (incorrectly) "BEGAN"; larger lettering. Sheets of 32 (4 × 8). (a) Imperf.*
22   7   ½ a. pale red   ..   1·40   6·50
    a. "BEGAM" (R.2/1) ..   9·00
    b. "NWAB" (R.3/4)   ..   9·00
(b) Perf
23   7   ½ a. pale red   ..   £250
    a. "BEGAM" (R.2/1) ..   £550
    b. "NWAB" (R.3/4)   ..   £550

8 (4 a.)

1886. *T* **8.** *T* **6** *redrawn. Sheets of 24 (4 × 6). The "M" of "BEGAM" is an inverted "W". The width of the stamps is rather greater than the height. (a) Wove paper. Imperf.*
24   8   4 a. yellow £650
    a. "EEGAM" (R.2/3–4, R.3/3–4, R.4/2, R.4/4, R.6/1)   £750
(b) Laid paper
25   8   4 a. yellow (*imperf*)   ..   7·00
    a. "EEGAM" (R.2/3–4, R.3/3–4, R.4/2, R.4/4, R.6/1)   10·00
26   4 a. yellow (*perf*)   ..   2·75   12·00
    a. "EEGAM" (R.2/3–4, R.3/3–4, R.4/2, R.4/4, R.6/1)   5·00   16·00

1889. *T* **6** *again redrawn. Sheets of 32 (4×8) lettered "BEGAN."*
27   ¼ a. black (*perf*)   ..   1·00   3·75
    a. "EEGAN" (R.7/3)   ..   10·00   21·00
    b. Imperf between (horiz pair)   £200
28   ¼ a. black (*imperf*)   ..   1·10   3·50
    a. "EEGAN" (R.7/3)   ..   12·00   21·00

9 (¼ a.)

1889–90. *T* **9.** *T* **6** *again redrawn. Sheets of 24 (4 × 6), all with "M" like an inverted "W". Wove paper. (a) Imperf.*
29   9   ¼ a. black   ..   ..   1·10   90
30   1 a. brown   ..   ..   1·00   3·50
    a. "EEGAM" (R.2/3) ..   10·00   18·00
    b. "BBGAM" (R.3/1) ..   10·00   18·00
31   2 a. blue   85   1·25
    a. "BBEGAM" (R.1/2) ..   6·50   10·00
    b. "NAWAH" (R.4/2) ..   6·50   10·00
32   4 a. orange-yellow   ..   1·25   2·25
29/32 ..   ..   ..   *Set of 4* 3·75   7·00
(b) Perf
33   9   ¼ a. black   ..   ..   1·25   2·25
34   1 a. brown   ..   ..   3·00   4·25
    a. "EEGAM" (R.2/3) ..   18·00   24·00
    b. "BBGAM" (R.3/1) ..   18·00   24·00
35   2 a. blue ..   ..   ..   1·00   1·60
    a. "BBEGAM" (R.1/2) ..   6·50   13·00
    b. "NAWAH" (R.4/2) ..   6·50   13·00
36   4 a. orange-yellow   ..   1·75   4·50
33/6   ..   ..   ..   *Set of 4* 6·25 11·50
   Nos. 32 and 36 are nearly square, in many cases rather larger in height than in width.

1891. *As last, but sheets of 32 (4 × 8).*
37   9   ½ a. red (*imperf*) ..   ..   1·25   2·25
38   ½ a. red (*perf*)   85   3·25

1894–98. *T* **6** *again redrawn; (a) Sheets of 24 (4 × 6), almost all showing a character inside the octagon below, as in T* **9.** *Wove paper.*
39   1 a. deep brown (*imperf*)   ..   4·75   2·25
    a. Red-brown   ..   ..   26·00
    b. Printed both sides   ..   —   £425
41   1 a. deep brown (*perf*).   ..   4·25   2·25

10 (1 a.)

(b) As Nos. 39/41, but printed from a new stone showing the lines blurred and shaky. Wove paper. Imperf (1898)
42   10   1 a. purple-brown   ..   2·00   2·75
    a. "NAWAH" (R.4/1)   ..   13·00 17·00
43   1 a. purple-brown/*buff* ..   2·00   2·75
    a. "NAWAH" (R.4/1)   ..   13·00 17·00
    b. Printed on both sides   ..
   The above are known without embossing.

11 (¼ a.)

1895. *Sheets of 8 (2 × 4), lettered "EEGAM". White laid paper.*
44   11   ¼ a. black (*imperf*)   ..   2·25   1·50
    a. "A" inserted (R.4/2)..   6·50   5·00
45   ¼ a. black (*perf*)   ..   65·00 30·00
    a. "NAW B" (R.4/2)   ..   £225 £150
   On the perf stamp the second "A" in "NAWAB" was missing on R.4/2 in the setting. This letter was later inserted for the imperf printing varying progressively from small to large.

12 (½ a.)

1895. *Narrow label at bottom. Sheets of 8 (2 × 4), lettered "W W" for "H H". Laid paper.*
46   12   ½ a. black (*imperf*)   ..   1·00   1·50

12a

1895. *Sheets of 8 (2 × 4). Laid paper.*
47   12a   ½ a. red (*imperf*)   ..   1·25   1·25
   No. 47 is a combination of Types 1 and 6, having the double outer frame to the octagon and the value in one form only.

13 (¼ a.)   (14 (¼ a.)

1884. *Sheets of 32 (4 × 8). Perf.*
48   13   ¼ a. blue-green   ..   £130 £160
    a. "JAN" (R.2/1–2, R.3/1, R.3/3–4, R.4/1–3, R.5/1–3) ..   £130 £160
    b. "BEGM" (R.2/3–4)   ..   £350
    c. "NWAB" and "JAN" (R.3/2) ..   £600
    ca. "NWAB" and "JN" (R.5/4) ..   £600
    d. "SHAHAN" (R.4/4)   ..   £600
    e. "JAHA" (R.6/2–4)   ..   £275

1895. *T* **14**, *double-lined frame round each stamp. Sheets of 6 (2 × 3), lettered "JAN". Laid paper.*
49   14   ¼ a. bright green (*imperf*)   ..   3·00   9·00

15 (½ a.)   16 (¼ a.)

1884. *Sheets of 32 (4 × 8). Laid paper.*
50   15   ¼ a. blue-green (*imperf*)..   95·00 £110
    a. "NWAB" (R.1/1)   ..   £300
    b. "SAH" (R.1/4)   ..   £300
    c. "NAWA" and "JANAN" (R.3/2) ..   £300
51   ¼ a. blue-green (*perf*)   ..   55   2·50
    a. "NWAB" (R.1/1)   ..   3·25
    b. "SAH" (R.1/4)   ..   3·25
    c. "NAWA" and "JANAN" (R.3/2) ..   3·25
    d. Imperf between (vert pair)..   £200
52   ½ a. black (*imperf*)   ..   1·75   1·25
    a. "NWAB" (R.1/1)   ..   7·50
    b. "SAH" (R.1/4)   ..   7·50
    c. "NAWA" and "JANAN" (R.3/2) ..   7·50
53   ½ a. black (*perf*)   45   1·75
    a. "NWAB" (R.1/1)   ..   3·00
    b. "SAH" (R.1/4)   ..   3·00
    c. "NAWA" and "JANAN" (R.3/2) ..   3·00
   The ¼ a. of this issue is in *blue-green*, or *greenish blue*. Both values were printed from the same stone, the value alone being altered. There are therefore the same varieties of each. These are the only stamps of this design on laid paper.
   Both values show the "N" of "NAWAB" reversed on R.1/1–4, R.2/1–4, R.3/1–4 and the "N" of "JAHAN" reversed on R.1/1–4, R.2/1–4, R.3/4.

1886. *T* **15** *redrawn. Sheets of 32 (4 × 8). Wove paper.*
54   ¼ a. green (*imperf*)   40   2·00
    a. "NAWA" (R.6/3–4)   ..   1·50
    b. "NWAB" (R.1/1)   ..   2·50
    c. "NWABA" (R.7/4)   ..   2·50
    d. "NAWA" (R.6/2)   ..   2·50
    e. "BEGAAM" and "NWABA" (R.7/3)   2·50
55   ¼ a. green (*perf*)   ..   ..   1·50   2·75
    a. "NAWA" (R.6/3–4)   ..   6·00
    b. "NWAB" (R.1/1)   ..   9·50
    c. "NWABA" (R.7/4)   ..   9·50
    d. "NAWAA" (R.6/2)   ..   9·50
    e. "BEGAAM" and "NWABA" (R.7/3)   9·50
    f. Imperf between (horiz pair)   £130
56   ½ a. red (*imperf*)   45   80
    a. "SAH" (R.1/4)   ..   3·50
    b. "NAWABA" (R.6/3–4)   ..   2·75
   The ¼ a. varies from *yellow-green* to *deep green*.
   All examples of the ¼ a. value show the "N" of "NAWAB" reversed. On the same value the "N" of "JAHAN" is reversed on all positions except R.3/2, R.4/1, R.4/3. On the ½ a. both "N"s are always reversed.

1888. *T* **15** *again redrawn. Sheets of 32 (4 × 8), letters in upper angles smaller. "N" of "NAWAB" correct. Wove paper.*

57	¼ a. deep green (*imperf*)				45	85
	a. "SAH" (R.6/2)				3·50	4·75
	b. "NAWA" (R.4/4)				3·50	4·75
58	¼ a. deep green (*perf*)				75	1·50
	a. "SAH" (R.6/2)					4·25
	b. "NAWA" (R.4/4)					4·25
	c. Imperf between (vert pair)					£180

Nos. 50 to 58 have the dash under the letter "JA" as in No. 14.

1891. *T* **15** *again redrawn. Sheets of 32 (4 × 8), lettered "NWAB". Wove paper. (a) Imperf.*

59	½ a. red				85	65
	a. "SAH" (R.2/4)				3·50	

(b) P 3 to 4½, or about 7

60	½ a. red				60	85
	a. "SAH" (R.2/4)				4·50	

Nos. 59 and 60 have the comma under "JA". The "N" of "JAHAN" is reversed on R.1/1–3, R.2/1–2.

1894. *T* **15** *again redrawn; letters in corners larger than in 1888, value in very small characters. Sheets of 32 (4 × 8), all with "G" in left-hand lower corner. Wove paper.*

61	¼ a. green (*imperf*)				70	70
	a. "NAWAH" (R.4/4)				5·50	6·00
	b. Value in brackets (R.1/1)				5·50	6·00
62	¼ a. green (*perf*)				1·75	1·50
	a. "NAWAH" (R.4/4)				9·00	9·00
	b. Value in brackets (R.1/1)				9·00	9·00

Nos. 61 and 62 have neither the dash nor the comma under "JA".

1896. *T* **16**; *oval narrower, stops after "H.H.", space after "NAWAB". The line down the centre is under the first "H" of "SHAH" or between "HA" instead of being under the second "H" or between "AH". Sheets of 32 (4 × 8). Wove paper. Imperf.*

63	**16**	¼ a. bright green			40	40
	a. "SHAN" (R.1/1)				3·00	
64	¼ a. pale green				40	35
	a. "SHAN" (R.1/1)				3·00	
65	¼ a. black				30	30
	a. "SHAN" (R.1/1)				3·00	

1899. *T* **15** *redrawn. Sheets of 32 (4 × 8), the first "A" of "NAWAB" always absent. Numerous defective and malformed letters. Wove paper. Imperf.*

66	½ a. black				2·75	3·75
	a. "NWASBAHJANNI" (R.2/4)			16·00	19·00
	b. "SBAH" (R.3/3, R.4/3–4, R.5/1–2, R.6/4)		7·00	9·00
	c. "SBAN" (R.8/2)				16·00	19·00
	d. "NWIB" (R.3/2)				16·00	19·00
	e. "BEIAM" (R.4/4)				16·00	19·00
	f. "SHH" (R.6/3)				16·00	19·00
	g. "SBAH" and "BBGAM" (R.3/4)			16·00	19·00
	h. "BBGAM" (R.1/3)				16·00	19·00

17 (8 a.)

18 (¼ a.)

1890. *T* **17.** *Sheets of 10 (2 × 5). Single-line frame to each stamp.*

(a) Wove paper

67	**17**	8 a. slate-green (*imperf*)			35·00	65·00
	a. "HAH" (R.3/1, R.4/1, R.5/1)			50·00	
	b. "JABAN" (R.2/2)				50·00	
68	8 a. slate-green (*perf*)				35·00	65·00
	a. "HAH" (R.3/1, R.4/1, R.5/1)			50·00	
	b. "JABAN" (R.2/2)				50·00	

(b) Thin laid paper

69	**17**	8 a. green-black (*imperf*)			45·00	85·00
	a. "HAH" (R.3/1, R.4/1, R.5/1)			65·00	
	b. "JABAN" (R.2/2)				65·00	
70	8 a. green-black (*perf*)				45·00	85·00
	a. "HAH" (R.3/1, R.4/1, R.5/1)			65·00	
	b. "JABAN" (R.2/2)				65·00	

The "N" of "NAWAB" is reversed on R.5/2 and the "N" of "JAHAN" on R.1/1–2, R.2/2, R.3/2, R.4/2 and R.5/2.

1893. *T* **17** *redrawn. No frame to each stamp, but a frame to the sheet. Sheets of 10 (2 × 5). (a) Wove paper.*

71	8 a. green-black (*imperf*)				16·00	16·00
72	8 a. green-black (*perf*)				21·00	27·00

(b) Thin laid paper. Imperf

73	8 a. green-black				£130	£150

1898. *Printed from a new stone. Lettering irregular. Sheets of 10 (2×5). Wove paper. Imperf.*

74	8 a. green-black				28·00	40·00
	a. Reversed "E" in "BEGAM" (R.1/2, R.3/2)		65·00	
75	8 a. black				28·00	40·00
	a. Reversed "E" in "BEGAM" (R.1/2, R.3/2)		65·00	

1896–1901. *Sheets of 32 (4×8). (a) Wove paper. Imperf.*

76	**18**	¼ a. black			70	70

(b) Printed from a new stone, lines shaky (1899)

77	**18**	¼ a. black			1·60	1·60

(c) The same, on thick wove paper (1901)

78	**18**	¼ a. black			£500	£500

Nawab Sultan Jahan Begam, 16 June 1901–17 May 1926

19 (¼ a.)

20

1902. *T* **19.** *With the octagonal embossed device of the previous issues. Sheets of 16 (4 × 4) ¼ a. or 8 (2 × 4) others. Thin, yellowish wove paper. Imperf.*

79	**19**	¼ a. rose			3·75	6·00
80	¼ a. rose-red				1·60	3·75
81	½ a. black				2·25	4·50
	a. Printed both sides				£450	
82	1 a. brown				3·50	10·00
83	1 a. red-brown				2·75	9·00
84	2 a. blue				5·50	8·50
85	4 a. orange				45·00	75·00
86	4 a. yellow				30·00	60·00
87	8 a. lilac				65·00	£120
88	1 r. rose				£170	£225
79/88					Set of 7	£250	£375

1903. *With a circular embossed device. Sheets of 16 (4×4) ¼ a. (two plates) or 8 (2×4) (others). Wove paper.*

89	**19**	¼ a. rose-red			80	3·00
	a. Laid paper				60	4·75
90	¼ a. red				70	2·75
	a. Laid paper				30	3·75
91	½ a. black				65	3·50
	a. Laid paper				70	4·75
92	1 a. brown				1·10	4·25
	a. Laid paper				65·00	
93	1 a. red-brown				3·75	
	a. Laid paper					
94	2 a. blue				3·50	17·00
	a. Laid paper				£110	
95	4 a. orange (*laid paper*)				£170	£170
96	4 a. yellow				14·00	40·00
	a. Laid paper				90·00	85·00
97	8 a. lilac				35·00	90·00
	a. Laid paper				£950	
98	1 r. rose				50·00	£120
	a. Laid paper				£850	
89/98					Set of 7	95·00	£250

1903. *No. 71 optd with initial of the new Begam, either 6 or 11 mm long, in red.*

99	8 a. green-black				75·00	75·00
	a. Opt inverted				£170	£170

Some of the previous stamps remained on sale (and probably in use) after the issue of the series of 1902, and some of these were afterwards put on sale with the new form of embossing; fresh plates were made of some of the old designs, in imitation of the earlier issues, and impressions from these were also sold with the new embossed device. We no longer list these doubtful items.

(Recess Perkins, Bacon & Co)

1908. *P 13½.*

100	**20**	1 a. green			2·75	2·75
	a. Printed both sides			£100	
	b. Imperf (pair)					

The ordinary postage stamps of Bhopal became obsolete on 1 July 1908.

OFFICIAL STAMPS

SERVICE	SERVICE
(O 1)	(O 2)

(Recess and optd Perkins, Bacon)

1908–11. *As T* **20**, *but inscribed "H.H. BEGUM'S SERVICE" at left. No wmk. P 13 to 14. Overprinted. (a) With Type O 1.*

O301	½ a. yellow-green				1·75	10
	a. Imperf (pair)				£100	
	b. Pair, one without overprint			£400	
	c. Opt double, one inverted			£110	
	ca. Ditto. Imperf (pair)				£130	
	d. Opt inverted				£120	£120
	e. Imperf between (horiz pair)			£450	
O302	1 a. carmine-red				3·25	35
	a. Opt inverted				75·00	75·00
	b. Imperf (pair)				90·00	
	c. Red				4·00	10
O303	2 a. ultramarine				20·00	10
	a. Imperf (pair)				55·00	
O304	4 a. brown (1911)				8·50	25
O301/4					Set of 4	30·00	50

(b) With Type O 2

O305	½ a. yellow-green				4·25	40
O306	1 a. carmine-red				7·00	90
O307	2 a. ultramarine				3·00	40
	a. Opt inverted				25·00	
O308	4 a. brown (1911)				70·00	50
	a. Opt inverted				20·00	65·00
	b. Opt double				90·00	
	c. Imperf (pair)				80·00	
	d. Imperf (pair) and opt inverted			80·00	
O305/8					Set of 4	75·00	2·00

The two overprints differ in the shape of the letters, noticeably in the "R".

MINIMUM PRICE

The minimum price quote is 10p which represents a handling charge rather than a basis for valuing common stamps. For further notes about prices see introductory pages.

Nawab Mohammad Hamidullah Khan

17 May 1926 to transfer of administration to India, 1 June 1949

SERVICE

(O 3)	(O 4)

(Des T. I. Archer. Litho Indian Govt Ptg Wks, Nasik)

1930 (1 July)–**31.** *Type O* **4** (25½ × 30½ mm) *optd with Type O* **3**. *P* 14.

O309	O **4**	½ a. sage-green (1931)			7·00	85
O310	1 a. carmine-red				8·00	15
O311	2 a. ultramarine				7·50	40
O312	4 a. chocolate				6·50	60
O309/12					Set of 4	26·00	1·75

The ½ a., 2 a. and 4 a. are inscribed "POSTAGE" at left.

(Litho Perkins, Bacon)

1932–34. *As Type O* **4** (21 × 25 mm), *but inscr* "POSTAGE" *at left. Optd with Type O* **1**. *(a)* "BHOPAL STATE" *at right. P* 13.

O313	¼ a. orange				2·50	50
	a. Perf 11½ (1933)				4·50	20
	b. Perf 14 (1934)				10·00	30
	c. Perf 13½ (1934)				12·00	30
	ca. Vert pair, one without opt			£110	

(b) "BHOPAL GOVT" *at right. P* 13½

O314	½ a. yellow-green				4·00	10
O315	1 a. carmine-red				7·00	15
	a. Vert pair, one without opt			£200	
O316	2 a. ultramarine				7·00	45
O317	4 a. chocolate				5·50	80
	a. Perf 14 (1934)				12·00	40
O313/17					Set of 5	23·00	1·10

No. O317 is comb-perforated and No. O317a line-perforated.

¼A	THREE PIES	ONE ANNA
(O 5)	(O 6)	(O 7)

1935–36. *Nos. O314, O316 and O317 surch as Types O* **5** *to O* **7**.

O318	O **5**	¼ a. on ½ a. yellow-green (R.)		19·00	11·00
	a. Surch inverted				£120	75·00
	b. Vert pair. Nos. O318/19			29·00	18·00
	ba. Ditto. Surch inverted			£250	£140
O319	O **6**	3 p. on ½ a. yellow-green (R.)		2·50	2·75
	a. "THEEE PIES" (R. 7/10)			55·00	45·00
	b. "THRFE" for "THREE" (R. 10/6)	55·00	45·00
	c. Surch inverted				55·00	38·00
O320	O **5**	¼ a. on 2 a. ultramarine (R.)		19·00	13·00
	a. Surch inverted				£120	60·00
	b. Vert pair. Nos. O320/1			29·00	20·00
	ba. Ditto. Surch inverted			£250	£130
O321	O **6**	3 p. on 2 a. ultramarine (R.)		3·25	3·00
	a. Surch inverted				55·00	35·00
	b. "THEEE PIES" (R. 7/10)			55·00	42·00
	ba. Ditto. Surch inverted			£375	£375
	c. "THRFE" for "THREE" (R. 10/6)	55·00	42·00
	ca. Ditto. Surch inverted			£375	£375
O322	O **5**	¼ a. on 4 a. chocolate (R.)		£650	£190
	a. Vert pair. Nos O322 and O324	£900	£350
O323		¼ a. on 4 a. chocolate (No. O317a/ Blk.) (5.5.36)	50·00	18·00
	a. Vert pair. Nos. O323 and O325	70·00	30·00
O324	O **6**	3 p. on 4 a. chocolate (R.)		75·00	40·00
	a. "THEEE PIES" (R. 7/10)			£375	£325
	b. "THRFE" for "THREE" (R. 10/6)	£375	£325
O325		3 p. on 4 a. chocolate (No. O317a) (Blk.) (25.5.36)	2·50	2·50
	a. "THRER" for "THREE" (R. 8/2)	£225	£150
	b. "FHREE" for "THREE" (R.3/10, 10/1)			£250	£200
	c. "PISE" for "PIES" (R. 10/10)	£375	£300
	d. "PIFS" for "PIES" (R. 7/9)	£225	£170
O326	O **7**	1 a. on ½ a. yellow-green (V.)		2·75	1·50
	a. Surch inverted				60·00	40·00
	b. First "N" in "ANNA" inverted (R. 4/5)			65·00	50·00
	ba. Ditto. Surch inverted			£375	£350
O327		1 a. on 2 a. ultramarine (R.)		2·25	1·75
	a. Surch inverted				60·00	35·00
	b. First "N" in "ANNA" inverted (R. 4/5)			60·00	50·00
	ba. Ditto. Surch inverted			£375	£350
O327d		1 a. on 2 a. ultramarine (V.)		42·00	42·00
	da. Surch inverted				85·00	85·00
	db. First "N" in "ANNA" inverted (R. 4/5)			£375	£375
	dc. Ditto. Surch inverted			£600	£600
O328		1 a. on 2 a. ultram (Blk.) (25.5.36)	70	1·10
	a. "ANNO"				£950	
O329		1 a. on 4 a. chocolate (B.)		3·75	3·75
	a. First "N" in "ANNA" inverted (R. 4/5)			70·00	55·00
	b. Perf 14				7·00	3·50
	ba. Ditto. First "N" in "ANNA" inverted (R. 4/5)			£150	80·00

Nos. O318 to O325 are arranged in composite sheets of 100 (10 × 10). The two upper horizontal rows of each value are surcharged as Type O **5** and the next five rows as Type O **6**. The remaining three rows are also surcharged as Type O **6** but in a slightly narrower setting.

The surcharge on No. O323 differs from Type O **5** in the shape of the figures and letter.

O 8

(Des T. I. Archer. Litho Indian Govt Ptg Wks, Nasik (No. O330).
Typo Bhopal Govt Ptg Wks (others))

1935–39. *As Type O 8.*

(a) *Litho. Inscr* "BHOPAL GOVT POSTAGE". *Optd* "SERVICE".
(13½ *mm*). *P* 13½

O330	1 a. 3 p. blue and claret		3·00	35

(b) *Typo. Inscr* "BHOPAL STATE POSTAGE". *Optd* "SERVICE"
(11 *mm*). *P* 12

O331	1 a. 6 p. blue and claret (1937)		1·50	35
	a. Imperf between (pair)		£110	£120
	b. Opt omitted		£100	80·00
	c. Opt double, one inverted		£275	£275
	d. Imperf (pair)		†	£100
	e. Blue printing double		†	95·00
O332	1 a. 6 p. claret (1939)		4·00	70
	a. Imperf between (pair)		£110	£120
	b. Opt omitted		—	£225
	c. Opt double, one inverted		—	£225
	d. Opt double		—	£250

PRINTERS. From No. O333 all issues were printed by the Bhopal
Govt Ptg Wks in typography.

O 9   O 10 The Moti Mahal

1936 (July)–38. *Optd* "SERVICE". *P* 12.

O333	O 9	¼ a. orange (Br.)		90	20
		a. Imperf between (vert pair)		£120	
		ab. Imperf between (horiz pair)		†	£190
		b. Opt inverted		£225	£170
		c. Black opt		7·00	75
		ca. Opt inverted		†	£225
		cb. Opt double		†	£200
O334		¼ a. yellow (Br.) (1938)		2·00	60
O335		1 a. scarlet		1·25	10
		a. Imperf between (horiz pair)		90·00	85·00
		b. Imperf between (vert pair)		†	£160
		c. Imperf between (block of four)		£225	£225
		d. Imperf vert (horiz pair)		†	95·00

1936–49. *As Type O 10 (various palaces). P* 12.

(a) *Optd* "SERVICE" (13½ *mm*)

O336	½ a. purple-brown and yellow-green			70	55
	a. Imperf between (vert pair)			†	£130
	ab. Imperf between (horiz pair)			†	£130
	b. Opt double			£190	£130
	c. Frame double			95·00	15·00
	d. *Purple-brown and green* (1938)			70	30

(b) *Optd* "SERVICE" (11 *mm*)

O337	2 a. brown and blue (1937)			1·40	30
	a. Imperf between (vert pair)			†	£190
	ab. Imperf between (horiz pair)			†	£140
	b. Opt inverted			£200	£200
	c. Pair, one without opt			£375	
	d. As c. but opt inverted			£550	
O338	2 a. green and violet (1938)			6·50	25
	a. Imperf between (horiz pair)			†	£140
	b. Imperf between (vert strip of 3)			95·00	£140
	c. Frame double			†	£150
	d. Centre double			†	£150
O339	4 a. blue and brown (1937)			2·75	50
	a. Imperf between (horiz pair)			†	£375
	b. Opt omitted			†	£190
	c. Opt double			†	£120
	d. Centre double			†	£200
	e. *Blue and reddish brown* (1938)			2·75	55
	ea. Frame double			†	£150
O340	8 a. bright purple and blue (1938)			3·75	75
	a. Imperf between (vert pair)			†	£225
	b. Opt omitted			†	£100
	c. Opt double			†	£120
	d. Imperf vert (horiz pair) and opt omitted			†	£180
	e. Imperf (pair) and opt omitted			†	£180
O341	1 r. blue and reddish purple (Br.) (1938)			12·00	5·00
	a. Imperf horiz (vert pair)			†	£800
	b. Opt in black (1942)			13·00	4·00
	ba. *Light blue and bright purple*			32·00	27·00
	bb. Laid paper			£425	£450
O336/41			*Set of 6*	24·00	5·50

(c) *Optd* "SERVICE" (11½ *mm*) *with serifs*

O342	1 r. dull blue and bright purple (Blk.) (1949)			40·00	65·00
	a. "SREVICE" for "SERVICE" (R. 6/6)			£130	£170
	b. "SERVICE" omitted			£550	

(d) *Optd* "SERVICE" (13½ *mm*) *with serifs*

O343	8 a. bright purple and blue (1949)			60·00	85·00
	a. "SERAICE" for "SERVICE" (R. 6/5)			£250	£350
	b. Fig "1" for "I" in "SERVICE" (R. 7/1)			£250	£350

The ½ a. is inscr "BHOPAL GOVT" below the arms, other values
have "BHOPAL STATE".

Designs:—(37½ × 22½ *mm*) 2 a. The Moti Masjid; 4 a. Taj
Mahal and Be-Nazir Palaces. (39 × 24 *mm*)—8 a. Ahmadabad
Palace. (45½ × 27½ *mm*)—1 r. Rait Ghat.

O 11 Tiger   O 13 The Moti Mahal

1940. *As Type O 11 (animals). P* 12.

O344	¼ a. bright blue		2·75	80
O345	1 a. bright purple (Spotted Deer)		15·00	1·00

1941. *As Type O 8 but coloured centre inscr* "SERVICE"; *bottom
frame inscr* "BHOPAL STATE POSTAGE". *P* 12.

O346	1 a. 3 p. emerald-green		80	80
	a. Imperf between (pair)		£325	£325

1944–47. *As Type O 13 (various palaces). P* 12.

O347	½ a. green		85	50
	a. Imperf (pair)		†	65·00
	b. Imperf between (vert pair)		†	£120
	c. Doubly printed		†	£100
O348	2 a. violet		6·00	2·50
	a. Imperf (pair)		†	65·00
	c. *Bright purple* (1945)		1·75	2·25
	d. *Mauve* (1947)		11·00	12·00
	e. Error. Chocolate (imperf)		£120	£120
O349	4 a. chocolate		3·75	1·10
	a. Imperf (pair)		†	80·00
	b. Imperf vert (horiz pair)		†	£150
	c. Doubly printed		†	£120
O347/9		*Set of 3*	5·75	3·50

Design inscr "BHOPAL STATE":—2 a. The Moti Masjid; 4 a. Be-
Nazir Palaces.

O 14 Arms of Bhopal   **2 As.**   **2 As.**

                       (O 15)   (O 16)

1944–49. *P* 12.

O350	O 14	3 p. bright blue		65	30
		a. Imperf between (vert pair)	80·00	85·00	
		b. Imperf between (horiz pair)		†	£150
		c. Stamp doubly printed		42·00	
O351		9 p. chestnut (*shades*) (1945)		7·00	2·00
		a. Imperf (pair)		†	£130
		b. *Orange-brown*		2·00	2·50
O352		1 a. purple (1945)		3·75	90
		a. Imperf horiz (vert pair)		†	£225
		b. *Violet* (1946)		6·50	1·90
O353		1½ a. claret (1945)		1·25	50
		a. Imperf between (horiz pair)		†	£200
		b. Imperf between (vert pair)			
O354		3 a. yellow		7·50	8·00
		a. Imperf (pair)		†	£130
		b. Imperf horiz (vert pair)		†	£170
		c. Imperf vert (horiz pair)			
		d. *Orange-brown* (1949)		70·00	65·00
O355		6 a. carmine (1945)		11·00	30·00
		a. Imperf (pair)		†	£140
		b. Imperf horiz (vert pair)		†	£170
		c. Imperf vert (horiz pair)		†	£170
O350/5			*Set of 6*	23·00	38·00

1949 (July). *Surch with Type O 15. P* 12.

O356	O 14	2 a. on 1½ a. claret		2·25	5·00
		a. Stop omitted		12·00	20·00
		b. Imperf (pair)		£150	£170
		ba. Stop omitted (pair)		£425	£450
		c. "2" omitted (in pair with normal)	£500		

The "stop omitted" variety occurs on positions 60 and 69 in the
sheet of 81.

1949. *Surch with Type O 16. Imperf.*

O357	O 14	2 a. on 1½ a. claret		£550	£550
		a. Perf 12		£550	£550

Three different types of "2" occur in the setting of Type O 16.

BHOR

PRICES FOR STAMPS ON COVER	
Nos. 1/2	*from* × 40
No. 3	*from* × 6

GUM. The stamps of Bhor were issued without gum.

Pandit Shankar Rao, 1871–1922

1   2

1879. *Handstamped. Very thick to thin native paper. Imperf.*

1	1	½ a. carmine (*shades*)		1·75	3·50
		a. Tête-bêche (pair)		£600	
2	2	1 a. carmine (*shades*)		3·50	5·00

3

1901. *Typo. Wove paper. Imperf.*

3	3	½ a. red		9·00	30·00

BIJAWAR

PRICES FOR STAMPS ON COVER
The stamps of Bijawar are very rare used on cover.

Maharaja Sarwant Singh, 1899–1941

1   2

(Typo Lakshmi Art Ptg Works, Bombay)

1935 (1 July)–36. (a) *P* 11.

1	1	3 p. brown		4·25	3·00
		a. Imperf (pair)		6·50	
		b. Imperf between (vert pair)		85·00	
		c. Imperf horiz (vert pair)		50·00	
2		6 p. carmine		4·00	3·00
		a. Imperf (pair)		85·00	
		b. Imperf between (vert pair)		80·00	
		c. Imperf between (horiz pair)		85·00	£120
		d. Imperf horiz (vert pair)		85·00	
3		9 p. violet		4·50	3·50
		a. Imperf (pair)		£140	
		b. Imperf between (vert pair)		85·00	
		c. Imperf between (horiz pair)		80·00	
		d. Imperf horiz (vert pair)		80·00	
4		1 a. blue		5·00	4·00
		a. Imperf (pair)		85·00	
		b. Imperf between (vert pair)		85·00	
		c. Imperf between (horiz pair)		£120	
		d. Imperf horiz (vert pair)		85·00	
		e. Imperf vert (horiz strip of 3)		£140	
5		2 a. deep green		5·50	4·75
		a. Imperf (pair)		£100	
		b. Imperf horiz (vert pair)		11·00	
		c. Imperf between (vert pair)		35·00	
		d. Imperf between (horiz pair)		50·00	80·00
1/5			*Set of 5*	21·00	16·00

(b) *Roul* 7 (1936)

6	1	3 p. brown		2·75	2·75
		a. Printed on gummed side		£400	
7		6 p. carmine		4·25	15·00
8		9 p. violet		5·50	75·00
9		1 a. blue		7·00	80·00
10		2 a. deep green		7·50	85·00
6/10			*Set of 5*	24·00	£225

1937 (May). *Typo. P* 9.

11	2	4 a. orange		8·00	60·00
		a. Imperf between (vert pair)		£140	
		b. Imperf (pair)		£200	
12		6 a. lemon		8·50	60·00
		a. Imperf between (vert pair)		£140	
		b. Imperf (pair)		£200	
13		8 a. emerald-green		9·00	75·00
		a. Imperf (pair)		£225	
14		12 a. greenish blue		9·00	75·00
		a. Imperf (pair)		£250	
15		1 r. bright violet		29·00	£110
		a. "1 Rs" for "1 R" (R. 1/2)		48·00	£300
		b. Imperf (pair)		£300	
		ba. "1 Rs" for "1 R" (R. 1/2)		£850	
11/15			*Set of 5*	55·00	£350

The stamps of Bijawar were withdrawn in 1941.

BUNDI

PRICES FOR STAMPS ON COVER	
No. 1	*from* × 2
No. 2	*from* × 4
Nos. 3/53	*from* × 10
Nos. 54/63	*from* × 5
Nos. 64/78	*from* × 2
Nos. 79/92	*from* × 10
Nos. O1/52	*from* × 15
Nos. O53/9	*from* × 20

GUM. Nos. 1/17 were issued without gum.

ILLUSTRATIONS. Types 1/10 and 12/19 are shown actual size.

In Nos. 1 to 17 characters denoting the value are below the
dagger, except in Nos. 2a, 11 and 17.
All Bundi stamps until 1914 are imperforate.

Maharao Raja Raghubir Singh, 1889–1927

1

1894 (May).   *Each stamp with a distinct frame and the stamps not connected by the framing lines. Three vertical lines on dagger. Laid or wove paper.*
1   1   ½ a. slate-grey £4750 £1600
     a. Last two letters of value below the
     rest ..   ..   † £3500

2 (Block of four stamps)

1894 (Dec).   *Stamps joined together, with no space between them. Two vertical lines on dagger. Thin wove paper.*
2   2   ½ a. slate-grey   ..   ..   ..   30·00 32·00
     a. Value at top, name below ..   £170 £190
     b. Right upper ornament omitted ..   £1400 £1400
     c. Last two letters of value below the
     rest £1000 £1000
     d. Left lower ornament omitted   ..   £1400 £1400

3

1896 (Nov).   *Dagger shorter, lines thicker. Stamps separate. Laid paper.*
3   3   ½ a. slate-grey   ..   ..   ..   3·50   7·50
     a. Last two letters of value below the
     rest £300 £375

4 (1 anna)

5 (2 annas)

6 (2 annas)

1897–98.   *No shading in centre of blade of dagger. The stamps have spaces between them, but are connected by the framing lines, both vertically and horizontally. Laid paper.*

I. *Blade of dagger comparatively narrow, and either triangular, as in T 4 and 6, or with the left-hand corner not touching the bar behind it, as in T 5 (1897-98)*
4   4   1 a. Indian red   ..   ..   ..   8·00 18·00
5   5   1 a. red   ..   ..   ..   7·50 13·00
6   2 a. green   ..   ..   ..   9·50 18·00
7   6   2 a. yellow-green   ..   ..   9·00 19·00
8   5   4 a. green   ..   ..   ..   40·00 55·00
9   8 a. Indian red   ..   ..   70·00 £150
10   1 r. yellow/*blue* £160 £300
4/10   *Set of 5* £250 £475

7

II. *Blade varying in shape, but as a rule not touching the bar; value above and name below the dagger, instead of the reverse (Jan 1898)*
11   7   4 a. emerald-green   ..   ..   ..   26·00
     a. Yellow-green   ..   ..   17·00 40·00

8 (½ anna)   9 (8 annas)

III. *Blade wider and (except on the ½ a.) almost diamond shaped; it nearly always touches the bar (1898–1900)*
12   8   ½ a. slate-grey (5.2.98)   ..   ..   2·75   3·00
13   9   1 a. Indian red (7.98)   ..   ..   1·90   1·90
14   2 a. pale green (9.11.98)   ..   7·00 10·00
     a. First two characters of value (= two)
     omitted £1100 £1100
15   8 a. Indian red (7.98)   ..   ..   7·00 11·00
16   1 r. yellow/*blue* (7.98)   ..   21·00 32·00
     a. On wove paper   ..   ..   9·00 19·00
12/16a   *Set of 5* 25·00 40·00

10

IV. *Inscriptions as on No. 11; point of dagger to left (9.11.98)*
17   10   4 a. green   ..   ..   ..   18·00 22·00
     a. Yellow-green   ..   ..   9·00 13·00

All the above stamps are lithographed in large sheets, containing as many varieties of type as there are stamps in the sheets.

11 Raja protecting Sacred Cows

Type 11 was produced from separate clichés printed as a block of four. The same clichés were used for all values, but not necessarily in the same order within the block. The Devanagri inscriptions, "RAJ BUNDI" at top and the face value at bottom, were inserted into the basic clichés as required so that various differences exist within the 58 settings which have been identified.

The denominations may be identified from the following illustrations. The ½ a., 3 a. and rupee values can be easily distinguished by their colours.

Bottom tablets:—

पाव आना   एक आना
¼ a.   1 a.

दो आना   ढाई आना
2 a.   2½ a.

चार आना   छे आना
4 a.   6 a.

आठ आना   दस आना
8 a.   10 a.

बारह आना   एक रुपया
12 a.   1 r.

The nine versions of the inscriptions are as follows:

A   B

Top tablet

Type A.   Top tablet has inscription in two separate words with a curved line over the first character in the second. The second word has three characters. Bottom tablet has short line above the first character in the second word.

Type B.   Top tablet as Type A, but without the curved line over the first character in the second word. Bottom tablet as Type A.

C

Type C.   Top tablet as Type B, but with large loop beneath the first character in the second word. This loop is usually joined to the main character, but is sometimes detached as in the illustration. Bottom tablet as Type A.

D   E
Top tablet   Bottom tablet

Type D.   Top tablet in thinner lettering with the inscription shown as one word of six characters. The fourth character has a curved line above it, as in Type A, and a loop beneath, as in Type C. Bottom tablet as Type A, but thinner letters.

Type E.   Top tablet as Type C. Bottom tablet shows a redrawn first character to the second word. This has the line at top extending over the entire character.

F
Bottom tablet

Type F.   Top tablet as Type B. Bottom tablet as Type E, but first character in second word differs.

G   H

Type G.   Top tablet as Type C, but without dot over first character in second word. There are now four characters in the second word. Bottom tablet as Type E.

Type H.   Top tablet as Type G, but with characters larger and bolder. Bottom tablet as Type E, but with characters larger and bolder.

I

Type I.   Top tablet as Type H. Bottom tablet as Type E.

Some settings contained more than one inscription type within the block of four so that *se-tenant* examples are known of Type B with Type C (¼, 1, 2, 4, 8, 10 and 12 a.), Type C with Type E (¼, ½ and 4 a.) and Type E with Type F (½ and 4 a.). Type F only exists from this mixed setting.

1914 (Oct)–41.   *T* **11**. *Typo. Ungummed paper except for Nos. 73/8.*
     I. *Rouletted in colour*
     (a) Inscriptions as Type A. Thin wove paper (1916–23)
18   ½ a. black   ..   ..   ..   2·25 10·00
19   1 a. vermilion   ..   ..   3·25 17·00
20   2 a. emerald   ..   ..   3·25 26·00
     a. *Deep green (coarse ptg on medium wove paper)* (1923)   ..   ..   2·00   9·00
21   2½ a. chrome-yellow (*shades*) (1917)..   6·00 26·00
22   3 a. chestnut (1917) ..   ..   ..   15·00 28·00

23	4 a. yellow-green	..	.. ..	.. 17·00
24	6 a. cobalt (1917)	..	..	.. 17·00 65·00
25	1 r. reddish violet (1917)	..	..	.. 19·00 80·00

A special printing of the 1 a. took place in late 1917 in connection with the "OUR DAY" Red Cross Society Fund. This had the "RAJ BUNDI" inscription in the bottom tablet with the face value below it. The top tablet carried four Devanagri characters for "OUR DAY". No evidence has been found to suggest that this 1 a. stamp was used for postal purposes (*Price, £170 unused*).

(b) Inscriptions as Type B. Thin wove or pelure paper (1914–23)

25a	¼ a. cobalt (1916)	..	3·00 16·00
26	¼ a. ultramarine (*shades*) (1917)	..	1·75 4·25
	a. *Indigo* (1923)	..	2·75
	b. *Error. Black* (1923)	..	
27	½ a. black	..	2·75 6·00
28	1 a. vermilion (1915)	..	3·00 9·50
	a. *Carmine* (1923) ..		7·00 9·00
	b. *Red* (*shades*) (1923)		4·50 10·00
29	2 a. emerald (*shades*) (1915)		4·75 14·00
30	2½ a. olive-yellow (1917)		5·00 19·00
31	3 a. chestnut (1917)		4·75 26·00
32	4 a. apple-green (1915)		3·50 28·00
32a	4 a. olive-yellow (1917)		£120 £140
33	6 a. pale ultramarine (*shades*) (1917)		9·00 65·00
	a. *Deep ultramarine* (1917)		7·00
34	8 a. orange (1915)		7·50 70·00
35	10 a. olive-sepia (1917)		£225 £475
36	12 a. sage-green (1917)		£550
36a	1 r. lilac (*shades*) (1915)		24·00

(c) Inscriptions as Type C. Thin to medium wove paper (1917–41)

37	¼ a. ultramarine (*shades*) (1923)	..	4·75 5·50
	a. *Indigo* (1923)		4·75 7·00
	b. *Error. Black* (1923)		
	c. *Cobalt* (*medium wove paper*) (1937)		16·00 16·00
38	½ a. black		1·40 4·50
39	1 a. orange-red		13·00 18·00
	a. *Carmine* (1923) ..		11·00
	b. *Deep red* (*medium wove paper*) (1936)		15·00 15·00
40	2 a. emerald		8·00 19·00
	a. *Sage-green*		7·00 19·00
41	4 a. yellow-green (*shades*)		35·00 75·00
	a. *Olive-yellow*		90·00 £130
	b. *Bright apple-green* (*medium wove paper*) (1936)		£375 £225
42	8 a. reddish orange		9·00 50·00
43	10 a. brown-olive		16·00 65·00
	a. *Olive-sepia*		38·00 90·00
	b. *Yellow-brown*		60·00
44	4 a. sage-green		8·50 50·00
45	1 r. lilac		22·00 85·00
46	2 r. red-brown and black		50·00 £140
	a. *Chocolate and black* (*medium wove paper*) (1936)		60·00 £170
47	3 r. blue and red-brown		80·00 £180
	a. *Grey-blue and chocolate* (*medium wove paper*) (1941)		£100
	ab. Chocolate (inscriptions) inverted		£5500
48	4 r. emerald and scarlet		£170 £275
49	5 r. scarlet and emerald		£180 £300

(d) Inscriptions as Type D. Thin wove paper (1918?)

50	2½ a. buff (*shades*)	..	12·00 38·00
51	3 a. red-brown		18·00 20·00
	a. Semi-circle and dot omitted from 4th character		38·00 42·00
52	10 a. bistre..		26·00 80·00
	a. 4th character turned to left instead of downwards		45·00
53	12 a. grey-olive		32·00 85·00
	a. 4th character turned to left instead of downwards		60·00
	b. *Blackish green*		50·00
	ba. 4th character turned to left instead of downwards		80·00

(e) Inscriptions as Type E. (i) Medium wove paper (1930–37)

54	¼ a. deep slate	..	15·00 20·00
54a	¼ a. indigo (*thin wove paper*) (1935)		15·00 20·00
	b. *Cobalt* (1937)		15·00 15·00
55	½ a. black ..		9·50 11·00
56	1 a. carmine-red		19·00 24·00
57	3 a. chocolate (*shades*) (1936)		11·00 27·00
58	4 a. yellow-olive (1935)		£400 £180
	a. *Bright apple-green* (1936)		£400 £180
	ab. No tail to 4th character		£550 £275

(ii) Very thick wove paper (1930–32)

59	¼ a. indigo (1932)	..	16·00 21·00
60	½ a. black		70·00 75·00
61	1 a. bright scarlet (1931)		16·00 19·00
	a. *Carmine-red*		55·00 65·00

(iii) Thin horizontally laid paper (1935)

62	¼ a. indigo	..	4·50 15·00
63	1 a. scarlet-vermilion		7·00 21·00

Nos. 62 and 63 exist in *tête-bêche* blocks of four on the same or opposite sides of the paper.

(f) Inscriptions as Type F. Medium wove paper (1935)

63a	½ a. black	..	75·00
63b	4 a. yellow-olive		£700 £425

(g) Inscriptions as Type G. (i) Horizontally laid paper (1935)

64	½ a. black	..	85·00 85·00
	a. Vert laid paper ..		80·00 80·00
65	1 a. scarlet		70·00 50·00
66	4 a. bright green		20·00 38·00

(ii) Medium wove paper (1936)

66a	½ a. black	..	4·00 24·00
66b	4 a. yellow-green		£1000 £500

(h) Inscriptions as Type H. Medium wove paper (1935–41)

67	¼ a. ultramarine	..	1·75 7·00
68	½ a. black (1938)		75·00 75·00
69	1 a. deep red		6·50 28·00
	a. *Rosine* (1938)		15·00 30·00
70	4 a. emerald (1935)		18·00 27·00
71	4 r. yellow–green and vermilion (1941)		£180
72	5 r. vermilion and yellow-green (1941)		£250

No. 70 shows the currency spelt as "ANE" with the last letter missing and an accent over the Devanagari "N".

II. P 11.

(a) Inscriptions as Type H. Medium wove paper with gum (1939–41)

73	¼ a. ultramarine	..	25·00 38·00
	a. *Greenish blue* (1941)		1·75 48·00
74	½ a. black		30·00 30·00
75	1 a. scarlet-vermilion (1940)		£120 60·00
	a. *Rose* (1940)		12·00 50·00
76	2 a. yellow-green (1941)		16·00 75·00

(b) Inscriptions as Type I. Medium wove paper with gum (1940)

77	½ a. black	..	£120 95·00
78	2 a. bright apple-green		50·00 50·00

FISCAL USE. Collectors are warned that the low values of the later settings of Type **11** were extensively used for fiscal purposes. Stamps which have been fraudulently cleaned of pen-cancels, regummed or provided with forged postmarks are frequently met with. Particular care should be exercised with examples of Nos. 58/a, 64/5, 68/70, 74/5a and 77.

Maharao Raja Ishwari Singh, 1927–1945

20

1941–44. *Typo. P 11.*

79	**20**	3 p. bright blue	..	1·25 3·00
80		6 p. deep blue		3·00 4·50
81		1 a. orange-red		3·25 5·50
82		2 a. chestnut		4·50 12·00
		a. *Deep brown* (*no gum*) (1944)		13·00 15·00
83		4 a. bright green		9·00 35·00
84		8 a. dull green		11·00 12·00
85		1 r. deep blue		30·00 £180
79/85			Set of 7	55·00 £325

The first printing only of Nos. 79/85 is usual with gum; all further printings, including No. 82a, are without gum.

Maharao Raja Bahadur Singh, 1945–1971

21 Maharao Raja Bahadur Singh	22 Bundi

(Typo *Times of India* Press, Bombay)

1947. *P 11.*

86	**21**	¼ a. blue-green	..	1·25 24·00
87		½ a. violet		1·25 24·00
88		1 a. yellow-green		1·25 24·00
89		2 a. vermilion		1·25 45·00
90		4 a. orange		1·25 65·00
91	**22**	8 a. ultramarine		2·00
92		1 r. chocolate		13·00
86/92			Set of 7	19·00

On the 2 and 4 a. the Maharao is in Indian dress.

OFFICIAL STAMPS

PRICES. Prices for Nos. O1/52 are for unused examples. Used stamps are generally worth a small premium over the prices quoted.

वूंदी   **BUNDI**

(O 1)   (O 2)

सरविस   **SERVICE**

BUNDI

SERVICE

(O 3)

1915–41. *T 11 handstamped as Types O 1/3. Ungummed paper except Nos. O47/52.*

A. *Optd with Type O 1.* B. *Optd with Type O 2.* C. *Optd with Type O 3.*

I. Rouletted in colour

		A	B	C

(a) Inscriptions as Type A. Thin wove paper.

			A	B	C
O 1	½ a. black		£250	†	†
	a. Red opt		£225	†	†
O 1b	2 a. emerald		2·25	£225	†
	ba. *Deep green* (*coarse ptg on medium wove paper*)		6·50	13·00	£180
	bb. Red opt		12·00	11·00	†
O 2	2½ a. chrome-yellow (*shades*)..		2·50	12·00	£170
	a. Red opt		£130	£150	†

(a) Inscriptions as Type A. Thin wove paper.

		A	B	C
O 3	3 a. chestnut	3·00	18·00	†
	a. Green opt	£120	†	†
	b. Red opt	£160	£160	†
O 4	6 a. cobalt	24·00	26·00	£190
	a. Red opt	£180	£190	£200
O 5	1 r. reddish violet	40·00	40·00	†
	a. Red opt	£225	£250	†

(b) Inscriptions as Type B. Thin wove or pelure paper

		A	B	C
O 6	¼ a. ultramarine (*shades*)	1·60	1·75	7·50
	a. Red opt	1·25	4·00	£130
O 7	½ a. black	7·00	4·50	26·00
	a. Red opt	4·25	11·00	£140
O 8	1 a. vermilion	4·00	†	†
	a. Red opt		†	†
	b. *Carmine* ..	21·00	12·00	55·00
	c. *Red* (*shades*)		6·00	—
O 9	2 a. emerald (*shades*)	22·00	30·00	†
	a. Red opt		90·00	†
O 9b	4 a. chestnut (R.)		†	†
O10	4 a. apple-green	12·00	60·00	£180
	a. Red opt	£190	†	†
O10b	4 a. olive-yellow	£180	£190	†
	ba. Red opt		£375	†
O11	6 a. pale ultramarine (*shades*)	12·00	£150	†
	a. Red opt	£190	£190	†
	b. *Deep ultramarine*	55·00	70·00	†
	ba. Red opt	£180	£160	†
O12	8 a. orange	42·00	60·00	£200
	a. Red opt	£200	†	†
O13	10 a. olive-sepia	£170	£200	£400
	a. Red opt	£450	£475	£500
O14	12 a. sage-green	£140	£350	£425
	a. Red opt	†	†	£500
O14b	1 r. lilac	£250	†	†

(c) Inscriptions as Type C. Thin to medium wove paper.

		A	B	C
O15	¼ a. ultramarine (*shades*)	2·25	2·25	15·00
	a. Red opt	90	5·00	†
	b. Green opt	2·75	38·00	†
	c. *Cobalt* (*medium wove paper*)	50·00	48·00	£200
	ca. Red opt	38·00	10·00	£100
O16	½ a. black	6·50	3·00	11·00
	a. Red opt	75	8·00	£130
	b. Green opt	3·00	†	†
O17	1 a. orange-red	1·25	†	†
	a. *Carmine*	20·00	8·00	17·00
	b. *Deep red* (*medium wove paper*)	32·00	42·00	70·00
	ba. Red opt	†	£110	†
O18	2 a. emerald	5·00	12·00	60·00
	a. Red opt	†	75·00	†
	b. *Sage-green*	8·00	13·00	75·00
O19	4 a. yellow-green (*shades*)	8·50	65·00	†
	b. Red opt	†	†	†
	c. *Olive-yellow*	£100	£100	†
	ca. Red opt	£225	£225	†
O20	8 a. reddish orange	15·00	24·00	£190
	a. Red opt	£180	£275	†
O21	10 a. brown-olive	42·00	70·00	£200
	a. Red opt	£275	£275	£325
O22	12 a. sage-green	35·00	80·00	£325
	a. Red opt	£375	†	£375
O23	1 r. lilac	£110	†	†
	a. Red opt	£250	†	†
O24	2 r. red-brown and black	£325	£170	†
	a. Red opt	£700	†	†
	b. *Chocolate and black* (*medium wove paper*)	£475	£475	†
O25	3 r. blue and red-brown	£325	£200	†
	a. Red opt	£700	†	†
	b. *Grey-blue & chocolate* (*medium wove paper*)	£700	£700	†
	ba. Red opt	£750	†	†
O26	4 r. emerald and scarlet	£275	£300	†
O27	5 r. scarlet and emerald	£275	£300	†

(d) Inscriptions as Type D. Thin wove paper

		A	B	C
O28	2½ a. buff (*shades*)	15·00	18·00	†
	a. Red opt	£160	†	†
O29	3 a. red-brown	27·00	24·00	†
	a. Variety as No. 51a	48·00	45·00	†
	b. Red opt	†	£250	†
O30	10 a. bistre	35·00	65·00	£350
	a. Variety as No. 52a	60·00	£120	£475
	b. Red opt	£300	£400	†
O31	12 a. grey-olive	50·00	75·00	£300
	a. Variety as No. 53a	80·00	£130	£425
	b. Red opt	£300	£375	†
	ba. Variety as No. 53a	£400	†	†

(e) Inscriptions as Type E. (i) Medium wove paper

		A	B	C
O32	¼ a. deep slate	30·00	15·00	†
	a. Red opt	27·00	35·00	†
O32b	¼ a. indigo (*thin wove paper*)	28·00	32·00	†
	ba. Red opt	27·00	30·00	†
	bb. Green opt	65·00	70·00	†
	c. *Cobalt*	55·00	50·00	£200
	ca. Red opt	35·00	30·00	90·00
O33	½ a. black	32·00	12·00	†
	a. Red opt	22·00	10·00	†
	b. Green opt	£225	£160	†
O34	1 a. carmine-red	28·00	30·00	£200
O35	3 a. chocolate (*shades*)	£170	£110	£200
	a. Red opt	£350	£250	†
O35b	4 a. yellow-olive	†	£375	†
	ba. *Bright apple-green*	£650	†	†

(ii) Very thick wove paper

		A	B	C
O36	¼ a. indigo	9·00	12·00	†
	a. Red opt	18·00	38·00	†
O37	½ a. black	80·00	†	†
	a. Red opt	80·00	90·00	†
O38	1 a. bright scarlet	13·00	12·00	£180
	a. *Carmine-red*	90·00	65·00	†

(iii) Thin horizontally laid paper

		A	B	C
O39	¼ a. indigo	70·00	80·00	†
	a. Red opt	5·00	89·00	£160
O40	1 a. scarlet-vermilion	32·00	20·00	†
	a. Red opt	£200	£225	†

Nos. O39/40a exist in *tête-bêche* blocks of four on the same or opposite sides of the paper.

		A	B	C
(f) Inscriptions as Type F. Medium wove paper				
O40b	½ a. black			†
	ba. Red opt		£200	£300
O40c	4 a. yellow-olive			£500	†

(g) Inscriptions as Type G. (i) Horizontally laid paper

O41	½ a. black (red opt)	£110	£110	†
	a. Vert laid paper	£120	£120	†
	ab. Red opt	£150	60·00	£275
O42	4 a. bright green	£170	£150	†
	a. Red opt	£190	£250	†

(ii) Medium wove paper

O42b	½ a. black	£170	£180	†
	ba. Red opt	£225	£225	†

(h) Inscriptions as Type H. Medium wove paper

O43	¼ a. ultramarine	25·00	75·00	†
	a. Red opt	£160	£225	†
O44	½ a. black	90·00	£130	†
	a. Red opt	75·00	†	£350
O45	1 a. rosine	£150	£140	£325
O46	4 a. emerald	£130	£160	£325
	a. Red opt	£325		£325

II. *P* 11. *(a) Inscriptions as Type H. Medium wove paper with gum.*

O47	¼ a. ultramarine	45·00	75·00	£110
	a. Red opt	70·00	90·00	†
	b. Greenish blue	70·00	70·00	£170
	c. Ditto. Red opt	£170	†	†
O48	½ a. black	45·00	60·00	£275
	a. Red opt	85·00	£200	£150
O49	1 a. scarlet-vermilion	£200	£250	£400
	a. Stamp doubly printed	†	†	£850
	b. Rose	£120	£110	£275
O50	2 a. yellow-green	£325	£150	£200

(b) Inscriptions as Type I. Medium wove paper with gum

O51	½ a. black	£110	£225	£325
	a. Red opt	£250	£300	†
O52	2 a. bright apple-green	£275	£300	£500

Until 1941 it was the general practice to carry official mail free but some of the above undoubtedly exist postally used.

1941. *Nos. 79 to 85 optd* "SERVICE".

O53	20	3 p. bright blue (R.)	4·00	8·50
O54		6 p. deep blue (R.)	11·00	8·50
O55		1 a. orange-red (R.)	10·00	7·50
O56		2 a. brown	8·00	8·50
O57		4 a. bright green	26·00	70·00
O58		8 a. dull green	£100	£325
O59		1 r. deep blue (R.)	£130	£350
O53/9		*Set of 7*	£250	£700

Two different types of "R" occur in the "SERVICE" overprint. On five positions in the sheet of 12 the "R" shows a larger loop and a pointed diagonal leg.

Bundi became part of the Rajasthan Union by 15 April 1948.

BUSSAHIR (BASHAHR)

PRICES FOR STAMPS ON COVER	
Nos. 1/21	*from* × 8
Nos. 22/23	*from* × 2
Nos. 24/43	*from* × 8

Raja Shamsher Singh, 1850–1914

1   2   3

4   5   6

7   8   (9)

The initials are those of the Tika Raghunath Singh, son of the then Raja, who was the organiser and former director of the State Post Office.

(Litho at the Bussahir Press by Maulvi Karam Bakhsh, Rampur)

1895 (20 June). *Laid paper. Optd with T* 9 *in pale greenish blue* (B.), *rose* (R.), *mauve* (M.) *or lake* (L.). *With or without gum.*

(a) Imperf.

1	1	¼ a. pink (M.) (1.9.95)	£1000
		a. Monogram in rose	£1400
2	2	½ a. grey (R.)	£275
		a. Monogram in mauve	†
3	3	1 a. vermilion (M.)	£110
4	4	2 a. orange-yellow (M.)	35·00	£130
		a. Monogram in rose	75·00
		b. Monogram in lake	50·00
		c. Monogram in blue	£120

5	5	4 a. slate-violet (M.)	70·00
		a. Monogram in rose	90·00
		b. Monogram in lake	80·00
		c. Without monogram	£180
6	6	8 a. red-brown (M.)	70·00	£130
		a. Monogram in blue	90·00
		b. Monogram in lake	
		c. Without monogram	£170
		d. Thick paper	85·00
7	7	12 a. green (L.)	£180
		a. Monogram in mauve	
8	8	1 r. ultramarine (R.)	60·00
		a. Monogram in mauve	£120
		b. Monogram in lake	95·00
		c. Without monogram	£190

(b) Perf with a sewing machine; gauge and size of holes varying between 7 and 11½

9	1	¼ a. pink (B.)	38·00	80·00
		a. Monogram in mauve	—	£110
		b. Without monogram	£180	95·00
10	2	½ a. grey (R.)	16·00	90·00
		a. Without monogram	£375	
11	3	1 a. vermilion (M.)	17·00	75·00
		a. Without monogram		
12	4	2 a. orange-yellow (B.)	25·00	80·00
		a. Monogram in rose		
		b. Monogram in mauve	70·00	
		c. Without monogram	—	£170
13	5	4 a. slate-violet (B.)	17·00	85·00
		a. Monogram in rose	25·00	95·00
		b. Monogram in mauve	32·00	
		c. Without monogram	40·00	
14	6	8 a. red-brown (M.)	18·00	90·00
		a. Monogram in blue	42·00	£130
		b. Monogram in mauve	65·00	
		c. Without monogram	£100	
15	7	12 a. green (R.)	50·00	£110
		a. Monogram in mauve	90·00	
		b. Monogram in lake	85·00	
		c. Without monogram	£130	
16	8	1 r. ultramarine (R.)	30·00	90·00
		a. Monogram in mauve	80·00	
		b. Without monogram	£170	£250
9/16		*Set of 8*	£190	£650

1899. *As 1895, but pin-perf or rouletted.*

17	3	1 a. vermilion (M.)	£140	£160
18	4	2 a. orange-yellow (M.)	40·00	£100
		a. Monogram in lake	45·00	
		b. Monogram in mauve	65·00	
		c. Monogram in blue	90·00	
		d. Without monogram	£225	
19	5	4 a. slate-violet (L.)	£180	
		a. Monogram in rose	£225	
		b. Monogram in rose	£225	
		c. Monogram in mauve	£225	
20	7	12 a. green (R.)	£350	£400
21	8	1 r. ultramarine (R.)	£350	

Nos. 1 to 21 were in sheets of 24. They seem to have been overprinted and perforated as required. Those first issued for use were perforated, but they were subsequently supplied imperf, both to collectors and for use. Nos. 17 to 21 were some of the last supplies. No rule seems to have been observed as to the colour of the overprinted monogram; pale blue, rose and mauve were used from the first. The pale blue varies to greenish blue or blue-green, and appears quite green on the yellow stamps. The lake is possibly a mixture of the mauve and the rose—it is a quite distinct colour and apparently later than the others. Specimens without overprint are either remainders left in the Treasury or copies that have escaped accidentally; they have been found sticking to the backs of others that bore the overprint.

Varieties may also be found doubly overprinted, in two different colours.

10   11   12

T 11. Lines of shading above and at bottom left and right of shield.
T 12. White dots above shield and ornaments in bottom corners.

13   14

15   16

(Printed at the Bussahir Press by Maulvi Karam Bakhsh)

1896–97. *Wove paper. Optd with monogram* "R.S.", *T* 9, *in rose. Recess singly from line-engraved dies. With or without gum. Various perfs.*

22	10	¼ a. deep blue (1897)	£650
23	11	½ a. grey-blue (1897)	£475	£170
23a		½ a. deep blue (1897)	£225

No. 23 exists sewing-machine perf about 10 and also perf 14½–16. Nos. 22 and 23a are pin-perf.

1896–1900. *As Nos. 22/3, but lithographed in sheets of various sizes. No gum.*

(a) Imperf

24	10	¼ a. slate-violet (R.)	4·50
		a. Monogram in mauve	6·00
		b. Monogram in blue	8·00
		c. Monogram in lake	12·00
25	11	½ a. blue (shades) (R.)	5·00	12·00
		a. Monogram in mauve	5·50	12·00
		b. Monogram in lake	6·00	
		c. Without monogram		
		d. Laid paper (B.)	75·00	
		da. Monogram in lake		
26	13	1 a. olive (shades) (R.)	10·00	26·00
		a. Monogram in mauve	26·00	
		b. Monogram in lake	26·00	

(b) Pin-perf or rouletted

27	10	¼ a. slate-violet (R.)	13·00	12·00
		a. Monogram in lake	16·00	15·00
		b. Monogram in mauve	—	22·00
28	11	½ a. blue (shades) (R.)	8·50	23·00
		a. Monogram in mauve	11·00	24·00
		b. Monogram in lake	21·00	29·00
		c. Monogram in blue		
		d. Laid paper (M.)		
29	13	1 a. olive (shades) (R.)	16·00	
		a. Monogram in mauve	32·00	32·00
		b. Monogram in lake	35·00	35·00
30	14	2 a. orange-yellow (B.)	£375	£400

The ¼ a. and ½ a. are in sheets of 24, the 1 a. and 2 a. in blocks of 4.

1900–01. *¼ a., 1 a, colours changed; ½ a. redrawn type; 2 a. with dash before* "STATE" *and characters in lower left label; 4 a. new value. No gum.*

(a) Imperf

31	10	¼ a. vermilion (M.)	3·00	6·50
		a. Monogram in blue	3·50	6·00
		b. Without monogram		
31c	12	½ a. blue (M.)	7·00	17·00
		ca. Monogram in rose	22·00	
		cb. Without monogram	35·00	
32	13	1 a. vermilion (M.)	3·00	9·00
		a. Monogram in blue	5·00	6·50
		b. Monogram in lake		
		c. Without monogram	30·00	
33	15	2 a. ochre (M.) (9.00)	29·00	65·00
34		2 a. yellow (M.) (11.00)	29·00	
		a. Monogram in blue	32·00	70·00
		b. Without monogram	55·00	
35		2 a. orange (B.) (1.01)	38·00	65·00
		a. Monogram in mauve	38·00	60·00
		b. Without monogram	48·00	
36	16	4 a. claret (R.)	32·00	80·00
		a. Monogram in mauve	42·00	95·00
		b. Monogram in blue	55·00	£100
		c. Without monogram	29·00	

(b) Pin-perf or rouletted

37	10	¼ a. vermilion (M.)	2·50	6·50
		a. Monogram in blue	3·25	
		b. Without monogram		
37c	12	½ a. blue (M.)	32·00	42·00
38	13	1 a. vermilion (M.)	4·00	9·00
		a. Monogram in blue	7·00	7·50
39		1 a. brown-red (M.) (3.01)	—	£190
40	15	2 a. ochre (M.) (9.00)	40·00	
		a. Monogram in blue		
41		2 a. yellow (M.) (11.00)	30·00	55·00
		a. Monogram in rose	45·00	70·00
		b. Monogram in blue	50·00	80·00
42		2 a. orange (M.) (1.01)	40·00	48·00
		a. Monogram in mauve	55·00	60·00
		b. Without monogram	—	£130
43	16	4 a. claret (R.)	42·00	
		a. Monogram in blue	48·00	£100
		b. Monogram in mauve	70·00	

The ¼ a., ½ a. and 1 a. are in sheets of 24; the 2 a. in sheets of 50 differing throughout in the dash and the characters added at lower left; the 4 a. in sheets of 28.

(17)

The stamps formerly catalogued with large overprint "R.N.S." (T 17) are now believed never to have been issued for use.

Remainders are also found with overprint "P.S.", the initials of Padam Singh who succeeded Raghunath Singh in the direction of the Post Office, and with the original monogram "R.S." in a damaged state, giving it the appearance of a double-lined "R".

The stamps of Bussahir have been obsolete since 1 April 1901. Numerous remainders were sold after this date, and all values were later reprinted in the colours of the originals, or in fancy colours, from the original stones, or from new ones. Printings were also made from new types, similar to those of the second issue of the 8 a., 12 a., and 1 r. values, in sheets of 8.

Reprints are frequently found on laid paper.

Collectors are warned against obliterated copies bearing the Rampur postmark with date "19 MA 1900." Many thousand remainders and reprints were thus obliterated for export after the closing of the State Post Office.

CHARKHARI

PRICES FOR STAMPS ON COVER	
Nos. 1/4	*from* × 2
Nos. 5/26	*from* × 20
Nos. 27/44	*from* × 3
Nos. 45/53	*from* × 100
Nos. 54/5	*from* × 5
No. 56	*from* × 2

Maharaja Malkhan Singh, 1880–1908

1

¼ ½ **1 2 4**

¼ ½ **1 2 4**

The top row shows the figures of value used in the stamps of 1894–97, and the bottom row those for the 1904 issue. In the 4 a. the figure slopes slightly to the right in the first issue, and to the left in the second.

1894. *Typo from a single die. No gum. Imperf.*
1	1	¼ anna, rose	..	..	£950	£700
2		1 annas, dull green	..	..	£1600	£2250
3		2 annas, dull green	..	..	£1800	
4		4 annas, dull green	..	..	£1200	

Nos. 1/2 are known pin-perforated.

1897. *Inscr "ANNA". No gum. Imperf.*
5	1	¼ a. magenta	..	..	35·00	42·00
		a. Purple	..	..	2·50	3·00
		b. Violet	..	..	2·50	2·75
6		½ a. purple	..	..	2·50	3·50
		a. Violet	..	..	2·50	3·00
7	1	1 a. blue-green	..	..	4·75	7·00
		a. Turquoise-blue	..	..	4·00	4·50
		b. Indigo	..	..	11·00	18·00
8		2 a. blue-green	..	..	8·00	14·00
		a. Turquoise-blue	..	..	7·00	8·00
		b. Indigo	..	..	11·00	20·00
9		4 a. blue-green	..	..	8·00	15·00
		a. Turquoise-blue	..	..	6·00	9·00
		b. Indigo	..	..	21·00	32·00
		ba. Figure of value sideways			35·00	
5/9				*Set of 5*	20·00	25·00

Minor varieties may be found with the first "A" in "ANNA" not printed.

All values are known on various coloured papers, but these are proofs or trial impressions.

1904. *Numerals changed as illustrated above. No gum.*
10	1	¼ a. violet	..	..	1·75	2·50
11		½ a. violet	..	..	3·00	3·50
12		1 a. green	..	..	5·00	12·00
13		2 a. green	..	..	21·00	21·00
14		4 a. green	..	..	14·00	25·00
10/14				*Set of 5*	40·00	50·00

Stamps of this issue can be found showing part of the paper-maker's watermark. "Mercantile Script Extra Strong John Haddon & Co.".

Maharaja Jujhar Singh, 1908–1914

2 (Right-hand sword over left)

POSTAGE STAMP

Type I

POSTAGE STAMP

Type II

Type I. "P" of "POSTAGE" in same size as other letters. "E" small with long upper and lower arms. White dot often appears on one or both of the sword hilts.

Type II. "P" larger than the other letters. "E" large with short upper and lower arms. No dots occur on the hilts.

1909–19. *Litho in Calcutta. Wove paper. P 11. (a) Type I.*
15	2	1 p. chestnut	..	..	32·00	40·00
		a. Pale chestnut	..	..	2·75	38·00
		b. Orange-brown	..	..	3·00	38·00
16		1 p. turquoise-blue	..	..	40	45
		a. Imperf between (horiz pair)			£150	
		b. Greenish blue (1911)	..		80	90
		c. Pale turquoise-green	..		1·00	70
17		½ a. vermilion	..	..	1·50	90
		a. Imperf (pair)	..		£650	
		b. Deep rose-red	..		80	1·25
18		1 a. sage-green	..	..	1·75	1·90
		a. Yellow-olive	..		1·60	1·60
19		2 a. grey-blue	..	..	2·75	3·25
		a. Dull violet-blue	..		3·00	3·00
20		4 a. deep green	..	..	3·25	4·25
21		8 a. brown-red	..	..	6·50	14·00
22		1 r. pale chestnut	..	..	11·00	26·00
15a/22				*Set of 8*	26·00	80·00

(b) Type II.
24	2	1 p. turquoise-blue	..	..	2·50	2·50
25		½ a. vermilion	..	..	1·00	1·25
		b. Deep rose-red	..		3·75	3·75
26		1 a. yellow-olive (1919)	..		2·75	2·75
		a. Sage-green	..		1·60	1·60
24/6				*Set of 3*	4·50	4·75

No. 15, from the original printing, shows an upstroke to the "1", not present on other brown printings of this value.
See also Nos. 31/44.

3

POSTAGE STAMP
CHARKHARI STATE C.I.
JI
INDIA
BUNDELKHAND
चरखारी राज्य
1 PICE

4

POSTAGE STAMP
CHARKHARI STATE C.I.
JI
INDIA
BUNDELKHAND
चरखारीराज्य
1 PICE

"J͞I" below Swords.
Right sword overlaps left. Double frame lines.

"JI" below Swords.
Left sword overlaps right. Single frame line.

1912–17. *Handstamped. Wove paper. No gum. Imperf.*
27	3	1 p. violet	..	..	£400	70·00
		a. Dull purple	..		—	80·00
28	4	1 p. violet (1917)	..		7·00	5·00
		a. Dull purple	..		13·00	5·00
		b. Tête-bêche (pair)	..		70·00	70·00
		c. Laid paper	..		—	£250
		d. Pair, one stamp sideways			—	£110

Maharaja Ganga Singh, 1914–1920
Maharaja Arimardan Singh, 1920–1942

5 *(actual size 63 × 25 mm)*   6 (Left-hand sword over right)

1921. *Handstamped. No gum. (a) Wove paper. Imperf.*
29	5	1 a. violet	..	..	65·00	75·00
		a. Dull purple	..		80·00	85·00

(b) Laid paper. P 11.
30	5	1 a. violet	..	..	65·00	£110
		a. Imperf	..		£150	£160

(Typo State Ptg Press, Charkhari)

1930–45. *Wove paper. No gum. Imperf.*
31	6	1 p. deep blue	..		35	12·00
		a. Vert pair, top ptd inverted on back, bottom normal upright			13·00	
		b. Tête-bêche (vert pair)			£190	
		c. Perf 11×imperf (horiz pair) (1939)			35·00	35·00
		d. Bluish slate			21·00	
		e. Laid paper (1944)			—	£300
32		1 p. dull *to* light green *(pelure)* (1943)			42·00	£150
33		1 p. violet (1943)			14·00	£110
		a. Tête-bêche (vert pair)			50·00	
34		½ a. deep olive			85	12·00
35		½ a. red-brown (1940)			3·75	22·00
		a. Tête-bêche (vert pair)			£350	
36		½ a. black *(pelure)* (1943)			48·00	£130
37		½ a. red *(shades)* (1943)			17·00	32·00
		a. Tête-bêche (vert pair)			35·00	
		b. Laid paper (1944)			—	£275
38		½ a. grey-brown			60·00	75·00
39		1 a. green			60	12·00
		a. Emerald (1938)			27·00	45·00
40		1 a. chocolate (1940)			6·00	22·00
		a. Tête-bêche (vert pair)			75·00	
		b. Lake-brown			—	40·00
41		1 a. red (1940)			80·00	55·00
		a. Carmine			—	55·00
		b. Laid paper (1944)			—	£300
42		2 a. light blue			1·25	16·00
		a. Tête-bêche (vert pair)			9·50	
43		2 a. greenish grey (1941?)			38·00	50·00
		a. Tête-bêche (vert pair)			70·00	
		b. Laid paper (1944)			—	£325
		c. Greyish green			60·00	£110
43d		2 a. yellow-green (1945)			—	£450
44		4 a. carmine			3·50	18·00
		a. Tête-bêche (vert pair)			14·00	

There are two different versions of No. 37a, one with the stamps tête-bêche base to base and the other showing them top to top.

7 Imlia Palace   (8) ½ **As.**

(Typo Batliboi Litho Works, Bombay)

1931 (25 June). *T 7 and similar designs. P 11, 11½, 12 or compound.*
45	½ a. blue-green			90	10
	a. Imperf between (horiz pair)			35·00	11·00
	b. Imperf between (vert pair)			35·00	35·00
	c. Imperf horiz (vert pair)			35·00	
46	1 a. blackish brown			1·10	10
	a. Imperf between (horiz pair)			11·00	8·00
	b. Imperf between (vert pair)			12·00	8·00
	c. Imperf horiz (vert pair)			12·00	
47	2 a. violet			70	10
	a. Imperf between (horiz pair)			30·00	25·00
	b. Imperf between (vert pair)			30·00	25·00
	c. Imperf horiz (vert pair)			22·00	
	d. Doubly printed			8·50	
48	4 a. olive-green			90	15
	a. Imperf between (vert pair)			55·00	55·00
49	8 a. magenta			1·10	10
	a. Imperf between (horiz pair)			38·00	25·00
	b. Imperf between (vert pair)			38·00	30·00
	c. Imperf horiz (vert pair)			38·00	13·00
50	1 r. green and rose			1·50	15
	a. Imperf between (vert pair)			£100	£100
	b. Green (centre) omitted			—	£120

51	2 r. red and brown	..		3·00	20
	a. Imperf horiz (vert pair)			80·00	15·00
52	3 r. chocolate and blue-green	..		7·00	30
	a. Imperf between (horiz pair)			—	£150
	b. Tête-bêche (pair)			£160	20·00
	c. Chocolate (centre) omitted			20·00	
53	5 r. turquoise and purple	..		7·50	45
	a. Imperf between (horiz pair)			£150	
	b. Centre inverted			45·00	26·00
	c. Centre doubly printed			—	60·00
45/53			*Set of 9*	21·00	1·40

Designs:—½ a. The Lake; 2 a. Industrial School; 4 a. Bird's-eye view of City; 8 a. The Fort; 1 r. Guest House. 2 r. Palace Gate; 3 r. Temples at Rainpur; 5 r. Goverdhan Temple.

This issue was the subject of speculative manipulation, large stocks being thrown on the market cancelled-to-order at very low prices and unused at less than face value. The issue was an authorized one but was eventually withdrawn by the State authorities.

1939 (Dec)–**40.** *Nos. 21/2 surch as T 8.*
54	2	½ a. on 8 a. brown-red (1940)			26·00	£120
		a. No space between "½" and "As"			32·00	£120
		b. Surch inverted			£250	
		c. "1" of "½" inverted			£225	
55		1 a. on 1 r. chestnut (1940)			75·00	£300
		a. Surch inverted			£275	
56		"1 ANNA" on 1 r. chestnut	..		£500	£550

Maharaja Jaiendra Singh, 1942–1971

Charkhari became part of Vindhya Pradesh by 1 May 1948

COCHIN

(6 puttans = 5 annas. 12 pies = 1 anna; 16 annas = 1 rupee)

Stamps of Cochin were also valid on mail posted to Travancore.

<table>
<tr><td colspan="3">PRICES FOR STAMPS ON COVER</td></tr>
<tr><td>Nos. 1/3</td><td>from</td><td>× 30</td></tr>
<tr><td>Nos. 4/5</td><td>from</td><td>× 10</td></tr>
<tr><td>Nos. 6/6b</td><td>from</td><td>× 3</td></tr>
<tr><td>Nos. 7/9</td><td>from</td><td>× 20</td></tr>
<tr><td>Nos. 11/22</td><td>from</td><td>× 15</td></tr>
<tr><td>Nos. 26/128</td><td>from</td><td>× 8</td></tr>
<tr><td>Nos. O1/105</td><td>from</td><td>× 15</td></tr>
</table>

Raja Kerala Varma I, 1888–1895

COCHIN
HALF PUTTAN
1

COCHIN
TWO PUTTANS
2

(Dies eng P. Orr & Sons, Madras; typo Cochin Govt, Ernakulam)

1892 (13 Apr). *No wmk, or wmk large Umbrella in the sheet. P 12.*
1	1	½ put. buff	..	..	2·00	2·50
		a. Orange-buff	..		2·00	2·25
		b. Yellow	..		2·00	2·75
		c. Imperf (pair)	..			
2		1 put. purple	..		2·25	1·75
		a. Imperf between (vert pair)			†	£1900
3	2	2 put. deep violet	..		1·75	1·90
1/3				*Set of 3*	5·50	5·25

1893. *Laid paper. P 12.*
4	1	½ put. orange-buff	..		£450	£120
		a. Orange	..		—	£120
		b. Yellow	..		—	£120

WATERMARKS. Prior to the 1911–23 issue, printed by Perkins, Bacon & Co, little attention was paid to the position of the watermark. Inverted and sideways watermarks are frequently found in the 1898 and 1902–03 issues.

1894. *Wmk a small Umbrella on each stamp. P 12.*
5	1	½ put. buff	..	..	4·00	3·00
		a. Orange	..		1·50	1·25
		ab. Imperf (pair)				
		b. Yellow	..		3·25	1·00
6		1 put. purple	..		5·50	4·50
7	2	2 put. deep violet	..		3·00	3·25
		a. Imperf (pair)				
		b. Doubly printed				†
		c. Printed both sides				
		d. Tête-bêche (pair)			£2750	
5/7				*Set of 3*	9·00	8·00

The paper watermarked with a small umbrella is more transparent than that of the previous issue. The wmk is not easy to distinguish.

The 1 put. in deep violet was a special printing for fiscal use only.

Raja Rama Varma I, 1895-1914

1896 (End). *Similar to T 1, but 28×33 mm. P 12.*

(a) Wmk Arms and inscription in sheet
8	1 put. violet	..	..		65·00	65·00

(b) Wmk Conch Shell to each stamp
9	1 put. deep violet	..			18·00	30·00

Nos. 8/9 were intended for fiscal use, but are also known used for postal purposes.

3   4

5   6

1898. *Thin yellowish paper. Wmk small Umbrella on each stamp. With or without gum.* P 12.

11	3	3 pies, blue	..	..	1·00	90
		a. Imperf between (horiz pair)	..	£475	
		b. Imperf between (vert pair)		£600	
		c. Doubly printed	..	..		
12	4	½ put. green	..	..	1·50	60
		a. Imperf between (horiz pair)	..		
		b. Stamp sideways (in pair)	..		
13	5	1 put. pink	..	..	3·00	1·50
		a. Tête-bêche (pair)	..	£2250	£2000
		b. Laid paper	..	..	† £1600	
		ba. Laid paper. Tête-bêche (pair)		† £6500	
		c. Red	..	..	2·00	1·40
		d. Carmine-red	..	..	3·00	1·50
14	6	2 put. deep violet	..	..	3·00	1·75
		a. Imperf between (vert pair)		£450	
11/14	..	..	*Set of 4*	6·75	4·25

1902–03. *Thick white paper. Wmk small Umbrella on each stamp. With or without gum.* P 12.

16	3	3 pies, blue	..	..	45	10
		a. Doubly printed	..	..	—	£275
		b. Imperf between (horiz pair)		†	£550
17	4	½ put. green	..	..	85	30
		a. Stamp sideways (in pair)	..	£650	£650
		b. Doubly printed	..	..	—	£275
18	5	1 put. pink (1903)	..	..	1·60	10
		a. Tête-bêche (pair)	..	† £3000	
19	6	2 put. deep violet	..	..	1·90	40
		a. Doubly printed	..	..	£750	£300
16/19	..	..	*Set of 4*	4·25	80

2 (7)   **2** (7a)   **2** (7b)

1909. T 3 (*paper and perf of 1903*), *surch with* T 7. *Wmk is always sideways. No gum.*

22	3	2 on 3 pies, rosy mauve	..	..	15	30
		a. Surch Type 7 inverted	..	75·00	75·00
		b. Surch Type 7a	..	£600	£350
		c. Surch Type 7b	..	..		
		d. Stamps tête-bêche	..	£110	£130
		e. Stamps and surchs tête-bêche	..	£150	£170

Varieties a, d and e were caused by the inversion of one stamp (No. 7) in the plate and the consequent inversion of the corresponding surcharge to correct the error.

Types 7a and 7b were applied by handstamp to correct the omission of the surcharge on R. 3/2 in different settings. Other sheets show a handstamped version of Type 7.

8 Raja Rama Varma I   8a

(Recess Perkins, Bacon & Co)

1911–13. *Currency in pies and annas.* W 8a. P 14.

26	8	2 p. brown	..	..	30	10
		a. Imperf (pair)	..	..		
27		3 p. blue	..	..	35	10
		a. Perf 14×12½	..	27·00	2·50
		w. Wmk inverted	..		
28		4 p. green	..	..	1·25	10
		aw. Wmk inverted	..		
28b		4 p. apple-green	..	..	2·50	40
		bw. Wmk inverted	..		
29		9 p. carmine	..	..	1·10	10
		a. Wmk sideways	..		
30		1 a. brown-orange	..	..	2·25	10
31		1½ a. purple	..	..	5·00	45
32		2 a. grey (1913)	..	..	7·50	40
33		3 a. vermilion (1913)	..	..	30·00	32·00
26/33	..	..	*Set of 8*	42·00	32·00

No. 27a is line perforated. An example of the 3 a. has been reported line, rather than comb, perforated 14.

Raja (Maharaja from 1921) Rama Varma II, 1914–1932

9 Raja Rama Varma II   10

I   (2 p.)   II

I   (1 a.)   II

(Recess Perkins, Bacon & Co)

1916–30. W 8a. P 13½ to 14.

35	10	2 p. brown (Die I) (a)(b)(c)	..	..	4·75	10
		a. Imperf (pair)	..		£500	
		b. Die II (b)(c) (1930)	..		1·25	10
36		4 p. green (a)(b)	..	..	95	10
37		6 p. red-brown (a)(b)(c) (1922)	..	2·00	10
38		8 p. sepia (b) (1923)	..	..	1·40	10
39		9 p. carmine (a)	..	..	14·00	20
40		10 p. blue (b) (1923)	..	..	2·25	10
41	9	1 a. orange (Die I) (a)	..	11·00	75
		a. Die II (a)(b) (1922)	..	8·50	30
42	10	1½ a. purple (b) (1923)	..	2·25	15
43		2 a. grey (a)(b)(d)	..	..	4·25	10
44		2¼ a. yellow-green (a)(d) (1922)	..	4·00	2·50
45		3 a. vermilion (a)(b)	..	..	11·00	35
35/45		..	*Set of 11*	48·00	3·50

Four different perforating heads were used for this issue: (a) comb 13.9; (b) comb 13.6; (c) line 13.8; (d) line 14.2. Values on which each perforation occur are shown above. Stamps with perforation (a) are on hand-made paper, while the other perforations are on softer machine-made paper with a horizontal mesh.

2 **2** **2**

Two pies **Two pies** **Two pies**
(11)   (12)   (13)

2 **2**

Two Pies **Two Pies**
(14)   (15)

1922–29. T 8 (P 14), *surch with* T 11/15.

46	11	2 p. on 3 p. blue	..	..	40	30
		a. Surch double	..	£325	£325
47	12	2 p. on 3 p. blue	..	..	2·25	75
		a. Surch double	..	£500	
		b. "Pies" for "pies" (R. 4/8)	..	38·00	19·00
		ba. Surch double	..		
		c. Perf 12½ at foot	..		
48	13	2 p. on 3 p. blue (6.24)	..	3·00	35
		a. "Pies" for "pies" (R. 4/8)	..	48·00	16·00
		b. Perf 14×12½	..	14·00	16·00
		ba. Ditto. "Pies" for "pies" (R. 4/8)	£200	£225
49	14	2 p. on 3 p. blue (1929)	..	5·00	5·50
		a. Surch double	..	£300	
		b. Surch with Type 15	..	65·00	95·00
		ba. Ditto. Surch double	..	£1300	

There are four settings of these overprints. The first (July 1922) consisted of 39 stamps with Type 11, and 9 with Type 12, and in Type 11 the centre of the "2" is above the "o" of "Two". In the second setting (May 1924) there were 36 of Type 11 and 12 of Type 12, and the centre of the figure is above the space between "Two" and "Pies". The third setting (June 1924) consists of stamps with Type 13 only.

The fourth setting (1929) was also in sheets of 48, No. 49b being the first stamp in the fourth row.

No. 47c is from the bottom row of a sheet and was re-perforated 12½ line at foot as the bottom line of 14 perforations were too far from the design.

ONE ANNA
ഒരു അണ
(16)

Three Pies
3
(17)

ANCHAL &
REVENUE
(16)

�മൂന്ന പൈ
(17)

1928. *Surch with* T 16.

50	10	1 a. on 2¼ a. yellow-green (a)	..	5·00	12·00
		a. "REVENUF" for "REVENUE"	..	48·00	75·00
		b. Surch double	..		

1932–33. *Surch as* T 17. W 8a. P 13½.

51	10	3 p. on 4 p. green (b)	..	1·10	80
		a. "r" in "Three" inverted	..	†	£225
52		3 p. on 8 p. sepia (b)	..	1·10	2·00
53		9 p. on 10 p. blue (b)	..	1·50	2·50
51/3		..	*Set of 3*	3·25	4·75

Maharaja Rama Varma III, 1932–1941

18 Maharaja Rama Varma III

(Recess Perkins, Bacon & Co)

1933–38. T 18 (*but frame and inscription of 1 a. as* T 9). W 8a. P 13 × 13½.

54	18	2 p. brown (1936)	..	..	60	20
55		4 p. green	..	..	60	10
56		6 p. red-brown	..	..	70	10
57	—	1 a. brown-orange	..	..	70	10
58	18	1 a. 8 p. carmine	..	..	3·00	4·00
59		2 a. grey (1938)	..	..	4·25	55
60		2¼ a. yellow-green	..	..	1·50	10
61		3 a. vermilion (1938)	..	4·00	1·25
62		3 a. 4 p. violet	..	..	1·50	1·40
63		6 a. 8 p. sepia	..	..	1·75	9·00
64		10 a. blue	..	..	3·00	10·00
54/64		..	*Set of 11*	19·00	24·00

For stamps in this design, but lithographed, see Nos. 67/71.

1934. *Surcharged as* T 14. W 8a. P 13½.

65	10	6 p. on 8 p. sepia (R.) (b)	..	75	50
66		6 p. on 10 p. blue (R.) (b)	..	1·75	1·60

"DOUBLE PRINTS". The errors previously listed under this description are now identified as blanket offsets, a type of variety outside the scope of this catalogue. Examples occur on issues from 1938 onwards.

SPACING OF OVERPRINTS AND SURCHARGES. The typeset overprints issued from 1939 onwards show considerable differences in spacing. Except for specialists, however, these differences have little significance as they occur within the same settings and do not represent separate printings.

(Litho The Associated Printers, Madras)

1938. W 8a. P 11.

67	18	2 p. brown	..	..	1·00	35
		aw. Wmk inverted	..		
		b. Perf 13×13½	..	..	5·50	60
68		4 p. green	..	..	85	15
		aw. Wmk inverted	..		
		b. Perf 13×13½	..	..	8·00	13·00
69		6 p. red-brown	..	..	2·25	10
		aw. Wmk inverted	..		†	—
		b. Perf 13×13½	..	..	†	£2500
70		1 a. brown-orange	..	..	65·00	75·00
		aw. Wmk inverted	..		
		b. Perf 13×13½	..	..	75·00	80·00
71		2¼ a. sage-green	..	..	6·00	15
		a. Perf 13×13½	..	..	12·00	4·00
67/71		..	*Set of 5*	65·00	75·00

Most examples of Nos. 70/b were used fiscally. Collectors are warned against examples which have been cleaned and regummed or provided with forged postmarks.

ANCHAL **ANCHAL** **THREE PIES**
(19)   (19a)   (20)

SURCHARGED **ANCHAL**

ONE ANNA
THREE PIES **NINE PIES**
(21)   (22)

ANCHAL **ANCHAL**

NINE PIES **SURCHARGED**
NINE PIES
(23)   (24)

1939 (Jan). *Nos. 57 and 70 optd with* T 19/a.

72	18	1 a. brown-orange (recess) (T 19)	..	1·90	55
73		1 a. brown-orange (litho) (T 19)	..	£250	65
		aw. Wmk inverted	..		†	—
		b. Perf 13×13½	..	..	†	£275
74		1 a. brown-orange (litho) (T 19a)	..	75	1·60
		a. Perf 13×13½	..	..	10·00	50

In 1939 it was decided that there would be separate 1 a. stamps for revenue and postal purposes. The "ANCHAL" overprints were applied to stamps intended for postal purposes.

1942–44. T **18** *variously optd or surch.*

I. *Recess-printed stamp. No.* 58

75	3 p. on 1 a. 8 p. carmine (T 20)	..	..	£160	75·00
76	3 p. on 1 a. 8 p. carmine (T 21)	..	..	2·50	6·50
77	6 p. on 1 a. 8 p. carmine (T 20)	..	..	3·00	17·00
78	1 a. 3 p. on 1 a. 8 p. carmine (T 21)	..	..	1·00	30

II. *Lithographed stamps. Nos.* 68, 70 *and* 70b

79	3 p. on 4 p. (T 21)	..	..	5·50	3·50
	a. Perf 13×13½	..	..	13·00	3·50
80	6 p. on 4 p. (T 21)	..	..	£250	£170
	a. "SIX PIES" double	..	..	†	£700
81	6 p. on 1 a. (T 23)	..	..	£225	£150
	a. Perf 13×13½	..	..	90·00	48·00
82	9 p. on 1 a. (T 22)	..	..	95·00	£100
83	9 p. on 1 a. (T 23) (p 13×13½)	..	£180	30·00
84	9 p. on 1 a. (T 24) (p 13×13½)	..	14·00	4·50

Maharaja Kerala Varma II, 1941–1943

26 Maharaja Kerala Varma II

27 (*The actual measurement of this wmk is* 6¼ × 3⅝ *in.*)

(Litho The Associated Printers, Madras)

1943. *Frame of* 1 *a. inscr* "ANCHAL & REVENUE".
P 13×13½. (*a*) W 8*a*.

85	**26**	2 p. grey-brown	..	..	1·00	1·75
		a. Perf 11	..	..	†	£1700
85*b*		4 p. green	..	..	£475	£225
85*c*		1 a. brown-orange	..	..	80·00	90·00
85/*c*		..	..	Set of 3	£500	£275

(*b*) W **27**

86	**26**	2 p. grey-brown	..	..	25·00	1·75
		a. Perf 11	..	..	†	£2000
87		4 p. green	..	..	7·00	16·00
		a. Perf 11	..	..	3·00	3·25
88		6 p. red-brown	..	..	1·25	10
		a. Perf 11	..	..	8·00	1·40
89		9 p. ultramarine (*p* 11)	..	25·00	1·00
		a. Imperf between (horiz pair)	..	£1400
90		1 a. brown-orange	..	..	£200	£150
		a. Perf 11	..	..	21·00	40·00
91		2¼ a. yellow-green	..	..	20·00	1·75
		a. Perf 11	..	..	25·00	7·50

Part of W **27** appears on many stamps in each sheet, while others are entirely without wmk.

Although inscribed "ANCHAL (= Postage) & REVENUE" most examples of Nos. 85*c* and 90/*a* were used fiscally. Collectors are warned against examples which have been cleaned and regummed or provided with forged postmarks.

Maharaja Ravi Varma 1943-1946

1943. T **26** *variously optd or surch.* P 13×13½. (*a*) W 8*a*

92	3 p. on 4 p. (T 21)	..	..	50·00	16·00
92*a*	9 p. on 1 a. (T 23)	..	..	4·75	1·75
92*b*	9 p. on 1 a. (T 24)	..	..	3·75	2·00
92*c*	1 a. 3 p. on 1 a. (T 21)	..	—	£2750

(*b*) W **27**

93	2 p. on 6 p. (T 20)	..	..	75	2·50
	a. Perf 11	..	..	85	2·50
94	3 p. on 4 p. (T 20) (*p* 11)	..	2·50	10
95	3 p. on 4 p. (T 21)	..	..	3·25	10
96	3 p. on 6 p. (T 20)	..	..	85	20
	a. Perf 11	..	..	85	50
97	4 p. on 6 p. (T 20)	..	..	3·00	8·50

No. 92*c* is believed to be an error; a sheet of No. 85*b* having been included in a stock of No. O52 intended to become No. O66.

28 Maharaja Ravi Varma   **29**

I   II

(Litho The Associated Printers, Madras)

1944–48. W **27**. *No gum.* (*a*) Type I. P 11.

98	**28**	9 p. ultramarine (1944)	..	10·00	1·75

(*b*) Type II. P 13

98*a*	**28**	9 p. ultramarine (1946)	..	6·00	12·00
		ab. Perf 13 × 13½	..	30·00	2·50
99		1 a. 3 p. magenta (1948)	..	5·00	7·50
		a. Perf 13 × 13½	..	£160	35·00
100		1 a. 9 p. ultramarine (*shades*) (1948)	..	8·00	11·00
98*a*/100		..	Set of 3	17·00	19·00

Nos. 98*a*/100 are line-perforated, Nos. 98ab and 99a comb-perforated.

Maharaja Kerala Varma III, 1946–48

(Litho The Associated Printers, Madras)

1946–48. *Frame of* 1 *a. inscr* "ANCHAL & REVENUE". W **27**.
No gum (*except for stamps perf* 11). P 13.

101	**29**	2 p. chocolate	..	..	1·50	10
		a. Imperf horiz (vert pair)	..	£1300	£1300
		c. Perf 11	..	..	8·00	60
		d. Perf 11×13	..	..	£375	£140
102		3 p. carmine	..	..	50	10
103		4 p. grey-green	..	..	£1600	80·00
104		6 p. red-brown (1947)	..	20·00	3·00
		a. Perf 11	..	..	£150	3·00
105		9 p. ultramarine	..	..	50	10
		a. Imperf between (horiz pair)	..	†	£1400
106		1 a. orange (1948)	..	..	6·50	25·00
		a. Perf 11	..	..	£500
107		2 a. black	..	..	80·00	7·00
		a. Perf 11	..	..	£110	5·00
108		3 a. vermilion	..	..	50·00	50
101/8		..	Set of 8	£1600	£100

Although inscribed "ANCHAL (=Postage) & REVENUE" most examples of No. 106 were used fiscally.

The 1 a. 3 p. magenta, 1 a. 9 p. ultramarine and 2¼ a. yellow-green in Type **29** subsequently appeared surcharged or overprinted for official use. Examples of the 1 a. 3 p. magenta exist without overprint, but may have not been issued in this state (*Price £275 unused*).

30 Maharaja Kerala Varma III

Tail to turban flaw (R. 1/7)

(Litho The Associated Printers, Madras)

1948–50. W **27** (*upright or inverted*). P 11.

109	**30**	2 p. grey-brown	..	..	1·50	15
		a. Imperf vert (horiz pair)	..	†	£1300
110		3 p. carmine	..	..	75	15
		a. Imperf between (vert pair)	..	†	£1300
111		4 p. green	..	..	10·00	1·50
		a. Imperf vert (horiz pair)	..	£275	£325
112		6 p. chestnut	..	..	12·00	20
		a. Imperf vert (horiz pair)	..	£800
113		9 p. ultramarine	..	..	2·50	15
114		2 a. black	..	..	40·00	40
115		3 a. orange-red	..	..	50·00	50
		a. Imperf vert (horiz pair)	..	£1600
116		3 a. 4 p. violet (1950)	..	90·00	£350
		a. Tail to turban flaw	..	£250
109/16		..	Set of 8	£180	£350

Maharaja Rama Varma IV, 1948–1964

31 Chinese Nets   **32** Dutch Palace

(Litho The Associated Printers, Madras)

1949. W **27**. P 11.

117	**31**	2 a. black	..	..	3·25	5·00
		a. Imperf vert (horiz pair)	..	£425
118	**32**	2¼ a. green	..	..	2·50	4·50
		a. Imperf vert (horiz pair)	..	£425

SIX PIES

ആറു പൈ
(33)

പൈ Normal

പൈ Error

Due to similarities between two Malayalam characters some values of the 1948 provisional issue exist with an error in the second word of the Malayalam surcharge. On Nos. 119, 122 and O103 this occurs twice in the setting of 48. No. 125 shows four examples and No. O104b one. Most instances are as illustrated above, but in two instances on the setting for No. 125 the error occurs on the second character.

1949. *Surch as* T **33**. (i) *On* 1944–48 *issue*. P 13.

119	**28**	6 p. on 1 a. 3 p. magenta	..	3·00	3·25
		a. Incorrect character	..	24·00	24·00
120		1 a. on 1 a. 9 p. ultramarine (R.)	..	80	90

(ii) *On* 1946–48 *issue*

121	**29**	3 p. on 9 p. ultramarine	..	8·00	16·00
122		6 p. on 1 a. 3 p. magenta	..	10·00	11·00
		a. Surch double	..	†	£400
		b. Incorrect character	..	70·00	70·00
123		1 a. on 1 a. 9 p. ultramarine (R.)	..	3·00	1·50
		a. Surch in black	..	†	£2000
		b. Black surch with smaller native characters 7½ mm instead of 10 mm long	..	†	£2750

(iii) *On* 1948–50 *issue*

124	**30**	3 p. on 9 p. ultramarine	..	1·75	1·75
		a. Larger native characters 20 mm instead of 16½ mm long	..	2·25	50
		ab. Imperf between (vert pair)	..	†	£1200
		b. Surch double	..	£400
		c. Surch both sides	..	£325
125		3 p. on 9 p. ultramarine (R.)	..	3·00	2·25
		a. Incorrect character	..	17·00	14·00
126		6 p. on 9 p. ultramarine (R.)	..	75	40
119/26		..	Set of 8	27·00	32·00

The 9 p. ultramarine (T **29**) with 6 p. surcharge (T **33**) in red was prepared for use but not issued (*Price £250 unused*)

1949. *Surch as* T **20**. W **27**. P 13.

127	**29**	6 p. on 1 a. orange	..	55·00	£120
128		9 p. on 1 a. orange	..	70·00	£120

OFFICIAL STAMPS

On	ON	ON
O	G C	G C G
S	S	S
(O 1)	(O 2 Small "ON")	(O 3 "G" without serif)

1913. *Optd with Type* O **1** (3 p.) *or* O **2** (*others*).

O1	**8**	3 p. blue (R.)	..	..	£120	10
		a. Black opt	..	..	†	£1000
		b. Inverted "S"	..	..	—	48·00
		c. Opt double	..	..	†	£500
O2		4 p. green (*wmk sideways*)	..	8·00	10
		a. Opt inverted	..	..	—	£250
O3		9 p. carmine	..	..	85·00	10
		a. Wmk sideways	..	..	15·00	10
		w. Wmk inverted	..	..	†	75·00
O4		1½ a. purple	..	..	35·00	10
		a. Opt double	..	..	£450
O5		2 a. grey	..	..	13·00	10
O6		3 a. vermilion	..	..	48·00	30
O7		6 a. violet	..	..	40·00	2·00
O8		12 a. ultramarine	..	..	38·00	6·00
O9		1½ r. deep green	..	..	26·00	48·00
O1/9		..	Set of 9	£300	55·00

1919–33. *Optd as Type* O **3**.

O10	**10**	4 p. green (*a*) (*b*)	..	3·25	10
		a. Opt double	..	..	£375
O11		6 p. red-brown (*a*) (*b*) (1922)	..	6·00	10
		a. Opt double	..	..	—	£350
		w. Wmk inverted	..	..	†
O12		8 p. sepia (*b*) (1923)	..	11·00	10
O13		9 p. carmine (*a*) (*b*)	..	48·00	10
O14		10 p. blue (*b*) (1923)	..	12·00	10
O15		1½ a. purple (*a*) (1921)	..	5·50	10
O16		2 a. grey (*b*) (1923)	..	40·00	15
O17		2¼ a. yellow-green (*a*) (*b*) (1922)	..	11·00	10
		a. Opt double	..	..	†	£350
O18		3 a. vermilion (*a*) (*b*) (*c*)	..	15·00	25
		a. Opt inverted	..	..	†	£350
O19		6 a. violet (*a*) (*b*) (1924)	..	30·00	50
O19*a*		12 a. ultramarine (*a*) (*b*) (1929)	..	15·00	3·00
O19*b*		1½ r. deep green (*a*) (*b*) (1933)	..	22·00	85·00
O10/19*b*		..	Set of 12	£200	£450

All values exist showing a straight-backed "C" variety on R. 4/1.

8

ON   ON

C   G   C   G

Eight pies   S   S

(O **4** 27½ mm   (O **5** Straight back   (O **6** Circular "O";
high)   to "C")   "N" without serifs)

1923 (Jan)–24. *T* **8** *and* **10** *surch with Type O* **4.**

O20		8 p. on 9 p. carmine (No. O3)		£325	1·40
	a.	"Pies" for "pies" (R. 4/8)		£850	55·00
	b.	Wmk sideways		£130	20
	ba.	"Pies" for "pies" (R. 4/8)		£375	18·00
	c.	Surch double		†	£350
O21		8 p. on 9 p. carm (*a*) (*b*) (No. O13) (11.24)	70·00	10
	a.	"Pies" for "pies" (R. 4/8)		£180	12·00
	b.	Surch double		†	£275
	c.	Opt Type O 3 double		†	£275

Varieties with smaller "i" or "t" in "Eight" and small "i" in "Pies" are also known from a number of positions in the setting.

1925 (Apr). *T* **10** *surch as Type O* **4.**

O22		10 p. on 9 p. carmine (*b*) (No. O13)		65·00	65
	b.	Surch double		†	£275
	c.	Surch 25 mm high (*a*)		£160	90
	ca.	Surch double		†	£300

1929. *T* **8** *surch as Type O* **4.**

O23		10 p. on 9 p. carmine (No. O3a)		£800	8·50
	a.	Surch double		†	£375
	b.	Wmk upright		—	42·00

1929–31. *Optd with Type O* **5.**

O24	**10**	4 p. green (*b*) (1931)		22·00	1·25
	a.	Inverted "S"		£140	11·00
O25		6 p. red-brown (*b*) (*c*) (*d*) (1930)	13·00	10
	a.	Inverted "S"		80·00	40
O26		8 p. sepia (*b*) (1930)		6·00	10
	a.	Inverted "S"		48·00	4·50
O27		10 p. blue (*b*)		6·00	10
	a.	Inverted "S"		48·00	4·75
O28		2 a. grey (*b*) (1930)		24·00	15
	a.	Inverted "S"		£110	7·00
O29		3 a. vermilion (*b*) (1930)		8·00	15
	a.	Inverted "S"		75·00	7·50
O30		6 a. violet (*b*) (*d*) (1930)		65·00	3·00
	a.	Inverted "S"		£400	80·00
O24/30		..	*Set of 7*	£130	4·25

Pie3

No. O32b

1933. *Nos.* O26/7 *surch as T* **14,** *in red.*

O32	**10**	6 p. on 8 p. sepia (*b*)		2·00	10
	a.	Inverted "S"		18·00	4·25
	b.	"3" for "s" in "Pies"			
O33		6 p. on 10 p. blue (*b*)		4·00	10
	a.	Inverted "S"		38·00	3·75

The inverted "S" varieties occur on R.2/1 of one setting of this overprint only.

1933–38. *Recess-printed stamps of 1933–38 optd.*

(a) With Type O **5**

O34	**18**	4 p. green		2·00	10
O35		6 p. red-brown (1934)		2·25	10
O36		1 a. brown-orange		9·50	10
O37		1 a. 8 p. carmine		1·50	20
O38		2 a. grey		9·50	10
O39		2¼ a. yellow-green		4·00	10
O40		3 a. vermilion		35·00	10
O41		3 a. 4 p. violet		1·50	15
O42		6 a. 8 p. sepia		1·50	20
O43		10 a. blue		1·50	50
O34/43			*Set of 10*	60·00	1·50

(b) With Type O **6** *(typo)*

O44	**18**	1 a. brown-orange (1937)		35·00	45
O45		2 a. grey-black (1938)		21·00	1·10
O46		3 a. vermilion (1938)		10·00	1·10
O44/6			*Set of 3*	60·00	2·25

ON   ON

C   G   C   G

S   S

(O **7** Curved back   (O **8**)
to "c")

ON   ON   ON

C   G   C   G   C   G

S   S   S

(O **9** Circular   (O **10** Oval   (O **11**)
"O"; N with   "O")
serifs)

1938–44. *Lithographed stamps of 1938. W* **8a,** *optd.*

(a) With Type O **7** *or O* **8** *(1 a). P* 11

O47	**18**	4 p. green		22·00	1·60
	a.	Inverted "S"		26·00	1·60
	b.	Perf 13×13½		19·00	1·75
O48		6 p. red-brown		20·00	40
	a.	Inverted "S"		23·00	50
O49		1 a. brown-orange		£250	2·50
O50		2 a. grey-black		16·00	70
	a.	Inverted "S"		17·00	70

(b) With Type O **9** *(litho) or O* **10** *(6 p.)*

O51	**18**	6 p. red-brown (*p* 13×13½)		8·00	2·25
O52		1 a. brown-orange		1·00	10
O53		3 a. vermilion		2·75	70

(c) With Type O **11**

O53a	**18**	6 p. red-brown		£750	£325

The inverted "S" varieties, Nos. O47a, O48a and O50a, occur 21 times in the setting of 48.

1942–43. *Unissued stamps optd with Type O* **10.** *Litho. W* 27. *P* 11.

O54	**18**	4 p. green		60·00	13·00
	a.	Perf 13×13½		1·75	60
O55		6 p. red-brown		90·00	11·00
	a.	Perf 13×13½		18·00	90
	ab.	Optd both sides		†	£100
O56		1 a. brown-orange		16·00	5·00
	a.	Perf 13×13½		1·40	3·75
	ab.	Optd both sides			
O56b		2 a. grey-black (1943)		48·00	65
	a.	Opt omitted		†	£1200
O56c		2¼ a. sage-green (1943)		£900	4·25
O56d		3 a. vermilion (1943)		12·00	3·75

1943. *Official stamps variously surch with T* **20** *or* **21.**

(i) On 1½ a. purple, of 1919–33

O57	**10**	9 p. on 1½ a. (T **20**)		£400	20·00

(ii) On recess-printed 1 a. 8 p. carmine of 1933–44 (Type O **5** *opt)*

O58		4 p. on 1 a. 8 p. (T **21**)		4·50	75
O59		9 p. on 1 a. 8 p. (T **20**)		£100	26·00
O60		1 a. 9 p. on 1 a. 8 p. (T **20**)		1·75	1·60
O61		1 a. 9 p. on 1 a. 8 p. (T **21**)		80	30

(iii) On lithographed stamps of 1938–44. P 11. *(a) W* 8a

O62	**18**	3 p. on 4 p. (Types O **7** and **20**)		
		(*p* 13×13½)		19·00	5·00
	a.	Surch double		£300	£150
O63		3 p. on 4 p. (Types O **7** and **21**)		
		(*p* 13×13½)		85·00	45·00
O64		3 p. on 1 a. (Types O **9** and **20**)		1·75	2·25
O65		9 p. on 1 a. (Types O **9** and **20**)		£180	45·00
O66		1 a. 3 p. on 1 a. (Types O **9** and **21**)		£250	90·00

(b) W 27

O67	**18**	3 p. on 4 p. (Types O **10** and **20**)		
		(*p* 13×13½)		75·00	45·00
O67a		3 p. on 4 p. (Types O **10** and **21**)		
		(*p* 13×13½)		£450	
O67b		3 p. on 1 a. (Types O **10** and **20**)		£110	60·00
	ba.	Perf 13×13½		85·00	60·00

1944. *Optd with Type O* **10.** *W* 27. *P* 13×13½.

O68	**26**	4 p. green		18·00	2·75
	a.	Perf 11		£110	4·50
	b.	Perf 13		£250	65·00
O69		6 p. red-brown		1·10	10
	a.	Opt double		—	55·00
	b.	Perf 11		70	10
	ba.	Opt double		—	55·00
	c.	Perf 13		7·00	2·00
O70		1 a. brown-orange		£1600	45·00
O71		2 a. black		3·25	45
O72		2¼ a. yellow-green		2·00	45
	a.	Optd both sides		†	£110
O73		3 a. vermilion		5·50	45
	a.	Perf 11		5·40	40

Stamps perforated 13 × 13½ are from a comb machine; those perforated 13 from a line perforator.

1944. *Optd with Type O* **10** *and variously surch as Types* **20** *and* **21.** *W* 27.

O74	**26**	3 p. on 4 p. (T **20**)		1·75	10
	a.	Perf 11		5·50	45
	ab.	Optd Type O **10** on both sides		†	£120
O75		3 p. on 4 p. (T **21**)		3·75	30
	a.	Perf 11		£375	£160
O76		3 p. on 1 a. (T **20**)		14·00	3·00
O77		9 p. on 6 p. (T **20**)		6·00	1·50
	a.	Stamp printed both sides		
O78		9 p. on 6 p. (T **21**)		3·00	25
O79		1 a. 3 p. on 1 a. (T **20**)		5·00	90
O80		1 a. 3 p. on 1 a. (T **21**)		3·00	45
O74/80			*Set of 7*	32·00	5·50

1946–47. *Stamps of 1944–48 (Head Type II) optd with Type O* **10.** *P* 13.

O81	**28**	9 p. ultramarine		2·25	10
	a.	Stamp printed both sides		†	£350
	b.	Perf 13×13½		3·25	10
O82		1 a. 3 p. magenta (1947)		1·25	20
	a.	Opt double		19·00	12·00
	b.	Optd on both sides		
	ba.	Optd both sides, opt double and inverted on reverse		48·00	
O83		1 a. 9 p. ultramarine (1947)		40	70
	a.	Opt double			
O81/3			*Set of 3*	3·50	90

1948. *Stamps of 1946–48 and unissued values optd with Type O* **2.** *P* 13.

O84	**29**	3 p. carmine		50	10
	a.	Stamp printed both sides		†	—
O85		4 p. grey-green		23·00	4·50
O86		6 p. red-brown		4·50	60
O87		9 p. ultramarine		75	10
O88		1 a. 3 p. magenta		2·00	40
O89		1 a. 9 p. ultramarine		1·75	40
O90		2 a. black		13·00	2·50
O91		2¼ a. yellow-green		16·00	2·50
O84/91			*Set of 8*	55·00	10·00

1949. *Stamps of 1948–50 and unissued values optd with Type O* **7.**

O92	**30**	3 p. carmine		75	15
	a.	"C" for "G" in opt		8·50	3·00
O93		4 p. green		85	25
	a.	Imperf between (horiz or vert pair)		†	£1100
	b.	Optd on reverse		65·00	65·00
	c.	"C" for "G" in opt		11·00	4·25
O94		6 p. chestnut		2·25	10
	a.	Imperf between (vert pair)		†	£1200
	b.	"C" for "G" in opt		17·00	2·75
O95		9 p. ultramarine		2·00	10
	a.	"C" for "G" in opt		14·00	3·75
O96		2 a. black		85	15
	a.	"C" for "G" in opt		13·00	4·25
O97		2¼ a. yellow-green		2·25	4·25
	a.	"C" for "G" in opt		21·00	32·00
O98		3 a. orange-red		1·10	45
	a.	"C" for "G" in opt		16·00	8·00
O99		3 a. 4 p. violet		27·00	25·00
	a.	"C" for "G" in opt		£250	£250
	b.	Tail to turban flaw		£190	
O92/9			*Set of 8*	32·00	27·00

The "C" for "G" variety occurs on R. 1/4. Nos. O92/9, O103/4 and O104b also exist with a flat back to "G" which occurs twice in each sheet on R. 1/5 and R. 2/8.

No. O93 exists with watermark sideways, but can usually only be identified when in multiples.

1949. *Official stamps surch as T* **33.** *(i) On 1944 issue.*

O100	**28**	1 a. on 1 a. 9 p. ultramarine (R.)		60	40

(ii) On 1948 issue

O101	**29**	1 a. on 1 a. 9 p. ultramarine (R.)		16·00	12·00

(iii) On 1949 issue

O103	**30**	6 p. on 3 p. carmine		45	50
	a.	Imperf between (vert pair)		†	£800
	b.	Surch double		†	£275
	c.	"C" for "G" in opt		8·00	8·50
	d.	Incorrect character		8·00	8·50
O104		9 p. on 4 p. green (18 *mm* long)		55	1·50
	a.	Imperf between (horiz pair)		£650	£750
	b.	Larger native characters, 22 mm long		90	70
	ba.	Ditto. Imperf between (horiz pair)	£650	£650
	bb.	Incorrect character		15·00	12·00
	c.	"C" for "G" in opt		12·00	17·00
	ca.	Ditto. Larger native characters, 22 mm long		15·00	12·00
O100/4			*Set of 4*	16·00	12·00

No. O104 exists with watermark sideways, but can usually only be identified when in multiples.

1949. *No. 124a, but with lines of surch* 17½ *mm apart, optd* "SERVICE".

O105	**30**	3 p. on 9 p. ultramarine		60	55
	a.	Imperf between (horiz pair)		†	£1100

From 1 July 1949 Cochin formed part of the new state of Travancore-Cochin. Existing stocks of Cochin issues continued to be used in conjunction with stamps of Travancore surcharged in Indian currency.

DHAR

Raja (Maharaja from 1877) Anand Rao Puar III, 1857–1898

1   2

अर्धा बलड.   अर्धो लिबड.   आर्धा डबल.

No. 1c   No. 1d   No. 2

1897–1900. *Type-set. Colour-fugitive paper. With oval handstamp in black. No gum. Imperf.*

1	**1**	½ p. black/*red* (three characters at bottom left)		2·00	2·50
	a.	Handstamp omitted		£150	
	b.	Line below upper inscription (R. 2/2)	55·00	55·00
	c.	Character transposed (R. 2/3)		22·00	22·00
	d.	Character transposed (R. 2/5)		55·00	
2		½ p. black/*red* (four characters at bottom left)		2·00	2·75
	a.	Handstamp omitted		£180	
3		¼ a. black/*orange*		1·75	2·75
	a.	Handstamp omitted		£225	
4		½ a. black/*magenta*		3·00	3·75
	a.	Handstamp omitted		£225	£190
	b.	Line below upper inscription (R. 2/2)	£100	£110
5		1 a. black/*green*		6·00	10·00
	a.	Handstamp omitted		£400	
	b.	Printed both sides			
	c.	Line below upper inscription (R. 2/2)	£180	£190
6		2 a. black/*yellow*		21·00	32·00
	e.	Top right corner ornament transposed with one from top of frame (R. 2/5)	£100	£130
1/6			*Set of 6*	32·00	48·00

Nos. 1/6 were each issued in sheets of 10 (5 × 2), but may, on the evidence of a single sheet of the ½ pice value, have been printed in sheets of 20 containing two of the issued sheets *tête-bêche.*

Research has identified individual characteristics for stamps printed from each position in the sheet.

The same research suggests that the type remained assembled during the entire period of production, being amended as necessary to provide the different values. Seven main settings have been identified with changes sometimes occurring during their use which form sub-settings.

The distribution of stamps between the main settings was as follows:

Setting I—½ p.
Setting II—½ a., 1 a.
Setting III—1 a.
Setting IV—½ p., ½ a., 1 a.
Setting V—½ p.
Setting VI—½ p. (No. 2), ¼ a.
Setting VII—2 a.

The listed constant errors all occurred during Setting IV.

In No. 1c the three characters forming the second word in the lower inscription are transposed to the order (2) (3) (1) and in No. 1d to the order (3) (2) (1).

On Nos. 1b, 4b and 5c the line which normally appears above the upper inscription is transposed so that it appears below the characters.

All values show many other constant varieties including mistakes in the corner and border ornaments, and also both constant and non-constant missing lines, dots and characters.

Examples of complete forgeries and faked varieties on genuine stamps exist.

Raja (Maharaja from 1918) Udaji Rao Puar II, 1898–1926

(Typo at Bombay)

1898–1900. P 11 to 12.

7	2	½ a. carmine	..	..	..	3·00	5·00
		a. Imperf (pair) ..			..	38·00	
		b. Deep rose	..	..	..	2·50	4·75
8		1 a. claret	..	..	..	2·75	5·00
9		1 a. reddish violet	..	..	..	3·00	10·00
		a. Imperf between (horiz pair)			..	£400	
		b. Imperf (pair) ..			..	£100	
10		2 a. deep green	..	..	..	4·75	18·00
7/10					Set of 4	11·50	35·00

The stamps of Dhar have been obsolete since 31 March 1901.

DUNGARPUR

PRICES FOR STAMPS ON COVER
Nos. 1/15   *from* × 2

Maharawal Lakshman Singh, 1918–1971

1 State Arms

(Litho Shri Lakshman Bijaya Printing Press, Dungarpur)

1933–47. P 11.

1	1	¼ a. bistre-yellow	..	..	..	—	£120
2		¼ a. rose (1935)	..	..	..	—	£350
3		¼ a. red-brown (1937) ..		..	..	—	£225
4		1 a. pale turquoise-blue		..	..	—	£100
5		1 a. rose (1938)	..	..	..	—	£1100
6		1 a. 3 p. deep reddish violet (1935)		..		—	£160
7		2 a. deep dull green (1947)		..	..	—	£190
8		4 a. rose-red (1934)	..	..	..	—	£375

Nos. 2 and 5 are known in a *se-tenant* strip of 3, the centre stamp being the 1 a. value.

2   3   4

Maharawal Lakshman Singh

Three dies of ½ a. (*shown actual size*):

Die I. Size 21×25½ mm. Large portrait (head 5 mm and turban 7½ mm wide), correctly aligned (sheets of 12 and left-hand stamps in subsequent blocks of four *se-tenant* horizontally with Die II)

Die II. Size 20×24½ mm. Large portrait (head 4¾ mm and turban 7 mm wide), but with less detail at foot and with distinct tilt to left (right-hand stamps in sheets of four horizontally *se-tenant* with Die I)

Die III. Size 21×25½ mm. Small portrait (head 4½ mm and turban 6½ mm wide) (sheets of 4)

(Typo L.V. Indap & Co, Bombay)

1939–46. T 2 (various frames) and 3/4. Various perfs.

9	2	¼ a. orange (p 12, 11, 10½ or 10)	..	£375	50·00
10		½ a. verm (Die I) (p 12, 11 or 10½) (1940)	..	£170	38·00
		a. Die II (p 10½) (1944)	..	£170	48·00
		ab. Horiz pair. Die I and Die II	..	£375	120
		b. Die III (p 10) (1945)	..	£225	38·00
		c. Imperf between (vert pair)	..	†	£1700
11		1 a. deep blue (p 12, 11, 10½ or 10)	..	£160	29·00
12	3	1 a. 3 p. brt mauve (p 10½ or 10) (1944)		£425	150
13	4	1½ a. deep violet (p 10) (1946)	..	£450	150
14	2	2 a. brt green (p 12, pin perf 11½) (1943)		£500	£275
15		4 a. brown (p 12, 10½ or 10) (1940)	..	£425	120

Stamps perforated 12, 11 and 10½ were printed in sheets of 12 (4×3) which were imperforate along the top, bottom and, sometimes, at right so that examples exist with one or two adjacent sides imperforate. Stamps perforated 10 were printed in sheets of 4 either imperforate at top, bottom and right-hand side or fully perforated.

Dungarpur became part of Rajasthan by 15 April 1948.

DUTTIA (DATIA)

PRICES FOR STAMPS ON COVER
Nos. 1/15   —
Nos. 16/40   *from* × 20

All the stamps of Duttia were impressed with a circular handstamp (as a rule in *blue*) before issue.

This handstamp shows the figure of Ganesh in the centre, surrounded by an inscription in Devanagari reading "DATIYA STET POSTAJ 1893". Stamps could not be used for postage without this control mark.

PROCESS. Nos. 1/15 were type-set and printed singly. Nos. 16/40 were typo from plates comprising 8 or more clichés.

GUM. The stamps of Duttia (*except No. 25c*) were issued without gum.

Maharaja Bhawani Singh, 1857–1907

Rectangular labels each showing a double hand-drawn frame (in black for the 1 a. and in red for the others), face value in black and the Ganesh handstamp are known on thin cream (½ a.), rose (1 a.), orange (2 a.) or pale yellow (4 a.) paper. These are considered by some specialists to be the first stamps of Duttia, possibly issued during 1893, but the evidence for this is inconclusive.

1 (2 a.)   2 (½ a.)   3 (4 a.)
            Ganesh

1894?. Rosettes in lower corners. Control handstamp in blue. Imperf.

1	1	1½ a. black/green	..	..	..	£6000
2		2 a. grey-blue/yellow	..	..	..	£2500
		a. Handstamp in black	..	..	..	£2250

Only two examples of No. 1 have been reported. In both instances the Devanagari inscription was originally 8 a., but was amended in manuscript to ½ a.

1896. Control handstamp in blue. Imperf.

3	2	1 a. red	..	£2000	£2250
		a. Handstamp in black	..	£2000	£2250

1896. Control handstamp in blue. Imperf.

4	3	¼ a. black/orange	..	£3000
		a. Without handstamp	..	£2000
5		½ a. black/blue-green	..	£3500
		a. Without handstamp	..	£2000
6		2 a. black/yellow	..	£1900
		a. Without handstamp	..	£4250
7		4 a. black/rose	..	£1300

Two types of centre:

I   II

Type I. Small Ganesh. Height 13 mm. Width of statue 11 mm. Width of pedestal 8 mm.
Type II. Large Ganesh. Height 13½ mm. Width of statue 11½ mm. Width of pedestal 11½ mm. "Flag" in god's right hand; "angle" above left. All stamps also show dot at top right corner.

1897–98. Imperf.

8	2	½ a. black/green (I) (value in one group)		45·00	
		a. Tête-bêche (horiz pair)	..	£900	
		b. Value in two groups	..	16·00	£160
		ba. Tête-bêche (vert pair)	..	£950	
		bb. Type II (1898)	..	17·00	
9		1 a. black/white (I)	..	65·00	£180
		a. Tête-bêche (horiz pair)	..	£950	
		b. Laid paper	..	15·00	
		ba. Tête-bêche (vert pair)	..	£900	
		c. Type II (1898)	..	65·00	
		ca. Laid paper	..	17·00	
10		2 a. black/yellow (I)	..	21·00	£170
		a. On lemon	..	27·00	
		b. Type II (1898)	..	24·00	
11		4 a. black/rose (I)	..	18·00	£140
		a. Tête-bêche (horiz pair)	..	£250	
		b. Tête-bêche (vert pair)	..	£150	
		c. Doubly printed	..	£1400	
		d. Type II (1898)	..	20·00	

A used example of the 4 a. is known showing black roulettes at foot.

4 (½ a.)   5 (¼ a.)

1897. Name spelt "DATIA." Imperf.

12	4	½ a. black/green ..	..	60·00	£350
13		1 a. black/white	..	£130	
14		2 a. black/yellow	..	70·00	
		a. Tête-bêche (vert pair)	..	£3000	
15		4 a. black/rose	..	65·00	
		a. Tête-bêche (vert pair)	..	£3000	
12/15	..			Set of 4	£300

1899–1906.

(a) Rouletted in colour or in black, horizontally and at end of rows

16	5	¼ a. vermilion	..	..	2·75	
		a. Rose-red	..	..	1·90	
		b. Pale rose	..	..	1·75	
		c. Lake	..	..	3·25	12·00
		d. Carmine	..	..	3·00	
		e. Brownish red	..	..	7·00	
		ea. Tête-bêche (pair)	..		£3000	
17		½ a. black/blue-green	..	..	1·90	12·00
		a. On deep green	..	..	4·50	
		b. On yellow-green (pelure)	..	4·25	13·00
		c. On dull green (1906)	..	2·50	
18		1 a. black/white ..	..	..	2·25	12·00
19		2 a. black/lemon-yellow	..	..	7·00	
		a. On orange-yellow	..	..	9·00	
		b. On buff-yellow	..	..	2·25	14·00
		ba. Handstamp in black	..	8·00	
		bb. Without handstamp	..	£140	
		c. On pale yellow (1906)	..	2·75	14·00
20		4 a. black/deep rose	..	..	2·75	13·00
		a. Tête-bêche (pair)	..	..		
		b. Handstamp in black	..	11·00	
		c. Without handstamp	..	£140	

(b) Rouletted in colour between horizontal rows, but imperf at top and bottom and at ends of rows

20c	5	¼ a. brownish red	..	32·00	
21		1 a. black/white ..	..	12·00	

One setting of 16 (8×2) of the ¼ a. value (No. 16e) showed an inverted cliché at R. 1/2.

1904–5. *Without rouletting.*
22	5	¼ a. red	..	2·25	21·00
23		½ a. black/green	..	14·00	
24		1 a. black (1905)	..	9·50	25·00

Maharaja Govind Singh, 1907–1955

1911. *P 13½. Stamps very wide apart.*
25	5	¼ a. carmine	..	4·50	32·00
		a. Imperf horiz (vert pair)		£225	
		b. Imperf between (horiz pair)		£225	
		c. Stamps closer together (with gum) ..		6·50	23·00
		d. As c. Imperf vert (horiz pair)		£110	
25e		1 a. black		£750	

No. 25e was mainly used for fiscal purposes (*Price on piece,* £75), but one example has been seen used on a registered postcard.

1912? *Printed close together. (a) Coloured roulette×imperf*
26	5	½ a. black/green	..	6·50	

(b) Printed wide apart. P 13½×coloured roulette (¼ a.) or 13½×imperf (½ a.)
27	5	¼ a. carmine	..	4·75	25·00
28		½ a. black/dull green	..	10·00	29·00

1916. *Colours changed. Control handstamp in blue (Nos. 29/33) or black (No. 34). Imperf.*
29	5	¼ a. deep blue	..	5·50	16·00
30		½ a. green	..	4·50	18·00
31		1 a. purple	..	3·75	19·00
		a. Tête-bêche (vert pair)		22·00	
32		2 a. brown	..	11·00	23·00
33		2 a. lilac	..	5·00	22·00
		a. Handstamp in black		21·00	
		b. Without handstamp		£130	
34		4 a. Venetian red (date?)	..	70·00	

1918. *Colours changed. (a) Imperf.*
35	5	½ a. blue	..	2·75	12·00
36		1 a. pink	..	2·50	14·00
		a. Handstamp in black		5·50	

(b) P 11½
37	5	¼ a. black	..	3·75	16·00

1920. *Rouletted.*
38	5	¼ a. blue	..	1·90	8·50
		a. Roul × perf 7		35·00	35·00
		b. Imperf between (vert pair)		£500	
		c. Without handstamp		£110	
		d. Handstamp in black		5·50	
39		½ a. pink	..	2·25	13·00
		a. Roul × perf 7		£150	
		b. Without handstamp		£150	

1920?. *Rough perf about 7.*
40	5	½ a. dull red	..	9·50	25·00
		a. Handstamp in black		32·00	
		b. Without handstamp		£150	

The stamps of Duttia have been obsolete since 1 April 1921.

FARIDKOT

GUM. The stamps of Faridkot (Nos. N1/8) were issued without gum.

Raja Bikram Singh, 1874-1898

N 1 (1 folus)   N 2 (1 paisa)   N 3

1879–86. *Rough, handstamped impression. Imperf.*

(a) Native thick laid paper
N1	N 1	1 f. ultramarine	..	..	32·00	38·00
N2	N 2	1 p. ultramarine	..	..	90·00	95·00

(b) Ordinary laid paper
N3	N 1	1 f. ultramarine	..	..	14·00	16·00
N4	N 2	1 p. ultramarine	..	..	60·00	80·00

(c) Wove paper, thick to thinnish
N5	N 1	1 f. ultramarine	..	..	1·60	3·00
		a. Tête-bêche (pair)	..		£225	
N6	N 2	1 p. ultramarine	..	..	2·75	7·00
		a. Pair, one stamp sideways ..			£850	

(d) Thin wove whity brown paper
N7	N 2	1 p. ultramarine	..	..	28·00	30·00

(e) Wove paper
N8	N 3	1 p. ultramarine	..		1·25	
		a. Tête-bêche (pair)	..		£200	

It is doubtful whether stamps of Type N 3 were ever used for postage.

Impressions of these types in various colours, the ½ a. labels, and the later printings from re-engraved dies, were never in circulation at all.

Faridkot became a convention state and from 1887 used the Indian stamps overprinted which are listed under the Convention States.

HYDERABAD

The official title of the State in English was The Dominions of the Nizam and in Urdu "Sarkar-i-Asafia" (State of the successors of Asaf). This Urdu inscription appears in many of the designs.

Nawab Mir Mahbub Ali Khan Asaf Jah VI, 1869–1911

1   2

(Eng Mr. Rapkin. Plates by Nissen & Parker, London. Recess Mint, Hyderabad)

1869 (8 Sept.). *P 11½.*
1	1	1 a. olive-green	..	13·00	6·00
		a. Imperf between (horiz pair)	..	£110	
		b. Imperf horiz (vert pair)	..	£375	£100
		c. Imperf (pair)	..	£325	£325

Reprints in the colour of the issue, and also in fancy colours, were made in 1880 on white wove paper, perforated 12½. Fakes of No. 1c are known created by the removal of the outer perforations from examples of Nos. 1a/b.

1870 (16 May). *Locally engraved; 240 varieties of each value; wove paper. Recess. P 11½.*
2	2	½ a. brown	..	4·00	4·00
3		2 a. sage-green	..	42·00	38·00

Stamps exist showing traces of lines in the paper, but they do not appear to be printed on true laid paper.

Reprints of both values were made in 1880 on white wove paper, perforated 12½: the ½ a. in grey-brown, yellow-brown, sea-green, dull blue and carmine and the 2 a. in bright green and in blue-green.

3

A   2 a.   B
Normal   Variety

In A the coloured lines surrounding each of the four labels join a coloured circle round their inner edge, in B this circle is missing.

C   3 a.   D

C. Normal
D. Character ∧ omitted

Left side of central inscription omitted (Pl 4 R. 2/11)

Dot at top of central inscription omitted

Second dot in bottom label omitted

Centre dot in bottom label omitted

(Plates by Bradbury, Wilkinson & Co. Recess Mint, Hyderabad)

1871–1909. *(a) No wmk. (i) Rough perf 11½*
4	3	½ a. red-brown		18·00	19·00
5		1 a. purple-brown		£110	£120
6		2 a. green (A)		£750	
7		3 a. ochre-brown	..	32·00	42·00
8		4 a. slate	..	£140	£150
9		8 a. deep brown		£275	
10		12 a. dull blue		£275	

(ii) Pin perf 8–9
11	3	½ a. red-brown		—	£375
12		1 a. drab		£325	£160

(iii) P 12½
13	3	½ a. orange-brown	..	1·40	10
		a. Imperf vert (horiz pair)		† 80·00	
		ab. Imperf horiz (vert pair)		† £325	
		b. Orange	..	2·00	10
		c. Red-brown	..	1·40	10
		d. Brick-red	..	1·25	10
		da. Imperf vert (horiz pair)		† 80·00	
		db Doubly printed		† £160	
		e. Rose-red	..	1·60	15
		ea. Doubly printed		† £190	
		f. Error. Magenta	..	48·00	8·00
		g. Left side of central inscription omitted		£170	65·00
		h. Dot at top of central inscription omitted		40·00	2·25
14		1 a. purple-brown	..	4·00	4·00
		a. Doubly printed		£325	
		b. Drab		60	15
		ba. Imperf (pair)		—	£225
		bb. Doubly printed		£140	
		c. Grey-black	..	1·10	10
		d. Black (1909)	..	1·25	10
		da. Doubly printed		£325	
		db. Imperf vert (horiz pair)		† £475	
		dc. Imperf horiz (vert pair)		† £475	
		e. Dot at top of central inscription omitted		—	95·00
		f. Second dot in bottom label omitted		65·00	25·00
15		2 a. green (A)	..	2·25	15
		a. Deep green (A)	..	2·50	40
		b. Blue-green (A)	..	2·25	40
		ba. Blue-green (B)	..	£180	65·00
		c. Pale green (A)	..	2·25	15
		ca. Pale green (B)	..	£180	75·00
		d. Sage-green (A) (1909)	..	2·00	35
		da. Sage-green (B)	..	£130	45·00
		e. Dot at top of central inscription omitted		£170	80·00
		f. Centre dot in bottom panel omitted		85·00	32·00
16		3 a. ochre-brown (C)	..	1·75	1·10
		a. Character omitted (D)	..	£170	70·00
		b. Chestnut (C)	..	1·00	85
		ba. Character omitted (D)	..	£120	55·00
17		4 a. slate	..	4·50	1·75
		a. Imperf horiz (vert pair)	..	£650	£650
		b. Greenish grey	..	3·25	1·75
		ba. Imperf vert (horiz pair)	..	£700	
		c. Olive-green	..	3·00	85
18		8 a. deep brown	..	1·25	2·00
		a. Imperf vert (horiz pair)	..	£700	
19		12 a. pale ultramarine	..	3·00	4·50
		a. Grey-green	..	2·50	2·75
13/19			Set of 7	10·50	6·00

(b) W 7. P 12½
19b	3	1 a. black (1909)	..	90·00	9·50
19c		2 a. sage-green (A) (1909)		—	80·00
19d		12 a. bluish grey (1909?) ..		£800	

(4)   5

1898. *Surch with T 4. P 12½.*
20	3	¼ a. on ½ a. orange-brown	..	50	85
		a. Surch inverted		29·00	20·00
		b. Pair, one without surcharge		£375	
		c. Left side of central inscription omitted		£110	

(Des Khusrat Ullah. Recess Mint, Hyderabad)

1900 (20 Sept). *P 12½.*
21	5	¼ a. deep blue	..	4·00	2·75
		a. *Pale blue*	..	4·00	2·75

6   7

(Plates by Allan G. Wyon, London. Recess Mint, Hyderabad)

1905 (7 Aug). *W 7. P 12½.*
22	6	¼ a. dull blue	..	1·25	45
		a. Imperf (*pair*)	..	28·00	75·00
		b. *Dull ultramarine*	..	5·00	80
		ba. Perf 11 × 12½	..	22·00	22·00
		c. *Pale blue-green*	..	18·00	2·00
23		½ a. orange	..	4·00	35
		b. Perf 11	..		
		b. *Vermilion*	..	1·75	25
		ba. Imperf (*pair*)	..	26·00	75·00
		c. *Yellow*	..	60·00	16·00

1908–11. *W 7. P 12½.*
24	6	¼ a. grey	..	45	10
		a. Imperf between (*horiz pair*)		£190	£190
		b. Imperf between (*vert pair*)		†	£190
		c. Perf 11½, 12	..	2·00	35
		d. Perf 11	..	48·00	20·00
25		½ a. green	..	1·75	10
		a. Imperf between (*vert pair*)		£180	
		b. Perf 11½, 12	..	3·50	10
		c. Perf 13½	..	80·00	35·00
		d. *Pale green*	..	1·75	20
		da. Perf 11½, 12	..	3·50	10
		e. *Blue-green*	..	5·00	90
26		1 a. carmine	..	1·10	10
		a. Perf 11½, 12	..	4·00	50
		b. Perf 11	..	24·00	8·50
27		2 a. lilac	..	1·00	30
		a. Perf 11½, 12	..	3·50	1·10
		b. Perf 11	..	2·50	55
		c. Perf 13½	..	1·40	15
		ca. Imperf between (*horiz pair*)		†	£300
		cb. *Rose-lilac*	..	1·10	10
28		3 a. brown-orange (1909)	..	1·10	40
		a. Perf 11½, 12	..	7·50	2·00
		b. Perf 11	..	90	60
		c. Perf 13½	..	1·50	30
29		4 a. olive-green (1909)	..	1·10	45
		a. Perf 11½, 12	..	6·50	4·00
		b. Perf 11	..	28·00	9·00
		ba. Imperf between (*pair*)		£400	£400
		c. Perf 13½	..	90	30
30		8 a. purple (1911)	..	3·00	4·00
		a. Perf 11½, 12	..		
		b. Perf 11	..	1·75	2·50
		c. Perf 13½	..	1·10	35
31		12 a. blue-green (1911)	..	75·00	45·00
		a. Perf 11½, 12	..	9·50	12·00
		b. Perf 11	..		
		c. Perf 13½	..	3·00	1·50

The above perforations also exist compound.

Nawab Mir Osman Ali Khan Asaf Jah VII, 1911–1967

1912. *New plates engraved by Bradbury, Wilkinson & Co. W 7. P 12½.*
32	6	¼ a. grey-black	..	1·40	10
		a. Imperf horiz (*vert pair*)		†	£180
		b. Perf 11½, 12	..	60	35
		c. Perf 11	..	80	15
		ca. Imperf between (*horiz pair*)		†	£180
		cb. Imperf between (*vert pair*)		†	£180
		d. Perf 13½	..	30	10
33		¼ a. brown-purple (*shades*) (*p 13½*)		50	10
		a. Imperf horiz (*vert pair*)		†	£180
34		½ a. deep green	..	40	10
		a. Imperf between (*pair*)		†	£190
		b. Imperf (*pair*). Laid paper		80·00	60·00
		c. Perf 11½, 12	..	5·50	55
		d. Perf 11	..	8·00	10
		e. Perf 13½	..		

The above perforations also exist compound.

In Wyon's ¼ a. stamp the fraction of value is closer to the end of the label than in the B.W. issue. In the Wyon ¼ a. and ½ a. the value in English and the label below are further apart than in the B.W.

Wyon's ¼ a. measures 19½ × 20 mm and the ½ a. 19½ × 20½ mm; both stamps from the Bradbury plates measure 19¾ × 21½ mm.

---

8 Symbols   9

1915. *Inscr "Post & Receipt". W 7. P 13½.*
35	8	½ a. green	..	60	10
		a. Imperf between (*pair*)		65·00	70·00
		b. *Emerald-green*	..	3·00	10
		c. Perf 12½	..	5·50	35
		ca. Imperf between (*pair*)			
		cb. Imperf (*pair*)		£120	80·00
		d. Perf 11	..	60	10
		da. Imperf between (*pair*)		†	£170
36		1 a. carmine	..	80	10
		a. Imperf between (*pair*)		£160	
		b. *Scarlet*	..	1·00	10
		ba. Imperf between (*horiz pair*)		†	£170
		bb. Imperf between (*vert pair*)		†	£170
		c. Perf 12½	..	11·00	85
		ca. Imperf between (*pair*)			
		cb. Imperf (*pair*)		£160	£140
		cc. *Scarlet*			
		d. Perf 11	..	75	20
		da. *Scarlet*		—	18·00

The above perforations also exist compound.
For ½ a. claret, see No. 58.

1927 (1 Feb). *As W 7, but larger and sideways. P 13½.*
37	9	1 r. yellow	..	9·00	11·00

10 (4 pies)   11 (8 pies)

1930 (6 May). *Surch as T 10 and 11. W 7. P 13½.*
38	6	4 p. on ¼ a. grey-black (R.)	..	50·00	15·00
		a. Perf 11	..	†	£200
		b. Perf 12½	..	†	75·00
39		4 p. on ¼ a. brown-purple (R.)	..	25	10
		a. Imperf between (*pair*)		£400	£400
		b. Surch double		†	£180
		c. Perf 11	..	£400	
		d. Black surch ..	..	£425	£425
40	8	8 p. on ½ a. green (R.)	..	25	10
		a. Imperf between (*horiz pair*)		†	£190
		b. Perf 11	..	£275	£160
		c. Perf 12½	..	†	£275

12 Symbols   13 The Char Minar

14 Bidar College

(Plates by De La Rue. Recess Stamps Office, Hyderabad)

1931 (12 Nov)–**47.** *T 12 to 14 (and similar types). W 7. Wove paper. P 13½.*
41	12	4 p. black	..	30	10
		a. Laid paper (1947)	..	2·50	4·75
		b. Imperf (*pair*)	..	48·00	75·00
42		8 p. green	..	35	10
		a. Imperf between (*vert pair*) ..		—	£550
		b. Imperf (*pair*)	..	60·00	90·00
		c. Laid paper (1947)	..	3·00	4·25
43	13	1 a. brown (*shades*)	..	35	10
		a. Imperf between (*horiz pair*)		—	£550
44		2 a. violet (*shades*)	..	2·00	10
		a. Imperf (*pair*)	..	£130	£180
45		4 a. ultramarine	..	1·25	30
		a. Imperf (*pair*)	..	£140	£225
46		8 a. orange	..	4·00	2·50
		a. *Yellow-orange* (1944)	..	65·00	30·00
47	14	12 a. scarlet	..	4·00	8·50
48		1 r. yellow	..	4·00	10
41/8			*Set of 8*	14·50	13·00

Designs (*as T 14*): *Horiz*—2 a. High Court of Justice; 4 a. Osman Sagar Reservoir. *Vert*—8 a. Entrance to Ajanta Caves; 1 r. Victory Tower, Daulatabad.

Nos. 41a and 42c have a large sheet watermark "THE NIZAM's GOVERNMENT HYDERABAD DECCAN" and arms within a circle, but this does not appear on all stamps.

NEW INFORMATION

The editor is always interested to correspond with people who have new information that will improve or correct the Catalogue.

---

15 Unani General Hospital   16 Family Reunion

(Litho Indian Security Printing Press, Nasik)

1937 (13 Feb). *Various horiz designs as T 15, inscr "H.E.H. THE NIZAM'S SILVER JUBILEE". P 14.*
49		4 p. slate and violet	..	40	80
50		8 p. slate and brown	..	70	85
51		1 a. slate and orange-yellow	..	70	60
52		2 a. slate and green	..	90	3·00
49/52			*Set of 4*	2·50	4·75

Designs:—8 p. Osmania General Hospital; 1 a. Osmania University; 2 a. Osmania Jubilee Hall.

(Des T. I. Archer. Typo)

1945 (6 Dec). *Victory. W 7 (very faint). Wove paper. P 13½.*
53	16	1 a. blue	..	10	10
		a. Imperf between (*vert pair*) ..		£500	
		b. Laid paper	..	65	65

No. 53b shows the sheet watermark described beneath Nos. 41/8.

17 Town Hall   18 Power House, Hyderabad

(Des. T. I. Archer. Litho Government Press)

1947 (17 Feb). *Reformed Legislature. P 13½.*
54	17	1 a. black	..	70	1·00
		a. Imperf between (*pair*)		—	£700

(Des T. I. Archer. Typo)

1947–49. *As T 18 (inscr "H. E. H. THE NIZAM'S GOVT. POSTAGE"). W 7. P 13½.*
55		1 a. green	..	75	1·50
56		3 a. greenish blue	..	85	2·25
		a. *Bluish green*	..	1·50	50
57		6 a. sepia	..	3·00	10·00
		a. *Red-brown* (1949)	..	18·00	25·00
		ab. Imperf (*pair*)		£110	
55/7			*Set of 3*	4·25	12·50

Designs:—3 a. Kaktyai Arch, Warangal Fort; 6 a. Golkunda Fort.

1947. *As 1915 issue but colour changed. P 13½.*
58	8	½ a. claret	..	1·25	50
		a. Imperf between (*horizontal pair*)		—	£275
		b. Imperf between (*vert pair*)		—	£425

An Independence commemorative set of four, 4 p., 8 p., 1 a. and 2 a., was prepared in 1948, but not issued.

1948. *As T 12 ("POSTAGE" at foot). Recess. W 7. P 13½.*
59		6 p. claret	..	6·00	5·00

Following intervention by the forces of the Dominion of India during September 1948 the Hyderabad postal system was taken over by the Dominion authorities, operating as an agency of the India Post Office.

1949. *T 12 ("POSTAGE" at top). Litho. W 7. P 13½.*
60	12	2 p. bistre-brown	..	1·00	1·75
		a. Imperf between (*horizontal pair*)	..	†	£650
		b. Imperf (*pair*)	..	£325	£475

No. 60 was produced from a transfer taken from a plate of the 4 p., No. 41, with each impression amended individually.

OFFICIAL STAMPS

Official stamps became valid for postage within India from 1910.

(O1)   (O 1a)   (O 2)

1873. I. *Handstamped as Type O 1 in red.*
O1		1 a. olive-green	..	60·00	20·00
		a. Black opt	..		
O2	2	½ a. brown	..	—	£400
		a. Black opt	..		£400
O3		2 a. sage-green	..	—	£400
		a. Black opt	..		£130

At least ten different handstamps as Type O 1 were used to produce Nos. O1/17. These differ in the size, shape and spacing of the characters. The prices quoted are for the cheapest versions where more than one is known to exist on a particular stamp.

Imitations of these overprints on genuine stamps and on reprints are found horizontally or vertically in various shades of red, in magenta and in black.

II. *T* 3 *handstamped as Type* O 1 *in red.*

(a) Rough perf 11½

O 4	½ a. red-brown		—	£600
	a. Black opt			
O 5	1 a. purple-brown		—	£750
	a. Black opt		£130	£160
O 6	2 a. green (A)		—	£750
	a. Black opt			
O 7	4 a. slate		—	£850
	a. Black opt			
O 8	8 a. deep brown			
	a. Black opt		£850	£850
O 8b	12 a. dull blue		—	£850

(b) Pin perf 8–9

O 8c	1 a. drab (*black opt*)		6·50	85·00

(c) P 12½

O 9	½ a. red-brown		9·00	3·50
	a. Black opt		6·00	2·50
	ab. Left side of central inscription omitted		—	£120
	ac. Dot at top of central inscription omitted		—	35·00
O11	1 a. purple-brown		70·00	48·00
	a. Black opt		—	21·00
O12	1 a. drab		13·00	14·00
	a. Black opt		1·50	1·60
	ab. Second dot in bottom label omitted		75·00	75·00
O13	2 a. green (*to* deep) (A)		26·00	20·00
	a. Black opt		3·00	4·00
	ab. Inner circle missing (B)		—	£160
	ac. Centre dot in bottom label omitted		90·00	90·00
O14	3 a. ochre-brown		90·00	90·00
	a. Black opt		23·00	18·00
O15	4 a. slate		40·00	26·00
	a. Black opt		11·00	11·00
O16	8 a. deep brown		42·00	80·00
	a. Imperf vert (horiz pair)		£600	
	b. Black opt		30·00	24·00
O17	12 a. blue		65·00	90·00
	a. Black opt		35·00	50·00

The use of Official Stamps (Sarkari) was discontinued in 1878, but was resumed in 1909, when the current stamps were overprinted from a new die.

1909–11. *Optd with Type* O 1a. *(a) On Type* 3. *P* 12½.

O18	½ a. orange-brown		80·00	4·00
	a. Opt inverted		†	£350
O19	1 a. black		55·00	10
	a. Second dot in bottom label omitted		—	6·00
O20	2 a. sage-green (A)		65·00	30
	a. Optd on No. 15da (B)		—	10·00
	b. Stamp doubly printed		†	£140
	c. Centre dot in bottom label omitted		—	6·50
O20d	3 a. ochre-brown		3·00	1·00
	da. Character omitted (D)		—	£250
O20e	4 a. olive-green		£275	3·25
	ea. Perf 11½, 12		—	£250
O20f	8 a. deep brown		—	28·00
O20g	12 a. grey-green		—	60·00

(b) On Type 6 *(Wyon ptgs). P* 12½

O21	½ a. orange		—	1·75
	a. *Vermilion*		£100	15
	b. Opt inverted		†	£250
	c. Imperf between (vert pair)		†	£250
O22	½ a. green		13·00	10
	a. *Pale green*		13·00	10
	b. Opt inverted		†	55·00
	c. Imperf between (vert pair)		†	£180
	d. Imperf between (horiz pair)		†	£170
	e. Stamp doubly printed		—	£130
	f. Perf 11½, 12		12·00	30
	fa. *Pale green*		12·00	30
	fb. Opt inverted		†	55·00
	g. Perf 11		—	
	ga. *Pale green*		—	
	h. Perf 13½		—	55·00
O23	1 a. carmine		35·00	15
	a. Opt double		£160	
	b. Perf 11½, 12		48·00	30
	ba. Stamp doubly printed		—	£130
	c. Perf 11		—	5·50
O24	2 a. lilac		40·00	30
	a. Perf 11½, 12		75·00	4·00
	b. Perf 11		£350	
O25	3 a. brown-orange		90·00	9·00
	a. Opt inverted		†	£140
	b. Perf 11½, 12		£160	22·00
	c. Perf 11		£350	35·00
	d. Perf 13½		—	60·00
O26	4 a. olive-green (1911)		26·00	30
	a. Perf 11½, 12		75·00	3·25
	b. Perf 11		—	16·00
O27	8 a. purple (1911)		13·00	1·40
	a. Perf 11½, 12		80·00	5·00
	b. Perf 11		£350	£110
O28	12 a. blue-green (1911)		9·00	1·25
	a. Imperf between (horiz pair)		—	£650
	b. Perf 11½, 12		23·00	2·25
	c. Perf 11			

(c) On Type 6 *(Bradbury Wilkinson ptgs). P* 11

O28d	6 ½ a. deep green			£325

1911–12. *Optd with Type* O 2. *(a) Type* 6 *(Wyon printings). P* 13½ (8 *a.*, 12 *a.*) *or* 12½ (*others*).

O29	¼ a. grey		40·00	1·00
	a. Perf 11½, 12		20·00	30
	ab. Imperf between (vert pair)		†	£200
	b. Perf 11		70·00	30·00
	c. Perf 13½			
O30	½ a. pale green		30·00	1·00
	a. Perf 11½, 12		—	30
	b. Perf 13½			
O31	1 a. carmine		85	15
	a. Opt inverted		—	38·00
	b. Imperf horiz (vert pair)		†	£200
	c. Perf 11½, 12		5·50	15
	d. Perf 11		75	15
	e. Perf 13½			

O32	2 a. lilac		4·75	60
	a. Perf 11½, 12		18·00	2·00
	b. Perf 11		85	25
	c. Perf 13½		5·00	10
	ca. Imperf between (horiz pair)		†	£300
	cb. *Rose-lilac*		1·75	10
O33	3 a. brown-orange		15·00	2·00
	a. Opt inverted		†	70·00
	b. Perf 11½, 12		9·00	1·75
	ba. Opt inverted		†	75·00
	c. Perf 11		23·00	2·25
	ca. Opt inverted		†	70·00
	d. Perf 13½		15·00	35
	da. Opt inverted		†	60·00
O34	4 a. olive-green		10·00	1·25
	a. Opt inverted		—	70·00
	b. Perf 11½, 12		4·50	1·75
	ba. Opt inverted		—	75·00
	c. Perf 11		2·00	1·10
	d. Perf 13½		2·25	10
	da. Opt inverted		†	70·00
O35	8 a. purple		3·00	20
	a. Perf 11½, 12			
	b. Perf 11		£275	35·00
	c. Perf 12½		—	£300
O36	12 a. blue-green		11·00	60
	a. Perf 11½, 12			
	b. Perf 11			
	c. Perf 12½			

(b) Type 6 *(Bradbury, Wilkinson printings). P* 12½

O37	¼ a. grey-black		2·25	35
	a. Opt inverted		†	55·00
	b. Pair, one without opt			
	c. Imperf between (vert pair)		†	£170
	d. Perf 11½, 12		5·00	60
	da. Opt inverted		†	55·00
	db. Pair, one without opt			
	e. Perf 11		70	35
	ea. Opt sideways		†	55·00
	f. Perf 13½		2·25	10
	fa. Opt inverted		†	60·00
	fb. Pair, one without opt		†	£120
	fc. Imperf between (horiz pair)		†	£170
O38	¼ a. brown-purple (*shades*) (*p* 13½)		1·60	10
	a. Imperf horiz (vert pair)		†	£170
	b. Imperf between (horiz pair)		†	£180
	c. Perf 11			
O39	½ a. deep green		2·25	15
	a. Opt inverted		—	22·00
	b. Perf 11½, 12		6·50	90
	ba. Pair, one without opt		†	£120
	c. Perf 11		1·90	10
	ca. Opt inverted		—	25·00
	cb. Imperf horiz (vert pair)		†	£180
	d. Perf 13½		1·25	10
	da. Imperf between (horiz pair)		†	£150
	db. *Yellow-green*		—	50

1917–20. *T* 8 *optd with Type* O 2. *P* 13½.

O40	½ a. green		1·50	10
	a. Opt inverted		†	20·00
	b. Pair, one without opt		†	90·00
	c. Imperf between (horiz pair)		†	£120
	d. Imperf between (vert pair)		†	£150
	e. *Emerald-green*		2·75	40
	f. Perf 12½		—	3·50
	g. Perf 11		5·00	30
	ga. Opt inverted		†	22·00
	gb. Pair, one without opt			
O41	1 a. carmine		2·50	10
	a. Opt inverted		†	25·00
	b. Opt double		†	65·00
	c. Imperf horiz (vert pair)		†	£170
	d. Stamp printed double			
	e. *Scarlet* (1920)		85	10
	ea. Stamp printed double		†	£130
	eb. Imperf between (horiz pair)		†	£150
	ec. Imperf between (vert pair)		†	£150
	f. Perf 12½		—	3·50
	g. Perf 11		8·00	15
	ga. Opt inverted		†	16·00
	gb. *Scarlet* (1920)		—	21·00

1930–34. *T* 6 *and* 8 *optd as Type* O 2 *and surch at top of stamp, in red, as T* 10 *or* 11.

O42	4 p. on ¼ a. grey-black (O37f) (1934)		£200	17·00
O43	4 p. on ¼ a. brown-purple (O38)		65	10
	b. Imperf between (horiz pair)		†	£170
	c. Imperf between (vert pair)		†	£170
	d. Imperf horiz (vert pair)		†	£170
	e. Red surch double		†	85·00
	f. Black opt double		†	£180
O44	8 p. on ½ a. green (O40)		60	10
	c. Imperf between (horiz pair)		†	£170
	ca. Imperf between (vert pair)		†	£170
	d. Red surch double		†	85·00
	e. Stamp doubly printed		†	£170
	f. Black opt double		†	£180
O45	8 p. on ½ a. yellow-green (O39db)		35·00	45·00

For Nos. O42/5 the red surcharge was intended to appear on the upper part of the stamp, above the official overprint, Type O 2, but surcharge and overprint are not infrequently found superimposed on one another.

1934–44. *Nos.* 41/8 *optd with Type* O 2.

O46	4 p. black		1·00	10
	a. Imperf (pair)		60·00	
	b. Imperf between (vert pair)		£500	£500
	c. Imperf between (horiz pair)		—	£500
O47	8 p. green		40	10
	a. Opt inverted		†	£150
	b. Imperf between (horiz pair)		£500	
	c. Opt double		†	£120
	d. Imperf (pair)		£120	£150
O48	1 a. brown		60	10
	a. Imperf between (vert pair)		£400	£400
	b. Imperf between (horiz pair)		—	£400
	c. Imperf (pair)		£140	£180
	d. Opt double		—	£160
O49	2 a. violet		4·00	10
	a. Imperf between (horiz pair)		†	£900

O50	4 a. ultramarine		1·75	20
	a. Opt double		†	£375
	b. Imperf between (vert pair)		†	£950
O51	8 a. orange (1935)		8·00	50
	a. *Yellow-orange* (1944)		—	38·00
O52	12 a. scarlet (1935)		5·50	1·25
O53	1 r. yellow (1935)		13·00	2·00
O46/53		*Set of* 8	30·00	3·75

1947. *No.* 58 *optd with Type* O 2.

O54	8 ½ a. claret		9·00	5·50

1949. *No.* 60 *optd with Type* O 2.

O55	12 2 p. bistre-brown		7·00	6·00

1950. *No.* 59 *optd with Type* O 2.

O56	6 p. claret		8·50	17·00

IDAR

PRICES FOR STAMPS ON COVER

Nos. 1/2c	*from* × 2
Nos. 3/6	*from* × 3
Nos. F1/4	*from* × 2

Maharaja Himmat Singh, 1931–1960

1 Maharaja Himmat Singh **2**

(Typo M. N. Kothari & Sons, Bombay)

1932 (1 Oct)**–43.** *P* 11. *(a) White panels.*

1	1	½ a. light green		—	25·00
		a. *Pale yellow-green* (*thick paper*) (1939)	13·00	18·00
		b. *Emerald* (1941)		12·00	18·00
		ba. Imperf between (pair)		£950	
		c. *Yellow-green* (1943)		10·00	16·00
		ca. Imperf between (horiz pair)		£900	

(b) Coloured panels

2	1	½ a. pale yellow-green (*thick paper*) (1939)	22·00	22·00
		a. *Emerald* (1941)		17·00	19·00
		b. *Yellow-green* (1943)		9·50	18·00

In No. 2 the whole design is composed of half-tone dots. In No. 1 the dots are confined to the oval portrait.

(Typo P. G. Mehta & Co, Hitmatnagar)

1944 (21 Oct). *P* 12.

3	2	½ a. blue-green		2·00	50
		a. Imperf between (vert pair)		£250	
		b. *Yellow-green*		2·00	50·00
		ba. Imperf between (vert pair)		12·00	
4		1 a. violet		2·25	45·00
		a. Imperf (pair)		£200	
		b. Imperf vert (horiz pair)		£225	
5		2 a. blue		2·50	75·00
		a. Imperf between (vert pair)		75·00	
		b. Imperf between (horiz pair)		£190	
6		4 a. vermilion		2·75	80·00
		a. Doubly printed		£550	
3/6			*Set of* 4	8·50	£225

Nos. 1 to 6 are from booklet panes of 4 stamps, producing single stamps with one or two adjacent sides imperf.

The 4 a. violet is believed to be a colour trial.

POSTAL FISCAL STAMPS

F 1

1940 (?)**–45.** *Typo. P* 11 (*No.* F1) *or* 12 *on two or three sides.*

F1	—	1 a. violet		65·00	£100
F2	F 1	1 a. violet (1943)		—	£100
F3		1¼ a. on 1 a. violet		95·00	£200
F4		1¼ a. yellow-green (1945)		13·00	
		a. Imperf between (vert pair)		30·00	
		b. *Blue-green* (1945)		48·00	95·00

No. F1 shows the portrait as Type **1**. Used prices are for examples with postal cancellations. No. F3 shows a handstamped surcharge in Gujerati.

Idar became part of Bombay Province on 10 June 1948.

ALTERED CATALOGUE NUMBERS

Any Catalogue numbers altered from the last edition are shown as a list in the introductory pages.

INDORE

(HOLKAR STATE)

PRICES FOR STAMPS ON COVER	
Nos. 1/15	*from* × 20
Nos. 16/43	*from* × 6
Nos. S1/7	*from* × 40

Maharaja Tukoji Rao Holkar II, 1843–1886

1 Maharaja Tukoji Rao Holkar II

(Litho Waterlow & Sons)

1886 (6 Jan). *P* 15. *(a) Thick white paper.*
1	1	½ a. bright mauve		7·50	8·00

(b) Thin white or yellowish paper.
2	1	½ a. pale mauve		1·75	1·10
		a. Dull mauve		2·00	1·75

Maharaja Shivaji Rao Holkar, 1886–1903

2 Type I   2a Type II

TYPES 2 AND 2a. In addition to the difference in the topline character (marked by arrow), the two Types can be distinguished by the difference in the angles of the 6-pointed stars and the appearance of the lettering. In Type I the top characters are smaller and more cramped than the bottom; in Type II both are in the same style and similarly spaced.

1889 (Sept). *Handstamped. No gum. Imperf.*
3	2	½ a. black/*pink*		27·00	27·00
4	2a	½ a. black/*pink*		2·00	2·75
		a. *Tête-bêche* (pair)		£190	

3 Maharaja Shivaji   4 Maharaja Tukoji Holkar III 5
Rao Holkar

(Recess Waterlow)

1889–92. *Medium wove paper. P* 14 *to* 15.
5	3	¼ a. orange (9.2.92)		65	45
		a. Imperf between (horiz pair)	†	£550	
		b. Very thick wove paper		1·40	55
		c. *Yellow*		1·00	60
6		½ a. dull violet		1·50	60
		a. *Brown-purple*		80	15
		b. Imperf between (vert pair)		£500	
7		1 a. green (7.2.92)		90	50
		a. Imperf between (vert pair)		£750	
		b. Very thick wove paper		75·00	
8		2 a. vermilion (7.2.92)		3·25	1·00
		a. Very thick wove paper		5·00	3·00
5/8			*Set of* 4	5·00	1·75

Maharaja Tukoji Rao Holkar III, 1903–1926

(Recess Perkins, Bacon & Co)

1904–20. *P* 13½, 14.
9	4	¼ a. orange		30	10
10	5	½ a. lake (1909)		8·50	10
		a. *Brown-lake (shades)*		9·50	15
		b. Imperf (pair)		16·00	
11		1 a. green		1·60	10
		a. Imperf (pair)		£120	
		b. Perf 12½ (1920)	†	80·00	
12		2 a. brown		8·00	50
		a. Imperf (pair)		75·00	
13		3 a. violet		13·00	5·00
14		4 a. ultramarine		10·00	1·90
		a. *Dull blue*		5·00	1·10
9/14			*Set of* 6	32·00	6·25

 पाव आना.

(6)

7 Maharaja Yeshwant
Rao Holkar II

1905 (June). *No. 6a surch* "QUARTER ANNA" *in Devanagari, as T* 6.
15	3	¼ a. on ½ a. brown-purple		3·75	17·00

On 1 March 1908 the Indore State postal service was amalgamated with the Indian Imperial system. Under the terms of the agreement stamps showing the Maharaja would still be used for official mail sent to addresses within the state. Initially Nos. 9/14 were used for this purpose, the "SERVICE" overprints, Nos. S1/7, being withdrawn.

Maharaja Yeshwant Rao Holkar II, 1926–1961

(Recess Perkins, Bacon & Co)

1927–37. *P* 13 *to* 14.
16	7	¼ a. orange (a) (d) (e)		30	10
17		½ a. claret (a) (d) (e)		40	10
18		1 a. green (a) (d) (e)		90	10
19		1¼ a. green (c) (d) (1933)		1·50	25
20		2 a. sepia (a)		3·75	1·00
21		2 a. bluish green (d) (1936)		10·00	70
		a. Imperf (pair)		25·00	£110
22		3 a. deep violet (a)		1·50	9·00
23		3 a. Prussian blue (d) (1935?)		15·00	
		a. Imperf (pair)		30·00	£275
24		3½ a. violet (d) (1934)		4·75	9·50
		a. Imperf (pair)		50·00	£275
25		4 a. ultramarine (a)		3·25	3·25
26		4 a. yellow-brown (d) (1937)		22·00	1·50
		a. Imperf (pair)		30·00	£190
27		8 a. slate-grey (a)		5·50	4·50
28		8 a. red-orange (d) (1937)		16·00	19·00
29		12 a. carmine (d) (1934)		5·00	10·00
30	—	1 r. black and light blue (b)		8·00	14·00
31	—	2 r. black and cream (b)		35·00	35·00
32	—	5 r. black & brown-orange (b)		55·00	60·00

Nos. 30/32 are as Type 7, but larger, size 23 × 28 mm.
Five different perforating heads were used for this issue: (a) comb 13·6; (b) comb 13·9; (c) line 13·2; (d) line 13·8; (e) line 14·2. Values on which each perforation occur are indicated above.
Nos. 21a, 23a, 24a and 26a were specifically ordered by the state government in 1933 and are known used for postage *circa* 1938–42. A plate proof of the 1 r. in green and carmine is also known postally used (*Price of pair* £32 *unused,* £300 *used*).
Nos. 16/19 and 28/32 also exist as imperforate plate proofs, but these were never sent to India.

 QUARTER ANNA

(8)

9

1940 (1 Aug). *Surch in words as T* 8 *by Times of India Press, Bombay.*
33	7	¼ a. on 5 r. black and brown-orange (b)		7·50	85
		a. Surch double (Blk. + G.)	†	£400	
34		½ a. on 2 r. black and carmine (b)		11·00	1·75
35		1 a. on 1¼ a. green (c) (d) (e)		11·00	40
		b. Surch inverted (d)		90·00	
		c. Surch double (c)		£325	
33/5			*Set of* 3	27·00	2·75

(Typo "*Times of India*" Press, Bombay)

1941–46. *P* 11.
36	9	¼ a. red-orange		2·00	10
37		½ a. claret		1·60	10
38		1 a. green		8·00	10
39		1¼ a. yellow-green		14·00	45
		a. Imperf (pair)		£190	
40		2 a. turquoise-blue		11·00	1·00
41		4 a. yellow-brown (1946)		12·00	9·50

Larger size (23 × 28 *mm*)
42		2 r. black and carmine (1943)		9·00	£100
43		5 r. black and yellow-orange (1943)		9·00	£140
36/43			*Set of* 8	60·00	£225

OFFICIAL STAMPS

SERVICE	SERVICE
(S 1)	(S 2)

1904–6. *(a) Optd with Type* S 1.
S1	4	¼ a. orange (1906)		10	50
S2	5	½ a. lake		10	10
		a. Opt inverted		19·00	28·00
		b. Opt double		17·00	
		c. Imperf (pair)		55·00	
		d. *Brown-lake*		10	10
		da. Opt inverted		18·00	
		e. Pair, one without opt		£450	
S3		1 a. green		10	20
S4		2 a. brown (1905)		30	30
		a. Vert pair, one without opt		£700	
S5		3 a. violet (1906)		2·00	1·60
		a. Imperf (pair)		£325	
S6		4 a. ultramarine (1905)		3·00	1·50

(b) Optd with Type S 2
S7	5	½ a. lake		10	50
		a. Opt double		£325	
S1/7			*Set of* 6	5·00	3·75

Types S 1 and S 2 differ chiefly in the shape of the letter "R".

Indore became part of Madhya Bharat by 1 July 1948

JAIPUR

PRICES FOR STAMPS ON COVER	
No. 1	*from* × 3
No. 2	*from* × 2
Nos. 3/5	*from* × 10
Nos. 6/70	*from* × 4
Nos. 71/80	*from* × 6
Nos. O1/34	*from* × 8

Maharaja Sawai Madho Singh II, 1880–1922

1   1a   2

Chariot of the Sun God, Surya

Type 1 – Value at sides in small letters and characters. "HALF ANNA", shown as one word except for R. 1/1 and 1/3, measuring between 13½ and 15 mm. Sheets of 12 (4×3) with stamps 2 to 2½ mm apart.

Type 1a – Value in large letters and characters. "HALF ANNA", always with a gap between the two words, measuring between 14½ and 15½ mm. Sheets of 24 (4×6) with stamps 3 to 4 mm apart.

Type 2 – Value in large letters and characters. "HALF ANNA" measuring 16 to 17 mm. Both side inscriptions start below the inner frame line. Sheets of 24 (4×6) with stamps 1½ to 2 mm apart.

(Litho Durbar Press, Jaipur)

1904 (14 July). *Roughly perf* 14.
1	1	½ a. pale blue		90·00	£130
		a. *Ultramarine*		£130	£160
		b. Imperf, *ultramarine*		£350	
2	1a	½ a. grey-blue		£1200	£550
		a. Imperf		£350	£550
		b. *Ultramarine*	—	£325	
3	2	½ a. pale blue		2·75	4·50
		a. *Deep blue*		3·00	4·50
		b. *Ultramarine*		3·25	4·50
		c. Imperf		£300	£300
4	1	1 a. dull red		4·25	12·00
		a. *Scarlet*		4·25	12·00
5		2 a. pale green		3·50	10·00
		a. *Emerald-green*		3·75	

Nos. 1b, 2a and 3c are on gummed paper. Imperforate plate proofs also exist for Nos. 1/5, but these are ungummed.

3 Chariot of the Sun God, Surya

(Recess Perkins, Bacon & Co)

1904. *P* 12.
6	3	½ a. blue		3·25	6·50
		a. Perf 12½		20·00	14·00
		b. Perf comp of 12 and 12½		15·00	16·00
7		1 a. brown-red		48·00	48·00
		a. Perf 12½		£110	£110
		b. Perf comp of 12 and 12½		£120	£120
		c. *Carmine*		2·25	3·75
		ca. Imperf between (vert pair)		£400	£550
		cb. Perf comp of 12 and 12½		10·00	13·00
8		2 a. deep green		5·50	11·00
		a. Perf 12½		£120	85·00
		b. Perf comp of 12 and 12½		25·00	30·00

Nos. 6b, 7b, 7cb and 8b occur on the bottom two rows of sheets otherwise perforated 12.

1905–8. *Wmk* "JAs WRIGLEY & SON Ld. 219" "SPECIAL POSTAGE PAPER LONDON" *or* "PERKINS BACON & Co Ld LONDON" *in sheet. P* 13½.
9	3	¼ a. olive-yellow (1906)		55	45
10		½ a. blue (1906)		1·90	1·75
		a. *Indigo*		55	40
11		1 a. brown-red (1906)		4·75	4·25
		a. *Bright red* (1908)		1·90	40
12		2 a. deep green (1906)		1·00	75
13		4 a. chestnut		5·00	2·00
14		8 a. bright violet		3·00	2·75
15		1 r. yellow		16·00	16·00
		a. *Orange-yellow*		15·00	16·00
		b. *Yellow-ochre*		17·00	23·00
9/15			*Set of* 7	24·00	20·00

 ३ आना

4 Chariot of the Sun God,   (5)
Surya

(Typo Jaipur State Press)

1911. *Thin wove paper. No gum. Imperf.*

16	4	¼ a. green		1·75	2·50
		a. Printed double		6·00	
		ab. Ditto, one inverted			
		b. "¼" inverted in right upper corner (R. 1/2)		5·00	
		c. No stop after "STATE" (R. 3/1)		5·00	
17		¼ a. greenish yellow		30	60
		a. Printed double		2·00	
		b. "¼" inverted in right upper corner (R. 1/2)		1·50	
		c. No stop after "STATE" (R. 3/1)		1·50	
18		½ a. ultramarine		30	60
		a. Printed double		2·00	
		b. No stop after "STATE" (R. 3/1)		75	
		c. Large "J" in "JAIPUR" (R. 1/2)		75	
		d. "¹/₃" for "¹/₂" at lower left (R. 3/1)		1·50	
		e. "1½ a." at lower right (R. 3/2)		1·50	
19		½ a. grey-blue		1·50	1·50
		a. No stop after "STATE" (R. 3/1)		2·75	
		b. Large "J" in "JAIPUR" (R. 1/2)		2·75	
		c. "¹/₃" for "¹/₂" at lower left (R. 3/1)		3·25	
		d. "1½ a." at lower right (R. 3/2)		3·75	
20		1 a. rose-red		45	65
		a. Printed double		£180	
21		2 a. greyish green		2·25	5·50
		a. Deep green		2·00	5·50
		ab. Printed double		£180	

Issued in sheets of 6 (2×3). There are three recognised settings. Nos. 18d/e and 19c/d come from Setting B, and Nos. 16b/c, 17b/c, 18b/c and 19a/b from Setting C.
One sheet of the ¼ a. is known in blue.

(Typo Jaipur State Press)

1912–22. *Paper-maker's wmk "DORLING & CO. LONDON" in sheet.* P 11.

22	3	¼ a. pale olive-yellow		30	70
		a. Imperf horiz (vert pair)		£200	£200
		b. Imperf vert (horiz pair)		—	£160
23		¼ a. olive		35	90
		a. Imperf between (horiz pair)		£190	
		b. Imperf vert (horiz pair)		£200	
		c. Imperf horiz (vert pair)		£200	
		d. Tête-bêche (pair)		£275	
24		¼ a bistre		30	80
		a. Imperf between (horiz pair)		£190	
		b. Imperf between (vert pair)		†	£275
		c. Imperf horiz (vert pair)		†	£275
		d. Doubly printed		†	—
25		½ a. pale ultramarine		1·00	50
		a. Imperf vert (horiz pair)		†	£375
		b. Blue		1·10	45
		ba. Imperf between (horiz pair)		£325	
26		1 a. carmine (1918)		3·25	3·25
		a. Imperf between (vert pair)		†	£475
		b. Imperf horiz (vert pair)		†	£475
27		1 a. rose-red		1·90	6·50
		a. Imperf between (vert pair)		£500	
28		1 a. scarlet (1922)		1·75	1·60
		a. Imperf between (vert pair)		£500	£500
29		2 a. green (1918)		3·25	2·75
30		4 a. chocolate		3·50	5·50
31		4 a. pale brown		3·75	6·50
		a. Imperf vert (horiz pair)		£400	
22/31			Set of 5	9·00	10·00

Maharaja Sawai Man Singh II 1922–1970

1926. *Surch with T 5.*

32	3	3 a. on 8 a. bright violet (R.)		1·25	1·90
		a. Surch inverted		£170	£140
33		3 a. on 1 r. yellow (R.)		2·00	3·75
		a. Surch inverted		£375	£170
		c. Yellow-ochre		6·00	8·00

1928. *As 1913–18 issue. Wmk "DORLING & CO. LONDON" (½ a., 1 a., 2 a.) or "OVERLAND BANK" (all values) in sheet. No gum.* P 12.

34	3	½ a. ultramarine		3·00	4·00
		a. Perf comp of 12 and 11		13·00	8·00
35		1 a. rose-red		22·00	17·00
		a. Imperf between (vert pair)		£400	
36		1 a. scarlet		35·00	12·00
		a. Perf comp of 12 and 11		50·00	25·00
37		2 a. green		65·00	26·00
		a. Perf comp of 12 and 11		£160	55·00
38		8 a. bright violet			
39		1 r. orange-vermilion		£250	£375

The "OVERLAND BANK" paper has a coarser texture. The ½ a. and 2 a. values also exist on this paper perforated 11, but such stamps are difficult to distinguish from examples of Nos. 25 and 29.

6 Chariot of the Sun God, Surya

7 Maharaja Sawai Man Singh II

8 Sowar in Armour

(Des T. I. Archer. Litho Indian Security Printing Press, Nasik)

1931 (14 Mar). *Investiture of Maharaja. T 6/8 and similar designs. No wmk.* P 14.

40		¼ a. black and deep lake		90	1·25
41		½ a. black and violet		30	10
42		1 a. black and blue		5·00	5·50
43		2 a. black and buff		3·50	5·50
44		2½ a. black and carmine		28·00	45·00
45		3 a. black and myrtle		10·00	38·00
46		4 a. black and olive-green		12·00	40·00
47		6 a. black and deep blue		6·00	38·00
48		8 a. black and chocolate		10·00	55·00
49		1 r. black and pale olive		25·00	£160
50		2 r. black and yellow-green...		22·00	£170
51		5 r. black and purple		32·00	£180
40/51			Set of 12	£140	£650

Designs: *Vert*—1 a. Elephant and state banner; 2½ a. Common Peafowl; 8 a. Sireh-Deorhi Gate. *Horiz*—3 a. Bullock carriage; 4 a. Elephant carriage; 6 a. Albert Museum; 1 r. Chandra Mahal; 2 r. Amber Palace; 5 r. Maharajas Jai Singh and Man Singh.
Eighteen of these sets were issued for presentation purposes with a special overprint "INVESTITURE–MARCH 14, 1931" in red (*Price for set of 12 £2750, unused*).

10 Maharaja Sawai Man Singh II

One Rupee

(11)

(Des T. I. Archer. Litho Indian Security Printing Press, Nasik)

1932–46. P 14. (*a*) *Inscr* "POSTAGE & REVENUE".

52	10	1 a. black and blue		50	55
53		2 a. black and buff		1·75	1·10
54		4 a. black and grey-green		3·25	5·50
55		8 a. black and chocolate.		4·50	8·50
56		1 r. black and yellow-bistre		16·00	70·00
57		2 r. black and yellow-green		70·00	£275
52/7			Set of 6	85·00	£325

(*b*) *Inscr* "POSTAGE"

58	7	¼ a. black and brown-lake		30	15
59		¾ a. black and brown-red (1943?)		4·50	2·75
60		1 a. black and blue (1943?)		5·50	2·00
61		2 a. black and buff (1943?)		5·50	2·75
62		2½ a. black and carmine .		2·25	1·50
63		3 a. black and green		1·40	40
64		4 a. black and grey-green (1943?)		17·00	80·00
65		6 a. black and deep blue		2·25	18·00
		a. Black and pale blue (1946)..		6·50	45·00
66		8 a. black and chocolate (1946)..		14·00	75·00
67		1 r. black and yellow-bistre (1946)		20·00	£100
58/67			Set of 10	65·00	£250

1936. *Nos. 57 and 51 surch with T 11.*

68	10	1 r. on 2 r. black and yellow-green (R.)		6·00	65·00
69	—	1 r. on 5 r. black and purple		6·00	50·00

पाव आना

(12)

13 Maharaja and Amber Palace

1938 (Dec). *No. 41 surch* "QUARTER ANNA" *in Devanagari,* T 12.

70	7	¼ a. on ½ a. black and violet (R.)		9·00	12·00

(Recess D.L.R.)

1947 (Dec)–**48.** *Silver Jubilee of Maharaja's Accession to Throne. Various designs as T 13.* P 13½ × 14.

71		¼ a. red-brown and green (5.48)		70	2·75
72		½ a. green and violet		20	2·50
73		¾ a. black and lake (5.48)		70	3·25
74		1 a. red-brown and ultramarine		40	2·50
75		2 a. violet and scarlet		40	2·75
76		3 a. green and black (5.48)		90	3·75
77		4 a. ultramarine and brown		50	2·50
78		8 a. vermilion and brown		60	3·50
79		1 r. purple and green (5.48)		1·40	19·00
71/9			Set of 9	5·25	38·00

Designs:—¼ a. Palace Gate; ¾ a. Map of Jaipur; 1 a. Observatory; 2 a. Wind Palace; 3 a. Coat of Arms; 4 a. Amber Fort Gate; 8 a. Chariot of the Sun; 1 r. Maharaja's portrait between State flags.

3 PIES

(14)

1947 (Dec). *No. 41 surch with T 14.*

80	7	3 p. on ½ a. black and violet (R.)		14·00	22·00
		a. "PIE" for "PIES"		42·00	75·00
		b. Bars at left vertical.		55·00	85·00
		c. Surch inverted		35·00	32·00
		d. Surch inverted and "PIE" for "PIES"		£150	£140
		e. Surch double, one inverted.		48·00	45·00
		f. As variety e, but inverted surch showing "PIE" for "PIES"		£300	£275

There were three settings of Type 14, each applied to quarter sheets of 30 (6×5). No. 80a occurs in two of these settings on R.5/5 and one of these settings also shows No. 80b on R.6/1.

OFFICIAL STAMPS

SERVICE (O 1) SERVICE (O 2)

1928 (13 Nov)–**31.** T 3 *typographed. No gum (except for Nos. O6/a).* P 11, 12, *or compound.* Wmk "DORLING & CO. LONDON" (4 a.) *or* "OVERLAND BANK" (others). (*a*) *Optd with Type* O 1.

O 1		¼ a. olive		1·25	1·50
		a. Bistre		1·40	1·40
O 2		½ a. pale ultramarine (Blk.)		65	20
		a. Imperf between (horiz pair)		£275	£275
		b. Imperf between (vert pair)		†	£475
		c. Opt inverted		†	£325
		d. Opt double (R. and Blk.)		†	£400
O 3		½ a. pale ultramarine (R.) (13.10.30)		2·50	25
		a. Imperf horiz (vert pair)			
		b. Stamp doubly printed			
O 3c		1 a. rose-red		70	25
		d. Imperf between (horiz pair)		†	£475
O 4		1 a. scarlet		1·00	50
		a. Opt inverted		£500	£500
		b. Imperf between (horiz pair)		†	£500
O 5		2 a. green		65	40
		a. Imperf between (vert pair)		†	£550
		b. Imperf between (horiz pair)		£550	£550
O 6		4 a. pale brown (with gum)		3·50	1·75
		a. Chocolate (with gum)		2·00	1·75
O 7		8 a. bright violet (R.) (13.10.30)		16·00	48·00
O 8		1 r. orange-vermilion		32·00	£190

(*b*) *Optd with Type* O 2

O 9		½ a. ultramarine (Blk.) (11.2.31)		£190	15
		a. Imperf vert (horiz pair)		†	£600
O10		½ a. ultramarine (R.) (15.10.30)		£160	15
		a. Imperf between (vert pair)		†	£600
O11		8 a. bright violet (11.2.31)		£350	£170
O12		1 r. orange-vermilion (11.2.31)		£300	£225

SERVICE (O 3) आध आना (O 4)

1931–7. *Nos. 41/3 and 46 optd at Nasik with Type* O 3, *in red.*

O13	7	½ a. black and violet		30	10
O14		1 a. black and blue		£225	1·75
O15	8	2 a. black and buff (1936)		2·25	4·25
O16	—	4 a. black and olive-green (1937)		25·00	23·00
O13/16			Set of 4	£225	26·00

1932. *No. O5 surch with Type* O 4.

O17	3	½ a. on 2 a. green		£130	1·00

1932–7. *Nos. 52/6 optd at Nasik with Type* O 3, *in red.*

O18	10	1 a. black and blue		1·50	10
O19		2 a. black and buff		2·00	10
O20		4 a. black and grey-green (1937)		£225	5·50
O21		8 a. black and chocolate.		5·50	1·10
O22		1 r. black and yellow-bistre		14·00	15·00
O18/22			Set of 5	£225	19·00

1936–46. *Stamps of 1932–46, inscr* "POSTAGE".

(*a*) *Optd at Nasik with Type* O 3, *in red*

O23	7	¼ a. black and brown-lake (1936)		40	10
O24		¾ a. black and brown-red (1944)		1·50	40
O25		1 a. black and blue (1941?)		7·50	30
O26		2 a. black and buff (date?)		6·50	1·75
O27		2½ a. black and carmine (1946)		9·00	70·00
O28		4 a. black and grey-green (1942)		5·00	3·25
O29		8 a. black and chocolate (1943)		5·00	4·50
O30		1 r. black and yellow-bistre (date?)		£100	
O23/9			Set of 7	32·00	75·00

(*b*) *Optd locally as Type* O 2 (16 *mm long), in black*

O31	7	¼ a. black and red-brown (1936)		65·00	55·00

9 PIES

(O 5)

1947. *No. O25 surch with Type* O 5, *in red.*

O32	7	9 p. on 1 a. black and blue		2·50	2·50

1947 (Dec). *No. O13 surch as T 14, but* "3 PIES" *placed higher.*

O33	7	3 p. on ½ a. black and violet (R.)		4·00	10·00
		a. Surch double, one inverted.		35·00	35·00
		ab. "PIE" for "PIES" in inverted surcharge		£190	£200
		c. Surch inverted		—£1100	

1949. *No. O13 surch* "THREE-QUARTER ANNA" *in Devanagari, as T 12, but with two bars on each side.*

O34	7	¾ a. on ½ a. black and violet (R.)		13·00	13·00
		a. Surch double		—£1100	

There are three different types of surcharge in the setting of 30, which vary in one or other of the Devanagari characters.

Jaipur became part of Rajasthan by 7 April 1949.

JAMMU AND KASHMIR

PRICES FOR STAMPS ON COVER

Nos. 1/73	from × 3	
Nos. 74/84	from × 2	
No. 85	—	
Nos. 86/9	from × 2	
Nos. 90/101	from × 10	
Nos. 101b/23	from × 5	
Nos. 124/36	from × 10	
Nos. 138/9	from × 100	
Nos. 140/61a	from × 15	
Nos. 162/8	from × 5	
No. O1	from × 2	
Nos. O2/4	from × 4	
No. O5	—	
Nos. O6/14	from × 30	
Nos. O15/18		

ILLUSTRATIONS. Designs of Jammu and Kashmir are illustrated actual size.

Maharaja Ranbir Singh, 1857–1885

1 (½ a.)   2 (1 a.)

3 (4 a.)

Characters denoting the value (on the circular stamps only) are approximately as shown in the central circles of the stamps illustrated above.

These characters were taken from Punjabi merchants' notation and were not familiar to most of the inhabitants of the state. Type 1 was certainly the ½ anna value, but there has long been controversy over the correct face values of Types 2 and 3.

The study of surviving material suggests that, to some extent, this confusion involved contemporary post office officials. Although covers posted at Jammu, where the stamps were in use for twelve years, show Type 2 used as the 1 a. value and Type 3 as the 4 a., those originating from Srinagar (Kashmir) during 1866–68 show both Types 2 and 3 used as 1 a. stamps.

In the following listing we have followed contemporary usage at Jammu and this reflects the prevailing opinion amongst modern authorities.

GUM. The stamps of Jammu and Kashmir were issued without gum.

PRICES. Prices for the circular stamps, Nos. 1/49, are for cut-square examples. Cut-to-shape examples are worth from 10% to 20% of these prices, according to condition.

A. Handstamped in watercolours

1866 (23 Mar)–67. *Native paper, thick to thin, usually having the appearance of laid paper and tinted grey or brown. For Jammu and Kashmir.*

1	1	½ a. grey-black				£160	75·00
2	2	1 a. grey-black				£1200	£1000
3	3	4 a. grey-black				£1300	
4	2	1 a. royal blue				£550	£375
4a	1	½ a. ultramarine				£2250	£2250
5	2	1 a. ultramarine				£300	75·00
6	3	4 a. ultramarine				£600	£300
7		4 a. indigo (1867)				£1500	£850

1869–72. *Reissued for use in Jammu only.*

8	1	½ a. red				65·00	£275
9	2	1 a. red				£130	£200
10	3	4 a. red				50·00	90·00
11	1	½ a. orange-red				£475	£500
12	2	1 a. orange-red				£140	£225
13	3	4 a. orange-red				£110	£160
13a		4 a. carmine-red				£700	
13b	2	1 a. orange (1872)				£600	
13c	3	4 a. orange (1872)					

1874–76. *Special Printings.*

14	1	½ a. deep black				17·00	£150
		a. Tête-bêche (pair)				£350	
15	2	1 a. deep black				£200	
16	3	4 a. deep black				£200	
17	1	½ a. bright blue (1876)				£225	£300
18	2	1 a. bright blue (1876)				85·00	£275
19	3	4 a. bright blue (1876)				£140	
20	1	½ a. emerald-green				70·00	£180
21	2	1 a. emerald-green				75·00	£180
22	3	4 a. emerald-green				£170	£300
23a	1	½ a. yellow				£450	£550
24	2	1 a. yellow				£600	
25	3	4 a. yellow				£350	
25a		4 a. deep blue-black (1876)				£900	£550

These special printings were available for use, but little used.

B. Handstamped in oil colours. Heavy blurred prints

1877 (June)–78. *(a) Native paper.*

26	1	½ a. red			24·00	42·00
27	2	1 a. red			28·00	£150
28	3	4 a. red			£180	£400
29	1	½ a. black			24·00	42·00
32		½ a. slate-blue			£100	£170
34	2	1 a. slate-blue			20·00	£200
35	1	½ a. sage-green			£100	
36	2	1 a. sage-green			£110	
37	3	4 a. sage-green			£110	

(b) European laid paper, medium to thick

38	1	½ a. red			—	£600
39	3	4 a. red			£325	£350
41	1	½ a. black			19·00	42·00
		a. Printed both sides				
		b. Tête-bêche (pair)				£275
44		½ a. slate-blue			32·00	£200
45	2	1 a. slate-blue			42·00	£300
46	3	4 a. slate-blue			£550	£550
47		4 a. sage-green			£1000	
48	1	½ a. yellow			£100	

(c) Thick yellowish wove paper

49	1	½ a. red (1878)			—	£800

Forgeries exist of the ½ a. and 1 a. in types which were at one time supposed to be authentic.

Reprints and imitations (of which some of each were found in the official remainder stock) exist in a great variety of fancy colours, both on native paper, usually thinner and smoother than that of the originals, and on various thin European wove papers, on which the originals were never printed.

The imitations, which do not agree in type with the above illustrations, are also to be found on laid paper.

All the reprints, etc. are in oil colours or printer's ink. The originals in oil colour are usually blurred, particularly when on native paper. The reprints, etc. are usually clear.

FOR USE IN JAMMU

½ a.   ½ a.

1 a.   4   ½ a.

T 4 to 11 have a star at the top of the oval band; the characters denoting the value are in the upper part of the inner oval. All are dated 1923, corresponding with A.D. 1866.

T 4. Printed in blocks of four, three varieties of ½ anna and one of 1 anna.

1867. *In watercolour on native paper.*

52		½ a. grey-black			£600	£190
53		1 a. grey-black			£1800	£800
54		½ a. indigo			£250	£200
55		1 a. indigo			£500	£275
56		½ a. deep ultramarine			£200	£140
57		1 a. deep ultramarine			£475	£275
58		½ a. deep violet-blue			£140	75·00
59		1 a. deep violet-blue			£475	£275

1868 (May)–76. *In watercolour on native paper.*

60		½ a. red (shades) (1876)			4·75	2·50
61		1 a. red (shades) (1876)			11·00	8·00
62		½ a. orange-red			£170	55·00
63		1 a. orange-red			£500	£200
64		½ a. orange (1872)			85·00	90·00
65		1 a. orange (1872)			£1500	£950

1874–6. *Special printings; in watercolour on native paper.*

66		½ a. bright blue (1876)			£950	£225
67		1 a. bright blue (1876)			£300	£325
68		½ a. emerald-green			£1300	£800
69		1 a. emerald-green			£2250	£1400
69a		½ a. jet-black			£100	£130
69b		1 a. jet-black			£1200	£1000

1877 (June)–78. *In oil colour. (a) Native paper.*

70		½ a. red			8·50	5·50
71		1 a. red			25·00	19·00
72		½ a. brown-red (1878)			—	32·00
73		1 a. brown-red (1878)			—	95·00
74		½ a. black			†	£700
75		1 a. black			†	£1600
76		½ a. deep blue-black			†	£1100
77		1 a. deep blue-black			†	£3000

(b) Laid paper (medium or thick)

78		½ a. red			—	£750

(c) Thick wove paper

79		½ a. red			†	£375
80		1 a. red				

(d) Thin laid, bâtonné paper

84		½ a. red			†	£1000
85		1 a. red				£3000

The circular and rectangular stamps listed under the heading "Special Printings" did not supersede those in red, which was the normal colour for Jammu down to 1878. It is not known for what

---

reason other colours were used during that period, but these stamps were printed in 1874 or 1875 and were certainly put into use. The rectangular stamps were again printed in black (jet-black, as against the greyish black of the 1867 printings) at that time, and impressions of the two periods can also be distinguished by the obliterations, which until 1868 were in magenta and after that in black.

There are reprints of these, in oil colour, brown-red and bright blue, on native paper; they are very clearly printed, which is not the case with the originals in oil colour.

4a

1877 (Sept). *Provisional. Seal obliterator of Jammu handstamped in red watercolour on pieces of native paper, and used as a ½ anna stamp.*

86	4a	(½ a.) rose-red			—	£950

FOR USE IN KASHMIR

5

1866 (Sept(?). *Printed from a single die. Native laid paper.*

87	5	½ a. black			£2000	£300

Forgeries of this stamp are commonly found, copied from an illustration in *Le Timbre-Poste.*

6 (½ a.)   7 (1 a.)

1867. *Native laid paper.*

88	6	½ a. black			£950	£130
89	7	1 a. black			£1700	£350

Printed in sheets of 25 (5×5), the four top rows being ½ a. and the bottom row 1 a.

8 (¼ a.)

9 (2 a.)

10 (4 a.)

11 (8 a.)

1867–76. *Native laid paper.*

90	8	¼ a. black			2·00	2·25
91	6	½ a. ultramarine			2·00	1·00
92		½ a. violet-blue (1870)			3·75	2·25
93	7	1 a. ultramarine			£2750	£1200
94		1 a. orange (7.67)			7·50	8·00
95		1 a. brown-orange (1868)			9·50	7·50
96		1 a. orange-vermilion (1876)			11·00	8·00
97	9	2 a. yellow			10·00	12·00
98		2 a. buff			15·00	13·00
99	10	4 a. emerald-green			26·00	26·00
		a. Tête-bêche (pair)			£850	
100		4 a. sage-green			£225	£110
100a		4 a. myrtle-green			£550	£550
101	11	8 a. red (1868)			28·00	26·00
		a. Tête-bêche (pair)			£850	

Of the above, the ½ a. and 1 a. were printed from the same plate of 25 as Nos. 87/8, the ¼ a. and 2 a. from a new plate of 10 (5 × 2), the top row being ¼ a. and the lower 2 a., and the 4 a. and 8 a. from single dies. Varieties at one time catalogued upon European papers were apparently never put into circulation, though some of them were printed while these stamps were still in use.

Nos. 86 to 101 are in watercolour.

FOR USE IN JAMMU AND KASHMIR

In the following issues there are 15 varieties on the sheets of the ⅛ a., ¼ a. and ½ a.; 20 varieties of the 1 a. and 2 a. and 8 varieties of the 4 a. and 8 a. The value is in the lower part of the central oval.

12 (¼ a.)

13 (½ a.)

14 (1 a.)

15 (2 a.)

16 (4 a.)

17 (8 a.)

1878 (May)–**79.** *Provisional printings.*

I. Ordinary white laid paper, of varying thickness

(a) Rough perf 10 to 12 (i) or 13 to 16 (ii)

101*b*	12	¼ a. red (i)	..	..		
102	13	½ a. red (i)	..	..	12·00	14·00
103	14	1 a. red (i)	..	..	£950	
104	13	½ a. slate-violet (i)	..		70·00	50·00
104*a*	14	1 a. violet (ii)	..	..		
104*b*	15	2 a. violet (i)	..	..	£1300	

(b) Imperf

105	13	½ a. slate-violet (*shades*)		13·00	12·00
106	14	1 a. slate-purple	..	..	19·00	20·00
107		1 a. mauve	..	..	29·00	29·00
108	15	2 a. violet	..	..	20·00	20·00
109		2 a. bright mauve	..		27·00	25·00
110		2 a. slate-blue	..	..	38·00	38·00
111		2 a. dull blue	..	..	70·00	75·00
112	12	¼ a. red	..	..	17·00	13·00
113	13	½ a. red	..	..	7·00	7·00
114	14	1 a. red	..	..	6·50	7·00
115	15	2 a. red	..	..	55·00	55·00
116	16	4 a. red	..	..	£140	£120

II. Medium wove paper. (a) Rough perf 10 to 12

117	13	½ a. red	..	..	—	£170

(b) Imperf

117*b*	12	¼ a. red	..	..		
118	13	½ a. red	..	..	12·00	6·50
119	14	1 a. red	..	..	11·00	7·50
120	15	2 a. red	..	..	60·00	

III. Thick wove paper. Imperf

121	13	½ a. red	..	..	22·00	45·00
122	14	1 a. red	..	..	40·00	17·00
123	15	2 a. red	..	..	15·00	18·00

Of the above stamps those in red were intended for use in Jammu and those in shades of violet and blue for use in Kashmir.

1879. *Definitive issue. Thin wove paper, fine to coarse.*

(a) Rough perf 10 to 12

124	13	½ a. red	..	..	£190	£140

(b) Imperf

125	12	¼ a. red	..	..	2·50	2·75
126	13	½ a. red	..	..	50	55
		a. Bisected (¼ a.) on postcard		† £3000
127	14	1 a. red	..	..	2·00	2·60
128	15	2 a. red	..	..	2·75	3·50
129	16	4 a. red	..	..	6·50	6·50
130	17	8 a. red	..	..	6·50	7·50

The plates were transferred from Jammu to Srinagar in early 1881 when further printings in red and all orange stamps were produced.

1880 (Mar). *Provisional printing in watercolour on thin bâtonné paper. Imperf.*

130*a*	12	¼ a. ultramarine	..		£750	£450

1881–83. *As Nos. 124 to 130. Colour changed.*

(a) Rough perf 10 to 12

130*b*	13	½ a. orange	..	..		

(b) Imperf

131	12	¼ a. orange	..	..	8·00	9·50
132	13	½ a. orange	..	..	18·00	12·00
133	14	1 a. orange	..	..	17·00	9·00
		a. Bisected (½ a.) (on cover)		† £3250

134	15	2 a. orange	..	..	14·00	9·00
135	16	4 a. orange	..	..	26·00	40·00
136	17	8 a. orange	..	..	50·00	60·00

Nos. 126a and 133a were used at Leh between April and July 1883.

Nos. 125/30 and 132/6 were re-issued between 1890 and 1894 and used concurrently with the stamps which follow. Such re-issues can be identified by the "three circle" cancellations, introduced in December 1890.

18 (⅛ a.)

1883–94. *New colours. Thin wove papers, toned, coarse to fine, or fine white (1889). Imperf.*

138	18	⅛ a. yellow-brown	..	..	70	1·00
139		⅛ a. yellow	..	..	70	1·00
140	12	¼ a. sepia	..	..	60	45
141		¼ a. brown	..	..	55	45
		a. Double impression	..		£1100	
142		¼ a. pale brown	..	..	55	45
		a. Error. Green	..	..	50·00	
143	13	½ a. dull blue	..	..	4·25	
144		½ a. bright blue	..	..	40·00	
145		½ a. vermillion	..	..	90	35
146		½ a. rose	..	..	90	60
147		½ a. orange-red	..	..	85	35
148	14	1 a. greenish grey	..	..	65	50
149		1 a. bright green	..	..	75	75
		a. Double impression	..			
150		1 a. dull green	..	..	65	50
151		1 a. blue-green	..	..	1·00	
152	15	2 a. red/*yellow*	..	..	1·25	90
153		2 a. red/*yellow-green*	..		2·00	2·50
154		2 a. red/*deep green*	..		10·00	10·00
155	16	4 a. deep green	..	..	2·50	3·25
156		4 a. green	..	..	2·75	3·00
157		4 a. pale green	..	..	2·75	3·25
158		4 a. sage-green	..	..	3·00	
159	17	8 a. pale blue	..	..	5·00	7·00
159*a*		8 a. deep blue	..	..	8·00	9·00
160		8 a. bright blue	..	..	7·00	8·50
161		8 a. indigo-blue	..		8·50	10·00
161*a*		8 a. slate-lilac	..		10·00	15·00

Well-executed forgeries of the ¼ a. to 8 a. have come from India, mostly postmarked; they may be detected by the type, which does not agree with any variety on the genuine sheets, and also, in the low values, by the margins being filled in with colour, all but a thin white frame round the stamp. The forgeries of the 8 a. are in sheets of eight like the originals.

Other forgeries of nearly all values also exist, showing all varieties of type. All values are on thin, coarse wove paper.

In February 1890, a forgery, in watercolour, of the ½ a. orange on thin wove or on thin laid paper appeared, and many have been found genuinely used during 1890 and 1891 (*Price* £3).

Nos. 143 and 144 were never issued.

Examples of the ¼ a. brown, ½ a. orange-red and 1 a. green on wove paper exist with clean-cut perf 12.

There is a reference in the Jammu and Kashmir State Administration Report covering 1890–91 to the re-introduction of perforating and the machine-gumming of paper at the Jammu printing works.

The few known examples, the ¼ a. being only recorded used, the others unused or used, would appear to date from this period, but there is, as yet, no direct confirmation as to their status.

Maharaja Partap Singh, 1885–1925

1887–94. *Thin creamy laid paper. Imperf.*

162	18	⅛ a. yellow	..	..	38·00	45·00
163	12	¼ a. brown	..	..	9·00	6·00
164	13	½ a. brown-red (March 1887)		—	60·00
165		½ a. orange-red	..	..	6·50	4·75
166	14	1 a. grey-green	..	..	£100	£100
168	17	8 a. blue (*Printed in watercolour*)		£150	£150
		a. On wove paper	..	..	£100	£100

19

T **19** represents a ¼ a. stamp, which exists in sheets of twelve varieties, in *red* and *black*, on thin wove and laid papers, also in *red* on native paper, but which does not appear ever to have been issued for use. It was first seen in 1886.

The ¼ a. *brown* and the 4 a. *green* both exist on ordinary white laid paper and the ½ a. *red* on native paper. None of these are known to have been in use.

OFFICIAL STAMPS

1878. *I. White laid paper. (a) Rough perf 10 to 12.*

O1	13	½ a. black	..	..	—£1200	

		(b) Imperf				
O2	13	½ a. black	..	..	90·00	85·00
O3	14	1 a. black	..	..	55·00	55·00
O4	15	2 a. black	..	..	50·00	45·00

II. Medium wove paper. Imperf

O5	14	1 a. black	..	..	£200	

1880–94. *Thin wove papers, toned, coarse to fine, or fine white (1889). Imperf.*

O 6	12	¼ a. black	..	..	65	70
		a. Double print	..		£180	
O 7	13	½ a. black	..	..	15	30
		a. Printed both sides		£400	
O 8	14	1 a. black	..	..	20	45
O 9	15	2 a. black	..	..	30	40
O10	16	4 a. black	..	..	35	70
O11	17	8 a. black	..	..	1·00	1·00

1887–94. *Thin creamy laid paper. Imperf.*

O12	12	¼ a. black	..	..	5·00	5·00
O13	13	½ a. black	..	..	3·00	3·25
O14	14	1 a. black	..	..	1·50	2·25
O15	15	2 a. black	..	..	12·00	
O16	16	4 a. black	..	..	48·00	50·00
O17	17	8 a. black	..	..	28·00	45·00

1889. *Stout white wove paper. Imperf.*

O18	12	¼ a. black	..	..	£180	£110

The stamps of Jammu and Kashmir have been obsolete since 1 November 1894.

JASDAN

PRICES FOR STAMPS ON COVER	
Nos. 1/2	*from* × 2
No. 3	*from* × 3
Nos. 4/6	*from* × 4

Darbar Ala Khachar, 1919–1971

1 Sun

(Typo L. V. Indap & Co, Bombay)

1942 (15 Mar)–**47.** *Stamps from booklet panes. Various perfs.*

1	1 a. deep myrtle-green (*p* 10½×*imperf*)		£650	£425
2	1 a. light green (*p* 12×*imperf*)		£375	£425
3	1 a. light green (*p* 10½×*imperf*) (1943)		£100	£130
4	1 a. pale yellow-green (*p* 8½×*imperf*)		12·00	95·00
5	1 a. dull yellow-green (*p* 10) (1946)		17·00	£110
6	1 a. bluish green (*p* 9) (1947)		13·00	95·00

Nos. 1/4 were issued in panes of four with the stamps imperforate on one or two sides; Nos. 5/6 were in panes of eight perforated all round.

A 1 a. rose with the arms of Jasdan in the centre is a fiscal stamp.

Jasdan was merged with the United State of Kathiawar (later Saurashtra) by 15 April 1948.

JHALAWAR

PRICES FOR STAMPS ON COVER	
Nos. 1/2	*from* × 25

Maharaj Rana Zalim Singh, 1875–1896

(Figure of an Apsara, "RHEMBA", a dancing nymph of the Hindu Paradise)

1 (1 paisa)   **2** (¼ anna)

1886–90. *Typo in horizontal strips of 12. Laid paper. No gum.*

1	1	1 p. yellow-green	..	..	3·25	8·50
		a. Blue-green	..	..	75·00	30·00
2	2	¼ a. green (*shades*)	..	..	70	1·60

The stamps formerly listed as on wove paper are from sheets on laid paper, with the laid paper lines almost invisible.

The Maharaj Rana was deposed in 1896 and much of the state's territory transferred to Kotah on 1 January 1899.

Raj (Maharaj from 1918) Rana Bhawani Singh, 1899–1929

The stamps of Jhalawar have been obsolete since 1 November 1900.

JIND

ILLUSTRATIONS. Designs of Jind are illustrated actual size.

Raja Raghubir Singh, 1864–1887

J 1 (½ a.) J 2 (1 a.)

J 3 (2 a.) J 4 (4 a.)

J 5 (8 a.)

(Litho Jind State Rajah's Press, Sungroor)

1874. *Thin yellowish paper. Imperf.*

J1	J 1	½ a. blue	..	..	6·00	2·75
		a. No frame to value. (Retouched all over)	..	£250	£140
J2	J 2	1 a. rosy mauve	..	..	7·00	6·00
J3	J 3	2 a. yellow	..	..	1·00	3·25
J4		2 a. brown-buff	..	..	£140	80·00
J5	J 4	4 a. green	..	..	18·00	6·00
J6	J 5	8 a. dull purple	..	£450	£120
J6a		8 a. bluish violet	..	£160	70·00
J7		8 a. slate-blue	..	£130	60·00

Nos. J1/7 were produced from two stones. Those from the first stone had rather blurred impressions, but those from the second are clearer with a conspicuous white frame around the value. Nos. J4 and J8/13 were only printed from the second stone.

1876. *Bluish laid card-paper. No gum. Imperf.*

J 8	J 1	½ a. blue	..	..	60	3·25
J 9	J 2	1 a. purple	..	..	1·40	7·50
J10	J 3	2 a. brown	..	..	2·50	10·00
J11	J 4	4 a. green	..	..	1·50	10·00
J11a	J 5	8 a. bluish violet	..	8·00	20·00
J12		8 a. slate-blue	..	7·00	10·00
J13		8 a. steel-blue	..	9·00	15·00

Stocks of the ½ a. (No. J8) and 2 a. (No. J4) were perforated 12 in 1885 for use as fiscal stamps.

J 6 (¼ a.) J 7 (½ a.)

J 8 (1 a.) J 9 (2 a.)

J 10 (4 a.) J 11 (8 a.)

(Litho Jind State Rajah's Press, Sungroor)

1882–85. *Types **J 6** to **J 11**. 25 varieties of each value. No gum.*

A. *Imperf* (1882–4). (a) *Thin yellowish wove paper.*

J15	¼ a. buff (*shades*)	..	..	30	1·50
J16	¼ a. red-brown	..	..	30	1·25
	a. Doubly printed	..	42·00	
J17	½ a. lemon	..	..	90	1·75
J18	½ a. buff	..	..	1·75	1·50
J19	½ a. brown-buff	..	..	70	60
J20	1 a. brown (*shades*)	..	1·60	3·25
J21	2 a. blue	..	..	1·75	7·00
J22	2 a. deep blue	..	2·25	1·00
J23	4 a. sage-green	..	1·25	90
J24	4 a. blue-green	..	1·75	2·75
J25	8 a. red	..	..	5·00	4·25

(b) *Various thick laid papers*

J26	¼ a. brown-buff	..	..	1·25	
J27	½ a. lemon	..	..	1·25	
J28	½ a. brown-buff	..	..		
J29	1 a. brown	..	..	1·25	2·50
J30	2 a. blue	..	..	18·00	21·00
J31	8 a. red	..	..	2·50	9·50

(c) *Thick white wove paper*

J32	¼ a. brown-buff	..	..	12·00	
J33	½ a. brown-buff	..	..	27·00	
J34	1 a. brown	..	..	3·75	
J35	8 a. red	..	..	4·75	9·00

B. *Perf* 12 (1885). (a) *Thin yellowish wove paper*

J36	¼ a. buff (*shades*)	..	..	60	2·50
	a. Doubly printed	..	85·00	
J37	¼ a. red-brown	..	..	3·50	
J38	½ a. lemon	..	..	£100	£100
J39	½ a. buff	..	..	45	3·50
J40	½ a. brown-buff	..	3·00	4·25
J41	1 a. brown (*shades*)	..	2·50	4·50
J42	2 a. blue	..	..	3·25	8·50
J43	2 a. deep blue	..	2·75	5·50
J44	4 a. sage-green	..	5·00	9·00
J45	4 a. blue-green	..	2·00	
	a. Imperf vert (horiz pair)	£500	
J46	8 a. red	..	..	9·00	

(b) *Various thick laid papers*

J47	¼ a. brown-buff	..	..	6·00	
J48	½ a. lemon	..	..	90·00	22·00
J49	1 a. brown	..	..	1·50	
J50	2 a. blue	..	..	20·00	23·00
J51	8 a. red	..	..	2·50	7·00

(c) *Thick white wove paper*

J52	1 a. brown	..	..		
J53	8 a. red	..	..	9·50	

The perforated stamps ceased to be used for postal purposes in July 1885, but were used as fiscals to at least the mid-1920s. Other varieties exist, but they must either be fiscals or reprints, and it is not quite certain that all those listed above were issued as early as 1885.

Jind became a Convention State and from 1 July 1885 used overprinted Indian stamps.

KISHANGARH

GUM. The stamps of Kishangarh were issued without gum, *except* for Nos. 42/50 and O 17/24.

Maharaja Sardul Singh, 1879–1900

1

1899. *Medium wove paper. Typo from a plate of eight impressions.*

1	1	1 a. green (*imperf*)	..	..	21·00	55·00
2		1 a. green (*pin-perf*)	..		65·00	

1900. *Thin white wove paper. Printed from a single die. Imperf.*

3	1	1 a. blue	..	..	£400

ILLUSTRATIONS. Types **2** to **10a** are shown actual size.

2 (¼ a.) 3 (½ a.)

---

4 (1 a.) 5 (2 a.)
            Maharaja Sardul Singh

6 (4 a.) 7 (1 r.)

8 (2 r.) 9 (5 r.)

1899–1901. *Thin white wove paper.* (a) *Imperf.*

4	2	¼ a. green	..	..	£500	
5		¼ a. carmine	..	..	6·50	
		a. *Rose-pink*	..	..	90	1·60
6		¼ a. magenta	..	..	5·00	5·00
		a. Doubly printed	..	80·00	
7	3	½ a. lilac	..	..	£100	£180
8		½ a. red	..	..	£1800	£1100
9		½ a. green	..	..	26·00	30·00
10		½ a. pale yellow-olive	..	40·00	40·00
11		½ a. slate-blue	..	32·00	32·00
		a. Pair, one stamp sideways	£1000	
		b. *Deep blue*	..	..	6·00	7·00
		c. *Light blue*	..	..	1·40	1·50
12	4	1 a. slate	..	..	4·25	4·75
		a. Laid paper	..	38·00	
12b		1 a. pink	..	..	50·00	£150
13		1 a. mauve	..	..	5·50	8·00
		a. Laid paper	..	32·00	
14		1 a. brown-lilac	..	1·10	90
		a. Laid paper	..	28·00	
15	5	2 a. dull orange	..	4·25	4·50
		a. Laid paper	..	£400	£375
16	6	4 a. chocolate	..	5·50	
		a. *Lake-brown*	..	5·50	9·00
		b. *Chestnut*	..	..	5·50	9·00
		c. Laid paper (*shades*)	..	55·00	55·00
17	7	1 r. brown-lilac	..	20·00	25·00
18		1 r. dull green	..	18·00	30·00
19	8	2 r. brown-red	..	70·00	90·00
		a. Laid paper	..	55·00	
20	9	5 r. mauve	..	..	60·00	70·00
		a. Laid paper	..	60·00	

(b) *Pin-perf* 12½ *or* 14

21	2	¼ a. green	..	..	£200	£350
		a. Imperf between (pair)	£1000	
22		¼ a. carmine	..	..	4·00	5·00
		a. *Rose-pink*	..	..	25	40
		ab. *Tête-bêche* (horiz pair)	£700	
		b. *Rose*	..	..		
23		¼ a. magenta	..	..	5·00	7·00
		a. *Bright purple*	..	..		
		ab. Doubly printed	..		
24	3	½ a. green	..	..	17·00	22·00
		a. Imperf between (pair)	£160	
25		½ a. pale yellow-olive	..	13·00	16·00
		a. Imperf vert (horiz pair)	£160	
		b. Imperf between (horiz pair)	†	£275
26		½ a. deep blue	..	..	1·90	3·25
		a. *Light blue*	..	..	75	50
		ab. Doubly printed	..	£100	£100
27	4	1 a. slate	..	..	4·50	3·00
		a. Laid paper	..	35·00	18·00
27b		1 a. pink	..	..	60·00	£170
28		1 a. mauve	..	..	85	1·60
		a. Laid paper	..	35·00	13·00
29		1 a. brown-lilac	..	75	1·00
		a. Laid paper	..	32·00	13·00
30	5	2 a. dull orange	..	4·00	5·00
31	6	4 a. chocolate	..	2·00	5·00
		a. *Lake-brown*	..	2·50	5·00
		b. *Chestnut*	..	..	3·50	5·50
		c. Laid paper (*shades*)	..	45·00	42·00
32	7	1 r. dull green	..	10·00	15·00
		a. Laid paper	..	70·00	
33		1 r. pale olive-yellow	..	£650	
34	8	2 r. brown-red	..	38·00	48·00
		a. Laid paper	..	40·00	
35	9	5 r. mauve	..	..	32·00	48·00
		a. Laid paper	..	60·00	

All the above, both imperf and pin-perf, were printed singly, sometimes on paper with spaces marked in pencil. They exist in vertical *tête-bêche* pairs imperf between from the centre of the sheet. *Prices from* 3 × *normal, unused.* No. 22ab is an error.

FISCAL STAMPS. Many of the following issues were produced in different colours for fiscal purposes. Such usage is indicated by the initials "M.C.", punched hole or violet Stamp Office handstamp.

Maharaja Madan Singh, 1900–1926

10 (¼ a.) 10a (1 r.)

1901. *Toned wove paper. Pin-perf.*

36	10	¼ a. dull pink	..	..	8·00	6·00
37	4	1 a. violet	..	..	40·00	27·00
38	10a	1 r. dull green	..	..	14·00	16·00
36/8				*Set of 3*	55·00	45·00

Nos. 36/8 were printed in sheets of 24. Sheets of the 1 r. were always torn to remove R. 5/4 where the cliché is believed to have been defective.

The 1 a. (No. 37) differs from T 4 in having an inscription in native characters below the words "ONE ANNA".

11 (½ a.) 12 Maharaja Sardul Singh

1903. *Litho. Thick white wove glazed paper. Imperf.*

39	11	½ a. pink	..	..	8·50	3·00
		a. Printed both sides	..	†	£950	
40	12	2 a. dull yellow	..	..	3·00	5·50

12a (8 a.)

1904. *Printed singly. Thin paper. Pin-perf.*

41	12a	8 a. grey	..	..	5·00	7·50
		a. Tête-bêche (vert pair)	..		26·00	
		b. Doubly printed	..		£110	

13 Maharaja Madan Singh 14

(Recess Perkins Bacon & Co)

1904–10. *With gum. P 12½.*

42	13	¼ a. carmine	..	..	45	45
		a. Perf 13½ (1910)	..		45	45
		b. Perf 12×12½	..		75·00	
43		½ a. chestnut	..	..	1·60	85
		a. Perf 13½ (1906)	..		50	30
44		1 a. blue	..	..	3·50	2·25
		a. Perf 13½ (1906)	..		1·50	1·40
45		2 a. orange-yellow	..		13·00	7·00
		a. Perf 13½ (1907)	..		17·00	14·00
46		4 a. brown	..		19·00	16·00
		a. Perf 13½ (1907)	..		11·00	14·00
		b. Perf 12	..		45·00	38·00
47		8 a. violet (1905)	..		6·00	17·00
48		1 r. green	..		22·00	28·00
49		2 r. olive-yellow	..		22·00	£100
50		5 r. purple-brown	..		21·00	£130
42/50				*Set of 9*	85·00	£275

Stamps in other columns, all perforated 13½, are colour trials.

1912. *Printed from half-tone blocks. No ornaments to left and right of value in English; large ornaments on either side of value in Hindi. Small stop after "STATE". (a) Thin wove paper. Rouletted.*

51	14	2 a. deep violet ("TWO ANNA")	..		3·25	7·50
		a. Tête-bêche (vert pair)	..		8·00	
		b. Imperf (pair)	..		£275	

No. 51 is printed in four rows, each inverted in respect to that above and below it.

(b) Thick white chalk-surfaced paper. Imperf.

52	14	2 a. lilac ("TWO ANNA")	..		£1200	£600

(c) Thick white chalk-surfaced paper. Rouletted in colour (Medallion only in half-tone)

53	14	¼ a. ultramarine	..		14·00	14·00

1913. *No ornaments on either side of value in English. Small ornaments in bottom label. With stop after "STATE". Thick white chalk-surfaced paper. Rouletted.*

54	14	2 a. purple ("TWO ANNAS")	..		2·50	5·00

15

No. 59e. This occurs on R. 3/3 on one setting only

2 TWO ANNAS 2 **2 TWO ANNAS 2**
No. 60. Small figures No. 60b. Large figures

(Typo Diamond Soap Works, Kishangarh)

1913 (Aug). *Thick surfaced paper. Half-tone centre. Type-set inscriptions. Rouletted. Inscr "KISHANGARH".*

59	15	¼ a. pale blue	..		20	90
		a. Imperf (pair)	..		7·00	
		b. Roul × imperf (horiz pair)			25·00	
		ba. Imperf between (horiz pair)			42·00	
		c. "OUARTER" (R. 4/4)	..		5·00	7·00
		ca. As last, imperf (pair)	..		28·00	
		cb. As last, roul × imperf			55·00	
		d. "KISHANGAHR" (R. 2/3)	..		5·00	7·00
		da. As last, imperf (pair)	..		28·00	
		db. As last, roul × imperf			55·00	
		dc. As last, imperf between (horiz pair)			85·00	
		e. Character omitted	..		7·00	7·00
		ea. As last, imperf (pair)	..		32·00	
60		2 a. purple	..		7·00	18·00
		a. "KISHANGAHR" (R. 2/3)	..		50·00	90·00
		b. Large figures "2"	..		32·00	55·00

1913–16. *Stamps printed far apart, horizontally and vertically, otherwise as No. 54, except as noted below.*

63	14	¼ a. blue	..		20	45
64		½ a. green (1915)	..		20	80
		a. Printed both sides	..		£200	
		b. Imperf (pair)	..		£150	£150
		c. Emerald-green (1916)	..		1·75	3·50
65		1 a. red	..		1·00	2·50
		a. Without stop*	..		1·25	4·50
		ab. Imperf (pair)	..		£180	
66		2 a. purple ("TWO ANNAS") (1915)	..		6·00	7·00
67		4 a. bright blue	..		6·00	8·00
68		8 a. brown	..		7·00	38·00
69		1 r. mauve	..		15·00	£100
		a. Imperf (pair)	..		£275	
70		2 r. deep green	..		75·00	£200
71		5 r. brown	..		75·00	£350
63/71				*Set of 9*	£170	£600

*For this issue, ornaments were added on either side of the English value (except in the ¼ a.) and the inscription in the right label was without stop, except in the case of No. 65.

In Nos. 70 and 71 the value is expressed as "RUPIES" instead of "RUPEES".

Initial printings of the ¼ a., 1 a. and 4 a. values were in sheets of 20 containing two panes of 10 separated by a central gutter margin. Stamps from these sheets measure 20×25½ mm and have heavier screening dots on the perforation margins than on the designs. Subsequent printings of these stamps, and of other values in the set, were from single pane sheets of 20 on which the designs measured 19½×23¾ mm and with the screening dots uniform across the sheet.

Maharaja Yagyanarayan Singh, 1926–1939

16 Maharaja Yagyanarayan Singh 17

1928–36. *Thick surfaced paper. Typo. Pin-perf.*

72	16	¼ a. light blue	..		70	2·00
73		½ a. yellow-green	..		2·25	1·25
		a. Deep green	..		2·75	2·75
		ab. Imperf (pair)	..		75·00	75·00
		ac. Imperf between (vert or horiz pair)			90·00	90·00
74	17	1 a. carmine	..		65	1·50
		a. Imperf (pair)	..		£140	£100
75		2 a. purple	..		3·00	7·50
75a		2 a. magenta (1936)	..		6·00	11·00
		ab. Imperf (pair)	..		£200	
76	16	4 a. chestnut	..		1·40	1·75
		a. Imperf (pair)	..		£120	
77		8 a. violet	..		3·50	23·00
78		1 r. light green	..		12·00	45·00
79		2 r. lemon-yellow (1929)	..		26·00	£140
80		5 r. claret (1929)	..		30·00	£160
		a. Imperf (pair)	..		£100	
72/80				*Set of 9*	70·00	£350

The 4 a. to 5 r. are slightly larger than, but otherwise similar to, the ¼ a. and ½ a. The 8 a. has a dotted background covering the whole design.

Maharaja Sumar Singh, 1939–1971

1943–47. *As last, but thick, soft, unsurfaced paper. Poor impression. Typo. Pin-perf.*

81	16	¼ a. pale dull blue (1945)	..		3·75	8·50
		a. Imperf (pair)	..		32·00	
82		¼ a. greenish blue (1947)	..		1·60	7·00
		a. Imperf (pair)	..		28·00	

83	16	½ a. deep green (1944)	..		90	2·00
		a. Imperf (pair)	..		25·00	25·00
		b. Imperf between (vert or horiz pair)			42·00	
84		½ a. yellow-green (1946)	..		4·75	7·00
		a. Imperf (pair)	..		28·00	28·00
		b. Imperf between (vert or horiz pair)			42·00	
85	17	1 a. carmine-red (1944)	..		6·50	2·75
		a. Double print	..		£300	
		b. Imperf (pair)	..		28·00	28·00
		c. Imperf between (vert or horiz pair)			42·00	
		d. Red-orange (1947)	..		60·00	24·00
		da. Imperf (pair)	..		95·00	75·00
86		2 a. bright magenta	..		7·50	13·00
		a. Imperf (pair)	..		55·00	60·00
87		2 a. maroon (1947)	..		65·00	16·00
		a. Imperf (pair)	..		42·00	42·00
		b. Imperf between (vert or horiz pair)			75·00	
88	16	4 a. brown (1944)	..		22·00	16·00
		a. Imperf (pair)	..			
89		8 a. violet (1945)	..		45·00	£110
90		1 r. green (1945)	..		50·00	£120
		a. Imperf (pair)	..		£170	£250
90b		2 r. yellow (date?)	..		£375	
		ba. Imperf (pair)	..		£375	
91		5 r. claret (1945)	..		£425	£450
		a. Imperf (pair)	..		£275	

OFFICIAL STAMPS

(O 1)

1918. *Handstamped with Type O 1.*

(a) Stamps of 1899–1901. (i) Imperf

O 1	2	¼ a. green	..		—	£160
O 2		¼ a. rose-pink	..		—	6·00
		a. Pair, one without opt			—	60·00
O 3	4	1 a. mauve	..		—	50·00
O 3a		1 a. brown-lilac	..		40·00	5·50
		a. Pair, one without opt			—	60·00
O 4	6	4 a. chocolate	..		—	85·00

(ii) Pin-perf

O 5	2	¼ a. green	..		—	£120
O 6		¼ a. rose-pink	..		2·25	60
		a. Pair, one without opt			70·00	32·00
		b. Stamp doubly printed			90·00	60·00
O 7	3	½ a. light blue	..		£130	35·00
O 8	4	1 a. mauve	..		32·00	1·50
O 9		1 a. brown-lilac	..		30·00	1·50
O10	5	2 a. dull orange	..		—	£120
O11	6	4 a. chocolate	..		42·00	16·00
		a. Pair, one without opt			—	65·00
O12	7	1 r. dull green	..		£130	95·00
O13	8	2 r. brown-red	..		—	£750
O14	9	5 r. mauve	..		—	£1500

(b) Stamp of 1901

O14a	10a	1 r. dull green	..		—	£500

(c) Stamps of 1903 and 1904

O15	12	2 a. dull yellow	..		60·00	5·00
		a. Stamp printed both sides			†	£750
		b. Red opt	..		£325	£180
O16	12a	8 a. grey	..		60·00	22·00
		a. Red opt	..		—	£160

(d) Stamps of 1904–5. P 13½ (¼ a. to 4 a.) or 12½ (others)

O17	13	¼ a. carmine	..		—	£225
O18		½ a. chestnut	..		75	35
		a. Pair, one without opt			—	40·00
O19		1 a. blue	..		7·00	4·00
		a. Red opt	..		21·00	7·00
		b. Pair, one without opt			—	50·00
O20		2 a. orange-yellow	..		—	£800
O21		4 a. brown	..		45·00	18·00
		a. Red opt	..		55·00	28·00
O22		8 a. violet	..		£250	£160
		a. Red opt	..		—	£170
O23		1 r. green	..		£500	£450
		a. Red opt	..		—	£425
O24		5 r. purple-brown	..			

(e) Stamps of 1913

O25	15	¼ a. pale blue	..			6·00
		a. Imperf (pair)	..			85·00
		b. Roul×imperf (horiz pair)				£140
		c. "OUARTER"	..			22·00
		ca. As last, imperf (pair)				£130
		d. "KISHANGAHR"	..			22·00
		da. As last, imperf (pair)				£130
		e. Character omitted	..			22·00
		ea. As last, imperf (pair)				£130
O26	14	2 a. purple (No. 54)	..		—	85·00
		a. Red opt	..		£120	20·00
O27	15	2 a. purple	..		£375	£400
		a. "KISHANGAHR"	..		£700	
		b. Large figures "2"			£500	£550

(f) Stamps of 1913–16

O28	14	¼ a. blue	..		50	50
		a. Red opt	..		2·00	1·75
O29		½ a. green	..		75	75
		a. Pair, one without opt			—	50·00
		b. Red opt	..		3·25	1·80
		ba. Pair, one without opt			—	£100
O30		1 a. red	..		8·50	4·50
		a. Without stop	..		1·00	1·00
		ab. Red opt	..		£120	75·00
O31		2 a. purple	..		6·00	4·00
		a. Red opt	..		£120	65·00
		b. Pair, one without opt			—	55·00
O32		4 a. bright blue	..		20·00	15·00
		a. Red opt	..		—	30·00

O33	14	8 a. brown	..	95·00	40·00
		a. Red opt	..	—	85·00
O34		1 r. mauve ..	..	£300	£300
O35		2 r. deep green	..	..	
O36		5 r. brown	..	..	£1300

This overprint is found inverted as often as it is upright; and many other "errors" exist.

Kishangarh became part of Rajasthan by 15 April 1948.

LAS BELA

> ### PRICES FOR STAMPS ON COVER
> Nos. 1/12 *from* × 8

Mir Kamal Khan, 1896–1926

1	2

(Litho Thacker & Co, Bombay)

1897–98. *Thick paper.* P 11½.
1	1	½ a. black on *white*	..	20·00	13·00

1898–1900. P 11½.
2	1	½ a. black on *greyish blue* (1898)	..	13·00	8·00
3		½ a. black on *greenish grey* (1899)	..	11·00	7·00
		a. "BFLA" for "BELA" ..	..	£140	
		b. Imperf between (horiz strip of 3)	..		
4		½ a. black on *thin white surfaced paper*			
		(1899)	..	23·00	35·00
5		½ a. black on *slate* (1900)	..	25·00	38·00
		a. Imperf between (horiz pair) ..	..	£750	

1901–2. P 11½.
6	1	½ a. black on *pale grey*	..	10·00	8·00
		a. "BFLA" for "BELA" ..	..	£100	£140
7		½ a. black on *pale green* (1902) ..	..	18·00	19·00
8	2	1 a. black on *orange*	..	15·00	17·00

There are at least 14 settings of the above ½ a. stamps, the sheets varying from 16 to 30 stamps.

No. 6a occurred on R.3/2 of the July 1901 printing in sheets of 16 (4×4).

1904 (Feb–Nov). *Stamps printed wider apart.* P 11½.
11	1	½ a. black on *pale blue*	..	10·00	6·50
		a. Imperf between (pair) ..	..	£650	
		b. Imperf between (horiz strip of 3)	..	£900	
		c. Perf 12½ (Nov)	..	13·00	8·00
12		½ a. black on *pale green*	..	10·00	6·50
		c. Perf 12½ (Nov)	..	13·00	8·00

There are five plates of the above two stamps, each consisting of 18 (3×6) varieties.

All the coloured papers of the ½ a. show coloured fibres, similar to those in granite paper.

The stamps of Las Bela have been obsolete since 1 April 1907.

MORVI

> ### PRICES FOR STAMPS ON COVER
> Nos. 1/19 *from* × 6

Thakur (Maharaja from 1926) Lakhdirji, 1922–48

1	2	3

Maharaja Lakhdirji

1931 (1 April). *Typo.* P 12.

(a) *Printed in blocks of four. Stamps 10 mm apart (Nos. 1/2) or 6½ mm apart (No. 3). Perf on two or three sides*
1	1	3 p. deep red	..	3·00	14·00
2		½ a. blue ..	..	21·00	29·00
3		2 a. yellow-brown	..	80·00	
1/3			Set of 3	95·00	

(b) *Printed in two blocks of four. Stamps 5½ mm apart. Perf on four sides*
4	1	3 p. bright scarlet	..	4·75	16·00
		a. Error. Dull blue	..	4·00	16·00
		b. Ditto. Double print	..	£600	
		c. Ditto. Printed on gummed side	..	£600	
5		½ a. dull blue	..	2·25	9·50
		a. Chalk-surfaced paper	..	1·90	9·50
6		1 a. brown-red	..	3·25	19·00
7		2 a. yellow-brown	..	6·00	26·00
4/7			Set of 4	12·00	60·00

Nos. 1/3 were supplied to post offices in panes of four sewn into bundles with interleaving.

1932–33. *Horizontal background lines wider apart and portrait smaller than in T 1. Typo.* P 11.
8	2	3 p. carmine-rose (*shades*)	..	2·25	7·50
9		6 p. green	..	4·25	9·50
		a. Imperf between (horiz pair)	..	£1800	
		b. Emerald-green	..	3·00	7·50
10		1 a. ultramarine (*to deep*)	..	2·25	8·00
		a. Imperf between (vert pair)	..	£1400	
11		2 a. bright violet (1933) ..	..	10·00	28·00
		a. Imperf between (vert pair) ..	..	£1400	
8/11			Set of 4	16·00	45·00

1934. *Typo. London ptg.* P 14.
12	3	3 p. carmine	..	1·60	1·75
13		6 p. emerald-green	..	80	60
14		1 a. purple-brown	..	1·10	8·00
		a. Imperf between (horiz pair)	..	† £1300	
15		2 a. bright violet	..	2·50	16·00
12/15			Set of 4	5·50	27·00

1935–48. *Typo. Morvi Press ptg. Rough perf* 11.
16	3	3 p. scarlet (*shades*)	..	70	2·50
		a. Imperf between (horiz pair)	..	£1300	
17		6 p. grey-green	..	75	2·00
		a. Emerald-green	..	5·50	23·00
18		1 a. brown	..	12·00	14·00
		a. Pale yellow-brown	..	16·00	25·00
		b. Chocolate	..	22·00	30·00
19		2 a. dull violet (*to deep*)	..	2·50	15·00
16/19			Set of 4	30·00	30·00

Nos. 17a, 18a and 18b were issued between 1944 and 1948.

Maharaja Mahendra Singh, 1948–1957

Morvi was merged with the United State of Kathiawar (later Saurashtra) by 15 April 1948.

NANDGAON

> ### PRICES FOR STAMPS ON COVER
> The stamps of Nandgaon are very rare used on cover.

GUM. The stamps of Nandgaon were issued without gum.

Raja Mahant Balram Das, 1883–1897

1	2 (½ a.)

(Litho at Poona)

1891. *Imperf.*
1	1	½ a. blue ..	..	4·00	£110
		a. Dull blue	..	4·25	
2		2 a. rose	..	18·00	£325

The few covers in existence franked with Nos. 1/2 have undated manuscript cancellations, but other forms are known on loose examples.

The state was under Imperial administration from January 1888 to November 1891 and it is possible that Nos. 1/2 may have appeared in late 1887.

Last character in top line omitted

(Typo Balram Press, Raj-Nandgaon)

1893 (1 Jan)–**94.** *Printed in sheets of* 16 (4×4). *Imperf.*

(a) *Stamps printed wide apart (8 to 10 mm) without wavy lines between them. Thin, toned wove paper*
3	2	½ a. dull *to* deep green	..	8·50	55·00
4		2 a. red	..	7·50	55·00
		a. Thick paper			
		b. Dull rose	..	7·50	55·00

(b) *Stamps printed closer together (4 to 7 mm) with wavy lines between them. Thin, white wove paper* (1894)
5	2	½ a. green	..	20·00	45·00
		a. Last character in top line omitted			
		(R.4/3)	..	80·00	
		b. Thick paper			
		ba. Last character in top line omitted			
6		1 a. rose	..	40·00	90·00
		a. Thick paper			
		b. Thick laid paper			
		ba. Thin laid paper	..	£200	

There were three settings of Type **2** with a number of separate printings made from the third:

Setting I – Nos. 3, 4, 4a, 4b, O2
Setting II – Nos. 5, 5b, 6, 6a, 6b
Setting III – Nos. 5, 6ba, O3, O3a, O4, O4a, O5 and subsequent reprints

The same clichés were used for all values with the face value inscriptions changed. These exist in two different sizes with both occurring on the 1 a., the small on the 1 a. and the large on the 2 a. except for No. O5 which has the small type.

The ordinary postage stamps of Nandgaon became obsolete on 1 July 1894.

OFFICIAL STAMPS

(O 1)

("M.B.D." = Mahant Balram Das)

1893. *Handstamped with ruler's initials in oval.* Type O 1, *in purple.*
O1	1	½ a. blue	..	..	£350
O2		2 a. rose	..	..	£650

1894. *Handstamped with* Type O 1 *in purple.*

(a) *Stamps printed wide apart (8 to 10 mm) without wavy lines between them. Thin, toned wove paper*
O3	2	2 a. red	..	20·00	90·00

(b) *Stamps printed closer together (4 to 7 mm) with wavy lines between them. Thin, white wove paper*
O4	2	½ a. yellow-green	..	4·50	7·50
		a. Sage-green	..	6·00	
O5		1 a. rose (*shades*)	..	7·50	26·00
		a. Thin laid paper	..	10·00	65·00
O6		2 a. rose (*shades*)	..	6·00	16·00

Further printings took place in 1895 after the Official stamps were withdrawn from postal use on 31 December 1894. These were all on thin, white wove paper with the ½ a. and 2 a. in slightly different shades and the 1 a. in brown or ultramarine.

There is a forgery of the handstamp, Type O 1, which shows 8 mm between the two ornaments below the initials instead of the normal 4 mm.

NAWANAGAR

> ### PRICES FOR STAMPS ON COVER
> | No. | 1 | *from* × 20 |
> |---|---|---|
> | No. | 2 | *from* × 8 |
> | Nos. | 3/4 | *from* × 3 |
> | No. | 5 | — |
> | Nos. | 6/12 | — |
> | Nos. | 13/15 | *from* × 100 |
> | Nos. | 16/18 | — |

GUM. The stamps of Nawanagar were issued without gum.

Jam Vibhaji 1882–1895

1 (1 docra)	2 (2 docra)	3 (3 docra)

1877. *Typo in sheets of* 32 (4×8 *or* 8×4). *Laid paper.* (a) *Imperf*
1	1	1 doc. blue (*shades*)	..	50	22·00
		a. Tête-bêche (pair)	..	£1000	
		b. Doubly printed	..	80·00	

(b) *Perf* 12½ (*line*)
2	1	1 doc. slate-blue	..	60·00	£100
		a. Perf 11 (harrow) ..	..	65·00	
		ab. Tête-bêche (pair)	..	£1300	

The inverted clichés which cause the *tête-bêche* pairs come from different settings and occur on R. 3/2 (No. 1a) or R. 4/4 (No. 2ab) of sheets of 32 (4×8).

1877. T 2 *and* 3. *Type-set in black. Wove paper. Thick horizontal and vertical frame lines. Stamp* 19 mm *wide.*
3		1 doc. *deep mauve*	..	..	£3000	£160
		a. Stamp 14½–15 mm wide	..	†	£275	
		b. Stamp 16 mm wide	..	†	£200	
4		2 doc. *green* ..	..	£3000	£1500	
5		3 doc. *yellow*	..	£3000	£1500	

1880. *As last, but thin frame lines, as illustrated. Stamp* 15 *to* 18 mm *wide.*
6		1 doc. *deep mauve* ..	..	2·25	7·00
		a. On rose	..	2·25	
		ab. Stamp 14 mm wide	..	2·25	5·00
7		1 doc. *magenta* (stamp 14 mm wide)	..	2·25	
8		2 doc. *yellow-green*	..	3·00	9·00
		a. On blue-green	..	5·50	
		b. Error. Yellow	..	£325	
		c. Stamp 14 mm wide	..	3·00	7·50
		ca. On blue-green	..	7·00	

9		3 doc. *orange-yellow*	..	..	8·00
		a. *On yellow*	..	3·75	13·00
		ab. On laid paper		..	90·00
		b. Stamp 14 mm wide. *On yellow*		4·25	8·50
		ba. On laid paper		..	42·00

There are several different settings of each value of this series.

No. 8b occurs in the sheet of the 3 doc. value from one setting only.

4 (1 docra)

1893. *Typo in sheets of 36. P 12. (a) Thick paper.*

10	4	1 doc. black	..	..	1·75	
		a. Imperf (pair)	..	..	£475	
11		3 doc. orange	..	..	2·25	

(b) Thick laid paper

12	4	1 doc. black	..	..	£450	

(c) Thin wove paper

13	4	1 doc. black *to grey*	..	75	3·75
		a. Imperf between (pair)	..	£400	
		b. Imperf (pair)	..	£375	
14		2 doc. green	..	80	4·25
		a. Imperf (pair)	..	£400	
		b. Imperf between (vert pair)	£425	
15		3 doc. orange-yellow	..	1·25	7·50
		a. Imperf between (pair)	£425	
		b. *Orange*	..	80	7·00
		ba. Imperf (pair)	..	£400	
		bb. Imperf vert (horiz pair)	£425	
		bc. Imperf between (horiz pair)	£425	

(d) Thin, soft wove paper

16	4	1 doc. black	..	..		
17		2 doc. deep green	..	..	2·50	
18		3 doc. brown-orange	..	..	3·50	

Cancellations for postal purposes were intaglio seals, applied in black. Other forms of cancellation were only used on remainders.

The stamps of Nawanagar became obsolete on 1 January 1895.

NEPAL

Nepal being an independent state, its stamps will be found listed in Part 21 (*South-East Asia*) of this catalogue.

ORCHHA

PRICES FOR STAMPS ON COVER

Nos. 1/2	
Nos. 3/7	*from* × 8
Nos. 8/30	*from* × 50
Nos. 31/45	*from* × 4

A set of four stamps, ½ a. red, 1 a. violet, 2 a. yellow and 4 a. deep blue-green, in a design similar to T **2**, was prepared in 1897 with State authority but not put into use. These exist both imperforate and pin-perforated. (*Price for set of 4, £16 unused or c.t.o.*)

Maharaja Partab Singh, 1874–1930

1   **2**

(T **1/2** litho Shri Pratap Prabhakar)

1913. *Background to arms unshaded. Very blurred impression. Wove paper. No gum. Imperf.*

1	1	½ a. green	..	..	30·00	80·00
2		1 a. red	..	..	19·00	

1914–35. *Background shaded with short horizontal lines. Clearer impression. Wove paper. No gum. Imperf.*

3	2	¼ a. bright ultramarine	..	1·25	3·25
		a. Grey-blue	..	35	3·25
		b. Deep blue	..	1·60	3·25
		ba. Laid paper	..	£550	
4		½ a. green (*shades*)	..	50	3·75
		a. Dull green	..	1·50	4·00
		b. Apple-green	..	2·25	3·50
5		1 a. scarlet	..	2·50	6·00
		a. Laid paper	..	—	£350
		b. Indian red	..	1·75	8·00
		c. Carmine	..	2·50	3·75
		ca. Laid paper (1935)	£200	£250
6		2 a. red-brown (1916)	..	4·50	19·00
		a. Light brown	..	11·00	19·00
		b. Chestnut	..	18·00	20·00
7		4 a. ochre (1917)	..	9·50	28·00
		a. Yellow-orange	..	8·00	28·00
		b. Yellow	..	8·00	24·00
3/7			*Set of 5*	13·50	48·00

There are two sizes of T **2** in the setting of 8 (4 × 2). In each value stamps from the upper row are slightly taller than those from the lower.

Maharaja Vir Singh II, 1930–1956

3 Maharaja Vir Singh II **4**

(Typo Lakshmi Art Ptg Wks, Bombay)

1935 (1 Apr). *Thick, chalk-surfaced wove paper. P 9½, 10, 10×9½, 11, 11×9½, 11½, 11½×11, 11½×12, 12 or 12×11.*

8	3	¼ a. purple and slate	..	1·40	2·25
		a. Imperf between (vert pair)	..	
		b. Ordinary paper	..	35	1·40
		ba. Imperf between (vert pair)	..	11·00	
		bb. Imperf vert (horiz pair)	..	65·00	
		bc. Imperf horiz (vert pair)	..	65·00	
9		½ a. olive-grey and emerald	..	50	85
		a. Imperf (pair)	..	75·00	
10		¾ a. magenta and deep myrtle-green	50	95
		a. Imperf (pair)	..	75·00	
11		1 a. myrtle-green and purple-brown	50	75
		a. Imperf (pair)	..	65·00	65·00
		b. Imperf horiz (vert pair)	..	
		c. Imperf vert (horiz pair)	..	
12		1¼ a. slate and mauve	..	45	80
		a. Imperf between (horiz pair)	75·00	£200
		b. Imperf between (vert pair)	75·00	
		c. Frame doubly printed	..	75·00	
13		1½ a. brown and scarlet	..	45	85
		a. Imperf between (vert pair)	75·00	
		b. Imperf between (horiz pair)	75·00	
14		2 a. blue and red-orange	..	45	85
		a. Imperf (pair)	..	12·00	
		b. Imperf between (horiz pair)	75·00	
15		2½ a. olive-brown and dull orange	65	90
		a. Imperf (pair)	..	12·00	
		b. Imperf between (horiz pair)	75·00	
16		3 a. bright blue and magenta	..	65	95
		a. Imperf (pair)	..	75·00	£100
		b. Imperf (pair)	..	75·00	
17		4 a. deep reddish purple and sage-green	65	2·75
		a. Imperf (pair)	..	8·50	
		b. Imperf between (vert pair)	..	75·00	
		c. Imperf vert (horiz pair)	..	75·00	
18		6 a. black and pale ochre	..	70	2·75
		a. Imperf (pair)	..	8·50	
19		8 a. brown and purple	..	1·50	3·00
		a. Imperf (pair)	..	8·50	
		b. Imperf between (vert pair)	..	85·00	
20		12 a. bright emerald and bright purple	1·00	3·25
		a. Imperf (pair)	..	8·50	
		b. Imperf between (vert pair)	..	85·00	
21		12 a. pale greenish blue and bright purple	23·00	48·00
22		1 r. chocolate and myrtle-green	..	80	4·00
		a. Imperf (pair)	..	9·00	
		b. Imperf between (vert pair)	75·00	
23	4	1 r. chocolate and myrtle-green	..	5·00	10·00
		a. Imperf (pair)	..	85·00	
		b. Imperf between (horiz pair)	£100	
24	3	2 r. purple-brown and bistre-yellow	2·75	10·00
		a. Imperf (pair)	..	9·00	
25		3 r. black and greenish blue	..	1·50	10·00
		a. Imperf (pair)	..	9·00	
26		4 r. black and brown	..	2·50	11·00
		a. Imperf (pair)	..	9·00	
27		5 r. bright blue and plum	..	3·00	12·00
		a. Imperf (pair)	..	9·00	
28		10 r. bronze-green and cerise	..	7·00	18·00
		a. Imperf (pair)	..	12·00	
		b. Imperf between (horiz pair)	95·00	
29		15 r. black and bronze-green	..	12·00	42·00
		a. Imperf (pair)	..	12·00	
30		25 r. red-orange and blue	..	16·00	48·00
		a. Imperf (pair)	..	15·00	
8/20, 22/30			*Set of 22*	50·00	£160

Values to 5 r. except the 1 a., are inscribed "POSTAGE", and the remaining values "POSTAGE & REVENUE".

The central portrait of Type **3** is taken from a half-tone block and consists of large square dots. The portrait of Type **4** has a background of lines.

Owing to a lack of proper State control considerable quantities of these stamps circulated at below face value and the issue was subsequently withdrawn, supplies being exchanged for the 1939–42 issue. We are, however, now satisfied that the lower values at least did genuine postal duty until 1939.

Used prices are for stamps cancelled-to-order, postally used examples being worth considerably more.

5 Maharaja Vir Singh II **6**

(Litho Indian Security Printing Press, Nasik)

1939–42? *P 13½ × 14 (T* **5**) *or 14 × 13½ (T* **6**).

31	5	¼ a. chocolate	..	2·50	48·00
32		½ a. yellow-green	..	2·75	40·00
33		¾ a. bright blue	..	2·75	65·00
34		1 a. scarlet	..	2·75	13·00
35		1¼ a. blue	..	2·75	65·00
36		1½ a. mauve	..	3·00	80·00
37		2 a. vermilion	..	2·75	48·00
38		2½ a. turquoise-green	..	2·75	£140
39		3 a. slate-violet	..	4·00	75·00

40	5	4 a. slate	..	..	5·00	21·00
41		8 a. magenta	..	..	8·50	£140
42	6	1 r. grey-green	..	..	15·00	
43		2 r. bright violet	..	..	32·00	£375
44		5 r. yellow-orange	..	..	90·00	
45		10 r. turquoise-green (1942)	..	£350	
46		15 r. slate-lilac (date ?)	..	£7500	
47		25 r. claret (date ?)	..	£5500	

Orchha became part of Vindhya Pradesh by 1 May 1948.

POONCH

PRICES FOR STAMPS ON COVER

Nos. 1/2	*from* × 3
Nos. 3/63	*from* × 10
Nos. O1/10	*from* × 30

Poonch was ruled by a junior branch of the Jammu and Kashmir princely family and, by treaty, was subject to the "advice and consent" of the Maharaja of that state.

The Poonch postal service operated an office at Kahuta in the Punjab which acted as the office of exchange between the state post and that of British India.

GUM. The stamps of Poonch were issued without gum, except for some examples of Nos. 7/10.

The stamps of Poonch are all imperforate, and handstamped in watercolours.

ILLUSTRATIONS. Designs of Poonch are illustrated actual size.

Raja Moti Singh, 1852–1892

1   **2**

1876. *T* **1** *(22 × 21 mm). Yellowish white, wove paper.*

1		6 p. red	..	..	£3250	£100

1877. *As T* **1** *(19 × 17 mm). Same paper.*

1a		½ a. red	..	..	£5500	£2250

1879. *T* **2** *(21 × 19 mm). Same paper.*

2		½ a. red	..	..	—	£2000

3 (½ a.)   **4** (1 a.)

5 (2 a.)   **6** (4 a.)

1880. *Yellowish white, wove paper.*

3	3	½ a. red	..	..	38·00	16·00
4	4	1 a. red	..	..	65·00	38·00
5	5	2 a. red	..	..	£110	80·00
6	6	4 a. red	..	..	£120	90·00

1884. *Toned wove bâtonné paper.*

7	3	½ a. red	..	..	4·00	4·00
8	4	1 a. red	..	..	14·00	
9	5	2 a. red	..	..	13·00	16·00
10	6	4 a. red	..	..	26·00	26·00

These are sometimes found gummed.

7 (1 pice)

1884–87. *Various papers. (a) White laid bâtonné or ribbed bâtonné.*

11	7	1 p. red	..	14·00	16·00
		a. Pair, one stamp sideways	£150	
12	3	½ a. red	..	1·75	2·50
13	4	1 a. red	..	2·25	
14	5	2 a. red	..	6·00	7·50
15	6	4 a. red	..	8·00	

			(b) Thick white laid paper		
22	7	1 p. red	.. ..	38·00	
23	3	½ a. red	.. .. ..	55·00	
24	4	1 a. red	.. .. ..	55·00	
25	5	2 a. red	.. .. ..	55·00	
26	6	4 a. red	.. .. ..	65·00	

(c) Yellow wove bâtonné

27	7	1 p. red		2·50	2·50
		a. Pair, one stamp sideways		28·00	
28	3	½ a. red		3·00	4·00
29	4	1 a. red		27·00	
30	5	2 a. red		5·50	7·50
31	6	4 a. red		2·75	3·00

(d) Orange-buff wove bâtonné

32	7	1 p. red		1·60	2·00
		a. Pair, one stamp sideways	20·00		24·00
		b. Tête-bêche (pair)		32·00	
33	3	½ a. red		17·00	
34	5	2 a. red		60·00	
35	6	4 a. red		14·00	

(e) Yellow laid paper

36	7	1 p. red		1·25	2·50
		a. Pair, one stamp sideways		17·00	
		b. Tête-bêche (pair)		24·00	
37	3	½ a. red		2·25	
38	4	1 a. red		28·00	
39	5	2 a. red		38·00	38·00
40	6	4 a. red		30·00	

(f) Yellow laid bâtonné

41	7	1 p. red	8·50	6·50

(g) Buff laid or ribbed bâtonné paper thicker than (d)

42	4	1 a. red	45·00
43	6	4 a. red	48·00

(h) Blue-green laid paper (1887)

44	3	½ a. red	27·00	
45	4	1 a. red	2·00	3·50
46	5	2 a. red	22·00	
47	6	4 a. red	42·00	

(i) Yellow-green laid paper

48	3	½ a. red	2·25

(j) Blue-green wove bâtonné

49	7	1 p. red	30·00	27·00
49a	3	½ a. red	£700	
50	4	1 a. red	1·25	2·25

(k) Lavender wove bâtonné

51	4	1 a. red	60·00	
52	5	2 a. red	1·50	2·25

(l) Blue wove bâtonné

53	7	1 p. red	2·00	1·50
		a. Pair, one stamp sideways	19·00	
		b. Tête-bêche (pair)	27·00	
54	4	1 a. red	£325	

(m) Various coloured papers

55	7	1 p. red/grey-blue laid	6·50	4·25
56	7	1 p. red/lilac laid	45·00	48·00
		a. Pair, one stamp sideways	£275	£275
		b. Tête-bêche (pair)	£250	

1888. *Printed in aniline rose on various papers.*

57	7	1 p. on blue wove bâtonné	3·25	
		a. Tête-bêche (pair)	55·00	
58		1 p. on buff laid	10·00	
59	3	½ a. on white laid	16·00	
60	4	1 a. on green laid	12·00	13·00
61		1 a. on green wove bâtonné	6·00	6·00
62	5	2 a. on lavender wove bâtonné	5·50	5·50
63	6	4 a. on yellow laid	12·00	13·00
		a. Pair, one stamp sideways	£500	
		b. Tête-bêche (pair)	£500	

OFFICIAL STAMPS

Raja Baldeo Singh, 1892–1918

1887. (a) White laid bâtonné paper

O 1	7	1 p. black	1·75	1·90
		a. Pair, one stamp sideways	13·00	15·00
		b. Tête-bêche (pair)	16·00	
O 2	3	½ a. black	1·75	2·75
O 3	4	1 a. black	1·60	1·75
O 4	5	2 a. black	2·75	2·75
O 5	6	4 a. black	4·50	7·50

(b) White toned wove bâtonné paper

O 6	7	1 p. black	1·75	
		a. Pair, one stamp sideways	27·00	
		b. Tête-bêche (pair)	38·00	
O 7	3	½ a. black	2·25	2·50
		a. Pair, one stamp sideways	£850	
O 8	4	1 a. black	14·00	13·00
O 9	5	2 a. black	6·00	6·00
O10	6	4 a. black	9·50	

RAJASTHAN

Rajasthan was formed in 1948–49 from a number of States in Rajputana; these included Bundi, Jaipur and Kishangarh, whose posts continued to function more or less separately until ordered by the Indian Government to close on 1 April 1950.

PRICES FOR STAMPS ON COVER	
Nos. 1/7	*from* × 15
Nos. 8/10	
Nos. 11/12	*from* × 5
Nos. 13/14	
Nos. 15/25	*from* × 4
Nos. 26/42	*from* × 3
No. 43	
Nos. 44/60	*from* × 3
No. 61	*from* × 5
Nos. 62/5	

BUNDI

(1)

1949. *Nos. 86/92 of Bundi.* (a) Handstamped with T **1**.

A. In black. B. In violet. C. In blue

				A	B	C
1	¼ a. blue-green		4·75	4·50	24·00
	a. Pair, one without opt		£170	†	†
2	½ a. violet		3·50	3·00	27·00
	a. Pair, one without opt		†	£180	†
3	1 a. yellow-green		4·50	9·50	28·00
	a. Pair, one without opt		†	£180	†
4	2 a. vermilion		8·00	20·00	—
5	4 a. orange		29·00	23·00	70·00
6	8 a. ultramarine		4·00	6·00	45·00
7	1 r. chocolate		—	£160	60·00

The above prices are for unused, used stamps being worth about six times the unused prices. Most of these handstamps are known, sideways, inverted or double.

(b) Machine-printed as T **1** in black

8	¼ a. blue-green		
9	½ a. violet		
10	1 a. yellow-green		
11	2 a. vermilion	4·00	55·00
	a. Opt inverted	£250	
12	4 a. orange	2·00	55·00
	a. Opt double	£225	
13	8 a. ultramarine	25·00	
	a. Opt inverted	£450	
	b. Opt double	£375	
14	1 r. chocolate	7·50	

JAIPUR

राजस्थान

RAJASTHAN

(2)

1950 (26 Jan). *T* **7** *of Jaipur optd with T* **2**.

15	¼ a. black and brown-lake (No. 58) (B.)	3·75	13·00
16	½ a. black and violet (No. 41) (R.)	3·25	14·00
17	¾ a. black and brown-red (No. 59) (Blue-blk.)	6·00	16·00
	a. Opt in pale blue	14·00	32·00
18	1 a. black and blue (No. 60) (R.)	4·00	29·00
19	2 a. black and buff (No. 61) (R.)	6·50	38·00
20	2½ a. black and carmine (No. 62) (B.)	7·00	18·00
21	3 a. black and green (No. 63) (R.)	7·50	42·00
22	4 a. black and grey-green (No. 64) (R.)	7·50	48·00
23	6 a. black and pale blue (No. 65a) (R.)	8·50	75·00
24	8 a. black and chocolate (No. 66) (R.)	12·00	95·00
25	1 r. black and yellow-bistre (No. 67) (R.)	13·00	£140
15/25		70·00	£475

KISHANGARH

1948–49. *Various stamps of Kishangarh handstamped with T* **1** *in red.*

(a) On stamps of 1899–1901

26	¼ a. rose-pink (No. 5a) (B.)		£150	
26a	¼ a. rose-pink (No. 22a)		—	£140
27	½ a. deep blue (No. 26)		£250	
29	1 a. brown-lilac (No. 29)		14·00	38·00
	b. Imperf (pair)		40·00	80·00
	c. Violet handstamp		—	£225
	d. Black handstamp		—	£275
30	4 a. chocolate (No. 31)		55·00	75·00
	a. Violet handstamp		—	£325
31	1 r. dull green (No. 32)		£170	£180
31a	2 r. brown-red (No. 34)		£200	
32	5 r. mauve (No. 35)		£190	£190

(b) On stamps of 1904–10

33	13	½ a. chestnut		—	95·00
33a		1 a. blue		—	£130
34		4 a. brown		13·00	
		a. Blue handstamp		£160	
35	12a	8 a. grey		75·00	£120
36	13	8 a. violet		11·00	
37		1 r. green		11·00	
38		2 r. olive-yellow		18·00	
39		5 r. purple-brown		23·00	
		a. Blue handstamp		£275	

(c) On stamps of 1912–16

40	14	½ a. green (No. 64)		—	£120
41		1 a. red		—	£120
42		2 a. deep violet (No. 51)		£250	
43		2 a. purple (No. 66)		2·50	5·50
44		4 a. bright blue		£325	
45		8 a. brown		5·00	
		a. Pair, one without handstamp		£250	
46		1 r. mauve		10·00	
47		2 r. deep green		10·00	
48		5 r. brown		£225	

(d) On stamps of 1928–36

49	16	½ a. yellow-green	90·00	
49a		2 a. magenta	—	£225
50		4 a. chestnut	£140	
51		8 a. violet	6·00	50·00
		a. Pair, one without handstamp	£225	
52		1 r. light green	20·00	
53		2 r. lemon-yellow	14·00	
54		5 r. claret	15·00	

(e) On stamps of 1943–47

55	16	¼ a. pale dull blue	65·00	65·00
56		¼ a. greenish blue	38·00	38·00
		a. Imperf (pair)	£150	
57		½ a. deep green	25·00	27·00
		a. Violet handstamp	—	£140
57b		½ a. yellow-green	35·00	38·00
		ba. Imperf (pair)	£150	
		bb. Blue handstamp	—	£140
58	17	1 a. carmine-red	38·00	38·00
		a. Violet handstamp	—	£150
58b		1 a. orange-red (imperf)	95·00	
		ba. Blue handstamp	£100	
59		2 a. bright magenta	£110	£110
60		2 a. maroon (imperf)	£120	
61	16	4 a. brown	2·00	6·00
62		8 a. violet	15·00	45·00
63		1 r. green	6·00	
64		2 r. yellow	90·00	
65		5 r. claret	50·00	

A 1 a. value in deep violet-blue was issued for revenue purposes, but is known postally used (*Price £60 used*).

RAJPIPLA

PRICES FOR STAMPS ON COVER	
No. 1	*from* × 25
Nos. 2/3	

Maharana Ganbhir Singh, 1860–1897

1 (1 pice)	2 (2 a.)	3 (4 a.)

1880. *Litho. With or without gum (1 p.) or no gum (others). P* 11 (1 p.) *or* 12½.

1	1	1 p. blue	2·00	24·00
2	2	2 a. green	22·00	65·00
		a. Imperf between (pair)	£550	£550
3	3	4 a. red	11·00	40·00
1/3		Set of 3	32·00	£120

These stamps became obsolete in 1886.

SHAHPURA

PRICES FOR STAMPS ON COVER	
Nos. 1/4	*from* × 2
No. F1	*from* × 2

DATES. Those quoted are of first known use.

Rajadhiraj Nahar Singh, 1870–1932

RAJ SHAHPURA Postage 1 pice	RAJ SHAHPURA 1 pice
1	2

1914–17. *Typo.*

1	1	1 p. carmine/bluish grey (p 11)	—	£275
2		1 p. carmine/drab (imperf) (1917)	—	£425

Some examples of No. 1 are imperforate on one side or on two adjacent sides.

1920–28. *Typo. Imperf.*

3	2	1 p. carmine/drab (1928)	—	£475
4		1 a. black/pink	—	£475

POSTAL FISCAL

Rajadhiraj Umaid Singh, 1932–1947

Rajadhiraj Sudarshan Deo, 1947–1971

F 1

1932–47. *Typo. P* 11, 11½ *or* 12.

F1	F **1**	1 a. red (*shades*)	..	50·00	£130
		a. Pin-perf 7 (1947)			

Nos. F1/a were used for both fiscal and postal purposes. Manuscript cancellations must be assumed to be fiscal, unless on cover showing other evidence of postal use. The design was first issued for fiscal purposes in 1898.

Shahpura became part of Rajasthan by 15 April 1948.

SIRMOOR

PRICES FOR STAMPS ON COVER

The stamps of Sirmoor are very rare used on cover.

Raja Shamsher Parkash, 1886–1898

1 (1 pice)   **2**   **3 Raja Shamsher Parkash**

1878 (June)**–80.** *Litho. P* 11½.

1	1	1 p. pale green	..	9·00	£225
2		1 p. blue (on *laid paper*) (1880) ..		4·00	£140
		a. Imperf between (pair)	..	£300	
		b. Imperf (pair)	..	£300	

(Litho at Calcutta)

1892. *Thick wove paper. P* 11½.

3	**2**	1 p. yellow-green	..	65	70
		a. Imperf between (vert pair)	..	70·00	
		b. Deep green	..	55	60
		ba. Imperf between (vert pair)	..	70·00	70·00
4		1 p. blue	..	65	65
		a. Imperf between (vert pair)	..	60·00	60·00
		b. Imperf between (horiz pair)	..	60·00	60·00
		c. Imperf vert (horiz pair)	..	60·00	
		d. Imperf (pair)	..	75·00	

These were originally made as reprints, about 1891, to supply collectors, but there being very little demand for them they were put into use. The design was copied (including the perforations) from an illustration in a dealer's catalogue.

A   **B**

C   **D**

There were seven printings of stamps as Type **3**, all in sheets of 70 (10×7) and made up from groups of transfers which can be traced through minor varieties.

Printings I to V and VII of the 3 p. and 6 p. are as Types A and C (both with large white dots evenly spaced between the ends of the upper and lower inscriptions).

Printing VI is as Type B (small white dots and less space) and Type D (large white dots unevenly positioned between the inscriptions).

(Litho Waterlow)

1885–96. *P* 14 *to* 15.

5	**3**	3 p. chocolate (A) ..	..	55	30
		a. Brown (B) (1896)	..	30	35
6		3 p. orange (A) (1888)	..	1·50	20
		a. Type B (1896)		30	20
		ab. Imperf (pair) ..	..	£550	
7		6 p. blue-green (C)	..	4·00	2·50
		a. Green (C) (1888)	..	95	50
		b. Bright green (C) (1891)	..	60·00	60·00
		c. Deep green (C) (1894)	..	40	25
		d. Yellowish green (D) (1896)	..	40	1·50
8		1 a. bright blue	..	2·25	2·50
		a. Dull blue (1891)	..	6·50	4·50
		b. Steel-blue (1891)	..	85·00	85·00
		c. Grey-blue (1894)	..	2·25	1·00
		d. Slate-blue (1896)	..	50	1·75
9		2 a. pink	..	4·25	10·00
		a. Carmine (1894)	..	3·50	3·00
		b. Rose-red (1896)	..	3·25	4·00

Composition of the various printings was as follows:
Printing I   – Nos. 5, 7, 8 and 9
Printing II – Nos. 6 and 7a
Printing III – Nos. 6, 7b and 8a
Printing IV – Nos. 5, 6, 7a and 8b
Printing V – Nos. 6, 7c, 8c and 9a
Printing VI – Nos. 5a, 6a, 7d, 8d and 9b
Printing VII – Only exists overprinted "On S. S. S." (Nos. 78/81).

NEW INFORMATION

The editor is always interested to correspond with people who have new information that will improve or correct the Catalogue.

---

4 Indian Elephant   **5 Raja Shamsher Parkash**

(Recess Waterlow & Sons)

1894–99. *P* 12 *to* 15 *and compounds.*

22	**4**	3 p. orange-brown	..	1·60	30
23		6 p. green	..	75	30
		a. Imperf between (vert pair)	..	£1400	
24		1 a. blue ..	..	2·75	80
25		2 a. rose	..	1·25	1·00
26		3 a. yellow-green	..	15·00	28·00
27		4 a. deep green	..	7·50	14·00
28		8 a. deep blue	..	11·00	19·00
29		1 r. vermilion	..	26·00	45·00
22/9			*Set of* 8	60·00	95·00

Raja Surindra Bikram Parkash, 1898–1911

(Recess Waterlow & Sons)

1899. *P* 13 *to* 15.

30	**5**	3 a. yellow-green	..	1·60	19·00
31		4 a. deep green	..	2·25	13·00
32		8 a. deep blue	..	4·25	12·00
33		1 r. vermilion	..	8·00	32·00
30/3		..	*Set of* 4	14·50	70·00

OFFICIAL STAMPS

NOTE. The varieties occurring in the machine-printed "On S.S.S." overprints may, of course, also be found in the inverted and double overprints, and many of them are known thus.

Roman figures denote printings of the basic stamps (Nos. 7/21). Where more than one printing was overprinted the prices quoted are for the commonest.

I. MACHINE-PRINTED

On

S.   S.

S.

(11)

1890. *Optd with T* **11.** (*a*) *In black.*

50	**3**	6 p. green (C)	..	£900	£900
		a. Stop before first "S"	..		
51		2 a. pink	..	50·00	£140
		a. Stop before first "S"	..	£130	

(*b*) *In red*

52	**3**	6 p. green (C)	..	17·00	2·50
		a. Stop before first "S"	..	55·00	25·00
53		1 a. bright blue	..	40·00	12·00
		a. Stop before first "S"	..	£110	60·00
		b. Opt inverted	..	£1000	£550

(*c*) *Doubly optd in red and in black*

53c	**3**	6 p. green (C)	..	£950	£950
		ca. Stop before first "S"	..	£2250	£2250

Nos. 50, 52 and 53c are from Printing II and the remainder from Printing I.

On   **On**

S.   S.   S.   S.

S.   S.

(12)   **(13)**

1891. *Optd with T* **12.** (*a*) *In black.*

54	**3**	3 p. orange (A)	..	2·25	35·00
		a. Opt inverted	..	£425	
55		6 p. green (C)	..	1·50	1·50
		a. Opt double	..	£170	
		b. No stop after lower "S"	..	22·00	22·00
		c. Raised stop before lower "S"	..	£150	£110
56		1 a. bright blue	..	£275	£350
57		2 a. pink	..	13·00	48·00

(*b*) *In red*

58	**3**	6 p. green (C)	..	26·00	3·00
		a. Opt inverted	..	£200	£170
		b. Opt double	..	£200	£180
59		1 a. bright blue	..	19·00	26·00
		a. Opt inverted	..	†	£425
		b. Opt double	..	†	£425
		c. No stop after lower "S"	..	£160	£170

(*c*) *In black and red*

59d	**3**	6 p. green (C)	..		£900

Nos. 54/5, 58 and 59d are from Printing II and the others from Printing I.

1892–97. *Optd with T* **13.** (*a*) *In black.*

60	**3**	3 p. orange (A)	..	50	40
		a. Type B	..	3·00	60
		b. Opt inverted	..	£225	
		c. First "S" inverted and stop raised	..	5·00	5·00
		d. No stop after lower "S"	..	5·00	5·00
		e. Raised stop after second "S"	..	35·00	16·00
		f. Vertical pair, Types **12** and **13**	..	95·00	
61		6 p. green (C)	..	5·50	1·00
		a. Deep green (C)	..	1·60	50
		b. First "S" inverted and stop raised	..	32·00	14·00
		c. Raised stop after second "S"	..	32·00	12·00
		d. No stop after lower "S"	..	42·00	17·00
		e. Opt double	..	£475	
62		1 a. steel-blue	..		
		a. Grey-blue	..	8·00	1·00
		b. Opt double	..	£350	
		c. First "S" inverted and stop raised	..	32·00	10·00
		d. No stop after lower "S"	..	£130	48·00
		e. Raised stop after second "S"	..	55·00	12·00
63		2 a. pink	..	10·00	16·00
		a. Carmine	..	7·00	7·00
		b. Opt inverted	..	£600	£600
		c. First "S" inverted and stop raised	..	35·00	35·00
		d. No stop after lower "S"	..	35·00	35·00
		e. Raised stop after second "S"	..	£150	£150

(*b*) *In red*

64	**3**	6 p. green (C)	..	3·50	50
		a. Bright green (C)	..	7·00	1·00
		b. Opt inverted	..	£100	90·00
		c. First "S" inverted and stop raised	..	20·00	5·00
		d. Vertical pair, Types **12** and **13**	..	95·00	95·00
65		1 a. bright blue	..	15·00	3·00
		a. Steel-blue	..	11·00	1·00
		b. Opt inverted	..	£190	£150
		c. Opt double	..	£250	
		d. First "S" inverted and stop raised	..	30·00	8·00
		e. No stop after lower "S"	..	30·00	8·00

(*c*) *Doubly overprinted in black and red*

65f	**3**	6 p. bright green (C)	..	—	£850
		fa. Green (C). Red opt inverted		†	£1100

The printings used for this issue were as follows:
Printing I   – Nos. 63 and 65
Printing II – Nos. 60, 64 and 65fa
Printing III – Nos. 60, 64a and 65f
Printing IV – Nos. 61, 62 and 64
Printing V – Nos. 60, 61a, 62a and 63a
Printing VI – No. 60a

There are seven settings of this overprint, the first of which was a composite setting of 20 (10×2), with examples of Type **12** in the upper row. The inverted "S" and the missing stop occur in the 3rd and 6th settings with the latter also including the raised stop after second "S".

On   **On**

S.   S.   S.   S.

S.   S.

(14)   **(15)**

1896–97. *Optd as T* **14.**

66	**3**	3 p. orange (B) (1897)	..	8·00	1·25
		a. Comma after first "S"	..	42·00	30·00
		b. Opt inverted	..		
		c. Opt double	..	†	£475
67		6 p. deep green (C)	..	5·50	60
		a. Yellowish green (D)	..	—	2·25
		b. Comma after first "S"	..	45·00	18·00
		c. Comma after lower "S"	..	£140	18·00
		d. "S" at right inverted	..	£140	42·00
68		1 a. grey-blue	..	7·00	1·25
		a. Comma after first "S"	..	60·00	22·00
		b. Comma after lower "S"	..	£160	22·00
		c. "S" at right inverted	..	—	45·00
69		2 a. carmine (1897)	..	17·00	14·00
		a. Comma after first "S"	..	£120	£120

Nos. 66 and 67a are from Printing VI and the remainder from Printing V.

There are four settings of this overprint, (1) 23 mm high, includes the comma after lower "S"; (2) and (3) 25 mm high, with variety, comma after first "S"; (4) 25 mm high, with variety, "S" at right inverted.

1898 (Nov). *Optd with T* **15.**

70	**3**	6 p. deep green (C)	..	£160	7·00
		a. Yellowish green (D)	..	£150	5·50
		b. Small "S" at right	..	£250	25·00
		c. Comma after lower "S"	..	—	50·00
		d. Lower "S" inverted and stop raised	..	—	50·00
71		1 a. grey-blue	..	£170	12·00
		a. Small "S" at right	..	£275	40·00
		b. Small "S" without stop	..	—	£180

No. 70a is from Printing VI and the others Printing V.

There are two settings of this overprint. Nos. 70a and 71a/b occur in the first setting, and Nos. 70b/c in the second setting.

On   **On**

S.   S.   S.   S.

S.   S.

(16)   **(17)**

1899 (July).   *Optd with T* **16.**

| 72 | 3 | 3 p. orange (B) | .. | .. | .. | £190 | 6·50 |
| 73 | | 6 p. deep green (C) | .. | .. | .. | — | 17·00 |

No. 72 is from Printing VI and No. 73 from Printing V.

1899 (Dec)–**1900.**   *Optd as T* **17.**

74	3	3 p. orange (B)	..	..	..	—	5·00
		a. Raised stop after lower "S"	..	..	†	55·00
		b. Comma after first "S"	..	..	†	£160
		c. No stop after first "S"	..	..	†	95·00
75		6 p. deep green (C)	..	..	..	—	5·00
		a. Yellowish green (D)	..	..	†	7·00
		b. Raised stop after lower "S"	..	..	†	55·00
		c. Comma after first "S"	..	..	†	£150
76	1 a.	bright blue	..	..	..	†	£130
		a. Grey-blue	..	..	†	7·00
		b. Slate-blue	..	..		8·50
		c. Raised stop after lower "S"	..	..	†	80·00
		d. Comma after first "S"	..	..	†	£170
		e. No stop after first "S"	..	..	†	95·00
77	2 a.	carmine	..	..	..	†	£100
		a. Raised stop after lower "S"	..	..	†	£400

There are two settings of this overprint: (1) 22 mm high, with raised stop variety; (2) 23 mm high, with "comma" and "no stop" varieties.

The printings used for this issue were as follows:
Printing I – No. 76
Printing V – Nos. 75, 76a and 77
Printing VI – Nos. 74, 75a and 76b

(18)   (19)

(Optd by Waterlow & Sons)

1900.   *Optd with T* **18.**

78	3	3 p. orange	..	..	..	2·25	5·00
79		6 p. green	..	..	..	40	45
80		1 a. blue ..	..	..	..	35	50
81		2 a. carmine	..	..	..	3·25	55·00

Nos. 78/81 were from Printing VII which was not issued without the overprint.

II. HANDSTAMPED

The words "On" and each letter "S" struck separately (except for Type **22** which was applied at one operation).

1894.   *Handstamped with T* **19.** (*a*) *In black.*

82	3	3 p. orange (A)	..	..	..	3·00	3·75
		a. "On" only	..	..	65·00	
83		6 p. green (C)	..	..	..	5·00	6·00
		a. Deep green (C)	..	..	8·50	11·00
		b. "On" only	..	..	65·00	65·00
84	1 a.	bright blue	..	..	..	38·00	28·00
		a. Dull blue	..	..	12·00	14·00
		b. Steel-blue	..	..		
		c. Grey-blue	..	..	12·00	11·00
		d. "On" only	..	..	—	90·00
85	2 a.	carmine	..	..	..	17·00	17·00
		a. "On" only	..	..	£100	

(*b*) *In red*

| 86 | 3 | 6 p. green (C) | .. | .. | .. | 95·00 | £100 |
| 86a | | 1 a. grey-blue | .. | .. | .. | £275 | £275 |

The printings used for this issue were as follows:
Printing I – No. 84
Printing III – No. 84a
Printing IV – Nos. 83, 84b and 86
Printing V – Nos. 82, 83a, 84c, 85 and 86a

1896.   *Handstamped with letters similar to those of T* **13,** *with stops, but irregular.*

87	3	3 p. orange (A)	..	..	..	80·00	65·00
		a. Type B	..	..		
88		6 p. green (C)	..	..	..		
		a. Deep green (C)	..	..	70·00	60·00
		b. "On" omitted ..	..	..	£130	
88c		1 a. grey-blue	..	..	..	85·00	85·00
89		2 a. carmine	..	..	..	£140	

Printings used for this issue were as follows:
Printing II – No. 88
Printing III – No. 87
Printing IV – No. 88
Printing V – Nos. 87, 88a, 88c and 89
Printing VI – No. 87a

1897.   *Handstamped with letters similar to those of T* **14,** *with stops, but irregular.*

90	3	3 p. orange (B)	..	..	..	8·50	17·00
91		6 p. deep green (C)	..	..	45·00	50·00
		a. "On" only	..	..	..	£100	
92		1 a. grey-blue	..	..	..	£190	£190
		a. "On" only	..	..	..	£100	
93		2 a. carmine	..	..	..	90·00	90·00

No. 90 was from Printing VI and the remainder from Printing V.

1897.   *Handstamped with letters similar to those of T* **16,** *with stops, but irregular.*

| 93a | 3 | 6 p. deep green (C) | .. | .. | £110 | 90·00 |

No. 93a is from Printing V.

---

(20)   (21)

1896.   (*a*) *Handstamped with T* **20.**

| 94 | 3 | 3 p. orange (A) | .. | .. | .. | 55·00 | 60·00 |
| 95 | | 2 a. carmine | .. | .. | .. | 60·00 | 65·00 |

(*b*) *Handstamped with T* **21.**

96	3	3 p. orange (A)	..	..	£150	£160
97		6 p. bright green (C)	..	..	£180	
98		1 a. bright blue	..	..	..	£180	
		a. Dull blue	..	..		
98b		2 a. carmine	..	..	..	£190	

No. 98 comes from Printing I, No. 98a from Printing III, No. 97 possibly from Printing IV and the remainder from Printing V.

(22)   (23)

(*c*) *Handstamped with T* **22.**

99	3	3 p. orange (B)	..	..	..	£120	
100		6 p. deep green (C)	..	..	£170	
101		1 a. grey-blue	..	..	..	£225	
101a		2 a. carmine	..	..	..	£300	

No. 99 is from Printing VI and the others from Printing V.

1899.   *Handstamped with T* **23.**

102	3	3 p. orange (A)	..	..	..	—	£130
		a. Type B	..	..	19·00	7·00
103		6 p. green (C)	..	..	..		
		a. Deep green (C)	..	..	21·00	15·00
		b. Yellowish green (D)	..	..	15·00	16·00
104	1 a.	bright blue	..	..	..	—	85·00
		a. Grey-blue	..	..	40·00	35·00
105	2 a.	pink ..	..	..	..		
		a. Carmine	..	..	40·00	22·00
		b. Rose-red	..	..	48·00	32·00
		c. "On" only	..	..	—	£120

Printings used for this issue were as follows:
Printing I   – Nos. 104 and 105
Printing IV – Nos. 102 and 103
Printing V – Nos. 102, 103a, 104a and 105a
Printing VI – Nos. 102a, 103b and 105b

(24)

1901 (?).   *Handstamped with T* **24.**

| 105d | 3 | 6 p. yellowish green (D) | .. | .. | — | £300 |

From Printing VI

III. MIXED MACHINE-PRINTED AND HANDSTAMPED

1896.   (*i*) *Handstamped "On" as in T* **19,** *and machine-printed opt T* **13** *complete.*

| 106 | 3 | 6 p. green (C) | .. | .. | .. | — | £400 |

(*ii*) *Handstamped opt as T* **14,** *and machine-printed opt T* **13** *complete*

| 107 | 3 | 6 p. deep green (C) | .. | .. | .. | | |

No. 106 is from Printing IV and No. 107 from Printing V. Various other types of these handstamps are known to exist, but in the absence of evidence of their authenticity we do not list them. It is stated that stamps of T **4** were never officially overprinted.

The stamps of Sirmoor have been obsolete since 1 April 1902.

PRICES OF SETS

Set prices are given for many issues, generally those containing three stamps or more. Definitive sets include one of each value or major colour change, but do not cover different perforations, die types or minor shades. Where a choice is possible the set prices are based on the cheapest versions of the stamps included in the listings.

SORUTH

PRICES FOR STAMPS ON COVER

Nos. 1/2	*from* × 5
Nos. 4/4a	—
Nos. 5/7	*from* × 1
No. 8	*from* × 3
No. 9	*from* × 1
Nos. 10/11	*from* × 5
No. 11e	*from* × 1
No. 12	*from* × 4
No. 13	*from* × 5
Nos. 14/15	*from* × 3
Nos. 16/24	*from* × 20
Nos. 33/6	*from* × 50
Nos. 37/8	*from* × 50
Nos. 40/1	*from* × 10
Nos. 42/57	*from* × 10
Nos. O1/13	*from* × 20
No. 58	*from* × 15
No. 59	*from* × 6
No. 60	*from* × 10
No. 61	*from* × 6
Nos. O14/22	*from* × 10

The name "Saurashtra", corrupted to "Sorath" or "Soruth", was originally used for all the territory later known as Kathiawar. Strictly speaking the name should have been applied only to a portion of Kathiawar including the state of Junagadh. As collectors have known these issues under the heading of "Soruth" for so long, we retain the name.

GUM. Nos. 1/47 of Soruth were issued without gum.

JUNAGADH

Nawab Mahabat Khan II, 1851–1882

(Currency 40 dokras or 16 annas = 1 koree)

1

(="Saurashtra Post 1864–65")

1864 (Nov).   *Handstamped in water-colour. Imperf.*

1	1	(1 a.) black/green (laid)	..	..	£650	55·00
2		(1 a.) black/azure to grey (wove)	..	—	£150
4		(1 a.) black/cream (laid)	..	..	†	£1100
4a		(1 a.) black/cream (wove)	..	..	—	£700

ILLUSTRATIONS. Types 2 to 11 are shown actual size.

2 (1 a.) (Devanagri numeral)   3 (1 a.) (Gujarati numeral)

4 (4 a.) (Devanagri numeral)   5 (4 a.) (Gujarati numeral)

Differences in first character of bottom line on Nos. 8/a:

Type A "u"   Type B "ka"
(error)   (correct)

(Type-set Nitiprakash Ptg Press, Junagadh)

1868 (June)–**75.**   *Designs as T* **2** *to* **5.** *Imperf.*

A. *Inscriptions in Gujarati characters. Wove paper*

| 5 | | 1 a. black/yellowish | .. | .. | .. | † | £5500 |

B. *Inscriptions in Devanagri characters (as in the illustrations)*

I. *Accents over first letters in top and bottom lines. Wove paper*

6		1 a. red/green	..	..	..	†	£2000
7		1 a. red/blue	..	..	..	†	£2000
8		1 a. black/pink (first character in bottom line as Type A)	..	†	£850
8a		1 a. black/pink (first character in bottom line as Type B)	..	£700	£100
9		2 a. black/yellow (1869)	..	..	†	£3000

II. *Accents over second letters in top and bottom lines*

(a) Wove paper

10	2	1 a. black/*pink* (1869)	..	£375	48·00
		a. Printed both sides	..	†	—
		b. First two characters in last word of bottom line omitted (R. 4/1)		—	£475

(b) Laid paper

11	2	1 a. black/*azure* (1870)	..	70·00	8·00
		a. Final character in both top and bottom lines omitted (R. 1/1)		—	£130
		b. First two characters in last word of bottom line omitted (R. 4/1)		—	95·00
		c. Doubly printed	..	†	£650
		d. *Se-tenant* pair. Nos. 11/12	..	£275	£100
11e		1 a. black/*white*		†	£3000
12	3	1 a. black/*azure* (1870)	..	£160	17·00
		a. Printed both sides	..	†	£750
		b. Final character in bottom line omitted (R. 1/1)		—	95·00
		c. Accent omitted from last word in bottom line (R. 5/2, 5/4)		—	75·00
		d. Large numeral (R. 4/1)	..	£475	£140
		e. First character in middle line omitted (R. 2/4)		—	£225
		f. Central two characters in middle line omitted (R. 2/4)		—	£400
13		1 a. red/*white* (1875)	..	16·00	18·00
		a. First two characters in bottom line omitted (R. 5/1)		80·00	£100
14	5	4 a. black/*white*	..	£200	£375
		a. First two characters in last word of bottom line omitted (R. 4/1)		£850	
		b. Final character in bottom line omitted (R. 5/2)		£1400	
15	4	4 a. black/*white*	..	£110	£180
		a. Final character in bottom line omitted (R. 1/1)		£425	

The settings of Nos. 5/7 are unknown.

Nos. 10/15, and probably Nos. 8/9, were printed in sheets of 20 (4×5). The same type was used throughout, but changes occurred as the loose type was amended.

Specialists now recognise four main settings for the 1 a., one of which was amended for the 2 a. and another for the 4 a. There are sub-settings within each of these groups:

1 a. Setting I (pink wove paper) (No. 8)
　Setting II (pink wove paper) (No. 8a)
　Setting III (pink wove paper) (No. 10)
　Setting IV (Devanagri numerals only) (pink wove paper) (Nos. 10/b)
　Setting IVA (Devanagri numerals only) (azure vertical laid paper) (Nos. 11, 11b)
　Setting IVB (Devanagri and Gujarati numerals mixed) (azure horizontal laid paper) (Nos. 11/a, 11d, 12)
　Setting IVC (Devanagri and Gujarati numerals mixed) (azure or white vertical laid paper) (Nos. 11, 11c/d, 11e, 12/b, 12e/f)
　Setting IVD (Devanagri and Gujarati numerals mixed) (azure vertical laid paper) (Nos. 11, 11d, 12, 12d)
　Setting IVE (Gujarati numerals only) (white vertical laid paper) (Nos. 13/a)
2 a. Setting I (probably derived from 1 a. Setting II) (yellow wove paper) (No. 9)
4 a. Setting IA (Gujarati numerals only) (white vertical laid paper) (Nos. 14/a)
　Setting IB (Devanagri numerals only) (white horizontal laid paper) (No. 15)
　Setting 1C (Devanagri numerals only) (white vertical laid paper) (Nos. 15/a)
　Setting ID (only Gujarati numerals so far identified) (white vertical laid paper) (Nos. 14, 14b)

Settings IVA/D of the 1 a. were subsequently adapted to form settings IA/D of the 4 a.

The two known examples of No. 8 both come from the top row of the sheet. Marginal inscriptions indicate that No. 8a is from a separate setting.

Official imitations, consisting of 1 a. carmine-red on white wove and white laid, 1 a. black on blue wove, 4 a. black on white wove, 4 a. black on blue wove, 4 a. red on white laid—all imperforate; 1 a. carmine-red on white laid, 1 a. black on blue wove, 4 a. black on white laid and blue wove—all perforated 12, were made in 1890. Entire sheets of originals have 20 stamps (4×5), the imitations only 4 or 16.

6	7

(Typo Nitiprakash Ptg Press, Junagadh)

1878 (16 Jan)**–86.** *Laid paper with the lines wide apart. Imperf.*

16	6	1 a. green	..	50	30
		a. Printed both sides	..	£450	
		b. Laid lines close together (1886)		50	30
17	7	4 a. vermilion	..	1·50	1·00
		a. Printed both sides	..	£500	
		b. *Scarlet/bluish*	..	2·50	2·00
18		4 a. brown	..	8·00	

Nawab Bahadur Khan III, 1882–1892

1886. *P 12. (a) On toned laid paper with the lines close together*

19	6	1 a. green	..	15	15
		a. Imperf vert (horiz pair)	..	95·00	
		b. Doubly printed	..		£375
		c. Error. Blue	..	£600	£600
		d. On bluish white laid paper	..	2·50	3·50
		da. Imperf between (pair)	..	£150	
		e. *Emerald-green*	..	2·25	2·25
20	7	4 a. red	..	1·25	60
		a. On bluish white laid paper	..	8·00	12·00
		b. *Carmine*	..	2·25	1·75
21		4 a. brown	..	6·00	

(b) Wove paper

22	6	1 a. green	..	1·50	65
		a. Imperf (pair)	..	55·00	75·00
		b. Error. Blue	..		£600
		c. Imperf horiz (vert pair)	..	£110	
23	7	4 a. red	..	3·75	7·00
		a. Imperf (pair)	..	£140	£170
24		4 a. brown	..	10·00	

There is a very wide range of colours in both values. The laid paper, on which imperforate printings continued to appear until 1912, is found both vertical and horizontal.

The 1 a. was originally issued in sheets of 15 (5×3), but later appeared in sheets of 20 (5×4) with marginal inscriptions. Stamps were sometimes printed in double sheets showing two impressions of the plate printed *tête-bêche* on the same or opposite sides of the paper.

The 4 a. was in horizontal strips of 5. No. 19 exists as a sheet of 10 (5×2), with two impressions of the plate printed *tête-bêche*, and No. 23 in a similar sized sheet but with both impressions upright.

Nawab Rasul Khan 1892–1911
Nawab Mahabat Khan III, 1911–1959

(Indian currency)

Three pies.	One anna.
ત્રણ પાઇ.	એક આના.
(8)	(9)

1913 (1 Jan). *Surch in Indian currency with T 8 or 9. P 12.*

(a) On toned wove paper

33	6	3 p. on 1 a. emerald-green	..	15	20
		a. Imperf (pair)	..	£325	
		b. Imperf between (horiz pair)	..	£275	
34	7	1 a. on 4 a. red	..	1·60	4·25
		a. Imperf (pair)	..	£600	
		b. Capital "A" in "Anna"	..	6·00	
		c. Surch inverted	..	£650	
		d. Imperf between (horiz pair)			

(b) On white wove paper

35	6	3 p. on 1 a. emerald-green	..	15	20
		a. Imperf between (pair)			
		b. Surch inverted	..	35·00	20·00
		c. Surch double	..	†	—
36	7	1 a. on 4 a. carmine	..	1·60	4·25
		a. Imperf (pair)	..	£700	
		b. Surch both sides	..	£700	
		c. Capital "A" in "Anna"	..	13·00	

(c) On white laid paper

37	6	3 p. on 1 a. emerald-green	..	75·00	30·00
		a. Imperf (pair)	..	—	£325
		b. Larger English surch (21 mm long with capital "p" in "Pies") inverted	..	†	£1300
38	7	1 a. on 4 a. red	..	7·00	40·00
		a. Capital "A" in "Anna"	..	£200	
		b. Surch inverted	..	£650	
		c. Surch double	..	£650	
		d. Surch double, one inverted	..	£650	

The 1 a. surcharge with capital "A" in "Anna" comes from a separate setting.

10	11

(Dies eng Thacker & Co, Bombay. Typo Junagadh State Press)

1914 (1 Sept). *New plates. T 6/7 redrawn as T 10/11. Wove paper. P 12.*

40	10	3 p. green	..	45	35
		a. Imperf (pair)	..	4·75	16·00
		b. Imperf vert (horiz pair)	..	70·00	
		c. Laid paper	..	3·00	1·50
		ca. Imperf (pair)	..	12·00	22·00
		d. Error. Red (imperf)	..	†	£1500
41	11	1 a. red	..	70	1·10
		a. Imperf (pair)	..	18·00	60·00
		b. Imperf between (pair)	..	£375	
		c. Laid paper	..	£275	95·00

12　Nawab Mahabat Khan III　13

(Dies eng Popatlal Bhimji Pandya. Typo Junagadh State Press)

1923 (1 Sept). *Blurred impression. Laid paper. Pin-perf 12.*

42	12	1 a. red	..	3·00	7·50

Sheets of 16 stamps (8×2).
This setting was later printed on wove paper, but single examples cannot readily be distinguished from No. 46b.

ત્રણ પાઇ	ત્રણ પાઇ
(14)	(14a)

1923 (1 Sept). *Surch with T 14.*

43	12	3 p. on 1 a. red	..	3·25	7·00
		a. Surch with T 14a	..	3·75	10·00

Four stamps in the setting have surch. T 14a, i.e. with top of last character curved to right.

1923 (Oct). *Blurred impression. Wove paper. Pin-perf 12, small holes.*

44	13	3 p. mauve	..	35	40

Sheets of 16 (4×4).

1924. *Clear impression. Wove paper. P 12, large holes.*

45	13	3 p. mauve (1.24)	..	80	35
46	12	1 a. red (4.24)	..	5·00	5·50
		a. Imperf (pair)	..	42·00	
		b. Pin perf	..	2·50	2·75

The first plate of the 3 p., which printed No. 44, produced unsatisfactory impressions, so it was replaced by a second plate, producing two panes of 16 (4×4), from which No. 45 comes. Sheets printed from the first plate had very large margins.

The 1 a. is also from a new plate, giving a clearer impression. Sheets of 16 stamps (4×4).

1929. *Clear impressions. Laid paper. P 12, large holes.*

47	13	3 p. mauve	..	3·75	2·75
		a. Imperf (pair)	..	3·00	22·00
		b. Perf 11	..	6·00	5·00
		ba. Imperf between (horiz pair)	..	3·00	18·00

Sheets of two panes of 16 (4×4).
The laid paper shows several sheet watermarks.

15　Junagadh City

16　Gir Lion	17　Nawab Mahabat Khan III

18　Kathi Horse

(Des Amir Sheikh Mahamadbhai. Litho Indian Security Printing Press, Nasik)

1929 (1 Oct). *Inscr "POSTAGE". P 14.*

49	15	3 p. black and blackish green	..	60	10
50	16	½ a. black and deep blue	..	5·00	10
51	17	1 a. black and carmine	..	3·50	85
52	18	2 a. black and dull orange	..	9·00	1·75
		a. *Grey and dull yellow*	..	26·00	1·75
53	15	3 a. black and carmine	..	3·25	6·50
54	16	4 a. black and purple	..	12·00	19·00
55	18	8 a. black and yellow-green	..	10·00	19·00
56	17	1 r. black and pale blue	..	4·25	19·00
49/56			*Set of 8*	42·00	60·00

1935. *As T 17, but inscr "POSTAGE AND REVENUE". P 14.*

57	17	1 a. black and carmine	..	4·50	90

OFFICIAL STAMPS

SARKARI

(O 1)

1929 (1 Oct). *Optd with Type O 1, in vermilion, at Nasik.*

O1	15	3 p. black and blackish green	..	1·00	15
		a. Red opt	..	75	10
O2	16	½ a. black and deep blue	..	1·75	10
		a. Red opt	..	2·75	30
O3	17	1 a. black and carmine (No. 51)	..	2·50	30
		a. Red opt	..	1·50	15
O4	18	2 a. black and dull orange	..	2·50	70
		a. *Grey and dull yellow*	..	16·00	60
		b. Red opt	..	23·00	2·50
O5	15	3 a. black and carmine	..	60	30
		a. Red opt	..	15·00	1·50
O6	16	4 a. black and purple	..	2·00	40
		a. Red opt	..	19·00	2·25
O7	18	8 a. black and yellow-green	..	2·00	1·50
O8	17	1 r. black and pale blue	..	2·50	14·00
O1/8			*Set of 8*	12·50	15·00

SARKARI　　SARKARI

(O 2)　　(O 3)

1932. *Optd with Types O 2 (3 a., 1 r.) or O 3 (others), all in red, at Junagadh State Press.*

O 9	15	3 a. black and carmine	..	75·00	7·00
		a. Optd with Type O 3	..	17·00	13·00
O10	16	4 a. black and purple	..	24·00	15·00
O11	18	8 a. black and yellow-green	..	26·00	18·00
O12	17	1 r. black and pale blue	..	95·00	95·00
		a. Optd with Type O 3	..	21·00	60·00

1938. *No. 57 optd with Type O 1, in vermilion.*

O13	17	1 a. black and carmine	..	.. 12·00	1·90
		a. Brown-red opt	..	.. 9·50	1·40

The state was occupied by Indian troops on 9 November 1947 following the flight of the Nawab to Pakistan.

UNITED STATE OF SAURASHTRA

The administration of Junagadh state was assumed by the Government of India on 7 November 1947. An Executive Council took office on 1 June 1948.

Under the new Constitution of India the United State of Saurashtra was formed on 15 February 1948, comprising 221 former states and estates of Kathiawar, including Jasdan, Morvi, Nawanagar and Wadhwan, but excluding Junagadh. A referendum was held by the Executive Council of Junagadh which then joined the United State on 20 January 1949. It is believed that the following issues were only used in Junagadh.

The following issues were surcharged at the Junagadh State Press.

POSTAGE & REVENUE

ONE ANNA
(19)

Postage & Revenue

ONE ANNA
(20)

1949. *Stamps of 1929 surch. (a) With T 19 in red.*

58	16	1 a. on ½ a. black and deep blue (6.49)		9·00	4·50
		a. Surch double		†	£425
		b. "AFNA" for "ANNA" and inverted "N" in "REVENUE"			£1600
		c. Larger first "A" in "ANNA" (R. 2/5)		80·00	60·00

(b) With T 20 in green

59	18	1 a. on 2 a. grey and dull yellow (2.49)		9·50	20·00
		a. "evenue" omitted		—	£425

A number of other varieties occur on No. 58, including: small "V" in "REVENUE" (R. 2/3); small "N" in "REVENUE" (R. 2/4, 3/4); small "E" in "POSTAGE" (R. 3/2); thick "A" in "POSTAGE" (R. 4/4); inverted "N" in "REVENUE" and small second "A" in "ANNA" (R. 4/5); small "O" in "ONE" (R. 5/1); small "V" and "U" in "REVENUE" (R. 6/3); small "N" in "ONE" (R. 7/2).

In No. 59 no stop after "ANNA" is known on R. 1/4, 4/2, 7/4 and 8/3 and small "N" in "ONE" on R. 2/4.

21

(Typo Waterlow)

1949 (Sept). *Court Fee stamps of Bhavnagar state optd "SAURASHTRA" and further optd "U.S.S. REVENUE & POSTAGE" as in T 21, in black. P 11.*

60	21	1 a. purple		8·00	8·50
		a. "POSTAGE" omitted (R. 1/2)		£250	180
		b. Opt double		£250	£300

The Count Fee stamps were in sheets of 80 (8×10) and were overprinted in a setting of 40 applied twice to each sheet.

Minor varieties include small "S" in "POSTAGE" (R. 2/1 of the setting); small "N" in "REVENUE" (R. 2/7); small "U" in "REVENUE" (R. 3/2); small "V" in "REVENUE" (R. 3/8, 5/5); and small "O" in "POSTAGE" (R. 4/7).

Various missing stop varieties also occur.

POSTAGE & REVENUE
ONE ANNA
(22)

1950 (2 Mar). *Stamp of 1929 surch with T 22.*

61	15	1 a. on 3 p. black and blackish green		48·00	50·00
		a. "P" of "POSTAGE" omitted (R. 8/1)		£550	£550
		b. "O" of "ONE" omitted (R. 6/1)			£700

Other minor varieties include small second "A" in "ANNA" (R. 1/2); small "S" in "POSTAGE" with small "V" in "REVENUE" (R. 3/4, 6/1) and small "V" in "REVENUE" (R. 2/3, 3/1).

OFFICIAL STAMPS

1948 (July–Dec). *Nos. O4/O7 surch "ONE ANNA" (2¼ mm high) by Junagadh State Press.*

O14	18	1 a. on 2 a. grey & dull yellow (B.)		£5000	20·00
O15	15	1 a. on 3 a. black and carmine (Aug)		£1700	45·00
		a. Surch double		†	£1600
O16	16	1 a. on 4 a. black and purple (Dec)		£275	40·00
		a. "ANNE" for "ANNA" (R. 5/4)		£2000	£350
		b. "ANNN" for "ANNA" (R. 7/5)		£2000	£350
O17	18	1 a. on 8 a. black & yellow-green (Dec)		£250	30·00
		a. "ANNE" for "ANNA" (R. 5/4)		£2000	£275
		b. "ANNN" for "ANNA" (R. 7/5)		£2000	£275

Numerous minor varieties of fount occur in this surcharge.

1948 (Nov). *Handstamped "ONE ANNA" (4 mm high).*

O18	17	1 a. on 1 r. (No. O8)		£950	29·00
O19		1 a. on 1 r. (No. O12a)		£350	32·00
		a. Optd on No. O12		—	50·00

A used copy of No. O12a is known surcharged in black as on Nos. O14/17. This may have come from a proof sheet.

1949 (Jan). *Postage stamps optd with Type O 3, in red.*

O20	15	3 p. black and blackish green		£225	10·00
O21	16	½ a. black and deep blue		£500	10·00
O22	18	1 a. on 2 a. grey and dull yellow (No. 59)		60·00	18·00

Various wrong fount letters occur in the above surcharges.

MANUSCRIPT OVERPRINTS. Nos. 49, 50, 57, 58, 59 and 60 are known with manuscript overprints reading "Service" or "SARKARI" (in English or Gujerati script), usually in red. Such provisionals were used at Gadhda and Una between June and December 1949 (*Price from £85 each, used on piece*).

The United State of Saurashtra postal service was incorporated into that of India on 30 March 1950.

TRAVANCORE

PRICES FOR STAMPS ON COVER	
Nos. 1/77	*from* × 10
Nos. O1/108	*from* × 15

(16 cash = 1 chuckram; 28 chuckrams = 1 rupee)

"Anchel" or "Anchal" = Post Office Department.

The stamps of Travancore were valid on mail posted to Cochin.

PRINTERS. All stamps of Travancore were printed by the Stamp Manufactory, Trivandrum, *unless otherwise stated.*

PRINTING METHODS. The dies were engraved on brass from which electrotypes were made and locked together in a forme for printing the stamps. As individual electrotypes became worn they were replaced by new ones and their positions in the forme were sometimes changed. This makes it difficult to plate the early issues. From 1901 plates were made which are characterised by a frame (or "Jubilee" line) round the margins of the sheets.

Up to the 6 cash of 1910 the dies were engraved by Dharmalingham Asari.

SHADES. We list only the main groups of shades but there are many others in view of the large number of printings and the use of fugitive inks. Sometimes shade variation is noticeable within the same sheet.

Maharaja Rama Varma X, 1885–1924

1 Conch or Chank Shell

1888 (16 Oct). *As T 1, but each value differs slightly. Laid paper. P 12.*

1	1	1 ch. ultramarine (*shades*)		3·50	2·75
2		2 ch. red		3·25	8·00
3		4 ch. green		14·00	11·00
1/3		Set of 3		18·00	19·00

The paper bears a large sheet watermark showing a large conch shell surmounted by "GOVERNMENT" in large outline letters, in an arch with "OF TRAVANCORE" at foot in a straight line. Many stamps in the sheet are without watermark.

These stamps on laid paper in abnormal colours are proofs.

2

A   B   C

Three forms of watermark Type 2.
(*as seen from the back of the stamp*)

WATERMARKS AND PAPERS.

Type A appeared upright on early printings of the 1, 2 and 4 ch. values on odd-sized sheets which did not fit the number of shells. Later it was always sideways with 15 mm between the shells on standard-sized sheets of 84 (14 × 6) containing 60 shells (10 × 6). It therefore never appears centred on the stamps and it occurs on hand-made papers only.

Type B is similar in shape but can easily be distinguished as it is invariably upright, with 11 mm between the shells, and is well centred on the stamps. It also occurs only on handmade papers. It was introduced in 1904 and from 1914, when Type A was brought back into use, it was employed concurrently until 1924.

Type C is quite different in shape and occurs on machine-made papers. There are two versions. The first, in use from 1924 to 1939, has 84 shells 11 mm apart and is always sideways and well centred. The second, introduced in 1929 and believed not to have been used after 1930, has 60 shells (12 × 5) 15 mm apart and is invariably badly centred so that some stamps in the sheet are without watermark. This second version is normally found upright, but a few sideways watermark varieties are known and listed as Nos. 35g, 37c, O31j and O32i. We do not distinguish between the two versions of Type C in the lists, but stamps known to exist in the second version are indicated in footnotes. The machine-made paper is generally smoother and of more even texture.

NO WATERMARK VARIETIES. Some of these were formerly listed but we have now decided to omit them as they do not occur in full sheets. They arise in the following circumstances: (a) on sheets with wmk A; (b) on sheets with the wide-spaced form of wmk C; and (c) on late printings of the pictorial issues of 1939–46. They are best collected in pairs, with and without watermark.

DATES OF ISSUE. In the absence of more definite information the dates quoted usually refer to the first reported date of new printings on different watermarks but many were not noted at the time and the dates of these are indicated by a query. Dated postmarks on single stamps are difficult to find.

3   4   5

6   7   8

1889–1904. *Wove paper. Wmk A (upright or sideways). P 12 (sometimes rough).*

4	1	½ ch. slate-lilac (1894)		2·00	50
		a. Doubly printed		†	£190
		b. *Reddish lilac*		60	£190
		ba. Imperf between (vert pair)		£190	£190
		bb. Doubly printed		†	£190
		c. *Purple* (1899)		1·10	20
		ca. Doubly printed		†	£190
		d. *Dull purple* (1904)		1·40	20
5	5	¾ ch. black (14.3.01)		2·75	80
6	1	1 ch. ultramarine		1·40	15
		a. *Tête-bêche* (pair)		£2000	£2000
		b. Doubly printed		†	£325
		c. Imperf vert (horiz pair)		†	£325
		d. Imperf between (vert pair)		†	£325
		e. *Pale ultramarine* (1892)		2·50	20
		f. *Violet-blue* (1901)		3·00	40
7		2 ch. salmon (1890)		4·00	1·00
		a. *Rose* (1891)		3·25	30
		ab. Imperf (pair)		†	£350
		b. *Pale pink* (1899)		2·75	35
		ba. Imperf between (vert pair)		£130	
		bb. Doubly printed		£190	
		c. *Red* (1904)		2·75	15
		ca. Imperf between (horiz pair)		†	£250
8		4 ch. green		3·00	70
		a. *Yellow-green* (1901)		2·25	45
		b. *Dull green* (1904)		6·00	1·00
		ba. Doubly printed		†	£325

Nos. 6, 6d, 7 and 8 occur with the watermark upright and sideways. No. 7a is known only with the watermark upright. The remainder exist only with the watermark sideways.

The sheet sizes were as follows:

½ ch. 56 (14 × 4) except for No. 4d which was 84 (14 × 6), initially without border, later with border.

¾ ch. 84 (14 × 6) with border.

1 ch. No. 6, 80 (10 × 8) and later 84 (14 × 6) without border and then with border; No. 6d, 96 (16 × 6); No. 6e, 84 (14 × 6) with border.

2 ch. No. 7, 80 (10 × 8); No. 7a, 70 (10 × 7); Nos. 7b, 7c, 60 (10 × 6).

4 ch. No. 8, 60 (10 × 6); Nos. 8a/b, 84 (14 × 6) with border.

After 1904 all stamps in Types 3 to 8 were in standard-sized sheets of 84 (14 × 6) with border.

For later printings watermarked Type A, see Nos. 23/30.

1904–20. *Wmk B, upright (centred). P 12, sometimes rough.*

9	3	4 ca. pink (11.08)		25	10
		a. Imperf between (vert pair)		£180	£180
10	1	6 ca. chestnut (2.10)		30	10
		a. Imperf between (horiz pair)		†	£180
11		½ ch. reddish lilac		1·00	10
		a. *Reddish violet* (6.10)		75	10
		b. *Lilac*		1·10	30
		c. "CHUCRRAM" (R. 5/6)		5·00	3·25
		d. Imperf horiz (vert pair)		†	£130

12	4	10 ca. pink (1920)	..	24·00	5·00
13	5	¾ ch. black	..	1·25	25
14	1	1 ch. bright blue			
		a. *Blue*	..	3·00	30
		b. *Deep blue*	..	3·00	30
		c. *Indigo* (8.10) ..	..	75	10
		d. *Chalky blue* (1912) ..	..	4·00	60
15		1¼ ch. claret (*shades*) (10.14) ..		50	45
		a. Imperf between (horiz pair) ..		£190	£190
16		2 ch. salmon	..	18·00	6·00
		a. *Red* (8.10)	..	50	10
17	6	3 ch. violet (11.3.11) ..	..	2·50	20
		a. Imperf between (vert pair) ..		£180	£180
		b. Imperf between (vert strip of 3)		†	£250
18	1	4 ch. dull green		9·00	3·50
		a. *Slate-green*		1·25	35
19	7	7 ch. claret (1916) ..	..	1·75	45
		a. Error. Carmine-red ..		—	50·00
20	8	14 ch. orange-yellow (1916) ..		2·40	1·40
		a. Imperf vert (horiz strip of 3) ..		£400	

(9)   1 C   (10)

1906. *Surch as T 9. Wmk* B.

21	1	1¼ on ½ ch. reddish lilac ..	..	30	30
		a. *Reddish violet* ..	..	30	20
		b. *Lilac*	..	50	30
		c. "CHUCRRAM" (R.5/6) ..		3·50	3·25
		d. Surch inverted ..	..	42·00	28·00
22		⅜ on ½ ch. reddish lilac ..	..	20	35
		a. *Reddish violet* ..	..	20	35
		b. *Lilac*	..	20	35
		c. "CHUCRRAM" (R.5/6) ..		3·25	3·50
		d. Surch inverted ..	..	—	40·00
		e. Surch double ..	..		
		f. "8" omitted ..	..	—	40·00

1914–22. *Reversion to wmk* A (*sideways*). *P* 12 (*sometimes rough*).

23	3	4 ca. pink (1915) ..	..	7·50	60
24	4	5 ca. olive-bistre (30.10.21) ..		70	10
		a. Imperf between (horiz pair) ..		42·00	48·00
		b. Imperf between (horiz strip of 3)		85·00	90·00
		c. "TRAVANCOPE" ..		—	8·00
25	1	6 ca. orange-brown (2.15) ..		5·00	35
26		½ ch. reddish violet (12.14) ..		2·25	30
		a. "CHUCRRAM" (R.5/6) ..		9·00	3·50
		b. Imperf between (horiz pair) ..		£140	
27	4	10 ca. pink (26.10.21) ..		35	10
28	1	1 ch. grey-blue (5.22) ..		8·00	1·60
		a. *Deep blue*		8·00	1·60
29		1¼ ch. claret (12.19) ..		9·50	30
30	6	3 ch. reddish lilac (8.22) ..		9·50	1·50

1921 (Mar). *Surch as T 10. Wmk* A.

31	3	1 c. on 4 ca. pink ..	..	15	15
		a. Surch inverted ..	..	19·00	9·00
32	1	5 c. on 1 ch. grey-blue (R.) ..		90	10
		a. *Deep blue*		90	10
		b. Stamp printed both sides ..		†	£180
		c. Imperf between (vert pair) ..		†	£160
		d. Surch inverted ..	..	13·00	8·00
		e. Surch double ..	..	40·00	30·00
		f. On wmk B. *Deep blue* ..		20·00	20·00

ALBINO OVERPRINT VARIETIES. Stamps with overprint double, one albino are frequently found in the provisional and official issues of Travancore, and are only worth a small premium over the normal prices.

Maharaja Bala Rama Varma XI, 1924–1971

1924–39. *Wmk* C. *Machine-made paper. P* 12.

33	4	5 ca. olive-bistre (18.6.25) ..		10·00	2·50
		a. Imperf between (horiz pair) ..		£120	
		b. "TRAVANCOPE" ..		—	13·00
34		5 ca. chocolate (1930) ..		2·50	20
		a. Imperf between (horiz pair) ..		35·00	
		b. Imperf between (vert pair) ..		†	£110
35	1	6 ca. brown-red (3.24) ..		4·25	10
		a. Imperf between (horiz pair) ..		21·00	22·00
		b. Imperf between (vert pair) ..		85·00	85·00
		c. Printed both sides ..		50·00	
		d. Perf 12½		4·25	50
		e. Perf comp of 12 and 12½ ..		8·00	4·00
		f. Perf 12½×11 ..		—	75·00
		g. Wmk sideways ..		—	14·00
36		½ ch. reddish violet (date?) ..		4·25	4·25
		a. "CHUCRRAM" (R. 5/6) ..		32·00	
37	4	10 ca. pink (8.24) ..		2·00	10
		a. Imperf between (horiz pair) ..		70·00	70·00
		b. Imperf between (vert pair) ..		21·00	23·00
		c. Wmk sideways (16.9.28) ..		—	5·50
38	5	¾ ch. black (4.10.32) ..		9·00	50
39		¾ ch. mauve (16.11.32) ..		35	10
		a. Imperf between (horiz pair) ..		†	£120
		b. Perf 12½ (8.37) ..		8·50	70
		ba. Imperf between (horiz pair) ..		£110	
		c. Perf comp of 12 and 12½ ..		12·00	5·00
40		¾ ch. reddish violet (1939) ..		3·00	70
		a. Perf 12½		4·50	60
		b. Perf comp of 12 and 12½ ..		7·50	2·25
		c. Perf 11		—	75·00
		d. Perf comp of 12 and 11 ..		—	75·00
41	1	1 ch. slate-blue (8.26) ..		2·75	30
		a. *Indigo*		4·00	20
		b. Imperf between (horiz pair) ..		†	£160
		c. Imperf between (vert pair) ..		†	£160
		d. Perf 12½		13·00	1·10

42	1	1½ ch. rose (1932) ..		2·50	10
		a. Imperf between (horiz strip of 3)		£160	
		b. Perf 12½ ..		21·00	2·75
		c. Perf comp of 12 and 12½ ..		—	26·00
43		2 ch. carmine-red (4.6.29) ..		4·50	30
44	6	3 ch. violet (4.25) ..		6·50	15
		a. Imperf between (vert pair) ..		85·00	85·00
		b. Perf 12½ ..		—	11·00
		c. Perf comp of 12 and 12½ ..		—	24·00
45	1	4 ch. grey-green (5.4.34) ..		6·00	45
46	7	7 ch. claret (1925) ..		8·50	1·75
		a. Doubly printed ..		†	£300
		b. *Carmine-red* (date?) ..		65·00	55·00
		c. *Brown-purple* (1932) ..		14·00	4·25
		ca. Perf 12½ ..		8·50	14·00
		cb. Perf comb of 12 and 12½ ..		8·50	14·00
46d	8	14 ch. orange-yellow (date?) ..		40·00	
		da. Perf 12½ ..		—	£180

It is believed that the 12½ perforation and the perf 12 and 12½ compound were introduced in 1937 and that the 11 perforation came later, probably in 1939.

The 5 ca. chocolate, 6 ca., 10 ca. and 3 ch. also exist on the wide-spaced watermark (60 shells to the sheet of 84).

11 Sri Padmanabha Shrine

12 State Chariot   13 Maharaja Bala Rama Varma XI

(Des M. R. Madhawan Unnithan. Plates by Calcutta Chromotype Co. Typo Stamp Manufactory, Trivandrum)

1931 (6 Nov). *Coronation. Cream or white paper. Wmk* C. *P* 11½, 12.

47	11	6 ca. black and green ..		1·00	1·00
		a. Imperf between (horiz pair) ..		£180	£200
48	12	10 ca. black and ultramarine ..		90	40
		a. Imperf between (vert pair) ..		†	£350
49	13	3 ch. black and purple ..		2·00	1·75
47/9		.. .. *Set of* 3		3·50	2·75

1 C   1 C

(14)   (15)   16 Maharaja Bala Rama Varma XI and Subramania Shrine

1932 (14 Jan).   (i) *Surch as T* 14. (*a*) *Wmk* A (*sideways*).

50	1	1 c. on 1¼ ch. claret ..		15	50
		a. Imperf between (horiz pair) ..		85·00	
		b. Surch inverted ..		4·25	6·50
		c. Surch double ..		26·00	26·00
		d. Pair, one without surch ..		80·00	90·00
		e. "c" omitted ..		45·00	45·00
51		2 c. on 1¼ ch. claret ..		15	15
		a. Surch inverted ..		4·25	6·50
		b. Surch double ..		26·00	
		c. Surch double, one inverted ..		55·00	
		d. Surch treble ..		60·00	
		e. Surch treble, one inverted ..		70·00	70·00
		f. Pair, one without surch ..		85·00	85·00
		g. "2" omitted ..		45·00	45·00
		h. "c" omitted ..		45·00	45·00
		i. Imperf between (horiz pair) ..		85·00	
		j. Imperf between (vert pair) ..		90·00	

(*b*) *Wmk* B (*upright*)

52	1	1 c. on 1¼ ch. claret ..		75	85
		a. Surch inverted ..		19·00	
		b. Surch double ..		35·00	
53		2 c. on 1¼ ch. claret ..		6·00	6·00
		a. Imperf between (horiz pair) ..		£110	

(*c*) *Wmk* C

54	1	1 c. on 1¼ ch. claret ..		13·00	14·00
		a. Surch inverted ..		48·00	48·00
55		2 c. on 1¼ ch. claret ..		20·00	15·00

(ii) *Surch as T* 10. *Wmk* B

56	1	2 c. on 1¼ ch. claret ..		3·75	13·00

1932 (5 Mar)   *Surch as T* 15. *Wmk* C.

57	4	1 c. on 5 ca. chocolate ..		15	15
		a. Imperf between (horiz pair) ..		£100	
		b. Surch inverted ..		7·50	10·00
		c. Surch inverted on back only ..		55·00	
		d. Pair, one without surch ..		85·00	
		e. "1" omitted ..		38·00	
		f. "C" omitted ..		—	38·00
		g. "TRAVANCOPE" ..		8·50	
58		1 c. on 5 ca. slate-purple ..		1·10	15
		a. Surch inverted ..		†	£160
		b. "1" inverted ..		70·00	70·00
59		2 c. on 10 ca. pink ..		15	15
		a. Imperf between (horiz pair) ..		90·00	
		b. Surch inverted ..		5·00	7·50
		c. Surch double ..		19·00	21·00
		d. Surch double, one inverted ..		50·00	50·00
		e. Surch double, both inverted ..		38·00	

No. 58 was not issued without the surcharge.

(Plates by Indian Security Printing Press, Nasik. Typo Stamp Manufactory, Trivandrum)

1937 (29 Mar). *Temple Entry Proclamation. T* 16 *and similar horiz designs. Wmk* C. *P* 12.

60		6 ca. carmine ..		60	70
		a. Imperf between (horiz strip of 3)		£400	
		b. Perf 12½ ..		1·10	1·50
		c. Compound perf ..		25·00	25·00
61		12 ca. bright blue ..		1·40	20
		a. Perf 12½ ..		2·00	60
		ab. Imperf between (vert pair) ..		£375	
		c. Compound perf ..		40·00	
62		1½ ch. yellow-green ..		1·00	70
		a. Imperf between (vert pair) ..		£300	
		b. Perf 12½ ..		21·00	5·00
		c. Compound perf ..			
63		3 ch. violet ..		2·75	1·40
		a. Perf 12½ ..		3·50	1·90
60/3		.. .. *Set of* 4		5·25	2·75

Designs:—Maharaja's portrait and temples—12 ca. Sri Padmanabha; 1½ ch. Mahadeva; 3 ch. Kanyakumari.

COMPOUND PERFS. This term covers stamps perf compound of 12½ and 11, 12 and 11 or 12 and 12½, and where two or more combinations exist the prices are for the commonest. Such compounds can occur on values which do not exist perf 12 all round.

17 Lake Ashtamudi   18 Maharaja Bala Rama Varma XI

(Des Nilakantha Pellai. Plates by Indian Security Printing Press, Nasik. Typo Stamp Manufactory, Trivandrum)

1939 (9 Nov). *Maharaja's 27th Birthday. T* 17/18 *and similar designs. Wmk* C. *P* 12½.

64		1 ch. yellow-green ..		3·25	10
		a. Imperf between (horiz pair) ..		20·00	
		b. Perf 11 ..		7·00	10
		ba. Imperf between (vert pair) ..		30·00	35·00
		bb. Imperf between (vert strip of 3)		20·00	32·00
		c. Perf 12 ..		14·00	75
		ca. Imperf between (horiz pair) ..		20·00	
		cb. Imperf between (vert pair) ..		30·00	
		d. Compound perf ..		17·00	1·90
		da. Imperf between (vert pair) ..		85·00	
65		1½ ch. scarlet ..		1·60	1·90
		a. Doubly printed ..		£190	
		b. Imperf between (horiz pair) ..		25·00	
		c. Imperf between (vert pair) ..		20·00	
		d. Perf 11 ..		3·00	17·00
		da. Imperf horiz (vert pair) ..		8·00	
		e. Perf 12 ..		23·00	3·00
		f. Perf 13½ ..		13·00	48·00
		g. Compound perf ..		32·00	4·25
		h. Imperf (pair) ..		30·00	
66		2 ch. orange ..		3·75	75
		a. Perf 11 ..		12·00	35
		b. Perf 12 ..		70·00	3·75
		c. Compound perf ..		70·00	4·50
67		3 ch. brown ..		4·75	10
		a. Doubly printed ..		—	£100
		b. Imperf between (horiz pair) ..		32·00	45·00
		c. Perf 11 ..		15·00	30
		ca. Doubly printed ..		40·00	48·00
		d. Perf 12 ..		29·00	2·25
		da. Imperf between (vert pair) ..		£100	£100
		e. Compound perf ..		22·00	1·00
68		4 ch. red ..		3·75	40
		a. Perf 11 ..		24·00	50
		b. Perf 12 ..		22·00	4·75
		c. Compound perf ..		£110	90·00
69		7 ch. pale blue ..		6·50	12·00
		a. Perf 11 ..		55·00	22·00
		ab. *Blue* ..		55·00	20·00
		b. Compound perf ..		70·00	25·00
70		14 ch. turquoise-green ..		6·00	38·00
		a. Perf 11 ..		7·50	65·00
64/70		.. .. *Set of* 7		27·00	48·00

Designs: Vert as T 18—1½ ch., 3 ch. Portraits of Maharaja in different frames. *Horiz as T* 17—4 ch. Sri Padmanabha Shrine; 7 ch. Cape Comorin; 14 ch. Pachipari Reservoir.

19 Maharaja and Aruvikara Falls   (20) 2 CASH

(Des Nilakantha Pellai. Plates by Indian Security Printing Press, Nasik. Typo Stamp Manufactory, Trivandrum)

1941 (20 Oct). *Maharaja's 29th Birthday. T* 19 *and similar horiz design. Wmk* C. *P* 12½.

71		6 ca. blackish violet ..		4·50	10
		a. Perf 11 ..		4·50	10
		ab. Imperf between (vert pair) ..		20·00	
		ac. Imperf horiz (vert pair) ..		32·00	45·00
		b. Perf 12 ..		16·00	1·00
		ba. Imperf between (horiz pair) ..		24·00	
		bb. Imperf between (vert pair) ..		32·00	
		bc. Imperf between (vert strip of 3)		21·00	
		c. Compound perf ..		4·75	80

72	¾ ch. brown	..	..	4·75	15
	a. Perf 11			6·50	15
	ab. Imperf between (horiz pair)	..		£100	
	ac. Imperf between (vert pair)	..		26·00	35·00
	ad. Imperf between (vert strip of 3)			23·00	
	ae. Block of four imperf between (horiz and				
	vert)	..	..	£140	
	b. Perf 12	..	..	38·00	6·50
	c. Compound perf	..	..	9·00	1·10

Design:—¾ ch. Maharaja and Marthanda Varma Bridge, Alwaye.

1943 (17 Sept). *Nos. 65, 71 (colour changed) and 72 surch as T* **20**. *P* 12½.

73	2 ca. on 1½ ch. scarlet	..		1·10	45
	a. Imperf between (vert pair)			32·00	
	b. "2" omitted	..		£180	£180
	c. "CA" omitted	..		£275	
	d. "ASH" omitted	..		£275	
	e. Perf 11	..		30	20
	ea. "CA" omitted	..		£275	
	f. Compound perf	..		55	85
	fa. Imperf between (vert pair)			95·00	
	fb. "2" omitted	..		£190	
74	4 ca. on ¾ ch. brown	..		2·75	1·00
	a. Perf 11	..		3·00	20
	b. Perf 12	..		—	90·00
	c. Compound perf	..		3·75	1·00
75	8 ca. on 6 ca. scarlet	..		3·50	10
	a. Perf 11	..		2·25	10
	ab. Imperf between (horiz pair)			30·00	
	b. Perf 12	..		—	65·00
	c. Compound perf	..		10·00	5·00
73/5	.. ..	*Set of 3*		4·75	45

21 Maharaja Bala Rama Varma XI

SPECIAL (22)

(Des Nilakantha Pellai. Plates by Indian Security Printing Press, Nasik. Typo Stamp Manufactory, Trivandrum)

1946 (24 Oct). *Maharaja's 34th Birthday. Wmk* C. *P* 12½.

76	21	8 ca. carmine	..	20·00	2·75
		a. Perf 11	..	65	85
		b. Perf 12	..	28·00	2·50
		ba. Imperf between (horiz pair)	..	30·00	42·00
		bb. Imperf between (horiz strip of 3)	45·00	
		c. Compound perf			

1946. *No.* O103 *revalidated for ordinary postage with opt T* **22**, *in orange. P* 12½.

77	19	6 ca. blackish violet	..	6·00	2·25
		a. Perf 11	..	28·00	5·00
		b. Compound perf	..	6·00	5·00

OFFICIAL STAMPS

GUM. Soon after 1911 the Official stamps were issued without gum. Thus only the initial printings of the 1, 2, 3 and 4 ch. values were gummed. As Nos. O38/9, O41/2 and O95 were overprinted on stamps intended for normal postage these, also, have gum.

PRINTINGS. Sometimes special printings of postage stamps were made specifically for overprinting for Official use, thus accounting for Official stamps appearing with watermarks or in shades not listed in the postage issues.

SETTINGS. These are based on the study of complete sheets of 84, and the measurements given are those of the majority of stamps on the sheet. Examples are known showing different measurements as each overprint was set individually in loose type, but these are not included in the listings.

On   On

S S   S S

(O 1)   (O 2)

Rounded "O"

1911 (16 Aug)–30. *Contemporary stamps optd with Type* O 1 (13 *mm wide*). *P* 12, *sometimes rough.* (*a*) *Wmk* B (*upright*) (16.8.11–21).

O 1	3	4 ca. pink (1916)	..	20	10
		a. Opt inverted	..	†	65·00
		b. Opt double	..	95·00	75·00
		c. "S S" inverted	..	25·00	15·00
		d. Imperf (pair)	..	£180	£180
		e. Stamp doubly printed	..	†	£180
O 2	1	6 ca. chestnut (date ?)	..	30·00	30·00
O 3		½ ch. reddish lilac (R.) (1919)	70	35
		a. "CHUCRRAM" (R.5/6)	..	8·50	4·50
O 4	4	10 ca. pink (1921)	..	13·00	2·50
		a. "O" inverted	..	35·00	8·00
		b. Left "S" inverted	..	35·00	8·00
		c. Right "S" inverted	..	35·00	8·00
		d. Opt inverted	..	†	90·00
O 5	1	1 ch. chalky blue (R.)	..	55	10
		a. Imperf between (vert pair)	†	£160	
		b. Opt inverted	..	7·00	4·25
		c. Opt double	..	60·00	50·00
		d. "nO" for "On"	..	75·00	75·00
		e. "O" inverted	..	6·50	2·00
		f. Left "S" inverted	..	6·50	2·00
		g. Right "S" inverted	..	6·50	2·00
		h. "S S" inverted	..	—	38·00

O 6	1	2 ch. red	..	35	10
		a. Opt inverted	..	8·00	8·00
		b. "O" inverted	..	7·50	1·25
		c. Left "S" inverted	..	6·00	1·10
		d. Right "S" inverted	..	8·00	1·50
O 7		2 ch. red (B.) (date ?)	..	—	80·00
O 8	6	3 ch. violet	..	35	10
		a. Imperf between (vert pair)	£140	£140
		b. Imperf vert (horiz pair)	£120	
		c. Opt inverted	..	10·00	10·00
		d. Opt double	..	60·00	60·00
		e. Right "S" inverted	..	4·50	1·00
		f. Right "S" omitted	..	85·00	85·00
		g. Left "S" omitted	..	85·00	85·00
O 9		3 ch. violet (B.) (date ?)	£110	55·00
O10	1	4 ch. slate-green	..	55	10
		a. Imperf between (pair)	£160	£160
		b. Opt inverted	..	38·00	12·00
		c. Opt double	..	80·00	80·00
		d. "O" inverted	..	9·00	2·40
		e. Left "S" inverted	..	8·50	2·75
		f. Right "S" inverted	..	9·00	3·25
		g. Left "S" omitted	..	85·00	85·00
O11		4 ch. slate-green (B.) (1921)	—	45·00
		a. "O" inverted	..	—	£100
		b. Left "S" inverted	..	—	£100
		c. Right "S" inverted	..	—	£100

(*b*) *Wmk* A (*sideways*) (1919–25)

O12	3	4 ca. pink	..	3·50	15
		a. Imperf (pair)	..	£200	£200
		b. Opt inverted	..	48·00	16·00
		c. "O" inverted	..	26·00	8·00
		d. Left "S" inverted	..	26·00	8·00
		e. Right "S" inverted	..	26·00	8·00
O13		4 ca. pink (B.) (1921)	..	32·00	75
		a. "O" inverted	..	—	19·00
O14	4	5 ca. olive-bistre (1921)	..	50	10
		a. Opt inverted	..	12·00	9·00
		b. "O" inverted	..	4·50	1·40
		c. Left "S" inverted	..	4·50	1·40
		d. Right "S" inverted	..	4·50	1·40
O15	1	6 ca. orange-brown (1921)	..	30	10
		a. Imperf between (vert pair)	†	£150
		b. Opt inverted	..	10·00	8·50
		c. Opt double	..	55·00	55·00
		d. "O" inverted	..	5·50	1·50
		e. Left "S" inverted	..	5·50	1·25
		f. Right "S" inverted	..	5·50	1·50
O16		6 ca. orange-brown (B.) (1921)	8·50	1·50
		a. "O" inverted	..	90·00	90·00
		b. "O" inverted	..	42·00	14·00
		c. Left "S" inverted	..	42·00	14·00
		d. Right "S" inverted	..	42·00	14·00
O17		½ ch. reddish violet (R.) (date?)	95	15
		a. Reddish lilac (date?)	..	95	15
		b. Imperf between (horiz pair)	£100	£100
		c. Imperf between (vert pair)	48·00	48·00
		d. Stamp doubly printed	..	48·00	
		e. Opt inverted	..	9·00	3·00
		f. Opt double, both inverted	£100	
		g. "CHUCRRAM" (R. 5/6)	..	6·50	2·75
		h. "On" omitted	..	—	95·00
		i. Right "S" inverted	..	—	21·00
		j. Right "S" omitted	..	—	95·00
O18	4	10 ca. pink (3.21)	..	55	10
		a. Scarlet (1925?)	..	—	9·50
		b. Opt inverted	..	—	17·00
		c. Opt double	..	75·00	60·00
		d. "O" inverted	..	7·50	2·50
		e. "S" inverted	..	6·50	1·75
		f. Right "S" inverted	..	7·50	2·50
		g. Imperf between (horiz pair)	—	£110
O19		10 ca. pink (B.) (date?)	..	55·00	13·00
		a. Opt inverted	..	—	70·00
		b. "O" inverted	..	—	42·00
O20	1	1 ch. grey-blue (R.) (date?)	..	4·00	60
		a. Deep blue	..	4·25	80
		b. "O" inverted	..	30·00	8·00
		c. Left "S" inverted	..	30·00	8·50
		d. "On" omitted	..		
		e. Opt inverted	..	†	45·00
O21		1¼ ch. claret (12.19)	..	40	10
		ca. Stamp doubly printed	..	—	£190
		b. Opt inverted	..	9·00	8·00
		c. Opt double	..	45·00	
		d. "O" inverted	..	10·00	2·00
		e. Left "S" inverted	..	12·00	3·00
		f. Right "S" inverted	..	12·00	3·00
		g. Error. Carmine	..	50·00	
O22		1¼ ch. claret (B.) (1921)	..	—	55·00
		a. "O" inverted	..	—	£120
		b. Left "S" inverted	..	—	£120
		c. Right "S" inverted	..	—	£120

(*c*) *Wmk* C (1925–30)

O23	4	5 ca. olive-bistre (1926)	..	40	35
		a. Imperf between (horiz pair)	£150	£150
		b. Opt inverted	..	15·00	12·00
		c. "O" inverted	..	4·50	2·50
		d. Left "S" inverted	..	4·50	2·50
		e. Right "S" inverted	..	4·50	2·50
O23*f*		5 ca. chocolate (1930)	..	45·00	
		fa. Opt inverted	..	—	£100
O24		10 ca. pink (1926)	..	3·50	15
		a. Imperf between (vert pair)	—	£140
		b. Opt inverted	..	55·00	55·00
		c. "O" inverted	..	19·00	2·25
		d. Left "S" inverted	..	19·00	2·50
		e. Right "S" inverted	..	19·00	2·50
		f. Stamp doubly printed	..		
		g. Opt double	..	†	85·00
O25	1	1¼ ch. claret (1926)	..	11·00	40
		a. "O" inverted	..	35·00	3·50
		b. Left "S" inverted	..	40·00	5·00
		c. Right "S" inverted	..	40·00	5·00
		d. Opt double	..	†	85·00
O26	7	7 ch. claret	..	1·50	30
		a. "O" inverted	..	14·00	3·50
		b. Left "S" inverted	..	14·00	3·50
		c. Right "S" inverted	..	14·00	3·50
		d. Error. Carmine-red	..	60·00	

O27	8	14 ch. orange-yellow	..	2·00	40
		a. "O" inverted	..	14·00	3·00
		b. Left "S" inverted	..	14·00	3·00
		c. Right "S" inverted	..	14·00	3·75

1926–30. *Contemporary stamps optd with Type* O 2 (16½ *mm wide*). *Wmk* C. *P* 12.

O28	4	5 ca. olive-bistre	..	2·25	30
		a. Right "S" inverted	..	13·00	4·00
		b. Left "S" inverted	..	15·00	4·50
O29		5 ca. chocolate (1930)	..	25	40
		a. Imperf between (vert pair)	†	£180
		b. Opt inverted	..	17·00	
		c. "O" inverted	..	3·50	3·50
		d. Left "S" inverted	..	3·50	3·50
O30	1	6 ca. brown-red (date?)	..	4·50	1·00
		a. "O" inverted	..	20·00	6·00
		b. Left "S" inverted	..	20·00	6·00
		c. Opt double	..	†	£110
O31	4	10 ca. pink	..	30	10
		a. Imperf between (horiz pair)	55·00	55·00
		b. Imperf between (vert pair)	42·00	42·00
		c. Imperf vert (horiz strip of 3)	†	£110
		d. Opt inverted	..	9·00	9·00
		e. "Ou" for "On"	..	40·00	40·00
		f. "O" inverted	..	4·25	1·50
		g. Left "S" inverted	..	3·75	1·40
		h. Right "S" inverted	..	3·75	1·25
		i. Left "S" omitted	..	38·00	38·00
		j. Wmk sideways	..	19·00	7·50
O32	1	1¼ ch. claret (shades)	..	1·60	30
		a. Imperf between (horiz pair)	80·00	85·00
		b. Imperf between (vert pair)	85·00	90·00
		c. Opt inverted	..	21·00	21·00
		d. "O" inverted	..	17·00	3·75
		e. Left "S" inverted	..	17·00	3·75
		f. Right "S" inverted	..	17·00	3·75
		g. Left "S" omitted	..	95·00	95·00
		h. Right "S" omitted	..	95·00	95·00
		i. Wmk sideways	..	—	7·50
O33	6	3 ch. violet	..	8·00	70
		a. Opt inverted	..	†	£110
		b. "O" inverted	..	40·00	16·00
		c. "O" omitted	..	75·00	75·00
		d. "Ou" for "On"	..	£120	£120
		e. Left "S" inverted	..	—	30·00
O34	7	7 ch. claret (date?)	..	£100	2·25
O35	8	14 ch. orange-yellow	..	42·00	85
		a. Imperf between (vert pair)	£375	
		b. "O" inverted	..	£100	8·50

The 5 ca. olive-bistre, 3 ch. and 7 ch. exist only with the normal watermark spaced 11 mm; the 5 ca. chocolate and 14 ch. exist only with the wide 15 mm spacing; the 6 ca., 10 ca. and 1¼ ch. exist in both forms.

On On On

S S S S S S

(O 3) (O 4) (O 5)

Italic "S S"

1930. *Wmk* C. *P* 12. (*a*) *Optd with Type* O 3.

O36	4	10 ca. pink		£180	£120
O37	1	1¼ ch. carmine-rose		3·25	3·25

(*b*) *Optd with Type* O 4

O38	5	¾ ch. black (R.)		35	30
		a. Left "S" omitted	..	75·00	
		b. Right "S" omitted	..	75·00	
		c. Large roman "S" at left	..	—	75·00

(*c*) *Optd with Type* O 5

O39	5	¾ ch. black (R.)		35	15
		a. Opt inverted	..	†	£160
		b. "n" omitted	..	80·00	80·00
O40	1	4 ch. slate-green (R.)	..	28·00	12·00

On   On

On

S S S S S

(O 6) (O 7) (O 8)

Oval "O"

1930–39 (?). *Contemporary stamps overprinted. P* 12.

(*a*) *With Type* O 6 (16 *mm high*) (i) *Wmk* A

O41	3	4 ca. pink		19·00	35·00
		a. Large right "S" as Type O 2	85·00	£140

(ii) *Wmk* B

O42	3	4 ca. pink		19·00	40·00
		a. Large right "S" as Type O 2	90·00	£150

(iii) *Wmk* C

O43	1	6 ca. brown-red (1932)		35	10
		a. Opt inverted	..	19·00	
		b. Opt double	..	42·00	42·00
		c. "O" inverted	..	8·00	5·00
O44	4	10 ca. pink	..	1·75	1·25
O45	5	¾ ch. mauve (1933)	..	3·25	10
		a. Imperf between (horiz pair)	80·00	55·00
		b. Imperf between (horiz strip of 3)	†	£100
		c. Imperf between (vert pair)	†	£85·00
		d. Stamp doubly printed	..	†	£140
		e. Perf 12½	..	6·50	40
		f. Perf comp of 12 and 12½	13·00	1·50
		g. Right "S" inverted	..	—	20·00
O46	1	1¼ ch. carmine-rose	..	10·00	1·75
		a. Opt double	..	95·00	75·00
		b. Large right "S" as Type O 2	90·00	48·00
O47		4 ch. grey-green	..	1·60	4·00

O48	**1**	4 ch. grey-green (R.) (27.10.30) ..		70	20

O48 **1** 4 ch. grey-green (R.) (27.10.30) .. 70 20
   a. Imperf between (horiz pair) .. 95·00 95·00
   b. Opt double .. 25·00 25·00
   c. "O" inverted .. 28·00 17·00
   d. Large right "S" as Type O 2 .. 42·00 28·00
   e. Imperf between (vert pair) .. 95·00
O49 **8** 14 ch. orange-yellow (1931) .. 6·50 1·75
   a. Imperf between (vert pair) .. † £120
For the 1½ ch. and 3 ch., and for Nos. O43 and O48/9 but perf 12½, see Nos. O66/70 (new setting combining Types O 6 and O 8).

(b) With Type O 7 (14 mm high). Wmk C
O50 **3** 4 ca. pink .. 11·00 26·00
   a. "O" inverted .. 40·00 70·00
O51 **4** 5 ca. chocolate (1932) .. 19·00 9·00
   a. Opt inverted .. 65·00 65·00
O52 **1** 6 ca. brown-red .. 20 10
   a. Imperf between (vert pair) .. 48·00 48·00
   b. Opt inverted .. 26·00
   c. Opt double .. † 55·00
   d. "nO" for "On" .. 95·00 95·00
   e. Right "S" inverted .. 17·00 12·00
   f. Left "S" omitted .. — 70·00
   g. Large "n" as Type O 5 .. 20·00 12·00
   h. Large italic left "S" as Type O 5 .. 20·00 12·00
   i. Perf 12½ .. — 6·50
   j. Perf compound of 12 and 12½ .. — 15·00
O53 ½ ch. reddish violet (1932) .. 30 15
   a. "CHUCRRAM" (R.5/6) .. 7·50 5·50
   b. "Ou" for "On" .. 50·00 50·00
   c. Left "S" omitted .. — 90·00
   d. "O" of "On" omitted .. £130
O54 ½ ch. reddish violet (R.) (1935) .. 20 10
   a. Imperf between (vert pair) .. 95·00 95·00
   b. "CHUCRRAM" (R.5/6) .. 3·25 3·00
   c. Left "S" inverted .. 19·00 17·00
O55 **4** 10 ca. pink (date?) .. 3·25 1·60
   a. Imperf between (horiz pair) .. 12·00 17·00
   b. Imperf between (vert pair) .. 10·00 16·00
   c. "O" inverted .. 26·00 18·00
   d. Right "S" inverted .. 26·00 18·00
O56 **5** ¾ ch. mauve (1933?) .. 30 15
   a. Imperf between (vert pair) .. † £100
   b. "Ou" for "On" .. 55·00 55·00
   c. "O" inverted .. 20·00 17·00
   d. Right "S" inverted .. — 17·00
   e. Opt double .. † 95·00
   f. Perf comp of 12 and 12½ .. 21·00 13·00
O57 **1** 1 ch. deep blue (R.) (1935) .. 1·60 35
   a. Slate-blue .. 90 20
   b. Imperf between (horiz pair) .. 90·00 90·00
   c. Imperf between (vert pair) .. 25·00 32·00
   d. Perf 12½ .. 8·00 3·00
   e. Perf comp of 12 and 12½ .. 16·00 5·50
O58 1¼ ch. claret .. 1·25 1·25
O59 1½ ch. rose (1933) .. 40 10
   a. Imperf between (vert pair) .. † £110
   b. Opt double .. 70·00 70·00
   c. "O" inverted .. 4·00 2·50
   e. Large "n" as type O 5 .. 48·00 22·00
   f. Large italic left "S" as Type O 5 .. 48·00 22·00
   g. Left "S" inverted .. — 20·00
   h. Perf 12½ .. — 9·00
   i. Perf comp of 12 and 12½ .. — 17·00
   ia. Stamp doubly printed .. † £150
O60 **6** 3 ch. reddish violet (1933) .. 1·10 60
   a. "O" inverted .. 16·00 7·50
   b. Opt double .. † 80·00
O61 3 ch. violet (R.) (1934) .. 70 10
   a. Imperf between (horiz pair) .. 70·00 42·00
   b. Imperf between (vert pair) .. 60·00 40·00
   c. Opt inverted .. † 42·00
   d. "O" inverted .. 17·00 12·00
   e. Perf 12½ .. — 2·00
   ea. Imperf between (vert pair) .. † £140
   f. Perf comp of 12 and 12½ .. — 10·00
   fa. Imperf between (horiz pair) .. † £140
   g. "Ou" for "On" .. — 70·00
O62 **1** 4 ch. grey-green (1934) .. — £250
O63 4 ch. grey-green (R.) (1935?) .. 80 20
   a. "Ou" for "On" .. 50·00 40·00
O64 **7** 7 ch. claret (*shades*) .. 1·10 30
   a. Imperf between (vert pair) .. 27·00 35·00
   b. "O" inverted .. 40·00 19·00
   c. Left "S" inverted .. 40·00 19·00
   d. Perf 12½ .. — 6·50
   e. Perf comp of 12 and 12½ .. — 7·50
   ea. Imperf between (vert pair) .. † 85·00
   eb. Imperf between (vert strip of 3) .. £110 £110
O65 **8** 14 ch. orange (1933) .. 1·60 40
   a. Imperf between (horiz pair) .. 30·00 40·00
   b. Imperf between (vert pair) .. £110
   c. Opt inverted .. † £275

(c) New setting combining Type O 8 (18 mm high) in top row with Type O 6 (16 mm high) for remainder. Wmk C (dates?)
A. Type O 8.
O66A **1** 6 ca. brown-red .. 6·50 3·00
   a. Perf 12½ .. 6·50 3·00
O67A 1½ ch. rose .. 30·00 4·50
   a. Perf 12½ .. 38·00 7·50
O68A **6** 3 ch. violet (R.) .. 45·00 8·00
   a. Perf 12½ .. 55·00 16·00
   b. Perf compound of 12 and 12½ .. 80·00 19·00
O69A **1** 4 ch. grey-green (R.) .. 45·00 22·00
   a. Perf 12½ .. 45·00 16·00
O70A **8** 14 ch. orange-yellow .. 42·00 12·00
   a. Perf 12½ .. 45·00 12·00
B. Type O 6
O66Ba **1** 6 ca. brown-red (p 12½) .. 2·75 80
   ab. Imperf between (vert pair) .. 85·00 85·00
   ac. "O" inverted .. 16·00 8·50
   g. Perf comp of 12 and 12½ .. — 15·00
O67B 1½ ch. rose .. 7·50 35
   a. Perf 12½ .. 12·00 50
   ab. "O" inverted .. 42·00 16·00
   c. Perf comp of 12 and 12½ .. — 18·00
O68B **6** 3 ch. violet (R.) .. 80·00 80
   a. Perf 12½ .. 14·00 80
   b. Perf comp of 12 and 12½ .. 23·00 5·00
O69Ba **1** 4 ch. grey-green (R.) (p 12½) .. 6·50 2·25
   ab. Imperf between (horiz pair) .. † £150
   ac. "O" inverted .. 80·00 35·00
O70Ba **8** 14 ch. orange-yellow (p 12½) .. 10·00 75

Nos. O66/70A/B in vertical *se-tenant* pairs are very scarce. As with the postage issues it is believed that the 12½ and compound perforations were issued between 1937 and 1939.

1 ch

8 c **1 ch**
(O 9) Wrong fount "1 c" (R.6/7)

1932. *Official stamps surch as T 14 or with Type O 9. P 12.*
(a) With opt Type O 1 (i) Wmk A
O71 **4** 6 c. on 5 ca. olive-bistre .. 35·00 17·00
   a. "O" inverted .. £110 48·00
   b. Left "S" inverted .. £110 48·00
   c. Right "S" inverted .. £110 48·00
(ii) Wmk C
O72 **4** 6 c. on 5 ca. olive-bistre .. 18·00 6·50
   a. "O" inverted .. 48·00 17·00
   b. Left "S" inverted .. 48·00 17·00
   c. Right "S" inverted .. 48·00 17·00
O73 12 c. on 10 ca. pink .. £100
(b) With opt Type O 2. Wmk C
O74 **4** 6 c. on 5 ca. olive-bistre .. 1·60 1·00
   a. Opt and surch inverted .. 40·00
   b. Surch inverted .. 50·00
   c. Left "S" inverted .. 13·00 4·75
   d. Right "S" inverted .. 13·00 4·75
   e. "6" omitted .. — 75·00
O75 6 c. on 25 ca. chocolate .. 20 25
   a. Surch inverted .. 9·00 9·50
   b. Surch double .. 90·00
   c. Surch double, one inverted .. 90·00
   d. "O" inverted .. 4·00 4·00
   e. Left "S" inverted .. 4·00 4·00
   f. Pair, one without surch .. £200
O76 12 c. on 10 ca. pink .. 1·25 40
   a. Opt inverted .. 11·00 11·00
   b. Surch inverted .. 7·00 7·00
   c. Opt and surch inverted .. 28·00 28·00
   d. Pair, one without surch .. £250
   e. "O" inverted .. 6·50 3·25
   f. Left "S" inverted .. 5·00 2·50
   g. "Ou" for "On" .. 70·00 70·00
   h. Right "S" inverted .. 5·00 2·50
   i. "c" omitted (R. 6/1) .. 48·00 48·00
O77 **1** 1 ch. 8 c. on 1¼ ch. claret .. 2·00 90
   a. Surch inverted .. † 70·00
   b. "O" inverted .. 8·50 3·75
   c. Left "S" inverted .. 8·50 3·75
   d. Right "S" inverted .. 8·50 3·75
   e. Wrong fount "1 c" .. 23·00 17·00
(c) With opt Type O 3. Wmk C
O78 **4** 12 c. on 10 ca. pink .. † £300
O79 **1** 1 ch. 8 c. on 1¼ ch. carmine-rose .. 48·00 30·00
   a. "n" omitted .. £180
   b. Wrong fount "1 c" .. £170 £120
(d) With opt Type O 6. Wmk C
O80 **4** 12 c. on 10 ca. pink .. 80·00 18·00
O81 **1** 1 ch. 8 c. on 1¼ ch. carmine-rose .. 90·00 16·00
   a. Wrong fount "1 c" .. £225 70·00
   b. "h" omitted
   c. Brown-red .. — 16·00
(e) With opt Type O 7. Wmk C
O82 **4** 6 c. on 5 ca. chocolate .. 20 25
   a. Opt inverted .. 65·00 65·00
   b. Surch inverted .. 11·00 12·00
   c. Right "S" omitted .. 90·00 90·00
   d. Two quads for right "S" .. £450
   e. Right "S" inverted .. 22·00
O83 12 c. on 10 ca. pink .. 20 15
   a. Opt inverted .. 7·00 7·00
   b. Surch inverted .. 6·00 6·00
   c. Opt and surch inverted .. 30·00 30·00
   d. Opt double .. † 80·00
   e. "O" inverted .. 15·00 15·00
   f. Right "S" inverted .. 15·00 15·00
   g. "On" omitted .. — 85·00
   h. "n" omitted .. — 85·00
   i. "c" omitted (R. 6/1) .. 29·00 29·00
   j. Surch double .. † 80·00
O84 **1** 1 ch. 8 c. on 1¼ ch. claret .. 35 25
   a. Imperf between (vert pair) .. † £200
   b. Opt omitted .. † £375
   c. Surch inverted .. 14·00 14·00
   d. Surch double .. 60·00
   e. "O" inverted .. 4·50 2·75
   f. Wrong fount "1 c" .. 18·00 15·00

SERVICE **SERVICE** **SERVICE**
(O 10) (O 11) **8 CASH**
13 mm ("R" 13½ mm (O 12)
with curved ("R" with
tail) straight tail)

1939–41. *Nos. 35 and 40 with type-set opt, Type O 10. P 12½.*
O85 **1** 6 ca. brown-red (1941) .. 70 20
   a. Perf 11 .. 1·25 75
   b. Perf 12 .. 70 30
   c. Compound perf .. 70 1·10
O86 **5** ¾ ch. reddish violet .. 90·00 48·00
   a. Perf 12 .. 21·00 1·25
   b. Compound perf .. 85·00 48·00

1939 (9 Nov). *Maharaja's 27th Birthday. Nos. 64/70 with type-set opt, Type O 10. P 12½.*
O87 1 ch. yellow-green .. 3·75 25
O88 1½ ch. scarlet .. 3·75 75
   a. "SESVICE" .. 80·00 26·00
   b. Perf 12 .. 30·00 5·50
   ba. "SESVICE" .. — 95·00
   bb. Imperf between (horiz pair) .. † £130
   c. Compound perf .. 9·00 1·75

O89 2 ch. orange .. 3·75 4·25
   a. "SESVICE" .. 95·00 £110
   b. Compound perf .. 70·00 70·00
O90 3 ch. brown .. 3·00 20
   a. "SESVICE" .. 60·00 21·00
   b. Perf 12 .. 16·00 45
   ba. "SESVICE" .. £150 42·00
   c. Compound perf .. 7·00 2·75
O91 4 ch. red .. 7·50 3·00
O92 7 ch. pale blue .. 8·50 1·90
O93 14 ch. turquoise-green .. 11·00 3·00
O87/93 *Set of 7* 38·00 12·00

1940 (?)–45. *Nos. 40a and 42b optd with Type O 11 from stereos. P 12½.*
O94 **5** ¾ ch. reddish violet .. 10·00 20
   a. Imperf between (horiz pair) .. £100
   b. Perf 11 .. 50·00 1·10
   c. Perf 12 .. 15·00 20
   d. Compound perf .. 42·00 75
O95 **1** 1½ ch. rose (1945) .. 13·00 8·00
   a. Perf 12 .. 4·50 1·00
   b. Compound perf .. 18·00 12·00

1942 (?). *Nos. 64/70 optd with Type O 11 from stereos. P 12½.*
O 96 1 ch. yellow-green .. 75 10
   a. Imperf between (vert pair) .. 42·00 45·00
   b. Opt inverted .. † 38·00
   c. Opt double .. 21·00
   d. Perf 11 .. 60 10
   da. Imperf between (vert pair) .. 27·00
   db. Opt double .. 85·00 85·00
   e. Perf 12 .. 2·75 50
   ea. Imperf between (vert pair) .. 80·00 80·00
   eb. Stamp doubly printed .. £110
   ec. Opt inverted .. † 85·00
   ed. Opt double .. 23·00
   f. Compound perf .. 5·50 1·00
   fa. Imperf between (vert pair) .. † £110
O 97 1½ ch. scarlet .. 2·75 10
   a. Imperf between (horiz pair) .. 50·00
   b. Perf 11 .. 1·10 15
   ba. Imperf between (vert pair) .. 85·00 85·00
   bb. Imperf between (vert strip of 3) .. 65·00
   bc. Imperf between (horiz pair) .. † 90·00
   c. Perf 12 .. 4·25 50
   ca. Imperf between (vert strip of 3) .. £110
   d. Compound perf .. 2·00 30
   e. Imperf (pair) .. 26·00
O 98 2 ch. orange .. 1·00 30
   a. Perf 11 .. 6·50 1·00
   ab. Imperf between (vert pair)
   b. Perf 12 .. 70·00 70·00
   ba. Imperf between (vert pair) .. £275 £275
   c. Compound perf .. 70·00 70·00
O 99 3 ch. brown .. 60 10
   a. Imperf between (vert pair)
   b. Perf 11 .. 1·75 10
   c. Perf 12 .. 4·00 1·40
   ca. Imperf between (vert pair) .. £200 £200
   d. Compound perf .. 14·00 75
O100 4 ch. red .. 1·75 65
   a. Perf 11 .. 2·75 45
   b. Perf 12 .. 13·00 3·50
   c. Compound perf .. 55·00 20·00
O101 7 ch. pale blue .. 5·50 35
   a. Perf 11 .. 4·50 3·50
   b. Perf 12 .. 17·00 6·50
   c. Compound perf .. 14·00 4·50
   d. Blue (p 11) .. 8·50 4·00
   da. Imperf between (vert pair) .. 6·50 4·00
   db. Compound perf .. 21·00 14·00
O102 14 ch. turquoise-green .. 9·50 20
   a. Perf 11 .. 9·50 1·50
   b. Perf 12 .. 7·50 2·40
   c. Compound perf .. 48·00 6·00
O96/102 *Set of 7* 15·00 1·90

1942. *Maharaja's 29th Birthday. Nos 71/2 optd with Type O 11. P 12½.*
O103 6 ca. blackish violet .. 40 40
   a. Perf 11 .. 70 80
   b. Perf 12 .. 48·00 4·50
   c. Compound perf .. 1·50 1·00
O104 ¾ ch. brown .. 3·00 10
   a. Imperf between (vert pair) .. † £250
   b. Perf 11 .. 5·50 10
   c. Perf 12 .. 48·00 1·75
   d. Compound perf .. 6·50 85

1943. *Surch with Type O 12. P 12½.*
O105 **19** 8 ca. on 6 ca. scarlet .. 1·75 20
   a. Perf 11 .. 1·25 10
   ab. Surch inverted .. † £700
   b. Compound perf .. 5·50 1·25

1945. *Nos. 73/4 optd with Type O 11. P 12½.*
O106 2 ca. on 1½ ch. scarlet .. 50 50
   a. Perf 11 .. 45 15
   ab. Pair, one without surch .. £225
   b. Compound perf .. 70 1·00
   ba. "2" omitted .. £200 £100
   c. Perf 12
O107 4 ca. on ¾ ch. brown .. 2·25 30
   a. Perf 11 .. 1·25 20
   b. Compound perf .. 1·40 1·00

1947. *Maharaja's 34th Birthday. Optd with Type O 11. P 11.*
O108 **21** 8 ca. carmine .. 1·75 70
   a. Imperf between (horiz pair) .. 35·00
   ab. Imperf between (vert pair) .. † £120
   b. Opt double .. † £170
   c. Perf 12½ .. 3·50 1·00
   ca. Stamp doubly printed .. 30·00
   d. Perf 12 .. 3·50 1·40
   da. Stamp doubly printed .. 38·00

From 1 July 1949 Travancore formed part of the new State of Travancore-Cochin and stamps of Travancore surcharged in Indian currency were used.

TRAVANCORE-COCHIN

On 1 July 1949 the United State of Travancore and Cochin was formed ("U.S.T.C.") and the name was changed to State of Travancore-Cochin ("T.C.") by the new constitution of India on 26 January 1950.

> **PRICES FOR STAMPS ON COVER**
> Nos. 1/13   *from* × 8
> Nos. O1/17   *from* × 15

NO WATERMARK VARIETIES. These were formerly listed but we have now decided to omit them as they do not occur in full sheets. They are best collected in pairs, with and without watermarks.

COMPOUND PERFS. The notes above Type **17** of Travancore also apply here.

VALIDITY OF STAMPS. From 6 June 1950 the stamps of Travancore-Cochin were valid on mail from both Indian and state post offices to destinations in India and abroad.

ONE ANNA
ഒരണ
(1)

2 p. on 6 ca.

രണ്ട പൈെസ   രണ്ട രപൈെസ

Normal	1st character of 2nd group as 1st character of 1st group (Rt pane R.14/2)

1949 (1 July). *Stamps of Travancore surch in* "PIES" *or* "ANNAS" *as T* **1**. *P* 12½.

1	19	2 p. on 6 ca. blackish violet (R.)	2·00	90
		a. Surch inverted	32·00	
		b. Character error	£100	70·00
		c. "O" inverted	25·00	13·00
		d. Perf 11	1·25	20
		da. Imperf between (vert pair)	£110	£110
		db. Pair, one without surch	85·00	
		dc. Character error	95·00	70·00
		dd. "O" inverted	26·00	13·00
		e. Perf 12	40	20
		ea. Imperf between (horiz pair)	48·00	
		eb. Imperf between (vert pair)	5·00	13·00
		ec. Surch inverted	75·00	
		ed. Character error	£100	70·00
		ee. Imperf between (vert strip of 3)	32·00	
		ef. Block of four imperf between (horiz and vert)	45·00	
		eg. "O" inverted	26·00	13·00
		f. Perf 14	†	£400
		g. Imperf (pair)	8·50	
		h. Compound perf	—	30·00
2	21	4 p. on 8 ca. carmine	1·10	30
		a. Surch inverted	38·00	
		b. "S" inverted	75·00	38·00
		c. Perf 11	1·60	30
		ca. Imperf between (vert pair)	£120	£120
		cb. Surch inverted	75·00	
		cc. Pair, one without surch	90·00	
		cd. "FOUP" for "FOUR"	£120	85·00
		ce. "S" inverted	75·00	38·00
		d. Perf 12	45	30
		da. Imperf between (vert pair)	17·00	
		db. Pair, one without surch	85·00	
		dc. "FOUP" for "FOUR"	£100	80·00
		dd. "S" inverted	80·00	45·00
		de. Surch inverted	95·00	
		e. Imperf (pair)	70·00	
		f. Compound perf	—	30·00
		g. Perf 13½	†	£425
3	17	½ a. on 1 ch. yellow-green	2·50	30
		a. "NANA" for "ANNA" (Lt pane R.3/3)	£120	85·00
		b. Inverted "H" in "HALF"	—	75·00
		c. Imperf between (vert pair)	†	£100
		d. Perf 11	1·75	20
		da. Imperf between (vert pair)	26·00	
		db. Surch inverted	†	£140
		dc. "NANA" for "ANNA" (Lt pane R.3/3)	£140	95·00
		dd. Inverted "H" in "HALF"	—	80·00
		e. Perf 12	65	40
		ea. Imperf between (horiz pair)	38·00	42·00
		eb. Imperf between (vert pair)	4·50	11·00
		ec. Surch inverted	5·00	
		ed. "NANA" for "ANNA" (Lt pane R.3/3)	£160	£100
		ee. Block of four imperf between (horiz and vert)	42·00	
		f. Perf 14	†	£375
		g. Imperf (pair)	8·50	18·00
		h. Compound perf	—	28·00
4	18	1 a. on 2 ch. orange	2·75	30
		a. Perf 11	55	20
		ab. Surch double	50·00	
		b. Perf 12	2·75	50
		ba. Imperf between (horiz pair)	6·00	
		bb. Imperf between (vert pair)	4·25	11·00
		bc. Block of four imperf between (horiz and vert)	42·00	
		c. Perf 13½	£140	2·00
		d. Imperf (pair)	8·50	
		e. Compound perf	32·00	22·00
5	—	2 a. on 4 ch. red (68)	2·25	60
		a. Surch inverted	†	£200
		b. "O" inverted	30·00	16·00
		c. Perf 11	2·25	60
		ca. "O" inverted	—	18·00
		d. Perf 12	1·75	55
		da. "O" inverted	35·00	18·00
		e. Compound perf	35·00	26·00

6	18	3 a. on 7 ch. pale blue (69)	8·50	3·75
		a. Perf 11	4·50	2·00
		ab. *Blue*	48·00	4·50
		ac. "3" omitted	†	£400
		b. Perf 12	8·00	2·75
		c. Compound perf	—	48·00
		ca. *Blue*	—	65·00
7	—	6 a. on 14 ch. turquoise-green (70)	11·00	18·00
		a. Accent omitted from native surch (Rt pane R.13/4)	£180	£190
		b. Perf 11	9·00	16·00
		ba. Accent omitted from native surch (Rt pane R.13/4)	£180	£190
		c. Perf 12	11·00	17·00
		ca. Accent omitted from native surch (Rt pane R. 13/4)	£190	£200
		d. Compound perf	25·00	27·00
		da. Accent omitted from native surch (Rt pane R.13/4)	£275	
		e. Imperf (pair)		
1/7			*Set of 7*	15·50	17·50

There are two settings of the ½ a. surcharge. In one the first native character is under the second downstroke of the "H" and in the other it is under the first downstroke of the "A" of "HALF". They occur on stamps perf 12½, 11 and 12 equally commonly and also on the Official stamps.

U.S.T.C.   T.-C.   SIX PIES
(2)   (3)   (4)

1949. *No.* 106 *of Cochin optd with T* **2**.

8	29	1 a. orange	4·50	50·00
		a. No stop after "S" (R. 1/6)	70·00	
		b. Raised stop after "T" (R. 4/1)	70·00	

1950 (1 Apr). *No.* 106 *of Cochin optd with T* **3**.

9	29	1 a. orange	5·50	48·00
		a. No stop after "T"	50·00	
		b. Opt inverted	£190	
		ba. No stop after "T"	£1500	

The no stop variety occurs on No. 5 in the sheet and again on No. 8 in conjunction with a short hyphen.

1950 (1 Apr). *No.* 9 *surch as T* **4**.

10	29	6 p. on 1 a. orange	2·75	35·00
		a. No stop after "T" (R. 1/5)	17·00	
		b. Error. Surch on No. 8	25·00	
		ba. No stop after "S"	£200	
		bb. Raised stop after "T"	£200	
11		9 p. on 1 a. orange	2·00	30·00
		a. No stop after "T" (R. 1/5)	17·00	
		b. Error. Surch on No. 8	£160	
		ba. No stop after "S"	£600	
		bb. Raised stop after "T"	£600	

5 Conch or Chank Shell   6 Palm Trees

(Litho Indian Security Printing Press, Nasik)

1950 (24 Oct). *W* **69** *of India. P* 14.

12	5	2 p. rose-carmine	1·50	1·40
13	6	4 p. ultramarine	2·25	11·00

The ordinary issues of Travancore-Cochin became obsolete on 1 July 1951.

OFFICIAL STAMPS

VALIDITY. Travancore-Cochin official stamps were valid for use throughout India from 30 September 1950.

SERVICE   SERVICE
(O 1)   (O 2)

1949 (1 July)–**51**. *Stamps of Travancore surch with value as T* **1** *and optd* "SERVICE". *No gum. P* 12½. (a) *With Type* O **1**.

(i) *Wmk C of Travancore*

O 1	19	2 p. on 6 ca. blackish violet (R.)	1·00	20
		a. Imperf between (vert pair)	£120	£120
		b. Character error (Rt pane R. 14/2)	32·00	24·00
		c. "O" inverted	21·00	10·00
		d. Pair, one without surch	£110	
		e. Perf 11	70	20
		ea. Imperf between (vert pair)	£120	£120
		eb. Character error (Rt pane R. 14/2)	42·00	32·00
		ec. "O" inverted	21·00	12·00
		f. Perf 12	35	20
		fa. Imperf between (horiz pair)	7·50	17·00
		fb. Imperf between (vert pair)	6·00	
		fc. Character error (Rt pane R.14/2)	35·00	28·00
		fd. "O" inverted	21·00	
		fe. Block of four imperf between (horiz and vert)	25·00	42·00
		g. Imperf (pair)	8·50	18·00
		ga. Character error (Rt pane R. 14/2)	£170	

O 2	21	4 p. on 8 ca. carmine	2·00	55
		a. "FOUB" for "FOUR" (Lt pane R. 2/3)	£150	95·00
		b. Perf 11	1·90	30
		ba. "FOUB" for "FOUR" (Lt pane R. 2/3)	80·00	32·00
		c. Perf 12	1·90	55
		ca. "FOUB" for "FOUR" (Lt pane R. 2/3)	90·00	50·00
		d. Compound perf	17·00	17·00
O 3	17	½ a. on 1 ch. yellow-green	50	25
		a. Pair, one without surch	70·00	
		b. Surch inverted	24·00	
		c. "NANA" for "ANNA" (Lt pane R. 3/3)	£170	60·00
		d. Perf 11	1·00	25
		da. Pair, one without surch	£100	
		db. Surch inverted	55·00	
		dc. "NANA" for "ANNA" (Lt pane R. 3/3)	£160	70·00
		e. Perf 12	8·00	2·00
		ea. "NANA" for "ANNA" (Lt pane R. 3/3)	£300	£140
		eb. Pair, one without surch	90·00	
		ec. Surch inverted on back only	£180	
		f. Compound perf	—	21·00
O 4	18	1 a. on 2 ch. orange	16·00	5·00
		a. Surch inverted	85·00	
		b. Pair, one without surch	£475	
		c. Perf 11	14·00	7·50
O 5	—	2 a. on 4 ch. red (68)	1·00	60
		b. Perf 11	4·00	60
		ba. Surch inverted	£500	
		bb. "O" inverted	—	32·00
		c. Perf 12	4·75	3·75
		ca. "O" inverted	—	55·00
		cb. Pair, one without surch	£190	
		d. Compound perf	—	27·00
		e. Imperf (pair)	12·00	
O 6	—	3 a. on 7 ch. pale blue (69)	4·00	1·40
		a. Imperf between (vert pair)	17·00	
		b. *Blue*	30·00	5·50
		c. Perf 11	2·40	90
		ca. *Blue*	30·00	5·50
		d. Perf 12	2·50	3·50
		da. Imperf between (horiz pair)	15·00	
		db. Imperf between (vert pair)	8·00	
		dc. Block of four imperf between (horiz and vert)	35·00	
		dd. *Blue*	30·00	5·00
		e. Imperf (pair)	11·00	
O 7	—	6 a. on 14 ch. turquoise-green (70)	11·00	6·00
		a. Imperf between (vert pair)	27·00	
		b. Perf 11	9·50	5·00
		c. Perf 12	40·00	6·00
		ca. Imperf between (horiz pair)	24·00	
		cb. Imperf between (vert pair)	29·00	
		cc. Block of four imperf between (horiz and vert)	55·00	
		d. Imperf (pair)	14·00	
O1/7			*Set of 7*	27·00	11·00

(ii) *W* **27** *of Cochin*

O 8	19	2 p. on 6 ca. blackish violet (R.)	30	1·10
		a. Type O **1** double	18·00	
		b. Perf 11	75	1·25
		c. Perf 12	45	1·10
O 9	—	2 a. on 4 ch. red (68)	1·25	85
		a. Perf 11	60	65
		ab. Imperf between (vert pair)	£190	£190
		b. Compound perf	—	30·00

(b) *With Type* O **2**
(i) *Wmk C of Travancore*

O10	21	4 p. on 8 ca. carmine	30	20
		a. "FOUB" for "FOUR" (Lt pane R.2/3)	95·00	38·00
		b. 2nd "E" of "SERVICE" in wrong fount	—	48·00
		c. "S" in "PIES" inverted	—	50·00
		d. Imperf between (vert pair)	†	£100
		e. Perf 11	30	20
		ea. Imperf between (horiz pair)	4·50	
		eb. Imperf between (vert pair)	27·00	
		ec. "FOUB" for "FOUR" (Lt pane R.2/3)	90·00	32·00
		ed. 2nd "E" of "SERVICE" in wrong fount	£100	50·00
		ee. "S" in "PIES" inverted	—	55·00
		ef. Block of four imperf between (horiz and vert)	32·00	
		f. Perf 12	30	20
		fa. Imperf between (horiz pair)	4·00	
		fb. Imperf between (vert pair)	2·00	
		fc. Block of four imperf between (horiz and vert)	12·00	21·00
		fd. "FOUB" for "FOUR" (Lt pane R.2/3)	£110	40·00
		ff. 2nd "E" of "SERVICE" in wrong fount	95·00	48·00
		fg. "FOUK" for "FOUR"	†	£375
		g. Perf 13½	3·25	1·25
		h. Compound perf	8·00	8·00
		i. Imperf (pair)	6·00	
		ia. 2nd "E" of "SERVICE" in wrong fount	£130	
O11	17	½ a. on 1 ch. yellow-green	50	20
		a. "AANA" for "ANNA" (Rt pane R.13/1)	£140	60·00
		b. Perf 11	30	20
		ba. Imperf between (horiz pair)	55·00	55·00
		bb. Imperf between (vert pair)	8·00	
		bc. Block of four imperf between (horiz and vert)	48·00	
		bd. "AANA" for "ANNA" (Rt pane R.13/1)	75·00	40·00
		c. Perf 12	60	15
		ca. Imperf between (horiz pair)	3·50	
		cb. Imperf between (vert pair)	3·50	8·50
		cc. "AANA" for "ANNA" (Rt pane R.13/1)	90·00	55·00
		cd. Block of four imperf between (horiz and vert)	23·00	
		d. Compound perf	20·00	15·00
		da. "AANA" for "ANNA" (Rt pane R.13/1)	—	£160
		e. Imperf (pair)	6·00	15·00

O12	**18**	1 a. on 2 ch. orange	.. ..	40	30
		a. Imperf between (vert pair)	..	†	£110
		ab. Imperf between (horiz pair)	..	†	£110
		b. Perf 11	.. ..	2·25	50
		ba. Imperf between (horiz pair)	..	6·00	15·00
		bb. Imperf between (vert pair)	..	70·00	70·00
		c. Perf 12	.. ..	40	20
		ca. Imperf between (horiz pair)	..	6·00	
		cb. Imperf between (vert pair)	..	3·50	9·00
		cc. Block of four imperf between (horiz and vert)	..	20·00	
		d. Compound perf	.. ..	24·00	16·00
		e. Imperf (pair)	..	14·00	
O13	–	2 a. on 4 ch. red (68)	..	2·50	80
		a. "O" inverted (Lt pane R. 14/3)		60·00	35·00
		b. Perf 11	.. ..	1·50	1·10
		ba. "O" inverted (Lt pane R. 14/3)		50·00	35·00
		c. Perf 12	.. ..	7·50	1·10
		ca. Imperf between (vert pair)	..	£120	£130
		cb. "O" inverted (Lt pane R. 14/3)		95·00	35·00
		d. Compound perf	..	23·00	13·00
O14	–	3 a. on 7 ch. pale blue (69)	..	5·50	1·10
		a. "S" inverted in "SERVICE" (Lt pane R.6/3)		75·00	32·00
		b. First "E" inverted (Lt pane R.7/4)		£170	£130
		c. "C" inverted (Lt pane R.4/1 and 5/1)		90·00	75·00
		d. Second "E" inverted (Lt pane R.3/2)		£160	£120
		e. Perf 11	.. ..	1·50	1·10
		ea. "S" inverted in "SERVICE" (Lt pane R.6/3)		50·00	32·00
		f. Perf 12	.. ..	3·75	1·60
		fa. "S" inverted in "SERVICE" (Lt pane R.6/3)		£130	80·00
		g. Compound perf	..	—	40·00
		h. Imperf (pair)	..	38·00	
O15	–	6 a. on 14 ch. turquoise-green (70)	..	1·50	3·25
		a. Accent omitted from native surch		16·00	13·00
		b. "S" inverted in "SERVICE" (Lt pane R.6/3)		70·00	42·00
		c. Perf 11	.. ..	11·00	3·25
		ca. Accent omitted from native surch		60·00	22·00
		cb. "S" inverted in "SERVICE" (Lt pane R.6/3)		£130	50·00
		d. Perf 12	.. ..	42·00	4·50
		da. Accent omitted from native surch		£130	30·00
		db. "S" inverted in "SERVICE" (Lt pane R.6/3)		£275	65·00
		e. Compound perf	..	70·00	70·00
O10/15			*Set of 6*	5·00	5·00

(ii) W 27 of Cochin

O16	**17**	½ a. on 1 ch. yellow-green	..	1·25	65
		a. Perf 11	.. ..	40	35
		b. Perf 12	.. ..	17·00	8·50
		c. Compound perf	..	11·00	3·00
O17	**18**	1 a. on 2 ch. orange	..	65	65
		a. Perf 11	.. ..	50	40
		b. Perf 12	.. ..	11·00	4·00
		c. Perf 13½	.. ..	2·00	1·00
		d. Compound perf	..	5·00	3·00

Nos. O2, O10, O12 and O17 have the value at top in English and at bottom in native characters with "SERVICE" in between. All others have "SERVICE" below the surcharge.

Type O **2** was overprinted at one operation with the surcharges.

Nos. O10b, O10ed, O10ff and O10ia, show the second "E" of "SERVICE" with serifs matching those on the surcharge.

The "accent omitted" varieties on No. O15 occur on Left pane R. 5/1, 11/4 and Right pane R. 1/4, 12/4, 14/1 and 13/4.

The Official stamps became obsolete in September 1951.

WADHWAN

PRICES FOR STAMPS ON COVER	
No. 1	*from* × 30
No. 2	—
Nos. 3/6	*from* × 30

Thakur Bal Singh, 1885–1910

1

1888–94. *Litho.* (a) *Thin toned wove paper*

1	1	1½ pice, black (I, III) (p 12½ *large holes*)	..	14·00	48·00
		a. Imperf between (vert pair) (I)	..		
		b. Pin-perf 6½ irregular (I)		85·00	
		c. Compound of 12½ and pin-perf 6½ (I)		£150	
2		½ pice, black (II). (p 12½ *irregular small holes*)	..	32·00	

(b) *Medium toned wove paper*

3	1	1½ pice, black (III) (p 12½)	..	8·50	38·00
4		½ pice, black (V) (p 12)	..	7·50	8·50

(c) *Thick off-white or toned wove paper*

5	1	1½ pice, black (IV, VI) (p 12) (7.92)		6·00	7·00
		a. Perf compound of 12 and 11 (IV)		15·00	38·00
6		½ pice, black (VII) (*fine impression*) (p 12) (1894)		6·50	20·00

Sheets from the Stone IV printing had at least one horizontal line of perforations gauging 11, normally between the bottom two rows of the sheet.

These stamps were lithographed from seven different stones taken from a single die. Brief details of the individual stones are as follows:

Stone I – No. 1. Sheet size not known, but possibly 28 (4×7). Sheet margins imperforate

Stone II – No. 2. Sheets of 42 (7×6) with imperforate margins

Stone III – Nos. 1 (thin paper) and 3 (medium paper). Sheets of 40 (4×10) with imperforate margins

Stone IV – Nos. 5/a. Sheets of 32 (4×8) with imperforate margins at top and right

Stone V – No. 4. Sheets of 20 (4×5) with imperforate margins at top, right and bottom

Stone VI – No. 5. Sheets of 30 (5×6) with all margins perforated

Stone VII – No. 6. Sheets of 32 (4×8) with all margins perforated. Much finer impression than the other stones

Stamps from stones I and II come with or without the dot before "STATE". Those from the later stones always show the dot. The shading on the pennant above the shield can also be used in stone identification. Stamps from stones I to III show heavy shading on the pennant, but this is less evident on stone IV and reduced further to a short line or dot on stones V to VII. There is a ")" hairline after "HALF" on the majority of stamps from Stone III.

The stamps of Wadhwan became obsolete on 1 January 1895.

Ionian Islands

The British occupation of the Ionian Islands was completed in 1814 and the archipelago was placed under the protection of Great Britain by the Treaty of Paris of 9 November 1815. The United States of the Ionian Islands were given local self-government, which included responsibility for the postal services. Crowned-circle handstamps were, however, supplied in 1844, although it is believed these were intended for use on prepaid mail to foreign destinations.

Examples of the Great Britain 1855 1d. red-brown stamp are known used at Corfu, cancelled as No. CC2, but it is believed that these originate from mail sent by the British garrison.

For illustrations of the handstamp types see BRITISH POST OFFICES ABROAD notes, following GREAT BRITAIN.

CEPHALONIA
CROWNED-CIRCLE HANDSTAMPS
CC1 CC 1 CEPHALONIA (19.4.1844) .. Price on cover £1000

CORFU
CROWNED-CIRCLE HANDSTAMPS
CC2 CC 1 CORFU (19.4.1844) .. .. Price on cover £500
CC3 CC 1 CORFU (G. or B.) (1844) .. Price on cover —

ZANTE
CROWNED-CIRCLE HANDSTAMPS
CC4 CC 1 ZANTE (G. or B.) (19.4.1844) .. Price on cover £1000
Nos. CC1/2 were later, circa 1860/1, struck in green (Cephalonia) or red (Corfu).

It is believed that examples of No. CC4 in black are from an unauthorised use of this handstamp which is now on display in the local museum. A similar handstamp, but without "PAID AT" was introduced in 1861.

PRICES FOR STAMPS ON COVER
Nos. 1/3   from × 10

PERKINS BACON "CANCELLED". For notes on these handstamps, showing "CANCELLED" between horizontal bars forming an oval, see Catalogue Introduction.

1

(Eng. C. Jeens. Recess Perkins, Bacon & Co)
1859 (15 June). Imperf.
1 1 (½d.) orge (no wmk) (H/S "CANCELLED" in oval £5000) .. .. 80·00 £500
2 (1d.) blue (wmk "2") (H/S "CANCELLED" in oval £5000) .. .. 20·00 £180
3 (2d.) carm (wmk "1") (H/S "CANCELLED" in oval £4500) .. .. 15·00 £180

On 30 May 1864, the islands were ceded to Greece, and these stamps became obsolete.
Great care should be exercised in buying used stamps, on or off cover, as forged postmarks are plentiful.

Iraq

Indian post offices were opened at Baghdad and Basra, then part of the Turkish Empire, on 1 January 1868. Unoverprinted stamps of India were used, Baghdad being allocated numeral cancellations "356", "18" and "K-6", and Basra (also spelt Bussorah, Busreh, Busrah, Busra) "357", "19" and "1/K-6". Both offices closed on 30 September 1914, but Basra re-opened the following month when Indian stamps overprinted "I.E.F." were used.

(Currency. 16 annas = 1 rupee)

I. ISSUES FOR BAGHDAD

PRICES FOR STAMPS ON COVER
Nos 1/25   from × 6

BRITISH OCCUPATION
British and Indian troops occupied the port of Basra on 22 November 1914 to protect the oil pipeline. They then advanced up the rivers, and after a hard campaign took Baghdad from the Turks on 11 March 1917.

IN BRITISH **BAGHDAD** OCCUPATION
2 Ans
(1)

1917 (1 Sept). Stamps of Turkey, surch as T 1 in three operations.
(a) Pictorial designs of 1914. T 32, etc., and 31
1 32 ¼ a. on 2 pa. claret (Obelisk) .. 95·00 £110
2 34 ¼ a. on 5 pa. dull purple (Leander's Tower) 70·00 75·00
3 36 ½ a. on 10 pa. green (Lighthouse garden) .. £550 £600
4 31 ½ a. on 10 pa. green (Mosque of Selim) .. £850 £1000
5 37 1 a. on 20 pa. red (Castle) .. £325 £350
   a. "IN BRITISH" omitted £5000
   a. Value omitted £4750
   b. "OCCUPATION" double £1300
6 38 2 a. on 1 pi. bright blue (Mosque) .. £120 £150
(b) As (a), but overprinted with small five-pointed Star
7 37 1 a. on 20 pa. red (B.) .. £170 £190
   a. "OCCUPATION" omitted £4250
   b. "BAGHDAD" omitted £1300
8 38 2 a. on 1 pi. bright blue (R.) .. £2250 £3000
(c) Postal Jubilee stamps (Old G.P.O.). P 12½
9 60 ½ a. on 10 pa. carmine .. £300 £325
   a. Perf 13½ £650 £700
10 1 a. on 20 pa. blue .. £3000
   a. Value omitted £6000
   b. Perf 13½ £700 £850
11 2 a. on 1 pi. black and violet .. £140 £150
   a. "BAGHDAD" omitted £4250
   b. Perf 13½ 70·00 80·00
(d) T 30 (G.P.O., Constantinople) with opt T 26.
12 30 2 a. on 1 pi. ultramarine .. £275 £400
   a. "IN BRITISH" omitted £5500
(e) Stamps optd with six-pointed Star and Arabic date "1331" within Crescent. T 53 (except No. 16, which has five-pointed Star and Arabic "1332", T 57)
13 30 ½ a. on 10 pa. green (R.) .. 70·00 75·00
14 1 a. on 20 pa. rose .. £300 £325
   a. Value omitted £3750 £3750
   b. Optd with T 26 (Arabic letter "B") also .. £4250 £4250
15 23 1 a. on 20 pa. rose (No. 554a) .. £350 £375
   a. Value omitted £5500
16 21 1 a. on 20 pa. carmine (No. 732) .. £2750 £3500
17 30 2 a. on 1 pi. ultramarine (R.) .. 80·00 95·00
   a. "BAGHDAD" omitted † —
18 21 2 a. on 1 pi. dull blue (No. 543) (R.) .. £130 £140
   a. "OCCUPATION" omitted £5500
(f) Stamps with similar opt, but date between Star and Crescent (Nos. 19 and 22, T 54; others T 55, five-pointed Star)
19 23 ½ a. on 10 pa. grey-green (No. 609a) (R.) 85·00 90·00
   a. "OCCUPATION" omitted £4500
20 60 ½ a. on 10 pa. carmine (p 12½) (B.) .. £120 £130
   a. Perf 13½ £250 £275
21 30 1 a. on 20 pa. rose .. 80·00 £100
22 28 1 a. on 20 pa. rose (Plate II) (No. 617) .. £300 £350
23 15 1 a. on 10 pa. on 20 pa. claret (No. 630) .. £150 £150
   a. "OCCUPATION" omitted £4750 £4750
24 30 2 a. on 1 pi. ultramarine (R.) .. £130 £140
   a. "OCCUPATION" omitted £4750
   b. "BAGHDAD" omitted £4750
25 28 2 a. on 1 pi. ultramarine (Pl. II) (No. 645) £1100 £1300
The last group (f) have the Crescent obliterated by hand in violet-black ink, as this included the inscription, "Tax for the relief of children of martyrs".

II. ISSUES FOR MOSUL

PRICES FOR STAMPS ON COVER
Nos. 1/8   from × 40

BRITISH OCCUPATION
A British and Indian force occupied Mosul on 1 November 1918.
As the status of the vilayet was disputed stocks of "IRAQ IN BRITISH OCCUPATION" surcharges were withdrawn in early 1919 and replaced by Nos. 1/8.

POSTAGE

I.E.F. 'D'

1 Anna   4 4
(1)   I II

Two types of tougra in central design:
(a) Large "tougra" or sign-manual of El Ghazi 7 mm high.
(b) Smaller "tougra" of Sultan Rechad 5½ mm high.

Two types of 4 a. surcharge:
I. Normal "4". Apostrophes on D 3½ mm apart.
II. Small "4". Apostrophes on D 4½ mm apart.

1919 (28 Jan). Turkish Fiscal stamps surch as T 1 by Govt Press, Baghdad. P 11½ (½ a.), 12 (1 a.), or 12½ (others).
1 ½ a. on 1 pi. green and red .. 1·60 1·60
2 1 a. on 20 pa. black/red (a) .. 1·40 1·75
   a. Imperf between (horiz pair) .. £600
   b. Surch double .. £600
   c. "A" of "Anna" omitted .. £200
3 1 a. on 20 pa. black/red (b) .. 4·00 3·00
   b. Surch double .. £600
4 2½ a. on 1 pi. mauve and yellow (b) .. 1·50 1·50
   a. No bar to fraction (R. 2/4) .. 28·00 40·00
   b. Surch double .. £650
5 3 a. on 20 pa. green (a) .. 1·60 3·25
6 3 a. on 20 pa. green and orange (b) .. 32·00 50·00
7 4 a. on 1 pi. deep violet (a) (I) .. 3·00 3·50
   a. "4" omitted .. £1400
   c. Surch double .. £800
7d 4 a. on 1 pi. deep violet (a) (II) .. 8·00 10·00
   da. Surch double, one with "4" omitted .. £2250

---

8 8 a. on 10 pa. lake (a) .. 4·00 5·00
   a. Surch inverted .. £600 £700
   b. Surch double .. £500 £600
   c. No apostrophe after "D" (R. 1/5) 24·00 35·00
   d. Surch inverted. No apostrophe after "D"
   e. "na" of "Anna" omitted .. £250
   f. Error. 8 a. on 1 pi. deep violet .. £1700
No. 4a occurs on some sheets only. No. 8c comes from the first setting only.
Nos. 1/8 were replaced by "IRAQ IN BRITISH OCCUPATION" surcharges during 1921.

In December 1925 the League of Nations awarded the vilayet of Mosul to Iraq.

III. ISSUES FOR IRAQ

PRICES FOR STAMPS ON COVER
Nos. 1/18   from × 4
Nos. 41/154   from × 2
Nos. O19/171   from × 2

BRITISH OCCUPATION

IN BRITISH **IRAQ** OCCUPATION
1 An.
(1)

A   B

1918 (1 Sept)–**21**. Turkish pictorial issue of 1914, surch as T 1 by Bradbury Wilkinson. P 12.
(a) No wmk. Tougra as A (1 Sept 1918–20)
1 34 ¼ a. on 5 pa. dull purple .. 30 80
2 36 ½ a. on 10 pa. green .. 30 15
3 37 1 a. on 20 pa. red .. 30 10
4 34 1½ a. on 5 pa. dull purple (1920) .. 3·00 50
5 38 2½ a. on 1 pi. bright blue .. 90 1·25
   a. Surch inverted .. £3500
6 39 3 a. on 1½ pi. grey and rose .. 80 25
   a. Surch double (Bk. + R.) .. £1500 £2250
7 40 4 a. on 1¾ pi. red-brown and grey .. 80 25
   a. Centre inverted .. †£15000
8 41 6 a. on 2 pi. black and green .. 1·60 1·25
9 42 8 a. on 2½ pi. green and orange .. 90 60
   a. Surch inverted .. † £9000
10 43 12 a. on 5 pi. deep lilac .. 1·75 3·00
11 44 1 r. on 10 pi. red-brown .. 2·25 1·40
12 45 2 r. on 25 pi. yellow-green .. 7·50 2·50
13 46 5 r. on 50 pi. rose .. 20·00 20·00
14 47 10 r. on 100 pi. indigo .. 48·00 17·00
1/14   Set of 14 75·00 42·00
1/3, 5/14 Perf "Specimen" .. Set of 13 £250
(b) No wmk. Tougra as B (one device instead of two) (1921)
15 44 1 r. on 10 pi. red-brown .. £100 24·00
(c) Wmk Mult Script CA (sideways on ½ a., 1½ a.) (1921)
16 36 ½ a. on 10 pa. green .. 1·00 1·40
17 34 1½ a. on 5 pa. dull purple .. 1·00 95
18 45 2 r. on 25 pi. yellow-green .. 13·00 11·00
16/18   Set of 3 13·50 12·00
16/18 Optd "Specimen" .. Set of 3 50·00
Designs: Horiz—5 pa. Leander's Tower; 10 pa. Lighthouse-garden, Stamboul; 20 pa. Castle of Europe; 1 pi. Mosque of Sultan Ahmed; 1½ pi. Martyrs of Liberty Monument; 1¾ pi. Fountains of Suleiman; 2 pi. Cruiser Hamidiye; 2½ pi. Candilli, Bosphorus; 5 pi. Former Ministry of War; 10 pi. Sweet Waters of Europe; 25 pi. Suleiman Mosque; 50 pi. Bosphorus at Rumeli Hisar; 100 pi. Sultan Ahmed's Fountain.
The original settings of Nos. 1/18 showed the surcharge 27 mm wide, except for the 2½ a. (24 mm), 4 a. (26½ mm), 6 a. (32 mm), 8 a. (30½ mm), 12 a. (33 mm), 1 r. (31½ mm), 2 r. (30 mm) and 5 r. (32 mm). The 6 a., 8 a. and 5 r. also exist from a subsequent setting on which the surcharge was 27½ mm wide.
Nos. 2, 3, 5, 6 and 7/9 are known bisected and used on philatelic covers. All such covers have Makinah or F.P.O. 339 cancellations.
During January 1923 an outbreak of cholera in Baghdad led to the temporary use for postal purposes of the above issue overprinted "REVENUE".

LEAGUE OF NATIONS MANDATE

On 25 April 1920 the Supreme Council of the Allies assigned to the United Kingdom a mandate under the League of Nations to administer Iraq.
The Emir Faisal, King of Syria in 1920, was proclaimed King of Iraq on 23 August 1921.

King Faisal I
23 August 1921–8 September 1933

2 Sunni Mosque, Muadhdham   3 Winged Cherub

4 Allegory of Date Palm

(Des Miss Edith Cheesman (½ a., 1 a., 4 a., 6 a., 8 a., 2 r., 5 r., 10 r.), Mrs. C. Garbett (Miss M. Maynard) (others). Typo (1 r.) or recess (others) Bradbury, Wilkinson)

1923 (1 June)–25. *T 2/4 and similar designs. Wmk Mult Script CA (sideways on 2 a., 4 a., 8 a., 5 r.). P 12.*

41	2	½ a. olive-green	..	60	10
42	–	1 a. brown	..	1·00	10
43	3	1½ a. lake	..	50	10
44	–	2 a. orange-buff	..	50	10
45	–	3 a. grey-blue (1923)	..	85	15
46	–	4 a. violet	..	1·75	30
47	–	6 a. greenish blue	..	1·00	30
48	–	8 a. olive-bistre	..	2·00	30
49	4	1 r. brown and blue-green	..	3·00	1·00
50	2	2 r. black	..	12·00	7·00
51	–	2 r. olive-bistre (1925)	..	30·00	3·25
52	–	5 r. orange	..	26·00	13·00
53	–	10 r. lake	..	32·00	20·00
41/53			*Set of 13*	95·00	40·00
41/53 Optd "Specimen"			*Set of 13*	£225	

Designs: *Horiz (as T 2)*—1 a. Gufas on the Tigris. (30×24 mm) —2 a. Bull from Babylonian wall-sculpture, 6 a., 10 r. Shiah Mosque, Kadhimain. (34×24 mm)—3 a. Arch of Ctesiphon. *Vert (as T 3)*—4 a., 8 a., 5 r. Tribal Standard, Dulaim Camel Corps.
  With the exception of Nos. 49 and 50, later printings of these stamps and of No. 78 are on a thinner paper.

10	11	12

King Faisal I

(Recess Bradbury, Wilkinson)

1927 (1 Apr). *Wmk Mult Script CA. P 12.*

78	10	1 r. red-brown (Optd S. £30)	..	6·00	50

See note below No. 53.

(Recess Bradbury Wilkinson)

1931 (17 Feb). *Wmk Mult Script CA (sideways on 1 r. to 25 r.). P 12.*

80	11	½ a. green	..	80	10
81	–	1 a. red-brown	..	90	10
82	–	1½ a. scarlet	..	80	30
83	–	2 a. orange	..	80	10
84	–	3 a. blue	..	80	10
85	–	4 a. slate-purple	..	1·25	1·10
86	–	6 a. greenish blue	..	1·25	60
87	–	8 a. deep green	..	1·25	1·75
88	12	1 r. chocolate	..	3·00	1·25
89	–	2 r. yellow-brown	..	5·50	4·00
90	–	5 r. orange	..	18·00	30·00
91	–	10 r. scarlet	..	50·00	70·00
92	–	25 r. violet	..	£500	£650
80/91			*Set of 12*	75·00	95·00
80/92 Perf "Specimen"			*Set of 13*	£500	

(New Currency. 1000 fils = 1 dinar)

(13)	(14)

Normal "SIN"	Error "SAD" (R. 8/16 of second setting)

(Surcharged at Govt Ptg Wks, Baghdad)

1932 (1 Apr). *Nos. 80/92 and 46 surch in "Fils" or "Dinar" as T 13 or 14.*

106	11	2 f. on ½ a. green (R.)	..	20	10
107	–	3 f. on ½ a. green	..	20	10
		a. Surch double	..	£140	
		b. Surch inverted	..	£140	
		c. Arabic letter "SAD" instead of "SIN"	..	20·00	20·00
108	–	4 f. on 1 a. red-brown (G.)	..	1·75	25
109	–	5 f. on 1 a. red-brown	..	40	10
		a. Inverted Arabic "5" (R. 8/11)	..	27·00	32·00
		b. Surch inverted	..	£250	
110	–	8 f. on 1½ a. scarlet	..	35	30
		a. Surch inverted	..	£140	
111	–	10 f. on 2 a. orange	..	35	10
		a. Inverted Arabic "1" (R. 8/13)	..	18·00	18·00
		b. No space between "10" and "Fils"	..	35	10
112	–	15 f. on 3 a. blue	..	85	1·00
113	–	20 f. on 4 a. slate-purple	..	1·25	1·25
		a. Surch inverted	..	£250	

114	–	25 f. on 4 a. violet (No. 46)	..	1·75	3·00
		a. "Flis" for "Fils" (R. 2/1, 10/8, 10/15)	..	£300	£350
		b. Inverted Arabic "5" (R. 10/7, 10/14)	..	£350	£450
		c. Vars a and b in *se-tenant* pair	..	£700	
		d. Error. 20 f. on 4 a. violet (R. 10/1, 10/9)	..	£1200	
115	11	30 f. on 6 a. greenish blue	..	1·50	60
		a. Error. 80 f. on 6 a. greenish blue	..	£1000	
116	–	40 f. on 8 a. deep green	..	2·25	2·50
117	12	75 f. on 1 r. chocolate	..	1·75	2·50
		a. Inverted Arabic "5"	..	30·00	38·00
118	–	100 f. on 2 r. yellow-brown	..	5·50	3·75
119	–	200 f. on 5 r. orange	..	11·00	17·00
120	–	½ d. on 10 r. scarlet	..	£600	£650
		a. No bar in English "½"	..	48·00	75·00
		b. Scarlet-vermilion	..	£600	£130
121	10	1 d. on 25 r. violet	..	80·00	£130
106/121			*Set of 16*	£130	£200

Nos. 106/13 and 115/16 were in sheets of 160 (16×10), No. 114 sheets of 150 (15×10) and Nos. 117/121 sheets of 100 (10×10). There were three settings of the surcharge for the 3 f. and two settings for the 5, 10, 25, 40, 100 and 200 f. Nos. 109a and 111a come from the first setting and Nos. 107c, 111b and 114a/b come from the second.
  No. 109a can be easily identified as it shows the point of the Arabic numeral at the foot of the surcharge.
  All 10 f. stamps from the second setting are as No. 111b except for R. 4/7–8 and 15–16 where the spacing is the same as for the first setting (Type 13).
  No. 114d shows "20" instead of "25". Many examples of this error were removed from the sheets before issue. The Arabic value "25" was unaltered.
  No. 115a shows the error in the English face value only.
  No. 117a occurs on R. 1/2, 1/7 and a third position in the first vertical row not yet identified.
  No. 120a occurs on R. 10/1, one position in the first horizontal row and another in the second.
  No. 120b was a special printing of No. 91 which does not exist unsurcharged.

15

1932 (9 May). *T 10 to 12, but with values altered to "FILS" or "DINAR" as in T 15. Wmk Mult Script CA (sideways on 50 f. to 1 d.). P 12.*

138	11	2 f. ultramarine	..	40	10
139	–	3 f. green	..	40	10
140	–	4 f. brown-purple	..	40	10
141	–	5 f. grey-green	..	50	10
142	–	8 f. scarlet	..	1·00	10
143	–	10 f. yellow	..	1·00	10
144	–	15 f. blue	..	1·00	10
145	–	20 f. orange	..	1·00	40
146	–	25 f. mauve	..	1·00	10
147	–	30 f. bronze-green	..	1·75	15
148	–	40 f. violet	..	1·00	10
149	12	50 f. brown	..	1·00	20
150	–	75 f. dull ultramarine	..	2·00	2·00
151	–	100 f. deep green	..	3·50	70
152	–	200 f. scarlet	..	12·00	3·25
153	10	½ d. deep blue	..	35·00	32·00
154	–	1 d. claret	..	65·00	65·00
138/154			*Set of 17*	£110	95·00
138/54 Perf "Specimen"			*Set of 17*	£180	

OFFICIAL STAMPS

ON STATE SERVICE

(O 2)

1920 (1 May)–23. *As Nos. 1/18, but surch includes additional wording "ON STATE SERVICE" as Type O 2 in black.*

(a) No wmk. Tougra as A (1920)

O19	36	½ a. on 10 pa. blue-green	..	3·75	1·00
O20	37	1 a. on 20 pa. red	..	1·50	60
O21	34	1½ a. on 5 pa. purple-brown	..	8·50	2·00
O22	38	2½ a. on 1 pi. blue.	..	1·75	2·25
O23	39	4 a. on 1½ pi. black and rose	..	9·00	80
O24	40	4 a. on 1¾ pi. red-brown and grey-blue	..	11·00	2·50
O25	41	8 a. on 2 pi. black and green	..	12·00	4·75
O26	42	8 a. on 2½ pi. yellow-green & orge-brn	..	11·00	2·75
O27	43	1 r. on 5 pi. purple	..	8·50	4·75
O28	44	1 r. on 10 pi. red-brown	..	9·00	4·25
O29	45	2 r. on 25 pi. olive-green	..	18·00	10·00
O30	46	5 r. on 50 pi. rose-carmine	..	32·00	23·00
O31	47	10 r. on 100 pi. slate-blue	..	50·00	65·00
O19/31			*Set of 13*	£160	£110

(b) No wmk. Tougra as B (No. 15) (1922)

O32	44	1 r. on 10 pi. red-brown..	..	20·00	7·00

(c) Wmk Mult Script CA (sideways on ½ a. to 8 a.) (1921–23)

O33	36	½ a. on 10 pa. green	..	80	80
O34	37	1 a. on 20 pa. red	..	2·00	80
O35	34	1½ a. on 5 pa. purple-brown	..	2·00	55
O36	40	4 a. on 1¾ pi. red-brown and grey-blue	..	2·00	1·00
O37	41	6 a. on 2 pi. black and green (10.3.23)	..	11·00	70·00
O38	42	8 a. on 2½ pi. yellow-green & orge-brn	..	3·00	2·00
O39	43	12 a. on 5 pi. purple (10.3.23)	..	14·00	55·00
O40	45	2 r. on 25 pi. olive-green (10.3.23)	..	45·00	70·00
O33/40			*Set of 8*	70·00	£180
O33/40 Optd "Specimen"..			*Set of 8*	£120	

Nos. O25/6, O30 and O37/8 only exist from the setting with the surcharge 27½ mm wide.

ON		
	STATE	
ON STATE SERVICE		SERVICE
(O 6)		(O 7)

1923. *Optd with Types O 6 (horiz designs) or O 7 (vert designs).*

O54	2	½ a. olive-green	..	90	40
O55	–	1 a. brown	..	90	10

O56	3	1½ a. lake	..	1·75	60
O57	–	2 a. orange-buff	..	1·75	20
O58	–	3 a. grey-blue	..	2·50	85
O59	–	4 a. violet	..	3·50	50
O60	–	6 a. greenish blue	..	3·75	1·25
O61	–	8 a. olive-bistre	..	4·00	1·75
O62	4	1 r. brown and blue-green	..	6·00	1·25
O63	2	2 r. black (R.)	..	20·00	8·00
O64	–	5 r. orange	..	48·00	26·00
O65	–	10 r. lake	..	70·00	48·00
O54/65			*Set of 12*	£140	80·00
O54/65 Optd "Specimen"			*Set of 12*	£200	

ON STATE SERVICE / ON STATE SERVICE

(O 8)   (O 9)

1924–25. *Optd with Types O 8 (horiz designs) or O 9 (vert designs).*

O66	2	½ a. olive-green	..	85	10
O67	–	1 a. brown	..	60	10
O68	3	1½ a. lake	..	70	20
O69	–	2 a. orange-buff	..	1·00	10
O70	–	3 a. grey-blue	..	1·25	10
O71	–	4 a. violet	..	3·25	30
O72	–	6 a. greenish blue	..	1·75	20
O73	–	8 a. olive-bistre	..	2·50	35
O74	4	1 r. brown and blue-green	..	9·50	1·00
O75	2	2 r. olive-bistre (1925)	..	27·00	3·75
O76	–	5 r. orange	..	45·00	42·00
O77	–	10 r. lake	..	65·00	42·00
O66/77			*Set of 12*	£140	80·00
O66/77 Optd "Specimen"			*Set of 12*	£200	

1927 (1 Apr). *Optd with Type O 9.*

O79	10	1 r. red-brown (Optd S. £30)	..	5·50	1·75

ON STATE SERVICE

ON STATE SERVICE / رسمي

(O 12)   (O 13)

1931. *Optd. (a) As Type O 12.*

O 93	11	½ a. green	..	50	2·75
O 94	–	1 a. red-brown	..	70	10
O 95	–	1½ a. scarlet	..	4·50	17·00
O 96	–	2 a. orange	..	70	10
O 97	–	3 a. blue	..	85	85
O 98	–	4 a. slate-purple	..	95	1·00
O 99	–	6 a. greenish blue	..	4·00	15·00
O100	–	8 a. deep green	..	4·00	15·00

(b) As Type O 13, horizontally

O101	12	1 r. chocolate	..	13·00	14·00
O102	–	2 r. yellow-brown	..	20·00	50·00
O103	–	5 r. orange	..	40·00	90·00
O104	–	10 r. scarlet	..	70·00	£150

(c) As Type O 13, vertically upwards

O105	10	25 r. violet	..	£550	£700
O93/104			*Set of 12*	£140	£325
O93/105 Perf "Specimen"..			*Set of 13*	£500	

1932 (1 Apr). *Official issues of 1924–25 and 1931 surch in "FILS" or "DINAR", as T 13 or 14.*

O122	11	3 f. on ½ a. green	..	3·25	3·25
		a. Pair, one without surch ..		£250	
O123	–	4 f. on 1 a. red-brown (G.)	..	2·25	10
O124	–	5 f. on 1 a. red-brown	..	2·25	10
		a. Inverted Arabic "5" (R. 8/11)	..	40·00	£300
O125	3	8 f. on 1½ a. lake (No. O68)	..	3·75	50
O126	11	10 f. on 2 a. orange	..	2·50	10
		a. Inverted Arabic "1" (R. 8/13)	..	32·00	25·00
		b. "10" omitted	..	†£1500	
		c. No space between "10" and "Fils"	..	2·50	10
O127	–	15 f. on 3 a. blue	..	3·50	1·00
O128	–	20 f. on 4 a. slate-purple	..	3·50	1·40
O129	–	25 f. on 4 a. slate-purple	..	3·75	1·50
O130	–	30 f. on 6 a. greenish blue (No. O72)	..	3·75	1·75
O131	11	40 f. on 8 a. deep green	..	3·75	3·50
		a. "Flis" for "Fils" (R. 7/5, 7/13)	..	£200	£275
O132	12	50 f. on 1 r. chocolate	..	3·75	3·50
		a. Inverted Arabic "5" (R. 1/2)	..	65·00	75·00
O133	–	75 f. on 1 r. chocolate	..	6·00	6·00
		a. Inverted Arabic "5"	..	45·00	55·00
O134	2	100 f. on 2 r. olive-bistre (surch at top)	..	11·00	3·50
		a. Surch at foot	..	12·00	9·00
O135	–	200 f. on 5 r. orange (No. O76)	..	20·00	20·00
O136	–	½ d. on 10 r. lake (No. O77)	..	50·00	70·00
		a. No bar in English "½" (R. 2/10)	..	£650	£750
O137	10	1 d. on 25 r. violet	..	85·00	£140
O122/37			*Set of 16*	£180	£225

Nos. O122/4, O126/9 and O131 were in sheets of 160 (16×10), Nos. O130, O134 and 150 (10×15), No. O135 150 (15×10) and Nos. O125, O132/3 and O137 in sheets of 100 (10×10). There was a second setting of the surcharge for the 3 f. (equivalent to the third postage setting), 10 f. to 25 f., 40 f. to 100 f. and 1 d. Nos. O126c, O131a and O134a come from the second setting.
  All 100 f. stamps from the second setting are as No. O134a. For notes on other varieties see below No. 121.

1932 (9 May). Optd. (a) As Type O 12.

O155	11	2 f. ultramarine	1·25	10
O156		3 f. green	1·25	10
O157		4 f. brown-purple	1·25	10
O158		5 f. grey-green	1·25	10
O159		8 f. scarlet	1·25	10
O160		10 f. yellow	2·00	10
O161		15 f. blue	2·25	10
O162		20 f. orange	2·25	15
O163		25 f. mauve	2·25	15
O164		30 f. bronze-green	3·25	20
O165		40 f. violet	4·25	20

(b) As Type O 13, horizontally

O166	12	50 f. brown	3·00	20
O167		75 f. dull ultramarine	2·25	90
O168		100 f. deep green	10·00	1·25
O169		200 f. scarlet	19·00	6·50

(c) As Type O 13, vertically upwards

O170	10	½d. deep blue	12·00	22·00
O171		1 d. claret	50·00	75·00
O155/71		Set of 17	£110	95·00
O155/71 Perf "Specimen"		Set of 17	£300	

The British Mandate was given up on 3 October 1932 and Iraq became an independent kingdom. Later issues will be found listed in Part 19 (*Middle East*) of this catalogue.

Ireland (Republic)

All the issues of Ireland are listed together here, in this section of the Gibbons Catalogue, purely as a matter of convenience to collectors.

PRICES FOR STAMPS ON COVER TO 1945

Nos. 1/15	from × 5
Nos. 17/21	from × 3
Nos. 26/9a	from × 5
Nos. 30/43	from × 4
Nos. 44/6	—
Nos. 47/63	from × 5
Nos. 64/6	from × 3
Nos. 67/70	from × 6
Nos. 71/82	from × 2
Nos. 83/8	from × 3
Nos. 89/98	from × 2
Nos. 99/104	from × 3
Nos. 105/37	from × 2
Nos. D1/4	from × 7
Nos. D5/14	from × 6

PROVISIONAL GOVERNMENT
16 January—6 December 1922
Stamps of Great Britain overprinted. T 104/8, W 100; T 109, W 110

(1) RialtaR SeaLaDaċ na hÉireann 1922

(2) RialtaR SeaLaDaċ na hÉireann 1922.

(3) RialtaR SeaLaDaċ na hÉireann 1922

("Provisional Government of Ireland, 1922")

1922 (17 Feb–July). T 104 to 108 (W 100) and 109 of Great Britain overprinted in black.

(a) With T 1, by Dollard Printing House Ltd. Optd in black*

1	105	½d. green	1·00	40
		a. Opt inverted	£400	£550
2	104	1d. scarlet	1·50	35
		a. Opt inverted	£250	£300
		b. Opt double, both inverted, one albino	£350	
		c. Opt double	†	—
		w. Wmk inverted	—	£150
3		1d. carmine-red	2·75	60
4		2½d. bright blue	1·75	4·50
		a. Red opt (1 Apr)	1·00	3·50
5	106	3d. bluish violet	4·25	3·75
6		4d. grey-green	3·50	10·00
		a. Red opt (1 Apr)	8·50	15·00
		b. Carmine opt (July)	40·00	65·00
7	107	5d. yellow-brown	4·00	8·50
		x. Wmk reversed	—	£200
8	108	9d. agate	11·00	21·00
		a. Opt double, one albino		
		b. Red opt (1 Apr)	14·00	17·00
		c. Carmine opt (July)	80·00	85·00
9		10d. turquoise-blue	8·50	40·00
1/9		Set of 8	30·00	75·00

*All values except 2½d. and 4d. are known with greyish black overprint, but these appear to be trials.

The carmine overprints on the 4d. and 9d. may have been produced by Alex Thom & Co. Ltd. There was a further

overprinting of the 2½d. at the same time, but this is difficult to distinguish.

The ½d. with red overprint is a trial or proof printing (*Price £150*).

Bogus inverted T 1 overprints exist on the 2d., 4d., 9d and 1s. values.

(b) With T 2, by Alex Thom & Co Ltd.

10	105	1½d. red-brown	1·40	85
		a. Error. "PENCF"	£350	£275
		w. Wmk inverted	—	£120
		x. Wmk reversed	—	£120
12	106	2d. orange (Die I)	2·50	50
		a. Opt inverted	£180	£250
		w. Wmk inverted	—	£100
		x. Wmk reversed	—	£120
13		2d. orange (Die II)	2·25	50
		a. Opt inverted	£300	£400
		w. Wmk inverted	—	£120
14	107	6d. reddish pur (*chalk-surfaced paper*)	11·00	14·00
15	108	1s. bistre-brown	11·00	9·00
10/15		Set of 5	25·00	22·00

Varieties occur throughout the T 2 overprint in the relative positions of the lines of the overprint, the "R" of "Rialtas" being over either the "Se" or "S" of "Sealadac" or intermediately.

(c) With T 3 by Dollard Printing House Ltd

17	109	2s. 6d. chocolate-brown	35·00	65·00
18		2s. 6d. reddish brown	50·00	75·00
19		5s. rose-red	60·00	£120
21		10s. dull grey-blue	£120	£250
17/21		Set of 3	£190	£400

1922 (19 June–Aug). Optd as T 2, in black, by Harrison & Sons, for use in horiz and vert coils.

26	105	½d. green	2·25	10·00
27	104	1d. scarlet	2·75	6·50
28	105	1½d. red-brown (21.6)	4·00	35·00
29	106	2d. bright orange (Die I)	18·00	29·00
29a		2d. bright orange (Die II) (August)	19·00	26·00
		ay. Wmk inverted and reversed	—	£200
26/9a		Set of 5	40·00	95·00

The Harrison overprint measures 15×17 mm (maximum) against the 14½×16 mm of T 2 (Thom printing) and is a much bolder black than the latter, while the individual letters are taller, the "i" of "Rialtas" being specially outstanding as it extends below the foot of the "R".

The "R" of "Rialtas" is always over the "Se" of "Sealadac".

1922. Optd by Thom.

(a) As T 2 but bolder, in dull to shiny blue-black or red (June–Nov)

30	105	½d. green	2·00	80
31	104	1d. scarlet	1·50	50
		a. "Q" for "O" (No. 357ab)	£1200	£1100
		b. Reversed "Q" for "O" (No. 357ac)	£350	£250
32	105	1½d. red-brown	3·50	3·25
33	106	2d. orange (Die I)	18·00	1·50
34		2d. orange (Die II)	2·75	50
		y. Wmk inverted and reversed	£120	£120
35	104	2½d. blue (R.)	6·00	18·00
36	106	3d. violet	2·50	2·00
		y. Wmk inverted and reversed	75·00	75·00
37		4d. grey-green (R.)	3·25	5·00
38	107	5d. yellow-brown	4·25	9·00
39		6d. reddish pur (*chalk-surfaced paper*)	8·00	3·25
		w. Wmk inverted	75·00	50·00
40	108	9d. agate (R.)	12·00	15·00
41		9d. olive-green (R.)	4·75	32·00
42		10d. turquoise-blue	26·00	50·00
43		1s. bistre-brown	8·50	12·00
30/43		Set of 14	85·00	£140

Both 2d. stamps exist with the overprint inverted but there remains some doubt as to whether they were issued.

These Thom printings are distinguishable from the Harrison printings by the size of the overprint, and from the previous Thom printings by the intensity and colour of the overprint, the latter being best seen when the stamp is looked through with a strong light behind it.

(b) As with T 3, but bolder, in shiny blue-black (Oct–Dec)

44	109	2s. 6d. chocolate-brown	£180	£250
45		5s. rose-red	£170	£275
46		10s. dull grey-blue	£850	£1000
44/6		Set of 3	£1100	£1400

The above differ from Nos. 17/21 not only in the bolder impression and colour of the ink but also in the "h" and "é" of "héireann" which are closer together and horizontally aligned.

(4) RialtaR SeaLaDaċ na hÉireann 1922.

Saorstát Éireann 1922
(5 Wide date)
("Irish Free State 1922")

1922 (21 Nov–Dec). Optd by Thom with T 4 (*wider setting*) in shiny blue-black.

47	105	½d. green	1·00	1·75
		a. Opt in jet-black	£100	90·00
48	104	1d. scarlet	4·25	2·50
49	105	1½d. red-brown (4 December)	3·00	10·00
50	106	2d. orange (Die II)	9·00	7·00
51	108	1s. olive-bistre (4 December)	55·00	48·00
47/51		Set of 5	55·00	60·00

The overprint T 4 measures 15¾ × 16 mm (maximum).

OMNIBUS ISSUES

Details, together with prices for complete sets, of the various Omnibus issues from the 1935 Silver Jubilee series to date are included in a special section following Zimbabwe at the end of Volume 2.

IRISH FREE STATE
6 December 1922—29 December 1937

1922 (Dec)–23.

(a) Optd by Thom with T 5, in dull to shiny blue-black or red

52	105	½d. green	1·25	30
		a. No accent in "Saorstat"	£1000	£900
		b. Accent inserted by hand	85·00	95·00
53	104	1d. scarlet	75	40
		aa. No accent in "Saorstat"	£7000	£5000
		a. No accent and final "t" missing	£6000	£4500
		b. Accent inserted by hand	£130	£150
		c. Accent and "t" inserted	£225	£250
		d. Reversed "Q" for "O" (No. 357ac)	£300	£250
54	105	1½d. red-brown	3·50	8·50
55	106	2d. orange (Die II)	1·25	1·00
56	104	2½d. bright blue (R.) (6.1.23)	6·50	8·00
		a. No accent	£140	£170
57	106	3d. bluish violet (6.1.23)	3·50	11·00
		a. No accent	£250	£275
58		4d. grey-green (R.) (16.1.23)	3·25	6·50
		a. No accent	£150	£170
59	107	5d. yellow-brown	3·50	4·75
60		6d. reddish pur (*chalk-surfaced paper*)	2·00	2·00
		a. Accent inserted by hand	£700	£700
		y. Wmk inverted and reversed	50·00	30·00
61	108	9d. olive-green (R.)	3·00	5·50
		a. No accent	£250	£275
62		10d. turquoise-blue	16·00	50·00
63		1s. bistre-brown	7·00	11·00
		a. No accent	£5500	£6500
		b. Accent inserted by hand	£600	£650
64	109	2s. 6d. chocolate-brown	35·00	55·00
		a. Major Re-entry	£850	£950
		b. No accent	£350	£400
		c. Accent reversed	£425	£475
65		5s. rose-red	65·00	£120
		a. No accent	£450	£500
		b. Accent reversed	£550	£600
66		10s. dull grey-blue	£140	£275
		a. No accent	£2000	£2500
		b. Accent reversed	£2750	£3500
52/66		Set of 15	£380	£500

The accents inserted by hand are in dull black. The reversed accents are grave (thus "à") instead of acute ("á"). A variety with "S" of "Saorstat" directly over "é" of "éireann", instead of to left, may be found in all values except the 2½d. and 4d. In the 2s. 6d., 5s. and 10s. it is very slightly to the left in the "S" over "é" variety, bringing the "à" of "Saorstat" directly above the last "n" of "éireann".

(b) Optd with T 5, in dull or shiny blue-black, by Harrison, for use in horiz or vert coils (7.3.23)

67		½d. green	1·75	10·00
		a. Long "1" in "1922"	20·00	48·00
		y. Wmk inverted and reversed		
68		1d. scarlet	4·00	10·00
		a. Long "1" in "1922"	75·00	£140
69		1½d. red-brown	6·00	40·00
		a. Long "1" in "1922"	85·00	£225
70		2d. orange (Die II)	6·50	9·00
		a. Long "I" in "1922"	27·00	45·00
		w. Wmk inverted	—	£150
67/70		Set of 4	16·00	60·00

In the Harrison overprint the characters are rather bolder than those of the Thom overprint, and the foot of the "1" of "1922" is usually rounded instead of square. The long "1" in "1922" has a serif at foot. The second "e" in "éireann" appears to be slightly raised.

PRINTERS. The following and all subsequent issues to No. 148 were printed at the Government Printing Works, Dublin, *unless otherwise stated*.

6 "Sword of Light"   7 Map of Ireland   8 Arms of Ireland

9 Celtic Cross   10

(Des J. J. O'Reilly, T 6; J. Ingram, T 7; Miss M. Girling, T 8; and Miss L. Williams, T 9. Typo. Plates made by Royal Mint, London)

1922 (6 Dec)–34. W 10. P 15×14.

71	6	½d. bright green (20.4.23)	90	90
		a. Imperf × perf 14, wmk sideways (11.34)	20·00	45·00
		w. Wmk inverted	30·00	15·00
72	7	1d. carmine (23.2.23)	1·00	10
		c. Perf 15 × imperf (single perf) (1933)	85·00	£160
		c. Perf 15 × imperf (7.34)	15·00	40·00
		cw. Wmk inverted		
		d. Booklet pane. Three stamps plus three printed labels (21.8.31)	£225	
		dw. Wmk inverted		
73		1½d. claret (2.2.23)	1·60	2·00
		w. Wmk inverted		
74		2d. grey-green (6.12.22)	1·50	10
		a. Imperf × perf 14, wmk sideways (11.34)	38·00	70·00
		b. Perf 15 × imperf (1934)	£8500	£1500
		w. Wmk inverted	20·00	5·00
		y. Wmk inverted and reversed	30·00	7·00

75	8	2½d. red-brown (7.9.23)	.. .. ..	4·00	3·75
		w. Wmk inverted	.. .. ..	50·00	8·00
76	9	3d. ultramarine (16.3.23)	.. ..	2·00	75
		w. Wmk inverted	.. .. ..	65·00	12·00
77	8	4d. slate-blue (28.9.23)	.. ..	2·00	3·25
		w. Wmk inverted	.. .. ..	75·00	25·00
78	6	5d. deep violet (11.5.23)	.. ..	8·00	9·50
79		6d. claret (21.12.23)	.. .. ..	4·00	3·50
		w. Wmk inverted	.. .. ..	£110	25·00
80	8	9d. deep violet (26.10.23)	.. ..	13·00	8·00
		w. Wmk inverted	.. ..		
81	9	10d. brown (11.5.23)	.. .. ..	9·00	18·00
		w. Wmk inverted	.. ..		
82	6	1s. light blue (15.6.23)	.. ..	17·00	5·50
		w. Wmk inverted	.. ..		
71/82			Set of 12	55·00	50·00

No. 72a is imperf vertically except for a single perf at each top corner. It was issued for use in automatic machines.
See also Nos. 111/22 and 227/8.

SAORSTÁT ÉIREANN 1922

(11 Narrow Date) 12 Daniel O'Connell

1925 (Aug)–28. T 109 of Great Britain (Bradbury, Wilkinson printing) optd at the Government Printing Works, Dublin or by Harrison and Sons. (a) With T 11 in black or grey-black (25.8.25).

83	2s. 6d. chocolate-brown	.. ..	38·00	80·00
	a. Wide and narrow date (pair) (1927)			£250
84	5s. rose-red	.. .. ..	50·00	£120
	a. Wide and narrow date (pair) (1927)			£400
85	10s. dull grey-blue	.. ..	£110	£275
	a. Wide and narrow date (pair) (1927)			£1000
83/5		Set of 3	£180	£425

The varieties with wide and narrow date *se-tenant* are from what is known as the "composite setting," in which some stamps showed the wide date, as T 5, while in others the figures were close together, as in T 11.
Single specimens of this printing with wide date may be distinguished from Nos. 64 to 66 by the colour of the ink, which is black or grey-black in the composite setting and blue-black in the Thom printing.
The type of the "composite" overprint usually shows distinct signs of wear.

(b) As T 5 (wide date) in black (1927–28)

86	2s. 6d. chocolate-brown (9.12.27)	..	42·00	42·00
	a. Circumflex accent over "a"	..	£200	£250
	b. No accent over "a"	.. ..	£350	£375
	c. Flat accent on "a"	.. ..	£300	£350
87	5s. rose-red (2.28)	.. ..	60·00	80·00
	a. Circumflex accent over "a"	..	£325	£375
	b.	.. ..	£400	£450
	c. Flat accent on "a"	.. ..	£300	£250
88	10s. dull grey-blue (15.2.28)	..	£150	£170
	a. Circumflex accent over "a"	..	£800	£900
	c. Flat accent on "a"	.. ..	£900	£1000
86/8		Set of 3	£225	£250

This printing can be distinguished from the Thom overprints in dull black, by the clear, heavy impression (in deep black) which often shows in relief on the back of the stamp.
The variety showing a circumflex accent over the "a" occurred on R.9/2. The overprint in this position finally deteriorated to such an extent that some examples of the 2s. 6d. were without accent (No. 86b). A new cliché was then introduced with the accent virtually flat and which also showed damage to the "a" and the crossbar of the "t".

(Des L. Whelan. Typo.)
1929 (22 June). Catholic Emancipation Centenary. W10. P 15 × 14.

89	12	2d. grey-green	.. ..	50	45
90		3d. blue	.. ..	4·00	8·50
91		9d. bright violet	.. ..	4·00	4·00
89/91			Set of 3	7·50	11·50

13 Shannon Barrage 14 Reaper

(Des E. L. Lawrenson. Typo.)
1930 (15 Oct). Completion of Shannon Hydro-Electric Scheme. W 10. P 15 × 14.

92	13	2d. agate	.. ..	80	55

(T 14 and 15 des G. Atkinson. Typo.)
1931 (12 June). Bicentenary of the Royal Dublin Society. W 10. P 15 × 14.

93	14	2d. blue	.. ..	65	30

15 The Cross of Cong 16 Adoration of the Cross 17 Hurler

1932 (12 May). International Eucharistic Congress. W 10. P 15×14.

94	15	2d. grey-green	.. ..	1·00	30
		w. Wmk inverted			
95		3d. blue	.. ..	2·25	5·00

(T 16 to 19 des R. J. King. Typo)
1933 (18 Sept). "Holy Year". W 10. P 15 × 14.

96	16	2d. grey-green	.. ..	1·25	15
97		3d. blue	..	2·50	2·00

1934 (27 July). Golden Jubilee of the Gaelic Athletic Association. W 10. P 15 × 14.

98	17	2d. green		75	55

1935 (Mar–July). T 109 of Great Britain (Waterlow printings) optd as T 5 (wide date), at the Government Printing Works, Dublin.

99	109	2s. 6d. chocolate (No. 450)	45·00	48·00
	a. Flat accent on "a" (R. 9/2)	..	£225	£200
100	5s. bright rose-red (No. 451)	..	80·00	80·00
	a. Flat accent on "a" (R. 9/2)	..	£300	£250
101	10s. indigo (No. 452)	..	£350	£350
	a. Flat accent on "a" (R. 9/2)	..	£900	£750
99/101		Set of 3	£425	£425

18 St. Patrick 19 Ireland and New Constitution

1937 (8 Sept). W 10. P 14×15.

102	18	2s. 6d. emerald-green	.. ..	£140	65·00
		w. Wmk inverted	..	£600	£225
103		5s. maroon	.. ..	£180	£110
		w. Wmk inverted	..	£500	£225
104		10s. deep blue	.. ..	£140	50·00
		w. Wmk inverted	..		
102/4			Set of 3	£425	£200

See also Nos. 123/5.

EIRE

29 December 1937—17 April 1949

1937 (29 Dec). Constitution Day. W 10. P 15×14.

105	19	2d. claret	.. ..	1·00	20
		w. Wmk inverted	..	—	£180
106		3d. blue	.. ..	4·00	3·75

For similar stamps see Nos. 176/7.

20 Father Mathew

(Des S. Keating. Typo.)
1938 (1 July). Centenary of Temperance Crusade. W 10. P 15 × 14.

107	20	2d. agate	.. ..	1·50	30
		w. Wmk inverted	..		
108		3d. blue	.. ..	8·50	6·00

21 George Washington, American Eagle and Irish Harp 22

(Des G. Atkinson. Typo.)
1939 (1 Mar). 150th Anniv of U.S. Constitution and Installation of First U.S. President. W 10. P 15 × 14.

109	21	2d. scarlet	.. ..	1·75	65
110		3d. blue	..	3·25	4·25

SIZE OF WATERMARK. T 22 can be found in various sizes from about 8 to 10 mm high. This is due to the use of two different dandy rolls supplied by different firms and to the effects of paper shrinkage and other factors such as pressure and machine speed.

COVER PRICES

Cover factors are quoted at the beginning of each country for most issues to 1945. An explanation of the system can be found on page x. The factors quoted do not, however, apply to philatelic covers.

White line above left value tablet joining horizontal line to ornament (R. 3/7)

1940–68. Typo. W 22. P 15×14 or 14×15 (2s. 6d. to 10s.).

111	6	½d. bright green (24.11.40)	..	2·00	40
		w. Wmk inverted	..	50·00	6·50
112	7	1d. carmine (26.10.40)	..	30	10
		aw. Wmk inverted	..	1·75	30
		b. From coils. Perf 14×imperf (9.40)		60·00	65·00
		c. From coils. Perf 15×imperf (20.3.46)		35·00	15·00
		cw. Wmk inverted	..	35·00	15·00
		d. Booklet pane. Three stamps plus three printed labels			£1500
		dw. Wmk inverted			
113		1½d. claret (1.40)	..	14·00	30
		w. Wmk inverted	..	32·00	7·50
114		2d. grey-green (1.40)	..	30	10
		w. Wmk inverted	..	2·25	75
115	8	2½d. red-brown (3.41)	..	9·00	15
		w. Wmk inverted	..	20·00	4·00
116	9	3d. blue (12.40)	..	60	10
		w. Wmk inverted	..	3·50	50
117	8	4d. slate-blue (12.40)	..	55	10
		w. Wmk inverted	..	14·00	2·75
118	6	5d. deep violet (7.40)	..	65	10
		w. Wmk inverted	..	26·00	1·50
119		6d. claret (3.42)	..	2·25	50
		aw. Wmk inverted	..	18·00	3·00
		b. Chalk-surfaced paper (1967)		1·25	20
		bw. Wmk inverted	..	13·00	2·50
119c		8d. scarlet (12.9.49)	..	80	80
		cw. Wmk inverted	..	32·00	10·00
120	8	9d. deep violet (7.40)	..	1·50	80
		w. Wmk inverted	..	9·50	2·00
121	9	10d. brown (7.40)	..	60	80
		w. Wmk inverted	..	10·00	3·50
121b		11d. rose (12.9.49)	..	1·50	2·25
122	6	1s. light blue (6.40)	..	70·00	17·00
		w. Wmk inverted	..	£600	£150
123	18	2s. 6d. emerald-green (10.2.43)		40·00	1·25
		aw. Wmk inverted	..	85·00	20·00
		b. Chalk-surfaced paper (1968?)		1·50	2·25
		bw. Wmk inverted	..	28·00	4·00
124		5s. maroon (15.12.42)	..	40·00	3·00
		a. Line flaw			
		bw. Wmk inverted	..	£160	32·00
		c. Chalk-surfaced paper (1968?)		13·00	4·00
		ca. Purple	..	6·00	7·50
		cb. Line flaw	..	95·00	
		cw. Wmk inverted	..	35·00	9·00
125		10s. deep blue (7.45)	..	60·00	6·00
		aw. Wmk inverted	..	£180	70·00
		b. Chalk-surfaced paper (1968)		19·00	12·00
		ba. Blue	..	7·00	16·00
		bw. Wmk inverted	..	£130	60·00
111/25			Set of 17	£100	30·00

There is a wide range of shades and also variation in paper used in this issue.
See also Nos. 227/8.

1941 I gcuimhne aiséirge 1916

(23 Trans "In memory of the rising of 1916") 24 Volunteer and G.P.O., Dublin

1941 (12 Apr). 25th Anniv of Easter Rising (1916). Provisional issue. T 7 and 9 (2d. in new colour), optd with T 23.

126	7	2d. orange (G.)	..	1·00	50
127	9	3d. blue (V.)	..	24·00	9·50

(Des V. Brown. Typo.)
1941 (27 Oct). 25th Anniv of Easter Rising (1916). Definitive issue. W 22. P 15 × 14.

128	24	2½d. blue-black	..	70	60

25 Dr. Douglas Hyde 26 Sir William Rowan Hamilton 27 Bro. Michael O'Clery

(Des S. O'Sullivan. Typo.)
1943 (31 July). 50th Anniv of Founding of Gaelic League. W 22. P 15 × 14.

129	25	½d. green	.. ..	40	30
130		2½d. claret	..	1·25	10

(Des S. O'Sullivan from a bust by Hogan. Typo.)
1943 (13 Nov). Centenary of Announcement of Discovery of Quaternions. W 22. P 15 × 14.

131	26	½d. green	.. ..	40	40
		w. Wmk inverted			
132		2½d. brown	..	1·75	10

(Des R. J. King. Typo)

1944 (30 June). *Tercentenary of Death of Michael O'Clery. (Commemorating the "Annals of the Four Masters"). W 22 (sideways*). P* 14×15.

133	27	½d. emerald-green	10	10
		w. Wmk facing right	55	20
134		1s. red-brown	70	10
		w. Wmk facing right	2·25	50

*The normal sideways watermark shows the top of the e facing left, *as seen from the back of the stamp.*

Although issued as commemoratives these two stamps were kept in use as part of the current issue, replacing Nos. 111 and 122.

28 Edmund Ignatius Rice

29 "Youth Sowing Seeds of Freedom"

(Des S. O'Sullivan. Typo)

1944 (29 Aug). *Death Centenary of Edmund Rice (founder of Irish Christian Brothers). W 22. P* 15 × 14.

135	28	2½d. slate	60	45
		w. Wmk inverted		

(Des R. J. King. Typo)

1945 (15 Sept). *Centenary of Death of Thomas Davis (founder of Young Ireland Movement). W 22. P* 15 × 14.

136	29	2½d. blue	1·00	25
		w. Wmk inverted	—	£130
137		6d. claret	6·00	3·75

30 "Country and Homestead"

(Des R. J. King. Typo)

1946 (16 Sept). *Birth Centenaries of Davitt and Parnell (land reformers). W 22. P* 15 × 14.

138	30	2½d. scarlet	1·50	20
139		3d. blue	2·75	3·50

31 Angel Victor over Rock of Cashel

(Des R. J. King. Recess Waterlow (1d. to 1s. 3d. until 1961), D.L.R. (8d., 1s. 3d. from 1961 and 1s. 5d.))

1948 (7 Apr)—**65.** *Air. T* **31** *and similar horiz designs. W* **22.** *P* 15 (1s. 5d.) or 15 × 14 (others).

140	31	1d. chocolate (4.4.49)	1·50	3·50
141	—	3d. blue	3·00	2·25
142	—	6d. magenta	80	1·50
		aw. Wmk inverted		
142b	—	8d. lake-brown (13.12.54)	6·00	7·00
143	—	1s. green (4.4.49)	80	1·50
143a	31	1s. 3d. red-orange (13.12.54)	7·00	1·25
		aw. Wmk inverted	£550	£250
143b		1s. 5d. deep ultramarine (1.4.65)	2·75	1·00
140/3b		*Set of* 7	20·00	16·00

Designs:—3d., 8d. Lough Derg; 6d. Croagh Patrick; 1s. Glendalough.

35 Theobald Wolfe Tone

(Des K. Uhlemann. Typo)

1948 (19 Nov). *150th Anniv of Insurrection. W* **22.** *P* 15×14.

144	35	2½d. reddish purple	1·00	10
		w. Wmk inverted		
145		3d. violet	3·25	3·25

REPUBLIC OF IRELAND
18 April 1949

36 Leinster House and Arms of Provinces

37 J. C. Mangan

(Des Muriel Brandt. Typo)

1949 (21 Nov). *International Recognition of Republic. W* **22.** *P* 15 × 14.

146	36	2½d. reddish brown	1·50	10
147		3d. bright blue	5·50	4·25

(Des R. J. King. Typo)

1949 (5 Dec). *Death Centenary of James Clarence Mangan (poet). W* **22.** *P* 15 × 14.

148	37	1d. green	1·50	20
		w. Wmk inverted		

38 Statue of St. Peter, Rome

39 Thomas Moore

40 Irish Harp

(Recess Waterlow & Sons)

1950 (11 Sept). *Holy Year. W* **22.** *P* 12½.

149	38	2½d. violet	1·00	40
150		3d. blue	8·00	8·50
151		9d. brown	8·00	10·00
149/51		*Set of* 3	15·00	17·00

PRINTERS. Nos. 152 to 200 were recess-printed by De La Rue & Co, Dublin, *unless otherwise stated.*

(Eng W. Vacek)

1952 (10 Nov). *Death Centenary of Thomas Moore (poet). W* **22.** *P* 13.

152	39	2½d. reddish purple	50	10
153		3½d. deep olive-green	1·75	2·75

(Des F. O'Ryan. Typo Government Printing Works, Dublin)

1953 (9 Feb). *"An Tostal" (Ireland at Home) Festival. W* **22** (sideways). *P* 14 × 15.

154	40	2½d. emerald-green	1·75	35
155		1s. 4d. blue	15·00	24·00

41 Robert Emmet

42 Madonna and Child (Della Robbia)

43 Cardinal Newman (first Rector)

(Eng L. Downey)

1953 (21 Sept). *150th Death Anniv of Emmet (patriot). W* **22.** *P* 13.

156	41	3d. deep bluish green	3·75	15
157		1s. 3d. carmine	42·00	9·50

(Eng A. R. Lane)

1954 (24 May). *Marian Year. W* **22.** *P* 15.

158	42	3d. blue	1·50	10
159		5d. myrtle-green	2·75	5·50

(Des L. Whelan. Typo Govt Printing Works, Dublin)

1954 (19 July). *Centenary of Founding of Catholic University of Ireland. W* **22.** *P* 15 × 14.

160	43	2d. bright purple	1·50	10
		w. Wmk inverted	—	£180
161		1s. 3d. blue	16·00	6·00

44 Statue of Commodore Barry

45 John Redmond

46 Thomas O'Crohan

(Des and eng H. Woyty-Wimmer)

1956 (16 Sept). *Barry Commemoration. W* **22.** *P* 15.

162	44	3d. slate-lilac	1·50	10
163		1s. 3d. deep blue	5·50	9·00

1957 (11 June). *Birth Centenary of John Redmond (politician). W* **22.** *P* 14 × 15.

164	45	3d. deep blue	1·00	10
165		1s. 3d. brown-purple	8·00	15·00

1957 (1 July). *Birth Centenary of Thomas O'Crohan (author). W* **22.** *P* 14 × 15.

166	46	2d. maroon	1·50	15
		a. Wmk sideways	†	—
167		5d. violet	1·50	5·50

47 Admiral Brown

48 "Father Wadding" (Ribera)

49 Tom Clarke

(Des S. O'Sullivan. Typo Govt Printing Works, Dublin)

1957 (23 Sept). *Death Centenary of Admiral William Brown. W* **22.** *P* 15 × 14.

168	47	3d. blue	2·25	20
169		1s. 3d. carmine	30·00	16·00

1957 (25 Nov). *300th Death Anniv of Father Luke Wadding (theologian). W* **22.** *P* 15.

170	48	3d. deep blue	2·00	10
171		1s. 3d. lake	15·00	8·50

1958 (28 July). *Birth Centenary of Thomas J. ("Tom") Clarke (patriot). W* **22.** *P* 15.

172	49	3d. deep green	2·50	10
173		1s. 3d. red-brown	5·00	13·00

50 Mother Mary Aikenhead

51 Arthur Guinness

(Eng Waterlow. Recess Imprimerie Belge de Securité, Brussels subsidiary of Waterlow & Sons)

1958 (20 Oct). *Death Centenary of Mother Mary Aikenhead (foundress of Irish Sisters of Charity). W* **22.** *P* 15 × 14.

174	50	3d. Prussian blue	1·75	10
175		1s. 3d. rose-carmine	15·00	10·00

(Typo Govt Printing Works, Dublin)

1958 (29 Dec). *21st Anniv of the Irish Constitution. W* **22.** *P* 15 × 14.

176	19	3d. brown	1·25	10
177		5d. emerald-green	2·25	4·50

1959 (20 July). *Bicentenary of Guinness Brewery. W* **22.** *P* 15.

178	51	3d. brown-purple	3·00	10
179		1s. 3d. blue	11·00	12·00

52 "The Flight of the Holy Family"

(Des K. Uhlemann)

1960 (20 June). *World Refugee Year. W* **22.** *P* 15.

180	52	3d. purple	50	10
181		1s. 3d. sepia	75	3·25

53 Conference Emblem

(Des P. Rahikainen)

1960 (19 Sept). *Europa. W* **22.** *P* 15.

182	53	6d. light brown	4·00	3·00
183		1s. 3d. violet	10·00	20·00

The ink of No. 183 is fugitive.

NEW INFORMATION

The editor is always interested to correspond with people who have new information that will improve or correct the Catalogue.

54 Dublin Airport, De
Havilland D.H.84 Dragon
Mk 2 *Iolar* and Boeing 720

55 St. Patrick

(Des J. Flanagan and D. R. Lowther)

1961 (26 June). *25th Anniv of Aer Lingus.* W **22**. P 15.
184	**54**	6d. blue	..	..	1·00	3·25
		w. Wmk inverted	..	..	1·50	4·75
185		1s. 3d. green	..	..	1·50	4·75

(Recess B.W.)

1961 (25 Sept). *Fifteenth Death Centenary of St. Patrick.* W **22**.
P 14½.
186	**55**	3d. blue ..	..	..	1·00	10
187		8d. purple	..	..	2·00	5·50
188		1s. 3d. green	..	..	2·00	1·60
186/8	..	..	..	Set of 3	4·50	6·50

56 John O'Donovan and
Eugene O'Curry

(Recess B.W.)

1962 (26 Mar). *Death Centenaries of O'Donovan and O'Curry
(scholars).* W **22**. P 15.
189	**56**	3d. carmine	..	..	30	10
190		1s. 3d. purple	..	..	1·25	2·25

57 Europa "Tree"

(Des L. Weyer)

1962 (17 Sept). *Europa.* W **22**. P 15.
191	**57**	6d. carmine-red	..	..	50	1·00
192		1s. 3d. turquoise	..	..	90	1·50

58 Campaign Emblem

(Des K. Uhlemann)

1963 (21 Mar). *Freedom from Hunger.* W **22**. P 15.
193	**58**	4d. deep violet	..	..	50	10
194		1s. 3d. scarlet ..	..	..	1·75	2·75

59 "Co-operation"

(Des A. Holm)

1963 (16 Sept). *Europa.* W **22**. P 15.
195	**59**	6d. carmine	..	..	75	75
196		1s. 3d. blue	..	..	2·00	3·75

60 Centenary Emblem

(Des P. Wildbur. Photo Harrison & Sons)

1963 (2 Dec). *Centenary of Red Cross.* W **22**. P 14½ × 14.
197	**60**	4d. red and grey	..	..	50	10
198		1s. 3d. red, grey and light emerald	..	1·25	2·25

61 Wolfe Tone

(Des P. Wildbur)

1964 (13 Apr). *Birth Bicentenary of Wolfe Tone (revolutionary).*
W **22**. P 15.
199	**61**	4d. black	..	..	50	10
200		1s. 3d. ultramarine	..	..	1·90	2·25

62 Irish Pavilion at Fair

(Des A. Devane. Photo Harrison & Sons)

1964 (20 July). *New York World's Fair.* W **22**. P 14½ × 14.
201	**62**	5d. blue-grey, brown, violet & yellow-ol	50	10
		a. Brown omitted*		£1200
202		1s. 5d. blue-grey, brown, turquoise-blue and light yellow-green	2·25	3·75

*No. 201a comes from the top row of a sheet and shows part of the
brown cross which would appear in the sheet margin. As the second
horizontal row was normal it would appear that the brown cylinder
was incorrectly registered.

63 Europa "Flower"

64 "Waves of Communication"

(Des G. Bétemps. Photo Harrison)

1964 (14 Sept). *Europa.* W **22** (*sideways*). P 14 × 14½.
203	**63**	8d. olive-green and blue	..	1·00	1·25
204		1s. 5d. red-brown and orange	..	3·00	2·75

(Des P. Wildbur. Photo Harrison)

1965 (17 May). *I.T.U. Centenary.* W **22**. P 14½ × 14.
205	**64**	3d. blue and green	..	..	40	10
206		8d. black and green	..	..	1·40	2·00

PRINTERS. Nos. 207 onwards were photogravure-printed by
the Stamping Branch of the Revenue Commissioners, Dublin
unless otherwise stated.

65 W. B. Yeats (poet)   **66** I.C.Y. Emblem

(Des R. Kyne, from drawing by S. O'Sullivan)

1965 (14 June). *Yeats' Birth Centenary.* W **22** (*sideways*). P 15.
207	**65**	5d. black, orange-brown and deep green	30	10
208		1s. 5d. black, grey-green and brown	2·25	1·75

1965 (16 Aug). *International Co-operation Year.* W **22**. P 15.
209	**66**	3d. ultramarine and new blue ..	..	60	10
210		10d. deep brown and brown	..	1·00	3·00

67 Europa "Sprig"

(Des H. Karlsson)

1965 (27 Sept). *Europa.* W **22**. P 15.
211	**67**	8d. black and brown-red	..	1·00	1·00
212		1s. 5d. purple and light turquoise-blue	3·25	3·50

68 James Connolly

69 "Marching to Freedom"

(Des E. Delaney (No. 216), R. Kyne, after portraits by S. O'Sullivan
(others))

1966 (12 Apr). *50th Anniv of Easter Rising.* T **68/9** *and similar
horiz portraits.* W **22**. P 15.
213		3d. black and greenish blue ..	..	35	10
		a. Horiz pair. Nos. 213/14 ..	..	70	2·50
214		3d. black and bronze-green	..	35	10
215		5d. black and yellow-olive	..	35	10
		a. Horiz pair. Nos. 215/16 ..	..	70	2·50
216		5d. black, orange and blue-green	..	35	10
217		7d. black and light orange-brown	..	40	2·25
		a. Horiz pair. Nos. 217/18 ..	..	80	7·50
218		7d. black and blue-green	..	40	2·25
219		1s. 5d. black and turquoise	..	40	1·50
		a. Horiz pair. Nos. 219/20 ..	..	80	9·00
220		1s. 5d. black and bright green	..	40	1·50
213/20			Set of 8	2·75	7·00

Designs:—No. 213, Type **68**; No. 214, Thomas J. Clarke; No. 215,
P. H. Pearse; No. 216, Type **69**; No. 217, Eamonn Ceannt; No. 218,
Sean MacDiarmada; No. 219, Thomas MacDonagh; No. 220,
Joseph Plunkett.
Nos. 213/14, 215/16, 217/18 and 219/20 were each printed
together, *se-tenant*, in horizontal pairs throughout the sheet.

76 R. Casement   **77** Europa "Ship"

(Des R. Kyne)

1966 (3 Aug). *50th Death Anniv of Roger Casement (patriot).* W **22**
(*sideways*). P 15.
221	**76**	5d. black	..	..	15	10
222		1s. red-brown	..	..	30	50

(Des R. Kyne, after G. and J. Bender)

1966 (26 Sept). *Europa.* W **22** (*sideways*). P 15.
223	**77**	7d. emerald and orange	..	35	40
224		1s. 5d. emerald and light grey ..	..	90	1·00

78 Interior of Abbey (from lithograph)   **79** Cogwheels

1966 (8 Nov). *750th Anniv of Ballintubber Abbey.* W **22**. P 15.
225	**78**	5d. red-brown ..	..	..	10	10
226		1s. black	..	..	20	25

1966–67. *As Nos. 116, 118 but photo. Smaller design* (17×21
mm). *Chalk-surfaced paper.* W **22**. P 15.
227	**9**	3d. blue (1.8.67)	..	..	40	15
228	**6**	5d. bright violet (1.12.66)	..	30	15
		w. Wmk inverted (from booklets)	..	1·75	1·25

No. 228 was only issued in booklets at first but was released in
sheets on 1.4.68 in a slightly brighter shade. In the sheet stamps
the lines of shading are more regular.

(Des O. Bonnevalle)

1967 (2 May). *Europa.* W **22** (*sideways*). P 15.
229	**79**	7d. light emerald, gold and pale cream	30	40
230		1s. 5d. carmine-red, gold and pale cream	70	1·00

COVER PRICES

Cover factors are quoted at the beginning of each
country for most issues to 1945. An explanation of
the system can be found on page x. The factors
quoted do not, however, apply to philatelic covers.

80 Maple Leaves

(Des P. Hickey)

1967 (28 Aug). *Canadian Centennial.* W **22**. P 15.
231 80 5d. multicoloured 10 10
232   1s. 5d. multicoloured 20 75

81 Rock of Cashel (from photo by Edwin Smith)

1967 (25 Sept). *International Tourist Year.* W **22** (*inverted*). P 15.
233 81 7d. sepia 15 20
234   10d. slate-blue 15 40

82 1 c. Fenian Stamp Essay   **83** 24 c. Fenian Stamp Essay

1967 (23 Oct). *Centenary of Fenian Rising.* W **22** (*sideways*). P 15.
235 82 5d. black and light green 10 10
236 83 1s. black and light pink 20 30

84 Jonathan Swift   **85** Gulliver and Lilliputians

(Des M. Byrne)

1967 (30 Nov). *300th Birth Anniv of Jonathan Swift.* W **22** (*sideways*). P 15.
237 84 3d. black and olive-grey 10 10
238 85 1s. 5d. blackish brown and pale blue .. 20 30

86 Europa "Key"

(Des H. Schwarzenbach and M. Biggs)

1968 (29 Apr). *Europa.* W **22**. P 15.
239 86 7d. brown-red, gold and brown.. .. 25 50
240   1s. 5d. new blue, gold and brown .. 40 1·00

87 St Mary's Cathedral, Limerick

(Des from photo by J. J. Bambury. Recess B.W.)

1968 (26 Aug). *800th Anniv of St. Mary's Cathedral, Limerick.* W **22**. P 15.
241 87 5d. Prussian blue 10 10
242   10d. yellow-green 20 60

NEW INFORMATION

The editor is always interested to correspond with people who have new information that will improve or correct the Catalogue.

88 Countess Markievicz   **89** James Connolly

1968 (23 Sept). *Birth Centenary of Countess Markievicz (patriot).* W **22**. P 15.
243 88 3d. black 10 10
244   1s. 5d. deep blue and blue .. 20 20

1968 (23 Sept). *Birth Centenary of James Connolly (patriot).* W **22** (*sideways*). P 15.
245 89 6d. deep brown and chocolate .. 15 50
246   1s. blcksh grn, apple-grn & myrtle-grn 15 10

90 Stylised Dog (brooch)   **91** Stag

92 Winged Ox (Symbol of St. Luke)

93 Eagle (Symbol of St. John The Evangelist)

(Des H. Gerl)

1968–70. *Pence values expressed with "p".* W **22** (*sideways* on ¹/₂d. to 1s. 9d.*). P 15.
247 90 ¹/₂d. red-orange (7.6.69) 10 30
248   1d. pale yellow-green (7.6.69) .. 15 10
         a. Coil stamp. Perf 14×15 (8.70?) .. 90 3·00
249   2d. light ochre (14.10.68) .. 50 10
         a. Coil stamp. Perf 14×15 (8.70?) .. 90 3·75
250   3d. blue (7.6.69) 35 10
         a. Coil stamp. Perf 14×15 (8.70?) .. 90 3·75
251   4d. deep brown-red (31.3.69) .. 30 10
252   5d. myrtle-green (31.3.69) .. 40 35
253   6d. bistre-brown (24.2.69) .. 30 10
         w. Wmk e facing right .. 5·50 1·75
254 91 7d. brown and yellow (7.6.69) .. 45 3·50
255   8d. chocolate & orge-brown (14.10.68) 45 1·25
256   9d. slate-blue and olive-green (24.2.69) 50 10
257   10d. chocolate and bluish violet (31.3.69) 1·50 1·50
258   1s. chocolate and red-brown (31.3.69) 40 10
259   1s. 9d. black & lt turquoise-bl (24.2.69) 4·00 1·50
260 92 2s. 6d. multicoloured (14.10.68) .. 1·75 30
261   5s. multicoloured (24.2.69) .. 3·00 1·50
262 93 10s. multicoloured (14.10.68) .. 4·50 3·75
247/62   *Set of 16* 16·00 12·50

*The normal sideways watermark shows the top of the e facing left, *as seen from the back of the stamp.*
The 1d., 2d., 3d., 5d., 6d., 9d., 1s. and 2s. 6d. exist with PVA gum as well as gum arabic. The coil stamps exist on PVA only, and the rest on gum arabic only.
See also Nos. 287/301, 339/59 and 478/83.

94 Human Rights Emblem   **95** Dail Eireann Assembly

1968 (4 Nov). *Human Rights Year.* W **22** (*sideways*). P 15.
263 94 5d. yellow, gold and black 15 10
264   7d. yellow, gold and red 15 40

(Des M. Byrne)

1969 (21 Jan). *50th Anniv of Dail Eireann (First National Parliament).* W **22**. P 15 × 14½.
265 95 6d. myrtle-green 15 10
266   9d. Prussian blue 15 30

96 Colonnade   **97** Quadruple I.L.O. Emblems

(Des L. Gasbarra and G. Belli; adapted Myra Maguire)

1969 (28 Apr). *Europa.* W **22**. P 15.
267 96 9d. grey, ochre and ultramarine .. 40 1·10
268   1s. 9d. grey, gold and scarlet .. 70 1·40

(Des K. C. Dăbczewski)

1969 (14 July). *50th Anniv of International Labour Organization.* W **22** (*sideways*). P 15.
269 97 6d. black and grey 20 10
270   9d. black and yellow 20 25

98 "The Last Supper and Crucifixion" (Evie Hone Window, Eton Chapel)

(Des R. Kyne)

1969 (1 Sept). *Contemporary Irish Art (1st issue).* W **22** (*sideways*). P 15 × 14½.
271 98 1s. multicoloured .. .. 30 1·50
See also Nos. 280, 306, 317, 329, 362, 375, 398, 408, 452, 470 and 498.

99 Mahatma Gandhi

1969 (2 Oct). *Birth Centenary of Mahatma Gandhi.* W **22**. P 15.
272 99 6d. black and green 20 10
273   1s. 9d. black and yellow .. 30 90

100 Symbolic Bird in Tree

(Des D. Harrington)

1970 (23 Feb). *European Conservation Year.* W **22**. P 15.
274 100 6d. bistre and black 20 10
275   9d. slate-violet and black .. 25 80

101 "Flaming Sun"

(Des L. le Brocquy)

1970 (4 May). *Europa.* W **22**. P 15.
276 101 6d. bright violet and silver .. 30 10
277   9d. brown and silver .. .. 45 1·25
278   1s. 9d. deep olive-grey and silver .. 65 2·00
276/8   *Set of 3* 1·25 3·00

102 "Sailing Boats"
(Peter Monamy)

103 "Madonna of
Eire" (Mainie Jellett)

(Des P. Wildbur and P. Scott)

1970 (13 July). *250th Anniv of Royal Cork Yacht Club.* W **22.**
P 15.

279	102	4d. multicoloured		15	10

1970 (1 Sept). *Contemporary Irish Art (2nd issue).* W **22** (*sideways*). *P* 15.

280	103	1s. multicoloured		15	20

104 Thomas
MacCurtain

106 Kevin Barry

(Des P. Wildbur)

1970 (26 Oct). *50th Death Anniversaries of Irish Patriots.* T **104** *and similar vert design.* W **22** (*sideways*). *P* 15.

281	9d. black, bluish violet and greyish black		50	25
	a. Pair. Nos. 281/2		1·00	2·50
282	9d. black, bluish violet and greyish black		50	25
283	2s. 9d. black, new blue and greyish black		1·40	1·50
	a. Pair. Nos. 283/4		2·75	11·00
284	2s. 9d. black, new blue and greyish black		1·40	1·50
281/4	*Set of 4*		3·50	3·25

Designs:—Nos. 281 and 283, Type **104**; others, Terence MacSwiney.

Nos. 281/2 and 283/4 were each printed together, *se-tenant*, in horizontal and vertical pairs throughout the sheet.

(Des P. Wildbur)

1970 (2 Nov). *50th Death Anniv of Kevin Barry (patriot).* W **22** (*inverted*). *P* 15.

285	106	6d. olive-green		30	10
286		1s. 2d. royal blue		40	1·10

106a Stylized Dog
(Brooch)

107 "Europa Chain"

Two types of 10 p.:
I. Outline and markings of the ox in lilac.
II. Outline and markings in brown.

1971 (15 Feb)–**75.** *Decimal Currency. Designs as Nos. 247/62 but with "p" omitted as in T* **106a.** W **22** (*sideways* on* 10, 12, 20 *and* 50p.). *P* 15.

287	106a	½p. bright green		10	10
		a. Wmk sideways		4·50	10·00
		ab. Booklet pane of 6		25·00	
		aw. Wmk e facing right		4·50	10·00
		awb. Booklet pane of 6		25·00	
288		1p. blue		40	10
		a. Coil stamp. Perf 14×14½		65	60
		b. Coil strip. Nos. 288a, 289a and 291a *se-tenant*		1·00	
		c. Wmk sideways		35	40
		ca. Booklet pane of 6		1·50	
		cb. Booklet pane. No. 288c×5 plus one *se-tenant* label (11.3.74)		1·50	
		cw. Wmk e facing right		35	40
		cwa. Booklet pane of 6		1·50	
		cwb. Booklet pane. No. 288cw×5 plus one *se-tenant* label (11.3.74)		1·50	
289		1½p. lake-brown		15	15
		a. Coil stamp. Perf 14×14½		20	50
		b. Coil strip. Nos. 289a, 291a, 294a and 290a *se-tenant* (24.2.72)		1·00	
		c. Coil strip. Nos. 289a×2, 290a and 295ab *se-tenant* (29.1.74)		1·00	
290		2p. myrtle-green		15	10
		a. Coil stamp. Perf 14×14½ (24.2.72)		20	40
		b. Wmk sideways (27.1.75)		50	50
		ba. Booklet pane. No. 290b×5 plus one *se-tenant* label		1·50	
		bw. Wmk e facing right		50	50
		bwa. Booklet pane. No. 290bw×5 plus one *se-tenant* label		1·50	

291	106a	2½p. sepia		15	10
		a. Coil stamp. Perf 14×14½ (20.2.71)		30	85
		b. Wmk sideways		1·00	1·25
		ba. Booklet pane of 6		5·00	
		bw. Wmk e facing right		1·00	1·25
		bwa. Booklet pane of 6		5·00	
292		3p. cinnamon		15	10
293		3½p. orange-brown		15	10
294		4p. pale bluish violet		15	10
		a. Coil stamp. Perf 14×14½ (24.2.72)		70	60
295	91	5p. brown and yellow-olive		70	20
295a	106a	5p. bright yellow-green (29.1.74)		3·50	45
		ab. Coil stamp. Perf 14×14½ (29.1.74)		80	90
		ac. Wmk sideways (11.3.74)		60	80
		ad. Booklet pane. No. 295ac×5 plus one *se-tenant* label		2·00	
		ada. Booklet pane imperf vert			
		ae. Booklet pane. No. 295ac×6		6·00	
		awc. Wmk e facing right		60	80
		awd. Booklet pane. No. 295awc×5 plus one *se-tenant* label		2·00	
		awe. Booklet pane. No. 295awc×6		6·00	
296	91	6p. blackish brown and slate		3·50	30
296a		7p indigo and olive-green (29.1.74)		4·00	1·00
297		7½p. chocolate and reddish lilac		50	85
298		9p. black and turquoise-green		75	35
299	92	10p. multicoloured (I)		15·00	10·00
299a		10p. multicoloured (II)		15·00	70
299b		12p. multicoloured (29.1.74)		60	80
300		20p. multicoloured		75	10
301	93	50p. multicoloured		1·75	65
287/301		*Set of 18*	26·00	5·25

Nos. 287a/awb, 288c/cwb, 290b/bwa, 291b/bwa and 295ac/awe come from Booklet Nos. SB20/4. The sideways watermark has the top of the e pointing left, and the sideways inverted has it pointing right, *when seen from the back of the stamp.* Stamps with one, or two adjoining, sides imperf come from these booklets.

See also Nos. 339/59 and 478/83.

(Des H. Haflidason; adapted P. Wildbur)

1971 (3 May). *Europa.* W **22** (*sideways*). *P* 15.

302	107	4p. sepia and olive-yellow		50	10
303		6p. black and new blue		1·75	2·25

108 J. M. Synge

109 "An Island Man"
(Jack B. Yeats)

(Des R. Kyne from a portrait by Jack B. Yeats)

1971 (19 July). *Birth Centenary of J. M. Synge (playwright).* W **22.** *P* 15.

304	108	4p. multicoloured		15	10
305		10p. multicoloured		60	80

(Des P. Wildbur)

1971 (30 Aug). *Contemporary Irish Art (3rd issue). Birth Centenary of J. B. Yeats (artist).* W **22.** *P* 15.

306	109	6p. multicoloured		55	55

110 Racial Harmony
Symbol

111 "Madonna and
Child" (statue by
J. Hughes)

(Des P. Wildbur. Litho Harrison)

1971 (18 Oct). *Racial Equality Year. No wmk. P* 14 × 14½.

307	110	4p. red		20	10
308		10p. black		50	75

(Des R. Kyne)

1971 (15 Nov). *Christmas.* W **22.** *P* 15.

309	111	2½p. black, gold and deep bluish green		10	10
310		6p. black, gold and ultramarine		55	65

112 Heart

(Des L. le Brocquy)

1972 (7 Apr). *World Health Day.* W **22** (*sideways*). *P* 15.

311	112	2½p. gold and brown		30	15
312		12p. silver and grey		1·10	1·75

113 "Communications"

(Des P. Huovinen and P. Wildbur)

1972 (1 May). *Europa.* W **22** (*sideways*). *P* 15.

313	113	4p. orange, black and silver		1·25	25
314		6p. blue, black and silver		3·25	4·75

114 Dove and Moon

115 "Black Lake"
(Gerard Dillon)

(Des P. Scott)

1972 (1 June). *The Patriot Dead, 1922–23.* W **22.** *P* 15.

315	114	4p. grey-blue, light orange & deep blue		10	10
316		6p. dp yellow-grn, lemon & dp dull grn		45	40

(Des P. Wildbur)

1972 (10 July). *Contemporary Irish Art (4th issue).* W **22** (*sideways*). *P* 15.

317	115	3p. multicoloured		50	35

116 "Horseman"
(Carved Slab)

117 Madonna and Child
(from Book of Kells)

(Des P. Scott)

1972 (28 Aug). *50th Anniv of Olympic Council of Ireland.* W **22.** *P* 15.

318	116	3p. bright yellow, black and gold		15	10
319		6p. salmon, black and gold		55	60

WATERMARK. All issues from here onwards are on unwatermarked paper.

(Des P. Scott)

1972 (16 Oct). *Christmas. P* 15.

320	117	2½p. multicoloured (*shades*)		10	10
321		4p. multicoloured		20	10
322		12p. multicoloured		55	65
320/2		*Set of 3*		75	70

118 2d. Stamp of
1922

119 Celtic Head Motif

(Des Stamping Branch of the Revenue Commissioners, Dublin)

1972 (6 Dec). *50th Anniv of the First Irish Postage Stamp. P* 15.

323	118	6p. light grey and grey-green		30	60
MS324		72 × 104 mm. No. 323 × 4		6·50	11·00

(Des L. le Brocquy)

1973 (1 Jan). *Entry into European Communities. P* 15.
325 119 6p. multicoloured 40 90
326 12p. multicoloured .. .. .. 60 1·10

120 Europa "Posthorn"

(Des L. Anisdahl; adapted R. Kyne)

1973 (30 Apr). *Europa. P* 15.
327 120 4p. bright blue 50 10
328 6p. black .. .. .. 1·25 2·00

121 "Berlin Blues II" (W. Scott)   **122** Weather Map

(Adapted by R. Scott)

1973 (9 Aug). *Contemporary Irish Art (5th issue). P* 15 × 14½.
329 121 5p. ultramarine and grey-black .. 40 30

(Des R. Ballagh)

1973 (4 Sept). *I.M.O./W.M.O. Centenary. P* 14½ × 15.
330 122 3½p. multicoloured 30 10
331 12p. multicoloured .. .. 80 2·00

123 Tractor ploughing   **124** "Flight into Egypt"
(Jan de Cock)

(Des P. Scott)

1973 (5 Oct). *World Ploughing Championships, Wellington Bridge. P* 15 × 14½.
332 123 5p. multicoloured 15 10
333 7p. multicoloured 75 50

(Des D. Kiely. Litho ("EIRE" and face value) and photo (3½p.) or photo (12p.))

1973 (1 Nov). *Christmas. P* 15.
334 124 3½p. multicoloured 15 10
335 12p. multicoloured .. .. 1·10 1·50

125 Daunt Island Lightship   **126** "Edmund Burke"
and *Mary Stanford*   (statue by J. H. Foley)
(Ballycotton lifeboat), 1936

(Des M. Byrne from painting by B. Gribble)

1974 (28 Mar). *150th Anniv of Royal National Lifeboat Institution. P* 15 × 14½.
336 125 5p. multicoloured 30 30

(Des P. Wildbur)

1974 (29 Apr). *Europa. P* 14½ × 15.
337 126 5p. black and pale violet-blue .. 50 10
338 7p. black and light emerald .. 2·25 2·50

NEW INFORMATION

The editor is always interested to correspond with people who have new informations that will improve or correct the Catalogue.

Two types of 50p.:

Type I. Fine screen (Cyls 1)

Type II. Coarse screen (Cyls 2)

1974–83. *Designs as Nos. 287 etc. No wmk. P* 15.
339 106a ½p. bright green (5.6.78) 30 10
340 1p. blue (21.2.75) 10 10
    a. Coil stamp. Perf 14×14½ (21.3.77) 60 70
    b. Coil strip. Nos. 340a, 341a×2 and 344a *se-tenant* (21.3.77) 1·90
341 2p. myrtle-green (7.4.76) .. 10 10
    a. Coil stamp. Perf 14×14½ (21.3.77) 40 50
342 3p. cinnamon (21.2.75) .. 10 10
343 3½p. orange-brown (9.10.74) .. 2·75 4·00
344 5p. bright yellow-green (16.8.74) 60 10
    a. Coil stamp. Perf 14×14½ (21.3.77) 85 1·40
345 91 6p. blackish brn & slate (16.10.74) 90 1·75
346 106a 6p. slate (17.6.75) .. 20 10
347 91 7p. indigo and olive-green (27.9.74) 90 35
348 106a 7p. deep yellow-green (17.6.75) 35 10
    a. Booklet pane. No. 348×5 plus *se-tenant* label (21.3.77) 11·00
349 91 8p. dp brown & dp orge-brn (17.6.75) 75 50
350 106a 8p. chestnut (14.7.76) .. 30 10
351 91 9p. black & turquoise-green (12.74) 90 30
352 106a 9p. greenish slate (14.7.76) 30 10
352a 9½p. vermilion (3.12.79) .. 35 20
353 92 10p. multicoloured (II) (12.74) 1·50 30
354 91 10p. black and violet-blue (14.7.76) 85 10
354a 106a 10p. deep mauve (8.6.77) 70 10
355 91 11p. black and rose-carmine (14.7.76) 45 30
355a 12p. black and bright green (8.6.77) 55 10
355b 106a 12p. yellowish green (26.3.80) 30 10
355c 91 13p. reddish brn & red-brn (26.3.80) 40 1·25
356 92 15p. multicoloured (12.74) 55 40
356a 106a 15p. ultramarine (10.7.80) 40 10
356b 91 16p. black & dull yellow-grn (10.7.80) 40 80
356c 92 17p. multicoloured (8.6.77) 50 50
357 20p. multicoloured (13.6.74) 50 15
358 93 50p. multicoloured (I) (12.74) 70 30
    a. Type II (1983) .. .. 1·75 2·50
359 £1 multicoloured (17.6.75) 1·25 30
339/59 Set of 29 15·00 10·50
For 18p., 19p., 22p., 24p., 26p. and 29p. values printed by lithography, see Nos. 478/83.
Stamps with one or two sides imperf come from the booklet pane.

127 "Oliver Goldsmith"   **128** "Kitchen Table"
(statue by J. H. Foley)   (Norah McGuiness)

(Des P. Wildbur)

1974 (24 June). *Death Bicentenary of Oliver Goldsmith (writer). P* 14½ × 15.
360 127 3½p. black and olive-yellow .. 15 10
361 12p. black and bright yellowish green .. 60 1·00

(Design adapted by Norah McGuiness. Photo Harrison)

1974 (19 Aug). *Contemporary Irish Art (6th issue). P* 14 × 14½.
362 128 5p. multicoloured 35 30

129 Rugby Players   **130** U.P.U. "Postmark"

(Design adapted from Irish Press photograph. Eng C. Slania. Recess (3½p.) or recess and photo (12p.) Harrison)

1974 (9 Sept). *Centenary of Irish Rugby Football Union. P* 14½ × 14.
363 129 3½p. greenish black 30 10
    a. Deep greenish blue .. 7·50 3·50
364 12p. multicoloured .. .. 1·75 2·75
No. 363a is from a second printing using a recut plate on which the engraving was deeper.

(Des R. Ballagh)

1974 (9 Oct). *Centenary of Universal Postal Union. P* 14½ × 15.
365 130 5p. light yellowish green and black .. 25 10
366 7p. light ultramarine and black .. 35 80

131 "Madonna and Child"   **132** "Peace"
(Bellini)

(Des P. Wildbur)

1974 (14 Nov). *Christmas. P* 14½ × 15.
367 131 5p. multicoloured 15 10
368 15p. multicoloured 60 90

(Des Alexandra Wejchert)

1975 (24 Mar). *International Women's Year. P* 14½ × 15.
369 132 8p. brt reddish purple & ultramarine .. 25 75
370 15p. ultramarine and bright green .. 50 1·25

133 "Castletown Hunt" (R. Healy)

(Des R. Kyne)

1975 (28 Apr). *Europa. P* 15 × 14½.
371 133 7p. grey-black 75 15
372 9p. dull blue-green .. .. 1·25 2·50

134 Putting

(Des from photographs by J. McManus. Litho ("EIRE" and face value) and photo.)

1975 (26 June). *Ninth European Amateur Golf Team Championship, Killarney. P* 15 × 14½.
373 134 6p. multicoloured (*shades*) .. 75 45
374 – 9p. multicoloured (*shades*) .. 1·50 1·50
The 9p. is similar to T **134** but shows a different view of the putting green.

135 "Bird of Prey" (sculpture by   **136** Nano Nagle (founder)
Oisin Kelly)   and Waifs

(Design adapted by the artist)

1975 (28 July). *Contemporary Irish Art (7th issue).* P 15×14½.
375 135 15p. yellow-brown 65 75

(Des Kilkenny Design Workshops)

1975 (1 Sept). *Bicentenary of Presentation Order of Nuns.* P 14½ × 15.
376 136 5p. black and pale blue.. .. 20 10
377 7p. black and light stone 30 30

137 Tower of St. Anne's Church, Shandon
138 St. Oliver Plunkett (commemorative medal by Imogen Stuart)

(Des P. Scott)

1975 (6 Oct). *European Architectural Heritage Year. T 137 and similar vert design.* P 12½.
378 137 5p. blackish brown 20 10
379 6p. multicoloured 40 85
380 — 7p. steel-blue 40 10
381 — 9p. multicoloured 45 80
378/81 .. .. .. Set of 4 1·25 1·75
Design:—Nos. 380/1, Interior of Holycross Abbey, Co. Tipperary.

(Design adapted by the artist. Recess Harrison)

1975 (13 Oct). *Canonisation of Oliver Plunkett.* P 14 × 14½.
382 138 7p. black 15 10
383 15p. chestnut 55 45

139 "Madonna and Child" (Fra Filippo Lippi)
140 James Larkin (from a drawing by Sean O'Sullivan)

(Des P. Wildbur)

1975 (13 Nov). *Christmas.* P 15.
384 139 5p. multicoloured 15 10
385 7p. multicoloured 15 10
386 10p. multicoloured 45 30
384/6 .. .. .. Set of 3 65 40

(Des P. Wildbur. Litho)

1976 (21 Jan). *Birth Centenary of James Larkin (Trade Union leader).* P 14½×15.
387 140 7p. deep bluish green and pale grey 20 10
388 11p. sepia and yellow-ochre .. 40 55

141 Alexander Graham Bell
142 1847 Benjamin Franklin Essay

(Des R. Ballagh)

1976 (10 Mar). *Telephone Centenary.* P 14½ × 15.
389 141 9p. multicoloured 20 10
390 15p. multicoloured 45 50

(Des L. le Brocquy; graphics by P. Wildbur. Litho Irish Security Stamp Printing Ltd)

1976 (17 May). *Bicentenary of American Revolution. T 142 and similar horiz designs.* P 14½ × 14.
391 7p. ultramarine, light red and silver 15 10
a. Silver (inscr) omitted .. † £225
392 8p. ultramarine, light red and silver 20 1·10
393 9p. violet-blue, orange and silver .. 20 10
394 15p. light rose-red, grey-blue and silver 30 75
a. Silver (face-value and inscr) omitted £550 £650
391/4 .. .. .. Set of 4 75 1·75
MS395 95 × 75 mm. Nos. 391/4 .. 4·50 8·00
a. Silver omitted £1600
Designs:—7p. Thirteen stars; 8p. Fifty stars; 9, 15p. Type 142.
No. MS395 exists with the sheet margins overprinted in blue to commemorate "Stampa 76", the Irish National Stamp Exhibition.

143 Spirit Barrel

(Des P. Hickey)

1976 (1 July). *Europa. Irish Delft. T 143 and similar horiz design. Multicoloured.* P 15 × 14.
396 9p. Type 143 .. .. .. 40 20
397 11p. Dish .. .. 70 1·60

144 "The Lobster Pots, West of Ireland" (Paul Henry)

(Des R. McGrath)

1976 (30 Aug). *Contemporary Irish Art (8th issue).* P 15.
398 144 15p. multicoloured 60 60

145 Radio Waves

(Des G. Shepherd and A. O'Donnell. Litho De La Rue Smurfit Ltd, Dublin)

1976 (5 Oct). *50th Anniv of Irish Broadcasting Service. T 145 and similar vert design. Chalk-surfaced paper.* P 14½×14 (9p.) or 14×14½ (11p.).
399 9p. light new blue and bottle-green .. 20 10
400 11p. agate, orange-red and light new blue 60 1·00
Design:—11p. Transmitter, radio waves and globe.

146 "The Nativity" (Lorenzo Monaco)

(Des R. McGrath)

1976 (11 Nov). *Christmas.* P 15×14½.
401 146 7p. multicoloured 15 10
402 9p. multicoloured 15 10
403 15p. multicoloured 55 55
401/3 .. .. .. Set of 3 75 65

147 16th Century Manuscript
148 Ballynahinch, Galway

(Des P. Hickey)

1977 (9 May). *Centenaries of National Library (8p.) and National Museum (10p.). T 147 and similar horiz design. Multicoloured.* P 15 × 14½.
404 8p. Type 147 .. .. .. 30 30
405 10p. Prehistoric stone 40 35

(Des E. van der Grijn. Litho Irish Security Stamp Printing Ltd)

1977 (27 June). *Europa. T 148 and similar vert design. Multicoloured.* P 14 × 15.
406 10p. Type 148 .. .. .. 30 25
407 12p. Lough Tay, Wicklow .. .. 95 1·50

ALTERED CATALOGUE NUMBERS

Any Catalogue numbers altered from the last edition are shown as a list in the introductory pages.

149 "Head" (Louis le Brocquy)
150 Guide and Tents

(Design adapted by the artist. Litho Irish Security Stamp Ptg Ltd)

1977 (8 Aug). *Contemporary Irish Art (9th issue).* P 14 × 14½.
408 149 17p. multicoloured 55 75

(Des R. Ballagh)

1977 (22 Aug). *Scouting and Guiding. T 150 and similar horiz design. Multicoloured.* P 15 × 14½.
409 8p. Type 150 .. .. .. 35 10
410 17p. Tent and Scout saluting .. .. 75 1·75

151 "The Shanachie" (drawing by Jack B. Yeats)
152 "Electricity" (Golden Jubilee of Electricity Supply Board)

(Des L. Miller (10p.), R. Ballagh (12p.). Litho Irish Security Stamp Printing Ltd)

1977 (12 Sept). *Anniversaries. T 151 and similar horiz design.* P 14 × 14½ (10p.) or 14½ × 14 (12p.).
411 10p. black 25 15
412 12p. black .. .. 35 1·00
Designs and events:—10p. Type 151 (Golden jubilee of Irish Folklore Society; 12p. The philosopher Eriugena (1100th death anniv).

(Des R. Ballagh (10p.), P. Hickey (12p.), B. Blackshaw (17p.). Photo Stamping Branch of the Revenue Commissioners (12p.); Litho Irish Security Stamp Ptg Ltd (others))

1977 (10 Oct). *Golden Jubilees. T 152 and similar horiz designs.* P 15 × 14½ (12p.) or 15 × 14 (others).
413 10p. multicoloured 15 10
414 12p. multicoloured .. .. 30 1·40
415 17p. grey-black and grey-brown .. 40 85
413/15 .. .. .. Set of 3 75 2·10
Designs:—12p. Bulls (from contemporary coinage) (Jubilee of Agricultural Credit Corporation); 17p. Greyhound (Jubilee of greyhound track racing).

153 "The Holy Family" (Giorgione)
154 Junkers W.33 *Bremen* in Flight

(Des R. McGrath)

1977 (3 Nov). *Christmas.* P 14½ × 15.
416 153 8p. multicoloured 15 10
417 9p. multicoloured 15 10
418 17p. multicoloured .. .. 55 1·25
416/18 .. .. .. Set of 3 75 1·25

(Des R. Ballagh. Litho Irish Security Stamp Ptg Ltd)

1978 (13 Apr). *50th Anniv of First East–West Transatlantic Flight.* P 14 × 14½.
419 154 10p. bright blue and black .. 20 15
420 17p. olive-brown and black .. 35 1·10
The 17p. is as T 154, but shows a different sky and sea.

155 Spring Gentian
156 Catherine McAuley

(Des Wendy Walsh. Litho Irish Security Stamp Ptg Ltd)

1978 (12 June). *Wild Flowers.* T **155** and similar vert designs. Multicoloured. P 14 × 15.

421	8p. Type **155**		20	40
422	10p. Strawberry tree		25	15
423	11p. Large-flowered Butterwort		30	50
424	17p. St. Dabeoc's Heath		40	2·00
421/4		Set of 4	1·00	2·75

(Des R. Ballagh (10p.), R. Kyne (11p.), E. van der Grijn (17p.). Litho Irish Security Stamp Ptg Ltd)

1978 (18 Sept). *Anniversaries and Events.* T **156** and similar multicoloured designs. P 14½ × 14 (11p.) or 14 × 14½ (others).

425	10p. Type **156**		20	10
426	11p. Doctor performing vaccination (horiz)		30	80
427	17p. "Self Portrait"		40	1·10
425/7		Set of 3	80	1·75

Events:—10p. Birth bicentenary of Catherine McAuley (founder of Sisters of Mercy); 11p. Global eradication of Smallpox; 17p. Birth centenary of Sir William Orpen (painter).

157 Diagram of Drilling Rig   **158** Farthing

(Des R. Ballagh. Litho Irish Security Stamp Ptg Ltd)

1978 (18 Oct). *Arrival Onshore of Natural Gas.* P 14 × 14½.

428	**157**	10p. maroon, turquoise-green and bistre	30	30

(Des P. Wildbur and R. Mercer)

1978 (26 Oct). *50th Anniv of Irish Currency.* T **158** and similar horiz designs. P 15 × 14½.

429	8p. black, copper and deep bluish green		20	20
430	10p. black, silver and blue-green		25	10
431	11p. black, copper and chocolate		25	50
432	17p. black, silver and deep blue		40	1·00
429/32		Set of 4	1·00	1·60

Designs:—10p. Florin; 11p. Penny; 17p. Half-crown.

159 "The Virgin and Child" (Guercino)   **160** Conolly Folly, Castletown

(Des P. Wildbur)

1978 (16 Nov). *Christmas.* P 14½ × 15.

433	**159**	8p. purple-brown, gold and pale turquoise-green	15	10
434		10p. purple-brown, chocolate and pale turquoise-green	15	10
435		17p. purple-brown, deep blue-green and pale turquoise-green	45	1·40
433/5		Set of 3	65	1·40

(Des R. McGrath)

1978 (6 Dec). *Europa. Architecture.* T **160** and similar horiz design. P 15 × 14½.

436	10p. lake-brown and red-brown		30	15
437	11p. green and deep green		30	1·00

Design:—11p. Dromoland Belvedere.

161 Athletes in Cross-country Race   **162** "European Communities" (in languages of member nations)

(Des R. Mercer. Litho Irish Security Stamp Ptg Ltd)

1979 (20 Aug). *7th World Cross-country Championships, Limerick.* P 14½ × 14.

438	**161**	8p. multicoloured	20	30

(Des P. Wildbur)

1979 (20 Aug). *First Direct Elections to European Assembly.* P 14½ × 15.

439	**162**	10p. dull turquoise-green	15	15
440		11p. reddish violet	15	35

163 Sir Rowland Hill   **164** Winter Wren (*Troglodytes troglodytes*)

(Des C. Harrison. Litho Irish Security Stamp Ptg Ltd)

1979 (20 Aug). *Death Centenary of Sir Rowland Hill.* P 14 × 14½.

441	**163**	17p. black, brownish grey and red	30	60

(Des Wendy Walsh. Litho Irish Security Stamp Ptg Ltd)

1979 (30 Aug). *Birds.* T **164** and similar horiz designs. Multicoloured. P 14½ × 14.

442	8p. Type **164**		40	70
443	10p. Great Crested Grebe (*Podiceps cristatus*)		40	15
444	11p. White-fronted Goose (*Anser albifrons flavirostris*)		45	70
445	17p. Peregrine Falcon (*Falco peregrinus*)		70	2·00
442/5		Set of 4	1·75	3·25

165 "A Happy Flower" (David Gallagher)

(Des P. Wildbur. Litho Irish Security Stamp Ptg Ltd)

1979 (13 Sept). *International Year of the Child. Paintings by Children.* T **165** and similar multicoloured designs. P 14 × 14½ (11p.) or 14½ × 14 (others).

446	10p. Type **165**		20	10
447	11p. "Myself and My Skipping Rope" (Lucy Norman) (vert)		25	60
448	17p. "Swans on a Lake" (Nicola O'Dwyer)		35	85
446/8		Set of 3	70	1·40

166 Pope John Paul II

(Des P. Byrne. Litho Irish Security Stamp Ptg Ltd)

1979 (29 Sept). *Visit of Pope John Paul II.* P 14½ × 14.

449	**166**	12p. multicoloured	30	20

167 Brother and Child

(Des R. Kyne (9½p.), P. Scott (11p.), R. Mercer (20p.). Photo Stamping Branch of the Revenue Commissioners, Dublin (11p.), Litho Irish Security Stamp Ptg Ltd (others))

1979 (4 Oct). *Commemorations.* T **167** and similar designs. P 14½ × 14 (9½p.), 14½ × 15 (11p.) or 14 × 14½ (others).

450	9½p. black and pale claret		20	10
451	11p. black, reddish orange and bright blue		20	70
452	20p. multicoloured		40	1·40
450/2		Set of 3	70	2·00

Designs and commemorations: Horiz—9½p. Type **167** (Centenary of Hospitaller Order of St. John of God in Ireland); 20p. "Seated Figure" (sculpture by F. E. McWilliam) (Contemporary Irish Art (10th issue)). Vert—11p. Windmill and Sun (International Energy Conservation Month).

PRICES OF SETS

Set prices are given for many issues, generally those containing three stamps or more. Definitive sets include one of each value or major colour change, but do not cover different perforations, die types or minor shades. Where a choice is possible the set prices are based on the cheapest versions of the stamps included in the listings.

168 Patrick Pearse, "Liberty" and General Post Office, Dublin   **169** Madonna and Child (panel painting from Domnach Airgid Shrine)

(Des R. Ballagh)

1979 (10 Nov). *Birth Centenary of Patrick Pearse (patriot).* P 15 × 14½.

453	**168**	12p. multicoloured	30	15

(Des Ewa Gargulinska)

1979 (15 Nov). *Christmas.* P 14½ × 15.

454	**169**	9½p. multicoloured	15	10
455		20p. multicoloured	30	55

170 Bianconi Long Car, 1836   **171** John Baptist de la Salle (founder)

(Des P. Wildbur. Litho Irish Security Stamp Ptg Ltd)

1979 (6 Dec). *Europa. Communications.* T **170** and similar horiz design. Multicoloured. P 14½ × 14.

456	12p. Type **170**		20	30
457	13p. Transatlantic cable, Valentia, 1866		30	1·40

(Des P. Wildbur. Litho Irish Security Stamp Ptg Ltd)

1980 (19 Mar). *Centenary of arrival of De La Salle Order.* P 14 × 14½.

458	**171**	12p. multicoloured	30	30

172 George Bernard Shaw   **173** Stoat

(Des P. Byrne. Litho Irish Security Stamp Ptg Ltd)

1980 (7 May). *Europa. Personalities.* T **172** and similar multicoloured design. P 14 × 14½.

459	12p. Type **172**		40	50
460	13p. Oscar Wilde (28 × 38 mm)		40	1·00

(Des Wendy Walsh. Litho Irish Security Stamp Ptg Ltd)

1980 (30 July). *Wildlife.* T **173** and similar vert designs. Multicoloured. P 14 × 14½.

461	12p. Type **173**		20	40
462	15p. Arctic Hare		20	15
463	16p. Red Fox		20	50
464	25p. Red Deer		30	1·40
461/4		Set of 4	80	2·25
MS465	73 × 97 mm. Nos. 461/4		1·00	2·75

No. **MS**465 exists with the sheet margins overprinted to commemorate "STAMPA 80", the Irish National Stamp Exhibition, in black or red, and for the Dublin Stamp Show, 1992, in red.

174 Playing Bodhran and Whistle   **175** Sean O'Casey

(Des J. Dixon and P. Wildbur. Litho Irish Security Stamp Ptg Ltd)

1980 (25 Sept). *Traditional Music and Dance. T **174** and similar vert designs. Multicoloured.* P 14 × 14½.
466	12p. Type 174			15	10
467	15p. Playing Uilleann pipes	..	..	20	15
468	25p. Dancing	..	..	35	1·10
466/8	..	*Set of 3*		65	1·25

(Des P. Wildbur (12p.), P. Scott (25p.). Litho Irish Security Stamp Ptg Ltd)

1980 (23 Oct). *Commemorations. T **175** and similar vert design.* P 14 × 14½.
469	12p. multicoloured			15	10
470	25p. black, buff and drab			30	55

Designs and commemorations:—12p. Type 175 (Birth centenary of Sean O'Casey (playwright)); 25p. "Gold Painting No. 57" (Patrick Scott) (Contemporary Irish Art (11th issue)).

176 Nativity Scene (painting by Geraldine McNulty)

177 Boyle Air-pump, 1659

(Des P. Wildbur)

1980 (13 Nov). *Christmas.* P 14½ × 15.
471	**176** 12p. multicoloured			15	10
472	15p. multicoloured	..	..	20	10
473	25p. multicoloured			40	1·25
471/3	..	*Set of 3*		65	1·25

(Des P. Wildbur. Litho Irish Security Stamp Ptg Ltd)

1981 (12 Mar). *Irish Science and Technology. T **177** and similar vert designs. Multicoloured.* P 14 × 14½.
474	12p. Type 177			20	10
475	15p. Ferguson tractor, 1936			25	10
476	16p. Parsons turbine, 1884	..	..	25	90
477	25p. Holland submarine, 1878			30	1·25
474/7	..	*Set of 4*		90	2·10

(Litho Irish Security Stamp Ptg Ltd)

1981 (27 Apr)–**82**. *No wmk.* P 14 × 14½.
478	**106a** 18p. dull claret	..	..	45	50
479	19p. light blue			55	1·75
480	22p. dull turquoise-blue (1.9.81)			65	10
481	24p. drab (29.10.81)		..	75	95
482	26p. blue-green (1.4.82)			1·50	40
483	29p. purple (1.4.82)			1·75	2·00
478/83	..	*Set of 6*		5·00	5·00

178 "The Legend of the Cock and the Pot"

179 Cycling

(Des P. Byrne. Litho Irish Security Stamp Ptg Ltd)

1981 (4 May). *Europa. Folklore. Paintings by Maria Simonds-Gooding. T **178** and similar vert design.* P 14 × 14½.
491	18p. black, orange-yellow and carmine	..	25	10
492	19p. black, yellow-orange and yellow		35	70

Design:—19p. "The Angel with the Scales of Judgement".

(Des R. Ballagh. Litho Irish Security Stamp Ptg Ltd)

1981 (24 June). *50th Anniv of "An Óige" (Irish Youth Hostel Association). T **179** and similar multicoloured designs.* P 14 × 14½ (15, 30p.) or 14½ × 14 (others).
493	15p. Type 179			25	40
494	18p. Hill-walking (horiz)			25	10
495	19p. Mountaineering (horiz)			25	95
496	30p. Rock-climbing			40	95
493/6	..	*Set of 4*		1·00	2·25

180 Jeremiah O'Donovan Rossa
181 "Railway Embankment" (W. J. Leech)

(Des C. Harrison. Litho Irish Security Stamp Ptg Ltd)

1981 (31 Aug). *Birth Anniv of Jeremiah O'Donovan Rossa (politician).* P 14 × 14½.
497	**180** 15p. multicoloured			30	30

(Des P. Wildbur. Litho Irish Security Stamp Ptg Ltd)

1981 (31 Aug). *Contemporary Irish Art (12th issue).* P 14½ × 14.
498	**181** 30p. multicoloured	..	..	60	60

182 James Hoban and White House
183 "Arkle" (steeplechaser)

(Des B. Thompson. Litho Irish Security Stamp Ptg Ltd)

1981 (29 Sept). *150th Death Anniv of James Hoban (White House architect).* P 14½ × 14.
499	**182** 18p. multicoloured	..	..	30	30

(Des Wendy Walsh and P. Wildbur. Litho Irish Security Stamp Ptg Ltd)

1981 (23 Oct). *Famous Irish Horses. T **183** and similar horiz designs. Multicoloured. Ordinary paper (18p.) or chalk-surfaced paper (others).* P 14½ × 14.
500	18p. Type 183	..	..	40	1·00
	a. Pair. Nos. 500/1			80	2·00
501	18p. "Boomerang" (showjumper)		40	1·00
502	22p. "King of Diamonds" (Draught horse)	40	30
503	24p. "Ballymoss" (flatracer)		40	70
504	36p. "Coosheen Finn" (Connemara pony)	60	1·00
500/4	..	*Set of 5*		2·00	3·50

The 18p values were printed together, *se-tenant*, in horizontal and vertical pairs throughout the sheet.

184 "Nativity" (F. Barocci)
185 Eviction Scene

(Des P. Wildbur. Litho Irish Security Stamp Ptg Ltd)

1981 (19 Nov). *Christmas. Chalk-surfaced paper.* P 14 × 14½.
505	**184** 18p. multicoloured			20	10
506	22p. multicoloured			25	10
507	36p. multicoloured	..	..	45	2·00
505/7	..	*Set of 3*		80	2·00

(Des R. Mercer (18p.), P. Wildbur (22p.). Litho Irish Security Stamp Ptg Ltd)

1981 (10 Dec). *Anniversaries. T **185** and similar multicoloured design. Chalk-surfaced paper.* P 14 × 14½ (18p.) or 14½ × 14 (22p.).
508	18p. Type 185	..	..	35	25
509	22p. Royal Dublin Society emblem (horiz)	40	30

Anniversaries—18p. Centenary of Land Law (Ireland) Act; 22p. 250th of Royal Dublin Society (organization for the advancement of agriculture, industry, art and science).

186 Upper Lake, Killarney National Park
187 "The Stigmatization of St Francis" (Sassetta)

(Des P. Wildbur. Litho Irish Security Stamp Ptg Ltd)

1982 (26 Feb). *50th Anniv of Killarney National Park. T **186** and similar horiz design. Multicoloured.* P 14½ × 14.
510	18p. Type 186			35	20
511	36p. Eagle's Nest			65	1·60

(Des P. Wildbur (22p.), M. Craig (24p.). Litho Irish Security Stamp Ptg Ltd)

1982 (2 Apr). *Religious Anniversaries. T **187** and similar horiz design. Chalk-surfaced paper.* P 14 × 14½ (22p.) or 14½ × 14 (24p.).
512	22p. multicoloured			35	15
513	24p. olive-brown			40	80

Designs and anniversaries:—22p. Type 187 (800th birth anniv of St Francis of Assisi (founder of Franciscan Order)); 24p. Francis Makemie (founder of American Presbyterianism) and old Presbyterian Church, Ramelton, Co Donegal (300th anniv of ordination).

188 The Great Famine, 1845–50
189 Pádraic Ó Conaire (writer) (Birth Centenary)

(Des P. Wildbur. Litho Irish Security Stamp Ptg Ltd)

1982 (4 May). *Europa. Historic Events. T **188** and similar design. Chalk-surfaced paper.* P 14 × 14½ (26p.) or 14½ × 14 (29p.).
514	26p. black and stone			80	50
515	29p. multicoloured	..	..	80	2·00

Design: *Horiz*—29p. The coming of Christianity to Ireland.

(Des P. Wildbur. Litho Irish Security Stamp Ptg Ltd)

1982 (16 June). *Anniversaries of Cultural Figures. T **189** and similar vert designs. Chalk-surfaced paper.* P 14 × 14½.
516	22p. black and light blue			25	30
517	26p. black and sepia	..	..	30	30
518	29p. black and blue			40	1·25
519	44p. black and greenish grey	..	50	1·75
516/19	..	*Set of 4*		1·25	3·25

Designs and anniversaries—26p. James Joyce (writer) (Birth centenary); 29p. John Field (musician) (Birth bicentenary); 44p. Charles Kickham (writer) (Death centenary).

190 Porbeagle Shark (Lamna nasus)
191 St. Patrick (Galway hooker)

(Des Wendy Walsh and P. Wildbur. Litho Irish Security Stamp Ptg Ltd)

1982 (29 July). *Marine Life. T **190** and similar horiz designs. Multicoloured. Chalk-surfaced paper.* P 14½ × 14.
520	22p. Type 190			55	1·25
521	22p. Common European Oyster (Ostrea edulis)		55	1·25
522	26p. Atlantic Salmon (Salmo salar)		70	30
523	29p. Dublin Bay Prawn (Nephrops norvegicus)		70	2·25
520/3	..	*Set of 4*		2·25	4·50

(Des P. Wildbur. Litho Irish Security Stamp Ptg Ltd)

1982 (21 Sept). *Irish Boats. T **191** and similar multicoloured designs. Ordinary paper (26p.) or chalk-surfaced paper (others).* P 14 × 14½ (Nos. 524 and 527) or 14½ × 14 (others).
524	22p. Type 191			60	1·25
525	22p. Currach (horiz)			60	1·25
526	26p. Asgard II (cadet brigantine) (horiz)		60	30
527	29p. Howth 17 foot yacht			60	2·25
524/7	..	*Set of 4*		2·25	4·50

192 "Irish House of Commons" (painting by Francis Wheatley)
193 "Madonna and Child" (sculpture)

(Des P. Wildbur (22p.) or R. Ballagh (26p.). Litho Irish Security Stamp Ptg Ltd)

1982 (14 Oct). *Bicentenary of Grattan's Parliament (22p.) and Birth Centenary of Eamon de Valera (26p.). T **192** and similar multicoloured design.* P 14½ × 14 (22p.) or 14 × 14½ (26p.).
528	22p. Type 192			35	1·25
529	26p. Eamon de Valera (vert)			40	40

(Des P. Wildbur. Litho Irish Security Stamp Ptg Ltd)

1982 (11 Nov). *Christmas.* P 14 × 14½.
530	**193** 22p. multicoloured			30	90
531	26p. multicoloured	..	..	30	35

NEW INFORMATION

The editor is always interested to correspond with people who have new information that will improve or correct the Catalogue.

194 Aughnanure Castle   195 Ouzel Galley Goblet

(Des M. Craig and P. Wildbur. Litho Irish Security Stamp Ptg Ltd)

1982 (15 Dec)–**90**. *Irish Architecture. T* **194** *and similar designs. Chalk-surfaced paper* (24, 28, 32, 37, 39, 46p., £1 (*No.* 550b), £2) *or ordinary paper* (*others*) *P* 15×14 (15, 20, 22, 23, 24, 26, 39, 46, 50p., £1 (*No.* 550), £2, £5) *or* 14×15 (*others*).

532	1p. dull violet-blue (6.7.83)		10	10
	a. Chalk-surfaced paper (9.87)		40	40
533	2p. deep yellow-green (6.7.83)		20	10
	a. Chalk-surfaced paper (27.6.85)		50	40
	ab. Booklet pane. Nos. 533a, 543a and 545a, each × 2		4·50	
	ac. Booklet pane. Nos. 533a, 543a and 545a, each × 4		7·50	
	ad. Booklet pane. Nos. 533a×2, 535b×3, 544a×3 and 545c×4 (8.9.86)		7·50	
	ae. Booklet pane. Nos. 533a×4, 535b, 544a×2 and 545c×5 (24.11.88)		8·00	
534	3p. black (6.7.83)		20	10
	a. Chalk-surfaced paper (2.88)		90	90
535	4p. maroon (16.3.83)		20	10
	a. Booklet pane. Nos. 535×3, 543×4 and 1 label (15.8.83)		2·00	
	b. Chalk-surfaced paper (9.7.84)		40	40
	ba. Booklet pane. Nos. 535b×3, 543a×5 and 545a×4		5·00	
	c. Perf 13½ (3.5.90)		3·00	4·00
	ca. Booklet pane. Nos. 535c×3, 545b, 752ab×2 and 754ab×2		23·00	
536	5p. olive-sepia (6.7.83)		30	10
	a. Chalk-surfaced paper (8.87)		70	30
537	6p. deep grey-blue (16.3.83)		30	15
	a. Chalk-surfaced paper (11.85)		1·75	1·75
538	7p. dull yellow-green (16.3.83)		30	15
	a. Chalk-surfaced paper (3.88)		2·00	2·00
539	10p. black (6.7.83)		30	10
	a. Chalk-surfaced paper (3.87)		85	30
540	12p. purple-brown (6.7.83)		30	30
	a. Chalk-surfaced paper (5.87)		3·25	3·25
541	15p. deep yellow-green (6.7.83)		45	35
542	20p. deep brown-purple (16.3.83)		50	45
	a. Chalk-surfaced paper (12.84)		1·75	1·75
543	22p. chalky blue		50	10
	a. Chalk-surfaced paper (9.7.84)		1·75	50
544	23p. yellow-green (16.3.83)		85	80
544a	24p. bistre-brown (27.6.85)		1·25	35
	ab. Ordinary paper (9.87)		3·50	2·00
545	26p. blackish brown		75	10
	a. Chalk-surfaced paper (9.7.84)		1·25	30
	b. Perf 13½ (3.5.90)		5·00	6·50
545c	28p. maroon (27.6.85)		75	45
	ca. Ordinary paper (10.87)		9·00	9·00
546	29p. deep yellow-green		90	65
547	30p. black (16.3.83)		70	70
	a. Chalk-surfaced paper (3.87)		70	90
	b. Perf 13½ (3.5.90)		5·00	6·50
	ba. Booklet pane. Nos. 547b, 754ab and 774a/5a		9·00	
	bb. Booklet pane. Nos. 547b×2, 754ab×2 and 774a		11·00	
547c	32p. bistre-brown (1.5.86)		1·75	2·50
	ca. Ordinary paper (9.90)		5·00	7·00
547d	37p. chalky blue (27.6.85)		90	1·60
547e	39p. maroon (1.5.86)		2·25	2·75
548	44p. black and grey		90	90
	a. Chalk-surfaced paper (4.85)		3·25	3·00
548b	46p. olive-green and brownish grey (1.5.86)		5·00	2·00
	ba. Ordinary paper (9.87)		15·00	15·00
549	50p. dull ultramarine and grey (16.3.83)		1·00	65
	a. Chalk-surfaced paper (12.84)		2·50	90
550	£1 bistre-brown and grey		3·75	3·00
	a. Chalk-surfaced paper (9.84)		10·00	7·50
550b	£1 chalky blue & brownish grey (27.6.85)		3·25	1·25
	ba. Ordinary paper (1.88)		16·00	16·00
550c	£2 grey-olive and black (26.7.88)		4·25	4·50
551	£5 crimson and grey		10·00	5·00
	a. Chalk-surfaced paper (8.87)		30·00	30·00
532/51		*Set of 28*	35·00	24·00

Designs: *Horiz* (as *T* **194**)—1p. to 5p. Central Pavilion, Dublin Botanic Gardens; 6p. to 12p. Dr. Steevens' Hospital, Dublin; 28p. to 37p. St. MacDara's Church. (37×21 *mm*)—46p., £1 (*No.* 550) Cahir Castle: 50p., £2 Casino, Marino; £5 Central Bus Station, Dublin. *Vert* (as *T* **194**— 15p. to 22p. Type **194**; 23p. to 26p., 39p. Cormac's Chapel. (21×37 *mm*)—44p., £1 (*No.* 550b) Killarney Cathedral.

The following stamps first appeared in booklet panes, but were later issued in sheets: Nos. 533a (7.86), 535b (7.85), 543a (10.84) and 545a (1.85).

Nos. 533ab/ae and 535a/ba show the horizontal edges of the panes imperforate so that 2, 22 and 26p. values from them exist imperforate at top, bottom, left or right, the 4p. at top or bottom the 24p. at right and the 28p. at top.

No. 535ba comes from a £2 Discount booklet and shows "Booklet Stamp" printed over the gum on the reverse of each stamp.

Nos. 535c, 545b and 547b are on ordinary paper and come from the 1990 150th Anniversary of the Penny Black £6 booklet. Examples of Nos. 535c, 545b and 752ab from the right-hand column of booklet pane No. 535ca are imperforate at right (4p.) or top (others). In booklet pane No. 547bb Nos. 547b and 754ab are imperforate at right.

Booklet pane No. 547ba exists with the margins overprinted to commemorate "New Zealand 1990" International Stamp Exhibition Auckland, and No. 547bb with the margins overprinted in blue for "STAMPA 90", the Irish National Stamp Exhibition.

Nos. 550/a were withdrawn without warning on 14 November 1984 after the authorities had discovered forged examples of the

£1 stamp used in P.O. savings books. Such forgeries, which it is believed were not used for postal purposes, are line perforated 14.75 or 12 instead of the 14.75×14 comb perforation of the genuine and also show the foot of the "1" rounded instead of square.

(Des P. Wildbur (22p.), C. Harrison (26p.). Litho Irish Security Stamp Ptg Ltd)

1983 (23 Feb). *Bicentenaries of Dublin Chamber of Commerce* (22p.) *and Bank of Ireland* (26p.). *T* **195** *and similar multicoloured design. P* 14 × 14½ (22p.) *or* 14½ × 14 (26p.).

552	22p. Type **195**		30	55
553	26p. Bank of Ireland building (*horiz*)		35	35

196 Pádraig O Siochfhradha (writer and teacher) (Birth cent)   197 Neolithic Carved Pattern, Newgrange Tomb

(Des C. Harrison (26p.), R. Ballagh (29p.). Litho Irish Security Stamp Ptg Ltd)

1983 (7 Apr). *Anniversaries. T* **196** *and similar vert design. Multicoloured. P* 14 × 14½.

554	26p. Type **196**		50	75
555	29p. Young Boys' Brigade member (Centenary)		60	1·50

(Des L. le Brocquy (26p.), P. Wildbur (29p.). Litho Irish Security Stamp Ptg Ltd)

1983 (4 May). *Europa. T* **197** *and similar horiz design. P* 14½ × 14.

556	26p. grey-black and gold		1·75	50
557	29p. black, blackish brown and gold		4·00	5·00

Design:—29p. Sir William Rowan Hamilton's formulae for the multiplication of quaternions.

198 Kerry Blue Terrier

(Des Wendy Walsh and L. Miller. Litho Irish Security Stamp Ptg Ltd)

1983 (23 June). *Irish Dogs. T* **198** *and similar horiz designs. Multicoloured. P* 14½ × 14.

558	22p. Type **198**		65	35
559	26p. Irish Wolfhound		75	45
560	26p. Irish Water Spaniel		75	45
561	29p. Irish Terrier		95	2·25
562	44p. Irish Setters		1·40	2·50
558/62		*Set of 5*	4·00	5·00
MS563	142 × 80 mm. Nos. 558/62		6·00	8·00

No. **MS563** exists with the sheet margins overprinted in blue to commemorate "STAMPA 83", the Irish National Stamp Exhibition.

199 Animals (Irish Society for the Prevention of Cruelty to Animals)   200 Postman with Bicycle

(Des Wendy Walsh (No. 564), B. Murphy (No. 566), K. Uhlemann (No. 567), R. Ballagh (others). Litho Irish Security Stamp Ptg Ltd)

1983 (11 Aug). *Anniversaries and Commemorations. T* **199** *and similar designs. P* 14½ × 14 (*Nos.* 564, 566) *or* 14 × 14½ (*others*).

564	199	22p. multicoloured	50	1·00
565	—	22p. multicoloured	50	1·00
566	—	26p. multicoloured	50	60
567	—	26p. multicoloured	50	60
568	—	44p. grey-blue and black	75	2·00
564/8			*Set of 5* 2·50	4·75

Designs: *Vert*—No. 565, Sean Mac Diarmada (patriot) (Birth cent); No. 567, "St. Vincent de Paul in the Streets of Paris" (150th anniv of Society of St. Vincent de Paul); No. 568, "Andrew Jackson" (Frank McKelvey) (President of the United States). *Horiz*—No. 566, "100" (Centenary of Industrial Credit Company).

(Des R. Ballagh. Litho Irish Security Stamp Ptg Ltd)

1983 (15 Sept). *World Communications Year. T* **200** *and similar vert design. Multicoloured. P* 14 × 14½.

569	22p. Type **200**		55	75
570	29p. Dish antenna		70	2·00

201 Weaving   202 "La Natividad" (R. van der Weyden)

(Des R. Mercer. Litho Irish Security Stamp Ptg Ltd)

1983 (13 Oct). *Irish Handicrafts. T* **201** *and similar vert designs. Multicoloured. P* 14 × 14½.

571	22p. Type **201**		40	50
572	26p. Basketmaking		40	35
573	29p. Irish crochet		45	1·25
574	44p. Harpmaking		70	2·00
571/4		*Set of 4*	1·75	3·50

(Des and litho Irish Security Stamp Ptg Ltd)

1983 (30 Nov). *Christmas. P* 14 × 14½.

575	202	22p. multicoloured	35	30
576		26p. multicoloured	40	30

203 Dublin and Kingstown Railway Steam Locomotive *Princess*

(Des C. Rycroft. Litho Irish Security Stamp Ptg Ltd)

1984 (30 Jan). *150th Anniv of Irish Railways. T* **203** *and similar horiz designs. Multicoloured. Ordinary paper* (23p., 26p. *and miniature sheet*) *or chalk-surfaced paper* (*others*). *P* 15×14.

577	23p. Type **203**		75	1·25
578	26p. Great Southern Railway steam locomotive *Macha*		75	35
579	29p. Great Northern Railway steam locomotive No. 87 *Kestrel*		85	1·75
580	44p. Coras Iompair Eireann two-car electric unit		1·10	2·25
577/80		*Set of 4*	3·00	5·00
MS581	129×77 mm. Nos. 577/80		4·75	7·00

No. **MS581** exists with the sheet margins overprinted in black to commemorate "STAMPA 84", the Irish National Stamp Exhibition.

204 Sorbus hibernica

(Des Wendy Walsh and P. Wildbur. Litho Irish Security Stamp Ptg Ltd)

1984 (1 Mar). *Irish Trees. T* **204** *and similar horiz designs. Multicoloured. P* 15 × 14.

582	22p. Type **204**		65	70
583	26p. *Taxus baccata fastigiata*		70	40
584	29p. *Salix hibernica*		85	2·00
585	44p. *Betula pubescens*		1·10	2·75
582/5		*Set of 4*	3·00	5·25

205 St. Vincent's Hospital, Dublin

(Des B. Donegan, adapted by C. Vis (26p.), B. Murphy (44p.). Litho Irish Security Stamp Ptg Ltd)

1984 (12 Apr). *150th Anniv of St. Vincent's Hospital and Bicentenary of Royal College of Surgeons. T* **205** *and similar horiz design. Multicoloured. P* 15 × 14.

586	26p. Type **205**		50	30
587	44p. Royal College and logo		90	1·50

206 C.E.P.T. 25th Anniversary Logo

(Des J. Larrivière. Litho Irish Security Stamp Ptg Ltd)

1984 (10 May). *Europa.* P 15 × 14.
588 206 26p. blue, deep dull blue and black .. 1·75 50
589 29p. light green, blue-green and black .. 2·25 2·75

207 Flags on Ballot Box   **208** John McCormack

(Des R. Ballagh. Litho Irish Security Stamp Ptg Ltd)

1984 (10 May). *Second Direct Elections to European Assembly.* P 15 × 14.
590 207 26p. multicoloured 50 70

(Des R. Mercer and J. Sharpe. Litho Irish Security Stamp Ptg Ltd)
1984 (6 June). *Birth Centenary of John McCormack (tenor).* P 14 × 15.
591 208 22p. multicoloured 50 70

209 Hammer-throwing

(Des L. le Brocquy and P. Wildbur. Litho Irish Security Stamp Ptg Ltd)

1984 (21 June). *Olympic Games, Los Angeles. T 209 and similar horiz designs.* P 15 × 14.
592 22p. deep mauve, black and gold 35 80
593 26p. violet, black and gold 40 65
594 29p. bright blue, black and gold .. .. 60 1·25
592/4 .. .. .. *Set of 3* 1·25 2·50
Designs:—26p. Hurdling; 29p. Running.

210 Hurling   **211** Galway Mayoral Chain (500th Anniv of Mayoral Charter)

(Des C. Harrison. Litho Irish Security Stamp Ptg Ltd)

1984 (23 Aug). *Centenary of Gaelic Athletic Association. T 210 and similar multicoloured design.* P 15 × 14 (22p.) or 14 × 15 (26p.).
595 22p. Type 210 .. .. 50 90
596 26p. Irish football (vert) 60 90

(Des P. Wildbur. Litho Irish Security Stamp Ptg Ltd)

1984 (18 Sept). *Anniversaries. T 211 and similar multicoloured design.* P 14 × 15 (26p.) or 15 × 14 (44p.).
597 26p. Type 211 .. .. 35 50
598 44p. St. Brendan (from 15th-cent Bodleian manuscript) (1500th birth anniv) (horiz) 75 1·50

212 Hands passing Letter   **213** "Virgin and Child" (Sassoferrato)

(Litho Irish Security Stamp Ptg Ltd)

1984 (19 Oct). *Bicentenary of the Irish Post Office.* P 15 × 14.
599 212 26p. multicoloured 60 70

(Des O'Connor O'Sullivan Advertising (17p.), P. Wildbur (others). Litho Irish Security Stamp Ptg Ltd)

1984 (26 Nov). *Christmas. T 213 and similar multicoloured design. Chalk-surfaced paper.* P 15 × 14 (17p.) or 14 × 15 (others).
600 17p. Christmas star (horiz) 45 80
601 22p. Type 213 .. .. .. 45 1·25
602 26p. Type 213 .. .. .. 65 40
600/2 .. .. *Set of 3* 1·40 2·25
No. 600 represented a special concession rate for Christmas card postings to addresses within Ireland and Great Britain between 26 November and 8 December 1984.

214 "Love" and Heart-shaped Balloon   **215** Dunsink Observatory (Bicentenary)

(Des Susan Dubsky (22p.), Patricia Jorgensen (26p.). Litho Irish Security Stamp Ptg Ltd)

1985 (31 Jan). *Greetings Stamps. T 214 and similar multicoloured design. Chalk-surfaced paper.* P 15 × 14 (22p.) or 14 × 15 (26p.).
603 22p. Type 214 .. .. 50 75
604 26p. Bouquet of hearts and flowers (vert) 60 75

(Des R. Ballagh (22, 44p.), K. Thomson (26p.), M. Lunt (37p.). Litho Irish Security Stamp Ptg Ltd)

1985 (14 Mar). *Anniversaries. T 215 and similar designs. Multicoloured. Chalk-surfaced paper.* P 15 × 14 (26p.) or 14 × 15 (others).
605 22p. Type 215 .. .. 50 50
606 26p. "A Landscape at Tivoli, Cork, with Boats" (Nathaniel Grogan) (800th anniv of City of Cork) (horiz) 50 30
607 37p. Royal Irish Academy (Bicentenary) .. 70 1·75
608 44p. Richard Crosbie's balloon flight (Bicentenary of first aeronautic flight by an Irishman) .. .. 80 1·75
605/8 .. .. .. *Set of 4* 2·25 3·75

216 *Polyommatus icarus*   **217** Charles Villiers Stanford (composer)

(Des I. Loe. Litho Irish Security Stamp Ptg Ltd)

1985 (11 Apr). *Butterflies. T 216 and similar vert designs. Multicoloured. Chalk-surfaced paper.* P 14 × 15.
609 22p. Type 216 .. .. .. 1·25 1·00
610 26p. Vanessa atalanta .. .. 1·25 70
611 28p. Gonepteryx rhamni .. .. 1·50 2·75
612 44p. Eurodryas aurinia .. .. 2·00 3·00
609/12 .. .. .. *Set of 4* 5·50 6·75

(Des P. Hickey and J. Farrar. Litho Irish Security Stamp Ptg Ltd)

1985 (16 May). *Europa. Irish Composers. T 217 and similar horiz design. Multicoloured. Chalk-surfaced paper.* P 15 × 14.
613 22p. Type 217 .. .. .. 2·00 50
614 37p. Turlough Carolan (composer and lyricist) .. .. .. 4·00 5·50

218 George Frederick Handel   **219** U.N. Patrol of Irish Soldiers, Congo, 1960 (25th Anniv. of Irish Participation in U.N. Peace-keeping Force)

(Des K. Uhlemann and J. Farrar. Litho Irish Security Stamp Ptg Ltd)

1985 (16 May). *European Music Year. Composers. T 218 and similar vert designs. Multicoloured. Chalk-surfaced paper.* P 14 × 15.
615 22p. Type 218 .. .. .. 1·25 2·50
a. Pair. Nos. 615/16 .. .. 2·50 5·00
616 22p. Guiseppe Domenico Scarlatti .. 1·25 2·50
617 26p. Johann Sebastian Bach .. .. 1·50 1·50
615/17 .. .. .. *Set of 3* 3·50 5·00
Nos. 615/16 were printed together, se-tenant, in horizontal and vertical pairs throughout the sheet.

(Des B. Donegan and J. Farrar (22p.), R. Ballagh (26p.), B. Donegan (44p.). Litho Irish Security Stamp Ptg Ltd)

1985 (20 June). *Anniversaries. T 219 and similar multicoloured designs. Chalk-surfaced paper.* P 15 × 14 (22p.) or 14 × 15 (others).
618 22p. Type 219 .. .. .. 65 80
619 26p. Thomas Ashe (patriot) (Birth cent) (vert) 65 60
620 44p. "Bishop George Berkeley" (James Lathan) (philosopher) (300th birth anniv) (vert) .. .. 1·00 3·00
618/20 .. .. *Set of 3* 2·10 4·00

220 Group of Young People

(Des J. Farrar and N. Mooney. Litho Irish Security Stamp Ptg Ltd)

1985 (1 Aug). *International Youth Year. T 220 and similar multicoloured design. Chalk-surfaced paper.* P 15 × 14 (22p.) or 14 × 15 (26p.).
621 22p. Type 220 .. .. .. 55 50
622 26p. Students and young workers (vert) .. 55 50

221 Visual Display Unit

(Des B. Donegan (44p.), C. Rycraft (others). Litho Irish Security Stamp Ptg Ltd)

1985 (3 Oct). *Industrial Innovation. T 221 and similar horiz designs. Multicoloured. Chalk-surfaced paper.* P 15 × 14.
623 22p. Type 221 .. .. .. 65 75
624 26p. Turf cutting with hand tool and with modern machinery 70 55
625 44p. "The Key Man" (Sean Keating) (150th anniv of Institution of Engineers of Ireland) .. .. .. 1·25 2·50
623/5 .. .. .. *Set of 3* 2·40 3·50

222 Lighted Candle and Holly   **223** "Virgin and Child in a Landscape" (Adrian van Ijsenbrandt)

(Des R. Mahon (No. 626). Litho Irish Security Stamp Ptg Ltd)

1985 (26 Nov). *Christmas. T 222 and designs as T 223 showing paintings. Multicoloured. Chalk-surfaced paper.* P 15 × 14 (26p.) or 14 × 15 (others).
626 22p. Type 222 .. .. .. 75 65
a. Sheetlet. No. 626 × 16 .. .. 11·00
627 22p. Type 223 .. .. .. 90 2·50
a. Pair. Nos. 627/8 .. .. 1·75 5·00
628 26p. "The Holy Family" (Murillo) .. 90 2·50
629 26p. "The Adoration of the Shepherds" (Louis le Nain) (horiz) 90 25
626/9 .. .. .. *Set of 4* 3·00 5·50
No. 626 was only issued in sheetlets of 16 sold at £3, providing a discount of 52p. off the face value of the stamps.
Nos. 627/8 were printed together, se-tenant, in horizontal and vertical pairs throughout the sheet.

224 Stylised Love Bird with Letter   **225** Hart's Tongue Fern

(Des R. Hoek (22p.), T. Monaghan (26p.). Litho Irish Security Stamp Ptg Ltd)

1986 (30 Jan). *Greetings Stamps. T 224 and similar vert design. Multicoloured. Chalk-surfaced paper.* P 14 × 15.
630 22p. Type 224 .. .. .. 55 90
631 26p. Heart-shaped pillar-box 55 90

(Des I. Loe. Litho Irish Security Stamp Ptg Ltd)

1986 (20 Mar). *Ferns. T 255 and similar vert designs. Multi-coloured. Chalk-surfaced paper.* P 14 × 15.
632	24p. Type 225		70	70
633	28p. Rusty-back Fern		80	70
634	46p. Killarney Fern		1·25	2·10
632/4		*Set of 3*	2·50	3·25

226 "Harmony between Industry and Nature"   227 Boeing 747-200 over Globe showing Aer Lingus Routes

(Des G. van Gelderen. Litho Irish Security Stamp Ptg Ltd)

1986 (1 May). *Europa. Protection of the Environment. T 226 and similar multicoloured design. Chalk-surfaced paper.* P 14 × 15 (28p.) or 15 × 14 (39p.)
635	28p. Type 226		1·75	50
636	39p. *Vanessa atalanta* (butterfly) and tractor in field ("Preserve hedgerows") (*horiz*)		3·25	5·00

(Des R. Ballagh. Litho Irish Security Stamp Ptg Ltd)

1986 (27 May). *50th Anniv of Aer Lingus (airline). T 227 and similar horiz design. Multicoloured. Chalk-surfaced paper.* P 15 × 14.
637	28p. Type 227		1·40	75
638	46p. De Havilland D.H.84 Dragon Mk 2 *Iolar* (first aircraft)		1·90	3·00

228 Grand Canal at Robertstown   229 Severn (19th-century paddle-steamer)

(Des B. Matthews. Litho Irish Security Stamp Ptg Ltd)

1986 (27 May). *Irish Waterways. T 228 and similar multi-coloured designs. Chalk-surfaced paper.* P 14 × 15 (28p.) or 15 × 14 (others).
639	24p. Type 228		1·00	1·00
640	28p. Fishing in County Mayo (*vert*)		1·25	1·00
641	30p. Motor cruiser on Lough Derg		1·50	2·50
639/41		*Set of 3*	3·25	4·00

(Des C. Rycraft. Litho Irish Security Stamp Ptg Ltd)

1986 (10 July). *150th Anniv of British and Irish Steam Packet Company. T 229 and similar horiz design. Multicoloured.* P 15 × 14.
642	24p. Type 229		75	1·00
643	28p. M.V. *Leinster* (modern ferry)		85	60

230 Kish Lighthouse and Bell 206B Jet Ranger III Helicopter   231 J. P. Nannetti (first president) and Linotype Operator (Dublin Council of Trade Unions Centenary)

(Des R. Ballagh. Litho Irish Security Stamp Printing Ltd)

1986 (10 July). *Irish Lighthouses. T 230 and similar vert design. Multicoloured.* P 14 × 15.
644	24p. Type 230		75	75
645	30p. Fastnet Lighthouse		1·75	2·75

(Des R. Ballagh (Nos. 646/7), M. Cameron (No. 648), A. Mazer (Nos. 649/50). Litho Irish Security Stamp Ptg Ltd)

1986 (21 Aug). *Anniversaries and Commemorations. T 231 and similar designs. Ordinary paper (24p.) or chalk-surfaced paper (others).* P 14 × 15 (Nos. 646/7, 649) or 15 × 14 (others).
646	24p. multicoloured		50	90
647	28p. black and brownish grey		60	60
648	28p. multicoloured		60	80
649	30p. multicoloured		65	1·00
650	46p. multicoloured		70	1·75
646/50		*Set of 5*	2·75	4·75

Designs: *Vert*—No. 647, Arthur Griffith (statesman); No. 649, Clasped hands (International Peace Year). *Horiz*—No. 648, Woman surveyor (Women in Society); No. 650, Peace dove (International Peace Year).

232 William Mulready and his Design for 1840 Envelope   233 "The Adoration of the Shepherds" (Francesco Pascucci)

(Des C. Harrison (24p.), A. Mazer from aquatints by M. A. Hayes (others). Litho Irish Security Stamp Ptg Ltd)

1986 (2 Oct). *Birth Bicentenaries of William Mulready (artist) (24p.) and Charles Bianconi (originator of Irish mail coach service) (others). T 232 and similar multicoloured designs. Chalk-surfaced paper.* P 14 × 15 (28p.) or 15 × 14 (others).
651	24p. Type 232		65	70
652	28p. Bianconi car outside Hearns Hotel, Clonmel (*vert*)		75	55
653	39p. Bianconi car on the road		1·25	1·75
651/3		*Set of 3*	2·40	2·75

(Des C. O'Neill (21p.). Litho Irish Security Stamp Ptg Ltd)

1986 (20 Nov). *Christmas. T 233 and similar multicoloured design. Chalk-surfaced paper.* P 15 × 14 (21p.) or 14 × 15 (28p.).
654	21p. Type 233		1·10	1·40
	a. Sheetlet. No. 654 × 12			12·00
655	28p. "The Adoration of the Magi" (Frans Francken III) (*vert*)		65	60

No. 654 was only issued in sheetlets of 12 sold at £2·50, providing a discount of 2p. off the face value of the stamps.

234 "Butterfly and Flowers" (Tara Collins)   235 Cork Electric Tram

(Litho Irish Security Stamp Ptg Ltd)

1987 (27 Jan). *Greetings Stamps. Children's Paintings. T 234 and similar multicoloured design. Chalk-surfaced paper.* P 15 × 14 (24p.) or 14 × 15 (28p.).
656	24p. Type 234		70	1·25
657	28p. "Postman on Bicycle delivering Hearts" (Brigid Teehan) (*vert*)		80	1·25

(Des C. Rycraft. Litho Irish Security Stamp Ptg Ltd)

1987 (4 Mar). *Irish Trams. T 235 and similar horiz designs. Multicoloured. Chalk-surfaced paper.* P 15 × 14.
658	24p. Type 235		65	65
659	28p. Dublin standard tram No. 291		70	85
660	30p. Howth (Great Northern Railway) tram		80	2·00
661	46p. Galway horse tram		1·25	2·25
658/61		*Set of 4*	3·00	5·00
MS662	131×85 mm. Nos. 658/61		4·25	6·50

No. MS662 exists with the sheet margins overprinted in red for "HAFNIA 87" and in black for "STAMPA 87".

236 Ships from Crest (Bicentenary of Waterford Chamber of Commerce)   237 Bord na Mona Headquarters and "The Turf Cutter" sculpture (John Behan), Dublin

(Des K. Uhlemann (24p.), J Farrer (28p.), A. Mazer and Wendy Walsh (30p.), M. Cameron (39p.). Litho Irish Security Stamp Ptg Ltd)

1987 (9 Apr). *Anniversaries. T 236 and similar designs. Chalk-surfaced paper.* P 14 × 15 (30p.) or 15 × 14 (others).
663	24p. black, ultramarine and deep grey-green		70	60
664	28p. multicoloured		70	60
665	30p. multicoloured		70	1·75
666	39p. multicoloured		75	2·00
663/6		*Set of 4*	2·50	4·50

Designs: *Horiz*—28p. Canon John Hayes and symbols of agriculture and development (Birth centenary and 50th anniv of Muintir na Tire Programme); 39p. Mother Mary Martin and International Missionary Training Hospital, Drogheda (50th anniv of Medical Missionaries of Mary). *Vert*—30p. *Calceolaria burbidgei* and College crest (300th anniv of Trinity College Botanic Gardens, Dublin).

(Des M. Lunt. Litho Harrison)

1987 (14 May). *Europa. Modern Architecture. T 237 and similar horiz design. Multicoloured.* P 15 × 14.
667	28p. Type 237		1·50	60
668	39p. St. Mary's Church, Cong		3·50	5·00

238 Kerry Cow   239 Fleadh Nua, Ennis

(Des B. Driscoll. Litho Irish Security Stamp Ptg Ltd)

1987 (2 July). *Irish Cattle. T 238 and similar horiz designs. Multicoloured. Chalk-surfaced paper.* P 15 × 14.
669	24p. Type 238		70	75
670	28p. Friesian cow and calf		85	60
671	30p. Hereford bullock		90	2·25
672	39p. Shorthorn bull		1·00	2·25
669/72		*Set of 4*	3·00	5·25

(Des R. Ballagh. Litho Irish Security Stamp Ptg Ltd)

1987 (27 Aug). *Festivals. T 239 and similar multicoloured designs. Chalk-surfaced paper.* P 14 × 15 (*vert*) or 15 × 14 (*horiz*).
673	24p. Type 239		65	70
674	28p. Rose of Tralee International Festival		70	60
675	30p. Wexford Opera Festival (*horiz*)		80	2·00
676	46p. Ballinasloe Horse Fair (*horiz*)		1·10	2·00
673/6		*Set of 4*	3·00	4·75

240 Flagon (1637), Arms and Anniversary Ornament (1987) (350th Anniv of Dublin Goldsmiths' Company)   241 Scenes from "The Twelve Days of Christmas" (carol)

(Des B. Donegan (No. 677), R. Ballagh (No. 678), A. Mazer and Breda Mathews (No. 679), Libby Carton (No. 680). Litho Harrison (46p.) or Irish Security Stamp Ptg Ltd (others))

1987 (1 Oct). *Anniversaries and Commemorations. T 240 and similar designs. Ordinary paper (46p.) or chalk-surfaced paper (others).* P 15 × 14 (*horiz*) or 14 × 15 (*vert*).
677	240 24p. multicoloured		55	80
678	— 24p. grey and black		55	80
679	— 28p. multicoloured		65	60
680	— 46p. multicoloured		1·00	1·10
677/80		*Set of 4*	2·50	3·00

Designs: *Vert*—24p. (No. 678) Cathal Brugha (statesman); 46p. Woman chairing board meeting (Women in Society). *Horiz*—28p. Arms of Ireland and inscription (50th anniv of Constitution).

(Des M. Cameron (21p.), A. Mazer (others). Litho Irish Security Stamp Ptg Ltd)

1987 (17 Nov). *Christmas. T 241 and similar multicoloured designs. Chalk-surfaced paper.* P 15 × 14 (21p.) or 14 × 15 (others).
681	21p. Type 241		60	1·00
	a. Sheetlet. No. 681 × 14			7·50
682	24p. The Nativity (detail, late 15th-cent Waterford Vestments) (*vert*)		75	1·00
683	28p. Figures from Neapolitan crib, *c* 1850 (*vert*)		75	80
681/3		*Set of 3*	1·90	2·50

No. 681 represents a special rate for greetings cards within Ireland and to all E.E.C. countries. It was only issued in sheetlets of 14 stamps and 1 label sold at £2·90, providing an additional discount of 4p. off the face value of the stamps.

242 Acrobatic Clowns spelling "LOVE"   243 "Robert Burke" (Sidney Nolan) and Map of Burke and Wills Expedition Route

(Des M. Cameron (24p.), Aislinn Adams (28p.). Litho Irish Security Stamp Ptg Ltd)

1988 (27 Jan). *Greetings Stamps. T 242 and similar multi-coloured design. Chalk-surfaced paper.* P 15 × 14 (24p.) or 14 × 15 (28p.).
684	24p. Type 242		60	60
685	28p. Pillar box and hearts (*vert*)		65	65

(Des A. Mazer. Litho Irish Security Stamp Ptg Ltd)

1988 (1 Mar). *Bicentenary of Australian Settlement. T 243 and similar horiz design. Multicoloured. Chalk-surfaced paper.* P 15 × 14.
686	24p. Type 243		40	60
687	46p. "Eureka Stockade" (mural detail, Sidney Nolan)		85	1·75

244 Past and Present Buildings of Dublin

245 Showjumping

(Des S. Conlin. Litho Irish Security Stamp Ptg Ltd)

1988 (1 Mar). *Dublin Millennium. Chalk-surfaced paper. P 15×14.*

688	244	28p. multicoloured		45	55
		a. Booklet pane. No. 688 × 4		1·75	

No. 688a was printed with either Irish or English inscriptions in the centre of the pane and came from £2.24 stamp booklets. Loose panes could also be purchased from the Philatelic Bureau, Dublin, and its agents. They exist overprinted for "STAMPA 88" (in blue on Irish version and red on English) and "Sydpex 88" (both green on gold).

(Des Ann Flynn Litho Irish Security Stamp Ptg Ltd)

1988 (7 Apr). *Olympic Games, Seoul. T 245 and similar horiz design. Multicoloured. Chalk-surfaced paper. P 15×14.*

689		28p. Type 245		1·00	1·40
		a. Sheetlet. Nos. 689/90, each × 5		9·00	
690		28p. Cycling		1·00	1·40

Nos. 689/90 were printed together, *se-tenant*, in a sheetlet containing five of each design and two stamp-size labels.

246 William T. Cosgrave (statesman)

247 Air Traffic Controllers and Airbus Industrie A320

(Des R. Ballagh (24p.), J. Farrer (30p.), K. Uhlemann (50p.). Litho Irish Security Stamp Ptg Ltd)

1988 (7 Apr). *Anniversaries and Events. T 246 and similar designs. Chalk-surfaced paper. P 14×15 (vert) or 15×14 (horiz).*

691		24p. brownish grey and black		45	45
692		30p. multicoloured		80	1·00
693		50p. multicoloured		1·00	1·90
691/3			Set of 3	2·00	3·00

Designs: *Horiz*—30p. Members with casualty and ambulance (50th anniv of Order of Malta Ambulance Corps). *Vert*—50p. Barry Fitzgerald (actor) (Birth centenary).

(Des C. Rycraft (28p.), M. Cameron (39p.). Litho Irish Security Stamp Ptg Ltd)

1988 (12 May). *Europa. Transport and Communications. T 247 and similar horiz design. Multicoloured. Chalk-surfaced paper. P 15×14.*

694		28p. Type 247		1·25	55
695		39p. Globe with stream of letters from Ireland to Europe		1·75	2·50

248 *Sirius* (paddle-steamer) (150th anniv of regular transatlantic steamship services)

249 Cottonweed

(Des C. Rycraft. Litho Irish Security Stamp Ptg Ltd)

1988 (12 May). *Transatlantic Transport Anniversaries. T 248 and similar horiz design. Multicoloured. Chalk-surfaced paper. P 15×14.*

696		24p. Type 248		75	50
697		46p. Short S.20 seaplane *Mercury* and Short S.21 flying boat *Maia* (Short-Mayo composite aircraft) (50th anniv of first commercial transatlantic flight)		1·50	2·75

(Des Frances Poskitt. Litho Irish Security Stamp Ptg Ltd)

1988 (21 June). *Endangered Flora of Ireland. T 249 and similar vert designs. Multicoloured. Chalk-surfaced paper. P 14×15.*

698		24p. Type 249		65	55
699		25p. Hart's Saxifrage		75	55
700		46p. Purple Milk-Vetch		1·10	2·00
698/700			Set of 3	2·25	2·75

250 Garda on Duty

251 Computer and Abacus (Institute of Chartered Accountants in Ireland Centenary)

(Des D. Teskey. Litho Irish Security Stamp Ptg Ltd)

1988 (23 Aug). *Irish Security Forces. T 250 and similar horiz designs. Multicoloured. Chalk-surfaced paper. P 15×14.*

701		28p. Type 250		60	1·00
		a. Strip of 4. Nos. 701/4		2·25	
702		28p. Army unit with personnel carrier		60	1·00
703		28p. Navy and Air Corps members with *Eithne* (helicopter patrol vessel)		60	1·00
704		28p. Army and navy reservists		60	1·00
701/4			Set of 4	2·25	3·50

Nos. 701/4 were printed together, both horizontally and vertically *se-tenant*, throughout the sheet of 20 (4×5).

(Des C. Rycraft (24p.), K. King and A. Mazer (46p.). Litho Irish Security Stamp Ptg Ltd)

1988 (6 Oct). *Anniversaries. T 251 and similar multicoloured design. Chalk-surfaced paper. P 14×15 (24p.) or 15×14 (46p.).*

705		24p. Type 251		40	40
706		46p. *Duquesa Santa Ana* off Donegal (*horiz*) (400th anniv of Spanish Armada)		1·25	1·25

252 "President Kennedy" (James Wyeth)

253 St. Kevin's Church, Glendalough

(Des A. Mazer. Litho Irish Security Stamp Ptg Ltd)

1988 (24 Nov). *25th Death Anniv of John F. Kennedy (American statesman). Chalk-surfaced paper. P 15×14.*

707	252	28p. multicoloured		70	80

(Des Ann Flynn (21p.), B. Donegan (others). Litho Irish Security Stamp Ptg Ltd)

1988 (24 Nov). *Christmas. T 253 and similar vert designs. Multicoloured. Chalk-surfaced paper. P 14×15.*

708		21p. Type 253		80	80
		a. Sheetlet. No. 708 × 14		10·00	
709		24p. The Adoration of the Magi		50	60
710		28p. The Flight into Egypt		60	55
711		46p. The Holy Family		90	2·25
708/11			Set of 4	2·50	3·75

No. 708 represents a special rate for greetings cards within Ireland and to all E.E.C. countries. It was only issued in sheetlets of 14 stamps and 1 label sold at £2.90, providing an additional discount of 4p. off the face value of the stamps.

The designs of Nos. 709/11 are from a 15th-century French Book of Hours.

254 Spring Flowers spelling "Love" in Gaelic

255 Italian Garden, Garinish Island

(Des Susan Dubsky (24p.), A. Mazer (28p.). Litho Irish Security Stamp Ptg Ltd)

1989 (24 Jan). *Greetings Stamps. T 254 and similar multicoloured design. Chalk-surfaced paper. P 15×14 (24p.) or 14×15 (28p.).*

712		24p. Type 254		60	55
713		28p. "The Sonnet" (William Mulready) (*vert*)		65	55

(Des Frances Poskitt. Litho Irish Security Stamp Ptg Ltd)

1989 (11 Apr). *National Parks and Gardens. T 255 and similar horiz designs. Multicoloured. Chalk-surfaced paper. P 14×15.*

714		24p. Type 255		80	55
715		28p. Lough Veagh, Glenveagh National Park		95	55
716		32p. Barnaderg Bay, Connemara National Park		1·00	1·25
717		50p. St. Stephen's Green, Dublin		1·50	1·75
714/17			Set of 4	3·75	3·75

256 "Silver Stream", 1908

257 Ring-a-ring-a-roses

(Des C. Rycraft. Litho Irish Security Stamp Ptg Ltd)

1989 (11 Apr). *Classic Irish Cars. T 256 and similar horiz designs. Multicoloured. Chalk-surfaced paper. P 15×14.*

718		24p. Type 256		50	55
		a. Booklet pane. Nos. 718/19, each ×2		2·75	
		b. Booklet pane. No. 718/21		2·75	
719		28p. Benz "Comfortable", 1898		50	55
720		39p. "Thomond", 1929		1·25	1·50
721		46p. Chambers' 8 h.p. model, 1905		1·50	1·60
718/21			Set of 4	3·25	3·75

Booklet panes Nos. 718a/b come from £2.41 stamp booklets and stamps from them have one or two adjacent sides imperforate. Such panes were also available loose from the Philatelic Bureau, Dublin, and its agents

(Des C. Harrison. Litho Irish Security Stamp Ptg Ltd)

1989 (11 May). *Europa. Children's Games. T 257 and similar horiz design. Multicoloured. Chalk-surfaced paper. P 15×14.*

722		28p. Type 257		75	75
723		39p. Hopscotch		1·00	2·25

Nos. 722/3 were each issued in sheets of 10 showing additional illustrations in the left-hand sheet margin.

258 Irish Red Cross Flag (50th anniv)

259 Saints Kilian, Totnan and Colman (from 12th-century German manuscript)

(Des Q Design (24p.), R. Hoek (28p.). Litho Irish Security Stamp Ptg Ltd)

1989 (11 May). *Anniversaries and Events. T 258 and similar vert design. Chalk-surfaced paper. P 14×15.*

724		24p. vermilion and black		55	60
725		28p. new blue, black and lemon		1·10	1·10

Design:—28p. Circle of twelve stars (Third direct elections to European Parliament).

(Des P. Effert. Litho Irish Security Stamp Ptg Ltd)

1989 (15 June). *1300th Death Anniv of Saints Kilian, Totnan and Colman. Chalk-surfaced paper. P 13½.*

726	259	28p. multicoloured		65	1·10
		a. Booklet pane. No. 726×4 with margins all round		2·50	

A stamp in a similar design was issued by West Germany. No. 726a exists with text in Irish, English, German or Latin on the pane margin.

260 19th-century Mail Coach passing Cashel

261 Crest and 19th-century Dividers (150th anniv of Royal Institute of Architects of Ireland)

(Des Katie O'Sullivan and B. Donegan. Litho Irish Security Stamp Ptg Ltd)

1989 (27 July). *Bicentenary of Irish Mail Coach Service. Chalk-surfaced paper. P 15×14.*

727	260	28p. multicoloured		1·00	75

(Des R. Ballagh (24p.), A. Mazer (28p.), K. Uhlemann (30p.), Carey Clarke (46p.). Litho Irish Security Stamp Ptg Ltd)

1989 (27 July). *Anniversaries and Commemorations. T 261 and similar designs. Chalk-surfaced paper. P 15×14 (30p.) or 14×15 (others).*

728		24p. grey and black		60	55
729		28p. multicoloured		65	55
730		30p. multicoloured		1·40	1·75
731		46p. orange-brown		1·60	1·75
728/31			Set of 4	3·75	4·25

Designs: *Vert*—24p. Sean T. O'Kelly (statesman) (drawing by Sean O'Sullivan); 46p. Jawaharlal Nehru (Birth centenary). *Horiz*—30p. Margaret Burke-Sheridan (soprano) (portrait by De Gennaro) and scene from *La Bohème* (Birth centenary).

262 "NCB Ireland" rounding
Cape Horn" (Des Fallon)

263 Willow/Red Grouse

(Des I. Caulder. Litho Irish Security Stamp Ptg Ltd)

1989 (31 Aug). *First Irish Entry in Whitbread Round the World Yacht Race. Chalk-surfaced paper.* P 15×14.
732 **262** 28p. multicoloured .. .. .. 1·25 1·25

(Des R. Ward. Litho Irish Security Stamp Ptg Ltd)

1989 (5 Oct). *Game Birds. T 263 and similar square designs. Multicoloured. Chalk-surfaced paper.* P 13½.
733 24p. Type **263** .. .. .. 1·00 55
734 28p. Lapwing .. .. .. 1·10 55
735 39p. Woodcock .. .. .. 1·40 2·25
736 46p. Ring-necked Pheasant .. 1·50 2·25
733/6 *Set of* 4 4·50 5·00
MS737 128×92 mm. Nos. 733/6 .. 4·50 5·50
No. **MS737** exists overprinted on the margins to commemorate "STAMPA 89", the Irish National Stamp Exhibition.

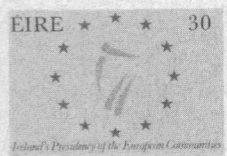

264 "The Annunciation"

265 Logo (Ireland's
Presidency of the European
Communities)

(Des Jacinta Fitzgerald (21p.), J. McEvoy from 13th-century Flemish Psalter (others). Litho Irish Security Stamp Ptg Ltd)

1989 (14 Nov). *Christmas. T 264 and similar vert designs. Multicoloured. Chalk-surfaced paper.* P 14×15.
738 21p. Children decorating crib .. 75 75
   a. Sheetlet. No. 738×14 .. .. 9·50
739 24p. Type **264** 85 60
740 28p. "The Nativity" 90 55
741 46p. "The Adoration of the Magi" .. 1·75 2·50
738/41 *Set of* 4 3·75 4·00
No. 738 represents a special rate for greetings cards within Ireland and to all E.E.C. countries. It was only issued in sheetlets of 14 stamps and 1 label sold at £2.90, providing an additional discount of 4p. off the face value of the stamps.

(Des B. Donegan (30p.), Q Design (50p.). Litho Irish Security Stamp Ptg Ltd)

1990 (9 Jan). *European Events. T 265 and similar horiz design. Multicoloured. Chalk-surfaced paper.* P 15×14.
742 30p. Type **265** 75 60
743 50p. Logo and outline map of Ireland (European Tourism Year) .. 2·00 3·00

266 Dropping
Messages from
Balloon

267 Silver
Kite Brooch

(Des Aislinn Adams (26p.), Patricia Sleeman and R. Vogel (30p.). Litho Irish Security Stamp Ptg Ltd)

1990 (30 Jan). *Greetings Stamps. T 266 and similar vert design. Chalk-surfaced paper.* P 14×15.
744 26p. multicoloured .. .. 1·25 1·25
745 30p. rosine, pale buff and reddish brown .. 1·25 1·25
Design:—30p. Heart and "Love" drawn in lipstick.

PRICES OF SETS

Set prices are given for many issues, generally those containing three stamps or more. Definitive sets include one of each value or major colour change, but do not cover different perforations, die types or minor shades. Where a choice is possible the set prices are based on the cheapest versions of the stamps included in the listings.

Two Types of 20, 28, 52p.:

A. Irish Security Stamp Ptg Ltd printing (coarse background screen. Less distinct centre detail)

B. Enschedé printing (fine background screen. Clear centre detail)

Two Types of £1, £2, £3:

C. Irish Security Stamp
Ptg Ltd printing

D. Enschedé printing

(Des M. Craig and Q Design. Litho Walsall (Nos. 748c, 755b), Enschedé (Nos. 751b, 753b, 762b, 763b, 764b, 765b) or Irish Security Stamp Ptg Ltd (others))

1990 (8 Mar)–**97**. *Irish Heritage and Treasures. T 267 and similar designs. Chalk-surfaced paper (5, 20, 26, 28, 30, 32, 37, 38, 41, 44, 50, 52p., £1, £5) or ordinary paper (others). P 14×15 (10, 20, 30, 32p, £5) or 15×14 (others).*
746 1p. black and new blue (26.7.90) .. 10 10
   a. Chalk-surfaced paper (10.91) 40 40
747 2p. black and bright red-orange (26.7.90) 10 10
   a. Chalk-surfaced paper (15.11.90) 10 10
   ab. Booklet pane. Nos. 747a, 748b×3, 752 and 754×2 plus label .. 3·00
   ac. Booklet pane. Nos. 747a×2, 755×2 and 820 (17.10.91) .. 4·00
748 4p. black and bluish violet (26.7.90) .. 10 10
   a. Booklet pane. Nos. 748 and 755a×3 (16.11.95) .. 2·00
   b. Chalk-surfaced paper (15.11.90) 75 1·00
   ba. Booklet pane. Nos. 748b×3, 753×4 plus label (17.10.91) .. 4·00
   bb. Booklet pane. Nos. 748b and 1084×3 (6.3.97) .. 1·60
   c. Perf 13×13½. Chalk-surfaced paper (24.9.93) .. 10 10
   ca. Booklet pane. Nos. 748c and 755b×3 (4p. at bottom right) .. 2·00
   cb. Ditto, but 4p., at top left (2.3.94) 2·00
749 5p. black and bright green (29.1.91) 15 10
   a. Ordinary paper (5.92) .. 1·25 1·00
750 10p. black and bright red-orange (26.7.90) 20 25
   a. Chalk-surfaced paper (9.93) 1·25 1·00
751 20p. black and lemon (A) (29.1.91) 35 40
   a. Ordinary paper (3.92) .. 1·50 1·50
   b. Type B (Enschedé ptg) (16.11.95) 1·25 1·00
752 26p. black and bluish violet .. 45 50
   a. Ordinary paper (5.90) .. 2·75 1·50
   ab. Perf 13½ (3.5.90) .. 4·00 5·00
753 28p. black & bright red-orange (A) (3.4.91) 50 55
   a. Ordinary paper (5.91) .. 2·25 2·25
   b. Type B (Enschedé ptg) (16.11.95) 1·25 1·00
754 30p. black and new blue .. 55 60
   a. Ordinary paper (5.90) .. 1·75 1·75
   ab. Perf 13½ (3.5.90) .. 4·00 5·00
755 32p. black and bright green .. 60 65
   a. Ordinary paper (5.90) .. 2·00 2·00
   b. Perf 13½×13. Chalk-surfaced paper (24.9.93) .. 90 90
756 34p. black and lemon (26.7.90) .. 1·00 1·00
757 37p. brownish black & brt green (3.4.91) 1·25 1·25
   a. Ordinary paper (11.91) .. 3·25 3·75
758 38p. black and bluish violet (3.4.91) 1·25 1·25
   a. Ordinary paper (5.95) .. 3·00 3·00
758b 40p. black and new blue (14.5.92) 1·25 1·25
   ba. Chalk-surfaced paper (9.93) 3·50 3·50
759 41p. black and bright red-orange 80 75
   a. Ordinary paper (10.90) .. 3·50 3·50
760 44p. agate and lemon (3.4.91) .. 85 80
760a 45p. black and bluish violet (14.5.92) 1·25 1·50
761 50p. black and lemon .. .. 1·25 1·50
   a. Ordinary paper (5.90) .. 3·75 3·75
762 52p. black and new blue (A) (3.4.91) 1·50 1·50
   a. Ordinary paper (2.96) .. 12·00 12·00
   b. Type B (Enschedé ptg) (16.11.95) 1·75 1·75
763 £1 black and lemon (C) .. 1·75 1·90
   a. Ordinary paper (5.90) .. 15·00 4·00
   b. Type D (Enschedé ptg) (16.11.95) 3·25 3·00
764 £2 black and bright green (C) (26.7.90) 3·50 3·75
   a. Chalk-surfaced paper (9.93) 10·00 10·00
   b. Type D (Enschedé ptg) (chalk-surfaced paper) (16.11.95) 6·00 6·00
765 £5 black and new blue (29.1.91) 9·00 9·25
   a. Ordinary paper (10.97) .. 30·00 35·00
   b. Type D (Enschedé ptg) (16.11.95) 15·00 15·00
746/65 *Set of* 22 25·00 26·00
Designs: *Vert (as T 267)*—1p., 2p. Type **267**; 4p., 5p. Dunamase Food Vessel; 26p., 28p. Lismore Crozier; 34p., 37p., 38p., 40p. Gleninsheen Collar; 41p., 44p., 45p. Silver thistle brooch; 50p., 52p. Broighter Boat. (22×38 mm)—£5 St. Patrick's Bell Shrine. *Horiz (as T 267)*—10p. Derrinboy Armlets; 20p. Gold dress fastener; 30p. Enamelled latchet brooch; 32p.

Broighter Collar. (38×22 *mm*)—£1 Ardagh Chalice; £2 Tara Brooch.
Nos. 747a and 748b were initially only available from booklet pane No. 747ab, but were subsequently issued in sheet form during March (4p.) and October (2p.) 1991. Nos. 748c and 755b only occur from booklet panes Nos. 748ca/cb.
With the exception of Nos. 747ac and 748ba each of the listed booklet panes shows either the upper and lower edges (Nos. 748a, 747ab) or the three outer edges of the pane imperforate. Booklet panes Nos. 535ca and 547bb, which include Nos. 752ab and 754ab, and also Nos. 747ac and 748ba each show stamps from the right-hand vertical row imperforate at top, right or at foot depending on the format of the design. The following variations exist:
   2p. Imperf at left (booklet pane No. 747ab)
      Imperf at foot (booklet pane No. 747ac)
   4p. Imperf at left or right (booklet pane No. 747ab)
      Imperf at left (booklet panes Nos. 748a, 748bb)
      Imperf at foot (booklet pane No. 748ba)
      Imperf at foot and left (p 13×13½) (booklet pane No. 748ca)
      Imperf at right (p 13×13½) (booklet pane No. 748cb)
   26p. Imperf at top (p 13½) (booklet pane No. 535ca)
      Imperf at foot and left (booklet pane No. 747ab)
   28p. Imperf at foot (booklet pane No. 748ba)
   30p. Imperf at right (p 13½) (booklet pane No. 547bb)
      Imperf at top or top and right (booklet pane No. 747ab)
   32p. Imperf at right (booklet pane No. 747ac)
      Imperf at top or foot (booklet pane No. 748a)
      Imperf at top, top and right or foot (p 13½×13) (booklet pane No. 748ca)
      Imperf at top and right, foot and right or foot (p 13½×x 13) (booklet pane No. 748cb)
For 4, 28 and 32p. stamps in same designs as Nos. 748, 753 and 755, but printed in photogravure, see Nos. 808/10.
For 32p. value as No. 755, but 27×20 mm and self-adhesive see No. 823.

268 Posy of Flowers

269 Player
heading Ball

(Des M. Cameron. Litho Irish Security Stamp Ptg Ltd)

1990 (22 Mar). *Greetings Stamps. T 268 and similar vert designs. Multicoloured.* P 14×15.
766 26p. Type **268** .. .. .. 2·00 2·50
   a. Booklet pane. Nos. 766/9 .. 7·50
767 26p. Birthday presents .. .. 2·00 2·50
768 30p. Flowers, ribbon and horseshoe 2·00 2·50
769 30p. Balloons .. .. .. 2·00 2·50
766/9 *Set of* 4 7·50 9·00
Nos. 766/9 come from £1.98 discount stamp booklets.
Booklet pane No. 766a exists with the 26p. values at left or right and the right-hand stamp (either No. 767 or 769) imperforate at right. The booklet pane also contains 8 small greetings labels.

(Des C. Harrison. Litho Irish Security Stamp Ptg Ltd)

1990 (5 Apr). *World Cup Football Championship, Italy. T 269 and similar vert design. Multicoloured. Chalk-surfaced paper.* P 14×15.
770 30p. Type **269** .. .. .. 1·50 2·00
   a. Sheetlet. Nos. 770/1, each × 4 11·00
771 30p. Tackling .. .. .. 1·50 2·00
Nos. 770/1 were printed together, *se-tenant*, in a sheetlet of 8 stamps and 1 central stamp-size label.

270 Battle of the Boyne, 1690

(Des S. Conlin. Litho Irish Security Stamp Ptg Ltd)

1990 (5 Apr). *300th Anniv of the Williamite Wars (1st issue). T 270 and similar horiz designs. Multicoloured. Chalk-surfaced paper.* P 13½.
772 30p. Type **270** .. .. .. 1·25 1·75
   a. Pair. Nos. 772/3 .. .. 2·25 3·25
773 30p. Siege of Limerick, 1690 .. 1·25 1·75
Nos. 772/3 were printed together, *se-tenant*, in horizontal and vertical pairs throughout the sheet.
See also Nos. 806/7.

271 1990 Irish Heritage
30p. Stamp and 1840
Postmark

272 General Post
Office, Dublin

(Des Q Design. Litho Irish Security Stamp Ptg Ltd)

1990 (3 May). *150th Anniv of the Penny Black.* T **271** *and similar horiz design. Multicoloured. Chalk-surfaced paper.* P 15×14.
774 30p. Type **271** 90 90
   a. Ordinary paper .. .. 1·75 3·00
   ab. Booklet pane. Nos. 774a/5a, each × 2 7·00
775 50p. Definitive stamps of 1922, 1969, 1982
   and 1990 .. .. .. 1·25 2·00
   a. Ordinary paper .. .. 1·75 3·00
Nos. 774a and 775a were only issued in booklets.
In booklet pane No. 774ab one example of each value is imperforate at right.
Booklet pane No. 774ab exists with the margins overprinted in red in connection with "STAMPA 90", the Irish National Stamp Exhibition.
For other booklet panes containing Nos. 774a/5a see Nos. 547ba/bb.

(Des P. Keogh. Litho Irish Security Stamp Ptg Ltd)

1990 (3 May). *Europa. Post Office Buildings.* T **272** *and similar vert design. Multicoloured.* P 14 × 15.
776 30p. Type **272** .. .. .. 1·00 60
777 41p. Westport Post Office, County Mayo 1·40 2·75
Nos. 776/7 were each printed in sheets of 10 stamps and 2 stamp-size labels.

273 Medical Missionary giving Injection

274 Narcissus "Foundling" and Japanese Gardens, Tully

(Des I. Calder (26, 50p.), R. Ballagh (30p.). Litho Irish Security Stamp Ptg Ltd)

1990 (21 June). *Anniversaries and Events.* T **273** *and similar designs.* P 15×14 (*horiz*) or 14×15 (*vert*).
778 26p. multicoloured 80 30
779 30p. black .. .. .. 1·00 2·25
780 50p. multicoloured .. .. 1·00 1·25
          Set of 3 2·50 3·50
Designs: *Vert*—30p. Michael Collins (statesman) (Birth centenary). *Horiz*—Missionaries working at water pump (Irish missionary service).

(Des I. Loe. Litho Irish Security Stamp Ptg Ltd)

1990 (30 Aug). *Garden Flowers.* T **274** *and similar vert designs. Multicoloured.* P 14×15.
781 26p. Type **274** 60 55
   a. Booklet pane. Nos. 781/2, each × 2 4·00
   b. Booklet pane. Nos. 781/4 4·00
782 30p. *Rosa x hibernica* and Malahide Castle gardens 70 80
783 41p. *Primula* "Rowallane Rose" and Rowallane garden .. .. 1·40 2·00
784 50p. *Erica erigena* "Irish Dusk" and Palm House, National Botanical Gardens 1·75 2·25
781/4 .. .. *Set of 4* 4·00 5·00
Both booklet panes show the stamps as horizontal rows of four imperforate at top and at right. Stamps from the right of the pane, 30p. on No. 781a, 50p. on No. 781b, are imperforate at top and right with the other values imperforate at top only.
No. 781a exists overprinted in blue for Collectors' Road Shows at Waterford and Galway.

Frama label

Klussendorf label

Amiel Pitney/Bowes label

MACHINE LABELS. For a trial period of three months from 8 October 1990 labels in the above designs, ranging in value from 1p. to £99.99, were available from the head post offices at Dublin (Frama), Limerick (Klussendorf) and Cork (Amiel Pitney/Bowes). The Amiel Pitney/Bowes machine (Cork) was taken out of service on 31 January 1991. The other two machines were withdrawn on 31 May 1991.

NEW INFORMATION

The editor is always interested to correspond with people who have new information that will improve or correct the Catalogue.

275 *Playboy of the Western World* (John Synge)

276 Nativity

(Des R. Ballagh. Litho Irish Security Stamp Ptg Ltd)

1990 (18 Oct). *Irish Theatre.* T **275** *and similar horiz designs. Multicoloured.* P 13½.
785 30p. Type **275** .. .. .. 1·25 1·75
   a. Horiz strip of 4. Nos. 785/8 .. 4·50
786 30p. *Juno and the Paycock* (Sean O'Casey) 1·25 1·75
787 30p. *The Field* (John Keane) .. 1·25 1·75
788 30p. *Waiting for Godot* (Samuel Beckett) 1·25 1·75
785/8 .. .. *Set of 4* 4·50 6·00
Nos. 785/8 were printed together in sheets of 20 (4×5), producing horizontal *se-tenant* strips of 4 and vertical *se-tenant* pairs for Nos. 785 and 788 or 786/7.

(Des Pamela Leonard (No. 789), B. Cronin (others). Litho Irish Security Stamp Ptg Ltd)

1990 (15 Nov). *Christmas.* T **276** *and similar vert designs. Multicoloured. Chalk-surfaced paper* (50p.) *or ordinary paper* (*others*). P 14×15.
789 26p. Child praying by bed .. 70 80
   a. Sheetlet. No. 789×12 .. 7·50
790 26p. Type **276** 70 60
791 30p. Madonna and Child .. 90 90
792 50p. Adoration of the Magi .. 1·60 2·25
789/92 .. .. .. *Set of 4* 3·50 4·00
No. 789 was only issued in sheetlets of 12 sold at £2·86, providing a discount of 26p. off the face value of the stamps.

277 Hearts in Mail Sack and Postman's Cap

278 Starley "Rover" Bicycle, 1886

(Des Liz Manning (26p.), Louise Mullally (30p.). Litho Irish Security Stamp Ptg Ltd)

1991 (29 Jan). *Greetings Stamps.* T **277** *and similar vert design. Multicoloured. Chalk-surfaced paper.* P 14×15.
793 26p. Type **277** .. .. .. 85 1·00
794 30p. Boy and girl kissing .. 90 1·00

(Des E. Patton. Litho Irish Security Stamp Ptg Ltd)

1991 (5 Mar). *Early Bicycles.* T **278** *and similar vert designs. Multicoloured. Chalk-surfaced paper.* P 14×15.
795 26p. Type **278** 80 60
796 30p. Child's horse tricycle, 1875 .. 90 1·00
797 50p. "Penny Farthing", 1871 .. 1·60 2·00
795/7 .. .. .. *Set of 3* 3·00 3·25
MS798 113×72 mm. Nos. 795/7 .. 3·00 3·50
No. **MS**798 exists with privately-applied marginal overprints for the "Collectorex 91" Exhibition, Dublin, the I.P.T.A. Collectors' Road Show, Birr (both in black) and "STAMPA 91" Exhibition, Dublin (in red or blue).

279 Cuchulainn (statue by Oliver Sheppard) and Proclamation

280 Scene from *La Traviata* (50th anniv of Dublin Grand Opera Society)

(Des I. Calder. Litho Irish Security Stamp Ptg Ltd)

1991 (3 Apr). *75th Anniv of Easter Rising. Chalk-surfaced paper.* P 15×14.
799 279 32p. multicoloured .. .. 85 1·40

(Des K. Uhlemann (28p.), M. Craig and I. Calder (32p.), M. Craig (44p.), M. Craig and Q Design (52p.). Litho Irish Security Stamp Ptg Ltd)

1991 (11 Apr). *"Dublin 1991 European City of Culture".* T **280** *and similar horiz designs. Multicoloured. Chalk-surfaced paper.* P 13½ (52p.) or 15×14 (*others*).
800 28p. Type **280** 65 80
   a. Booklet pane. Nos. 800/2 .. 3·75
   b. Booklet pane. Nos. 800/3 .. 3·75

801 32p. City Hall and European Community emblem .. .. .. 85 1·50
802 44p. St. Patrick's Cathedral (800th anniv) 90 1·60
803 52p. Custom House (bicent) (41×24 *mm*) 1·00 1·60
800/3 .. .. *Set of 4* 3·00 5·00

281 *Giotto* Spacecraft approaching Halley's Comet

(Des C. Rycraft. Litho Irish Security Stamp Ptg Ltd)

1991 (14 May). *Europa. Europe in Space.* T **281** *and similar horiz design. Multicoloured.* P 15×14.
804 32p. Type **281** .. .. .. 1·00 1·00
805 44p. Hubble Telescope orbiting Earth 1·50 3·00
Nos. 804/5 were each issued in sheetlets of 10 (2×5) with illustrations of space launches on enlarged left hand margins.

282 Siege of Athlone

283 John A. Costello (statesman)

(Des S. Conlin. Litho Irish Security Stamp Ptg Ltd)

1991 (14 May). *300th Anniv of the Williamite Wars* (2nd issue). T **282** *and similar horiz design. Multicoloured. Chalk-surfaced paper.* P 15×14.
806 28p. Type **282** .. .. .. 90 1·40
   a. Pair. Nos. 806/7 .. .. 1·75 2·75
807 28p. Generals Ginkel and Sarsfield (signatories of Treaty of Limerick) 90 1·40
Nos. 806/7 were printed together, *se-tenant*, in horizontal and vertical pairs throughout the sheet.

1991 (14 May). *As Nos. 748, 753 and 755, but printed in photogravure by Enschedé. Chalk-surfaced paper.* P 14×15 (32p.) or 15×14 (*others*).
808 4p. black and bluish violet .. 10 10
   a. Booklet pane. Nos. 808×2, 809 and 810×2 plus label .. 1·60
809 28p. black and reddish orange .. 45 50
810 32p. black and bright green .. 50 50
808/10 .. .. .. *Set of 3* 1·10 1·25
Nos. 808/10 were only available in £1 stamp booklets. Booklet pane No. 808a has imperforate outer edges giving stamps imperforate at left or right (4p.), at left and foot (28p.) and at top and right (32p.).

(Des R. Ballagh (28p.), Q Design (others). Litho Irish Security Stamp Ptg Ltd)

1991 (2 July). *Anniversaries.* T **283** *and similar designs. Chalk-surfaced paper* (28p.). P 15×14 (52p.) or 14×15 (*others*).
811 28p. black 70 70
812 32p. multicoloured .. .. 85 1·00
813 52p. multicoloured .. .. 1·40 2·50
811/13 .. .. .. *Set of 3* 2·75 3·75
Designs: *Vert*—28p. Type **283** (Birth centenary) (drawing by Sean O'Sullivan); 32p. "Charles Stewart Parnell" (Sydney Hall) (Death centenary). *Horiz*—52p. Meeting of United Irishmen (Bicentary).

284 Player on 15th Green, Portmarnock (Walker Cup)

285 Wicklow Cheviot

(Des E. Patton. Litho Irish Security Stamp Ptg Ltd)

1991 (3 Sept). *Golf Commemorations.* T **284** *and similar multicoloured design. Chalk-surfaced paper* (32p.). P 15×14 (28p.) or 14×15 (32p.).
814 28p. Type **284** .. .. .. 1·00 75
815 32p. Logo and golfer of 1900 (Centenary of Golfing Union of Ireland) (*vert*) 1·25 1·00

(Des Pamela Leonard. Litho Irish Security Stamp Ptg Ltd)

1991 (3 Sept). *Irish Sheep.* T **285** *and similar multicoloured designs. Chalk-surfaced paper.* P 15×14 (52p.) or 14×15 (*others*).
816 32p. Type **285** .. .. .. 1·00 80
817 38p. Donegal Blackface .. 1·40 1·75
818 52p. Galway (*horiz*) .. .. 2·00 3·50
816/18 .. .. .. *Set of 3* 4·00 5·50

286 Boatyard   287 The Annunciation

(Des C. Rycraft. Litho Irish Security Stamp Ptg Ltd)

1991 (17 Oct). *Fishing Fleet. T 286 and similar horiz designs. Multicoloured. Chalk-surfaced paper.* P 15×14.

819	28p. Type 286		60	65
	a. Booklet pane. Nos. 819/22		4·00	
	b. Booklet pane. Nos. 819/20 each × 2		4·00	
820	32p. Traditional inshore trawlers		70	80
821	44p. Inshore lobster pot boat		1·40	2·25
822	52p. *Veronica* (fish factory ship)		1·75	2·50
819/22		*Set of 4*	4·00	5·50

In booklet pane No. 819a the 32p. and 52p. values are imperforate at right.

Booklet pane No. 819a exists with the gutter margin overprinted in connection with the "PHILANIPPON '91" International Stamp Exhibition, Tokyo.

For a further booklet pane including No. 820 see No. 747ac.

(Litho Printset-Cambec Pty Ltd, Australia (No. 823) or Irish Security Stamp Ptg Ltd (No. 823a))

1991 (31 Oct)–**95**. *As No. 755, but larger, 27×21 mm, and self-adhesive.* P 11½.

823	32p. black and bright green		65	80
	a. Perf 10×9 (8.6.95)		65	90

Examples of No. 823 have rounded perforations at each corner of the stamp and pointed die-cut "teeth". No. 823a shows a perforation at each corner and has rounded teeth. Initially both printers showed the stamps separate on the backing paper, but from September 1996 printings of No. 823a retained the surplus self-adhesive paper around each stamp. Printings from July 1992 contained "reminder" labels inserted 20 stamps and 10 stamps from the end of the coil.

Nos. 823/a were only available in coils of 100, or as strips of 3 from the Philatelic Bureau.

(Des Q. Design (No. 827), T. Gayer (others). Litho Irish Security Stamp Ptg Ltd)

1991 (14 Nov). *Christmas. T 287 and similar vert designs. Chalk-surfaced paper.* P 14×15.

827	28p. multicoloured		80	85
	a. Sheetlet. No. 827×13		10·00	
828	28p. dull ultramarine, sage-green and black		75	65
829	32p. scarlet and black		85	75
830	52p. multicoloured		1·60	2·50
827/30		*Set of 4*	3·50	4·25

Designs:—No. 827, Three Kings; No. 828, Type 287; No. 829, The Nativity; No. 830, Adoration of the Kings.

No. 827 was only issued in sheetlets of 13 stamps and two labels (at the centre of rows 1 and 2) sold at £3.36 providing a discount of 28p. off the face value of the stamps.

288 Multicoloured Heart   289 Healthy Family on Apple

(Des T. Monaghan (28p.), R. Ballagh (32p.). Litho Irish Security Stamp Ptg Ltd)

1992 (28 Jan). *Greetings Stamps. T 288 and similar multicoloured design.* P 15×14 (28p.) or 14×15 (32p.).

831	28p. Type 288		85	95
832	32p. "LOVE" at end of rainbow (vert)		95	1·10

(Des Pamela Leonard. Litho Irish Security Stamp Ptg Ltd)

1992 (25 Feb). *"Healthy Living" Campaign.* P 14×15.

833	289 28p. multicoloured		85	85

290 Boxing

(Des C. Harrison. Litho Irish Security Stamp Ptg Ltd)

1992 (25 Feb). *Olympic Games, Barcelona. T 290 and similar horiz design.* P 15×14.

834	32p. Type 290		75	90
835	44p. Sailing		1·00	2·50
MS836	130×85 mm. Nos. 834/5×2		4·50	5·00
	a. On chalk-surfaced paper		£170	

No. MS836 exists overprinted in black on the margin in connection with the "World Columbian Stamp Expo '92", Chicago. The chalk-surfaced paper variety is only known with this marginal overprint.

291 *Mari* (cog) and 14th-century Map

(Des C. Rycraft. Litho Irish Security Stamp Ptg Ltd)

1992 (2 Apr). *Irish Maritime Heritage. T 291 and similar multicoloured design. Chalk-surfaced paper.* P 15×14 (32p) or 14×15 (52p).

837	32p. Type 291		1·00	90
838	52p. *Ovoca* (trawler) and chart (vert)		1·50	2·75

292 Chamber Logo and Commercial Symbols   293 Cliffs and Cove

(Des E. Patton. Litho Irish Security Stamp Ptg Ltd)

1992 (2 Apr). *Bicentenary of Galway Chamber of Commerce and Industry. Chalk-surfaced paper.* P 15×14.

839	292 28p. multicoloured		70	85

(Des Pamela Leonard. Litho Irish Security Stamp Ptg Ltd)

1992 (2 Apr). *Greetings Stamps. T 293 and similar vert designs. Multicoloured. Chalk-surfaced paper.* P 14×15.

840	28p. Type 293		75	1·10
	a. Booklet pane. Nos. 840/3		2·75	
841	28p. Meadow		75	1·10
842	32p. Fuchsia and Honeysuckle		75	1·10
843	32p. Lily pond and dragonfly		75	1·10
840/3		*Set of 4*	2·75	4·00

Nos. 840/3 come from £2.40 stamp booklets.

Booklet pane No. 840a exists with the 28p. values at left or right and has the right-hand stamp (either No. 841 or 843) imperforate at right. The booklet pane also contains 8 small greetings labels.

Booklet pane No. 840a exists overprinted on the margin for Regional Stamp Shows at Sligo and Waterford.

MACHINE LABELS. Frama labels in the above design, providing values from 1p. to £99·99, were introduced at head post offices in Dublin (001), Cork (003), Limerick (004) and Galway (005) on 6 April 1992. The system was extended to Bray (008), Killarney (009) and Sligo (007) on 20 July 1992, and to Kilkenny (010) and Waterford (006) on 7 September when a second machine (002) was also provided at Dublin. Both the Dublin machines were relocated to Dublin Airport in August 1994. The Killarney machine was out of use by the end of 1998 and the two at Dublin Airport were withdrawn on 28 July 1999.

294 Fleet of Columbus

(Des S. Conlin. Litho Irish Security Stamp Ptg Ltd)

1992 (14 May). *Europa. 500th Anniv of Discovery of America by Columbus. T 294 and similar horiz design. Multicoloured.* P 15×14.

844	32p. Type 294		75	90
845	44p. Columbus landing in the New World		1·25	2·50

Nos. 844/5 were each issued in sheetlets of 10 (2×5) with illustrated left or right margins.

295 Irish Immigrants

(Des Pamela Leonard. Litho Irish Security Stamp Ptg Ltd)

1992 (14 May). *Irish Immigrants in the Americas. T 295 and similar horiz design. Multicoloured.* P 13½.

846	52p. Type 295		1·60	1·75
	a. Pair. Nos. 846/7		3·00	3·50
847	52p. Irish soldiers, entertainers and politicians		1·60	1·75

Nos. 846/7 were printed together, *se-tenant*, in horizontal and vertical pairs throughout the sheet.

296 Pair of Pine Martens

(Des R. Ward. Litho Irish Security Stamp Ptg Ltd)

1992 (9 July). *Endangered Species. Pine Marten. T 296 and similar horiz designs. Multicoloured.* P 15×14.

848	28p. Type 296		1·00	1·00
849	32p. Marten on branch		1·00	80
850	44p. Female with kittens		1·60	1·50
851	52p. Marten catching Great Tit		2·00	1·75
848/51		*Set of 4*	5·00	4·25

297 "The Rotunda and New Rooms" (James Malton)

(Des J. McEvoy (28, 44p.), E. Patton (32, 52p.). Litho Irish Security Stamp Ptg Ltd)

1992 (2 Sept). *Dublin Anniversaries. T 297 and similar multicoloured designs. Chalk-surfaced paper (32p.).* P 15×14 (28, 44p.) or 13½×14 (32, 52p.).

852	28p. Type 297		70	65
853	32p. Trinity College Library (28×45 mm)		1·00	1·00
854	44p. "Charlemont House"		1·10	2·00
855	52p. Trinity College main gate (28×45 mm)		1·40	2·25
852/5		*Set of 4*	3·75	5·50

Anniversaries:—28, 44p. Bicentenary of publication of Malton's "Views of Dublin"; 32, 52p. 400th anniv of founding of Trinity College.

298 European Star and Megalithic Dolmen   299 Farm Produce

(Des R. Ballagh. Litho Irish Security Stamp Ptg Ltd)

1992 (15 Oct). *Single European Market.* P 15×14.

856	298 32p. multicoloured		70	80
	a. Booklet pane. No. 856×4		3·00	
	b. Booklet pane. No. 856×3		3·00	

Three versions of booklet pane No. 856a exist showing the stamps arranged as a block of 4, as singles or in two vertical pairs. The first two versions exist overprinted for "STAMPA '92" (in blue on the block of four pane and in red on the other).

The booklet panes also exist overprinted for Regional Stamp Shows at Galway, Dundalk, Kilkenny and Limerick.

(Des Frances Poskitt. Litho Irish Security Stamp Ptg Ltd)

1992 (15 Oct). *Irish Agriculture. T 299 and similar vert designs. Multicoloured.* P 14×15.

857	32p. Type 299		1·00	1·25
	a. Horiz strip of 4. Nos. 857/60		3·50	
858	32p. Dairy and beef herds		1·00	1·25
859	32p. Harvesting cereals		1·00	1·25
860	32p. Market gardening		1·00	1·25
857/60		*Set of 4*	3·50	4·50

Nos. 857/60 were printed together, *se-tenant*, in horizontal strips of 4 throughout the sheet with each strip forming a composite design.

ALTERED CATALOGUE NUMBERS

Any Catalogue numbers altered from the last edition are shown as a list in the introductory pages.

300 "The Annunciation" (from illuminated manuscript)

301 Queen of Hearts

(Des Frances Poskitt (No. 861), J. McEvoy (others). Litho Irish Security Stamp Ptg Ltd)

1992 (19 Nov). *Christmas. T 300 and similar vert designs. Multicoloured. Chalk-surfaced paper. P 14×15.*
861	28p.	Congregation entering church	80	65
	a.	Sheetlet. No. 861×13	9·00	
862	28p.	Type 300	80	65
863	32p.	"Adoration of the Shepherds" (Da Empoli)	1·10	1·00
864	52p.	"Adoration of the Magi" (Rottenhammer)	1·40	1·50
861/4		*Set of 4*	3·75	3·50

No. 861 was only issued in sheetlets of 13 stamps and two labels (at the centre of rows 1 and 2) sold at £3.36 providing a discount of 28p. off the face value of the stamps.

(Des C. Harrison (28p.), Q. Design (32p.) Litho Irish Security Stamp Ptg Ltd)

1993 (26 Jan). *Greetings Stamps. T 301 and similar multicoloured design. Chalk-surfaced paper. P 14×15 (28p.) or 15×14 (32p.).*
865	28p.	Type 301	75	75
866	32p.	Hot air balloon trailing hearts (*horiz*)	85	85

302 "Evening at Tangier" (Sir John Lavery)

(Des. E. Patton. Litho Irish Security Stamp Ptg Ltd)

1993 (4 Mar). *Irish Impressionist Painters. T 302 and similar multicoloured designs. Chalk-surfaced paper. P 13.*
867	28p.	Type 302	75	60
	a.	Booklet pane. Nos. 867/70 with margins all round	5·00	
	b.	Booklet pane. Nos. 867/8 with margins all round	2·75	
868	32p.	"The Goose Girl" (William Leech)	80	65
869	44p.	"La Jeune Bretonne" (Roderic O'Conor) (*vert*)	1·25	1·60
	a.	Booklet pane. Nos. 869/70 with margins all round	2·75	
870	52p.	"Lustre Jug" (Walter Osborne) (*vert*)	1·75	2·25
867/70		*Set of 4*	4·00	4·50

Booklet pane No. 867a exists in two slightly different versions, one containing two se-tenant pairs and the other the stamps perforated individually.

The booklet panes exist overprinted in the margin in connection with Regional Stamp Shows at Mullingar, Tralee (overprint reads "Summer Regional Show"), Cork and Letterkenny. No. 867b also comes with a blue marginal overprint for "STAMPA 93".

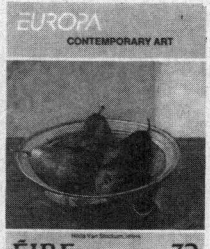

303 Bee Orchid

304 "Pears in a Copper Pan" (Hilda van Stockum)

(Des I. Loe. Litho Irish Security Stamp Ptg Ltd)

1993 (20 Apr). *Irish Orchids. T 303 and similar vert designs. Multicoloured. P 14×15.*
871	28p.	Type 303	90	60
872	32p.	O'Kelly's Orchid	1·00	80
873	38p.	Dark Red Helleborine	1·60	2·25
874	52p.	Irish Lady's Tresses	1·90	2·75
871/4		*Set of 4*	4·75	5·75
MS875	130×71 mm. Nos. 871/4		4·75	6·00

No. MS875 exists overprinted in red on the margin in connection with "STAMPA 93". This miniature sheet was also re-issued with a wider upper margin, showing the Irish and Thai flags, for the "Bangkok '93" International Stamp Exhibition. Such sheets were only available from the Philatelic Bureau and the An Post stand at the exhibition.

(Des E. Patton. Litho Irish Security Stamp Ptg Ltd)

1993 (18 May). *Europa. Contemporary Art. T 304 and similar vert design. Multicoloured. Chalk-surfaced paper. P 13.*
876	32p.	Type 304	75	75
877	44p.	"Arrieta Orzola" (Tony O'Malley)	1·10	1·10

Nos. 876/7 were each issued in sheetlets of 10 stamps and two labels (in positions 1 and 4 of the top row).

305 Cultural Activities

(Des K. Uhlemann and B. Donegan. Litho Irish Security Stamp Ptg Ltd)

1993 (8 July). *Centenary of Conradh Na Gaelige (cultural organization). T 305 and similar multicoloured design. Chalk-surfaced paper. P 15×14 (32p.) or 14×15 (52p.).*
878	32p.	Type 305	85	75
879	52p.	Illuminated manuscript cover (*vert*)	1·50	1·50

306 Diving

(Des C. Harrison. Litho Irish Security Stamp Ptg Ltd)

1993 (8 July). *Centenary of Irish Amateur Swimming Association. T 306 and similar horiz design. Multicoloured. Chalk-surfaced paper. P 15×14.*
880	32p.	Type 306	1·00	1·25
	a.	Horiz pair. Nos. 880/1	2·00	2·50
881	32p.	Swimming	1·00	1·25

Nos. 880/1 were printed together, *se-tenant*, in horizontal pairs throughout the sheet.

307 Nurse with Patient and Hospital Buildings (250th anniv of Royal Hospital, Donnybrook)

(Des K. Uhlemann (28p.), Q Design (32p.), C. Rycraft (44p.), P. Monahan (52p.). Litho Irish Security Stamp Ptg Ltd)

1993 (2 Sept). *Anniversaries and Events. T 307 and similar multicoloured designs. Chalk-surfaced paper. P 15×14 (28p., 44p.), 14×15 (32p.) or 13½ (52p.).*
882	28p.	Type 307	80	60
883	32p.	College building and crest (Bicent of St. Patrick's College, Carlow) (*vert*)	80	65
884	44p.	Map of Neolithic field system, Céide (Opening of interpretative centre)	1·25	1·40
885	52p.	Edward Bunting (musicologist) (150th death anniv) (25×42 mm)	1·40	1·60
882/5		*Set of 4*	3·75	3·75

308 Great Northern Railways Gardner at Drogheda

309 The Annunciation

(Des C. Rycraft. Litho Irish Security Stamp Ptg Ltd)

1993 (12 Oct). *Irish Buses. T 308 and similar horiz designs. Multicoloured. Chalk-surfaced paper. P 15×14.*
886	28p.	Type 308	60	65
	a.	Booklet pane. Nos. 886/7, each × 2	3·25	
	b.	Booklet pane. Nos. 886/9	3·25	
887	32p.	C.I.E. Leyland Titan at College Green, Dublin	65	70
888	52p.	Horse-drawn omnibus at Old Baal's Bridge, Limerick	1·50	2·00
	a.	Horiz pair. Nos. 888/9	3·00	4·00
889	52p.	Char-a-banc at Lady's View, Killarney	1·50	2·00
886/9		*Set of 4*	4·75	4·75

Nos. 888/9 were printed together, *se-tenant*, in horizontal pairs throughout the sheet.

Booklet panes Nos. 886a/b come from £2.84 stamp booklets and have the outer edges of the pane imperforate.

(Des Pamela Leonard (No. 890), C. Harrison (others). Litho Irish Security Stamp Ptg Ltd)

1993 (16 Nov). *Christmas. T 309 and similar multicoloured designs. Chalk-surfaced paper. P 14×15 (No. 890) or 15×14 (others).*
890	28p.	The Flight into Egypt (*vert*)	60	65
	a.	Sheetlet. No. 890×13	5·75	
891	28p.	Type 309	60	55
892	32p.	Holy Family	70	70
893	52p.	Adoration of the shepherds	1·60	2·25
890/3		*Set of 4*	3·25	3·75

No. 890 was only issued in sheetlets of 13 stamps and two labels (at the centre of rows 1 and 2) sold at £3.36 providing a discount of 28p. off the face value of the stamps.

310 Airplane skywriting "Love"

311 Smiling Sun

(Des Jean Colton (28p.), E. Rainsberry (32p.) Litho Questa)

1994 (27 Jan). *Greetings Stamps. T 310 and similar multicoloured design. Chalk-surfaced paper. P 15×14 (28p.) or 14×15 (32p.).*
894	28p.	Type 310	75	75
895	32p.	Couple within heart (*vert*)	85	85

(Des S. Young. Litho Irish Security Stamp Ptg)

1994 (27 Jan). *Greetings Booklet Stamps. T 311 and similar vert designs. Multicoloured. P 14×15.*
896	32p.	Type 311	85	90
	a.	Booklet pane. No. 896/9	3·00	
897	32p.	Smiling daisy	85	90
898	32p.	Smiling heart	85	90
899	32p.	Smiling rose	85	90
896/9		*Set of 4*	3·00	3·25

Nos. 896/9 come from £2.56 stamp booklets.

Booklet pane No. 896a exists with the right-hand stamp (either No. 897 or 899) imperforate at right. Each booklet pane also contains 8 small greeting labels.

The booklet pane also exists overprinted for Regional Stamp Shows at Cork and Letterkenny and from the Dublin International Stamp and Card Show.

(Des S. Young. Litho Irish Security Stamp Ptg Ltd)

1994 (18 Feb). *"Hong Kong '94" International Stamp Exhibition. Chinese New Year ("Year of the Dog"). P 14×15.*
MS900	137×34 mm. Nos. 896/8		4·25	5·00

The example of No. 898 in the above miniature sheet is imperforate at right.

312 Stylised Logo of Macra na Feirme (50th anniv)

(Des K. and R. Uhlemann (28p.), Creative Inputs (32p.), E. Patton (38, 52p.). Litho Irish Security Stamp Ptg Ltd)

1994 (2 Mar). *Anniversaries and Events. T 312 and similar horiz designs. Chalk-surfaced paper. P 15×14.*
901	28p.	gold and deep ultramarine	75	65
902	32p.	multicoloured	1·25	75
903	38p.	multicoloured	1·25	1·75
904	52p.	black, cobalt and bright blue	1·40	2·00
901/4		*Set of 4*	4·25	4·75

Designs: (38×35 mm)—32p. "The Taking of Christ" (Caravaggio) (Loan of painting to National Gallery). (37½×27 mm)—38p. Sir Horace Plunkett with 19th-century milk carts and modern tankers (Centenary of Irish Co-operative Organisation Society); 52p. Congress emblem (Centenary of Irish Congress of Trade Unions).

313 St. Brendan visiting Iceland

(Des C. Harrison. Litho Irish Security Stamp Ptg, Ltd)

1994 (18 Apr). *Europa. St. Brendan's Voyages. T 313 and similar horiz design. Multicoloured. Chalk-surfaced paper. P 15×14.*
905	32p.	Type 313	75	70
906	44p.	St. Brendan discovering Faroe Islands	1·50	2·00
MS907	82×76 mm. Nos. 905/6		2·25	2·75

Nos. 905/6 were each issued in sheetlets of 10 (2×5) with enlarged illustrated left margins.

No. MS907 also exists overprinted in blue on the margins in connection with "Stampa '94".

314 First Meeting of Dail, 1919

315 Irish and Argentine Footballers

(Des R. Hoek. Litho Irish Security Stamp Ptg Ltd)

1994 (27 Apr). *Parliamentary Anniversaries. T* **314** *and similar horiz design. Multicoloured. Chalk-surfaced paper. P* 15×14.

908	32p. Type 314 (75th anniv)		90	1·00
	a. Booklet pane. Nos. 908/9, each × 2		3·00	
	b. Booklet pane. Nos. 908/9		1·50	
909	32p. European Parliament (4th direct elections)		90	1·00

Booklet panes Nos. 908a/b come from £1.92 stamp booklets and have the outer edges of the panes imperforate. Booklet pane No. 908a contains examples of No. 908 either imperforate at top or at right and foot, and No. 909 imperforate at foot or at top and right. In booklet pane No. 908b No. 908 is imperforate at right and No. 909 fully perforated.

(Des J. Donohoe (Nos. 910/11), E. Patton (others). Litho Irish Security Stamp Ptg Ltd (Nos. 910/11) or Enschedé (others))

1994 (31 May). *Sporting Anniversaries and Events. T* **315** *and similar multicoloured designs. Chalk-surfaced paper (Nos. 910/11) or* P 14×15 *(Nos. 910/11) or* 13×13½ *(others).*

910	32p. Type 315		80	1·00
	a. Sheetlet. Nos. 910/11, each × 4		6·00	
911	32p. Irish and German footballers		80	1·00
912	32p. Irish and Dutch women's hockey match (*horiz*)		1·25	1·00
913	52p. Irish and English women's hockey match (*horiz*)		1·50	2·00
910/13		*Set of 4*	4·00	4·50

Anniversaries and Events:—Nos. 910/11, World Cup Football Championship, U.S.A.; No. 912, Women's Hockey World Cup, Dublin; No. 913, Centenary of Irish Ladies' Hockey Union.

Nos. 910/11 were printed together, *se-tenant*, in sheetlets of 8 stamps and one central label.

316 *Arctia caja*

317 Statue of Edmund Rice and Class

(Des I. Loe)

1994 (12 July). *Moths. T* **316** *and similar horiz designs. Multicoloured. (a) Litho Irish Security Stamp Ptg Ltd. Chalk-surfaced paper. P* 15×14.

914	28p. Type 316		65	60
915	32p. *Calamia tridens*		75	70
916	38p. *Saturnia pavonia*		90	1·10
917	52p. *Deilephila elpenor*		1·50	2·00
914/17		*Set of 4*	3·50	4·00
MS918	120×71 mm. Nos. 914/17		3·50	4·00

(b) *Litho Printset-Cambec Pty Ltd, Australia. Self-adhesive. Chalk-surfaced paper. P* 11½

919	32p. *Calamia tridens*		90	1·25
920	32p. Type 316		90	1·25
921	32p. *Deilephila elpenor*		90	1·25
922	32p. *Saturnia pavonia*		90	1·25
919/22		*Set of 4*	3·25	4·50

No. MS918 also exists with the "Philakorea '94" International Stamp Exhibition, Seoul, logo added at bottom right and also comes overprinted in black for Collectors' Road Show, Sligo, or in red for "Stampa '94".

Nos. 919/22 are smaller, 34×22 mm, and occur, *se-tenant*, in strips of 4 or rolls of 100 with the surplus self-adhesive paper around each stamp removed.

(Des S. Conlin (No. 923), Design Factory (Nos. 925, 927), E. Patton (Nos. 924, 926). Litho Walsall (Nos. 925, 927), Irish Security Stamp Ptg Ltd (others))

1994 (6 Sept). *Anniversaries and Events. T* **317** *and similar multicoloured designs. Chalk-surfaced paper. P* 13½ *(No.* 923*),* 14 *(Nos.* 925, 927*),* 14×15 *(No.* 924*) or* 15×14 *(No.* 926*).*

923	28p. St. Laurence Gate, Drogheda (41½×25 mm)		70	80
924	32p. Type 317		75	1·10
925	32p. Edmund Burke (politician)		75	1·10
926	52p. Vickers FB-27 Vimy and map (*horiz*)		1·25	1·40
927	52p. Eamonn Andrews (broadcaster)		1·50	1·50
923/7		*Set of 5*	4·50	5·50

Anniversaries and Events:—No. 923, 800th anniv of Drogheda; No. 924, 150th death anniv of Edmund Rice (founder of Irish Christian Brothers); Nos. 925, 927, The Irish abroad; No. 926, 75th anniv of Alcock and Brown's first Transatlantic flight.

318 George Bernard Shaw (author) and *Pygmalion* Poster

319 The Annunciation (ivory plaque)

(Des R. Ballagh. Litho Irish Security Stamp Ptg Ltd)

1994 (18 Oct). *Irish Nobel Prizewinners. T* **318** *and similar horiz designs. Multicoloured. Chalk-surfaced paper. P* 15×14.

928	28p. Type 318		60	75
	a. Pair. Nos. 928/9		1·10	1·50
	b. Booklet pane. Nos. 928/9 and 930×2 with margins all round		3·00	
	c. Booklet pane. Nos. 928/31 with margins all round		3·00	
	d. Booklet pane. Nos. 928/30 with margins all round		3·00	
929	28p. Samuel Beckett (author) and pair of boots		60	75
930	32p. Sean MacBride (human rights campaigner) and peace doves		70	75
	a. Booklet pane. Nos. 930 and 931×2 with margins all round		3·00	
931	52p. William Butler Yeats (poet) and poem		1·10	1·75
928/31		*Set of 4*	2·75	3·50

Nos. 928/9 were printed together, *se-tenant*, in horizontal and vertical pairs throughout the sheet.

The booklet panes also exist overprinted for Regional Stamp Shows at Waterford, Galway, Athlone and Kilkenny.

(Des Pamela Leonard (No. 932), Q Design (others). Litho Irish Security Stamp Ptg Ltd)

1994 (17 Nov). *Christmas. T* **319** *and similar vert designs. Chalk-surfaced paper. P* 14×15.

932	28p. Nativity		70	60
	a. Sheetlet. No. 932×13		8·00	
933	28p. Type 319		70	60
934	32p. Flight into Egypt (wood carving)		80	70
935	52p. Nativity (ivory plaque)		1·10	2·00
932/5		*Set of 4*	3·00	3·50

No. 932 was only issued in sheetlets of 13 stamps and two labels (at the centre of rows 1 and 2) sold at £3.36 providing a discount of 28p. off the face value of the stamps.

320 Tree of Hearts

321 West Clare Railway Steam Locomotive No. 1 *Kilkee* at Kilrush Station

(Des Bridget Flinn. Litho Irish Security Stamp Ptg Ltd)

1995 (24 Jan). *Greetings Stamps. T* **320** *and similar vert designs. Multicoloured. Chalk-surfaced paper. P* 14×15.

936	32p. Type 320		80	95
	a. Booklet pane. Nos. 936/7		3·00	
937	32p. Teddy bear holding balloon		80	95
938	32p. Clown juggling hearts		80	95
939	32p. Bouquet of flowers		80	95
936/9		*Set of 4*	3·00	3·50

Nos. 937/9 were only available from £2.56 stamp booklets containing two examples of No. 936a. This pane, which also includes 8 small greetings labels, exists in two different forms with either No. 936 at left and No. 938 at right or No. 937 at left and No. 939 at right. In each instance the right-hand stamp is imperforate at right.

(Des Bridget Flynn. Litho Irish Security Stamp Ptg Ltd)

1995 (24 Jan). *Chinese New Year ("Year of the Pig"). P* 14×15.

MS940	137×74 mm. Nos. 936, 938/9		2·75	3·50

The example of No. 939 in the above miniature sheet is imperforate at right.

(Des C. Rycraft. Litho Irish Security Stamp Ptg Ltd)

1995 (28 Feb). *Transport. Narrow Gauge Railways. T* **321** *and similar horiz designs. Multicoloured. Chalk-surfaced paper. P* 15×14.

941	28p. Type 321		75	60
942	32p. County Donegal Railway tank locomotive No. 2 *Blanche* at Donegal Station		90	90
943	38p. Cork and Muskerry Railway tank locomotive No. 1 *City of Cork* on Western Road, Cork		1·25	1·75
944	52p. Cavan and Leitrim tank locomotive No. 3 *Lady Edith* on Arigna Tramway		1·75	2·50
941/4		*Set of 4*	4·25	5·25
MS945	127×83 mm. Nos. 941/4		4·50	5·50

No. MS945 also exists with the "Singapore '95" International Stamp Exhibition logo added.

322 English and Irish Rugby Players

(Des C. Harrison. Litho Walsall)

1995 (6 Apr). *World Cup Rugby Championship, South Africa. T* **322** *and similar horiz design. Multicoloured. Chalk-surfaced paper. P* 14.

946	32p. Type 322		75	75
947	52p. Australian and Irish players		1·25	1·75
MS948	108×77 mm. £1 Type 322		2·50	2·75

No. MS948 also exists overprinted for Regional Stamp Shows at Limerick and Letterkenny.

323 Peace Dove and Skyscrapers

324 Soldiers of the Irish Brigade and Memorial Cross

(Des R. Ballagh)

1995 (6 Apr). *Europa. Peace and Freedom. T* **323** *and similar horiz design. Multicoloured. Chalk-surfaced paper. (a) Litho Irish Security Stamp Ptg Ltd. P* 15×14.

949	32p. Type 323		85	75
950	44p. Peace dove and map of Europe and North Africa		1·40	2·00

(b) *Litho Printset Cambec Pty Ltd, Melbourne. Self-adhesive. P* 11½

951	32p. Type 323		90	90
952	32p. As No. 950		90	90

Nos. 949/50 were issued in sheetlets of 10 (2×5) with illustrated left margins.

Nos. 951/2 are smaller, 34½×23 mm, and occur, *se-tenant*, in pairs or rolls of 100 with the surplus self-adhesive paper around each stamps removed.

(Des E. Daniels. Photo Belgian Post Office Ptg Wks, Malines)

1995 (15 May). *250th Anniv of Battle of Fontenoy. Chalk-surfaced paper. P* 11½.

953	**324** 32p. multicoloured		80	80

325 Irish Brigade, French Army, 1745

326 Guglielmo Marconi and Original Radio Transmitter

(Des D. McAllister. Litho Irish Security Stamp Ptg Ltd)

1995 (15 May). *Military Uniforms. T* **325** *and similar vert designs. Multicoloured. Chalk-surfaced paper. P* 14×15.

954	28p. Type 325		70	60
	a. Booklet pane. Nos. 954/5, each × 2		3·25	
	b. Booklet pane. Nos. 954/5 and 957/8		3·25	
	c. Booklet pane. Nos. 954/5 and 957		3·25	
	d. Booklet pane. Nos. 954/5 and 958		3·25	
955	32p. Tercio Irlanda, Spanish army in Flanders, 1605		80	75
956	32p. Royal Dublin Fusiliers, 1914		80	75
957	38p. St. Patrick's Battalion, Papal Army, 1860		1·10	1·25
958	52p. 69th Regiment, New York State Militia, 1861		1·10	1·75
954/8		*Set of 5*	4·50	4·50

Booklet panes Nos. 954a/b come with the two right-hand stamps (Nos. 954/5 or 955 and 958) imperforate at right.

The booklet panes also exist overprinted for Regional Stamp Shows at Sligo, Waterford and Galway and for "Stampa '95" (two panes).

(Des E. Jünger (No. 959), S. Young (No. 960). Litho Irish Security Stamp Ptg Ltd)

1995 (8 June). *Centenary of Radio. T* **326** *and similar horiz design. Multicoloured. Chalk-surfaced paper. P* 13½.

959	32p. Type 326		90	1·25
	a. Pair. Nos. 959/60		1·75	2·50
960	32p. Traditional radio dial		90	1·25

Nos. 959/60 were printed together, *se-tenant*, in horizontal and vertical pairs throughout the sheet.

327 Bartholomew Mosse
(founder) and Hospital
Building

(Des A. May (No. 961), S. Woulfe Flanagan (No. 962), Q Design
(No. 963), Creative Inputs (No. 964). Litho Questa (Nos.
961/2) or Irish Security Stamp Ptg Ltd (others))

1995 (27 July). *Anniversaries. T **327** and similar
multicoloured designs. Chalk-surfaced paper. P 15×14 (Nos.
961), 14½×14 (No. 962), 14½×14 (No. 963) or 13½ (No. 964).*
961 28p. Type **327** (250th anniv of Rotunda
     Hospital) 70 70
962 32p. St. Patrick's House, Maynooth College
     (Bicent) (25×41 *mm*) 80 80
963 32p. Laurel wreath and map of Europe
     (50th anniv of end of Second World
     War) 80 80
964 52p. Geological map of Ireland (150th anniv
     of Geological Survey of Ireland)
     (32½×32½ *mm*) .. .. 1·25 1·50
961/4 .. .. *Set of 4* 3·25 3·50

328 Natterjack Toad

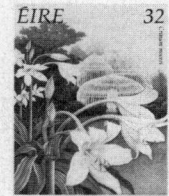

329 Crinum moorei

(Des I. Loe. Litho Irish Security Stamp Ptg Ltd)

1995 (1 Sept). *Reptiles and Amphibians. T **328** and similar
horiz designs. Chalk-surfaced paper. (a) P 15×14.*
965 32p. Type **328** .. .. 1·00 1·25
     a. Horiz strip. Nos. 965/8 .. 3·50
966 32p. Common Lizards .. .. 1·00 1·25
967 32p. Smooth Newts .. .. 1·00 1·25
968 32p. Common Frog .. .. 1·00 1·25
965/8 .. .. .. *Set of 4* 3·50 4·50
     (b) Self-adhesive. P 9½.
969 32p. Type **328** .. .. 1·00 1·25
970 32p. Common Lizard .. .. 1·00 1·25
971 32p. Smooth Newt .. .. 1·00 1·25
972 32p. Common Frog .. .. 1·00 1·25
969/72 .. .. .. *Set of 4* 3·50 4·50
Nos. 965/8 were printed together, *se-tenant*, in horizontal
strips of 4 with the backgrounds forming a composite design.
Nos. 969/72 are smaller, 34×23 mm, and occur, *se-tenant*, in
strips of 4 or rolls of 100 with the surplus self-adhesive paper
around each stamp removed.

(Des Frances Poskitt. Litho Irish Security Stamp Ptg Ltd)

1995 (9 Oct). *Bicentenary of National Botanic Gardens,
Glasnevin. Flowers. T **329** and similar vert designs.
Multicoloured. Chalk-surfaced paper. P 14×15.*
973 32p. Type **329** 85 70
     a. Booklet pane. Nos. 973×2 and 974/5 4·50
     b. Booklet pane. Nos. 973/5 .. 4·50
974 38p. *Sarracenia × moorei* .. 1·10 1·10
975 44p. *Solanum crispum* "Glasnevin" .. 1·50 2·50
973/5 .. .. .. *Set of 3* 3·00 3·75
Booklet panes Nos. 973a/b come from £2.60 stamp booklets
and have the outer edges of the pane imperforate so that
examples of each value exist imperforate on one or two sides.

330 Anniversary Logo and
Irish United Nations Soldier

(Des Jarlath Hayes. Litho Enschedé)

1995 (19 Oct). *50th Anniv of United Nations. T **330** and
similar horiz design. Multicoloured. Chalk-surfaced paper.
P 13×13½.*
976 32p. Type **330** 80 70
977 52p. Emblem and "UN" .. 1·25 1·40
Nos. 976/7 were each issued in sheets of 10 (2×5) with
enlarged illustrated left margins.

COVER PRICES

Cover factors are quoted at the beginning of each
country for most issues to 1945. An explanation of
the system can be found on page x. The factors
quoted do not, however, apply to philatelic covers.

331 "Adoration of the Shepherds"
(illuminated manuscript)
(Benedetto Bardone)

332 Zig and Zag on
Heart

(Des Q Design. Litho Irish Security Stamp Ptg Ltd)

1995 (16 Nov). *Christmas. T **331** and similar horiz designs.
Multicoloured. Chalk-surfaced paper. P 15×14.*
978 28p. Adoration of the Magi .. 70 65
     a. Sheetlet. No. 978×13 .. 8·25
979 28p. Type **331** 70 65
980 32p. "Adoration of the Magi" (illuminated
     manuscript) (Bardone) .. 80 70
981 52p. "The Holy Family" (illuminated
     manuscript) (Bardone) .. 1·40 1·90
978/81 .. .. .. *Set of 4* 3·25 3·50
No. 978 was issued in sheetlets of 13 stamps and two
labels (at centre of rows 1 and 2) sold at £3.36 providing a
discount of 28p. off the face value of the stamps.

(Des Double Z Enterprises. Litho Irish Security Stamp Ptg Ltd)

1996 (23 Jan). *Greetings Stamps. T **332** and similar vert
designs. Multicoloured. Chalk-surfaced paper. P 14×15.*
982 32p. Type **332** 95 50
     a. Booklet pane. Nos. 982/5 .. 4·25
983 32p. Zig and Zag waving .. 1·25 1·25
984 32p. Zig and Zag in space suits .. 1·25 1·25
985 32p. Zig and Zag wearing hats .. 1·25 1·25
982/5 .. .. .. *Set of 4* 4·25 3·75
Nos. 983/5 were only issued in £2.56 stamp booklets. No. 982
was available from sheets and booklets.
Booklet pane No. 982a, which also includes eight small
greetings labels, exists in two different forms with either No.
982 or 984 at right. In each instance the right-hand stamp is
imperforate at right.

(Des Double Z Enterprises. Litho Irish Security Stamp Ptg Ltd)

1996 (23 Jan). *Chinese New Year ("Year of the Rat"). Chalk-
surfaced paper. P 14×15.*
MS986 130×74 mm. Nos. 982, 984/5 .. 3·00 3·00
The example of No. 982 in No. MS986 is imperforate at right.
No. MS986 also exists overprinted for the Collectors' Road
Show at Kilkenny.

333 Wheelchair
Athlete

334 Before the Start,
Fairyhouse Race Course

(Des C. Harrison. Litho Irish Security Stamp Ptg Ltd)

1996 (1 Feb). *Olympic and Paralympic Games, Atlanta. T **333**
and similar vert designs. Multicoloured. Chalk-surfaced
paper. P 14×15.*
987 28p. Type **333** 70 65
988 32p. Running 80 80
     a. Strip of 3. Nos. 988/90 .. 2·25
989 32p. Throwing the discus .. 80 80
990 32p. Single kayak 80 80
987/90 .. .. .. *Set of 4* 2·75 2·75
Nos. 988/90 were printed together, *se-tenant*, as horizontal
and vertical strips of 3 in sheets of 9.

(Des P. Curling and Q Design. Litho Irish Security Stamp Ptg
Ltd)

1996 (12 Mar). *Irish Horse Racing. T **334** and similar horiz
designs. Multicoloured. Chalk-surfaced paper. P 15×14.*
991 28p. Type **334** 70 65
     a. Booklet pane. Nos. 991×2 and 992/3 4·25
992 32p. Steeplechase, Punchestown .. 80 80
     a. Pair. Nos. 992/3 .. 1·60 1·60
     b. Booklet pane. Nos. 992/5 .. 4·25
     c. Booklet pane. Nos. 992×2 and 994 4·25
993 32p. On the Flat, The Curragh .. 80 80
     a. Booklet pane. Nos. 993×2 and 995 4·25
994 38p. Steeplechase, Galway .. 1·25 1·25
995 52p. After the race, Leopardstown .. 1·50 1·50
991/5 .. .. .. *Set of 4* 4·50 4·50
Nos. 992/3 were printed together, *se-tenant*, in horizontal and
vertical pairs throughout the sheet.
Booklet pane Nos. 991a, 992b/c and 993a come from £4.92
stamp booklets with the right-hand edge of the panes
imperforate. The complete booklet contains two examples of No.
992 and one each of Nos. 991, 993 and 995 imperforate at right.
The booklet panes also exist overprinted for Collectors' Road
Shows at Cork (No. 992c), Limerick (No. 991a) or Sligo (No.
993a) and for "Stampa '96" (No. 992c).
For designs as Nos. 992/3 in miniature sheet see No. MS1003.

335 Irish and French Coloured
Ribbons merging

336 Louie Bennett
(suffragette)

(Des R. Ballagh. Litho Irish Security Stamp Ptg Ltd)

1996 (12 Mar). *"L'Imaginaire Irlandais" Festival of
Contemporary Irish Arts, France. Chalk-surfaced paper.
P 15×14.*
996 335 32p. multicoloured .. 80 80

(Des S. Young)

1996 (2 Apr). *Europa. Famous Women. T **336** and similar
horiz design. Multicoloured.*
     (a) Litho Questa. P 15×14.
997 336 32p. deep reddish violet .. 80 70
998 44p. myrtle-green .. 1·10 1·25
     (b) Litho Irish Security Stamp Ptg Ltd. Self-adhesive. P 9½.
999 336 32p. deep reddish violet .. 90 1·25
1000 32p. dull green .. 90 1·25
Design:—Nos. 998, 1000, Lady Augusta Gregory (playwright).
Nos. 997/8 were each issued in sheetlets of 10 (2×5) with
enlarged illustrated left margins.
Nos. 999/1000 are smaller, 34×23 mm, and occur, *se-tenant*,
in rolls of 100 with the surplus self-adhesive paper around each
stamp removed.

337 Newgrange Passage Tomb
(Boyne Valley World
Heritage Site)

(Des L. Belton (28p.), Q Design (32p.). Litho Walsall)

1996 (2 Apr). *Anniversaries and Events. T **337** and similar
horiz design. Multicoloured. Chalk-surfaced paper. P 14.*
1001 28p. grey-brown and black .. 85 60
1002 32p. multicoloured .. 90 90
Designs:—32p. Children playing (50th anniv of U.N.I.C.E.F.).

(Litho Irish Security Stamp Printing Ltd)

1996 (18 May). *"CHINA '96" 9th Asian International Stamp
Exhibition, Peking. Sheet 120×95 mm containing Nos. 992/3.
Chalk-surfaced paper. P 15×14.*
MS1003 32p. Steeplechase, Punchestown; 32p.
On the Flat, The Curragh .. 2·50 3·00

338 Stanley Woods

339 Michael Davitt
(founder of The
Land League)

(Des J. Dunne. Litho Questa)

1996 (30 May). *Isle of Man Tourist Trophy Motorcycle Races.
Irish Winners. T **338** and similar horiz designs. Multicoloured. Chalk-surfaced paper. P 14.*
1004 32p. Type **338** 80 70
1005 44p. Artie Bell .. .. 1·25 1·50
1006 50p. Alec Bennett .. .. 1·50 1·75
1007 52p. Joey and Robert Dunlop .. 1·50 1·75
1004/7 .. .. .. *Set of 4* 4·50 5·25
MS1008 100×70 mm. 50p. As 52p. .. 1·50 1·75
No. MS1008 also exists overprinted for "Stampa '96" and for
the Collectors' Road Show at Dundalk.

(Des R. Ballagh (28p.), J. Tobin (32p.), C. Harrison (38p.),
L. Belton (52p.). Litho Enschedé)

1996 (4 July). *Anniversaries and Events. T **339** and similar
multicoloured designs. Chalk-surfaced paper. P 13½×13
(28p.) or 13×13½ (others).*
1009 28p. Type **339** (150th birth anniv) .. 70 60
1010 32p. Presidency logo (Ireland's Presidency
     of European Union) (*horiz*) .. 80 70
1011 38p. Thomas McLaughlin (hydro-electric
     engineer) and Ardnacrusha Power
     Station (Birth centenary) (*horiz*) 1·00 1·10
1012 52p. Mechanical peat harvester (50th
     anniv of Bord na Móna) (*horiz*) 1·60 1·75
1009/12 .. .. .. *Set of 4* 3·75 3·75

340 *Ciara* (coastal patrol vessel) 341 Blind Woman with Child

(Des G. Fallon. Litho Irish Security Stamp Ptg Ltd)

1996 (18 July). *50th Anniv of Irish Naval Service. T* **340** *and similar multicoloured designs. Chalk-surfaced paper. P* 14×15 (52p.) *or* 15×14 (*others*).

1013	32p. Type **340**		80	70
	a. Booklet pane. No. 1013×3		2·75	
	b. Booklet pane. Nos. 1013/15		2·75	
1014	44p. *Cliona* (corvette)		1·40	1·50
1015	52p. *M-1* (motor torpedo boat) (*vert*)		1·50	1·60
1013/15		*Set of 3*	3·25	3·50

Booklet panes Nos. 1013a/b come from £2.24 stamp booklets. Stamps from No. 1013a have either one or two adjacent sides imperforate and those from No. 1013b are imperforate at foot (32, 44p.) or at right and foot (52p.).

The booklet panes also exist overprinted for "Stampa '96" (No. 1013b) or for the Collectors' Road Shows at Galway (No. 1013b) and Waterford (No. 1013a).

(Des E. Patton. Litho Irish Security Stamp Ptg Ltd)

1996 (3 Sept). *People with Disabilities. T* **341** *and similar vert design. Multicoloured. Chalk-surfaced paper. P* 14×15.

1016	28p. Type **341**		55	60
	a. Pair. Nos. 1016/7		1·10	
1017	28p. Man in wheelchair playing bowls		55	60

Nos. 1016/17 were printed together, *se-tenant*, in horizontal and vertical pairs throughout the sheet.

342 Green-winged Teal

(Des R. Ward. Litho Irish Security Stamp Ptg Ltd)

1996 (24 Sept). *Freshwater Ducks. T* **342** *and similar horiz designs. Multicoloured. Chalk-surfaced paper. P* 15×14.

1018	32p. Type **342**		85	70
1019	38p. Common Shoveler		1·00	1·00
1020	44p. European Wigeon		1·25	1·50
1021	52p. Mallard		1·50	1·75
1018/21		*Set of 4*	4·25	4·50
MS1022	127×85 mm. Nos. 1018/21		4·25	4·75

343 Scene from *Man of Aran* 344 Visit of the Magi

(Des J. Reddy. Litho Irish Security Stamp Ptg Ltd)

1996 (17 Oct). *Centenary of Irish Cinema. T* **343** *and similar horiz designs. Multicoloured. Chalk-surfaced paper. P* 13½.

1023	32p. Type **343**		85	90
	a. Strip of 4. Nos. 1023/6		3·00	
1024	32p. *My Left Foot*		85	90
1025	32p. *The Commitments*		85	90
1026	32p. *The Field*		85	90
1023/6		*Set of 4*	3·00	3·25

Nos. 1023/6 were printed together, *se-tenant*, in vertical and horizontal strips of 4 throughout the sheet.

(Des T. Monaghan (No. 1027), E. Patton (others). Litho Irish Security Stamp Ptg Ltd)

1996 (19 Nov). *Christmas. T* **344** *and similar vert designs from 16th-century Book of Hours (Nos. 1028/30). Multicoloured. Chalk-surfaced paper (Nos. 1028/30). P* 14×15.

1027	28p. The Holy Family		75	60
	a. Sheetlet. No. 1027×15		10·00	
1028	28p. Type **344**		60	60
1029	32p. The Annunciation		80	80
1030	52p. The Shepherds receiving news of Christ's birth		1·40	1·60
1027/30		*Set of 4*	3·25	3·25

No. 1027 was only issued in sheetlets of 15 stamps sold at £3.92 providing a discount of 28p. off the face value of the stamps.

345 Magpie 346 Pair of Doves

(Des K. Mullarney)

1997 (16 Jan)–*99. Birds. T* **345** *and similar multicoloured designs.*

(a) *Litho Walsall (Nos. 1038ac, 1053ac, 1054ac, 1055ac, 1057ac, 1058ac) or Irish Security Stamp Ptg Ltd (others). Chalk-surfaced paper* (1p., 2p., 4p., 10p., 20p., 30p. (*Nos.* 1039/52), £5) *or ordinary paper* (*others*). *P* 15×14 (5p., 28p., 40p., 50p., £1, £5) *or* 14×15 (*others*)

(i) *Size* 21×24 *mm* (*vert*) *or* 24×21 *mm* (*horiz*)

1031	1p. Type **345** (27.8.97)		10	10
1032	2p. Gannet (27.8.97)		10	10
1033	4p. Corncrake (27.8.97)		10	10
	a. Ordinary paper (3.98)		40	40
1034	5p. Wood Pigeon (*horiz*) (2.4.98)		10	10
	a. Chalk-surfaced paper (9.98)		40	40
1035	10p. Kingfisher (27.8.97)		15	20
1036	20p. Lapwing (27.8.97)		30	35
1037	28p. Blue Tit (*horiz*)		45	50
	a. Chalk-surfaced paper (10.97)		75	75
1038	30p. Blackbird (2.4.98)		45	50
	a. Chalk-surfaced paper (4.98)		1·25	90
	ab. Booklet pane. Nos. 1038a and 1039, each × 5 (4.9.98)		6·50	
	ac. Perf 14 (phosphor frame) (17.11.98)		45	50
	ap. Phosphor frame (25.1.99)		45	
	aq. Sheetlet. Nos. 1038ap, 1039p and 1040/52 (16.2.99)		6·25	
	ar. Booklet pane. Nos. 1038ap and 1039p, each × 5 (25.1.99)		4·50	
	p. Phosphor frame (*ordinary paper*) (6.12.99)		45	50
1039	30p. Goldcrest (4.9.98)		45	50
	p. Phosphor frame (25.1.99)		45	50
1040	30p. Stonechat (*phosphor frame*) (16.2.99)		45	50
1041	30p. Lapwing (*phosphor frame*) (16.2.99)		45	50
1042	30p. Gannet (*phosphor frame*) (16.2.99)		45	50
1043	30p. Corncrake (*phosphor frame*) (16.2.99)		45	50
1044	30p. Type **345** (*phosphor frame*) (16.2.99)		45	50
1045	30p. Kingfisher (*phosphor frame*) (16.2.99)		45	50
1046	30p. Peregrine Falcon (*phosphor frame*) (16.2.99)		45	50
1047	30p. Barn Owl (*phosphor frame*) (16.2.99)		45	50
1048	30p. Robin (*phosphor frame*) (16.2.99)		45	50
1049	30p. Song Thrush (*phosphor frame*) (16.2.99)		45	50
1050	30p. Wren (*phosphor frame*) (16.2.99)		45	50
1051	30p. Pied Wagtail (*phosphor frame*) (16.2.99)		45	50
1052	30p. Puffin (*phosphor frame*) (16.2.99)		45	50
1053	32p. Robin		50	55
	a. Chalk-surfaced paper (10.97)		1·00	1·00
	ac. Perf 14 (phosphor frame) (17.11.98)		50	55
	p. Phosphor frame (30.6.99)		50	55
	pa. Booklet pane. No. 1053p×5, plus 5 airmail labels		2·50	
1054	35p. Stonechat (2.4.98)		50	55
	a. Chalk-surfaced paper (4.98)		1·60	1·10
	ac. Perf 14 (phosphor frame) (17.11.98)		50	55
1055	40p. Ringed Plover (*horiz*) (2.4.98)		60	65
	ac. Perf 14. Chalk-surfaced paper (phosphor frame) (17.11.98)		60	65
1056	44p. Puffin		70	75
1057	45p. Song Thrush (2.4.98)		70	75
	a. Chalk-surfaced paper (9.98)		1·90	1·25
	ac. Perf 14 (phosphor frame) (17.11.98)		70	75
	ap. Phosphor frame (30.6.99)		70	75
	apa. Booklet pane. No. 1057ap×4, plus 4 labels		2·75	
	p. Phosphor frame (*ordinary paper*) (18.5.99)		70	75
	pa. Booklet pane. No. 1057p×4, plus 4 labels (30.6.99)		2·75	
1058	50p. European Sparrow Hawk (*horiz*) (2.4.98)		80	85
	a. Chalk-surfaced paper (8.98)		2·00	1·25
	ac. Perf 14 (phosphor frame) (17.11.98)		80	85
1059	52p. Barn Owl		80	85

(ii) *Size* 24×45 *mm* (*vert*) *or* 45×24 *mm* (*horiz*)

1060	£1 Greenland White-fronted Goose		1·60	1·75
	a. Chalk-surfaced paper (11.98)		2·50	1·90
1061	£2 Pintail (*horiz*) (2.4.98)		3·25	3·50
	a. Chalk-surfaced paper (6.99)		3·25	3·50
1062	£5 Shelduck (28.8.97)		8·00	8·25
	a. Ordinary paper (9.98)		15·00	11·00
1031/62		*Set of 32*	27·00	29·00

(b) *Booklet stamps. Litho Irish Security Stamp Ptg Ltd. Size* 21×17 (5p.) *or* 17×21 *mm* (*others*). *Chalk-surfaced paper* (4p., 30p. (*No.* 1083), 32p.) *or ordinary paper* (*others*). *P* 14×15 (5p.) *or* 15×14 (*others*)

1080	4p. Corncrake (6.12.97)		10	10
	a. Booklet pane. Nos. 1080 and 1085×3		1·75	
1081	5p. Wood Pigeon (*horiz*) (2.4.98)		10	10
	a. Booklet pane. Nos. 1081×2 and 1082×3 plus label		1·75	
	b. Chalk-surfaced paper (16.2.99)		10	10
	ba. Booklet pane. Nos. 1081b×2 and 1083×3 plus label		1·75	
1082	30p. Blackbird (2.4.98)		45	50
1083	30p. Goldcrest ("all-over" phosphor) (16.2.99)		45	50
1084	32p. Robin (6.3.97)		50	55
1085	32p. Peregrine Falcon (6.12.97)		50	55

(c) *Self-adhesive. Size* 25×30 *mm.*

(i) *Litho Irish Stamp Security Ptg Ltd. P* 9×10

1086	30p. Goldcrest (2.4.98)		85	85
	a. Vert pair. Nos. 1086/7		1·60	1·60
	p. Phosphor frame (14.12.98)		45	50
	pa. Vert pair. Nos. 1086p/7p		90	1·00
1087	30p. Blackbird (2.4.98)		85	85
	p. Phosphor frame (14.12.98)		45	50
1088	32p. Peregrine Falcon (6.3.97)		1·00	1·00
	a. Vert pair. Nos. 1088/9		2·00	2·00
1089	32p. Robin (6.3.97)		1·00	1·00

(ii) *Litho SNP Cambec, Melbourne. P* 11½

1090	30p. Goldcrest (2.4.98)		85	85
	a. Vert pair. Nos. 1090/1		1·60	1·60
	p. Phosphor frame (17.11.98)		45	50
	pa. Vert pair. Nos. 1090p/1p		90	1·00
1091	30p. Blackbird (2.4.98)		85	85
	p. Phosphor frame (17.11.98)		45	50
1092	32p. Peregrine Falcon (4.97)		1·00	1·25
	a. Vert pair. Nos. 1092/3		2·00	2·50
1093	32p. Robin (4.97)		1·00	1·25

No. 1039 was only issued in £3 stamp booklets which show the upper and lower edges of the pane imperforate and a margin at either end.

The sheet stamps with phosphor frames and No. 1038ar show the actual designs slightly reduced to provide a clear 2 mm border on which the phosphor frame appears.

The sheetlet, No. 1038aq, repeats the vertical designs from other values in the set. The designs showing the Wren and Pied Wagtail will only occur in the sheetlet. It also exists overprinted for the Collectors' Road Show at Limerick.

Nos. 748bb (containing No. 1084), 1080a, 1081a and 1081ab show the upper and lower edges of the panes imperforate. On booklet pane No. 1081ba the three 30p. have "all-over" phosphor, but this does not extend to the two 5p. stamps or the label.

Booklet panes Nos. 1053pa, 1057apa and 1057pa show the stamps as a horizontal row with margins on three sides and the airmail labels attached at right.

Nos. 1086/7, 1088/9, 1090/1 and 1092/3 were produced in rolls of 100, each containing two designs. Those printed by Irish Stamp Security Ptg Ltd retain the surplus self-adhesive paper around each stamp, but this was removed for those produced in Australia.

Nos. 1086p/7p show the actual designs slightly reduced and the inscriptions repositioned to provide a clear 2 mm border on which the phosphor frame appears.

The sheetlet of 30p. designs, No. 1038aq, also exists overprinted on the margins for Collectors Road Shows at Limerick (in black), Cork (in red), Killarney (in green), Sligo (in deep blue), and Galway (in maroon).

For £2 value in miniature sheet see No. **MS**1131.

(Des Double Z Enterprises. Litho Irish Security Stamp Ptg Ltd)

1997 (28 Jan). *Greetings Stamps. T* **346** *and similar vert designs. Multicoloured. Chalk-surfaced paper. P* 14×15.

1100	32p. Type **346**		85	50
	a. Booklet pane. No. 1100/3		3·75	
1101	32p. Cow jumping over moon		1·10	1·10
1102	32p. Pig going to market		1·10	1·10
1103	32p. Cockerel		1·10	1·10
1100/3		*Set of 4*	3·75	3·50

Nos. 1101/3 were only issued in £2.56 stamp booklets. No. 1100 was available from sheets and booklets.

Booklet pane No. 1100a, which also includes eight small greetings labels, exists in two forms with No. 1101 either at left or right. In each instance the right-hand stamp, No. 1101 or No. 1103, is imperforate at right.

(Des Double Z Enterprises. Litho Irish Security Stamp Ptg Ltd)

1997 (28 Jan). *"HONG KONG '97" International Stamp Exhibition. Chinese New Year ("Year of the Ox"). Chalk-surfaced paper. P* 14×15.

MS1104 124×74 mm. Nos. 1101/3 2·40 2·40

The example of No. 1103 in No. **MS**1104 is imperforate at right.

No. **MS**1104 also exists overprinted for the Collectors' Road Show at Limerick.

347 Troops on Parade 348 Grey Seals

(Des Q Design. Litho Irish Security Stamp Ptg Ltd)

1997 (18 Feb–6 Dec). *75th Anniv of Irish Free State. T* **347** *and similar horiz designs. Multicoloured. Chalk-surfaced paper. P* 15×14.

1105	28p. Page from the "Annals of the Four Masters", quill and 1944 ½d. O'Clery stamp (27 Aug)		55	55
1106	32p. Type **347**		60	65
	a. Pair. Nos. 1106/7		1·25	1·25
1107	32p. The Dail, national flag and Constitution		60	65
1108	32p. Athlete, footballer and hurling players (3 Apr)		60	65
	a. Pair. Nos. 1108/9		1·25	1·25
1109	32p. Singer, violinist and bodhran player (3 Apr)		60	65
1110	32p. Stained glass window and 1929 9d. O'Connell stamp (27 Aug)		60	60
1111	32p. G.P.O., Dublin, and 1923 2d. map stamp (6 Dec)		60	60
1112	52p. Police personnel and Garda badge		1·00	1·25
	a. Pair. Nos. 1112/13		2·00	2·50

1113	52p.	The Four Courts and Scales of Justice	1·00	1·25
1114	52p.	Currency, blueprint and food-processing plant (3 Apr)	1·00	1·25
	a.	Pair. Nos. 1114/15	2·00	2·50
1115	52p.	Books, palette and Seamus Heaney manuscript (3 Apr)	1·00	1·25
1116	52p.	Air Lingus airliner and 1965 1s. 5d air stamp (27 Aug)	1·00	95
1105/16		Set of 12	8·25	9·00
MS1117		174×209 mm. As Nos. 1105/16, but each with face value of 32p. (6 Dec)	6·50	7·50

Nos. 1106/7, 1108/9, 1112/13 and 1114/15 were each printed together, *se-tenant*, in horiz or vert pairs throughout the sheets.

(Des Rosemary Davis. Litho Irish Security Stamp Ptg Ltd)

1997 (6 Mar). *Marine Mammals. T **348** and similar multicoloured designs. Chalk-surfaced paper. P 14×15 (28p., 32p.) or 15×14 (others).*

1118	28p.	Type **348**	75	60
1119	32p.	Bottle-nosed Dolphins ..	85	80
1120	44p.	Harbour Porpoises (*horiz*) ..	1·25	1·25
1121	52p.	Killer Whale (*horiz*) ..	1·40	1·50
1118/21		Set of 4	3·75	3·75
MS1122		150×68 mm. As Nos. 1118/21. P 15	4·25	4·25

No. MS1122 also exists overprinted for the Collectors' Road Show at Dublin.

349 Dublin Silver Penny of 997

(Des Creative Inputs. Litho Irish Security Stamp Ptg Ltd)

1997 (3 Apr). *Millenary of Irish Coinage. Chalk-surfaced paper. P 15×14.*

1123	**349**	32p. multicoloured ..	65	65

350 "The Children of Lir"

(Des P. Lynch)

1997 (14 May). *Europa. Tales and Legends. T **350** and similar horiz design. Multicoloured. (a) Litho Walsall. Chalk-surfaced paper. P 14.*

1124	32p.	Type **350**	70	60
1125	44p.	Oisin and Niamh	1·00	1·40

(b) Litho Irish Security Stamp Ptg Ltd. Self-adhesive. P 9½.

1126	32p.	Type **350**	70	70
	a.	Horiz pair. Nos. 1126/7	1·40	1·40
1127	32p.	Oisin and Niamh ..	70	70
1124/7		Set of 4	2·75	2·75

Nos. 1124/5 were each issued in sheetlets of 10 (2×5) with enlarged illustrated left margins.

Nos. 1126/7, which are smaller 36×25 mm, occur in rolls of 100.

351 Emigrants waiting to board Ship

(Des Q Design. Litho Irish Security Stamp Ptg Ltd)

1997 (14 May). *150th Anniv of The Great Famine. T **351** and similar horiz designs. Chalk-surfaced paper. P 15×14.*

1128	28p.	dp dull blue, verm & pale yellow-ochre	75	60
1129	32p.	reddish orange, deep dull blue and pale yellow-ochre ..	90	70
1130	52p.	brown, dp dull blue & pale yell-ochre	1·40	1·40
1128/30		Set of 3	2·75	2·40

Designs—32p. Family and dying child; 52p. Irish Society of Friends soup kitchen.

(Des K. Mullarney. Litho Irish Security Stamp Ptg Ltd)

1997 (29 May). *"Pacific '97" International Stamp Exhibition, San Francisco. Sheet, 100×70 mm, containing No. 1061. Multicoloured. Chalk-surfaced paper. P 14.*

MS1131		£2 Pintail (48×26 mm) ..	4·50	5·00

COVER PRICES

Cover factors are quoted at the beginning of each country for most issues to 1945. An explanation of the system can be found on page x. The factors quoted do not, however, apply to philatelic covers.

---

352 Kate O'Brien (novelist) (birth centenary)

353 The Baily Lighthouse

(Des Creative Inputs. Litho Irish Security Stamp Ptg Ltd (No. 1133) or Walsall (others))

1997 (1 July). *Anniversaries. T **352** and similar vert designs. Multicoloured. Chalk-surfaced paper. P 14×15 (No. 1133), 14½ (No. 1134) or 14 (others).*

1132	28p.	Type **352**	60	70
1133	28p.	St. Columba crossing to Iona (stained glass window) (1400th death anniv)	60	70
1134	32p.	"Daniel O'Connell" (J. Haverty) (politician) (150th death anniv) (27×49 mm)	70	70
1135	52p.	"John Wesley" (N. Hone) (founder of Methodism) (250th anniv of first visit to Ireland)	1·25	1·60
1132/5		Set of 4	2·75	3·25

(Des Design Image. Litho Irish Security Stamp Ptg Ltd)

1997 (1 July). *Lighthouses. T **353** and similar multicoloured designs. Chalk-surfaced paper. P 15×14 (32p.) or 14×15 (others).*

1136	32p.	Type **353**	80	80
	a.	Pair. Nos. 1136/7 ..	1·60	1·60
	b.	Booklet pane. Nos. 1136×2 and 1137	2·75	
	c.	Booklet pane. Nos. 1136/7, each × 2	2·75	
	d.	Perf 15 ..	1·10	1·40
	da.	Booklet pane. Nos. 1136d/9d	4·00	
1137	32p.	Tarbert ..	80	80
	d.	Perf 15 ..	1·10	1·40
1138	38p.	Hookhead (*vert*) ..	85	85
	d.	Perf 15 ..	1·10	1·40
	da.	Booklet pane. Nos. 1138d/9d	2·75	
1139	50p.	The Fastnet (*vert*) ..	1·10	1·25
	d.	Perf 15 ..	1·10	1·40
1136/9		Set of 4	3·25	3·25

Nos. 1136/7 were printed together, *se-tenant*, in horizontal or vertical pairs throughout the sheet.

Nos. 1136d/9d only exist from booklet panes Nos. 1136da and 1138da.

The booklet panes also exist overprinted for Collectors' Road Shows at Sligo (No. 1136b), Tralee (No. 1138da), Galway (No. 1136c) or Limerick (No. 1136da) and also for "Stampa '97" (Nos. 1136b/c, 1136da and 1138da).

354 Commemorative Cross

355 Dracula and Bat

(Des L. Rafael. Litho Irish Security Stamp Ptg Ltd)

1997 (12 Sept). *Ireland–Mexico Joint Issue. 150th Anniv of Mexican St. Patrick's Battalion. Ordinary paper. P 13½.*

1140	**354**	32p. multicoloured ..	55	60

(Des Passmore Design. Litho Irish Security Stamp Ptg Ltd)

1997 (1 Oct). *Centenary of Publication of Bram Stoker's Dracula. T **355** and similar multicoloured designs. Chalk-surfaced paper. P 14×15 (vert) or 15×14 (horiz).*

1141	28p.	Type **355**	60	55
1142	32p.	Dracula and female victim ..	65	60
1143	38p.	Dracula emerging from coffin (*horiz*)	80	80
1144	52p.	Dracula and wolf (*horiz*) ..	1·10	1·10
1141/4		Set of 4	2·75	2·75
MS1145		150×90 mm. As Nos. 1141/4. P 15	3·25	3·25

A second miniature sheet, 75×55 mm, containing No. 1142, was only available as a promotional item connected with the purchase of funsize bars of various Mars products or at face value from the Philatelic Bureau.

356 "The Nativity" (Kevin Kelly)

357 Christmas Tree

(Des Creative Inputs (Nos. 1146/8). Q. Design (No. 1149). Litho Irish Security Stamp Ptg Ltd)

1997 (18 Nov). *Christmas. (a) Stained Glass Windows. T **356** and similar vert designs. Multicoloured. Chalk-surfaced paper. P 14×15.*

1146	28p.	Type **356**	60	55
1147	32p.	"The Nativity" (Sarah Purser and A. E. Child) ..	70	65
1148	52p.	"The Nativity" (A. E. Child) ..	1·25	1·40
1146/8		Set of 3	2·25	2·40

(b) Self-adhesive booklet stamp. P 9×10

1149	28p.	Type **357** ..	55	65
	a.	Booklet pane. No. 1149×20 ..	11·00	

No. 1149 as only available from £5.32 stamp booklets.

358 Holding Heart

359 Lady Mary Heath and Avro Avian over Pyramids

(Des B. Asprey. Litho Irish Security Stamp Ptg Ltd)

1998 (26 Jan). *Greetings Stamps (1st series). T **358** and similar vert designs based on the "love is..." cartoon characters of Kim Casali. Multicoloured. Chalk-surfaced paper. P 14×15.*

1150	32p.	Type **358**	70	50
	a.	Booklet pane. Nos. 1150/3 ..	2·50	
1151	32p.	Receiving letter ..	70	1·00
1152	32p.	Sitting on log	70	1·00
1153	32p.	With birthday presents ..	70	1·00
1150/3		Set of 4	2·50	3·25

Nos. 1151/3 were only available from £2.56 stamp booklets containing two examples of No. 1150a. This pane exists in two different forms with either No. 1150 at right and No. 1153 at left or No. 1152 at right and No. 1151 at left. In each instance the right-hand stamp is imperforate at right. No. 1150 is available from both sheets and booklets.

For 30p values in these designs see Nos. 1173/6

(Des B. Asprey. Litho Irish Security Stamp Ptg Ltd)

1998 (26 Jan). *Chinese New Year ("Year of the Tiger"). Chalk-surfaced paper. P 14×15.*

MS1154		124×73 mm. As Nos. 1151/3. ..	2·25	2·50

The example of No. 1152 in No. MS1154 is imperforate at right.

(Des V. Killowry. Litho Irish Security Stamp Ptg Ltd)

1998 (24 Feb). *Pioneers of Irish Aviation. T **359** and similar horiz designs. Multicoloured. Chalk-surfaced paper. P 15×14.*

1155	28p.	Type **359**	60	55
	a.	Booklet pane. Nos. 1155/8 ..	3·00	
	b.	Booklet pane. Nos. 1155/6 each × 2	3·00	
1156	32p.	Col. James Fitzmaurice and Junkers W. 33 *Bremen* over Labrador	65	60
	a.	Booklet pane. Nos. 1156×2 and 1157	3·00	
	b.	Booklet pane. Nos. 1156 and 1158×2	3·00	
1157	44p.	Captain J. P. Saul and Fokker FVIIa/3m *Southern Cross* ..	1·25	1·25
1158	52p.	Captain Charles Blair and Sikorsky V-s 44 (flying boat) ..	1·50	1·50
1155/8		Set of 4	3·50	3·50

Booklet panes Nos. 1155b and 1156a/b have margins all round. On No. 1155a there are margins on three sides, but the two right-hand stamps (Nos. 1156 and 1158) are each imperforate at right.

360 Show-jumping

(Des P. Curling. Litho Irish Security Stamp Ptg Ltd)

1998 (2 Apr). *Equestrian Sports. T **360** and similar multicoloured designs. Chalk-surfaced paper. P 14×15 (45p.) or 15×14 (others).*

1159	30p.	Type **360**	70	60
1160	32p.	Three-day eventing ..	75	65
1161	40p.	Gymkhana	90	1·25
1162	45p.	Dressage (*vert*) ..	90	1·25
1159/62		Set of 4	3·25	3·25
MS1163		126×84 mm. Nos. 1159/62 ..	3·00	3·25

361 Figure of "Liberty"

(Des R. Ballagh. Litho Irish Security Stamp Printing Ltd)

1998 (6 May). *Bicentenary of United Irish Rebellion. T **361** and similar horiz designs. Multicoloured. Chalk-surfaced paper. P 15×14.*

1164	30p. Type **361**	90	90
	a. Horiz strip of 3. Nos. 1164/6	2·40	
1165	30p. United Irishman	90	90
1166	30p. French soldiers	90	90
1167	45p. Wolfe Tone	1·00	1·25
	a. Horiz pair. Nos. 1167/8	2·00	2·50
1168	45p. Henry Joy McCracken	1·00	1·25
1164/8	*Set of 5*	4·25	4·75

Nos. 1164/6 and 1167/8 were each printed together, horizontally *se-tenant*, in strips of 3 (30p.) or in pairs (45p.) throughout sheets of 12.

362 Gathering of the Boats, Kinvara

(Des J. Dunne. Litho Irish Security Stamp Ptg Ltd)

1998 (6 May). *Europa. Festivals. T **362** and similar horiz design. Multicoloured. (a) P 15×14*

1169	30p. Type **362**	70	80
1170	40p. Puck Fair, Killorglin	80	95

(b) Self-adhesive. Chalk-surfaced paper. P 9½

1171	30p. Type **362**	65	70
1172	30p. Puck Fair, Killorglin	65	70

Nos. 1169/70 were each issued in sheetlets of 10 (2×5) with enlarged illustrated left margins.
Nos. 1171/2, which are smaller 34×23 mm, occur in rolls of 100 with the surplus self-adhesive paper retained.

1998 (6 May). *Greetings Stamps (2nd series). Vert designs as Nos. 1150/3, but with changed face value. Multicoloured. Chalk-surfaced paper. P 14×15.*

1173	30p. As No. 1153	70	80
	a. Booklet pane. Nos. 1173/6	2·50	
1174	30p. As No. 1152	70	80
1175	30p. As No. 1151	70	80
1176	30p. Type **358**	70	80
1173/6	*Set of 4*	2·50	3·00

Nos. 1173/6 were only available from £2·40 stamp booklets containing two examples of No. 1173a. This pane exists in two different forms with either No. 1176 at right and No. 1173 at left or No. 1174 at right and No. 1175 at left. In each instance the right-hand stamp is imperforate at right.

363 Cyclists rounding Bend

(Des C. Harrison. Litho Irish Security Stamp Ptg Ltd)

1998 (2 June). *Visit of "Tour de France" Cycle Race to Ireland. T **363** and similar horiz designs. Multicoloured. Chalk-surfaced paper. P 15×14.*

1177	30p. Type **363**	70	70
	a. Horiz strip of 4. Nos. 1177/80	2·50	
1178	30p. Two cyclists ascending hill	70	70
1179	30p. "Green jersey" cyclist and other competitor	70	70
1180	30p. "Yellow jersey" (race leader)	70	70
1177/80	*Set of 4*	2·50	2·50

Nos. 1177/80 were printed together, *se-tenant*, in horizontal strips of 4 throughout the sheet.

364 Voter and Local Councillors of 1898

365 Asgard II (cadet brigantine)

(Des J. Dunne. Litho Irish Security Stamp Ptg Ltd)

1998 (2 June). *Democracy Anniversaries. T **364** and similar horiz designs. Multicoloured. Chalk-surfaced paper. P 15×14.*

1181	30p. Type **364** (Cent of Local Government (Ireland) Act)	60	60
1182	32p. European Union flag and harp symbol (25th anniv of Ireland's entry into European Community)	65	65
1183	35p. Woman voter and suffragettes, 1898 (Cent of women's right to vote in local elections)	75	75
1184	45p. Irish Republic flag (50th anniv of Republic of Ireland Act)	1·00	1·00
1181/4	*Set of 4*	2·75	2·75

(Des FOR Design. Litho Irish Security Stamp Ptg Ltd)

1998 (20 July). *Cutty Sark International Tall Ships Race, Dublin. T **365** and similar multicoloured designs. Chalk-surfaced paper.*

(a) P 14×15 (30p.) or 15×14 (45p, £1)

1185	30p. Type **365**	55	60
	a. Pair. Nos. 1185/6	1·10	1·25
	b. Perf 15	65	75
	ba. Booklet pane. Nos. 1185b×2 and 1186b with margins all round	2·25	
1186	30p. U.S.C.G. *Eagle* (cadet barque)	55	60
	b. Perf 15	65	75
	ba. Booklet pane. Nos. 1186b/8b with margins all round	2·25	
1187	45p. *Boa Esperanza* (replica caravel) (horiz)	80	85
	b. Perf 15	1·00	1·60
1188	£1 *Royalist* (training brigantine) (horiz)	1·75	1·90
	b. Perf 15	1·75	1·90
1185/8	*Set of 4*	3·50	3·75

(b) Self-adhesive. P 9½

1189	30p. *Boa Esperanza* (horiz)	55	60
	a. Strip of 4. Nos. 1189/92	2·10	
1190	30p. Type **365**	55	60
1191	30p. U.S.C.G. *Eagle*	55	60
1192	30p. *Royalist* (horiz)	55	60
1189/92	*Set of 4*	2·10	2·25

Nos. 1185b/8b were only available from £2·65 stamp booklets.
Nos. 1189/92 are smaller, 34×23 or 23×34 mm, and occur, *se-tenant*, in strips of 4 or rolls of 100 with the surplus self-adhesive paper around each stamp retained.
Nos. 1185ba and 1186ba also exist overprinted for "Stampa 98".

366 Ashworth Pillarbox (1856)

367 Mary Immaculate College, Limerick

(Des M. Craig. Litho Irish Security Stamp Ptg Ltd)

1998 (3 Sept). *Irish Postboxes. T **366** and similar vert designs. Multicoloured. Chalk-surfaced paper. P 15×14.*

1193	30p. Type **366**	55	65
	a. Horiz strip of 4. Nos. 1193/6	2·10	
1194	30p. Irish Free State wallbox (1922)	55	65
1195	30p. Double pillarbox (1899)	55	65
1196	30p. Penfold pillarbox (1866)	55	65
1193/6	*Set of 4*	2·10	2·40

Nos. 1193/6 were printed together, *se-tenant*, in horizontal strips of 4 throughout the sheet of 12.

(Des J. McPartlin (45p), E. Patton (others). Litho Irish Security Stamp Ptg Ltd)

1998 (3 Sept). *Anniversaries. T **367** and similar multicoloured designs. Chalk-surfaced paper. P 14×15 (40p.) or 15×14 (others).*

1197	30p. Type **367** (centenary)	65	60
1198	40p. Newtown School, Waterford (bicent) (vert)	80	90
1199	45p. Trumpeters (50th anniv of Universal Declaration of Human Rights)	95	1·10
1197/9	*Set of 3*	2·25	2·40

(Des FOR Design. Litho Irish Security Stamp Ptg Ltd)

1998 (4 Sept). *"Portugal '98" International Stamp Exhibition, Lisbon. Sheet, 101×71 mm, containing design as No. 1187. Chalk-surfaced paper. P 15×14.*

MS1200	£2 *Boa Esperanza* (caravel) (horiz)	3·50	3·75

368 Cheetah

(Des F. O'Conner. Litho Walsall)

1998 (8 Oct). *Endangered Animals. T **368** and similar multicoloured designs. P 14.*

1201	30p. Type **368**	75	75
	a. Horiz pair. Nos. 1201/2	1·50	1·50
1202	30p. Scimitar-horned Oryx	75	75
1203	40p. Golden Lion Tamarin (vert)	1·00	1·00
1204	45p. Tiger (vert)	1·25	1·25
1201/4	*Set of 4*	3·25	3·25
MS1205	150×90 mm. As Nos. 1201/4. P 15	3·25	3·25

Nos. 1201/4 were printed together, *se-tenant*, in horizontal pairs throughout the sheet.
No. MS1205 also exists with an enlarged top margin overprinted for "Stampa '98" National Stamp Exhibition, Dublin.

369 The Holy Family

370 Choir Boys

(Des P. Lynch (Nos. 1206/8), J. Laffan (No. 1209))

1998 (17 Nov). *Christmas. (a) Litho Irish Security Stamp Ptg Ltd. T **369** and similar vert designs. Multicoloured. Chalk-surfaced paper. P 14×15.*

1206	30p. Type **369**	60	60
1207	32p. Shepherds	65	65
1208	45p. Three Kings	85	1·10
1206/8	*Set of 3*	1·90	2·10

(b) Litho SNP Cambec, Australia. Self-adhesive. Phosphor frame. P 11½

1209	30p. Type **370**	55	60
	a. Booklet pane. No. 1209×20	11·00	

No. 1209, on which the phosphor frame appears greenish yellow under U.V. light, was only available from £5·40 stamp booklets.

371 Puppy and Heart

372 Micheál Mac Liammóir

(Des M. Connor. Litho Irish Security Stamp Ptg Ltd)

1999 (26 Jan). *Greetings Stamps. Pets. T **371** and similar vert designs. Multicoloured. Chalk-surfaced paper. Phosphor frame. P 14×15.*

1210	30p. Type **371**	45	50
	a. Booklet pane. Nos. 1210/13	1·75	
1211	30p. Kitten and ball of wool	45	50
1212	30p. Goldfish	45	50
1213	30p. Rabbit with lettuce leaf	45	50
1210/13	*Set of 4*	1·75	2·00

Nos. 1211/13, on which the phosphor appears green under U.V. light, were only available from £2·40 stamp booklets containing two examples of No. 1210a. This pane exists in two different forms with either No. 1210 at left and No. 1213 at right or No. 1213 at left and No. 1210 at right. In each instance the right-hand stamp is imperforate at right. No. 1210 is available from both sheets and booklets.

(Des M. Connor. Litho Irish Security Stamp Ptg Ltd)

1999 (26 Jan). *Chinese New Year ("Year of the Rabbit"). Chalk-surfaced paper. Phosphor frame. P 14×15.*

MS1214	124×74 mm. Nos. 1211/13	1·60	1·75

The example of No. 1213 is imperforate at right.

(Des Creative Inputs. Litho Irish Security Stamp Ptg Ltd)

1999 (16 Feb). *Irish Actors and Actresses. T **372** and similar vert designs. Multicoloured. Chalk-surfaced paper. Phosphor frame. P 14×15.*

1215	30p. black and yellow-brown	60	60
1216	45p. black and bright green	90	1·00
1217	50p. black and ultramarine	95	1·10
1215/17	*Set of 3*	2·25	2·40

Designs: 45p. Siobhán McKenna; 50p. Noel Purcell.

373 Irish Emigrant Ship

374 Polly Woodside (barque)

(Des H. Paine and T. Mann. Litho Irish Security Stamp Ptg Ltd)

1999 (26 Feb). *Ireland–U.S.A. Joint Issue. Irish Emigration. Chalk-surfaced paper. Phosphor frame. P 15×14.*

1218	**373** 45p. multicoloured	80	85

A stamp in a similar design was issued by the U.S.A.

(Des V. Killowry. Litho Walsall)

1999 (19 Mar). *Maritime Heritage. T* **374** *and similar multi-coloured designs. Chalk-surfaced paper. Phosphor frame.*
P 14.

1219	30p. Type **374**	70	60
1220	35p. *Ilen* (schooner)	75	70
1221	45p. R.N.L.I. "Cromer" class lifeboat (*horiz*)	65	65
1222	£1 *Titanic* (liner) (*horiz*)	2·00	2·25
1219/22	*Set of* 4	4·00	4·00
MS1223	150×90 mm. No. 1222×2. No phosphor frame	3·50	3·75

On Nos. 1219/22, the phosphor shows green under U.V. light.
No. **MS**1223 also exists overprinted for "Australia '99" International Stamp Exhibition, Melbourne, in gold, "Stampania '99", Dublin, in deep blue and "Stampa '99" National Stamp Exhibition, Dublin, in red.

(Litho SNP Ausprint)

1999 (19 Mar). *Ireland—Australia Joint Issue. Polly Woodside* (*barque*). *Sheet* 137×72 *mm. Multicoloured. Phosphorised paper. P* 14×14½.

MS1224	45 c. Type **603** of Australia; 30p. Type **374** (*No.* MS1224 *was sold at* 52p. *in Ireland*)	95	1·00

No. **MS**1224 includes the "Australia '99" emblem on the sheet margin and was postally valid in Ireland to the value of 30p. The same miniature sheet was also available in Australia.

375 Sean Lemass | 376 European Currency Emblem

(Des Creative Inputs. Litho Irish Security Stamp Ptg Ltd)

1999 (29 Apr). *Birth Centenary of Sean Lemass* (*politician*). *Chalk-surfaced paper. Phosphor frame. P* 14×15.

1225	**375**	30p. black and deep bluish green	60	65

(Des Creative Inputs. Litho Irish Security Stamp Ptg Ltd)

1999 (29 Apr). *Introduction of Single European Currency. Chalk-surfaced paper. Phosphor frame. P* 15×14.

1226	**376**	30p. multicoloured	60	65

The face value of No. 1226 is shown in both Irish and Euro currencies.

377 European Flags | 378 Swans, Kilcolman Nature Reserve

(Des J. McPartlin. Litho Irish Security Stamp Ptg Ltd)

1999 (29 Apr). *50th Anniv of Council of Europe. Chalk-surfaced paper. Phosphor frame. P* 14×15.

1227	**377**	45p. multicoloured	80	85

(Des F. O'Connor. Litho Irish Security Stamp Ptg Ltd)

1999 (29 Apr). *Europa. Parks and Gardens. T* **378** *and similar horiz design. Chalk-surfaced paper. Phosphor frame.*

(a) P 15×14

1228	30p. Type **378**	70	50
1229	40p. Fallow Deer, Phoenix Park	90	1·00

(b) Self-adhesive. P 9½

1230	30p. Type **378**	65	65
1231	30p. Fallow Deer, Phoenix Park	65	65

Nos. 1228/9 were each issued in sheets of 10 (2×5) with enlarged illustrated left margins.
Nos. 1230/1, which are smaller, 34×23 mm, were only available in rolls of 100 on which the surplus self-adhesive paper was retained.

379 Father James Cullen and St. Francis Xavier Church, Dublin | 380 Elderly Man and Child using Computer

---

(Des Creative Inputs. Litho Irish Security Stamp Ptg Ltd)

1999 (15 June). *Centenary of Pioneer Total Abstinence Association. Chalk-surfaced paper. Phosphor frame. P* 14×15.

1232	**379**	32p. olive-brown, bistre and black	60	65

(Des C. Harrison. Litho Irish Security Stamp Ptg Ltd)

1999 (15 June). *International Year of Older Persons. Chalk-surfaced paper. Phosphor frame. P* 15×14.

1233	**380**	30p. multicoloured	60	65

381 Postal Van, 1922

(Des Creative Inputs. Litho Irish Security Stamp Ptg Ltd)

1999 (15 June). *125th Anniv of Universal Postal Union. T* **381** *and similar horiz design. Chalk-surfaced paper. Phosphor frame. P* 15×14.

1234	30p. grey-green and slate-green	65	65
	a. Pair. Nos. 1234/5	1·25	1·25
1235	30p. multicoloured	65	65

Designs:—No. 1234, Type **381**; No. 1235, Modern postal lorries.
Nos. 1234/5 were printed together, *se-tenant*, in horizontal or vertical pairs throughout sheets of 16.

382 Danno Keeffe

(Des F. O'Connor)

1999 (17 Aug). *Gaelic Athletic Association "Millennium Football Team". T* **382** *and similar horiz designs. Multicoloured. Phosphor frame. Chalk-surfaced paper.*

(a) Litho Irish Security Stamp Ptg Ltd. P 15×14

1236	30p. Type **382**	45	50
	a. Sheetlet. Nos. 1236/50 plus label	6·75	
1237	30p. Enda Colleran	45	50
1238	30p. Joe Keohane	45	50
1239	30p. Seán Flanagan	45	50
1240	30p. Seán Murphy	45	50
1241	30p. John Joe Reilly	45	50
1242	30p. Martin O'Connell	45	50
1243	30p. Mick O'Connell	45	50
1244	30p. Tommy Murphy	45	50
1245	30p. Seán O'Neill	45	50
1246	30p. Seán Purcell	45	50
1247	30p. Pat Spillane	45	50
1248	30p. Mikey Sheehy	45	50
1249	30p. Tom Langan	45	50
1250	30p. Kevin Heffernan	45	50
1236/50	*Set of* 15	6·75	7·50

(b) Self-adhesive booklet stamps. Litho SNP Ausprint, Australia. P 11½

1251	30p. Danno Keeffe	45	50
	a. Booklet pane. Nos. 1251, 1253, 1255, 1258, 1262×2 and 1263×2	3·50	
1252	30p. Enda Colleran	45	50
	a. Booklet pane. Nos. 1252, 1254, 1261 and 1264, each × 2	3·50	
1253	30p. Joe Keohane	45	50
1254	30p. Seán Flanagan	45	50
1255	30p. Seán Murphy	45	50
1256	30p. John Joe Reilly	45	50
	a. Booklet pane. Nos. 1256 and 1260, each × 4	3·50	
1257	30p. Martin O'Connell	45	50
	a. Booklet pane. Nos. 1257×3, 1259×2 and 1265×3	3·50	
1258	30p. Mick O'Connell	45	50
1259	30p. Tommy Murphy	45	50
1260	30p. Seán O'Neill	45	50
1261	30p. Seán Purcell	45	50
1262	30p. Pat Spillane	45	50
1263	30p. Mikey Sheehy	45	50
1264	30p. Tom Langan	45	50
1265	30p. Kevin Heffernan	45	50
1251/65	*Set of* 15	6·75	7·50

Nos. 1236/50 were issued together, *se-tenant*, in sheetlets of 15 stamps and a label. No. 1236a also exists imperforate from a framed limited edition sold at £30. Such imperforate sheetlets were overprinted "NOT VALID FOR POSTAGE" on the reverse and stamps from them should not, according to An Post, be postmarked.
No. 1236a also exists with the margins overprinted in black for "Stampa '99" National Stamp Exhibition, Dublin.
Nos. 1251/65 are smaller, 33×23 mm, and were only issued in four different £2·40 stamp booklets in which the surplus self-adhesive paper around each stamp was retained.

NEW INFORMATION

The editor is always interested to correspond with people who have new information that will improve or correct the Catalogue.

---

383 Douglas DC3 | 384 Mammoth

(Des V. Killowry. Litho Irish Security Stamp Ptg Ltd)

1999 (9 Sept). *Commercial Aviation. T* **383** *and similar horiz designs. Multicoloured. Chalk-surfaced paper. Phosphor frame. P* 15×14.

1266	30p. Type **383**	45	50
	a. Booklet pane. No. 1266×4, with margins all around	1·75	
	b. Booklet pane. Nos. 1266/9, with margins all around	2·25	
	c. Booklet pane. Nos. 1266/7, each × 2, with margins all around	1·90	
	d. Booklet pane. Nos. 1266×2 and 1268, with margins all around	1·50	
1267	32p. Britten Norman Islander	50	55
1268	40p. Boeing 707	60	65
1269	45p. Lockheed Constellation	70	75
1266/9	*Set of* 4	2·25	2·50

Booklet pane No. 1266d exists overprinted for "Stampa '99" National Stamp Exhibition, Dublin.

(Des F. O'Connor. Litho Irish Security Stamp Ptg Ltd)

1999 (11 Oct). *Extinct Irish Animals. T* **384** *and similar multicoloured designs. Chalk-surfaced paper. Phosphor frame.*

(a) P 14×15 (30p.) *or* 15×14 (45p.)

1270	30p. Type **384**	45	50
	a. Pair. Nos. 1270/1	90	
1271	30p. Giant Deer	45	50
1272	45p. Wolves (*horiz*)	70	75
	a. Pair. Nos. 1272/3	1·40	
1273	45p. Brown Bear (*horiz*)	70	75
1270/3	*Set of* 4	2·25	2·50
MS1274	150×63 mm. Nos. 1270/3. Without phosphor frame	2·75	2·75

(b) Self-adhesive. P 15

1275	30p. Brown Bear (*horiz*)	45	50
	a. Horiz strip of 4. Nos. 1275/8	1·75	
1276	30p. Type **384**	45	50
1277	30p. Wolves (*horiz*)	45	50
1278	30p. Giant Deer	45	50
1275/8	*Set of* 4	1·75	2·00

Nos. 1270/1 and 1272/3 were each printed together, *se-tenant*, in horizontal or vertical pairs throughout sheets of 16.
Nos. 1275/8, which are smaller, 36×25 mm (*horiz*) or 25×36 mm (*vert*), occur, *se-tenant*, in strips of 4 or rolls of 100 with the surplus self-adhesive paper around each stamp retained.

385 Holy Family | 386 Grace Kelly (American actress)

(Des P. Lynch. Litho Irish Security Stamp Ptg Ltd)

1999 (4 Nov). *Christmas. Children's Nativity Plays. T* **385** *and similar multicoloured designs. Chalk-surfaced paper. Phosphor frame. (a) Horiz designs. P* 15×14

1279	30p. Type **385**	45	50
1280	32p. Visit of the Shepherds	50	55
1281	45p. Adoration of the Magi	70	75
1279/81	*Set of* 3	1·60	1·75

(b) Self-adhesive. Vert design, 16×26 *mm. P* 9½

1282	30p. Angel	55	60
	a. Booklet pane. No. 1282×20	11·00	

(Des FOR Design. Litho Irish Security Stamp Ptg Ltd)

1999 (31 Dec). *New Millennium (1st issue). Famous People of the 20th Century. T* **386** *and similar vert designs. Multicoloured. Chalk-surfaced paper. Phosphor frame. P* 14×15.

1283	30p. Type **386**	45	50
	a. Sheetlet. Nos. 1283/8×2	5·50	
1284	30p. Jesse Owens (American athlete)	45	50
1285	30p. John F. Kennedy (former American President)	45	50
1286	30p. Mother Teresa (missionary)	45	50
1287	30p. John McCormack (tenor)	45	50
1288	30p. Nelson Mandela (South African statesman)	45	50
1283/8	*Set of* 6	2·75	3·00

Nos. 1283/8 were printed together, *se-tenant*, as two separate blocks of 6 in sheetlets of 12 with enlarged illustrated margins.
See also Nos. 1289/94 and 1300/5.

387 Ruined Castle
(Norman Invasion, 1169)

388 Frog Prince

(Des FOR Design. Litho Irish Security Stamp Ptg Ltd)

2000 (1 Jan). *New Millennium (2nd issue). Irish Historic Events. T* **387** *and similar horiz designs. Multicoloured. Chalk-surfaced paper. Phosphor frame. P* 15×14.

1289	30p. Type **387**	45	50
	a. Sheetlet. Nos. 1289/95×2	5·50	
1290	30p. Flight of the Earls, 1607	45	50
1291	30p. Opening of Irish Parliament, 1782	45	50
1292	30p. Eviction (formation of the Land League)	45	50
1293	30p. First four Irish Prime Ministers (Irish Independence)	45	50
1294	30p. Irish soldier and personnel carrier (U.N. Peace-keeping)	45	50
1289/94	*Set of 6*	2·75	3·00

Nos. 1289/94 were issued in the same format as Nos. 1283/8.

(Des B. Castle. Litho Irish Security Stamp Ptg Ltd)

2000 (26 Jan). *Greetings Stamps. Mythical Creatures. T* **388** *and similar vert designs. Multicoloured. Chalk-surfaced paper. Phosphor frame. P* 14×15.

1295	30p. Type **388**	45	50
	a. Booklet pane. Nos. 1295/8	1·75	
	b. Booklet pane. Nos. 1295 and 1298	90	
1296	30p. Pegasus	45	50
1297	30p. Unicorn	45	50
1298	30p. Dragon	45	50
1295/8	*Set of 4*	1·75	2·00

No. 1295 was available from both sheets and booklets, but Nos. 1296/8 come from £3 booklets only.

The examples of No. 1295 in the booklet panes are imperforate at right. Booklet pane No. 1295a includes 8 greetings labels in horizontal rows above and below the stamps and No. 1295b 14 similar labels in the same position and as a block of 10 at left.

(Des B. Castle. Litho Irish Security Stamp Ptg Ltd)

2000 (26 Jan). *Chinese New Year ("Year of the Dragon"). Chalk-surfaced paper. Phosphor frame. P* 14×15.

MS1299	124×74 mm. Nos. 1296/8	1·25	1·40

On No. **MS**1299 No. 1298 is imperforate at right.

389 Revd. Nicholas
Callan (electrical
scientist)

390 *Jeanie Johnston*
(emigrant ship)

(Des FOR Design. Litho Irish Security Stamp Ptg Ltd)

2000 (29 Feb). *New Millennium (3rd issue). Discoveries. T* **389** *and similar vert designs. Multicoloured. Chalk-surfaced paper. Phosphor frame. P* 14×15.

1300	30p. Type **389**	45	50
	a. Sheetlet. Nos. 1300/5×2	5·50	
1301	30p. Birr Telescope	45	50
1302	30p. Thomas Edison (inventor of light bulb)	45	50
1303	30p. Albert Einstein (mathematical physicist)	45	50
1304	30p. Marie Curie (physicist)	45	50
1305	30p. Galileo (astronomer and mathematician)	45	50
1300/5	*Set of 6*	2·75	3·00

Nos. 1300/5 were printed in a similar format as Nos. 1283/8.

(Des V. Killowry. Litho Irish Security Stamp Ptg Ltd)

2000 (9 Mar). *Completion of Jeanie Johnston Replica. Chalk-surfaced paper. Phosphor frame. P* 15×14.

1306 **390**	30p. multicoloured	45	50

STAMP BOOKLETS

Nos. SB1 to SB24 are stitched. Subsequent booklets have their panes attached by the selvedge, *unless otherwise stated.*

B 1 Harp and Monogram

B 2 Harp and "EIRE"

1931 (21 Aug)**–40.** *Black on red cover as Type B **1**.*
SB1 2s. booklet containing six ½d., six 2d. (Nos. 71, 74), each in block of 6, and nine 1d. (No. 72) in block of 6 and pane of 3 stamps and 3 labels (No. 72d or 72dw) .. .. *From* £1900
  Edition Nos.:—31–1, 31–2, 32–3, 33–4, 33–5, 34–6, 34–7, 35–8, 35–9, 36–10, 36–11, 37–12, 37–13, 37–14, 15–38, 16–38, 17–38,
    a. Cover as Type B **2**
  Edition Nos.:—18–39, 19–39, 20–39, 21–40, 22–40

1940. *Black on red cover as Type B **2**.*
SB2 2s. booklet containing six ½d., six 2d. (Nos. 71, 74), each in block of 6, and nine 1d. (No. 72) in block of 6 and pane of 3 stamps and 3 labels (No. 112d or 112dw) £6500
  Edition No.:—22–40

1940. *Black on red cover as Type B **2**.*
SB3 2s. booklet containing six ½d., six 2d. (Nos. 111, 114), each in block of 6, and nine 1d. (No. 112) in block of 6 and pane of 3 stamps and 3 labels (No. 112d or 112dw) £6500
  Edition No.:—23–40

1941–44. *Black on red cover as Type B **2**.*
SB4 2s. booklet containing twelve ½d., six 1d. and six 2d. (Nos. 111/12, 114) in blocks of 6 .. .. £750
  Edition Nos.:—24–41, 25–42, 26–44

B 3

1945. *Black on red cover as Type B **3**.*
SB5 2s. booklet containing twelve ½d., six 1d. and six 2d. (Nos. 111/12, 114) in blocks of 6 .. £650
  Edition No.:—27–45

1946. *Black on buff cover as Type B **2**.*
SB6 2s. booklet containing twelve ½d., six 1d. and six 2d. (Nos. 111/12, 114) in blocks of 6 .. .. £475
  Edition No.:—28–46

1946–47. *Black on buff cover as Type B **2**.*
SB7 2s. booklet containing twelve ½d., six 1d. and six 2d. (Nos. 133, 112, 114) in blocks of 6 .. *From* £225
  Edition Nos.:—29–46, 30–47

B 4 Harp only

1948–50. *Black on red cover as Type B **4**.*
SB8 2s. 6d. booklet containing six ½d., twelve 1d. and six 2½d. (Nos. 133, 112, 115) in blocks of 6 .. £130
  Edition Nos.:—31–48, 32–49, 33–50

1951–53. *Black on buff cover as Type B **4**.*
SB9 2s. 6d. booklet containing six ½d., twelve 1d. and six 2½d. (Nos. 133, 112, 115) in blocks of 6 .. 50·00
  Edition Nos.:—34–51, 35–52, 36–53

1954 (24 Nov). *Black on buff cover as Type B **4**.*
SB10 4s. booklet containing six ½d., six 1½d. and twelve 3d. (Nos. 133, 113, 116) in blocks of 6 £100
  Edition No.:—37–54

1956 (17 Dec). *Black on buff cover as Type B **4**.*
SB11 4s. booklet containing twelve 1d. and twelve 3d. (Nos. 112, 116) in blocks of 6 .. .. 60·00
  Edition No.:—38–56

B 5

1958–61. *Black on buff cover as Type B **5**.*
SB12 4s. booklet containing twelve 1d. and twelve 3d. (Nos. 112, 116) in blocks of 6 .. .. 60·00
  Edition Nos.:—39–58, 40–59, 41–60, 42–61

1962 (23 Oct)**–63.** *Black on buff cover as Type B **5**.*
SB13 3s. booklet containing six 2d. and six 4d. (Nos. 114, 117) in blocks of 6 .. .. *From* 50·00
  Edition Nos.:—43–62, 44–63 (June)

B 6

1964 (Sept). *Red on yellow cover as Type B **6**.*
SB14 3s. booklet containing twelve 1d. and six 4d. (Nos. 112, 117) in blocks of 6 .. .. .. 35·00

B 7

1966 (1–9 Dec). *Covers as Type B **7** in red (No. SB15), blue (No. SB16) or green (No SB17).*
SB15 2s. 6d. booklet containing six 2d. and six 3d. (Nos. 114, 116) in blocks of 6 (9 Dec) .. 17·00
SB16 2s. 6d. booklet containing six 5d. (No. 228) in block of 6 (9 Dec) .. .. 13·00
SB17 5s. booklet containing twelve 5d. (No. 228) in blocks of 6 .. .. 26·00

B 8

1969 (12 Sept). *Plain blue-green cover as Type B **8**.*
SB18 6s. booklet containing twelve 6d. (No. 253) in blocks of six .. .. 40·00

1971 (15 Feb). *Plain slate-green cover as Type B **8**.*
SB19 30p. booklet containing six ½p., twelve 1p. and six 2½p. in panes of 6 (Nos. 287ab or 287awb, 288ca or 288cwa, 291ba or 291bwa) 32·00

1974 (11 Mar). *Green cover as Type B **8**.*
SB20 50p. booklet containing ten 5p. in panes of 5 stamps and 1 label (No. 295ad or 295adw) 18·00

1974 (11 Mar). *Blue cover as Type B **8**.*
SB21 50p. booklet containing five 1p. in pane of 5 stamps and 1 label (No. 288cb or 288cwb), six 2½p. and six 5p. in panes of 6 (Nos. 291ba or 291bwa, 295ae or 295awe) .. 9·00

1975 (27 Jan). *Covers as Type B **8**, in rose (No. SB22) or light grey (No. SB23).*
SB22 40p. booklet containing five 1p., 2p. and 5p. each in panes of 5 stamps and 1 label (Nos. 288cb or 288cwb, 290ba or 290bwa, 295ad or 295awd) .. .. 3·00
SB23 70p. booklet containing ten 2p. and 5p. each in panes of 5 stamps and 1 label (Nos. 290ba or 290bwa, 295ad or 295awd) .. .. 3·75

1977 (21 Mar). *Yellow-olive cover similar to Type B **8**.*
SB24 50p. booklet containing five 1p., 2p. and 7p. each in panes of 5 stamps and 1 label (Nos. 288cb or 288cwb, 290ba or 290bwa, 348a) .. 9·00

B 9 Four Courts

1983 (15 Aug). *Yellow-green cover as Type B **9**.*
SB25 £1 booklet containing se-tenant pane of 7 stamps and 1 label (No. 535a) .. .. 2·00
  No. SB25 was an experimental issue available from two machines, accepting two 50p. coins, at the G.P.O. Dublin, and from the Philatelic Bureau.

B 10

1984 (9 July). *Dull green, greenish yellow and black cover as Type B **10**.*
SB26 £2 booklet containing se-tenant pane of 12 (No. 535ba) .. .. 5·00
  No. SB26 actually contains £2.26 worth of stamps, but was sold at a discount of 26p. by the Irish Post Office from 9 July until 10 August.

B 11 Custom House, Dublin, in 19th Century

1985 (27 June). *Yellowish green cover as Type B **11**.*
SB27 £1 booklet containing se-tenant pane of 6 (No. 533ab) .. .. 4·50

B 12

1985 (27 June). *Bright green cover as Type B **12**.*
SB28 £2 booklet containing se-tenant pane of 12 (No. 533ac) .. .. 7·50

B 13

1986 (8 Sept). *Black, light green and pale yellow cover as Type B **13**.*
SB29 £2 booklet containing se-tenant pane of 12 (No. 533ad) .. .. 7·50

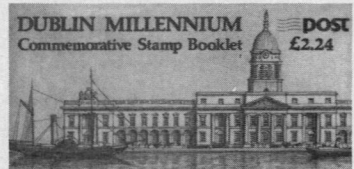

B 14 Custom House, Dublin
(Illustration further reduced. Actual size 137×70 mm)

1988 (1 Mar). *Dublin Millenium. Multicoloured cover as Type B 14.*
SB30 £2.24, booklet containing eight 24p. in panes of 4 (No. 688a) (one inscr in Irish, one in English) 4·00
No. SB30 also exists with the booklet cover overprinted for "SPRING STAMPEX 1988", "7 Internationale Briefmarken-Messe" (Essen), "FINLANDIA 88" and "SYDPEX 88" exhibitions.

1988 (24 Nov). *Maroon and black cover as Type B 11, but showing Courthouse, Cork.*
SB31 £2 booklet containing *se-tenant* pane of 12 (No. 533ae) .. .. 8·00

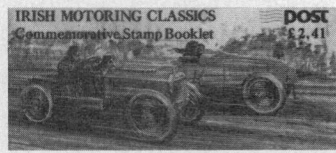

B 15 Gordon Bennett Race, 1903
(Illustration further reduced. Actual size 132×60 mm)

1989 (11 Apr). *Irish Motoring Classics. Multicoloured cover as Type B 15.*
SB32 £2.41, booklet containing two different *se-tenant* panes of 4 (Nos. 718a/b) .. .. .. 5·50

B 16 8th-century Gilt-silver Brooch
(Illustration further reduced. Actual size 160×100 mm)

1989 (15 June). *1300th Death Anniv of Saints Kilian, Totnan and Colman. Multicoloured cover as Type B 16.*
SB33 £4.48, booklet containing sixteen 28p. in panes of 4 (No. 726a) .. .. 9·50
No. SB33 exists overprinted for "PHILEXFRANCE 89" or "WORLD STAMP EXPO '89".

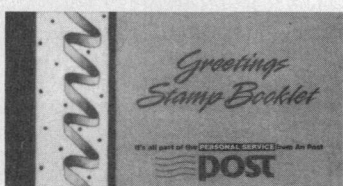

B 17 *(Illustration further reduced. Actual size 136×74 mm)*

1990 (22 Mar). *Greetings Booklet. Multicoloured cover as Type B 17. Stitched.*
SB34 £1.98, booklet containing two *se-tenant* panes of 4 (No. 766a) and eight greetings labels .. 15·00
No. SB34 was sold at £1.98, providing a discount of 26p. off the face value of the stamps.

B 18 *(Illustration further reduced. Actual size 161×99 mm)*

1990 (3 May). *150th Anniv of the Penny Black. Multicoloured cover as Type B 18. Stitched.*
SB35 £6 booklet containing *se-tenant* panes of 8, 4 and 5 (Nos. 535ca, 547ba/bb and pane of 4 (No. 774a) 35·00
No. SB25 exists overprinted for "Stamp World London 90" exhibition.

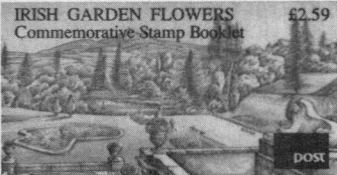

B 19 Garden at Powerscourt, Co. Wicklow
(Illustration further reduced. Actual size 150×75 mm)

1990 (30 Aug). *Garden Flowers. Multicoloured cover as Type B 19. Stitched.*
SB36 £2.59, booklet containing two different *se-tenant* panes of 4 (Nos. 781a/b) .. .. 8·00

B 20 7th-century Tara Brooch

1990 (15 Nov). *Irish Heritage. Black and bright blue cover as Type B 20.*
SB37 £1 booklet containing *se-tenant* pane of 7 stamps and 1 label (No. 747ab) .. .. 3·00

B 21 View of Dublin
(Illustration further reduced. Actual size 140×85 mm)

1991 (11 Apr). *"Dublin 1991 European City of Culture". Multicoloured cover as Type B 21.*
SB38 £2.60, booklet containing two different *se-tenant* panes of 3 (Nos. 800a/b) .. .. 7·50

B 22 Ardagh Chalice

1991 (14 May)–**92.** *Covers as Type B 22.*
SB39 £1 booklet containing *se-tenant* pane of 5 stamps and 1 label (No. 808a) (black and green cover as Type B 22) .. .. 1·75
SB40 £1 booklet containing *se-tenant* pane of 5 stamps and 1 label (No. 808a) (black and orange-yellow cover showing St. Patrick's Bell Shrine) (25.2.92) .. .. 1·75

B 23 *(Illustration further reduced. Actual size 161×99 mm)*

1991 (17 Oct). *Fishing Fleet. Multicoloured cover as Type B 23. Stitched.*
SB41 £5 booklet containing *se-tenant* panes of 5 and 7 and 1 label (Nos. 747ac, 748ba) and two different *se-tenant* panes of 4 (Nos. 819a/b) 14·00

B 24 *(Illustration further reduced. Actual size 138×75 mm)*

1992 (2 Apr). *Greetings Booklet. Multicoloured cover as Type B 24. Stitched.*
SB42 £2.40, booklet containing two *se-tenant* panes of 4 (No. 840a) and eight greetings labels .. 5·50

B 25 *(Illustration further reduced. Actual size 161×100 mm)*

1992 (15 Oct). *Single European Market. Deep bluish violet and greenish yellow cover as Type B 25. Stitched.*
SB43 £4.80, booklet containing fifteen 32p. in three panes of 4 (No. 856a) and one pane of 3 (No. 856b) .. .. 11·00

B 26 "Banks of the Seine, near Paris" (N. Hone)
(Illustration further reduced. Actual size 161×100 mm)

1993 (4 Mar). *Irish Impressionist Painters. Multicoloured cover as Type B 26. Stitched.*
SB44 £4.68, booklet containing four *se-tenant* panes (Nos. 867a×2, 867b and 869a) .. 10·00

B 27 Lismore Crozier

1993 (24 Sept)–**95.** *Covers as Type B 27.*
SB45 £1 booklet containing *se-tenant* pane of 4 (No. 748ca) (bright greenish blue cover as Type B 27) .. .. 1·75
SB46 £1 booklet containing *se-tenant* pane of 4 (No. 748cb) (black and bright vermilion cover showing enamelled latchet brooch) (2.3.94) 1·75
SB46a £1 booklet containing *se-tenant* pane of 4 (No. 748cb) (black and bright orange-red cover showing Gleninsheen Collar) (28.2.95) 1·75
SB46b £1 booklet containing *se-tenant* pane of 4 (No. 748a) (black and bright reddish violet cover showing Broighter Collar) (16.11.95) .. 1·75

B 28 Front and Side View of Dublin Bus Leyland Olympian
(Illustration further reduced. Actual size 131×61 mm)

1993 (12 Oct). *Irish Buses. Multicoloured cover as Type B 28. Stitched.*
SB47 £2.84, booklet containing two different *se-tenant* panes (Nos. 886a/b) .. .. 6·50

B 29 *(Illustration further reduced. Actual size 138×75 mm)*

1994 (27 Jan). *Greetings Booklet. Multicoloured cover as Type B 29. Stitched.*
SB48 £2.56, booklet containing two *se-tenant* panes of four 32p. (No. 896a) .. .. .. 6·00

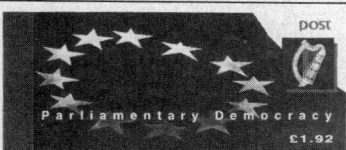

B 30 (*Illustration further reduced. Actual size 137×60 mm*)

1994 (27 Apr). *Parliamentary Anniversaries. Multicoloured cover as Type B 30. Stitched.*
SB49 £1.92, booklet containing two different *se-tenant* panes (Nos. 908a/b) (Stitched) . . 4·50

B 31 (*Illustration further reduced. Actual size 161×101 mm*)

1994 (18 Oct). *Irish Nobel Prizewinners. Multicoloured cover as Type B 31. Stitched.*
SB50 £4.84, booklet containing four different *se-tenant* panes (Nos. 928b/d and 930a) . . 11·50

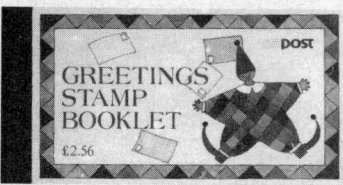

B 32 (*Illustration further reduced. Actual size 138×75 mm*)

1995 (24 Jan). *Greetings Booklet. Multicoloured cover as Type B 32. Stitched.*
SB51 £2.56, booklet containing two *se-tenant* panes of four 32p. (No. 936a) . . . . 6·00

B 33 Blessing before Battle
(*Illustration further reduced. Actual size 161×100 mm*)

1995 (15 May). *Military Uniforms. Multicoloured cover as Type B 33. Stitched.*
SB52 £4.80, booklet containing four different *se-tenant* panes (Nos. 954a/d) . . . . 12·00

B 34 (*Illustration further reduced. Actual size 140×82 mm*)

1995 (9 Oct). *Bicentenary of National Botanic Gardens, Glasnevin. Multicoloured cover as Type B 34. Stitched.*
SB53 £2.60, booklet containing two different *se-tenant* panes (Nos. 973a/b) . . . . 9·00

MINIMUM PRICE

The minimum price quote is 10p which represents a handling charge rather than a basis for valuing common stamps. For further notes about prices see introductory pages.

B 35 (*Illustration further reduced. Actual size 137×74 mm*)

1996 (23 Jan). *Greetings Booklet. Multicoloured cover as Type B 35. Stitched.*
SB54 £2.56, booklet containing two *se-tenant* panes of four 32p. (No. 982a) . . . . 8·50

B 36 Steeplechasing
(*Illustration further reduced. Actual size 161×100 mm*)

1996 (12 Mar). *Irish Horse Racing. Multicoloured cover as Type B 36. Stitched.*
SB55 £4.92, booklet containing four different *se-tenant* panes (Nos. 991a, 992b/c and 993a) . . 16·00

B 37 Coastal Patrol Vessel and Sailor
(*Illustration further reduced. Actual size 150×90 mm*)

(Des Design Image)

1996 (18 July). *50th Anniv of Irish Naval Service. Multicoloured cover as Type B 37. Stitched.*
SB56 £2.24, booklet containing pane of three 32p. and pane of three values *se-tenant* (Nos. 1013a/b) 5·50

B 38 Farmyard Animals
(*Illustration further reduced. Actual size 137×73 mm*)

1997 (28 Jan). *Greetings Booklet. Multicoloured cover as Type B 38. Stitched.*
SB57 £2.56, booklet containing two *se-tenant* panes of four 32p. (No. 1100a) . . . . 7·50

B 39 Robin

1997 (6 Mar). *Birds. Multicoloured cover as Type B 39. Stamps attached by selvedge.*
SB58 £1 booklet containing pane of 4 (2×2) (No. 748bb) . . . . . . 1·75

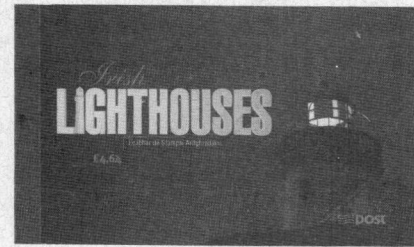

B 40 The Baily Lighthouse
(*Illustration further reduced. Actual size 160×100 mm*)

1997 (1 July). *Lighthouses. Multicoloured cover as Type B 40. Stitched.*
SB59 £4.64, booklet containing four different, *se-tenant*, panes (Nos. 1136b/c, 1136da and 1138da) . . . . 11·00

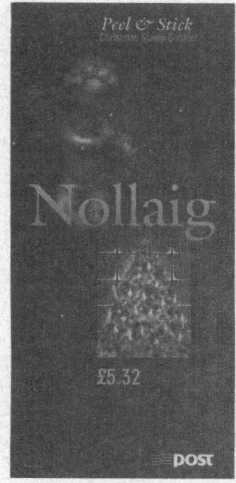

B 41 Christmas Tree

1997 (18 Nov). *Christmas. Multicoloured cover as Type B 41. Self-adhesive.*
SB60 £5.32, booklet containing pane of twenty 28p. (2×10) (No. 1149a) . . . . 11·00
No. SB60 was sold at £5.32 providing a discount of 28p. off the face value of the stamps.

1997 (6 Dec). *Multicoloured cover as Type B 39 showing Peregrine Falcon. Stamps attached by selvedge.*
SB61 £1 booklet containing pane of 4 (2×2) (No. 1080a) . . . . . . 1·75

B 42 On Swing
(*Illustration further reduced. Actual size 138×74 mm*)

1998 (26 Jan). *Greetings Booklet. Multicoloured cover as Type B 42. Stitched.*
SB62 £2.56, booklet containing two different *se-tenant* panes of four 32p. (No. 1150a) . . 5·00

B 43 Early Aeroplane and Map
(*Illustration further reduced. Actual size 160×100 mm*)

1998 (24 Feb). *Pioneers of Irish Aviation. Multicoloured cover as Type B 43. Stitched.*
SB63 $5.20, booklet containing four different, *se-tenant*, panes (Nos. 1155a/b and 1156a/b) 11·00

B 44 Blackbird

1998 (2 Apr). *Multicoloured cover as Type B 44. Stamps attached by selvedge.*
SB64   £1 booklet containing pane of 5 stamps and 1 label (No. 1081a)   ..   ..   ..   1·60

1998 (6 May).   *Greetings Booklet. Multicoloured cover as Type B 42, but inscribed "LETTER POST" in green border at foot. Stitched.*
SB65   £2.40, booklet containing two different se-tenant panes of four 30p. (No. 1173a)   ..   ..   4·00

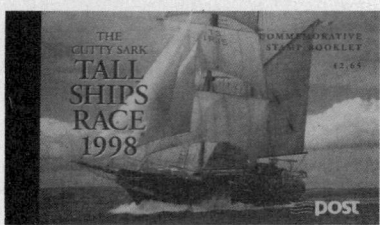

B 45 *Asgard II* (cadet brigantine)
(Illustration further reduced. Actual size 138×89 mm)

1998 (20 July).   Cutty Sark *International Tall Ships Race, Dublin. Multicoloured cover as Type B 45. Stitched.*
SB66   £2.65, booklet containing two different se-tenant panes of 3 (Nos. 1185ba and 1186ba)   ..   4·50

B 46 *Blackbird*

1998 (4 Sept).–**99**.   *Multicoloured cover as Type B 46. Stamps attached by selvedge.*
SB67   £3 booklet containing pane of 10 (5×2) 30p. stamps (No. 1038ab)   ..   ..   ..   6·50
    a. Containing pane No. 1038ar (stamps with phosphor frames) (25.1.99)   ..   4·75
No. SB67 exists overprinted for "Stampa '99" National Stamp Exhibition, Dublin, in red.

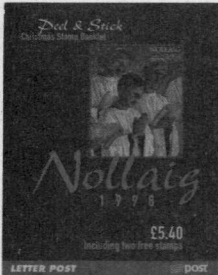

B 47 *Choir Boys*

1998 (17 Nov).   *Christmas. Multicoloured cover as Type B 47. Self-adhesive.*
SB68   £5.40, booklet containing pane of twenty 30p. (5×4) (No. 1209a)   ..   ..   11·00
No. SB68 was sold at £5.40 providing a discount of 60p. off the face value of the stamps.

B 48 *Domestic Pets*
(Illustration further reduced. Actual size 139×73 mm)

1999 (26 Jan).   *Greetings Booklet. Pets. Multicoloured cover as Type B 48. Stitched.*
SB69   £2.40, booklet containing two different se-tenant panes of four 30p. (No. 1210a)   ..   ..   4·00

B 49 *Goldcrest*

1999 (16 Feb).   *Multicoloured cover as Type B 49. Stamps attached by selvedge.*
SB70   £1 booklet containing pane of 5 stamps and 1 label (No. 1081ba)   ..   ..   ..   1·60

B 50 *Dublin*

1999 (30 June).   *Multicoloured covers as Type B 50. Stamps attached by selvedge.*
SB71   £1.60, booklet containing pane of five 32p. plus 5 airmail labels (No. 1053pa)   ..   ..   2·50
SB72   £1.80, booklet containing pane of four 45p. and 4 airmail labels (No. 1057pa) (cover showing ornamental garden)   ..   ..   ..   2·75
    a. Containing stamps on chalk-surfaced paper (No. 1057apa)   ..   ..   2·75

B 51 "the Kingdom"

1999 (17 Aug).   *Gaelic Athletics Association "Millennium Football Team". Multicoloured covers as Type B 51. Self-adhesive.*
SB73   £2.40, booklet containing pane of 8 stamps (No. 1251a) (cover as Type B 51)   ..   ..   3·50
SB74   £2.40, booklet containing pane of 8 stamps (No. 1252a) (cover inscr "the West awake")   ..   3·50
SB75   £2.40, booklet containing pane of 8 stamps (No. 1256a) (cover inscr "ulster abú")   ..   3·50
SB76   £2.40, booklet containing pane of 8 stamps (No. 1257a) (cover inscr "Kings of Leinster")   ..   3·50

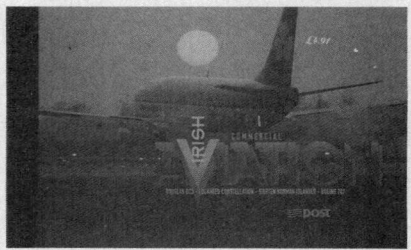

B 52 *Boeing 707*
(Illustration further reduced. Actual size 160×100 mm)

1999 (9 Sept).   *Commercial Aviation. Multicoloured cover as Type B 52. Stitched.*
SB77   £4.91, booklet containing four different se-tenant panes of 3 (No. 1266d) or 4 (Nos. 1266a/c)   ..   8·00

The new-issue supplement to this Catalogue appears each month in

GIBBONS
STAMP MONTHLY

—from your newsagent or by postal subscription— sample copy and details on request.

B 53 *Angel*

1999 (4 Nov).   *Christmas. Multicoloured cover as Type B 53. Self-adhesive.*
SB78   £5.40, booklet containing pane of twenty 30p. (2×10) (No. 1282a)   ..   ..   ..   11·00
No. SB78 was sold at £5.40 providing a discount of 60p. off the face value of the stamps.

B 54
(Illustration further reduced. Actual size 138×75 mm)

2000 (26 Jan).   *Greetings Stamps. Mythical Creatures. Multicoloured cover as Type B 54. Stitched.*
SB79   £3 booklet containing three se-tenant panes of 30p. (Nos. 1295a×2 and 1295b)   ..   ..   4·75

POSTAGE DUE STAMPS

From 1922 to 1925 Great Britain postage due stamps in both script and block watermarks were used without overprint.

D 1   D 2   D 3

(Des Ruby McConnell. Typo Govt Printing Works, Dublin)

1925 (20 Feb). *W 10. P 14×15.*

D1	D 1	½d. emerald-green	..	12·00	16·00
D2		1d. carmine	..	15·00	3·00
		a. Wmk sideways	..	£600	£250
		w. Wmk inverted	..	£250	30·00
D3		2d. deep green	..	28·00	5·50
		a. Wmk sideways	..	45·00	15·00
		w. Wmk inverted	..	70·00	23·00
D4		6d. plum	..	6·00	6·50
D1/4		..	*Set of 4*	55·00	28·00

1940–70. *W 22. P 14×15.*

D 5	D 1	½d. emerald-green (1942)	..	35·00	22·00
		w. Wmk inverted	..	£250	£130
D 6		1d. carmine (1941) ..	..	1·50	70
		w. Wmk inverted	..	55·00	6·50
D 7		1½d. vermilion (1953)	..	1·75	6·50
		w. Wmk inverted	..	15·00	21·00
D 8		2d. deep green (1940)	..	2·75	70
		w. Wmk inverted	..	20·00	6·50
D 9		3d. blue (10.11.52)	..	2·25	2·75
		w. Wmk inverted	..	6·00	5·00
D10		5d. blue-violet (3.3.43)	..	4·50	3·00
		w. Wmk inverted	..	6·50	7·00
D11		6d. plum (21.3.60)	..	3·00	2·00
		a. Wmk sideways (1968)	..	80	95
D12		8d. orange (30.10.62)	..	8·50	8·00
		w. Wmk inverted	..	17·00	18·00
D13		10d. bright purple (27.1.65)	..	8·50	7·50
D14		1s. apple-green (10.2.69)	..	6·00	9·00
		a. Wmk sideways (1970)	..	70·00	8·50
D5/14		..	*Set of 10*	65·00	55·00

1971 (15 Feb). *As Nos. D5/14, but with values in decimal currency and colours changed. W 22. P 14 × 15.*

D15	D 1	1p. sepia	..	30	60
		a. Wmk sideways ..	..	1·75	1·50
		w. Wmk inverted	..	1·25	1·75
D16		1½p. light emerald	..	60	1·50
D17		3p. stone	..	90	2·00
		w. Wmk inverted	..	1·25	2·00
D18		4p. orange	..	90	1·25
D19		5p. greenish blue	..	95	3·00
		w. Wmk inverted	..	2·25	3·50
D20		7p. bright yellow	..	40	3·50
		w. Wmk inverted	..	1·50	3·50
D21		8p. scarlet ..	..	40	2·75
D15/21		..	*Set of 7*	3·75	13·00

1978 (20 Mar). *As Nos. D17/19, but no wmk. Chalk-surfaced paper. P 14×15.*

D22	D 1	3p. stone	..	1·50	5·00
D23		4p. orange	..	6·00	8·00
D24		5p. greenish blue	..	1·50	4·00
D22/4		..	*Set of 3*	8·00	15·00

1980 (11 June)–**85.** *Photo. Chalk-surfaced paper. P 15.*

D25	D 2	1p. apple green	..	30	55
D26		2p. dull blue	..	30	55
D27		4p. myrtle-green	..	40	55
D28		6p. flesh	..	40	70
D29		8p. chalky blue	..	40	75
D30		18p. green	..	75	1·25
D31		20p. Indian red (22.8.85)	..	2·25	4·50
D32		24p. bright yellowish green	..	75	2·00
D33		30p. deep violet blue (22.8.85)	..	3·00	5·50
D34		50p. cerise (22.8.85)	..	3·75	6·50
D25/34		..	*Set of 10*	11·00	20·00

The 1p. to 18p. are on white paper and the 20p., 30p. and 50p. on cream. The 24p. value exists on both types of paper.

(Des Q Design. Litho Irish Security Stamp Ptg Ltd)

1988 (6 Oct). *Chalk-surfaced paper. P 14 × 15.*

D35	D 3	1p. black, orange-vermilion & lemon	10	10
D36		2p. black, orange-verm & purple-brn	10	10
D37		3p. black, orange-vermilion and plum	10	10
D38		4p. black, orange-vermilion & brt vio	10	10
D39		5p. black, orge-vermilion & royal blue	10	10
D40		17p. black, orange-verm & dp yell-grn	30	35
D41		20p. black, orange-vermilion & slate-bl	35	40
D42		24p. black, orange-verm & dp turq-grn	40	45
D43		30p. black, orange-vermilion & dp grey	50	55
D44		50p. black, orge-verm & brownish grey	90	95
D45		£1 black, orge-vermilion & bistre-brn	1·75	1·90
D35/45		..	*Set of 11*	4·50	5·00

PRICES OF SETS

Set prices are given for many issues, generally those containing three stamps or more. Definitive sets include one of each value or major colour change, but do not cover different perforations, die types or minor shades. Where a choice is possible the set prices are based on the cheapest versions of the stamps included in the listings.

From 20 September 1993 labels in the above style were used to indicate postage due charges in the Dublin 2 delivery area. They are dispensed by a Pitney/Bowes machine, in much the same way as a meter mark, and can show any face value between 1p. and I£99.99. Such labels are not normally postmarked. Labels with face values of 32p. and 50p. were sold to collectors by the Philatelic Bureau.

THOMOND AND LONG ISLAND

Labels inscribed "Principality of Thomond" appeared on the philatelic market in the early 1960s. Thomond is the name of a district in western Ireland. The area does not have its own administration or postal service and the labels were not recognised by the Department of Posts & Telegraphs, Dublin.

Local carriage labels were issued for Long Island, County Cork in April 1973; they were intended to cover the cost of taking mail from the island to the nearest mainland post office. A local service operated for a few weeks before it was suppressed by the Irish Post Office. As the stamps were not accepted for national or international mail they are not listed here.

Addenda and Corrigenda

GREAT BRITAIN

Add to Nos. 2125/8:

(Photo Walsall)

P 14×14½

2126a **1439** (1st) greenish yellow, magenta, pale
new blue, blk & silver (26.5.2000) 40 45
ab. Booklet pane. Nos. 2126a and
2139 with margins all round 80

No. 2126a was only available from £2.70 Millennium stamp booklets. The sheet stamp in the same design, issued 18 January 2000, had a face value of 26p. and was printed in photogravure by Questa. The previously-issued version of No. 2139 from sheets was printed in photogravure by De La Rue.

(Des J. Matthews. Photo De La Rue)

2000 (22 May). *"Stamp Show 2000" International Stamp Exhibition, London. Jeffrey Matthews Colour Palette. Sheet, 124×70 mm, containing stamps as T 367 together with two labels. Phosphorised paper. P 15×14 (with one elliptical hole on each vertical side).*

MS2146 4p. new blue; 5p. dull red-brown; 6p.
yellow-olive; 10p. dull orange; 31p. dp mauve; 39p.
brt magenta; 64p. turquoise-green; £1 bluish violet 5·00 5·25

The £1 value is printed in Iriodin ink which gives a shiny effect to the solid part of the background behind the Queen's head.

1459
(Illustration reduced. Actual size 121×89 mm)

(Des Delaney Design Consultants. Photo De La Rue)

2000 (23 May). *"Stamp Show 2000" International Stamp Exhibition, London. "Her Majesty's Stamps". Sheet 121×89 mm. Phosphorised paper. P 15×14 (with one elliptical hole on each vertical side of stamps as T 1437).*

MS2147 **1459** (1st) olive-brown (Type *1437*) × 4; £1
slate-green (as Type *163*) 3·50 3·75

The £1 value is an adaption of the 1953 Coronation 1s. 3d. stamp originally design by Edmund Dulac.

1460 Children playing (Millennium Greens Project)

1461 Millennium Bridge, Gateshead

1462 Daisies (Mile End Park, London)

1463 African Hut and Thatched Cottage ("On the Meridian Line" Project)

(Photo (2nd, 45p.) or litho (1st, 65p.) Walsall)

2000 (6 June). *Millennium Projects (6th series). "People and Places" (others). One phosphor band (2nd) or two phosphor bands (others). P 14×14½.*

2148 **1460** (2nd) bistre-yellow, bright magenta,
new blue, grey-black and silver 30 35
2149 **1461** (1st) deep ultramarine, silver, black,
new blue, brt mag & greenish yell 40 45

2150 **1462** 45p. greenish yellow, mag, pale new
bl, grey-blk, silver & dp turq-grn 70 75
2151 **1463** 65p. silver, black, new blue, bright
magenta and greenish yellow 1·00 1·10
2148/51 .. *Set of 4* 2·40 2·50

1464 Raising the Stone (Strangford Stone, Killyleagh)

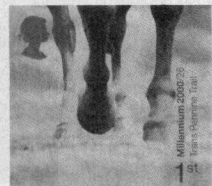
1465 Horse's Hooves (Trans Pennine Trail, Derbyshire)

1466 Cyclist (Kingdom of Fife Cycle Ways, Scotland)

1467 Bluebell Wood (Groundwork's "Changing Places" Project)

(Photo Enschedé)

2000 (4 July). *Millennium Projects (7th series). "Stone and Soil". One phosphor band (2nd) or two phosphor bands (others). P 14×14½.*

2152 **1464** (2nd) brownish black, grey-blk & silver 30 35
2153 **1465** (1st) greenish yellow, bright magenta,
new blue, grey-blk, silver & grey 40 45
2154 **1466** 45p. brownish black, grey-black,
black and silver 70 75
2155 **1467** 65p. greenish yellow, bright magenta,
new blue black and silver 1·00 1·10
2152/5 .. *Set of 4* 2·40 2·50

Isle of Man

185 Harrison's Chronometer, 1735, and Map

186 Duke and Duchess of York on Wedding Day, 1923

(Des E. Cassidy. Litho Cartor)

2000 (24 Jan). *"The Story of Time". T 185 and similar vert designs. Multicoloured. P 13×13½.*

869 **185** 22p. Type **185** 45 50
870 26p. Daniels' chronometer, 2000, and clock
face 50 55
871 29p. Harrison's chronometer, 1767, map and
clock 60 65
872 34p. Mudge's chronometer, 1769, and steam
locomotives 70 75
873 38p. Arnold's chronometer, 1779, and map of
Africa 75 80
874 44p. Earnshaw's chronometer, 1780, and map
of Caribbean 90 95
869/74 .. *Set of 6* 3·75 4·00

(Des E.D.L. Litho B.D.T.)

2000 (29 Feb). *"Queen Elizabeth the Queen Mother's Century". T 186 and similar horiz designs. Multicoloured (except 26p. and 30p.). P 14.*

875 **186** 22p. Type **186** 45 50
a. Horiz strip of 3. Nos. 875/7 1·50
876 26p. Queen Elizabeth with Princess Elizabeth,
1940 (sepia and black) 50 55
877 30p. King George VI and Queen Elizabeth
visiting troops, 1944 (sepia and black) 60 65
878 44p. Queen Mother and Queen Elizabeth, 1954 85 90
a. Horiz strip of 3. Nos. 878/80 3·00
879 52p. Queen Mother with Prince Charles, 1985 1·00 1·10
880 64p. Queen Mother, 1988 1·25 1·25
875/80 .. *Set of 6* 4·50 4·75
MS881 100×70 mm. £1 Queen Mother visiting Isle
of Man (74×49 mm) 2·00 2·10

Nos. 875/7 and 878/80 were each printed together, *se-tenant*, as horizontal strips of 3 in sheets of 12 (3×4).

Jersey

210 "Ocean Adventure" (Gemma Carré)

(Litho Questa)

2000 (9 May). *"Stampin' the Future" (children's stamp design competition) Winners. T 210 and similar horiz designs. Multicoloured. P 14.*

929 **210** 22p. Type **210** 45 50
930 22p. "Solar Power" (Chantal Varley-Best) 45 50
931 22p. "Floating City and Space Cars" (Nicola
Singleton) 45 50
932 22p. "Conservation" (Carly Logan) .. 45 50
929/32 .. *Set of 4* 1·75 2·00
MS933 150×100 mm. Nos. 929/32 .. 1·75 2·00

211 "Jersey in Europe"

(Des A. Copp (26p.), J.-P. Cousin (34p.). Litho Cartor)

2000 (9 May). *Europa. T 211 and similar multicoloured design. P 13½×13.*

934 26p. Type **211** 50 55
935 34p. "Building Europe" (29×39 mm) .. 70 75

ANGUILLA

189 Library and Resource Centre

(Litho Cot Printery Ltd, Barbados)

1999 (10 Nov). *Modern Architecture. T 189 and similar horiz designs. Multicoloured. P 14×14½.*

1039 30 c. Type **189** 15 20
1040 65 c. Parliamentary building and Court
House 30 35
1041 $1 Caribbean Commercial Bank .. 45 50
1042 $1.50, Police Headquarters 65 70
1043 $1.90, Post Office 80 85
1039/43 .. *Set of 5* 2·25 2·50

190 Beach Barbecue and Fireworks

(Litho Cartor)

1999 (13 Dec). *Christmas and New Millennium. T 190 and similar horiz designs. Multicoloured. P 13½.*

1044 30 c. Type **190** 15 20
1045 $1 Musicians around globe .. 45 50
1046 $1.50, Family at Christmas dinner 65 70
1047 $1.90, Celebrations around decorated
shrub 80 85
1044/7 .. *Set of 4* 2·00 2·25

191 Shoal Bay (East)

(Litho Cartor)

1999 (31 Dec). *Beaches. T* **191** *and similar horiz designs. Multicoloured. P* 12.

1048	15 c. Type 191	..	..	10	15
1049	30 c. Maundys Bay	..	..	15	20
1050	$1 Rendezvous Bay	..	..	45	50
1051	$1.50, Meads Bay	..	..	65	70
1052	$1.90, Little Bay	..	..	80	85
1053	$2 Sandy Ground	..	..	85	90
1048/53			Set of 6	3·00	3·25
MS1054	144×144 mm. Nos. 1048/53	..	..	3·00	3·25

ASCENSION

190 Baby Turtles

(Des Crown Agents. Litho Questa)

2000 (8 Mar). *Turtle Project on Ascension. T* **190** *and similar horiz designs. Multicoloured. W w* **14** *(sideways). P* 13½×14.

795	15p. Type 190	..	..	30	35
796	35p. Turtle on beach	..	..	70	75
797	40p. Turtle with tracking device	..	80	85
798	50p. Turtle heading for sea	..	1·00	1·10
795/8			Set of 4	2·75	3·00
MS799	197×132 mm. 25p. Head of turtle; 25p. Type 190; 25p. Turtle on beach; 25p. Turtle entering sea (each 40×26 mm). P 14			2·00	2·10

AUSTRALIA

CORRECTION: Nos. 1863c/6c to become 1863d/6d

Add to Nos. 1863/6: *P* 11½

(Litho SNP Ausprint)

(1863   45 c. Type **605**)

	c. Booklet pane. Nos. 1863/6, each × 5 (8.7.99)	..	..	7·00

The surplus self-adhesive paper is retained on No. 1863c.

619 Scenes from *Cloudstreet* (play) (Perth Festival)	**620** Coast Banksia, False Sarsaparilla and Swamp Bloodwood (plants)

(Des W. Rankin. Litho McPherson's Ptg Group, Mulgrave)

2000 (24 Feb). *Arts Festivals. T* **619** *and similar vert designs. Multicoloured. P* 14½×14.

1955	45 c. Type 619	..	..	35	40
	a. Horiz strip of 5. Nos. 1955/9	..	1·75	
1956	45 c. Belgian dancers from Rosas Company (Adelaide Festival)	..		35	40
1957	45 c. "Guardian Angel" (sculpture) and dancer (Sydney Festival)	..		35	40
1958	45 c. Musician and Balinese dancer (Melbourne Festival)	..		35	40
1959	45 c. Members of Vusa Dance Company of South Africa (Brisbane Festival)	..		35	40
1955/9			Set of 5	1·75	2·00

Nos. 1955/9 were printed together, *se-tenant*, in horizontal strips of 5.

(Des Marg Towt. Litho SNP Ausprint)

2000 (23 Mar). *Gardens. T* **620** *and similar vert designs. Multicoloured.* (a) *Phosphorised paper. P* 14½×14

1960	45 c. Type 620	..	..	35	40
	a. Horiz strip of 5. Nos. 1960/4	..	1·75	
1961	45 c. Eastern Spinebill on Swamp Bottlebrush in foreground	..		35	40
1962	45 c. Border of Cannas	..		35	40
1963	45 c. Roses, lake and ornamental bridge	..		35	40
1964	45 c. Hibiscus with bandstand in background	..		35	40
1960/4			Set of 5	1·75	2·00

(b) *Self-adhesive. Phosphor frame. P* 11½

1965	45 c. Type 620	..	..	35	40
	a. Strip of 5. Nos. 1965/9	..	1·75	
	b. Booklet pane. Nos. 1965/9, each × 2	3·50		
1966	45 c. Eastern Spinebill on Swamp Bottlebrush in foreground	..		35	40
1967	45 c. Border of Cannas	..		35	40
1968	45 c. Roses, lake and ornamental bridge	..		35	40
1969	45 c. Hibiscus with bandstand in background	..		35	40
1965/9			Set of 5	1·75	2·00

Nos. 1960/4 were printed together, *se-tenant*, as horizontal strips of 5 in sheets of 10 (2×5).

Nos. 1965/9 are smaller, 21×33 mm, and were issued either as rolls of 100, on which the surplus self-adhesive paper was removed, or in booklets of 10 on which the surplus paper was retained. On both versions the phosphor frame shows pink under U.V. light.

621 Queen Elizabeth II in 1996	**622** Medals and Korean Landscape

(Des C. McPartlin. Litho McPherson's Ptg Group, Mulgrave)

2000 (13 Apr). *Queen Elizabeth II's Birthday. P* 14×14½.

1970	621	45 c. multicoloured	..	35	40

(Des B. Sadgrove. Litho McPherson's Ptg Group, Mulgrave)

2000 (18 Apr). *50th Anniv of Korean War. P* 14×14½.

1971	622	45 c. multicoloured	..	35	40

STAMP BOOKLETS

CORRECTION: Re-number Nos. SB131/3 to SB132/4

1999 (8 July). *Multicoloured cover as Type B* **56** *showing Hibbertia scandens. Flowers. Self-adhesive.*

SB131	$9 booklet containing pane of 20 45 c. (No. 1863c)	..	..	7·00

B 66 Flowers

2000 (23 Mar). *Gardens. Multicoloured cover as Type B* **66**. *Self-adhesive.*

SB135	$4.50, booklet containing pane of 10 45 c. (No. 1965b)	..	3·50

The cover of No. SB135 is allegedly impregnated with the scent of new mown grass.

Christmas Island

101 Yeow Jian Min

(Des C. McPartlin. Litho SNP Ausprint)

2000 (13 Apr). *New Millennium. "Face of Christmas Island". T* **101** *and similar vert designs. Multicoloured. P* 14½×14.

479	45 c. Type 101	..	..	35	40
	a. Horiz strip of 5. Nos. 479/83	..	1·75	
480	45 c. Ida Chin (school girl)	..		35	40
481	45 c. Ho Tak Wah (elderly man)	..		35	40
482	45 c. Thomas Faul and James Neill (young boys)	..		35	40
483	45 c. Siti Sanniah Kawi (mother of three)		35	40
479/83			Set of 5	1·75	2·00

Nos. 479/83 were printed together, *se-tenant*, as horizontal strips of 5 in sheets of 50 (2×25).

MINIMUM PRICE

The minimum price quote is 10p which represents a handling charge rather than a basis for valuing common stamps. For further notes about prices see introductory pages.

Cocos (Keeling) Islands

83 Ratma Anthoney

(Des Lisa Christensen. Litho SNP Ausprint)

2000 (13 Apr). *New Millennium. "Face of Cocos (Keeling) Islands". T* **83** *and similar horiz designs. Multicoloured. P* 14×14½.

384	45 c. Type 83	..		35	40
	a. Horiz strip of 5. Nos. 384/8	..	1·75	
385	45 c. Nakia Haji Dolman (school girl)	..	35	40
386	45 c. Muller Eymin (elderly man)	..	35	40
387	45 c. Courtney Press (toddler)	..	35	40
388	45 c. Mhd. Abu-Yazid (school boy)	..	35	40
384/8			Set of 5	1·75	2·00

Nos. 384/8 were printed together, *se-tenant*, as horizontal strips of 5 in sheets of 50 (2×25).

Norfolk Island

(Des D. Miller. Litho Cartor)

1999 (12 Oct). *"Queen Elizabeth the Queen Mother's Century". Horiz designs as T* **187** *of Ascension. Multicoloured (except* $1.20). *P* 13½.

712	45 c. Inspecting bomb damage, Buckingham Palace, 1940		35	40
713	45 c. At Abergeldy Castle sale of work, 1955		35	40
714	75 c. Queen Mother, Queen Elizabeth and Prince William, 1994		60	65
715	$1.20, Inspecting the King's Regiment (black)		90	95
712/15			Set of 4	2·25	2·40
MS716	145×70 mm. $3 Queen Elizabeth, 1937, and Amy Johnson's flight to Australia, 1930		2·40	2·50

207 Bishop George Augustus Selwyn	**208** Basket of Food (Thanksgiving)

(Des Tracey Yager. Litho B.D.T.)

1999 (10 Nov). *Christmas. 150th Anniv of Melanesian Mission. T* **207** *and similar vert designs. Multicoloured (except* 75 c.). *P* 14.

717	45 c. Type 207		35	40
	a. Horiz strip of 5. Nos. 717/21	..	3·00	
718	45 c. Bishop John Coleridge Patteson		35	40
719	75 c. "150 YEARS MELANESIAN MISSION" (black)		60	65
720	$1.05, Stained-glass windows	..	80	85
721	$1.20, Southern Cross (missionary ship) and religious symbols		90	95
717/21			Set of 5	3·00	3·25

Nos. 717/21 were printed together, *se-tenant*, in horizontal strips of 5 throughout the sheet with the backgrounds forming a composite design.

(Des R. Pennycuick. Litho Photopress International, Norfolk Island)

2000 (31 Jan). *Festivals. T* **208** *and similar horiz design. Roul* 5½.

722	5 c. black and ultramarine	..	10	10
	a. Booklet pane. Nos. 722/3 each × 5	40	
723	5 c. black and ultramarine	..	10	10

Design—No. 723, Musician playing guitar (Country Music Festival).

Nos. 722/3 were only issued in $2 stamp booklets containing four panes of 10 (2×5) showing the two designs *se-tenant* horizontally.

209 Dragon	**210** Domestic Goose

(Des Mary Butterfield. Litho B.D.T.)

2000 (7 Feb). *Chinese New Year ("Year of the Dragon"). Sheet* 106×86 mm. *P* 13×13½.

MS724	209	$2 multicoloured	..	1·60	1·75

ADDENDA

(Des Tracey Yager. Litho Southern Colour Print, Dunedin)

2000 (18 Feb). *Ducks and Geese. T* **210** *and similar square designs. Multicoloured. P* 14½.

725	45 c. Type 210		35	40
726	75 c. Pacific Black Duck		60	65
727	$1.05, Mallard Drake		80	85
728	$1.20, Aylesbury Duck		90	95
725/8		Set of 4	2·50	2·75

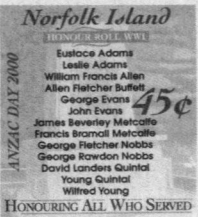

211 Honour Roll for First World War

(Des Photopress International. Litho Questa)

2000 (25 Apr). *Anzac Day. T* **211** *and similar vert design. Multicoloured. P* 14×15.

729	45 c. Type 211		35	40
730	75 c. Honour rolls for Second World War and Korea		60	65

STAMP BOOKLETS

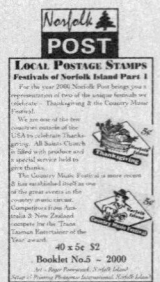

B 9
(*Illustration reduced. Actual size 92×168 mm*)

2000 (31 Jan). *Festivals. Bright ultramarine and bright carmine cover as Type B* **9**. *Stamps attached by selvedge.*

SB12	$2 booklet containing four panes of ten 5 c. (No. 722a)			1·60

BAHAMAS

241 Gold Medal Winning Bahamas Women's Relay Team

(Des N. Shewring. Litho Questa)

2000 (22 Feb). *"The Golden Girls" (winners of* 4×100 *metre Relay at I.A.A.F. World Track and Field Championships '99, Spain. Sheet* 100×55 *mm. W w* **14** *(sideways). P* 14½.

MS1216	241	$2 multicoloured	2·40	2·50

BARBADOS

240 Globe and Barbados Flag

(Des G. Vasarhelyi. Litho Questa)

2000 (8 Feb). *New Millennium. Sheet* 90×80 *mm. W w* **14** *(sideways). P* 14.

MS1152	240	$3 multicoloured	1·90	2·00

BELIZE

224 "Holy Family with Jesus and St. John" (School of Rubens)	225 Iguana

(Litho Questa)

1999 (6 Dec). *Christmas. Religious Paintings. T* **224** *and similar vert designs. Multicoloured. W w* 14. *P* 14.

1250	25 c. Type 224		15	20
1251	60 c. "Holy Family with St. John" (unknown artist)		40	45
1252	75 c. "Madonna and Child with St. John and Angel" (unknown artist)		45	50
1253	$1 "Madonna with Child and St. John" (Andrea del Salerno)		60	65
1250/3		Set of 4	1·50	1·60

(Des Doreen McGuiness. Litho Questa)

2000 (15 Feb). *Wildlife. T* **225** *and similar horiz designs. Multicoloured. W w* 14 *(sideways). P* 14.

1254	5 c. Type 225		10	10
1255	10 c. Gibnut		10	10
1256	15 c. Howler Monkey		10	15
1257	25 c. Collared Anteater		15	20
1258	30 c. Hawksbill Turtle		20	25
1259	50 c. Red Brocket Antelope		30	35
1260	60 c. Jaguar		35	40
1261	75 c. American Manatee		45	50
1262	$1 Crocodile		60	65
1263	$2 Baird's Tapir		1·25	1·40
1264	$5 Collared Peccary		3·00	3·25
1265	$10 Boa Constrictor		6·25	6·50
1254/65		Set of 12	12·50	13·50

BRITISH VIRGIN ISLANDS

223 King Henry VII

(Des Crown Agents. Litho Walsall)

2000 (29 Feb). *"Stamp Show 2000" International Stamp Exhibition, London. Kings and Queens of England. T* **223** *and similar vert designs. Multicoloured. W w* 14. *P* 14.

1036	60 c. Type 223		70	75
	a. Sheetlet. Nos. 1036/41		4·00	
1037	60 c. Lady Jane Grey		70	75
1038	60 c. King Charles I		70	75
1039	60 c. King William III		70	75
1040	60 c. King George III		70	75
1041	60 c. King Edward VII		70	75
1036/41		Set of 6	4·00	4·50

Nos. 1036/41 were printed together, *se-tenant*, in sheetlets of 6 with an enlarged illustrated right-hand margin.

CANADA

719 Portia White (singer)	720 Millennium Partnership Programme Logo

---

(Des F. and B. Ross, A. Dunkelman, R. Willms and Y. Laroche (No. **MS**1952); J. Michaud, P. Haslip, Geneviève Caron and C. Malenfant (**MS**1953); T. Gregoraschuk, M. Serre, D. Fortin, G. Fok and Alexis Brothers, Sheri Hancock and Hélène L'Heureux (2) (**MS**1954); K. Tsetsekas and G. Kehrig, H. Chung, D. Corriveau, P. Scott and Glenda Rissman, B. Canning and M. Waddell (**MS**1955) Litho Ashton-Potter Canada)

1999 (17 Dec). *Millennium Collection (1st series). Entertainment and Arts. Miniature sheets, each* 108×112 *mm, containing T* **719** *and similar vert designs. Multicoloured. Fluorescent frame. P* 13½.

MS1952	46 c. Type **719**; 46 c. Glenn Gould (pianist); 46 c. Guy Lombardo (conductor of "Royal Canadians"); 46 c. Félix Leclerc (musician, playwright and actor)	1·60	1·75
MS1953	46 c. Artists looking at painting (Royal Canadian Academy of Arts); 46 c. Cloud, stave and pencil marks (The Canada Council); 46 c. Man with video camera (National Film Board of Canada); 46 c. News-reader (Canadian Broadcasting Corporation	1·60	1·75
MS1954	46 c. Calgary Stampede; 46 c. Circus performers; 46 c. Ice hockey (Hockey Night); 46 c. Goalkeeper (Ice hockey live from The Forum)	1·60	1·75
MS1955	46 c. IMAX cinema; 46 c. Computer image (Softimage); 46 c. Ted Rogers Sr ("Plugging in the Radio"); 46 c. Sir William Stephenson (inventor of radio facsimile system)	1·60	1·75
MS1952/5	Set of 4 sheets	6·25	7·00

In addition to Nos. **MS**1952/5 these designs were also available in a presentation album showing two stamps per page.

(Des karacters design group. Litho C.B.N.)

2000 (1 Jan). *Canada Millennium Partnership Programme. Fluorescent frame. P* 13×12½.

1956	720	46 c. brt red, myrtle-green & lt grey-bl	40	45

721 Chinese Dragon

(Des K. Fung and K. Woo. Litho and embossed Ashton-Potter Canada)

2000 (5 Jan). *Chinese New Year ("Year of the Dragon"). Fluorescent frame. P* 12½.

1957	721	46 c. multicoloured	40	45
MS1958		150×85 mm **721** 95 c. mult. P 13½	80	85

(Des R. Tibbles, P.-Y. Pelletier, Koo Creative Group Inc, and L. Cable (No. **MS**1959); L. Fishauf, Louise Delisle and J.-C. Guénette, Stéphane Huot, and T. Yakobina (No. **MS**1960); R. Bellemare, Margaret Issenman and Bonnie Ross, Letterbox Design Group, and Circle Design Incorporated (No. **MS**1961); F. Blais, Orange, F. Dallaire and B. Leduc, and Gaynor and D. Sarty (No. **MS**1962). Litho Ashton-Potter Canada)

2000 (17 Jan). *Millennium Collection (2nd series). Charities, Medical Pioneers, Peace-keepers and Social Reforms. Miniature sheets, each* 108×112 *mm, containing vert designs as T* **719**. *Multicoloured. Fluorescent frame. P* 13½.

MS1959	46 c. Providing equipment (Canadian International Development Agency); 46 c. Dr. Lucille Teasdale (medical missionary); 46 c. Terry Fox (Marathon of Hope); 46 c. Delivering meal (Meals on Wheels)	1·60	1·75
MS1960	46 c. Sir Frederick Banting (discovery of insulin); 46 c. Armand Frappier (developer of BCG vaccine); 46 c. Dr. Hans Selye (research into stress); 46 c. "Dr. Maude Abbott" (pathologist) (M. Bell Eastlake)	1·60	1·75
MS1961	46 c. Senator Raoul Dandurand (diplomat); 46 c. Pauline Vanier and Elizabeth Smellie (nursing pioneers); 46 c. Lester B. Pearson (diplomat); 46 c. One-legged man (Ottawa Convention on Banning Landmines)	1·60	1·75
MS1962	46 c. Nun and surgeon (medical care); 46 c. "Women are Persons" (sculpture by Barbara Paterson) (Appointment of women senators); 46 c. Alphonse and Dorimène Desjardins (People's bank movement); 46 c. Father Moses Coady (Adult education pioneer)	1·60	1·75
MS1959/62	Set of 4 sheets	6·25	7·00

In addition to Nos. **MS**1959/62, these designs were also available in a presentation album showing two stamps per page.

722 Wayne Gretzky (ice-hockey player)	723 Judges and Supreme Court Building

(Des D. Fell and V. McIndoe. Litho C.B.N.)

2000 (5 Feb). *50th National Hockey League All-Star Game. T 722 and similar square designs. Multicoloured. Fluorescent circular frame around central design. P 13.*

1963	46 c. Type 722	40	45
	a. Sheetlet. Nos. 1963/8	2·40	
1964	46 c. Gordie Howe (No. 9 in white jersey)	40	45
1965	46 c. Maurice Richard (No. 9 in blue and red jersey)	40	45
1966	46 c. Doug Harvey (No. 2)	40	45
1967	46 c. Bobby Orr (No. 4)	40	45
1968	46 c. Jacques Plante (No. 1)	40	45
1963/8	*Set of 6*	2·40	2·50

Nos. 1963/8 were printed together, *se-tenant*, in sheetlets of 6 with portraits of the players shown on the sheet margins alongside the individual stamps.

(Des R. Harder, S. Bhandari and G. Khayat, J. Skipp and J. Evans and S. Slipp (No. **MS1969**); I. Drolet, B. Tsang, P. Fontaine, and Zabolotney Graphic Design (**MS1970**); Susan Warr, H. Deppe and F. Ross, B. Kierstead, K. Sollows and G. Tuck and L. Holloway (**MS1971**); D. Bartsch, P. Fontaine, Lise Giguère and G. Ludwig (**MS1972**); Debbie Adams, D. Page and T. Hawkins, T. Nokes and R. Harder (**MS1973**). Litho Ashton-Potter Canada)

2000 (17 Feb). *Millennium Collection (3rd series). First Inhabitants, Great Thinkers, Culture and Literary Legends, and Charitable Foundations. Miniature sheets, each 108×112 mm, containing vert designs as T 719. Multicoloured. Fluorescent frame. P 13½.*

MS1969	46 c. Pontiac (Ottawa chief); 46 c. Tom Longboat (long-distance runner); 46 c. "Inuit Shaman" (sculpture by Paul Toolooktook); 46 c. Shaman and patient (Indian medicine)	1·60 1·75
MS1970	46 c. Prof. Marshall McLuhan (media philosopher); 46 c. Northrop Frye (literary critic); 46 c. Roger Lemelin (novelist); 46 c. Prof. Hilda Marion Neatby (educator)	1·60 1·75
MS1971	46 c. Bow of Viking longship (L'Anse aux Meadows World Heritage Site); 46 c. Immigrant family (Pier 21 monument); 46 c. Neptune mask (Neptune Theatre, Halifax); 46 c. Auditorium and actor (The Stratford Festival)	1·60 1·75
MS1972	46 c. W. O. Mitchell (writer); 46 c. Gratien Gélinas (actor, producer and playwright); 46 c. Text and fountain pen (Cercle du Livre de France); 46 c. Harlequin and roses (Harlequin Books)	1·60 1·75
MS1973	46 c. Hart Massey (Massey Foundation); 46 c. Izaak Walton Killam and Dorothy Killam; 46 c. Eric Lafferty Harvie (Glenbow Foundation); 46 c. Macdonald Stewart Foundation	1·60 1·75
MS1969/73	*Set of 5 sheets*	8·00 8·75

In addition to Nos. **MS1969/73**, these designs were also available in a presentation album showing two stamps per page.

(Des P. Leduc and R. Bellemare. Litho Ashton-Potter Canada)

2000 (1 Mar). *Birds (5th series). Horiz designs as T 643. Multicoloured. Fluorescent frame. (a) P 12½×13*

1974	46 c. Canadian Warbler	40	45
	a. Horiz strip of 4. Nos. 1974/7	1·60	
1975	46 c. Osprey	40	45
1976	46 c. Pacific Loon	40	45
1977	46 c. Blue Jay	40	45
1974/7	*Set of 4*	1·60	1·75

(b) Self-adhesive. P 11½

1978	46 c. Canadian Warbler	40	45
	a. Booklet pane. Nos. 1978/81, each × 3	4·75	
1979	46 c. Osprey	40	45
1980	46 c. Pacific Loon	40	45
1981	46 c. Blue Jay	40	45
1978/81	*Set of 4*	1·60	1·75

Nos. 1974/7 were printed together, *se-tenant*, as horizontal strips of 4 in sheets of 20 (4×5).

Nos. 1978/81 were only available from $5.52 stamp booklets.

(Des Taylor/Sprules Corporation and P. Sayers, M. Koudis, D. Preston Smith and P.-M. Brunelle and J. Hudson (No. **MS1982**); Susan Scott, N. Smith, Monique Dufour and Sophie LaFortune and Doreen Colonello and S. Ash (**MS1983**); T. Telmet and M. Barac, S. Slipp and D. Preston Smith, J. LeBlanc and Bonnie Ross and Michèle Cayer and T. Kapas (**MS1984**); K. van der Leek and A. McKinley, E. Roch, T. Yakobina and N. Skinner, J. Gault and N.C.K Engineering (**MS1985**). Litho Ashton-Potter Canada)

2000 (17 Mar). *Millennium Collection (4th series). Canadian Agriculture, Commerce and Technology. Miniature sheets, each 108×112 mm, containing vert designs as T 719. Multicoloured. Fluorescent frame. P 13½.*

MS1982	46 c. Sir Charles Saunders (developer of Marquis wheat); 46 c. Baby (Pablum baby food); 46 c. Dr. Archibald Gowanlock Huntsman (frozen fish pioneer); 46 c. Oven chips and field of potatos (McCain Frozen Foods)	1·60 1·75
MS1983	46 c. Early trader and Indian (Hudson's Bay Company); 46 c. Satelite over earth (Bell Canada Enterprises); 46 c. Jos. Louis biscuits and Vachon family (Vachon Family Bakery); 46 c. Bread and eggs (George Weston Limited)	1·60 1·75
MS1984	46 c. George Klein and cog wheels (inventor of electric wheelchair and microsurgical staple gun); 46 c. Abraham Gesner (developer of kerosene); 46 c. Alexander Graham Bell (inventor of telephone); 46 c. Joseph-Armand Bombardier (inventor of snowmobile)	1·60 1·75
MS1985	46 c. Workers and steam locomotive (Rogers Pass rail tunnel); 46 c. Manic 5 dam (Manicouagan River hydro-electric project); 46 c. Mobile Servicing System for International Space Station (Canadian Space Program); 46 c. CN Tower (World's tallest building)	1·60 1·75
MS1982/5	*Set of 4 sheets*	6·25 7·00

In addition to Nos. **MS1982/5**, these designs were also available in a presentation album showing two stamps per page.

(Des C. Le Sauter. Litho C.B.N.)

2000 (10 Apr). *125th Anniv of Supreme Court of Canada. Fluorescent frame. P 12½×13.*

1986	723 46 c. multicoloured	40	45

STAMP BOOKLETS

2000 (1 Mar). *Birds (5th series). Multicoloured cover as Type B 62. Self-adhesive.*

SB238	$5.52, booklet containing pane of 12 46 c. (No. 1978a)	4·75

CAYMAN ISLANDS

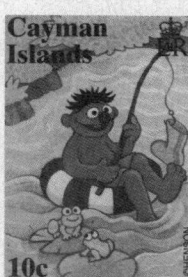

202 Ernie fishing from Rubber Ring

(Des Children's Television Workshop. Litho Questa)

2000 (15 Mar). *Sesame Street (children's T.V. programme). T 202 and similar vert designs. Multicoloured. W w 14 (inverted on 20 c.). P 14½×15.*

915	10 c. Type 202	15	20
916	20 c. Grover flying	30	35
	a. Sheetlet. Nos. 916/24	2·50	
917	20 c. Zoe in airplane	30	35
918	20 c. Oscar the Grouch in balloon	30	35
919	20 c. The Count on motorbike	30	35
920	20 c. Big Bird rollerskating	30	35
921	20 c. Cookie Monster heading for Cookie Factory	30	35
922	20 c. Type 202	30	35
923	20 c. Bert in rowing boat	30	35
924	20 c. Elmo snorkeling	30	35
925	30 c. As No. 920	45	50
915/25	*Set of 11*	3·00	3·50
MS926	139×86 mm. 20 c. Elmo with stamps.		
	Wmk inverted	30	35

Nos. 916/24 were printed together, *se-tenant*, in sheetlets of 9 with the backgrounds forming a composite design.

CYPRUS

330 Woman's Silhouette with Stars and Globe

331 Necklace, 4500–4000 B.C.

(Des G. Theophylaktou. Litho Oriental Press, Bahrain)

2000 (2 Mar). *Miss Universe Beauty Contest, Cyprus. Sheet, 80×65 mm containing T 330 and similar vert design. Multicoloured. P 13½×13.*

MS983	15 c. Type 330; 35 c. Statue of Aphrodite and apple	35 40

(Des A. Koutas. Litho Oriental Press, Bahrain)

2000 (30 Mar). *Jewellery. T 331 and similar multicoloured designs. P 14.*

984	10 c. Type 331	25	30
985	15 c. Gold earrings, 3rd-cent B.C.	35	40
986	20 c. Gold earring from Lampousa, 6th–7th-cent	45	50
987	25 c. Brooch, 19th-cent	55	60
988	30 c. Gold cross, 6th–7th-cent	65	70
989	35 c. Necklace, 18th–19th-cent	75	80
990	40 c. Gold earring, 19th-cent	85	90
991	50 c. Spiral hair ring, 5th–4th-cent B.C.	1·10	1·25
992	75 c. Gold-plated silver plaques from Gialia, 700–600 B.C. (*horiz*)	1·50	1·60
993	£1 Gold frontlet from Egkomi, 14th–13th-cent B.C. (*horiz*)	2·10	2·25
994	£2 Gold necklace from Egkomi, 13th-cent B.C. (*horiz*)	4·25	4·50
995	£3 Buckles, 19th-cent (*horiz*)	6·50	6·75
984/95	*Set of 12*	19·00	20·00

OMNIBUS ISSUES

Details, together with prices for complete sets, of the various Omnibus issues from the 1935 Silver Jubilee series to date are included in a special section following Zimbabwe at the end of Volume 2.

DOMINICA

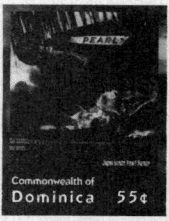

339 Leonardo Fibonacci (mathematician, 1202)

340 Bombing of Pearl Harbor, 1941

(Litho Cartor)

1999 (31 Dec). *New Millennium. People and Events of Thirteenth Century (1200–50). T 339 and similar multicoloured designs. P 12½.*

2703	55 c. Type 339	25	30
	a. Sheetlet. Nos. 2703/19	4·25	
2704	55 c. St Francis of Assisi (founder of Franciscan Order, 1207)	25	30
2705	55 c. Mongol horsemen (Conquest of China, 1211)	25	30
2706	55 c. Children with banner (Children's Crusade, 1212)	25	30
2707	55 c. King John signing Magna Carta, 1215	25	30
2708	55 c. University class (foundation of Salamanca University, 1218)	25	30
2709	55 c. Snorre Sturlusson (author of the Edda, 1222)	25	30
2710	55 c. Ma Yuan (Chinese painter) in garden (died 1224)	25	30
2711	55 c. Genghis Khan (Mongol Emperor) (died 1227)	25	30
2712	55 c. Student and Buddha (establishment of Zen Buddhism in Japan, 1227)	25	30
2713	55 c. Galleys (The Sixth Crusade, 1228)	25	30
2714	55 c. Seals (Lübeck–Hamburg Treaty, 1230)	25	30
2715	55 c. Cardinal and angel (Holy Inquisition, 1231)	25	30
2716	55 c. Palace interior (conquest of Cordoba, 1236)	25	30
2717	55 c. San Marino (town founded, 1243)	25	30
2718	55 c. Maimonides (Jewish philosopher) (died 1204) (59×39 mm)	25	30
2719	55 c. Notre Dame Cathedral, Paris (completed 1250)	25	30
2703/19	*Set of 17*	4·25	5·00

Nos. 2703/19 were printed together, *se-tenant*, in sheetlets of 17 including a central label (59×39 mm) and inscribed left margin.

(Des Spotlight Designs. Litho Cartor)

1999 (31 Dec). *New Millennium. People and Events of Twentieth Century (1940–49). T 340 and similar multicoloured designs. P 12½.*

2720	55 c. Type 340	25	30
	a. Sheetlet. Nos. 2720/36	4·25	
2721	55 c. Sir Winston Churchill (British Prime Minister, 1940)	25	30
2722	55 c. Children in front of set (start of television broadcasting in U.S.A., 1940)	25	30
2723	55 c. Anne Frank (Holocaust, 1942)	25	30
2724	55 c. Troops wading ashore (D-Day, 1944)	25	30
2725	55 c. Churchill, Roosevelt and Stalin (Yalta Conference, 1945)	25	30
2726	55 c. U. N. Headquarters, New York (United Nations Organization, 1945)	25	30
2727	55 c. American G.I. and concentration camp (Surrender of Germany, 1945)	25	30
2728	55 c. Hoisting the Red Flag on the Reichstag (Fall of Berlin, 1945)	25	30
2729	55 c. "Eniac" (first operational computer, 1946)	25	30
2730	55 c. Indian with flag (Independence of India, 1947)	25	30
2731	55 c. Early transistor, 1947	25	30
2732	55 c. Mahatma Gandhi assassinated, 1948	25	30
2733	55 c. Israelis with flag (Establishment of Israel, 1948)	25	30
2734	55 c. Aircraft and children (Berlin Airlift, 1948)	25	30
2735	55 c. Atomic bomb test, New Mexico, 1948 (59×39 mm)	25	30
2736	55 c. Great Wall of China (People's Republic established, 1949)	25	30
2720/36	*Set of 17*	4·25	5·00

Nos. 2720/36 were printed together, *se-tenant*, in sheetlets of 17 including a central label (59×39 mm) and inscribed left margin.

No. 2732 is inscribed "Ghandi" in error.

341 "Dragon flying in the Mist" (Chen Rong)

(Des Y. Lee ($1.50), W. Wu ($4). Litho Questa)

2000 (5 Feb). *Chinese New Year ("Year of the Dragon"). T* **341** *and similar multicoloured design.* P 13½×14.
2737	$1.50, Type 341		65	70
	a. Sheetlet of 4		2·50	
MS2738	80×60 mm. $4 Red dragon (*horiz*).			
	P 14×13½		1·75	1·90

No. 2737 was printed in sheetlets of 4 with an enlarged illustrated and inscribed right margin.

GAMBIA

307 Flowers forming Top of Head   308 Betty Boop

(Des R. Silvers. Litho Questa)

1999 (31 Dec). *Faces of the Millennium: Diana, Princess of Wales.* T **307** *and similar vert designs showing collage of miniature flower photographs. Multicoloured.* P 13½×14.
3231	3 d. Type 307 (face value at left)		35	40
	a. Sheetlet. Nos. 3231/8		2·75	
3232	3 d. Top of head (face value at right)		35	40
3233	3 d. Ear (face value at left)		35	40
3234	3 d. Eye and temple (face value at right)		35	40
3235	3 d. Cheek (face value at left)		35	40
3236	3 d. Cheek (face value at right)		35	40
3237	3 d. Blue background (face value at left)		35	40
3238	3 d. Chin (face value at right)		35	40
3231/8		*Set of 8*	2·75	3·00

Nos. 3231/8 were printed together, *se-tenant*, in sheetlets of 8 with the stamps arranged in two vertical columns separated by a gutter also containing miniature photographs. When viewed as a whole the sheetlet forms a portrait of Diana, Princess of Wales.

2000 (14 Jan). *Betty Boop* (*cartoon character*). T **308** *and similar vert designs. Multicoloured. Litho.* P 13½.
3239	5 d. Type 308		60	65
	a. Sheetlet. Nos. 3239/47		5·25	
3240	5 d. In full-length gown		60	65
3241	5 d. In t-shirt and dungarees		60	65
3242	5 d. In cropped trousers, sleeveless shirt and tie		60	65
3243	5 d. Sitting in wicker chair		60	65
3244	5 d. In ripped purple trousers, orange t-shirt and gilet		60	65
3245	5 d. In fur coat		60	65
3246	5 d. In pink crinoline		60	65
3247	5 d. In the gym		60	65
3239/47		*Set of 9*	5·25	5·75
MS3248	Two sheets, each 140×89 mm. (a) 25 d.			
	In the bath; (b) 25 d. With chin on hand			
		Set of 2 sheets	6·00	6·25

Nos. 3239/47 were printed together, *se-tenant*, in sheetlets of 9.

(Des Dreamscape Studios. Litho Cartor)

2000 (28 Jan). *New Millennium. People and Events of Fifteenth Century (1450–1500). Multicoloured designs as* T **339** *of Dominica.* P 12½.
3249	2 d. Leonardo da Vinci's first design for flying machine, 1480		20	25
	a. Sheetlet. Nos. 3249/65		3·25	
3250	2 d. Johann Gutenberg (first printed Bible, 1455)		20	25
3251	2 d. Capital "B" (first colour printing, 1457)		20	25
3252	2 d. Ivan III ("the Great") becomes Grand Prince of Moscow, 1462		20	25
3253	2 d. Walls under attack (Fall of Constantinople, 1453)		20	25
3254	2 d. Great Wall of China rebuilt, 1488		20	25
3255	2 d. Lorenzo de Medici (ruler of Florence) and "Pieta" (sculpture), 1479		20	25
3256	2 d. King Henry VII of England (Foundation of Tudor dynasty, 1485)		20	25
3257	2 d. Sailing ship and meeting with Indians (Vasco da Gama's voyage to India, 1497)		20	25
3258	2 d. King Ferdinand V and Queen Isabella I (Union of Aragon and Castile, 1479)		20	25
3259	2 d. Foetus (birth of Erasmus (Dutch scholar),1466)		20	25
3260	2 d. Sailing ship and Cross of St. George (John Cabot's voyage to North America, 1497)		20	25
3261	2 d. King Henry VI and Richard, Duke of Gloucester (War of the Roses, 1455)		20	25
3262	2 d. Bartalomeu Dias and map (Discovery of Cape of Good Hope, 1487)		20	25
3263	2 d. Matthias Hunyadi (crowned King of Hungary, 1458)		20	25
3264	2 d. Christopher Columbus (Discovery of the Americas, 1492) (59×39 mm)		20	25
3265	2 d. Girolamo Savonarola (religious reformer) (executed 1498)		20	25
3249/65		*Set of 17*	3·25	4·25

Nos. 3249/65 were printed together, *se-tenant*, in sheetlets of 17 including a central label (59×39 mm) and inscribed left margin.

(Des Spotlight Designs. Litho Cartor)

2000 (28 Jan). *New Millennium. People and Events of Twentieth Century (1900–09). Multicoloured designs as* T **340** *of Dominica.* P 12½.
3266	3 d. Max Planck (Quantum Theory of Energy, 1900)		35	40
	a. Sheetlet. Nos. 3266/82		5·75	
3267	3 d. Zeppelin in hangar (invention of rigid airship, 1900)		35	40
3268	3 d. Guglielmo Marconi (first transatlantic radio message, 1901)		35	40
3269	3 d. Funeral of Queen Victoria, 1901		35	40
3270	3 d. Alfred Nobel (first Nobel Prizes awarded, 1901)		35	40
3271	3 d. British infantry advancing (end of Boer War, 1902)		35	40
3272	3 d. Wright Brothers and aircraft (first flight, 1903)		35	40
3273	3 d. Early teddy bear, 1903		35	40
3274	3 d. Panama Canal locks under construction, 1904		35	40
3275	3 d. Albert Einstein (Theory of Relativity, 1905)		35	40
3276	3 d. Crowd with flags (unrest in Russia, 1905)		35	40
3277	3 d. Rescue squad and collapsed building, San Francisco earthquake, 1906		35	40
3278	3 d. Louis Lumiere (development of colour photography, 1907)		35	40
3279	3 d. "Les Demoiselles d'Avignon" (Pablo Picasso), 1907		35	40
3280	3 d. Robert Peary (conquest of North Pole, 1909)		35	40
3281	3 d. Henry Ford and first Model T, 1908 (59×39 mm)		35	40
3282	3 d. Planting sapling (foundation of first Jewish kibbutz in Palestine, 1909)		35	40
3266/82		*Set of 17*	5·75	6·75

Nos. 3266/82 were printed together, *se-tenant*, in sheetlets of 17 including a central label (59×39 mm) and inscribed left margin.

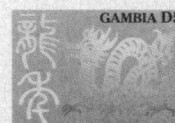

309 Dragon

(Des Y. Lee. Litho Cartor)

2000 (5 Feb). *Chinese New Year ("Year of the Dragon"). T* **309** *and similar horiz designs. Multicoloured.* P 15×14½.
3283	5 d. Type 309		60	65
	a. Sheetlet. Nos. 3283/6		2·40	
3284	5 d. Multicoloured dragon		60	65
3285	5 d. Purple dragon		60	65
3286	5 d. Brown dragon		60	65
3283/6		*Set of 4*	2·40	2·50
MS3287	106×76 mm. 15 d. Coiled dragon			
	(39×24 mm). P 14		1·75	1·90

Nos. 3283/6 were printed together, *se-tenant*, in sheetlets of 4.

GHANA

Add to Nos. 1639a/45:

Three types of 100 c.:

I. Cross bars of "A"'s in "GHANA" slope to left. Line in currency abbreviation upright. "CAPE COAST CASTLE" 9 mm long (No. 1643)

II. Inscriptions re-drawn. Cross bars of "A" slope to right. Line in currency abbreviation upright. "CAPE COAST CASTLE" 10 mm long (No. 1643b)

III. Inscription again re-drawn. Cross bars of "A" slope to right. Line in currency abbreviation diagonal. "CAPE COAST CASTLE" 13 mm long (No. 1643c)

(1643	100 c. Cape Coast Castle (*horiz*) (I) (12.12.91)		
	c. Type III (1999)		

578 Black-faced Impala

(Des W. Still. Litho Questa)

2000 (28 Feb). *African Wildlife.* T **578** *and similar multicoloured designs.* P 14.
2966	300 c. Type 578		10	15
2967	500 c. Cheetah		15	20
2968	1000 c. Wildebeest		35	40
2969	1100 c. Chimpanzee (*vert*)		40	45
	a. Sheetlet. Nos. 2969/76		3·00	
2970	1100 c. Boomslang Tree Snake (*vert*)		40	45
2971	1100 c. Vulture (*vert*)		40	45
2972	1100 c. Leopard (*vert*)		40	45
2973	1100 c. African Rhinoceros (*vert*)		40	45
2974	1100 c. Zebra (*vert*)		40	45
2975	1100 c. Crowned Crane (*vert*)		40	45
2976	1100 c. Female Lesser Kudu (*vert*)		40	45
2977	1200 c. Purple Roller (*vert*)		45	50
	a. Sheetlet. Nos. 2977/84		3·50	
2978	1200 c. Pelicans (*vert*)		45	50
2979	1200 c. Egrets (*vert*)		45	50
2980	1200 c. Orange-breasted Waxbill (*vert*)		45	50
2981	1200 c. Giraffe (*vert*)		45	50
2982	1200 c. African Buffalo (*vert*)		45	50
2983	1200 c. Elephant (*vert*)		45	50
2984	1200 c. African Lion (*vert*)		45	50
2985	3000 c. Hippopotamus		1·10	1·25
2966/85		*Set of 20*	8·00	9·50
MS2986	Two sheets, each 76×106 mm. (a)			
	7000 c. Ostrich; (b) 7000 c. Young Waterbuck			
		Set of 2 sheets	4·75	5·00

Nos. 2969/76 and 2977/84 were each printed together, *se-tenant*, in sheetlets of 8 with the backgrounds forming composite designs.

GRENADA

469 Christmas Rose

(Litho Questa)

1999 (17 Dec). *Christmas.* T **469** *and similar multicoloured designs.* P 14.
3893	20 c. Type 469		10	10
3894	75 c. Tulip		35	40
3895	90 c. Pear		40	45
3896	$1 Hibiscus		45	50
3897	$4 Lily		1·75	1·90
3893/7		*Set of 5*	3·00	3·25
MS3898	106×91 mm. $6 "The Nativity" (Botticelli) (*horiz*)		2·50	2·75

(Des R. Silvers. Litho Questa)

1999 (31 Dec). *Faces of the Millennium: Diana, Princess of Wales. Vert designs as* T **307** *of Gambia showing collage of miniature flower photographs. Multicoloured.* P 13½×14.
3899	$1 Top of head (face value at left)		45	50
	a. Sheetlet. Nos. 3899/3906		3·50	
3900	$1 Top of head (face value at right)		45	50
3901	$1 Ear (face value at left)		45	50
3902	$1 Eye and temple (face value at right)		45	50
3903	$1 Cheek (face value at left)		45	50
3904	$1 Cheek (face value at right)		45	50
3905	$1 Blue background (face value at left)		45	50
3906	$1 Chin (face value at right)		45	50
3899/3906		*Set of 8*	3·50	4·00

Nos. 3899/906 were printed together, *se-tenant*, in sheetlets of 8 with the stamps arranged in two vertical columns separated by a gutter also containing miniature photographs. When viewed as a whole the sheetlet forms a portrait of Diana, Princess of Wales.

Grenadines of Grenada

138 George Raft   139 "Sputnik I", 1957

(Des Michelle Amatrula and D. Keren. Litho Questa)

1999 (20 Aug). *Early Cinema Actors.* T **138** *and similar designs.* P 14.
2788	$1 multicoloured		45	50
	a. Sheetlet. Nos. 2788/95		3·50	
2789	$1 lavender-grey and grey-black		45	50
2790	$1 brownish grey and brownish black		45	50
2791	$1 multicoloured		45	50
2792	$1 multicoloured		45	50
2793	$1 grey-black and bluish grey		45	50
2794	$1 grey-black, bluish grey & brownish grey		45	50
2795	$1 multicoloured		45	50
2796	$2 multicoloured		85	90
	a. Sheetlet. Nos. 2796/9		3·25	
2797	$2 grey-black and grey		85	90
2798	$2 multicoloured		85	90
2799	$2 grey-black and grey		85	90
2788/99		*Set of 12*	6·75	7·50
MS2800	$6 multicoloured		2·50	2·75

Designs (As Type **138**)—No. 2788, Type 138; No. 2791, Fatty Arbuckle; No. 2792, Buster Keaton; No. 2795, Harold Lloyd; No. 2796, James Cagney; No. 2798, Edward G. Robinson. MS2800, Charlie Chaplin. (53×39 mm) No. 2789, George Raft in *Scarface*; No. 2790, Fatty Arbuckle with nurse; No. 2793, Buster Keaton on locomotive cow-catcher; No. 2794, Harold Lloyd hanging on clockface; No. 2797, James Cagney in *The Public Enemy*; No. 2799, Edward G. Robinson in *Little Caesar*.

Nos. 2788/95 and 2796/9 were each printed together, *se-tenant*, in sheetlets of 8 or 4 with illustrated and inscribed margins.

(Des G. Capasso. Litho Questa)

1999 (8 Oct). *Space Exploration. T* **139** *and similar multi-coloured designs. P* 14.
2801	$1.50, Type **139**	65	70
	a. Sheetlet. Nos. 2801/6	3·75	
2802	$1.50, "Explorer I", 1958	65	70
2803	$1.50, "Telstar I" satellite, 1962	65	70
2804	$1.50, "Maristat I", 1976	65	70
2805	$1.50, Long Duration Exposure facility, 1984	65	70
2806	$1.50, Hubble Space Telescope, 1990	65	70
2807	$1.50, X-15 rocket plane, 1960 (*vert*)	65	70
	a. Sheetlet. Nos. 2807/12	3·75	
2808	$1.50, "Freedom 7" rocket, 1961 (*vert*)	65	70
2809	$1.50, "Friendship 7", 1962 (*vert*)	65	70
2810	$1.50, "Gemini 4" rocket and Edward H. White, 1965 (*vert*)	65	70
2811	$1.50, Saturn V rocket and Edwin E. Aldrin stepping onto Moon, 1969 (*vert*)	65	70
2812	$1.50, Lunar Rover, "Apollo 15" mission, 1971 (*vert*)	65	70
2801/12		*Set of* 12	7·50 8·25

MS2813 Two sheets, each 110×85 mm. (a) $6 "Mars Pathfinder", 1997 (55×42 *mm*); (b) $6 Space shuttle *Columbia*, 1981 (55×42 *mm*)
Set of 2 *sheets* 5·00 5·25

Nos. 2801/6 and 2807/12 were each printed together, *se-tenant*, in sheetlets of 6 with the backgrounds forming composite designs.

140 Kirk Douglas   **141** Elvis Presley

(Litho Questa)

1999 (11 Oct). *Kirk Douglas (American actor). T* **140** *and similar vert designs. Multicoloured. P* 13½×14.
2814	$1.50, Type **140**	65	70
	a. Sheetlet. Nos. 2814/19	3·75	
2815	$1.50, As a boxer in *Champion*	65	70
2816	$1.50, As Van Gogh in *Lust for Life*	65	70
2817	$1.50, With white hair and wearing black shirt	65	70
2818	$1.50, In French uniform for *Paths of Glory*	65	70
2819	$1.50, As a cowboy in *The Bad and the Beautiful*	65	70
2814/19		*Set of* 6	3·75 4·00

MS2820 93×106 mm. $6 As Spartacus   2·50 2·75

Nos. 2814/19 were printed together, *se-tenant*, in sheetlets of 6 with illustrated and inscribed margins.

(Litho Questa)

1999 (11 Oct). *Elvis Presley Commemoration. T* **141** *and similar vert designs. Each lavender-grey, silver and black. P* 13½×14.
2821	$1.50, Type **141**	65	70
	a. Sheetlet. Nos. 2821/6	3·75	
2822	$1.50, Resting chin on hand	65	70
2823	$1.50, Wearing roll-neck sweater	65	70
2824	$1.50, Leaning against brick wall	65	70
2825	$1.50, Singing into microphone	65	70
2826	$1.50, Singing with eyes closed	65	70
2821/6		*Set of* 6	3·75 4·00

Nos. 2821/6 were printed together, *se-tenant*, in sheetlets of 6 with enlarged illustrated and inscribed top and right margins.

Christmas 1999
142 Poinsettia and Candle

(Litho Questa)

1999 (23 Nov). *Christmas. Foliage and Candles. T* **142** *and similar multicoloured designs. P* 13½×14.
2827	15 c. Type **142**	10	15
2828	35 c. Holly	15	20
2829	75 c. Fir tree	35	40
2830	$1.50, Ivy	65	70
2831	$3 Geranium	1·25	1·40
2827/31		*Set of* 5	2·50 2·75

MS2832 83×108 mm. $6 The Adoration of the Magi (*horiz*). P 14   2·50 2·75

Nos. 2827/31 were issued in separate sheets with each stamp accompanied by a *se-tenant* half-size label.

No. 2829 is inscribed "FUR TREE" in error

GUYANA

564 "Washington in Battle"

1997 (14 Mar). *Bicentenary of George Washington's Retirement from United States Presidency. T* **564** *and similar vert designs. Multicoloured. Litho. P* 13½×14 ($60) *or imperf* ($300).
4911	$60 Type **564**	40	45
	a. Sheetlet. Nos. 4911/22 and 4935	4·75	
4912	$60 "Washington taking Presidential Oath"	40	45
4913	$60 "Washington seated in Armchair" (engraving after Chappel)	40	45
4914	$60 "Col. Washington of the Virginia Militia" (Charles W. Peale)	40	45
4915	$60 "George Washington" (Rembrandt Peale)	40	45
4916	$60 "Washington addressing Constitutional Convention" (Junius B. Stearns)	40	45
4917	$60 "Washington on his way to Continental Congress"	40	45
4918	$60 "Washington on a White Charger" (John Faed)	40	45
4919	$60 "Washington surveying" (engraving by G. R. Hall)	40	45
4920	$60 "Washington praying at Valley Forge" (bas-relief)	40	45
4921	$60 "Death of Gen. Mercer at Battle of Princeton" (John Trumbull)	40	45
4922	$60 "Washington taking Command at Cambridge"	40	45
4923	$60 "Washington before Battle of Trenton" (John Trumbull)	40	45
	a. Sheetlet. Nos. 4923/34 and 4936	4·75	
4924	$60 "Washington and his Family at Mount Vernon" (Alonzo Chappel)	40	45
4925	$60 "Washington's Inauguration" (Chappel)	40	45
4926	$60 "Washington" (Adolph Ulrich Wertmuller)	40	45
4927	$60 "Washington accepts Commission as Commander-in-Chief" (Currier & Ives lithograph)	40	45
4928	$60 "Washington" (mezzotint by Sartain)	40	45
4929	$60 "Mount Vernon"	40	45
4930	$60 "Washington with Farm Workers" (print by Junius B. Stearns)	40	45
4931	$60 "Wedding of Nellie Custis" (Ogden)	40	45
4932	$60 "Washington crossing the Delaware" (Leutze)	40	45
4933	$60 "Washington and Gen. Braddock"	40	45
4934	$60 "Washington's Birthplace" (Currier & Ives lithograph)	40	45
4935	$300 "George Washington" (Gilbert Stuart) (66×91 *mm*)	2·00	2·10
4936	$300 "Washington at Yorktown" (James Peale) (66×91 *mm*)	2·00	2·10
4911/36		*Set of* 26	13·50 15·00

Nos. 4911/22 with 4935, and 4923/34 with 4936, were each printed together in sheetlets containing twelve $60 designs *se-tenant* and a single $300 value imperforate within an enlarged right-hand margin.

565 Pres. Kennedy and "Eternal Flame"

(Litho Questa)

1997 (14 Mar). *80th Birth Anniv of Pres. John F. Kennedy. P* 13½×14.
4937	**565** $50 bluish violet	35	40

No. 4937 is in the same design as the U.S.A. Memorial Issue of 1964.

(Des M. Friedman and Dena Rubin. Litho Questa)

1997 (2 Apr). *50th Anniv of U.N.E.S.C.O. Multicoloured designs as T* **374** *of Antigua. P* 14×13½ (*horiz*) *or* 13½×14 (*vert*).
4938	$20 Hall at Horyu-ji, Japan	15	20
4939	$25 Coastline, Scandola Nature Reserve, France	20	25
4940	$25 Great Wall turret, China	20	25
4941	$35 Bedroom in the Residenz, Wurzburg, Germany	20	25
4942	$60 Monastery of Batalha, Portugal	40	45
4943	$60 Cathedral of Aquisgrán, Aachen, Germany (*vert*)	40	45
	a. Sheetlet. Nos. 4943/50	3·00	
4944	$60 Trier Cathedral, Germany (*vert*)	40	45
4945	$60 Column of Augusta Treveror, Trier (*vert*)	40	45

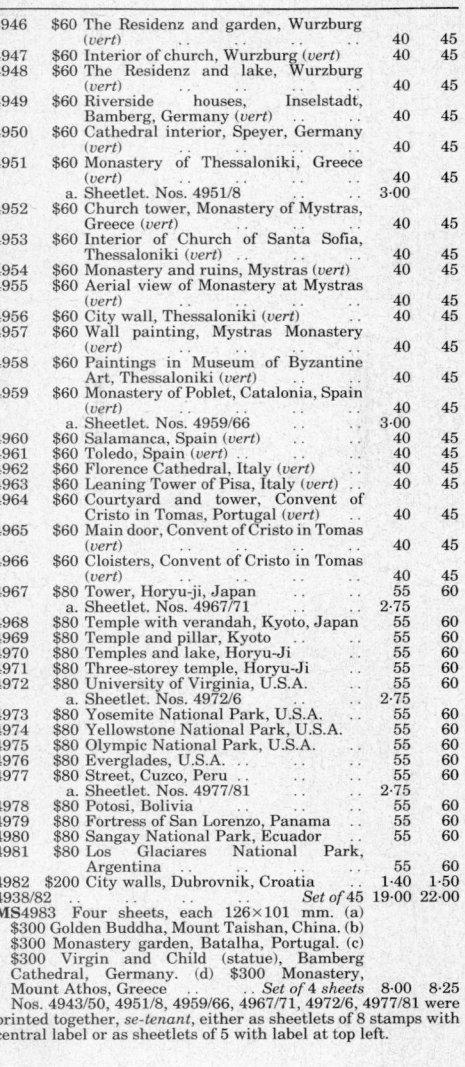

4946	$60 The Residenz and garden, Wurzburg (*vert*)	40	45
4947	$60 Interior of church, Wurzburg (*vert*)	40	45
4948	$60 The Residenz and lake, Wurzburg (*vert*)	40	45
4949	$60 Riverside houses, Inselstadt, Bamberg, Germany (*vert*)	40	45
4950	$60 Cathedral interior, Speyer, Germany (*vert*)	40	45
4951	$60 Monastery of Thessaloniki, Greece (*vert*)	40	45
	a. Sheetlet. Nos. 4951/8	3·00	
4952	$60 Church tower, Monastery of Mystras, Greece (*vert*)	40	45
4953	$60 Interior of Church of Santa Sofia, Thessaloniki (*vert*)	40	45
4954	$60 Monastery and ruins, Mystras (*vert*)	40	45
4955	$60 Aerial view of Monastery at Mystras (*vert*)	40	45
4956	$60 City wall, Thessaloniki (*vert*)	40	45
4957	$60 Wall painting, Mystras Monastery (*vert*)	40	45
4958	$60 Paintings in Museum of Byzantine Art, Thessaloniki (*vert*)	40	45
4959	$60 Monastery of Poblet, Catalonia, Spain (*vert*)	40	45
	a. Sheetlet. Nos. 4959/66	3·00	
4960	$60 Salamanca, Spain (*vert*)	40	45
4961	$60 Toledo, Spain (*vert*)	40	45
4962	$60 Florence Cathedral, Italy (*vert*)	40	45
4963	$60 Leaning Tower of Pisa, Italy (*vert*)	40	45
4964	$60 Courtyard and tower, Convent of Cristo in Tomas, Portugal (*vert*)	40	45
4965	$60 Main door, Convent of Cristo in Tomas (*vert*)	40	45
4966	$60 Cloisters, Convent of Cristo in Tomas (*vert*)	40	45
4967	$80 Tower, Horyu-ji, Japan	55	60
	a. Sheetlet. Nos. 4967/71	2·75	
4968	$80 Temple with verandah, Kyoto, Japan	55	60
4969	$80 Temple and pillar, Kyoto	55	60
4970	$80 Temples and lake, Horyu-Ji	55	60
4971	$80 Three-storey temple, Horyu-Ji	55	60
4972	$80 University of Virginia, U.S.A.	55	60
	a. Sheetlet. Nos. 4972/6	2·75	
4973	$80 Yosemite National Park, U.S.A.	55	60
4974	$80 Yellowstone National Park, U.S.A.	55	60
4975	$80 Olympic National Park, U.S.A.	55	60
4976	$80 Everglades, U.S.A.	55	60
4977	$80 Street, Cuzco, Peru	55	60
	a. Sheetlet. Nos. 4977/81	2·75	
4978	$80 Potosi, Bolivia	55	60
4979	$80 Fortress of San Lorenzo, Panama	55	60
4980	$80 Sangay National Park, Ecuador	55	60
4981	$80 Los Glaciares National Park, Argentina	55	60
4982	$200 City walls, Dubrovnik, Croatia	1·40	1·50
4938/82		*Set of* 45	19·00 22·00

MS4983 Four sheets, each 126×101 mm. (a) $300 Golden Buddha, Mount Taishan, China. (b) $300 Monastery garden, Batalha, Portugal. (c) $300 Virgin and Child (statue), Bamberg Cathedral, Germany. (d) $300 Monastery, Mount Athos, Greece.   *Set of* 4 *sheets* 8·00 8·25

Nos. 4943/50, 4951/8, 4959/66, 4967/71, 4972/6, 4977/81 were printed together, *se-tenant*, either as sheetlets of 8 stamps with central label or as sheetlets of 5 with label at top left.

566 *Morchella*   **567** Pineapple Lily
hortensis

(Litho Questa)

1997 (2 Apr). *Fungi of the World. T* **566** *and similar vert designs. Multicoloured. P* 14.
4984	$6 Type **566**	10	10
4985	$20 *Boletus chyrsenteron*	15	20
4986	$25 *Hygrophorus agathosmus*	20	25
4987	$30 *Cortinarius violaceus*	20	25
4988	$35 *Acanthocystis geogenius*	20	25
4989	$60 *Mycena polygramma*	40	45
4990	$80 *Coprinus picaceus*	55	60
	a. Sheetlet. Nos. 4990/5	3·25	
4991	$80 *Stropharia umbonatescens*	55	60
4992	$80 *Paxillus involutus*	55	60
4993	$80 *Amanita inaurata*	55	60
4994	$80 *Lepiota rhacodes*	55	60
4995	$80 *Russula amoena*	55	60
4996	$80 *Volvaria volvacea*	55	60
	a. Sheetlet. Nos. 4996/5001	3·25	
4997	$80 *Psalliota augusta*	55	60
4998	$80 *Tricholoma aurantium*	55	60
4999	$80 *Pholiota spectabilis*	55	60
5000	$80 *Cortinarius armillatus*	55	60
5001	$80 *Agrocybe dura*	55	60
5002	$200 *Hebeloma radicosum*	1·40	1·50
5003	$300 *Coprinus comatus*	2·00	2·10
4984/5003		*Set of* 20	11·00 12·00

MS5004 Two sheets, each 76×105 mm. (a) $300 *Pholiota mutabilis*. (b) $300 *Amanita muscaria*.
Set of 2 *sheets* 4·00 4·25

Nos. 4990/5 and 4996/5001 were each printed together, *se-tenant*, in sheetlets of 6.

ADDENDA

(Des Courtney Ryan (Nos. 5020/5), Rina Lyamphe (others). Litho Questa)

1997 (2 Apr). *Flowers.* T **567** *and similar vert designs. Multicoloured.* P 14.

5005	$6 Type **567**	..	..	10	10
5006	$6 Blue Columbine	..	..	10	10
5007	$20 Petunia	..	..	15	20
5008	$25 Lily of the Nile	..	..	20	25
5009	$30 Bird of Paradise	..	..	20	25
5010	$35 African Daisy	..	..	20	25
5011	$60 Cape Daisy	..	..	40	45
5012	$60 Monarch Slipperwort	..	..	40	45
	a. Sheetlet. Nos. 5012/19	..	..	3·00	
5013	$60 Passion Flower	..	..	40	45
5014	$60 Butterfly Iris	..	..	40	45
5015	$60 Red-hot Poker	..	..	40	45
5016	$60 Water Lily "Dir G. T. Moore"	..	..	40	45
5017	$60 Painted Tongue "Superbissima"	..		40	45
5018	$60 Canariensis Orchid	..	..	40	45
5019	$60 Annual Chrysanthemum	..		40	45
5020	$80 Tulips	..	..	55	60
	a. Sheetlet. Nos. 5020/5	..	..	3·25	
5021	$80 Liatris	..	..	55	60
5022	$80 Roses	..	..	55	60
5023	$80 Gerber Daisies	..	..	55	60
5024	$80 Sunflowers	..	..	55	60
5025	$80 Chrysanthemums	..	..	55	60
5026	$80 Gazania	..	..	55	60
5027	$80 Cape Water Lily	..	..	55	60
5028	$200 Insigne Lady's Slipper	..	..	1·40	1·50
5005/28		*Set of 24*		10·00	11·00
MS5029	105×75 mm. $300 Petunias	..		2·00	2·10

Nos. 5012/19 and 5020/5 were each printed together, *se-tenant*, in sheetlets of 8 or 6.

INDIA

1457 Kalki Krishnamurthy

1458 Ramdhari Sinha

1999 (9 Sept). *Kalki Krishnamurthy Commemoration.* P 14.
1861 **1457** 3 r. violet-grey 15 15

1999 (14 Sept). *Ramdhari Sinha "Dinkar" (writer) Commemoration.* P 13½.
1862 **1458** 3 r. light brown and light new blue .. 15 15

1459 Jhaverchand Kalidas Meghani and Graves

1460 Rambrikish Benipuri and Statue of Horse

1999 (14 Sept). *Jhaverchand Kalidas Meghani Commemoration.* P 13½×13.
1863 **1459** 3 r. Indian red and dull yellowish green 15 15

1999 (14 Sept). *Rambrikish Benipuri Commemoration.* P 13½×13.
1864 **1460** 3 r. brown and yellow-brown .. 15 15

1461 Kazi Nazrul Islam

1462 Arati Gupta

1999 (14 Sept). *Birth Centenary of Kazi Nazrul Islam (Bengali poet).* P 13.
1865 **1461** 3 r. sepia and yellow 15 15

1999 (29 Sept). *Arari Gupta (swimmer) Commemoration.* P 13.
1866 **1462** 3 r. multicoloured 15 15

The new-issue supplement to this Catalogue appears each month in

GIBBONS
STAMP MONTHLY

—from your newsagent or by postal subscription—
sample copy and details on request.

1463 Lionesses

1464 A. D. Shroff

1999 (4 Oct). *Endangered Species. Asiatic Lion.* T **1463** *and similar horiz designs. Multicoloured.* P 13½×13.

1867	3 r. Type **1463**	..	15	15
1868	3 r. Lions and lionesses lying down		15	15
1869	3 r. Lioness with cubs	..	15	15
1870	15 r. Two lions	..	40	45
1867/70		*Set of 4*	85	90

1999 (9 Oct). *A. D. Shroff Commemoration.* P 13×13½.
1871 **1464** 3 r. yellowish green and yellow-ochre 15 15

1465 A. B. Walawalkar and Map

1466 Chhaganlal K. Parekh and Medical Staff with Child

1999 (9 Oct). *A. B. Walawalkar Commemoration.* P 13×13½.
1872 **1465** 3 r. reddish purple 15 15

1999 (9 Oct). *Chhaganlal K. Parekh (doctor) Commemoration.* P 13.
1873 **1466** 3 r. Prussian blue and orange-brown 15 15

1467 Dr. T. M. A. Pai and Hospital

1468 Chhau Dance Masks

1999 (9 Oct). *20th Death Anniv of Dr. T. M. A. Pai.* P 13.
1874 **1467** 3 r. chocolate and stone .. 15 15

1999 (9 Oct). *125th Anniv of Universal Postal Union.* T **1468** *and similar multicoloured designs.* P 13½×13 (horiz) or 13×13½ (vert).

1875	3 r. Type **1468**	..	15	15
1876	3 r. Elephant and horseman (Rathva wall painting) (*vert*)		15	15
1877	3 r. Man ploughing (Muria ritual collar)		15	15
1878	15 r. Angami ornament (*vert*)		40	45
1875/8		*Set of 4*	85	90

1469 Veerapandia Kattabomman

1470 Ustad Allauddin Khan Saheb (sarod player)

1999 (16 Oct). *Death Bicentenary of Veerapandia Kattabomman (ruler of Panchalankuruchi).* P 13×13½.
1879 **1469** 3 r. yellow-green 15 15

(Des R. Pasricha (No. 1880))

1999 (19 Oct). *Modern Masters of Indian Classical Music.* T **1470** *and similar horiz design. Multicoloured.* P 13½×14.
1880 3 r. Type **1470** 15 15
1881 3 r. Musiri Subramania Iyer (singer) .. 15 15

1471 Brigadier Rajinder Singh

1472 Elephant and Rhinoceros

1999 (27 Oct). *Birth Centenary of Brigadier Rajinder Singh (first recipient of M.V.C. medal).* P 13×13½.
1882 **1471** 3 r. slate-purple 15 15

(Des Rishikesh Gohain)

1999 (14 Nov). *Children's Day.* P 14.
1883 **1472** 3 r. multicoloured 15 15

1473 Dam and Pumping Station

1474 Supreme Court, New Delhi

1999 (23 Nov). *Sri Sathya Sai Water Supply Project.* P 13.
1884 **1473** 3 r. multicoloured 15 15

(Des S. Bhatnagar)

1999 (26 Nov). *50th Anniv of Supreme Court of India.* P 13.
1885 **1474** 3 r. multicoloured 15 15

1475 A. Vaidyanatha Iyer and Temple Tower

1476 Aspects of Thermal Power

1999 (9 Dec). *March of Progress.* T **1475** *and similar horiz designs.* P 13½×13.

1886	3 r. Indian red	..	15	15
1887	3 r. red-brown and green	..	15	15
1888	3 r. buff and grey-black	..	15	15
1889	3 r. reddish brown & dull yellowish green		15	15
1886/9		*Set of 4*	60	60

Designs:—No. 1886, Type **1475**; No. 1887, Dr. Punjabrao Deshmukh and symbols of agriculture; No. 1888, Indulal Kanaiyalal Yagnik and newspaper; No. 1889, P. Kakkan and machinery.

1999 (14 Dec). *Centenary of Thermal Power.* P 13½×13.
1890 **1476** 3 r. chocolate and brown-ochre .. 15 15

1477 Hindustan Times Front Pages from 1950 and 1999

1478 Three Faces ("Small Family by Choice")

1999 (16 Dec). *75th Anniv of Hindustan Times Newspaper.* P 13½×13.
1891 **1477** 15 r. multicoloured 40 45

1999 (18 Dec). *50th Anniv of Family Planning Association of India.* P 14.
1892 **1478** 3 r. multicoloured 15 15

1479 Hand inside Flame in front of Cross

1480 Tabo Monastery and Mountains

1999 (25 Dec). *2000th Birth Anniv of Jesus Christ.* P 13½×14.
1893 **1479** 3 r. multicoloured 15 15

1999 (31 Dec). *Tabo Monastery Commemoration.* T **1480** *and similar horiz design. Multicoloured.* P 13.
1894 5 r. Type **1480** 15 20
a. Horiz pair. Nos. 1894/5 45
1895 10 r. Traditional scene 30 35
Nos. 1894/5 were printed together, *se-tenant*, as horizontal pairs within the sheet.

1481 Agni II Rocket and Dove   **1482** Sunrise

2000 (1 Jan). *41st Anniv of Defence Research and Development Organisation. Litho.* P 13×13½.
1896 **1481** 3 r. multicoloured 15 15

2000 (1 Jan). *New Millennium.* P 13½×13.
1897 **1482** 3 r. multicoloured 15 15

Note: The first Supplement recording new stamps not in this catalogue or the Addenda appeared in the September 2000 number of *Gibbons Stamp Monthly*.

Notes

Index